AHA Members $299.00
Nonmembers $446.00
AHA Item Number 010021
Telephone ORDERS 1–800–AHA–2626

ISSN 0094–8969
ISBN–13: 978–1–55648–457–5

# Contents

**Section**

v   Acknowledgements and Advisements

vi   Introduction

ix   AHA Offices, Officers, and Historical Data

## A  Hospitals Institutional and Associate Members

A1   Contents of Section A

2   AHA Guide Hospital Listing Requirements

3   Explanation of Hospital Listings

5   Annual Survey

13   Hospitals in the United States, by State

805   Hospitals in Areas Associated with the United States, by Area

813   U.S. Government Hospitals Outside the United States, by Area

814   Index of Hospitals

877   Index of Health Care Professionals

1106   AHA Membership Categories

1107   Other Institutional Members

1112   Associate Members

## B  Networks, Health Care Systems and Alliances

B1   Contents of Section B

2   Introduction

3   Statistics for Multihospital Health Care Systems and their Hospitals

4   Health Care Systems and their Hospitals

151   Headquarters of Health Care Systems, Geographically

160   Networks and their Hospitals

176   Alliances

**Section**

# C

Indexes

**C**1   Abbreviations Used in the AHA Guide

2   Index

## Acknowledgements

The AHA Guide® to the Health Care Field is published annually by Health Forum LLC, an affiliate of the American Hospital Association. Contributions are made by Information Systems and Technology, Member Relations, Office of the President, Office of the Secretary, Printing Services Group, AHA Resource Center and the following participants:

| | |
|---|---|
| Jed Cusimano | Kimberly Jackson |
| Grant Denten | Peter Kralovec |
| Dianna Doyle | Mary Krzywicki |
| DeAnn Ellis | Andrea Liebig |
| Joan Finn | Denise Loggins |
| Deanna Frazier | Gail Lovinger |
| Jennifer Gillespie | Bethany Parnell |
| Tan Harris | Susan Sheffey |
| Estella Heard | Elaine Singh |
| Clisby Jackson | Christopher Gonzales |
| Danny Jackson | Armelle Otou Minkala |

Health Forum LLC acknowledges the cooperation given by many professional groups and government agencies in the health care field, particularly the following: American College of Surgeons; American Medical Association; Council of Teaching Hospitals of the Association of American Medical Colleges; The Joint Commission; DNV Healthcare Inc.; Center for Improvement in Healthcare Quality; Commission on Accreditation of Rehabilitation Facilities; American Osteopathic Association, Centers for Medicare & Medicaid Services; and various offices within the U.S. Department of Health and Human Services.

## Advisements

The data published here should be used with the following advisements: The data is based on replies to an annual survey that seeks a variety of information, not all of which is published in this book. The information gathered by the survey includes specific services, but not all of each hospital's services. Therefore, the data does not reflect an exhaustive list of all services offered by all hospitals. For information on the availability of additional data and products, please contact Health Forum LLC at 800/821–2039, or visit our web site.

Health Forum LLC does not assume responsibility for the accuracy of information voluntarily reported by the individual institutions surveyed. **The purpose of this publication is to provide basic data reflecting the delivery of health care in the United States and associated areas, and is not to serve as an official and all inclusive list of services offered by individual hospitals. The information reflected is based on data collected as of September 12, 2020.**

## An Introduction to AHA Guide

Welcome, and thank you for purchasing the 2021 edition of *AHA Guide®*. This section is designed to aid you in using the book. While the primary focus of *AHA Guide* is on hospitals, it also contains information on other areas of the health care field, divided across its two major sections:

A.  Hospitals
B.  Health care systems, networks, and alliances

The information contained within this publication was compiled using AHA membership, and the AHA Annual Survey of Hospitals. *AHA Guide* is the leading hospital directory and represents hospitals with or without AHA membership.

Additional information contained in the front of AHA Guide includes:

- A section by section table of contents
- Recognition of the source of data in the *Acknowledgements and Advisements* section
- Information on AHA's history as well as a listing of our awards in *AHA Offices, Officers, Historical Data, and Awards*

Open the front cover and *AHA Guide* begins with the *2021 AHA Guide Code Chart*. This two page section (front and back) explains how to find and understand the most important elements of each hospital's listing.

The *Code Chart* is a very useful tool to have when reading. It allows new users to become familiar with the data, and it aids returning users in understanding the new design and layout of *AHA Guide*. At the top of the chart, there is a sample listing. If you have used this publication before, you will notice the new columnar listing of all hospital entries by city. The city and county names are highlighted in gray, and all hospitals within the city follow. After the hospital name, you will find the address, telephone number, approval, facility and service codes, and health care systems to which the hospital belongs. Following this are the chief administrators and classifications for the hospital.

Utilization data for the hospital is found in the box at the bottom of each hospital's entry in *AHA Guide*.

The chart further demonstrates how to understand these important elements:

1.  **Approval codes** refer to certifications held by a hospital; they represent information supplied by various national approving and reporting bodies. For example, code A–3 indicates accreditation under one of the programs of the Accreditation Council for Graduate Medical Education, evidence that the hospital has been approved for participation in residency training.

2.  **Health Care System names** reference specific health care system headquarters to which the hospital belongs. The presence of a system name indicates that the hospital is a member. If no names are listed, the hospital does not belong to a system.

3.  **Titles of Chief Administrators** including the Chief Executive Officer and, when available, other C-Suite officers such as the Chief Financial Officer, Chief Information Officer, Chief Medical Officer, Chief Operating Officer, Chief Human Resources Officer, and Chief Nursing Officer.

4.  **Classification** refers to two items in *AHA Guide*. **Control** classification indicates the organization that operates the hospital, and **Service** classification refers to the type of service the hospital offers. Previously, this section utilized numerical codes corresponding with a literal value, but the new design of *AHA Guide* bypasses the codes and

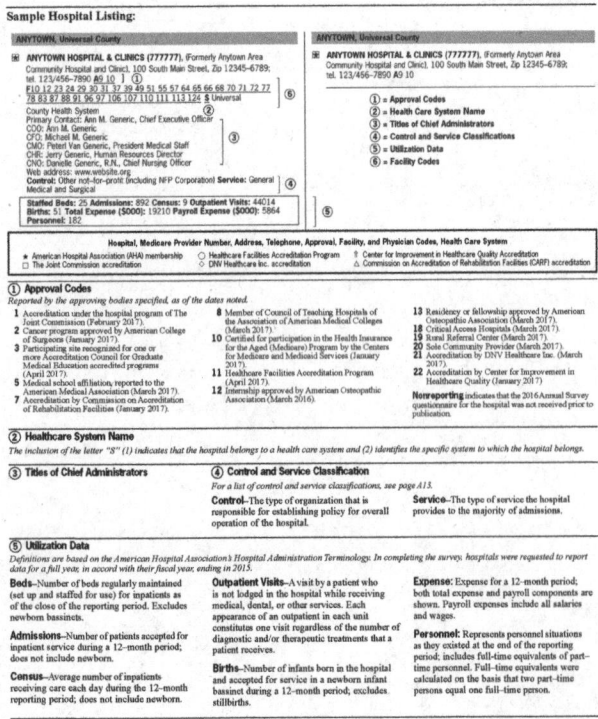

**2021 AHA Guide Code Chart**

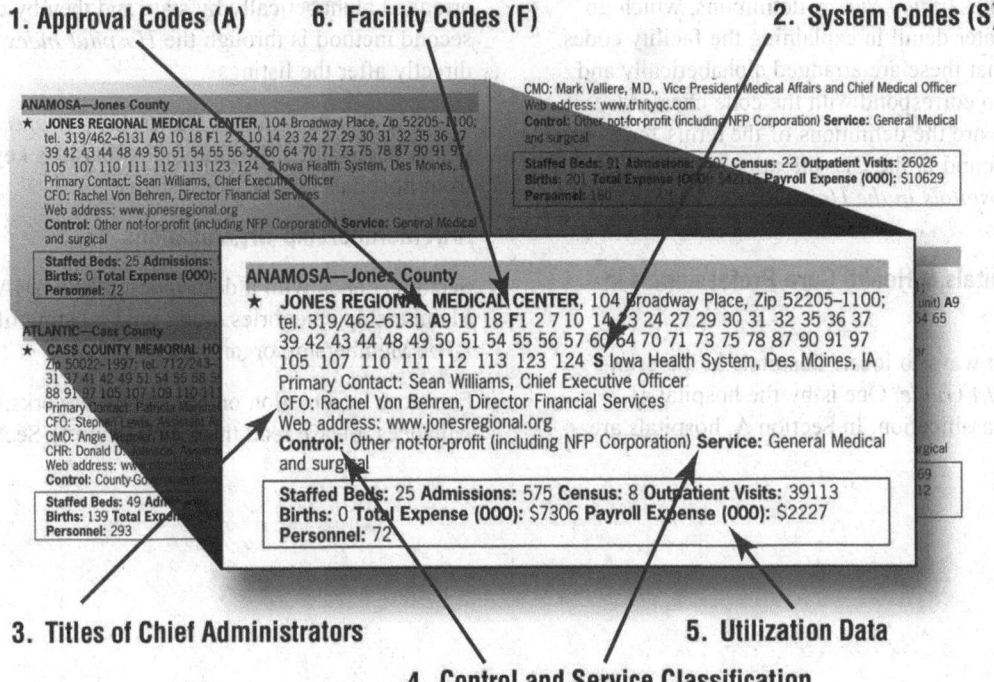

**1. Approval Codes (A)**     **6. Facility Codes (F)**     **2. System Codes (S)**

**3. Titles of Chief Administrators**     **5. Utilization Data**

**4. Control and Service Classification**

instead displays the literal classifications for control and service.

- **Control:** In this section, organizations are divided among nonfederal government hospitals, nongovernment not-for-profit hospitals, investor owned for-profit hospitals, and federal government hospitals.
- **Service:** This section displays the primary type of service that a hospital offers. The most common value is general hospital. Among the other services listed in this section are specialties such as psychiatric hospitals or children's hospitals.

5. **Utilization Data** contains the statistics related to the day-to-day and cumulative operation of the hospital. The information included in this section consists of:

- **Beds:** Number of beds regularly maintained.
- **Admissions:** Amount of patients accepted for inpatient services over a 12-month period.
- **Census:** Average number of patients receiving care each day.
- **Outpatient Visits:** Amount of visits by patients not lodged in the hospital while receiving care.

- **Births:** Number of infants born in the hospital and accepted for service in a newborn infant bassinet.
- **Expense:** Includes all expenses (including payroll) that the hospital had over the 12- month period.
- **Personnel:** Represents personnel situations as they existed at the end of the reporting period. In this area, full time equivalency is calculated on the basis that two part-time persons equal one full-time person.

6. **Facility codes** provide a description of the specific services offered by a hospital. Code F-14, for instance, indicates that the hospital contains a Blood Donor Center.

### How To Use This Book

Section A begins with the *AHA Guide Hospital Listing Requirements*. This explains the requisite accreditations or characteristics a hospital must meet to be included in *AHA Guide*.

After this there is *An Explanation of the Hospital Listings*. These two pages review the information included in the Code Chart and are a vital resource in identifying the information, symbols, and codes for each hospital's listing.

Next up are the *Annual Survey* definitions, which go into even greater detail in explaining the facility codes. Please note that these are arranged alphabetically and numerically to correspond with the code chart. Also included here are the definitions of the terms for Control and Service found in the Classification section. The listings of *Hospitals in the United States, by State* follow the definitions.

### Finding Hospitals & Health Care Professionals in Section A

There are two ways to locate hospitals in the print version of *AHA Guide*. One is by the hospital's geographic classification. In Section A, hospitals are arranged alphabetically by state and then by city. The second method is through the *Hospital Index* that appears directly after the listings.

There is also an *Index of Health Care Professionals* which begins after the first index that lists key people from hospitals and health systems.

### AHA Membership Organizations

Section A ends with a description of the AHA Membership categories along with a listing of various AHA Membership organizations.

For more information on Systems, Networks, and Alliances, please read the introduction to Section B.

# AHA Offices, Officers, and Historical Data

**Chicago:** 155 N. Wacker Drive, Chicago, IL 60606; tel. 312/422-3000

**Washington:** 800 10th Street, N.W., Two CityCenter, Suite 400, Washington, DC 20001; tel. 202/638-1100

**Chair of the Board of Trustees:**
Rod Hochman, M.D., Providence St. Joseph Health, 1801 Lind Ave SW, Renton, WA 98057
**Chair-Elect of the Board of Trustees:** Wright L. Lassiter III, Henry Ford Health System, One Ford Place, Detroit, MI 48202

**Immediate Past Chair:** Melinda L. Estes, M.D., Saint Luke's Health System, 901 East 104th Street, Kansas City, MO 64131
**President & CEO:** Richard J. Pollack , 800 10th Street, NW, Two CityCenter, Suite 400, Washington, DC 20001
**Senior Vice President and Secretary:** Gail Lovinger Goldblatt, 155 N. Wacker Drive, Chicago, IL 60606

**Senior Vice President, Association Services and Chief Financial Officer:** Christina Fisher, 155 N. Wacker Drive, Chicago, IL 60606
**Executive Vice President and Chief Operating Officer:** M. Mchelle Hood, 155 N. Wacker Drive, Chicago, IL 60606

## Past Presidents/Chairs†

| | | | | | |
|---|---|---|---|---|---|
| 1899 | ★James S. Knowles | 1940 | ★Fred G. Carter, M.D. | 1981 | ★Bernard J. Lachner |
| 1900 | ★James S. Knowles | 1941 | ★B. W. Black, M.D. | 1982 | ★Stanley R. Nelson |
| 1901 | ★Charles S. Howell | 1942 | ★Basil C. MacLean, M.D. | 1983 | ★Elbert E. Gilbertson |
| 1902 | ★J. T. Duryea | 1943 | ★James A. Hamilton | 1984 | Thomas R. Matherlee |
| 1903 | ★John Fehrenbatch | 1944 | ★Frank J. Walter | 1985 | ★Jack A. Skarupa |
| 1904 | ★Daniel D. Test | 1945 | ★Donald C. Smelzer, M.D. | 1986 | Scott S. Parker |
| 1905 | ★George H. M. Rowe, M.D. | 1946 | ★Peter D. Ward, M.D. | 1987 | Donald C. Wegmiller |
| 1906 | ★George P. Ludlam | 1947 | ★John H. Hayes | 1988 | ★Eugene W. Arnett |
| 1907 | ★Renwick R. Ross, M.D. | 1948 | ★Graham L. Davis | 1989 | ★Edward J. Connors |
| 1908 | ★Sigismund S. Goldwater, M.D. | 1949 | ★Joseph G. Norby | 1990 | David A. Reed |
| 1909 | ★John M. Peters, M.D. | 1950 | ★John N. Hatfield | 1991 | C. Thomas Smith |
| 1910 | ★H. B. Howard, M.D. | 1951 | ★Charles F. Wilinsky, M.D. | 1992 | ★D. Kirk Oglesby, Jr. |
| 1911 | ★W. L. Babcock, M.D. | 1952 | ★Anthony J. J. Rourke, M.D. | 1993 | Larry L. Mathis |
| 1912 | ★Henry M. Hurd, M.D. | 1953 | ★Edwin L. Crosby, M.D. | 1994 | Carolyn C. Roberts |
| 1913 | ★F. A. Washburn, M.D. | 1954 | ★Ritz E. Heerman | 1995 | Gail L. Warden |
| 1914 | ★Thomas Howell, M.D. | 1955 | ★Frank R. Bradley | 1996 | Gordon M. Sprenger |
| 1915 | ★William O. Mann, M.D. | 1956 | ★Ray E. Brown | 1997 | Reginald M. Ballantyne III |
| 1916 | ★Winford H. Smith, M.D. | 1957 | ★Albert W. Snoke, M.D. | 1998 | John G. King |
| 1917 | ★Robert J. Wilson, M.D. | 1958 | ★Tol Terrell | 1999 | Fred L. Brown |
| 1918 | ★A. B. Ancker, M.D. | 1959 | ★Ray Amberg | 2000 | ★Carolyn Boone Lewis |
| 1919 | ★A. R. Warner, M.D. | 1960 | ★Russell A. Nelson, M.D. | 2001 | Gary A. Mecklenburg |
| 1920 | ★Joseph B. Howland, M.D. | 1961 | ★Frank S. Groner | 2002 | Sr. Mary Roch Rocklage, RSM |
| 1921 | ★Louis B. Baldwin, M.D. | 1962 | ★Jack Masur, M.D. | 2003 | ★Dennis R. Barry |
| 1922 | ★George O'Hanlon, M.D. | 1963 | ★T. Stewart Hamilton, M.D. | 2004 | David L. Bernd |
| 1923 | ★Asa S. Bacon | 1964 | ★Stanley A. Ferguson | 2005 | George F. Lynn |
| 1924 | ★Malcolm T. MacEachern, M.D. | 1965 | ★Clarence E. Wonnacott | January–April 2006 | Richard J. Umbdenstock |
| 1925 | ★E. S. Gilmore | 1966 | ★Philip D. Bonnet, M.D. | April–December 2006 | George F. Lynn |
| 1926 | ★Arthur C. Bachmeyer, M.D. | 1967 | ★George E. Cartmill | 2007 | Kevin E. Lofton |
| 1927 | ★R. G. Brodrick, M.D. | 1968 | ★David B. Wilson, M.D. | 2008 | William D. Petasnick |
| 1928 | ★Joseph C. Doane, M.D. | 1969 | ★George William Graham, M.D. | 2009 | Thomas M. Priselac |
| 1929 | ★Louis H. Burlingham, M.D. | 1970 | ★Mark Berke | 2010 | Richard P. de Filippi |
| 1930 | ★Christopher G. Parnall, M.D. | 1971 | ★Jack A. L. Hahn | 2011 | John W. Bluford |
| 1931 | ★Lewis A. Sexton, M.D. | 1972 | ★Stephen M. Morris | 2012 | Teri G. Fontenot |
| 1932 | ★Paul H. Fesler | 1973 | ★John W. Kauffman | 2013 | Benjamin K. Chu, MD |
| 1933 | ★George F. Stephens, M.D. | 1974 | ★Horace M. Cardwell | 2014 | James H. Hinton |
| 1934 | ★Nathaniel W. Faxon, M.D. | 1975 | ★Wade Mountz | 2015 | Jonathan B. Perlin, MD, PhD |
| 1935 | ★Robert Jolly | 1976 | ★H. Robert Cathcart | 2016 | Jim Skogsbergh |
| 1936 | ★Robin C. Buerki, M.D. | 1977 | ★John M. Stagl | 2017 | Eugene A. Woods |
| 1937 | ★Claude W. Munger, M.D. | 1978 | ★Samuel J. Tibbitts | 2018 | Nancy Howell Agee |
| 1938 | ★Robert E. Neff | 1979 | W. Daniel Barker | 2019 | Brian Gragnolati |
| 1939 | ★G. Harvey Agnew, M.D. | 1980 | ★Sister Irene Kraus | | |

## Chief Executive Officers

| | | | | | |
|---|---|---|---|---|---|
| 1917–18 | ★William H. Walsh, M.D. | 1954–72 | ★Edwin L. Crosby, M.D. | 1991–2007 | ★Richard J. Davidson |
| 1919–24 | ★Andrew Robert Warner, M.D. | 1972 | ★Madison B. Brown, M.D. (acting) | 2007–2015 | Richard J. Umbdenstock |
| 1925–27 | ★William H. Walsh, M.D. | 1972–86 | ★J. Alexander McMahon | 2015 | Richard J. Pollack (current) |
| 1928–42 | ★Bert W. Caldwell, M.D. | 1986–91 | Carol M. McCarthy, Ph.D., J.D. | | |
| 1943–54 | ★George Bugbee | 1991 | ★Jack W. Owen (acting) | | |

★Deceased

## Distinguished Service Award

The award recognizes significant lifetime contributions and service to health care institutions and associations.

| | | | | | |
|---|---|---|---|---|---|
| 1934 | Matthew O. Foley | 1967 | Rev. John J. Flanagan, S.J. | 1995 | Scott S. Parker |
| 1939 | Malcolm T. MacEachern, M.D. | 1968 | Stanley W. Martin | 1996 | John A. Russell |
| 1940 | Sigismund S. Goldwater, M.D. | 1969 | T. Stewart Hamilton, M.D. | 1997 | D. Kirk Oglesby, Jr. |
| 1941 | Frederic A. Washburn, M.D. | 1970 | Charles Patteson Cardwell, Jr. | 1998 | Henry B. Betts, M.D. |
| 1942 | Winford H. Smith, M.D. | 1971 | Mark Berke | 1999 | Mitchell T. Rabkin, M.D. |
| 1943 | Arthur C. Bachmeyer, M.D. | 1972 | Stanley A. Ferguson | 2000 | Gail L. Warden |
| 1944 | Rt. Rev. Msgr. Maurice F. Griffin, LL.D. | 1973 | Jack A. L. Hahn | 2001 | Gordon M. Sprenger |
| 1945 | Asa S. Bacon | 1974 | George William Graham, M.D. | 2002 | Carolyn Boone Lewis |
| 1946 | George F. Stephens, M.D. | 1975 | George E. Cartmill | 2003 | C. Thomas Smith |
| 1947 | Robin C. Buerki, M.D. | 1976 | D. O. McClusky, Jr. | 2004 | Michael C. Waters |
| 1948 | James A. Hamilton | 1977 | Boone Powell | 2005 | John G. King |
| 1949 | Claude W. Munger, M.D. | 1978 | Richard J. Stull | 2006 | Gary A. Mecklenburg |
| 1950 | Nathaniel W. Faxon, M.D. | 1979 | Horace M. Cardwell | | Sr. Mary Roch Rocklage, RSM |
| 1951 | Bert W. Caldwell, M.D. | 1980 | Donald W. Cordes | 2007 | Richard J. Davidson |
| 1952 | Fred G. Carter, M.D. | 1981 | Sister Mary Brigh Cassidy | 2008 | Fred L. Brown |
| 1953 | Basil C. MacLean, M.D. | 1982 | R. Zach Thomas, Jr. | 2009 | George F. Lynn |
| 1954 | George Bugbee | 1983 | H. Robert Cathcart | 2010 | James J. Mongan, M.D. |
| 1955 | Joseph G. Norby | 1984 | Matthew F. McNulty, Jr., Sc.D. | 2011 | Thomas C. Royer, M.D. |
| 1956 | Charles F. Wilinsky, M.D. | 1985 | J. Alexander McMahon | 2012 | Karen Davis, Ph.D. |
| 1957 | John H. Hayes | 1986 | Sister Irene Kraus | 2013 | Thomas C. Dolan, Ph.D., FACHE |
| 1958 | John N. Hatfield | 1987 | W. Daniel Barker | 2014 | Thomas M. Priselac |
| 1959 | Edwin L. Crosby, M.D. | 1988 | Elbert E. Gilbertson | 2015 | Richard P. de Filippi |
| 1960 | Oliver G. Pratt | 1989 | Donald G. Shropshire | 2016 | William Petasnick |
| 1961 | E. M. Bluestone, M.D. | 1990 | John W. Colloton | 2017 | Richard J. Umbdenstock |
| 1962 | Mother Loretto Bernard, S.C., R.N. | 1991 | Carol M. McCarthy, Ph.D., J.D. | 2018 | C. Duane Dauner |
| 1963 | Ray E. Brown | 1992 | David H. Hitt | 2019 | Ralph W. Muller |
| 1964 | Russell A. Nelson, M.D. | 1993 | Edward J. Connors | 2020 | Teri Fontento |
| 1965 | Albert W. Snoke, M.D. | | Jack W. Owen | | |
| 1966 | Frank S. Groner | 1994 | George Adams | | |

†On June 3, 1972, the House of Delegates changed the title of the chief elected officer to chairman of the Board of Trustees, and the title of president was conferred on the chief executive officer of the Association.

# Award of Honor

Awarded to individuals, organizations, or groups to recognize an exemplary contribution to the health and well being of the people through leadership on a major health policy or social initiative.

| | | | | | |
|---|---|---|---|---|---|
| 1966 | Senator Lister Hill | 1998 | John E. Curley, Jr. | 2010 | Jack Bovender |
| 1967 | Emory W. Morris, D.D.S. | | National Civic League | 2011 | Cary Medical Center, Caribou, ME |
| 1971 | Special Committee on Provision of Health Services | 1999 | Joseph Cardinal Bernardin, Literacy Volunteers of | 2012 | Ronald McDonald House Charities |
| | (staff also) | | America | | The Schwartz Center for Compassionate Healthcare |
| 1982 | Walter J. McNerney | 2000 | Institute for Safe Medication Practices | 2013 | George C. Halvorson |
| 1989 | Ruth M. Rothstein | 2001 | Dennis R. Barry | | Reach Out and Read |
| 1990 | Joyce C. Clifford, R.N. | 2002 | Donald M. Berwick, M.D. | 2014 | Rhonda Anderson, RN |
| 1991 | Haynes Rice | 2003 | Steven A. Schroeder, M.D. | | Ohio Hospital Association |
| 1992 | Donald W. Dunn | | Dan S. Wilford | 2015 | Spencer C. Johnson |
| | Ira M. Lane, Jr. | 2004 | Ron J. Anderson, M.D. | | Robert Wood Johnson Foundation |
| 1993 | Elliott C. Roberts, Sr. | | Johnson & Johnson | 2016 | Henry J. Kaiser Family Foundation |
| | William A. Spencer, M.D. | 2005 | Sr. Mary Jean Ryan | 2017 | Joel T. Allison |
| 1994 | Robert A. Derzon | 2006 | Jordan J. Cohen, M.D. | | Doug Leonard |
| 1995 | Russell G. Mawby, Ph.D. John K. Springer | | James W. Varnum | 2018 | Ronald R. Peterson |
| 1996 | Stephen J. Hegarty | 2007 | Edward A. Eckenhoff | | Sister Carol Keehan |
| | Mothers Against Drunk Driving (MADD) | | Stanley F. Hupfeld | 2019 | Darrell G. Kirch, M.D. |
| 1997 | Paul B. Batalden, M.D. | 2008 | Regina M. Benjamin, MD, MBA Alfred G. Stubblefield | | John Bluford |
| | Habitat for Humanity International | 2009 | The Center to Advance Palliative Care Paul B. Hofmann, Dr.PH | 2020 | March of Dimes |

# Justin Ford Kimball Innovators Award

Recognition to individuals or organizations that have made outstanding, innovative contributions to health care financing and/or delivery that improves access or coordination of care.

| | | | | | |
|---|---|---|---|---|---|
| 1958 | E. A. van Steenwyk | 1975 | Earl H. Kammer | 1997 | Harvey Pettry |
| 1959 | George A. Newbury | 1976 | J. Ed McConnell | | D. David Sniff |
| 1960 | C. Rufus Rorem, Ph.D. | 1978 | Edwin R. Werner | 1998 | Montana Health Research and Education Foundation |
| 1961 | James E. Stuart | 1979 | Robert M. Cunningham, Jr. | 1999 | Kenneth W. Kizer, M.D. |
| 1962 | Frank Van Dyk | 1981 | Maurice J. Norby | 2002 | David M. Lawrence, M.D. |
| 1963 | William S. McNary | 1982 | Robert E. Rinehimer | 2003 | Lowell C. Kruse |
| 1964 | Frank S. Groner | 1983 | John B. Morgan, Jr. | 2006 | Spencer Foreman, M.D. |
| 1965 | J. Douglas Colman | 1984 | Joseph F. Duplinsky | 2009 | On Lok |
| 1967 | Walter J. McNerney | 1985 | David W. Stewart | 2012 | Thomas S. Nesbitt, M.D. |
| 1968 | John W. Paynter | 1988 | Ernest W. Saward, M.D. | 2015 | Glenn D. Steele, Jr., MD |
| 1970 | Edwin L. Crosby, M.D. | 1990 | James A. Vohs | 2016 | Dan Wolterman |
| 1971 | H. Charles Abbott | 1993 | John C. Lewin, M.D. | 2017 | James W. Weinstein, DO |
| 1972 | John R. Mannix | 1994 | Donald A. Brennan | 2018 | Nicholas Wolter, M.D. |
| 1973 | Herman M. Somers | 1995 | E. George Middleton, Jr. | 2020 | Bernard Tyson (posthumous) |
| 1974 | William H. Ford, Ph.D. | | Glenn R. Mitchell | | |

# Board of Trustees Award

Individuals or groups who have made substantial and noteworthy contributions to the work of the American Hospital Association.

| | | | | | |
|---|---|---|---|---|---|
| 1959 | Joseph V. Friel | | Robert W. O'Leary | 2003 | J. Richard Gaintner, M.D. |
| | John H. Hayes | | Jack W. Owen | | Donald A. Wilson |
| 1960 | Duncan D. Sutphen, Jr. | 1984 | Howard J. Berman | 2004 | Richard L. Clarke |
| 1963 | Eleanor C. Lambertsen, R.N., Ed.D. | | O. Ray Hurst | | Thelma Traut |
| 1964 | John R. Mannix | | James R. Neely | 2005 | Merrill Gappmayer |
| 1965 | Albert G. Hahn | 1985 | James E. Ferguson | | Leo Greenawalt |
| | Maurice J. Norby | | Cleveland Rodgers | 2006 | Robert L. Harman |
| 1966 | Madison B. Brown, M.D. | 1986 | Rex N. Olsen | | Kenneth G. Stella |
| | Kenneth Williamson | 1987 | Michael Lesparre | 2007 | Deborah Freund, Ph.D. |
| 1967 | Alanson W. Wilcox | 1988 | Barbara A. Donaho, R.N. | | Michael D. Stephens |
| 1968 | E. Dwight Barnett, M.D. | 1989 | Walter H. MacDonald | 2008 | James R. Castle |
| 1969 | Vane M. Hoge, M.D. | | Donald R. Newkirk | 2009 | Richard M. Knapp, Ph.D. |
| | Joseph H. McNinch, M.D. | 1990 | William T. Robinson | 2010 | Fred Hessler |
| 1972 | David F. Drake, Ph.D. | 1992 | Jack C. Bills | | John G. O'Brien |
| | Paul W. Earle | | Anne Hall Davis | 2011 | Carolyn F. Scanlan |
| | Michael Lesparre | 1993 | Theodore C. Eickhoff, M.D. | | Charlotte S. Yeh, MD |
| | Andrew Pattullo | | Stephen W. Gamble | 2012 | Larry S. Gage |
| 1973 | Tilden Cummings | | Yoshi Honkawa | | Larry McAndrews |
| | Edmond J. Lanigan | 1994 | Roger M. Busfield, Jr., Ph.D. | 2013 | Jeffrey D. Selberg |
| 1974 | James E. Hague | 1995 | Stephen E. Dorn | 2014 | Russell D. Harrington, Jr. |
| | Sister Marybelle | | William L. Yates | | Daniel Sisto |
| 1975 | Helen T. Yast | 1996 | Leigh E. Morris | 2015 | Todd C. Linden |
| 1976 | Boynton P. Livingston | | John Quigley | | R. Timothy Rice |
| | James Ludlam | 1998 | John D. Leech | 2016 | Sandra Bennett Bruce |
| | Helen McGuire | 1999 | Sister Carol Keehan | | Michael G. Rock, M.D. |
| 1979 | Newton J. Jacobson | | C. Edward McCauley | 2017 | Kris A. Doody, RN |
| | Edward W. Weimer | | Stephen Rogness | | Daniel L. Gross, RN |
| 1980 | Robert B. Hunter, M.D. | 2000 | Dennis May | 2018 | Ian Morrison |
| | Samuel J. Tibbitts | 2001 | Spencer C. Johnson | 2019 | Jeanette Clough Bruce Bailey |
| 1981 | Vernon A. Knutson | 2002 | Michael M. Mitchel | 2020 | Nicholas Tejeda |
| | John E. Sullivan | | Victor L. Campbell | | Ninfa Saunders |
| 1982 | John Bigelow | | Joseph A. Parker | | |

# Citation for Meritorious Service

| | | | | | |
|---|---|---|---|---|---|
| 1968 | F. R. Knautz | | Gordon McLachlan | 1983 | David M. Kinzer |
| | Sister Conrad Mary, R.N. | 1977 | Theodore Cooper, M.D. | 1984 | Donald L. Custis, M.D. |
| 1971 | Hospital Council of Southern California | 1979 | Norman D. Burkett | 1985 | John A. D. Cooper, M.D. |
| 1972 | College of Misericordia, Dallas, PA | | John L. Quigley | | Imperial Council of the Ancient Arabic Order of the |
| 1973 | Madison B. Brown, M.D. | | William M. Whelan | | Nobles of the Mystic Shrine for North America |
| | Samuel J. Tibbitts | 1980 | Sister Grace Marie Hiltz | 1986 | Howard F. Cook |
| 1975 | Kenneth B. Babcock, M.D. | | Leo J. Gehrig, M.D. | 1987 | David H. Hitt |
| | Sister Mary Maurita Sengelaube | 1981 | Richard Davi | | Lucile Packard |
| 1976 | Chaiker Abbis | | Pearl S. Fryar | | |
| | Susan Jenkins | 1982 | Jorge Brull Nater | | |

This citation is no longer awarded

# Dick Davidson NOVA Award

This award honors effective, collaborative programs focused on improving community health status.

## 1994

**Health Partners of Philadelphi (PA):** Albert Einstein Medical Center, Episcopal Hospital, Frankford Hospital, Medical College of Pennsylvania Hospital, St. Christopher's Hospital for Children, Temple University Hospital

**Decker Family Development Center:** Children's Hospital Medical Center of Akron (OH)
**Denver (CO) School–Based Clinics:** The Children's Hospital

**Basic Health Plan:** Dominican Network; Mount Carmel Hospital, Colville, WA; St. Joseph's Hospital, Chewelah, WA; and Holy Family Hospital, Spokane, WA
**HealthLink:** Lakes Region General Hospital, Laconia, NH

## 1995

**Bladen Community Care Network:** Bladen County Hospital, Elizabethtown, NC
**Building a Healthier Community:** Community– Kimball Health Care System, Toms River, NJ ʻ

**Injury Prevention Program:** Harlem Hospital Center, New York City, NY
**The Community Ministries & Outreach Program:** Reaching Out to Our Vickery/Meadow Neighborhood: Presbyterian Healthcare System, Dallas, TX

**"CHOICES":** Shriners Hospitals for Crippled Children, Tampa, FL

## 1996

**Lincoln and Sunnyslope:** John C. Lincoln Hospital and Health Center, Sunnyslope, AZ
**Growing into Life Task Force:** Aiken (SC) Regional Medical Centers

**People Caring for People:** Beatrice (NE) Community Hospital and Health Center
**Injury Prevention Center of the Greater Dayton (OH) Area:** The Children's Medical Center, Good Samaritan Hospital and Health Center, Grandview Hospital, Kettering Memorial

Hospital, Miami Valley Hospital, and St. Elizabeth Medical Center
**Family Road:** Hutzel Hospital, Detroit, MI

## 1997

**Health Promotion Schools of Excellence Program:** Alliant Health System and Kosair Children's Hospital, Louisville, KY
**Health, Outreach, Prevention, and Education (HOPE):** Health First Holmes Regional Medical Center, Melbourne, FL

**Healthy Community Initiative:** Roper Care Alliance, Charleston, SC
**Obstetrical Care and Prenatal Counseling Program:** St. Alexius Medical Center, Bismarck, ND

**HIV/AIDS Neighborhood Service Program:** Yale–New Haven Hospital, New Haven, CT

## 1998

**Partners for a Healthier Community:** Evergreen Community Health Care, Group Health Cooperative of Puget Sound, Overlake Hospital Medical Center, Providence Health System/Medalia HealthCare, Seattle, WA
**Glenwood–Lyndale Community Clinic:** Hennepin County Medical Center, Minneapolis, MN

**Greater Dallas (TX) Injury Prevention Center:** Parkland Health & Hospital System, Children's Medical Center of Dallas, Baylor Health Care System, Methodist Hospitals of Dallas, and Presbyterian Healthcare System
**Network of Trust:** Phoebe Putney Memorial Hospital, Albany, GA

**The Lauderdale Court:** A Community Partnership:St. Joseph Hospital and Health Centers, Memphis, TN

## 1999

**Making a Case for Community Health:** Middletown (OH) Regional Hospital
**The Family Resource Center:** Mount Carmel Medical Center, Pittsburgh, KS

**The Health Neighborhood Project:** St. Patrick Hospital, Missoula, MT
**Kids for Health:** Washington Regional Medical Center, Fayetteville, AR

**Children's Village:** Yakima Memorial Hospital, Yakima, WA

## 2000

**Community Healthcare Network:** Columbus (GA) Regional Healthcare System
**Pasadena County Asthma Project:** Huntington Memorial Hospital, Pasadena, CA

**Ashe County Health Council "Health Carolinias Task Force":** Ashe Memorial Hospital, Jefferson, NC
**Caritas–Connection Project:** St. Mary's Hospital, Passaic, NJ

**Correctional Health Care Program:** Baystate Health System, Springfield, MA

## 2001

**J.C. Lewis Health Center:** Memorial Health and St. Joseph's Candler Health System, Savannah, GA
**Project C.A.R.E.:** Mercy Medical Center, Canton, OH

**TeenHealthFX.com:** Atlantic Health System, Florham Park, NJ
**Vista ElderCARE:** Vista Health, Waukegan, IL

**Western Village Enterprise School:** INTEGRIS Health, Oklahoma City, OK

## 2002

**Chester Community Connections:** Crozer– Keystone Health System, Springfield, PA
**The Hope Street Family Center:** California Hospital Medical Center, Los Angeles, CA

**Mobile Health Outreach Ministry:** St. Vincent's Health System, Jacksonville, FL
**Operation Access:** Kaiser Foundation Hospitals, Oakland; Sutter Health, Sacramento; San Francisco General Hospital,

San Francisco; St. Rose Hospital, Hayward; and Santa Rosa Memorial Hospital, Santa Rosa, CA
**Wilmington Health Access for Teens:** New Hanover Health Network, Wilmington, NC

## 2003

**C.O.A.C.H. for Kids:** Cedars–Sinai Medical Center, Los Angeles, CA
**Community Action Network:** Trinity Regional Medical Center, Fort Dodge, IA

**Hearts N' Health:** Glendale Adventist Medical Center, Glendale, CA
**Saint Joseph Health Center:** Saint Joseph Regional Medical Center, South Bend, IN

**St. Mary Medical Center Bensalem Ministries:** St. Mary Medical Center, Langhorne, PA

## 2004

**Better Beginnings:** Brockton Hospital, Brockton, MA
**Buffalo County Community Health Partners:** Good Samaritan Health Systems, Kearney, NE

**Quad City Health Initiative:** Genesis Health System, Davenport, IA and Trinity Regional Health System, Rock Island, IL
**Quality of Life in the Truckee Meadows:** Washoe Health System, Reno, NV

**Solano Coalition for Better Health, Inc.:** NorthBay Healthcare Group, Fairfield, CA; Sutter Solano Medical Center, Vallejo, CA; and Kaiser Permanente, Martinez, CA

## 2005

**Children's Health Connection:** McKay-Dee Hospital Center, Ogden, UT
**Palmetto Health's Vision Health Initiative:** Palmetto Health, Columbia, SC

**Project Dulce, Whittier Institute for Diabetes:** Scripps Health, San Diego, CA
**Toledo/Lucas County CareNet:** Mercy Health Partners, ProMedica Health System, and Medical University of Ohio, all of Toledo, OH and St. Luke's Hospital, Maumee, O

**Volunteer Health Advisor (VHA) Program:** Cambridge Health Alliance, Cambridge, MA

## 2006

**Healthy Learners, Columbia, SC:** Allendale County Hospital, Fairfax, SC; McLeod Medical Center–Dillon, Dillon, SC; Sisters of Charity Providence Hospitals, Columbia, SC; and Self Regional Healthcare, Greenwood, SC

**Primary Care Access Network (PCAN):** Health Central, Ocoee, FL; Florida Hospital, Winter Park, FL; and Orlando Regional Healthcare, Orlando, FL **ProHealth Care Community Health Outreach Initiative:** ProHealth Care, Waukesha, WI

**St. Joseph Mobile Health Services:** Saint Joseph HealthCare Inc., Lexington, KY
**Yonkers Childhood Health Initiative:** St. John's Riverside, Yonkers, NY

## 2007

**Medical-Legal Partnership for Children:** Boston Medical Center, Boston, MA
**NOW (Nutritional Options for Wellness) Program:** Spectrum Health, Grand Rapids, MI
**Richland Care:** Palmetto Health, Columbia, SC

**Trauma Nurses Talk Tough:** Legacy Health System, Portland, OR
**UMass Memorial Medical Center Healthy Youth Development Initiative:** UMass Memorial Health Care, Worcester, MA

**Youth Health Partnership-Patee Market Youth Dental Clinic:** Heartland Health, St. Joseph, MO

**2008**
**Partnership for Community Health:** California Pacific
Medical Center, San Francisco, CA
**Every Child Succeeds:** Cincinnati Children's Hospital Medical
Center, Cincinnati, OH

**Memorial Hermann Health Centers for Schools:**
Memorial Hermann, Houston, TX
**Nutrition Center of Maine:** Saint Mary's Health System,
Lewiston, ME

**ENERGIZE! Pediatric Diabetes Intervention Program:**
WakeMed Health & Hospitals, Raleigh, NC

---

**2009**
**Lighten Up 4 Life:** Mission Health System, Asheville, NC
**Project BRIEF:** Jacobi Medical Center and North Central
Bronx Hospital, Bronx, NY

**Really Awesome Health (RAH) and Wholesome Routines:**
Duke Raleigh Hospital, Raleigh, NC

**Student Success Jobs Program:** Brigham and Women's
Hospital, Boston, MA
**Taos First Steps Program:** Holy Cross Hospital, Taos, NM

---

**2010**
**Community-Based Alternatives to the Emergency
Room:** Lee Memorial Health System, Fort Meyers, FL
**Health-e-Access Telemedicine:** University of Rochester
Medical Center, Rochester, NY

**Healthy Futures:** Munson Healthcare System, Traverse
City, MI
**Healthy San Francisco:** San Francisco General Hospital,
University of California Medical Center, Chinese Hospital,
California Pacific Medical Center, Saint Francis Memorial

Hospital, St. Mary's Medical Center, and Kaiser Permanente,
San Francisco, CA
**Pediatric Asthma Program:** Sinai Health System, Chicago,
IL

---

**2011**
**Emergency Department Consistent Care Program:**
Providence St. Peter Hospital, Olympia, WA
**Integrated Community Nursing Program at Parkview
Health:** Parkview Health, Fort Wayne, IN

**Milwaukee Health Care Partnership:** Aurora Health Care,
Children's Hospital & Health System, Inc., Columbia St. Mary's,
and Froedtert Health, all of Milwaukee, WI, and Wheaton
Franciscan Healthcare, Glendale, WI

**The Diabetes Collaborative:** Northwestern Memorial
Hospital, Chicago, IL
**Rochester Youth Violence Partnership:** University of
Rochester Medical Center and Rochester General Health
System, Rochester, NY

---

**2012**
**The Beth Embraces Wellness: An Integrated Approach
to Prevention in the Community:** Newark Beth Israel
Medical Center and Children's Hospital of New Jersey, Newark,
NJ

**CARE Network:** St. Joseph Health Queen of the Valley
Medical Center, Napa, CA
**Fitness in the City:** Boston Children's Hospital, Boston, MA
**Puff City:** Henry Ford Health System, Detroit, MI

**Rural Health Initiative:** Shawano Medical Center of
ThedaCare, Shawano, WI

---

**2013**
**Bangor Beacon Community:** EMHS, Brewer, ME
and St. Joseph Healthcare, Bangor, ME
**Chippewa Health Improvement Partnership
(CHIP):** St. Joseph's Hospital, Chippewa Falls, WI

**Core Health Program of Healthier Communities:**
Spectrum Health, Grand Rapids, MI
**Free Preventive Screenings Program:** Good Samaritan
Hospital, Vincennes, IN

**Hope Clinic and Pharmacy:** Ephraim McDowell Health,
Danville, KY

---

**2014**
**FirstReach:** FirstHealth of the Carolinas, Pinehurst, NC
**Children's Hospital Center for Pediatric Medicine Asthma
Action Team:** Greenville Health System, Greenville, SC

**Let's Go!** The Barbara Bush Children's Hospital at Maine
Medical Center, Portland, ME
**Hearts Beat Back:** The Heart of New Ulm (HONU) Project:
New Ulm Medical Center, part of Allina Health, New Ulm, MN

**Finney County Community Health Coalition:** St. Catherine
Hospital, Garden City, KS

---

**2015**
**Activate Whittier:** PIH Health, Whittier, Calif. And Kaiser
Permanente Downey Medical Center, Downey, CA
**Bithlo Transformation Effort:** Florida Hospital, Orlando, FL

**Blood Pressure Advocate Program:** University of
Rochester Medical Center, Rochester, NY
**Community Health: Healthy Eating:** Presbyterian Healthcare
Services, Albuquerque, NM

**Mayor's Healthy City Initiative (Healthy BR):** Baton Rouge
General Medical Center, Ochsner Medical Center-Baton Rouge,
Our Lady of the Lake Regional Medical Center and Woman's
Hospital, Baton Rouge, LA

---

**2016**
**Baylor Scott & White Health's Diabetes Health and
Wellness Institute at the Juanita J. Craft Recreation
Center:** Baylor Scott & White Health, Dallas, TX

**Building a Healthy Community Initiative, East Ocean
View:** Bon Secours Hampton Roads Health System, Norfolk, VA
**Memorial Hermann Mobile Dental Program:** Memorial
Hermann Health System, Houston, TX

**Spectrum Health Healthier Communities – Strong
Beginnings:** Spectrum Health, Grand Rapids, MI
**Get Healthy, Live Well:** Tanner Health System, Carrollton, GA

---

**2017**
**Morrison County Community-Based Care Coordination:**
CHI St. Gabriel's Health, Little Falls, MN
**The Health and Wellness Alliance Asthma Collaboration:**
Children's Health, Dallas, TX

**Healthy Youth Transitions:** Memorial Healthcare System,
Hollywood, FL
**Pediatric Care-A-Van:** Norwegian American Hospital,
Chicago, IL

**Palmetto Health Dental Health Initiative:** Palmetto Health,
Columbia, SC

---

**2018**
**Unity Center for Behavioral Health:** Adventist
Health, Kaiser Permanente, Legacy Health, Oregon
Health & Science University, Portland, OR
**Annapolis Community Health Partnership:** Anne
Arundel Medical Center, Annapolis, MD

**Enos Park Access to Care Collaborative:** HSHS
St. John's Hospital and Memorial Medical Center,
Springfield, IL
**Kids Teaching Kids:** Medical City Healthcare,
Dallas, TX

**Healthy Kids Express:** St. Louis Children's
Hospital, St. Louis, MO

---

**2019**
**Stark County Toward Health Resiliency for
Infant Vitality and Equality (THRIVE):** Aultman
Hospital and Canton City Public Health, Canton, OH

**Project Ujima:** Children's Hospital of Wisconsin,
Milwaukee, WI
**Women-Inspired Neighborhood Network:** Henry
Ford Health System, Detroit, MI

**House of Mercy Homeless Center:** Mercyhealth,
Janesville, WI
**Transforming Communities Initiative:** Trinity
Health, Livonia, MI

---

**2020**
**Eagle Valley Behavioral Health:** Vail Health, Vail, Colo.
**Hackensack Meridian School of Medicine at
Seton Hall University:** Edison, N.J.

**Supportive Housing for the Homeless:** Baltimore
City Hospitals, Baltimore, Md.
**Healthy Roanoke Valley:** Carilion Clinic, Roanoke, Va.

**Mothers in Recovery,** Memorial Healthcare
System, Hollywood, Fla.

---

# The Carolyn Boone Lewis Living the Vision Award

Organizations and individuals living AHA's vision of a society of healthy communities where all individuals reach their highest potential for health.

| | | | | | |
|---|---|---|---|---|---|
| 1998 | Memorial Healthcare System, Hollywood, FL Baptist Health System, Montgomery, AL | 2003 | Franklin Memorial Hospital, Farmington, ME | | Cheshire Medical Center/Dartmouth–Hitchcock Keene, Keene, NH |
| 1999 | Robert A. DeVries, Battle Creek, MI Memorial Health System, South Bend, IN | 2004 | Jamaica Hospital Medical Center, Jamaica, NY | 2014 | TPR Collaborative, MD |
| | | 2005 | Fairbanks Memorial Hospital, Fairbanks, AK Boston Medical Center, Boston, MA | 2016 | Saint Elizabeth's Medical Center, Wabasha, MN |
| 2000 | Rockingham Memorial Hospital, Harrisonburg, VA | 2010 | Lehigh Valley Health Network, Allentown, PA | | |
| 2001 | Salina Regional Health Center, Salina, KS | 2011 | Alaska Native Tribal Health Consortium, Anchorage, AK | | |
| 2002 | Health Improvement Collaborative of Greater Cincinnati, Cincinnati, OH | 2013 | St. Joseph's Hospital Health Center, Syracuse, NY | | |

This citation is no longer awarded

© 2021 AHA Guide

# Circle of Life Award

This award celebrates innovation in palliative and end-of-life care.

## 2000

Improving Care through the End of Life, Franciscan Health System, Gig Harbor, WA

The Hospice of The Florida Suncoast, Largo, FL

Louisiana State Penitentiary Hospice Program, Angola, LA

## 2001

Department of Pain Medicine and Palliative Care, Beth Israel Medical Center, New York, NY

Palliative CareCenter & Hospice of the North Shore, Evanston, IL

St. Joseph's Manor, Trumbull, CT

## 2002

Children's Program of San Diego Hospice and Children's Hospital and Health Center of San Diego, San Diego, CA Hospice of the Bluegrass, Lexington, KY

Project Safe Conduct, Hospice of the Western Reserve and Ireland Cancer Center, Cleveland, OH

**Special Circle of Life Award** Population–based Palliative Care Research Network (PoPCRN), Denver, CO

## 2003

Hospice & Palliative CareCenter, Winston–Salem, NC

Providence Health System, Portland, OR

University of California Davis Health System, Sacramento, CA

## 2004

Hope Hospice and Palliative Care, Fort Myers, FL St. Mary's Healthcare System for Children, Bayside, NY

University of Texas M.D. Anderson Cancer Center Palliative Care, Houston, TX

## 2005

High Point Regional Health System, High Point, NC

Palliative and End-of-life Care Program, Hoag Memorial Hospital Presbyterian, Newport Beach, CA

Thomas Palliative Care Unit, VCU Massey Cancer Center, Richmond, VA

## 2006

Continuum Hospice Care, New York, NY

Mercy Supportive Care, St. Joseph Mercy Oakland, Pontiac, MI

Transitions and Life Choices, Fairview Health Services, Minneapolis, MN

## 2007

UCSF Palliative Care Program, San Francisco, CA Covenant Hospice, Pensacola, FL

Woodwell: A Program of Presbyterian SeniorCare and Family Hospice and Palliative Care, Oakmont, PA

## 2008

Children's Hospitals and Clinics of Minnesota, Pain and Palliative Care Program, Minneapolis, MN

Haven Hospice, Gainesville, FL

The Pediatric Advanced Care Team, The Children's Hospital of Philadelphia, Philadelphia, PA

## 2009

Four Seasons, Flat Rock, NC

Oregon Health and Science University Palliative Medicine & Comfort Care Program, Portland, OR

Wishard Health Services Palliative Care Program, Indianapolis, IN

## 2010

Department of Veteran Affairs, VA New York/New Jersey Healthcare Network, Brooklyn, NY

Kansas City Hospice & Palliative Care, Kansas City, MO Snohomish Palliative Partnership, Everett, WA

## 2011

The Center for Hospice & Palliative Care, Cheektowaga, NY

Gilchrist Hospice Care, Hunt Valley, MD

St. John Providence Health System, Detroit, MI

## 2012

Haslinger Family Pediatric Palliative Care Center, Akron Children's Hospital, Akron, OH

Calvary Hospital, Bronx, NY Sharp HealthCare, San Diego, CA

## 2013

The Denver Hospice and Optio Health Services, Denver, CO

Hertzberg Palliative Care Institute at the Mount Sinai Medical Center, New York, NY

UnityPoint Health, Iowa and Illinois

## 2014

OACIS/Palliative Medicine, Lehigh Valley Health Network, Allentown, PA

Supportive & Palliative Care, Baylor Health Care System, Dallas, TX

Yakima Valley Memorial Hospital, Yakima, WA

## 2015

Care Dimensions, Danvers, MA

## 2016

Bon Secours Palliative Medicine, Richmond, VA

Cambia Palliative Care Center of Excellence at UW Medicine, Seattle, WA

Susquehanna Health Hospice and Palliative Care, Williamsport, PA

## 2017

Bluegrass Care Navigators, formerly Hospice of the Bluegrass, Lexington, KY

Providence TrinityCare Hospice, Providence Little Company of Mary Medical Center Torrance and Providence Institute for Human Caring, Torrance, CA

## 2018

Hospice of the Valley, Phoenix, AZ

Western Connecticut Health Network, Danbury, CT

Penn Wissahickon Hospice and Caring Way, Philadelphia, PA

## 2019

Western Reserve Navigator, Hospice of the Western Reserve, Cleveland, OH

Palliative Care Services, UCHealth University of Colorado Hospital, Aurora, CO

University Health System Palliative Care Team, San Antonio, TX

## 2020

Caring Circle, Spectrum Health Lakeland, St. Joseph, MI

Choices and Champions, Novant Health, Winston-Salem, NC

# The American Hospital Association Quest for Quality Prize*

Honoring Leadership and Innovation in Patient Care Quality, Safety, and Commitment

## 2002
Missouri Baptist Medical Center, St. Louis, MO

**Finalist:** Fairview Hospital, Greater, Barrington, MA

**Finalist:** Minnesota Children's Hospital and Clinics, Minneapolis, MN

## 2003
Abington Memorial Hospital, Abington, PA

**Finalist:** Beaumont Hospitals, Royal Oak, MI

**Finalist:** University of Wisconsin Hospital and Clinics, Madison, WI

## 2004
Sentara Norfolk General Hospital, Norfolk, VA

**Finalist:** The Johns Hopkins Hospital, Baltimore, MD

**Finalist:** Mary Lanning Memorial Hospital, Hastings, NE

## 2005
North Mississippi Medical Center, Tupelo, MS

**Finalist:** El Camino Hospital, Mountain View, CA

**Finalist:** NewYork-Presbyterian Hospital, New York, NY

## 2006
Cincinnati Children's Hospital Medical Center, Cincinnati, OH

## 2007
Columbus Regional Hospital, Columbus, IN

**Finalist:** Cedars-Sinai Medical Center, Los Angeles, CA

**Finalist:** INTEGRIS Baptist Medical Center, Oklahoma City, OK

## 2008
Munson Medical Center, Traverse City, MI

**Finalist:** University of Michigan Hospitals & Health Centers, Ann Arbor, MI

## 2009
Bronson Methodist Hospital, Kalamazoo, MI

**Finalist:** Beth Israel Deaconess Medical Center, Boston, MA

## 2010
McLeod Regional Medical Center, Florence, SC

**Finalist:** Henry Ford Hospital, Detroit, MI

## 2011
Memorial Regional Hospital, Hollywood, FL

**Finalist:** AtlantiCare Regional Medical Center, Atlantic City, NJ

**Finalist:** Northwestern Memorial Hospital, Chicago, IL

## 2012
University Hospitals Case Medical Center, Cleveland, OH

**Finalist:** Lincoln Medical and Mental Health Center, Bronx, NY

**Finalist:** University of North Carolina Hospitals, Chapel Hill, NC and Life Choices, Fairview Health Services, Minneapolis, MN

## 2013
Beth Israel Deaconess Medical Center, Boston, MA

**Finalist:** Franklin Woods Community Hospital, Johnson City, TN

## 2014
VCU Medical Center, Richmond, VA

**Finalist:** Carolinas Medical Center-Northeast, Concord, NC

## 2015
Children's Hospital Colorado in Aurora, CO

**Finalist:** Duke University Hospital, Durham, NC

## 2016
Memorial Medical Center, Springfield, IL

**Finalist:** Memorial Hermann Greater Heights, Houston, TX

## 2018
Northwell Health, New Hyde Park, NY

**Finalist:** Anne Arundel Medical Center, Annapolis, MD

**Finalist:** Aurora Health Care, Milwaukee, WI

## 2019
Carolinas Rehabilitation, Charlotte, NC

**Finalist:** Finalist: Mission Health, Asheville, NC

(*This award was sponsored from 2001-2016 by McKesson. RLDatix is the current sponsor.)

# Foster G. McGaw Prize

Honors health delivery organizations that have demonstrated exceptional commitment to community service.

| Year | Organization | Year | Organization | Year | Organization |
|---|---|---|---|---|---|
| 1986 | Lutheran Medical Center, Brooklyn, NY | 1997 | Bladen County Hospital Rural Health Network, Elizabethtown, NC | 2010 | Allegiance Health, Jackson, MI |
| 1987 | Copley Hospital, Morrisville, VT Mount Sinai Hospital, Hartford, CT | | | 2011 | Mt. Ascutney Hospital and Health Center, Windsor, VT |
| 1988 | MetroHealth System, Cleveland, OH | 1998 | Allina Health System, Minneapolis, MN | 2012 | St. Joseph's/Candler Health System, Savannah, GA |
| 1989 | Greater Southeast Healthcare System, Washington, DC | 1999 | LAC+USC Healthcare Network, Los Angeles, CA | 2013 | Crozer–Keystone Health System, Delaware County, PA |
| 1990 | Mount Zion Medical Center of The University of California-San Francisco, San Francisco, CA | 2000 | Kaweah Delta Health Care District, Visalia, CA | 2014 | Palmetto Health, Columbia, SC |
| | | 2001 | Memorial Hospital of South Bend, South Bend, IN | 2015 | Massachusetts General Hospital, Boston |
| 1991 | Franklin Regional Hospital, Franklin, NH | 2002 | John C. Lincoln Health Network, Phoenix, AZ | 2016 | Spectrum Health, Grand Rapids, MI |
| 1992 | Mount Sinai Hospital Medical Center of Chicago, Chicago, IL | 2003 | Phoebe Putney Memorial Hospital, Albany, GA | 2017 | Yale New Haven Hospital, New Haven, CT |
| | | 2004 | Henry Ford Health System, Detroit, MI | 2018 | Penn Medicine Lancaster General Health, Lancaster County, PA |
| 1993 | The Cambridge Hospital, Cambridge, MA | 2005 | Venice Family Clinic, Venice, CA | | |
| 1994 | Parkland Memorial Hospital, Dallas, TX | 2006 | Memorial Healthcare System, Hollywood, FL | 2019 | ProMedica, Toledo, OH |
| 1995 | Our Lady of Lourdes Medical Center, Camden, NJ | 2007 | Harborview Medical Center, Seattle, WA | | |
| 1996 | St. Mary's Hospital, Rochester, NY | 2008 | St. Mary's Health System, Lewiston, ME | | |
| | | 2009 | Heartland Health, St. Joseph, MO | | |

# Dick Davidson Quality Milestone Award for Allied Association Leadership

The award recognizes state, regional or metropolitan hospital association leadership in improving health care quality.

| | | | | | |
|---|---|---|---|---|---|
| **2011** | Michigan Health & Hospital Association | **2013** | Florida Hospital Association | **2015** | Minnesota Hospital Association |
| | South Carolina Hospital Association | | Tennessee Hospital Association | **2016** | Maryland Hospital Association |
| **2012** | Iowa Hospital Association | **2014** | Connecticut Hospital Association | **2017** | California's Hospital Quality Institute |
| | Washington State Hospital Association | | Wisconsin Hospital Association | **2018** | Missouri Hospital Association |

This citation is no longer awarded

# Carolyn Boone Lewis Equity of Care Award

The award is presented to hospitals or care systems that are noteworthy leaders and examples to the field in the area of equitable care.

| | |
|---|---|
| **2014** | Massachusetts General Hospital, Boston, MA |
| **2015** | Henry Ford Health System, Detroit, MI |
| | Robert Wood Johnson University Hospital, New Brunswick, NJ |
| **2016** | Cleveland Clinic, Cleveland, OH |
| **2017** | Kaiser Permanente, Oakland, CA |
| **2018** | Navicent Health, Macon, GA |
| **2019** | Anne Arundel Medical Center, Annapolis, MD |
| **2020** | Cone Health - Greensboro, N.C. |

**A2** AHA Guide Hospital Listing Requirements

3 Explanation of Hospital Listings

5 Annual Survey

13 Hospitals in the United States, by State

805 Hospitals in Areas Associated with the United States, by Area

813 U.S. Government Hospitals Outside the United States, by Area

814 Index of Hospitals

877 Index of Health Care Professionals

1106 AHA Membership Categories

1107 Other Institutional Members
1107 *Institutional Member Hospitals*
1108 *Associated University Programs in Health Administration*
1109 *Hospital Schools of Nursing*
1110 *Nonhospital Preacute and Postacute Care Facilities*
1111 *Provisional Hospitals*

1112 Associate Members
1112 *Ambulatory Centers and Home Care Agencies*
1112 *Blue Cross Plans*
1113 *Other Associate Members*

An institution is considered a hospital by the American Hospital Association if it is licensed as general or specialty hospital by the appropriate state agency, and accredited as a hospital by one of the following organizations: The Joint Commission; Healthcare Facilities Accreditation Program (HFAP); accreditation by DNV GL Healthcare; Center for Improvement in Healthcare Quality accreditation; or Medicare certified as a provider of acute service under Title 18 of the Social Security Act.

## Types of Hospitals

Hospitals are listed as one of four types of hospitals: general, special, rehabilitation and chronic disease, or psychiatric. The following definitions of function by type of hospital and special requirements are:

### General

The primary function of the institution is to provide patient services, diagnostic and therapeutic, for a variety of medical conditions. A general hospital also shall provide:

- diagnostic x–ray services with facilities and staff for a variety of procedures
- clinical laboratory service with facilities and staff for a variety of procedures and with anatomical pathology services regularly and conveniently available
- operating room service with facilities and staff.

### Special

The primary function of the institution is to provide diagnostic and treatment services for patients who have specified medical conditions, both surgical and nonsurgical. A special hospital also shall provide:

- such diagnostic and treatment services as may be determined by the Executive Committee of the Board of Trustees of the American Hospital Association to be appropriate for the specified medical conditions for which medical services are provided shall be maintained in the institution with suitable facilities and staff. If such conditions do not normally require diagnostic x–ray service, laboratory service, or operating room service, and if any such services are therefore not maintained in the institution, there shall be written arrangements to make them available to patients requiring them.
- clinical laboratory services capable of providing tissue diagnosis when offering pregacy termination services.

### Rehabilitation and Chronic Disease

The primary function of the institution is to provide diagnostic and treatment services to handicapped or disabled individuals requiring restorative and adjustive services. A rehabilitation and chronic disease hospital also shall provide:

- arrangements for diagnostic x–ray services, as required, on a regular and conveniently available basis
- arrangements for clinical laboratory service, as required on a regular and conveniently available basis
- arrangements for operating room service, as required, on a regular and conveniently available basis
- a physical therapy service with suitable facilities and staff in the institution

- an occupational therapy service with suitable facilities and staff in the institution
- arrangements for psychological and social work services on a regular and conveniently available basis
- arrangements for educational and vocational services on a regular and conveniently available basis
- written arrangements with a general hospital for the transfer of patients who require medical, obstetrical, or surgical services not available in the institution.

### Psychiatric

The primary function of the institution is to provide diagnostic and treatment services for patients who have psychiatric–related illnesses. A psychiatric hospital also shall provide:

- arrangements for clinical laboratory service, as required, on a regular and conveniently available basis
- arrangements for diagnostic x–ray services, as required on a regular and conveniently available basis
- psychiatric, psychological, and social work service with facilities and staff in the institution
- arrangements for electroencephalograph services, as required, on a regular and conveniently available basis
- written arrangements with a general hospital for the transfer of patients who require medical, obstetrical, or surgical services not available in the institution

The American Hospital Association may, at the sole discretion of the Executive Committee of the Board of Trustees, grant, deny, or withdraw the listing of an institution.

---

\* Physician–Term used to describe an individual with an M.D. or D.O. degree who is fully licensed to practice medicine in all its phases.

‡ The completed records in general shall contain at least the following: the patient's identifying data and consent forms, medical history, record of physical examination, physicians' progress notes, operative notes, nurses' notes, routine x–ray and laboratory reports, doctors' orders, and final diagnosis.

## Sample Hospital Listing:

**ANYTOWN, Universal County**

☒ **ANYTOWN HOSPITAL & CLINICS (777777)**, (Formerly Anytown Area
Community Hospital and Clinic), 100 South Main Street, Zip 12345–6789;
tel. 123/456–7890 **A**9 10 ] ①
**F**10 12 23 24 29 30 31 37 39 49 51 55 57 64 65 66 68 70 71 72 77
78 83 87 88 91 96 97 106 107 110 111 113 124 **S** Universal
County Health System ⑥
② 
Primary Contact: Ann M. Generic, Chief Executive Officer
COO: Ann M. Generic
CFO: Michael M. Generic
CMO: Peterl Van Generic, President Medical Staff ③
CHR: Jerry Generic, Human Resources Director
CNO: Danielle Generic, R.N., Chief Nursing Officer
Web address: www.website.org
**Control:** Other not–for–profit (including NFP Corporation) **Service:** General ④
Medical and Surgical

**Staffed Beds:** 25 **Admissions:** 892 **Census:** 9 **Outpatient Visits:** 44014
**Births:** 51 **Total Expense ($000):** 19210 **Payroll Expense ($000):** 5864 ⑤
**Personnel:** 182

**ANYTOWN, Universal County**

☒ **ANYTOWN HOSPITAL & CLINICS (777777)**, (Formerly Anytown Area
Community Hospital and Clinic), 100 South Main Street, Zip 12345–6789;
tel. 123/456–7890 **A**9 10

① = **Approval Codes**
② = **Health Care System Name**
③ = **Titles of Chief Administrators**
④ = **Control and Service Classifications**
⑤ = **Utilization Data**
⑥ = **Facility Codes**

**Hospital, Medicare Provider Number, Address, Telephone, Approval, Facility, and Health Care System**

★ American Hospital Association (AHA) membership   ○ Healthcare Facilities Accreditation Program   ⇑ Center for Improvement in Healthcare Quality Accreditation
□ The Joint Commission accreditation   ◇ DNV Healthcare Inc. accreditation   △ Commission on Accreditation of Rehabilitation Facilities (CARF) accreditation

## ① Approval Codes

*Reported by the approving bodies specified, as of the dates noted.*

**1** Accreditation under the hospital program of The
Joint Commission (February 2020).
**2** Cancer program approved by American College
of Surgeons (March 2020).
**3** Participating site recognized for one or
more Accreditation Council for Graduate
Medical Education accredited programs
(March 2020).
**5** Medical school affiliation, reported to the
American Medical Association (February 2020).
**7** Accreditation by Commission on Accreditation
of Rehabilitation Facilities (January 2020).

**8** Member of Council of Teaching Hospitals of
the Association of American Medical Colleges
(February 2020).
**10** Certified for participation in the Health Insurance
for the Aged (Medicare) Program by the Centers
for Medicare and Medicaid Services.
**11** American Osteopathic Association (AOA)
(February 2020).
**18** Critical Access Hospitals (June 2020).
**19** Rural Referral Center.
**20** Sole Community Provider.
**21** Accreditation by DNV Healthcare Inc. (February
2020).

**22** Accreditation by Center for Improvement in
Healthcare Quality (January 2020).

**Nonreporting** indicates that the 2019 Annual Survey
questionnaire for the hospital was not received prior to
publication.

## ② Healthcare System Name

*The inclusion of the letter "S" (1) indicates that the hospital belongs to a health care system and (2) identifies the specific system to which the hospital belongs.*

## ③ Titles of Chief Administrators

## ④ Control and Service Classification

*For a list of control and service classifications, see page A12.*

**Control**–The type of organization that is
responsible for establishing policy for overall
operation of the hospital.

**Service**–The type of service the hospital
provides to the majority of admissions.

## ⑤ Utilization Data

*Definitions are based on the American Hospital Association's Hospital Administration Terminology. In completing the survey, hospitals were requested to report data for a full year, in accord with their fiscal year, ending in 2019.*

**Beds**–Number of beds regularly maintained
(set up and staffed for use) for inpatients as
of the close of the reporting period. Excludes
newborn bassinets.

**Admissions**–Number of patients accepted for
inpatient service during a 12–month period;
does not include newborn.

**Census**–Average number of inpatients
receiving care each day during the 12–month
reporting period; does not include newborn.

**Outpatient Visits**–A visit by a patient who
is not lodged in the hospital while receiving
medical, dental, or other services. Each
appearance of an outpatient in each unit
constitutes one visit regardless of the number of
diagnostic and/or therapeutic treatments that a
patient receives.

**Births**–Number of infants born in the hospital
and accepted for service in a newborn infant
bassinet during a 12–month period; excludes
stillbirths.

**Expense:** Expense for a 12–month period;
both total expense and payroll components are
shown. Payroll expenses include all salaries
and wages.

**Personnel:** Represents personnel situations
as they existed at the end of the reporting
period; includes full-time equivalents of part–
time personnel. Full–time equivalents were
calculated on the basis that two part–time
persons equal one full–time person.

## Sample Hospital Listing:

**ANYTOWN, Universal County**

⊠ **ANYTOWN HOSPITAL & CLINICS (777777)**, (Formerly Anytown Area Community Hospital and Clinic), 100 South Main Street, Zip 12345–6789; tel. 123/456–7890 **A**9 10 ] ①
**F**10 12 23 24 29 30 31 37 39 49 51 55 57 64 65 66 68 70 71 72 77 78 83 87 88 91 96 97 106 107 110 111 113 124 **S** Universal } ⑥
County Health System ②
Primary Contact: Ann M. Generic, Chief Executive Officer
COO: Ann M. Generic
CFO: Michael M. Generic
CMO: Peterl Van Generic, President Medical Staff ③
CHR: Jerry Generic, Human Resources Director
CNO: Danielle Generic, R.N., Chief Nursing Officer
Web address: www.website.org
**Control:** Other not–for–profit (including NFP Corporation) **Service:** General ] ④
Medical and Surgical

**Staffed Beds:** 25 **Admissions:** 892 **Census:** 9 **Outpatient Visits:** 44014
**Births:** 51 **Total Expense ($000):** 19210 **Payroll Expense ($000):** 5864
**Personnel:** 182
⑤

**ANYTOWN, Universal County**

⊠ **ANYTOWN HOSPITAL & CLINICS (777777)**, (Formerly Anytown Area Community Hospital and Clinic), 100 South Main Street, Zip 12345–6789; tel. 123/456–7890 **A**9 10

① = Approval Codes
② = Health Care System Name
③ = Titles of Chief Administrators
④ = Control and Service Classifications
⑤ = Utilization Data
⑥ = Facility Codes

**Hospital, Medicare Provider Number, Address, Telephone, Approval, Facility, and Health Care System**

★ American Hospital Association (AHA) membership    ○ Healthcare Facilities Accreditation Program    ⇑ Center for Improvement in Healthcare Quality Accreditation
□ The Joint Commission accreditation    ◇ DNV Healthcare Inc. accreditation    △ Commission on Accreditation of Rehabilitation Facilities (CARF) accreditation

## ⑥ Facility Codes

*Provided directly by the hospital; for definitions, see page A6.*

### (Numerical Order)

1 Acute long-term care
2 Adult day care program
3 Airborne infection isolation room
4 Alcoholism-drug abuse or dependency inpatient services
5 Alcoholism-drug abuse or dependency outpatient services
6 Alzheimer center
7 Ambulance services
8 Ambulatory surgery center
9 Arthritis treatment center
10 Assisted living
11 Auxiliary
12 Bariatric/weight control services
13 Birthing room-LDR room-LDRP room
14 Blood donor center
15 Breast cancer screening/mammograms
16 Burn care services
17 Cardiac intensive care
18 Adult cardiology services
19 Pediatric cardiology services
20 Adult diagnostic catheterization
21 Pediatric diagnostic catheterization
22 Adult interventional cardiac catheterization
23 Pediatric interventional cardiac catheterization
24 Adult cardiac surgery
25 Pediatric cardiac surgery
26 Adult cardiac electrophysiology
27 Pediatric cardiac electrophysiology
28 Cardiac rehabilitation
29 Case management
30 Chaplaincy/pastoral care services
31 Chemotherapy
32 Children's wellness program
33 Chiropractic services
34 Community health education
35 Community outreach
36 Complementary and alternative medicine services
37 Computer assisted orthopedic surgery (CAOS)
38 Crisis prevention
39 Dental services
40 On-campus emergency department
41 Pediatric emergency department
42 Off-campus emergency department
43 Trauma center (certified)
44 Enabling services
45 Optical colonoscopy
46 Endoscopic ultrasound
47 Ablation of Barrett's esophagus
48 Esophageal impedance study
49 Endoscopic retrograde cholangiopancreatography (ERCP)
50 Enrollment assistance services
51 Extracorporeal shock wave lithotripter (ESWL)
52 Fertility clinic
53 Fitness center
54 Freestanding outpatient care center
55 Genetic testing/counseling
56 Geriatric services
57 Health fair
58 Health research
59 Health screenings
60 Hemodialysis
61 HIV–AIDS services
62 Home health services
63 Hospice program
64 Hospital–based outpatient care center services
65 Immunization program
66 Indigent care clinic
67 Intermediate nursing care
68 Linguistic/translation services
69 Meal delivery services
70 Medical surgical intensive care services
71 Mobile health services
72 Neonatal intensive care
73 Neonatal intermediate care
74 Neurological services
75 Nutrition programs
76 Obstetrics
77 Occupational health services
78 Oncology services
79 Orthopedic services
80 Other special care
81 Outpatient surgery
82 Pain management program
83 Inpatient palliative care unit
84 Palliative care program
85 Patient controlled analgesia (PCA)
86 Patient education center
87 Patient representative services
88 Pediatric intensive care services
89 Pediatric medical–surgical care
90 Physical rehabilitation inpatient services
91 Assistive technology center
92 Electrodiagnostic services
93 Physical rehabilitation outpatient services
94 Prosthetic and orthotic services
95 Robot-assisted walking therapy
96 Simulated rehabilitation environment
97 Primary care department
98 Psychiatric care
99 Psychiatric pediatric care
100 Psychiatric consultation–liaison services
101 Psychiatric education services
102 Psychiatric emergency services
103 Psychiatric geriatric services
104 Psychiatric outpatient services
105 Psychiatric partial hospitalization services
106 Psychiatric residential treatment
107 CT scanner
108 Diagnostic radioisotope facility
109 Electron beam computed tomography (EBCT)
110 Full–field digital mammography (FFDM)
111 Magnetic resonance imaging (MRI)
112 Intraoperative magnetic resonance imaging
113 Magnetoencephalography (MEG)
114 Multi–slice spiral computed tomography (MSCT) (<64 slice CT)
115 Multi–slice spiral computed tomography (64 + slice CT)
116 Positron emission tomography (PET)
117 Positron emission tomography/CT (PET/CT)
118 Single photon emission computerized tomography (SPECT)
119 Ultrasound
120 Image–guided radiation therapy (IGRT)
121 Intensity–modulated radiation therapy (IMRT)
122 Proton beam therapy
123 Shaped beam radiation therapy
124 Stereotactic radiosurgery
125 Retirement housing
126 Robotic surgery
127 Rural health clinic
128 Skilled nursing care
129 Sleep center
130 Social work services
131 Sports medicine
132 Support groups
133 Swing bed services
134 Teen outreach services
135 Tobacco treatment/cessation program
136 Bone marrow transplant services
137 Heart transplant
138 Kidney transplant
139 Liver transplant
140 Lung transplant
141 Tissue transplant
142 Other transplant
143 Transportation to health services
144 Urgent care center
145 Virtual colonoscopy
146 Volunteer services department
147 Women's health center/services
148 Wound management services
149 Violence prevention programs for the workplace
150 Violence prevention programs for the community
151 Alcoholism-chemical dependency pediatric services
152 Alcoholism-chemical dependency partial hospitalization services
153 Psychiatric intensive outpatient services
154 Telehealth
155 Air ambulance services
156 Diabetes prevention program
157 Employment support services
158 Supportive housing services

*Each year, an annual survey of hospitals is conducted by the American Hospital Association through its Health Forum affiliate.*

*The facilities and services found below are provided by the hospital. For data products reflecting the services provided by a hospital through its health care system, or network or through a formal arrangement with another provider contact Health Forum at 800/821–2039, or visit www.healthforum.com.*

*The AHA Guide to the Health Care Field does not include all data collected from the 2019 Annual Survey. Requests for purchasing other Annual Survey data should be directed to Health Forum LLC, an affiliate of the American Hospital Association, 155 N. Wacker Drive, Chicago, IL 60606, 800/821–2039.*

## Definitions of Facility Codes

1. **Acute long–term care.** Provides specialized acute hospital care to medically complex patients who are critically ill, have multisystem complications and/or failure, and require hospitalization averaging 25 days, in a facility offering specialized treatment programs and therapeutic intervention on a 24–hour/7 day a week basis.

2. **Adult day care program.** Program providing supervision, medical and psychological care, and social activities for older adults who live at home or in another family setting, but cannot be alone or prefer to be with others during the day. May include intake assessment, health monitoring, occupational therapy, personal care, noon meal, and transportation services.

3. **Airborne infection isolation room.** A single–occupancy room for patient care where environmental factors are controlled in an effort to minimize the transmission of those infectious agents, usually spread person to person by droplet nuclei associated with coughing and inhalation. Such rooms typically have specific ventilation requirements for controlled ventilation, air pressure and filtration.

4. **Alcoholism–drug abuse or dependency inpatient unit.** Provides diagnosis and therapeutic services to patients with alcoholism or other drug dependencies. Includes care for inpatient/residential treatment for patients whose course of treatment involves more intensive care than provided in an outpatient setting or where patient requires supervised withdrawal.

5. **Alcoholism–drug abuse or dependency outpatient unit.** Organized hospital services that provide medical care and/or rehabilitative treatment services to outpatients for whom the primary diagnosis is alcoholism or other chemical dependency.

6. **Alzheimer center.** Facility that offers care to persons with Alzheimer's disease and their families through an integrated program of clinical services, research, and education.

7. **Ambulance services.** Provision of ambulance services to the ill and injured who require medical attention on a scheduled or unscheduled basis.

8. **Ambulatory surgery center.** Facility that provides care to patients requiring surgery who are admitted and discharged on the same day. Ambulatory surgery centers are distinct from same day surgical units within the hospital outpatient departments for purposes of Medicare payments.

9. **Arthritis treatment center.** Specifically equipped and staffed center for the diagnosis and treatment of arthritis and other joint disorders.

10. **Assisted living.** A special combination of housing, supportive services, personalized assistance and health care designed to respond to the individual needs of those who need help in activities of daily living and instrumental activities of daily living. Supportive services are available, 24 hours a day, to meet scheduled and unscheduled needs, in a way that promotes maximum independence and dignity for each resident and encourages the involvement of a resident's family, neighbor and friends.

11. **Auxiliary.** A volunteer community organization formed to assist the hospital in carrying out its purpose and to serve as a link between the institution and the community.

12. **Bariatric/weight control services.** Bariatrics is the medical practice of weight reduction.

13. **Birthing room–LDR room–LDRP room.** A single room–type of maternity care with a more homelike setting for families than the traditional three–room unit (labor/delivery/recovery) with a separate postpartum area. A birthing room combines labor and delivery in one room. An LDR room accommodates three stages in the birthing process—labor, delivery, and recovery. An LDRP room accommodates all four stages of the birth process—labor, delivery, recovery and postpartum.

14. **Blood donor center.** A facility that performs, or is responsible for the collection, processing, testing or distribution of blood and components.

15. **Breast cancer screening/mammograms**. Mammography screening–the use of breast x–ray to detect unsuspected breast cancer in asymptomatic women. Diagnostic mammography–the x–ray imaging of breast tissue in symptomatic women who are considered to have a substantial likelihood of having breast cancer already.

16. **Burn care services**. Provides care to severely burned patients. Severely burned patients are those with any of the following: 1. Second–degree burns of more than 25% total body surface area for adults or 20% total body surface area for children; 2. Third–degree burns of more than 10% total body surface area; 3. Any severe burns of the hands, face, eyes, ears or feet or; 4. All inhalation injuries, electrical burns, complicated burn injuries involving fractures and other major traumas, and all other poor risk factors.

17. **Cardiac intensive care.** Provides patient care of a more specialized nature than the usual medical and surgical care, on the basis of

physicians' orders and approved nursing care plans. The unit is staffed with specially trained nursing personnel and contains monitoring and specialized support or treatment equipment for patients who, because of heart seizure, one-heart surgery, or other life-threatening conditions, require intensified, comprehensive observation and care. May include myocardial infarction, pulmonary care, and heart transplant units.

18. **Adult cardiology services.** An organized clinical service offering diagnostic and interventional procedures to manage the full range of adult heart conditions.

19. **Pediatric cardiology services.**

20. **Adult diagnostic catheterization.** (also called coronary angiography or coronary arteriography) is used to assist in diagnosing complex heart conditions. Cardiac angiography involves the insertion of a tiny catheter up into the artery in the groin then carefully threading the catheter up into the aorta where the coronary arteries originate. Once the catheter is in place, a dye is injected which allows the cardiologist to see the size, shape and distribution of the coronary arteries. These images are used to diagnose heart disease and to determine, among other things, whether or not surgery is indicated.

21. **Pediatric diagnostic catheterization.** (also called coronary angiography or coronary arteriography) is used to assist in diagnosing complex heart conditions. Cardiac angiography involves the insertion of a tiny catheter up into the artery in the groin then carefully threading the catheter up into the aorta where the coronary arteries originate. Once the catheter is in place, a dye is injected which allows the cardiologist to see the size, shape and distribution of coronary arteries. These images are used to diagnose heart disease and to determine, among other things, whether or not surgery is indicated.

22. **Adult interventional cardiac catheterization.** Nonsurgical procedure that utilizes the same basic principles as diagnostic catheterization and then uses advanced the techniques to improve the heart's function. It can be less invasive alternative to heart surgery.

23. **Pediatric diagnostic catheterization.** Nonsurgical procedure that utilizes the same

basic principles as diagnostic cathereterization and then uses advanced the techniques to improve the heart's function. It can be less invasive alternative to heart surgery.

24. **Adult cardiac surgery.** Includes minimally invasive procedures that include surgery done with only a small incision or no incision at all, such as through a laparoscope or an endoscope and more invasive major surgical procedures that include open chest and open heart surgery.

25. **Pediatric cardiac surgery.** Includes minimally invasive procedures that include surgery done with only a small incision or no incision at all, such as through a laparoscope or an endoscope and more invasive major surgical procedures that include open chest and open heart surgery defibrillator implantation and follow-up.

26. **Adult cardiac electrophysiology.** Evaluation and management of patients with complex rhythm or conduction abnormalities, including diagnostic testing, treatment of arrhythmias by catheter ablation or drug therapy, and pacemaker/defibrillator implantation and follow-up.

27. **Pediatric cardiac electrophysiology.**

28. **Cardiac rehabilitation.** A medically supervised program to help heart patients recover quickly and improve their overall physical and mental functioning. The goal is to reduce risk of another cardiac event or to keep an already present heart condition from getting worse. Cardiac rehabilitation programs include: counseling to patients, an exercise program, helping patients modify risk factors such as smoking and high blood pressure, providing vocational guidance to enable the patient to return to work, supplying information on physical limitations and lending emotional support.

29. **Case management.** A system of assessment, treatment planning, referral and follow-up that ensures the provision of comprehensive and continuous services and the coordination of payment and reimbursement for care.

30. **Chaplaincy/pastoral care services.** A service ministering religious activities and providing pastoral counseling to patients, their families, and staff of a health care organization.

31. **Chemotherapy.** An organized program for the treatment of cancer by the use of drugs or chemicals.

32. **Children's wellness program.** A program that encourages improved health status and a healthful lifestyle of children through health education, exercise, nutrition and health promotion.

33. **Chiropractic services.** An organized clinical service including spinal manipulation or adjustment and related diagnostic and therapeutic services.

34. **Community health education.** Education that provides health information to individuals and populations as well as support for personal, family and community health decisions with the objective of improving health status.

35. **Community outreach.** A program that systematically interacts with the community to identify those in need of services, alerting persons and their families to the availability of services, locating needed services, and enabling persons to enter the service delivery system.

36. **Complementary and alternative medicine services.** Organized hospital services or formal arrangements to providers that provide care or treatment not based solely on traditional western allopathic medical teachings as instructed in most U.S. medical schools. Includes any of the following; acupuncture, chiropractic, homeopathy, osteopathy, diet and lifestyle changes, herbal medicine, massage therapy, etc.

37. **Computer assisted orthopedic surgery (CAOS).** Orthopedic surgery using computer technology, enabling three-dimensional graphic models to visualize a patient's anatomy.

38. **Crisis prevention.** Services provided in order to promote physical and mental well being and the early identification of disease and ill health prior to the onset and recognition of symptoms so as to permit early treatment.

39. **Dental services.** An organized dental service, not necessarily involving special facilities, that provides dental or oral services to inpatients or outpatients.

40. **On-campus emergency department.** Hospital facilities for the provision of unscheduled outpatient services to patients whose conditions require immediate care. Must be staffed 24 hours a day.

41. **Pediatric emergency department.** Hospital facilities for the provision of unscheduled outpatient services to patients whose conditions require immediate care.

42. **Off-campus emergency department.** A facility owned and operated by the hospital but physically separate from the hospital for the provision of unscheduled outpatient services to patients whose conditions require immediate care. A freestanding ED is not physically connected to a hospital but has all the necessary emergency staffing and equipment on site.

43. **Trauma center (certified).** A facility certified to provide emergency and specialized intensive care to critically ill and injured patients.

44. **Enabling services.** A program that is designed to help the patient access health care services by offering any of the following linguistic services, transportation services, and/or referrals to local social services agencies.

45. **Optical colonoscopy.** An examination of the interior of the colon using a long, flexible, lighted tube with a small built-in camera.

46. **Endoscopic ultrasound.** Specially designed endoscope that incorporates an ultrasound transducer used to obtain detailed images of organs in the chest and abdomen. The endoscope can be passed through the mouth or the anus. When combined with needle biopsy the procedure can assist in diagnosis and staging of cancer.

47. **Ablation of Barrett's esophagus.** Premalignant condition that can lead to adenocarcinoma of the esophagus. The non surgical ablation of the premalignant tissue in Barrett's esophagus by the application of thermal energy or light through an endoscope passed from the mouth into the esophagus.

48. **Esophageal impedance study.** A test in which a catheter is placed through the nose into the esophagus to measure whether gas or liquids are passing from the stomach into the esophagus and causing symptoms.

49. **Endoscopic retrograde cholangiopancreatography (ERCP).** A procedure in which a catheter is introduced through an endoscope into the bile ducts and pancreatic ducts. Injection of contrast materials permits detailed x–ray of these structures. The procedure is used diagnostically as well as therapeutically to relieve obstruction or remove stones

50. **Enrollment assistance services.** A program that provides enrollment assistance for patients who are potentially eligible for public health insurance programs such as Medicaid, State Children's Health Insurance, or local/state indigent care programs. The specific services offered could include explanation of benefits, assist applicants in completing the application and locating all relevant documents, conduct eligibilty interviews, and/or forward applications and documentation to state/local social service or health agency.

51. **Extracorporeal shock wave lithotripter (ESWL).** A medical device used for treating stones in the kidney or urethra. The device disintegrates kidney stones noninvasively through the transmission of acoustic shock waves directed at the stones.

52. **Fertility clinic.** A specialized program set in an infertility center that provides counseling and education as well as advanced reproductive techniques such as: injectable therapy, reproductive surgeries, treatment for endometriosis, male factor infertility, tubal reversals, in vitro fertilization (IVF), donor eggs, and other such services to help patients achieve successful pregnancies.

53. **Fitness center.** Provides exercise, testing, or evaluation programs and fitness activities to the community and hospital employees.

54. **Freestanding outpatient care center.** A facility owned and operated by the hospital, but physically separate from the hospital, that provides various medical treatments on an outpatient basis only. In addition to treating minor illnesses or injuries, the center will stabilize seriously ill or injured patients before transporting them to a hospital. Laboratory and radiology services are usually available.

55. **Genetic testing/counseling.** A service equipped with adequate laboratory facilities and directed by a qualified physician to advise parents and prospective parents on potential problems in cases of genetic defects. A genetic test is the analysis of human DNA, RNA, chromosomes, proteins, and certain metabolites in order to detect heritable disease– related genotypes, mutations, phenotypes, or karyotypes for clinical purposes. Genetic tests can have diverse purposes, including the diagnosis of genetic diseases in newborns, children, and adults; the identification of future health risks; the prediction of drug responses; and the assessment of risks to future children.

56. **Geriatric services.** The branch of medicine dealing with the physiology of aging and the diagnosis and treatment of disease affecting the aged. Services could include: Adult day care program; Alzheimer's diagnostic–assessment services; Comprehensive geriatric assessment; Emergency response system; Geriatric acute care unit; and/or Geriatric clinics.

57. **Health fair.** Community health education events that focus on the prevention of disease and promotion of health through such activities as audiovisual exhibits and free diagnostic services.

58. **Health research.** Organized hospital research program in any of the following areas: basic research, clinical research, community health research, and/or research on innovative health care delivery.

59. **Health screenings.** A preliminary procedure, such as a test or examination to detect the most characteristic sign or signs of a disorder that may require further investigation.

60. **Hemodialysis.** Provision of equipment and personnel for the treatment of renal insufficiency on an inpatient or outpatient basis.

61. **HIV–AIDS services.** Services may include one or more of the following: HIV–AIDS unit (special unit or team designated and equipped specifically for diagnosis, treatment, continuing care planning, and counseling services for HIV–AIDS patients and their families.) General inpatient care for HIV–AIDS (inpatient diagnosis and treatment for human immunodeficiency virus and acquired immunodeficiency syndrome patients, but dedicated unit is not available.) Specialized outpatient program for HIV–AIDS (special outpatient program providing diagnostic, treatment, continuing care planning, and counseling

for HIV–AIDS patients and their families.)

62. **Home health services.** Service providing nursing, therapy, and health–related homemaker or social services in the patient's home.

63. **Hospice program.** A program providing palliative care, chiefly medical relief of pain and supportive services, addressing the emotional, social, financial, and legal needs of terminally ill patients and their families. Care can be provided in a variety of settings, both inpatient and at home.

64. **Hospital–based outpatient care center services.** Organized hospital health care services offered by appointment on an ambulatory basis. Services may include outpatient surgery, examination, diagnosis, and treatment of a variety of medical conditions on a nonemergency basis, and laboratory and other diagnostic testing as ordered by staff or outside physician referral.

65. **Immunization program.** Program that plans, coordinates and conducts immunization services in the community.

66. **Indigent care clinic.** Health care services for uninsured and underinsured persons where care is free of charge or charged on a sliding scale. This would include "free clinics" staffed by volunteer practitioners, but could also be staffed by employees with sponsoring health care organizations subsidizing the cost of service.

67. **Intermediate nursing care.** Provides health–related services (skilled nursing care and social services) to residents with a variety of physical conditions or functional disabilities. These residents do not require the care provided by a hospital or skilled nursing facility, but do need supervision and support services.

68. **Linguistic/translation services.** Services provided by the hospital designed to make health care more accessible to non–English speaking patients and their physicians.

69. **Meal delivery services.** A hospital sponsored program which delivers meals to people, usually the elderly, who are unable to prepare their own meals. Low cost, nutritional meals are delivered to individuals' homes on a regular basis.

70. **Medical surgical intensive care services.** Provides patient care of a more intensive nature than the usual medical and surgical care, on the basis of physicians' orders and approved nursing care plans. These units are staffed with specially trained nursing personnel and contain monitoring and specialized support equipment of patients who, because of shock, trauma, or other life–threatening conditions, require intensified, comprehensive observation and care. Includes mixed intensive care units.

71. **Mobile health services.** Vans and other vehicles used to deliver primary care services.

72. **Neonatal intensive care.** A unit that must be separate from the newborn nursery providing intensive care to all sick infants including those with the very lowest birth weights (less that 1500 grams). NICU has potential for providing mechanical ventilation, neonatal surgery, and special care for the sickest infants born in the hospital or transferred from another institution. A full–time neonatologist serves    as director of the NICU.

73. **Neonatal intermediate care.** A unit that must be separate from the normal newborn nursery and that provides intermediate and/or recovery care and some specialized services, including immediate resuscitation, intravenous therapy, and capacity for prolonged oxygen therapy and monitoring.

74. **Neurological services.** Services provided by the hospital dealing with the operative and nonoperative management of disorders of the central, peripheral, and autonomic nervous system.

75. **Nutrition programs.** Those services within a health care facility which are designed to provide inexpensive, nutritionally sound meals to patients.

76. **Obstetrics.** Levels should be designated: (1) unit provides services for uncomplicated maternity and newborn cases; (2) unit provides services for uncomplicated cases, the majority of complicated problems, and special neonatal services; and (3) unit provides services for all serious illnesses and abnormalities and is supervised by a full–time maternal/ fetal specialist.

77. **Occupational health services.** Includes services designed to protect the safety of employees from hazards in the work environment.

78. **Oncology services.** Inpatient and outpatient services for patients with cancer, including comprehensive care, support and guidance in addition to patient education and preventiion, chemotherapy, counseling, and other treatment methods.

79. **Orthopedic services.** Services provided for the prevention or correction of injuries or disorders of the skeletal system and associated muscles, joints, and ligaments.

80. **Other special care.** Provides care to patients requiring care more intensive than that provided in the acute area, yet not sufficiently intensive to require admission to an intensive care unit. Patients admitted to the area are usually transferred here from an intensive care unit once their condition has improved. These units are sometimes referred to as definitive observation, step–down, or progressive care units.

81. **Outpatient surgery.** Scheduled surgical services provided to patients who do not remain in the hospital overnight. The surgery may be performed in operating suites also used for inpatient surgery, specially designated surgical suites for outpatient surgery, or procedure rooms within an outpatient care facility.

82. **Pain management program.** A hospital wide formalized program that includes staff education for the management of chronic and acute pain based on guidelines and protocols like those developed by the agency for Health Care Policy Research, etc.

83. **Inpatient palliative care unit.** An inpatient palliative care ward is a physically discreet, inpatient nursing unit where the focus is palliative care. The patient care focus is on symptom relief for complex patients who may be continuing to undergo primary treatment. Care is delivered by palliative medicine specialists.

84. **Palliative care program.** An organized program providing specialized medical care, drugs or therapies for the management of acute or chronic pain and/or the control of symptoms adminstered by specially trained physicians and

other clinicians; and supportive care services, such as counseling on advanced directives, spiritual care, and social services, to patients with advanced disease and their families.

85. **Patient controlled analgesia (PCA).** Patient Controlled Analgesia (PCA) is intravenously administered pain medicine under the patient's control. The patient has a button on the end of a cord than can be pushed at will, whenever more pain medicine is desired. This button will only deliver more pain medicine at pre-determined intervals, as programmed by the doctor's order.

86. **Patient education center.** Written goals and objectives for the patient and/or family related to therapeutic regimens, medical procedures, and self care.

87. **Patient representative services.** Organized hospital services providing personnel through whom patients and staff can seek solutions to institutional problems affecting the delivery of high–quality care and services.

88. **Pediatric intensive care services.** Provides care to pediatric patients that is of a more intensive nature than that usually provided to pediatric patients. The unit is staffed with specially trained personnel and contains monitoring and specialized support equipment for treatment of patients who, because of shock, trauma, or other life–threatening conditions, require intensified, comprehensive observation and care.

89. **Pediatric medical–surgical care.** Provides acute care to pediatric settings) or in a traditional setting (gymnasium) using motor learning principles.

90. **Physical rehabilitation inpatient services.** Provides care encompassing a comprehensive array of restoration services for the disabled and all support services necessary to help patients attain their maximum functional capacity.

91. **Assistive technology center.** A program providing access to specialized hardware and software with adaptations allowing individuals greater independence with mobility, dexterity, or increased communication options.

92. **Electrodiagnostic services.** Diagnostic testing services for nerve and muscle function including services such as nerve

conduction studies and needle electromyography.

93. **Physical rehabilitation outpatient services.** Outpatient program providing medical, health–related, therapy, social, and/or vocational services to help disabled persons attain or retain their maximum functional capacity.

94. **Prosthetic and orthotic services.** Services providing comprehensive prosthetic and orthotic evaluation, fitting, and training.

95. **Robot-assisted walking therapy.** A form of physical therapy that uses a courts, public health nurses, welfare agencies, clergy and so forth. The purpose is to expand the mental health knowledge and competence of personnel not working in the mental health field and to promote good mental health through improved understanding, attitudes, and behavioral patterns.

96. **Simulated rehabilitation environment.** Rehabilitation focused on retraining functional skills in a contextually appropriate environment (simulated home and community settings) or in a traditional setting (gymnasium) using motor learning principles.

97. **Primary care department.** A unit or clinic within the hospital that provides primary care services (e.g. general pediatric care, general internal medicine, family practice and gynecology) through hospital–salaried medical and or nursing staff, focusing on evaluating and diagnosing medical problems and providing medical treatment on an outpatient basis.

98. **Psychiatric care.** Provides acute or long–term care to emotionally disturbed patients, including patients admitted for diagnosis and those admitted for treatment of psychiatric problems, on the basis of physicians' orders and approved nursing care plans. Long–term care may include intervention, and assistance to persons suffering acute emotional or mental distress.

99. **Psychiatric pediatric care.** The branch of medicine focused on the diagnosis, treatment, and prevention of mental, emotional, and behavioral disorders in pediatric patients.

100. **Psychiatric consultation–liaison services.** Provides organized psychiatric consultation/liaison services to nonpsychiatric

hospital staff and/or department on psychological aspects of medical care that may be generic or specific to individual patients.

101. **Psychiatric education services.** Provides psychiatric educational services to community agencies and workers such as schools, police, courts, public health nurses, welfare agencies, clergy and so forth. The purpose is to expand the mental health knowledge and competence of personnel not working in the mental health field and to promote good mental health through improved understanding, attitudes, and behavioral patterns.

102. **Psychiatric emergency services.** Services or facilities available on a 24–hour basis to provide immediate unscheduled outpatient care, diagnosis, evaluation, crisis intervention, and assistance to persons suffering acute emotional or mental distress.

103. **Psychiatric geriatric services.** Provides care to emotionally disturbed elderly patients, including those admitted for diagnosis and those admitted for treatment.

104. **Psychiatric outpatient services.** Provides medical care, including diagnosis and treatment of psychiatric outpatients.

105. **Psychiatric partial hospitalization services.** Organized hospital services of intensive day/evening outpatient services of three hours or more duration, distinguished from other outpatient visits of one hour.

106. **Psychiatric residential treatment.**

107. **CT scanner.** Computed tomographic scanner for head and whole body scans.

108. **Diagnostic radioisotope facility.** The use of radioactive isotopes (Radiopharmaceutical) as tracers or indicators to detect an abnormal condition or disease.

109. **Electron beam computed tomography (EBCT).** A high tech computed tomography scan used to detect coronary artery disease by measuring coronary calcifications. This imaging procedure uses electron beams which are magnetically steered to produce a visual of the coronary artery and the images are produced faster than conventional CT scans.

110. **Full–field digital mammography (FFDM).** Combines the x–ray generators and tubes used in analog screen–film mammography (SFM) with a detector plate that converts the x–rays into a digital signal.

111. **Magnetic resonance imaging (MRI).** The use of a uniform magnetic field and radio frequencies to study tissue and structure of the body. This procedure enables the visualization of biochemical activity of the cell in vivo without the use of ionizing radiation, radioisotopic substances, or high–frequency sound.

112. **Intraoperative magnetic resonance imaging.** An integrated surgery system which provides an MRI system in an operating room. The system allows for immediate evaluation of the degree to tumor resection while the patient is undergoing a surgical resection. Intraoperative MRI exists when a MRI (low–field or high–field) is placed in the operating theater and is used during surgical resection without moving the patient from the operating room to the diagnostic imaging suite.

113. **Magnetoencephalography (MEG).** A noninvasive neurophysiological measurement tool used to study magnetic fields generated by neuronal activity of the brain. MEG provides direct information about the dynamics of evoked and spontaneous neural activity and the location of their sources in the brain. The primary uses of MEG include assisting surgeons in localizing the source of epilepsy, sensory mapping and the study of brain function. When it is combined with structural imaging, it is known as magnetic source imaging (MSI).

114. **Multi–slice spiral computed tomography (MSCT) (<64 slice CT).** A specialized computed tomography cycles per second to visualize internal body structures.

115. **Multi–slice spiral computed tomography (64 + slice CT).** Involves the acquisition of volumetric tomographic x–ray absorption data expressed in Hounsfield units using multiple rows of detectors. 64+ systems reconstruct the equivalent of 64 or greater slices to cover the imaged volume.

116. **Positron emission tomography (PET).** A nuclear medicine imaging technology which uses radioactive (positron emitting) isotopes created in a cyclotron or generator and computers to produce composite pictures of the brain and heart at work. PET scanning produces sectional images depicting metabolic activity or blood flow rather than anatomy.

117. **Positron emission tomography/ CT (PET/CT).** Provides metabolic functional information for the monitoring of chemotherapy, radiotherapy and surgical planning.

118. **Single photon emission computerized tomography (SPECT).** A nuclear medicine imaging technology that combines existing technology of gamma camera imaging with computed tomographic imaging technology to provide a more precise and clear image.

119. **Ultrasound.** The use of acoustic waves above the range of 20,000 cycles per second to visualize internal body structures.

120. **Image–guided radiation therapy (IGRT).** Automated system for image–guided radiation therapy that enables clinicians to obtain high–resolution x–ray images to pinpoint tumor sites, adjust patient positioning when necessary, and complete a treatment, all within the standard treatment time slot, allowing for more effective cancer treatments.

121. **Intensity–modulated radiation Therapy (IMRT).** A type of three–dimensional radiation therapy, which improves the targeting of treatment delivery in a way that is likely to decrease damage to normal tissues and allows varying intensities diagnosis of genetic diseases in newborns, children, and adults; the identification of future health risks; arrange for acute and long term care through affiliated institutions.

122. **Proton beam therapy.** A form of radiation therapy which administers proton beams. While producing the same biologic effects as x–ray beams, the energy distribution of protons differs from conventional x–ray beams in that they can be more precisely focused in tissue volumes in a three–dimensional pattern resulting in less surrounding tissue damage than conventional radiation therapy permitting administration of higher doses.

123. **Shaped beam radiation therapy.** A precise, non–invasive treatment that involves targeting beams of radiation that mirror the exact size and shape of a tumor at a specific area of a tumor to shrink or destroy cancerous cells. This procedure delivers a therapeutic dose of radiation that conforms precisely to the shape of the tumor, thus minimizing the risk to nearby tissues.

124. **Stereotactic radiosurgery.** Stereotactic radiosurgery (SRS) is a radiotherapy modality that delivers a high dosage of radiation to a discrete treatment area in as few as one treatment session. Includes gamma knife, cyberknife, etc.

125. **Retirement housing.** A facility which provides social activities to senior citizens, usually retired persons, who do not require health care but some short–term skilled nursing care may be provided. A retirement center may furnish housing and may also have acute hospital and long–term care facilities, or it may arrange for acute and long term care through affiliated institutions.

126. **Robotic surgery.** The use of mechanical guidance devices to remotely manipulate surgical instrumentation.

127. **Rural health clinic.** A clinic located in a rural, medically under-served area in the United States that has a separate reimbursement structure from the standard medical office under the Medicare and Medicaid programs.

128. **Skilled nursing care.** Provides non–acute medical and skilled nursing care services, therapy, and social services under the supervision of a licensed registered nurse on a 24–hour basis.

129. **Sleep center.** Specially equipped and staffed center for the diagnosis and treatment of sleep disorders.

130. **Social work services.** Services may include one or more of the following: Organized social work services (services that are properly directed and sufficiently staffed by qualified individuals who provide assistance and counseling to patients and their families in dealing with social, emotional, and environmental problems associated with illness or disability, often in the context of financial or discharge planning coordination.) Outpatient social work services (social work services provided in ambulatory care areas.) Emergency department social work services (social work services provided to emergency department patients by social workers dedicated to the emergency department or on call.)

131. **Sports medicine.** Provision of diagnostic screening and assessment and clinical and rehabilitation services for the prevention and treatment of sports–related injuries.

132. **Support groups.** A hospital sponsored program which allows a group of individuals with the same or similar problems who meet periodically to share experiences, problems, and solutions, in order to support each other.

133. **Swing bed services.** A hospital bed that can be used to provide either acute or long–term care depending on community or patients needs. To be eligible a hospital must have a Medicare provider agreement in place, have fewer than 100 beds, be located in a rural area, not have a 24 hour nursing service waiver in effect, have not been terminated from the program in the prior two years, and meet various service conditions.

134. **Teen outreach services.** A program focusing on the teenager which encourages an improved health status and a healthful lifestyle including physical, emotional, mental, social, spiritual and economic health through education, exercise, nutrition and health promotion.

135. **Tobacco treatment/cessation program.** Organized hospital services with the purpose of ending tobacco–use habits of patients addicted to tobacco/nicotine.

136.–142. **Transplant services.** The branch of medicine that transfers an organ or tissue from one person to another or from one body part to another to replace a diseased structure or to restore function or to change appearance. Services could include: Bone marrow transplant program (136. Bone marrow); heart (137. Heart transplant), kidney (138. Kidney transplant), liver (139. Liver transplant) lung (140. Lung transplant), tissue (141. Tissue transplant). Please include heart/lung or other multi- transplant surgeries inn other (142. Other Transplant).

143. **Transportation to health services.** A long–term care support service designed to assist the mobility of the elderly. Some programs offer improved financial access by offering reduced rates and barrier–free buses or vans with ramps and lifts to assist the elderly or handicapped; others offer subsidies for public transport systems or operate mini–bus services

144. **Urgent care center.** A facility that provides care and treatment for problems that are not life–threatening but require attention over the short term. These units function like emergency rooms but are separate from hospitals with which they may have backup affiliation arrangements.

145. **Virtual colonoscopy.** Noninvasive screening procedure used to visualize, analyze and detect cancerous or potentially cancerous polyps in the colon.

146. **Volunteer services department.** An organized hospital department responsible for coordinating the services of volunteers working within the institution.

147. **Women's center.** An area set aside for coordinated education and treatment services specifically for and promoted by women as provided by this special unit. Services may or may not include obstetrics but include a range of services other than OB.

148. **Wound management services.** Services for patients with chronic wounds and non–healing wounds often resulting from diabetes, poor circulation, improper seating and immunocompromising conditions. The goals are to progress chronic wounds through stages of healing, reduce and eliminate infections, increase physical function to minimize complications from current wounds and prevent future chronic wounds. Wound management services are provided on an inpatient or outpatient basis, depending on the intensity of service needed.

149. **Violence prevention programs for the workplace.** A violence prevention program with goals and objectives for preventing workplace violence against staff and patients.

150. **Violence prevention programs for the community.** An organized program that attempts to make a positive impact on the type(s) of violence a community is experiencing. For example, it can assist victims of violent crimes, e.g., rape, or incidents, e.g., bullying, to hospital or to community services to prevent further victimization or retaliation. A program that targets the underlying circumstances that contribute to violence such as poor housing, insufficient job training, and/or substance abuse through means such as direct involvement and support, education, mentoring, anger management, crisis intervention and training programs would also qualify.

151. **Alcoholism-chemical dependency pediatric services.** Provides diagnosis and therapeutic services to pediatric patients with alcoholism or other drug dependencies. Includes care for inpatient/ residential treatment for patients whose course of treatment involves more intensive care than provided in an outpatient setting or where patient requires supervised withdrawal.

152. **Alcoholism-chemical dependency partial hospitalization services.** Organized hospital services providing intensive day/evening outpatient services of three hour or more duration, distinguished from other outpatient visits of one hour.

153. **Psychiatric intensive outpatient services.** A prescribed course of treatment in which the patient receives outpatient care no less than three times a week (which might include more than one service/day).

154. **Telehealth.** A broad variety of technologies and tactics to deliver virtual medical, public health, health education delivery, and support services using telecommunications technologies. Telehealth is used more commonly as it describes the wide range of diagnosis and management, education, and other related fields of health care. This includes, but are not limited to: dentistry, counseling, physical and occupational therapy, home health, chronic disease monitoring and management, disaster management, and consumer and professional education, and remote patient monitoring.

155. **Air ambulance services.** Aircraft and especially a helicopter equipped for transporting the injured or sick. Most air ambulances carry critically ill or injured patients, whose condition could rapidly change for the worse.

156. **Diabetes prevention program.** Program to prevent or delay the onset of type 2 diabetes by offering evidence-based lifestyle changes based on research studies, which showed modest behavior changes helped individuals with prediabetes reduce their risk of developing type 2 diabetes.

157. **Employment support services.** Services designed to support individuals with significant disabilities to seek and maintain employment.

158. **Supportive housing services.** A hospital program that provides decent, safe, affordable, community-based housing with flexible support services designed to help the individual or family stay housed and live a more productive life in the community.

## Control and Service Classifications

### Control

#### Government, nonfederal
State
County
City
City–county
Hospital district or authority

#### Nongovernment not-for-profit
Church operated
Other

#### Investor–owned (for–profit)
Individual
Partnership
Corporation

#### Department of Defense, Government, federal*
Public Health Service other than 47
Veterans Affairs

#### Osteopathic
Church operated Other not–for–profit
Other
Individual for–profit
Partnership for–profit
Corporation for–profit

### Service

General medical and surgical
Hospital unit of an institution (prison hospital, college infirmary, etc.)
Hospital unit within a facility for persons with intellectual disabilities
Surgical
Psychiatric
Tuberculosis and other respiratory diseases
Cancer
Heart
Obstetrics and gynecology

Eye, ear, nose, and throat
Rehabilitation
Orthopedic
Chronic disease
Other specialty
Children's general
Children's hospital unit of an institution
Children's psychiatric
Children's tuberculosis and other respiratory diseases
Children's eye, ear, nose, and throat

Children's rehabilitation
Children's orthopedic
Children's chronic disease
Children's other specialty
Intellectual disabilities
Long–Term Acute Care
Alcoholism and other chemical dependency
Children's Long–Term Acute Care
Children's Cancer
Children's Heart

---

* Starting with the 2018 Annual Survey, Air Force, Army, and Navy are now rolled up into the Department of Defense.

# ALABAMA

## ALABASTER—Shelby County

☐ **NOLAND HOSPITAL SHELBY (012013)**, 1000 First Street North, 3rd Floor,
Zip 35007–8703; tel. 205/620–8641, (Nonreporting) **A**1 10 **S** Noland Health
Services, Inc., Birmingham, AL
Primary Contact: Laura S. Wills, Administrator
Web address: www.nolandhospitals.com
**Control:** Other not–for–profit (including NFP Corporation) **Service:** Acute long–
term care hospital

**Staffed Beds:** 52

⊠ **SHELBY BAPTIST MEDICAL CENTER (010016)**, 1000 First Street North,
Zip 35007–8703; tel. 205/620–8100, (Nonreporting) **A**1 10 **F**3 8 11 12 13 15
17 18 20 22 24 26 28 29 30 31 34 35 40 43 45 47 48 49 50 57 59 64 70 72
74 75 76 77 79 81 82 84 85 87 93 98 103 107 108 110 111 114 115 118
119 124 126 127 129 130 131 135 146 147 148 149 156 157 **P**6 **S** TENET
Healthcare Corporation, Dallas, TX
Primary Contact: Daniel Listi, Chief Executive Officer
COO: Megan Drake, Chief Operating Officer
CFO: Jennifer Pittman, Chief Financial Officer
CMO: Jade Brice Roshell, M.D., Chief Medical Officer
CIO: Mike Nighman, Facility Coordinator Information Systems
CHR: Cindy Nicholson, Director Human Resources
CNO: Susan Bria, Chief Nursing Officer
Web address: www.brookwoodbaptisthealth.com
**Control:** Corporation, Investor–owned (for–profit) **Service:** General medical and
surgical

**Staffed Beds:** 231 **Admissions:** 12074 **Census:** 163 **Outpatient
Visits:** 96609 **Births:** 947 **Total Expense ($000):** 160122 **Payroll Expense
($000):** 54658

**SHELBY MEDICAL CENTER** See Shelby Baptist Medical Center

## ALEXANDER CITY—Tallapoosa County

☐ **RUSSELL MEDICAL (010065)**, 3316 Highway 280, Zip 35010–3369, Mailing
Address: P.O. Box 939, Zip 35011–0939; tel. 256/329–7100, (Nonreporting) **A**1
3 5 10 19 **F**3 11 13 15 18 20 22 28 29 30 31 34 35 40 43 45 50 51 53 57 59
60 64 67 68 74 75 76 77 78 79 80 81 82 85 89 93 102 107 108 110 111 115
116 119 121 123 126 129 131 132 133 143 144 146 148 149 154
Primary Contact: Lother E. Peace III, President and Chief Executive Officer
CFO: J. Matthew Fisher, Chief Financial Officer
CMO: Michele Goldhagen, M.D., Chief Medical Officer
CIO: Donna Carter, Chief Information Officer and Security Officer
CHR: Holly Williams, Human Resources Director
Web address: www.russellmedcenter.com
**Control:** Other not–for–profit (including NFP Corporation) **Service:** General
medical and surgical

**Staffed Beds:** 69 **Admissions:** 2191 **Census:** 10 **Outpatient Visits:** 95791
**Births:** 349 **Total Expense ($000):** 76281 **Payroll Expense ($000):** 25287
**Personnel:** 526

**RUSSELL MEDICAL CENTER** See Russell Medical

## ANDALUSIA—Covington County

⊠ **ANDALUSIA HEALTH (010036)**, 849 South Three Notch Street,
Zip 36420–5325, Mailing Address: P.O. Box 760, Zip 36420–1214;
tel. 334/222–8466, (Nonreporting) **A**1 10 **F**3 8 13 15 18 20 29 34 35 40 45 46
57 59 64 70 76 79 81 85 107 108 110 111 115 118 119 128 131 133 146
154 **S** LifePoint Health, Brentwood, TN
Primary Contact: Clint Kendall, R.N., Chief Executive Officer
CFO: Shirley M Smith, Chief Financial Officer
CIO: Matthew Perry, Director Information Systems
CHR: Brian Woods, Human Resources Director
CNO: Pam Aud, Chief Clinical Officer
Web address: www.andalusiahealth.com
**Control:** Corporation, Investor–owned (for–profit) **Service:** General medical and
surgical

**Staffed Beds:** 78 **Admissions:** 2819 **Census:** 28 **Outpatient Visits:** 40580
**Births:** 322 **Total Expense ($000):** 36417 **Payroll Expense ($000):** 12816
**Personnel:** 288

**ANDALUSIA REGIONAL HOSPITAL** See Andalusia Health

## ANNISTON—Calhoun County

**LONG TERM HOSPITAL OF ANNISTON** See Noland Hospital Anniston

☐ **NOLAND HOSPITAL ANNISTON (012011)**, 400 East 10th Street, 4th Fl,
Zip 36207–4716; tel. 256/741–6141, (Nonreporting) **A**1 10 **S** Noland Health
Services, Inc., Birmingham, AL
Primary Contact: Trina Woods, Administrator
Web address: www.nolandhealth.com
**Control:** Other not–for–profit (including NFP Corporation) **Service:** Acute long–
term care hospital

**Staffed Beds:** 38

**REGIONAL MEDICAL CENTER - ANNISTON** See RMC Anniston

⊠ **RMC ANNISTON (010078)**, 400 East Tenth Street, Zip 36207–4716, Mailing
Address: P.O. Box 2208, Zip 36202–2208; tel. 256/235–5121, (Nonreporting) **A**1
2 10 19 **S** Regional Medical Center, Anniston, AL
Primary Contact: Louis A. Bass, Chief Executive Officer
COO: Tripp Johnson, Assistant Vice President Operations
CFO: Mark D. North, Chief Financial Officer
CMO: David Zinn, M.D., Vice President Medical Affairs
CIO: Pete Furlow, Chief Information Officer
CHR: Doug Scott, Vice President Human Resources
CNO: Elaine Davis, Chief Nursing Officer and Vice President Patient Services
Web address: www.rmccares.org
**Control:** Hospital district or authority, Government, Nonfederal **Service:** General
medical and surgical

**Staffed Beds:** 276

☐ **RMC-STRINGFELLOW MEMORIAL HOSPITAL (010038)**, 301 East 18th Street,
Zip 36207–3952; tel. 256/235–8900, (Nonreporting) **A**1 10 **S** Regional Medical
Center, Anniston, AL
Primary Contact: Joe Weaver, Chief Executive Officer
CIO: Peggy Henderson, Director Health Information
CHR: Tamatha Johnson, Director Human Resources
Web address: www.stringfellowmemorial.com
**Control:** Corporation, Investor–owned (for–profit) **Service:** General medical and
surgical

**Staffed Beds:** 88

**STRINGFELLOW MEMORIAL HOSPITAL** See RMC-Stringfellow Memorial Hospital

---

**Hospital, Medicare Provider Number, Address, Telephone, Approval, Facility, and Physician Codes, Health Care System**

★ American Hospital Association (AHA) membership  ○ Healthcare Facilities Accreditation Program  ⇑ Center for Improvement in Healthcare Quality Accreditation
☐ The Joint Commission accreditation  ◇ DNV Healthcare Inc. accreditation  △ Commission on Accreditation of Rehabilitation Facilities (CARF) accreditation

## ASHLAND—Clay County

**CLAY COUNTY HOSPITAL (010073)**, 83825 Highway 9, Zip 36251–7981,
Mailing Address: P.O. Box 1270, Zip 36251–1270; tel. 256/354–2131,
(Nonreporting) **A**10
Primary Contact: Joel W. Tate, FACHE, Chief Executive Officer
CFO: Kerry W Tomlin, Associate Administrator
CMO: David Hensleigh, Director Medical Staff
CIO: Patrick Smith, Director Information Technology
CHR: Linda T Smith, Director Human Resources
CNO: Charles Griffin, Director of Nursing
Web address: www.claycountyhospital.com
**Control**: County, Government, Nonfederal **Service**: General medical and surgical

**Staffed Beds:** 129

**CLAY COUNTY HOSPITAL & NRSG HM** See Clay County Hospital

## ATHENS—Limestone County

☐ **ATHENS-LIMESTONE HOSPITAL (010079)**, 700 West Market Street,
Zip 35611–2457, Mailing Address: P.O. Box 999, Zip 35612–0999;
tel. 256/233–9292, (Nonreporting) **A**1 5 10 **F**3 7 8 11 13 15 18 28 29 34 35 40
43 46 48 50 51 53 54 56 57 58 59 64 68 70 73 75 76 77 79 81 82 85 86 87
89 93 98 107 108 109 110 111 114 115 118 119 129 130 131 132 143 144
146 147 148 149 154 **S** Huntsville Hospital Health System, Huntsville, AL
Primary Contact: David Pryor, President
COO: Randy Comer, Chief Operating Officer
CFO: Randy Comer, Chief Financial Officer
CMO: Jon Bignault, M.D., Chief of Staff
CIO: Kim Hoback, Supervisor Information Systems
CHR: Rachel Frey, Director Human Resources
CNO: Jan Lenz, Chief Nursing Officer
Web address: www.athenslimestonehospital.com
**Control**: Hospital district or authority, Government, Nonfederal **Service**: General medical and surgical

**Staffed Beds:** 71 **Admissions:** 3735 **Census:** 35 **Outpatient Visits:** 137794
**Births:** 419 **Total Expense ($000):** 94208 **Payroll Expense ($000):** 36076
**Personnel:** 786

**NORTH ALABAMA SPECIALTY HOSPITAL (012014)**, 700 West Market Street,
2 South, Zip 35611–2457; tel. 256/262–6767, (Nonreporting) **A**10 22
Primary Contact: Gene Smith, Chief Executive Officer
Web address: www.amgnash.com
**Control**: Corporation, Investor–owned (for–profit) **Service**: Acute long–term care hospital

**Staffed Beds:** 31

## ATMORE—Escambia County

**ATMORE COMMUNITY HOSPITAL (010169)**, 401 Medical Park Drive,
Zip 36502–3091; tel. 251/368–2500, (Nonreporting) **A**10 **S** Infirmary Health
System, Mobile, AL
Primary Contact: Suzanne McGill, Interim Chief Executive Officer
COO: Brad Lowery, Director of Operations
CFO: Keith Strickling, Chief Financial Officer
CHR: Linda Lowrey, Human Resources Officer
CNO: Suzanne McGill, Director of Nursing
Web address: www.atmorehealth.org/
**Control**: Other not–for–profit (including NFP Corporation) **Service**: General medical and surgical

**Staffed Beds:** 33

**GREENLAWN HOSPITAL** See Atmore Community Hospital

## BAY MINETTE—Baldwin County

**NORTH BALDWIN HOSPITAL** See North Baldwin Infirmary

**NORTH BALDWIN INFIRMARY (010129)**, 1815 Hand Avenue, Zip 36507–4110,
Mailing Address: P.O. Box 1409, Zip 36507–1409; tel. 251/937–5521,
(Nonreporting) **A**10 **S** Infirmary Health System, Mobile, AL
Primary Contact: Benjamin K. Hansert, Administrator
CFO: J Patrick Murphy, Chief Financial Officer
Web address: www.mobileinfirmary.org
**Control**: Other not–for–profit (including NFP Corporation) **Service**: General medical and surgical

**Staffed Beds:** 50

## BESSEMER—Jefferson County

☐ **MEDICAL WEST (010114)**, 995 Ninth Avenue SW, Zip 35022–4527;
tel. 205/481–7000, (Nonreporting) **A**1 3 10 **F**3 11 13 15 18 20 28 29 30 31
33 34 40 42 43 45 49 50 53 54 57 59 60 64 68 70 74 75 76 77 78 79 81 82
85 86 90 92 93 94 96 98 100 101 102 103 104 107 108 110 111 114 115
118 119 129 130 132 143 146 147 148 149 154 **P**6 **S** UAB Health System,
Birmingham, AL
Primary Contact: Brian Keith. Pennington, President and Chief Executive Officer
COO: Sean Tinney, FACHE, Chief Operating Officer
CFO: Brandon H Slocum, Senior Vice President and Chief Financial Officer
CMO: Conrad De Los Santos, President Medical Staff
CIO: Bob Duckworth, Director Information Systems
CHR: Gannon Davis, Director Human Resources
CNO: Pamela Spencer Autrey, R.N., Ph.D., MSN, Chief Nursing Officer
Web address: www.medicalwesthospital.org
**Control**: Hospital district or authority, Government, Nonfederal **Service**: General medical and surgical

**Staffed Beds:** 231 **Admissions:** 7489 **Census:** 113 **Outpatient**
**Visits:** 243050 **Births:** 365 **Total Expense ($000):** 129808 **Payroll Expense**
**($000):** 52816 **Personnel:** 1072

**UAB MEDICAL WEST** See Medical West

## BIRMINGHAM—Jefferson County

**BAPTIST PRINCETON** See Princeton Baptist Medical Center

☒ **BIRMINGHAM VETERANS AFFAIRS MEDICAL CENTER**, 700 South 19th Street,
Zip 35233–1927; tel. 205/933–8101, (Nonreporting) **A**1 2 3 5 8 **F**3 15 17 18 24
26 28 29 30 31 33 34 35 36 37 38 39 40 45 46 47 48 49 54 56 57 58 59 60
62 63 64 70 74 75 77 78 79 81 82 83 84 85 86 87 91 92 93 94 95 96 97 100
101 102 104 107 108 109 110 111 112 113 114 115 116 117 118 119 120
126 127 129 130 132 133 135 138 143 146 147 148 149 153 154 156 157 **S**
Department of Veterans Affairs, Washington, DC
Primary Contact: Stacy J. Vasquez, Chief Executive Officer
COO: Phyllis J. Smith, Associate Director
CFO: Mary S Mitchell, Chief Resource Management Services
CMO: William F Harper, M.D., Chief of Staff
CIO: Antonia Mohamed, Acting Chief Information Officer
CHR: Jacqueline Caron, Chief Human Resources
CNO: Cynthia Cleveland, Ph.D., R.N., Associate Director for Patient Care Services
and Nurse Executive
Web address: www.birmingham.va.gov/
**Control**: Veterans Affairs, Government, federal **Service**: General medical and surgical

**Staffed Beds:** 139 **Admissions:** 7673 **Census:** 96 **Outpatient**
**Visits:** 862170 **Total Expense ($000):** 607413 **Payroll Expense**
**($000):** 218351 **Personnel:** 2754

☒ △ **BROOKWOOD BAPTIST MEDICAL CENTER (010139)**, 2010 Brookwood
Medical Center Drive, Zip 35209–6875; tel. 205/877–1000, (Nonreporting) **A**1 2
3 5 7 10 **S** TENET Healthcare Corporation, Dallas, TX
Primary Contact: Timothy Puthoff, Chief Executive Officer
COO: Kathy Healy-Collier, Chief Operating Officer
CFO: Ken Hendren, Chief Financial Officer
CMO: Vish Sachdev, M.D., Chief Medical Officer
CIO: Manuel Price, Director Information Systems
CHR: Ronnelle Stewart, Chief Human Resources Officer
CNO: Robbie Hindman, Chief Nursing Officer
Web address: www.https://www.brookwoodbaptisthealth.com/
**Control**: Corporation, Investor–owned (for–profit) **Service**: General medical and surgical

**Staffed Beds:** 607

*Many Facility Codes have changed. Please refer to the AHA Guide Code Chart.*

**BROOKWOOD MEDICAL CENTER** See Brookwood Baptist Medical Center

✠ **CHILDREN'S OF ALABAMA (013300)**, 1600 Seventh Avenue South,
Zip 35233–1785; tel. 205/638–9100, (Nonreporting) **A**1 3 5 10 **F**3 7 8 9 11 12
16 17 19 20 21 22 23 25 27 28 29 30 31 32 34 35 36 37 38 39 40 41 43 44
46 48 50 54 55 57 58 59 60 61 64 65 68 72 74 75 77 78 79 80 81 82 84 85
86 87 88 89 91 92 93 94 95 96 97 98 99 100 101 102 104 107 108 109 111
114 115 116 117 118 119 126 129 130 131 132 134 135 136 137 138 139
142 146 148 149 154 155 156
Primary Contact: Wm. Michael. Warren Jr, President and Chief Executive Officer
COO: Tom Shufflebarger, Chief Operating Officer
CFO: Dawn Walton, Chief Financial Officer
CMO: Crayton A Fargason, M.D., Medical Director
CIO: Robert Sarnecki, Interim Chief Information Officer
CHR: Douglas B Dean, Chief Human Resources Officer
CNO: Deb Wesley, MSN, Chief Nursing Officer
Web address: www.childrensal.org
**Control:** Other not–for–profit (including NFP Corporation) **Service:** Children's
general medical and surgical

**Staffed Beds: 341 Admissions: 15111 Census: 257 Outpatient
Visits: 684092 Births: 0 Total Expense ($000): 713965 Payroll Expense
($000): 295266 Personnel: 4033**

✠ **ENCOMPASS HEALTH LAKESHORE REHABILITATION HOSPITAL (013025)**,
3800 Ridgeway Drive, Zip 35209–5599; tel. 205/868–2000, (Nonreporting)
**A**1 10 **F**3 29 35 68 75 86 87 90 91 95 96 130 132 **S** Encompass Health
Corporation, Birmingham, AL
Primary Contact: Michael Bartell, Chief Executive Officer
CFO: Kimberly Thrasher, Controller
CMO: Michael Rosemore, M.D., Medical Director
CHR: Julie Smith, Director Human Resources
CNO: April Cobb, Chief Nursing Officer
Web address: www.encompasshealth.com/lakeshorerehab
**Control:** Corporation, Investor–owned (for–profit) **Service:** Rehabilitation

**Staffed Beds: 100 Admissions: 2680 Census: 87 Outpatient Visits: 3572
Births: 0 Total Expense ($000): 47726 Payroll Expense ($000): 18997
Personnel: 345**

✠ **GRANDVIEW MEDICAL CENTER (010104)**, 3690 Grandview Parkway,
Zip 35243–3326; tel. 205/971–1000, (Nonreporting) **A**1 3 10 **S** Community
Health Systems, Inc., Franklin, TN
Primary Contact: Drew Mason, Chief Executive Officer
COO: Justin O. Bryant, Chief Operating Officer
CFO: Michael Cotton, Chief Financial Officer
CMO: David Wynne, President Medical Staff
CIO: Tim Townes, Director Information Systems
CHR: Jeri Wink, Director Human Resources
CNO: Sherry Cole, Chief Nursing Officer
Web address: www.grandviewhealth.com
**Control:** Corporation, Investor–owned (for–profit) **Service:** General medical and
surgical

**Staffed Beds: 379**

**HEALTHSOUTH LAKESHORE REHABILITATION HOSPITAL** See Encompass
Health Lakeshore Rehabilitation Hospital

**HEALTHSOUTH MEDICAL CENTER** See UAB Highlands

☐ **HILL CREST BEHAVIORAL HEALTH SERVICES (014000)**, 6869 Fifth Avenue
South, Zip 35212–1866; tel. 205/833–9000, (Nonreporting) **A**1 10 **S** Universal
Health Services, Inc., King of Prussia, PA
Primary Contact: Jennifer Synder, Chief Executive Officer
CFO: Mark Teske, Chief Financial Officer
Web address: www.hillcrestbhs.com
**Control:** Corporation, Investor–owned (for–profit) **Service:** Psychiatric

**Staffed Beds: 80**

**HILL CREST HOSPITAL** See Hill Crest Behavioral Health Services

**LONG TERM HOSPITAL OF BIRMINGHAM** See Noland Hospital Birmingham

**MEDICAL CENTER EAST** See St. Vincent's East

☐ **NOLAND HOSPITAL BIRMINGHAM (012009)**, 50 Medical Park East Drive, 8th
Floor, Zip 35235; tel. 205/808–5100, (Nonreporting) **A**1 10 **S** Noland Health
Services, Inc., Birmingham, AL
Primary Contact: Laura S. Wills, Administrator
COO: Sharon Engle, Director Clinical Services
CMO: Mark Middlebrooks, M.D., Medical Director
CHR: Ashley Clark, Coordinator Human Resources
CNO: Rachel Chapman, Nurse Manager
Web address: www.nolandhealth.com
**Control:** Other not–for–profit (including NFP Corporation) **Service:** Acute long–
term care hospital

**Staffed Beds: 45**

✠ **PRINCETON BAPTIST MEDICAL CENTER (010103)**, 701 Princeton Avenue
SW, Zip 35211–1303; tel. 205/783–3000, (Nonreporting) **A**1 2 3 5 10 **S** TENET
Healthcare Corporation, Dallas, TX
Primary Contact: Michael Neuendorf, Chief Executive Officer
CFO: Amanda Dyle, Chief Financial Officer
CMO: Alan Craig, M.D., Chief Medical Officer
CHR: Jason Hatter, Chief Human Resource Officer
CNO: Paula Davenport, Chief Nursing Officer
Web address: www.bhsala.com
**Control:** Church operated, Nongovernment, not–for–profit **Service:** General
medical and surgical

**Staffed Beds: 315**

✠ **SELECT SPECIALTY HOSPITAL-BIRMINGHAM (012008)**, 2010 Brookwood
Medical Center Drive, 3rd Floor, Zip 35209–6804; tel. 205/599–4600,
(Nonreporting) **A**1 10 **S** Select Medical Corporation, Mechanicsburg, PA
Primary Contact: Clifton Quinn, Chief Executive Officer
CMO: Allan Goldstein, M.D., Medical Director and Chief of Staff
Web address: www.birmingham.selectspecialtyhospitals.com
**Control:** Corporation, Investor–owned (for–profit) **Service:** Acute long–term care
hospital

**Staffed Beds: 38**

**ST VINCENT'S HOSPITAL** See St. Vincent's Birmingham

✠ **ST. VINCENT'S BIRMINGHAM (010056)**, 810 St Vincent's Drive,
Zip 35205–1695, Mailing Address: P.O. Box 12407, Zip 35202–2407;
tel. 205/939–7000, (Nonreporting) **A**1 2 3 5 10 **F**3 11 13 15 17 18 20 22 24 26
28 29 30 31 34 35 37 40 43 45 53 57 58 59 60 62 68 70 72 74 76 77 78 79
81 82 84 85 86 87 91 93 94 107 110 111 114 119 120 121 123 124 126 131
132 135 146 147 149 **S** Ascension Healthcare, Saint Louis, MO
Primary Contact: Andrew Gnann, President
COO: Andy Davis, Chief Operating Officer
CFO: Wilma Newton, Executive Vice President and Chief Financial Officer
CMO: Gregory L James, D.O., Chief Medical Officer
CIO: Timothy Stettheimer, Vice President and Chief Information Officer
CHR: Michelle Galipeau, Director Human Resources
Web address: www.stvhs.com
**Control:** Other not–for–profit (including NFP Corporation) **Service:** General
medical and surgical

**Staffed Beds: 409 Admissions: 20616 Census: 241 Outpatient
Visits: 167047 Births: 3777 Total Expense ($000): 429178 Payroll
Expense ($000): 108065 Personnel: 1664**

✠ **ST. VINCENT'S EAST (010011)**, 50 Medical Park East Drive, Zip 35235–9987;
tel. 205/838–3000, (Nonreporting) **A**1 2 3 5 10 **F**3 11 12 13 15 17 18 20 22
24 26 28 29 30 31 35 40 43 44 45 46 47 49 50 51 53 57 59 70 72 74 76
77 78 79 81 85 86 87 90 93 98 100 102 103 107 108 111 114 118 119 120
121 123 124 129 130 132 135 146 147 149 **S** Ascension Healthcare, Saint
Louis, MO
Primary Contact: Suzannah Campbell, President
CFO: Jan DiCesare, Vice President Financial Operations
CMO: Frank Malensek, M.D., Chief Medical Officer
CIO: Beverly Golightly, Director Information Technology
CHR: Carol Maietta, Vice President Human Resources and Chief Learning Officer
CNO: Amy Shelton, Chief Nursing Officer
Web address: www.stvhs.com
**Control:** Other not–for–profit (including NFP Corporation) **Service:** General
medical and surgical

**Staffed Beds: 362 Admissions: 14932 Census: 251 Outpatient
Visits: 106175 Births: 0 Total Expense ($000): 222133 Payroll Expense
($000): 65986 Personnel: 996**

---

**Hospital, Medicare Provider Number, Address, Telephone, Approval, Facility, and Physician Codes, Health Care System**

★ American Hospital Association (AHA) membership
☐ The Joint Commission accreditation
○ Healthcare Facilities Accreditation Program
◇ DNV Healthcare Inc. accreditation
⇑ Center for Improvement in Healthcare Quality Accreditation
△ Commission on Accreditation of Rehabilitation Facilities (CARF) accreditation

**THE CHILDREN'S HOSPITAL OF ALABAMA** See Children's of Alabama

**TRINITY MEDICAL CENTER** See Grandview Medical Center

**UAB HIGHLANDS** See University of Alabama Hospital, Birmingham

**UNIVERSITY OF ALA HOSPITAL** See University of Alabama Hospital

✉ **UNIVERSITY OF ALABAMA HOSPITAL (010033)**, 619 19th Street South,
Zip 35249–1900; tel. 205/934–4011, (Includes UAB HIGHLANDS, Mailing
address: 1201 11th Avenue South, Birmingham, Alabama, Zip 35205–5299;
tel. 205/930–7000; Anthony Patterson, FACHE, Chief Operating Officer)
(Nonreporting) **A**1 2 3 5 8 10 **F**3 4 5 7 8 9 11 12 13 15 16 17 18 20 22 24 26
27 28 29 30 31 33 34 35 36 37 38 39 40 41 42 43 44 45 46 47 48 49 50 52
53 54 55 56 57 58 59 60 61 62 64 65 66 68 70 71 72 73 74 75 76 77 78 79
81 82 83 84 85 86 87 90 91 92 93 94 95 96 97 98 99 100 101 102 103 104
105 107 108 110 111 113 114 115 116 117 118 119 120 121 123 124 126
129 130 131 132 135 136 137 138 139 140 141 142 143 144 145 146 147
148 149 152 153 154 155 156 157 **S** UAB Health System, Birmingham, AL
Primary Contact: Reid F. Jones, Chief Executive Officer
CMO: Loring Rue, M.D., Senior Vice President, Quality Patient Safety and Clinical
Effectiveness
CIO: Joan Hicks, Chief Information Officer
CHR: Alesia Jones, Chief Human Resources Officer
CNO: Terri Lyn Poe, Chief Nursing Officer
Web address: www.uabmedicine.org
**Control**: State, Government, Nonfederal **Service**: General medical and surgical

**Staffed Beds**: 1188 **Admissions**: 52644 **Census**: 1038 **Outpatient
Visits**: 799105 **Births**: 4433 **Total Expense ($000)**: 1892729 **Payroll
Expense ($000)**: 649627 **Personnel**: 12877

**VETERANS AFFAIRS MEDICAL CENTER** See Birmingham Veterans Affairs
Medical Center

### BOAZ—Marshall County

**BOAZ-ALBERTVILLE MEDICAL CTR** See Marshall Medical Center South

☐ **MARSHALL MEDICAL CENTER SOUTH (010005)**, U S Highway 431
North, Zip 35957–0999, Mailing Address: P.O. Box 758, Zip 35957–0758;
tel. 256/593–8310, (Data for 273 days) (Nonreporting) **A**1 5 10 19 **F**3 7 9 11 12
13 15 18 20 22 26 28 29 31 32 34 35 37 40 43 45 46 49 50 51 53 54 57 59
64 68 70 74 75 76 77 78 79 81 84 85 86 87 89 92 93 100 107 108 110 111
114 115 117 119 121 123 129 130 131 132 135 141 146 147 148 149 154 **S**
Marshall Health System, Guntersville, AL
Primary Contact: Cheryl M. Hays, FACHE, Chief Executive Officer
CFO: Taylor Walker, Chief Financial Officer
Web address: www.mmcenters.com//index.php/facilities/marshall_south
**Control**: Hospital district or authority, Government, Nonfederal **Service**: General
medical and surgical

**Staffed Beds**: 107 **Admissions**: 3170 **Census**: 52 **Outpatient
Visits**: 205506 **Births**: 518 **Total Expense ($000)**: 76264 **Payroll Expense
($000)**: 30732 **Personnel**: 728

### BREWTON—Escambia County

☐ **D. W. MCMILLAN MEMORIAL HOSPITAL (010099)**, 1301 Belleville
Avenue, Zip 36426–1306, Mailing Address: P.O. Box 908, Zip 36427–0908;
tel. 251/867–8061, (Nonreporting) **A**1 10
Primary Contact: Rick Owens, Administrator
CIO: Ian Vickery, Director Information Technology
CHR: Autherine Davis, Director Human Resources
CNO: Bob Ellis, Director of Nursing
Web address: www.dwmmh.org
**Control**: Hospital district or authority, Government, Nonfederal **Service**: General
medical and surgical

**Staffed Beds**: 49

### BUTLER—Choctaw County

**CHOCTAW GENERAL HOSPITAL (011304)**, 401 Vanity Fair Avenue,
Zip 36904–3032; tel. 205/459–9100, (Nonreporting) **A**10 18 **S** Rush Health
Systems, Meridian, MS
Primary Contact: J W. Cowan, Administrator
Web address: www.choctawgeneral.com/cgh/
**Control**: Other not-for-profit (including NFP Corporation) **Service**: General
medical and surgical

**Staffed Beds**: 25

### CENTRE—Cherokee County

**CHEROKEE MEDICAL CENTER** See Floyd Cherokee Medical Center

✉ **FLOYD CHEROKEE MEDICAL CENTER (010022)**, 400 Northwood Drive,
Zip 35960–1023; tel. 256/927–5531, (Nonreporting) **A**1 10 **S** Floyd Healthcare
Management, Rome, GA
Primary Contact: David T. Early, FACHE, Chief Executive Officer
CFO: Zac Allen, CPA, Chief Financial Officer
CHR: Marlene Benefield, Director Human Resources
CNO: Tifani Kinard, Chief Nursing Officer
Web address: www.cherokeemedicalcenter.com
**Control**: Other not-for-profit (including NFP Corporation) **Service**: General
medical and surgical

**Staffed Beds**: 45

### CENTREVILLE—Bibb County

**BIBB MEDICAL CENTER (010058)**, 208 Pierson Avenue, Zip 35042–2918;
tel. 205/926–4881, (Total facility includes 131 beds in nursing home–type unit)
(Nonreporting) **A**3 5 10 13 **F**3 7 11 13 15 29 30 31 34 35 40 45 46 50 53 54
56 57 59 64 65 66 69 71 75 76 77 80 81 86 87 93 97 107 115 119 125 127
128 130 133 135 143 144 146 148 149 150 154 156 158 **P**6
Primary Contact: Joseph Marchant, Administrator
CFO: Heather Desmond, Chief Financial Officer
CMO: John Meigs, M.D., JrChief of Staff
CHR: Karen Daniel, Director Human Resources
Web address: www.bibbmedicalcenter.com
**Control**: Hospital district or authority, Government, Nonfederal **Service**: General
medical and surgical

**Staffed Beds**: 166 **Admissions**: 1146 **Census**: 122 **Outpatient
Visits**: 48964 **Births**: 76 **Total Expense ($000)**: 20310 **Payroll Expense
($000)**: 9243 **Personnel**: 243

### CHATOM—Washington County

**WASHINGTON COUNTY HOSPITAL (011300)**, 14600 St Stephens
Avenue, Zip 36518–9998, Mailing Address: P.O. Box 1299, Zip 36518–1299;
tel. 251/847–2223, (Nonreporting) **A**10 18
Primary Contact: Teresa G. Grimes, Chief Executive Officer
CMO: Steve Donald, M.D., Chief of Staff
CIO: Brady Wright, Information Technology Network Administrator
CHR: Linda Randolph, Director Personnel Services
CNO: Michelle Alford, R.N., MSN, Director of Nursing
Web address: www.wchnh.org
**Control**: County, Government, Nonfederal **Service**: General medical and surgical

**Staffed Beds**: 20

**WASHINGTON COUNTY HOSPITAL AND NURSING HOME** See Washington
County Hospital

### CLANTON—Chilton County

✉ **ST. VINCENT'S CHILTON HOSPITAL (010173)**, 2030 Lay Dam Road,
Zip 35045; tel. 205/258–4400, (Nonreporting) **A**1 10 **F**3 11 15 29 30 35 40 43
45 46 50 59 60 64 68 70 79 81 82 85 87 93 107 108 110 111 119 130 135
146 148 149 **S** Ascension Healthcare, Saint Louis, MO
Primary Contact: Andrew Gnann, President
Web address: www.https://www.stvhs.com/chilton/
**Control**: Other not-for-profit (including NFP Corporation) **Service**: General
medical and surgical

**Staffed Beds**: 36 **Admissions**: 717 **Census**: 7 **Outpatient Visits**: 30484
**Births**: 0 **Total Expense ($000)**: 23459 **Payroll Expense ($000)**: 7111
**Personnel**: 106

*Many Facility Codes have changed. Please refer to the AHA Guide Code Chart.*
© 2021 AHA Guide

## CULLMAN—Cullman County

**CULLMAN MEDICAL CENTER** See Cullman Regional Medical Center

✜ **CULLMAN REGIONAL MEDICAL CENTER (010035)**, 1912 Alabama Highway 157, Zip 35055, Mailing Address: P.O. Box 1108, Zip 35056–1108; tel. 256/737–2000, (Nonreporting) **A**1 3 10 **F**3 7 8 12 13 15 18 20 22 26 28 29 30 34 35 37 40 43 45 46 49 50 51 53 54 57 59 62 63 64 68 70 71 75 76 79 81 82 84 85 86 87 89 93 97 107 108 110 111 114 115 118 119 120 126 129 130 131 132 133 134 135 144 146 147 148 149 156 157
Primary Contact: James Clements, Chief Executive Officer
COO: Nesha Donaldson, Chief Operating Officer
CMO: William E. Smith, M.D., Chief Medical Officer
CIO: Nancy Zavatchen, Director Information Technology
CHR: Toni Geddings, Director Human Resources
CNO: Charna Brown, Chief Nursing Officer
Web address: www.crmchospital.com
**Control**: Other not-for-profit (including NFP Corporation) **Service**: General medical and surgical

**Staffed Beds:** 145 **Admissions:** 7746 **Census:** 78 **Outpatient Visits:** 103181 **Births:** 665 **Total Expense ($000):** 118133 **Payroll Expense ($000):** 48655 **Personnel:** 1067

## DADEVILLE—Tallapoosa County

**LAKE MARTIN COMMUNITY HOSPITAL (010052)**, 201 Mariarden Road, Zip 36853–6251, Mailing Address: P.O. Box 629, Zip 36853–0629; tel. 256/825–7821, (Nonreporting) **A**10
Primary Contact: Michael D. Bruce, Chief Executive Officer
CHR: Karen Treadwell, Director Human Resources
Web address: www.lakemartincommunityhospital.com
**Control**: Partnership, Investor–owned (for–profit) **Service**: General medical and surgical

**Staffed Beds:** 25

**LAKESHORE COMMUNITY HOSPITAL** See Lake Martin Community Hospital

## DAPHNE—Baldwin County

★ **EASTPOINTE HOSPITAL (014017)**, 7400 Roper Lane, Zip 36526–5274; tel. 251/378–6500, (Nonreporting) **A**5 10 **F**29 98 106 130 143 **S** AltaPointe Health Systems, Mobile, AL
Primary Contact: Philip L. Cusa, Hospital Director
CFO: Kevin Markham, Chief Financial Officer
CMO: Sandra K Parker, M.D., Chief Medical Officer
CIO: Steve Dolan, Chief Information Officer
CHR: Alicia Donoghue, Director Human Resources
Web address: www.altapointe.org/eastpointe.php
**Control**: Other not-for-profit (including NFP Corporation) **Service**: Psychiatric

**Staffed Beds:** 50 **Admissions:** 778 **Census:** 39 **Outpatient Visits:** 0 **Total Expense ($000):** 9120 **Payroll Expense ($000):** 5885 **Personnel:** 143

## DECATUR—Morgan County

**DECATUR GENERAL HOSPITAL-WEST** See Decatur Morgan Hospital-West

**DECATUR MORGAN HOSPITAL** See Decatur Morgan Hospital Parkway Campus

☐ **DECATUR MORGAN HOSPITAL (010085)**, 1201 Seventh Street SE, Zip 35601–3303, Mailing Address: P.O. Box 2239, Zip 35609–2239; tel. 256/341–2000, (Includes DECATUR MORGAN HOSPITAL PARKWAY CAMPUS, Mailing address: 1874 Beltline Road SW, Decatur, Alabama, Zip 35601–5509, P O Box 2239, Zip 35609–2239, tel. 256/350–2211; DECATUR MORGAN HOSPITAL-WEST, Mailing address: 2205 Beltline Road SW, Decatur, Alabama, Zip 35601–3687, P O Box 2240, Zip 35609–2240, tel. 256/306–4000), (Nonreporting) **A**1 3 5 10 **S** Huntsville Hospital Health System, Huntsville, AL
Primary Contact: Kelli Powers, President
CFO: Danny Crowe, Chief Financial Officer
CMO: Allen J Schmidt, M.D., President, Medical Staff
CIO: Mark Megehee, Vice President and Chief Information Officer
CNO: Anita Walden, Vice President and Chief Nursing Officer
Web address: www.decaturgeneral.org
**Control**: Hospital district or authority, Government, Nonfederal **Service**: General medical and surgical

**Staffed Beds:** 110

## DEMOPOLIS—Marengo County

**BRYAN W. WHITFIELD MEMORIAL HOSPITAL (010112)**, 105 U S Highway 80 East, Zip 36732–3616, Mailing Address: P.O. Box 890, Zip 36732–0890; tel. 334/289–4000, (Nonreporting) **A**3 10 20 **S** UAB Health System, Birmingham, AL
Primary Contact: Douglas L. Brewer, Chief Executive Officer
COO: Dereck Morrison, Assistant Administrator
CFO: Doug A. Brooker, Chief Financial Officer
CMO: John G. Kahler, M.D., Radiologist
Web address: www.bwwmh.com
**Control**: Hospital district or authority, Government, Nonfederal **Service**: General medical and surgical

**Staffed Beds:** 47

## DOTHAN—Houston County

✜ **ENCOMPASS HEALTH REHABILITATION HOSPITAL OF DOTHAN (013030)**, 1736 East Main Street, Zip 36301–3040, Mailing Address: P.O. Box 6708, Zip 36302–6708; tel. 334/712–6333, (Nonreporting) **A**1 10 **S** Encompass Health Corporation, Birmingham, AL
Primary Contact: Margaret A. Futch, Chief Executive Officer
CFO: Heath Watson, Controller
CHR: Lydia Christion, Director Human Resources
Web address: www.encompasshealth.com/dothanrehab
**Control**: Corporation, Investor–owned (for–profit) **Service**: Rehabilitation

**Staffed Beds:** 51

✜ **FLOWERS HOSPITAL (010055)**, 4370 West Main Street, Zip 36305–4000, Mailing Address: P.O. Box 6907, Zip 36302–6907; tel. 334/793–5000, (Nonreporting) **A**1 3 10 19 **S** Community Health Systems, Inc., Franklin, TN
Primary Contact: Jeffrey M. Brannon, Chief Executive Officer
COO: Matthew H Blevins, Chief Operating Officer
CFO: Talana Bell, Chief Financial Officer
CIO: Matthew Garrett, Director Information Systems
CHR: Jennifer Odom, Interim Director Human Resources
CNO: Dan L Cumbie, Chief Nursing Officer
Web address: www.flowershospital.com
**Control**: Corporation, Investor–owned (for–profit) **Service**: General medical and surgical

**Staffed Beds:** 147

**HEALTHSOUTH REHABILITATION HOSPITAL** See Encompass Health Rehabilitation Hospital of Dothan

☐ **LAUREL OAKS BEHAVIORAL HEALTH CENTER (014013)**, 700 East Cottonwood Road, Zip 36301–3644; tel. 334/794–7373, (Nonreporting) **A**1 10 **S** Universal Health Services, Inc., King of Prussia, PA
Primary Contact: Derek Johnson, Chief Executive Officer
CMO: Nelson Handol, M.D., Medical Director
CHR: Lorrie Evans, Director Human Resources
Web address: www.laureloaksbhc.com
**Control**: Corporation, Investor–owned (for–profit) **Service**: Children's hospital psychiatric

**Staffed Beds:** 38

**LONG TERM HOSPITAL OF DOTHAN** See Noland Hospital Dothan

☐ **NOLAND HOSPITAL DOTHAN (012010)**, 1108 Ross Clark Circle, 4th Floor, Zip 36301–3022; tel. 334/699–4300, (Nonreporting) **A**1 10 **S** Noland Health Services, Inc., Birmingham, AL
Primary Contact: Kaye Burk, Administrator
Web address: www.nolandhealth.com
**Control**: Other not-for-profit (including NFP Corporation) **Service**: Acute long–term care hospital

**Staffed Beds:** 38

---

**Hospital, Medicare Provider Number, Address, Telephone, Approval, Facility, and Physician Codes, Health Care System**

★ American Hospital Association (AHA) membership
☐ The Joint Commission accreditation
○ Healthcare Facilities Accreditation Program
◇ DNV Healthcare Inc. accreditation
⇑ Center for Improvement in Healthcare Quality Accreditation
△ Commission on Accreditation of Rehabilitation Facilities (CARF) accreditation

⇑ **SOUTHEAST ALABAMA MEDICAL CENTER (010001)**, 1108 Ross Clark Circle, Zip 36301–3024, Mailing Address: P.O. Box 6987, Zip 36302–6987; tel. 334/793–8111, (Nonreporting) **A**3 5 10 21
Primary Contact: Richard O. Sutton, FACHE, Chief Executive Officer
COO: Charles C Brannen, Senior Vice President and Chief Operating Officer
CFO: Derek Miller, Senior Vice President and Chief Financial Officer
CMO: Charles Harkness, D.O., Vice President Medical Affairs
CIO: Eric Allen Daffron, Division Director, Information Systems
CHR: Tony Welch, Vice President Human Resources
CNO: Diane Buntyn, MSN, R.N., Vice President Patient Care Services
Web address: www.samc.org
**Control**: Hospital district or authority, Government, Nonfederal **Service**: General medical and surgical

| Staffed Beds: 387 |
| --- |

### ENTERPRISE—Coffee County

**HUMANA HOSPITAL-ENTERPRISE** See Medical Center Enterprise

✠ **MEDICAL CENTER ENTERPRISE (010049)**, 400 North Edwards Street, Zip 36330–2510; tel. 334/347–0584, (Nonreporting) **A**1 10 **F**3 11 13 15 18 26 28 29 30 34 35 40 45 50 57 59 60 65 68 70 76 79 81 82 87 93 107 108 110 111 115 118 119 129 130 133 146 147 148 154 **S** Community Health Systems, Inc., Franklin, TN
Primary Contact: Suzanne Woods, Chief Executive Officer
CFO: Greg McGilvray, Chief Financial Officer
CMO: Patrick Lett, M.D., Medical Doctor
CIO: Stephen Smothers, Director Information Systems
CHR: Toni Kaminski, Director Human Resources
CNO: Barry Eads, R.N., Chief Nursing Officer
Web address: www.mcehospital.com
**Control**: Corporation, Investor–owned (for–profit) **Service**: General medical and surgical

| Staffed Beds: 99 Admissions: 3954 Census: 30 Outpatient Visits: 68673 Births: 973 Total Expense ($000): 49637 Payroll Expense ($000): 18092 Personnel: 351 |
| --- |

### EUFAULA—Barbour County

**LAKEVIEW COMMUNITY HOSPITAL** See Medical Center Barbour

**MEDICAL CENTER BARBOUR (010069)**, 820 West Washington Street, Zip 36027–1899; tel. 334/688–7000, (Nonreporting) **A**10 20
Primary Contact: Lynn M. Mergen, Chief Executive Officer
CFO: Michael Reynolds, Chief Financial Officer
CHR: Cindy Griffin, Director Human Resources
CNO: Missy Thomas, Chief Nursing Officer
Web address: www.medctrbarbour.org
**Control**: Hospital district or authority, Government, Nonfederal **Service**: General medical and surgical

| Staffed Beds: 47 |
| --- |

### EUTAW—Greene County

**GREENE COUNTY HEALTH SYSTEM (010051)**, 509 Wilson Avenue, Zip 35462–1099; tel. 205/372–3388, (Nonreporting) **A**10
Primary Contact: Marcia Pugh, Chief Executive Officer
Web address: www.gcheutaw.com
**Control**: County, Government, Nonfederal **Service**: General medical and surgical

| Staffed Beds: 92 |
| --- |

**GREENE COUNTY HOSPITAL** See Greene County Health System

### EVERGREEN—Conecuh County

**EVERGREEN MED CTR** See Evergreen Medical Center

**EVERGREEN MEDICAL CENTER (010148)**, 101 Crestview Avenue, Zip 36401–3333, Mailing Address: P.O. Box 706, Zip 36401–0706; tel. 251/578–2480, (Nonreporting) **A**10 **F**4 15 32 34 35 40 41 45 46 47 48 49 50 53 57 59 62 64 65 66 75 81 82 83 84 86 87 93 94 97 107 108 110 111 114 119 127 130 132 133 134 135 144 146 147 148 150 151 154 157 **S** Gilliard Health Services, Montgomery, AL
Primary Contact: Tom McLendon, Administrator
CFO: Sharon Jones, Chief Financial Officer
CMO: William Farmer, M.D., Chief of Staff
CHR: Tracey Rhodes, Coordinator Human Resources
CNO: Angie Hendrix, Director of Nursing
Web address: www.evergreenmedical.org
**Control**: Corporation, Investor–owned (for–profit) **Service**: General medical and surgical

| Staffed Beds: 44 Admissions: 1435 Census: 17 Outpatient Visits: 2356 Births: 0 Total Expense ($000): 13067 Payroll Expense ($000): 5965 Personnel: 143 |
| --- |

### FAIRHOPE—Baldwin County

☐ **THOMAS HOSPITAL (010100)**, 750 Morphy Avenue, Zip 36532–1812, Mailing Address: P.O. Box 929, Zip 36533–0929; tel. 251/928–2375, (Nonreporting) **A**1 2 3 10 19 **S** Infirmary Health System, Mobile, AL
Primary Contact: Ormand P. Thompson, President
COO: Douglas Garner, Vice President
CMO: Michael McBrearty, M.D., Vice President Medical Affairs
CNO: Julie Rowell, R.N., Chief Nursing Officer
Web address: www.thomashospital.com
**Control**: Other not–for–profit (including NFP Corporation) **Service**: General medical and surgical

| Staffed Beds: 136 |
| --- |

### FAYETTE—Fayette County

**FAYETTE COUNTY HOSPITAL & HOME** See Fayette Medical Center

☐ **FAYETTE MEDICAL CENTER (010045)**, 1653 Temple Avenue North, Zip 35555–1314, Mailing Address: P O Drawer 710, Zip 35555–0710; tel. 205/932–5966, (Total facility includes 122 beds in nursing home–type unit) (Nonreporting) **A**1 10 **F**3 11 15 28 29 30 34 40 50 57 59 64 68 70 74 75 81 89 93 107 110 111 114 116 119 127 128 130 132 133 146 154 **S** DCH Health System, Tuscaloosa, AL
Primary Contact: Donald J. Jones, FACHE, Administrator
CFO: Jeff Huff, Assistant Administrator Finance
CHR: Felicia Solomon-Owens, Director Human Resources
Web address: www.dchsystem.com
**Control**: Hospital district or authority, Government, Nonfederal **Service**: General medical and surgical

| Staffed Beds: 167 Admissions: 696 Census: 124 Outpatient Visits: 49540 Births: 0 Total Expense ($000): 26111 Payroll Expense ($000): 11926 Personnel: 196 |
| --- |

### FLORENCE—Lauderdale County

**ELIZA COFFEE MEMORIAL HOSPITAL** See North Alabama Medical Center

✠ **NORTH ALABAMA MEDICAL CENTER (010006)**, 1701 Veterans Drive, Zip 35630–6033; tel. 256/629–1000, (Nonreporting) **A**1 3 5 10 19 **F**3 13 15 17 18 20 22 24 26 28 29 34 35 40 43 49 50 54 56 57 60 64 68 70 73 74 75 76 77 79 80 81 83 84 85 86 87 89 90 97 98 107 108 110 111 115 117 119 126 127 129 130 135 145 146 147 148 156 **S** LifePoint Health, Brentwood, TN
Primary Contact: Russell Pigg, Chief Executive Officer
COO: Mike Howard, Chief Operating Officer
CFO: Steve E. Hobbs, Chief Financial Officer
CMO: Oliver Matthews, M.D., Chief Medical Officer
CIO: Raul Velez, Information Technology Director
CHR: Cheryl Lee, Human Resources Director
Web address: www.https://namccares.com/
**Control**: Corporation, Investor–owned (for–profit) **Service**: General medical and surgical

| Staffed Beds: 321 Admissions: 15383 Census: 178 Outpatient Visits: 111313 Births: 1396 Total Expense ($000): 157238 Payroll Expense ($000): 55962 Personnel: 1290 |
| --- |

### FOLEY—Baldwin County

**SOUTH BALDWIN HOSPITAL** See South Baldwin Regional Medical Center

✠ **SOUTH BALDWIN REGIONAL MEDICAL CENTER (010083)**, 1613 North McKenzie Street, Zip 36535–2299; tel. 251/949–3400, (Nonreporting) **A**1 3 5 10 19 **F**3 12 13 15 18 20 28 29 30 31 34 35 37 38 40 43 45 49 50 51 54 57 59 60 64 65 66 68 70 74 75 76 77 79 81 82 85 86 87 93 107 108 110 111 115 116 117 118 119 126 129 130 131 132 133 134 135 144 146 147 148 149 154 156 **S** Community Health Systems, Inc., Franklin, TN
Primary Contact: Daniel McKinney, Chief Executive Officer
CFO: Brad Hardcastle, Chief Financial Officer
CMO: Lee Eslava, Chief Medical Officer
CHR: Pamela J Brunson, Director Human Resources
CNO: Margaret Roley, Chief Nursing Officer
Web address: www.southbaldwinrmc.com
**Control**: Corporation, Investor–owned (for–profit) **Service**: General medical and surgical

| Staffed Beds: 112 Admissions: 7032 Census: 68 Outpatient Visits: 119849 Births: 634 Personnel: 618 |
| --- |

**FORT PAYNE—Dekalb County**

**DEKALB MEDICAL CENTER** See Dekalb Regional Medical Center

☐ **DEKALB REGIONAL MEDICAL CENTER (010012)**, 200 Medical Center Drive, Zip 35968–3458, Mailing Address: P.O. Box 680778, Zip 35968–1608; tel. 256/845–3150, (Nonreporting) **A**1 10 20 **S** Quorum Health, Brentwood, TN
Primary Contact: Patrick Trammell, Chief Executive Officer
CFO: Phillip Fouts, Chief Financial Officer
CMO: Anthony Sims, M.D., Chief of Staff
CIO: Joseph Helms, Director Information Systems
CHR: Kim Reed, Director Human Resources
CNO: Angela Bennett, Chief Nursing Officer
Web address: www.dekalbregional.com
**Control**: Corporation, Investor–owned (for–profit) **Service**: General medical and surgical

**Staffed Beds: 115**

**GADSDEN—Etowah County**

**BAPTIST MEMORIAL HOSPITAL** See Gadsden Regional Medical Center

⊞ **ENCOMPASS HEALTH REHABILITATION HOSPITAL OF GADSDEN (013032)**, 801 Goodyear Avenue, Zip 35903–1133; tel. 256/439–5000, (Nonreporting) **A**1 10 **S** Encompass Health Corporation, Birmingham, AL
Primary Contact: Kayla Feazell, Chief Executive Officer
COO: Kayla Feazell, Chief Executive Officer
CFO: Lori Norman, Chief Financial Officer
CMO: Vladimir Slutsker, Medical Director
CIO: Lori Norman, Chief Financial Officer
CHR: Rhonda Young, Human Resource Director
CNO: Barry Eads, R.N., Chief Nursing Officer
Web address: www.encompasshealth.com/gadsdenrehab
**Control**: Corporation, Investor–owned (for–profit) **Service**: Rehabilitation

**Staffed Beds: 44**

⊞ **GADSDEN REGIONAL MEDICAL CENTER (010040)**, 1007 Goodyear Avenue, Zip 35903–1195; tel. 256/494–4000, (Nonreporting) **A**1 2 10 **S** Community Health Systems, Inc., Franklin, TN
Primary Contact: Corey Ewing, Chief Executive Officer
COO: Josh Hester, Chief Operating Officer
CFO: Kandi Garmany, Interim Chief Financial Officer
CMO: John Pirani, M.D., Chief Medical Officer
CIO: Glenn Phillips, Director Information Systems
CHR: Allison Casey, Director
CNO: Martha Seahorn, Chief Nursing Officer
Web address: www.gadsdenregional.com
**Control**: Corporation, Investor–owned (for–profit) **Service**: General medical and surgical

**Staffed Beds: 279**

**HEALTHSOUTH REHABILITATION OF GADSDEN** See Encompass Health Rehabilitation Hospital of Gadsden

**HOLY NAME OF JESUS MED CTR** See Riverview Regional Medical Center

**MOUNTAIN VIEW BAPTIST HOSPITAL** See Mountain View Hospital

☐ **MOUNTAIN VIEW HOSPITAL (014006)**, 3001 Scenic Highway, Zip 35904–3047, Mailing Address: P.O. Box 8406, Zip 35902–8406; tel. 256/546–9265, (Nonreporting) **A**1 10
Primary Contact: Jeremy Bradshaw, Chief Executive Officer
COO: Sara Romano, R.N., Vice President
CFO: Mary Jensen, Controller
CMO: G Michael Shehi, M.D., Medical Director
CHR: Dave Jensen, Director Human Resources, Performance Improvement and Risk Management
Web address: www.mtnviewhospital.com
**Control**: Corporation, Investor–owned (for–profit) **Service**: Psychiatric

**Staffed Beds: 68**

☐ **RIVERVIEW REGIONAL MEDICAL CENTER (010046)**, 600 South Third Street, Zip 35901–5399; tel. 256/543–5200, (Nonreporting) **A**1 10 **S** Prime Healthcare, Ontario, CA
Primary Contact: John Langlois, Chief Executive Officer
CIO: Jay Terrell, Manager Management Information Systems
CHR: Leslie Morton, Manager Human Resources
Web address: www.riverviewregional.com
**Control**: Corporation, Investor–owned (for–profit) **Service**: General medical and surgical

**Staffed Beds: 280**

**GENEVA—Geneva County**

**WIREGRASS HOSPITAL** See Wiregrass Medical Center

**WIREGRASS MEDICAL CENTER (010062)**, 1200 West Maple Avenue, Zip 36340–1694; tel. 334/684–3655, (Nonreporting) **A**10
Primary Contact: Jeffrey M. Brannon, Chief Executive Officer
CFO: Janet Smith, Chief Financial Officer
CHR: Tim Tidwell, Human Resources Director
CNO: Ashley Tanner, Director of Nursing
Web address: www.wiregrassmedicalcenter.org
**Control**: Hospital district or authority, Government, Nonfederal **Service**: General medical and surgical

**Staffed Beds: 147**

**GREENSBORO—Hale County**

**HALE COUNTY HOSPITAL (010095)**, 508 Green Street, Zip 36744–2316; tel. 334/624–3024, (Nonreporting) **A**10
Primary Contact: Shay Fondren, Administrator
Web address: www.halecountyhospital.com
**Control**: Hospital district or authority, Government, Nonfederal **Service**: General medical and surgical

**Staffed Beds: 20**

**GREENVILLE—Butler County**

**L. V. STABLER MEMORIAL HOSPITAL** See Regional Medical Center of Central Alabama

☐ **REGIONAL MEDICAL CENTER OF CENTRAL ALABAMA (010150)**, 29 L V Stabler Drive, Zip 36037–3800; tel. 334/382–2671, (Nonreporting) **A**1 5 10
Primary Contact: Chad French, Chief Executive Officer
CFO: David Wilcox, Chief Financial Officer
CMO: Norman F McGowin, M.D., IIIChief of Staff
CIO: Doug Burkett, Manager Information Technology
CHR: Robert Foster, Director Human Resources
CNO: Kimberli Weaver, Chief Nursing Officer
Web address: www.lvstabler.com
**Control**: City, Government, Nonfederal **Service**: General medical and surgical

**Staffed Beds: 61**

**GROVE HILL—Clarke County**

★ **GROVE HILL MEMORIAL HOSPITAL (010091)**, 295 South Jackson Street, Zip 36451–3231, Mailing Address: P.O. Box 935, Zip 36451–0935; tel. 251/275–3191, (Nonreporting) **A**10
Primary Contact: Doug Tanner, Chief Executive Officer
CFO: Alyson Overstreet, Chief Financial Officer
CMO: Eniola Fagbongbe, M.D., Chief Medical Staff
CIO: Aaron Harrell, Director
CHR: Aubrey Sheffield, Administrative Assistant Human Resources and Public Relations
CNO: Karen Coleman, Director of Nursing
Web address: www.grovehillmemorial.org
**Control**: City, Government, Nonfederal **Service**: General medical and surgical

**Staffed Beds: 34**

**GUNTERSVILLE—Marshall County**

**GUNTERSVILLE-ARAB MED CENTER** See Marshall Medical Center North

**MARSHALL MEDICAL CENTER NORTH (010010)**, 8000 Alabama Highway 69, Zip 35976; tel. 256/753–8000, (Data for 273 days) (Nonreporting) **A**5 10 **F**3 11 12 13 15 26 28 29 32 34 35 37 38 40 43 45 49 50 51 53 54 57 59 64 68 70 74 75 76 77 79 81 82 85 86 87 89 92 93 98 100 102 104 107 108 110 111 114 115 119 130 131 132 135 141 146 147 149 154 **S** Marshall Health System, Guntersville, AL
Primary Contact: Cheryl M. Hays, FACHE, Chief Executive Officer
COO: Cheryl M Hays, FACHE, Chief Operating Officer
CFO: Taylor Walker, Chief Financial Officer
CMO: Victor Sparks, M.D., Chief of Staff
CIO: David Mize, Director of Information Technology
CHR: Sabrina Weaver, Director of Human Resources
CNO: Kathy Woodruff, R.N., MSN, Chief Nursing Officer
Web address: www.mmcenters.com
**Control**: Hospital district or authority, Government, Nonfederal **Service**: General medical and surgical

**Staffed Beds: 76 Admissions: 2580 Census: 49 Outpatient Visits: 84009 Births: 339 Total Expense ($000): 46193 Payroll Expense ($000): 20794 Personnel: 382**

---

| Hospital, Medicare Provider Number, Address, Telephone, Approval, Facility, and Physician Codes, Health Care System |
| --- |

★ American Hospital Association (AHA) membership
☐ The Joint Commission accreditation
○ Healthcare Facilities Accreditation Program
◇ DNV Healthcare Inc. accreditation
⇑ Center for Improvement in Healthcare Quality Accreditation
△ Commission on Accreditation of Rehabilitation Facilities (CARF) accreditation

**HALEYVILLE—Winston County**

**BURDICK WEST MEDICAL CENTER** See Lakeland Community Hospital

☒ **LAKELAND COMMUNITY HOSPITAL (010125)**, Highway 195 East, Zip 35565–9536, Mailing Address: P.O. Box 780, Zip 35565–0780; tel. 205/486–5213, (Nonreporting) **A**1 10
Primary Contact: Ashley Pool, Chief Executive Officer
CFO: Penny Westmoreland, Chief Financial Officer
Web address: www.https://lakelandcommunityhospital.com
**Control:** Hospital district or authority, Government, Nonfederal **Service:** General medical and surgical

Staffed Beds: 59

**HAMILTON—Marion County**

**MARION REGIONAL MEDICAL CENTER** See North Mississippi Medical Center-Hamilton

☒ **NORTH MISSISSIPPI MEDICAL CENTER-HAMILTON (010044)**, 1256 Military Street South, Zip 35570–5003; tel. 205/921–6200, (Nonreporting) **A**1 10 **S** North Mississippi Health Services, Inc., Tupelo, MS
Primary Contact: Robert Trimm, Administrator
CMO: Jarred Sartain, M.D., President Medical Staff
CHR: Anne Lawler, Director Human Resources
CNO: Jennifer Cagle, Director of Nursing
Web address: www.nmhs.net
**Control:** Other not–for–profit (including NFP Corporation) **Service:** General medical and surgical

Staffed Beds: 15

**HUNTSVILLE—Madison County**

**BEHAVIORAL HEALTHCARE CENTER AT HUNTSVILLE** See Unity Psychiatric Care-Huntsville

**COLUMBIA MED CTR OF HUNTSVILLE** See Crestwood Medical Center

☒ **CRESTWOOD MEDICAL CENTER (010131)**, One Hospital Drive, Zip 35801–3403; tel. 256/429–4000, (Nonreporting) **A**1 5 10 **F**3 11 12 13 15 17 18 20 22 26 28 29 30 31 34 35 40 43 45 46 47 48 49 50 51 54 56 57 58 59 60 64 65 68 70 73 74 75 76 77 78 79 81 85 86 87 89 93 97 107 108 110 111 114 115 119 126 129 130 131 132 135 145 146 147 148 149 154 156 157 **S** Community Health Systems, Inc., Franklin, TN
Primary Contact: Pamela Hudson, M.D., Chief Executive Officer
COO: Bobby Ginn, Chief Operating Officer
CFO: Sherry J Jones, Chief Financial Officer
CHR: David A Brown, Human Resources Director
CNO: Martha Delaney Walls, R.N., MSN, Chief Nursing Officer
Web address: www.crestwoodmedcenter.com
**Control:** Corporation, Investor–owned (for–profit) **Service:** General medical and surgical

Staffed Beds: 180 **Admissions:** 11432 **Census:** 112 **Outpatient Visits:** 115965 **Births:** 1297 **Total Expense ($000):** 198446 **Payroll Expense ($000):** 62078 **Personnel:** 1202

☒ **ENCOMPASS REHABILITATION HOSPITAL OF NORTH ALABAMA (013029)**, 107 Governors Drive SW, Zip 35801–4326; tel. 256/535–2300, (Nonreporting) **A**1 10 **S** Encompass Health Corporation, Birmingham, AL
Primary Contact: Douglas H. Beverly, Chief Executive Officer
Web address: www.encompasshealth.com/huntsvillerehab
**Control:** Corporation, Investor–owned (for–profit) **Service:** Rehabilitation

Staffed Beds: 70

**HEALTHSOUTH REHABILITATION HOSPITAL OF NORTH ALABAMA** See Encompass Rehabilitation Hospital of North Alabama

☐ **HUNTSVILLE HOSPITAL (010039)**, 101 Sivley Road SW, Zip 35801–4470; tel. 256/265–1000, (Includes HUNTSVILLE HOSPITAL FOR WOMEN AND CHILDREN, Mailing address: 911 Big Cove Road SE, Huntsville, Alabama, Zip 35801–3784; tel. 256/265–1000; MADISON HOSPITAL, Mailing address: 8375 Highway 72 West, Madison, Alabama, Zip 35758–9573; tel. 256/265–2012; Mary Lynne Wright, R.N., President), (Nonreporting) **A**1 2 3 5 10 **F**5 7 8 12 13 14 15 17 18 19 20 21 22 23 24 25 26 28 29 30 31 35 37 38 40 41 43 46 49 50 51 53 54 56 57 59 60 63 64 68 70 71 72 73 76 78 79 80 81 82 84 85 86 87 88 89 93 98 100 101 102 103 107 108 109 110 111 114 115 116 117 118 119 126 129 130 131 142 145 146 147 148 154 157 **P**6 **S** Huntsville Hospital Health System, Huntsville, AL
Primary Contact: David S. Spillers, Chief Executive Officer
COO: Jeff Samz, Chief Operating Officer
CFO: Kelli Powers, Chief Financial Officer
CMO: Robert Chappell, M.D., Chief Medical Officer and Chief Quality Officer
CIO: Rick Corn, Chief Information Officer
CHR: Andrea P Rosler, Vice President Human Resources
CNO: Karol Jones, Chief Nursing Officer
Web address: www.huntsvillehospital.org
**Control:** Hospital district or authority, Government, Nonfederal **Service:** General medical and surgical

Staffed Beds: 949 **Admissions:** 48788 **Census:** 662 **Outpatient Visits:** 873863 **Births:** 5415 **Total Expense ($000):** 1009244 **Payroll Expense ($000):** 378603 **Personnel:** 8041

**HUNTSVILLE HOSPITAL EAST** See Huntsville Hospital for Women and Children

**UNITY PSYCHIATRIC CARE-HUNTSVILLE (014018)**, 5315 Millennium Drive NW, Zip 35806–2458; tel. 256/964–6700, (Nonreporting) **A**10 **S** Tennessee Health Management, Parsons, TN
Primary Contact: Bradley Moss, Administrator
Web address: www.thmgt.com/locations/behavioral-healthcare-center-at-huntsville
**Control:** Corporation, Investor–owned (for–profit) **Service:** Psychiatric

Staffed Beds: 20

**JACKSON—Clarke County**

**JACKSON MEDICAL CENTER (010128)**, 220 Hospital Drive, Zip 36545–2459, Mailing Address: P.O. Box 428, Zip 36545–0428; tel. 251/246–9021, (Nonreporting) **A**10 **S** Gilliard Health Services, Montgomery, AL
Primary Contact: Jennifer M. Ryland, R.N., Chief Executive Officer
COO: Jennifer M Ryland, R.N., Chief Administrative Officer
CHR: Kathy Jones, Director Human Resources
Web address: www.jacksonmedicalcenter.org
**Control:** Partnership, Investor–owned (for–profit) **Service:** General medical and surgical

Staffed Beds: 26

**VAUGHN JACKSON MEDICAL CTR** See Jackson Medical Center

**JASPER—Walker County**

☒ **WALKER BAPTIST MEDICAL CENTER (010089)**, 3400 Highway 78 East, Zip 35501–8907, Mailing Address: P.O. Box 3547, Zip 35502–3547; tel. 205/387–4000, (Nonreporting) **A**1 10 20 **S** TENET Healthcare Corporation, Dallas, TX
Primary Contact: Michael Neuendorf, Chief Executive Officer
CFO: Amanda Dyle, Chief Financial Officer
CIO: Kenny Horton, Director Information Systems
CHR: Pat Morrow, Director Human Resources
Web address: www.bhsala.com
**Control:** Church operated, Nongovernment, not–for–profit **Service:** General medical and surgical

Staffed Beds: 158

**WALKER REGIONAL MEDICAL CENTER** See Walker Baptist Medical Center

**LUVERNE—Crenshaw County**

☐ **BEACON CHILDREN'S HOSPITAL (014015)**, 150 Hospital Drive, Zip 36049; tel. 334/335–5040, (Nonreporting) **A**1 10
Primary Contact: Shannon Hudson, Interim Chief Executive Officer
Web address: www.beaconchildrenshospital.com
**Control:** Other not–for–profit (including NFP Corporation) **Service:** Children's hospital psychiatric

Staffed Beds: 28

*Many Facility Codes have changed. Please refer to the AHA Guide Code Chart.*

**CRENSHAW BAPTIST HOSPITAL** See Crenshaw Community Hospital

**CRENSHAW COMMUNITY HOSPITAL (010008)**, 101 Hospital Circle, Zip 36049–7344; tel. 334/335–3374, (Nonreporting) **A**10
Primary Contact: David L. Hughes, Administrator
COO: Victoria Lawrenson, Chief Operating Officer
CMO: Charles Tompkins, M.D., Chief of Staff
CHR: Patricia Jarry, Manager Human Resources
Web address: www.crenshawcommunityhospital.com
**Control:** Corporation, Investor–owned (for–profit) **Service:** General medical and surgical

**Staffed Beds:** 65

### MADISON—Madison County

**BRADFORD HEALTH SERVICES AT HUNTSVILLE**, 1600 Browns Ferry Road, Zip 35758–9601, Mailing Address: P.O. Box 1488, Zip 35758–0176; tel. 256/461–7272, (Nonreporting) **S** Bradford Health Services, Birmingham, AL
Primary Contact: Bob Hinds, Executive Director
Web address: www.bradfordhealth.com
**Control:** Corporation, Investor–owned (for–profit) **Service:** Alcoholism and other chemical dependency

**Staffed Beds:** 84

**BRADFORD PARKSIDE AT MADISON** See Bradford Health Services at Huntsville

### MOBILE—Mobile County

★ **BAYPOINTE BEHAVIORAL HEALTH (014014)**, 5800 Southland Drive, Zip 36693–3313; tel. 251/661–0153, (Nonreporting) **A**3 5 10 **F**38 98 99 100 101 106 130 132 154 **P**6 **S** AltaPointe Health Systems, Mobile, AL
Primary Contact: Jarett Crum, Hospital Director
Web address: www.altapointe.org
**Control:** Other not–for–profit (including NFP Corporation) **Service:** Children's hospital psychiatric

**Staffed Beds:** 60 **Admissions:** 1486 **Census:** 46 **Outpatient Visits:** 0 **Births:** 0 **Total Expense ($000):** 9861 **Payroll Expense ($000):** 7244 **Personnel:** 193

☐ **INFIRMARY LONG TERM ACUTE CARE HOSPITAL (012006)**, 5 Mobile Infirmary Circle, Zip 36607–3513, Mailing Address: P.O. Box 2226, Zip 36652–2226; tel. 251/660–5239, (Nonreporting) **A**1 10 **S** Infirmary Health System, Mobile, AL
Primary Contact: Susanne Marmande, Administrator
Web address: www.theinfirmary.com/
**Control:** Other not–for–profit (including NFP Corporation) **Service:** Acute long–term care hospital

**Staffed Beds:** 38

☐ △ **MOBILE INFIRMARY MEDICAL CENTER (010113)**, 5 Mobile Infirmary Drive North, Zip 36607–3513, Mailing Address: P.O. Box 2144, Zip 36652–2144; tel. 251/435–2400, (Includes ROTARY REHABILITATION HOSPITAL, Mailing address: 5 Mobile Infirmary Circle, Mobile, Alabama, Zip 36607, P O Box 2144, Zip 36652, tel. 251/435–3400), (Nonreporting) **A**1 2 3 5 7 10 **S** Infirmary Health System, Mobile, AL
Primary Contact: Joe Stough, Interim President
CFO: Joe Denton, Executive Vice President and Chief Financial Officer
CMO: John Dixon, Chief Medical Officer
CIO: Eddy Stephens, Vice President Information Technology
CHR: Sheila Young, Vice President Human Resources
Web address: www.infirmaryhealth.org
**Control:** Other not–for–profit (including NFP Corporation) **Service:** General medical and surgical

**Staffed Beds:** 554

⊞ **PROVIDENCE HOSPITAL (010090)**, 6801 Airport Boulevard, Zip 36608–3785, Mailing Address: P.O. Box 850429, Zip 36685–0429; tel. 251/633–1000, (Nonreporting) **A**1 2 3 5 10 **F**1 3 4 11 13 15 16 17 18 20 22 24 26 28 29 30 31 34 35 40 44 45 49 50 51 53 54 55 57 58 59 60 61 64 65 67 68 70 72 73 74 75 76 77 78 79 80 81 82 83 84 85 86 87 88 89 90 92 93 96 98 102 107 108 110 111 114 115 117 119 120 121 124 126 128 129 130 131 132 135 146 148 149 154 **P**5 6 **S** Ascension Healthcare, Saint Louis, MO
Primary Contact: Todd S. Kennedy, President and Chief Executive Officer
COO: C Susan Cornejo, Chief Operating Officer
CMO: William M Lightfoot, M.D., Vice President Medical Services
CHR: Christopher Cockrell, Executive Director Human Resources
CNO: Peter Lindquist, Vice President and Chief Nursing Officer
Web address: www.providencehospital.org
**Control:** Church operated, Nongovernment, not–for–profit **Service:** General medical and surgical

**Staffed Beds:** 305 **Admissions:** 13779 **Census:** 192 **Outpatient Visits:** 149222 **Births:** 1557 **Total Expense ($000):** 210384 **Payroll Expense ($000):** 59245 **Personnel:** 1446

**ROTARY REHABILITATION HOSPITAL** See Mobile Infirmary Medical Center, Mobile

☐ **SPRINGHILL MEMORIAL HOSPITAL (010144)**, 3719 Dauphin Street, Zip 36608–1798, Mailing Address: P.O. Box 8246, Zip 36689–0246; tel. 251/344–9630, (Nonreporting) **A**1 10
Primary Contact: Jeffery M. St Clair, President and Chief Executive Officer
COO: Rene Areaux, Vice President and Chief Operating Officer
CFO: Jan Grigsby, Vice President and Chief Financial Officer
CMO: Liston Jones, M.D., Medical Director
CIO: Mark Kilborn, Director Information Systems
CHR: Daniela Batchelor, Director Human Resources
CNO: Paul Read, R.N., MSN, Vice President and Chief Nursing Officer
Web address: www.springhillmedicalcenter.com
**Control:** Corporation, Investor–owned (for–profit) **Service:** General medical and surgical

**Staffed Beds:** 219

**UNIVERSITY OF SOUTH ALABAMA MEDICAL CENTER** See USA Health University Hospital

**USA CHILDREN'S AND WOMEN'S HOSPITAL** See USA Health Children's & Women's Hospital

⊞ **USA HEALTH CHILDREN'S & WOMEN'S HOSPITAL (013301)**, 1700 Center Street, Zip 36604–3301; tel. 251/415–1000, (Nonreporting) **A**1 3 5 10 **F**7 11 13 15 21 27 29 31 40 41 48 49 52 55 58 59 64 72 73 74 75 76 77 78 79 81 85 86 87 88 89 93 107 111 114 126 130 146 147 157 **S** USA Health, Mobile, AL
Primary Contact: Chris Jett, Administrator
COO: Alan Whaley, Chief Operating Officer
CFO: Traci Jones, Chief Financial Officer
CMO: Michael Chang, M.D., Chief Medical Officer
CIO: Dan Howard, Chief Information Officer
CHR: Janice Rehm, Manager Human Resources
CNO: Scotty Roberson, Assistant Administrator and Chief Nursing Officer
Web address: www.usahealthsystem.com/usacwh
**Control:** State, Government, Nonfederal **Service:** Other specialty treatment

**Staffed Beds:** 172 **Admissions:** 9667 **Census:** 166 **Outpatient Visits:** 68080 **Births:** 2537 **Total Expense ($000):** 150568 **Payroll Expense ($000):** 57876 **Personnel:** 1077

⊞ **USA HEALTH UNIVERSITY HOSPITAL (010087)**, 2451 University Hospital Drive, Zip 36617–2293; tel. 251/471–7000, (Nonreporting) **A**1 2 3 5 8 10 **F**3 11 12 16 17 18 20 22 24 26 29 31 34 40 43 45 46 47 48 49 57 58 59 61 64 65 70 74 78 79 80 81 85 87 107 108 111 114 115 119 120 121 124 126 130 131 132 145 146 148 149 **S** USA Health, Mobile, AL
Primary Contact: Sam Dean, Administrator
CFO: Traci Jones, Chief Financial Officer
CIO: Mark Lauteren, Chief Information Officer
CHR: Anita Shirah, Director Human Resources
CNO: Lisa Mestas, Associate Administrator and System Chief Nursing Officer
Web address: www.usahealthsystem.com/usamc
**Control:** State, Government, Nonfederal **Service:** General medical and surgical

**Staffed Beds:** 203 **Admissions:** 10685 **Census:** 162 **Outpatient Visits:** 66080 **Births:** 9 **Total Expense ($000):** 253188 **Payroll Expense ($000):** 102076 **Personnel:** 1655

---

**MONROEVILLE—Monroe County**

☒ **MONROE COUNTY HOSPITAL (010120)**, 2016 South Alabama Avenue, Zip 36460–3044, Mailing Address: P.O. Box 886, Zip 36461–0886; tel. 251/575–3111, (Nonreporting) **A**1 10 20
Primary Contact: Wes Nall, Interim Chief Executive Officer
CFO: Wes Nall, Chief Financial Officer
CMO: David Stallworth, M.D., Chief of Staff
CIO: Jody Falkenberry, Director Information Systems
CHR: Tara Nowling, Director Human Resources
CNO: Barbara Harned, R.N., MSN, Chief Nursing Officer
Web address: www.mchcare.com
**Control**: Hospital district or authority, Government, Nonfederal **Service**: General medical and surgical

| Staffed Beds: 44 |
| --- |

**MONTGOMERY—Montgomery County**

**BAPTIST MEDICAL CENTER** See Baptist Medical Center South

☐ **BAPTIST MEDICAL CENTER EAST (010149)**, 400 Taylor Road, Zip 36117–3512, Mailing Address: P.O. Box 241267, Zip 36124–1267; tel. 334/747–8330, (Nonreporting) **A**1 3 5 10 **F**3 11 12 13 15 29 30 34 35 40 44 45 47 49 50 56 57 60 63 70 72 74 75 76 77 79 81 82 85 86 87 89 90 93 94 107 108 111 114 115 119 126 129 130 132 135 146 147 148 154 **S** Baptist Health, Montgomery, AL
Primary Contact: Jeff G. Rains, Chief Executive Officer
CFO: Christine Bruton, Chief Financial Officer
CHR: Kay R Bennett, Vice President Human Resources
Web address: www.baptistfirst.org
**Control**: Hospital district or authority, Government, Nonfederal **Service**: General medical and surgical

| Staffed Beds: 150 Admissions: 11127 Census: 133 Outpatient Visits: 121363 Births: 3574 Total Expense ($000): 124598 Payroll Expense ($000): 50131 Personnel: 982 |
| --- |

☐ **BAPTIST MEDICAL CENTER SOUTH (010023)**, 2105 East South Boulevard, Zip 36116–2409, Mailing Address: Box 11010, Zip 36111–0010; tel. 334/288–2100, (Nonreporting) **A**1 2 3 5 10 **F**3 5 11 13 15 17 18 20 22 24 26 28 29 30 31 34 35 37 40 43 44 45 46 47 49 50 56 57 58 59 60 63 64 68 70 72 74 75 77 78 79 81 82 84 85 86 87 93 94 98 100 101 102 103 104 107 108 110 111 114 115 116 117 118 119 126 129 130 131 132 135 146 147 148 153 154 **S** Baptist Health, Montgomery, AL
Primary Contact: J Peter. Selman, FACHE, Chief Executive Officer
CFO: Melissa Johnson, Chief Financial Officer
CMO: Donovan Kendrick, M.D., Chief Medical Officer
CIO: Steve Miller, Director Information Systems
CHR: Kay R Bennett, System Director Human Resources
CNO: Karen McCaa, R.N., Vice President Patient Care Services and Chief Nursing Officer
Web address: www.baptistfirst.org
**Control**: Hospital district or authority, Government, Nonfederal **Service**: General medical and surgical

| Staffed Beds: 371 Admissions: 17196 Census: 265 Outpatient Visits: 338223 Births: 720 Total Expense ($000): 462184 Payroll Expense ($000): 117420 Personnel: 2042 |
| --- |

**CENTRAL ALABAMA VA HEALTH CARE SYSTEM-MONTGOMERY DIVISION** See Montgomery Division

**CENTRAL ALABAMA VA HLTH CARE** See Central Alabama Veterans Health Care System

☒ **CENTRAL ALABAMA VETERANS HEALTH CARE SYSTEM**, 215 Perry Hill Road, Zip 36109–3798; tel. 334/272–4670, (Includes MONTGOMERY DIVISION, Mailing address: 215 Perry Hill Road, Montgomery, Alabama, Zip 36109–3798; tel. 334/272–4670; TUSKEGEE DIVISION, Mailing address: 2400 Hospital Road, Tuskegee, Alabama, Zip 36083–5001; tel. 334/727–0550), (Nonreporting) **A**1 3 **F**2 3 7 11 34 39 40 45 46 47 48 49 50 54 56 57 59 61 62 63 64 65 66 68 70 75 77 79 81 82 83 84 86 87 90 91 93 94 97 98 100 101 105 106 107 108 111 114 115 116 117 118 119 127 128 129 130 132 133 135 143 146 147 148 149 153 154 155 156 157 158 **S** Department of Veterans Affairs, Washington, DC
Primary Contact: Linda Lake Boyle, R.N., MSN, Director
CFO: Debra Nicholson, Manager Finance
CMO: Cliff Robinson, M.D., Chief of Staff
CIO: Rhoda Tyson, Chief Information Officer
CHR: Janice Hardy, Chief Human Resource Management Service
Web address: www.centralalabama.va.gov/
**Control**: Veterans Affairs, Government, federal **Service**: General medical and surgical

| Staffed Beds: 313 Admissions: 1279 Census: 125 Outpatient Visits: 475737 Births: 0 Total Expense ($000): 362525 Payroll Expense ($000): 128632 Personnel: 1844 |
| --- |

**COLUMBIA MONTGOMERY MED CTR** See Baptist Medical Center East

☒ **ENCOMPASS HEALTH REHABILITATION HOSPITAL OF MONTGOMERY (013028)**, 4465 Narrow Lane Road, Zip 36116–2900; tel. 334/284–7700, (Nonreporting) **A**1 10 **F**3 9 28 29 34 35 56 57 59 74 75 77 86 90 95 96 97 130 131 132 143 146 148 149 **S** Encompass Health Corporation, Birmingham, AL
Primary Contact: Randy Thompson, Chief Executive Officer
CFO: Heath Watson, Controller
CMO: Jeffrey Eng, M.D., Medical Director
CIO: Anidra Billingslea, Health Insurance Management
CHR: Kim McDaniel, Director Human Resources
CNO: Gretchen Vercher, Chief Nursing Officer
Web address: www.encompasshealth.com/montgomeryrehab
**Control**: Corporation, Investor–owned (for–profit) **Service**: Rehabilitation

| Staffed Beds: 70 Admissions: 1989 Census: 65 Outpatient Visits: 0 Births: 0 Total Expense ($000): 26748 Payroll Expense ($000): 13386 |
| --- |

**HEALTHSOUTH REHABILITATION HOSPITAL OF MONTGOMERY** See Encompass Health Rehabilitation Hospital of Montgomery

☒ **JACKSON HOSPITAL AND CLINIC (010024)**, 1725 Pine Street, Zip 36106–1117; tel. 334/293–8000, (Nonreporting) **A**1 3 5 10 19 **F**12 13 15 17 18 20 22 24 26 29 30 31 34 35 40 45 46 48 49 54 55 57 59 64 68 70 74 75 76 77 78 79 81 82 83 84 85 86 87 89 97 107 108 110 111 115 116 117 118 119 126 129 130 132 135 144 146 147 148 149 154 156
Primary Contact: Joe B. Riley, FACHE, President and Chief Executive Officer
COO: Michael James, Chief Operations Officer
CFO: Paul Peiffer, Chief Financial Officer and Vice President
CHR: Gilbert Darrington, Director Human Resources
Web address: www.jackson.org
**Control**: Other not–for–profit (including NFP Corporation) **Service**: General medical and surgical

| Staffed Beds: 262 Admissions: 14426 Census: 194 Outpatient Visits: 135145 |
| --- |

**LONG TERM CARE HOSPITAL** See Noland Hospital Montgomery

**MONTGOMERY DIVISION** See Central Alabama Veterans Health Care System, Montgomery

☐ **NOLAND HOSPITAL MONTGOMERY (012007)**, 1725 Pine Street, 5 North, Zip 36106–1109; tel. 334/240–0532, (Nonreporting) **A**1 10 **S** Noland Health Services, Inc., Birmingham, AL
Primary Contact: William Elsesser, Administrator
Web address: www.nolandhealth.com
**Control**: Other not–for–profit (including NFP Corporation) **Service**: Acute long–term care hospital

| Staffed Beds: 65 |
| --- |

**MOULTON—Lawrence County**

☐ **LAWRENCE MEDICAL CENTER (010059)**, 202 Hospital Street, Zip 35650–1218, Mailing Address: P.O. Box 39, Zip 35650–0039; tel. 256/974–2200, (Nonreporting) **A**1 10 **S** Huntsville Hospital Health System, Huntsville, AL
Primary Contact: Dean A. Griffin, Chief Executive Officer
CFO: Jim Crawford, Chief Financial Officer
CIO: Jeremy Duncan, Director Information Systems
CHR: Diane K Secor, Director Human Resources
Web address: www.lawrencemedicalcenter.com
**Control**: County, Government, Nonfederal **Service**: General medical and surgical

| Staffed Beds: 43 |
| --- |

**LAWRENCE MEDICAL CTR** See Lawrence Medical Center

**MUSCLE SHOALS—Colbert County**

**MEDICAL CENTER SHOALS** See Shoals Hospital

☒ **SHOALS HOSPITAL (010157)**, 201 Avalon Avenue, Zip 35661–2805, Mailing Address: P.O. Box 3359, Zip 35662–3359; tel. 256/386–1600, (Nonreporting) **A**1 10 **S** LifePoint Health, Brentwood, TN
Primary Contact: Kidada Hawkins, Chief Executive Officer
CFO: Steve E. Hobbs, Chief Financial Officer
CMO: Terry true, M.D., Chief of Staff
CIO: William Johnson, Director Information Systems
CHR: Nancy Bowling, Director Human Resources
Web address: www.shoalshospital.com
**Control**: Hospital district or authority, Government, Nonfederal **Service**: General medical and surgical

| Staffed Beds: 137 |
| --- |

*Many Facility Codes have changed. Please refer to the AHA Guide Code Chart.*

## NORTHPORT—Tuscaloosa County

**NORTHPORT HOSPITAL-DCH** See Northport Medical Center

## ONEONTA—Blount County

**MEDICAL CENTER BLOUNT** See St. Vincent'S Blount

⊠ **ST. VINCENT'S BLOUNT (011305)**, 150 Gilbreath, Zip 35121–2827, Mailing Address: P.O. Box 1000, Zip 35121–0013; tel. 205/274–3000, (Nonreporting) **A**1 10 18 **F**3 11 15 18 29 30 35 40 45 46 50 57 59 60 64 70 81 85 87 93 97 107 108 110 111 119 127 133 135 146 149 **S** Ascension Healthcare, Saint Louis, MO
Primary Contact: Suzannah Campbell, President
CFO: Jennifer Kingry, Chief Financial Officer
CMO: David R Wilson, M.D., Chief of Staff
CIO: John Laliberte, Chief Information Officer
CHR: Kristin L. Costanzo, Direct-In-Market Lead Human Relations Partner
CNO: Kira Schnittker, Director of Nursing
Web address: www.stvhs.com
**Control:** Other not–for–profit (including NFP Corporation) **Service:** General medical and surgical

**Staffed Beds:** 25 **Admissions:** 839 **Census:** 12 **Outpatient Visits:** 38808 **Births:** 0 **Total Expense ($000):** 18932 **Payroll Expense ($000):** 7003 **Personnel:** 104

## OPELIKA—Lee County

⊠ **EAST ALABAMA MEDICAL CENTER (010029)**, 2000 Pepperell Parkway, Zip 36801–5452; tel. 334/749–3411, (Includes EAST ALABAMA MEDICAL CENTER-LANIER, Mailing address: 4800 48th Street, Valley, Alabama, Zip 36854–3666; tel. 334/756–9180; Greg Nichols, Chief Executive Officer) (Total facility includes 216 beds in nursing home–type unit) **A**1 2 10 19 **F**3 7 11 13 15 17 18 20 22 24 26 28 29 30 31 34 35 40 43 45 47 48 50 53 54 57 58 59 60 61 64 68 70 73 75 76 77 78 79 81 82 84 85 86 89 90 93 94 98 99 100 102 107 110 111 114 115 116 117 119 120 121 123 124 125 126 128 129 130 131 132 135 146 148 149 154 156
Primary Contact: Laura D. Grill, R.N., Chief Executive Officer
COO: Sarah Nunnelly, Executive Vice President and Chief Operating Officer
CFO: Sam Price, Executive Vice President Finance/Chief Financial Officer
CMO: William Golden, M.D., Chief Medical Officer
CIO: Sarah Gray, Vice President Information Services
CHR: Susan Johnston, Vice President Human Resources
CNO: Jane Fullum, Vice President Patient Care Services
Web address: www.eamc.org
**Control:** Hospital district or authority, Government, Nonfederal **Service:** General medical and surgical

**Staffed Beds:** 532 **Admissions:** 16939 **Census:** 415 **Outpatient Visits:** 202126 **Births:** 2086 **Total Expense ($000):** 404839 **Payroll Expense ($000):** 160971 **Personnel:** 3298

## OPP—Covington County

**MIZELL MEMORIAL HOSPITAL (010007)**, 702 Main Street, Zip 36467–1626, Mailing Address: P.O. Box 1010, Zip 36467–1010; tel. 334/493–3541, (Nonreporting) **A**10
Primary Contact: Jana Wyatt, Chief Executive Officer
CFO: Amy Bess, Chief Financial Officer
CIO: Elizabeth Cook, Chief Information Officer
CHR: Dianne Morrison, Director Human Resources
CNO: Steven Skeen, R.N., Chief Nursing Officer
Web address: www.mizellmh.com
**Control:** Other not–for–profit (including NFP Corporation) **Service:** General medical and surgical

**Staffed Beds:** 59

## OZARK—Dale County

**DALE COUNTY HOSPITAL** See Dale Medical Center

**DALE MEDICAL CENTER (010021)**, 126 Hospital Avenue, Zip 36360–2080; tel. 334/774–2601, (Nonreporting) **A**10
Primary Contact: Vernon Johnson, Administrator
CFO: Brad Hull, Chief Financial Officer
CMO: Steve Brandt, M.D., Chief of Staff
CHR: Sheila Dunn, Assistant Administrator Human Resources
Web address: www.dalemedical.org
**Control:** Corporation, Investor–owned (for-profit) **Service:** General medical and surgical

**Staffed Beds:** 69

## PELHAM—Shelby County

☐ **ENCOMPASS HEALTH REHABILITATION HOSPITAL OF SHELBY COUNTY (013031)**, 900 Oak Mountain Commons Lane, Zip 35124; tel. 205/216–7600, (Nonreporting) **A**1 10 **F**29 35 68 75 79 87 90 91 95 96 130 **S** Encompass Health Corporation, Birmingham, AL
Primary Contact: Nathan Ford, Chief Executive Officer
Web address: www.encompasshealth.com/shelbycountyrehab
**Control:** Corporation, Investor–owned (for-profit) **Service:** Rehabilitation

**Staffed Beds:** 34 **Admissions:** 866 **Census:** 27 **Outpatient Visits:** 0 **Births:** 0 **Total Expense ($000):** 12888 **Payroll Expense ($000):** 5991 **Personnel:** 116

## PELL CITY—St. Clair County

**ST CLAIR REGIONAL HOSPITAL** See St. Vincent'S St. Clair

⊠ **ST. VINCENT'S ST. CLAIR (010130)**, 7063 Veterans Parkway, Zip 35125–1499; tel. 205/814–2105, (Nonreporting) **A**1 10 **F**3 11 15 29 30 35 40 43 45 46 50 59 60 64 68 70 79 81 82 85 87 93 107 108 110 111 119 130 135 146 148 149 **S** Ascension Healthcare, Saint Louis, MO
Primary Contact: Suzannah Campbell, President
CFO: Jason Lynn, Director Finance
Web address: www.stvhs.com
**Control:** Other not–for–profit (including NFP Corporation) **Service:** General medical and surgical

**Staffed Beds:** 40 **Admissions:** 1856 **Census:** 20 **Outpatient Visits:** 52696 **Births:** 0 **Total Expense ($000):** 25228 **Payroll Expense ($000):** 9763 **Personnel:** 143

## PHENIX CITY—Russell County

☐ **JACK HUGHSTON MEMORIAL HOSPITAL (010168)**, 4401 Riverchase Drive, Zip 36867–7483; tel. 334/732–3000, (Nonreporting) **A**1 3 5 10 13 **F**3 29 40 45 70 79 81 89 107 111 115 119 130 131
Primary Contact: Mark A. Baker, Chief Executive Officer
COO: Rachel H. Crenshaw, Chief Operating Officer
CFO: Angela Shelton, Chief Financial Officer
CMO: James F. Zumstein, M.D., Chief of Medicine
CHR: Lana Thomas-Folds, System Director Human Resources
CNO: Sylvia Thomas, Chief Nursing Officer
Web address: www.hughston.com
**Control:** Corporation, Investor–owned (for-profit) **Service:** General medical and surgical

**Staffed Beds:** 35 **Admissions:** 3196 **Census:** 17 **Outpatient Visits:** 18512 **Births:** 0 **Total Expense ($000):** 61413 **Payroll Expense ($000):** 16125 **Personnel:** 284

⊠ **REGIONAL REHABILITATION HOSPITAL (013033)**, 3715 Highway 280/431 North, Zip 36867; tel. 334/732–2200, (Nonreporting) **A**1 10 **F**3 9 28 29 34 56 57 59 61 64 65 74 75 77 79 86 90 93 95 96 97 130 132 143 148 149 **S** Encompass Health Corporation, Birmingham, AL
Primary Contact: Lora Davis, FACHE, Chief Executive Officer
CFO: Bobby Edmondson, Controller
CMO: Nitin Desei, M.D., Medical Director
CIO: Jacki Cuevas, Director Health Information Services
CHR: Cindy Glynn, Director Human Resources
CNO: Wendy Lee, Chief Nursing Officer
Web address: www.regionalrehabhospital.com
**Control:** Corporation, Investor–owned (for-profit) **Service:** Rehabilitation

**Staffed Beds:** 58 **Admissions:** 1668 **Census:** 56 **Outpatient Visits:** 3424 **Total Expense ($000):** 20344 **Payroll Expense ($000):** 11151 **Personnel:** 193

**SUMMIT HOSPITAL** See Jack Hughston Memorial Hospital

---

| Hospital, Medicare Provider Number, Address, Telephone, Approval, Facility, and Physician Codes, Health Care System |
| --- |

★ American Hospital Association (AHA) membership
☐ The Joint Commission accreditation
○ Healthcare Facilities Accreditation Program
◇ DNV Healthcare Inc. accreditation
⇑ Center for Improvement in Healthcare Quality Accreditation
△ Commission on Accreditation of Rehabilitation Facilities (CARF) accreditation

## PRATTVILLE—Autauga County

**NORTHRIDGE MEDICAL CENTER** See Prattville Baptist Hospital

☐ **PRATTVILLE BAPTIST HOSPITAL (010108)**, 124 South Memorial Drive, Zip 36067–3619, Mailing Address: P.O. Box 681630, Zip 36068–1638; tel. 334/365–0651, (Nonreporting) **A**1 10 **F**3 11 15 18 29 30 34 35 40 44 45 50 56 57 59 60 63 64 68 70 74 75 77 81 82 84 85 86 87 107 111 115 119 129 132 146 154 **S** Baptist Health, Montgomery, AL
Primary Contact: Eric Morgan, Chief Executive Officer
CFO: LaDonna McDaniel, Financial Manager
CIO: B Blaine Brown, Vice President and General Counsel
CHR: Kymberli Skipper, Manager Human Resources
Web address: www.baptistfirst.org/facilities/prattville-baptist-hospital/default.aspx
**Control**: Hospital district or authority, Government, Nonfederal **Service**: General medical and surgical

**Staffed Beds**: 55 **Admissions**: 2895 **Census**: 34 **Outpatient Visits**: 83178 **Births**: 0 **Total Expense ($000)**: 47820 **Payroll Expense ($000)**: 17058 **Personnel**: 320

## RED BAY—Franklin County

★ **RED BAY HOSPITAL (011302)**, 211 Hospital Road, Zip 35582–3858, Mailing Address: P.O. Box 490, Zip 35582–0490; tel. 256/356–9532, (Nonreporting) **A**5 10 18 **F**7 11 15 29 34 35 40 53 57 59 68 77 85 87 93 97 107 110 114 119 127 130 131 133 135 157 **S** Huntsville Hospital Health System, Huntsville, AL
Primary Contact: Sherry Jolley, Director of Operations and Nursing
CFO: Penny Westmoreland, Chief Financial Officer
CMO: Kristy Crandell, M.D., Medical Staff President
CHR: Amy Leigh Bishop, Director Human Resources
CNO: Margaret Thorn, Interim Director of Nursing
Web address: www.redbayhospital.com
**Control**: Hospital district or authority, Government, Nonfederal **Service**: General medical and surgical

**Staffed Beds**: 22 **Admissions**: 401 **Census**: 7 **Outpatient Visits**: 9754 **Births**: 0 **Total Expense ($000)**: 9656 **Payroll Expense ($000)**: 4076 **Personnel**: 112

## RUSSELLVILLE—Franklin County

☐ **RUSSELLVILLE HOSPITAL (010158)**, 15155 Highway 43, Zip 35653–1975, Mailing Address: P.O. Box 1089, Zip 35653–1089; tel. 256/332–1611, (Nonreporting) **A**1 10 **S** Curae Health, Clinton, TN
Primary Contact: Christine R. Stewart, FACHE, Chief Executive Officer
CFO: Penny Westmoreland, Chief Financial Officer
CHR: Stephen Proctor, Director of Human Resources/Risk
CNO: Belinda Johnson, R.N., Chief Nursing Officer/Chief Clinical Officer
Web address: www.russellvillehospital.com
**Control**: Partnership, Investor–owned (for–profit) **Service**: General medical and surgical

**Staffed Beds**: 92

**RUSSELLVILLE MEDICAL CENTER** See Russellville Hospital

## SCOTTSBORO—Jackson County

☐ **HIGHLANDS MEDICAL CENTER (010061)**, 380 Woods Cove Road, Zip 35768–2428, Mailing Address: P.O. Box 1050, Zip 35768–1050; tel. 256/259–4444, (Nonreporting) **A**1 5 10 20
Primary Contact: John D. Anderson, FACHE, Interim Chief Executive Officer
CFO: Dan Newell, Chief Financial Officer
CIO: Doug Newby, Chief Information Officer
CHR: Susanna S Sivley, Chief Personnel Officer
Web address: www.highlandsmedcenter.com
**Control**: Hospital district or authority, Government, Nonfederal **Service**: General medical and surgical

**Staffed Beds**: 92

**JACKSON COUNTY HOSPITAL** See Highlands Medical Center

## SELMA—Dallas County

**SELMA REGIONAL MEDICAL CENTER** See Vaughan Regional Medical Center

✉ **VAUGHAN REGIONAL MEDICAL CENTER (010118)**, 1015 Medical Center Parkway, Zip 36701–6352; tel. 334/418–4100, (Nonreporting) **A**1 3 5 10 **S** LifePoint Health, Brentwood, TN
Primary Contact: J. David. McCormack, Chief Executive Officer
CFO: Tyler Adkins, Chief Financial Officer
CMO: Walid Freij, M.D., Chief of Staff
CIO: Matthew McHugh, Director Information Services
CHR: Dionne Williams, Director Human Resources
CNO: Patricia Hannon, Chief Nursing Officer
Web address: www.vaughanregional.com
**Control**: Corporation, Investor–owned (for–profit) **Service**: General medical and surgical

**Staffed Beds**: 149

## SHEFFIELD—Colbert County

☐ **HELEN KELLER HOSPITAL (010019)**, 1300 South Montgomery Avenue, Zip 35660–6334, Mailing Address: P.O. Box 610, Zip 35660–0610; tel. 256/386–4196, (Nonreporting) **A**1 5 10 **F**3 7 8 11 13 15 18 20 21 28 29 30 31 34 35 37 40 45 47 49 50 51 53 57 59 60 64 65 68 70 74 75 76 77 78 79 80 81 82 83 84 85 86 87 89 91 92 93 94 107 108 110 111 114 115 117 118 119 126 129 130 131 132 135 145 146 147 148 149 154 157 **S** Huntsville Hospital Health System, Huntsville, AL
Primary Contact: Kyle Buchanan, President
CFO: Morris S Strickland, Chief Financial Officer
CHR: Pam Bryant, Director Human Resources
Web address: www.helenkeller.com
**Control**: Hospital district or authority, Government, Nonfederal **Service**: General medical and surgical

**Staffed Beds**: 143 **Admissions**: 7032 **Census**: 75 **Outpatient Visits**: 93530 **Births**: 746 **Total Expense ($000)**: 113460 **Payroll Expense ($000)**: 42784 **Personnel**: 915

**HELEN KELLER MEMORIAL HOSPITAL** See Helen Keller Hospital

## SYLACAUGA—Talladega County

**COOSA VALLEY BAPTIST MED CTR** See Coosa Valley Medical Center

☐ **COOSA VALLEY MEDICAL CENTER (010164)**, 315 West Hickory Street, Zip 35150–2996; tel. 256/401–4000, (Nonreporting) **A**1 10
Primary Contact: Glenn C. Sisk, President
CFO: Janice Brown, Chief Financial Officer
CIO: Sandra Murchison, Director Medical Records
CHR: Christy Knowles, Chief Human Resources Officer
Web address: www.cvhealth.net
**Control**: Other not–for–profit (including NFP Corporation) **Service**: General medical and surgical

**Staffed Beds**: 101

## TALLADEGA—Talladega County

**CITIZENS BAPTIST MED CTR** See Citizens Baptist Medical Center

✉ **CITIZENS BAPTIST MEDICAL CENTER (010101)**, 604 Stone Avenue, Zip 35160–2217, Mailing Address: P.O. Box 978, Zip 35161–0978; tel. 256/362–8111, (Nonreporting) **A**1 10 19 **S** TENET Healthcare Corporation, Dallas, TX
Primary Contact: Frank D. Thomas, Chief Executive Officer
CFO: Zach Abercrombie, Chief Financial Officer
CHR: Sandra Willis, Director of Human Resources
CNO: Ann McEntire, MSN, R.N., Chief Nursing Officer
Web address: www.brookwoodbaptisthealth.org
**Control**: Church operated, Nongovernment, not–for–profit **Service**: General medical and surgical

**Staffed Beds**: 72

## TALLASSEE—Elmore County

**COMMUNITY HOSPITAL (010034)**, 805 Friendship Road, Zip 36078–1234; tel. 334/283–6541, (Nonreporting) **A**10
Primary Contact: Jennie R. Rhinehart, Administrator and Chief Executive Officer
Web address: www.chal.org
**Control**: Other not–for–profit (including NFP Corporation) **Service**: General medical and surgical

**Staffed Beds**: 47

*Many Facility Codes have changed. Please refer to the AHA Guide Code Chart.*

## TROY—Pike County

**EDGE REGIONAL MEDICAL CENTER** See Troy Regional Medical Center

☐ **TROY REGIONAL MEDICAL CENTER (010126)**, 1330 Highway 231 South, Zip 36081–3058; tel. 334/670–5000, (Nonreporting) **A**1 10
Primary Contact: Amy Minor, Interim Chief Executive Officer
CFO: Janet Smith, Chief Financial Officer
CMO: Paul Dulaney, M.D., Chief of Staff
CIO: Michael Moore, Director Information Systems
CHR: Beth Nissen, Director Human Resources
CNO: Amy Minor, Chief Nursing Officer
Web address: www.troymedicalcenter.com
**Control:** Corporation, Investor–owned (for–profit) **Service:** General medical and surgical

**Staffed Beds:** 43

## TUSCALOOSA—Tuscaloosa County

☐ **BRYCE HOSPITAL (014007)**, 200 University Boulevard, Zip 35401–1294; tel. 205/507–8299, (Nonreporting) **A**1 5 10
Primary Contact: Shelia Penn, Facility Director
CFO: Wendell Summerville, Chief Financial Officer
CMO: Cynthia Moore Sledge, M.D., Medical Director
CIO: Ronene Howell, Director Health Information Management
CHR: Jim Elliott, Director Human Resources
Web address: www.mh.alabama.gov/
**Control:** State, Government, Nonfederal **Service:** Psychiatric

**Staffed Beds:** 820

☐ **DCH REGIONAL MEDICAL CENTER (010092)**, 809 University Boulevard East, Zip 35401–2029; tel. 205/759–7111, (Includes NORTHPORT MEDICAL CENTER, Mailing address: 2700 Hospital Drive, Northport, Alabama, Zip 35476–3360; tel. 205/333–4500; Luke Standeffer, Administrator), (Nonreporting) **A**1 2 3 5 10 20 **F**3 11 12 13 15 17 18 20 22 24 26 28 29 30 31 34 40 43 44 45 46 48 49 50 58 59 60 62 64 70 72 74 75 76 77 78 79 81 82 84 85 86 87 89 90 98 100 101 102 103 107 108 110 111 114 115 117 118 119 120 121 123 124 126 129 130 146 147 148 156 **S** DCH Health System, Tuscaloosa, AL
Primary Contact: Paul Betz, FACHE, Administrator
CFO: Nina Dusang, Vice President Finance and Chief Financial Officer
CMO: Kenneth Aldridge, M.D., Vice President Medical Affairs
CIO: Kim Ligon, Director Information Services
CHR: Peggy Sease, Vice President Human Resources
CNO: Lorraine Yehlen, R.N., Vice President Patient Care Services
Web address: www.dchsystem.com
**Control:** Hospital district or authority, Government, Nonfederal **Service:** General medical and surgical

**Staffed Beds:** 687 **Admissions:** 31539 **Census:** 471 **Outpatient Visits:** 556791 **Births:** 3364 **Total Expense ($000):** 503720 **Payroll Expense ($000):** 203510 **Personnel:** 3779

**LONG TERM HOSPITAL OF TUSCALOOSA** See Noland Hospital Tuscaloosa

**MARY S HARPER GERIATRIC PSYCHIATRIC CENTER** See Mary S Harper Geriatric Psychiatry Center

☐ **MARY S HARPER GERIATRIC PSYCHIATRY CENTER (014012)**, 200 University Boulevard, Zip 35401–1250; tel. 205/759–0900, (Nonreporting) **A**1 3 10
Primary Contact: Beverly White, MS, Facility Director
CFO: Sarah Mitchell, Director Finance
CMO: Robin Barton Lariscy, M.D., Medical Director
CIO: Sarah Mitchell, Director Finance
CHR: Jim Elliott, Director Human Resources
Web address: www.mh.alabama.gov
**Control:** Corporation, Investor–owned (for–profit) **Service:** Psychiatric

**Staffed Beds:** 96

☐ **NOLAND HOSPITAL TUSCALOOSA (012012)**, 809 University Blvd E, 4th Fl, Zip 35401–2029; tel. 205/759–7241, (Nonreporting) **A**1 10 **S** Noland Health Services, Inc., Birmingham, AL
Primary Contact: Jack Gibson, Administrator
Web address: www.nolandhealth.com
**Control:** Other not–for–profit (including NFP Corporation) **Service:** Acute long–term care hospital

**Staffed Beds:** 32

☐ **TAYLOR HARDIN SECURE MEDICAL FACILITY (014011)**, 1301 Jack Warner Parkway, Zip 35404–1060; tel. 205/556–7060, (Nonreporting) **A**1 10
Primary Contact: Barbara Jackson, Ed.D., Acting Facility Director
Web address: www.mh.alabama.gov/
**Control:** Corporation, Investor–owned (for–profit) **Service:** Psychiatric

**Staffed Beds:** 114

⊠ **TUSCALOOSA VETERANS AFFAIRS MEDICAL CENTER**, 3701 Loop Road East, Zip 35404–5015; tel. 205/554–2000, (Nonreporting) **A**1 5 **S** Department of Veterans Affairs, Washington, DC
Primary Contact: John F. Merkle, Medical Center Director
COO: Gary D Trende, FACHE, Associate Director
CFO: Angelia Stevenson, Manager Finance
CMO: Carlos E. Berry, M.D., Acting Chief of Staff
Web address: www.tuscaloosa.va.gov
**Control:** Veterans Affairs, Government, federal **Service:** Psychiatric

**Staffed Beds:** 305

**VETERANS AFFAIRS MEDICAL CENTER** See Tuscaloosa Veterans Affairs Medical Center

## TUSKEGEE—Macon County

**CENTRAL ALABAMA VETERANS AFFAIRS HEALTH CARE SYSTEM-TUSKEGEE DIVISION** See Tuskegee Division

**TUSKEGEE DIVISION** See Central Alabama Veterans Health Care System, Montgomery

## UNION SPRINGS—Bullock County

☐ **BULLOCK COUNTY HOSPITAL (010110)**, 102 West Conecuh Avenue, Zip 36089–1303; tel. 334/738–2140, (Nonreporting) **A**10 20
Primary Contact: Sharon Lee, Chief Executive Officer
COO: Victoria Lawrenson, Chief Operating Officer
CMO: Maria Bernardo, M.D., Chief of Staff
Web address: www.unionspringsalabama.com/
**Control:** Corporation, Investor–owned (for–profit) **Service:** General medical and surgical

**Staffed Beds:** 54

## VALLEY—Chambers County

**LANIER HEALTH SERVICES** See East Alabama Medical Center-Lanier

## WARRIOR—Jefferson County

**BRADFORD HEALTH SERVICES AT BIRMINGHAM LODGE** See Bradford Health Services at Warrior Lodge

**BRADFORD HEALTH SERVICES AT WARRIOR LODGE**, 1189 Allbritt Road, Zip 35180, Mailing Address: P.O. Box 129, Zip 35180–0129; tel. 205/647–1945, (Nonreporting) **S** Bradford Health Services, Birmingham, AL
Primary Contact: Roy M. Ramsey, Executive Director
Web address: www.bradfordhealth.com
**Control:** Corporation, Investor–owned (for–profit) **Service:** Alcoholism and other chemical dependency

**Staffed Beds:** 100

## WEDOWEE—Randolph County

**TANNER MEDICAL CENTER/EAST ALABAMA (011306)**, 1032 South Main Street, Zip 36278–7428; tel. 256/357–2111, (Nonreporting) **A**10 18 **S** Tanner Health System, Carrollton, GA
Primary Contact: Jerry Morris, Administrator
Web address: www.tanner.org/eastalabama
**Control:** County, Government, Nonfederal **Service:** General medical and surgical

**Staffed Beds:** 26

**WEDOWEE HOSPITAL** See Tanner Medical Center/East Alabama

---

**Hospital, Medicare Provider Number, Address, Telephone, Approval, Facility, and Physician Codes, Health Care System**

★ American Hospital Association (AHA) membership
☐ The Joint Commission accreditation
○ Healthcare Facilities Accreditation Program
◇ DNV Healthcare Inc. accreditation
⇑ Center for Improvement in Healthcare Quality Accreditation
△ Commission on Accreditation of Rehabilitation Facilities (CARF) accreditation

---

### WETUMPKA—Elmore County

**CENTRAL ALABAMA MED CENTER** See Elmore Community Hospital

**ELMORE COMMUNITY HOSPITAL (010097)**, 500 Hospital Drive,
Zip 36092–1625, Mailing Address: P.O. Box 130, Zip 36092–0003;
tel. 334/567–4311, (Nonreporting) **A**10
Primary Contact: Michael Bruce, Chief Executive Officer
CFO: Michael Bruce, Chief Financial Officer
CHR: Cindy Futral, Director Human Resources
Web address: www.ivycreekhealth.com/hospital/elmore-community-hospital/
**Control**: Partnership, Investor–owned (for–profit) **Service**: General medical and surgical

| **Staffed Beds: 49** |
|---|

### WINFIELD—Marion County

☐ **NORTHWEST MEDICAL CENTER (010086)**, 1530 U S Highway 43,
Zip 35594–5056; tel. 205/487–7000, (Nonreporting) **A**1 10 **F**3 15 18 29 30 34
40 41 43 45 50 53 56 57 59 64 68 70 75 77 79 80 81 83 85 87 98 100 102
103 104 107 108 110 111 115 119 127 129 130 133 135 146 149 154 **S**
Curae Health, Clinton, TN
Primary Contact: Robert Henger, Chief Executive Officer
CFO: Glenda Reyes, Chief Financial Officer
CMO: David Corbett, M.D., Chief of Staff
Web address: www.https://northwestmedcenter.net/
**Control**: Hospital district or authority, Government, Nonfederal **Service**: General medical and surgical

| **Staffed Beds: 56 Admissions: 1109 Census: 17 Outpatient Visits: 43578** |
|---|
| **Births: 0 Total Expense ($000): 25930 Payroll Expense ($000): 11721** |
| **Personnel: 210** |

**NORTHWEST MEDICAL CTR** See Northwest Medical Center

### YORK—Sumter County

**HILL HOSPITAL OF SUMTER COUNTY (010138)**, 751 Derby Drive,
Zip 36925–2121; tel. 205/392–5263, (Nonreporting) **A**10
Primary Contact: Loretta Wilson, Administrator
CFO: Joyce Wedgeworth, Financial Clerk
CMO: Gary Walton, M.D., Chief Medical Officer
CNO: Cynthia Brown, Director of Nursing
**Control**: Other not–for–profit (including NFP Corporation) **Service**: General medical and surgical

| **Staffed Beds: 33** |
|---|

**HILL HOSPITAL OF YORK** See Hill Hospital of Sumter County

*Many Facility Codes have changed. Please refer to the AHA Guide Code Chart.*

© 2021 AHA Guide

# ALASKA

## ANCHORAGE—Anchorage County

☒ **ALASKA NATIVE MEDICAL CENTER (020026)**, 4315 Diplomacy Drive, Zip 99508–5926; tel. 907/563–2662, (Nonreporting) **A**1 3 5 10
Primary Contact: Roald Helgesen, Chief Executive Officer
CMO: Paul Franke, M.D., Chief Medical Officer
CHR: Sonya Conant, Senior Director Human Resources
Web address: www.dhss.alaska.gov/dbh/Pages/api/default.aspx
**Control**: Other not–for–profit (including NFP Corporation) **Service**: General medical and surgical

**Staffed Beds:** 172

**ALASKA PSYCHIATRIC HOSPITAL** See Alaska Psychiatric Institute

☐ **ALASKA PSYCHIATRIC INSTITUTE (024002)**, 3700 Piper Street, Zip 99508–4677; tel. 907/269–7100, (Nonreporting) **A**1 10
Primary Contact: John E. Lee, Interim Chief Executive Officer
COO: Gavin H Carmichael, FACHE, Chief Operating Officer
CFO: Gavin H Carmichael, FACHE, Chief Operating Officer
CMO: Claudette A. Zarema, M.D., Medical Officer
CIO: Stephen Schneider, Manager Information Services
CHR: Katie E. Gratrix, Administrative Assistant III
CNO: Sharon Bergstedt, Director of Nursing
Web address: www.hss.state.ak.us/dbh/API/
**Control**: State, Government, Nonfederal **Service**: Psychiatric

**Staffed Beds:** 80

☒ **ALASKA REGIONAL HOSPITAL (020017)**, 2801 Debarr Road, Zip 99508–2997; tel. 907/264–1754, (Nonreporting) **A**1 2 10 **S** HCA Healthcare, Nashville, TN
Primary Contact: Julie Taylor, FACHE, Chief Executive Officer
COO: Victor Rosenbaum, Chief Operating Officer
CFO: Lynn Kennington, Chief Financial Officer
CMO: David Cadogan, Chief Medical Officer
CIO: Gene Kaplanis, Director Information Technology
CHR: Tammy Kaminski, Director Human Resources
CNO: Linda Doughty, Chief Nursing Officer
Web address: www.alaskaregional.com
**Control**: Corporation, Investor–owned (for–profit) **Service**: General medical and surgical

**Staffed Beds:** 250

**COLUMBIA ALASKA REGIONAL HOSP** See Alaska Regional Hospital

☒ **NORTH STAR BEHAVIORAL HEALTH SYSTEM (024001)**, 2530 DeBarr Circle, Zip 99508–2948; tel. 907/258–7575, (Includes NORTH STAR BEHAVIORAL HEALTH, Mailing address: 1650 South Bragaw, Anchorage, Alaska, Zip 99508–3467; tel. 907/258–7575), (Nonreporting) **A**1 5 10 **S** Universal Health Services, Inc., King of Prussia, PA
Primary Contact: Alan Barnes, Interim Chief Executive Officer
CFO: Alan Barnes, Chief Financial Officer
CMO: Ruth Dukoff, M.D., Medical Director
CIO: Brian O'Connell, Director Information Services
CHR: Sabrina Ben, Director Human Resources
CNO: Brandy Proctor, Director of Nursing
Web address: www.northstarbehavioral.com
**Control**: Corporation, Investor–owned (for–profit) **Service**: Psychiatric

**Staffed Beds:** 200

**NORTH STAR BEHAVIORAL HLTH SYS** See North Star Behavioral Health System

**NORTH STAR HLTH SYST** See North Star Behavioral Health

**PHS ALASKA NATIVE MED CENTER** See Alaska Native Medical Center

☒ **PROVIDENCE ALASKA MEDICAL CENTER (020001)**, 3200 Providence Drive, Zip 99508–4615, Mailing Address: P.O. Box 196604, Zip 99519–6604; tel. 907/562–2211, (Includes CHILDREN'S HOSPITAL AT PROVIDENCE, Mailing address: 3200 Providence Drive, Anchorage, Alaska, Zip 99508; tel. 907/212–3130), (Nonreporting) **A**1 3 5 10 13 **F**3 11 12 13 17 18 19 20 21 22 24 25 26 28 29 30 31 32 34 35 38 39 40 41 43 45 46 47 49 50 53 55 56 57 58 59 60 62 63 65 67 68 70 72 74 75 76 77 78 79 81 82 83 84 85 86 87 88 90 92 93 94 97 98 100 101 102 104 105 107 108 111 115 118 119 120 121 123 124 126 130 131 132 146 148 149 154 156 **S** Providence St. Joseph Health, Renton, WA
Primary Contact: Ella M. Goss, MSN, R.N., Chief Executive Officer
CFO: Anthony Dorsch, Chief Financial Officer
CMO: Roy Davis, M.D., Chief Medical Officer
CIO: Stephanie Morton, Chief Information Officer
CHR: Scott Jungwirth, Chief Human Resources Officer
Web address: www.alaska.providence.org/locations/p/pamc
**Control**: Church operated, Nongovernment, not–for–profit **Service**: General medical and surgical

**Staffed Beds:** 401 **Admissions:** 15587 **Census:** 293 **Outpatient Visits:** 403167 **Births:** 2499 **Total Expense ($000):** 470896 **Payroll Expense ($000):** 221172

**PROVIDENCE HOSPITAL** See Providence Alaska Medical Center

☒ **ST. ELIAS SPECIALTY HOSPITAL (022001)**, 4800 Cordova Street, Zip 99503–7218; tel. 907/561–3333, (Nonreporting) **A**1 10 **F**1 3 18 28 29 30 60 65 75 77 86 107 114 119
Primary Contact: Jessica Oswald, Chief Executive Officer
CFO: Andrew Fitch, Chief Financial Officer
Web address: www.st-eliashospital.com
**Control**: Corporation, Investor–owned (for–profit) **Service**: Acute long–term care hospital

**Staffed Beds:** 56 **Admissions:** 236 **Census:** 29 **Outpatient Visits:** 0 **Births:** 0 **Total Expense ($000):** 30038 **Payroll Expense ($000):** 11575 **Personnel:** 195

**THE CHILDREN'S HOSPITAL AT PROVIDENCE** See Children's Hospital at Providence

## BARROW—North Slope County

**PHS ALASKA NATIVE HOSPITAL** See Samuel Simmonds Memorial Hospital

☒ **SAMUEL SIMMONDS MEMORIAL HOSPITAL (021312)**, 7000 Uulu Street, Zip 99723, Mailing Address: P.O. Box 29, Zip 99723–0029; tel. 907/852–4611, (Nonreporting) **A**1 10 18
Primary Contact: Richard Hall, Chief Executive Officer
CMO: Devon Allen, M.D., Chief of Medical Staff
Web address: www.arcticslope.org
**Control**: Other not–for–profit (including NFP Corporation) **Service**: General medical and surgical

**Staffed Beds:** 14

## BETHEL—Bethel County

**PHS YUKON-KUSKOKWIM DELTA HOSP** See Yukon-Kuskokwim Delta Regional Hospital

☒ **YUKON-KUSKOKWIM DELTA REGIONAL HOSPITAL (020018)**, 700 Chief Eddie Hoffman Highway, Zip 99559–3000, Mailing Address: P.O. Box 528, Zip 99559–0528; tel. 907/543–6300, (Nonreporting) **A**1 3 5 10
Primary Contact: Dan Winkelman, President and Chief Executive Officer
CFO: Tommy Tompkins, Vice President, Finance and Chief Financial Officer
CIO: William Pearch, Chief Information Officer
Web address: www.ykhc.org
**Control**: Other not–for–profit (including NFP Corporation) **Service**: General medical and surgical

**Staffed Beds:** 37

---

**Hospital, Medicare Provider Number, Address, Telephone, Approval, Facility, and Physician Codes, Health Care System**

★ American Hospital Association (AHA) membership ○ Healthcare Facilities Accreditation Program ⇑ Center for Improvement in Healthcare Quality Accreditation
☐ The Joint Commission accreditation ◇ DNV Healthcare Inc. accreditation △ Commission on Accreditation of Rehabilitation Facilities (CARF) accreditation

**AK**

## CORDOVA—Valdez-Cordova County

**CORDOVA COMMUNITY HOSPITAL** See Cordova Community Medical Center

★ **CORDOVA COMMUNITY MEDICAL CENTER (021307)**, 602 Chase Avenue, Zip 99574, Mailing Address: P.O. Box 160, Zip 99574–0160; tel. 907/424–8000, (Nonreporting) **A**10 18
Primary Contact: Randall Draney, Chief Executive Officer and Chief Financial Officer
CFO: Randall Draney, Chief Executive Officer and Chief Financial Officer
CMO: Hannah Sanders, M.D., Medical Director
CHR: Kim Wilson, Human Resources Coordinator
CNO: Kelly Kedzierski, R.N., Director of Nursing
Web address: www.cdvcmc.com
**Control**: City, Government, Nonfederal **Service**: General medical and surgical

**Staffed Beds**: 23

## DILLINGHAM—Dillingham County

⊠ **BRISTOL BAY AREA HEALTH CORPORATION (021309)**, 6000 Kanakanak Road, Zip 99576, Mailing Address: P.O. Box 130, Zip 99576–0130; tel. 907/842–5201, (Nonreporting) **A**1 3 10 18
Primary Contact: Robert J. Clark, President and Chief Executive Officer
COO: Lucrecia Scotford, Executive Vice President and Chief Operations Officer
CFO: David Morgan, Vice President and Chief Financial Officer
CMO: Arnold Loera, M.D., Clinical Director
CIO: Bill Wilcox, Chief Information Technology Officer
CHR: John Davis, Chief Human Resources Officer
CNO: Starla Fox, Director of Nursing
Web address: www.bbahc.org
**Control**: Other not–for–profit (including NFP Corporation) **Service**: General medical and surgical

**Staffed Beds**: 16

**KANAKANAK HOSPITAL** See Bristol Bay Area Health Corporation

## ELMENDORF AFB—Anchorage County

⊠ **U. S. AIR FORCE REGIONAL HOSPITAL**, 5955 Zeamer Avenue, Zip 99506–3702; tel. 907/580–3006, (Nonreporting) **A**1 **S** Department of the Air Force, Washington, DC
Primary Contact: Major Mark Lamey, Commander
COO: ColonelRebecca Seese, Chief Operating Officer
CFO: MajorFelicia Burks, Chief Financial Officer
CMO: ColonelMarriner Oldham, M.D., Chief Medical Officer
CIO: MajorPhillip Oliphant, Chief Information Officer
CHR: Mark Clark, Human Resources Liaison
Web address: www.elmendorf.af.mil/
**Service**: General medical and surgical

**Staffed Beds**: 64

## FAIRBANKS—Fairbanks North Star County

⊠ **FAIRBANKS MEMORIAL HOSPITAL (020012)**, 1650 Cowles Street, Zip 99701–5998; tel. 907/452–8181, (Total facility includes 90 beds in nursing home–type unit) **A**1 2 3 5 10 **F**3 11 13 15 17 18 20 22 28 29 30 31 34 35 40 41 43 45 48 50 51 54 59 60 62 63 64 67 68 70 72 75 76 77 79 81 84 85 86 87 89 93 98 102 107 108 110 111 114 115 118 119 120 121 123 126 128 129 130 135 146 147 148 149
Primary Contact: Shelley Ebenal, Chief Executive Officer
COO: Clint Brooks, Chief Operating Officer
CFO: Steve Leslie, Chief Financial Officer
CIO: Carl J Kegley, System Director Information Technology
CHR: Nicole Welch, Chief Human Resources Officer
CNO: Karen Justin-Tanner, R.N., Chief Nursing Officer
Web address: www.https://www.foundationhealth.org/fmh
**Control**: Other not–for–profit (including NFP Corporation) **Service**: General medical and surgical

**Staffed Beds**: 217 **Admissions**: 4307 **Census**: 121 **Outpatient Visits**: 343716 **Births**: 986 **Total Expense ($000)**: 256050 **Payroll Expense ($000)**: 113767 **Personnel**: 1332

## FORT WAINWRIGHT—Fairbanks North Star County

⊠ **BASSETT ARMY COMMUNITY HOSPITAL**, 1060 Gaffney Road, Box 7400, Zip 99703–5001, Mailing Address: 1060 Gaffney Road, Box 7440, Zip 99703–5001; tel. 907/361–4000, (Nonreporting) **A**1 3 **S** Department of the Army, Office of the Surgeon General, Falls Church, VA
Primary Contact: Colonel Constance Jenkins, Commander
CMO: ColonelLeo Bennett, M.D., Deputy Commander Clinical Services
CHR: Terri Morefield, Deputy Chief Human Resources Division
Web address: www.alaska.amedd.army.mil
**Service**: General medical and surgical

**Staffed Beds**: 21

## HOMER—Kenai Peninsula County

★ **SOUTH PENINSULA HOSPITAL (021313)**, 4300 Bartlett Street, Zip 99603–7000; tel. 907/235–8101, (Total facility includes 28 beds in nursing home–type unit) (Nonreporting) **A**10 18 **F**3 11 13 15 29 31 32 34 35 40 46 54 57 59 62 64 67 70 75 76 77 79 81 82 93 97 100 104 107 110 111 115 119 129 130 133 147 148 154 156 **P**6 8
Primary Contact: Ryan K. Smith, Chief Executive Officer
CMO: Sarah Spencer, M.D., Chief of Staff
CIO: Jim Bartilson, Manager Information Systems
CNO: Von Kilpatrick, Chief Nursing Officer
Web address: www.sphosp.org
**Control**: Other not–for–profit (including NFP Corporation) **Service**: General medical and surgical

**Staffed Beds**: 50 **Admissions**: 812 **Census**: 32 **Outpatient Visits**: 78519 **Births**: 135 **Total Expense ($000)**: 75239 **Payroll Expense ($000)**: 34292 **Personnel**: 379

## JUNEAU—Juneau County

**BARTLETT MEMORIAL HOSPITAL** See Bartlett Regional Hospital

⊠ **BARTLETT REGIONAL HOSPITAL (020008)**, 3260 Hospital Drive, Zip 99801–7808; tel. 907/796–8900, (Nonreporting) **A**1 5 10 20 **F**3 4 5 13 15 28 29 31 34 36 37 38 40 43 45 50 51 57 59 64 70 75 76 77 81 82 85 86 87 91 93 98 100 101 102 104 105 107 108 110 111 114 115 119 129 130 132 135 148 149 150 152 153 154 156 157
Primary Contact: Charles E. Bill, Chief Executive Officer
CFO: Kevin Benson, Chief Financial Officer
CMO: Sharon Fisher, M.D., Chief of Staff
CIO: Martha Palicka, Director Information Systems
CHR: Dallas Hargrave, Human Resources Director
CNO: William Gardner, Chief Clinical Officer
Web address: www.bartletthospital.org
**Control**: City, Government, Nonfederal **Service**: General medical and surgical

**Staffed Beds**: 73 **Admissions**: 2297 **Census**: 37 **Outpatient Visits**: 31531 **Births**: 325 **Total Expense ($000)**: 104301 **Payroll Expense ($000)**: 48853

## KETCHIKAN—Ketchikan Gateway County

⇧ **KETCHIKAN GENERAL HOSPITAL** See Peacehealth Ketchikan Medical Center

★ ⇧ **PEACEHEALTH KETCHIKAN MEDICAL CENTER (021311)**, 3100 Tongass Avenue, Zip 99901–5746; tel. 907/225–5171, (Total facility includes 25 beds in nursing home–type unit) (Nonreporting) **A**5 10 18 21 **F**13 30 40 62 70 75 76 79 81 107 111 119 128 129 130 154 **S** PeaceHealth, Vancouver, WA
Primary Contact: Joe Mark, Interim Chief Administrator
CFO: Ken Tonjes, Chief Financial Officer
CMO: Peter Rice, M.D., Medical Director
CIO: Tim Walker, Manager Information Services
CHR: Lanetta Lundberg, Vice President Culture and People
Web address: www.peacehealth.org
**Control**: Other not–for–profit (including NFP Corporation) **Service**: General medical and surgical

**Staffed Beds**: 50 **Admissions**: 1020 **Census**: 30 **Outpatient Visits**: 43578 **Births**: 169 **Total Expense ($000)**: 60611 **Payroll Expense ($000)**: 29152 **Personnel**: 316

## KODIAK—Kodiak Island County

**PROVIDENCE KODIAK ISLAND HOSP** See Providence Kodiak Island Medical Center

⊠ **PROVIDENCE KODIAK ISLAND MEDICAL CENTER (021306)**, 1915 East Rezanof Drive, Zip 99615–6602; tel. 907/486–3281, (Nonreporting) **A**1 10 18 **S** Providence St. Joseph Health, Renton, WA
Primary Contact: Regina L. Bishop, Administrator
COO: Brenda Zawacki, Chief Operating Manager
CFO: Timothy Hocum, Chief Financial Officer
CMO: Steve Smith, M.D., Chief of Staff
CIO: David Johnson, Manager Information Services
CNO: LeeAnn Horn, Chief Nurse Executive
Web address: www.providence.org
**Control**: Other not–for–profit (including NFP Corporation) **Service**: General medical and surgical

**Staffed Beds**: 25

*Many Facility Codes have changed. Please refer to the AHA Guide Code Chart.*
© 2021 AHA Guide

## KOTZEBUE—Northwest Arctic County

☐ **MANIILAQ HEALTH CENTER (021310)**, 436 5th Avenue, Zip 99752–0043, Mailing Address: P.O. Box 43, Zip 99752–0043; tel. 907/442–7344, (Nonreporting) **A**1 10 18
Primary Contact: Tim J. Gilbert, President and Administrator
COO: Timothy Schuerch, President and Chief Executive Officer
CFO: Lucy Nelson, Director Finance, Vice President
CMO: Patricia Clancy, M.D., Director Medical Services
CIO: Eugene Smith, Chief Information Officer
CHR: Gerty Gallahom, Director Human Resources
CNO: CommanderDonna K Biagioni, R.N., MSN, Director of Nursing
Web address: www.maniilaq.org
**Control:** Other not–for–profit (including NFP Corporation) **Service:** General medical and surgical

**Staffed Beds:** 17

**MANIILAQ MEDICAL CENTER** See Maniilaq Health Center

## NOME—Nome County

✠ **NORTON SOUND REGIONAL HOSPITAL (021308)**, Bering Straits, Zip 99762, Mailing Address: P.O. Box 966, Zip 99762–0966; tel. 907/443–3311, (Nonreporting) **A**1 10 18
Primary Contact: Angela Gorn, Vice President
COO: Roy Agloinga, Chief Administrative Officer
CMO: David Head, M.D., Chief Medical Staff
CIO: Dan Bailey, Director Information Systems
CHR: Tiffany Martinson, Director Human Resources
Web address: www.nortonsoundhealth.org
**Control:** Other not–for–profit (including NFP Corporation) **Service:** General medical and surgical

**Staffed Beds:** 36

## PALMER—Matanuska-Susitna County

✠ **MAT-SU REGIONAL MEDICAL CENTER (020006)**, 2500 South Woodworth Loop, Zip 99645–8984, Mailing Address: P.O. Box 1687, Zip 99645–1687; tel. 907/861–6000, (Nonreporting) **A**1 3 10 20 **S** Community Health Systems, Inc., Franklin, TN
Primary Contact: David Wallace, Chief Executive Officer
CMO: Christopher Sahlstrom, M.D., Chief of Staff
CIO: Bryan Meurer, Director Information Systems
CHR: Cathy Babuscio, Director Human Resources
CNO: Emily Stevens, Chief Nursing Officer
Web address: www.matsuregional.com
**Control:** Partnership, Investor–owned (for–profit) **Service:** General medical and surgical

**Staffed Beds:** 74

**VALLEY HOSPITAL** See Mat-Su Regional Medical Center

## PETERSBURG—Petersburg County

**PETERSBURG GENERAL MED CTR** See Petersburg Medical Center

★ **PETERSBURG MEDICAL CENTER (021304)**, 103 Fram Street, Zip 99833, Mailing Address: Box 589, Zip 99833–0589; tel. 907/772–4291, (Nonreporting) **A**10 18
Primary Contact: Phil A. Hofstetter, Chief Executive Officer
CFO: Doran Hammett, Chief Financial Officer
CHR: Cynthia Newman, Manager Human Resources
CNO: Jennifer Bryner, Director Nursing
Web address: www.pmcak.org
**Control:** City, Government, Nonfederal **Service:** General medical and surgical

**Staffed Beds:** 27

## SEWARD—Kenai Peninsula County

★ **PROVIDENCE SEWARD MEDICAL CENTER (021302)**, 417 First Avenue, Zip 99664, Mailing Address: P.O. Box 365, Zip 99664–0365; tel. 907/224–5205, (Total facility includes 40 beds in nursing home–type unit) (Nonreporting) **A**10 18 **F**3 29 30 40 43 67 68 75 77 93 94 107 119 130 133 148 150 154 **P**6 **S** Providence St. Joseph Health, Renton, WA
Primary Contact: Robert A. Rang, R.N., MSN, Chief Executive Officer
CMO: Amy Bukac, M.D., Medical Director
CNO: Heather McKean, Director of Patient Care Services
Web address: www.providence.org
**Control:** City, Government, Nonfederal **Service:** General medical and surgical

**Staffed Beds:** 46 **Admissions:** 94 **Census:** 37 **Outpatient Visits:** 2251 **Births:** 0 **Total Expense ($000):** 19702 **Payroll Expense ($000):** 11793 **Personnel:** 138

**SEWARD GENERAL HOSPITAL** See Providence Seward Medical Center

## SITKA—Sitka County

**SEARHC MT EDGECUMBE HOSPITAL** See Searhc Mt. Edgecumbe Hospital

✠ **SEARHC MT. EDGECUMBE HOSPITAL (021314)**, 222 Tongass Drive, Zip 99835–9416; tel. 907/966–2411, (Nonreporting) **A**1 5 10 18
Primary Contact: Charles Clement, Chief Executive Officer
COO: Daniel P Neumeister, Senior Vice President and Chief Operating Officer
CFO: Barbara Searls, Chief Financial Officer
CMO: David Vastola, Medical Director
CIO: Bob Cita, Chief Information Officer
CHR: Peggy Bernhardt-Kadlec, Chief Human Resources Officer
CNO: Patricia L Giampa, Chief Nursing Officer
Web address: www.searhc.org
**Control:** Other not–for–profit (including NFP Corporation) **Service:** General medical and surgical

**Staffed Beds:** 25

## SOLDOTNA—Kenai Peninsula County

**CENTRAL PENINSULA GENERAL HOSPITAL** See Central Peninsula Hospital

✠ **CENTRAL PENINSULA HOSPITAL (020024)**, 250 Hospital Place, Zip 99669–6999; tel. 907/714–4404, (Total facility includes 60 beds in nursing home–type unit) (Nonreporting) **A**1 3 10 20 **F**3 4 5 11 13 15 28 29 30 31 34 35 36 38 40 45 46 47 48 49 50 51 57 59 65 68 70 74 75 76 77 78 79 81 82 84 85 86 87 93 97 105 106 107 108 110 111 115 119 128 129 130 131 132 133 134 135 145 146 147 148 149 152 153 154 155 156 **P**6
Primary Contact: Richard Davis, Chief Executive Officer
CMO: Gregg Motonaga, M.D., Chief of Staff
CIO: Bryan Downs, Director Information Systems
CHR: John Dodd, Vice President Human Resources
Web address: www.cpgh.org
**Control:** Other not–for–profit (including NFP Corporation) **Service:** General medical and surgical

**Staffed Beds:** 119 **Admissions:** 2725 **Census:** 84 **Outpatient Visits:** 133287 **Births:** 331 **Total Expense ($000):** 163771 **Payroll Expense ($000):** 69912 **Personnel:** 792

## VALDEZ—Valdez-Cordova County

★ **PROVIDENCE VALDEZ MEDICAL CENTER (021301)**, 911 Meals Avenue, Zip 99686–0550, Mailing Address: P.O. Box 550, Zip 99686–0550; tel. 907/835–2249, (Nonreporting) **A**5 10 18 **S** Providence St. Joseph Health, Renton, WA
Primary Contact: Jeremy O'Neil, Administrator
CMO: John Cullen, M.D., Chief of Staff and Medical Director Long Term Care
CHR: Maureen Radotich, Director Human Resources
Web address: www.providence.org/alaska
**Control:** City, Government, Nonfederal **Service:** General medical and surgical

**Staffed Beds:** 11

**VALDEZ COMMUNITY HOSPITAL** See Providence Valdez Medical Center

## WRANGELL—Wrangell County

**WRANGELL GENERAL HOSPITAL** See Wrangell Medical Center

★ **WRANGELL MEDICAL CENTER (021305)**, First Avenue & Bennett Street, Zip 99929, Mailing Address: P.O. Box 1081, Zip 99929–1081; tel. 907/874–7000, (Nonreporting) **A**10 18
Primary Contact: Leatha N. Merculieff, Hospital Administrator
CIO: Cathy Gross, Director Health Information Management Systems
CNO: Sherri Austin, MSN, R.N., Chief Nursing Officer
Web address: www.wrangellmedicalcenter.org/
**Control:** City, Government, Nonfederal **Service:** General medical and surgical

**Staffed Beds:** 22

---

| Hospital, Medicare Provider Number, Address, Telephone, Approval, Facility, and Physician Codes, Health Care System | | |
|---|---|---|
| ★ American Hospital Association (AHA) membership | ○ Healthcare Facilities Accreditation Program | ⇑ Center for Improvement in Healthcare Quality Accreditation |
| ☐ The Joint Commission accreditation | ◇ DNV Healthcare Inc. accreditation | △ Commission on Accreditation of Rehabilitation Facilities (CARF) accreditation |

# ARIZONA

## APACHE JUNCTION—Pinal County

**APACHE JUNCTION HOSPITAL** See Banner Goldfield Medical Center

✉ **BANNER GOLDFIELD MEDICAL CENTER (030134)**, 2050 West Southern Avenue, Zip 85120–7305; tel. 480/733–3300, (Nonreporting) **A**1 10 **F**3 18 29 30 34 35 40 45 49 59 60 65 67 68 75 79 81 82 85 87 100 107 108 111 115 119 126 130 131 135 146 147 148 149 154 156 **P**8 **S** Banner Health, Phoenix, AZ
Primary Contact: Robert Gardner, Chief Executive Officer
CFO: Tracy French, Chief Financial Officer
CMO: Jason Brown, M.D., Chief Medical Officer
CHR: Rebecca McLaughlin, Chief Human Resource Officer
CNO: Terresa Ann Paulus, Chief Nursing Officer
Web address: www.bannerhealth.com/Locations/Arizona/
Banner+Goldfield+Medical+Center/_Welcome+to+Banner+Goldfield.htm
**Control**: Other not–for–profit (including NFP Corporation) **Service**: General medical and surgical

**Staffed Beds**: 20 **Admissions**: 731 **Census**: 6 **Outpatient Visits**: 24330 **Births**: 0 **Total Expense ($000)**: 20228 **Payroll Expense ($000)**: 7482 **Personnel**: 88

## AVONDALE—Maricopa County

☐ **COPPER SPRINGS HOSPITAL (034032)**, 10550 West McDowell Road, Zip 85392–4864; tel. 602/314–7800, (Includes COPPER SPRINGS EAST, Mailing address: 3755 Rome Street, Gilbert, Arizona, Zip 85295; tel. 480/667–5500; Beckie Shauinger, Chief Executive Officer), (Nonreporting) **A**1 **F**5 30 38 68 98 100 101 104 106 152
Primary Contact: Jessica Black, Chief Executive Officer
Web address: www.coppersspringshealth.com
**Control**: Corporation, Investor–owned (for–profit) **Service**: Psychiatric

**Staffed Beds**: 72 **Admissions**: 3621 **Census**: 71 **Births**: 0

## BENSON—Cochise County

★ **BENSON HOSPITAL (031301)**, 450 South Ocotillo Street, Zip 85602–6403, Mailing Address: P.O. Box 2290, Zip 85602–2290; tel. 520/586–2261, (Nonreporting) **A**10 18 **F**3 11 29 30 34 35 40 43 50 54 57 59 64 75 77 86 87 93 107 111 114 119 132 133 146 148
Primary Contact: Julia Strange, Chief Executive Officer
COO: Teresa Vincifora, Chief Operating Officer
CFO: Ken Goranson, Chief Financial Officer
CMO: Barbara Hartley, Chief Medical Officer
CIO: Rob Roberts, Director Information Technology
CHR: Ashley Dickey, Director Human Resources
Web address: www.bensonhospital.org
**Control**: Other not–for–profit (including NFP Corporation) **Service**: General medical and surgical

**Staffed Beds**: 22 **Admissions**: 283 **Census**: 5 **Births**: 0

## BISBEE—Cochise County

★ **COPPER QUEEN COMMUNITY HOSPITAL (031312)**, 101 Cole Avenue, Zip 85603–1399; tel. 520/432–5383, (Nonreporting) **A**10 18 **F**3 7 11 18 29 30 34 40 42 45 46 50 57 62 67 77 81 90 92 93 97 107 108 110 111 119 146 154 155
Primary Contact: Robert L. Seamon, Chief Executive Officer
COO: Daniel Roe, M.D., Chief Operating Officer
CFO: James Ehasz, Chief Financial Officer
CIO: David Chmura, Chief Information Officer
CHR: Virginia Martinez, Director Human Resources
CNO: Sadie Maestas, Interim Chief Nursing Officer
Web address: www.cqch.org
**Control**: Other not–for–profit (including NFP Corporation) **Service**: General medical and surgical

**Staffed Beds**: 14 **Admissions**: 373 **Census**: 4 **Outpatient Visits**: 68681 **Births**: 0 **Total Expense ($000)**: 35122 **Payroll Expense ($000)**: 17183 **Personnel**: 271

## BULLHEAD CITY—Mohave County

**BULLHEAD COMMUNITY HOSPITAL** See Western Arizona Regional Medical Center

✉ **WESTERN ARIZONA REGIONAL MEDICAL CENTER (030101)**, 2735 Silver Creek Road, Zip 86442–8303; tel. 928/763–2273, (Nonreporting) **A**1 10 19 **F**3 8 11 13 15 18 20 22 28 29 34 35 40 43 45 50 54 56 57 59 64 65 68 69 70 75 76 77 79 80 81 82 85 87 93 97 102 107 108 110 111 114 115 118 119 130 131 144 146 147 148 149 154 156 157 **S** Community Health Systems, Inc., Franklin, TN
Primary Contact: Michael J Stenger, Chief Executive Officer
CFO: Christopher Frysztak, CPA, Chief Financial Officer
CNO: Emily Stevens, Chief Nursing Officer
Web address: www.warmc.com
**Control**: Corporation, Investor–owned (for–profit) **Service**: General medical and surgical

**Staffed Beds**: 106 **Admissions**: 4889 **Census**: 55 **Outpatient Visits**: 82282 **Births**: 287 **Personnel**: 538

## CASA GRANDE—Pinal County

✉ **BANNER CASA GRANDE MEDICAL CENTER (030016)**, 1800 East Florence Boulevard, Zip 85122–5399; tel. 520/381–6300, (Nonreporting) **A**1 10 **F**3 13 15 18 20 22 29 30 34 40 41 43 45 46 47 48 49 57 68 70 73 75 76 77 79 81 85 87 93 107 111 114 115 116 119 126 129 130 131 135 141 146 147 148 149 154 **P**8 **S** Banner Health, Phoenix, AZ
Primary Contact: Brian Kellar, Chief Executive Officer
CMO: Devin Minior, M.D., Chief Medical Officer
CHR: Carol D'Souza, Chief Human Resources Officer
CNO: Dan Lingle, Chief Nursing Officer
Web address: www.https://www.bannerhealth.com/locations/casa-grande/banner-casa-grande-medical-center
**Control**: Other not–for–profit (including NFP Corporation) **Service**: General medical and surgical

**Staffed Beds**: 123 **Admissions**: 5871 **Census**: 67 **Outpatient Visits**: 144418 **Births**: 730 **Total Expense ($000)**: 123016 **Payroll Expense ($000)**: 44135 **Personnel**: 581

**CASA GRANDE REGIONAL MEDICAL CENTER** See Banner Casa Grande Medical Center

## CHANDLER—Maricopa County

☐ **ARIZONA ORTHOPEDIC SURGICAL HOSPITAL (030112)**, 2905 West Warner Road, Suite 1, Zip 85224–1674; tel. 480/603–9000, (Nonreporting) **A**1 10 **S** United Surgical Partners International, Addison, TX
Primary Contact: Patricia K. Alice, Chief Executive Officer
CFO: Shalen Young, Chief Financial Officer
CMO: Randall Hardison, M.D., Chief Medical Officer
CIO: John Langenfeld, Medical Records Coordinator
CNO: Caroline Herpfer, Chief Nursing Officer
Web address: www.azosh.com
**Control**: Corporation, Investor–owned (for–profit) **Service**: Surgical

**Staffed Beds**: 24

**CHANDLER REGIONAL HOSPITAL** See Chandler Regional Medical Center

✉ **CHANDLER REGIONAL MEDICAL CENTER (030036)**, 1955 West Frye Road, Zip 85224–6282; tel. 480/728–3000, (Nonreporting) **A**1 3 5 10 19 **F**3 8 11 12 13 15 17 18 20 22 24 26 28 29 30 31 32 34 35 37 40 41 42 43 44 45 46 47 48 49 50 51 54 57 58 59 60 64 65 66 68 70 71 72 73 74 75 76 77 78 79 81 82 83 84 85 86 87 93 96 107 108 110 111 114 115 119 126 130 131 132 135 143 144 146 147 148 156 **S** CommonSpirit Health, Chicago, IL
Primary Contact: Mark F. Slyter, FACHE, President and Chief Operating Officer
COO: Mark F. Slyter, FACHE, President and Chief Operating Officer
CFO: Mark Kem, Vice President Finance and Chief Financial Officer
CMO: Terry J Happel, M.D., Vice President and Chief Medical Officer
CHR: Renea Brunke, Vice President Human Resources
CNO: Peg Smith, Vice President and Chief Nursing Officer
Web address: www.chandlerregional.com
**Control**: Other not–for–profit (including NFP Corporation) **Service**: General medical and surgical

**Staffed Beds**: 338 **Admissions**: 25386 **Census**: 279 **Outpatient Visits**: 194558 **Births**: 3528

*Many Facility Codes have changed. Please refer to the AHA Guide Code Chart.*

☐ **DIGNITY HEALTH EAST VALLEY REHABILITATION HOSPITAL (033040)**, 1515 West Chandler Boulevard, Zip 85224–6141; tel. 602/594–5400, (Nonreporting) **A**1 **S** Kindred Healthcare, Louisville, KY
Primary Contact: Alvin Wendt, Acting Chief Executive Officer
Web address: www.dignityhealthevrehab.com
**Control:** Partnership, Investor–owned (for–profit) **Service:** Rehabilitation

**Staffed Beds:** 50

☐ **OASIS BEHAVIORAL HEALTH - CHANDLER (034029)**, 2190 North Grace Boulevard, Zip 85225–3416; tel. 480/917–9301, (Nonreporting) **A**1 **S** Acadia Healthcare Company, Inc., Franklin, TN
Primary Contact: James Gallagher, Chief Executive Officer
CFO: Dino Quarante, CPA, Chief Financial Officer
CHR: Barbara Mitchell, Director Human Resources
CNO: Charissa Davis, Chief Nursing Officer and Director of Nursing
Web address: www.obhhospital.com/about/location
**Control:** Corporation, Investor–owned (for–profit) **Service:** Psychiatric

**Staffed Beds:** 146

### CHINLE—Apache County

⊞ **CHINLE COMPREHENSIVE HEALTH CARE FACILITY (030084)**, Highway 191, Zip 86503, Mailing Address: Highway 191 Hospital Drive, Zip 86503–8000; tel. 928/674–7001, (Nonreporting) **A**1 5 10 **F**3 15 29 30 34 35 36 38 39 40 44 45 50 53 54 57 59 61 64 65 68 70 71 75 76 77 81 82 85 87 89 93 97 100 104 107 110 111 114 119 130 132 135 143 146 147 149 150 153 154 156 **S** U. S. Indian Health Service, Rockville, MD
Primary Contact: Darlene Chee, Acting Chief Executive Officer
CFO: Philene Tyler, Chief Finance Officer
CMO: Eric Ritchie, M.D., Clinical Director
CIO: Perry Francis, Supervisory Information Technology Specialist
CHR: Lorraine Begaye, Supervisory Human Resource Specialist
Web address: www.ihs.gov
**Control:** PHS, Indian Service, Government, federal **Service:** General medical and surgical

**Staffed Beds:** 60 **Admissions:** 1533 **Census:** 13 **Outpatient Visits:** 323825 **Births:** 489

### COTTONWOOD—Yavapai County

⇑ **MARCUS J LAWRENCE MED CENTER** See Verde Valley Medical Center

⇑ **VERDE VALLEY MEDICAL CENTER (030007)**, 269 South Candy Lane, Zip 86326–4170; tel. 928/639–6000, (Nonreporting) **A**3 5 10 13 20 21 **F**3 11 13 15 18 20 22 28 29 30 31 32 34 35 40 42 44 45 47 48 49 50 51 53 54 57 58 59 60 61 63 64 68 70 75 76 77 78 79 81 84 85 86 87 91 92 93 94 96 97 100 101 102 107 108 110 111 114 115 118 119 120 121 123 124 129 130 131 132 135 145 146 147 148 149 154 **S** Northern Arizona Healthcare, Flagstaff, AZ
Primary Contact: Barbara Firminger, Chief Administrative Officer
CFO: Jeffrey Treasure, Chief Financial Officer, Northern Arizona Healthcare
CMO: Amy Gottschalk, M.D., Chief Medical Officer, Verde Valley Medical Center; Vice President Quality, Northern Arizona Healthcare
CIO: Marilynn Black, Chief Information Officer, Northern Arizona Healthcare
CHR: Ronald Haase, Chief Human Resources Officer, Northern Arizona Healthcare
CNO: Lori A Stevens, MSN, R.N., Interim Chief Nursing Officer
Web address: www.https://nahealth.com/
**Control:** Other not–for–profit (including NFP Corporation) **Service:** General medical and surgical

**Staffed Beds:** 87 **Admissions:** 4308 **Census:** 50 **Outpatient Visits:** 34707 **Births:** 490 **Total Expense ($000):** 131395 **Payroll Expense ($000):** 50489 **Personnel:** 888

### FLAGSTAFF—Coconino County

⇑ **FLAGSTAFF MEDICAL CENTER (030023)**, 1200 North Beaver Street, Zip 86001–3118; tel. 928/779–3366, (Nonreporting) **A**3 5 10 21 **F**3 5 7 8 11 12 13 15 17 18 19 20 22 24 26 29 30 31 32 34 35 36 38 40 43 44 45 46 47 48 49 50 51 53 54 57 58 59 60 61 64 68 70 72 74 75 76 77 78 79 81 84 85 86 87 88 89 91 92 93 94 96 97 98 100 101 102 103 104 105 107 108 110 111 114 115 118 119 120 121 123 124 126 130 131 132 135 146 147 148 149 152 154 155 **S** Northern Arizona Healthcare, Flagstaff, AZ
Primary Contact: Florence (Flo). Spyrow, Chief Administrative Officer
CFO: Jeffrey Treasure, Chief Financial Officer, Northern Arizona Healthcare
CMO: Richard Neff, M.D., Interim Chief Medical Officer
CIO: Marilynn Black, Chief Information Officer, Northern Arizona Healthcare
CHR: Ronald Haase, Chief Human Resources Officer, Northern Arizona Healthcare
Web address: www.nahealth.com
**Control:** Other not–for–profit (including NFP Corporation) **Service:** General medical and surgical

**Staffed Beds:** 264 **Admissions:** 11717 **Census:** 166 **Outpatient Visits:** 53115 **Births:** 1048 **Total Expense ($000):** 404230 **Payroll Expense ($000):** 136521 **Personnel:** 1910

☐ **GUIDANCE CENTER (034023)**, 2187 North Vickey Street, Zip 86004–6121; tel. 928/527–1899, (Nonreporting) **A**1 10
Primary Contact: Lauren Lauder, Chief Executive Officer
CFO: Steve Finch, Chief Financial Officer
CMO: Chris Linskey, M.D., Acting Chief Medical Officer
CIO: John Crockett, Chief Information Officer
Web address: www.tgcaz.org
**Control:** Other not–for–profit (including NFP Corporation) **Service:** Psychiatric

**Staffed Beds:** 16

☐ **REHABILITATION HOSPITAL OF NORTHERN ARIZONA (033041)**, 1851 North Gemini Drive, Zip 86001–1607; tel. 928/774–7070, (Nonreporting) **A**1 **S** Ernest Health, Inc., Albuquerque, NM
Primary Contact: Chris LaFontsee, Chief Executive Officer
Web address: www.ernesthealth.com/gallery-item/rehabilitation-hospital-of-northern-arizona/
**Control:** Corporation, Investor–owned (for–profit) **Service:** Rehabilitation

**Staffed Beds:** 40

### FORT DEFIANCE—Apache County

**FORT DEFIANCE INDIAN HEALTH SERVICE HOSPITAL** See Tsehootsooi Medical Center

★ **TSEHOOTSOOI MEDICAL CENTER (030071)**, Highway 12 & Bonito Drive, Zip 86504, Mailing Address: P.O. Box 649, Zip 86504–0649; tel. 928/729–8000, (Nonreporting) **A**3 5 10
Primary Contact: Sandi Aretino, M.D., Chief Executive Officer
COO: Valonia Hardy, Chief Healthy Living Officer
CFO: Rachel Sorrell, Chief Financial Officer
CMO: Michael Tutt, M.D., Chief Medical Officer
CIO: Virgil Chavez, Director Information Technology
CHR: Vivian Santistevan, Chief Human Resources
CNO: Tori Davidson, R.N., Chief Nursing Officer
Web address: www.fdihb.org
**Control:** Public Health Service other than 47, Government, federal **Service:** General medical and surgical

**Staffed Beds:** 39

### FORT MOHAVE—Mohave County

⊞ **VALLEY VIEW MEDICAL CENTER (030117)**, 5330 South Highway 95, Zip 86426–9225; tel. 928/788–2273, (Nonreporting) **A**1 10 **F**3 8 11 13 15 18 20 22 29 45 50 51 56 59 64 70 76 77 81 85 87 90 93 107 108 111 114 115 116 117 119 135 144 149 154 **S** LifePoint Health, Brentwood, TN
Primary Contact: Feliciano Jiron, Chief Executive Officer
CFO: Emma Canlas, Chief Financial Officer
CIO: Monique Murphy-Mijares, Chief Information Officer
CHR: Bonnie Guerrero, Director Human Resources
CNO: Lesa Lock, Chief Nursing Officer
Web address: www.valleyviewmedicalcenter.net
**Control:** Corporation, Investor–owned (for–profit) **Service:** General medical and surgical

**Staffed Beds:** 84 **Admissions:** 2258 **Census:** 23

### GANADO—Apache County

⊞ **SAGE MEMORIAL HOSPITAL (031309)**, Highway 264, Zip 86505, Mailing Address: P.O. Box 457, Zip 86505–0457; tel. 928/755–4500, (Nonreporting) **A**1 10 18
Primary Contact: Christi J. El-Meligi, Chief Executive Officer
COO: Netrisha Dalgai, Director of Operations
CHR: Gary Pahe, Manager Human Resources
CNO: Ernasha McIntosh, Interim Director of Nursing
Web address: www.sagememorial.com
**Control:** Other not–for–profit (including NFP Corporation) **Service:** General medical and surgical

**Staffed Beds:** 24

---

**Hospital, Medicare Provider Number, Address, Telephone, Approval, Facility, and Physician Codes, Health Care System**

★ American Hospital Association (AHA) membership
☐ The Joint Commission accreditation
○ Healthcare Facilities Accreditation Program
◇ DNV Healthcare Inc. accreditation
⇑ Center for Improvement in Healthcare Quality Accreditation
△ Commission on Accreditation of Rehabilitation Facilities (CARF) accreditation

**AZ**

### GILBERT—Maricopa County

⊞ **BANNER GATEWAY MEDICAL CENTER (030122)**, 1900 North Higley Road, Zip 85234–1604; tel. 480/543–2000, (Nonreporting) **A**1 3 10 **F**3 8 12 13 15 18 29 30 31 34 35 36 40 44 45 46 47 49 50 51 55 57 58 59 60 63 68 70 72 74 75 76 77 78 79 81 85 87 93 102 107 108 110 111 114 116 117 118 119 120 121 124 126 130 132 134 136 141 142 146 147 148 149 154 **P**8 **S** Banner Health, Phoenix, AZ
Primary Contact: Lamont M. Yoder, R.N., MSN, FACHE, Chief Executive Officer
COO: James R Powell, Associate Administrator
CFO: Thomas M Matenaer, Chief Financial Officer
CMO: Nikunj Doshi, D.O., Chief Medical Officer
CHR: Michele Mustacchia, Chief Human Resources Officer
CNO: Debra Adornetto-Garcia, MSN, R.N., Chief Nursing Officer
Web address: www.bannerhealth.com/Locations/Arizona/ Banner+Gateway+Medical+Center/
**Control**: Other not–for–profit (including NFP Corporation) **Service**: General medical and surgical

**Staffed Beds:** 177 **Admissions:** 13355 **Census:** 153 **Outpatient Visits:** 366018 **Births:** 4460 **Total Expense ($000):** 406257 **Payroll Expense ($000):** 110279

⊞ **MERCY GILBERT MEDICAL CENTER (030119)**, 3555 South Val Vista Road, Zip 85297–7323; tel. 480/728–8000, (Nonreporting) **A**1 10 19 **F**3 8 11 12 13 15 18 20 22 26 28 29 30 31 32 34 35 37 38 40 41 42 44 45 46 47 49 50 51 57 58 59 60 64 65 66 68 70 73 74 75 76 77 78 79 81 82 83 84 85 86 87 96 100 101 102 103 107 108 110 111 114 115 119 126 129 130 131 132 135 144 145 146 147 148 156 **S** CommonSpirit Health, Chicago, IL
Primary Contact: Mark F. Slyter, FACHE, President and Chief Operating Officer
COO: Mark F. Slyter, FACHE, President and Chief Operating Officer
CFO: Chuck Sowers, Vice President Finance and Chief Financial Officer
CIO: Larissa Spraker, Vice President Business Development and Chief Strategy Officer
CHR: Anita Harger, Director Human Resources
Web address: www.mercygilbert.org
**Control**: Other not–for–profit (including NFP Corporation) **Service**: General medical and surgical

**Staffed Beds:** 197 **Admissions:** 15229 **Census:** 152 **Outpatient Visits:** 91027 **Births:** 3526 **Total Expense ($000):** 281686 **Payroll Expense ($000):** 96815

### GLENDALE—Maricopa County

⊞ **ABRAZO ARROWHEAD CAMPUS (030094)**, 18701 North 67th Avenue, Zip 85308–7100; tel. 623/561–1000, (Includes ABRAZO ARIZONA HEART HOSPITAL, Mailing address: 1930 East Thomas Road, Phoenix, Arizona, Zip 85016; tel. 602/532–1000; Jeff Patterson, Chief Executive Officer), (Nonreporting) **A**1 3 5 10 **F**3 13 17 18 20 22 24 26 28 29 30 31 34 35 37 40 42 45 48 49 50 51 54 57 58 59 60 64 68 70 72 74 75 76 77 78 79 81 93 102 107 108 111 114 115 119 126 130 131 132 148 154 **S** TENET Healthcare Corporation, Dallas, TX
Primary Contact: Jeff Patterson, Chief Executive Officer
CMO: Patrick Smith, M.D., Chief Medical Officer
CHR: Sharon M Chadwick, Director Human Resources
Web address: www.arrowheadhospital.com
**Control**: Corporation, Investor–owned (for–profit) **Service**: General medical and surgical

**Staffed Beds:** 217 **Admissions:** 16651 **Census:** 169 **Outpatient Visits:** 86619 **Births:** 3241 **Total Expense ($000):** 295537 **Payroll Expense ($000):** 106859

**ARROWHEAD HOSPITAL** See Abrazo Arrowhead Campus

☐ **AURORA BEHAVIORAL HEALTH SYSTEM WEST (034024)**, 6015 West Peoria Avenue, Zip 85302–1213; tel. 623/344–4400, (Nonreporting) **A**1 10 **F**4 5 10 11 29 30 34 35 38 44 50 57 68 75 86 87 98 101 102 104 105 130 132 134 135 146 151 152 153 154 **S** Signature Healthcare Services, Corona, CA
Primary Contact: Bruce Waldo, Chief Executive Officer
CFO: Rebekah Francis, JD, Chief Financial Officer
CHR: Vicki Thomsen, Director Human Resources
CNO: Lori Milus, R.N., MSN, Director of Nursing
Web address: www.aurorabehavioral.com
**Control**: Corporation, Investor–owned (for–profit) **Service**: Psychiatric

**Staffed Beds:** 100 **Admissions:** 4718 **Census:** 85 **Outpatient Visits:** 6775 **Births:** 0 **Total Expense ($000):** 20236 **Payroll Expense ($000):** 12600

**AURORA PHOENIX HOSPITAL** See Aurora Behavioral Health System West

⊞ **BANNER THUNDERBIRD MEDICAL CENTER (030089)**, 5555 West Thunderbird Road, Zip 85306–4696; tel. 602/865–5555, (Includes BANNER BEHAVIORAL HEALTH CENTER-THUNDERBIRD CAMPUS, Mailing address: 5555 West Thunderbird Road, Glendale, Arizona, Zip 85306; tel. 602/588–5555, MSN), (Nonreporting) **A**1 3 5 17 18 19 20 22 24 26 28 29 30 31 32 34 35 40 41 43 45 46 49 50 51 59 60 61 64 65 68 70 71 72 74 75 76 77 78 79 81 84 85 87 88 89 98 100 101 102 104 107 108 109 111 112 114 115 116 117 118 119 120 121 122 123 124 126 129 130 132 134 135 145 146 147 148 149 150 153 154 **P**8 **S** Banner Health, Phoenix, AZ
Primary Contact: Debbie Flores, Chief Executive Officer
CFO: Richard Miller, Administrator Finance
CMO: Kathryn Perkins, M.D., Chief Medical Officer
CHR: Laura Witt, Administrator Human Resources
Web address: www.https://www.bannerhealth.com/locations/glendale/banner-thunderbird-medical-center
**Control**: Other not–for–profit (including NFP Corporation) **Service**: General medical and surgical

**Staffed Beds:** 555 **Admissions:** 26141 **Census:** 351 **Outpatient Visits:** 452957 **Births:** 5090 **Total Expense ($000):** 486208 **Payroll Expense ($000):** 175763 **Personnel:** 2701

⊞ **ENCOMPASS HEALTH VALLEY OF THE SUN REHABILITATION HOSPITAL (033032)**, 13460 North 67th Avenue, Zip 85304–1042; tel. 623/878–8800, (Nonreporting) **A**1 10 **F**29 62 64 75 90 93 132 **S** Encompass Health Corporation, Birmingham, AL
Primary Contact: Beth Bacher, Chief Executive Officer
CFO: Kathryn Haney, Controller
CMO: Michael Kravetz, M.D., Medical Director
CHR: Danette Garcia, Director Human Resources
CNO: Stephanie Palmer, Chief Nursing Officer
Web address: www.https://www.encompasshealth.com/valleyofthesunrehab
**Control**: Corporation, Investor–owned (for–profit) **Service**: Rehabilitation

**Staffed Beds:** 75 **Admissions:** 1095 **Census:** 41 **Births:** 0

**ENCOMPASS VALLEY OF THE SUN REHABILITATION HOSPITAL** See Encompass Health Valley of The Sun Rehabilitation Hospital

**SAMARITAN BEHAVIORAL HLTH CTR** See Banner Behavioral Health Center-Thunderbird Campus

**THUNDERBIRD SAMARITAN MED CTR** See Banner Thunderbird Medical Center

### GLOBE—Gila County

**COBRE VALLEY COMMUNITY HOSPITAL** See Cobre Valley Regional Medical Center

★ **COBRE VALLEY REGIONAL MEDICAL CENTER (031314)**, 5880 South Hospital Drive, Zip 85501–9454; tel. 928/425–3261, (Nonreporting) **A**10 18 **S** HealthTech Management Services, Brentwood, TN
Primary Contact: Neal Jensen, Chief Executive Officer
CFO: Frank Napier, Interim Chief Financial Officer
CIO: Sharon Bennett, Manager Information Systems
CHR: Rita Murphy, Director Human Resources
Web address: www.cvrmc.org
**Control**: Other not–for–profit (including NFP Corporation) **Service**: General medical and surgical

**Staffed Beds:** 25

### GOODYEAR—Maricopa County

⊞ **ABRAZO WEST CAMPUS (030110)**, 13677 West McDowell Road, Zip 85395–2635; tel. 623/882–1500, (Nonreporting) **A**1 3 5 10 **S** TENET Healthcare Corporation, Dallas, TX
Primary Contact: Christina E. Oh, Chief Executive Officer
COO: Jeffrey Dossett, Chief Operating Officer
CFO: Asja DiMuria, Chief Financial Officer
CNO: Scott David Morey, Chief Nursing Officer
Web address: www.abrazohealth.com
**Control**: Corporation, Investor–owned (for–profit) **Service**: General medical and surgical

**Staffed Beds:** 106

**WEST VALLEY HOSPITAL** See Abrazo West Campus

⊞ **WESTERN REGIONAL MEDICAL CENTER (030138)**, 14200 West Celebrate Life way, Zip 85338–3005; tel. 623/207–3000, (Nonreporting) **A**1 10 **F**3 15 18 29 30 31 63 64 68 70 75 78 81 82 84 85 87 100 107 108 110 111 114 115 116 117 118 119 120 121 123 126 130 135 146 **S** Cancer Treatment Centers of America, Schaumburg, IL
Primary Contact: Robert Gould, President and Chief Executive Officer
Web address: www.cancercenter.com/western-hospital.cfm
**Control**: Corporation, Investor–owned (for–profit) **Service**: Cancer

**Staffed Beds:** 11 **Admissions:** 557 **Census:** 7 **Outpatient Visits:** 0 **Births:** 0

*Many Facility Codes have changed. Please refer to the AHA Guide Code Chart.*
© 2021 AHA Guide

## GREEN VALLEY—Cochise County

⇑ **GREEN VALLEY HOSPITAL** See Santa Cruz Valley Regional Hospital

⇑ **SANTA CRUZ VALLEY REGIONAL HOSPITAL (030137)**, 4455 South I-19 Frontage Road, Zip 85614; tel. 520/393–4700, (Nonreporting) **A**21 **F**18 20 22 29 30 34 35 40 45 48 57 70 75 79 81 93 107 108 111 114 119 126 133 146 148 154
Primary Contact: Kelly Adams, Chief Executive Officer
CFO: Sara Ghali, Chief Financial Officer
CNO: Mona R. Smith, Chief Nursing Officer
Web address: www.https://scvrhaz.com/
**Control:** Partnership, Investor–owned (for–profit) **Service:** General medical and surgical

**Staffed Beds:** 49 **Admissions:** 2240 **Census:** 10 **Outpatient Visits:** 20103 **Births:** 2 **Total Expense ($000):** 45971 **Payroll Expense ($000):** 15837

## KEAMS CANYON—Navajo County

⊞ **HOPI HEALTH CARE CENTER (031305)**, Highway 264 Mile Marker 388, Zip 86042, Mailing Address: P.O. Box 4000, Polacca, Zip 86042–4000; tel. 928/737–6000, (Nonreporting) **A**1 3 5 10 18 **S** U. S. Indian Health Service, Rockville, MD
Primary Contact: Mose Herne, Chief Executive Officer
COO: Leonard H Lopez, Chief Operating Officer
CFO: Dorothy Sulu, Budget Analyst
CMO: Darren Vicenti, M.D., Clinical Director
CHR: Trudy Begay, Human Resources Specialist
Web address: www.ihs.gov/index.asp
**Control:** PHS, Indian Service, Government, federal **Service:** General medical and surgical

**Staffed Beds:** 15

**USPHS INDIAN HOSPITAL** See Hopi Health Care Center

## KINGMAN—Mohave County

★ ⇑ **KINGMAN REGIONAL MEDICAL CENTER (030055)**, 3269 North Stockton Hill Road, Zip 86409–3691; tel. 928/757–2101, (Nonreporting) **A**3 5 10 13 21 **F**11 17 20 22 24 28 29 30 31 32 33 34 35 36 40 43 45 46 47 48 53 57 59 60 62 63 64 65 68 69 70 75 76 77 78 79 81 82 83 84 85 86 87 89 90 92 93 96 97 100 107 108 114 115 117 118 119 121 129 130 131 132 143 144 145 146 147 148
Primary Contact: C. William McConnell, Ph.D., Chief Executive Officer
COO: Ryan Kennedy, Chief Operating Officer
CFO: Timothy D Blanchard, Chief Financial Officer
CMO: Thomas Gaughan, M.D., Chief Medical Officer
CIO: Arek Shennar, Chief Information Officer
CHR: Anita Harger, Chief Human Resource Officer
CNO: James Wells, R.N., Chief Nursing Officer
Web address: www.azkrmc.com
**Control:** Hospital district or authority, Government, Nonfederal **Service:** General medical and surgical

**Staffed Beds:** 160 **Admissions:** 7244 **Census:** 89

## LAKE HAVASU CITY—Mohave County

⊞ **HAVASU REGIONAL MEDICAL CENTER (030069)**, 101 Civic Center Lane, Zip 86403–5683; tel. 928/855–8185, (Nonreporting) **A**1 10 **S** LifePoint Health, Brentwood, TN
Primary Contact: Michael N. Patterson, Chief Executive Officer
CFO: Christina DiMambro, Chief Financial Officer
CMO: Michael Rosen, M.D., Chief Medical Officer
CIO: Linda Toy, Director Information Systems
Web address: www.havasuregional.com
**Control:** Corporation, Investor–owned (for–profit) **Service:** General medical and surgical

**Staffed Beds:** 162

**HAVASU SAMARITAN REG HOSP** See Havasu Regional Medical Center

## LAKESIDE—Navajo County

☐ **CCC AT PINEVIEW HOSPITAL (034027)**, 1920 West Commerce Drive, Zip 85929; tel. 928/368–4110, (Nonreporting) **A**1 10
Primary Contact: Rosemary Anderson, Administrator
Web address: www.ccc-az.org
**Control:** Other not–for–profit (including NFP Corporation) **Service:** Psychiatric

**Staffed Beds:** 16

## LAVEEN—Maricopa County

☐ **DIGNITY HEALTH ARIZONA GENERAL HOSPITAL (030136)**, 7171 South 51st Avenue, Zip 85339–2923; tel. 623/584–5100, (Nonreporting) **A**1 **S** CommonSpirit Health, Chicago, IL
Primary Contact: Jane E. Hanson, R.N., Chief Executive Officer
CFO: Anthony Cirocco, Chief Financial Officer
CMO: Fred Johnson, M.D., Chief Medical Officer
CNO: Victoria Nugent, Chief Nursing Officer
Web address: www.dignityhealth.org/arizonageneral/
**Control:** Other not–for–profit (including NFP Corporation) **Service:** Acute long–term care hospital

**Staffed Beds:** 16

## MESA—Maricopa County

☐ **ARIZONA SPINE AND JOINT HOSPITAL (030107)**, 4620 East Baseline Road, Zip 85206–4624; tel. 480/832–4770, (Nonreporting) **A**1 10 **F**29 34 77 79 81 82 85 111 146 **S** National Surgical Healthcare, Chicago, IL
Primary Contact: Todd Greene, Chief Executive Officer
CHR: Diane Hearne, Director Human Resources
CNO: Stacy Hayes, R.N., Chief Nursing Officer
Web address: www.azspineandjoint.com
**Control:** Corporation, Investor–owned (for–profit) **Service:** Orthopedic

**Staffed Beds:** 23 **Admissions:** 1589 **Census:** 5 **Births:** 0

**BANNER BAYWOOD HEART HOSPITAL** See Banner Heart Hospital

⊞ **BANNER BAYWOOD MEDICAL CENTER (030088)**, 6644 East Baywood Avenue, Zip 85206–1797; tel. 480/321–2000, (Nonreporting) **A**1 10 **F**3 15 18 29 30 31 34 35 36 37 40 43 44 45 46 47 48 49 50 51 56 57 58 59 60 61 63 64 65 68 70 74 75 77 78 79 81 82 84 85 86 87 90 92 94 96 97 100 102 107 108 110 111 115 118 119 126 129 130 135 146 147 148 149 154 156 **P**8 **S** Banner Health, Phoenix, AZ
Primary Contact: Lamont M. Yoder, R.N., MSN, FACHE, Chief Executive Officer
CFO: Derek Lythgoe, Chief Financial Officer
CMO: Michael P O'Connor, M.D., Chief Medical Officer
CIO: Lori Matthews, Vice President Information Technology System
CHR: Tiffany Werner, Senior Human Resource Business Partner
CNO: Kelley Kieffer, Chief Nursing Officer
Web address: www.bannerhealth.com/locations/Arizona/banner+baywood+medical+center
**Control:** Other not–for–profit (including NFP Corporation) **Service:** General medical and surgical

**Staffed Beds:** 359 **Admissions:** 14787 **Census:** 204 **Outpatient Visits:** 273639 **Births:** 0 **Total Expense ($000):** 260693 **Payroll Expense ($000):** 91402 **Personnel:** 1457

**BANNER CHILDREN'S HOSPITAL** See Cardon Children's Medical Center

⊞ **BANNER DESERT MEDICAL CENTER (030065)**, 1400 South Dobson Road, Zip 85202–4707; tel. 480/412–3000, (Includes CARDON CHILDREN'S MEDICAL CENTER, Mailing address: 1400 South Dobson Road, Mesa, Arizona, Zip 85202–4707; tel. 480/412–3000; Justin Bradshaw, Chief Executive Officer; SAMARITAN BEHAVIORAL HEALTH CENTER-DESERT SAMARITAN MEDICAL CENTER, Mailing address: 2225 West Southern Avenue, Mesa, Arizona, Zip 85202; tel. 602/464–4000), (Nonreporting) **A**1 3 5 10 **F**3 9 11 13 17 18 19 20 21 22 23 24 25 26 27 28 29 30 31 32 34 35 36 37 40 41 43 45 46 47 48 49 50 51 56 58 59 60 61 63 64 68 70 72 74 75 76 77 78 79 81 84 85 86 87 88 89 91 92 96 100 107 108 111 114 115 118 119 120 121 123 124 126 129 130 133 135 146 147 148 149 154 **P**8 **S** Banner Health, Phoenix, AZ
Primary Contact: Laura Robertson, R.N., Chief Executive Officer
COO: Cristal Mackay, Chief Operating Officer
CFO: Scott Leckey, Chief Financial Officer
CMO: Tanya Kne, M.D., Chief Medical Officer
CIO: Stacey Hinkle, Director Information Technology
CHR: Kevin McVeigh, Chief Human Resources Officer
Web address: www.bannerhealth.com/Locations/Arizona/Banner+Desert+Medical+Center
**Control:** Other not–for–profit (including NFP Corporation) **Service:** General medical and surgical

**Staffed Beds:** 595 **Admissions:** 35335 **Census:** 474 **Outpatient Visits:** 471150 **Births:** 4034 **Total Expense ($000):** 636067 **Payroll Expense ($000):** 222465 **Personnel:** 2468

---

| | |
|---|---|
| Hospital, Medicare Provider Number, Address, Telephone, Approval, Facility, and Physician Codes, Health Care System | |
| ★ American Hospital Association (AHA) membership | ○ Healthcare Facilities Accreditation Program |
| ☐ The Joint Commission accreditation | ◇ DNV Healthcare Inc. accreditation |
| ⇑ Center for Improvement in Healthcare Quality Accreditation | △ Commission on Accreditation of Rehabilitation Facilities (CARF) accreditation |

**BANNER HEART HOSPITAL (030105)**, 6750 East Baywood Avenue, Zip 85206–1749; tel. 480/854–5000, (Nonreporting) **A**1 3 10 **F**3 17 18 20 22 24 26 28 29 30 34 35 36 40 44 50 57 58 59 60 63 68 75 81 82 84 85 86 87 102 119 130 132 146 149 154 156 **P**8 **S** Banner Health, Phoenix, AZ
Primary Contact: Lamont M. Yoder, R.N., MSN, FACHE, Chief Executive Officer
CFO: Derek Lythgoe, Chief Financial Officer
CMO: Paul Hurst, M.D., Chief Medical Officer
CHR: Tiffany Werner, Senior Human Resource Business Partner
CNO: Kelley Kieffer, Chief Nursing Officer
Web address: www.https://www.bannerhealth.com/locations/mesa/banner-heart-hospital
**Control:** Other not–for–profit (including NFP Corporation) **Service:** Heart

| | |
|---|---|
| **Staffed Beds:** 111 **Admissions:** 5034 **Census:** 60 **Outpatient Visits:** 60018 **Births:** 0 **Total Expense ($000):** 127894 **Payroll Expense ($000):** 31719 **Personnel:** 387 | |

**CARDON CHILDREN'S MEDICAL CENTER** See Banner Desert Medical Center, Mesa

**DESERT SAMARITAN MEDICAL CTR** See Banner Desert Medical Center

**ENCOMPASS HEALTH REHABILITATION HOSPITAL OF EAST** See Encompass Health Rehabilitation Hospital of East Valley

**ENCOMPASS HEALTH REHABILITATION HOSPITAL OF EAST VALLEY (033037)**, 5652 East Baseline Road, Zip 85206–4713; tel. 480/567–0350, (Nonreporting) **A**1 10 **S** Encompass Health Corporation, Birmingham, AL
Primary Contact: Elizabeth Gibson, Chief Executive Officer
CMO: Martin Yee, M.D., Medical Director
CHR: Nancy Pickler, Director of Human Resources
CNO: Hope Dunn, Chief Nursing Officer
Web address: www.https://www.encompasshealth.com/eastvalleyrehab
**Control:** Corporation, Investor–owned (for–profit) **Service:** Rehabilitation

| |
|---|
| **Staffed Beds:** 60 |

**KPC PROMISE HOSPITAL OF PHOENIX (032006)**, 433 East 6th Street, Zip 85203–7104; tel. 480/427–3000, (Nonreporting) **A**10 **S** KPC Healthcare, Inc., Santa Ana, CA
Primary Contact: Wayne Kinsey, Chief Executive Officer
COO: Wendy Larson, Chief Clinical Officer
CFO: Theo Clark, Director Financial Services
CMO: Syed Shahryar, M.D., Medical Director
CHR: Christie Brea, Manager Human Resources
Web address: www.phoenix.kpcph.com/
**Control:** Corporation, Investor–owned (for–profit) **Service:** Acute long–term care hospital

| |
|---|
| **Staffed Beds:** 40 |

⇈ **MOUNTAIN VISTA MEDICAL CENTER (030121)**, 1301 South Crismon Road, Zip 85209–3767; tel. 480/358–6100, (Nonreporting) **A**3 5 10 13 21 **F**6 7 8 9 11 12 13 14 15 18 20 22 24 26 29 30 31 34 35 37 38 40 43 45 50 51 56 57 68 70 72 74 76 79 81 87 93 94 96 98 100 102 103 107 108 110 111 114 119 126 130 131 143 146 147 148 **S** Steward Health Care System, LLC, Dallas, TX
Primary Contact: William J. Comer, President
CNO: Elizabeth Kearney, R.N., Chief Nursing Officer
Web address: www.https://www.mvmedicalcenter.org/
**Control:** Corporation, Investor–owned (for–profit) **Service:** General medical and surgical

| |
|---|
| **Staffed Beds:** 178 **Admissions:** 6825 **Census:** 84 |

**PROMISE HOSPITAL OF PHOENIX** See Kpc Promise Hospital of Phoenix

**SAMARITAN BEHAVELBACK HOSPITAL** See Samaritan Behavioral Health Center-Desert Samaritan Medical Center

**SAMARITAN BEHAVIORAL HEALTH CENTER-DESERT SAMARITAN MEDICAL CENTER** See Banner Desert Medical Center, Mesa

**VALLEY LUTHERAN MEDICAL CENTER** See Banner Baywood Medical Center

**NOGALES—Santa Cruz County**

**CARONDELET HOLY CROSS HOSPITAL (031313)**, 1171 West Target Range Road, Zip 85621–2415; tel. 520/285–3000, (Nonreporting) **A**1 5 10 18 **F**3 13 29 30 31 32 34 35 40 50 51 56 57 59 64 65 68 70 75 76 77 79 81 85 86 87 89 93 107 111 119 130 132 133 134 135 146 149 156 **S** TENET Healthcare Corporation, Dallas, TX
Primary Contact: Debbie Knapheide, MSN, Site Administrator, Chief Nursing Officer and Chief Operating Officer
COO: Debbie Knapheide, MSN, Site Administrator, Chief Nursing Officer and Chief Operating Officer
CFO: Alan Strauss, Chief Financial Officer
CMO: Roy Farrell, M.D., Chief Medical Officer
CNO: Debbie Knapheide, MSN, Site Administrator, Chief Nursing Officer and Chief Operating Officer
Web address: www.carondelet.org
**Control:** Corporation, Investor–owned (for–profit) **Service:** General medical and surgical

| | |
|---|---|
| **Staffed Beds:** 25 **Admissions:** 1171 **Census:** 7 **Outpatient Visits:** 45131 **Births:** 700 **Total Expense ($000):** 27242 **Payroll Expense ($000):** 12800 | |

**CARONDELET HOLY CROSS HOSPITAL** See Carondelet Holy Cross Hospital

**ORO VALLEY—Pima County**

**NORTHWEST MEDICAL CENTER, ORO VALLEY** See Oro Valley Hospital

**ORO VALLEY HOSPITAL (030114)**, 1551 East Tangerine Road, Zip 85755–6213; tel. 520/901–3500, (Nonreporting) **A**1 10 **F**3 15 17 20 22 29 30 34 35 37 40 42 45 49 50 54 57 59 60 64 70 74 75 77 79 81 85 86 87 90 93 96 98 100 103 107 108 109 110 111 114 115 118 119 126 129 130 144 146 154 **S** Community Health Systems, Inc., Franklin, TN
Primary Contact: Jennifer Schomburg, Chief Administrative Officer
CFO: Maurene Polashek, Chief Financial Officer
CNO: Julie Hunt, R.N., MS, Chief Nursing Officer
Web address: www.orovalleyhospital.com
**Control:** Individual, Investor–owned (for–profit) **Service:** General medical and surgical

| |
|---|
| **Staffed Beds:** 146 **Admissions:** 6110 **Census:** 63 **Births:** 0 |

**PAGE—Coconino County**

**PAGE HOSPITAL (031304)**, 501 North Navajo Drive, Zip 86040, Mailing Address: P.O. Box 1447, Zip 86040–1447; tel. 928/645–2424, (Nonreporting) **A**1 10 18 **F**29 34 35 40 43 57 63 71 76 80 81 84 85 93 97 107 108 115 127 133 146 148 **P**8 **S** Banner Health, Phoenix, AZ
Primary Contact: Susan Eubanks, Chief Executive Officer
CFO: Darcy Robertson, Chief Financial Officer
CMO: Thomas Wood, M.D., Chief Medical Officer
CIO: Paul Caldwell, Facility Coordinator Information Technology Customer Relations
CHR: Ed Franklin, Chief Human Resources Officer
Web address: www.bannerhealth.com/Locations/Arizona/Page+Hospital
**Control:** Other not–for–profit (including NFP Corporation) **Service:** General medical and surgical

| | |
|---|---|
| **Staffed Beds:** 25 **Admissions:** 343 **Census:** 2 **Outpatient Visits:** 27186 **Births:** 146 **Total Expense ($000):** 17916 **Payroll Expense ($000):** 8370 **Personnel:** 133 | |

**PARKER—La Paz County**

○ **LA PAZ REGIONAL HOSPITAL (031317)**, 1200 West Mohave Road, Zip 85344–6349; tel. 928/669–9201, (Nonreporting) **A**10 11 18
Primary Contact: Kevin Brown, Chief Executive Officer
CFO: Carl J. Flanagan, Chief Financial Officer
CMO: Jack Dunn, M.D., Chief of Staff
CHR: Regina M Martinez, Director Human Resources
CNO: Maria Martinez, Chief Nursing Officer
Web address: www.lapazhospital.org
**Control:** Other not–for–profit (including NFP Corporation) **Service:** General medical and surgical

| |
|---|
| **Staffed Beds:** 25 |

**PARKER COMMUNITY HOSPITAL** See La Paz Regional Hospital

**PHS INDIAN HOSPITAL** See U.S. Public Health Service Indian Hospital

**U. S. PUBLIC HEALTH SERVICE INDIAN HOSPITAL (031307)**, 12033 Agency Road, Zip 85344–7718; tel. 928/669–2137, (Nonreporting) **A**1 10 18 **S** U. S. Indian Health Service, Rockville, MD
Primary Contact: Elizabeth Helsel, Chief Executive Officer
CFO: Robin Tahbo, Financial Management Officer
CMO: Laurence Norick, M.D., Clinical Director
CIO: JayLynn Saavedra, Chief Information Officer
Web address: www.ihs.gov
**Control:** PHS, Indian Service, Government, federal **Service:** General medical and surgical

| |
|---|
| **Staffed Beds:** 20 |

**PAYSON—Gila County**

**BANNER PAYSON MEDICAL CENTER (031318)**, 807 South Ponderosa Street, Zip 85541–5599; tel. 928/474–3222, (Nonreporting) **A**1 3 5 10 18 **F**3 13 15 18 29 31 35 36 38 40 43 45 50 51 54 64 68 70 71 74 75 76 77 78 79 81 83 85 86 89 91 100 102 107 108 110 111 115 119 130 132 133 135 145 146 147 148 149 154 157 **P**8 **S** Banner Health, Phoenix, AZ
Primary Contact: Lance Porter, Chief Executive Officer
CFO: Peter Finelli, Chief Financial Officer
CMO: John Vandruff, M.D., Chief of Staff
CIO: Nick Vandermeer, Director Information Systems
CHR: Shawn M. Thomas, Director Human Resources
CNO: Hartland Hintze, Chief Nursing Officer
Web address: www.paysonhospital.com
**Control:** Other not–for–profit (including NFP Corporation) **Service:** General medical and surgical

| | |
|---|---|
| **Staffed Beds:** 25 **Admissions:** 1380 **Census:** 11 **Outpatient Visits:** 57431 **Births:** 139 **Total Expense ($000):** 45304 **Payroll Expense ($000):** 13375 **Personnel:** 238 | |

**PAYSON REGIONAL MEDICAL CENTER** See Banner Payson Medical Center

*Many Facility Codes have changed. Please refer to the AHA Guide Code Chart.*

© 2021 AHA Guide

AZ

**AZ**

**PEORIA—Maricopa County**

**CURAHEALTH PHOENIX** See Curahealth Phoenix, Phoenix

**KINDRED HOSPITAL ARIZONA-NORTHWEST PHOENIX** See Curahealth Phoenix

**PERIDOT—Gila County**

✠ **SAN CARLOS APACHE HEALTHCARE CORPORATION (030077)**, 103 Medicine Way Road, Zip 85542; tel. 928/475–1400, (Nonreporting) **A**1 10 **F**3 5 12 15 18 19 29 34 35 36 39 40 43 44 50 53 54 55 56 57 58 59 61 64 65 66 68 69 74 75 77 79 82 86 87 91 93 94 96 97 100 107 110 111 114 115 119 120 127 129 130 135 147 148 149 154 156 157 **P**6 **S** U. S. Indian Health Service, Rockville, MD
Primary Contact: Victoria D. Began, R.N., MS, President and Chief Executive Officer
CFO: Vivie Hosteenez, Chief Financial Officer
CMO: Douglas Brinkerhoff, M.D., Clinical Director
CIO: Nimmy Mathews, Acting Director Quality Management
CHR: Shirley M Boni, Administrative Officer
Web address: www.ihs.gov
**Control:** Federal, Government, federal **Service:** General medical and surgical

| Staffed Beds: 12 Admissions: 477 Census: 4 Outpatient Visits: 160803 |
| Total Expense ($000): 95828 Payroll Expense ($000): 41530 |

**U. S. PUBLIC HEALTH SERVICE INDIAN HOSPITAL** See San Carlos Apache Healthcare Corporation

**PHOENIX—Maricopa County**

✠ **ABRAZO CENTRAL CAMPUS (030030)**, 2000 West Bethany Home Road, Zip 85015–2443; tel. 602/249–0212, (Includes ABRAZO MESA HOSPITAL, Mailing address: 5750 East Baseline Rod, Mesa, Arizona, Zip 85206; tel. 602/833–6900; Edgar Staren, M.D., Interim Chief Executive Officer), (Nonreporting) **A**1 3 5 10 **F**3 15 18 20 22 26 29 30 31 34 35 40 41 44 45 46 48 49 50 51 57 58 59 60 63 64 70 74 75 77 78 79 80 81 82 85 87 107 108 110 111 114 119 120 121 124 126 129 130 132 135 146 148 149 154 157 **S** TENET Healthcare Corporation, Dallas, TX
Primary Contact: Edgar Staren, M.D., Interim Chief Executive Officer
CFO: Paul Hymel, Chief Financial Officer
CHR: Dana George, Chief Human Resources Officer
Web address: www.abrazohealth.com
**Control:** Corporation, Investor–owned (for–profit) **Service:** General medical and surgical

| Staffed Beds: 180 Admissions: 7446 Census: 94 Outpatient Visits: 60058 |
| Births: 0 Total Expense ($000): 129602 Payroll Expense ($000): 56600 |
| Personnel: 697 |

✠ **ABRAZO SCOTTSDALE CAMPUS (030083)**, 3929 East Bell Road, Zip 85032–2196; tel. 602/923–5000, (Nonreporting) **A**1 10 **F**3 11 12 18 20 22 26 28 29 30 34 35 37 40 41 43 44 45 48 49 50 51 57 59 60 63 64 68 70 75 77 79 81 82 85 87 93 97 107 108 111 114 119 126 130 131 132 135 146 148 149 154 157 **S** TENET Healthcare Corporation, Dallas, TX
Primary Contact: Edgar Staren, M.D., Interim Chief Executive Officer
CFO: Jeffrey Zyla, Chief Financial Officer
CHR: Kendrick Russell, Chief Human Resources Officer
CNO: Vicki Lynn Huber, R.N., MSN, Chief Nursing Officer
Web address: www.abrazoscottsdale.com
**Control:** Corporation, Investor–owned (for–profit) **Service:** General medical and surgical

| Staffed Beds: 116 Admissions: 5540 Census: 53 Outpatient Visits: 42902 |
| Births: 0 Total Expense ($000): 93471 Payroll Expense ($000): 36773 |
| Personnel: 432 |

**ARIZONA CHILDREN'S CENTER MARICOPA MEDICAL CENTER** See Arizona Children's Center

**ARIZONA HEART HOSPITAL** See Abrazo Arizona Heart Hospital

☐ **ARIZONA STATE HOSPITAL (034021)**, 2500 East Van Buren Street, Zip 85008–6079; tel. 602/244–1331, (Nonreporting) **A**1 3 5 10
Primary Contact: Aaron Bowen, Chief Executive Officer
CHR: Jeanine Decker, Manager Human Resources
Web address: www.https://www.azdhs.gov/az-state-hospital/index.php
**Control:** State, Government, Nonfederal **Service:** Psychiatric

| Staffed Beds: 299 |

✠ **BANNER - UNIVERSITY MEDICAL CENTER PHOENIX (030002)**, 1111 East McDowell Road, Zip 85006–2666, Mailing Address: P.O. Box 2989, Zip 85062–2989; tel. 602/239–2000, (Nonreporting) **A**1 3 5 8 10 **F**3 6 9 11 12 13 15 17 18 20 22 24 26 28 29 30 31 34 35 36 37 38 40 43 44 45 46 47 48 49 50 51 54 55 56 57 58 59 60 61 64 65 66 68 70 72 73 74 75 76 77 78 79 81 82 84 85 86 87 90 91 92 93 94 96 97 98 100 101 102 104 107 108 109 110 111 114 115 118 119 120 121 122 123 124 126 129 130 131 132 135 137 138 139 146 147 148 149 151 154 156 **S** Banner Health, Phoenix, AZ
Primary Contact: Daniel Post, Chief Executive Officer
CFO: Kathy Kotin, Chief Financial Officer
CMO: Paul Stander, M.D., Chief Medical Officer
CIO: Michael S Warden, Senior Vice President Information Technology
CHR: Michael Fleming, Chief People Officer
Web address: www.bannerhealth.com/Locations/Arizona/Banner+Good+Samaritan+Medical+Center
**Control:** Other not–for–profit (including NFP Corporation) **Service:** General medical and surgical

| Staffed Beds: 745 Admissions: 33643 Census: 530 Outpatient |
| Visits: 402325 Births: 5955 Total Expense ($000): 942128 Payroll |
| Expense ($000): 275563 Personnel: 3722 |

**BANNER ESTRELLA MEDICAL** See Banner Estrella Medical Center

✠ **BANNER ESTRELLA MEDICAL CENTER (030115)**, 9201 West Thomas Road, Zip 85037–3332; tel. 623/327–4000, (Nonreporting) **A**1 3 5 10 **F**3 11 12 13 18 20 22 24 28 29 30 31 34 35 36 37 38 40 41 43 44 45 46 49 50 51 57 58 59 60 61 63 64 68 70 72 74 75 76 77 78 79 81 82 83 84 85 86 87 96 102 107 108 111 115 118 119 126 130 131 132 135 144 145 146 147 148 149 154 157 **P**8 **S** Banner Health, Phoenix, AZ
Primary Contact: Courtney Ophaug, FACHE, Chief Executive Officer
COO: Gary Foster, R.N., Associate Administrator
CFO: Dean Shepardson, Chief Financial Officer
CHR: Wendy Labadie, Chief Human Resource Officer
CNO: Sheri Dahlstrom, R.N., Chief Nursing Officer
Web address: www.bannerhealth.com/Locations/Arizona/Banner+Estrella+Medical+Center/
**Control:** Other not–for–profit (including NFP Corporation) **Service:** General medical and surgical

| Staffed Beds: 317 Admissions: 18253 Census: 202 Outpatient |
| Visits: 282184 Births: 5059 Total Expense ($000): 286761 Payroll |
| Expense ($000): 105095 Personnel: 1506 |

**BANNER GOOD SAMARITAN MEDICAL CENTER** See Banner - University Medical Center Phoenix

**CARL T HAYDEN VET AFFAIRS CTR** See Phoenix Veterans Affairs Health Care System

**CHILDREN'S HEALTH CENTER ST. JOSEPH'S HOSPITAL AND MEDICAL CENTER** See Children's Health Center

☐ **CURAHEALTH PHOENIX (032000)**, 40 East Indianola Avenue, Zip 85012–2059; tel. 602/280–7000, (Includes CURAHEALTH PHOENIX, Mailing address: 13216 North Plaza Del Rio Boulevard, Peoria, Arizona, Zip 85381–4907; tel. 623/974–5463; Karen Shammas, Chief Executive Officer), (Nonreporting) **A**1 10 **S** Curahealth Hospitals, Garland, TX
Primary Contact: Karen Cawley, Chief Executive Officer
Web address: www.curahealth.com
**Control:** Corporation, Investor–owned (for–profit) **Service:** Acute long–term care hospital

| Staffed Beds: 58 |

⇑ **DEER VALLEY MEDICAL CENTER** See Honorhealth Deer Valley Medical Center

**HAVEN BEHAVIORAL HOSPITAL OF PHOENIX (034020)**, 1201 South 7th Avenue, Suite 200, Zip 85007–4076; tel. 623/236–2000, (Nonreporting) **A**10 **S** Haven Behavioral Healthcare, Nashville, TN
Primary Contact: Amy Gerberry, Chief Executive Officer
CHR: Erin McEldowney, Manager Human Resources
CNO: Debbie Swiers, Director of Nursing
Web address: www.havenbehavioral.com
**Control:** Corporation, Investor–owned (for–profit) **Service:** Psychiatric

| Staffed Beds: 45 |

---

| **Hospital, Medicare Provider Number, Address, Telephone, Approval, Facility, and Physician Codes, Health Care System** | | |
|---|---|---|
| ★ American Hospital Association (AHA) membership | ○ Healthcare Facilities Accreditation Program | ⇑ Center for Improvement in Healthcare Quality Accreditation |
| ☐ The Joint Commission accreditation | ◇ DNV Healthcare Inc. accreditation | △ Commission on Accreditation of Rehabilitation Facilities (CARF) accreditation |

**AZ**

**HAVEN SENIOR HORIZONS** See Haven Behavioral Hospital of Phoenix

★ ⇑ **HONORHEALTH DEER VALLEY MEDICAL CENTER (030092)**, 19829 North 27th Avenue, Zip 85027–4002; tel. 623/879–6100, (Nonreporting) **A**3 5 10 19 21 **S** HonorHealth, Scottsdale, AZ
Primary Contact: David Price, Chief Executive Officer
CMO: Mary Ann Turley, D.O., Medical Director
CHR: Frank L Cummins, Vice President Human Resources
Web address: www.jcl.com
**Control**: Other not–for–profit (including NFP Corporation) **Service**: General medical and surgical

**Staffed Beds: 204**

★ ⇑ **HONORHEALTH JOHN C. LINCOLN MEDICAL CENTER (030014)**, 250 East Dunlap Avenue, Zip 85020–2825; tel. 602/943–2381, (Nonreporting) **A**3 5 10 19 21 **S** HonorHealth, Scottsdale, AZ
Primary Contact: Gary E. Baker, Chief Executive Officer
CMO: Christopher Shearer, M.D., Chief Medical Officer
Web address: www.jcl.com
**Control**: Other not–for–profit (including NFP Corporation) **Service**: General medical and surgical

**Staffed Beds: 262**

⇑ **JOHN C. LINCOLN MEDICAL CENTER** See Honorhealth John C. Lincoln Medical Center

**KINDRED HOSPITAL ARIZONA-PHOENIX** See Curahealth Phoenix

**LOS NINOS HOSPITAL (033301)**, 2601 East Thomas Road, Zip 85016–7827; tel. 602/424–9880, (Nonreporting) **A**10
Primary Contact: John Widder, Director
Web address: www.losninoshospital.com
**Control**: Other not–for–profit (including NFP Corporation) **Service**: Children's other specialty

**Staffed Beds: 15**

⇑ **MARICOPA INTEGRATED HEALTH SYSTEM** See Valleywise Health

✠ **MAYO CLINIC HOSPITAL (030103)**, 5777 East Mayo Boulevard, Zip 85054–4502; tel. 480/342–2000, (Nonreporting) **A**1 2 3 5 8 10 19 **F**3 8 9 11 12 14 15 17 18 20 22 24 26 28 29 30 31 34 35 36 37 39 40 44 45 46 47 48 49 50 51 53 54 55 56 57 58 59 60 61 64 65 67 68 70 74 75 77 78 79 80 81 82 83 84 85 86 87 90 92 93 96 97 100 104 107 108 110 111 112 114 115 116 117 118 119 120 121 122 123 124 126 129 130 131 132 135 136 137 138 139 141 142 145 146 147 148 149 154 **P**6 **S** Mayo Clinic, Rochester, MN
Primary Contact: Richard Gray, M.D., Vice President Operations
CFO: Jeffrey R Froisland, Chief Financial Officer
CMO: Alyssa B Chapital, M.D., Medical Director, Mayo Clinic Hospital
CIO: Paul Lenko, Section Head Information Technology
CHR: Nichelle A Baker, Chair Human Resources
CNO: Teresa Connolly, R.N., Chief Nursing Officer
Web address: www.mayoclinic.org/arizona/
**Control**: Other not–for–profit (including NFP Corporation) **Service**: General medical and surgical

**Staffed Beds: 280 Admissions: 16939 Census: 224 Outpatient Visits: 74162 Births: 0 Personnel: 3739**

☐ **OASIS HOSPITAL (030131)**, 750 North 40th Street, Zip 85008–6486; tel. 602/797–7700, (Nonreporting) **A**1 3 5 10
Primary Contact: Tim Bogardus, Chief Executive Officer
Web address: www.oasishospital.com
**Control**: Partnership, Investor–owned (for–profit) **Service**: Orthopedic

**Staffed Beds: 64**

**PHOENIX BAPTIST HOSPITAL** See Abrazo Central Campus

✠ △ **PHOENIX CHILDREN'S HOSPITAL (033302)**, 1919 East Thomas Road, Zip 85016–7710; tel. 602/933–1000, (Nonreporting) **A**1 3 5 7 10 **F**3 8 11 15 17 19 21 23 25 27 29 30 31 32 34 35 37 38 39 40 41 43 44 46 48 49 50 54 55 57 58 59 60 61 64 65 66 68 71 72 73 74 75 77 78 79 81 82 84 85 86 87 88 89 90 91 92 93 94 96 97 98 99 100 101 102 104 105 107 108 111 113 114 115 116 117 118 119 129 130 131 132 134 136 137 138 139 144 146 148 153 157 **P**6
Primary Contact: Robert L. Meyer, President and Chief Executive Officer
COO: Betsy Kuzas, Executive Vice President and Chief Operating Officer
CFO: Douglas Myers, Executive Vice President and Chief Financial Officer
CMO: H. Stacy Nicholson, M.D., M.P.H., Physician in Chief
CIO: David Higginson, Executive Vice President and Chief Administrative Officer
CHR: Lisa Phelps, Senior Vice President, Human Resources
CNO: Julie Bowman, Senior Vice President, Patient Care and Chief Nursing Officer
Web address: www.phoenixchildrens.com
**Control**: Other not–for–profit (including NFP Corporation) **Service**: Children's general medical and surgical

**Staffed Beds: 403 Admissions: 14232 Census: 241 Outpatient Visits: 367610 Births: 0 Total Expense ($000): 957776 Payroll Expense ($000): 438514 Personnel: 4632**

✠ **PHOENIX VETERANS AFFAIRS HEALTH CARE SYSTEM**, 650 East Indian School Road, Zip 85012–1892; tel. 602/277–5551, (Nonreporting) **A**1 3 5 **S** Department of Veterans Affairs, Washington, DC
Primary Contact: Alyshia Smith, R.N., Interim Director
CFO: Christine Hollingsworth, Chief Financial Officer
CMO: Maureen McCarthy, M.D., Chief of Staff
Web address: www.phoenix.va.gov/
**Control**: Veterans Affairs, Government, federal **Service**: General medical and surgical

**Staffed Beds: 197**

☐ **QUAIL RUN BEHAVIORAL HEALTH (034031)**, 2545 West Quail Avenue, Zip 85027–2418; tel. 602/455–5700, (Nonreporting) **A**1
Primary Contact: David Carnahan, Chief Executive Officer
Web address: www.quailrunbehavioral.com/
**Control**: Other not–for–profit (including NFP Corporation) **Service**: Psychiatric

**Staffed Beds: 102**

✠ **SELECT SPECIALTY HOSPITAL-PHOENIX (032001)**, 350 West Thomas Road, 3rd Floor Main, Zip 85013–4409; tel. 602/406–6810, (Nonreporting) **A**1 10 **F**1 29 75 77 87 148 **S** Select Medical Corporation, Mechanicsburg, PA
Primary Contact: Karen Cawley, Chief Executive Officer
Web address: www.https://phoenix.selectspecialtyhospitals.com
**Control**: Corporation, Investor–owned (for–profit) **Service**: Acute long–term care hospital

**Staffed Beds: 48 Admissions: 537 Census: 41 Outpatient Visits: 0 Births: 0 Total Expense ($000): 25829 Payroll Expense ($000): 11688 Personnel: 182**

★ **SELECT SPECIALTY HOSPITAL-PHOENIX DOWNTOWN (032005)**, 1012 East Wiletta Street, 4th Floor, Zip 85006; tel. 602/839–6550, (Nonreporting) **F**1 29 75 77 87 148 **S** Select Medical Corporation, Mechanicsburg, PA
Primary Contact: David Selman, Chief Executive Officer
Web address: www.selectmedicalcorp.com
**Control**: Corporation, Investor–owned (for–profit) **Service**: Acute long–term care hospital

**Staffed Beds: 32 Admissions: 326 Census: 24 Outpatient Visits: 0 Births: 0 Total Expense ($000): 15381 Payroll Expense ($000): 7213 Personnel: 95**

**SELECT SPECIALTY HOSPITAL-PHOENIX DOWNTOWN** See Select Specialty Hospital-Phoenix

✠ △ **ST. JOSEPH'S HOSPITAL AND MEDICAL CENTER (030024)**, 350 West Thomas Road, Zip 85013–4496, Mailing Address: P.O. Box 2071, Zip 85001–2071; tel. 602/406–3000, (Includes CHILDREN'S HEALTH CENTER, Mailing address: 350 West Thomas Road, Phoenix, Arizona, Zip 85013–4409; tel. 623/974–5463; ST. JOSEPH'S WESTGATE MEDICAL CENTER, Mailing address: 7300 North 99th Avenue, Glendale, Arizona, Zip 85307–3003; tel. 602/406–0000; Gabrielle Finley-Hazle, President and Chief Executive Officer), (Nonreporting) **A**1 3 5 7 10 19 **F**2 3 6 7 10 11 12 13 15 17 18 20 22 24 26 29 30 31 32 34 35 36 37 38 39 40 41 42 43 44 45 46 47 48 49 50 51 53 54 55 56 57 58 59 60 61 62 64 65 66 68 70 71 72 73 74 75 76 77 78 79 80 81 82 84 85 86 87 90 91 92 93 95 97 100 101 102 104 107 108 110 111 112 113 114 115 117 118 119 120 121 123 124 126 127 130 131 132 134 135 138 139 140 141 142 143 144 145 146 147 148 149 150 153 154 156 157 158 **P**6 **S** CommonSpirit Health, Chicago, IL
Primary Contact: Gabrielle Finley-Hazle, President and Chief Executive Officer
CMO: Edward Donahue, M.D., Chief Medical Officer
CHR: Maureen Sterbach, Vice President Human Resources
CNO: Julie Ward, MSN, R.N., Chief Nursing Officer
Web address: www.stjosephs-phx.org
**Control**: Other not–for–profit (including NFP Corporation) **Service**: General medical and surgical

**Staffed Beds: 609 Admissions: 31626 Census: 451 Outpatient Visits: 689445 Births: 5108 Total Expense ($000): 1232270 Payroll Expense ($000): 478999 Personnel: 5067**

☐ **ST. LUKE'S BEHAVIORAL HEALTH CENTER (034013)**, 1800 East Van Buren, Zip 85006–3742; tel. 602/251–8546, (Nonreporting) **A**1 10 **S** Steward Health Care System, LLC, Dallas, TX
Primary Contact: Gregory L. Jahn, R.N., Chief Executive Officer
CFO: Ruby Majhail, Chief Financial Officer
CHR: Amy M Howell, Director Human Resources
Web address: www.https://www.stlukesbehavioralhealth.org/
**Control**: Corporation, Investor–owned (for–profit) **Service**: Psychiatric

**Staffed Beds: 85**

**THE CORE INSTITUTE SPECIALTY HOSPITAL (030108)**, 6501 North 19th Avenue, Zip 85015–1646; tel. 602/795–6020, (Nonreporting) **A**1 3 10
Primary Contact: Rona Curphy, Chief Executive Officer
CFO: Barbara Chacon, Chief Financial Officer
CMO: Christopher A. Yeung, M.D., Chief of Staff
CHR: Sherrie A Wagner, Manager Human Resources
CNO: Deborah Roberts, R.N., Chief Nursing Officer
Web address: www.thecoreinstitutehospital.com/
**Control:** Corporation, Investor–owned (for–profit) **Service:** Surgical

Staffed Beds: 33

**THE SURGICAL HOSPITAL OF PHOENIX** See The Core Institute Specialty Hospital

☒ **U. S. PUBLIC HEALTH SERVICE PHOENIX INDIAN MEDICAL CENTER (030078)**, 4212 North 16th Street, Zip 85016–5389; tel. 602/263–1200, (Nonreporting) **A**1 3 5 10 **S** U. S. Indian Health Service, Rockville, MD
Primary Contact: Deanna Dick, Chief Executive Officer
CFO: Geraldine Harney, Chief Financial Officer
CMO: Dave Civic, M.D., Associate Director Clinical Services
CIO: Vina Montour, Director Information Technology
CHR: Betty Weston, Chief Human Resources Officer
Web address: www.ihs.gov
**Control:** PHS, Indian Service, Government, federal **Service:** General medical and surgical

Staffed Beds: 127

**USPHS PHOENIX INDIAN MED CTR** See U.S. Public Health Service Phoenix Indian Medical Center

**VALLEY HOSPITAL** See Valley Hospital Phoenix

☐ **VALLEY HOSPITAL PHOENIX (034026)**, 3550 East Pinchot Avenue, Zip 85018–7434; tel. 602/957–4000, (Nonreporting) **A**1 5 10 **S** Universal Health Services, Inc., King of Prussia, PA
Primary Contact: Lloyd Noble, Chief Executive Officer
Web address: www.valleyhospital-phoenix.com
**Control:** Corporation, Investor–owned (for–profit) **Service:** Psychiatric

Staffed Beds: 122

★ ⇑ **VALLEYWISE HEALTH (030022)**, 2601 East Roosevelt Street, Zip 85008–4956; tel. 602/344–5011, (Includes Arizona Children's Center, Mailing address: 2601 East Roosevelt Street, Phoenix, Arizona, Zip 85008–4973; tel. 602/344–5051), (Nonreporting) **A**3 8 10 21
Primary Contact: Stephen A. Purves, FACHE, President and Chief Executive Officer
COO: Kris Gaw, Executive Vice President and Chief Operating Officer
CFO: Kathleen Benaquista, Executive Vice President and Chief Financial Officer
CMO: John Hitt, M.D., Executive Vice President and Chief Medical Officer
CIO: Kelly Summers, Chief Information Officer
CHR: Marshall Jones, Senior Vice President Human Resources
CNO: Sherry Stotler, R.N., MSN, Chief Nursing Officer
Web address: www.mihs.org
**Control:** County, Government, Nonfederal **Service:** General medical and surgical

Staffed Beds: 544

**PRESCOTT—Yavapai County**

**NORTHERN ARIZONA VA HEALTH CARE SYSTEM** See Northern Arizona Veterans Affairs Health Care System

☒ **NORTHERN ARIZONA VETERANS AFFAIRS HEALTH CARE SYSTEM**, 500 Highway 89 North, Zip 86313–5000; tel. 928/445–4860, (Nonreporting) **A**1 **S** Department of Veterans Affairs, Washington, DC
Primary Contact: Jean J. Gurga, Medical Center Director
COO: James Belmont, Associate Director
CFO: Ame Callahan, Acting Manager Resource Management Service
CMO: A Panneer Selvam, M.D., Chief of Staff
CIO: Scott McCrimmon, Manager Information Technology
CHR: Jane Lewerke, Manager Human Resources
Web address: www.prescott.va.gov/
**Control:** Veterans Affairs, Government, federal **Service:** General medical and surgical

Staffed Beds: 147

★ **YAVAPAI REGIONAL MEDICAL CENTER (030012)**, 1003 Willow Creek Road, Zip 86301–1668; tel. 928/445–2700, (Includes YAVAPAI REGIONAL MEDICAL CENTER - EAST, Mailing address: 7700 East Florentine Road, Prescott Valley, Arizona, Zip 86314–2245; tel. 928/445–2700; John R. Amos, Chief Executive Officer), (Nonreporting) **A**5 10 20 **F**3 11 13 15 17 18 20 22 24 26 28 29 30 31 32 34 35 40 45 46 50 53 54 57 59 60 64 68 70 71 72 74 75 76 77 78 79 81 82 84 85 86 87 89 91 93 107 108 111 114 116 117 118 119 130 131 132 135 146 147 148 154 156 **P**6
Primary Contact: John R. Amos, President and Chief Executive Officer
COO: Larry P Burns JrChief Operating Officer
CFO: Lee Livin, Chief Financial Officer
CMO: Anthony Torres, M.D., Chief Medical Officer
CHR: Mark Timm, Executive Director Human Resources
CNO: Diane Drexler, R.N., Chief Nursing Officer
Web address: www.yrmc.org
**Control:** Other not–for–profit (including NFP Corporation) **Service:** General medical and surgical

Staffed Beds: 206 Admissions: 11737 Census: 114 Outpatient Visits: 162439 Births: 1016 Total Expense ($000): 362537 Payroll Expense ($000): 136661 Personnel: 1363

**PRESCOTT VALLEY—Yavapai County**

☐ **MOUNTAIN VALLEY REGIONAL REHABILITATION HOSPITAL (033036)**, 3700 North Windsong Drive, Zip 86314–1253; tel. 928/759–8800, (Nonreporting) **A**1 10 **S** Ernest Health, Inc., Albuquerque, NM
Primary Contact: Judy Baum, Chief Executive Officer
CFO: Mark A. Roth, Chief Financial Officer
CMO: Alan S. Berman, M.D., Medical Director
CHR: Troy Eagar, Director Human Resources
CNO: Leah Walters, R.N., Director of Nursing
Web address: www.mvrrh.ernesthealth.com
**Control:** Corporation, Investor–owned (for–profit) **Service:** Rehabilitation

Staffed Beds: 16

**WINDHAVEN PSYCHIATRIC HOSPITAL (034025)**, 3347 North Windsong Drive, Zip 86314–2283, Mailing Address: 3343 North Windsong Drive, Zip 86314–1213; tel. 928/445–5211, (Nonreporting) **A**10 **F**50 54 98 100 152
Primary Contact: Tamara Player, Chief Executive Officer
COO: Pamela Pierce, Deputy Chief Executive Officer
CFO: Doug Oliver, Chief Financial Officer
CMO: Shane Russell-Jenkins, M.D., Medical Director
CIO: Laura Norman, Chief Development and Information Officer
CHR: Pamela Pierce, Deputy Chief Executive Officer
CNO: Esther Grear, Director Hospital Social Work and Assistant Hospital Administrator
Web address: www.wygc.org
**Control:** Other not–for–profit (including NFP Corporation) **Service:** Psychiatric

Staffed Beds: 16 Admissions: 698 Census: 13 Total Expense ($000): 38154 Payroll Expense ($000): 7482

**SACATON—Pinal County**

☐ **HUHUKAM MEMORIAL HOSPITAL (031308)**, 483 West Seed Farm Road, Zip 85147, Mailing Address: P.O. Box 38, Zip 85147–0001; tel. 602/528–1200, (Nonreporting) **A**1 3 5 10 18
Primary Contact: Anthony Santiago, Chief Executive Officers
COO: Pamela Thompson, Chief Operations Officer
CMO: Noel Habib, M.D., Chief Medical Officer
CHR: Michael Freeman, Director Human Resources
Web address: www.grhc.org
**Control:** Other not–for–profit (including NFP Corporation) **Service:** General medical and surgical

Staffed Beds: 15

**PHS INDIAN HOSPITAL** See Huhukam Memorial Hospital
SAFFORD-Graham County

**MT GRAHAM COMMUNITY HOSPITAL** See Mt. Graham Regional Medical Center

★ **MT. GRAHAM REGIONAL MEDICAL CENTER (030068)**, 1600 South 20th Avenue, Zip 85546–4097; tel. 928/348–4000, (Nonreporting) **A**3 5 10 20
Primary Contact: Roland Knox, Chief Executive Officer
CFO: Keith Bryce, Vice President Finance and Chief Financial Officer
CIO: Anthon Ellsworth, Director Information Technology
CHR: Irvan Wick"" Lewis, Vice President Human Resources
CNO: Lori Burress, Vice President Patient Services and Chief Nursing Officer
Web address: www.mtgraham.org
**Control:** Other not–for–profit (including NFP Corporation) **Service:** General medical and surgical

Staffed Beds: 49

**AZ**

### SAN TAN VALLEY—Pinal County

⊞ **BANNER IRONWOOD MEDICAL CENTER (030130)**, 37000 North Gantzel Road, Zip 85140–7303; tel. 480/394–4000, (Nonreporting) **A**1 10 **F**3 13 18 29 30 35 40 45 49 50 53 67 68 70 73 75 76 81 87 100 107 115 119 130 135 146 147 148 149 154 156 **P**8 **S** Banner Health, Phoenix, AZ
Primary Contact: Robert Gardner, Chief Executive Officer
CFO: Tracy French, Chief Financial Officer
CMO: Darren West, M.D., Interim Chief Medical Officer
CHR: Janine Polito, Chief Human Resources Officer
CNO: Terresa Ann Paulus, Chief Nursing Officer
Web address: www.bannerhealth.com/Locations/Arizona/Banner+Ironwood/
**Control**: Other not–for–profit (including NFP Corporation) **Service**: General medical and surgical

**Staffed Beds**: 53 **Admissions**: 3871 **Census**: 33 **Outpatient Visits**: 77532
**Births**: 1175 **Total Expense ($000)**: 81337 **Payroll Expense ($000)**: 29597
**Personnel**: 429

### SCOTTSDALE—Maricopa County

⊞ **BANNER BEHAVIORAL HEALTH HOSPITAL - SCOTTSDALE (034004)**, 7575 East Earll Drive, Zip 85251–6915; tel. 480/941–7500, (Nonreporting) **A**1 3 10 **F**4 5 29 30 34 35 38 44 50 57 68 75 86 87 98 99 101 102 104 130 132 134 135 146 149 153 **P**8 **S** Banner Health, Phoenix, AZ
Primary Contact: William Southwick, R.N., MS, Chief Executive Officer
CFO: Michael A. Cimino JrChief Financial Officer
CMO: Gagandeep Singh, M.D., Chief Medical Officer Behavioral Health
CHR: Zsaber Gere, Chief Human Resource Officer
CNO: Cherri Anderson, Chief Nursing Officer
Web address: www.https://www.bannerhealth.com/locations/scottsdale/banner-behavioral-health-hospital
**Control**: Other not–for–profit (including NFP Corporation) **Service**: Psychiatric

**Staffed Beds**: 128 **Admissions**: 7238 **Census**: 116 **Outpatient Visits**: 7493
**Births**: 0 **Total Expense ($000)**: 48057 **Payroll Expense ($000)**: 22588
**Personnel**: 392

**BANNER BEHAVIORAL HLTH CTR** See Banner Behavioral Health Hospital - Scottsdale

**EMCOMPASS HEALTH SCOTTSDALE REHABILITATION HOSPITAL** See Encompass Health Rehabilitation Hospital of Scottsdale

⊞ **ENCOMPASS HEALTH REHABILITATION HOSPITAL OF SCOTTSDALE (033025)**, 9630 East Shea Boulevard, Zip 85260–6267; tel. 480/551–5400, (Nonreporting) **A**1 10 **S** Encompass Health Corporation, Birmingham, AL
Primary Contact: Kenneth Bell, Chief Executive Officer
CFO: Lisa Barrick, Controller
CMO: Keith W Cunningham, M.D., Medical Director
CHR: Mary Beth Giczi, Director Human Resources
CNO: Diane M Caruso, MSN, Chief Nursing Officer
Web address: www.https://www.encompasshealth.com/locations/scottsdalerehab
**Control**: Corporation, Investor–owned (for–profit) **Service**: Rehabilitation

**Staffed Beds**: 60

⊞ △ **HONORHEALTH REHABILITATION HOSPITAL (033038)**, 8850 East Pima Center Parkway, Zip 85258–4619; tel. 480/800–3900, (Nonreporting) **A**1 3 5 7 10 **F**3 28 29 34 35 38 50 56 57 59 60 68 74 75 79 82 84 86 87 90 91 92 94 96 100 101 119 130 132 143 148 149 156 **S** Select Medical Corporation, Mechanicsburg, PA
Primary Contact: Scott R. Keen, Chief Executive Officer
Web address: www.scottsdale-rehab.com/
**Control**: Partnership, Investor–owned (for–profit) **Service**: Rehabilitation

**Staffed Beds**: 50 **Admissions**: 1186 **Census**: 43 **Outpatient Visits**: 0
**Births**: 0 **Personnel**: 140

★ ⇑ **HONORHEALTH SCOTTSDALE OSBORN MEDICAL CENTER (030038)**, 7400 East Osborn Road, Zip 85251–6403; tel. 480/882–4000, (Nonreporting) **A**3 5 8 10 21 **S** HonorHealth, Scottsdale, AZ
Primary Contact: Kimberly Post, Senior Vice President and Chief Executive Officer
CMO: James Burke, M.D., Senior Vice President and Chief Medical Officer
CIO: James R Cramer, Vice President and Chief Information Officer
Web address: www.shc.org
**Control**: Other not–for–profit (including NFP Corporation) **Service**: General medical and surgical

**Staffed Beds**: 347

★ ⇑ **HONORHEALTH SCOTTSDALE SHEA MEDICAL CENTER (030087)**, 9003 East Shea Boulevard, Zip 85260–6771; tel. 480/323–3000, (Nonreporting) **A**2 3 5 10 19 21 **S** HonorHealth, Scottsdale, AZ
Primary Contact: Gary E. Baker, Senior Vice President and Chief Executive Officer
CMO: James Burke, M.D., Senior Vice President and Chief Medical Officer
CIO: James R Cramer, Vice President and Chief Information Officer
Web address: www.shc.org
**Control**: Other not–for–profit (including NFP Corporation) **Service**: General medical and surgical

**Staffed Beds**: 409

★ ⇑ **HONORHEALTH SCOTTSDALE THOMPSON PEAK MEDICAL CENTER (030123)**, 7400 East Thompson Peak Parkway, Zip 85255–4109; tel. 480/324–7000, (Nonreporting) **A**3 5 10 21 **F**3 5 20 22 24 26 29 30 31 34 35 37 40 45 46 49 50 51 57 58 59 70 77 78 79 81 82 107 110 111 112 119 126 130 131 132 133 134 135 143 144 145 146 147 148 149 150 **S** HonorHealth, Scottsdale, AZ
Primary Contact: David Price, Chief Executive Officer
COO: Bruce Pearson, Senior Vice President and Chief Operating Officer
CFO: Alice H Pope, Chief Financial Officer
CMO: Stephanie Jackson, M.D., Vice President and Chief Medical Officer
CIO: Charles Scully, Chief Information Officer
CHR: Wendy Crawford, Chief Human Resource Officer
CNO: Kimberly Post, Senior Vice President and Chief Clinical Officer
Web address: www.shc.org
**Control**: Other not–for–profit (including NFP Corporation) **Service**: General medical and surgical

**Staffed Beds**: 92 **Admissions**: 7451 **Census**: 65

**SCOTTSDALE HEALTHCARE REHABILITATION HOSPITAL** See Honorhealth Rehabilitation Hospital

⇑ **SCOTTSDALE OSBORN MEDICAL CENTER** See Honorhealth Scottsdale Osborn Medical Center

⇑ **SCOTTSDALE SHEA MEDICAL CENTER** See Honorhealth Scottsdale Shea Medical Center

⇑ **SCOTTSDALE THOMPSON PEAK MEDICAL CENTER** See Honorhealth Scottsdale Thompson Peak Medical Center

### SELLS—Pima County

**PHS INDIAN HOSPITAL** See U.S. Public Health Service Indian Hospital-Sells

⊞ **U. S. PUBLIC HEALTH SERVICE INDIAN HOSPITAL-SELLS (030074)**, Highway 86 & Topawa Road, Zip 85634, Mailing Address: P.O. Box 548, Zip 85634–0548; tel. 520/383–7251, (Nonreporting) **A**1 10 **S** U. S. Indian Health Service, Rockville, MD
Primary Contact: Troy Klarkowski, Administrator and Chief Executive Officer
COO: Diane Shanley, Deputy Service Unit Director
CFO: Vivian Draper, Chief Financial Officer
CNO: Donna Hobbs, Nurse Executive
Web address: www.ihs.gov
**Control**: PHS, Indian Service, Government, federal **Service**: General medical and surgical

**Staffed Beds**: 12

### SHOW LOW—Navajo County

**NAVAPACHE REGIONAL MED CENTER** See Summit Healthcare Regional Medical Center

★ **SUMMIT HEALTHCARE REGIONAL MEDICAL CENTER (030062)**, 2200 East Show Low Lake Road, Zip 85901–7800; tel. 928/537–4375, (Nonreporting) **A**2 3 5 10 20 **F**8 11 13 15 18 20 22 28 29 30 31 32 34 35 36 38 40 41 43 45 46 47 54 55 57 59 62 64 65 68 70 71 73 75 76 77 78 79 81 82 84 91 92 93 97 100 104 107 108 110 111 114 115 118 119 121 127 129 130 132 133 144 146 147 148 149 154 156 **P**6
Primary Contact: Ronald L. McArthur, Chief Executive Officer
COO: Doug Gilchrist, Chief Operating Officer
CFO: David Rothenberger, Chief Financial Officer
CMO: Alan Neil DeWitt, Chief Medical Officer
CIO: Aaron Young, Chief Information Officer
CHR: Connie Kakavas, Chief Human Resources Officer
CNO: Cynthia Ebert-Loomis, R.N., Chief Nursing Officer
Web address: www.summithealthcare.net
**Control**: Other not–for–profit (including NFP Corporation) **Service**: General medical and surgical

**Staffed Beds**: 89 **Admissions**: 5042 **Census**: 38 **Outpatient Visits**: 73287
**Births**: 816 **Total Expense ($000)**: 213117 **Payroll Expense ($000)**: 95105

### SIERRA VISTA—Cochise County

⊞ **CANYON VISTA MEDICAL CENTER (030043)**, 5700 East Highway 90, Zip 85635–9110; tel. 520/263–2000, (Nonreporting) **A**1 3 5 10 13 20 **S** LifePoint Health, Brentwood, TN
Primary Contact: Bob Gomes, FACHE, President and Chief Executive Officer
COO: Ashley L. Johnson, Chief Operations Officer
CIO: Jorge Moreno, Director Information Technology Operations
CHR: Traci Meyer, Director Human Resources
Web address: www.canyonvistamedicalcenter.com/
**Control**: Corporation, Investor–owned (for–profit) **Service**: General medical and surgical

**Staffed Beds**: 100

**SIERRA VISTA REGIONAL HEALTH CENTER** See Canyon Vista Medical Center

*Many Facility Codes have changed. Please refer to the AHA Guide Code Chart.*   © 2021 AHA Guide

## SPRINGERVILLE—Apache County

**WHITE MOUNTAIN COMM HOSPITAL** See White Mountain Regional Medical Center

**WHITE MOUNTAIN REGIONAL MEDICAL CENTER (031315)**, 118 South Mountain Avenue, Zip 85938–5104; tel. 928/333–4368, (Nonreporting) **A**10 18
Primary Contact: Gregory J. Was, CPA, Chief Executive Officer
CFO: James Hamblin, Chief Financial Officer
CMO: Scott Hamblin, M.D., President Medical Staff
Web address: www.wmrmc.com
**Control:** Other not–for–profit (including NFP Corporation) **Service:** General medical and surgical

**Staffed Beds:** 20

## SUN CITY—Maricopa County

**BANNER BOSWELL HOSPITAL** See Banner Boswell Medical Center

⊞ **BANNER BOSWELL MEDICAL CENTER (030061)**, 10401 West Thunderbird Boulevard, Zip 85351–3004; tel. 623/832–4000, (Nonreporting) **A**1 2 3 5 10 **F**3 9 11 15 17 18 20 22 24 26 28 29 30 31 34 35 36 37 40 43 44 45 46 47 48 49 50 51 53 56 57 58 59 60 61 63 64 65 69 70 74 75 77 78 79 81 84 85 86 87 90 91 92 93 94 96 107 108 110 111 114 115 117 119 120 121 124 126 128 130 131 132 135 141 145 146 147 148 149 154 157 **P**8 **S** Banner Health, Phoenix, AZ
Primary Contact: Sharon Lind, MSN, FACHE, Chief Executive Officer
CFO: Jeremy Williams, Chief Financial Officer
CMO: Kathryn Perkins, M.D., Chief Medical Officer
CHR: Brenda Dietrich, Chief Human Resources Officer
Web address: www.bannerhealth.com/locations/sun-city/banner-boswell-medical-center
**Control:** Other not–for–profit (including NFP Corporation) **Service:** General medical and surgical

**Staffed Beds:** 436 **Admissions:** 16348 **Census:** 262 **Outpatient Visits:** 304595 **Births:** 0 **Total Expense ($000):** 336550 **Payroll Expense ($000):** 108990

## SUN CITY WEST—Maricopa County

**BANNER DEL E WEBB HOSPITAL** See Banner Del E. Webb Medical Center

⊞ **BANNER DEL E. WEBB MEDICAL CENTER (030093)**, 14502 West Meeker Boulevard, Zip 85375–5299; tel. 623/524–4000, (Nonreporting) **A**1 3 5 10 **F**3 4 5 9 11 13 15 18 20 22 28 29 30 31 34 35 36 37 38 40 43 44 45 46 49 50 51 53 54 56 57 58 59 60 61 63 64 65 70 74 75 76 77 78 79 80 81 84 85 86 87 90 91 92 93 94 96 98 100 101 102 103 104 107 108 110 111 114 115 118 119 126 130 131 132 135 141 145 146 147 148 149 153 154 157 **P**8 **S** Banner Health, Phoenix, AZ
Primary Contact: Sharon Lind, MSN, FACHE, Chief Executive Officer
COO: Nathan Shinagawa, Chief Operating Officer
CFO: Dan Stimpson, Chief Financial Officer
CMO: Scott Anderson, Chief Medical Officer
CHR: Carole Smith, Senior Human Resource Business Partner
CNO: Nancy Adamson, Chief Nursing Officer
Web address: www.bannerhealth.com/Locations/Arizona/Banner+Del+Webb+Medical+Center/
**Control:** Other not–for–profit (including NFP Corporation) **Service:** General medical and surgical

**Staffed Beds:** 433 **Admissions:** 18936 **Census:** 249 **Outpatient Visits:** 295715 **Births:** 2032 **Total Expense ($000):** 284909 **Payroll Expense ($000):** 102058 **Personnel:** 1469

## SURPRISE—Maricopa County

**AVENIR BEHAVIORAL HEALTH CENTER (034035)**, 16561 North Parkview Place, Zip 85374–7499; tel. 489/900–2790, (Nonreporting)
Primary Contact: Burton Carriker, Chief Executive Officer
Web address: www.https://www.avenirseniorliving.com/
**Control:** Partnership, Investor–owned (for–profit) **Service:** Psychiatric

**Staffed Beds:** 32

**COBALT REHABILITATION HOSPITAL (033039)**, 13060 West Bell Road, Zip 85378–1200; tel. 623/499–9100, (Nonreporting) **A**10 22
Primary Contact: Sharon Noe, Chief Executive Officer
Web address: www.colbaltrehab.com
**Control:** Corporation, Investor–owned (for–profit) **Service:** Rehabilitation

**Staffed Beds:** 40

## TEMPE—Maricopa County

☐ **AURORA BEHAVIORAL HEALTH SYSTEM EAST (034028)**, 6350 South Maple Street, Zip 85283–2857; tel. 480/345–5400, (Nonreporting) **A**1 3 5 10 **S** Signature Healthcare Services, Corona, CA
Primary Contact: Bruce Waldo, Chief Executive Officer
CFO: Rebekah Francis, JD, Chief Financial Officer
CMO: Tariq Ghafoor, Medical Director
CHR: Vicki Thomsen, Director Human Resources
CNO: Dawn Whitmore EsqDirector of Nursing
Web address: www.auroraarizona.com
**Control:** Partnership, Investor–owned (for–profit) **Service:** Psychiatric

**Staffed Beds:** 70

**AURORA TEMPE HOSPITAL** See Aurora Behavioral Health System East

**TEMPE ST. LUKE'S HOSPITAL**, 1500 South Mill Avenue, Zip 85281–6699; tel. 480/784–5510, (Nonreporting) **S** Steward Health Care System, LLC, Dallas, TX
Primary Contact: Jenifer Midgett, President and Chief Executive Officer
Web address: www.tempestlukeshospital.com
**Service:** General medical and surgical

**Staffed Beds:** 110

## TUBA CITY—Coconino County

**TUBA CITY INDIAN MEDICAL CTR** See Tuba City Regional Health Care Corporation

⊞ **TUBA CITY REGIONAL HEALTH CARE CORPORATION (030073)**, 167 Main Street, Zip 86045–0611, Mailing Address: P.O. Box 600, Zip 86045–0600; tel. 928/283–2501, (Nonreporting) **A**1 3 5 10
Primary Contact: Lynette Bonar, FACHE, R.N., Chief Executive Officer
CFO: Christine Keyonnie, CPA, Chief Financial Officer
CMO: Holly Van Dyk, M.D., Interim Chief Medical Officer
CIO: Shawn Davis, Chief Information Officer
CHR: George Hunter, Interim Chief Human Resources Officer
CNO: Alvina Rosales, R.N., Chief Nursing Officer
Web address: www.tchealth.org
**Control:** Other not–for–profit (including NFP Corporation) **Service:** General medical and surgical

**Staffed Beds:** 53

## TUCSON—Pima County

⊞ **BANNER - UNIVERSITY MEDICAL CENTER SOUTH (030111)**, 2800 East Ajo Way, Zip 85713–6289; tel. 520/874–2000, (Nonreporting) **A**1 3 5 10 **F**3 11 18 20 22 29 30 34 36 40 43 45 47 48 51 54 56 58 59 60 61 64 65 66 68 70 71 74 75 77 79 81 82 84 85 86 87 92 97 98 99 100 101 102 103 104 107 108 111 114 115 119 130 131 132 135 146 148 149 154 156 **P**8 **S** Banner Health, Phoenix, AZ
Primary Contact: Sarah Frost, Chief Executive Officer
CFO: Jeff Buehrle, Chief Financial Officer
CMO: David Sheinbein, Chief Medical Officer
CIO: Ryan K Smith, Senior Vice President Information Technology
CHR: Jennifer L Sherwood, Division, Human Resource Business Partner
CNO: Cathy Townsend, Chief Nursing Officer
Web address: www.bannerhealth.com
**Control:** Other not–for–profit (including NFP Corporation) **Service:** General medical and surgical

**Staffed Beds:** 245 **Admissions:** 7775 **Census:** 114 **Outpatient Visits:** 143848 **Births:** 0 **Total Expense ($000):** 196474 **Payroll Expense ($000):** 56752 **Personnel:** 1090

⊞ **BANNER - UNIVERSITY MEDICAL CENTER TUCSON (030064)**, 1501 North Campbell Avenue, Zip 85719; tel. 520/694–0111, (Includes DIAMOND CHILDREN'S HOSPITAL, Mailing address: 1501 North Campbell Avenue, Tucson, Arizona, Zip 85724–0001; tel. 520/694–0111), (Nonreporting) **A**1 2 3 5 8 10 19 **F**3 11 12 13 15 16 17 18 19 20 21 22 23 24 25 26 27 28 29 30 31 34 35 40 41 43 44 46 47 49 50 51 53 54 55 56 57 58 59 60 61 64 65 68 70 71 72 73 74 75 76 77 78 79 80 81 82 84 85 87 88 89 92 97 100 107 108 110 111 112 114 115 116 117 118 119 126 129 130 131 132 135 136 137 138 140 141 142 145 146 147 148 149 154 **P**8 **S** Banner Health, Phoenix, AZ
Primary Contact: Sarah Frost, Chief Executive Officer
CFO: Misty Hansen, Chief Financial Officer
CMO: Andreas Theodorou, Chief Medical Officer
CIO: Dan Critchley, Chief Information Officer
Web address: www.https://www.bannerhealth.com/locations/tucson/banner-university-medical-center-tucson
**Control:** Other not–for–profit (including NFP Corporation) **Service:** General medical and surgical

**Staffed Beds:** 583 **Admissions:** 22407 **Census:** 371 **Outpatient Visits:** 440190 **Births:** 1785 **Total Expense ($000):** 842760 **Payroll Expense ($000):** 227647 **Personnel:** 2936

---

**Hospital, Medicare Provider Number, Address, Telephone, Approval, Facility, and Physician Codes, Health Care System**

★ American Hospital Association (AHA) membership
☐ The Joint Commission accreditation
○ Healthcare Facilities Accreditation Program
◇ DNV Healthcare Inc. accreditation
⇧ Center for Improvement in Healthcare Quality Accreditation
△ Commission on Accreditation of Rehabilitation Facilities (CARF) accreditation

**BANNER - UNIVERSITY MEDICAL CENTER TUCSON BANNER - UNIVERSITY MEDICAL CENTER SOUTH** See Banner - University Medical Center Tucson

**BANNER - UNIVERSITY OF ARIZONA MEDICAL CENTER - SOUTH CAMPUS** See Banner - University Medical Center South

**CARONDELET ST. JOSEPH'S HOSPITAL (030011)**, 350 North Wilmot Road, Zip 85711–2678; tel. 520/873–3000, (Nonreporting) **A**1 5 10 19 **F**3 5 12 13 18 20 22 24 28 29 30 31 34 35 38 40 44 45 46 47 49 50 57 59 60 64 68 69 70 72 74 75 76 77 78 79 81 82 83 84 85 86 87 90 92 93 98 100 101 102 104 107 108 114 115 118 119 126 129 130 132 135 145 146 147 148 156 **S** TENET Healthcare Corporation, Dallas, TX
Primary Contact: Frank L. Molinaro, Chief Executive Officer
CFO: Alan Strauss, Chief Financial Officer
CMO: Donald Denmark, M.D., Chief Medical Officer
CIO: Sally Zambrello, Chief Information Officer
CHR: Igor Shegolev, Vice President Human Resources
CNO: Robin Conklin, R.N., Chief Nursing Officer
Web address: www.carondelet.org
**Control**: Corporation, Investor–owned (for–profit) **Service**: General medical and surgical

**Staffed Beds:** 486 **Admissions:** 15724 **Census:** 185 **Outpatient Visits:** 90054 **Births:** 2027 **Total Expense ($000):** 249050 **Payroll Expense ($000):** 96961

△ **CARONDELET ST. MARY'S HOSPITAL (030010)**, 1601 West St Mary's Road, Zip 85745–2682; tel. 520/872–3000, (Nonreporting) **A**1 5 7 10 19 **F**3 12 15 17 18 20 22 24 26 28 29 30 31 34 38 40 44 45 46 47 49 50 51 53 56 57 58 59 60 64 68 70 74 77 78 79 81 82 84 85 86 87 90 92 93 96 98 100 101 102 103 107 108 110 111 114 115 118 119 126 129 130 131 132 146 148 149 156 157 **S** TENET Healthcare Corporation, Dallas, TX
Primary Contact: Frank L. Molinaro, Chief Executive Officer
COO: Ryan Harper, Chief Operating Officer
CMO: William Ellert, M.D., Medical Director
CHR: Ricky Russell, Chief Human Resource Officer
CNO: Jennifer Roy, R.N., Chief Nursing Officer
Web address: www.carondelet.org
**Control**: Corporation, Investor–owned (for–profit) **Service**: General medical and surgical

**Staffed Beds:** 300 **Admissions:** 11581 **Census:** 151 **Outpatient Visits:** 80179 **Births:** 0 **Total Expense ($000):** 193977 **Payroll Expense ($000):** 75858

**CHG HOSPITAL TUCSON, LLC (032004)**, 7220 East Rosewood Drive, Zip 85710–1350; tel. 520/546–4595, (Nonreporting) **A**1 10 22 **S** Cornerstone Healthcare Group, Dallas, TX
Primary Contact: Debora Bornmann, Chief Executive Officer
CFO: Kurt Schultz, Group Chief Financial Officer
CMO: Sassan Momtazbakhsh, M.D., Medical Director
CHR: Deborah Darcy, Human Resources
CNO: Ritche Berdal, Chief Nursing Officer
Web address: www.chghospitals.com
**Control**: Corporation, Investor–owned (for–profit) **Service**: Acute long–term care hospital

**Staffed Beds:** 32

**CORNERSTONE HOSPITAL OF SOUTHEAST ARIZONA** See Chg Hospital Tucson, LLC

**CURAHEALTH TUCSON (032002)**, 355 North Wilmot Road, Zip 85711–2601; tel. 520/584–4500, (Nonreporting) **A**1 10 **S** Curahealth Hospitals, Garland, TX
Primary Contact: Camie Overton, Chief Executive Officer
CMO: Sunil Natrajan, M.D., Medical Director
CNO: Globert Empedrad, Chief Clinical Officer
Web address: www.curahealth.com
**Control**: Corporation, Investor–owned (for–profit) **Service**: Acute long–term care hospital

**Staffed Beds:** 51

**ENCOMPASS HEALTH REHABILITATION HOSPITAL OF NORTHWEST TUCSON (033029)**, 1921 West Hospital Drive, Zip 85704–7806; tel. 520/742–2800, (Nonreporting) **A**1 10 **F**3 29 34 59 64 69 90 93 95 96 130 131 132 143 148 **S** Encompass Health Corporation, Birmingham, AL
Primary Contact: Jeffrey Christensen, Chief Executive Officer
CFO: Kaleigh Hotchkiss, Controller
CMO: Susan R. Bulen, M.D., Medical Director
CHR: Neil Cullen, Director Human Resources
CNO: Virginia Ragonese-Green, Chief Nursing Officer
Web address: www.https://www.encompasshealth.com/northwesttucsonrehab
**Control**: Corporation, Investor–owned (for–profit) **Service**: Rehabilitation

**Staffed Beds:** 60 **Admissions:** 941 **Census:** 32 **Births:** 0

**ENCOMPASS HEALTH REHABILITATION INSTITUTE OF TUCSON (033028)**, 2650 North Wyatt Drive, Zip 85712–6108; tel. 520/325–1300, (Nonreporting) **A**1 3 5 10 **F**29 34 35 62 90 93 96 130 132 **S** Encompass Health Corporation, Birmingham, AL
Primary Contact: Jeffrey Christensen, Chief Executive Officer
CFO: Mary Donovan, Controller
CMO: Jon Larson, M.D., Medical Director
CHR: Dawn Mosier, Director Human Resources
Web address: www.https://www.encompasshealth.com/rehabinstituteoftucson
**Control**: Corporation, Investor–owned (for–profit) **Service**: Rehabilitation

**Staffed Beds:** 80 **Admissions:** 1716 **Census:** 59 **Births:** 0

**HEALTHSOUTH REHABILITATION HOSPITAL OF SOUTHERN ARIZONA** See Encompass Health Rehabilitation Hospital of Northwest Tucson

**HEALTHSOUTH REHABILITATION INSTITUTE OF TUCSON** See Encompass Health Rehabilitation Institute of Tucson

**KINDRED HOSPITAL-TUCSON** See Curahealth Tucson

**NORTHWEST HOSPITAL** See Northwest Medical Center

**NORTHWEST MEDICAL CENTER (030085)**, 6200 North La Cholla Boulevard, Zip 85741–3599; tel. 520/742–9000, (Nonreporting) **A**1 5 10 **S** Community Health Systems, Inc., Franklin, TN
Primary Contact: Jennifer Schomburg, Chief Executive Officer
CFO: Ronald Patrick, Chief Financial Officer
CIO: David Bullock, Director Information Services
CNO: Kay Stubbs, Chief Nursing Officer
Web address: www.northwestmedicalcenter.com
**Control**: Corporation, Investor–owned (for–profit) **Service**: General medical and surgical

**Staffed Beds:** 270

**PALO VERDE BEHAVIORAL HEALTH (034030)**, 2695 North Craycroft Road, Zip 85712–2244; tel. 520/322–2888, (Nonreporting) **A**1 3 5 10 **S** Universal Health Services, Inc., King of Prussia, PA
Primary Contact: Jill Scheckel, Ph.D., Chief Executive Officer
CFO: Richard N England, Chief Financial Officer
CHR: Michelle Carrasco, Director Human Resources
Web address: www.paloverdebh.com/
**Control**: Other not–for–profit (including NFP Corporation) **Service**: Psychiatric

**Staffed Beds:** 48

**PALO VERDE MENTAL HEALTH SERVICES** See Palo Verde Behavioral Health

## TUCSON—Pinal County

**SIERRA TUCSON**, 39580 South Lago Del Oro Parkway, Zip 85739–1091; tel. 520/624–4000, (Nonreporting) **A**3 5 **S** CRC Health Group, Inc., Cupertino, CA
Primary Contact: Jaime W. Vinck, MC, Chief Executive Officer
COO: Stephen P Fahey, Executive Director
CFO: Amy Fritton, Controller
CMO: Jerome Lerner, M.D., Medical Director
CHR: Betty Dickens, Director Human Resources
CNO: Sue Menzie, R.N., Director Patient Care
Web address: www.sierratucson.com
**Control**: Corporation, Investor–owned (for–profit) **Service**: Alcoholism and other chemical dependency

**Staffed Beds:** 139

## TUCSON—Pima County

**SONORA BEHAVIORAL HEALTH HOSPITAL (034022)**, 6050 North Corona Road, #3, Zip 85704–1096; tel. 520/469–8700, (Nonreporting) **A**1 10 **S** Acadia Healthcare Company, Inc., Franklin, TN
Primary Contact: Edeli Kinsala, Chief Executive Officer
CMO: Steven Bupp, M.D., Medical Director
CHR: Ciria Soto, Director Human Resources
CNO: Angel Payne, Clinical Director, Director of Nursing
**Control**: Corporation, Investor–owned (for–profit) **Service**: Psychiatric

**Staffed Beds:** 106

**SOUTHERN ARIZONA VA HEALTHCARE** See Southern Arizona Veterans Affairs Health Care System

☒ △ **SOUTHERN ARIZONA VETERANS AFFAIRS HEALTH CARE SYSTEM**, 3601 Sout 6th Avenue, Zip 85723–0002, Mailing Address: 3601 South 6th Avenue, Zip 85723–0002; tel. 520/792–1450, (Nonreporting) **A**1 3 5 7 **F**3 4 5 15 18 20 22 24 26 28 29 30 31 33 34 35 36 38 39 40 44 45 46 49 52 53 54 56 57 58 59 60 61 63 64 65 66 70 71 74 75 77 78 79 80 81 82 83 84 85 86 87 90 91 92 93 94 96 97 98 100 101 102 103 104 105 106 107 108 110 111 112 115 116 117 118 119 126 127 128 129 130 132 135 143 146 147 148 149 150 152 153 154 156 157 158 **P**6 **S** Department of Veterans Affairs, Washington, DC
Primary Contact: Jennifer S. Gutowski, FACHE, Director
CMO: Jayendra H Shah, M.D., Chief Medical Officer
CIO: John Walston, Chief Information Officer
CHR: Patrice Craig, Manager Human Resources
Web address: www.tucson.va.gov
**Control:** Veterans Affairs, Government, federal **Service:** General medical and surgical

**Staffed Beds: 328 Admissions: 9306 Census: 229 Outpatient Visits: 377000 Births: 1 Personnel: 2518**

**ST JOSEPH'S HOSP & HLTH CTR** See Carondelet St. Joseph's Hospital

**ST MARY'S HOSPITAL & HLTH CNTR** See Carondelet St. Mary's Hospital

**TMC FOR CHILDREN** See Tmc Healthcare, Tucson

**TMC HEALTHCARE** See Tmc Healthcare

☒ **TMC HEALTHCARE (030006)**, 5301 East Grant Road, Zip 85712–2874; tel. 520/324–5461, (Includes TMC FOR CHILDREN, Mailing address: 5301 East Grant Road, Tucson, Arizona, Zip 85712–2805; tel. 520/327–5461; Judy F. Rich, MSN, R.N., President and Chief Executive Officer), (Nonreporting) **A**1 3 5 10 19 **F**3 11 12 13 15 17 18 19 20 22 24 25 26 27 28 29 30 31 32 34 35 37 40 41 45 46 47 48 49 50 53 54 55 56 57 58 59 63 64 65 66 68 72 74 75 76 77 78 79 80 81 82 84 85 87 88 89 93 98 102 103 107 108 110 111 114 115 118 119 124 126 127 129 130 132 135 144 146 147 148 149 154 156 157 **P**3 6
Primary Contact: Judy F. Rich, MSN, R.N., President and Chief Executive Officer
COO: Karen Mlawsky, Senior Vice President and Chief Operations Officer
CFO: Stephen Bush, Chief Financial Officer
CMO: Rick Anderson, M.D., Senior Vice President and Chief Medical Officer
CIO: Frank Marini, Senior Vice President and Chief Information Officer
CHR: Alex Horvath, Vice President and Chief Human Resources Officer
CNO: Mimi Coomler, R.N., Vice President and Chief Nursing Officer
Web address: www.tmcaz.com
**Control:** Other not–for–profit (including NFP Corporation) **Service:** General medical and surgical

**Staffed Beds: 595 Admissions: 35500 Census: 416 Outpatient Visits: 184970 Births: 5009 Total Expense ($000): 571959 Payroll Expense ($000): 228532 Personnel: 3904**

**WHITERIVER—Navajo County**

☐ **U. S. PUBLIC HEALTH SERVICE INDIAN HOSPITAL-WHITERIVER (030113)**, 200 West Hospital Drive, Zip 85941–0860, Mailing Address: State Route 73, Box 860, Zip 85941–0860; tel. 928/338–4911, (Nonreporting) **A**1 3 5 10 **S** U. S. Indian Health Service, Rockville, MD
Primary Contact: Michelle Martinez, Chief Executive Officer
COO: Brian Campbell, Director Professional Services
CFO: Desdemona Leslie, Finance Officer
CMO: John Umhau, M.D., Clinical Director
CIO: Russell Barker, Information Officer
CHR: Lena Fasthorse, Supervisor Human Resource
CNO: Jana Towne, Nurse Executive
Web address: www.ihs.gov
**Control:** PHS, Indian Service, Government, federal **Service:** General medical and surgical

**Staffed Beds: 35**

**USPHS INDIAN HOSPITAL** See U.S. Public Health Service Indian Hospital-Whiteriver

**WICKENBURG—Maricopa County**

★ **WICKENBURG COMMUNITY HOSPITAL (031300)**, 520 Rose Lane, Zip 85390–1447; tel. 928/684–5421, (Nonreporting) **A**10 18
Primary Contact: James Tavary, Chief Executive Officer
CFO: Jackie Lundblad, Chief Financial Officer
CMO: Todd Kravetz, Chief of Staff
CIO: Blue Beckham, Interim Chief Information Officer
CHR: Dede Schmallen, Chief Human Resources Officer
CNO: Linda Rankin, Chief Nursing Officer
Web address: www.wickhosp.com
**Control:** Other not–for–profit (including NFP Corporation) **Service:** General medical and surgical

**Staffed Beds: 19**

**WICKENBURG REGIONAL MED CTR** See Wickenburg Community Hospital

**WILLCOX—Cochise County**

★ **NORTHERN COCHISE COMMUNITY HOSPITAL (031302)**, 901 West Rex Allen Drive, Zip 85643–1009; tel. 520/384–3541, (Nonreporting) **A**10 18 **F**11 15 29 34 35 40 43 57 59 65 75 77 87 90 93 100 107 110 111 115 119 127 128 133 149
Primary Contact: Monica Sheldon, Chief Executive Officer
COO: Bill Hopkins, Director of Operations
CFO: Carol Holden, Chief Financial Officer
CMO: Dawn Walker, D.O., Chief of Staff
CHR: Jennifer Cochran, Director Human Relations
CNO: C. Renae Dineen, Chief Nursing Officer
Web address: www.ncch.com
**Control:** Hospital district or authority, Government, Nonfederal **Service:** General medical and surgical

**Staffed Beds: 24 Admissions: 225 Census: 2 Births: 0**

**WINSLOW—Navajo County**

**LITTLE COLORADO MEDICAL CENTER (031311)**, 1501 Williamson Avenue, Zip 86047–2797; tel. 928/289–4691, (Nonreporting) **A**3 10 18
Primary Contact: John J. Dempsey, Chief Executive Officer
CFO: Gina Reffner, Chief Financial Officer
CMO: Perry Mitchell, M.D., Chief of Staff
CIO: Jacob Garcia, Chief Information Officer
CHR: Nina L Ferguson, Director Human Resources
Web address: www.lcmcwmh.com
**Control:** Other not–for–profit (including NFP Corporation) **Service:** General medical and surgical

**Staffed Beds: 25**

**WINSLOW MEMORIAL HOSPITAL** See Little Colorado Medical Center

**YUMA—Yuma County**

★ ⇑ **YUMA REGIONAL MEDICAL CENTER (030013)**, 2400 South Avenue 'A', Zip 85364–7170; tel. 928/344–2000, (Nonreporting) **A**2 3 5 10 21 **F**3 8 12 13 15 18 20 22 24 26 28 29 30 31 32 34 35 40 41 45 46 47 48 49 50 54 57 58 59 64 68 70 72 74 75 76 77 78 79 81 82 83 84 85 86 87 89 97 104 107 108 109 110 111 112 114 115 116 117 118 119 120 121 122 123 124 126 130 132 144 146 147 148 149 154
Primary Contact: Robert Trenschel, D.O., FACHE, M.P.H., President and Chief Executive Officer
CFO: David Willie, Chief Financial Officer
CMO: Bharat Magu, M.D., Chief Medical Officer
CIO: Fred Peet, Chief Information Officer
CHR: Randal M. Etzler, Chief Human Resources Officer
CNO: Deb Aders, MS, R.N., Vice President Patient Care Services, Chief Nursing Officer
Web address: www.yumaregional.org
**Control:** Other not–for–profit (including NFP Corporation) **Service:** General medical and surgical

**Staffed Beds: 406 Admissions: 16952 Census: 172 Outpatient Visits: 354075 Births: 3323 Total Expense ($000): 478538 Payroll Expense ($000): 192252 Personnel: 2317**

**YUMA REHABILITATION HOSPITAL** See Yuma Rehabilitation Hospital, A Partnership of Encompass Health and Yrmc

☒ **YUMA REHABILITATION HOSPITAL, A PARTNERSHIP OF ENCOMPASS HEALTH AND YRMC (033034)**, 901 West 24th Street, Zip 85364–6384; tel. 928/726–5000, (Nonreporting) **A**1 10 **S** Encompass Health Corporation, Birmingham, AL
Primary Contact: Ian Hodge, Chief Executive Officer
CMO: Bapu Aluri, M.D., Chief Medical Officer
CHR: Linda Woen, Director Human Resources
CNO: Kristin Parra, Chief Nursing Officer
Web address: www.https://www.encompasshealth.com/yumarehab
**Control:** Corporation, Investor–owned (for–profit) **Service:** Rehabilitation

**Staffed Beds: 41**

---

| **Hospital, Medicare Provider Number, Address, Telephone, Approval, Facility, and Physician Codes, Health Care System** | | |
|---|---|---|
| ★ American Hospital Association (AHA) membership | ○ Healthcare Facilities Accreditation Program | ⇑ Center for Improvement in Healthcare Quality Accreditation |
| ☐ The Joint Commission accreditation | ◇ DNV Healthcare Inc. accreditation | △ Commission on Accreditation of Rehabilitation Facilities (CARF) accreditation |

# ARKANSAS

**AR**

## ARKADELPHIA—Clark County

★ **BAPTIST HEALTH MEDICAL CENTER-ARKADELPHIA (041321)**, 3050 Twin Rivers Drive, Zip 71923–4299; tel. 870/245–2622, (Nonreporting) **A**10 18 **F**3 11 13 15 29 30 34 35 40 41 43 45 46 50 57 59 64 65 68 69 70 75 76 79 81 85 87 93 96 97 102 107 110 111 114 119 127 129 130 131 133 135 146 148 154 156 **S** Baptist Health, Little Rock, AR
Primary Contact: Tony Hardage, PharmD, Assistant Vice President and Administrator
CFO: Robert C Roberts, Vice President and Chief Financial Officer
CMO: Eddie Phillips, M.D., Chief Medical Officer
CIO: David House, Vice President and Chief Information Officer
CHR: Anthony Kendall, Vice President Human Resources
Web address: www.baptist-health.com/locations/accesspoint.aspx?accessPointID=187
**Control:** Other not–for–profit (including NFP Corporation) **Service:** General medical and surgical

Staffed Beds: 25 Admissions: 1203 Census: 11 Outpatient Visits: 38527 Births: 376 Total Expense ($000): 23972 Payroll Expense ($000): 9461 Personnel: 159

**BAPTIST MED CTR ARKADELPHIA** See Baptist Health Medical Center-Arkadelphia

## ASHDOWN—Little River County

★ **LITTLE RIVER MEMORIAL HOSPITAL (041320)**, 451 West Locke Street, Zip 71822–3325; tel. 870/898–5011, (Nonreporting) **A**10 18 **F**3 40 56 59 62 65 77 93 97 107 110 115 119 133 **P**5
Primary Contact: James Dowell, Administrator and Chief Executive Officer
CFO: Jackie Rainey, Chief Financial Officer
CIO: Mitchell Jones, Director Information Technology
CHR: Vicki Keener, Administrative Assistant and Director Human Resources
CNO: Cynthia Metzger, Chief Nursing and Operations Officer
**Control:** Other not–for–profit (including NFP Corporation) **Service:** General medical and surgical

Staffed Beds: 25 Admissions: 96 Census: 1 Outpatient Visits: 12098 Births: 0 Total Expense ($000): 9822 Payroll Expense ($000): 5784 Personnel: 126

## BARLING—Sebastian County

☐ **VALLEY BEHAVIORAL HEALTH SYSTEM (044006)**, 10301 Mayo Drive, Zip 72923–1660; tel. 479/494–5700, (Nonreporting) **A**1 10 **F**29 34 35 75 87 98 99 100 101 102 105 130 135 153 154 **P**6 **S** Acadia Healthcare Company, Inc., Franklin, TN
Primary Contact: Andrea Norman, Chief Executive Officer
CFO: Paul D Ervin, Chief Financial Officer
CMO: Richard Livingston, M.D., Medical Director
CHR: Patricia J Moore, Director Human Resource
CNO: Landon Horton, Director of Nursing
Web address: www.valleybehavioral.com
**Control:** State, Government, Nonfederal **Service:** Psychiatric

Staffed Beds: 114 Admissions: 2170 Census: 71 Outpatient Visits: 11544 Births: 0 Total Expense ($000): 13429 Payroll Expense ($000): 7750 Personnel: 166

**VISTA HEALTH OF FORT SMITH** See Valley Behavioral Health System

## BATESVILLE—Independence County

★ **WHITE RIVER MEDICAL CENTER (040119)**, 1710 Harrison Street, Zip 72501–7303, Mailing Address: P.O. Box 2197, Zip 72503–2197; tel. 870/262–1200, (Nonreporting) **A**3 5 10 **S** White River Health System, Batesville, AR
Primary Contact: Gary Paxson, MS, R.N., President and Chief Executive Officer
CFO: Shawna Ives, CPA, Chief Financial Officer
CMO: Doug Bernard, M.D., Chief Medical Officer
CIO: Jeff Reifsteck, Assistant Vice President Chief Information Officer
CHR: Lindsey Castelberry, Vice President Human Resources and General Counsel
CNO: Terri Bunch, MSN, R.N., MSN, Chief Nursing Officer
Web address: www.whiteriverhealthsystem.com
**Control:** Other not–for–profit (including NFP Corporation) **Service:** General medical and surgical

Staffed Beds: 210

## BENTON—Saline County

**RIVENDELL BEHAVIORAL HEALTH** See Rivendell Behavioral Health Services of Arkansas

☐ **RIVENDELL BEHAVIORAL HEALTH SERVICES OF ARKANSAS (044007)**, 100 Rivendell Drive, Zip 72019–9100; tel. 501/316–1255, (Nonreporting) **A**1 10 **S** Universal Health Services, Inc., King of Prussia, PA
Primary Contact: Ballard Sheppard, Ph.D., Chief Executive Officer
CFO: Mike Rainbolt, Chief Financial Officer
Web address: www.rivendellofarkansas.com
**Control:** Corporation, Investor–owned (for–profit) **Service:** Children's hospital psychiatric

Staffed Beds: 80

★ **SALINE MEMORIAL HOSPITAL (040084)**, 1 Medical Park Drive, Zip 72015–3354; tel. 501/776–6000, (Nonreporting) **A**5 10 **F**3 7 11 12 13 15 18 20 22 26 29 34 35 39 40 43 56 57 59 62 63 70 75 76 77 79 81 82 85 87 90 98 103 107 108 110 111 114 115 118 119 129 130 132 135 146 147 148 149 154 **P**6 8 **S** LifePoint Health, Brentwood, TN
Primary Contact: Michael K. Stewart, Chief Executive Officer
COO: Carla Robertson, Chief Operating Officer and Chief Financial Officer
CFO: Carla Robertson, Chief Operating Officer and Chief Financial Officer
CIO: Andy Dick, Director Information Services
CHR: Carol Matthews, Director Human Resources
CNO: Katie Lea, Chief Nursing Officer
Web address: www.salinememorial.org
**Control:** Corporation, Investor–owned (for–profit) **Service:** General medical and surgical

Staffed Beds: 133 Admissions: 6193 Census: 70 Outpatient Visits: 106864 Births: 467 Total Expense ($000): 107366 Payroll Expense ($000): 45978 Personnel: 529

## BENTONVILLE—Benton County

**BATES MEDICAL CENTER** See Northwest Medical Center - Bentonville

## BERRYVILLE—Carroll County

⊞ **MERCY HOSPITAL BERRYVILLE (041329)**, 214 Carter Street, Zip 72616–4303; tel. 870/423–3355, (Nonreporting) **A**1 10 18 **S** Mercy, Chesterfield, MO
Primary Contact: VonDa Moore, Administrator
CFO: Sherry Clouse Day, Vice President Finance
CHR: Taya James, Director
CNO: Michele Gann, Vice President Patient Services
Web address: www.https://www.mercy.net/newsroom/mercy-hospital-berryville-quick-facts/
**Control:** Church operated, Nongovernment, not–for–profit **Service:** General medical and surgical

Staffed Beds: 25

**ST. JOHN'S HOSPITAL-BERRYVILLE** See Mercy Hospital Berryville

*Many Facility Codes have changed. Please refer to the AHA Guide Code Chart.*

## BLYTHEVILLE—Mississippi County

**BAPTIST MEMORIAL HOSPITAL** See Great River Medical Center

✠ **GREAT RIVER MEDICAL CENTER (040069)**, 1520 North Division Street, Zip 72315–1448, Mailing Address: P.O. Box 108, Zip 72316–0108; tel. 870/838–7300, (Nonreporting) **A**1 5 10 **F**3 13 15 29 34 40 43 45 48 53 57 68 70 76 81 89 90 92 93 107 108 110 111 114 119 148 149 154
Primary Contact: Chris Lee. Raymer, MSN, Chief Executive Officer
COO: Paul Pieffer, Chief Operating Officer
CFO: Randy Nichols, Chief Financial Officer
CIO: Tammy Bratcher, Director System Information Technology
CHR: Cheri Blurton, SPHR,SHRM-SCP, Director Human Resources, HIPAA Privacy Officer
CNO: Felicia Pierce, R.N., Chief Nursing Officer
Web address: www.mchsys.org
**Control:** County, Government, Nonfederal **Service:** General medical and surgical

| | |
|---|---|
| **Staffed Beds:** 73 **Admissions:** 1486 **Census:** 10 **Outpatient Visits:** 29935 **Births:** 346 **Total Expense ($000):** 23142 **Payroll Expense ($000):** 9530 **Personnel:** 222 | |

## BOONEVILLE—Logan County

**BOONEVILLE COMMUNITY HOSPITAL** See Mercy Hospital Booneville

★ **MERCY HOSPITAL BOONEVILLE (041318)**, 880 West Main Street, Zip 72927–3443; tel. 479/675–2800, (Nonreporting) **A**10 18 **F**3 11 15 35 40 43 45 57 59 62 64 65 68 81 85 107 119 127 133 148 149 **P**8 **S** Mercy, Chesterfield, MO
Primary Contact: Teresa Williams, R.N., Regional Administrator
CMO: Michael Miranda, Chief of Staff
CHR: Doris Whitaker, Vice President and Manager
CNO: Kimberly Russell, Chief Nursing Officer
Web address: www.https://www.mercy.net/practice/mercy-hospital-booneville/our-locations/
**Control:** Church operated, Nongovernment, not-for-profit **Service:** General medical and surgical

| | |
|---|---|
| **Staffed Beds:** 25 **Admissions:** 372 **Census:** 4 **Outpatient Visits:** 14911 **Births:** 0 **Total Expense ($000):** 15670 **Payroll Expense ($000):** 5403 **Personnel:** 69 | |

## CALICO ROCK—Izard County

**COMMUNITY MEDICAL CENTER OF IZARD COUNTY** See Izard County Medical Center

**IZARD COUNTY MEDICAL CENTER (041306)**, 61 Grasse Street, Zip 72519–7013, Mailing Address: P.O. Box 438, Zip 72519–0438; tel. 870/297–3726, (Nonreporting) **A**10 18
Primary Contact: Kim Skidmore, Chief Executive Officer
COO: Cathy Franks RNChief Operating Officer
CMO: Bethany Knight, M.D., Chief of Staff
CIO: Quentin Wildhagen, Systems Administrator
CHR: Crystal R Moody, Director Human Resources
CNO: Dana Hicks, Director of Nursing
Web address: www.cmcofic.org
**Control:** Other not-for-profit (including NFP Corporation) **Service:** General medical and surgical

| | |
|---|---|
| **Staffed Beds:** 25 | |

## CAMDEN—Ouachita County

★ **OUACHITA COUNTY MEDICAL CENTER (040050)**, 638 California Avenue SW, Zip 71701–4699, Mailing Address: P.O. Box 797, Zip 71711–0797; tel. 870/836–1000, (Nonreporting) **A**10 20 **F**3 4 5 7 11 13 15 18 20 22 26 29 31 34 35 40 41 43 45 50 57 59 62 63 64 69 70 75 76 79 81 85 87 89 93 100 102 107 108 110 111 114 115 119 127 129 130 132 133 135 144 146 147 148 149 150 152 154
Primary Contact: Peggy L. Abbott, President and Chief Executive Officer
CFO: Robert Anders, Chief Financial Officer
CIO: Kenny Frachiseur, Chief Information Officer
CHR: Mary Bridges, Director Human Resources
CNO: Diane Isaacs, Director of Nursing
Web address: www.ouachitamedcenter.com
**Control:** Other not-for-profit (including NFP Corporation) **Service:** General medical and surgical

| | |
|---|---|
| **Staffed Beds:** 67 **Admissions:** 1876 **Census:** 13 **Outpatient Visits:** 47776 **Births:** 236 **Total Expense ($000):** 33120 **Payroll Expense ($000):** 14055 **Personnel:** 372 | |

**OUACHITA MEDICAL CENTER** See Ouachita County Medical Center

## CLARKSVILLE—Johnson County

**JOHNSON REGIONAL HOSPITAL** See Johnson Regional Medical Center

★ **JOHNSON REGIONAL MEDICAL CENTER (040002)**, 1100 East Poplar Street, Zip 72830–4419, Mailing Address: P.O. Box 738, Zip 72830–0738; tel. 479/754–5454, (Nonreporting) **A**10 **F**3 7 11 13 15 29 34 35 40 45 50 51 57 62 64 68 70 75 76 77 79 81 85 90 91 93 96 98 103 104 107 108 110 111 115 119 129 130 131 132 147 148 153 154
Primary Contact: Michael A. Dorsey, FACHE, Chief Executive Officer
CFO: Joe Jeans, CPA, Chief Financial Officer
CIO: Andy Altenburger, Chief Information Officer
CHR: Amy Powell, Director Human Resources
CNO: Nancy Hill, R.N., Chief Nursing Officer
Web address: www.jrmc.com
**Control:** Other not-for-profit (including NFP Corporation) **Service:** General medical and surgical

| | |
|---|---|
| **Staffed Beds:** 90 **Admissions:** 2145 **Census:** 30 **Outpatient Visits:** 48498 **Births:** 308 **Total Expense ($000):** 39038 **Payroll Expense ($000):** 18559 **Personnel:** 331 | |

## CLINTON—Van Buren County

**OZARK HEALTH MEDICAL CENTER (041313)**, Highway 65 South, Zip 72031–9045, Mailing Address: P.O. Box 206, Zip 72031–0206; tel. 501/745–7000, (Total facility includes 118 beds in nursing home–type unit) (Nonreporting) **A**10 18 **F**3 11 15 28 29 34 35 40 43 45 57 59 62 64 65 75 79 81 93 107 110 111 114 119 128 132 133 146 156
Primary Contact: David Deaton, FACHE, Chief Executive Officer
CFO: Mike Deaton, Chief Financial Officer
CMO: Steve Schoettle, M.D., Chief Medical Staff
CHR: Sally D Cassell, Manager Human Resources
CNO: Edna Prosser, Chief Nursing Officer
Web address: www.ozarkhealthinc.com
**Control:** Other not-for-profit (including NFP Corporation) **Service:** General medical and surgical

| | |
|---|---|
| **Staffed Beds:** 143 **Admissions:** 635 **Census:** 86 **Outpatient Visits:** 26565 **Births:** 0 **Total Expense ($000):** 28810 **Payroll Expense ($000):** 13091 **Personnel:** 285 | |

**VAN BUREN COUNTY MEM HOSPITAL** See Ozark Health Medical Center

## CONWAY—Faulkner County

✠ **BAPTIST HEALTH MEDICAL CENTER - CONWAY (040154)**, 1555 Exchange Avenue, Zip 72032–7824; tel. 501/585–2000, (Nonreporting) **A**1 3 10 **F**3 13 15 18 20 22 28 29 30 35 40 43 45 46 51 59 60 64 68 70 74 76 77 79 81 85 87 91 96 107 108 110 111 115 118 119 126 130 133 135 147 148 149 **S** Baptist Health, Little Rock, AR
Primary Contact: Tim Bowen, Vice President and Administrator
CNO: Stephana Loyd, Vice President, Chief Nursing Officer
Web address: www.baptist-health.com/location/baptist-health-medical-center-conway-conway
**Control:** Other not-for-profit (including NFP Corporation) **Service:** General medical and surgical

| | |
|---|---|
| **Staffed Beds:** 111 **Admissions:** 3727 **Census:** 33 **Outpatient Visits:** 45906 **Births:** 337 **Total Expense ($000):** 85541 **Payroll Expense ($000):** 20580 **Personnel:** 359 | |

☐ **CONWAY BEHAVIORAL HEALTH HOSPITAL (044022)**, 2255 Sturgis Road, Zip 72034–8029; tel. 501/858–3048, (Nonreporting) **A**1 **S** Acadia Healthcare Company, Inc., Franklin, TN
Primary Contact: Anthony Guild, Chief Executive Officer
CFO: Kimberly Hibschman, Chief Financial Officer
CMO: Thomas Stinnett, M.D., Chief Medical Officer
CHR: Levi J. King, Director Human Resources
CNO: Beth Williams, R.N., Chief Nursing Officer
Web address: www.conwaybh.com
**Control:** Corporation, Investor–owned (for–profit) **Service:** Psychiatric

| | |
|---|---|
| **Staffed Beds:** 80 | |

---

| Hospital, Medicare Provider Number, Address, Telephone, Approval, Facility, and Physician Codes, Health Care System | | |
|---|---|---|
| ★ American Hospital Association (AHA) membership | ○ Healthcare Facilities Accreditation Program | ⇑ Center for Improvement in Healthcare Quality Accreditation |
| ☐ The Joint Commission accreditation | ◇ DNV Healthcare Inc. accreditation | △ Commission on Accreditation of Rehabilitation Facilities (CARF) accreditation |

**CONWAY REGIONAL HOSPITAL** See Conway Regional Medical Center

☒ **CONWAY REGIONAL MEDICAL CENTER (040029)**, 2302 College Avenue, Zip 72034–6297; tel. 501/329–3831, (Nonreporting) **A**1 3 10 **F**3 8 11 12 13 15 17 18 20 22 24 26 28 29 30 31 34 35 37 40 43 45 46 49 50 51 53 56 57 59 61 62 64 70 74 75 76 77 78 79 81 82 85 87 89 97 98 103 104 107 108 110 111 115 118 119 126 127 129 130 131 135 144 146 147 148 149 154 156 157 **P**5 8
Primary Contact: Matthew Troup, FACHE, President and Chief Executive Officer
COO: Alan Finley, Chief Operating Officer
CFO: Troy Brooks, Chief Financial Officer
CMO: James France, M.D., Chief of Staff
CHR: Richard Tyler, Corporate Director Human Resources
CNO: Jacquelyn Wilkerson, R.N., Chief Nursing Officer
Web address: www.conwayregional.org
**Control**: Other not–for–profit (including NFP Corporation) **Service**: General medical and surgical

**Staffed Beds**: 150 **Admissions**: 8261 **Census**: 95 **Outpatient Visits**: 120517 **Births**: 1655 **Total Expense ($000)**: 190328 **Payroll Expense ($000)**: 75267 **Personnel**: 1281

**CONWAY REGIONAL REHAB HOSPITAL** See Conway Regional Rehabilitation Hospital

**CONWAY REGIONAL REHABILITATION HOSPITAL (043033)**, 2210 Robinson Avenue, Zip 72034–4943; tel. 501/932–3500, (Nonreporting) **A**10 **F**3 29 90 91 96 130 132 143 149 154 156 **P**8
Primary Contact: Alicia Kunert, MS, R.N., Executive Director
COO: Christy Scroggin, Director Operations and Human Resources
CMO: Roy Denton, M.D., Chief Medical Officer
CNO: Darrallyn Webb, R.N., Chief Nursing Officer
Web address: www.conwayregional.org
**Control**: Partnership, Investor–owned (for–profit) **Service**: Rehabilitation

**Staffed Beds**: 26 **Admissions**: 424 **Census**: 15 **Outpatient Visits**: 0 **Births**: 0 **Total Expense ($000)**: 5681 **Payroll Expense ($000)**: 1714 **Personnel**: 34

★ **ASHLEY COUNTY MEDICAL CENTER (041323)**, 1015 Unity Road, Zip 71635–9443, Mailing Address: P.O. Box 400, Zip 71635–0400; tel. 870/364–4111, (Nonreporting) **A**5 10 18 **F**3 11 13 15 18 29 31 34 35 40 45 50 53 56 57 59 62 64 68 70 75 76 77 78 79 81 85 93 98 100 103 104 107 108 110 111 115 119 127 129 130 132 133 148 153 154 156
Primary Contact: Phillip K. Gilmore, Ph.D., FACHE, Chief Executive Officer
CFO: Bill Couch, Chief Financial Officer
CMO: Brad Walsh, M.D., Chief of Staff
CIO: Dan Austin, Manager Data Processing
CHR: Shirley White, Director Human Resources
CNO: Emily Bendinelli, Director of Nurses
Web address: www.acmconline.org
**Control**: Other not–for–profit (including NFP Corporation) **Service**: General medical and surgical

**Staffed Beds**: 33 **Admissions**: 811 **Census**: 8 **Outpatient Visits**: 32176 **Births**: 158 **Total Expense ($000)**: 42636 **Payroll Expense ($000)**: 18069 **Personnel**: 337

**ASHLEY MEMORIAL HOSPITAL** See Ashley County Medical Center

**CHAMBERS MEMORIAL HOSPITAL (040011)**, 719 Detroit Avenue, Zip 72833–9607, Mailing Address: P.O. Box 639, Zip 72833–0639; tel. 479/495–2241, (Nonreporting) **A**10 20 **F**3 11 15 29 34 35 40 43 45 57 59 62 66 75 77 81 87 93 96 97 98 103 107 110 114 119 128 130 133 154 **P**6
Primary Contact: Mike McCoy, Chief Executive Officer
CMO: Philip Tippin, M.D., Chief Medical Officer
CIO: Ken Masters, Director Information Technology
CNO: Michele Shoptaw, Director of Nursing
Web address: www.chambershospital.com
**Control**: Other not–for–profit (including NFP Corporation) **Service**: General medical and surgical

**Staffed Beds**: 42 **Admissions**: 1638 **Census**: 19 **Outpatient Visits**: 39188 **Births**: 0 **Total Expense ($000)**: 20609 **Payroll Expense ($000)**: 10135 **Personnel**: 225

**YELL COUNTY HOSPITAL** See Chambers Memorial Hospital

**DARDANELLE HOSPITAL YELL COUNTY** See Dardanelle Regional Medical Center

**DARDANELLE REGIONAL MEDICAL CENTER (041302)**, 200 North Third Street, Zip 72834–3802, Mailing Address: P.O. Box 578, Zip 72834–0578; tel. 479/229–4677, (Nonreporting) **A**10 18
Primary Contact: Alan Finley, Chief Executive Officer
CMO: William P Scott, M.D., Chief of Staff
CHR: Kathy Hastin-Hulsey, Administrative Assistant Human Resources
Web address: www.https://www.dardanelleregional.org
**Control**: Corporation, Investor–owned (for–profit) **Service**: General medical and surgical

**Staffed Beds**: 35

**DEWITT CITY HOSPITAL** See Dewitt Hospital

★ **DEWITT HOSPITAL (041314)**, 1641 South Whitehead Drive, Zip 72042–9481, Mailing Address: P.O. Box 32, Zip 72042–0032; tel. 870/946–3571, (Total facility includes 40 beds in nursing home–type unit) (Nonreporting) **A**10 18 **F**3 7 11 14 15 34 40 43 55 57 59 65 87 90 107 111 119 127 128 129 130 133 145 149
Primary Contact: Brian F. Miller, Chief Executive Officer
CFO: Brandon Cotten, Chief Financial Officer
CMO: Stan Burleson, M.D., Chief Medical Staff
CIO: Brian Brooks, Information Manager
CHR: Alisa Brown, Administrative Assistant
CNO: Jerrilyn Horton, R.N., Chief Nursing Officer
Web address: www.dhnh.org
**Control**: Other not–for–profit (including NFP Corporation) **Service**: General medical and surgical

**Staffed Beds**: 65 **Admissions**: 210 **Census**: 36 **Outpatient Visits**: 8180 **Births**: 0 **Total Expense ($000)**: 11173 **Payroll Expense ($000)**: 6310 **Personnel**: 91

**DELTA MEMORIAL HOSPITAL (041326)**, 811 South Highway 65, Zip 71639–3006, Mailing Address: P.O. Box 887, Zip 71639–0887; tel. 870/382–4303, (Nonreporting) **A**5 10 18
Primary Contact: Ashley Anthony, R.N., Chief Executive Officer
CMO: Thomas Lewellen, D.O., Chief of Staff
CIO: Chris McTigrit, Manager Information Technology
CHR: Doris Fortenberry, Coordinator Human Resources
CNO: Dana Miles, Chief Nursing Officer and Chief Clinical Officer
Web address: www.deltamem.org
**Control**: Other not–for–profit (including NFP Corporation) **Service**: General medical and surgical

**Staffed Beds**: 25

☒ **MEDICAL CENTER OF SOUTH ARKANSAS (040088)**, 700 West Grove Street, Zip 71730–4416; tel. 870/863–2000, (Nonreporting) **A**1 3 5 10 **F**3 11 13 15 17 18 20 22 24 29 31 34 40 41 43 45 46 50 56 57 59 64 65 70 73 76 78 79 80 81 82 85 89 90 93 96 102 107 108 110 111 115 118 119 130 146 147 149 152 **P**7 8 **S** Community Health Systems, Inc., Franklin, TN
Primary Contact: Scott Street, Chief Executive Officer
CFO: Dale Maddox, Chief Financial Officer
CMO: Misty Kneeland, Chief Medical Officer
CIO: Rob Robison, Director Information Technology
CHR: LaKeitha Davis, Director Human Resources
CNO: Kathy Degenstein Gartman, Chief Nursing Officer
Web address: www.themedcenter.net
**Control**: Corporation, Investor–owned (for–profit) **Service**: General medical and surgical

**Staffed Beds**: 121 **Admissions**: 3683 **Census**: 42 **Outpatient Visits**: 64487 **Births**: 647 **Total Expense ($000)**: 63903 **Payroll Expense ($000)**: 22995 **Personnel**: 378

AR

## EUREKA SPRINGS—Carroll County

**EUREKA SPRINGS HOSPITAL (041304)**, 24 Norris Street, Zip 72632–3541; tel. 479/253–7400, (Nonreporting) **A**10 18 **F**3 29 34 40 43 47 57 83 84 91 93 107 115 119 128 133 148 154 **S** Allegiance Health Management, Shreveport, LA
Primary Contact: Kathy Hall, Interim Chief Executive Officer
CFO: Taylor Smith, Chief Financial Officer
CMO: John House, M.D., Chief of Staff
CIO: Drew Wood, Director Information Technology
CHR: Jodi Smith, Administrative Assistant Human Resources
Web address: www.eurekaspringshospital.com
**Control**: Corporation, Investor–owned (for–profit) **Service**: General medical and surgical

**Staffed Beds**: 15 **Admissions**: 179 **Census**: 2 **Outpatient Visits**: 4794
**Births**: 0 **Total Expense ($000)**: 7636 **Payroll Expense ($000)**: 2740
**Personnel**: 65

## FAYETTEVILLE—Washington County

☒ **ENCOMPASS HEALTH REHABILITATION HOSPITAL, A PARTNER OF WASHINGTON REGIONAL (043032)**, 153 East Monte Painter Drive, Zip 72703–4002; tel. 479/444–2200, (Nonreporting) **A**1 10 **S** Encompass Health Corporation, Birmingham, AL
Primary Contact: Kevin J. Clement, Chief Executive Officer
CFO: Corey Thomason, Controller
CMO: Borian Matinchev, M.D., Medical Director
CNO: Miriam Irvin, CNO
Web address: www.https://www.encompasshealth.com/fayettevillerehab
**Control**: Corporation, Investor–owned (for–profit) **Service**: Rehabilitation

**Staffed Beds**: 80

**HEALTHSOUTH REHABILITATION HOSPITAL** See Encompass Health Rehabilitation Hospital, A Partner of Washington Regional

☒ **NORTHWEST HEALTH PHYSICIANS' SPECIALTY HOSPITAL (040152)**, 3873 North Parkview Drive, Zip 72703–6286; tel. 479/571–7070, (Nonreporting) **A**1 3 10 **F**3 12 29 40 45 68 79 81 82 85 86 107 111 114 119 131 135 **S** Community Health Systems, Inc., Franklin, TN
Primary Contact: Denten Park, Chief Executive Officer
CFO: Jermaine Bucknor, Chief Financial Officer
CNO: Tim Kimball, Chief Nursing Officer
Web address: www.pshfay.com
**Control**: Corporation, Investor–owned (for–profit) **Service**: Surgical

**Staffed Beds**: 20 **Admissions**: 1328 **Census**: 7 **Outpatient Visits**: 12698
**Births**: 0 **Total Expense ($000)**: 37640 **Payroll Expense ($000)**: 7615
**Personnel**: 118

**PHYSICIANS' SPECIALTY HOSPITAL** See Northwest Health Physicians' Specialty Hospital

☒ **SPRINGWOODS BEHAVIORAL HEALTH HOSPITAL (044019)**, 1955 West Truckers Drive, Zip 72704–5637; tel. 479/973–6000, (Nonreporting) **A**1 10 **F**3 29 34 35 38 56 57 98 99 100 103 105 130 132 134 135 143 144 147 149 150 152 153 157 **S** Universal Health Services, Inc., King of Prussia, PA
Primary Contact: Jordon Babcock, Chief Executive Officer
Web address: www.springwoodsbehavioral.com
**Control**: Corporation, Investor–owned (for–profit) **Service**: Psychiatric

**Staffed Beds**: 80 **Admissions**: 2393 **Census**: 42 **Outpatient Visits**: 2709
**Births**: 0 **Total Expense ($000)**: 16517 **Payroll Expense ($000)**: 7334
**Personnel**: 188

☐ **VANTAGE POINT OF NORTHWEST ARKANSAS (044004)**, 4253 North Crossover Road, Zip 72703–4596; tel. 479/521–5731, (Nonreporting) **A**1 10 **S** Acadia Healthcare Company, Inc., Franklin, TN
Primary Contact: Megan Wedgworth, Chief Executive Officer
CFO: Ben Winbery, Chief Financial Officer
CMO: Norman Snyder, M.D., Medical Director
CIO: Margaret Brown, Director Medical Records
CHR: Kathy Vickers, Director Human Resources
CNO: Suzette Branscum, Director of Nursing
Web address: www.vantagepointnwa.com
**Control**: Corporation, Investor–owned (for–profit) **Service**: Psychiatric

**Staffed Beds**: 114

**VETERANS ADM MEDICAL CENTER** See Veterans Health Care System of The Ozarks

☒ **VETERANS HEALTH CARE SYSTEM OF THE OZARKS**, 1100 North College Avenue, Zip 72703–1944; tel. 479/443–4301, (Nonreporting) **A**1 3 5 **F**3 5 29 30 31 34 35 36 38 39 40 45 57 59 60 62 63 64 70 74 75 77 78 79 81 82 83 84 86 87 93 94 97 98 100 101 102 104 105 106 107 111 115 118 119 127 129 130 132 135 143 146 147 148 149 151 152 153 154 156 157 158 **S** Department of Veterans Affairs, Washington, DC
Primary Contact: Kelvin L. Parks, Interim Director
CMO: Bonnie Baker, M.D., Chief Medical Services
CIO: Michael Gracie, Chief Information Officer
CHR: Kathryn L Barker, Chief Human Resources Management
Web address: www.fayettevillear.va.gov
**Control**: Veterans Affairs, Government, federal **Service**: General medical and surgical

**Staffed Beds**: 52 **Admissions**: 1966 **Census**: 27 **Outpatient Visits**: 604747
**Births**: 0 **Personnel**: 1178

**VISTA HEALTH** See Vantage Point of Northwest Arkansas

☒ **WASHINGTON REGIONAL MEDICAL CENTER (040004)**, 3215 North Hills Boulevard, Zip 72703–4424; tel. 479/463–1000, (Nonreporting) **A**1 3 5 10 **F**3 11 13 17 18 20 22 24 26 28 29 30 31 34 35 40 43 45 48 49 50 56 57 58 59 60 62 63 64 68 70 71 72 74 75 76 77 78 79 80 81 84 85 86 87 93 100 102 107 108 111 115 119 126 129 130 132 135 141 146 147 148 149 154 157 **P**1 6
Primary Contact: J. Larry. Shackelford, CPA, President and Chief Executive Officer
COO: Birch G. Wright, Chief Operating Officer and Administrator
CFO: Dan Eckels, Chief Financial Officer
CMO: David Ratcliff, M.D., Chief Medical Affairs
CIO: Becky Magee, Chief Information Officer
CHR: Laurie Morrow, Executive Director Human Resources
CNO: Meredith Green, Senior Vice President and Chief Nursing Officer
Web address: www.wregional.com
**Control**: Other not–for–profit (including NFP Corporation) **Service**: General medical and surgical

**Staffed Beds**: 366 **Admissions**: 16468 **Census**: 173 **Outpatient Visits**: 159635 **Births**: 2502 **Total Expense ($000)**: 303189 **Payroll Expense ($000)**: 115335 **Personnel**: 2766

## FORDYCE—Dallas County

**DALLAS COUNTY HOSPITAL** See Dallas County Medical Center

★ **DALLAS COUNTY MEDICAL CENTER (041317)**, 201 Clifton Street, Zip 71742–3099; tel. 870/352–6300, (Nonreporting) **A**10 18
Primary Contact: Kenneth Sanders, Administrator and Chief Executive Officer
CFO: Billie Launius, Director Business Finance
CMO: Michael Payne, M.D., Chief of Staff
CHR: Audrey Allen, Coordinator Benefits
CNO: Hollie Raney, Director of Nursing
Web address: www.dallascountymedicalcenter.com
**Control**: County, Government, Nonfederal **Service**: General medical and surgical

**Staffed Beds**: 25

## FORREST CITY—St. Francis County

**FORREST CITY MED CENTER** See Forrest City Medical Center

☐ **FORREST CITY MEDICAL CENTER (040019)**, 1601 Newcastle Road, Zip 72335–2218; tel. 870/261–0000, (Nonreporting) **A**1 10 20 **F**3 7 13 15 29 30 34 40 43 45 50 56 57 70 76 77 81 85 87 89 91 92 93 98 100 102 103 107 108 109 110 111 112 114 119 129 130 135 145 146 147 148 154 **S** Quorum Health, Brentwood, TN
Primary Contact: John Ballard, Ph.D., FACHE, Chief Executive Officer
CFO: Misty Gates, Chief Financial Officer
CMO: James DeRossitt, M.D., Chief of Staff
CIO: David Shaw, Director Information Technology
CHR: Sherry McLaughlin, Director Human Resources
CNO: Leslie Harris, MSN, R.N., Chief Nursing Officer
Web address: www.forrestcitymedicalcenter.com
**Control**: Corporation, Investor–owned (for–profit) **Service**: General medical and surgical

**Staffed Beds**: 55 **Admissions**: 2305 **Census**: 21 **Outpatient Visits**: 36802
**Births**: 783 **Total Expense ($000)**: 30872 **Payroll Expense ($000)**: 11018
**Personnel**: 222

---

**Hospital, Medicare Provider Number, Address, Telephone, Approval, Facility, and Physician Codes, Health Care System**

★ American Hospital Association (AHA) membership
☐ The Joint Commission accreditation
○ Healthcare Facilities Accreditation Program
◇ DNV Healthcare Inc. accreditation
⇑ Center for Improvement in Healthcare Quality Accreditation
△ Commission on Accreditation of Rehabilitation Facilities (CARF) accreditation

**AR**

### FORT SMITH—Sebastian County

⊞ **BAPTIST HEALTH - FORT SMITH (040055)**, 1001 Towson Avenue, Zip 72901–4921, Mailing Address: P.O. Box 2406, Zip 72917–7006; tel. 479/441–4000, (Nonreporting) **A**1 3 10 19 **F**3 8 12 13 14 15 17 18 20 22 24 26 28 29 30 31 34 35 40 43 45 46 47 48 49 50 51 53 54 56 58 59 60 64 67 68 70 72 74 75 76 77 78 79 81 82 85 86 87 89 93 97 98 103 107 108 109 110 111 112 113 114 115 116 117 119 120 121 122 123 124 126 129 130 144 146 147 148 154 156 **P**8 **S** Baptist Health, Little Rock, AR
Primary Contact: Kimberly J. Miller, FACHE, President, Western Region
COO: Aimee Arzoumanian, Chief Operating Officer
CMO: Katherine Irish-Clardy, M.D., Chief Medical Officer
CIO: Tom Sallis, Director Information Systems
CHR: Robert Freeman, Director Human Resources
CNO: Stephanie Whitaker, Chief Nursing Officer
Web address: www.https://www.sparkshealth.com/
**Control**: Other not–for–profit (including NFP Corporation) **Service**: General medical and surgical

Staffed Beds: 281 Admissions: 13421 Census: 168 Outpatient Visits: 181363 Births: 466 Total Expense ($000): 236239 Payroll Expense ($000): 69237 Personnel: 1087

☐ **CHRISTUS DUBUIS HOSPITAL OF FORT SMITH (042008)**, 7301 Rogers Avenue, 4th Floor, Zip 72903–4100; tel. 479/314–4900, (Nonreporting) **A**1 10 **S** LHC Group, Lafayette, LA
Primary Contact: Nancy Owens, Administrator
CFO: Paul Veillon, CPA, Chief Financial Officer
Web address: www.christusdubuis.org/fortsmith
**Control**: Church operated, Nongovernment, not–for–profit **Service**: Acute long–term care hospital

Staffed Beds: 25

**CHRISTUS DUBUIS HOSPITAL OF FORT SMITH** See Christus Dubuis Hospital of Fort Smith

⊞ **ENCOMPASSS HEALTH REHABILITATION HOSPITAL OF FORT SMITH (043028)**, 1401 South 'J' Street, Zip 72901–5155; tel. 479/785–3300, (Nonreporting) **A**1 10 **F**29 30 34 77 90 91 94 95 96 130 132 149 157 **S** Encompass Health Corporation, Birmingham, AL
Primary Contact: Dawn Watts, Chief Executive Officer
CFO: Brenda Forbes, Controller
CMO: Cygnet Schroeder, D.O., Medical Director
CHR: S Janette Daniels, Director Human Resources
Web address: www.healthsouthfortsmith.com
**Control**: Corporation, Investor–owned (for–profit) **Service**: Rehabilitation

Staffed Beds: 60 Admissions: 1522 Census: 49 Outpatient Visits: 0 Births: 0 Total Expense ($000): 16586 Payroll Expense ($000): 9765 Personnel: 111

**HEALTHSOUTH REHABILITATION HOSPITAL OF FORT SMITH** See Encompasss Health Rehabilitation Hospital of Fort Smith

⊞ **MERCY HOSPITAL FORT SMITH (040062)**, 7301 Rogers Avenue, Zip 72903–4189, Mailing Address: P.O. Box 17000, Zip 72917–7000; tel. 479/314–6000, (Includes MERCY ORTHOPEDIC HOSPITAL FORT SMITH, Mailing address: 3601 South 79th Street, Fort Smith, Arkansas, Zip 72903–6255; tel. 479/709–8500; Ryan T. Gehrig, FACHE, President), (Nonreporting) **A**1 2 3 10 13 19 **F**3 12 13 15 18 20 22 24 26 28 29 30 31 32 34 35 36 38 40 42 43 44 45 48 49 50 53 54 56 57 58 59 60 61 62 63 64 65 68 70 71 72 74 75 76 77 78 79 81 82 83 84 85 86 87 89 90 91 93 95 96 102 107 108 109 110 111 114 115 116 117 119 120 121 123 124 129 130 131 134 135 143 146 147 148 149 154 156 157 **P**8 **S** Mercy, Chesterfield, MO
Primary Contact: Ryan T. Gehrig, FACHE, President
COO: Ryan Christopher Geib, Chief Operating Officer
CFO: Greta Wilcher, Senior Vice President and Chief Financial Officer
CMO: David Hunton, M.D., Chief Medical Officer
CHR: Bryan Brown, Executive Director
CNO: Marianne Rataj, Chief Nursing Officer
Web address: www.mercy.net/fortsmithar
**Control**: Church operated, Nongovernment, not–for–profit **Service**: General medical and surgical

Staffed Beds: 356 Admissions: 16992 Census: 201 Outpatient Visits: 307359 Births: 2441 Total Expense ($000): 313166 Payroll Expense ($000): 113576 Personnel: 1706

⊞ **SELECT SPECIALTY HOSPITAL-FORT SMITH (042006)**, 1001 Towson Avenue, 6 Central, Zip 72901–4921; tel. 479/441–3960, (Nonreporting) **A**1 10 **F**1 3 29 34 45 46 57 74 75 78 79 94 148 **S** Select Medical Corporation, Mechanicsburg, PA
Primary Contact: Shannon Grams, Chief Executive Officer
Web address: www.https://fortsmith.selectspecialtyhospitals.com/
**Control**: Corporation, Investor–owned (for–profit) **Service**: Acute long–term care hospital

Staffed Beds: 34 Admissions: 264 Census: 18 Outpatient Visits: 0 Births: 0 Total Expense ($000): 10079 Payroll Expense ($000): 4475 Personnel: 66

**SPARKS REGIONAL MEDICAL CENTER** See Baptist Health - Fort Smith

**ST. EDWARD MERCY MEDICAL CENTER** See Mercy Hospital Fort Smith

### GRAVETTE—Benton County

**OZARKS COMMUNITY HOSPITAL (041331)**, 1101 Jackson Street Sw, Zip 72736–9121; tel. 479/787–5291, (Nonreporting) **A**10 18 **F**1 2 3 29 34 35 36 40 44 45 50 56 57 59 64 65 74 75 77 79 81 82 85 87 90 91 93 96 97 100 104 107 111 115 119 127 128 129 130 131 133 143 148 153 154 157
Primary Contact: Paul Taylor, Administrator
Web address: www.ochonline.com/
**Control**: Corporation, Investor–owned (for–profit) **Service**: General medical and surgical

Staffed Beds: 25 Admissions: 561 Census: 19 Outpatient Visits: 101901 Births: 0 Total Expense ($000): 50572 Payroll Expense ($000): 19898 Personnel: 260

### HARRISON—Boone County

**NORTH ARKANSAS MEDICAL CENTER** See North Arkansas Regional Medical Center

★ **NORTH ARKANSAS REGIONAL MEDICAL CENTER (040017)**, 620 North Main Street, Zip 72601–2911; tel. 870/414–4000, (Nonreporting) **A**10 **F**3 7 11 13 15 17 18 28 29 30 31 32 34 35 39 40 41 43 45 50 53 56 57 59 62 63 64 65 68 70 73 75 76 77 78 79 81 85 86 87 89 93 97 98 102 103 107 108 110 111 114 115 118 119 120 121 127 129 130 131 132 135 144 146 147 148 149 154 156 157 **P**8
Primary Contact: Vincent Leist, President and Chief Executive Officer
CFO: Deana Thomas, Vice President Finance and Chief Financial Officer
CIO: William J Bogle, Director Information Systems
CNO: Sammie Cribbs, Vice President Clinical Services and Chief Nursing Officer
Web address: www.narmc.com
**Control**: Other not–for–profit (including NFP Corporation) **Service**: General medical and surgical

Staffed Beds: 113 Admissions: 4543 Census: 28 Outpatient Visits: 109391 Births: 547 Total Expense ($000): 103186 Payroll Expense ($000): 41423 Personnel: 816

### HEBER SPRINGS—Cleburne County

★ **BAPTIST HEALTH MEDICAL CENTER-HEBER SPRINGS (041312)**, 1800 Bypass Road, Zip 72543–9135; tel. 501/887–3000, (Nonreporting) **A**10 18 **F**3 8 11 15 28 29 31 34 35 40 43 45 48 50 57 59 64 68 75 77 78 79 81 85 93 96 97 102 107 110 111 115 116 117 118 119 127 129 131 133 143 146 149 154 156 157 **S** Baptist Health, Little Rock, AR
Primary Contact: Kevin L. Storey, Vice President and Administrator
Web address: www.baptist-health.com/maps-directions/bhmc-heber-springs
**Control**: Other not–for–profit (including NFP Corporation) **Service**: General medical and surgical

Staffed Beds: 25 Admissions: 687 Census: 7 Outpatient Visits: 37952 Births: 0 Total Expense ($000): 22238 Payroll Expense ($000): 7715 Personnel: 151

**BAPTIST MEDICAL CENTER** See Baptist Health Medical Center-Heber Springs

### HELENA—Phillips County

☐ **HELENA REGIONAL MEDICAL CENTER (040085)**, 1801 Martin Luther King Drive, Zip 72342, Mailing Address: P.O. Box 788, Zip 72342–0788; tel. 870/338–5800, (Nonreporting) **A**1 10 20 **F**3 11 13 15 29 34 40 50 59 62 70 76 81 86 87 89 91 93 97 107 108 111 113 114 119 129 130 132 133 135 145 146 147 148 **S** Quorum Health, Brentwood, TN
Primary Contact: Amy Rice, Chief Executive Officer
CFO: Amy Rice, Chief Financial Officer
CIO: Christopher Hunt, Director, Information Technologies, FISO
CHR: Juril Fonzie, Director Human Resources
CNO: Steven W. Brackeen, Chief Nursing Officer
Web address: www.helenarmc.com
**Control**: Corporation, Investor–owned (for–profit) **Service**: General medical and surgical

Staffed Beds: 45 Admissions: 1132 Census: 8 Outpatient Visits: 39585 Births: 204 Total Expense ($000): 23994 Payroll Expense ($000): 9444 Personnel: 139

*Many Facility Codes have changed. Please refer to the AHA Guide Code Chart.*

## HOPE—Hempstead County

⚘ **MEDICAL PARK HOSPITAL** See Wadley Regional Medical Center at Hope

⚘ **WADLEY REGIONAL MEDICAL CENTER AT HOPE (040153)**, 2001 South Main Street, Zip 71801–8194; tel. 870/722–3800, (Nonreporting) **A**10 21 **F**3 15 18 29 34 35 40 50 56 57 59 64 70 86 93 98 103 107 110 111 114 119 127 130 **S** Steward Health Care System, LLC, Dallas, TX
Primary Contact: Thomas D. Gilbert, FACHE, Chief Executive Officer
CFO: Bonny Sorensen, Chief Financial Officer
CIO: Matt Kesterson, Director Information Services
CHR: Debby Butler, Director Human Resources
CNO: Shelly Strayhorn, R.N., Chief Nursing Officer
Web address: www.wadleyhealthathope.com
**Control:** Corporation, Investor–owned (for–profit) **Service:** General medical and surgical

**Staffed Beds:** 79 **Admissions:** 879 **Census:** 12 **Outpatient Visits:** 23370 **Births:** 0 **Total Expense ($000):** 14191 **Payroll Expense ($000):** 6167 **Personnel:** 122

## HOT SPRINGS—Garland County

⊞ **CHI ST. VINCENT HOT SPRINGS (040026)**, 300 Werner Street, Zip 71913–6406; tel. 501/622–1000, (Nonreporting) **A**1 2 5 10 19 **F**3 11 12 13 15 18 20 22 24 26 28 29 30 31 34 35 37 38 40 43 46 47 49 50 56 57 59 62 64 66 68 69 70 71 74 75 76 77 78 79 81 82 85 86 87 89 93 97 102 107 108 110 111 114 115 116 117 118 119 120 121 123 124 130 132 135 146 147 148 154 156 157 **P**6 **S** CommonSpirit Health, Chicago, IL
Primary Contact: Douglas B. Ross, M.D., President
CFO: Shawn Barnett, Senior Vice President and Chief Financial Officer
CIO: Tracy Kirby, Assistant Vice President Business Relationship Management
CNO: Bryan Williams, R.N., Vice President Patient Care Services
Web address: www.chistvincent.com/Hospitals/st-vincent-hot-springs
**Control:** Church operated, Nongovernment, not–for–profit **Service:** General medical and surgical

**Staffed Beds:** 241 **Admissions:** 11578 **Census:** 137 **Outpatient Visits:** 191160 **Births:** 987 **Total Expense ($000):** 193157 **Payroll Expense ($000):** 68237 **Personnel:** 1042

⊞ **CHI ST. VINCENT HOT SPRINGS REHABILITATION HOSPITAL (043035)**, 1636 Higdon Ferry Road, Zip 71913–6912; tel. 501/651–2000, (Nonreporting) **A**1 **S** Encompass Health Corporation, Birmingham, AL
Primary Contact: Janette Daniels, Chief Executive Officer
Web address: www.https://www.encompasshealth.com
**Control:** Corporation, Investor–owned (for–profit) **Service:** Rehabilitation

**Staffed Beds:** 40

⊞ △ **NATIONAL PARK MEDICAL CENTER (040078)**, 1910 Malvern Avenue, Zip 71901–7799; tel. 501/321–1000, (Nonreporting) **A**1 7 10 19 **F**3 11 12 13 15 17 18 20 22 24 28 29 30 31 34 35 40 45 46 47 48 49 56 57 59 64 70 73 74 75 76 78 79 81 85 87 89 90 92 98 103 107 110 111 115 119 124 130 131 132 146 148 156 **P**4 **S** LifePoint Health, Brentwood, TN
Primary Contact: Joann Ettien, R.N., MS, Interim Chief Executive Officer
COO: Brian Bell, Associate Administrator and Chief Operating Officer
CFO: Mike Long, Chief Financial Officer
CMO: Robert Breving, M.D., Chief of Staff
CIO: Brian Coffman, Director Information System
CHR: Tina Albright, Director Human Resources
CNO: Patsy Sue Crumpton, R.N., Chief Nursing Officer
Web address: www.nationalparkmedical.com
**Control:** Corporation, Investor–owned (for–profit) **Service:** General medical and surgical

**Staffed Beds:** 181 **Admissions:** 7018 **Census:** 104 **Outpatient Visits:** 56600 **Births:** 397 **Total Expense ($000):** 97836 **Payroll Expense ($000):** 33808 **Personnel:** 592

**NATIONAL PARK MEDICAL CTR** See National Park Medical Center

**ST. VINCENT HOSPITAL HOT SPRINGS** See Chi St. Vincent Hot Springs

## HOT SPRINGS NATIONAL PARK—Garland County

**CHRISTUS DUBUIS HOSPITAL OF HOT SPRINGS** See Christus Dubuis Hospital of Hot Springs

⊞ **CHRISTUS DUBUIS HOSPITAL OF HOT SPRINGS (042004)**, 300 Werner Street, 3rd Floor East, Zip 71913–6406; tel. 501/609–4300, (Nonreporting) **A**1 10 **F**1 3 29 130 135 **P**8 **S** LHC Group, Lafayette, LA
Primary Contact: Kathy DeVore, R.N., Administrator
CFO: Paul Veillon, CPA, Chief Financial Officer
CIO: David Cook, Manager Information Systems
Web address: www.christusdubuis.org/hotsprings
**Control:** Partnership, Investor–owned (for–profit) **Service:** Acute long–term care hospital

**Staffed Beds:** 27 **Admissions:** 224 **Census:** 13 **Outpatient Visits:** 0 **Births:** 0 **Total Expense ($000):** 4727 **Payroll Expense ($000):** 3303 **Personnel:** 39

**LEVI ARTHRITIS HOSPITAL** See Levi Hospital

★ **LEVI HOSPITAL (040132)**, 300 Prospect Avenue, Zip 71901–4097; tel. 501/624–1281, (Nonreporting) **A**5 10 **F**3 40 57 59 64 93 98 102 104 130 131 132 153
Primary Contact: Patrick G. McCabe Jr, FACHE, President and Chief Executive Officer
CFO: Stuart Lisko, Vice President, Chief Financial Officer and Compliance Officer
CMO: P Ross Bandy, M.D., Chief Medical Officer and Chief of Staff
CIO: Stuart Lisko, Vice President, Chief Financial Officer and Compliance Officer
CHR: Susan Kramer, Director of Human Resources
CNO: Steven Boyd, R.N., Nurse Executive
Web address: www.levihospital.com
**Control:** Other not–for–profit (including NFP Corporation) **Service:** Psychiatric

**Staffed Beds:** 35 **Admissions:** 909 **Census:** 13 **Outpatient Visits:** 16833 **Births:** 0 **Total Expense ($000):** 8305 **Payroll Expense ($000):** 4448 **Personnel:** 95

## JONESBORO—Craighead County

**ARKANSAS CONTINUED CARE HOSPITAL (042013)**, 3024 Red Wolf Boulevard, Zip 72401–7415; tel. 870/819–4040, (Nonreporting) **A**22 **F**1 3 29 **S** Community Hospital Corporation, Plano, TX
Primary Contact: Vincent Gore, Chief Executive Officer
**Control:** Corporation, Investor–owned (for–profit) **Service:** Acute long–term care hospital

**Staffed Beds:** 44 **Admissions:** 222 **Census:** 18 **Outpatient Visits:** 0 **Births:** 0 **Total Expense ($000):** 11680 **Payroll Expense ($000):** 3824 **Personnel:** 52

⊞ **ENCOMPASS HEALTH REHABILITATION HOSPITAL OF JONESBORO (043029)**, 1201 Fleming Avenue, Zip 72401–4311, Mailing Address: P.O. Box 1680, Zip 72403–1680; tel. 870/932–0440, (Nonreporting) **A**1 10 **S** Encompass Health Corporation, Birmingham, AL
Primary Contact: Donna Harris, Chief Executive Officer
CFO: Allan Jones, Controller
CMO: Virendar Verma, M.D., Medical Director
CHR: Tammy Barley, Director, Human Resources
CNO: Becky Kimble, R.N., Chief Nursing Officer
Web address: www.https://www.encompasshealth.com/jonesbororehab
**Control:** Corporation, Investor–owned (for–profit) **Service:** Rehabilitation

**Staffed Beds:** 67

**Hospital, Medicare Provider Number, Address, Telephone, Approval, Facility, and Physician Codes, Health Care System**

★ American Hospital Association (AHA) membership
□ The Joint Commission accreditation
○ Healthcare Facilities Accreditation Program
◇ DNV Healthcare Inc. accreditation
⚘ Center for Improvement in Healthcare Quality Accreditation
△ Commission on Accreditation of Rehabilitation Facilities (CARF) accreditation

© 2021 AHA Guide    *Many Facility Codes have changed. Please refer to the AHA Guide Code Chart.*    Hospitals **A47**

**HEALTHSOUTH REHABILITATION HOSPITAL OF JONESBORO** See Encompass Health Rehabilitation Hospital of Jonesboro

☒ **NEA BAPTIST MEMORIAL HOSPITAL (040118)**, 4800 East Johnson Avenue, Zip 72401–8413; tel. 870/936–1000, (Nonreporting) **A**1 2 3 5 10 **F**3 11 12 13 15 17 18 20 22 24 26 28 29 30 31 34 39 40 43 45 46 48 49 57 58 59 60 74 75 76 77 78 79 81 82 84 85 86 87 90 93 96 97 107 108 110 111 115 119 120 121 123 124 126 129 130 135 146 148 **S** Baptist Memorial Health Care Corporation, Memphis, TN
Primary Contact: Samuel Lynd, Administrator and Chief Executive Officer
COO: Melanie Edens, Chief Operating Officer
CFO: Kyle Sanders, Chief Financial Officer
CMO: Stephen Woodruff, M.D., Chief Medical Officer
CIO: Terry Crider, Information Technology Site Manager
CHR: James Keller, Director Human Resources
CNO: Paula Grimes, R.N., MSN, Chief Nursing Officer
Web address: www.https://www.baptistonline.org/locations/nea
**Control**: Other not–for–profit (including NFP Corporation) **Service**: General medical and surgical

**Staffed Beds:** 228 **Admissions:** 12399 **Census:** 145 **Outpatient Visits:** 113572 **Births:** 1071 **Total Expense ($000):** 216007 **Payroll Expense ($000):** 61035 **Personnel:** 1040

**NEA MEDICAL CENTER** See Nea Baptist Memorial Hospital

**ST BERNARDS REGIONAL MED CTR** See St. Bernards Medical Center

☒ **ST. BERNARDS MEDICAL CENTER (040020)**, 225 East Jackson Avenue, Zip 72401–3119; tel. 870/207–4100, (Nonreporting) **A**1 2 3 5 10 13 19 **F**3 5 11 12 13 15 17 18 19 20 22 24 26 27 28 29 30 31 32 34 35 38 39 40 43 44 45 46 48 49 50 51 53 54 55 56 57 58 59 60 62 63 64 66 68 70 71 72 74 75 76 77 78 79 81 82 83 84 85 86 87 89 91 92 93 97 98 100 101 102 103 104 107 108 109 110 111 114 115 116 117 118 119 120 121 123 124 126 129 130 131 132 134 135 141 145 146 147 148 149 154 156 157
Primary Contact: Michael K. Givens, FACHE, Administrator
CFO: Ben Barylske, Chief Financial Officer
CMO: Kasey Holder, M.D., Vice President Medical Affairs
CIO: Josh Melton, Chief Information Officer
CHR: Lori J. Smith, Vice President Human Resources
CNO: Angie B. Smith, Chief Nursing Officer
Web address: www.stbernards.info
**Control**: Church operated, Nongovernment, not–for–profit **Service**: General medical and surgical

**Staffed Beds:** 386 **Admissions:** 19075 **Census:** 238 **Outpatient Visits:** 360521 **Births:** 1379 **Total Expense ($000):** 359553

**LAKE VILLAGE—Chicot County**

**CHICOT MEMORIAL HOSPITAL** See Chicot Memorial Medical Center

★ **CHICOT MEMORIAL MEDICAL CENTER (041328)**, 2729 Highway 65 and 82 South, Zip 71653; tel. 870/265–5351, (Nonreporting) **A**10 18 **F**3 7 11 15 29 34 35 39 40 43 49 53 57 59 62 64 66 68 75 77 80 81 82 85 86 87 93 97 107 110 111 119 127 129 130 132 133 146 147 148 154 **P**6
Primary Contact: Luther J. Lewis, FACHE, Chief Executive Officer
CFO: Vicki Allen, Chief Financial Officer
CMO: Michael Bradley Mayfield, M.D., Chief of Staff
CIO: David Andrews, Manager Information Systems
CNO: Eric Selby, R.N., Chief Nursing Officer
Web address: www.chicotmemorial.com
**Control**: Other not–for–profit (including NFP Corporation) **Service**: General medical and surgical

**Staffed Beds:** 25 **Admissions:** 572 **Census:** 9 **Outpatient Visits:** 20708 **Births:** 0 **Total Expense ($000):** 19016 **Payroll Expense ($000):** 8797 **Personnel:** 152

**SOUTHEAST REHABILITATION HOSPITAL (043034)**, 905 Borgognoni Road, Zip 71653, Mailing Address: P.O. Box 743, Zip 71653; tel. 870/265–4333, (Nonreporting) **A**10 **F**3 29 34 35 56 57 59 64 65 90 91 127 133 148 154 156 **P**5
Primary Contact: Catherine M. Waldrop, Administrator
CNO: Michael Vaughn, Director of Nursing
Web address: www.southeastrehab.com
**Control**: Partnership, Investor–owned (for–profit) **Service**: Rehabilitation

**Staffed Beds:** 10 **Admissions:** 225 **Census:** 6 **Outpatient Visits:** 0 **Births:** 0 **Total Expense ($000):** 3360 **Payroll Expense ($000):** 2303 **Personnel:** 63

**LITTLE ROCK—Pulaski County**

☒ **ARKANSAS CHILDREN'S HOSPITAL (043300)**, 1 Children's Way, Zip 72202–3500; tel. 501/364–1100, (Nonreporting) **A**1 3 5 10 **F**3 7 11 16 17 19 21 23 25 27 28 29 30 31 32 34 35 38 39 40 41 43 45 46 48 49 50 53 54 55 57 58 59 60 64 68 72 74 75 77 78 79 80 81 82 84 85 86 87 88 89 90 91 92 93 94 96 97 102 107 108 111 113 115 119 126 129 130 131 132 134 135 136 137 138 146 149 150 154 155 156 **P**4 8
Primary Contact: Marcella Doderer, FACHE, President and Chief Executive Officer
COO: Chanda Cashen Chacon, Executive Vice President and Chief Operating Officer
CFO: Gena Wingfield, Senior Vice President and Chief Financial Officer
CMO: Greg Sharp, M.D., Senior Vice President and Chief Medical Officer
CIO: Jonathan Goldberg, Senior Vice President and Chief Information Officer
CHR: Jimmy Duncan, Senior Vice President and Chief People Officer
CNO: Lee Anne Eddy, Senior Vice President and Chief Nursing Officer
Web address: www.archildrens.org
**Control**: Other not–for–profit (including NFP Corporation) **Service**: Children's general medical and surgical

**Staffed Beds:** 336 **Admissions:** 16177 **Census:** 225 **Outpatient Visits:** 374181 **Births:** 0 **Total Expense ($000):** 532671 **Payroll Expense ($000):** 210115 **Personnel:** 3589

☐ **ARKANSAS HEART HOSPITAL (040134)**, 1701 South Shackleford Road, Zip 72211–4335; tel. 501/219–7000, (Nonreporting) **A**1 3 5 10 **F**3 11 12 17 18 20 22 24 26 28 29 30 34 35 40 45 46 50 53 54 57 59 64 68 75 81 87 107 108 111 115 119 127 130 135 148 154 156 **P**4
Primary Contact: Bruce Murphy, M.D., President and Chief Executive Officer
Web address: www.arheart.com
**Control**: Partnership, Investor–owned (for–profit) **Service**: Heart

**Staffed Beds:** 110 **Admissions:** 6440 **Census:** 60 **Outpatient Visits:** 223510 **Births:** 0 **Total Expense ($000):** 211468 **Payroll Expense ($000):** 57435 **Personnel:** 1337

☐ **ARKANSAS STATE HOSPITAL (044011)**, 305 South Palm Street, Zip 72205–5432; tel. 501/686–9000, (Nonreporting) **A**1 3 10 **F**11 29 30 50 57 59 65 75 86 87 97 98 99 101 102 106 130 132 135 143 146 149 154 **P**6
Primary Contact: James Scoggins, Interim Chief Executive Officer
CFO: Gary W Hollis, Comptroller
CMO: Steven Domon, M.D., Medical Director
CIO: Tina Grissom, Chief Information Technology Officer
CHR: Donna Sadler, Director Human Resources
CNO: James Scoggins, Director of Nursing
Web address: www.https://humanservices.arkansas.gov/about-dhs/dbhs/arkansas-state-hospital
**Control**: State, Government, Nonfederal **Service**: Psychiatric

**Staffed Beds:** 222 **Admissions:** 377 **Census:** 165 **Outpatient Visits:** 107 **Births:** 0 **Total Expense ($000):** 49200 **Payroll Expense ($000):** 22314 **Personnel:** 639

★ **BAPTIST HEALTH EXTENDED CARE HOSPITAL (042012)**, 9601 Baptist Health Drive, Zip 72205–7202; tel. 501/202–1070, (Nonreporting) **A**10 **F**1 3 29 31 77 85 87 130 148 158 **S** Baptist Health, Little Rock, AR
Primary Contact: Greg Stubblefield, President
CFO: Brent Beaulieu, Chief Financial Officer
CMO: Alexander Orsini, M.D., Medical Director
CIO: David House, Vice President
CHR: Cathy C. Dickinson, Chief Human Resources
CNO: Christopher Cox, Chief Nursing Officer
Web address: www.https://www.baptist-health.com/location/baptist-health-extended-care-hospital/
**Control**: Other not–for–profit (including NFP Corporation) **Service**: Acute long–term care hospital

**Staffed Beds:** 36 **Admissions:** 341 **Census:** 26 **Outpatient Visits:** 0 **Births:** 0 **Total Expense ($000):** 16361 **Payroll Expense ($000):** 7121 **Personnel:** 90

*Many Facility Codes have changed. Please refer to the AHA Guide Code Chart.*

© 2021 AHA Guide

**AR**

☒ **BAPTIST HEALTH MEDICAL CENTER-LITTLE ROCK (040114)**, 9601 Baptist Health Drive, Zip 72205-7299; tel. 501/202-2000, (Nonreporting) **A**1 3 5 10 **F**3 4 7 8 11 12 13 15 17 18 20 22 24 26 28 29 30 31 32 34 35 36 37 38 40 43 44 45 46 47 48 49 50 54 56 57 58 59 60 61 64 65 68 70 72 73 74 75 76 77 78 79 81 82 84 85 86 87 89 92 98 100 101 102 103 104 107 110 111 114 115 118 119 126 129 130 131 132 134 135 137 141 143 146 147 148 149 154 **S** Baptist Health, Little Rock, AR
Primary Contact: Greg Crain, FACHE, Senior Vice President and Administrator
CFO: Robert C Roberts, Senior Vice President Financial Services
CMO: Anthony Bennett, M.D., Chief Clinical Affairs
CIO: David House, Vice President and Chief Information Officer
CHR: Anthony Kendall, Vice President Human Resources
CNO: Michele Diedrich, R.N., Vice President Nursing Officer, Vice President Patient Care
Web address: www.baptist-health.org/maps-directions/bhmc-lr
**Control:** Other not-for-profit (including NFP Corporation) **Service:** General medical and surgical

**Staffed Beds:** 657 **Admissions:** 30173 **Census:** 466 **Outpatient Visits:** 154310 **Births:** 3208 **Total Expense ($000):** 541038 **Payroll Expense ($000):** 168994 **Personnel:** 2837

☒ △ **BAPTIST HEALTH REHABILITATION INSTITUTE (043026)**, 9501 Baptist Health Drive, Zip 72205-6225; tel. 501/202-7000, (Nonreporting) **A**1 3 5 7 10 **F**29 30 34 35 50 53 64 75 86 87 90 91 93 95 96 130 132 143 **S** Baptist Health, Little Rock, AR
Primary Contact: Julie Nix, Vice President and Administrator
CFO: Robert C Roberts, Senior Vice President
CIO: David House, Vice President and Chief Information Officer
CHR: Anthony Kendall, Vice President Human Resources
Web address: www.baptist-health.com/locations/accesspoint.aspx?accessPointID=202
**Control:** Other not-for-profit (including NFP Corporation) **Service:** Rehabilitation

**Staffed Beds:** 120 **Admissions:** 1482 **Census:** 52 **Outpatient Visits:** 101839 **Births:** 0 **Total Expense ($000):** 32527 **Payroll Expense ($000):** 15380 **Personnel:** 223

**BAPTIST MEDICAL CENTER** See Baptist Health Medical Center-Little Rock

**BAPTIST REHAB INSTITUTE** See Baptist Health Rehabilitation Institute

**BHC PINNACLE POINTE HOSPITAL** See Pinnacle Pointe Hospital

☒ △ **CENTRAL ARKANSAS VETERANS HEALTHCARE SYSTEM**, 4300 West Seventh Street, Zip 72205-5446; tel. 501/257-1000, (Includes NORTH LITTLE ROCK DIVISION, Mailing address: 2200 Fort Roots Drive, North Little Rock, Arkansas, Zip 72114-1706; tel. 501/661-1202) (Total facility includes 152 beds in nursing home-type unit) **A**1 2 3 5 7 8 **F**2 3 5 8 15 17 18 20 22 26 28 29 30 31 33 34 35 36 38 39 40 44 45 46 47 49 50 51 52 53 54 55 56 57 58 59 60 61 62 63 64 65 66 68 70 71 74 75 77 78 79 81 82 83 84 85 86 87 91 92 93 94 95 96 97 98 100 101 102 103 104 105 106 109 110 111 114 115 119 120 126 127 128 129 130 132 133 135 143 144 145 146 147 148 149 150 152 153 154 156 157 158 **S** Department of Veterans Affairs, Washington, DC
Primary Contact: Margie A. Scott, M.D., Director
CFO: ColonelNate Todd, Chief Financial Officer
CIO: Jim Hall, Acting Chief Information Officer
CHR: Richard Nelson, Chief of Human Resources Management Services
Web address: www.littlerock.va.gov/
**Control:** Veterans Affairs, Government, federal **Service:** General medical and surgical

**Staffed Beds:** 551 **Admissions:** 11476 **Census:** 338 **Outpatient Visits:** 1200000 **Births:** 0 **Total Expense ($000):** 684285 **Payroll Expense ($000):** 278710 **Personnel:** 3346

☒ **CHI ST. VINCENT INFIRMARY MEDICAL CENTER (040007)**, Two St Vincent Circle, Zip 72205-5499; tel. 501/552-3000, (Nonreporting) **A**1 5 10 **F**3 11 15 17 18 20 22 24 26 28 29 30 31 34 35 37 39 40 43 44 45 46 47 48 49 50 51 53 54 56 57 59 60 61 62 64 67 68 70 74 75 77 78 79 80 81 82 84 85 86 87 91 93 96 97 98 100 102 103 104 107 108 111 114 115 116 117 118 119 126 129 130 132 135 143 144 146 148 149 154 156 157 **P**6 7 **S** CommonSpirit Health, Chicago, IL
Primary Contact: Chad S. Aduddell, Market Chief Executive Officer
CFO: Shawn Barnett, Senior Vice President and Chief Financial Officer
CMO: Gerry Jones, M.D., Chief Medical Officer
CIO: Tracy Kirby, Assistant Vice President Business Relationship Management
CNO: Kathy E. Neely, R.N., Interim Vice President Patient Care Services
Web address: www.chistvincent.com/
**Control:** Church operated, Nongovernment, not-for-profit **Service:** General medical and surgical

**Staffed Beds:** 307 **Admissions:** 17274 **Census:** 259 **Outpatient Visits:** 160485 **Births:** 437 **Total Expense ($000):** 409012 **Payroll Expense ($000):** 166701 **Personnel:** 1707

**CORNERSTONE HOSPITAL OF LITTLE ROCK (042010)**, 2 Saint Vincent Circle, 6th Floor, Zip 72205-5423; tel. 501/265-0600, (Nonreporting) **A**10 22 **F**1 3 29 85 **S** Cornerstone Healthcare Group, Dallas, TX
Primary Contact: James H. Rogers, FACHE, Chief Executive Officer
CNO: Joy Miller, Chief Nursing Officer
Web address: www.chghospitals.com/littlerock/
**Control:** Corporation, Investor-owned (for-profit) **Service:** Acute long-term care hospital

**Staffed Beds:** 30 **Admissions:** 370 **Census:** 26 **Outpatient Visits:** 0 **Births:** 0 **Total Expense ($000):** 10906 **Payroll Expense ($000):** 5965 **Personnel:** 89

**CORNERSTONE HOSPITAL OF NORTH LITTLE ROCK** See Cornerstone Hospital of Little Rock

☐ **PINNACLE POINTE HOSPITAL (044013)**, 11501 Financial Center Parkway, Zip 72211-3715; tel. 501/223-3322, (Nonreporting) **A**1 10 **F**5 29 34 35 38 50 75 87 98 99 101 102 106 130 134 143 154 **S** Universal Health Services, Inc., King of Prussia, PA
Primary Contact: Shane Frazier, Chief Executive Officer
CFO: Gina Dailey, Chief Financial Officer
CMO: Ben Nimmo, M.D., Medical Director
CIO: James L Howe, Director Human Resources
CHR: James L Howe, Director Human Resources
CNO: Bobby Alexander, R.N., Chief Nursing Officer
Web address: www.pinnaclepointehospital.com
**Control:** Corporation, Investor-owned (for-profit) **Service:** Children's hospital psychiatric

**Staffed Beds:** 127 **Admissions:** 2981 **Census:** 107 **Outpatient Visits:** 0 **Births:** 0 **Total Expense ($000):** 20503 **Payroll Expense ($000):** 11916 **Personnel:** 248

**ST. VINCENT INFIRMARY MEDICAL CENTER** See Chi St. Vincent Infirmary Medical Center

☒ **UAMS MEDICAL CENTER (040016)**, 4301 West Markham Street, Zip 72205-7101; tel. 501/686-7000, (Nonreporting) **A**1 3 5 8 10 **F**3 5 11 12 13 15 17 18 20 22 24 26 29 30 31 34 37 38 40 43 44 45 46 47 48 49 50 51 52 53 54 55 56 57 58 59 60 61 64 68 70 71 72 73 74 75 76 77 78 79 80 81 82 84 85 86 87 91 92 93 94 96 97 98 99 100 101 102 103 104 105 106 107 108 110 111 114 115 116 117 118 119 120 121 123 124 126 127 129 130 131 132 135 136 138 139 141 142 146 147 148 149 153 154 156 **P**6 Primary Contact: Stephen Mette, M.D., Interim Chief Executive Officer
COO: Timothy Hill, Chief Operating Officer
CFO: William Bowes, Chief Financial Officer
CMO: Nicholas P Lang, M.D., Chief Medical Officer
CHR: Jeff Risinger, Director Human Resources
CNO: Mary Helen Forrest, R.N., Chief Nursing Officer
Web address: www.uams.edu/medcenter
**Control:** State, Government, Nonfederal **Service:** General medical and surgical

**Staffed Beds:** 519 **Admissions:** 24950 **Census:** 411 **Outpatient Visits:** 568842 **Births:** 3454 **Total Expense ($000):** 1063259 **Payroll Expense ($000):** 439692 **Personnel:** 5829

**UNIVERSITY HOSP OF ARKANSAS** See UAMS Medical Center

**VETERANS AFFAIRS MED CENTER** See Central Arkansas Veterans Healthcare System

**MAGNOLIA—Columbia County**

**MAGNOLIA HOSPITAL** See Magnolia Regional Medical Center

★ **MAGNOLIA REGIONAL MEDICAL CENTER (040067)**, 101 Hospital Drive, Zip 71753-2415, Mailing Address: P.O. Box 629, Zip 71754-0629; tel. 870/235-3000, (Nonreporting) **A**3 10 20 **F**3 11 13 15 29 31 34 35 40 43 45 50 59 62 64 70 76 81 87 93 107 108 110 111 115 119 129 130 132 133 146 147 148 149
Primary Contact: Rex Jones, Chief Executive Officer
CFO: Roxane Stewart, Chief Financial Officer
CMO: James W Chambliss, Chief of Staff
CHR: Laura Akkub, Director Human Resources
CNO: Stephanie Schmittou, MSN, R.N., Chief Nursing Officer
Web address: www.magnoliarmc.org
**Control:** City, Government, Nonfederal **Service:** General medical and surgical

**Staffed Beds:** 36 **Admissions:** 999 **Census:** 8 **Outpatient Visits:** 24022 **Births:** 130 **Total Expense ($000):** 22629 **Payroll Expense ($000):** 10230 **Personnel:** 206

---

**Hospital, Medicare Provider Number, Address, Telephone, Approval, Facility, and Physician Codes, Health Care System**

★ American Hospital Association (AHA) membership　○ Healthcare Facilities Accreditation Program　⇑ Center for Improvement in Healthcare Quality Accreditation
☐ The Joint Commission accreditation　◇ DNV Healthcare Inc. accreditation　△ Commission on Accreditation of Rehabilitation Facilities (CARF) accreditation

## MALVERN—Hot Spring County

★ **BAPTIST HEALTH MEDICAL CENTER-HOT SPRING COUNTY (040076)**, 1001 Schneider Drive, Zip 72104–4811; tel. 501/332–1000, (Nonreporting) **A**10 **F**3 11 12 15 29 30 34 35 40 43 45 57 59 64 70 75 81 93 98 102 106 107 110 111 115 119 130 132 133 146 152 154 155 156 **S** Baptist Health, Little Rock, AR
Primary Contact: Tony Hardage, PharmD, Interim Chief Executive Officer
CMO: Allen Gerber, M.D., Chief of Staff
CHR: Kelli Hopkins, Director Human Resources
CNO: Dee Schall, R.N., Chief Nursing Officer
Web address: www.https://www.baptist-health.com/location/baptist-health-medical-center-hot-spring-county-hot-spring-county
**Control:** Other not–for–profit (including NFP Corporation) **Service:** General medical and surgical

**Staffed Beds:** 72 **Admissions:** 2032 **Census:** 25 **Outpatient Visits:** 22459 **Births:** 0 **Total Expense ($000):** 21871 **Payroll Expense ($000):** 9050 **Personnel:** 164

**H.S.C. MEDICAL CENTER** See Baptist Health Medical Center-Hot Spring County

## MAUMELLE—Pulaski County

☐ **METHODIST BEHAVIORAL HOSPITAL OF ARKANSAS (044017)**, 1601 Murphy Drive, Zip 72113–6187; tel. 501/803–3388, (Nonreporting) **A**1 10 **F**98 99 104 153 154 **P**5
Primary Contact: Andy Altom, President and Chief Executive Officer
Web address: www.https://www.methodistfamily.org/
**Control:** Other not–for–profit (including NFP Corporation) **Service:** Children's hospital psychiatric

**Staffed Beds:** 60 **Admissions:** 1975 **Census:** 51 **Outpatient Visits:** 92800 **Births:** 0 **Total Expense ($000):** 22164 **Payroll Expense ($000):** 8611 **Personnel:** 110

## MCGEHEE—Desha County

★ **MCGEHEE HOSPITAL (041308)**, 900 South Third, Zip 71654–2562, Mailing Address: P.O. Box 351, Zip 71654–0351; tel. 870/222–5600, (Nonreporting) **A**10 18 **F**3 11 29 40 57 59 64 68 107 114 119 132 133 135 146 154
Primary Contact: Terry Lee. Amstutz, FACHE, Chief Executive Officer
CFO: Teresa Morgan, Chief Financial Officer
CMO: James Young, M.D., Chief of Staff
CIO: Shaun Perry, Chief Information Officer
CNO: Sarah Calvert, Chief Nursing Officer
Web address: www.mymcgeheehospital.org/
**Control:** Other not–for–profit (including NFP Corporation) **Service:** General medical and surgical

**Staffed Beds:** 25 **Admissions:** 246 **Census:** 3 **Outpatient Visits:** 19989 **Births:** 0 **Total Expense ($000):** 12365 **Payroll Expense ($000):** 5510 **Personnel:** 133

**MCGEHEE-DESHA COUNTY HOSPITAL** See Mcgehee Hospital

## MENA—Polk County

**MENA MEDICAL CENTER** See Mena Regional Health System

★ **MENA REGIONAL HEALTH SYSTEM (040015)**, 311 North Morrow Street, Zip 71953–2516; tel. 479/394–6100, (Nonreporting) **A**5 10 20 **F**3 4 11 13 15 29 30 34 35 40 43 45 56 57 59 64 68 70 75 76 77 79 81 86 87 90 91 93 96 98 100 101 103 104 107 108 110 111 115 119 127 129 130 131 144 146 147 149 **P**8
Primary Contact: Jay Quebedeaux, FACHE, Chief Executive Officer
CFO: Mark Henke, Chief Financial Officer
CMO: Richard Lochala, Chief of Staff
CIO: Nicholas Dunn, Director Information Systems
CHR: Chandler Cox, Director Human Resources
CNO: Teresa Wise, R.N., Chief Nursing Officer
Web address: www.menaregional.com
**Control:** City, Government, Nonfederal **Service:** General medical and surgical

**Staffed Beds:** 65 **Admissions:** 1472 **Census:** 23 **Outpatient Visits:** 47806 **Births:** 280 **Total Expense ($000):** 30216 **Payroll Expense ($000):** 15604 **Personnel:** 306

## MONTICELLO—Drew County

★ **DREW MEMORIAL HEALTH SYSTEM (040051)**, 778 Scogin Drive, Zip 71655–5729; tel. 870/367–2411, (Nonreporting) **A**5 10 20 **F**11 13 15 18 29 30 31 34 35 50 57 59 62 68 70 75 76 77 78 79 81 85 86 87 93 94 96 100 102 107 111 115 119 128 129 130 132 133 135 143 147 148 153 154 156
Primary Contact: Scott G. Barrilleaux, FACHE, Chief Executive Officer
COO: Wade Smith, Chief Operating Officer
CFO: Melodie Colwell, Chief Financial Officer
CMO: Julia Nichoson, M.D., Chief Medical Officer
CIO: Rusty Bryant, Director Information Technology
CHR: Seth Givens, Chief Human Resource Officer
CNO: Jonathan Schell, Chief Nursing Officer
Web address: www.drewmemorial.org
**Control:** Other not–for–profit (including NFP Corporation) **Service:** General medical and surgical

**Staffed Beds:** 49 **Admissions:** 2249 **Census:** 20 **Outpatient Visits:** 53176 **Births:** 361 **Total Expense ($000):** 36364 **Payroll Expense ($000):** 14817 **Personnel:** 354

**DREW MEMORIAL HOSPITAL** See Drew Memorial Health System

## MORRILTON—Conway County

★ **CHI ST. VINCENT MORRILTON (041324)**, 4 Hospital Drive, Zip 72110–4510; tel. 501/977–2300, (Nonreporting) **A**10 18 **F**3 11 15 18 29 30 34 40 43 44 45 57 59 62 63 64 77 79 80 81 85 87 93 104 107 108 110 111 119 127 129 130 132 133 143 145 146 148 154 **P**6 **S** CommonSpirit Health, Chicago, IL
Primary Contact: Leslie Arnold, Chief Executive Officer and Administrator
CFO: Shawn Barnett, Senior Vice President and Chief Financial Officer
CIO: Tracy Kirby, Assistant Vice President Business Relationship Management
CNO: Kathy E. Neely, R.N., Interim Vice President Patient Care Services
Web address: www.chistvincent.com/Hospitals/st-vincent-morrilton
**Control:** Church operated, Nongovernment, not–for–profit **Service:** General medical and surgical

**Staffed Beds:** 25 **Admissions:** 634 **Census:** 8 **Outpatient Visits:** 29542 **Births:** 0 **Total Expense ($000):** 20630 **Payroll Expense ($000):** 8702 **Personnel:** 126

**ST. VINCENT MORRILTON** See Chi St. Vincent Morrilton

## MOUNTAIN HOME—Baxter County

**BAXTER COUNTY REGIONAL HOSP** See Baxter Regional Medical Center

★ **BAXTER REGIONAL MEDICAL CENTER (040027)**, 624 Hospital Drive, Zip 72653–2955; tel. 870/508–1000, (Nonreporting) **A**10 **F**7 11 13 15 17 18 20 22 24 28 29 30 31 34 40 43 45 46 47 49 53 56 57 59 62 63 64 70 74 76 77 78 79 81 82 85 86 87 89 90 93 96 97 98 100 103 107 108 110 111 114 115 116 117 119 124 126 127 129 130 132 135 146 147 148 149 154 156 **P**6 8
Primary Contact: Ron Peterson, FACHE, President and Chief Executive Officer
COO: David R. Fox, Vice President and Chief Operating Officer
CFO: Debbie Henry, Vice President and Chief Financial Officer
CHR: Karen Adams, Vice President Human Resources
Web address: www.baxterregional.org
**Control:** Other not–for–profit (including NFP Corporation) **Service:** General medical and surgical

**Staffed Beds:** 185 **Admissions:** 9699 **Census:** 91 **Outpatient Visits:** 135810 **Births:** 672 **Total Expense ($000):** 231186 **Payroll Expense ($000):** 92493 **Personnel:** 1656

## MOUNTAIN VIEW—Stone County

**STONE CNTY MEDICAL CENTER** See Stone County Medical Center

★ **STONE COUNTY MEDICAL CENTER (041310)**, 2106 East Main Street, Zip 72560–6439, Mailing Address: P.O. Box 510, Zip 72560–0510; tel. 870/269–4361, (Nonreporting) **A**5 10 18 **F**3 11 15 28 29 34 40 43 45 57 59 64 79 81 85 93 107 110 111 114 119 128 133 135 146 147 148 154 **S** White River Health System, Batesville, AR
Primary Contact: Kevin Spears, Chief Executive Officer
CFO: Phillip Hacker, Chief Financial Officer
CHR: Gary McDonald, Associate Administrator Human Resources
CNO: Terri Bunch, MSN, R.N., MSN, Chief Nursing Officer
Web address: www.whiteriverhealthsystem.com/doctors/facilities/stone-county-medical-center
**Control:** Other not–for–profit (including NFP Corporation) **Service:** General medical and surgical

**Staffed Beds:** 25 **Admissions:** 548 **Census:** 5 **Outpatient Visits:** 29774 **Births:** 0 **Total Expense ($000):** 14361 **Payroll Expense ($000):** 6233 **Personnel:** 122

*Many Facility Codes have changed. Please refer to the AHA Guide Code Chart.*

## NASHVILLE—Howard County

★ **HOWARD MEMORIAL HOSPITAL (041311)**, 130 Medical Circle,
Zip 71852–8606; tel. 870/845–4400, (Nonreporting) **A**5 10 18 **F**3 11 15 28 29
30 34 35 40 43 45 50 53 57 64 65 70 77 81 85 87 93 97 107 108 110 115
119 133 146 156 **P**6
Primary Contact: Debra J. Wright, R.N., Chief Executive Officer
CFO: William J Craig, CPA, Chief Financial Officer
CMO: John Hearnsberger, M.D., Chief of Staff
CHR: Gayla Lacefield, Director Human Resources
CNO: Alesha Danielle Collins, MSN, R.N., Chief Nursing Officer
Web address: www.howardmemorial.com
**Control:** Other not–for–profit (including NFP Corporation) **Service:** General
medical and surgical

**Staffed Beds:** 20 **Admissions:** 644 **Census:** 7 **Outpatient Visits:** 38107
**Births:** 0 **Total Expense ($000):** 25232 **Payroll Expense ($000):** 11401
**Personnel:** 202

## NEWPORT—Jackson County

**HARRIS HOSPITAL** See Unity Health Harris Medical Center

## NORTH LITTLE ROCK—Pulaski County

**ARKANSAS SURGICAL HOSPITAL (040147)**, 5201 North Shore Drive,
Zip 72118–5312; tel. 501/748–8000, (Nonreporting) **A**10 **F**3 29 30 35 40 59 64
74 75 78 79 81 82 85 86 87 107 111 114 119 130 131 144 148 149
Primary Contact: Carrie Helm, Chief Executive Officer
CFO: Charles Powell, Chief Financial Officer
CMO: Kenneth A Martin, M.D., Chief of Staff
CIO: Scott Davis, Manager Information Technology
CNO: Judy Jones, Chief Clinical Officer
Web address: www.ArkSurgicalHospital.com
**Control:** Corporation, Investor–owned (for–profit) **Service:** General medical and surgical

**Staffed Beds:** 49 **Admissions:** 3437 **Census:** 19 **Outpatient Visits:** 17700
**Births:** 0 **Total Expense ($000):** 55947 **Payroll Expense ($000):** 14711
**Personnel:** 261

**BAPTIST HEALTH BAPTIST MEM CTR** See Baptist Health Medical Center - North
Little Rock

⊞ △ **BAPTIST HEALTH MEDICAL CENTER - NORTH LITTLE ROCK (040036)**,
3333 Springhill Drive, Zip 72117–2922; tel. 501/202–3000, (Nonreporting) **A**1 3
5 7 10 **F**3 8 11 13 15 17 18 20 22 24 26 28 29 30 31 38 40 43 45 46 47 48
49 50 53 54 56 59 60 64 65 70 74 75 76 77 78 79 81 85 86 87 89 90 93 94
107 108 110 111 114 115 118 119 124 126 128 129 130 135 144 146 147
148 **S** Baptist Health, Little Rock, AR
Primary Contact: Mike Perkins, Vice President and Administrator
COO: Doug Weeks, FACHE, Executive Vice President and Chief Operations Officer
CFO: Robert C Roberts, Senior Vice President Financial Services
CMO: Eddie Phillips, M.D., Chief Medical Affairs
CIO: David House, Vice President and Chief Information Officer
CHR: Cathy C. Dickinson, Vice President Human Resources
CNO: Kelley Hamby, Vice President Patient Care
Web address: www.https://www.baptist-health.com/location/baptist-health-medical-
center-north-little-rock-north-little-rock
**Control:** Other not–for–profit (including NFP Corporation) **Service:** General
medical and surgical

**Staffed Beds:** 177 **Admissions:** 11115 **Census:** 137 **Outpatient
Visits:** 110059 **Births:** 1260 **Total Expense ($000):** 192998 **Payroll
Expense ($000):** 64096 **Personnel:** 1018

**BRIDGEWAY** See The Bridgeway

**CENTRAL ARKANSAS VETERANS AFFAIRS HEALTHCARE SYSTEM, EUGENE
TOWBIN HEALTHCARE CENTER** See North Little Rock Division

**NORTH LITTLE ROCK DIVISION** See Central Arkansas Veterans Healthcare
System, Little Rock

☐ **THE BRIDGEWAY (044005)**, 21 Bridgeway Road, Zip 72113–9516;
tel. 501/771–1500, (Nonreporting) **A**1 10 **F**4 5 34 56 98 99 101 102 103 104 105
106 149 151 152 153 154 **S** Universal Health Services, Inc., King of Prussia, PA
Primary Contact: Sherrie James, R.N., Chief Executive Officer
CFO: Fred Woods, Chief Financial Officer
CMO: Philip L Mizell, M.D., Medical Director
CHR: Neely Robison, Director Human Resources
Web address: www.thebridgeway.com
**Control:** Corporation, Investor–owned (for–profit) **Service:** Psychiatric

**Staffed Beds:** 124 **Admissions:** 3952 **Census:** 79 **Outpatient Visits:** 5227
**Births:** 0 **Total Expense ($000):** 25532 **Payroll Expense ($000):** 11344
**Personnel:** 156

## OSCEOLA—Mississippi County

**BAPTIST MEMORIAL HOSP-OSCEOLA** See South Mississippi County Regional
Medical Center

⊞ **SOUTH MISSISSIPPI COUNTY REGIONAL MEDICAL CENTER (041316)**, 611
West Lee Avenue, Zip 72370–3001, Mailing Address: P.O. Box 108, Blytheville,
Zip 72316–0108; tel. 870/563–7000, (Nonreporting) **A**1 10 18 **F**3 29 34 40 43
45 81 90 107 114 133 135 148 149 154
Primary Contact: Chris Lee. Raymer, MSN, Chief Executive Officer
COO: Paul Pieffer, Chief Operating Officer
CFO: Randy Nichols, Chief Financial Officer
CMO: Pratapji Thakor, M.D., Chief of Staff
CIO: Tammy Bratcher, Director Information Technology
CHR: Cheri Blurton, SPHR,SHRM-SCP, Director Human Resources
CNO: Felicia Pierce, R.N., Chief Nursing Officer
Web address: www.mchsys.org
**Control:** County, Government, Nonfederal **Service:** General medical and surgical

**Staffed Beds:** 25 **Admissions:** 397 **Census:** 5 **Outpatient Visits:** 13700
**Births:** 0 **Total Expense ($000):** 10546 **Payroll Expense ($000):** 4201
**Personnel:** 58

## OZARK—Franklin County

★ **MERCY HOSPITAL OZARK (041303)**, 801 West River Street, Zip 72949–3023;
tel. 479/667–4138, (Nonreporting) **A**10 18 **F**3 15 35 40 43 45 57 59 64 65 68
81 85 107 119 129 133 148 149 **P**8 **S** Mercy, Chesterfield, MO
Primary Contact: Teresa Williams, R.N., Regional Administrator
COO: Brent Hubbard, FACHE, Chief Operating Officer
CMO: John Lachowsky, M.D., Chief Medical Officer
CIO: Tiana Bolduc, Chief Information Officer
Web address: www.https://www.mercy.net/practice/mercy-hospital-ozark/
**Control:** Church operated, Nongovernment, not–for–profit **Service:** General
medical and surgical

**Staffed Beds:** 25 **Admissions:** 301 **Census:** 3 **Outpatient Visits:** 12707
**Births:** 0 **Total Expense ($000):** 11424 **Payroll Expense ($000):** 4589
**Personnel:** 49

**MERCY HOSPITAL-TURNER MEMORIAL** See Mercy Hospital Ozark

## PARAGOULD—Greene County

**ARKANSAS METHODIST HOSPITAL** See Arkansas Methodist Medical Center

⊞ △ **ARKANSAS METHODIST MEDICAL CENTER (040039)**, 900 West
Kingshighway, Zip 72450–5942, Mailing Address: P.O. Box 339, Zip 72451–0339;
tel. 870/239–7000, (Nonreporting) **A**1 5 7 10 19 **F**3 7 10 11 13 15 18 20 22
28 29 32 34 35 40 43 45 49 50 51 53 54 57 59 62 64 68 70 75 76 79 81 85
86 87 89 90 93 97 107 108 110 111 114 115 119 124 125 129 130 131 132
133 135 144 146 147 148 154 156 **P**8
Primary Contact: Barry L. Davis, FACHE, President and Chief Executive Officer
COO: Jason Masingale, Chief Operating Officer
CFO: Brad Bloemer, Vice President Finance and Chief Financial Officer
CMO: Joel Epperson, M.D., Chief of Staff
CIO: Dan Austin, Director Information Technology
CHR: Kevin Thielemier, Director Human Resources
CNO: Lana R Williams, Chief Nursing Officer
Web address: www.arkansasmethodist.org
**Control:** Other not–for–profit (including NFP Corporation) **Service:** General
medical and surgical

**Staffed Beds:** 125 **Admissions:** 4143 **Census:** 45 **Outpatient
Visits:** 142754 **Births:** 500 **Total Expense ($000):** 71269 **Payroll Expense
($000):** 31799 **Personnel:** 649

## PARIS—Logan County

★ **MERCY HOSPITAL PARIS (041300)**, 500 East Academy, Zip 72855–4040;
tel. 479/963–6101, (Nonreporting) **A**10 18 **F**3 15 35 40 43 45 57 59 64 65 68
81 85 107 119 127 129 133 148 149 **P**8 **S** Mercy, Chesterfield, MO
Primary Contact: Teresa Williams, R.N., Regional Administrator
COO: Brent Hubbard, FACHE, Chief Operating Officer
Web address: www.https://www.mercy.net/practice/mercy-hospital-paris/
**Control:** Church operated, Nongovernment, not–for–profit **Service:** General
medical and surgical

**Staffed Beds:** 16 **Admissions:** 254 **Census:** 3 **Outpatient Visits:** 28258
**Births:** 0 **Total Expense ($000):** 10914 **Payroll Expense ($000):** 4998
**Personnel:** 61

**NORTH LOGAN MERCY HOSPITAL** See Mercy Hospital Paris

---

**Hospital, Medicare Provider Number, Address, Telephone, Approval, Facility, and Physician Codes, Health Care System**

★ American Hospital Association (AHA) membership ○ Healthcare Facilities Accreditation Program ⇑ Center for Improvement in Healthcare Quality Accreditation
☐ The Joint Commission accreditation ◇ DNV Healthcare Inc. accreditation △ Commission on Accreditation of Rehabilitation Facilities (CARF) accreditation

## PIGGOTT—Clay County

★ **PIGGOTT COMMUNITY HOSPITAL (041330)**, 1206 Gordon Duckworth Drive, Zip 72454–1911; tel. 870/598–3881, (Nonreporting) **A**10 18 **F**3 7 8 29 30 34 35 40 43 45 46 57 59 62 64 65 71 77 81 82 86 87 93 107 111 114 119 127 129 130 132 133 135 143 146 148 153 154 156 **P**8
Primary Contact: James L. Magee, Executive Director
CFO: Linda Ort, Chief Financial Officer
Web address: www.piggottcommunityhospital.com
**Control**: City, Government, Nonfederal **Service**: General medical and surgical

> **Staffed Beds**: 25 **Admissions**: 770 **Census**: 7 **Outpatient Visits**: 20855
> **Births**: 0 **Total Expense ($000)**: 22458 **Payroll Expense ($000)**: 9501
> **Personnel**: 220

## PINE BLUFF—-Jefferson County

★ △ **JEFFERSON REGIONAL MEDICAL CENTER (040071)**, 1600 West 40th Avenue, Zip 71603–6301; tel. 870/541–7100, (Nonreporting) **A**3 5 7 10 20 **F**3 8 11 13 15 17 18 20 22 28 29 30 31 34 35 38 40 43 45 46 48 49 50 51 53 54 56 57 59 60 61 64 65 70 72 73 74 75 76 77 78 79 81 82 85 86 87 89 90 93 94 96 97 98 100 101 102 105 107 108 110 111 114 115 116 117 118 119 124 130 131 132 135 143 144 145 146 147 148 149 154 156 157 **P**6 7
Primary Contact: Brian N. Thomas, President and Chief Executive Officer
CFO: Jeremy Jeffery, Regional Chief Financial Officer
CMO: Reid Pierce, M.D., Chief Medical Officer
CIO: Patrick Neece, Chief Information Officer
CHR: M Daryl Scott, Assistant Vice President
CNO: Louise Hickman, R.N., Vice President of Patient Care Services
Web address: www.jrmc.org
**Control**: Other not–for–profit (including NFP Corporation) **Service**: General medical and surgical

> **Staffed Beds**: 258 **Admissions**: 9812 **Census**: 133 **Outpatient Visits**: 227347 **Births**: 664 **Total Expense ($000)**: 200713 **Payroll Expense ($000)**: 82025 **Personnel**: 1366

## POCAHONTAS—Randolph County

**FIVE RIVERS MEDICAL CENTER** See St. Bernards Five Rivers

**ST. BERNARDS FIVE RIVERS (040047)**, 2801 Medical Center Drive, Zip 72455–9436; tel. 870/892–6000, (Data for 273 days) (Nonreporting) **A**10 20 **F**3 4 8 11 29 30 34 38 40 43 45 50 57 59 62 68 70 77 79 81 85 87 89 93 97 98 103 104 107 111 115 119 127 129 133 146 148 151 154 157
Primary Contact: Jeremy D. Capps, R.N., Chief Executive Officer
CFO: Joey Radcliff, Chief Financial Officer
CHR: Anita Dickson, Director Human Resources
CNO: Paula Lewis, Interim Chief Nursing Officer
Web address: www.https://www.stbernards.info/
**Control**: Other not–for–profit (including NFP Corporation) **Service**: General medical and surgical

> **Staffed Beds**: 37 **Admissions**: 646 **Census**: 12 **Outpatient Visits**: 18366
> **Births**: 0 **Total Expense ($000)**: 11252 **Payroll Expense ($000)**: 5678
> **Personnel**: 175

## ROGERS—Benton County

✉ **MERCY HOSPITAL ROGERS (040010)**, 2710 Rife Medical Lane, Zip 72758–1452; tel. 479/338–8000, (Nonreporting) **A**1 3 5 10 **F**3 7 8 11 12 13 15 17 18 20 22 24 26 28 29 30 34 35 40 42 43 45 46 48 49 54 57 59 62 64 68 70 71 72 74 75 76 77 79 81 82 84 85 86 87 93 104 107 108 110 111 114 115 118 119 129 130 131 135 146 147 148 149 153 154 155 156 157 **S** Mercy, Chesterfield, MO
Primary Contact: Eric Pianalto, Chief Executive Officer
COO: Charlotte Rankin, R.N., Chief Operating Officer
CFO: Benny Stover, Vice President Finance
CMO: Chris Johnson, M.D., Chief of Staff
CHR: Rick Barclay, Vice President Support Services
Web address: www.https://www.mercy.net/practice/mercy-hospital-northwest-arkansas/
**Control**: Church operated, Nongovernment, not–for–profit **Service**: General medical and surgical

> **Staffed Beds**: 194 **Admissions**: 11295 **Census**: 114 **Outpatient Visits**: 278578 **Births**: 1581 **Total Expense ($000)**: 226763 **Payroll Expense ($000)**: 81658 **Personnel**: 1338

**MERCY MEDICAL CENTER** See Mercy Hospital Rogers

## RUSSELLVILLE—Pope County

✉ **SAINT MARY'S REGIONAL MEDICAL CENTER (040041)**, 1808 West Main Street, Zip 72801–2724; tel. 479/968–2841, (Nonreporting) **A**1 10 19 **F**3 8 11 13 15 18 20 22 26 29 35 40 43 45 53 59 60 68 70 75 76 77 79 80 81 85 87 90 93 98 102 105 107 108 110 111 114 115 119 120 121 123 129 130 145 146 147 149 154 157 **S** LifePoint Health, Brentwood, TN
Primary Contact: Bob Honeycutt, Chief Executive Officer
COO: Scott Bailey, Chief Operating Officer
CFO: Wendell VanEs, Chief Financial Officer
CMO: Vickie Henderson, M.D., Chief Medical Officer
CHR: Connie Gragg, Director Human Resources
CNO: Carol Gore, MSN, R.N., Chief Nursing Officer
Web address: www.saintmarysregional.com
**Control**: Corporation, Investor–owned (for–profit) **Service**: General medical and surgical

> **Staffed Beds**: 136 **Admissions**: 5709 **Census**: 69 **Outpatient Visits**: 50581
> **Births**: 842 **Total Expense ($000)**: 76721 **Payroll Expense ($000)**: 28129
> **Personnel**: 487

**ST MARY'S REGIONAL MEDICAL CTR** See Saint Mary's Regional Medical Center

## SALEM—Fulton County

**FULTON COUNTY HOSPITAL (041322)**, 679 North Main Street, Zip 72576–9451; Mailing Address: P.O. Box 517, Zip 72576–0517; tel. 870/895–2691, (Nonreporting) **A**10 18 **F**3 7 11 28 29 30 34 43 45 57 59 64 87 107 114 119 133 146 148 154
Primary Contact: Curren Everett, Chief Executive Officer
Web address: www.fultoncountyhospital.org
**Control**: County, Government, Nonfederal **Service**: General medical and surgical

> **Staffed Beds**: 25 **Admissions**: 502 **Census**: 5 **Outpatient Visits**: 8345
> **Births**: 0 **Total Expense ($000)**: 8970 **Payroll Expense ($000)**: 4368

## SEARCY—White County

**ADVANCED CARE HOSPITAL OF WHITE COUNTY (042011)**, 1200 South Main Street, Zip 72143–7321; tel. 501/278–3155, (Nonreporting) **A**10 **F**1 3 29 85 130 148
Primary Contact: Terri L. Parsons, Administrator
CMO: Miguel Aguinaga, M.D., FACS, Medical Director
CNO: Mistie Vannatter, Chief Nursing Officer
Web address: www.https://unity-health.org/advanced-care
**Control**: Other not–for–profit (including NFP Corporation) **Service**: Acute long–term care hospital

> **Staffed Beds**: 27 **Admissions**: 154 **Census**: 10 **Outpatient Visits**: 0
> **Births**: 0 **Total Expense ($000)**: 5190 **Payroll Expense ($000)**: 2624
> **Personnel**: 46

★ **UNITY HEALTH WHITE COUNTY MEDICAL CENTER (040014)**, 3214 East Race Avenue, Zip 72143–4810; tel. 501/268–6121, (Includes UNITY HEALTH HARRIS MEDICAL CENTER, Mailing address: 1205 McLain Street, Newport, Arkansas, Zip 72112–3533; tel. 870/523–8911; Steven B. Webb, FACHE, President and Chief Executive Officer; UNITY HEALTH SPECIALTY CARE, Mailing address: 1200 South Main Street, Searcy, Arkansas, Zip 72143–7397; tel. 501/278–3100; Steven B. Webb, FACHE, President and Chief Executive Officer), (Nonreporting) **A**3 5 10 **F**3 11 13 15 17 18 20 22 28 29 30 31 34 35 38 39 40 43 45 50 51 57 58 59 64 65 68 69 70 74 75 76 77 78 79 81 85 86 87 90 93 95 98 100 102 103 104 105 107 108 110 111 114 115 119 126 129 130 132 134 135 144 146 147 148 152 154 157 **P**3 6
Primary Contact: Steven B. Webb, FACHE, President and Chief Executive Officer
CFO: Stuart Hill, Vice President and Treasurer
CMO: John Henderson, M.D., Chief Medical Officer
CIO: Phil Miller, Chief Information Officer
CHR: Pamela G Williams, Director Human Resources
CNO: Peggy Turner, Assistant Vice President and Director of Nursing
Web address: www.unity-health.org
**Control**: Other not–for–profit (including NFP Corporation) **Service**: General medical and surgical

> **Staffed Beds**: 229 **Admissions**: 13889 **Census**: 162 **Outpatient Visits**: 110719 **Births**: 1251 **Total Expense ($000)**: 258974 **Payroll Expense ($000)**: 123979 **Personnel**: 1931

**WHITE COUNTY MEDICAL CENTER** See Unity Health White County Medical Center

**WHITE COUNTY MEDICAL CENTER - SOUTH CAMPUS** See Unity Health Specialty Care

## SHERWOOD—Pulaski County

★ **CHI ST. VINCENT MEDICAL CENTER-NORTH (040137)**, 2215 Wildwood Avenue, Zip 72120–5089; tel. 501/552–7100, (Nonreporting) **A**10 **F**3 11 15 18 20 22 26 29 30 34 35 40 43 44 45 50 53 57 58 64 68 70 74 79 82 85 87 107 110 111 114 115 118 119 129 130 146 149 150 154 **P**6 **S** CommonSpirit Health, Chicago, IL
Primary Contact: Shawn Barnett, President and Chief Executive Officer
CFO: Shawn Barnett, Senior Vice President and Chief Financial Officer
Web address: www.stvincenthealth.com
**Control:** Church operated, Nongovernment, not–for–profit **Service:** General medical and surgical

> **Staffed Beds:** 68 **Admissions:** 2259 **Census:** 24 **Outpatient Visits:** 32066 **Births:** 0 **Total Expense ($000):** 42029 **Payroll Expense ($000):** 15506 **Personnel:** 299

⊞ **CHI ST. VINCENT SHERWOOD REHABILITATION HOSPITAL (043031)**, 2201 Wildwood Avenue, Zip 72120–5074; tel. 501/834–1800, (Nonreporting) **A**1 10 **F**3 29 50 87 90 91 94 95 96 130 132 135 143 148 149 **S** Encompass Health Corporation, Birmingham, AL
Primary Contact: Lisa Watson, Chief Executive Officer
CFO: Stacy Shilling, Controller
CMO: Kevin J. Collins, M.D., Medical Director
CNO: Carolynn Whitley, Chief Nursing Officer
Web address: www.stvincentrehabhospital.com/
**Control:** Corporation, Investor–owned (for–profit) **Service:** Rehabilitation

> **Staffed Beds:** 80 **Admissions:** 1984 **Census:** 63 **Outpatient Visits:** 0 **Births:** 0 **Total Expense ($000):** 24841 **Payroll Expense ($000):** 13472 **Personnel:** 231

**ST. VINCENT MEDICAL CENTER-NORTH** See Chi St. Vincent Medical Center-North

**ST. VINCENT REHABILITATION HOSPITAL** See Chi St. Vincent Sherwood Rehabilitation Hospital

## SILOAM SPRINGS—Benton County

**SILOAM SPRINGS MEMORIAL HOSPITAL** See Siloam Springs Regional Hospital

⊞ **SILOAM SPRINGS REGIONAL HOSPITAL (040001)**, 603 North Progress Avenue, Zip 72761–4352; tel. 479/215–3000, (Nonreporting) **A**1 10 **F**3 8 11 15 28 29 30 34 35 40 42 43 45 46 57 59 68 70 75 76 79 81 82 85 87 89 91 93 107 110 111 119 129 130 131 132 133 146 149 154 156 **P**6 **S** Community Health Systems, Inc., Franklin, TN
Primary Contact: Adam Bracks, Chief Executive Officer
CFO: Todd Williams, Chief Financial Officer
CMO: Ashish Mathur, M.D., Chief of Staff
CHR: Cindy Ruffing, Director Human Resources
CNO: Maria Wleklinski, Chief Nursing Officer
Web address: www.ssrh.net
**Control:** Corporation, Investor–owned (for–profit) **Service:** General medical and surgical

> **Staffed Beds:** 44 **Admissions:** 1738 **Census:** 12 **Outpatient Visits:** 58352 **Births:** 546 **Total Expense ($000):** 34099 **Payroll Expense ($000):** 13839 **Personnel:** 200

## SPRINGDALE—Washington County

⊞ **ARKANSAS CHILDREN'S NORTHWEST (043301)**, 2601 Gene George Boulevard, Zip 72762; tel. 479/725–6800, (Nonreporting) **A**1 **F**3 29 30 31 32 34 38 40 41 44 50 55 57 59 64 68 74 75 77 78 79 81 85 86 87 89 93 97 102 107 111 115 119 130 132 146 149 150 154 156 **P**4 8
Primary Contact: Trisha Montague, MSN, R.N., Senior Vice President and Chief Administrator
**Control:** Other not–for–profit (including NFP Corporation) **Service:** Children's general medical and surgical

> **Staffed Beds:** 24 **Admissions:** 2225 **Census:** 12 **Outpatient Visits:** 58393 **Births:** 0 **Total Expense ($000):** 56416 **Payroll Expense ($000):** 18939 **Personnel:** 336

**NORTHWEST MEDICAL CENTER** See Northwest Medical Center - Springdale

⊞ **NORTHWEST MEDICAL CENTER - SPRINGDALE (040022)**, 609 West Maple Avenue, Zip 72764–5394, Mailing Address: P.O. Box 47, Zip 72765–0047; tel. 479/751–5711, (Includes NORTHWEST MEDICAL CENTER - BENTONVILLE, Mailing address: 3000 Medical Center Parkway, Bentonville, Arkansas, Zip 72712; tel. 479/553–1000; Denten Park, Chief Executive Officer; WILLOW CREEK WOMEN'S HOSPITAL, Mailing address: 4301 Greathouse Springs Road, Johnson, Arkansas, Zip 72741–0544, P O Box 544, Zip 72741–0544, tel. 479/684–3000; Denten Park, Chief Executive Officer), (Nonreporting) **A**1 3 5 10 **F**3 7 8 11 12 13 15 18 20 22 24 26 28 29 30 37 40 42 43 45 46 47 48 49 50 51 52 54 56 60 61 70 71 72 74 76 77 79 81 82 85 86 87 90 91 92 93 96 98 102 107 108 110 111 114 115 118 119 124 126 129 130 131 135 141 146 147 148 154 156 **P**5 8 **S** Community Health Systems, Inc., Franklin, TN
Primary Contact: Hans Driessnack, Chief Executive Officer
COO: Tom Sledge, Chief Operating Officer
CMO: James Tanner, M.D., Chief Medical Officer
CIO: Mark Bokon, Chief Information Officer
CNO: Karen Y Labonte, Chief Nursing Officer
Web address: www.https://www.northwesthealth.com/nmc-springdale
**Control:** Corporation, Investor–owned (for–profit) **Service:** General medical and surgical

> **Staffed Beds:** 366 **Admissions:** 14141 **Census:** 170 **Outpatient Visits:** 137807 **Births:** 2774 **Total Expense ($000):** 230192 **Payroll Expense ($000):** 76024 **Personnel:** 1109

⊞ **REGENCY HOSPITAL OF NORTHWEST ARKANSAS - SPRINGDALE (042009)**, 609 West Maple Avenue, 6th Fl, Zip 72764; tel. 479/757–2600, (Nonreporting) **A**1 10 **F**1 3 29 84 130 148 **S** Select Medical Corporation, Mechanicsburg, PA
Primary Contact: Lisa Muskrat, Chief Executive Officer
COO: Ruth Jones, Chief Clinical Officer
CMO: Gary Templeton, M.D., Medical Director
CHR: Melissa Ross-Cole, Director Human Resources
Web address: www.regencyhospital.com
**Control:** Corporation, Investor–owned (for–profit) **Service:** Acute long–term care hospital

> **Staffed Beds:** 25 **Admissions:** 224 **Census:** 16 **Outpatient Visits:** 0 **Births:** 0 **Total Expense ($000):** 9810 **Payroll Expense ($000):** 4467 **Personnel:** 74

**REGENCY HOSPITAL OF SPRINGDALE** See Regency Hospital of Northwest Arkansas - Springdale

## STUTTGART—Arkansas County

★ **BAPTIST HEALTH MEDICAL CENTER-STUTTGART (040072)**, 1703 North Buerkle Road, Zip 72160–1905, Mailing Address: P.O. Box 1905, Zip 72160–1905; tel. 870/673–3511, (Nonreporting) **A**10 **F**3 11 13 15 18 29 30 34 35 39 40 43 45 53 57 59 64 68 75 76 78 79 81 85 87 97 107 110 111 114 119 127 129 130 132 133 135 146 148 154 156 157 **S** Baptist Health, Little Rock, AR
Primary Contact: Kevin L. Storey, President
CMO: Michael Oltmann, M.D., Chief Medical Officer
CIO: Warren Horton, Information Technologist
CNO: Lauren Reynolds, Associate Director of Nursing
Web address: www.https://www.baptist-health.com/location/baptist-health-medical-center-stuttgart-stuttgart
**Control:** Church operated, Nongovernment, not–for–profit **Service:** General medical and surgical

> **Staffed Beds:** 41 **Admissions:** 1020 **Census:** 9 **Outpatient Visits:** 23628 **Births:** 192 **Total Expense ($000):** 28943 **Payroll Expense ($000):** 10216 **Personnel:** 135

**STUTTGART MEMORIAL HOSPITAL** See Baptist Health Medical Center-Stuttgart

## TEXARKANA—Miller County

☐ **RIVERVIEW BEHAVIORAL HEALTH (044020)**, 701 Arkansas Boulevard, Zip 71854–2105; tel. 870/772–5028, (Nonreporting) **A**1 10 **S** Acadia Healthcare Company, Inc., Franklin, TN
Primary Contact: Allison De Bruycker, Chief Executive Officer
CFO: Kimberly Hibschman, Chief Financial Officer
CIO: Jim Cruson, Chief Information Officer
CHR: Roberta Bachman, Director Human Resources
CNO: Carrie Gray, Director of Nursing
Web address: www.riverviewbehavioralhealth.com
**Control:** Corporation, Investor–owned (for–profit) **Service:** Psychiatric

> **Staffed Beds:** 62

**VISTA HEALTH TEXARKANA** See Riverview Behavioral Health

---

| **Hospital, Medicare Provider Number, Address, Telephone, Approval, Facility, and Physician Codes, Health Care System** | | |
|---|---|---|
| ★ American Hospital Association (AHA) membership | ○ Healthcare Facilities Accreditation Program | ⇑ Center for Improvement in Healthcare Quality Accreditation |
| ☐ The Joint Commission accreditation | ◇ DNV Healthcare Inc. accreditation | △ Commission on Accreditation of Rehabilitation Facilities (CARF) accreditation |

## VAN BUREN—Crawford County

⊞ **BAPTIST HEALTH - VAN BUREN (040018)**, East Main and South 20th Streets, Zip 72956–5715, Mailing Address: P.O. Box 409, Zip 72957–0409; tel. 479/474–3401, (Nonreporting) **A**1 10 **F**3 29 30 40 43 45 64 68 70 81 89 107 108 111 119 151 **S** Baptist Health, Little Rock, AR
Primary Contact: Kimberly J. Miller, FACHE, President, Western Region
CHR: James Ford, Director Human Resources
Web address: www.https://www.sparkshealth.com/
**Control:** Other not–for–profit (including NFP Corporation) **Service:** General medical and surgical

**Staffed Beds:** 17 **Admissions:** 834 **Census:** 6 **Outpatient Visits:** 34437
**Births:** 0 **Total Expense ($000):** 18324 **Payroll Expense ($000):** 6136
**Personnel:** 85

**SPARKS MEDICAL CENTER - VAN BUREN** See Baptist Health - Van Buren

## WALDRON—Scott County

**MERCY HOSPITAL OF SCOTT COUNTY** See Mercy Hospital Waldron

★ **MERCY HOSPITAL WALDRON (041305)**, 1341 West 6th Street, Zip 72958–7642; tel. 479/637–4135, (Nonreporting) **A**10 18 **F**3 15 35 40 43 45 57 59 64 65 68 81 85 107 119 127 129 133 148 149 **P**8 **S** Mercy, Chesterfield, MO
Primary Contact: Teresa Williams, R.N., Regional Administrator
COO: Brent Hubbard, FACHE, Chief Operating Officer
CFO: Greta Wilcher, Senior Vice President and Chief Financial Officer
CNO: Nick Hunt, Interim Director of Nursing
Web address: www.https://www.mercy.net/practice/mercy-hospital-waldron/
**Control:** Church operated, Nongovernment, not–for–profit **Service:** General medical and surgical

**Staffed Beds:** 24 **Admissions:** 276 **Census:** 3 **Outpatient Visits:** 17580
**Births:** 0 **Total Expense ($000):** 11685 **Payroll Expense ($000):** 5056
**Personnel:** 65

## WALNUT RIDGE—Lawrence County

⊞ **LAWRENCE MEMORIAL HOSPITAL (041309)**, 1309 West Main, Zip 72476–1430, Mailing Address: P.O. Box 839, Zip 72476–0839; tel. 870/886–1200, (Total facility includes 150 beds in nursing home–type unit) (Nonreporting) **A**1 5 10 18 **F**3 11 15 29 32 34 35 40 45 46 47 57 59 84 85 87 97 107 110 111 114 119 127 128 129 130 133 135 146
Primary Contact: Josh Conlee, President
COO: Junior Briner, Chief Operating Officer
CFO: Vanessa Wagner, Chief Financial Officer
CMO: Kevin M. Diamond, M.D., Chief Medical Officer
CIO: Josh Wise, Director Information Technology
CHR: Charles Walker, Director Human Resource
CNO: Rosalind C Casillas, Chief Nursing Officer
Web address: www.lawrencehealth.net
**Control:** Other not–for–profit (including NFP Corporation) **Service:** General medical and surgical

**Staffed Beds:** 175 **Admissions:** 937 **Census:** 140 **Outpatient Visits:** 35147
**Births:** 0 **Total Expense ($000):** 27008 **Payroll Expense ($000):** 11357
**Personnel:** 224

## WARREN—Bradley County

★ **BRADLEY COUNTY MEDICAL CENTER (041327)**, 404 South Bradley Street, Zip 71671–3493; tel. 870/226–3731, (Nonreporting) **A**10 18
Primary Contact: Steve Henson, Chief Executive Officer
CFO: Brandon Gorman, Chief Financial Officer
CMO: Joe H Wharton, M.D., Chief of Staff
CHR: Brooke Hatch, Director Human Resource
CNO: Sarah Tucker, Chief Nursing Officer
Web address: www.bradleycountymedicalcenter.com
**Control:** Other not–for–profit (including NFP Corporation) **Service:** General medical and surgical

**Staffed Beds:** 33

**BRADLEY COUNTY MEM HOSPITAL** See Bradley County Medical Center

## WEST MEMPHIS—Crittenden County

⊞ **BAPTIST MEMORIAL HOSPITAL - CRITTENDEN, INC. (040156)**, 2100 North 7th Street, Zip 72301–2017; tel. 870/394–7800, (Nonreporting) **A**1 2 **F**3 8 11 15 29 30 31 34 35 40 44 45 50 57 59 65 68 78 79 81 91 100 102 107 108 111 115 119 154 **P**6 **S** Baptist Memorial Health Care Corporation, Memphis, TN
Primary Contact: Brian Welton, Chief Executive Officer and Administrator
Web address: www.baptistonline.org
**Control:** Other not–for–profit (including NFP Corporation) **Service:** General medical and surgical

**Staffed Beds:** 11 **Admissions:** 499 **Census:** 3 **Outpatient Visits:** 25667
**Births:** 3

☐ **PERIMETER BEHAVIORAL HOSPITAL OF WEST MEMPHIS (044021)**, 600 North Seventh Street, Zip 72301–3235; tel. 870/394–7100, (Nonreporting) **A**1 **S** Perimeter Healthcare, Alpharetta, GA
Primary Contact: Barbara Radebaugh, Chief Executive Officer
Web address: www.https://www.perimeterhealthcare.com
**Control:** Corporation, Investor–owned (for–profit) **Service:** Psychiatric

**Staffed Beds:** 24

## WYNNE—Cross County

**CROSSBRIDGE COMMUNITY HOSPITAL** See Crossridge Community Hospital

⊞ **CROSSRIDGE COMMUNITY HOSPITAL (041307)**, 310 South Falls Boulevard, Zip 72396–3013, Mailing Address: P.O. Box 590, Zip 72396–0590; tel. 870/238–3300, (Nonreporting) **A**1 10 18 **F**1 3 4 11 15 16 17 28 34 35 40 57 59 62 64 67 68 69 70 72 73 80 81 88 89 90 93 98 107 110 111 114 119 128 130 133 146 148
Primary Contact: Gary R. Sparks, Administrator
COO: Bryan Mattes, Associate Administrator
CFO: Janice Morris, Accountant
CIO: Gail Copeland, Director Management Information Systems
CHR: Bertha Ragle, Director Personnel
CNO: Amelia Davis, Director of Nursing
Web address: www.https://www.stbernards.info
**Control:** Church operated, Nongovernment, not–for–profit **Service:** General medical and surgical

**Staffed Beds:** 15 **Admissions:** 664 **Census:** 8 **Outpatient Visits:** 19440
**Births:** 0 **Total Expense ($000):** 16032 **Payroll Expense ($000):** 6632
**Personnel:** 129

*Many Facility Codes have changed. Please refer to the AHA Guide Code Chart.*     © 2021 AHA Guide

AR

# CALIFORNIA

## ALAMEDA—Alameda County

✠ **ALAMEDA HOSPITAL (050211)**, 2070 Clinton Avenue, Zip 94501–4397; tel. 510/522–3700, (Total facility includes 181 beds in nursing home–type unit) (Nonreporting) **A**1 3 5 10 **F**3 11 15 17 18 29 31 34 35 36 39 40 43 46 50 57 58 59 70 77 78 79 81 82 83 85 93 97 107 108 110 114 118 119 128 130 131 132 146 147 148 **S** Alameda Health System, San Leandro, CA
Primary Contact: Delvecchio Finley, Chief Executive Officer
CFO: Robert C Anderson, Interim Chief Financial Officer
CMO: Aika Sharma, M.D., President Medical Staff
CIO: Robert Lundy-Paine, Director Information Systems
CHR: Phyllis Weiss, Director Human Resources
Web address: www.alamedahealthsystem.org
**Control:** Hospital district or authority, Government, Nonfederal **Service:** General medical and surgical

**Staffed Beds:** 215 **Admissions:** 2997 **Census:** 212 **Outpatient Visits:** 31809 **Births:** 0 **Total Expense ($000):** 107980 **Payroll Expense ($000):** 58722 **Personnel:** 558

## ALHAMBRA—Los Angeles County

**ALHAMBRA HOSPITAL** See Alhambra Hospital Medical Center

☐ **ALHAMBRA HOSPITAL MEDICAL CENTER (050281)**, 100 South Raymond Avenue, Zip 91801–3199, Mailing Address: P.O. Box 510, Zip 91802–2510; tel. 626/570–1606, (Nonreporting) **A**1 10 **S** AHMC & Healthcare, Inc., Alhambra, CA
Primary Contact: Iris Lai, Chief Executive Officer
CFO: Linda Marsh, Vice President Financial Services and Chief Financial Officer
CMO: Stephen Chen, M.D., Chief Medicare
CIO: Johnson Legaspi, Director Information Systems
CHR: Elizabeth Sabandit, Director Human Resources
CNO: Eleanor Martinez, Chief Nursing Officer
Web address: www.alhambrahospital.com
**Control:** Partnership, Investor–owned (for–profit) **Service:** General medical and surgical

**Staffed Beds:** 144

## ALTURAS—Modoc County

★ **MODOC MEDICAL CENTER (051330)**, 228 West McDowell Avenue, Zip 96101–3934; tel. 530/233–5131, (Nonreporting) **A**10 18
Primary Contact: Kevin Kramer, Chief Executive Officer
CMO: Ed Richert, M.D., Chief of Staff
CHR: Diane Hagelthorn, Human Resources Generalist
Web address: www.modocmedicalcenter.org
**Control:** County, Government, Nonfederal **Service:** General medical and surgical

**Staffed Beds:** 87

## ANAHEIM—Orange County

☐ **AHMC ANAHEIM REGIONAL MEDICAL CENTER (050226)**, 1111 West La Palma Avenue, Zip 92801–2881; tel. 714/774–1450, (Nonreporting) **A**1 10 **S** AHMC & Healthcare, Inc., Alhambra, CA
Primary Contact: Richard Castro, Chief Executive Officer
COO: Mary Anne Monje, Chief Operations Officer
CFO: Mary Anne Monje, Chief Financial Officer
CMO: Amitabh Prakash, M.D., Chief Medical Officer
CIO: Jeff DesRoches, Director Information Systems
CHR: Jason Jaquez, Human Resource Director
CNO: Lisa Hahn, R.N., Chief Nursing Officer
Web address: www.anaheimregionalmc.com
**Control:** Other not–for–profit (including NFP Corporation) **Service:** General medical and surgical

**Staffed Beds:** 223

☐ **ANAHEIM GLOBAL MEDICAL CENTER (050744)**, 1025 South Anaheim Boulevard, Zip 92805–5806; tel. 714/533–6220, (Nonreporting) **A**1 10 **S** KPC Healthcare, Inc., Santa Ana, CA
Primary Contact: Jamie Yoo, Chief Executive Officer
CFO: John Collins, Chief Financial Officer
CMO: Beena Shah, M.D., Chief of Staff and Chief Medical Officer
CNO: Bonita Wells Veal, Chief Nursing Officer
Web address: www.anaheim-gmc.com
**Control:** Corporation, Investor–owned (for–profit) **Service:** General medical and surgical

**Staffed Beds:** 188

**ANAHEIM REGIONAL MEDICAL CENTER** See Ahmc Anaheim Regional Medical Center

**COLUMBIA WEST ANAHEIM MED CTR** See West Anaheim Medical Center

**KAISER PERMANENTE ANAHEIM MEDICAL CENTER** See Kaiser Permanente Orange County Anaheim Medical Center

✠ **KAISER PERMANENTE ORANGE COUNTY ANAHEIM MEDICAL CENTER (050609)**, 3440 East La Palma Avenue, Zip 92806–2020; tel. 714/644–2000, (Includes ORANGE COUNTY IRVINE MEDICAL CENTER, Mailing address: 6640 Alton Parkway, Irvine, California, Zip 92618; tel. 949/932–5000; Mark E Costa, Executive Director), (Nonreporting) **A**1 3 5 10 **F**3 8 13 15 18 19 20 22 29 30 31 35 36 37 40 44 45 46 47 48 49 50 51 53 55 56 57 59 60 61 62 63 64 65 66 68 70 72 74 75 76 77 78 79 80 81 82 84 85 86 87 89 92 93 100 107 108 110 111 114 115 119 130 135 146 148 149 150 154 155 156 157 **S** Kaiser Foundation Hospitals, Oakland, CA
Primary Contact: Mark E. Costa, Executive Director
COO: Margie Harrier, MSN, R.N., Medical Center Chief Operations Officer
CFO: Marcus Hoffman, Area Chief Financial Officer
CMO: Nancy Gin, M.D., Area Associate Medical Director
CIO: James Brady, Area Information Officer
CHR: Jocelyn A. Herrera, Director Human Resources
CNO: Martha Dispoto, R.N., IChief Nurse Executive, Anaheim Medical Center
Web address: www.kp.org
**Control:** Other not–for–profit (including NFP Corporation) **Service:** General medical and surgical

**Staffed Beds:** 478 **Admissions:** 24177 **Census:** 255 **Outpatient Visits:** 424535 **Births:** 6691 **Personnel:** 3651

☐ **WEST ANAHEIM MEDICAL CENTER (050426)**, 3033 West Orange Avenue, Zip 92804–3183; tel. 714/827–3000, (Nonreporting) **A**1 3 5 10 13 **S** Prime Healthcare, Ontario, CA
Primary Contact: Allen Stefanek, Chief Executive Officer
CFO: Kora Guoyavatin, Chief Financial Officer
CMO: Hassan Alkhouli, M.D., Chief Medical Officer
CIO: Vic Mahan, Director Information Technology
CHR: Stephanie Sioson, Director Human Resources
Web address: www.westanaheimmedctr.com
**Control:** Partnership, Investor–owned (for–profit) **Service:** General medical and surgical

**Staffed Beds:** 219

**WESTERN MEDICAL CENTER ANAHEIM** See Anaheim Global Medical Center

---

**Hospital, Medicare Provider Number, Address, Telephone, Approval, Facility, and Physician Codes, Health Care System**

★ American Hospital Association (AHA) membership
☐ The Joint Commission accreditation
○ Healthcare Facilities Accreditation Program
◇ DNV Healthcare Inc. accreditation
⇧ Center for Improvement in Healthcare Quality Accreditation
△ Commission on Accreditation of Rehabilitation Facilities (CARF) accreditation

## ANTIOCH—Contra Costa County

**ANTIOCH MEDICAL CENTER** See Kaiser Permanente Antioch Medical Center

☒ **KAISER PERMANENTE ANTIOCH MEDICAL CENTER (050760)**, 4501 Sand Creek Road, Zip 94531–8687; tel. 925/813–6500, (Nonreporting) **A**1 2 5 10 **F**3 11 13 15 18 26 30 31 34 37 39 40 41 45 49 56 60 63 64 68 70 73 74 75 76 78 79 80 81 82 84 85 86 87 100 107 108 110 111 114 115 118 119 120 121 123 124 126 130 135 146 149 154 **S** Kaiser Foundation Hospitals, Oakland, CA
Primary Contact: Colleen McKeown, Senior Vice President and Area Manager
CFO: Kerry Easthope, Area Finance Officer
CMO: Dale Poppert, M.D., Chief of Staff
CIO: Mical Cayton, Area Information Officer
CHR: Davida Lindsay-Bell, Area Human Resources Leader
CNO: Janet Jule, Chief Nurse Executive
Web address: www.https://health.kaiserpermanente.org/wps/portal/facility/100382
**Control:** Other not–for–profit (including NFP Corporation) **Service:** General medical and surgical

**Staffed Beds:** 150 **Admissions:** 7404 **Census:** 63 **Outpatient Visits:** 153362 **Births:** 1822 **Personnel:** 757

☒ **SUTTER DELTA MEDICAL CENTER (050523)**, 3901 Lone Tree Way, Zip 94509–6253; tel. 925/779–7200, (Nonreporting) **A**1 5 10 **S** Sutter Health, Sacramento, CA
Primary Contact: Sherie C. Hickman, Chief Executive Officer
CFO: Julie Peterson, Chief Financial Officer
CMO: Anupam Mapara, M.D., Chief of Staff
CIO: Kathy Frederickson, Information Systems Site Lead
CHR: Noemi Whitehead, Administrative Director Human Resources
Web address: www.sutterdelta.org
**Control:** Other not–for–profit (including NFP Corporation) **Service:** General medical and surgical

**Staffed Beds:** 132

**SUTTER DELTA MEMORIAL HOSPITAL** See Sutter Delta Medical Center

## APPLE VALLEY—San Bernardino County

**ST. JOSEPH HEALTH ST. MARY** See St. Mary Medical Center

☒ **ST. MARY MEDICAL CENTER (050300)**, 18300 Highway 18, Zip 92307–2206, Mailing Address: P.O. Box 7025, Zip 92307–0725; tel. 760/242–2311, (Nonreporting) **A**1 3 5 10 **F**8 11 18 20 22 28 29 30 40 45 46 50 68 70 71 72 75 76 77 81 83 84 89 93 107 108 111 115 119 126 130 146 147 148 156 **P**2 3 5 **S** Providence St. Joseph Health, Renton, WA
Primary Contact: Randall Castillo, Chief Executive Officer
CFO: Tracey Fernandez, Chief Financial Officer
CMO: Riad Z. Abdelkarim, M.D., Vice President and Chief Medical Officer
CIO: Doug Kleine, IT Director
CHR: Jean Holtman, Vice President, Human Resources
CNO: Marilyn Drone, R.N., MSN, Vice President, CNO
Web address: www.stmaryapplevalley.com/
**Control:** Church operated, Nongovernment, not–for–profit **Service:** General medical and surgical

**Staffed Beds:** 213 **Admissions:** 13837 **Census:** 175 **Outpatient Visits:** 97685 **Births:** 1766 **Total Expense ($000):** 236684 **Payroll Expense ($000):** 132011 **Personnel:** 1476

## ARCADIA—Los Angeles County

**METHODIST HOSPITAL** See Methodist Hospital of Southern California

☒ **METHODIST HOSPITAL OF SOUTHERN CALIFORNIA (050238)**, 300 West Huntington Drive, Zip 91007–3473, Mailing Address: P.O. Box 60016, Zip 91066–6016, (Nonreporting) **A**1 2 3 10 **F**3 12 13 14 17 18 20 22 24 26 28 29 30 31 34 35 37 38 40 45 46 48 49 50 51 55 56 57 58 59 60 64 65 68 70 72 74 75 76 77 78 79 81 82 84 85 86 87 90 92 94 96 107 108 110 111 114 115 119 130 132 135 146 147 148 156
Primary Contact: Dan F. Ausman, President and Chief Executive Officer
COO: Steven A. Sisto, Senior Vice President and Chief Operating Officer
CFO: William E. Grigg, Senior Vice President and Chief Financial Officer
CHR: Gwen Chambers, Executive Director Human Resources
Web address: www.methodisthospital.org
**Control:** Other not–for–profit (including NFP Corporation) **Service:** General medical and surgical

**Staffed Beds:** 294 **Admissions:** 15403 **Census:** 211 **Outpatient Visits:** 76811 **Births:** 1525 **Total Expense ($000):** 269905 **Payroll Expense ($000):** 139255 **Personnel:** 1331

## ARCATA—Humboldt County

○ **MAD RIVER COMMUNITY HOSPITAL (050028)**, 3800 Janes Road, Zip 95521–4788, Mailing Address: P.O. Box 1115, Zip 95518–1115; tel. 707/822–3621, (Nonreporting) **A**10 11
Primary Contact: Douglas A. Shaw, Chief Executive Officer
CFO: Michael Young, Chief Financial Officer
CMO: Bonnie MacEvoy, Chief of Staff
CIO: Jedd Rudd, Director of Ancillary Services and Safety
CNO: Sara Isaacson, Chief Nursing Officer
Web address: www.madriverhospital.com
**Control:** Corporation, Investor–owned (for–profit) **Service:** General medical and surgical

**Staffed Beds:** 42

## ARROYO GRANDE—San Luis Obispo County

**AMI ARROYO GRANDE COMM HOSP** See Arroyo Grande Community Hospital

★ **ARROYO GRANDE COMMUNITY HOSPITAL (050016)**, 345 South Halcyon Road, Zip 93420–3896; tel. 805/489–4261, (Nonreporting) **A**10
Primary Contact: Sue Andersen, Chief Executive Officer
CHR: Ami Padilla, Director Human Resources
Web address: www.arroyograndehospital.org
**Control:** Other not–for–profit (including NFP Corporation) **Service:** General medical and surgical

**Staffed Beds:** 67

## ATASCADERO—San Luis Obispo County

☐ **ATASCADERO STATE HOSPITAL**, 10333 El Camino Real, Zip 93422–5808, Mailing Address: P.O. Box 7001, Zip 93423–7001; tel. 805/468–2000, (Nonreporting) **A**1
Primary Contact: Bob Hushing-Kline, Hospital Administrator
COO: David Landrum, Chief Police Services
CFO: Janie Pagnini, Administrator Accounting
CMO: David Fennell, M.D., Acting Medical Director
CIO: James Grover, Manager Data Processing
CHR: Elizabeth Andres, Director Human Resources
CNO: Liz Souza, Coordinator Nursing Services
Web address: www.dmh.ca.gov/statehospitals/atascadero
**Control:** State, Government, Nonfederal **Service:** Psychiatric

**Staffed Beds:** 1184

## AUBURN—Placer County

**AUBURN FAITH COMMUNITY HOSP** See Sutter Auburn Faith Hospital

☒ **SUTTER AUBURN FAITH HOSPITAL (050498)**, 11815 Education Street, Zip 95602–2410; tel. 530/888–4500, (Nonreporting) **A**1 2 5 10 **S** Sutter Health, Sacramento, CA
Primary Contact: Mitchell J. Hanna, Chief Executive Officer
CFO: Gary Hubschman, Administrative Director Finance
CMO: John Mesic, M.D., Chief Medical Officer
CIO: Tom Ream, Regional Chief Information Officer
CHR: Yvette Martinez, Director Human Resources
Web address: www.sutterhealth.org
**Control:** Other not–for–profit (including NFP Corporation) **Service:** General medical and surgical

**Staffed Beds:** 72

## AVALON—Los Angeles County

**AVALON MUNICIPAL HOSPITAL** See Catalina Island Medical Center

★ **CATALINA ISLAND MEDICAL CENTER (051307)**, 100 Falls Canyon Road, Zip 90704, Mailing Address: P.O. Box 1563, Zip 90704–1563; tel. 310/510–0700, (Nonreporting) **A**10 18 **F**3 11 28 34 36 40 50 57 64 65 75 93 96 107 113 119 127 128 130 133 134 146 154 **P**5
Primary Contact: Jason Paret, Chief Executive Officer
COO: Stacie Amarantos, Chief Operating Officer
CFO: John Lovrich, Chief Financial Officer
CMO: Laura Ulibarri, M.D., Chief of Staff
CIO: Leah Keeline, Clinical Informatics Specialist
CHR: Lilly Hernandez, Human Resources Director
CNO: Stacie Amarantos, Chief Operating Officer
Web address: www.catalinaislandmedicalcenter.org
**Control:** Other not–for–profit (including NFP Corporation) **Service:** General medical and surgical

**Staffed Beds:** 12 **Admissions:** 15 **Census:** 8 **Outpatient Visits:** 22318 **Births:** 0 **Total Expense ($000):** 11607 **Payroll Expense ($000):** 3955 **Personnel:** 69

**CA**

*Many Facility Codes have changed. Please refer to the AHA Guide Code Chart.*

**BAKERSFIELD—Kern County**

☒ **ADVENTIST HEALTH BAKERSFIELD (050455)**, 2615 Chester Avenue, Zip 93301–2014, Mailing Address: P.O. Box 2615, Zip 93303–2615; tel. 661/395–3000, (Nonreporting) **A**1 2 10 **F**3 8 11 12 13 15 18 20 22 24 26 28 29 30 31 34 35 36 40 45 46 47 48 49 50 51 54 55 56 57 59 64 65 70 71 72 74 75 76 77 78 79 81 82 84 85 86 87 89 91 107 108 110 111 114 115 116 117 118 119 120 121 123 124 126 130 131 132 135 146 147 148 149 154 156 **P**3 7 **S** Adventist Health, Roseville, CA
Primary Contact: Sharlet Briggs, Ph.D., Market Chief Executive Officer and President
COO: Sharlet Briggs, Ph.D., Chief Operating Officer
CFO: Brent Soper, Chief Financial Officer
CHR: Marlene Kreidler, Executive Director Human Resources
Web address: www.sanjoaquinhospital.org
**Control:** Church operated, Nongovernment, not–for–profit **Service:** General medical and surgical

**Staffed Beds:** 254 **Admissions:** 16902 **Census:** 186 **Outpatient Visits:** 144502 **Births:** 2607 **Total Expense ($000):** 411970 **Payroll Expense ($000):** 113241 **Personnel:** 1677

☐ **BAKERSFIELD BEHAVIORAL HEALTHCARE HOSPITAL (054155)**, 5201 White Lane, Zip 93309; tel. 877/755–4907, (Nonreporting) **A**1 10 **S** Signature Healthcare Services, Corona, CA
Primary Contact: Jeff Chinn, Interim Chief Executive Officer
Web address: www.https://www.bakersfieldbehavioral.com/
**Control:** Other not–for–profit (including NFP Corporation) **Service:** Psychiatric

**Staffed Beds:** 60

☐ **BAKERSFIELD HEART HOSPITAL (050724)**, 3001 Sillect Avenue, Zip 93308–6337; tel. 661/316–6000, (Nonreporting) **A**1 10
Primary Contact: Michelle Oxford, Chief Operating Officer, Acting Chief Executive Officer
COO: Michelle Oxford, Chief Operating Officer, Acting Chief Executive Officer
CFO: Vickie Scharr, Chief Financial Officer
CMO: Brijesh Bhambi, M.D., Chief Medical Officer
CIO: Peter Mayer, Director Information Systems
CHR: Linda Hansen, Director Human Resources
Web address: www.bakersfieldhearthospital.com
**Control:** Partnership, Investor–owned (for–profit) **Service:** Heart

**Staffed Beds:** 47

☒ **BAKERSFIELD MEMORIAL HOSPITAL (050036)**, 420 34th Street, Zip 93301–2237; tel. 661/327–1792, (Nonreporting) **A**1 3 5 10 13 **F**3 11 13 15 16 17 18 20 22 24 26 28 29 30 31 37 40 45 50 58 60 68 70 72 74 75 76 77 78 79 81 84 85 86 88 89 93 107 108 109 111 114 115 119 120 124 126 130 146 147 148 149 156 **S** CommonSpirit Health, Chicago, IL
Primary Contact: Ken Keller, President and Chief Executive Officer
COO: Bruce Peters, Vice President and Chief Operating Officer
CFO: Jesica Hanson, Vice President and Chief Financial Officer
CMO: Rodney Mark Root, D.O., Vice President Medical Affairs
CHR: Sheri Comaianni, Vice President Human Resources
Web address: www.bakersfieldmemorial.org
**Control:** Other not–for–profit (including NFP Corporation) **Service:** General medical and surgical

**Staffed Beds:** 401 **Admissions:** 17216 **Census:** 187 **Outpatient Visits:** 157558 **Births:** 3194 **Total Expense ($000):** 475331 **Payroll Expense ($000):** 166504 **Personnel:** 1553

☒ **ENCOMPASS HEALTH REHABILITATION HOSPITAL OF BAKERSFIELD (053031)**, 5001 Commerce Drive, Zip 93309–0689; tel. 661/323–5500, (Nonreporting) **A**1 10 **S** Encompass Health Corporation, Birmingham, AL
Primary Contact: Martha Samora, R.N., FACHE, Chief Executive Officer
CFO: Robert Mosesian, Controller
CMO: Chris Yoon, M.D., Medical Director
CHR: Lori Brackett, Director Human Resources
CNO: Kathleen Szura, R.N., Chief Nursing Officer
Web address: www.healthsouthbakersfield.com
**Control:** Corporation, Investor–owned (for–profit) **Service:** Rehabilitation

**Staffed Beds:** 70

☐ **GOOD SAMARITAN HOSPITAL (050257)**, 901 Olive Drive, Zip 93308–4144, Mailing Address: P.O. Box 85002, Zip 93380–5002; tel. 661/215–7500, (Nonreporting) **A**1 10 **F**3 29 35 45 60 64 70 75 81 82 85 98 100 103 107 115 117 119 130 135 148 **P**1
Primary Contact: Amandeep Basra, Chief Administrative Officer
CFO: Gerrie Halbrook, Chief Financial Officer
CMO: Matab Singh, Chief of Staff
CNO: Toby Davis, Chief Nursing Officer
Web address: www.goodsamhospital.com
**Control:** Partnership, Investor–owned (for–profit) **Service:** General medical and surgical

**Staffed Beds:** 64 **Admissions:** 1709 **Census:** 25 **Outpatient Visits:** 7306 **Births:** 0 **Total Expense ($000):** 29337 **Payroll Expense ($000):** 11286 **Personnel:** 317

**GOOD SAMARITAN HOSPITAL-NORTH** See Good Samaritan Hospital

**HEALTHSOUTH BAKERSFIELD REHABILITATION HOSPITAL** See Encompass Health Rehabilitation Hospital of Bakersfield

☐ **KERN MEDICAL (050315)**, 1700 Mount Vernon Avenue, Zip 93306–4018; tel. 661/326–2000, (Nonreporting) **A**1 2 3 5 10
Primary Contact: Russell V. Judd, Chief Executive Officer
COO: Jared Leavitt, Chief Operating Officer
CFO: Andrew Cantu, Chief Financial Officer
CMO: Glenn Goldis, Chief Medical Officer
CHR: Lisa K. Hockersmith, Vice President Human Resources
CNO: Toni Smith, Chief Nursing Officer
Web address: www.kernmedical.com
**Control:** County, Government, Nonfederal **Service:** General medical and surgical

**Staffed Beds:** 188

**KERN MEDICAL CENTER** See Kern Medical

**MEMORIAL CENTER** See Bakersfield Behavioral Healthcare Hospital

**MERCY HOSPITAL** See Mercy Hospitals of Bakersfield

☒ **MERCY HOSPITALS OF BAKERSFIELD (050295)**, 2215 Truxtun Avenue, Zip 93301–3698, Mailing Address: P.O. Box 119, Zip 93302–0119; tel. 661/632–5000, (Includes MERCY SOUTHWEST HOSPITAL, Mailing address: 400 Old River Road, Bakersfield, California, Zip 93311; tel. 661/663–6000), (Nonreporting) **A**1 3 10 **F**11 12 13 15 26 29 30 31 34 35 36 40 44 45 46 47 48 49 51 54 57 59 62 64 65 68 69 70 71 72 74 75 76 77 78 79 81 84 85 86 87 92 97 100 101 102 107 108 110 111 112 113 114 115 116 117 118 119 120 121 122 124 126 130 131 132 135 146 147 148 149 154 **S** CommonSpirit Health, Chicago, IL
Primary Contact: Bruce Peters, Chief Executive Officer
CFO: Rodney Winegarner, Chief Financial Officer
CIO: Jeff Vague, Regional Manager Information Systems
CHR: Jay King, Vice President Human Resources
Web address: www.mercybakersfield.org
**Control:** Other not–for–profit (including NFP Corporation) **Service:** General medical and surgical

**Staffed Beds:** 204 **Admissions:** 11638 **Census:** 113 **Outpatient Visits:** 120168 **Births:** 2672 **Total Expense ($000):** 323597 **Payroll Expense ($000):** 120801 **Personnel:** 1398

**SAN JOAQUIN COMMUNITY HOSPITAL** See Adventist Health Bakersfield

**BALDWIN PARK—Los Angeles County**

**BALDWIN PARK MEDICAL CENTER** See Kaiser Permanente Baldwin Park Medical Center

☒ **KAISER PERMANENTE BALDWIN PARK MEDICAL CENTER (050723)**, 1011 Baldwin Park Boulevard, Zip 91706–5806; tel. 626/851–1011, (Nonreporting) **A**1 3 10 **F**3 6 9 13 15 29 30 31 32 34 35 38 40 41 44 46 50 53 54 56 57 59 60 61 62 63 64 65 66 68 70 72 74 75 76 77 78 79 81 82 83 84 85 86 87 92 93 94 97 107 108 110 111 112 114 115 116 117 118 119 130 131 132 135 144 146 147 148 149 154 156 157 **S** Kaiser Foundation Hospitals, Oakland, CA
Primary Contact: Margaret H. Pierce, Executive Director
COO: Payman Roshan, Chief Operating Officer
CFO: Rebecca Wheeler, Director Finance
CMO: John Bigley, M.D., Medical Director
CIO: Linda C Salazar, Information Technology Leader
CNO: Michelle Nowicki, R.N., MSN, Chief Nurse Executive
Web address: www.kp.org
**Control:** Other not–for–profit (including NFP Corporation) **Service:** General medical and surgical

**Staffed Beds:** 257 **Admissions:** 10338 **Census:** 102 **Outpatient Visits:** 407747 **Births:** 3139 **Personnel:** 1648

⊞ **KINDRED HOSPITAL-BALDWIN PARK (052045)**, 14148 Francisquito Avenue, Zip 91706–6120; tel. 626/388–2700, (Nonreporting) **A**1 3 10 **S** Kindred Healthcare, Louisville, KY
Primary Contact: Larry Foster, R.N., MSN, Chief Executive Officer
COO: Dina Garrow, Chief Nursing Officer and Chief Operating Officer
CFO: Christine Saltonstall, Chief Financial Officer
CMO: Anil Gupta, M.D., Chief of Staff
CHR: Antoinette Bibal, Director Human Resources
CNO: Dina Garrow, Chief Nursing Officer and Chief Operating Officer
Web address: www.khbaldwinpark.com
**Control**: Corporation, Investor–owned (for–profit) **Service**: Acute long–term care hospital

| Staffed Beds: 91 |
|---|

**VISTA HOSPITAL OF SAN GABRIEL VALLEY** See Kindred Hospital-Baldwin Park

### BANNING—Riverside County

★ **SAN GORGONIO MEMORIAL HOSPITAL (050054)**, 600 North Highland Springs Avenue, Zip 92220–3046; tel. 951/845–1121, (Nonreporting) **A**10 22 **F**3 8 11 13 15 18 28 29 30 34 35 40 45 49 50 56 57 68 70 76 79 81 82 85 87 104 107 108 110 111 115 119 130 146 147 148 149
Primary Contact: Steven R. Barron Esq, Chief Executive Officer
CFO: David Recupero, Chief Financial Officer
CIO: Duane Cicchelli, Director, Information Technology Services
CHR: Annah Karam, Director Human Resources
CNO: Pat Brown, R.N., Chief Nursing Officer
Web address: www.sgmh.org
**Control**: Hospital district or authority, Government, Nonfederal **Service**: General medical and surgical

| Staffed Beds: 79 Admissions: 2857 Census: 27 Outpatient Visits: 51355 Births: 268 Total Expense ($000): 80792 Payroll Expense ($000): 35263 Personnel: 675 |
|---|

**SAN GORGONIO MEMORIAL HOSPTIAL** See San Gorgonio Memorial Hospital

### BARSTOW—San Bernardino County

☐ **BARSTOW COMMUNITY HOSPITAL (050298)**, 820 East Mountain View Street, Zip 92311–3004; tel. 760/256–1761, (Nonreporting) **A**1 10 20 **F**3 11 13 15 18 20 22 24 29 40 45 46 47 48 49 50 64 70 75 76 79 81 86 87 107 111 114 119 **S** Quorum Health, Brentwood, TN
Primary Contact: Kolbe Sheridan, Chief Executive Officer
CFO: Carrie Howell, Chief Financial Officer
CIO: Scott Bullock, Director Information Systems
CNO: Donna M Smith, Chief Nursing Officer
Web address: www.barstowhospital.com
**Control**: Corporation, Investor–owned (for–profit) **Service**: General medical and surgical

| Staffed Beds: 30 Admissions: 1972 Census: 15 Outpatient Visits: 46116 Births: 343 Total Expense ($000): 46482 Payroll Expense ($000): 19030 Personnel: 309 |
|---|

### BERKELEY—Alameda County

**ALTA BATES SUMMIT MEDICAL CENTER** See Alta Bates Summit Medical Center-Alta Bates Campus

⊞ **ALTA BATES SUMMIT MEDICAL CENTER-ALTA BATES CAMPUS (050305)**, 2450 Ashby Avenue, Zip 94705–2067; tel. 510/204–4444, (Includes ALTA BATES MEDICAL CENTER-HERRICK CAMPUS, Mailing address: 2001 Dwight Way, Berkeley, California, Zip 94704; tel. 510/204–4444), (Nonreporting) **A**1 3 5 10 **S** Sutter Health, Sacramento, CA
Primary Contact: David D. Clark, FACHE, Chief Executive Officer
CFO: Robert Petrina, Chief Financial Officer
CMO: John Gentile, M.D., Vice President Medical Affairs
Web address: www.altabatessummit.org/
**Control**: Other not–for–profit (including NFP Corporation) **Service**: General medical and surgical

| Staffed Beds: 416 |
|---|

**HERRICK HOSPITAL & HLTH CENTER** See Alta Bates Medical Center-Herrick Campus

### BIG BEAR LAKE—San Bernardino County

★ **BEAR VALLEY COMMUNITY HOSPITAL (051335)**, 41870 Garstin Drive, Zip 92315, Mailing Address: P.O. Box 1649, Zip 92315–1649; tel. 909/866–6501, (Nonreporting) **A**10 18 **S** QHR Health, Brentwood, TN
Primary Contact: John P. Friel, Chief Executive Officer
CFO: Garth Hamblin, Chief Financial Officer
CMO: Steven Knapik, M.D., Chief of Staff
CHR: Erin Wilson, Human Resource Director
CNO: Kerri Jex, R.N., Chief Nursing Officer
Web address: www.bvchd.com
**Control**: Hospital district or authority, Government, Nonfederal **Service**: General medical and surgical

| Staffed Beds: 30 |
|---|

### BISHOP—Inyo County

⊞ **NORTHERN INYO HOSPITAL (051324)**, 150 Pioneer Lane, Zip 93514–2599; tel. 760/873–5811, (Nonreporting) **A**1 5 10 18
Primary Contact: Kelli Davis, Interim Chief Executive Officer
COO: Kelli Huntsinger, Chief Operating Officer
CMO: William Timbers, M.D., Interim Chief Medical Officer
CIO: Adam Taylor, Manager Information Technology
CHR: Georgan L. Stottlemyre, Chief Human Relations Officer
CNO: Tracy Aspel, Chief Nursing Officer
Web address: www.nih.org
**Control**: Hospital district or authority, Government, Nonfederal **Service**: General medical and surgical

| Staffed Beds: 25 |
|---|

### BLYTHE—Riverside County

⇑ **PALO VERDE HOSPITAL (050423)**, 250 North First Street, Zip 92225–1702; tel. 760/922–4115, (Nonreporting) **A**10 20 21
Primary Contact: Sandra J. Anaya, R.N., Chief Executive Officer
CFO: Christa Ronde, Assistant Chief Financial Officer
CMO: Hossain Sahlolbei, M.D., Chief of Staff
CIO: Jerome Learson, Manager Information Technology and Chief Security Officer
CHR: Myrna Davis, Manager Human Resources
CNO: Nena Foreman, Chief Nursing Officer
Web address: www.paloverdehospital.org
**Control**: Hospital district or authority, Government, Nonfederal **Service**: General medical and surgical

| Staffed Beds: 42 |
|---|

### BRAWLEY—Imperial County

★ ⇑ **PIONEERS MEMORIAL HEALTHCARE DISTRICT (050342)**, 207 West Legion Road, Zip 92227–7780; tel. 760/351–3333, (Nonreporting) **A**3 10 21 **F**3 13 15 18 29 30 31 34 40 45 46 49 50 51 54 57 60 64 68 70 72 74 76 78 79 80 81 82 85 89 93 107 110 111 115 117 119 127 130 144 146 147 148
Primary Contact: Lawrence E. Lewis, Chief Executive Officer
COO: Stephen J Campbell, Chief Operating Officer
CFO: Roger Armstrong, Interim Chief Financial Officer
CMO: Kestutis V Kuraitis, M.D., Chief of Staff
CIO: Kathleen S. McKernan, Director Information Systems
CHR: Julie Cunningham, Associate Administrator and Chief Human Resources Officer
CNO: Robyn Atadero, R.N., Chief Nursing Officer
Web address: www.pmhd.org
**Control**: Hospital district or authority, Government, Nonfederal **Service**: General medical and surgical

| Staffed Beds: 107 Admissions: 5146 Census: 52 Outpatient Visits: 166533 Births: 1691 Total Expense ($000): 132852 Payroll Expense ($000): 53570 |
|---|

⇑ **PIONEERS MEMORIAL HOSPITAL** See Pioneers Memorial Healthcare District

### BREA—Orange County

⊞ **KINDRED HOSPITAL-BREA (052039)**, 875 North Brea Boulevard, Zip 92821–2699; tel. 714/529–6842, (Nonreporting) **A**1 10 **S** Kindred Healthcare, Louisville, KY
Primary Contact: Kevin Chavez, Chief Executive Officer
COO: Denise Jenkins, Chief Clinical Officer
CFO: John Browne, Assistant Administrator Finance
CMO: Jyotika Wali, M.D., Chief of Staff
Web address: www.kindredhospitalbrea.com/
**Control**: Corporation, Investor–owned (for–profit) **Service**: Acute long–term care hospital

| Staffed Beds: 48 |
|---|

**VENCOR HOSPITAL-BREA** See Kindred Hospital-Brea

*Many Facility Codes have changed. Please refer to the AHA Guide Code Chart.*  © 2021 AHA Guide

## BURBANK—Los Angeles County

⊞ △ **PROVIDENCE SAINT JOSEPH MEDICAL CENTER (050235)**, 501 South Buena Vista Street, Zip 91505–4866; tel. 818/843–5111, (Nonreporting) **A**1 2 3 5 7 10 19 **F**3 11 12 13 15 17 18 20 22 24 26 28 29 30 31 34 35 36 39 40 41 44 45 46 47 48 49 50 51 53 54 55 56 57 58 59 62 63 64 65 70 72 74 75 76 77 78 79 81 82 83 84 85 86 87 90 92 93 96 97 100 101 107 108 110 111 114 115 116 117 118 119 120 121 122 123 126 130 131 132 143 145 146 147 148 149 154 156 **S** Providence St. Joseph Health, Renton, WA
Primary Contact: Kelly Linden, Chief Executive Officer
CFO: Glenn Bales, Chief Financial Officer
CMO: Nick Testa, M.D., Chief Medical Officer
CIO: Anne Marie Brody, Director Information Systems Customer Service
CHR: LaDonna Najieb, Service Area Director Human Resources
CNO: Elizabeth Hart, R.N., MSN, Chief Nursing Officer
Web address: www.providence.org
**Control:** Church operated, Nongovernment, not–for–profit **Service:** General medical and surgical

**Staffed Beds:** 385 **Admissions:** 15714 **Census:** 195 **Outpatient Visits:** 250760 **Births:** 2140 **Total Expense ($000):** 328118 **Payroll Expense ($000):** 152109 **Personnel:** 1877

**SAINT JOSEPH MEDICAL CENTER** See Providence Saint Joseph Medical Center

## BURLINGAME—San Mateo County

**MILLS-PENINSULA HEALTH SERVICE** See Mills-Peninsula Health Services

⊞ **MILLS-PENINSULA HEALTH SERVICES (050007)**, 1501 Trousdale Drive, Zip 94010–3282; tel. 650/696–5400, (Includes MILLS HEALTH CENTER, Mailing address: 100 South San Mateo Drive, San Mateo, California, Zip 94401; tel. 650/696–4400; Janet Wagner, R.N., Chief Executive Officer; MILLS-PENINSULA MEDICAL CENTER, Mailing address: 1501 Trousdale Drive, Burlingame, California, Zip 94010–3205; tel. 650/696–5400; Janet Wagner, R.N., Chief Executive Officer), (Nonreporting) **A**1 3 10 **S** Sutter Health, Sacramento, CA
Primary Contact: Janet Wagner, R.N., Chief Executive Officer
COO: Dolores S. Gomez, R.N., Chief Operating Officer
CFO: Catherine Messman, Chief Financial Officer
CMO: Ranjit Hundal, M.D., Chief Medical Executive
CIO: Michael Reandeau, Chief Information Officer
CHR: Claudia Christensen, Director, Human Resources
CNO: Vicki White, R.N., MS, Chief Nurse Executive
Web address: www.mills-peninsula.org
**Control:** Other not–for–profit (including NFP Corporation) **Service:** General medical and surgical

**Staffed Beds:** 266

**PENINSULA HOSPITAL** See Mills-Peninsula Medical Center

## CAMARILLO—Ventura County

**PLEASANT VALLEY HOSPITAL** See St. John's Pleasant Valley Hospital

⊞ **ST. JOHN'S PLEASANT VALLEY HOSPITAL (050616)**, 2309 Antonio Avenue, Zip 93010–1414; tel. 805/389–5800, (Nonreporting) **A**1 10 **S** CommonSpirit Health, Chicago, IL
Primary Contact: Darren W. Lee, President and Chief Executive Officer
COO: Richard Montmeny, Vice President Professional Services, On-Site Administrator
CFO: Donald P Bernard, Chief Financial Officer
CMO: Sahin Yanik, M.D., Vice President Medical Associate
CIO: Jeff Perry, Director Information Technology
CHR: Ed Gonzales, Vice President Human Resources
CNO: Dana Littlepage, Interim Chief Nursing Officer
Web address: www.dignityhealth.org/pleasantvalley
**Control:** Other not–for–profit (including NFP Corporation) **Service:** General medical and surgical

**Staffed Beds:** 127

## CAMP PENDLETON—San Diego County

**NAVAL HOSPITAL** See Naval Hospital Camp Pendleton

⊞ **NAVAL HOSPITAL CAMP PENDLETON**, 200 Mercy Circle, Zip 92055–5191, Mailing Address: P.O. Box 555191, Zip 92055–5191; tel. 760/725–1304, (Nonreporting) **A**1 3 5 **S** Bureau of Medicine and Surgery, Department of the Navy, Falls Church, VA
Primary Contact: Captain Shelley K. Perkins, Commanding Officer
CFO: CommanderGordon Blighton, Director Resource Management
CIO: Gabe Vallido, Chief Information Officer
CHR: LieutenantJet Ramos, Head Staff Administration
Web address: www.https://www.med.navy.mil/sites/cpen/newSite/Pages/default.aspx
**Service:** General medical and surgical

**Staffed Beds:** 72

## CARMICHAEL—Sacramento County

**MERCY SAN JUAN HOSPITAL** See Mercy San Juan Medical Center

⊞ **MERCY SAN JUAN MEDICAL CENTER (050516)**, 6501 Coyle Avenue, Zip 95608–0306; tel. 916/537–5000, (Nonreporting) **A**1 2 3 5 10 **F**3 8 11 12 13 17 20 26 28 29 30 31 35 36 37 40 43 45 46 47 48 49 62 63 64 65 68 70 72 74 75 76 77 78 79 81 82 84 89 100 104 107 108 109 111 114 115 119 126 130 132 135 146 148 149 153 154 **S** CommonSpirit Health, Chicago, IL
Primary Contact: Michael Korpiel, FACHE, Chief Executive Officer
COO: Paul R Luehrs, Chief Operating Officer
CFO: Robert Pascuzzi, Chief Financial Officer
CMO: Mark Owens, M.D., Vice President Medical Affairs
CHR: Donna Utley, Vice President Human Resources
Web address: www.mercysanjuan.org
**Control:** Other not–for–profit (including NFP Corporation) **Service:** General medical and surgical

**Staffed Beds:** 370 **Admissions:** 20323 **Census:** 256 **Outpatient Visits:** 102577 **Births:** 2025 **Total Expense ($000):** 683234 **Payroll Expense ($000):** 264792

## CASTRO VALLEY—Alameda County

⊞ **EDEN MEDICAL CENTER (050488)**, 20103 Lake Chabot Road, Zip 94546–5305; tel. 510/537–1234, (Nonreporting) **A**1 2 3 5 10 **S** Sutter Health, Sacramento, CA
Primary Contact: Patricia Ryan, Chief Executive Officer
Web address: www.edenmedcenter.org
**Control:** Other not–for–profit (including NFP Corporation) **Service:** General medical and surgical

**Staffed Beds:** 130

## CEDARVILLE—Modoc County

★ **SURPRISE VALLEY HEALTH CARE DISTRICT (051308)**, 741 North Main Street, Zip 96104, Mailing Address: P.O. Box 246, Zip 96104–0246; tel. 530/279–6111, (Nonreporting) **A**10 18
Primary Contact: William Bostic, Interim Administrator
CFO: Renae Sweet, Chief Financial Officer
CMO: Chuck Colas, M.D., Medical Director
CHR: William Bostic, Administrative Assistant Human Resources
Web address: www.https://sites.google.com/view/s-v-health-care-district/home
**Control:** Hospital district or authority, Government, Nonfederal **Service:** General medical and surgical

**Staffed Beds:** 4

**SURPRISE VALLEY HEALTHCARE DISTRICT** See Surprise Valley Health Care District

## CERRITOS—Los Angeles County

**COLLEGE HOSPITAL** See College Hospital Cerritos

☐ **COLLEGE HOSPITAL CERRITOS (054055)**, 10802 College Place, Zip 90703–1579; tel. 562/924–9581, (Nonreporting) **A**1 10 **S** College Health Enterprises, Santa Fe Springs, CA
Primary Contact: Stephen Witt, President and Chief Executive Officer
CFO: Roderick Bell, Chief Financial Officer
CHR: Holly Risha, Administrative Director Human Resources
Web address: www.collegehospitals.com
**Control:** Corporation, Investor–owned (for–profit) **Service:** Psychiatric

**Staffed Beds:** 187

---

| Hospital, Medicare Provider Number, Address, Telephone, Approval, Facility, and Physician Codes, Health Care System |
|---|
| ★ American Hospital Association (AHA) membership    ○ Healthcare Facilities Accreditation Program    ⇑ Center for Improvement in Healthcare Quality Accreditation |
| ☐ The Joint Commission accreditation    ◇ DNV Healthcare Inc. accreditation    △ Commission on Accreditation of Rehabilitation Facilities (CARF) accreditation |

## CHESTER—Plumas County

**SENECA DISTRICT HOSPITAL** See Seneca Healthcare District

★ **SENECA HEALTHCARE DISTRICT (051327)**, 130 Brentwood Drive,
Zip 96020–0737, Mailing Address: P.O. Box 737, Zip 96020–0737;
tel. 530/258–2151, (Nonreporting) **A**5 10 18
Primary Contact: Steve Boline, Acting Administrator and Chief Executive Officer
CFO: Carlene Slusher, Director Finance
CMO: Dana Ware, M.D., Chief of Staff
CIO: Elizabeth Steffen, Director Information Technology
CHR: James Kooyman, Human Resources Manager
CNO: Karen Turner, Chief Nursing Officer
Web address: www.senecahospital.org
**Control:** Hospital district or authority, Government, Nonfederal **Service:** General
medical and surgical

| Staffed Beds: 26 |
| --- |

## CHICO—Butte County

**CHICO COMMUNITY HOSPITAL** See Enloe Medical Center-Cohasset

✠ **ENLOE MEDICAL CENTER (050039)**, 1531 Esplanade, Zip 95926–3386;
tel. 530/332–7300, (Includes ENLOE MEDICAL CENTER-COHASSET, Mailing
address: 560 Cohasset Road, Chico, California, Zip 95926; tel. 530/332–7300),
(Nonreporting) **A**1 10 **F**3 7 8 11 12 13 17 18 19 20 22 24 26 28 29 30 31 34
35 36 38 39 40 43 44 45 46 49 50 51 54 57 59 61 62 63 64 65 68 69 70 73
74 75 76 77 78 79 80 81 82 84 85 87 89 90 91 92 93 94 96 98 100 102 107
108 109 111 114 115 116 117 118 119 120 121 123 124 126 130 131 132
143 144 146 147 148 149 155 157
Primary Contact: Michael C. Wiltermood, President and Chief Executive Officer
CMO: Forrest Olson, M.D., Chief Medical Officer
CHR: Carol Linscheid, Vice President Human Resources
Web address: www.enloe.org
**Control:** Other not–for–profit (including NFP Corporation) **Service:** General
medical and surgical

| Staffed Beds: 246 Admissions: 20269 Census: 240 Outpatient |
| --- |
| Visits: 337710 Births: 1943 Total Expense ($000): 655049 Payroll |
| Expense ($000): 226337 Personnel: 3302 |

## CHINO—San Bernardino County

**BHC CANYON RIDGE HOSPITAL** See Canyon Ridge Hospital

☐ **CANYON RIDGE HOSPITAL (054111)**, 5353 'G' Street, Zip 91710–5250;
tel. 909/590–3700, (Nonreporting) **A**1 3 10 **F**3 5 29 98 99 100 101 102 103
104 105 130 132 133 134 135 143 149 152 153 154 **S** Universal Health
Services, Inc., King of Prussia, PA
Primary Contact: Stephanie Bernier, Chief Executive Officer
CFO: Burt Harris, Chief Financial Officer
CMO: Mir Ali-Khan, M.D., Medical Director
CIO: Maria Patterson, Manager Health Information Management
CHR: Ericca Lopez, Director Human Resources
Web address: www.canyonridgehospital.com
**Control:** Corporation, Investor–owned (for–profit) **Service:** Psychiatric

| Staffed Beds: 107 Admissions: 5693 Census: 100 Outpatient |
| --- |
| Visits: 12488 Births: 0 Total Expense ($000): 28859 Payroll Expense |
| ($000): 12505 Personnel: 186 |

**CHINO VALLEY HOSPITAL** See Chino Valley Medical Center

○ **CHINO VALLEY MEDICAL CENTER (050586)**, 5451 Walnut Avenue,
Zip 91710–2672; tel. 909/464–8600, (Nonreporting) **A**3 5 10 11 12 13 **F**3 15
34 40 51 61 64 70 79 81 84 85 97 107 108 110 111 114 115 119 120 130
146 148 149 154 **S** Prime Healthcare, Ontario, CA
Primary Contact: Tim Moran, Chief Executive Officer
CIO: Vic Mahan, Chief Information Officer
Web address: www.cvmc.com
**Control:** Corporation, Investor–owned (for–profit) **Service:** General medical and
surgical

| Staffed Beds: 112 Admissions: 4727 Census: 43 Outpatient Visits: 48635 |
| --- |
| Births: 0 Total Expense ($000): 80843 Payroll Expense ($000): 35396 |
| Personnel: 560 |

## CHOWCHILLA—Madera County

**CHOWCHILLA DISTRICT MEMORIAL HOSPITAL** See Chowchilla Skilled Nursing
and Rehabilitation Facillity

## CHULA VISTA—San Diego County

**BAYVIEW HOSP & MENTAL SYSTEM** See Bayview Behavioral Health Campus

**COMM HOSP OF CHULA VISTA** See Sharp Chula Vista Medical Center

**SCRIPPS MEMORIAL HOSPITAL** See Scripps Mercy Hospital Chula Vista

**SCRIPPS MERCY HOSPITAL CHULA VISTA** See Scripps Mercy Hospital, San Diego

✠ **SHARP CHULA VISTA MEDICAL CENTER (050222)**, 751 Medical Center Court,
Zip 91911–6699; tel. 619/502–5800, (Total facility includes 100 beds in nursing
home–type unit) (Nonreporting) **A**1 2 10 **F**8 10 11 12 13 15 17 18 19 20 22 24 26
28 29 30 31 34 35 40 45 46 47 49 51 53 54 57 59 60 63 64 65 70 72 75 76 77
78 79 81 82 84 85 86 87 93 107 108 114 115 119 120 121 123 124 126 128
130 132 143 146 147 148 154 156 **P**3 5 **S** Sharp HealthCare, San Diego, CA
Primary Contact: Pablo Velez, R.N., Ph.D., Chief Executive Officer
CMO: Lynn Welling, M.D., Chief Medical Officer
CHR: Zoe Gardner, Manager Human Resources
Web address: www.sharp.com
**Control:** Other not–for–profit (including NFP Corporation) **Service:** General
medical and surgical

| Staffed Beds: 343 Admissions: 16229 Census: 280 Outpatient |
| --- |
| Visits: 160219 Births: 2252 Total Expense ($000): 420829 Payroll |
| Expense ($000): 172504 Personnel: 1858 |

## CLEARLAKE—Lake County

✠ **ADVENTIST HEALTH CLEAR LAKE (051317)**, 15630 18th Avenue,
Zip 95422–9336, Mailing Address: P.O. Box 6710, Zip 95422;
tel. 707/994–6486, (Nonreporting) **A**1 3 10 18 **F**29 30 33 34 35 39 40 45
50 57 64 70 76 77 79 81 82 85 86 87 92 93 96 97 100 107 108 110 111
114 115 119 127 129 130 132 133 146 148 149 154 **S** Adventist Health,
Roseville, CA
Primary Contact: David Santos, President and Chief Executive Officer
COO: David Santos, President Chief Executive Officer
CFO: Carlton Jacobson, Vice President of Finance
CMO: Marc Shapiro, M.D., Chief Medical Officer
CIO: Cambria Wheeler, Communications and Marketing
CHR: Audrey Barrall, Director Human Resources
CNO: Colleen Assavapisitkul, MSN, RN, HCAP, R.N., Patient Care Executive
Web address: www.adventisthealth.org
**Control:** Church operated, Nongovernment, not–for–profit **Service:** General
medical and surgical

| Staffed Beds: 25 Admissions: 1381 Census: 16 Outpatient Visits: 225503 |
| --- |
| Births: 148 Total Expense ($000): 114751 Payroll Expense ($000): 32840 |

**ST. HELENA HOSPITAL CLEAR LAKE** See Adventist Health Clear Lake

## CLOVIS—Fresno County

☐ **CLOVIS COMMUNITY MEDICAL CENTER (050492)**, 2755 Herndon Avenue,
Zip 93611–6801; tel. 559/324–4000, (Nonreporting) **A**1 3 10 **S** Community
Medical Centers, Fresno, CA
Primary Contact: Craig Castro, Chief Executive Officer
CFO: Tracy Kiritani, Vice President and Chief Financial Officer
CIO: George Vasquez, Chief Technology Officer
CHR: Ginny Burdick, Senior Vice President and Chief Human Resources Officer
Web address: www.communitymedical.org
**Control:** Other not–for–profit (including NFP Corporation) **Service:** General
medical and surgical

| Staffed Beds: 109 |
| --- |

**COMMUNITY MEDICAL CTR-CLOVIS** See Clovis Community Medical Center

## COLTON—San Bernardino County

✠ **ARROWHEAD REGIONAL MEDICAL CENTER (050245)**, 400 North Pepper
Avenue, Zip 92324–1819; tel. 909/580–1000, (Nonreporting) **A**1 3 5 10 13 **F**3 8
15 16 18 20 22 28 29 30 31 32 34 35 36 39 40 43 45 47 49 50 51 52 54 55
56 57 60 64 66 68 70 71 72 74 75 76 77 78 79 81 82 84 85 86 87 91 92 93
97 98 100 101 102 107 108 110 111 114 115 116 118 119 120 121 130 132
135 146 147 148 149 150 **P**5
Primary Contact: William L. Gilbert, Hospital Director
CFO: Arvind Oswal, Chief Financial Officer
CIO: Andrew Lerman, Interim Chief Information Officer
CHR: Susan Peterson, Human Resources Director
CNO: Nanette Buenavidez, Chief Nursing Officer
Web address: www.arrowheadmedcenter.org
**Control:** County, Government, Nonfederal **Service:** General medical and surgical

| Staffed Beds: 456 Admissions: 21102 Census: 328 Outpatient |
| --- |
| Visits: 355639 Births: 2974 Total Expense ($000): 678669 Payroll |
| Expense ($000): 218105 Personnel: 3138 |

**SAN BERNARDINO CNTY MED CENTER** See Arrowhead Regional Medical Center

*Many Facility Codes have changed. Please refer to the AHA Guide Code Chart.*
© 2021 AHA Guide

CA

## CONCORD—Contra Costa County

⊠ **JOHN MUIR BEHAVIORAL HEALTH CENTER (054131)**, 2740 Grant Street, Zip 94520–2265; tel. 925/674–4100, (Nonreporting) **A**1 10 **S** John Muir Health, Walnut Creek, CA
Primary Contact: Cindy Bolter, Chief Nursing and Operations Officer
COO: Arman Danielyan, M.D., Chief of Staff
CFO: Christian Pass, Senior Vice President and Chief Financial Officer
CMO: O B Towery, M.D., Chief of Staff
CIO: Jim Wesley, Senior Vice President and Chief Information Officer
CHR: Lisa Foust, Senior Vice President Human Resources
CNO: Cindy Bolter, Chief Nursing and Operations Officer
Web address: www.johnmuirhealth.com
**Control:** Other not–for–profit (including NFP Corporation) **Service:** Psychiatric

**Staffed Beds:** 73

**JOHN MUIR BEHAVIORAL HLTH** See John Muir Behavioral Health Center

⊠ **JOHN MUIR MEDICAL CENTER, CONCORD (050496)**, 2540 East Street, Zip 94520–1906; tel. 925/682–8200, (Nonreporting) **A**1 2 3 5 10 **F**3 12 15 17 18 20 22 24 26 28 29 30 31 34 37 39 40 41 44 45 46 47 48 49 50 55 56 57 58 59 61 64 68 70 74 75 77 78 79 80 81 82 83 84 85 86 87 93 100 102 107 108 110 115 118 119 120 121 123 126 130 132 141 145 146 148 149 156 157 **P**3 7 **S** John Muir Health, Walnut Creek, CA
Primary Contact: Jane Willemsen, President and Chief Administrative Officer
COO: Michael S Thomas, President and Chief Administrative Officer
CFO: Christian Pass, Interim Chief Financial Officer
CMO: John Merson, M.D., Chief of Staff
CIO: Jon Russell, Senior Vice President and Chief Information Officer
CHR: Lisa Foust, Senior Vice President Human Resources
CNO: Donna Brackley, R.N., MSN, Senior Vice President Patient Care Services
Web address: www.johnmuirhealth.com
**Control:** Other not–for–profit (including NFP Corporation) **Service:** General medical and surgical

**Staffed Beds:** 215 **Admissions:** 11872 **Census:** 151 **Outpatient Visits:** 123896 **Births:** 0 **Total Expense ($000):** 498254 **Payroll Expense ($000):** 180590 **Personnel:** 1010

**MOUNT DIABLO MEDICAL CENTER** See John Muir Medical Center, Concord

## CORONA—Riverside County

**CIRCLE CITY MEDICAL CENTER** See Corona Regional Medical Center-Rehabilitation

☐ **CORONA REGIONAL MEDICAL CENTER (050329)**, 800 South Main Street, Zip 92882–3400; tel. 951/737–4343, (Includes CORONA REGIONAL MEDICAL CENTER-REHABILITATION, Mailing address: 730 Magnolia Avenue, Corona, California, Zip 92879; tel. 951/736–7200; Mark H Uffer, Chief Executive Officer), (Nonreporting) **A**1 3 10 **F**3 12 13 15 18 20 22 26 29 30 34 35 40 45 46 47 48 49 50 57 59 62 63 64 65 67 70 75 76 79 81 84 85 87 98 100 101 102 104 105 106 107 108 110 111 114 115 119 128 130 143 146 147 148 149 154 157 **S** Universal Health Services, Inc., King of Prussia, PA
Primary Contact: Mark H. Uffer, Chief Executive Officer
COO: Alistair M Machoka, Chief Operating Officer
CMO: Paul Niu, Chief Medical Officer
CIO: De'Niro Pankey, Director Information Systems
CHR: Dale Cole, Director, Human Resources
CNO: Phyllis Snyder, Chief Nursing Officer
Web address: www.coronaregional.com
**Control:** Individual, Investor–owned (for–profit) **Service:** General medical and surgical

**Staffed Beds:** 238 **Admissions:** 9662 **Census:** 153 **Outpatient Visits:** 74679 **Births:** 925 **Total Expense ($000):** 157388 **Payroll Expense ($000):** 78419 **Personnel:** 1025

## CORONADO—San Diego County

**CORONADO HOSPITAL** See Sharp Coronado Hospital and Healthcare Center

⊠ **SHARP CORONADO HOSPITAL AND HEALTHCARE CENTER (050234)**, 250 Prospect Place, Zip 92118–1999; tel. 619/522–3600, (Total facility includes 108 beds in nursing home–type unit) (Nonreporting) **A**1 5 10 **F**3 8 11 15 29 30 34 35 36 37 40 41 45 46 47 49 53 57 58 59 60 64 65 68 70 74 75 77 79 81 82 84 85 86 87 91 93 107 111 114 119 126 128 130 132 135 146 148 149 154 **S** Sharp HealthCare, San Diego, CA
Primary Contact: Susan Stone, R.N., Ph.D., Senior Vice President and Chief Executive Officer
CFO: Victoria Day, Chief Financial Officer and Vice President of Ancillary Services
CHR: Rachel Davis, Director
CNO: Christopher Walker, Chief Nursing Officer and Operating Officer
Web address: www.sharp.com
**Control:** Other not–for–profit (including NFP Corporation) **Service:** General medical and surgical

**Staffed Beds:** 181 **Admissions:** 2542 **Census:** 117 **Outpatient Visits:** 81221 **Births:** 0 **Total Expense ($000):** 109960 **Payroll Expense ($000):** 47691 **Personnel:** 447

## COSTA MESA—Orange County

☐ **COLLEGE HOSPITAL COSTA MESA (050543)**, 301 Victoria Street, Zip 92627–7131; tel. 949/642–2734, (Nonreporting) **A**1 10 **S** College Health Enterprises, Santa Fe Springs, CA
Primary Contact: Susan L. Taylor, JD, Chief Executive Officer
CFO: Dale Bracy, Chief Financial Officer
CMO: Michael Schwartz, M.D., Chief of Staff
CIO: Eladio Aldana, Manager Information Systems
CHR: Sharon DuBruyne, Director Human Resources
Web address: www.collegehospitals.com/cosHome
**Control:** Corporation, Investor–owned (for–profit) **Service:** Psychiatric

**Staffed Beds:** 122

**FAIRVIEW DEVELOPMENTAL CENTER (050548)**, 2501 Harbor Boulevard, Zip 92626; tel. 714/957–5000, (Nonreporting) **A**10
Primary Contact: Cheryl Bright, Executive Director
Web address: www.dds.ca.gov/fairview/index.cfm
**Control:** State, Government, Nonfederal **Service:** Intellectual disabilities

**Staffed Beds:** 237

## COVINA—Los Angeles County

**AURORA BEHAVIORAL HEALTHCARE** See Aurora Charter Oak Hospital

☐ **AURORA CHARTER OAK HOSPITAL (054069)**, 1161 East Covina Boulevard, Zip 91724–1599; tel. 626/966–1632, (Nonreporting) **A**1 10 **S** Signature Healthcare Services, Corona, CA
Primary Contact: Todd A. Smith, Chief Executive Officer
COO: Sheila Cordova, Director Clinical Services and Chief Operating Officer
CMO: Adib Bitar, M.D., Medical Director
CHR: Christine de la Paz, Director Human Resources
CNO: Sheila Cordova, Chief Operating Officer and Chief Nursing Officer
Web address: www.charteroakhospital.com
**Control:** Corporation, Investor–owned (for–profit) **Service:** Psychiatric

**Staffed Beds:** 146

**CITRUS VALLEY MEDICAL CENTER-INTER COMMUNITY CAMPUS** See Emanate Health Inter-Community Hospital

⊠ △ **EMANATE HEALTH INTER-COMMUNITY HOSPITAL (050382)**, 210 West San Bernardino Road, Zip 91723–1515, Mailing Address: P.O. Box 6108, Zip 91722–5108; tel. 626/331–7331, (Includes CITRUS VALLEY MEDICAL CENTER-INTER-COMMUNITY CAMPUS, Mailing address: 210 West San Bernardino Road, Covina, California, Zip 91723–1515, P O Box 6108, Zip 91722–5108, tel. 626/331–7331; Robert H Curry, President and Chief Executive Officer; CITRUS VALLEY MEDICAL CENTER-QUEEN OF THE VALLEY CAMPUS, Mailing address: 1115 South Sunset Avenue, West Covina, California, Zip 91790–3940, P O Box 1980, Zip 91793–1980, tel. 626/962–4011; Robert H Curry, President and Chief Executive Officer), (Nonreporting) **A**1 3 7 10 **S** Emanate Health, Covina, CA
Primary Contact: Robert H. Curry, President and Chief Executive Officer
CFO: Roger Sharma, Executive Vice President/Chief Financial Officer
CIO: Daniel J Nash, Chief Information Officer
CHR: Ryan Burke EsqVice President, Human Resources
CNO: Melissa Howard, Chief Nurse Executive, ICH & FPH
Web address: www.cvhp.org
**Control:** Other not–for–profit (including NFP Corporation) **Service:** General medical and surgical

**Staffed Beds:** 320

**INTER-COMMUNITY MED CENTER** See Citrus Valley Medical Center-Inter-Community Campus

### CRESCENT CITY—Del Norte County

✠ **SUTTER COAST HOSPITAL (050417)**, 800 East Washington Boulevard, Zip 95531–8359; tel. 707/464–8511, (Nonreporting) **A**1 10 20 **S** Sutter Health, Sacramento, CA
Primary Contact: Mitchell J. Hanna, Chief Executive Officer
CNO: Rose Corcoran, R.N., Chief Nursing Executive
Web address: www.sutterhealth.org
**Control**: Other not–for–profit (including NFP Corporation) **Service**: General medical and surgical

**Staffed Beds:** 49

### CULVER CITY—Los Angeles County

**BROTMAN MEDICAL CENTER** See Southern California Hospital at Culver City

**SOUTHERN CALIFORNIA HOSPITAL AT CULVER CITY (050752)**, 3828 Delmas Terrace, Zip 90232–6806; tel. 310/836–7000, (Nonreporting) **A**10 **S** Prospect Medical Holdings, Los Angeles, CA
Primary Contact: Michael R. Klepin, Chief Executive Officer
CFO: Vincent Rubin, Chief Financial Officer
CMO: Martha Sonnenberg, M.D., Chief of Staff
CIO: Carrie Bonar, Chief Information Officer
CHR: Betty J Harris, Director Human Resources
Web address: www.sch-culvercity.com
**Control**: Corporation, Investor–owned (for–profit) **Service**: General medical and surgical

**Staffed Beds:** 239

### DALY CITY—San Mateo County

☐ **SETON MEDICAL CENTER (050289)**, 1900 Sullivan Avenue, Zip 94015–2229; tel. 650/992–4000, (Total facility includes 199 beds in nursing home–type unit) (Nonreporting) **A**1 2 10 **F**3 8 15 17 18 20 22 24 26 29 30 31 34 35 37 39 40 44 45 46 48 49 50 54 56 57 58 59 60 64 66 68 70 74 75 77 78 79 81 82 84 85 86 87 92 93 96 98 100 102 103 107 108 110 111 114 116 117 118 119 120 121 123 124 126 128 130 132 135 141 143 146 147 148 149 154 156 **P**3 **S** Verity Health System, Los Angeles, CA
Primary Contact: Mark Fratzke, R.N., President and Chief Executive Officer
COO: Stephanie Mearns, Vice President Patient Care Services and Chief Nurse Executive
CFO: Richard Wood, Chief Financial Officer
CMO: Timothy Ranney, M.D., Chief Medical Officer
CHR: Patricia White, Vice President Human Resources
CNO: Mark R Brown, Chief Nursing Officer
Web address: www.setonmedicalcenter.org
**Control**: Other not–for–profit (including NFP Corporation) **Service**: General medical and surgical

**Staffed Beds:** 446 **Admissions:** 5320 **Census:** 245 **Outpatient Visits:** 118414 **Births:** 0 **Total Expense ($000):** 294682 **Payroll Expense ($000):** 122247 **Personnel:** 891

### DAVIS—Yolo County

✠ **SUTTER DAVIS HOSPITAL (050537)**, 2000 Sutter Place, Zip 95616–6201, Mailing Address: P.O. Box 1617, Zip 95617–1617; tel. 530/756–6440, (Nonreporting) **A**1 3 5 10 **S** Sutter Health, Sacramento, CA
Primary Contact: Rachael McKinney, FACHE, Chief Executive Officer
CFO: Patti Pilgrim, Chief Financial Officer
CMO: Deven Merchant, M.D., Chief Medical Executive
CHR: Don Hartman, Director Human Resources
CNO: Tamara Davis, R.N., Chief Nurse Executive Officer
Web address: www.sutterhealth.org
**Control**: Other not–for–profit (including NFP Corporation) **Service**: General medical and surgical

**Staffed Beds:** 48

### DELANO—Kern County

○ **DELANO REGIONAL MEDICAL CENTER (050608)**, 1401 Garces Highway, Zip 93215–3690, Mailing Address: P.O. Box 460, Zip 93216–0460; tel. 661/725–4800, (Nonreporting) **A**10 11
Primary Contact: David Butler, Chief Executive Officer
CFO: Bahram Ghaffari, President
CIO: Sandy Bakich, Director Information Management
CHR: Del Garbanzos, Director Human Resources
CNO: Amy Scroggs, Chief Nursing Officer
Web address: www.drmc.com
**Control**: Other not–for–profit (including NFP Corporation) **Service**: General medical and surgical

**Staffed Beds:** 100

### DOWNEY—Los Angeles County

**DOWNEY MEDICAL CENTER** See Kaiser Permanente Downey Medical Center

**DOWNEY REGIONAL MEDICAL CENTER** See PIH Health Hospital - Downey

✠ **KAISER PERMANENTE DOWNEY MEDICAL CENTER (050139)**, 9333 Imperial Highway, Zip 90242–2812; tel. 562/657–9000, (Nonreporting) **A**1 3 5 10 **F**2 3 5 11 12 14 15 29 30 31 32 33 34 38 39 40 41 44 45 46 47 48 49 50 51 52 53 54 55 56 57 58 59 60 61 62 63 64 65 66 68 70 71 72 73 74 75 76 77 78 79 81 82 83 84 85 86 87 88 89 93 94 96 97 100 102 104 107 108 110 111 114 115 119 126 129 130 131 132 134 135 141 144 146 147 148 149 150 153 154 156 **P**6 **S** Kaiser Foundation Hospitals, Oakland, CA
Primary Contact: James Branchick, R.N., MS, Senior Vice President and Area Manager
CNO: Patricia J Clausen, R.N., Chief Nurse Executive
Web address: www.kaiserpermanente.org
**Control**: Other not–for–profit (including NFP Corporation) **Service**: General medical and surgical

**Staffed Beds:** 352 **Admissions:** 16089 **Census:** 184 **Outpatient Visits:** 232452 **Births:** 4232 **Personnel:** 3311

**LAC-RANCHO LOS AMIGOS CENTER** See Rancho Los Amigos National Rehabilitation Center

★ **PIH HEALTH HOSPITAL - DOWNEY (050393)**, 11500 Brookshire Avenue, Zip 90241–4917; tel. 562/904–5000, (Nonreporting) **A**3 5 10 12 13 22 **F**3 8 11 13 15 17 18 20 22 24 26 29 30 35 40 41 45 46 49 50 51 59 60 64 68 70 74 76 79 81 84 85 87 91 92 93 97 100 102 107 111 114 115 119 130 143 146 147 148 149 154 156 **S** PIH Health, Whittier, CA
Primary Contact: James R. West, President and Chief Executive Officer
CFO: Greg Williams, Chief Financial Officer
CIO: Jason Fischer, Chief Information Officer
CHR: Sherri Hollingsworth, Chief Human Resources Officer
CNO: Ceonne Houston-Raasikh, Chief Nursing Officer
Web address: www.PIHHealth.org
**Control**: Other not–for–profit (including NFP Corporation) **Service**: General medical and surgical

**Staffed Beds:** 156 **Admissions:** 9260 **Census:** 87 **Outpatient Visits:** 77043 **Births:** 959 **Total Expense ($000):** 170452 **Payroll Expense ($000):** 71473 **Personnel:** 1090

☐ △ **RANCHO LOS AMIGOS NATIONAL REHABILITATION CENTER (050717)**, 7601 East Imperial Highway, Zip 90242–3496; tel. 562/401–7111, (Nonreporting) **A**1 3 5 7 10 **S** Los Angeles County-Department of Health Services, Los Angeles, CA
Primary Contact: Aries Limbaga, R.N., Chief Executive Officer
COO: Benjamin Ovando, Chief Operations Officer
CFO: Robin Bayus, Chief Financial Officer
CMO: Mindy Aisen, M.D., Chief Medical Officer
CIO: Francis Tang, Chief Information Officer
CHR: Elizabeth Jacobi, Associate Director Human Resources
Web address: www.rancho.org
**Control**: County, Government, Nonfederal **Service**: Rehabilitation

**Staffed Beds:** 207

### DUARTE—Los Angeles County

**CITY OF HOPE NATIONAL MEDICAL CENTER** See City of Hope's Helford Clinical Research Hospital

✠ **CITY OF HOPE'S HELFORD CLINICAL RESEARCH HOSPITAL (050146)**, 1500 East Duarte Road, Zip 91010–3012; tel. 626/256–4673, (Nonreporting) **A**1 2 3 5 8 10 **F**3 8 11 14 15 18 19 29 30 31 34 35 36 38 39 44 45 46 47 49 50 55 56 57 58 59 60 61 63 64 68 70 74 75 77 78 79 80 81 82 84 85 86 87 88 89 91 92 93 94 96 100 101 104 107 108 110 111 114 115 116 117 118 119 120 121 123 124 126 130 132 135 136 142 144 145 146 147 148 149 154 156 158 **P**3
Primary Contact: Robert Stone, President and Chief Executive Officer
COO: Jeff E. Walker, Chief Operating Officer
CFO: Jennifer Parkhurst, Chief Financial Officer
CMO: William D. Boswell, M.D., JrChief Medical Officer
CIO: Mark Hulse, MSN, Chief Digital Officer
CHR: Stephanie Neuvirth, Chief Human Resource and Diversity Officer
Web address: www.cityofhope.org
**Control**: Other not–for–profit (including NFP Corporation) **Service**: Cancer

**Staffed Beds:** 215 **Admissions:** 6661 **Census:** 206 **Outpatient Visits:** 280197 **Births:** 0 **Total Expense ($000):** 1349466 **Payroll Expense ($000):** 443593 **Personnel:** 4546

*Many Facility Codes have changed. Please refer to the AHA Guide Code Chart.*

CA

**EL CENTRO—Imperial County**

✠ **EL CENTRO REGIONAL MEDICAL CENTER (050045)**, 1415 Ross Avenue, Zip 92243–4398; tel. 760/339–7100, (Nonreporting) **A**1 3 10
Primary Contact: Adolphe Edward, Chief Executive Officer
COO: Tomas Virgen, R.N., MSN, Chief Operating Officer
CFO: Kathleen Farmer, Assistant Administrator Finance and Chief Financial Officer
CIO: John Gaede, Director Information Systems
CHR: Bill Moore, Chief Human Resources
Web address: www.ecrmc.org
**Control:** City, Government, Nonfederal **Service:** General medical and surgical

**Staffed Beds:** 161

**ELDRIDGE—Sonoma County**

**SONOMA DEVELOPMENTAL CENTER (050547)**, 15000 Arnold Drive, Zip 95431–8900, Mailing Address: P.O. Box 1493, Zip 95431–1493; tel. 707/938–6000, (Nonreporting) **A**10
Primary Contact: Aleana Carreon, Executive Director
COO: Karen Clark, Director Administrative Services
CMO: Carol Castillo, Medical Director
CHR: Brenda Dukes, Director Human Resources
Web address: www.dds.ca.gov/sonoma
**Control:** State, Government, Nonfederal **Service:** Intellectual disabilities

**Staffed Beds:** 546

**ENCINITAS—San Diego County**

✠ **SCRIPPS MEMORIAL HOSPITAL-ENCINITAS (050503)**, 354 Santa Fe Drive, Zip 92024–5182, Mailing Address: P.O. Box 230817, Zip 92023–0817; tel. 760/633–6501, (Nonreporting) **A**1 10 **F**3 8 13 14 15 18 20 22 26 29 30 31 34 35 44 45 46 49 50 54 57 58 59 64 65 68 70 74 75 76 77 78 79 81 82 84 85 86 87 90 91 92 93 94 95 96 100 107 108 110 111 114 115 118 119 126 130 131 132 141 146 148 156 **S** Scripps Health, San Diego, CA
Primary Contact: Carl J. Etter, Chief Executive and Senior Vice President
COO: Jan Zachry, R.N., Vice President Administrator and Chief Operations Executive
CFO: Sharon Creal, Vice President Financial Operations
CHR: Steve Rust, Director, Human Resources
CNO: Jan Zachry, R.N., Vice President Administrator and Chief Operations Executive
Web address: www.scripps.org
**Control:** Other not–for–profit (including NFP Corporation) **Service:** General medical and surgical

**Staffed Beds:** 171 **Admissions:** 12319 **Census:** 133 **Outpatient Visits:** 97412 **Births:** 1821 **Total Expense ($000):** 288154 **Payroll Expense ($000):** 115111 **Personnel:** 1328

**SCRIPPS OCEANVIEW CONV HOSP** See Evergreen Encinitas Health Care Center

**ENCINO—Los Angeles County; See Los Angeles**

**ENCINO-TARZANA REG MED CENTER** See Encino Hospital Medical Center

**ESCONDIDO—San Diego County**

**PALOMAR MEDICAL CENTER** See Palomar Medical Center Escondido

✠ △ **PALOMAR MEDICAL CENTER ESCONDIDO (050115)**, 2185 West Citracado Parkway, Zip 92029–4159; tel. 760/739–3000, (Nonreporting) **A**1 3 7 10 **S** Palomar Health, Escondido, CA
Primary Contact: Mariellena Sudak, R.N., MSN, Vice President and Chief Nursing Officer
CMO: Duane Buringrud, M.D., Chief Medical and Quality Officer
CIO: Prudence August, Chief Information Officer
CHR: Brenda C Turner, Chief Human Resources Officer
CNO: Mariellena Sudak, R.N., MSN, Vice President and Chief Nursing Officer
Web address: www.palomarhealth.org
**Control:** Hospital district or authority, Government, Nonfederal **Service:** General medical and surgical

**Staffed Beds:** 344

**EUREKA—Humboldt County**

**HUMBOLDT COUNTY MENTAL HEALTH (054124)**, 720 Wood Street, Zip 95501–4413; tel. 707/268–2900, (Nonreporting) **A**10
Primary Contact: Jet L. DeKruse, Administrator
CMO: Harpreet Duggal, M.D., Medical Director, Department of Health and Human Services
CNO: Sherry Gallagher, Director Nursing, Department of Health and Human Services
Web address: www.https://co.humboldt.ca.us/hhs/mhb/
**Control:** County, Government, Nonfederal **Service:** Psychiatric

**Staffed Beds:** 16

**SEMPERVIRENS PSYCHIATRIC HEALTH FACILITY** See Humboldt County Mental Health

**ST. JOSEPH HOSPITAL** See St. Joseph Hospital Eureka

✠ **ST. JOSEPH HOSPITAL EUREKA (050006)**, 2700 Dolbeer Street, Zip 95501–4799; tel. 707/445–8121, (Includes GENERAL HOSPITAL, Mailing address: 2200 Harrison Avenue, Eureka, California, Zip 95501–3299; tel. 707/445–5111), (Nonreporting) **A**1 2 3 10 19 **F**3 8 11 12 13 15 17 18 20 22 24 26 28 29 30 31 35 39 40 43 45 46 47 48 49 53 54 62 63 64 68 70 72 74 75 76 78 79 81 82 84 85 86 87 89 90 93 96 107 108 110 111 114 115 118 119 120 121 123 124 129 130 131 146 148 152 154 **P**5 **S** Providence St. Joseph Health, Renton, WA
Primary Contact: Roberta Luskin-Hawk, M.D., Chief Executive
CFO: Michel Riccioni, Chief Financial Officer
CMO: Mathew Miller, M.D., Vice President and Chief Medical Officer
CIO: Wendy Thorpe, Area Director Information Systems
CHR: Linda Cook, Vice President Human Resources
CNO: Carol Reeder, R.N., Chief Nursing Officer
Web address: www.stjosepheureka.org
**Control:** Church operated, Nongovernment, not–for–profit **Service:** General medical and surgical

**Staffed Beds:** 153 **Admissions:** 7137 **Census:** 104 **Outpatient Visits:** 172249 **Births:** 438 **Total Expense ($000):** 188624 **Payroll Expense ($000):** 97595 **Personnel:** 1171

**FAIRFIELD—Solano County**

✠ **NORTHBAY MEDICAL CENTER (050367)**, 1200 B. Gale Wilson Boulevard, Zip 94533–3587; tel. 707/646–5000, (Includes NORTHBAY VACAVALLEY HOSPITAL, Mailing address: 1000 Nut Tree Road, Vacaville, California, Zip 95687–4100; tel. 707/624–7000; Aimee Brewer, President, NorthBay Healthcare Group), (Nonreporting) **A**1 2 5 10 **F**2 3 6 8 11 13 17 18 20 22 24 28 29 30 31 34 35 36 40 41 43 44 45 46 49 50 51 53 54 55 56 57 59 62 63 64 65 70 72 74 75 76 77 78 79 80 81 82 84 85 87 89 92 93 94 97 100 102 105 107 114 115 117 118 119 120 121 123 124 126 129 130 131 132 144 146 147 148 149 154 156 157
Primary Contact: Aimee Brewer, President, NorthBay Healthcare Group
CFO: Arthur E DeNio, Vice President and Chief Financial Officer
CMO: Seth Kaufman, M.D., Chief Medical Officer
CIO: Christopher Timbers, Vice President and Chief Information Officer
CNO: Traci A Duncan, R.N., Vice President, Chief Nursing Officer
Web address: www.northbay.org
**Control:** Other not–for–profit (including NFP Corporation) **Service:** General medical and surgical

**Staffed Beds:** 192 **Admissions:** 9931 **Census:** 132 **Outpatient Visits:** 365907 **Births:** 1108 **Total Expense ($000):** 634609 **Payroll Expense ($000):** 262793 **Personnel:** 2033

**FALL RIVER MILLS—Shasta County**

★ **MAYERS MEMORIAL HOSPITAL DISTRICT (051305)**, 43563 Highway 299 East, Zip 96028–0459, Mailing Address: P.O. Box 459, Zip 96028–0459; tel. 530/336–5511, (Nonreporting) **A**10 18
Primary Contact: Louis James. Ward, Interim Chief Executive Officer
COO: Louis James Ward, Chief Operating Officer
CFO: Travis Lakey, Chief Financial Officer
CMO: Thomas Watson, M.D., Chief of Staff
CIO: Chris Broadway, Manager Information Technology
CHR: Julie Thompson, Manager Personnel and Payroll
CNO: Sherry Wilson, R.N., Chief Nursing Officer
Web address: www.mayersmemorial.com
**Control:** Hospital district or authority, Government, Nonfederal **Service:** General medical and surgical

**Staffed Beds:** 109

CA

---

**Hospital, Medicare Provider Number, Address, Telephone, Approval, Facility, and Physician Codes, Health Care System**

★ American Hospital Association (AHA) membership    ○ Healthcare Facilities Accreditation Program    ⇧ Center for Improvement in Healthcare Quality Accreditation
□ The Joint Commission accreditation    ◇ DNV Healthcare Inc. accreditation    △ Commission on Accreditation of Rehabilitation Facilities (CARF) accreditation

## FOLSOM—Sacramento County

**KINDRED HOSPITAL-SACRAMENTO** See Vibra Hospital of Sacramento

☒ **MERCY HOSPITAL OF FOLSOM (050414)**, 1650 Creekside Drive, Zip 95630-3400; tel. 916/983-7400, (Nonreporting) **A**1 5 10 **F**3 8 11 12 13 29 30 34 35 36 37 39 40 49 57 59 60 64 66 68 70 74 75 76 77 79 81 82 84 85 86 93 107 108 114 115 118 119 130 132 146 147 148 154 **P**3 4 5 **S** CommonSpirit Health, Chicago, IL
Primary Contact: Randall W. Ross, FACHE, President and Chief Executive Officer
CMO: Robert Allen, M.D., Chief Medical Officer
CHR: Anthony Robinson, Manager, Human Resources
CNO: Josh Freilich, Vice President and Chief Nurse Executive
Web address: www.mercyfolsom.org
**Control**: Church operated, Nongovernment, not-for-profit **Service**: General medical and surgical

**Staffed Beds:** 106 **Admissions:** 6904 **Census:** 67 **Outpatient Visits:** 56877 **Births:** 723 **Total Expense ($000):** 206121 **Payroll Expense ($000):** 79999 **Personnel:** 750

☒ **VIBRA HOSPITAL OF SACRAMENTO (052033)**, 330 Montrose Drive, Zip 95630-2720; tel. 916/351-9151, (Nonreporting) **A**1 10 **S** Vibra Healthcare, Mechanicsburg, PA
Primary Contact: Kimberly C. Long, R.N., MSN, Chief Executive Officer
CFO: Todd Scott, Chief Financial Officer
CMO: S. Kwon Lee, M.D., Chief of Staff
CHR: Glenda Franco, Director, Human Resources
Web address: www.vhsacramento.com
**Control**: Corporation, Investor-owned (for-profit) **Service**: Acute long-term care hospital

**Staffed Beds:** 58

## FONTANA—San Bernardino County

**FONTANA MEDICAL CENTER** See Kaiser Permanente Fontana Medical Center

☒ **KAISER PERMANENTE FONTANA MEDICAL CENTER (050140)**, 9961 Sierra Avenue, Zip 92335-6794; tel. 909/427-5000, (Includes KAISER PERMANENTE ONTARIO MEDICAL CENTER, Mailing address: 2295 South Vineyard Avenue, Ontario, California, Zip 91761-7925; tel. 909/724-5000; Greg Christian, Sr Vice President, Area Manager - San Bernardino County Area), (Nonreporting) **A**1 3 5 10 **F**3 8 11 12 13 15 17 18 20 22 24 26 29 30 31 35 36 40 41 44 45 46 48 49 50 51 53 56 57 58 59 60 61 62 63 64 65 68 70 72 73 74 75 76 77 78 79 81 82 84 85 86 87 88 89 92 100 102 107 108 110 111 114 115 116 117 118 119 126 130 131 132 135 136 141 143 145 146 148 149 154 **S** Kaiser Foundation Hospitals, Oakland, CA
Primary Contact: Greg Christian, Senior Vice President, Area Manager - San Bernardino County Area
COO: Ken Rivers, Chief Operating Officer, Fontana Medical Center
CFO: Trish Lopez, Area Chief Financial Officer
CMO: Timothy Jenkins, M.D., Area Medical Director and Chief of Staff
CIO: Heather Raymond, Area Public Relations Director
CHR: Irene Ruiz, Area Human Resources Director
CNO: Raye M. Burkhardt, Chief Nurse Executive
Web address: www.kaiserpermanente.org
**Control**: Other not-for-profit (including NFP Corporation) **Service**: General medical and surgical

**Staffed Beds:** 490 **Admissions:** 30872 **Census:** 350 **Outpatient Visits:** 186771 **Births:** 7137 **Personnel:** 4187

## FORT BRAGG—Mendocino County

☒ **MENDOCINO COAST DISTRICT HOSPITAL (051325)**, 700 River Drive, Zip 95437-5495; tel. 707/961-1234, (Nonreporting) **A**1 10 18 **S** Adventist Health, Roseville, CA
Primary Contact: Wayne Allen, Interim Chief Executive Officer
CFO: Mike Ellis, Chief Financial Officer
CMO: John Kermen, D.O., Chief Medical Staff
CIO: Jeff Edwards, Manager Information Services
CNO: Bonnie Kittner, R.N., Chief Nursing Officer
Web address: www.mcdh.org
**Control**: Hospital district or authority, Government, Nonfederal **Service**: General medical and surgical

**Staffed Beds:** 25

## FORT IRWIN—San Bernardino County

☒ **WEED ARMY COMMUNITY HOSPITAL**, Inner Loop Road and 4th Street, Building 166, Zip 92310-5065, Mailing Address: P.O. Box 105109, Zip 92310-5109; tel. 760/380-3108, (Nonreporting) **A**1 **S** Department of the Army, Office of the Surgeon General, Falls Church, VA
Primary Contact: Colonel Larry O. France, Commander
CIO: Michael Haenelt, Chief Information Management
Web address: www.https://www.irwin.amedd.army.mil/
**Service**: General medical and surgical

**Staffed Beds:** 27

## FORTUNA—Humboldt County

☒ **REDWOOD MEMORIAL HOSPITAL (051318)**, 3300 Renner Drive, Zip 95540-3198; tel. 707/725-3361, (Nonreporting) **A**1 10 18 **S** Providence St. Joseph Health, Renton, WA
Primary Contact: Roberta Luskin-Hawk, M.D., Chief Executive
COO: Joseph J Rogers, Vice President and Chief Operating Officer
CHR: Bob Sampson, Vice President Human Resources
Web address: www.redwoodmemorial.org/
**Control**: Church operated, Nongovernment, not-for-profit **Service**: General medical and surgical

**Staffed Beds:** 25

## FOUNTAIN VALLEY—Orange County

☒ **FOUNTAIN VALLEY REGIONAL HOSPITAL AND MEDICAL CENTER (050570)**, 17100 Euclid Street, Zip 92708-4043; tel. 714/966-7200, (Nonreporting) **A**1 2 5 10 **F**3 8 12 13 17 18 20 22 24 26 29 30 31 34 36 40 45 49 50 54 56 57 60 63 68 70 72 73 74 75 76 77 78 79 81 82 84 85 87 88 89 100 107 108 111 114 115 118 119 126 130 132 146 147 148 149 154 156 **S** TENET Healthcare Corporation, Dallas, TX
Primary Contact: Kenneth D. McFarland, Chief Executive Officer
COO: Edward Littlejohn, Chief Operating Officer
CFO: Ken Jordan, Chief Financial Officer
CMO: Daniel Hilton, M.D., Chief of Staff
CIO: Freddie Sanchez, Director Information Systems
CHR: Connie Worden, Chief Human Resources Officer
CNO: Kristin Christophersen, Chief Nursing Officer
Web address: www.fountainvalleyhospital.com
**Control**: Corporation, Investor-owned (for-profit) **Service**: General medical and surgical

**Staffed Beds:** 380 **Admissions:** 18875 **Census:** 233 **Outpatient Visits:** 67223 **Births:** 2825 **Total Expense ($000):** 339288 **Payroll Expense ($000):** 151429 **Personnel:** 1547

**FOUNTAIN VLY REG HOSP** See Fountain Valley Regional Hospital and Medical Center

☒ **MEMORIALCARE, ORANGE COAST MEMORIAL MEDICAL CENTER (050678)**, 9920 Talbert Avenue, Zip 92708-5115; tel. 714/378-7000, (Nonreporting) **A**1 2 10 **F**3 8 11 12 13 15 18 20 22 24 26 28 29 31 34 35 38 40 44 45 46 47 48 49 50 51 53 55 56 57 58 59 64 65 68 70 72 74 75 76 77 78 79 81 82 84 85 86 87 93 107 108 110 111 114 115 116 117 118 119 124 126 130 131 132 135 143 145 146 147 149 154 157 **P**3 5 **S** MemorialCare, Fountain Valley, CA
Primary Contact: Marcia Manker, Chief Executive Officer
COO: Emily Randle, Vice President Operations
CFO: Steve McNamara, Chief Financial Officer
CIO: Scott Raymond, Director Information Systems
CHR: Michelle Gutierrez, Executive Director Human Resources
CNO: Dale Vital, Chief Nursing Officer
Web address: www.memorialcare.org
**Control**: Other not-for-profit (including NFP Corporation) **Service**: General medical and surgical

**Staffed Beds:** 218 **Admissions:** 11962 **Census:** 117 **Outpatient Visits:** 98299 **Births:** 1462 **Total Expense ($000):** 326356 **Payroll Expense ($000):** 88738 **Personnel:** 1137

**ORANGE COAST MEMORIAL MEDICAL CENTER** See Memorialcare, Orange Coast Memorial Medical Center

## FREMONT—Alameda County

**BHC FREMONT HOSPITAL** See Fremont Hospital

☒ **FREMONT HOSPITAL (054110)**, 39001 Sundale Drive, Zip 94538-2005; tel. 510/796-1100, (Nonreporting) **A**1 10 **S** Universal Health Services, Inc., King of Prussia, PA
Primary Contact: Tricia Williams, Chief Executive Officer
CMO: Vikas Duvvuri, M.D., Medical Director
CHR: Tom Piz, Director Human Resources
Web address: www.fremonthospital.com
**Control**: Corporation, Investor-owned (for-profit) **Service**: Psychiatric

**Staffed Beds:** 148

**CA**

**FREMONT MEDICAL CENTER** See Kaiser Permanente Fremont Medical Center

☒ **KAISER PERMANENTE FREMONT MEDICAL CENTER (050512)**, 39400 Paseo Padre Parkway, Zip 94538–2310; tel. 510/248–3000, (Nonreporting) **A**1 2 3 5 10 **F**3 11 12 15 18 20 34 39 40 44 49 56 60 63 64 68 70 74 75 78 79 80 81 82 84 85 86 87 98 100 103 107 108 110 111 114 115 118 119 130 135 146 149 154 **S** Kaiser Foundation Hospitals, Oakland, CA
Primary Contact: Victoria O'Gorman, Administrator
Web address: www.kp.org
**Control**: Other not–for–profit (including NFP Corporation) **Service**: General medical and surgical

Staffed Beds: 100 Admissions: 3900 Census: 39 Outpatient
Visits: 254594 Births: 13 Personnel: 579

**WASHINGTON HEALTH CARE DIST** See Washington Hospital Healthcare System

☒ **WASHINGTON HOSPITAL HEALTHCARE SYSTEM (050195)**, 2000 Mowry Avenue, Zip 94538–1746; tel. 510/797–1111, (Nonreporting) **A**1 2 10 19 **F**18 19 20 22 24 28 29 30 31 34 35 38 40 45 46 49 54 55 57 59 60 71 74 75 76 77 78 79 81 82 84 85 87 89 100 107 111 112 114 115 116 117 119 120 121 123 130 132 135 144 146 147 148 149 154 156 157
Primary Contact: Kimberly Hartz, Chief Executive Officer
COO: Edward J Fayen, Associate Administrator Operations and Support
CFO: Chris Henry, Associate Administrator and Chief Financial Officer
CMO: Albert Brooks, M.D., Chief Medical Staff Services
CIO: Robert Thorwald, Chief Information Officer
CHR: Bryant Welch, Chief Human Resources
CNO: Stephanie Williams, R.N., Chief Nursing Officer
Web address: www.whhs.com
**Control**: Hospital district or authority, Government, Nonfederal **Service**: General medical and surgical

Staffed Beds: 288 Admissions: 11984 Census: 146 Outpatient
Visits: 137959 Births: 1542 Personnel: 2617

**FRENCH CAMP—San Joaquin County**

☐ **SAN JOAQUIN GENERAL HOSPITAL (050167)**, 500 West Hospital Road, Zip 95231–9693, Mailing Address: P.O. Box 1020, Stockton, Zip 95201–3120; tel. 209/468–6000, (Nonreporting) **A**1 3 5 10
Primary Contact: David K. Culberson, Chief Executive Officer
CFO: Ron Kreutner, Chief Financial Officer
CMO: Sheela Kapre, M.D., Chief Medical Officer
CIO: Don Johnston, Chief Information Officer
CHR: Lisa M Lopez, Director Human Resources
CNO: Erlinda Bolor, R.N., Chief Nursing Officer
Web address: www.sjgeneral.org/
**Control**: County, Government, Nonfederal **Service**: General medical and surgical

Staffed Beds: 110

**FRESNO—Fresno County**

**CEDAR VISTA HOSPITAL** See Community Behavioral Health Center

**COMMUNITY BEHAVIORAL HEALTH CENTER**, 7171 North Cedar Avenue, Zip 93720–3311; tel. 559/449–8000, (Nonreporting) **S** Community Medical Centers, Fresno, CA
Primary Contact: Craig Wagoner, Chief Executive Officer
CFO: Stephen Walter, Senior Vice President and Chief Financial Officer
CMO: Tom Utecht, M.D., Senior Vice President and Chief Quality Officer
CIO: George Vasquez, Vice President Information Services
CHR: Ginny Burdick, Vice President Human Resources
CNO: Karen L Buckley, R.N., Chief Nursing Officer
Web address: www.communitymedical.org
**Control**: Corporation, Investor–owned (for–profit) **Service**: Psychiatric

Staffed Beds: 61

**COMMUNITY MEDICAL CENTER** See Community Regional Medical Center

☐ **COMMUNITY REGIONAL MEDICAL CENTER (050060)**, 2823 Fresno Street, Zip 93721–1324, Mailing Address: P.O. Box 1232, Zip 93715–1232; tel. 559/459–6000, (Nonreporting) **A**1 3 5 8 10 **S** Community Medical Centers, Fresno, CA
Primary Contact: Craig Wagoner, Chief Executive Officer
CFO: Stephen Walter, Senior Vice President and Chief Financial Officer
CMO: Tom Utecht, M.D., Chief Medical Officer
CIO: Craig Castro, Chief Information Officer
CHR: Ginny Burdick, Vice President Human Resources
Web address: www.communitymedical.org
**Control**: Other not–for–profit (including NFP Corporation) **Service**: General medical and surgical

Staffed Beds: 852

**FRESNO HEART AND SURGICAL HOSPITAL (050732)**, 15 East Audubon Drive, Zip 93720–1542; tel. 559/433–8000, (Nonreporting) **A**3 10 **S** Community Medical Centers, Fresno, CA
Primary Contact: Ben Armfield, Associate Administrator
CFO: Ben Armfield, Chief Financial Officer
CMO: Tom Utecht, M.D., Corporate Chief Quality Officer
CIO: George Vasquez, Corporate Chief Information Officer
CHR: Julie Adair, Interim Corporate Chief Human Resources Officer
CNO: Heather Rodriguez, Chief Nursing Officer
Web address: www.fresnoheartandsurgical.org
**Control**: Corporation, Investor–owned (for–profit) **Service**: Heart

Staffed Beds: 60

**FRESNO HEART HOSPITAL** See Fresno Heart and Surgical Hospital

**FRESNO MEDICAL CENTER** See Kaiser Permanente Fresno Medical Center

**FRESNO SURGERY CENTER** See Fresno Surgical Hospital

☐ **FRESNO SURGICAL HOSPITAL (050708)**, 6125 North Fresno Street, Zip 93710–5207; tel. 559/431–8000, (Nonreporting) **A**1 10
Primary Contact: Kristine Kassahn, Chief Executive Officer
CFO: Bruce Cecil, Chief Financial Officer
CMO: Bruce Witmer, M.D., Medical Director
CHR: Laura Patillo, Manager Human Resources
Web address: www.fresnosurgicalhospital.com
**Control**: Partnership, Investor–owned (for–profit) **Service**: Surgical

Staffed Beds: 16

☒ **KAISER PERMANENTE FRESNO MEDICAL CENTER (050710)**, 7300 North Fresno Street, Zip 93720–2942; tel. 559/448–4500, (Nonreporting) **A**1 2 3 5 10 **F**3 11 12 13 15 18 26 30 31 34 39 40 41 45 49 56 60 64 68 70 72 73 74 75 76 78 79 80 81 82 84 85 86 87 100 107 108 110 111 114 115 118 119 130 135 146 149 154 **P**6 **S** Kaiser Foundation Hospitals, Oakland, CA
Primary Contact: Debbie Hemker, Senior Vice President and Area Manager
CFO: Paula Armstrong, Chief Financial Officer
CMO: Smita Rouillard, M.D., Physician in Chief
CIO: Patty Thompson, Area Compliance Officer
CHR: Mike Silveira, Director Human Resources Business Partners
CNO: Karen S Strauman, R.N., Chief Nurse Executive
Web address: www.kaiserpermanente.org
**Control**: Other not–for–profit (including NFP Corporation) **Service**: General medical and surgical

Staffed Beds: 169 Admissions: 8576 Census: 84 Outpatient
Visits: 282662 Births: 1617 Personnel: 733

☒ **SAINT AGNES MEDICAL CENTER (050093)**, 1303 East Herndon Avenue, Zip 93720–3397; tel. 559/450–3000, (Nonreporting) **A**1 2 3 5 10 **S** Trinity Health, Livonia, MI
Primary Contact: Nancy Hollingsworth, R.N., MSN, President and Chief Executive Officer
COO: Mark T Bateman, Interim Chief Operating Officer
CFO: Phil Robinson, Chief Financial Officer
CMO: Stephen Soldo, M.D., Chief Medical Officer
CIO: Irfan Ali, Director Information Services
CHR: Stacy Vaillancourt, Vice President Marketing, Communications, Advocacy and Human Resources
Web address: www.samc.com
**Control**: Church operated, Nongovernment, not–for–profit **Service**: General medical and surgical

Staffed Beds: 436

CA

**Hospital, Medicare Provider Number, Address, Telephone, Approval, Facility, and Physician Codes, Health Care System**

★ American Hospital Association (AHA) membership
☐ The Joint Commission accreditation
○ Healthcare Facilities Accreditation Program
◇ DNV Healthcare Inc. accreditation
⇑ Center for Improvement in Healthcare Quality Accreditation
△ Commission on Accreditation of Rehabilitation Facilities (CARF) accreditation

⊞ △ **SAN JOAQUIN VALLEY REHABILITATION HOSPITAL (053032)**, 7173 North Sharon Avenue, Zip 93720–3329; tel. 559/436–3600, (Nonreporting) **A**1 7 10 **S** Vibra Healthcare, Mechanicsburg, PA
Primary Contact: Mary Jo Jacobson, Chief Executive Officer
CFO: Margaret Casarez, Chief Financial Officer
CMO: Michael Azevedo, M.D., Medical Director
CIO: Christi Rolff, Director Business Development
CHR: Jennifer Morrow, Director Human Resources
Web address: www.sanjoaquinrehab.com
**Control**: Corporation, Investor–owned (for–profit) **Service**: Rehabilitation

**Staffed Beds:** 62

**ST AGNES MEDICAL CENTER** See Saint Agnes Medical Center

⊞ **VETERANS AFFAIRS CENTRAL CALIFORNIA HEALTH CARE SYSTEM**, 2615 East Clinton Avenue, Zip 93703–2223; tel. 559/225–6100, (Nonreporting) **A**1 3 5 **S** Department of Veterans Affairs, Washington, DC
Primary Contact: Stephen R. Bauman, Medical Center Director
CMO: Wessel H. Meyer, M.D., Chief of Staff
CHR: Sandra Stein, Chief Human Resources Management
Web address: www.fresno.va.gov/
**Control**: Veterans Affairs, Government, federal **Service**: General medical and surgical

**Staffed Beds:** 117

**VETERANS AFFAIRS MED CENTER** See Veterans Affairs Central California Health Care System

## FULLERTON—Orange County

**ST JUDE HOSP & REHAB CENTER** See St. Jude Medical Center

⊞ △ **ST. JUDE MEDICAL CENTER (050168)**, 101 East Valencia Mesa Drive, Zip 92835–3875; tel. 714/992–3000, (Nonreporting) **A**1 2 3 5 7 10 **F**2 3 8 9 11 13 15 18 20 22 24 26 28 29 30 31 34 35 36 38 39 40 44 45 46 47 48 49 50 51 53 54 55 56 57 58 59 60 61 62 63 64 65 66 68 70 71 72 73 74 75 76 77 78 79 81 82 83 84 85 86 87 90 91 92 93 94 95 96 97 100 101 102 107 108 109 110 111 112 114 115 116 117 118 119 120 121 123 124 126 129 130 131 132 134 135 143 145 146 147 148 149 154 156 157 **S** Providence St. Joseph Health, Renton, WA
Primary Contact: Brian Helleland, Chief Executive Officer
CFO: Ed Salvador, Chief Financial Officer
CMO: Eugene P. Kim, M.D., Chief Medical Officer
CHR: Mark Jablonski, Vice President Mission Integration
CNO: Linda Jenkins, R.N., Vice President Patient Care Services
Web address: www.stjudemedicalcenter.org
**Control**: Church operated, Nongovernment, not–for–profit **Service**: General medical and surgical

**Staffed Beds:** 320 **Admissions:** 14590 **Census:** 186 **Outpatient Visits:** 519441 **Births:** 2393 **Total Expense ($000):** 519666 **Payroll Expense ($000):** 195937 **Personnel:** 2169

## GARBERVILLE—Humboldt County

★ **JEROLD PHELPS COMMUNITY HOSPITAL (051309)**, 733 Cedar Street, Zip 95542–3292; tel. 707/923–3921, (Total facility includes 8 beds in nursing home–type unit) (Nonreporting) **A**10 18 **F**10 34 35 40 41 50 57 59 62 65 66 68 77 97 107 110 119 127 128 133 135 143 149 154 156 **P**5
Primary Contact: Matthew Rees, Administrator
COO: Kent Scown, Director Operations and Information Services
CFO: Harry Jasper, Chief Financial Officer
CMO: Marcin Matuszkiewicz, M.D., Chief of Staff and Medical Director
CIO: Kent Scown, Director Operations and Information Services
CHR: Dee Way, Director Human Resources
CNO: Sarah Beach, Director of Nursing
Web address: www.shchd.org
**Control**: Hospital district or authority, Government, Nonfederal **Service**: General medical and surgical

**Staffed Beds:** 17 **Admissions:** 114 **Census:** 11 **Outpatient Visits:** 9617 **Births:** 0 **Total Expense ($000):** 11579 **Payroll Expense ($000):** 5142 **Personnel:** 85

**SO HUMBOLDT COMM HLTHCARE DIST** See Jerold Phelps Community Hospital

## GARDEN GROVE—Orange County

**GARDEN GROVE HOSP & MED CTR** See Garden Grove Hospital and Medical Center

☐ **GARDEN GROVE HOSPITAL AND MEDICAL CENTER (050230)**, 12601 Garden Grove Boulevard, Zip 92843–1959; tel. 714/537–5160, (Nonreporting) **A**1 3 10 **S** Prime Healthcare, Ontario, CA
Primary Contact: Richard M. Rowe, PharmD, Chief Executive Officer
CFO: Kora Guoyavatin, Chief Financial Officer
CMO: Hassan Alkhouli, M.D., Chief Medical Officer
CIO: Vic Mahan, Director Information Systems
CHR: Stephanie Sioson, Director Human Resources
CNO: Wanda Ruben, R.N., Chief Nursing Officer
Web address: www.gardengrovehospital.com
**Control**: Corporation, Investor–owned (for–profit) **Service**: General medical and surgical

**Staffed Beds:** 167

## GARDENA—Los Angeles County

**KINDRED HOSPITAL OF SOUTH BAY** See Kindred Hospital South Bay

⊞ **KINDRED HOSPITAL SOUTH BAY (052050)**, 1246 West 155th Street, Zip 90247–4062; tel. 310/323–5330, (Nonreporting) **A**1 10 **S** Kindred Healthcare, Louisville, KY
Primary Contact: Michael D. Kerr, Chief Executive Officer
CHR: Michelle Parra, Director Human Resources
Web address: www.khsouthbay.com/
**Control**: Corporation, Investor–owned (for–profit) **Service**: Acute long–term care hospital

**Staffed Beds:** 84

⊞ **MEMORIAL HOSPITAL OF GARDENA (050468)**, 1145 West Redondo Beach Boulevard, Zip 90247–3528; tel. 310/532–4200, (Nonreporting) **A**1 10 **S** Avanti Hospitals, El Segundo, CA
Primary Contact: Kathy Wojno, R.N., MSN, Administrator
CFO: Daniel R Heckathorne, Chief Financial Officer
CMO: Nosratian Farshao, M.D., Chief Medical Staff
CHR: Matthew Kempiak, Director Human Resources and Administrative Services
CNO: Glenda Luce, Chief Nursing Officer
Web address: www.mhglax.com/
**Control**: Corporation, Investor–owned (for–profit) **Service**: General medical and surgical

**Staffed Beds:** 172

## GILROY—Santa Clara County

**ST LOUISE REGIONAL HOSPITAL** See St. Louise Regional Hospital

☐ **ST. LOUISE REGIONAL HOSPITAL (050688)**, 9400 No Name Uno, Zip 95020–3528; tel. 408/848–2000, (Nonreporting) **A**1 10
Primary Contact: John Hennelly, Chief Executive Officer
COO: Carol Furgurson, Chief Operating Officer
CFO: Nicole Thomson, Chief Financial Officer
CMO: Arthur Douville, M.D., Chief Medical Officer
CIO: Dick Hutsell, Vice President Information Technology Services
CHR: Lin Velasquez, Vice President Human Resources
CNO: Marilyn Gerrior, R.N., MSN, Chief Nursing Executive
Web address: www.https://slrh.sccgov.org/Pages/home.aspx
**Control**: County, Government, Nonfederal **Service**: General medical and surgical

**Staffed Beds:** 93

## GLENDALE—Los Angeles County

⊞ **ADVENTIST HEALTH GLENDALE (050239)**, 1509 Wilson Terrace, Zip 90048; tel. 818/409–8000, (Nonreporting) **A**1 2 3 5 10 **F**3 4 5 8 12 13 15 17 18 20 22 24 26 28 29 30 31 32 34 35 36 37 39 40 44 45 46 47 48 49 50 53 54 57 58 59 63 64 65 68 71 72 73 74 75 76 77 78 79 81 82 83 84 85 86 87 90 91 92 93 96 98 100 101 102 104 105 106 107 108 109 110 111 114 115 118 119 120 121 124 126 128 129 130 131 132 135 145 146 147 148 149 152 154 156 **S** Adventist Health, Roseville, CA
Primary Contact: Alice H. Issai, President
COO: Liz Cochran, Operations Executive
CFO: Eric Krueger, Finance Officer
CMO: Steven Brass, Medical Officer
CIO: Sharon Correa, Chief Information Officer
CNO: Jinhee Nguyen, Patient Care Executive
Web address: www.https://www.adventisthealth.org/glendale/
**Control**: Other not–for–profit (including NFP Corporation) **Service**: General medical and surgical

**Staffed Beds:** 502 **Admissions:** 20003 **Census:** 261 **Outpatient Visits:** 137498 **Births:** 1560 **Total Expense ($000):** 510547 **Payroll Expense ($000):** 151431 **Personnel:** 1512

*Many Facility Codes have changed. Please refer to the AHA Guide Code Chart.* © 2021 AHA Guide

**GLENDALE ADVENTIST MEDICAL CENTER** See Adventist Health Glendale

☒ **GLENDALE MEMORIAL HOSPITAL AND HEALTH CENTER (050058)**, 1420 South Central Avenue, Zip 91204–2594; tel. 818/502–1900, (Nonreporting) **A1** 10 19 **S** CommonSpirit Health, Chicago, IL
Primary Contact: Jill Welton, President and Chief Executive Officer
COO: Brad Grote, Chief Operating Officer
CFO: Rebecca Cheng, Chief Financial Officer
CIO: Brian Gregor, Manager Information Technology Operations
CHR: Nga Nguyen, Manager Human Resources and Organizational Development
CNO: Jason Black EsqVice President and Chief Nursing Officer
Web address: www.glendalememorial.com
**Control:** Other not–for–profit (including NFP Corporation) **Service:** General medical and surgical

| Staffed Beds: 334 |
| --- |

★ ⇑ **USC VERDUGO HILLS HOSPITAL (050124)**, 1812 Verdugo Boulevard, Zip 91208–1409; tel. 818/790–7100, (Nonreporting) **A3** 10 21 **F3** 11 12 13 15 17 18 26 28 29 30 34 35 37 38 40 41 45 46 47 48 49 50 51 53 56 57 59 64 65 68 70 72 74 75 76 77 78 79 81 83 85 87 93 94 96 98 100 101 102 103 104 107 108 110 111 115 119 126 128 130 131 132 135 145 146 147 148 149 153 **P6 S** Keck Medicine of USC, Los Angeles, CA
Primary Contact: Keith Hobbs, Chief Executive Officer
COO: Kenny Pawlek, Chief Operating Officer
CMO: Stephanie Hall, M.D., Chief Medical Officer
CHR: Eva Herberger, Administrator Human Resources
CNO: Theresa Murphy, Chief Nursing Officer
Web address: www.uscvhh.org
**Control:** Other not–for–profit (including NFP Corporation) **Service:** General medical and surgical

| Staffed Beds: 154 Admissions: 6370 Census: 89 Outpatient Visits: 69690 Births: 366 Total Expense ($000): 138575 Payroll Expense ($000): 66729 Personnel: 706 |
| --- |

⇑ **VERDUGO HILLS HOSPITAL** See USC Verdugo Hills Hospital

### GLENDORA—Los Angeles County

**EAST VALLEY HOSPITAL MEDICAL CENTER** See Glendora Community Hospital

☒ **EMANATE HEALTH FOOTHILL PRESBYTERIAN HOSPITAL (050597)**, 250 South Grand Avenue, Zip 91741–4218; tel. 626/963–8411, (Nonreporting) **A1** 3 10 **F3** 7 11 13 15 17 18 29 30 31 34 35 40 41 44 45 49 50 51 60 64 68 70 74 75 76 77 78 79 81 85 86 87 89 107 108 114 119 130 131 143 146 154 **S** Emanate Health, Covina, CA
Primary Contact: Robert H. Curry, President and Chief Executive Officer
COO: Elvia Foulke, Executive Vice President and Chief Operating Officer
CMO: John DiMare, M.D., Medical Director
CIO: David McCobb, Chief Information Officer
Web address: www.cvhp.org/Our_Facilities/Foothill_Presbyterian.aspx
**Control:** Other not–for–profit (including NFP Corporation) **Service:** General medical and surgical

| Staffed Beds: 67 Admissions: 5426 Census: 64 Outpatient Visits: 63984 Births: 490 Total Expense ($000): 108514 Payroll Expense ($000): 40716 Personnel: 475 |
| --- |

**FOOTHILL PRESBYTERIAN HOSPITAL** See Emanate Health Foothill Presbyterian Hospital

**GLENDORA COMMUNITY HOSPITAL (050205)**, 150 West Route 66, Zip 91740–6207; tel. 626/852–5000, (Nonreporting) **A10 F13** 29 40 45 64 70 79 81 93 98 100 101 103 119 126 130 **S** Prime Healthcare, Ontario, CA
Primary Contact: Sofia Abrina, R.N., Chief Executive Officer
CFO: Robert Bonner, Chief Financial Officer
CMO: Oliver Solomon, M.D., Chief Medical Officer
CIO: Jeffrey Cox, Chief Information Officer
CHR: Diana Cancel, Director Human Resources
CNO: Mary Ann Bennett, Chief Nursing Officer
Web address: www.evhmc.com
**Control:** Other not–for–profit (including NFP Corporation) **Service:** General medical and surgical

| Staffed Beds: 128 Admissions: 1422 Census: 30 Outpatient Visits: 59605 Births: 0 Total Expense ($000): 27857 Payroll Expense ($000): 12214 Personnel: 155 |
| --- |

### GRASS VALLEY—Nevada County

☒ **SIERRA NEVADA MEMORIAL HOSPITAL (050150)**, 155 Glasson Way, Zip 95945–5723, Mailing Address: P.O. Box 1029, Zip 95945–1029; tel. 530/274–6000, (Nonreporting) **A1** 2 10 19 **F3** 7 13 15 28 29 31 34 35 40 44 45 46 49 50 56 62 64 65 68 70 76 77 78 81 84 85 92 93 102 107 108 110 111 114 115 118 119 120 124 130 132 146 147 148 149 154 **S** CommonSpirit Health, Chicago, IL
Primary Contact: Brian Evans Esq, M.D., President and Chief Executive Officer
CFO: Carolyn Canady, Chief Financial Officer
CMO: Jeffrey M. Rosenburg, Chief Medical Officer
CHR: Terri Labriola, Human Resources Officer
CNO: Jill McWilliams, Chief Nursing Officer
Web address: www.snmh.org
**Control:** Other not–for–profit (including NFP Corporation) **Service:** General medical and surgical

| Staffed Beds: 104 Admissions: 4951 Census: 52 Outpatient Visits: 93441 Births: 465 Total Expense ($000): 173794 Payroll Expense ($000): 74274 Personnel: 659 |
| --- |

### GREENBRAE—Marin County

**MARIN GENERAL HOSPITAL** See Marinhealth Medical Center

☒ **MARINHEALTH MEDICAL CENTER (050360)**, 250 Bon Air Road, Zip 94904–1784, Mailing Address: P.O. Box 8010, San Rafael, Zip 94912–8010; tel. 415/925–7000, (Nonreporting) **A1** 2 **F2** 3 8 13 15 18 20 22 24 26 29 30 31 34 35 36 37 40 43 45 46 47 48 49 51 57 60 63 64 68 70 73 74 75 76 77 78 79 81 82 84 85 87 89 98 100 104 105 107 108 110 111 112 114 115 118 119 120 121 122 123 124 126 130 132 141 146 148 149 153 154 156 157 **P3** 5
Primary Contact: Lee Domanico, Chief Executive Officer
CFO: Eric Brettner, Chief Financial Officer
CMO: Joel Sklar, M.D., Chief Medical Officer
CIO: Mark Zielazinski, Chief Information and Technology Integration Officer
CHR: Linda Lang, Chief Human Resources Officer
Web address: www.maringeneral.org
**Control:** Hospital district or authority, Government, Nonfederal **Service:** General medical and surgical

| Staffed Beds: 235 Admissions: 8100 Census: 115 Outpatient Visits: 143380 Births: 1233 Total Expense ($000): 426577 Payroll Expense ($000): 187757 Personnel: 1447 |
| --- |

### GRIDLEY—Butte County

⇑ **BIGGS-GRIDLEY MEMORIAL HOSPITAL** See Orchard Hospital

★ ⇑ **ORCHARD HOSPITAL (051311)**, 240 Spruce Street, Zip 95948–2216, Mailing Address: P.O. Box 97, Zip 95948–0097; tel. 530/846–5671, (Nonreporting) **A**10 18 21
Primary Contact: Steve Lee. Stark, Chief Executive Officer
COO: Tracy Atkins, Chief Operating and Nursing Officer
CFO: Kristina Sanke, Chief Financial Officer
CMO: Henry Starkes, M.D., Medical Director
CIO: John Helvey, Chief Information Officer
CNO: Tracy Atkins, Chief Operating and Nursing Officer
Web address: www.orchardhospital.com
**Control:** Other not–for–profit (including NFP Corporation) **Service:** General medical and surgical

| Staffed Beds: 45 |
| --- |

### HANFORD—Kings County

☒ **ADVENTIST HEALTH HANFORD (050121)**, 115 Mall Drive, Zip 93230–3513; tel. 559/582–9000, (Includes ADVENTIST MEDICAL CENTER-SELMA, Mailing address: 1141 Rose Avenue, Selma, California, Zip 93662–3241; tel. 559/891–1000; Richard L Rawson, President and Chief Executive Officer), (Nonreporting) **A1** 3 5 10 **S** Adventist Health, Roseville, CA
Primary Contact: Wayne Ferch, President and Chief Executive Officer
CIO: Michael Aubry, Director Information Systems
Web address: www.adventisthealthcv.com/hospital_newhanfordhospital.aspx
**Control:** Church operated, Nongovernment, not–for–profit **Service:** General medical and surgical

| Staffed Beds: 199 |
| --- |

**ADVENTIST MEDICAL CENTER - HANFORD** See Adventist Health Hanford

CA

★ **CENTRAL VALLEY GENERAL HOSPITAL (050196)**, 1025 North Douty Street, Zip 93230–3722, Mailing Address: P.O. Box 480, Zip 93232–2113; tel. 559/583–2100, (Nonreporting) **A**10 **S** Adventist Health, Roseville, CA
Primary Contact: Wayne Ferch, President and Chief Executive Officer
Web address: www.hanfordhealth.com
**Control**: Corporation, Investor–owned (for–profit) **Service**: General medical and surgical

| Staffed Beds: 49 |
| --- |

**SACRED HEART HOSP & CNTR** See Central Valley General Hospital

### HARBOR CITY—Los Angeles County

⊞ **KAISER PERMANENTE SOUTH BAY MEDICAL CENTER (050411)**, 25825 Vermont Avenue, Zip 90710–3599; tel. 310/325–5111, (Nonreporting) **A**1 3 5 10 **F**2 3 5 6 9 11 12 13 15 28 29 30 31 32 34 35 36 39 40 44 45 46 47 48 49 50 51 53 54 55 56 57 58 59 60 61 63 64 65 66 68 70 72 74 75 76 77 78 79 81 82 85 86 87 91 92 93 94 96 97 100 107 108 110 111 114 115 116 117 118 119 130 131 132 134 135 144 146 147 148 149 150 154 156 157 **P**6 **S** Kaiser Foundation Hospitals, Oakland, CA
Primary Contact: Margie Harrier, MSN, R.N., Senior Vice President and Area Manager
Web address: www.kaiserpermanente.org
**Control**: Other not–for–profit (including NFP Corporation) **Service**: General medical and surgical

| Staffed Beds: 257 **Admissions:** 10387 **Census:** 106 **Outpatient Visits:** 157969 **Births:** 2543 **Personnel:** 1648 |
| --- |

**SOUTH BAY MEDICAL CENTER** See Kaiser Permanente South Bay Medical Center

### HAYWARD—Alameda County

☐ **ST. ROSE HOSPITAL (050002)**, 27200 Calaroga Avenue, Zip 94545–4383; tel. 510/264–4000, (Nonreporting) **A**1 10 **S** Alecto Healthcare, Irvine, CA
Primary Contact: Aman Dhuper, President and Chief Executive Officer
CFO: Michael Taylor, Vice President Financial Services and Chief Financial Officer
CMO: Charles S Feldstein, M.D., Vice President Medical Affairs
CHR: John Davini, Vice President
Web address: www.srhca.org
**Control**: Church operated, Nongovernment, not–for–profit **Service**: General medical and surgical

| Staffed Beds: 150 |
| --- |

### HEALDSBURG—Sonoma County

☐ **HEALDSBURG DISTRICT HOSPITAL (051321)**, 1375 University Avenue, Zip 95448–3382; tel. 707/431–6500, (Total facility includes 17 beds in nursing home–type unit) (Nonreporting) **A**1 10 18 **F**3 8 15 18 29 30 34 35 40 45 46 48 50 51 54 57 59 64 65 68 70 74 75 77 79 81 82 85 87 93 97 104 107 110 111 115 119 128 130 133 146 147 148 149 153 154
Primary Contact: James P. Schuessler, Chief Executive Officer
COO: Regina Novello, R.N., Chief Operating Officer
CFO: John S Parigi IllInterim Chief Financial Officer
CMO: Judy Widger, M.D., Chief of Staff
CIO: Steven Hansen, Director Information Technology
CHR: Kristina Holloway, Chief Human Resources Officer
CNO: Susan G Spoelma, MSN, R.N., Chief Nursing Officer
Web address: www.nschd.org
**Control**: Hospital district or authority, Government, Nonfederal **Service**: General medical and surgical

| Staffed Beds: 38 **Admissions:** 797 **Census:** 22 **Outpatient Visits:** 43257 **Births:** 0 **Total Expense ($000):** 58618 **Payroll Expense ($000):** 23665 |
| --- |

**NORTH SONOMA COUNTY HEALTHCARE DISTRICT** See Healdsburg District Hospital

### HEMET—Riverside County

☐ **HEMET VALLEY MEDICAL CENTER (050390)**, 1117 East Devonshire Avenue, Zip 92543–3083; tel. 951/652–2811, (Nonreporting) **A**1 3 5 10 12 13 **S** Physicians for Healthy Hospitals, Hemet, CA
Primary Contact: Dan C. McLaughlin, Chief Hospital Executive Officer
CFO: John R Collins, Chief Financial Officer
CMO: Sumanta Chaudhuri, M.D., Chief Medical Officer
CHR: Michele Bird, Chief Human Resources Officer
CNO: Kathryn McLaughlin, Chief Nursing Officer
Web address: www.physiciansforhealthyhospitals.com
**Control**: Hospital district or authority, Government, Nonfederal **Service**: General medical and surgical

| Staffed Beds: 238 |
| --- |

### HOLLISTER—San Benito County

☐ **HAZEL HAWKINS MEMORIAL HOSPITAL (050296)**, 911 Sunset Drive, Zip 95023–5695; tel. 831/637–5711, (Includes WILLIAM AND INEZ MABIE SKILLED NURSING FACILITY, Mailing address: 911 Sunset Drive, Hollister, California, Zip 95023; tel. 408/637–5711), (Nonreporting) **A**1 10
Primary Contact: Ken Underwood, Chief Executive Officer
CFO: Mark Robinson, Associate Administrator and Chief Financial Officer
CIO: Julio Gil, Manager Information Services
CHR: Ysidro Gallardo, Associate Administrator Human Resources
Web address: www.hazelhawkins.com
**Control**: Hospital district or authority, Government, Nonfederal **Service**: General medical and surgical

| Staffed Beds: 181 |
| --- |

**HAZEL HAWKINS MEMORIAL HOSPITAL** See William and Inez Mabie Skilled Nursing Facility

**SAN BENITO HOSPITAL DISTRICT** See Hazel Hawkins Memorial Hospital

### HUNTINGTON BEACH—Orange County

☐ **HUNTINGTON BEACH HOSPITAL (050526)**, 17772 Beach Boulevard, Zip 92647–6896; tel. 714/843–5000, (Nonreporting) **A**1 10 **S** Prime Healthcare, Ontario, CA
Primary Contact: Richard M. Rowe, PharmD, Chief Executive Officer
CFO: Alan H Smith, Chief Financial Officer
CMO: Hassan Alkhouli, M.D., Medical Director
CIO: Adam Morquecho, Director Information Technology
CHR: Stephanie Sioson, Director Human Resources
Web address: www.hbhospital.com
**Control**: Other not–for–profit (including NFP Corporation) **Service**: General medical and surgical

| Staffed Beds: 102 |
| --- |

**HUNTINGTON BEACH MEDICAL CTR** See Huntington Beach Hospital

### HUNTINGTON PARK—Los Angeles County

**COMMUNITY AND MISSION HOSPITALS OF HUNTINGTON PARK** See Community Hospital of Huntington Park

★ ○ **COMMUNITY HOSPITAL OF HUNTINGTON PARK (050091)**, 2623 East Slauson Avenue, Zip 90255–2926; tel. 323/583–1931, (Nonreporting) **A**10 11 **S** Avanti Hospitals, El Segundo, CA
Primary Contact: Patricia Rives, R.N., MSN, Chief Executive Officer
CFO: Cheryl Tong, Corporate Chief Financial Officer
CMO: Jose Rivas, M.D., Chief of Staff
CIO: Jason Cervantes, Corporate Chief Information Officer
CHR: Paul Celuch, Corporate Human Resources Director
CNO: Lisa Jacobson, Director of Nursing
Web address: www.avantihospitals.com/community-hospital-of-huntington-park
**Control**: Corporation, Investor–owned (for–profit) **Service**: General medical and surgical

| Staffed Beds: 81 |
| --- |

### INDIO—Riverside County

⊞ **JFK MEMORIAL HOSPITAL (050534)**, 47111 Monroe Street, Zip 92201–6799; tel. 760/347–6191, (Nonreporting) **A**1 10 **F**3 8 18 20 29 30 34 35 37 40 46 47 48 49 50 54 56 57 59 68 70 74 76 78 79 81 85 87 89 97 107 108 111 118 119 126 130 146 148 154 156 **S** TENET Healthcare Corporation, Dallas, TX
Primary Contact: Gary Honts, Chief Executive Officer
CFO: Mike King, Chief Financial Officer and Chief Operating Officer
CHR: Raymond Konieczek, Chief Human Resources Officer
CNO: Heather Adams, Chief Nursing Officer
Web address: www.jfkmemorialhosp.com
**Control**: Corporation, Investor–owned (for–profit) **Service**: General medical and surgical

| Staffed Beds: 145 **Admissions:** 6972 **Census:** 53 **Outpatient Visits:** 59915 **Births:** 1949 **Total Expense ($000):** 121300 **Payroll Expense ($000):** 54234 |
| --- |

**JOHN F. KENNEDY MEMORIAL HOSPITAL** See Jfk Memorial Hospital

*Many Facility Codes have changed. Please refer to the AHA Guide Code Chart.*
© 2021 AHA Guide

**CA**

## INGLEWOOD—Los Angeles County

**CENTINELA FREEMAN MED CENTER** See Centinela Hospital Medical Center

☐ **CENTINELA HOSPITAL MEDICAL CENTER (050739)**, 555 East Hardy Street, Zip 90301–4011, Mailing Address: P.O. Box 720, Zip 90312–6720; tel. 310/673–4660, (Nonreporting) **A**1 10 **S** Prime Healthcare, Ontario, CA
Primary Contact: Linda Bradley, Chief Executive Officer
CFO: Paul Sennett, Chief Financial Officer
CMO: Paryus Patel, M.D., Chief Medical Officer
CIO: Martin Cordova, Director Information Services
CHR: George Akopyan, Director Human Resources
CNO: Mohammad Abdelnaser, Chief Nursing Officer
Web address: www.centinelamed.com
**Control:** Corporation, Investor–owned (for–profit) **Service:** General medical and surgical

| **Staffed Beds:** 369 |
| --- |

## IRVINE—Orange County

⇑ **HOAG ORTHOPEDIC INSTITUTE (050769)**, 16250 Sand Canyon Avenue, Zip 92618–3714; tel. 949/517–3149, (Nonreporting) **A**3 10 21
Primary Contact: Carlos Prietto, President and Chief Executive Officer
CMO: Robert Gorab, M.D., Chief Medical Officer
Web address: www.https://www.orthopedichospital.com/
**Control:** Other not–for–profit (including NFP Corporation) **Service:** Orthopedic

| **Staffed Beds:** 70 |
| --- |

**KAISER FOUNDATION HOSPITAL - ORANGE COUNTY** See Orange County Irvine Medical Center

**ORANGE COUNTY IRVINE MEDICAL CENTER** See Kaiser Permanente Orange County Anaheim Medical Center, Anaheim

## JACKSON—Amador County

**AMADOR HOSPITAL** See Sutter Amador Hospital

✠ **SUTTER AMADOR HOSPITAL (050014)**, 200 Mission Boulevard, Zip 95642–2564; tel. 209/223–7500, (Nonreporting) **A**1 5 10 20 **S** Sutter Health, Sacramento, CA
Primary Contact: Thomas C. Dickson, Chief Executive Officer
CFO: Brett Moore, CPA, Assistant Administrator Finance
CMO: Ron Hood, M.D., Chief of Staff
CIO: Joy Bailey, Director Information Technology
CHR: Beverly Revels, Director Human Resources
CNO: Nikki Allen, Patient Care Executive
Web address: www.sutteramador.org
**Control:** Other not–for–profit (including NFP Corporation) **Service:** General medical and surgical

| **Staffed Beds:** 52 |
| --- |

## JOSHUA TREE—San Bernardino County

✠ **HI-DESERT MEDICAL CENTER (050279)**, 6601 White Feather Road, Zip 92284; tel. 760/366–3711, (Nonreporting) **A**1 10 20 **S** TENET Healthcare Corporation, Dallas, TX
Primary Contact: Karen Faulis, Chief Executive Officer
COO: David Cooke, R.N., Chief Operating Officer
CMO: Jeffrey Seip, M.D., Chief Medical Staff
CIO: Darrell Goodman, Chief Information Officer
CHR: Nicole Smith, Director Human Resources
CNO: David Cooke, R.N., Chief Operating Officer
Web address: www.hdmc.org
**Control:** Corporation, Investor–owned (for–profit) **Service:** General medical and surgical

| **Staffed Beds:** 179 |
| --- |

**HI-DESERT MEDICAL CENTER** See Hi-Desert Medical Center

## KENTFIELD—Marin County

✠ **KENTFIELD HOSPITAL (052043)**, 1125 Sir Francis Drake Boulevard, Zip 94904–1455; tel. 415/456–9680, (Nonreporting) **A**1 10 **S** Vibra Healthcare, Mechanicsburg, PA
Primary Contact: Varun Chauhan, Chief Executive Officer
CFO: Stephanie Lawrence, Chief Financial Officer
CMO: Curtis Roebken, M.D., Chief Medical Staff
CHR: Julene English, Director Human Resources
Web address: www.kentfieldrehab.com
**Control:** Corporation, Investor–owned (for–profit) **Service:** Acute long–term care hospital

| **Staffed Beds:** 60 |
| --- |

**KENTFIELD REHABILITATION AND SPECIALTY HOSPITAL** See Kentfield Hospital

## KING CITY—Monterey County

**GEORGE L. MEE MEMORIAL HOSPITAL** See Mee Memorial Hospital

☐ **MEE MEMORIAL HOSPITAL (050189)**, 300 Canal Street, Zip 93930–3431; tel. 831/385–6000, (Total facility includes 48 beds in nursing home–type unit) (Nonreporting) **A**1 5 10 20 **F**3 13 15 29 32 40 45 55 59 60 65 68 70 75 76 82 89 90 93 97 107 110 111 114 119 127 128 130 133 146 147 148 154
Primary Contact: R. Michael. Hutchinson, Chief Executive Officer
CFO: Gary L Wangsmo, Chief Financial Officer
CMO: Schindelheim Roy, M.D., Chief of Staff
CIO: Mike McNamara, Chief Information Officer
CHR: Karen Wong, Chief Human Resources Officer
Web address: www.meememorial.com
**Control:** Other not–for–profit (including NFP Corporation) **Service:** General medical and surgical

| **Staffed Beds:** 76 **Admissions:** 1206 **Census:** 23 **Outpatient Visits:** 106159 **Births:** 267 **Total Expense ($000):** 70403 **Payroll Expense ($000):** 21829 **Personnel:** 325 |
| --- |

## LA JOLLA—San Diego County

**GREEN HOSP OF SCRIPPS CLINIC** See Scripps Green Hospital

✠ **SCRIPPS GREEN HOSPITAL (050424)**, 10666 North Torrey Pines Road, Zip 92037–1093; tel. 858/455–9100, (Nonreporting) **A**1 3 5 8 10 **F**3 8 11 12 14 15 17 18 20 22 24 26 29 30 31 34 35 36 37 44 45 46 47 49 50 51 54 57 58 59 61 64 68 70 74 75 77 78 79 80 81 82 84 85 86 87 93 107 108 110 111 115 118 119 120 121 123 124 126 130 131 132 136 138 139 141 142 146 148 156 157 **S** Scripps Health, San Diego, CA
Primary Contact: Carl J. Etter, Chief Executive Officer
CFO: Richard Rothberger, Corporate Executive Vice President and Chief Financial Officer
CMO: James LaBelle, M.D., Chief Medical Officer
CIO: Andy Crowder, Chief Information Officer and Corporate Senior Vice President
CHR: Victor Buzachero, Corporate Senior Vice President for Innovation, Human Resources and Performance Management
Web address: www.scrippshealth.org
**Control:** Other not–for–profit (including NFP Corporation) **Service:** General medical and surgical

| **Staffed Beds:** 150 **Admissions:** 8298 **Census:** 78 **Outpatient Visits:** 110301 **Births:** 0 **Total Expense ($000):** 277472 **Payroll Expense ($000):** 90255 **Personnel:** 1055 |
| --- |

**SCRIPPS MEM HOSP - LA JOLLA** See Scripps Memorial Hospital-La Jolla

---

| Hospital, Medicare Provider Number, Address, Telephone, Approval, Facility, and Physician Codes, Health Care System |
| --- |
| ★ American Hospital Association (AHA) membership  ○ Healthcare Facilities Accreditation Program  ⇑ Center for Improvement in Healthcare Quality Accreditation<br>☐ The Joint Commission accreditation  ◇ DNV Healthcare Inc. accreditation  △ Commission on Accreditation of Rehabilitation Facilities (CARF) accreditation |

⊞ **SCRIPPS MEMORIAL HOSPITAL-LA JOLLA (050324)**, 9888 Genesee Avenue, Zip 92037–1200, Mailing Address: P.O. Box 28, Zip 92038–0028; tel. 858/626–4123, (Nonreporting) **A**1 3 5 10 **F**3 8 11 12 13 14 15 17 18 20 22 24 26 28 29 30 31 34 35 40 43 44 45 46 48 49 50 51 53 54 55 57 58 59 64 65 68 70 74 75 76 77 78 79 81 82 84 85 86 87 91 92 93 94 100 101 102 107 108 110 111 114 115 116 117 118 119 124 126 130 132 141 145 146 147 148 156 157 **S** Scripps Health, San Diego, CA
Primary Contact: Carl J. Etter, Chief Executive Officer
COO: Cindy Steckel, Ph.D., R.N., Vice President Chief Nurse and Operations Executive
CFO: Alan Mandal, Vice President Financial Operations
CMO: James LaBelle, M.D., Chief Medical Officer
CHR: Shelly Blazakis, Director Human Resources Services
CNO: Cindy Steckel, Ph.D., R.N., Vice President Chief Nurse and Operations Executive
Web address: www.scripps.org/locations/hospitals__scripps-memorial-hospital-la-jolla
**Control**: Other not–for–profit (including NFP Corporation) **Service**: General medical and surgical

**Staffed Beds:** 365 **Admissions:** 19216 **Census:** 235 **Outpatient Visits:** 106638 **Births:** 3293 **Total Expense ($000):** 644239 **Payroll Expense ($000):** 214773 **Personnel:** 2433

**SCRIPPS TORREY PINES CONV HOSP** See Evergreen of La Jolla

**UC SAN DIEGO SHILEY EYE CENTER** See UC San Diego Shiley Eye Institute

### LA MESA—San Diego County

☐ **ALVARADO PARKWAY INSTITUTE BEHAVIORAL HEALTH SYSTEM (054075)**, 7050 Parkway Drive, Zip 91942–1535; tel. 619/465–4411, (Nonreporting) **A**1 10
Primary Contact: Megan Montgomery-West, Chief Executive Officer
CFO: Chad Engbrecht, Chief Financial Officer
CMO: R. Bradley Sanders, D.O., Executive Medical Director
CNO: Bonnie Asada, Chief Nursing Officer
Web address: www.apibhs.com
**Control**: Partnership, Investor–owned (for–profit) **Service**: Psychiatric

**Staffed Beds:** 66

**GROSSMONT HOSPITAL** See Sharp Grossmont Hospital

⊞ △ **SHARP GROSSMONT HOSPITAL (050026)**, 5555 Grossmont Center Drive, Zip 91942–3019, Mailing Address: PO Box 158, Zip 91944–0158; tel. 619/740–6000, (Total facility includes 30 beds in nursing home–type unit) (Nonreporting) **A**1 2 3 7 10 **F**3 5 8 11 12 13 15 17 18 20 22 24 26 28 29 30 31 34 35 37 38 40 44 45 46 47 48 49 50 51 54 55 56 57 58 59 60 61 62 63 64 65 68 70 72 74 75 76 77 78 79 80 81 82 84 85 87 90 91 92 93 94 96 98 100 101 102 103 104 106 107 108 109 111 114 115 116 117 118 119 120 121 123 124 126 128 129 130 132 135 143 146 147 148 149 153 154 156 **P**3 5 **S** Sharp HealthCare, San Diego, CA
Primary Contact: Scott Evans, PharmD, FACHE, Senior Vice President and Chief Executive Officer
COO: Maryann Cone, Chief Operating Officer
CFO: Kari Cornicelli, Chief Financial Officer
CMO: Michael Murphy, M.D., JD, Chief Medical Officer
CIO: Kenneth Lawonn, Senior Vice President and Chief Information Officer
Web address: www.sharp.com
**Control**: Other not–for–profit (including NFP Corporation) **Service**: General medical and surgical

**Staffed Beds:** 524 **Admissions:** 28606 **Census:** 383 **Outpatient Visits:** 478217 **Births:** 2963 **Total Expense ($000):** 756479 **Payroll Expense ($000):** 316390 **Personnel:** 3214

### LA MIRADA—Los Angeles County

⊞ **KINDRED HOSPITAL-LA MIRADA (052038)**, 14900 East Imperial Highway, Zip 90638–2172; tel. 562/944–1900, (Includes KINDRED HOSPITAL SAN GABRIEL VALLEY, Mailing address: 845 North Lark Ellen Avenue, West Covina, California, Zip 91791–1069; tel. 626/339–5451; Anthony Nguyen, Chief Executive Officer; KINDRED HOSPITAL SANTA ANA, Mailing address: 1901 North College Avenue, Santa Ana, California, Zip 92706–2334; tel. 714/564–7800; Rick Rufino, Chief Executive Officer), (Nonreporting) **A**1 3 10 **F**1 3 4 16 17 28 29 45 46 47 48 50 60 65 67 70 72 73 74 75 76 77 79 80 82 83 84 87 88 89 90 91 92 94 95 96 98 107 109 111 114 115 116 117 118 119 128 130 143 154 157 **S** Kindred Healthcare, Louisville, KY
Primary Contact: David Kowalski, Chief Executive Officer
CFO: Rishab Punjabi, Chief Financial Officer
CMO: Prakash Chandra Patel, M.D., Chief of Staff
CHR: Susan Bergquist, Human Resources Generalist
CNO: Esperanza Sanchez, Chief Clinical Officer
Web address: www.kindredlamirada.com/
**Control**: Corporation, Investor–owned (for–profit) **Service**: Acute long–term care hospital

**Staffed Beds:** 118 **Admissions:** 600 **Census:** 49 **Outpatient Visits:** 0 **Births:** 0 **Total Expense ($000):** 22984 **Payroll Expense ($000):** 15500 **Personnel:** 220

### LA PALMA—Orange County

☐ **LA PALMA INTERCOMMUNITY HOSPITAL (050580)**, 7901 Walker Street, Zip 90623–1764; tel. 714/670–7400, (Nonreporting) **A**1 10 **S** Prime Healthcare, Ontario, CA
Primary Contact: Michael Sarian, Interim Chief Executive Officer
CFO: Alan H Smith, Chief Financial Officer
CMO: Sami Shoukair, M.D., Chief Medical Officer
CIO: Vic Mahan, Director Information Technology
CHR: Stephanie Sioson, Director Human Resources
CNO: Hilda Manzo-Luna, Chief Nursing Officer
Web address: www.lapalmaintercommunityhospital.com
**Control**: Other not–for–profit (including NFP Corporation) **Service**: General medical and surgical

**Staffed Beds:** 140

### LAGUNA BEACH—Orange County

**SOUTH COAST MEDICAL CENTER** See Mission Hospital Laguna Beach

### LAGUNA HILLS—Orange County

⊞ **SADDLEBACK MEDICAL CENTER (050603)**, 24451 Health Center Drive, Zip 92653–3689; tel. 949/837–4500, (Nonreporting) **A**1 3 5 10 **F**3 11 13 14 15 18 20 22 24 26 28 29 30 31 34 35 36 38 40 44 45 46 47 48 49 50 51 53 54 55 56 57 58 59 62 63 64 65 68 70 72 74 75 76 77 78 79 81 84 85 86 87 93 94 107 108 110 111 115 116 117 118 119 120 121 123 124 126 130 132 135 141 142 143 145 146 147 148 149 154 157 **P**3 5 **S** MemorialCare, Fountain Valley, CA
Primary Contact: Marcia Manker, Chief Executive Officer
COO: Ryan Olsen, Chief Operating Officer
CFO: Aaron Coley, Chief Financial Officer, Orange County
CMO: Kathleen Sullivan, M.D., Chief of Staff
CIO: J Scott Joslyn, Senior Vice President and Chief Information Officer
CHR: Michelle Gutierrez, Executive Director Human Resources, Orange County
CNO: Brandi Cassingham, Chief Nursing Officer
Web address: www.memorialcare.org
**Control**: Other not–for–profit (including NFP Corporation) **Service**: General medical and surgical

**Staffed Beds:** 250 **Admissions:** 11939 **Census:** 111 **Outpatient Visits:** 217815 **Births:** 2293 **Total Expense ($000):** 340579 **Payroll Expense ($000):** 97762 **Personnel:** 1279

**SADDLEBACK MEMORIAL MEDICAL CENTER** See Saddleback Medical Center

### LAKE ARROWHEAD—San Bernardino County

⊞ **MOUNTAINS COMMUNITY HOSPITAL (051312)**, 29101 Hospital Road, Zip 92352–9706, Mailing Address: P.O. Box 70, Zip 92352–0070; tel. 909/336–3651, (Nonreporting) **A**1 10 18
Primary Contact: Charles Harrison, Chief Executive Officer
COO: Terry Pena, Chief Operating Officer and Chief Nursing Officer
CFO: Yvonne Waggener, Chief Financial Officer
CMO: Walter M. Maier, Chief of Staff
CIO: Patrick Miller, Technology Coordinator
CHR: Julie Atwood, Director Human Resources
CNO: Terry Pena, Chief Operating Officer and Chief Nursing Officer
Web address: www.mchcares.com
**Control**: Hospital district or authority, Government, Nonfederal **Service**: General medical and surgical

**Staffed Beds:** 37

**SAN BERNARDINO MOUNTAINS COMMUNITY HOSPITAL DISTRICT** See Mountains Community Hospital

### LAKE ISABELLA—Kern County

**KERN VALLEY HEALTHCARE DISTRICT (051314)**, 6412 Laurel Avenue, Zip 93240–9529, Mailing Address: P.O. Box 1628, Zip 93240–1628; tel. 760/379–2681, (Nonreporting) **A**10 18
Primary Contact: Timothy McGlew, Chief Executive Officer
CFO: Chester Beedle, Chief Financial Officer
CMO: Gary A Finstad, M.D., Chief of Staff
CIO: Paul Quinn, Information Systems Manager
CHR: Debra Hoffman, Human Resources Manager
CNO: Mark Gordon, Chief Nursing Officer
Web address: www.kvhd.org
**Control**: Hospital district or authority, Government, Nonfederal **Service**: General medical and surgical

**Staffed Beds:** 99

**KERN VALLEY HOSPITAL DISTRICT** See Kern Valley Healthcare District

**CA**

*Many Facility Codes have changed. Please refer to the AHA Guide Code Chart.*
© 2021 AHA Guide

## LAKEPORT—Lake County

**LAKESIDE COMMUNITY HOSPITAL** See Sutter Lakeside Hospital

✠ **SUTTER LAKESIDE HOSPITAL (051329)**, 5176 Hill Road East, Zip 95453–6300; tel. 707/262–5000, (Nonreporting) **A**1 10 18 **S** Sutter Health, Sacramento, CA
Primary Contact: Scott Knight, Chief Administrative Officer
CFO: Linnea Humble, Director of Finance
CMO: Diane Pege, M.D., Vice President Medical Affairs
CIO: Jack Buell, Director Information Services
CHR: Brenda DeRamus, Manager Human Resources
CNO: Teresa Campbell, R.N., Chief Nursing Executive
Web address: www.sutterlakeside.org
**Control:** Other not–for–profit (including NFP Corporation) **Service:** General medical and surgical

| Staffed Beds: 25 |
|---|

## LAKEWOOD—Los Angeles County

**DOCTORS HOSPITAL OF LAKEWOOD** See Lakewood Regional Medical Center

✠ **LAKEWOOD REGIONAL MEDICAL CENTER (050581)**, 3700 East South Street, Zip 90712–1498, Mailing Address: P.O. Box 6070, Zip 90712; tel. 562/531–2550, (Nonreporting) **A**1 10 **F**3 11 15 17 18 20 22 24 26 29 30 34 35 38 40 45 49 50 51 57 59 64 68 70 74 75 77 79 81 85 87 93 107 108 109 111 115 118 119 120 126 130 132 143 146 148 149 154 **S** TENET Healthcare Corporation, Dallas, TX
Primary Contact: John A. Grah, FACHE, Chief Executive Officer
COO: Michael Paul Amos, Chief Operating Officer
CFO: Eric Delgado, Chief Financial Officer
CIO: Pat Pierce, Director Information Systems
CHR: Mary Okuhara, Chief Human Resource Officer
CNO: Terri Newton, Chief Nursing Officer
Web address: www.lakewoodregional.com
**Control:** Corporation, Investor–owned (for–profit) **Service:** General medical and surgical

| Staffed Beds: 111 Admissions: 8717 Census: 113 Outpatient Visits: 59355 Births: 0 Total Expense ($000): 179101 Payroll Expense ($000): 81257 Personnel: 847 |
|---|

## LANCASTER—Los Angeles County

**ANTELOPE VALLEY HOSP** See Antelope Valley Hospital

✠ **ANTELOPE VALLEY HOSPITAL (050056)**, 1600 West Avenue 'J', Zip 93534–2894; tel. 661/949–5000, (Nonreporting) **A**1 2 3 5 10
Primary Contact: Edward Mirzabegian, Chief Executive Officer
COO: Colette Menzel, Ph.D., Chief Operating Officer and Chief Financial Officer
CFO: Colette Menzel, Ph.D., Chief Operating Officer and Chief Financial Officer
CMO: Radha Krishnan, M.D., Chief Medical Officer
CIO: Dale Lepper, Chief Information Officer
CHR: George Leisher JrChief Human Resources Officer
CNO: Jack J Burke, MS, R.N., Chief Operating Officer and Chief Nursing Officer
Web address: www.avhospital.org
**Control:** Hospital district or authority, Government, Nonfederal **Service:** General medical and surgical

| Staffed Beds: 368 |
|---|

## LEMOORE—Kings County

**NAVAL HOSPITAL** See Naval Hospital Lemoore

★ **NAVAL HOSPITAL LEMOORE**, 937 Franklin Avenue, Zip 93246–0001; tel. 559/998–4481, (Nonreporting) **S** Bureau of Medicine and Surgery, Department of the Navy, Falls Church, VA
Primary Contact: Captain Kristen Attenbury, Commanding Officer
CFO: Thomas M Brui, Director Resource Management
CMO: Scott Cota, M.D., Director Medical Services
CIO: Victor Dela Torre, Command Legal Officer
CHR: Billy Newman, Department Head
Web address: www.med.navy.mil/sites/nhlem/Pages/index.aspx
**Service:** General medical and surgical

| Staffed Beds: 16 |
|---|

## LIVERMORE—Kings County

**VA PALO ALTO HEALTH CARE SYSTEM-LIVERMORE DIVISION** See Veterans Affairs Palo Alto Health Care System, Livermore Division

## LIVERMORE—Alameda County

**VALLEY MEMORIAL** See Stanford Health Care - Valleycare, Pleasanton

**VALLEYCARE MEDICAL CENTER** See Valley Memorial

**VETERANS AFFAIRS PALO ALTO HEALTH CARE SYSTEM, LIVERMORE DIVISION** See VA Palo Alto Health Care System, Palo Alto

## LODI—San Joaquin County

**ADVENTIST HEALTH LODI** See Adventist Health Lodi Memorial

✠ **ADVENTIST HEALTH LODI MEMORIAL (050336)**, 975 South Fairmont Avenue, Zip 95240–5118, Mailing Address: P.O. Box 3004, Zip 95241–1908; tel. 209/334–3411, (Includes LODI MEMORIAL HOSPITAL WEST, Mailing address: 800 South Lower Sacramento Road, Lodi, California, Zip 95242; tel. 209/333–0211), (Nonreporting) **A**1 5 10 **F**2 3 8 11 12 13 15 18 20 26 28 29 30 31 32 34 35 40 41 45 46 47 48 49 50 51 53 54 56 57 59 60 62 64 65 66 68 70 72 74 75 76 77 79 81 82 84 85 90 93 96 97 107 108 111 115 118 119 126 127 129 130 131 132 134 135 144 146 147 148 149 150 154 156 157 **P**7 8 **S** Adventist Health, Roseville, CA
Primary Contact: Daniel Wolcott, President and Chief Executive Officer
CFO: Terry Deak, Chief Financial Officer
CHR: Mark T Wallace, Director Human Resources
CNO: Debbie Moreno, R.N., Patient Care Executive
Web address: www.https://www.adventisthealth.org/lodi-memorial/
**Control:** Other not–for–profit (including NFP Corporation) **Service:** General medical and surgical

| Staffed Beds: 194 Admissions: 8283 Census: 83 Outpatient Visits: 75264 Births: 1051 Total Expense ($000): 243955 Payroll Expense ($000): 75365 Personnel: 847 |
|---|

**DOCTORS HOSPITAL OF LODI** See Lodi Memorial Hospital West

## LOMA LINDA—San Bernardino County

**CALIFORNIA HEART AND SURGICAL HOSPITAL** See Loma Linda University Heart & Surgical Hospital

**JERRY L. PETTIS MEMORIAL VETERANS MEDICAL CENTER** See Veterans Affairs Loma Linda Healthcare System

**LOMA LINDA UNIV COMM MED CTR** See Loma Linda University East Campus Hospital

☐ **LOMA LINDA UNIVERSITY CHILDREN'S HOSPITAL (050778)**, 11234 Anderson Street, Zip 92354–2804; tel. 909/558–8000, (Nonreporting) **A**1 3 5 10 **F**3 11 13 19 25 27 29 30 31 32 34 43 44 45 46 50 54 55 57 58 59 60 61 64 65 68 72 74 75 76 77 78 79 80 81 82 84 85 86 87 88 89 97 119 126 130 132 134 136 137 138 141 146 147 148 149 150 154 156 **S** Loma Linda University Adventist Health Sciences Center, Loma Linda, CA
Primary Contact: Kerry Heinrich, JD, Chief Executive Officer
COO: Trevor Wright, Chief Operating Officer
CFO: Angela Lalas, Senior Vice President, Finance
CMO: Richard Chinnock, Chief Medical Officer, LLUCH
CIO: Mark Zirkelbach, Chief Information Officer
CHR: Lizette O Norton, Vice President, Human Resources
CNO: Helen Staples-Evans, Chief Nursing Officer, LLUCH
Web address: www.llu.edu/lluch
**Control:** Other not–for–profit (including NFP Corporation) **Service:** General medical and surgical

| Staffed Beds: 343 Admissions: 14472 Census: 230 Outpatient Visits: 75639 Births: 3140 Total Expense ($000): 434015 Payroll Expense ($000): 164097 Personnel: 1592 |
|---|

**LOMA LINDA UNIVERSITY HEART & SURGICAL HOSPITAL** See Loma Linda University Medical Center, Loma Linda

---

| Hospital, Medicare Provider Number, Address, Telephone, Approval, Facility, and Physician Codes, Health Care System |
|---|

★ American Hospital Association (AHA) membership    ○ Healthcare Facilities Accreditation Program    ⇑ Center for Improvement in Healthcare Quality Accreditation
☐ The Joint Commission accreditation    ◇ DNV Healthcare Inc. accreditation    △ Commission on Accreditation of Rehabilitation Facilities (CARF) accreditation

**CA**

✠ △ **LOMA LINDA UNIVERSITY MEDICAL CENTER (050327)**, 11234 Anderson Street, Zip 92354–2804, Mailing Address: P.O. Box 2000, Zip 92354–0200; tel. 909/558–4000, (Includes LOMA LINDA UNIVERSITY EAST CAMPUS HOSPITAL, Mailing address: 25333 Barton Road, Loma Linda, California, Zip 92354–3053; tel. 909/558–6000; LOMA LINDA UNIVERSITY HEART & SURGICAL HOSPITAL, Mailing address: 26780 Barton Road, Loma Linda, California, Zip 92354; tel. 909/583–2900), (Nonreporting) **A**1 2 3 5 7 8 10 **F**2 3 8 11 12 15 17 18 20 21 22 23 24 26 27 28 29 30 31 34 35 37 40 41 43 44 45 46 47 48 49 50 51 54 57 58 59 60 61 62 64 65 68 70 74 75 77 78 79 81 82 84 85 86 87 90 91 92 93 94 95 96 102 107 108 110 111 114 115 117 118 119 120 121 122 123 124 126 129 130 132 136 137 138 139 141 142 143 144 146 147 148 149 150 154 156 157 **S** Loma Linda University Adventist Health Sciences Center, Loma Linda, CA
Primary Contact: Kerry Heinrich, JD, Chief Executive Officer
COO: Trevor Wright, Chief Operating Officer
CMO: H Roger Hadley, M.D., Vice President, Medical Affairs
CIO: Mark Zirkelbach, Chief Information Officer
CNO: Judith Storfjell, Ph.D., R.N., Senior Vice President and Chief Nursing Officer
Web address: www.llumc.edu
**Control**: Other not–for–profit (including NFP Corporation) **Service**: General medical and surgical

**Staffed Beds**: 533 **Admissions**: 24148 **Census**: 374 **Outpatient Visits**: 686007 **Births**: 0 **Total Expense ($000)**: 1373025 **Payroll Expense ($000)**: 381110 **Personnel**: 5331

☐ **TOTALLY KIDS REHABILITATION HOSPITAL (053038)**, 1720 Mountain View Avenue, Zip 92354–1727; tel. 909/796–6915, (Nonreporting) **A**1
Primary Contact: Doug Padgett, President and Chief Executive Officer
Web address: www.https://totallykids.com/
**Control**: Corporation, Investor–owned (for–profit) **Service**: Rehabilitation

**Staffed Beds**: 25

✠ △ **VETERANS AFFAIRS LOMA LINDA HEALTHCARE SYSTEM**, 11201 Benton Street, Zip 92357–1000; tel. 909/825–7084, (Nonreporting) **A**1 2 3 5 7 8 **S** Department of Veterans Affairs, Washington, DC
Primary Contact: Andrew Welch, Interim Director
COO: Shane Elliott, Associate Director Administration
CFO: Eric C Sorenson, Chief Financial Officer
CMO: Dwight Evans, M.D., Chief of Staff
CIO: Doug Wirthgen, Facility Chief Information Officer
CHR: Eugene Wylie, Chief Human Resources Officer
CNO: Anne Gillespie, R.N., Associate Director Patient Care and Nursing Services
Web address: www.lomalinda.va.gov
**Control**: Veterans Affairs, Government, federal **Service**: General medical and surgical

**Staffed Beds**: 268

### LOMPOC—Santa Barbara County

**LOMPOC HEALTHCARE DISTRICT** See Lompoc Valley Medical Center

★ **LOMPOC VALLEY MEDICAL CENTER (050110)**, 1515 East Ocean Avenue, Zip 93436–7092, Mailing Address: P.O. Box 1058, Zip 93438–1058; tel. 805/737–3300, (Nonreporting) **A**10 22
Primary Contact: Steven Popkin, Chief Executive Officer
COO: Naishadh Buch, Chief Operating Officer
CFO: Robert M Baden, Chief Financial Officer
CMO: Randall Michel, M.D., Chief of Staff
CIO: Jim White, Chief Information Officer
CHR: Edwin R Braxton, Director Human Resources
CNO: Yvette Renee Cope, Chief Nurse Executive
Web address: www.lompocvmc.com
**Control**: Hospital district or authority, Government, Nonfederal **Service**: General medical and surgical

**Staffed Beds**: 170

### LONE PINE—Inyo County

**SOUTHERN INYO HEALTHCARE DIST** See Southern Inyo Healthcare District

**SOUTHERN INYO HEALTHCARE DISTRICT (051302)**, 501 East Locust Street, Zip 93545–1009, Mailing Address: P.O. Box 1009, Zip 93545–1009; tel. 760/876–5501, (Nonreporting) **A**10 18
Primary Contact: Brian Cotter, Chief Operating Officer
CFO: Marise Andrade, Controller
CIO: Phyllis Gregory, Registered Health Information Administrator
CHR: Nancy Erickson, Human Resource Director
CNO: Colleen Wilson, Chief Nursing Officer
Web address: www.sihd.org
**Control**: Hospital district or authority, Government, Nonfederal **Service**: General medical and surgical

**Staffed Beds**: 4

### LONG BEACH—Los Angeles County

⇑ **COLLEGE MEDICAL CENTER (050776)**, 2776 Pacific Avenue, Zip 90806–2613; tel. 562/595–1911, (Nonreporting) **A**3 5 10 12 13 21
Primary Contact: Joseph Avelino, Chief Executive Officer
COO: Jennifer Ensminger, Chief Operating Officer
CFO: Jim Canedo, Chief Financial Officer
CMO: Luke Watson, M.D., Chief of Staff
CIO: Rohan Corea, Director Healthcare Information Technology
CHR: Ann Mattia Schiller, Vice President Human Resources
Web address: www.collegemedicalcenter.com/
**Control**: Other not–for–profit (including NFP Corporation) **Service**: General medical and surgical

**Staffed Beds**: 137

✠ △ **LONG BEACH MEDICAL CENTER (050485)**, 2801 Atlantic Avenue, Zip 90806–1701, Mailing Address: P.O. Box 1428, Zip 90801–1428; tel. 562/933–2000, (Nonreporting) **A**1 2 3 5 7 8 10 **F**3 8 9 11 12 14 15 17 18 20 22 24 26 28 29 30 31 34 35 36 37 38 39 40 43 44 45 47 48 49 50 52 53 55 56 57 58 59 61 63 64 65 68 70 74 75 77 78 79 81 82 84 85 86 87 90 93 96 97 107 108 110 111 114 115 116 117 118 119 120 121 123 124 126 128 129 130 131 132 135 141 142 143 144 146 147 148 149 150 154 156 157 **P**3 5 **S** MemorialCare, Fountain Valley, CA
Primary Contact: John Bishop, Chief Executive Officer
COO: Ikenna Mmeje, Chief Operating Officer
CFO: Yair Katz, Chief Financial Officer
CMO: Susan Melvin, D.O., Chief Medical Officer
CIO: Danny Asaoka, Executive Director Information Systems
CHR: Marcie Atchison, Vice President Human Resources
CNO: Susan B Herman, MSN, R.N., Chief Nursing Officer
Web address: www.memorialcare.org/LongBeach
**Control**: Other not–for–profit (including NFP Corporation) **Service**: General medical and surgical

**Staffed Beds**: 458 **Admissions**: 21808 **Census**: 285 **Outpatient Visits**: 224346 **Births**: 0 **Total Expense ($000)**: 662279 **Payroll Expense ($000)**: 201566 **Personnel**: 2705

**LONG BEACH MEMORIAL MEDICAL CENTER** See Long Beach Medical Center

**MEMORIALCARE, MILLER CHILDREN'S & WOMEN'S HOSPITAL LONG BEACH** See Miller Children's & Women's Hospital Long Beach

☐ **MILLER CHILDREN'S & WOMEN'S HOSPITAL LONG BEACH (053309)**, 2801 Atlantic Avenue, Zip 90806–1701; tel. 562/933–5437, (Nonreporting) **A**1 2 3 5 10 **F**3 11 12 13 14 15 19 21 23 25 27 29 30 31 32 34 35 36 37 38 40 41 43 44 45 47 48 49 50 52 53 54 55 57 58 59 61 64 65 66 68 72 74 75 76 77 78 79 81 82 84 85 86 87 88 89 93 96 97 107 108 111 114 115 116 117 118 119 120 121 123 124 126 129 130 132 134 135 141 142 143 144 146 147 148 149 154 156 157 **P**3 5 **S** MemorialCare, Fountain Valley, CA
Primary Contact: John Bishop, Chief Executive Officer
COO: Tamra Kaplan, PharmD, Chief Operating Officer
CFO: Yair Katz, Chief Financial Officer
CMO: Graham Tse, M.D., Chief Medical Officer
CIO: Danny Asaoka, Executive Director Information Systems
CHR: Marcie Atchison, Vice President Human Resources
CNO: Antonio M. Garcia, Chief Nursing Officer
Web address: www.memorialcare.org
**Control**: Other not–for–profit (including NFP Corporation) **Service**: Children's general medical and surgical

**Staffed Beds**: 371 **Admissions**: 15205 **Census**: 185 **Outpatient Visits**: 94397 **Births**: 4116 **Total Expense ($000)**: 434504 **Payroll Expense ($000)**: 136848 **Personnel**: 1208

⇑ **PACIFIC HOSPITAL OF LONG BEACH** See College Medical Center

**ST. MARY MEDICAL CENTER** See St. Mary Medical Center Long Beach

✠ **ST. MARY MEDICAL CENTER LONG BEACH (050191)**, 1050 Linden Avenue, Zip 90813–3321, Mailing Address: P.O. Box 887, Zip 90801–0887; tel. 562/491–9000, (Nonreporting) **A**1 3 5 10 **F**3 12 13 15 17 18 19 20 22 24 25 26 28 29 30 31 32 34 35 38 39 40 41 43 45 46 47 48 49 50 54 55 56 57 59 61 64 65 66 68 70 71 72 74 75 76 77 78 79 80 81 82 84 85 86 87 89 90 92 96 97 100 104 107 108 110 111 115 118 119 120 121 122 123 126 130 131 143 145 146 147 148 153 156 **P**5 **S** CommonSpirit Health, Chicago, IL
Primary Contact: Carolyn P. Caldwell, FACHE, President and Chief Executive Officer
COO: Bonnie Panlasigui, Chief Operating Officer
CFO: Leon Choiniere, Vice President, Chief Financial Officer
CIO: David Ung, Site Director
CHR: Denise Livingston, Director Human Resources
CNO: Gloria Carter, Chief Nurse Executive Officer
Web address: www.stmarymedicalcenter.org
**Control**: Other not–for–profit (including NFP Corporation) **Service**: General medical and surgical

**Staffed Beds**: 307 **Admissions**: 12052 **Census**: 161 **Outpatient Visits**: 128868 **Births**: 1881 **Total Expense ($000)**: 357032 **Payroll Expense ($000)**: 135457 **Personnel**: 1252

*Many Facility Codes have changed. Please refer to the AHA Guide Code Chart.*

**CA**

✠ △　**VA LONG BEACH HEALTHCARE SYSTEM**, 5901 East 7th Street, Zip 90822–5201; tel. 562/826–8000, (Nonreporting) **A**1 3 5 7 8 **S** Department of Veterans Affairs, Washington, DC
Primary Contact: Walt Dannenberg, Director
COO: Anthony DeFrancesco, Associate Director
CFO: Michael J Rupert, Chief Financial Officer
CMO: Sandor Szabo, M.D., Ph.D., M.P.H., Chief of Staff
CIO: Rodney Sagmit, Chief Information Management
CHR: Mary E McCartan, Manager Human Resources
Web address: www.longbeach.va.gov/
**Control**: Veterans Affairs, Government, federal **Service**: General medical and surgical

| Staffed Beds: 335 |
| --- |

**VETERANS AFFAIRS LONG BEACH HEALTHCARE SYSTEM** See VA Long Beach Healthcare System

## LOS ALAMITOS—Orange County

✠　**LOS ALAMITOS MEDICAL CENTER (050551)**, 3751 Katella Avenue, Zip 90720–3164; tel. 562/598–1311, (Nonreporting) **A**1 10 **F**3 11 15 17 18 20 22 26 28 29 30 31 34 35 37 40 45 49 50 51 54 56 57 58 59 64 65 66 68 70 74 75 77 78 79 81 82 84 85 86 87 92 102 107 108 110 114 115 117 119 120 121 122 123 124 126 146 148 154 156 **S** TENET Healthcare Corporation, Dallas, TX
Primary Contact: Kent G. Clayton, Chief Executive Officer
COO: Clay Farell, Chief Operation Officer
CFO: Dave Vickers, Chief Financial Officer
CMO: Nirav Patel, M.D., Chief of Staff
CIO: Sally Andrada, Chief Information Officer
CHR: Mark Fisher, Chief Human Resources Officer
CNO: Judy Chabot, Chief Nursing Officer
Web address: www.losalamitosmedctr.com
**Control**: Corporation, Investor–owned (for–profit) **Service**: General medical and surgical

| Staffed Beds: 120 Admissions: 8122 Census: 110 Outpatient Visits: 86801 Births: 235 Total Expense ($000): 193540 Payroll Expense ($000): 83290 |
| --- |

## LOS ANGELES—Los Angeles County

**(Mailing Addresses - Canoga Park, Encino, Granada Hills, Harbor City, Hollywood, Mission Hills, North Hollywood, Northridge, Panorama City, San Pedro, Sepulveda, Sherman Oaks, Sun Valley, Sylmar, Tarzana, Van Nuys, West Hills, West Los Angeles, Woodland Hills)**

✠　**ADVENTIST HEALTH WHITE MEMORIAL (050103)**, 1720 Cesar Chavez Avenue, Zip 90033–2414; tel. 323/268–5000, (Total facility includes 27 beds in nursing home–type unit) (Nonreporting) **A**1 2 3 5 8 10 **F**17 70 72 76 88 89 90 98 128 **S** Adventist Health, Roseville, CA
Primary Contact: John Raffoul, Chief Executive Officer
CIO: Ralf Weissenberger, Director Information Systems
CHR: Natasha Milatovich, Association Vice President Human Resources
CNO: Patricia Stone, R.N., MSN, Senior Vice President Operations and Chief Nursing Officer
Web address: www.whitememorial.com
**Control**: Church operated, Nongovernment, not–for–profit **Service**: General medical and surgical

| Staffed Beds: 353 Admissions: 19628 Census: 248 Outpatient Visits: 80867 Births: 3490 Total Expense ($000): 474986 Payroll Expense ($000): 136410 |
| --- |

**BARLOW HOSPITAL** See Barlow Respiratory Hospital

✠　**BARLOW RESPIRATORY HOSPITAL (052031)**, 2000 Stadium Way, Zip 90026–2696; tel. 213/250–4200, (Nonreporting) **A**1 10 **F**1 3 14 29 30 35 45 46 60 68 91 107 111 119 130 148 **P**6
Primary Contact: Amit Mohan, President and Chief Executive Officer
CFO: Edward Engesser, Chief Financial Officer and Chief Information Officer
CMO: David Nelson, M.D., Medical Director
CIO: Edward Engesser, Chief Financial Officer and Chief Information Officer
CHR: Rashawn Woods, Vice President Human Resources
CNO: Gladys D'Souza, Chief Nursing Officer
Web address: www.barlow2000.org
**Control**: Other not–for–profit (including NFP Corporation) **Service**: Acute long–term care hospital

| Staffed Beds: 105 Admissions: 960 Census: 77 Outpatient Visits: 0 Births: 0 Total Expense ($000): 63359 Payroll Expense ($000): 27677 Personnel: 431 |
| --- |

**CALIF MED CENTER-LOS ANGELES** See California Hospital Medical Center

✠　**CALIFORNIA HOSPITAL MEDICAL CENTER (050149)**, 1401 South Grand Avenue, Zip 90015–3010; tel. 213/748–2411, (Nonreporting) **A**1 3 5 10 **F**3 13 15 17 18 20 22 24 26 29 30 31 34 35 40 43 45 49 50 51 57 58 59 60 64 68 70 71 72 74 75 76 77 78 79 81 82 84 85 87 89 97 100 102 104 107 108 110 111 114 115 118 119 123 132 134 135 136 146 147 148 149 150 154 156 **S** CommonSpirit Health, Chicago, IL
Primary Contact: Alina Moran, President
CFO: Rebecca Cheng, Chief Financial Officer
CMO: Joseph Nussbaum, M.D., Chief of Staff
CIO: David Ung, Director, Information Technology
CHR: Kristin Anderson, Director, Human Resources
CNO: Valarie McPherson, MSN, Chief Nursing Executive
Web address: www.chmcla.org
**Control**: Other not–for–profit (including NFP Corporation) **Service**: General medical and surgical

| Staffed Beds: 318 Admissions: 18945 Census: 207 Outpatient Visits: 104417 Births: 3227 Total Expense ($000): 446624 Payroll Expense ($000): 159622 Personnel: 1773 |
| --- |

✠ △　**CALIFORNIA REHABILITATION INSTITUTE (053039)**, 2070 Century Park East, Zip 90067–1907; tel. 424/363–1000, (Nonreporting) **A**1 3 7 10 **F**29 30 34 44 50 68 77 87 90 92 94 96 100 130 132 148 **S** Select Medical Corporation, Mechanicsburg, PA
Primary Contact: Scott T. Rotsted, Chief Executive Officer
Web address: www.californiarehabinstitute.com/
**Control**: Corporation, Investor–owned (for–profit) **Service**: Rehabilitation

| Staffed Beds: 138 Admissions: 3137 Census: 121 Outpatient Visits: 0 Births: 0 Personnel: 456 |
| --- |

✠　**CEDARS-SINAI MEDICAL CENTER (050625)**, 8700 Beverly Boulevard, Zip 90048–1865; tel. 310/423–5000, (Nonreporting) **A**1 2 3 5 8 10 19 **F**3 8 9 11 12 13 14 15 17 18 19 20 21 22 23 24 25 26 27 28 29 30 31 32 34 35 36 37 39 40 41 43 44 45 46 47 48 49 50 51 52 54 55 56 57 58 59 60 61 64 65 66 68 69 70 71 72 74 75 76 77 78 79 81 82 83 84 85 86 87 88 89 91 92 93 96 97 100 102 107 108 109 110 111 112 113 114 115 116 117 118 119 120 121 123 124 126 130 131 132 134 135 136 137 138 139 140 141 142 145 146 147 148 149 150 154 **P**3 5 6 **S** Cedars-Sinai Health System, West Hollywood, CA
Primary Contact: Thomas M. Priselac, President and Chief Executive Officer
COO: Jeffrey A. Smith, Executive Vice President Hospital Operations and Chief Operating Officer
CFO: Edward M Prunchunas, Executive Vice President and Chief Financial Officer
CMO: Richard V. Riggs, M.D., Senior Vice President Medical Affairs and Chief Medical Officer
CIO: Darren Dworkin, Senior Vice President Enterprise Information Systems and Chief Information Officer
CHR: Andrew Ortiz, Senior Vice President, Human Resources and Organization Development
CNO: David R Marshall, R.N., Ph.D., Senior Vice President, Chief Nursing Executive
Web address: www.cedars-sinai.edu
**Control**: Other not–for–profit (including NFP Corporation) **Service**: General medical and surgical

| Staffed Beds: 886 Admissions: 50646 Census: 734 Outpatient Visits: 893378 Births: 6270 Total Expense ($000): 3146176 Payroll Expense ($000): 1175645 Personnel: 13257 |
| --- |

**CHILDRENS HOSP LOS ANGELES** See Children's Hospital Los Angeles

---

**CA**

**△ CHILDREN'S HOSPITAL LOS ANGELES (053302)**, 4650 West Sunset Boulevard, Zip 90027–6062, Mailing Address: 4650 West Sunset Boulevard, MS #1, Zip 90027–6062; tel. 323/660–2450, (Nonreporting) **A**1 3 5 7 8 10 **F**3 7 8 9 11 14 15 17 19 21 23 25 27 28 29 30 31 32 34 35 36 37 38 39 40 41 43 44 45 46 47 48 49 50 54 55 57 58 59 60 61 64 65 68 70 72 73 74 75 77 78 79 80 81 82 83 84 86 87 88 89 90 91 92 93 94 95 107 111 115 116 117 118 119 120 121 122 124 126 129 130 131 132 134 136 137 138 139 140 141 146 148 154 155 156 157
Primary Contact: Paul S. Viviano, President and Chief Executive Officer
CFO: Lannie Tonnu, Senior Vice President and Chief Financial Officer
CMO: Brent Polk, M.D., Chair Department of Pediatrics and Vice President Academic Affairs
CIO: TJ Malseed, Vice President and Chief Information Officer
CHR: Myra Gregorian, Vice President and Chief Human Resources Officer
CNO: Mary Dee Hacker, R.N., Vice President, Patient Care Services and Chief Nursing Officer
Web address: www.chla.org
**Control:** Other not–for–profit (including NFP Corporation) **Service:** Children's general medical and surgical

**Staffed Beds:** 379 **Admissions:** 17716 **Census:** 324 **Outpatient Visits:** 382886 **Births:** 0 **Total Expense ($000):** 1254873 **Payroll Expense ($000):** 493128 **Personnel:** 5843

**□ EAST LOS ANGELES DOCTORS HOSPITAL (050641)**, 4060 Whittier Boulevard, Zip 90023–2526; tel. 323/268–5514, (Nonreporting) **A**1 10 **S** Avanti Hospitals, El Segundo, CA
Primary Contact: Gerald B. Clute, Chief Executive Officer
CFO: Steven Blake, Corporate Chief Financial Officer
CMO: Janine King, M.D., Chief of Staff
CIO: Jason Cervantes, Chief Information Officer
CHR: Paul Celuch, Chief Human Resource Officer
CNO: Kimberly Frazier, R.N., Chief Nursing Officer
Web address: www.avantihospitals.com
**Control:** Corporation, Investor–owned (for–profit) **Service:** General medical and surgical

**Staffed Beds:** 127

**□ ENCINO HOSPITAL MEDICAL CENTER (050158)**, 16237 Ventura Boulevard, Zip 91436–2272; tel. 818/995–5000, (Nonreporting) **A**1 10 **S** Prime Healthcare, Ontario, CA
Primary Contact: Bockhi Park, Chief Executive Officer
CFO: Kanner Tillman, Chief Financial Officer
CMO: Muhammad Anwar, M.D., Chief Medical Officer
CIO: Edward Barrera, Director Communications
CHR: Barbara Back, Manager Human Resources
CNO: Vilma L Dinham, R.N., Chief Nursing Officer
Web address: www.encinomed.com
**Control:** Other not–for–profit (including NFP Corporation) **Service:** General medical and surgical

**Staffed Beds:** 78

**GATEWAYS HOSP & MNTL HLTH CNTR** See Gateways Hospital and Mental Health Center

**○ GATEWAYS HOSPITAL AND MENTAL HEALTH CENTER (054028)**, 1891 Effie Street, Zip 90026–1793; tel. 323/644–2000, (Nonreporting) **A**10 11
Primary Contact: Philip Wong, PsyD, Chief Executive Officer
COO: Philip Wong, PsyD, Chief Operating Officer
CMO: Imani Walker, M.D., Medical Director
CIO: Rozelle DeVera, Director of Information Systems
CHR: Vahan Demlakian, Director of Human Resources
Web address: www.gatewayshospital.org
**Control:** Other not–for–profit (including NFP Corporation) **Service:** Psychiatric

**Staffed Beds:** 55

**□ GOOD SAMARITAN HOSPITAL (050471)**, 1225 Wilshire Boulevard, Zip 90017–2395; tel. 213/977–2121, (Nonreporting) **A**1 3 5 10 **F**3 7 8 11 13 15 17 18 20 22 23 24 26 28 29 30 31 34 35 40 44 45 46 47 48 49 51 53 57 58 59 64 65 68 70 72 74 75 76 77 78 79 81 84 85 86 87 90 93 107 108 110 111 114 115 117 118 119 120 121 123 124 126 129 130 131 132 146 148 149 156 **P**5 7 **S** PIH Health, Whittier, CA
Primary Contact: Andrew B. Leeka, President and Chief Executive Officer
COO: Phillip Wolfe, Vice President of Professional Operations
CFO: Alan Ino, Chief Financial Officer
CMO: Margaret Bates, Chief of Staff
CIO: Dean Campbell, Vice President Information Services and Chief Information Officer
CHR: Lexie Schuster, Vice President Human Resources
CNO: Margaret Pfeiffer, R.N., MSN, Vice President Patient Care Services
Web address: www.goodsam.org
**Control:** Other not–for–profit (including NFP Corporation) **Service:** General medical and surgical

**Staffed Beds:** 402 **Admissions:** 12873 **Census:** 190 **Outpatient Visits:** 75708 **Births:** 2640 **Total Expense ($000):** 383105 **Payroll Expense ($000):** 124539 **Personnel:** 1358

**HOLLYWOOD COMMUNITY HOSPITAL** See Southern California Hospital at Hollywood

**⊞ HOLLYWOOD PRESBYTERIAN MEDICAL CENTER (050063)**, 1300 North Vermont Avenue, Zip 90027–6306; tel. 213/413–3000, (Nonreporting) **A**1 3 10 **F**3 8 13 15 17 18 20 22 24 26 29 30 31 34 40 41 45 46 49 50 51 56 57 59 60 61 64 68 70 72 74 75 76 77 78 79 80 81 85 87 89 90 92 96 97 107 108 110 111 115 119 126 130 146 147 148 149 154
Primary Contact: Robert Allen, President and Chief Executive Officer
COO: Wontae Cha, Chief Operating Officer
CIO: Steve Giles, Chief Information Officer
CHR: George Leisher JrVice President Human Resources
CNO: Farideh Ara, Interim Chief Nursing Officer
Web address: www.hollywoodpresbyterian.com
**Control:** Partnership, Investor–owned (for–profit) **Service:** General medical and surgical

**Staffed Beds:** 434 **Admissions:** 13305 **Census:** 222 **Outpatient Visits:** 61508 **Births:** 2756 **Total Expense ($000):** 296079 **Payroll Expense ($000):** 130655 **Personnel:** 1239

**HOSPITAL OF THE GOOD SAMARITAN** See Good Samaritan Hospital

**KAISER FOUNDATION MENTAL HEALTH CENTER** See Kaiser Permanente Los Angeles Medical Center, Los Angeles

**⊞ KAISER PERMANENTE LOS ANGELES MEDICAL CENTER (050138)**, 4867 Sunset Boulevard, Zip 90027–5961; tel. 323/783–4011, (Includes KAISER FOUNDATION MENTAL HEALTH CENTER, Mailing address: 765 West College Street, Los Angeles, California, Zip 90012; tel. 213/580–7200), (Nonreporting) **A**1 3 5 8 10 **F**3 7 8 13 15 17 18 19 20 21 22 23 24 26 29 30 31 34 35 36 38 40 44 45 46 47 49 50 51 52 54 55 56 57 58 59 60 61 62 63 64 65 66 68 70 72 74 75 76 77 78 79 81 82 83 84 85 86 87 88 89 92 93 97 98 99 101 102 103 104 105 107 108 109 110 111 113 114 115 116 117 118 119 120 121 122 123 124 126 129 130 131 132 135 144 146 147 148 149 150 153 154 156 157 **P**6 **S** Kaiser Foundation Hospitals, Oakland, CA
Primary Contact: William N. Grice, Executive Director
COO: Derek Berz, Chief Operating Officer
CFO: Brad Malsed, Area Chief Financial Officer
CMO: Michael Tome, M.D., Medical Director
CIO: David Strickland, Area Information Officer
CHR: Paul J Martin, Director Human Resources
Web address: www.kaiserpermanente.org
**Control:** Other not–for–profit (including NFP Corporation) **Service:** General medical and surgical

**Staffed Beds:** 528 **Admissions:** 34151 **Census:** 413 **Outpatient Visits:** 98911 **Births:** 2739 **Personnel:** 5919

**⊞ KAISER PERMANENTE WEST LOS ANGELES MEDICAL CENTER (050561)**, 6041 Cadillac Avenue, Zip 90034–1700; tel. 323/857–2201, (Nonreporting) **A**1 3 5 10 **F**3 6 11 12 13 15 29 30 31 32 34 35 37 40 41 44 45 46 47 48 49 50 55 56 57 58 59 60 61 64 65 68 70 72 73 74 75 76 78 79 80 81 82 84 85 87 100 101 107 108 110 111 114 115 116 117 119 126 130 132 135 146 148 149 150 154 158 **P**6 **S** Kaiser Foundation Hospitals, Oakland, CA
Primary Contact: Georgina R. Garcia, R.N., Executive Director
CMO: Fred Alexander, M.D., Medical Director
CIO: Gregory M Sincock, Information Technology Leader
Web address: www.kaiserpermanente.org
**Control:** Other not–for–profit (including NFP Corporation) **Service:** General medical and surgical

**Staffed Beds:** 265 **Admissions:** 9062 **Census:** 91 **Outpatient Visits:** 297265 **Births:** 1915 **Personnel:** 1413

*Many Facility Codes have changed. Please refer to the AHA Guide Code Chart.*
© 2021 AHA Guide

⊞ **KECK HOSPITAL OF USC (050696)**, 1500 San Pablo Street, Zip 90033–5313;
tel. 323/442–8500, (Nonreporting) **A**1 3 5 8 10 **F**3 6 8 9 11 12 14 15 17 18 20
22 24 26 29 30 31 34 35 36 37 38 39 43 44 45 46 47 48 49 50 51 52 53 54
55 56 57 58 59 60 61 64 65 66 68 70 71 74 75 77 78 79 81 82 84 85 86 87
90 91 92 93 94 95 96 97 100 101 104 107 108 109 110 111 112 113 114
115 116 117 118 119 124 126 129 130 131 132 135 137 138 139 140 141
142 144 145 146 147 148 149 150 154 156 157 **P**6 **S** Keck Medicine of USC,
Los Angeles, CA
Primary Contact: Rodney B. Hanners, Chief Executive Officer
CMO: Stephanie Hall, M.D., Chief Medical Officer
CIO: Timothy James Malseed, Chief Information Officer
CHR: Matthew McElrath, Chief Human Resources Officer
CNO: Annette Sy, Chief Nursing Officer
Web address: www.https://www.keckmedicine.org/
**Control:** Other not–for–profit (including NFP Corporation) **Service:** General
medical and surgical

**Staffed Beds:** 401 **Admissions:** 12025 **Census:** 226 **Outpatient
Visits:** 364896 **Births:** 0 **Total Expense ($000):** 1194584 **Payroll Expense
($000):** 386006 **Personnel:** 3986

**KEDREN COMMUNITY MENTAL HEALTH CENTER (054083)**, 4211 South
Avalon Boulevard, Zip 90011–5699; tel. 323/233–0425, (Nonreporting) **A**3 10
Primary Contact: John H. Griffith, Ph.D., President and Chief Executive Officer
COO: Madeline Valencerina, Chief Operating Officer
CFO: Rizwan A. Uraizee, Chief Financial Officer
CMO: Frank L. Williams, Executive Vice President/ Medical Director
CNO: Essie Adams, Director of Nursing
Web address: www.kedren.org/
**Control:** Other not–for–profit (including NFP Corporation) **Service:** Psychiatric

**Staffed Beds:** 72

⊞ **KINDRED HOSPITAL-LOS ANGELES (052032)**, 5525 West Slauson Avenue,
Zip 90056–1067; tel. 310/642–0325, (Nonreporting) **A**1 10 **S** Kindred
Healthcare, Louisville, KY
Primary Contact: Fiona Basa-Reyes, Chief Executive Officer
CFO: Charles Natcher, Chief Financial Officer
Web address: www.kindredhospitalla.com/
**Control:** Corporation, Investor–owned (for–profit) **Service:** Acute long–term care
hospital

**Staffed Beds:** 81

⊞ **LA DOWNTOWN MEDICAL CENTER, LLC (050763)**, 1711 West Temple
Street, Zip 90026–5421; tel. 213/989–6100, (Includes LA DOWNTOWN MEDICAL
CENTER, LLC -INGLESIDE CAMPUS, Mailing address: 7500 East Hellman Avenue,
Rosemead, California, Zip 91770; tel. 626/288–1160), (Nonreporting) **A**1 10
Primary Contact: Bill Nelson, Chief Executive Officer
CFO: John Cowles, Chief Financial Officer
CMO: Louis Acosta, M.D., Chief of Staff
CIO: Scott Musack, Chief Information Officer
CHR: Sylvia Cloud, Director Human Resources
Web address: www.https://ladowntownmc.com/
**Control:** Corporation, Investor–owned (for–profit) **Service:** General medical and
surgical

**Staffed Beds:** 229

**LAC/UNIVERSITY OF SOUTHERN CALIFORNIA MEDICAL CENTER** See
Lac+Usc Medical Center

**LAC+USC MEDICAL CENTER (050373)**, 2051 Marengo Street,
Zip 90033–1352; tel. 323/409–1000, (Includes GENERAL HOSPITAL, Mailing
address: 1200 North State Street, Los Angeles, California, Zip 90033;
tel. 626/288–1160; WOMEN'S AND CHILDREN'S HOSPITAL, Mailing
address: 1240 North Mission Road, Los Angeles, California, Zip 90033;
tel. 626/288–1160), (Nonreporting) **A**2 3 5 10 **S** Los Angeles County-Department
of Health Services, Los Angeles, CA
Primary Contact: Jorge Orozco, Chief Executive Officer
COO: Henry Ornelas, Chief Operating Officer
CFO: Mark Corbet, Interim Chief Financial Officer
CMO: Brad Spellberg, M.D., Chief Medical Officer
CIO: Oscar Autelli, Chief Information Officer
CHR: Elizabeth Jacobi, Human Resources Director
CNO: Isabel Milan, R.N., Chief Nursing Officer
Web address: www.lacusc.org
**Control:** County, Government, Nonfederal **Service:** General medical and surgical

**Staffed Beds:** 538

**LOS ANGELES COMMUNITY HOSPITAL** See Los Angeles Community Hospital at
Los Angeles

☐ **LOS ANGELES COMMUNITY HOSPITAL AT LOS ANGELES (050663)**,
4081 East Olympic Boulevard, Zip 90023–3330; tel. 323/267–0477, (Includes
LOS ANGELES COMMUNITY HOSPITAL OF NORWALK, Mailing address: 13222
Bloomfield Avenue, Norwalk, California, Zip 90650; tel. 562/863–4763),
(Nonreporting) **A**1 10 **F**3 18 29 40 45 46 49 50 64 65 70 75 79 81 92 98 100
107 119 128 130 148 149 **S** Prospect Medical Holdings, Los Angeles, CA
Primary Contact: Omar Ramirez, Chief Executive Officer
CFO: Johnnette Chong, Chief Financial Officer
Web address: www.altacorp.com/altacorp/our-hospitals/lach-menu.html
**Control:** Corporation, Investor–owned (for–profit) **Service:** General medical and
surgical

**Staffed Beds:** 212 **Admissions:** 10349 **Census:** 152 **Outpatient
Visits:** 16141 **Births:** 0 **Total Expense ($000):** 113100 **Payroll Expense
($000):** 51600 **Personnel:** 743

**LOS ANGELES COUNTY CENTRAL JAIL HOSPITAL**, 441 Bauchet Street,
Zip 90012–2906; tel. 213/473–6100, (Nonreporting)
Primary Contact: Tom Flaherty, Assistant Administrator
**Control:** County, Government, Nonfederal **Service:** Hospital unit of an institution
(prison hospital, college infirmary, etc.)

**Staffed Beds:** 190

**LOS ANGELES MEDICAL CENTER** See Kaiser Permanente Los Angeles Medical
Center

☐ **MARTIN LUTHER KING, JR. COMMUNITY HOSPITAL (050779)**, 1680 East
120th Street, Zip 90059–3026; tel. 424/338–8000, (Nonreporting) **A**1 5 10
Primary Contact: Elaine Batchlor, M.D., M.P.H. Chief Executive Officer
COO: Myrna Allen, R.N., MS, Chief Operating and Nursing Officer
CMO: John Fisher, M.D., Chief Medical Officer
CIO: Sajid Ahmed, Chief Information and Innovation Officer
CHR: Susan M Burrows, Vice President Human Resources
CNO: Myrna Allen, R.N., MS, Chief Operating and Nursing Officer
Web address: www.mlkcommunityhospital.org/
**Control:** Other not–for–profit (including NFP Corporation) **Service:** General
medical and surgical

**Staffed Beds:** 131

⇧ **MIDWAY HOSPITAL MEDICAL CENTER** See Olympia Medical Center

☐ **MIRACLE MILE MEDICAL CENTER (050751)**, 6000 San Vicente Boulevard,
Zip 90036–4404; tel. 323/930–1040, (Nonreporting) **A**1 10
Primary Contact: Gil Tepper, M.D., Chief Executive Officer
COO: Liz Cheever, Administrator
CFO: Bert Roberts, Controller
CMO: Gil Tepper, M.D., Chief of Staff
CIO: Jonathan Lindell, Director Information Technology
CHR: Liz Cheever, Administrator
CNO: Melody Bradley, Chief Nursing Officer
Web address: www.miraclemilemedicalcenter.com
**Control:** Individual, Investor–owned (for–profit) **Service:** General medical and surgical

**Staffed Beds:** 17

⇧ **OLYMPIA MEDICAL CENTER (050742)**, 5900 West Olympic Boulevard,
Zip 90036–4671; tel. 310/657–5900, (Nonreporting) **A**10 21 **S** Alecto
Healthcare, Irvine, CA
Primary Contact: Matthew Williams, R.N., Chief Executive Officer
CFO: Matthew Williams, R.N., Chief Financial Officer
CMO: Panch Jeyakumar, M.D., Chief of Staff
CIO: Jason Williams, Director Information Systems
CHR: Joseph Ambrosini, Director Human Resources
CNO: Sylvia A Ventura, R.N., MS, Chief Nursing Officer
Web address: www.olympiamc.com
**Control:** Partnership, Investor–owned (for–profit) **Service:** General medical and
surgical

**Staffed Beds:** 204

**CA**

**CA**

**QUEEN OF ANGELS-HOLLYWOOD CTR** See Hollywood Presbyterian Medical Center

⊞ **RONALD REAGAN UCLA MEDICAL CENTER (050262)**, 757 Westwood Plaza, Zip 90095–8358; tel. 310/825–9111, (Includes MATTEL CHILDREN'S HOSPITAL, Mailing address: 757 Westwood Plaza, Los Angeles, California, Zip 90095; tel. 310/825–9111), (Nonreporting) **A**1 3 5 8 10 19 **F**3 6 7 8 9 11 12 13 14 15 17 18 19 20 21 22 23 24 25 26 27 28 29 30 31 32 34 35 36 37 39 40 41 43 44 45 46 47 48 49 50 51 52 54 55 56 57 58 59 61 62 64 65 66 68 70 71 72 74 75 76 77 78 79 81 82 84 85 86 87 88 89 92 93 94 96 97 102 107 108 110 111 112 113 114 115 116 117 118 119 120 121 123 124 126 129 130 131 132 135 136 137 138 139 140 141 142 143 145 146 147 148 149 154 156 **P**6 **S** University of California Systemwide Administration, Oakland, CA
Primary Contact: Johnese Spisso, Chief Executive Officer
COO: Richard Azar, Chief Operation Officer
CFO: Paul Staton, Chief Financial Officer
CMO: Robert Cherry, M.D., Chief Medical and Quality Officer
CIO: Michael Pfeffer, Chief Information Officer
CHR: Susi Takeuchi, Chief Human Resources and Organization Development Officer
CNO: Karen A Grimley, Chief Nursing Executive
Web address: www.uclahealth.org
**Control:** State, Government, Nonfederal **Service:** General medical and surgical

**Staffed Beds: 445 Admissions: 23011 Census: 452 Outpatient Visits: 585022 Births: 1601 Total Expense ($000): 2103698 Payroll Expense ($000): 766745 Personnel: 8084**

**SILVER LAKE MEDICAL CENTER** See La Downtown Medical Center, LLC

☐ **SOUTHERN CALIFORNIA HOSPITAL AT HOLLYWOOD (050135)**, 6245 De Longpre Avenue, Zip 90028–9001; tel. 323/462–2271, (Includes SOUTHERN CALIFORNIA HOSPITAL AT VAN NUYS, Mailing address: 14433 Emelita Street, Van Nuys, California, Zip 91401; tel. 818/787–1511), (Nonreporting) **A**1 10 **S** Prospect Medical Holdings, Los Angeles, CA
Primary Contact: Bruce P. Grimshaw, FACHE, Chief Executive Officer
Web address: www.hollywoodcommunityhospital.org/
**Control:** Corporation, Investor–owned (for–profit) **Service:** General medical and surgical

**Staffed Beds: 45**

⊞ **STEWART & LYNDA RESNICK NEUROPSYCHIATRIC HOSPITAL AT UCLA (054009)**, 150 UCLA Medical Plaza, Zip 90095–8353; tel. 310/825–9989, (Nonreporting) **A**1 3 10 **F**3 5 6 29 30 35 40 43 55 56 64 68 86 87 98 99 100 101 102 103 104 105 130 132 134 147 149 153 154 **P**1 **S** University of California Systemwide Administration, Oakland, CA
Primary Contact: Peter Whybrow, M.D., Chief Executive Officer
COO: Ruth Irwin, Associate Director Clinical Operations
CFO: Ronald Anthony Davis, Chief Financial Officer - UCLA Hospital System
CMO: Thomas Strouse, M.D., Medical Director and Professor of Clinical Psych
CIO: Michael Pfeffer, M.D., Chief Medical Informatics Officer, UCLA Health
CHR: Monica Rodriguez, Director of Human Resources
CNO: Patricia Matos, Chief Nursing Officer
Web address: www.semel.ucla.edu/resnick
**Control:** State, Government, Nonfederal **Service:** Psychiatric

**Staffed Beds: 74 Admissions: 1927 Census: 68 Outpatient Visits: 19551 Births: 0 Total Expense ($000): 78312 Payroll Expense ($000): 41445 Personnel: 373**

**UNIVERSITY OF CALIFORNIA LOS ANGELES MEDICAL CENTER** See Ronald Reagan UCLA Medical Center

**UNIVERSITY OF CALIFORNIA LOS ANGELES NEUROPSYCHIATRIC HOSPITAL** See Stewart & Lynda Resnick Neuropsychiatric Hospital at UCLA

**UNIVERSITY OF SOUTHERN CALIFORNIA-NORRIS CANCER HOSPITAL** See USC Norris Comprehensive Cancer Center

⊞ **USC NORRIS COMPREHENSIVE CANCER CENTER (050660)**, 1441 Eastlake Avenue, Zip 90089–0112; tel. 323/865–3000, (Nonreporting) **A**1 2 3 5 8 10 **F**3 11 15 18 29 30 31 34 35 36 38 39 44 45 46 47 48 49 50 51 54 55 56 57 58 59 60 61 64 65 68 70 74 75 77 78 79 81 82 84 85 86 87 92 93 94 97 100 101 104 107 108 109 110 111 115 118 119 120 121 123 124 126 130 132 134 135 136 145 146 147 148 149 150 154 156 157 **P**6 **S** Keck Medicine of USC, Los Angeles, CA
Primary Contact: Rodney B. Hanners, Chief Executive Officer
COO: Tarek Salaway, Chief Operating Officer
CMO: Stephanie Hall, M.D., Medical Director
CHR: Matthew McElrath, Chief Human Resources Officer
CNO: Annette Sy, Chief Nursing Officer
Web address: www.uscnorriscancerhospital.org
**Control:** Other not–for–profit (including NFP Corporation) **Service:** Cancer

**Staffed Beds: 60 Admissions: 1582 Census: 40 Outpatient Visits: 147686 Births: 0 Total Expense ($000): 218304 Payroll Expense ($000): 61468 Personnel: 573**

**USC UNIVERSITY HOSPITAL** See Keck Hospital of Usc

⊞ △ **VA GREATER LOS ANGELES HEALTHCARE SYSTEM**, 11301 Wilshire Boulevard, Zip 90073–1003; tel. 310/478–3711, (Nonreporting) **A**1 3 5 7 8 **S** Department of Veterans Affairs, Washington, DC
Primary Contact: Steven E. Braverman, M.D., Director
COO: Susan Shyshka, Associate Director
CFO: Joseph Schmitt, Chief Financial Officer
CIO: Eugene Archey, Chief Information Technology
CHR: Brenda Cabunoc, Chief Human Resources
Web address: www.losangeles.va.gov/
**Control:** Veterans Affairs, Government, federal **Service:** General medical and surgical

**Staffed Beds: 708**

**VENCOR HOSPITAL-LOS ANGELES** See Kindred Hospital-Los Angeles

**VETERANS AFFAIRS GREATER LOS ANGELES HEALTHCARE SYSTEM** See VA Greater Los Angeles Healthcare System

**WEST LOS ANGELES MEDICAL CENTER** See Kaiser Permanente West Los Angeles Medical Center

**WHITE MEMORIAL MEDICAL CENTER** See Adventist Health White Memorial

**WOMEN'S HOSPITAL** See Women's and Children's Hospital

**LOS BANOS—Merced County**

**LOS BANOS COMMUNITY HOSPITAL** See Memorial Hospital Los Banos

⊞ **MEMORIAL HOSPITAL LOS BANOS (050528)**, 520 West 'I' Street, Zip 93635–3498; tel. 209/826–0591, (Nonreporting) **A**1 10 20 **S** Sutter Health, Sacramento, CA
Primary Contact: Doug Archer, Administrator
CFO: Timothy J Noakes, Chief Financial Officer
CHR: Shawn Garcia, Manager Human Resources
CNO: Kristie Marion, Chief Nurse Executive
Web address: www.memoriallosbanos.org/
**Control:** Other not–for–profit (including NFP Corporation) **Service:** General medical and surgical

**Staffed Beds: 44**

**LOS GATOS—Santa Clara County**

**COMMUNITY HOSPITAL OF LOS GATOS** See El Camino Hospital Los Gatos

**LYNWOOD—Los Angeles County**

☐ **ST. FRANCIS MEDICAL CENTER (050104)**, 3630 East Imperial Highway, Zip 90262–2636; tel. 310/900–8900, (Nonreporting) **A**1 3 10 **S** Prime Healthcare, Ontario, CA
Primary Contact: Eleanor Ramirez, R.N., MS, Interim President and Chief Executive Officer
CFO: Anil Jain, Chief Financial Officer
CMO: Rahul Dhawan, M.D., Chief Medical Officer
CIO: Judi Binderman, Chief Information Technology Officer and Chief Medical Informatics Officer
CHR: Laura Kato, Vice President Human Resources
Web address: www.https://stfrancis.verity.org/SFMC/
**Control:** Church operated, Nongovernment, not–for–profit **Service:** General medical and surgical

**Staffed Beds: 323**

**MADERA—Madera County**

○ **MADERA COMMUNITY HOSPITAL (050568)**, 1250 East Almond Avenue, Zip 93637–5696; tel. 559/675–5555, (Nonreporting) **A**3 10 11 19
Primary Contact: Karen Paolinelli, Chief Executive Officer
CFO: Mark Foote, Chief Financial Officer
CIO: Stuart Bispham, Director, Information Technology and Security Officer
CHR: Melissa Bushey, Director, Human Resources
CNO: Jane Winning, Chief Nursing Officer
Web address: www.maderahospital.org
**Control:** Other not–for–profit (including NFP Corporation) **Service:** General medical and surgical

**Staffed Beds: 106**

*Many Facility Codes have changed. Please refer to the AHA Guide Code Chart.* © 2021 AHA Guide

⊠ △ **VALLEY CHILDREN'S HEALTHCARE (053300)**, 9300 Valley Children's Place, Zip 93636–8761; tel. 559/353–3000, (Nonreporting) **A**1 3 5 7 8 10 **F**3 8 9 11 19 21 23 25 27 28 29 30 31 32 34 35 38 40 41 43 44 46 48 49 50 54 55 57 58 59 60 61 62 64 65 68 72 73 74 75 77 78 79 81 82 84 85 86 87 88 89 90 93 94 107 108 111 114 115 119 126 127 129 130 131 132 134 146 147 148 149 **P**3
Primary Contact: Todd A. Suntrapak, President and Chief Executive Officer
COO: Debra A Flores, R.N., MS, President and Chief Operating Officer
CFO: Michele Waldron, Senior Vice President and Chief Financial Officer
CMO: David Christensen, M.D., Senior Vice President and Chief Medical Officer
CIO: Kevin Shimamoto, Vice President and Chief Informational Officer
CHR: Nat Ponticello, Vice President Human Resources
CNO: Beverly P. Hayden-Pugh, R.N., Senior Vice President and Chief Nursing Officer
Web address: www.valleychildrens.org
**Control:** Other not–for–profit (including NFP Corporation) **Service:** Children's general medical and surgical

**Staffed Beds:** 358 **Admissions:** 12139 **Census:** 202 **Outpatient Visits:** 285493 **Births:** 0 **Total Expense ($000):** 623081 **Payroll Expense ($000):** 213482 **Personnel:** 2858

**VALLEY CHILDREN'S HOSPITAL** See Valley Children's Healthcare

## MAMMOTH LAKES—Mono County

⇑ **CENTINELA MAMMOTH HOSPITAL** See Mammoth Hospital

⇑ **MAMMOTH HOSPITAL (051303)**, 85 Sierra Park Road, Zip 93546–2073, Mailing Address: P.O. Box 660, Zip 93546–0660; tel. 760/934–3311, (Nonreporting) **A**3 5 10 18 21
Primary Contact: Thomas Parker, Chief Executive Officer
CFO: Melanie Van Winkle, Chief Financial Officer
CMO: Yuri Parisky, M.D., Chief of Staff
CIO: Mark Lind, Chief Information Officer
CHR: Sarah Vigilante, Manager Human Resources
CNO: Kathleen Alo, Chief Nursing Officer
Web address: www.mammothhospital.com
**Control:** Hospital district or authority, Government, Nonfederal **Service:** General medical and surgical

**Staffed Beds:** 17

## MANTECA—San Joaquin County

⊠ **DOCTORS HOSPITAL OF MANTECA (050118)**, 1205 East North Street, Zip 95336–4900; tel. 209/823–3111, (Nonreporting) **A**1 10 **F**3 11 12 13 15 29 31 34 35 40 44 45 49 50 51 64 75 76 78 79 81 85 102 107 108 110 111 115 116 117 118 119 126 130 132 146 147 148 149 154 **S** TENET Healthcare Corporation, Dallas, TX
Primary Contact: Murali Naidu, M.D., Chief Executive Officer
CFO: Ryan Marshall, Chief Financial Officer
CHR: Traci Holzer, Chief Human Resources Officer
CNO: Beverly Fick, Chief Nursing Officer
Web address: www.doctorsmanteca.com
**Control:** Corporation, Investor–owned (for–profit) **Service:** General medical and surgical

**Staffed Beds:** 56 **Admissions:** 3834 **Census:** 43 **Outpatient Visits:** 65012 **Births:** 482 **Total Expense ($000):** 102292 **Payroll Expense ($000):** 44340 **Personnel:** 459

⊠ **KAISER PERMANENTE MANTECA MEDICAL CENTER (050748)**, 1777 West Yosemite Avenue, Zip 95337–5187; tel. 209/825–3700, (Includes MODESTO MEDICAL CENTER, Mailing address: 4601 Dale Road, Modesto, California, Zip 95356–9718; tel. 209/735–5000; Corwin N Harper, Administrator), (Nonreporting) **A**1 2 5 10 **F**3 11 15 18 20 26 28 29 30 31 34 39 40 41 45 49 50 55 56 57 58 59 60 61 63 64 65 68 70 72 73 74 75 76 78,79 81 82 84 85 86 102 107 108 110 111 114 115 118 119 129 130 131 134 135 144 146 147 148 149 154 156 **P**6 **S** Kaiser Foundation Hospitals, Oakland, CA
Primary Contact: Corwin N. Harper, Senior Vice President and Area Manager
COO: Corwin N Harper, Senior Vice President and Area Manager
CFO: Debra L Brown, Area Financial Officer
CMO: Moses D Elam, M.D., Physician-in-Chief
CIO: Tom J Osteen, Director Area Technology
CHR: Pat McKeldin, Human Resource Business Partner
Web address: www.kaiserpermanente.org
**Control:** Other not–for–profit (including NFP Corporation) **Service:** General medical and surgical

**Staffed Beds:** 213 **Admissions:** 13054 **Census:** 131 **Outpatient Visits:** 214190 **Births:** 3675 **Personnel:** 3321

**MANTECA MEDICAL CENTER** See Kaiser Permanente Manteca Medical Center

## MARINA DEL REY—Los Angeles County

**CENTINELA FREEMAN REGIONAL MEDICAL CENTER, MARINA CAMPUS**
See Marina Del Rey Hospital

⊠ **MARINA DEL REY HOSPITAL (050740)**, 4650 Lincoln Boulevard, Zip 90292–6306; tel. 310/823–8911, (Nonreporting) **A**1 10 **S** Cedars-Sinai Health System, West Hollywood, CA
Primary Contact: Paulette Heitmeyer, Administrator and Chief Operating Officer
COO: Phyllis Buchart, Chief Operating Officer
CFO: Stephen A Hargett, Senior Vice President and Chief Financial Officer
CNO: Joanne Laguna-Kennedy, Vice President of Hospital Operations and Chief Nursing Officer
Web address: www.marinahospital.com
**Control:** Corporation, Investor–owned (for–profit) **Service:** General medical and surgical

**Staffed Beds:** 145

## MARIPOSA—Mariposa County

**JOHN C FREMONT DISTRICT HEALTH** See John C. Fremont Healthcare District

★ **JOHN C. FREMONT HEALTHCARE DISTRICT (051304)**, 5189 Hospital Road, Zip 95338–9524, Mailing Address: P.O. Box 216, Zip 95338–0216; tel. 209/966–3631, (Nonreporting) **A**10 18
Primary Contact: Matthew Matthiessen, Chief Executive Officer
CFO: Joseph O'Malley, Interim Chief Financial Officer
CMO: Kenneth P Smith, Chief Medical Officer
CHR: Martha Robichaux, Chief Human Resources Officer
CNO: Thomas Wilkinson, R.N., Chief Nursing Officer
Web address: www.jcf-hospital.com
**Control:** Hospital district or authority, Government, Nonfederal **Service:** General medical and surgical

**Staffed Beds:** 33

## MARTINEZ—Contra Costa County

⊠ **CONTRA COSTA REGIONAL MEDICAL CENTER (050276)**, 2500 Alhambra Avenue, Zip 94553–3156; tel. 925/370–5000, (Nonreporting) **A**1 2 3 10
Primary Contact: Anna M. Roth, R.N., MS, M.P.H., Chief Executive Officer
COO: Timothy Thompson-Cook, Chief Operating Officer
CFO: Patrick Godley, Chief Financial Officer
CMO: David Goldstein, M.D., Chief Medical Officer
CNO: Jaspreet Benepal, Chief Nursing Officer
Web address: www.cchealth.org/medical_center/
**Control:** County, Government, Nonfederal **Service:** General medical and surgical

**Staffed Beds:** 113

**KAISER FOUNDATION HOSPITAL** See Kaiser Permanente Walnut Creek Medical Center, Walnut Creek

**KAISER PERMANENTE MEDICAL CNTR** See Kaiser Foundation Hospital

**MERRITHEW MEMORIAL HOSPITAL** See Contra Costa Regional Medical Center

## MARYSVILLE—Yuba County

⊠ **ADVENTIST HEALTH AND RIDEOUT (050133)**, 726 Fourth Street, Zip 95901–5600; tel. 530/749–4300, (Includes FREMONT MEDICAL CENTER, Mailing address: 970 Plumas Street, Yuba City, California, Zip 95991–4087; tel. 530/751–4000), (Nonreporting) **A**1 2 5 10 20 **S** Adventist Health, Roseville, CA
Primary Contact: Richard Rawson, Chief Executive Officer
COO: Cyndy Gordon, Chief Operating Officer
CFO: Diane Moon, Chief Financial Officer
CMO: Azad Sheikh, Chief Medical Officer
CIO: Daniel Chibaya, Chief Information Officer
CHR: Bart R Minsky, Interim Vice President Human Resources
CNO: Inna Makievsky, Interim Chief Nursing Officer
Web address: www.frhg.org
**Control:** Other not–for–profit (including NFP Corporation) **Service:** General medical and surgical

**Staffed Beds:** 219

**RIDEOUT MEMORIAL HOSPITAL** See Adventist Health and Rideout

## MENLO PARK—San Mateo County

☒ **MENLO PARK SURGICAL HOSPITAL (050754)**, 570 Willow Road, Zip 94025–2617; tel. 650/324–8500, (Nonreporting) **A**1 10 **S** Sutter Health, Sacramento, CA
Primary Contact: Jeanette Engle-Ramirez, Chief Executive Officer
CMO: Andrew Gutow, M.D., Medical Director
CNO: Marjorie Eckford, Chief Nursing Officer
Web address: www.pamf.org/mpsh
**Control**: Other not–for–profit (including NFP Corporation) **Service**: General medical and surgical

| Staffed Beds: 16 |

**RECOVERY INN OF MENLO PARK** See Menlo Park Surgical Hospital

## MERCED—Merced County

**MERCY MED CTR MERCED, DOWNTOWN** See Mercy Medical Center Merced-Dominican Campus

☒ **MERCY MEDICAL CENTER MERCED (050444)**, 333 Mercy Avenue, Zip 95340–8319; tel. 209/564–5000, (Includes MERCY MEDICAL CENTER MERCED-DOMINICAN CAMPUS, Mailing address: 2740 'M' Street, Merced, California, Zip 95340–2880; tel. 209/384–6444; Charles Kassis, President), (Nonreporting) **A**1 3 5 10 19 **F**3 8 13 15 18 20 22 28 29 30 32 34 35 40 41 44 45 46 49 50 54 57 59 62 64 65 66 68 70 74 75 76 77 79 81 84 85 86 87 93 96 97 107 108 110 111 115 118 119 126 127 130 132 135 146 148 149 154 156 **P**3 **S** CommonSpirit Health, Chicago, IL
Primary Contact: Charles Kassis, President
CFO: Michael Strasser, Vice President and Chief Financial Officer
CMO: Robert Streeter, M.D., Vice President Medical Affairs
CIO: Daniel Andresen, Chief information Officer
CHR: Julie Rocha, Vice President Human Resources
CNO: Greg Rouleau, Vice President Nursing
Web address: www.mercymercedcares.org
**Control**: Other not–for–profit (including NFP Corporation) **Service**: General medical and surgical

| Staffed Beds: 186 Admissions: 12167 Census: 125 Outpatient Visits: 200228 Births: 2498 Total Expense ($000): 313327 Payroll Expense ($000): 116358 Personnel: 1287 |

## MISSION HILLS—Los Angeles County

**HOLY CROSS MEDICAL CENTER** See Providence Holy Cross Medical Center

☒ △ **PROVIDENCE HOLY CROSS MEDICAL CENTER (050278)**, 15031 Rinaldi Street, Zip 91345–1207; tel. 818/365–8051, (Total facility includes 48 beds in nursing home–type unit) (Nonreporting) **A**1 2 7 10 19 **F**3 8 11 13 15 17 18 20 22 24 26 28 29 30 31 34 35 36 40 41 43 44 45 46 49 50 54 55 56 57 58 59 60 61 64 65 68 70 71 72 74 75 76 77 78 79 81 82 83 84 85 87 90 93 94 97 105 107 108 110 111 114 115 116 117 119 120 121 123 124 126 128 130 131 132 133 143 146 147 148 149 150 153 154 156 157 **P**3 5 **S** Providence St. Joseph Health, Renton, WA
Primary Contact: Bernard Klein, M.D., Chief Executive
CMO: Rex Hoffman, M.D., Chief Medical Officer
CHR: Pam Stahl, Regional Chief Human Resources Officer
CNO: Jodi Hein, Chief Nursing Officer
Web address: www.https://california.providence.org/holy-cross/Pages/default.aspx
**Control**: Church operated, Nongovernment, not–for–profit **Service**: General medical and surgical

| Staffed Beds: 377 Admissions: 17365 Census: 231 Outpatient Visits: 326596 Births: 3116 Total Expense ($000): 359850 Payroll Expense ($000): 170434 Personnel: 1636 |

## MISSION VIEJO—Orange County

**CHILDREN'S HOSPITAL AT MISSION** See Choc Children's at Mission Hospital

☐ **CHOC CHILDREN'S AT MISSION HOSPITAL (053306)**, 27700 Medical Center Road, Zip 92691–6426; tel. 949/347–8400, (Nonreporting) **A**1 10 **F**3 11 36 72 74 79 81 85 88 89 92 129 154
Primary Contact: Kimberly C. Cripe, President and Chief Executive Officer
COO: Matthew S Gerlach, Chief Operating Officer
CFO: Kerri Ruppert Schiller, Senior Vice President and Chief Financial Officer
CMO: Maria Minon, M.D., Vice President Medical Affairs and Chief Medical Officer
CIO: John Henderson, Chief Information Officer
CHR: Thomas Capizzi, Vice President Human Resources
Web address: www.choc.org
**Control**: Other not–for–profit (including NFP Corporation) **Service**: Children's general medical and surgical

| Staffed Beds: 54 Admissions: 2071 Census: 21 Outpatient Visits: 22137 Births: 0 Total Expense ($000): 58310 Payroll Expense ($000): 11427 Personnel: 106 |

**MISSION HOSPITAL** See Mission Hospital Mission Viejo

☒ △ **MISSION HOSPITAL MISSION VIEJO (050567)**, 27700 Medical Center Road, Zip 92691–6474; tel. 949/364–1400, (Includes MISSION HOSPITAL LAGUNA BEACH, Mailing address: 31872 Coast Highway, Laguna Beach, California, Zip 92651–6775; tel. 949/499–1311; Seth R. Teigen, Chief Executive Officer), (Nonreporting) **A**1 2 3 5 7 10 **F**3 4 5 8 11 13 14 15 17 18 20 22 24 26 28 29 30 31 32 34 35 36 37 38 39 40 41 43 44 45 46 48 49 50 51 53 54 55 57 58 59 64 65 68 70 72 74 75 76 77 78 79 80 81 82 84 85 86 87 88 90 93 96 98 100 102 104 105 107 108 110 111 114 115 116 117 118 119 120 121 123 126 129 130 131 132 134 135 141 142 146 147 148 149 150 152 153 154 **P**3 5 **S** Providence St. Joseph Health, Renton, WA
Primary Contact: Seth R. Teigen, Chief Executive Officer
COO: Terrence Wooten, Vice President of Operations, Support Services
CFO: Eileen Haubl, Senior Vice President and Chief Financial Officer
CMO: Linda Sieglen, M.D., Chief Medical Officer
CIO: Bill Russell, Senior Chief Information Officer
CHR: Terri Covert, Vice President Human Resources
CNO: Jennifer Cord, R.N., Chief Nursing Officer
Web address: www.mission4health.com
**Control**: Church operated, Nongovernment, not–for–profit **Service**: General medical and surgical

| Staffed Beds: 290 Admissions: 18430 Census: 213 Outpatient Visits: 447627 Births: 2388 Total Expense ($000): 530452 Payroll Expense ($000): 215674 Personnel: 2280 |

## MODESTO—Stanislaus County

⇑ **CENTRAL VALLEY SPECIALTY HOSPITAL (052055)**, 730 17th Street, Zip 95354–1209; tel. 209/248–7700, (Nonreporting) **A**10 21
Primary Contact: Gia Smith, Chief Executive Officer
Web address: www.centralvalleyspecialty.org/CVSH/
**Control**: Partnership, Investor–owned (for–profit) **Service**: Acute long–term care hospital

| Staffed Beds: 36 |

**DOCTORS MEDICAL CENTER** See Doctors Medical Center of Modesto

☒ **DOCTORS MEDICAL CENTER OF MODESTO (050464)**, 1441 Florida Avenue, Zip 95350–4418, Mailing Address: P.O. Box 4138, Zip 95352–4138; tel. 209/578–1211, (Nonreporting) **A**1 2 3 10 **F**3 5 12 13 15 17 18 20 22 24 26 28 29 30 31 34 35 40 43 45 46 47 48 49 50 51 55 56 57 58 59 60 61 63 64 65 70 72 73 74 75 76 77 78 79 80 81 82 84 85 87 89 98 100 101 102 103 104 105 107 108 111 113 114 115 119 126 130 135 146 147 148 149 152 156 157 **S** TENET Healthcare Corporation, Dallas, TX
Primary Contact: Warren J. Kirk, Chief Executive Officer
CFO: Greg Berry, Chief Financial Officer
CMO: Gabrielle Gaspar, M.D., Chief Medical Officer
CHR: Michele Bava, Director Human Resources
CNO: Cheryl Harless, Chief Nursing Officer
Web address: www.dmc-modesto.com
**Control**: Corporation, Investor–owned (for–profit) **Service**: General medical and surgical

| Staffed Beds: 461 Admissions: 25791 Census: 371 Outpatient Visits: 160243 Births: 3380 Total Expense ($000): 585053 Payroll Expense ($000): 249060 Personnel: 2481 |

☒ **ENCOMPASS HEALTH REHABILITATION HOSPITAL OF MODESTO (053040)**, 1303 Mable Avenue, Zip 95355; tel. 209/857–3400, (Nonreporting) **A**1 10 **F**3 29 75 90 96 149 **S** Encompass Health Corporation, Birmingham, AL
Primary Contact: Seth Rogers, Chief Executive Officer
CFO: Seth Rogers, Controller
CMO: Greg A. Vigna, M.D., Medical Director
CHR: Tina Reed, Director of Human Resources
CNO: Mark Dinardo, Chief Nursing Officer
Web address: www.healthsouthmodesto.com/
**Control**: Corporation, Investor–owned (for–profit) **Service**: Rehabilitation

| Staffed Beds: 35 Admissions: 877 Census: 32 Outpatient Visits: 0 Births: 0 Total Expense ($000): 20134 Payroll Expense ($000): 10603 Personnel: 148 |

*Many Facility Codes have changed. Please refer to the AHA Guide Code Chart.*

**HEALTHSOUTH REHABILITATION HOSPITAL OF MODESTO** See Encompass Health Rehabilitation Hospital of Modesto

**KAISER FOUNDATION HOSPITAL** See Modesto Medical Center

**MEMORIAL HOSPITALS ASSOCIATION** See Memorial Medical Center

✠ **MEMORIAL MEDICAL CENTER (050557)**, 1700 Coffee Road, Zip 95355–2869, Mailing Address: P.O. Box 942, Zip 95353–0942; tel. 209/526–4500, (Includes MEMORIAL MEDICAL CENTER, Mailing address: 1700 Coffee Road, Modesto, California, Zip 95355, Box 942, Zip 95353, tel. 209/526–4500), (Nonreporting) **A**1 2 10 **S** Sutter Health, Sacramento, CA
Primary Contact: Eugene Patrizio, Chief Executive Officer
COO: Steve Mitchell, Chief Operating Officer
CFO: Eric Dalton, Chief Financial Officer
CIO: Patrick Anderson, Chief Information Officer
CHR: Paula Rafala, Director, Human Resources
CNO: Sandra Proctor, R.N., MS, Chief Nurse Executive
Web address: www.memorialmedicalcenter.org
**Control:** Other not–for–profit (including NFP Corporation) **Service:** General medical and surgical

**Staffed Beds:** 220

**MODESTO MEDICAL CENTER** See Kaiser Permanente Manteca Medical Center, Manteca

**STANISLAUS SURGERY CENTER** See Stanislaus Surgical Hospital

★ **STANISLAUS SURGICAL HOSPITAL (050726)**, 1421 Oakdale Road, Zip 95355–3356; tel. 209/572–2700, (Nonreporting) **A**10 **S** Sutter Health, Sacramento, CA
Primary Contact: Douglas V. Johnson, Chief Executive Officer
CFO: Richard Hart, Chief Financial Officer
CMO: Wesley Kinzie, M.D., Chief of Staff
CIO: Richard Hart, Chief Financial Officer
CHR: Tyson Hubbard, Director Human Resources
CNO: Susan Gonzalez, Director of Clinical Services
Web address: www.stanislaussurgical.com
**Control:** Individual, Investor–owned (for–profit) **Service:** General medical and surgical

**Staffed Beds:** 23

### MONROVIA—Los Angeles County

**MONROVIA COMMUNITY HOSPITAL** See Monrovia Memorial Hospital

○ **MONROVIA MEMORIAL HOSPITAL (052054)**, 323 South Heliotrope Avenue, Zip 91016–2914; tel. 626/408–9800, (Nonreporting) **A**10 11
Primary Contact: Ron Kupferstein, Chief Executive Officer
Web address: www.monroviamemorial.com
**Control:** Partnership, Investor–owned (for–profit) **Service:** Acute long–term care hospital

**Staffed Beds:** 49

### MONTCLAIR—San Bernardino County

**DOCTORS HOSPITAL MEDICAL CTR** See Montclair Hospital Medical Center

☐ **MONTCLAIR HOSPITAL MEDICAL CENTER (050758)**, 5000 San Bernardino Street, Zip 91763–2326; tel. 909/625–5411, (Nonreporting) **A**1 3 5 10 12 13 **F**13 29 40 70 76 81 93 107 115 119 130 **S** Prime Healthcare, Ontario, CA
Primary Contact: Sofia Abrina, R.N., Administrator
CFO: Robert Bonner, Chief Financial Officer
CMO: Joseph Hourany, Chief Medical Officer
CNO: Gail Aviado, Chief Nursing Officer
Web address: www.montclair-hospital.com
**Control:** Other not–for–profit (including NFP Corporation) **Service:** General medical and surgical

**Staffed Beds:** 102 **Admissions:** 2781 **Census:** 25 **Outpatient Visits:** 34256 **Births:** 243 **Total Expense ($000):** 47586 **Payroll Expense ($000):** 22456 **Personnel:** 383

### MONTEBELLO—Los Angeles County

⇑ **BEVERLY HOSPITAL (050350)**, 309 West Beverly Boulevard, Zip 90640–4308; tel. 323/726–1222, (Nonreporting) **A**10 21 **F**3 13 15 18 20 22 24 29 30 31 34 35 40 41 45 49 50 51 57 59 60 65 68 70 72 74 75 76 77 78 79 81 86 89 107 108 110 111 115 118 119 130 132 135 143 146 147 148 149 150 154 156 **P**5
Primary Contact: Alice Cheng, President and Chief Executive Officer
CFO: Larry Pugh, Vice President and Chief Financial Officer
CMO: Kenneth L. Cohen, M.D., Chief Medical Officer
CIO: James Jaworski, Chief Information Officer
CHR: George Holtz, Adminstrative Director Human Resources
Web address: www.beverly.org
**Control:** Other not–for–profit (including NFP Corporation) **Service:** General medical and surgical

**Staffed Beds:** 202 **Admissions:** 10924 **Census:** 111 **Outpatient Visits:** 59113 **Births:** 741 **Total Expense ($000):** 194165 **Payroll Expense ($000):** 59478 **Personnel:** 739

### MONTEREY—Monterey County

**COMM HOSP FDN** See Community Hospital of The Monterey Peninsula

✠ △ **COMMUNITY HOSPITAL OF THE MONTEREY PENINSULA (050145)**, 23625 Holman Highway, Zip 93940–5902, Mailing Address: Box 'HH', Zip 93942–6032; tel. 831/624–5311, (Total facility includes 28 beds in nursing home–type unit) (Nonreporting) **A**1 2 7 10 **F**3 5 11 12 13 15 17 18 20 22 24 26 28 29 30 31 32 34 35 37 40 44 45 46 47 48 49 50 51 53 54 57 58 59 60 61 62 63 64 66 68 70 71 73 74 75 76 77 78 79 81 82 83 84 85 86 87 89 90 91 92 93 94 96 98 99 100 101 102 103 104 105 107 110 111 114 115 116 117 118 119 120 121 123 124 126 128 129 130 132 134 135 145 146 148 149 150 153 154 156 **P**5 6
Primary Contact: Steven J. Packer, M.D., President and Chief Executive Officer
CFO: Laura Zehm, Vice President and Chief Financial Officer
CMO: Anthony D Chavis, M.D., Vice President Enterprise Medical Officer, Community Hospital Foundation
Web address: www.chomp.org
**Control:** Other not–for–profit (including NFP Corporation) **Service:** General medical and surgical

**Staffed Beds:** 248 **Admissions:** 13621 **Census:** 175 **Outpatient Visits:** 370003 **Births:** 1104 **Total Expense ($000):** 611371 **Payroll Expense ($000):** 230438 **Personnel:** 1943

### MONTEREY PARK—Los Angeles County

☐ **GARFIELD MEDICAL CENTER (050737)**, 525 North Garfield Avenue, Zip 91754–1205; tel. 626/573–2222, (Nonreporting) **A**1 10 **S** AHMC & Healthcare, Inc., Alhambra, CA
Primary Contact: Patrick A. Petre, Chief Executive Officer
COO: Herbert Villafuerte, Chief Operating Officer/Chief Nursing Officer
CFO: Steve Maekawa, Chief Financial Officer
CMO: Thomas Lam, Chief Medical Officer
CIO: Angelica Ching, Director Information Systems
CHR: Darcy Castro, Director Human Resources
CNO: Herbert Villafuerte, Chief Operating Officer and Chief Nursing Officer
Web address: www.garfieldmedicalcenter.com
**Control:** Partnership, Investor–owned (for–profit) **Service:** General medical and surgical

**Staffed Beds:** 195

☐ **MONTEREY PARK HOSPITAL (050736)**, 900 South Atlantic Boulevard, Zip 91754–4780; tel. 626/570–9000, (Nonreporting) **A**1 10 **S** AHMC & Healthcare, Inc., Alhambra, CA
Primary Contact: Philip A. Cohen, Chief Executive Officer
COO: Ericka Smith, Chief Operating Officer
CFO: Daniel Song, Chief Financial Officer
CMO: Ruben Ramirez, M.D., Chief of Staff
CIO: Angelica Ching, Director Information Systems
CHR: Gretchen Lindeman, Director of Human Resources
CNO: Shirley Tang, R.N., Chief Nursing Officer
Web address: www.montereyparkhosp.com
**Control:** Partnership, Investor–owned (for–profit) **Service:** General medical and surgical

**Staffed Beds:** 101

---

**Hospital, Medicare Provider Number, Address, Telephone, Approval, Facility, and Physician Codes, Health Care System**

★ American Hospital Association (AHA) membership
☐ The Joint Commission accreditation
○ Healthcare Facilities Accreditation Program
◇ DNV Healthcare Inc. accreditation
⇑ Center for Improvement in Healthcare Quality Accreditation
△ Commission on Accreditation of Rehabilitation Facilities (CARF) accreditation

**CA**

## MORENO VALLEY—Riverside County

☒ **KAISER PERMANENTE MORENO VALLEY MEDICAL CENTER (050765)**, 27300 Iris Avenue, Zip 92555–4800; tel. 951/243–0811, (Nonreporting) **A**1 3 10 **F**3 13 15 29 30 35 40 44 45 46 49 50 59 60 64 65 68 70 71 72 74 75 76 77 78 79 81 82 84 85 87 97 100 101 102 104 107 108 109 110 111 115 117 119 130 135 144 146 148 149 154 156 157 **P**6 **S** Kaiser Foundation Hospitals, Oakland, CA
Primary Contact: Vita M. Willett, Senior Vice President, Area Manager
COO: Corey A Seale, Chief Operating Officer
CFO: JiJi Abraham, Area Chief Financial Officer
CMO: Frank M. Flowers, M.D., Area Medical Director
CIO: Alfred T Velasquez, Area Information Officer
CHR: Cheryl M Witt, Human Resources Director
**Control**: Other not–for–profit (including NFP Corporation) **Service**: General medical and surgical

| | |
|---|---|
| **Staffed Beds:** 94 **Admissions:** 4425 **Census:** 39 **Outpatient Visits:** 64322 **Births:** 1413 **Personnel:** 467 | |

**MORENO VALLEY COMMUNITY HOSPITAL** See Kaiser Permanente Moreno Valley Medical Center

**RIVERSIDE COUNTY REGIONAL MEDICAL CENTER** See Riverside University Health System-Medical Center

☒ **RIVERSIDE UNIVERSITY HEALTH SYSTEM-MEDICAL CENTER (050292)**, 26520 Cactus Avenue, Zip 92555–3911; tel. 951/486–4000, (Nonreporting) **A**1 3 5 10 12 13
Primary Contact: Jennifer Cruikshank, R.N., Chief Executive Officer
CFO: Christopher Hans, Chief Financial Officer
CMO: Arnold Tabuenca, M.D., Medical Director
CNO: Judi Nightingale, R.N., Dr.PH, Chief Nursing Officer
Web address: www.ruhealth.org/en-us
**Control**: County, Government, Nonfederal **Service**: General medical and surgical

| | |
|---|---|
| **Staffed Beds:** 439 | |

## MOSS BEACH—San Mateo County

**ST CATHERINE HOSP ON HALF MOON** See Seton Medical Center Coastside

## MOUNT SHASTA—Siskiyou County

☒ **MERCY MEDICAL CENTER MOUNT SHASTA (051319)**, 914 Pine Street, Zip 96067–2143; tel. 530/926–6111, (Nonreporting) **A**1 10 18 **F**3 11 13 15 29 30 35 40 43 50 53 56 57 59 62 63 64 68 70 75 76 77 79 81 82 84 93 107 108 110 111 114 118 119 121 127 130 131 132 133 143 146 148 149 154 **S** CommonSpirit Health, Chicago, IL
Primary Contact: Rodger Page, President
CMO: David Holst, M.D., Chief of Staff
CHR: Michelle Michl, Director Human Resources
CNO: Lisa Hubbard, Vice President and Chief Nursing Executive
Web address: www.mercymtshasta.org
**Control**: Other not–for–profit (including NFP Corporation) **Service**: General medical and surgical

| | |
|---|---|
| **Staffed Beds:** 33 **Admissions:** 1002 **Census:** 8 **Outpatient Visits:** 60622 **Births:** 126 **Total Expense ($000):** 59514 **Payroll Expense ($000):** 24436 **Personnel:** 235 | |

**MERCY MEDICAL CENTER MT SHASTA** See Mercy Medical Center Mount Shasta

## MOUNTAIN VIEW—Santa Clara County

**CAMINO HEALTHCARE** See El Camino Hospital

☒ △ **EL CAMINO HOSPITAL (050308)**, 2500 Grant Road, Zip 94040–4302, Mailing Address: P.O. Box 7025, Zip 94039–7025; tel. 650/940–7000, (Includes EL CAMINO HOSPITAL LOS GATOS, Mailing address: 815 Pollard Road, Los Gatos, California, Zip 95032–1438; tel. 408/378–6131), (Nonreporting) **A**1 2 3 7 10
Primary Contact: Dan Woods, Chief Executive Officer
COO: James D Griffith, Chief Operating Officer
CFO: Iftikhar Hussain, Chief Financial Officer
CMO: Mark C. Adams, M.D., Chief Medical Officer
CIO: Deborah Muro, Chief Information Officer
CHR: Kathryn M Fisk, Chief Human Resources Officer
CNO: Cheryl Reinking, R.N., MS, Chief Nursing Officer
Web address: www.elcaminohospital.org
**Control**: Hospital district or authority, Government, Nonfederal **Service**: General medical and surgical

| | |
|---|---|
| **Staffed Beds:** 420 | |

## MURRIETA—Riverside County

☐ **LOMA LINDA UNIVERSITY MEDICAL CENTER-MURRIETA (050770)**, 28062 Baxter Road, Zip 92563–1401; tel. 951/290–4000, (Nonreporting) **A**1 3 10 **F**3 11 13 15 18 20 22 24 26 28 29 30 31 34 35 40 44 45 46 47 48 49 50 54 57 58 59 60 61 64 65 68 70 72 74 75 76 77 78 79 81 82 85 86 87 91 92 93 107 108 110 111 114 115 117 118 119 120 121 123 126 130 132 146 147 148 149 154 **S** Loma Linda University Adventist Health Sciences Center, Loma Linda, CA
Primary Contact: Peter Baker, Senior Vice President and Administrator
COO: Richard M Tibbits, Vice President and Chief Operating Officer
CFO: James Uli, Chief Financial Officer
CMO: Jeff Conner, M.D., Chief Medical Staff
Web address: www.llumcmurrieta.org
**Control**: Other not–for–profit (including NFP Corporation) **Service**: General medical and surgical

| | |
|---|---|
| **Staffed Beds:** 111 **Admissions:** 9378 **Census:** 98 **Outpatient Visits:** 172634 **Births:** 1112 **Total Expense ($000):** 227766 **Payroll Expense ($000):** 67997 **Personnel:** 911 | |

**SHARP HEALTHCARE MURRIETA** See Rancho Springs Medical Center

☒ **SOUTHWEST HEALTHCARE SYSTEM (050701)**, 25500 Medical Center Drive, Zip 92562–5965; tel. 951/696–6000, (Includes INLAND VALLEY MEDICAL CENTER, Mailing address: 36485 Inland Valley Drive, Wildomar, California, Zip 92595–9700; tel. 951/677–1111; Bradley D Neet, FACHE, Chief Executive Officer; RANCHO SPRINGS MEDICAL CENTER, Mailing address: 25500 Medical Center Drive, Murrieta, California, Zip 92562–5965; tel. 951/696–6000), (Nonreporting) **A**1 3 10 **F**3 8 11 12 13 15 29 30 34 35 37 40 43 45 49 50 51 57 59 68 70 72 74 76 77 79 81 84 85 87 93 96 100 102 107 108 110 111 115 119 126 130 132 134 146 147 149 154 155 **S** Universal Health Services, Inc., King of Prussia, PA
Primary Contact: Bradley D. Neet, FACHE, Chief Executive Officer
COO: Jared Giles, Chief Operating Officer
CFO: Jon Zilkow, Chief Financial Officer
CMO: Reza Vaezazizi, M.D., Chief of Staff
CIO: Jeffrey Upcraft, Director Information Services
CHR: Della G Stange, Director Human Resources
CNO: Kristen Johnson, Chief Nursing Officer
Web address: www.swhealthcaresystem.com/
**Control**: Corporation, Investor–owned (for–profit) **Service**: General medical and surgical

| | |
|---|---|
| **Staffed Beds:** 231 **Admissions:** 16563 **Census:** 160 **Outpatient Visits:** 116247 **Births:** 3091 **Total Expense ($000):** 253135 **Payroll Expense ($000):** 109836 **Personnel:** 1271 | |

## NAPA—Napa County

**DEPARTMENT OF STATE HOSPITALS-NAPA** See Napa State Hospital

☐ **NAPA STATE HOSPITAL (054122)**, 2100 Napa-Vallejo Highway, Zip 94558–6293; tel. 707/253–5000, (Nonreporting) **A**1 3 5 10 **F**30 39 53 56 59 61 67 68 78 98 128 130 132 135 146 149 154 **P**6
Primary Contact: Dolly Matteucci, Executive Director
COO: Dolly Matteucci, Executive Director
Web address: www.dmh.ca.gov
**Control**: State, Government, Nonfederal **Service**: Psychiatric

| | |
|---|---|
| **Staffed Beds:** 1284 **Admissions:** 851 **Census:** 1253 **Outpatient Visits:** 0 **Births:** 0 **Total Expense ($000):** 351265 **Payroll Expense ($000):** 215661 **Personnel:** 2324 | |

**QUEEN OF THE VALLEY HOSPITAL** See Queen of The Valley Medical Center

☒ **QUEEN OF THE VALLEY MEDICAL CENTER (050009)**, 1000 Trancas Street, Zip 94558–2906, Mailing Address: P.O. Box 2340, Zip 94558–0688; tel. 707/252–4411, (Nonreporting) **A**1 2 10 19 **S** Providence St. Joseph Health, Renton, WA
Primary Contact: Larry Coomes, Chief Executive Officer
COO: Vincent Morgese, M.D., Executive Vice President, Chief Operating Officer and Chief Medical Officer
CFO: Michel Riccioni, Vice President and Chief Financial Officer, Northern California Region
CMO: Vincent Morgese, M.D., Executive Vice President, Chief Operating Officer and Chief Medical Officer
CHR: Robert A Eisen, Vice President Human Resources, Northern California Region
Web address: www.thequeen.org
**Control**: Church operated, Nongovernment, not–for–profit **Service**: General medical and surgical

| | |
|---|---|
| **Staffed Beds:** 208 | |

*Many Facility Codes have changed. Please refer to the AHA Guide Code Chart.*

© 2021 AHA Guide

## NATIONAL CITY—San Diego County

☐ △ **PARADISE VALLEY HOSPITAL (050024)**, 2400 East Fourth Street,
Zip 91950–2099; tel. 619/470–4321, (Includes BAYVIEW BEHAVIORAL
HEALTH CAMPUS, Mailing address: 330 Moss Street, Chula Vista, California,
Zip 91911–2005; tel. 619/470–4321; Neerav Jadeja, Administrator),
(Nonreporting) **A**1 7 10 **S** Prime Healthcare, Ontario, CA
Primary Contact: Neerav Jadeja, Chief Executive Officer
CFO: Becky Levy, Chief Financial Officer
CMO: Rosemarie Lim, M.D., Chief Medical Officer
CIO: Allan Tojino, Director, Information Systems
CHR: Lorraine Villegas, Manager Human Resources
CNO: Gemma Rama-Banaag, R.N., MSN, Chief Nursing Officer
Web address: www.paradisevalleyhospital.org
**Control:** Corporation, Investor–owned (for–profit) **Service:** General medical and
surgical

**Staffed Beds:** 256

## NEEDLES—San Bernardino County

**COLORADO RIVER MEDICAL CENTER (051323)**, 1401 Bailey Avenue,
Zip 92363–3198; tel. 760/326–7100, (Nonreporting) **A**10 18
Primary Contact: Steve Kelley. Lopez, Chief Executive Officer
COO: Knaya Tabora, Chief Operating Officer and Chief Nursing Officer
CFO: Steve Kelley Lopez, Chief Financial Officer
CMO: Robert Strecker, M.D., Chief of Staff
CIO: Ron Chieffo, Chief Information Officer
CHR: Pam Barrett, Human Resources Director
CNO: Knaya Tabora, Chief Operating Officer and Chief Nursing Officer
Web address: www.crmccares.com
**Control:** City, Government, Nonfederal **Service:** General medical and surgical

**Staffed Beds:** 25

**NEEDLES-DESERT COMMUNITIES HSP** See Colorado River Medical Center

## NEWPORT BEACH—Orange County

★ ᐃ **HOAG MEMORIAL HOSPITAL PRESBYTERIAN (050224)**, One Hoag
Drive, Zip 92663–4120, Mailing Address: P.O. Box 6100, Zip 92658–6100;
tel. 949/764–4624, (Includes HOAG HOSPITAL IRVINE, Mailing address: 16200
Sand Canyon Avenue, Irvine, California, Zip 92618–3714; tel. 949/764–8240),
(Nonreporting) **A**3 5 10 21 **F**3 4 5 8 11 13 14 15 17 18 20 22 24 26 28 29 30
31 34 35 36 37 40 44 45 46 47 48 49 50 51 52 53 54 55 57 58 59 64 65 68
70 72 74 75 76 77 78 79 80 81 82 84 85 86 87 90 92 93 94 96 97 100 101
102 104 107 108 109 110 111 113 114 115 116 117 118 119 120 121 123
124 126 129 130 131 132 134 135 141 143 144 145 146 147 148 149 150
152 154 156 **P**2 7 **S** Providence St. Joseph Health, Renton, WA
Primary Contact: Robert Braithwaite, President and Chief Executive Officer
COO: Michael Ricks, Chief Operating Officer
CFO: Andrew Guarni, Chief Financial Officer
CIO: Patrick Anderson, Chief Information Officer and Senior Vice President
CHR: Jan L Blue, Vice President Human Resources
CNO: Richard A Martin, MSN, R.N., Senior Vice President and Chief Nursing Officer
Web address: www.hoaghospital.org
**Control:** Other not–for–profit (including NFP Corporation) **Service:** General
medical and surgical

**Staffed Beds:** 588 **Admissions:** 37328 **Census:** 384 **Outpatient
Visits:** 489670 **Births:** 6976 **Total Expense ($000):** 1209588 **Payroll
Expense ($000):** 430998 **Personnel:** 5407

**NEWPORT BAY HOSPITAL (054135)**, 1501 East 16th Street, Zip 92663–5924;
tel. 949/650–9750, (Nonreporting) **A**10
Primary Contact: James E. Parkhurst, President and Chief Executive Officer
COO: Garry Hardwick, R.N., Chief Operating Officer
CFO: Rocky Gentner, Chief Financial Officer
CMO: Jason Kellogg, M.D., Chief of Staff
CIO: Nina Swenson, Director Business Services
CHR: Phyllis Parkhurst, Vice President Support Services
CNO: Diana Hakenson, Director of Patient Care Services
Web address: www.newportbayhospital.com
**Control:** Corporation, Investor–owned (for–profit) **Service:** Psychiatric

**Staffed Beds:** 34

**NORTH BAY HOSPITAL** See Newport Bay Hospital

## NORTH HOLLYWOOD—Los Angeles County

**ST. ELIZABETH TOLUCA LAKE CONVALESCENT HOSPITAL** See Providence
St. Elizabeth Care Center

## NORTHRIDGE—Los Angeles County

⊠ △ **NORTHRIDGE HOSPITAL MEDICAL CENTER (050116)**, 18300 Roscoe
Boulevard, Zip 91328–4167; tel. 818/885–8500, (Nonreporting) **A**1 2 3 5 7 10
**F**3 5 11 13 15 17 18 20 22 24 26 28 29 30 31 34 35 37 38 40 41 43 45 46
49 57 59 60 61 64 68 70 72 74 75 76 77 78 79 81 82 84 85 87 89 90 93 95
97 98 99 104 105 107 108 110 111 114 115 117 119 120 121 126 130 132
146 147 148 152 153 154 **S** CommonSpirit Health, Chicago, IL
Primary Contact: Paul Watkins, JD, President
COO: Betsy Hart, Chief Operating Officer
CFO: Douglas Brown, Chief Financial Officer
CMO: Mark Dumais, M.D., Chief Medical Officer
CHR: Susan Paulsen, Director Human Resources
CNO: Resha T Holman, Chief Nurse Executive Officer
Web address: www.northridgehospital.org
**Control:** Other not–for–profit (including NFP Corporation) **Service:** General
medical and surgical

**Staffed Beds:** 394 **Admissions:** 15005 **Census:** 187 **Outpatient
Visits:** 103815 **Births:** 637 **Total Expense ($000):** 424766 **Payroll Expense
($000):** 164092 **Personnel:** 1518

**NORTHRIDGE HOSPITAL MEDICAL CENTER-ROSCOE BOULEVARD CAMPUS**
See Northridge Hospital Medical Center

## NORWALK—Los Angeles County

**COAST PLAZA DOCTORS HOSPITAL** See Coast Plaza Hospital

☐ **COAST PLAZA HOSPITAL (050771)**, 13100 Studebaker Road,
Zip 90650–2500; tel. 562/868–3751, (Nonreporting) **A**1 10 **S** Avanti Hospitals, El
Segundo, CA
Primary Contact: Patrick W. Rafferty, Chief Executive Officer
CMO: Galal S Gough, M.D., Chief of Staff
CIO: Linda K Roman, Administrator
Web address: www.avantihospitals.com/coast-plaza-hospital
**Control:** Corporation, Investor–owned (for–profit) **Service:** General medical and
surgical

**Staffed Beds:** 123

☐ **DSH METROPOLITAN (054133)**, 11401 Bloomfield Avenue, Zip 90650–2015;
tel. 562/863–7011, (Nonreporting) **A**1 10
Primary Contact: Michael Barsom, M.D., Executive Director
CFO: Maybelle Manlagnit, Senior Accounting Officer
CIO: Paul Mello, Manager Data Processing
CHR: Jorge Banuedos, Director Human Resources
Web address: www.dmh.ca.gov
**Control:** State, Government, Nonfederal **Service:** Psychiatric

**Staffed Beds:** 657

**LOS ANGELES COMMUNITY HOSPITAL OF NORWALK** See Los Angeles
Community Hospital at Los Angeles, Los Angeles

**METROPOLITAN STATE HOSPITAL** See Dsh Metropolitan

**NORWALK COMMUNITY HOSPITAL** See Los Angeles Community Hospital of
Norwalk

## NOVATO—Marin County

⊠ **NOVATO COMMUNITY HOSPITAL (050131)**, 180 Rowland Way,
Zip 94945–5009, Mailing Address: P.O. Box 1108, Zip 94948–1108;
tel. 415/209–1300, (Nonreporting) **A**1 10 **S** Sutter Health, Sacramento, CA
Primary Contact: Michael L. Purvis, Chief Executive Officer
CMO: Barbara Nylund, M.D., Chief of Staff
CIO: Kathryn Graham, Director Communications and Community Relations
CHR: Diana G Johnson, Acting Chief Human Resources Officer
Web address: www.novatocommunity.sutterhealth.org
**Control:** Other not–for–profit (including NFP Corporation) **Service:** General
medical and surgical

**Staffed Beds:** 40

---

**Hospital, Medicare Provider Number, Address, Telephone, Approval, Facility, and Physician Codes, Health Care System**

★ American Hospital Association (AHA) membership   ○ Healthcare Facilities Accreditation Program   ᐃ Center for Improvement in Healthcare Quality Accreditation
☐ The Joint Commission accreditation   ◇ DNV Healthcare Inc. accreditation   △ Commission on Accreditation of Rehabilitation Facilities (CARF) accreditation

**CA**

## OAKDALE—Stanislaus County

⊞ **OAK VALLEY HOSPITAL (050067)**, 350 South Oak Avenue, Zip 95361–3581; tel. 209/847–3011, (Nonreporting) **A**1 10
Primary Contact: John McCormick, President and Chief Executive Officer
CMO: Blackhart Bruce, M.D., Chief of Staff
CIO: Sherry Peral, Director Information Systems
CHR: Brian Beck,PHR,MHROD, Vice President Human Resources
CNO: Joann L. Saporito, R.N., Vice President Nursing Services
Web address: www.oakvalleycares.org
**Control:** Hospital district or authority, Government, Nonfederal **Service:** General medical and surgical

| Staffed Beds: 150 |
|---|

**OAK VALLEY HOSPITAL DISTRICT** See Oak Valley Hospital

## OAKLAND—Alameda County

**ALAMEDA HEALTH SYSTEM** See Highland Hospital

**ALTA BATE SUMMIT MED CENTER** See Alta Bates Summit Medical Center - Summit Campus

⊞ △ **ALTA BATES SUMMIT MEDICAL CENTER - SUMMIT CAMPUS (050043)**, 350 Hawthorne Avenue, Zip 94609–3100; tel. 510/655–4000, (Nonreporting) **A**1 2 7 10 **S** Sutter Health, Sacramento, CA
Primary Contact: David D. Clark, FACHE, Chief Executive Officer
CMO: John Gentile, M.D., Vice President Medical Affairs
CHR: Mark Beiting, Vice President Human Resources
Web address: www.altabatessummit.com
**Control:** Other not–for–profit (including NFP Corporation) **Service:** General medical and surgical

| Staffed Beds: 427 |
|---|

⊞ △ **HIGHLAND HOSPITAL (050320)**, 1411 East 31st Street, Zip 94602–1018; tel. 510/437–4800, (Includes FAIRMONT HOSPITAL, Mailing address: 15400 Foothill Boulevard, San Leandro, California, Zip 94578–1009; tel. 510/895–4200; Richard Espinoza, Chief Administrative Officer; JOHN GEORGE PSYCHIATRIC HOSPITAL, Mailing address: 2060 Fairmont Drive, San Leandro, California, Zip 94578–1001; tel. 510/346–1300; Guy C Qvistgaard, Chief Executive Officer) (Total facility includes 109 beds in nursing home–type unit) **A**1 3 5 7 10 **F**3 5 8 11 13 15 18 20 22 23 30 32 34 35 36 38 39 40 43 44 45 46 49 50 54 56 57 58 59 60 61 64 65 66 68 70 71 73 74 75 76 77 78 79 81 82 84 85 86 87 90 92 93 94 96 97 98 100 101 102 104 105 107 111 112 114 115 119 128 130 132 134 135 142 143 144 146 147 148 152 153 154 156 157 **S** Alameda Health System, San Leandro, CA
Primary Contact: Delvecchio Finley, Chief Executive Officer
CFO: Marion Schales, Chief Financial Officer
CMO: Sang-ick Chang, M.D., M.P.H., Chief Medical Officer
CHR: Jeanette L Louden Corbett, Chief Human Resources Officer
Web address: www.alamedahealthsystem.org
**Control:** Hospital district or authority, Government, Nonfederal **Service:** General medical and surgical

| Staffed Beds: 372 Admissions: 12848 Census: 352 Outpatient Visits: 409635 Births: 1270 Total Expense ($000): 893114 Payroll Expense ($000): 394380 Personnel: 3222 |
|---|

⊞ **KAISER PERMANENTE OAKLAND MEDICAL CENTER (050075)**, 3600 Broadway, Zip 94611–5693; tel. 510/752–1000, (Includes KAISER PERMANENTE RICHMOND MEDICAL CENTER, Mailing address: 901 Nevin Avenue, Richmond, California, Zip 94801–2555; tel. 510/307–1500; Jeffrey A Collins, M.D., Chief Executive Officer), (Nonreporting) **A**1 2 5 8 10 **F**3 11 12 13 15 18 19 20 21 22 23 25 26 27 29 30 31 34 37 39 40 41 45 47 48 49 50 51 56 60 63 64 68 70 72 73 74 75 76 78 79 80 81 82 84 85 86 87 88 89 100 107 108 110 111 112 114 115 117 118 119 120 121 123 124 126 130 135 146 149 154 **S** Kaiser Foundation Hospitals, Oakland, CA
Primary Contact: Jeffrey A. Collins, M.D., Senior Vice President and Area Manager
CFO: Dennis Morris, Area Finance Officer
CMO: John Loftus, M.D., Chief of Staff
CIO: Johnny Law, Area Information Officer
CHR: Rick Mead, Human Resources Leader
CNO: Charlene Boyer, Chief Nursing Officer
Web address: www.kaiserpermanente.org
**Control:** Other not–for–profit (including NFP Corporation) **Service:** General medical and surgical

| Staffed Beds: 365 Admissions: 21714 Census: 254 Outpatient Visits: 384164 Births: 3079 Personnel: 2649 |
|---|

**OAKLAND MEDICAL CENTER** See Kaiser Permanente Oakland Medical Center

☐ **TELECARE HERITAGE PSYCHIATRIC HEALTH CENTER (054146)**, 2633 East 27th Street, Zip 94601–1912; tel. 510/535–5115, (Nonreporting) **A**1 10
Primary Contact: Anne L. Bakar, President and Chief Executive Officer
Web address: www.tbhcare.com/
**Control:** Partnership, Investor–owned (for–profit) **Service:** Psychiatric

| Staffed Beds: 26 |
|---|

⊞ **UCSF BENIOFF CHILDREN'S HOSPITAL OAKLAND (053301)**, 747 52nd Street, Zip 94609–1859; tel. 510/428–3000, (Nonreporting) **A**1 3 5 10
Primary Contact: Michael Anderson, M.D., President
CFO: Ted Wang, Chief Financial Officer
CIO: Don Livsey, Vice President and Chief Information Officer
Web address: www.childrenshospitaloakland.org
**Control:** Other not–for–profit (including NFP Corporation) **Service:** Children's general medical and surgical

| Staffed Beds: 190 |
|---|

**USCF BENIOFF CHILDREN'S HOSPITAL OAKLAND** See UCSF Benioff Children's Hospital Oakland

## OCEANSIDE—San Diego County

⊞ **TRI-CITY MEDICAL CENTER (050128)**, 4002 Vista Way, Zip 92056–4593; tel. 760/724–8411, (Nonreporting) **A**1 3 5 10
Primary Contact: Steve Dietlin, Chief Executive Officer
CMO: Scott Worman, Chief of Staff
CIO: Kim Cook, Interim Clinical Applications Services Manager
CHR: Esther Beverly, Vice President Human Resources
CNO: Sharon A Schultz, Chief Nurse Executive and Vice President
Web address: www.tricitymed.org
**Control:** Hospital district or authority, Government, Nonfederal **Service:** General medical and surgical

| Staffed Beds: 330 |
|---|

## OJAI—Ventura County

⇑ **OJAI VALLEY COMMUNITY HOSPITAL (051334)**, 1306 Maricopa Highway, Zip 93023–3163; tel. 805/646–1401, (Nonreporting) **A**10 18 21 **S** Community Memorial Health System, Ventura, CA
Primary Contact: Haady Lashkari, Chief Administrative Officer
CFO: David Glyer, Vice President Finance
CIO: Mark Turner, Manager Information Technology
CHR: Deborah Gallagher, Manager Human Resources
Web address: www.cmhshealth.org/locations/ojai-valley-community-hospital/
**Control:** Other not–for–profit (including NFP Corporation) **Service:** General medical and surgical

| Staffed Beds: 96 |
|---|

## ONTARIO—San Bernardino County

⊞ **KINDRED HOSPITAL-ONTARIO (052037)**, 550 North Monterey Avenue, Zip 91764–3399; tel. 909/391–0333, (Nonreporting) **A**1 10 **S** Kindred Healthcare, Louisville, KY
Primary Contact: Natalie Merckens, Chief Executive Officer
CFO: Omar Oregel, Controller
CMO: Marc Lynch, D.O., Chief of Staff
CHR: Laurel Scharber, Administrative Assistant and Coordinator Human Resources
CNO: Holly Ramos, R.N., Chief Clinical Officer
Web address: www.khontario.com/
**Control:** Corporation, Investor–owned (for–profit) **Service:** Acute long–term care hospital

| Staffed Beds: 81 |
|---|

**ONTARIO MEDICAL CENTER** See Kaiser Permanente Ontario Medical Center

**VENCOR HOSPITAL-ONTARIO** See Kindred Hospital-Ontario

## ORANGE—Orange County

☐ **CHAPMAN GLOBAL MEDICAL CENTER (050745)**, 2601 East Chapman Avenue, Zip 92869–3296; tel. 714/633–0011, (Nonreporting) **A**1 10 **S** KPC Healthcare, Inc., Santa Ana, CA
Primary Contact: Ada Yeh, Chief Executive Officer
CFO: John Collins, Corporate Chief Financial Officer
CMO: Gary Bennett, M.D., Chief of Medical Staff
CHR: Cynthia Garren-Oster, Human Resources Manager
CNO: Ada Yeh, Chief Operating Officer and Chief Nursing Officer
Web address: www.Chapmanglobalmedicalcenter.com
**Control:** Corporation, Investor–owned (for–profit) **Service:** General medical and surgical

| Staffed Beds: 100 |
|---|

**CHAPMAN MEDICAL CENTER** See Chapman Global Medical Center

**CHILDRENS HOSP OF ORANGE CNTY** See Children's Hospital of Orange County

☐ **CHILDREN'S HOSPITAL OF ORANGE COUNTY (053304)**, 1201 West La Veta Avenue, Zip 92868–4203, Mailing Address: PO Box 5700, Zip 92863–5700; tel. 714/997–3000, (Nonreporting) **A**1 3 5 10 **F**3 14 17 19 21 23 25 27 29 30 31 32 34 35 39 40 41 43 50 55 57 58 59 60 61 64 65 66 68 71 72 74 75 77 78 79 81 82 84 85 86 87 88 89 91 92 93 97 98 99 100 101 102 104 107 111 113 114 115 118 119 121 123 126 129 130 131 132 134 136 144 146 149 153 154 **P**3 5
Primary Contact: Kimberly C. Cripe, President and Chief Executive Officer
COO: Matthew S Gerlach, Chief Operating Officer
CFO: Kerri Ruppert Schiller, Senior Vice President and Chief Financial Officer
CMO: Maria Minon, M.D., Vice President Medical Affairs and Chief Medical Officer
CIO: John Henderson, Vice President and Chief Information Officer
CHR: Mamoon Syed, Vice President Human Resources
CNO: Melanie Patterson, R.N., Vice President Patient Care Services and Chief Nursing Officer
Web address: www.choc.org
Control: Other not–for–profit (including NFP Corporation) Service: Children's general medical and surgical

Staffed Beds: 334 Admissions: 13055 Census: 193 Outpatient Visits: 684712 Births: 0 Total Expense ($000): 826289 Payroll Expense ($000): 238316 Personnel: 3152

⇑ **HEALTHBRIDGE CHILDREN'S HOSPITAL (053308)**, 393 South Tustin Street, Zip 92866–2501; tel. 714/289–2400, (Nonreporting) **A**10 21 **S** Nexus Health Systems, Houston, TX
Primary Contact: Alex Villarruz, Chief Executive Officer
CIO: Roberta Consolver, Chief Information Officer
Control: Partnership, Investor–owned (for–profit) Service: Rehabilitation

Staffed Beds: 27

⇑ **HEALTHBRIDGE CHILDRENS REHABILITATION HOSPITAL** See Healthbridge Children's Hospital

**ST. JOSEPH HOSPITAL** See St. Joseph Hospital Orange

⊠ **ST. JOSEPH HOSPITAL ORANGE (050069)**, 1100 West Stewart Drive, Zip 92868–3849, Mailing Address: P.O. Box 5600, Zip 92863–5600; tel. 714/633–9111, (Nonreporting) **A**1 2 3 5 10 **F**3 5 8 12 13 15 17 18 19 20 22 24 26 28 29 30 31 34 35 37 38 40 41 42 44 45 46 47 48 49 50 51 53 54 55 57 58 59 60 63 64 65 68 69 70 74 75 76 77 78 79 80 81 82 84 85 86 87 91 92 93 98 100 101 102 104 105 107 108 109 110 111 113 114 115 116 117 118 119 120 121 123 124 126 129 130 131 132 135 138 141 146 147 148 149 152 153 154 156 157 **P**3 5 **S** Providence St. Joseph Health, Renton, WA
Primary Contact: Jeremy Zoch, Chief Executive
COO: Jeremy Zoch, Executive Vice President and Chief Operating Officer
CFO: Kristi Liberatore, Vice President and Chief Financial Officer
CMO: Scott Rusk, M.D., Chief Medical Officer
CIO: Jeremy Zoch, Executive Vice President and Chief Operating Officer
CHR: Mary P Leahy, Regional Vice President, Chief Human Resources Officer
CNO: Katie Skelton, MSN, R.N., Vice President Nursing and Chief Nursing Officer
Web address: www.sjo.org
Control: Church operated, Nongovernment, not–for–profit Service: General medical and surgical

Staffed Beds: 379 Admissions: 20373 Census: 229 Outpatient Visits: 341146 Births: 4860 Total Expense ($000): 620859 Payroll Expense ($000): 219915 Personnel: 2362

**UC IRVINE MEDICAL CENTER** See UCI Medical Center

⊠ **UCI MEDICAL CENTER (050348)**, 101 The City Drive South, Zip 92868–3298; tel. 714/456–6011, (Nonreporting) **A**1 2 5 8 10 19 **F**3 6 8 9 11 12 13 14 15 16 17 18 19 20 21 22 24 26 27 28 29 30 31 32 34 35 36 37 39 40 41 43 44 45 46 47 48 49 50 51 52 53 54 55 56 57 58 59 60 61 63 64 65 66 68 70 71 72 73 74 75 76 77 78 79 80 81 82 84 85 88 89 90 91 92 93 96 97 98 99 100 101 102 103 104 105 107 108 110 111 114 115 116 117 118 119 120 121 123 124 126 129 130 131 132 134 135 138 141 142 144 145 146 147 148 149 150 153 154 156 **P**4 6 **S** University of California Systemwide Administration, Oakland, CA
Primary Contact: Chad T. Lefteris, Chief Executive Officer
COO: Chad T. Lefteris, Chief Operating Officer
CFO: Ajay Sial, Chief Financial Officer, UC Irvine Health
CMO: William Wilson, M.D., Chief Medical Officer
CIO: Charles H Podesta, Chief Information Officer
CHR: Ramona Agrela, Associate Chancellor & Chief Human Resources Executive
CNO: Sonia Lane, Interim Chief Nursing Officer
Web address: www.ucirvinehealth.org
Control: State, Government, Nonfederal Service: General medical and surgical

Staffed Beds: 402 Admissions: 22142 Census: 348 Outpatient Visits: 747187 Births: 1540 Total Expense ($000): 1234471 Payroll Expense ($000): 452767 Personnel: 4592

## OROVILLE—Butte County

**OROVILLE HOSPITAL (050030)**, 2767 Olive Highway, Zip 95966–6118; tel. 530/533–8500, (Nonreporting) **A**10 **F**3 5 8 11 13 15 17 18 20 26 27 28 29 30 31 32 33 34 35 36 38 39 40 41 44 45 46 47 48 49 50 51 52 54 56 57 58 59 60 61 62 63 64 65 66 68 70 74 75 76 77 78 79 81 82 83 84 85 86 87 91 93 94 96 97 100 101 102 104 107 108 110 111 114 115 116 117 118 119 120 121 123 124 126 127 129 130 131 132 134 135 143 144 145 146 147 148 149 153 154 156
Primary Contact: Robert J. Wentz, President and Chief Executive Officer
COO: Scott Chapple, Chief Operating Officer
CFO: Ashok Khanchandani, Chief Financial Officer
CMO: Mathew N. Fine, M.D., Chief Medical Officer
CIO: Denise LeFevre, Chief Information Officer
CHR: Scott Chapple, Chief Operating Officer
CNO: Carol Speer-Smith, R.N., Chief Nursing Officer
Web address: www.orovillehospital.com
Control: Other not–for–profit (including NFP Corporation) Service: General medical and surgical

Staffed Beds: 153 Admissions: 13854 Census: 132 Outpatient Visits: 676125 Births: 488 Total Expense ($000): 315676 Payroll Expense ($000): 118666 Personnel: 1584

## OXNARD—Ventura County

⊠ **ST. JOHN'S REGIONAL MEDICAL CENTER (050082)**, 1600 North Rose Avenue, Zip 93030–3723; tel. 805/988–2500, (Nonreporting) **A**1 2 3 5 10 **S** CommonSpirit Health, Chicago, IL
Primary Contact: Darren W. Lee, President and Chief Executive Officer
CFO: Donald P Bernard, Chief Financial Officer
CMO: Sahin Yanik, M.D., Vice President Medical Administration
CIO: Jeff Perry, Director Information Technology
CHR: Ed Gonzales, Vice President Human Resources
Web address: www.stjohnshealth.org
Control: Other not–for–profit (including NFP Corporation) Service: General medical and surgical

Staffed Beds: 139

## PALM SPRINGS—Riverside County

⊠ △ **DESERT REGIONAL MEDICAL CENTER (050243)**, 1150 North Indian Canyon Drive, Zip 92262–4872; tel. 760/323–6511, (Nonreporting) **A**1 2 3 5 7 10 13 **S** TENET Healthcare Corporation, Dallas, TX
Primary Contact: Michele Finney, Chief Executive Officer
COO: James Santucci, Chief Operating Officer
CFO: Judi Stimson, Chief Financial Officer
CMO: Charles Anderson, M.D., Chief Medical Officer
CIO: Robert Klingseis, Director Information Systems
CHR: James Kelley, Chief Human Resources Officer
CNO: Beverly Fick, Chief Nursing Officer
Web address: www.desertregional.com
Control: Individual, Investor–owned (for–profit) Service: General medical and surgical

Staffed Beds: 382

**DESERT REGIONAL MEDICAL CTR** See Desert Regional Medical Center

---

**Hospital, Medicare Provider Number, Address, Telephone, Approval, Facility, and Physician Codes, Health Care System**

★ American Hospital Association (AHA) membership ○ Healthcare Facilities Accreditation Program ⇑ Center for Improvement in Healthcare Quality Accreditation
☐ The Joint Commission accreditation ◇ DNV Healthcare Inc. accreditation △ Commission on Accreditation of Rehabilitation Facilities (CARF) accreditation

**CA**

**CA**

## PALMDALE—Los Angeles County

**LANCASTER COMMUNITY HOSPITAL** See Palmdale Regional Medical Center, Lancaster

**PALMDALE REGIONAL MEDICAL CENTER**A1 10 F3 11 12 18 20 22 24 26 29 31 34 35 40 41 45 46 47 48 49 50 56 57 60 63 64 68 70 74 78 79 81 85 87 90 93 96 102 107 108 111 114 115 119 126 130 132 135 146 148 149 154
CFO: Kurt Broten, Chief Financial Officer
CIO: Roy Singleton, Director Computer Information Systems
CHR: Karen Hickling, Director Human Resources
Web address: www.palmdaleregional.com

☐ **PALMDALE REGIONAL MEDICAL CENTER (050204)**, 38600 Medical Center Drive, Zip 93551–4483; tel. 661/382–5000, (Nonreporting) A1 10 F3 11 12 18 20 22 24 26 29 31 34 35 40 41 45 46 47 48 49 50 56 57 60 63 64 68 70 74 78 79 81 85 87 90 93 96 102 107 108 111 114 115 119 126 130 132 135 146 148 149 154 S Universal Health Services, Inc., King of Prussia, PA
Primary Contact: Richard Allen, Chief Executive Officer
CFO: Kurt Broten, Chief Financial Officer
CIO: Roy Singleton, Director Computer Information Systems
CHR: Karen Hickling, Director Human Resources
Web address: www.palmdaleregional.com
**Control**: Corporation, Investor–owned (for–profit) **Service**: General medical and surgical

**Staffed Beds**: 184 **Admissions**: 8599 **Census**: 93 **Outpatient Visits**: 77445 **Births**: 0 **Total Expense ($000)**: 167019 **Payroll Expense ($000)**: 64778 **Personnel**: 834

## PALO ALTO—Santa Clara County

⊞ **LUCILE PACKARD CHILDREN'S HOSPITAL STANFORD (053305)**, 725 Welch Road, Zip 94304–1614; tel. 650/497–8000, (Nonreporting) A1 3 5 10 F3 7 8 11 12 13 17 19 25 27 28 29 30 31 32 34 35 36 38 39 44 45 46 47 48 49 50 52 54 55 57 58 59 60 61 64 65 66 68 71 72 73 74 75 76 77 78 79 81 82 84 85 86 87 88 89 91 92 93 96 97 99 100 101 104 107 108 109 111 112 113 114 115 116 118 119 124 126 129 130 131 132 134 136 137 138 139 140 141 142 144 145 146 148 149 154 156 P3
Primary Contact: Paul A. King, President and Chief Executive Officer
COO: Rick Majzun, FACHE, Chief Operating Officer
CMO: Dennis Lund, M.D., Chief Medical Officer
CIO: Kim Roberts, Chief Strategy Officer
CHR: Greg Souza, Vice President Human Resources
CNO: Kelly M Johnson, Chief Nursing Officer
Web address: www.stanfordchildrens.org
**Control**: Other not–for–profit (including NFP Corporation) **Service**: Children's general medical and surgical

**Staffed Beds**: 337 **Admissions**: 13643 **Census**: 250 **Outpatient Visits**: 98412 **Births**: 4418 **Total Expense ($000)**: 1419039 **Payroll Expense ($000)**: 496834 **Personnel**: 4500

**LUCILE SALTER PACKARD CHILDREN'S HOSPITAL STANFORD** See Lucile Packard Children's Hospital Stanford

⊞ **STANFORD HEALTH CARE (050441)**, 300 Pasteur Drive, Suite H3200, Zip 94304–2203; tel. 650/723–4000, (Nonreporting) A1 3 5 8 10 F3 5 6 8 9 11 12 14 15 17 18 20 22 24 26 28 29 30 31 34 35 36 37 38 39 40 41 43 45 46 47 48 49 52 54 55 56 57 58 59 60 61 65 68 70 74 75 77 79 80 81 82 84 85 86 87 92 93 95 96 97 98 100 102 103 104 107 108 110 111 114 115 117 118 119 120 121 123 124 126 129 130 131 132 135 136 137 138 139 140 141 142 145 146 147 148 149 154 155 156 P3 5 6 S Stanford Health Care, Palo Alto, CA
Primary Contact: David Entwistle, President and Chief Executive Officer
COO: Quinn McKenna, Chief Operating Officer
CFO: Daniel Morrissette, Chief Financial Officer
CMO: Norman Rizk, M.D., Chief Medical Officer
CIO: Pravene Nath, Chief Information Officer
CHR: Kety Duron, Vice President Human Resources
CNO: Nancy Lee, R.N., MSN, Vice President Patient Care Services and Chief Nursing Officer
Web address: www.stanfordhealthcare.org
**Control**: Other not–for–profit (including NFP Corporation) **Service**: General medical and surgical

**Staffed Beds**: 477 **Admissions**: 27393 **Census**: 427 **Outpatient Visits**: 1673680 **Births**: 0 **Total Expense ($000)**: 4213404 **Payroll Expense ($000)**: 1277306 **Personnel**: 11726

**STANFORD HOSPITAL AND CLINICS** See Stanford Health Care

⊞ △ **VA PALO ALTO HEALTH CARE SYSTEM**, 3801 Miranda Avenue, Zip 94304–1207; tel. 650/493–5000, (Includes PALO ALTO DIVISION, Mailing address: 3801 Miranda Avenue, Palo Alto, California, Zip 94304–1207; tel. 650/493–5000; VETERANS AFFAIRS PALO ALTO HEALTH CARE SYSTEM, LIVERMORE DIVISION, Mailing address: 4951 Arroyo Road, Livermore, California, Zip 94550; tel. 510/447–2560) (Total facility includes 377 beds in nursing home–type unit) A1 2 3 5 7 F3 4 5 8 9 12 15 17 18 20 22 24 26 28 29 30 31 33 34 35 36 37 38 39 40 44 45 46 47 49 50 51 53 54 55 56 57 58 59 60 61 62 63 64 65 66 67 68 70 71 74 75 77 78 79 80 81 82 83 84 85 86 87 90 91 92 93 94 95 96 97 98 100 101 102 103 104 105 106 107 108 110 111 114 115 116 117 118 119 126 127 128 129 130 131 132 135 143 144 146 147 148 149 152 153 154 156 157 158 S Department of Veterans Affairs, Washington, DC
Primary Contact: Thomas J. Fitzgerald III, Director
CFO: Mel Niese, Chief Fiscal Service
CMO: Lawrence Leung, M.D., Chief of Staff
CIO: Doug Wirthgen, Chief Information Officer
CHR: Lori Peery, Chief Human Resource Management Services
Web address: www.paloalto.va.gov/
**Control**: Veterans Affairs, Government, federal **Service**: General medical and surgical

**Staffed Beds**: 768 **Admissions**: 7128 **Census**: 493 **Outpatient Visits**: 949240 **Births**: 0 **Total Expense ($000)**: 1166996 **Payroll Expense ($000)**: 484442 **Personnel**: 4936

**VETERANS AFFAIRS MED CENTER** See Palo Alto Division

**VETERANS AFFARIS PALO ALTO HEALTH CARE SYSTEM** See VA Palo Alto Health Care System

## PANORAMA CITY—Los Angeles County

⊞ **KAISER PERMANENTE PANORAMA CITY MEDICAL CENTER (050137)**, 13652 Cantara Street, Zip 91402–5497; tel. 818/375–2000, (Nonreporting) A1 3 5 10 F3 7 11 13 15 18 29 30 31 32 34 35 37 38 40 41 44 45 46 48 49 50 51 54 55 56 57 58 59 60 61 62 63 64 65 66 68 70 72 74 75 77 78 79 81 82 84 85 86 87 92 97 101 102 104 107 108 110 111 115 116 117 118 119 124 126 129 130 131 132 135 141 143 144 146 147 148 149 154 156 157 S Kaiser Foundation Hospitals, Oakland, CA
Primary Contact: Payman Roshan, Senior Vice President and Area Manager
COO: Laura Gallardo, Chief Operating Officer
CFO: Karla Valle, Area Chief Financial Officer
CMO: James Lau, M.D., Area Medical Director
CIO: Earle Johnson, Area Information Officer
CHR: Carole L Erken, Human Resources Leader
Web address: www.kaiserpermanente.org
**Control**: Other not–for–profit (including NFP Corporation) **Service**: General medical and surgical

**Staffed Beds**: 218 **Admissions**: 8426 **Census**: 85 **Outpatient Visits**: 173070 **Births**: 2532 **Personnel**: 724

☐ **MISSION COMMUNITY HOSPITAL (050704)**, 14850 Roscoe Boulevard, Zip 91402–4677; tel. 818/787–2222, (Nonreporting) A1 3 5 10
Primary Contact: James Theiring, Chief Executive Officer
CFO: Mihi Lee, Chief Financial Officer
CMO: Glenn Marshak, M.D., Chief of Staff
CIO: Eric Rivers, Chief Information Officer
CHR: Carolyn Fish, Director Human Resources
CNO: Gwendolyn Dianne Wagner, R.N., MSN, Chief Nursing Officer
Web address: www.mchonline.org
**Control**: Other not–for–profit (including NFP Corporation) **Service**: General medical and surgical

**Staffed Beds**: 145

**PANORAMA CITY MEDICAL CENTER** See Kaiser Permanente Panorama City Medical Center

**SAN FERNANDO COMMUNITY HOSP** See Mission Community Hospital

## PARAMOUNT—Los Angeles County

⊞ **KINDRED HOSPITAL PARAMOUNT (052046)**, 16453 South Colorado Avenue, Zip 90723–5011; tel. 562/531–3110, (Nonreporting) A1 10 S Kindred Healthcare, Louisville, KY
Primary Contact: Mark Apodaca, Chief Executive Officer
Web address: www.promiseeastla.com
**Control**: Corporation, Investor–owned (for–profit) **Service**: Acute long–term care hospital

**Staffed Beds**: 148

**PROMISE HOSPITAL OF EAST LOS ANGELES, SUBURBAN MEDICAL CENTER CAMPUS** See Kindred Hospital Paramount

*Many Facility Codes have changed. Please refer to the AHA Guide Code Chart.* © 2021 AHA Guide

**CA**

## PASADENA—Los Angeles County

**AURORA LAS ENCINAS HOSPITAL** See Las Encinas Hospital

☒ **HUNTINGTON HOSPITAL (050438)**, 100 West California Boulevard,
Zip 91105–3097, Mailing Address: P.O. Box 7013, Zip 91109–7013;
tel. 626/397–5000, (Nonreporting) **A**1 2 3 5 8 10 19
Primary Contact: Lori J. Morgan, M.D., President and Chief Executive Officer
CFO: Steven Mohr, Senior Vice President and Chief Financial Officer
CMO: Paula Verrette, M.D., Senior Vice President Quality and Physician Services
and Chief Medical Officer
CIO: Debbie Tafoya, Vice President and Chief Information Officer
CHR: Debbie Ortega, Chief Human Resource Officer and Vice President
Administrative Services
CNO: Gloria Sanchez-Rico, Chief Nursing Officer and Vice President
Web address: www.huntingtonhospital.com
**Control:** Other not-for-profit (including NFP Corporation) **Service:** General
medical and surgical

**Staffed Beds:** 619

**HUNTINGTON MEMORIAL HOSPITAL** See Huntington Hospital

☐ **LAS ENCINAS HOSPITAL (054078)**, 2900 East Del Mar Boulevard,
Zip 91107–4399; tel. 626/795–9901, (Nonreporting) **A**1 10 **F**4 5 29 32 54 98 99
100 104 105 130 132 152 153 **P**6 **S** Signature Healthcare Services, Corona, CA
Primary Contact: Trevor Asmus, Chief Executive Officer
CMO: Daniel Suzuki, M.D., Medical Director
CIO: Eric Kim, Chief Information Officer
CHR: Veronica Herrera, Director Human Resources
Web address: www.lasencinashospital.com
**Control:** Individual, Investor-owned (for-profit) **Service:** Psychiatric

**Staffed Beds:** 118 **Admissions:** 4960 **Census:** 80 **Outpatient Visits:** 8010
**Births:** 0 **Total Expense ($000):** 28090 **Payroll Expense ($000):** 15604
**Personnel:** 240

## PATTON—San Bernardino County

☐ **DSH PATTON**, 3102 East Highland Avenue, Zip 92369–7813;
tel. 909/425–7000, (Nonreporting) **A**1 3 5
Primary Contact: Harry Oreol, Acting Chief Executive Officer
CFO: Kathleen Gamble, Fiscal Officer
CMO: George Christison, M.D., Medical Director
CIO: Cindy Barrett, Administrative Assistant
CHR: Nancy Varela, Director Human Resources
Web address: www.dmh.cahwnet.gov/statehospitals/patton
**Control:** State, Government, Nonfederal **Service:** Psychiatric

**Staffed Beds:** 1527

**PATTON STATE HOSPITAL** See Dsh Patton

## PERRIS—Riverside County

**KINDRED HOSPITAL OF RIVERSIDE** See Kindred Hospital Riverside

☒ **KINDRED HOSPITAL RIVERSIDE (052052)**, 2224 Medical Center Drive,
Zip 92571–2638; tel. 951/436–3535, (Nonreporting) **A**1 10 **S** Kindred
Healthcare, Louisville, KY
Primary Contact: William Mitchell, Chief Executive Officer and Administrator
COO: Guay Khim Fugate, Chief Operations Officer
CFO: John Browne, Senior Chief Financial Officer
CHR: Tom Wright, Director Human Resources
Web address: www.khriverside.com
**Control:** Corporation, Investor-owned (for-profit) **Service:** Acute long-term care
hospital

**Staffed Beds:** 40

## PETALUMA—Sonoma County

☒ **PETALUMA VALLEY HOSPITAL (050136)**, 400 North McDowell Boulevard,
Zip 94954–2366; tel. 707/778–1111, (Nonreporting) **A**1 10
Primary Contact: David Southerland, Vice President of Operations
CFO: Michel Riccioni, Chief Financial Officer
CIO: Patrick Wylie, Director Information Systems
Web address: www.stjosephhealth.org/About-Us/Facilities/Petaluma-Valley-Hospital.aspx
**Control:** Other not-for-profit (including NFP Corporation) **Service:** General
medical and surgical

**Staffed Beds:** 51

## PLACENTIA—Orange County

**PLACENTIA LINDA HOSPITAL** See Placentia-Linda Hospital

☒ **PLACENTIA-LINDA HOSPITAL (050589)**, 1301 North Rose Drive,
Zip 92870–3899; tel. 714/993–2000, (Nonreporting) **A**1 10 **F**3 12 17 18 20 22
29 30 34 35 40 41 45 49 50 51 56 57 59 60 64 65 68 70 74 75 77 79 81 82
84 85 86 87 93 97 107 108 110 111 114 119 126 130 132 135 144 145 146
148 149 154 156 **S** TENET Healthcare Corporation, Dallas, TX
Primary Contact: Bryan R. Rogers, Group Chief Executive Officer
COO: Dwayne Richardson, Chief Operating Officer
CFO: Kelsie Blackwell, Chief Financial Officer
CIO: Eleanor Laneaux, Director Information Systems
CHR: Michelle Miller, Chief Human Resources
CNO: Rhonda Sausedo, Chief Nursing Officer
Web address: www.placentialinda.com
**Control:** Corporation, Investor-owned (for-profit) **Service:** General medical and
surgical

**Staffed Beds:** 74 **Admissions:** 3081 **Census:** 29 **Outpatient Visits:** 53483
**Births:** 0 **Total Expense ($000):** 85683 **Payroll Expense ($000):** 34056
**Personnel:** 312

## PLACERVILLE—El Dorado County

**MARSHALL HOSPITAL CENTER** See Marshall Medical Center

☒ **MARSHALL MEDICAL CENTER (050254)**, 1100 Marshall Way,
Zip 95667–5722; tel. 530/622–1441, (Total facility includes 10 beds in nursing
home-type unit) (Nonreporting) **A**1 2 5 10 **F**3 5 8 11 12 13 15 18 20 28 29 30
31 34 35 40 43 46 49 50 51 54 56 57 59 62 64 65 70 74 75 76 77 78 79 81
84 85 87 93 97 100 104 107 108 110 111 115 116 117 119 126 127 128
130 131 135 146 147 148 149 154 156 **P**3
Primary Contact: Siri Nelson, Chief Executive Officer
COO: Shannon Truesdell, Chief Operating Officer
CFO: Laurie Eldridge, Chief Financial Officer
CMO: Rajiv Pathak, Chief of Staff
CIO: Mike Jones, Executive Director
CHR: Scott M Comer, Vice President Human Resources
CNO: Kathy Blair Krejci, Chief Nursing Officer
Web address: www.marshallmedical.org
**Control:** Other not-for-profit (including NFP Corporation) **Service:** General
medical and surgical

**Staffed Beds:** 119 **Admissions:** 5134 **Census:** 65 **Outpatient
Visits:** 419324 **Births:** 454 **Total Expense ($000):** 272985 **Payroll Expense
($000):** 98427 **Personnel:** 1262

## PLEASANTON—Alameda County

☒ **STANFORD HEALTH CARE - VALLEYCARE (050283)**, 5555 West Las
Positas Boulevard, Zip 94588–4000; tel. 925/847–3000, (Includes VALLEY
MEMORIAL, Mailing address: 1111 East Stanley Boulevard, Livermore, California,
Zip 94550–4115; tel. 925/447–7000) (Total facility includes 22 beds in nursing
home-type unit) **A**1 2 10 **F**3 8 11 12 13 15 17 18 20 22 24 26 28 29 30 31 34
35 40 45 47 49 50 53 54 57 59 60 64 68 70 72 74 75 76 77 78 79 81 82 85
89 93 107 110 111 116 119 126 128 130 131 132 144 146 147 155 156 157
**S** Stanford Health Care, Palo Alto, CA
Primary Contact: Tracey Lewis-Taylor, Chief Operating Officer
COO: Tracey Lewis-Taylor, Chief Operating Officer
CMO: David Svec, M.D., Chief Medical Officer
CIO: Bob Woods, Chief Information Officer
CHR: Chris Faber, Human Resources Analyst
Web address: www.valleycare.com
**Control:** Other not-for-profit (including NFP Corporation) **Service:** General
medical and surgical

**Staffed Beds:** 193 **Admissions:** 6855 **Census:** 94 **Outpatient
Visits:** 219841 **Births:** 1423 **Total Expense ($000):** 297860 **Payroll
Expense ($000):** 122692 **Personnel:** 1037

**VALLEYCARE MEDICAL CENTER** See Stanford Health Care - Valleycare

---

**Hospital, Medicare Provider Number, Address, Telephone, Approval, Facility, and Physician Codes, Health Care System**

★ American Hospital Association (AHA) membership ○ Healthcare Facilities Accreditation Program ⇑ Center for Improvement in Healthcare Quality Accreditation
☐ The Joint Commission accreditation ◇ DNV Healthcare Inc. accreditation △ Commission on Accreditation of Rehabilitation Facilities (CARF) accreditation

## POMONA—Los Angeles County

☒ △ **CASA COLINA HOSPITAL AND CENTERS FOR HEALTHCARE (050782)**, 255 East Bonita Avenue, Zip 91767–1923, Mailing Address: P.O. Box 6001, Zip 91769–6001; tel. 909/596–7733, (Nonreporting) **A**1 3 5 7 10 13 **F**2 3 15 18 26 28 29 30 34 35 37 38 44 45 46 48 49 50 53 54 56 57 58 59 64 68 70 74 75 79 81 82 85 86 87 90 91 92 93 95 96 97 104 107 108 110 111 115 118 119 126 130 131 132 134 146 147 148 149 154 158
Primary Contact: Felice L. Loverso, Ph.D., President and Chief Executive Officer
CFO: David Morony, Chief Financial Officer
CMO: Christopher Chalian, M.D., Medical Director
CIO: Ross Lesins, Chief Information Officer
CHR: Karen Du Pont, Chief Human Resource Officer
CNO: Kathryn Johnson, Chief Nursing Officer
Web address: www.casacolina.org
**Control**: Other not–for–profit (including NFP Corporation) **Service**: Rehabilitation

**Staffed Beds**: 99 **Admissions**: 2531 **Census**: 72 **Outpatient Visits**: 108786 **Births**: 0 **Total Expense ($000)**: 84992 **Payroll Expense ($000)**: 39447 **Personnel**: 591

**CASA COLINA HOSPITAL AND HEALTH SYSTEMS** See Casa Colina Hospital and Centers for Healthcare

☒ **POMONA VALLEY HOSPITAL MEDICAL CENTER (050231)**, 1798 North Garey Avenue, Zip 91767–2918; tel. 909/865–9500, (Nonreporting) **A**1 2 3 5 10 **F**3 11 13 15 17 18 20 22 24 26 28 29 30 31 34 35 40 41 43 45 46 47 49 50 51 53 54 55 57 58 59 60 61 63 64 68 69 70 72 74 75 76 77 78 79 81 84 85 87 89 92 93 107 108 110 111 114 115 116 117 118 119 120 121 123 124 126 129 130 131 132 134 145 146 147 148 149 154 156 **P**5 7
Primary Contact: Richard E. Yochum, FACHE, President and Chief Executive Officer
CFO: Michael Nelson, Executive Vice President and Chief Financial Officer
CMO: Kenneth Nakamoto, M.D., Vice President Medical Affairs
CIO: Kent Hoyos, Chief Information Officer
CHR: Ray Inge, Vice President Human Resources
CNO: Darlene Scafiddi, R.N., MSN, Vice President Nursing and Patient Care Services
Web address: www.pvhmc.org
**Control**: Other not–for–profit (including NFP Corporation) **Service**: General medical and surgical

**Staffed Beds**: 412 **Admissions**: 20164 **Census**: 244 **Outpatient Visits**: 438479 **Births**: 5560 **Total Expense ($000)**: 639239 **Payroll Expense ($000)**: 290360 **Personnel**: 2400

## PORTERVILLE—Tulare County

**PORTERVILLE DEVELOPMENTAL CENTER (050546)**, 26501 Avenue 140, Zip 93257–9109, Mailing Address: P.O. Box 2000, Zip 93258–2000; tel. 559/782–2222, (Nonreporting) **A**10
Primary Contact: Theresa Billeci, Executive Director
COO: Betty Davis, Director Administrative Services
CFO: Karen Warren, Fiscal Officer
CMO: Joseph Mendoza, M.D., Medical Director
CIO: Vincent Chandler, Director Information Services
CHR: Shawna Gregg, Director Human Resources
CNO: Tom Shelton, Coordinator of Nursing Services
Web address: www.pdc.dds.ca.gov
**Control**: State, Government, Nonfederal **Service**: Intellectual disabilities

**Staffed Beds**: 484

**SIERRA VIEW DISTRICT HOSPITAL** See Sierra View Medical Center

☐ **SIERRA VIEW MEDICAL CENTER (050261)**, 465 West Putnam Avenue, Zip 93257–3320; tel. 559/784–1110, (Total facility includes 35 beds in nursing home–type unit) (Nonreporting) **A**1 10 **F**3 8 13 15 20 22 29 30 31 34 35 40 45 49 54 57 59 60 65 68 70 72 75 76 78 79 81 83 84 85 87 89 93 107 108 110 111 114 115 118 119 120 121 123 124 130 132 135 144 146 147 148 149 156
Primary Contact: Donna J. Hefner, R.N., President and Chief Executive Officer
CFO: John Chivers, Senior Vice President Finance
CIO: Traci Follett, Director Clinical Informatics
CHR: Sharon Brown, Vice President Human Resources
Web address: www.sierra-view.com
**Control**: Hospital district or authority, Government, Nonfederal **Service**: General medical and surgical

**Staffed Beds**: 158 **Admissions**: 6227 **Census**: 99 **Outpatient Visits**: 171611 **Births**: 1467 **Total Expense ($000)**: 151788 **Payroll Expense ($000)**: 55884 **Personnel**: 857

## PORTOLA—Plumas County

**EASTERN PLUMAS HEALTH CARE (051300)**, 500 First Avenue, Zip 96122–9406; tel. 530/832–6500, (Nonreporting) **A**10 18
Primary Contact: Thomas P. Hayes, Chief Executive Officer
CFO: Katherine Pairish, Chief Financial Officer
CMO: Eric Bugna, M.D., Chief of Staff
CHR: Cathy Conant, Chief Human Resources and Personnel
Web address: www.ephc.org
**Control**: Hospital district or authority, Government, Nonfederal **Service**: General medical and surgical

**Staffed Beds**: 75

**EASTERN PLUMAS HEALTH CARE DISTRICT** See Eastern Plumas Health Care

## POWAY—San Diego County

☒ **PALOMAR MEDICAL CENTER POWAY (050636)**, 15615 Pomerado Road, Zip 92064–2460; tel. 858/613–4000, (Nonreporting) **A**1 10 **S** Palomar Health, Escondido, CA
Primary Contact: Cheryl Olson, Vice President
CIO: David Pape, Vice President, Information Technology
CHR: Brenda C Turner, Chief Human Resources Officer
Web address: www.pph.org
**Control**: Hospital district or authority, Government, Nonfederal **Service**: General medical and surgical

**Staffed Beds**: 201

**POMERADO HOSPITAL** See Palomar Medical Center Poway

## QUINCY—Plumas County

☐ **PLUMAS DISTRICT HOSPITAL (051326)**, 1065 Bucks Lake Road, Zip 95971–9599; tel. 530/283–2121, (Nonreporting) **A**1 5 10 18
Primary Contact: JoDee Tittle, Chief Executive Officer
CMO: Vincent Frantz, M.D., Chief of Staff
CIO: Brenda Compton, Manager Information Technology
CHR: Denise Harding, Director Human Resources
Web address: www.pdh.org
**Control**: Hospital district or authority, Government, Nonfederal **Service**: General medical and surgical

**Staffed Beds**: 25

## RANCHO CUCAMONGA—San Bernardino County

☒ **KINDRED HOSPITAL RANCHO (052049)**, 10841 White Oak Avenue, Zip 91730–3811; tel. 909/581–6400, (Nonreporting) **A**1 10 **S** Kindred Healthcare, Louisville, KY
Primary Contact: Lerenda Johnson, Interim Chief Executive Officer
COO: Jody Knox, Chief Operating Officer
Web address: www.khrancho.com
**Control**: Corporation, Investor–owned (for–profit) **Service**: Acute long–term care hospital

**Staffed Beds**: 55

**RANCHO SPECIALTY HOSPITAL** See Kindred Hospital Rancho

## RANCHO MIRAGE—Riverside County

☒ **EISENHOWER HEALTH (050573)**, 39000 Bob Hope Drive, Zip 92270–3221; tel. 760/340–3911, (Nonreporting) **A**1 2 3 5 8 10 **F**2 3 9 11 12 15 17 18 20 22 24 26 28 29 30 31 34 35 37 40 41 45 46 47 49 50 53 54 56 57 58 59 60 61 64 65 68 70 74 75 77 78 79 81 82 84 85 86 87 89 93 97 100 101 102 104 107 108 109 110 111 112 114 115 118 119 120 121 123 124 126 129 130 131 132 135 143 144 145 146 147 148 149 156 **P**3
Primary Contact: G Aubrey. Serfling, President and Chief Executive Officer
COO: Martin Massiello, Executive Vice President and Chief Operating Officer
CFO: Ken Wheat, Senior Vice President and Chief Financial Officer
CMO: Alan Williamson, M.D., Chief Medical Officer
CIO: David Perez, Vice President and Chief Information Officer
CHR: Liz Guignier, Vice President Human Resources
CNO: Ann R Mostofi, MSN, R.N., Vice President Patient Care and Chief Nursing Officer
Web address: www.emc.org
**Control**: Other not–for–profit (including NFP Corporation) **Service**: General medical and surgical

**Staffed Beds**: 345 **Admissions**: 19620 **Census**: 190 **Outpatient Visits**: 850483 **Births**: 0 **Total Expense ($000)**: 814338 **Payroll Expense ($000)**: 267343 **Personnel**: 3229

CA

**EISENHOWER MEDICAL CENTER** See Eisenhower Health

☐ **VIBRA REHABILITATION HOSPITAL RANCHO MIRAGE (053041)**, 70077 Ramon Road, Zip 92270–5201; tel. 760/671–3425, (Nonreporting) **A**1
Primary Contact: Joshua Bowie, Chief Executive Officer
Web address: www.https://www.vibrahealthcare.com/rancho-mirage/
**Control**: Corporation, Investor–owned (for–profit) **Service**: Rehabilitation

**Staffed Beds: 50**

### RED BLUFF—Tehama County

⊞ **ST. ELIZABETH COMMUNITY HOSPITAL (050042)**, 2550 Sister Mary Columba Drive, Zip 96080–4397; tel. 530/529–8000, (Nonreporting) **A**1 10 20 **S** CommonSpirit Health, Chicago, IL
Primary Contact: Jordan Wright, Chief Executive Officer
CFO: Kim Miranda, Chief Financial Officer
CMO: James DeSoto, M.D., Vice President Medical Affairs
CIO: Henry Niessink, Senior Manager Information Technology Systems
CHR: Denise Little, Director Human Resources
Web address: www.mercy.org
**Control**: Church operated, Nongovernment, not–for–profit **Service**: General medical and surgical

**Staffed Beds: 65**

### REDDING—Shasta County

**MERCY MEDICAL CENTER** See Mercy Medical Center Redding

⊞ **MERCY MEDICAL CENTER REDDING (050280)**, 2175 Rosaline Avenue, Zip 96001–2549, Mailing Address: P.O. Box 496009, Zip 96049–6009; tel. 530/225–6000, (Nonreporting) **A**1 2 3 5 10 **F**2 3 7 11 13 15 17 18 20 22 24 28 29 30 31 34 35 37 40 43 45 46 47 48 49 50 54 57 59 61 62 63 64 66 68 70 72 75 76 77 78 79 81 82 84 85 89 91 97 107 108 111 114 115 118 119 126 130 132 135 143 144 145 146 147 148 149 154 **S** CommonSpirit Health, Chicago, IL
Primary Contact: G. Todd. Smith, Chief Executive Officer
COO: Patrick Varga, Chief Operating Officer
CFO: Joseph D'Angina, Chief Financial Officer
CMO: James DeSoto, M.D., Vice President Medical Affairs
CIO: Henry Niessink, Regional Director Information Technology Services
CNO: Kimberly Shaw, Vice President Patient Care and Chief Nursing Executive
Web address: www.mercy.org
**Control**: Church operated, Nongovernment, not–for–profit **Service**: General medical and surgical

**Staffed Beds: 260 Admissions: 13996 Census: 172 Outpatient Visits: 159331 Births: 1942 Total Expense ($000): 466620 Payroll Expense ($000): 164048 Personnel: 1726**

**NORTHERN CALIFORNIA REHABILITATION HOSPITAL** See Vibra Hospital of Northern California

**PATIENTS' HOSPITAL OF REDDING (050697)**, 2900 Eureka Way, Zip 96001–0220; tel. 530/225–8700, (Nonreporting) **A**10
Primary Contact: Shari Lejsek, Administrator
CFO: Kim Needles, Manager Business Office
CMO: James Tate, M.D., Chief of Staff
CIO: Kim Cameron, Manager Health Information Services
CHR: Brenda Meline, Manager Human Resources
CNO: Diane Rieke, Director Patient Care Services
Web address: www.patientshospital.com
**Control**: Individual, Investor–owned (for–profit) **Service**: Surgical

**Staffed Beds: 10**

**REDDING MEDICAL CENTER** See Shasta Regional Medical Center

☐ **SHASTA REGIONAL MEDICAL CENTER (050764)**, 1100 Butte Street, Zip 96001–0853, Mailing Address: P.O. Box 496072, Zip 96049–6072; tel. 530/244–5400, (Nonreporting) **A**1 5 10 **S** Prime Healthcare, Ontario, CA
Primary Contact: Casey Fatch, Chief Executive Officer
COO: Becky Levy, Chief Operating Officer
CFO: Becky Levy, Chief Financial Officer
CMO: Marcia McCampbell, M.D., Chief Medical Officer
CIO: Tony VanBoekel, Director Information Systems
CHR: Andrew Torge, Director Human Resources
Web address: www.shastaregional.com
**Control**: Corporation, Investor–owned (for–profit) **Service**: General medical and surgical

**Staffed Beds: 100**

⊞ **VIBRA HOSPITAL OF NORTHERN CALIFORNIA (052047)**, 2801 Eureka Way, Zip 96001–0222; tel. 530/246–9000, (Nonreporting) **A**1 10 **S** Vibra Healthcare, Mechanicsburg, PA
Primary Contact: Emily DeFillipo, Chief Executive Officer
COO: Sheba Saelee, Chief Clinical Office and Chief Operating Officer
CFO: Rebecca Andrews, Chief Financial Officer
CMO: Nanda Kumar, M.D., Chief of Staff
CIO: Mark Cardenas, Director Plant Operations
Web address: www.norcalrehab.com
**Control**: Corporation, Investor–owned (for–profit) **Service**: Acute long–term care hospital

**Staffed Beds: 88**

### REDLANDS—San Bernardino County

⊞ **LOMA LINDA UNIVERSITY BEHAVIORAL MEDICINE CENTER (054093)**, 1710 Barton Road, Zip 92373–5304; tel. 909/558–9200, (Nonreporting) **A**1 3 5 10 **F**4 5 29 30 34 44 50 57 87 98 99 100 101 103 104 105 130 132 134 135 152 153 154 **S** Loma Linda University Adventist Health Sciences Center, Loma Linda, CA
Primary Contact: Edward Field, Administrator
COO: Ruthita J Fike, Chief Executive Officer
CMO: William Murdoch, M.D., Medical Director
CIO: Mark Zirkelback, Chief Information Officer
CHR: Mark Hubbard, Vice President Risk Management
CNO: Norie Lee Reyes Bencito Acaac, R.N., MS, Executive Director
Web address: www.llu.edu
**Control**: Other not–for–profit (including NFP Corporation) **Service**: Psychiatric

**Staffed Beds: 89 Admissions: 4074 Census: 71 Outpatient Visits: 48236 Births: 0 Total Expense ($000): 43815 Payroll Expense ($000): 21058 Personnel: 325**

⊞ **REDLANDS COMMUNITY HOSPITAL (050272)**, 350 Terracina Boulevard, Zip 92373–0742, Mailing Address: P.O. Box 3391, Zip 92373–0742; tel. 909/335–5500, (Total facility includes 16 beds in nursing home–type unit) (Nonreporting) **A**1 10 **F**3 11 13 15 20 28 29 30 31 34 35 40 45 46 47 49 54 57 59 62 63 64 65 66 70 72 74 75 76 77 78 79 81 82 84 85 87 93 96 97 98 102 104 105 107 108 110 111 115 117 119 120 121 123 126 128 130 132 143 146 147 148 154 **P**5
Primary Contact: James R. Holmes, President and Chief Executive Officer
CFO: Michelle Mok, Chief Financial Officer
CHR: Lisa Guzman, Human Resource Vice President
CNO: Lauren Spilsbury, R.N., MSN, Vice President for Patient Care Services
Web address: www.redlandshospital.org
**Control**: Other not–for–profit (including NFP Corporation) **Service**: General medical and surgical

**Staffed Beds: 229 Admissions: 12668 Census: 132 Outpatient Visits: 180700 Births: 2079 Total Expense ($000): 346023 Payroll Expense ($000): 120255 Personnel: 1565**

### REDWOOD CITY—San Mateo County

⊞ **KAISER PERMANENTE REDWOOD CITY MEDICAL CENTER (050541)**, 1100 Veterans Boulevard, Zip 94063–2087; tel. 650/299–2000, (Nonreporting) **A**1 3 5 10 **F**3 8 11 13 15 18 20 26 28 29 30 31 34 35 39 40 41 45 49 50 55 56 57 58 59 60 61 62 63 64 68 70 73 74 75 76 77 78 79 80 81 82 84 85 86 87 100 107 108 110 111 114 115 118 119 130 135 146 148 149 154 156 **S** Kaiser Foundation Hospitals, Oakland, CA
Primary Contact: Michelle Gaskill–Hames, R.N., Senior Vice President & Area Manager
COO: Sheila Gilson, R.N., Chief Operating Officer
CFO: Doug Reynolds, Area Finance Officer
CMO: William Firtch, M.D., Physician in Chief
CHR: Kimberly A Seitz, Area Human Resources Leader
CNO: Jodi B. Galli, R.N., Chief Nursing Officer
Web address: www.kaiserpermanente.org
**Control**: Other not–for–profit (including NFP Corporation) **Service**: General medical and surgical

**Staffed Beds: 153 Admissions: 8564 Census: 79 Outpatient Visits: 58604 Births: 2138 Personnel: 818**

**REDWOOD CITY MEDICAL CENTER** See Kaiser Permanente Redwood City Medical Center

**SEQUOIA DISTRICT HOSPITAL** See Sequoia Hospital

CA

---

**Hospital, Medicare Provider Number, Address, Telephone, Approval, Facility, and Physician Codes, Health Care System**

★ American Hospital Association (AHA) membership
☐ The Joint Commission accreditation
○ Healthcare Facilities Accreditation Program
◇ DNV Healthcare Inc. accreditation
⇑ Center for Improvement in Healthcare Quality Accreditation
△ Commission on Accreditation of Rehabilitation Facilities (CARF) accreditation

✠ **SEQUOIA HOSPITAL (050197)**, 170 Alameda De Las Pulgas, Zip 94062–2799; tel. 650/369–5811, (Nonreporting) **A**1 10 **F**11 12 13 15 18 20 22 24 26 28 29 30 31 32 34 35 37 40 45 46 49 50 53 57 59 60 64 68 70 74 75 76 77 78 79 81 84 86 87 92 93 94 107 108 110 111 115 118 119 120 121 123 124 126 130 132 135 146 147 149 154 156 **P**3 5 **S** CommonSpirit Health, Chicago, IL
Primary Contact: Bill Graham, President
CFO: Kim Osborn, Chief Financial Officer
CMO: Anita Chandrasena, M.D., Vice President Medical Affairs
CIO: Ian Vallely, Information Technology Site Leader
CHR: Linde Cheema, Vice President Human Resources
CNO: Sherie Ambrose, Chief Nurse Executive
Web address: www.sequoiahospital.org
**Control**: Other not-for-profit (including NFP Corporation) **Service**: General medical and surgical

**Staffed Beds**: 114 **Admissions**: 5470 **Census**: 55 **Outpatient Visits**: 72802 **Births**: 1293 **Total Expense ($000)**: 288831 **Payroll Expense ($000)**: 92151 **Personnel**: 730

### REEDLEY—Fresno County

✠ **ADVENTIST HEALTH REEDLEY (050192)**, 372 West Cypress Avenue, Zip 93654–2199; tel. 559/638–8155, (Nonreporting) **A**1 3 10 **S** Adventist Health, Roseville, CA
Primary Contact: Wayne Ferch, President and Chief Executive Officer
CFO: Teresa Jacques, Interim Chief Financial Officer
CMO: Todd Spencer, M.D., Chief Medical Staff
CIO: Valerie Alvarez, Executive Assistant
CHR: Ramona Alvarado, Interim Manager Human Resources
Web address: www.https://www.adventisthealth.org/reedley/
**Control**: Hospital district or authority, Government, Nonfederal **Service**: General medical and surgical

**Staffed Beds**: 49

**ADVENTIST MEDICAL CENTER-REEDLEY** See Adventist Health Reedley

### RESEDA—Los Angeles County

☐ **JOYCE EISENBERG-KEEFER MEDICAL CENTER (054147)**, 7150 Tampa Avenue, Zip 91335–3700; tel. 818/774–3000, (Total facility includes 239 beds in nursing home–type unit) (Nonreporting) **A**1 10 **F**2 3 29 30 34 35 39 50 53 56 63 65 68 69 74 75 77 82 84 98 103 128 130 132 143 146 148 149 154
Primary Contact: Molly Forrest, President and Chief Executive Officer
CNO: Haya Berci, Executive Director of Nursing
Web address: www.jha.org
**Control**: Other not-for-profit (including NFP Corporation) **Service**: Psychiatric

**Staffed Beds**: 249 **Admissions**: 412 **Census**: 240 **Outpatient Visits**: 0 **Births**: 0 **Total Expense ($000)**: 42024 **Payroll Expense ($000)**: 19191 **Personnel**: 410

### RICHMOND—Contra Costa County

**KAISER PERMANENTE RICHMOND MEDICAL CENTER** See Kaiser Permanente Oakland Medical Center, Oakland

**RICHMOND MEDICAL CENTER** See Kaiser Permanente Richmond Medical Center

### RIDGECREST—Kern County

⇑ **RIDGECREST COMMUNITY HOSPITAL** See Ridgecrest Regional Hospital

★ ⇑ **RIDGECREST REGIONAL HOSPITAL (051333)**, 1081 North China Lake Boulevard, Zip 93555–3130; tel. 760/446–3551, (Total facility includes 125 beds in nursing home–type unit) (Nonreporting) **A**10 18 21 **F**7 8 15 18 28 29 30 31 32 33 34 35 39 40 43 45 46 50 57 59 62 63 64 65 68 69 70 71 75 76 77 78 79 81 82 84 85 86 87 89 93 94 97 107 108 109 110 111 112 113 114 115 116 117 118 119 127 128 129 130 132 133 135 143 144 146 147 148 149 154 155
Primary Contact: James A. Suver, FACHE, Chief Executive Officer
CFO: John Chivers, Chief Financial Officer
CHR: Michelle Lemke, Administrator Human Resources and Support Services
Web address: www.rrh.org
**Control**: Other not-for-profit (including NFP Corporation) **Service**: General medical and surgical

**Staffed Beds**: 197 **Admissions**: 1869 **Census**: 81 **Outpatient Visits**: 197874 **Births**: 410 **Total Expense ($000)**: 126579 **Payroll Expense ($000)**: 45751

### RIVERSIDE—Riverside County

✠ **KAISER PERMANENTE RIVERSIDE MEDICAL CENTER (050686)**, 10800 Magnolia Avenue, Zip 92505–3000; tel. 951/353–2000, (Nonreporting) **A**1 3 5 10 **F**3 13 15 17 28 29 30 31 34 35 40 44 45 46 49 50 51 53 59 60 62 63 64 65 68 70 71 72 74 75 76 77 78 79 81 82 84 85 86 87 89 92 93 97 100 102 107 108 109 110 111 114 115 116 117 118 119 130 131 132 135 143 144 146 147 148 149 150 154 156 157 **P**6 **S** Kaiser Foundation Hospitals, Oakland, CA
Primary Contact: Vita M. Willett, Executive Director
COO: Robin D. Mackenroth, Chief Operating Officer
CFO: JiJi Abraham, Chief Financial Officer
CMO: Frank M. Flowers, M.D., Area Medical Director
CIO: Alfred T Velasquez, Area Information Officer
CHR: Michelle Skipper, Director Human Resources
CNO: Rosemary M Butler, R.N., MSN, Chief Nurse Executive
Web address: www.kaiserpermanente.org
**Control**: Other not-for-profit (including NFP Corporation) **Service**: General medical and surgical

**Staffed Beds**: 226 **Admissions**: 10194 **Census**: 118 **Outpatient Visits**: 297912 **Births**: 3287 **Personnel**: 1440

☐ **PACIFIC GROVE HOSPITAL (054130)**, 5900 Brockton Avenue, Zip 92506–1862; tel. 951/275–8400, (Nonreporting) **A**1 3 5 10 **S** Acadia Healthcare Company, Inc., Franklin, TN
Primary Contact: Nichol Sheffield, Chief Executive Officer
Web address: www.pacificgrovehospital.com
**Control**: Corporation, Investor–owned (for–profit) **Service**: Psychiatric

**Staffed Beds**: 68

**PARKVIEW COMM HOSP & MED CTR** See Parkview Community Hospital Medical Center

☐ **PARKVIEW COMMUNITY HOSPITAL MEDICAL CENTER (050102)**, 3865 Jackson Street, Zip 92503–3998; tel. 951/688–2211, (Nonreporting) **A**1 10 **S** AHMC & Healthcare, Inc., Alhambra, CA
Primary Contact: Steven Popkin, Chief Executive Officer
COO: Robert Brown, Chief Operating Officer
CFO: Nancy Wilson, Chief Financial Officer
CMO: Serafin Salazar, M.D., Chief of Staff
CIO: John Ciccarelli, Director Information Technology
CHR: Ilyssa DeCasperis, Director of Human Resources
Web address: www.pchmc.org
**Control**: Other not-for-profit (including NFP Corporation) **Service**: General medical and surgical

**Staffed Beds**: 193

**RIVERSIDE CENTER FOR BEHAVIORAL MEDICINE** See Pacific Grove Hospital

✠ **RIVERSIDE COMMUNITY HOSPITAL (050022)**, 4445 Magnolia Avenue, Zip 92501–4199; tel. 951/788–3000, (Nonreporting) **A**1 2 3 5 10 **S** HCA Healthcare, Nashville, TN
Primary Contact: Jacqueline DeSouza-Van Blaricum, President and Chief Executive Officer
COO: Daniel Bowers, Chief Operating Officer
CFO: Todd LaCaze, Chief Financial Officer
CMO: David Tito, M.D., President Medical Staff
CIO: Cae Swanger, Chief Information Officer
CHR: Tammy Kaminski, Vice President Human Relations
CNO: Annette June Greenwood, Chief Nursing Officer
Web address: www.riversidecommunityhospital.com
**Control**: Corporation, Investor–owned (for–profit) **Service**: General medical and surgical

**Staffed Beds**: 478

**RIVERSIDE MEDICAL CENTER** See Kaiser Permanente Riverside Medical Center

### ROSEMEAD—Los Angeles County

**ALHAMBRA HOSPITAL** See Bhc Alhambra Hospital

☐ **BHC ALHAMBRA HOSPITAL (054032)**, 4619 North Rosemead Boulevard, Zip 91770–1478, Mailing Address: P.O. Box 369, Zip 91770–0369; tel. 626/286–1191, (Nonreporting) **A**1 3 10 **S** Universal Health Services, Inc., King of Prussia, PA
Primary Contact: Peggy Minnick, R.N., Chief Executive Officer
CFO: Craig Corley, Chief Financial Officer
CMO: Wakelin McNeel, Medical Director
CIO: Debbie Irvin, Director Health Information Management
CHR: Venus Taylor, Director Human Resources
Web address: www.bhcalhambra.com
**Control**: Corporation, Investor–owned (for–profit) **Service**: Psychiatric

**Staffed Beds**: 97

**SILVER LAKE MEDICAL CENTER-INGLESIDE HOSPITAL** See La Downtown Medical Center, LLC -Ingleside Campus

**CA**

*Many Facility Codes have changed. Please refer to the AHA Guide Code Chart.*

**ROSEVILLE—Placer County**

☒ **KAISER PERMANENTE ROSEVILLE MEDICAL CENTER (050772)**, 1600 Eureka Road, Zip 95661–3027; tel. 916/784–4000, (Nonreporting) **A**1 2 3 5 10 **F**1 3 4 8 13 15 16 17 18 20 22 26 27 28 29 30 31 34 39 40 41 45 49 50 51 55 56 57 58 59 62 63 64 67 68 70 72 73 74 75 76 77 78 79 80 82 84 85 86 88 89 90 98 107 108 110 111 114 115 117 118 119 120 121 123 124 128 130 135 146 148 149 154 **P**6 **S** Kaiser Foundation Hospitals, Oakland, CA
Primary Contact: Gregory A. Adams, Chief Executive Officer and Chairman
Web address: www.kp.org
**Control:** Other not–for–profit (including NFP Corporation) **Service:** General medical and surgical

**Staffed Beds: 340 Admissions: 23524 Census: 251 Outpatient Visits: 201193 Births: 6709 Personnel: 4273**

**ROSEVILLE HOSPITAL** See Sutter Roseville Medical Center

**ROSEVILLE MEDICAL CENTER** See Kaiser Permanente Roseville Medical Center

☒ △ **SUTTER ROSEVILLE MEDICAL CENTER (050309)**, One Medical Plaza Drive, Zip 95661–3037; tel. 916/781–1000, (Nonreporting) **A**1 2 5 7 10 **S** Sutter Health, Sacramento, CA
Primary Contact: Brian Alexander, Chief Executive Officer
COO: Dionne Miller, Chief Operating Officer
CFO: Gary Hubschman, Administrative Director Finance
CMO: Stuart Bostrom, M.D., Director Medical Affairs
CIO: Nancy Turner, Director Communications
CHR: Lynda Dasaro, Director Human Resources
CNO: Barbara J Nelson, Ph.D., R.N., Chief Nursing Executive
Web address: www.sutterroseville.org
**Control:** Other not–for–profit (including NFP Corporation) **Service:** General medical and surgical

**Staffed Beds: 328**

**SACRAMENTO—Sacramento County**

**BHC HERITAGE OAKS HOSPITAL** See Heritage Oaks Hospital

**BHC SIERRA VISTA HOSPITAL** See Sierra Vista Hospital

☐ **HERITAGE OAKS HOSPITAL (054104)**, 4250 Auburn Boulevard, Zip 95841–4164; tel. 916/489–3336, (Nonreporting) **A**1 3 5 10 **S** Universal Health Services, Inc., King of Prussia, PA
Primary Contact: Shawn Silva, Chief Executive Officer
CFO: Art Wong, Chief Financial Officer
CMO: Joseph Sison, M.D., Medical Director
CHR: Lisa Myers, Director Human Resources
Web address: www.heritageoakshospital.com
**Control:** Corporation, Investor–owned (for–profit) **Service:** Psychiatric

**Staffed Beds: 120**

☒ **KAISER PERMANENTE SACRAMENTO MEDICAL CENTER (050425)**, 2025 Morse Avenue, Zip 95825–2100; tel. 916/973–5000, (Nonreporting) **A**1 2 3 5 10 **F**3 11 15 17 18 20 26 30 34 39 40 41 45 46 47 49 56 60 63 64 68 70 74 75 78 79 80 81 82 84 85 86 87 100 107 108 110 111 114 115 118 119 120 121 123 124 130 135 146 149 154 **P**6 **S** Kaiser Foundation Hospitals, Oakland, CA
Primary Contact: Sandy Sharon, Senior Vice President and Area Manager
CFO: Jim Eldridge, Area Financial Officer
CMO: Chris Palkowski, M.D., Physician in Chief
CIO: Philip Fasano, Chief Information Officer
CHR: Gay Westfall, Senior Vice President Human Resources
Web address: www.kp.org
**Control:** Other not–for–profit (including NFP Corporation) **Service:** General medical and surgical

**Staffed Beds: 200 Admissions: 12176 Census: 139 Outpatient Visits: 265909 Births: 0 Personnel: 3408**

☒ **KAISER PERMANENTE SOUTH SACRAMENTO MEDICAL CENTER (050674)**, 6600 Bruceville Road, Zip 95823–4691; tel. 916/688–2430, (Nonreporting) **A**1 3 5 10 **F**3 11 12 13 15 18 20 22 26 30 31 34 35 37 39 40 41 43 44 45 49 50 51 56 60 62 63 64 68 70 73 74 75 76 78 79 81 82 84 85 86 87 100 107 108 110 111 114 115 117 118 126 130 135 144 146 149 150 154 **P**6 **S** Kaiser Foundation Hospitals, Oakland, CA
Primary Contact: Patricia M. Rodriguez, Senior Vice President and Area Manager
CFO: Kevin L Smith, Area Finance Officer
CIO: Michelle Odell, Director of Public Affairs
CHR: James Kevin Peterson, Human Resources Leader
CNO: Terri Owensby, R.N., Chief Nursing Executive
Web address: www.kp.org
**Control:** Other not–for–profit (including NFP Corporation) **Service:** General medical and surgical

**Staffed Beds: 241 Admissions: 15386 Census: 159 Outpatient Visits: 222194 Births: 2860 Personnel: 3301**

☒ △ **MERCY GENERAL HOSPITAL (050017)**, 4001 'J' Street, Zip 95819–3600; tel. 916/453–4545, (Nonreporting) **A**1 2 3 5 7 10 **F**3 8 11 13 15 17 18 20 22 24 26 28 30 31 34 35 36 37 38 39 40 44 45 46 47 48 49 50 51 53 56 57 58 59 61 62 63 64 66 67 68 70 74 75 76 77 78 79 81 82 84 85 86 87 90 91 92 93 94 96 100 102 107 108 111 114 115 118 119 124 126 130 131 132 135 141 142 143 145 146 149 154 157 **P**3 5 **S** CommonSpirit Health, Chicago, IL
Primary Contact: Edmundo Castaneda, President
COO: Clare Lee, Chief Operating Officer
CFO: Bonnie Jenkins, Chief Financial Officer
CHR: Cyndi Kirch, Vice President Human Resources
CNO: Allison Cotterill, Chief Nursing Officer
Web address: www.mercygeneral.org
**Control:** Other not–for–profit (including NFP Corporation) **Service:** General medical and surgical

**Staffed Beds: 277 Admissions: 14657 Census: 162 Outpatient Visits: 103033 Births: 973 Total Expense ($000): 598272 Payroll Expense ($000): 200782 Personnel: 1606**

**METHODIST HOSPITAL** See Methodist Hospital of Sacramento

☒ **METHODIST HOSPITAL OF SACRAMENTO (050590)**, 7500 Hospital Drive, Zip 95823–5477; tel. 916/423–3000, (Total facility includes 171 beds in nursing home–type unit) (Nonreporting) **A**1 3 5 10 **F**3 8 12 13 17 29 30 34 35 40 44 45 48 49 50 51 57 60 66 70 72 74 75 76 79 81 85 87 91 92 93 96 97 107 111 114 115 119 128 130 132 146 147 148 149 154 **P**3 **S** CommonSpirit Health, Chicago, IL
Primary Contact: Phyllis Baltz, Chief Executive Officer
COO: Anita J Kennedy, Vice President Operations
CFO: Bonnie Jenkins, Chief Financial Officer
CMO: Amir Sweha, M.D., Vice President Medical Administration
CHR: Cyndi Kirch, Vice President Human Resources
CNO: Martina Evans-Harrison, R.N., MSN, Chief Nurse Executive
Web address: www.methodistsacramento.org
**Control:** Other not–for–profit (including NFP Corporation) **Service:** General medical and surgical

**Staffed Beds: 329 Admissions: 10126 Census: 247 Outpatient Visits: 89488 Births: 1490 Total Expense ($000): 312825 Payroll Expense ($000): 127495 Personnel: 758**

**SACRAMENTO MEDICAL CENTER** See Kaiser Permanente Sacramento Medical Center

☐ **SHRINERS HOSPITALS FOR CHILDREN-NORTHERN CALIFORNIA (053311)**, 2425 Stockton Boulevard, Zip 95817–2215; tel. 916/453–2000, (Nonreporting) **A**1 3 5 10 **S** Shriners Hospitals for Children, Tampa, FL
Primary Contact: Margaret Bryan, Administrator
COO: Margaret Bryan, Administrator
CFO: William Dalby, Director Fiscal Services
CIO: John Bevel, Manager Information Systems
CHR: Deborah Rubens, Director Human Resources
Web address: www.shrinershospitalsforchildren.org/Hospitals/Locations/NorthernCalifornia.aspx
**Control:** Other not–for–profit (including NFP Corporation) **Service:** Children's general medical and surgical

**Staffed Beds: 60**

**SHRINERS HOSPS FOR CHILD** See Shriners Hospitals for Children-Northern California

---

**Hospital, Medicare Provider Number, Address, Telephone, Approval, Facility, and Physician Codes, Health Care System**

★ American Hospital Association (AHA) membership
☐ The Joint Commission accreditation
○ Healthcare Facilities Accreditation Program
◇ DNV Healthcare Inc. accreditation
⇑ Center for Improvement in Healthcare Quality Accreditation
△ Commission on Accreditation of Rehabilitation Facilities (CARF) accreditation

☐ **SIERRA VISTA HOSPITAL (054087)**, 8001 Bruceville Road, Zip 95823–2329; tel. 916/288–0300, (Nonreporting) **A**1 10 **S** Universal Health Services, Inc., King of Prussia, PA
Primary Contact: Mike Zauner, Chief Executive Officer
COO: Ixel Morell, Chief Operating Officer
CFO: Nicole Samuel, Chief Financial Officer
CMO: Alok Banga, M.D., Medical Director
CNO: Gwen Hubbard, Chief Nursing Officer
Web address: www.sierravistahospital.com
**Control**: Corporation, Investor–owned (for–profit) **Service**: Psychiatric

**Staffed Beds**: 171

**SOUTH SACRAMENTO MEDICAL CENTER** See Kaiser Permanente South Sacramento Medical Center

⊞ **SUTTER CENTER FOR PSYCHIATRY (054096)**, 7700 Folsom Boulevard, Zip 95826–2608; tel. 916/386–3000, (Nonreporting) **A**1 3 10 **S** Sutter Health, Sacramento, CA
Primary Contact: John W. Boyd, PsyD, Chief Executive Officer
CFO: Pamela Ansley, Director Finance
CMO: Cindy Thygeson, M.D., Director Medical Affairs
CHR: Kristin Daniels, Manager Human Resources
Web address: www.sutterpsychiatry.org
**Control**: Other not–for–profit (including NFP Corporation) **Service**: Psychiatric

**Staffed Beds**: 71

**SUTTER COMMUNITY HOSPITALS** See Sutter Medical Center, Sacramento

⊞ **SUTTER MEDICAL CENTER, SACRAMENTO (050108)**, 2801 'L' Street, Zip 95816–5680; tel. 916/454–3333, (Includes SUTTER CHILDREN'S CENTER, Mailing address: 5151 F Street, Sacramento, California, Zip 95819–3223; tel. 800/478–8837; SUTTER GENERAL HOSPITAL, Mailing address: 2801 'L' Street, Sacramento, California, Zip 95816; tel. 916/454–2222), (Nonreporting) **A**1 2 3 5 10 **S** Sutter Health, Sacramento, CA
Primary Contact: David Cheney, Chief Executive Officer
CFO: Richard SooHoo, Chief Financial Officer
CMO: Muhammed Afzal, M.D., Chief of Staff
CIO: Jim Mills, Regional Director Information Technology
CHR: Colleen Peschel, Director Human Resources
CNO: Marchelle M McGriff, Chief Nursing Executive
Web address: www.sutterhealth.org
**Control**: Other not–for–profit (including NFP Corporation) **Service**: General medical and surgical

**Staffed Beds**: 523

**UNIV OF CALIF, DAVIS MED CTR** See University of California, Davis Medical Center

⊞ **UNIVERSITY OF CALIFORNIA, DAVIS MEDICAL CENTER (050599)**, 2315 Stockton Boulevard, Zip 95817–2282; tel. 916/734–2011, (Includes UNIVERSITY OF CALIFORNIA DAVIS CHILDREN'S HOSPITAL, Mailing address: 2315 Stockton Boulevard, Sacramento, California, Zip 95817–2201; tel. 800/282–3284), (Nonreporting) **A**1 2 3 5 8 10 **F**3 5 6 8 9 11 12 13 15 16 17 18 19 20 21 22 23 24 25 26 27 28 29 30 31 32 34 35 36 37 38 39 40 41 43 44 45 46 47 48 49 50 51 53 54 55 56 57 58 59 60 61 62 63 64 65 66 68 70 72 73 74 75 76 77 78 79 81 82 83 84 85 86 87 88 89 90 91 92 93 94 95 96 97 99 100 101 102 103 104 107 108 110 111 114 115 116 117 118 119 120 121 123 124 126 129 130 131 132 134 135 138 141 145 146 147 148 149 150 153 154 156 157 **P**6 **S** University of California Systemwide Administration, Oakland, CA
Primary Contact: Brad Simmons, Interim Chief Executive Officer
COO: Brad Simmons, Chief Operating Officer
CFO: Timothy Maurice, Chief Financial Officer
CMO: J. Douglas Kirk, M.D., Chief Medical Officer
CIO: John Cook, Interim Chief Information Officer
CHR: Stephen Chilcott, Associate Director Human Resources
CNO: Toby Marsh, MSN, R.N., Interim Chief Patient Care Services Officer
Web address: www.ucdmc.ucdavis.edu
**Control**: Other not–for–profit (including NFP Corporation) **Service**: General medical and surgical

**Staffed Beds**: 617 **Admissions**: 31819 **Census**: 529 **Outpatient Visits**: 1157757 **Births**: 1410 **Total Expense ($000)**: 2352197 **Payroll Expense ($000)**: 937657 **Personnel**: 8882

**SAINT HELENA—Napa County**

⊞ **ADVENTIST HEALTH ST. HELENA (050013)**, 10 Woodland Road, Zip 94574–9554; tel. 707/963–3611, (Nonreporting) **A**1 10 **F**3 8 15 17 18 20 22 24 26 28 29 30 31 34 35 36 37 40 45 47 50 51 53 56 57 58 59 60 64 65 70 74 75 76 77 78 79 81 82 84 85 86 87 92 97 98 100 101 102 103 104 105 107 108 110 111 115 117 119 120 121 126 130 131 135 146 147 148 153 154 156 157 **S** Adventist Health, Roseville, CA
Primary Contact: Steven Herber, M.D., FACS, President and Chief Executive Officer
COO: Hal Chilton, Senior Vice President and Chief Operating Officer
CMO: Timothy Lyons, M.D., Chief Medical Officer
CIO: David Noll, Director
CHR: Audrey Barrall, Director Human Resources
CNO: Nia Lendaris, MS, R.N., Regional Vice President Patient Care
Web address: www.sthelenahospital.org
**Control**: Church operated, Nongovernment, not–for–profit **Service**: General medical and surgical

**Staffed Beds**: 81 **Admissions**: 4526 **Census**: 67 **Outpatient Visits**: 44080 **Births**: 207

**ST. HELENA HOSPITAL NAPA VALLEY** See Adventist Health St. Helena

**SALINAS—Monterey County**

⊞ △ **NATIVIDAD MEDICAL CENTER (050248)**, 1441 Constitution Boulevard, Zip 93906–3100, Mailing Address: P.O. Box 81611, Zip 93912–1611; tel. 831/647–7611, (Nonreporting) **A**1 3 5 7 10
Primary Contact: Gary Gray, D.O., Chief Executive Officer
CMO: Craig Walls, M.D., Ph.D., Chief Medical Officer
CIO: Ari Entin, Chief Information Officer
CHR: Lawanda Janine Bouyea, Director Human Resources
Web address: www.natividad.com
**Control**: County, Government, Nonfederal **Service**: General medical and surgical

**Staffed Beds**: 157

**SALINAS VALLEY MEM HOSPITAL** See Salinas Valley Memorial Healthcare System

⊞ **SALINAS VALLEY MEMORIAL HEALTHCARE SYSTEM (050334)**, 450 East Romie Lane, Zip 93901–4098; tel. 831/757–4333, (Nonreporting) **A**1 2 10 19 **F**3 7 9 13 15 17 18 20 22 24 26 28 29 30 31 34 35 37 40 45 46 49 50 51 54 55 57 58 59 64 65 68 70 72 74 75 76 77 78 79 81 84 85 86 87 89 93 96 102 107 108 110 111 114 115 118 119 124 126 127 129 130 132 146 148 149 156
Primary Contact: Pete Delgado, President and Chief Executive Officer
COO: Henry Ornelas, Chief Operating Officer
CFO: Augustine Lopez, Chief Financial Officer
CMO: Allen Radner, M.D., Chief Medical Officer
CIO: Audrey Parks, Chief Information Officer
CHR: Michelle Childs, Chief Human Resources Officer
CNO: Christie McGuire, R.N., Chief Nursing Officer
Web address: www.svmh.com
**Control**: Hospital district or authority, Government, Nonfederal **Service**: General medical and surgical

**Staffed Beds**: 263 **Admissions**: 11145 **Census**: 127 **Outpatient Visits**: 121725 **Births**: 1718 **Total Expense ($000)**: 469891 **Payroll Expense ($000)**: 207726 **Personnel**: 1640

**SAN ANDREAS—Calaveras County**

⊞ **MARK TWAIN MEDICAL CENTER (051332)**, 768 Mountain Ranch Road, Zip 95249–9998; tel. 209/754–3521, (Nonreporting) **A**1 10 18 **F**3 8 15 29 30 34 35 40 45 50 57 59 68 69 70 77 78 79 81 85 87 93 97 100 107 110 111 115 119 127 130 133 146 147 149 154 157 **P**6 **S** CommonSpirit Health, Chicago, IL
Primary Contact: Doug Archer, President and Chief Executive Officer
CFO: Jacob Lewis, Chief Financial Officer
CHR: Nancy Vargas, Director Human Resources
Web address: www.marktwainhospital.com
**Control**: Church operated, Nongovernment, not–for–profit **Service**: General medical and surgical

**Staffed Beds**: 25 **Admissions**: 917 **Census**: 9 **Outpatient Visits**: 76803 **Births**: 0 **Total Expense ($000)**: 69335 **Payroll Expense ($000)**: 27793 **Personnel**: 367

**MARK TWAIN ST. JOSEPH'S HOSPITAL** See Mark Twain Medical Center

**SAN BERNARDINO—San Bernardino County**

☒ △ **BALLARD REHABILITATION HOSPITAL (053037)**, 1760 West 16th Street, Zip 92411–1160; tel. 909/473–1200, (Nonreporting) **A**1 7 10 **S** Vibra Healthcare, Mechanicsburg, PA
Primary Contact: Mary Miles. Hunt, Chief Executive Officer
CMO: Van Chen, M.D., Medical Director
CNO: Chris Bauman, Director of Nursing
Web address: www.ballardrehab.com
**Control:** Corporation, Investor–owned (for–profit) **Service:** Rehabilitation

**Staffed Beds:** 60

☒ **COMMUNITY HOSPITAL OF SAN BERNARDINO (050089)**, 1805 Medical Center Drive, Zip 92411–1214; tel. 909/887–6333, (Nonreporting) **A**1 10 **S** CommonSpirit Health, Chicago, IL
Primary Contact: June Collison, President
COO: Victoria Selby MHA, BSNVice President, Ancillary and Support Services
CFO: Dave Evans, Chief Financial Officer
CMO: Andrew Fragen, M.D., Chief Medical Officer
CIO: James Borrenpohl, Market Site Director
CHR: Deena Marano, Human Resources Director
CNO: Roz Nolan, Interim Chief Nursing Officer
Web address: www.dignityhealth.org/san-bernardino
**Control:** Other not–for–profit (including NFP Corporation) **Service:** General medical and surgical

**Staffed Beds:** 379

**ROBERT H. BALLARD REHABILITATION HOSPITAL** See Ballard Rehabilitation Hospital

**SAN BERNARDINO COMMUNITY HOSP** See Community Hospital of San Bernardino

☒ **ST. BERNARDINE MEDICAL CENTER (050129)**, 2101 North Waterman Avenue, Zip 92404–4855; tel. 909/883–8711, (Nonreporting) **A**1 3 5 10 **S** CommonSpirit Health, Chicago, IL
Primary Contact: Douglas V. Kleam, President
CFO: Paul Steinke, Chief Financial Officer
CMO: Betty Daniels, M.D., Chief of Staff
CIO: James Croker, Director Information Systems
CHR: Dee Webb, Vice President Human Resources
Web address: www.stbernardinemedicalcenter.com
**Control:** Other not–for–profit (including NFP Corporation) **Service:** General medical and surgical

**Staffed Beds:** 342

**SAN DIEGO—San Diego County**

☐ **ALVARADO HOSPITAL MEDICAL CENTER (050757)**, 6655 Alvarado Road, Zip 92120–5208; tel. 619/287–3270, (Nonreporting) **A**1 10 **S** Prime Healthcare, Ontario, CA
Primary Contact: Robin Gomez, R.N., MSN, Administrator
CMO: Larry Emdur, D.O., Chief Medical Officer
CIO: Wayne Bartlett, Director Information Systems
CHR: Sara Turner, Director Human Resources
CNO: Peggy Jezsu, Chief Nursing Officer
Web address: www.alvaradohospital.com
**Control:** Corporation, Investor–owned (for–profit) **Service:** General medical and surgical

**Staffed Beds:** 137

**ALVARADO MEDICAL CENTER** See Alvarado Hospital Medical Center

☐ **AURORA BEHAVIORAL HEALTHCARE SAN DIEGO (054095)**, 11878 Avenue of Industry, Zip 92128–3490; tel. 858/487–3200, (Nonreporting) **A**1 10 **S** Signature Healthcare Services, Corona, CA
Primary Contact: Alain Azcona, Chief Executive Officer
COO: Barbara Kennison, Director Clinical Services
CFO: Gene Fantano, Chief Financial Officer
CMO: Thomas Flanagan, M.D., Medical Director
CIO: Alain Azcona, Director Business Development
CHR: Susan Haas, Director Human Resources
Web address: www.sandiego.aurorabehavioral.com/
**Control:** Corporation, Investor–owned (for–profit) **Service:** Psychiatric

**Staffed Beds:** 80

**AURORA SAN DIEGO HOSPITAL** See Aurora Behavioral Healthcare San Diego

☒ **KAISER PERMANENTE SAN DIEGO MEDICAL CENTER (050515)**, 4647 Zion Avenue, Zip 92120–2507; tel. 619/528–5000, (Includes KAISER PERMANENTE SAN DIEGO MEDICAL CENTER, Mailing address: 9455 Clairemont Mesa Boulevard, San Diego, California, Zip 92123–1297; tel. 800/282–3284; Jane Finley, Senior Vice President and Area Manager), (Nonreporting) **A**1 3 5 10 **F**3 6 8 9 11 13 15 18 19 26 28 29 30 31 32 34 35 37 38 40 41 42 45 46 47 48 49 50 51 54 56 57 60 61 64 65 68 70 72 74 75 76 77 78 79 81 82 84 85 86 87 89 94 97 100 102 104 107 108 110 111 114 115 116 117 118 119 126 130 131 143 146 148 149 154 156 157 **S** Kaiser Foundation Hospitals, Oakland, CA
Primary Contact: Jane Finley, Senior Vice President & Area Manager
COO: Sam Totah, Chief Operating Officer
CFO: Lynette Seid, Area Chief Financial Officer
CMO: Paul E Bernstein, M.D., Area Medical Director
CIO: Laura Sullivant, Area Chief Information Officer
CHR: Jocelyn A. Herrera, Human Resources Director
CNO: Anne Marie Watkins, R.N., Chief Nurse Executive
Web address: www.kaiserpermanente.org
**Control:** Other not–for–profit (including NFP Corporation) **Service:** General medical and surgical

**Staffed Beds:** 563 **Admissions:** 24936 **Census:** 270 **Outpatient Visits:** 233416 **Births:** 4951 **Personnel:** 3861

☒ **KINDRED HOSPITAL-SAN DIEGO (052036)**, 1940 El Cajon Boulevard, Zip 92104–1096; tel. 619/543–4500, (Nonreporting) **A**1 10 **F**1 3 29 107 119 130 148 **S** Kindred Healthcare, Louisville, KY
Primary Contact: Kerry Ashment, Chief Executive Officer
CMO: Davies Wong, M.D., Medical Director
CHR: Jody Dewen Moore, District Director Human Resources
CNO: Maureen Bodine, Chief Clinical Officer
Web address: www.kindredsandiego.com
**Control:** Corporation, Investor–owned (for–profit) **Service:** Acute long–term care hospital

**Staffed Beds:** 60 **Admissions:** 511 **Census:** 51 **Outpatient Visits:** 0 **Births:** 0 **Total Expense ($000):** 37999 **Payroll Expense ($000):** 17442 **Personnel:** 151

**MESA VISTA HOSPITAL** See Sharp Mesa Vista Hospital

**NAVAL MEDICAL CENTER** See Naval Medical Center San Diego

☒ **NAVAL MEDICAL CENTER SAN DIEGO**, 34800 Bob Wilson Drive, Zip 92134–5000; tel. 619/532–6400, (Nonreporting) **A**1 2 3 5 **S** Bureau of Medicine and Surgery, Department of the Navy, Falls Church, VA
Primary Contact: Captain Joel A. Roos, Commanding Officer
CFO: CommanderThomas J. Piner, Director for Resources Management
CIO: Lieutenant CommanderRyan Jarmer, Chief Information Officer
Web address: www.med.navy.mil/sites/nmcsd/Pages/default.aspx
**Service:** General medical and surgical

**Staffed Beds:** 285

☐ **RADY CHILDREN'S HOSPITAL - SAN DIEGO (053303)**, 3020 Childrens Way, Zip 92123–4223; tel. 858/576–1700, (Total facility includes 38 beds in nursing home–type unit) (Nonreporting) **A**1 3 5 10 **F**1 3 4 7 8 9 10 11 16 17 19 20 21 22 23 24 25 26 27 28 29 30 31 32 34 35 36 38 39 40 41 43 45 46 47 48 50 51 54 55 57 58 59 60 61 62 63 64 65 66 67 68 70 71 72 73 74 75 77 78 79 80 81 82 83 84 85 86 87 88 89 90 91 92 93 94 98 99 100 101 102 104 107 108 111 114 115 118 119 122 124 128 129 130 131 132 133 134 135 136 137 138 143 144 145 146 148 149 150 153 154 155 156 **P**3 5
Primary Contact: Patricio A. Frias, M.D., President and Chief Executive Officer
COO: Meg Norton, Executive Vice President and Chief Administrative Officer
CFO: Roger Roux, Chief Financial Officer
CMO: Irvin A Kaufman, M.D., Chief Medical Officer
CIO: Albert Oriol, Vice President Information Management and Chief Information Officer
CHR: Mamoon Syed, Vice President Human Resources
CNO: Mary Fagan, MSN, R.N., Chief Nursing Officer
Web address: www.rchsd.org
**Control:** Other not–for–profit (including NFP Corporation) **Service:** Children's general medical and surgical

**Staffed Beds:** 524 **Admissions:** 20320 **Census:** 308 **Outpatient Visits:** 543939 **Births:** 0 **Total Expense ($000):** 1211 **Payroll Expense ($000):** 400 **Personnel:** 4243

**RADY CHILDREN'S HOSPITAL AND HEALTH CENTER** See Rady Children's Hospital - San Diego

---

**Hospital, Medicare Provider Number, Address, Telephone, Approval, Facility, and Physician Codes, Health Care System**

★ American Hospital Association (AHA) membership
☐ The Joint Commission accreditation
○ Healthcare Facilities Accreditation Program
◇ DNV Healthcare Inc. accreditation
⇑ Center for Improvement in Healthcare Quality Accreditation
△ Commission on Accreditation of Rehabilitation Facilities (CARF) accreditation

☐ **SAN DIEGO COUNTY PSYCHIATRIC HOSPITAL (054114)**, 3853 Rosecrans Street, Zip 92110–3115, Mailing Address: P.O. Box 85524, Zip 92186–5524; tel. 619/692–8211, (Nonreporting) **A**1 10
Primary Contact: Izabela Karmach, R.N., Administrator
COO: Izabela Karmach, R.N., Administrator
CFO: Raul J Loyo-Rodriguez, Administrative Analyst III
CMO: Michael Krelstein, M.D., Medical Director
CIO: Linda Cannon, Chief Medical Records Services
CHR: Francisco Puentes, Human Resource Officer
Web address: www.sdcounty.ca.gov
**Control:** County, Government, Nonfederal **Service:** Psychiatric

**Staffed Beds:** 357

**SAN DIEGO MEDICAL CENTER** See Kaiser Permanente San Diego Medical Center

☒ **SCRIPPS MERCY HOSPITAL (050077)**, 4077 Fifth Avenue, Zip 92103–2105; tel. 619/294–8111, (Includes SCRIPPS MERCY HOSPITAL CHULA VISTA, Mailing address: 435 'H' Street, Chula Vista, California, Zip 91912–6617, P O Box 1537, Zip 91910–1537, tel. 619/691–7000; Thomas A Gammiere, Chief Executive Officer), (Nonreporting) **A**1 3 5 10 19 **F**3 8 11 12 13 14 15 17 18 20 22 24 26 28 29 30 31 32 34 35 39 40 43 44 45 46 49 50 51 54 56 58 59 61 64 65 66 68 70 73 74 75 76 77 78 79 81 82 84 85 86 87 92 93 97 98 100 101 102 103 107 108 110 111 114 115 119 126 130 132 134 135 141 146 147 148 154 156 157 **S** Scripps Health, San Diego, CA
Primary Contact: Thomas A. Gammiere, Chief Executive, Senior Vice President
CFO: Edward Turk, Vice President Finance
CMO: Davis Cracroft, M.D., Senior Director Medical Affairs
CIO: Drexel DeFord, Chief Information Officer
Web address: www.scrippshealth.org
**Control:** Other not–for–profit (including NFP Corporation) **Service:** General medical and surgical

**Staffed Beds:** 392 **Admissions:** 31036 **Census:** 386 **Outpatient Visits:** 175767 **Births:** 3754 **Total Expense ($000):** 769037 **Payroll Expense ($000):** 302578 **Personnel:** 3487

**SCRIPPS MERCY MEDICAL CENTER** See Scripps Mercy Hospital

☒ **SELECT SPECIALTY HOSPITAL - SAN DIEGO (052044)**, 555 Washington Street, Zip 92103–2294; tel. 619/260–8300, (Nonreporting) **A**1 10 **S** Select Medical Corporation, Mechanicsburg, PA
Primary Contact: Yameeka Jones, Chief Executive Officer
CFO: Mike Gonzales, Chief Financial Officer
CMO: John Fox, M.D., Medical Director
CHR: Tania Khalique, Director Human Resources
Web address: www.vhsandiego.com/
**Control:** Corporation, Investor–owned (for–profit) **Service:** Acute long–term care hospital

**Staffed Beds:** 80

**SHARP MARY BIRCH HOSPITAL FOR WOMEN** See Sharp Mary Birch Hospital for Women and Newborns

★ **SHARP MARY BIRCH HOSPITAL FOR WOMEN AND NEWBORNS (050722)**, 3003 Health Center Drive, Zip 92123–2700; tel. 858/939–3400, (Nonreporting) **A**10 **F**3 11 13 29 30 31 34 36 44 50 58 59 64 65 68 72 73 75 76 77 80 81 85 86 87 119 126 130 132 146 147 148 149 **S** Sharp HealthCare, San Diego, CA
Primary Contact: Trisha Khaleghi, Senior Vice President and Chief Executive Officer
CFO: Kari Cornicelli, Chief Financial Officer
CMO: Colleen McNally, M.D., Chief Medical Officer
CHR: Connie Duquette, Director Human Resources
CNO: Maria Carmen Colombo, R.N., Chief Nursing Officer
Web address: www.sharp.com
**Control:** Other not–for–profit (including NFP Corporation) **Service:** General medical and surgical

**Staffed Beds:** 206 **Admissions:** 9970 **Census:** 137 **Outpatient Visits:** 17115 **Births:** 7741 **Total Expense ($000):** 197747 **Payroll Expense ($000):** 86402 **Personnel:** 792

**SHARP MEMORIAL HOSP** See Sharp Memorial Hospital

☒ △ **SHARP MEMORIAL HOSPITAL (050100)**, 7901 Frost Street, Zip 92123–2701; tel. 858/939–3400, (Nonreporting) **A**1 2 7 10 **F**3 11 12 15 17 18 20 22 24 26 28 29 30 31 34 35 36 40 43 44 45 46 49 50 54 55 56 57 58 59 62 64 65 68 70 74 75 77 78 79 80 81 82 84 85 86 87 90 93 94 96 107 108 109 110 114 115 116 117 118 119 120 121 124 126 129 130 131 132 135 137 138 142 143 145 146 148 149 156 **S** Sharp HealthCare, San Diego, CA
Primary Contact: Tim Smith, Senior Vice President and Chief Executive Officer
COO: Janie Kramer, Chief Operating Officer
CFO: Kari Cornicelli, Chief Financial Officer
CMO: Geoffrey Stiles, M.D., Chief Medical Officer
CIO: Kenneth Lawonn, Senior Vice President and Chief Information Officer
CHR: Connie Duquette, Director Human Resources
CNO: Pamela Wells, R.N., MSN, Chief Nursing Officer
Web address: www.sharp.com
**Control:** Other not–for–profit (including NFP Corporation) **Service:** General medical and surgical

**Staffed Beds:** 459 **Admissions:** 23145 **Census:** 311 **Outpatient Visits:** 364461 **Births:** 0 **Total Expense ($000):** 811494 **Payroll Expense ($000):** 308615 **Personnel:** 3594

☒ **SHARP MESA VISTA HOSPITAL (054145)**, 7850 Vista Hill Avenue, Zip 92123–2717; tel. 858/278–4110, (Includes SHARP MCDONALD CENTER, Mailing address: 7989 Linda Vista Road, San Diego, California, Zip 92111–5106; tel. 858/637–6920; Trisha Khaleghi, Chief Executive Officer), (Nonreporting) **A**1 5 10 **F**3 4 5 11 29 30 31 34 35 40 44 49 50 56 57 58 59 64 68 87 98 99 100 101 102 103 104 105 130 132 135 143 146 149 150 152 153 **S** Sharp HealthCare, San Diego, CA
Primary Contact: Trisha Khaleghi, Senior Vice President and Chief Executive Officer
CFO: Tony Guerra, Chief Financial Officer
CMO: Fadi Nicolas, M.D., Chief Medical Officer
CIO: Kenneth Lawonn, Senior Vice President Information Systems
CHR: Rick Grossman, Senior Vice President and General Counsel
CNO: Maria Carmen Colombo, R.N., Chief Nursing Officer
Web address: www.sharp.com
**Control:** Other not–for–profit (including NFP Corporation) **Service:** Psychiatric

**Staffed Beds:** 174 **Admissions:** 5363 **Census:** 134 **Outpatient Visits:** 90974 **Births:** 0 **Total Expense ($000):** 94210 **Payroll Expense ($000):** 52067 **Personnel:** 590

**UC SAN DIEGO HEALTH** See UC San Diego Medical Center—Hillcrest

☒ **UC SAN DIEGO MEDICAL CENTER—HILLCREST (050025)**, 200 West Arbor Drive, Zip 92103–9000; tel. 619/543–6222, (Includes THORNTON HOSPITAL, Mailing address: 9300 Campus Point Drive, La Jolla, California, Zip 92037–1300; tel. 858/657–7000; UC SAN DIEGO SHILEY EYE INSTITUTE, Mailing address: 9415 Campus Point Drive, Room 2411 Dept Of, Department of Ophthalmology, Mail Code 0946, La Jolla, California, Zip 92093–0946, 9415 Campus Point Drive, Zip 92093–0946, tel. 858/534–6290; Karen Anisko Ryan, Director Business Development and Communications), (Nonreporting) **A**1 3 5 8 10 **F**3 5 6 8 9 11 12 13 15 16 17 18 20 22 24 26 28 29 30 31 34 35 36 37 40 43 44 45 46 47 48 49 50 51 52 54 55 56 57 58 59 60 61 63 64 65 66 68 70 72 73 74 75 76 77 78 79 80 81 82 83 84 85 86 87 91 92 93 94 96 97 98 100 101 102 103 104 107 108 109 110 111 112 113 114 115 116 117 118 119 120 121 123 124 126 129 130 131 132 136 137 138 139 140 141 142 144 145 146 147 148 149 153 154 158 **P**8 **S** University of California Systemwide Administration, Oakland, CA
Primary Contact: Patty Maysent, Chief Executive Officer
COO: Margarita Baggett, MSN, R.N., Interim Chief Operating Officer
CFO: Lori Donaldson, Chief Financial Officer
CMO: Angela Scioscia, M.D., Chief Medical Officer
CIO: Ed Babakanian, Chief Information Officer
CHR: William J Murin, Chief Human Resources Officer
CNO: Margarita Baggett, MSN, R.N., Chief Nursing Officer
Web address: www.https://health.ucsd.edu
**Control:** State, Government, Nonfederal **Service:** General medical and surgical

**Staffed Beds:** 776 **Admissions:** 33605 **Census:** 587 **Outpatient Visits:** 1004954 **Births:** 3364 **Total Expense ($000):** 2196016 **Payroll Expense ($000):** 684700 **Personnel:** 7799

*Many Facility Codes have changed. Please refer to the AHA Guide Code Chart.*

CA

⊞ △ **VA SAN DIEGO HEALTHCARE SYSTEM**, 3350 LaJolla Village Drive, Zip 92161–0002; tel. 858/552–8585, (Total facility includes 18 beds in nursing home–type unit) (Nonreporting) **A**1 3 5 7 **F**2 3 4 5 8 9 10 11 12 15 18 20 22 24 26 29 30 31 34 35 36 37 38 39 40 44 45 46 47 48 49 50 52 53 54 56 57 58 59 60 61 62 63 64 65 66 68 70 71 74 75 77 78 79 80 81 82 83 84 85 86 87 90 91 92 93 94 95 96 97 98 100 101 102 103 104 106 107 108 110 111 114 115 116 117 118 119 126 128 129 130 131 132 133 135 143 146 147 148 149 153 154 156 157 **P**6 **S** Department of Veterans Affairs, Washington, DC
Primary Contact: Robert M. Smith, M.D., Director
COO: Cynthia Abair, Associate Director
CFO: Ronald Larson, Chief Financial Officer
CIO: Ruey Keller, Acting Chief Information Officer
CHR: Stephanie Wright, Director Human Resources Management
Web address: www.sandiego.va.gov
**Control:** Veterans Affairs, Government, federal **Service:** General medical and surgical

**Staffed Beds: 256 Admissions:** 7167 **Census:** 194 **Outpatient Visits:** 984462 **Births:** 0 **Total Expense ($000):** 746841 **Payroll Expense ($000):** 311456 **Personnel:** 5419

**VENCOR HOSPITAL–SAN DIEGO** See Kindred Hospital–San Diego

**VETERANS AFFAIRS SAN DIEGO HEALTHCARE SYSTEM** See VA San Diego Healthcare System

**VIBRA HOSPITAL OF SAN DIEGO** See Select Specialty Hospital – San Diego

**SAN DIMAS—Los Angeles County**

**SAN DIMAS COMM HOSPITAL** See San Dimas Community Hospital

☐ **SAN DIMAS COMMUNITY HOSPITAL (050588)**, 1350 West Covina Boulevard, Zip 91773–3219; tel. 909/599–6811, (Nonreporting) **A**1 10 **F**3 13 15 29 30 40 45 46 49 50 56 70 74 76 79 81 85 107 108 110 114 119 126 130 146 148 149 **S** Prime Healthcare, Ontario, CA
Primary Contact: Parrish Scarboro, Chief Executive Officer
CFO: Edward Matthews, Chief Financial Officer
CMO: Rajnish Jandial, M.D., Chief Medical Officer
CIO: Jeffrey Cox, Director Information Technology
CHR: Kristina Mack, Manager, Human Resources
CNO: Holly Nagatoshi, R.N., Chief Nursing Officer
Web address: www.sandimashospital.com/
**Control:** Corporation, Investor–owned (for–profit) **Service:** General medical and surgical

**Staffed Beds: 101 Admissions:** 3427 **Census:** 35 **Outpatient Visits:** 21320 **Births:** 498 **Total Expense ($000):** 55806 **Payroll Expense ($000):** 22283 **Personnel:** 313

**SAN FRANCISCO—San Francisco County**

⊞ **CALIFORNIA PACIFIC MEDICAL CENTER (050047)**, 2333 Buchanan Street, Zip 94115–1925, Mailing Address: P.O. Box 7999, Zip 94120–7999; tel. 415/600–6000, (Nonreporting) **A**1 2 3 5 8 10 **S** Sutter Health, Sacramento, CA
Primary Contact: Warren S. Browner, M.D., M.P.H., Chief Executive Officer
COO: Hamila Kownacki, Chief Operating Officer
CFO: Henry Yu, Vice President Finance and Chief Financial Officer
CMO: Vernon Giang, M.D., Chief Medical Executive
CIO: Ann Barr, Chief Information Officer - Bay Area
CHR: Edward Battista, Vice President Human Resources
CNO: Diana M. Karner, R.N., MSN, Chief Nursing Officer
Web address: www.cpmc.org
**Control:** Other not–for–profit (including NFP Corporation) **Service:** General medical and surgical

**Staffed Beds: 640**

⊞ △ **CALIFORNIA PACIFIC MEDICAL CENTER-DAVIES CAMPUS (050008)**, Castro and Duboce Streets, Zip 94114; tel. 415/600–6000, (Nonreporting) **A**1 3 5 7 **S** Sutter Health, Sacramento, CA
Primary Contact: Mary Lanier, Vice President, Post Acute Services and Site Administrator
Web address: www.cpmc.org
**Control:** Other not–for–profit (including NFP Corporation) **Service:** General medical and surgical

**Staffed Beds: 154**

⊞ **CALIFORNIA PACIFIC MEDICAL CENTER-ST. LUKE'S CAMPUS (050055)**, 3555 Cesar Chavez Street, Zip 94110–4403; tel. 415/600–6000, (Nonreporting) **A**1 5 10 **S** Sutter Health, Sacramento, CA
Primary Contact: Warren S. Browner, M.D., M.P.H., Chief Executive Officer
COO: Hamila Kownacki, Chief Operating Officer
CFO: Henry Yu, Vice President Finance and Chief Financial Officer
CMO: Vernon Giang, M.D., Chief Medical Executive
CIO: Ann Barr, Chief Information Officer - Bay Area
CHR: Edward Battista, Vice President Human Resources
CNO: Diana M. Karner, R.N., MSN, Chief Nursing Executive
Web address: www.stlukes-sf.org
**Control:** Other not–for–profit (including NFP Corporation) **Service:** General medical and surgical

**Staffed Beds: 165**

⊞ **CHINESE HOSPITAL (050407)**, 845 Jackson Street, Zip 94133–4899; tel. 415/982–2400, (Nonreporting) **A**1 10
Primary Contact: Jian Q. Zhang, Chief Executive Officer
CFO: Paul Ziegele, Chief Financial Officer
CMO: William Chung, M.D., Chief of Staff
CIO: Keith Minard, Chief Information Officer
CHR: Lydia Mahr-Chan, Director of Human Resources
CNO: Antonia Lendaris, Chief Nursing Operations Officer
Web address: www.chinesehospital-sf.org
**Control:** Other not–for–profit (including NFP Corporation) **Service:** General medical and surgical

**Staffed Beds: 65**

**DAVIES MEDICAL CENTER** See California Pacific Medical Center-Davies Campus

**JEWISH HOME OF SAN FRANCISCO (054089)**, 302 Silver Avenue, Zip 94112–1510; tel. 415/334–2500, (Nonreporting) **A**3 10
Primary Contact: Daniel R. Ruth, President and Chief Executive Officer
COO: Kevin Ward, Chief Operating Officer
CFO: Victor E Meinke, Chief Financial Officer
CNO: Edwin Cabigao, Chief Nursing Officer
Web address: www.jhsf.org
**Control:** Other not–for–profit (including NFP Corporation) **Service:** Psychiatric

**Staffed Beds: 374**

⊞ **KAISER PERMANENTE SAN FRANCISCO MEDICAL CENTER (050076)**, 2425 Geary Boulevard, Zip 94115–3358; tel. 415/833–2000, (Nonreporting) **A**1 2 3 5 10 **F**3 11 13 15 17 18 20 22 24 26 30 31 34 37 39 40 41 45 46 49 56 60 63 64 68 70 72 73 74 75 76 78 79 80 81 82 84 85 86 87 89 100 107 108 110 111 114 115 118 119 126 130 135 146 149 154 **P**6 **S** Kaiser Foundation Hospitals, Oakland, CA
Primary Contact: Ronald Groepper, Senior Vice President and Area Manager
COO: Helen Archer-Duste, Chief Operating Officer
CFO: Alex Khoo, Interim Area Finance Officer
CMO: Robert Mithun, M.D., Physician in Chief
CIO: Peti Arunamata, Interim Area Director Information Technology
CHR: Diane J Easterwood, Human Resources Business Partner
Web address: www.kaiserpermanente.org
**Control:** Other not–for–profit (including NFP Corporation) **Service:** General medical and surgical

**Staffed Beds: 239 Admissions:** 11958 **Census:** 155 **Outpatient Visits:** 73501 **Births:** 2907 **Personnel:** 1434

**LAGUNA HONDA HOSP & REHAB CNTR** See Laguna Honda Hospital and Rehabilitation Center

★ **LAGUNA HONDA HOSPITAL AND REHABILITATION CENTER (050668)**, 375 Laguna Honda Boulevard, Zip 94116–1499; tel. 415/759–2300, (Nonreporting) **A**10
Primary Contact: Margaret A. Rykowski, Acting Chief Executive Officer
COO: Michael R Llewellyn, Chief Operating Officer
CFO: Tess Navarro, Chief Financial Officer
CMO: Colleen Riley, M.D., Medical Director
CIO: Pat Skala, Chief Information Officer
CHR: Willie Ramirez, Manager Labor Relations
Web address: www.lagunahonda.org/
**Control:** City–county, Government, Nonfederal **Service:** Rehabilitation

**Staffed Beds: 780**

**CA**

---

**Hospital, Medicare Provider Number, Address, Telephone, Approval, Facility, and Physician Codes, Health Care System**

★ American Hospital Association (AHA) membership  ○ Healthcare Facilities Accreditation Program  ⇑ Center for Improvement in Healthcare Quality Accreditation
☐ The Joint Commission accreditation  ◇ DNV Healthcare Inc. accreditation  △ Commission on Accreditation of Rehabilitation Facilities (CARF) accreditation

**CA**

⊠ △ **SAINT FRANCIS MEMORIAL HOSPITAL (050152)**, 900 Hyde Street, Zip 94109–4899, Mailing Address: P.O. Box 7726, Zip 94120–7726; tel. 415/353–6000, (Nonreporting) **A**1 3 5 7 10 **S** CommonSpirit Health, Chicago, IL
Primary Contact: David Klein, M.D., President
CFO: Alan Fox, Chief Financial Officer
CHR: Richard Mead, Senior Director Human Resources
Web address: www.saintfrancismemorial.org
**Control**: Other not–for–profit (including NFP Corporation) **Service**: General medical and surgical

| Staffed Beds: 239 |
|---|

**SAN FRANCISCO GENERAL HOSPITAL AND TRAUMA CENTER** See Zuckerberg San Francisco General Hospital and Trauma Center

**SAN FRANCISCO MEDICAL CENTER** See Kaiser Permanente San Francisco Medical Center

⊠ **SAN FRANCISCO VA MEDICAL CENTER**, 4150 Clement Street, Zip 94121–1545; tel. 415/221–4810, (Total facility includes 120 beds in nursing home–type unit) (Nonreporting) **A**1 3 5 **F**3 5 8 9 10 11 12 18 20 22 24 26 28 29 30 31 33 34 35 36 37 38 39 40 44 45 46 47 48 49 50 51 54 55 56 57 58 59 60 61 62 63 64 65 66 68 70 71 74 75 77 78 79 81 82 83 84 85 86 87 91 92 93 94 96 97 100 101 102 104 105 107 111 114 115 116 117 118 119 120 126 127 129 130 131 132 135 143 144 146 147 148 149 153 154 156 157 158 **S** Department of Veterans Affairs, Washington, DC
Primary Contact: Bonnie S. Graham, Director
CFO: Brian Kelly, Acting Chief Fiscal Service
CMO: C. Diana Nicoll, M.D., Ph.D., Chief of Staff
CIO: Ryan Chun, Information Resources Management
CHR: Jerry Mills, Chief Human Resources Management Services
CNO: Shirley Pikula, MSN, Associate Director Patient Center Care
Web address: www.sanfrancisco.va.gov/
**Control**: Veterans Affairs, Government, federal **Service**: General medical and surgical

| Staffed Beds: 232 Admissions: 3558 Census: 200 Outpatient Visits: 526676 Births: 0 Total Expense ($000): 736487 Payroll Expense ($000): 322728 Personnel: 3137 |
|---|

**SAN FRANCISO VA MEDICAL CENTER** See San Francisco Va Medical Center

**ST FRANCIS MEMORIAL HOSPITAL** See Saint Francis Memorial Hospital

**ST MARY'S MEDICAL CENTER** See St. Mary's Medical Center

**ST. LUKE'S HOSPITAL** See California Pacific Medical Center-St. Luke's Campus

⊠ △ **ST. MARY'S MEDICAL CENTER (050457)**, 450 Stanyan Street, Zip 94117–1079; tel. 415/668–1000, (Nonreporting) **A**1 2 3 5 7 10 **S** CommonSpirit Health, Chicago, IL
Primary Contact: David Klein, M.D., President and Chief Executive Officer
COO: Deborah Kolhede, Vice President and Chief Operating Officer
CMO: Francis Charlton, M.D., JrChief Medical Staff
CHR: Barbara Morrissett, Vice President Human Resources
CNO: Barbara Eusebio, R.N., JD, Vice President, Chief Nurse Executive
Web address: www.stmarysmedicalcenter.com
**Control**: Other not–for–profit (including NFP Corporation) **Service**: General medical and surgical

| Staffed Beds: 232 |
|---|

**UCSF CHILDREN'S HOSPITAL** See UCSF Benioff Children's Hospital

⊠ **UCSF MEDICAL CENTER (050454)**, 500 Parnassus Avenue, Zip 94143–0296, Mailing Address: 500 Parnassus Avenue, Box 0296, Zip 94143–0296; tel. 415/476–1000, (Includes UCSF BENIOFF CHILDREN'S HOSPITAL, Mailing address: 500 Parnassus Avenue, San Francisco, California, Zip 94143–2203, 505 Parnassus Avenue, Zip 94143–2203, tel. 888/689–8273; Michael Anderson, M.D., President; UCSF MEDICAL CENTER MISSION BAY, Mailing address: 1975 4th Street, San Francisco, California, Zip 94158–2351; tel. 415/353–3000), (Nonreporting) **A**1 2 3 5 8 10 **F**3 6 7 8 9 11 12 13 14 15 17 18 19 20 21 22 23 24 25 26 27 28 29 30 31 32 33 34 35 36 37 38 39 40 41 43 44 45 46 47 48 49 50 51 52 53 54 55 56 57 58 59 60 61 63 64 65 66 68 70 71 72 74 75 76 77 78 79 81 82 83 84 85 86 87 88 89 90 91 92 93 94 96 97 98 99 100 101 102 103 104 105 107 108 110 111 112 113 114 115 116 117 118 119 120 121 123 124 126 129 130 131 132 134 135 136 137 138 139 140 141 142 143 144 145 146 147 148 149 150 153 154 155 156 **P**3 6 7 **S** University of California Systemwide Administration, Oakland, CA
Primary Contact: Mark R. Laret, Chief Executive Officer
COO: Ken M Jones, Chief Operating Officer
CFO: Raju Iyer, Senior Vice President and Chief Financial Officer
CMO: Josh Adler, M.D., Chief Medical Officer
CIO: Joe Bergfort, Chief Information Officer
CHR: David Odato, Chief Administrative and Chief Human Resources Officer
CNO: Sheila Antrum, R.N., President
Web address: www.ucsfhealth.org
**Control**: Other not–for–profit (including NFP Corporation) **Service**: General medical and surgical

| Staffed Beds: 820 Admissions: 35667 Census: 665 Outpatient Visits: 1358107 Births: 3090 Total Expense ($000): 4338852 Payroll Expense ($000): 1433988 Personnel: 13620 |
|---|

**UNIV OF CA SAN FRANCISCO** See UCSF Medical Center

⊠ **ZUCKERBERG SAN FRANCISCO GENERAL HOSPITAL AND TRAUMA CENTER (050228)**, 1001 Potrero Avenue, Zip 94110–3518; tel. 628/206–8000, (Total facility includes 26 beds in nursing home–type unit) (Nonreporting) **A**1 2 3 5 10 **F**3 13 15 18 20 22 29 30 31 34 35 36 38 39 40 41 43 44 45 46 47 49 50 57 58 59 60 61 64 65 68 70 71 72 73 74 75 76 77 78 79 81 82 83 84 85 86 87 89 92 93 94 97 98 100 102 105 107 108 110 111 115 119 128 129 130 131 132 135 144 146 147 148 149 150 154 157
Primary Contact: Susan P. Ehrlich, M.D., Chief Executive Officer
COO: Tosan O. Boyo, Chief Operating Officer
CFO: Valerie Inouye, Chief Financial Officer
CMO: Todd May, M.D., Chief Medical Officer
CIO: Winona Windolovich, Associate Chief Information Officer
CHR: Karen Hill, Departmental Personnel Officer
CNO: Terry Dentoni, Chief Nursing Officer
Web address: www.zuckerbergsanfranciscogeneral.org/
**Control**: City–county, Government, Nonfederal **Service**: General medical and surgical

| Staffed Beds: 296 Admissions: 15830 Census: 299 Outpatient Visits: 589444 Births: 1067 Total Expense ($000): 993809 Payroll Expense ($000): 387761 |
|---|

**SAN GABRIEL—Los Angeles County**

☐ **SAN GABRIEL VALLEY MEDICAL CENTER (050132)**, 438 West Las Tunas Drive, Zip 91776–1216, Mailing Address: P.O. Box 1507, Zip 91778–1507; tel. 626/289–5454, (Nonreporting) **A**1 3 10 **S** AHMC & Healthcare, Inc., Alhambra, CA
Primary Contact: Jonathon F. Aquino, Chief Executive Officer
CFO: Andrew Grim, Chief Financial Officer
CIO: Bernie Sauer, Director Information Technology
CHR: Victor Voisard, Director Human Resources
CNO: Gail Freeman, Chief Nursing Officer
Web address: www.sgvmc.org
**Control**: Partnership, Investor–owned (for–profit) **Service**: General medical and surgical

| Staffed Beds: 273 |
|---|

**SAN JOSE—Santa Clara County**

**COLUMBIA GOOD SAMARITAN HOSP** See Good Samaritan Hospital

⊠ **GOOD SAMARITAN HOSPITAL (050380)**, 2425 Samaritan Drive, Zip 95124–3997, Mailing Address: P.O. Box 240002, Zip 95154–2402; tel. 408/559–2011, (Nonreporting) **A**1 2 10 **S** HCA Healthcare, Nashville, TN
Primary Contact: Joseph DeSchryver, Chief Executive Officer
CFO: Lana Arad, Chief Financial Officer
CMO: Bruce Wilbur, M.D., Chief Medical Officer
CIO: Darrell O'Dell, Director Information Services
CHR: Edward Battista, Vice President Human Resources
CNO: Darina Kavanagh, R.N., MSN, Chief Nursing Officer
Web address: www.goodsamsanjose.com
**Control**: Corporation, Investor–owned (for–profit) **Service**: General medical and surgical

| Staffed Beds: 474 |
|---|

⊠ **KAISER PERMANENTE SAN JOSE MEDICAL CENTER (050604)**, 250 Hospital Parkway, Zip 95119–1199; tel. 408/972–7000, (Nonreporting) **A**1 2 3 5 10 **F**3 11 13 15 18 20 22 26 30 31 34 39 40 41 45 46 49 56 60 63 64 68 70 73 74 75 76 78 79 80 81 82 84 85 86 87 100 107 108 110 111 114 115 118 119 130 135 146 149 154 **S** Kaiser Foundation Hospitals, Oakland, CA
Primary Contact: Irene Chavez, Senior Vice President and Area Manager
COO: Samyukt Bajaj, Chief Operating Officer
CFO: Stephen L Kalsman, Area Finance Officer
CMO: Efren Rosas, M.D., Physician in Chief
CIO: Greg Tuck, Area Information Officer
CHR: Lina Slack, Human Resources Leader
CNO: Shanthi Margoschis, M.D., Chief Nurse Executive
Web address: www.kaiserpermanente.org
**Control**: Other not–for–profit (including NFP Corporation) **Service**: General medical and surgical

| Staffed Beds: 247 Admissions: 12090 Census: 117 Outpatient Visits: 160393 Births: 2596 Personnel: 2825 |
|---|

☐ **O'CONNOR HOSPITAL (050153)**, 2105 Forest Avenue, Zip 95128–1471; tel. 408/947–2500, (Nonreporting) **A**1 2 3 5 10
Primary Contact: Meenesh Bhimani, M.D., Hospital Executive
CMO: Arthur Douville, M.D., Chief Medical Officer
CIO: Richard Hutsell, Vice President and Chief Information Officer, Daughters of Charity Health System
CHR: Julie Hatcher, Vice President Human Resources
CNO: Dawn Marie Goeringer, Chief Clinical Care Officer
Web address: www.https://och.sccgov.org/Pages/home.aspx
**Control**: County, Government, Nonfederal **Service**: General medical and surgical

**Staffed Beds: 202**

☒ **REGIONAL MEDICAL CENTER OF SAN JOSE (050125)**, 225 North Jackson Avenue, Zip 95116–1603; tel. 408/259–5000, (Nonreporting) **A**1 10 **S** HCA Healthcare, Nashville, TN
Primary Contact: Tomi S. Ryba, President and Chief Executive Officer
COO: Brian J Knecht, Chief Operating Officer
CFO: Fred Ashworth, Chief Financial Officer
CMO: William Scott, M.D., Vice President Medical Affairs
CIO: Shirley Joyal, Director Information Systems
CHR: Nancy Clark, Vice President Human Resources
Web address: www.regionalmedicalsanjose.com
**Control**: Partnership, Investor–owned (for–profit) **Service**: General medical and surgical

**Staffed Beds: 264**

☐ **SAN JOSE BEHAVORIAL HEALTH (054154)**, 455 Silicon Valley Boulevard, Zip 95138–1858; tel. 888/210–2484, (Nonreporting) **A**1 10 **S** Acadia Healthcare Company, Inc., Franklin, TN
Primary Contact: Rob Marsh, Chief Executive Officer
Web address: www.sanjosebh.com
**Control**: Corporation, Investor–owned (for–profit) **Service**: Psychiatric

**Staffed Beds: 80**

**SAN JOSE MEDICAL CENTER** See Kaiser Permanente San Jose Medical Center

**SAN JOSE REGIONAL MEDICAL CTR** See Regional Medical Center of San Jose

☐ △ **SANTA CLARA VALLEY MEDICAL CENTER (050038)**, 751 South Bascom Avenue, Zip 95128–2699; tel. 408/885–5000, (Nonreporting) **A**1 3 5 7 10
Primary Contact: Paul E. Lorenz, Chief Executive Officer
COO: Benita McLarin, Chief Operating Officer
CMO: Jeffrey Arnold, M.D., Chief Medical Officer
CIO: Lee Herrmann, Chief Healthcare Technology Officer
CHR: David Manson, Manager Human Resources
CNO: Trudy Johnson, R.N., RNChief Nursing Officer
Web address: www.scvmed.org
**Control**: County, Government, Nonfederal **Service**: General medical and surgical

**Staffed Beds: 481**

**SANTA CLARA VLY HLTH SYSTEM** See Santa Clara Valley Medical Center

### SAN LEANDRO—Alameda County

**ALAMEDA COUNTY MEDICAL CENTER-FAIRMONT CAMPUS** See Fairmont Hospital

**COLUMBIA SAN LEANDRO HOSP** See San Leandro Hospital

**FAIRMONT HOSPITAL** See Highland Hospital, Oakland

☒ **KAISER PERMANENTE SAN LEANDRO MEDICAL CENTER (050777)**, 2500 Merced Street, Zip 94577–4201; tel. 510/454–1000, (Nonreporting) **A**1 3 10 **F**3 11 13 15 18 26 30 31 34 39 40 41 45 49 56 60 63 64 68 70 72 73 74 75 76 78 79 80 81 82 84 85 86 87 100 107 108 110 111 114 115 117 118 119 130 135 146 149 154 **S** Kaiser Foundation Hospitals, Oakland, CA
Primary Contact: Thomas S. Hanenburg, Senior Vice President and Area Manager
Web address: www.kaiserpermanente.org
**Control**: Other not–for–profit (including NFP Corporation) **Service**: General medical and surgical

**Staffed Beds: 206 Admissions: 12189 Census: 121 Outpatient Visits: 162483 Births: 3982 Personnel: 1245**

☒ **KINDRED HOSPITAL-SAN FRANCISCO BAY AREA (052034)**, 2800 Benedict Drive, Zip 94577–6840; tel. 510/357–8300, (Nonreporting) **A**1 10 **S** Kindred Healthcare, Louisville, KY
Primary Contact: Jacob M. McCarty, Chief Executive Officer
CFO: Ziba Aflak, Chief Financial Officer
CHR: Erin Greene, Coordinator Human Resources
CNO: Emily Gard, Chief Clinical Officer
Web address: www.kindredhospitalsfba.com
**Control**: Corporation, Investor–owned (for–profit) **Service**: Acute long–term care hospital

**Staffed Beds: 99**

**KINDRED HOSPITAL-SAN LEANDRO** See Kindred Hospital-San Francisco Bay Area

☐ **SAN LEANDRO HOSPITAL (050773)**, 13855 East 14th Street, Zip 94578–2600; tel. 510/357–6500, (Nonreporting) **A**1 3 5 10 **F**3 11 15 18 29 30 31 34 35 40 44 45 50 51 57 59 60 67 68 70 73 76 77 79 81 87 107 108 110 111 114 119 128 130 146 **S** Alameda Health System, San Leandro, CA
Primary Contact: James E T. Jackson, M.P.H., Chief Administrative Officer
Web address: www.sanleandrohospital.org
**Control**: Hospital district or authority, Government, Nonfederal **Service**: General medical and surgical

**Staffed Beds: 48 Admissions: 2658 Census: 32 Outpatient Visits: 32285 Births: 0 Total Expense ($000): 78617 Payroll Expense ($000): 44803 Personnel: 356**

☐ **WILLOW ROCK CENTER (054149)**, 2050 Fairmont Drive, Zip 94578–1001; tel. 510/895–5502, (Nonreporting) **A**1 10
Primary Contact: Anne L. Bakar, President and Chief Executive Officer
Web address: www.tbhcare.com
**Control**: County, Government, Nonfederal **Service**: Psychiatric

**Staffed Beds: 16**

### SAN LUIS OBISPO—San Luis Obispo County

**CALIFORNIA MENS COLONY CORRECTIONAL TREATMENT CENTER**, Highway 1, Zip 93409–8101, Mailing Address: P.O. Box 8101, Zip 93403–8101; tel. 805/547–7913, (Nonreporting)
Primary Contact: Teresa Macias, Administrator
CFO: William Cook, Associate Warden Business Service
CIO: Terry Knight, Public Information Officer and Administrative Assistant
Web address: www.yaca.ca.gov/visitors/fac_prison_cmc.html
**Control**: State, Government, Nonfederal **Service**: Hospital unit of an institution (prison hospital, college infirmary, etc.)

**Staffed Beds: 39**

**CALIFORNIA MENS COLONY HOSPITAL** See California Mens Colony Correctional Treatment Center

☒ **FRENCH HOSPITAL MEDICAL CENTER (050232)**, 1911 Johnson Avenue, Zip 93401–4197; tel. 805/543–5353, (Nonreporting) **A**1 2 10 **S** CommonSpirit Health, Chicago, IL
Primary Contact: Alan Iftiniuk, Chief Executive Officer
COO: Julia Fogelson, R.N., Chief Operating Officer and Chief Nursing Executive
CFO: Debbie Wettlaufer, Chief Financial Officer
CMO: Andrea Tackett, Chief of Staff
CIO: Cyndi Lang, Director Information Services
CHR: Clara Ramirez, Manager
CNO: Julia Fogelson, R.N., Chief Operating Officer and Chief Nursing Executive
Web address: www.frenchmedicalcenter.org
**Control**: Other not–for–profit (including NFP Corporation) **Service**: General medical and surgical

**Staffed Beds: 72**

**SIERRA VISTA REG MED CTR** See Sierra Vista Regional Medical Center

**CA**

---

**Hospital, Medicare Provider Number, Address, Telephone, Approval, Facility, and Physician Codes, Health Care System**

★ American Hospital Association (AHA) membership
☐ The Joint Commission accreditation
○ Healthcare Facilities Accreditation Program
◇ DNV Healthcare Inc. accreditation
⇑ Center for Improvement in Healthcare Quality Accreditation
△ Commission on Accreditation of Rehabilitation Facilities (CARF) accreditation

✠ **SIERRA VISTA REGIONAL MEDICAL CENTER (050506)**, 1010 Murray Avenue, Zip 93405–1806, Mailing Address: P.O. Box 1367, Zip 93405; tel. 805/546–7600, (Nonreporting) **A**1 2 10 19 **F**11 13 18 19 20 29 31 34 35 39 40 45 46 47 48 49 50 51 57 59 64 65 68 74 75 77 78 79 81 85 107 108 111 115 119 126 130 132 146 148 149 154 157 **S** TENET Healthcare Corporation, Dallas, TX
Primary Contact: Mark P. Lisa, FACHE, Chief Executive Officer
COO: Eleze Armstrong, Chief Operating Officer
CFO: Scott Wartelle, Chief Financial Officer
CIO: Robert Leonard, Director Information Services
CHR: Kristin Flynn, Chief Human Resources Officer
CNO: Nicki E Edwards, Ph.D., R.N., Interim Chief Nursing Officer
Web address: www.sierravistaregional.com
**Control:** Corporation, Investor–owned (for–profit) **Service:** General medical and surgical

**Staffed Beds:** 74 **Admissions:** 5764 **Census:** 67 **Outpatient Visits:** 40882 **Births:** 1095 **Total Expense ($000):** 139950 **Payroll Expense ($000):** 69794 **Personnel:** 1244

### SAN MATEO—San Mateo County

**MILLS HEALTH CENTER** See Mills-Peninsula Health Services, Burlingame

**MILLS HOSPITAL** See Mills Health Center

**SAN MATEO COUNTY GENERAL HOSP** See San Mateo Medical Center

☐ **SAN MATEO MEDICAL CENTER (050113)**, 222 West 39th Avenue, Zip 94403–4398; tel. 650/573–2222, (Nonreporting) **A**1 3 5 10
Primary Contact: Chester Kunnappilly, M.D., Interim Chief Executive Officer
COO: John Thomas, Chief Operating Officer
CFO: David S McGrew, Chief Financial Officer
CMO: Susan Fernyak, M.D., Interim Chief Medical Officer & Chief Quality Officer
CIO: Michael Aratow, M.D., Chief Information Officer
CHR: Angela Gonzales, Manager Human Resources
CNO: Joan G Spicer, R.N., Chief Nursing Officer
Web address: www.sanmateomedicalcenter.org
**Control:** County, Government, Nonfederal **Service:** General medical and surgical

**Staffed Beds:** 90

### SAN PEDRO—Los Angeles County

✠ △ **PROVIDENCE LITTLE COMPANY OF MARY MEDICAL CENTER SAN PEDRO (050078)**, 1300 West Seventh Street, Zip 90732–3505; tel. 310/832–3311, (Total facility includes 125 beds in nursing home–type unit) (Nonreporting) **A**1 7 10 **F**2 3 4 5 11 13 14 15 17 18 29 30 32 34 35 40 41 44 45 49 50 51 56 57 59 60 63 64 65 66 68 70 71 72 73 74 75 76 77 78 79 81 82 84 85 86 87 88 90 92 93 94 95 96 98 100 101 102 103 104 107 108 110 111 114 119 120 123 128 130 131 132 135 145 146 147 149 150 153 154 **S** Providence St. Joseph Health, Renton, WA
Primary Contact: Garry M. Olney, Chief Executive Officer
CFO: Elizabeth Zuanich, Chief Financial Officer
CMO: Richard Glimp, M.D., Chief Medical Officer
CIO: Kim Brant-Lucich, Director, Information Systems
CHR: Melissa Baker, Director, Human Resources
Web address: www.https://california.providence.org/san-pedro
**Control:** Church operated, Nongovernment, not–for–profit **Service:** General medical and surgical

**Staffed Beds:** 318 **Admissions:** 5133 **Census:** 203 **Outpatient Visits:** 130244 **Births:** 146 **Total Expense ($000):** 142498 **Payroll Expense ($000):** 81778 **Personnel:** 1007

**PROVIDENCE LITTLE COMPANY OF MARY MEDICAL CENTER SAN PEDRO HOSPITAL** See Providence Little Company of Mary Medical Center San Pedro

### SAN RAFAEL—Marin County

✠ **KAISER PERMANENTE SAN RAFAEL MEDICAL CENTER (050510)**, 99 Montecillo Road, Zip 94903–3397; tel. 415/444–2000, (Nonreporting) **A**1 5 10 **F**3 11 15 18 20 26 30 31 34 35 39 41 44 45 49 54 56 60 61 62 64 66 68 70 74 75 77 78 79 81 82 84 85 86 87 100 102 107 108 110 111 114 115 118 119 130 135 146 148 149 154 **S** Kaiser Foundation Hospitals, Oakland, CA
Primary Contact: Tarek Salaway, Senior Vice President and Area Manager
COO: Kimberly Colonnelli, Chief Operating Officer and Chief Nurse Executive
CFO: Diane Hernandez, Area Finance Officer
CMO: Naveen Kumar, M.D., Physician-in-Chief
CIO: Stanley Dobrawa, Area Information Officer
CNO: Kimberly Colonnelli, Chief Operating Officer and Chief Nurse Executive
Web address: www.kaiserpermanente.org
**Control:** Other not–for–profit (including NFP Corporation) **Service:** General medical and surgical

**Staffed Beds:** 116 **Admissions:** 3774 **Census:** 42 **Outpatient Visits:** 136989 **Births:** 1 **Personnel:** 540

**SAN RAFAEL MEDICAL CENTER** See Kaiser Permanente San Rafael Medical Center

### SAN RAMON—Contra Costa County

✠ **SAN RAMON REGIONAL MEDICAL CENTER (050689)**, 6001 Norris Canyon Road, Zip 94583–5400; tel. 925/275–9200, (Nonreporting) **A**1 5 10 **F**3 8 11 13 15 18 20 22 24 26 28 29 30 31 34 35 37 40 45 46 47 48 49 53 57 59 64 70 72 75 76 77 78 79 81 85 86 87 93 107 108 110 118 119 126 130 131 146 147 148 149 **S** TENET Healthcare Corporation, Dallas, TX
Primary Contact: Ann Lucena, Chief Executive Officer
CFO: Beenu Chadha, Chief Financial Officer
CIO: Anthony Abbate, Director of Information Services
CHR: Dennis Mills, Chief Human Resources Officer
CNO: Wendy Sirivar, Chief Nurse Officer
Web address: www.sanramonmedctr.com
**Control:** Partnership, Investor–owned (for–profit) **Service:** General medical and surgical

**Staffed Beds:** 123 **Admissions:** 4644 **Census:** 49 **Outpatient Visits:** 64826 **Births:** 440 **Total Expense ($000):** 153490 **Payroll Expense ($000):** 72051

### SANTA ANA—Orange County

**COASTAL COMMUNITIES HOSPITAL** See South Coast Global Medical Center

☐ **ORANGE COUNTY GLOBAL MEDICAL CENTER, INC. (050746)**, 1001 North Tustin Avenue, Zip 92705–3577; tel. 714/953–3500, (Nonreporting) **A**1 3 5 10 **S** KPC Healthcare, Inc., Santa Ana, CA
Primary Contact: Ann Abe, Interim Chief Executive Officer
COO: Ann Abe, Administrator and Chief Operating Officer
CFO: John Collins, Chief Financial Officer
CMO: Steven Bui, M.D., Chief of Staff
CIO: Charles Flack, Interim Chief Information Officer
CHR: Terry Bohn, Director, Human Resources
CNO: Sandra Moreno, Chief Nursing Officer
Web address: www.orangecounty-gmc.com
**Control:** Corporation, Investor–owned (for–profit) **Service:** General medical and surgical

**Staffed Beds:** 282

☐ **SOUTH COAST GLOBAL MEDICAL CENTER (050747)**, 2701 South Bristol Street, Zip 92704–6278; tel. 714/754–5454, (Nonreporting) **A**1 10 **S** KPC Healthcare, Inc., Santa Ana, CA
Primary Contact: Ada Yeh, Chief Executive Officer
CFO: John Collins, Chief Financial Officer
CHR: Cynthia Garren-Oster, Human Resource Manager
Web address: www.SouthCoast-GMC.com
**Control:** Corporation, Investor–owned (for–profit) **Service:** General medical and surgical

**Staffed Beds:** 178

**SPECIALTY HOSP OF SANTA ANA** See Kindred Hospital Santa Ana

**WESTERN MEDICAL CENTER-SANTA ANA** See Orange County Global Medical Center, Inc.

### SANTA BARBARA—Santa Barbara County

**COTTAGE REHABILITATION HOSPITAL** See Santa Barbara Cottage Hospital, Santa Barbara

**GOLETA VALLEY COMM HOSPITAL** See Goleta Valley Cottage Hospital

✠ **GOLETA VALLEY COTTAGE HOSPITAL (050357)**, 351 South Patterson Avenue, Zip 93111–2496, Mailing Address: Box 6306, Zip 93160–6306; tel. 805/967–3411, (Nonreporting) **A**1 10 **F**8 11 12 15 29 40 65 68 70 75 79 81 107 110 114 119 124 130 148 149 **S** Cottage Health, Santa Barbara, CA
Primary Contact: Ronald C. Werft, President and Chief Executive Officer
COO: Steven A Fellows, Executive Vice President and Chief Operating Officer
CFO: Joan Bricher, Senior Vice President Finance and Chief Financial Officer
CMO: Edmund Wroblewski, M.D., Vice President Medical Affairs and Chief Medical Officer
CIO: Alberto Kywi, Chief Information Officer
CHR: Patrice Ryan, Vice President Human Resources
Web address: www.sbch.org
**Control:** Other not–for–profit (including NFP Corporation) **Service:** General medical and surgical

**Staffed Beds:** 28 **Admissions:** 1946 **Census:** 11 **Outpatient Visits:** 53045 **Births:** 0 **Total Expense ($000):** 80965 **Payroll Expense ($000):** 31295 **Personnel:** 297

**REHAB INST AT SANTA BARBARA** See Cottage Rehabilitation Hospital

**SANTA BARBARA COTTAGE HOSP** See Santa Barbara Cottage Hospital

*Many Facility Codes have changed. Please refer to the AHA Guide Code Chart.* © 2021 AHA Guide

✠ △ **SANTA BARBARA COTTAGE HOSPITAL (050396)**, 400 West Pueblo Street, Zip 93105–4390, Mailing Address: P.O. Box 689, Zip 93102–0689; tel. 805/682–7111, (Includes COTTAGE CHILDREN'S HOSPITAL, Mailing address: 400 West Pueblo Street, Santa Barbara, California, Zip 93105–4353; tel. 877/247–3260; COTTAGE REHABILITATION HOSPITAL, Mailing address: 2415 De la Vina Street, Santa Barbara, California, Zip 93105–3819; tel. 805/687–7444; Melinda Staveley, President and Chief Executive Officer), (Nonreporting) **A**1 2 3 5 7 10 **F**3 4 5 8 11 12 13 15 17 18 20 22 24 26 28 29 30 31 34 35 40 43 45 46 50 53 54 57 58 59 60 64 65 68 70 72 74 75 76 77 78 79 81 84 86 88 89 90 91 92 93 96 98 100 102 103 104 106 107 110 111 114 115 117 119 126 130 132 135 146 148 149 151 152 153 154 155 156 **S** Cottage Health, Santa Barbara, CA
Primary Contact: Ronald C. Werft, President and Chief Executive Officer
COO: Steven A Fellows, Executive Vice President and Chief Operating Officer
CFO: Joan Bricher, Senior Vice President Finance and Chief Financial Officer
CMO: Edmund Wroblewski, M.D., Vice President Medical Affairs and Chief Medical Officer
CIO: Alberto Kywi, Chief Information Officer
CHR: Patrice Ryan, Vice President Human Resources
CNO: Herb J Geary, Vice President Patient Care Services and Chief Nursing Officer
Web address: www.cottagehealthsystem.org
Control: Other not-for-profit (including NFP Corporation) Service: General medical and surgical

Staffed Beds: 392 Admissions: 18522 Census: 252 Outpatient Visits: 126409 Births: 2117 Total Expense ($000): 709005 Payroll Expense ($000): 280422 Personnel: 2646

**SANTA BARBARA COUNTY PSYCHIATRIC HEALTH FACILITY (054125)**, 315 Camino Del Remedio, Zip 93110–1332; tel. 805/681–5244, (Nonreporting) **A**10
Primary Contact: Ole Behrendtsen, M.D., Interim Director
CFO: Michael C. Evans, Chief Executive Officer and Deputy Director of Finance and Administration
CMO: Ole Behrendtsen, M.D., Medical Director
CIO: Dana Fahey, Manager Management Information Systems
CHR: Elena Molelus, Manager Human Resources
Web address: www.countyofsb.org
Control: County, Government, Nonfederal Service: Psychiatric

Staffed Beds: 16

### SANTA CLARA—Santa Clara County

✠ **KAISER PERMANENTE SANTA CLARA MEDICAL CENTER (050071)**, 700 Lawrence Expressway, Zip 95051–5173; tel. 408/851–1000, (Nonreporting) **A**1 2 3 5 10 **F**3 11 13 15 17 18 19 20 22 24 26 27 30 31 34 37 39 40 41 45 49 56 60 63 64 68 70 72 74 75 76 78 79 81 82 84 85 86 87 88 100 107 110 111 114 115 117 118 119 120 121 123 126 130 135 146 149 154 **P**6 **S** Kaiser Foundation Hospitals, Oakland, CA
Primary Contact: Christopher L. Boyd, Senior Vice President and Area Manager
CFO: Tim O'Connor, Area Finance Officer
CMO: Susan Smarr, M.D., Physician-in-Chief
CIO: Scott May, Area Director Technology
CHR: Robert Hyde, Human Resources Business Partner
Web address: www.kaiserpermanente.org
Control: Other not-for-profit (including NFP Corporation) Service: General medical and surgical

Staffed Beds: 327 Admissions: 18814 Census: 222 Outpatient Visits: 215357 Births: 4701 Personnel: 4558

**SANTA CLARA MEDICAL CENTER** See Kaiser Permanente Santa Clara Medical Center

### SANTA CRUZ—Santa Cruz County

✠ **DOMINICAN HOSPITAL (050242)**, 1555 Soquel Drive, Zip 95065–1794; tel. 831/462–7700, (Nonreporting) **A**1 2 10 **S** CommonSpirit Health, Chicago, IL
Primary Contact: Nanette Mickiewicz, M.D., President
COO: Chris Wernke, Chief Operating Officer
CFO: Rick Harron, Chief Financial Officer
CMO: Freddie Weinstein, M.D., Chief Medical Officer
CIO: Lee Vanderpool, Vice President
CHR: Vicki Miranda, Vice President Human Resources
Web address: www.dominicanhospital.org
Control: Church operated, Nongovernment, not-for-profit Service: General medical and surgical

Staffed Beds: 223

**DOMINICAN SANTA CRUZ HOSPITAL** See Dominican Hospital

☐ **SANTA CRUZ COUNTY PSYCHIATRIC HEALTH FACILITY (054152)**, 2250 Soquel Avenue, Zip 95062–1402; tel. 831/600–2801, (Nonreporting) **A**1
Web address: www.https://www.telecarecorp.com/santa-cruz-psychiatric-health-facility
Control: Corporation, Investor–owned (for–profit) Service: Psychiatric

Staffed Beds: 16

✠ **SUTTER MATERNITY AND SURGERY CENTER OF SANTA CRUZ (050714)**, 2900 Chanticleer Avenue, Zip 95065–1816; tel. 831/477–2200, (Nonreporting) **A**1 10 **S** Sutter Health, Sacramento, CA
Primary Contact: Trina White, President and Chief Executive Officer
CFO: Bonnie Liang, Divisional Finance Officer
CMO: Joseph Fabry, D.O., Chief of Staff
CIO: Ann Barr, Chief Information Officer, Sutter Health Bay Area
CHR: Maynard Jenkins, Regional Vice President Human Resources
CNO: Sherri Stout-Torres, R.N., Chief Nursing Executive
Web address: www.suttersantacruz.org
Control: Other not-for-profit (including NFP Corporation) Service: Other specialty treatment

Staffed Beds: 30

### SANTA MARIA—Santa Barbara County

**MARIAN MEDICAL CENTER** See Marian Regional Medical Center

✠ **MARIAN REGIONAL MEDICAL CENTER (050107)**, 1400 East Church Street, Zip 93454–5906; tel. 805/739–3000, (Nonreporting) **A**1 2 3 5 10 **S** CommonSpirit Health, Chicago, IL
Primary Contact: Kerin A. Mase, President and Chief Executive Officer
COO: Mark Allen, Chief Operating Officer
CFO: Sue Andersen, Vice President and Service Area and Chief Financial Officer
CMO: Chuck Merrill, M.D., Vice President Medical Affairs
CIO: Patricia Haase, Director Information Technology and Communications
CHR: Ed Gonzales, Vice President Human Resources
CNO: Candice Monge, R.N., Chief Nurse Executive Officer
Web address: www.marianmedicalcenter.org
Control: Church operated, Nongovernment, not-for-profit Service: General medical and surgical

Staffed Beds: 286

### SANTA MONICA—Los Angeles County

✠ **PROVIDENCE SAINT JOHN'S HEALTH CENTER (050290)**, 2121 Santa Monica Boulevard, Zip 90404–2091; tel. 310/829–5511, (Nonreporting) **A**1 2 3 10 19 **F**3 8 11 15 18 20 22 24 26 29 30 31 32 34 35 36 37 39 40 44 45 46 47 48 49 50 58 59 60 64 70 72 74 75 76 77 78 79 80 81 82 84 85 86 87 93 96 107 108 110 111 114 115 118 119 120 121 123 124 126 130 131 132 135 146 147 148 149 154 156 **S** Providence St. Joseph Health, Renton, WA
Primary Contact: Marcel C. Loh, FACHE, Chief Executive Officer
CFO: James Uli, Chief Financial Officer
CMO: Donald Larsen, M.D., Chief Medical Officer
CIO: Martha Ponce, Director Information Technologies and Telecommunications
CHR: Laura Morton Rowe, Director of Human Resources
CNO: Dawna Hendel, R.N., Chief Nursing Officer and Vice President Patient Care Services
Web address: www.providence.org/saintjohns
Control: Church operated, Nongovernment, not-for-profit Service: General medical and surgical

Staffed Beds: 234 Admissions: 13001 Census: 147 Outpatient Visits: 189431 Births: 2008 Total Expense ($000): 335147 Payroll Expense ($000): 139793 Personnel: 1528

**SAINT JOHN'S HEALTH CENTER** See Providence Saint John's Health Center

**SANTA MONICA-UCLA MEDICAL CENTER AND ORTHOPAEDIC HOSPITAL** See UCLA Medical Center-Santa Monica

✠ **UCLA MEDICAL CENTER-SANTA MONICA (050112)**, 1250 16th Street, Zip 90404–1249; tel. 310/319–4000, (Nonreporting) **A**1 3 5 10 19 **F**3 8 9 11 12 13 15 18 20 22 24 26 29 30 31 34 35 36 37 39 40 41 45 46 47 48 49 50 51 52 54 55 56 57 58 59 62 64 65 68 70 72 74 75 76 78 79 81 82 83 84 85 86 87 89 93 96 97 102 107 108 110 111 114 115 116 117 118 119 130 131 143 145 146 147 149 154 156 **P**6 **S** University of California Systemwide Administration, Oakland, CA
Primary Contact: Richard Azar, Chief Operating Officer
COO: Robert Azar, Chief Operating Officer
CFO: Paul Staton, Chief Financial Officer
CMO: James Atkinson, M.D., Medical Director
CIO: Virginia McFerran, Chief Information Officer
CHR: Mark Speare, Senior Associate Director Patient Relations and Human Resources
Web address: www.healthcare.ucla.edu
**Control**: State, Government, Nonfederal **Service**: General medical and surgical

**Staffed Beds**: 281 **Admissions**: 15325 **Census**: 210 **Outpatient Visits**: 192356 **Births**: 1610 **Total Expense ($000)**: 644268 **Payroll Expense ($000)**: 211050 **Personnel**: 1801

### SANTA ROSA—Sonoma County

☐ **AURORA SANTA ROSA HOSPITAL (054151)**, 1287 Fulton Road, Zip 95401–4923; tel. 707/800–7700, (Nonreporting) **A**1 10 **S** Signature Healthcare Services, Corona, CA
Primary Contact: Susan Rose, Chief Executive Officer
Web address: www.aurorasantarosa.com
**Control**: Corporation, Investor–owned (for–profit) **Service**: Rehabilitation

**Staffed Beds**: 95

✠ **KAISER PERMANENTE SANTA ROSA MEDICAL CENTER (050690)**, 401 Bicentennial Way, Zip 95403–2192; tel. 707/393–4000, (Nonreporting) **A**1 2 3 5 10 **F**3 8 11 13 15 18 26 30 31 34 35 39 40 41 44 45 49 53 54 56 60 61 62 64 66 68 70 73 74 75 76 77 78 79 81 82 84 85 86 87 89 100 102 107 108 110 111 114 115 118 119 130 135 146 148 149 154 **S** Kaiser Foundation Hospitals, Oakland, CA
Primary Contact: Tarek Salaway, Senior Vice President and Area Manager
COO: Vicky Locey, R.N., MSN, Chief Operating Officer and Chief Nursing Executive
CFO: Diane Hernandez, Area Finance Officer
CMO: Michael Shulman, Pysician-in-Chief
CIO: Stanley Dobrawa, Area Information Officer
CHR: Anna Krajna-Matherly, Human Resources Leader
CNO: Vicky Locey, R.N., MSN, Chief Operating Officer and Chief Nursing Executive
Web address: www.kaiserpermanente.org
**Control**: Other not–for–profit (including NFP Corporation) **Service**: General medical and surgical

**Staffed Beds**: 173 **Admissions**: 9753 **Census**: 97 **Outpatient Visits**: 123353 **Births**: 1859 **Personnel**: 965

**SANTA ROSA MEDICAL CENTER** See Kaiser Permanente Santa Rosa Medical Center

✠ **SANTA ROSA MEMORIAL HOSPITAL (050174)**, 1165 Montgomery Drive, Zip 95405–4897, Mailing Address: P.O. Box 522, Zip 95402–0522; tel. 707/546–3210, (Nonreporting) **A**1 2 3 10 19 **F**2 3 8 11 15 17 18 20 22 24 26 29 30 31 32 34 35 40 42 43 45 46 47 49 50 54 58 59 62 63 64 65 66 68 70 71 72 74 75 76 77 78 79 81 82 83 84 85 86 87 89 90 93 94 100 104 107 108 110 111 114 115 116 117 118 119 120 123 126 129 130 132 143 144 146 148 149 150 153 **S** Providence St. Joseph Health, Renton, WA
Primary Contact: Tyler Hedden, Interim Chief Executive Officer
COO: Tyler Hedden, Chief Operating Officer
CFO: John Peters, Interim Chief Financial Officer
CMO: Chad Krilich, M.D., Chief Medical Officer
CIO: Greg Summers, Regional Director, Field Technical Services
CHR: Jamie Welsh, Interim Chief Human Resources Officer
CNO: Vicki White, Chief Nursing Officer
Web address: www.stjosephhealth.org
**Control**: Other not–for–profit (including NFP Corporation) **Service**: General medical and surgical

**Staffed Beds**: 283 **Admissions**: 12627 **Census**: 187 **Outpatient Visits**: 162435 **Births**: 519 **Total Expense ($000)**: 484324 **Payroll Expense ($000)**: 193007 **Personnel**: 1618

**SUTTER MEDICAL CENTER OF SANTA ROSA, CHANATE CAMPUS** See Sutter Santa Rosa Regional Hospital

✠ **SUTTER SANTA ROSA REGIONAL HOSPITAL (050291)**, 30 Mark West Springs Road, Zip 95403; tel. 707/576–4000, (Includes WARRACK CAMPUS, Mailing address: 2449 Summerfield Road, Santa Rosa, California, Zip 95405–7815; tel. 707/576–4200), (Nonreporting) **A**1 2 3 5 10 **S** Sutter Health, Sacramento, CA
Primary Contact: Dan Peterson, Chief Executive Officer
CMO: William Carroll, M.D., Chief Medical Executive
Web address: www.sutterhealth.org
**Control**: Other not–for–profit (including NFP Corporation) **Service**: General medical and surgical

**Staffed Beds**: 84

**WARRACK HOSPITAL CAMPUS** See Warrack Campus

### SEBASTOPOL—Sonoma County

⇑ **PALM DRIVE HOSPITAL** See Sonoma West Medical Center

⇑ **SONOMA WEST MEDICAL CENTER (052057)**, 501 Petaluma Avenue, Zip 95472–4215; tel. 707/823–8511, (Nonreporting) **A**10 21
Primary Contact: John Peleuses, Interim Chief Executive Officer
CFO: Robert Heinemeier, Interim Chief Financial Officer
Web address: www.sonomawesthealth.org/
**Control**: Hospital district or authority, Government, Nonfederal **Service**: Acute long–term care hospital

**Staffed Beds**: 37

### SELMA—Fresno County

**SELMA COMMUNITY HOSPITAL** See Adventist Medical Center-Selma

### SHERMAN OAKS—Los Angeles County

**SHERMAN OAKS HOSP** See Sherman Oaks Hospital

☐ **SHERMAN OAKS HOSPITAL (050755)**, 4929 Van Nuys Boulevard, Zip 91403–1777; tel. 818/981–7111, (Nonreporting) **A**1 5 10 **S** Prime Healthcare, Ontario, CA
Primary Contact: Bockhi Park, Chief Executive Officer
CFO: Daniel Leon, Chief Financial Officer
CMO: Michael Malamed, M.D., Chief of Staff
Web address: www.shermanoakshospital.com
**Control**: Other not–for–profit (including NFP Corporation) **Service**: General medical and surgical

**Staffed Beds**: 90

### SIMI VALLEY—Ventura County

✠ **ADVENTIST HEALTH SIMI VALLEY (050236)**, 2975 North Sycamore Drive, Zip 93065–1277; tel. 805/955–6000, (Nonreporting) **A**1 2 10 **F**3 8 11 13 15 18 20 22 24 26 29 30 31 32 34 35 36 40 41 44 45 46 49 50 51 54 56 57 58 59 62 63 64 65 68 70 72 74 75 76 77 78 79 81 82 84 85 86 87 93 96 97 100 101 102 107 108 110 111 114 115 116 117 118 119 120 121 123 126 130 131 132 134 141 144 146 147 148 149 150 154 **P**3 4 **S** Adventist Health, Roseville, CA
Primary Contact: Jennifer Swenson, President and Chief Executive Officer
COO: Caroline Esparza, R.N., Sr. VP, COO & CNO
CFO: Brian Anderson, Chief Financial Officer
CMO: John Dingilian, M.D., Chief Medical Officer
CIO: Bridget Nakamura, Director Information Systems
CHR: Susan Crabtree, Director Human Resources
CNO: Caroline Esparza, R.N., Senior Vice President, Chief Operating Officer and Chief Nurse Officer
Web address: www.simivalleyhospital.com
**Control**: Other not–for–profit (including NFP Corporation) **Service**: General medical and surgical

**Staffed Beds**: 144 **Admissions**: 7555 **Census**: 80 **Outpatient Visits**: 74775 **Births**: 472 **Total Expense ($000)**: 141856 **Payroll Expense ($000)**: 51157 **Personnel**: 715

**SIMI VALLEY HOSPITAL** See Adventist Health Simi Valley

**CA**

*Many Facility Codes have changed. Please refer to the AHA Guide Code Chart.*

© 2021 AHA Guide

**SOLVANG—Santa Barbara County**

⊞ **SANTA YNEZ VALLEY COTTAGE HOSPITAL (051331)**, 2050 Viborg Road, Zip 93463–2295; tel. 805/688–6431, (Nonreporting) **A**1 10 18 **F**11 15 18 28 40 45 57 68 75 81 85 107 111 114 119 143 146 149 **S** Cottage Health, Santa Barbara, CA
Primary Contact: Ronald C. Werft, President and Chief Executive Officer
COO: Steven A Fellows, Executive Vice President and Chief Operating Officer
CFO: Brett Tande, Chief Financial Officer
CMO: Edmund Wroblewski, M.D., Vice President Medical Affairs and Chief Medical Officer
CHR: Patrice Ryan, Vice President Human Resources
CNO: Herb J Geary, Chief Nursing Officer
Web address: www.cottagehealthsystem.org
**Control:** Other not–for–profit (including NFP Corporation) **Service:** General medical and surgical

**Staffed Beds:** 11 **Admissions:** 182 **Census:** 1 **Outpatient Visits:** 23385 **Births:** 0 **Total Expense ($000):** 18639 **Payroll Expense ($000):** 9369 **Personnel:** 82

**SANTA YNEZ VALLEY HOSPITAL** See Santa Ynez Valley Cottage Hospital

**SONOMA—Sonoma County**

**SONOMA VALLEY HOSPITAL (050090)**, 347 Andrieux Street, Zip 95476–6811, Mailing Address: P.O. Box 600, Zip 95476–0600; tel. 707/935–5000, (Nonreporting) **A**5 10 22
Primary Contact: Kelly Mather, Chief Executive Officer
CFO: Jeanette Tarver, Director of Finance
CMO: Sabrina Kidd, M.D., Chief Medical Officer
CIO: Fe Sendaydiego, Director Information Systems
CHR: Paula M Davis, Chief Human Resources Officer
CNO: Leslie Lovejoy, R.N., Ph.D., Chief Nursing and Quality Officer
Web address: www.https://www.sonomavalleyhospital.org/
**Control:** Hospital district or authority, Government, Nonfederal **Service:** General medical and surgical

**Staffed Beds:** 65

**SONORA—Tuolumne County**

⊞ **ADVENTIST HEALTH SONORA (050335)**, 1000 Greenley Road, Zip 95370–4819; tel. 209/536–5000, (Total facility includes 68 beds in nursing home–type unit) (Nonreporting) **A**1 10 **F**3 8 11 13 15 17 18 20 28 29 30 31 34 35 37 39 40 45 49 53 54 56 57 59 62 63 64 66 70 75 76 77 78 79 81 82 84 85 86 87 89 93 94 96 97 104 107 108 110 111 114 115 117 118 119 120 121 123 126 127 128 129 130 131 132 133 143 144 145 146 148 149 154 156 **S** Adventist Health, Roseville, CA
Primary Contact: Michelle Fuentes, President
CFO: Greg McCulloch, CPA, Vice President of Finance and Chief Financial Officer
CMO: Ed Clinite, D.O., Chief of Staff
CIO: Manty Drews, Chief Information Officer
CNO: Julie Kline, R.N., Senior Vice President Patient Services
Web address: www.sonoramedicalcenter.org/
**Control:** Church operated, Nongovernment, not–for–profit **Service:** General medical and surgical

**Staffed Beds:** 152 **Admissions:** 4368 **Census:** 107 **Outpatient Visits:** 418189 **Births:** 531 **Total Expense ($000):** 262904 **Payroll Expense ($000):** 74264 **Personnel:** 1022

**SONORA REGIONAL MEDICAL CENTER** See Adventist Health Sonora

**SOUTH EL MONTE—Los Angeles County**

☐ **GREATER EL MONTE COMMUNITY HOSPITAL (050738)**, 1701 Santa Anita Avenue, Zip 91733–3411; tel. 626/579–7777, (Nonreporting) **A**1 10 **S** AHMC & Healthcare, Inc., Alhambra, CA
Primary Contact: Stanley Toy Jr, M.D., Chief Executive Officer
COO: Jose Ortega, Chief Operating Officer
CFO: Michael Chung, Chief Financial Officer
CMO: Dilip Patel, M.D., Chief of Staff
CIO: Jay Geldhof, Director Information Systems
CHR: Jason Jaquez, Director Human Resources
CNO: Evelyn Calubaquib, Chief Nursing Officer
Web address: www.greaterelmonte.com
**Control:** Hospital district or authority, Government, Nonfederal **Service:** General medical and surgical

**Staffed Beds:** 117

**SOUTH LAKE TAHOE—El Dorado County**

**BARTON HEALTHCARE SYSTEM** See Barton Memorial Hospital

⊞ **BARTON MEMORIAL HOSPITAL (050352)**, 2170 South Avenue, Zip 96150–7026, Mailing Address: P.O. Box 9578, Zip 96158–9578; tel. 530/541–3420, (Total facility includes 48 beds in nursing home–type unit) (Nonreporting) **A**1 3 5 10 20 **F**3 8 11 13 15 18 29 30 32 34 35 38 40 43 45 46 47 48 49 50 54 57 59 62 63 64 65 66 68 70 75 76 77 79 81 82 83 84 85 86 87 89 90 92 93 94 96 97 100 104 107 109 110 111 112 113 114 115 116 117 118 119 121 122 123 124 126 127 128 129 130 131 132 135 143 144 146 147 148 149
Primary Contact: Clint Purvance, M.D., President and Chief Executive Officer
CFO: Kelly Neiger, Chief Financial Officer
CMO: Matthew Wonnacott, M.D., Chief Medical Officer
CIO: Jason Roberts, Director of Information Services
CHR: Elizabeth Stork, Chief Human Resources Officer
CNO: Julie B Clayton, Chief Nursing Officer
Web address: www.bartonhealth.org
**Control:** Other not–for–profit (including NFP Corporation) **Service:** General medical and surgical

**Staffed Beds:** 111 **Admissions:** 2016 **Census:** 63 **Outpatient Visits:** 193007 **Births:** 301 **Total Expense ($000):** 130465 **Payroll Expense ($000):** 55822 **Personnel:** 915

**SOUTH SAN FRANCISCO—San Mateo County**

⊞ **KAISER PERMANENTE SOUTH SAN FRANCISCO (050070)**, 1200 El Camino Real, Zip 94080–3208; tel. 650/742–2000, (Nonreporting) **A**1 3 5 10 **F**3 11 12 15 18 26 30 31 34 39 40 41 45 49 56 60 63 64 68 70 74 75 77 78 79 80 81 82 84 85 86 87 89 90 93 100 107 108 110 111 114 115 118 119 120 121 123 124 130 135 146 148 149 154 **P**6 **S** Kaiser Foundation Hospitals, Oakland, CA
Primary Contact: Ronald Groepper, Senior Vice President and Area Manager
CMO: Michelle Caughey, M.D., Physician in Chief
CIO: Angel Shew, Director Area Technology
CHR: Sharon Barncord, Human Resource Business Partner
Web address: www.kaiserpermanente.org
**Control:** Other not–for–profit (including NFP Corporation) **Service:** General medical and surgical

**Staffed Beds:** 120 **Admissions:** 5476 **Census:** 56 **Outpatient Visits:** 101017 **Births:** 0 **Personnel:** 664

**SOUTH SAN FRANCISCO MEDICAL CENTER** See Kaiser Permanente South San Francisco

**STOCKTON—San Joaquin County**

☐ **DAMERON HOSPITAL (050122)**, 525 West Acacia Street, Zip 95203–2484; tel. 209/944–5550, (Nonreporting) **A**1 5 10 **F**3 8 12 17 18 20 22 24 29 40 45 49 54 60 64 70 75 77 79 80 81 82 85 107 108 111 115 119 130 132 146 148 149
Primary Contact: Lorraine P. Auerbach, FACHE, President and Chief Executive Officer
COO: Michael Glasberg, Senior Vice President, Chief Operating Officer
CFO: Elizabeth R Propp, Vice President Finance and Chief Financial Officer
CMO: Bradley Reinke, M.D., Vice President Medical Affairs and Chief Medical Officer
CIO: David Kerrins, Vice President Information Services and Chief Information Officer
CNO: Denise J. Hair, Vice President of Nursing Services and Chief Nursing Officer
Web address: www.dameronhospital.org
**Control:** Other not–for–profit (including NFP Corporation) **Service:** General medical and surgical

**Staffed Beds:** 170 **Admissions:** 3403 **Census:** 39 **Outpatient Visits:** 95101 **Births:** 0 **Total Expense ($000):** 151571 **Payroll Expense ($000):** 48831 **Personnel:** 471

**ST JOSEPH'S PARKSIDE HOSPITAL** See St. Joseph's Behavioral Health Center

**CA**

---

| Hospital, Medicare Provider Number, Address, Telephone, Approval, Facility, and Physician Codes, Health Care System |
|---|
| ★ American Hospital Association (AHA) membership   ○ Healthcare Facilities Accreditation Program   ⇑ Center for Improvement in Healthcare Quality Accreditation |
| ☐ The Joint Commission accreditation   ◇ DNV Healthcare Inc. accreditation   △ Commission on Accreditation of Rehabilitation Facilities (CARF) accreditation |

⊞ **ST. JOSEPH'S BEHAVIORAL HEALTH CENTER (054123)**, 2510 North California Street, Zip 95204–5568; tel. 209/461–2000, (Nonreporting) **A**1 10 **F**5 29 35 38 98 100 101 103 104 105 130 132 143 146 152 153 154 **S** CommonSpirit Health, Chicago, IL
Primary Contact: Paul Rains, R.N., MSN, President
CFO: Doreen Hartmann, Chief Financial Officer
CMO: David Robinson, D.O., Medical Director
CHR: Nancy Vargas, Chief Human Resources
CNO: Benny Lee Lucas JrChief Nursing Executive
Web address: www.stjosephscanhelp.org
**Control:** Other not–for–profit (including NFP Corporation) **Service:** Psychiatric

**Staffed Beds:** 35 **Admissions:** 2002 **Census:** 32 **Outpatient Visits:** 8905 **Births:** 0 **Total Expense ($000):** 20494 **Payroll Expense ($000):** 10655 **Personnel:** 122

⊞ **ST. JOSEPH'S MEDICAL CENTER (050084)**, 1800 North California Street, Zip 95204–6019, Mailing Address: P.O. Box 213008, Zip 95213–9008; tel. 209/943–2000, (Nonreporting) **A**1 2 3 5 10 19 **S** CommonSpirit Health, Chicago, IL
Primary Contact: Donald J. Wiley, President and Chief Executive Officer
COO: Michaell Rose, Chief Operating Officer
CFO: Nikki Ochoa, Interim Chief Financial Officer
CIO: Randall Gamino, Director Perot Site
CHR: Nancy Vargas, Vice President Human Resources
Web address: www.stjosephsCARES.org
**Control:** Church operated, Nongovernment, not–for–profit **Service:** General medical and surgical

**Staffed Beds:** 273

### SUN CITY—Riverside County

☐ **MENIFEE VALLEY MEDICAL CENTER (050684)**, 28400 McCall Boulevard, Zip 92585–9537; tel. 951/679–8888, (Nonreporting) **A**1 3 10 **S** Physicians for Healthy Hospitals, Hemet, CA
Primary Contact: Dan C. McLaughlin, Chief Executive Officer
CMO: Sumanta Chaudhuri, M.D., Chief Medical Officer
CHR: Michele Bird, Chief Human Resources Officer
Web address: www.menifeevalleymedicalcenter.com/
**Control:** Hospital district or authority, Government, Nonfederal **Service:** General medical and surgical

**Staffed Beds:** 84

### SUN VALLEY—Los Angeles County

☐ **PACIFICA HOSPITAL OF THE VALLEY (050378)**, 9449 San Fernando Road, Zip 91352–1489; tel. 818/767–3310, (Nonreporting) **A**1 10 **S** Southwest Healthcare System, Scottsdale, AZ
Primary Contact: Ayman Mousa, R.N., Ph.D., Chief Executive Officer
COO: Daniel Santos, Director Ancillary Services
CFO: Eileen Fisler, Chief Financial Officer
CMO: Joseph Eipe, M.D., Chief Medical Officer
CIO: Mubashir Hashmi, Chief Information Officer
CHR: Patti Alonzo, Manager Human Resources
CNO: Janet B. Latto, Chief Nursing Officer and Disaster Officer
Web address: www.pacificahospital.com
**Control:** Corporation, Investor–owned (for–profit) **Service:** General medical and surgical

**Staffed Beds:** 231

### SUSANVILLE—Lassen County

⊞ **BANNER LASSEN MEDICAL CENTER (051320)**, 1800 Spring Ridge Drive, Zip 96130–6100; tel. 530/252–2000, (Nonreporting) **A**1 5 10 18 **F**3 15 15 29 34 40 43 45 50 59 68 76 79 81 85 87 93 107 110 111 114 119 129 130 149 **P**8 **S** Banner Health, Phoenix, AZ
Primary Contact: Sandy Dugger, Chief Executive Officer
CFO: Jon R McMillan, Chief Financial Officer
CMO: Hal Meadows, M.D., Chief Medical Officer
CIO: Randy Moore, Chief Information Officer
CHR: Ruth Smith, Division Human Resources Business Partner
CNO: Claudia Helmes, R.N., Chief Nursing Officer
Web address: www.https://www.bannerhealth.com/locations/susanville/banner-lassen-medical-center
**Control:** Other not–for–profit (including NFP Corporation) **Service:** General medical and surgical

**Staffed Beds:** 25 **Admissions:** 1001 **Census:** 10 **Outpatient Visits:** 51847 **Births:** 238 **Total Expense ($000):** 38354 **Payroll Expense ($000):** 17181 **Personnel:** 183

**LASSEN COMMUNITY HOSPITAL** See Banner Lassen Medical Center

### SYLMAR—Los Angeles County

☐ **LAC-OLIVE VIEW-UCLA MEDICAL CENTER (050040)**, 14445 Olive View Drive, Zip 91342–1438; tel. 818/364–1555, (Nonreporting) **A**1 3 5 10 **F**3 7 13 15 18 20 22 26 29 30 31 34 40 44 45 46 48 49 50 51 55 57 58 59 60 61 62 63 64 65 68 70 72 74 75 76 77 78 79 80 81 82 84 85 87 89 93 94 97 98 100 102 104 107 108 110 111 114 115 116 117 118 119 126 129 130 143 144 146 147 148 149 154 156 **S** Los Angeles County-Department of Health Services, Los Angeles, CA
Primary Contact: Judith Maass, Chief Executive Officer
COO: Niloo Shahi, Chief Operating Officer
CFO: Anthony Gray, Chief Financial Officer
CMO: Shannon Thyne, Chief Medical Officer
CIO: Susan Aintablian, Chief Information Officer
CHR: Thomas Beggane, Manager Human Resources
CNO: Dellone Pascascio, Chief Nursing Officer
Web address: www.dhs.lacounty.gov/wps/portal/dhs/oliveview
**Control:** County, Government, Nonfederal **Service:** General medical and surgical

**Staffed Beds:** 202 **Admissions:** 11508 **Census:** 192 **Outpatient Visits:** 253158 **Births:** 700 **Total Expense ($000):** 827965 **Payroll Expense ($000):** 251495 **Personnel:** 2638

**OLIVE VIEW-UCLA MEDICAL CTR** See Lac-Olive View-UCLA Medical Center

### TARZANA—Los Angeles County

**ENCINO-TARZANA REG MED CENTER** See Providence Tarzana Medical Center

⊞ **PROVIDENCE TARZANA MEDICAL CENTER (050761)**, 18321 Clark Street, Zip 91356–3521; tel. 818/881–0800, (Nonreporting) **A**1 10 **F**3 7 8 13 15 17 18 19 20 22 24 26 28 29 30 31 34 35 37 40 41 44 45 46 49 50 51 54 56 57 58 59 63 64 70 72 74 75 76 77 78 79 81 82 83 84 85 86 87 88 89 107 108 110 111 114 115 118 119 126 130 131 132 143 146 147 148 149 154 **P**3 5 **S** Providence St. Joseph Health, Renton, WA
Primary Contact: Dale Surowitz, Chief Executive
COO: Phyllis Bushart, R.N., Chief Operating Officer
CMO: Howard Z Davis, M.D., Chief Medical Officer
CIO: Alex Nury, Chief Information Officer
CHR: Beverly Murray, Director of Human Resources
CNO: Deborah Carver, Chief Nursing Officer
Web address: www.providence.org/tarzana
**Control:** Church operated, Nongovernment, not–for–profit **Service:** General medical and surgical

**Staffed Beds:** 229 **Admissions:** 12728 **Census:** 125 **Outpatient Visits:** 159123 **Births:** 2504 **Total Expense ($000):** 233013 **Payroll Expense ($000):** 110248 **Personnel:** 1237

### TEHACHAPI—Kern County

**ADVENTIST HEALTH MEDICAL CENTER - TEHACHAPI VALLEY** See Adventist Health Tehachapi Valley

★ **ADVENTIST HEALTH TEHACHAPI VALLEY (051301)**, 115 West 'E' Street, Zip 93561–1607, Mailing Address: P.O. Box 1900, Zip 93581–1900; tel. 661/823–3000, (Nonreporting) **A**10 18 **S** Adventist Health, Roseville, CA
Primary Contact: David Eastman, Interim Chief Executive Officer
CFO: Chester Beedle, Interim Chief Financial Officer
CMO: Susan Cribbs, D.O., Chief of Staff
CIO: Dusty Colvard, Manager Information Technology
CHR: Susan Nelson-Jones, Director Human Resources
CNO: Juliana Kay Kirby, R.N., MSN, Chief Nursing Officer
Web address: www.tvhd.org
**Control:** Hospital district or authority, Government, Nonfederal **Service:** General medical and surgical

**Staffed Beds:** 24

### TEMECULA—Riverside County

⊞ **TEMECULA VALLEY HOSPITAL (050775)**, 31700 Temecula Parkway, Zip 92592–5896; tel. 951/331–2216, (Nonreporting) **A**1 3 10 **S** Universal Health Services, Inc., King of Prussia, PA
Primary Contact: Darlene Wetton, R.N., Chief Executive Officer
CNO: Janet L Ruffin, R.N., Chief Nursing Officer
Web address: www.temeculavalleyhospital.com
**Control:** Corporation, Investor–owned (for–profit) **Service:** General medical and surgical

**Staffed Beds:** 140

*Many Facility Codes have changed. Please refer to the AHA Guide Code Chart.*

**TEMPLETON—San Luis Obispo County**

✠ **TWIN CITIES COMMUNITY HOSPITAL (050633)**, 1100 Las Tablas Road,
Zip 93465–9796; tel. 805/434–3500, (Nonreporting) **A**1 10 **F**3 13 29 30 34 40
45 49 50 55 56 57 59 60 64 68 70 74 75 76 77 79 81 85 87 91 107 111 114
115 119 130 132 146 148 149 154 **S** TENET Healthcare Corporation, Dallas, TX
Primary Contact: Mark P. Lisa, FACHE, Chief Executive Officer
COO: Mike Lane, Chief Operating Officer
CFO: Scott Wartelle, Chief Financial Officer
CHR: Diane M McCluskey, Chief Human Resources Officer
CNO: Robert Cook, Chief Nursing Officer
Web address: www.twincitieshospital.com
**Control:** Corporation, Investor–owned (for–profit) **Service:** General medical and
surgical

Staffed Beds: 49 Admissions: 4462 Census: 45 Outpatient Visits: 43834
Births: 557 Total Expense ($000): 96495 Payroll Expense ($000): 42933
Personnel: 439

**THOUSAND OAKS—Ventura County**

✠ **LOS ROBLES HOSPITAL AND MEDICAL CENTER (050549)**, 215 West
Janss Road, Zip 91360–1899; tel. 805/370–4421, (Includes THOUSAND OAKS
SURGICAL HOSPITAL, Mailing address: 401 Rolling Oaks Drive, Thousand Oaks,
California, Zip 91361–1050; tel. 805/497–2727; Natalie Mussi, President and
Chief Executive Officer), (Nonreporting) **A**1 2 10 **S** HCA Healthcare, Nashville, TN
Primary Contact: Natalie Mussi, President and Chief Executive Officer
COO: Austin Lane Manning, Chief Operating Officer
CMO: Hannah Grossman, M.D., Chief Medical Officer
CIO: Alex Bryer, Director Information Management
CHR: Geoff Washburn, Vice President Human Resources
Web address: www.losrobleshospital.com
**Control:** Corporation, Investor–owned (for–profit) **Service:** General medical and
surgical

Staffed Beds: 382

**LOS ROBLES REGIONAL MED CENTER** See Los Robles Hospital and Medical
Center

**TORRANCE—Los Angeles County**

**AMI DEL AMO HOSPITAL** See Del Amo Hospital

☐ **DEL AMO HOSPITAL (054053)**, 23700 Camino Del Sol, Zip 90505–5000;
tel. 310/530–1151, (Nonreporting) **A**1 10 **S** Universal Health Services, Inc., King
of Prussia, PA
Primary Contact: Steven Hytry, PsyD, Chief Executive Officer
CFO: Norma Hudson, Chief Financial Officer
Web address: www.delamohospital.com
**Control:** Corporation, Investor–owned (for–profit) **Service:** Psychiatric

Staffed Beds: 70

☐ **HARBOR-UCLA MEDICAL CENTER (050376)**, 1000 West Carson Street,
Zip 90502–2059; tel. 310/222–2345, (Nonreporting) **A**1 2 3 5 8 10 **S** Los
Angeles County-Department of Health Services, Los Angeles, CA
Primary Contact: Kimberly McKenzie, R.N., MSN, Interim Chief Executive Officer
COO: Kimberly McKenzie, R.N., MSN, Chief Nursing Officer and Chief Operations
Officer
CFO: Jody Nakasuji, Chief Financial Officer
CMO: Timothy Van Natta, M.D., Chief Medical Officer
CIO: Sandy Mungovan, Chief Information Officer
CHR: Karyl Smith, Director Human Resources
CNO: Kimberly McKenzie, R.N., MSN, Chief Nursing Officer and Chief Operations
Officer
Web address: www.harbor-ucla.org
**Control:** County, Government, Nonfederal **Service:** General medical and surgical

Staffed Beds: 373

**LAC-HARBOR-UNIVERSITY OF CALIFORNIA AT LOS ANGELES MEDICAL
CENTER** See Harbor-UCLA Medical Center

**PROVIDENCE LITTLE COMPANY OF MARY MEDICAL CENTER** See
Providence Little Company of Mary Medical Center - Torrance

✠ **PROVIDENCE LITTLE COMPANY OF MARY MEDICAL CENTER - TORRANCE
(050353)**, 4101 Torrance Boulevard, Zip 90503–4664; tel. 310/540–7676,
(Total facility includes 77 beds in nursing home–type unit) (Nonreporting) **A**1 2 10
**F**3 11 12 13 14 15 18 19 20 22 24 26 28 29 30 31 34 35 37 39 40 41 44 45
46 49 50 51 54 55 57 58 59 60 61 62 63 64 68 70 72 74 75 76 77 78 79 81 82
84 85 86 87 89 91 92 93 94 100 107 108 110 111 114 115 116 117 118 119
120 121 123 126 128 130 131 132 143 145 146 147 148 149 150 154 156 **S**
Providence St. Joseph Health, Renton, WA
Primary Contact: Garry M. Olney, Chief Executive Officer
CFO: Elizabeth Zuanich, Chief Financial Officer
CMO: Richard Glimp, M.D., Chief Medical Officer
CIO: Andrea Flores, Director, Information Systems
CHR: Melissa Baker, Director, Human Resources
CNO: Michael Jongsma, R.N., Chief Nursing Officer
Web address: www.providence.org
**Control:** Church operated, Nongovernment, not-for-profit **Service:** General
medical and surgical

Staffed Beds: 386 Admissions: 16787 Census: 187 Outpatient
Visits: 307593 Births: 2699 Total Expense ($000): 333367 Payroll
Expense ($000): 161901 Personnel: 1920

✠ **TORRANCE MEMORIAL MEDICAL CENTER (050351)**, 3330 Lomita Boulevard,
Zip 90505–5073; tel. 310/325–9110, (Total facility includes 40 beds in nursing
home–type unit) (Nonreporting) **A**1 2 10 **F**3 5 8 9 11 12 13 14 15 16 17 18 19
20 22 24 26 28 29 30 31 32 34 35 36 37 39 40 41 44 45 46 47 48 49 50 51
53 54 55 56 57 58 59 60 61 62 63 64 68 70 72 74 75 76 77 78 79 81 82 83
84 85 86 87 89 91 92 93 96 100 107 108 109 110 111 114 115 116 117 118 119
120 121 123 124 126 128 129 130 132 134 135 141 143 145 146 147 148
149 154 156 **P**2 3 **S** Cedars-Sinai Health System, West Hollywood, CA
Primary Contact: Craig Leach, President and Chief Executive Officer
CFO: Bill Larson, Vice President Finance and Chief Financial Officer
CMO: John McNamara, M.D., Senior Vice President, Chief Medical Officer
CIO: Bernadette Reid, Vice President, Information Technology and Chief Information
Officer
CHR: Linda Dobie, R.N., JD, Vice President, Legal Affairs
CNO: Mary Wright, Senior Vice President, Patient Services
Web address: www.torrancememorial.org
**Control:** Other not-for-profit (including NFP Corporation) **Service:** General
medical and surgical

Staffed Beds: 436 Admissions: 26451 Census: 305 Outpatient
Visits: 454995 Births: 2569 Total Expense ($000): 652514 Payroll
Expense ($000): 259635 Personnel: 3294

**TRACY—San Joaquin County**

✠ **SUTTER TRACY COMMUNITY HOSPITAL (050313)**, 1420 North Tracy
Boulevard, Zip 95376–3497; tel. 209/835–1500, (Nonreporting) **A**1 10 **S** Sutter
Health, Sacramento, CA
Primary Contact: David M. Thompson, Chief Executive Officer
CFO: Eric Dalton, Chief Financial Officer
CIO: Catherine M Larsen, Director Marketing
CHR: Melanie Wallace, Manager Human Resources
Web address: www.suttertracy.org
**Control:** Other not-for-profit (including NFP Corporation) **Service:** General
medical and surgical

Staffed Beds: 33

**TRACY COMM MEMORIAL HOSPITAL** See Sutter Tracy Community Hospital

**TRAVIS AFB—Solano County**

**DAVID GRANT MEDICAL CENTER** See David Grant Usaf Medical Center

✠ **DAVID GRANT USAF MEDICAL CENTER**, 101 Bodin Circle, Zip 94535–1809;
tel. 707/423–7300, (Nonreporting) **A**1 3 5 **S** Department of the Air Force,
Washington, DC
Primary Contact: Lieutenant Michael Higgins, Commander
CFO: MajorJonathan Richards, Chief Financial Officer
CMO: ColonelChris Scharenbrock, M.D., Chief Medical Staff
Web address: www.travis.af.mil/units/dgmc/index.asp
**Service:** General medical and surgical

Staffed Beds: 116

**CA**

### TRUCKEE—Nevada County

★ ○ **TAHOE FOREST HOSPITAL DISTRICT (051328)**, 10121 Pine Avenue, Zip 96161–4856, Mailing Address: P.O. Box 759, Zip 96160–0759; tel. 530/587–6011, (Nonreporting) **A**2 3 5 10 11 18 **S** Tahoe Forest Health System, Truckee, CA
Primary Contact: Harry Weis, Chief Executive Officer
COO: Judy Newland, R.N., Chief Operating Officer
CFO: Crystal Betts, Chief Financial Officer
CMO: Shawni Coll, D.O., Chief Medical Officer
CIO: Jake Dorst, Chief Information Officer
CHR: Alex MacLennan, Chief Human Resources Officer
CNO: Karen Baffone, R.N., Chief Nursing Officer
Web address: www.tfhd.com
**Control**: Hospital district or authority, Government, Nonfederal **Service**: General medical and surgical

**Staffed Beds**: 62

### TULARE—Tulare County

★ ⇑ **ADVENTIST HEALTH - TULARE (050359)**, 869 North Cherry Street, Zip 93274–2287; tel. 559/688–0821, (Nonreporting) **A**10 21 **S** Adventist Health, Roseville, CA
Primary Contact: Randy Dodd, President
COO: Alan Germany, Chief Operating Officer
CFO: Michael Bernstein, Chief Financial Officer
CMO: Pradeep Kamboj, M.D., Chief Medical Staff
CIO: Jim Peelgren, Chief Information Officer
CHR: John Barbadian, Vice President Human Resources
CNO: Patricia Mathewson, Chief Nursing Officer
Web address: www.tulareregional.org
**Control**: Hospital district or authority, Government, Nonfederal **Service**: General medical and surgical

**Staffed Beds**: 103

⇑ **TULARE REGIONAL MEDICAL CENTER** See Adventist Health - Tulare

### TURLOCK—Stanislaus County

☒ **EMANUEL MEDICAL CENTER (050179)**, 825 Delbon Avenue, Zip 95382–2016; tel. 209/667–4200, (Nonreporting) **A**1 5 10 **S** TENET Healthcare Corporation, Dallas, TX
Primary Contact: Lani Dickinson, Chief Executive Officer
CFO: Anil Jain, Interim Chief Financial Officer
CIO: Beth Walker, Director, Information Technology
CHR: Dianna Romo, Director, Human Resources
CNO: Sharon Perry, Chief Nursing Officer
Web address: www.emanuelmedicalcenter.org
**Control**: Church operated, Nongovernment, not–for–profit **Service**: General medical and surgical

**Staffed Beds**: 209

### TUSTIN—Orange County

☒ **ENCOMPASS HEALTH REHABILITATION HOSPITAL OF TUSTIN (053034)**, 14851 Yorba Street, Zip 92780–2925; tel. 714/832–9200, (Nonreporting) **A**1 5 10 **S** Encompass Health Corporation, Birmingham, AL
Primary Contact: Diana Hanyak, Chief Executive Officer
CFO: Paula Redmond, Controller
CMO: Ann Vasile, M.D., Medical Director
CHR: JoAnn Roiz, Director Human Resources
CNO: LaDonna Butler EsqChief Nursing Officer
Web address: www.tustinrehab.com
**Control**: Corporation, Investor–owned (for–profit) **Service**: Rehabilitation

**Staffed Beds**: 48

☐ **FOOTHILL REGIONAL MEDICAL CENTER (050780)**, 14662 Newport Avenue, Zip 92780–6064; tel. 714/838–9600, (Nonreporting) **A**1 10 **S** Prospect Medical Holdings, Los Angeles, CA
Primary Contact: Barbara Schneider, R.N., Chief Executive Officer
COO: Kara Bourne, R.N., MSN, Chief Nursing Officer and Chief Operating Officer
CIO: Darla Kennedy, Chief Information Officer
CHR: Aprille Major, Director Human Resources
Web address: www.hfcis.cdph.ca.gov/longtermcare/Facility.aspx?fac=060000013
**Control**: Corporation, Investor–owned (for–profit) **Service**: Acute long–term care hospital

**Staffed Beds**: 127

**HEALTHSOUTH TUSTIN REHABILITATION HOSPITAL** See Encompass Health Rehabilitation Hospital of Tustin

**NEWPORT SPECIALTY HOSPITAL** See Foothill Regional Medical Center

### TWENTYNINE PALMS—San Bernardino County

**NAVAL HOSPITAL** See Robert E. Bush Naval Hospital

☒ **ROBERT E. BUSH NAVAL HOSPITAL**, 1145 Sturgis Road, Zip 92278, Mailing Address: Box 788250, MCAGCC, Zip 92278–8250; tel. 760/830–2190, (Nonreporting) **A**1 3 **S** Bureau of Medicine and Surgery, Department of the Navy, Falls Church, VA
Primary Contact: Captain Jay C. Sourbeer, Commanding Officer
CHR: Virginia Ward, Human Resources Officer
CNO: CaptainSandra Mason, MSN, R.N., Director Nursing Services and Senior Nurse Executive
Web address: www.med.navy.mil/sites/nhtp/Pages/default.aspx
**Service**: General medical and surgical

**Staffed Beds**: 29

### UKIAH—Mendocino County

☒ ⇑ **ADVENTIST HEALTH UKIAH VALLEY (050301)**, 275 Hospital Drive, Zip 95482–4531; tel. 707/462–3111, (Nonreporting) **A**1 3 5 10 21 **F**3 8 11 12 13 15 18 29 30 31 32 34 35 36 38 40 44 45 46 48 49 50 51 54 57 59 60 64 65 68 70 72 75 76 77 78 79 81 82 84 85 86 87 93 94 97 107 108 110 111 114 115 116 117 118 119 127 130 131 132 135 144 146 147 148 **P**3 **S** Adventist Health, Roseville, CA
Primary Contact: Gwen Matthews, R.N., MSN, Chief Executive Officer
CHR: Rebecca Ryan, Interim Director Human Resources and Employee Health
Web address: www.adventisthealth.org
**Control**: Church operated, Nongovernment, not–for–profit **Service**: General medical and surgical

**Staffed Beds**: 50 **Admissions**: 4192 **Census**: 34 **Outpatient Visits**: 134241 **Births**: 759 **Total Expense ($000)**: 197878 **Payroll Expense ($000)**: 48872 **Personnel**: 612

⇑ **UKIAH VALLEY MEDICAL CENTER** See Adventist Health Ukiah Valley

### UPLAND—San Bernardino County

**SAN ANTONIO COMMUNITY HOSPITAL** See San Antonio Regional Hospital

☒ **SAN ANTONIO REGIONAL HOSPITAL (050099)**, 999 San Bernardino Road, Zip 91786–4920; tel. 909/985–2811, (Nonreporting) **A**1 2 3 5 10 **F**3 8 11 13 15 17 18 20 22 24 26 28 29 31 35 38 40 45 46 49 50 54 57 59 60 61 64 65 69 70 72 74 75 76 77 78 79 80 81 82 83 84 85 86 87 89 91 92 93 94 107 108 110 111 114 115 118 119 121 123 124 130 132 146 147 148 157
Primary Contact: John T. Chapman, Interim President and Chief Executive Officer
COO: John T. Chapman, Chief Operative Officer
CFO: Wah Chung Hsu, Senior Vice President Finance
CMO: Edward DiGiamarino, M.D., President of Medical Staff
CIO: Kamel Pandya, Director Information Services
CHR: La Donna Najieb, Vice President, Human Resources
CNO: Gudrun Moll, R.N., MSN, Chief Nursing Officer
Web address: www.sarh.org
**Control**: Other not–for–profit (including NFP Corporation) **Service**: General medical and surgical

**Staffed Beds**: 363 **Admissions**: 18049 **Census**: 198 **Outpatient Visits**: 247015 **Births**: 2265 **Total Expense ($000)**: 394111 **Payroll Expense ($000)**: 166255 **Personnel**: 1936

### VACAVILLE—Solano County

**CALIFORNIA MEDICAL FACILITY**, 1600 California Drive, Zip 95687; tel. 707/448–6841, (Nonreporting)
Primary Contact: David Horch, Chief Executive
CMO: Raymond Andreasen, M.D., Chief Medical Officer-Inpatient
Web address: www.cya.ca.gov/visitors/fac_prison_cmf.html
**Control**: State, Government, Nonfederal **Service**: Hospital unit of an institution (prison hospital, college infirmary, etc.)

**Staffed Beds**: 215

☒ **KAISER PERMANENTE VACAVILLE MEDICAL CENTER (050767)**, 1 Quality Drive, Zip 95688–9494; tel. 707/624–4000, (Nonreporting) **A**1 2 3 5 10 **F**3 11 13 15 18 26 30 31 34 39 40 41 43 45 49 56 60 64 68 70 74 75 76 78 79 81 82 84 85 86 87 100 107 108 110 111 114 115 118 119 130 135 146 149 154 **S** Kaiser Foundation Hospitals, Oakland, CA
Primary Contact: Norair Jemjemian, Senior Vice President and Area Manager
Web address: www.kp.org
**Control**: Other not–for–profit (including NFP Corporation) **Service**: General medical and surgical

**Staffed Beds**: 140 **Admissions**: 6344 **Census**: 71 **Outpatient Visits**: 145378 **Births**: 1378 **Personnel**: 1438

**NORTHBAY VACAVALLEY HOSPITAL** See Northbay Vacavalley Hospital

**NORTHBAY VACAVALLEY HOSPITAL** See Northbay Medical Center, Fairfield

**VACAVILLE MEDICAL CENTER** See Kaiser Permanente Vacaville Medical Center

*Many Facility Codes have changed. Please refer to the AHA Guide Code Chart.* © 2021 AHA Guide

## VALENCIA—Los Angeles County

⊞ **HENRY MAYO NEWHALL HOSPITAL (050624)**, 23845 McBean Parkway, Zip 91355–2083; tel. 661/200–2000, (Nonreporting) **A**1 10 **F**3 8 11 13 15 17 18 20 22 24 26 28 29 30 31 34 35 38 40 41 43 45 49 50 55 57 59 60 64 70 72 74 76 77 78 79 81 82 84 85 86 87 90 93 98 100 102 107 108 110 115 119 126 130 132 135 146 147 148
Primary Contact: Roger E. Seaver, President and Chief Executive Officer
COO: John V Schleif, Senior Vice President and Chief Operating Officer
CFO: Ted Sirotta, Senior Vice President and Chief Financial Officer
CMO: Kingman Ho, M.D., Senior Vice President, Chief Medical and Care Innovation Officer
CIO: Ray Moss, Vice President and Chief Information Officer
CHR: Mark Puleo, Vice President and Chief Human Resources Officer
CNO: Jennifer Castaldo, R.N., Vice President, Patient Care and Chief Nursing Officer
Web address: www.henrymayo.com
**Control**: Other not–for–profit (including NFP Corporation) **Service**: General medical and surgical

**Staffed Beds: 238 Admissions: 12473 Census: 154 Outpatient Visits: 121493 Births: 1372 Total Expense ($000): 340137 Payroll Expense ($000): 136761 Personnel: 1633**

**HENRY MAYO NEWHALL MEMORIAL HOSPITAL** See Henry Mayo Newhall Hospital

## VALLEJO—Solano County

⊞ **ADVENTIST HEALTH ST. HELENA (054074)**, 525 Oregon Street, Zip 94590–3201; tel. 707/648–2200, (Nonreporting) **A**1 5 10 **F**29 30 50 64 65 68 98 104 105 130 146 153 154 **S** Adventist Health, Roseville, CA
Primary Contact: Steven Herber, M.D., FACS, President and Chief Executive Officer
CFO: Edward A McDonald, Chief Financial Officer
Web address: www.sthelenahospitals.org/location/center-for-behavioral-health
**Control**: Other not–for–profit (including NFP Corporation) **Service**: Psychiatric

**Staffed Beds: 61 Admissions: 2079 Census: 54 Outpatient Visits: 0 Births: 0**

⊞ △ **KAISER PERMANENTE VALLEJO MEDICAL CENTER (050073)**, 975 Sereno Drive, Zip 94589–2441; tel. 707/651–1000, (Nonreporting) **A**1 2 3 5 7 10 **F**3 11 13 15 18 20 22 26 30 31 34 39 40 41 45 48 49 56 60 64 68 70 73 74 75 76 78 79 81 82 84 85 86 87 90 100 107 108 110 111 114 115 118 119 130 135 146 149 154 **S** Kaiser Foundation Hospitals, Oakland, CA
Primary Contact: Corwin N. Harper, Senior Vice President and Area Manager
COO: Karen Grisnak, R.N., Chief Operating Officer and Assistant Administrator Quality Services
CMO: Steven Stricker, M.D., Physician in Chief
CIO: Gale Austin-Moore, Director Area Technology
CHR: Sherri Stegge, Director Human Resources
Web address: www.kaiserpermanente.org
**Control**: Other not–for–profit (including NFP Corporation) **Service**: General medical and surgical

**Staffed Beds: 248 Admissions: 8607 Census: 98 Outpatient Visits: 168517 Births: 1720 Personnel: 2235**

**ST. HELENA HOSPITAL CENTER FOR BEHAVIORAL HEALTH** See Adventist Health St. Helena

⊞ **SUTTER SOLANO MEDICAL CENTER (050101)**, 300 Hospital Drive, Zip 94589–2574, Mailing Address: P.O. Box 3189, Zip 94590–0669; tel. 707/554–4444, (Nonreporting) **A**1 2 5 10 **S** Sutter Health, Sacramento, CA
Primary Contact: Abhishek Dosi, Chief Executive Officer
CHR: Jean Willhite, Director Human Resources
Web address: www.suttersolano.org
**Control**: Other not–for–profit (including NFP Corporation) **Service**: General medical and surgical

**Staffed Beds: 108**

**VALLEJO MEDICAL CENTER** See Kaiser Permanente Vallejo Medical Center

## VAN NUYS—Los Angeles County

**HOLLYWOOD COMMUNITY HOSPITAL OF VAN NUYS** See Southern California Hospital at Van Nuys

**SOUTHERN CALIFORNIA HOSPITAL AT VAN NUYS** See Southern California Hospital at Hollywood, Los Angeles

★ △ ⇑ **VALLEY PRESBYTERIAN HOSPITAL (050126)**, 15107 Vanowen Street, Zip 91405–4597; tel. 818/782–6600, (Nonreporting) **A**7 10 21
Primary Contact: Gustavo A. Valdespino, President and Chief Executive Officer
COO: Lori Cardle, Senior Vice President, Chief Operating Officer
CFO: Janice Klostermeier, Senior Vice President and Chief Financial Officer
CMO: Clyde Wesp, M.D., Chief Medical Officer
CIO: Jeff Allport, Vice President, Chief Information Officer
CHR: Deborah Gac, Vice President Human Resources
CNO: Lori Burnell, R.N., Ph.D., Senior Vice President and Chief Nursing Officer
Web address: www.valleypres.org
**Control**: Other not–for–profit (including NFP Corporation) **Service**: General medical and surgical

**Staffed Beds: 350**

## VENTURA—Ventura County

**AURORA VISTA DEL MAR HOSPITAL** See Vista Del Mar Hospital

⇑ **COMMUNITY MEMORIAL HEALTH SYSTEM** See Community Memorial Hospital

★ ⇑ **COMMUNITY MEMORIAL HOSPITAL (050394)**, 147 North Brent Street, Zip 93003–2809; tel. 805/652–5011, (Includes COMMUNITY MEMORIAL HOSPITAL, Mailing address: 147 North Brent Street, Ventura, California, Zip 93003–2854; tel. 805/652–5011), (Nonreporting) **A**2 3 5 10 13 21 **S** Community Memorial Health System, Ventura, CA
Primary Contact: Gary Wilde, President and Chief Executive Officer
COO: Adam Thunell, Chief Operating Officer and Vice President Operations
CFO: David Glyer, Vice President Finance
CMO: Stanley Frochtzwajg, M.D., Chief Medical Officer
CIO: Ron Sandifer, Chief Information Officer
CHR: Diany Klein, Vice President Human Resources
Web address: www.cmhshealth.org
**Control**: Other not–for–profit (including NFP Corporation) **Service**: General medical and surgical

**Staffed Beds: 284**

⊞ **VENTURA COUNTY MEDICAL CENTER (050159)**, 300 Hillmont Avenue, Zip 93003–3099; tel. 805/652–6000, (Nonreporting) **A**1 2 3 5 10
Primary Contact: John Fankhauser, M.D., Chief Executive Officer
CMO: Bryan Wong, M.D., Medical Director
CIO: Terry Theobald, Chief Information Officer
CHR: Tim Rhyne, Personnel Officer
CNO: Susan Scott, Chief Nurse Executive
Web address: www.vchca.org
**Control**: County, Government, Nonfederal **Service**: General medical and surgical

**Staffed Beds: 160**

☐ **VISTA DEL MAR HOSPITAL (054077)**, 801 Seneca Street, Zip 93001–1411; tel. 805/653–6434, (Nonreporting) **A**1 10 **S** Signature Healthcare Services, Corona, CA
Primary Contact: Jenifer Nyhuis, Chief Executive Officer
CFO: Kurt Broten, Chief Financial Officer
CMO: Steve Ruths, M.D., Chief Medical Officer
Web address: www.vistadelmarhospital.com
**Control**: Corporation, Investor–owned (for–profit) **Service**: Psychiatric

**Staffed Beds: 87**

**CA**

## VICTORVILLE—San Bernardino County

○ **DESERT VALLEY HOSPITAL (050709)**, 16850 Bear Valley Road, Zip 92395–5795; tel. 760/241–8000, (Nonreporting) **A**10 11 **S** Prime Healthcare, Ontario, CA
Primary Contact: Fred Hunter, R.N., Chief Executive Officer
COO: Luis Leon, Chief Operating Officer
CFO: Martin Mansukhani, Chief Financial Officer
CIO: Sreekant Gotti, Director Information Systems
Web address: www.dvmc.com
**Control:** Corporation, Investor–owned (for–profit) **Service:** General medical and surgical

**Staffed Beds: 110**

**VICTOR VALLEY COMMUNITY HOSPITAL** See Victor Valley Global Medical Center

☐ **VICTOR VALLEY GLOBAL MEDICAL CENTER (050517)**, 15248 Eleventh Street, Zip 92395–3704; tel. 760/245–8691, (Nonreporting) **A**1 10
Primary Contact: Lori Burns, Administrator
COO: Doreen Dann, R.N., Chief Operating Officer
CIO: Joe Archer, Chief Information Officer
CHR: Cesar Lugo, Director Human Resources
Web address: www.vvgmc.com
**Control:** Other not–for–profit (including NFP Corporation) **Service:** General medical and surgical

**Staffed Beds: 101**

## VISALIA—Tulare County

**KAWEAH DELTA HEALTH CARE DISTRICT** See Kaweah Delta Medical Center

⊠ △ **KAWEAH DELTA MEDICAL CENTER (050057)**, 400 West Mineral King Avenue, Zip 93291–6263; tel. 559/624–2000, (Includes SOUTH CAMPUS, Mailing address: 1633 South Court Street, Visalia, California, Zip 93277; tel. 559/624–6090) (Total facility includes 60 beds in nursing home–type unit) **A**1 3 5 7 10 **F**3 13 15 17 18 20 22 24 26 28 29 30 31 34 35 40 41 43 45 49 50 51 53 54 56 57 59 60 62 63 64 65 68 70 73 74 75 76 77 78 79 81 82 84 85 86 87 89 90 93 97 98 100 101 102 103 104 107 108 110 111 114 115 116 117 118 119 123 124 126 127 128 129 130 131 132 134 135 144 146 147 148 149 156 157 **P**3
Primary Contact: Gary K. Herbst, Chief Executive Officer
COO: Thomas J Rayner, Senior Vice President and Chief Operating Officer
CFO: Malinda Tupper, Vice President and Chief Financial Officer
CIO: Doug Leeper, Chief Information Officer
CHR: Dianne E Cox, Vice President of Human Resources
CNO: Regina Sawyer, Vice President Chief Nursing Officer
Web address: www.kaweahdelta.org
**Control:** Hospital district or authority, Government, Nonfederal **Service:** General medical and surgical

**Staffed Beds: 437 Admissions: 27674 Census: 472 Outpatient Visits: 857724 Births: 4895 Total Expense ($000): 737365 Payroll Expense ($000): 287902 Personnel: 4561**

**VISALIA COMMUNITY HOSPITAL** See South Campus

## WALNUT CREEK—Contra Costa County

⊠ △ **JOHN MUIR MEDICAL CENTER, WALNUT CREEK (050180)**, 1601 Ygnacio Valley Road, Zip 94598–3194; tel. 925/939–3000, (Nonreporting) **A**1 2 3 5 7 10 **F**3 11 13 15 18 19 20 22 24 26 28 29 30 31 32 34 35 37 39 40 41 43 44 45 46 47 48 49 50 54 55 56 57 58 59 61 62 64 65 68 70 72 74 75 76 77 78 79 80 81 82 83 84 85 86 87 88 89 90 91 93 95 96 100 102 107 108 110 118 119 120 121 123 124 126 130 131 132 141 145 146 147 148 149 150 154 156 157 **P**3 7 **S** John Muir Health, Walnut Creek, CA
Primary Contact: Jane Willemsen, President and Chief Administrative Officer
COO: Raymond Nassief, Senior Vice President, Hospital Operations and Support Services
CFO: Christian Pass, Senior Vice President & Chief Financial Officer
CMO: Irving Pike, M.D., Senior Vice President and Chief Medical Officer
CIO: Jon Russell, Senior Vice President & Chief Information Officer
CHR: Lisa Foust, Senior Vice President, Human Resources
CNO: Michelle Anne Lopes, MSN, R.N., Senior Vice President, Patient Care Services & Chief Nursing Officer
Web address: www.https://www.johnmuirhealth.com/
**Control:** Other not–for–profit (including NFP Corporation) **Service:** General medical and surgical

**Staffed Beds: 420 Admissions: 19896 Census: 285 Outpatient Visits: 373580 Births: 2802 Total Expense ($000): 897023 Payroll Expense ($000): 315313 Personnel: 1960**

⊠ **KAISER PERMANENTE WALNUT CREEK MEDICAL CENTER (050072)**, 1425 South Main Street, Zip 94596–5300; tel. 925/295–4000, (Includes KAISER FOUNDATION HOSPITAL, Mailing address: 200 Muir Road, Martinez, California, Zip 94553–4696; tel. 510/372–1000), (Nonreporting) **A**1 2 3 5 10 **F**3 11 13 15 18 20 22 26 30 31 34 39 40 41 45 49 56 60 63 64 68 70 73 74 75 76 78 79 80 81 82 84 85 86 87 89 100 107 108 110 111 114 115 118 119 120 121 123 124 130 135 146 149 154 **P**6 **S** Kaiser Foundation Hospitals, Oakland, CA
Primary Contact: Colleen McKeown, Senior Vice President and Area Manager
CFO: Yakesun Wing, Business Strategy and Finance Leader
Web address: www.kaiserpermanente.org
**Control:** Other not–for–profit (including NFP Corporation) **Service:** General medical and surgical

**Staffed Beds: 233 Admissions: 11540 Census: 132 Outpatient Visits: 140231 Births: 3139 Personnel: 1597**

**WALNUT CREEK MEDICAL CENTER** See Kaiser Permanente Walnut Creek Medical Center

## WATSONVILLE—Santa Cruz County

⊠ **WATSONVILLE COMMUNITY HOSPITAL (050194)**, 75 Nielson Street, Zip 95076–2468; tel. 831/724–4741, (Nonreporting) **A**1 10
Primary Contact: Sean Fowler, Chief Executive Officer
CFO: Rachel Jones, Chief Financial Officer
CIO: Sergio Nell, Director Information Systems
CNO: Donna Salvi, Chief Nursing Officer
Web address: www.watsonvillehospital.com
**Control:** Other not–for–profit (including NFP Corporation) **Service:** General medical and surgical

**Staffed Beds: 106**

## WEAVERVILLE—Trinity County

**MOUNTAIN COMMUNITY MED SERVS** See Trinity Hospital

**TRINITY HOSPITAL (051315)**, 60 Easter Avenue, Zip 96093, Mailing Address: P.O. Box 1229, Zip 96093–1229; tel. 530/623–2687, (Nonreporting) **A**10 18
Primary Contact: Aaron Rogers, Chief Executive Officer
CFO: Jennifer Van Matre, Chief Financial Officer
CMO: Daniel Harwood, M.D., Chief of Staff
CIO: Jake Odom, Chief Information Officer
CHR: Elizabeth Reeder, Director Human Resources
CNO: Belen Manybanseng, R.N., Chief Nursing Officer
Web address: www.mcmedical.org
**Control:** Hospital district or authority, Government, Nonfederal **Service:** General medical and surgical

**Staffed Beds: 47**

## WEST COVINA—Los Angeles County

**DOCTORS HOSPITAL OF WEST COVINA** See West Covina Medical Center

**QUEEN OF THE VALLEY HOSPITAL** See Citrus Valley Medical Center-Queen of The Valley Campus

**SPECIALTY HOSPITAL** See Kindred Hospital San Gabriel Valley

☐ **WEST COVINA MEDICAL CENTER (050096)**, 725 South Orange Avenue, Zip 91790–2614; tel. 626/338–8481, (Nonreporting) **A**1 10
Primary Contact: Gerald H. Wallman, Administrator
CFO: Kami Horvat, Chief Financial Officer
CMO: Erich Pollak, M.D., Chief of Staff
CHR: Lourdes Meza, Coordinator Human Resources
CNO: Guadalupe Ojeda, R.N., Chief Nursing Officer
**Control:** Corporation, Investor–owned (for–profit) **Service:** General medical and surgical

**Staffed Beds: 46**

## WEST HILLS—Los Angeles County

⊠ **WEST HILLS HOSPITAL AND MEDICAL CENTER (050481)**, 7300 Medical Center Drive, Zip 91307–1900; tel. 818/676–4000, (Nonreporting) **A**1 10 **S** HCA Healthcare, Nashville, TN
Primary Contact: Mark Miller, FACHE, Chief Executive Officer
COO: Isaiah Zirkle, Chief Operating Officer
CFO: David Cantrell, CPA, Vice President and Chief Financial Officer
CMO: Yale D. Podnos, M.D., Chief Medical Officer
CHR: Diana Steel, Vice President Human Resources
CNO: Janeen Gallego, Chief Nursing Officer
Web address: www.westhillshospital.com
**Control:** Corporation, Investor–owned (for–profit) **Service:** General medical and surgical

**Staffed Beds: 260**

**WEST HILLS MEDICAL CENTER** See West Hills Hospital and Medical Center

*Many Facility Codes have changed. Please refer to the AHA Guide Code Chart.* © 2021 AHA Guide

## WESTMINSTER—Orange County

**KINDRED HOSPITAL-ORANGE COUNTY** See Kindred Hospital-Westminster

☒ **KINDRED HOSPITAL-WESTMINSTER (052035)**, 200 Hospital Circle, Zip 92683–3910; tel. 714/893–4541, (Nonreporting) **A**1 10 **S** Kindred Healthcare, Louisville, KY
Primary Contact: Julie Myers, Chief Executive Officer
CFO: Dale Wagner, Chief Financial Officer
Web address: www.khwestminster.com/
**Control**: Corporation, Investor–owned (for–profit) **Service**: Acute long–term care hospital

**Staffed Beds: 109**

## WHITTIER—Los Angeles County

☒ **PIH HEALTH HOSPITAL - WHITTIER (050169)**, 12401 Washington Boulevard, Zip 90602–1099; tel. 562/698–0811, (Total facility includes 26 beds in nursing home–type unit) (Nonreporting) **A**1 2 3 5 10 22 **F**1 3 8 11 12 13 15 18 20 22 24 26 28 29 30 31 34 38 40 45 46 49 50 54 55 56 57 58 59 60 61 62 63 64 65 68 70 72 74 75 76 77 78 79 81 84 85 86 87 90 93 94 96 97 100 107 108 110 111 114 115 116 117 118 119 120 121 123 128 130 131 132 135 143 146 147 148 149 154 156 157 **S** PIH Health, Whittier, CA
Primary Contact: James R. West, President and Chief Executive Officer
COO: Reanna Thompson, R.N., Chief Operating Officer and Chief Nursing Officer
CFO: Greg Williams, Chief Financial Officer
CMO: Rosalio J Lopez, M.D., Senior Vice President and Chief Medical Officer
CIO: Jason Fischer, Chief Information Officer
CNO: Ramona Pratt, Chief Nursing Officer
Web address: www.PIHHealth.org
**Control**: Other not–for–profit (including NFP Corporation) **Service**: General medical and surgical

**Staffed Beds: 255 Admissions: 19008 Census: 213 Outpatient Visits: 390814 Births: 1700 Total Expense ($000): 581390 Payroll Expense ($000): 210649 Personnel: 3114**

**PIH HEALTH HOSPITAL-WHITTIER** See PIH Health Hospital - Whittier

☐ **WHITTIER HOSPITAL MEDICAL CENTER (050735)**, 9080 Colima Road, Zip 90605–1600; tel. 562/945–3561, (Nonreporting) **A**1 10 **S** AHMC & Healthcare, Inc., Alhambra, CA
Primary Contact: Richard Castro, Chief Executive Officer
COO: Mary Anne Monje, Chief Financial Officer and Chief Operating Officer
CFO: Mary Anne Monje, Chief Financial Officer and Chief Operating Officer
CIO: Jay Geldhof, Director Information Systems
CHR: Terry Jaqua, Human Resources Director
CNO: Sarkis Vartanian, Chief Nursing Officer
Web address: www.whittierhospital.com
**Control**: Corporation, Investor–owned (for–profit) **Service**: General medical and surgical

**Staffed Beds: 100**

## WILDOMAR—Riverside County

**INLAND VALLEY REG MEDICAL CTR** See Inland Valley Medical Center

## WILLITS—Mendocino County

☒ **ADVENTIST HEALTH HOWARD MEMORIAL (051310)**, One Marcela Drive, Zip 95490–4298; tel. 707/459–6801, (Nonreporting) **A**1 3 10 18 **F**11 15 29 30 34 35 40 57 59 68 70 75 79 81 93 97 107 110 111 115 119 127 131 132 133 135 146 147 148 **P**3 **S** Adventist Health, Roseville, CA
Primary Contact: Jason Wells, President and Chief Executive Officer
CFO: Judson Howe, Chief Financial Officer
CMO: Kimberly Faucher, M.D., Chief Medical Officer
CIO: Cecilia Winiger, Community Outreach and Communication Manager
CHR: Darcy De Leon, Executive Director, Human Resources
CNO: Karen M Scott, Vice President Patient Care
Web address: www.howardhospital.com
**Control**: Church operated, Nongovernment, not–for–profit **Service**: General medical and surgical

**Staffed Beds: 25 Admissions: 1774 Census: 18 Outpatient Visits: 64169 Births: 0 Total Expense ($000): 76255 Payroll Expense ($000): 22827 Personnel: 305**

**FRANK R. HOWARD MEMORIAL HOSPITAL** See Adventist Health Howard Memorial

## WILLOWS—Glenn County

**GLENN GENERAL HOSPITAL** See Glenn Medical Center

**GLENN MEDICAL CENTER (051306)**, 1133 West Sycamore Street, Zip 95988–2745; tel. 530/934–1800, (Nonreporting) **A**10 18
Primary Contact: Timothy M. Moran, Chief Executive Officer
CFO: John Lovrich, Chief Financial Officer
CHR: Deborah McMillan, Director Human Resources
CNO: Timothy Speek IDirector of Nursing
Web address: www.glennmed.org
**Control**: Other not–for–profit (including NFP Corporation) **Service**: General medical and surgical

**Staffed Beds: 15**

## WOODLAND—Yolo County

☒ **WOODLAND HEALTHCARE (050127)**, 1325 Cottonwood Street, Zip 95695–5199; tel. 530/662–3961, (Nonreporting) **A**1 5 10 **F**2 3 11 13 18 20 26 28 29 30 31 34 35 40 45 46 47 49 50 51 56 57 58 59 60 61 64 68 70 72 74 75 76 78 79 81 82 84 85 86 87 89 98 100 102 103 107 108 111 114 115 116 117 119 129 130 131 132 135 146 147 148 149 154 155 **S** CommonSpirit Health, Chicago, IL
Primary Contact: Edmundo Castaneda, President and Chief Executive Officer
CMO: Sarada Mylavarapu, M.D., Chief Medical Officer
Web address: www.woodlandhealthcare.org
**Control**: Church operated, Nongovernment, not–for–profit **Service**: General medical and surgical

**Staffed Beds: 105 Admissions: 5021 Census: 42 Outpatient Visits: 60537 Births: 644 Total Expense ($000): 193608 Payroll Expense ($000): 71721 Personnel: 639**

**WOODLAND MEMORIAL HOSPITAL** See Woodland Healthcare

## WOODLAND HILLS—Los Angeles County

☒ **KAISER PERMANENTE WOODLAND HILLS MEDICAL CENTER (050677)**, 5601 DeSoto Avenue, Zip 91367–6798; tel. 818/719–2000, (Nonreporting) **A**1 3 5 10 **F**3 6 8 9 12 13 15 18 28 29 30 31 32 34 35 38 40 41 44 45 46 48 49 50 51 52 53 54 55 56 57 58 59 60 61 63 64 65 68 70 73 74 75 76 77 78 79 80 81 82 84 85 86 87 90 92 93 97 100 102 104 107 108 110 111 114 115 116 117 119 124 129 130 131 132 134 135 141 144 146 147 148 149 150 153 154 156 157 158 **P**6 **S** Kaiser Foundation Hospitals, Oakland, CA
Primary Contact: Murtaza Sanwari, Senior Vice President and Area Manager
COO: Richard Trogman, FACHE, Chief Operating Officer
CFO: Marilou Cheung, Assistant Administrator Finance
CMO: Gregory Kelman, M.D., Area Medical Director
CIO: Earle Johnson, Area Information Officer
CHR: Cathy Cousineau, Director Human Resources
CNO: Nancy Tankel, R.N., Chief Nurse Executive
Web address: www.kaiserpermanente.org
**Control**: Other not–for–profit (including NFP Corporation) **Service**: General medical and surgical

**Staffed Beds: 185 Admissions: 7828 Census: 80 Outpatient Visits: 136203 Births: 1729 Personnel: 1648**

☐ **MOTION PICTURE AND TELEVISION FUND HOSPITAL AND RESIDENTIAL SERVICES (050552)**, 23388 Mulholland Drive, Zip 91364–2792; tel. 818/876–1888, (Nonreporting) **A**1 3 10
Primary Contact: Bob Beitcher, Chief Executive Officer
COO: David Asplund, Chief Operating Officer
CFO: Frank Guarrera, Executive Vice President and Chief Financial Officer
CHR: Nancy Rubin, Vice President Human Resources
Web address: www.mptvfund.org
**Control**: Other not–for–profit (including NFP Corporation) **Service**: General medical and surgical

**Staffed Beds: 20**

**WOODLAND HILLS MEDICAL CENTER** See Kaiser Permanente Woodland Hills Medical Center

---

**Hospital, Medicare Provider Number, Address, Telephone, Approval, Facility, and Physician Codes, Health Care System**

★ American Hospital Association (AHA) membership    ○ Healthcare Facilities Accreditation Program    ⇑ Center for Improvement in Healthcare Quality Accreditation
☐ The Joint Commission accreditation    ◇ DNV Healthcare Inc. accreditation    △ Commission on Accreditation of Rehabilitation Facilities (CARF) accreditation

## YREKA—Siskiyou County

☒ **FAIRCHILD MEDICAL CENTER (051316)**, 444 Bruce Street, Zip 96097–3450;
tel. 530/842–4121, (Nonreporting) **A**1 10 18
Primary Contact: Jonathon Andrus, Chief Executive Officer
CFO: Kelly Martin, Chief Financial Officer
CMO: Moudy Youssef, M.D., Chief Medical Officer
CIO: Randy Ferguson, Information Systems Manager
CHR: Joann Sarmento, Manager Human Resources
CNO: Susan Westphal, Assistant Administrator, Patient Care Services
Web address: www.fairchildmed.org
**Control**: Other not–for–profit (including NFP Corporation) **Service**: General
medical and surgical

| Staffed Beds: 25 |
|---|

**FAIRFIELD MEDICAL CENTER** See Fairchild Medical Center

## YUBA CITY—Sutter County

**FREMONT MEDICAL CENTER** See Adventist Health and Rideout, Marysville

☐ **SUTTER SURGICAL HOSPITAL - NORTH VALLEY (050766)**, 455 Plumas
Boulevard, Zip 95991–5074; tel. 530/749–5700, (Nonreporting) **A**1 5 10 **S**
Sutter Health, Sacramento, CA
Primary Contact: Shawndra Simpson, Interim Chief Executive Officer
CHR: Michelle Guina, Manager Human Resources
CNO: David Cooke, R.N., Chief Nursing Officer
Web address: www.sshnv.org
**Control**: Partnership, Investor–owned (for–profit) **Service**: Surgical

| Staffed Beds: 14 |
|---|

CA

# COLORADO

CO

## ALAMOSA—Alamosa County

★ **SAN LUIS VALLEY HEALTH (060008)**, 106 Blanca Avenue, Zip 81101–2393; tel. 719/589–2511, (Nonreporting) **A**3 10 20 **F**3 8 13 15 18 29 30 31 32 33 34 35 38 40 43 44 45 53 54 56 57 59 60 65 68 70 74 75 76 77 78 79 81 82 84 85 87 93 97 107 108 110 111 115 116 117 118 119 127 129 130 131 132 133 146 147 148 154 156 157 **S** San Luis Valley Health, Alamosa, CO
Primary Contact: Konnie Martin, Chief Executive Officer
COO: Patti Thompson, Chief Operating Officer
CFO: Shane Mortensen, Chief Financial Officer
CMO: Carmelo Hernandez, M.D., Chief Medical Officer
CIO: Chuck Laufle, Director of Information Services
CHR: Mandy Lee Crockett, Director Human Resources
Web address: www.sanluisvalleyhealth.org
**Control**: Other not–for–profit (including NFP Corporation) **Service**: General medical and surgical

**Staffed Beds**: 49 **Admissions**: 2561 **Census**: 24 **Outpatient Visits**: 151915 **Births**: 437 **Total Expense ($000)**: 97987 **Payroll Expense ($000)**: 47112

**SAN LUIS VALLEY HEALTH REGIONAL MEDICAL CENTER** See San Luis Valley Health

## ASPEN—Pitkin County

✉ **ASPEN VALLEY HOSPITAL (061324)**, 0401 Castle Creek Road, Zip 81611–1159; tel. 970/925–1120, (Nonreporting) **A**1 10 18
Primary Contact: David Ressler, Chief Executive Officer
CFO: Ginette Sebenaler, Associate Chief Financial Officer
CMO: J Christopher Beck, D.O., President Medical Staff
CIO: Ginny Dyche, Director Community Relations
CHR: Alicia Miller, Director Human Resources
CNO: Elaine Gerson, Chief Clinical Officer and General Counsel
Web address: www.avhaspen.org
**Control**: Hospital district or authority, Government, Nonfederal **Service**: General medical and surgical

**Staffed Beds**: 25

**ASPEN VALLEY HOSPITAL DISTRICT** See Aspen Valley Hospital

## AURORA—Arapahoe County

**AURORA REGIONAL MEDICAL CENTER** See South Campus

## AURORA—Adams County

✉ **CHILDREN'S HOSPITAL COLORADO (063303)**, 13123 East 16th Avenue, Zip 80045–7106; tel. 720/777–1234, (Includes CHILDREN'S HOSPITAL OF COLORADO AT MEMORIAL, Mailing address: 1400 East Boulder Street, Colorado Springs, Colorado, Zip 80909–5533; tel. 719/365–5000; Greg Raymond, Regional Vice President, Southern Colorado), (Nonreporting) **A**1 3 5 8 10 **F**3 11 12 13 14 17 19 21 23 25 27 28 29 30 31 32 34 35 36 38 39 40 41 43 44 45 46 48 49 50 53 54 55 58 59 60 61 64 65 66 68 71 72 74 75 76 77 78 79 80 81 82 84 85 86 87 88 89 91 92 93 95 96 97 98 99 100 101 102 104 107 108 111 114 115 116 117 119 126 129 130 131 132 134 136 137 138 139 141 144 146 147 148
Primary Contact: Jena Hausmann, President and Chief Executive Officer
COO: David Biggerstaff, Chief Operating Officer
CFO: Jeff Harrington, Chief Financial Officer
CMO: Joan Bothner, M.D., Chief Medical Officer
CIO: Dana Moore, Chief Information Officer
CNO: Patricia Givens, R.N., Chief Nursing Officer
Web address: www.thechildrenshospital.org
**Control**: Other not–for–profit (including NFP Corporation) **Service**: Children's general medical and surgical

**Staffed Beds**: 486 **Admissions**: 16541 **Census**: 305

**COLUMBIA PRESBYTERIAN MED CTR** See Medical Center of Aurora North

## AURORA—Arapahoe County

✉ **KINDRED HOSPITAL-AURORA (062013)**, 700 Potomac Street 2nd Floor, Zip 80011–6844; tel. 720/857–8333, (Nonreporting) **A**1 10 **S** Kindred Healthcare, Louisville, KY
Primary Contact: Marc Lemon, Chief Executive Officer
CMO: Eric Yaeger, M.D., Chief Medical Officer
CHR: Becky Small, Chief Human Resources Officer
CNO: Paul Green, Chief Clinical Officer
Web address: www.khaurora.com/
**Control**: Corporation, Investor–owned (for–profit) **Service**: Acute long–term care hospital

**Staffed Beds**: 37

✉ **MEDICAL CENTER OF AURORA (060100)**, 1501 South Potomac Street, Zip 80012–5411; tel. 303/695–2600, (Includes MEDICAL CENTER OF AURORA NORTH, Mailing address: 700 Potomac Street, Aurora, Colorado, Zip 80011–6792; tel. 303/363–7200; MEDICAL CENTER OF AURORA, Mailing address: 700 Potomac Street, Aurora, Colorado, Zip 80011; tel. 303/360–3030; Ryan Simpson, President and Chief Executive Officer; SOUTH CAMPUS, Mailing address: 1501 South Potomac, Aurora, Colorado, Zip 80012; tel. 303/695–2600), (Nonreporting) **A**1 2 3 5 10 **S** HCA Healthcare, Nashville, TN
Primary Contact: Ryan Simpson, President and Chief Executive Officer
CFO: Bryce DeHaven, Chief Financial Officer
CMO: Dianne McCallister, M.D., Chief Medical Officer
CNO: John Roque, MSN, R.N., Chief Nursing Officer
Web address: www.auroramed.com
**Control**: Corporation, Investor–owned (for–profit) **Service**: General medical and surgical

**Staffed Beds**: 360

**MEDICAL CENTER OF AURORA-SOUTH** See Medical Center of Aurora

## AURORA—Adams County

✉ **SPALDING REHABILITATION HOSPITAL (063027)**, 900 Potomac Steet, Zip 80011–6716; tel. 303/367–1166, (Nonreporting) **A**1 10 **S** HCA Healthcare, Nashville, TN
Primary Contact: Ryan Simpson, President and Chief Executive Officer
COO: Debbie Petersen, R.N., Chief Operating Officer and Chief Nursing Officer
CFO: Joyce Webber, Chief Financial Officer
CHR: Donna Greeley, Director Human Resources
CNO: John Roque, MSN, R.N., Chief Nursing Officer
Web address: www.spaldingrehab.com
**Control**: Partnership, Investor–owned (for–profit) **Service**: Rehabilitation

**Staffed Beds**: 100

**THE CHILDREN'S HOSPITAL** See Children's Hospital Colorado

## AURORA—Arapahoe County

**TRIUMPH HOSPITAL AURORA** See Kindred Hospital-Aurora

---

**Hospital, Medicare Provider Number, Address, Telephone, Approval, Facility, and Physician Codes, Health Care System**

★ American Hospital Association (AHA) membership   ○ Healthcare Facilities Accreditation Program   ⇑ Center for Improvement in Healthcare Quality Accreditation
☐ The Joint Commission accreditation   ◇ DNV Healthcare Inc. accreditation   △ Commission on Accreditation of Rehabilitation Facilities (CARF) accreditation

**CO**

## AURORA—Adams County

**UNIV OF COLORADO HOSPITAL** See University of Colorado Hospital

☒ **UNIVERSITY OF COLORADO HOSPITAL (060024)**, 12401 East 17th Avenue,
MS F417, Zip 80045–2545; tel. 720/848–0000, (Nonreporting) **A**1 2 3 5 8 10
**F**3 4 5 6 8 9 11 12 13 14 15 16 17 18 20 22 24 26 28 29 30 31 33 34 35 36
37 38 39 40 42 43 44 45 46 47 48 49 50 52 53 54 55 56 57 58 59 60 61 63
64 65 68 70 71 72 74 75 76 77 78 79 80 81 82 84 85 86 87 90 91 92 93 96
97 98 100 101 102 103 104 105 106 107 108 109 110 111 112 113 114 115
116 117 118 119 120 121 123 124 126 129 130 131 132 134 135 136 137
138 139 140 141 142 145 146 147 148 149 150 152 153 154 156 157 **S**
UCHealth, Fort Collins, CO
Primary Contact: Christopher A. Gessner, President and Chief Executive Officer
COO: Thomas Gronow, Chief Operating Officer
CFO: Barbara Carveth, Chief Financial Officer
CMO: Jean Kutner, M.D., Chief Medical Officer
CIO: Steve Hess, Vice President Information Services and Chief Information Officer
CNO: Katherine Howell, Chief Nursing Officer
Web address: www.uchealth.org
**Control**: Hospital district or authority, Government, Nonfederal **Service**: General
medical and surgical

> **Staffed Beds:** 829 **Admissions:** 32727 **Census:** 582 **Outpatient**
> **Visits:** 1480093 **Births:** 3685 **Total Expense ($000):** 1812359 **Payroll**
> **Expense ($000):** 534354 **Personnel:** 7145

## BOULDER—Boulder County

☒ **BOULDER COMMUNITY HEALTH (060027)**, 4747 Arapahoe Ave,
Zip 80303–1133, Mailing Address: P.O. Box 9019, Zip 80301–9019;
tel. 303/415–7000, (Includes BOULDER COMMUNITY FOOTHILLS HOSPITAL,
Mailing address: 4747 Arapahoe Avenue, Boulder, Colorado, Zip 80303–1133,
P O Box 9047, Zip 80301–9047, tel. 720/854–7000; Robert Vissers, M.D.,
President and Chief Executive Officer), (Nonreporting) **A**1 **F**3 5 7 8 13 15
18 20 22 24 26 28 29 30 31 34 35 36 37 40 42 43 45 46 49 50 54 56 59 60
61 62 64 65 68 70 72 74 75 76 77 78 79 81 84 85 87 93 94 96 97 98 100
101 102 104 107 109 110 111 114 115 118 119 126 130 132 144 146 147
148 149 153 154 155 **P**4 5 6
Primary Contact: Robert Vissers, M.D., President and Chief Executive Officer
CFO: Bill Munson, Vice President and Chief Financial Officer
CNO: Jacqueline M Attlesey-Pries, MS, R.N., Chief Nursing Officer, Vice President
Web address: www.bch.org
**Control**: Other not–for–profit (including NFP Corporation) **Service**: General
medical and surgical

> **Staffed Beds:** 167 **Admissions:** 7815 **Census:** 86 **Outpatient**
> **Visits:** 385742 **Births:** 653 **Total Expense ($000):** 369352 **Payroll Expense**
> **($000):** 164620 **Personnel:** 2086

**BOULDER COMMUNITY HOSPITAL** See Boulder Community Health

## BRIGHTON—Adams County

☒ **PLATTE VALLEY MEDICAL CENTER (060004)**, 1600 Prairie Center Parkway,
Zip 80601–4006; tel. 303/498–1600, (Nonreporting) **A**1 5 10 **F**3 5 7 13 15 18
20 22 26 28 29 30 31 34 35 40 43 45 49 57 65 68 70 73 74 75 76 77 78 79
81 85 87 90 92 93 107 108 110 111 115 119 130 132 135 146 147 148 149
152 154 **P**6 **S** SCL Health, Broomfield, CO
Primary Contact: John R. Hicks, President and Chief Executive Officer
COO: Kurt G Gensert, FACHE, R.N., Vice President Operations
CFO: Harold Dupper, Chief Financial Officer
CMO: Kirk Quackenbush, M.D., Chief of Staff
CIO: Timothy Brannigan, Director Information Services
CHR: Jackie J. Dunkin, Director Human Resources
Web address: www.pvmc.org
**Control**: Other not–for–profit (including NFP Corporation) **Service**: General
medical and surgical

> **Staffed Beds:** 97 **Admissions:** 3111 **Census:** 30 **Outpatient Visits:** 97204
> **Births:** 745 **Total Expense ($000):** 135853 **Payroll Expense ($000):** 40473
> **Personnel:** 530

## BROOMFIELD—Denver County

☐ **UCHEALTH BROOMFIELD HOSPITAL (060129)**, 11820 Destination Drive,
Zip 80021; tel. 303/460–6000, (Nonreporting) **A**1 3 **F**3 7 9 14 15 29 30 35 40
43 50 56 61 64 68 75 76 77 79 81 85 87 90 96 100 102 107 115 119 130
131 146 148 154 **S** UCHealth, Fort Collins, CO
Primary Contact: Lonnie Cramer, President
Web address: www.uchealth.org/pages/OHAM/OrgUnitDetails.aspx?
**Control**: Other not–for–profit (including NFP Corporation) **Service**: General
medical and surgical

> **Staffed Beds:** 40 **Admissions:** 291 **Census:** 6 **Outpatient Visits:** 5282
> **Births:** 0 **Total Expense ($000):** 44064 **Payroll Expense ($000):** 12103
> **Personnel:** 126

## BRUSH—Morgan County

☒ **EAST MORGAN COUNTY HOSPITAL (061303)**, 2400 West Edison Street,
Zip 80723–1640; tel. 970/842–6200, (Nonreporting) **A**1 10 18 **F**3 13 15 28 29
34 35 36 40 41 43 45 50 53 56 57 59 65 68 75 76 77 79 80 81 85 86 87 89
93 96 97 107 108 110 111 114 115 119 127 128 130 131 132 133 141 146
147 148 149 154 155 156 **P**8 **S** Banner Health, Phoenix, AZ
Primary Contact: Linda Thorpe, Chief Executive Officer
CFO: Edith Pemberton, Chief Financial Officer
CHR: Cynthia Wentworth, Chief Human Resource Officer
CNO: Linda Lyn Roan, Chief Nursing Officer
Web address: www.emchbrush.com
**Control**: Other not–for–profit (including NFP Corporation) **Service**: General
medical and surgical

> **Staffed Beds:** 22 **Admissions:** 493 **Census:** 4 **Outpatient Visits:** 47965
> **Births:** 119 **Total Expense ($000):** 32123 **Payroll Expense ($000):** 14697
> **Personnel:** 156

## BURLINGTON—Kit Carson County

★ **KIT CARSON COUNTY HEALTH SERVICE DISTRICT (061313)**, 286 16th
Street, Zip 80807–1697; tel. 719/346–5311, (Nonreporting) **A**10 18
Primary Contact: Darcy Howard, Interim Chief Executive Officer
CMO: Bong Pham, Chief Medical Officer
CIO: Paul Velasco, IT Manager
CHR: Robin Konecne, Manager Human Resources
CNO: Kandi Kuper, Chief Nursing Officer
Web address: www.kcchsd.org
**Control**: Hospital district or authority, Government, Nonfederal **Service**: General
medical and surgical

> **Staffed Beds:** 19

**KIT CARSON COUNTY MEMORIAL HOSPITAL** See Kit Carson County Health
Service District

## CANON CITY—Fremont County

**ST THOMAS BENEDICTINE HLTH CTR** See St. Thomas More Hospital

☒ **ST. THOMAS MORE HOSPITAL (061344)**, 1338 Phay Avenue,
Zip 81212–2302; tel. 719/285–2000, (Nonreporting) **A**1 10 18 **F**3 8 11 12 13
15 28 29 30 34 35 40 43 51 53 57 59 64 66 70 75 76 77 79 81 85 86 87 93
97 107 108 110 111 119 127 129 130 131 132 133 146 147 148 149 154 **P**6
**S** CommonSpirit Health, Chicago, IL
Primary Contact: Kristi Olson, Chief Executive Officer
COO: Dennis Bruens, Vice President Operations
CFO: Gwenyth Howard, Vice President Finance
CMO: Kern Low, M.D., Chief Medical Officer
CIO: Jillian Maes, Director Marketing and Public Relations
CHR: Janet Reedy, Manager Human Resources
CNO: James Woodard, Chief Nursing Officer
Web address: www.stmhospital.org
**Control**: Church operated, Nongovernment, not–for–profit **Service**: General
medical and surgical

> **Staffed Beds:** 25 **Admissions:** 1774 **Census:** 15 **Outpatient Visits:** 46749
> **Births:** 221 **Total Expense ($000):** 45460 **Payroll Expense ($000):** 15880
> **Personnel:** 344

## CASTLE ROCK—Douglas County

☒ **CASTLE ROCK ADVENTIST HOSPITAL (060125)**, 2350 Meadows Boulevard,
Zip 80109–8405; tel. 720/455–5000, (Nonreporting) **A**1 3 10 **F**3 11 13 15 18
20 22 29 30 32 34 35 37 38 40 41 43 44 45 48 49 50 53 57 59 60 62 64 65
67 68 70 72 74 75 76 77 79 81 85 86 87 91 93 101 102 107 108 110 111
114 115 118 119 129 130 131 135 146 147 148 154 156 **P**6 **S** AdventHealth,
Altamonte Springs, FL
Primary Contact: Brandon M. Nudd, Chief Executive Officer
CFO: Jeremy Pittman, Chief Financial Officer
Web address: www.castlerockhospital.org
**Control**: Church operated, Nongovernment, not–for–profit **Service**: General
medical and surgical

> **Staffed Beds:** 53 **Admissions:** 3577 **Census:** 28 **Outpatient Visits:** 42499
> **Births:** 897 **Total Expense ($000):** 88159 **Payroll Expense ($000):** 30962
> **Personnel:** 447

## CHEYENNE WELLS—Cheyenne County

**CHEYENNE COUNTY HOSPITAL** See Keefe Memorial Hospital

*Many Facility Codes have changed. Please refer to the AHA Guide Code Chart.*
© 2021 AHA Guide

★ **KEEFE MEMORIAL HOSPITAL (061343)**, 602 North 6th Street West, Zip 80810, Mailing Address: P.O. Box 578, Zip 80810–0578; tel. 719/767–5661, (Nonreporting) **A**10 18
Primary Contact: Stella Worley, Interim Chief Executive Officer
CFO: Stella Worley, Director of Finance
CMO: Christine Connolly, M.D., Chief of Staff
CIO: Jeanne Moffat, Manager Information Technology
CHR: Carrie Rico, Chief Human Resource Officer
CNO: Jesse Smith, Director of Nursing
Web address: www.keefememorial.com
**Control**: County, Government, Nonfederal **Service**: General medical and surgical

**Staffed Beds:** 11

### COLORADO SPRINGS—El Paso County

**CEDAR SPRINGS BEHAVIORAL HEALTH SYSTEM** See Cedar Springs Hospital

☐ **CEDAR SPRINGS HOSPITAL (064009)**, 2135 Southgate Road, Zip 80906–2693; tel. 719/633–4114, (Nonreporting) **A**1 10 **S** Universal Health Services, Inc., King of Prussia, PA
Primary Contact: David Franklin, Chief Executive Officer
CFO: Cynthia D Deboer, Chief Financial Officer
CMO: Larry Shores, M.D., Executive Medical Director
CHR: Jessica McCoy, Director Human Resources
CNO: Jodi Mattson, Director of Nursing
Web address: www.cedarspringsbhs.com
**Control**: Corporation, Investor–owned (for–profit) **Service**: Psychiatric

**Staffed Beds:** 110

⊞ **ENCOMPASS HEALTH REHABILITATION HOSPITAL OF COLORADO SPRINGS (063030)**, 325 Parkside Drive, Zip 80910–3134; tel. 719/630–8000, (Nonreporting) **A**1 10 **S** Encompass Health Corporation, Birmingham, AL
Primary Contact: Stephen Schaefer, Chief Executive Officer
CFO: Stephanie Davis, Controller
CHR: Diana Crepeau, Director Human Resources
CNO: Cindy Nordell, Chief Nursing Officer
Web address: www.healthsouthcoloradosprings.com
**Control**: Corporation, Investor–owned (for–profit) **Service**: Rehabilitation

**Staffed Beds:** 60

**HEALTHSOUTH REHABILITATION HOSPITAL OF COLORADO SPRINGS** See Encompass Health Rehabilitation Hospital of Colorado Springs

**MEMORIAL HOSPITAL FOR CHILDREN** See Children's Hospital of Colorado at Memorial

**MEMORIAL HOSPITAL NORTH** See Uchealth Memorial Hospital North

☐ **PEAK VIEW BEHAVIORAL HEALTH (064026)**, 7353 Sisters Grove, Zip 80923–2615; tel. 719/444–8484, (Nonreporting) **A**1 3 10 **F**4 5 29 35 38 54 56 98 99 100 101 103 104 105 152 153 **S** Strategic Behavioral Health, LLC, Memphis, TN
Primary Contact: Ty Meredith, Chief Executive Officer
Web address: www.strategicbh.com/peakview.html
**Control**: Corporation, Investor–owned (for–profit) **Service**: Psychiatric

**Staffed Beds:** 112 **Admissions:** 4190 **Census:** 77 **Outpatient Visits:** 15376 **Births:** 0 **Personnel:** 262

**PENROSE HOSPITALS** See Penrose Hospital

**PENROSE-ST FRANCIS HLTH SYSTEM** See Penrose-St. Francis Health Services

⊞ **PENROSE-ST. FRANCIS HEALTH SERVICES (060031)**, 2222 North Nevada Avenue, Zip 80907–6799; tel. 719/776–5000, (Includes PENROSE HOSPITAL, Mailing address: 2222 North Nevada Avenue, Colorado Springs, Colorado, Zip 80907; tel. 719/776–5000; Brian Erling, M.D., Chief Executive Officer; ST. FRANCIS MEDICAL CENTER, Mailing address: 6001 East Woodmen Road, Colorado Springs, Colorado, Zip 80923–2601; tel. 719/776–5000; Brian Erling, M.D., Chief Executive Officer), (Nonreporting) **A**1 3 5 10 **F**3 5 11 12 13 14 15 17 18 20 22 24 26 28 29 30 31 34 35 36 37 38 39 40 41 43 44 45 46 47 48 49 50 52 53 54 55 56 57 58 59 61 62 64 65 68 70 71 72 74 75 76 77 78 79 81 82 84 85 86 87 89 90 91 92 93 94 96 97 100 101 102 107 108 110 114 115 118 119 120 121 123 124 126 127 129 130 131 132 135 144 146 147 148 149 150 154 **S** CommonSpirit Health, Chicago, IL
Primary Contact: Brian Erling, M.D., Chief Executive Officer
COO: Lonnie Cramer, Chief Operating Officer
CFO: Danny Reeves, Chief Financial Officer
CMO: David Dull, M.D., Chief Medical Officer
CHR: James Humphrey, Vice President Talent Resources and Human Resources for South Side Operating Group
CNO: Cynthia Latney, Chief Nursing Officer
Web address: www.penrosestfrancis.org
**Control**: Church operated, Nongovernment, not–for–profit **Service**: General medical and surgical

**Staffed Beds:** 444 **Admissions:** 26746 **Census:** 315

**ST FRANCIS HEALTH CENTER** See St. Francis Medical Center

☐ **UCHEALTH GRANDVIEW HOSPITAL (060130)**, 5623 Pulpit Peak View, Zip 80918; tel. 719/272–3600, (Nonreporting) **A**1 **F**3 29 30 34 35 37 40 50 64 68 70 75 79 81 85 86 87 100 107 115 119 130 131 149 154 157 **P**5 **S** UCHealth, Fort Collins, CO
Primary Contact: Joel P. Yuhas, FACHE, Chief Executive Officer
Web address: www.https://www.uchealth.org/Pages/OHAM/OrgUnitDetails.aspx?OrganizationalUnitId=514
**Control**: Other not–for–profit (including NFP Corporation) **Service**: General medical and surgical

**Staffed Beds:** 22 **Admissions:** 914 **Census:** 5 **Outpatient Visits:** 19895 **Births:** 0 **Total Expense ($000):** 39657 **Payroll Expense ($000):** 10331 **Personnel:** 113

**UCHEALTH MEMORIAL** See Uchealth Memorial Hospital

⊞ **UCHEALTH MEMORIAL HOSPITAL (060022)**, 1400 East Boulder Street, Zip 80909–5599; tel. 719/365–5000, (Includes UCHEALTH MEMORIAL HOSPITAL NORTH, Mailing address: 4050 Briargate Parkway, Colorado Springs, Colorado, Zip 80909, 1400 East Boulder Street, Zip 80909, tel. 719/365–5000; Joel P. Yuhas, FACHE, President and Chief Executive Officer), (Nonreporting) **A**1 3 5 10 **F**3 5 7 9 11 12 13 14 15 17 18 20 22 24 26 28 29 30 31 34 35 36 37 38 39 40 41 42 43 44 45 46 47 48 49 50 54 55 56 57 58 59 61 63 64 65 68 70 72 74 75 76 77 78 79 81 82 84 85 86 87 90 92 93 96 97 100 102 107 108 109 110 111 114 115 116 117 118 119 120 121 123 124 126 129 130 131 132 135 144 146 148 149 154 156 157 **P**6 **S** UCHealth, Fort Collins, CO
Primary Contact: Joel P. Yuhas, FACHE, President and Chief Executive Officer
COO: Cherie Gorby, Chief Operating Officer
CFO: Dan Rieber, Chief Financial Officer
CMO: Jose Melendez, M.D., Chief Medical Officer
CHR: Jeffrey Johnson, Vice President
CNO: Kay J Miller, R.N., MSN, Chief Nursing Officer
Web address: www.uchealth.org/southerncolorado
**Control**: Other not–for–profit (including NFP Corporation) **Service**: General medical and surgical

**Staffed Beds:** 459 **Admissions:** 27131 **Census:** 341 **Outpatient Visits:** 611455 **Births:** 4684 **Total Expense ($000):** 733984 **Payroll Expense ($000):** 283562 **Personnel:** 3657

### CORTEZ—Montezuma County

★ ⇑ **SOUTHWEST HEALTH SYSTEM (061327)**, 1311 North Mildred Road, Zip 81321–2299; tel. 970/565–6666, (Nonreporting) **A**10 18 21
Primary Contact: Anthony G. Sudduth, CPA, Chief Executive Officer
CHR: Travis Parker, Director Human Resources
Web address: www.swhealth.org
**Control**: Other not–for–profit (including NFP Corporation) **Service**: General medical and surgical

**Staffed Beds:** 25

⇑ **SOUTHWEST MEMORIAL HOSPITAL** See Southwest Health System

---

**Hospital, Medicare Provider Number, Address, Telephone, Approval, Facility, and Physician Codes, Health Care System**

★ American Hospital Association (AHA) membership
☐ The Joint Commission accreditation
○ Healthcare Facilities Accreditation Program
◇ DNV Healthcare Inc. accreditation
⇑ Center for Improvement in Healthcare Quality Accreditation
△ Commission on Accreditation of Rehabilitation Facilities (CARF) accreditation

**CO**

## CRAIG—Moffat County

★ ⇑ **MEMORIAL REGIONAL HEALTH (061314)**, 750 Hospital Loop, Zip 81625–8750; tel. 970/824–9411, (Nonreporting) **A**10 18 21 **F**3 7 11 15 18 29 30 31 32 34 35 40 43 45 46 47 48 50 51 54 56 57 59 62 63 65 67 68 70 75 77 79 81 82 83 84 87 90 93 97 107 108 110 111 112 114 119 128 129 130 131 132 133 135 146 147 148 156 157
Primary Contact: Andrew J. Daniels, Chief Executive Officer
COO: Jennifer Riley, Vice President Operations
CFO: Kelsea Henry, Chief Financial Officer
CMO: Scott Ellis, D.O., Chief Medical Officer
CIO: Bryan Curtis, Chief Information Officer
CNO: Amy Peck, R.N., Chief Nursing Officer
Web address: www.thememorialhospital.com
**Control**: County, Government, Nonfederal **Service**: General medical and surgical

**Staffed Beds**: 25 **Admissions**: 1015 **Census**: 9 **Outpatient Visits**: 25000 **Births**: 0

⇑ **THE MEMORIAL HOSPITAL AT CRAIG** See Memorial Regional Health

## DEL NORTE—Rio Grande County

★ **RIO GRANDE HOSPITAL (061301)**, 310 County Road 14, Zip 81132–8719; tel. 719/657–2510, (Nonreporting) **A**10 18
Primary Contact: Arlene Harms, Chief Executive Officer
CFO: Greg Porter, Chief Financial Officer
CMO: Heidi E Helgeson, M.D., Chief Medical Officer
CIO: Denise Fietek, Information Technology
CHR: Paula Warner-Pacheco, Chief Human Resources
CNO: Candice Allen, Director of Nursing
Web address: www.rio-grande-hospital.org/
**Control**: Other not–for–profit (including NFP Corporation) **Service**: General medical and surgical

**Staffed Beds**: 17

## DELTA—Delta County

★ ⇑ **DELTA COUNTY MEMORIAL HOSPITAL (060071)**, 1501 East 3rd Street, Zip 81416–2815, Mailing Address: P.O. Box 10100, Zip 81416–0008; tel. 970/874–7681, (Nonreporting) **A**10 21 **F**3 8 9 13 15 28 29 30 31 34 40 43 45 50 57 59 62 70 75 76 77 78 79 81 85 87 90 93 107 108 110 111 115 119 129 135 141 144 146 147 148
Primary Contact: Matthew M. Heyn, Chief Executive Officer
CFO: Larry Vincent, Chief Financial Officer
CMO: John P Knutson, M.D., Chief Medical Staff
CIO: Mitch Van Scoyk, Manager Information Systems
Web address: www.deltahospital.org
**Control**: Hospital district or authority, Government, Nonfederal **Service**: General medical and surgical

**Staffed Beds**: 49 **Admissions**: 1436 **Census**: 13

## DENVER—Denver, Adams AND Arapaho Coun County

**COLORADO ACUTE LONG TERM HOSPITAL** See Pam Specialty Hospital of Denver

☐ **COLORADO MENTAL HEALTH INSTITUTE AT FORT LOGAN (064003)**, 3520 West Oxford Avenue, Zip 80236–3197; tel. 303/866–7066, (Nonreporting) **A**1 3 5 10
Primary Contact: David M. Polunas, Director
CFO: Sabina Genesio, Finance Officer for Institutes
CMO: Bruce Leonard, M.D., Medical Director and Chief of Psychiatry
CNO: Nancy Kehiayan, Director of Nursing
Web address: www.cdhs.state.co.us/cmhifl
**Control**: State, Government, Nonfederal **Service**: Psychiatric

**Staffed Beds**: 297

**COLUMBIA PRESBY-ST LUKE'S CTR** See Presbyterian/St. Luke's Medical Center

**COLUMBIA ROSE MEDICAL CENTER** See Rose Medical Center

⊞ **DENVER HEALTH (060011)**, 777 Bannock Street, Zip 80204–4507, Mailing Address: 777 Bannock Street, MC0278, Zip 80204–4507; tel. 303/436–6000, (Nonreporting) **A**1 3 5 8 10 **F**3 5 7 8 11 12 13 15 18 19 20 22 26 28 29 30 31 32 34 35 36 37 38 39 40 41 42 43 44 45 46 49 50 52 53 54 55 56 57 58 59 60 61 64 65 66 68 70 71 72 74 75 76 77 78 79 80 81 82 84 85 86 87 88 89 90 92 93 94 96 97 98 99 100 101 102 103 104 107 108 110 111 114 115 118 119 127 129 130 131 132 134 135 143 144 146 147 148 149 153 154 156
Primary Contact: Robin D. Wittenstein, Ed.D., Chief Executive Officer
CFO: Peg Burnette, Chief Financial Officer
CMO: Connie Price, M.D., Chief Medical Officer
CIO: Jeff Pelot, Interim Chief Information Officer
CHR: Tim Hansen, Interim Chief Human Resource Officer
CNO: Kathy Boyle, R.N., Ph.D., Chief Nursing Officer
Web address: www.denverhealth.org
**Control**: Hospital district or authority, Government, Nonfederal **Service**: General medical and surgical

**Staffed Beds**: 431 **Admissions**: 21206 **Census**: 307 **Outpatient Visits**: 935703 **Births**: 3519 **Total Expense ($000)**: 1076348 **Payroll Expense ($000)**: 544635 **Personnel**: 6659

**DENVER HEALTH MEDICAL CENTER** See Denver Health

**EXEMPLA SAINT JOSEPH HOSPITAL** See Saint Joseph Hospital

**FORT LOGAN MENTAL HLTH CENTER** See Colorado Mental Health Institute at Fort Logan

⊞ **KINDRED HOSPITAL-DENVER (062009)**, 1920 High Street, Zip 80218–1213; tel. 303/320–5871, (Nonreporting) **A**1 10 **S** Kindred Healthcare, Louisville, KY
Primary Contact: Janelle Kircher, R.N., MSN, Chief Executive Officer
CFO: Tim Stecker, Chief Financial Officer
CMO: Eric Yaeger, M.D., Medical Director
Web address: www.kh-denver.com
**Control**: Corporation, Investor–owned (for–profit) **Service**: Acute long–term care hospital

**Staffed Beds**: 68

⊞ **NATIONAL JEWISH HEALTH (060107)**, 1400 Jackson Street, Zip 80206–2762; tel. 303/388–4461, (Nonreporting) **A**1 3 5 8 10 **F**3 9 11 12 18 20 28 29 30 31 32 34 35 36 44 45 46 48 50 53 54 55 57 58 59 61 62 64 65 66 68 70 74 75 77 78 84 86 87 89 90 93 96 97 98 99 100 101 104 107 108 111 114 115 116 117 118 119 127 129 130 132 134 135 143 145 146 147 149 154 156 **P**6
Primary Contact: Michael Salem, M.D., President and Chief Executive Officer
COO: Ron Berge, Executive Vice President and Chief Operating Officer
CFO: Christine Forkner, Executive Vice President and Chief Financial Officer
CMO: Gary Cott, M.D., Executive Vice President Medical and Clinical Services
CIO: Lots Pook, Chief Information Officer
CHR: Sarah Taylor, Chief Human Resources
CNO: Jeff Downing, R.N., MS, Chief Nursing Officer
Web address: www.njhealth.org
**Control**: Other not–for–profit (including NFP Corporation) **Service**: Tuberculosis and other respiratory diseases

**Staffed Beds**: 76 **Admissions**: 50 **Census**: 1 **Outpatient Visits**: 112251 **Births**: 0 **Total Expense ($000)**: 280740 **Payroll Expense ($000)**: 138862 **Personnel**: 1583

**NATL JEWISH MED & RES CTR** See National Jewish Health

⊞ **PAM SPECIALTY HOSPITAL OF DENVER (062012)**, 1690 Meade Street, Zip 80204–1552, Mailing Address: 1690 North Meade Street, Zip 80204–1552; tel. 303/264–6900, (Data for 92 days) (Nonreporting) **A**1 10 **F**1 107 **S** Post Acute Medical, LLC, Enola, PA
Primary Contact: Cindy Chaney, Chief Executive Officer
Web address: www.https://postacutemedical.com/facilities/find-facility/specialty-hospitals/PAM-Specialty-Hospital-of-Denver
**Control**: Partnership, Investor–owned (for–profit) **Service**: Acute long–term care hospital

**Staffed Beds**: 63 **Admissions**: 72 **Census**: 42 **Outpatient Visits**: 0 **Births**: 0 **Total Expense ($000)**: 6424 **Payroll Expense ($000)**: 2639 **Personnel**: 88

*Many Facility Codes have changed. Please refer to the AHA Guide Code Chart.* © 2021 AHA Guide

⊞ **PORTER ADVENTIST HOSPITAL (060064)**, 2525 South Downing Street, Zip 80210–5876; tel. 303/778–1955, (Nonreporting) **A**1 3 5 10 **F**3 4 5 6 8 11 15 17 18 20 22 24 26 28 29 30 31 34 35 36 37 38 39 40 43 44 45 46 47 48 49 50 53 54 55 56 58 59 60 63 64 65 68 70 74 75 77 78 79 81 82 83 84 85 86 87 90 91 92 93 94 96 97 98 100 101 102 103 104 105 107 108 109 110 111 112 114 115 116 117 118 119 120 121 122 123 124 125 126 130 131 132 135 141 142 144 146 147 148 153 155 156 **P**6 **S** AdventHealth, Altamonte Springs, FL
Primary Contact: Todd Folkenberg, Chief Executive Officer
COO: David Dookeeram, Chief Operating Officer
CFO: Andrew Gaasch, Chief Financial Officer
CHR: Oz Muller, Director Human Resources
Web address: www.porterhospital.org/poh/home/
**Control**: Church operated, Nongovernment, not–for–profit **Service**: General medical and surgical

| Staffed Beds: 228 Admissions: 8846 Census: 124 Outpatient Visits: 63493 Births: 0 Total Expense ($000): 262019 Payroll Expense ($000): 85302 Personnel: 1277 |
|---|

**PORTER CARE HOSPITAL** See Porter Adventist Hospital

⊞ **PRESBYTERIAN/ST. LUKE'S MEDICAL CENTER (060014)**, 1719 East 19th Avenue, Zip 80218–1281; tel. 720/754–6000, (Includes ROCKY MOUNTAIN HOSPITAL FOR CHILDREN, Mailing address: 1719 East 19th Avenue, Denver, Colorado, Zip 80218–1235; tel. 720/754–1000; Maureen Tarrant, President and Chief Executive Officer), (Nonreporting) **A**1 2 3 5 10 **F**3 11 12 13 14 18 19 20 21 22 23 24 25 26 27 28 29 30 31 34 35 36 37 40 41 45 46 47 48 49 50 52 53 54 55 56 58 59 60 61 64 65 68 70 72 73 74 75 76 77 78 79 81 82 84 85 86 87 89 91 92 93 94 95 96 97 102 107 108 111 114 115 116 117 118 119 120 121 123 126 129 130 131 132 136 138 139 146 147 148 156 **S** HCA Healthcare, Nashville, TN
Primary Contact: Maureen Tarrant, President and Chief Executive Officer
CFO: Shari Collier, Chief Financial Officer
CMO: Stephen Cobb, M.D., Chief Medical Officer
CIO: Jason Brakenhoff, Director Information Services
CHR: Keri Moore, Vice President Human Resources and Support Services
CNO: Amanda Veit, R.N., Chief Nursing Officer
Web address: www.pslmc.com
**Control**: Corporation, Investor–owned (for–profit) **Service**: General medical and surgical

| Staffed Beds: 359 Admissions: 12087 Census: 226 |
|---|

⊞ **ROSE MEDICAL CENTER (060032)**, 4567 East Ninth Avenue, Zip 80220–3941; tel. 303/320–2121, (Nonreporting) **A**1 2 3 5 10 **F**3 8 11 12 13 15 17 18 20 22 24 26 28 29 30 31 34 35 36 40 41 42 44 45 46 49 50 52 53 54 58 59 60 61 63 64 65 68 70 71 72 74 75 76 77 78 79 81 82 84 85 86 87 91 92 93 96 97 100 101 102 107 108 110 111 112 114 115 116 117 118 119 120 121 122 123 126 129 130 131 132 135 146 147 148 149 154 **S** HCA Healthcare, Nashville, TN
Primary Contact: Hollie Seeley, Interim Chief Executive Officer and Chief Operating Officer
COO: Hollie Seeley, Chief Operating Officer
CFO: Jac Connelly, Chief Financial Officer
CMO: Andrew Ziller, M.D., Chief Medical Officer
CIO: Dave Trevathan, Director Information Systems
CHR: Clarence McDavid, Vice President Human Resources
CNO: Lynne Wagner, R.N., Chief Nursing Officer
Web address: www.rosebabies.com
**Control**: Corporation, Investor–owned (for–profit) **Service**: General medical and surgical

| Staffed Beds: 248 Admissions: 11083 Census: 114 Outpatient Visits: 103650 |
|---|

⊞ **SAINT JOSEPH HOSPITAL (060028)**, 1375 East 19th Avenue, Zip 80218–1126; tel. 303/837–7111, (Nonreporting) **A**1 2 3 5 8 10 **F**3 8 11 12 13 15 18 20 22 24 26 28 29 30 31 34 35 37 40 42 43 45 46 49 50 53 55 58 60 63 64 66 68 70 71 72 74 75 76 77 78 79 81 82 84 85 87 93 107 108 110 111 115 116 117 119 120 121 123 124 126 130 145 146 149 154 156 157 **P**6 **S** SCL Health, Broomfield, CO
Primary Contact: Jameson Smith, President
COO: Barbara A. Jahn, Chief Operating Officer
CFO: Alice W. Rigdon, Vice President Finance
CMO: Shawn Dufford, M.D., Vice President Medical Affairs and Chief Medical Officer
CHR: William R Gould, Vice President Human Resources
Web address: www.saintjosephdenver.org/
**Control**: Other not–for–profit (including NFP Corporation) **Service**: General medical and surgical

| Staffed Beds: 379 Admissions: 19226 Census: 251 Outpatient Visits: 135233 Births: 4242 Total Expense ($000): 560866 Payroll Expense ($000): 175180 Personnel: 2310 |
|---|

**VENCOR HOSPITAL–DENVER** See Kindred Hospital–Denver

⊞ △ **VETERANS AFFAIRS EASTERN COLORADO HEALTH CARE SYSTEM**, 1055 Clermont Street, Zip 80220–3877; tel. 303/399–8020, (Nonreporting) **A**1 5 7 **S** Department of Veterans Affairs, Washington, DC
Primary Contact: Michael T. Kilmer, Director
CMO: Ellen Mangione, M.D., Chief of Staff
CIO: Don Huckaby, Chief Information Management Service
CHR: Lorene Connel, Chief Human Resources Management Service
Web address: www.denver.va.gov/
**Control**: Veterans Affairs, Government, federal **Service**: General medical and surgical

| Staffed Beds: 271 |
|---|

**VETERANS AFFAIRS MED CENTER** See Veterans Affairs Eastern Colorado Health Care System

**DURANGO—La Plata County**

**ANIMAS SURGICAL HOSPITAL (060117)**, 575 Rivergate Lane, Zip 81301–7487; tel. 970/247–3537, (Nonreporting) **A**10
Primary Contact: Brett Gosney, Chief Executive Officer
Web address: www.animassurgical.com/
**Control**: Corporation, Investor–owned (for–profit) **Service**: Surgical

| Staffed Beds: 12 |
|---|

**MERCY MEDICAL CENTER** See Mercy Regional Medical Center

⊞ **MERCY REGIONAL MEDICAL CENTER (060013)**, 1010 Three Springs Boulevard, Zip 81301–8296; tel. 970/247–4311, (Nonreporting) **A**1 10 20 **F**3 11 13 15 18 20 22 24 26 27 28 29 30 31 35 36 40 43 45 49 50 55 59 60 61 70 74 75 76 78 79 81 83 84 85 87 93 94 96 97 107 108 111 115 119 120 126 127 129 130 131 132 133 135 144 146 147 148 149 150 154 155 156 **P**6 **S** CommonSpirit Health, Chicago, IL
Primary Contact: Michael Murphy, Interim Chief Executive Officer
CFO: Jane Strobel, Vice President and Chief Financial Officer
CMO: William Plauth, M.D., Vice President Operations and Chief Medical Officer
CIO: Neil Stock, Director Technology and Facilities
CHR: Cathy Roberts, Vice President Mission Integration and Human Resources
CNO: Nancy Gerilyn Hoyt, R.N., Vice President Operations/Clinical and Chief Nursing Officer
Web address: www.mercydurango.org
**Control**: Church operated, Nongovernment, not–for–profit **Service**: General medical and surgical

| Staffed Beds: 82 Admissions: 4290 Census: 39 Outpatient Visits: 127376 Births: 732 Total Expense ($000): 149374 Payroll Expense ($000): 46151 Personnel: 771 |
|---|

| Hospital, Medicare Provider Number, Address, Telephone, Approval, Facility, and Physician Codes, Health Care System | | |
|---|---|---|
| ★ American Hospital Association (AHA) membership | ○ Healthcare Facilities Accreditation Program | ⇑ Center for Improvement in Healthcare Quality Accreditation |
| ☐ The Joint Commission accreditation | ◇ DNV Healthcare Inc. accreditation | △ Commission on Accreditation of Rehabilitation Facilities (CARF) accreditation |

## EADS—Kiowa County

★ **WEISBROD MEMORIAL COUNTY HOSPITAL (061300)**, 1208 Luther Street, Zip 81036, Mailing Address: P.O. Box 817, Zip 81036–0817; tel. 719/438–5401, (Nonreporting) **A**10 18 **F**7 29 30 32 34 40 57 59 64 65 75 82 84 87 93 96 97 107 119 127 133 135 143 148 156
Primary Contact: Charlene Korrell, Chief Executive Officer
CFO: Shannon Dixon, Manager Business Office
CMO: Jeff Waggoner, M.D., Chief of Staff
CHR: Shannon Dixon, Manager Business Office
CNO: Wendy McDowell, R.N., Director of Nursing
Web address: www.kchd.org
**Control**: Hospital district or authority, Government, Nonfederal **Service**: General medical and surgical

**Staffed Beds**: 25 **Admissions**: 70 **Census**: 1 **Births**: 0 **Total Expense ($000)**: 8011 **Payroll Expense ($000)**: 3601

**WEISBROD MEMORIAL HOSPITAL** See Weisbrod Memorial County Hospital

## ENGLEWOOD—Arapahoe County

**COLUMBIA SWEDISH MEDICAL CTR** See Swedish Medical Center

⊠ **CRAIG HOSPITAL (062011)**, 3425 South Clarkson Street, Zip 80113–2899; tel. 303/789–8000, (Nonreporting) **A**1 3 5 10 **F**29 30 34 35 44 50 53 57 58 59 64 74 75 77 81 86 87 90 91 93 95 96 130 132 135 146 148 149 157
Primary Contact: Jandel Allen-Davis, President and Chief Executive Officer
CFO: Daniel Frank, Chief Financial Officer
CMO: Thomas E Balazy, M.D., Medical Director
CHR: Stacy L Abel, Vice President People and Culture
CNO: Diane Reinhard, R.N., Vice President of Patient Care Services
Web address: www.craighospital.org
**Control**: Other not–for–profit (including NFP Corporation) **Service**: Rehabilitation

**Staffed Beds**: 92 **Admissions**: 476 **Census**: 78 **Outpatient Visits**: 17908 **Births**: 0 **Total Expense ($000)**: 116083 **Payroll Expense ($000)**: 56838 **Personnel**: 1009

☐ **DENVER SPRINGS (064028)**, 8835 American Way, Zip 80112–7056; tel. 720/643–4300, (Nonreporting) **A**1 10 **S** Springstone, Louisville, KY
Primary Contact: Mark Littrell, Chief Executive Officer
Web address: www.denversprings.com/
**Control**: Other not–for–profit (including NFP Corporation) **Service**: Psychiatric

**Staffed Beds**: 96

⊠ **SWEDISH MEDICAL CENTER (060034)**, 501 East Hampden Avenue, Zip 80113–2702; tel. 303/788–5000, (Nonreporting) **A**1 2 3 5 10 **S** HCA Healthcare, Nashville, TN
Primary Contact: Ryan Tobin, President and Chief Executive Officer
CFO: Kathy Ashenfelter, Chief Financial Officer
CMO: Monique Butler, Chief Medical Officer
CIO: Jeff Schnoor, Director Information Systems
CHR: Lisa Morris, Vice President Human Resources
CNO: Shari Chavez, Chief Nursing Officer
Web address: www.swedishhospital.com
**Control**: Partnership, Investor–owned (for–profit) **Service**: General medical and surgical

**Staffed Beds**: 408

## ESTES PARK—Larimer County

⇧ **ESTES PARK MEDICAL CENTER (061312)**, 555 Prospect Avenue, Zip 80517–6312, Mailing Address: P.O. Box 2740, Zip 80517–2740; tel. 970/586–2317, (Nonreporting) **A**10 18 21
Primary Contact: Vern Carda, Chief Executive Officer
CFO: Tim Cashman, Chief Financial Officer
CMO: Paul Fonken, M.D., Chief of Staff
CIO: Gary Hall, Vice President of Information Technology
CHR: Randy Brigham, Chief Human Resource Officer
Web address: www.epmedcenter.com
**Control**: Hospital district or authority, Government, Nonfederal **Service**: General medical and surgical

**Staffed Beds**: 79

## FORT CARSON—El Paso County

**EVAN'S U S ARMY COMM HOSPITAL** See Evans U.S. Army Community Hospital

⊠ **EVANS U. S. ARMY COMMUNITY HOSPITAL**, 1650 Cochrane Circle, Building 7500, Zip 80913–4613; tel. 719/526–7200, (Nonreporting) **A**1 3 **S** Department of the Army, Office of the Surgeon General, Falls Church, VA
Primary Contact: Colonel Patrick M. Garman, Commander
COO: Lieutenant ColonelSteven D. Hankins, Chief Operating Officer
CFO: MajorBradley Robinson, Chief Financial Officer
CHR: Lieutenant ColonelLory Gurr, Chief Human Resources Division
Web address: www.https://evans.amedd.army.mil/
**Service**: General medical and surgical

**Staffed Beds**: 68

## FORT COLLINS—Larimer County

⊠ **BANNER FORT COLLINS MEDICAL CENTER (060126)**, 4700 Lady Moon Drive, Zip 80528–4426; tel. 970/821–4000, (Nonreporting) **A**1 **F**3 13 15 18 29 30 34 35 36 38 40 43 45 47 57 59 60 70 74 76 77 79 81 84 85 86 87 89 105 107 108 111 114 115 119 130 135 146 149 154 **P**8 **S** Banner Health, Phoenix, AZ
Primary Contact: Hoyt Skabelund, Chief Executive Officer
COO: Marilyn Fain, R.N., MSN, Chief Operating Officer
CFO: Lori Sehrt, Associate Chief Financial Officer Northern Colorado
CMO: Bert Honea, M.D., Associate Chief Medical Officer Northern Colorado
CHR: Kelly Hurt, Chief Human Resources Officer Northern Colorado and Western Region
CNO: Roberta Bean, R.N., Associate Chief Nursing Officer
Web address: www.bannerhealth.com/Locations/Colorado/Banner+Fort+Collins+Medical+Center
**Control**: Other not–for–profit (including NFP Corporation) **Service**: General medical and surgical

**Staffed Beds**: 23 **Admissions**: 1322 **Census**: 10 **Outpatient Visits**: 35524 **Births**: 403 **Total Expense ($000)**: 47113 **Payroll Expense ($000)**: 12936 **Personnel**: 162

**POUDRE VALLEY HOSPITAL** See Uchealth Poudre Valley Hospital

⊠ **UCHEALTH POUDRE VALLEY HOSPITAL (060010)**, 1024 South Lemay Avenue, Zip 80524–3998, Mailing Address: 2315 East Harmony Road, Suite 200, Zip 80528; tel. 970/495–7000, (Includes MOUNTAIN CREST HOSPITAL, Mailing address: 4601 Corbett Drive, Fort Collins, Colorado, Zip 80525; tel. 970/270–4800), (Nonreporting) **A**1 3 5 10 **F**3 5 7 9 11 12 13 14 15 18 20 22 24 26 28 29 30 31 32 34 35 36 38 39 40 42 43 45 46 47 49 50 53 54 55 56 58 59 61 63 64 65 66 68 69 70 72 73 74 75 76 77 78 79 80 81 82 84 85 87 88 90 93 96 97 98 99 100 101 102 103 104 105 107 108 111 114 115 118 119 120 121 122 123 124 126 129 130 131 132 135 143 144 146 148 149 150 151 152 153 154 156 157 **P**6 **S** UCHealth, Fort Collins, CO
Primary Contact: Kevin L. Unger, Ph.D., FACHE, President and Chief Executive Officer
COO: Ryan Rohman, MSN, R.N., Chief Operating Officer
CFO: Stephanie Doughty, Chief Financial Officer
CIO: Fernando Pedroza, Vice President Information Technology
Web address: www.uchealth.org
**Control**: Other not–for–profit (including NFP Corporation) **Service**: General medical and surgical

**Staffed Beds**: 305 **Admissions**: 15235 **Census**: 174 **Outpatient Visits**: 369846 **Births**: 1897 **Total Expense ($000)**: 515431 **Payroll Expense ($000)**: 193207 **Personnel**: 2261

## FORT MORGAN—Morgan County

⊠ **COLORADO PLAINS MEDICAL CENTER (060044)**, 1000 Lincoln Street, Zip 80701–3298; tel. 970/867–3391, (Nonreporting) **A**1 3 10 20 **S** LifePoint Health, Brentwood, TN
Primary Contact: Kevin Zachary, Chief Executive Officer
CFO: Christina Patton, Chief Financial Officer
CHR: Janet Brinkman, Director Human Resources
CNO: Sonya Bass, MS, Chief Nursing Officer
Web address: www.coloradoplainsmedicalcenter.com
**Control**: Corporation, Investor–owned (for–profit) **Service**: General medical and surgical

**Staffed Beds**: 50

**FORT MORGAN COMMUNITY HOSPITAL** See Colorado Plains Medical Center

**FRISCO—Summit County**

✠ **ST. ANTHONY SUMMIT MEDICAL CENTER (060118)**, 340 Peak One Drive, Zip 80443, Mailing Address: P.O. Box 738, Zip 80443–0738; tel. 970/668–3300, (Nonreporting) **A**1 10 **F**3 13 15 29 30 34 35 40 43 45 57 59 66 68 70 75 76 77 79 81 82 84 85 97 107 110 111 119 129 130 132 133 146 147 **S** CommonSpirit Health, Chicago, IL
Primary Contact: Lee Boyles, Chief Executive Officer
CNO: Trixie VanderSchaaff, Chief Nursing Officer
Web address: www.summitmedicalcenter.org
**Control:** Church operated, Nongovernment, not–for–profit **Service:** General medical and surgical

| | |
|---|---|
| **Staffed Beds:** 34 **Admissions:** 1294 **Census:** 9 **Outpatient Visits:** 25468 **Births:** 384 **Total Expense ($000):** 57708 **Payroll Expense ($000):** 18196 **Personnel:** 355 | |

**FRUITA—Mesa County**

★ **COLORADO CANYONS HOSPITAL AND MEDICAL CENTER (061302)**, 300 West Ottley Avenue, Zip 81521–2118, Mailing Address: P.O. Box 130, Zip 81521–0130; tel. 970/858–9871, (Nonreporting) **A**10 18 **F**3 9 10 15 29 30 34 35 36 40 41 43 45 50 53 54 56 57 59 64 65 67 68 74 75 77 79 81 82 85 86 87 90 93 97 107 110 111 115 119 128 129 130 131 132 133 143 144 146 148 149 154 **P**5
Primary Contact: Korrey Klein, M.D., President and Chief Executive Offricer
CMO: Christopher Wibblesman, M.D., Chief of Staff
CIO: Derrick Diddle, Chief Information Officer
CHR: Kelly Murphy, Vice President Human Resources
CNO: Lori Henderson, Chief Nursing Officer, Vice President Clinical
Web address: www.fhw.org
**Control:** Other not–for–profit (including NFP Corporation) **Service:** General medical and surgical

| | |
|---|---|
| **Staffed Beds:** 25 **Admissions:** 501 **Census:** 16 **Outpatient Visits:** 69347 **Births:** 0 **Total Expense ($000):** 45329 **Payroll Expense ($000):** 18722 **Personnel:** 197 | |

**FAMILY HEALTH WEST** See Colorado Canyons Hospital and Medical Center

**GLENWOOD SPRINGS—Garfield County**

✠ **VALLEY VIEW HOSPITAL (060075)**, 1906 Blake Avenue, Zip 81601–4259; tel. 970/945–6535, (Nonreporting) **A**1 2 10 20
Primary Contact: Brian Murphy, M.D., Chief Executive Officer
COO: Daniel Biggs, Chief Operating Officer
CFO: Charles Crevling, Chief Financial Officer
CMO: David Brooks, M.D., Chief Medical Officer
CHR: Dan E. Deaton, Executive Director Human Resources
CNO: Dawn Sculco, Chief Nursing Officer
Web address: www.vvh.org
**Control:** Other not–for–profit (including NFP Corporation) **Service:** General medical and surgical

| | |
|---|---|
| **Staffed Beds:** 49 | |

**GRAND JUNCTION—Mesa County**

**COLORADO WEST PSYCHIATRIC HOSPITAL** See West Springs Hospital

✠ **COMMUNITY HOSPITAL (060054)**, 2351 G Road, Zip 81505; tel. 970/242–0920, (Nonreporting) **A**1 2 10 **F**12 15 18 20 22 28 30 31 34 35 36 37 40 41 43 45 46 47 48 49 50 51 52 54 55 56 59 60 64 65 68 70 75 76 77 78 79 81 82 85 86 87 91 92 93 94 97 107 108 110 111 114 115 117 119 120 121 129 130 131 132 135 144 146 147 148 154 156 157 **P**1 **S** QHR Health, Brentwood, TN
Primary Contact: Chris Thomas, FACHE, President and Chief Executive Officer
CMO: Donald Nicolay, M.D., Chief Medical Officer
CIO: Bart Butzine, Director Information Technology
Web address: www.yourcommunityhospital.com
**Control:** Other not–for–profit (including NFP Corporation) **Service:** General medical and surgical

| | |
|---|---|
| **Staffed Beds:** 44 **Admissions:** 1500 **Census:** 27 **Births:** 500 | |

**GRAND JUNCTION VETERANS AFFAIRS MEDICAL CENTER** See Grand Junction Veterans Health Care System

✠ **GRAND JUNCTION VETERANS HEALTH CARE SYSTEM**, 2121 North Avenue, Zip 81501–6428; tel. 970/242–0731, (Nonreporting) **A**1 **S** Department of Veterans Affairs, Washington, DC
Primary Contact: Patrick Hull, Acting Director
COO: Patricia A Hitt, Associate Director
CFO: Laquita Gruver, Fiscal Officer
CMO: William R Berryman, M.D., Chief of Staff
CIO: Craig Frerichs, Chief Information Technology Service
CHR: William Chester, Manager Human Resources
Web address: www.grandjunction.va.gov/
**Control:** Veterans Affairs, Government, federal **Service:** General medical and surgical

| | |
|---|---|
| **Staffed Beds:** 23 | |

✠ **ST. MARY'S HOSPITAL AND MEDICAL CENTER (060023)**, 2635 North 7th Street, Zip 81501–8209, Mailing Address: P.O. Box 1628, Zip 81502–1628; tel. 970/298–2273, (Nonreporting) **A**1 2 3 5 10 **F**3 5 7 11 13 14 15 17 18 19 20 22 24 26 28 29 30 31 34 35 37 40 43 45 46 48 49 50 51 54 55 57 58 59 60 61 64 65 68 69 70 71 72 74 75 76 77 78 79 81 82 84 85 86 87 89 90 91 92 93 96 97 107 108 109 110 111 113 114 115 116 117 119 120 121 122 123 124 126 129 130 131 132 135 143 145 146 147 148 149 154 155 156 **P**6 **S** SCL Health, Broomfield, CO
Primary Contact: Bryan L. Johnson, President
COO: Reza Kaleel, Executive Vice President and Chief Operating Officer
CFO: Terri Chinn, Vice President Finance
CIO: John Bullard, Director Information Technology
CHR: Judy White House, FACHE, Vice President Human Resources
CNO: Shelley Peterson, R.N., Vice President Patient Services and Chief Nursing Officer
Web address: www.stmarygj.com
**Control:** Other not–for–profit (including NFP Corporation) **Service:** General medical and surgical

| | |
|---|---|
| **Staffed Beds:** 309 **Admissions:** 12597 **Census:** 185 **Outpatient Visits:** 185434 **Births:** 1434 **Total Expense ($000):** 423742 **Payroll Expense ($000):** 121722 **Personnel:** 1848 | |

**ST. MARY'S MEDICAL CENTER** See St. Mary's Hospital and Medical Center

**WEST SPRINGS HOSPITAL (064023)**, 515 28 3/4 Road, Zip 81501–5016; tel. 970/263–4918, (Nonreporting) **A**10
Primary Contact: Sharon Raggio, President and Chief Executive Officer
COO: Brandi Kroese, Director Operations
CFO: John Rattle, Chief Financial Officer
CMO: Jules Rosen, M.D., Chief Medical Officer
CIO: Charles Andrews, Director Information Technology
CHR: Karen Birmingham, Director Human Resources
CNO: Deborah Sharpe, R.N., Director of Nursing
Web address: www.WestSpringsHospital.org
**Control:** Other not–for–profit (including NFP Corporation) **Service:** Psychiatric

| | |
|---|---|
| **Staffed Beds:** 32 | |

**GREELEY—Weld County**

✠ **NORTH COLORADO MEDICAL CENTER (060001)**, 1801 16th Street, Zip 80631–5154; tel. 970/352–4121, (Nonreporting) **A**1 2 3 5 10 **F**3 7 8 11 13 15 16 18 20 22 24 26 28 29 30 31 34 35 36 38 40 42 43 44 46 49 50 51 53 54 55 57 58 59 60 61 64 65 68 70 72 73 74 75 76 77 78 79 80 81 82 83 84 85 86 87 89 93 96 100 102 107 108 110 111 114 115 116 117 118 119 120 121 126 129 130 131 132 135 141 146 148 149 154 155 156 **P**8 **S** Banner Health, Phoenix, AZ
Primary Contact: Hoyt Skabelund, Chief Executive Officer
COO: Wendy Sparks, Chief Operating Officer
CFO: Mary McCabe, Chief Financial Officer
CHR: Jeannie Gallagher, Chief Human Resource Officer
CNO: Tiffany Erin Hettinger, Associate Chief Nursing Officer
Web address: www.ncmcgreeley.com
**Control:** Other not–for–profit (including NFP Corporation) **Service:** General medical and surgical

| | |
|---|---|
| **Staffed Beds:** 369 **Admissions:** 9705 **Census:** 125 **Outpatient Visits:** 338747 **Births:** 1445 **Total Expense ($000):** 351172 **Payroll Expense ($000):** 105357 **Personnel:** 1696 | |

**CO**

---

**Hospital, Medicare Provider Number, Address, Telephone, Approval, Facility, and Physician Codes, Health Care System**

★ American Hospital Association (AHA) membership
□ The Joint Commission accreditation
○ Healthcare Facilities Accreditation Program
◇ DNV Healthcare Inc. accreditation
⇑ Center for Improvement in Healthcare Quality Accreditation
△ Commission on Accreditation of Rehabilitation Facilities (CARF) accreditation

☐ **UCHEALTH GREELEY**, 6767 29th Street, Zip 80634–5474; tel. 970/652–2000, (Nonreporting) **A**1 **S** UCHealth, Fort Collins, CO
Primary Contact: Marilyn Schock, President
CNO: Kay J Miller, R.N., MSN, Chief Nursing Officer
Web address: www.https://www.uchealth.org/locations/uchealth-greeley-medical-clinic/
**Control**: Other not–for–profit (including NFP Corporation) **Service**: General medical and surgical

**Staffed Beds: 25**

### GUNNISON—Gunnison County

⌧ **GUNNISON VALLEY HOSPITAL (061320)**, 711 North Taylor Street, Zip 81230–2296; tel. 970/641–1456, (Nonreporting) **A**1 10 18
Primary Contact: Robert J. Santilli, Chief Executive Officer
CFO: Mark L. VanderVeer, Chief Financial Officer
CIO: Trevor Smith, Chief Management Information Services
CHR: Christina Lovelace, Director Human Resources
CNO: Andrew Bertapelle, Chief Nursing Officer
Web address: www.gvh-colorado.org
**Control**: County, Government, Nonfederal **Service**: General medical and surgical

**Staffed Beds: 24**

### HAXTUN—Phillips County

★ **HAXTUN HOSPITAL DISTRICT (061304)**, 235 West Fletcher Street, Zip 80731–2737; tel. 970/774–6123, (Nonreporting) **A**10 18
Primary Contact: Dewane Pace, President and Chief Executive Officer
CFO: Rick Lee Nader, Chief Financial Officer
CMO: Colby Jolley, D.O., Acting Chief of Staff
CIO: Andrea Evers, Director Information Technology
CNO: Gail Phelps, R.N., Chief Nursing Officer
Web address: www.haxtunhealth.org
**Control**: Hospital district or authority, Government, Nonfederal **Service**: General medical and surgical

**Staffed Beds: 25**

### HIGHLANDS RANCH—Douglas County

☐ **UCHEALTH HIGHLANDS RANCH HOSPITAL**, 1500 Park Central Drive, Zip 80129–6688; tel. 720/848–0000, (Nonreporting) **A**1 **S** UCHealth, Fort Collins, CO
Primary Contact: Diane M. Cookson, President
CMO: Tom Purcell, Chief Medical Officer
Web address: www.https://www.uchealth.org/locations/uchealth-highlands-ranch-hospital/
**Control**: Other not–for–profit (including NFP Corporation) **Service**: General medical and surgical

**Staffed Beds: 72**

### HOLYOKE—Phillips County

★ **MELISSA MEMORIAL HOSPITAL (061305)**, 1001 East Johnson Street, Zip 80734–1854; tel. 970/854–2241, (Nonreporting) **A**10 18
Primary Contact: Catherine S. Harshbarger, R.N., Interim Chief Executive Officer
CFO: Jason McCormick, Interim Chief Financial Officer
CMO: Dennis Jelden, M.D., Chief of Staff
CIO: David Bickford, Chief Information Officer
CHR: Sharon Greenman, Director Human Resources
CNO: Pat Notter, R.N., Chief Nursing Officer and Director Quality
Web address: www.melissamemorial.org
**Control**: Hospital district or authority, Government, Nonfederal **Service**: General medical and surgical

**Staffed Beds: 13**

### HUGO—Lincoln County

★ **LINCOLN COMMUNITY HOSPITAL AND NURSING HOME (061306)**, 111 6th Street, Zip 80821–0248, Mailing Address: P.O. Box 248, Zip 80821–0248; tel. 719/743–2421, (Total facility includes 35 beds in nursing home–type unit) (Nonreporting) **A**10 18 **F**7 8 10 13 15 29 34 35 40 43 59 62 63 64 71 78 79 81 82 84 89 90 93 97 107 111 115 119 128 130 133 147 154
Primary Contact: Kevin M. Stansbury, Chief Executive Officer
CMO: Mark Olson, M.D., Chief of Staff
CIO: Michael Gaskins, Director Information Technology
CHR: Susan Petersen, Human Resources
CNO: Dan Walker, Chief Nursing Officer
Web address: www.lincolncommunityhospital.com
**Control**: County, Government, Nonfederal **Service**: General medical and surgical

**Staffed Beds:** 45 **Admissions:** 286 **Census:** 21 **Outpatient Visits:** 5671 **Births:** 0 **Total Expense ($000):** 18878 **Payroll Expense ($000):** 8181 **Personnel:** 131

### JOHNSTOWN—Larimer County

☐ **CLEAR VIEW BEHAVIORAL HEALTH (064027)**, 4770 Larimer Parkway, Zip 80534; tel. 970/461–5061, (Nonreporting) **A**1 10 **S** Strategic Behavioral Health, LLC, Memphis, TN
Primary Contact: Sharon Pendlebury, Chief Executive Officer
Web address: www.clearviewbh.com/
**Control**: Corporation, Investor–owned (for–profit) **Service**: Children's hospital psychiatric

**Staffed Beds: 92**

☐ **NORTHERN COLORADO LONG TERM ACUTE HOSPITAL (062017)**, 4401 Union Street, Zip 80534; tel. 970/619–3663, (Nonreporting) **A**1 10 **S** Ernest Health, Inc., Albuquerque, NM
Primary Contact: Blake Sims, Chief Executive Officer
Web address: www.ncltah.ernesthealth.com/
**Control**: Partnership, Investor–owned (for–profit) **Service**: Acute long–term care hospital

**Staffed Beds: 40**

☐ **NORTHERN COLORADO REHABILITATION HOSPITAL (063033)**, 4401 Union Street, Zip 80534–2800; tel. 970/619–3400, (Nonreporting) **A**1 10 **S** Ernest Health, Inc., Albuquerque, NM
Primary Contact: Brenda Simon, Chief Executive Officer
CFO: Bonnie Cushman, Chief Financial Officer
CMO: Revelyn Arrogante, M.D., Medical Director
CHR: Amy Lauridsen, Director Human Resources
CNO: Mark Smith, Director Nursing Operations
Web address: www.ncrh.ernesthealth.com
**Control**: Corporation, Investor–owned (for–profit) **Service**: Rehabilitation

**Staffed Beds: 40**

### JULESBURG—Sedgwick County

**SEDGWICK COUNTY HEALTH CENTER (061310)**, 900 Cedar Street, Zip 80737–1199; tel. 970/474–3323, (Total facility includes 52 beds in nursing home–type unit) (Nonreporting) **A**10 18 **F**3 10 13 32 40 43 45 53 56 57 59 64 65 66 67 68 76 77 81 89 93 107 111 114 119 127 128 130 133 145 148 154
Primary Contact: Nick Goshe, Chief Executive Officer
CFO: Karla Dunker, Chief Financial Officer
CMO: Donald Regier, M.D., Chief Medical Officer
CHR: Sonja Bell, Coordinator Human Resources
Web address: www.schealth.org/
**Control**: County, Government, Nonfederal **Service**: General medical and surgical

**Staffed Beds:** 67 **Admissions:** 180 **Census:** 52 **Outpatient Visits:** 14230 **Births:** 17 **Total Expense ($000):** 11999 **Payroll Expense ($000):** 5974 **Personnel:** 96

**SEDGWICK COUNTY MEM HOSPITAL** See Sedgwick County Health Center

### KREMMLING—Grand County

★ **MIDDLE PARK HEALTH-KREMMLING (061318)**, 214 South Fourth Street, Zip 80459, Mailing Address: P.O. Box 399, Zip 80459–0399; tel. 970/724–3442, (Includes MIDDLE PARK MEDICAL CENTER - GRANBY, Mailing address: 1000 Granby Park Drive South, Granby, Colorado, Zip 80446, P.O. Box 399, Kremmling, Zip 80446, tel. 970/887–5800; Jason Cleckler, Chief Executive Officer), (Nonreporting) **A**10 18
Primary Contact: Jason Cleckler, Chief Executive Officer
CMO: Thomas C. Coburn, M.D., Chief Medical Officer
CHR: Jason Bryan, Director Human Resources
CNO: Debra Plemmons, Chief Nursing Officer
Web address: www.mpmc.org
**Control**: Hospital district or authority, Government, Nonfederal **Service**: General medical and surgical

**Staffed Beds: 10**

**MIDDLE PARK MEDICAL CENTER-KREMMLING** See Middle Park Health-Kremmling

### LA JARA—Conejos County

**CONEJOS COUNTY HOSPITAL** See San Luis Valley Health Conejos County Hospital

**CO**

**★ SAN LUIS VALLEY HEALTH CONEJOS COUNTY HOSPITAL (061308)**, 19021 U S Highway 285, Zip 81140–0639, Mailing Address: P.O. Box 639, Zip 81140–0639; tel. 719/274–5121, (Nonreporting) **A**10 18 **S** San Luis Valley Health, Alamosa, CO
Primary Contact: Kelly Gallegos, Administrator
CFO: Shane Mortensen, Chief Financial Officer
CIO: Kathy Rogers, Vice President Marketing
CHR: Mandy Lee Crockett, Director Human Resources
CNO: Tandra Dunn, Director of Nursing
Web address: www.sanluisvalleyhealth.org/locations/conejos-county-hospital
**Control**: Hospital district or authority, Government, Nonfederal **Service**: General medical and surgical

**Staffed Beds: 17**

## LA JUNTA—Otero County

**✠ ARKANSAS VALLEY REGIONAL MEDICAL CENTER (061336)**, 1100 Carson Avenue, Zip 81050–2799; tel. 719/383–6000, (Nonreporting) **A**1 10 18 **S** QHR Health, Brentwood, TN
Primary Contact: Lynn Crowell, Chief Executive Officer
CMO: Kent E. Gay, M.D., Chief of Medical Staff
CIO: Heidi Gearhart, Director Information Systems
CHR: Kelsey B. Brundage, Director Human Resources
CNO: Carrie Cutrell, Chief Nursing Officer
Web address: www.avrmc.org
**Control**: Other not–for–profit (including NFP Corporation) **Service**: General medical and surgical

**Staffed Beds: 106**

## LAFAYETTE—Boulder County

**EXEMPLA GOOD SAMARITAN MEDICAL CENTER** See Good Samaritan Medical Center

**✠ GOOD SAMARITAN MEDICAL CENTER (060116)**, 200 Exempla Circle, Zip 80026–3370; tel. 303/689–4000, (Nonreporting) **A**1 2 10 **F**3 11 12 13 15 18 20 22 26 28 29 30 31 32 34 35 36 40 41 43 45 46 47 49 50 51 60 64 68 70 72 74 75 76 77 78 79 80 81 84 85 86 87 91 92 93 100 102 107 108 110 111 114 115 117 118 119 120 121 123 124 126 130 132 135 143 146 147 148 149 150 154 156 **P**6 **S** SCL Health, Broomfield, CO
Primary Contact: Jennifer Alderfer, President
COO: Beth Forsyth, Chief Operating Officer
CFO: John Higgins, Vice President and Chief Financial Officer
CMO: Todd Mydler, M.D., Vice President and Chief Medical Officer
CHR: Amy Pacey, Vice President Human Resources
CNO: Susan Kerschen, MS, R.N., Vice President and Chief Nursing Officer
Web address: www.goodsamaritancolorado.org/
**Control**: Other not–for–profit (including NFP Corporation) **Service**: General medical and surgical

**Staffed Beds: 175 Admissions: 11796 Census: 135 Outpatient Visits: 85439 Births: 1748 Total Expense ($000): 291763 Payroll Expense ($000): 88099 Personnel: 1156**

## LAKEWOOD—Jefferson County

**✠ ORTHOCOLORADO HOSPITAL (060124)**, 11650 West 2nd Place, Zip 80228–1527; tel. 720/321–5000, (Nonreporting) **A**1 10 **S** CommonSpirit Health, Chicago, IL
Primary Contact: Jude Torchia, Chief Executive Officer
Web address: www.orthocolorado.org
**Control**: Partnership, Investor–owned (for–profit) **Service**: Orthopedic

**Staffed Beds: 48**

**ST. ANTHONY CENTRAL HOSPITAL** See St. Anthony Hospital, Lakewood

**ST. ANTHONY HOSPITAL A**1 3 5 10 **F**3 7 11 15 17 18 20 22 24 26 28 29 30 31 34 35 36 38 40 42 43 45 46 47 48 49 50 53 56 57 59 63 64 65 66 68 70 74 75 77 78 79 80 81 82 84 85 87 90 92 93 96 102 107 108 110 111 114 115 116 117 118 119 126 129 130 131 132 134 135 144 146 147 148 149 154 155 **P**6
CMO: Brian Erling, M.D., Group Chief Medical Officer
CHR: Michelle Fornier-Johnson, Group Vice President Human Resources
Web address: www.stanthonyhosp.org

**✠ ST. ANTHONY HOSPITAL (060015)**, 11600 West Second Place, Zip 80228–1527; tel. 720/321–0000, (Nonreporting) **A**1 3 5 10 **F**3 7 11 15 17 18 20 22 24 26 28 29 30 31 34 35 36 38 40 42 43 45 46 47 48 49 50 53 56 57 59 63 64 65 66 68 70 74 75 77 78 79 80 81 82 84 85 87 90 92 93 96 102 107 108 110 111 114 115 116 117 118 119 126 129 130 131 132 134 135 144 146 147 148 149 154 155 **P**6 **S** CommonSpirit Health, Chicago, IL
Primary Contact: Kevin Jenkins, Chief Executive Officer
CMO: Brian Erling, M.D., Group Chief Medical Officer
CHR: Michelle Fornier-Johnson, Group Vice President Human Resources
Web address: www.stanthonyhosp.org
**Control**: Church operated, Nongovernment, not–for–profit **Service**: General medical and surgical

**Staffed Beds: 237 Admissions: 12205 Census: 170 Outpatient Visits: 88207 Births: 0 Total Expense ($000): 339998 Payroll Expense ($000): 101793 Personnel: 1613**

## LAMAR—Prowers County

**★ ⇑ PROWERS MEDICAL CENTER (061323)**, 401 Kendall Drive, Zip 81052–3993; tel. 719/336–4343, (Nonreporting) **A**10 18 21 **F**3 11 13 15 18 20 28 29 31 34 35 40 44 45 50 56 57 59 62 64 65 66 68 76 77 78 79 81 85 86 93 96 97 107 111 115 119 127 130 131 132 133 135 146 147 148 154 **S** QHR Health, Brentwood, TN
Primary Contact: Karen L. Bryant, Chief Executive Officer
CFO: Audrey Kane, Interim Chief Financial Officer
CMO: Barry Portner, M.D., Chief of Staff
CIO: Jason Spano, Director of Information Technology
Web address: www.prowersmedical.com
**Control**: Hospital district or authority, Government, Nonfederal **Service**: General medical and surgical

**Staffed Beds: 25 Admissions: 650 Census: 7 Outpatient Visits: 50127 Births: 151 Total Expense ($000): 31747 Payroll Expense ($000): 12699**

## LAS ANIMAS—Bent County

**VETERANS AFFAIRS MED CENTER** See Southern Colorado Healthcare System

## LEADVILLE—Lake County

**⇑ ST VINCENT GENERAL HOSPITAL** See St. Vincent General Hospital District

**★ ⇑ ST. VINCENT GENERAL HOSPITAL DISTRICT (061319)**, 822 West 4th Street, Zip 80461–3897; tel. 719/486–0230, (Nonreporting) **A**10 18 21 **F**3 7 29 34 35 40 44 50 57 59 64 87 93 97 107 116 117 119 129 130 133 143 146 148 157
Primary Contact: Gary Campbell, Chief Executive Officer
CMO: Gary Petry, M.D., Chief of Staff
CHR: Cheryl Snider, Director Human Resources
CNO: Von Kilpatrick, Chief Nursing Officer
Web address: www.svghd.org
**Control**: Hospital district or authority, Government, Nonfederal **Service**: General medical and surgical

**Staffed Beds: 8 Admissions: 130 Census: 1 Outpatient Visits: 7858 Births: 1**

## LITTLETON—Arapahoe County

**✠ ENCOMPASS HEALTH REHABILITATION HOSPITAL OF LITTLETON (063034)**, 1001 West Mineral Avenue, Zip 80120–4507; tel. 303/334–1100, (Nonreporting) **A**1 10 **S** Encompass Health Corporation, Birmingham, AL
Primary Contact: David H. Shefte, Chief Executive Officer
CFO: Liz Freudenberg, Chief Financial Officer
CMO: Jill Castro, M.D., Medical Director
CHR: Sarah Thomas, Director of Human Resources
Web address: www.healthsouthdenver.com
**Control**: Corporation, Investor–owned (for–profit) **Service**: Rehabilitation

**Staffed Beds: 28**

CO

## LITTLETON—Jefferson County

**FEDERAL CORRECTIONAL INSTITUTE HOSPITAL**, 9595 West Quincy Street, Zip 80123–1159; tel. 303/985–1566, (Nonreporting)
Primary Contact: Mike Hudson, Administrator
**Control**: Department of Justice, Government, federal **Service**: Hospital unit of an institution (prison hospital, college infirmary, etc.)

**Staffed Beds:** 6

## LITTLETON—Arapahoe County

**HEALTHSOUTH REHABILITATION HOSPITAL OF LITTLETON** See Encompass Health Rehabilitation Hospital of Littleton

## LITTLETON—Douglas County

☐ **HIGHLANDS BEHAVIORAL HEALTH SYSTEM (064024)**, 8565 South Poplar Way, Zip 80130–3602; tel. 720/348–2800, (Nonreporting) **A**1 10 **S** Universal Health Services, Inc., King of Prussia, PA
Primary Contact: Elicia Bunch, Chief Executive Officer
Web address: www.highlandsbhs.com
**Control**: Corporation, Investor–owned (for–profit) **Service**: Psychiatric

**Staffed Beds:** 86

## LITTLETON—Arapahoe County

☒ **LITTLETON ADVENTIST HOSPITAL (060113)**, 7700 South Broadway Street, Zip 80122–2628; tel. 303/730–8900, (Nonreporting) **A**1 3 5 10 **F**3 11 13 15 17 18 20 22 26 29 30 31 34 35 36 39 40 41 42 43 44 45 46 47 48 49 50 53 54 55 57 58 59 64 68 70 72 74 75 76 77 78 79 81 82 83 84 85 86 87 89 91 92 93 97 107 108 110 111 114 115 116 117 118 119 120 121 126 130 131 132 135 146 147 148 156 **P**6 **S** AdventHealth, Altamonte Springs, FL
Primary Contact: Jillyan McKinney, Chief Executive Officer
COO: Geoff Lawton, Vice President Operations
CFO: Cheryl Curry, Chief Financial Officer
CMO: Lawrence Wood, M.D., Chief Medical Officer
CHR: Rita K Arthur, Director Human Resources
CNO: Rhonda Ward, R.N., MSN, Chief Nursing Officer
Web address: www.centura.org
**Control**: Church operated, Nongovernment, not–for–profit **Service**: General medical and surgical

**Staffed Beds:** 159 **Admissions:** 10061 **Census:** 112 **Outpatient Visits:** 61704 **Births:** 1364 **Total Expense ($000):** 225171 **Payroll Expense ($000):** 75244 **Personnel:** 1004

**PORTER CARE HOSPITAL-LITTLETON** See Littleton Adventist Hospital

## LONE TREE—Douglas County

☒ **SKY RIDGE MEDICAL CENTER (060112)**, 10101 Ridge Gate Parkway, Zip 80124–5522; tel. 720/225–1000, (Nonreporting) **A**1 2 3 5 10 12 13 **F**3 8 12 13 15 17 18 20 22 26 28 29 30 31 34 35 36 37 40 41 42 43 44 45 46 47 48 49 50 54 57 58 59 64 70 72 74 75 76 77 78 79 81 82 84 85 86 87 89 93 107 108 111 114 115 116 117 118 119 120 121 123 126 129 130 131 132 135 146 147 148 149 154 157 **P**5 **S** HCA Healthcare, Nashville, TN
Primary Contact: Kirk McCarty, R.N., MSN, Chief Executive Officer
CFO: Craig Sammons, Chief Financial Officer
CMO: David Markenson, M.D., Chief Medical Officer
CIO: Evan Tice, Director Information Technology and Systems
CHR: Jim Ritchey, Director Human Resources
CNO: Marian Savitsky, R.N., Chief Nursing Officer
Web address: www.skyridgemedcenter.com
**Control**: Corporation, Investor–owned (for–profit) **Service**: General medical and surgical

**Staffed Beds:** 272 **Admissions:** 16180 **Census:** 152 **Outpatient Visits:** 106142 **Births:** 3347 **Personnel:** 1105

## LONGMONT—Boulder County

☒ **LONGMONT UNITED HOSPITAL (060003)**, 1950 Mountain View Avenue, Zip 80501–3162; tel. 303/651–5111, (Nonreporting) **A**1 10 **F**3 11 13 15 18 20 22 26 28 29 30 31 33 36 37 38 40 42 43 44 45 47 48 49 50 53 54 56 57 59 61 64 65 68 70 73 74 75 76 77 78 79 81 82 84 85 86 87 89 92 93 102 107 108 110 111 114 115 118 119 121 123 126 129 130 131 132 144 146 147 148 149 150 154 156 **P**6 **S** CommonSpirit Health, Chicago, IL
Primary Contact: Christina Johnson, M.D., Chief Executive Officer
COO: Andrew Ritz, Chief Operatiang Officer
CHR: Warren Laughlin, Vice President Human Resources
CNO: Mary Hillard, MSN, R.N., Chief Nursing Officer
Web address: www.luhcares.org
**Control**: Other not–for–profit (including NFP Corporation) **Service**: General medical and surgical

**Staffed Beds:** 131 **Admissions:** 4423 **Census:** 51 **Outpatient Visits:** 69531 **Births:** 539 **Total Expense ($000):** 139293 **Payroll Expense ($000):** 45684 **Personnel:** 555

## LONGMONT—Weld County

☐ **UCHEALTH LONGS PEAK HOSPITAL (060128)**, 1750 East Ken Pratt Boulevard, Zip 80504–5311; tel. 970/237–7850, (Nonreporting) **A**1 **F**3 7 8 9 11 12 13 14 15 18 20 22 29 30 34 35 38 40 43 45 46 49 50 56 70 74 75 76 77 79 81 85 87 100 102 107 108 111 115 117 118 119 126 129 130 131 135 143 146 147 148 149 154 **P**6 **S** UCHealth, Fort Collins, CO
Primary Contact: Lonnie Cramer, President
Web address: www.https://www.uchealth.org/locations/uchealth-longs-peak-hospital/
**Control**: Other not–for–profit (including NFP Corporation) **Service**: General medical and surgical

**Staffed Beds:** 51 **Admissions:** 2730 **Census:** 25 **Outpatient Visits:** 26549 **Births:** 692 **Total Expense ($000):** 98437 **Payroll Expense ($000):** 34591 **Personnel:** 454

## LOUISVILLE—Boulder County

☒ **AVISTA ADVENTIST HOSPITAL (060103)**, 100 Health Park Drive, Zip 80027–9583; tel. 303/673–1000, (Nonreporting) **A**1 3 10 **F**3 8 11 13 15 17 18 20 22 28 29 30 31 34 40 42 43 44 45 47 48 49 50 56 59 60 62 63 64 68 70 72 74 75 76 77 79 81 82 84 85 86 87 90 93 107 108 111 114 115 119 126 129 130 131 132 135 146 147 157 **P**6 **S** AdventHealth, Altamonte Springs, FL
Primary Contact: Isaac Sendros, Chief Executive Officer
CMO: David Ehrenberger, M.D., Chief Medical Officer
CHR: Becky Ortega, Manager Human Resources
CNO: Lavah Boyers Lowe, Chief Nursing Officer
Web address: www.avistahospital.org
**Control**: Church operated, Nongovernment, not–for–profit **Service**: General medical and surgical

**Staffed Beds:** 114 **Admissions:** 4659 **Census:** 40 **Outpatient Visits:** 41797 **Births:** 2324 **Total Expense ($000):** 105575 **Payroll Expense ($000):** 36292 **Personnel:** 506

**CENTENNIAL PEAKS HEALTH** See Centennial Peaks Hospital

☐ **CENTENNIAL PEAKS HOSPITAL (064007)**, 2255 South 88th Street, Zip 80027–9716; tel. 303/673–9990, (Nonreporting) **A**1 10 **S** Universal Health Services, Inc., King of Prussia, PA
Primary Contact: Sean Forster, Interim Chief Executive Officer
COO: Lisa Strub, Chief Operating Officer
CFO: Tim Ryan, Chief Financial Officer
CMO: Konoy Mandal, M.D., Medical Director
CHR: Suzanne Martinez, Director Human Resources
CNO: Donia L Andersen, Director of Nursing
Web address: www.centennialpeaks.com
**Control**: Other not–for–profit (including NFP Corporation) **Service**: Psychiatric

**Staffed Beds:** 104

**PORTERCARE HOSPITAL - AVISTA** See Avista Adventist Hospital

CO

*Many Facility Codes have changed. Please refer to the AHA Guide Code Chart.*

CO

## LOVELAND—Larimer County

☒ **MCKEE MEDICAL CENTER (060030)**, 2000 Boise Avenue, Zip 80538–4281;
tel. 970/669–4640, (Nonreporting) **A**1 2 10 **F**2 3 8 11 13 14 15 18 20 22 26 28
29 30 31 34 35 36 40 43 44 50 56 59 60 62 64 65 68 70 74 75 77 78 79 81
84 85 87 92 93 97 105 107 108 110 111 114 115 119 120 121 123 124 126
130 132 143 146 147 148 149 154 **P**8 **S** Banner Health, Phoenix, AZ
Primary Contact: Hoyt Skabelund, Chief Executive Officer
COO: Julie Klein, Chief Operations Officer
CFO: Lori Sehrt, Chief Financial Officer
CMO: Bert Honea, M.D., Medical Director
CIO: Steve Rains, Director Information Services
CHR: Jeannie Gallagher, jeanie.gallagher@bannerhealth.com
CNO: Kelly Sturler, Chief Nursing Officer
Web address: www.mckeeloveland.com
**Control**: Other not–for–profit (including NFP Corporation) **Service**: General
medical and surgical

**Staffed Beds**: 73 **Admissions**: 2817 **Census**: 24 **Outpatient Visits**: 175759
**Births**: 442 **Total Expense ($000)**: 121342 **Payroll Expense ($000)**: 35582
**Personnel**: 499

**MEDICAL CENTER OF THE ROCKIES** See Uchealth Medical Center of The
Rockies

☒ **UCHEALTH MEDICAL CENTER OF THE ROCKIES (060119)**, 2500 Rocky
Mountain Avenue, Zip 80538–9004; tel. 970/624–2500, (Nonreporting) **A**1 3 5
10 **F**3 8 9 11 13 14 15 17 18 20 22 24 26 28 29 30 31 34 35 38 40 42 43 45
46 49 50 58 59 61 63 64 65 68 70 71 73 74 75 76 77 78 79 80 81 82 84 85
87 93 100 102 107 110 111 114 115 116 118 119 126 129 130 132 135 143 146
149 154 156 157 **S** UCHealth, Fort Collins, CO
Primary Contact: Kevin L. Unger, Ph.D., FACHE, President and Chief Executive
Officer
COO: Ryan Rohman, MSN, R.N., Chief Operating Officer
CFO: Stephanie Doughty, Chief Financial Officer
CMO: William Neff, M.D., Chief Medical Officer
CIO: Steve Hess, Vice President & Chief Information Officer
Web address: www.medctrrockies.org
**Control**: Other not–for–profit (including NFP Corporation) **Service**: General
medical and surgical

**Staffed Beds**: 220 **Admissions**: 12089 **Census**: 134 **Outpatient
Visits**: 109484 **Births**: 1684 **Total Expense ($000)**: 449470 **Payroll
Expense ($000)**: 130822 **Personnel**: 1463

## MEEKER—Rio Blanco County

**PIONEERS HOSP OF RIO BLANCO** See Pioneers Medical Center

★ **PIONEERS MEDICAL CENTER (061325)**, 100 Pioneers Medical Center Drive,
Zip 81641–3181; tel. 970/878–5047, (Nonreporting) **A**10 18 **S** QHR Health,
Brentwood, TN
Primary Contact: Liz Sellers, R.N., MSN, Chief Executive Officer
COO: Karen Iacuone, Chief Nursing Officer and Chief Operating Officer
CFO: James W Worrell, Chief Financial Officer
CMO: Christopher Williams, M.D., Chief of Staff
CIO: Curtis Cooper, Manager Information Systems
CHR: Twyla Jensen, Director Human Resources
CNO: Karen Iacuone, Chief Nursing Officer
Web address: www.pioneershospital.org
**Control**: Hospital district or authority, Government, Nonfederal **Service**: General
medical and surgical

**Staffed Beds**: 40

## MONTROSE—Montrose County

☒ **MONTROSE MEMORIAL HOSPITAL (060006)**, 800 South Third Street,
Zip 81401–4212; tel. 970/249–2211, (Nonreporting) **A**1 10 20 **F**3 13 15 18 20
22 28 29 30 31 34 35 40 43 44 45 46 50 51 57 59 64 68 70 72 74 75 76 77
78 79 81 82 85 89 90 92 93 96 107 108 110 111 115 118 119 126 129 130
132 135 146 147 148 149 154 **P**1 5 **S** QHR Health, Brentwood, TN
Primary Contact: James R. Kiser II, Chief Executive Officer
COO: Mary E Snyder, Chief Operations Officer
CFO: Stephan A Wilson, Chief Financial Officer
CMO: Richard Shannon, M.D., Chief of Staff
CIO: Carlos Lovera, Director Information Systems
CHR: Kathy McKie, Director Human Resources
Web address: www.montrosehospital.com
**Control**: Other not–for–profit (including NFP Corporation) **Service**: General
medical and surgical

**Staffed Beds**: 62 **Admissions**: 2880 **Census**: 24 **Outpatient Visits**: 119053
**Births**: 374 **Total Expense ($000)**: 115802 **Payroll Expense ($000)**: 42887
**Personnel**: 749

## PAGOSA SPRINGS—Archuleta County

**PAGOSA MOUNTAIN HOSPITAL** See Pagosa Springs Medical Center

**PAGOSA SPRINGS MEDICAL CENTER (061328)**, 95 South Pagosa Boulevard,
Zip 81147–8329; tel. 970/731–3700, (Nonreporting) **A**10 18 **F**3 7 11 15 18 29
30 31 32 34 35 38 40 43 45 50 54 56 57 59 61 64 65 66 68 74 78 79 81 82
84 85 86 87 89 90 93 97 100 102 104 107 110 111 115 119 127 128 130
131 133 135 143 144 145 146 147 148 154 156 157
Primary Contact: Rhonda Webb, M.D., Chief Executive Officer
Web address: www.pagosaspringsmedicalcenter.org/
**Control**: Hospital district or authority, Government, Nonfederal **Service**: General
medical and surgical

**Staffed Beds**: 11 **Admissions**: 377 **Census**: 3 **Outpatient Visits**: 67335
**Births**: 0 **Total Expense ($000)**: 35538 **Payroll Expense ($000)**: 18652
**Personnel**: 221

## PARKER—Douglas County

☒ **PARKER ADVENTIST HOSPITAL (060114)**, 9395 Crown Crest Boulevard,
Zip 80138–8573; tel. 303/269–4000, (Nonreporting) **A**1 3 5 10 **F**3 11 12 13 15
18 20 22 29 30 31 34 35 36 37 38 40 42 43 45 46 47 48 49 50 54 55 57 59
64 70 72 73 74 75 76 77 78 79 81 82 83 84 85 87 93 96 97 102 107 110
111 114 115 116 117 118 119 120 121 123 126 130 131 132 146 147 148
156 **P**6 **S** AdventHealth, Altamonte Springs, FL
Primary Contact: Michael Goebel, Chief Executive Officer
COO: Leanne Naso, Chief Operating Officer
CFO: Jonathan Fisher, Chief Financial Officer
CMO: Devin Bateman, M.D., Chief Medical Officer
CNO: Andrea Narvaez, R.N., Chief Nursing Officer
Web address: www.parkerhospital.org
**Control**: Church operated, Nongovernment, not–for–profit **Service**: General
medical and surgical

**Staffed Beds**: 152 **Admissions**: 8231 **Census**: 84 **Outpatient Visits**: 79345
**Births**: 1130 **Total Expense ($000)**: 212641 **Payroll Expense
($000)**: 66229 **Personnel**: 1043

## PUEBLO—Pueblo County

☐ **COLORADO MENTAL HEALTH INSTITUTE AT PUEBLO (064001)**, 1600 West
24th Street, Zip 81003–1499; tel. 719/546–4000, (Nonreporting) **A**1 3 5 10
Primary Contact: Ron Hale, Superintendent
CFO: Jim Duff, Chief Financial Officer
CMO: Al Singleton, M.D., Chief Psychiatry and Chief Medical Staff
CIO: Eunice Wolther, Public Information Officer
CHR: Mary Young, Director Human Resources
Web address: www.cdhs.state.co.us/cmhip
**Control**: State, Government, Nonfederal **Service**: Psychiatric

**Staffed Beds**: 514

**COLORADO STATE HOSPITAL** See Colorado Mental Health Institute at Pueblo

**PARKVIEW EPISCOPAL MED CENTER** See Parkview Medical Center

---

✠ △ **PARKVIEW MEDICAL CENTER (060020)**, 400 West 16th Street,
Zip 81003–2781; tel. 719/584–4000, (Nonreporting) **A**1 3 5 7 10 13 **F**2 3 4 5
11 13 15 17 18 20 22 24 26 28 29 30 31 34 35 37 38 40 42 43 45 46 48 49
50 51 53 54 56 57 58 59 62 64 70 72 74 75 76 78 79 81 82 84 85 86 87 89
90 92 93 94 95 96 97 98 99 100 101 102 103 104 107 108 110 111 114 115
119 126 129 130 131 132 135 141 146 147 148 151 156 157 **P**6 8
Primary Contact: Leslie Barnes, Chief Executive Officer
COO: Darrin Smith, Chief Operating Officer
CFO: Leslie Barnes, Chief Financial Officer
CMO: Steve Nafziger, M.D., Vice President Medical Affairs
CIO: Steve Shirley, Chief Information Officer
CNO: Linda Flores, R.N., MSN, Vice President Nursing Services
Web address: www.parkviewmc.org
**Control**: Other not–for–profit (including NFP Corporation) **Service**: General
medical and surgical

> **Staffed Beds: 341 Admissions: 16611 Census: 223 Outpatient
> Visits: 246864 Births: 1949 Total Expense ($000): 355718 Payroll
> Expense ($000): 144531 Personnel: 3556**

**ST MARY-CORWIN REG MED CENTER** See St. Mary-Corwin Medical Center

✠ **ST. MARY-CORWIN MEDICAL CENTER (060012)**, 1008 Minnequa Avenue,
Zip 81004–3798; tel. 719/557–4000, (Nonreporting) **A**1 3 5 10 13 **F**3 15 18 29
30 31 34 35 40 43 45 47 48 49 50 53 55 57 59 64 68 70 78 79 81 85 86 87
107 108 109 110 111 114 115 117 119 120 121 123 124 126 130 132 135
146 148 149 154 **P**6 **S** CommonSpirit Health, Chicago, IL
Primary Contact: Michael Cafasso, Chief Executive Officer
COO: Michael Cafasso, Chief Operating Officer
CFO: Janiece McNichols, Chief Financial Officer
CMO: Kern Low, M.D., Chief Medical Officer
CHR: Timea Kennedy, Director Human Resources
Web address: www.stmarycorwin.org
**Control**: Church operated, Nongovernment, not–for–profit **Service**: General
medical and surgical

> **Staffed Beds: 42 Admissions: 2028 Census: 22 Outpatient Visits: 75122
> Births: 0 Total Expense ($000): 110618 Payroll Expense ($000): 33112
> Personnel: 547**

### RANGELY—Rio Blanco County

★ **RANGELY DISTRICT HOSPITAL (061307)**, 225 Eagle Crest Drive,
Zip 81648–2104; tel. 970/675–5011, (Total facility includes 14 beds in nursing
home–type unit) (Nonreporting) **A**10 18 **F**3 7 8 10 15 18 19 35 39 40 41 45 57
59 62 64 65 68 69 81 84 89 93 97 104 107 114 133 148 153 154
Primary Contact: Kyle Wren, Chief Executive Officer
COO: Bernard Rice, Chief Compliance Officer
CFO: Jim Dillon, Chief Financial Officer
CMO: Abigail R. Urish, M.D., Chief of Staff
CHR: Cynthia S. Stults, Executive Assistant and Human Resources Director
CNO: Sharma Vaughn EsqChief Nursing Officer
Web address: www.rangelyhospital.com
**Control**: Hospital district or authority, Government, Nonfederal **Service**: General
medical and surgical

> **Staffed Beds: 18 Admissions: 71 Census: 14 Outpatient Visits: 10994
> Births: 0 Total Expense ($000): 17796 Payroll Expense ($000): 7076
> Personnel: 129**

### RIFLE—Garfield County

**CLAGETT MEMORIAL HOSPITAL** See Grand River Hospital District

★ **GRAND RIVER HOSPITAL DISTRICT (061317)**, 501 Airport Road,
Zip 81650–8510, Mailing Address: P.O. Box 912, Zip 81650–0912;
tel. 970/625–1510, (Total facility includes 50 beds in nursing home–type unit)
(Nonreporting) **A**10 18 **F**3 11 12 15 29 31 32 34 35 36 38 39 40 41 43 45 50
55 57 59 64 68 69 75 77 78 79 81 85 87 93 96 97 107 108 110 111 115 119
127 128 129 130 131 132 133 144 146 147 148 149 156 157 **P**6
Primary Contact: James Coombs, Chief Executive Officer
COO: Bill Noel, Chief Operating Officer
CFO: Cris Bolin, Chief Financial Officer
CMO: Kevin Coleman, M.D., Chief Medical Officer
CIO: Diana Murray, Director Information Systems
CHR: Dawn Hodges, Director Human Resources
CNO: Stacy Pemberton, Chief Nursing Officer
Web address: www.grhd.org
**Control**: Hospital district or authority, Government, Nonfederal **Service**: General
medical and surgical

> **Staffed Beds: 62 Admissions: 660 Census: 47 Outpatient Visits: 118532
> Births: 0 Total Expense ($000): 89643 Payroll Expense ($000): 40261
> Personnel: 536**

### SALIDA—Chaffee County

★ **HEART OF THE ROCKIES REGIONAL MEDICAL CENTER (061322)**, 1000
Rush Drive, Zip 81201–9627, Mailing Address: P.O. Box 429, Zip 81201–0429;
tel. 719/530–2200, (Nonreporting) **A**10 18 **F**3 5 11 13 15 28 29 31 34 35 40
43 45 50 53 54 57 59 64 68 70 74 75 76 77 78 79 81 82 85 87 91 93 97 102
104 107 110 111 115 119 127 129 130 131 132 133 135 146 147 148
156 **P**5
Primary Contact: Robert A. Morasko, Chief Executive Officer
CFO: Lesley Fagerberg, Vice President Fiscal Services
CMO: Daniel Wardrop, M.D., Medical Director
CIO: Andy Waldbart, Department Manager
CHR: Barbara Lutz, Vice President Human Resources
CNO: Linda Johnson, R.N., Vice President, Patient Services Risk Management and
Chief Nursing Officer
Web address: www.hrrmc.com
**Control**: Hospital district or authority, Government, Nonfederal **Service**: General
medical and surgical

> **Staffed Beds: 25 Admissions: 1097 Census: 11 Outpatient Visits: 109982
> Births: 116 Total Expense ($000): 75818 Payroll Expense ($000): 33926
> Personnel: 451**

### SPRINGFIELD—Baca County

**SOUTHEAST COLORADO HOSPITAL** See Southeast Colorado Hospital District

★ **SOUTHEAST COLORADO HOSPITAL DISTRICT (061311)**, 373 East Tenth
Avenue, Zip 81073–1699; tel. 719/523–4501, (Total facility includes 56 beds in
nursing home–type unit) (Nonreporting) **A**10 18 **F**3 6 7 11 28 29 40 45 50 57
62 63 66 67 68 81 91 97 114 119 127 130 133 135 148 154 **S** QHR Health,
Brentwood, TN
Primary Contact: David Engel, Chief Executive Officer and Administrator
CFO: Dorothy Burke, Chief Financial Officer
CMO: Andrea Wismann, M.D., Chief of Staff
CIO: Chris Westphal, Chief Information Technology Officer
CHR: Sherrilyn Turner, Director Human Resources
CNO: Cecelia Deen EsqChief Nursing Officer
Web address: www.sechosp.org
**Control**: Hospital district or authority, Government, Nonfederal **Service**: General
medical and surgical

> **Staffed Beds: 79 Admissions: 287 Census: 53 Outpatient Visits: 38385
> Births: 0 Total Expense ($000): 14890 Payroll Expense ($000): 6139
> Personnel: 198**

### STEAMBOAT SPRINGS—Routt County

✠ **UCHEALTH YAMPA VALLEY MEDICAL CENTER (060049)**, 1024 Central Park
Drive, Zip 80487–8813; tel. 970/879–1322, (Nonreporting) **A**1 10 20 **F**3 9 11
13 14 15 18 28 29 31 34 35 36 37 38 40 43 45 46 48 50 57 59 61 64 65 68
70 73 74 75 76 77 78 79 81 82 84 85 86 87 93 97 102 107 110 111 115 119
126 129 130 131 132 133 135 146 147 148 149 154 156 **S** UCHealth, Fort
Collins, CO
Primary Contact: Soniya Fidler, MS, President
CMO: Laura Sehnert, M.D., Chief Medical Officer
CHR: Dallis Howard-Crow, Chief Human Resources Officer
Web address: www.https://www.uchealth.org/locations/uchealth-yampa-valley-
medical-center/
**Control**: Other not–for–profit (including NFP Corporation) **Service**: General
medical and surgical

> **Staffed Beds: 39 Admissions: 1281 Census: 8 Outpatient Visits: 63719
> Births: 271 Total Expense ($000): 100095 Payroll Expense ($000): 36117
> Personnel: 474**

**YAMPA VALLEY MEDICAL CENTER** See Uchealth Yampa Valley Medical Center

### STERLING—Logan County

**STERLING REGIONAL MEDCENTER** See Sterling Regional Medcenter

**CO**

✠ **STERLING REGIONAL MEDCENTER (060076)**, 615 Fairhurst Street, Zip 80751–4523; tel. 970/522–0122, (Nonreporting) **A**1 3 10 20 **F**3 13 15 18 28 29 34 35 40 43 45 57 59 64 65 70 76 77 78 79 81 85 87 91 93 96 97 107 108 110 111 115 119 120 121 127 129 130 131 146 147 148 149 154 **P**8 **S** Banner Health, Phoenix, AZ
Primary Contact: Wade Tyrell, Chief Executive Officer and Chief Nursing Officer
CFO: Nathan Nichols, Director of Finance
CMO: Jeff Bacon, D.O., Chief Medical Officer
CNO: Wade Alan Tyrrell RNChief Executive Officer and Chief Nursing Officer
Web address: www.https://www.bannerhealth.com/locations/sterling/sterling-regional-medcenter
**Control:** Other not–for–profit (including NFP Corporation) **Service:** General medical and surgical

**Staffed Beds:** 25 **Admissions:** 1030 **Census:** 8 **Outpatient Visits:** 69017 **Births:** 210 **Total Expense ($000):** 50349 **Payroll Expense ($000):** 16823 **Personnel:** 231

**THORNTON—Adams County**

✠ **NORTH SUBURBAN MEDICAL CENTER (060065)**, 9191 Grant Street, Zip 80229–4341; tel. 303/451–7800, (Nonreporting) **A**1 3 5 10 **S** HCA Healthcare, Nashville, TN
Primary Contact: Daphne G. David, President and Chief Executive Officer
CIO: Marty Hoesch, Director Information Systems
CHR: Dena Schmaedecke, Vice President Human Resources
Web address: www.northsuburban.com
**Control:** Corporation, Investor–owned (for–profit) **Service:** General medical and surgical

**Staffed Beds:** 157

**NORTH SUBURBAN MEDICALCENTER** See North Suburban Medical Center

**VIBRA HOSPITAL DENVER** See Vibra Hospital of Denver

✠ **VIBRA HOSPITAL OF DENVER (062014)**, 8451 Pearl Street, Zip 80229–4804; tel. 303/288–3000, (Nonreporting) **A**1 10 **S** Vibra Healthcare, Mechanicsburg, PA
Primary Contact: Lamar McBride, Chief Executive Officer
CMO: John Buckley, M.D., President Medical Staff
Web address: www.vhdenver.com
**Control:** Corporation, Investor–owned (for–profit) **Service:** Acute long–term care hospital

**Staffed Beds:** 71

☐ **VIBRA REHABILITATION HOSPITAL OF DENVER (063035)**, 8451 Pearl Street, Suite 101, Zip 80229–4803; tel. 303/301–8700, (Nonreporting) **A**1
Primary Contact: Craig A. Hoover, Chief Executive Officer
Web address: www.https://www.vibrahealthcare.com
**Control:** Corporation, Investor–owned (for–profit) **Service:** Rehabilitation

**Staffed Beds:** 31

**TRINIDAD—Las Animas County**

**MOUNT SAN RAFAEL HOSPITAL** See Mt. San Rafael Hospital

★ **MT. SAN RAFAEL HOSPITAL (061321)**, 410 Benedicta Avenue, Zip 81082–2093; tel. 719/846–9213, (Nonreporting) **A**10 18 **F**3 15 28 29 32 34 35 40 43 45 46 47 48 50 59 64 65 66 75 79 81 82 87 90 93 97 107 110 111 115 119 127 129 133 135 146 147 148 149 150 154 156 157
Primary Contact: John Tucker, Chief Executive Officer
CFO: Calvin Carey, Chief Financial Officer
CIO: Michael Archuleta, Chief Information Technology Officer
CHR: Tammy Rogers, Director Human Resources
CNO: Mandy Shaiffer, Chief Nursing Officer
Web address: www.msrhc.org
**Control:** Other not–for–profit (including NFP Corporation) **Service:** General medical and surgical

**Staffed Beds:** 18 **Admissions:** 408 **Census:** 7 **Outpatient Visits:** 41860 **Births:** 0 **Total Expense ($000):** 32812 **Payroll Expense ($000):** 16677 **Personnel:** 209

**VAIL—Eagle County**

✠ **VAIL HEALTH (060096)**, 181 West Meadow Drive, Zip 81657–5242, Mailing Address: P.O. Box 40000, Zip 81658–7520; tel. 970/476–2451, (Nonreporting) **A**1 3 10 20 **F**3 11 13 15 17 18 20 22 24 26 28 29 30 31 34 39 40 42 43 45 46 50 51 54 55 57 59 64 68 70 72 74 75 76 77 78 79 81 82 85 86 87 89 91 92 93 94 107 108 109 110 111 115 116 117 119 120 121 123 129 130 131 135 141 142 143 144 145 146 147 148 149 154 156 **P**6
Primary Contact: William Cook, President and Chief Executive Officer
CFO: Ted Sirotta, Chief Financial Officer
CMO: Barry Hammaker, M.D., Chief Medical Officer and Chief Clinical Officer
CIO: Brian Foster, Chief Information Officer
CHR: Rick Smith, Senior Vice President Human Resources and Chief Administrative Officer
CNO: Sheila Sherman, Vice President Patient Care Services
Web address: www.vvmc.com
**Control:** Other not–for–profit (including NFP Corporation) **Service:** General medical and surgical

**Staffed Beds:** 53 **Admissions:** 1983 **Census:** 14 **Outpatient Visits:** 131396 **Births:** 417 **Total Expense ($000):** 242155 **Payroll Expense ($000):** 64863 **Personnel:** 886

**VAIL VALLEY HEALTH HOSPITAL** See Vail Health

**WALSENBURG—Huerfano County**

**HUERFANO MEDICAL CENTER** See Spanish Peaks Regional Health Center

★ **SPANISH PEAKS REGIONAL HEALTH CENTER (061316)**, 23500 U S Highway 160, Zip 81089–9524; tel. 719/738–5100, (Total facility includes 120 beds in nursing home–type unit) (Nonreporting) **A**10 18 **F**7 15 26 27 28 29 30 32 34 35 40 43 45 50 57 59 64 65 66 67 68 77 79 81 93 96 97 107 110 115 119 127 132 133 134 135 143 146 147 148 155 156 157 **S** QHR Health, Brentwood, TN
Primary Contact: Kay L. Whitley, President and Chief Executive Officer
CMO: Michael A. Moll, M.D., Chief Medical Officer and Chief of Staff
CHR: Tony Marostica, Chief Compliance and Human Resource Officer
CNO: Mary Cope, R.N., Chief Clinical Officer
Web address: www.sprhc.org
**Control:** Hospital district or authority, Government, Nonfederal **Service:** General medical and surgical

**Staffed Beds:** 140 **Admissions:** 277 **Census:** 95 **Outpatient Visits:** 17209 **Births:** 0 **Total Expense ($000):** 16583 **Payroll Expense ($000):** 9151

**WESTMINSTER—Adams County**

✠ **ST. ANTHONY NORTH HEALTH CAMPUS (060104)**, 14300 Orchard Parkway, Zip 80023–9206; tel. 720/627–0000, (Nonreporting) **A**1 3 5 10 **F**3 11 13 15 18 20 22 26 28 29 30 31 34 35 36 40 42 43 45 46 49 51 54 55 57 59 60 63 64 65 68 70 74 75 76 77 78 79 81 82 84 85 87 91 92 93 97 102 107 108 110 111 114 115 119 130 131 132 135 142 146 147 148 149 150 155 **P**6 **S** CommonSpirit Health, Chicago, IL
Primary Contact: Constance Schmidt, FACHE, R.N., Chief Executive Officer
CFO: Alison Mizer, Chief Financial Officer
CHR: Robert Archibold, Director, Human Resources
CNO: Carol A Butler, R.N., MSN, VP Patient Care Services & Operations
Web address: www.https://www.centura.org/locations/st-anthony-north-health-campus?utm_source=yext&utm_medium=organic_google&utm_term=ST_ANTHONY_NORTH_HEALTH_CAMPUS&utm_content=facilities_landing_page
**Control:** Church operated, Nongovernment, not–for–profit **Service:** General medical and surgical

**Staffed Beds:** 100 **Admissions:** 5996 **Census:** 53 **Outpatient Visits:** 75702 **Births:** 911 **Total Expense ($000):** 153387 **Payroll Expense ($000):** 48016 **Personnel:** 800

**ST. ANTHONY NORTH HOSPITAL** See St. Anthony North Health Campus

**WHEAT RIDGE—Jefferson County**

**EXEMPLA LUTHERAN MEDICAL CENTER** See Lutheran Medical Center

---

**Hospital, Medicare Provider Number, Address, Telephone, Approval, Facility, and Physician Codes, Health Care System**

★ American Hospital Association (AHA) membership    ○ Healthcare Facilities Accreditation Program    ⇑ Center for Improvement in Healthcare Quality Accreditation
☐ The Joint Commission accreditation    ◇ DNV Healthcare Inc. accreditation    △ Commission on Accreditation of Rehabilitation Facilities (CARF) accreditation

CO

☒ **LUTHERAN MEDICAL CENTER (060009)**, 8300 West 38th Avenue,
Zip 80033–6005; tel. 303/425–4500, (Includes EXEMPLA WEST PINES,
Mailing address: 3400 Lutheran Parkway, Wheat Ridge, Colorado, Zip 80033;
tel. 303/467–4000), (Nonreporting) **A**1 2 3 10 **F**3 4 5 11 12 13 15 18 20 22 24
26 28 29 30 31 33 35 36 40 43 45 47 48 49 50 55 56 58 59 60 61 63 64 68
70 71 72 74 75 76 77 78 79 81 83 84 85 86 87 94 98 100 101 102 103 104
105 106 107 108 110 111 114 115 119 120 121 123 124 126 129 130 132
146 147 148 149 152 153 154 157 **P**6 **S** SCL Health, Broomfield, CO
Primary Contact: Grant Wicklund, SCL Health Regional President, Western Colorado
and President, Lutheran Medical Center
CFO: Karen Scremin, Vice President Finance
CHR: Scott Day, Vice President Human Resources
CNO: Geraldine Towndrow, R.N., Senior Vice President Nursing
Web address: www.https://www.sclhealth.org/locations/lutheran-medical-center/
**Control**: Other not–for–profit (including NFP Corporation) **Service**: General
medical and surgical

> **Staffed Beds:** 368 **Admissions:** 14805 **Census:** 190 **Outpatient
> Visits:** 177544 **Births:** 1902 **Total Expense ($000):** 380552 **Payroll
> Expense ($000):** 125930 **Personnel:** 1627

**WEST PINES AT LUTHERAN MED CTR** See Exempla West Pines

**WOODLAND PARK—Teller County**

**PIKES PEAK REGIONAL HOSPITAL** See Uchealth Pikes Peak Regional Hospital

☐ **UCHEALTH PIKES PEAK REGIONAL HOSPITAL (061326)**, 16420 West
Highway 24, Zip 80863; tel. 719/687–9999, (Nonreporting) **A**1 10 18 **F**3 15
29 30 34 40 41 43 45 50 57 59 64 65 68 75 77 79 80 81 85 87 93 97 107
110 111 114 119 129 131 133 146 148 **S** Steward Health Care System, LLC,
Dallas, TX
Primary Contact: Ron Fitch, Chief Executive Officer
CFO: Robin Ruff, Chief Financial Officer
CMO: Richard Malyszek, M.D., Chief of Staff
CHR: Arianne Randolph, Director Human Resources
Web address: www.https://www.uchealth.org/locations/uchealth-pikes-peak-
regional-hospital/
**Control**: Corporation, Investor–owned (for–profit) **Service**: General medical and
surgical

> **Staffed Beds:** 15 **Admissions:** 492 **Census:** 6

**WRAY—Yuma County**

★ **WRAY COMMUNITY DISTRICT HOSPITAL (061309)**, 1017 West 7th Street,
Zip 80758–1420; tel. 970/332–4811, (Nonreporting) **A**3 10 18
Primary Contact: John Hart, Chief Executive Officer
CMO: Monte Uyemura, M.D., Chief of Staff
Web address: www.wraycommunitydistricthospital.com/
**Control**: Hospital district or authority, Government, Nonfederal **Service**: General
medical and surgical

> **Staffed Beds:** 15

**YUMA—Yuma County**

★ **YUMA DISTRICT HOSPITAL (061315)**, 1000 West 8th Avenue,
Zip 80759–2641; tel. 970/848–5405, (Nonreporting) **A**10 18
Primary Contact: Beth Saxton, R.N., Chief Executive Officer
CFO: Rick Korf, Chief Financial Officer
CMO: John Wolz, M.D., Chief Medical Staff
CIO: Jason Hawley, Director of Information Services and Security
CHR: Gini Adams, Director Employee and Public Relations
Web address: www.yumahospital.org
**Control**: Hospital district or authority, Government, Nonfederal **Service**: General
medical and surgical

> **Staffed Beds:** 12

# CONNECTICUT

## BRANFORD—New Haven County

☐ **THE CONNECTICUT HOSPICE (070038)**, 100 Double Beach Road,
Zip 06405–4909; tel. 203/315–7500, (Nonreporting) **A**1 3 5 10
Primary Contact: Barbara Pearce, Interim Chief Executive Officer
Web address: www.hospice.com
**Control:** Other not-for-profit (including NFP Corporation) **Service:** Other specialty treatment

**Staffed Beds:** 52

## BRIDGEPORT—Fairfield County

✠ **BRIDGEPORT HOSPITAL (070010)**, 267 Grant Street, Zip 06610–2805,
Mailing Address: P.O. Box 5000, Zip 06610–0120; tel. 203/384–3000, (Includes
MILFORD HOSPITAL, Mailing address: 300 Seaside Avenue, Milford, Connecticut,
Zip 06460–4603; tel. 203/876–4000; Lloyd Friedman, M.D., Interim President
and Chief Operating Officer), (Nonreporting) **A**1 2 3 5 8 10 **F**3 5 6 8 11 12 13 14
15 16 17 18 20 22 24 26 28 29 30 31 32 34 35 36 37 38 39 40 41 42 43 44
45 46 47 48 49 50 51 52 54 55 56 57 58 59 61 62 64 65 66 68 70 74 75 76
78 79 80 81 82 84 85 86 87 93 96 97 98 101 102 103 104 107 108 110 111
114 115 116 117 118 119 120 121 123 124 126 129 130 131 132 134 144
145 146 147 148 149 153 154 **S** Yale New Haven Health, New Haven, CT
Primary Contact: Anne Diamond, President
CFO: Patrick McCabe, Senior Vice President Finance and Chief Financial Officer
CMO: Michael Ivy, M.D., Senior Vice President for Medical Affairs and Chief Medical Officer
CIO: Daniel Barchi, Senior Vice President, Technical Services and Chief Information Officer
CHR: Melissa Turner, Senior Vice President Human Resources
CNO: MaryEllen Kosturko, R.N., Senior Vice President Patient Care Operations and Chief Nursing Officer
Web address: www.bridgeporthospital.org
**Control:** Other not-for-profit (including NFP Corporation) **Service:** General medical and surgical

**Staffed Beds:** 423 **Admissions:** 20700 **Census:** 329 **Outpatient Visits:** 341878 **Births:** 2406 **Total Expense ($000):** 585419 **Payroll Expense ($000):** 187000 **Personnel:** 2628

**GRTR BRIDGEPORT COMM HLTH CTR** See Southwest Connecticut Mental Health System

☐ **SOUTHWEST CONNECTICUT MENTAL HEALTH SYSTEM (074012)**, 1635
Central Avenue, Zip 06610–2717; tel. 203/551–7400, (Nonreporting) **A**1 10 **S**
Connecticut Department of Mental Health and Addiction Services, Hartford, CT
Primary Contact: Alicia Feller, Chief Executive Officer
COO: Fran Giannini, Associate Director
CMO: Robert Berger, M.D., Medical Director
CIO: Paula Zwally, Director Quality Improvement Services and Compliance
CHR: Irena Baj-Wright, Director Human Resources
Web address: www.ct.gov/dmhas/cwp/view.asp?a=2946&q=378936
**Control:** State, Government, Nonfederal **Service:** Psychiatric

**Staffed Beds:** 62

✠ **ST. VINCENT'S MEDICAL CENTER (070028)**, 2800 Main Street,
Zip 06606–4292; tel. 203/576–6000, (Includes ST. VINCENT'S BEHAVIORAL
HEALTH, Mailing address: 47 Long Lots Road, Westport, Connecticut,
Zip 06880–3800; tel. 203/221–8813), (Nonreporting) **A**1 2 3 5 10 **F**3 11 12 13
15 18 20 22 24 26 28 29 30 31 34 35 36 37 38 40 43 44 45 46 47 48 49 50
51 54 55 56 57 58 59 61 64 65 70 71 72 74 75 76 77 78 79 80 81 82 84 85
86 87 90 96 97 98 99 100 101 102 104 107 108 110 111 114 115 116 117
118 119 120 121 122 123 124 126 130 132 135 144 145 146 147 148 149
150 153 154 **P**8 **S** Hartford HealthCare, Hartford, CT
Primary Contact: Vincent DiBattista, Senior Vice President, Fairfield Region President
COO: Brooke Karlsen, MSN, R.N., Regional Vice President, Operations
CFO: Christopher Given, Regional Vice President, Finance
CMO: Dan Gottschall, Vice President, Medical Officer
CNO: Dale Danowski, R.N., Vice President, Patient Care Services
Web address: www.stvincents.org
**Control:** Other not-for-profit (including NFP Corporation) **Service:** General medical and surgical

**Staffed Beds:** 337 **Admissions:** 12710 **Census:** 211 **Outpatient Visits:** 213438 **Births:** 729 **Total Expense ($000):** 468036 **Payroll Expense ($000):** 174059 **Personnel:** 1772

## BRISTOL—Hartford County

✠ **BRISTOL HEALTH (070029)**, 41 Brewster Road, Zip 06010–5161, Mailing
Address: P.O. Box 977, Zip 06011–0977; tel. 860/585–3000, (Nonreporting) **A**1
5 10
Primary Contact: Kurt A. Barwis, FACHE, President and Chief Executive Officer
COO: Robert Smanik, Vice President of Operatoins
CFO: Richard Braam, Vice President, Operations and Chief Financial Officer
CHR: Christine Laprise, Vice President of Human Resources
CNO: Chris Ann Meaney, Vice President of Patient Care Service and Chief Nursing Officer
Web address: www.https://www.bristolhealth.org/
**Control:** Other not-for-profit (including NFP Corporation) **Service:** General medical and surgical

**Staffed Beds:** 110

**BRISTOL HOSPITAL** See Bristol Health

## DANBURY—Fairfield County

✠ **DANBURY HOSPITAL (070033)**, 24 Hospital Avenue, Zip 06810–6099;
tel. 203/739–7000, (Includes NEW MILFORD HOSPITAL, Mailing address: 21 Elm
Street, New Milford, Connecticut, Zip 06776–2993; tel. 860/355–2611; John M
Murphy, M.D., President and Chief Executive Officer, Western Connecticut Health
Network), (Nonreporting) **A**1 2 3 5 8 10 **F**3 5 8 9 12 13 14 15 18 20 22 24 26
28 29 30 31 32 34 35 36 37 38 39 40 41 43 44 45 46 47 49 50 51 54 55 56
57 58 59 61 64 65 66 68 70 72 73 74 75 76 77 78 79 81 82 83 84 85 86 87
89 90 93 96 97 98 100 101 102 104 105 107 108 110 111 114 115 117 118
119 120 121 123 124 126 129 130 131 132 134 135 145 146 147 148 149
153 154 156 **S** Nuvance Health, Danbury, CT
Primary Contact: Sharon Adams, President
COO: Sharon Adams, Chief Operating Officer
CFO: Steven Rosenberg, Chief Financial Officer
CMO: Patricia Tietjen, M.D., Vice President, Medical Affairs
CIO: Kathleen DeMatteo, Chief Information Officer
CHR: Cathy Frierson, Chief Human Resource Officer
CNO: Sharon Adams, Chief Nursing Officer
Web address: www.danburyhospital.org
**Control:** Other not-for-profit (including NFP Corporation) **Service:** General medical and surgical

**Staffed Beds:** 286 **Admissions:** 19889 **Census:** 240 **Outpatient Visits:** 376995 **Births:** 2027 **Total Expense ($000):** 654854 **Payroll Expense ($000):** 224434 **Personnel:** 2011

CT

**DERBY—New Haven County**

☒ **GRIFFIN HOSPITAL (070031)**, 130 Division Street, Zip 06418–1326;
tel. 203/735–7421, (Nonreporting) **A**1 2 3 5 10 **F**3 12 13 15 18 28 29 30 31 34
35 36 38 40 45 49 50 53 54 56 57 58 59 64 65 66 68 70 71 74 75 76 77 78
79 81 82 84 85 86 87 91 92 93 94 96 97 98 100 101 102 104 107 108 110
111 114 115 118 119 120 121 123 124 126 129 130 131 132 134 135 143
146 147 148 149 152 153 154 156 **P**3 8
Primary Contact: Patrick Charmel, President and Chief Executive Officer
CMO: Kenneth V Schwartz, M.D., Medical Director
CIO: George Tomas, Director Information Services
CHR: Steve Mordecai, Director Human Resources
CNO: Barbara J Stumpo, R.N., Vice President Patient Care Services
Web address: www.griffinhealth.org
**Control:** Other not–for–profit (including NFP Corporation) **Service:** General
medical and surgical

**Staffed Beds:** 111 **Admissions:** 6364 **Census:** 80 **Outpatient**
**Visits:** 192426 **Births:** 530 **Total Expense ($000):** 189139 **Payroll Expense**
**($000):** 72310 **Personnel:** 1322

**FARMINGTON—Hartford County**

☒ **UCONN, JOHN DEMPSEY HOSPITAL (070036)**, 263 Farmington Avenue,
Zip 06032–1941; tel. 860/679–2000, (Nonreporting) **A**1 2 3 5 8 10 12 13 **F**3 7
8 11 13 15 18 20 22 24 26 29 30 31 34 35 36 37 38 39 40 45 46 47 48 49
50 51 52 53 54 55 56 57 58 59 60 61 64 65 67 68 70 74 75 76 77 78 79 81
82 84 85 86 87 91 92 93 94 98 100 101 102 103 104 105 107 108 110 111
114 115 116 117 118 119 120 121 123 124 126 130 131 132 135 144 145
146 147 148 149 153 157 **P**6
Primary Contact: Andrew Agwunobi, M.D., Chief Executive Officer
COO: Kevin Larsen, Associate Vice President, Business and Ancillary Services
CFO: Jeffrey Geoghegan, Chief Financial Officer
CMO: Richard Simon, M.D., Chief of Staff
CIO: Jonathan Carroll, Chief Information Officer
CHR: Carolle Andrews, Vice President, Interim Human Resources Officer
CNO: Ann Marie Capo, R.N., Chief Nursing Officer, Vice President, Quality and
Patient Services
Web address: www.uchc.edu
**Control:** State, Government, Nonfederal **Service:** General medical and surgical

**Staffed Beds:** 186 **Admissions:** 9065 **Census:** 113 **Outpatient**
**Visits:** 346321 **Births:** 829 **Total Expense ($000):** 486888 **Payroll Expense**
**($000):** 143755 **Personnel:** 1458

**UNIV OF CONN HEALTH CENTER** See UCONN, John Dempsey Hospital

**GREENWICH—Fairfield County**

☒ **GREENWICH HOSPITAL (070018)**, 5 Perryridge Road, Zip 06830–4697;
tel. 203/863–3000, (Nonreporting) **A**1 2 3 5 8 10 **F**3 5 11 12 13 14 15 18 20
22 26 28 29 30 31 32 34 35 36 37 38 39 40 41 44 45 46 47 48 49 50 51 52
53 54 55 56 57 58 59 61 64 65 66 68 70 72 74 75 76 78 79 80 81 82 84 85
86 87 89 91 93 96 97 100 101 102 104 107 108 110 111 114 115 116 117
118 119 120 121 123 124 126 129 130 131 132 134 135 146 147 148 149
154 156 157 **S** Yale New Haven Health, New Haven, CT
Primary Contact: Norman G. Roth, President
COO: Diane Kelly, Chief Operating Officer
CFO: Eugene Colucci, Vice President Finance
CMO: A Michael Marino, M.D., Senior Vice President Medical Administration
Web address: www.greenhosp.org
**Control:** Other not–for–profit (including NFP Corporation) **Service:** General
medical and surgical

**Staffed Beds:** 184 **Admissions:** 11213 **Census:** 127 **Outpatient**
**Visits:** 277357 **Births:** 2635 **Total Expense ($000):** 393993 **Payroll**
**Expense ($000):** 136028 **Personnel:** 1417

**HARTFORD—Hartford County**

☒ **CONNECTICUT CHILDREN'S MEDICAL CENTER (073300)**, 282 Washington
Street, Zip 06106–3322; tel. 860/545–9000, (Nonreporting) **A**1 3 5 10 **F**3 8 11
12 19 21 23 25 27 29 30 31 32 34 35 36 37 38 39 40 41 43 44 45 46 47 48
49 50 51 54 55 57 58 59 60 61 62 63 64 65 68 72 74 75 78 79 81 82 84 85
86 87 88 89 91 92 93 96 97 99 100 101 102 104 105 107 111 114 115 119
126 129 130 131 132 134 143 146 148 149 150 154 156 157 **P**3
Primary Contact: James E. Shmerling, President and Chief Executive Officer
COO: Gil Peri, President and Chief Operating Officer
CFO: Gerald J Boisvert, Vice President and Chief Financial Officer
CMO: Paul Dworkin, M.D., Physician–in–Chief
CIO: Jung Park, Interim Chief Information Officer
CHR: Elizabeth Rudden, Vice President Human Resources
Web address: www.connecticutchildrens.org/
**Control:** Other not–for–profit (including NFP Corporation) **Service:** Children's
general medical and surgical

**Staffed Beds:** 185 **Admissions:** 5687 **Census:** 123 **Outpatient**
**Visits:** 202852 **Births:** 0 **Total Expense ($000):** 356007 **Payroll Expense**
**($000):** 152728 **Personnel:** 2510

☒ **HARTFORD HOSPITAL (070025)**, 80 Seymour Street, Zip 06102–8000,
Mailing Address: P.O. Box 5037, Zip 06102–5037; tel. 860/545–5000, (Includes
INSTITUTE OF LIVING, Mailing address: 400 Washington Street, Hartford,
Connecticut, Zip 06106–3392; tel. 860/545–7000) (Total facility includes 104
beds in nursing home–type unit) **A**1 2 3 5 8 10 **F**2 3 5 6 7 8 9 10 11 12 13 15
17 18 20 22 24 26 28 29 30 31 34 35 36 37 38 39 40 43 44 45 46 47 48
49 50 51 52 53 54 55 56 57 58 59 60 61 63 64 65 66 68 70 71 74 75 76
77 78 79 80 81 82 83 84 85 86 87 90 91 92 93 94 95 96 97 98 99 100 101
102 103 104 105 106 107 108 110 111 112 114 115 116 117 118 119 120
121 123 124 125 126 128 129 130 131 132 133 134 135 137 138 139 141
143 145 146 147 148 149 150 152 153 154 155 156 157 **P**6 **S** Hartford
HealthCare, Hartford, CT
Primary Contact: Bimal Patel, President
CMO: Stuart Markowitz, M.D., Chief Medical Officer
CIO: Stephan O'Neill, Vice President Information Services
CHR: Richard McAloon, Vice President Human Resources
Web address: www.harthosp.org
**Control:** Other not–for–profit (including NFP Corporation) **Service:** General
medical and surgical

**Staffed Beds:** 982 **Admissions:** 43669 **Census:** 780 **Outpatient**
**Visits:** 505669 **Births:** 3672 **Total Expense ($000):** 1477933 **Payroll**
**Expense ($000):** 518393 **Personnel:** 5601

☒ **MOUNT SINAI REHABILITATION HOSPITAL (073025)**, 490 Blue Hills Avenue,
Zip 06112–1513; tel. 860/714–3500, (Nonreporting) **A**1 10 **S** Trinity Health,
Livonia, MI
Primary Contact: Robert J. Krug, M.D., Chief Executive Officer
CFO: David Bittner, Chief Financial Officer
Web address: www.stfranciscare.org
**Control:** Other not–for–profit (including NFP Corporation) **Service:** Rehabilitation

**Staffed Beds:** 32

**NEWINGTON CHILDREN'S HOSPITAL** See Connecticut Children's Medical Center

**REHAB HOSP OF CONNECTICUT** See Mount Sinai Rehabilitation Hospital

☒ **SAINT FRANCIS HOSPITAL AND MEDICAL CENTER (070002)**, 114 Woodland
Street, Zip 06105–1208; tel. 860/714–4000, (Nonreporting) **A**1 2 3 5 8 10 19
**F**3 8 11 12 13 15 17 18 20 22 24 26 28 29 30 31 34 35 36 38 39 40 43 45
46 47 48 49 50 53 54 55 56 57 58 59 61 64 65 66 67 68 70 72 74 75 76 77
78 79 81 82 84 85 86 87 91 92 93 94 95 96 97 98 99 100 101 102 104 107
108 110 111 115 117 118 119 120 121 123 124 126 129 130 131 132 135
146 147 148 150 154 **P**8 **S** Trinity Health, Livonia, MI
Primary Contact: John F. Rodis, M.D., President
CFO: Jennifer S. Schneider, Vice President of Finance
CMO: Michael Grey, M.D., Interim Chief Medical Officer
CIO: Linda L. Shanley, Vice President, Chief Information Officer
CHR: Dennis W. Sparks, Vice President of Human Resources
Web address: www.saintfranciscare.com
**Control:** Church operated, Nongovernment, not–for–profit **Service:** General
medical and surgical

**Staffed Beds:** 412 **Admissions:** 28275 **Census:** 360 **Outpatient**
**Visits:** 264535 **Births:** 2828 **Total Expense ($000):** 844404 **Payroll**
**Expense ($000):** 218763 **Personnel:** 3978

**MANCHESTER—Hartford County**

☐ **MANCHESTER MEMORIAL HOSPITAL (070027)**, 71 Haynes Street,
Zip 06040–4188; tel. 860/646–1222, (Nonreporting) **A**1 2 3 5 10 12 13 **S**
Prospect Medical Holdings, Los Angeles, CA
Primary Contact: Deborah K. Weymouth, FACHE, Chief Executive Officer
CFO: Michael D. Veillette, Senior Vice President and Chief Financial Officer
CMO: Joel R Reich, M.D., Senior Vice President Medical Affairs
CIO: Richard Daigle, Chief Information Officer
CHR: Natalie Cook, Administrative Director of Human Resources
CNO: Mary Powers, R.N., MSN, Senior Vice President and Chief Nursing Officer
Web address: www.echn.org
**Control:** Other not–for–profit (including NFP Corporation) **Service:** General
medical and surgical

**Staffed Beds:** 156

CT

**MANSFIELD CENTER—Tolland County**

✠ **NATCHAUG HOSPITAL (074008)**, 189 Storrs Road, Zip 06250–1683;
tel. 860/456–1311, (Nonreporting) **A**1 10 **F**2 3 4 5 29 34 44 50 56 75 77 87 98
99 100 101 104 105 106 130 132 135 149 151 152 153 154 **P**6 **S** Hartford
HealthCare, Hartford, CT
Primary Contact: Patricia Rehmer, MSN, FACHE, President
COO: David Klein, Ph.D., Vice President Operations, Behavioral Health Network
CFO: Paul V Maloney, Vice President Finance, Behavioral Health Network
CMO: Deborah Weidner, Medical Director
CIO: Mark Olson, Interim Chief Information Officer, Behavioral Health Network
CHR: Janet Keown, Vice President Human Resources, Behavioral Health Network
CNO: Justin Sleeper, Vice President Clinical Operations, Behavioral Health Network
Web address: www.natchaug.org
**Control**: Other not–for–profit (including NFP Corporation) **Service**: Psychiatric

| | |
|---|---|
| **Staffed Beds:** 57 **Admissions:** 1966 **Census:** 55 **Outpatient Visits:** 223066 **Births:** 0 **Total Expense ($000):** 54859 **Payroll Expense ($000):** 29932 **Personnel:** 387 | |

**MERIDEN—New Haven County**

✠ **MIDSTATE MEDICAL CENTER (070017)**, 435 Lewis Avenue, Zip 06451–2101;
tel. 203/694–8200, (Nonreporting) **A**1 10 **F**3 11 12 13 15 18 26 28 29 30 31
34 35 36 38 39 40 44 45 46 47 48 49 50 51 53 54 56 57 59 61 63 64 68 70
74 75 76 78 79 81 82 84 85 86 87 97 102 107 108 110 111 114 115 117
118 119 120 121 123 124 126 129 130 131 132 144 145 146 147 148 149
154 157 **P**6 **S** Hartford HealthCare, Hartford, CT
Primary Contact: Gary C. Havican, President
CMO: Kenneth R Kurz, M.D., Chief of Staff
CIO: Jennifer Comerford, Manager Information Services
CHR: Ken Cesca, Vice President Human Resources
Web address: www.midstatemedical.org
**Control**: Other not–for–profit (including NFP Corporation) **Service**: General
medical and surgical

| | |
|---|---|
| **Staffed Beds:** 97 **Admissions:** 9531 **Census:** 102 **Outpatient Visits:** 145137 **Births:** 762 **Total Expense ($000):** 294733 **Payroll Expense ($000):** 76889 **Personnel:** 953 | |

**VETERANS MEMORIAL MED CENTER** See Midstate Medical Center

**MIDDLETOWN—Middlesex County**

☐ **ALBERT J. SOLNIT PSYCHIATRIC CENTER - SOUTH CAMPUS (074015)**, 915
River Road, Zip 06457–3921, Mailing Address: P.O. Box 2792, Zip 06457–9292;
tel. 860/704–4000, (Nonreporting) **A**1 3 5 10
Primary Contact: Michelle Sarofin, Superintendent
CFO: Connie Tessarzik, Business Manager
CMO: Lesley Siegel, M.D., Medical Director
CIO: Andrew J A Kass, M.D., Assistant Superintendent
Web address: www.ct.gov/
**Control**: State, Government, Nonfederal **Service**: Children's hospital psychiatric

| | |
|---|---|
| **Staffed Beds:** 50 | |

☐ **CONNECTICUT VALLEY HOSPITAL (074003)**, 1000 Silver Street,
Zip 06457–3947; tel. 860/262–5000, (Includes WHITING FORENSIC HOSPITAL,
Mailing address: 70 O'Brien Drive, Middletown, Connecticut, Zip 6457, Box 70,
Zip 06457–3942; tel. 860/262–5400; Michael A Norko, M.D., Acting Chief
Executive Officer), (Nonreporting) **A**1 3 5 10 **F**4 29 30 34 36 39 50 53 56 57 58
59 60 65 68 74 75 77 82 84 86 87 91 96 97 98 100 101 103 106 119 130
132 135 146 148 149 **S** Connecticut Department of Mental Health and Addiction
Services, Hartford, CT
Primary Contact: Helene M. Vartelas, MSN, Chief Executive Officer
COO: John D'Eramo, Chief Operating Officer
CFO: Cindy Butterfield, Director, Fiscal and Administrative Services
CMO: Thomas Pisano, M.D., Chief Professional Services
CIO: Kathryn Connelly, Manager Information Technology
CHR: Cheryl Thompson, Facility Director Human Resources
CNO: Jerilynn Lamb-Pagone, Nurse Executive
Web address: www.ct.gov/dmhas/cwp/view.asp?a=3519&q=416778
**Control**: State, Government, Nonfederal **Service**: Psychiatric

| | |
|---|---|
| **Staffed Beds:** 361 **Admissions:** 3576 **Census:** 325 **Outpatient Visits:** 0 **Births:** 0 | |

✠ **MIDDLESEX HOSPITAL (070020)**, 28 Crescent Street, Zip 06457–3650;
tel. 860/358–6000, (Nonreporting) **A**1 2 3 5 10 **F**3 5 7 8 12 13 15 18 20 26 28
29 30 31 32 34 35 36 37 38 40 42 45 46 47 48 49 50 51 54 55 57 58 59 60
61 62 63 64 65 68 70 74 75 76 77 78 79 81 82 83 84 85 86 87 92 93 94 97
98 100 101 102 104 105 107 108 110 111 114 115 116 117 118 119 120
121 123 124 126 129 130 131 132 134 135 143 145 146 147 148 149 152
153 154 **P**6
Primary Contact: Vincent G. Capece Jr, M.D., President and Chief Executive Officer
CFO: Susan Martin, Chief Financial Officer and Vice President, Finance
CMO: Jesse Wagner, M.D., Chief Medical Officer and Vice President, Quality and
Patient Safety
CIO: Evan Jackson, Chief Information Officer and Vice President, Planning and
Business Development
CHR: Donna Stroneski, Vice President, Human Resources
CNO: Jacquelyn Calamari, MSN, MS, Chief Nursing Officer and Vice President,
Patient Care Services
Web address: www.middlesexhealth.org
**Control**: Other not–for–profit (including NFP Corporation) **Service**: General
medical and surgical

| | |
|---|---|
| **Staffed Beds:** 233 **Admissions:** 12049 **Census:** 141 **Outpatient Visits:** 637701 **Births:** 983 **Total Expense ($000):** 409865 **Payroll Expense ($000):** 193934 **Personnel:** 1940 | |

**MIDDLESEX MEMORIAL HOSPITAL** See Middlesex Hospital

**RIVERVIEW HOSPITAL FOR CHILDREN AND YOUTH** See Albert J. Solnit
Psychiatric Center - South Campus

**WHITING FORENSIC DIVISION OF CONNECTICUT VALLEY HOSPITAL** See
Whiting Forensic Hospital

**WHITING FORENSIC HOSPITAL** See Connecticut Valley Hospital, Middletown

**NEW BRITAIN—Hartford County**

✠ **HOSPITAL FOR SPECIAL CARE (072004)**, 2150 Corbin Avenue,
Zip 06053–2298; tel. 860/223–2761, (Nonreporting) **A**1 3 5 10
Primary Contact: Lynn Ricci, President and Chief Executive Officer
CFO: Laurie A Whelan, Senior Vice President Finance and Chief Financial Officer
CMO: J. Kevin Shushtari, M.D., Chief Medical Officer
CIO: Stan Jankowski, Vice President and Chief Information Officer
CHR: Nancy M Martone, Vice President and Chief Human Resources Officer
Web address: www.hfsc.org
**Control**: Other not–for–profit (including NFP Corporation) **Service**: Acute long–
term care hospital

| | |
|---|---|
| **Staffed Beds:** 228 | |

**NEW BRITAIN GENERAL HOSPITAL** See New Britain General

**NEW BRITAIN MEMORIAL HOSPITAL** See Hospital for Special Care

✠ **THE HOSPITAL OF CENTRAL CONNECTICUT (070035)**, 100 Grand
Street, Zip 06052–2017, Mailing Address: P.O. Box 100, Zip 06052–2017;
tel. 860/224–5011, (Includes BRADLEY MEMORIAL, Mailing address: 81 Meriden
Avenue, Southington, Connecticut, Zip 06489–3297; tel. 860/276–5000; NEW
BRITAIN GENERAL, Mailing address: 100 Grand Street, New Britain, Connecticut,
Zip 06052–2017, P O Box 100, Zip 06050–0100, tel. 860/224–5011),
(Nonreporting) **A**1 2 3 5 10 **F**3 11 12 13 15 18 20 22 26 28 29 30 31 34 35 38
40 44 45 49 50 51 53 54 57 58 59 60 61 64 65 66 68 70 72 74 75 76 77 78
79 81 84 85 86 87 93 97 98 100 101 102 104 105 107 108 110 111 114 115
117 118 119 120 121 123 124 126 129 130 132 135 144 146 147 148 149
153 154 156 157 **P**6 **S** Hartford HealthCare, Hartford, CT
Primary Contact: Gary C. Havican, President
CFO: Brian Rogoz, Vice President Finance and Treasurer
CIO: Frank Pinto, Chief Information Officer
CHR: Elizabeth A Lynch, Vice President Human Resources
Web address: www.thocc.org
**Control**: Other not–for–profit (including NFP Corporation) **Service**: General
medical and surgical

| | |
|---|---|
| **Staffed Beds:** 188 **Admissions:** 12640 **Census:** 178 **Outpatient Visits:** 453564 **Births:** 1638 **Total Expense ($000):** 408494 **Payroll Expense ($000):** 148484 **Personnel:** 1683 | |

**NEW CANAAN—Fairfield County**

**SILVER HILL FOUNDATION HOSP** See Silver Hill Hospital

---

**Hospital, Medicare Provider Number, Address, Telephone, Approval, Facility, and Physician Codes, Health Care System**

★ American Hospital Association (AHA) membership  ○ Healthcare Facilities Accreditation Program  ⇑ Center for Improvement in Healthcare Quality Accreditation
☐ The Joint Commission accreditation  ◇ DNV Healthcare Inc. accreditation  △ Commission on Accreditation of Rehabilitation Facilities (CARF) accreditation

CT

☐ **SILVER HILL HOSPITAL (074014)**, 208 Valley Road, Zip 06840–3899; tel. 203/966–3561, (Nonreporting) **A1** 10
Primary Contact: Andrew J. Gerber, M.D., Ph.D., President and Chief Executive Officer
COO: Elizabeth Moore, Chief Operating Officer
CFO: Ruurd Leegstra, Chief Financial Officer
CMO: Andrew J. Gerber, M.D., Ph.D., President and Medical Director
CIO: Maria Klinga, Director Management Information Systems
CHR: Rich Juliana, Director Human Resources
Web address: www.silverhillhospital.org
**Control**: Other not–for–profit (including NFP Corporation) **Service**: Psychiatric

| Staffed Beds: 121 |
|---|

### NEW HAVEN—New Haven County

☐ **CONNECTICUT MENTAL HEALTH CENTER (074011)**, 34 Park Street, Zip 06519–1109, Mailing Address: P.O. Box 1842, Zip 06508–1842; tel. 203/974–7144, (Nonreporting) **A1** 3 5 10 **S** Connecticut Department of Mental Health and Addiction Services, Hartford, CT
Primary Contact: Michael Sernyak, M.D., Director
COO: Robert Cole, Chief Operating Officer
CFO: Robert Cole, Chief Operating Officer
CMO: Jeanne Steines, D.O., Medical Director
CIO: Paul Moore, Chief Information Officer
CHR: Carolyn Wallace, Director Human Resources
Web address: www.ct.gov/dmhas/cwp/view.asp?a=2906&q=334596
**Control**: State, Government, Nonfederal **Service**: Psychiatric

| Staffed Beds: 32 |
|---|

**HOSPITAL OF SAINT RAPHAEL** See Yale-New Haven Hospital-Saint Raphael Campus

**YALE PSYCHIATRIC INSTITUTE** See Yale-New Haven Psychiatric Hospital

⊞ **YALE-NEW HAVEN HOSPITAL (070022)**, 20 York Street, Zip 06510–3202; tel. 203/688–4242, (Includes YALE-NEW HAVEN CHILDREN'S HOSPITAL, Mailing address: 1 Park Street, New Haven, Connecticut, Zip 06504–8901; tel. 203/688–4242; Cynthia Sparer, Senior Vice President and Executive Director Women's & Children; YALE-NEW HAVEN HOSPITAL-SAINT RAPHAEL CAMPUS, Mailing address: 1450 Chapel Street, New Haven, Connecticut, Zip 06511–4405; tel. 203/789–3000; Richard D'Aquila, President; YALE-NEW HAVEN PSYCHIATRIC HOSPITAL, Mailing address: 184 Liberty Street, New Haven, Connecticut, Zip 06519–1625; tel. 203/688–9704; Eusebio Mark Sevilla, R.N., MSN, Executive Director), (Nonreporting) **A**1 2 3 5 8 10 19 **F**3 5 6 9 11 12 13 14 15 17 18 19 20 21 22 23 24 25 26 27 28 29 30 31 32 34 35 36 37 38 39 40 41 42 43 44 45 46 47 48 49 50 51 52 53 54 55 56 57 58 59 61 64 65 66 68 70 72 73 74 75 76 77 78 79 80 81 82 84 85 86 87 88 89 90 91 92 93 94 96 97 98 99 100 101 102 103 104 105 107 108 109 110 111 112 114 115 116 117 118 119 120 121 123 124 126 129 130 131 132 134 135 136 137 138 139 141 142 143 144 145 146 147 148 149 153 154 156 **S** Yale New Haven Health, New Haven, CT
Primary Contact: Marna P. Borgstrom, Chief Executive Officer
CFO: Vincent Tammaro, Chief Financial Officer
CMO: Thomas Balcezak, M.D., Senior Vice President Medical Affairs and Chief Medical Officer
CIO: Lisa Stump, Interim Chief Information Officer
CHR: Kevin A Myatt, Senior Vice President Human Resources
CNO: Patricia Sue Fitzsimons, R.N., Ph.D., Senior Vice President Patient Services
Web address: www.ynhh.org
**Control**: Other not–for–profit (including NFP Corporation) **Service**: General medical and surgical

| Staffed Beds: 1455 Admissions: 69953 Census: 1255 Outpatient Visits: 1514333 Births: 5684 Total Expense ($000): 3004510 Payroll Expense ($000): 961013 Personnel: 12791 |
|---|

### NEW LONDON—New London County

**LAWRENCE & MEMORIAL HOSPITAL** See Lawrence + Memorial Hospital

⊞ △ **LAWRENCE + MEMORIAL HOSPITAL (070007)**, 365 Montauk Avenue, Zip 06320–4769; tel. 860/442–0711, (Nonreporting) **A**1 2 3 5 7 10 19 **F**3 11 13 15 17 18 19 20 22 26 28 29 30 31 34 35 38 39 40 41 42 44 46 49 50 51 54 55 57 59 60 63 64 65 68 70 72 74 75 76 77 78 79 81 82 84 85 86 87 89 90 91 92 93 96 98 100 101 102 104 107 108 110 111 114 115 116 117 118 119 120 121 123 124 126 129 130 131 132 146 147 148 149 153 154 **S** Yale New Haven Health, New Haven, CT
Primary Contact: Patrick Green, FACHE, President and Chief Executive Officer
CFO: Seth Van Essendelft, Vice President and Chief Financial Officer
CMO: Oliver Mayorga, M.D., Chief Medical Officer
CIO: Kimberly Kalajainen, Vice President Operations and Chief Information Officer
CHR: Donna Epps, Vice President and Chief Human Resources Officer
CNO: Caren Lewis, R.N., Chief Nursing Officer
Web address: www.lmhospital.org
**Control**: Other not–for–profit (including NFP Corporation) **Service**: General medical and surgical

| Staffed Beds: 251 Admissions: 12969 Census: 191 Outpatient Visits: 314564 Births: 1316 Total Expense ($000): 366267 Payroll Expense ($000): 145945 Personnel: 1483 |
|---|

### NORWALK—Fairfield County

⊞ **NORWALK HOSPITAL (070034)**, 34 Maple Street, Zip 06850–3894; tel. 203/852–2000, (Nonreporting) **A**1 2 3 5 8 10 **F**3 5 7 8 11 12 13 15 17 18 20 22 26 28 29 30 31 34 35 36 39 40 43 44 45 46 47 48 49 50 51 54 55 57 58 59 64 66 68 70 72 74 75 76 77 78 79 80 81 82 84 85 87 89 93 96 97 98 100 101 102 104 105 107 108 110 111 114 115 117 118 119 120 121 123 124 126 129 130 131 132 135 145 146 148 149 153 154 **S** Nuvance Health, Danbury, CT
Primary Contact: Peter Cordeau, President
CFO: Michael Kruzick, Acting Chief Financial Officer
CMO: Michael Marks, M.D., Chief of Staff
CHR: Anthony Aceto, Vice President Human Resources
Web address: www.norwalkhospital.org
**Control**: Other not–for–profit (including NFP Corporation) **Service**: General medical and surgical

| Staffed Beds: 161 Admissions: 11428 Census: 130 Outpatient Visits: 228932 Births: 1127 Total Expense ($000): 374714 Payroll Expense ($000): 125013 Personnel: 1249 |
|---|

### NORWICH—New London County

⊞ **THE WILLIAM W. BACKUS HOSPITAL (070024)**, 326 Washington Street, Zip 06360–2740; tel. 860/889–8331, (Nonreporting) **A**1 3 5 10 19 **F**3 9 11 12 13 15 18 20 26 28 29 30 31 34 35 36 37 40 43 45 46 49 50 51 54 57 58 59 61 63 64 65 70 71 72 73 74 75 76 78 79 80 81 82 84 85 86 87 89 92 93 97 98 100 101 102 104 105 107 108 110 111 114 115 116 117 118 119 120 121 126 130 132 134 135 144 145 146 147 148 149 153 154 157 **P**6 **S** Hartford HealthCare, Hartford, CT
Primary Contact: Donna Handley, President
COO: Carolyn Trantalis, R.N., MSN, Regional Vice President, Clinical Services and Operations
CFO: Anthony Mastroianni, Regional Vice President Finance
CMO: Robert Sidman, M.D., Regional Vice President, Medical Affairs
CIO: Angie Mathieu, System Director Information Technology and Regional Chief Information Officer
CHR: Karen James, Regional Director, Human Resources
CNO: Carolyn Trantalis, R.N., MSN, Regional Vice President, Clinical Services and Operations
Web address: www.backushospital.org
**Control**: Other not–for–profit (including NFP Corporation) **Service**: General medical and surgical

| Staffed Beds: 183 Admissions: 10026 Census: 136 Outpatient Visits: 204931 Births: 875 Total Expense ($000): 343018 Payroll Expense ($000): 118683 Personnel: 1203 |
|---|

### PUTNAM—Windham County

☐ **DAY KIMBALL HOSPITAL (070003)**, 320 Pomfret Street, Zip 06260–1836; tel. 860/928–6541, (Nonreporting) **A**1 2 5 10
Primary Contact: Kyle Kramer, Chief Executive Officer
CFO: Paul Beaudoin, Chief Financial Officer
CMO: John Graham, M.D., Vice President Medical Affairs
CIO: Odile Romanick, Chief information Officer
CHR: Jeffrey T. Corrigan, Vice President Human Resources
CNO: John O'Keefe, Chief Nursing Officer
Web address: www.daykimball.org
**Control**: Other not–for–profit (including NFP Corporation) **Service**: General medical and surgical

| Staffed Beds: 62 |
|---|

*Many Facility Codes have changed. Please refer to the AHA Guide Code Chart.*  © 2021 AHA Guide

**ROCKY HILL—Hartford County**

**CONNECTICUT VETERANS HOME AND HOSPITAL (072006)**, 287 West Street, Zip 06067–3501; tel. 860/616–3606, (Nonreporting) **A**10
Primary Contact: Seam Connolly, Commissioner
CFO: Michael Clark, Fiscal Administrative Manager
CMO: Vamseedhar Alla, M.D., Director Medical Staff
CIO: Sheri DeVaux, Information Technology Manager
CHR: Noreen Sinclair, Human Resources Administrator
CNO: Jeff Lord, Director of Nursing
Web address: www.ct.gov/ctva
**Control**: State, Government, Nonfederal **Service**: Acute long–term care hospital

**Staffed Beds**: 125

**VETERANS HOME AND HOSPITAL** See Connecticut Veterans Home and Hospital

**SHARON—Litchfield County**

☐ **SHARON HOSPITAL (070004)**, 50 Hospital Hill Road, Zip 06069–2096, Mailing Address: P.O. Box 789, Zip 06069–0789; tel. 860/364–4000, (Data for 273 days) (Nonreporting) **A**1 3 10 20 **F**3 13 15 18 28 29 30 34 35 36 40 44 45 46 48 49 50 56 57 59 65 68 70 74 75 76 77 79 81 82 84 85 87 93 97 98 100 102 103 107 108 110 111 115 119 120 130 131 132 135 146 147 148 149 154 157 **S** Health Quest Systems, Inc., LaGrangeville, NY
Primary Contact: Mark Hirko, M.D., President
CMO: Michael Parker, M.D., Chief of Staff
CHR: Kathleen Berlinghoff, Director Human Resources
Web address: www.sharonhospital.com
**Control**: Other not–for–profit (including NFP Corporation) **Service**: General medical and surgical

**Staffed Beds**: 60 **Admissions**: 1416 **Census**: 25 **Outpatient Visits**: 58833 **Births**: 135 **Total Expense ($000)**: 42474 **Payroll Expense ($000)**: 22495 **Personnel**: 301

**SOMERS—Tolland County**

**CONNECTICUT DEPARTMENT OF CORRECTION'S HOSPITAL**, 100 Bilton Road, Zip 06071–1059, Mailing Address: P.O. Box 100, Zip 06071–0100; tel. 860/749–8391, (Nonreporting)
Primary Contact: Edward A. Blanchette, M.D., Director
**Control**: State, Government, Nonfederal **Service**: Hospital unit of an institution (prison hospital, college infirmary, etc.)

**Staffed Beds**: 29

**SOUTHINGTON—Hartford County**

**BRADLEY MEMORIAL** See The Hospital of Central Connecticut, New Britain

**BRADLEY MEMORIAL HOSPITAL AND HEALTH CENTER** See Bradley Memorial

**STAFFORD SPRINGS—Tolland County**

☒ **JOHNSON MEMORIAL HOSPITAL (070008)**, 201 Chestnut Hill Road, Zip 06076–4005; tel. 860/684–4251, (Nonreporting) **A**1 10 **S** Trinity Health, Livonia, MI
Primary Contact: Stuart E. Rosenberg, President
CFO: John Grish, Chief Financial Officer
CMO: Ian Tucker, M.D., Vice President Medical Affairs
CHR: Donna M Megliola, Assistant Vice President
CNO: Patricia Jagoe, Assistant Vice President Patient Care
Web address: www.jmmc.com
**Control**: Other not–for–profit (including NFP Corporation) **Service**: General medical and surgical

**Staffed Beds**: 78

**JOHNSON MEMORIAL MEDICAL CENTER** See Johnson Memorial Hospital

**STAMFORD—Fairfield County**

**STAMFORD HEALTH SYSTEM** See Stamford Hospital

☒ **STAMFORD HOSPITAL (070006)**, One Hospital Plaza, Zip 6902, Mailing Address: P.O. Box 9317, Zip 06904–9317; tel. 203/276–1000, (Nonreporting) **A**1 2 3 5 10 **F**3 8 12 13 15 18 19 20 22 24 26 28 29 30 31 32 34 35 36 37 38 40 41 43 44 45 46 47 48 49 50 52 53 54 55 56 57 58 59 60 61 64 66 68 70 72 74 75 76 77 78 79 81 82 84 85 86 87 89 90 91 92 93 95 96 97 98 100 107 108 110 111 114 115 116 117 118 119 120 121 123 124 126 129 130 131 132 135 144 145 146 147 148 149 150 154 157 **P**3 7
Primary Contact: Kathleen A. Silard, R.N., MS, FACHE, President and Chief Executive Officer
COO: Jonathan T Bailey, Chief Operating Officer
CFO: Kevin Gage, Chief Financial Officer
CMO: Sharon Kiely, M.D., Senior Vice President Medical Affairs and Chief Medical Officer
CIO: Steven Sakovits, Vice President Information Systems and Chief Information Officer
CHR: Elaine Guglielmo, Vice President Human Resources and Organizational Development
CNO: Ellen M Komar, R.N., Vice President Patient Care Services and Chief Nursing Officer
Web address: www.stamhealth.org
**Control**: Other not–for–profit (including NFP Corporation) **Service**: General medical and surgical

**Staffed Beds**: 305 **Admissions**: 13725 **Census**: 192 **Outpatient Visits**: 495313 **Births**: 2299 **Total Expense ($000)**: 567898 **Payroll Expense ($000)**: 224543 **Personnel**: 3188

**TORRINGTON—Litchfield County**

☒ **CHARLOTTE HUNGERFORD HOSPITAL (070011)**, 540 Litchfield Street, Zip 06790–6679, Mailing Address: P.O. Box 988, Zip 06790–0988; tel. 860/496–6666, (Nonreporting) **A**1 10 **F**3 5 8 11 13 15 18 28 29 30 31 32 34 35 37 38 40 41 42 44 45 47 48 49 50 51 53 54 57 59 64 68 70 74 75 76 77 78 79 81 82 84 85 86 87 89 93 98 100 102 104 105 107 108 110 111 115 117 118 119 120 121 123 129 130 131 132 146 149 152 153 154 **P**3 6 **S** Hartford HealthCare, Hartford, CT
Primary Contact: Daniel J. McIntyre, President
CFO: Susan Schapp, Vice President Finance and Treasurer
CMO: Mark Prete, M.D., Vice President Medical Affairs
CHR: R James Elliott, Vice President Human Resources
Web address: www.charlottehungerford.org
**Control**: Other not–for–profit (including NFP Corporation) **Service**: General medical and surgical

**Staffed Beds**: 72 **Admissions**: 5261 **Census**: 71 **Outpatient Visits**: 282857 **Births**: 377 **Total Expense ($000)**: 141984 **Payroll Expense ($000)**: 65664 **Personnel**: 709

**THE CHARLOTTE HUNGERFORD HOSPITAL** See Charlotte Hungerford Hospital

**VERNON—Tolland County**

☐ **ROCKVILLE GENERAL HOSPITAL (070012)**, 31 Union Street, Zip 06066–3160; tel. 860/872–0501, (Nonreporting) **A**1 5 10 **S** Prospect Medical Holdings, Los Angeles, CA
Primary Contact: Deborah K. Weymouth, FACHE, Chief Executive Officer
CFO: Michael D. Veillette, Senior Vice President and Chief Financial Officer
CMO: Joel R Reich, M.D., Senior Vice President Medical Affairs
CIO: Richard Daigle, Chief Information Officer
CHR: Natalie Cook, Administrative Director, Human Resources
CNO: Mary Powers, R.N., MSN, Senior Vice President and Chief Nursing Officer
Web address: www.echn.org
**Control**: Other not–for–profit (including NFP Corporation) **Service**: General medical and surgical

**Staffed Beds**: 47

**WALLINGFORD—New Haven County**

**GAYLORD HOSPITAL** See Gaylord Specialty Healthcare

CT

☐ △ **GAYLORD SPECIALTY HEALTHCARE (072003)**, 50 Gaylord Farm Road, Zip 06492–7048, Mailing Address: P.O. Box 400, Zip 06492–7048; tel. 203/284–2800, (Nonreporting) **A**1 3 5 7 10 **F**1 29 30 31 34 35 36 50 53 54 56 57 58 59 60 64 74 75 79 84 85 86 87 91 93 94 95 96 107 114 119 130 131 132 135 146 148 149 154 **P**5
Primary Contact: Sonja LaBarbera, President and Chief Executive Officer
CFO: Art Tedesco, Interim Chief Financial Officer
CMO: Stephen Holland, M.D., Vice President Chief Medical Officer and Medical Director
CIO: Gerry Maroney, Chief Information Officer and Security Officer
CHR: Wally G Harper, Vice President Human Resources
CNO: Lisa Kalafus, MSN, R.N., Chief Nursing Officer
Web address: www.gaylord.org
**Control**: Other not–for–profit (including NFP Corporation) **Service**: Acute long–term care hospital

**Staffed Beds**: 122 **Admissions**: 1415 **Census**: 108 **Outpatient Visits**: 86877 **Births**: 0 **Total Expense ($000)**: 80145 **Payroll Expense ($000)**: 45172 **Personnel**: 490

**MASONIC HEALTHCARE CENTER** See Masonicare Health Center

★ **MASONICARE HEALTH CENTER (070039)**, 22 Masonic Avenue, Zip 06492–3048, Mailing Address: P.O. Box 70, Zip 06492–7001; tel. 203/679–5900, (Nonreporting) **A**5 10
Primary Contact: Jon–Paul Venoit, President and Chief Executive Officer
COO: Jon–Paul Venoit, Chief Operating Officer
CFO: Raymond Scott Thelen, Vice President and Chief Financial Officer
CMO: Ronald Schwartz, M.D., Medical Director
CIO: Michael Nichols, Chief Information Officer
CHR: Edward Dooling, Vice President, Human Resources
CNO: Patti Russell, Vice President Nursing
Web address: www.masonicare.org
**Control**: Other not–for–profit (including NFP Corporation) **Service**: Other specialty treatment

**Staffed Beds**: 65

### WATERBURY—New Haven County

⊞ **SAINT MARY'S HOSPITAL (070016)**, 56 Franklin Street, Zip 06706–1281; tel. 203/709–6000, (Nonreporting) **A**1 2 3 5 10 **F**3 5 8 11 12 13 14 15 17 18 20 22 24 26 28 29 30 31 34 35 37 38 40 41 42 43 44 45 46 48 49 50 51 54 55 56 57 59 64 65 66 70 72 74 75 76 77 78 79 80 81 82 83 84 85 86 87 91 92 93 97 98 100 101 102 104 105 106 107 108 110 111 115 118 119 120 126 129 130 131 132 135 144 146 147 148 149 152 153 154 157 **P**8 **S** Trinity Health, Livonia, MI
Primary Contact: Steven E. Schneider, M.D., President
COO: Charles Flinn, Vice President, Chief Operating Officer
CFO: Ralph W Becker, Vice President, Chief Financial Officer
CIO: Michael Novak, Vice President, Operations and Chief Information Officer
CHR: M Clark Kearney, Vice President Human Resources
CNO: Elizabeth Bozzuto, R.N., Chief Nursing Officer and Vice President
Web address: www.stmh.org
**Control**: Church operated, Nongovernment, not–for–profit **Service**: General medical and surgical

**Staffed Beds**: 187 **Admissions**: 9914 **Census**: 112 **Outpatient Visits**: 289425 **Births**: 677 **Total Expense ($000)**: 289359 **Payroll Expense ($000)**: 85963 **Personnel**: 1558

**ST MARY'S HOSPITAL** See Saint Mary's Hospital

☐ **WATERBURY HOSPITAL (070005)**, 64 Robbins Street, Zip 06708–2600; tel. 203/573–6000, (Nonreporting) **A**1 2 3 5 10 **F**3 5 9 12 13 15 17 18 20 22 24 26 28 29 30 31 34 35 38 40 41 43 44 45 47 49 50 51 53 55 57 59 61 64 68 70 72 73 74 75 76 78 79 81 82 84 85 87 96 97 98 100 101 102 104 105 107 108 110 115 119 126 129 130 131 132 135 145 146 147 148 149 152 153 156 157 **S** Prospect Medical Holdings, Los Angeles, CA
Primary Contact: Lester P. Schindel, Interim Chief Executive Officer
CFO: Colleen M Scott, Vice President Finance
CMO: David Puzzuto, M.D., Vice President Medical Affairs and Chief Medical Officer
CIO: Michael J Cemeno, Chief Information Officer
CHR: Diane Woolley, Vice President Human Resources
CNO: Sandra Ladarola, Chief Nursing Officer
Web address: www.waterburyhospital.org
**Control**: Corporation, Investor–owned (for–profit) **Service**: General medical and surgical

**Staffed Beds**: 176 **Admissions**: 11783 **Census**: 161 **Outpatient Visits**: 160656 **Births**: 1065 **Total Expense ($000)**: 207997 **Payroll Expense ($000)**: 82936 **Personnel**: 1550

### WEST HARTFORD—Hartford County

**HEBREW CENTER FOR HEALTH REHABILITATION** See Hebrew Senior Care

★ **HEBREW SENIOR CARE (070040)**, 1 Abrahms Boulevard, Zip 06117–1525; tel. 860/523–3800, (Nonreporting) **A**10
Primary Contact: Denise Peterson, R.N., FACHE, President and Chief Executive Officer
COO: Marcia H Hickey, Senior Vice President Operations
CFO: David Houle, Executive Vice President and Chief Financial Officer
CMO: Ava Pannullo, M.D., Vice President Medical Services and Physician in Chief
CHR: Sam Vogt, Manager Human Resources
Web address: www.hebrewhealthcare.org
**Control**: Other not–for–profit (including NFP Corporation) **Service**: Other specialty treatment

**Staffed Beds**: 45

### WEST HAVEN—New Haven County

⊞ **VETERANS AFFAIRS CONNECTICUT HEALTHCARE SYSTEM**, 950 Campbell Avenue, Zip 06516–2770; tel. 203/932–5711, (Includes WEST HAVEN DIVISION, Mailing address: 950 Campbell Avenue, West Haven, Connecticut, Zip 06516–2700; tel. 203/932–5711), (Nonreporting) **A**1 2 3 5 8 **F**2 3 5 12 18 20 22 24 26 27 28 29 30 31 33 34 35 36 39 40 44 45 46 47 48 49 50 53 54 55 56 57 58 59 60 61 62 63 64 65 66 68 70 74 75 77 78 79 80 81 82 83 84 85 86 87 91 92 93 94 96 97 98 100 101 102 103 104 105 106 107 108 111 115 116 117 118 119 126 128 129 130 131 132 135 143 144 145 146 147 148 149 153 154 156 157 158 **S** Department of Veterans Affairs, Washington, DC
Primary Contact: Alfred Montoya, Director
CFO: Joseph LaMadeleine, Chief Financial Officer
CMO: Michael Ebert, M.D., Chief of Staff
CIO: Joseph Erdos, M.D., Chief Information Officer
CHR: Mark Bain, Chief Human Resources
Web address: www.connecticut.va.gov
**Control**: Veterans Affairs, Government, federal **Service**: General medical and surgical

**Staffed Beds**: 177 **Admissions**: 3724 **Census**: 105 **Outpatient Visits**: 784712 **Births**: 0 **Total Expense ($000)**: 1052114 **Payroll Expense ($000)**: 300706 **Personnel**: 2944

**VETERANS AFFAIRS CONNECTICUT HEALTHCARE SYSTEM-NEW HAVEN DIVISION** See Veterans Affairs Connecticut Healthcare System

**VETERANS AFFAIRS MEDICAL CENTER** See West Haven Division

### WESTPORT—Fairfield County

**HALL-BROOKE HOSPITAL, A DIVISION OF HALL-BROOKE BEHAVIORAL HEALTH SERVICES** See St. Vincent'S Behavioral Health

**ST. VINCENT'S BEHAVIORAL HEALTH** See St. Vincent'S Medical Center, Bridgeport

### WILLIMANTIC—Windham County

**WINDHAM COMMUNITY MEMORIAL HOSPITAL** See Windham Hospital

⊞ **WINDHAM HOSPITAL (070021)**, 112 Mansfield Avenue, Zip 06226–2040; tel. 860/456–9116, (Nonreporting) **A**1 5 10 **F**2 3 6 8 11 13 15 18 28 29 30 31 32 34 35 36 40 43 45 48 50 51 53 54 56 57 59 60 61 64 65 66 68 72 73 75 76 77 78 79 81 82 85 86 87 90 93 94 98 99 100 102 107 108 110 111 115 116 117 118 119 126 129 130 131 132 134 135 144 146 147 148 149 151 154 157 **P**6 **S** Hartford HealthCare, Hartford, CT
Primary Contact: Donna Handley, President
COO: Carolyn Trantalis, R.N., MSN, Chief Operating Officer, East Region
CFO: Daniel E Lohr, Regional Vice President Finance
CMO: Nadia Nashid, M.D., Chief of Staff
CHR: Theresa L Buss, Regional Vice President Human Resources
Web address: www.windhamhospital.org
**Control**: Other not–for–profit (including NFP Corporation) **Service**: General medical and surgical

**Staffed Beds**: 42 **Admissions**: 2614 **Census**: 27 **Outpatient Visits**: 81458 **Births**: 100 **Total Expense ($000)**: 105694 **Payroll Expense ($000)**: 36792 **Personnel**: 393

*Many Facility Codes have changed. Please refer to the AHA Guide Code Chart.*

# DELAWARE

## DOVER—Kent County

✠ △ **BAYHEALTH MEDICAL CENTER (080004)**, 640 South State Street, Zip 19901–3530; tel. 302/674–4700, (Includes BAYHEALTH MEDICAL CENTER AT KENT GENERAL, Mailing address: 640 South State Street, Dover, Delaware, Zip 19901–3597; tel. 203/932–5711; BAYHEALTH MEDICAL CENTER, MILFORD MEMORIAL HOSPITAL, Mailing address: 21 West Clarke Avenue, Milford, Delaware, Zip 19963–1840, P O Box 199, Zip 19963–0199, tel. 302/430–5738; Michael Ashton, Administrator), (Nonreporting) **A**1 2 3 5 7 10 **F**3 8 11 12 13 15 17 18 20 22 24 26 28 29 30 31 32 34 35 38 40 41 42 43 44 45 47 48 49 50 51 53 54 55 57 58 59 60 61 64 67 68 70 72 73 74 75 76 77 78 79 81 82 84 85 86 87 88 89 90 93 94 98 99 100 101 102 103 104 107 108 110 111 114 115 117 118 119 120 121 123 124 126 129 130 131 132 134 135 144 146 147 148
Primary Contact: Terry Murphy, President and Chief Executive Officer
COO: Deborah Watson, Senior Vice President and Chief Operating Officer
CFO: Mike Tretina, Senior Vice President and Chief Financial Officer
CMO: Gary M Siegelman, M.D., MSC, Senior Vice President and Chief Medical Officer
CIO: Richard Mohnk, Vice President Corporate Services
CHR: Shana Ross, Vice President Human Resources
CNO: Brenda Blain, MSN, Senior Vice President and Chief Nursing Executive
Web address: www.bayhealth.org
**Control**: Other not–for–profit (including NFP Corporation) **Service**: General medical and surgical

**Staffed Beds: 385 Admissions: 20203 Census: 283 Outpatient Visits:** 616156 **Births:** 2193 **Total Expense ($000):** 633770 **Payroll Expense ($000):** 298284 **Personnel:** 2981

☐ **DOVER BEHAVIORAL HEALTH SYSTEM (084004)**, 725 Horsepond Road, Zip 19901–7232; tel. 302/741–0140, (Nonreporting) **A**1 10 **S** Universal Health Services, Inc., King of Prussia, PA
Primary Contact: Jean-Charles Constant, Administrator
Web address: www.doverbehavioral.com
**Control**: Corporation, Investor–owned (for–profit) **Service**: Psychiatric

**Staffed Beds:** 80

**KENT GENERAL HOSPITAL** See Bayhealth Medical Center at Kent General

☐ **PAM REHABILITATION HOSPITAL OF DOVER (083027)**, 1240 Mckee Road, Zip 19904–1381; tel. 302/672–5800, (Nonreporting) **A**1
Primary Contact: Ted Werner, Chief Executive Officer
Web address: www.https://postacutemedical.com/facilities/find-facility/rehabilitation-hospitals/pam-rehabilitation-hospital-dover
**Control**: Corporation, Investor–owned (for–profit) **Service**: Rehabilitation

**Staffed Beds:** 34

## GEORGETOWN—Sussex County

☐ **SUN BEHAVIORAL DELAWARE (084005)**, 21655 Biden Avenue, Zip 19947–4573; tel. 302/604–5600, (Nonreporting) **A**1
Primary Contact: Ann Wayne, Chief Executive Officer
Web address: www.https://sunbehavioral.com/delaware/
**Control**: Corporation, Investor–owned (for–profit) **Service**: Psychiatric

**Staffed Beds:** 90

**SUN BEHAVIORAL DELEWARE** See Sun Behavioral Delaware

## LEWES—Sussex County

✠ **BEEBE HEALTHCARE (080007)**, 424 Savannah Road, Zip 19958–1462; tel. 302/645–3300, (Nonreporting) **A**1 2 3 10 19 **F**3 11 12 13 15 17 18 20 22 24 28 29 30 31 34 35 40 43 45 46 49 51 54 56 57 59 62 64 68 70 74 75 76 77 78 79 81 82 84 85 87 89 93 96 97 107 108 110 111 114 115 117 118 119 120 121 123 124 130 146 147 148 154 156 **P**6
Primary Contact: David A. Tam, M.D., FACHE, President
COO: Richard Schaffner, Executive Vice President and Chief Operating Officer
CFO: Paul Pernice, Vice President Finance
CMO: Jeffrey Hawtof, M.D., Vice President Medical Operations and Informatics
CIO: Michael Maksymow, Vice President Information Systems
CHR: Catherine Halen, Vice President Human Resources
Web address: www.beebemed.org
**Control**: Other not–for–profit (including NFP Corporation) **Service**: General medical and surgical

**Staffed Beds: 155 Admissions: 10655 Census: 123 Outpatient Visits:** 440652 **Births:** 668 **Total Expense ($000):** 364854 **Payroll Expense ($000):** 134374 **Personnel:** 2338

**BEEBE MEDICAL CENTER** See Beebe Healthcare

## MIDDLETOWN—New Castle County

✠ **ENCOMPASS HEALTH REHABILITATION HOSPITAL OF MIDDLETOWN (083026)**, 250 East Hampden Road, Zip 19709–5303; tel. 302/464–3400, (Nonreporting) **A**1 10 **F**3 29 90 95 96 146 148 149 **S** Encompass Health Corporation, Birmingham, AL
Primary Contact: Mathew Gooch, Chief Executive Officer
CFO: Lisa Trimble, Controller
CMO: Ashish Khandelwal, M.D., Medical Director
CHR: Anitra Jones, Director Human Resources
CNO: Rebecca Boney, R.N., Chief Nursing Officer
Web address: www.encompasshealth.com/middletownrehab
**Control**: Corporation, Investor–owned (for–profit) **Service**: Rehabilitation

**Staffed Beds: 37 Admissions: 1121 Census: 36 Outpatient Visits:** 0 **Births:** 0 **Total Expense ($000):** 14499 **Payroll Expense ($000):** 8786 **Personnel:** 145

**HEALTHSOUTH REHABILITATION HOSPITAL OF MIDDLETOWN** See Encompass Health Rehabilitation Hospital of Middletown

## MILFORD—Sussex County

**BAYHEALTH MEDICAL CENTER, MILFORD MEMORIAL HOSPITAL** See Bayhealth Medical Center, Dover

**MILFORD MEMORIAL HOSPITAL** See Bayhealth Medical Center, Milford Memorial Hospital

## NEW CASTLE—New Castle County

☐ **DELAWARE PSYCHIATRIC CENTER (084001)**, 1901 North Dupont Highway, Zip 19720–1199; tel. 302/255–2700, (Nonreporting) **A**1 3 5 10
Primary Contact: Norman Vetter, Chief Executive Officer, Division of Substance Abuse and Mental Health
CIO: James Nau, Manager Computer and Applications Support
Web address: www.dhss.delaware.gov
**Control**: State, Government, Nonfederal **Service**: Psychiatric

**Staffed Beds:** 166

**DELAWARE STATE HOSPITAL** See Delaware Psychiatric Center

☐ **MEADOW WOOD BEHAVIORAL HEALTH SYSTEM (084003)**, 575 South Dupont Highway, Zip 19720–4606; tel. 302/328–3330, (Nonreporting) **A**1 10 **S** Acadia Healthcare Company, Inc., Franklin, TN
Primary Contact: Bill A. Mason, Chief Executive Officer
CFO: Maria Valdenegro, Chief Financial Officer
Web address: www.meadowwoodhospital.com
**Control**: Corporation, Investor–owned (for–profit) **Service**: Psychiatric

**Staffed Beds:** 53

**MEADOW WOOD HOSPITAL** See Meadow Wood Behavioral Health System

**Hospital, Medicare Provider Number, Address, Telephone, Approval, Facility, and Physician Codes, Health Care System**

★ American Hospital Association (AHA) membership
☐ The Joint Commission accreditation
○ Healthcare Facilities Accreditation Program
◇ DNV Healthcare Inc. accreditation
⇑ Center for Improvement in Healthcare Quality Accreditation
△ Commission on Accreditation of Rehabilitation Facilities (CARF) accreditation

© 2021 AHA Guide          *Many Facility Codes have changed. Please refer to the AHA Guide Code Chart.*          Hospitals **A127**

## NEWARK—New Castle County

**CHRISTIANA CARE HEALTH SYSTEM** See Christianacare

☒ △ **CHRISTIANACARE (080001)**, 4755 Ogletown-Stanton Road, Zip 19718–0002, Mailing Address: P.O. Box 6001, Zip 19718; tel. 302/733–1000, (Nonreporting) **A**1 2 3 5 7 8 10 **F**2 3 5 6 7 8 11 12 13 15 17 18 20 22 24 26 28 29 30 31 32 34 35 36 37 38 39 40 41 42 43 44 45 46 47 48 49 50 53 54 55 56 57 58 59 60 61 62 64 65 66 68 70 72 74 75 76 77 78 79 80 81 82 84 85 86 87 89 90 92 93 94 96 97 98 100 101 102 104 107 108 110 111 114 115 117 118 119 120 121 123 124 126 129 130 131 132 134 135 136 138 143 144 145 146 147 148 149 150 154 155 156 157 **S** ChristianaCare, Wilmington, DE
Primary Contact: Janice E. Nevin, M.D., M.P.H., Chief Executive Officer
CFO: Rob McMurray, Chief Financial Officer
CMO: Kenneth L Silverstein, M.D., Chief Clinical Officer
CIO: Randall Gaboriault, Chief Information Officer
CHR: Christopher Cowan, Senior Vice President and Chief Human Resources Officer
CNO: Richard Cuming, R.N., MSN, Ed.D., Chief Nurse Executive
Web address: www.christianacare.org
**Control**: Other not–for–profit (including NFP Corporation) **Service**: General medical and surgical

**Staffed Beds**: 1074 **Admissions**: 53121 **Census**: 836 **Outpatient Visits**: 620939 **Births**: 6035 **Total Expense ($000)**: 1922428 **Payroll Expense ($000)**: 937277 **Personnel**: 10899

☐ **ROCKFORD CENTER (084002)**, 100 Rockford Drive, Zip 19713–2121; tel. 302/996–5480, (Nonreporting) **A**1 3 10 **F**5 98 99 103 104 105 154 **S** Universal Health Services, Inc., King of Prussia, PA
Primary Contact: John F. McKenna, Chief Executive Officer and Managing Director
CFO: Kumar Purohit, Chief Financial Officer
CMO: Saurabh Gupta, Chief Medical Officer
CHR: Jessi Stewart, Director Human Resources
CNO: Michelle Singletary-Twyman, Chief Nursing Officer
Web address: www.rockfordcenter.com
**Control**: Corporation, Investor–owned (for–profit) **Service**: Psychiatric

**Staffed Beds**: 138 **Admissions**: 4709 **Census**: 134 **Outpatient Visits**: 16271 **Births**: 0

## SEAFORD—Sussex County

☒ **TIDALHEALTH NANTICOKE (080006)**, 801 Middleford Road, Zip 19973–3636; tel. 302/629–6611, (Nonreporting) **A**1 2 10 **F**3 12 13 15 18 20 22 28 29 30 31 34 35 37 40 43 45 49 50 54 57 59 64 65 70 74 75 76 77 78 79 81 84 85 86 87 89 93 107 108 111 114 115 119 120 121 123 126 129 130 132 135 144 146 147 148 149 150 154 156 157 **S** TidalHealth, Salisbury, MD
Primary Contact: Penny Short, R.N., President
CFO: Denise Jester, Chief Financial Officer
CMO: Harry C. Anthony, M.D., Chief Medical Officer
CIO: Charles Palmer, Director Information Technology
CNO: Ray Fulkrod, Chief Nursing Officer
Web address: www.nanticoke.org
**Control**: Other not–for–profit (including NFP Corporation) **Service**: General medical and surgical

**Staffed Beds**: 99 **Admissions**: 5538 **Census**: 55 **Outpatient Visits**: 152124 **Births**: 871 **Total Expense ($000)**: 146033 **Payroll Expense ($000)**: 48552 **Personnel**: 912

## WILMINGTON—New Castle County

☒ △ **ALFRED I. DUPONT HOSPITAL FOR CHILDREN (083300)**, 1600 Rockland Road, Zip 19803–3616, Mailing Address: Box 269, Zip 19899–0269; tel. 302/651–4000, (Nonreporting) **A**1 2 3 5 7 10 **F**7 11 12 17 18 19 21 23 25 27 28 29 30 31 32 34 35 36 37 39 40 41 43 44 45 47 48 50 53 54 55 56 57 58 59 60 61 64 65 66 68 72 74 75 77 78 79 80 81 82 84 85 87 88 89 90 92 93 94 96 97 99 100 101 102 104 107 111 113 114 115 116 118 119 126 127 129 130 131 132 134 136 137 138 139 143 144 146 148 149 154 156 157 **P**3 **S** Nemours, Jacksonville, FL
Primary Contact: Jay S. Greenspan, M.D., Chief Executive Officer
CFO: William N Britton, Associate Administrator Finance
CMO: Brent R King, Chief Medical Officer and Chief Physician
Web address: www.nemours.org
**Control**: Other not–for–profit (including NFP Corporation) **Service**: Children's general medical and surgical

**Staffed Beds**: 208 **Admissions**: 8311 **Census**: 146 **Outpatient Visits**: 188154 **Total Expense ($000)**: 491617 **Payroll Expense ($000)**: 176611 **Personnel**: 1939

**DUPONT HOSPITAL FOR CHILDREN** See Alfred I. Dupont Hospital for Children

☒ **SELECT SPECIALTY HOSPITAL-WILMINGTON (082000)**, 701 North Clayton Street, 5th Floor, Zip 19805–3948; tel. 302/421–4545, (Nonreporting) **A**1 10 **F**1 18 29 74 79 130 148 **S** Select Medical Corporation, Mechanicsburg, PA
Primary Contact: Donna Gares, R.N., FACHE, MSN, Chief Executive Officer
CFO: David Huffman, Vice President and Controller
CMO: Hummayun Ismail, M.D., Medical Director
CHR: Barbara A Foster, Regional Human Resources Director
Web address: www.wilmington.selectspecialtyhospitals.com
**Control**: Corporation, Investor–owned (for–profit) **Service**: Acute long–term care hospital

**Staffed Beds**: 35 **Admissions**: 288 **Census**: 30 **Outpatient Visits**: 0 **Births**: 0 **Total Expense ($000)**: 18322 **Payroll Expense ($000)**: 8675 **Personnel**: 90

☒ **ST. FRANCIS HOSPITAL (080003)**, 701 North Clayton Street, Zip 19805, Mailing Address: P.O. Box 2500, Zip 19805–0500; tel. 302/421–4100, (Nonreporting) **A**1 2 3 5 10 **S** Trinity Health, Livonia, MI
Primary Contact: Brandon Harvath, President and Chief Operating Officer
CIO: Paul W Rowe, Director Information Technology
CHR: Charlene J Wilson, Vice President Human Resources
Web address: www.stfrancishealthcare.org
**Control**: Other not–for–profit (including NFP Corporation) **Service**: General medical and surgical

**Staffed Beds**: 154

**VETERANS AFFAIRS MEDICAL CENTER** See Wilmington Veterans Affairs Medical Center

☒ **WILMINGTON VETERANS AFFAIRS MEDICAL CENTER**, 1601 Kirkwood Highway, Zip 19805–4989; tel. 302/994–2511, (Nonreporting) **A**1 3 5 **S** Department of Veterans Affairs, Washington, DC
Primary Contact: Robert W. Callahan Jr, Interim Director
CFO: Mary Ann Kozel, Chief Fiscal
CMO: Enrique Guttin, M.D., FACS, Chief of Staff
CIO: Scott Vlars, Chief Information Technology Services
CHR: Louis McCloskey, Chief Human Resources
Web address: www.va.gov/wilmington
**Control**: Veterans Affairs, Government, federal **Service**: General medical and surgical

**Staffed Beds**: 60

*Many Facility Codes have changed. Please refer to the AHA Guide Code Chart.* © 2021 AHA Guide

# DISTRICT OF COLUMBIA

**WASHINGTON—District of Columbia County**

**BRIDGEPOINT HOSPITAL CAPITOL HILL (092002)**, 223 7th Street, NE, Zip 20002–7045; tel. 202/546–5700, (Nonreporting) **A**10 22 **S** BridgePoint Healthcare, Portsmouth, NH
Primary Contact: James Linhares, Chief Executive Officer
COO: Michelle Mullen, Chief Clinical Officer
CFO: Michael Grubb, Senior Chief Financial Officer
CMO: Harminder Sandhu, M.D., Chief of Staff
CHR: Toni Wright, Director Human Resources
CNO: Adedayo Ekundayo, Ph.D., Director of Nursing
Web address: www.bridgepointhealthcare.com/
**Control**: Corporation, Investor–owned (for–profit) **Service**: Acute long–term care hospital

**Staffed Beds:** 177

**BRIDGEPOINT HOSPITAL NATIONAL HARBOR (092003)**, 4601 Martin Luther King Jr Avenue, SW, Zip 20032–1131; tel. 202/574–5700, (Nonreporting) **A**10 19 22 **S** BridgePoint Healthcare, Portsmouth, NH
Primary Contact: Swenda Moreh, Interim Chief Executive Officer
COO: Swenda Moreh, Vice President and Chief Operating Officer
CFO: Michael Grubb, Chief Financial Officer
CMO: Khosrow Davachi, Chief Medical Officer
CHR: Antoninette Saldivar, Vice President, Human Resources
CNO: Diane White, Chief Clinical Officer and Chief Nursing Officer
Web address: www.bridgepointhealthcare.com/
**Control**: Corporation, Investor–owned (for–profit) **Service**: Acute long–term care hospital

**Staffed Beds:** 82

**BRIDGEPOINT HOSPITAL-CAPITOL HILL** See Bridgepoint Hospital Capitol Hill

**BRIDGEPOINT HOSPITAL-NATIONAL HARBOR** See Bridgepoint Hospital National Harbor

**CHILDREN'S NATIONAL HEALTH SYSTEM** See Children's National Hospital

**CHILDREN'S NATIONAL HOSPITAL (093300)**, 111 Michigan Avenue NW, Zip 20010–2916; tel. 202/476–5000, (Nonreporting) **A**1 3 5 8 10 **F**3 5 7 8 11 12 14 17 18 19 21 23 25 27 29 30 31 32 34 35 36 38 39 40 41 42 43 44 45 46 48 49 50 51 54 55 57 58 59 60 61 64 65 66 68 71 72 74 75 77 78 79 81 82 83 84 85 86 87 88 89 91 92 93 94 96 97 98 99 100 102 104 105 106 107 111 112 115 116 117 118 119 126 129 130 131 132 134 136 137 138 141 142 146 148 155 156 157 **P**6
Primary Contact: Kurt Newman, M.D., President and Chief Executive Officer
COO: Kathleen Gorman, MSN, R.N., Executive Vice President Patient Care Services and Chief Operating Officer
CMO: Mark L Batshaw, M.D., Physician-in-Chief, Executive Vice President and Chief Academic Officer
CIO: Brian Jacobs, M.D., Vice President Chief Information Officer and Chief Medical Information Officer
CHR: Darryl Varnado, Executive Vice President and Chief People Officer
CNO: Linda Talley, MS, R.N., Vice President and Chief Nursing Officer
Web address: www.childrensnational.org
**Control**: Other not–for–profit (including NFP Corporation) **Service**: Children's general medical and surgical

**Staffed Beds:** 323 **Admissions:** 15989 **Census:** 267 **Outpatient Visits:** 560566 **Births:** 0 **Total Expense ($000):** 1117141 **Payroll Expense ($000):** 615518 **Personnel:** 5361

△ **GEORGE WASHINGTON UNIVERSITY HOSPITAL (090001)**, 900 23rd Street NW, Zip 20037–2342; tel. 202/715–4000, (Nonreporting) **A**1 2 3 5 7 8 10 **F**3 8 11 12.13 15 17 18 20 22 24 26 29 31 34 35 37 38 40 43 44 45 46 47 48 49 51 53 54 55 56 57 58 59 60 61 63 64 65 68 70 71 72 74 75 76 77 78 79 80 81 82 84 85 86 87 90 91 92 93 94 96 98 102 107 108 110 111 114 115 116 117 118 119 120 121 123 124 126 129 130 131 132 134 135 136 138 141 146 147 148 149 150 154 156 **S** Universal Health Services, Inc., King of Prussia, PA
Primary Contact: Kimberly Russo, Chief Executive Officer
CFO: Richard Davis, Chief Financial Officer
CMO: Gary Little, M.D., Medical Director
CIO: Louis Duhe, Senior Director Information Technology
CHR: Erin Fagan, Manager Human Resources
Web address: www.gwhospital.com
**Control**: Partnership, Investor–owned (for–profit) **Service**: General medical and surgical

**Staffed Beds:** 395 **Admissions:** 21533 **Census:** 336 **Outpatient Visits:** 206696 **Births:** 3243 **Personnel:** 2852

**GREATER SOUTHEAST COMM HOSP** See United Medical Center

**HOSPITAL FOR SICK CHILDREN** See The Hsc Pediatric Center

**HOWARD UNIVERSITY HOSPITAL (090003)**, 2041 Georgia Avenue NW, Zip 20060–0002; tel. 202/865–6100, (Nonreporting) **A**1 3 5 8 10 **S** Adventist HealthCare, Gaithersburg, MD
Primary Contact: Anita L.A. Jenkins, FABC, Chief Executive Officer
CFO: Ed Gyimah, Chief Financial Officer
CMO: Shelly McDonald-Pinkett, Chief Medical Officer
CIO: Becky Quammen, Chief Information Officer
CHR: Jeronica Goodwin, Senior Director Human Resources
CNO: Shirley Evers-Manly, Chief Nursing Officer
Web address: www.huhealthcare.com
**Control**: Other not–for–profit (including NFP Corporation) **Service**: General medical and surgical

**Staffed Beds:** 217

**MEDSTAR GEORGETOWN UNIVERSITY HOSPITAL (090004)**, 3800 Reservoir Road NW, Zip 20007–2197; tel. 202/444–2000, (Nonreporting) **A**1 2 3 5 8 10 **F**3 6 7 9 11 13 15 18 20 26 29 30 31 32 34 35 36 37 38 39 40 41 44 45 46 47 48 49 50 51 54 55 56 57 58 59 60 61 63 64 65 66 68 70 71 72 74 75 76 77 78 79 80 81 82 84 85 86 87 88 89 92 93 97 98 100 101 102 103 104 105 107 108 110 111 114 115 116 117 118 119 120 121 122 123 124 126 129 130 131 132 134 135 136 138 139 141 142 145 146 147 148 149 150 154 156 **P**1 6 **S** MedStar Health, Columbia, MD
Primary Contact: Michael Sachtleben, President
CFO: Paul Warda, Chief Financial Officer
CMO: Lisa Boyle, M.D., Vice President Medical Affairs and Medical Director
CIO: John Rasmussen, Vice President for Information Technology
CHR: Mary Jo Schweickhardt, Vice President Human Resources
CNO: Eileen Brennan Ferrell, MS, R.N., Vice President and Chief Nursing Officer
Web address: www.georgetownuniversityhospital.org
**Control**: Other not–for–profit (including NFP Corporation) **Service**: General medical and surgical

**Staffed Beds:** 408 **Admissions:** 15760 **Census:** 332 **Outpatient Visits:** 720168 **Births:** 980 **Total Expense ($000):** 1083033 **Payroll Expense ($000):** 485185 **Personnel:** 4504

**MEDSTAR GEORGETOWN UNIVERSITY HOSPITAL** See Medstar Georgetown University Hospital

DC

---

**Hospital, Medicare Provider Number, Address, Telephone, Approval, Facility, and Physician Codes, Health Care System**

★ American Hospital Association (AHA) membership  ○ Healthcare Facilities Accreditation Program  ⇑ Center for Improvement in Healthcare Quality Accreditation
□ The Joint Commission accreditation  ◇ DNV Healthcare Inc. accreditation  △ Commission on Accreditation of Rehabilitation Facilities (CARF) accreditation

✠ △ **MEDSTAR NATIONAL REHABILITATION HOSPITAL (093025)**, 102 Irving Street NW, Zip 20010–2949; tel. 202/877–1000, (Nonreporting) **A**1 3 5 7 10 **F**9 11 28 29 30 34 35 36 44 50 54 56 57 58 59 60 64 68 74 75 77 78 79 82 86 87 90 91 92 93 94 95 96 100 119 129 130 131 132 134 146 148 149 154 157 **P**1 6 **S** MedStar Health, Columbia, MD
Primary Contact: John D. Rockwood, President
CFO: Michael Boemmel, Vice President and Chief Financial Officer
CMO: Michael R Yochelson, M.D., Vice President and Medical Director
CHR: Pamela Ashby, Vice President Human Resources
CNO: Rosemary C Welch, R.N., Vice President and Chief Nursing Officer
Web address: www.medstarnrh.org
**Control**: Other not–for–profit (including NFP Corporation) **Service**: Rehabilitation

**Staffed Beds**: 137 **Admissions**: 1948 **Census**: 94 **Outpatient Visits**: 452215 **Births**: 0 **Total Expense ($000)**: 139636 **Payroll Expense ($000)**: 83493 **Personnel**: 1384

**MEDSTAR NATIONAL REHABILITATION NETWORK** See Medstar National Rehabilitation Hospital

✠ **MEDSTAR WASHINGTON HOSPITAL CENTER (090011)**, 110 Irving Street NW, Zip 20010–3017; tel. 202/877–7000, (Nonreporting) **A**1 2 3 5 8 10 **F**3 5 12 13 15 16 17 18 20 22 24 26 27 28 29 30 31 34 35 37 38 39 40 43 44 45 46 47 48 49 50 51 54 55 56 57 58 59 61 62 64 65 66 68 70 72 73 74 75 76 77 78 79 80 81 82 84 85 86 87 92 97 98 100 101 102 103 104 107 108 110 111 114 115 116 117 118 119 120 121 123 124 126 130 131 132 134 135 137 146 147 148 149 150 153 154 156 157 **P**1 6 **S** MedStar Health, Columbia, MD
Primary Contact: Gregory J. Argyros, M.D., Senior Vice President and President
COO: Robert Ross, Chief Operating Officer
CFO: William Gayne, Chief Financial Officer
CIO: Joe Brothman, Assistant Vice President, Information Systems
CHR: James P Hill, Senior Vice President Administrative Services
CNO: Susan E. Eckert, R.N., MSN, Senior Vice President and Chief Nursing Officer
Web address: www.whcenter.org
**Control**: Other not–for–profit (including NFP Corporation) **Service**: General medical and surgical

**Staffed Beds**: 758 **Admissions**: 37223 **Census**: 653 **Outpatient Visits**: 456449 **Births**: 3002 **Total Expense ($000)**: 1325114 **Payroll Expense ($000)**: 582087 **Personnel**: 5667

**MEDSTAR WASHINGTON HOSPITAL CENTER** See Medstar Washington Hospital Center

☐ **PSYCHIATRIC INSTITUTE OF WASHINGTON (094004)**, 4228 Wisconsin Avenue NW, Zip 20016–2138; tel. 202/885–5600, (Nonreporting) **A**1 3 5 10
Primary Contact: Corey Odol, Director Business Development
COO: Carol Desjeunes, Vice President and Chief Operating Officer
CFO: Aarti Subramanian, Vice President and Chief Financial Officer
CMO: Howard Hoffman, M.D., Medical Director
CIO: Ray Santina, Director Information Systems
CHR: Dawn Hatterer-Hoag, Director Human Resources
Web address: www.psychinstitute.com
**Control**: Corporation, Investor–owned (for–profit) **Service**: Psychiatric

**Staffed Beds**: 124

★ **SAINT ELIZABETHS HOSPITAL (094001)**, 1100 Alabama Avenue SE, Zip 20032–4540; tel. 202/299–5000, (Nonreporting) **A**3 5 10
Primary Contact: Mark J. Chastang, M.P.H., Chief Executive Officer
COO: K. Singh Taneja, Chief Operating Officer
CFO: Steward Beckham, Director, Chief Operating Officer
CMO: Phillip Candilis, M.D., Director, Medical Affairs
CIO: Mark Larkins, Interim Chief Information Officer
CHR: Frankie Wheeler, Director, Human Resources
CNO: Lori Ann Yerrell-Garrett, Interim Chief Nursing Executive
Web address: www.dmh.dc.gov/
**Control**: City, Government, Nonfederal **Service**: Psychiatric

**Staffed Beds**: 292

✠ **SIBLEY MEMORIAL HOSPITAL (090005)**, 5255 Loughboro Road NW, Zip 20016–2633; tel. 202/537–4000, (Total facility includes 45 beds in nursing home–type unit) (Nonreporting) **A**1 3 5 10 **F**3 6 10 12 13 15 20 29 30 31 34 35 36 37 38 44 45 46 47 48 49 50 53 55 57 58 59 64 68 70 73 74 75 76 77 78 79 81 82 84 85 86 87 91 92 93 96 97 98 100 101 102 104 107 108 109 110 111 113 114 115 116 117 118 119 120 121 122 123 126 129 130 132 135 146 147 148 149 154 157 **P**6 **S** Johns Hopkins Health System, Baltimore, MD
Primary Contact: Hasan A. Zia, Interim President and Chief Executive Officer
COO: Sanjay K Saha, Chief Operating Officer
CFO: Marty Basso, Chief Financial Officer
CMO: Hasan A. Zia, Vice President of Medical Affairs and Chief Medical Officer
CIO: Christopher T Timbers, Chief Information Officer
CHR: Queenie C. Plater, Vice President, Human Resources National Capital Region Johns Hopkins Medicine
CNO: Lynn Meuer, Interim Chief Nursing Officer
Web address: www.sibley.org
**Control**: Other not–for–profit (including NFP Corporation) **Service**: General medical and surgical

**Staffed Beds**: 273 **Admissions**: 12435 **Census**: 161 **Outpatient Visits**: 142735 **Births**: 4237 **Total Expense ($000)**: 396902 **Payroll Expense ($000)**: 141049 **Personnel**: 2092

**ST. ELIZABETHS HOSPITAL** See Saint Elizabeths Hospital

✠ **THE HSC PEDIATRIC CENTER**, 1731 Bunker Hill Road NE, Zip 20017–3096; tel. 202/832–4400, (Total facility includes 3 beds in nursing home–type unit) (Nonreporting) **A**1 3 **F**3 12 29 30 32 34 35 44 50 54 64 65 68 71 75 79 80 84 86 90 91 93 94 96 104 128 130 132 134 143 146 148
Primary Contact: Debbie C. Holson, R.N., MSN, Chief Operating Officer
COO: Debbie C Holson, R.N., MSN, Chief Operating Officer
CFO: Ray Vicks, Senior Vice President, Finance and Chief Financial Officer
CMO: Andrew Metinko, M.D., Chief Medical Officer
CIO: Khalil Bouharoun, Chief Information Officer
CHR: Lynne Hostetter, Vice President Human Resources
Web address: www.hscpediatriccenter.org/
**Control**: Other not–for–profit (including NFP Corporation) **Service**: Children's chronic disease

**Staffed Beds**: 57 **Admissions**: 212 **Census**: 26 **Outpatient Visits**: 22301 **Births**: 0 **Total Expense ($000)**: 39127 **Payroll Expense ($000)**: 14216 **Personnel**: 208

✠ **UNITED MEDICAL CENTER (090008)**, 1310 Southern Avenue SE, Zip 20032–4623; tel. 202/574–6000, (Nonreporting) **A**1 5 10
Primary Contact: Colene Y. Daniel, MS, M.P.H., FACHE, Chief Executive Officer
COO: Marcela Maamari, Chief Operating Officer
CFO: Lilian Chukwuma, Chief Financial Officer
CMO: Eric Li, M.D., Chief Medical Officer
CIO: Alan Johnson, Interim Chief Information Officer
CHR: Eric M. Johnson, Director
Web address: www.united-medicalcenter.com
**Control**: Other not–for–profit (including NFP Corporation) **Service**: General medical and surgical

**Staffed Beds**: 354

**VETERANS AFFAIRS MEDICAL CENTER** See Washington DC Veterans Affairs Medical Center

✠ △ **WASHINGTON DC VETERANS AFFAIRS MEDICAL CENTER**, 50 Irving Street NW, Zip 20422–0002; tel. 202/745–8000, (Nonreporting) **A**1 2 3 5 7 **S** Department of Veterans Affairs, Washington, DC
Primary Contact: Adam M. Robinson, Acting Director
CFO: Frank Filosa, Fiscal Manager
CIO: Amanda Graves, Chief Information Systems
Web address: www.washingtondc.va.gov/
**Control**: Veterans Affairs, Government, federal **Service**: General medical and surgical

**Staffed Beds**: 291

DC

*Many Facility Codes have changed. Please refer to the AHA Guide Code Chart.* © 2021 AHA Guide

# FLORIDA

## ALTAMONTE SPRINGS—Seminole County

**ADVENTHEALTH ALTAMONTE SPRINGS** See Adventhealth Orlando, Orlando

☒ **ENCOMPASS HEALTH REHABILITATION HOSPITAL OF ALTAMONTE SPRINGS (103045)**, 831 South State Road 434, Zip 32714–3502; tel. 407/587–8600, (Nonreporting) **A**1 10 **F**3 29 74 75 79 82 86 90 91 96 130 132 148 149 **S** Encompass Health Corporation, Birmingham, AL
Primary Contact: Michael Thomas, Chief Executive Officer
Web address: www.healthsouthaltamontesprings.com
**Control**: Corporation, Investor–owned (for–profit) **Service**: Rehabilitation

**Staffed Beds**: 60 **Admissions**: 1546 **Census**: 56 **Outpatient Visits**: 0
**Births**: 0 **Total Expense ($000)**: 21707 **Payroll Expense ($000)**: 11185
**Personnel**: 194

**FLORIDA HOSPITAL-ALTAMONTE** See Adventhealth Altamonte Springs

**HEALTHSOUTH REHABILITATION HOSPITAL OF ALTAMONTE SPRINGS** See Encompass Health Rehabilitation Hospital of Altamonte Springs

## APALACHICOLA—Franklin County

**EMERALD COAST HOSPITAL** See George E. Weems Memorial Hospital

★ **GEORGE E. WEEMS MEMORIAL HOSPITAL (101305)**, 135 Avenue G, Zip 32320–1613, Mailing Address: P.O. Box 580, Zip 32329–0580; tel. 850/653–8853, (Nonreporting) **A**10 18
Primary Contact: David Walker, Interim Chief Executive Officer
CHR: Ginny Griner, Director Human Resources
Web address: www.weemsmemorial.com
**Control**: Partnership, Investor–owned (for–profit) **Service**: General medical and surgical

**Staffed Beds**: 10

## APOPKA—Orange County

**ADVENTHEALTH APOPKA** See Adventhealth Orlando, Orlando

**FLORIDA HOSPITAL-APOPKA** See Adventhealth Apopka

## ARCADIA—Desoto County

☒ **DESOTO MEMORIAL HOSPITAL (100175)**, 900 North Robert Avenue, Zip 34266–8712, Mailing Address: P.O. Box 2180, Zip 34265–2180; tel. 863/494–3535, (Nonreporting) **A**1 10 20 **F**3 5 11 15 28 29 34 35 40 45 46 54 55 57 62 64 65 68 70 74 75 77 78 79 81 82 85 87 93 100 101 103 104 107 108 110 111 114 119 120 130 135 146 148 149 153 154
Primary Contact: Vincent A. Sica, President and Chief Executive Officer
CFO: Dan Hogan, Chief Financial Officer
CMO: Steven Mishkind, M.D., Chief of Staff
CIO: Kristen Spahr, Director of Marketing
CHR: Lois Hilton, Director Human Resources
CNO: Joseph La Cava, Chief Nursing Officer and Director of Anesthesia
Web address: www.dmh.org
**Control**: Hospital district or authority, Government, Nonfederal **Service**: General medical and surgical

**Staffed Beds**: 45 **Admissions**: 882 **Census**: 9 **Outpatient Visits**: 77186
**Births**: 0 **Total Expense ($000)**: 35185 **Payroll Expense ($000)**: 13667
**Personnel**: 267

**DESOTO MEMORIAL HOSPITAL** See Desoto Memorial Hospital

## ATLANTIS—Palm Beach County

**J. F. K. MEDICAL CENTER** See Jfk Medical Center

☒ **JFK MEDICAL CENTER (100080)**, 5301 South Congress Avenue, Zip 33462–1197; tel. 561/965–7300, (Includes JFK MEDICAL CENTER NORTH CAMPUS, Mailing address: 2201 45th Street, West Palm Beach, Florida, Zip 33407–2047; tel. 561/842–6141; Gina Melby, Chief Executive Officer), (Nonreporting) **A**1 3 5 10 **S** HCA Healthcare, Nashville, TN
Primary Contact: Gina Melby, Chief Executive Officer
CFO: Jim Leamon, Chief Financial Officer
CIO: Jane Stewart, Director Information Services
CHR: Trudy Bromley, Vice President Human Resources
Web address: www.jfkmc.com
**Control**: Corporation, Investor–owned (for–profit) **Service**: General medical and surgical

**Staffed Beds**: 803

## AVENTURA—Miami—Dade County

☒ **AVENTURA HOSPITAL AND MEDICAL CENTER (100131)**, 20900 Biscayne Boulevard, Zip 33180–1407; tel. 305/682–7000, (Nonreporting) **A**1 2 3 5 10 **S** HCA Healthcare, Nashville, TN
Primary Contact: David LeMonte, Chief Executive Officer
COO: Luanne Ansaldo, Chief Operating Officer
CFO: Jalima Hernandez, Chief Financial Officer
CHR: April Radden, Vice President of Human Resources
CNO: Jesse Gabuat, Chief Nursing Officer
Web address: www.aventurahospital.com
**Control**: Corporation, Investor–owned (for–profit) **Service**: General medical and surgical

**Staffed Beds**: 407

**COLUMBIA AVENTURA HOSPITAL** See Aventura Hospital and Medical Center

## BARTOW—Polk County

**BARTOW MEMORIAL HOSPITAL** See Bartow Regional Medical Center

☒ **BARTOW REGIONAL MEDICAL CENTER (100121)**, 2200 Osprey Boulevard, Zip 33830–3308; tel. 863/533–8111, (Nonreporting) **A**1 10 **F**3 11 12 15 18 20 22 29 30 34 35 40 44 45 46 49 50 51 57 59 60 64 68 70 74 75 77 78 79 81 82 84 85 86 87 93 107 108 110 111 114 115 118 119 126 129 130 131 132 135 145 146 147 148 149 154 156 **P**6 **S** Trinity Health, Livonia, MI
Primary Contact: Karen Kerr, R.N., President
CFO: Michael Boscia, Chief Financial Officer
CMO: Stuart Patterson, M.D., Chief of Staff
CIO: Vilakon Champavannarath, Director Information Systems
CHR: Marie Horton, Director Associate Relations
Web address: www.bartowregional.com
**Control**: Other not–for–profit (including NFP Corporation) **Service**: General medical and surgical

**Staffed Beds**: 72 **Admissions**: 3375 **Census**: 33 **Outpatient Visits**: 42748
**Births**: 0 **Total Expense ($000)**: 60531 **Payroll Expense ($000)**: 22238
**Personnel**: 344

## BAY PINES—Pinellas County

☒ △ **BAY PINES VETERANS AFFAIRS HEALTHCARE SYSTEM**, 10000 Bay Pines Boulevard, Zip 33744–8200, Mailing Address: P.O. Box 5005, Zip 33744–5005; tel. 727/398–6661, (Nonreporting) **A**1 2 3 5 7 **S** Department of Veterans Affairs, Washington, DC
Primary Contact: Paul M. Russo, FACHE, Director
COO: Kris Brown, Associate Director
CFO: Jeanine Ergle, Chief Financial Officer
CMO: George F Van Buskirk, M.D., Chief of Staff
CIO: John Williams, Chief Information Officer
CHR: Paula Buchele, Chief Human Resources
Web address: www.baypines.va.gov/
**Control**: Veterans Affairs, Government, federal **Service**: General medical and surgical

**Staffed Beds**: 396

**BAY PINES VETERANS AFFAIRS MEDICAL CENTER** See Bay Pines Veterans Affairs Healthcare System

---

| **Hospital, Medicare Provider Number, Address, Telephone, Approval, Facility, and Physician Codes, Health Care System** |
|---|

★ American Hospital Association (AHA) membership    ○ Healthcare Facilities Accreditation Program    ⇑ Center for Improvement in Healthcare Quality Accreditation
□ The Joint Commission accreditation    ◇ DNV Healthcare Inc. accreditation    △ Commission on Accreditation of Rehabilitation Facilities (CARF) accreditation

FL

## BELLE GLADE—Palm Beach County

**GLADES GENERAL HOSPITAL** See Lakeside Medical Center

☒ **LAKESIDE MEDICAL CENTER (100130)**, 39200 Hooker Highway,
Zip 33430–5368; tel. 561/996–6571, (Nonreporting) **A**1 5 10 13
Primary Contact: Janet Moreland, Hospital Administrator
COO: Darcy Davis, Chief Financial Officer
CFO: Darcy Davis, Chief Financial Officer
CMO: Ron Wiewora, M.D., Chief Medical Officer
Web address: www.lakesidemedical.org
**Control**: Hospital district or authority, Government, Nonfederal **Service**: General medical and surgical

| Staffed Beds: 70 |
|---|

## BELLEAIR—Pinellas County

**MORTON PLANT REHAB & NRSG CNTR** See Morton Plant Rehabilitation Center

## BLOUNTSTOWN—Calhoun County

**CALHOUN-LIBERTY HOSIPTAL** See Calhoun-Liberty Hospital

**CALHOUN-LIBERTY HOSPITAL (101304)**, 20370 NE Burns Avenue,
Zip 32424–1045, Mailing Address: P.O. Box 419, Zip 32424–0419;
tel. 850/674–5411, (Nonreporting) **A**10 18 **S** Alliant Management Services, Louisville, KY
Primary Contact: Janet Kinney, Chief Executive Officer
CFO: Nathan Ebersole, Controller
CIO: Michael Flowers, Director Information Management
CHR: Lynn Pitts, Director Human Resources
CNO: Debra Summers, Chief Nursing Officer
Web address: www.calhounlibertyhospital.com
**Control**: Other not–for–profit (including NFP Corporation) **Service**: General medical and surgical

| Staffed Beds: 25 |
|---|

## BOCA RATON—Palm Beach County

**BOCA RATON COMMUNITY HOSPITAL** See Boca Raton Regional Hospital

☐ **BOCA RATON REGIONAL HOSPITAL (100168)**, 800 Meadows Road,
Zip 33486–2368; tel. 561/955–7100, (Nonreporting) **A**1 2 3 5 10 **F**3 8 11 13 15
17 18 20 22 24 26 28 29 30 31 34 35 36 37 39 40 44 45 46 47 48 49 50 51
53 54 55 56 57 58 59 60 61 62 64 66 70 71 72 73 74 75 76 77 78 79 80 81
82 84 85 86 87 92 93 95 96 97 100 102 107 108 109 110 111 112 114 115
116 117 118 119 120 121 123 124 126 130 131 132 135 144 145 146 147
148 149 154 156 **P**6
Primary Contact: Lincoln S. Mendez, Chief Executive Officer
COO: Mindy Shikiar, MSN, Chief Operating Officer
CFO: Dawn Javersack, Vice President and Chief Financial Officer
CMO: Charles Posternack, M.D., Vice President
CIO: Robin Hildwein, Chief Information Officer
CHR: Mindy Raymond, Vice President Human Resources
CNO: Melissa Ann Durbin, R.N., MSN, Chief Nursing Officer
Web address: www.brrh.com
**Control**: Other not–for–profit (including NFP Corporation) **Service**: General medical and surgical

| Staffed Beds: 374 Admissions: 19385 Census: 241 Outpatient Visits: 286436 Births: 2529 Total Expense ($000): 521438 Payroll Expense ($000): 167336 Personnel: 2827 |
|---|

☒ **WEST BOCA MEDICAL CENTER (100268)**, 21644 State Road 7,
Zip 33428–1899; tel. 561/488–8000, (Nonreporting) **A**1 3 5 10 **S** TENET
Healthcare Corporation, Dallas, TX
Primary Contact: George Rizzuto, CPA, Chief Executive Officer
COO: Ryan Lee, Chief Operating Officer
CFO: Brook Thomas, Chief Financial Officer
CMO: Jack L Harari, M.D., Chief Medical Officer
CIO: Lauren Spagna, Marketing Director
CHR: Stephanie Sherman, Chief Human Resources Officer
CNO: Ruth Schwarzkopf, Chief Nursing Officer
Web address: www.westbocamedctr.com
**Control**: Corporation, Investor–owned (for–profit) **Service**: General medical and surgical

| Staffed Beds: 195 |
|---|

## BONIFAY—Holmes County

☐ **DOCTORS MEMORIAL HOSPITAL (101307)**, 2600 Hospital Drive,
Zip 32425–4264, Mailing Address: P.O. Box 188, Zip 32425–0188;
tel. 850/547–8000, (Nonreporting) **A**1 10 18
Primary Contact: Joann Baker, Administrator
CFO: Celia F Ward, Controller and Chief Financial Officer
CMO: Leisa Bailey, M.D., Chief of Staff
CIO: Rohan Anderson, Chief Information Officer
CHR: Christy Booth, Chief Human Resources Officer
CNO: Karla Rockwell, Director of Nursing
Web address: www.doctorsmemorial.org
**Control**: Hospital district or authority, Government, Nonfederal **Service**: General medical and surgical

| Staffed Beds: 20 |
|---|

## BOYNTON BEACH—Palm Beach County

☒ △ **BETHESDA HOSPITAL EAST (100002)**, 2815 South Seacrest Boulevard,
Zip 33435–7995; tel. 561/737–7733, (Includes BETHESDA HOSPITAL WEST,
Mailing address: 9655 West Boynton Beach Boulevard, Boynton Beach, Florida,
Zip 33472–4421; tel. 561/336–7000; Nelson Lazo, Chief Executive Officer),
(Nonreporting) **A**1 3 5 7 10 **F**3 8 11 12 13 17 18 19 20 22 24 26 28 29 30 31
40 41 44 45 46 47 48 49 50 51 56 59 68 70 72 74 75 76 77 78 79 81 82 84
85 87 88 89 90 92 93 96 107 108 109 110 111 114 115 116 117 118 119
120 121 124 126 129 130 131 132 135 146 147 148 149 **P**6 **S** Baptist Health
South Florida, Coral Gables, FL
Primary Contact: Nelson Lazo, Chief Executive Officer
COO: Ela C Lena, Administrator and Vice President Operations
CFO: Joanne Aquilina, Vice President Finance and Chief Financial Officer
CMO: Albert Biehl, M.D., Vice President Medical Affairs
CIO: Leslie Albright, Vice President Information Systems
CHR: Regina Bellucy, Vice President Human Resources
CNO: Tracy Edelstein, MSN, R.N., Vice President and Chief Nursing Officer
Web address: www.bethesdaweb.com
**Control**: Other not–for–profit (including NFP Corporation) **Service**: General medical and surgical

| Staffed Beds: 481 Admissions: 20907 Census: 284 Outpatient Visits: 264954 Births: 2631 Total Expense ($000): 325284 Payroll Expense ($000): 126466 Personnel: 1911 |
|---|

**BETHESDA MEMORIAL HOSPITAL** See Bethesda Hospital East

## BRADENTON—Manatee County

☒ △ **BLAKE MEDICAL CENTER (100213)**, 2020 59th Street West,
Zip 34209–4669; tel. 941/792–6611, (Nonreporting) **A**1 2 3 5 7 10 **S** HCA
Healthcare, Nashville, TN
Primary Contact: Randy Currin, Chief Executive Officer
COO: Lisa Nummi, MSN, R.N., Chief Operating Officer
CFO: Andrew Smith, Chief Financial Officer
CMO: Alan Harmatz, M.D., Chief Medical Officer
CIO: Shannon Piatkowski, Director Information Technology
CHR: Veronica Lequeux, Vice President Human Resources
CNO: Kimberly Kay Hatchel, Chief Nursing Officer
Web address: www.blakemedicalcenter.com
**Control**: Corporation, Investor–owned (for–profit) **Service**: General medical and surgical

| Staffed Beds: 383 |
|---|

**CENTERSTONE HOSPITAL (104040)**, 2020 26th Avenue East,
Zip 34208–7753, Mailing Address: P.O. Box 9478, Zip 34206–9478;
tel. 941/782–4600, (Nonreporting) **A**3 5 10 13
Primary Contact: Melissa Larkin-Skinner, Chief Executive Officer
CFO: Sean Gingras, CPA, Chief Financial Officer
CMO: Ranjay Halder, M.D., Chief Medical Director
CIO: Heidi L Blair, Vice President Administration
CHR: Colleen O'Connor, Director Human Resources
Web address: www.manateeglens.org
**Control**: Individual, Investor–owned (for–profit) **Service**: Other specialty treatment

| Staffed Beds: 62 |
|---|

**COLUMBIA BLAKE MEDICAL CENTER** See Blake Medical Center

*Many Facility Codes have changed. Please refer to the AHA Guide Code Chart.*

FL

☐ **LAKEWOOD RANCH MEDICAL CENTER (100299)**, 8330 Lakewood Ranch Boulevard, Zip 34202–5174; tel. 941/782–2100, (Nonreporting) **A**1 10 **S** Universal Health Services, Inc., King of Prussia, PA
Primary Contact: Andrew Guz, Chief Executive Officer
COO: Linda S Widra, FACHE, Ph.D., R.N., Chief Operating Officer
CFO: Gerald Christine, Chief Financial Officer
CHR: Trish Morales, Director Human Resources
Web address: www.lakewoodranchmedicalcenter.com
**Control**: Corporation, Investor–owned (for–profit) **Service**: General medical and surgical

**Staffed Beds:** 120

**MANATEE GLENS HOSPITAL AND ADDICTION CENTER** See Centerstone, Hospital

☐ **MANATEE MEMORIAL HOSPITAL (100035)**, 206 Second Street East, Zip 34208–1000; tel. 941/746–5111, (Nonreporting) **A**1 2 3 5 10 12 13 **S** Universal Health Services, Inc., King of Prussia, PA
Primary Contact: Kevin DiLallo, Chief Executive Officer
COO: Camie Patterson, Chief Operating Officer
CFO: Mark A Tierney, Chief Financial Officer
CMO: Eric Deppert, M.D., Chief Medical Officer
CIO: Troy Beaubien, Director Information Services
CHR: Sheree Threewits, Director Human Resources
Web address: www.manateememorial.com
**Control**: Partnership, Investor–owned (for–profit) **Service**: General medical and surgical

**Staffed Beds:** 319

**MANATEE PALMS YOUTH SERVICES** See Suncoast Behavioral Health Center

☐ **SUNCOAST BEHAVIORAL HEALTH CENTER (104078)**, 4480 51st Street West, Zip 34210–2855; tel. 941/251–5000, (Nonreporting) **A**1 10 **S** Universal Health Services, Inc., King of Prussia, PA
Primary Contact: Brandy Hamilton, Chief Executive Officer
CFO: Linda Weymouth, Chief Financial Officer
CMO: Randolph Hemsath, M.D., Medical Director
CNO: Janey Sweeney, Chief Nursing Officer
Web address: www.suncoastbhc.com
**Control**: Corporation, Investor–owned (for–profit) **Service**: Children's hospital psychiatric

**Staffed Beds:** 60

### BRANDON—Hillsborough County

☒ **BRANDON REGIONAL HOSPITAL (100243)**, 119 Oakfield Drive, Zip 33511–5779; tel. 813/681–5551, (Nonreporting) **A**1 3 5 10 **S** HCA Healthcare, Nashville, TN
Primary Contact: Bland Eng, Chief Executive Officer
COO: Liz Durrence, Chief Operating Officer
CFO: Gary Searls, Chief Financial Officer
CMO: Joseph C. Corcoran, D.O., Chief Medical Officer
CIO: Aaron Fountain, Chief Information Officer
CHR: Doug Goodman, Vice President Human Resources
CNO: William Kyle Thrift, Chief Nursing Officer
Web address: www.brandonhospital.com
**Control**: Corporation, Investor–owned (for–profit) **Service**: General medical and surgical

**Staffed Beds:** 422

**BRANDON REGIONAL MEDICAL CTR** See Brandon Regional Hospital

### BROOKSVILLE—Hernando County

☒ **BAYFRONT HEALTH BROOKSVILLE (100071)**, 17240 Cortez Boulevard, Zip 34601–8921, Mailing Address: P.O. Box 37, Zip 34605–0037; tel. 352/796–5111, (Includes BAYFRONT HEALTH SPRING HILL, Mailing address: 10461 Quality Drive, Spring Hill, Florida, Zip 34609–9634; tel. 352/688–8200; Michael Irvin, Chief Executive Officer), (Nonreporting) **A**1 10 **S** Community Health Systems, Inc., Franklin, TN
Primary Contact: Kenneth R. Wicker, FACHE, Chief Executive Officer
COO: Scott Hartsell, Chief Operating Officer
CFO: Matthew Seagroves, Chief Financial Officer
CMO: Mohammad A Joud, M.D., Chief of Staff
CIO: Lee Burch, Director Management Information Systems
CHR: Claudia L Jack, Director Associate Relations
Web address: www.brooksvilleregionalhospital.org
**Control**: Corporation, Investor–owned (for–profit) **Service**: General medical and surgical

**Staffed Beds:** 120

**BROOKSVILLE REGIONAL HOSPITAL** See Bayfront Health Brooksville

**COLUMBIA REGIONAL MED CTR** See Oak Hill Hospital

☒ **ENCOMPASS HEALTH REHABILITATION HOSPITAL OF SPRING HILL (103042)**, 12440 Cortez Boulevard, Zip 34613–2628; tel. 352/592–4250, (Nonreporting) **A**1 10 **S** Encompass Health Corporation, Birmingham, AL
Primary Contact: Jeffrey Alexander, Chief Executive Officer
CFO: Kimberly Lunt, Controller
CMO: Mira Zelin, D.O., Medical Director
CIO: Myra Merillo, Supervisor Health Information Management
CHR: Mary Salamanca, Director Human Resources
Web address: www.healthsouthspringhill.com
**Control**: Corporation, Investor–owned (for–profit) **Service**: Rehabilitation

**Staffed Beds:** 80

**GREENBRIER HOSPITAL** See Springbrook Hospital

**HEALTHSOUTH REHABILITATION HOSPITAL OF SPRING HILL** See Encompass Health Rehabilitation Hospital of Spring Hill

☒ **OAK HILL HOSPITAL (100264)**, 11375 Cortez Boulevard, Zip 34613–5409; tel. 352/596–6632, (Nonreporting) **A**1 2 3 10 13 **S** HCA Healthcare, Nashville, TN
Primary Contact: Mickey Smith, Chief Executive Officer
COO: Leanne Salazar, Chief Operating Officer
CFO: Matt Romero, Chief Financial Officer
CMO: Ed Nast, M.D., Chief Medical Officer
CHR: Charles Snider, Vice President Human Resources
CNO: Elizabeth Adams, R.N., Chief Nursing Officer
Web address: www.oakhillhospital.com
**Control**: Corporation, Investor–owned (for–profit) **Service**: General medical and surgical

**Staffed Beds:** 280

☐ **SPRINGBROOK HOSPITAL (104057)**, 7007 Grove Road, Zip 34609–8610; tel. 352/596–4306, (Nonreporting) **A**1 10 **S** Oglethorpe Recovery and Behavioral Hospitals, Tampa, FL
Primary Contact: Mercy Estevez, Chief Executive Officer
Web address: www.springbrookhospital.org/
**Control**: Other not–for–profit (including NFP Corporation) **Service**: Psychiatric

**Staffed Beds:** 66

**FL**

---

| Hospital, Medicare Provider Number, Address, Telephone, Approval, Facility, and Physician Codes, Health Care System |

★ American Hospital Association (AHA) membership ○ Healthcare Facilities Accreditation Program ⇧ Center for Improvement in Healthcare Quality Accreditation
☐ The Joint Commission accreditation ◇ DNV Healthcare Inc. accreditation △ Commission on Accreditation of Rehabilitation Facilities (CARF) accreditation

© 2021 AHA Guide     *Many Facility Codes have changed. Please refer to the AHA Guide Code Chart.*     Hospitals **A133**

## CAPE CORAL—Lee County

★ ⇑ **CAPE CORAL HOSPITAL (100244)**, 636 Del Prado Boulevard, Zip 33990–2695; tel. 239/424–2000, (Nonreporting) **A**10 21 **F**3 11 13 14 18 28 29 30 34 35 40 45 46 48 49 50 51 53 56 57 59 60 66 68 70 74 75 76 77 79 81 82 84 85 86 87 93 94 102 107 108 111 114 119 129 130 132 135 146 147 148 156 **S** Lee Health, Fort Myers, FL
Primary Contact: Lawrence Antonucci, M.D., President and Chief Executive Officer
CFO: Ben Spence, Chief Financial Officer
CMO: Mark Greenberg, M.D., Chief Medical Officer
CIO: Mike Smith, Chief Information Officer
CHR: Jon C Cecil, Chief Human Resource Officer
CNO: Lisa Sgarlata, MSN, Chief Patient Care Officer
Web address: www.leememorial.org
**Control:** Hospital district or authority, Government, Nonfederal **Service:** General medical and surgical

**Staffed Beds:** 291 **Admissions:** 16142 **Census:** 188 **Outpatient Visits:** 225905 **Births:** 1327 **Total Expense ($000):** 187746 **Payroll Expense ($000):** 80751 **Personnel:** 1330

## CELEBRATION—Osceola County

**ADVENTHEALTH CELEBRATION** See Adventhealth Orlando, Orlando

**FLORIDA HOSPITAL CELEBRATION HEALTH** See Adventhealth Celebration

## CHATTAHOOCHEE—Gadsden County

**FLORIDA STATE HOSPITAL (104000)**, U S Highway 90 East, Zip 32324–1000, Mailing Address: P.O. Box 1000, Zip 32324–1000; tel. 850/663–7536, (Nonreporting) **A**10
Primary Contact: Marguerite J. Morgan, Administrator
CFO: Bill Jones, Chief Financial Officer
CMO: Josefina Balulga, M.D., Clinical Director
CIO: Wesley Pelham
CHR: Keri Bassett, Human Resources Business Partner
Web address: www.dcf.state.fl.us/institutions/fsh
**Control:** State, Government, Nonfederal **Service:** Psychiatric

**Staffed Beds:** 987

## CHIPLEY—Washington County

☐ **NORTHWEST FLORIDA COMMUNITY HOSPITAL (101308)**, 1360 Brickyard Road, Zip 32428–6303, Mailing Address: P.O. Box 889, Zip 32428–0889; tel. 850/638–1610, (Nonreporting) **A**1 10 18 **S** Alliant Management Services, Louisville, KY
Primary Contact: Michael A. Kozar, Chief Executive Officer
CFO: Marcey Black, Chief Financial Officer
CHR: Shelia Schiefelbein, Coordinator Human Resources
CNO: Joan Beard, Chief Nursing Officer
Web address: www.nfch.org
**Control:** Corporation, Investor–owned (for–profit) **Service:** General medical and surgical

**Staffed Beds:** 59

## CLEARWATER—Pinellas County

**MORTON F PLANT HOSPITAL** See Morton Plant Hospital

☒ **MORTON PLANT HOSPITAL (100127)**, 300 Pinellas Street, Zip 33756–3804, Mailing Address: P.O. Box 210, Zip 33757–0210; tel. 727/462–7000, (Total facility includes 120 beds in nursing home–type unit) (Nonreporting) **A**1 2 3 5 10 **F**3 6 11 13 15 17 18 20 22 24 26 28 29 30 31 34 35 36 37 38 40 42 44 45 46 47 48 49 50 51 53 54 55 56 57 58 59 60 61 62 63 64 65 66 68 70 72 74 75 76 77 78 79 80 81 82 84 85 86 87 91 92 93 98 100 101 102 107 108 110 111 112 114 115 118 119 120 121 123 124 126 128 129 130 131 132 135 143 145 146 147 148 149 154 156 **P**6 **S** Morton Plant Mease Health Care, Clearwater, FL
Primary Contact: Lou Galdieri, R.N., President
CFO: Carl Tremonti, Chief Financial Officer
CMO: Jeff Jensen, D.O., Vice President, Medical Affairs
CIO: Timothy Thompson, Senior Vice President and Chief Information Officer
CHR: Angel Brown, Director Human Resources
CNO: Thomas Doria, Vice President Patient Services - West
Web address: www.mortonplant.com
**Control:** Other not–for–profit (including NFP Corporation) **Service:** General medical and surgical

**Staffed Beds:** 650 **Admissions:** 29157 **Census:** 345 **Outpatient Visits:** 413279 **Births:** 2231 **Total Expense ($000):** 604604 **Payroll Expense ($000):** 173024 **Personnel:** 3126

**PSYCHIATRIC HOSP OF FLORIDA** See Windmoor Healthcare of Clearwater

☐ **WINDMOOR HEALTHCARE OF CLEARWATER (104017)**, 11300 U S 19 North, Zip 33764; tel. 727/541–2646, (Nonreporting) **A**1 10 **S** Universal Health Services, Inc., King of Prussia, PA
Primary Contact: Joshua Rodriguez, Chief Executive Officer
Web address: www.windmoor.com
**Control:** Corporation, Investor–owned (for–profit) **Service:** Psychiatric

**Staffed Beds:** 100

## CLERMONT—Lake County

☐ **SOUTH LAKE HOSPITAL (100051)**, 1900 Don Wickham Drive, Zip 34711–1979; tel. 352/394–4071, (Total facility includes 30 beds in nursing home–type unit) (Nonreporting) **A**1 3 10 **F**3 8 11 13 15 18 20 22 26 28 29 30 31 32 34 35 40 42 45 46 47 48 49 50 51 53 54 57 59 60 62 64 68 70 74 75 76 77 78 79 81 82 85 86 87 89 92 93 107 108 110 111 114 115 116 117 119 120 121 124 126 128 130 131 132 135 146 147 148 149 154 156 **P**6 **S** Orlando Health, Orlando, FL
Primary Contact: John Moore, FACHE, President
COO: Paul Johns, Chief Operating Officer
CFO: Lance Sewell, Chief Financial Officer
CHR: Stephanie Stapelfeldt, Director, Human Resources
CNO: Bonnie Onofre, Chief Nursing Officer
Web address: www.southlakehospital.com
**Control:** Other not–for–profit (including NFP Corporation) **Service:** General medical and surgical

**Staffed Beds:** 170 **Admissions:** 14089 **Census:** 153 **Outpatient Visits:** 169010 **Births:** 820 **Total Expense ($000):** 234910 **Payroll Expense ($000):** 88253 **Personnel:** 1357

**SOUTH LAKE MEMORIAL HOSPITAL** See South Lake Hospital

## CLEWISTON—Hendry County

**HENDRY REGIONAL MED CENTER** See Hendry Regional Medical Center

☒ **HENDRY REGIONAL MEDICAL CENTER (101309)**, 524 West Sagamore Avenue, Zip 33440–3514; tel. 863/902–3000, (Nonreporting) **A**1 10 18 **F**3 11 15 29 34 35 40 45 50 57 59 64 65 68 70 75 77 81 82 85 91 93 97 107 110 111 114 119 127 133 135 146 **S** QHR Health, Brentwood, TN
Primary Contact: R D Williams, Chief Executive Officer
CFO: John Beltz, Chief Financial Officer
CMO: Leonard Carroll, M.D., Chief of Staff
CIO: Harrington Fuller, Information Technology Director
CHR: Lisa Miller, Director Human Resources
CNO: Rebecca Springer, MSN, R.N., Chief Nursing Officer
Web address: www.hendryregional.org
**Control:** Hospital district or authority, Government, Nonfederal **Service:** General medical and surgical

**Staffed Beds:** 25 **Admissions:** 444 **Census:** 3 **Outpatient Visits:** 36033 **Births:** 0 **Total Expense ($000):** 32360 **Payroll Expense ($000):** 14318 **Personnel:** 238

## COCOA BEACH—Brevard County

**CAPE CANAVERAL HOSPITAL** See Health First Cape Canaveral Hospital

☒ **HEALTH FIRST CAPE CANAVERAL HOSPITAL (100177)**, 701 West Cocoa Beach Causeway, Zip 32931–5595, Mailing Address: P.O. Box 320069, Zip 32932–0069; tel. 321/799–7111, (Nonreporting) **A**1 10 **F**3 11 13 15 18 20 22 26 29 30 31 34 39 40 41 45 46 49 50 54 59 60 62 64 68 70 74 75 76 77 78 79 80 81 85 86 87 92 93 102 107 108 110 111 114 118 119 129 130 132 141 146 147 148 149 154 **P**6 **S** Health First, Inc., Rockledge, FL
Primary Contact: Brett A. Esrock, FACHE, President
COO: Deborah Angerami, Chief Operating Officer, Health First Community Hospitals
CFO: Joseph G Felkner, Senior Vice President Finance and Chief Financial Officer
CMO: Lee Scheinbart, M.D., Vice President Medical Affairs, Health First Community Hospitals
CIO: Alex Popowycz, Senior Vice President and Chief Information Officer
CHR: Paula Just, Chief Human Resources Officer
CNO: Connie Bradley, R.N., MSN, FACHE, Chief Nursing Officer
Web address: www.health-first.org
**Control:** Other not–for–profit (including NFP Corporation) **Service:** General medical and surgical

**Staffed Beds:** 144 **Admissions:** 7298 **Census:** 76 **Outpatient Visits:** 116638 **Births:** 706 **Total Expense ($000):** 143309 **Payroll Expense ($000):** 64493 **Personnel:** 560

*Many Facility Codes have changed. Please refer to the AHA Guide Code Chart.*

FL

## CORAL GABLES—Miami—Dade County

⊠ **BAPTIST HEALTH SOUTH FLORIDA, DOCTORS HOSPITAL (100296)**, 5000 University Drive, Zip 33146–2094; tel. 786/308–3000, (Nonreporting) **A**1 3 5 10 **F**3 11 18 29 30 31 34 35 37 38 40 44 45 47 49 50 57 58 59 60 63 64 68 70 74 75 77 78 79 80 81 82 84 85 86 87 90 93 94 100 102 107 108 111 115 119 124 126 130 131 132 135 141 146 148 149 150 154 157 **S** Baptist Health South Florida, Coral Gables, FL
Primary Contact: Javier Hernandez-Lichtl, Chief Executive Officer
CFO: Maria J Yanez, Chief Financial Officer
Web address: www.baptisthealth.net
**Control**: Other not–for–profit (including NFP Corporation) **Service**: General medical and surgical

**Staffed Beds: 126 Admissions: 5666 Census: 67 Outpatient Visits: 66646 Births: 0 Total Expense ($000): 187876 Payroll Expense ($000): 61228 Personnel: 839**

⊠ **CORAL GABLES HOSPITAL (100183)**, 3100 Douglas Road, Zip 33134–6914; tel. 305/445–8461, (Nonreporting) **A**1 10 **S** TENET Healthcare Corporation, Dallas, TX
Primary Contact: Cristina Jimenez, Chief Executive Officer
COO: Madison Workman, Chief Operating Officer
CFO: Henry Capote, Interim Chief Financial Officer
CMO: Pedro Friarte, Director of Physician Services
CIO: Mercy Hermosa, Director of Information System
CHR: Ana Paguaga, Director of Human Resources
Web address: www.coralgableshospital.com
**Control**: Corporation, Investor–owned (for–profit) **Service**: General medical and surgical

**Staffed Beds: 256**

**DOCTORS' HOSPITAL** See Baptist Health South Florida, Doctors Hospital

**VENCOR HOSPITAL-CORAL GABLES** See Kindred Hospital South Florida-Coral Gables

## CORAL SPRINGS—Broward County

⊠ **BROWARD HEALTH CORAL SPRINGS (100276)**, 3000 Coral Hills Drive, Zip 33065–4108; tel. 954/344–3000, (Nonreporting) **A**1 3 10 **F**3 11 12 13 15 18 26 29 30 31 32 34 35 40 41 44 45 47 48 49 50 51 56 57 58 59 60 61 62 63 64 68 70 72 74 75 76 77 78 79 80 81 82 84 85 86 87 88 89 93 96 100 107 108 111 115 118 119 126 129 130 131 132 135 141 146 147 148 149 154 157 **S** Broward Health, Fort Lauderdale, FL
Primary Contact: Jared M. Smith, Chief Executive Officer
COO: Michael Leopold, Chief Operating Officer
CFO: Onel Rodriguez, Chief Financial Officer
CMO: Kutty Chandran, M.D., Regional Medical Officer
CNO: Carolyn Lizann Carter, Chief Nursing Officer
Web address: www.browardhealth.org
**Control**: Hospital district or authority, Government, Nonfederal **Service**: General medical and surgical

**Staffed Beds: 220 Admissions: 10907 Census: 120 Outpatient Visits: 125437 Births: 2190 Total Expense ($000): 165037 Payroll Expense ($000): 66242 Personnel: 937**

**CORAL SPRINGS MEDICAL CENTER** See Broward Health Coral Springs

## CRESTVIEW—Okaloosa County

⊠ **NORTH OKALOOSA MEDICAL CENTER (100122)**, 151 Redstone Avenue SE, Zip 32539–6026; tel. 850/689–8100, (Nonreporting) **A**1 10 **F**3 8 11 13 15 18 20 22 28 29 30 34 35 40 45 49 50 51 54 59 60 64 70 75 76 79 81 85 86 87 89 90 107 108 110 111 114 115 116 117 118 119 126 127 129 130 131 132 146 147 148 149 150 154 156 157 **S** Community Health Systems, Inc., Franklin, TN
Primary Contact: Ronnie Daves, Chief Executive Officer
CFO: Jim Andrews, Chief Financial Officer
CMO: Michael Foley, M.D., Chief Medical Officer
CIO: Jenny Zeitler, Network Administrator
CHR: Melody M Miller-Collette, Director Human Resources
CNO: Nina Perez, R.N., MSN, Chief Nursing Officer
Web address: www.northokaloosa.com
**Control**: Corporation, Investor–owned (for–profit) **Service**: General medical and surgical

**Staffed Beds: 110 Admissions: 4880 Census: 55 Outpatient Visits: 85696 Births: 478 Total Expense ($000): 90196 Payroll Expense ($000): 27094 Personnel: 458**

**NORTH OKALOOSA MEDICAL CTR** See North Okaloosa Medical Center

## CRYSTAL RIVER—Citrus County

**SEVEN RIVERS COMMUNITY HOSP** See Seven Rivers Regional Medical Center

⊠ **SEVEN RIVERS REGIONAL MEDICAL CENTER (100249)**, 6201 North Suncoast Boulevard, Zip 34428–6712; tel. 352/795–6560, (Nonreporting) **A**1 10 19 **S** Community Health Systems, Inc., Franklin, TN
Primary Contact: Linda Stockton, Chief Executive Officer
CFO: Vickie Magurean, Chief Financial Officer
CHR: Joann Mramor, Director Human Resources
CNO: Cynthia Heitzman, R.N., Chief Nursing Officer
Web address: www.srrmc.com
**Control**: Corporation, Investor–owned (for–profit) **Service**: General medical and surgical

**Staffed Beds: 128**

## CUTLER BAY—Miami—Dade County

⊠ **ENCOMPASS HEALTH REHABILITATION HOSPITAL OF MIAMI (103038)**, 20601 Old Cutler Road, Zip 33189–2400; tel. 305/251–3800, (Nonreporting) **A**1 10 **S** Encompass Health Corporation, Birmingham, AL
Primary Contact: Luis R. Allende Ruiz, Chief Executive Officer
CFO: Reyna Hernandez, Chief Financial Officer
CIO: Miguel Cruz, Medical Staff Credentialing Coordinator
CHR: Susan Riley, Director Human Resources
CNO: Ellen Romanowski, Chief Nursing Officer
Web address: www.healthsouthmiami.com
**Control**: Corporation, Investor–owned (for–profit) **Service**: Rehabilitation

**Staffed Beds: 60**

**HEALTHSOUTH REHABILITATION HOSPITAL OF MIAMI** See Encompass Health Rehabilitation Hospital of Miami

## DADE CITY—Pasco County

⊠ **ADVENTHEALTH DADE CITY (100211)**, 13100 Fort King Road, Zip 33525–5294; tel. 352/521–1100, (Total facility includes 45 beds in nursing home–type unit) (Nonreporting) **A**1 10 **F**12 18 20 22 26 29 30 40 45 64 70 74 75 77 79 81 82 84 93 107 111 115 119 126 128 129 154 **S** AdventHealth, Altamonte Springs, FL
Primary Contact: Amanda Maggard, Chief Executive Officer
CFO: Ann Barr, Interim Chief Financial Officer
CMO: Petros Tsambiras, M.D., Chief of Staff
CIO: Cheryl Kaufman, Director Health Information Management
CHR: Tabatha Wallace, Director Human Resources
Web address: www.floridahospital.com/dade-city
**Control**: Church operated, Nongovernment, not–for–profit **Service**: General medical and surgical

**Staffed Beds: 120 Admissions: 2517 Census: 24 Outpatient Visits: 21082 Births: 0 Total Expense ($000): 46496 Payroll Expense ($000): 16875 Personnel: 505**

**FLORIDA HOSPITAL DADE CITY** See Adventhealth Dade City

## DAVENPORT—Polk County

⊠ **ADVENTHEALTH HEART OF FLORIDA (100137)**, 40100 Highway 27, Zip 33837–5906; tel. 863/422–4971, (Nonreporting) **A**1 10 19 **F**3 12 13 15 18 20 22 26 28 29 30 34 35 37 40 42 45 46 49 50 51 57 59 60 64 68 70 74 75 76 77 79 81 82 85 86 87 89 92 93 96 100 107 108 110 111 114 115 119 126 130 131 132 135 146 147 148 149 154 156 **P**5 **S** AdventHealth, Altamonte Springs, FL
Primary Contact: Brian Adams, Chief Executive Officer
CFO: Tonja Mosley, Chief Financial Officer
CMO: Claudio Manubens, M.D., Chief of Staff
CIO: Louis Jones, Director Management Information Systems
CHR: Joan Allard, Director Human Resources
CNO: Dottie Mileto, Chief Nursing Officer
Web address: www.heartofflorida.com
**Control**: Other not–for–profit (including NFP Corporation) **Service**: General medical and surgical

**Staffed Beds: 193 Admissions: 7918 Census: 90 Outpatient Visits: 80566 Births: 761 Total Expense ($000): 135637 Payroll Expense ($000): 45186 Personnel: 713**

**HEART OF FLORIDA REGIONAL MEDICAL CENTER** See Adventhealth Heart of Florida

**FL**

---

**Hospital, Medicare Provider Number, Address, Telephone, Approval, Facility, and Physician Codes, Health Care System**

★ American Hospital Association (AHA) membership
☐ The Joint Commission accreditation
○ Healthcare Facilities Accreditation Program
◇ DNV Healthcare Inc. accreditation
⇑ Center for Improvement in Healthcare Quality Accreditation
△ Commission on Accreditation of Rehabilitation Facilities (CARF) accreditation

## DAYTONA BEACH—Volusia County

☒ △ **ADVENTHEALTH DAYTONA BEACH (100068)**, 301 Memorial Medical Parkway, Zip 32117–5167; tel. 386/676–6000, (Nonreporting) **A**1 2 7 10 **F**3 11 12 13 15 17 18 20 22 24 26 28 29 30 31 32 34 35 40 41 45 46 47 49 50 53 54 57 58 59 65 70 72 74 75 76 77 78 79 80 81 85 86 87 89 90 91 92 93 96 97 107 108 109 110 111 112 114 115 116 117 119 120 121 123 124 126 130 131 132 135 146 147 148 149 154 **P**6 **S** AdventHealth, Altamonte Springs, FL
Primary Contact: Ed Noseworthy, Chief Executive Officer
COO: Darlinda Copeland, Chief Operating Officer
CFO: Debora Thomas, Chief Financial Officer
CMO: Kris David Gray, Chief Medical Officer
CHR: Opal R Howard, Executive Director Human Resources
CNO: Michele Goeb-Burkett, R.N., MSN, Chief Nursing Officer
Web address: www.floridahospitalmemorial.org
**Control**: Church operated, Nongovernment, not–for–profit **Service**: General medical and surgical

**Staffed Beds**: 362 **Admissions**: 17538 **Census**: 250 **Outpatient Visits**: 353672 **Births**: 1501 **Total Expense ($000)**: 383886 **Payroll Expense ($000)**: 151343 **Personnel**: 2273

**FLORIDA HOSPITAL MEMORIAL MEDICAL CENTER** See Adventhealth Daytona Beach

**HALIFAX BEHAVIORAL CENTER** See Halifax Behavioral Services

**HALIFAX COMMUNITY HEALTH SYST** See Halifax Health Medical Center of Daytona Beach

☐ △ **HALIFAX HEALTH MEDICAL CENTER OF DAYTONA BEACH (100017)**, 303 North Clyde Morris Boulevard, Zip 32114–2700; tel. 386/425–4000, (Includes HALIFAX BEHAVIORAL SERVICES, Mailing address: 841 Jimmy Ann Drive, Daytona Beach, Florida, Zip 32117–4599; tel. 386/425–3900; HALIFAX HEALTH MEDICAL CENTER OF PORT ORANGE, Mailing address: 1041 Dunlawton Avenue, Port Orange, Florida, Zip 32127; tel. 386/425–4700; Ann Martorano, Chief Operating Officer), (Nonreporting) **A**1 3 5 7 10 **F**3 8 12 13 14 17 18 19 20 22 24 26 28 29 30 31 32 34 35 37 39 40 41 42 43 45 46 47 49 50 53 55 57 58 59 60 64 65 66 70 72 74 75 76 77 78 79 81 82 85 86 87 88 89 90 91 92 93 94 96 97 98 99 100 101 102 103 104 105 107 108 111 114 115 118 119 120 121 123 124 126 131 132 134 135 138 143 144 145 146 147 148 149 153 154 155 156 157 **P**6
Primary Contact: Jeff Feasel, President and Chief Executive Officer
COO: Mark Billings, Chief Operating Officer
CFO: Eric Peburn, Chief Financial Officer
CMO: Margaret Crossman, M.D., Chief Medical Officer
CIO: Tom Stafford, Chief Information Officer
CHR: Kimberly Fulcher, Chief Human Resources Officer
CNO: Catherine Luchsinger, MSN, Chief Nursing Officer
Web address: www.halifax.org
**Control**: Hospital district or authority, Government, Nonfederal **Service**: General medical and surgical

**Staffed Beds**: 673 **Admissions**: 24243 **Census**: 367 **Outpatient Visits**: 270634 **Births**: 1729 **Total Expense ($000)**: 513538 **Payroll Expense ($000)**: 209313 **Personnel**: 2779

☒ **SELECT SPECIALTY HOSPITAL DAYTONA BEACH (102030)**, 301 Memorial Medical Parkway, 11th Floor, Zip 32117–5167; tel. 386/231–3436, (Nonreporting) **A**1 10 **S** Select Medical Corporation, Mechanicsburg, PA
Primary Contact: Adrianne Lutes, Chief Executive Officer
Web address: www.daytonabeach.selectspecialtyhospitals.com
**Control**: Corporation, Investor–owned (for–profit) **Service**: Acute long–term care hospital

**Staffed Beds**: 34

## DEERFIELD BEACH—Broward County

☒ △ **BROWARD HEALTH NORTH (100086)**, 201 East Sample Road, Zip 33064–3502; tel. 954/941–8300, (Nonreporting) **A**1 3 7 10 **F**3 6 11 15 17 18 20 22 29 30 31 34 35 37 40 43 44 45 46 48 49 50 51 56 57 58 59 60 61 64 65 66 68 70 74 75 77 78 79 80 81 82 84 85 86 87 90 93 96 100 107 108 110 111 114 115 119 126 129 130 131 132 141 146 148 149 154 157 **S** Broward Health, Fort Lauderdale, FL
Primary Contact: Alice Taylor, R.N., MSN, Chief Executive Officer
COO: Susan Newton, Chief Operating Officer
CFO: Kim Braxl-Cole, Chief Financial Officer
CMO: Narendra Maheshwari, M.D., Chief of Staff
CNO: Bettiann S Ruditz, MS, R.N., Chief Nursing Officer
Web address: www.browardhealth.org
**Control**: Hospital district or authority, Government, Nonfederal **Service**: General medical and surgical

**Staffed Beds**: 331 **Admissions**: 13346 **Census**: 198 **Outpatient Visits**: 100506 **Births**: 0 **Total Expense ($000)**: 256400 **Payroll Expense ($000)**: 90959 **Personnel**: 1196

**NORTH BROWARD MEDICAL CENTER** See Broward Health North

## DEFUNIAK SPRINGS—Walton County

**HEALTHMARK REGIONAL MEDICAL CENTER** See Healthmark Regional Medical Center

**HEALTHMARK REGIONAL MEDICAL CENTER (100081)**, 4413 US Highway 331 South, Zip 32435–6307; tel. 850/951–4500, (Nonreporting) **A**10 **F**3 29 34 35 40 45 46 48 50 55 56 59 62 66 70 75 81 82 86 97 107 111 114 115 119 127 130 133 135 143 146 149 152 **P**5
Primary Contact: James H. Thompson, Ph.D., FACHE, Owner and Chief Executive Officer
COO: Gerald C Beard, Chief Operating Officer
CFO: Jim Brewer, M.P.H., Chief Financial Officer
CMO: Edward Tenewitz, M.D., Chief of Staff
CIO: Ray Downs, Senior Staff Accountant
CHR: Debra Tiller, Director Personnel and Administrative Secretary
Web address: www.healthmarkregional.com
**Control**: Individual, Investor–owned (for–profit) **Service**: General medical and surgical

**Staffed Beds**: 50 **Admissions**: 458 **Census**: 5 **Outpatient Visits**: 15676

## DELAND—Volusia County

☒ **ADVENTHEALTH DELAND (100045)**, 701 West Plymouth Avenue, Zip 32720–3236; tel. 386/943–4522, (Nonreporting) **A**1 2 10 **F**3 4 11 13 15 18 20 22 26 28 29 30 31 34 35 40 45 46 47 48 49 50 51 53 54 57 59 60 64 66 68 70 74 75 76 77 78 79 80 81 82 84 85 86 87 93 97 98 100 101 102 107 108 109 110 111 112 114 115 116 117 118 119 120 121 124 126 129 130 131 132 135 146 147 148 149 154 156 **S** AdventHealth, Altamonte Springs, FL
Primary Contact: Lorenzo Brown, Chief Executive Officer
COO: Samuel Aguero, Chief Operating Officer
CFO: Kyle Glass, Chief Financial Officer
CMO: Samuel Edwards, M.D., Chief of Staff
CIO: Kevin Piper, Director Information Systems
CNO: Patricia Ann Stark, R.N., CNO
Web address: www.fhdeland.org
**Control**: Other not–for–profit (including NFP Corporation) **Service**: General medical and surgical

**Staffed Beds**: 164 **Admissions**: 9242 **Census**: 100 **Outpatient Visits**: 109814 **Births**: 484 **Total Expense ($000)**: 160333 **Payroll Expense ($000)**: 64905 **Personnel**: 866

**FLORIDA HOSPITAL DELAND** See Adventhealth Deland

## DELRAY BEACH—Palm Beach County

☒ △ **DELRAY MEDICAL CENTER (100258)**, 5352 Linton Boulevard, Zip 33484–6580; tel. 561/498–4440, (Includes FAIR OAKS PAVILION, Mailing address: 5440 Linton Boulevard, Delray Beach, Florida, Zip 33484–6578; tel. 561/495–1000; PINECREST REHABILITATION HOSPITAL, Mailing address: 5360 Linton Boulevard, Delray Beach, Florida, Zip 33484–6538; tel. 561/495–0400), (Nonreporting) **A**1 3 5 7 10 **F**3 4 11 12 15 17 18 20 22 24 26 28 29 30 31 34 35 37 38 40 42 43 45 46 49 50 51 56 57 58 59 60 64 65 74 75 77 78 79 80 81 82 83 84 85 87 90 91 93 94 96 97 98 100 101 102 103 104 107 108 111 115 118 119 126 129 130 132 135 143 146 147 148 151 154 157 **S** TENET Healthcare Corporation, Dallas, TX
Primary Contact: Margaret Gill, Chief Executive Officer
COO: Stephen Garner, Chief Operating Officer
CMO: Anthony Dardano, M.D., Chief Medical Officer
CIO: Robens Rosena, Director Information Systems
CHR: Shannon Wills, Director Human Resources
Web address: www.delraymedicalctr.com
**Control**: Corporation, Investor–owned (for–profit) **Service**: General medical and surgical

**Staffed Beds**: 536 **Admissions**: 21855 **Census**: 324 **Outpatient Visits**: 94412 **Births**: 0 **Personnel**: 1445

**FAIR OAKS HOSPITAL** See Fair Oaks Pavilion

## DUNEDIN—Pinellas County

☒ **BAYCARE ALLIANT HOSPITAL (102021)**, 601 Main Street, Zip 34698–5848; tel. 727/736–9991, (Nonreporting) **A**1 10 **F**1 3 28 29 34 35 36 57 130 148 154 **S** Trinity Health, Livonia, MI
Primary Contact: Jacqueline Arocho, Administrator
CFO: John Proni, CPA, Manager Finance and Operations
CMO: Leonard Dunn, M.D., Chief Medical Officer
CHR: Darlene Shelton, Coordinator Team Resources
Web address: www.baycare.org
**Control**: Other not–for–profit (including NFP Corporation) **Service**: Acute long–term care hospital

**Staffed Beds**: 34 **Admissions**: 373 **Census**: 26 **Outpatient Visits**: 0 **Births**: 0 **Total Expense ($000)**: 18056 **Payroll Expense ($000)**: 8378 **Personnel**: 107

*Many Facility Codes have changed. Please refer to the AHA Guide Code Chart.*

✠ **MEASE DUNEDIN HOSPITAL (100043)**, 601 Main Street, Zip 34698–5891; tel. 727/733–1111, (Nonreporting) **A**1 10 **F**3 11 12 15 18 26 29 30 31 34 35 37 38 40 44 45 49 50 56 57 59 60 62 63 64 68 70 74 75 78 79 81 84 85 86 87 98 99 100 102 103 107 108 110 111 114 118 119 130 132 135 143 145 146 149 154 156 **P**6 **S** Trinity Health, Livonia, MI
Primary Contact: Matthew Novak, President
CFO: Carl Tremonti, Chief Financial Officer
CMO: Tony Schuster, M.D., Vice President of Physician Services
CIO: Tim Thompson, Senior Vice President, Information Services and Chief Information Officer
CHR: Kyle J Barr, Senior Vice President, Chief Team Resources Officer
CNO: Thomas Doria, Vice President, Patient Services and Chief Nursing Officer
Web address: www.mpmhealth.com
**Control**: Other not–for–profit (including NFP Corporation) **Service**: General medical and surgical

**Staffed Beds**: 120 **Admissions**: 6578 **Census**: 80 **Outpatient Visits**: 38384 **Births**: 0 **Total Expense ($000)**: 100144 **Payroll Expense ($000)**: 37487 **Personnel**: 579

**MEASE HOSPITAL DUNEDIN** See Mease Dunedin Hospital

## EGLIN AFB—Okaloosa County

✠ **U. S. AIR FORCE REGIONAL HOSPITAL**, 307 Boatner Road, Suite 114, Zip 32542–1282; tel. 850/883–8221, (Nonreporting) **A**1 3 5 **S** Department of the Air Force, Washington, DC
Primary Contact: Colonel Pamela Smith, Commander
Web address: www.eglin.af.mil
**Service**: General medical and surgical

**Staffed Beds**: 57

## ENGLEWOOD—Sarasota County

**COLUMBIA ENGLEWOOD COMM HOSP** See Englewood Community Hospital

✠ **ENGLEWOOD COMMUNITY HOSPITAL (100267)**, 700 Medical Boulevard, Zip 34223–3978; tel. 941/475–6571, (Nonreporting) **A**1 10 **S** HCA Healthcare, Nashville, TN
Primary Contact: Michael Ehrat, Chief Executive Officer
COO: Alex Chang, Chief Operating Officer
CFO: Vickie Magurean, Chief Financial Officer
CMO: L. Craig McAskill, M.D., Chief Medical Officer
CNO: Kathleen Pace, MSN, R.N., Chief Nursing Officer
Web address: www.englewoodcommunityhospital.com
**Control**: Corporation, Investor–owned (for–profit) **Service**: General medical and surgical

**Staffed Beds**: 100

## FERNANDINA BEACH—Nassau County

✠ **BAPTIST MEDICAL CENTER NASSAU (100140)**, 1250 South 18th Street, Zip 32034–3098; tel. 904/321–3500, (Nonreporting) **A**1 10 **F**3 11 13 15 18 26 28 29 30 34 35 40 45 49 64 70 74 76 79 81 82 85 91 92 93 102 107 108 110 111 114 115 119 124 129 132 146 148 149 **S** Baptist Health, Jacksonville, FL
Primary Contact: Edward T. Hubel, FACHE, President
CFO: Patricia K Hausauer, Director Finance
CHR: Erin Jackson, Human Resources Specialist
Web address: www.baptistjax.com/locations/baptist-medical-center-nassau
**Control**: Other not–for–profit (including NFP Corporation) **Service**: General medical and surgical

**Staffed Beds**: 52 **Admissions**: 3329 **Census**: 30 **Outpatient Visits**: 62241 **Births**: 368 **Total Expense ($000)**: 65770 **Payroll Expense ($000)**: 19262 **Personnel**: 360

**BAPTIST MEDICAL CENTER-NASSAU** See Baptist Medical Center Nassau

## FORT LAUDERDALE—Broward County

**BROWARD GENERAL MEDICAL CENTER** See Broward Health Medical Center

✠ **BROWARD HEALTH IMPERIAL POINT (100200)**, 6401 North Federal Highway, Zip 33308–1495; tel. 954/776–8500, (Nonreporting) **A**1 3 10 **F**3 11 12 15 18 20 22 29 30 31 34 35 40 44 45 49 50 51 53 56 57 58 59 60 64 68 70 75 77 78 79 80 81 82 85 86 87 93 98 100 102 103 107 108 110 111 114 115 119 126 130 132 146 147 148 149 157 **P**6 **S** Broward Health, Fort Lauderdale, FL
Primary Contact: Randy Gross, Chief Executive Officer
COO: Netonua Reyes, MSN, Chief Operating Officer and Chief Nursing Officer
CFO: Joseph Paul, Chief Financial Officer
CNO: Netonua Reyes, MSN, Chief Operating Officer and Chief Nursing Officer
Web address: www.browardhealth.org
**Control**: Hospital district or authority, Government, Nonfederal **Service**: General medical and surgical

**Staffed Beds**: 193 **Admissions**: 7508 **Census**: 107 **Outpatient Visits**: 74419 **Births**: 0 **Total Expense ($000)**: 120494 **Payroll Expense ($000)**: 45316 **Personnel**: 788

✠ **BROWARD HEALTH MEDICAL CENTER (100039)**, 1600 South Andrews Avenue, Zip 33316–2510; tel. 954/355–4400, (Includes CHRIS EVERT CHILDRENS HOSPITAL, Mailing address: 1600 South Andrews Avenue, Fort Lauderdale, Florida, Zip 33316–2510; tel. 954/355–4400; Calvin E Glidewell Jr, Chief Executive Officer), (Nonreporting) **A**1 3 5 10 13 **F**3 11 12 13 15 17 18 19 20 22 24 26 28 29 30 31 32 34 35 36 38 39 40 41 43 44 45 46 47 48 49 50 53 54 55 56 57 58 59 61 62 63 65 66 70 71 72 73 74 75 76 77 78 79 80 81 82 83 84 85 86 87 88 89 93 94 97 98 101 102 107 108 109 110 111 113 114 115 117 118 119 120 121 126 129 130 131 132 134 135 139 141 146 147 148 149 150 154 156 157 **P**2 **S** Broward Health, Fort Lauderdale, FL
Primary Contact: Heather Havericak, Chief Executive Officer
COO: Natassia Orr, Chief Operating Officer
CFO: Alexander Fernandez, Chief Financial Officer
CMO: Joshua D. Lenchus, Chief Medical Officer
CHR: Dionne Wong, Vice President and Chief Human Resources Officer
CNO: Robyn Farrington, Chief Nursing Officer
Web address: www.browardhealth.org
**Control**: Hospital district or authority, Government, Nonfederal **Service**: General medical and surgical

**Staffed Beds**: 614 **Admissions**: 24590 **Census**: 393 **Outpatient Visits**: 203062 **Births**: 3644 **Total Expense ($000)**: 519661 **Payroll Expense ($000)**: 182460 **Personnel**: 2710

✠ **HOLY CROSS HOSPITAL (100073)**, 4725 North Federal Highway, Zip 33308–4668, Mailing Address: P.O. Box 23460, Zip 33307–3460; tel. 954/771–8000, (Nonreporting) **A**1 2 3 5 10 **F**3 8 11 12 13 15 17 18 20 22 24 26 28 29 30 31 34 35 36 37 40 44 45 46 47 48 49 50 51 53 54 55 56 57 58 59 61 62 64 65 66 67 70 72 74 75 76 77 78 79 81 82 84 85 87 90 91 92 93 95 96 97 100 107 108 109 110 111 115 117 118 119 120 121 123 124 126 130 131 132 134 135 144 145 146 147 149 154 156 157 **P**6 **S** Trinity Health, Livonia, MI
Primary Contact: Mark Doyle, President and Chief Executive Officer
CFO: Ronald Brandenburg, Vice President and Chief Financial Officer
CMO: Eduardo Locatelli, M.D., Interim Chief Medical Officer
CNO: Taren Ruggiero, R.N., MSN, Vice President and Chief Nursing Officer
Web address: www.holy-cross.com
**Control**: Other not–for–profit (including NFP Corporation) **Service**: General medical and surgical

**Staffed Beds**: 365 **Admissions**: 16687 **Census**: 219 **Outpatient Visits**: 187414 **Births**: 939 **Total Expense ($000)**: 352262 **Payroll Expense ($000)**: 125895 **Personnel**: 2637

**IMPERIAL POINT MEDICAL CENTER** See Broward Health Imperial Point

**KINDRED HOSP-FORT LAUDERDALE** See Kindred Hospital South Florida-Fort Lauderdale

✠ **KINDRED HOSPITAL SOUTH FLORIDA-FORT LAUDERDALE (102010)**, 1516 East Las Olas Boulevard, Zip 33301–2399; tel. 954/764–8900, (Includes KINDRED HOSPITAL SOUTH FLORIDA-CORAL GABLES, Mailing address: 5190 SW Eighth Street, Coral Gables, Florida, Zip 33134–2495; tel. 305/445–1364; Al Molina, Chief Executive Officer; KINDRED HOSPITAL SOUTH FLORIDA-HOLLYWOOD, Mailing address: 1859 Van Buren Street, Hollywood, Florida, Zip 33020–5127; tel. 954/920–9000; Roberta Moss, Chief Executive Officer), (Nonreporting) **A**1 10 **S** Kindred Healthcare, Louisville, KY
Primary Contact: Theodore L. Welding, Chief Executive Officer
CFO: Dean Card, Chief Financial Officer
Web address: www.khfortlauderdale.com/
**Control**: Corporation, Investor–owned (for–profit) **Service**: Acute long–term care hospital

**Staffed Beds**: 123

**NORTH SHORE MEDICAL CENTER, FLORIDA MEDICAL CENTER CAMPUS** See Florida Medical Center - A Campus of North Shore

FL

## FORT MYERS—Lee County

**CHILDREN'S HOSPITAL OF SOUTHWEST FLORIDA** See Golisano Children's Hospital of Southwest Florida

**GOLISANO CHILDREN'S HOSPITAL OF SOUTHWEST FLORIDA** See Lee Memorial Hospital, Fort Myers

★ ⇑ **GULF COAST MEDICAL CENTER (100220)**, 13681 Doctor's Way, Zip 33912–4300; tel. 239/343–1000, (Nonreporting) **A**10 21 **F**3 11 13 14 20 28 29 40 45 46 49 51 60 70 74 77 79 81 84 85 86 87 93 102 107 108 111 114 115 118 119 128 130 146 154 156 **S** Lee Health, Fort Myers, FL
Primary Contact: Lawrence Antonucci, M.D., President and Chief Executive Officer
CFO: Ben Spence, Chief Financial Officer
CMO: Mark Greenberg, M.D., Medical Director
CIO: Mike Smith, Chief Information Officer
CHR: Jon C Cecil, Chief Human Resource Officer
CNO: Lisa Sgarlata, MSN, Chief Patient Care Officer
Web address: www.leememorial.org
**Control:** Hospital district or authority, Government, Nonfederal **Service:** General medical and surgical

**Staffed Beds:** 431 **Admissions:** 20437 **Census:** 270 **Outpatient Visits:** 73791 **Births:** 532 **Total Expense ($000):** 297462 **Payroll Expense ($000):** 112652 **Personnel:** 1823

⇑ **LEE MEMORIAL HEALTH SYSTEM** See Lee Memorial Hospital

★ △ ⇑ **LEE MEMORIAL HOSPITAL (100012)**, 2776 Cleveland Avenue, Zip 33901–5855, Mailing Address: P.O. Box 2218, Zip 33902–2218; tel. 239/343–2000, (Includes GOLISANO CHILDREN'S HOSPITAL OF SOUTHWEST FLORIDA, Mailing address: 9981 South HealthPark Drive, Fort Myers, Florida, Zip 33908; tel. 239/343–5437; HEALTHPARK MEDICAL CENTER, Mailing address: 9981 South HealthPark Drive, Fort Myers, Florida, Zip 33908; tel. 239/433–7799; THE REHABILITATION HOSPITAL, Mailing address: 2776 Cleveland Avenue, Fort Myers, Florida, Zip 33901; tel. 239/343–3900), (Nonreporting) **A**2 3 5 7 10 21 **F**3 11 12 13 14 15 17 18 19 20 21 22 24 26 28 29 30 31 32 34 40 41 43 45 46 48 49 51 53 54 55 56 57 58 59 60 68 69 70 72 74 75 76 77 78 79 81 82 84 85 86 87 88 89 90 93 94 100 102 104 107 108 110 111 114 115 116 117 119 126 128 129 130 131 132 135 136 146 147 148 156 **S** Lee Health, Fort Myers, FL
Primary Contact: Lawrence Antonucci, M.D., President and Chief Executive Officer
CFO: Ben Spence, Chief Financial Officer
CMO: Alex Daneshmand, D.O., Chief Patient Safety Officer
CIO: Mike Smith, Chief Information Officer
CHR: Jon C Cecil, Chief Human Resource Officer
CNO: Donna Giannuzzi, R.N., Chief Nursing Officer
Web address: www.leememorial.org
**Control:** Hospital district or authority, Government, Nonfederal **Service:** General medical and surgical

**Staffed Beds:** 874 **Admissions:** 41327 **Census:** 551 **Outpatient Visits:** 192269 **Births:** 4173 **Total Expense ($000):** 1404580 **Payroll Expense ($000):** 693981 **Personnel:** 8547

☐ **PARK ROYAL HOSPITAL (104074)**, 9241 Park Royal Drive, Zip 33908–9204; tel. 239/985–2700, (Nonreporting) **A**1 10 **F**4 98 103 105 152 153 154 **S** Acadia Healthcare Company, Inc., Franklin, TN
Primary Contact: Coleby Wright, Chief Executive Officer
CFO: Amy Ciampa, Chief Financial Officer
CHR: Robert Raynor, Human Resources Director
Web address: www.ParkRoyalHospital.com
**Control:** Corporation, Investor–owned (for–profit) **Service:** Psychiatric

**Staffed Beds:** 114 **Admissions:** 3653 **Census:** 82 **Outpatient Visits:** 6989 **Births:** 0 **Total Expense ($000):** 19303 **Payroll Expense ($000):** 9200 **Personnel:** 187

★ **PROMISE HOSPITAL OF FORT MYERS (102029)**, 3050 Champion Ring Road, Zip 33905–5599; tel. 239/313–2900, (Nonreporting) **A**10 **S** Select Medical Corporation, Mechanicsburg, PA
Primary Contact: Patrick G. Ryan, Chief Executive Officer
Web address: www.https://fortmyers.selectspecialtyhospitals.com/
**Control:** Corporation, Investor–owned (for–profit) **Service:** Acute long–term care hospital

**Staffed Beds:** 60

## FORT PIERCE—St. Lucie County

**HARBOUR SHORES OF LAWNWOOD** See Lawnwood Pavilion

**LAWNWOOD REGIONAL MEDICAL CENTER** See Lawnwood Regional Medical Center & Heart Institute

☒ △ **LAWNWOOD REGIONAL MEDICAL CENTER & HEART INSTITUTE (100246)**, 1700 South 23rd Street, Zip 34950–4803; tel. 772/461–4000, (Includes LAWNWOOD PAVILION, Mailing address: 1860 North Lawnwood Circle, Fort Pierce, Florida, Zip 34950, P O Box 1540, Zip 34954–1540, tel. 361/466–1500), (Nonreporting) **A**1 3 7 10 **S** HCA Healthcare, Nashville, TN
Primary Contact: Eric Goldman, Chief Executive Officer
CFO: Robert Dunwoody, Chief Financial Officer
CIO: Eric Castle, Director Information Services
CHR: Pam Burchell, Director Human Resources
Web address: www.lawnwoodmed.com
**Control:** Corporation, Investor–owned (for–profit) **Service:** General medical and surgical

**Staffed Beds:** 392

## FORT WALTON BEACH—Okaloosa County

**COLUMBIA FORT WALTON BEACH MED** See Fort Walton Beach Medical Center

☒ △ **FORT WALTON BEACH MEDICAL CENTER (100223)**, 1000 Mar-Walt Drive, Zip 32547–6795; tel. 850/862–1111, (Nonreporting) **A**1 2 7 10 **S** HCA Healthcare, Nashville, TN
Primary Contact: Mitchell P. Mongell, FACHE, Chief Executive Officer
CFO: Jeffrey Steve Moore, Chief Financial Officer
CMO: ColonelTama Van Decar, M.D., Chief Medical Officer
CIO: Amy Caldeira, Director Information Technology and Systems
CHR: Julia Truman, Vice President Human Resources
CNO: Caroline Stewart, Chief Nursing Officer
Web address: www.fwbmc.com
**Control:** Corporation, Investor–owned (for–profit) **Service:** General medical and surgical

**Staffed Beds:** 267

## GAINESVILLE—Alachua County

**COLUMBIA NORTH FL REG MED CTR** See North Florida Regional Medical Center

**MALCOM RANDALL VETERANS AFFAIRS MEDICAL CENTER** See Gainesville Veterans Affairs Medical Center

☒ **NORTH FLORIDA REGIONAL MEDICAL CENTER (100204)**, 6500 Newberry Road, Zip 32605–4392, Mailing Address: P.O. Box 147006, Zip 32614–7006; tel. 352/333–4000, (Nonreporting) **A**1 2 3 5 10 **S** HCA Healthcare, Nashville, TN
Primary Contact: Eric Lawson, Chief Executive Officer
CFO: Stewart Whitmore, Chief Financial Officer
CMO: Joseph Parra, M.D., Chief Medical Officer
CIO: Eric Strand, Director Information Services
CHR: Jane Fuller, Vice President Human Resources
CNO: Natalie Ransom, Chief Nursing Officer
Web address: www.nfrmc.com
**Control:** Corporation, Investor–owned (for–profit) **Service:** General medical and surgical

**Staffed Beds:** 432

☒ **NORTH FLORIDA/SOUTH GEORGIA VETERAN'S HEALTH SYSTEM**, 1601 SW Archer Road, Zip 32608–1135; tel. 352/376–1611, (Includes GAINESVILLE VETERANS AFFAIRS MEDICAL CENTER, Mailing address: 1601 SW Archer Road, Gainesville, Florida, Zip 32608–1197; tel. 352/376–1611; LAKE CITY VETERANS AFFAIRS MEDICAL CENTER, Mailing address: 619 South Marion Avenue, Lake City, Florida, Zip 32025–5898; tel. 386/755–3016) (Total facility includes 28 beds in nursing home–type unit) **A**1 3 5 **F**3 4 5 12 15 17 18 29 30 34 35 36 38 39 40 42 44 45 54 55 56 57 58 59 62 63 64 65 66 68 70 75 77 79 81 82 83 84 85 86 87 91 92 93 94 97 98 100 101 102 103 104 105 106 107 108 111 119 127 128 129 130 132 135 143 144 145 146 147 148 149 152 153 154 156 157 **S** Department of Veterans Affairs, Washington, DC
Primary Contact: Thomas Wisnieski, FACHE, Director
COO: Thomas Sutton, Associate Director
CFO: Jim Taylor, Chief Business Office
CMO: Brad Bender, M.D., Chief of Staff
CIO: Deborah Michel-Ogborn, Chief Information Resource Management
CHR: Michelle Manderino, Chief Human Resources
Web address: www.northflorida.va.gov
**Control:** Veterans Affairs, Government, federal **Service:** General medical and surgical

**Staffed Beds:** 324 **Admissions:** 17891 **Census:** 235 **Outpatient Visits:** 1277970 **Births:** 0 **Total Expense ($000):** 1225900 **Payroll Expense ($000):** 467027

*Many Facility Codes have changed. Please refer to the AHA Guide Code Chart.*

FL

⊞ **SELECT SPECIALTY HOSPITAL-GAINESVILLE (102022)**, 1600 SW Archer Road, 5th Floor, Zip 32610; tel. 352/337-3240, (Nonreporting) **A**1 3 10 **S** Select Medical Corporation, Mechanicsburg, PA
Primary Contact: Ronnie Wagley, Market Chief Executive Officer
Web address: www.gainesville.selectspecialtyhospitals.com/
**Control:** Corporation, Investor-owned (for-profit) **Service:** Acute long-term care hospital

**Staffed Beds:** 44

**SHANDS AT THE UNIVERSITY OF FLORIDA** See UF Health Shands Hospital

**SHANDS AT VISTA** See UF Health Shands Psychiatric Hospital

**SHANDS CHILDRENS HOSPITAL** See UF Health Shands Children's Hospital

**SHANDS REHAB HOSPITAL** See UF Health Rehab Hospital

⊞ **UF HEALTH REHAB HOSPITAL (103046)**, 2708 Southwest Archer Road, Zip 32608-1316; tel. 352/265-5499, (Nonreporting) **A**1 10 **F**28 29 35 43 51 54 75 87 90 91 96 100 130 132 146 148 149 154 156 157 **S** Select Medical Corporation, Mechanicsburg, PA
Primary Contact: Marina T. Cecchini, Administrator
CFO: William J Robinson, Senior Vice President and Chief Financial Officer
Web address: www.https://ufhealth.org/uf-health-shands-rehab-hospital
**Control:** Corporation, Investor-owned (for-profit) **Service:** Rehabilitation

**Staffed Beds:** 60 **Admissions:** 1010 **Census:** 36 **Outpatient Visits:** 0
**Births:** 0 **Personnel:** 104

⊞ △ **UF HEALTH SHANDS HOSPITAL (100113)**, 1600 SW Archer Road, Zip 32610-3003, Mailing Address: PO Box 100326, Zip 32610-0326; tel. 352/265-0111, (Includes UF HEALTH SHANDS CANCER HOSPITAL, Mailing address: 1515 SW Archer Road, Gainesville, Florida, Zip 32608-1134, PO Box 100326, Zip 32610-0326, tel. 352/265-0111; Edward Jimenez, Chief Executive Officer; UF HEALTH SHANDS CHILDREN'S HOSPITAL, Mailing address: 1600 SW Archer Road, Gainesville, Florida, Zip 32610-3003, PO Box 100326, Zip 32610-0326, tel. 352/265-0111; Edward Jimenez, Chief Executive Officer; UF HEALTH SHANDS PSYCHIATRIC HOSPITAL, Mailing address: 4101 NW 89th Boulevard, Gainesville, Florida, Zip 32606; tel. 352/265-5481; Roxane Harcourt, Interim Administrator), (Nonreporting) **A**1 2 3 5 7 8 10 **F**2 3 4 5 6 7 9 11 12 13 15 16 17 18 19 20 21 22 23 24 25 26 27 28 29 30 31 32 34 35 36 37 38 39 40 41 42 43 44 45 46 47 48 49 50 51 52 53 54 55 56 57 58 59 60 61 62 63 64 65 66 68 69 70 72 73 74 75 76 77 78 79 80 81 82 83 84 85 86 87 88 89 91 92 93 94 96 97 98 99 100 101 102 103 104 107 108 109 110 111 112 114 115 116 117 118 119 120 121 123 124 126 129 130 131 132 134 135 136 137 138 139 140 141 142 143 144 145 146 147 148 149 150 152 154 155 156 157 **P**6 **S** UF Health Shands, Gainesville, FL
Primary Contact: Edward Jimenez, Chief Executive Officer
CFO: James J. Kelly JrSenior Vice President and Chief Financial Officer
CMO: Parker Gibbs, M.D., Chief Medical Officer
CHR: Janet L. Christie, Senior Vice President Human Resources
CNO: Irene Alexaitis, R.N., Vice President of Nursing and Patient Services and Chief Nursing Officer
Web address: www.https://ufhealth.org/
**Control:** Other not-for-profit (including NFP Corporation) **Service:** General medical and surgical

**Staffed Beds:** 1015 **Admissions:** 50791 **Census:** 855 **Outpatient Visits:** 1116995 **Births:** 2787 **Total Expense ($000):** 1498796 **Payroll Expense ($000):** 545009 **Personnel:** 9315

**GREEN COVE SPRINGS—Clay County**

⊞ **KINDRED HOSPITAL NORTH FLORIDA (102015)**, 801 Oak Street, Zip 32043-4317; tel. 904/284-9230, (Nonreporting) **A**1 10 **S** Kindred Healthcare, Louisville, KY
Primary Contact: Susan Drago, R.N., Chief Executive Officer
CFO: Rickie Simmons, Controller
CMO: Uriel Nazario, M.D., Chief of Medical Staff
CIO: Rick Chapman, Chief Information Officer
CNO: Ashley McRae, Chief Clinical Officer
Web address: www.khnorthflorida.com
**Control:** Corporation, Investor-owned (for-profit) **Service:** Acute long-term care hospital

**Staffed Beds:** 80

**KINDRED HOSPITAL-NORTH FLORIDA** See Kindred Hospital North Florida

**GULF BREEZE—Santa Rosa County**

★ ⇑ **GULF BREEZE HOSPITAL (100266)**, 1110 Gulf Breeze Parkway, Zip 32561-4884; tel. 850/934-2000, (Nonreporting) **A**3 10 21 **F**3 8 11 15 18 26 29 30 35 40 43 44 45 49 50 54 57 59 64 68 70 74 75 77 78 79 81 82 84 85 86 91 93 107 110 111 114 119 120 121 123 130 131 132 143 146 147 148 **P**6 **S** Baptist Health Care Corporation, Pensacola, FL
Primary Contact: Scott Raynes, President
CFO: Kerry Vermillion, Senior Vice President Finance and Chief Financial Officer
Web address: www.ebaptisthealthcare.org/GulfBreezeHospital/
**Control:** Other not-for-profit (including NFP Corporation) **Service:** General medical and surgical

**Staffed Beds:** 65 **Admissions:** 3895 **Census:** 38 **Outpatient Visits:** 117081 **Births:** 0 **Total Expense ($000):** 87335 **Payroll Expense ($000):** 27602 **Personnel:** 362

**HIALEAH—Miami-Dade County**

**AMI PALMETTO GENERAL HOSPITAL** See Palmetto General Hospital

⊞ **HIALEAH HOSPITAL (100053)**, 651 East 25th Street, Zip 33013-3878; tel. 305/693-6100, (Nonreporting) **A**1 5 10 **S** TENET Healthcare Corporation, Dallas, TX
Primary Contact: Michael J. Bell, Chief Executive Officer
COO: Lourdes Camps, Chief Operating Officer
CFO: Gary Nymoen, Chief Financial Officer
CMO: Orlando Garcia, M.D., Chief Medical Officer
CHR: Yamila Herrera, Director Human Resources
CNO: Maribel Torres, Chief Nursing Officer
Web address: www.hialeahhosp.com
**Control:** Corporation, Investor-owned (for-profit) **Service:** General medical and surgical

**Staffed Beds:** 191

**LARKIN COMMUNITY HOSPITAL** See Larkin Community Hospital-Palm Springs Campus

☐ **LARKIN COMMUNITY HOSPITAL-PALM SPRINGS CAMPUS (100050)**, 1475 West 49th Street, Zip 33012-3275, Mailing Address: P.O. Box 2804, Zip 33012-2804; tel. 305/558-2500, (Nonreporting) **A**1 3 5 10 12 13
Primary Contact: Nicholas T. Smith, Chief Executive Officer
CFO: Tony Milian, Chief Financial Officer
CHR: Lourdes Anton, Director Human Resources
Web address: www.larkinhospital.com
**Control:** Corporation, Investor-owned (for-profit) **Service:** General medical and surgical

**Staffed Beds:** 130

⊞ **PALMETTO GENERAL HOSPITAL (100187)**, 2001 West 68th Street, Zip 33016-1898; tel. 305/823-5000, (Nonreporting) **A**1 3 5 10 13 **S** TENET Healthcare Corporation, Dallas, TX
Primary Contact: Ana J. Mederos, Chief Executive Officer
COO: Michele Thoman, Chief Operating Officer
CFO: Oscar Vicente, Chief Financial Officer
CMO: Anais Cortes, Chief of Staff
CHR: Elizabeth Camarena, Chief Human Resource Officer
CNO: Kathleen Guido, Chief Nursing Officer
Web address: www.palmettogeneral.com
**Control:** Corporation, Investor-owned (for-profit) **Service:** General medical and surgical

**Staffed Beds:** 360

**HIALEAH—Dade County**

**SOUTHERN WINDS HOSPITAL** See Westchester General Hospital, Miami

**HOLLYWOOD—Broward County**

**HOLLYWOOD MEDICAL CENTER** See Memorial Regional Hospital South

**HOLLYWOOD PAVILION** See Larkin Community Hospital Behavioral Health Services

**KINDRED HOSPITAL-HOLLYWOOD** See Kindred Hospital South Florida-Hollywood

FL

---

**Hospital, Medicare Provider Number, Address, Telephone, Approval, Facility, and Physician Codes, Health Care System**

★ American Hospital Association (AHA) membership
☐ The Joint Commission accreditation
○ Healthcare Facilities Accreditation Program
◇ DNV Healthcare Inc. accreditation
⇑ Center for Improvement in Healthcare Quality Accreditation
△ Commission on Accreditation of Rehabilitation Facilities (CARF) accreditation

☐ **LARKIN COMMUNITY HOSPITAL BEHAVIORAL HEALTH SERVICES (104079)**, 1201 North 37th Avenue, Zip 33021–5498; tel. 954/962–1355, (Nonreporting) **A**1 3 10
Primary Contact: Iris Berges, Chief Executive Officer
COO: Christopher Gabel, Chief Operating Officer
CFO: Rocky Davidson, Chief Financial Officer
CHR: Len Alpert, Director Human Resources
Web address: www.hollywoodpavilion.com
**Control**: Corporation, Investor–owned (for–profit) **Service**: Psychiatric

**Staffed Beds**: 50

**MEMORIAL HOSPITAL** See Memorial Regional Hospital

☒ △ **MEMORIAL REGIONAL HOSPITAL (100038)**, 3501 Johnson Street, Zip 33021–5421; tel. 954/987–2000, (Includes JOE DIMAGGIO CHILDREN'S HOSPITAL, Mailing address: 1005 Joe DiMaggio Drive, Hollywood, Florida, Zip 33021–5426; tel. 954/987–2000; Caitlin Beck Stella, Chief Executive Officer; MEMORIAL REGIONAL SOUTH, Mailing address: 3600 Washington Street, Hollywood, Florida, Zip 33021–8216; tel. 954/966–4500; Douglas Zaren, FACHE, Administrator and CEO), (Nonreporting) **A**1 2 3 5 7 10 **F**1 3 4 5 11 12 13 15 16 17 18 19 20 21 22 23 24 25 26 27 28 29 30 31 32 34 37 38 39 40 41 43 44 45 46 47 49 50 51 53 55 56 57 58 59 60 61 64 65 66 67 68 70 71 72 73 74 75 76 77 78 79 80 81 82 85 87 88 89 90 93 95 96 97 98 99 100 101 102 103 104 107 108 110 111 114 115 118 119 120 121 123 126 128 130 131 132 134 135 137 138 145 146 147 148 149 150 153 **S** Memorial Healthcare System, Hollywood, FL
Primary Contact: Judy Frum, Interim Chief Executive Officer
COO: Judy Frum, Chief Operating Officer
CFO: Walter Bussell, Chief Financial Officer
CMO: Donald Kim, M.D., Chief Medical Officer
CIO: Jeffrey S. Sturman, Senior Vice President and Chief Information Officer
CHR: Margie Vargas, Chief Human Resources Officer
CNO: Leslie Pollart, R.N., Chief Nursing Officer
Web address: www.mhs.net
**Control**: Hospital district or authority, Government, Nonfederal **Service**: General medical and surgical

**Staffed Beds**: 1013 **Admissions**: 35779 **Census**: 636 **Outpatient Visits**: 478436 **Births**: 5325 **Total Expense ($000)**: 992479 **Payroll Expense ($000)**: 419699 **Personnel**: 5652

☐ **SOUTH FLORIDA STATE HOSPITAL (104001)**, 800 East Cypress Drive, Zip 33025–4543; tel. 954/392–3000, (Nonreporting) **A**1 10
Primary Contact: Lee Packer, Administrator
Web address: www.geocarellc.com/Locations/SouthFloridaStateHospital
**Control**: State, Government, Nonfederal **Service**: Psychiatric

**Staffed Beds**: 355

**HOMESTEAD—Miami–Dade County**

☒ △ **BAPTIST HEALTH SOUTH FLORIDA, HOMESTEAD HOSPITAL (100125)**, 975 Baptist Way, Zip 33033–7600; tel. 786/243–8000, (Nonreporting) **A**1 7 10 **F**3 11 13 15 18 19 26 29 30 34 35 40 41 44 45 49 50 51 53 57 58 59 60 61 63 64 68 70 71 74 75 76 77 78 79 80 81 82 84 85 86 87 89 90 91 93 95 96 100 102 107 108 110 111 115 119 129 130 132 134 135 141 145 146 147 148 149 150 154 156 **S** Baptist Health South Florida, Coral Gables, FL
Primary Contact: Kenneth R. Spell, Chief Executive Officer
CFO: David Abercrombie, Controller
CMO: Mark A. Hernandez, M.D., President Medical Staff
CIO: Mimi Taylor, Corporate Vice President Information Technology
CHR: Adriene McCoy, Corporate Vice President
CNO: Ana Cabrera, Interim Chief Nursing Officer
Web address: www.baptisthealth.net
**Control**: Other not–for–profit (including NFP Corporation) **Service**: General medical and surgical

**Staffed Beds**: 147 **Admissions**: 7727 **Census**: 81 **Outpatient Visits**: 110424 **Births**: 1251 **Total Expense ($000)**: 228123 **Payroll Expense ($000)**: 81010 **Personnel**: 1109

**SMH HOMESTEAD HOSPITAL** See Baptist Health South Florida, Homestead Hospital

**HUDSON—Pasco County**

☒ **REGIONAL MEDICAL CENTER BAYONET POINT (100256)**, 14000 Fivay Road, Zip 34667–7199; tel. 727/869–5400, (Nonreporting) **A**1 2 3 5 10 12 13 **S** HCA Healthcare, Nashville, TN
Primary Contact: Regina Temple, President and Chief Executive Officer
COO: Paige Laughlin, Chief Operating Officer
CFO: Thomas Lawhorne, Chief Financial Officer
CMO: Joseph Pino, M.D., Chief Medical Officer
CIO: Mike Wilms, Director Information Systems
CHR: Geoffrey A. Washburn, Vice President
CNO: Melanie Wetmore, MSN, R.N., Chief Nursing Officer
Web address: www.rmchealth.com
**Control**: Corporation, Investor–owned (for–profit) **Service**: General medical and surgical

**Staffed Beds**: 290

**REGIONAL MEDICAL CENTER-BAYONET POINT** See Regional Medical Center Bayonet Point

**INVERNESS—Citrus County**

☒ **CITRUS MEMORIAL HEALTH SYSTEM (100023)**, 502 West Highland Boulevard, Zip 34452–4754; tel. 352/726–1551, (Nonreporting) **A**1 3 10 19 **S** HCA Healthcare, Nashville, TN
Primary Contact: Ginger Carroll, Chief Executive Officer
COO: George Mavros, Chief Operating Officer
CFO: Christopher Green, Chief Financial Officer
CMO: Raylene Platel, M.D., Chief Medical Officer
CIO: Nick Brooks, Director of Information Systems
CHR: Lee Glotzback, Director Human Resources
CNO: Caroline Stewart, Chief Nursing Officer
Web address: www.citrusmh.com
**Control**: Other not–for–profit (including NFP Corporation) **Service**: General medical and surgical

**Staffed Beds**: 204

**CITRUS MEMORIAL HOSPITAL** See Citrus Memorial Health System

**JACKSONVILLE—Duval County**

**BAPTIST MEDICAL CENTER** See Baptist Medical Center Jacksonville

☒ **BAPTIST MEDICAL CENTER JACKSONVILLE (100088)**, 800 Prudential Drive, Zip 32207–8202; tel. 904/202–2000, (Includes BAPTIST MEDICAL CENTER SOUTH, Mailing address: 14550 St Augustine Road, Jacksonville, Florida, Zip 32258–2160; tel. 904/821–6000; Nicole B. Thomas, President; WOLFSON CHILDREN'S HOSPITAL, Mailing address: 800 Prudential Drive, Jacksonville, Florida, Zip 32207; tel. 904/202–8000; Michael D Aubin, President), (Nonreporting) **A**1 2 3 5 10 **F**3 5 6 8 11 12 13 15 17 18 19 20 21 22 23 24 25 26 27 28 29 30 31 32 34 35 36 37 38 39 40 41 42 45 46 47 48 49 50 51 53 54 55 56 57 58 59 60 61 62 64 68 70 72 73 74 75 76 77 78 79 81 82 85 86 87 88 89 92 93 94 98 99 100 101 102 103 104 105 107 108 109 110 111 112 113 114 115 116 117 118 119 120 121 123 124 126 129 130 132 134 135 136 145 146 147 148 149 153 154 155 156 157 **S** Baptist Health, Jacksonville, FL
Primary Contact: Michael A. Mayo, FACHE, President
CFO: Scott Wooten, Senior Vice President and Chief Financial Officer
CMO: Keith L Stein, M.D., Senior Vice President Medical Affairs and Chief Medical Officer
CIO: Roland Garcia, Senior Vice President and Chief Information Officer
CHR: M. Beth Mehaffey, Senior Vice President Human Resources
Web address: www.e-baptisthealth.com
**Control**: Other not–for–profit (including NFP Corporation) **Service**: General medical and surgical

**Staffed Beds**: 955 **Admissions**: 40964 **Census**: 568 **Outpatient Visits**: 635261 **Births**: 5064 **Total Expense ($000)**: 1201875 **Payroll Expense ($000)**: 330589 **Personnel**: 5206

**BROOKS REHABILITATION HOSP** See Brooks Rehabilitation Hospital

*Many Facility Codes have changed. Please refer to the AHA Guide Code Chart.*

⊠ △ **BROOKS REHABILITATION HOSPITAL (103039)**, 3599 University Boulevard South, Zip 32216–4252; tel. 904/345-7600, (Nonreporting) **A**1 3 5 7 10 **F**3 28 29 30 38 44 50 64 74 75 77 78 79 82 86 87 90 91 93 94 95 96 97 130 148 149 **P**6
Primary Contact: Douglas M. Baer, Chief Executive Officer
COO: Michael Spigel, Executive Vice President & Chief Operating Officer
CMO: Trevor Paris, M.D., Medical Director
CIO: Karen Green, Chief Information Officer
CHR: Karen Gallagher, Vice President Human Resources and Learning
CNO: Joanne Hoertz, Vice President of Nursing
Web address: www.brookshealth.org
**Control**: Other not–for–profit (including NFP Corporation) **Service**: Rehabilitation

**Staffed Beds**: 146 **Admissions**: 3049 **Census**: 138 **Outpatient Visits**: 248203 **Births**: 0 **Total Expense ($000)**: 78150 **Payroll Expense ($000)**: 28965 **Personnel**: 494

☐ **CURAHEALTH JACKSONVILLE (102012)**, 4901 Richard Street, Zip 32207–7328; tel. 904/425–0500, (Nonreporting) **A**1 10 **S** Curahealth Hospitals, Garland, TX
Primary Contact: Jerry Deller, Chief Executive Officer
CFO: Joshua Szostek, Chief Financial Officer
CMO: Wendell H Williams, M.D., JrMedical Director
CIO: Patrick Adesso, Director Information Technology and Systems
CHR: Lisa Ayala, R.N., Director Human Resources
Web address: www.specialtyhospitaljax.com
**Control**: Corporation, Investor–owned (for–profit) **Service**: Acute long–term care hospital

**Staffed Beds**: 62

⊞ **MAYO CLINIC HOSPITAL IN FLORIDA (100151)**, 4500 San Pablo Road South, Zip 32224–1865; tel. 904/953–2000, (Nonreporting) **A**1 2 3 5 8 10 **F**3 6 7 8 9 11 12 14 15 18 20 22 24 26 28 29 30 31 34 35 36 37 40 44 45 46 47 48 49 50 51 54 55 56 57 58 59 60 61 64 65 68 70 74 75 77 78 79 80 81 82 84 85 86 87 92 93 96 97 100 102 104 107 108 109 110 111 112 115 116 117 118 119 120 121 123 124 126 129 130 131 132 135 136 137 138 139 140 141 142 145 146 147 148 149 150 154 156 **P**6 **S** Mayo Clinic, Rochester, MN
Primary Contact: Kent Thielen, M.D., Vice President Operations
CFO: Kevin Lockett, Interim Chief Financial Officer
CMO: David Thiel, M.D., Medical Director
CIO: John Crooks, Chair Information Services
CHR: Rosemary McMullan, Chief Human Resources
CNO: Ryannon Frederick, Chief Nursing Officer
Web address: www.mayoclinic.org/jacksonville/
**Control**: Other not–for–profit (including NFP Corporation) **Service**: General medical and surgical

**Staffed Beds**: 304 **Admissions**: 16512 **Census**: 231 **Outpatient Visits**: 64909 **Births**: 0 **Personnel**: 3390

**MAYO CLINIC JACKSONVILLE** See Mayo Clinic Hospital in Florida

**MEMORIAL HOSP OF JACKSONVILLE** See Memorial Hospital Jacksonville

⊞ **MEMORIAL HOSPITAL JACKSONVILLE (100179)**, 3625 University Boulevard South, Zip 32216–4207; tel. 904/702-6111, (Nonreporting) **A**1 2 3 5 10 **S** HCA Healthcare, Nashville, TN
Primary Contact: Bradley S. Talbert, FACHE, President and Chief Executive Officer
COO: Cory Darling, Chief Operating Officer
CMO: John Lazenby, M.D., Chief Medical Officer
CIO: Patrick Adesso, Director Information Technology and Systems
CHR: Stuart Thompson, Vice President Human Resources
CNO: Suzanne Woods, Senior Vice President of Nursing
Web address: www.memorialhospitaljax.com
**Control**: Corporation, Investor–owned (for–profit) **Service**: General medical and surgical

**Staffed Beds**: 454

**NAVAL HOSPITAL** See Naval Hospital Jacksonville

⊠ **NAVAL HOSPITAL JACKSONVILLE**, 2080 Child Street, Zip 32214–5000; tel. 904/542–7300, (Nonreporting) **A**1 3 5 **S** Bureau of Medicine and Surgery, Department of the Navy, Falls Church, VA
Primary Contact: Captain Matthew Case, MSC, USN, Commanding Officer
CFO: Lieutenant CommanderMichael Gregonis, Comptroller
CMO: CaptainChristopher Quarles, M.D., Director Medical Services
CIO: Mike Haytaian, Head Director Information Resources Management
CHR: CaptainRuby Tennyson, Director Administration
Web address: www.med.navy.mil/SITES/NAVALHOSPITALJAX/Pages/default.aspx
**Service**: General medical and surgical

**Staffed Beds**: 64

☐ **RIVER POINT BEHAVIORAL HEALTH (104016)**, 6300 Beach Boulevard, Zip 32216–2782; tel. 904/724–9202, (Nonreporting) **A**1 10 **S** Universal Health Services, Inc., King of Prussia, PA
Primary Contact: Kevin McGee, Chief Executive Officer
CFO: Jenni Stackhouse, Chief Financial Officer
CIO: Bill Willis, Director Information Technology
CHR: Cathy Calhoun, Director Human Resources
Web address: www.riverpointbehavioral.com
**Control**: Corporation, Investor–owned (for–profit) **Service**: Psychiatric

**Staffed Beds**: 92

**SHANDS JACKSONVILLE MEDICAL CENTER** See UF Health Jacksonville

**SPECIALTY HOSPITAL JACKSONVILLE** See Curahealth Jacksonville

**ST JOHNS RIVER HOSPITAL** See River Point Behavioral Health

**ST. LUKE'S HOSPITAL** See St. Vincent'S Medical Center Southside

**ST. VINCENT'S MEDICAL CENTER** See St. Vincent'S Medical Center Riverside

⊞ **ST. VINCENT'S MEDICAL CENTER RIVERSIDE (100040)**, 1 Shircliff Way, Zip 32204–4748, Mailing Address: P.O. Box 2982, Zip 32203–2982; tel. 904/308–7300, (Nonreporting) **A**1 2 3 5 10 **F**3 12 13 15 17 18 20 22 24 26 28 29 30 31 34 37 40 44 45 46 47 48 49 53 55 57 58 61 64 65 70 72 74 76 78 79 81 85 86 87 91 93 107 108 110 111 114 115 117 118 119 120 121 123 124 126 130 131 132 146 147 149 154 156 **S** Ascension Healthcare, Saint Louis, MO
Primary Contact: Thomas J. VanOsdol, Chief Executive Officer
CIO: Ann Carey, Vice President and Chief Information Officer
CHR: Michelle Adamolekun, Chief Human Resource Officer
CNO: Lorraine Keith, Chief Nursing Officer
Web address: www.jaxhealth.com
**Control**: Church operated, Nongovernment, not–for–profit **Service**: General medical and surgical

**Staffed Beds**: 479 **Admissions**: 22120 **Census**: 268 **Outpatient Visits**: 151333 **Births**: 1747 **Total Expense ($000)**: 457892 **Payroll Expense ($000)**: 120119 **Personnel**: 1841

⊞ **ST. VINCENT'S MEDICAL CENTER SOUTHSIDE (100307)**, 4201 Belfort Road, Zip 32216–1431; tel. 904/296–3700, (Nonreporting) **A**1 3 5 10 **F**3 12 13 15 18 20 22 26 29 30 31 34 40 44 47 49 50 57 60 61 64 65 70 72 74 76 78 79 81 85 86 87 93 96 102 107 108 110 111 114 115 119 126 128 129 130 131 132 146 147 149 154 156 **S** Ascension Healthcare, Saint Louis, MO
Primary Contact: Thomas J. VanOsdol, Chief Executive Officer
CIO: Ann Carey, Chief Information Officer
CHR: Kaye W Lunsford, System Director Human Resources
CNO: Lorraine Keith, Chief Nursing Officer
Web address: www.jaxhealth.com
**Control**: Church operated, Nongovernment, not–for–profit **Service**: General medical and surgical

**Staffed Beds**: 260 **Admissions**: 10336 **Census**: 107 **Outpatient Visits**: 60873 **Births**: 1584 **Total Expense ($000)**: 173391 **Payroll Expense ($000)**: 43675 **Personnel**: 625

**FL**

---

**Hospital, Medicare Provider Number, Address, Telephone, Approval, Facility, and Physician Codes, Health Care System**

★ American Hospital Association (AHA) membership ☐ The Joint Commission accreditation ○ Healthcare Facilities Accreditation Program ◇ DNV Healthcare Inc. accreditation ⇑ Center for Improvement in Healthcare Quality Accreditation △ Commission on Accreditation of Rehabilitation Facilities (CARF) accreditation

⊞ **UF HEALTH JACKSONVILLE (100001)**, 655 West Eighth Street, Zip 32209–6595; tel. 904/244–0411, (Total facility includes 56 beds in nursing home–type unit) (Nonreporting) **A**1 3 5 8 10 **F**3 5 8 11 13 15 17 18 20 22 24 26 28 29 30 31 32 34 35 36 37 38 40 41 43 44 45 46 47 49 50 51 53 54 55 56 57 58 59 60 61 62 63 64 65 66 68 70 71 72 73 74 75 76 77 78 79 80 81 82 84 85 86 87 88 91 92 93 94 96 97 98 100 101 102 103 104 107 108 109 110 111 114 115 116 117 118 119 120 121 123 124 126 128 129 130 131 132 134 135 141 145 146 147 148 149 150 154 156 157 **S** UF Health Shands, Gainesville, FL
Primary Contact: Leon L. Haley Jr, M.D., Chief Executive Officer
COO: Greg Miller, Senior Vice President Operations
CFO: William Ryan, Vice President and Chief Financial Officer
CMO: David Vukich, M.D., Senior Vice President, Chief Medical Officer and Chief Quality Officer
CIO: Kari Cassel, Senior Vice President and Chief Information Officer
CHR: Lesli Ward, Vice President Human Resources
CNO: Patrice Jones, R.N., MSN, Vice President and Chief Nursing Officer
Web address: www.ufhealthjax.org/
**Control**: Other not–for–profit (including NFP Corporation) **Service**: General medical and surgical

**Staffed Beds: 644 Admissions: 26775 Census: 458 Outpatient Visits: 564146 Births: 3573 Total Expense ($000): 759445 Payroll Expense ($000): 268890 Personnel: 4429**

☐ **WEKIVA SPRINGS (104069)**, 3947 Salisbury Road, Zip 32216–6115; tel. 904/296–3533, (Nonreporting) **A**1 3 10 **S** Universal Health Services, Inc., King of Prussia, PA
Primary Contact: Sheila Carr, Chief Executive Officer
Web address: www.wekivacenter.com
**Control**: Other not–for–profit (including NFP Corporation) **Service**: Psychiatric

**Staffed Beds: 60**

**WEKIVA SPRINGS CENTER FOR WOMEN** See Wekiva Springs

### JACKSONVILLE BEACH—Duval County

⊞ **BAPTIST MEDICAL CENTER BEACHES (100117)**, 1350 13th Avenue South, Zip 32250–3205; tel. 904/627–2900, (Nonreporting) **A**1 10 **F**3 8 11 13 15 18 20 28 29 30 34 35 36 40 45 49 50 53 54 56 57 59 61 64 74 75 76 77 78 79 80 81 82 85 86 93 107 108 110 111 114 115 116 118 119 126 129 130 146 147 148 155 156 157 **S** Baptist Health, Jacksonville, FL
Primary Contact: Joseph M. Mitrick, FACHE, President
CFO: Scott Wooten, Senior Vice President and Chief Financial Officer
CMO: Keith L Stein, M.D., Chief Medical Officer
CIO: Roland Garcia, Senior Vice President and Chief Information Officer
CHR: Dana Voiselle, Director Human Resources and Community Relations
Web address: www.community.e-baptisthealth.com/bmc/beaches/index.html
**Control**: Other not–for–profit (including NFP Corporation) **Service**: General medical and surgical

**Staffed Beds: 135 Admissions: 7650 Census: 75 Outpatient Visits: 89598 Births: 932 Total Expense ($000): 116790 Payroll Expense ($000): 35489 Personnel: 645**

**BAPTIST ST VINCENT'S BEACHES** See Baptist Medical Center Beaches

### JAY—Santa Rosa County

★ **JAY HOSPITAL (100048)**, 14114 Alabama Street, Zip 32565–1219; tel. 850/675–8000, (Nonreporting) **A**10 **F**3 11 15 29 30 35 40 45 48 50 59 64 75 81 85 90 93 107 108 110 114 119 127 128 130 133 **S** Baptist Health Care Corporation, Pensacola, FL
Primary Contact: Michael T. Hutchins, Administrator
CFO: Keith Strickling, Chief Accountant
CMO: C David Smith, M.D., Chief Medical Officer
CHR: Heather Suggs, Manager Human Resources
CNO: Patsy Jackson, Director of Nursing
Web address: www.bhcpns.org/jayhospital/
**Control**: Other not–for–profit (including NFP Corporation) **Service**: General medical and surgical

**Staffed Beds: 21 Admissions: 527 Census: 9 Outpatient Visits: 18360 Births: 0 Total Expense ($000): 13332 Payroll Expense ($000): 6289 Personnel: 91**

### JUPITER—Palm Beach County

**JUPITER HOSPITAL** See Jupiter Medical Center

⊞ **JUPITER MEDICAL CENTER (100253)**, 1210 South Old Dixie Highway, Zip 33458–7299; tel. 561/263–2234, (Nonreporting) **A**1 2 10
Primary Contact: Amit Rastogi, M.D., Chief Executive
COO: Steven Seeley, Vice President, Chief Operating Officer, Chief Nursing Officer
CFO: Dale E Hocking, Chief Financial Officer
CIO: Thomas Schoenig, Chief Information Officer
CHR: Peter Gloggner, Chief Human Resources Officer
CNO: Steven Seeley, Vice President, Chief Operating Officer, Chief Nursing Officer
Web address: www.jupitermed.com
**Control**: Other not–for–profit (including NFP Corporation) **Service**: General medical and surgical

**Staffed Beds: 207**

### KEY WEST—Monroe County

**LOWER FLORIDA KEYS HEALTH SYST** See Lower Keys Medical Center

⊞ **LOWER KEYS MEDICAL CENTER (100150)**, 5900 College Road, Zip 33040–4396, Mailing Address: P.O. Box 9107, Zip 33041–9107; tel. 305/294–5531, (Includes DE POO HOSPITAL, Mailing address: 1200 Kennedy Drive, Key West, Florida, Zip 33041; tel. 305/294–4692), (Nonreporting) **A**1 10 **S** Community Health Systems, Inc., Franklin, TN
Primary Contact: David Clay, Chief Executive Officer
CFO: Maureen Henslee, Chief Financial Officer
CMO: Jerome Covington, M.D., Chief Medical Officer
Web address: www.lkmc.com
**Control**: Corporation, Investor–owned (for–profit) **Service**: General medical and surgical

**Staffed Beds: 90**

### KISSIMMEE—Osceola County

**ADVENTHEALTH KISSIMMEE** See Adventhealth Orlando, Orlando

**FLORIDA HOSPITAL KISSIMMEE** See Adventhealth Kissimmee

**OSCEOLA MEDICAL CENTER** See Osceola Regional Medical Center

⊞ **OSCEOLA REGIONAL MEDICAL CENTER (100110)**, 700 West Oak Street, Zip 34741–4996; tel. 407/846–2266, (Nonreporting) **A**1 2 3 5 8 10 **S** HCA Healthcare, Nashville, TN
Primary Contact: Davide M. Carbone, FACHE, Chief Executive Officer
COO: Steve Gordon, Chief Operating Officer
CFO: Carrie Biggar, Chief Financial Officer
CMO: Joseph Mazzola, M.D., Chief Medical Officer
CIO: Carrie Biggar, Chief Financial Officer
CHR: Sylvia Lollis, Director Human Resources
CNO: Barbara K Watson, Chief Nursing Officer
Web address: www.osceolaregional.com
**Control**: Corporation, Investor–owned (for–profit) **Service**: General medical and surgical

**Staffed Beds: 404**

⊞ **POINCIANA MEDICAL CENTER (100320)**, 325 Cypress Parkway, Zip 34758; tel. 407/530–2000, (Nonreporting) **A**1 10 **S** HCA Healthcare, Nashville, TN
Primary Contact: Christopher Cosby, Chief Executive Officer
CFO: Chris Conn, Chief Financial Officer
CNO: Sharon Dillard, Chief Nursing Officer
Web address: www.poincianamedicalcenter.com
**Control**: Corporation, Investor–owned (for–profit) **Service**: General medical and surgical

**Staffed Beds: 76**

### LAKE BUTLER—Union County

**LAKE BUTLER HOSPITAL (101303)**, 850 East Main Street, Zip 32054–1353, Mailing Address: P.O. Box 748, Zip 32054–0748; tel. 386/496–2323, (Nonreporting) **A**10 18 **F**3 29 34 40 57 59 64 75 77 91 93 107 115 119 127 130 133 135 143 148
Primary Contact: Pamela B. Howard, R.N., Chief Executive Officer, Administrator and Risk Manager
COO: Jennifer Thomas, Chief Operating Officer and Director of Public Relations
CFO: Paula Webb, Chief Financial Officer and Compliance Officer
CMO: Cynthia Larimer, M.D., Chief of Staff
CIO: Diane Cason, Chief Information Officer, Controller and Director Human Resources
CNO: Mandy Dicks, Director of Nursing
Web address: www.lakebutlerhospital.com
**Control**: Corporation, Investor–owned (for–profit) **Service**: General medical and surgical

**Staffed Beds: 25 Admissions: 164 Census: 7 Outpatient Visits: 8157 Births: 0 Total Expense ($000): 8927 Payroll Expense ($000): 5236 Personnel: 126**

FL

**LAKE BUTLER HOSPITAL HAND SURGERY CENTER** See Lake Butler Hospital

**NORTH FL RECEPTION CTR HOSP** See Reception and Medical Center

**RECEPTION AND MEDICAL CENTER**, State Road 231 South, Zip 32054, Mailing Address: P.O. Box 628, Zip 32054–0628; tel. 386/496–6000, (Nonreporting)
Primary Contact: Maxine Streeter, Administrator
Web address: www.dc.state.fl.us
**Control**: State, Government, Nonfederal **Service**: Hospital unit of an institution (prison hospital, college infirmary, etc.)

**Staffed Beds:** 120

## LAKE CITY—Columbia County

**COLUMBIA LAKE CITY MEDICAL CTR** See Lake City Medical Center

☒ **LAKE CITY MEDICAL CENTER (100156)**, 340 NW Commerce Drive, Zip 32055–4709; tel. 386/719–9000, (Nonreporting) **A**1 10 **S** HCA Healthcare, Nashville, TN
Primary Contact: Rick Naegler, Chief Executive Officer
COO: Jennifer B Adams, Chief Operating Officer and Chief Financial Officer
CFO: Jennifer B Adams, Chief Operating Officer and Chief Financial Officer
CMO: Miguel Tepedino, M.D., Chief Medicine
CIO: Taylor Dickerson, Chief Information Officer
CHR: Steve Gordon, Director Human Resources
Web address: www.lakecitymedical.com
**Control**: Corporation, Investor–owned (for–profit) **Service**: General medical and surgical

**Staffed Beds:** 91

**VETERANS AFFAIRS MEDICAL CENTER** See Lake City Veterans Affairs Medical Center

## LAKE WALES—Polk County

☒ **ADVENTHEALTH LAKE WALES (100099)**, 410 South 11th Street, Zip 33853–4256; tel. 863/676–1433, (Nonreporting) **A**1 10 **F**3 11 15 18 20 29 30 34 35 40 45 46 49 50 56 57 59 64 68 70 74 75 77 79 81 82 85 86 87 92 93 96 98 101 103 107 108 110 111 114 115 119 124 131 132 146 148 149 154 156 **S** AdventHealth, Altamonte Springs, FL
Primary Contact: Brian Adams, Chief Executive Officer
COO: Rebecca Brewer, FACHE, Chief Operating Officer
CMO: Sunil Nihalani, M.D., Chief Medical Staff
CIO: Erwin Jaropillo, Director Information Systems
CHR: Renee Latterner, Director Human Resources
CNO: Jennifer Huston, Chief Nursing Officer
Web address: www.lakewalesmedicalcenter.com
**Control**: Other not–for–profit (including NFP Corporation) **Service**: General medical and surgical

**Staffed Beds:** 150 **Admissions:** 5868 **Census:** 72 **Outpatient Visits:** 47221 **Births:** 0 **Total Expense ($000):** 62813 **Payroll Expense ($000):** 24978 **Personnel:** 432

**LAKE WALES MEDICAL CENTER** See Adventhealth Lake Wales

## LAKE WORTH—Palm Beach County

☒ **SELECT SPECIALTY HOSPITAL-PALM BEACH (102023)**, 3060 Melaleuca Lane, Zip 33461–5174; tel. 561/357–7200, (Nonreporting) **A**1 10 **S** Select Medical Corporation, Mechanicsburg, PA
Primary Contact: Larry Melby, Chief Executive Officer
Web address: www.selectspecialtyhospitals.com/company/locations/palmbeach.aspx
**Control**: Corporation, Investor–owned (for–profit) **Service**: Acute long–term care hospital

**Staffed Beds:** 60

## LAKELAND—Polk County

**LAKELAND REGIONAL HEALTH** See Lakeland Regional Health Medical Center

☒ △ **LAKELAND REGIONAL HEALTH MEDICAL CENTER (100157)**, 1324 Lakeland Hills Blvd, Zip 33805–4543, Mailing Address: P.O. Box 95448, Zip 33804–5448; tel. 863/687–1100, (Nonreporting) **A**1 2 3 5 7 10 19 **F**3 4 13 18 20 22 24 26 28 29 30 31 34 37 38 40 41 43 44 45 46 47 49 51 55 56 57 58 59 60 61 64 65 66 70 72 74 75 76 77 78 79 81 82 83 84 85 86 87 88 89 90 93 95 96 98 99 100 101 102 103 107 108 109 110 111 114 115 118 119 120 121 123 124 126 130 131 132 135 143 146 147 148 149 154 156
Primary Contact: Timothy Regan, M.D., President and Chief Medical Officer
COO: Sarah Bhagat, Chief Operating Officer and Vice President of Organizational Effectiveness
CFO: Evan Jones, Executive Vice President and Chief Financial Officer
CMO: Timothy Regan, M.D., President and Chief Medical Officer
CIO: Elizabeth Kerns, Senior Vice President and Chief Information Officer
CHR: Scott Dimmick, Senior Vice President and Chief Human Resources Officer
Web address: www.mylrh.org
**Control**: Other not–for–profit (including NFP Corporation) **Service**: General medical and surgical

**Staffed Beds:** 841 **Admissions:** 45231 **Census:** 556 **Outpatient Visits:** 329162 **Births:** 3393 **Total Expense ($000):** 691161 **Payroll Expense ($000):** 259528 **Personnel:** 4402

## LAND O'LAKES—Pasco County

☒ **ADVENTHEALTH CONNERTON (102026)**, 9441 Health Center Drive, Zip 34637–5837; tel. 813/903–3701, (Nonreporting) **A**1 10 **F**1 3 4 16 17 29 30 31 34 67 68 70 72 73 74 79 80 88 89 90 91 98 107 119 128 146 148 **S** AdventHealth, Altamonte Springs, FL
Primary Contact: Denyse Bales-Chubb, President and Chief Executive Officer
COO: Debora Martoccio, R.N., Chief Operating Officer
CMO: Sharad Patel, M.D., Medical Director
Web address: www.https://www.adventhealth.com/hospital/adventhealth-connerton
**Control**: Church operated, Nongovernment, not–for–profit **Service**: Acute long–term care hospital

**Staffed Beds:** 77 **Admissions:** 649 **Census:** 47 **Outpatient Visits:** 0 **Births:** 0 **Total Expense ($000):** 29753 **Payroll Expense ($000):** 12916 **Personnel:** 201

**FLORIDA HOSPITAL AT CONNERTON LONG TERM ACUTE CARE** See Adventhealth Connerton

## LARGO—Pinellas County

**COLUMBIA LARGO MEDICAL CENTER** See Largo Medical Center

☒ **ENCOMPASS HEALTH REHABILITATION HOSPITAL OF LARGO (103037)**, 901 North Clearwater-Largo Road, Zip 33770–4126; tel. 727/586–2999, (Nonreporting) **A**1 10 **S** Encompass Health Corporation, Birmingham, AL
Primary Contact: Tripp Smith, Chief Executive Officer
CFO: Judith Johnson, Controller
CMO: Richard A Liles, M.D., Medical Director
CHR: Jackie Chalk, Director Human Resources
CNO: Pattie Brenner, R.N., Chief Nursing Officer
Web address: www.healthsouthlargo.com
**Control**: Corporation, Investor–owned (for–profit) **Service**: Rehabilitation

**Staffed Beds:** 70

**HEALTHSOUTH REHABILITATION HOSPITAL OF LARGO** See Encompass Health Rehabilitation Hospital of Largo

☒ **LARGO MEDICAL CENTER (100248)**, 201 14th Street SW, Zip 33770–3133; tel. 727/588–5200, (Includes LARGO MEDICAL CENTER - INDIAN ROCKS, Mailing address: 2025 Indian Rocks Road, Largo, Florida, Zip 33774–1096, P O Box 2025, Zip 33779–2025, tel. 727/581–9474), (Nonreporting) **A**1 2 3 5 10 12 13 **S** HCA Healthcare, Nashville, TN
Primary Contact: Adam Rudd, Chief Executive Officer
COO: Wyatt Chocklett, Chief Operating Officer
CFO: Glenn Romig, Chief Financial Officer
CMO: David Weiland, M.D., Chief Medical Officer
CIO: David Saly, Director, Information Services
CNO: Brenda Simpson, R.N., Chief Nursing Officer
Web address: www.largomedical.com
**Control**: Corporation, Investor–owned (for–profit) **Service**: General medical and surgical

**Staffed Beds:** 455

**SUN COAST HOSPITAL** See Largo Medical Center - Indian Rocks

---

**Hospital, Medicare Provider Number, Address, Telephone, Approval, Facility, and Physician Codes, Health Care System**

★ American Hospital Association (AHA) membership
☐ The Joint Commission accreditation
○ Healthcare Facilities Accreditation Program
◇ DNV Healthcare Inc. accreditation
⇑ Center for Improvement in Healthcare Quality Accreditation
△ Commission on Accreditation of Rehabilitation Facilities (CARF) accreditation

FL

## LAUDERDALE LAKES—Broward County

**ST. ANTHONY'S REHABILITATION HOSPITAL (103027)**, 3485 NW 30th Street, Zip 33311–1890; tel. 954/739–6233, (Nonreporting) **A**10 **S** Catholic Health Services, Lauderdale Lakes, FL
Primary Contact: Joseph M. Catania, Chief Executive Officer
COO: James Ball, Chief Operating Officer, Executive
CFO: David D'Amico
CMO: Mark Reiner, Chief Medical Office, Executive
CIO: Dario Achury, Director of Information Management
CHR: Barbara Griffith, Vice President Human Resources
Web address: www.catholichealthservices.org
**Control:** Church operated, Nongovernment, not–for–profit **Service:** Rehabilitation

Staffed Beds: 26

## LEESBURG—Lake County

**LEESBURG REGIONAL MEDICAL CENTER (100084)**, 600 East Dixie Avenue, Zip 34748–5999; tel. 352/323–5762, (Nonreporting) **A**1 10 **F**3 11 13 15 17 18 20 22 24 26 28 29 30 31 34 35 40 45 47 48 49 53 54 57 59 64 68 70 74 75 76 77 78 79 81 82 84 85 87 89 93 96 98 103 106 107 108 110 111 114 115 116 119 130 132 135 144 146 147 149 154 156 **P**1 **S** UF Health Shands, Gainesville, FL
Primary Contact: Donald G. Henderson, FACHE, President and Chief Executive Officer
COO: David Berger, M.D., Senior Vice President and Chief Operating Officer
CFO: Diane P Harden, Chief Financial Officer
CIO: David Steele, Vice President Chief Information Officer
CHR: Amie A Richason, Vice President Human Resources
CNO: Joshua Fleming, Vice President Chief Clinical Officer
Web address: www.centralfloridahealth.org
**Control:** Other not–for–profit (including NFP Corporation) **Service:** General medical and surgical

Staffed Beds: 329 Admissions: 13081 Census: 169 Outpatient Visits: 73574 Births: 1072 Personnel: 1433

**LIFESTREAM BEHAVIORAL CENTER (104018)**, 2020 Tally Road, Zip 34748–3426, Mailing Address: P.O. Box 491000, Zip 34749–1000; tel. 352/315–7500, (Nonreporting) **A**10
Primary Contact: Jonathan M. Cherry, President and Chief Executive Officer
COO: David Braughton, Chief Operating Officer
CFO: Carol Dozier, Chief Financial Officer
CMO: T. J. Valente, M.D., Medical Director
CIO: Chad Heim, Management Information System Director
CHR: Ben Hargrove, Human Resources Director
Web address: www.lsbc.net
**Control:** Other not–for–profit (including NFP Corporation) **Service:** Psychiatric

Staffed Beds: 46

## LEHIGH ACRES—Lee County

**EAST POINTE HOSPITAL** See Lehigh Regional Medical Center

☐ **LEHIGH REGIONAL MEDICAL CENTER (100107)**, 1500 Lee Boulevard, Zip 33936–4835; tel. 239/369–2101, (Nonreporting) **A**1 10 **S** Prime Healthcare, Ontario, CA
Primary Contact: Gary C. Bell, LFACHE, Chief Executive Officer
CFO: Osman Gruhonjic, Chief Financial Officer
CMO: Joe Lemmons, D.O., Chief of Staff
CIO: Jeff Hampton, Director Information Systems
CHR: Mary Gray, Director Human Resources
CNO: Julie G Banker, R.N., MSN, Chief Nursing Officer
Web address: www.lehighregional.com
**Control:** Corporation, Investor–owned (for–profit) **Service:** General medical and surgical

Staffed Beds: 88

## LONGWOOD—Seminole County

**ORLANDO REGIONAL SOUTH SEMINOLE HOSPITAL** See Orlando Health South Seminole Hospital

## LOXAHATCHEE—Palm Beach County

**COLUMBIA PALMS WEST HOSPITAL** See Palms West Hospital

**PALMS WEST HOSPITAL (100269)**, 13001 Southern Boulevard, Zip 33470–9203; tel. 561/798–3300, (Nonreporting) **A**1 3 5 10 **S** HCA Healthcare, Nashville, TN
Primary Contact: Joshua DeTillio, Chief Executive Officer
COO: Lorna Kernivan, Chief Operating Officer
CFO: Steven Burroughs, Chief Financial Officer
CIO: Martha Stinson, Director of Information Technology
CHR: Marcy Mills-Mathews, Director Human Resources
Web address: www.palmswesthospital.com
**Control:** Corporation, Investor–owned (for–profit) **Service:** General medical and surgical

Staffed Beds: 204

## LUTZ—Hillsborough County

**JOSEPH'S HOSPITAL -NORTH** See St. Joseph's Hospital - North

## MACCLENNY—Baker County

**ED FRASER MEMORIAL HOSPITAL (100134)**, 159 North Third Street, Zip 32063–2103, Mailing Address: P.O. Box 484, Zip 32063–0484; tel. 904/259–3151, (Nonreporting) **A**10 20
Primary Contact: Edward Anderson, Chief Executive Officer
CFO: W. Steve Dudley, CPA, Chief Financial Officer
CMO: Mark Hardin, M.D., Medical Director
CIO: Ernie Waller, Director Information Technology
CHR: Stacey Conner, Human Resources Director
CNO: Valerie Markos, Chief Nursing Officer
Web address: www.bcmedsvcs.com
**Control:** Other not–for–profit (including NFP Corporation) **Service:** General medical and surgical

Staffed Beds: 68

**ED FRASER MEMORIAL HOSPITAL AND BAKER COMMUNITY HEALTH CENTER** See Ed Fraser Memorial Hospital

## MADISON—Madison County

**MADISON COUNTY MEMORIAL HOSPITAL (101311)**, 224 NW Crane Avenue, Zip 32340–2561; tel. 850/973–2271, (Nonreporting) **A**10 18
Primary Contact: Tammy Stevens, Chief Executive Officer
CMO: Brett Perkins, M.D., Medical Staff
CIO: Patrick Stiff, Coordinator Information Technology
CHR: Cindi Burnett, Chief Human Resources Officer
Web address: www.mcmh.us/
**Control:** Other not–for–profit (including NFP Corporation) **Service:** General medical and surgical

Staffed Beds: 25

## MARATHON—Monroe County

**FISHERMEN'S HOSPITAL (101312)**, 3301 Overseas Highway, Zip 33050–2329; tel. 305/743–5533, (Nonreporting) **A**1 10 18 **F**3 11 29 30 34 35 40 44 50 57 59 64 68 75 77 84 85 87 90 93 107 114 119 130 135 146 149 150 154 **P**8 **S** Baptist Health South Florida, Coral Gables, FL
Primary Contact: Rick Freeburg, Chief Executive Officer
COO: Lynn Mauck, R.N., Chief Operating Officer and Chief Nursing Officer
CFO: H D Cannington, Interim Chief Financial Officer
CMO: Harlan Pettit, M.D., Chief of Medical Staff
CIO: Patrick Stitt, Director of Information Systems
CHR: Chris Fletcher, Director of Human Resources
CNO: Lynn Mauck, R.N., Chief Operating Officer and Chief Nursing Officer
Web address: www.fishermenshospital.org
**Control:** Other not–for–profit (including NFP Corporation) **Service:** General medical and surgical

Staffed Beds: 4 Admissions: 19 Census: 1 Outpatient Visits: 12460 Births: 0 Total Expense ($000): 20173 Payroll Expense ($000): 6030 Personnel: 76

## MARGATE—Broward County

**COLUMBIA NORTHWEST MEDICAL CTR** See Northwest Medical Center

**FL**

✠ **NORTHWEST MEDICAL CENTER (100189)**, 2801 North State Road 7, Zip 33063–5727; tel. 954/974–0400, (Nonreporting) **A**1 3 5 10 **S** HCA Healthcare, Nashville, TN
Primary Contact: Erica Gulrich, Chief Executive Officer
CFO: Ananda Rampat, Chief Financial Officer
CMO: Jose Martinez, M.D., Chief Medical Officer
CIO: David Irizarri, Director Information Technology
CHR: Lynda Bryan, Vice President Human Resources
CNO: Sandra Emeott, R.N., Chief Nursing Officer
Web address: www.northwestmed.com
**Control:** Corporation, Investor–owned (for–profit) **Service:** General medical and surgical

**Staffed Beds:** 283

**MARIANNA—Jackson County**

✠ **JACKSON HOSPITAL (100142)**, 4250 Hospital Drive, Zip 32446–1917, Mailing Address: P.O. Box 1608, Zip 32447–5608; tel. 850/526–2200, (Nonreporting) **A**1 10 20 **F**3 11 13 15 20 28 29 30 31 34 35 40 45 50 53 54 57 59 70 75 76 78 79 81 85 86 87 93 97 107 108 110 111 114 118 119 120 127 130 132 133 135 146 147 148 154 **S** QHR Health, Brentwood, TN
Primary Contact: James Platt, Chief Executive Officer
CFO: Kevin Rovito, Chief Financial Officer
CMO: Steven Walter Spence, M.D., Chief Medical Officer
CIO: Jamie Hussey, Chief Information Officer
CHR: Brooke G Donaldson, Assistant Administrator Human Resources
CNO: Robbin K Pumphrey, Chief Nursing Officer
Web address: www.jacksonhosp.com
**Control:** Hospital district or authority, Government, Nonfederal **Service:** General medical and surgical

**Staffed Beds:** 68 **Admissions:** 2581 **Census:** 35 **Outpatient Visits:** 72146 **Births:** 327 **Total Expense ($000):** 59067 **Payroll Expense ($000):** 26627 **Personnel:** 616

**MELBOURNE—Brevard County**

☐ **CIRCLES OF CARE (104024)**, 400 East Sheridan Road, Zip 32901–3184; tel. 321/722–5200, (Nonreporting) **A**1 10
Primary Contact: David L. Feldman, President and Chief Executive Officer
CFO: David L Feldman, Executive Vice President and Treasurer
CMO: Jose Alvarez, M.D., Chief Medical Staff
CHR: Linda Brannon, Vice President Human Resources
Web address: www.circlesofcare.org
**Control:** Other not–for–profit (including NFP Corporation) **Service:** Psychiatric

**Staffed Beds:** 134

**DEVEREUX HOSPITAL AND CHILDREN'S CENTER OF FLORIDA**, 8000 Devereux Drive, Zip 32940–7907; tel. 321/242–9100, (Nonreporting) **S** Devereux, Villanova, PA
Primary Contact: Steven Murphy, Executive Director
COO: Eva Horner, Assistant Executive Director Operations
CFO: Kelly Messer, Director of Finance
CMO: Manal Durgin, Network Medical Director
CIO: Diana Deitrick, Director Information Services
CHR: Tim Dillion, Vice President of Human Resources
Web address: www.devereux.org
**Control:** Other not–for–profit (including NFP Corporation) **Service:** Children's hospital psychiatric

**Staffed Beds:** 100

✠ **HEALTH FIRST HOLMES REGIONAL MEDICAL CENTER (100019)**, 1350 South Hickory Street, Zip 32901–3224; tel. 321/434–7000, (Nonreporting) **A**1 10 **F**3 11 13 17 18 20 22 24 26 29 30 31 34 39 40 41 43 45 46 49 50 54 56 59 60 64 68 70 72 74 75 76 77 78 79 80 81 82 84 85 86 87 89 92 93 102 107 108 111 113 114 119 126 130 132 141 146 148 149 154 155 **P**6 **S** Health First, Inc., Rockledge, FL
Primary Contact: Brett A. Esrock, FACHE, Chief Executive Officer
CFO: Joseph G Felkner, Executive Vice President/Chief Financial Officer
CMO: Mark Rosenbloom, M.D., Vice President of Medical Affairs
CIO: Dustin Leek, Vice President of Enterprise Technology Services
CHR: Paula Just, Chief Human Resources Officer
CNO: Barbara Seymour, Vice President of Nursing
Web address: www.health-first.org
**Control:** Other not–for–profit (including NFP Corporation) **Service:** General medical and surgical

**Staffed Beds:** 514 **Admissions:** 30585 **Census:** 390 **Outpatient Visits:** 220476 **Births:** 3046 **Total Expense ($000):** 518781 **Payroll Expense ($000):** 186292 **Personnel:** 2294

☐ **HEALTH FIRST VIERA HOSPITAL (100315)**, 8745 North Wickham Road, Zip 32940–5997; tel. 321/434–9164, (Nonreporting) **A**1 10 **F**3 12 15 18 20 29 30 31 34 39 40 41 45 46 47 48 49 50 54 59 60 64 68 70 74 75 77 79 80 81 85 86 87 93 102 107 108 110 111 115 117 118 119 126 129 130 141 146 148 149 154 **P**6 **S** Health First, Inc., Rockledge, FL
Primary Contact: Brett A. Esrock, FACHE, President
COO: Deborah Angerami, Chief Operating Officer
CFO: Joseph G Felkner, Chief Financial Officer
CMO: Scott Gettings, M.D., Senior Vice President and Chief Medical Officer
CIO: Alex Popowycz, Chief Information Officer
CHR: Paula Just, Chief Human Resources Officer
CNO: Connie Bradley, R.N., MSN, FACHE, Senior Vice President and Chief Nursing Officer
Web address: www.vierahospital.org
**Control:** Other not–for–profit (including NFP Corporation) **Service:** General medical and surgical

**Staffed Beds:** 84 **Admissions:** 5135 **Census:** 49 **Outpatient Visits:** 81801 **Births:** 0 **Total Expense ($000):** 105891 **Payroll Expense ($000):** 37561 **Personnel:** 407

**HEALTHSOUTH SEA PINES REHABILITATION HOSPITAL** See Sea Pines Rehabilitation Hospital

**HOLMES REGIONAL MEDICAL CENTER** See Health First Holmes Regional Medical Center

✠ **KINDRED HOSPITAL MELBOURNE (102027)**, 765 West Nasa Boulevard, Zip 32901–1815; tel. 321/733–5725, (Nonreporting) **A**1 10 **S** Kindred Healthcare, Louisville, KY
Primary Contact: Pamela R. Reed, Chief Executive Officer
Web address: www.khmelbourne.com
**Control:** Corporation, Investor–owned (for–profit) **Service:** Acute long–term care hospital

**Staffed Beds:** 60

☐ **MELBOURNE REGIONAL MEDICAL CENTER (100291)**, 250 North Wickham Road, Zip 32935–8625; tel. 321/752–1200, (Nonreporting) **A**1 10 **S** Steward Health Care System, LLC, Dallas, TX
Primary Contact: Ron Gicca, Chief Executive Officer
CFO: Dale Armour, Chief Financial Officer
Web address: www.wuesthoff.com/locations/wuesthoff-medical-center-melbourne
**Control:** Corporation, Investor–owned (for–profit) **Service:** General medical and surgical

**Staffed Beds:** 119

✠ **SEA PINES REHABILITATION HOSPITAL (103034)**, 101 East Florida Avenue, Zip 32901–8301; tel. 321/984–4600, (Nonreporting) **A**1 10 **S** Encompass Health Corporation, Birmingham, AL
Primary Contact: Denise B. McGrath, Chief Executive Officer
CFO: Dana Edwards, Chief Financial Officer
CMO: Juan Lebron, M.D., Medical Director
CHR: James L Henry, Director Human Resources
CNO: Lisa Truman, Chief Nursing Officer
Web address: www.healthsouthseapines.com
**Control:** Corporation, Investor–owned (for–profit) **Service:** Rehabilitation

**Staffed Beds:** 90

**VIERA HOSPITAL** See Health First Viera Hospital

**WUESTHOFF MEDICAL CENTER - MELBOURNE** See Melbourne Regional Medical Center

**FL**

---

**Hospital, Medicare Provider Number, Address, Telephone, Approval, Facility, and Physician Codes, Health Care System**

★ American Hospital Association (AHA) membership
☐ The Joint Commission accreditation
○ Healthcare Facilities Accreditation Program
◇ DNV Healthcare Inc. accreditation
⇑ Center for Improvement in Healthcare Quality Accreditation
△ Commission on Accreditation of Rehabilitation Facilities (CARF) accreditation

**MIAMI—Miami—Dade County**

⊞ △ **BAPTIST HEALTH SOUTH FLORIDA, BAPTIST HOSPITAL OF MIAMI (100008)**, 8900 North Kendall Drive, Zip 33176–2197; tel. 786/596–1960, (Includes BAPTIST CHILDREN'S HOSPITAL, Mailing address: 8900 North Kendall Drive, Miami, Florida, Zip 33176–2118; tel. 786/596–1960; Albert Leon Boulenger, R.N., Chief Executive Officer), (Nonreporting) **A**1 2 7 10 **F**3 11 13 15 17 18 19 20 22 24 26 28 29 30 31 32 34 35 36 38 39 40 41 44 45 46 47 48 49 50 51 53 54 55 56 57 58 59 60 61 63 64 68 70 72 73 74 75 76 77 78 79 80 81 82 84 85 86 87 88 89 90 91 92 93 94 96 100 102 107 108 109 110 111 112 115 116 117 118 119 120 121 122 123 124 126 130 132 135 136 141 144 145 146 147 148 149 150 154 156 157 **S** Baptist Health South Florida, Coral Gables, FL
Primary Contact: Patricia M. Rosello, Chief Executive Officer
CFO: Ralph E Lawson, Executive Vice President and Chief Financial Officer
CMO: Mark J Hauser, M.D., Chief Medical Officer
CIO: Mimi Taylor, Corporate Vice President Information Technology
CHR: Adriene McCoy, Chief Human Resource Officer
CNO: Becky Montesino-King, MS, R.N., MSN, Vice President and Chief Nursing Officer
Web address: www.baptisthealth.net
**Control**: Other not–for–profit (including NFP Corporation) **Service**: General medical and surgical

**Staffed Beds: 720 Admissions: 31156 Census: 534 Outpatient Visits: 555335 Births: 4052 Total Expense ($000): 1161902 Payroll Expense ($000): 353041 Personnel: 5432**

⊞ **BAPTIST HEALTH SOUTH FLORIDA, SOUTH MIAMI HOSPITAL (100154)**, 6200 SW 73rd Street, Zip 33143–4679; tel. 786/662–4000, (Nonreporting) **A**1 3 10 **F**3 5 11 12 13 15 16 17 18 19 20 22 24 26 28 29 30 31 34 35 36 40 44 45 46 48 49 50 51 52 53 54 57 58 59 60 61 63 64 66 68 70 72 73 74 75 76 77 78 79 80 81 82 84 85 86 87 90 91 93 94 96 100 102 107 108 110 111 115 118 119 126 130 132 135 141 144 146 147 148 149 150 152 154 157 **S** Baptist Health South Florida, Coral Gables, FL
Primary Contact: William M. Duquette, Chief Executive Officer
COO: Jeanette Stone, Vice President Operations
CFO: Erik Long, Controller
CMO: Jeremy Tabak, M.D., President Medical Staff
CIO: Mimi Taylor, Vice President Information Technology
CHR: Diana Montenegro, Director Human Resources
CNO: Kathy Sparger, R.N., MSN, Chief Nursing Officer
Web address: www.baptisthealth.net
**Control**: Other not–for–profit (including NFP Corporation) **Service**: General medical and surgical

**Staffed Beds: 336 Admissions: 14953 Census: 198 Outpatient Visits: 277118 Births: 4056 Total Expense ($000): 459523 Payroll Expense ($000): 157458 Personnel: 1861**

⊞ **BAPTIST HEALTH SOUTH FLORIDA, WEST KENDALL BAPTIST HOSPITAL (100314)**, 9555 SW 162nd Avenue, Zip 33196–6408; tel. 786/467–2000, (Nonreporting) **A**1 3 10 **F**3 11 13 18 19 29 30 31 34 35 38 40 41 42 44 45 49 50 51 53 57 58 59 60 63 64 68 70 71 74 75 76 77 78 79 80 81 82 84 85 86 87 90 93 100 102 107 108 111 114 115 119 126 130 131 132 135 145 146 147 148 149 150 154 **S** Baptist Health South Florida, Coral Gables, FL
Primary Contact: Lourdes Boue, Chief Executive Officer
CFO: Odalys Remigio, Assistant Vice President, Finance
CMO: Juan-Carlos Verdeja, M.D., President of Medical Staff
CHR: Hilde Zamora de Aguero, Human Resources Site Director
CNO: Denise H. Harris, R.N., MSN, Chief Nursing Officer
Web address: www.baptisthealth.net/en/facilities/West-Kendall-Baptist-Hospital/Pages/default.aspx
**Control**: Other not–for–profit (including NFP Corporation) **Service**: General medical and surgical

**Staffed Beds: 133 Admissions: 8104 Census: 93 Outpatient Visits: 103528 Births: 892 Total Expense ($000): 212424 Payroll Expense ($000): 76649 Personnel: 1004**

**CEDARS MEDICAL CENTER** See University of Miami Hospital

**DEERING HOSPITAL** See Jackson South Community Hospital

**HIGHLAND PARK HOSPITAL** See Jackson Behavioral Health Hospital

**HOLTZ CHILDREN'S HOSPITAL JACKSON MEMORIAL HOSPITAL** See Holtz Children's Hospital

**JACKSON BEHAVIORAL HEALTH HOSPITAL** See Jackson Health System, Miami

☐ **JACKSON HEALTH SYSTEM (100022)**, 1611 NW 12th Avenue, Zip 33136–1005; tel. 305/585–1111, (Includes HOLTZ CHILDREN'S HOSPITAL, Mailing address: 1611 NW 12th Avenue, Miami, Florida, Zip 33136–1005; tel. 305/585–5437; Don S Steigman, Chief Executive Officer; JACKSON BEHAVIORAL HEALTH HOSPITAL, Mailing address: 1695 NW Ninth Avenue, Miami, Florida, Zip 33136–1409; tel. 305/324–4357; Nicolette B Tessler, Chief Executive Officer of Behavioral Health Hospital; JACKSON MEMORIAL HOSPITAL, Mailing address: 1611 NW 12th Avenue, Miami, Florida, Zip 33136; tel. 305/585–1111; David Zambrana, Ph.D., R.N., Executive Vice President Hospital Operations; JACKSON NORTH MEDICAL CENTER, Mailing address: 160 NW 170th Street, North Miami Beach, Florida, Zip 33169–5576; tel. 305/651–1100; Roy L. Hawkins Jr, Senior Vice President and Chief Executive Officer; JACKSON SOUTH COMMUNITY HOSPITAL, Mailing address: 9333 SW 152nd Street, Miami, Florida, Zip 33157–1780; tel. 305/251–2500; Georgina Diaz, Chief Executive Officer) (Total facility includes 343 beds in nursing home–type unit) **A**1 3 5 8 10 19 **F**3 4 5 8 10 11 12 13 15 16 17 18 19 20 21 22 23 24 25 26 27 28 29 30 31 32 34 35 38 39 40 41 43 44 45 46 49 50 54 55 56 57 58 59 60 61 64 65 66 68 70 71 72 73 74 75 76 77 78 79 80 81 82 83 84 85 86 87 88 89 90 93 94 96 97 98 99 100 101 102 103 104 107 108 110 111 115 117 118 119 120 121 123 124 126 128 130 131 132 134 135 136 137 138 139 140 141 142 144 146 147 148 149 154 157 **P**6
Primary Contact: Carlos A. Migoya, President and Chief Executive Officer
COO: Don S Steigman, Chief Operating Officer
CFO: Mark T Knight, Executive Vice President and Chief Financial Officer
CMO: Peter G Paige, Chief Medical Officer
CIO: Michael A Garcia, Vice President and Chief Information Officer
CHR: Julie Staub, Chief Human Resources Officer
Web address: www.jacksonhealth.org
**Control**: County, Government, Nonfederal **Service**: General medical and surgical

**Staffed Beds: 2112 Admissions: 63290 Census: 1524 Outpatient Visits: 3368547 Births: 6010 Total Expense ($000): 2064175 Payroll Expense ($000): 958630 Personnel: 9154**

**JACKSON MEMORIAL HOSPITAL** See Jackson Health System

**JACKSON SOUTH COMMUNITY HOSPITAL** See Jackson Health System, Miami

**JAMES M JACKSON MEMORIAL HOSP** See Jackson Memorial Hospital

**JEWISH HOME & HOSP FOR AGED** See Miami Jewish Home and Hospital for Aged

**KENDALL MEDICAL CENTER** See Kendall Regional Medical Center

⊞ **KENDALL REGIONAL MEDICAL CENTER (100209)**, 11750 Bird Road, Zip 33175–3530; tel. 305/223–3000, (Nonreporting) **A**1 3 5 10 **S** HCA Healthcare, Nashville, TN
Primary Contact: Brandon Haushalter, Chief Executive Officer
COO: Corey Lovelace, Chief Operating Officer
CFO: Robert Grace, Chief Financial Officer
CIO: Matt Hernandez, Director of Information Technology and System
CHR: Knicole S White, Vice-President, Human Resources
CNO: Maria Villa, Interim Chief Nursing Officer
Web address: www.kendallmed.com
**Control**: Partnership, Investor–owned (for–profit) **Service**: General medical and surgical

**Staffed Beds: 417**

**MEADOWBROOK REHAB HOSPITAL** See West Gables Rehabilitation Hospital

**MERCY HOSPITAL** See Mercy Hospital - A Campus of Plantation General Hospital

⇧ **MIAMI CHILDREN'S HOSPITAL** See Nicklaus Children's Hospital

☐ **MIAMI JEWISH HOME AND HOSPITAL FOR AGED (100277)**, 5200 NE Second Avenue, Zip 33137–2706; tel. 305/751–8626, (Nonreporting) **A**1 3 5 10
Primary Contact: Jeffrey P. Freimark, Chief Executive Officer
CFO: Lisa Jo Desmarteau, Chief Financial Officer
CMO: Brian Kiedrowski, M.D., Chief Medical Director
CHR: Larry McDonald, Director Human Resources
Web address: www.mjhha.org
**Control**: Other not–for–profit (including NFP Corporation) **Service**: General medical and surgical

**Staffed Beds: 32**

*Many Facility Codes have changed. Please refer to the AHA Guide Code Chart.*

✉ △ **MIAMI VETERANS AFFAIRS HEALTHCARE SYSTEM**, 1201 NW 16th Street, Zip 33125–1624; tel. 305/575–7000, (Total facility includes 110 beds in nursing home–type unit) (Nonreporting) **A**1 3 5 7 **F**2 3 4 5 6 9 10 15 17 18 20 22 24 26 28 29 30 31 33 34 35 36 38 39 40 44 45 46 47 48 49 51 54 56 57 58 59 60 61 62 63 64 65 66 70 74 75 77 78 79 81 82 83 84 85 86 87 90 91 92 93 94 96 97 98 100 101 102 103 104 105 106 107 108 110 111 114 115 116 117 118 119 120 121 123 124 126 128 129 130 132 135 143 145 146 147 148 149 150 152 153 154 156 157 158 **S** Department of Veterans Affairs, Washington, DC
Primary Contact: Kalautie JangDhari, Director
COO: Lance Davis, PharmD, Associate Director
CFO: Albert Tucker, Chief Financial Officer
CMO: Vincent DeGennaro, M.D., Chief of Staff
CIO: Anthony Brooks, Chief Information Officer
CHR: Loyman Marin, Chief Human Resources
CNO: Marcia C Lysaght, R.N., MSN, Associate Director Patient Care Services
Web address: www.miami.va.gov/
**Control**: Veterans Affairs, Government, federal **Service**: General medical and surgical

**Staffed Beds: 284 Admissions: 7919 Census: 218 Outpatient Visits: 796848 Births: 0 Personnel: 2578**

★ ⇑ **NICKLAUS CHILDREN'S HOSPITAL (103301)**, 3100 SW 62nd Avenue, Zip 33155–3009; tel. 305/666–6511, (Nonreporting) **A**2 3 5 8 10 21 **F**3 7 11 13 17 18 19 20 21 22 23 24 25 26 27 29 30 31 32 34 35 39 40 41 43 44 45 46 47 48 49 50 53 54 55 57 58 59 60 61 64 65 68 71 72 74 75 76 77 78 79 80 81 82 85 86 87 88 89 91 93 94 96 97 98 99 100 101 102 104 105 107 108 109 111 112 115 116 117 118 119 126 129 130 131 132 136 142 143 144 145 146 148 149 153 154 155 156 157 158
Primary Contact: Matthew Love, Interim Chief Executive Officer
COO: Martha McGill, Executive Vice President and Chief Operating Officer
CFO: Arianna Urquia, Chief Financial Officer
CMO: Deise Granado-Villar, M.D., Chief Medical Officer and Senior Vice President Medical Affairs
CIO: Edward Martinez, Chief Information Officer
CHR: Michael S. Kushner, Senior Vice President and Chief Talent Officer
CNO: Jacqueline Gonzalez, Senior Vice President and Chief Nursing Officer
Web address: www.mch.com
**Control**: Other not–for–profit (including NFP Corporation) **Service**: Children's general medical and surgical

**Staffed Beds: 291 Admissions: 21801 Census: 173 Outpatient Visits: 449515 Births: 11 Total Expense ($000): 670034 Payroll Expense ($000): 215737 Personnel: 3821**

✉ **NORTH SHORE MEDICAL CENTER (100029)**, 1100 NW 95th Street, Zip 33150–2098; tel. 305/835–6000, (Includes FLORIDA MEDICAL CENTER - A CAMPUS OF NORTH SHORE, Mailing address: 5000 West Oakland Park Boulevard, Fort Lauderdale, Florida, Zip 33313–1585; tel. 954/735–6000; Trey Abshier, Chief Executive Officer), (Nonreporting) **A**1 3 10 **S** TENET Healthcare Corporation, Dallas, TX
Primary Contact: Mark Racicot, Chief Executive Officer
COO: Shana Crittenden, Chief Operating Officer
CFO: Howard Brown, Chief Financial Officer
CMO: Marcia Bierman, M.D., Chief of Staff
CIO: Luis Estrada, Director Multifacility Information Systems
CHR: Carmen Gomez, Director Human Resources
Web address: www.northshoremedical.com
**Control**: Corporation, Investor–owned (for–profit) **Service**: General medical and surgical

**Staffed Beds: 816**

**SELECT SPECIALTY HOSP OF MIAMI** See Select Specialty Hospital-Miami

✉ **SELECT SPECIALTY HOSPITAL-MIAMI (102001)**, 955 NW 3rd Street, Zip 33128–1274; tel. 305/416–5700, (Nonreporting) **A**1 10 **S** Select Medical Corporation, Mechanicsburg, PA
Primary Contact: Loretta Sheffield, Chief Executive Officer
Web address: www.selectspecialtyhospitals.com/company/locations/miami.aspx
**Control**: Corporation, Investor–owned (for–profit) **Service**: Acute long–term care hospital

**Staffed Beds: 47**

✉ **UNIVERSITY OF MIAMI HOSPITAL AND CLINICS (100079)**, 1475 NW 12th Avenue, Zip 33136–1002; tel. 305/689–5511, (Includes BASCOM PALMER EYE INSTITUTE-ANNE BATES LEACH EYE HOSPITAL, Mailing address: 900 NW 17th Street, Miami, Florida, Zip 33136–1199, Box 016880, Zip 33101–6880, tel. 305/326–6000; Michael B Gittelman, Administrator; UNIVERSITY OF MIAMI HOSPITAL, Mailing address: 1400 NW 12th Avenue, Miami, Florida, Zip 33136–1003; tel. 305/325–5511; Michael B Gittelman, Chief Executive Officer), (Nonreporting) **A**1 2 3 5 8 10 **F**3 8 11 12 15 17 18 20 22 24 26 28 29 30 31 34 35 36 37 38 39 40 44 45 46 47 48 49 50 51 53 54 55 56 57 58 59 60 61 63 64 66 68 70 71 74 75 77 78 79 80 81 82 83 84 85 86 87 90 92 93 94 96 98 100 102 104 107 108 110 111 114 115 117 118 119 120 121 123 124 126 129 130 131 132 135 136 141 145 146 147 148 149 156 157
Primary Contact: Kymberlee Jean. Manni, Chief Executive Officer
COO: Kymberlee Jean Manni, Chief Operating Officer
CFO: Harry Rohrer, Chief Financial Officer
CMO: W Jarrad Goodwin, M.D., Director
CIO: David Reis, Ph.D., Interim Chief Information Officer
Web address: www.uhealthsystem.com
**Control**: Other not–for–profit (including NFP Corporation) **Service**: Cancer

**Staffed Beds: 558 Admissions: 18854 Census: 304 Outpatient Visits: 956351 Births: 0 Total Expense ($000): 1450895 Payroll Expense ($000): 280313 Personnel: 4150**

**VETERANS AFFAIRS MEDICAL CENTER** See Miami Veterans Affairs Healthcare System

✉ △ **WEST GABLES REHABILITATION HOSPITAL (103036)**, 2525 SW 75th Avenue, Zip 33155–2800; tel. 305/262–6800, (Nonreporting) **A**1 3 7 10 **F**29 34 74 75 77 82 86 87 90 93 94 95 96 130 131 132 135 148 149 **S** Select Medical Corporation, Mechanicsburg, PA
Primary Contact: Walter Concepcion, Chief Executive Officer
CFO: Sara Reohr, Regional Controller
CMO: Jose L Vargas, M.D., Medical Director
CHR: Barbara Etchason, HR Manager
CNO: Lucia Benjamin, Chief Nursing Officer
Web address: www.westgablesrehabhospital.com/
**Control**: Corporation, Investor–owned (for–profit) **Service**: Rehabilitation

**Staffed Beds: 60 Admissions: 1555 Census: 59 Outpatient Visits: 0 Births: 0 Personnel: 140**

☐ ○ **WESTCHESTER GENERAL HOSPITAL (100284)**, 2500 SW 75th Avenue, Zip 33155–2805; tel. 305/264–5252, (Includes SOUTHERN WINDS HOSPITAL, Mailing address: 4225 West 20th Street, Hialeah, Florida, Zip 33012–5835; tel. 305/558–9700), (Nonreporting) **A**1 3 5 10 11 13 **F**3 15 18 29 40 45 49 56 65 70 74 75 77 78 79 81 85 87 98 100 102 103 107 108 110 114 115 119 130
Primary Contact: Rodolfo R. Garcia, Chief Executive Officer
CFO: Joel Snook, Chief Financial Officer
CMO: Rogelio Zaldivar, M.D., Medical Director
CHR: Jennifer Ricardo, Director of Human Resources
Web address: www.westchesterhospital.com
**Control**: Corporation, Investor–owned (for–profit) **Service**: General medical and surgical

**Staffed Beds: 125 Admissions: 3981 Census: 67 Outpatient Visits: 25831 Births: 0 Total Expense ($000): 45382 Payroll Expense ($000): 22181 Personnel: 501**

**MIAMI BEACH—Dade County**

**MIAMI HEART CAMPUS AT MOUNT SINAI MEDICAL CENTER** See Mount Sinai Medical Center, Miami Beach

**MIAMI HEART INST & MED CTR** See Miami Heart Campus at Mount Sinai Medical Center

FL

---

| | | |
|---|---|---|
| Hospital, Medicare Provider Number, Address, Telephone, Approval, Facility, and Physician Codes, Health Care System | | |

★ American Hospital Association (AHA) membership ○ Healthcare Facilities Accreditation Program ⇑ Center for Improvement in Healthcare Quality Accreditation
☐ The Joint Commission accreditation ◇ DNV Healthcare Inc. accreditation △ Commission on Accreditation of Rehabilitation Facilities (CARF) accreditation

## MIAMI BEACH—Miami—Dade County

☐ △ **MOUNT SINAI MEDICAL CENTER (100034)**, 4300 Alton Road, Zip 33140–2948; tel. 305/674–2121, (Includes MIAMI HEART CAMPUS AT MOUNT SINAI MEDICAL CENTER, Mailing address: 4701 North Meridian Avenue, Miami Beach, Florida, Zip 33140–2910; tel. 305/672–1111), (Nonreporting) **A**1 2 3 5 7 8 10 **F**1 2 3 4 6 8 9 12 13 14 15 16 17 18 19 20 22 24 26 28 29 30 31 34 35 36 37 38 39 40 41 42 44 45 46 47 48 49 50 51 53 54 55 56 57 58 59 60 61 62 63 64 65 66 67 68 70 71 72 73 74 75 76 77 78 79 80 81 82 84 85 86 87 88 89 90 91 92 93 96 97 98 100 101 102 103 104 105 107 108 110 111 114 115 118 119 120 121 123 124 126 128 129 130 131 132 135 141 143 145 146 147 148 149 152 154 156 157 158 **P**6
Primary Contact: Steven D. Sonenreich, President and Chief Executive Officer
COO: Angel Pallin, Senior Vice President of Operations
CFO: Alex A Mendez, Executive Vice President of Operations and Chief Financial Officer
CMO: Robert Goldszer, M.D., Senior Vice President and Chief Medical Officer
CIO: Tom Gillette, Senior Vice President and Chief Information Officer
CHR: Georgia McLean, Director Human Resources
CNO: Karen W Moyer, R.N., Senior Vice President and Chief Nursing Officer
Web address: www.msmc.com
**Control**: Other not–for–profit (including NFP Corporation) **Service**: General medical and surgical

**Staffed Beds**: 609 **Admissions**: 24712 **Census**: 355 **Outpatient Visits**: 246595 **Births**: 2639 **Total Expense ($000)**: 643286 **Payroll Expense ($000)**: 285118 **Personnel**: 3974

## MIAMI LAKES—Miami—Dade County

**PROMISE HOSPITAL OF MIAMI** See Select Specialty Hospital-Miami Lakes

★ **SELECT SPECIALTY HOSPITAL-MIAMI LAKES (102031)**, 14001 NW 82nd Avenue, Zip 33016–1561; tel. 786/609–9200, (Nonreporting) **A**10 **S** Select Medical Corporation, Mechanicsburg, PA
Primary Contact: Brian Soares, Chief Executive Officer
Web address: www.promise-miami.com
**Control**: Corporation, Investor–owned (for–profit) **Service**: Acute long–term care hospital

**Staffed Beds**: 60

## MIDDLEBURG—Clay County

⊞ **ST. VINCENT'S MEDICAL CENTER CLAY COUNTY (100321)**, 1670 St. Vincent's Way, Zip 32068–8427, Mailing Address: 1670 St. Vincents Way, Zip 32068–8447; tel. 904/602–1000, (Nonreporting) **A**1 10 **F**3 13 15 18 20 22 29 30 34 37 40 44 49 57 61 64 65 70 74 76 79 81 84 85 86 87 93 107 108 110 111 114 115 118 119 124 130 131 132 146 147 149 156 **S** Ascension Healthcare, Saint Louis, MO
Primary Contact: James Machado, President
Web address: www.jaxhealth.com/
**Control**: Church operated, Nongovernment, not–for–profit **Service**: General medical and surgical

**Staffed Beds**: 106 **Admissions**: 6948 **Census**: 61 **Outpatient Visits**: 69630 **Births**: 626 **Total Expense ($000)**: 102045 **Payroll Expense ($000)**: 29134 **Personnel**: 413

## MILTON—Santa Rosa County

⊞ **SANTA ROSA MEDICAL CENTER (100124)**, 6002 Berryhill Road, Zip 32570–5062; tel. 850/626–7762, (Nonreporting) **A**1 10 **S** Community Health Systems, Inc., Franklin, TN
Primary Contact: Doug Sills, Chief Executive Officer
CFO: Jared Whipkey, Chief Financial Officer
CIO: Rick Payne, Director Information Systems
CHR: Christopher Foreman, Director Human Resources
CNO: Trish Davis, Chief Nursing Officer
Web address: www.santarosamedicalcenter.org
**Control**: Corporation, Investor–owned (for–profit) **Service**: General medical and surgical

**Staffed Beds**: 68

**WEST FLORIDA COMMUNITY CARE CENTER (104027)**, 5500 Stewart Street, Zip 32570–4304; tel. 850/983–5500, (Nonreporting) **A**10
Primary Contact: Meredith Olsen, Administrator
Web address: www.https://www.elakeviewcenter.org/WFCCC
**Control**: Other not–for–profit (including NFP Corporation) **Service**: Psychiatric

**Staffed Beds**: 100

## MIRAMAR—Broward County

⊞ **MEMORIAL HOSPITAL MIRAMAR (100285)**, 1901 SW 172nd Avenue, Zip 33029–5592; tel. 954/538–5000, (Nonreporting) **A**1 10 **F**3 11 13 15 29 30 32 34 40 41 44 45 49 50 55 57 59 64 68 70 72 74 75 76 77 79 81 82 84 85 87 91 93 107 108 110 111 114 115 119 126 130 131 132 145 146 147 149 **S** Memorial Healthcare System, Hollywood, FL
Primary Contact: Grisel Fernandez-Bravo, R.N., Administrator and Chief Executive Officer
CFO: Judy Sada, Chief Financial Officer
CMO: Stanley Marks, M.D., FACS, Chief Medical Officer
CIO: Forest Blanton, Senior VP and Chief Information Officer
CHR: Ray Kendrick, Chief Human Resources Officer
CNO: Denise Reynolds, Chief Nursing Officer
Web address: www.mhs.net
**Control**: Hospital district or authority, Government, Nonfederal **Service**: General medical and surgical

**Staffed Beds**: 178 **Admissions**: 9067 **Census**: 90 **Outpatient Visits**: 140539 **Births**: 3792 **Total Expense ($000)**: 159919 **Payroll Expense ($000)**: 78857 **Personnel**: 832

## MIRAMAR BEACH—Walton County

⊞ **SACRED HEART HOSPITAL ON THE EMERALD COAST (100292)**, 7800 Highway 98 West, Zip 32550; tel. 850/278–3000, (Nonreporting) **A**1 10 **F**8 13 15 18 20 22 24 26 28 29 30 31 34 35 40 45 46 49 51 59 60 64 68 70 74 76 77 78 79 80 81 84 85 87 93 107 108 110 111 114 115 116 117 118 119 124 126 130 131 132 146 147 148 154 156 **S** Ascension Healthcare, Saint Louis, MO
Primary Contact: Henry Stovall, Regional President
CMO: Gary M. Pablo, M.D., Chief Medical Officer
CNO: Barbara Fontaine, Vice President, Nursing
Web address: www.sacredheartemerald.org
**Control**: Other not–for–profit (including NFP Corporation) **Service**: General medical and surgical

**Staffed Beds**: 76 **Admissions**: 5341 **Census**: 46 **Outpatient Visits**: 96996 **Births**: 1407 **Total Expense ($000)**: 109232 **Payroll Expense ($000)**: 30822 **Personnel**: 402

## NAPLES—Collier County

**LANDMARK HOSPITAL OF SOUTHWEST FLORIDA (102032)**, 1285 Creekside Boulevard East, Zip 34108; tel. 239/529–1800, (Nonreporting) **A**10 22 **S** Landmark Hospitals, Cape Girardeau, MO
Primary Contact: Susan P. Bailey, R.N., Chief Executive Officer
Web address: www.https://www.landmarkhospitals.com/critical-care-hospital-system/critical-care-hospital-southwest-florida/
**Control**: Partnership, Investor–owned (for–profit) **Service**: Acute long–term care hospital

**Staffed Beds**: 50

⊞ **NCH BAKER HOSPITAL (100018)**, 350 Seventh Street North, Zip 34102–5754, Mailing Address: P.O. Box 413029, Zip 34101–3029; tel. 239/624–4000, (Includes NCH NORTH NAPLES HOSPITAL, Mailing address: 11190 Health Park Blvd, Naples, Florida, Zip 34110–5729, 11190 Health Park Boulevard, Zip 34110–5729, tel. 239/552–7000), (Nonreporting) **A**1 2 3 5 10 **F**8 9 11 12 13 14 15 17 18 19 20 22 24 26 28 29 30 31 32 34 35 37 40 41 42 44 45 46 47 48 49 50 53 56 57 59 64 68 70 72 74 75 76 77 78 79 81 82 84 85 86 87 88 89 90 91 92 93 95 96 98 100 102 103 107 108 110 111 114 115 116 117 119 126 131 135 145 146 147 148 149 154 156 **P**6
Primary Contact: Paul C. Hiltz, FACHE, Chief Executive Officer
COO: Phillip C Dutcher, Chief Operating Officer
CFO: Mike Stephens, Chief Financial Officer
CMO: Doug Ardion, M.D., Chief Medical Officer
CHR: John McGirl, Chief Human Resources Officer
CNO: Michele Thoman, Chief Nursing Officer
Web address: www.nchmd.org
**Control**: Other not–for–profit (including NFP Corporation) **Service**: General medical and surgical

**Staffed Beds**: 676 **Admissions**: 30993 **Census**: 385 **Outpatient Visits**: 346742 **Births**: 3430 **Total Expense ($000)**: 509745 **Payroll Expense ($000)**: 204799 **Personnel**: 3100

**NCH DOWNTOWN NAPLES HOSPITAL** See NCH Baker Hospital

FL

⊞ **PHYSICIANS REGIONAL - PINE RIDGE (100286)**, 6101 Pine Ridge Road, Zip 34119–3900; tel. 239/348–4000, (Includes PHYSICIANS REGIONAL, Mailing address: 8300 Collier Boulevard, Naples, Florida, Zip 34114; tel. 239/354–6000; C Scott Campbell, Market Chief Executive Officer), (Nonreporting) **A**1 3 10 19 **S** Community Health Systems, Inc., Franklin, TN
Primary Contact: Scott Lowe, Market Chief Executive Officer
COO: Susan Takacs, Market Chief Operating Officer
CFO: Ken Warriner, Market Chief Financial Officer
CHR: Jill Gaffoli, Director Human Resources
Web address: www.physiciansregional.com
**Control**: Corporation, Investor–owned (for–profit) **Service**: General medical and surgical

**Staffed Beds:** 70

**PHYSICIANS REGIONAL MEDICAL CENTER** See Physicians Regional

**PHYSICIANS REGIONAL MEDICAL CENTER - PINE RIDGE** See Physicians Regional - Pine Ridge

☐ **THE WILLOUGH AT NAPLES (104063)**, 9001 Tamiami Trail East, Zip 34113–3304; tel. 239/775–4500, (Nonreporting) **A**1 10
Primary Contact: Kathleen Melo, Administrator
CFO: Steve Baldwin, Vice President Finance
Web address: www.thewilloughatnaples.com/
**Control**: Corporation, Investor–owned (for–profit) **Service**: Psychiatric

**Staffed Beds:** 80

**WILLOUGH HEALTHCARE SYSTEM** See The Willough at Naples

### NEW PORT RICHEY—Pasco County

⊞ △ **MORTON PLANT NORTH BAY HOSPITAL (100063)**, 6600 Madison Street, Zip 34652–1900; tel. 727/842–8468, (Nonreporting) **A**1 7 10 **F**3 11 18 20 22 28 29 30 31 34 35 40 44 45 49 50 57 58 59 63 64 68 70 74 75 78 79 81 84 85 86 87 90 93 94 96 98 99 100 102 107 108 110 111 114 115 118 119 129 130 131 132 135 143 146 147 149 154 156 **P**6 **S** Morton Plant Mease Health Care, Clearwater, FL
Primary Contact: Brandon May, President
CFO: Carl Tremonti, Chief Financial Officer
CMO: Jeff Jensen, D.O., Vice President, Medical Affairs
CIO: Timothy Thompson, Senior Vice President and Chief Information Officer
CHR: Kyle J Barr, Senior Vice President, Chief Team Resources Officer
CNO: Thomas Doria, Vice President and Patient Services - West
Web address: www.mpmhealth.com
**Control**: Other not–for–profit (including NFP Corporation) **Service**: General medical and surgical

**Staffed Beds:** 217 **Admissions:** 12711 **Census:** 173 **Outpatient Visits:** 50494 **Births:** 0 **Total Expense ($000):** 159835 **Payroll Expense ($000):** 62987 **Personnel:** 969

**MORTON PLANT-MEASE-NORTH BAY** See Morton Plant North Bay Hospital

### NEW SMYRNA BEACH—Volusia County

⊞ **ADVENTHEALTH NEW SMYRNA BEACH (100014)**, 401 Palmetto Street, Zip 32168–7399; tel. 386/424–5000, (Nonreporting) **A**1 10 **F**3 11 15 18 20 22 28 29 30 31 34 35 40 45 46 49 50 57 59 60 66 68 70 74 75 78 79 81 84 93 107 108 110 111 114 115 119 120 121 135 146 148 154 **P**6 **S** AdventHealth, Altamonte Springs, FL
Primary Contact: Dennis Hernandez, Chief Executive Officer
COO: Steven W Harrell, FACHE, Chief Operating Officer
CFO: Al W Allred, Chief Financial Officer
CMO: Dennis Hernandez, Chief Medical Officer
CIO: Calvin Patrick IIDirector Information Services
CHR: Nancy K Evolga, Director Human Resources
CNO: Linda G Breum, R.N., MSN, Chief Nursing Officer
Web address: https://www.floridahospital.com/new-smyrna
**Control**: Church operated, Nongovernment, not–for–profit **Service**: General medical and surgical

**Staffed Beds:** 109 **Admissions:** 5448 **Census:** 64 **Outpatient Visits:** 76366 **Births:** 0 **Total Expense ($000):** 122934 **Payroll Expense ($000):** 46057 **Personnel:** 579

**FLORIDA HOSPITAL NEW SMYRNA** See Adventhealth New Smyrna Beach

### NICEVILLE—Okaloosa County

**COLUMBIA TWIN CITIES HOSPITAL** See Twin Cities Hospital

⊞ **TWIN CITIES HOSPITAL (100054)**, 2190 Highway 85 North, Zip 32578–1045; tel. 850/678–4131, (Nonreporting) **A**1 10 **S** HCA Healthcare, Nashville, TN
Primary Contact: David Whalen, Chief Executive Officer
CFO: Mark Day, Chief Financial Officer
CHR: Cyndi Ronca, Director Human Resources
Web address: www.tchealthcare.com
**Control**: Corporation, Investor–owned (for–profit) **Service**: General medical and surgical

**Staffed Beds:** 65

### NORTH MIAMI—Miami—Dade County

☐ **ST. CATHERINE'S REHABILITATION HOSPITAL (103026)**, 1050 NE 125th Street, Zip 33161–5881; tel. 305/357–1735, (Nonreporting) **A**1 10 **S** Catholic Health Services, Lauderdale Lakes, FL
Primary Contact: Jaime Gonzalez, Administrator
COO: Jim Ball, Chief Operating Officer
CFO: Mary Jo Frick, Director Finance
CMO: Miriam Feliz, M.D., Medical Director
Web address: www.catholichealthservices.org
**Control**: Other not–for–profit (including NFP Corporation) **Service**: Rehabilitation

**Staffed Beds:** 60

**VILLA MARIA HOSPITAL** See St. Catherine's Rehabilitation Hospital

### NORTH MIAMI BEACH—Miami—Dade County

**JACKSON NORTH MEDICAL CENTER** See Jackson Health System, Miami

**PARKWAY REGIONAL MED CENTER** See Jackson North Medical Center

### OAKLAND PARK—Broward County

☐ **FORT LAUDERDALE BEHAVIORAL HEALTH CENTER (104026)**, 5757 North Dixie Highway, Zip 33301–2393; tel. 954/734–2000, (Nonreporting) **A**1 10 **S** Universal Health Services, Inc., King of Prussia, PA
Primary Contact: Manuel R. Llano, Chief Executive Officer
COO: Miguel Fernandez, Chief Operating Officer
CFO: Burt Harris, Chief Financial Officer
CMO: Jared Gaines, M.D., Chief Medical Officer
CHR: Carlos A Gato, Director of Human Resources
CNO: Jillian Wirzman, Cheif Nursing Officer
Web address: www.ftlauderdalebehavioral.com
**Control**: Corporation, Investor–owned (for–profit) **Service**: Psychiatric

**Staffed Beds:** 100

**FORT LAUDERDALE HOSPITAL** See Fort Lauderdale Behavioral Health Center

### OCALA—Marion County

⊞ **ADVENTHEALTH OCALA (100062)**, 1500 SW 1st Avenue, Zip 34471–6504, Mailing Address: P.O. Box 6000, Zip 34478–6000; tel. 352/351–7200, (Nonreporting) **A**1 5 10 19 **F**3 12 13 17 18 20 22 24 26 28 29 30 31 34 35 37 38 40 41 42 45 46 47 49 50 51 53 57 58 59 60 64 65 68 70 72 74 75 76 77 78 79 80 81 83 84 85 86 87 89 91 92 93 96 100 107 108 111 114 115 119 126 127 130 132 133 135 146 147 148 156 157 **S** AdventHealth, Altamonte Springs, FL
Primary Contact: Joe Johnson, FACHE, Chief Executive Officer
COO: Philoron A. Wright, FACHE, IIChief Operating Officer
CFO: Eric LaChance, Chief Financial Officer
CMO: Lon McPherson, M.D., Senior Vice President Medical Affairs and Chief Quality Officer
CIO: Carl Candullo, Chief Information Officer
CNO: Pamela W Michell, R.N., Vice President, Chief Nursing Officer
Web address: www.munroeregional.com
**Control**: Other not–for–profit (including NFP Corporation) **Service**: General medical and surgical

**Staffed Beds:** 357 **Admissions:** 16983 **Census:** 216 **Outpatient Visits:** 130029 **Births:** 2444 **Total Expense ($000):** 322833 **Payroll Expense ($000):** 105453 **Personnel:** 1629

**COLUMBIA OCALA REG MED CTR** See Ocala Regional Medical Center

FL

⊞ **ENCOMPASS HEALTH REHABILITATION HOSPITAL OF OCALA (103043)**, 2275 SW 22nd Lane, Zip 34471–7710; tel. 352/282–4000, (Nonreporting) **A**1 10 **S** Encompass Health Corporation, Birmingham, AL
Primary Contact: Karthik Muthu, Chief Executive Officer
CFO: Sammy King, Controller
CMO: Amy Clunn, M.D., Medical Director
CHR: Tracy Sapp, Director Human Resources
CNO: Wendy Milam, Chief Nursing Officer
Web address: www.healthsouthocala.com
**Control**: Corporation, Investor–owned (for–profit) **Service**: Rehabilitation

**Staffed Beds**: 60

**FLORIDA HOSPITAL OCALA** See Adventhealth Ocala

**HEALTHSOUTH REHABILITATION HOSPITAL OF OCALA** See Encompass Health Rehabilitation Hospital of Ocala

⊞ **KINDRED HOSPITAL OCALA (102019)**, 1500 SW 1st Avenue, Zip 34471–6504; tel. 352/369–0513, (Nonreporting) **A**1 10 **S** Kindred Healthcare, Louisville, KY
Primary Contact: Merlene Bhoorasingh, Administrator
CFO: Dean Cocchi, Chief Financial Officer
Web address: www.kindredocala.com/
**Control**: Corporation, Investor–owned (for–profit) **Service**: Acute long–term care hospital

**Staffed Beds**: 31

⊞ **OCALA REGIONAL MEDICAL CENTER (100212)**, 1431 SW First Avenue, Zip 34471–6500, Mailing Address: P.O. Box 2200, Zip 34478–2200; tel. 352/401–1000, (Includes WEST MARION COMMUNITY HOSPITAL, Mailing address: 4600 SW 46th Court, Ocala, Florida, Zip 34474; tel. 352/291–3000; Gabe Bullaro, Chief Executive Officer), (Nonreporting) **A**1 2 3 5 10 13 **S** HCA Healthcare, Nashville, TN
Primary Contact: Chad Christianson, Chief Executive Officer
CMO: Art Osberg, M.D., Chief Medical Officer
CIO: Brandon Holbert, Director, Information Services
CHR: Wayne Nielsen, Director Human Resources
Web address: www.ocalaregional.com
**Control**: Corporation, Investor–owned (for–profit) **Service**: General medical and surgical

**Staffed Beds**: 430

**TEN BROECK HOSPITAL-OCALA** See The Vines

☐ **THE VINES (104071)**, 3130 SW 27th Avenue, Zip 34471–4306; tel. 352/671–3130, (Nonreporting) **A**1 10 **F**4 5 38 40 98 100 102 105 132 135 147 151 152 153 154 **S** Universal Health Services, Inc., King of Prussia, PA
Primary Contact: Stephen Quintyne, Chief Executive Officer
Web address: www.thevineshospital.com
**Control**: Corporation, Investor–owned (for–profit) **Service**: Psychiatric

**Staffed Beds**: 98 **Admissions**: 4005 **Census**: 66 **Outpatient Visits**: 0 **Births**: 0 **Total Expense ($000)**: 18937 **Payroll Expense ($000)**: 7519 **Personnel**: 148

**OCOEE—Orange County**

**HEALTH CENTRAL** See Health Central Hospital

⊞ **HEALTH CENTRAL HOSPITAL (100030)**, 10000 West Colonial Drive, Zip 34761–3499; tel. 407/296–1000, (Total facility includes 228 beds in nursing home–type unit) (Nonreporting) **A**1 3 10 **F**3 6 8 11 12 15 17 18 20 22 26 28 29 30 34 35 37 40 42 45 46 48 49 50 51 57 59 60 64 65 68 74 75 79 80 81 82 85 86 87 93 107 108 110 111 115 118 119 126 128 130 131 132 135 146 147 148 149 150 154 156 157 **S** Orlando Health, Orlando, FL
Primary Contact: Mark A. Marsh, President
COO: Rick Smith, Chief Operating Officer
CFO: Michael E Mueller, Chief Financial Officer
CMO: Antonio Velardi, M.D., Chief Quality Officer
CIO: John T Sills, Chief Information Officer
CHR: Karen Frenier, Chief Human Resources Officer
CNO: Christina Marie McGuirk, R.N., Chief Nursing Officer
Web address: www.orlandohealth.com/facilities/health-central-hospital
**Control**: Other not–for–profit (including NFP Corporation) **Service**: General medical and surgical

**Staffed Beds**: 439 **Admissions**: 14290 **Census**: 353 **Outpatient Visits**: 115838 **Births**: 0 **Total Expense ($000)**: 236253 **Payroll Expense ($000)**: 94479 **Personnel**: 1120

**OKEECHOBEE—Okeechobee County**

**COLUMBIA RAULERSON HOSPITAL** See Raulerson Hospital

⊞ **RAULERSON HOSPITAL (100252)**, 1796 Highway 441 North, Zip 34972–1918, Mailing Address: P.O. Box 1307, Zip 34973–1307; tel. 863/763–2151, (Nonreporting) **A**1 10 20 **S** HCA Healthcare, Nashville, TN
Primary Contact: Brian Melear, Chief Executive Officer
CFO: Terry L Brown, Chief Financial Officer
CMO: Arif Shakoor, Chief of Staff
CIO: Tim Hearing, Associate Information Technology Director
CHR: Cynthia Jackson, Vice President Human Resources
CNO: Adam Kless, Chief Nursing Officer
Web address: www.raulersonhospital.com
**Control**: Corporation, Investor–owned (for–profit) **Service**: General medical and surgical

**Staffed Beds**: 100

**ORANGE CITY—Volusia County**

⊞ **ADVENTHEALTH FISH MEMORIAL (100072)**, 1055 Saxon Boulevard, Zip 32763–8468; tel. 386/917–5000, (Nonreporting) **A**1 10 **F**3 11 15 18 20 22 24 26 28 29 30 31 34 35 37 40 42 45 46 48 49 50 54 59 60 64 68 70 74 75 77 78 79 81 82 85 87 91 92 93 100 104 107 108 109 110 111 114 115 116 117 118 119 120 121 129 130 135 146 147 148 154 **S** AdventHealth, Altamonte Springs, FL
Primary Contact: Robert Deininger, Chief Executive Officer
COO: Danielle Johnson, Chief Operating Officer
CFO: Eric Osterly, Chief Financial Officer
CMO: Stephen Knych, M.D., Chief Medical Officer
CHR: Jannina Garcia, Director of Human Resources
CNO: Jennifer Shull, R.N., Chief Nursing Officer
Web address: www.fhfishmemorial.org
**Control**: Other not–for–profit (including NFP Corporation) **Service**: General medical and surgical

**Staffed Beds**: 197 **Admissions**: 10080 **Census**: 124 **Outpatient Visits**: 92136 **Births**: 0 **Total Expense ($000)**: 163353 **Payroll Expense ($000)**: 61843

**FLORIDA HOSPITAL FISH MEMORIAL** See Adventhealth Fish Memorial

**ORANGE PARK—Clay County**

**COLUMBIA ORANGE PARK MED CTR** See Orange Park Medical Center

⊞ **ORANGE PARK MEDICAL CENTER (100226)**, 2001 Kingsley Avenue, Zip 32073–5156; tel. 904/639–8500, (Nonreporting) **A**1 3 5 10 **F**3 13 15 17 18 20 22 24 26 29 30 31 32 34 35 37 38 40 41 42 43 45 46 47 48 49 50 56 57 58 60 61 68 70 72 74 75 76 77 78 79 81 82 84 85 88 90 93 98 100 102 104 105 107 108 110 111 114 115 119 126 130 132 135 146 147 153 154 **S** HCA Healthcare, Nashville, TN
Primary Contact: Lisa R. Valentine, Chief Executive Officer
CFO: Chris Glenn, Chief Financial Officer
CMO: Bradley Shumaker, Chief Medical Officer
CHR: Brad Coburn, Vice President, Human Resources
CNO: Kathy Hester, Chief Nursing Officer
Web address: www.opmedical.com
**Control**: Corporation, Investor–owned (for–profit) **Service**: General medical and surgical

**Staffed Beds**: 314 **Admissions**: 20438 **Census**: 268 **Outpatient Visits**: 149007 **Births**: 1842 **Personnel**: 1397

**ORLANDO—Orange County**

★ ⇧ **ADVENTHEALTH ORLANDO (100007)**, 601 East Rollins Street, Zip 32803–1248; tel. 407/303–6611, (Includes ADVENTHEALTH ALTAMONTE SPRINGS, Mailing address: 601 East Altamonte Drive, Altamonte Springs, Florida, Zip 32701; tel. 407/830–4321; David Ottati, Regional Chief Executive Officer; ADVENTHEALTH APOPKA, Mailing address: 201 North Park Avenue, Apopka, Florida, Zip 32703; tel. 407/889–1000; Tim Clark, Chief Executive Officer; ADVENTHEALTH CELEBRATION, Mailing address: 400 Celebration Place, Celebration, Florida, Zip 34747; tel. 407/303–4000; Douglas Harcombe, Chief Executive Officer; ADVENTHEALTH EAST ORLANDO, Mailing address: 7727 Lake Underhill Drive, Orlando, Florida, Zip 32822; tel. 407/277–8110; Adventhealth for Children, Mailing address: 601 East Rollins Street, Orlando, Florida, Zip 32803–1248; tel. 407/303–9732; Lars D Houmann, President; ADVENTHEALTH KISSIMMEE, Mailing address: 2269 Santa Lucia St, Kissimmee, Florida, Zip 34743, 2450 North Orange Blossom Trai, Zip 34741, tel. 407/846–4343; William Haupt, Administrator; ADVENTHEALTH WINTER PARK, Mailing address: 200 North Lakemont Avenue, Winter Park, Florida, Zip 32792–3273; tel. 407/646–7000; Justin Birmele, Chief Executive Officer), (Nonreporting) **A**2 3 5 8 10 21 **F**3 6 7 8 9 11 12 13 15 17 18 19 20 21 22 23 24 25 26 27 28 29 30 31 32 34 35 36 40 41 42 44 45 46 47 48 49 50 51 53 54 55 56 57 58 59 60 61 62 63 64 65 66 67 68 70 71 72 73 74 75 76 77 78 79 80 81 82 83 84 85 87 88 89 90 93 95 96 97 98 100 101 102 107 108 109 110 111 112 113 114 115 116 117 118 119 120 121 123 124 126 128 129 130 131 132 134 135 136 137 138 139 140 141 142 146 147 148 154 155 156 157 **P**6 **S** AdventHealth, Altamonte Springs, FL
Primary Contact: Daryl Tol, President and Chief Executive Officer
COO: Brian Paradis, Chief Operating Officer
CFO: Eddie Soler, Chief Financial Officer
CMO: David Moorhead, M.D., Chief Medical Officer
CHR: Sheryl Dodds, Chief Clinical Officer
Web address: www.floridahospital.com/orlando
**Control:** Other not–for–profit (including NFP Corporation) **Service:** General medical and surgical

**Staffed Beds:** 3890 **Admissions:** 146072 **Census:** 1868 **Outpatient Visits:** 1230876 **Births:** 13290 **Total Expense ($000):** 3480495 **Payroll Expense ($000):** 1208548 **Personnel:** 19854

**ARNOLD PALMER CHILDREN'S HOSPITAL** See Arnold Palmer Hospital for Children

**ARNOLD PALMER HOSPITAL FOR CHILDREN** See Orlando Regional Medical Center, Orlando

**ASPIRE HEALTH PARTNERS (104067)**, 1800 Mercy Drive, Zip 32808–5646; tel. 407/875–3700, (Nonreporting) **A**10 **F**5 29 35 38 75 98 100 102 104 106 130 132 133 134 135 153 154
Primary Contact: Jerry Kassab, President and Chief Executive Officer
Web address: www.lakesidecares.org
**Control:** Other not–for–profit (including NFP Corporation) **Service:** Psychiatric

**Staffed Beds:** 56 **Admissions:** 2794 **Census:** 40 **Outpatient Visits:** 0 **Births:** 0 **Total Expense ($000):** 6585 **Payroll Expense ($000):** 3099 **Personnel:** 67

☐ **CENTRAL FLORIDA BEHAVIORAL HOSPITAL (104072)**, 6601 Central Florida Parkway, Zip 32821–8064; tel. 407/370–0111, (Nonreporting) **A**1 3 10 **S** Universal Health Services, Inc., King of Prussia, PA
Primary Contact: Vickie Lewis, Chief Executive Officer
CFO: Marsha Burick, Chief Financial Officer
Web address: www.centralfloridabehavioral.com
**Control:** Other not–for–profit (including NFP Corporation) **Service:** Psychiatric

**Staffed Beds:** 126

⇧ **FLORIDA HOSPITAL** See Adventhealth Orlando

**FLORIDA HOSPITAL EAST ORLANDO** See Adventhealth East Orlando

**FLORIDA HOSPITAL FOR CHILDREN-WALT DISNEY PAVILION** See Adventhealth for Children

**LAKESIDE BEHAVIORAL HEALTHCARE-PRINCETON PLAZA** See Aspire Health Partners

⊞ **NEMOURS CHILDREN'S HOSPITAL (103304)**, 13535 Nemours Parkway, Zip 32827–7402; tel. 407/567–4000, (Nonreporting) **A**1 3 5 10 **F**3 17 19 21 23 25 27 29 30 31 32 34 35 40 41 45 46 48 50 53 55 57 58 59 60 64 65 68 72 73 74 75 77 78 79 80 81 82 84 85 86 87 88 89 90 91 92 93 94 96 97 100 107 108 111 115 119 120 121 130 131 146 149 154 156 **S** Nemours, Jacksonville, FL
Primary Contact: Randall W. Hartley, Interim President
COO: Randall W Hartley, Chief Operating Officer
CFO: Rodney McKendree, Senior Vice President and Chief Financial Officer
CMO: Andre Hebra, M.D., Chief Medical Officer
CIO: Bernard Rice, Chief Information Officer
CHR: Theresa M Young, Senior Vice President Human Resources
CNO: Helen M Case, Chief Nursing Officer
Web address: www.nemours.org
**Control:** Other not–for–profit (including NFP Corporation) **Service:** Children's general medical and surgical

**Staffed Beds:** 108 **Admissions:** 3617 **Census:** 69 **Outpatient Visits:** 85350 **Births:** 0 **Total Expense ($000):** 235389 **Payroll Expense ($000):** 78224 **Personnel:** 1040

⊞ △ **ORLANDO REGIONAL MEDICAL CENTER (100006)**, 52 West Underwood Street, Zip 32806; tel. 407/841–5111, (Includes ARNOLD PALMER HOSPITAL FOR CHILDREN, Mailing address: 92 West Miller Street, Orlando, Florida, Zip 32806; tel. 407/649–6960; Cary D'Ortona, President; ORLANDO HEALTH SOUTH SEMINOLE HOSPITAL, Mailing address: 555 West State Road 434, Longwood, Florida, Zip 32750–4999; tel. 407/767–1200; Karen Frenier, President; WINNIE PALMER HOSPITAL FOR WOMEN AND BABIES, Mailing address: 83 West Miller Street, Orlando, Florida, Zip 32806; tel. 321/843–9792; Kelly Nierstedt, President), (Nonreporting) **A**1 2 3 5 7 10 **F**3 4 7 8 11 12 13 15 16 17 18 19 20 21 22 23 24 25 26 27 28 29 30 31 34 35 36 37 40 41 42 43 44 45 46 47 48 49 50 51 54 55 57 58 59 60 61 62 64 68 70 71 72 73 74 75 76 77 78 79 80 81 82 84 85 86 87 88 89 90 91 92 93 94 95 96 98 99 100 101 102 104 107 108 110 111 114 115 116 117 118 119 120 121 122 123 124 126 127 129 130 131 132 134 135 143 145 146 147 148 149 152 154 155 156 157 **S** Orlando Health, Orlando, FL
Primary Contact: Mark A. Jones, President
COO: Carlos Carrasco, Chief Operating Officer
CFO: Steve Miglietta, Chief Financial Officer
CMO: Charles Heard, M.D., Chief of Staff
CIO: Rick Schooler, Vice President and Chief Information Officer
CHR: Greg Thompson, Corporate Director, Human Resources
CNO: Jayne Willis, Vice President, System Chief Nurse Executive
Web address: www.orlandohealth.com/facilities/orlando-regional-medical-center
**Control:** Other not–for–profit (including NFP Corporation) **Service:** General medical and surgical

**Staffed Beds:** 1342 **Admissions:** 92324 **Census:** 1235 **Outpatient Visits:** 784567 **Births:** 14111 **Total Expense ($000):** 2254431 **Payroll Expense ($000):** 829262 **Personnel:** 14875

**ORLANDO REGIONAL MEDICAL CNTR** See Orlando Regional Medical Center

☐ **ORLANDO VA MEDICAL CENTER**, 13800 Veterans Way, Zip 32827–7403; tel. 407/631–1000, (Total facility includes 120 beds in nursing home–type unit) (Nonreporting) **A**1 3 5 8 **F**3 5 11 15 18 20 26 28 29 30 31 33 34 35 36 38 39 40 44 45 46 47 48 49 50 51 54 56 57 58 59 60 61 62 63 64 65 68 70 71 74 75 77 78 79 81 82 83 84 85 86 87 93 94 97 98 100 101 102 104 105 106 107 108 110 111 115 117 118 119 120 121 123 126 128 129 130 132 135 145 146 147 148 149 150 152 153 154 156 157 158 **S** Department of Veterans Affairs, Washington, DC
Primary Contact: Timothy J. Cooke, Medical Center Director and Chief Executive Officer
Web address: www.orlando.va.gov
**Control:** Veterans Affairs, Government, federal **Service:** General medical and surgical

**Staffed Beds:** 370 **Admissions:** 6180 **Census:** 201 **Outpatient Visits:** 1760215 **Births:** 0 **Total Expense ($000):** 960772 **Payroll Expense ($000):** 385313 **Personnel:** 5345

**FL**

---

**Hospital, Medicare Provider Number, Address, Telephone, Approval, Facility, and Physician Codes, Health Care System**

★ American Hospital Association (AHA) membership   ○ Healthcare Facilities Accreditation Program   ⇧ Center for Improvement in Healthcare Quality Accreditation
☐ The Joint Commission accreditation   ◇ DNV Healthcare Inc. accreditation   △ Commission on Accreditation of Rehabilitation Facilities (CARF) accreditation

⊞ **SELECT SPECIALTY HOSPITAL-ORLANDO (102003)**, 2250 Bedford Road, Zip 32803–1443; tel. 407/303–7869, (Includes SELECT SPECIALTY HOSPITAL-ORLANDO SOUTH, Mailing address: 5579 South Orange Avenue, Orlando, Florida, Zip 32809–3493; tel. 407/241–4800), (Nonreporting) **A**1 10 **S** Select Medical Corporation, Mechanicsburg, PA
Primary Contact: Theodore Mena, Chief Executive Officer
Web address: www.selectspecialtyhospitals.com/company/locations/orlando.aspx
**Control**: Corporation, Investor–owned (for–profit) **Service**: Acute long–term care hospital

| Staffed Beds: 75 |
|---|

**SELECT SPECIALTY HOSPITAL-ORLANDO NORTH** See Select Specialty Hospital-Orlando

**WINNIE PALMER HOSPITAL FOR WOMEN AND BABIES** See Orlando Regional Medical Center, Orlando

**OVIEDO—Seminole County**

⊞ **OVIEDO MEDICAL CENTER (100329)**, 8300 Red Bug Lake Road, Zip 32765–6801; tel. 407/890–2273, (Nonreporting) **A**1 10 **S** HCA Healthcare, Nashville, TN
Primary Contact: Kenneth C. Donahey, Chief Executive Officer
CFO: Jay Pettus, Chief Financial Officer
CNO: John Voight, Chief Nursing Officer
Web address: www.oviedomedicalcenter.com
**Control**: Other not–for–profit (including NFP Corporation) **Service**: General medical and surgical

| Staffed Beds: 64 |
|---|

**OXFORD—Sumter County**

★ **PROMISE HOSPITAL OF FLORIDA AT THE VILLAGES (102028)**, 5050 County Road 472, Zip 34484; tel. 352/689–6400, (Nonreporting) **A**10 **S** Select Medical Corporation, Mechanicsburg, PA
Primary Contact: Hoyt Ross, Chief Executive Officer
CNO: Janice M McCoy, MS, R.N., Chief Clinical Officer
Web address: www.promise-villages.com
**Control**: Corporation, Investor–owned (for–profit) **Service**: Acute long–term care hospital

| Staffed Beds: 40 |
|---|

**PALATKA—Putnam County**

**COLUMBIA PUTNAM MEDICAL CENTER** See Putnam Community Medical Center

⊞ **PUTNAM COMMUNITY MEDICAL CENTER (100232)**, 611 Zeagler Drive, Zip 32177–3810; tel. 386/328–5711, (Nonreporting) **A**1 10 **S** HCA Healthcare, Nashville, TN
Primary Contact: Mark J. Dooley, Chief Executive Officer
CFO: Stewart Whitmore, Chief Financial Officer
CIO: Yvette A Jones, Health Information Management Director
CHR: John Schneider, Human Resources Director
CNO: Kari Bolin, Chief Nursing Officer
Web address: www.pcmcfl.com
**Control**: Corporation, Investor–owned (for–profit) **Service**: General medical and surgical

| Staffed Beds: 99 |
|---|

**PALM BAY—Brevard County**

☐ **HEALTH FIRST PALM BAY HOSPITAL (100316)**, 1425 Malabar Road NE, Zip 32907–2506; tel. 321/434–8000, (Nonreporting) **A**1 10 **F**3 11 12 15 18 20 22 29 30 34 37 39 40 41 45 47 49 50 59 60 64 68 70 74 75 77 79 80 81 85 86 87 93 102 107 108 110 111 114 119 126 130 132 141 146 148 149 153 154 **P**6 **S** Health First, Inc., Rockledge, FL
Primary Contact: Brett A. Esrock, FACHE, President
COO: Deborah Angerami, Chief Operating Officer, Health First Community Hospitals
CFO: Joseph G Felkner, Executive Vice President and Chief Financial Officer
CMO: Lee Scheinbart, M.D., Vice President Medical Affairs, Health First Community Hospitals
CIO: Alex Popowycz, Senior Vice President and Chief Information Officer
CHR: Paula Just, Chief Human Resources Officer
CNO: Connie Bradley, R.N., MSN, FACHE, Chief Nursing Officer
Web address: www.health-first.org/hospitals_services/pbch/index.cfm
**Control**: Other not–for–profit (including NFP Corporation) **Service**: General medical and surgical

| Staffed Beds: 120 Admissions: 6857 Census: 72 Outpatient Visits: 85850 Births: 0 Total Expense ($000): 108666 Payroll Expense ($000): 44012 Personnel: 515 |
|---|

**PALM BAY HOSPITAL** See Health First Palm Bay Hospital

**PALM BEACH GARDENS—Palm Beach County**

**AMI PALM BEACH GARDENS MED CTR** See Palm Beach Gardens Medical Center

⊞ **PALM BEACH GARDENS MEDICAL CENTER (100176)**, 3360 Burns Road, Zip 33410–4323; tel. 561/622–1411, (Nonreporting) **A**1 5 10 **F**3 11 15 17 18 20 22 24 26 28 29 34 35 40 45 49 50 57 58 59 64 67 70 74 77 79 81 85 87 92 93 94 96 107 108 110 111 115 118 119 126 130 131 132 135 146 148 149 **S** TENET Healthcare Corporation, Dallas, TX
Primary Contact: Teresa C. Urquhart, Chief Executive Officer
CFO: Judi Stimson, Chief Financial Officer
CIO: James Vega, Director Information Systems
CHR: Kevin Caracciolo, Chief Human Resources Officer
CNO: Patricia Rosenberg, R.N., MSN, Chief Nursing Officer
Web address: www.pbgmc.com
**Control**: Corporation, Investor–owned (for–profit) **Service**: General medical and surgical

| Staffed Beds: 202 Admissions: 10246 Census: 137 Outpatient Visits: 59958 Births: 0 Total Expense ($000): 202299 Payroll Expense ($000): 59693 Personnel: 806 |
|---|

**PALM COAST—Flagler County**

⊞ **ADVENTHEALTH PALM COAST (100118)**, 60 Memorial Medical Parkway, Zip 32164–5980; tel. 386/586–2000, (Nonreporting) **A**1 2 10 **F**3 8 11 15 18 20 22 28 29 30 31 34 35 37 40 45 46 47 48 49 50 51 54 57 59 60 62 63 64 68 70 74 75 77 78 79 81 84 85 86 87 91 93 96 97 107 108 109 110 111 114 115 116 117 119 120 121 123 124 126 130 131 132 135 145 146 147 148 154 **S** AdventHealth, Altamonte Springs, FL
Primary Contact: Ronald Jimenez, M.D., Chief Executive Officer
COO: JoAnne King, Chief Operating Officer
CFO: Cory Domayer, Chief Financial Officer
CMO: Ron Thomas, M.D., Chief Medical Officer
CHR: Joshua I Champion, Director
CNO: Robert Davis, Chief Nursing Officer
Web address: www.floridahospitalflagler.com/
**Control**: Church operated, Nongovernment, not–for–profit **Service**: General medical and surgical

| Staffed Beds: 99 Admissions: 8253 Census: 93 Outpatient Visits: 183634 Births: 0 Total Expense ($000): 192408 Payroll Expense ($000): 81178 Personnel: 1050 |
|---|

**FLORIDA HOSPITAL FLAGLER** See Adventhealth Palm Coast

**PANAMA CITY—Bay County**

**BAY MEDICAL CENTER SACRED HEART HEALTH SYSTEM** See Bay Medical Sacred Heart

⊞ **BAY MEDICAL SACRED HEART (100026)**, 615 North Bonita Avenue, Zip 32401–3600, Mailing Address: P.O. Box 59515, Zip 32412–0515; tel. 850/769–1511, (Data for 282 days) (Nonreporting) **A**1 10 **F**3 17 18 20 22 24 26 28 29 30 35 40 42 43 45 46 49 51 54 64 70 74 77 79 81 87 92 93 107 108 111 114 115 119 126 154 **S** Ascension Healthcare, Saint Louis, MO
Primary Contact: Heath Evans, President
CHR: Donna Baird, Vice President Corporate Services
CNO: Jan Thornton, Chief Nursing Officer
Web address: www.baymedical.org
**Control**: Other not–for–profit (including NFP Corporation) **Service**: General medical and surgical

| Staffed Beds: 74 Admissions: 6424 Census: 113 Outpatient Visits: 101083 Births: 173 Total Expense ($000): 201855 Payroll Expense ($000): 65349 Personnel: 576 |
|---|

☐ **EMERALD COAST BEHAVIORAL HOSPITAL (104073)**, 1940 Harrison Avenue, Zip 32405–4542; tel. 850/763–0017, (Nonreporting) **A**1 10 **S** Universal Health Services, Inc., King of Prussia, PA
Primary Contact: Tim Bedford, Chief Executive Officer
CFO: Michael J Zenone, Chief Financial Officer
CMO: Roy Deal, Chief Medical Officer
CNO: Michael B Barbour, Chief Nursing Officer
Web address: www.emeraldcoastbehavioral.com
**Control**: Corporation, Investor–owned (for–profit) **Service**: Psychiatric

| Staffed Beds: 86 |
|---|

**FL**

*Many Facility Codes have changed. Please refer to the AHA Guide Code Chart.*

© 2021 AHA Guide

⊠ **ENCOMPASS HEALTH REHABILITATION HOSPITAL OF PANAMA CITY (103040)**, 1847 Florida Avenue, Zip 32405–4640; tel. 850/914–8600, (Nonreporting) **A**1 10 **F**3 28 29 34 57 59 68 75 77 86 87 90 95 96 130 131 132 148 156 **S** Encompass Health Corporation, Birmingham, AL
Primary Contact: Tony N. Bennett, Chief Executive Officer
CFO: Bradley Tilghman, Controller
CMO: Michael Hennigan, M.D., Medical Director
CHR: Traci Powell, Director Human Resources
CNO: Sharon Hamilton, Chief Nursing Officer
Web address: www.healthsouthpanamacity.com
**Control**: Corporation, Investor–owned (for–profit) **Service**: Rehabilitation

**Staffed Beds**: 75 **Admissions**: 1312 **Census**: 48 **Outpatient Visits**: 0
**Births**: 0 **Total Expense ($000)**: 20384 **Payroll Expense ($000)**: 10656
**Personnel**: 196

**GULF COAST MEDICAL CENTER** See Gulf Coast Regional Medical Center

⊠ **GULF COAST REGIONAL MEDICAL CENTER (100242)**, 449 West 23rd Street, Zip 32405–4593, Mailing Address: P.O. Box 15309, Zip 32406–5309; tel. 850/769–8341, (Nonreporting) **A**1 2 10 **S** HCA Healthcare, Nashville, TN
Primary Contact: Brad Griffin, Chief Executive Officer
COO: Holly Jackson, Chief Operating Officer
CFO: Laurie Haynes, Chief Financial Officer
CHR: Tracy McGlon, Director Human Resources
CNO: Brian Pinelle, R.N., Chief Nursing Officer
Web address: www.egulfcoastmedical.com
**Control**: Corporation, Investor–owned (for–profit) **Service**: General medical and surgical

**Staffed Beds**: 223

**HEALTHSOUTH EMERALD COAST REHABILITATION HOSPITAL** See Encompass Health Rehabilitation Hospital of Panama City

★ **SELECT SPECIALTY HOSPITAL-PANAMA CITY (102017)**, 615 North Bonita Avenue, 3rd Floor, Zip 32401–3623; tel. 850/767–3180, (Nonreporting) **A**10 **S** Select Medical Corporation, Mechanicsburg, PA
Primary Contact: Randal S. Hamilton, Chief Executive Officer
CMO: Amir Manzoor, M.D., Medical Director
Web address: www.selectspecialtyhospitals.com/company/locations/panamacity.aspx
**Control**: Corporation, Investor–owned (for–profit) **Service**: Acute long–term care hospital

**Staffed Beds**: 30

### PEMBROKE PINES—Broward County

⊠ **MEMORIAL HOSPITAL PEMBROKE (100230)**, 7800 Sheridan Street, Zip 33024–2536; tel. 954/883–8482, (Nonreporting) **A**1 5 10 **F**3 12 29 30 34 40 44 45 46 47 48 49 50 51 59 64 65 66 70 74 75 77 79 81 82 84 85 86 87 107 108 111 115 119 126 130 132 141 144 146 148 149 154 **S** Memorial Healthcare System, Hollywood, FL
Primary Contact: Joseph Stuczynski, Administrator and Chief Executive Officer
CMO: Stanley Marks, M.D., FACS, Chief Medical Officer
CIO: Forest Blanton, Chief Information Officer
CNO: Judy Frum, Chief Nursing Officer
Web address: www.memorialpembroke.com/
**Control**: Hospital district or authority, Government, Nonfederal **Service**: General medical and surgical

**Staffed Beds**: 190 **Admissions**: 6696 **Census**: 88 **Outpatient Visits**: 98111
**Births**: 0 **Total Expense ($000)**: 145438 **Payroll Expense ($000)**: 69711
**Personnel**: 947

⊠ **MEMORIAL HOSPITAL WEST (100281)**, 703 North Flamingo Road, Zip 33028–1014; tel. 954/436–5000, (Nonreporting) **A**1 2 3 5 10 **F**3 12 13 15 17 18 22 26 28 29 30 31 34 35 36 40 41 45 46 47 49 53 55 56 57 58 60 68 70 72 74 75 76 78 79 81 82 85 87 91 93 107 108 110 111 114 115 119 120 121 123 124 126 130 131 132 136 145 146 147 **S** Memorial Healthcare System, Hollywood, FL
Primary Contact: Leah A. Carpenter, Administrator and Chief Executive Officer
CFO: Walter Bussell, Chief Financial Officer
CMO: Eric Freling, M.D., Director Medical Staff Affairs
CIO: Forest Blanton, Chief Information Officer
CHR: Maria Naranjo, Director Human Resources
Web address: www.mhs.net
**Control**: Hospital district or authority, Government, Nonfederal **Service**: General medical and surgical

**Staffed Beds**: 485 **Admissions**: 20789 **Census**: 290 **Outpatient Visits**: 298517 **Births**: 4037 **Total Expense ($000)**: 483239 **Payroll Expense ($000)**: 182653 **Personnel**: 2290

**PEMBROKE PINES HOSPITAL** See Memorial Hospital Pembroke

### PENSACOLA—Escambia County

★ ⇑ **BAPTIST HOSPITAL (100093)**, 1000 West Moreno Street, Zip 32501–2316, Mailing Address: P.O. Box 17500, Zip 32522–7500; tel. 850/434–4011, (Nonreporting) **A**2 3 10 21 **F**3 8 11 12 13 15 17 18 20 22 24 26 28 29 30 31 34 35 40 43 45 46 47 48 49 50 51 54 55 56 57 58 59 60 61 63 64 70 71 74 75 76 77 78 79 80 81 82 84 85 86 87 91 92 93 97 98 99 100 101 102 103 104 107 108 110 111 114 115 116 117 118 119 120 121 123 126 130 131 132 146 147 148 **P**6 **S** Baptist Health Care Corporation, Pensacola, FL
Primary Contact: Scott Raynes, President
CFO: Sharon Nobles, Interim Chief Financial Officer
CMO: Mike Oleksyk, M.D., Vice President and Chief Medical Officer
CIO: Steven Sarros, Vice President and Chief Information Officer
CHR: Darlene Stone, Vice President Human Resources
CNO: Cynde Gamache, R.N., Vice President and Chief Nursing Officer
Web address: www.ebaptisthealthcare.org
**Control**: Other not–for–profit (including NFP Corporation) **Service**: General medical and surgical

**Staffed Beds**: 340 **Admissions**: 17492 **Census**: 241 **Outpatient Visits**: 300792 **Births**: 883 **Total Expense ($000)**: 414148 **Payroll Expense ($000)**: 113129 **Personnel**: 1601

**NAVAL HOSPITAL** See Naval Hospital Pensacola

★ **NAVAL HOSPITAL PENSACOLA**, 6000 West Highway 98, Zip 32512–0003; tel. 850/505–6601, (Nonreporting) **A**3 5 **S** Bureau of Medicine and Surgery, Department of the Navy, Falls Church, VA
Primary Contact: Captain David Webster, Commanding Officer
COO: CommanderDevin Morrison, Director for Administration
CMO: CommanderCarolyn Rice, M.D., Director Medical Services
CIO: Lieutenant CommanderWilliam Berg, Chief Information Officer
CHR: CommanderDevin Morrison, Director for Administration
CNO: CaptainAmy Tarbay, Director Nursing Services
Web address: www.https://www.med.navy.mil/sites/pcola
**Service**: General medical and surgical

**Staffed Beds**: 28

**REHABILITATION INSTITUTE OF WEST FLORIDA** See West Florida Rehabilitation Institute

**SACRED HEART HOSPITAL OF PENSACOLA** See Sacred Heart Hospital Pensacola

FL

⊞ **SACRED HEART HOSPITAL PENSACOLA (100025)**, 5151 North Ninth Avenue, Zip 32504–8795, Mailing Address: P.O. Box 2700, Zip 32513–2700; tel. 850/416–7000, (Nonreporting) **A**1 2 3 5 10 **F**3 8 11 12 13 15 17 18 19 20 21 22 24 26 28 29 30 31 34 35 40 41 43 44 45 46 47 48 49 50 54 55 57 58 59 60 61 65 68 70 72 73 74 75 76 77 78 79 81 82 84 85 87 88 89 92 93 96 97 107 108 110 111 112 114 115 119 120 124 126 130 131 132 135 138 146 147 148 149 154 156 **S** Ascension Healthcare, Saint Louis, MO
Primary Contact: Dawn Rudolph, President
COO: Terri Smith, Chief Operating Officer
CFO: C Susan Cornejo, Chief Financial Officer
CMO: Peter Jennings, M.D., Chief Medical Officer
CIO: Donna Roach, Chief Information Officer
CHR: Michelle Adamolekun, Vice President Human Resource Market Lead Florida/Alabama Ministry Market
Web address: www.https://healthcare.ascension.org/Locations/Florida/FLPEN/Pensacola-Sacred-Heart-Hospital-Pensacola
**Control**: Other not–for–profit (including NFP Corporation) **Service**: General medical and surgical

| | |
|---|---|
| **Staffed Beds**: 465 **Admissions**: 24645 **Census**: 329 **Outpatient Visits**: 349352 **Births**: 4133 **Total Expense ($000)**: 440805 **Payroll Expense ($000)**: 132126 **Personnel**: 2084 | |

⊞ **SELECT SPECIALTY HOSPITAL-PENSACOLA (102024)**, 7000 Cobble Creek Drive, Zip 32504–8638; tel. 850/473–4800, (Nonreporting) **A**1 10 **S** Select Medical Corporation, Mechanicsburg, PA
Primary Contact: Adam Principe, Chief Executive Officer
CMO: John Bray, M.D., Medical Director
Web address: www.https://pensacola.selectspecialtyhospitals.com/
**Control**: Corporation, Investor–owned (for–profit) **Service**: Acute long–term care hospital

**Staffed Beds**: 75

⊞ △ **WEST FLORIDA HOSPITAL (100231)**, 8383 North Davis Highway, Zip 32514–6088; tel. 850/494–4000, (Includes THE PAVILION, Mailing address: 8383 North Davis Highway, Pensacola, Florida, Zip 32523, P O Box 18900, Zip 32523, tel. 904/494–5000; WEST FLORIDA REHABILITATION INSTITUTE, Mailing address: 8383 North Davis Highway, Pensacola, Florida, Zip 32514, P O Box 18900, Zip 32523, tel. 850/494–6000), (Nonreporting) **A**1 2 3 7 10 **S** HCA Healthcare, Nashville, TN
Primary Contact: Gay Nord, Chief Executive Officer
COO: Jessica O'Neal, Chief Operating Officer
CFO: Randy Butler, Chief Financial Officer
CMO: Terry Stallings, M.D., Chief Medical Officer
CIO: Jeff Amerson, Director Information System
CHR: Wanda Salley, Vice President Human Resources
CNO: Karen White-Trevino, Chief Nursing Officer
Web address: www.westfloridahospital.com
**Control**: Corporation, Investor–owned (for–profit) **Service**: General medical and surgical

**Staffed Beds**: 515

**WEST FLORIDA REG MED CENTER** See West Florida Hospital

**WEST FLORIDA REHABILITATION INSTITUTE** See West Florida Hospital, Pensacola

## PERRY—Taylor County

**CREST MEDICAL CENTER-PERRY** See Doctor's Memorial Hospital

**DOCTOR'S MEMORIAL HOSPITAL (100106)**, 333 North Byron Butler Parkway, Zip 32347–2300; tel. 850/584–0800, (Nonreporting) **A**10 20
Primary Contact: Thomas J. Stone, FACHE, Chief Executive Officer
CIO: Kyle Wright, Management Information System Director
CHR: Sherry Blanton, Human Resource Director
CNO: Ashley Beagle, Director of Nursing
Web address: www.doctorsmemorial.com
**Control**: Other not–for–profit (including NFP Corporation) **Service**: General medical and surgical

**Staffed Beds**: 24

## PLANT CITY—Hillsborough County

⊞ **SOUTH FLORIDA BAPTIST HOSPITAL (100132)**, 301 North Alexander Street, Zip 33563–4303; tel. 813/757–1200, (Nonreporting) **A**1 10 **F**3 11 12 13 15 18 20 22 28 29 30 31 34 35 37 40 41 44 45 47 48 49 50 51 57 59 60 64 68 70 71 74 75 76 77 78 79 80 81 83 84 85 87 93 107 108 110 111 114 115 118 119 124 126 130 131 132 135 145 146 147 148 154 156 **S** Trinity Health, Livonia, MI
Primary Contact: Karen Kerr, R.N., President
COO: Beth Tancredo, Director Operations
CFO: Carl Tremonti, Chief Financial Officer
CMO: Mark Vaaler, M.D., Chief Medical Officer
CIO: Tim Thompson, Senior Vice President, Chief Information Officer
CHR: Pat Lipton, Director Team Resources
CNO: Teresa Colletti, Director Patient Services
Web address: www.https://baycare.org/sfbh
**Control**: Other not–for–profit (including NFP Corporation) **Service**: General medical and surgical

| | |
|---|---|
| **Staffed Beds**: 141 **Admissions**: 7045 **Census**: 65 **Outpatient Visits**: 60214 **Births**: 560 **Total Expense ($000)**: 128634 **Payroll Expense ($000)**: 44822 **Personnel**: 669 | |

## PLANTATION—Broward County

**COLUMBIA PLANTATION GEN HOSP** See Plantation General Hospital

**COLUMBIA WESTSIDE REG MED CTR** See Westside Regional Medical Center

⊞ △ **PLANTATION GENERAL HOSPITAL (100167)**, 401 NW 42nd Avenue, Zip 33317–2882; tel. 954/587–5010, (Includes MERCY HOSPITAL - A CAMPUS OF PLANTATION GENERAL HOSPITAL, Mailing address: 3663 South Miami Avenue, Miami, Florida, Zip 33133–4237; tel. 305/854–4400; David Donaldson, Chief Executive Officer), (Nonreporting) **A**1 2 3 5 7 10 **S** HCA Healthcare, Nashville, TN
Primary Contact: Madeline Nava, Chief Executive Officer
CFO: Irfan Mirza, Chief Financial Officer
CIO: Mia McGlynn, Director Management Information Systems
CHR: Jennifer Allen, Vice President Human Resources
CNO: Jesse Gabuat, Chief Nursing Officer
Web address: www.plantationgeneral.com/
**Control**: Corporation, Investor–owned (for–profit) **Service**: General medical and surgical

**Staffed Beds**: 752

⊞ **WESTSIDE REGIONAL MEDICAL CENTER (100228)**, 8201 West Broward Boulevard, Zip 33324–2701; tel. 954/473–6600, (Nonreporting) **A**1 3 5 10 **S** HCA Healthcare, Nashville, TN
Primary Contact: Barbara Simmons, R.N., Chief Executive Officer
COO: Shana Sappington-Crittenden, Chief Operating Officer
CFO: Kevin Corcoran, Chief Financial Officer
CMO: Brian Weinstein, M.D., Chief of Staff
CIO: Andres Blanco, Director Management Information Systems
CHR: Maria Rivera, Director Human Resources
Web address: www.westsideregional.com
**Control**: Corporation, Investor–owned (for–profit) **Service**: General medical and surgical

**Staffed Beds**: 250

## PORT CHARLOTTE—Charlotte County

⊞ **BAYFRONT HEALTH PORT CHARLOTTE (100077)**, 2500 Harbor Boulevard, Zip 33952–5000; tel. 941/766–4122, (Nonreporting) **A**1 10 **S** Community Health Systems, Inc., Franklin, TN
Primary Contact: Eric Kaplan, Interim Chief Executive Officer and Chief Operating Officer
COO: Eric Kaplan, Chief Operating Officer
CFO: Jeffrey Mullis, Interim Chief Financial Officer
CMO: Thomas Noone, M.D., Chief Medical Officer
CHR: Karen Gardiner, Human Resources Director
CNO: Debra Clark, Chief Nursing Officer
Web address: www.bayfrontcharlotte.com
**Control**: Corporation, Investor–owned (for–profit) **Service**: General medical and surgical

**Staffed Beds**: 254

**COLUMBIA FAWCETT MEM HOSP** See Fawcett Memorial Hospital

*Many Facility Codes have changed. Please refer to the AHA Guide Code Chart.* © 2021 AHA Guide

✠ △ **FAWCETT MEMORIAL HOSPITAL (100236)**, 21298 Olean Boulevard, Zip 33952-6765; tel. 941/629-1181, (Nonreporting) **A**1 2 7 10 **S** HCA Healthcare, Nashville, TN
Primary Contact: Michael Ehrat, Interim Chief Executive Officer
CFO: Vickie Magurean, Chief Financial Officer
CMO: Mark Callman, M.D., Chief Medical Officer
CHR: Linda Bryan, Vice President Human Resources
CNO: Brandy Hershberger, Chief Nursing Officer
Web address: www.fawcetthospital.com
**Control**: Corporation, Investor-owned (for-profit) **Service**: General medical and surgical

| Staffed Beds: 237 |
| --- |

**PEACE RIVER REGIONAL MEDICAL CENTER** See Bayfront Health Port Charlotte

### PORT ORANGE—Volusia County

**HALIFAX HOSPITAL PORT ORANGE** See Halifax Health Medical Center of Port Orange

### PORT ST JOE—Gulf County

✠ **SACRED HEART HOSPITAL ON THE GULF (100313)**, 3801 East Highway 98, Zip 32456-5318; tel. 850/229-5600, (Nonreporting) **A**1 10 **F**29 30 40 68 77 79 81 85 87 93 107 110 111 114 119 127 130 131 132 133 146 156 **S** Ascension Healthcare, Saint Louis, MO
Primary Contact: Henry Stovall, Regional President
CMO: Gary M. Pablo, M.D., Chief Medical Officer
CNO: Robin M. Godwin, MSN, Vice President of Nursing
Web address: www.sacred-heart.org/gulf/
**Control**: Other not-for-profit (including NFP Corporation) **Service**: General medical and surgical

| Staffed Beds: 12 Admissions: 405 Census: 4 Outpatient Visits: 31794 |
| --- |
| Births: 0 Total Expense ($000): 18160 Payroll Expense ($000): 5829 |
| Personnel: 70 |

### PORT ST LUCIE—St. Lucie County

**COLUMBIA MED CTR-PORT ST LUCIE** See St. Lucie Medical Center

**PORT SAINT LUCIE HOSPITAL** See Port St. Lucie Hospital

☐ **PORT ST. LUCIE HOSPITAL (104070)**, 2550 SE Walton Road, Zip 34952-7168; tel. 772/335-0400, (Nonreporting) **A**1 10 **S** Oglethorpe Recovery and Behavioral Hospitals, Tampa, FL
Primary Contact: Patrick Kiley, Administrator
Web address: www.portstluciehospitalinc.com
**Control**: Other not-for-profit (including NFP Corporation) **Service**: Psychiatric

| Staffed Beds: 75 |
| --- |

✠ **ST. LUCIE MEDICAL CENTER (100260)**, 1800 SE Tiffany Avenue, Zip 34952-7521; tel. 772/335-4000, (Nonreporting) **A**1 3 5 10 **S** HCA Healthcare, Nashville, TN
Primary Contact: Jay Finnegan, Chief Executive Officer
COO: Calvin Thomas IVChief Operating Officer
CFO: Kevin Keeling, Chief Financial Officer
Web address: www.stluciemed.com
**Control**: Corporation, Investor-owned (for-profit) **Service**: General medical and surgical

| Staffed Beds: 229 |
| --- |

**TRADITION MEDICAL CENTER** See Cleveland Clinic Tradition Hospital

### PUNTA GORDA—Charlotte County

✠ **BAYFRONT HEALTH PUNTA GORDA (100047)**, 809 East Marion Avenue, Zip 33950-3819, Mailing Address: P.O. Box 51-1328, Zip 33951-1328; tel. 941/639-3131, (Nonreporting) **A**1 10 **F**34 40 45 53 57 59 60 77 79 81 82 87 91 93 100 104 107 111 115 119 130 148 154 **S** Community Health Systems, Inc., Franklin, TN
Primary Contact: Eric Kaplan, Interim Chief Executive Officer
CNO: Russell Schroeder, Chief Nursing Officer
Web address: www.bayfrontcharlotte.com
**Control**: Corporation, Investor-owned (for-profit) **Service**: General medical and surgical

| Staffed Beds: 190 Admissions: 5695 Census: 87 Births: 0 |
| --- |

**CHARLOTTE REGIONAL MEDICAL CENTER** See Bayfront Health Punta Gorda

### RIVERVIEW—Hillsborough County

**JOSEPH'S HOSPITAL SOUTH** See St. Joseph's Hospital-South

### RIVIERA BEACH—Palm Beach County

✠ **KINDRED HOSPITAL THE PALM BEACHES (102025)**, 5555 West Blue Heron Boulevard, Zip 33418-7813; tel. 561/840-0754, (Nonreporting) **A**1 10 **S** Kindred Healthcare, Louisville, KY
Primary Contact: Elayne Lopreato, Chief Executive Officer
CFO: Dean Card, Chief Financial Officer
CNO: Elayne Lopreato, Chief Clinical Officer
Web address: www.khthepalmbeaches.com/
**Control**: Corporation, Investor-owned (for-profit) **Service**: Acute long-term care hospital

| Staffed Beds: 70 |
| --- |

### ROCKLEDGE—Brevard County

☐ **ROCKLEDGE REGIONAL MEDICAL CENTER (100092)**, 110 Longwood Avenue, Zip 32955-2887, Mailing Address: P.O. Box 565002, Mail Stop 1, Zip 32956-5002; tel. 321/636-2211, (Nonreporting) **A**1 10 **S** Steward Health Care System, LLC, Dallas, TX
Primary Contact: Andrew Romine, Chief Executive Officer
CFO: Jonathan R Immordino, Chief Financial Officer
CMO: Vinay Mehindru, M.D., Medical Director
CIO: David Barnhart, Director Information Systems
CHR: Marchita H Marino, Vice President Human Resources
CNO: Mary Sue Zinsmeister, Chief Nursing Officer
Web address: www.wuesthoff.org
**Control**: Corporation, Investor-owned (for-profit) **Service**: General medical and surgical

| Staffed Beds: 215 |
| --- |

**WUESTHOFF MEDICAL CENTER - ROCKLEDGE** See Rockledge Regional Medical Center

### SAFETY HARBOR—Pinellas County

✠ **MEASE COUNTRYSIDE HOSPITAL (100265)**, 3231 McMullen Booth Road, Zip 34695-6607; tel. 727/725-6111, (Nonreporting) **A**1 2 3 10 **F**3 11 13 15 17 18 20 22 26 28 29 30 31 32 34 35 37 38 40 41 44 45 46 49 50 51 55 56 57 59 60 62 63 64 68 70 72 74 75 76 77 78 79 81 84 85 86 87 89 92 93 107 108 110 111 114 115 116 117 118 119 126 129 130 131 132 135 143 145 146 147 148 149 154 156 **P**6 **S** Trinity Health, Livonia, MI
Primary Contact: Matthew Novak, President
CFO: Carl Tremonti, Chief Financial Officer
CMO: Tony Schuster, M.D., Vice President of Physician Services
CIO: Tim Thompson, Senior Vice President, Informant Services and Chief Information Officer
CHR: Kyle J Barr, Senior Vice President, Chief Team Resources Officer
CNO: Thomas Doria, Vice President, Patient Services and Chief Nursing Officer
Web address: www.mpmhealth.com
**Control**: Other not-for-profit (including NFP Corporation) **Service**: General medical and surgical

| Staffed Beds: 311 Admissions: 17760 Census: 202 Outpatient |
| --- |
| Visits: 138758 Births: 2064 Total Expense ($000): 317268 Payroll |
| Expense ($000): 106964 Personnel: 1611 |

**MEASE HOSPITAL COUNTRYSIDE** See Mease Countryside Hospital

### SAINT AUGUSTINE—St. Johns County

☐ **FLAGLER HOSPITAL (100090)**, 400 Health Park Boulevard, Zip 32086-5784; tel. 904/819-5155, (Nonreporting) **A**1 2 5 10 20
Primary Contact: Jason P. Barrett, Chief Executive Officer
CFO: Lynda I Kirker, Chief Financial Officer
CMO: Douglas Dew, M.D., President Medical Staff
CIO: Bill Rieger, Chief Information Officer
CHR: Jeff Hurley, Vice President Human Resources
Web address: www.flaglerhospital.org
**Control**: Other not-for-profit (including NFP Corporation) **Service**: General medical and surgical

| Staffed Beds: 204 |
| --- |

**FL**

---

| Hospital, Medicare Provider Number, Address, Telephone, Approval, Facility, and Physician Codes, Health Care System |
| --- |
| ★ American Hospital Association (AHA) membership ○ Healthcare Facilities Accreditation Program ⇑ Center for Improvement in Healthcare Quality Accreditation |
| ☐ The Joint Commission accreditation ◇ DNV Healthcare Inc. accreditation △ Commission on Accreditation of Rehabilitation Facilities (CARF) accreditation |

## SAINT CLOUD—Osceola County

**ST CLOUD HOSPITAL** See St. Cloud Regional Medical Center

☒ **ST. CLOUD REGIONAL MEDICAL CENTER (100302)**, 2906 17th Street, Zip 34769–6099; tel. 407/892–2135, (Nonreporting) **A**1 10 **F**3 15 18 20 22 29 30 34 35 40 45 46 49 51 57 59 70 74 75 77 78 79 81 82 85 86 87 91 93 94 96 97 107 108 110 111 115 119 130 146 154 **S** Orlando Health, Orlando, FL
Primary Contact: Brent Burish, Chief Executive Officer
COO: Andrea Thomas, Chief Operating Officer
CFO: Carl Caley, Chief Financial Officer
CIO: James Devlin, Director Information Systems
CHR: Jennifer Harmon, Director of Human Resources
CNO: Perry Horne, Chief Nursing Officer
Web address: www.stcloudregional.com
**Control**: Corporation, Investor–owned (for–profit) **Service**: General medical and surgical

**Staffed Beds**: 84 **Admissions**: 4354 **Census**: 46 **Outpatient Visits**: 38425 **Births**: 0 **Total Expense ($000)**: 58993 **Payroll Expense ($000)**: 23339

☐ **THE BLACKBERRY CENTER (104081)**, 91 Beehive Circle, Zip 34769–1432, Mailing Address: St. Cloud, tel. 321/805–5090, (Nonreporting) **A**1 **S** Oglethorpe Recovery and Behavioral Hospitals, Tampa, FL
Primary Contact: Rick Bennett, Director
Web address: www.blackberrycenter.com
**Control**: Corporation, Investor–owned (for–profit) **Service**: Psychiatric

**Staffed Beds**: 64

## SAINT PETERSBURG—Pinellas County

☒ **BAYFRONT HEALTH ST. PETERSBURG (100032)**, 701 Sixth Street South, Zip 33701–4891; tel. 727/823–1234, (Nonreporting) **A**1 3 5 10 **S** Community Health Systems, Inc., Franklin, TN
Primary Contact: Sharon Hayes, Chief Executive Officer
COO: Austin Brown, Chief Operating Officer
CFO: Eric Smith, Chief Financial Officer
CIO: Kevin Murphy, Director, Information Technology Services
CHR: Jim Reames, Director Human Resources
CNO: Karen Long, R.N., FACHE, Vice President Nursing
Web address: www.bayfrontstpete.com
**Control**: Corporation, Investor–owned (for–profit) **Service**: General medical and surgical

**Staffed Beds**: 480

**BAYFRONT MEDICAL CENTER** See Bayfront Health St. Petersburg

☒ **JOHNS HOPKINS ALL CHILDREN'S HOSPITAL (103300)**, 501 6th Avenue South, Zip 33701–4634; tel. 727/898–7451, (Nonreporting) **A**1 3 5 8 10 **F**3 11 12 17 18 19 20 21 22 23 24 25 26 27 29 30 31 32 34 35 36 37 39 40 41 43 44 45 46 47 48 49 50 54 55 57 58 59 60 61 62 64 65 68 72 73 74 75 77 78 79 81 82 84 85 87 93 98 100 102 103 107 108 110 111 114 115 117 118 119 121 123 124 126 129 130 131 132 135 146 147 148 154 **P**6 **S** Johns Hopkins Health System, Baltimore, MD
Primary Contact: Thomas D. Kmetz, Interim Chief Executive Officer
CFO: Nancy Templin, Vice President Finance and Chief Financial Officer
CMO: Michael Epstein, M.D., Senior Vice President Medical Affairs
CIO: John McLendon, Vice President and Chief Information Officer
CHR: Jay Kuhns, Vice President Human Resources
CNO: Melissa Macogay, Vice President and Chief Nursing Officer
Web address: www.allkids.org
**Control**: Other not–for–profit (including NFP Corporation) **Service**: Children's general medical and surgical

**Staffed Beds**: 259 **Admissions**: 6288 **Census**: 148 **Outpatient Visits**: 354631 **Births**: 0 **Total Expense ($000)**: 516629 **Payroll Expense ($000)**: 192126 **Personnel**: 3290

**JOHNS HOPKINS ALL CHILDREN'S HOSPITALA** See Johns Hopkins All Children's Hospital

**KINDRED HOSPITAL BAY AREA** See Kindred Hospital-Bay Area St. Petersburg

☒ **NORTHSIDE HOSPITAL (100238)**, 6000 49th Street North, Zip 33709–2145; tel. 727/521–4411, (Nonreporting) **A**1 3 5 10 13 **S** HCA Healthcare, Nashville, TN
Primary Contact: Valerie L. Powell-Stafford, Chief Executive Officer
COO: Peter Kennedy, Chief Operating Officer
CFO: Peggy Gatliff, Chief Financial Officer
CMO: Ira Siegman, M.D., Chief Medical Officer
CIO: Kirk Hendrick, Director Information Systems
CHR: Maggie Miklos, Director Human Resources
CNO: John Polisknowski, Chief Nursing Officer
Web address: www.northsidehospital.com
**Control**: Corporation, Investor–owned (for–profit) **Service**: General medical and surgical

**Staffed Beds**: 288

**NORTHSIDE HOSPITAL AND HEART INSTITUTE** See Northside Hospital

☒ **PALMS OF PASADENA HOSPITAL (100126)**, 1501 Pasadena Avenue South, Zip 33707–3798; tel. 727/381–1000, (Nonreporting) **A**1 10 **S** HCA Healthcare, Nashville, TN
Primary Contact: Michael Irvin, Chief Executive Officer
COO: Raynard Ware, Vice President of Opeartions
CFO: Maria Caruso, Chief Financial Officer
CMO: Ron Rasmussen, M.D., Chief Medical Officer
CIO: Danny Waters, Director, Information Services
CHR: Megan Joy Whalen, Vice President, Human Resources
CNO: Susan Laber, R.N., Chief Nursing Officer
Web address: www.palmspasadena.com
**Control**: Corporation, Investor–owned (for–profit) **Service**: General medical and surgical

**Staffed Beds**: 307

**ST PETERSBURG MEDICAL CENTER** See St. Petersburg General Hospital

☒ **ST. ANTHONY'S HOSPITAL (100067)**, 1200 Seventh Avenue North, Zip 33705–1388, Mailing Address: P.O. Box 12588, Zip 33733–2588; tel. 727/825–1100, (Nonreporting) **A**1 2 5 10 **F**3 6 11 12 15 17 18 20 22 26 28 29 30 31 34 35 37 40 44 45 46 47 49 51 57 59 60 63 64 68 70 74 75 77 78 79 81 84 85 87 93 98 100 102 103 107 108 110 111 114 115 117 118 119 121 123 124 126 129 130 131 132 135 146 148 149 154 156 **P**6 **S** Trinity Health, Livonia, MI
Primary Contact: M. Scott Smith, President
CFO: Carl Tremonti, Chief Financial Officer
CMO: John Haffner, M.D., Chief Medical Officer
CIO: Tim Thompson, Senior Vice President and Chief Informatics Officer
CHR: Kristen A Betts, Director Team Resources
CNO: Thomas Doria, Vice President and Patient Services West
Web address: www.stanthonys.com/
**Control**: Other not–for–profit (including NFP Corporation) **Service**: General medical and surgical

**Staffed Beds**: 358 **Admissions**: 21629 **Census**: 279 **Outpatient Visits**: 119384 **Births**: 0 **Total Expense ($000)**: 388611 **Payroll Expense ($000)**: 130812 **Personnel**: 1972

☒ **ST. PETERSBURG GENERAL HOSPITAL (100180)**, 6500 38th Avenue North, Zip 33710–1629; tel. 727/384–1414, (Nonreporting) **A**1 2 3 5 10 12 13 **S** HCA Healthcare, Nashville, TN
Primary Contact: Kenneth R. Wicker, FACHE, Chief Executive Officer
COO: Stephanie McNulty, Chief Operating Officer
CFO: Shawn Gregory, Chief Financial Officer
CMO: Mitchell Rubinstein, M.D., Chief Medical Officer
CHR: Jennifer B Robinson, Vice President Human Resources
CNO: JoAnne Cattell, Chief Nursing Officer
Web address: www.stpetegeneral.com
**Control**: Corporation, Investor–owned (for–profit) **Service**: General medical and surgical

**Staffed Beds**: 215

## SANFORD—Seminole County

☒ △ **CENTRAL FLORIDA REGIONAL HOSPITAL (100161)**, 1401 West Seminole Boulevard, Zip 32771–6764; tel. 407/321–4500, (Nonreporting) **A**1 7 10 **S** HCA Healthcare, Nashville, TN
Primary Contact: Trey Abshier, Chief Executive Officer
CFO: Richard Read, Chief Financial Officer
CIO: Jerry Ballard, Director Information Systems
CHR: Linda V Smith, Vice President Human Resources
CNO: Maria Calloway, R.N., MSN, Chief Nursing Officer
Web address: www.centralfloridaregional.com
**Control**: Corporation, Investor–owned (for–profit) **Service**: General medical and surgical

**Staffed Beds**: 221

**COLUMBIA MEDICAL CTR SANFORD** See Central Florida Regional Hospital

*Many Facility Codes have changed. Please refer to the AHA Guide Code Chart.*

FL

## SARASOTA—Sarasota County

**COLUMBIA DOCTORS HOSPITAL** See Doctors Hospital of Sarasota

**COMPLEX CARE HOSPITAL AT RIDGELAKE** See Pam Specialty Hospital of Sarasota

☒ **DOCTORS HOSPITAL OF SARASOTA (100166)**, 5731 Bee Ridge Road, Zip 34233–5056; tel. 941/342–1100, (Nonreporting) **A**1 10 **F**3 5 11 15 18 20 22 26 28 29 31 34 35 37 38 40 41 42 45 46 49 50 51 54 57 59 60 64 65 70 74 75 77 78 79 80 81 85 86 87 93 98 100 101 103 104 105 107 108 110 111 114 119 126 130 131 132 134 135 136 141 145 146 147 148 149 150 152 153 154 157 **S** HCA Healthcare, Nashville, TN
Primary Contact: Robert C. Meade, Chief Executive Officer
COO: Allyssa Tobitt, Chief Operating Officer
CFO: Charles Schwaner IIIChief Financial Officer
CMO: Michael Schandorf-Lartey, M.D., Chief Medical Officer
CHR: Theresa Levering, Director Human Resources
CNO: Kathy Mitchell, R.N., Chief Nursing Officer
Web address: www.doctorsofsarasota.com
**Control:** Corporation, Investor–owned (for–profit) **Service:** General medical and surgical

**Staffed Beds: 155 Admissions:** 8814 **Census:** 100 **Outpatient Visits:** 59661 **Births:** 0 **Total Expense ($000):** 141296 **Payroll Expense ($000):** 41427 **Personnel:** 494

☒ △ **ENCOMPASS HEALTH REHABILITATION HOSPITAL OF SARASOTA (103031)**, 6400 Edgelake Drive, Zip 34240–8813; tel. 941/921–8600, (Nonreporting) **A**1 7 10 **S** Encompass Health Corporation, Birmingham, AL
Primary Contact: Marcus Braz, Chief Executive Officer
CFO: Barbara Bierut, Chief Financial Officer
CMO: Alexander De Jesus, M.D., Medical Director
CHR: Brenda Benner, Director Human Resources
Web address: www.healthsouthsarasota.com
**Control:** Corporation, Investor–owned (for–profit) **Service:** Rehabilitation

**Staffed Beds: 96**

**HEALTHSOUTH REHABILITATION HOSPITAL OF SARASOTA** See Encompass Health Rehabilitation Hospital of Sarasota

☒ **PAM SPECIALTY HOSPITAL OF SARASOTA (102018)**, 6150 Edgelake Drive, Zip 34240–8803; tel. 941/342–3000, (Nonreporting) **A**1 10 **S** Post Acute Medical, LLC, Enola, PA
Primary Contact: Jacob McGuirt, Chief Executive Officer
Web address: www.lifecare-hospitals.com/hospital.php?id=23
**Control:** Corporation, Investor–owned (for–profit) **Service:** Acute long–term care hospital

**Staffed Beds: 40**

☐ △ **SARASOTA MEMORIAL HEALTH CARE SYSTEM (100087)**, 1700 South Tamiami Trail, Zip 34239–3555; tel. 941/917–9000, (Nonreporting) **A**1 2 3 5 7 8 10 **F**3 6 8 11 12 13 15 17 18 19 20 22 24 26 28 29 30 31 32 34 35 36 37 38 39 40 42 43 44 45 46 47 48 49 50 51 53 54 55 56 57 58 59 60 61 64 66 68 70 72 73 74 75 76 77 78 79 80 81 82 84 85 86 87 89 90 91 92 93 95 96 97 98 99 100 101 102 107 108 110 111 114 115 117 118 119 124 126 129 130 131 132 134 135 143 144 145 146 147 148 149 150 154 156 **P**5 8
Primary Contact: David Verinder, President and Chief Executive Officer
COO: David Verinder, President and Chief Executive Officer
CFO: Bill Woeltjen, Chief Financial Officer
CMO: James Fiorica, M.D., Chief Medical Officer
CIO: Denis Baker, Chief Information Officer
CHR: Laurie Bennett, Director Human Resources
CNO: Connie Andersen, R.N., MS, Chief Nursing Officer
Web address: www.smh.com
**Control:** Hospital district or authority, Government, Nonfederal **Service:** General medical and surgical

**Staffed Beds: 788 Admissions:** 43120 **Census:** 543 **Outpatient Visits:** 583845 **Births:** 4012 **Total Expense ($000):** 776459 **Payroll Expense ($000):** 311958 **Personnel:** 6082

**SARASOTA MEMORIAL HOSPITAL** See Sarasota Memorial Health Care System

## SEBASTIAN—Indian River County

**SEBASTIAN HOSPITAL** See Sebastian River Medical Center

☐ **SEBASTIAN RIVER MEDICAL CENTER (100217)**, 13695 North U S Hwy 1, Zip 32958–3230, Mailing Address: Box 780838, Zip 32978–0838; tel. 772/589–3186, (Nonreporting) **A**1 10 **S** Steward Health Care System, LLC, Dallas, TX
Primary Contact: Ronald L. Bierman, President
CFO: John McEachern, Controller
CMO: Ralph Geiger, M.D., Chief of Staff
CHR: Kam Storey, Director Human Resources
CNO: Ralph Taylor, Chief Nursing Officer
Web address: www.https://www.sebastianrivermedical.org/
**Control:** Corporation, Investor–owned (for–profit) **Service:** General medical and surgical

**Staffed Beds: 154**

## SEBRING—Highlands County

☒ **ADVENTHEALTH SEBRING (100109)**, 4200 Sun'n Lake Boulevard, Zip 33872–1986, Mailing Address: P.O. Box 9400, Zip 33871–9400; tel. 863/314–4466, (Includes FLORIDA HOSPITAL LAKE PLACID, Mailing address: 1210 US 27 North, Lake Placid, Florida, Zip 33852–7948; tel. 863/465–3777; Eric Stevens, Chief Executive Officer), (Nonreporting) **A**1 3 10 19 **F**3 11 13 15 18 20 22 24 26 28 29 30 34 35 37 40 45 46 49 50 53 54 57 58 59 60 62 64 70 75 76 78 79 81 86 87 89 104 107 108 110 111 114 115 116 117 118 119 120 121 123 126 127 129 130 131 132 146 147 148 149 153 154 156 **P**6 **S** AdventHealth, Altamonte Springs, FL
Primary Contact: Randy Surber, Chief Executive Officer
CFO: Rosalie Oliver, Chief Financial Officer
CMO: Jorge F Gonzalez, M.D., Chief Medical Officer
CNO: Gloria N Santos, R.N., MS, Chief Nursing Officer
Web address: www.floridahospital.com/heartland/our-location
**Control:** Church operated, Nongovernment, not–for–profit **Service:** General medical and surgical

**Staffed Beds: 180 Admissions:** 10808 **Census:** 120 **Outpatient Visits:** 153370 **Births:** 1012 **Total Expense ($000):** 213878 **Payroll Expense ($000):** 89364 **Personnel:** 1245

**FLORIDA HOSPITAL HEARTLAND MEDICAL CENTER** See Adventhealth Sebring

☒ **HIGHLANDS REGIONAL MEDICAL CENTER (100049)**, 3600 South Highlands Avenue, Zip 33870–5495, Mailing Address: Drawer 2066, Zip 33871–2066; tel. 863/385–6101, (Nonreporting) **A**1 10 19 **S** HCA Healthcare, Nashville, TN
Primary Contact: Jason Kimbrell, Chief Executive Officer
CFO: Paul Damron, Chief Financial Officer
CIO: Nate Johnson, Chief Information Officer
CHR: Brenda Dane, Director, Human Resources
CNO: Adam Kless, Chief Nursing Officer
Web address: www.highlandsregional.com
**Control:** Corporation, Investor–owned (for–profit) **Service:** General medical and surgical

**Staffed Beds: 126**

## SOUTH MIAMI—Miami–Dade County

**LARKIN COMMUNITY HOSPITAL** See Larkin Community Hospital-South Miami Campus

☐ **LARKIN COMMUNITY HOSPITAL-SOUTH MIAMI CAMPUS (100181)**, 7031 SW 62nd Avenue, Zip 33143–4781; tel. 305/284–7500, (Nonreporting) **A**1 3 5 10 12 13
Primary Contact: Sandra Sosa-Guerrero, Chief Executive Officer
COO: George J Michel, Chief Operating Officer
CFO: Edgar Castillo, Chief Financial Officer
CMO: Mario Almeida-Suarez, M.D., Chief of Staff
CIO: Orlando Suarez, Director Information Technology
CHR: Carolina Pena, Assistant Director Administrator
CNO: Mercedes Perez, Vice President Nursing
Web address: www.larkinhospital.com
**Control:** Individual, Investor–owned (for–profit) **Service:** General medical and surgical

**Staffed Beds: 146**

---

**Hospital, Medicare Provider Number, Address, Telephone, Approval, Facility, and Physician Codes, Health Care System**

★ American Hospital Association (AHA) membership
☐ The Joint Commission accreditation
○ Healthcare Facilities Accreditation Program
◇ DNV Healthcare Inc. accreditation
⇈ Center for Improvement in Healthcare Quality Accreditation
△ Commission on Accreditation of Rehabilitation Facilities (CARF) accreditation

FL

## SPRING HILL—Hernando County

**SPRING HILL REGIONAL HOSPITAL** See Bayfront Health Spring Hill

## STUART—Martin County

☒ **CLEVELAND CLINIC MARTIN NORTH HOSPITAL (100044)**, 200 SE Hospital Avenue, Zip 34994–2346, Mailing Address: P.O. Box 9010, Zip 34995–9010; tel. 772/287–5200, (Includes CLEVELAND CLINIC MARTIN SOUTH HOSPITAL, Mailing address: 2100 SE Salerno Road, Stuart, Florida, Zip 34997; tel. 772/223–2300; Mark E Robitaille, FACHE, President and Chief Executive Officer; CLEVELAND CLINIC TRADITION HOSPITAL, Mailing address: 10000 SW Innovation Way, Port St Lucie, Florida, Zip 34987–2111; tel. 772/345–8100; Mark E Robitaille, FACHE, President and Chief Executive Officer), (Nonreporting) **A**1 2 10 **F**3 8 11 12 13 15 17 18 20 22 24 26 28 29 30 31 34 35 36 37 40 42 45 46 47 48 49 50 51 53 55 59 60 64 65 68 70 72 74 75 76 77 78 79 81 82 85 86 87 91 92 93 94 95 107 108 110 111 112 114 115 118 119 120 121 122 123 124 126 129 130 132 135 143 146 148 149 154 156 **P**6 **S** Cleveland Clinic Health System, Cleveland, OH
Primary Contact: Robert L. Lord, JD, President and Chief Executive Officer
CFO: Chuck Cleaver, Vice President and Chief Financial Officer
CMO: Fernando Petry, M.D., Vice President and Chief Medical Officer
CIO: Edmund Collins, Chief Information Officer
CHR: Angie L Metcalf, Vice President and Chief Human Resource Officer
CNO: Mary Elizabeth Flippo, R.N., MSN, Vice President and Chief Nursing Officer
Web address: www.martinhealth.org
**Control:** Other not–for–profit (including NFP Corporation) **Service:** General medical and surgical

**Staffed Beds:** 507 **Admissions:** 27089 **Census:** 318 **Outpatient Visits:** 163623 **Births:** 1772 **Total Expense ($000):** 488117 **Payroll Expense ($000):** 213486 **Personnel:** 4119

☒ **ENCOMPASS HEALTH REHABILITATION HOSPITAL AN AFFILIATE OF MARTIN HEALTH (103044)**, 5850 SE Community Drive, Zip 34997–6420; tel. 772/324–3500, (Nonreporting) **A**1 10 **S** Encompass Health Corporation, Birmingham, AL
Primary Contact: Ivette Miranda, Chief Executive Officer
CFO: Dawn Salas, Controller
CMO: Stephen L Chastain, M.D., Chief Medical Officer
CHR: Donna Holder-Hooper, Chief Human Resource Officer
CNO: Charmaine Blanchard, Chief Nursing Officer
Web address: www.healthsouthmartin.com
**Control:** Corporation, Investor–owned (for–profit) **Service:** Rehabilitation

**Staffed Beds:** 54

**HEALTHSOUTH REHABILITATION HOSPITAL AT MARTIN HEALTH** See Encompass Health Rehabilitation Hospital An Affiliate of Martin Health

**MARTIN HEALTH SYSTEM** See Cleveland Clinic Martin North Hospital

**MARTIN MEMORIAL HOSPITAL SOUTH** See Cleveland Clinic Martin South Hospital

## SUN CITY CENTER—Hillsborough County

**COLUMBIA SOUTH BAY HOSPITAL** See South Bay Hospital

☒ **SOUTH BAY HOSPITAL (100259)**, 4016 Sun City Center Blvd, Zip 33573–5298; tel. 813/634–3301, (Nonreporting) **A**1 10 **S** HCA Healthcare, Nashville, TN
Primary Contact: Daniel Bender, Chief Executive Officer
CFO: Warren Pate, Chief Financial Officer
CMO: Joseph C. Corcoran, D.O., Chief Medical Officer
CIO: Eric Young, Director Information Technology and Systems
CHR: Stacie Novosel, Vice President, Human Resources
CNO: Marcy Frisina, Chief Nursing Officer
Web address: www.southbayhospital.com/
**Control:** Corporation, Investor–owned (for–profit) **Service:** General medical and surgical

**Staffed Beds:** 138

## SUNRISE—Broward County

☒ **ENCOMPASS HEALTH REHABILITATION HOSPITAL OF SUNRISE (103028)**, 4399 North Nob Hill Road, Zip 33351–5899; tel. 954/749–0300, (Nonreporting) **A**1 3 10 **S** Encompass Health Corporation, Birmingham, AL
Primary Contact: Michael S. Roffelsen, Chief Executive Officer
CFO: Ruth Goodstein, Controller
CMO: Scott Tannenbaum, M.D., Medical Director
CIO: Angela Manning, Director Health Information Services
CHR: Barbara Dunkiel, Director Human Resources
CNO: Omaira D. Riano, Chief Nursing Officer
Web address: www.healthsouthsunrise.com
**Control:** Corporation, Investor–owned (for–profit) **Service:** Rehabilitation

**Staffed Beds:** 126

**HEALTHSOUTH SUNRISE REHABILITATION HOSPITAL** See Encompass Health Rehabilitation Hospital of Sunrise

## TALLAHASSEE—Leon County

☒ **CAPITAL REGIONAL MEDICAL CENTER (100254)**, 2626 Capital Medical Boulevard, Zip 32308–4499; tel. 850/325–5000, (Nonreporting) **A**1 2 10 **S** HCA Healthcare, Nashville, TN
Primary Contact: Alan Seesee, Chief Executive Officer
CMO: Steve West, M.D., Chief Medical Officer
CIO: Robert A Steed, Director Information Systems
CHR: Louise Truitt, Vice President Human Resources
Web address: www.capitalregionalmedicalcenter.com
**Control:** Individual, Investor–owned (for–profit) **Service:** General medical and surgical

**Staffed Beds:** 270

**EASTSIDE PSYCHIATRIC HOSPITAL (104059)**, 2634 Capital Circle NE, Zip 32308–4106; tel. 850/523–3333, (Nonreporting) **A**10
Primary Contact: Jay A. Reeve, Ph.D., President and Chief Executive Officer
COO: Sue Conger, Chief Operating Officer
CFO: Virginia Kelly, Chief Financial Officer
CMO: Ludmila de Faria, M.D., Chief Medical Officer
CIO: Thad Moorer, Chief Information Officer
CHR: Candy Landry, Chief Human Resource Officer
CNO: Judy Goreau, R.N., Director of Nursing
Web address: www.apalacheecenter.org
**Control:** Other not–for–profit (including NFP Corporation) **Service:** Psychiatric

**Staffed Beds:** 24

☒ **ENCOMPASS HEALTH REHABILITATION HOSPITAL OF TALLAHASSEE (103033)**, 1675 Riggins Road, Zip 32308–5315; tel. 850/656–4800, (Nonreporting) **A**1 10 **S** Encompass Health Corporation, Birmingham, AL
Primary Contact: K. Dale. Neely, FACHE, Chief Executive Officer
CFO: Jennifer Spooner, Controller
CMO: Robert Rowland, M.D., Medical Director
CIO: Michael Spangler, Health Information Management Services Supervisor
CHR: Carol Bugayong, Human Resources Director
CNO: Elizabeth Squires, R.N., Chief Nursing Officer
Web address: www.healthsouthtallahassee.com
**Control:** Corporation, Investor–owned (for–profit) **Service:** Rehabilitation

**Staffed Beds:** 76

**HEALTHSOUTH REHABILITATION HOSPITAL OF TALLAHASSEE** See Encompass Health Rehabilitation Hospital of Tallahassee

☒ **SELECT SPECIALTY HOSPITAL-TALLAHASSEE (102020)**, 1554 Surgeons Drive, Zip 32308–4631; tel. 850/219–6950, (Nonreporting) **A**1 10 **S** Select Medical Corporation, Mechanicsburg, PA
Primary Contact: Jay Faherty, Chief Executive Officer
Web address: www.tallahassee.selectspecialtyhospitals.com/
**Control:** Corporation, Investor–owned (for–profit) **Service:** Acute long–term care hospital

**Staffed Beds:** 29

**TALLAHASSEE COMMUNITY HOSPITAL** See Capital Regional Medical Center

**TALLAHASSEE MEM REG MED CENTER** See Tallahassee Memorial Healthcare

☒ **TALLAHASSEE MEMORIAL HEALTHCARE (100135)**, 1300 Miccosukee Road, Zip 32308–5054; tel. 850/431–1155, (Total facility includes 42 beds in nursing home–type unit) (Nonreporting) **A**1 2 3 5 10 **F**2 3 5 8 11 12 15 17 18 19 20 22 24 26 28 29 30 31 34 35 37 40 42 43 46 47 48 49 50 51 53 54 55 56 57 58 59 60 61 62 64 65 68 70 72 73 74 75 76 77 78 79 80 81 82 84 85 86 87 88 89 91 93 96 97 98 99 100 102 103 104 107 108 110 113 114 115 117 118 119 120 121 123 124 126 127 128 129 130 131 132 135 143 144 146 147 148 149 154 156 **P**6
Primary Contact: G. Mark. O'Bryant, President and Chief Executive Officer
COO: Jason H Moore, Vice President and Chief Operating Officer
CFO: William A Giudice, Vice President and Chief Financial Officer
CMO: Dean Watson, M.D., Chief Medical Officer
CIO: Don Lindsey, Vice President and Chief Information Officer
CHR: Steven W Adriaanse, Vice President and Chief Human Resources Officer
Web address: www.tmh.org
**Control:** Other not–for–profit (including NFP Corporation) **Service:** General medical and surgical

**Staffed Beds:** 495 **Admissions:** 29284 **Census:** 421 **Outpatient Visits:** 859615 **Births:** 3733 **Total Expense ($000):** 755897 **Payroll Expense ($000):** 315143 **Personnel:** 5109

FL

## TAMARAC—Broward County

**COLUMBIA UNIVERSITY HOSPITAL** See University Hospital and Medical Center

☒ **UNIVERSITY HOSPITAL AND MEDICAL CENTER (100224)**, 7201 North University Drive, Zip 33321–2996; tel. 954/721–2200, (Includes UNIVERSITY PAVILION, Mailing address: 7425 North University Drive, Tamarac, Florida, Zip 33328; tel. 305/722–9933), (Nonreporting) **A**1 3 5 10 **S** HCA Healthcare, Nashville, TN
Primary Contact: Ben Harris, Chief Executive Officer
CFO: Aurelio Gonzalez, Chief Financial Officer
CMO: Ran Abrahamy, M.D., Chief of Staff
CIO: Tom Scharff, Director Information Services
Web address: www.uhmchealth.com
**Control:** Corporation, Investor–owned (for–profit) **Service:** General medical and surgical

| Staffed Beds: 317 |
| --- |

## TAMPA—Hillsborough County

☒ ○ **ADVENTHEALTH CARROLLWOOD (100069)**, 7171 North Dale Mabry Highway, Zip 33614–2665; tel. 813/932–2222, (Nonreporting) **A**1 3 10 11 **F**3 12 15 18 20 22 26 29 30 34 35 40 44 45 46 47 48 49 50 51 57 58 59 60 65 70 71 74 75 79 81 82 87 107 108 110 111 115 116 117 118 119 126 130 133 143 146 148 149 157 **S** AdventHealth, Altamonte Springs, FL
Primary Contact: Erika Skula, President and Chief Executive Officer
COO: Mary C Whillock, R.N., MS, Associate Nursing Officer and Chief Operating Officer
CFO: Chris Sauder, Vice President and Chief Financial Officer
CNO: Deborah W Kumar, MSN, Chief Nursing Officer
Web address: www.https://www.floridahospital.com/carrollwood
**Control:** Church operated, Nongovernment, not–for–profit **Service:** General medical and surgical

| Staffed Beds: 95 Admissions: 5707 Census: 60 Outpatient Visits: 51177 Births: 0 Total Expense ($000): 145065 Payroll Expense ($000): 41193 Personnel: 534 |
| --- |

☒ △ ⇑ **ADVENTHEALTH TAMPA (100173)**, 3100 East Fletcher Avenue, Zip 33613–4688; tel. 813/971–6000, (Nonreporting) **A**1 2 3 5 7 10 21 **F**3 11 12 13 15 17 18 19 20 21 22 24 25 26 27 28 29 30 31 34 35 37 40 41 42 44 45 46 47 48 49 50 54 57 58 59 60 64 65 70 72 74 75 76 77 78 79 80 81 82 84 85 86 87 88 89 90 91 92 93 96 105 107 108 109 110 111 112 114 115 116 117 118 119 120 121 123 124 126 129 130 132 135 143 144 146 147 148 149 152 156 **S** AdventHealth, Altamonte Springs, FL
Primary Contact: Denyse Bales-Chubb, Chief Executive Officer
COO: Dick Tibbits, Vice President and Chief Operating Officer
CFO: Tyson Davis, Chief Financial Officer
CMO: Brad Bjornstad, M.D., Vice President and Chief Medical Officer
CHR: Dick Tibbits, Vice President and Chief Operating Officer
CNO: Theresa Trivette, R.N., Chief Nursing Officer
Web address: www.floridahospital.com/tampa
**Control:** Other not–for–profit (including NFP Corporation) **Service:** General medical and surgical

| Staffed Beds: 536 Admissions: 22048 Census: 338 Outpatient Visits: 133960 Births: 2295 Total Expense ($000): 525085 Payroll Expense ($000): 162266 Personnel: 2582 |
| --- |

**AMI MEMORIAL HOSPITAL OF TAMPA** See Memorial Hospital of Tampa

**FLORIDA HOSPITAL CARROLLWOOD** See Adventhealth Carrollwood

⇑ **FLORIDA HOSPITAL TAMPA** See Adventhealth Tampa

☒ **H. LEE MOFFITT CANCER CENTER AND RESEARCH INSTITUTE (100271)**, 12902 Magnolia Drive, Zip 33612–9497; tel. 813/745–4673, (Nonreporting) **A**1 2 3 5 10 **F**3 8 15 26 29 30 31 34 35 36 37 38 44 45 46 47 49 50 54 55 56 57 58 59 64 68 70 71 74 75 77 78 79 80 81 82 84 85 86 87 91 92 93 96 97 100 101 103 104 107 108 110 111 114 115 117 118 119 120 121 123 124 126 130 132 135 136 144 145 146 147 148 149 154 **P**6
Primary Contact: Tim Adams, Interim Chief Executive Officer and President
COO: John A Kolosky, Executive Vice President and Chief Operating Officer
CFO: Yvette Tremonti, Chief Financial Officer
CMO: Bob Keenan, Chief Medical Officer
CIO: Dave Summitt, Chief Information Security Officer
CHR: Mariana Bugallo-Muros, Vice President Chief Human Resources Officer
CNO: Jane Fusilero, Vice President Chief Nursing Officer
Web address: www.moffitt.org
**Control:** Other not–for–profit (including NFP Corporation) **Service:** Cancer

| Staffed Beds: 206 Admissions: 9465 Census: 170 Outpatient Visits: 450116 Births: 0 Total Expense ($000): 1431060 Payroll Expense ($000): 551865 Personnel: 6459 |
| --- |

**JAMES A. HALEY VETERANS' HOSPITAL** See James A. Haley Veterans' Hospital-Tampa

☒ △ **JAMES A. HALEY VETERANS' HOSPITAL-TAMPA**, 13000 Bruce B Downs Boulevard, Zip 33612–4745; tel. 813/972–2000, (Total facility includes 64 beds in nursing home–type unit) (Nonreporting) **A**1 3 5 7 8 **F**3 5 9 12 15 17 18 20 22 24 26 28 29 30 31 33 34 35 36 38 39 40 45 46 47 48 49 50 51 53 54 55 56 57 58 59 60 61 62 63 64 65 70 71 74 75 77 78 79 80 81 82 83 84 85 86 87 90 91 92 93 94 95 96 97 98 100 101 102 104 105 107 108 109 110 111 113 114 115 116 117 118 119 120 121 123 126 127 128 129 130 131 132 135 143 144 146 147 148 149 152 153 154 156 157 158 **S** Department of Veterans Affairs, Washington, DC
Primary Contact: Joe Battle, Director
CFO: Robert Konkel, Manager Finance
CMO: Edward Cutolo, M.D., JrChief of Staff
CIO: Jose Seymour, Chief Information Resource Management
CHR: Andrew Sutton, Chief, Human Resources Management Service
CNO: Laureen Doloresco, R.N., Associate Director for Patient Care and Nursing Services
Web address: www.tampa.va.gov/
**Control:** Veterans Affairs, Government, federal **Service:** General medical and surgical

| Staffed Beds: 499 Admissions: 11046 Census: 368 Outpatient Visits: 1437900 Births: 0 Personnel: 915 |
| --- |

☒ **KINDRED HOSPITAL BAY AREA-TAMPA (102009)**, 4555 South Manhattan Avenue, Zip 33611–2397; tel. 813/839–6341, (Includes KINDRED HOSPITAL-BAY AREA ST. PETERSBURG, Mailing address: 3030 Sixth Street South, Saint Petersburg, Florida, Zip 33705–3720; tel. 727/894–8719; Paul Schrank, Chief Executive Officer), (Nonreporting) **A**1 10 **S** Kindred Healthcare, Louisville, KY
Primary Contact: Cindy Jackson, Chief Executive Officer
CFO: Frank Billy, Chief Financial Officer
CHR: Deborah Basria, Human Resources Payroll Administrator
Web address: www.khtampa.com/
**Control:** Corporation, Investor–owned (for–profit) **Service:** Acute long–term care hospital

| Staffed Beds: 73 |
| --- |

☒ **KINDRED HOSPITAL CENTRAL TAMPA (102013)**, 4801 North Howard Avenue, Zip 33603–1411; tel. 813/874–7575, (Nonreporting) **A**1 10 **S** Kindred Healthcare, Louisville, KY
Primary Contact: Suthanthira M. Ratnasamy, R.N., FACHE, Chief Executive Officer
CFO: John Miner, Chief Financial Officer
Web address: www.kindredcentraltampa.com/
**Control:** Corporation, Investor–owned (for–profit) **Service:** Acute long–term care hospital

| Staffed Beds: 109 |
| --- |

**KINDRED HOSPITAL-CENTRAL TAMPA** See Kindred Hospital Central Tampa

**KINDRED HOSPITAL-TAMPA** See Kindred Hospital Bay Area-Tampa

☒ **MEMORIAL HOSPITAL OF TAMPA (100206)**, 2901 Swann Avenue, Zip 33609–4057; tel. 813/873–6400, (Includes TAMPA COMMUNITY HOSPITAL, Mailing address: 6001 Webb Road, Tampa, Florida, Zip 33615–3291; tel. 813/888–7060), (Nonreporting) **A**1 5 10 **S** HCA Healthcare, Nashville, TN
Primary Contact: Sonia I. Wellman, Chief Executive Officer
COO: Cathy Edmisten, Chief Operating Officer
CFO: Shelley V Kolseth, Chief Financial Officer
CMO: Christos Politis, M.D., Chief Medical Officer
CIO: John Riton, Director Information Services
Web address: www.memorialhospitaltampa.com
**Control:** Corporation, Investor–owned (for–profit) **Service:** General medical and surgical

| Staffed Beds: 384 |
| --- |

**SHRINERS HOSPITALS FOR CHILDREN-TAMPA (103303)**, 12502 USF Pine Drive, Zip 33612–9499; tel. 813/972–2250, (Nonreporting) **A**3 5 10 **S** Shriners Hospitals for Children, Tampa, FL
Primary Contact: Fleury Yelvington, Administrator
CFO: Ruth Gregos, Director Finance
CMO: Maureen Maciel, M.D., Chief of Staff
CHR: Amy Schenker, Human Resources Director
Web address: www.shrinershospitalsforchildren.org/Hospitals/Locations/Tampa.aspx
**Control:** Other not–for–profit (including NFP Corporation) **Service:** Children's orthopedic

| Staffed Beds: 60 |
| --- |

---

**Hospital, Medicare Provider Number, Address, Telephone, Approval, Facility, and Physician Codes, Health Care System**

★ American Hospital Association (AHA) membership  ○ Healthcare Facilities Accreditation Program  ⇑ Center for Improvement in Healthcare Quality Accreditation
□ The Joint Commission accreditation  ◇ DNV Healthcare Inc. accreditation  △ Commission on Accreditation of Rehabilitation Facilities (CARF) accreditation

**FL**

**SHRINERS HOSPS FOR CRPLD CHILD** See Shriners Hospitals for Children-Tampa

**ST. JOSEPH'S CHILDREN'S HOSPITAL OF TAMPA** See St. Joseph's Children's Hospital

⊞ **ST. JOSEPH'S HOSPITAL (100075)**, 3001 West Martin Luther King Jr. Boulevard, Zip 33607–6387, Mailing Address: P.O. Box 4227, Zip 33677–4227; tel. 813/870–4000, (Includes ST. JOSEPH'S CHILDREN'S HOSPITAL, Mailing address: 3001 Dr Martin Luther King Jr Boulevard, Tampa, Florida, Zip 33607; tel. 813/554–8500; Sarah Naumowich, President; ST. JOSEPH'S HOSPITAL - NORTH, Mailing address: 4211 Van Dyke Road, Lutz, Florida, Zip 33558–8005; tel. 813/443–7000; Paula McGinnis, Chief Executive Officer; ST. JOSEPH'S HOSPITAL BEHAVIORAL HEALTH CENTER, Mailing address: 4918 North Habana Avenue, Tampa, Florida, Zip 33614–6815; tel. 813/870–4300; ST. JOSEPH'S HOSPITAL-SOUTH, Mailing address: 6901 Simmons Loop, Riverview, Florida, Zip 33578–9498; tel. 813/302–8000; Philip Minden, President; ST. JOSEPH'S WOMEN'S HOSPITAL, Mailing address: 3030 West Dr Martin L King Boulevard, Tampa, Florida, Zip 33607–6394; tel. 813/872–2950; Sarah Naumowich, President), (Nonreporting) **A**1 2 3 5 10 **F**3 7 11 12 13 15 17 18 19 20 21 22 23 24 25 26 27 28 29 30 31 32 34 35 36 37 39 40 41 43 44 45 46 48 49 50 51 57 58 59 61 63 64 65 66 68 70 71 72 73 74 75 76 78 79 81 82 84 85 86 87 88 89 92 93 94 98 99 100 101 102 107 108 110 111 112 114 115 116 117 118 119 120 121 123 124 126 127 129 130 131 132 134 135 143 145 146 147 148 149 150 154 156 **P**6 **S** Trinity Health, Livonia, MI
Primary Contact: Kimberly Guy, President
CFO: Ron Beamon, Chief Financial Officer
CMO: Peter Charvat, M.D., Chief Medical Officer
CIO: Tim Thompson, Senior Vice President and Chief Information Officer
CHR: Kris Betts, Director Team Resources
CNO: Joanne Mayer
Web address: www.sjbhealth.org
**Control:** Other not–for–profit (including NFP Corporation) **Service:** General medical and surgical

**Staffed Beds:** 1062 **Admissions:** 56561 **Census:** 695 **Outpatient Visits:** 610066 **Births:** 6907 **Total Expense ($000):** 1150649 **Payroll Expense ($000):** 383402 **Personnel:** 5963

**ST. JOSEPH'S WOMEN'S HOSPITAL - TAMPA** See St. Joseph's Women's Hospital

**TAMPA GENERAL HEALTHCARE** See Tampa General Hospital

★ △ **TAMPA GENERAL HOSPITAL (100128)**, 1 Tampa General Circle, Zip 33606–3571, Mailing Address: P.O. Box 1289, Zip 33601–1289; tel. 813/844–7000, (Includes TAMPA GENERAL HOSPITAL CHILDREN'S MEDICAL CENTER, Mailing address: 1 Tampa General Circle, Tampa, Florida, Zip 33606–3571; tel. 813/844–7000), (Nonreporting) **A**3 5 7 8 10 **F**3 4 7 8 9 11 12 13 15 16 17 18 19 20 22 24 26 28 29 30 31 32 34 35 36 37 38 39 40 41 42 43 44 45 46 47 48 49 50 52 53 54 55 56 57 58 59 60 61 62 63 64 65 66 68 69 70 72 73 74 75 76 77 78 79 81 82 83 84 85 86 87 88 89 90 91 92 93 94 95 96 97 99 100 101 102 103 107 108 109 110 111 112 114 115 116 117 118 119 120 121 123 124 126 129 130 132 134 135 137 138 139 140 141 142 143 144 145 146 147 148 149 150 154 155 156 157
Primary Contact: John D. Couris, Chief Executive Officer
COO: Kelly Cullen, R.N., Executive Vice President and Chief Operating Officer
CFO: Mark A Runyon, Chief Financial Officer
CMO: Sally Houston, M.D., Executive Vice President and Chief Medical Officer
CIO: Scott Arnold, Senior Vice President Information Systems
CHR: Chris Roederer, Senior Vice President Human Resources
CNO: Janet Davis, R.N., MS, Senior Vice President and Chief Nursing Officer
Web address: www.tgh.org
**Control:** Other not–for–profit (including NFP Corporation) **Service:** General medical and surgical

**Staffed Beds:** 1007 **Admissions:** 53477 **Census:** 796 **Outpatient Visits:** 510271 **Births:** 6371 **Total Expense ($000):** 1433702 **Payroll Expense ($000):** 524879 **Personnel:** 7762

**TOWN AND COUNTRY HOSPITAL** See Tampa Community Hospital

**TARPON SPRINGS—Pinellas County**

⊞ **ADVENTHEALTH NORTH PINELLAS (100055)**, 1395 South Pinellas Avenue, Zip 34689–3790; tel. 727/942–5000, (Total facility includes 32 beds in nursing home–type unit) (Nonreporting) **A**1 5 10 **F**3 11 15 17 18 20 22 26 28 29 30 31 34 35 37 38 40 41 42 45 46 49 50 51 54 56 57 59 64 65 68 70 74 75 76 78 79 81 85 87 93 97 107 108 110 111 114 115 116 117 119 126 128 129 130 131 132 146 148 149 154 **S** AdventHealth, Altamonte Springs, FL
Primary Contact: Jason Dunkel, President and Chief Executive Officer
CFO: Caleb Heinrich, Chief Financial Officer
CMO: Michael Longley, M.D., Chief Medical Officer
CIO: Brett Peterson, Director of Information Services
CHR: Vernon Elarbee, Director of Human Resources
CNO: Jennifer Segur, Chief Nursing Officer and Chief Clinical Officer
Web address: www.fhnorthpinellas.com/
**Control:** Church operated, Nongovernment, not–for–profit **Service:** General medical and surgical

**Staffed Beds:** 187 **Admissions:** 5784 **Census:** 83 **Outpatient Visits:** 49725 **Births:** 0 **Total Expense ($000):** 122466 **Payroll Expense ($000):** 39178

**FLORIDA HOSPITAL NORTH PINELLAS** See Adventhealth North Pinellas

**TAVARES—Lake County**

⊞ **ADVENTHEALTH WATERMAN (100057)**, 1000 Waterman Way, Zip 32778–5266; tel. 352/253–3333, (Nonreporting) **A**1 2 10 **F**3 11 13 15 17 18 20 22 24 26 28 29 30 31 32 34 35 40 41 45 46 47 49 50 54 57 59 62 64 66 70 74 75 76 77 78 79 81 84 85 86 87 89 90 91 93 107 108 110 111 114 115 116 117 118 119 120 121 123 124 126 130 132 143 146 147 148 149 154 156 157 **P**8 **S** AdventHealth, Altamonte Springs, FL
Primary Contact: Abel Biri, Chief Executive Officer
COO: Anita Young, Chief Operating Officer
CFO: Terri Warren, Chief Financial Officer
CMO: Vinay Mehindru, M.D., Vice President/Chief Medical Officer
CHR: Madge Springer, Director Human Resources
CNO: Michael Stimson, Chief Nursing Officer
Web address: www.fhwat.org
**Control:** Church operated, Nongovernment, not–for–profit **Service:** General medical and surgical

**Staffed Beds:** 300 **Admissions:** 13653 **Census:** 165 **Outpatient Visits:** 134757 **Births:** 577 **Total Expense ($000):** 243989 **Payroll Expense ($000):** 90944 **Personnel:** 1800

**FLORIDA HOSPITAL WATERMAN** See Adventhealth Waterman

**TAVERNIER—Monroe County**

⊞ **BAPTIST HEALTH SOUTH FLORIDA, MARINERS HOSPITAL (101313)**, 91500 Overseas Highway, Zip 33070–2547; tel. 305/434–3000, (Nonreporting) **A**1 10 18 **F**3 11 15 18 28 29 30 31 34 35 40 44 45 50 51 53 57 59 63 64 68 70 74 75 77 78 79 81 84 85 87 93 107 108 110 111 114 119 129 130 131 132 133 135 146 147 148 149 150 154 156 **P**8 **S** Baptist Health South Florida, Coral Gables, FL
Primary Contact: Rick Freeburg, Chief Executive Officer
CFO: David Abercrombie, Controller
CIO: Mimi Taylor, Vice President Information Technology
CHR: John Williamson, Human Resources Site Manager
Web address: www.baptisthealth.net/en/facilities/mariners-hospital/Pages/default. aspx
**Control:** Other not–for–profit (including NFP Corporation) **Service:** General medical and surgical

**Staffed Beds:** 25 **Admissions:** 466 **Census:** 4 **Outpatient Visits:** 35572 **Births:** 0 **Total Expense ($000):** 50015 **Payroll Expense ($000):** 16505 **Personnel:** 196

**THE VILLAGES—Sumter County**

**THE VILLAGES HEALTH SYSTEM** See The Villages Regional Hospital

⊞ △ **THE VILLAGES REGIONAL HOSPITAL (100290)**, 1451 El Camino Real, Zip 32159–0041; tel. 352/751–8000, (Nonreporting) **A**1 2 5 7 10 **F**3 11 15 18 20 22 24 26 28 29 30 31 34 35 40 45 49 51 57 59 64 68 70 74 75 77 78 79 81 84 85 87 90 92 93 96 97 107 108 111 114 115 119 126 130 132 135 146 147 149 150 154 156 **P**1 **S** UF Health Shands, Gainesville, FL
Primary Contact: Donald G. Henderson, FACHE, President and Chief Executive Officer
CFO: Diane P Harden, Senior Vice President and Chief Financial Officer
CHR: Amie A Richason, Vice President Human Resources
CNO: Mary Jane Curry-Pelyak, R.N., Vice President and Chief Clinical Officer
Web address: www.cfhalliance.org
**Control:** Other not–for–profit (including NFP Corporation) **Service:** General medical and surgical

**Staffed Beds:** 307 **Admissions:** 13144 **Census:** 180 **Outpatient Visits:** 48580 **Births:** 0 **Personnel:** 882

**TITUSVILLE—Brevard County**

☐ **PALM POINT BEHAVIORAL HEALTH (104082)**, 2355 Truman Scarborough Way, Zip 32796–1310; tel. 321/603–6550, (Nonreporting) **A**1
Primary Contact: Thomas J. Mahle, Chief Executive Officer
Web address: www.palmpointbehavioral.com
**Control:** Corporation, Investor–owned (for–profit) **Service:** Psychiatric

**Staffed Beds:** 74

☐ **PARRISH MEDICAL CENTER (100028)**, 951 North Washington Avenue, Zip 32796–2163; tel. 321/268–6111, (Nonreporting) **A**1 2 5 10
Primary Contact: George Mikitarian Jr, FACHE, President and Chief Executive Officer
CFO: Timothy Skeldon, Senior Vice President and Chief Financial Officer
CMO: Lisa Alexanda, M.D., Vice President Medical Affairs
CIO: William Moore, Chief Information Officer
Web address: www.parrishmed.com
**Control:** Hospital district or authority, Government, Nonfederal **Service:** General medical and surgical

**Staffed Beds:** 210

*Many Facility Codes have changed. Please refer to the AHA Guide Code Chart.*

FL

## TRINITY—Pasco County

**COMMUNITY HOSPITAL** See Medical Center of Trinity, Trinity

✠ **MEDICAL CENTER OF TRINITY (100191)**, 9330 State Road 54, Zip 34655–1808; tel. 727/834–4900, (Nonreporting) **A**1 2 3 10 **S** HCA Healthcare, Nashville, TN
Primary Contact: Leigh Massengill, Chief Executive Officer
COO: Sally Seymour, Chief Operating Officer
CFO: Michael Wyers, Chief Financial Officer
CMO: Elbert Barnes, M.D., Chief Medical Officer
CIO: Kurt Hornung, Director
CHR: Christena Miano, Vice President, Human Resources
CNO: Nancy Maysilles, R.N., Chief Nursing Officer
Web address: www.medicalcentertrinity.com
**Control:** Corporation, Investor–owned (for–profit) **Service:** General medical and surgical

| **Staffed Beds:** 340 |
| --- |

## VENICE—Sarasota County

✠ **VENICE REGIONAL BAYFRONT HEALTH (100070)**, 540 The Rialto, Zip 34285–2900; tel. 941/485–7711, (Nonreporting) **A**1 10 **F**3 8 11 12 15 17 18 20 22 24 26 28 29 34 35 37 40 45 46 47 49 50 51 54 56 57 59 64 70 74 77 79 81 82 85 87 93 96 107 108 110 111 114 115 118 119 126 129 130 146 148 149 154 156 157 **S** Community Health Systems, Inc., Franklin, TN
Primary Contact: Beryl Ramsey, FACHE, Interim Chief Executive Officer
COO: Benjamin Brodersen, Chief Operating Officer
CFO: Danny Warren, Chief Financial Officer
CIO: Eloy Rivas, Director of Information Systems
CHR: John Ware, Director of Human Resources
CNO: Dawn Beljin, R.N., Chief Nursing Officer
Web address: www.veniceregional.com
**Control:** Corporation, Investor–owned (for–profit) **Service:** General medical and surgical

| **Staffed Beds:** 221 **Admissions:** 8332 **Census:** 94 **Outpatient Visits:** 100275 **Births:** 0 **Total Expense ($000):** 154298 **Payroll Expense ($000):** 51957 **Personnel:** 756 |
| --- |

**VENICE REGIONAL MEDICAL CENTER** See Venice Regional Bayfront Health

## VERO BEACH—Indian River County

✠ **CLEVELAND CLINIC INDIAN RIVER HOSPITAL (100105)**, 1000 36th Street, Zip 32960–6592; tel. 772/567–4311, (Includes BEHAVIORAL HEALTH CENTER, Mailing address: 1190 37th Street, Vero Beach, Florida, Zip 32960–6507; tel. 772/563–4666; Jeffrey L Susi, President and Chief Executive Officer), (Nonreporting) **A**1 2 10 **F**3 11 12 13 15 17 18 20 22 24 26 28 29 30 31 34 35 37 40 44 45 46 47 48 49 50 51 57 58 59 60 61 64 70 74 75 76 77 78 79 80 81 82 84 85 87 89 92 93 96 97 98 99 100 101 102 103 104 107 108 110 111 114 115 116 117 118 119 121 124 126 129 130 131 132 135 144 146 147 148 154 **S** Cleveland Clinic Health System, Cleveland, OH
Primary Contact: Gregory Rosencrance, Chief Executive Officer
COO: Ralph Turner, Chief Operating Officer
CFO: Greg Gardner, Senior Vice President and Chief Financial Officer
CMO: Charles Mackett, M.D., Senior Vice President and Chief Medical Officer
CIO: William Neil, Vice President and Chief Information Officer
Web address: www.https://www.indianrivermedicalcenter.com/
**Control:** Other not–for–profit (including NFP Corporation) **Service:** General medical and surgical

| **Staffed Beds:** 220 **Admissions:** 16583 **Census:** 174 **Outpatient Visits:** 109259 **Births:** 1015 **Total Expense ($000):** 237918 **Payroll Expense ($000):** 93164 **Personnel:** 1617 |
| --- |

✠ **ENCOMPASS HEALTH REHABILITATION HOSPITAL OF TREASURE COAST (103032)**, 1600 37th Street, Zip 32960–4863; tel. 772/778–2100, (Nonreporting) **A**1 10 **S** Encompass Health Corporation, Birmingham, AL
Primary Contact: Michael Kissner, Chief Executive Officer
CFO: Kevin Hardy, Chief Financial Officer
CMO: Jimmy Wayne Lockhart, M.D., Medical Director
CHR: Linda Rinehart, Director Human Resources
Web address: www.healthsouthtreasurecoast.com
**Control:** Corporation, Investor–owned (for–profit) **Service:** Rehabilitation

| **Staffed Beds:** 80 |
| --- |

**HEALTHSOUTH TREASURE COAST REHABILITATION HOSPITAL** See Encompass Health Rehabilitation Hospital of Treasure Coast

**INDIAN RIVER MEDICAL CENTER** See Cleveland Clinic Indian River Hospital

## WAUCHULA—Hardee County

✠ **ADVENTHEALTH WAUCHULA (101300)**, 533 West Carlton Street, Zip 33873–3407; tel. 863/773–3101, (Nonreporting) **A**1 10 18 **F**29 30 34 40 57 58 59 107 110 111 119 127 130 131 133 149 156 **P**6 **S** AdventHealth, Altamonte Springs, FL
Primary Contact: Denise Grimsley, R.N., Vice President and Administrator
CFO: Rosalie Oliver, Senior Vice President and Chief Financial Officer
CMO: Jorge F Gonzalez, M.D., Vice President and Chief Nursing Officer
CIO: Jeff McDonald, Information Technology Manager
CHR: Michelle F. Myers, Director Human Resources
CNO: Gloria N Santos, R.N., MS, Vice President and Chief Nursing Officer
Web address: www.fh.floridahospital.com/heartland/home.aspx
**Control:** Church operated, Nongovernment, not–for–profit **Service:** General medical and surgical

| **Staffed Beds:** 25 **Admissions:** 735 **Census:** 24 **Outpatient Visits:** 24352 **Births:** 0 **Total Expense ($000):** 24299 **Payroll Expense ($000):** 9518 **Personnel:** 135 |
| --- |

**FLORIDA HOSPITAL WAUCHULA** See Adventhealth Wauchula

## WELLINGTON—Palm Beach County

☐ **WELLINGTON REGIONAL MEDICAL CENTER (100275)**, 10101 Forest Hill Boulevard, Zip 33414–6199; tel. 561/798–8500, (Nonreporting) **A**1 3 5 10 13 **F**3 7 8 12 13 15 17 18 20 22 29 31 34 35 40 42 54 57 58 59 67 70 72 73 74 75 76 77 78 79 81 82 85 86 87 90 93 96 107 110 111 112 114 115 116 117 119 121 124 126 130 131 132 135 144 146 147 148 149 154 157 **S** Universal Health Services, Inc., King of Prussia, PA
Primary Contact: Pamela S. Tahan, Chief Executive Officer
CFO: Tonja Mosley, Chief Financial Officer
CMO: Richard Hays, M.D., Chief Medical Officer
CIO: Pierre Bergeron, Information Services Director
CHR: Mary Jo Caracciolo, Human Resource Director
CNO: Asenath Cassel, Chief Nursing Officer
Web address: www.wellingtonregional.com
**Control:** Corporation, Investor–owned (for–profit) **Service:** General medical and surgical

| **Staffed Beds:** 235 **Admissions:** 13135 **Census:** 152 **Outpatient Visits:** 70238 **Births:** 1984 **Total Expense ($000):** 175191 **Payroll Expense ($000):** 64966 **Personnel:** 859 |
| --- |

## WESLEY CHAPEL—Pasco County

★ ⇑ **ADVENTHEALTH WESLEY CHAPEL (100319)**, 2600 Bruce B Downs Bouelvard, Zip 33544–9207; tel. 813/929–5000, (Nonreporting) **A**5 10 21 **F**3 11 13 15 18 20 22 26 28 29 30 34 35 40 42 45 46 49 51 53 57 59 64 70 74 75 76 77 79 81 85 87 93 107 108 109 110 111 115 117 119 120 126 130 132 145 146 147 148 149 154 **S** AdventHealth, Altamonte Springs, FL
Primary Contact: Erik Wangsness, Chief Executive Officer
Web address: www.https://www.floridahospital.com/wesley-chapel
**Control:** Other not–for–profit (including NFP Corporation) **Service:** General medical and surgical

| **Staffed Beds:** 145 **Admissions:** 8190 **Census:** 67 **Outpatient Visits:** 79154 **Births:** 731 **Total Expense ($000):** 194509 **Payroll Expense ($000):** 61452 **Personnel:** 880 |
| --- |

⇑ **FLORIDA HOSPITAL WESLEY CHAPEL** See Adventhealth Wesley Chapel

☐ **NORTH TAMPA BEHAVIORAL HEALTH (104075)**, 29910 State Road 56, Zip 33543–8800; tel. 813/922–3300, (Nonreporting) **A**1 10 **S** Acadia Healthcare Company, Inc., Franklin, TN
Primary Contact: Clint Hauger, Chief Executive Officer
Web address: www.northtampabehavioralhealth.com
**Control:** Corporation, Investor–owned (for–profit) **Service:** Psychiatric

| **Staffed Beds:** 78 |
| --- |

## WEST PALM BEACH—Palm Beach County

**CHILDREN'S HOSPITAL AT ST. MARY'S MEDICAL CENTER** See Palm Beach Children's Hospital

**GOOD SAMARITAN HOSPITAL** See Good Samaritan Medical Center

---

**Hospital, Medicare Provider Number, Address, Telephone, Approval, Facility, and Physician Codes, Health Care System**

★ American Hospital Association (AHA) membership ○ Healthcare Facilities Accreditation Program ⇑ Center for Improvement in Healthcare Quality Accreditation
☐ The Joint Commission accreditation ◇ DNV Healthcare Inc. accreditation △ Commission on Accreditation of Rehabilitation Facilities (CARF) accreditation

**FL**

**⊞ GOOD SAMARITAN MEDICAL CENTER (100287)**, 1309 North Flagler Drive, Zip 33401–3499; tel. 561/655–5511, (Nonreporting) **A**1 2 5 10 **F**3 12 13 15 18 20 22 26 29 30 31 34 35 40 42 45 46 49 50 51 54 55 56 57 58 59 60 68 70 72 74 75 76 77 78 79 81 82 84 85 86 87 93 107 108 110 111 114 115 119 126 129 130 131 132 146 147 154 157 **S** TENET Healthcare Corporation, Dallas, TX
Primary Contact: Sheri Montgomery, Acting Chief Executive Officer
COO: Tony Bajak, Chief Operating Officer
CFO: Taylor Guittap, Chief Financial Officer
CIO: James Dailey, Director Information Services
CNO: Joe Lopez-Cepero, Chief Nursing Officer
Web address: www.goodsamaritanmc.com
**Control**: Corporation, Investor–owned (for–profit) **Service**: General medical and surgical

**Staffed Beds: 225 Admissions: 10212 Census: 127 Outpatient Visits: 129926 Births: 562 Total Expense ($000): 177780 Payroll Expense ($000): 64699 Personnel: 962**

**JEROME GOLDEN CENTER FOR BEHAVIORAL HEALTH, INC. (104008)**, 1041 45th Street, Zip 33407–2494; tel. 561/383–8000, (Nonreporting) **A**10
Primary Contact: Linda De Piano, Ph.D., Chief Executive Officer
CFO: America Cordoves, Controller
CMO: Suresh Rajpara, M.D., Chief Medical Officer
CIO: Iris Garcia, Director, Information Services
CHR: Nadine Wilson, Manager, Human Resources
CNO: Holly Horvath, Director of Nursing
Web address: www.goldenctr.org
**Control**: Other not–for–profit (including NFP Corporation) **Service**: Psychiatric

**Staffed Beds: 44**

**OAKWOOD CENTER OF THE PALM BEACHES, INC.** See Jerome Golden Center for Behavioral Health, Inc.

**ST MARY'S HOSPITAL** See St. Mary's Medical Center

**⊞ △ ST. MARY'S MEDICAL CENTER (100288)**, 901 45th Street, Zip 33407–2495; tel. 561/844–6300, (Includes PALM BEACH CHILDREN'S HOSPITAL, Mailing address: 901 45th Street, West Palm Beach, Florida, Zip 33407; tel. 561/844–6300), (Nonreporting) **A**1 3 5 7 10 **F**3 8 13 15 17 18 19 20 29 30 31 32 34 35 37 39 40 41 43 45 46 47 48 49 50 51 56 57 58 59 60 61 64 70 72 73 74 75 76 77 78 79 81 84 85 86 87 88 89 90 91 92 93 94 96 97 98 100 101 102 107 108 110 111 114 115 119 130 131 132 135 146 147 148 149 156 157 **S** TENET Healthcare Corporation, Dallas, TX
Primary Contact: David O'Brien, Interim Chief Executive Officer
COO: David O'Brien, Chief Operating Officer
CFO: Michelle Cartwright, Chief Financial Officer
CMO: Jeffrey Davis, D.O., Chief Medical Officer
CIO: Rich Avato, Director
CHR: Thomas J Piszczatoski, Chief Human Resource Officer
CNO: Donna Small, R.N., Chief Nursing Officer
Web address: www.stmarysmc.com
**Control**: Corporation, Investor–owned (for–profit) **Service**: General medical and surgical

**Staffed Beds: 460 Admissions: 18979 Census: 281 Outpatient Visits: 119710 Births: 3346 Total Expense ($000): 305112 Payroll Expense ($000): 120782 Personnel: 1650**

**VETERANS AFFAIRS MEDICAL CENTER** See West Palm Beach Veterans Affairs Medical Center

**⊞ WEST PALM BEACH VETERANS AFFAIRS MEDICAL CENTER**, 7305 North Military Trail, Zip 33410–6400; tel. 561/422–8262, (Nonreporting) **A**1 3 5 **S** Department of Veterans Affairs, Washington, DC
Primary Contact: Donna Katen-Bahensky, Director
CFO: Lori Hancock, Chief Business Officer
CMO: Deepak Mandi, M.D., Chief of Staff
CIO: Karen Gabaldon, Chief Management Information Systems
CHR: David Green, Chief Human Resources
Web address: www.westpalmbeach.va.gov/
**Control**: Veterans Affairs, Government, federal **Service**: General medical and surgical

**Staffed Beds: 300**

**WEST PALM HOSPITAL** See Jfk Medical Center North Campus

**⊞ CLEVELAND CLINIC FLORIDA (100289)**, 2950 Cleveland Clinic Boulevard, Zip 33331–3602; tel. 954/659–5000, (Nonreporting) **A**1 2 3 5 10 **F**3 7 8 9 11 12 15 17 18 20 22 24 26 28 29 30 31 34 35 36 37 39 40 41 44 45 46 47 48 49 50 51 54 55 56 57 58 59 60 61 63 64 65 68 70 71 74 75 77 78 79 80 81 82 84 85 86 87 91 92 93 96 97 100 107 108 109 110 111 114 115 116 117 118 119 120 121 123 124 126 129 130 131 132 135 137 138 139 141 145 146 147 148 149 154 155 156 **P**6 **S** Cleveland Clinic Health System, Cleveland, OH
Primary Contact: Wael Barsoum, M.D., President
CMO: Raul Rosenthal, M.D., Interim Chief of Staff
CIO: John Santangelo, Director Information Technology
CHR: Carl McDonald, Senior Director, Human Resources
CNO: Kerry Major, R.N., MSN, Chief Nursing Officer
Web address: www.clevelandclinic.org/florida
**Control**: Other not–for–profit (including NFP Corporation) **Service**: General medical and surgical

**Staffed Beds: 206 Admissions: 14402 Census: 176 Outpatient Visits: 54043 Births: 0 Total Expense ($000): 340518 Payroll Expense ($000): 117271 Personnel: 3015**

**CLEVELAND CLINIC HOSPITAL** See Cleveland Clinic Florida

**⊞ △ WINTER HAVEN HOSPITAL (100052)**, 200 Avenue F NE, Zip 33881–4193; tel. 863/293–1121, (Nonreporting) **A**1 3 7 10 19 **F**3 11 13 14 15 17 18 20 22 24 26 28 29 30 31 34 37 40 45 47 49 57 58 59 60 64 68 70 72 74 75 76 77 78 79 81 82 84 85 86 87 93 94 98 100 101 102 104 107 108 109 110 111 114 115 118 119 120 121 122 123 126 130 132 135 144 146 147 148 156 **S** Trinity Health, Livonia, MI
Primary Contact: Stephen A. Nierman, President
COO: Jacques Vasconcellos, Director, Operations
CFO: Ron Beamon, Vice President, Chief Financial Officer
CMO: Vincent Gatto, M.D., Chief Medical Officer
CIO: Cal Cole, Director Information Systems
CHR: Tina Howard, Manager, Team Member Relations
Web address: www.winterhavenhospital.org
**Control**: Other not–for–profit (including NFP Corporation) **Service**: General medical and surgical

**Staffed Beds: 361 Admissions: 21596 Census: 257 Outpatient Visits: 170042 Births: 1952 Total Expense ($000): 352098 Payroll Expense ($000): 130578 Personnel: 2114**

**ADVENTHEALTH WINTER PARK** See Adventhealth Orlando, Orlando

**WINTER PARK MEMORIAL HOSPITAL** See Adventhealth Winter Park

**⊞ ADVENTHEALTH ZEPHYRHILLS (100046)**, 7050 Gall Boulevard, Zip 33541–1399; tel. 813/788–0411, (Nonreporting) **A**1 5 10 **F**13 15 18 20 22 26 29 40 45 50 64 70 74 76 79 81 82 84 97 107 108 111 112 116 117 119 126 146 147 148 **S** AdventHealth, Altamonte Springs, FL
Primary Contact: Amanda Maggard, President and Chief Executive Officer
COO: Donald E Welch, Chief Operating Officer
CFO: Bill Heinrich, Chief Financial Officer
CMO: Hugar McNamee, D.O., Chief Medical Officer
CIO: Kelley Sasser, Director Information Systems
CHR: Laura Asaftei, Administrative Director
CNO: Gwen Alonso, Chief Nursing Officer
Web address: www.fhzeph.org
**Control**: Church operated, Nongovernment, not–for–profit **Service**: General medical and surgical

**Staffed Beds: 149 Admissions: 9402 Census: 97 Outpatient Visits: 92726 Births: 512 Total Expense ($000): 162490 Payroll Expense ($000): 62531 Personnel: 946**

**FLORIDA HOSPITAL ZEPHYRHILLS** See Adventhealth Zephyrhills

FL

# GEORGIA

## ADEL—Cook County

**COOK MEDICAL CENTER-A CAMPUS OF TIFT REGIONAL MEDICAL CENTER**
See Southwell Medical

✠ **SOUTHWELL MEDICAL (110101)**, 260 MJ Taylor Road, Zip 31620–3485;
tel. 229/896–8000, (Total facility includes 95 beds in nursing home–type unit)
(Nonreporting) **A**1 10 **F**11 15 29 30 34 35 45 56 57 59 63 64 65 68 75 77 81
84 85 86 87 93 97 98 101 103 104 107 108 110 111 114 119 127 129 130
133 135 146 147 148 149 154 156 **P**6 **S** Tift Regional Health System, Tifton, GA
Primary Contact: Christopher Dorman, Chief Executive Officer
COO: Kim Wills, Chief Operating Officer
CIO: Barry Medley, Director Information Systems
CHR: Shirley Padgett, Director Human Resources
Web address: www.cookmedicalcenter.com
**Control:** Other not–for–profit (including NFP Corporation) **Service:** General
medical and surgical

> **Staffed Beds:** 155 **Admissions:** 508 **Census:** 94 **Outpatient Visits:** 12572
> **Births:** 0 **Total Expense ($000):** 18247 **Payroll Expense ($000):** 9271
> **Personnel:** 233

## ALBANY—Dougherty County

**PALMYRA MEDICAL CENTERS** See Phoebe North

★ ⇑ **PHOEBE PUTNEY MEMORIAL HOSPITAL (110007)**, 417 West Third
Avenue, Zip 31701–1943, Mailing Address: P.O. Box 3770, Zip 31706–3770;
tel. 229/312–4100, (Includes PHOEBE NORTH, Mailing address: 2000 Palmyra
Road, Albany, Georgia, Zip 31701–1528, P O Box 1908, Zip 31702–1908,
tel. 229/434–2000), (Nonreporting) **A**2 3 5 10 21 **F**3 5 11 12 13 15 17 18 20
22 24 26 28 29 30 31 34 35 40 44 45 46 49 50 51 53 54 55 56 57 58 59 60
61 62 63 64 68 70 72 73 74 75 76 77 78 79 81,82 83 84 85 86 87 89 90 91
92 93 94 96 97 98 100 101 102 103 104 105 107 108 110 111 114 115 116
117 118 119 120 121 123 124 126 127 129 130 131 132 134 135 136 144
145 146 147 148 149 153 154 **S** Phoebe Putney Health System, Albany, GA
Primary Contact: Scott Steiner, FACHE, Chief Executive Officer
COO: Joe Austin, Executive Vice President and Chief Operating Officer
CFO: Brian Church, Senior Vice President and Chief Financial Officer
CMO: Steven Kitchen, M.D., Chief Medical Officer
CIO: Jesse Diaz, Chief Information Officer
CHR: Tony Welch, Senior Vice President and Chief Human Resources Officer
CNO: Laura Shearer, R.N., MSN, Senior Vice President and Chief Nursing Officer
Web address: www.phoebeputney.com
**Control:** Other not–for–profit (including NFP Corporation) **Service:** General
medical and surgical

> **Staffed Beds:** 442 **Admissions:** 18520 **Census:** 296 **Outpatient
> Visits:** 1190706 **Births:** 2142 **Total Expense ($000):** 568742 **Payroll
> Expense ($000):** 152891 **Personnel:** 2536

## ALMA—Bacon County

**BACON COUNTY HOSPITAL** See Bacon County Hospital and Health System

✠ **BACON COUNTY HOSPITAL AND HEALTH SYSTEM (111327)**, 302
South Wayne Street, Zip 31510–2922, Mailing Address: P O Drawer 1987,
Zip 31510–0987; tel. 912/632–8961, (Nonreporting) **A**1 10 18
Primary Contact: Cindy R. Turner, Chief Executive Officer
COO: Cindy R Turner, Chief Executive Officer
CFO: Kyle Kimmel, Chief Financial Officer
CMO: Lou Ellen Hutcheson, M.D., Chief of Staff
CIO: Neil O'Steen, Director Information Technology
CHR: Kerry Hancock, Director Human Resources
CNO: Deanna Hoff, R.N., Director of Nursing
Web address: www.baconcountyhospital.com
**Control:** Other not–for–profit (including NFP Corporation) **Service:** General
medical and surgical

> **Staffed Beds:** 113

## AMERICUS—Sumter County

★ ⇑ **PHOEBE SUMTER MEDICAL CENTER (110044)**, 126 Highway, 280
West, Zip 31719, Mailing Address: 126 Highway 280 West, Zip 31719;
tel. 229/924–6011, (Nonreporting) **A**10 21 **F**3 11 12 13 15 18 28 29 31 32 34
35 39 40 45 50 53 55 57 59 60 63 64 65 68 70 71 75 76 78 79 81 85 86 87
92 93 100 107 108 110 111 115 119 127 129 131 132 135 146 147 149 154
156 **S** Phoebe Putney Health System, Albany, GA
Primary Contact: Brandi Lunneborg, Chief Executive Officer
CHR: Cassandra Haynes Aldridge, Chief Human Resources Officer
CNO: Susan Bruns, Chief Nursing Officer
Web address: www.phoebesumter.org
**Control:** Hospital district or authority, Government, Nonfederal **Service:** General
medical and surgical

> **Staffed Beds:** 54 **Admissions:** 2895 **Census:** 30 **Outpatient Visits:** 78411
> **Births:** 419 **Total Expense ($000):** 76277 **Payroll Expense ($000):** 27439
> **Personnel:** 514

⇑ **SUMTER REGIONAL HOSPITAL EAST** See Phoebe Sumter Medical Center

## ATHENS—Clarke County

⇑ **ATHENS REGIONAL MEDICAL CENTER** See Piedmont Athens Regional Medical
Center

**LANDMARK HOSPITAL OF ATHENS (112017)**, 775 Sunset Drive,
Zip 30606–2211; tel. 706/425–1500, (Nonreporting) **A**10 22 **S** Landmark
Hospitals, Cape Girardeau, MO
Primary Contact: Vivian Goff, R.N., Chief Executive Officer
Web address: www.landmarkhospitals.com
**Control:** Individual, Investor–owned (for–profit) **Service:** Acute long–term care
hospital

> **Staffed Beds:** 42

⇑ **PIEDMONT ATHENS REGIONAL MEDICAL CENTER (110074)**, 1199 Prince
Avenue, Zip 30606–2797; tel. 706/475–7000, (Nonreporting) **A**2 3 5 10 21 **F**3 8
13 15 17 18 20 22 24 26 28 29 30 31 32 34 35 36 40 43 45 46 47 48 49 50
51 54 55 56 57 58 59 60 61 62 64 66 68 70 71 72 73 74 76 77 78 79 80 81
83 84 85 86 87 89 91 92 93 94 96 100 102 107 108 110 111 114 115 116
117 118 119 120 121 123 124 126 129 130 131 132 135 144 145 146 147
148 156 **S** Piedmont Healthcare, Roswell, GA
Primary Contact: Michael Burnett, Chief Executive Officer
COO: Jason Smith, Chief Operating Officer
CFO: Wendy J. Cook, Chief Financial Officer
CMO: Robert Sinyard, M.D., Chief Medical Officer
CIO: Louis H. Duhe, Executor Director, Information Services
CHR: Robert D. Finch, Director, Human Resources
CNO: Tamara Jackson, Chief Nursing Officer
Web address: www.https://www.piedmont.org/locations/piedmont-athens
**Control:** Other not–for–profit (including NFP Corporation) **Service:** General
medical and surgical

> **Staffed Beds:** 345 **Admissions:** 18802 **Census:** 258 **Outpatient
> Visits:** 295373 **Births:** 2240 **Personnel:** 2699

GA

---

**Hospital, Medicare Provider Number, Address, Telephone, Approval, Facility, and Physician Codes, Health Care System**

★ American Hospital Association (AHA) membership ○ Healthcare Facilities Accreditation Program ⇑ Center for Improvement in Healthcare Quality Accreditation
□ The Joint Commission accreditation ◇ DNV Healthcare Inc. accreditation △ Commission on Accreditation of Rehabilitation Facilities (CARF) accreditation

**ST MARY'S HOSPITAL** See St. Mary's Health Care System

☒ △ **ST. MARY'S HEALTH CARE SYSTEM (110006)**, 1230 Baxter Street, Zip 30606–3791; tel. 706/389–3000, (Nonreporting) **A**1 3 5 7 10 19 **F**3 11 12 13 15 18 20 22 26 28 29 30 31 34 35 40 41 45 46 47 48 49 50 53 54 57 59 61 62 63 64 68 70 73 74 75 76 77 79 80 81 83 84 85 87 89 90 92 93 107 110 111 114 115 118 119 126 129 130 131 132 135 141 145 146 147 148 149 156 **S** Trinity Health, Livonia, MI
Primary Contact: D. Montez. Carter, Chief Executive Officer
CFO: Marty Hutson, Chief Financial Officer
CMO: Bruce Middendorf, M.D., Chief Medical Officer
CIO: Kerry Vaughn, Chief Information Officer
CHR: Jeff English, Vice President Human Resources
CNO: Titus E. Gambrell, Vice President and Chief Nursing Officer
Web address: www.stmarysathens.com
**Control**: Church operated, Nongovernment, not–for–profit **Service**: General medical and surgical

**Staffed Beds**: 173 **Admissions**: 10940 **Census**: 140 **Outpatient Visits**: 220623 **Births**: 1522 **Total Expense ($000)**: 214176 **Payroll Expense ($000)**: 75623 **Personnel**: 1073

### ATLANTA—Fulton AND De Kalb County

☐ **ANCHOR HOSPITAL (114032)**, 5454 Yorktowne Drive, Zip 30349–5317; tel. 770/991–6044, (Nonreporting) **A**1 10 **F**98 102 103 105 153 154 **S** Universal Health Services, Inc., King of Prussia, PA
Primary Contact: Luis Betances, Chief Executive Officer
CFO: John Kim, Chief Financial Officer
CMO: Shailesh Patel, M.D., Medical Director
CIO: Chris Hill, Information Technology
CHR: Danna Nordin, Director Human Resources
CNO: Angelica Jackson, Director of Nursing
Web address: www.anchorhospital.com
**Control**: Corporation, Investor–owned (for–profit) **Service**: Psychiatric

**Staffed Beds**: 124 **Admissions**: 3691 **Census**: 90 **Outpatient Visits**: 8445 **Births**: 0 **Total Expense ($000)**: 24367 **Payroll Expense ($000)**: 11394 **Personnel**: 247

**ATLANTA MEDICAL CENTER** See Wellstar Atlanta Medical Center

**ATLANTA MEDICAL CENTER - SOUTH CAMPUS** See Wellstar Atlanta Medical Center - South Campus

**CHARTER ANCHOR HOSPITAL** See Anchor Hospital

**CHARTER BEHAVIORAL HLTH SYSTEM** See Peachford Behavioral Health System

☐ △ **CHILDREN'S HEALTHCARE OF ATLANTA (113300)**, 1600 Tullie Circle, NE, Zip 30329–2303; tel. 404/785–7000, (Includes CHILDREN'S HEALTHCARE OF ATLANTA AT EGLESTON, Mailing address: 1600 Tullie Circle, Atlanta, Georgia, Zip 30329; tel. 404/325–6000; CHILDREN'S HEALTHCARE OF ATLANTA AT HUGHES SPALDING, Mailing address: 35 Jesse Hill Jr Drive, SE, Atlanta, Georgia, Zip 30303–3032; tel. 404/785–9500; CHILDREN'S HEALTHCARE OF ATLANTA AT SCOTTISH RITE, Mailing address: 1001 Johnson Ferry Road NE, Atlanta, Georgia, Zip 30342–1600; tel. 404/256–5252), (Nonreporting) **A**1 3 5 7 8 10
Primary Contact: Donna W. Hyland, President and Chief Executive Officer
COO: Carolyn Kenny, Executive Vice President Clinical Care
CFO: Ruth Fowler, Senior Vice President and Chief Financial Officer
CMO: Daniel Salinas, M.D., Senior Vice President and Chief Medical Officer
CIO: Allana Cummings, Chief Information Officer
CHR: Linda Matzigkeit, Senior Vice President Human Resources
Web address: www.choa.org
**Control**: Other not–for–profit (including NFP Corporation) **Service**: Children's general medical and surgical

**Staffed Beds**: 496

**EGLESTON CHILDREN'S HOSPITAL** See Children's Healthcare of Atlanta at Egleston

**EMORY CRAWFORD LONG HOSPITAL** See Emory University Hospital Midtown

☒ △ **EMORY REHABILITATION HOSPITAL (113031)**, 1441 Clifton Road NE, Zip 30322–1004; tel. 404/712–5512, (Nonreporting) **A**1 7 10 **F**11 29 30 34 35 36 50 56 58 64 68 74 75 77 79 82 85 86 87 90 93 94 95 96 130 131 132 135 146 148 149 **S** Emory Healthcare, Atlanta, GA
Primary Contact: Michael Eric. Garrard, FACHE, Chief Executive Officer
CMO: S. Byron Milton, M.D., Medical Director
CHR: Janine Diaz, Human Resources Manager
CNO: Deborah Almauhy, R.N., Chief Nursing Officer
Web address: www.emoryhealthcare.org/rehabilitation
**Control**: Partnership, Investor–owned (for–profit) **Service**: Rehabilitation

**Staffed Beds**: 46 **Admissions**: 1015 **Census**: 41 **Outpatient Visits**: 28260 **Births**: 0 **Total Expense ($000)**: 26477 **Payroll Expense ($000)**: 15152 **Personnel**: 167

☒ **EMORY SAINT JOSEPH'S HOSPITAL OF ATLANTA (110082)**, 5665 Peachtree Dunwoody Road NE, Zip 30342–1701; tel. 678/843–7001, (Nonreporting) **A**1 2 3 5 10 11 12 15 17 18 20 22 24 26 28 29 30 31 34 35 37 40 44 45 46 47 49 50 51 53 54 55 57 58 59 60 64 68 70 74 75 77 78 79 81 82 84 85 86 87 100 102 107 108 110 111 115 117 118 119 120 121 123 124 126 130 132 135 145 146 147 148 149 156 **S** Emory Healthcare, Atlanta, GA
Primary Contact: Heather Dexter, Chief Executive Officer
CFO: JoAnn Manning, Chief Financial Officer
CMO: Thomas P. McGahan, M.D., Chief Medical Officer
CHR: Jeanne Landry, Vice President Human Resources
Web address: www.emoryhealthcare.org/locations/hospitals/emory-saint-josephs-hospital/
**Control**: Other not–for–profit (including NFP Corporation) **Service**: General medical and surgical

**Staffed Beds**: 352 **Admissions**: 18879 **Census**: 246 **Outpatient Visits**: 133749 **Births**: 0 **Total Expense ($000)**: 439999 **Payroll Expense ($000)**: 156343 **Personnel**: 1910

☒ **EMORY UNIVERSITY HOSPITAL (110010)**, 1364 Clifton Road NE, Zip 30322; tel. 404/712–2000, (Includes EMORY UNIVERSITY ORTHOPAEDIC AND SPINE HOSPITAL, Mailing address: 1455 Montreal Road, Tucker, Georgia, Zip 30084; tel. 404/251–3600; June Conner, R.N., Chief Operating Officer; EMORY WESLEY WOODS GERIATRIC HOSPITAL, Mailing address: 1821 Clifton Road NE, Atlanta, Georgia, Zip 30329–4021; tel. 404/728–6200; Matthew Wain, Chief Executive Officer), (Nonreporting) **A**1 2 3 5 8 10 **F**3 11 14 15 17 18 20 22 24 26 29 30 31 34 35 36 38 39 40 44 45 46 47 48 49 50 55 56 57 58 59 60 61 63 64 68 70 74 75 77 78 79 80 81 82 84 85 86 87 90 92 93 98 100 101 102 103 104 105 107 108 110 111 114 115 116 117 118 119 120 121 123 124 126 129 130 131 132 135 136 137 138 139 140 141 142 145 146 147 148 149 153 154 156 **S** Emory Healthcare, Atlanta, GA
Primary Contact: Matthew Wain, Chief Executive Officer
CFO: Carla Chandler, Vice President and Chief Financial Officer
CMO: Chad W.M. Ritenour, M.D., Chief Medical Officer
CIO: Sheila M Sanders, Chief Information Officer
CHR: Melanie DeGennaro, Vice President of Human Resources
CNO: Nancye R. Feistritzer, Chief Nursing Officer
Web address: www.emoryhealthcare.org
**Control**: Other not–for–profit (including NFP Corporation) **Service**: General medical and surgical

**Staffed Beds**: 645 **Admissions**: 29112 **Census**: 541 **Outpatient Visits**: 207634 **Births**: 0 **Total Expense ($000)**: 978360 **Payroll Expense ($000)**: 324472 **Personnel**: 4304

☒ **EMORY UNIVERSITY HOSPITAL MIDTOWN (110078)**, 550 Peachtree Street NE, Zip 30308–2247; tel. 404/686–4411, (Nonreporting) **A**1 2 3 5 8 10 **F**3 11 12 13 14 15 17 18 20 22 24 26 29 30 31 34 35 36 38 40 44 45 46 47 48 49 50 51 52 55 57 58 59 60 61 63 64 68 70 72 73 74 75 76 77 78 79 81 82 84 85 86 87 92 93 100 101 102 107 108 110 111 114 115 116 117 118 119 120 121 123 124 126 130 131 132 135 141 146 147 149 154 156 157 **S** Emory Healthcare, Atlanta, GA
Primary Contact: Daniel Owens, Chief Executive Officer
CMO: James P Steinberg, M.D., Chief Medical Officer
CIO: Dedra Cantrell, Chief Information Officer
CHR: Dallis Howard-Crow, Chief Human Resources Officer
Web address: www.emoryhealthcare.org
**Control**: Other not–for–profit (including NFP Corporation) **Service**: General medical and surgical

**Staffed Beds**: 532 **Admissions**: 29863 **Census**: 399 **Outpatient Visits**: 297038 **Births**: 5705 **Total Expense ($000)**: 1000858 **Payroll Expense ($000)**: 273246 **Personnel**: 3349

☒ **GRADY MEMORIAL HOSPITAL (110079)**, 80 Jesse Hill Jr Drive SE, Zip 30303–3031, Mailing Address: P.O. Box 26189, Zip 31329–0386; tel. 404/616–1000, (Total facility includes 296 beds in nursing home–type unit) (Nonreporting) **A**1 2 3 5 8 10 **F**2 3 5 7 13 15 16 18 20 22 24 26 29 30 31 34 35 38 39 40 43 45 46 47 49 50 51 52 53 54 55 56 57 58 59 60 61 62 64 65 66 68 70 72 73 74 75 76 77 78 79 81 82 84 85 86 87 93 94 97 98 100 101 102 103 104 105 106 107 108 109 110 111 112 113 114 115 116 117 118 119 120 121 126 128 129 130 132 134 135 143 144 146 147 148 153 154 155 156 157
Primary Contact: John M. Haupert, FACHE, President and Chief Executive Officer
COO: Rhonda A Scott, Ph.D., R.N., Chief Operating Officer
CFO: Mark Meyer, Chief Financial Officer
CMO: Robert Jansen, M.D., Chief Medical Officer
CIO: Ben McKeeby, Senior Vice President and Chief Information Officer
CHR: Larry A. Callahan, Senior Vice President Human Resources
CNO: Jacqueline Herd, Executive Vice President and Chief Nursing Officer
Web address: www.gradyhealthsystem.org
**Control**: Other not–for–profit (including NFP Corporation) **Service**: General medical and surgical

**Staffed Beds**: 1060 **Admissions**: 34251 **Census**: 945 **Outpatient Visits**: 724631 **Births**: 2676 **Total Expense ($000)**: 1302842 **Payroll Expense ($000)**: 478190 **Personnel**: 6319

GA

*Many Facility Codes have changed. Please refer to the AHA Guide Code Chart.*
© 2021 AHA Guide

**KINDRED HOSPITAL-ATLANTA** See Select Specialty Hospital Midtown Atlanta

✠ **NORTHSIDE HOSPITAL (110161)**, 1000 Johnson Ferry Road NE, Zip 30342–1611; tel. 404/851–8000, (Nonreporting) **A**1 2 3 10 **F**3 5 8 11 12 13 15 17 18 20 22 26 28 29 30 31 34 35 37 40 44 45 46 47 48 49 50 54 55 57 58 59 60 64 68 70 71 72 73 74 75 76 77 78 79 80 81 82 84 85 86 87 93 100 104 107 108 110 111 114 115 117 118 119 120 121 123 124 126 129 130 131 132 135 136 144 145 146 147 148 156 **S** Northside Healthcare System, Atlanta, GA
Primary Contact: Robert Quattrocchi, President and Chief Executive Officer
CFO: Debbie Mitcham, Chief Financial Officer
CIO: Tina Wakim, Vice President Information
Web address: www.northside.com
**Control**: Other not–for–profit (including NFP Corporation) **Service**: General medical and surgical

**Staffed Beds:** 506 **Admissions:** 31266 **Census:** 377 **Outpatient Visits:** 2115172 **Births:** 15442 **Total Expense ($000):** 2249853 **Payroll Expense ($000):** 670482 **Personnel:** 9579

☐ **PEACHFORD BEHAVIORAL HEALTH SYSTEM (114010)**, 2151 Peachford Road, Zip 30338–6599; tel. 770/455–3200, (Nonreporting) **A**1 10 **S** Universal Health Services, Inc., King of Prussia, PA
Primary Contact: Matthew Crouch, Chief Executive Officer and Managing Director
COO: Sharon Stackhouse, Assistant Administrator and Director Risk Management
CFO: April Hughes, Chief Financial Officer
CMO: Asaf Aleem, M.D., Medical Director
CHR: Clay Boyles, Director Human Resources
Web address: www.peachfordhospital.com
**Control**: Corporation, Investor–owned (for–profit) **Service**: Psychiatric

**Staffed Beds:** 246

⇑ **PIEDMONT HOSPITAL (110083)**, 1968 Peachtree Road NW, Zip 30309–1281; tel. 404/605–5000, (Nonreporting) **A**2 3 5 10 21 **F**3 8 11 12 13 15 17 18 20 22 24 26 28 29 30 31 34 35 40 44 45 46 47 48 49 50 51 53 54 55 56 57 58 59 60 61 63 64 65 68 70 72 73 74 75 76 77 78 79 81 82 84 85 86 87 92 93 107 108 110 111 114 115 116 117 118 119 120 121 123 124 126 129 130 131 132 135 137 138 139 141 142 145 146 147 148 149 154 156 **P**1 6 **S** Piedmont Healthcare, Roswell, GA
Primary Contact: Patrick M. Battey, FACS, M.D., Chief Executive Officer
CFO: Sheryl Klink, Chief Financial Officer
CMO: Mark Cohen, M.D., Chief Medical Officer
CHR: Vicki A Cansler, Chief Human Resource Officer
CNO: Kelly Hulsey, MSN, R.N., Chief Nursing Officer
Web address: www.piedmont.org
**Control**: Other not–for–profit (including NFP Corporation) **Service**: General medical and surgical

**Staffed Beds:** 512 **Admissions:** 26462 **Census:** 384 **Outpatient Visits:** 362462 **Births:** 2661 **Personnel:** 3453

**SAINT JOSEPH'S HOSPITAL OF ATLANTA** See Emory Saint Joseph's Hospital of Atlanta

**SCOTTISH RITE CHILDREN'S CTR** See Children's Healthcare of Atlanta at Scottish Rite

✠ **SELECT SPECIALTY HOSPITAL MIDTOWN ATLANTA (112004)**, 705 Juniper Street NE, Zip 30308–1307; tel. 404/873–2871, (Nonreporting) **A**1 10 **S** Select Medical Corporation, Mechanicsburg, PA
Primary Contact: Adriene Kinnaird, Chief Executive Officer
CFO: Michael Nelson, Chief Financial Officer
CMO: David N. DeRuyter, M.D., President Medical Staff
CHR: Armetria Gibson, Human Resources Generalist
CNO: Annette Harrilson, Chief Clinical Officer
Web address: www.selectspecialtyhospitals.com/
**Control**: Partnership, Investor–owned (for–profit) **Service**: Acute long–term care hospital

**Staffed Beds:** 72

☐ △ **SHEPHERD CENTER (112003)**, 2020 Peachtree Road NW, Zip 30309–1465; tel. 404/352–2020, (Nonreporting) **A**1 3 5 7 10 **F**3 10 11 29 30 34 35 36 44 50 53 54 57 58 59 64 65 70 74 75 77 79 82 86 87 90 91 92 93 94 95 96 97 107 111 119 130 131 132 134 143 146 148 149 157 **P**6
Primary Contact: Sarah Morrison, President and Chief Executive Officer
COO: Jamie Shepherd, Chief Operating Officer
CFO: Stephen B Holleman, Chief Financial Officer
CMO: Donald P Leslie, M.D., Medical Director
CIO: Brian Barnette, Chief Information Officer
CHR: Lorie Hutcheson, Vice President of Human Resources
CNO: Tamara King, R.N., MSN, Chief Nurse Executive
Web address: www.https://www.shepherd.org
**Control**: Other not–for–profit (including NFP Corporation) **Service**: Rehabilitation

**Staffed Beds:** 132 **Admissions:** 935 **Census:** 130 **Outpatient Visits:** 69494 **Births:** 0 **Total Expense ($000):** 245378 **Payroll Expense ($000):** 106082 **Personnel:** 1454

**SHEPHERD SPINAL CENTER** See Shepherd Center

**VERITAS COLLABORATIVE**, 6600 Peachtree Dunwoody Road, Embassy Row, Building 400, Suite 150, Zip 30328–6773; tel. 770/871–3730, (Nonreporting) **A**3
Primary Contact: Mederic D. McLaughlin, Executive Director
Web address: www.https://veritascollaborative.com
**Control**: Partnership, Investor–owned (for–profit) **Service**: Psychiatric

**Staffed Beds:** 50

✠ **WELLSTAR ATLANTA MEDICAL CENTER (110115)**, 303 Parkway Drive NE, Zip 30312–1212; tel. 404/265–4000, (Includes WELLSTAR ATLANTA MEDICAL CENTER - SOUTH CAMPUS, Mailing address: 1170 Cleveland Avenue, Atlanta, Georgia, Zip 30344–3665; tel. 404/466–1170; Daniel Jackson, Vice President, Administrator), (Nonreporting) **A**1 3 5 8 10 **F**3 11 12 13 15 17 18 20 22 24 26 28 29 30 31 34 35 36 37 38 40 43 44 45 46 50 53 54 56 57 59 60 61 64 65 66 68 70 72 73 74 75 76 77 78 79 81 84 85 86 87 90 93 96 97 98 101 102 103 106 107 108 110 111 114 118 126 129 130 132 134 144 146 147 148 149 150 154 156 **S** WellStar Health System, Marietta, GA
Primary Contact: Stuart D. Downs, R.N., Interim President
CFO: Jason K Limbaugh, Vice President and Chief Financial Officer
CMO: Albert Barrocas, M.D., Chief Medical Officer
CIO: Mike Sharp, Interim Director
CHR: Detra Bickerstaff, Vice President, Human Resources
CNO: Stuart D. Downs, R.N., Vice President and Chief Operating Officer
Web address: www.atlantamedcenter.com
**Control**: Other not–for–profit (including NFP Corporation) **Service**: General medical and surgical

**Staffed Beds:** 506 **Admissions:** 17755 **Census:** 286 **Outpatient Visits:** 194175 **Births:** 2306 **Personnel:** 1893

**WESLEY WOODS CENTER** See Wesley Woods Health Center

**WESLEY WOODS GERIATRIC HOSPITAL OF EMORY UNIVERSITY** See Emory Wesley Woods Geriatric Hospital

### AUGUSTA—Richmond County

✠ **AUGUSTA UNIVERSITY MEDICAL CENTER (110034)**, 1120 15th Street, Zip 30912–0004; tel. 706/721–0211, (Includes CHILDREN'S HOSPITAL OF GEORGIA, Mailing address: 1446 Harper Street, Augusta, Georgia, Zip 30912–0012; tel. 706/721–5437; Katrina Keefer, Chief Operating Officer), (Nonreporting) **A**1 2 3 8 10 **F**3 6 9 11 12 13 14 15 17 18 19 20 21 22 23 24 25 26 27 28 29 30 31 32 34 35 36 38 40 41 43 44 45 46 47 48 49 50 51 54 55 56 58 59 60 61 64 65 66 68 70 72 73 74 75 76 77 78 79 81 82 85 86 87 88 89 92 93 97 99 100 101 102 103 104 107 108 111 112 113 115 116 117 118 119 120 121 123 124 126 127 129 130 131 132 134 135 136 138 141 142 143 146 147 148 154 156
Primary Contact: Katrina Keefer, Chief Executive Officer
COO: Timothy Gaillard, Chief Operating Officer
CFO: Katrina Keefer, Interim Chief Financial Officer
CMO: Phillip Coule, M.D., Chief Medical Officer
CIO: Michael Casdorph, Ph.D., Chief Information Officer
CHR: Susan Norton, Vice President Human Resources
CNO: Laura E Brower, R.N., MSN, Chief Nursing Officer
Web address: www.grhealth.org
**Control**: Other not–for–profit (including NFP Corporation) **Service**: General medical and surgical

**Staffed Beds:** 466 **Admissions:** 20331 **Census:** 331 **Outpatient Visits:** 571333 **Births:** 1489 **Total Expense ($000):** 747405 **Payroll Expense ($000):** 219106 **Personnel:** 3339

**GA**

---

**Hospital, Medicare Provider Number, Address, Telephone, Approval, Facility, and Physician Codes, Health Care System**

★ American Hospital Association (AHA) membership
☐ The Joint Commission accreditation
○ Healthcare Facilities Accreditation Program
◇ DNV Healthcare Inc. accreditation
⇑ Center for Improvement in Healthcare Quality Accreditation
△ Commission on Accreditation of Rehabilitation Facilities (CARF) accreditation

⊞ △ **CHARLIE NORWOOD VETERANS AFFAIRS MEDICAL CENTER**, 1 Freedom Way, Zip 30904–6285; tel. 706/733–0188, (Nonreporting) **A**1 2 3 5 7 8 **S** Department of Veterans Affairs, Washington, DC
Primary Contact: Robin E. Jackson, Ph.D., Interim Acting Director
COO: John D Stenger, Acting Associate Director
CFO: Earline Corder, Chief Fiscal
CIO: Sandy Williford, Chief Health Information Management and Revenue Administration
CHR: Roger W Buterbaugh, Chief Human Resources Officer
Web address: www.augusta.va.gov/
**Control**: Veterans Affairs, Government, federal **Service**: General medical and surgical

**Staffed Beds**: 338

⊞ △ **DOCTORS HOSPITAL (110177)**, 3651 Wheeler Road, Zip 30909–6426; tel. 706/651–3232, (Nonreporting) **A**1 2 3 5 7 10 **F**3 12 13 14 15 16 18 20 22 24 26 29 34 35 36 37 38 39 40 41 43 44 45 46 47 48 49 50 51 54 56 57 58 59 60 64 68 70 71 72 74 75 76 77 78 79 81 82 84 85 86 87 88 89 90 93 94 95 96 97 100 102 107 108 110 111 114 115 116 117 118 119 120 121 123 124 126 130 131 132 135 143 146 147 148 149 154 157 **S** HCA Healthcare, Nashville, TN
Primary Contact: Douglas Welch, Chief Executive Officer
CIO: Dona Hornung, Director Information and Technology Services
Web address: www.doctors-hospital.net
**Control**: Corporation, Investor–owned (for–profit) **Service**: General medical and surgical

**Staffed Beds**: 288 **Admissions**: 16394 **Census**: 233 **Outpatient Visits**: 119825 **Births**: 2175 **Personnel**: 1242

**DOCTORS HOSPITAL OF AUGUSTA** See Doctors Hospital

☐ **EAST CENTRAL REGIONAL HOSPITAL (114029)**, 3405 Mike Padgett Highway, Zip 30906–3897; tel. 706/790–2011, (Includes EAST CENTRAL REGIONAL HOSPITAL, Mailing address: 100 Myrtle Boulevard, Gracewood, Georgia, Zip 30812–1299; tel. 706/790–2011), (Nonreporting) **A**1 3 5 10 **F**29 34 38 39 59 65 67 75 77 98 101 102 128 130 132 135 **P**6
Primary Contact: Paul Brock, Administrator
CFO: Candace Walker, Chief Financial Officer
Web address: www.dbhdd.ga.gov
**Control**: State, Government, Nonfederal **Service**: Psychiatric

**Staffed Beds**: 308 **Admissions**: 731 **Census**: 283 **Outpatient Visits**: 0 **Births**: 0 **Total Expense ($000)**: 69580 **Payroll Expense ($000)**: 23713 **Personnel**: 968

**GEORGIA REG HOSP AT AUGUSTA** See East Central Regional Hospital

**GEORGIA REGENTS MEDICAL CENTER** See Augusta University Medical Center

**HEALTHSOUTH WALTON REHABILITATION HOSPITAL** See Walton Rehabilitation Hospital

**MCG CHILDREN'S MEDICAL CENTER** See Children's Hospital of Georgia

**SELECT SPECIALTY HOSPITAL** See Select Specialty Hospital-Augusta

⊞ **SELECT SPECIALTY HOSPITAL-AUGUSTA (112013)**, 1537 Walton Way, Zip 30904–3764; tel. 706/731–1200, (Nonreporting) **A**1 10 **S** Select Medical Corporation, Mechanicsburg, PA
Primary Contact: E Rick. Lowe, FACHE, Chief Executive Officer
CHR: Terrie Richardson, Coordinator Human Resources
CNO: Kim Pippin, Chief Nursing Officer
Web address: www.augusta.selectspecialtyhospitals.com
**Control**: Corporation, Investor–owned (for–profit) **Service**: Acute long–term care hospital

**Staffed Beds**: 80

**TRINITY HOSPITAL OF AUGUSTA** See University Hospital Summerville

**UNIVERSITY HEALTH CARE SYSTEM** See University Hospital

⊞ **UNIVERSITY HOSPITAL (110028)**, 1350 Walton Way, Zip 30901–2629; tel. 706/722–9011, (Includes UNIVERSITY HOSPITAL SUMMERVILLE, Mailing address: 2260 Wrightsboro Road, Augusta, Georgia, Zip 30904–4726; tel. 706/481–7000; James R Davis, Chief Executive Officer), (Nonreporting) **A**1 2 3 5 10 **F**3 12 13 15 17 18 20 22 24 26 28 29 30 31 34 35 37 38 40 41 44 48 49 50 54 55 56 57 59 60 62 64 68 70 71 72 73 74 75 76 77 78 79 80 81 82 83 84 85 86 87 89 93 96 100 107 108 110 111 114 115 116 117 118 119 126 129 130 132 134 135 146 147 148 149 150 154 156 **P**8 **S** University Health Care System, Augusta, GA
Primary Contact: James R. Davis, Chief Executive Officer
CFO: David Belkoski, Senior Vice President and Chief Financial Officer
CMO: William L Farr, M.D., Chief Medical Officer
CIO: Shirley Gabriel, Vice President and Chief Information Officer
CHR: Laurie Ott, Vice President Human Resources and President University Health Care Foundation
Web address: www.universityhealth.org
**Control**: Other not–for–profit (including NFP Corporation) **Service**: General medical and surgical

**Staffed Beds**: 568 **Admissions**: 26220 **Census**: 362 **Outpatient Visits**: 590260 **Births**: 3247 **Total Expense ($000)**: 515564 **Payroll Expense ($000)**: 181879 **Personnel**: 2671

**VETERANS AFFAIRS MEDICAL CENTER** See Charlie Norwood Veterans Affairs Medical Center

⊞ **WALTON REHABILITATION HOSPITAL (113030)**, 1355 Independence Drive, Zip 30901–1037; tel. 706/724–7746, (Nonreporting) **A**1 5 10 **S** Encompass Health Corporation, Birmingham, AL
Primary Contact: Eric Crossan, Chief Executive Officer
CMO: Pamela Salazar, M.D., Chief of Staff
CIO: Ann Keller, Supervisor Health Information Management
CHR: Volante Henderson, Director Human Resources
CNO: Lynn Beaulieu, Chief Nursing Officer
Web address: www.healthsouthwalton.com/
**Control**: Corporation, Investor–owned (for–profit) **Service**: Rehabilitation

**Staffed Beds**: 58

### AUSTELL—Cobb County

**PROMINA COBB HOSPITAL** See Wellstar Cobb Hospital

⊞ △ **WELLSTAR COBB HOSPITAL (110143)**, 3950 Austell Road, Zip 30106–1121; tel. 470/732–4000, (Nonreporting) **A**1 2 3 7 10 **F**3 4 5 11 13 15 16 17 18 20 22 26 28 29 30 31 38 40 41 44 45 46 48 49 50 51 53 54 55 58 59 60 61 64 65 66 68 70 72 73 74 75 76 77 78 79 81 82 84 85 86 87 90 93 94 96 97 98 100 101 102 104 105 106 107 108 110 111 114 115 119 120 121 123 124 126 129 130 131 132 135 141 144 146 147 148 149 153 154 156 **S** WellStar Health System, Marietta, GA
Primary Contact: Callie Andrews, President
CFO: Darold Etheridge, Vice President and Chief Financial Officer
CMO: Thomas McNamara, D.O., Vice President Medical Affairs
CIO: Jonathan B Morris, M.D., Senior Vice President and Chief Information Officer
CHR: Danyale Ziglor, Vice President
CNO: Kay Kennedy, Chief Nurse Executive
Web address: www.wellstar.org
**Control**: Other not–for–profit (including NFP Corporation) **Service**: General medical and surgical

**Staffed Beds**: 372 **Admissions**: 20416 **Census**: 259 **Outpatient Visits**: 244824 **Births**: 3146 **Personnel**: 2402

### BAINBRIDGE—Decatur County

⇑ **MEMORIAL HOSPITAL AND MANOR (110132)**, 1500 East Shotwell Street, Zip 39819–4256; tel. 229/246–3500, (Nonreporting) **A**10 21
Primary Contact: James M. Lambert, FACHE, Chief Executive Officer
COO: Lee Harris, Assistant Administrator Support Services
CFO: Karen Faircloth, Chief Financial Officer
CMO: Shawn Surratt, M.D., Chief of Staff
CIO: Nelda Moore, Director Data Processing
CHR: Angel Sykes, Director Human Resources
CNO: Cynthia Vickers, R.N., Assistant Administrator for Nursing Services
Web address: www.mh-m.org
**Control**: Hospital district or authority, Government, Nonfederal **Service**: General medical and surgical

**Staffed Beds**: 80

## BAXLEY—Appling County

⇧ **APPLING GENERAL HOSPITAL** See Appling Healthcare System

★ ⇧ **APPLING HEALTHCARE SYSTEM (110071)**, 163 East Tollison Street, Zip 31513–0120; tel. 912/367–9841, (Nonreporting) **A**10 20 21
Primary Contact: Randy Crawford, Chief Executive Officer
COO: Judy M Long, R.N., MS, Chief Nursing Officer and Chief Operating Officer
CFO: Raymond J. Leadbetter JrRevenue Cycle Consultant
CMO: Garland Martin, M.D., Chief of Staff
CIO: Gary Gower, Chief Information Officer
CHR: Carla McLendon, Director Human Resources
CNO: Judy M Long, R.N., MS, Chief Nursing Officer and Chief Operating Officer
Web address: www.appling-hospital.org
**Control**: County, Government, Nonfederal **Service**: General medical and surgical

| **Staffed Beds:** 150 |
| --- |

## BLAIRSVILLE—Union County

★ ⇧ **UNION GENERAL HOSPITAL (110051)**, 35 Hospital Road, Zip 30512–3139; tel. 706/745–2111, (Total facility includes 150 beds in nursing home–type unit) (Nonreporting) **A**10 20 21 **F**3 7 11 13 15 28 29 30 34 35 40 45 46 47 48 49 50 53 57 59 64 70 76 77 79 81 82 85 86 87 93 96 107 108 110 111 114 115 119 120 127 131 132 135 143 146 147 148 149 157 **S** Union General Hospital, Inc., Blairsville, GA
Primary Contact: Kevin Bierschenk, Chief Executive Officer
COO: Lewis Kelley, Chief Operating Officer
CFO: Stephanie L Fletcher, CPA, Chief Financial Officer
CMO: Andre Schaeffer, M.D., Chief of Staff
CIO: Mike Johnston, Director Facilities Operations
CHR: Kathy Hood, Administrative Assistant Human Resources
CNO: Julia Barnett, Chief Nursing Officer
Web address: www.uniongeneralhospital.com
**Control**: Other not–for–profit (including NFP Corporation) **Service**: General medical and surgical

| **Staffed Beds:** 195 **Admissions:** 3188 **Census:** 169 **Outpatient Visits:** 71583 **Births:** 580 **Total Expense ($000):** 85960 **Payroll Expense ($000):** 37247 **Personnel:** 831 |
| --- |

## BLAKELY—Early County

⇧ **LIFEBRITE COMMUNITY HOSPITAL OF EARLY (111314)**, 11740 Columbia Street, Zip 39823–2574; tel. 229/723–4241, (Nonreporting) **A**10 18 21 **S** LifeBrite Hospital Group, LLC, Lilburn, GA
Primary Contact: Ginger Cushing, Chief Executive Officer
Web address: www.pchearly.com
**Control**: Corporation, Investor–owned (for–profit) **Service**: General medical and surgical

| **Staffed Beds:** 152 |
| --- |

⇧ **PIONEER COMMUNITY HOSPITAL OF EARLY** See Lifebrite Community Hospital of Early

## BLUE RIDGE—Fannin County

☐ **FANNIN REGIONAL HOSPITAL (110189)**, 2855 Old Highway 5, Zip 30513–6248; tel. 706/632–3711, (Nonreporting) **A**1 10 **S** Quorum Health, Brentwood, TN
Primary Contact: Jason L. Jones, R.N., Chief Executive Officer
CFO: Phillip Fouts, Chief Financial Officer
CMO: Dillon D Miller, M.D., Chief Medical Officer
CIO: Timothy Snider, Manager Information Systems
CHR: Terrasina Ensley, Director Human Resources
Web address: www.fanninregionalhospital.com
**Control**: Corporation, Investor–owned (for–profit) **Service**: General medical and surgical

| **Staffed Beds:** 50 |
| --- |

## BRASELTON—Hall County

**NORTHEAST GEORGIA MEDICAL CENTER BRASELTON**, 1400 River Place, Zip 30517–5600; tel. 770/219–9000, (Nonreporting) **A**3 **S** Northeast Georgia Health System, Gainesville, GA
Primary Contact: Carol H. Burrell, Chief Executive Officer
Web address: www.nghs.com/locations/braselton
**Control**: Other not–for–profit (including NFP Corporation) **Service**: General medical and surgical

| **Staffed Beds:** 100 |
| --- |

## BREMEN—Haralson County

⊞ **HIGGINS GENERAL HOSPITAL (111320)**, 200 Allen Memorial Drive, Zip 30110–2012; tel. 770/824–2000, (Nonreporting) **A**1 10 18 **S** Tanner Health System, Carrollton, GA
Primary Contact: Jerry Morris, Administrator
CFO: Carol Crews, Chief Financial Officer
CMO: Bill Waters, M.D., Chief Medical Officer
CIO: Terri Lee, Chief Information Officer
CHR: Shari W Gainey, Human Resource Director
CNO: B. J. Brock, Nursing Director
Web address: www.tanner.org/Main/HigginsGeneralHospitalBremen.aspx
**Control**: Other not–for–profit (including NFP Corporation) **Service**: General medical and surgical

| **Staffed Beds:** 23 |
| --- |

**TANNER HIGGINS GENERAL HOSPITAL** See Higgins General Hospital

## BRUNSWICK—Glynn County

⊞ **SOUTHEAST GEORGIA HEALTH SYSTEM BRUNSWICK CAMPUS (110025)**, 2415 Parkwood Drive, Zip 31520–4722, Mailing Address: P.O. Box 1518, Zip 31521–1518; tel. 912/466–7000, (Total facility includes 278 beds in nursing home–type unit) (Nonreporting) **A**1 2 10 **F**3 6 8 11 12 13 15 17 18 20 22 26 28 29 30 31 34 35 37 40 44 45 46 47 48 49 50 51 54 57 59 64 66 68 70 71 74 75 76 77 78 79 81 84 85 86 87 89 91 93 94 96 100 107 108 110 111 114 115 117 119 120 121 124 126 129 131 132 135 144 146 147 148 149 156 **P**5 **S** Southeast Georgia Health System, Brunswick, GA
Primary Contact: Michael D. Scherneck, President and Chief Executive Officer
COO: Christy D Jordan, R.N., JD, Chief Operating Officer/Legal Counsel
CFO: John A Miliazzo, Vice President and Chief Financial Officer
CIO: Charles Bumgardner, Director Information Systems
CHR: Kelli Reale, Vice President Human Resources
CNO: Judith Henson, Vice President Patient Care Services
Web address: www.sghs.org
**Control**: Other not–for–profit (including NFP Corporation) **Service**: General medical and surgical

| **Staffed Beds:** 532 **Admissions:** 13155 **Census:** 428 **Outpatient Visits:** 253064 **Births:** 1221 **Total Expense ($000):** 364663 **Payroll Expense ($000):** 168836 **Personnel:** 2242 |
| --- |

**SOUTHEAST GEORGIA REG MED CTR** See Southeast Georgia Health System Brunswick Campus

## BRYON—Peach County

★ ⇧ **MEDICAL CENTER OF PEACH COUNTY, NAVICENT HEALTH (111310)**, 1960 Highway 247 Connector, Zip 31008; tel. 478/654–2000, (Nonreporting) **A**10 18 21 **S** Navicent Health, Macon, GA
Primary Contact: Laura Gentry, Administrator
CFO: Lisa Urbistondo, Chief Financial Officer
CMO: Crystal Brown, M.D., Medical Director
CNO: Brenda Goodman, Chief Nursing Officer
Web address: www.navicenthealth.org
**Control**: Hospital district or authority, Government, Nonfederal **Service**: General medical and surgical

| **Staffed Beds:** 25 |
| --- |

⇧ **PEACH REGIONAL MEDICAL CENTER** See Medical Center of Peach County, Navicent Health

## BUENA VISTA—Marion County

**MARION MEMORIAL HOSPITAL** See Marion Memorial Nursing Home

## CAIRO—Grady County

⊞ **GRADY GENERAL HOSPITAL (110121)**, 1155 Fifth Street SE, Zip 39828–3142, Mailing Address: P.O. Box 360, Zip 39828–0360; tel. 229/377–1150, (Nonreporting) **A**1 10 **F**3 11 13 15 28 29 30 39 40 45 57 59 68 76 77 79 81 85 93 107 111 119 128 133 154 **S** Archbold Medical Center, Thomasville, GA
Primary Contact: Crystal Wells, Administrator
COO: Jim Carter, Chief Operating Officer
CFO: Skip Hightower, Chief Financial Officer
CIO: Tracy Gray, Chief Information Officer
CHR: Michelle Pledger, Coordinator Human Resources
Web address: www.archbold.org
**Control**: Other not–for–profit (including NFP Corporation) **Service**: General medical and surgical

| **Staffed Beds:** 39 **Admissions:** 1209 **Census:** 15 **Outpatient Visits:** 85762 **Births:** 221 **Total Expense ($000):** 24813 **Payroll Expense ($000):** 9150 **Personnel:** 136 |
| --- |

**GA**

---

**Hospital, Medicare Provider Number, Address, Telephone, Approval, Facility, and Physician Codes, Health Care System**

★ American Hospital Association (AHA) membership    ○ Healthcare Facilities Accreditation Program    ⇧ Center for Improvement in Healthcare Quality Accreditation
☐ The Joint Commission accreditation    ◇ DNV Healthcare Inc. accreditation    △ Commission on Accreditation of Rehabilitation Facilities (CARF) accreditation

## CALHOUN—Gordon County

☒ ○ **ADVENTHEALTH GORDON (110023)**, 1035 Red Bud Road,
Zip 30701–2082, Mailing Address: P.O. Box 12938, Zip 30703–7013;
tel. 706/629–2895, (Nonreporting) **A**1 2 10 11 19 **F**3 7 11 13 15 18 20 29 30
31 34 35 37 40 46 57 59 62 64 70 75 76 77 78 79 81 82 85 86 87 93 107
108 111 115 119 120 121 123 129 130 135 144 146 147 148 154 **P**1 6 8 **S**
AdventHealth, Altamonte Springs, FL
Primary Contact: Michael Murrill, President and Chief Executive Officer
COO: Karen Steely, Chief Operating Officer
CMO: Will Theus, M.D., Chief of Staff
CHR: Jeni Hasselbrack, Director Human Resources
CNO: Amy Jordan, Chief Nursing Officer/Vice President of Nursing
Web address: www.gordonhospital.com
**Control:** Church operated, Nongovernment, not–for–profit **Service:** General
medical and surgical

**Staffed Beds:** 83 **Admissions:** 4107 **Census:** 45 **Outpatient Visits:** 268765
**Births:** 517 **Total Expense ($000):** 151894 **Payroll Expense ($000):** 63858
**Personnel:** 1174

**GORDON HOSPITAL** See Adventhealth Gordon

## CAMILLA—Mitchell County

☒ **MITCHELL COUNTY HOSPITAL (111331)**, 90 East Stephens Street,
Zip 31730–1836, Mailing Address: P.O. Box 639, Zip 31730–0639;
tel. 229/336–5284, (Total facility includes 156 beds in nursing home–type unit)
(Nonreporting) **A**1 10 18 **F**3 15 29 30 35 40 41 50 54 57 58 59 68 93 100
102 107 110 111 114 119 127 128 133 135 154 **S** Archbold Medical Center,
Thomasville, GA
Primary Contact: James Womack, Administrator
CFO: Skip Hightower, Senior Vice President and Chief Financial Officer
CIO: Tracy Gray, Chief Information Officer
CHR: Vickie County-Teemer, Coordinator Human Resources
CNO: Carla Beasley, Director of Nursing
Web address: www.archbold.org
**Control:** Other not–for–profit (including NFP Corporation) **Service:** General
medical and surgical

**Staffed Beds:** 181 **Admissions:** 487 **Census:** 168 **Outpatient Visits:** 28018
**Births:** 0 **Total Expense ($000):** 30295 **Payroll Expense ($000):** 14321
**Personnel:** 270

## CANTON—Cherokee County

☒ **NORTHSIDE HOSPITAL-CHEROKEE (110008)**, 450 Northside Cherokee
Boulevard, Zip 30115–8015, Mailing Address: P.O. Box 906, Zip 30169–0906;
tel. 770/720–5100, (Nonreporting) **A**1 10 **F**3 8 11 12 13 15 18 20 22 26 28
29 30 31 34 35 40 44 45 49 50 54 55 57 59 60 64 68 70 73 74 75 76 77 78
79 81 82 84 85 86 87 93 107 108 110 111 114 117 118 119 120 121 123
124 126 129 130 131 132 144 145 146 147 148 156 **S** Northside Healthcare
System, Atlanta, GA
Primary Contact: William M. Hayes, Chief Executive Officer
COO: Mike Patterson, Director of Operations
CFO: Brian Jennette, Chief Financial Officer
CMO: Alexander Kessler, M.D., Chief of Staff
CIO: Bill Dunford, Manager
CHR: Roslyn Roberts, Manager
Web address: www.northside.com
**Control:** Other not–for–profit (including NFP Corporation) **Service:** General
medical and surgical

**Staffed Beds:** 130 **Admissions:** 10561 **Census:** 143 **Outpatient
Visits:** 398312 **Births:** 2027 **Total Expense ($000):** 403351 **Payroll
Expense ($000):** 159185 **Personnel:** 2374

**R T JONES HOSPITAL** See Northside Hospital-Cherokee

## CARROLLTON—Carroll County

**TANNER MEDICAL CENTER** See Tanner Medical Center-Carrollton

☒ **TANNER MEDICAL CENTER-CARROLLTON (110011)**, 705 Dixie Street,
Zip 30117–3818; tel. 770/836–9666, (Nonreporting) **A**1 2 10 **S** Tanner Health
System, Carrollton, GA
Primary Contact: Loy M. Howard, Chief Operating Officer
CFO: Carol Crews, Chief Financial Officer
CMO: William Waters, M.D., IVChief Medical Officer
CNO: Deborah Matthews, Chief Nursing Officer
Web address: www.tanner.org
**Control:** Other not–for–profit (including NFP Corporation) **Service:** General
medical and surgical

**Staffed Beds:** 142

## CARTERSVILLE—Bartow County

☒ **CARTERSVILLE MEDICAL CENTER (110030)**, 960 Joe Frank Harris Parkway,
Zip 30120–2129; tel. 770/382–1530, (Nonreporting) **A**1 2 3 5 10 **S** HCA
Healthcare, Nashville, TN
Primary Contact: J. Christopher. Mosley, Chief Executive Officer
COO: Lori Rakes, Chief Operating Officer
CNO: Jan Tidwell, Chief Nursing Officer
Web address: www.cartersvillemedical.com
**Control:** Corporation, Investor–owned (for-profit) **Service:** General medical and surgical

**Staffed Beds:** 119

**EMORY CARTERSVILLE MEDICAL CTR** See Cartersville Medical Center

## CEDARTOWN—Polk County

**COLUMBIA POLK GENERAL HOSPITAL** See Polk Medical Center

☒ **POLK MEDICAL CENTER (111330)**, 2360 Rockmart Highway,
Zip 30125–6029; tel. 770/748–2500, (Nonreporting) **A**1 10 18 **F**3 15 28 29
30 34 35 40 43 50 56 57 59 64 68 75 77 81 93 103 107 108 110 114 119
130 132 133 135 143 144 146 147 148 149 154 156 **S** Floyd Healthcare
Management, Rome, GA
Primary Contact: Tifani Kinard, Administrator and Chief Nursing Officer
CFO: Rick Sheerin, Chief Financial Officer
CHR: Jeanna Smith, Administrative Assistant and Human Resources Officer
CNO: Tifani Kinard, Administrator and Chief Nursing Officer
Web address: www.polkhospital.org
**Control:** Hospital district or authority, Government, Nonfederal **Service:** General
medical and surgical

**Staffed Beds:** 25 **Admissions:** 595 **Census:** 21 **Outpatient Visits:** 39674
**Births:** 0 **Total Expense ($000):** 24489 **Payroll Expense ($000):** 10299
**Personnel:** 154

## CHATSWORTH—Murray County

☒ **ADVENTHEALTH MURRAY (110050)**, 707 Old Dalton Ellijay Road,
Zip 30705–2060, Mailing Address: P.O. Box 1406, Zip 30705–1406;
tel. 706/695–4564, (Nonreporting) **A**1 10 **F**3 7 15 29 30 34 35 40 57 59 64 79
81 93 107 111 115 119 146 **P**6 8 **S** AdventHealth, Altamonte Springs, FL
Primary Contact: Michael Murrill, President and Chief Executive Officer
COO: Karen Steely, Chief Operating Officer
CMO: Blaine Minor, M.D., Chief of Staff
CIO: Jose C Rios, Director Information Services
CHR: Brandy Rymer, Coordinator Human Resources
CNO: Susan Shook, Interim Chief Executive Officer
Web address: www.murraymedical.org/
**Control:** Church operated, Nongovernment, not–for–profit **Service:** General
medical and surgical

**Staffed Beds:** 12 **Admissions:** 625 **Census:** 5 **Outpatient Visits:** 78481
**Births:** 0 **Total Expense ($000):** 32355 **Payroll Expense ($000):** 12600
**Personnel:** 273

**MURRAY MEDICAL CENTER** See Adventhealth Murray

## CLAXTON—Evans County

⇑ **EVANS MEMORIAL HOSPITAL (110142)**, 200 North River Street,
Zip 30417–1659, Mailing Address: P.O. Box 518, Zip 30417–0518;
tel. 912/739–2611, (Nonreporting) **A**10 21
Primary Contact: William H. Lee, Chief Executive Officer
CFO: John Wiggins, Chief Financial Officer
CMO: Kyle Parks, M.D., Chief of Staff
CIO: Steve Schmidt, Director Information Systems
CHR: Gina Waters, Director Human Resources
CNO: Nikki NeSmith, Chief Nursing Officer
Web address: www.evansmemorialhospital.org/
**Control:** Hospital district or authority, Government, Nonfederal **Service:** General
medical and surgical

**Staffed Beds:** 10

## CLAYTON—Rabun County

**MOUNTAIN LAKES MEDICAL CENTER (111336)**, 162 Legacy Point,
Zip 30525–5354; tel. 706/782–3100, (Nonreporting) **A**10 18 **F**12 30 40 45 47
49 64 68 70 79 81 82 85 93 102 107 111 114 115 130 133 135 154
Primary Contact: Tammy L. Coll, Chief Executive Officer
CFO: Jimmy Norman, Chief Financial Officer
CHR: Charles Harbaugh, Director Human Resources
Web address: www.mountainlakesmedicalcenter.com
**Control:** Partnership, Investor–owned (for-profit) **Service:** General medical and surgical

**Staffed Beds:** 16 **Admissions:** 350 **Census:** 35 **Outpatient Visits:** 15,684
**Births:** 0

**RABUN COUNTY HOSPITAL** See Mountain Lakes Medical Center

**GA**

## COCHRAN—Bleckley County

⇧ **BLECKLEY MEMORIAL HOSPITAL (111302)**, 145 East Peacock Street, Zip 31014–7846, Mailing Address: P.O. Box 536, Zip 31014–0536; tel. 478/934–6211, (Nonreporting) **A**10 18 21
Primary Contact: Jon Green, R.N., Chief Executive Officer
COO: John Roland, R.N., Chief Operating Officer and Chief Nursing Officer
CFO: Sandra Herndon, CPA, Chief Financial Officer
CIO: Scott Wynne, Chief Information Officer Director
CHR: Jean Allen, Human Resources Director
CNO: John Roland, R.N., Chief Operating Officer and Chief Nursing Officer
Web address: www.bleckleymemorial.com
**Control:** Hospital district or authority, Government, Nonfederal **Service:** General medical and surgical

| Staffed Beds: 25 |
|---|

## COLQUITT—Miller County

⇧ **MILLER COUNTY HOSPITAL (111305)**, 209 North Cuthbert Street, Zip 39837–3518, Mailing Address: P.O. Box 7, Zip 39837–0007; tel. 229/758–3385, (Total facility includes 191 beds in nursing home–type unit) (Nonreporting) **A**10 18 21 **F**3 15 28 29 32 34 35 40 44 45 50 56 57 59 66 68 75 81 83 84 85 86 87 89 97 107 110 115 119 127 128 129 130 132 133 135 148 149 154 156 158
Primary Contact: Robin Rau, Chief Executive Officer
CFO: Jill Brown, Chief Financial Officer
CMO: William Swofford, M.D., Chief of Staff
CIO: Keith Lovering, Information Technician
CHR: Karie Spence, Director Human Resources
CNO: Shawn Whittaker, Chief Nursing Officer
Web address: www.millercountyhospital.com
**Control:** Hospital district or authority, Government, Nonfederal **Service:** General medical and surgical

| Staffed Beds: 216 Admissions: 698 Census: 192 Outpatient Visits: 49119 Births: 0 Total Expense ($000): 47323 Payroll Expense ($000): 24036 Personnel: 561 |
|---|

## COLUMBUS—Muscogee County

**BRADLEY CENTER** See Bradley Center of St. Francis

**BRADLEY CENTER OF ST. FRANCIS** See St. Francis Hospital

**COLUMBUS SPECIALTY HOSPITAL (112012)**, 616 19th Street, Zip 31901–1528, Mailing Address: P.O. Box 910, Zip 31902–0910; tel. 706/494–4075, (Nonreporting) **A**10
Primary Contact: William Eckstein, Chief Executive Officer and Chief Financial Officer
CFO: William Eckstein, Chief Executive Officer and Chief Financial Officer
CHR: Myra Whitley, Vice President, Human Resources
Web address: www.columbusspecialtyhospital.net
**Control:** Other not–for–profit (including NFP Corporation) **Service:** Acute long–term care hospital

| Staffed Beds: 33 |
|---|

**DOCTORS SPECIALTY HOSPITAL** See Midtown Medical Center West

**NORTHSIDE MEDICAL CENTER** See Piedmont Columbus Regional Northside

**PIEDMONT COLUMBUS REGIONAL** See Piedmont Columbus Regional Midtown

☐ **PIEDMONT COLUMBUS REGIONAL MIDTOWN (110064)**, 710 Center Street, Zip 31901–1527, Mailing Address: P.O. Box 951, Zip 31902–0951; tel. 706/571–1000, (Includes MIDTOWN MEDICAL CENTER WEST, Mailing address: 616 19th Street, Columbus, Georgia, Zip 31901–1528, P O Box 2188, Zip 31902–2188, tel. 706/494–4262; Ryan Chandler, Chief Executive Officer), (Nonreporting) **A**1 2 3 5 10 13 **F**3 11 12 13 18 20 22 29 30 31 34 35 38 40 41 43 44 45 46 47 48 49 50 51 55 56 57 58 59 60 61 64 65 66 68 70 72 73 74 75 76 77 78 79 81 82 85 86 87 88 89 92 93 94 97 102 107 108 111 114 115 116 117 119 120 121 123 124 126 130 131 132 135 146 147 148 149 156 **S** Piedmont Healthcare, Roswell, GA
Primary Contact: M. Scott. Hill, President and Chief Executive Officer
COO: Bill Tustin, Chief Operating Officer
CMO: Chris Edwards, M.D., Chief Medical Officer
Web address: www.columbusregional.com
**Control:** Other not–for–profit (including NFP Corporation) **Service:** General medical and surgical

| Staffed Beds: 510 Admissions: 16226 Census: 222 Outpatient Visits: 259217 Births: 2695 Total Expense ($000): 326860 Payroll Expense ($000): 114528 |
|---|

☐ **PIEDMONT COLUMBUS REGIONAL NORTHSIDE (110200)**, 100 Frist Court, Zip 31909–3578, Mailing Address: P.O. Box 7188, Zip 31908–7188; tel. 706/494–2100, (Nonreporting) **A**1 3 10 **F**3 11 29 30 32 34 35 38 40 44 45 50 57 59 60 61 64 65 68 70 71 74 75 77 79 81 82 85 86 87 90 92 93 94 96 97 107 108 111 119 129 130 131 135 146 149 156 **S** Piedmont Healthcare, Roswell, GA
Primary Contact: M. Scott. Hill, President and Chief Executive Officer
COO: Laura Drew, Chief Operating Officer
CFO: Roland Thacker, Chief Financial Officer
CMO: Chris Edwards, M.D., Chief Medical Officer
CIO: Douglas Colburn, Chief Information Officer
CHR: Becky Augustyniak, Director Human Resources
Web address: www.columbusregional.com
**Control:** Other not–for–profit (including NFP Corporation) **Service:** General medical and surgical

| Staffed Beds: 100 Admissions: 3891 Census: 50 Outpatient Visits: 33593 Births: 0 Total Expense ($000): 73226 Payroll Expense ($000): 22158 Personnel: 362 |
|---|

**ST FRANCIS HOSPITAL, INC** See St. Francis Hospital

⊞ **ST. FRANCIS HOSPITAL (110129)**, 2122 Manchester Expressway, Zip 31904–6878, Mailing Address: P.O. Box 7000, Zip 31908–7000; tel. 706/596–4000, (Includes BRADLEY CENTER OF ST. FRANCIS, Mailing address: 2000 16th Avenue, Columbus, Georgia, Zip 31906–0308; tel. 706/320–3700), (Nonreporting) **A**1 5 10 **S** LifePoint Health, Brentwood, TN
Primary Contact: Melody Trimble, Chief Executive Officer
COO: Alan E George, Chief Operating Officer
CFO: Greg Hembree, Senior Vice President and Chief Financial Officer
CMO: Bobbi Farber, M.D., Chief Medical Officer
CIO: Jonathon R Jager, Chief Information Officer
CHR: E Rick Lowe, FACHE, Operations Support Risk Management and Compliance
CNO: Charlene Falgout, Chief Nursing Officer
Web address: www.mystfrancis.com
**Control:** Other not–for–profit (including NFP Corporation) **Service:** General medical and surgical

| Staffed Beds: 302 |
|---|

☐ **WEST CENTRAL GEORGIA REGIONAL HOSPITAL (114013)**, 3000 Schatulga Road, Zip 31907–3117, Mailing Address: P.O. Box 12435, Zip 31917–2435; tel. 706/568–5000, (Nonreporting) **A**1 10 **F**39 98 130 135 149
Primary Contact: John L. Robertson, Administrator
COO: Marcia Capshaw, Chief Operating Officer
CFO: John Frederick, Chief Financial Officer
CMO: David Morton, M.D., Clinical Director
CIO: Karen Fisher-Ford, Director of Health Information Management
CHR: Peri Johnson, Human Resources Director
CNO: Nicolise Claassens, Nurse Executive
Web address: www.dbhdd.georgia.gov/west-central-georgia-regional-hospital-columbus
**Control:** State, Government, Nonfederal **Service:** Psychiatric

| Staffed Beds: 194 Admissions: 225 Census: 70 Outpatient Visits: 0 Births: 0 Personnel: 552 |
|---|

## COMMERCE—Jackson County

**BJC MEDICAL CENTER** See Northridge Medical Center

⊞ **NORTHRIDGE MEDICAL CENTER (110040)**, 70 Medical Center Drive, Zip 30529–1078; tel. 706/335–1000, (Nonreporting) **A**1 10
Primary Contact: Jerry R. Wise, Chief Executive Officer
CMO: Narasimhulu Neelagaru, M.D., Chief of Staff
Web address: www.northridgemc.com
**Control:** Partnership, Investor–owned (for–profit) **Service:** General medical and surgical

| Staffed Beds: 207 |
|---|

GA

## CONYERS—Rockdale County

☐ **PIEDMONT ROCKDALE HOSPITAL (110091)**, 1412 Milstead Avenue NE, Zip 30012–3877; tel. 770/918–3000, (Nonreporting) **A**1 5 10 **F**3 11 13 15 18 20 22 26 28 29 30 34 35 36 44 45 46 47 49 57 59 70 72 75 76 77 79 81 85 86 87 93 94 107 108 110 111 114 115 118 119 126 130 131 132 135 145 146 147 148 149 154 **S** Piedmont Healthcare, Roswell, GA
Primary Contact: Richard Tanzella, Chief Executive Officer
COO: Blake Watts, Chief Operating Officer
CFO: Diane Roth, Chief Financial Officer
CMO: Lisa Gillespie, M.D., Chief Medical Officer
CIO: Gail Waldo, Director Information Technology
CHR: Marianne Freeman, Vice President Human Resources
CNO: Eleanor Post, R.N., Chief Nursing Officer
Web address: www.rockdalemedicalcenter.org
**Control**: Other not–for–profit (including NFP Corporation) **Service**: General medical and surgical

**Staffed Beds**: 158 **Admissions**: 8892 **Census**: 114 **Outpatient Visits**: 100856 **Births**: 1712 **Personnel**: 839

**ROCKDALE MEDICAL CENTER** See Piedmont Rockdale Hospital

## CORDELE—Crisp County

**CRISP COUNTY HOSPITAL** See Crisp Regional Hospital

☒ **CRISP REGIONAL HOSPITAL (110104)**, 902 North Seventh Street, Zip 31015–3234; tel. 229/276–3100, (Total facility includes 243 beds in nursing home–type unit) (Nonreporting) **A**1 3 5 10 20 **F**3 11 13 15 29 30 31 34 35 40 43 44 45 48 49 50 51 54 56 57 58 59 60 61 62 63 64 65 68 70 71 75 76 77 78 79 81 84 85 86 87 89 90 93 96 97 107 108 110 111 114 115 117 118 125 126 127 128 129 130 132 133 135 144 146 147 148 149 154 156 **P**6 8
Primary Contact: Steven Gautney, Chief Executive Officer
COO: Mary Jim Montgomery, R.N., MSN, FACHE, Chief Operating Officer
CFO: Jessica Y Carter, Chief Financial Officer
CMO: David Kavtaradze, M.D., Chief of Staff
CHR: George M Laurin, Interim Director Human Resources
CNO: Marsha L. Mulderig, R.N., MSN, Chief Nursing Officer
Web address: www.crispregional.org
**Control**: Other not–for–profit (including NFP Corporation) **Service**: General medical and surgical

**Staffed Beds**: 316 **Admissions**: 3064 **Census**: 161 **Outpatient Visits**: 103877 **Births**: 246 **Personnel**: 470

## COVINGTON—Newton County

⇑ **NEWTON MEDICAL CENTER** See Piedmont Newton Hospital

⇑ **PIEDMONT NEWTON HOSPITAL (110018)**, 5126 Hospital Drive, Zip 30014–2567; tel. 770/786–7053, (Nonreporting) **A**10 21 **F**3 7 11 13 15 18 20 28 29 30 34 35 39 44 45 47 49 50 51 53 54 57 59 60 68 70 73 75 76 79 81 85 93 107 108 110 111 114 115 119 130 131 143 146 147 148 149 154 156 157 **S** Piedmont Healthcare, Roswell, GA
Primary Contact: David Kent, Chief Executive Officer
CFO: Lauren Matthews, Chief Financial Officer
CMO: B. Carter Rogers, Chief of Staff
CIO: Brad Collier, Director
CHR: Greg H Richardson, Assistant Administrator Human Resources
CNO: Jeremiah Bame, R.N., Chief Nursing Officer
Web address: www.newtonmedical.com
**Control**: Other not–for–profit (including NFP Corporation) **Service**: General medical and surgical

**Staffed Beds**: 103 **Admissions**: 5257 **Census**: 49 **Outpatient Visits**: 85615 **Births**: 721 **Personnel**: 579

## CUMMING—Forsyth County

**BAPTIST MEDICAL CENTER** See Northside Hospital-Forsyth

☒ **NORTHSIDE HOSPITAL-FORSYTH (110005)**, 1200 Northside Forsyth Drive, Zip 30041–7659; tel. 770/844–3200, (Nonreporting) **A**1 10 **F**3 8 11 12 13 15 18 20 22 26 28 29 30 31 34 35 37 40 44 45 48 49 50 54 55 57 59 60 64 68 70 72 73 74 75 76 77 78 79 81 82 84 85 86 87 93 107 108 110 111 114 115 117 118 119 120 121 123 124 126 129 130 131 132 135 144 145 146 147 148 156 **S** Northside Healthcare System, Atlanta, GA
Primary Contact: Skip Putnam, Chief Executive Officer
COO: Lynn Jackson, Chief Operating Officer
CFO: Eric Caldwell, Director Finance
CNO: Carolyn Booker, Chief Nursing Officer
Web address: www.northside.com
**Control**: Other not–for–profit (including NFP Corporation) **Service**: General medical and surgical

**Staffed Beds**: 319 **Admissions**: 16036 **Census**: 221 **Outpatient Visits**: 679838 **Births**: 3185 **Total Expense ($000)**: 536435 **Payroll Expense ($000)**: 214402 **Personnel**: 2976

## CUTHBERT—Randolph County

⇑ **PATTERSON HOSPITAL** See Southwest Georgia Regional Medical Center

★ ⇑ **SOUTHWEST GEORGIA REGIONAL MEDICAL CENTER (111300)**, 361 Randolph Street, Zip 39840–6127; tel. 229/732–2181, (Nonreporting) **A**10 18 21 **S** Phoebe Putney Health System, Albany, GA
Primary Contact: Kim Gilman, Chief Executive Officer and Chief Nursing Officer
CFO: Candace Guarnieri, Chief Financial Officer
CNO: Kim Gilman, Chief Executive Officer and Chief Nursing Officer
Web address: www.phoebeputney.com/
**Control**: Hospital district or authority, Government, Nonfederal **Service**: General medical and surgical

**Staffed Beds**: 25

## DAHLONEGA—Lumpkin County

⇑ **NORTHEAST GEORGIA MEDICAL CENTER LUMPKIN (110237)**, 227 Mountain Drive, Zip 30533–1606; tel. 770/219–9000, (Nonreporting) **A**21 **S** Northeast Georgia Health System, Gainesville, GA
Primary Contact: Carol H. Burrell, Chief Executive Officer
Web address: www.https://www.nghs.com/locations/lumpkin/
**Control**: Other not–for–profit (including NFP Corporation) **Service**: General medical and surgical

**Staffed Beds**: 49

⇑ **NORTHEAST GEORGIA MEDICAL CENTER-LUMPKIN** See Northeast Georgia Medical Center Lumpkin

## DALTON—Whitfield County

☒ **HAMILTON MEDICAL CENTER (110001)**, 1200 Memorial Drive, Zip 30720–2529, Mailing Address: P.O. Box 1168, Zip 30722–1168; tel. 706/272–6000, (Nonreporting) **A**1 2 10 19
Primary Contact: Jeffrey D. Myers, President and Chief Executive Officer
COO: Sandra D. McKenzie, Executive Vice President and Chief Operating Officer
CFO: Gary L Howard, Senior Vice President and Chief Financial Officer
CMO: Andrew C. Bland, M.D., Vice President and Chief Medical Officer
CIO: John M Forrester, Director Information Services
CHR: Jason Hopkins, Director, Human Resources
CNO: Cathy Ferguson, R.N., MSN, Vice President and Chief Nursing Officer
Web address: www.hamiltonhealth.com
**Control**: Other not–for–profit (including NFP Corporation) **Service**: General medical and surgical

**Staffed Beds**: 227

## DECATUR—Dekalb County

☒ **ATLANTA VETERANS AFFAIRS MEDICAL CENTER**, 1670 Clairmont Road, Zip 30033–4004; tel. 404/321–6111, (Total facility includes 110 beds in nursing home–type unit) (Nonreporting) **A**1 3 5 8 **F**3 5 17 18 20 22 24 26 29 30 31 34 35 36 38 39 40 45 46 47 48 49 52 54 55 56 57 58 59 60 61 62 63 64 65 66 70 74 75 77 78 79 81 82 83 84 85 86 87 91 92 93 94 96 97 98 100 101 102 103 104 107 108 111 114 115 116 117 118 119 120 121 123 127 129 130 132 135 143 144 145 146 147 148 149 153 154 156 157 **S** Department of Veterans Affairs, Washington, DC
Primary Contact: Ann R. Brown, M.D., Director
CFO: Pamela Watkins, Chief Financial Officer
CMO: David Bower, M.D., Chief of Staff
CIO: William Brock, Chief Information Officer
CHR: Zeta Ferguson, Chief Human Resources
CNO: Sandy Leake, MSN, R.N., Associate Director, Nursing and Patient Care Services
Web address: www.atlanta.va.gov/
**Control**: Veterans Affairs, Government, federal **Service**: General medical and surgical

**Staffed Beds**: 273 **Admissions**: 8875 **Census**: 289 **Outpatient Visits**: 1243099 **Births**: 0 **Total Expense ($000)**: 955718 **Payroll Expense ($000)**: 541274 **Personnel**: 5478

*Many Facility Codes have changed. Please refer to the AHA Guide Code Chart.* © 2021 AHA Guide

**DEKALB MEDICAL AT DOWNTOWN DECATUR** See Emory Long-Term Acute Care

**DEKALB MEDICAL AT NORTH DECATUR** See Emory Decatur Hospital

⊞ **EMORY DECATUR HOSPITAL (110076)**, 2701 North Decatur Road, Zip 30033–5995; tel. 404/501–1000, (Nonreporting) **A**1 2 3 10 **F**3 11 12 13 15 20 22 26 28 29 30 31 34 35 38 40 44 46 48 49 50 51 53 55 57 58 59 60 68 70 72 73 74 75 76 77 78 79 81 82 84 85 86 87 90 93 96 98 100 102 104 107 108 110 111 114 115 116 117 119 120 121 123 124 126 129 130 131 132 135 146 147 148 154 156 **P**1 **S** Emory Healthcare, Atlanta, GA
Primary Contact: Jim Forstner, Chief Executive Officer
CFO: Robin Nichols, Interim Chief Financial Officer
CIO: Beth Patino, Chief Information Officer
CHR: LeRoy Walker, Vice President Human Resources
CNO: Susan Breslin, R.N., MSN, Vice President Patient Care Services and Chief Nursing Officer
Web address: www.dekalbmedical.org
**Control:** Other not–for–profit (including NFP Corporation) **Service:** General medical and surgical

**Staffed Beds:** 472 **Admissions:** 19323 **Census:** 262 **Outpatient Visits:** 154440 **Births:** 3444 **Total Expense ($000):** 339647 **Payroll Expense ($000):** 177838 **Personnel:** 2431

☐ **EMORY LONG-TERM ACUTE CARE (112006)**, 450 North Candler Street, Zip 30030–2671; tel. 404/501–6700, (Nonreporting) **A**1 5 10 **F**1 18 29 30 45 48 50 60 68 74 75 78 84 85 91 94 100 119 130 135 149 **P**1 **S** Emory Healthcare, Atlanta, GA
Primary Contact: Jim Forstner, Chief Executive Officer
CMO: David Snyder, M.D., Chief of Staff
CHR: Tom Crawford, Vice President Human Resources
Web address: www.dekalbmedicalcenter.org
**Control:** Other not–for–profit (including NFP Corporation) **Service:** Acute long–term care hospital

**Staffed Beds:** 50 **Admissions:** 326 **Census:** 31 **Outpatient Visits:** 0 **Births:** 0 **Total Expense ($000):** 21161 **Payroll Expense ($000):** 10662 **Personnel:** 170

☐ **GEORGIA REGIONAL HOSPITAL AT ATLANTA (114019)**, 3073 Panthersville Road, Zip 30034–3828; tel. 404/243–2100, (Nonreporting) **A**1 3 5 10
Primary Contact: Gilbert Scott, Regional Hospital Administrator
COO: Sonny Slate, Chief Operating Officer
CFO: Reginald Jones, Business Manager
CMO: Emile Risby, M.D., Clinical Director
CIO: Elfie Early, Manager Data Services
CHR: Lorraine Farr, Manager Human Resources
Web address: www.atlantareg.dhr.state.ga.us
**Control:** State, Government, Nonfederal **Service:** Psychiatric

**Staffed Beds:** 319

**VETERANS AFFAIRS MEDICAL CENTER** See Atlanta Veterans Affairs Medical Center

**DEMOREST—Habersham County**

⇑ **HABERSHAM COUNTY MEDICAL CENTER** See Habersham Medical Center

★ ⇑ **HABERSHAM MEDICAL CENTER (110041)**, 541 Historic Highway 441, Zip 30535–3118, Mailing Address: P.O. Box 37, Zip 30535–0037; tel. 706/754–2161, (Nonreporting) **A**10 21
Primary Contact: Stephen Tyler. Williams, Chief Executive Officer
COO: Michael Gay, Chief Operating Officer
CFO: Barbara Duncan, Chief Financial Officer
CMO: Josh Garrett, Chief of Staff
CHR: Ryan Snow, Director Human Resources
Web address: www.habershammedical.com/
**Control:** Hospital district or authority, Government, Nonfederal **Service:** General medical and surgical

**Staffed Beds:** 137

**DONALSONVILLE—Seminole County**

⇑ **DONALSONVILLE HOSPITAL (110194)**, 102 Hospital Circle, Zip 39845–1199; tel. 229/524–5217, (Nonreporting) **A**10 21
Primary Contact: Charles H. Orrick, Administrator
CFO: James Moody, Chief Financial Officer
CMO: C O Walker, M.D., Chief of Staff
CHR: Jo Adams, Director Human Resources
**Control:** Other not–for–profit (including NFP Corporation) **Service:** General medical and surgical

**Staffed Beds:** 140

**DOUGLAS—Coffee County**

⇑ **COFFEE REGIONAL HOSPITAL** See Coffee Regional Medical Center

★ ⇑ **COFFEE REGIONAL MEDICAL CENTER (110089)**, 1101 Ocilla Road, Zip 31533–2207, Mailing Address: P.O. Box 1287, Zip 31534–1287; tel. 912/384–1900, (Nonreporting) **A**10 20 21 **F**3 7 11 13 15 18 20 22 26 28 29 30 31 34 35 39 40 41 44 45 47 50 51 53 54 56 57 59 60 61 64 65 66 68 71 74 75 77 78 79 81 82 85 86 87 92 93 97 107 108 110 111 114 115 119 124 127 130 131 132 133 135 143 146 147 148 149 156
Primary Contact: Vicki Lewis, R.N., MS, FACHE, President and Chief Executive Officer
CFO: Lavonda Cravey, Chief Financial Officer
CHR: Laura Bloom, Director Human Resources
Web address: www.coffeeregional.org
**Control:** Other not–for–profit (including NFP Corporation) **Service:** General medical and surgical

**Staffed Beds:** 88 **Admissions:** 4511 **Census:** 47 **Outpatient Visits:** 93740 **Births:** 547 **Total Expense ($000):** 100725 **Payroll Expense ($000):** 37618 **Personnel:** 658

**DOUGLASVILLE—Douglas County**

**INNER HARBOUR** See Youth Villages Inner Harbour Campus

**PROMINA DOUGLAS HOSPITAL** See Wellstar Douglas Hospital

⊞ **WELLSTAR DOUGLAS HOSPITAL (110184)**, 8954 Hospital Drive, Zip 30134–2282; tel. 770/949–1500, (Nonreporting) **A**1 2 10 **F**3 11 13 15 18 20 22 28 29 30 31 37 38 40 44 45 48 49 50 51 53 54 58 59 60 61 64 68 70 74 75 76 77 78 79 81 82 84 85 86 87 93 94 102 107 108 110 111 114 115 117 118 119 126 129 130 132 135 146 147 148 154 156 **S** WellStar Health System, Marietta, GA
Primary Contact: Craig A. Owens, President
CFO: Bradley Greene, Chief Financial Officer
CMO: Noel Holtz, M.D., Chief Medical Officer
CHR: Danyale Ziglor, Vice President
Web address: www.wellstar.org
**Control:** Other not–for–profit (including NFP Corporation) **Service:** General medical and surgical

**Staffed Beds:** 108 **Admissions:** 6713 **Census:** 75 **Outpatient Visits:** 129067 **Births:** 448 **Personnel:** 821

**YOUTH VILLAGES INNER HARBOUR CAMPUS**, 4685 Dorsett Shoals Road, Zip 30135–4999; tel. 770/942–2391, (Nonreporting)
Primary Contact: Patrick Lawler, Chief Executive Officer
CFO: J Steve Lewis, Director Finance
CIO: Laura Sellers, Director Information Systems
CHR: Sherry Kollmeyer, Vice President Human Resources
Web address: www.innerharbour.org
**Control:** Other not–for–profit (including NFP Corporation) **Service:** Children's hospital psychiatric

**Staffed Beds:** 190

**DUBLIN—Laurens County**

⊞ **CARL VINSON VETERANS AFFAIRS MEDICAL CENTER**, 1826 Veterans Boulevard, Zip 31021–3620; tel. 478/272–1210, (Nonreporting) **A**1 3 **S** Department of Veterans Affairs, Washington, DC
Primary Contact: David Whitmer, FACHE, Director
COO: Gerald M DeWorth, Associate Director
CFO: Kimberly Johnson-Miller, Chief Financial Officer
CMO: Christopher Blasy, D.O., Chief of Staff
CIO: Mark Cowart, Facility Chief Information Officer
CHR: Kurt Oster, Human Resources Officer
CNO: Connie Hampton, R.N., Associate Director for Patient Care Services
Web address: www.dublin.va.gov/
**Control:** Veterans Affairs, Government, federal **Service:** General medical and surgical

**Staffed Beds:** 178

---

| **Hospital, Medicare Provider Number, Address, Telephone, Approval, Facility, and Physician Codes, Health Care System** |
|---|
| ★ American Hospital Association (AHA) membership    ○ Healthcare Facilities Accreditation Program    ⇑ Center for Improvement in Healthcare Quality Accreditation |
| ☐ The Joint Commission accreditation    ◇ DNV Healthcare Inc. accreditation    △ Commission on Accreditation of Rehabilitation Facilities (CARF) accreditation |

**GA**

**COLUMBIA FAIRVIEW PARK HOSP** See Fairview Park Hospital

⊠ **FAIRVIEW PARK HOSPITAL (110125)**, 200 Industrial Boulevard,
Zip 31021–2997, Mailing Address: P.O. Box 1408, Zip 31040–1408;
tel. 478/275–2000, (Nonreporting) **A**1 3 10 19 **S** HCA Healthcare, Nashville, TN
Primary Contact: Donald R. Avery, FACHE, President and Chief Executive Officer
CFO: Ted Short, Chief Financial Officer
CMO: George E. Harrison, M.D., Chief Medical Officer
CIO: Marsha Morris, Manager Information Services
CHR: Jeff Bruton, Director Human Resources
CNO: Donna Trickey, R.N., Chief Nursing Officer
Web address: www.fairviewparkhospital.com
**Control**: Corporation, Investor–owned (for–profit) **Service**: General medical and surgical

**Staffed Beds:** 190

**VETERANS AFFAIRS MEDICAL CTR** See Carl Vinson Veterans Affairs Medical Center

### DULUTH—De Kalb County

**GWINNETT MEDICAL CENTER-DULUTH** See Northside Hospital - Duluth

**NORTHSIDE HOSPITAL - DULUTH** See Northside Hospital - Gwinnett, Lawrenceville

### EAST POINT—Fulton County

★ **REGENCY HOSPITAL OF SOUTH ATLANTA (112014)**, 1170 Cleveland Avenue,
4th Floor, Zip 30344–3615; tel. 404/466–6250, (Nonreporting) **A**3 10 **S** Select Medical Corporation, Mechanicsburg, PA
Primary Contact: Michelle Tenhengel-deVille, Chief Executive Officer
Web address: www.regencyhospital.com
**Control**: Corporation, Investor–owned (for–profit) **Service**: Acute long–term care hospital

**Staffed Beds:** 40

### EASTMAN—Dodge County

⇑ **DODGE COUNTY HOSPITAL (110092)**, 901 Griffin Avenue, Zip 31023–6720,
Mailing Address: PO BOX 4309, Zip 31023–4309; tel. 478/374–4000,
(Nonreporting) **A**10 21 **F**3 11 13 15 29 30 31 40 45 57 59 64 69 70 75 76 79 81 85 86 98 103 107 108 110 111 114 119 146 147
Primary Contact: LaDon Toole, Chief Executive Officer
CFO: Jan Hamrick, Chief Financial Officer
CIO: Victor Woodard, Manager Information Technology
CHR: Wendy Selph, Director Human Resources
CNO: Sandra M. Campbell, R.N., Chief Nursing Officer
Web address: www.dodgecountyhospital.com
**Control**: Hospital district or authority, Government, Nonfederal **Service**: General medical and surgical

**Staffed Beds:** 35 **Admissions:** 1422 **Census:** 24 **Outpatient Visits:** 30149
**Births:** 83 **Total Expense ($000):** 19769 **Payroll Expense ($000):** 9196
**Personnel:** 239

### EATONTON—Putnam County

☐ **PUTNAM GENERAL HOSPITAL (111313)**, 101 Lake Oconee Parkway,
Zip 31024–6054; tel. 706/485–2711, (Nonreporting) **A**1 10 18 **F**3 11 15 18 28 29 34 35 40 45 47 51 57 59 64 68 80 81 89 90 93 107 108 110 111 114 119 128 129 133 146
Primary Contact: Alan Horton, Administrator
CFO: Judy Ware, Chief Financial Officer
CMO: Omar Akhras, M.D., Chief of Staff
CIO: Marcel Lundy, Chief Information Officer
CHR: Jeanine Martinez, Director Human Resources
CNO: Pam Douglas, Chief Nursing Officer
Web address: www.putnamgeneral.com
**Control**: Hospital district or authority, Government, Nonfederal **Service**: General medical and surgical

**Staffed Beds:** 25 **Admissions:** 442 **Census:** 10 **Outpatient Visits:** 18962
**Births:** 0 **Total Expense ($000):** 17764 **Payroll Expense ($000):** 5305
**Personnel:** 117

### ELBERTON—Elbert County

☐ **ELBERT MEMORIAL HOSPITAL (111337)**, 4 Medical Drive, Zip 30635–1897;
tel. 706/283–3151, (Nonreporting) **A**1 10 18 20 **F**3 11 15 29 40 45 50 53 57 59 70 77 79 81 87 93 102 107 110 115 119 128 130 133 146 147 **P**6
Primary Contact: Kerry A. Trapnell, Chief Executive Officer
CIO: Greg Fields, Director Information Technology
CHR: Georgian Walton, Director Human Resources
CNO: Tammy Harlow, Chief Nursing Officer
Web address: www.emhcare.net
**Control**: Hospital district or authority, Government, Nonfederal **Service**: General medical and surgical

**Staffed Beds:** 35 **Admissions:** 567 **Census:** 8 **Outpatient Visits:** 22624
**Births:** 0 **Total Expense ($000):** 13746 **Payroll Expense ($000):** 5488
**Personnel:** 130

### FAYETTEVILLE—Fayette County

⇑ **FAYETTE COMMUNITY HOSPITAL** See Piedmont Fayette Hospital

⇑ **PIEDMONT FAYETTE HOSPITAL (110215)**, 1255 Highway 54 West,
Zip 30214–4526; tel. 770/719–7000, (Nonreporting) **A**2 3 10 21 **S** Piedmont Healthcare, Roswell, GA
Primary Contact: Stephen D. Porter, Chief Executive Officer
COO: Nathan Nipper, Chief Operating Officer
CFO: Scott A. Wolfe, Chief Financial Officer
CMO: Angela Swayne, M.D., Chief Medical Officer
CIO: Geoffrey Brown, Chief Information Officer
CHR: Holly Sawyer, Director and Human Resources Business Partner
CNO: Merry Heath, Chief Nursing Officer
Web address: www.piedmont.org
**Control**: Other not–for–profit (including NFP Corporation) **Service**: General medical and surgical

**Staffed Beds:** 210

### FITZGERALD—Ben Hill County

⇑ **DORMINY MEDICAL CENTER (110073)**, 200 Perry House Road,
Zip 31750–8857, Mailing Address: P.O. Box 1447, Zip 31750–1447;
tel. 229/424–7100, (Nonreporting) **A**10 21
Primary Contact: Staci Mims, Chief Executive Officer
CFO: Paige Wynn, Chief Financial Officer
CMO: Davey Herring, M.D., Chief Medical Officer
CIO: Chris Ward, Director Management Information Systems
CHR: Denise Steverson, Director Human Resources
CNO: Staci Mims, Chief Nursing Officer
Web address: www.dorminymedical.org
**Control**: Hospital district or authority, Government, Nonfederal **Service**: General medical and surgical

**Staffed Beds:** 58

### FORSYTH—Monroe County

⇑ **MONROE COUNTY HOSPITAL (111318)**, 88 Martin Luther King Jr Drive,
Zip 31029–1682, Mailing Address: P.O. Box 1068, Zip 31029–1068;
tel. 478/994–2521, (Nonreporting) **A**3 10 18 21
Primary Contact: Lorraine Smith, Chief Executive Officer
CFO: Judy King Ware, Chief Financial Officer
CMO: Jeremy Goodwin, M.D., President, Medical Staff
CIO: Tiffany Purmont, Supervisor Medical Records
CHR: Deborah Flowers, Director Human Resources
CNO: Casey Fleckenstein, Nurse Manager
Web address: www.monroehospital.org
**Control**: Hospital district or authority, Government, Nonfederal **Service**: General medical and surgical

**Staffed Beds:** 25

### FORT BENNING—Muscogee County

⊠ **MARTIN ARMY COMMUNITY HOSPITAL**, 7950 Martin Loop, Zip 31905–5648,
Mailing Address: 7950 Martin Loop, B9200, Room 010, Zip 31905–5648;
tel. 706/544–2516, (Nonreporting) **A**1 3 5 **S** Department of the Army, Office of the Surgeon General, Falls Church, VA
Primary Contact: Colonel Marie Dominguez, Commander
CHR: MajorBernita Hightower, Chief Human Resources
Web address: www.martin.amedd.army.mil
**Service**: General medical and surgical

**Staffed Beds:** 57

**GA**

## FORT GORDON—Richmond County

✉ **DWIGHT DAVID EISENHOWER ARMY MEDICAL CENTER**, 300 West Hospital Road, Zip 30905–5741; tel. 706/787–5811, (Nonreporting) **A**1 3 5 **S** Department of the Army, Office of the Surgeon General, Falls Church, VA
Primary Contact: Colonel John P. Lamoureux, Commander
CMO: ColonelJames M Baunchalk, Deputy Chief Clinical Services
CIO: MajorJoseph A Ponce, Chief Information Management
CHR: Elizabeth Shelt, Civilian Personnel Officer
Web address: www.ddeamc.amedd.army.mil
**Service**: General medical and surgical

**Staffed Beds:** 107

## FORT OGLETHORPE—Catoosa County

★ **CHI MEMORIAL HOSPITAL - GEORGIA (110236)**, 100 Gross Crescent Circle, Zip 30742–3669; tel. 706/858–2000, (Nonreporting) **A**10 22 **F**7 18 29 30 34 35 40 44 45 46 48 57 64 68 78 81 87 107 114 115 119 121 130 146 149 **P**3 6 7 8 **S** CommonSpirit Health, Chicago, IL
Primary Contact: Angie Hullander, Administrator and Special Operations
COO: Kevin Hopkins, Vice President of Operations
CFO: Farrell Hayes, Chief Financial Officer
CMO: John Erdman, M.D., Chief of Staff
CIO: Ruth Wright-Whitaker, Director Information Services
CHR: Cathy Hulsey, Manager of Human Resources
CNO: Sandra Siniard, Vice President of Patient Care Services
Web address: www.memorial.org/chi-memorial-hospital-georgia
**Control**: Church operated, Nongovernment, not–for–profit **Service**: General medical and surgical

**Staffed Beds:** 35 **Admissions:** 439 **Census:** 4 **Outpatient Visits:** 30768 **Births:** 0 **Total Expense ($000):** 21461 **Payroll Expense ($000):** 8113 **Personnel:** 166

**CORNERSTONE MEDICAL CENTER** See Chi Memorial Hospital - Georgia

## GAINESVILLE—Hall County

★ △ ⇑ **NORTHEAST GEORGIA MEDICAL CENTER (110029)**, 743 Spring Street NE, Zip 30501–3899; tel. 770/219–3553, (Total facility includes 252 beds in nursing home–type unit) (Nonreporting) **A**2 3 5 7 10 19 21 **F**3 4 7 11 12 13 15 17 18 20 22 24 26 28 29 30 31 34 35 38 40 43 44 45 46 47 48 49 50 51 54 56 57 58 59 60 61 63 64 66 68 70 72 73 74 75 76 77 78 79 81 82 83 84 85 86 87 89 90 93 98 99 100 101 104 105 107 110 111 114 115 116 117 119 120 121 123 124 126 128 129 130 131 132 143 144 146 147 148 149 151 152 153 154 156 **S** Northeast Georgia Health System, Gainesville, GA
Primary Contact: Carol H. Burrell, Chief Executive Officer
CFO: Brian D Steines, Chief Financial Officer
CMO: Sam Johnson, M.D., Chief Medical Officer
CIO: Chris Paravate, Chief Information Officer
CHR: Deborah Weber, Chief Human Resource Officer
CNO: Brenda Simpson, Chief Nursing Officer
Web address: www.nghs.com
**Control**: Other not–for–profit (including NFP Corporation) **Service**: General medical and surgical

**Staffed Beds:** 887 **Admissions:** 38088 **Census:** 719 **Outpatient Visits:** 430285 **Births:** 4708 **Personnel:** 5267

## GRACEWOOD—Richmond County

**EAST CENTRAL REGIONAL HOSP** See East Central Regional Hospital

**EAST CENTRAL REGIONAL HOSPITAL** See East Central Regional Hospital, Augusta

## GREENSBORO—Greene County

**GOOD SAMARITAN HOSPITAL** See St. Mary's Good Samaritan Hospital

✉ **ST. MARY'S GOOD SAMARITAN HOSPITAL (111329)**, 5401 Lake Oconee Parkway, Zip 30642–4232; tel. 706/453–7331, (Nonreporting) **A**1 3 10 18 **F**3 11 15 18 26 29 30 34 35 40 45 50 51 57 64 65 68 74 75 77 79 81 85 87 93 107 108 115 119 130 132 133 146 147 154 156 157 **S** Trinity Health, Livonia, MI
Primary Contact: Tanya M. Adcock, President
CMO: Dave Ringer, M.D., Chief of Staff
CNO: Kimberly Tyler, Director of Nursing
Web address: www.stmarysgoodsam.org
**Control**: Church operated, Nongovernment, not–for–profit **Service**: General medical and surgical

**Staffed Beds:** 25 **Admissions:** 1092 **Census:** 14 **Outpatient Visits:** 42680 **Births:** 0 **Total Expense ($000):** 25168 **Payroll Expense ($000):** 8475 **Personnel:** 157

## GRIFFIN—Spalding County

**SPALDING REGIONAL HOSPITAL** See Wellstar Spalding Regional Hospital

✉ **WELLSTAR SPALDING REGIONAL HOSPITAL (110031)**, 601 South Eighth Street, Zip 30224–4294, Mailing Address: P O Drawer 'V', Zip 30224–1168; tel. 770/228–2721, (Nonreporting) **A**1 10 **F**3 7 11 13 15 18 20 22 29 30 31 34 35 40 45 49 50 53 54 57 59 64 70 73 75 76 77 78 79 80 81 85 87 89 93 107 108 110 111 114 115 119 129 130 146 147 148 **S** WellStar Health System, Marietta, GA
Primary Contact: Tamara Ison, Senior Vice President and President
COO: Tamara Ison, Chief Operating Officer
CMO: Philip Osehobo, M.D., Chief Medical Officer
CIO: Steve Brown, Director Information Systems
CHR: Amanda Remington, Director Human Resources
CNO: Wadra McCullough, Chief Nursing Officer
Web address: www.spaldingregional.com
**Control**: Other not–for–profit (including NFP Corporation) **Service**: General medical and surgical

**Staffed Beds:** 160 **Admissions:** 8741 **Census:** 96 **Outpatient Visits:** 112406 **Births:** 1096 **Personnel:** 757

## HAWKINSVILLE—Pulaski County

⇑ **TAYLOR REGIONAL HOSPITAL (110135)**, Macon Highway, Zip 31036, Mailing Address: P.O. Box 1297, Zip 31036–7297; tel. 478/783–0200, (Nonreporting) **A**10 21
Primary Contact: Jon Green, R.N., Chief Executive Officer
CFO: Lisa Halliday, Director Accounting Services
CMO: Al Baggett, M.D., Interim Chief of Staff
CIO: Dawn Warnock, Director Medical Records
Web address: www.taylorregional.org
**Control**: Other not–for–profit (including NFP Corporation) **Service**: General medical and surgical

**Staffed Beds:** 57

## HAZLEHURST—Jeff Davis County

⇑ **JEFF DAVIS HOSPITAL (111333)**, 163 South Tallahassee Street, Zip 31539–2921, Mailing Address: P.O. Box 1690, Zip 31539–1690; tel. 912/375–7781, (Nonreporting) **A**10 18 21 **F**15 29 30 40 45 57 68 70 77 81 85 97 98 103 107 115 119 133 143 149 153 154
Primary Contact: Barry Bloom, Chief Executive Officer
CFO: Cathy Cason, Chief Financial Officer
CIO: Brian Fowler, Information Technology Director
CHR: Brenda McEachin, Human Resources Director
CNO: Allen Crawford, Chief Nursing Officer
Web address: www.jeffdavishospital.org
**Control**: Hospital district or authority, Government, Nonfederal **Service**: General medical and surgical

**Staffed Beds:** 25 **Admissions:** 442 **Census:** 7 **Outpatient Visits:** 20722 **Births:** 0 **Total Expense ($000):** 14678 **Payroll Expense ($000):** 6426 **Personnel:** 173

## HIAWASSEE—Towns County

⇑ **CHATUGE REGIONAL HOSPITAL AND NURSING HOME (111324)**, 110 Main Street, Zip 30546–3408, Mailing Address: P.O. Box 509, Zip 30546–0509; tel. 706/896–2222, (Total facility includes 112 beds in nursing home–type unit) (Nonreporting) **A**10 18 21 **F**3 11 15 29 30 34 40 45 56 57 59 64 65 70 75 77 81 82 86 87 92 93 97 98 100 103 104 107 108 110 111 115 119 127 128 130 132 133 135 144 146 148 149 **S** Union General Hospital, Inc., Blairsville, GA
Primary Contact: Ryan Snow, Administrator
CFO: Tim Henry, Accountant
CMO: Robert F Stahlkuppe, M.D., Chief of Staff
CIO: Walt Stafford, Director Information Technology
CHR: Rita Bradshaw, Director Human Resources
Web address: www.chatugeregionalhospital.org
**Control**: Hospital district or authority, Government, Nonfederal **Service**: General medical and surgical

**Staffed Beds:** 150 **Admissions:** 961 **Census:** 121 **Outpatient Visits:** 22809 **Births:** 0 **Total Expense ($000):** 28469 **Payroll Expense ($000):** 14531 **Personnel:** 307

⇑ **HOSP AUTHORITY OF TOWNS CNTY** See Chatuge Regional Hospital and Nursing Home

**GA**

---

## HINESVILLE—Liberty County

**LIBERTY MEMORIAL HOSPITAL** See Liberty Regional Medical Center

**LIBERTY REGIONAL MEDICAL CENTER (111335)**, 462 Elma G Miles Parkway, Zip 31313–4000, Mailing Address: P.O. Box 919, Zip 31310–0919; tel. 912/369–9400, (Nonreporting) **A**10 18
Primary Contact: Tammy Mims, Chief Executive Officer
CFO: Derek Rozier, Chief Financial Officer
CNO: Donna R. Cochrane, Chief Nursing Officer
Web address: www.libertyregional.org
**Control**: Hospital district or authority, Government, Nonfederal **Service**: General medical and surgical

**Staffed Beds: 25**

✉ **WINN ARMY COMMUNITY HOSPITAL**, 1061 Harmon Avenue, Zip 31314–5641, Mailing Address: 1061 Harmon Avenue, Suite 2311B, Zip 31314–5641; tel. 912/435–6965, (Nonreporting) **A**1 5 **S** Department of the Army, Office of the Surgeon General, Falls Church, VA
Primary Contact: Colonel Kirk W. Eggleston, Commanding Officer
CIO: Arthur N Kirshner, Chief Information Management
CHR: MajorYvette McCrea, Chief Human Resources
CNO: ColonelSharon Brown, Deputy Commander Nursing
Web address: www.winn.amedd.army.mil/
**Service**: General medical and surgical

**Staffed Beds: 37**

## HIRAM—Paulding County

**PROMINA PAULDING MEM MED CTR** See Wellstar Paulding Hospital

✉ **WELLSTAR PAULDING HOSPITAL (110042)**, 2518 Jimmy Lee Smith Parkway, Zip 30141; tel. 470/644–7000, (Total facility includes 182 beds in nursing home–type unit) (Nonreporting) **A**1 10 **F**3 11 15 18 20 28 29 30 31 37 38 40 41 44 45 49 50 53 54 55 59 61 64 68 70 75 77 78 79 80 81 82 85 86 87 93 102 107 108 110 111 114 118 119 120 121 123 124 128 129 130 135 146 148 154 156 **S** WellStar Health System, Marietta, GA
Primary Contact: John Kueven, Senior Vice President and President
COO: Lindsay Rehn, Executive Director of Financial Operations
CFO: Lindsay Rehn, Executive Director of Financial Operations
CMO: Guillermo Pierluisi, Vice President of Medical Affairs
CHR: Jessica Bedsole, Director, Human Resources
CNO: Vicky Hogue, R.N., Vice President Patient Services and Chief Nursing Officer
Web address: www.wellstar.org
**Control**: Other not–for–profit (including NFP Corporation) **Service**: General medical and surgical

**Staffed Beds: 294 Admissions: 8445 Census: 248 Outpatient Visits: 144003 Births: 0 Personnel: 975**

## HOMERVILLE—Clinch County

★ ⇑ **CLINCH MEMORIAL HOSPITAL (111308)**, 1050 Valdosta Highway, Zip 31634–9701, Mailing Address: P.O. Box 516, Zip 31634–0516; tel. 912/487–5211, (Nonreporting) **A**10 18 21
Primary Contact: Angela Ammons, Administrator
COO: Wallace D Mincey, Chief Executive Officer
CFO: Teressia Shook, Chief Financial Officer
CMO: Samuel Cobarrubias, M.D., Chief of Staff
CIO: Shelly Studebaker, Human Resources Assistant
CHR: Shelly Studebaker, Human Resources Assistant
CNO: Kellie Register, Director of Nursing
Web address: www.clinchmh.org
**Control**: County, Government, Nonfederal **Service**: General medical and surgical

**Staffed Beds: 25**

## JACKSON—Butts County

**SYLVAN GROVE HOSPITAL** See Wellstar Sylvan Grove Hospital

★ **WELLSTAR SYLVAN GROVE HOSPITAL (111319)**, 1050 McDonough Road, Zip 30233–1599; tel. 770/775–7861, (Nonreporting) **A**10 18 **F**29 34 35 40 50 57 59 68 77 93 107 119 133 **S** WellStar Health System, Marietta, GA
Primary Contact: Tamara Ison, Senior Vice President and President
CFO: Tamara Ison, Chief Financial Officer
CIO: Steve Brown, Chief Information Officer
CHR: Amanda Remington, Director Human Resources
Web address: www.sylvangrovehospital.com
**Control**: Other not–for–profit (including NFP Corporation) **Service**: General medical and surgical

**Staffed Beds: 24 Admissions: 358 Census: 13 Outpatient Visits: 17184 Births: 0 Personnel: 82**

## JASPER—Pickens County

⇑ **PIEDMONT MOUNTAINSIDE HOSP** See Piedmont Mountainside Hospital

⇑ **PIEDMONT MOUNTAINSIDE HOSPITAL (110225)**, 1266 Highway 515 South, Zip 30143–4872; tel. 706/692–2441, (Nonreporting) **A**10 21 **F**3 13 15 20 28 29 34 35 40 42 45 46 49 53 57 59 64 70 75 76 77 79 81 85 107 108 110 111 114 115 119 124 129 130 132 135 146 148 149 154 **S** Piedmont Healthcare, Roswell, GA
Primary Contact: Denise Ray, Chief Executive Officer
CMO: Moiz Master, M.D., Medical Director of Quality
CIO: Geoffrey Brown, Chief Information Officer
CHR: Frank Leist, Human Resources Manager
CNO: Michelle Breitfelder, Chief Nursing Officer
Web address: www.https://www.piedmont.org
**Control**: Other not–for–profit (including NFP Corporation) **Service**: General medical and surgical

**Staffed Beds: 52 Admissions: 3481 Census: 37 Outpatient Visits: 82317 Births: 287 Personnel: 410**

## JESUP—Wayne County

☐ **WAYNE MEMORIAL HOSPITAL (110124)**, 865 South First Street, Zip 31545–0210, Mailing Address: P.O. Box 410, Zip 31598–0410; tel. 912/427–6811, (Nonreporting) **A**1 10 20
Primary Contact: Joseph P. Ierardi, Chief Executive Officer
CFO: Greg Jones, Chief Financial Officer
CMO: Dan Collipp, M.D., Chief of Staff
CIO: Deborah Six, Coordinator Data Processing
CHR: John Mclwain, Director Human Resources
Web address: www.wmhweb.com
**Control**: County, Government, Nonfederal **Service**: General medical and surgical

**Staffed Beds: 84**

## JOHNS CREEK—Fulton County

**EMORY DUNWOODY MEDICAL CTR** See Emory Johns Creek Hospital

✉ **EMORY JOHNS CREEK HOSPITAL (110230)**, 6325 Hospital Parkway, Zip 30097–5775; tel. 678/474–7000, (Nonreporting) **A**1 2 3 5 10 **F**3 11 12 13 15 18 20 22 26 29 30 31 34 35 36 40 45 49 50 54 55 57 58 59 60 64 68 70 72 73 74 75 76 77 78 79 81 82 84 85 86 87 93 100 101 102 107 108 110 111 115 116 117 119 126 129 130 131 132 141 146 147 148 149 154 156 **S** Emory Healthcare, Atlanta, GA
Primary Contact: Marilyn Margolis, MSN, Chief Executive Officer
COO: Laurie Hansen, Vice President of Operations
CFO: JoAnn Manning, Chief Financial Officer
CMO: Adedapo Odetoyinbo, M.D., Chief Medical Office
CHR: Hannah Henry, Interim Vice President of Human Resources
CNO: Heather Redrick, Chief Nursing Officer
Web address: www.emoryjohnscreek.com
**Control**: Other not–for–profit (including NFP Corporation) **Service**: General medical and surgical

**Staffed Beds: 118 Admissions: 8400 Census: 98 Outpatient Visits: 89071 Births: 1359 Total Expense ($000): 171277 Payroll Expense ($000): 62420 Personnel: 820**

## KENNESAW—Cobb County

**DEVEREUX ADVANCED BEHAVIORAL HEALTH GEORGIA**, 1291 Stanley Road NW, Zip 30152–4359; tel. 770/427–0147, (Nonreporting) **A**3 **F**98 106 **S** Devereux, Villanova, PA
Primary Contact: Gwendolyn Skinner, Operational Vice President
COO: Mary H Esposito, Assistant Executive Director
CFO: Kathy Goggin, Director of Finance
CMO: Yolanda Graham, M.D., Medical Director
CIO: Sam Maguta, Coordinator Information Systems
CHR: Rudie Delien, Director of Human Resources
CNO: Debra Sharpton, Director of Nursing
Web address: www.devereuxga.org
**Control**: Other not–for–profit (including NFP Corporation) **Service**: Psychiatric

**Staffed Beds: 110 Admissions: 176 Census: 78 Outpatient Visits: 53 Births: 0 Total Expense ($000): 23102 Payroll Expense ($000): 12706 Personnel: 360**

**DEVEREUX GEORGIA TREATMENT NETWORK** See Devereux Advanced Behavioral Health Georgia

**GA**

*Many Facility Codes have changed. Please refer to the AHA Guide Code Chart.*
© 2021 AHA Guide

## LAGRANGE—Troup County

**WELLSTAR WEST GEORGIA MEDICAL CENTER (110016)**, 1514 Vernon Road, Zip 30240-4131; tel. 706/882-1411, (Total facility includes 260 beds in nursing home-type unit) (Nonreporting) **A**1 2 10 19 **F**3 11 12 13 15 18 20 22 26 28 29 30 31 34 35 40 44 47 48 49 50 51 56 57 58 59 62 63 64 66 68 70 73 74 75 76 77 78 79 80 81 82 84 85 86 87 89 92 93 96 107 108 110 111 114 115 119 120 121 123 124 126 128 129 130 132 135 146 147 148 149 154 **S** WellStar Health System, Marietta, GA
Primary Contact: Coleman Foss, Chief Executive Officer
COO: Charis L Acree, Vice President and Chief Operating Officer
CFO: Paul R Perrotti, CPA, Chief Financial Officer
CIO: Alan Whitehouse, Chief Information Officer
CHR: Tommy Britt, Vice President of Human Resources
CNO: Tracy Gynther, R.N., Vice President and Chief Nursing Officer
Web address: www.wghealth.org/
**Control:** Other not-for-profit (including NFP Corporation) **Service:** General medical and surgical

**Staffed Beds:** 390 **Admissions:** 8089 **Census:** 320 **Outpatient Visits:** 121091 **Births:** 979 **Personnel:** 1221

**WEST GEORGIA HEALTH** See Wellstar West Georgia Medical Center

## LAKELAND—Lanier County

**LOUIS SMITH MEMORIAL HOSPITAL** See South Georgia Medical Center Lanier Campus

**SOUTH GEORGIA MEDICAL CENTER LANIER CAMPUS (111326)**, 116 West Thigpen Avenue, Zip 31635-1011; tel. 229/482-3110, (Nonreporting) **A**1 10 18 **F**3 15 29 34 35 40 57 59 68 75 77 107 119 129 130 133 135 149 **S** South Georgia Medical Center, Valdosta, GA
Primary Contact: Geoff Hardy, Administrator
CFO: Libby Flemming, Controller and Chief Information Officer
CMO: Bruce Herrington, M.D., Chief Medical Officer
CIO: Libby Flemming, Controller and Chief Information Officer
CHR: Vicki Dinkins, Director Human Resources
Web address: www.sgmc.org
**Control:** Hospital district or authority, Government, Nonfederal **Service:** General medical and surgical

**Staffed Beds:** 25 **Admissions:** 196 **Census:** 6 **Outpatient Visits:** 14186 **Births:** 0 **Total Expense ($000):** 9215 **Payroll Expense ($000):** 3882 **Personnel:** 81

## LAVONIA—Franklin County

**ST. MARY'S SACRED HEART HOSPITAL (110027)**, 367 Clear Creek Parkway, Zip 30553-4173; tel. 706/356-7800, (Nonreporting) **A**1 10 **F**3 11 13 15 18 29 30 34 35 40 49 50 53 57 59 70 74 75 76 79 81 85 87 93 107 108 110 111 115 119 129 130 132 149 154 **S** Trinity Health, Livonia, MI
Primary Contact: Jeff English, President
CIO: Tim Vickery, Chief Information Officer
CHR: Lauren Papka, Chief Administrative Officer
CNO: Evelyn Murphy, Chief Nursing Officer
Web address: www.stmaryssacredheart.org/
**Control:** Church operated, Nongovernment, not-for-profit **Service:** General medical and surgical

**Staffed Beds:** 41 **Admissions:** 1893 **Census:** 18 **Outpatient Visits:** 49339 **Births:** 294 **Total Expense ($000):** 35331 **Payroll Expense ($000):** 13818 **Personnel:** 235

**TY COBB REGIONAL MEDICAL CENTER** See St. Mary's Sacred Heart Hospital

## LAWRENCEVILLE—Gwinnett County

**NORTHSIDE HOSPITAL - GWINNETT (110087)**, 1000 Medical Center Boulevard, Zip 30046-7694, Mailing Address: P.O. Box 348, Zip 30046-0348; tel. 678/312-1000, (Includes GWINNETT MEDICAL CENTER, Mailing address: 1000 Medical Center Boulevard, Lawrenceville, Georgia, Zip 30245, Box 348, Zip 30246, tel. 678/312-1000; Debbie Mitcham, President and Chief Executive Officer; NORTHSIDE HOSPITAL - DULUTH, Mailing address: 3620 Howell Ferry Road, Duluth, Georgia, Zip 30096; tel. 678/312-6800; Debbie Mitcham, President and Chief Executive Officer) (Total facility includes 89 beds in nursing home-type unit) **A**1 2 3 5 8 10 **F**3 8 11 12 13 15 17 18 20 22 24 26 28 29 30 31 34 35 36 37 38 40 41 43 44 45 46 47 48 49 50 53 54 55 56 58 59 64 67 68 70 71 72 73 74 75 76 77 78 79 81 82 84 85 87 90 93 96 97 107 108 110 111 114 115 116 117 118 119 126 128 129 130 131 132 134 135 146 147 148 149 157 **S** Northside Healthcare System, Atlanta, GA
Primary Contact: Debbie Mitcham, President and Chief Executive Officer
COO: Mary Shepherd, Chief Operating Officer
CFO: Shannon A Banna, Chief Financial Officer
CIO: Ashley Petit, Chief Information Officer
CHR: Bridget Green, Chief Human Resources Officer
CNO: Pamela Garland, R.N., Chief Nursing Officer
Web address: www.gwinnettmedicalcenter.org
**Control:** Other not-for-profit (including NFP Corporation) **Service:** General medical and surgical

**Staffed Beds:** 556 **Admissions:** 28380 **Census:** 492 **Outpatient Visits:** 368159 **Births:** 4401 **Total Expense ($000):** 751848 **Payroll Expense ($000):** 299690 **Personnel:** 4693

**NORTHSIDE HOSPITAL GWINNETT** See Northside Hospital - Gwinnett

**SUMMITRIDGE HOSPITAL (114004)**, 250 Scenic Highway, Zip 30046-5675; tel. 678/442-5800, (Nonreporting) **A**1 10 **F**4 5 98 99 102 103 104 105 152 153 154
Primary Contact: Vernell Nunn, Chief Executive Officer
Web address: www.summitridgehospital.net
**Control:** Corporation, Investor-owned (for-profit) **Service:** Psychiatric

**Staffed Beds:** 96 **Admissions:** 4137 **Census:** 88 **Outpatient Visits:** 8057 **Births:** 0 **Total Expense ($000):** 18165 **Payroll Expense ($000):** 10581 **Personnel:** 144

## LITHONIA—Dekalb County

**DEKALB MEDICAL AT HILLANDALE** See Emory Hillandale Hospital

**EMORY HILLANDALE HOSPITAL (110226)**, 2801 DeKalb Medical Parkway, Zip 30058-4996; tel. 404/501-8000, (Nonreporting) **A**1 10 **F**3 15 18 20 22 26 28 29 30 34 35 38 40 44 49 50 51 57 59 60 61 68 70 74 75 77 78 79 81 82 84 85 86 87 93 96 100 107 111 121 129 130 131 132 135 148 149 156 **P**1 **S** Emory Healthcare, Atlanta, GA
Primary Contact: Jim Forstner, Chief Executive Officer
CMO: Duane Barclay, D.O., Chief Medical Officer
CIO: Mark Trocino, Chief Information Officer
CHR: Tom Crawford, Vice President Human Resources
Web address: www.dekalbmedical.org
**Control:** Other not-for-profit (including NFP Corporation) **Service:** General medical and surgical

**Staffed Beds:** 70 **Admissions:** 4377 **Census:** 52 **Outpatient Visits:** 96740 **Births:** 0 **Total Expense ($000):** 76304 **Payroll Expense ($000):** 34647 **Personnel:** 500

## LOUISVILLE—Jefferson County

**JEFFERSON HOSPITAL (110100)**, 1067 Peachtree Street, Zip 30434-1599; tel. 478/625-7000, (Nonreporting) **A**10 20 21
Primary Contact: Wendy Martin, Chief Executive Officer
CFO: LieutenantJohn Graham, Chief Financial Officer
CMO: James Polhill, M.D., Chief Medical Officer
CHR: Catherine Hall, Manager Human Resources
CNO: Stacey Smith, R.N., Director of Nursing
Web address: www.jeffersonhosp.com
**Control:** City-county, Government, Nonfederal **Service:** General medical and surgical

**Staffed Beds:** 37

**GA**

## MACON—Bibb County

⇑ **CENTRAL GEORGIA REHABILITATION HOSPITAL** See Rehabilitation Hospital, Navicent Health

**CHILDREN'S HOSPITAL** See Children's Hospital, Navicent Health

⊠ **COLISEUM MEDICAL CENTERS (110164)**, 350 Hospital Drive, Zip 31217–3871; tel. 478/765–7000, (Includes COLISEUM CENTER FOR BEHAVIORAL HEALTH, Mailing address: 340 Hospital Drive, Macon, Georgia, Zip 31217–3838; tel. 478/741–1355; Stephen J. Daugherty, Interim Chief Executive Officer), (Nonreporting) **A**1 2 3 5 10 **S** HCA Healthcare, Nashville, TN
Primary Contact: Stephen J. Daugherty, Chief Executive Officer
COO: Kelly Lindsay, Chief Operating Officer
CFO: Scott Anderton, Chief Financial Officer
CIO: Joan Morstad, Director Information Systems
CHR: Laura Booras, Vice President Human Resources
Web address: www.coliseumhealthsystem.com
**Control**: Corporation, Investor–owned (for–profit) **Service**: General medical and surgical

**Staffed Beds:** 310

⊠ **COLISEUM NORTHSIDE HOSPITAL (110201)**, 400 Charter Boulevard, Zip 31210–4853, Mailing Address: P.O. Box 4627, Zip 31208–4627; tel. 478/757–8200, (Nonreporting) **A**1 10 **S** HCA Healthcare, Nashville, TN
Primary Contact: Greg Caples, Chief Executive Officer
CFO: Elmer Polite, Chief Financial Officer
CHR: Louise Truitt, Human Resource Director
CNO: Patricia Derrico, FACHE, R.N., Chief Nursing Officer
Web address: www.coliseumhealthsystem.com
**Control**: Corporation, Investor–owned (for–profit) **Service**: General medical and surgical

**Staffed Beds:** 103

**COLISEUM PSYCHIATRIC CENTER** See Coliseum Center for Behavioral Health

**COLUMBIA COLISEUM MED CTRS** See Coliseum Medical Centers

**MACON NORTHSIDE HOSPITAL** See Coliseum Northside Hospital

⇑ **MEDICAL CENTER OF CENTRAL GEORGIA** See Medical Center, Navicent Health

★ ⇑ **MEDICAL CENTER, NAVICENT HEALTH (110107)**, 777 Hemlock Street, Zip 31201–2155; tel. 478/633–1000, (Includes CHILDREN'S HOSPITAL, NAVICENT HEALTH, Mailing address: 888 Pine Street, Macon, Georgia, Zip 31201–2155; tel. 478/633–1000), (Nonreporting) **A**2 3 5 8 10 21 **F**3 7 8 11 12 13 14 15 17 18 20 22 24 26 28 29 30 31 32 34 35 36 39 40 43 44 45 46 47 48 49 50 51 53 54 56 57 58 59 60 61 62 63 64 65 66 68 70 72 73 74 75 76 77 78 79 80 81 82 83 84 85 86 87 88 89 92 93 94 97 98 100 101 102 104 107 108 110 111 114 115 119 126 130 132 135 143 144 145 146 147 148 149 150 154 **S** Navicent Health, Macon, GA
Primary Contact: Ninfa M. Saunders, President and Chief Executive Officer
COO: Susan Harris, R.N., Chief Operating Officer
CFO: Rhonda S. Perry, Chief Financial Officer
CMO: Christopher Hendry, M.D., Chief Medical Officer
CIO: Ed Brown, Chief Information Officer
CHR: Bernard J Price, Chief Human Resources Officer
CNO: Tracey Blalock, MSN, R.N., Chief Nurse Executive
Web address: www.https://www.navicenthealth.org/
**Control**: Other not–for–profit (including NFP Corporation) **Service**: General medical and surgical

**Staffed Beds:** 586 **Admissions:** 31324 **Census:** 522 **Outpatient Visits:** 415669 **Births:** 2661

⊠ **REGENCY HOSPITAL OF CENTRAL GEORGIA (112016)**, 535 Coliseum Drive, Zip 31217–0104; tel. 478/803–7300, (Nonreporting) **A**1 10 **S** Select Medical Corporation, Mechanicsburg, PA
Primary Contact: Wayne B. Boutwell, Chief Executive Officer
Web address: www.regencyhospital.com
**Control**: Corporation, Investor–owned (for–profit) **Service**: Acute long–term care hospital

**Staffed Beds:** 60

★ ⇑ **REHABILITATION HOSPITAL, NAVICENT HEALTH (113029)**, 3351 Northside Drive, Zip 31210–2587; tel. 478/201–6500, (Nonreporting) **A**3 10 21 **F**11 33 35 36 56 57 60 64 68 74 75 79 90 91 92 93 94 96 130 131 132 143 148 149 154 **S** Navicent Health, Macon, GA
Primary Contact: Regina Tipton, Hospital Administrator
COO: Darren Pearce, Executive Director
CFO: Beverly Owens, Controller
CMO: Allison Scheetz, M.D., Medical Director
Web address: www.navicenthealth.org/service-center/rehabilitation-hospital-navicent-health
**Control**: Other not–for–profit (including NFP Corporation) **Service**: Rehabilitation

**Staffed Beds:** 58 **Admissions:** 1153 **Census:** 45 **Outpatient Visits:** 19358 **Births:** 0

## MADISON—Morgan County

☐ **MORGAN MEMORIAL HOSPITAL (111304)**, 1077 South Main Street, Zip 30650–2073; Mailing Address: P.O. Box 860, Zip 30650–0860; tel. 706/342–1667, (Nonreporting) **A**1 10 18
Primary Contact: Ralph A. Castillo, CPA, Chief Executive Officer
CFO: Kyle Wilkinson, Chief Financial Officer
CMO: Dan Zant, M.D., Chief of Staff
CIO: Patrick Cook, Vice President Support Services
CHR: Sarah Phillips, Manager Human Resources
CNO: Beth O'Neill, Chief Nursing Officer
Web address: www.mmh.org
**Control**: Hospital district or authority, Government, Nonfederal **Service**: General medical and surgical

**Staffed Beds:** 25

## MARIETTA—Cobb County

**PROMINA WINDY HILL HOSPITAL** See Wellstar Windy Hill Hospital

**PROMINA-KENNESTONE HOSPITAL** See Wellstar Kennestone Hospital

⊠ △ **WELLSTAR KENNESTONE HOSPITAL (110035)**, 677 Church Street, Zip 30060–1148; tel. 770/793–5000, (Nonreporting) **A**1 2 3 5 7 10 **F**3 10 11 12 13 15 17 18 20 22 24 26 28 29 30 31 34 36 37 38 40 41 43 44 45 46 47 48 49 50 51 53 54 55 58 59 60 61 64 66 68 70 72 73 74 75 76 77 78 79 80 81 82 84 85 86 87 89 90 93 94 96 97 100 102 107 108 110 111 114 115 116 117 118 119 120 121 123 124 125 126 129 130 132 141 146 147 148 154 156 **S** WellStar Health System, Marietta, GA
Primary Contact: Mary Chatman, Ph.D., R.N., Senior Vice President and President
COO: Constance Bradley, FACHE, R.N., Vice President and Chief Operating Officer
CFO: Anthony James (Jim) Budzinski, R.N., IIExecutive Vice President and Chief Financial Officer
CMO: Vikrum Reddy, M.D., Vice President and Chief Medical Officer
CIO: Shalima Pannikode, Senior Vice President and Chief Information and Digital Officer
CHR: David A Jones, JD, Executive Vice President of Human Resources and Organizational Learning
Web address: www.wellstar.org
**Control**: Other not–for–profit (including NFP Corporation) **Service**: General medical and surgical

**Staffed Beds:** 657 **Admissions:** 42980 **Census:** 561 **Outpatient Visits:** 456747 **Births:** 5314 **Personnel:** 4338

⊠ **WELLSTAR WINDY HILL HOSPITAL (112007)**, 2540 Windy Hill Road, Zip 30067–8632; tel. 770/644–1000, (Nonreporting) **A**1 2 10 **F**1 11 15 28 29 30 44 45 50 51 60 61 64 68 75 77 79 81 82 85 86 87 93 100 101 107 108 110 111 114 118 119 129 130 131 135 141 146 147 148 156 **S** WellStar Health System, Marietta, GA
Primary Contact: Mary Chatman, Ph.D., R.N., Chief Executive Officer
CFO: Marsha Burke, Senior Vice President and Chief Financial Officer
CMO: Larry Haldeman, M.D., Executive Vice President and Chief Medical Officer
CIO: Leigh Cox, Chief Information Officer
Web address: www.wellstar.org
**Control**: Other not–for–profit (including NFP Corporation) **Service**: Acute long–term care hospital

**Staffed Beds:** 19 **Admissions:** 279 **Census:** 24 **Outpatient Visits:** 151381 **Births:** 0 **Personnel:** 310

## METTER—Candler County

★ ⇑ **CANDLER COUNTY HOSPITAL (111334)**, 400 Cedar Street, Zip 30439–3338, Mailing Address: P.O. Box 597, Zip 30439–0597; tel. 912/685–5741, (Nonreporting) **A**10 18 21
Primary Contact: Michael Purvis, Chief Executive Officer
COO: David Flanders, Chief Operating Officer
CFO: Will Bennett, Chief Financial Officer
CNO: Linda G. Coleman, Chief Nursing Officer
Web address: www.candlercountyhospital.com
**Control**: Hospital district or authority, Government, Nonfederal **Service**: General medical and surgical

**Staffed Beds:** 25

**GA**

*Many Facility Codes have changed. Please refer to the AHA Guide Code Chart.*
© 2021 AHA Guide

## MILLEDGEVILLE—Baldwin County

☐ **CENTRAL STATE HOSPITAL**, 2450 Vinson Highway, Zip 31062–0001;
tel. 478/445–4128, (Nonreporting) **A**1 3 **F**30 39 59 75 77 86 87 97 98 100 130
132 149
Primary Contact: Gilbert Sutton Jr, Regional Hospital Administrator/ Chief Executive
Officer
COO: Terry McGee, Chief Operations Officer
CMO: Scott VanSant, M.D., Chief Medical Officer
CIO: Betsy Bradley, Coordinator Performance Improvement
CHR: Myra Holloway, Director Human Resources Management
Web address: www.https://dbhdd.georgia.gov/be-caring/central-state-hospital-csh-
milledgeville-ga
**Control**: State, Government, Nonfederal **Service**: Psychiatric

**Staffed Beds:** 182 **Admissions:** 184 **Census:** 176 **Outpatient Visits:** 0
**Births:** 0 **Total Expense ($000):** 57395 **Payroll Expense ($000):** 24403
**Personnel:** 619

★ ⇑ **NAVICENT HEALTH BALDWIN (110150)**, 821 North Cobb Street,
Zip 31061–2351, Mailing Address: P.O. Box 690, Zip 31059–0690;
tel. 478/454–3505, (Nonreporting) **A**10 19 21 **S** Navicent Health, Macon, GA
Primary Contact: Todd Dixon, R.N., Chief Executive Officer
CFO: Brenda Qualls, Chief Financial Officer
CMO: Douglas Brewer, M.D., Chief Medical Officer
CNO: Deborah Block, Vice President Nursing and Chief Nursing Officer
Web address: www.navicenthealth.org/nhb/home
**Control**: Other not-for-profit (including NFP Corporation) **Service**: General
medical and surgical

**Staffed Beds:** 90

⇑ **OCONEE REGIONAL MEDICAL CENTER** See Navicent Health Baldwin

## MILLEN—Jenkins County

**JENKINS COUNTY MEDICAL CENTER (111311)**, 931 East Winthrope Avenue,
Zip 30442–1839; tel. 478/982–4221, (Nonreporting) **A**10 18 **S** National Surgical
Healthcare, Chicago, IL
Primary Contact: Earl S. Whiteley, FACHE, Chief Executive Officer
CFO: Cindy Bierschenk, Director of Financial Services
CIO: Christian Rekowski, Information Technology Director
CHR: Natalie Tambon, Director of Human Resources
CNO: Sharon Lagina Evans, R.N., Assistant Chief Nursing Officer
Web address: www.https://jenkinsmedicalcenter.com/
**Control**: Hospital district or authority, Government, Nonfederal **Service**: General
medical and surgical

**Staffed Beds:** 25

**OPTIM MEDICAL CENTER - JENKINS** See Jenkins County Medical Center

## MONROE—Walton County

⇑ **CLEARVIEW REGIONAL MEDICAL CENTER** See Piedmont Walton Hospital

⇑ **PIEDMONT WALTON HOSPITAL (110046)**, 2151 West Spring Street,
Zip 30655–3115, Mailing Address: PO BOX 1346, Zip 30655–1346;
tel. 770/267–8461, (Nonreporting) **A**10 21 **S** Piedmont Healthcare, Roswell, GA
Primary Contact: Larry W. Ebert Jr, Chief Executive Officer
CFO: Jeffrey Mullis, Interim Chief Financial Officer
CMO: Robert Sinyard, M.D., Chief Medical Officer
CIO: Cory Crayton, Director of Information Systems
CHR: Michele Monsrud, Director Human Resources
CNO: Sharon H Queen, R.N., Chief Nursing Officer
Web address: www.https://www.piedmont.org/locations/piedmont-walton/home
**Control**: Corporation, Investor-owned (for-profit) **Service**: General medical and
surgical

**Staffed Beds:** 52

⊞ **RIDGEVIEW INSTITUTE (114037)**, 709 Breedlove Drive, Zip 30655–2055;
tel. 844/350–8800, (Nonreporting) **A**1
Primary Contact: Amy Alexander, Chief Executive Officer
Web address: www.https://ridgeviewinstitute.com/
**Control**: Other not-for-profit (including NFP Corporation) **Service**: Psychiatric

**Staffed Beds:** 88

## MONTEZUMA—Macon County

⇑ **FLINT RIVER COMMUNITY HOSPITAL (110190)**, 509 Sumter Street,
Zip 31063–1733, Mailing Address: P.O. Box 770, Zip 31063–2502;
tel. 478/472–3100, (Nonreporting) **A**10 21
Primary Contact: Michael C. Patterson, Chief Executive Officer
CMO: Quincy Jordan, M.D., Chief of Staff
CHR: Vicki Stotts, Coordinator Human Resources
CNO: Lee Hughes, R.N., Chief Nursing Officer
Web address: www.flintriverhospital.com/
**Control**: Corporation, Investor-owned (for-profit) **Service**: General medical and
surgical

**Staffed Beds:** 49

## MONTICELLO—Jasper County

**JASPER MEMORIAL HOSPITAL (111303)**, 898 College Street,
Zip 31064–1258; tel. 706/468–6411, (Total facility includes 55 beds in nursing
home–type unit) (Nonreporting) **A**10 18 **F**11 18 29 34 40 57 59 65 77 93 97 107
119 128 133 146 148 149
Primary Contact: Jan Gaston, Administrator
CFO: Stuart Abney, Controller
CHR: Laura E Hudgins, Assistant Administrator
CNO: Robin Carey, Director of Nursing
Web address: www.jaspermemorialhospital.org
**Control**: Other not-for-profit (including NFP Corporation) **Service**: General
medical and surgical

**Staffed Beds:** 67 **Admissions:** 105 **Census:** 57 **Outpatient Visits:** 6705
**Births:** 0 **Total Expense ($000):** 12976 **Payroll Expense ($000):** 6053
**Personnel:** 143

## MOULTRIE—Colquitt County

⊞ **COLQUITT REGIONAL MEDICAL CENTER (110105)**, 3131 South Main
Street, Zip 31768–6925, Mailing Address: P.O. Box 40, Zip 31776–0040;
tel. 229/985–3420, (Nonreporting) **A**1 3 5 10 13 **F**3 7 11 12 13 15 17 20 29 30
31 32 34 35 40 45 47 48 49 56 57 59 60 61 62 63 65 68 70 74 75 76 77 78
79 81 82 85 86 87 89 91 93 97 107 108 110 111 115 119 126 127 129 130
131 132 133 135 143 146 147 148
Primary Contact: James L. Matney, President and Chief Executive Officer
COO: Greg K Johnson, Chief Operating Officer
CFO: Shamb Purohit, Chief Financial Officer
CMO: Andy Wills, M.D., Medical Director
CIO: Bill Bishop, Chief Information Officer
CHR: Dawn Johns, Director Human Resources
CNO: Dena Zinker, MSN, R.N., Vice President Patient Services
Web address: www.colquittregional.com
**Control**: Hospital district or authority, Government, Nonfederal **Service**: General
medical and surgical

**Staffed Beds:** 99 **Admissions:** 4793 **Census:** 55 **Outpatient Visits:** 158110
**Births:** 496 **Total Expense ($000):** 127036 **Payroll Expense ($000):** 54066
**Personnel:** 1132

**TURNING POINT CARE CENTER** See Turning Point Hospital

**TURNING POINT HOSPITAL (110209)**, 3015 Veterans Parkway South,
Zip 31788–6705, Mailing Address: P.O. Box 1177, Zip 31776–1177;
tel. 229/985–4815, (Nonreporting) **A**10 **F**4 5 29 30 50 71 87 98 100 130 135
143 149 152 **S** Universal Health Services, Inc., King of Prussia, PA
Primary Contact: Judy H. Payne, Chief Executive Officer
COO: Michael James, Chief Operating Officer
CFO: Edwin Bennett, Controller
CMO: Muhammad M Alam, M.D., Medical Director
CHR: Michelle Hamilton, Human Resource Manager
CNO: Heather Hightower, Director of Nursing
Web address: www.turningpointcare.com
**Control**: Corporation, Investor-owned (for-profit) **Service**: Alcoholism and other
chemical dependency

**Staffed Beds:** 69 **Admissions:** 3852 **Census:** 60 **Outpatient Visits:** 106831
**Births:** 0 **Total Expense ($000):** 27995 **Payroll Expense ($000):** 17221
**Personnel:** 249

**GA**

---

| Hospital, Medicare Provider Number, Address, Telephone, Approval, Facility, and Physician Codes, Health Care System |

★ American Hospital Association (AHA) membership
☐ The Joint Commission accreditation
○ Healthcare Facilities Accreditation Program
◇ DNV Healthcare Inc. accreditation
⇑ Center for Improvement in Healthcare Quality Accreditation
△ Commission on Accreditation of Rehabilitation Facilities (CARF) accreditation

## NASHVILLE—Berrien County

**BERRIEN COUNTY HOSPITAL** See South Georgia Medical Center Berrien Campus

⊞ **SOUTH GEORGIA MEDICAL CENTER BERRIEN CAMPUS (110234)**, 1221 East McPherson Avenue, Zip 31639–2326; tel. 229/433–8600, (Nonreporting) **A**1 10 **F**15 29 34 35 40 57 59 75 77 84 87 91 98 100 102 103 107 110 115 119 130 135 149 150 154 **S** South Georgia Medical Center, Valdosta, GA
Primary Contact: Richard Huth, Administrator
Web address: www.sgmc.org/
**Control**: Hospital district or authority, Government, Nonfederal **Service**: General medical and surgical

**Staffed Beds**: 39 **Admissions**: 284 **Census**: 8 **Outpatient Visits**: 13392
**Births**: 0

## NEWNAN—Coweta County

⊞ **ENCOMPASS HEALTH REHABILITATION HOSPITAL OF NEWNAN (113032)**, 2101 East Newnan Crossing Boulevard, Zip 30265–2406; tel. 678/552–6200, (Nonreporting) **A**1 10 **S** Encompass Health Corporation, Birmingham, AL
Primary Contact: Shawn Bright, Chief Executive Officer
Web address: www.https://encompasshealth.com/locations/newnanrehab/
**Control**: Corporation, Investor–owned (for–profit) **Service**: Rehabilitation

**Staffed Beds**: 50

⇑ **NEWNAN HOSPITAL** See Piedmont Newnan Hospital

⇑ **PIEDMONT NEWNAN HOSPITAL (110229)**, 745 Poplar Road, Zip 30265–1618; tel. 770/400–1000, (Nonreporting) **A**2 10 21 **S** Piedmont Healthcare, Roswell, GA
Primary Contact: Michael Robertson, Chief Executive Officer
COO: Nathan Nipper, Vice President and Chief Operating Officer
CFO: John Miles, Chief Financial Officer
CMO: Jeffrey R Folk, M.D., Vice President Medical Affairs and Chief Medical Officer
CIO: Henry Scott, Executive Director, Technical Services
CHR: Clay Boyles, Executive Director, Human Resources
CNO: Jennifer Key, Chief Nursing Officer
Web address: www.piedmont.org/locations/piedmont-newnan/pnh-home
**Control**: Other not–for–profit (including NFP Corporation) **Service**: General medical and surgical

**Staffed Beds**: 146

☐ **SOUTHEASTERN REGIONAL MEDICAL CENTER (110233)**, 600 Celebrate Life Parkway, Zip 30265–8000; tel. 770/400–6000, (Nonreporting) **A**1 2 10 **F**3 8 15 18 29 30 31 33 35 36 45 46 47 49 55 58 64 67 70 75 77 78 81 82 85 86 87 93 107 108 109 110 111 114 115 116 117 118 119 120 121 123 124 130 132 135 146 148 149 154 **S** Cancer Treatment Centers of America, Schaumburg, IL
Primary Contact: Anne Meisner, MSN, President and Chief Executive Officer
CFO: Scott Walker, Chief Financial Officer
CNO: Gloria V. Barnes, MSN, Assistant Vice President Patient Care Services
Web address: www.cancercenter.com/southeastern-hospital.cfm
**Control**: Corporation, Investor–owned (for–profit) **Service**: Cancer

**Staffed Beds**: 50 **Admissions**: 1431 **Census**: 17 **Outpatient Visits**: 37307
**Births**: 0 **Personnel**: 713

## NORCROSS—Gwinnett County

**LAKEVIEW BEHAVIORAL HEALTH**, 1 Technology Parkway South, Zip 30092–2928; tel. 678/713–2600, (Nonreporting) **A**3 **S** Acadia Healthcare Company, Inc., Franklin, TN
Primary Contact: Deagan Watson, Chief Executive Officer
Web address: www.lakeviewbehavioralhealth.com
**Control**: Corporation, Investor–owned (for–profit) **Service**: Psychiatric

**Staffed Beds**: 70

## OCILLA—Irwin County

⇑ **IRWIN COUNTY HOSPITAL (110130)**, 710 North Irwin Avenue, Zip 31774–5011; tel. 229/468–3800, (Nonreporting) **A**10 21
Primary Contact: Paige Wynn, Administrator
CFO: Tami Gray, Chief Financial Officer
CMO: Ashfaq Saiyed, M.D., Medical Director
CHR: Becky Edwards, Manager Human Resources
Web address: www.irwincntyhospital.com
**Control**: County, Government, Nonfederal **Service**: General medical and surgical

**Staffed Beds**: 64

## PERRY—Houston County

★ ⇑ **PERRY HOSPITAL (110153)**, 1120 Morningside Drive, Zip 31069–2906; tel. 478/987–3600, (Nonreporting) **A**10 21 **F**3 11 15 18 29 30 34 35 40 45 46 50 57 59 61 64 68 70 75 79 81 82 85 86 87 89 93 100 107 110 111 115 119 129 130 131 132 133 134 135 146 149 **S** Houston Healthcare System, Warner Robins, GA
Primary Contact: David Campbell, Administrator
COO: Charles G Briscoe, FACHE, Chief Operating Officer
CFO: Sean Whilden, Chief Financial Officer
CMO: Larry D. Stewart JrChief Medical Officer and Vice President, Medical Affairs
CHR: Michael O'Hara, Senior Executive Director
CNO: Melinda D. Hartley, R.N., Vice President Patient Care Services
Web address: www.hhc.org
**Control**: Other not–for–profit (including NFP Corporation) **Service**: General medical and surgical

**Staffed Beds**: 39 **Admissions**: 1326 **Census**: 17 **Outpatient Visits**: 47561
**Births**: 0 **Total Expense ($000)**: 26363 **Payroll Expense ($000)**: 9998
**Personnel**: 200

## QUITMAN—Brooks County

⊞ **BROOKS COUNTY HOSPITAL (111332)**, 903 North Court Street, Zip 31643–1315, Mailing Address: P.O. Box 5000, Zip 31643–5000; tel. 229/263–4171, (Nonreporting) **A**1 10 18 **F**15 29 30 34 40 87 93 107 110 119 133 146 149 154 **S** Archbold Medical Center, Thomasville, GA
Primary Contact: Nancy M. Williams, R.N., Administrator
CFO: Skip Hightower, Chief Financial Officer
CMO: Michael Sopt, M.D., Chief of Staff
CHR: Janet Eldridge, Director Human Resources and Personnel
CNO: June Furney, R.N., Director of Nursing
Web address: www.archbold.org
**Control**: Other not–for–profit (including NFP Corporation) **Service**: General medical and surgical

**Staffed Beds**: 25 **Admissions**: 439 **Census**: 16 **Outpatient Visits**: 15358
**Births**: 0 **Total Expense ($000)**: 10479 **Payroll Expense ($000)**: 5234
**Personnel**: 93

## REIDSVILLE—Tattnall County

⇑ **DOCTORS HOSPITAL OF TATTNALL** See Optim Medical Center - Tattnall

★ ⇑ **OPTIM MEDICAL CENTER - TATTNALL (111323)**, 247 South Main Street, Zip 30453–4605; tel. 912/557–1000, (Nonreporting) **A**10 18 21 **S** National Surgical Healthcare, Chicago, IL
Primary Contact: Rob Snipes, Administrator
Web address: www.optimmedicalcenter.com
**Control**: Corporation, Investor–owned (for–profit) **Service**: Orthopedic

**Staffed Beds**: 25

## RIVERDALE—Clayton County

**CLAYTON GENERAL HOSPITAL** See Southern Regional Medical Center

☐ **RIVERWOODS BEHAVIORAL HEALTH SYSTEM (114035)**, 233 Medical Center Drive, Zip 30274–2640; tel. 770/991–8500, (Nonreporting) **A**1 5 10 **S** Acadia Healthcare Company, Inc., Franklin, TN
Primary Contact: Patricia Hamilton, Chief Executive Officer
COO: Jenifer Harcourt, Chief Operating Officer
CFO: Tricia Nelson, Chief Financial Officer
CIO: Hema Patel, Director Medical Records
CHR: Tareka Beasley, Director Human Resources
Web address: www.riverwoodsbehavioral.com
**Control**: Corporation, Investor–owned (for–profit) **Service**: Psychiatric

**Staffed Beds**: 75

☐ **SOUTHERN REGIONAL MEDICAL CENTER (110165)**, 11 Upper Riverdale Road SW, Zip 30274–2615; tel. 770/991–8000, (Nonreporting) **A**1 10 **S** Prime Healthcare, Ontario, CA
Primary Contact: Charlotte W. Dupre, Chief Executive Officer
COO: Therese O Sucher, Senior Vice President Operations
CFO: Richard G Stovall, Senior Vice President Fiscal Services and Chief Financial Officer
CMO: Willie Cochran, M.D., JrChief of Staff
CIO: Karen Moore, Vice President Information Technology and Chief Information Officer
CHR: Norma Adams, Director Human Resources
Web address: www.southernregional.org
**Control**: Other not–for–profit (including NFP Corporation) **Service**: General medical and surgical

**Staffed Beds**: 331

*Many Facility Codes have changed. Please refer to the AHA Guide Code Chart.*

© 2021 AHA Guide

## ROME—Floyd County

**COLUMBIA REDMOND REG MED CTR** See Redmond Regional Medical Center

✉ **FLOYD MEDICAL CENTER (110054)**, 304 Turner McCall Boulevard,
Zip 30165–5621, Mailing Address: P.O. Box 233, Zip 30162–0233;
tel. 706/509–5000, (Nonreporting) **A**1 2 3 5 10 19 **F**3 4 5 6 7 8 9 11 12 13 15
17 18 20 22 26 28 29 30 31 32 34 35 36 37 38 39 40 43 44 45 46 48 49 50
51 53 54 56 57 58 59 61 63 64 65 66 68 70 71 72 73 74 75 76 77 78 79 81
82 84 85 86 87 89 90 93 96 97 98 100 101 102 104 105 107 108 110 111
114 115 118 119 129 130 131 132 134 135 143 144 146 147 148 149 152
153 154 156 **S** Floyd Healthcare Management, Rome, GA
Primary Contact: Kurt Stuenkel, FACHE, President and Chief Executive Officer
COO: Warren Alston Rigas, Executive Vice President and Chief Operating Officer
CFO: Rick Sheerin, Vice President Fiscal Services
CMO: Joseph Biuso, M.D., Vice President and Chief of Medical Affairs
CIO: Jeff Buda, Chief Information Officer
CHR: Beth Bradford, Director Human Resources
CNO: Sheila Bennett, R.N., Vice President & Chief Nursing Officer
Web address: www.floyd.org
**Control**: Other not–for–profit (including NFP Corporation) **Service**: General
medical and surgical

**Staffed Beds: 327 Admissions: 15928 Census: 213 Outpatient
Visits: 299256 Births: 2192 Total Expense ($000): 457037 Payroll
Expense ($000): 192613 Personnel: 2043**

✉ **REDMOND REGIONAL MEDICAL CENTER (110168)**, 501 Redmond Road,
Zip 30165–1415, Mailing Address: P.O. Box 107001, Zip 30164–7001;
tel. 706/291–0291, (Nonreporting) **A**1 2 3 5 10 13 19 **S** HCA Healthcare,
Nashville, TN
Primary Contact: John Quinlivan, Chief Executive Officer
COO: David Bradley Stockton, Chief Operating Officer
CFO: Kenneth Metteauer, Chief Financial Officer
CMO: Julie Coffman Barnes, M.D., Chief Medical Officer
CIO: Brad Treglown, Director Information Systems
CHR: Patsy Adams, Vice President Human Resources
CNO: Stephanie Jones, R.N., Chief Nursing Officer
Web address: www.redmondregional.com
**Control**: Corporation, Investor–owned (for–profit) **Service**: General medical and
surgical

**Staffed Beds: 230**

## ROSWELL—Fulton County

**NORTH FULTON REGIONAL HOSPITAL** See Wellstar North Fulton Hospital

✉ **WELLSTAR NORTH FULTON HOSPITAL (110198)**, 3000 Hospital Boulevard,
Zip 30076–3899; tel. 770/751–2500, (Nonreporting) **A**1 2 3 10 13 15 18
20 22 26 28 29 30 31 34 35 37 40 43 45 48 49 55 57 59 63 67 68 70 73 74
75 76 77 78 79 81 82 85 86 87 90 91 92 93 107 108 110 111 114 115 118
119 126 130 132 141 146 147 148 152 **S** WellStar Health System, Marietta, GA
Primary Contact: Jon-Paul Croom, President
COO: Lindsey Petrini, Chief Operating Officer
CFO: Felix Sotoizaguirre, Chief Financial Officer
CMO: Karim Godamunne, M.D., Chief Medical Officer
CHR: Susan Brown, Chief Human Resources Officer
CNO: Nancy Melcher, Chief Nursing Officer
Web address: www.nfultonhospital.com
**Control**: Other not–for–profit (including NFP Corporation) **Service**: General
medical and surgical

**Staffed Beds: 173 Admissions: 7703 Census: 100 Outpatient
Visits: 85039 Births: 1030 Personnel: 792**

## SAINT MARYS—Camden County

**SOUTHEAST GA HLTH SYST CAMDEN** See Southeast Georgia Health System
Camden Campus

✉ **SOUTHEAST GEORGIA HEALTH SYSTEM CAMDEN CAMPUS (110146)**, 2000
Dan Proctor Drive, Zip 31558–3810; tel. 912/576–6200, (Nonreporting) **A**1 10
20 **F**3 11 13 15 18 29 30 31 34 35 40 45 46 47 48 49 50 57 59 64 68 70 71
75 76 77 78 79 81 85 86 87 93 94 107 108 110 111 114 116 117 119 120
129 130 131 132 146 149 **S** Southeast Georgia Health System, Brunswick, GA
Primary Contact: Howard W. Sepp Jr, Vice-President and Administrator
CFO: John Milazzo, Chief Financial Officer
CMO: Robert Bernasek, M.D., Chief Medical Officer
CIO: Charles Bumgardner, Director
CNO: Judith Henson, Vice President, Patient Care Services
Web address: www.sghs.org
**Control**: Other not–for–profit (including NFP Corporation) **Service**: General
medical and surgical

**Staffed Beds: 40 Admissions: 1936 Census: 18 Outpatient Visits: 85416
Births: 627 Total Expense ($000): 46898 Payroll Expense ($000): 17443
Personnel: 290**

## SAINT SIMONS ISLAND—Glynn County

**FOCUS BY-THE-SEA** See Saint Simons By-The-Sea Hospital

☐ **SAINT SIMONS BY-THE-SEA HOSPITAL (114016)**, 2927 Demere Road,
Zip 31522–1620; tel. 912/638–1999, (Nonreporting) **A**1 10 **S** Universal Health
Services, Inc., King of Prussia, PA
Primary Contact: Chris Little, Chief Executive Officer
CMO: Kim Masters, M.D., Medical Director
CIO: Chisty Mosely, Director Information Management
Web address: www.ssbythesea.com
**Control**: Corporation, Investor–owned (for–profit) **Service**: Psychiatric

**Staffed Beds: 101**

## SANDERSVILLE—Washington County

**WASHINGTON COUNTY REG HOSP** See Washington County Regional Medical
Center

☐ **WASHINGTON COUNTY REGIONAL MEDICAL CENTER (110086)**, 610
Sparta Road, Zip 31082–1860, Mailing Address: P.O. Box 636, Zip 31082–0636;
tel. 478/240–2000, (Nonreporting) **A**1 10 20
Primary Contact: Antoine Poythress, Interim Chief Executive Officer
CFO: Antoine Poythress, Chief Financial Officer
CMO: Rob Gatliff, Chief of Medical Staff
CHR: Misty Ivey, Human Resources Manager
CNO: Pamela Stewart, Director of Nursing
Web address: www.wcrmc.com
**Control**: Hospital district or authority, Government, Nonfederal **Service**: General
medical and surgical

**Staffed Beds: 116**

## SAVANNAH—Chatham County

✉ △ **CANDLER HOSPITAL (110024)**, 5353 Reynolds Street, Zip 31405–6015;
tel. 912/819–6000, (Total facility includes 11 beds in nursing home–type unit)
(Nonreporting) **A**1 7 10 **F**2 3 11 13 15 18 20 29 30 31 32 34 35 36 38 39 40
44 45 46 47 48 49 50 53 54 57 58 59 60 61 64 65 68 70 71 73 74 75 76 77
78 80 81 82 84 85 86 87 89 90 93 94 96 107 108 110 111 114 117 119 120
121 123 124 126 128 129 130 131 132 135 146 147 148 149 156 **P**6 8
Primary Contact: Paul P. Hinchey, President and Chief Executive Officer
CFO: Gregory J Schaack, CPA, Vice President and Chief Financial Officer
CMO: James Scott, M.D., Vice President Medical Affairs
CIO: George Evans, Vice President and Chief Information Officer
CHR: Don Stubbs, Vice President Human Resources
CNO: Sherry Danello, MSN, R.N., Vice President and Chief Nursing Officer
Web address: www.sjchs.org
**Control**: Church operated, Nongovernment, not–for–profit **Service**: General
medical and surgical

**Staffed Beds: 264 Admissions: 11132 Census: 164 Outpatient
Visits: 295262 Births: 2733 Total Expense ($000): 320090 Payroll
Expense ($000): 110080 Personnel: 1786**

**GA**

---

| Hospital, Medicare Provider Number, Address, Telephone, Approval, Facility, and Physician Codes, Health Care System |
|---|

★ American Hospital Association (AHA) membership    ○ Healthcare Facilities Accreditation Program    ⇧ Center for Improvement in Healthcare Quality Accreditation
☐ The Joint Commission accreditation    ◇ DNV Healthcare Inc. accreditation    △ Commission on Accreditation of Rehabilitation Facilities (CARF) accreditation

**CHARTER BEHAVIORAL HLTH SYSTEM** See Coastal Harbor Treatment Center

☐ **COASTAL HARBOR TREATMENT CENTER (114008)**, 1150 Cornell Avenue, Zip 31406–2702; tel. 912/354–3911, (Nonreporting) **A**1 3 10 **F**4 5 98 99 100 103 104 105 106 152 153 154 **S** Universal Health Services, Inc., King of Prussia, PA
Primary Contact: Sally Perry, Chief Executive Officer
COO: Ray Heckerman, Chief Executive Officer and Managing Director
CFO: Brad Lavoie, Chief Financial Officer
CMO: Reemon Bishara, M.D., Medical Director
CHR: Kellie Carlson, Director Human Resources
CNO: Jillisa Thornton, Director of Nursing
Web address: www.coastalharbor.com
**Control**: Corporation, Investor-owned (for–profit) **Service**: Psychiatric

**Staffed Beds:** 191 **Admissions:** 3741 **Census:** 140 **Outpatient Visits:** 21480 **Births:** 0 **Total Expense ($000):** 26909 **Payroll Expense ($000):** 14906 **Personnel:** 285

✜ **ENCOMPASS HEALTH REHABILITATION HOSPITAL OF SAVANNAH (113033)**, 6510 Seawright DR, Zip 31406–2752; tel. 800/622–7269, (Nonreporting) **A**1 10 **S** Encompass Health Corporation, Birmingham, AL
Primary Contact: Kathy Kleinsteuber, Chief Executive Officer
Web address: www.rehabilitationhospitalsavannah.com
**Control**: Corporation, Investor-owned (for–profit) **Service**: Rehabilitation

**Staffed Beds:** 50

**GEORGE AND MARIE BACKUS CHILDREN'S HOSPITAL** See Memorial Children's Hospital

☐ **GEORGIA REGIONAL HOSPITAL AT SAVANNAH (114028)**, 1915 Eisenhower Drive, Zip 31406–5098; tel. 912/356–2011, (Nonreporting) **A**1 3 10
Primary Contact: Andy Mannich, Regional Administrator
COO: Thomas F Kurtz JrChief Operating Officer
CFO: Janet Edenfield, Director Financial Services
CMO: Donald Manning, M.D., Clinical Director
CHR: Jamekia Powers, Assistant Director Human Resources
Web address: www.dbhdd.georgia.gov/georgia-regional-hospital-savannah
**Control**: State, Government, Nonfederal **Service**: Psychiatric

**Staffed Beds:** 105

**LANDMARK HOSPITAL OF SAVANNAH (112018)**, 800 East 68th Street, Zip 31405–4710; tel. 912/298–1000, (Nonreporting) **A**10 22 **S** Landmark Hospitals, Cape Girardeau, MO
Primary Contact: John Salandi, Chief Executive Officer
Web address: www.landmarkhospitals.com/savannah
**Control**: Partnership, Investor-owned (for–profit) **Service**: Acute long-term care hospital

**Staffed Beds:** 50

✜ **MEMORIAL HEALTH (110036)**, 4700 Waters Avenue, Zip 31404–6283, Mailing Address: P.O. Box 23089, Zip 31403–3089; tel. 912/350–8000, (Includes MEMORIAL CHILDREN'S HOSPITAL, Mailing address: 4700 Waters Avenue, Savannah, Georgia, Zip 31404–6220, PO Box 23089, Zip 31403–3089, tel. 912/350–7337), (Nonreporting) **A**1 2 3 8 10 **S** HCA Healthcare, Nashville, TN
Primary Contact: Shayne George, Chief Executive Officer
COO: Matthew Steven Hasbrouck, Chief Operating Officer
CFO: Laura Dow, Chief Financial Officer
CMO: Ramon V Meguiar, M.D., Chief Medical Officer
CIO: Kathryn McClellan, Chief Information Officer
CHR: Alisa R Griner, Director, Human Resources
CNO: Todd Isbell, R.N., MSN, Chief Nursing Officer
Web address: www.memorialhealth.com
**Control**: Other not-for-profit (including NFP Corporation) **Service**: General medical and surgical

**Staffed Beds:** 622

**MEMORIAL HEALTH SYSTEM** See Memorial Health

**REHABILITATION HOSPITAL OF SAVANNAH** See Encompass Health Rehabilitation Hospital of Savannah

✜ **SELECT SPECIALTY HOSPITAL-SAVANNAH (112011)**, 5353 Reynolds Street, 4 South, Zip 31405–6015; tel. 912/819–7982, (Nonreporting) **A**1 10 **S** Select Medical Corporation, Mechanicsburg, PA
Primary Contact: Greg Wuchter, R.N., MSN, Chief Executive Officer
Web address: www.savannah.selectspecialtyhospitals.com
**Control**: Corporation, Investor-owned (for–profit) **Service**: Acute long-term care hospital

**Staffed Beds:** 40

**ST. JOSEPH'S CANDLER HOSPITAL** See Candler Hospital

☐ △ **ST. JOSEPH'S HOSPITAL (110043)**, 11705 Mercy Boulevard, Zip 31419–1791; tel. 912/819–4100, (Total facility includes 11 beds in nursing home–type unit) (Nonreporting) **A**1 2 7 10 **F**2 3 11 15 17 18 20 22 24 26 28 29 30 34 35 36 37 38 39 40 41 44 45 49 50 56 57 58 59 60 65 70 74 75 77 79 80 81 82 84 85 86 90 94 96 107 108 110 111 114 115 119 126 128 130 131 132 135 146 148 149 150 **P**6 8
Primary Contact: Paul P. Hinchey, President and Chief Executive Officer
COO: Kyle McCann, Chief Operating Officer
CFO: Gregory J Schaack, CPA, Vice President and Chief Financial Officer
CMO: James Scott, M.D., Vice President Medical Affairs
CIO: Nolan Henessee, Vice President and Chief Information Officer
CHR: Steve Pound, Vice President Human Resources
CNO: Sherry Danello, MSN, R.N., Vice President and Chief Nursing Officer
Web address: www.sjchs.org
**Control**: Church operated, Nongovernment, not-for-profit **Service**: General medical and surgical

**Staffed Beds:** 231 **Admissions:** 18878 **Census:** 174 **Outpatient Visits:** 98486 **Births:** 0 **Total Expense ($000):** 251081 **Payroll Expense ($000):** 87943 **Personnel:** 1124

**ST. JOSEPH'S/CANDLER, ST. JOSEPH'S HOSPITAL** See St. Joseph's Hospital

**SMYRNA—Cobb County**

✜ **RIDGEVIEW INSTITUTE (114012)**, 3995 South Cobb Drive SE, Zip 30080–6397; tel. 770/434–4567, (Nonreporting) **A**1 3 10
Primary Contact: Margaret P. Collier, Chief Executive Officer
CFO: Ruth Jenkins, Chief Financial Officer
CMO: Thomas Bradford Johns, M.D., Medical Director
CIO: Lynn Leger, Director Information Systems
CHR: Betty Sonderman, Manager Human Resources
Web address: www.ridgeviewinstitute.com
**Control**: Other not-for-profit (including NFP Corporation) **Service**: Psychiatric

**Staffed Beds:** 110

**SNELLVILLE—Gwinnett County**

✜ **EASTSIDE MEDICAL CENTER (110192)**, 1700 Medical Way, Zip 30078–2195; tel. 770/979–0200, (Nonreporting) **A**1 2 10 **S** HCA Healthcare, Nashville, TN
Primary Contact: Trent Lind, Chief Executive Officer
COO: John Hoover, Chief Operating Officer
CMO: Michael O'Neill, M.D., Chief Medical Officer
CIO: Pattie Page, Director Marketing and Public Relations
CNO: Tracey Smithson, MSN, R.N., Chief Nursing Officer
Web address: www.eastsidemedical.com
**Control**: Corporation, Investor-owned (for–profit) **Service**: General medical and surgical

**Staffed Beds:** 310

**EMORY EASTSIDE MEDICAL CENTER** See Eastside Medical Center

**SPRINGFIELD—Effingham County**

**EFFINGHAM COUNTY HOSP & ECF** See Effingham Hospital

✜ **EFFINGHAM HOSPITAL (111306)**, 459 Highway 119 South, Zip 31329–3021, Mailing Address: P.O. Box 386, Zip 31329–0386; tel. 912/754–6451, (Total facility includes 105 beds in nursing home–type unit) (Nonreporting) **A**1 10 18 **F**3 6 11 15 29 34 35 40 43 45 50 57 59 74 77 81 85 97 107 110 111 114 119 126 127 128 130 132 133 135 146 147 154 **P**6
Primary Contact: Francine Baker-Witt, R.N., Chief Executive Officer
CFO: Matthew Moore, Director of Financial Reporting
CMO: Claude Sanks, Chief Medical Staff
CIO: Mary Pizzino, Chief Information Officer
CHR: Marie Murphy, Director Human Resources
CNO: Betsy Smith, Chief Nursing Officer
Web address: www.effinghamhospital.org
**Control**: Hospital district or authority, Government, Nonfederal **Service**: General medical and surgical

**Staffed Beds:** 130 **Admissions:** 1145 **Census:** 102 **Outpatient Visits:** 68493 **Births:** 0 **Total Expense ($000):** 60253 **Payroll Expense ($000):** 21167 **Personnel:** 410

**GA**

## STATESBORO—Bulloch County

**BULLOCH MEMORIAL HOSPITAL** See East Georgia Regional Medical Center

⊞ **EAST GEORGIA REGIONAL MEDICAL CENTER (110075)**, 1499 Fair Road, Zip 30458–1683, Mailing Address: P.O. Box 1048, Zip 30459–1048; tel. 912/486–1000, (Nonreporting) **A**1 10 **S** Community Health Systems, Inc., Franklin, TN
Primary Contact: Stephen G. Pennington, Chief Executive Officer
COO: Erin Smith, Chief Operating Officer
CFO: Eric Roach, Chief Financial Officer
CMO: Alan Scott, M.D., Chief of Staff
CIO: Brian Girardeau, Director Information System
CHR: Michael Black, Director Human Resources
CNO: Marie Burdette, Chief Nursing Officer
Web address: www.eastgeorgiaregional.com
**Control:** Corporation, Investor–owned (for–profit) **Service:** General medical and surgical

**Staffed Beds:** 149

**WILLINGWAY HOSPITAL**, 311 Jones Mill Road, Zip 30458–4765; tel. 912/764–6236, (Nonreporting)
Primary Contact: Cherie Tolley, Chief Executive Officer
CMO: Robert W Mooney, M.D., Medical Director
Web address: www.willingway.com
**Control:** Corporation, Investor–owned (for–profit) **Service:** Alcoholism and other chemical dependency

**Staffed Beds:** 40

## STOCKBRIDGE—Henry County

⇑ **HENRY MEDICAL CENTER** See Piedmont Henry Hospital

⇑ **PIEDMONT HENRY HOSPITAL (110191)**, 1133 Eagle's Landing Parkway, Zip 30281–5099; tel. 678/604–1000, (Nonreporting) **A**2 10 21 **F**3 8 11 13 15 18 20 22 26 28 29 30 31 34 35 40 45 49 54 55 57 59 61 64 70 72 73 74 75 76 77 78 79 81 82 84 85 86 87 93 94 100 107 108 110 111 114 115 118 119 120 121 123 130 132 135 146 147 148 154 156 **S** Piedmont Healthcare, Roswell, GA
Primary Contact: Lily Henson, M.D., Chief Executive Officer
COO: James Atkins, PharmD, Chief Operating Officer
CFO: Wesley James, Chief Financial Officer
CHR: Jana Warren, Human Resources Business Partner
CNO: Paula Yvonne Butts, Chief Nursing Officer
Web address: www.piedmont.org
**Control:** Other not–for–profit (including NFP Corporation) **Service:** General medical and surgical

**Staffed Beds:** 258 **Admissions:** 15507 **Census:** 185 **Outpatient Visits:** 160003 **Births:** 1663 **Personnel:** 1527

## SWAINSBORO—Emanuel County

⇑ **EMANUEL MEDICAL CENTER (110109)**, 117 Kite Road, Zip 30401–3231, Mailing Address: P.O. Box 879, Zip 30401–0879; tel. 478/289–1100, (Nonreporting) **A**10 20 21
Primary Contact: Damien Scott, Chief Executive Officer
CFO: Jessica Johnson, Chief Financial Officer
CMO: Daryl McCartney, M.D., President Medical Staff
CIO: Tony Waters, Chief Information Officer
CHR: Jinny Newman, Director Human Resources
CNO: Ginger Hall, Chief Nursing Officer
Web address: www.emanuelmedical.org
**Control:** Hospital district or authority, Government, Nonfederal **Service:** General medical and surgical

**Staffed Beds:** 91

⇑ **EMANUEL MEDICAL HOSPITAL** See Emanuel Medical Center

## SYLVANIA—Screven County

**OPTIM MEDICAL CENTER - SCREVEN (111312)**, 215 Mims Road, Zip 30467–2097; tel. 912/564–7426, (Nonreporting) **A**10 18 **S** National Surgical Healthcare, Chicago, IL
Primary Contact: Suzanne Doscher, FACHE, Chief Executive Officer
CFO: Neil Orrill, Director of Finance
CMO: Heywood Kyle Gay, M.D., Physician
CIO: Christian Rekowski, Information Technology Manager
CHR: Natalie Tambon, Director of Human Resources
CNO: Sharon Lagina Evans, R.N., Assistant Chief Nursing Officer
Web address: www.optimhealth.com
**Control:** County, Government, Nonfederal **Service:** General medical and surgical

**Staffed Beds:** 25

**SCREVEN COUNTY HOSPITAL** See Optim Medical Center - Screven

## SYLVESTER—Worth County

⇑ **BAPTIST HOSPITAL, WORTH COUNTY** See Phoebe Worth Medical Center

★ ⇑ **PHOEBE WORTH MEDICAL CENTER (111328)**, 807 South Isabella Street, Zip 31791–7554, Mailing Address: P.O. Box 545, Zip 31791–0545; tel. 229/776–6961, (Nonreporting) **A**10 18 21 **S** Phoebe Putney Health System, Albany, GA
Primary Contact: Kim Gilman, Chief Executive Officer
CFO: Candace Guarnieri, Chief Financial Officer
CMO: Natu M Patel, M.D., Chief of Staff
CHR: Mandy Gordon, Human Resource Coordinator
CNO: Kim Gilman, Chief Nursing Officer
Web address: www.phoebeputney.com
**Control:** Other not–for–profit (including NFP Corporation) **Service:** General medical and surgical

**Staffed Beds:** 18

## THOMASTON—Upson County

⇑ **UPSON REGIONAL MED CTR** See Upson Regional Medical Center

★ ⇑ **UPSON REGIONAL MEDICAL CENTER (110002)**, 801 West Gordon Street, Zip 30286–3426, Mailing Address: P.O. Box 1059, Zip 30286–0027; tel. 706/647–8111, (Nonreporting) **A**10 21 **F**11 13 15 20 21 22 23 28 29 30 31 34 35 36 40 45 46 49 50 57 59 61 64 68 70 76 78 79 80 81 82 85 86 87 89 98 103 107 108 109 111 114 115 118 119 124 130 131 132 135 148 154 156 **S** HealthTech Management Services, Brentwood, TN

Primary Contact: Jeffrey S. Tarrant, FACHE, Chief Executive Officer
CFO: John Williams, Chief Financial Officer
CIO: Johnathan Buice, Chief Information Officer
CHR: Laura Stokes, Human Resources Director
CNO: Lane Harrington, Chief Nursing Officer
Web address: www.urmc.org
**Control:** Other not–for–profit (including NFP Corporation) **Service:** General medical and surgical

**Staffed Beds:** 93 **Admissions:** 3730 **Census:** 45 **Outpatient Visits:** 72635 **Births:** 372 **Total Expense ($000):** 77761 **Payroll Expense ($000):** 29772 **Personnel:** 648

**GA**

---

**Hospital, Medicare Provider Number, Address, Telephone, Approval, Facility, and Physician Codes, Health Care System**

★ American Hospital Association (AHA) membership
☐ The Joint Commission accreditation
○ Healthcare Facilities Accreditation Program
◇ DNV Healthcare Inc. accreditation
⇑ Center for Improvement in Healthcare Quality Accreditation
△ Commission on Accreditation of Rehabilitation Facilities (CARF) accreditation

## THOMASVILLE—Thomas County

**JOHN D ARCHBOLD MEMRIAL HOSP** See John D. Archbold Memorial Hospital

✠ **JOHN D. ARCHBOLD MEMORIAL HOSPITAL (110038)**, 915 Gordon Avenue, Zip 31792–6614, Mailing Address: P.O. Box 1018, Zip 31799–1018; tel. 229/228–2000, (Total facility includes 64 beds in nursing home–type unit) (Nonreporting) **A**1 2 10 19 **F**3 8 11 12 13 15 18 20 22 26 28 29 30 31 32 34 35 38 40 43 45 46 47 48 49 50 51 54 56 57 58 59 60 61 62 63 64 65 66 70 74 75 76 77 78 79 80 81 82 84 85 86 87 90 91 92 93 96 97 98 100 101 102 103 104 107 108 110 111 114 115 116 117 118 120 121 123 124 126 128 129 130 131 132 135 143 144 145 146 147 148 149 154 **S** Archbold Medical Center, Thomasville, GA
Primary Contact: J. Perry Mustian, President and Chief Executive Officer
CFO: Skip Hightower, Senior Vice President and Chief Financial Officer
CIO: Tracy Gray, Senior Vice President Information Services
CHR: Zachariah P Wheeler, Senior Vice President Human Resources
CNO: Amy Griffin, Vice President Patient Care Services
Web address: www.archbold.org
**Control**: Other not–for–profit (including NFP Corporation) **Service**: General medical and surgical

**Staffed Beds: 305 Admissions: 11060 Census: 226 Outpatient Visits: 204765 Births: 651 Total Expense ($000): 250371 Payroll Expense ($000): 86496 Personnel: 1666**

## THOMSON—McDuffie County

**MCDUFFIE REGIONAL MEDICAL CENTER** See University Hospital Mcduffie

✠ **UNIVERSITY HOSPITAL MCDUFFIE (110111)**, 2460 Washington Road, NE, Zip 30824; tel. 706/595–1411, (Nonreporting) **A**1 10 **F**3 11 15 29 30 40 45 50 59 64 68 79 81 85 87 107 110 114 119 130 132 133 146 148 149 **S** University Health Care System, Augusta, GA
Primary Contact: Bob Kepshire, R.N., MS, Administrator and Chief Nursing Officer
CFO: Dave Belkoski, Chief Financial Officer
CNO: Bob Kepshire, R.N., MS, Administrator and Chief Nursing Officer
Web address: www.universityhealth.org/mcduffie
**Control**: Other not–for–profit (including NFP Corporation) **Service**: General medical and surgical

**Staffed Beds: 22 Admissions: 729 Census: 15 Outpatient Visits: 36796 Births: 1 Total Expense ($000): 20142 Payroll Expense ($000): 6081 Personnel: 135**

## TIFTON—Tift County

**TIFT REGIONAL HEALTH SYSTEM** See Tift Regional Medical Center

✠ **TIFT REGIONAL MEDICAL CENTER (110095)**, 901 East 18th Street, Zip 31794–3648, Mailing Address: Drawer 747, Zip 31793–0747; tel. 229/382–7120, (Nonreporting) **A**1 2 5 10 19 **F**3 8 9 11 12 13 15 18 20 22 26 28 29 30 31 33 34 35 40 45 47 49 50 51 54 57 59 60 63 64 68 70 74 75 76 77 78 79 81 82 84 85 86 87 89 92 93 97 100 104 107 108 110 111 114 115 118 119 120 121 123 126 129 130 131 132 135 143 144 146 147 148 149 154 156 **P**6 **S** Tift Regional Health System, Tifton, GA
Primary Contact: Christopher Dorman, President and Chief Executive Officer
CFO: Dennis L Crum, Senior Vice President and Chief Financial Officer
CMO: William Guest, M.D., Senior Vice President and Chief Medical Officer
CIO: Guy McAllister, Vice President and Chief Information Officer
CHR: Lori S Folsom, Assistant Vice President Human Resources
CNO: Carol Smith, Vice President Patient Care and Chief Nursing Officer
Web address: www.tiftregional.com
**Control**: Other not–for–profit (including NFP Corporation) **Service**: General medical and surgical

**Staffed Beds: 181 Admissions: 9232 Census: 125 Outpatient Visits: 212659 Births: 1406 Total Expense ($000): 372648 Payroll Expense ($000): 158458 Personnel: 2203**

## TOCCOA—Stephens County

☐ **STEPHENS COUNTY HOSPITAL (110032)**, 163 Hospital Drive, Zip 30577–6820; tel. 706/282–4200, (Nonreporting) **A**1 10
Primary Contact: Michael Hester, Chief Executive Officer
CFO: Jeff Laird, Controller
CHR: Diane Hardeman, Director Personnel
CNO: Faye M Taylor, R.N., Director of Nursing
Web address: www.stephenscountyhospital.com
**Control**: Hospital district or authority, Government, Nonfederal **Service**: General medical and surgical

**Staffed Beds: 188**

## VALDOSTA—Lowndes County

☐ **GREENLEAF BEHAVIORAL HEALTH HOSPITAL (114036)**, 2209 Pineview Drive, Zip 31602–7316; tel. 229/247–4357, (Nonreporting) **A**1 10 **S** Acadia Healthcare Company, Inc., Franklin, TN
Primary Contact: Bryan D. Adams, Chief Executive Officer
Web address: www.greenleafcounseling.net
**Control**: Corporation, Investor–owned (for–profit) **Service**: Psychiatric

**Staffed Beds: 103**

**GREENLEAF CENTER** See Greenleaf Behavioral Health Hospital

**SMITH HOSPITAL** See Smith Northview Hospital

✠ **SOUTH GEORGIA MEDICAL CENTER (110122)**, 2501 North Patterson Street, Zip 31602–1735, Mailing Address: P.O. Box 1727, Zip 31603–1727; tel. 229/333–1000, (Includes SMITH NORTHVIEW HOSPITAL, Mailing address: 4280 North Valdosta Road, Valdosta, Georgia, Zip 31602, P O Box 10010, Zip 31604, tel. 229/671–2000; Leonard Carter, Campus Administrator), (Nonreporting) **A**1 2 10 19 **S** South Georgia Medical Center, Valdosta, GA
Primary Contact: Ronald Dean, Chief Executive Officer
CFO: Grant Byers, Senior Vice President and Chief Financial Officer
CMO: Brian Dawson, Senior Vice President and Chief Medical Officer
CIO: Bob Foster, Chief Information Officer
CNO: Randy Smith, Senior Vice President and Chief Nursing Officer
Web address: www.sgmc.org
**Control**: Other not–for–profit (including NFP Corporation) **Service**: General medical and surgical

**Staffed Beds: 302**

## VIDALIA—Toombs County

⇑ **DR JOHN M MEADOWS MEM HOSPITAL** See Meadows Regional Medical Center

★ ⇑ **MEADOWS REGIONAL MEDICAL CENTER (110128)**, One Meadows Parkway, Zip 30474–8759, Mailing Address: P.O. Box 1048, Zip 30475–1048; tel. 912/535–5555, (Nonreporting) **A**10 20 21
Primary Contact: Alan Kent, Chief Executive Officer
COO: James Nixon, Chief Operating Officer
CFO: Tony O'Steen, Chief Financial Officer
CMO: Karen McColl, M.D., Chief Medical Officer
CIO: Charles Bondurant, Chief Information Officer
CNO: Jeffrey M Harden, Chief Nursing Officer
Web address: www.meadowsregional.org
**Control**: Other not–for–profit (including NFP Corporation) **Service**: General medical and surgical

**Staffed Beds: 57**

## VILLA RICA—Carroll County

✠ **TANNER MEDICAL CENTER-VILLA RICA (110015)**, 601 Dallas Highway, Zip 30180–1202; tel. 770/456–3000, (Includes WILLOWBROOKE AT TANNER, Mailing address: 20 Herrell Road, Villa Rica, Georgia, Zip 30180–5527; tel. 770/812–3266; Paula Gresham, Vice President, Hospital Administrator), (Nonreporting) **A**1 10 **S** Tanner Health System, Carrollton, GA
Primary Contact: Eric Dalton, Administrator
CFO: Carol Crews, Senior Vice President and Chief Financial Officer
CMO: William Waters, M.D., IVExecutive Vice President
CIO: Terri Lee, Chief Information Officer
CHR: Shari W Gainey, Chief Human Resource Officer
CNO: Deborah Matthews, Senior Vice President
Web address: www.tanner.org
**Control**: Other not–for–profit (including NFP Corporation) **Service**: General medical and surgical

**Staffed Beds: 118**

## WARM SPRINGS—Meriwether County

**BAPTIST MERIWETHER HOSPITAL** See Warm Springs Medical Center

**ROOSEVELT WARM SPRINGS REHABILITATION AND SPECIALTY HOSPITALS** See Roosevelt Warm Springs Rehabilitation and Specialty Hospitals - Ltac

☐ **ROOSEVELT WARM SPRINGS REHABILITATION AND SPECIALTY HOSPITALS - LTAC (112000)**, 6135 Roosevelt Highway, Zip 31830–2757, Mailing Address: P.O. Box 280, Zip 31830–2757; tel. 706/655–5291, (Nonreporting) **A**1 10
Primary Contact: David L. Mork Jr, Chief Executive Officer
CFO: Susan Wilder, Director Financial Services
CMO: Carlos Parrado, M.D., SrChief Medical Officer
CHR: Laura Stokes, Director Human Resources
CNO: Cathy Harbin, Chief Nursing Officer
Web address: www.augustahealth.org/roosevelt-warm-springs/rwsh
**Control**: State, Government, Nonfederal **Service**: Acute long–term care hospital

**Staffed Beds: 28**

GA

*Many Facility Codes have changed. Please refer to the AHA Guide Code Chart.* © 2021 AHA Guide

**ROOSEVELT WARM SPRINGS REHABILITATION AND SPECIALTY HOSPITALS - REHAB** See Roosevelt Warm Springs Rehabilitation Hospital - Rehab

✠ **ROOSEVELT WARM SPRINGS REHABILITATION HOSPITAL - REHAB (113028)**, 6135 Roosevelt Highway, Zip 31830–2757, Mailing Address: P.O. Box 280, Zip 31830–0280; tel. 706/655–5515, (Nonreporting) **A**1 10
Primary Contact: David L. Mork Jr, Chief Executive Officer
CFO: Susan Wilder, Director Financial Services
CMO: Ara Chitchyan, M.D., Medical Director
CIO: Christen Carter, Director Public Relations
CHR: Laura Stokes, Director Human Resources
CNO: Cathy Harbin, Chief Nursing Officer
Web address: www.augustahealth.org/roosevelt-warm-springs/rwsh
**Control:** State, Government, Nonfederal **Service:** Rehabilitation

**Staffed Beds:** 32

✠ **WARM SPRINGS MEDICAL CENTER (111316)**, 5995 Spring Street, Zip 31830–2149, Mailing Address: P.O. Box 8, Zip 31830–0008; tel. 706/655–3331, (Nonreporting) **A**1 10 18
Primary Contact: Karen Daniel, Chief Executive Officer
CFO: Patrick Flynn, Chief Financial Officer
CMO: Alan Thompson, M.D., President Medical Staff
CIO: Milo Varnadoe, Director Information Systems
CHR: Theresa Passarelli, Human Resources Generalist
CNO: Lynda Ligon, Chief Nursing Officer
Web address: www.warmspringsmc.org
**Control:** Hospital district or authority, Government, Nonfederal **Service:** General medical and surgical

**Staffed Beds:** 104

### WARNER ROBINS—Houston County

★ ⇑ **HOUSTON MEDICAL CENTER (110069)**, 1601 Watson Boulevard, Zip 31093–3431, Mailing Address: P.O. Box 2886, Zip 31099–2886; tel. 478/922–4281, (Nonreporting) **A**3 5 10 13 21 **F**3 8 11 13 15 18 20 22 26 28 29 30 31 34 35 38 40 44 45 46 49 50 57 59 60 61 64 68 70 73 74 75 76 78 79 81 82 83 84 85 86 87 89 93 98 100 102 103 107 108 110 111 115 118 119 126 129 130 131 132 134 135 144 146 147 148 149 150 156 **S** Houston Healthcare System, Warner Robins, GA
Primary Contact: Charles G. Briscoe, FACHE, Interim President and Chief Executive Officer
COO: Charles G Briscoe, FACHE, Chief Operating Officer
CFO: Sean Whilden, Chief Financial Officer
CIO: George Curtis, Chief Information Officer
CHR: Michael O'Hara, Senior Executive Director Human Resources
Web address: www.hhc.org
**Control:** Other not–for–profit (including NFP Corporation) **Service:** General medical and surgical

**Staffed Beds:** 237 **Admissions:** 13327 **Census:** 167 **Outpatient Visits:** 245798 **Births:** 1891 **Total Expense ($000):** 225976 **Payroll Expense ($000):** 87358 **Personnel:** 1722

### WASHINGTON—Wilkes County

☐ **WILLS MEMORIAL HOSPITAL (111325)**, 120 Gordon Street, Zip 30673–1602, Mailing Address: P.O. Box 370, Zip 30673–0370; tel. 706/678–2151, (Nonreporting) **A**1 10 18
Primary Contact: Tracie Haughey, Chief Executive Officer and Chief Financial Officer
CFO: Tracie Haughey, Chief Executive Officer and Chief Financial Officer
CMO: Robert J. Williams, M.D., Chief Medical Staff
CIO: David Harper, Chief Information Officer
CHR: Susan Pope, Director Human Resources
CNO: Angie Radford, R.N., Director of Nursing
Web address: www.willsmemorialhospital.com
**Control:** Hospital district or authority, Government, Nonfederal **Service:** General medical and surgical

**Staffed Beds:** 25

### WAYCROSS—Ware County

✠ **MEMORIAL SATILLA HEALTH (110003)**, 1900 Tebeau Street, Zip 31501–6357, Mailing Address: P.O. Box 139, Zip 31502–0139; tel. 912/283–3030, (Nonreporting) **A**1 3 5 10 **S** HCA Healthcare, Nashville, TN
Primary Contact: Bobby McCullough, Chief Executive Officer
COO: Mark Roberts, Chief Operating Officer
CFO: Patrick Sloan, Chief Financial Officer
CIO: Barry Rudd, Chief Information Officer
CHR: Brigitte Churchill, Director of Human Resources
CNO: Holli Sweat, Associate Administrator and Chief Nursing Officer
Web address: www.memorialsatillahealth.com/
**Control:** Other not–for–profit (including NFP Corporation) **Service:** General medical and surgical

**Staffed Beds:** 231

**SATILLA REGIONAL MEDICAL CENTER** See Memorial Satilla Health

### WAYNESBORO—Burke County

**BURKE COUNTY HOSPITAL** See Burke Medical Center

☐ **BURKE MEDICAL CENTER (110113)**, 351 Liberty Street, Zip 30830–9686; tel. 706/554–4435, (Nonreporting) **A**1 10
Primary Contact: Tiffany G. Varnadoe, Chief Executive Officer and Chief Financial Officer
CFO: Karen ONeal, Chief Financial Officer
CHR: Kim Anthony, Director Human Resources
CNO: Debra Burch, Chief Nursing Officer
Web address: www.burkemedical.net
**Control:** Hospital district or authority, Government, Nonfederal **Service:** General medical and surgical

**Staffed Beds:** 40

### WINDER—Barrow County

⇑ **BARROW REGIONAL MEDICAL CENTER** See Northeast Georgia Medical Center Barrow

★ ⇑ **NORTHEAST GEORGIA MEDICAL CENTER BARROW (110045)**, 316 North Broad Street, Zip 30680–2150, Mailing Address: P.O. Box 688, Zip 30680–0688; tel. 770/867–3400, (Nonreporting) **A**10 21 **F**3 11 15 29 30 34 35 38 40 44 45 50 57 59 60 68 70 74 75 77 79 81 82 85 107 108 110 111 114 115 118 119 124 130 131 132 135 143 146 147 148 149 154 156 **S** Northeast Georgia Health System, Gainesville, GA
Primary Contact: Chad Hatfield, Chief Executive Officer
CMO: Jon Horn, M.D., Chief of Staff
CIO: Cory Crayton, Director Information Systems
CHR: Carlotta Hannah Newman, Human Resources Manager
CNO: Heather Standard, Chief Nursing Officer
Web address: www.barrowregional.com
**Control:** Other not–for–profit (including NFP Corporation) **Service:** General medical and surgical

**Staffed Beds:** 30 **Admissions:** 1385 **Census:** 12 **Outpatient Visits:** 31409 **Births:** 0 **Personnel:** 184

**GA**

# HAWAII

## AIEA—Honolulu County

**KAPIOLANI MEDICAL CENTER AT PALI MOMI** See Pali Momi Medical Center

☒ **PALI MOMI MEDICAL CENTER (120026)**, 98-1079 Moanalua Road,
Zip 96701–4713; tel. 808/486–6000, (Nonreporting) **A**1 2 3 5 10 **F**3 12 15 18
20 22 26 29 31 34 35 36 40 43 44 45 46 47 48 50 54 58 59 61 63 64 65 68 70
74 75 77 78 79 80 81 84 85 86 87 92 107 108 110 111 115 118 119 126
130 132 135 146 148 149 154 156 **P**8 **S** Hawaii Pacific Health, Honolulu, HI
Primary Contact: Martha Smith, Executive Vice President
CFO: David Okabe, Executive Vice President, Chief Financial Officer and Treasurer
CMO: James Kakuda, M.D., Chief of Staff
CIO: Steve Robertson, Senior Vice President
CHR: Gail Lerch, R.N., Vice President Human Resources
CNO: Brigitte McKale, MSN, FACHE, Vice President and Chief Nurse Executive
Web address: www.palimomi.org
**Control**: Other not–for–profit (including NFP Corporation) **Service**: General
medical and surgical

> **Staffed Beds:** 118 **Admissions:** 5683 **Census:** 90 **Outpatient**
> **Visits:** 242567 **Births:** 0 **Total Expense ($000):** 248663 **Payroll Expense**
> **($000):** 87510 **Personnel:** 966

## EWA BEACH—Honolulu County

**HAWAII MEDICAL CENTER-WEST** See Queen's Medical Center - West Oahu

**KAHI MOHALA BEHAVIORAL HEALTH** See Sutter Health Kahi Mohala

☒ **SUTTER HEALTH KAHI MOHALA (124001)**, 91-2301 Old Fort Weaver Road,
Zip 96706–3602; tel. 808/671–8511, (Nonreporting) **A**1 3 10 **S** Sutter Health,
Sacramento, CA
Primary Contact: Claudia Crist, Chief Executive Officer
CFO: Quin Ogawa, Chief Financial Officer
CMO: Steven Chaplin, M.D., Medical Director
CHR: Christina Enoka, Director Human Resources and Risk Management
CNO: Charles St. Louis, Director of Patient Care Services
Web address: www.kahimohala.org
**Control**: Other not–for–profit (including NFP Corporation) **Service**: Psychiatric

> **Staffed Beds:** 76

## HILO—Hawaii County

**HILO HOSPITAL** See Hilo Medical Center

☒ **HILO MEDICAL CENTER (120005)**, 1190 Waianuenue Avenue,
Zip 96720–2089; tel. 808/932–3000, (Nonreporting) **A**1 3 5 10 20 **S** Hawaii
Health Systems Corporation, Honolulu, HI
Primary Contact: Dan Brinkman, R.N., Chief Executive Officer
COO: Dan Brinkman, R.N., Chief Operating Officer
CMO: Ted Peskin, M.D., Acute Care Medical Director
CIO: Money Atwal, Chief Information Officer
CHR: Holly Ka'akimaka, Director Human Resources
CNO: Arthur Sampaga, Chief Nursing Officer
Web address: www.https://www.hilomedicalcenter.org/
**Control**: State, Government, Nonfederal **Service**: General medical and surgical

> **Staffed Beds:** 199

## HONOKAA—Hawaii County

★ **HALE HO'OLA HAMAKUA (121307)**, 45-547 Plumeria Street, Zip 96727–6902;
tel. 808/932–4100, (Nonreporting) **A**10 18 **S** Hawaii Health Systems Corporation,
Honolulu, HI
Primary Contact: Denise Mackey, Administrator
CMO: Bruce Graves, M.D., Chief of Staff
CNO: Gayle Green, Director of Nursing
Web address: www.halehoolahamakua.org
**Control**: State, Government, Nonfederal **Service**: General medical and surgical

> **Staffed Beds:** 77

**HONOKAA HOSPITAL** See Hale Ho'Ola Hamakua

## HONOLULU—Honolulu County

**KAISER FOUNDATION HOSPITAL** See Kaiser Permanente Medical Center

☒ **KAISER PERMANENTE MEDICAL CENTER (120011)**, 3288 Moanalua Road,
Zip 96819–1469; tel. 808/432–0000, (Nonreporting) **A**1 2 3 5 10 **F**3 12 13 15
17 18 19 20 21 22 24 26 29 30 31 32 34 35 36 38 40 41 45 46 47 48 49 50
51 54 55 56 57 58 59 60 61 62 64 65 68 70 72 74 75 76 77 78 79 80 81
82 83 84 85 86 87 88 92 93 94 97 100 101 104 107 108 110 111 115 119
126 129 130 131 134 135 146 148 149 154 **S** Kaiser Foundation Hospitals,
Oakland, CA
Primary Contact: Sam E. Balukoff, Hospital Administrator
CFO: Thomas Risse, Chief Financial Officer and Vice President Business Services
CMO: Keith Ogasawara, M.D., Associate Medical Director and Professional Chief
of Staff
CIO: Donna Scannell, Vice President Information Technology
CHR: Jean Melnikoff, Vice President Human Resources
CNO: Kecia Kelly, R.N., Chief Nurse Executive
Web address: www.kaiserpermanente.org
**Control**: Other not–for–profit (including NFP Corporation) **Service**: General
medical and surgical

> **Staffed Beds:** 295 **Admissions:** 11959 **Census:** 188 **Outpatient**
> **Visits:** 62189 **Births:** 1489 **Total Expense ($000):** 444355 **Payroll Expense**
> **($000):** 154894 **Personnel:** 1631

☐ **KAPIOLANI MEDICAL CENTER FOR WOMEN & CHILDREN (123300)**, 1319
Punahou Street, Zip 96826–1001; tel. 808/983–6000, (Nonreporting) **A**1 2 3 5
10 **S** Hawaii Pacific Health, Honolulu, HI
Primary Contact: Martha Smith, Chief Executive Officer
CFO: David Okabe, Senior Vice President, Chief Financial Officer and Treasurer
CIO: Steve Robertson, Vice President
CHR: Gail Lerch, R.N., Vice President
Web address: www.kapiolani.org
**Control**: Other not–for–profit (including NFP Corporation) **Service**: Children's
general medical and surgical

> **Staffed Beds:** 185

☒ **KUAKINI MEDICAL CENTER (120007)**, 347 North Kuakini Street,
Zip 96817–2381; tel. 808/536–2236, (Nonreporting) **A**1 2 3 5 10 **F**3 15 17 18
20 22 24 26 28 29 31 34 35 40 45 46 49 57 58 59 60 64 68 70 74 75 77 78
79 80 81 82 84 85 86 87 107 108 110 111 115 117 118 119 120 121 129
130 131 132 135 145 146 147 148 149 **P**1
Primary Contact: Gary K. Kajiwara, President and Chief Executive Officer
CFO: Quin Ogawa, Vice President Finance and Chief Financial Officer
CMO: Nobuyuki Miki, M.D., Vice President Medical Services and Chief Medical
Officer
CIO: Gary K Kajiwara, President and Chief Executive Officer
CHR: Ann N. Choy, Manager Human Resources and Payroll
CNO: Virginia Walker, Vice President Nursing Services and Chief Nursing Officer
Web address: www.kuakini.org
**Control**: Other not–for–profit (including NFP Corporation) **Service**: General
medical and surgical

> **Staffed Beds:** 100 **Admissions:** 3479 **Census:** 59 **Outpatient Visits:** 46919
> **Births:** 0 **Total Expense ($000):** 138158 **Payroll Expense ($000):** 51542
> **Personnel:** 797

**LEAHI HOSPITAL (122001)**, 3675 Kilauea Avenue, Zip 96816–2398;
tel. 808/733–8000, (Nonreporting) **A**10 **S** Hawaii Health Systems Corporation,
Honolulu, HI
Primary Contact: Derek Akiyoshi, Chief Executive Officer
CFO: Edward Chu, Chief Financial Officer
CMO: Albert Yazawa, M.D., Regional Medical Director
CHR: Russel Higa, JD, Regional Director Human Resources
CNO: Amy Vasunaga, Chief Nurse Executive
Web address: www.hhsc.org
**Control**: State, Government, Nonfederal **Service**: Acute long–term care hospital

> **Staffed Beds:** 126

**HI**

*Many Facility Codes have changed. Please refer to the AHA Guide Code Chart.*

**QUEEN'S MEDICAL CENTER** See The Queen's Medical Center

⊞ **REHABILITATION HOSPITAL OF THE PACIFIC (123025)**, 226 North Kuakini Street, Zip 96817–2488; tel. 808/531–3511, (Nonreporting) **A**1 10 **F**3 28 29 34 36 44 54 57 58 64 68 74 75 77 79 82 87 90 91 93 94 96 130 131 132 135 143 146 147 148
Primary Contact: Timothy J. Roe, M.D., President and Chief Executive Officer
CFO: Wendy Manuel, Vice President and Chief Financial Officer
CMO: Shari Ann Oshiro, Chief Medical Director
CHR: Lori Yoshioka, Director of Human Resources
CNO: Brenda Hiromoto, Director of Nursing
Web address: www.rehabhospital.org
**Control**: Other not–for–profit (including NFP Corporation) **Service**: Rehabilitation

**Staffed Beds:** 82 **Admissions:** 2038 **Census:** 65 **Outpatient Visits:** 40936 **Births:** 0 **Total Expense ($000):** 52462 **Payroll Expense ($000):** 26835 **Personnel:** 355

☐ **SHRINERS HOSPITALS FOR CHILDREN–HONOLULU (123301)**, 1310 Punahou Street, Zip 96826–1099; tel. 808/941–4466, (Nonreporting) **A**1 3 5 10 **S** Shriners Hospitals for Children, Tampa, FL
Primary Contact: Anton C. Smith, Administrator
CFO: Patricia Miyasawa, CPA, Director Fiscal Service
CMO: Craig Ono, M.D., Chief of Staff
CIO: Gregory A Wolf, Director Information Systems
CHR: Derek Ito, Director Human Resources
CNO: Andrea Kubota, R.N., MSN, Director Patient Care Services and Nurse Executive
Web address: www.shrinershospitalsforchildren.org/honolulu
**Control**: Other not–for–profit (including NFP Corporation) **Service**: Children's orthopedic

**Staffed Beds:** 16

**SHRINERS HOSPS FOR CRPLD CHILD** See Shriners Hospitals for Children-Honolulu

**STRAUB CLINIC & HOSPITAL** See Straub Medical Center

☐ **STRAUB MEDICAL CENTER (120022)**, 888 South King Street, Zip 96813–3097; tel. 808/522–4000, (Nonreporting) **A**1 2 3 5 10 **F**3 9 15 16 18 20 21 22 23 24 26 27 28 29 31 34 35 40 44 45 46 47 48 49 50 54 56 57 58 59 61 63 64 65 68 70 74 75 77 78 79 80 81 84 85 86 87 92 93 97 100 102 104 107 108 110 111 115 119 129 130 131 132 135 144 145 146 147 148 149 154 156 **P**6 8 **S** Hawaii Pacific Health, Honolulu, HI
Primary Contact: Art Gladstone, R.N., Chief Executive Officer
COO: Maureen Flannery, Vice President Clinic Operations
CFO: David Okabe, Executive Vice President, Chief Financial Officer and Treasurer
CMO: Randy Yates, M.D., Chief Medical Officer
CIO: Steve Robertson, Executive Vice President and Chief Information Officer
CHR: Gail Lerch, R.N., Executive Vice President Human Resources
CNO: Patricia Boeckmann, R.N., Chief Operating Officer and Chief Nursing Officer
Web address: www.straubhealth.org
**Control**: Other not–for–profit (including NFP Corporation) **Service**: General medical and surgical

**Staffed Beds:** 113 **Admissions:** 6418 **Census:** 105 **Outpatient Visits:** 891896 **Births:** 0 **Total Expense ($000):** 482778 **Payroll Expense ($000):** 212806 **Personnel:** 1895

⊞ **THE QUEEN'S MEDICAL CENTER (120001)**, 1301 Punchbowl Street, Zip 96813–2499; tel. 808/691–5100, (Includes QUEEN'S MEDICAL CENTER - WEST OAHU, Mailing address: 91-2141 Fort Weaver Road, Ewa Beach, Hawaii, Zip 96706–1993; tel. 808/691–3000; Susan Murray, FACHE, Chief Operating Officer), (Nonreporting) **A**1 2 3 5 10 **F**3 4 5 11 12 13 15 17 18 20 22 24 26 28 29 30 31 34 35 37 38 39 40 43 44 45 46 47 48 49 51 54 55 56 57 58 59 60 61 62 63 64 66 68 70 73 74 75 76 77 78 79 81 82 84 85 86 87 89 93 96 97 98 99 100 101 102 104 105 107 108 110 111 115 117 118 119 120 121 124 126 129 130 131 132 134 135 139 142 143 146 147 148 149 150 151 152 153 154 156 **P**5 **S** Queen's Health Systems, Honolulu, HI
Primary Contact: Jill Hoggard Green, Ph.D., R.N., President and Chief Executive Officer
COO: Jason Chang, Executive Vice President and Chief Operating Officer
CFO: Michel Riccioni, Chief Financial Officer
CMO: Whitney Limm, M.D., Executive Vice President and Chief Physician Executive
CIO: Brian Yoshii, Vice President Information Technology and Chief Information Officer
CHR: Nona Tamanaha, Vice President Human Resources
CNO: Madeline Harris, R.N., Vice President and Chief Nursing Officer
Web address: www.queensmedicalcenter.org
**Control**: Other not–for–profit (including NFP Corporation) **Service**: General medical and surgical

**Staffed Beds:** 637 **Admissions:** 28376 **Census:** 490 **Outpatient Visits:** 585820 **Births:** 1481 **Total Expense ($000):** 1102717 **Payroll Expense ($000):** 431514 **Personnel:** 4337

⊞ **TRIPLER ARMY MEDICAL CENTER**, 1 Jarrett White Road, Zip 96859–5001; tel. 808/433–6661, (Nonreporting) **A**1 2 3 5 **F**1 3 4 5 7 8 11 12 13 14 15 17 18 19 20 22 24 26 27 28 29 30 31 32 33 34 35 36 38 39 40 41 43 45 46 47 48 49 50 52 53 54 55 56 57 58 59 60 61 64 65 67 68 69 70 72 74 75 76 77 78 79 80 81 82 84 85 86 87 88 89 92 93 94 97 98 100 101 102 104 105 106 107 108 110 111 114 115 116 117 118 119 120 121 123 124 126 127 128 129 130 131 132 133 134 135 141 143 144 145 146 147 148 149 153 154 155 156 157 **S** Department of the Army, Office of the Surgeon General, Falls Church, VA
Primary Contact: Colonel Martin Doperak, Commander
COO: MajorElias B. Lozano, Executive Officer
CFO: Lieutenant ColonelChristopher A. Wodarz, Chief, Resource Management Division
CMO: CaptainAndrew L. Findlay, Deputy Commander Clinical Services
CIO: Lieutenant ColonelDonna E Beed, Chief Information Management Division
CHR: ColonelJames N. Davidson, Troop Commander
CNO: ColonelJennifer L. Bedick, Deputy Commander Nursing
Web address: www.tamc.amedd.army.mil
**Control**: Department of Defense, Government, federal **Service**: General medical and surgical

**Staffed Beds:** 143 **Admissions:** 9491 **Census:** 107 **Outpatient Visits:** 998127 **Births:** 2194 **Total Expense ($000):** 493479 **Payroll Expense ($000):** 195643 **Personnel:** 4121

### KAHUKU—Honolulu County

**KAHUKU HOSPITAL** See Kahuku Medical Center

⊞ **KAHUKU MEDICAL CENTER (121304)**, 56-117 Pualalea Street, Zip 96731–2052; tel. 808/293–9221, (Nonreporting) **A**1 10 18
Primary Contact: Alan MacPhee, Chief Executive Officer
COO: Jerome Flores, Chief Financial Officer and Chief Operating Officer
CFO: Jerome Flores, Chief Financial Officer and Chief Operating Officer
CMO: P Douglas Nielson, M.D., Chief of Staff
Web address: www.kahuku.hhsc.org/
**Control**: Other not–for–profit (including NFP Corporation) **Service**: General medical and surgical

**Staffed Beds:** 21

### KAHULUI—Maui County

**HALE MAKUA** See Hale Makua Health Services

### KAILUA—Honolulu County

⊞ **ADVENTIST HEALTH CASTLE (120006)**, 640 Ulukahiki Street, Zip 96734–4454; tel. 808/263–5500, (Nonreporting) **A**1 3 10 **F**3 8 12 13 15 18 20 22 24 26 29 30 31 32 34 35 37 39 40 43 45 46 49 50 51 54 56 57 59 64 68 70 73 74 75 76 78 79 81 84 85 86 91 92 93 94 97 98 102 107 108 110 111 114 119 120 126 127 129 130 132 135 146 147 148 149 154 156 **P**6 8 **S** Adventist Health, Roseville, CA
Primary Contact: Kathryn A. Raethel, R.N., M.P.H., President and Chief Executive Officer
COO: Travis Clegg, Vice President, Operations
CFO: Heidar Thordarson, Chief Financial Officer
CMO: Alan Cheung, M.D., Vice President Medical Affairs
CHR: Todd Reese, Director Human Performance
CNO: Laura R. Westphal, R.N., Vice President Patient Care Services
Web address: www.castlemed.org
**Control**: Church operated, Nongovernment, not–for–profit **Service**: General medical and surgical

**Staffed Beds:** 150 **Admissions:** 7084 **Census:** 77 **Outpatient Visits:** 102871 **Births:** 973 **Total Expense ($000):** 171216 **Payroll Expense ($000):** 57107 **Personnel:** 871

**CASTLE MEDICAL CENTER** See Adventist Health Castle

**HI**

---

**Hospital, Medicare Provider Number, Address, Telephone, Approval, Facility, and Physician Codes, Health Care System**

★ American Hospital Association (AHA) membership   ○ Healthcare Facilities Accreditation Program   ⇑ Center for Improvement in Healthcare Quality Accreditation
☐ The Joint Commission accreditation   ◇ DNV Healthcare Inc. accreditation   △ Commission on Accreditation of Rehabilitation Facilities (CARF) accreditation

## KAMUELA—Hawaii County

**NORTH HAWAII COMMUNITY HOSPITAL** See Queen's North Hawaii Community Hospital

⊞ **QUEEN'S NORTH HAWAII COMMUNITY HOSPITAL (120028)**, 67-1125 Mamalahoa Highway, Zip 96743–8496; tel. 808/885–4444, (Nonreporting) **A**1 3 10 20 **F**3 8 13 15 18 26 29 30 31 34 35 36 40 41 43 44 45 46 49 50 53 54 57 59 62 64 68 70 75 76 77 78 79 81 85 86 87 93 97 102 107 108 110 111 115 119 130 131 132 146 147 148 154 156 157 **S** Queen's Health Systems, Honolulu, HI
Primary Contact: Cynthia Kamikawa, R.N., MSN, President
CFO: Michel Riccioni, Chief Financial Officer
CMO: Gary Goldberg, M.D., Chief Medical Officer
CNO: Miquel Noelani Simms, R.N., Chief Nursing Officer
Web address: www.nhch.com
**Control**: Other not–for–profit (including NFP Corporation) **Service**: General medical and surgical

**Staffed Beds**: 35 **Admissions**: 1697 **Census**: 15 **Outpatient Visits**: 87209 **Births**: 444 **Total Expense ($000)**: 72221 **Payroll Expense ($000)**: 27097 **Personnel**: 295

## KANEOHE—Honolulu County

☐ **HAWAII STATE HOSPITAL**, 45-710 Keaahala Road, Zip 96744–3597; tel. 808/247–2191, (Nonreporting) **A**1 3 5
Primary Contact: William J. May, Administrator
COO: Anthony Fraiola, Associate Administrator Administrative and Support Services
CFO: Stephen Teeter, Business Manager
CMO: James Westphal, M.D., AMHD Medical Director
CIO: John Jansen, Management Information Specialist
CHR: Karen Hara, Personnel Management Specialist
CNO: Lani Tsuneishi, Nursing Services Manager
Web address: www.hawaii.gov/health/
**Control**: State, Government, Nonfederal **Service**: Psychiatric

**Staffed Beds**: 178

## KAPAA—Kauai County

★ **SAMUEL MAHELONA MEMORIAL HOSPITAL (121306)**, 4800 Kawaihau Road, Zip 96746–1971; tel. 808/822–4961, (Nonreporting) **A**10 18 **S** Hawaii Health Systems Corporation, Honolulu, HI
Primary Contact: Lance Segawa, Chief Executive Officer
CFO: Michael Perel, Regional Chief Financial Officer
CMO: Gerald Tomory, M.D., Regional Medical Director
CIO: Sandra McMaster, Regional Chief Information Officer
CHR: Lani Aranio, Regional Director Human Resources
Web address: www.smmh.hhsc.org
**Control**: State, Government, Nonfederal **Service**: General medical and surgical

**Staffed Beds**: 80

## KAUNAKAKAI—Maui County

⊞ **MOLOKAI GENERAL HOSPITAL (121303)**, 280 Home Olu Place, Zip 96748–0408, Mailing Address: P.O. Box 408, Zip 96748–0408; tel. 808/553–5331, (Nonreporting) **A**1 10 18 **S** Queen's Health Systems, Honolulu, HI
Primary Contact: Janice Kalanihuia, President
CFO: Zessica L Apiki, Accountant
CMO: William Thomas, M.D., JrMedical Director Clinical and Internal Affairs
CIO: Sampson Wescoatt, Manager Information Technology
CHR: Alicia Teves, Coordinator Human Resources
Web address: www.queens.org
**Control**: Other not–for–profit (including NFP Corporation) **Service**: General medical and surgical

**Staffed Beds**: 15

## KEALAKEKUA—Hawaii County

⊞ **KONA COMMUNITY HOSPITAL (120019)**, 79-1019 Haukapila Street, Zip 96750–7920; tel. 808/322–9311, (Nonreporting) **A**1 10 20 **S** Hawaii Health Systems Corporation, Honolulu, HI
Primary Contact: Jay E. Kreuzer, FACHE, Chief Executive Officer
CFO: Dean Herzog, Chief Financial Officer
CMO: Richard McDowell, M.D., Medical Director
CHR: Kathryn Salomon, Director Human Resources
CNO: Patricia Kalua, Chief Nurse Executive
Web address: www.kch.hhsc.org
**Control**: Other not–for–profit (including NFP Corporation) **Service**: General medical and surgical

**Staffed Beds**: 94

**KONA HOSPITAL** See Kona Community Hospital

## KOHALA—Hawaii County

★ **KOHALA HOSPITAL (121302)**, 54-383 Hospital Road, Zip 96755, Mailing Address: P.O. Box 10, Kapaau, Zip 96755–0010; tel. 808/889–6211, (Nonreporting) **A**10 18 **S** Hawaii Health Systems Corporation, Honolulu, HI
Primary Contact: Jay E. Kreuzer, FACHE, Chief Executive Officer
CMO: Silvia Sonnenschein, M.D., Chief of Staff
Web address: www.koh.hhsc.org
**Control**: State, Government, Nonfederal **Service**: General medical and surgical

**Staffed Beds**: 28

## KULA—Maui County

★ **KULA HOSPITAL (121308)**, 100 Keokea Place, Zip 96790–7450; tel. 808/878–1221, (Nonreporting) **A**10 18 **S** Kaiser Foundation Hospitals, Oakland, CA
Primary Contact: Kerry Pitcher, Chief Executive Officer
CFO: Nerissa Garrity, Chief Financial Officer
CMO: Nicole Apoliona, M.D., Medical Director
Web address: www.https://www.mauihealthsystem.org/kula-hospital/
**Control**: Other not–for–profit (including NFP Corporation) **Service**: General medical and surgical

**Staffed Beds**: 6

## LANAI CITY—Maui County

★ **LANAI COMMUNITY HOSPITAL (121305)**, 628 Seventh Street, Zip 96763–0650, Mailing Address: P.O. Box 630650, Zip 96763–0650; tel. 808/565–8450, (Nonreporting) **A**10 18 **S** Kaiser Foundation Hospitals, Oakland, CA
Primary Contact: Kerry Pitcher, Administrator
Web address: www.https://www.mauihealthsystem.org/lanai-hospital/
**Control**: Other not–for–profit (including NFP Corporation) **Service**: General medical and surgical

**Staffed Beds**: 24

## LIHUE—Kauai County

☐ **WILCOX MEDICAL CENTER (120014)**, 3-3420 Kuhio Highway, Zip 96766–1099; tel. 808/245–1100, (Nonreporting) **A**1 2 10 20 **F**3 13 15 28 29 31 32 34 35 37 40 41 43 44 45 49 50 53 56 57 58 59 61 63 64 65 70 74 75 76 77 78 79 81 82 84 85 86 87 93 107 108 110 111 114 115 119 126 130 131 132 133 135 145 146 147 148 149 154 156 **S** Hawaii Pacific Health, Honolulu, HI
Primary Contact: Jen Chahanovich, President and Chief Executive Officer
CFO: David Okabe, Executive Vice President, Chief Financial Officer and Treasurer
CMO: Craig Netzer, M.D., President Medical Staff
CIO: Steve Robertson, Executive Vice President Revenue Cycle Management and Chief Information Officer
CNO: Mary Ann England, Chief Nurse Executive
Web address: www.wilcoxhealth.org
**Control**: Other not–for–profit (including NFP Corporation) **Service**: General medical and surgical

**Staffed Beds**: 65 **Admissions**: 3273 **Census**: 43 **Outpatient Visits**: 100187 **Births**: 460 **Total Expense ($000)**: 124751 **Payroll Expense ($000)**: 40053 **Personnel**: 485

**WILCOX MEMORIAL HOSPITAL** See Wilcox Medical Center

## PAHALA—Hawaii County

**KAU HOSPITAL** See Ka'U Hospital

★ **KA'U HOSPITAL (121301)**, 1 Kamani Street, Zip 96777, Mailing Address: P.O. Box 40, Zip 96777–0040; tel. 808/932–4200, (Nonreporting) **A**10 18 **S** Hawaii Health Systems Corporation, Honolulu, HI
Primary Contact: Merilyn Harris, Administrator
CMO: Clifford Field, M.D., Medical Director
Web address: www.hhsc.org
**Control**: State, Government, Nonfederal **Service**: General medical and surgical

**Staffed Beds**: 21

**HI**

*Many Facility Codes have changed. Please refer to the AHA Guide Code Chart.* © 2021 AHA Guide

## WAHIAWA—Honolulu County

✠ **WAHIAWA GENERAL HOSPITAL (120004)**, 128 Lehua Street, Zip 96786–2036;
tel. 808/621–8411, (Nonreporting) **A**1 3 5 10
Primary Contact: Brian Cunningham, Chief Executive Officer
CMO: Manuel Abundo, M.D., Chief of Staff
CIO: Jason Fujinaka, Manager Information System
CHR: Liflor Barrera, Manager Human Resources
CNO: Tammy Kohrer, Director of Nursing-Acute
Web address: www.wahiawageneral.org
**Control**: Other not–for–profit (including NFP Corporation) **Service**: General
medical and surgical

**Staffed Beds:** 160

## WAILUKU—Maui County

**MAUI MEDICAL MEMORIAL CENTER** See Maui Memorial Medical Center

✠ **MAUI MEMORIAL MEDICAL CENTER (120002)**, 221 Mahalani Street,
Zip 96793–2581; tel. 808/244–9056, (Nonreporting) **A**1 10 20 **F**3 8 11 12 15
18 20 22 24 26 28 29 30 31 34 35 36 39 40 43 46 47 48 49 50 51 53 57 59
60 64 68 70 75 76 77 78 79 81 84 85 87 89 93 98 102 104 105 107 108 110
111 114 115 119 124 130 132 135 141 142 146 148 149 **S** Kaiser Foundation
Hospitals, Oakland, CA
Primary Contact: Michael A. Rembis, FACHE, Chief Executive Officer
COO: Debbie Walsh, MSN, Chief Operating Officer
CIO: Dana Mendoza, Chief Information Officer
Web address: www.https://www.mauihealthsystem.org/maui-memorial/
**Control**: Other not–for–profit (including NFP Corporation) **Service**: General
medical and surgical

**Staffed Beds:** 214 **Admissions:** 13594 **Census:** 164 **Outpatient
Visits:** 81315 **Births:** 1540 **Total Expense ($000):** 311344 **Payroll Expense
($000):** 113142 **Personnel:** 1290

## WAIMEA—Kauai County

✠ **KAUAI VETERANS MEMORIAL HOSPITAL (121300)**, 4643 Waimea
Canyon Road, Zip 96796, Mailing Address: P.O. Box 337, Zip 96796–0337;
tel. 808/338–9431, (Nonreporting) **A**1 10 18 **S** Hawaii Health Systems
Corporation, Honolulu, HI
Primary Contact: Lance Segawa, Chief Executive Officer
CFO: Michael Perel, Regional Chief Financial Officer
CMO: Gerald Tomory, M.D., Regional Medical Director
CIO: Sandra McMaster, Regional Chief Information Officer
CHR: Solette Perry, Regional Director Human Resources
Web address: www.kvmh.hhsc.org
**Control**: State, Government, Nonfederal **Service**: General medical and surgical

**Staffed Beds:** 45

# IDAHO

## AMERICAN FALLS—Power County

⇑ **HARMS MEMORIAL HOSPITAL DISTRICT** See Power County Hospital District

★ ⇑ **POWER COUNTY HOSPITAL DISTRICT (131304)**, 510 Roosevelt Street, Zip 83211–1362, Mailing Address: P.O. Box 420, Zip 83211–0420; tel. 208/226–3200, (Nonreporting) **A**10 18 21
Primary Contact: Dallas Clinger, Administrator
COO: Rock Roy, Professional Services Director
CFO: Jeremy Claunch, Chief Financial Officer
CMO: Spencer Garrett Seibold, M.D., Chief of Medical Staff
CIO: Mindy Earl, Health Information Manager
CHR: Kendra Sweat, Director Human Resources
CNO: June Mortenson, R.N., Director of Nursing
Web address: www.pchd.net
**Control**: Hospital district or authority, Government, Nonfederal **Service**: General medical and surgical

**Staffed Beds:** 10

## ARCO—Butte County

⇑ **LOST RIVERS DISTRICT HOSPITAL** See Lost Rivers Medical Center

⇑ **LOST RIVERS MEDICAL CENTER (131324)**, 551 Highland Drive, Zip 83213–9771, Mailing Address: P.O. Box 145, Zip 83213–0145; tel. 208/527–8206, (Nonreporting) **A**5 10 18 21
Primary Contact: Brad Huerta, Chief Executive Officer and Administrator
CFO: Jon Smith, Chief Financial Officer
CMO: Jeffrey Haskell, M.D., Chief Medical Staff
CHR: Tina Akins, Director Human Resources
CNO: Geri Cammack, R.N., Director of Nursing
Web address: www.lostriversmedical.com
**Control**: Hospital district or authority, Government, Nonfederal **Service**: General medical and surgical

**Staffed Beds:** 43

## BLACKFOOT—Bingham County

⊠ **BINGHAM MEMORIAL HOSPITAL (131325)**, 98 Poplar Street, Zip 83221–1799; tel. 208/785–4100, (Nonreporting) **A**1 3 5 10 18
Primary Contact: Jake Erickson, Chief Executive Officer
CFO: Randy Nightengale, Chief Financial Officer
CIO: Robert Weis, Director Information Systems
CHR: Tara Preston, Director Human Resources
CNO: Carolyn Hansen, Chief Nursing Officer
Web address: www.binghammemorial.org
**Control**: Other not–for–profit (including NFP Corporation) **Service**: General medical and surgical

**Staffed Beds:** 85

⊠ **IDAHO DOCTOR'S HOSPITAL (130067)**, 350 North Meridian Street, Zip 83221–1625; tel. 208/782–0300, (Nonreporting) **A**1 10
Primary Contact: D. Jeffery. Daniels, Chief Executive Officer
COO: Dan Cochran, Chief Operating Officer
CIO: Robert Weis, Director Information Technology
CHR: Tara Preston, Director Human Resources
CNO: Nathan Buck, R.N., Nursing Manager
Web address: www.binghammemorial.org
**Control**: Corporation, Investor–owned (for–profit) **Service**: Obstetrics and gynecology

**Staffed Beds:** 8

☐ **STATE HOSPITAL SOUTH (134010)**, 700 East Alice Street, Zip 83221–4925, Mailing Address: P.O. Box 400, Zip 83221–0400; tel. 208/785–1200, (Nonreporting) **A**1 5 10
Primary Contact: James Price, Hospital Administrator
COO: Greg Horton, Director Support Services
CFO: Angela Loosli, Assistant Administrator, Operations
CMO: Kelly Palmer, D.O., Medical Director
CIO: Julie Sutton, Director Performance Improvement
CHR: Sheryl Donnelly, Human Resources Specialist
CNO: Randy Walker, Director Nursing Services
Web address: www.healthandwelfare.idaho.gov
**Control**: State, Government, Nonfederal **Service**: Psychiatric

**Staffed Beds:** 135

## BOISE-Ada County

**BHC INTERMOUNTAIN HOSPITAL** See Intermountain Hospital

**BOISE BEHAVIORAL HEALTH HOSPITAL** See Safe Haven Hospital of Treasure Valley

⊠ **BOISE VETERANS AFFAIRS MEDICAL CENTER**, 500 West Fort Street, Zip 83702–4598; tel. 208/422–1000, (Total facility includes 32 beds in nursing home–type unit) (Nonreporting) **A**1 3 5 **F**1 2 3 4 5 8 9 10 12 29 30 31 34 35 38 39 40 43 45 46 47 50 53 54 56 57 58 59 60 61 62 63 64 65 66 67 68 70 71 74 75 77 78 79 81 82 83 84 85 86 87 90 91 92 93 94 96 97 98 100 101 102 104 107 108 111 112 119 120 121 122 123 124 127 128 129 130 132 133 135 143 144 145 146 147 148 149 150 152 154 156 **S** Department of Veterans Affairs, Washington, DC
Primary Contact: David P. Wood, FACHE, Director
CFO: Ron Blanton, Chief Fiscal Services
CMO: Paul Lambert, M.D., Chief of Staff
CHR: Randy Turner, Chief Human Resource Management Services
Web address: www.boise.va.gov/
**Control**: Veterans Affairs, Government, federal **Service**: General medical and surgical

**Staffed Beds:** 92 **Admissions:** 3256 **Census:** 72 **Outpatient Visits:** 420579 **Births:** 0 **Total Expense ($000):** 289000 **Payroll Expense ($000):** 175000 **Personnel:** 1449

**COMPLEX CARE HOSPITAL OF IDAHO** See Vibra Hospital of Boise

**ELKS REHAB HOSPITAL** See St. Luke's Rehabilitation Hospital

**HEALTHSOUTH TREASURE VLY HOSP** See Treasure Valley Hospital

☐ **INTERMOUNTAIN HOSPITAL (134002)**, 303 North Allumbaugh Street, Zip 83704–9208; tel. 208/377–8400, (Nonreporting) **A**1 10 **S** Universal Health Services, Inc., King of Prussia, PA
Primary Contact: Jeffrey F. Morrell, Chief Executive Officer
CFO: JeDonne Hines, Chief Financial Officer
CMO: Charles Novak, M.D., Chief Medical Officer
CHR: Nancy Nelson, Director Human Resources
CNO: Jennifer Beaulieu, Director of Nursing
Web address: www.intermountainhospital.com
**Control**: Corporation, Investor–owned (for–profit) **Service**: Psychiatric

**Staffed Beds:** 140

**SAFE HAVEN HOSPITAL OF TREASURE VALLEY (134009)**, 8050 Northview Street, Zip 83704–7126; tel. 208/327–0504, (Nonreporting) **A**10 **S** Safe Haven Health Care, Pocatello, ID
Primary Contact: Scott Proctor, Chief Executive Officer
CMO: David Kent, M.D., Chief Medical Officer
CIO: Debra Alexander, Chief Information Officer
CHR: Kathy Cady, Coordinator Human Resources, Accounts Payable and Payroll
Web address: www.boisepsychhospital.com
**Control**: Corporation, Investor–owned (for–profit) **Service**: Psychiatric

**Staffed Beds:** 22

⊠ △ **SAINT ALPHONSUS REGIONAL MEDICAL CENTER (130007)**, 1055 N Curtis Rd, Zip 83706–1309, Mailing Address: 1055 North Curtis Road, Zip 83706–1309; tel. 208/367–2121, (Nonreporting) **A**1 2 3 5 7 10 **F**3 11 12 13 15 17 18 20 22 24 26 28 29 30 31 32 33 34 35 36 37 38 39 40 42 43 44 45 49 50 54 55 56 57 58 59 64 65 66 68 70 71 72 74 75 76 77 78 79 81 82 84 85 86 87 89 90 91 93 94 96 97 98 99 100 102 103 104 107 108 110 111 114 115 118 119 121 124 126 129 130 131 132 134 135 144 146 147 148 149 150 154 156 **S** Trinity Health, Livonia, MI
Primary Contact: David M. McFadyen, FACHE, President
CFO: Kenneth Fry, Chief Financial Officer
CMO: Steve Brown, M.D., Chief Quality Officer
CIO: Dwight Pond, TIS Boise
CHR: Teresa Sargent, Vice President Human Resources
CNO: Sherry Parks, R.N., MS, Chief Nursing Officer
Web address: www.saintalphonsus.org
**Control**: Other not–for–profit (including NFP Corporation) **Service**: General medical and surgical

**Staffed Beds:** 392 **Admissions:** 18356 **Census:** 244 **Outpatient Visits:** 1192319 **Births:** 1235 **Total Expense ($000):** 655823 **Payroll Expense ($000):** 273232 **Personnel:** 3695

ID

*Many Facility Codes have changed. Please refer to the AHA Guide Code Chart.*

☐ **SAINT ALPHONSUS REGIONAL REHABILITATION HOSPITAL—AN AFFILIATE OF ENCOMPASS HEALTH (133028)**, 711 North Curtis Road, Zip 83706–1445; tel. 208/605–3000, (Nonreporting) **A**1 **S** Encompass Health Corporation, Birmingham, AL
Primary Contact: Renee Hinson, Chief Executive Officer
Web address: www.https://www.encompasshealth.com/locations/boiserehab
**Control:** Corporation, Investor–owned (for–profit) **Service:** Rehabilitation

**Staffed Beds:** 40

☒ **ST. LUKE'S REGIONAL MEDICAL CENTER (130006)**, 190 East Bannock Street, Zip 83712–6241; tel. 208/381–2222, (Includes ST. LUKE'S CHILDREN'S HOSPITAL, Mailing address: 190 East Bannock Street, Boise, Idaho, Zip 83712–6241; tel. 208/381–2222; ST. LUKE'S MERIDIAN MEDICAL CENTER, Mailing address: 520 South Eagle Road, Meridian, Idaho, Zip 83642, 520 S Eagle Road, Zip 83642–6351, tel. 208/706–5000; Dennis Mesaros, Administrator), (Nonreporting) **A**1 2 3 5 10 **F**3 7 11 12 13 15 17 18 19 20 21 22 23 24 25 26 27 28 29 30 31 32 34 35 36 37 40 41 46 47 48 49 50 51 54 55 56 57 58 59 60 62 63 64 65 68 70 71 72 74 75 76 77 78 79 81 82 84 86 87 88 89 90 93 97 100 105 107 108 110 111 114 115 116 117 118 119 120 121 124 126 127 128 129 130 131 132 134 135 136 144 146 147 148 149 154 155 **P**5 **S** St. Luke's Health System, Boise, ID
Primary Contact: John Allen, Interim Chief Executive Officer, Vice President, Population Health
CFO: Jeff Taylor, Vice President Finance
CMO: Jim Souza, Chief Medical Officer
CIO: Reid Stephan, Chief Information Officer
CHR: Phillip Johnson, Vice President, Chief Human Resources Officer
CNO: Barbara Hocking, Chief Nursing Officer
Web address: www.https://www.stlukesonline.org/communities-and-locations/facilities/hospitals-and-medical-centers/st-lukes-boise-medical-center
**Control:** Other not–for–profit (including NFP Corporation) **Service:** General medical and surgical

**Staffed Beds:** 604 **Admissions:** 30066 **Census:** 351 **Outpatient Visits:** 1666352 **Births:** 5029 **Total Expense ($000):** 733832 **Payroll Expense ($000):** 252028 **Personnel:** 4855

★ △ **ST. LUKE'S REHABILITATION HOSPITAL (133025)**, 600 North Robbins Road, Zip 83702–4565, Mailing Address: P.O. Box 1100, Zip 83701–1100; tel. 208/489–4444, (Nonreporting) **A**5 7 10 **S** St. Luke's Health System, Boise, ID
Primary Contact: Nolan Hoffer, Senior Director
COO: Melissa Honsinger, Chief Operating Officer
CFO: Doug Lewis, Chief Financial Officer
CMO: Lee Kornfield, M.D., Medical Director
CIO: Scott Pyrah, Director Information Systems
CHR: Jim Atkins, Director Employee Services
Web address: www.idahoelksrehab.org
**Control:** Other not–for–profit (including NFP Corporation) **Service:** Rehabilitation

**Staffed Beds:** 30

☐ **TREASURE VALLEY HOSPITAL (130063)**, 8800 West Emerald Street, Zip 83704–8205; tel. 208/373–5000, (Nonreporting) **A**1 3 10
Primary Contact: Nick Genna, Administrator
CMO: Jeffrey Hessing, M.D., Medical Director
CHR: Kathleen Phelps, Director Human Resources
Web address: www.treasurevalleyhospital.com
**Control:** Corporation, Investor–owned (for–profit) **Service:** General medical and surgical

**Staffed Beds:** 9

**VETERANS AFFAIRS MEDICAL CENTER** See Boise Veterans Affairs Medical Center

☒ **VIBRA HOSPITAL OF BOISE (132002)**, 6651 West Franklin Road, Zip 83709–0914; tel. 877/801–2244, (Nonreporting) **A**1 3 10 **S** Vibra Healthcare, Mechanicsburg, PA
Primary Contact: Ryan Zumalt, Chief Executive Officer
Web address: www.vhboise.com
**Control:** Corporation, Investor–owned (for–profit) **Service:** Acute long–term care hospital

**Staffed Beds:** 60

**BONNERS FERRY—Boundary County**

★ ⇑ **BOUNDARY COMMUNITY HOSPITAL (131301)**, 6640 Kaniksu Street, Zip 83805–7532; tel. 208/267–3141, (Nonreporting) **A**10 18 21
Primary Contact: Preston Becker, Chief Executive Officer
CFO: Holly McDonald, Controller
CMO: Chuck Newhouse, M.D., Chief of Staff
CHR: Ann Coughlin, Director Human Resources
CNO: Tari Yourzek, Chief Nursing Officer
Web address: www.boundarycommunityhospital.org
**Control:** County, Government, Nonfederal **Service:** General medical and surgical

**Staffed Beds:** 48

⇑ **COMMUNITY HOSPITAL** See Boundary Community Hospital

**BURLEY—Cassia County**

☒ **CASSIA REGIONAL HOSPITAL (131326)**, 1501 Hiland Avenue, Zip 83318–2688; tel. 208/678–4444, (Nonreporting) **A**1 10 18 **F**3 7 11 13 15 18 29 30 31 34 35 37 38 39 40 44 50 57 59 63 64 65 68 70 75 76 77 78 79 81 85 86 87 89 92 93 96 97 100 102 107 108 110 111 115 118 119 129 130 131 132 135 141 143 146 147 148 149 154 156 157 **P**6 **S** Intermountain Healthcare, Inc., Salt Lake City, UT
Primary Contact: Ben Smalley, Administrator
CFO: Justin Wiser, Chief Financial Officer
CMO: Bernard Boehmer, M.D., Medical Director
CIO: Jared Gallup, Chief Information Officer
CHR: Eric Gochnour, Chief Human Resource Officer
CNO: Michele Pond-Bell, R.N., Nurse Administrator
Web address: www.cassiaregional.org
**Control:** Other not–for–profit (including NFP Corporation) **Service:** General medical and surgical

**Staffed Beds:** 25 **Admissions:** 1694 **Census:** 11 **Outpatient Visits:** 55238 **Births:** 585 **Total Expense ($000):** 51552 **Payroll Expense ($000):** 20745 **Personnel:** 289

**CASSIA REGIONAL MEDICAL CENTER** See Cassia Regional Hospital

**CALDWELL—Canyon County**

**WEST VALLEY MED CTR** See West Valley Medical Center

☒ **WEST VALLEY MEDICAL CENTER (130014)**, 1717 Arlington, Zip 83605–4802; tel. 208/459–4641, (Nonreporting) **A**1 3 5 10 **S** HCA Healthcare, Nashville, TN
Primary Contact: Elizabeth Hunsicker, Chief Executive Officer
COO: Jennifer Opsut, Interim Chief Operating Officer
CFO: Kate Fowler, Chief Financial Officer
CMO: Richard Augustus, M.D., Chief Medical Officer
CIO: Jason Martinez, Director Information Technology
CHR: Senta Cornelius, Director Human Resources
CNO: Edith E Irving, R.N., MS, FACHE, Chief Nursing Officer
Web address: www.westvalleymedctr.com
**Control:** Corporation, Investor–owned (for–profit) **Service:** General medical and surgical

**Staffed Beds:** 150

**CASCADE—Valley County**

**CASCADE MEDICAL CENTER (131308)**, 402 Lake Cascade Pkwy, Zip 83611–7702, Mailing Address: P.O. Box 1330, Zip 83611–1330; tel. 208/382–4242, (Nonreporting) **A**5 10 18 **F**11 28 29 32 34 35 40 41 53 57 59 64 65 66 87 89 93 94 97 102 107 119 127 133 154
Primary Contact: Tom Reinhardt, Chief Executive Officer
CFO: Penny Lancaster, Controller
CMO: Mikael Bedell, M.D., Medical Director
CNO: Teri Coombs, R.N., Director Nursing Services
Web address: www.cascademedicalcenter.net
**Control:** Hospital district or authority, Government, Nonfederal **Service:** General medical and surgical

**Staffed Beds:** 8 **Admissions:** 38 **Census:** 1 **Outpatient Visits:** 10467 **Births:** 0

**VALLEY COUNTY HOSPITAL** See Cascade Medical Center

**ID**

---

**Hospital, Medicare Provider Number, Address, Telephone, Approval, Facility, and Physician Codes, Health Care System**

★ American Hospital Association (AHA) membership
☐ The Joint Commission accreditation
○ Healthcare Facilities Accreditation Program
◇ DNV Healthcare Inc. accreditation
⇑ Center for Improvement in Healthcare Quality Accreditation
△ Commission on Accreditation of Rehabilitation Facilities (CARF) accreditation

© 2021 AHA Guide          *Many Facility Codes have changed. Please refer to the AHA Guide Code Chart.*          Hospitals **A189**

## COEUR D'ALENE—Kootenai County

★ ⛨ **KOOTENAI HEALTH (130049)**, 2003 Kootenai Health Way, Zip 83814–2677; tel. 208/625–4000, (Includes KOOTENAI BEHAVIORAL HEALTH, Mailing address: 2301 North Ironwood Place, Coeur D'Alene, Idaho, Zip 83814–2650; tel. 208/625–4800), (Nonreporting) **A**2 3 5 10 19 21 **F**3 4 5 9 11 13 14 15 17 18 20 22 24 26 28 29 30 31 32 34 35 37 40 41 43 44 45 46 47 48 49 50 51 53 54 56 57 58 59 60 63 64 65 68 70 71 72 74 75 76 78 79 81 82 83 84 85 86 87 89 91 93 95 96 97 98 99 100 101 102 104 107 108 110 111 114 115 116 117 119 121 124 126 127 129 130 131 132 135 143 145 146 148 149 154 156 **P**6
Primary Contact: Jon Ness, Chief Executive Officer
COO: Jeremy Evans, Vice President Operations
CFO: Kimberly Webb, Chief Financial Officer
CMO: Walter Fairfax, M.D., Chief Medical Officer
CHR: Daniel Klocko, Vice President Human Resources
CNO: Joan M. Simon, R.N., FACHE, Chief Nursing Officer
Web address: www.kh.org
**Control**: Hospital district or authority, Government, Nonfederal **Service**: General medical and surgical

**Staffed Beds: 329 Admissions: 16134 Census: 189 Outpatient Visits: 608511 Births: 1941 Total Expense ($000): 583707 Payroll Expense ($000): 258449 Personnel: 3233**

⛨ **KOOTENAI MEDICAL CENTER** See Kootenai Health

**NORTH IDAHO BEHAVIORAL HEALTH, DIVISION OF KOOTENAI MEDICAL CENTER** See Kootenai Behavioral Health

## COTTONWOOD—Idaho County

★ **ST. MARY'S HOSPITAL (131321)**, 701 Lewiston Street, Zip 83522–9750, Mailing Address: P.O. Box 137, Zip 83522–0137; tel. 208/962–3251, (Nonreporting) **A**5 10 18 **S** Essentia Health, Duluth, MN
Primary Contact: Lenne Bonner, President
CFO: Jyl Ruland, Chief Financial Officer
CHR: Debbie Schumacher, Chief Human Resource Officer
Web address: www.smh-cvhc.org/getpage.php?name=index
**Control**: Other not-for-profit (including NFP Corporation) **Service**: General medical and surgical

**Staffed Beds: 28**

## DRIGGS—Teton County

★ **TETON VALLEY HEALTH CARE (131313)**, 120 E Howard Avenue, Zip 83422–5112, Mailing Address: 120 East Howard Avenue, Zip 83422–5112; tel. 208/354–2383, (Nonreporting) **A**10 18 **F**3 15 18 29 30 31 34 35 38 39 40 41 43 45 50 55 56 57 59 64 65 68 74 75 77 78 79 81 82 84 85 87 93 97 100 102 104 107 110 111 114 119 127 131 133 135 146 147 148 154
Primary Contact: Keith Gnagey, Chief Executive Officer
CFO: Wesley D White, Chief Financial Officer
CMO: Nathan Levanger, M.D., Chief of Staff
CHR: Dory Harris, Director Human Resource
CNO: Angela Booker, Director of Nursing Services
Web address: www.tvhcare.org
**Control**: Other not-for-profit (including NFP Corporation) **Service**: General medical and surgical

**Staffed Beds: 13 Admissions: 174 Census: 2 Outpatient Visits: 37130 Births: 0 Total Expense ($000): 19256 Payroll Expense ($000): 9131**

**TETON VALLEY HOSPITAL AND SURGICENTER** See Teton Valley Health Care

## EMMETT—Gem County

⛨ **VALOR HEALTH (131318)**, 1202 East Locust Street, Zip 83617–2715; tel. 208/365–3561, (Nonreporting) **A**10 18 21
Primary Contact: Brad Turpen, FACHE, Chief Executive Officer
CHR: Susan Vahlberg, Director Employee and Community Relations
Web address: www.wkmh.org
**Control**: County, Government, Nonfederal **Service**: General medical and surgical

**Staffed Beds: 12**

⛨ **WALTER KNOX MEMORIAL HOSPITAL** See Valor Health

## GOODING—Gooding County

⛨ **GOODING COUNTY MEMORIAL HOSPITAL** See North Canyon Medical Center

★ ⛨ **NORTH CANYON MEDICAL CENTER (131302)**, 267 North Canyon Drive, Zip 83330–5500; tel. 208/934–4433, (Nonreporting) **A**5 10 18 21 **F**3 5 11 12 15 29 32 33 34 35 36 37 40 41 44 45 50 54 56 57 59 63 64 65 68 75 77 79 81 85 87 90 93 97 107 110 111 114 119 126 127 129 130 131 133 135 143 144 148 154 156 **P**6
Primary Contact: J'Dee Adams, Chief Executive Officer
CFO: Sara DeMoe, Chief Financial Officer
CMO: Jennifer Olsen, M.D., Chief of Staff
CIO: Margie McLeod, Director Information Technology
CHR: Sara Otto, Chief Compliance Officer
CNO: Lisa Mangum, Chief Nursing Officer
Web address: www.ncm-c.org
**Control**: Other not-for-profit (including NFP Corporation) **Service**: General medical and surgical

**Staffed Beds: 18 Admissions: 603 Census: 7 Outpatient Visits: 35454 Total Expense ($000): 31793 Payroll Expense ($000): 13082 Personnel: 214**

## GRANGEVILLE—Idaho County

**SYRINGA GENERAL HOSPITAL** See Syringa Hospital and Clinics

★ **SYRINGA HOSPITAL AND CLINICS (131315)**, 607 West Main Street, Zip 83530–1396; tel. 208/983–1700, (Nonreporting) **A**5 10 18 **F**3 7 13 29 34 35 40 45 50 57 59 63 64 65 76 81 85 87 93 97 102 107 115 119 127 130 131 133 146 148 156
Primary Contact: Abner King, Chief Executive Officer
CFO: Betty A Watson, Chief Financial Officer
CMO: Daniel Griffis, M.D., Chief Medical Officer
CIO: Darla Whitley, Manager Health Information Technology
CHR: Katy Eimers, Human Resources Officer
CNO: Cindy Daly, R.N., Director of Nursing
Web address: www.syringahospital.org
**Control**: Hospital district or authority, Government, Nonfederal **Service**: General medical and surgical

**Staffed Beds: 14 Admissions: 405 Census: 3 Births: 38 Total Expense ($000): 15692 Payroll Expense ($000): 8646 Personnel: 148**

## IDAHO FALLS—Bonneville County

**COLUMBIA EASTERN IDAHO REG MED** See Eastern Idaho Regional Medical Center

⊞ **EASTERN IDAHO REGIONAL MEDICAL CENTER (130018)**, 3100 Channing Way, Zip 83404–7533, Mailing Address: P.O. Box 2077, Zip 83403–2077; tel. 208/529–6111, (Nonreporting) **A**1 3 5 10 19 **S** HCA Healthcare, Nashville, TN
Primary Contact: Jeff Sollis, Chief Executive Officer
COO: Sandee Moore, Chief Operating Officer
CFO: Judd Taylor, Chief Financial Officer
CMO: R. Lee Biggs, M.D., Chief Medical Officer
CHR: Wendy Andersen, Director Human Resources
CNO: Ann Marie Kjosa, R.N., MSN, Chief Nursing Officer
Web address: www.eirmc.com
**Control**: Corporation, Investor-owned (for-profit) **Service**: General medical and surgical

**Staffed Beds: 318**

**MOUNTAIN VIEW HOSPITAL (130065)**, 2325 Coronado Street, Zip 83404–7407; tel. 208/557–2700, (Nonreporting) **A**3 5 10
Primary Contact: James Adamson, Chief Executive Officer
COO: Peter Fabrick, Vice President Clinical Operations
CHR: Eilene Horne, Manager Human Resources
Web address: www.mountainviewhospital.org
**Control**: Corporation, Investor-owned (for-profit) **Service**: General medical and surgical

**Staffed Beds: 22**

## JEROME—Jerome County

**ST. BENEDICTS FAMILY MEDICAL CENTER** See St. Luke's Jerome

★ **ST. LUKE'S JEROME (131310)**, 709 North Lincoln Street, Zip 83338–1851, Mailing Address: 709 North Lincoln Avenue, Zip 83338–1851; tel. 208/814–9500, (Nonreporting) **A**3 10 18 **F**7 13 15 29 30 32 34 39 40 45 56 57 59 64 65 68 76 77 81 87 92 97 100 107 110 111 114 119 127 130 133 146 147 148 152 154 155 **P**5 **S** St. Luke's Health System, Boise, ID
Primary Contact: Jill Howell, Chief Operating Officer and Chief Nursing Officer
CMO: Elizabeth Sugden, M.D., Chief Medical Officer
CHR: Mark Stevens, Director Human Resources
CNO: Jill Howell, Chief Nursing Officer
Web address: www.stlukesonline.org/jerome/
**Control**: Other not-for-profit (including NFP Corporation) **Service**: General medical and surgical

**Staffed Beds: 18 Admissions: 498 Census: 7 Outpatient Visits: 38712 Births: 168 Total Expense ($000): 13929 Payroll Expense ($000): 7649 Personnel: 121**

**ID**

*Many Facility Codes have changed. Please refer to the AHA Guide Code Chart.*
© 2021 AHA Guide

**KELLOGG—Shoshone County**

⇑ **SHOSHONE MEDICAL CENTER (131314)**, 25 Jacobs Gulch, Zip 83837–2023; tel. 208/784–1221, (Nonreporting) **A**10 18 21 **F**3 15 28 29 31 34 40 45 53 57 59 77 78 85 90 93 107 110 111 115 119 127 130 133 135 148 154
Primary Contact: Paul Lewis, Chief Executive Officer
CFO: Donja Erdman, Chief Financial Officer
CMO: David Lawhorn, M.D., Chief Medical Officer
CIO: John Wohlman, Manager Information Systems
CHR: Dana Hemphill, Manager Human Resources
CNO: Karen Mann, R.N., Chief Nursing Officer
Web address: www.shoshonehealth.com
**Control**: Hospital district or authority, Government, Nonfederal **Service**: General medical and surgical

**Staffed Beds:** 25 **Admissions:** 263 **Census:** 5 **Outpatient Visits:** 21013
**Total Expense ($000):** 13833 **Payroll Expense ($000):** 5605

**KETCHUM—Blaine County**

✠ **ST. LUKE'S WOOD RIVER MEDICAL CENTER (131323)**, 100 Hospital Drive, Zip 83340, Mailing Address: P.O. Box 100, Zip 83340–0100; tel. 208/727–8800, (Nonreporting) **A**1 5 10 18 **F**3 7 11 13 15 29 31 32 34 35 36 37 40 43 45 49 50 54 56 57 59 62 64 65 68 74 75 76 77 79 81 82 85 86 87 91 93 97 101 104 107 108 110 111 114 115 119 126 130 131 132 133 134 135 143 146 147 148 154 156 **P**5 **S** St. Luke's Health System, Boise, ID
Primary Contact: Carmen Jacobsen, Chief Operating Officer and Chief Nursing Officer
CNO: Suzanne Miller, R.N., MSN, Senior Director Patient Care Services and Nursing
Web address: www.slrmc.org
**Control**: Other not–for–profit (including NFP Corporation) **Service**: General medical and surgical

**Staffed Beds:** 25 **Admissions:** 1198 **Census:** 9 **Outpatient Visits:** 113034
**Births:** 180 **Total Expense ($000):** 44729 **Payroll Expense ($000):** 19184
**Personnel:** 285

**WOOD RIVER MEDICAL CENTER** See St. Luke's Wood River Medical Center

**LEWISTON—Nez Perce County**

✠ **ST. JOSEPH REGIONAL MEDICAL CENTER (130003)**, 415 Sixth Street, Zip 83501–2431; tel. 208/743–2511, (Nonreporting) **A**1 2 10 **S** LifePoint Health, Brentwood, TN
Primary Contact: Timothy R. Trottier, Chief Executive Officer
COO: Taylor Rudd, Chief Operating Officer
CFO: Thomas Safley, Chief Financial Officer
CHR: Susan Dokken, Chief Human Resources
CNO: Joan Agee, Vice President Patient Care Services
Web address: www.sjrmc.org
**Control**: Church operated, Nongovernment, not–for–profit **Service**: General medical and surgical

**Staffed Beds:** 123

**MALAD CITY—Oneida County**

**NELL J. REDFIELD MEMORIAL HOSPITAL (131303)**, 150 North 200 West, Zip 83252–1239, Mailing Address: Box 126, Zip 83252–0126; tel. 208/766–2231, (Nonreporting) **A**10 18
Primary Contact: John Williams, Administrator and Chief Executive Officer
CFO: Cindy Howard, Director Financial Services
CHR: Kathy Hubbard, Manager Human Resources
Web address: www.oneidahospital.com
**Control**: County, Government, Nonfederal **Service**: General medical and surgical

**Staffed Beds:** 11

**ONEIDA COUNTY HOSPITAL** See Nell J. Redfield Memorial Hospital

**MCCALL—Valley County**

★ **ST. LUKE'S MCCALL (131312)**, 1000 State Street, Zip 83638–3704; tel. 208/634–2221, (Nonreporting) **A**5 10 18 **F**3 8 9 11 13 15 30 31 32 34 35 36 38 40 43 45 46 50 57 59 64 66 75 77 79 81 85 86 87 93 97 107 111 115 119 127 130 132 133 134 135 146 147 148 149 154 156 **P**5 **S** St. Luke's Health System, Boise, ID
Primary Contact: Amber Green, R.N., Chief Operating Officer and Chief Nursing Officer
COO: Amber Green, R.N., Chief Operating Officer and Chief Nursing Officer
CFO: Matt Groenig, Vice President Finance
CNO: Amber Green, R.N., Chief Operating Officer and Chief Nursing Officer
Web address: www.https://www.stlukesonline.org/communities-and-locations/facilities/hospitals-and-medical-centers/st-lukes-mccall-medical-center
**Control**: Other not–for–profit (including NFP Corporation) **Service**: General medical and surgical

**Staffed Beds:** 15 **Admissions:** 614 **Census:** 4 **Outpatient Visits:** 58596
**Births:** 93 **Total Expense ($000):** 23032 **Payroll Expense ($000):** 10035
**Personnel:** 174

**ST. LUKE'S MCCALL HOSPITAL** See St. Luke's Mccall

**MERIDIAN—Ada County**

**ST. LUKE'S MERIDIAN MEDICAL CENTER** See St. Luke's Regional Medical Center, Boise

**MONTPELIER—Bear Lake County**

★ ⇑ **BEAR LAKE MEMORIAL HOSPITAL (131316)**, 164 South Fifth Street, Zip 83254–1597; tel. 208/847–1630, (Total facility includes 36 beds in nursing home–type unit) (Nonreporting) **A**10 18 21 **F**2 3 5 10 11 12 13 15 28 29 30 31 32 34 35 36 37 38 40 41 43 44 45 50 53 56 59 60 62 64 65 66 68 70 75 76 77 78 79 81 82 85 86 87 89 91 92 93 97 107 108 115 119 126 127 128 129 130 131 132 133 135 146 147 148 152 154 156
Primary Contact: Michael Blauer, Chief Executive Officer
Web address: www.blmhospital.com
**Control**: County, Government, Nonfederal **Service**: General medical and surgical

**Staffed Beds:** 57 **Admissions:** 332 **Census:** 36 **Outpatient Visits:** 61600
**Births:** 76 **Total Expense ($000):** 27102 **Payroll Expense ($000):** 13031
**Personnel:** 223

**MOSCOW—Latah County**

✠ **GRITMAN MEDICAL CENTER (131327)**, 700 South Main Street, Zip 83843–3056; tel. 208/882–4511, (Nonreporting) **A**1 10 18 **S** QHR Health, Brentwood, TN
Primary Contact: Kara Besst, President and Chief Executive Officer
CMO: Michael Patmas, M.D., Chief Medical Officer
CIO: Kane Francetich, Chief Information Officer
Web address: www.gritman.org
**Control**: Other not–for–profit (including NFP Corporation) **Service**: General medical and surgical

**Staffed Beds:** 25

**GRITMAN MEMORIAL HOSPITAL** See Gritman Medical Center

**MOUNTAIN HOME—Elmore County**

**ELMORE MEDICAL CENTER** See St. Luke's Elmore

✠ **ST. LUKE'S ELMORE (131311)**, 895 North Sixth East Street, Zip 83647–2207, Mailing Address: P.O. Box 1270, Zip 83647–1270; tel. 208/587–8401, (Total facility includes 28 beds in nursing home–type unit) (Nonreporting) **A**1 10 18 **F**3 7 11 13 15 29 30 34 35 40 50 57 59 64 68 75 77 81 85 87 97 107 111 115 119 127 128 129 130 133 135 146 147 149 154 **S** St. Luke's Health System, Boise, ID
Primary Contact: Lisa Melchiorre, R.N., MS, Chief Operating Officer and Chief Nursing Officer
COO: Lisa Melchiorre, R.N., MS, Chief Operating Officer and Chief Nursing Officer
CFO: Tricia Senger, Chief Financial Officer
CNO: Lisa Melchiorre, R.N., MS, Chief Operating Officer and Chief Nursing Officer
Web address: www.stlukesonline.org/elmore/
**Control**: Other not–for–profit (including NFP Corporation) **Service**: General medical and surgical

**Staffed Beds:** 49 **Admissions:** 877 **Census:** 28 **Outpatient Visits:** 62720
**Births:** 224 **Total Expense ($000):** 27160 **Payroll Expense ($000):** 12649
**Personnel:** 220

**NAMPA—Canyon County**

**MERCY MEDICAL CENTER** See Saint Alphonsus Medical Center - Nampa

**ID**

---

**Hospital, Medicare Provider Number, Address, Telephone, Approval, Facility, and Physician Codes, Health Care System**

★ American Hospital Association (AHA) membership   ○ Healthcare Facilities Accreditation Program   ⇑ Center for Improvement in Healthcare Quality Accreditation
□ The Joint Commission accreditation   ◇ DNV Healthcare Inc. accreditation   △ Commission on Accreditation of Rehabilitation Facilities (CARF) accreditation

✠ **SAINT ALPHONSUS MEDICAL CENTER - NAMPA (130013)**, 4300 East Flamingo Avenue, Zip 83686–6008; tel. 208/205–1000, (Nonreporting) **A**1 3 10 19 **F**3 8 11 12 13 14 15 18 20 22 28 29 30 31 32 34 35 37 39 40 41 42 43 44 45 50 51 57 59 64 65 66 68 69 70 71 72 75 76 77 78 79 81 82 85 86 87 92 107 108 110 111 115 118 119 120 121 123 126 129 130 132 133 134 135 141 143 145 146 147 148 149 154 **S** Trinity Health, Livonia, MI
Primary Contact: Travis Leach, President
CFO: Lannie Checketts, Chief Financial Officer
CMO: Dustan Hughes, M.D., Vice President Medical Affairs
CIO: Daniel Wright, Director Information Technology
CHR: Stefanie Thiel, Senior Human Resources Business Partner
CNO: Clint L Child, R.N., Chief Nursing Officer
Web address: www.https://www.saintalphonsus.org/nampa
**Control**: Church operated, Nongovernment, not–for–profit **Service**: General medical and surgical

| | |
|---|---|
| **Staffed Beds**: 106 **Admissions**: 5957 **Census**: 57 **Outpatient Visits**: 127530 **Births**: 1057 **Total Expense ($000)**: 150717 **Payroll Expense ($000)**: 48409 **Personnel**: 770 | |

☐ **ST. LUKE'S NAMPA (130071)**, 9850 West St.Luke's Drive, Zip 83687; tel. 208/505–2000, (Nonreporting) **A**1 3 10 **F**3 7 11 13 15 18 20 22 29 30 40 41 50 51 53 63 68 70 72 75 76 77 81 85 87 92 93 107 108 109 110 111 114 115 118 119 120 130 134 135 146 154 157 **P**5 **S** St. Luke's Health System, Boise, ID
Primary Contact: Joan Agee, Chief Operating Officer and Chief Nursing Officer
Web address: www.https://www.stlukesonline.org/communities-and-locations/facilities/hospitals-and-medical-centers/st-lukes-nampa-medical-center
**Control**: Other not–for–profit (including NFP Corporation) **Service**: General medical and surgical

| | |
|---|---|
| **Staffed Beds**: 81 **Admissions**: 3571 **Census**: 32 **Outpatient Visits**: 131863 **Births**: 878 **Total Expense ($000)**: 90564 **Payroll Expense ($000)**: 34022 **Personnel**: 558 | |

### OROFINO—Clearwater County

★ **CLEARWATER VALLEY HOSPITAL AND CLINICS (131320)**, 301 Cedar, Zip 83544–9029; tel. 208/476–4555, (Nonreporting) **A**10 18 **S** Essentia Health, Duluth, MN
Primary Contact: Lenne Bonner, President
CFO: Jyl Ruland, Chief Financial Officer
CMO: Kelly McGrath, Chief Medical Officer
CHR: Debbie Schumacher, Chief Human Resource Officer
Web address: www.smh-cvhc.org
**Control**: Other not–for–profit (including NFP Corporation) **Service**: General medical and surgical

| | |
|---|---|
| **Staffed Beds**: 23 | |

**STATE HOSPITAL NORTH**, 300 Hospital Drive, Zip 83544–9034; tel. 208/476–4511, (Nonreporting) **A**5 **F**98 106 154
Primary Contact: Todd Hurt, Administrator
CMO: Karla Eisele, M.D., Clinical Director
CIO: James Sarbacher, Chief Information Officer
CHR: Heather Vandenbark, Human Resources Specialist
Web address: www.healthandwelfare.idaho.gov
**Control**: State, Government, Nonfederal **Service**: Psychiatric

| | |
|---|---|
| **Staffed Beds**: 55 **Admissions**: 263 **Census**: 44 **Outpatient Visits**: 0 **Births**: 0 **Total Expense ($000)**: 9998 **Payroll Expense ($000)**: 5405 **Personnel**: 138 | |

### POCATELLO—Bannock County

**BEACON HOSPITAL AND REHABILITATION OF POCATELLO** See Safe Haven Hospital of Pocatello

✠ **PORTNEUF MEDICAL CENTER (130028)**, 777 Hospital Way, Zip 83201–5175; tel. 208/239–1000, (Nonreporting) **A**1 3 5 10 20 **F**3 8 11 12 13 15 17 18 19 20 22 24 26 28 29 31 34 35 37 39 40 43 44 45 46 47 48 49 50 56 57 58 59 61 64 65 68 70 71 72 74 75 76 77 78 79 80 81 82 85 86 87 88 89 90 93 96 97 98 100 101 102 104 107 108 109 110 111 114 115 118 119 120 121 123 124 126 127 129 130 132 143 146 149 156 **S** Ardent Health Services, Nashville, TN
Primary Contact: Jordan Herget, Chief Executive Officer
COO: Don Wadle, Vice President Clinical and Support Services
CFO: John Abreu, Vice President and Chief Financial Officer
CMO: Dan Snell, Chief Medical Officer
CHR: Don Wadle, Interim Director Human Resources
CNO: Angela Treasure, Chief Nursing Officer
Web address: www.portmed.org
**Control**: Corporation, Investor–owned (for–profit) **Service**: General medical and surgical

| | |
|---|---|
| **Staffed Beds**: 175 **Admissions**: 8134 **Census**: 92 **Outpatient Visits**: 278771 **Births**: 1208 **Total Expense ($000)**: 253127 **Payroll Expense ($000)**: 87363 **Personnel**: 1104 | |

**SAFE HAVEN HOSPITAL OF POCATELLO (134011)**, 2520 South 5th Avenue, Zip 83204–1923; tel. 208/232–2570, (Nonreporting) **A**10 **S** Safe Haven Health Care, Pocatello, ID
Primary Contact: Karen Neilson, Administrator
Web address: www.safehavenhealthcare.org/safehaven_hospital/index.html
**Control**: Individual, Investor–owned (for–profit) **Service**: Rehabilitation

| | |
|---|---|
| **Staffed Beds**: 87 | |

### POST FALLS—Kootenai County

☐ **NORTHERN IDAHO ADVANCED CARE HOSPITAL (132001)**, 600 North Cecil Road, Zip 83854–6200; tel. 208/262–2800, (Nonreporting) **A**1 10 **S** Ernest Health, Inc., Albuquerque, NM
Primary Contact: Una Alderman, Chief Executive Officer
Web address: www.niach.ernesthealth.com
**Control**: Corporation, Investor–owned (for–profit) **Service**: Acute long–term care hospital

| | |
|---|---|
| **Staffed Beds**: 40 | |

☐ **NORTHWEST SPECIALTY HOSPITAL (130066)**, 1593 East Polston Avenue, Zip 83854–5326; tel. 208/262–2300, (Nonreporting) **A**1 10 **F**3 37 45 46 47 48 49 50 64 68 74 75 77 79 81 82 85 91 97 107 111 119 126 129 130 144 147 157 **S** National Surgical Healthcare, Chicago, IL
Primary Contact: Rick Rasmussen, Chief Executive Officer
CIO: Craig McIntosh, Chief Information Officer
CHR: Gina Schneider, Director Human Resources
CNO: Christi Nance, R.N., MSN, Chief Nursing Officer
Web address: www.northwestspecialtyhospital.com
**Control**: Partnership, Investor–owned (for–profit) **Service**: Surgical

| | |
|---|---|
| **Staffed Beds**: 32 **Admissions**: 1365 **Census**: 7 **Births**: 0 | |

☐ △ **REHABILITATION HOSPITAL OF THE NORTHWEST (133027)**, 3372 East Jenalan Avenue, Zip 83854–7787; tel. 208/262–8700, (Nonreporting) **A**1 7 **S** Ernest Health, Inc., Albuquerque, NM
Primary Contact: Darby Brockette, Chief Executive Officer
Web address: www.ernesthealth.com
**Control**: Corporation, Investor–owned (for–profit) **Service**: Rehabilitation

| | |
|---|---|
| **Staffed Beds**: 25 | |

### PRESTON—Franklin County

**FRANKLIN COUNTY MED CENTER** See Franklin County Medical Center

★ **FRANKLIN COUNTY MEDICAL CENTER (131322)**, 44 North First East Street, Zip 83263–1399; tel. 208/852–0137, (Nonreporting) **A**5 10 18
Primary Contact: Darin Dransfield, Chief Executive Officer
CFO: Paul Smart, CPA, Chief Financial Officer
CHR: Courtney Dursteler, Chief Human Resources Officer
CNO: Patrica Bowles, R.N., Chief Nursing Officer
Web address: www.fcmc.org
**Control**: County, Government, Nonfederal **Service**: General medical and surgical

| | |
|---|---|
| **Staffed Beds**: 55 | |

### REXBURG—Madison County

★ ⇑ **MADISON MEMORIAL HOSPITAL (130025)**, 450 East Main Street, Zip 83440–2048, Mailing Address: P.O. Box 310, Zip 83440–0310; tel. 208/359–6900, (Nonreporting) **A**3 5 10 21 **F**3 11 28 31 34 35 39 40 41 43 45 54 57 59 60 65 68 70 72 75 76 77 78 79 81 82 85 87 89 91 93 97 107 108 111 115 118 119 126 129 130 131 146 147 148 149
Primary Contact: Rachel Ann. Gonzales, Chief Executive Officer
CFO: Troy Christensen, Chief Financial Officer
CMO: Clay Prince, M.D., Chief Medical Officer
CNO: Kevin K McEwan, MSN, R.N., Chief Nursing Officer
Web address: www.https://madisonmemorial.org/
**Control**: County, Government, Nonfederal **Service**: General medical and surgical

| | |
|---|---|
| **Staffed Beds**: 58 **Admissions**: 2404 **Census**: 18 **Outpatient Visits**: 45436 **Births**: 1378 **Total Expense ($000)**: 80849 **Payroll Expense ($000)**: 27064 **Personnel**: 504 | |

*Many Facility Codes have changed. Please refer to the AHA Guide Code Chart.*

© 2021 AHA Guide

**ID**

## RUPERT—Minidoka County

★ ⇧ **MINIDOKA MEMORIAL HOSPITAL (131319)**, 1224 Eighth Street, Zip 83350–1599; tel. 208/436–0481, (Total facility includes 43 beds in nursing home–type unit) (Nonreporting) **A**5 10 18 21 **F**3 7 8 11 15 29 30 34 35 37 40 45 50 56 57 59 62 63 64 65 68 70 75 77 79 81 83 84 85 86 87 97 107 108 111 114 119 127 128 130 131 132 133 134 143 146 147 148 149 154 156 157 **P**5
Primary Contact: Tom Murphy, Chief Executive Officer
CFO: Jason Gibbons, Chief Financial Officer
CMO: Kevin Owens, M.D., Chief Medical Officer
CIO: Brody Beck, Director Information Technology
CHR: Desiree Carr, Director Human Resources
CNO: Erinn Neilson, Chief Nursing Officer
Web address: www.minidokamemorial.com
**Control**: County, Government, Nonfederal **Service**: General medical and surgical

**Staffed Beds**: 72 **Admissions**: 559 **Census**: 43 **Outpatient Visits**: 21020
**Births**: 0 **Total Expense ($000)**: 29810 **Payroll Expense ($000)**: 17490
**Personnel**: 216

⇧ **MINIDOKA MEMORIAL HOSPITAL AND EXTENDED CARE FACILITY** See Minidoka Memorial Hospital

## SAINT MARIES—Benewah County

**BENEWAH COMMUNITY HOSPITAL (131317)**, 229 South Seventh Street, Zip 83861–1803; tel. 208/245–5551, (Nonreporting) **A**5 10 18
Primary Contact: Chuck Lloyd, Chief Executive Officer
CFO: Lori Minier, Chief Financial Officer
CMO: William Wheeler, M.D., Chief of Staff
CIO: Joseph Getchius, Director Information Technology
CHR: Marlana Martin, Director Human Resources
CNO: Rhonda Smith, Chief Nursing Officer
Web address: www.bchmed.org
**Control**: County, Government, Nonfederal **Service**: General medical and surgical

**Staffed Beds**: 19

## SALMON—Lemhi County

⇧ **STEELE MEMORIAL HOSPITAL** See Steele Memorial Medical Center

★ ⇧ **STEELE MEMORIAL MEDICAL CENTER (131305)**, 203 South Daisy Street, Zip 83467–4709; tel. 208/756–5600, (Nonreporting) **A**10 18 21 **S** QHR Health, Brentwood, TN
Primary Contact: Jeanine Gentry, Chief Executive Officer
CFO: Lionel J. Montoya, Chief Financial Officer
CMO: Richard Natelson, M.D., Chief of Staff
CHR: Libby Brittain, Director Human Resources
CNO: Lisa Loughran, Chief Nursing Officer
Web address: www.steelemh.org
**Control**: County, Government, Nonfederal **Service**: General medical and surgical

**Staffed Beds**: 18

## SANDPOINT—Bonner County

★ ⇧ **BONNER GENERAL HEALTH (131328)**, 520 North Third Avenue, Zip 83864–1507; tel. 208/263–1441, (Nonreporting) **A**10 18 21 **F**3 11 13 15 17 22 26 28 29 30 34 35 40 43 45 46 47 48 54 57 59 62 63 64 68 75 76 77 79 81 85 86 87 93 102 104 107 108 110 111 114 118 119 127 130 131 132 144 146 148 156
Primary Contact: Sheryl Rickard, Chief Executive Officer
CFO: John Hennessy, Chief Financial Officer
CMO: Samuel Uzabel, M.D., Chief Medical Officer
CIO: Jeremy Welser, Director Information Systems
CHR: Shannon Barnes, Chief Human Resource Officer
CNO: Tracy Lynn Autler, R.N., Chief Nursing and Quality Officer
Web address: www.bonnergeneral.org
**Control**: Other not–for–profit (including NFP Corporation) **Service**: General medical and surgical

**Staffed Beds**: 25 **Admissions**: 1737 **Census**: 11 **Outpatient Visits**: 70112
**Births**: 287 **Total Expense ($000)**: 58453 **Payroll Expense ($000)**: 25337
**Personnel**: 373

## SODA SPRINGS—Caribou County

⇧ **CARIBOU MEM HOSPITAL & NSG HM** See Caribou Memorial Hospital and Living Center

★ ⇧ **CARIBOU MEMORIAL HOSPITAL AND LIVING CENTER (131309)**, 300 South Third West, Zip 83276–1598; tel. 208/547–3341, (Total facility includes 30 beds in nursing home–type unit) (Nonreporting) **A**5 10 18 21 **F**70 76 81 **P**6
Primary Contact: Christina Thomas, Chief Executive Officer
CMO: John K Franson, M.D., Chief Medical Staff
CIO: Johnathan Inskeep, Chief Information Officer
CHR: Michael D Peck, Assistant Administrator
CNO: Brenda Bergholm, MSN, R.N., Chief Nursing Officer
Web address: www.cmhlc.org/
**Control**: County, Government, Nonfederal **Service**: General medical and surgical

**Staffed Beds**: 55 **Admissions**: 377 **Census**: 24 **Outpatient Visits**: 18057
**Births**: 38 **Total Expense ($000)**: 22313 **Payroll Expense ($000)**: 11354
**Personnel**: 171

## TWIN FALLS—Twin Falls County

⊠ △ **ST. LUKE'S MAGIC VALLEY MEDICAL CENTER (130002)**, 801 Pole Line Road West, Zip 83301–5810, Mailing Address: P.O. Box 409, Zip 83303–0409; tel. 208/814–1000, (Nonreporting) **A**1 3 5 7 10 **F**3 4 5 7 11 13 15 18 20 22 28 29 30 31 34 35 39 40 43 45 46 48 49 50 51 54 55 57 59 62 63 64 65 68 70 71 72 74 75 76 77 78 79 81 82 84 85 87 89 90 92 93 96 97 98 104 107 108 110 111 114 115 116 117 119 126 129 130 131 132 143 144 146 148 154 155 156 **P**5 **S** St. Luke's Health System, Boise, ID
Primary Contact: Michael A. Fenello, Vice President Population Health
CFO: Joshua Custer, Director Finance
CIO: Melissa Capps, Site Leader Information Technology
CHR: Mark Stevens, Senior Director Human Resources
CNO: Amy Bearden, R.N., MSN, Vice President Patient Care Services and Chief Nursing Officer
Web address: www.stlukesonline.org
**Control**: Other not–for–profit (including NFP Corporation) **Service**: General medical and surgical

**Staffed Beds**: 213 **Admissions**: 11054 **Census**: 113 **Outpatient Visits**: 608118 **Births**: 1749 **Total Expense ($000)**: 212364 **Payroll Expense ($000)**: 82537 **Personnel**: 1541

**ST. LUKE'S MAGIC VALLEY REGIONAL MEDICAL CENTER** See St. Luke's Magic Valley Medical Center

## WEISER—Washington County

⇧ **MEMORIAL HOSPITAL** See Weiser Memorial Hospital

★ ⇧ **WEISER MEMORIAL HOSPITAL (131307)**, 645 East Fifth Street, Zip 83672–2202; tel. 208/549–0370, (Nonreporting) **A**5 10 18 21 **F**3 11 13 29 34 35 40 43 45 46 56 57 59 65 68 75 76 79 81 82 85 91 97 107 115 119 127 129 130 131 133 135 147 148 149 154 **S** St. Luke's Health System, Boise, ID
Primary Contact: Steven D. Hale, FACHE, Chief Executive Officer
CFO: Mark Christensen, Chief Financial Officer
CMO: Torrey S. Nash, M.D., Chief of Medical Staff
CHR: Terri Kautz, Manager Human Resources
Web address: www.weisermemorialhospital.org
**Control**: Hospital district or authority, Government, Nonfederal **Service**: General medical and surgical

**Staffed Beds**: 18 **Admissions**: 328 **Census**: 2 **Outpatient Visits**: 17864
**Births**: 46 **Total Expense ($000)**: 17347 **Payroll Expense ($000)**: 6880
**Personnel**: 127

**ID**

---

**Hospital, Medicare Provider Number, Address, Telephone, Approval, Facility, and Physician Codes, Health Care System**

★ American Hospital Association (AHA) membership ○ Healthcare Facilities Accreditation Program ⇧ Center for Improvement in Healthcare Quality Accreditation
□ The Joint Commission accreditation ◇ DNV Healthcare Inc. accreditation △ Commission on Accreditation of Rehabilitation Facilities (CARF) accreditation

# ILLINOIS

## ALEDO—Mercer County

⊠ **GENESIS MEDICAL CENTER-ALEDO (141304)**, 409 NW Ninth Avenue, Zip 61231–1296; tel. 309/582–9100, (Nonreporting) **A**1 10 18 **F**3 11 15 28 29 34 40 45 56 59 64 81 82 87 89 93 94 97 104 107 108 110 115 119 127 128 130 131 133 144 146 149 154 **P**6 **S** Genesis Health System, Davenport, IA
Primary Contact: Ted Rogalski, Administrator
CFO: Mark G Rogers, Vice President, Finance and Chief Financial Officer
CMO: Julio Santiago, M.D., Chief of Staff
CIO: Robert Frieden, Vice President, Information Services and Chief Information Officer
CHR: Tammy Hagedorn, Chief Human Resource Officer
CNO: Heidi Hess, Chief Nursing Officer
Web address: www.genesishealth.com
**Control**: Other not–for–profit (including NFP Corporation) **Service**: General medical and surgical

> **Staffed Beds:** 22 **Admissions:** 144 **Census:** 3 **Outpatient Visits:** 16380 **Births:** 0 **Total Expense ($000):** 16720 **Payroll Expense ($000):** 6393 **Personnel:** 72

**MERCER COUNTY HOSPITAL** See Genesis Medical Center-Aledo

## ALTON—Madison County

⊠ **ALTON MEMORIAL HOSPITAL (140002)**, One Memorial Drive, Zip 62002–6722; tel. 618/463–7311, (Total facility includes 64 beds in nursing home–type unit) (Nonreporting) **A**1 5 10 **F**1 3 6 7 11 13 15 18 20 22 29 30 31 34 35 36 38 39 40 45 46 49 50 51 56 57 59 64 70 74 75 76 77 78 79 81 82 84 85 86 87 89 92 93 96 98 100 103 104 107 108 110 111 114 115 116 117 118 119 120 121 129 130 131 132 135 146 148 149 154 156 **P**6 **S** BJC HealthCare, Saint Louis, MO
Primary Contact: David A. Braasch, President
COO: Brad Goacher, Vice President Administration
CFO: Susan Koesterer, Vice President, Finance
CMO: Sebastian Rueckert, M.D., Vice President and Chief Medical Officer
CIO: Jerry Fox Jr Chief Information Officer
CHR: Bryan Hartwick, Vice President Human Resources
CNO: Debra Turpin, R.N., MSN, Vice President Patient Care Services and Chief Nursing Officer
Web address: www.altonmemorialhospital.org
**Control**: Other not–for–profit (including NFP Corporation) **Service**: General medical and surgical

> **Staffed Beds:** 224 **Admissions:** 8233 **Census:** 123 **Outpatient Visits:** 156313 **Births:** 843 **Total Expense ($000):** 151538 **Payroll Expense ($000):** 54659 **Personnel:** 817

☐ **ALTON MENTAL HEALTH CENTER (144016)**, 4500 College Avenue, Zip 62002–5099; tel. 618/474–3800, (Nonreporting) **A**1 10 **S** Division of Mental Health, Department of Human Services, Springfield, IL
Primary Contact: Brian E. Thomas, Administrator
CFO: Susan Shobe, Director Administration and Support Services
CMO: Claudia Kachigion, M.D., Medical Director
**Control**: State, Government, Nonfederal **Service**: Psychiatric

> **Staffed Beds:** 125

**ALTON MENTAL HLTH & DEV CTR** See Alton Mental Health Center

⊠ **OSF HEALTHCARE SAINT ANTHONY'S HEALTH CENTER (140052)**, 1 Saint Anthony's Way, Zip 62002–4579, Mailing Address: PO Box 340, Zip 62002–0340; tel. 618/465–2571, (Includes OSF HEALTHCARE SAINT CLARE'S HOSPITAL, Mailing address: 915 East Fifth Street, Alton, Illinois, Zip 62002–6434; tel. 618/463–5151), (Nonreporting) **A**1 2 10 **F**3 5 10 11 15 18 20 22 29 30 31 34 35 37 38 39 40 41 44 45 47 48 49 50 51 56 57 58 59 60 64 65 68 69 70 74 75 77 78 79 81 82 84 85 86 87 91 92 93 95 96 100 101 102 104 107 108 110 111 114 115 116 117 118 119 120 121 123 125 129 130 131 132 134 135 146 147 148 149 154 156 158 **S** OSF Healthcare, Peoria, IL
Primary Contact: Sister M. Mikela. Meidl, Interim President
COO: SisterM. Anselma Belongea, Chief Operating Officer
CFO: Mathew Hanley, Chief Financial Officer
CMO: Dennis Sands, Chief Medical Officer
CIO: Georgia Henke, Operational Account Manager
CHR: Robyn Grissom, Director of Human Resources
CNO: Colleen Becker, Chief Nursing Officer
Web address: www.osfsaintanthonys.org
**Control**: Church operated, Nongovernment, not–for–profit **Service**: General medical and surgical

> **Staffed Beds:** 49 **Admissions:** 2436 **Census:** 26 **Outpatient Visits:** 93057 **Births:** 0 **Total Expense ($000):** 81221 **Payroll Expense ($000):** 25187 **Personnel:** 469

**OSF SAINT ANTHONY'S HEALTH CENTER** See OSF Healthcare Saint Anthony's Health Center

**OSF SAINT CLARE'S HOSPITAL** See OSF Healthcare Saint Clare's Hospital

## ANNA—Union County

☐ **CHOATE MENTAL HEALTH CENTER (144038)**, 1000 North Main Street, Zip 62906–1699; tel. 618/833–5161, (Nonreporting) **A**1 10 **F**34 39 59 65 75 86 98 101 102 130 143 149 154 **S** Division of Mental Health, Department of Human Services, Springfield, IL
Primary Contact: Elaine Ray, Administrator
COO: Elaine Ray, Administrator
CMO: John Larcas, M.D., Acting Medical Director
CIO: Cindy Flamm, Manager Quality
CHR: Tammy Tellor, Acting Director Human Resources
**Control**: State, Government, Nonfederal **Service**: Psychiatric

> **Staffed Beds:** 79 **Admissions:** 82 **Census:** 39 **Outpatient Visits:** 147 **Births:** 0 **Total Expense ($000):** 41147 **Payroll Expense ($000):** 33363 **Personnel:** 107

**CHOATE MENTAL HLTH & DEV CTR** See Choate Mental Health Center

☐ **UNION COUNTY HOSPITAL (141342)**, 517 North Main Street, Zip 62906–1696; tel. 618/833–4511, (Total facility includes 22 beds in nursing home–type unit) (Nonreporting) **A**1 10 18 **F**3 4 11 15 28 29 34 35 40 45 49 50 57 59 64 68 75 77 81 85 87 93 97 107 110 111 114 119 127 129 130 133 146 148 **P**6 **S** Quorum Health, Brentwood, TN
Primary Contact: James R. Farris, FACHE, Chief Executive Officer
CFO: Terry Paligo, Chief Financial Officer
CMO: Christine Lucas, Chief of Staff
CIO: John Hegger, Director Information Systems
CHR: Tammy Davis, Director Human Resources
CNO: Tammy H. Wheaton, Interim Chief Nursing Officer
Web address: www.unioncountyhospital.com
**Control**: Corporation, Investor–owned (for–profit) **Service**: General medical and surgical

> **Staffed Beds:** 47 **Admissions:** 541 **Census:** 21 **Outpatient Visits:** 34416 **Births:** 0 **Total Expense ($000):** 22209 **Payroll Expense ($000):** 8826 **Personnel:** 122

**UNION COUNTY HOSPITAL DISTRICT** See Union County Hospital

## ARLINGTON HEIGHTS—Cook County

⊠ △ **NORTHWEST COMMUNITY HEALTHCARE (140252)**, 800 West Central Road, Zip 60005–2392; tel. 847/618–1000, (Nonreporting) **A**1 2 7 10 **F**2 3 5 8 11 12 13 15 18 20 22 24 26 28 29 30 31 34 35 37 38 39 40 43 44 45 46 47 48 49 50 53 54 55 56 57 59 61 62 63 64 65 68 70 71 72 73 74 75 76 77 78 79 81 82 85 86 87 89 90 91 92 93 94 96 97 98 99 100 101 102 103 104 105 106 107 108 110 111 114 115 116 117 118 119 120 121 123 124 126 129 130 131 132 135 144 145 146 147 148 149 152 153 154 156
Primary Contact: Stephen Scogna, President and Chief Executive Officer
COO: Michael Hartke, Executive Vice President, Chief Operating Officer
CFO: John Skeans, Chief Financial Officer
CMO: Alan Loren, M.D., Chief Medical Officer
CIO: Glen Malan, Vice President Information Technology and Chief Information Officer
CHR: Terry S Solem, Vice President of Human Resources
CNO: Eileen Gillespie, Chief Nursing Officer
Web address: www.nch.org
**Control**: Other not–for–profit (including NFP Corporation) **Service**: General medical and surgical

> **Staffed Beds:** 395 **Admissions:** 23016 **Census:** 288 **Outpatient Visits:** 513754 **Births:** 2499 **Total Expense ($000):** 488895 **Payroll Expense ($000):** 203212 **Personnel:** 3392

**NORTHWEST COMMUNITY HOSPITAL** See Northwest Community Healthcare

IL

## AURORA—Du Page and Kane Counties County

☒ **AMITA HEALTH MERCY MEDICAL CENTER (140174)**, 1325 North Highland Avenue, Zip 60506–1449; tel. 630/859–2222, (Nonreporting) **A**1 2 10 **F**3 5 12 13 15 18 20 22 24 26 28 29 30 31 34 35 36 38 40 43 45 46 49 56 57 59 61 65 68 70 75 76 77 78 79 81 85 86 87 89 93 97 98 99 100 101 102 103 104 105 107 111 114 115 119 125 126 130 132 135 144 146 147 153 **S** Ascension Healthcare, Saint Louis, MO
Primary Contact: Richard Roehr, Chief Executive Officer
COO: Roxann E Barber, Regional Ambulatory Care and Ancillary Services Officer
CFO: Kevin Larkin, Regional Chief Financial Officer
CMO: Anil Gopinath, FACHE, M.D., Regional Chief Medical Officer
CHR: Michael O'Rourke, Regional Human Resource Officer
CNO: Grace McBride, Regional Chief Nursing Officer
Web address: www.presencehealth.org/mercy/
**Control:** Church operated, Nongovernment, not–for–profit **Service:** General medical and surgical

**Staffed Beds:** 292 **Admissions:** 7447 **Census:** 92 **Outpatient Visits:** 79102 **Births:** 249 **Total Expense ($000):** 164143 **Payroll Expense ($000):** 46375 **Personnel:** 495

**PRESENCE MERCY MEDICAL CENTER** See Amita Health Mercy Medical Center

☒ △ **RUSH-COPLEY MEDICAL CENTER (140029)**, 2000 Ogden Avenue, Zip 60504–7222; tel. 630/978–6200, (Nonreporting) **A**1 2 3 5 7 10 **F**3 7 8 9 13 15 17 18 19 20 22 24 26 28 29 30 31 32 34 35 36 38 39 40 42 43 44 45 46 47 48 49 50 51 52 53 54 55 57 58 59 60 61 64 65 66 68 70 72 73 74 75 76 78 79 81 82 84 85 86 87 89 90 92 93 94 96 97 107 108 110 111 114 115 117 118 119 120 121 123 132 134 135 143 144 145 146 147 148 149 154 **P**6 **S** Rush University Medical Center, Chicago, IL
Primary Contact: Barry C. Finn, President and Chief Executive Officer
COO: John A Diederich, Senior Vice President Operations and Chief Operating Officer
CFO: Brenda VanWyhe, Senior Vice President Finance and Chief Financial Officer
CMO: Steve B Lowenthal, M.D., M.P.H., FACS, Senior Vice President Medical Affairs and Chief Medical Officer
CIO: Dennis DeMasie, Vice President Information Systems and Chief Information Officer
CNO: Mary Shilkaitis, Vice President Patient Care and Chief Nursing Officer
Web address: www.rushcopley.com
**Control:** Other not–for–profit (including NFP Corporation) **Service:** General medical and surgical

**Staffed Beds:** 210 **Admissions:** 11626 **Census:** 131 **Outpatient Visits:** 217832 **Births:** 2968 **Total Expense ($000):** 322422 **Payroll Expense ($000):** 127724 **Personnel:** 1798

**RUSH-COPLEY MEMORIAL HOSPITAL** See Rush-Copley Medical Center

## BARRINGTON—Lake County

★ ⇑ **ADVOCATE GOOD SHEPHERD HOSPITAL (140291)**, 450 West Highway 22, Zip 60010–1919; tel. 847/381–0123, (Nonreporting) **A**2 10 21 **F**3 11 12 13 15 17 18 20 22 24 26 28 29 30 31 34 35 36 37 40 43 45 46 47 48 49 50 54 57 59 63 64 65 68 70 74 75 76 77 78 79 81 82 83 84 85 87 89 92 93 94 96 100 107 108 110 111 114 115 116 117 118 119 120 121 123 124 126 129 130 131 132 135 144 146 148 154 156 **P**8 **S** Advocate Aurora Health, Downers Grove, IL
Primary Contact: Karen A. Lambert, President
CFO: George Teufel, Vice President Finance
CMO: Barry Rosen, M.D., Vice President Medical Management
CIO: Chuck Malik, Director Information Systems
CHR: Jason Spigner, Vice President Human Resources
CNO: Marianne D Araujo, R.N., Ph.D., FACHE, Vice President Nursing and Chief Nurse Executive
Web address: www.advocatehealth.com/gshp/
**Control:** Church operated, Nongovernment, not–for–profit **Service:** General medical and surgical

**Staffed Beds:** 176 **Admissions:** 9708 **Census:** 102 **Outpatient Visits:** 254697 **Births:** 1095 **Total Expense ($000):** 258536 **Payroll Expense ($000):** 78177 **Personnel:** 1354

⇑ **GOOD SHEPHERD HOSPITAL** See Advocate Good Shepherd Hospital

## BELLEVILLE—St. Clair County

★ ○ **MEMORIAL HOSPITAL (140185)**, 4500 Memorial Drive, Zip 62226–5399; tel. 618/233–7750, (Total facility includes 69 beds in nursing home–type unit) (Nonreporting) **A**3 10 11 **F**3 11 13 15 18 20 22 24 26 28 29 30 31 34 40 45 46 47 48 49 51 53 54 57 59 64 67 70 74 76 77 79 81 82 84 85 87 91 92 93 94 107 108 110 111 114 115 118 119 126 128 129 130 131 132 145 146 147 148 149 156 **S** BJC HealthCare, Saint Louis, MO
Primary Contact: Michael T. McManus, President
CFO: Jane Gusmano, Interim Vice President Finance
CMO: William Casperson, M.D., Vice President Medical Affairs
CIO: Jennifer Meinkoth, Executive Director, IS
CHR: John C Ziegler, FACHE, Vice President Human Resources
CNO: Teresa Halloran, Ph.D., R.N., Vice President Nursing Services
Web address: www.memhosp.com
**Control:** Other not–for–profit (including NFP Corporation) **Service:** General medical and surgical

**Staffed Beds:** 217 **Admissions:** 11883 **Census:** 194 **Outpatient Visits:** 164026 **Births:** 449 **Total Expense ($000):** 248179 **Payroll Expense ($000):** 102020 **Personnel:** 1545

## BENTON—Franklin County

**FRANKLIN HOSPITAL** See Franklin Hospital District

**FRANKLIN HOSPITAL DISTRICT (141321)**, 201 Bailey Lane, Zip 62812–1969; tel. 618/439–3161, (Nonreporting) **A**10 18 **F**11 15 29 34 35 40 45 56 57 59 63 68 75 77 81 97 107 115 119 127 130 133
Primary Contact: James Johnson, Chief Executive Officer
COO: Derek Johnson SrChief Operating Officer
CFO: Rikki S Bonthron, Chief Financial Officer
CMO: Richard Rethorst, Chief of Medical Staff
CIO: David Williams, Director Information Technology
CNO: Terri Hermann, R.N., Chief Nursing Officer
Web address: www.franklinhospital.net
**Control:** Hospital district or authority, Government, Nonfederal **Service:** General medical and surgical

**Staffed Beds:** 16 **Admissions:** 285 **Census:** 2 **Outpatient Visits:** 42838 **Births:** 0 **Total Expense ($000):** 19839 **Payroll Expense ($000):** 8442 **Personnel:** 200

## BERWYN—Cook County

☒ **MACNEAL HOSPITAL (140054)**, 3249 South Oak Park Avenue, Zip 60402–0715; tel. 708/783–9100, (Nonreporting) **A**1 2 3 5 8 10 19 **F**3 5 12 13 15 18 19 20 22 24 26 28 29 30 31 34 35 37 38 40 41 43 44 45 46 47 48 49 50 54 56 57 58 59 64 65 68 70 74 75 76 77 78 79 81 82 85 86 87 89 90 91 93 96 97 98 100 101 102 103 104 105 107 108 110 111 114 118 126 128 130 131 132 144 146 147 148 149 150 152 153 **P**5 6 **S** Trinity Health, Livonia, MI
Primary Contact: Mary Elizabeth. Cleary, President
CMO: Charles Bareis, M.D., Medical Director
CIO: Tom Haslett, Interim Chief Information Officer
Web address: www.macneal.com
**Control:** Other not–for–profit (including NFP Corporation) **Service:** General medical and surgical

**Staffed Beds:** 358 **Admissions:** 13474 **Census:** 174 **Outpatient Visits:** 232297 **Births:** 1088 **Personnel:** 1650

**UNITYHEALTH MACNEAL HOSPITAL** See Macneal Hospital

## BLOOMINGTON—Mclean County

☒ **OSF ST. JOSEPH MEDICAL CENTER (140162)**, 2200 East Washington Street, Zip 61701–4323; tel. 309/662–3311, (Total facility includes 12 beds in nursing home–type unit) (Nonreporting) **A**1 2 3 10 **F**3 11 12 13 15 18 20 22 24 26 28 30 31 34 35 37 40 43 45 49 50 51 53 54 57 59 60 61 64 65 68 70 74 75 76 77 78 79 81 82 84 85 86 87 89 92 93 96 97 107 108 110 111 114 115 118 119 126 127 128 129 130 131 132 135 144 146 147 148 149 150 154 156 157 **S** OSF Healthcare, Peoria, IL
Primary Contact: Lynn Fulton, President
CFO: John R Zell, Chief Financial Officer
CMO: Paul E Pedersen, M.D., Vice President and Chief Medical Officer
CHR: Kelley Wagner, Director Employee Relations
CNO: Toni Bishop-McWain, Chief Nursing Officer
Web address: www.osfstjoseph.org
**Control:** Church operated, Nongovernment, not–for–profit **Service:** General medical and surgical

**Staffed Beds:** 149 **Admissions:** 7335 **Census:** 78 **Outpatient Visits:** 168757 **Births:** 785 **Total Expense ($000):** 155671 **Payroll Expense ($000):** 49242 **Personnel:** 831

**ST JOSEPH MEDICAL CENTER** See OSF St. Joseph Medical Center

**IL**

---

**Hospital, Medicare Provider Number, Address, Telephone, Approval, Facility, and Physician Codes, Health Care System**

★ American Hospital Association (AHA) membership  ○ Healthcare Facilities Accreditation Program  ⇑ Center for Improvement in Healthcare Quality Accreditation
☐ The Joint Commission accreditation  ◇ DNV Healthcare Inc. accreditation  △ Commission on Accreditation of Rehabilitation Facilities (CARF) accreditation

## BOLINGBROOK—Will County

**ADVENTIST MEDICAL CENTER BOLINGBROOK** See Amita Health Adventist Medical Center Bolingbrook

☒ **AMITA HEALTH ADVENTIST MEDICAL CENTER BOLINGBROOK (140304)**, 500 Remington Boulevard, Zip 60440–4906; tel. 630/312–5000, (Nonreporting) **A**1 10 **F**3 12 13 15 18 20 22 28 29 30 31 34 35 37 40 41 43 44 45 46 49 50 54 56 57 59 61 64 70 73 74 76 78 79 81 82 85 86 87 98 100 101 102 103 107 108 110 111 114 115 119 130 132 146 147 149 154 **S** AdventHealth, Altamonte Springs, FL
Primary Contact: Bruce C. Christian, Chief Executive Officer
COO: Richard Roehr, Chief Operating Officer
CFO: Rebecca Mathis, Chief Financial Officer
CMO: Richard Carroll, M.D., Chief Medical officer
CIO: John McLendon, Senior Vice President and Chief Information Officer
CHR: Katie Baio, Human Resource Director
CNO: Obed Cruz, Vice President and Chief Nursing Officer
Web address: www.keepingyouwell.com/abh/
**Control:** Church operated, Nongovernment, not–for–profit **Service:** General medical and surgical

**Staffed Beds:** 134 **Admissions:** 6244 **Census:** 70 **Outpatient Visits:** 99753 **Births:** 861 **Total Expense ($000):** 112100 **Payroll Expense ($000):** 38328 **Personnel:** 449

## BREESE—Clinton County

☒ **HSHS ST. JOSEPH'S HOSPITAL (140145)**, 9515 Holy Cross Lane, Zip 62230–3618, Mailing Address: PO Box 99, Zip 62230–0099; tel. 618/526–4511, (Nonreporting) **A**1 10 **S** HSHS Hospital Sisters Health System, Springfield, IL
Primary Contact: Chris Klay, President and Chief Executive Officer
CFO: John Jeffries, Director Finance
CHR: Jed Driemeyer, Director of Human Resources
CNO: Zachary Yoder, Chief Nursing Officer
Web address: www.stjoebreese.com
**Control:** Church operated, Nongovernment, not–for–profit **Service:** General medical and surgical

**Staffed Beds:** 65

**ST. JOSEPH'S HOSPITAL** See Hshs St. Joseph's Hospital

## CANTON—Fulton County

**GRAHAM HOSPITAL** See Graham Hospital Association

☒ **GRAHAM HOSPITAL ASSOCIATION (140001)**, 210 West Walnut Street, Zip 61520–2497; tel. 309/647–5240, (Total facility includes 38 beds in nursing home–type unit) (Nonreporting) **A**1 3 10 20 **F**3 11 13 15 26 28 29 30 33 40 45 50 53 54 57 59 64 65 67 70 75 76 79 81 82 85 87 89 91 97 107 108 110 111 115 119 124 126 127 128 129 130 131 132 135 143 144 145 146 **P**3
Primary Contact: Robert G. Senneff, FACHE, President and Chief Executive Officer
CFO: Eric Franz, Vice President, Finance and Chief Financial Officer
CIO: Jim Schreiner, Chief Information Officer
CHR: Canise A McComb, Director Human Resources
CNO: Teresa L McConkey, MSN, R.N., Vice President of Nursing and Chief Nursing Officer
Web address: www.grahamhealthsystem.org
**Control:** Other not–for–profit (including NFP Corporation) **Service:** General medical and surgical

**Staffed Beds:** 87 **Admissions:** 2299 **Census:** 46 **Outpatient Visits:** 240476 **Births:** 226 **Total Expense ($000):** 88553 **Payroll Expense ($000):** 33886 **Personnel:** 647

## CARBONDALE—Jackson County

☒ **MEMORIAL HOSPITAL OF CARBONDALE (140164)**, 405 West Jackson Street, Zip 62901–1467, Mailing Address: P.O. Box 10000, Zip 62902–9000; tel. 618/549–0721, (Nonreporting) **A**1 2 3 5 10 13 19 **F**3 11 13 17 18 20 22 24 26 28 29 30 31 34 35 36 38 40 45 46 47 48 49 54 56 57 59 64 68 70 72 74 75 76 77 78 79 81 82 83 84 85 86 87 89 100 101 102 104 107 108 111 112 114 115 116 117 118 119 120 121 124 126 130 131 132 135 145 146 147 148 149 154 156 **P**1 **S** Southern Illinois Healthcare, Carbondale, IL
Primary Contact: Al Taylor, Vice President and Administrator
CFO: Michael Kasser, Vice President Chief Financial Officer and Treasurer
CMO: Marci Moore-Connelly, M.D., Vice President Chief Medical Officer
CIO: David Holland, Vice President Chief Innovation Officer
CHR: Pamela S Henderson, Vice President Human Resources
Web address: www.sih.net
**Control:** Other not–for–profit (including NFP Corporation) **Service:** General medical and surgical

**Staffed Beds:** 167 **Admissions:** 10492 **Census:** 100 **Outpatient Visits:** 136191 **Births:** 2181 **Total Expense ($000):** 308976 **Payroll Expense ($000):** 68712 **Personnel:** 1142

## CARLINVILLE—Macoupin County

★ ○ **CARLINVILLE AREA HOSPITAL (141347)**, 20733 North Broad Street, Zip 62626–1499; tel. 217/854–3141, (Nonreporting) **A**10 11 18 **F**11 15 28 29 34 35 40 45 64 77 79 81 91 93 107 110 115 127 129 133 148 149 150 154 **P**6 **S** HealthTech Management Services, Brentwood, TN
Primary Contact: Kenneth G. Reid, President and Chief Executive Officer
CFO: Mike Brown, Chief Financial Officer
CMO: Therese Polo, Medical Staff President
CIO: Jerod Cottingham, Director Information Systems
CHR: Tracy Koster, Director Human Resources
CNO: Sara McPeak, Chief Nursing Officer
Web address: www.cahcare.com
**Control:** Other not–for–profit (including NFP Corporation) **Service:** General medical and surgical

**Staffed Beds:** 25 **Admissions:** 502 **Census:** 7 **Outpatient Visits:** 26228 **Births:** 0 **Total Expense ($000):** 27327 **Payroll Expense ($000):** 11047 **Personnel:** 194

## CARROLLTON—Greene County

**THOMAS H. BOYD MEMORIAL HOSPITAL (141300)**, 800 School Street, Zip 62016–1498; tel. 217/942–6946, (Nonreporting) **A**10 18
Primary Contact: Deborah Campbell, Administrator
CHR: Lisa Eldridge, Human Resources Officer
**Control:** Other not–for–profit (including NFP Corporation) **Service:** General medical and surgical

**Staffed Beds:** 65

## CARTHAGE—Hancock County

☐ **MEMORIAL HOSPITAL (141305)**, 1454 North County Road 2050, Zip 62321–3551, Mailing Address: P.O. Box 160, Zip 62321–0160; tel. 217/357–8500, (Nonreporting) **A**1 10 18 **S** UnityPoint Health, West Des Moines, IA
Primary Contact: Ada Bair, Chief Executive Officer
COO: Florine Dixon, Chief Operating Officer
CFO: Teresa Smith, Chief Financial Officer
CIO: Syndi Horn, Director Information Systems
CHR: Dan Smith, Director Human Resources
Web address: www.mhtlc.org
**Control:** Other not–for–profit (including NFP Corporation) **Service:** General medical and surgical

**Staffed Beds:** 18

## CENTRALIA—Marion County

☒ **SSM HEALTH ST. MARY'S HOSPITAL CENTRALIA (140034)**, 400 North Pleasant Avenue, Zip 62801–3056; tel. 618/436–8000, (Nonreporting) **A**1 2 10 **F**3 5 11 12 13 15 18 20 22 26 28 29 30 31 32 34 35 37 38 40 44 45 46 50 51 54 56 57 59 60 61 64 68 70 73 74 75 76 77 78 79 80 81 82 84 85 86 87 89 90 91 92 93 94 98 99 100 101 102 103 104 105 107 108 110 111 114 118 119 120 121 123 127 129 130 131 132 135 144 146 147 148 149 152 153 156 157 **P**6 8 **S** SSM Health, Saint Louis, MO
Primary Contact: Damon R. Harbison, President
CFO: Matthew Kinsella, Chief Financial Officer
CMO: Rajendra Shroff, M.D., Administrative Medical Director
CIO: Steve Murphy, Director Information Systems
CHR: Brenda Alexander, System Vice President, Human Resources
CNO: Lisa DiMarco, Chief Nursing Officer
Web address: www.https://www.ssmhealth.com/locations/st-marys-hospital-centralia
**Control:** Church operated, Nongovernment, not–for–profit **Service:** General medical and surgical

**Staffed Beds:** 124 **Admissions:** 4748 **Census:** 55 **Outpatient Visits:** 206935 **Births:** 272 **Total Expense ($000):** 96376 **Payroll Expense ($000):** 32214 **Personnel:** 612

**ST. MARY'S HOSPITAL** See Ssm Health St. Mary's Hospital Centralia

*Many Facility Codes have changed. Please refer to the AHA Guide Code Chart.* © 2021 AHA Guide

IL

## CENTREVILLE—St. Clair County

☐ **TOUCHETTE REGIONAL HOSPITAL (140077)**, 5900 Bond Avenue, Zip 62207–2326; tel. 618/332–3060, (Nonreporting) **A**1 5 10 **F**3 11 13 15 18 29 30 39 40 45 47 50 55 62 64 70 75 76 79 81 85 87 92 98 101 102 104 105 107 108 114 119 129 130 135 143 146 148 149 150 153 156 **P**6
Primary Contact: Larry W. McCulley, President and Chief Executive Officer
COO: Tom Mikkelson, M.D., Interim Chief Operating Officer
CFO: John Majchrzak, Chief Financial Officer
CMO: Tom Mikkelson, M.D., Vice President Medical Affairs
Web address: www.touchette.org
**Control:** Other not–for–profit (including NFP Corporation) **Service:** General medical and surgical

**Staffed Beds:** 119 **Admissions:** 2277 **Census:** 23 **Outpatient Visits:** 43207 **Births:** 32 **Total Expense ($000):** 56935 **Payroll Expense ($000):** 23596 **Personnel:** 401

**TOUCHETTE REGIONAL HOSPITALS** See Touchette Regional Hospital

## CHAMPAIGN—Champaign County

**CARLE PAVILION** See The Pavilion

☐ **THE PAVILION (144029)**, 809 West Church Street, Zip 61820–3399; tel. 217/373–1700, (Nonreporting) **A**1 10 **S** Universal Health Services, Inc., King of Prussia, PA
Primary Contact: Joseph King, Acting Chief Executive Officer
CFO: Edith Frasca, Controller and Chief Financial Officer
Web address: www.pavilionhospital.com
**Control:** Corporation, Investor–owned (for–profit) **Service:** Psychiatric

**Staffed Beds:** 106

## CHESTER—Randolph County

☐ **CHESTER MENTAL HEALTH CENTER**, Chester Road, Zip 62233–0031, Mailing Address: Box 31, Zip 62233–0031; tel. 618/826–4571, (Nonreporting) **A**1 **S** Division of Mental Health, Department of Human Services, Springfield, IL
Primary Contact: Leah Hammel, Acting Administrator
CFO: Sarah Imhoff, Business Administrator
CMO: Maitra Rupa, M.D., Acting Medical Director
CIO: Anthony Young, Information Services Specialist
CHR: Kim Holsapple, Human Resource Specialist
CNO: Jennifer Klingeman, Director of Nursing
**Control:** State, Government, Nonfederal **Service:** Psychiatric

**Staffed Beds:** 245

☐ **MEMORIAL HOSPITAL (141338)**, 1900 State Street, Zip 62233–1116, Mailing Address: P.O. Box 609, Zip 62233–0609; tel. 618/826–4581, (Nonreporting) **A**1 10 18
Primary Contact: Brett Bollmann, Administrator
CFO: Gail Miesner, Chief Financial Officer
CMO: Alan Liefer, M.D., President Medical Staff
CIO: Becky Bunselmeyer, Director Information Services
CHR: May Rose, Director Human Resources
Web address: www.mhchester.com
**Control:** Hospital district or authority, Government, Nonfederal **Service:** General medical and surgical

**Staffed Beds:** 25

## CHICAGO—Cook County

**ADVOCATE BETHANY HOSPITAL** See RML Specialty Hospital

★ ⇑ **ADVOCATE ILLINOIS MASONIC MEDICAL CENTER (140182)**, 836 West Wellington Avenue, Zip 60657–5147; tel. 773/975–1600, (Nonreporting) **A**2 3 5 8 10 21 **F**3 5 12 13 15 17 18 19 20 22 24 26 28 29 30 31 34 35 37 38 40 43 44 45 46 47 48 49 50 53 54 55 56 59 60 61 64 66 68 70 71 72 73 74 75 76 77 78 79 81 82 84 85 86 87 89 90 92 93 96 97 98 100 101 102 104 107 110 111 114 115 116 117 118 119 120 121 123 124 126 129 130 131 132 134 135 141 143 146 147 148 149 153 154 **P**8 **S** Advocate Aurora Health, Downers Grove, IL
Primary Contact: Susan Nordstrom. Lopez, President
CFO: Jack Gilbert, Vice President Finance and Facilities
CMO: Clifton Clarke, Vice President Medical Management
CIO: Chuck Malik, Director Information Systems
CHR: Katie Bata, Vice President Human Resources
Web address: www.advocatehealth.com/masonic
**Control:** Other not–for–profit (including NFP Corporation) **Service:** General medical and surgical

**Staffed Beds:** 319 **Admissions:** 13715 **Census:** 179 **Outpatient Visits:** 223255 **Births:** 1921 **Total Expense ($000):** 393346 **Payroll Expense ($000):** 142352 **Personnel:** 2353

⇑ **ADVOCATE NORTH SIDE HEALTH** See Advocate Illinois Masonic Medical Center

★ ⇑ **ADVOCATE TRINITY HOSPITAL (140048)**, 2320 East 93rd Street, Zip 60617–3909; tel. 773/967–2000, (Nonreporting) **A**2 10 21 **F**3 13 15 18 20 22 24 26 28 29 30 31 34 35 40 45 46 49 50 53 55 56 57 59 60 63 64 65 68 70 74 75 76 77 78 79 81 82 84 87 89 92 93 107 110 111 114 115 119 130 132 135 146 148 154 156 **P**8 **S** Advocate Aurora Health, Downers Grove, IL
Primary Contact: Rashard Johnson, President
COO: Dan Doherty, Vice President, Operations
CFO: Maureen Morrison, Vice President, Finance
CMO: James Keller, M.D., Vice President, Medical Management
CIO: Bonita Brown-Roberts, Director Information Systems
CHR: Kristin Landini, Vice President, Human Resources
CNO: Jacquelyn Whitten, MSN, R.N., Chief Nursing Executive, Vice President of Nursing
Web address: www.https://www.advocatehealth.com/trin/
**Control:** Church operated, Nongovernment, not–for–profit **Service:** General medical and surgical

**Staffed Beds:** 142 **Admissions:** 7377 **Census:** 81 **Outpatient Visits:** 77217 **Births:** 628 **Total Expense ($000):** 154479 **Payroll Expense ($000):** 54293 **Personnel:** 825

⊠ △ **AMITA HEALTH RESURRECTION MEDICAL CENTER (140117)**, 7435 West Talcott Avenue, Zip 60631–3746; tel. 773/774–8000, (Nonreporting) **A**1 2 3 5 7 10 13 **F**3 11 13 15 17 18 19 20 22 24 26 28 29 30 31 34 35 37 38 39 40 41 45 46 47 49 50 53 57 58 59 60 62 64 66 68 70 73 74 75 76 78 79 81 82 83 84 85 86 87 89 90 93 96 97 100 107 108 110 111 113 114 115 117 118 119 120 121 123 124 126 130 131 132 133 135 146 147 148 154 **S** Ascension Healthcare, Saint Louis, MO
Primary Contact: Scott L. Teffeteller, SVP, Regional Operating Officer, Chicago Metro & President and CEO, AMITA Health Resurrection Medica
CFO: Colleen Koppenhaver, Interim Chief Financial Officer
CMO: David Bordo, M.D., Regional Chief Medical Officer and AMITA Health Chief Clinical Reliability Officer
CHR: Paula Zawojski, Regional Director, Human Resources
CNO: Trisha E. Musich, R.N., Regional Chief Nursing Officer, Chicago Metro
Web address: www.presencehealth.org
**Control:** Church operated, Nongovernment, not–for–profit **Service:** General medical and surgical

**Staffed Beds:** 337 **Admissions:** 12326 **Census:** 178 **Outpatient Visits:** 133281 **Births:** 982 **Total Expense ($000):** 231987 **Payroll Expense ($000):** 85169 **Personnel:** 899

⊠ **AMITA HEALTH SAINT JOSEPH HOSPITAL (140224)**, 2900 North Lake Shore Drive, Zip 60657–6274; tel. 773/665–3000, (Nonreporting) **A**1 2 3 5 10 **F**3 5 7 11 12 13 15 18 19 20 22 24 25 26 28 29 30 32 33 34 35 36 38 39 40 41 45 46 47 48 49 50 53 54 55 56 57 58 59 60 61 63 64 65 66 68 70 72 74 75 76 77 78 79 81 82 84 85 86 87 89 90 92 93 96 97 98 101 102 103 104 107 108 110 111 114 115 117 118 119 120 121 122 123 124 126 128 129 130 131 132 135 143 145 146 147 148 151 152 154 156 **P**8 **S** Ascension Healthcare, Saint Louis, MO
Primary Contact: James D. Baird, President
CFO: Stanley Kazmierczak, Controller
CMO: M Todd Grendon, M.D., President Medical Staff
CIO: George Chessum, Senior Vice President Information Systems and Chief Information Officer
CHR: Denise Brown, Vice President Human Resources
Web address: www.reshealth.org
**Control:** Church operated, Nongovernment, not–for–profit **Service:** General medical and surgical

**Staffed Beds:** 361 **Admissions:** 9783 **Census:** 141 **Outpatient Visits:** 78018 **Births:** 826 **Total Expense ($000):** 186001 **Payroll Expense ($000):** 67339 **Personnel:** 606

IL

---

**Hospital, Medicare Provider Number, Address, Telephone, Approval, Facility, and Physician Codes, Health Care System**

★ American Hospital Association (AHA) membership
☐ The Joint Commission accreditation
◯ Healthcare Facilities Accreditation Program
◇ DNV Healthcare Inc. accreditation
⇑ Center for Improvement in Healthcare Quality Accreditation
△ Commission on Accreditation of Rehabilitation Facilities (CARF) accreditation

⊠ **AMITA HEALTH SAINTS MARY & ELIZABETH MEDICAL CENTER (140180)**, 2233 West Division Street, Zip 60622–3086; tel. 312/770–2000, (Includes PRESENCE SAINTS MARY & ELIZABETH MEDICAL CENTER, CLAREMONT AVENUE, Mailing address: 1431 North Claremont Avenue, Chicago, Illinois, Zip 60622–1791; tel. 773/278–2000; Martin H. Judd, Regional President and Chief Executive Officer), (Nonreporting) **A**1 2 3 5 10 **F**2 3 4 13 15 18 19 20 22 24 26 28 29 30 31 32 34 35 36 38 40 45 46 47 49 50 52 57 58 59 60 64 65 66 68 70 74 75 76 77 78 79 81 82 84 85 86 87 89 90 91 92 93 94 96 98 99 100 101 102 103 107 108 110 111 114 115 116 117 119 120 121 123 126 128 129 130 132 135 143 146 147 148 149 151 154 **S** Ascension Healthcare, Saint Louis, MO
Primary Contact: Robert Dahl, President and Chief Executive Officer
CFO: Bob Cech, Regional Finance Officer
CMO: Laura Concannon, M.D., Regional Chief Medical Officer
CIO: Cheryl Rodenfels, System Vice President, IT Operations
CHR: Melanie Saenz, Regional Human Resources Officer
CNO: Suzanne Lambert, R.N., Regional Chief Nursing Officer and Support Services
Web address: www.presencehealth.org/presence-saints-mary-and-elizabeth-medical-center-chicago
**Control**: Church operated, Nongovernment, not–for–profit **Service**: General medical and surgical

**Staffed Beds**: 495 **Admissions**: 17015 **Census**: 263 **Outpatient Visits**: 161529 **Births**: 900 **Total Expense ($000)**: 331103 **Payroll Expense ($000)**: 114340

⊠ **ANN & ROBERT H. LURIE CHILDREN'S HOSPITAL OF CHICAGO (143300)**, 225 East Chicago Avenue, Zip 60611–2991; tel. 312/227–4000, (Nonreporting) **A**1 3 5 8 10 **F**3 8 9 11 12 17 18 19 20 21 22 23 24 25 26 27 28 29 30 31 32 34 35 36 37 38 39 40 41 43 44 45 46 48 49 50 51 52 54 55 57 58 59 60 61 63 64 65 68 71 72 74 75 78 79 81 82 84 85 86 87 88 89 91 92 93 94 96 97 98 99 100 101 102 104 105 107 108 111 115 116 117 119 124 126 129 130 131 132 134 136 137 138 139 141 142 144 146 148 149 150 154
Primary Contact: Thomas Shanley, President and Chief Executive Officer
COO: Michelle Stephenson, R.N., Executive Vice President & Chief Operations Officer
CFO: Ron Blaustein, Chief Financial Officer
CMO: Michael Kelleher, Chief Medical Officer
CIO: Lisa Dykstra, Senior Vice President and Chief Information Officer
CHR: Joani Duncan, Chief Human Resource Officer
CNO: Brian M Stahulak, R.N., Chief Nursing Officer
Web address: www.luriechildrens.org
**Control**: Other not–for–profit (including NFP Corporation) **Service**: Children's general medical and surgical

**Staffed Beds**: 336 **Admissions**: 10605 **Census**: 244 **Outpatient Visits**: 666858 **Births**: 0 **Total Expense ($000)**: 948494 **Payroll Expense ($000)**: 421908 **Personnel**: 6116

**BERNARD MITCHELL HOSPITAL** See University of Chicago Medical Center, Chicago

**CHICAGO LYING-IN (CLI)** See University of Chicago Medical Center, Chicago

**CHICAGO LYING-IN HOSPITAL** See Chicago Lying-In (CLI)

☐ **CHICAGO-READ MENTAL HEALTH CENTER (144010)**, 4200 North Oak Park Avenue, Zip 60634–1457; tel. 773/794–4000, (Nonreporting) **A**1 10 **S** Division of Mental Health, Department of Human Services, Springfield, IL
Primary Contact: Ellen Otomo, Interim Hospital Administrator
**Control**: State, Government, Nonfederal **Service**: Psychiatric

**Staffed Beds**: 200

**CHILDREN'S MEMORIAL HOSPITAL** See Ann & Robert H. Lurie Children's Hospital of Chicago

**COMER CHILDREN'S HOSPITAL** See University of Chicago Medical Center, Chicago

☐ **COMMUNITY FIRST MEDICAL CENTER (140251)**, 5645 West Addison Street, Zip 60634–4403; tel. 773/282–7000, (Nonreporting) **A**1 3 10
Primary Contact: Sheila Senn, PsyD, Chief Clinical and Administrative Officer
COO: Dennis FitzMaurice, Vice President, Professional Services
CFO: Richard Franco, Chief Financial Officer
CMO: David Bordo, M.D., Vice President and Chief Medical Officer
CIO: George Chessum, Senior Vice President and Chief Information Officer
CHR: Ivy McKinley, Regional Human Resources Officer
Web address: www.cfmedicalcenter.com
**Control**: Church operated, Nongovernment, not–for–profit **Service**: General medical and surgical

**Staffed Beds**: 279

☐ **GARFIELD PARK HOSPITAL (144039)**, 520 North Ridgeway Avenue, Zip 60624–1232; tel. 773/265–3700, (Nonreporting) **A**1 10 **F**98 99 101 102 104 105 130 132 135 153 154 **S** Universal Health Services, Inc., King of Prussia, PA
Primary Contact: Steven Airhart, Chief Executive Officer
CMO: Tina Mahera, M.D., Chief Medical Officer
CHR: Janice Clark, Manager Human Resources
Web address: www.garfieldparkhospital.com
**Control**: Corporation, Investor–owned (for–profit) **Service**: Children's hospital psychiatric

**Staffed Beds**: 88 **Admissions**: 1215 **Census**: 44 **Outpatient Visits**: 6903 **Births**: 0 **Total Expense ($000)**: 14252 **Payroll Expense ($000)**: 7070 **Personnel**: 136

☐ **HARTGROVE HOSPITAL (144026)**, 5730 West Roosevelt Road, Zip 60644–1580; tel. 773/413–1700, (Nonreporting) **A**1 3 10 **F**5 29 38 68 98 99 100 101 102 103 104 105 152 153 154 **S** Universal Health Services, Inc., King of Prussia, PA
Primary Contact: Steven Airhart, Chief Executive Officer
COO: Patrick Sanders, Chief Operating Officer
CFO: Joseph Remer, Chief Financial Officer
CMO: Teresa Poprawski, Chief Medical Officer
CHR: Alanna Barker, Director of Human Resources
CNO: Jody Bhambra, Chief Nursing Officer
Web address: www.hartgrovehospital.com
**Control**: Corporation, Investor–owned (for–profit) **Service**: Psychiatric

**Staffed Beds**: 160 **Admissions**: 4077 **Census**: 137 **Outpatient Visits**: 30762 **Births**: 0 **Total Expense ($000)**: 34386 **Payroll Expense ($000)**: 17022 **Personnel**: 282

★ ○ **HOLY CROSS HOSPITAL (140133)**, 2701 West 68th Street, Zip 60629–1882; tel. 773/884–9000, (Nonreporting) **A**3 10 11 **F**3 9 11 15 17 18 20 22 26 29 30 34 35 38 40 44 45 46 49 50 56 57 59 64 66 68 70 74 75 77 78 81 85 86 87 92 93 97 98 100 101 102 104 107 108 110 111 114 115 118 119 121 123 130 132 134 148 153 154 **S** Sinai Health System, Chicago, IL
Primary Contact: Lori Pacura, MSN, R.N., President
COO: Donnica Austin, Vice President, Operations
CFO: Charles Weis, Executive Vice President and Chief Financial Officer
CMO: James Richardson, Chief Medical Officer
CHR: Ann Hatches, Director, Human Resources
CNO: Deborah Davisson, MSN, Chief Nursing Officer and Vice President, Patient Care Services
Web address: www.holycrosshospital.org
**Control**: Other not–for–profit (including NFP Corporation) **Service**: General medical and surgical

**Staffed Beds**: 155 **Admissions**: 8433 **Census**: 111 **Outpatient Visits**: 69600 **Births**: 161 **Total Expense ($000)**: 120733 **Payroll Expense ($000)**: 54811 **Personnel**: 777

**INSTITUTE OF PSYCHIATRY** See Stone Institute of Psychiatry

**JACKSON PARK HOSPITAL** See Jackson Park Hospital and Medical Center

☐ **JACKSON PARK HOSPITAL AND MEDICAL CENTER (140177)**, 7531 Stony Island Avenue, Zip 60649–3993; tel. 773/947–7500, (Nonreporting) **A**1 3 10
Primary Contact: William Dorsey, M.D., Board Chairman and Chief Executive Officer
COO: Randall Smith, Executive Vice President
CFO: Nelson Vasquez, Vice President Finance
CMO: Bangalore Murthy, M.D., Director Medical Staff
CIO: Thomas Pankow, Chief Information Officer
CHR: Tracey Jones, Director Human Resources
Web address: www.jacksonparkhospital.org
**Control**: Other not–for–profit (including NFP Corporation) **Service**: General medical and surgical

**Staffed Beds**: 118

**JESSE BROWN VETERANS AFFAIRS CHICAGO HEALTH CARE SYSTEM** See Jesse Brown Veterans Affairs Medical Center

⊠ △ **JESSE BROWN VETERANS AFFAIRS MEDICAL CENTER**, 820 South Damen, Zip 60612–3776; tel. 312/569–8387, (Nonreporting) **A**1 3 5 7 8 **S** Department of Veterans Affairs, Washington, DC
Primary Contact: Rick Ament, Medical Center Director
COO: Michelle Blakely, FACHE, Ph.D., Associate Director
CFO: Kalpana Mehta, Chief Fiscal Services
CMO: Wendy W Brown, M.D., M.P.H., Chief of Staff
CIO: Howard Loewenstein, Chief Information Resource Management Services
CHR: Wayne Davis, Manager Human Resources
Web address: www.chicago.va.gov/
**Control**: Veterans Affairs, Government, federal **Service**: General medical and surgical

**Staffed Beds**: 207

*Many Facility Codes have changed. Please refer to the AHA Guide Code Chart.* © 2021 AHA Guide

**JOHN H. STROGER JR. HOSPITAL OF COOK COUNTY (140124)**, 1969 West Ogden Avenue, Zip 60612–3714; tel. 312/864–6000, (Nonreporting) **A**1 2 3 5 8 10 13 **F**3 5 11 13 15 16 17 18 19 20 22 24 29 30 31 34 35 36 38 39 40 41 43 44 45 46 47 48 49 50 51 52 54 55 56 57 58 59 60 61 64 65 68 70 72 74 75 76 77 78 79 81 82 84 85 86 87 88 89 91 92 93 94 97 99 100 101 102 103 104 107 108 110 111 114 115 118 119 120 121 122 123 129 130 132 134 135 143 146 147 148 149 154 156 **P**6 **S** Cook County Health and Hospitals System, Chicago, IL
Primary Contact: Debra D. Carey, Interim Chief Executive Officer
CFO: John R Morales, Chief Financial Officer
CMO: Claudia Fegan, M.D., Chief Medical Officer
CIO: Bala Hota, Interim Chief Information Officer
CHR: Paris I Partee, Associate Administrator and Director Human Resources
CNO: Antoinette Williams, Chief Nursing Officer
Web address: www.cookcountyhealth.net
**Control**: County, Government, Nonfederal **Service**: General medical and surgical

**Staffed Beds: 446 Admissions:** 15885 **Census:** 239 **Births:** 1037
**Total Expense ($000):** 957383 **Payroll Expense ($000):** 480461
**Personnel:** 4989

**JOHNSTON R. BOWMAN HEALTH CENTER** See Rush University Medical Center, Chicago

**KINDRED CHICAGO LAKESHORE** See Kindred Chicago-Central Hospital, Chicago

**KINDRED CHICAGO-CENTRAL HOSPITAL (142009)**, 4058 West Melrose Street, Zip 60641–4797; tel. 773/736–7000, (Includes KINDRED CHICAGO LAKESHORE, Mailing address: 6130 North Sheridan Road, Chicago, Illinois, Zip 60660; tel. 773/381–1222; Michael DeLaRosa, Chief Executive Officer; KINDRED HOSPITAL CHICAGO NORTH, Mailing address: 2544 West Montrose Avenue, Chicago, Illinois, Zip 60618–1589; tel. 773/267–2622; Richard Cerceo, Chief Executive Officer), (Nonreporting) **A**1 10 **S** Kindred Healthcare, Louisville, KY
Primary Contact: Al Wazwaz, Chief Executive Officer
COO: Joanne Garcia, Chief Operating Officer
CFO: Mary Treacy Shiff, Chief Financial Officer
Web address: www.khchicagocentral.com
**Control**: Corporation, Investor–owned (for-profit) **Service**: Acute long–term care hospital

**Staffed Beds:** 187

**KINDRED HOSPITAL - LAKESHORE** See Kindred Chicago Lakeshore

**KINDRED HOSPITAL CHICAGO NORTH** See Kindred Chicago-Central Hospital, Chicago

**KINDRED HOSPITAL-CHICAGO NORTH** See Kindred Hospital Chicago North

**LA RABIDA CHILDREN'S HOSPITAL (143301)**, 6501 South Promontory Drive, Zip 60649–1003; tel. 773/363–6700, (Nonreporting) **A**1 3 5 10 **F**3 29 32 34 35 38 41 50 57 59 64 65 74 79 82 85 86 87 89 91 93 94 96 97 99 100 101 104 119 130 132 134 143 144 146 148 149 156 **P**6
Primary Contact: Brenda J. Wolf, President and Chief Executive Officer
CFO: Mark Renfree, Chief Financial Officer
CMO: David Soglin, Chief Medical Officer
CIO: Sheelah Cabrera, Chief Information Officer
CHR: Frances Lefkow, Director Human Resources
Web address: www.larabida.org
**Control**: Other not–for–profit (including NFP Corporation) **Service**: Children's chronic disease

**Staffed Beds: 30 Admissions:** 262 **Census:** 27 **Outpatient Visits:** 33018
**Births:** 0 **Total Expense ($000):** 58517 **Payroll Expense ($000):** 30711
**Personnel:** 459

**LARABIDA CHILDREN'S HOSPITAL** See La Rabida Children's Hospital

★ ○ **LORETTO HOSPITAL (140083)**, 645 South Central Avenue, Zip 60644–5059; tel. 773/626–4300, (Nonreporting) **A**3 10 11 **F**3 4 5 15 18 20 29 30 34 35 39 40 41 43 45 46 50 57 58 59 61 64 68 70 74 75 78 79 81 82 85 86 87 91 92 93 97 98 100 102 104 107 108 110 111 115 119 130 132 135 143 144 146 147 148 149 153 154 156 157
Primary Contact: George Miller, President and Chief Executive Officer
CFO: Kenneth Mcghee, Vice President and Chief Financial Officer
CIO: Syed Haque, Vice President and Chief Information Officer
CHR: Tania A White, Director Human Resources
Web address: www.lorettohospital.org
**Control**: Other not–for–profit (including NFP Corporation) **Service**: General medical and surgical

**Staffed Beds: 177 Admissions:** 3902 **Census:** 49 **Outpatient Visits:** 45218
**Births:** 0 **Total Expense ($000):** 75765 **Payroll Expense ($000):** 35580
**Personnel:** 488

☐ **LOUIS A. WEISS MEMORIAL HOSPITAL (140082)**, 4646 North Marine Drive, Zip 60613–5759; tel. 773/878–8700, (Nonreporting) **A**1 2 3 5 10
Primary Contact: Mary Shehan, R.N., MSN, Chief Executive Officer
CFO: Jeffrey L Meigs, Chief Financial Officer
CIO: Thomas Crawford, Chicago Market Chief Information Officer
CHR: Keoni Nader, Director Human Resources
Web address: www.weisshospital.com
**Control**: Corporation, Investor–owned (for–profit) **Service**: General medical and surgical

**Staffed Beds:** 153

★ ○ **MERCY HOSPITAL AND MEDICAL CENTER (140158)**, 2525 South Michigan Avenue, Zip 60616–2333; tel. 312/567–2000, (Nonreporting) **A**2 3 5 10 11 **S** Trinity Health, Livonia, MI
Primary Contact: Carol L. Schneider, President and Chief Executive Officer
CFO: Eric Krueger, Chief Financial Officer
CMO: Michael McDonnell, M.D., Chief Medical Officer
CIO: John Romeo, Chief Information Officer
CHR: Nancy L Hill-Davis, Vice President Human Resources
Web address: www.mercy-chicago.org
**Control**: Other not–for–profit (including NFP Corporation) **Service**: General medical and surgical

**Staffed Beds:** 354

○ **METHODIST HOSPITAL OF CHICAGO (140197)**, 5025 North Paulina Street, Zip 60640–2772; tel. 773/271–9040, (Nonreporting) **A**10 11
Primary Contact: Joseph Chandy, Administrator
CFO: Jim Gregory, Controller
Web address: www.bethanymethodist.org
**Control**: Other not–for–profit (including NFP Corporation) **Service**: General medical and surgical

**Staffed Beds:** 189

**MOUNT SINAI HOSP MED CENTER** See Mount Sinai Hospital

**MOUNT SINAI HOSPITAL (140018)**, 1500 South Fairfield Avenue, Zip 60608–1729; tel. 773/542–2000, (Includes SINAI CHILDREN'S HOSPITAL, Mailing address: California Avenue at 15th Street, Chicago, Illinois, Zip 60608; tel. 773/542–2000; Karen Teitelbaum, President and Chief Executive Officer), (Nonreporting) **A**1 2 3 5 10 **F**3 9 11 12 13 15 17 18 19 20 22 24 26 29 30 31 34 35 38 40 43 44 45 46 50 56 57 59 60 61 64 66 68 70 72 74 75 76 78 79 81 85 86 87 97 98 100 101 102 104 107 108 110 111 114 115 118 119 121 123 130 132 134 135 143 147 154 **S** Sinai Health System, Chicago, IL
Primary Contact: Loren Chandler, President
CFO: Charles Weis, Chief Financial Officer
CMO: Mark Multach, M.D., Chief Medical Officer
CHR: Ann Hatches, Interim Director Human Resources
CNO: Michele A Mazurek, Interim Vice President Patient Care Services and Chief Nursing Officer
Web address: www.sinai.org
**Control**: Other not–for–profit (including NFP Corporation) **Service**: General medical and surgical

**Staffed Beds: 284 Admissions:** 10949 **Census:** 153 **Outpatient Visits:** 237742 **Births:** 1555 **Total Expense ($000):** 261405 **Payroll Expense ($000):** 102284 **Personnel:** 1576

---

**Hospital, Medicare Provider Number, Address, Telephone, Approval, Facility, and Physician Codes, Health Care System**

★ American Hospital Association (AHA) membership ○ Healthcare Facilities Accreditation Program ⇑ Center for Improvement in Healthcare Quality Accreditation
☐ The Joint Commission accreditation ◇ DNV Healthcare Inc. accreditation △ Commission on Accreditation of Rehabilitation Facilities (CARF) accreditation

IL

☒ **NORTHWESTERN MEMORIAL HOSPITAL (140281)**, 251 East Huron Street, Zip 60611–2908; tel. 312/926–2000, (Includes PRENTICE WOMEN'S HOSPITAL, Mailing address: 250 East Superior Street, Chicago, Illinois, Zip 60611; tel. 312/926–2000; STONE INSTITUTE OF PSYCHIATRY, Mailing address: 251 East Huron Street, Chicago, Illinois, Zip 60611; tel. 312/926–2000), (Nonreporting) **A**1 2 3 5 8 10 19 **F**3 4 5 6 9 11 12 13 14 15 17 18 20 22 24 26 28 29 30 31 33 34 35 36 37 38 39 40 43 44 45 46 47 48 49 50 51 52 54 55 56 57 58 59 60 61 64 65 66 68 70 72 73 74 75 76 77 78 79 80 81 82 84 85 86 87 92 93 94 96 97 98 100 101 102 103 104 107 108 110 111 112 114 115 116 117 118 119 120 121 123 124 126 129 130 131 132 134 135 136 137 138 139 140 141 142 144 145 146 147 148 149 150 153 154 156 157 **S** Northwestern Memorial HealthCare, Chicago, IL
Primary Contact: Julie L. Creamer, President, Northwestern Memorial Hospital and Senior Vice President Northwestern Memorial HealthCare
CFO: Francis D Fraher, Vice President, Finance, Northwestern Memorial Hospital
CMO: Gary Noskin, Senior Vice President and Chief Medical Officer, Northwestern Memorial Hospital
CIO: Carl Christensen, Senior Vice President and Chief Information Officer, Northwestern Memorial HealthCare
CHR: Michael Vivoda, Senior Vice President, Administration
CNO: Kristin Ramsey, R.N., Senior Vice President and Chief Nursing Executive, Northwestern Memorial Hospital
Web address: www.nm.org
**Control**: Other not–for–profit (including NFP Corporation) **Service**: General medical and surgical

**Staffed Beds: 894 Admissions: 47130 Census: 721 Outpatient Visits: 2067356 Births: 11894 Total Expense ($000): 3073437 Payroll Expense ($000): 940341 Personnel: 12260**

☒ ⇑ **NORWEGIAN AMERICAN HOSPITAL (140206)**, 1044 North Francisco Avenue, Zip 60622–2743; tel. 773/292–8200, (Nonreporting) **A**1 3 10 21
Primary Contact: Jose R. Sanchez, President and Chief Executive Officer
COO: Michelle Blakely, FACHE, Ph.D., Chief Operating Officer
CFO: Gary M Krugel, Chief Financial Officer
CIO: Stephen DePooter, Chief Information Officer
CHR: Neil Teatsorth, Vice President Human Resources
CNO: William Duffy, Interim Chief Nursing Officer
Web address: www.nahospital.org
**Control**: Other not–for–profit (including NFP Corporation) **Service**: General medical and surgical

**Staffed Beds: 195**

⇑ **NORWEGIAN-AMERICAN HOSPITAL** See Norwegian American Hospital

**PRENTICE WOMEN'S HOSPITAL** See Northwestern Memorial Hospital, Chicago

**PRESENCE OUR LADY OF THE RESURRECTION MEDICAL CENTER** See Community First Medical Center

**PRESENCE RESURRECTION MEDICAL CENTER** See Amita Health Resurrection Medical Center

**PRESENCE SAINT JOSEPH HOSPITAL** See Amita Health Saint Joseph Hospital

**PRESENCE SAINTS MARY & ELIZABETH MEDICAL CENTER** See Amita Health Saints Mary & Elizabeth Medical Center

☒ **PROVIDENT HOSPITAL OF COOK COUNTY (140300)**, 500 East 51st Street, Zip 60615–2494; tel. 312/572–2000, (Nonreporting) **A**1 3 5 10 **F**3 8 15 18 29 30 34 35 40 45 50 53 57 59 61 64 66 68 78 81 85 87 92 94 104 107 119 130 132 135 143 146 147 149 154 156 **P**6 **S** Cook County Health and Hospitals System, Chicago, IL
Primary Contact: Debra D. Carey, Interim Chief Executive Officer
CFO: Barbara Patterson, Chief Financial Officer
CMO: Aaron Hamb, M.D., Chief Medical Officer
CIO: Donna Hart, Chief Information Officer
Web address: www.ccbhs.org/pages/ProvidentHospitalofCookCounty.htm
**Control**: County, Government, Nonfederal **Service**: General medical and surgical

**Staffed Beds: 25 Admissions: 538 Census: 9 Births: 0 Personnel: 370**

**PROVIDENT MEDICAL CENTER** See Provident Hospital of Cook County

**REHABILITATION INSTITUTE OF CHICAGO** See Shirley Ryan Abilitylab

○ **ROSELAND COMMUNITY HOSPITAL (140068)**, 45 West 111th Street, Zip 60628–4294; tel. 773/995–3000, (Nonreporting) **A**10 11
Primary Contact: Timothy Egan, President and Chief Executive Officer
CFO: Marlo Kemp, Vice President and Chief Financial Officer
CMO: Alan Jackson, M.D., Medical Director
CIO: Mariusz Mazek, Vice President Information Technology and Chief Information Officer
CHR: Paulette Clark, Chief Human Resource Officer
CNO: Jeraldene Shaffer, MSN, Chief Nursing Officer
Web address: www.roselandhospital.org
**Control**: Other not–for–profit (including NFP Corporation) **Service**: General medical and surgical

**Staffed Beds: 134**

☒ △ **RUSH UNIVERSITY MEDICAL CENTER (140119)**, 1653 West Congress Parkway, Zip 60612–3833; tel. 312/942–5000, (Includes JOHNSTON R. BOWMAN HEALTH CENTER, Mailing address: 700 South Paulina, Chicago, Illinois, Zip 60612; tel. 312/942–7000; RUSH CHILDREN'S HOSPITAL, Mailing address: 1653 Wes Congress Parkway, Chicago, Illinois, Zip 60612–3833; tel. 888/352–7874), (Nonreporting) **A**1 2 3 5 7 8 10 **F**2 3 6 8 9 11 12 13 14 15 17 18 19 20 21 22 23 24 25 26 27 29 30 31 32 33 34 35 36 37 38 40 41 43 44 45 46 47 48 49 50 51 52 53 54 55 56 57 58 59 60 61 62 63 64 65 66 68 70 71 72 74 75 76 77 78 79 81 82 83 84 85 86 87 88 89 90 91 92 93 94 95 96 97 98 100 101 102 104 105 106 107 108 110 111 114 115 117 118 119 120 121 123 124 125 126 129 130 131 132 134 135 136 138 139 141 142 145 146 147 148 149 153 154 156 157 **P**8 **S** Rush University Medical Center, Chicago, IL
Primary Contact: Omar Lateef, D.O., Chief Executive Officer
CFO: John P Mordach, Senior Vice President and Chief Financial Officer
CIO: Lac Tran, Senior Vice President Information Services
CHR: Mary Ellen Schopp, Senior Vice President Human Resources
CNO: Angelique Richard, R.N., Ph.D., Vice President Clinical Nursing, Chief Nursing Officer and Associate Dean for Practice, College of Nursing
Web address: www.rush.edu
**Control**: Other not–for–profit (including NFP Corporation) **Service**: General medical and surgical

**Staffed Beds: 684 Admissions: 33676 Census: 493 Outpatient Visits: 603846 Births: 2325 Total Expense ($000): 2018915 Payroll Expense ($000): 870251 Personnel: 9650**

**RUSH-PRESBY-ST LUKE'S MED CTR** See Rush University Medical Center

□ **SAINT ANTHONY HOSPITAL (140095)**, 2875 West 19th Street, Zip 60623–3596; tel. 773/484–1000, (Nonreporting) **A**1 3 10 **F**3 13 15 18 19 29 30 31 32 34 35 40 41 44 49 50 51 54 59 60 64 65 68 70 74 75 76 77 79 81 82 84 85 86 87 89 93 97 98 100 101 102 107 108 110 111 114 115 118 119 130 131 132 143 144 146 147 148 149 150 154 157 **P**8
Primary Contact: Guy A. Medaglia, President and Chief Executive Officer
CFO: Justin Bynum, Chief Financial Officer
CIO: Mark Jennings, Chief Information Officer
CHR: Malinda Yvonne Carter, Vice President Human Resources
Web address: www.sahchicago.org
**Control**: Church operated, Nongovernment, not–for–profit **Service**: General medical and surgical

**Staffed Beds: 151 Admissions: 5827 Census: 73 Outpatient Visits: 106572 Births: 1477 Total Expense ($000): 112215 Payroll Expense ($000): 55332 Personnel: 977**

**SAINT BERNARD HOSPITAL** See St. Bernard Hospital and Health Care Center

**SAINT ELIZABETH HOSPITAL** See Presence Saints Mary & Elizabeth Medical Center, Claremont Avenue

**SCHWAB REHABILITATION CENTER** See Schwab Rehabilitation Hospital

☒ **SCHWAB REHABILITATION HOSPITAL (143025)**, 1401 South California Avenue, Zip 60608–1858; tel. 773/522–2010, (Nonreporting) **A**1 3 5 10 **F**1 11 29 30 34 35 44 50 57 59 60 64 66 68 74 86 87 90 91 92 93 94 96 97 100 119 131 132 143 150 **S** Sinai Health System, Chicago, IL
Primary Contact: Karen Teitelbaum, Chief Executive Officer
CFO: Charles Weis, Chief Financial Officer
CMO: Michelle Gittler, M.D., Medical Director
CNO: Mary A Gollinger, MS, R.N., Director of Nursing
Web address: www.schwabrehab.org
**Control**: Other not–for–profit (including NFP Corporation) **Service**: Rehabilitation

**Staffed Beds: 52 Admissions: 1158 Census: 49 Outpatient Visits: 8981 Births: 0 Total Expense ($000): 35516 Payroll Expense ($000): 18277 Personnel: 409**

☒ **SHIRLEY RYAN ABILITYLAB (143026)**, 345 East Erie Street, Zip 60611–2654, Mailing Address: 355 East Erie Street, Zip 60611–2654; tel. 312/238–1000, (Nonreporting) **A**1 3 5 8 10 **F**3 9 11 29 30 34 35 36 44 50 53 54 57 58 64 68 74 75 77 79 81 82 86 87 90 91 92 93 94 95 96 107 111 119 130 131 132 143 146 148 154 157 **P**6
Primary Contact: Joanne C. Smith, M.D., President and Chief Executive Officer
COO: Peggy Kirk, Senior Vice President Clinical Operations
CFO: Ed Case, Executive Vice President and Chief Financial Officer
CMO: James Sliwa, M.D., Chief Medical Officer
CIO: Tim McKula, Vice President Information Systems and Chief Information Officer
CHR: Lois Huggins, Chief Human Resources Officer and Senior Vice President Human Resources
CNO: Karen M Colby, MS, Chief Nursing Officer
Web address: www.ric.org
**Control**: Other not–for–profit (including NFP Corporation) **Service**: Rehabilitation

**Staffed Beds: 242 Admissions: 3352 Census: 206 Outpatient Visits: 234505 Births: 0 Total Expense ($000): 319721 Payroll Expense ($000): 160788 Personnel: 1918**

IL

**SHRINERS HOSP FOR CHILDREN** See Shriners Hospitals for Children-Chicago

☐ **SHRINERS HOSPITALS FOR CHILDREN-CHICAGO (143302)**, 2211 North Oak Park Avenue, Zip 60707–3392; tel. 773/622–5400, (Nonreporting) **A**1 3 5 10 **S** Shriners Hospitals for Children, Tampa, FL
Primary Contact: Mark L. Niederpruem, FACHE, Administrator
CFO: Philip Magid, Director Fiscal Services
CMO: Jeffrey D. Ackman, M.D., Chief of Staff
CHR: James E Pawlowicz, Director Human Resources
CNO: Terry Wheat, R.N., M.P.H., Director of Patient Care Services
Web address: www.shrinershospitalsforchildren.org/Hospitals/Locations/Chicago.aspx
**Control**: Other not–for–profit (including NFP Corporation) **Service**: Children's orthopedic

**Staffed Beds**: 36

○ **SOUTH SHORE HOSPITAL (140181)**, 8012 South Crandon Avenue, Zip 60617–1124; tel. 773/768–0810, (Nonreporting) **A**10 11
Primary Contact: Timothy Caveney, President
CFO: Scott Spencer, Chief Financial Officer
CMO: James Bob Achebe, M.D., President Medical Staff
CIO: Jim Ritchie, Director Management Information Systems
CHR: Roger Rak, Director Human Resources
CNO: Laura Gonzalez, Interim Chief Nurse Executive
Web address: www.southshorehospital.com
**Control**: Other not–for–profit (including NFP Corporation) **Service**: General medical and surgical

**Staffed Beds**: 136

**ST ANTHONY HOSPITAL** See Saint Anthony Hospital

☐ **ST. BERNARD HOSPITAL AND HEALTH CARE CENTER (140103)**, 326 West 64th Street, Zip 60621–3146; tel. 773/962–3900, (Nonreporting) **A**1 3 10
Primary Contact: Charles Holland, President and Chief Executive Officer
COO: Roland Abellera, Vice President and Chief Operating Officer
CFO: James P Porter, Chief Financial Officer
CNO: Evelyn Jones, R.N., Vice President Nursing Services
Web address: www.stbernardhospital.com
**Control**: Church operated, Nongovernment, not–for–profit **Service**: General medical and surgical

**Staffed Beds**: 100

**STROGER HOSP OF COOK COUNTY** See John H. Stroger Jr. Hospital of Cook County

★ ○ **SWEDISH COVENANT HOSPITAL (140114)**, 5145 North California Avenue, Zip 60625–3661; tel. 773/878–8200, (Nonreporting) **A**2 3 5 10 11 13 **S** NorthShore University HealthSystem, Evanston, IL
Primary Contact: Anthony Guaccio, President and Chief Executive Officer
COO: Jonathan Lind, Chief Operating Officer
CFO: Thomas J Garvey, Senior Vice President Operations and Chief Financial Officer
CMO: Bruce McNulty, Chief Medical Officer
CIO: Karen Sheehan, Vice President and Chief Information Officer
CNO: Kathryn Donofrio, Chief Nursing Officer
Web address: www.schosp.org
**Control**: Church operated, Nongovernment, not–for–profit **Service**: General medical and surgical

**Staffed Beds**: 267

**THOREK HOSPITAL AND MED CENTER** See Thorek Memorial Hospital

○ **THOREK MEMORIAL HOSPITAL (140115)**, 850 West Irving Park Road, Zip 60613–3077; tel. 773/525–6780, (Nonreporting) **A**3 10 11
Primary Contact: Edward Budd, President and Chief Executive Officer
COO: Peter N Kamberos, Chief Operating Officer
CMO: Ilona Carlos, M.D., President Medical Staff
CIO: Tony Vavarutsos, Director Information Systems
CHR: Brett Wakefield, Director Human Resources
CNO: Mary McCahill, Chief Nursing Officer
Web address: www.thorek.org
**Control**: Other not–for–profit (including NFP Corporation) **Service**: General medical and surgical

**Staffed Beds**: 134

⇑ **TRINITY HOSPITAL** See Advocate Trinity Hospital

**UNIVERSITY OF CHICAGO COMER CHILDREN'S HOSPITAL** See Comer Children's Hospital

**UNIVERSITY OF CHICAGO HOSP** See University of Chicago Medical Center

⊞ **UNIVERSITY OF CHICAGO MEDICAL CENTER (140088)**, 5841 South Maryland Avenue, Zip 60637–1443; tel. 773/702–1000, (Includes BERNARD MITCHELL HOSPITAL, Mailing address: 5815 South Maryland Avenue, Chicago, Illinois, Zip 60637, 5841 S. Maryland Ave., Zip 60637, tel. 773/702–1000; Sharon L O'Keefe, President, University of Chicago Medical Center; CHICAGO LYING-IN (CLI), Mailing address: 5815 South Maryland Avenue, Chicago, Illinois, Zip 60637, 5841 South Maryland Avenue, Zip 60637, tel. 773/702–1000; Sharon L O'Keefe, President, University of Chicago Medical Center; COMER CHILDREN'S HOSPITAL, Mailing address: 5721 South Maryland Avenue, Chicago, Illinois, Zip 60637, 5841 South Maryland Avenue, Zip 60637, tel. 773/702–1000; Sharon L O'Keefe, President, University of Chicago Medical Center) **A**1 2 3 5 8 10 19 **F**3 5 6 9 11 12 13 14 15 16 17 18 19 20 21 22 23 24 25 26 27 28 29 30 31 32 34 35 36 37 38 40 41 43 44 45 46 47 48 49 50 51 52 54 55 56 57 58 59 60 61 63 64 65 68 70 71 72 73 74 75 76 77 78 79 81 82 83 84 85 86 87 88 89 92 93 97 100 101 102 104 107 108 109 110 111 112 114 115 116 117 118 119 120 121 123 124 126 129 130 131 132 134 135 136 137 138 139 140 141 142 143 145 146 147 148 149 150 156 **P**1 **S** University of Chicago Medicine, Chicago, IL
Primary Contact: Thomas E. Jackiewicz, President
COO: Jason Keeler, Executive Vice President and Chief Operating Officer
CFO: Rich Silveria, Executive Vice President and Chief Financial Officer
CMO: Stephen Weber, M.D., Senior Vice President Clinical Effectiveness and Chief Medical Officer
CIO: Heather Nelson, Senior Vice President and Chief Information Officer
CHR: Bob Hanley, Senior Vice President and Chief Human Resources Officer
Web address: www.uchospitals.edu
**Control**: Other not–for–profit (including NFP Corporation) **Service**: General medical and surgical

**Staffed Beds**: 698 **Admissions**: 33705 **Census**: 599 **Outpatient Visits**: 739987 **Births**: 2750 **Total Expense ($000)**: 1940230 **Payroll Expense ($000)**: 677940 **Personnel**: 9658

⊞ **UNIVERSITY OF ILLINOIS HOSPITAL & HEALTH SCIENCES SYSTEM (140150)**, 1740 West Taylor Street, Zip 60612–7232; tel. 312/996–7000, (Nonreporting) **A**1 2 3 5 8 10 **F**3 9 12 13 15 17 18 19 20 21 22 23 24 25 26 28 29 30 31 32 34 35 37 38 39 40 41 45 46 47 48 49 50 52 54 55 56 57 58 59 60 61 64 65 66 68 70 72 74 75 76 77 78 79 81 82 84 85 86 87 88 89 91 92 93 96 97 98 99 100 101 102 103 104 107 108 110 111 114 115 116 117 118 119 120 121 123 124 126 129 130 131 132 134 135 136 138 139 141 142 144 145 146 147 148 149 150 154 156 157 **P**4
Primary Contact: Michael B. Zenn, Chief Executive Officer
COO: David Loffing, Chief Operating Officer
CMO: Bernard Pygon, M.D., Chief Medical Officer
CIO: Audrius Polikaitis, Chief Information Officer
Web address: www.hospital.uillinois.edu/
**Control**: State, Government, Nonfederal **Service**: General medical and surgical

**Staffed Beds**: 404 **Admissions**: 18739 **Census**: 310 **Outpatient Visits**: 712990 **Births**: 2084 **Total Expense ($000)**: 1025909 **Payroll Expense ($000)**: 353759 **Personnel**: 4542

**UNIVERSITY OF ILLINOIS MEDICAL CENTER AT CHICAGO** See University of Illinois Hospital & Health Sciences System

**VENCOR HOSP-CHICAGO CENTRAL** See Kindred Chicago-Central Hospital

**CLINTON—De Witt County**

**DR. JOHN WARNER HOSPITAL** See Warner Hospital and Health Services

**WARNER HOSPITAL AND HEALTH SERVICES (141303)**, 422 West White Street, Zip 61727–2272; tel. 217/935–9571, (Nonreporting) **A**10 18
Primary Contact: Paul Skowron, Chief Executive Officer
CFO: Donna Wisner, Chief Financial Officer
CMO: Brit Williams, M.D., President Medical Staff
CIO: Larry Schleicher, Manager Information Services
CHR: Sarah Gerke, Manager Human Resources
CNO: Heidi Cook, Chief Nursing Officer
Web address: www.djwhospital.com
**Control**: City, Government, Nonfederal **Service**: General medical and surgical

**Staffed Beds**: 25

---

Hospital, Medicare Provider Number, Address, Telephone, Approval, Facility, and Physician Codes, Health Care System

★ American Hospital Association (AHA) membership
☐ The Joint Commission accreditation
○ Healthcare Facilities Accreditation Program
◇ DNV Healthcare Inc. accreditation
⇑ Center for Improvement in Healthcare Quality Accreditation
△ Commission on Accreditation of Rehabilitation Facilities (CARF) accreditation

IL

## DANVILLE—Vermilion County

☒ **OSF SACRED HEART MEDICAL CENTER (140093)**, 812 North Logan, Zip 61832–3788; tel. 217/443–5000, (Nonreporting) **A**1 2 5 10 19 **F**3 13 15 18 20 26 28 29 30 31 35 40 45 46 47 48 49 59 60 64 68 70 74 75 76 78 79 81 82 87 89 92 93 94 96 97 102 107 108 110 111 114 115 118 119 120 121 122 123 124 129 130 132 146 147 148 154 **S** OSF Healthcare, Peoria, IL
Primary Contact: Jared Rogers, M.D., President and Chief Executive Officer
CFO: Lucas Morton, Regional Chief Financial Officer
CMO: Vincent Kucich, FACHE, FACS, M.D., Chief Medical Officer
CIO: Paula Keele, Manager Information Systems
CHR: Michael Zimmerman, Human Resource Officer
CNO: Molly Nicholson, MS, R.N., Vice President of Patient Care/Chief Nurse Executive
Web address: www.presencehealth.org/usmc
**Control:** Church operated, Nongovernment, not–for–profit **Service:** General medical and surgical

| | |
|---|---|
| **Staffed Beds:** 115 **Admissions:** 4956 **Census:** 48 **Outpatient Visits:** 67012 **Births:** 453 **Total Expense ($000):** 98404 **Payroll Expense ($000):** 29392 **Personnel:** 408 | |

**PRESENCE UNITED SAMARITANS MEDICAL CENTER** See OSF Sacred Heart Medical Center

☒ **VETERANS AFFAIRS ILLIANA HEALTH CARE SYSTEM**, 1900 East Main Street, Zip 61832–5198; tel. 217/554–3000, (Nonreporting) **A**1 3 5 **S** Department of Veterans Affairs, Washington, DC
Primary Contact: Diana Carranza, Interim Director
COO: Diana Carranza, Associate Director
CFO: Becky Tissier, Chief Fiscal Service
CMO: Khiem Tran, M.D., Acting Chief of Staff
CIO: Frank D. Jackson IIIFacility Chief Information Officer
CHR: Connie Ohl, Acting Chief Human Resources
Web address: www.danville.va.gov/
**Control:** Veterans Affairs, Government, federal **Service:** General medical and surgical

| | |
|---|---|
| **Staffed Beds:** 221 | |

**VETERANS AFFAIRS MED CENTER** See Veterans Affairs Illiana Health Care System

## DECATUR—Macon County

☒ △ **DECATUR MEMORIAL HOSPITAL (140135)**, 2300 North Edward Street, Zip 62526–4192; tel. 217/876–8121, (Nonreporting) **A**1 2 3 5 7 10 19 **F**3 8 11 12 13 15 18 19 20 22 24 26 28 29 30 31 34 35 37 40 43 45 46 47 48 49 51 53 54 56 57 58 59 60 61 62 63 64 65 69 70 71 73 74 75 76 77 78 79 81 82 84 85 86 87 89 91 92 93 94 96 97 98 100 102 103 104 107 108 110 111 112 114 115 116 117 118 119 120 121 123 124 126 129 130 131 132 135 141 143 144 145 146 147 148 149 153 154 156 **P**6 7 8 **S** Memorial Health System, Springfield, IL
Primary Contact: Drew Early, President and Chief Executive Officer
COO: John Ridley, Executive Vice President & Chief Operating Officer
CFO: Deborah L Bragg, Senior Vice President, Finance
CMO: Larry T Hegland, M.D., Chief Medical Officer
CHR: Kevin Horath, Vice President Human Resources
Web address: www.dmhcares.com
**Control:** Other not–for–profit (including NFP Corporation) **Service:** General medical and surgical

| | |
|---|---|
| **Staffed Beds:** 304 **Admissions:** 8574 **Census:** 99 **Outpatient Visits:** 270345 **Births:** 687 **Total Expense ($000):** 465650 **Payroll Expense ($000):** 140236 **Personnel:** 2013 | |

☒ △ **HSHS ST. MARY'S HOSPITAL (140166)**, 1800 East Lake Shore Drive, Zip 62521–3883; tel. 217/464–2966, (Nonreporting) **A**1 3 5 7 10 **F**2 3 5 7 11 13 15 18 20 22 28 29 30 31 34 35 40 44 45 50 54 56 57 59 64 66 70 74 75 76 77 78 79 81 82 85 86 87 89 90 91 92 93 96 98 99 100 101 102 103 104 107 108 110 111 114 119 120 121 123 124 126 129 130 131 132 141 146 148 149 150 **S** HSHS Hospital Sisters Health System, Springfield, IL
Primary Contact: Michael Hicks, President and Chief Executive Officer
CMO: Phil Barnell, Chief Medical Officer
CHR: Melissa Tipton, Human Resource Director
CNO: Robyn Reising, R.N., Chief Nursing Officer
Web address: www.stmarysdecatur.com
**Control:** Church operated, Nongovernment, not–for–profit **Service:** General medical and surgical

| | |
|---|---|
| **Staffed Beds:** 230 **Admissions:** 6171 **Census:** 81 **Outpatient Visits:** 129912 **Births:** 702 **Total Expense ($000):** 163581 **Payroll Expense ($000):** 52081 **Personnel:** 851 | |

**ST. MARY'S HOSPITAL** See Hshs St. Mary's Hospital

## DEKALB—DeKalb County

**KISHWAUKEE HOSPITAL** See Northwestern Medicine Kishwaukee Hospital

☒ **NORTHWESTERN MEDICINE KISHWAUKEE HOSPITAL (140286)**, 1 Kish Hospital Drive, Zip 60115–9602, Mailing Address: P.O. Box 707, Zip 60115–0707; tel. 815/756–1521, (Nonreporting) **A**1 2 10 **F**3 8 11 13 15 18 20 22 26 28 29 30 31 32 33 34 35 36 38 40 41 43 44 45 46 48 49 50 51 53 54 55 57 58 59 60 64 65 68 70 71 73 74 75 76 77 78 79 80 81 82 84 85 86 87 89 93 94 96 97 98 100 101 102 104 107 108 110 111 114 115 117 118 119 126 129 130 131 132 135 144 145 146 147 148 149 150 154 157 158 **S** Northwestern Memorial HealthCare, Chicago, IL
Primary Contact: Jay Anderson, President
COO: Brad Copple, Vice President, Operations
CFO: John Orsini, Senior Vice President, Chief Financial Officer
CMO: Michael Kulisz, D.O., Chief Medical Officer
CIO: Carl Christensen, Senior Vice President, Chief Information Officer
CHR: Michael Vivoda, Senior Vice President, Human Resources
CNO: Pamela Duffy, MSN, R.N., Vice President Operations and Chief Nursing Officer
Web address: www.nm.org
**Control:** Other not–for–profit (including NFP Corporation) **Service:** General medical and surgical

| | |
|---|---|
| **Staffed Beds:** 98 **Admissions:** 5252 **Census:** 55 **Outpatient Visits:** 400712 **Births:** 772 **Total Expense ($000):** 233924 **Payroll Expense ($000):** 84736 **Personnel:** 1470 | |

## DES PLAINES—Cook County

☒ **AMITA HEALTH HOLY FAMILY MEDICAL CENTER (142011)**, 100 North River Road, Zip 60016–1255; tel. 847/297–1800, (Nonreporting) **A**1 3 10 **F**1 3 5 15 18 29 30 34 35 45 46 50 53 57 59 60 63 64 65 66 81 82 84 85 87 92 93 107 110 111 118 119 124 129 130 132 135 141 143 146 147 148 149 150 154 **S** Ascension Healthcare, Saint Louis, MO
Primary Contact: Yolande Wilson-Stubbs, President
CFO: Gene Yakovenko, Director of Finance
CMO: David Bordo, M.D., Chief Medical Officer
CIO: David Lundal, Senior Vice President Information Systems and Chief Information Officer
CHR: Ivy McKinley, Director Human Resources
Web address: www.https://www.amitahealth.org/
**Control:** Church operated, Nongovernment, not–for–profit **Service:** Acute long–term care hospital

| | |
|---|---|
| **Staffed Beds:** 178 **Admissions:** 1522 **Census:** 88 **Outpatient Visits:** 17440 **Births:** 0 **Total Expense ($000):** 65604 **Payroll Expense ($000):** 28839 **Personnel:** 361 | |

☐ **CHICAGO BEHAVIORAL HOSPITAL (144040)**, 555 Wilson Lane, Zip 60016–4729; tel. 847/768–5430, (Nonreporting) **A**1 **F**5 98 100 101 102 103 104 105 152 153 154
Primary Contact: Anthony M. DeJoseph, PsyD, Chief Executive Officer
CMO: Shiraz Butt, M.D., Medical Director
CHR: Betty Barnes, Director Human Resources
CNO: Barbara Preib, Director of Nursing
Web address: www.maryvilleacademy.org
**Control:** Corporation, Investor–owned (for–profit) **Service:** Children's hospital psychiatric

| | |
|---|---|
| **Staffed Beds:** 138 **Admissions:** 4855 **Census:** 115 | |

**MARYVILLE BEHAVIORAL HEALTH HOSPITAL** See Chicago Behavioral Hospital

**PRESENCE HOLY FAMILY MEDICAL CENTER** See Amita Health Holy Family Medical Center

## DIXON—Lee County

★ **KATHERINE SHAW BETHEA HOSPITAL (140012)**, 403 East First Street, Zip 61021–3187; tel. 815/288–5531, (Nonreporting) **A**3 5 10 **F**3 11 13 15 18 20 22 28 29 30 34 35 38 39 40 44 45 46 47 50 54 56 57 59 61 62 64 65 69 70 74 75 76 79 81 82 85 86 87 89 91 92 93 94 96 97 98 101 102 104 107 108 110 111 112 115 119 127 129 130 131 132 135 145 146 147 148 149 150 154 156 157 **P**6
Primary Contact: David L. Schreiner, FACHE, President and Chief Executive Officer
CFO: Michael Kittoe, Chief Financial Officer
CMO: Pratip Nag, Vice President, Chief Medical Officer
CIO: Ray Sharp, Chief Information Officer
CHR: Christy Pierce, Director of Human Resources
CNO: Linda Clemen, Vice President and Chief Nursing Officer
Web address: www.ksbhospital.com
**Control:** Other not–for–profit (including NFP Corporation) **Service:** General medical and surgical

| | |
|---|---|
| **Staffed Beds:** 80 **Admissions:** 2648 **Census:** 27 **Outpatient Visits:** 263254 **Births:** 263 **Total Expense ($000):** 145963 **Payroll Expense ($000):** 64474 **Personnel:** 783 | |

*Many Facility Codes have changed. Please refer to the AHA Guide Code Chart.* © 2021 AHA Guide

**IL**

## DOWNERS GROVE—Dupage County

★ ⇑ **ADVOCATE GOOD SAMARITAN HOSPITAL (140288)**, 3815 Highland Avenue, Zip 60515–1590; tel. 630/275–5900, (Nonreporting) **A**2 5 10 21 **F**3 5 11 12 13 15 17 18 20 22 24 26 28 29 30 31 32 34 35 36 37 38 40 41 43 44 45 46 47 49 50 53 54 55 56 57 59 60 63 64 68 70 72 74 75 76 77 78 79 81 82 84 85 86 87 89 93 97 98 100 101 102 103 104 105 107 108 109 110 111 114 115 118 119 120 121 123 124 126 129 130 131 132 135 144 145 146 147 148 149 152 153 154 156 157 **P**1 6 **S** Advocate Aurora Health, Downers Grove, IL
Primary Contact: Nancy M. Tinsley, R.N., FACHE, President
COO: Sandi Churchill, Vice President Business Development and Operations, Professional Services
CFO: Mary Treacy-Shiff, Vice President Finance
CMO: Charles Derus, M.D., Vice President Medical Management
CHR: Elizabeth Calby, Vice President Human Resources
CNO: Susan K Okuno-Jones, Vice President Patient Care Services and Chief Nursing Executive
Web address: www.advocatehealth.com/gsam
**Control:** Church operated, Nongovernment, not–for–profit **Service:** General medical and surgical

**Staffed Beds:** 293 **Admissions:** 15484 **Census:** 177 **Outpatient Visits:** 114917 **Births:** 1762 **Total Expense ($000):** 326096 **Payroll Expense ($000):** 111824 **Personnel:** 1554

⇑ **GOOD SAMARITAN HOSPITAL** See Advocate Good Samaritan Hospital

## DU QUOIN—Perry County

⊠ **MARSHALL BROWNING HOSPITAL (141331)**, 900 North Washington Street, Zip 62832–1233, Mailing Address: P.O. Box 192, Zip 62832–0192; tel. 618/542–2146, (Nonreporting) **A**1 10 18 **F**3 11 15 28 29 34 35 40 57 59 81 93 97 107 114 119 125 127 129 133 144 148 154 156
Primary Contact: Dan Eaves, Chief Executive Officer
CFO: Brice Harsy, Chief Financial Officer
CIO: Brian Schandl, Chief Information Officer
CHR: Sarah J. Dickey, Human Resource Director
CNO: Laurie Kellerman, MSN, Chief Clinical Officer
Web address: www.marshallbrowninghospital.com
**Control:** Other not–for–profit (including NFP Corporation) **Service:** General medical and surgical

**Staffed Beds:** 25 **Admissions:** 384 **Census:** 6 **Births:** 0 **Total Expense ($000):** 25841 **Payroll Expense ($000):** 10389 **Personnel:** 199

## EFFINGHAM—Effingham County

⊠ **HSHS ST. ANTHONY'S MEMORIAL HOSPITAL (140032)**, 503 North Maple Street, Zip 62401–2099; tel. 217/342–2121, (Nonreporting) **A**1 2 5 10 19 **F**3 11 13 15 18 20 28 29 30 31 32 34 35 37 40 45 50 54 57 59 62 63 64 68 70 75 76 79 81 82 84 85 87 89 93 96 107 108 110 111 114 115 117 118 119 126 129 130 131 132 144 146 147 154 **S** HSHS Hospital Sisters Health System, Springfield, IL
Primary Contact: Theresa Rutherford, R.N., MS, FACHE, President and Chief Executive Officer
CFO: Dave Storm, Director Business Support
CNO: Kelly Sage, Chief Nursing Officer
Web address: www.stanthonyshospital.org
**Control:** Church operated, Nongovernment, not–for–profit **Service:** General medical and surgical

**Staffed Beds:** 123 **Admissions:** 4561 **Census:** 40 **Outpatient Visits:** 159644 **Births:** 741 **Total Expense ($000):** 132522 **Payroll Expense ($000):** 46799 **Personnel:** 718

**ST. ANTHONY'S MEMORIAL HOSPITAL** See Hshs St. Anthony's Memorial Hospital

## ELDORADO—Saline County

★ **FERRELL HOSPITAL (141324)**, 1201 Pine Street, Zip 62930–1634; tel. 618/273–3361, (Nonreporting) **A**10 18 **F**11 15 18 28 29 30 34 35 40 45 57 59 65 81 84 85 87 101 104 107 110 115 119 127 130 133 146 148 153
Primary Contact: Alisa Coleman, Chief Executive Officer
CFO: Kevin Fowler, Chief Financial Officer
CMO: Nate Oldham, M.D., Chief Medical Officer
CIO: Kristie McDaniel, Director Information Technology
CHR: Caleigh Bruce, Director of Human Resources/Chief Compliance Officer
CNO: Rachael Prather, Chief Nursing Officer
Web address: www.ferrellhosp.org
**Control:** Other not–for–profit (including NFP Corporation) **Service:** General medical and surgical

**Staffed Beds:** 25 **Admissions:** 598 **Census:** 8 **Outpatient Visits:** 74972 **Births:** 0 **Total Expense ($000):** 23697 **Payroll Expense ($000):** 11009 **Personnel:** 247

**FERRELL HOSPITAL COMMUNITY FDN** See Ferrell Hospital

## ELGIN—Kane County

★ ⇑ **ADVOCATE SHERMAN HOSPITAL (140030)**, 1425 North Randall Road, Zip 60123–2300; tel. 847/742–9800, (Nonreporting) **A**2 10 21 **F**3 11 13 15 18 20 22 24 26 28 29 30 31 34 35 38 40 41 43 45 46 47 48 49 50 54 57 59 64 65 68 70 71 73 74 75 76 77 78 79 81 82 84 85 87 89 92 93 100 102 107 108 110 111 114 115 116 117 118 119 120 121 123 126 129 130 132 135 144 146 147 148 149 154 **P**6 8 **S** Advocate Aurora Health, Downers Grove, IL
Primary Contact: Sheri De Shazo, R.N., President
CMO: Bruce Hyman, M.D., Vice President Clinical Performance
CHR: Melissa O'Neill, Vice President Human Resources
Web address: www.advocatehealth.com/sherman
**Control:** Other not–for–profit (including NFP Corporation) **Service:** General medical and surgical

**Staffed Beds:** 271 **Admissions:** 13727 **Census:** 146 **Outpatient Visits:** 303551 **Births:** 2261 **Total Expense ($000):** 286097 **Payroll Expense ($000):** 95650 **Personnel:** 1515

⊠ △ **AMITA HEALTH SAINT JOSEPH HOSPITAL (140217)**, 77 North Airlite Street, Zip 60123–4912; tel. 847/695–3200, (Nonreporting) **A**1 2 7 10 **F**5 11 12 17 18 20 22 24 26 28 29 30 31 34 35 36 37 38 40 43 44 49 50 53 54 56 57 58 59 60 61 62 63 64 65 68 69 70 74 75 77 78 79 81 82 84 85 86 87 90 93 94 96 97 98 99 100 101 102 103 104 105 107 108 111 114 115 117 119 120 121 123 124 130 132 134 135 143 146 147 148 153 **S** Ascension Healthcare, Saint Louis, MO
Primary Contact: Polly J. Davenport, FACHE, R.N., President and Chief Executive Officer
CFO: Kevin Larkin, Regional Chief Financial Officer
CIO: Trevor O'Malley, Site Manager
CHR: Michael O'Rourke, Regional Human Resources Lead
Web address: www.provena.org
**Control:** Church operated, Nongovernment, not–for–profit **Service:** General medical and surgical

**Staffed Beds:** 184 **Admissions:** 6467 **Census:** 94 **Outpatient Visits:** 68725 **Births:** 0 **Total Expense ($000):** 119891 **Payroll Expense ($000):** 39555 **Personnel:** 433

☐ **ELGIN MENTAL HEALTH CENTER (144037)**, 750 South State Street, Zip 60123–7692; tel. 847/742–1040, (Nonreporting) **A**1 3 5 10 **F**29 30 38 39 50 59 65 68 87 98 101 130 132 143 **S** Division of Mental Health, Department of Human Services, Springfield, IL
Primary Contact: Meredith Kiss, Administrator
CFO: Tajudeen Ibrahim, Interim Business Administrator
CMO: Malini Patel, M.D., Medical Director
CIO: Kelly Callahan, Public Information Officer
CHR: Darek Williams, Director Human Resources
Web address: www.dhs.state.il.us
**Control:** State, Government, Nonfederal **Service:** Psychiatric

**Staffed Beds:** 383 **Admissions:** 773 **Census:** 364 **Outpatient Visits:** 0 **Births:** 0 **Total Expense ($000):** 60751 **Personnel:** 653

**PRESENCE SAINT JOSEPH HOSPITAL** See Amita Health Saint Joseph Hospital

⇑ **SHERMAN HOSPITAL** See Advocate Sherman Hospital

---

IL

## ELK GROVE VILLAGE—Cook County

**ALEXIAN BROTHERS MEDICAL CENTER** See Amita Health Elk Grove Village

**ALEXIAN REHABILITATION HOSPITAL** See Amita Health Rehabilitation Hospital

✠ **AMITA HEALTH ELK GROVE VILLAGE (140258)**, 800 Biesterfield Road, Zip 60007–3397; tel. 847/437–5500, (Includes AMITA HEALTH REHABILITATION HOSPITAL, Mailing address: 935 Beisner Road, Elk Grove Village, Illinois, Zip 60007; tel. 847/640–5600; John Dunkin, Executive Director), (Nonreporting) **A**1 2 3 5 10 **F**3 10 11 12 13 15 17 18 19 20 22 23 24 26 27 28 29 30 31 34 35 37 38 39 40 41 42 43 44 45 46 47 48 49 50 54 55 57 59 63 64 70 73 74 76 78 79 81 82 84 85 86 87 89 90 91 92 93 95 96 97 98 103 107 108 110 111 114 115 116 117 118 119 120 121 124 126 129 130 132 135 143 145 146 147 148 149 154 156 157 **S** Ascension Healthcare, Saint Louis, MO
Primary Contact: Dia Nichols, President and Chief Executive Officer
COO: Laurence Dry, Chief Operating Officer, Acute Care Hospitals Northern Region
CFO: Henry Zeisel, Chief Financial Officer, Northern Region
CIO: Sherrie Russell, Senior Vice President & Chief Information Officer
CHR: Donald Russell, Senior Vice President and Chief Human Resources Officer
CNO: Chris Budzinsky, Vice President, Nursing and Chief Nursing Officer
Web address: www.AMITAHealth.org
**Control**: Church operated, Nongovernment, not–for–profit **Service**: General medical and surgical

**Staffed Beds**: 376 **Admissions**: 17516 **Census**: 260 **Outpatient Visits**: 308229 **Births**: 1867 **Total Expense ($000)**: 383329 **Payroll Expense ($000)**: 143224 **Personnel**: 1485

## ELMHURST—Dupage County

✠ **ELMHURST HOSPITAL (140200)**, 155 East Brush Hill Road, Zip 60126–5658; tel. 331/221–1000, (Nonreporting) **A**1 2 5 10 **F**3 12 13 15 18 19 20 22 24 26 28 29 30 31 34 35 36 37 38 39 40 41 43 44 45 46 47 48 49 50 54 55 57 58 59 61 63 64 65 70 73 74 75 76 77 78 79 81 82 84 85 86 87 91 92 93 96 97 100 101 102 103 107 108 110 111 115 117 119 120 121 126 129 130 131 132 135 144 146 147 148 149 154 156 **P**3 **S** Edward-Elmhurst Healthcare, Naperville, IL
Primary Contact: Pamela L. Dunley, MS, R.N., Chief Executive Officer
CMO: Daniel Sullivan, D.O., Chief Medical Officer, Vice President Medical Administration
CHR: Robert Blazek, System Director, Human Resources Business Partners
CNO: Jean Lydon, MS, R.N., System Vice President Operations, Chief Nursing Officer
Web address: www.eehealth.org
**Control**: Other not–for–profit (including NFP Corporation) **Service**: General medical and surgical

**Staffed Beds**: 266 **Admissions**: 17413 **Census**: 186 **Outpatient Visits**: 716875 **Births**: 2310 **Total Expense ($000)**: 475216 **Payroll Expense ($000)**: 135693 **Personnel**: 2250

**ELMHURST MEMORIAL HOSPITAL** See Elmhurst Hospital

## EUREKA—Woodford County

⇑ **EUREKA COMMUNITY HOSPITAL** See Eureka Hospital

★ ⇑ **EUREKA HOSPITAL (141309)**, 101 South Major Street, Zip 61530–1246; tel. 309/467–2371, (Nonreporting) **A**10 18 21 **F**3 15 18 28 29 30 34 35 39 40 44 45 50 56 57 59 64 65 67 68 74 75 77 78 79 81 82 85 86 87 90 93 97 107 108 110 111 114 119 127 128 129 130 132 133 144 146 149 154 156 157 **P**7 8 **S** Carle Health, Urbana, IL
Primary Contact: Colleen Kannaday, FACHE, President
CFO: Aron Klein, Vice President of Finance
CMO: Steven K Jones, M.D., Medical Director
CIO: David Harper, Director, Site Information Systems
CHR: Antonio Coletta, Vice President Human Resources
CNO: Nancy Allen, R.N., MS, Director, Patient Services and Chief Nursing Executive
Web address: www.advocatehealth.com/eureka/
**Control**: Church operated, Nongovernment, not–for–profit **Service**: General medical and surgical

**Staffed Beds**: 11 **Admissions**: 288 **Census**: 5 **Outpatient Visits**: 52809 **Births**: 0 **Total Expense ($000)**: 22240 **Payroll Expense ($000)**: 9418 **Personnel**: 116

## EVANSTON—Cook County

✠ **AMITA HEALTH SAINT FRANCIS HOSPITAL EVANSTON (140080)**, 355 Ridge Avenue, Zip 60202–3399; tel. 847/316–4000, (Nonreporting) **A**1 2 3 5 10 **F**3 11 12 13 15 18 20 22 24 26 28 29 30 31 34 35 38 40 41 42 43 44 45 47 48 49 56 57 58 59 60 61 64 68 70 74 75 76 77 78 79 81 82 84 85 86 87 91 92 93 97 100 107 108 110 111 114 115 117 118 119 120 121 123 125 126 129 130 131 132 146 147 148 154 156 **P**8 **S** Ascension Healthcare, Saint Louis, MO
Primary Contact: Kenneth Jones, President
CMO: David DiLoreto, M.D., Executive Vice President and Chief Medical Officer
CIO: George Chessum, Vice President Information Systems
CHR: Paul Skiem, Senior Vice President Human Resources
Web address: www.reshealth.org
**Control**: Church operated, Nongovernment, not–for–profit **Service**: General medical and surgical

**Staffed Beds**: 215 **Admissions**: 7430 **Census**: 83 **Outpatient Visits**: 85471 **Births**: 371 **Total Expense ($000)**: 163117 **Payroll Expense ($000)**: 53742 **Personnel**: 459

**EVANSTON HOSPITAL** See Northshore Evanston Hospital

✠ **NORTHSHORE UNIVERSITY HEALTH SYSTEM (140010)**, 2650 Ridge Avenue, Zip 60201–1613; tel. 847/570–2000, (Includes NORTHSHORE EVANSTON HOSPITAL, Mailing address: 2650 Ridge Avenue, Evanston, Illinois, Zip 60201–1797; tel. 847/570–2000; Douglas M Silverstein, President; NORTHSHORE GLENBROOK HOSPITAL, Mailing address: 2100 Pfingsten Road, Glenview, Illinois, Zip 60025; tel. 847/657–5800; Jesse Peterson Hall, President; NORTHSHORE HIGHLAND PARK HOSPITAL, Mailing address: 718 Glenview Avenue, Highland Park, Illinois, Zip 60035–2497; tel. 847/432–8000; Gabrielle Cummings, President; NORTHSHORE SKOKIE HOSPITAL, Mailing address: 9600 Gross Point Road, Skokie, Illinois, Zip 60076–1257; tel. 847/677–9600; David Rahija, FACHE, President), (Nonreporting) **A**1 2 3 5 8 10 **S** NorthShore University HealthSystem, Evanston, IL
Primary Contact: J. P. Gallagher, President and Chief Executive Officer
CFO: Doug Welday, Chief Financial Officer
CIO: Steven Smith, Chief Information Officer
CHR: Bill Luehrs, Chief Human Resources Officer
CNO: Nancy Semerdjian, R.N., Chief Nursing Officer
Web address: www.northshore.org
**Control**: Other not–for–profit (including NFP Corporation) **Service**: General medical and surgical

**Staffed Beds**: 663

**NORTHSHORE UNIVERSITY HEALTH SYSTEM EVANSTON HOSPITAL** See Northshore University Health System

**PRESENCE SAINT FRANCIS HOSPITAL** See Amita Health Saint Francis Hospital Evanston

## EVERGREEN PARK—Cook County

**OSF HEALTHCARE LITTLE COMPANY OF MARY MEDICAL** See OSF Healthcare Little Company of Mary Medical Center

☐ **OSF HEALTHCARE LITTLE COMPANY OF MARY MEDICAL CENTER (140179)**, 2800 West 95th Street, Zip 60805–2795; tel. 708/422–6200, (Nonreporting) **A**1 2 3 5 10 **F**3 4 5 11 12 13 15 18 20 22 26 28 29 30 31 34 35 36 38 40 41 45 46 47 49 50 54 56 57 59 60 62 63 64 65 70 71 72 74 75 76 77 78 79 81 82 83 84 85 86 87 92 93 94 98 100 101 102 104 105 107 108 110 111 114 115 119 120 121 124 126 129 130 131 132 133 135 144 146 147 148 149 150 152 153 154 156 157 **S** OSF Healthcare, Peoria, IL
Primary Contact: Kathleen Kinsella, President
COO: Mary Freyer, Chief Operating Officer
CFO: Robert Tarola, Chief Financial Officer
CMO: Kent A W Armbruster, M.D., Vice President Medical Affairs
CIO: Darryl Mazzuca, Director Management Information Systems
CHR: Colleen M. Rohan, Director Human Resources
CNO: Lisa DiMarco, Vice President Patient Care Service and Chief Nursing Officer
Web address: www.https://www.osfhealthcare.org/little-company-of-mary/
**Control**: Other not–for–profit (including NFP Corporation) **Service**: General medical and surgical

**Staffed Beds**: 251 **Admissions**: 11331 **Census**: 145 **Outpatient Visits**: 238772 **Births**: 967 **Total Expense ($000)**: 220621 **Payroll Expense ($000)**: 90765 **Personnel**: 1751

IL

## FAIRFIELD—Wayne County

✠ **FAIRFIELD MEMORIAL HOSPITAL (141311)**, 303 NW 11th Street,
Zip 62837–1203; tel. 618/842–2611, (Total facility includes 30 beds in nursing
home–type unit) (Nonreporting) **A**1 10 18 **F**3 11 15 18 35 38 40 41 45
46 50 56 57 59 62 64 65 69 70 71 75 77 81 82 85 86 87 93 97 102 104 107
108 110 111 115 119 124 127 128 129 130 132 135 144 146 149 153 154
156 **P**6
Primary Contact: Katherine Bunting Esq, Chief Executive Officer
COO: Dana Shantel Taylor, Chief Operating Officer
CFO: Amy Marsh, Chief Financial Officer
CMO: Wesley Thompson, M.D., President Medical Staff
CIO: Brad August, Director Information Systems
CHR: Jill VanHyning, Director of Human Resources
CNO: Christina Baker, Chief Nursing Officer
Web address: www.fairfieldmemorial.org
**Control:** Other not–for–profit (including NFP Corporation) **Service:** General
medical and surgical

| | |
|---|---|
| **Staffed Beds:** 55 **Admissions:** 648 **Census:** 25 **Outpatient Visits:** 42907 **Births:** 0 **Total Expense ($000):** 32032 **Payroll Expense ($000):** 14043 **Personnel:** 315 | |

## FLORA—Clay County

✠ **CLAY COUNTY HOSPITAL (141351)**, 911 Stacy Burk Drive, Zip 62839–3241,
Mailing Address: P.O. Box 280, Zip 62839–0280; tel. 618/662–2131,
(Nonreporting) **A**1 10 18 **S** SSM Health, Saint Louis, MO
Primary Contact: Robert R. Sellers, President
COO: Jamie Veach, Chief Operating Officer
CFO: Mike Hobbs, Chief Financial Officer
CMO: Colleen Murphy, M.D., Chief of Staff
CIO: Phil Bute, Manager Information Technology
CHR: Chelsea Musgrave, Director of Human Resources
Web address: www.claycountyhospital.org
**Control:** County, Government, Nonfederal **Service:** General medical and surgical

| | |
|---|---|
| **Staffed Beds:** 22 | |

## FOREST PARK—Cook County

**COLUMBIA RIVEREDGE HOSPITAL** See Riveredge Hospital

☐ **RIVEREDGE HOSPITAL (144009)**, 8311 West Roosevelt Road,
Zip 60130–2500; tel. 708/771–7000, (Nonreporting) **A**1 10 **F**98 99 100 101
102 103 104 105 106 153 154 **S** Universal Health Services, Inc., King of
Prussia, PA
Primary Contact: Carey Carlock, Chief Executive Officer
COO: Joseph Baw, Chief Operating Officer
CFO: Anne Kim, Chief Financial Officer
CMO: Aamir Safdar, M.D., Chief Medical Officer
CIO: Jocelyn Zavala, Senior Information Technology Coordinator
CHR: Joseph Rinke, Director of Human Resources
Web address: www.riveredgehospital.com
**Control:** Corporation, Investor–owned (for–profit) **Service:** Psychiatric

| | |
|---|---|
| **Staffed Beds:** 210 **Admissions:** 4583 **Census:** 125 | |

## FREEPORT—Stephenson County

★ **FHN MEMORIAL HOSPITAL (140160)**, 1045 West Stephenson Street,
Zip 61032–4899; tel. 815/599–6000, (Nonreporting) **A**10 **F**3 13 14 15 18 20 22
28 29 30 31 34 38 40 45 46 47 48 49 50 51 53 55 57 58 59 61 63 64 65 68
69 74 75 76 77 78 79 81 82 84 85 86 87 93 97 100 101 102 104 107 108
109 110 111 114 119 129 130 131 132 135 145 146 149 153 154 156 **P**6 8
Primary Contact: Mark Gridley, FACHE, President and Chief Executive Officer
COO: Kathryn J Martinez, Chief Operating Officer and Chief Nursing Officer
CFO: Michael Clark, Executive Vice President and Chief Financial Officer
CMO: Keith Martin, M.D., Chief Medical Officer
CIO: Mike Willams, Chief Information Officer
CHR: Leonard M Carter, Chief Human Resources Officer
CNO: Kathryn J Martinez, Chief Operating Officer and Chief Nursing Officer
Web address: www.fhn.org
**Control:** Other not–for–profit (including NFP Corporation) **Service:** General
medical and surgical

| | |
|---|---|
| **Staffed Beds:** 100 **Admissions:** 3787 **Census:** 38 **Outpatient Visits:** 107766 **Births:** 312 **Total Expense ($000):** 117322 **Payroll Expense ($000):** 35937 **Personnel:** 510 | |

**FREEPORT MEMORIAL HOSPITAL** See Fhn Memorial Hospital

## GALENA—Jo Daviess County

**GALENA-STAUSS HOSPITAL** See Midwest Medical Center

★ **MIDWEST MEDICAL CENTER (141302)**, One Medical Center Drive,
Zip 61036–1697; tel. 815/777–1340, (Nonreporting) **A**10 18
Primary Contact: Tracy Bauer, Chief Executive Officer
COO: Steve Busch, Chief Operating Officer
CMO: Grant Westenfelder, M.D., Chief Medical Officer
CHR: Melissa Conley, Director Human Resources
Web address: www.midwestmedicalcenter.org
**Control:** Corporation, Investor–owned (for–profit) **Service:** General medical and
surgical

| | |
|---|---|
| **Staffed Beds:** 25 | |

## GALESBURG—Knox County

☐ **GALESBURG COTTAGE HOSPITAL (140040)**, 695 North Kellogg Street,
Zip 61401–2885; tel. 309/343–8131, (Nonreporting) **A**1 10
Primary Contact: Sanjay Sharma, Chief Executive Officer
CFO: Gary Singer, Interim Chief Financial Officer
CMO: Mark Davis, M.D., President Medical Staff
CIO: Richard Tran, Director Information Technology
CHR: Michelle Dutton, Human Resources
CNO: Pam Davis, Chief Nursing Officer
Web address: www.cottagehospital.com
**Control:** Other not–for–profit (including NFP Corporation) **Service:** General
medical and surgical

| | |
|---|---|
| **Staffed Beds:** 119 | |

✠ **OSF ST. MARY MEDICAL CENTER (140064)**, 3333 North Seminary Street,
Zip 61401–1299; tel. 309/344–3161, (Nonreporting) **A**1 10 **F**3 11 13 15 18 26
28 29 30 32 34 35 40 44 45 46 49 50 51 53 56 57 59 64 65 70 75 76 79 81
82 84 85 87 89 91 92 93 96 102 107 108 110 111 115 118 119 129 130 131
132 146 149 154 **S** OSF Healthcare, Peoria, IL
Primary Contact: Lisa DeKezel, President
COO: Don Shadensack, Vice President Clinical Services
CFO: Curt Lipe, Vice President, Chief Financial Officer
CMO: Clifford G Martin, M.D., Regional Vice President and Chief Medical Officer
CIO: Becky Lynch, Manager Business Entity Management and Information Systems
CHR: Jenny Jacobs, Director Human Resources
CNO: Alice Snyder, Vice President, Chief Nursing Officer
Web address: www.osfstmary.org
**Control:** Church operated, Nongovernment, not–for–profit **Service:** General
medical and surgical

| | |
|---|---|
| **Staffed Beds:** 73 **Admissions:** 3539 **Census:** 37 **Outpatient Visits:** 102631 **Births:** 537 **Total Expense ($000):** 75321 **Payroll Expense ($000):** 26913 **Personnel:** 445 | |

**ST MARY MEDICAL CENTER** See OSF St. Mary Medical Center

## GENESEO—Henry County

★ ⇑ **HAMMOND-HENRY HOSPITAL (141319)**, 600 North College Avenue,
Zip 61254–1099; tel. 309/944–6431, (Total facility includes 38 beds in nursing
home–type unit) (Nonreporting) **A**10 18 21 **F**3 11 15 28 29 34 35 40 45 49 50
59 62 70 75 81 86 87 93 97 107 111 114 119 128 129 130 131 132 133 144
146 154 **P**6 **S** HealthTech Management Services, Brentwood, TN
Primary Contact: Mark Kuhn, Chief Executive Officer
CFO: Jodie Criswell, Vice President of Fiscal Services
CIO: Heather Henry, Information Technology Manager
CHR: Hazel Butter, Manager Human Resources
Web address: www.hammondhenry.com
**Control:** Hospital district or authority, Government, Nonfederal **Service:** General
medical and surgical

| | |
|---|---|
| **Staffed Beds:** 61 **Admissions:** 1008 **Census:** 44 **Outpatient Visits:** 126728 **Births:** 0 **Total Expense ($000):** 44566 **Payroll Expense ($000):** 18889 **Personnel:** 326 | |

IL

## GENEVA—Kane County

**DELNOR HOSPITAL** See Northwestern Medicine Delnor Hospital

☒ **NORTHWESTERN MEDICINE DELNOR HOSPITAL (140211)**, 300 Randall Road, Zip 60134–4200; tel. 630/208–3000, (Nonreporting) **A**1 2 3 5 10 **F**3 12 13 15 16 20 22 26 28 29 30 31 33 34 35 36 37 39 40 41 43 44 45 46 47 48 49 50 51 53 55 57 59 62 64 65 68 70 73 74 75 76 77 78 79 81 82 84 85 86 87 89 92 93 94 96 97 100 101 102 104 105 107 108 110 111 114 115 116 117 119 120 121 123 126 129 130 131 132 135 146 147 148 149 153 154 156 157 **S** Northwestern Memorial HealthCare, Chicago, IL
Primary Contact: Maureen A. Bryant, FACHE, President
COO: Michael B Johnson, Vice President, Operations
CFO: Matt Flynn, Vice President/Chief Finanical Officer
CMO: Mark Daniels, M.D., Vice President/Chief Medical Officer
CIO: Doug King, Senior Vice President and Chief Information Officer
CNO: Gina Reid Tinio, M.P.H., MS, Ph.D., Vice President, Chief Nurse Executive
Web address: www.nm.org
**Control:** Other not–for–profit (including NFP Corporation) **Service:** General medical and surgical

**Staffed Beds:** 159 **Admissions:** 8388 **Census:** 81 **Outpatient Visits:** 642479 **Births:** 1366 **Total Expense ($000):** 410856 **Payroll Expense ($000):** 145322 **Personnel:** 2033

## GIBSON CITY—Ford County

★ ⇑ **GIBSON AREA HOSPITAL AND HEALTH SERVICES (141317)**, 1120 North Melvin Street, Zip 60936–1477, Mailing Address: P.O. Box 429, Zip 60936–0429; tel. 217/784–4251, (Total facility includes 42 beds in nursing home–type unit) (Nonreporting) **A**10 18 21 **F**3 7 8 11 13 15 18 20 26 28 29 31 34 35 39 40 44 45 46 50 51 53 56 57 59 64 67 68 69 70 75 76 77 78 79 81 82 85 86 87 89 90 93 97 98 100 102 104 107 110 111 115 118 119 127 128 129 130 131 132 133 135 141 143 144 146 148 149 154 **P**8 **S** Alliant Management Services, Louisville, KY
Primary Contact: Robert C. Schmitt II, CPA, FACHE, Chief Executive Officer
COO: Robin Rose, R.N., Chief Operating and Clinical Officer
CFO: Matthew Ertel, Chief Financial Officer
CMO: Mark Spangler, M.D., Chief Medical Officer
CHR: Ty Royal, Executive Director of Human Resources and Support Services
CNO: Barb Meyer, Executive Director of Nursing
Web address: www.gibsonhospital.org
**Control:** Other not–for–profit (including NFP Corporation) **Service:** General medical and surgical

**Staffed Beds:** 67 **Admissions:** 981 **Census:** 44 **Outpatient Visits:** 144715 **Births:** 229 **Total Expense ($000):** 106449 **Payroll Expense ($000):** 50233 **Personnel:** 714

⇑ **GIBSON COMMUNITY HOSPITAL** See Gibson Area Hospital and Health Services

## GLENDALE HEIGHTS—DuPage County

**ADVENTIST MEDICAL CENTER GLENOAKS** See Amita Health Adventist Medical Center Glenoaks

☒ **AMITA HEALTH ADVENTIST MEDICAL CENTER GLENOAKS (140292)**, 701 Winthrop Avenue, Zip 60139–1403; tel. 630/545–8000, (Nonreporting) **A**1 10 **F**3 11 13 15 18 20 22 26 29 30 31 34 35 38 40 41 43 44 45 49 50 56 57 59 61 64 70 73 74 76 78 79 81 82 85 86 87 98 100 101 103 107 108 110 111 114 115 119 130 131 132 146 147 148 149 154 157 **S** AdventHealth, Altamonte Springs, FL
Primary Contact: Bruce C. Christian, President and Chief Executive Officer
COO: Richard Roehr, Vice President and Chief Operating Officer
CFO: Chase Aalborg, Vice President and Chief Financial Officer
CMO: Richard Carroll, M.D., Vice President and Chief Medical Officer
CIO: Sherrie Russell, AMITA Health Senior Vice President and Chief Information Officer
CHR: Donald Russell, AMITA Health Senior Vice President and Chief Human Resources Officer
CNO: Suzette Mahneke, Associate Vice President of Nursing
Web address: www.AMITAhealth.org
**Control:** Church operated, Nongovernment, not–for–profit **Service:** General medical and surgical

**Staffed Beds:** 143 **Admissions:** 5687 **Census:** 79 **Outpatient Visits:** 34480 **Births:** 363 **Total Expense ($000):** 80427 **Payroll Expense ($000):** 35031 **Personnel:** 367

## GLENVIEW—Cook County

**NORTHSHORE GLENBROOK HOSPITAL** See Northshore University Health System, Evanston

**NORTHSHORE UNIVERSITY HEALTHSYSTEM-GLENBROOK HOSPITAL** See Northshore Glenbrook Hospital

## GRANITE CITY—Madison County

☐ **GATEWAY REGIONAL MEDICAL CENTER (140125)**, 2100 Madison Avenue, Zip 62040–4799; tel. 618/798–3000, (Nonreporting) **A**1 10 **F**3 8 11 12 13 15 18 20 22 24 26 28 29 34 35 38 40 45 46 48 50 51 54 59 64 66 70 76 77 79 80 81 82 85 86 87 93 94 96 97 98 99 100 101 102 103 104 107 108 110 111 114 115 119 126 129 130 132 135 144 146 147 148 149 **S** Quorum Health, Brentwood, TN
Primary Contact: Bob Moore, FACHE, Chief Executive Officer
CMO: Mike Adams, M.D., Chief Medical Officer
CIO: Dennis Kampwerth, Director Management Information Systems
CHR: Reva S Weems, Director Human Resources
CNO: Sam R White, Chief Nursing Officer
Web address: www.gatewayregional.net
**Control:** Corporation, Investor–owned (for–profit) **Service:** General medical and surgical

**Staffed Beds:** 127 **Admissions:** 6453 **Census:** 86 **Outpatient Visits:** 230020 **Births:** 254 **Total Expense ($000):** 109177 **Payroll Expense ($000):** 33554 **Personnel:** 762

**ST ELIZABETH MEDICAL CENTER** See Gateway Regionval Medical Center

## GREENVILLE—Bond County

**GREENVILLE REGIONAL HOSPITAL** See Hshs Holy Family Hospital in Greenville

★ ○ **HSHS HOLY FAMILY HOSPITAL IN GREENVILLE (140137)**, 200 Healthcare Drive, Zip 62246–1154; tel. 618/664–1230, (Nonreporting) **A**10 11 **F**3 11 13 15 18 30 31 34 40 41 45 49 50 56 57 59 76 78 79 81 85 89 93 94 97 98 103 104 107 110 111 115 119 125 127 129 130 132 133 135 154 **S** HSHS Hospital Sisters Health System, Springfield, IL
Primary Contact: Kelly Sager, R.N., President and Chief Executive Officer
CFO: Mark S Ennen, Director of Finance
CHR: Vicki Kloeckner, Director Human Resources
CNO: Lorna Keaster, Interim Chief Nursing Officer
Web address: www.greenvilleregionalhospital.com
**Control:** Other not–for–profit (including NFP Corporation) **Service:** General medical and surgical

**Staffed Beds:** 42 **Admissions:** 1128 **Census:** 15 **Outpatient Visits:** 28530 **Births:** 162 **Total Expense ($000):** 34175 **Payroll Expense ($000):** 11328 **Personnel:** 192

## HARRISBURG—Saline County

☒ **HARRISBURG MEDICAL CENTER (140210)**, 100 Dr Warren Tuttle Drive, Zip 62946–2718, Mailing Address: P.O. Box 428, Zip 62946–0428; tel. 618/253–7671, (Nonreporting) **A**1 10 20 **F**3 8 11 15 28 29 30 31 34 40 45 50 56 57 59 61 62 64 75 77 78 79 81 85 87 91 93 94 97 98 100 101 102 103 104 107 108 110 114 119 127 129 130 131 133 146 154
Primary Contact: Donald Hutson, President and Chief Executive Officer
COO: Danny Lampley, Chief Operating Officer
CFO: June Hayes, Chief Financial Officer
CIO: Rick Pyle, Director Information Systems
CHR: Dorene L Ewell, Director of Human Resources and Development
CNO: Leslie Ferrell, Chief Nursing Officer
Web address: www.harrisburgmc.com
**Control:** Other not–for–profit (including NFP Corporation) **Service:** General medical and surgical

**Staffed Beds:** 69 **Admissions:** 2768 **Census:** 39 **Outpatient Visits:** 90950 **Births:** 0 **Total Expense ($000):** 59385 **Payroll Expense ($000):** 28721 **Personnel:** 531

*Many Facility Codes have changed. Please refer to the AHA Guide Code Chart.*

## HARVARD—Mchenry County

**MERCYHEALTH HOSPITAL AND MEDICAL CENTER** See Mercyhealth Hospital and Medical Center - Harvard

**☒ MERCYHEALTH HOSPITAL AND MEDICAL CENTER - HARVARD (141335)**, 901 Grant Street, Zip 60033–1898, Mailing Address: P.O. Box 850, Zip 60033–0850; tel. 815/943–5431, (Total facility includes 45 beds in nursing home–type unit) (Nonreporting) **A**1 10 18 **F**3 11 15 18 28 29 30 35 40 45 46 47 48 57 59 64 69 70 75 77 79 81 82 85 87 93 96 107 108 110 119 128 129 130 131 132 143 146 148 149 154 **P**6 **S** Mercy Health System, Janesville, WI
Primary Contact: Javon R. Bea, Chief Executive Officer
COO: Jennifer Hallatt, Chief Operating Officer
CFO: Shannon Dunphy-Alexander, Director
CMO: Tawfik Barakat, M.D., President, Medical Staff
CHR: Heather Niles, Director Human Resources Operations
CNO: Caryn Lynn Oleston, FACHE, MSN, R.N., Chief Nursing Officer
Web address: www.mercyhealthsystem.org
**Control**: Other not–for–profit (including NFP Corporation) **Service**: General medical and surgical

**Staffed Beds**: 58 **Admissions**: 602 **Census**: 47 **Outpatient Visits**: 58443 **Births**: 0 **Total Expense ($000)**: 24783 **Payroll Expense ($000)**: 9464 **Personnel**: 146

## HARVEY—Cook County

**⇑ INGALLS HOSPITAL** See Ingalls Memorial Hospital

**★ △ ⇑ INGALLS MEMORIAL HOSPITAL (140191)**, One Ingalls Drive, Zip 60426–3591; tel. 708/333–2300, (Nonreporting) **A**2 3 5 7 10 21 **S** University of Chicago Medicine, Chicago, IL
Primary Contact: Brian Sinotte, President
COO: Michael L Hicks, Senior Vice President and Chief Operating Officer
CFO: Michael Lawrence, Chief Financial Officer
CNO: Kathy Mikos, Vice President and Chief Nursing Officer
Web address: www.ingallshealthsystem.org
**Control**: Other not–for–profit (including NFP Corporation) **Service**: General medical and surgical

**Staffed Beds**: 199

## HAVANA—Mason County

**☒ MASON DISTRICT HOSPITAL (141313)**, 615 North Promenade Street, Zip 62644–1243, Mailing Address: P.O. Box 530, Zip 62644–0530; tel. 309/543–4431, (Nonreporting) **A**1 10 18
Primary Contact: Douglas D. Kosier, Chief Executive Officer
CMO: Tad A. Yetter, M.D., President Medical Staff
CIO: Aaron Coots, Information Technology Director
CHR: Anne Davis, Director Human Resources
CNO: Rhonda Hine, R.N., Interim Chief Nursing Executive
Web address: www.masondistricthospital.org
**Control**: Hospital district or authority, Government, Nonfederal **Service**: General medical and surgical

**Staffed Beds**: 20

## HAZEL CREST—Cook County

**★ ⇑ ADVOCATE SOUTH SUBURBAN HOSPITAL (140250)**, 17800 South Kedzie Avenue, Zip 60429–0989; tel. 708/799–8000, (Nonreporting) **A**3 10 21 **F**3 11 13 15 18 20 22 24 26 28 29 30 31 34 35 36 40 45 46 47 49 51 53 55 57 59 60 63 64 68 70 75 76 77 78 79 81 82 84 85 87 89 92 93 100 107 108 110 111 114 115 118 119 126 130 132 145 146 147 148 149 154 156 157 **P**8 **S** Advocate Aurora Health, Downers Grove, IL
Primary Contact: Rashard Johnson, President
COO: Karen Clark, MS, R.N., Vice President Operations
CFO: Brian Kelly, Vice President Finance
CMO: Richard Multack, D.O., Vice President Medical Management
CIO: Beth Turek, Site Manager Information Systems
CHR: Kristin Landini, Vice President Human Resources
CNO: Sharon A. Otten, Vice President Nursing
Web address: www.advocatehealth.com/ssub/
**Control**: Church operated, Nongovernment, not–for–profit **Service**: General medical and surgical

**Staffed Beds**: 222 **Admissions**: 9451 **Census**: 108 **Outpatient Visits**: 147640 **Births**: 791 **Total Expense ($000)**: 222094 **Payroll Expense ($000)**: 72301 **Personnel**: 1092

**⇑ SOUTH SUBURBAN HOSPITAL** See Advocate South Suburban Hospital

## HERRIN—Williamson County

**☐ HERRIN HOSPITAL (140011)**, 201 South 14th Street, Zip 62948–3631; tel. 618/942–2171, (Nonreporting) **A**1 5 10 **F**3 11 12 18 28 29 30 34 35 40 45 47 49 50 51 54 56 57 59 60 61 64 68 70 74 75 78 79 81 82 84 85 86 87 90 92 93 100 107 108 111 114 115 119 130 131 132 135 143 146 148 149 154 156 **P**1 **S** Southern Illinois Healthcare, Carbondale, IL
Primary Contact: Rodney Smith, Vice President and Administrator
CFO: Michael Kasser, Chief Financial Officer
CMO: Michelle Jenkins, M.D., President Medical Staff
CIO: David Holland, Chief Information Officer
CHR: Teresa A Lovellette, Manager Human Resources
Web address: www.sih.net
**Control**: Other not–for–profit (including NFP Corporation) **Service**: General medical and surgical

**Staffed Beds**: 114 **Admissions**: 6607 **Census**: 78 **Outpatient Visits**: 177186 **Births**: 0 **Total Expense ($000)**: 163802 **Payroll Expense ($000)**: 46698 **Personnel**: 925

## HIGHLAND—Madison County

**☒ HSHS ST. JOSEPH'S HOSPITAL (141336)**, 12866 Troxler Avenue, Zip 62249–1698; tel. 618/651–2600, (Nonreporting) **A**1 10 18 **F**3 8 11 15 26 27 28 29 30 34 35 37 40 41 44 45 47 49 51 53 57 59 64 70 75 79 81 84 86 87 93 97 107 108 110 111 114 119 124 126 129 130 131 132 133 135 143 146 147 154 157 **S** HSHS Hospital Sisters Health System, Springfield, IL
Primary Contact: John A. Ludwig, President and Chief Operating Officer
COO: Chris Govero, Director of Operations
CFO: David Nosacka, Southern Illinois Division Chief Financial Officer
CHR: Christie Silvey, Director People Services
CNO: Teresa Cornelius, R.N., Interim Chief Nursing Officer
Web address: www.stjosephshighland.com
**Control**: Church operated, Nongovernment, not–for–profit **Service**: General medical and surgical

**Staffed Beds**: 25 **Admissions**: 1329 **Census**: 16 **Outpatient Visits**: 59458 **Births**: 0 **Total Expense ($000)**: 42782 **Payroll Expense ($000)**: 12549 **Personnel**: 250

**ST. JOSEPH'S HOSPITAL** See Hshs St. Joseph's Hospital

## HIGHLAND PARK—Lake County

**NORTHSHORE HIGHLAND PARK HOSPITAL** See Northshore University Health System, Evanston

**NORTHSHORE UNIVERSITY HEALTHSYSTEM-HIGHLAND PARK HOSPITAL** See Northshore Highland Park Hospital

## HILLSBORO—Montgomery County

**☒ ⇑ HILLSBORO AREA HOSPITAL (141332)**, 1200 East Tremont Street, Zip 62049–1900; tel. 217/532–6111, (Nonreporting) **A**1 10 18 21 **F**2 3 10 15 28 29 30 34 35 40 56 57 59 64 65 75 77 79 81 85 86 87 89 92 93 94 97 100 104 107 110 111 115 125 129 130 131 133 135 146 148 149 **P**6 **S** HealthTech Management Services, Brentwood, TN
Primary Contact: Rex H. Brown, President and Chief Executive Officer
CFO: Terri L Carroll, Vice President Financial Services
CHR: Sharon Clark, Director Human Resources
Web address: www.hillsborohealth.org
**Control**: Other not–for–profit (including NFP Corporation) **Service**: General medical and surgical

**Staffed Beds**: 25 **Admissions**: 312 **Census**: 7 **Outpatient Visits**: 14905 **Births**: 0 **Total Expense ($000)**: 22708 **Payroll Expense ($000)**: 8423 **Personnel**: 193

**⇑ HILLSBORO HOSPITAL** See Hillsboro Area Hospital

## HINES—Cook County

**☒ △ EDWARD HINES, JR. VETERANS AFFAIRS HOSPITAL**, 5000 South Fifth Avenue, Zip 60141–3030, Mailing Address: P.O. Box 5000, Zip 60141–5000; tel. 708/202–8387, (Nonreporting) **A**1 2 3 5 7 **S** Department of Veterans Affairs, Washington, DC
Primary Contact: Steven E. Braverman, M.D., Director
CFO: Yolanda Martinez, Chief Fiscal Services
CMO: Jack Bulmash, M.D., Chief of Staff
CIO: Robert Tanjuakio, Chief Information Resources Management
CNO: Marianne Locke, R.N., MSN, Associate Director Patient Care Services
Web address: www.hines.va.gov/
**Control**: Veterans Affairs, Government, federal **Service**: General medical and surgical

**Staffed Beds**: 485

---

**Hospital, Medicare Provider Number, Address, Telephone, Approval, Facility, and Physician Codes, Health Care System**

★ American Hospital Association (AHA) membership  ○ Healthcare Facilities Accreditation Program  ⇑ Center for Improvement in Healthcare Quality Accreditation
☐ The Joint Commission accreditation  ◇ DNV Healthcare Inc. accreditation  △ Commission on Accreditation of Rehabilitation Facilities (CARF) accreditation

**IL**

**JOHN J MADDEN MENTAL HLTH CNTR** See John J. Madden Mental Health Center

☐ **JOHN J. MADDEN MENTAL HEALTH CENTER (144028)**, 1200 South First Avenue, Zip 60141–0800; tel. 708/338–7202, (Nonreporting) **A**1 3 5 10 **S** Division of Mental Health, Department of Human Services, Springfield, IL
Primary Contact: Edith Newman, Interim Administrator
CFO: Janice Evans, Chief Financial Officer
**Control:** State, Government, Nonfederal **Service:** Psychiatric

| Staffed Beds: 125 |
| --- |

**VETERANS AFFAIRS EDWARD HINES, JR. HOSPITAL** See Edward Hines, Jr. Veterans Affairs Hospital

### HINSDALE—DuPage County

**ADVENTIST MEDICAL CENTER - HINSDALE** See Amita Health Adventist Medical Center - Hinsdale

✠ **AMITA HEALTH ADVENTIST MEDICAL CENTER - HINSDALE (140122)**, 120 North Oak Street, Zip 60521–3890; tel. 630/856–6001, (Nonreporting) **A**1 2 3 5 10 13 **F**3 4 13 15 18 20 22 24 26 28 29 30 31 34 37 38 39 40 41 43 44 45 47 49 54 55 57 58 59 61 64 70 72 76 78 79 81 82 84 85 86 87 89 92 93 97 98 99 100 107 108 114 115 126 129 130 131 132 135 143 146 147 149 151 154 156 **S** AdventHealth, Altamonte Springs, FL
Primary Contact: Adam Maycock, Chief Executive Officer
CFO: Rebecca Mathis, Vice President and Chief Financial Officer
CMO: Bonny Chen, M.D., Vice President and Chief Medical Officer
CHR: Mary P Leurck, Human Resources Director
CNO: Mary S Murphy, MSN, Vice President and Chief Nursing Officer
Web address: www.AMITAhealth.org
**Control:** Church operated, Nongovernment, not–for–profit **Service:** General medical and surgical

| Staffed Beds: 261 Admissions: 11785 Census: 136 Outpatient Visits: 256059 Births: 2671 Total Expense ($000): 272384 Payroll Expense ($000): 90007 Personnel: 980 |
| --- |

**R M SPECIALTY HOSPITAL** See RML Specialty Hospital

✠ **RML SPECIALTY HOSPITAL (142010)**, 5601 South County Line Road, Zip 60521–4875; tel. 630/286–4000, (Includes RML SPECIALTY HOSPITAL, Mailing address: 3435 West Van Buren Street, Chicago, Illinois, Zip 60624–3312; tel. 773/826–6300; James R Prister, President and Chief Executive Officer), (Nonreporting) **A**1 3 5 10 **F**1 3 18 29 30 31 45 53 58 74 85 87 107 114 115 119 130 148 149
Primary Contact: James R. Prister, President and Chief Executive Officer
COO: Ken Pawola, Chief Operating Officer
CFO: Tom Pater, Chief Financial Officer
CMO: Patrick Fahey, M.D., Chief Medical Officer
CIO: Vincent S Vitali, Chief Information Officer
CHR: John Landstrom, Director Human Resources
CNO: Marti Edwards, MSN, R.N., Chief Nursing Officer
Web address: www.rmlspecialtyhospital.org
**Control:** Other not–for–profit (including NFP Corporation) **Service:** Acute long–term care hospital

| Staffed Beds: 184 Admissions: 1344 Census: 143 Outpatient Visits: 0 Births: 0 Total Expense ($000): 95719 Payroll Expense ($000): 47850 Personnel: 710 |
| --- |

### HOFFMAN ESTATES—Cook County

**ALEXIAN BROTHERS BEHAVIORAL HEALTH HOSPITAL** See Amita Health Alexian Brothers Behavioral Health Hospital

**ALEXIAN BROTHERS WOMEN & CHILDREN'S HOSPITAL** See Amita Health Women & Children's Hospital

✠ **AMITA HEALTH ALEXIAN BROTHERS BEHAVIORAL HEALTH HOSPITAL (144031)**, 1650 Moon Lake Boulevard, Zip 60169–1010; tel. 847/882–1600, (Nonreporting) **A**1 10 **F**5 29 64 98 99 100 101 102 103 104 105 130 132 151 152 153 154 **P**6 **S** Ascension Healthcare, Saint Louis, MO
Primary Contact: Clayton Ciha, President and Chief Executive Officer
COO: Christopher Novak, Chief Operating Officer
CFO: David Jones, Chief Financial Officer
CMO: Christopher D'Agostino, Chief Medical Officer
CIO: Sherrie Russell, Vice President and Chief Information Officer
CNO: Beth Jelesky, MSN, Chief Nursing Officer
Web address: www.abbhh.org
**Control:** Church operated, Nongovernment, not–for–profit **Service:** Psychiatric

| Staffed Beds: 141 Admissions: 4739 Census: 113 Outpatient Visits: 190526 Total Expense ($000): 88445 Payroll Expense ($000): 43755 |
| --- |

✠ **AMITA HEALTH HOFFMAN ESTATES (140290)**, 1555 Barrington Road, Zip 60169–1019; tel. 847/843–2000, (Includes AMITA HEALTH WOMEN & CHILDREN'S HOSPITAL, Mailing address: 1555 Barrington Road, Hoffman Estates, Illinois, Zip 60169–1019; tel. 847/843–2000; Kevin Rath, Vice President and Executive Director), (Nonreporting) **A**1 2 3 5 10 **F**3 8 11 12 13 15 18 19 20 22 26 29 30 31 32 34 35 37 39 40 41 42 43 44 45 46 47 48 49 50 51 54 55 57 59 63 64 70 72 74 76 77 78 79 81 82 84 85 86 87 89 93 107 108 110 111 114 115 118 119 120 121 124 126 130 132 145 146 147 148 149 154 156 157 **S** Ascension Healthcare, Saint Louis, MO
Primary Contact: Polly J. Davenport, FACHE, R.N., President and Chief Executive Officer
COO: Laurence Dry, Chief Operating Officer, Acute Care Hospitals Northern Region
CFO: Henry Zeisel, Chief Financial Officer, Northern Region
CIO: Sherrie Russell, Senior Vice President and Chief Information Officer
CHR: Donald Russell, Senior Vice President and Chief Human Resources Officer
CNO: Chris Budzinsky, Vice President Nursing and Chief Nursing Officer Alexian Brothers Acute Care Ministries
Web address: www.AMITAHealth.org
**Control:** Church operated, Nongovernment, not–for–profit **Service:** General medical and surgical

| Staffed Beds: 298 Admissions: 16631 Census: 188 Outpatient Visits: 249022 Births: 3306 Total Expense ($000): 266731 Payroll Expense ($000): 100028 Personnel: 1029 |
| --- |

**ST. ALEXIUS MEDICAL CENTER** See Amita Health Hoffman Estates

### HOOPESTON—Vermilion County

★ ⇑ **CARLE HOOPESTON REGIONAL HEALTH CENTER (141316)**, 701 East Orange Street, Zip 60942–1801; tel. 217/283–5531, (Nonreporting) **A**3 5 10 18 21 **F**3 15 29 35 40 45 57 59 65 79 81 85 89 90 93 107 108 110 111 115 119 128 133 **S** Carle Health, Urbana, IL
Primary Contact: Harry Brockus, Chief Executive Officer
CHR: Melodee Bowers, Director Human Resources
Web address: www.carle.org
**Control:** Other not–for–profit (including NFP Corporation) **Service:** General medical and surgical

| Staffed Beds: 13 Admissions: 377 Census: 4 Outpatient Visits: 11624 Births: 0 Total Expense ($000): 68575 Payroll Expense ($000): 18917 Personnel: 265 |
| --- |

⇑ **HOOPESTON REGIONAL HEALTH CENTER** See Carle Hoopeston Regional Health Center

### HOPEDALE—Tazewell County

**HOPEDALE HOSPITAL** See Hopedale Medical Complex

**HOPEDALE MEDICAL COMPLEX (141330)**, 107 Tremont Street, Zip 61747–7525, Mailing Address: PO Box 267, Zip 61747–7525; tel. 309/449–3321, (Total facility includes 54 beds in nursing home–type unit) (Nonreporting) **A**10 18 **F**10 18 28 29 30 32 34 35 40 45 48 49 50 51 53 56 57 59 64 65 67 70 74 78 79 81 82 93 97 107 110 111 115 119 129 130 131 133 145 146 147 148 149 157 158
Primary Contact: Alfred N. Rossi, M.D., Chief Executive Officer
COO: Mark F Rossi, Chief Operating Officer and General Counsel
CFO: Nicholas A. Penn, Chief Financial Officer
CHR: Andrea Halley, Vice President of Non-Clinical Operations/Director Human Resources
CNO: Timothy Sondag, Senior Nursing Officer
Web address: www.hopedalemc.com
**Control:** Other not–for–profit (including NFP Corporation) **Service:** General medical and surgical

| Staffed Beds: 84 Admissions: 503 Census: 52 Births: 0 Total Expense ($000): 29327 Payroll Expense ($000): 12524 Personnel: 259 |
| --- |

### HUNTLEY—McHenry County

**CENTEGRA HOSPITAL - HUNTLEY** See Northwestern Medicine Huntley

*Many Facility Codes have changed. Please refer to the AHA Guide Code Chart.*    © 2021 AHA Guide

**IL**

## JACKSONVILLE—Morgan County

⊞ **PASSAVANT AREA HOSPITAL (140058)**, 1600 West Walnut Street,
Zip 62650–1136; tel. 217/245–9541, (Total facility includes 15 beds in nursing
home–type unit) (Nonreporting) **A**1 10 **F**3 13 14 15 28 29 30 31 34 35 40 41 44
45 50 51 57 58 59 60 64 68 69 70 75 76 78 79 81 82 85 86 87 89 93 97 104
107 108 110 111 115 118 119 120 121 127 128 129 130 131 141 146 147
148 **S** Memorial Health System, Springfield, IL
Primary Contact: Scott Boston, R.N., MS, President and Chief Executive Officer
CFO: Paul Eddington, CPA, Affiliate Vice President and Chief Financial Officer
CMO: Anthony Griffin, M.D., Chief Medical Officer
CIO: James Krug, Affiliate Vice President, Information Systems and Support
Services
CHR: Dillon Woods, Director Human Resources
CNO: Leanna Wynn, Affiliate Vice President and Chief Nursing Officer
Web address: www.passavanthospital.com
**Control:** Church operated, Nongovernment, not–for–profit **Service:** General
medical and surgical

**Staffed Beds:** 103 **Admissions:** 3144 **Census:** 39 **Outpatient Visits:** 86290
**Births:** 386 **Total Expense ($000):** 101974 **Payroll Expense ($000):** 43809
**Personnel:** 653

## JERSEYVILLE—Jersey County

⊞ **JERSEY COMMUNITY HOSPITAL (140059)**, 400 Maple Summit Road,
Zip 62052–2028, Mailing Address: P.O. Box 426, Zip 62052–0426;
tel. 618/498–6402, (Nonreporting) **A**1 10 **F**3 7 8 11 15 18 26 28 29 34 35 36
38 40 41 45 46 47 48 50 51 53 54 56 57 59 64 65 68 70 75 79 81 82 83 84
85 87 97 100 101 104 107 110 111 115 119 127 129 130 133 146 147 148
149 154 156 **P**6
Primary Contact: Beth King, Chief Executive Officer
CMO: Michael McNear, M.D., Chief Medical Officer
CIO: Shane Winters, Chief Information Officer
CHR: Sharon K Sanford, Director Human Resources
CNO: Julie Smith, R.N., MSN, Director of Nursing
Web address: www.jch.org
**Control:** Hospital district or authority, Government, Nonfederal **Service:** General
medical and surgical

**Staffed Beds:** 46 **Admissions:** 775 **Census:** 7 **Outpatient Visits:** 49592
**Births:** 0 **Total Expense ($000):** 44254 **Payroll Expense ($000):** 20389
**Personnel:** 361

## JOLIET—Will County

⊞ △ **AMITA HEALTH SAINT JOSEPH MEDICAL CENTER (140007)**, 333 North
Madison Street, Zip 60435–8200; tel. 815/725–7133, (Nonreporting) **A**1 2 3 7
10 **F**3 11 12 13 15 17 18 20 22 24 26 28 29 30 31 32 34 35 36 38 39 40 41
43 44 45 46 47 49 50 53 54 56 57 58 59 60 61 64 65 68 70 72 74 75 76 77
78 79 80 81 82 84 85 86 87 89 90 92 93 96 97 98 99 100 101 102 103 105
107 108 110 111 114 115 118 119 120 121 123 124 126 129 130 131 132
134 135 143 145 146 147 149 154 **S** Ascension Healthcare, Saint Louis, MO
Primary Contact: Herbert Buchanan, President
CFO: Deb Schimerowski, Regional Finance Officer
CMO: Gary Lipinski, M.D., Chief Medical Officer
CHR: Monica Simzyk, Regional Human Resource Officer
CNO: Lynn Watson, Interim Chief Nursing Officer
Web address: www.presencehealth.org/stjoes
**Control:** Church operated, Nongovernment, not–for–profit **Service:** General
medical and surgical

**Staffed Beds:** 485 **Admissions:** 18157 **Census:** 232 **Outpatient
Visits:** 183241 **Births:** 847 **Total Expense ($000):** 309124 **Payroll Expense
($000):** 105321

**PRESENCE SAINT JOSEPH MEDICAL CENTER** See Amita Health Saint Joseph
Medical Center

## KANKAKEE—Kankakee County

⊞ **AMITA HEALTH ST. MARY'S HOSPITAL (140155)**, 500 West Court Street,
Zip 60901–3661; tel. 815/937–2400, (Nonreporting) **A**1 2 3 10 **F**3 5 11 12 13
15 18 20 22 26 28 29 30 31 32 34 35 36 38 39 40 43 44 45 46 47 48 49 50
54 56 57 58 59 60 61 64 65 68 70 74 75 76 77 78 79 81 82 84 85 86 87 89
92 93 97 98 100 101 102 103 104 105 107 108 110 111 114 115 119 120
121 123 129 130 131 132 135 143 146 147 149 152 153 154 **S** Ascension
Healthcare, Saint Louis, MO
Primary Contact: Chris Shride, President
CFO: Deb Schimerowski, Regional Chief Financial Officer
CMO: Kalisha Hill, M.D., Chief Medical Officer
CIO: Russell Soliman, Director Information Services
CHR: Monica Simzyk, Regional Chief Human Resources Officer
CNO: Karen M Gallagher, MSN, Chief Nursing Office, Vice President Operations
Web address: www.presencehealth.org/presence-st-marys-hospital-kankakee
**Control:** Church operated, Nongovernment, not–for–profit **Service:** General
medical and surgical

**Staffed Beds:** 182 **Admissions:** 5563 **Census:** 57 **Outpatient Visits:** 81809
**Births:** 325 **Total Expense ($000):** 107948 **Payroll Expense ($000):** 34275

**PRESENCE ST. MARY'S HOSPITAL** See Amita Health St. Mary's Hospital

⇑ **RIVERSIDE HEALTHCARE** See Riverside Medical Center

★ △ ⇑ **RIVERSIDE MEDICAL CENTER (140186)**, 350 North Wall Street,
Zip 60901–2901; tel. 815/933–1671, (Nonreporting) **A**2 3 5 7 10 21 **F**3 4 5 6 7
8 9 12 13 15 17 18 20 22 24 26 28 29 30 31 32 34 35 36 38 39 40 41 43 44
45 46 47 49 50 51 54 55 56 57 58 59 61 62 64 65 66 68 70 71 74 75 76 77
78 79 81 82 84 85 86 87 89 90 92 93 96 97 98 99 100 101 102 103 104 105
107 108 110 111 114 115 118 119 120 121 123 124 126 127 129 130 131
132 134 135 141 143 144 145 146 147 148 149 150 151 152 153 154 156
157
Primary Contact: Phillip M. Kambic, President and Chief Executive Officer
CFO: John Seal, Interim Chief Financial Officer Director Human Resources
CMO: Keith A Moss, Vice President & Chief Medical Informatics Officers
CIO: Kyle Hansen, Corporate Director Information Systems
CHR: Becky Kay Hinrichs, Vice President Human Resources
CNO: Michael Mutterer, Senior Vice President and Chief Nursing Officer
Web address: www.riversidehealthcare.org
**Control:** Other not–for–profit (including NFP Corporation) **Service:** General
medical and surgical

**Staffed Beds:** 300 **Admissions:** 11815 **Census:** 160 **Outpatient
Visits:** 608990 **Births:** 1090 **Total Expense ($000):** 366594 **Payroll
Expense ($000):** 168416 **Personnel:** 2328

## KEWANEE—Henry County

**KEWANEE HOSPITAL** See OSF Saint Luke Medical Center

★ **OSF SAINT LUKE MEDICAL CENTER (141325)**, 1051 West South
Street, Zip 61443–8354, Mailing Address: P.O. Box 747, Zip 61443–0747;
tel. 309/852–7500, (Nonreporting) **A**10 18 **F**3 11 15 29 30 32 34 35 36 38 40
45 50 57 59 64 65 66 70 75 77 78 79 81 82 85 86 87 92 93 96 97 108 110
111 115 119 127 129 130 131 132 133 135 146 147 148 149 154 156 **S** OSF
Healthcare, Peoria, IL
Primary Contact: Jacqueline D. Kernan, President
CFO: John Bowser, Vice President, Chief Financial Officer
CMO: Clifford G Martin, M.D., Regional Vice President and Chief Medical Officer
CHR: Renee A Salisbury, Director Human Resources
CNO: Shelley Wiborg, MS, R.N., Chief Nursing Officer
Web address: www.osfsaintluke.org
**Control:** Other not–for–profit (including NFP Corporation) **Service:** General
medical and surgical

**Staffed Beds:** 25 **Admissions:** 473 **Census:** 4 **Outpatient Visits:** 43479
**Births:** 0 **Total Expense ($000):** 33457 **Payroll Expense ($000):** 13126
**Personnel:** 154

IL

---

**Hospital, Medicare Provider Number, Address, Telephone, Approval, Facility, and Physician Codes, Health Care System**

★ American Hospital Association (AHA) membership    ◯ Healthcare Facilities Accreditation Program    ⇑ Center for Improvement in Healthcare Quality Accreditation
□ The Joint Commission accreditation    ◇ DNV Healthcare Inc. accreditation    △ Commission on Accreditation of Rehabilitation Facilities (CARF) accreditation

© 2021 AHA Guide    *Many Facility Codes have changed. Please refer to the AHA Guide Code Chart.*    Hospitals **A209**

## LA GRANGE—Cook County

**ADVENTIST MEDICAL CENTER LAGRANGE** See Amita Health Adventist Medical Center La Grange

⊞ **AMITA HEALTH ADVENTIST MEDICAL CENTER LA GRANGE (140065)**, 5101 South Willow Spring Road, Zip 60525–2600; tel. 708/245–9000, (Nonreporting) **A**1 2 3 5 10 **F**3 13 15 18 20 22 24 29 30 31 34 37 40 41 43 44 45 49 51 54 57 58 59 61 62 64 68 70 73 77 78 79 81 82 84 85 86 87 90 91 93 96 97 100 101 107 108 110 111 114 115 119 126 130 131 143 146 147 148 154 **S** AdventHealth, Altamonte Springs, FL
Primary Contact: Adam Maycock, Chief Executive Officer
CFO: Rebecca Mathis, Chief Financial Officer
CIO: Thomas Schoenig, Chief Information Officer
CHR: Garry Giertuga, Site Manager Human Resources
CNO: Mary S Murphy, MSN, Regional Chief Nursing Officer
Web address: www.keepingyouwell.com
**Control**: Church operated, Nongovernment, not–for–profit **Service**: General medical and surgical

> **Staffed Beds:** 200 **Admissions:** 7950 **Census:** 102 **Outpatient Visits:** 76351 **Births:** 0 **Total Expense ($000):** 111053 **Payroll Expense ($000):** 51701 **Personnel:** 525

## LAKE FOREST—Lake County

**NORTHWESTERN LAKE FOREST HOSPITAL** See Northwestern Medicine Lake Forest Hospital

⊞ **NORTHWESTERN MEDICINE LAKE FOREST HOSPITAL (140130)**, 1000 North Westmoreland Road, Zip 60045–1696, Mailing Address: 1000 N Westmoreland Road, Zip 60045–1658; tel. 847/234–5600, (Nonreporting) **A**1 2 3 5 10 **F**3 8 9 11 12 13 15 18 20 22 26 28 29 30 31 32 34 35 36 38 40 41 42 43 44 45 46 47 48 49 50 51 52 53 54 55 56 57 58 59 60 64 65 66 68 70 73 74 75 76 77 78 79 81 82 84 85 86 87 92 93 96 97 100 102 103 104 107 108 110 111 114 115 116 117 119 120 121 123 126 129 130 131 132 135 144 146 147 148 149 150 154 156 **S** Northwestern Memorial HealthCare, Chicago, IL
Primary Contact: Thomas J. McAfee, President, North Region
CFO: Richard A. Franco, Vice President and Chief Financial Officer
CMO: Jeffrey D. Kopin, Senior Vice President and Chief Medical Officer
CNO: Denise Majeski, MSN, R.N., Vice President Operations and Chief Nurse Executive
Web address: www.nm.org
**Control**: Other not–for–profit (including NFP Corporation) **Service**: General medical and surgical

> **Staffed Beds:** 120 **Admissions:** 9589 **Census:** 85 **Outpatient Visits:** 678851 **Births:** 1700 **Total Expense ($000):** 540146 **Payroll Expense ($000):** 197129 **Personnel:** 2345

## LAWRENCEVILLE—Lawrence County

**LAWRENCE COUNTY MEMORIAL HOSPITAL (141344)**, 2200 West State Street, Zip 62439–1852; tel. 618/943–1000, (Nonreporting) **A**10 18 **F**3 8 11 15 28 29 30 35 40 45 54 64 65 75 77 81 93 97 104 107 110 114 127 130 133 149 **P**6
Primary Contact: Donald Robbins, Chief Executive Officer
CFO: Larry Spore, Chief Financial Officer
CIO: Gary Theriac, Director Information Technology
CHR: Kim Alldredge, Director Human Resources
CNO: Rita Garvey, Chief Nursing Officer
Web address: www.lcmhosp.org
**Control**: Other not–for–profit (including NFP Corporation) **Service**: General medical and surgical

> **Staffed Beds:** 25 **Admissions:** 437 **Census:** 5 **Outpatient Visits:** 48118 **Births:** 0 **Total Expense ($000):** 17151 **Payroll Expense ($000):** 7592 **Personnel:** 147

## LIBERTYVILLE—Lake County

★ ⇑ **ADVOCATE CONDELL MEDICAL CENTER (140202)**, 801 South Milwaukee Avenue, Zip 60048–3199; tel. 847/362–2900, (Nonreporting) **A**2 10 21 **F**3 11 13 15 18 19 20 22 24 26 28 29 30 31 32 34 35 36 37 38 39 40 41 43 44 45 46 47 48 49 50 51 53 55 56 57 59 60 64 65 68 70 73 74 75 76 77 78 79 81 82 84 85 86 87 89 92 93 94 96 107 108 110 111 115 117 118 119 120 121 124 126 130 131 132 135 143 144 145 146 147 148 154 156 **P**8 **S** Advocate Aurora Health, Downers Grove, IL
Primary Contact: Matthew Lee. Primack, President
COO: Christian Wallis, Vice President Operations
CFO: Darrick Minzey, Vice President Finance
CMO: Debra Susie-Lattner, M.D., Vice President Medical Management
CIO: Rick Cornwall, HIT Site Coordinator
CHR: Sarah Stehly, Vice President Human Resources
CNO: Karen L. Hanson, Vice President Patient Care Services
Web address: www.advocatehealth.com/condell/
**Control**: Other not–for–profit (including NFP Corporation) **Service**: General medical and surgical

> **Staffed Beds:** 283 **Admissions:** 15446 **Census:** 191 **Outpatient Visits:** 212130 **Births:** 1107 **Total Expense ($000):** 310899 **Payroll Expense ($000):** 108834 **Personnel:** 1789

⇑ **CONDELL MEDICAL CENTER** See Advocate Condell Medical Center

## LINCOLN—Logan County

⊞ **ABRAHAM LINCOLN MEMORIAL HOSPITAL (141322)**, 200 Stahlhut Drive, Zip 62656–5066; tel. 217/732–2161, (Nonreporting) **A**1 5 10 18 **F**13 15 28 29 30 34 35 40 57 59 64 75 76 77 78 79 81 82 87 89 93 107 108 110 111 119 129 130 131 132 133 144 146 149 156 **P**5 **S** Memorial Health System, Springfield, IL
Primary Contact: Dolan Dalpoas, President and Chief Executive Officer
CMO: Amir J. Wahab, M.D., Medical Staff President
CIO: Keenan Leesman, Director Information Systems
CHR: Michelle Long, Regional Human Resource Manager
CNO: Roxanne Harling, Chief Nursing Officer
Web address: www.almh.org
**Control**: Other not–for–profit (including NFP Corporation) **Service**: General medical and surgical

> **Staffed Beds:** 25 **Admissions:** 759 **Census:** 12 **Outpatient Visits:** 46171 **Births:** 158 **Total Expense ($000):** 44721 **Payroll Expense ($000):** 18139 **Personnel:** 301

## LITCHFIELD—Montgomery County

⊞ **HSHS ST. FRANCIS HOSPITAL (141350)**, 1215 Franciscan Drive, Zip 62056–1799, Mailing Address: P.O. Box 1215, Zip 62056–0999; tel. 217/324–2191, (Nonreporting) **A**1 10 18 **F**3 8 11 13 15 18 28 29 30 31 34 35 40 44 45 46 50 56 57 59 64 68 70 74 75 76 77 78 79 81 82 85 86 87 92 93 107 111 114 117 118 119 129 131 132 133 134 135 146 147 149 154 **P**6 **S** HSHS Hospital Sisters Health System, Springfield, IL
Primary Contact: James Timpe, Chief Executive Officer
CFO: Marisa Murray, CPA, Director Finance
Web address: www.stfrancis-litchfield.org
**Control**: Church operated, Nongovernment, not–for–profit **Service**: General medical and surgical

> **Staffed Beds:** 25 **Admissions:** 1129 **Census:** 12 **Outpatient Visits:** 68901 **Births:** 223 **Total Expense ($000):** 40771 **Payroll Expense ($000):** 12907 **Personnel:** 236

**ST. FRANCIS HOSPITAL** See Hshs St. Francis Hospital

**IL**

## MACOMB—McDonough County

✠ **MCDONOUGH DISTRICT HOSPITAL (140089)**, 525 East Grant Street, Zip 61455–3318; tel. 309/833–4101, (Nonreporting) **A**1 10 20 **F**3 5 11 13 15 28 29 31 34 35 38 40 45 47 48 50 51 54 57 59 62 63 64 68 70 76 77 78 79 81 84 85 86 91 93 94 96 97 98 100 101 102 103 104 107 108 110 115 119 124 127 129 130 131 132 133 135 146 147 148 **P**8
Primary Contact: Brian E. Dietz, FACHE, President and Chief Executive Officer
CFO: William R Murdock, Vice President Finance
CMO: Edwin Card, President Medical Staff
CIO: Harlan T Baker, Chief Information Officer
CHR: Sara Robertson, Director of Human Resources
CNO: Wanda Foster, Vice President Nursing
Web address: www.mdh.org
**Control:** Hospital district or authority, Government, Nonfederal **Service:** General medical and surgical

**Staffed Beds:** 60 **Admissions:** 1558 **Census:** 18 **Outpatient Visits:** 202562 **Births:** 240 **Total Expense ($000):** 85197 **Payroll Expense ($000):** 37419 **Personnel:** 422

## MARION—Williamson County

☐ **HEARTLAND REGIONAL MEDICAL CENTER (140184)**, 3333 West DeYoung, Zip 62959–5884; tel. 618/998–7000, (Nonreporting) **A**1 10 **S** Quorum Health, Brentwood, TN
Primary Contact: M Edward. Cunningham, Chief Executive Officer
CFO: Jeff Thomas, Chief Financial Officer
CHR: Sam Hood, Director Human Resources
Web address: www.heartlandregional.com
**Control:** Corporation, Investor–owned (for–profit) **Service:** General medical and surgical

**Staffed Beds:** 92

**MARION MEMORIAL HOSPITAL** See Heartland Regional Medical Center

✠ **MARION VETERANS AFFAIRS MEDICAL CENTER**, 2401 West Main Street, Zip 62959–1188; tel. 618/997–5311, (Nonreporting) **A**1 **F**3 12 18 20 22 26 29 30 31 33 34 35 36 38 39 40 44 45 46 53 54 56 57 59 60 61 63 64 65 68 70 71 75 77 78 79 81 82 83 84 86 87 92 93 94 96 97 100 102 104 105 107 108 111 114 115 119 128 130 132 135 141 146 147 148 149 153 154 156 157 **S** Department of Veterans Affairs, Washington, DC
Primary Contact: Jo-Ann M. Ginsberg, R.N., MSN, Director
COO: Frank Kehus, Associate Director for Operations
CFO: Connie McDonald, Chief Financial Officer
CMO: Michael Ladwig, M.D., Chief of Staff
CIO: Adam Powell, Program Manager
CHR: Tim Hartwell, Chief Human Resources
CNO: Rose Burke, Associate Director Patient Care Services
Web address: www.marion.va.gov
**Control:** Veterans Affairs, Government, federal **Service:** General medical and surgical

**Staffed Beds:** 116 **Admissions:** 2018 **Census:** 16 **Outpatient Visits:** 35705 **Births:** 0 **Total Expense ($000):** 360374 **Payroll Expense ($000):** 128746 **Personnel:** 1535

**VETERANS AFFAIRS MEDICAL CENTER** See Marion Veterans Affairs Medical Center

## MARYVILLE—Madison County

✠ △ **ANDERSON HOSPITAL (140289)**, 6800 State Route 162, Zip 62062–8500; tel. 618/288–5711, (Nonreporting) **A**1 7 10 **F**3 11 13 15 18 20 22 28 29 30 31 34 35 40 49 57 59 62 64 70 74 75 76 78 79 81 85 90 93 107 110 111 115 117 118 119 120 121 123 126 129 130 132 144 146 147 148 149 154 156
Primary Contact: Keith Allen. Page, President and Chief Executive Officer
CFO: Michael Marshall, Vice President Finance and Chief Financial Officer
CMO: Charles A. Lane, Chief Medical Officer
CIO: Michael Ward, Director Information Services
CHR: Robin Steinmann, Chief Human Resources Officer
CNO: Lisa Klaustermeier, R.N., MSN, Chief Nursing Officer
Web address: www.andersonhospital.org
**Control:** Other not–for–profit (including NFP Corporation) **Service:** General medical and surgical

**Staffed Beds:** 131 **Admissions:** 7135 **Census:** 76 **Outpatient Visits:** 170587 **Births:** 1383 **Total Expense ($000):** 147545 **Payroll Expense ($000):** 57377 **Personnel:** 1263

**OLIVER ANDERSON HOSPITAL** See Anderson Hospital

## MATTOON—Coles County

✠ **SARAH BUSH LINCOLN HEALTH CENTER (140189)**, 1000 Health Center Drive, Zip 61938–9253; tel. 217/258–2525, (Nonreporting) **A**1 10 20 **F**3 11 12 13 15 18 20 22 28 29 30 31 32 34 35 36 38 39 40 44 45 49 50 53 54 56 57 59 61 62 63 64 65 66 68 69 70 71 74 75 76 77 78 79 81 82 84 85 86 87 89 93 97 98 100 101 102 104 105 107 110 111 115 117 119 120 121 123 126 127 129 130 131 132 134 135 144 145 146 147 148 149 154 156 **P**6
Primary Contact: Jerry Esker, President and Chief Executive Officer
COO: Kimberly Uphoff, Vice President Operations
CFO: Dennis Pluard, Vice President Finance and Support Services
CMO: James Hildebrandt, D.O., Vice President Medical Affairs
CIO: Brian Murphy, Vice President Information Systems
CHR: Debbie Saddoris, Vice President Human Resources
CNO: Sandra Miller, MSN, R.N., Interim Vice President, Patient Care Continuum and Chief Nursing Officer
Web address: www.sarahbush.org
**Control:** Other not–for–profit (including NFP Corporation) **Service:** General medical and surgical

**Staffed Beds:** 132 **Admissions:** 6907 **Census:** 63 **Outpatient Visits:** 535228 **Births:** 767 **Total Expense ($000):** 325668 **Payroll Expense ($000):** 149459 **Personnel:** 2246

**SARAH BUSH LINCOLN HEALTH SYST** See Sarah Bush Lincoln Health Center

## MAYWOOD—Cook County

**LOYOLA UNIV MEDICAL CENTER** See Loyola University Medical Center

✠ **LOYOLA UNIVERSITY MEDICAL CENTER (140276)**, 2160 South First Avenue, Zip 60153–3328; tel. 708/216–9000, (Includes RONALD MCDONALD CHILDREN'S HOSPITAL, Mailing address: 2160 South 1St Avenue, Maywood, Illinois, Zip 60153–3328; tel. 888/584–7888), (Nonreporting) **A**1 2 3 5 8 10 19 **F**3 5 6 7 8 9 11 12 13 14 15 16 17 18 19 20 21 22 23 24 25 26 27 28 29 30 31 32 33 34 35 36 37 38 39 40 41 43 44 45 46 47 48 49 50 51 54 55 56 57 58 59 60 61 64 65 66 68 70 71 72 73 74 75 76 77 78 79 80 81 82 84 85 86 87 88 89 91 92 93 94 96 97 100 101 102 104 107 108 110 111 114 115 116 117 118 119 120 121 124 126 129 130 131 132 134 135 136 137 138 139 140 141 142 143 144 145 146 147 148 149 150 154 155 **P**6 **S** Trinity Health, Livonia, MI
Primary Contact: Tad A. Gomez, President
COO: Richard Freeman, FACS, M.D., Chief Clinical Officer
CFO: Daniel Isacksen, Regional Chief Financial Officer
CMO: Kevin Smith, M.D., Interim Chief Medical Officer
CIO: Cynthia Davis, Interim Chief Financial Officer
CHR: Vicky Piper, Regional Vice President Human Resources
CNO: Peggy Norton-Rosko, R.N., Regional Chief Nursing Officer
Web address: www.loyolamedicine.org/Medical_Services/index.cfm
**Control:** Other not–for–profit (including NFP Corporation) **Service:** General medical and surgical

**Staffed Beds:** 524 **Admissions:** 22196 **Census:** 366 **Outpatient Visits:** 1433044 **Births:** 1263 **Personnel:** 6717

IL

---

**Hospital, Medicare Provider Number, Address, Telephone, Approval, Facility, and Physician Codes, Health Care System**

★ American Hospital Association (AHA) membership
☐ The Joint Commission accreditation
○ Healthcare Facilities Accreditation Program
◇ DNV Healthcare Inc. accreditation
⇑ Center for Improvement in Healthcare Quality Accreditation
△ Commission on Accreditation of Rehabilitation Facilities (CARF) accreditation

## MCHENRY—Mchenry County

**NORTHWESTERN MEDICINE MCHENRY** See Northwestern Medicine Mchenry

⊠ **NORTHWESTERN MEDICINE MCHENRY (140116)**, 4201 Medical Center Drive, Zip 60050–8409; tel. 815/344–5000, (Includes NORTHWESTERN MEDICINE HUNTLEY, Mailing address: 10400 Haligus Road, Huntley, Illinois, Zip 60142; tel. 224/654–0000; Thomas J. McAfee, Region President; NORTHWESTERN MEDICINE WOODSTOCK, Mailing address: 3701 Doty Road, Woodstock, Illinois, Zip 60098–7509, P O Box 1990, Zip 60098–1990, tel. 815/338–2500; Thomas J. McAfee, Region President), (Nonreporting) **A**1 2 3 5 10 **F**3 8 11 12 13 15 17 18 20 22 24 26 28 29 30 31 34 35 37 38 39 40 43 45 47 49 50 51 53 54 55 56 57 58 59 60 64 65 66 68 69 70 71 73 74 75 76 77 78 79 81 82 85 86 87 89 90 92 93 96 97 98 100 101 102 103 104 105 107 108 110 111 114 115 116 117 118 119 120 121 123 124 126 129 130 131 132 135 143 144 146 147 148 149 153 154 156 157 **S** Northwestern Memorial HealthCare, Chicago, IL
Primary Contact: Thomas J. McAfee, Region President
CFO: David Tomlinson, Executive Vice President Chief Financial Officer and Chief Information Officer
CMO: Irfan Hafiz, Vice President Medical Affairs
CIO: David Tomlinson, Executive Vice President Chief Financial Officer and Chief Information Officer
CHR: Bernadette S Szczepanski, Senior Vice President, Human Resources
Web address: www.centegra.org
**Control**: Other not–for–profit (including NFP Corporation) **Service**: General medical and surgical

**Staffed Beds**: 350 **Admissions**: 18247 **Census**: 219 **Outpatient Visits**: 700626 **Births**: 1752 **Total Expense ($000)**: 597253 **Payroll Expense ($000)**: 207649 **Personnel**: 3034

## MCLEANSBORO—Hamilton County

**HAMILTON MEMORIAL HOSPITAL** See Hamilton Memorial Hospital District

★ **HAMILTON MEMORIAL HOSPITAL DISTRICT (141326)**, 611 South Marshall Avenue, Zip 62859–1213, Mailing Address: P.O. Box 429, Mc Leansboro, Zip 62859–0429; tel. 618/643–2361, (Nonreporting) **A**10 18
Primary Contact: Victoria Woodrow, Chief Executive Officer
CFO: Kent Mitchell, Chief Financial Officer
CIO: Mark Todd, Senior Systems Administrator
CHR: Sheila Thompson, Director Human Resources
CNO: Patty Blazier, Chief Nursing Officer
Web address: www.hmhospital.org
**Control**: Hospital district or authority, Government, Nonfederal **Service**: General medical and surgical

**Staffed Beds**: 25

## MELROSE PARK—Cook County

⊠ △ **GOTTLIEB MEMORIAL HOSPITAL (140008)**, 701 West North Avenue, Zip 60160–1612; tel. 708/681–3200, (Nonreporting) **A**1 3 5 7 10 19 **F**2 3 11 12 15 18 20 22 24 26 28 29 30 31 34 35 36 39 40 43 44 45 47 49 50 53 54 56 57 59 60 64 65 68 70 74 75 77 78 79 81 85 86 87 89 90 92 93 96 97 98 103 107 108 110 111 114 116 117 118 119 126 128 129 130 131 132 143 144 145 146 147 148 149 150 **P**8 **S** Trinity Health, Livonia, MI
Primary Contact: Mary Elizabeth. Cleary, President
CFO: Ellyn Chin, Vice President Finance
CMO: Gerald Luger, M.D., President Medical Staff
CIO: Maurita Adler, Director Information Services
CHR: Brett Wakefield, Vice President Human Resources
Web address: www.gottliebhospital.org
**Control**: Other not–for–profit (including NFP Corporation) **Service**: General medical and surgical

**Staffed Beds**: 166 **Admissions**: 5975 **Census**: 109 **Outpatient Visits**: 101752 **Births**: 0 **Personnel**: 771

## MENDOTA—Lasalle County

**MENDOTA COMMUNITY HOSPITAL** See OSF Saint Paul Medical Center

★ **OSF SAINT PAUL MEDICAL CENTER (141310)**, 1401 East 12th Street, Zip 61342–9216; tel. 815/539–7461, (Nonreporting) **A**10 18 **F**3 11 15 28 29 30 31 34 40 49 57 59 64 69 70 77 78 79 81 82 85 93 107 110 111 115 127 129 130 133 146 154 **S** OSF Healthcare, Peoria, IL
Primary Contact: Dawn Trompeter, President
CMO: Leonardo Lopez, President Medical Staff
CHR: Kimberly Kennedy, Manager Human Resources
CNO: Heather Bomstad, MSN, R.N., Vice President Patient Care Services and Chief Nursing Officer
Web address: www.https://www.osfhealthcare.org/saint-paul
**Control**: Other not–for–profit (including NFP Corporation) **Service**: General medical and surgical

**Staffed Beds**: 25 **Admissions**: 425 **Census**: 5 **Outpatient Visits**: 33030 **Births**: 0 **Total Expense ($000)**: 31375 **Payroll Expense ($000)**: 11964 **Personnel**: 240

## METROPOLIS—Massac County

★ **MASSAC MEMORIAL HOSPITAL (141323)**, 28 Chick Street, Zip 62960–2467, Mailing Address: P.O. Box 850, Zip 62960–0850; tel. 618/524–2176, (Nonreporting) **A**10 18 **F**3 7 11 15 18 28 29 34 40 44 45 54 57 59 64 75 77 81 86 93 96 97 107 108 110 111 115 119 127 129 132 133 143 149 154 **P**6
Primary Contact: Rick Goins, Chief Executive Officer
CFO: Randy Rushing, Chief Financial Officer
CHR: Johnna Douglas, Human Resources Manager
Web address: www.massachealth.org
**Control**: Hospital district or authority, Government, Nonfederal **Service**: General medical and surgical

**Staffed Beds**: 25 **Admissions**: 566 **Census**: 7 **Outpatient Visits**: 15690 **Births**: 0 **Total Expense ($000)**: 24968 **Payroll Expense ($000)**: 10168 **Personnel**: 199

## MOLINE—Rock Island County

**TRINITY MOLINE** See Unitypoint Health - Trinity Moline

**UNITYPOINT HEALTH - TRINITY MOLINE** See Unitypoint Health - Trinity Rock Island, Rock Island

## MONMOUTH—Warren County

**COMMUNITY MEDICAL CENTER** See OSF Holy Family Medical Center

★ **OSF HOLY FAMILY MEDICAL CENTER (141318)**, 1000 West Harlem Avenue, Zip 61462–1007; tel. 309/734–3141, (Nonreporting) **A**10 18 **F**11 15 28 29 30 34 40 45 46 57 59 64 65 68 75 81 85 87 93 97 107 110 115 118 119 127 129 130 132 133 145 146 154 156 **S** OSF Healthcare, Peoria, IL
Primary Contact: Jackie Kernan, President
CFO: Theresa Springer, Chief Financial Officer
CMO: Clifford G Martin, M.D., Regional Vice President and Chief Medical Officer
CIO: Lew McCann, Director Management Information Systems
CHR: Jenny Jacobs, Director Human Resources
CNO: Shelley Wiborg, MS, R.N., Director of Nursing
Web address: www.osfholyfamily.org
**Control**: Church operated, Nongovernment, not–for–profit **Service**: General medical and surgical

**Staffed Beds**: 23 **Admissions**: 280 **Census**: 3 **Outpatient Visits**: 62830 **Births**: 0 **Total Expense ($000)**: 29299 **Payroll Expense ($000)**: 10534 **Personnel**: 110

## MONTICELLO—Piatt County

**JOHN AND MARY KIRBY HOSPITAL** See Kirby Medical Center

⊠ **KIRBY MEDICAL CENTER (141301)**, 1000 Medical Center Drive, Zip 61856–2116; tel. 217/762–2115, (Nonreporting) **A**1 10 18
Primary Contact: Steven D. Tenhouse, FACHE, Chief Executive Officer
COO: Mark Fred, R.N., Chief Operating Officer
CFO: Kimberly Alvis, CPA, Chief Financial Officer
CMO: Narain Mandhan, M.D., Chief Medical Officer
CIO: Mark Fred, R.N., Chief Operating Offier, Chief Information Officer
CHR: Andrew Buffenbarger, FACHE, Chief Compliance Officer, Director of Human Resources & Risk Management
CNO: Jennifer Moss, MS, R.N., Chief Clinical Officer
Web address: www.kirbyhealth.org
**Control**: Other not–for–profit (including NFP Corporation) **Service**: General medical and surgical

**Staffed Beds**: 16

IL

## MORRIS—Grundy County

**MORRIS HOSPITAL** See Morris Hospital & Healthcare Centers

★ ○ **MORRIS HOSPITAL & HEALTHCARE CENTERS (140101)**, 150 West High Street, Zip 60450–1497; tel. 815/942–2932, (Nonreporting) **A**2 10 11 **F**3 11 13 15 18 20 22 26 28 29 34 35 40 41 43 45 47 49 50 54 57 59 64 65 66 69 70 75 76 77 78 79 81 82 85 86 87 89 93 97 102 107 108 110 111 114 115 118 119 120 121 123 129 130 132 135 143 144 146 149 154 156 **P**6
Primary Contact: Mark B. Steadham, President and Chief Executive Officer
CFO: Mary Lou Tate, Chief Financial Officer
CHR: Erin Murphy-Frobish, Vice President Human Resources
CNO: Kimberly A. Landers, MS, R.N., Vice President Patient Care Services
Web address: www.morrishospital.org
**Control:** Other not–for–profit (including NFP Corporation) **Service:** General medical and surgical

**Staffed Beds:** 89 **Admissions:** 4001 **Census:** 39 **Outpatient Visits:** 386061 **Births:** 497 **Total Expense ($000):** 179421 **Payroll Expense ($000):** 82511 **Personnel:** 950

## MORRISON—Whiteside County

**MORRISON COMMUNITY HOSPITAL (141329)**, 303 North Jackson Street, Zip 61270–3042; tel. 815/772–4003, (Nonreporting) **A**10 18 **F**3 7 11 29 34 35 38 40 45 51 59 64 65 66 74 79 81 90 93 94 97 104 107 114 119 127 128 130 131 133 135 143 146 148 154 **P**6
Primary Contact: Pam Pfister, Chief Executive Officer
COO: Pam Pfister, Chief Executive Officer
CFO: Cami Megli, Controller
CMO: Duncan Dinkha, M.D., Chief of Staff
CIO: Pam Pfister, Chief Executive Officer
CHR: Amber L Temple, Director Human Resources
Web address: www.morrisonhospital.com
**Control:** Hospital district or authority, Government, Nonfederal **Service:** General medical and surgical

**Staffed Beds:** 23 **Admissions:** 281 **Census:** 9 **Outpatient Visits:** 29205 **Total Expense ($000):** 17535 **Payroll Expense ($000):** 8624 **Personnel:** 174

## MOUNT CARMEL—Wabash County

⊞ **WABASH GENERAL HOSPITAL (141327)**, 1418 College Drive, Zip 62863–2638; tel. 618/262–8621, (Nonreporting) **A**1 10 18 **S** Alliant Management Services, Louisville, KY
Primary Contact: Karissa Turner, President and Chief Executive Officer
COO: Karissa Turner, Vice President Operations
CFO: Lynn Leek, Executive Vice President of Finance and Chief Financial Officer
CMO: Levi McDaniel, M.D., Chief of Staff
CIO: Bobby Gage, Director Information Technology
CHR: Bridget Shepard, Vice President Human Resources
CNO: Tamara Gould, R.N., Vice President Clinical Services and Chief Nursing Officer
Web address: www.wabashgeneral.com
**Control:** County, Government, Nonfederal **Service:** General medical and surgical

**Staffed Beds:** 25

**WABASH GENERAL HOSPITAL DISTRICT** See Wabash General Hospital

## MOUNT VERNON—Jefferson County

☐ **CROSSROADS COMMUNITY HOSPITAL (140294)**, 8 Doctors Park Road, Zip 62864–6224; tel. 618/244–5500, (Nonreporting) **A**1 10 **F**3 11 12 15 18 29 30 34 35 40 45 46 50 57 59 70 77 79 81 85 92 93 94 107 110 115 119 126 127 129 130 131 145 146 149 154 156 **P**6 **S** Quorum Health, Brentwood, TN
Primary Contact: Amanda J. Basso, Chief Executive Officer
CIO: Bryan Delaney, Director Information Technology
CHR: Jessica Connaway, Director Human Resources
CNO: Stephanie Maines, Chief Nursing Officer
Web address: www.crossroadshospital.com
**Control:** Corporation, Investor–owned (for–profit) **Service:** General medical and surgical

**Staffed Beds:** 28 **Admissions:** 1180 **Census:** 9 **Outpatient Visits:** 41862 **Births:** 0 **Total Expense ($000):** 40842 **Payroll Expense ($000):** 12355 **Personnel:** 195

**GOOD SAMARITAN REGIONAL HEALTH CENTER** See Ssm Health Good Samaritan Hospital

⊞ **SSM HEALTH GOOD SAMARITAN HOSPITAL (140046)**, 1 Good Samaritan Way, Zip 62864–2402; tel. 618/242–4600, (Nonreporting) **A**1 2 5 10 19 **F**3 4 8 11 12 13 15 18 20 22 26 28 29 30 31 34 35 38 40 44 45 46 50 51 54 56 57 59 60 61 64 68 70 73 74 75 76 77 78 79 80 81 82 84 85 86 87 89 90 92 93 94 96 102 104 107 108 110 111 114 115 119 123 124 126 130 131 132 135 144 146 147 148 149 154 156 157 **P**6 8 **S** SSM Health, Saint Louis, MO
Primary Contact: Jeremy Bradford, President
COO: Mark A Clark, Vice President Operations
CFO: Deland Evischi, Regional Chief Financial Officer, Southern Illinois
CMO: Daniel Hoffman, M.D., Administrative Medical Director
CIO: Steve Murphy, FM-East Region IS
CHR: Thomas W Blythe, System Vice President Human Resources
CNO: Chris Adams, Vice President Patient Care Services
Web address: www.smgsi.com
**Control:** Church operated, Nongovernment, not–for–profit **Service:** General medical and surgical

**Staffed Beds:** 134 **Admissions:** 6995 **Census:** 83 **Outpatient Visits:** 253352 **Births:** 1087 **Total Expense ($000):** 179918 **Payroll Expense ($000):** 53834 **Personnel:** 934

## MURPHYSBORO—Jackson County

★ **ST. JOSEPH MEMORIAL HOSPITAL (141334)**, 2 South Hospital Drive, Zip 62966–3333; tel. 618/684–3156, (Nonreporting) **A**10 18 **F**3 11 18 28 29 30 31 34 35 40 45 49 50 56 57 59 64 74 75 77 78 79 81 82 84 85 86 87 93 104 107 111 114 119 129 130 132 133 135 146 148 154 156 **P**1 **S** Southern Illinois Healthcare, Carbondale, IL
Primary Contact: Susan Odle, Administrator
CMO: Emily Hanson, M.D., President, Medical Staff
CIO: David Holland, Vice President Information Services
CHR: Kelly Stevens, Manager Human Resources
Web address: www.sih.net
**Control:** Other not–for–profit (including NFP Corporation) **Service:** General medical and surgical

**Staffed Beds:** 25 **Admissions:** 587 **Census:** 12 **Outpatient Visits:** 74901 **Births:** 0 **Total Expense ($000):** 59031 **Payroll Expense ($000):** 14166 **Personnel:** 270

## NAPERVILLE-Dupage County

⊞ **EDWARD HOSPITAL (140231)**, 801 South Washington Street, Zip 60540–7499; tel. 630/527–3000, (Nonreporting) **A**1 2 10 **F**3 7 12 13 15 17 18 19 20 22 24 26 28 29 30 31 34 35 36 37 38 39 40 41 42 43 44 45 46 47 48 49 50 53 54 55 57 58 59 61 63 64 65 70 72 74 75 76 77 78 79 81 82 84 85 86 87 88 89 91 92 93 96 97 99 100 101 102 103 107 108 110 111 114 115 117 118 119 120 121 123 124 126 129 130 131 132 135 144 146 147 148 149 154 156 **S** Edward-Elmhurst Healthcare, Naperville, IL
Primary Contact: Joseph Dant, President and Chief Executive Officer
CFO: Denise Chamberlain, Executive Vice President, Chief Financial Officer
CMO: Robert Payton, Chief Medical Officer
CHR: Chris Devereux, Human Resources Director, Business Partner
CNO: Lynn Cochran, R.N., System Vice President Operations, Chief Nursing Officer
Web address: www.eehealth.org
**Control:** Other not–for–profit (including NFP Corporation) **Service:** General medical and surgical

**Staffed Beds:** 358 **Admissions:** 22042 **Census:** 241 **Outpatient Visits:** 1030498 **Births:** 3093 **Total Expense ($000):** 637857 **Payroll Expense ($000):** 187595 **Personnel:** 2432

**EDWARD HOSPITAL ASSOCIATION** See Edward Hospital

---

IL

✠ **LINDEN OAKS HOSPITAL (144035)**, 852 South West Street, Zip 60540–6400; tel. 630/305–5500, (Nonreporting) **A**1 10 **F**4 5 29 34 35 38 44 56 57 59 64 75 86 87 98 99 100 101 103 104 105 130 132 134 149 150 151 152 153 **S** Edward-Elmhurst Healthcare, Naperville, IL
Primary Contact: Gina Sharp, FACHE, President and Chief Executive Officer
CFO: Kristen Refness, Director, Financial Operations
CMO: Barry Rabin, M.D., Regional Medical Director
CIO: David Pickering, System Director, Applications
CHR: Lisa Dixon, Business Partner and Human Resource Director
CNO: Trish Fairbanks, R.N., Associate Vice President and Chief Nursing Officer
Web address: www.https://www.eehealth.org/services/behavioral-health
**Control**: Other not–for–profit (including NFP Corporation) **Service**: Psychiatric

> **Staffed Beds**: 108 **Admissions**: 4183 **Census**: 81 **Outpatient Visits**: 74550
> **Births**: 0 **Total Expense ($000)**: 53279 **Payroll Expense ($000)**: 31487
> **Personnel**: 474

**LINDEN OAKS HOSPITAL AT EDWARD** See Linden Oaks Hospital

### NASHVILLE—Washington County

✠ **WASHINGTON COUNTY HOSPITAL (141308)**, 705 South Grand Avenue, Zip 62263–1534; tel. 618/327–8236, (Total facility includes 28 beds in nursing home–type unit) (Nonreporting) **A**1 10 18 **F**11 15 28 29 34 40 50 57 59 64 65 75 77 81 85 93 97 107 115 119 127 132 133 145 146 148 154 156 **S** SSM Health, Saint Louis, MO
Primary Contact: Brian Kent. Monsma, President
CFO: Jennifer Venable, Chief Financial Officer
CMO: Alfonso Urdaneta, M.D., President Medical Staff
CIO: Kim Larkin, Chief Information Officer
CHR: Barbara Gowler, Human Resources Manager
CNO: Stacie Hodge, Director of Nursing
Web address: www.washingtoncountyhospital.org
**Control**: Hospital district or authority, Government, Nonfederal **Service**: General medical and surgical

> **Staffed Beds**: 42 **Admissions**: 206 **Census**: 27 **Outpatient Visits**: 32002
> **Births**: 0 **Total Expense ($000)**: 13742 **Payroll Expense ($000)**: 6014
> **Personnel**: 121

### NEW LENOX—Will County

✠ △ **SILVER CROSS HOSPITAL (140213)**, 1900 Silver Cross Boulevard, Zip 60451–9509; tel. 815/300–1100, (Nonreporting) **A**1 2 3 7 10 **F**3 13 15 18 20 22 24 26 28 29 30 34 35 37 40 42 43 44 45 46 47 48 49 50 51 54 56 57 58 59 60 62 64 65 68 70 71 73 74 75 76 78 79 81 84 85 86 87 89 90 97 107 108 109 110 111 112 113 114 115 116 117 119 120 121 122 123 124 126 129 130 131 132 135 144 145 146 147 148 149 150 154 156 157 **P**8
Primary Contact: Ruth A. Colby, President and Chief Executive Officer
COO: Mary Bakken, Executive Vice President and Chief Operating Officer
CFO: Vincent Pryor, Senior Vice President and Chief Financial Officer
CMO: Christopher Udovich, M.D., Chief of Staff
CIO: Kevin Lane, Vice President Information Systems
CHR: Mark Jepson, Vice President
CNO: Peggy Gricus, R.N., Vice President, Patient Care Services and Chief Nursing Officer
Web address: www.silvercross.org
**Control**: Other not–for–profit (including NFP Corporation) **Service**: General medical and surgical

> **Staffed Beds**: 300 **Admissions**: 20413 **Census**: 215 **Outpatient Visits**: 279601 **Births**: 2819 **Total Expense ($000)**: 385920 **Payroll Expense ($000)**: 134472 **Personnel**: 1815

**SILVER CROSS HOSPITAL A**1 2 3 7 10 **F**3 13 15 18 20 22 24 26 28 29 30 34 35 37 40 42 43 44 45 46 47 48 49 50 51 54 56 57 58 59 60 62 64 65 68 70 71 73 74 75 76 78 79 81 84 85 86 87 89 90 97 107 108 109 110 111 112 113 114 115 116 117 119 120 121 122 123 124 126 129 130 131 132 135 144 145 146 147 148 149 150 154 156 157 **P**8
Primary Contact: , R.N.
COO: Mary Bakken, Executive Vice President and Chief Operating Officer
CFO: Vincent Pryor, Senior Vice President and Chief Financial Officer
CMO: Christopher Udovich, M.D., Chief of Staff
CIO: Kevin Lane, Vice President Information Systems
CHR: Mark Jepson, Vice President
CNO: Peggy Gricus, R.N., Vice President, Patient Care Services and Chief Nursing Officer
Web address: www.silvercross.org

☐ **SILVER OAKS BEHAVIORAL HOSPITAL (144041)**, 1004 Pawlak Parkway, Zip 60451–9401; tel. 844/580–5000, (Nonreporting) **A**1
Primary Contact: Scott Hullinger, Chief Executive Officer
Web address: www.https://silveroaksbehavioralhospital.com
**Control**: Other not–for–profit (including NFP Corporation) **Service**: Psychiatric

> **Staffed Beds**: 100

### NORMAL—Mclean County

⇑ **ADVOCATE BROMENN REGIONAL MEDICAL CENTER** See Bromenn Medical Center

★ ⇑ **BROMENN MEDICAL CENTER (140127)**, 1304 Franklin Avenue, Zip 61761–3558, Mailing Address: P.O. Box 2850, Bloomington, Zip 61702–2850; tel. 309/454–1400, (Includes ADVOCATE BROMENN REGIONAL MEDICAL CENTER, Mailing address: 1304 Franklin Avenue, Normal, Illinois, Zip 61761–3558, PO Box 2850, Bloomington, Zip 61702–2850, tel. 309/454–1400; Colleen Kannaday, FACHE, President), (Nonreporting) **A**2 3 5 10 13 21 **F**2 3 4 5 11 12 13 15 18 20 22 24 26 28 29 30 31 32 34 35 37 38 39 40 43 44 45 49 50 51 54 55 57 59 64 65 66 68 70 73 74 75 76 77 78 79 81 82 84 85 86 87 89 90 93 96 97 98 100 101 102 103 107 108 110 111 114 115 118 119 126 129 130 131 132 135 141 146 147 148 149 152 154 156 157 **P**7 8 **S** Carle Health, Urbana, IL
Primary Contact: Colleen Kannaday, FACHE, President
CFO: Aron Klein, Vice President Finance
CMO: James Nevin, M.D., Vice President and Chief Medical Officer
CHR: Antonio Coletta, Vice President Human Resources
CNO: Laurie Round, MS, R.N., Vice President and Chief Nursing Officer
Web address: www.advocatehealth.com/bromenn
**Control**: Church operated, Nongovernment, not–for–profit **Service**: General medical and surgical

> **Staffed Beds**: 203 **Admissions**: 8685 **Census**: 94 **Outpatient Visits**: 122784 **Births**: 1412 **Total Expense ($000)**: 170165 **Payroll Expense ($000)**: 62269 **Personnel**: 1153

### NORMAL—McLean County

**BROMENN REGIONAL MEDICAL CENTER** See Advocate Bromenn Regional Medical Center

### NORTH CHICAGO—Lake County

✠ **CAPTAIN JAMES A. LOVELL FEDERAL HEALTH CARE CENTER**, 3001 Green Bay Road, Zip 60064–3049; tel. 847/688–1900, (Total facility includes 104 beds in nursing home–type unit) (Nonreporting) **A**1 3 5 8 **F**2 3 4 8 11 14 15 18 29 30 31 32 34 35 36 38 39 40 44 45 46 48 49 54 56 58 59 61 62 63 64 65 68 70 71 74 75 77 78 79 81 83 84 86 87 90 91 92 96 97 98 100 101 102 103 104 107 108 110 111 115 118 119 128 129 130 131 132 133 135 143 146 147 148 149 154 156 **S** Department of Veterans Affairs, Washington, DC
Primary Contact: Daniel Zomcheck, Interim Director
CFO: Barbara Meadows, Chief Financial Manager
CMO: Tariq Hassan, M.D., Associate Director of Patient Care
CIO: Jonathan Friedman, Public Affairs Officer
CHR: Amy Sanders, Chief Human Resources
CNO: Sarah Fouse, Associate Director of Patient Services
Web address: www.lovell.fhcc.va.gov
**Control**: Veterans Affairs, Government, federal **Service**: General medical and surgical

> **Staffed Beds**: 281 **Admissions**: 5051 **Census**: 198 **Outpatient Visits**: 785000 **Births**: 0 **Personnel**: 1824

**VETERANS AFFAIRS MEDICAL CENTER** See Captain James A. Lovell Federal Health Care Center

### NORTHLAKE—Cook County

✠ **KINDRED HOSPITAL CHICAGO-NORTHLAKE (142008)**, 365 East North Avenue, Zip 60164–2628; tel. 708/345–8100, (Nonreporting) **A**1 10 **S** Kindred Healthcare, Louisville, KY
Primary Contact: Brinsley Lewis, FACHE, Chief Executive Officer
CFO: Chona Aban, Controller
CMO: Maher Najjar, M.D., Medical Director
CNO: Maria Suvacarov, Chief Clinical Officer
Web address: www.kindrednorthlake.com/
**Control**: Corporation, Investor–owned (for–profit) **Service**: Acute long–term care hospital

> **Staffed Beds**: 94

**KINDRED HOSPITAL NORTHLAKE** See Kindred Hospital Chicago-Northlake

IL

## OAK LAWN—Cook County

★ ⇧ **ADVOCATE CHRIST MEDICAL CENTER (140208)**, 4440 West 95th Street, Zip 60453–2699; tel. 708/684–8000, (Includes ADVOCATE HOPE CHILDREN'S HOSPITAL, Mailing address: 4440 West 95th Street, Oak Lawn, Illinois, Zip 60453–2600; tel. 708/684–8000), (Nonreporting) **A**2 3 5 8 10 21 **F**3 4 5 8 9 11 13 15 17 18 19 20 21 22 23 24 25 26 27 28 29 30 31 32 34 35 37 38 39 40 41 43 44 45 46 47 48 49 50 52 54 55 56 57 58 59 60 61 62 63 64 65 66 68 70 71 72 74 75 76 77 78 79 81 82 84 85 86 87 88 89 90 92 93 96 97 98 100 101 102 103 104 105 107 108 109 110 111 114 115 116 117 118 119 120 121 123 124 126 130 131 132 134 135 137 138 140 141 143 145 146 147 148 149 152 154 156 **P**8 **S** Advocate Aurora Health, Downers Grove, IL
Primary Contact: Richard Heim, President
CFO: Robert Pekofske, Vice President Finance
CMO: Robert Stein, M.D., Vice President Medical Management
CIO: Brian Banbury, Director Site Information Systems
Web address: www.advocatehealth.com/christ
**Control**: Other not–for–profit (including NFP Corporation) **Service**: General medical and surgical

**Staffed Beds:** 796 **Admissions:** 43485 **Census:** 672 **Outpatient Visits:** 369613 **Births:** 4355 **Total Expense ($000):** 1126576 **Payroll Expense ($000):** 381983 **Personnel:** 5736

⇧ **ADVOCATE CHRIST MEDICAL CTR** See Advocate Christ Medical Center

## OAK PARK—Cook County

**OAK PARK HOSPITAL** See Rush Oak Park Hospital

⊞ **RUSH OAK PARK HOSPITAL (140063)**, 520 South Maple Avenue, Zip 60304–1097; tel. 708/383–9300, (Total facility includes 21 beds in nursing home–type unit) (Nonreporting) **A**1 3 5 10 **F**3 11 15 18 20 28 29 30 34 35 40 45 47 50 56 57 58 59 64 70 74 75 77 79 81 82 85 87 91 92 93 96 107 108 110 111 114 115 119 126 128 130 141 145 146 148 149 154 **P**8 **S** Rush University Medical Center, Chicago, IL
Primary Contact: Bruce M. Elegant, FACHE, President and Chief Executive Officer
COO: Robert S Spadoni, Vice President of Hospital Operations
CFO: Elvy Yap, Director of Finance
CMO: Michael R. Silver, M.D., Vice President Medical Affairs
CIO: Michael R. Silver, M.D., Chief Information Officer
CHR: Arlene Cruz, Director
Web address: www.roph.org
**Control**: Other not–for–profit (including NFP Corporation) **Service**: General medical and surgical

**Staffed Beds:** 108 **Admissions:** 4519 **Census:** 55 **Outpatient Visits:** 148768 **Births:** 0 **Total Expense ($000):** 136140 **Payroll Expense ($000):** 63905 **Personnel:** 811

**WEST SUBURBAN HOSP MED CENTER** See West Suburban Medical Center

☐ **WEST SUBURBAN MEDICAL CENTER (140049)**, 3 Erie Court, Zip 60302–2599; tel. 708/383–6200, (Nonreporting) **A**1 2 3 5 10 13
Primary Contact: Joseph Ottolino, Chief Executive Officer
CFO: Jennifer Lamont, Chief Financial Officer
CMO: Robert Chase, M.D., Physician Advisor
CHR: Nancy Gunnell, Chief Human Resource Officer
CNO: Roslyn J Lennon, R.N., MS, Chief Nursing Officer
Web address: www.westsuburbanmc.com/Home.aspx
**Control**: Corporation, Investor–owned (for–profit) **Service**: General medical and surgical

**Staffed Beds:** 172

## O'FALLON—St. Clair County

⊞ **HSHS ST. ELIZABETH'S HOSPITAL (140187)**, One St. Elizabeth's Boulevard, Zip 62269; tel. 618/234–2120, (Nonreporting) **A**1 3 5 10 **F**3 11 13 15 18 20 22 24 26 28 29 30 31 34 35 40 44 45 46 47 48 49 51 54 57 59 60 64 68 70 74 75 76 77 78 79 81 82 90 91 93 96 102 107 108 111 112 114 115 119 126 129 130 132 144 146 147 148 149 154 156 157 **S** HSHS Hospital Sisters Health System, Springfield, IL
Primary Contact: Patricia Fischer, FACHE, R.N., President and Chief Executive Officer
CFO: David Nosacka, Chief Financial Officer
CMO: Shelly Harkins, M.D., Chief Medical Officer
CIO: Leslee Martin, Manager Information Technology
CHR: Jason T Snow, Director People Services
Web address: www.steliz.org
**Control**: Church operated, Nongovernment, not–for–profit **Service**: General medical and surgical

**Staffed Beds:** 144 **Admissions:** 9484 **Census:** 112 **Outpatient Visits:** 175138 **Births:** 907 **Total Expense ($000):** 232026 **Payroll Expense ($000):** 63777 **Personnel:** 1381

**ST. ELIZABETH'S HOSPITAL** See Hshs St. Elizabeth's Hospital

## OLNEY—Richland County

★ ○ **CARLE RICHLAND MEMORIAL HOSPITAL (140147)**, 800 East Locust Street, Zip 62450–2553; tel. 618/395–2131, (Total facility includes 20 beds in nursing home–type unit) (Nonreporting) **A**10 11 20 **F**3 11 13 15 18 28 29 31 34 35 40 45 57 59 64 68 69 70 75 76 78 79 81 85 87 89 93 97 104 107 108 110 111 115 119 127 130 131 132 133 135 143 146 147 148 **S** Carle Health, Urbana, IL
Primary Contact: Harry Brockus, Chief Executive Officer
CMO: Brian Atwood, M.D., Associate Medical Director
CIO: Tim Gillespie, Manager Information Systems
CHR: Marsha Heath, Human Resources Manager
CNO: Gina R. Thomas, Chief Nursing Officer and Director of Patient Care Services
Web address: www.carlermh.com
**Control**: Other not–for–profit (including NFP Corporation) **Service**: General medical and surgical

**Staffed Beds:** 65 **Admissions:** 1802 **Census:** 39 **Outpatient Visits:** 46513 **Births:** 264 **Total Expense ($000):** 64738 **Payroll Expense ($000):** 29592 **Personnel:** 423

**RICHLAND MEMORIAL HOSPITAL** See Carle Richland Memorial Hospital

## OLYMPIA FIELDS—Cook County

★ ○ **FRANCISCAN HEALTH OLYMPIA FIELDS (140172)**, 20201 South Crawford Avenue, Zip 60461–1010; tel. 708/747–4000, (Includes FRANCISCAN HEALTH OLYMPIA FIELDS, Mailing address: 20201 Crawford Avenue, Olympia Fields, Illinois, Zip 60461–1010; tel. 708/747–4000), (Nonreporting) **A**3 5 10 11 12 13 **S** Franciscan Health, Mishawaka, IN
Primary Contact: Allan M. Spooner, President and Chief Executive Officer
CIO: Stephen Maes, Director Information Systems
Web address: www.franciscanalliance.org/hospitals/olympiafields/pages/default.aspx
**Control**: Church operated, Nongovernment, not–for–profit **Service**: General medical and surgical

**Staffed Beds:** 329

**FRANCISCAN ST. JAMES HOSPITAL AND HEALTH CENTERS** See Franciscan Health Olympia Fields

**ST. JAMES HOSPITALS AND HEALTH CENTERS - OLYMPIA FIELDS CAMPUS** See Franciscan Health Olympia Fields

IL

**Hospital, Medicare Provider Number, Address, Telephone, Approval, Facility, and Physician Codes, Health Care System**

★ American Hospital Association (AHA) membership   ○ Healthcare Facilities Accreditation Program   ⇧ Center for Improvement in Healthcare Quality Accreditation
☐ The Joint Commission accreditation   ◇ DNV Healthcare Inc. accreditation   △ Commission on Accreditation of Rehabilitation Facilities (CARF) accreditation

© 2021 AHA Guide        *Many Facility Codes have changed. Please refer to the AHA Guide Code Chart.*        Hospitals **A215**

## OTTAWA—Lasalle County

☒ **OSF SAINT ELIZABETH MEDICAL CENTER (140110)**, 1100 East Norris Drive, Zip 61350–1687; tel. 815/433–3100, (Nonreporting) **A**1 10 19 **F**3 11 13 15 18 28 29 30 34 35 40 42 45 48 49 53 56 57 59 68 70 75 76 77 79 81 82 84 85 86 87 93 94 98 99 100 101 102 103 104 105 107 108 110 111 115 116 117 118 119 120 121 129 130 131 132 135 143 144 146 148 149 153 154 155 156 157 **S** OSF Healthcare, Peoria, IL
Primary Contact: Kenneth Beutke, President
CFO: Brad Chamberlin, Director of Finance
CMO: Brian S Rosborough, M.D., Chief Medical Officer
CHR: Karen M Russell, Director of Employee Relations
CNO: Heather Bomstad, MSN, R.N., Vice President, Chief Nursing Officer
Web address: www.osfsaintelizabeth.org
**Control**: Church operated, Nongovernment, not–for–profit **Service**: General medical and surgical

**Staffed Beds**: 87 **Admissions**: 4241 **Census**: 39 **Outpatient Visits**: 156163 **Births**: 385 **Total Expense ($000)**: 105018 **Payroll Expense ($000)**: 42330 **Personnel**: 566

**OTTAWA REGIONAL HOSPITAL AND HEALTHCARE CENTER** See OSF Saint Elizabeth Medical Center

## PALOS HEIGHTS—Cook County

**PALOS COMMUNITY HOSPITAL** See Palos Health

☐ **PALOS HEALTH (140062)**, 12251 South 80th Avenue, Zip 60463–0930; tel. 708/923–4000, (Nonreporting) **A**1 2 5 10
Primary Contact: Terrence Moisan, M.D., Chief Executive Officer
CFO: Hugh Rose, Vice President Fiscal Management
CIO: Peggy Carroll, Chief Information Officer
CHR: Mary Denisienko, Vice President Human Resources
Web address: www.https://www.paloshealth.com/
**Control**: Other not–for–profit (including NFP Corporation) **Service**: General medical and surgical

**Staffed Beds**: 362

## PANA—Christian County

★ **PANA COMMUNITY HOSPITAL (141341)**, 101 East Ninth Street, Zip 62557–1785; tel. 217/562–2131, (Nonreporting) **A**10 18 **F**3 11 15 28 29 30 31 34 35 40 45 46 49 50 53 55 57 61 62 63 69 75 77 78 79 81 87 91 93 107 115 124 127 130 131 132 133 143 146 148 149 156
Primary Contact: Trina Casner, President and Chief Executive Officer
CFO: James Moon, Chief Financial Officer
CMO: Alan Frigy, M.D., President Medical Staff
CIO: Dianne Bailey, Chief Information Officer
CHR: Luann A Funk, Administrative Assistant and Manager Human Resources
CNO: Vickie Coen, Chief Clinical Officer and Nurse Executive
Web address: www.panahospital.com
**Control**: Other not–for–profit (including NFP Corporation) **Service**: General medical and surgical

**Staffed Beds**: 22 **Admissions**: 494 **Census**: 5 **Outpatient Visits**: 47118 **Births**: 0 **Total Expense ($000)**: 26277 **Payroll Expense ($000)**: 12221 **Personnel**: 241

## PARIS—Edgar County

☒ **PARIS COMMUNITY HOSPITAL (141320)**, 721 East Court Street, Zip 61944–2460; tel. 217/465–4141, (Nonreporting) **A**1 10 18 **F**3 7 12 15 18 28 29 30 31 32 34 35 40 45 47 50 56 57 59 64 65 69 74 75 77 78 79 81 82 85 86 87 93 96 97 107 108 109 110 111 115 119 124 127 129 130 131 132 133 135 143 144 146 147 148 149 150 154 156 157 **P**6 **S** Alliant Management Services, Louisville, KY
Primary Contact: Oliver Smith, President and Chief Executive Officer
CFO: Martin D. Adams, CPA, Vice President Finance and Chief Financial Officer
CMO: Anita Toussi, M.D., Chief Medical Officer
CIO: Ed Weeks, Manager Information Services
CHR: Nan Dunning, Human Resources Manager
CNO: Tiffany Turner, MSN, R.N., Vice President of Nursing and Chief Nursing Officer
Web address: www.pariscommunityhospital.com
**Control**: Other not–for–profit (including NFP Corporation) **Service**: General medical and surgical

**Staffed Beds**: 25 **Admissions**: 652 **Census**: 14 **Outpatient Visits**: 176252 **Births**: 0 **Total Expense ($000)**: 60911 **Payroll Expense ($000)**: 31984 **Personnel**: 391

## PARK RIDGE—Cook County

★ △ ⇑ **ADVOCATE LUTHERAN GENERAL HOSPITAL (140223)**, 1775 Dempster Street, Zip 60068–1174; tel. 847/723–2210, (Nonreporting) **A**2 3 5 7 8 10 13 21 **F**2 3 4 5 6 8 9 11 13 15 17 18 19 20 22 24 25 26 27 28 29 30 31 32 34 35 37 38 39 40 41 43 44 45 46 47 48 49 50 53 55 56 57 58 59 60 61 63 64 65 66 68 69 70 72 74 75 76 78 79 80 81 82 84 85 86 87 88 89 90 92 93 94 96 97 98 99 100 101 102 103 104 105 107 108 110 111 114 115 116 117 118 119 120 121 124 126 129 130 131 132 134 135 136 143 146 147 148 149 150 152 153 154 156 157 **P**6 8 **S** Advocate Aurora Health, Downers Grove, IL
Primary Contact: Terika Richardson, M.P.H., President
COO: Allyson Wyler, Vice President, Operations
CFO: Beth Hickey, Vice President, Finance
CMO: Leo Kelly, Vice President Medical Management
CIO: Mark Beitzel, Director Information Systems
CHR: Katie Bata, Vice President Human Resources
CNO: Jane Denten, MSN, R.N., Chief Nurse Executive
Web address: www.advocatehealth.com/luth/
**Control**: Other not–for–profit (including NFP Corporation) **Service**: General medical and surgical

**Staffed Beds**: 651 **Admissions**: 29056 **Census**: 456 **Outpatient Visits**: 355223 **Births**: 3573 **Total Expense ($000)**: 726521 **Payroll Expense ($000)**: 264045 **Personnel**: 5417

⇑ **LUTHERAN GENERAL HOSPITAL** See Advocate Lutheran General Hospital

## PEKIN—Tazewell County

**UNITY POINT HEALTH-PEKIN HOSPITAL** See Unitypoint Health-Pekin Hospital

☒ **UNITYPOINT HEALTH-PEKIN HOSPITAL (140120)**, 600 South 13th Street, Zip 61554–4936; tel. 309/347–1151, (Nonreporting) **A**1 10 **F**3 11 15 18 20 22 29 30 31 34 35 40 45 46 47 48 49 50 57 59 60 62 64 68 70 74 75 76 77 78 79 81 82 85 86 87 89 93 107 108 110 111 114 115 119 129 130 135 143 144 145 146 147 148 149 154 **S** UnityPoint Health, West Des Moines, IA
Primary Contact: Keith Knepp, M.D., President and Chief Executive Officer
COO: Jeanine R. Spain, R.N., MS, Vice President, Chief Operating Officer and Chief Nursing Officer
CFO: Steve Hall, Chief Financial Officer
CMO: Kathryn Kramer, M.D., President Medical Staff
CHR: Anne Dierker, Vice President Hospital Services
CNO: Jeanine R. Spain, R.N., MS, Vice President, Chief Operating Officer and Chief Nursing Officer
Web address: www.pekinhospital.org
**Control**: Other not–for–profit (including NFP Corporation) **Service**: General medical and surgical

**Staffed Beds**: 86 **Admissions**: 2219 **Census**: 24 **Outpatient Visits**: 101405 **Births**: 163 **Total Expense ($000)**: 50116 **Payroll Expense ($000)**: 18801 **Personnel**: 281

## PEORIA—Peoria County

**GREATER PEORIA SPECIALTY HOSPITAL** See Kindred Hospital Peoria

☒ **KINDRED HOSPITAL PEORIA (142013)**, 500 West Romeo B Garrett Avenue, Zip 61605–2301; tel. 309/680–1500, (Nonreporting) **A**1 10 **S** Kindred Healthcare, Louisville, KY
Primary Contact: Christopher Curry, Chief Executive Officer
CMO: Michael Peil, M.D., Chief Medical Director
Web address: www.khpeoria.com/
**Control**: Corporation, Investor–owned (for–profit) **Service**: Acute long–term care hospital

**Staffed Beds**: 50

*Many Facility Codes have changed. Please refer to the AHA Guide Code Chart.*

© 2021 AHA Guide

IL

✛ **OSF SAINT FRANCIS MEDICAL CENTER (140067)**, 530 NE Glen Oak Avenue, Zip 61637–0001; tel. 309/655–2000, (Includes CHILDREN'S HOSPITAL OF ILLINOIS, Mailing address: 530 NE Glen Oak Avenue, Peoria, Illinois, Zip 61637–0001; tel. 309/655–7171; Kelly Nierstedt, President), (Nonreporting) **A**1 2 3 5 8 10 **F**3 9 11 12 13 15 17 18 19 20 21 22 23 24 25 26 27 28 29 30 31 32 34 35 37 38 39 40 41 43 44 45 46 47 48 49 50 51 52 54 56 57 58 59 60 64 65 66 70 71 72 73 74 75 76 77 78 79 80 81 82 83 84 85 86 87 88 89 90 92 93 95 96 100 102 104 105 107 108 109 110 111 112 114 115 116 117 118 119 120 121 124 126 129 130 138 142 145 146 147 148 149 153 154 **S** OSF Healthcare, Peoria, IL
Primary Contact: Robert G. Anderson Jr, President
CFO: Ken Harbaugh, Vice President and Chief Financial Officer
CMO: Robert T. Sparrow, M.D., Vice President, Chief Medical Officer
CHR: Jacki L. Fugitt, Director Employee Relations
CNO: Jennifer Hopwood, Chief Nursing Officer, Vice President Patient Care
Web address: www.osfsaintfrancis.org
**Control**: Church operated, Nongovernment, not–for–profit **Service**: General medical and surgical

**Staffed Beds**: 629 **Admissions**: 34788 **Census**: 487 **Outpatient Visits**: 614174 **Births**: 2553 **Total Expense ($000)**: 943271 **Payroll Expense ($000)**: 339378 **Personnel**: 5276

**SAINT FRANCIS MEDICAL CENTER** See OSF Saint Francis Medical Center

✛ **UNITYPOINT HEALTH - PEORIA (140209)**, 221 NE Glen Oak Avenue, Zip 61636–4310; tel. 309/672–5522, (Nonreporting) **A**1 2 3 5 10 **F**3 9 11 12 13 15 17 18 20 22 24 26 29 30 31 32 34 35 36 38 40 43 44 45 46 47 48 49 50 53 54 56 57 58 59 60 62 63 64 68 70 74 75 76 77 78 79 81 82 84 85 86 87 89 90 92 93 96 98 99 100 101 102 104 105 107 108 110 111 114 115 116 117 118 119 120 121 126 127 129 130 131 132 134 135 136 143 144 145 146 147 148 149 150 154 156 **P**1 8 **S** UnityPoint Health, West Des Moines, IA
Primary Contact: Keith Knepp, M.D., President and Chief Executive Officer
COO: Jeanine R. Spain, R.N., MS, Vice President, Chief Operating Officer and Chief Nursing Officer
CFO: Robert Quin, Regional Vice President Finance, and Chief Financial Officer
CMO: Gary Knepp, D.O., Regional Chief Medical Officer and Chief Quality Officer
CHR: Joy Ledbetter, Regional Chief Human Resources Officer
CNO: Jeanine R. Spain, R.N., MS, Vice President, Chief Operating Officer and Chief Nursing Officer
Web address: www.unitypoint.org/peoria
**Control**: Other not–for–profit (including NFP Corporation) **Service**: General medical and surgical

**Staffed Beds**: 275 **Admissions**: 13526 **Census**: 193 **Outpatient Visits**: 451131 **Births**: 1714 **Total Expense ($000)**: 397329 **Payroll Expense ($000)**: 177035 **Personnel**: 2376

**UNITYPOINT HEALTH - METHODIST PROCTOR** See Unitypoint Health - Peoria

☐ **UNITYPOINT HEALTH - PROCTOR (140013)**, 5409 North Knoxville Avenue, Zip 61614–5069; tel. 309/691–1000, (Total facility includes 34 beds in nursing home–type unit) (Nonreporting) **A**1 3 5 10 **F**3 4 5 11 15 18 20 22 24 28 29 30 34 40 45 51 53 57 59 60 64 70 74 75 79 81 85 86 87 93 98 103 104 107 108 110 111 114 115 118 119 128 130 132 135 143 145 146 148 149 150 151 152 154 **P**1 8 **S** UnityPoint Health, West Des Moines, IA
Primary Contact: Keith Knepp, M.D., President and Chief Executive Officer
COO: Jeanine R. Spain, R.N., MS, Vice President, Chief Operating Officer and Chief Nursing Officer
CFO: Roger Armstrong, Vice President Finance and Chief Financial Officer
CHR: Linda K Buck, Vice President Human Resources
CNO: Jeanine R. Spain, R.N., MS, Vice President, Chief Operating Officer and Chief Nursing Officer
Web address: www.proctor.org
**Control**: Other not–for–profit (including NFP Corporation) **Service**: General medical and surgical

**Staffed Beds**: 135 **Admissions**: 4021 **Census**: 74 **Outpatient Visits**: 58005 **Births**: 0 **Total Expense ($000)**: 98123 **Payroll Expense ($000)**: 30928 **Personnel**: 517

**UNITYPOINT HEALTH-PROCTOR** See Unitypoint Health - Proctor

### PEORIA HEIGHTS—Peoria County

**SAINT CLAIRE HOME** See Saint Clare Home

### PERU—Lasalle County

★ **ILLINOIS VALLEY COMMUNITY HOSPITAL (140234)**, 925 West Street, Zip 61354–2757; tel. 815/223–3300, (Nonreporting) **A**10 **F**3 11 13 15 18 28 29 30 31 34 35 37 38 40 45 46 47 48 49 50 51 54 57 59 63 64 65 66 68 69 70 74 75 76 77 79 81 82 84 85 87 93 96 97 104 107 110 111 114 115 118 119 127 129 130 131 132 133 135 143 144 146 147 148 149 154 156 157 **P**8
Primary Contact: Tommy Hobbs, Chief Executive Officer
COO: Bobby Smith, Vice President Physician Services and Quality
CFO: Lisa Lynch, Chief Financial Officer
CMO: Mark Fernandez, M.D., Chief of Staff and President Medical Staff
CIO: Nancy McDonnell, Manager Information Systems
CHR: Mary Beth Herron, Director of Human Resources
CNO: Robert Fortney, MS, R.N., Chief Nursing Officer and Vice President of Patient Care
Web address: www.ivch.org
**Control**: Other not–for–profit (including NFP Corporation) **Service**: General medical and surgical

**Staffed Beds**: 49 **Admissions**: 2207 **Census**: 17 **Outpatient Visits**: 193522 **Births**: 370 **Total Expense ($000)**: 86725 **Payroll Expense ($000)**: 34866 **Personnel**: 494

### PINCKNEYVILLE—Perry County

★ **PINCKNEYVILLE COMMUNITY HOSPITAL (141307)**, 5383 State Route 154, Zip 62274–1099, Mailing Address: PO Box 437, Zip 62274–1099; tel. 618/357–2187, (Nonreporting) **A**10 18 **F**3 11 15 28 29 31 34 40 43 45 50 53 56 57 65 78 81 82 85 93 107 108 110 119 127 130 132 133 146 149 **P**6
Primary Contact: Randall W. Dauby, Chief Executive Officer
COO: Bradley Futrell, Chief Operating Officer
CFO: Kara Jo Carson, Chief Financial Officer
CIO: Jeff Roberts, Director Information Technology
CHR: Christie Gajewski, Director Human Resources
CNO: Eva Hopp, Chief Nurse Executive
Web address: www.pvillehosp.org/
**Control**: Hospital district or authority, Government, Nonfederal **Service**: General medical and surgical

**Staffed Beds**: 17 **Admissions**: 452 **Census**: 9 **Outpatient Visits**: 47118 **Births**: 0 **Total Expense ($000)**: 27238 **Payroll Expense ($000)**: 10739 **Personnel**: 199

### PITTSFIELD—Pike County

★ ⇧ **ILLINI COMMUNITY HOSPITAL (141315)**, 640 West Washington Street, Zip 62363–1350; tel. 217/285–2113, (Nonreporting) **A**10 18 21 **F**3 15 28 29 30 31 34 40 46 50 53 59 64 65 68 70 75 77 78 81 85 87 89 93 97 98 100 101 103 104 107 110 115 119 127 129 130 131 132 133 144 146 149 154 156 **P**6
Primary Contact: Kathy Hull, President and Chief Executive Officer
CFO: Tim Moore, Vice President Finance
CMO: Bashar Alzein, M.D., President Medical Staff
CHR: Becky Myers, Human Resources Specialist
CNO: Holly A Jones, Administrative Director Nursing Services
Web address: www.illinihospital.org
**Control**: Other not–for–profit (including NFP Corporation) **Service**: General medical and surgical

**Staffed Beds**: 25 **Admissions**: 498 **Census**: 7 **Outpatient Visits**: 9320 **Births**: 0 **Total Expense ($000)**: 26943 **Payroll Expense ($000)**: 10109

### PONTIAC—Livingston County

✛ **OSF SAINT JAMES - JOHN W. ALBRECHT MEDICAL CENTER (140161)**, 2500 West Reynolds, Zip 61764–9774; tel. 815/842–2828, (Nonreporting) **A**1 10 20 **F**3 8 11 13 15 18 28 29 30 32 34 35 40 45 50 51 56 57 59 64 68 70 75 76 81 82 84 85 86 87 89 90 91 93 107 110 111 115 117 118 119 128 129 130 131 132 133 135 146 147 148 149 154 156 **S** OSF Healthcare, Peoria, IL
Primary Contact: Bradley V. Solberg, FACHE, President
CFO: Paula Corrigan, Vice President and Chief Financial Officer
CMO: John M. Rinker, Chief Medical Officer
CNO: Elizabeth Davidson, R.N., Vice President, Patient Care Services
Web address: www.osfsaintjames.org
**Control**: Church operated, Nongovernment, not–for–profit **Service**: General medical and surgical

**Staffed Beds**: 42 **Admissions**: 1998 **Census**: 18 **Outpatient Visits**: 73695 **Births**: 208 **Total Expense ($000)**: 51726 **Payroll Expense ($000)**: 19114 **Personnel**: 300

**OSF SAINT JAMES HOSPITAL** See OSF Saint James - John W. Albrecht Medical Center

---

**Hospital, Medicare Provider Number, Address, Telephone, Approval, Facility, and Physician Codes, Health Care System**

★ American Hospital Association (AHA) membership
☐ The Joint Commission accreditation
○ Healthcare Facilities Accreditation Program
◇ DNV Healthcare Inc. accreditation
⇧ Center for Improvement in Healthcare Quality Accreditation
△ Commission on Accreditation of Rehabilitation Facilities (CARF) accreditation

IL

## PRINCETON—Bureau County

★ **PERRY MEMORIAL HOSPITAL (141337)**, 530 Park Avenue East,
Zip 61356–2598; tel. 815/875–2811, (Nonreporting) **A**10 18 **F**3 11 15 18 28
29 30 31 32 34 35 40 41 45 48 49 51 56 57 59 64 65 70 75 77 78 79 81 82
83 85 86 87 93 97 100 104 105 107 108 110 111 115 116 118 119 127 129
130 131 132 133 144 145 146 148 149 153 154 156 **P**1
Primary Contact: Patricia A. Luker, Interim Chief Executive Officer
COO: Chris J. Williams, FACHE, Vice President Operations
CFO: Mike DeFoe, Chief Financial Officer
CMO: T Doran, M.D., Chief of Staff
CIO: Karen Behrens, Director Technology Services
CHR: James Lewandowski, Vice President Human Resources
Web address: www.https://perrymemorial.org
**Control**: City, Government, Nonfederal **Service**: General medical and surgical

> **Staffed Beds**: 25 **Admissions**: 607 **Census**: 7 **Outpatient Visits**: 82536
> **Births**: 0 **Total Expense ($000)**: 47410 **Payroll Expense ($000)**: 19370
> **Personnel**: 311

## QUINCY—Adams County

★ △ ⇑ **BLESSING HOSPITAL (140015)**, Broadway at 11th Street,
Zip 62305–7005, Mailing Address: P.O. Box 7005, Zip 62305–7005;
tel. 217/223–1200, (Includes BLESSING HOSPITAL, Mailing address: Broadway
& 14th Street, Quincy, Illinois, Zip 62301, P O Box 7005, Zip 62305–7005,
tel. 217/223–1200) (Total facility includes 20 beds in nursing home–type unit) **A**2
3 5 7 10 13 21 **F**3 5 8 11 12 13 15 17 18 20 22 24 26 28 29 30 31 32 33 34
35 40 42 43 44 48 49 50 53 56 57 58 59 60 61 62 63 64 66 68 70 73 74 75
76 77 78 79 81 82 84 85 86 87 89 90 94 96 98 99 100 101 102 104 105 107
108 110 111 114 115 118 119 120 121 123 124 126 127 128 129 130 131
132 135 144 146 147 148 149 152 153 154 156
Primary Contact: Maureen A. Kahn, R.N., President and Chief Executive Officer
COO: Tim Moore, Chief Accounting Officer and Vice President Ancillary Services
and Finance
CFO: Patrick M Gerveler, Vice President Finance and Chief Financial Officer
CMO: George Liesmann, M.D., Chief Medical Officer
CNO: Jill K Mason, MS, R.N., Chief Nursing Officer
Web address: www.blessinghospital.org
**Control**: Other not–for–profit (including NFP Corporation) **Service**: General
medical and surgical

> **Staffed Beds**: 314 **Admissions**: 15041 **Census**: 184 **Outpatient
> Visits**: 289561 **Births**: 1072 **Total Expense ($000)**: 403016 **Payroll
> Expense ($000)**: 142234 **Personnel**: 2435

**ST MARY HOSPITAL** See Blessing Hospital

## RED BUD—Randolph County

☐ **RED BUD REGIONAL HOSPITAL (141348)**, 325 Spring Street,
Zip 62278–1105; tel. 618/282–3831, (Nonreporting) **A**1 10 18 **S** Quorum Health,
Brentwood, TN
Primary Contact: Shane Watson, Chief Executive Officer
CFO: Veronica Marin, Chief Financial Officer
CMO: Julie Kelley, M.D., Chief of Staff
CIO: Nick Behnken, IT Director
CHR: Lori Brooks, Director Human Resources
CNO: Jennifer Gregson, Chief Nursing Officer
Web address: www.redbudregional.com
**Control**: Corporation, Investor–owned (for–profit) **Service**: General medical and
surgical

> **Staffed Beds**: 140

**REDBUD REGIONAL HOSPITAL** See Red Bud Regional Hospital

## ROBINSON—Crawford County

★ ○ **CRAWFORD MEMORIAL HOSPITAL (141343)**, 1000 North Allen Street,
Zip 62454–1167; tel. 618/544–3131, (Nonreporting) **A**10 11 18 **F**3 11 12 13 15
28 31 34 40 46 53 59 62 64 76 79 80 81 82 85 93 97 100 107 108 111 115
119 127 129 130 131 132 133 146 147 154 **S** QHR Health, Brentwood, TN
Primary Contact: Douglas Florkowski, Chief Executive Officer
CFO: Richard Carlson, Chief Financial Officer
CMO: Gary Tennison, M.D., Chief of Staff
CIO: Tim Richard, IT Coordinator
CHR: Kristi Zane, Chief Human Resources Officer
CNO: Tammy Fralicker, MS, R.N., Chief Nursing Officer
Web address: www.crawfordmh.net
**Control**: Hospital district or authority, Government, Nonfederal **Service**: General
medical and surgical

> **Staffed Beds**: 25 **Admissions**: 826 **Census**: 9 **Outpatient Visits**: 34413
> **Births**: 202 **Total Expense ($000)**: 48228 **Payroll Expense ($000)**: 23227
> **Personnel**: 357

## ROCHELLE—Ogle County

⊞ **ROCHELLE COMMUNITY HOSPITAL (141312)**, 900 North Second Street,
Zip 61068–1764; tel. 815/562–2181, (Nonreporting) **A**1 10 18 **F**3 11 15 29 30
31 34 35 40 41 45 53 57 59 64 68 70 74 75 77 78 81 82 85 86 87 97 107
110 111 115 130 132 133 135 144 146 149 156 **P**6
Primary Contact: Daniel Schwanke, Interim Chief Executive Officer
COO: Karen Tracy, R.N., Chief Operating Officer
CFO: Lori Gutierrez, Chief Financial Officer
CMO: Michael Monfils, M.D., Chief of Medical Staff
CIO: Scott Stewart, Manager Information Services
CHR: Denise Bauer, Director of Human Resources
Web address: www.rcha.net
**Control**: Other not–for–profit (including NFP Corporation) **Service**: General
medical and surgical

> **Staffed Beds**: 17 **Admissions**: 360 **Census**: 3 **Outpatient Visits**: 39601
> **Births**: 1 **Total Expense ($000)**: 31940 **Payroll Expense ($000)**: 12263
> **Personnel**: 209

## ROCK ISLAND—Rock Island County

**ST ANTHONY CONTINUING CARE CTR** See St. Anthony's Continuing Care
Center

**TRINITY ROCK ISLAND** See Unitypoint Health - Trinity Rock Island

⊞ △ **UNITYPOINT HEALTH - TRINITY ROCK ISLAND (140280)**, 2701 17th
Street, Zip 61201–5393; tel. 309/779–5000, (Includes UNITYPOINT HEALTH
- TRINITY MOLINE, Mailing address: 500 John Deere Road, Moline, Illinois,
Zip 61265; tel. 309/779–5000), (Nonreporting) **A**1 5 7 10 **F**3 4 5 11 12 13 15
18 20 22 24 26 28 29 30 31 34 35 38 40 43 44 45 46 49 50 55 57 58 59 64
68 70 73 74 75 76 78 79 81 82 85 86 87 90 93 96 97 98 102 104 105 107
108 110 114 115 118 119 120 121 123 126 129 130 132 146 147 148 149
150 152 153 154 157 158 **S** UnityPoint Health, West Des Moines, IA
Primary Contact: Robert J. Erickson, President and Chief Executive Officer
COO: Barbara Weber, Chief Operating Officer
CFO: Katie A Marchik, Chief Financial Officer
CMO: Paul McLoone, M.D., Chief Medical Officer
CHR: Cara Fuller, Vice President Human Resources
CNO: Ginger L Renkiewicz, Chief Clinical Officer, Chief Nursing Executive, and Chief
Quality Officer
Web address: www.https://www.unitypoint.org
**Control**: Other not–for–profit (including NFP Corporation) **Service**: General
medical and surgical

> **Staffed Beds**: 325 **Admissions**: 12353 **Census**: 149 **Outpatient
> Visits**: 429725 **Births**: 1063 **Total Expense ($000)**: 325762 **Payroll
> Expense ($000)**: 126392 **Personnel**: 2077

## ROCKFORD—Winnebago County

⊞ **JAVON BEA HOSPITAL-ROCKTON (140239)**, 2400 North Rockton Avenue,
Zip 61103–3655; tel. 815/971–5000, (Includes MERCYHEALTH JAVON BEA
HOSPITAL - RIVERSIDE CAMPUS, Mailing address: 8201 East Riverside Boulevard,
Rockford, Illinois, Zip 61114–2300; tel. 815/971–7000; Javon R. Bea, President
and Chief Executive Officer), (Nonreporting) **A**1 2 3 5 10 **F**3 11 13 18 19 20 22
24 26 27 28 29 30 31 32 34 35 39 40 41 43 44 45 46 47 48 49 50 51 54 55
56 57 59 64 65 68 70 71 72 74 75 76 77 78 79 81 82 83 84 85 86 87 88 89
91 93 97 98 100 101 102 103 107 108 111 114 115 118 119 120 121 123
126 129 130 131 132 135 145 146 147 148 149 154 156 157 **P**6 **S** Mercy
Health System, Janesville, WI
Primary Contact: Javon R. Bea, President and Chief Executive Officer
COO: Sue Ripsch, Senior Vice President & Chief Operating Officer
CFO: John Cook, Senior Vice President & Chief Financial Officer
CMO: John T Dorsey, M.D., Vice President Physician Services and Chief Medical
Officer
CIO: Ruth Yarbrough, Vice President
CHR: Heidi Elsbree, Vice President People and Culture
CNO: Doreen Timm, MSN, Senior Director and Chief Nursing Officer
Web address: www.rhsnet.org
**Control**: Other not–for–profit (including NFP Corporation) **Service**: General
medical and surgical

> **Staffed Beds**: 282 **Admissions**: 13224 **Census**: 192 **Outpatient
> Visits**: 365245 **Births**: 2455 **Total Expense ($000)**: 258302 **Payroll
> Expense ($000)**: 135004 **Personnel**: 2223

**MERCYHEALTH HOSPITAL - ROCKTON AVENUE** See Javon Bea Hospital-
Rockton

*Many Facility Codes have changed. Please refer to the AHA Guide Code Chart.*

© 2021 AHA Guide

**IL**

✠ **OSF SAINT ANTHONY MEDICAL CENTER (140233)**, 5666 East State Street, Zip 61108–2425; tel. 815/226–2000, (Nonreporting) **A**1 2 3 5 10 **F**3 11 12 13 15 16 17 18 19 20 22 24 26 28 29 30 31 32 34 35 36 37 38 40 41 43 44 45 46 49 50 51 53 55 56 57 58 59 63 64 66 70 73 74 75 76 77 78 79 81 82 84 85 86 87 89 92 93 107 108 110 111 114 115 116 117 118 119 120 121 123 124 126 129 130 131 132 135 145 146 147 148 149 150 154 **P**6 **S** OSF Healthcare, Peoria, IL
Primary Contact: Paula A. Carynski, MS, R.N., President
COO: James Girardy, M.D., Vice President, Chief Surgical Officer
CFO: David Stenerson, Vice President and Chief Financial Officer
CMO: Harneet Bath, M.D., Vice President, Chief Medicine Officer
CIO: Kathy Peterson, Director Information Services
CHR: Karen C Brown, Vice President Chief Operating Officer
Web address: www.osfhealth.com
**Control:** Church operated, Nongovernment, not–for–profit **Service:** General medical and surgical

**Staffed Beds: 235 Admissions:** 11251 **Census:** 140 **Outpatient Visits:** 213704 **Births:** 421 **Total Expense ($000):** 338015 **Payroll Expense ($000):** 103236 **Personnel:** 1526

**SAINT ANTHONY MEDICAL CENTER** See OSF Saint Anthony Medical Center

✠ **SWEDISHAMERICAN - A DIVISION OF UW HEALTH (140228)**, 1401 East State Street, Zip 61104–2315; tel. 815/968–4400, (Nonreporting) **A**1 2 3 5 10 **F**3 5 13 15 17 18 20 22 24 26 28 29 30 31 34 35 36 38 39 40 43 44 45 46 48 49 50 51 56 57 58 59 60 61 63 64 65 68 70 71 72 73 74 76 77 78 79 81 84 85 86 87 89 92 93 98 99 100 102 105 107 108 110 111 115 118 119 126 129 130 132 135 146 147 148 149 154 156 **P**6
Primary Contact: Don Daniels, Executive Vice President and Chief Operating Officer
COO: Don Daniels, Executive Vice President and Chief Operating Officer
CFO: Patti DeWane, Vice President Finance and Treasurer
CMO: Mike Polizzotto, Chief Medical Officer
CIO: Sheryl Johnson, Chief Information Officer
CHR: Gerard Guinane, Vice President Human Resources
CNO: Ann M Gantzer, Ph.D., R.N., Vice President Patient Services and Chief Nursing Officer
Web address: www.swedishamerican.org
**Control:** Other not–for–profit (including NFP Corporation) **Service:** General medical and surgical

**Staffed Beds: 281 Admissions:** 14216 **Census:** 160 **Outpatient Visits:** 273004 **Births:** 1532 **Total Expense ($000):** 356503 **Payroll Expense ($000):** 139244 **Personnel:** 2148

**SWEDISHAMERICAN HOSPITAL, A DIVISION OF UW HEALTH** See Swedishamerican - A Division of Uw Health

**VAN MATRE ENCOMPASS HEALTH** See Van Matre Encompass Health Rehabilitation Hospital

✠ **VAN MATRE ENCOMPASS HEALTH REHABILITATION HOSPITAL (143028)**, 950 South Mulford Road, Zip 61108–4274; tel. 815/381–8500, (Nonreporting) **A**1 10 **S** Encompass Health Corporation, Birmingham, AL
Primary Contact: Jeffrey Reese, Chief Executive Officer
CMO: Stephen Talty, M.D., Medical Director
CIO: Angela Bergman, Director of Quality, Risk and Health Information Management
CNO: Chrisi Karcz, Chief Nursing Officer
Web address: www.healthsouth.com
**Control:** Corporation, Investor–owned (for–profit) **Service:** Rehabilitation

**Staffed Beds:** 61

★ **HARDIN COUNTY GENERAL HOSPITAL (141328)**, 6 Ferrell Road, Zip 62982, Mailing Address: P.O. Box 2467, Zip 62982–2467; tel. 618/285–6634, (Nonreporting) **A**10 18
Primary Contact: Roby D. Williams, Administrator
CFO: Janie Parker, Chief Financial Officer
CMO: Marcos N Sunga, M.D., Chief of Staff
CIO: Brian Casteel, Information Technology Technician
CHR: Joyce Shelby, Manager Human Resources
CNO: Courtney Spivey, Chief Nursing Officer
Web address: www.ilhcgh.org
**Control:** Other not–for–profit (including NFP Corporation) **Service:** General medical and surgical

**Staffed Beds:** 25

★ **SARAH D. CULBERTSON MEMORIAL HOSPITAL (141333)**, 238 South Congress Street, Zip 62681–1472; tel. 217/322–4321, (Nonreporting) **A**10 18
Primary Contact: John E. Kessler, Chief Executive Officer
CFO: Alan Palo, Chief Financial Officer
CMO: Marguerite Taillefer, M.D., Acting President Medical Staff
CIO: Dan Wise, Manager Information Technology
CNO: Lisa M Downs, R.N., Chief Nursing Officer
Web address: www.cmhospital.com
**Control:** Hospital district or authority, Government, Nonfederal **Service:** General medical and surgical

**Staffed Beds:** 22

**PUB HOSP OF THE TOWN OF SALEM** See Salem Township Hospital

★ ○ **SALEM TOWNSHIP HOSPITAL (141345)**, 1201 Ricker Drive, Zip 62881–4263; tel. 618/548–3194, (Nonreporting) **A**10 11 18
Primary Contact: Kendra Taylor, MSN, R.N., President and Chief Executive Officer
CFO: Alexander Nazarian, CPA, Chief Financial Officer
CMO: Gautam Jha, M.D., Chief of Staff
CIO: Steve Turner, Director Information Technology
CHR: Diane Boswell, Director Human Resources and Marketing
Web address: www.sthcares.org
**Control:** City–county, Government, Nonfederal **Service:** General medical and surgical

**Staffed Beds:** 22

✠ **NORTHWESTERN MEDICINE VALLEY WEST HOSPITAL (141340)**, 1302 North Main Street, Zip 60548–2587; tel. 815/786–8484, (Nonreporting) **A**1 10 18 **F**3 11 13 15 18 28 29 30 31 32 34 35 36 38 40 41 44 45 46 49 50 51 57 58 59 60 64 68 70 71 73 75 76 77 78 79 81 82 84 85 87 89 93 102 104 107 108 110 111 115 119 129 130 131 132 133 135 146 147 149 150 154 **S** Northwestern Memorial HealthCare, Chicago, IL
Primary Contact: Jay Anderson, President
COO: Brad Copple, Vice President Operations
CFO: Matthew J Flynn, Chief Financial Officer West Region
CMO: Michael Kulisz, D.O., Vice President, Chief Medical Officer
CIO: Heath Bell, Vice President, Information Services
CHR: Michael Vivoda, Senior Vice President Human Resources
CNO: Pamela Duffy, MSN, R.N., Vice President Operations and Chief Nursing Executive
Web address: www.nm.org
**Control:** Other not–for–profit (including NFP Corporation) **Service:** General medical and surgical

**Staffed Beds: 25 Admissions:** 729 **Census:** 6 **Outpatient Visits:** 41973 **Births:** 163 **Total Expense ($000):** 43550 **Payroll Expense ($000):** 12344 **Personnel:** 247

**VALLEY WEST HOSPITAL** See Northwestern Medicine Valley West Hospital

IL

## SHELBYVILLE—Shelby County

★ ⇑ **HSHS GOOD SHEPHERD HOSPITAL (140019)**, 200 South Cedar Street, Zip 62565–1838; tel. 217/774–3961, (Nonreporting) **A**10 20 21 **F**3 15 28 29 30 34 35 40 45 50 57 59 62 64 77 79 81 97 107 108 110 115 118 119 127 129 131 132 133 146 154 **S** HSHS Hospital Sisters Health System, Springfield, IL
Primary Contact: Aaron Puchbauer, President
CFO: Marilyn Sears, Chief Financial Officer
CMO: David Oligschlaeger, Medical Staff President
CIO: Ian Kuhlman, Manager Information Technology
CHR: Amy Koehler, Director Human Resources
CNO: Michelle Oliver, Chief Nursing Executive
Web address: www.mysmh.org
**Control**: Church operated, Nongovernment, not-for-profit **Service**: General medical and surgical

**Staffed Beds**: 30 **Admissions**: 382 **Census**: 4 **Outpatient Visits**: 21389
**Births**: 0 **Total Expense ($000)**: 16245 **Payroll Expense ($000)**: 5242
**Personnel**: 110

⇑ **SHELBY MEMORIAL HOSPITAL** See Hshs Good Shepherd Hospital

## SHILOH—St. Clair County

★ ○ **MEMORIAL HOSPITAL EAST (140307)**, 1404 Cross Street, Zip 62269–2988; tel. 618/607–1000, (Nonreporting) **A**10 11 **F**3 11 13 15 18 20 22 26 29 30 40 41 45 49 57 64 70 74 76 78 79 81 85 87 91 92 93 94 107 110 111 115 118 119 130 131 132 146 148 149 154 **S** BJC HealthCare, Saint Louis, MO
Primary Contact: Michael T. McManus, President
CFO: Jane Gusmano, Interim Vice President Finance
CMO: William Casperson, Vice President Medical Affairs
CIO: Jennifer Meinkoth, Executive Director I.S.
CHR: John C Ziegler, FACHE, Vice President Human Resources
CNO: Teresa Halloran, Ph.D., R.N., Vice President Nursing Services
Web address: www.memhospeast.com
**Control**: Other not-for-profit (including NFP Corporation) **Service**: General medical and surgical

**Staffed Beds**: 51 **Admissions**: 4177 **Census**: 39 **Outpatient Visits**: 78500
**Births**: 1076 **Total Expense ($000)**: 87191 **Payroll Expense ($000)**: 36037
**Personnel**: 511

## SILVIS—Rock Island County

**GENESIS MEDICAL CENTER, ILLINI CAMPUS** See Genesis Medical Center, Silvis

⊞ **GENESIS MEDICAL CENTER, SILVIS (140275)**, 801 Illini Drive, Zip 61282–1893; tel. 309/281–4000, (Nonreporting) **A**1 10 **F**3 7 13 15 18 20 22 26 28 29 30 31 34 35 40 43 45 46 47 50 51 53 59 64 65 68 70 75 76 77 78 79 81 85 87 107 108 110 111 114 116 119 129 130 135 146 147 149 157 **S** Genesis Health System, Davenport, IA
Primary Contact: Theresa Summers-Main, R.N., President
CFO: Mark G Rogers, Interim Vice President Finance and Chief Financial Officer
CMO: Peter Metcalf, M.D., President Medical Staff
CIO: Robert Frieden, Vice President Information Systems
CHR: Heidi Kahly-McMahon, Vice President Human Resources
Web address: www.genesishealth.com
**Control**: Other not-for-profit (including NFP Corporation) **Service**: General medical and surgical

**Staffed Beds**: 127 **Admissions**: 3299 **Census**: 26 **Outpatient Visits**: 179207 **Births**: 369 **Total Expense ($000)**: 84529 **Payroll Expense ($000)**: 24507 **Personnel**: 381

## SKOKIE—Cook County

**NORTHSHORE UNIVERSITY HEALTH SYSTEM SKOKIE HOSPITAL** See Northshore Skokie Hospital

## SPARTA—Randolph County

○ **SPARTA COMMUNITY HOSPITAL (141349)**, 818 East Broadway Street, Zip 62286–1820, Mailing Address: P.O. Box 297, Zip 62286–0297; tel. 618/443–2177, (Nonreporting) **A**10 11 18 **F**3 11 15 28 29 34 35 40 41 45 50 53 57 59 62 64 75 77 81 85 93 97 107 110 111 115 119 127 130 132 133 135 143 146 149 156
Primary Contact: Joann Emge, Chief Executive Officer
CMO: Mark Pruess, M.D., Chief Medical Staff
CIO: Susan Gutjahr, Reimbursement Specialist
CHR: Darla Shawgo, Director Human Resources
CNO: Lori Clinton, Chief Nursing Officer
Web address: www.spartahospital.com
**Control**: Hospital district or authority, Government, Nonfederal **Service**: General medical and surgical

**Staffed Beds**: 25 **Admissions**: 410 **Census**: 5 **Outpatient Visits**: 41536
**Births**: 0 **Total Expense ($000)**: 37355 **Payroll Expense ($000)**: 14760
**Personnel**: 271

## SPRING VALLEY—Bureau County

**ST. MARGARET'S HOSPITAL (140143)**, 600 East First Street, Zip 61362–1512; tel. 815/664–5311, (Nonreporting) **A**10 **F**3 11 13 15 28 29 30 31 32 34 35 37 38 40 44 45 46 47 49 53 57 58 59 63 70 74 75 76 77 79 81 82 84 85 87 93 96 107 108 110 111 115 118 119 125 129 130 131 132 133 135 143 144 146 147 148 149 154 156 157 **P**6 8 **S** Sisters of Mary of the Presentation Health System, Fargo, ND
Primary Contact: Tim Muntz, President and Chief Executive Officer
CFO: Kim D Santman, Vice President Finance
CIO: John Sabotta, Director Information Systems
CHR: Lisa R Blackburn, Director Human Resources
CNO: Mary Vega, R.N., MSN, Vice President Nursing
Web address: www.aboutsmh.org
**Control**: Church operated, Nongovernment, not-for-profit **Service**: General medical and surgical

**Staffed Beds**: 44 **Admissions**: 1843 **Census**: 17 **Outpatient Visits**: 299075
**Births**: 295 **Total Expense ($000)**: 90031 **Payroll Expense ($000)**: 38285
**Personnel**: 551

## SPRINGFIELD—Sangamon County

☐ **ANDREW MCFARLAND MENTAL HEALTH CENTER (144021)**, 901 East Southwind Road, Zip 62703–5125; tel. 217/786–6994, (Nonreporting) **A**1 10 **F**29 30 38 87 98 101 130 146 149 154 157 **S** Division of Mental Health, Department of Human Services, Springfield, IL
Primary Contact: Karen Schweighart, R.N., MS, Administrator
CFO: Jeff Frey, Business Administrator
CMO: Kasturi Kripakaran, M.D., Medical Director
CIO: Josh Kates, Information Technology Analyst
CNO: Frances Collins, Director of Nursing
**Control**: State, Government, Nonfederal **Service**: Psychiatric

**Staffed Beds**: 142 **Admissions**: 220 **Census**: 137 **Outpatient Visits**: 0
**Births**: 0 **Total Expense ($000)**: 22803 **Payroll Expense ($000)**: 18212
**Personnel**: 276

⊞ **HSHS ST. JOHN'S HOSPITAL (140053)**, 800 East Carpenter Street, Zip 62769–0002; tel. 217/544–6464, (Includes ST. JOHN'S CHILDREN'S HOSPITAL, Mailing address: 800 East Carpenter Street, Springfield, Illinois, Zip 62769; tel. 217/544–6464), (Nonreporting) **A**1 2 3 5 10 **F**3 11 13 15 17 18 20 22 24 26 28 29 30 31 34 35 36 37 39 40 41 43 44 45 46 47 48 49 50 51 53 54 56 57 58 59 60 61 62 63 64 68 70 72 74 75 76 77 78 79 81 82 83 84 85 86 87 88 89 92 93 94 96 104 107 110 111 114 115 117 118 119 120 121 122 123 124 126 129 130 131 132 135 146 147 148 149 150 154 157 **S** HSHS Hospital Sisters Health System, Springfield, IL
Primary Contact: Evert J. Kuiper, President and Chief Executive Officer
CFO: Patty Allen, St. John's Vice President Finance
CIO: Ryan Leach, Chief Information Officer
CHR: Becky Puclik, Division Chief People Officer
CNO: Allison Kay Paul, R.N., Chief Nursing Officer
Web address: www.st-johns.org
**Control**: Other not-for-profit (including NFP Corporation) **Service**: General medical and surgical

**Staffed Beds**: 422 **Admissions**: 18223 **Census**: 270 **Outpatient Visits**: 219675 **Births**: 2021 **Total Expense ($000)**: 555267 **Payroll Expense ($000)**: 159667 **Personnel**: 2927

☐ **LINCOLN PRAIRIE BEHAVIORAL HEALTH CENTER**, 5230 South Sixth Street, Zip 62703–5128; tel. 217/585–1180, (Nonreporting) **A**1 **S** Universal Health Services, Inc., King of Prussia, PA
Primary Contact: Kevin McGee, Interim Chief Executive Officer
CFO: Chris Statz, Chief Financial Officer
CMO: Pamela Campbell, M.D., Medical Director
CNO: Renae Hale, Chief Nursing Officer
Web address: www.lincolnprairiebhc.com/
**Control**: Corporation, Investor-owned (for-profit) **Service**: Children's hospital psychiatric

**Staffed Beds**: 97

*Many Facility Codes have changed. Please refer to the AHA Guide Code Chart.*   © 2021 AHA Guide

IL

⊠ △ **MEMORIAL MEDICAL CENTER (140148)**, 701 North First Street, Zip 62781–0001; tel. 217/788–3000, (Nonreporting) **A**1 2 5 7 8 10 **F**3 8 11 12 13 14 15 16 17 18 20 22 24 26 28 29 30 31 32 34 35 36 37 40 43 44 45 46 47 48 49 50 51 54 57 58 59 60 61 63 64 68 69 70 74 75 76 77 78 79 81 82 84 85 86 87 89 90 92 93 96 97 98 102 105 107 110 111 114 115 116 117 118 119 120 121 123 124 126 129 130 131 132 134 135 138 141 145 146 147 148 149 154 156 **P**5 **S** Memorial Health System, Springfield, IL
Primary Contact: Charles D. Callahan, Ph.D., President and Chief Executive Officer
CFO: Robert W Kay, Senior Vice President and Chief Financial Officer
CMO: Rajesh G. Govindaiah, M.D., Chief Medical Officer
CIO: Jerry Miller, Vice President, Information Services
CHR: Robert F Scott, Vice President and Chief Human Resources Officer
CNO: Marsha A Prater, Ph.D., R.N., Senior Vice President and Chief Nursing Officer
Web address: www.memorialmedical.com
**Control:** Other not–for–profit (including NFP Corporation) **Service:** General medical and surgical

**Staffed Beds:** 456 **Admissions:** 23699 **Census:** 319 **Outpatient Visits:** 428193 **Births:** 1440 **Total Expense ($000):** 696148 **Payroll Expense ($000):** 227217 **Personnel:** 3723

**ST. JOHN'S HOSPITAL** See Hshs St. John's Hospital

### STAUNTON—Macoupin County

**COMMUNITY HOSPITAL OF STAUNTON (141306)**, 400 Caldwell Street, Zip 62088–1499; tel. 618/635–2200, (Nonreporting) **A**10 18
Primary Contact: Susie Campbell, Chief Executive Officer
CFO: Brian Engelke, Chief Financial Officer
CMO: Joshua Poos, M.D., President Medical Staff
CIO: Cheryl Horner, Supervisor Data Processing
CHR: Marilyn Herbeck, Coordinator Human Resources
CNO: Roberta Brown, Chief Nursing Officer
Web address: www.stauntonhospital.org
**Control:** Other not–for–profit (including NFP Corporation) **Service:** General medical and surgical

**Staffed Beds:** 25

**COMMUNITY MEMORIAL HOSPITAL** See Community Hospital of Staunton

### STERLING—Whiteside County

⊠ **CGH MEDICAL CENTER (140043)**, 100 East LeFevre Road, Zip 61081–1279; tel. 815/625–0400, (Nonreporting) **A**1 10 **F**3 7 8 11 13 15 18 20 22 28 29 30 31 34 35 40 45 47 49 50 51 57 59 62 64 68 70 74 76 78 79 81 82 85 86 87 89 93 97 107 108 110 111 112 115 116 117 118 119 124 129 130 132 135 144 145 146 147 148 149 156 157 **P**6
Primary Contact: Paul Steinke, D.O., President and Chief Executive Officer
CFO: Ben Schaab, Vice President, Chief Financial Officer
CIO: Randy Davis, Vice President and Chief Information Officer
CHR: Paul Steinke, D.O., President and Chief Executive Officer
CNO: Kristie A Geil, Vice President, Chief Nursing Officer
Web address: www.cghmc.com
**Control:** City, Government, Nonfederal **Service:** General medical and surgical

**Staffed Beds:** 87 **Admissions:** 3944 **Census:** 36 **Outpatient Visits:** 378150 **Births:** 562 **Total Expense ($000):** 228456 **Payroll Expense ($000):** 97982 **Personnel:** 1166

### STREAMWOOD—Cook County

☐ **STREAMWOOD BEHAVIORAL HEALTH CENTER (144034)**, 1400 East Irving Park Road, Zip 60107–3203; tel. 630/837–9000, (Nonreporting) **A**1 10 **F**50 64 68 98 99 100 101 104 105 130 149 153 **S** Universal Health Services, Inc., King of Prussia, PA
Primary Contact: Ron Weglarz, Chief Executive Officer and Managing Director
CMO: Joseph McNally, M.D., Medical Director
CHR: Joseph Rinke, Director Human Resources
CNO: Olieth Lightbourne, Chief Nursing Officer
Web address: www.streamwoodhospital.com
**Control:** Corporation, Investor–owned (for–profit) **Service:** Psychiatric

**Staffed Beds:** 178 **Admissions:** 4245 **Census:** 123 **Outpatient Visits:** 28363 **Births:** 0 **Total Expense ($000):** 34607 **Payroll Expense ($000):** 17607 **Personnel:** 343

**STREAMWOOD HOSPITAL** See Streamwood Behavioral Health Center

### SYCAMORE—Dekalb County

⊠ **KINDRED HOSPITAL-SYCAMORE (142006)**, 225 Edward Street, Zip 60178–2137; tel. 815/895–2144, (Nonreporting) **A**1 10 **S** Kindred Healthcare, Louisville, KY
Primary Contact: Beverly Foster, Chief Executive Officer
CFO: Jay Schweikart, Chief Financial Officer
CMO: Manav Salwan, Medical Director
CNO: Beth Ann Navarro, Chief Clinical Officer
Web address: www.kindredhospitalsyc.com/
**Control:** Corporation, Investor–owned (for–profit) **Service:** Acute long–term care hospital

**Staffed Beds:** 69

**VENCOR HOSPITAL-SYCAMORE** See Kindred Hospital-Sycamore

### TAYLORVILLE—Christian County

**ST VINCENT MEMORIAL HOSPITAL** See Taylorville Memorial Hospital

⊠ **TAYLORVILLE MEMORIAL HOSPITAL (141339)**, 201 East Pleasant Street, Zip 62568–1597; tel. 217/824–3331, (Nonreporting) **A**1 3 5 10 18 **F**8 15 28 29 30 34 35 40 45 46 50 57 59 64 75 77 79 81 87 89 93 103 107 108 110 111 115 119 129 130 131 132 133 144 146 149 **P**5 **S** Memorial Health System, Springfield, IL
Primary Contact: Kimberly L. Bourne, President and Chief Executive Officer
CFO: Christine Goldesberry-Curry, Director of Strategic Finance-CAH
CHR: Michelle Long, Regional Human Resource Manager
CNO: Geri L. Kirkbride, Chief Nursing Officer (Interim)
Web address: www.taylorvillememorial.org
**Control:** Other not–for–profit (including NFP Corporation) **Service:** General medical and surgical

**Staffed Beds:** 25 **Admissions:** 820 **Census:** 14 **Outpatient Visits:** 34061 **Births:** 0 **Total Expense ($000):** 39727 **Payroll Expense ($000):** 16182 **Personnel:** 267

### URBANA—Champaign County

★ △ ⇑ **CARLE FOUNDATION HOSPITAL (140091)**, 611 West Park Street, Zip 61801–2529; tel. 217/383–3311, (Nonreporting) **A**2 3 5 7 8 10 13 21 **F**3 8 12 13 15 17 18 20 22 24 26 28 29 30 31 34 35 40 43 44 45 46 47 48 49 50 51 53 56 57 58 59 60 61 62 63 64 68 70 72 73 74 75 76 77 78 79 80 81 82 84 85 86 87 89 90 91 92 93 96 97 104 107 108 110 111 114 115 117 118 119 120 121 123 124 126 129 130 131 132 146 148 149 154 **S** Carle Health, Urbana, IL
Primary Contact: James C. Leonard, M.D., President and Chief Executive Officer
COO: John Snyder, Executive Vice President and System Chief Operating Officer
CFO: Dennis Hesch, Executive Vice President Finance, System Chief Financial Officer
CMO: Matthew Gibb, M.D., Executive Vice President and System Chief Medical Officer
CIO: Rick Rinehart, Vice President, Chief Information Officer
CHR: Laurence Fallon, JD, JD, Executive Vice President, Chief Legal and Human Resources Officer
CNO: Pamela Bigler, R.N., Senior Vice President of Clinical Partnerships and Programs
Web address: www.carle.org
**Control:** Other not–for–profit (including NFP Corporation) **Service:** General medical and surgical

**Staffed Beds:** 456 **Admissions:** 26151 **Census:** 342 **Outpatient Visits:** 1565180 **Births:** 2451 **Total Expense ($000):** 917787 **Payroll Expense ($000):** 239902 **Personnel:** 3972

IL

**Hospital, Medicare Provider Number, Address, Telephone, Approval, Facility, and Physician Codes, Health Care System**

★ American Hospital Association (AHA) membership
☐ The Joint Commission accreditation
○ Healthcare Facilities Accreditation Program
◇ DNV Healthcare Inc. accreditation
⇑ Center for Improvement in Healthcare Quality Accreditation
△ Commission on Accreditation of Rehabilitation Facilities (CARF) accreditation

© 2021 AHA Guide    *Many Facility Codes have changed. Please refer to the AHA Guide Code Chart.*    Hospitals **A221**

✠ **OSF HEART OF MARY MEDICAL CENTER (140113)**, 1400 West Park Street, Zip 61801–2396, Mailing Address: P.O. Box 6259, Peoria, Zip 61601; tel. 217/337–2000, (Nonreporting) **A**1 3 5 10 **F**3 8 12 13 15 18 20 22 24 26 28 29 30 35 40 45 46 47 48 49 57 59 60 64 68 70 73 74 75 76 79 81 82 84 87 89 90 92 94 96 97 98 100 102 107 108 110 111 112 113 114 115 119 126 130 132 146 147 148 154 **S** OSF Healthcare, Peoria, IL
Primary Contact: Jared Rogers, M.D., President and Chief Executive Officer
CFO: Lucas Morton, Regional Chief Financial Officer
CMO: Vincent Kucich, FACHE, FACS, M.D., Chief Medical Officer
CIO: Paula Keele, Manager Information Systems
CHR: Michael Zimmerman, Human Resource Officer
CNO: Molly Nicholson, MS, R.N., Chief Nurse Executive
Web address: www.presencehealth.org/covenant
**Control:** Church operated, Nongovernment, not–for–profit **Service:** General medical and surgical

**Staffed Beds:** 181 **Admissions:** 6210 **Census:** 69 **Outpatient Visits:** 41537 **Births:** 558 **Total Expense ($000):** 134285 **Payroll Expense ($000):** 39792 **Personnel:** 465

**OSF SACRED HEART MEDICAL CENTER** See OSF Heart of Mary Medical Center

### VANDALIA—Fayette County

✠ **FAYETTE COUNTY HOSPITAL (141346)**, 650 West Taylor Street, Zip 62471–1296; tel. 618/283–1231, (Nonreporting) **A**1 10 18 **S** Alliant Management Services, Louisville, KY
Primary Contact: Gregory D. Starnes, Chief Executive Officer
CFO: David H Wiesman, Interim Chief Financial Officer
CMO: Joseph Blaser, Chief Medical Officer
CIO: Gary Hood, Chief Information Officer
CHR: Susan Crawford, Manager Human Resources
CNO: Marci Barth, Chief Nursing Officer
Web address: www.fayettecountyhospital.org
**Control:** Corporation, Investor–owned (for–profit) **Service:** General medical and surgical

**Staffed Beds:** 110

**FAYETTE COUNTY HOSPITAL & LTC** See Fayette County Hospital

### WATSEKA—Iroquois County

☐ **IROQUOIS MEMORIAL HOSPITAL AND RESIDENT HOME (140167)**, 200 Fairman Avenue, Zip 60970–1644; tel. 815/432–5841, (Total facility includes 35 beds in nursing home–type unit) (Nonreporting) **A**1 3 10 20 **F**3 7 11 14 15 18 20 28 29 30 31 34 35 38 40 43 45 46 49 56 57 59 62 63 65 69 70 75 77 81 82 85 86 87 92 93 97 107 108 110 115 119 127 128 129 130 132 133 135 145 146 147 154 **P**4
Primary Contact: Don Williams, Chief Executive Officer
CFO: Dana Gilleland, Chief Financial Officer
CMO: John Tricou, M.D., Chief of Staff
CHR: Tera Bivins, Chief Human Resources Officer
CNO: Michelle Fairley, R.N., Chief Nursing Officer
Web address: www.imhrh.org
**Control:** Other not–for–profit (including NFP Corporation) **Service:** General medical and surgical

**Staffed Beds:** 60 **Admissions:** 406 **Census:** 32 **Outpatient Visits:** 27586 **Births:** 0 **Total Expense ($000):** 34353 **Payroll Expense ($000):** 14533 **Personnel:** 283

### WAUKEGAN—Lake County

☐ **LAKE BEHAVIORAL HOSPITAL (140033)**, 2615 Washington Street, Zip 60085–4988; tel. 847/249–3900, (Nonreporting) **A**1 10
Primary Contact: Cindy DeMarco, Chief Operating Officer
COO: Cindy DeMarco, Chief Operating Officer
CHR: Jackie Brewer, Director, Human Resources
CNO: Chad Carson, Director of Nursing
Web address: www.https://lakebehavioralhospital.com
**Control:** Corporation, Investor–owned (for–profit) **Service:** Psychiatric

**Staffed Beds:** 42

☐ **VISTA HEALTH (140084)**, 1324 North Sheridan Road, Zip 60085–2161; tel. 847/360–3000, (Nonreporting) **A**1 3 5 10 **S** Quorum Health, Brentwood, TN
Primary Contact: Norman F. Stephens, Chief Executive Officer
COO: Kim Needham, Assistant Chief Executive Officer
CFO: Kerry Hill, Chief Financial Officer
CMO: Daniel Liesen, M.D., Chief Medical Officer
CHR: Michael R Isaacs, Vice President Human Resources
Web address: www.vistahealth.com
**Control:** Corporation, Investor–owned (for–profit) **Service:** General medical and surgical

**Staffed Beds:** 190

**VISTA HEALTH** See Lake Behavioral Hospital

**VISTA MEDICAL CENTER EAST** See Vista Health

### WHEATON—Du Page County

**MARIANJOY REHABILITATION HOSPITAL** See Northwestern Medicine Marianjoy Rehabilitation Hospital

✠ △ **NORTHWESTERN MEDICINE MARIANJOY REHABILITATION HOSPITAL (143027)**, 26 West 171 Roosevelt Road, Zip 60187–0795, Mailing Address: P.O. Box 795, Zip 60187–0795; tel. 630/909–8000, (Total facility includes 14 beds in nursing home–type unit) (Nonreporting) **A**1 3 5 7 10 **F**3 11 29 30 34 35 36 44 50 53 54 57 58 60 64 68 74 75 77 79 82 86 87 90 91 92 93 94 95 96 119 128 130 131 132 143 146 148 149 154 **S** Northwestern Memorial HealthCare, Chicago, IL
Primary Contact: Julie L. Creamer, President
COO: John Brady, Vice President Physician Services and Organizational Planning
CMO: Jeffrey Oken, Vice President of Medical Affairs
CIO: Robert Sinickas, Director Information Services
CHR: Teresa Chapman, Vice President Human Resources
Web address: www.marianjoy.org
**Control:** Other not–for–profit (including NFP Corporation) **Service:** Rehabilitation

**Staffed Beds:** 127 **Admissions:** 2899 **Census:** 112 **Outpatient Visits:** 115392 **Births:** 0 **Total Expense ($000):** 90256 **Payroll Expense ($000):** 47293 **Personnel:** 644

### WINFIELD—Du Page County

**ALCOHOLISM TREATMENT CENTER** See Behavioral Health Center

**CENTRAL DUPAGE HOSPITAL** See Northwestern Medicine Central Dupage Hospital

✠ **NORTHWESTERN MEDICINE CENTRAL DUPAGE HOSPITAL (140242)**, 25 North Winfield Road, Zip 60190; tel. 630/933–1600, (Includes BEHAVIORAL HEALTH CENTER, Mailing address: 27 West 350 High Lake Road, Winfield, Illinois, Zip 60190; tel. 630/653–4000), (Nonreporting) **A**1 2 3 5 10 **F**3 4 5 6 7 8 9 11 12 13 15 17 18 19 20 22 24 26 28 29 30 31 32 34 35 36 37 38 39 40 41 43 44 45 46 47 48 49 50 54 55 56 57 58 59 60 62 64 65 68 70 71 72 73 74 75 76 77 78 79 81 82 84 85 86 87 88 89 91 92 93 94 96 97 98 99 100 101 102 103 104 105 107 108 110 111 112 114 115 116 117 118 119 120 121 122 123 124 126 129 130 131 132 135 144 145 146 147 148 149 152 153 154 156 157 **S** Northwestern Memorial HealthCare, Chicago, IL
Primary Contact: Kevin Poorten, President
CFO: John Orsini, Executive Vice President and Chief Financial Officer
CMO: Kevin Most, D.O., Chief Medical Officer
CIO: Daniel F Kinsella, Vice President and Chief Information Officer
Web address: www.nm.org
**Control:** Other not–for–profit (including NFP Corporation) **Service:** General medical and surgical

**Staffed Beds:** 419 **Admissions:** 21119 **Census:** 257 **Outpatient Visits:** 1503275 **Births:** 2842 **Total Expense ($000):** 1067662 **Payroll Expense ($000):** 360807 **Personnel:** 6748

### WOODSTOCK—Mchenry County

**NORTHWESTERN WOODSTOCK** See Northwestern Medicine Woodstock

### ZION—Lake County

**AMERICAN INTERNATIONAL HOSP** See Midwestern Regional Medical Center

✠ **MIDWESTERN REGIONAL MEDICAL CENTER (140100)**, 2520 Elisha Avenue, Zip 60099–2587; tel. 847/872–4561, (Nonreporting) **A**1 2 3 10 **S** Cancer Treatment Centers of America, Schaumburg, IL
Primary Contact: Scott Jones, President and Chief Executive Officer
COO: Pete Govorchin, Senior Vice President Operations
CFO: Cecilia Taylor, Chief Financial Officer
CMO: Bradford Tan, M.D., Chief Medical Officer
CHR: Amy VanStrien, Director Talent Operations
CNO: Jacklynn Lesniak, R.N., MS, Vice President Patient Care Services and Chief Nursing Officer
Web address: www.cancercenter.com
**Control:** Corporation, Investor–owned (for–profit) **Service:** Cancer

**Staffed Beds:** 72

*Many Facility Codes have changed. Please refer to the AHA Guide Code Chart.*

© 2021 AHA Guide

IL

# INDIANA

## ANDERSON—Madison County

⊞ **ASCENSION ST. VINCENT ANDERSON (150088)**, 2015 Jackson Street, Zip 46016–4339; tel. 765/649–2511, (Nonreporting) **A**1 2 10 **F**3 4 5 8 11 13 15 18 20 22 26 28 29 30 31 32 34 35 36 38 39 40 43 44 45 46 48 49 50 51 54 55 56 57 58 59 60 61 64 65 66 68 70 74 75 76 77 78 79 81 82 84 85 86 87 89 90 92 93 94 96 98 99 100 101 102 103 104 106 107 108 110 111 114 115 117 118 119 120 121 123 124 126 129 130 132 134 135 145 146 147 148 149 151 153 154 156 **S** Ascension Healthcare, Saint Louis, MO
Primary Contact: Nick Theohares, Executive Director, Operations
COO: Nick Theohares, Executive Director, Operations
CFO: Laura L Rose, Chief Financial Officer
CIO: Robert A. Pope, Director I
CHR: Ross Brodhead, Senior Director, Human Resource
Web address: www.stvincent.org/anderson
**Control:** Church operated, Nongovernment, not–for–profit **Service:** General medical and surgical

**Staffed Beds:** 152 **Admissions:** 5812 **Census:** 83 **Outpatient Visits:** 236061 **Births:** 401 **Total Expense ($000):** 176903 **Payroll Expense ($000):** 37938 **Personnel:** 476

⊞ **COMMUNITY HOSPITAL ANDERSON (150113)**, 1515 North Madison Avenue, Zip 46011–3453; tel. 765/298–4242, (Nonreporting) **A**1 2 10 **F**3 10 11 13 15 18 20 22 28 29 30 31 32 34 43 44 46 49 50 51 54 55 56 57 58 59 60 61 64 68 70 74 75 76 77 78 79 81 82 85 86 87 93 107 108 109 110 111 114 115 119 120 121 122 123 126 129 130 132 135 143 144 146 147 148 149 156 157 **S** Community Health Network, Indianapolis, IN
Primary Contact: Beth S. Tharp, R.N., President and Chief Executive Officer
COO: Sherry Sidwell, Chief Operating Officer, Vice President Integrated Support Services
CFO: John B. Harris, Vice President Finance and Chief Financial Officer
CNO: Marsha S Meckel, R.N., Vice President Clinical Services and Chief Nursing Executive
Web address: www.https://www.ecommunity.com/locations/community-hospital-anderson
**Control:** Other not–for–profit (including NFP Corporation) **Service:** General medical and surgical

**Staffed Beds:** 140 **Admissions:** 6656 **Census:** 71 **Outpatient Visits:** 234585 **Births:** 768 **Total Expense ($000):** 225859 **Payroll Expense ($000):** 69799 **Personnel:** 1119

**COMMUNITY HOSPITAL OF ANDERSON & MADISON COUNTY, INC.** See Community Hospital Anderson

**ST. VINCENT ANDERSON** See Ascension St. Vincent Anderson

## ANGOLA—Steuben County

★ **CAMERON MEMORIAL COMMUNITY HOSPITAL (151315)**, 416 East Maumee Street, Zip 46703–2015; tel. 260/665–2141, (Nonreporting) **A**10 18
Primary Contact: Connie McCahill, R.N., President and Chief Executive Officer
CFO: Wendy Stamper, Controller
CMO: Jon Alley, D.O., President Medical Staff
CIO: Kris Keen, Chief Information Officer
CHR: Nancy Covell, Director Human Resources
Web address: www.cameronmch.com
**Control:** Other not–for–profit (including NFP Corporation) **Service:** General medical and surgical

**Staffed Beds:** 25

## AUBURN—Dekalb County

**DEKALB HEALTH** See Parkview Dekalb Hospital

**NORTHEASTERN CENTER (154050)**, 1850 Wesley Road, Zip 46706–3653; tel. 260/927–0726, (Nonreporting) **A**10
Primary Contact: Jerry Hollister, Chief Executive Officer
Web address: www.necmh.org
**Control:** Other not–for–profit (including NFP Corporation) **Service:** Psychiatric

**Staffed Beds:** 16

★ **PARKVIEW DEKALB HOSPITAL (150045)**, 1316 East Seventh Street, Zip 46706–2515, Mailing Address: P.O. Box 542, Zip 46706–0542; tel. 260/925–4600, (Nonreporting) **A**10 **F**3 7 13 15 28 29 32 34 35 36 40 45 53 56 57 59 64 70 73 75 76 79 81 82 85 86 87 89 93 97 107 108 110 111 115 119 129 132 135 144 146 147 148 149 154 **P**6 **S** Parkview Health, Fort Wayne, IN
Primary Contact: Natasha Eicher, President and Chief Executive Officer
CMO: Emilio Vazquez, M.D., Chief Medical Officer
CIO: Ed Hobbs, Director Information Services
CNO: Donna S Wisemore, R.N., Vice President and Chief Nursing Officer
Web address: www.dekalbhealth.com
**Control:** Other not–for–profit (including NFP Corporation) **Service:** General medical and surgical

**Staffed Beds:** 57 **Admissions:** 1998 **Census:** 16 **Outpatient Visits:** 13815 **Births:** 40 **Total Expense ($000):** 12221 **Payroll Expense ($000):** 4216 **Personnel:** 271

## AVON—Hendricks County

**CLARIAN WEST MEDICAL CENTER** See Indiana University Health West Hospital

⊞ **INDIANA UNIVERSITY HEALTH WEST HOSPITAL (150158)**, 1111 North Ronald Reagan Parkway, Zip 46123–7085; tel. 317/217–3000, (Nonreporting) **A**1 2 3 5 10 **F**3 5 13 15 18 20 22 26 28 29 30 34 35 40 46 47 48 49 50 51 57 59 64 68 70 73 74 75 76 77 78 79 81 82 84 85 86 87 89 93 100 107 110 111 113 114 117 119 120 121 129 130 132 135 146 147 148 156 157 **S** Indiana University Health, Indianapolis, IN
Primary Contact: Paul J. Ivkovich, President
CMO: Andrew Nigh, M.D., Chief of Staff
CHR: Tamarah Brownlee, Vice President, Human Resources
CNO: Lisa Sparks, R.N., Chief Nursing Officer and Vice President Patient Care Services
Web address: www.iuhealth.org
**Control:** Other not–for–profit (including NFP Corporation) **Service:** General medical and surgical

**Staffed Beds:** 123 **Admissions:** 6829 **Census:** 84 **Outpatient Visits:** 180230 **Births:** 935 **Total Expense ($000):** 182343 **Payroll Expense ($000):** 52327 **Personnel:** 806

## BATESVILLE—Ripley County

**MARGARET MARY COMMUNITY HOSPITAL** See Margaret Mary Health

⊞ **MARGARET MARY HEALTH (151329)**, 321 Mitchell Avenue, Zip 47006–8909, Mailing Address: P.O. Box 226, Zip 47006–0226; tel. 812/934–6624, (Nonreporting) **A**1 2 10 18 **F**3 5 8 13 15 26 28 29 31 34 35 36 38 40 45 50 54 59 63 64 65 70 75 76 77 78 79 81 85 93 94 96 104 107 108 110 111 114 115 119 120 121 123 127 129 130 131 132 133 135 143 144 146 147 148 149 154 156
Primary Contact: Timothy L. Putnam, FACHE, President and Chief Executive Officer
CFO: Brian Daeger, Chief Financial Officer and Vice President Financial Services
CMO: Charles McGovern, Chief of Staff
CIO: Trisha Prickel, Information Systems Director
CHR: Kimberly Inscho, Vice President Human Resources and Marketing
CNO: Elizabeth Leising, Chief Nursing Officer and Vice President Patient Services
Web address: www.mmhealth.org
**Control:** Other not–for–profit (including NFP Corporation) **Service:** General medical and surgical

**Staffed Beds:** 25 **Admissions:** 1496 **Census:** 12 **Births:** 474 **Personnel:** 601

IN

---

**Hospital, Medicare Provider Number, Address, Telephone, Approval, Facility, and Physician Codes, Health Care System**

★ American Hospital Association (AHA) membership    ○ Healthcare Facilities Accreditation Program    ⇑ Center for Improvement in Healthcare Quality Accreditation
□ The Joint Commission accreditation    ◇ DNV Healthcare Inc. accreditation    △ Commission on Accreditation of Rehabilitation Facilities (CARF) accreditation

## BEDFORD—Lawrence County

**ASCENSION ST. VINCENT DUNN (151335)**, 1600 23rd Street, Zip 47421–4704; tel. 812/275–3331, (Nonreporting) **A**1 10 18 **F**3 12 13 15 18 28 29 30 34 35 40 45 50 53 64 65 66 76 77 81 82 85 86 87 107 108 109 111 115 119 133 135 146 148 149 **S** Ascension Healthcare, Saint Louis, MO
Primary Contact: George Zhang, Administrator
CFO: Crystal Plano, Controller
CMO: Deborah W Craton, M.D., Chief Medical Officer
CIO: Chad Damon, Contractor
CHR: Darci Medlock, Manager Human Resources
CNO: Michelle Dotts-McCool, Chief Nursing Officer
Web address: www.stvincent.org/St-Vincent-Dunn/Default.aspx
**Control**: Other not–for–profit (including NFP Corporation) **Service**: General medical and surgical

**Staffed Beds**: 35 **Admissions**: 685 **Census**: 5 **Outpatient Visits**: 40126 **Births**: 292 **Total Expense ($000)**: 22123 **Payroll Expense ($000)**: 5426

**ASCENSION ST. VINCENT DUNN HOSPITAL** See Ascension St. Vincent Dunn

**BEDFORD REGIONAL MEDICAL CENTER** See Indiana University Health Bedford Hospital

**INDIANA UNIVERSITY HEALTH BEDFORD HOSPITAL (151328)**, 2900 West 16th Street, Zip 47421–3583; tel. 812/275–1200, (Nonreporting) **A**1 2 10 18 **F**3 11 15 18 28 29 30 31 34 35 38 40 41 45 46 47 48 49 50 57 59 64 68 70 74 75 77 78 79 81 85 86 87 93 102 107 108 110 111 115 118 119 129 130 132 133 135 146 149 154 156 157 **S** Indiana University Health, Indianapolis, IN
Primary Contact: Bradford W. Dykes, President
CFO: Mike Craig, Vice President, Chief Financial Officer
CMO: Daniel Handel, M.D., Chief Medical Officer
CHR: Bruce Wade, Vice President Human Resources
CNO: Amy A Little, Vice President Patient Services
Web address: www.iuhealth.org
**Control**: Other not–for–profit (including NFP Corporation) **Service**: General medical and surgical

**Staffed Beds**: 25 **Admissions**: 1376 **Census**: 12 **Outpatient Visits**: 88973 **Births**: 0 **Total Expense ($000)**: 59741 **Payroll Expense ($000)**: 15398 **Personnel**: 227

## BLOOMINGTON—Monroe County

**BLOOMINGTON HOSPITAL** See Indiana University Health Bloomington Hospital

**BLOOMINGTON MEADOWS HOSPITAL (154041)**, 3600 North Prow Road, Zip 47404–1616; tel. 812/331–8000, (Nonreporting) **A**1 10 **S** Universal Health Services, Inc., King of Prussia, PA
Primary Contact: Christopher Dowers, Chief Executive Officer
CFO: Becky T. Nyberg, Chief Financial Officer
CMO: David Gilliam, M.D., Medical Director
CHR: Amanda Shettlesworth, Director Human Resources
CNO: Penny Caswell, Director of Nursing
Web address: www.bloomingtonmeadows.com
**Control**: Corporation, Investor–owned (for–profit) **Service**: Psychiatric

**Staffed Beds**: 71

**INDIANA UNIVERSITY HEALTH BLOOMINGTON HOSPITAL (150051)**, 601 West Second Street, Zip 47403–2317, Mailing Address: P.O. Box 1149, Zip 47402–1149; tel. 812/336–6821, (Nonreporting) **A**1 2 5 10 19 **F**3 5 7 8 11 12 17 18 19 20 22 24 26 28 29 30 31 32 34 35 38 40 43 45 46 47 48 49 50 53 54 55 57 59 61 62 63 64 65 69 70 72 75 76 77 78 79 81 82 84 85 86 87 89 90 92 93 94 97 98 100 101 102 104 107 108 111 114 115 119 120 121 124 126 129 130 131 132 135 143 144 146 147 148 149 153 154 156 158 **P**6 **S** Indiana University Health, Indianapolis, IN
Primary Contact: Brian T. Shockney, FACHE, President
CFO: Mike Craig, Chief Financial Officer
CMO: Daniel Handel, M.D., Vice President, Chief Medical Officer
CHR: Steven D Deckard, Vice President Human Resources
Web address: www.iuhealth.org
**Control**: Other not–for–profit (including NFP Corporation) **Service**: General medical and surgical

**Staffed Beds**: 290 **Admissions**: 12439 **Census**: 162 **Outpatient Visits**: 304882 **Births**: 1737 **Total Expense ($000)**: 352408 **Payroll Expense ($000)**: 112642 **Personnel**: 1744

**MEADOWS HOSPITAL** See Bloomington Meadows Hospital

**MONROE HOSPITAL (150164)**, 4011 South Monroe Medical Park Boulevard, Zip 47403–8000; tel. 812/825–1111, (Nonreporting) **A**1 10 **F**3 15 18 20 29 34 35 40 41 44 45 46 47 48 50 56 57 59 64 65 68 70 75 78 79 80 81 85 86 87 91 97 107 108 109 110 111 114 115 119 135 148 149 154 156 **P**5 **S** Prime Healthcare, Ontario, CA
Primary Contact: Nancy Bakewell, Administrator
CFO: Hilary Dolbee, Chief Financial Officer
CMO: Amandeep Singh, Chief Medical Officer
CIO: LaDonna Cagle, HIM Appeals Coordinator III
CHR: Karyn Batdorf, Director of Human Resources
CNO: Nancy Bakewell, Chief Nursing Officer
Web address: www.monroehospital.com
**Control**: Corporation, Investor–owned (for–profit) **Service**: General medical and surgical

**Staffed Beds**: 32 **Admissions**: 1078 **Census**: 10 **Outpatient Visits**: 28892 **Births**: 0 **Total Expense ($000)**: 29199 **Payroll Expense ($000)**: 10232 **Personnel**: 268

## BLUFFTON—Wells County

**BLUFFTON REGIONAL MEDICAL CENTER (150075)**, 303 South Main Street, Zip 46714–2503; tel. 260/824–3210, (Total facility includes 13 beds in nursing home–type unit) (Nonreporting) **A**1 10 19 **F**3 13 15 18 28 29 30 34 35 40 41 45 49 50 57 59 64 70 74 75 76 79 81 85 86 87 89 91 93 94 96 97 107 108 110 111 114 119 128 129 130 132 135 146 147 148 149 150 154 **S** Community Health Systems, Inc., Franklin, TN
Primary Contact: Julie Thompson, Chief Adminstrative Officer and Chief Nursing Officer
COO: Julie Thompson, Chief Operating Officer and Chief Nursing Officer
CFO: Larry W DeBolt, Chief Financial Officer
CMO: Harish Ardeshna, Pulmonologist & Chief Medical Officer
CHR: Patricia Sprinkle, Vice President, Human Resources
CNO: Julie Thompson, Chief Operating Officer and Chief Nursing Officer
Web address: www.blufftonregional.com
**Control**: Corporation, Investor–owned (for–profit) **Service**: General medical and surgical

**Staffed Beds**: 54 **Admissions**: 1088 **Census**: 16 **Outpatient Visits**: 50624 **Births**: 227 **Total Expense ($000)**: 38277 **Payroll Expense ($000)**: 13092 **Personnel**: 193

## BOONVILLE—Warrick County

**ASCENSION ST. VINCENT WARRICK (151325)**, 1116 Millis Avenue, Zip 47601–2204; tel. 812/897–4800, (Nonreporting) **A**1 10 18 **F**3 11 18 28 29 30 34 35 38 40 45 46 48 50 53 54 56 59 64 68 75 77 79 81 87 91 93 97 98 100 101 102 103 107 108 111 115 119 130 133 135 145 148 154 **S** Ascension Healthcare, Saint Louis, MO
Primary Contact: Marty Mattingly, Administrator
CFO: Crystal Heaton, Director of Finance
CNO: Karen Waters, Chief Nursing Officer
Web address: www.https://healthcare.ascension.org
**Control**: Other not–for–profit (including NFP Corporation) **Service**: General medical and surgical

**Staffed Beds**: 35 **Admissions**: 502 **Census**: 17 **Outpatient Visits**: 25217 **Births**: 0 **Total Expense ($000)**: 17317 **Payroll Expense ($000)**: 5060 **Personnel**: 93

**ST. VINCENT WARRICK** See Ascension St. Vincent Warrick

## BRAZIL—Clay County

**ASCENSION ST. VINCENT CLAY HOSPITAL (151309)**, 1206 East National Avenue, Zip 47834–2797, Mailing Address: 1206 East National Ave, Zip 47834–0489; tel. 812/442–2500, (Nonreporting) **A**1 10 18 **F**3 12 15 18 29 30 34 35 40 45 50 57 59 65 68 75 77 79 81 82 85 86 87 107 108 110 111 115 119 128 130 132 133 135 146 148 154 **S** Ascension Healthcare, Saint Louis, MO
Primary Contact: Jerry Laue, Administrator
CFO: Wayne Knight, Director Finance
CMO: Stephen Tharp, Regional Chief Medical Officer
CHR: Lainie Collins, Human Resources Partner
CNO: Paulette Sue Gaskill, Executive Director of Nursing
Web address: www.stvincent.org
**Control**: Church operated, Nongovernment, not–for–profit **Service**: General medical and surgical

**Staffed Beds**: 25 **Admissions**: 151 **Census**: 3 **Outpatient Visits**: 42266 **Total Expense ($000)**: 17373 **Payroll Expense ($000)**: 3649 **Personnel**: 62

**ST. VINCENT CLAY HOSPITAL** See Ascension St. Vincent Clay Hospital

IN

*Many Facility Codes have changed. Please refer to the AHA Guide Code Chart.* © 2021 AHA Guide

## BREMEN—Marshall County

★ **COMMUNITY HOSPITAL OF BREMEN (151300)**, 1020 High Road, Zip 46506–1093, Mailing Address: P.O. Box 8, Zip 46506–0008; tel. 574/546–2211, (Nonreporting) **A**10 18 **F**3 11 13 15 29 34 35 40 45 50 57 59 64 69 75 76 77 79 81 82 85 93 107 110 111 115 119 129 130 132 133 135 146 149 **S** Beacon Health System, South Bend, IN
Primary Contact: David Bailey, FACHE, Chief Executive Officer
CFO: Amy Lashbrook, Chief Financial Officer
CMO: Lindy Sergeant, Medical Staff President
CHR: Patricia Board, Vice President Human Resources
CNO: Sue Bettcher, R.N., Vice President of Nursing Services
Web address: www.bremenhospital.com
**Control**: Other not–for–profit (including NFP Corporation) **Service**: General medical and surgical

**Staffed Beds:** 21 **Admissions:** 341 **Census:** 5 **Outpatient Visits:** 47358
**Births:** 96 **Total Expense ($000):** 20045 **Payroll Expense ($000):** 8375
**Personnel:** 129

☐ **DOCTORS NEUROPSYCHIATRIC HOSPITAL AND RESEARCH INSTITUTE (154058)**, 417 South Whitlock Street, Zip 46506–1626; tel. 574/546–0330, (Nonreporting) **A**1 10 **F**3 98 110 114 116 130 154 **S** NeuroPsychiatric Hospitals, Mishawaka, IN
Primary Contact: Christy Gilbert, Interim Chief Executive Officer
**Control**: Individual, Investor–owned (for–profit) **Service**: Psychiatric

**Staffed Beds:** 37 **Admissions:** 815 **Census:** 34 **Outpatient Visits:** 0
**Births:** 0 **Total Expense ($000):** 8722 **Payroll Expense ($000):** 4644

## CARMEL—Hamilton County

⊞ **ASCENSION ST. VINCENT CARMEL HOSPITAL (150157)**, 13500 North Meridian Street, Zip 46032–1456; tel. 317/582–7000, (Nonreporting) **A**1 5 10 **F**3 12 13 15 29 30 34 35 36 37 40 44 45 49 50 54 57 59 61 64 68 69 70 72 75 76 78 79 80 81 85 87 92 93 107 108 110 111 119 126 130 135 146 147 148 149 **S** Ascension Healthcare, Saint Louis, MO
Primary Contact: Julie Manas, Regional President
COO: Daniel LaReau, Executive Director, Operations and Information
CFO: Robert A. Bates, Chief Financial Officer
CMO: Steven Priddy, M.D., VP of Physician Affairs/Chief Medical Officer
CIO: Daniel LaReau, Executive Director, Operations and Information
CHR: Ross Brodhead, Senior Director, Human Resources
CNO: Ted Eads, Interim Chief Nursing Officer
Web address: www.https://www.stvincent.org
**Control**: Other not–for–profit (including NFP Corporation) **Service**: General medical and surgical

**Staffed Beds:** 121 **Admissions:** 5113 **Census:** 49 **Outpatient Visits:** 87335
**Births:** 1609 **Total Expense ($000):** 120570 **Payroll Expense ($000):** 31470 **Personnel:** 332

**CLARIAN NORTH MEDICAL CENTER** See Indiana University Health North Hospital

**FRANCISCAN HEALTH - CARMEL** See Franciscan Health Carmel

○ **FRANCISCAN HEALTH CARMEL (150182)**, 12188B North Meridian Street, Zip 46032–4840; tel. 317/705–4500, (Nonreporting) **A**10 11 **S** Franciscan Health, Mishawaka, IN
Primary Contact: Stephen J. Wheatley, Director of Operations
CFO: Keith A. Lauter, Chief Financial Officer
CMO: Christopher Doehring, M.D., Vice President of Medical Affairs
CIO: Rebecca Merkel, Privacy Officer
CHR: Corey Baute, Vice President of Human Resource
CNO: Agnes Therady, MSN, FACHE, Vice President and Chief Nursing Officer
Web address: www.franciscanalliance.org/hospitals/carmel/Pages/default.aspx
**Control**: Other not–for–profit (including NFP Corporation) **Service**: General medical and surgical

**Staffed Beds:** 6

**INDIANA SPINE HOSPITAL**, 13219 North Meridian Street, Zip 46032–5480; tel. 317/795–2000, (Nonreporting) **A**12
Primary Contact: Barbara Bridges, R.N., Chief Nursing Officer
Web address: www.https://indianaspinehospital.com
**Control**: Corporation, Investor–owned (for–profit) **Service**: General medical and surgical

**Staffed Beds:** 20

⊞ **INDIANA UNIVERSITY HEALTH NORTH HOSPITAL (150161)**, 11700 North Meridian Avenue, Zip 46032–4656; tel. 317/688–2000, (Nonreporting) **A**1 3 5 10 **F**3 12 13 15 18 19 20 22 26 29 30 31 34 35 36 37 40 45 47 48 50 55 57 59 60 64 68 70 72 74 75 76 77 78 79 81 84 85 86 87 88 89 91 92 93 107 108 110 111 115 119 126 129 130 132 135 146 147 148 154 156 157 **S** Indiana University Health, Indianapolis, IN
Primary Contact: Alicia Schulhof, President and Chief Executive Officer
COO: Randall C. Yust, Chief Operating Officer and Chief Financial Officer
CFO: Randall C. Yust, Chief Operating Officer and Chief Financial Officer
CMO: Paul Calkins, M.D., Chief Medical Officer
CIO: Steve Bodenham, Senior Manager Clinical Engineering
CHR: Steven E Kile, Vice President Human Resources
Web address: www.iuhealth.org/north
**Control**: Other not–for–profit (including NFP Corporation) **Service**: General medical and surgical

**Staffed Beds:** 161 **Admissions:** 7472 **Census:** 86 **Outpatient Visits:** 141918 **Births:** 2335 **Total Expense ($000):** 211756 **Payroll Expense ($000):** 60108 **Personnel:** 901

**ST. VINCENT CARMEL HOSPITAL** See Ascension St. Vincent Carmel Hospital

## CLINTON—Vermillion County

○ **UNION HOSPITAL CLINTON (151326)**, 801 South Main Street, Zip 47842–2261; tel. 765/832–1234, (Nonreporting) **A**10 11 18 **F**3 11 15 18 29 30 34 35 40 45 50 57 59 64 65 68 70 75 81 85 86 87 91 93 97 107 108 110 115 119 130 132 133 146 156 157
Primary Contact: Stephanie Laws, Vice President, Administrator
CFO: Wayne Hutson, Chief Financial Officer
CMO: John Albrecht, Chief of Staff
CIO: Jack Hill, Vice President and Chief Operating Officer
Web address: www.myunionhospital.org/unionhospital/union-hospital-clinton
**Control**: Other not–for–profit (including NFP Corporation) **Service**: General medical and surgical

**Staffed Beds:** 21 **Admissions:** 619 **Census:** 5 **Outpatient Visits:** 41022
**Births:** 0 **Total Expense ($000):** 21299 **Payroll Expense ($000):** 6639
**Personnel:** 101

**WEST CENTRAL COMMUNITY HOSPITAL** See Union Hospital Clinton

## COLUMBIA CITY—Whitley County

⊞ **PARKVIEW WHITLEY HOSPITAL (150101)**, 1260 East State Road 205, Zip 46725–9492; tel. 260/248–9000, (Nonreporting) **A**1 10 **F**3 7 13 15 28 29 30 34 35 38 40 42 45 50 54 59 64 70 75 76 79 81 82 85 87 89 91 93 96 102 107 108 110 111 115 119 129 132 143 146 148 154 156 **P**6 **S** Parkview Health, Fort Wayne, IN
Primary Contact: Scott F. Gabriel, President
COO: Scott F Gabriel, President
CFO: Lisa Peppler, Financial Manager
CMO: Jeffrey Brookes, M.D., Medical Director
Web address: www.parkview.com
**Control**: Other not–for–profit (including NFP Corporation) **Service**: General medical and surgical

**Staffed Beds:** 30 **Admissions:** 1582 **Census:** 13 **Outpatient Visits:** 70014
**Births:** 405 **Total Expense ($000):** 74580 **Payroll Expense ($000):** 19496
**Personnel:** 281

**WHITLEY MEMORIAL HOSPITAL** See Parkview Whitley Hospital

## COLUMBUS—Bartholomew County

**BARTHOLOMEW COUNTY HOSPITAL** See Columbus Regional Hospital

★ ○ **COLUMBUS REGIONAL HOSPITAL (150112)**, 2400 East 17th Street, Zip 47201–5360; tel. 812/379–4441, (Nonreporting) **A**2 10 11 19 **F**3 7 11 12 13 15 18 20 22 24 26 28 29 30 31 34 35 38 39 40 45 46 47 49 50 51 53 58 59 70 73 74 75 76 77 78 79 81 85 86 87 89 90 93 97 98 100 101 102 107 108 110 111 114 115 117 118 119 120 121 123 124 126 129 130 131 132 135 146 147 148 149 154 156 **P**6
Primary Contact: Jim Bickel, President and Chief Executive Officer
CFO: Marlene Weatherwax, Vice President and Chief Financial Officer
CMO: Thomas Sonderman, M.D., Vice President and Chief Medical Officer
CIO: Steve Baker, Vice President and Chief Technology and Information Officer
CHR: Julie McGregor, Vice President, Human Resources and Organization Development
Web address: www.crh.org
**Control**: County, Government, Nonfederal **Service**: General medical and surgical

**Staffed Beds:** 235 **Admissions:** 8855 **Census:** 89 **Outpatient Visits:** 252407 **Births:** 1212 **Total Expense ($000):** 283092 **Payroll Expense ($000):** 86431 **Personnel:** 1613

---

| Hospital, Medicare Provider Number, Address, Telephone, Approval, Facility, and Physician Codes, Health Care System | | |
|---|---|---|
| ★ American Hospital Association (AHA) membership | ○ Healthcare Facilities Accreditation Program | ⇑ Center for Improvement in Healthcare Quality Accreditation |
| ☐ The Joint Commission accreditation | ◇ DNV Healthcare Inc. accreditation | △ Commission on Accreditation of Rehabilitation Facilities (CARF) accreditation |

**IN**

## CORYDON—Harrison County

★ ○ **HARRISON COUNTY HOSPITAL (151331)**, 1141 Hospital Drive N W,
Zip 47112–1774; tel. 812/738–4251, (Nonreporting) **A**10 11 18 **F**3 7 10 13 15
18 28 29 34 35 40 45 46 49 56 57 59 64 70 76 77 79 81 82 85 87 90 93 97
107 108 110 111 112 115 119 127 129 131 133 144 146 154 156
Primary Contact: Steven L. Taylor, Chief Executive Officer
CFO: Jeff Davis, Chief Financial Officer
CIO: Chuck Wiley, Manager Information Systems
CHR: Loren Haverstock, Manager Human Resources
CNO: Ruth Donahue, R.N., Chief Nursing Officer
Web address: www.hchin.org
**Control**: County, Government, Nonfederal **Service**: General medical and surgical

**Staffed Beds:** 25 **Admissions:** 1442 **Census:** 13 **Outpatient Visits:** 53283
**Births:** 399 **Total Expense ($000):** 59483 **Payroll Expense ($000):** 27711
**Personnel:** 493

## CRAWFORDSVILLE—Montgomery County

○ **FRANCISCAN HEALTH CRAWFORDSVILLE (150022)**, 1710 Lafayette Road,
Zip 47933–1099; tel. 765/362–2800, (Nonreporting) **A**10 11 **S** Franciscan
Health, Mishawaka, IN
Primary Contact: Terrence Klein, Ph.D., Vice President and Chief Operating Officer
COO: Terrence Klein, Ph.D., Vice President and Chief Operating Officer
CFO: Keith A. Lauter, Vice President Finance
Web address: www.stclaremedical.org
**Control**: Other not-for-profit (including NFP Corporation) **Service**: General
medical and surgical

**Staffed Beds:** 40

**FRANCISCAN ST. ELIZABETH HEALTH - CRAWFORDSVILLE** See Franciscan
Health Crawfordsville

## CROWN POINT—Lake County

○ **FRANCISCAN HEALTH CROWN POINT (150126)**, 1201 South Main Street,
Zip 46307–8483; tel. 219/738–2100, (Nonreporting) **A**2 10 11 **S** Franciscan
Health, Mishawaka, IN
Primary Contact: Daniel McCormick, M.D., President and Chief Executive Officer
CFO: Marc Golan, Chief Financial Officer
CIO: Tim Loosemore, Director
CNO: Carol E Schuster, R.N., Chief Nursing Officer and Vice President Patient Care
Services
Web address: www.franciscanalliance.org
**Control**: Church operated, Nongovernment, not-for-profit **Service**: General
medical and surgical

**Staffed Beds:** 254

**FRANCISCAN ST. ANTHONY HEALTH - CROWN POINT** See Franciscan Health
Crown Point

☐ **NEUROBEHAVIORAL HOSPITAL OF NW INDIANA (154065)**, 9330 Broadway,
Zip 46307–9830; tel. 219/648–2400, (Nonreporting) **A**1 **S** NeuroPsychiatric
Hospitals, Mishawaka, IN
Primary Contact: Bob Kedelis, Chief Executive Officer
Web address: www.https://www.neuropsychiatrichospitals.net
**Control**: Corporation, Investor-owned (for-profit) **Service**: Psychiatric

**Staffed Beds:** 70

○ **PINNACLE HOSPITAL (150166)**, 9301 Connecticut Drive, Zip 46307–7486;
tel. 219/756–2100, (Nonreporting) **A**10 11
Primary Contact: Haroon Naz, Chief Executive Officer
Web address: www.pinnaclehealthcare.net
**Control**: Partnership, Investor-owned (for-profit) **Service**: General medical and
surgical

**Staffed Beds:** 18

⊞ **VIBRA HOSPITAL OF NORTHWESTERN INDIANA (152028)**, 9509 Georgia
Street, Zip 46307–6518; tel. 219/472–2200, (Nonreporting) **A**1 10 **S** Vibra
Healthcare, Mechanicsburg, PA
Primary Contact: Craig L. Johnson, FACHE, Chief Executive Officer
CFO: Douglas Morris, Chief Financial Officer
CMO: Raja Devanathan, M.D., Chief Medical Officer
CNO: Robert Beard, Chief Clinical Officer
Web address: www.vhnwindiana.com/
**Control**: Corporation, Investor-owned (for-profit) **Service**: Acute long-term care
hospital

**Staffed Beds:** 40

## DANVILLE—Hendricks County

**HENDRICKS COMM HOSPITAL** See Hendricks Regional Health

★ ○ **HENDRICKS REGIONAL HEALTH (150005)**, 1000 East Main
Street, Zip 46122–1948, Mailing Address: P.O. Box 409, Zip 46122–0409;
tel. 317/745–4451, (Includes HENDRICKS REGIONAL HEALTH BROWNSBURG
HOSPITAL, Mailing address: 5492 N Ronald Reagan Pkwy, Brownsburg, Indiana,
Zip 46112–5618; tel. 317/456–9051; Kevin Speer, President and Chief Executive
Officer), (Nonreporting) **A**2 5 10 11 **F**3 8 9 11 13 15 17 18 20 22 28 29 30 31
32 34 35 38 40 41 42 43 44 45 46 47 48 50 53 54 55 56 57 58 59 60 64 65
68 70 73 74 75 76 77 78 79 81 82 83 84 85 86 87 89 90 92 93 94 96 97 107
108 110 111 115 117 118 119 120 121 127 128 129 130 131 132 135 144
145 146 147 148 149 150 154 156 **P**6
Primary Contact: Kevin Speer, President and Chief Executive Officer
CFO: Dennis Ressler, Vice President, Finance and Chief Financial Officer
CMO: Michelle Fenoughty, M.D., Chief Medical Officer, Vice President of Medical
Affairs
CIO: Todd Davis, Executive Director of Information Systems
CHR: Nancy Foster, Vice President, Human Resources
Web address: www.https://www.hendricks.org
**Control**: County, Government, Nonfederal **Service**: General medical and surgical

**Staffed Beds:** 133 **Admissions:** 6074 **Census:** 54 **Outpatient
Visits:** 317295 **Births:** 1333 **Total Expense ($000):** 371808 **Payroll
Expense ($000):** 153595 **Personnel:** 1864

## DECATUR—Adams County

**ADAMS COUNTY MEMORIAL HOSPITAL** See Adams Memorial Hospital

★ ○ **ADAMS MEMORIAL HOSPITAL (151330)**, 1100 Mercer Avenue,
Zip 46733–2303, Mailing Address: P.O. Box 151, Zip 46733–0151;
tel. 260/724–2145, (Total facility includes 195 beds in nursing home–type unit)
(Nonreporting) **A**10 11 18 **F**3 5 7 10 13 15 28 29 30 34 35 38 40 47 50 53 56
57 59 64 65 66 67 70 74 75 76 77 79 81 82 85 86 87 93 97 101 102 104
105 107 108 110 111 115 119 125 127 128 129 130 131 132 133 135 143
144 146 147 148 149 152 153 156
Primary Contact: Scott Smith, M.D., Chief Executive Officer and Chief Medical
Officer
CFO: Dane Wheeler, Chief Financial Officer
CMO: Scott Smith, M.D., Chief Medical Officer
CIO: Nick Nelson, Director Support Services
CHR: Alison Kukelhan, Manager Human Resources
CNO: Theresa Bradtmiller DNP, RN, MSN, R.N., Chief Nursing Officer
Web address: www.adamshospital.com
**Control**: County, Government, Nonfederal **Service**: General medical and surgical

**Staffed Beds:** 224 **Admissions:** 1412 **Census:** 154 **Outpatient
Visits:** 176972 **Births:** 202 **Total Expense ($000):** 88319 **Payroll Expense
($000):** 41480 **Personnel:** 706

## DYER—Lake County

○ △ **FRANCISCAN HEALTH DYER (150090)**, 24 Joliet Street,
Zip 46311–1799; tel. 219/865–2141, (Nonreporting) **A**3 7 10 11 **S** Franciscan
Health, Mishawaka, IN
Primary Contact: Patrick J. Maloney, Chief Executive Officer
**Control**: Church operated, Nongovernment, not-for-profit **Service**: General
medical and surgical

**Staffed Beds:** 341

**FRANCISCAN ST. MARGARET HEALTH - DYER** See Franciscan Health Dyer

## EAST CHICAGO—Lake County

⊞ **REGENCY HOSPITAL OF NORTHWEST INDIANA (152024)**, 4321 Fir Street,
4th Floor, Zip 46312–3049; tel. 219/392–7799, (Includes REGENCY HOSPITAL
OF PORTER COUNTY, Mailing address: 3630 Willow Creek Road, Portage,
Indiana, Zip 46368; tel. 219/364–3800), (Nonreporting) **A**1 10 **S** Select Medical
Corporation, Mechanicsburg, PA
Primary Contact: Eleyce Winn, Chief Executive Officer
Web address: www.regencyhospital.com/company/locations/indiana-northwest-
indiana.aspx
**Control**: Corporation, Investor-owned (for-profit) **Service**: Acute long-term care
hospital

**Staffed Beds:** 61

**ST CATHERINE HOSP OF CHICAGO** See St. Catherine Hospital

*Many Facility Codes have changed. Please refer to the AHA Guide Code Chart.*
© 2021 AHA Guide

□ △ **ST. CATHERINE HOSPITAL (150008)**, 4321 Fir Street, Zip 46312–3097; tel. 219/392–1700, (Nonreporting) **A**1 2 7 10 **S** Community Healthcare System, Hammond, IN
Primary Contact: Leo Correa, Chief Executive Officer and Administrator
COO: Craig Bolda, Chief Operating Officer
CMO: John Griep, M.D., Chief Medical Director
CIO: Gary Weiner, Chief Information Officer
CNO: Paula C Swenson, R.N., Vice President and Chief Nursing Officer
Web address: www.stcatherinehospital.org
**Control**: Other not–for–profit (including NFP Corporation) **Service**: General medical and surgical

**Staffed Beds**: 220

## ELKHART—Elkhart County

**ELKHART GENERAL HEALTHCARE SYSTEM** See Elkhart General Hospital

⊞ △ **ELKHART GENERAL HOSPITAL (150018)**, 600 East Boulevard, Zip 46514–2499, Mailing Address: P.O. Box 1329, Zip 46515–1329; tel. 574/294–2621, (Nonreporting) **A**1 2 7 10 **F**3 11 12 13 15 17 18 20 22 24 26 28 29 30 31 34 35 40 43 45 46 48 49 50 57 59 64 65 68 70 72 74 75 76 77 78 79 81 82 84 85 86 87 89 90 91 92 93 98 100 102 104 107 108 110 111 114 115 118 119 120 121 123 126 129 130 131 132 134 135 145 146 147 148 155 156 **P**1 4 6 8 **S** Beacon Health System, South Bend, IN
Primary Contact: Carl W. Risk II, President
CFO: Jeff Costello, Chief Financial Officer
CMO: Gene Grove, M.D., Chief of Staff
CIO: Mark Warlick, Chief Information Officer
CHR: Steven M Eller, Vice President Human Resources
Web address: www.egh.org
**Control**: Other not–for–profit (including NFP Corporation) **Service**: General medical and surgical

**Staffed Beds**: 247 **Admissions**: 10659 **Census**: 130 **Outpatient Visits**: 142865 **Births**: 1294 **Total Expense ($000)**: 265576 **Payroll Expense ($000)**: 88107 **Personnel**: 1516

## ELWOOD—Madison County

⊞ **ASCENSION ST. VINCENT MERCY (151308)**, 1331 South 'A' Street, Zip 46036–1942; tel. 765/552–4600, (Nonreporting) **A**1 2 10 18 **F**3 8 15 28 29 30 31 34 35 40 44 45 50 57 59 64 68 74 75 77 78 79 81 85 89 93 107 108 110 111 115 119 128 129 130 132 133 135 146 148 149 150 154 **S** Ascension Healthcare, Saint Louis, MO
Primary Contact: Ann C. Yates, R.N., MSN, Administrator and Chief Nursing Officer
CFO: John Arthur, Chief Financial Officer
CMO: Gary Brazel, M.D., Chief Medical Officer
CHR: Ross Brodhead, Manager Human Resources
CNO: Ann C Yates, R.N., MSN, Chief Nursing Officer
Web address: www.stvincent.org
**Control**: Other not–for–profit (including NFP Corporation) **Service**: General medical and surgical

**Staffed Beds**: 15 **Admissions**: 237 **Census**: 2 **Outpatient Visits**: 33430 **Births**: 0 **Total Expense ($000)**: 22840 **Payroll Expense ($000)**: 4777 **Personnel**: 58

**ST. VINCENT MERCY HOSPITAL** See Ascension St. Vincent Mercy

## EVANSVILLE—Vanderburgh County

⊞ △ **ASCENSION ST. VINCENT EVANSVILLE (150100)**, 3700 Washington Avenue, Zip 47714–0541; tel. 812/485–4000, (Nonreporting) **A**1 2 3 5 7 10 **F**3 7 8 11 12 13 15 17 18 19 20 22 24 26 28 29 30 31 32 34 35 36 37 39 40 41 43 45 46 47 48 49 50 51 53 54 55 56 57 58 59 60 61 64 65 68 70 71 72 74 75 76 77 78 79 81 82 83 84 85 86 87 88 89 90 91 92 93 96 98 100 101 102 107 108 110 111 114 115 116 117 118 119 126 129 130 131 132 134 135 143 144 146 147 148 149 150 154 156 157 **S** Ascension Healthcare, Saint Louis, MO
Primary Contact: Daniel A. Parod, President
COO: Gwynn Perlich, Chief Operating Officer
CFO: Craig Polkow, Vice President, Finance
CMO: Vernon Maas, M.D., Vice President, Medical Affairs
CIO: Jose Diaz, Director Information Systems
CNO: Darcy Ellison, R.N., MSN, Senior Vice President, Chief Nursing Officer and Inpatient Flow
Web address: www.stmarys.org
**Control**: Other not–for–profit (including NFP Corporation) **Service**: General medical and surgical

**Staffed Beds**: 432 **Admissions**: 15090 **Census**: 196 **Outpatient Visits**: 408106 **Births**: 1338 **Total Expense ($000)**: 478321 **Payroll Expense ($000)**: 100798 **Personnel**: 1791

**DEACONESS HOSPITAL** See Deaconess Midtown Hospital

★ ○ **DEACONESS MIDTOWN HOSPITAL (150082)**, 600 Mary Street, Zip 47710–1658; tel. 812/450–5000, (Includes DEACONESS CROSS POINTE CENTER, Mailing address: 7200 East Indiana Street, Evansville, Indiana, Zip 47715; tel. 812/476–7200; Cheryl Rietman, Chief Administrative Officer; DEACONESS GATEWAY HOSPITAL, Mailing address: 4007 Gateway Boulevard, Newburgh, Indiana, Zip 47630–8947; tel. 812/842–2000; Rebecca Malotte, Executive Director and Chief Nursing Officer), (Nonreporting) **A**2 3 5 10 11 **F**3 4 5 9 11 12 15 17 18 19 20 22 24 26 28 29 30 31 32 34 35 36 37 38 39 40 43 44 45 46 47 48 49 50 51 53 54 56 57 59 60 61 64 65 66 68 70 71 74 75 77 78 79 81 82 85 86 87 88 89 92 93 94 96 97 98 99 100 101 102 104 105 107 108 110 111 114 115 116 117 118 119 120 121 123 124 126 129 130 132 134 135 143 145 146 148 149 150 153 154 156 **P**1 6 8 **S** Deaconess Health System, Evansville, IN
Primary Contact: Shawn W. McCoy, Chief Executive Officer
CFO: Cheryl A Wathen, Interim Chief Financial Officer
CHR: Larry Pile, Director Human Resources
Web address: www.deaconess.com
**Control**: Other not–for–profit (including NFP Corporation) **Service**: General medical and surgical

**Staffed Beds**: 555 **Admissions**: 33132 **Census**: 413 **Outpatient Visits**: 586065 **Births**: 0 **Total Expense ($000)**: 887859 **Payroll Expense ($000)**: 293976 **Personnel**: 3955

**EVANSVILLE PSYCH CHILDREN CNTR** See Evansville Psychiatric Children Center

**EVANSVILLE PSYCHIATRIC CHILDREN CENTER (15J200)**, 3300 East Morgan Avenue, Zip 47715–2232; tel. 812/477–6436, (Nonreporting) **A**10 **F**29 32 35 38 98 99 101 106 130 **P**6
Primary Contact: Carlene Oliver, Superintendent
COO: Melinda Kendle, Manager Business Office
CMO: Shannon Jones, M.D., Medical Director and Attending Psychiatrist
CIO: David Wirtz, Supervisor Information Technology
CHR: Jennifer Sontz, Director Human Resources
CNO: Elizabeth Angermeier, Director of Nursing
Web address: www.ih.gov
**Control**: State, Government, Nonfederal **Service**: Children's hospital psychiatric

**Staffed Beds**: 20 **Admissions**: 27 **Census**: 12 **Outpatient Visits**: 0 **Births**: 0 **Total Expense ($000)**: 4346 **Payroll Expense ($000)**: 2381

□ **EVANSVILLE STATE HOSPITAL (154056)**, 3400 Lincoln Avenue, Zip 47714–0146; tel. 812/469–6800, (Nonreporting) **A**1 3 5 10
Primary Contact: Gene Schadler, Superintendent
CFO: Melinda Kendle, Director Fiscal Management
CMO: Melba Briones, M.D., Medical Director
CIO: David Wirtz, Senior LAN Administrator
CHR: Jennifer Sontz, Director Human Resources
**Control**: State, Government, Nonfederal **Service**: Psychiatric

**Staffed Beds**: 168

**IN**

---

⊞ **SELECT SPECIALTY HOSPITAL-EVANSVILLE (152014)**, 400 SE 4th Street, Zip 47713–1206; tel. 812/421–2500, (Nonreporting) **A**1 10 **S** Select Medical Corporation, Mechanicsburg, PA
Primary Contact: Kristy C. Bruner, Chief Executive Officer
Web address: www.selectspecialtyhospitals.com/company/locations/evansville.aspx
**Control:** Corporation, Investor–owned (for–profit) **Service:** Acute long–term care hospital

**Staffed Beds:** 51

**ST. VINCENT EVANSVILLE** See Ascension St. Vincent Evansville

### FISHERS—Hamilton County

⊞ **ASCENSION ST. VINCENT FISHERS (150181)**, 13861 Olio Road, Zip 46037–3487; tel. 317/415–9000, (Nonreporting) **A**1 10 **F3** 13 15 29 30 31 34 35 37 39 40 41 45 46 50 53 57 59 60 64 75 76 77 78 79 81 82 87 91 93 97 107 110 111 119 129 130 131 132 146 148 149 157 **S** Ascension Healthcare, Saint Louis, MO
Primary Contact: Julie Manas, Regional President
CMO: Craig Wilson, Chief Medical Officer
Web address: www.stvincent.org
**Control:** Other not–for–profit (including NFP Corporation) **Service:** General medical and surgical

**Staffed Beds:** 46 **Admissions:** 1338 **Census:** 9 **Outpatient Visits:** 60601
**Births:** 545 **Total Expense ($000):** 51254 **Payroll Expense ($000):** 12379
**Personnel:** 118

**IU HEALTH SAXONY HOSPITAL** See Indiana University Health Saxony Hospital

**ST. VINCENT FISHERS HOSPITAL** See Ascension St. Vincent Fishers

### FORT WAYNE—Allen County

⊞ **DUPONT HOSPITAL (150150)**, 2520 East Dupont Road, Zip 46825–1675; tel. 260/416–3000, (Nonreporting) **A**1 10 **F3** 8 13 15 18 29 30 34 35 39 40 45 50 56 57 58 59 60 64 65 68 70 72 74 75 76 77 78 79 81 82 83 84 85 86 87 88 107 110 111 114 115 118 119 126 129 130 131 132 135 141 146 147 148 154 157 **P5 S** Community Health Systems, Inc., Franklin, TN
Primary Contact: Lorenzo Suter, Chief Executive Officer
COO: Darrick Hoopingarner, Chief Operating Officer
CFO: Brian Schneider, Chief Financial Officer
CIO: Janis Gray, Chief Information Officer
CNO: Kimberly Fulkerson, Chief Nursing Officer
Web address: www.thedupontdifference.com
**Control:** Partnership, Investor–owned (for–profit) **Service:** General medical and surgical

**Staffed Beds:** 131 **Admissions:** 4818 **Census:** 52 **Outpatient Visits:** 73253
**Births:** 2340 **Total Expense ($000):** 140675 **Payroll Expense ($000):** 38117 **Personnel:** 578

**LUTHERAN HOSP OF INDIANA** See Lutheran Hospital of Indiana

⊞ **LUTHERAN HOSPITAL OF INDIANA (150017)**, 7950 West Jefferson Boulevard, Zip 46804–4140; tel. 260/435–7001, (Nonreporting) **A**1 2 3 5 10 **S** Community Health Systems, Inc., Franklin, TN
Primary Contact: Brady Dubois, Chief Executive Officer
CFO: Cully Chapman, Chief Financial Officer
CIO: Keith A. Neuman, Chief Information Officer
CHR: Maria Kurtz, Director Human Resources
CNO: Angela Logan, Chief Nursing Officer
Web address: www.lutheranhospital.com
**Control:** Corporation, Investor–owned (for–profit) **Service:** General medical and surgical

**Staffed Beds:** 407

**ORTHOPAEDIC HOSPITAL AT PARKVIEW NORTH** See Parkview Ortho Hospital

**ORTHOPAEDIC HOSPITAL OF LUTHERAN HEALTH** See Orthopaedic Hospital of Lutheran Health Network

⊞ **ORTHOPAEDIC HOSPITAL OF LUTHERAN HEALTH NETWORK (150168)**, 7952 West Jefferson Boulevard, Zip 46804–4140; tel. 260/435–2999, (Nonreporting) **A**1 10 **S** Community Health Systems, Inc., Franklin, TN
Primary Contact: Lorie Ailor, Chief Executive Officer, Chief Administrative Officer, Network Vice President Orthopedics and Sports
CFO: Amy Hochstetler, Chief Financial Officer
CMO: Kevin Rahn, President Medical Staff
CIO: Keith A. Neuman, Chief Information Officer
CHR: Maria Kurtz, Director Human Resources
CNO: Marci Hamilton, Chief Nursing Officer
Web address: www.theorthohospital.com
**Control:** Corporation, Investor–owned (for–profit) **Service:** Orthopedic

**Staffed Beds:** 43

⊞ **PARKVIEW ORTHO HOSPITAL (150167)**, 11130 Parkview Circle Drive, Zip 46845–1735; tel. 260/672–5000, (Nonreporting) **A**1 10 **F3** 8 29 30 34 50 58 65 68 75 79 81 82 84 85 86 87 90 91 93 94 96 107 111 119 131 135 141 149 **S** Parkview Health, Fort Wayne, IN
Primary Contact: Julie Fleck, Chief Operating Officer
Web address: www.parkview.com
**Control:** Corporation, Investor–owned (for–profit) **Service:** Orthopedic

**Staffed Beds:** 37 **Admissions:** 2687 **Census:** 12 **Outpatient Visits:** 9100
**Births:** 0 **Total Expense ($000):** 75023 **Payroll Expense ($000):** 13614
**Personnel:** 174

**PARKVIEW HOSPITAL** See Parkview Hospital Randallia

**PARKVIEW NORTH HOSPITAL** See Parkview Regional Medical Center

⊞ **PARKVIEW REGIONAL MEDICAL CENTER (150021)**, 11109 Parkview Plaza Drive, Zip 46845–1701; tel. 260/266–1000, (Includes PARKVIEW HOSPITAL RANDALLIA, Mailing address: 2200 Randallia Drive, Fort Wayne, Indiana, Zip 46805–4699; tel. 260/373–4000; Marlon Wardlow, Chief Operating Officer; PARKVIEW REGIONAL MEDICAL CENTER, Mailing address: 11109 Parkview Plaza Drive, Fort Wayne, Indiana, Zip 46845; tel. 260/266–1000), (Nonreporting) **A**1 2 3 10 **F3** 5 7 11 12 13 14 15 17 18 19 20 22 24 26 28 29 30 31 32 34 35 39 40 41 43 44 45 46 47 48 49 50 51 53 54 55 56 57 58 59 60 61 62 63 64 65 67 68 70 72 74 75 76 78 79 80 81 82 83 84 85 86 87 88 89 90 91 92 93 95 96 98 99 100 101 102 103 104 105 107 108 109 111 114 115 118 119 120 121 123 124 126 129 130 131 132 135 141 146 147 148 149 152 153 154 155 156 **P6 S** Parkview Health, Fort Wayne, IN
Primary Contact: Ben Miles, President
COO: John Bowen, Chief Operating Officer
CNO: Erin L LaCross, R.N., Chief Nursing Officer
Web address: www.parkview.com
**Control:** Other not–for–profit (including NFP Corporation) **Service:** General medical and surgical

**Staffed Beds:** 738 **Admissions:** 39884 **Census:** 547 **Outpatient Visits:** 628334 **Births:** 3707 **Total Expense ($000):** 1190197 **Payroll Expense ($000):** 298453 **Personnel:** 4330

⊞ △ **REHABILITATION HOSPITAL OF FORT WAYNE (153030)**, 7970 West Jefferson Boulevard, Zip 46804–4140; tel. 260/435–6100, (Nonreporting) **A**1 7 10 **F**29 30 60 68 69 90 94 96 130 132 146 148 **S** Community Health Systems, Inc., Franklin, TN
Primary Contact: Ryan Cassedy, Chief Administrative Officer
COO: Shelley Boxell, R.N., Interim Chief Operating Officer
CFO: Edward Romero, Chief Financial Officer
CMO: Preeti Dembla, Chief Medical Officer and Medical Director
CIO: Janis Gray, Chief Information Officer
CHR: Deborah Giardina, Director Human Resources and Medical Staff Services
CNO: Shelley Boxell, R.N., Chief Nursing Officer
Web address: www.rehabhospital.com
**Control:** Corporation, Investor–owned (for–profit) **Service:** Rehabilitation

**Staffed Beds:** 36 **Admissions:** 740 **Census:** 26 **Births:** 0

**ST JOSEPH HEALTH SYSTEM** See St. Joseph Hospital

⊞ **ST. JOSEPH HOSPITAL (150047)**, 700 Broadway, Zip 46802–1493; tel. 260/425–3000, (Nonreporting) **A**1 3 10 **S** Community Health Systems, Inc., Franklin, TN
Primary Contact: Lisa Dolan, Interim Chief Executive Officer
COO: Vince Green, Chief Operating Officer
CHR: Steve Heggen, Administrative Director Human Resources
Web address: www.stjoehospital.com
**Control:** Corporation, Investor–owned (for–profit) **Service:** General medical and surgical

**Staffed Beds:** 162

**VET AFF NORTHERN IN HLTH CARE** See Veterans Affairs Northern Indiana Health Care System

*Many Facility Codes have changed. Please refer to the AHA Guide Code Chart.* © 2021 AHA Guide

IN

⊞ **VETERANS AFFAIRS NORTHERN INDIANA HEALTH CARE SYSTEM**, 2121 Lake Avenue, Zip 46805–5100; tel. 260/426–5431, (Includes VETERANS AFFAIRS NORTHERN INDIANA HEALTH CARE SYSTEM-MARION CAMPUS, Mailing address: 1700 East 38th Street, Marion, Indiana, Zip 46953–4589; tel. 765/674–3321), (Nonreporting) **A**1 **S** Department of Veterans Affairs, Washington, DC
Primary Contact: Michael Hershmann, Medical Center Director
COO: Helen Rhodes, R.N., Associate Director Operations
CFO: Jay H Vandermark, Chief Financial Officer
CMO: Ajay Dhawan, M.D., Chief of Staff
CIO: David Troyer, Chief Information Officer
CHR: Brian Flynn, Chief Human Resources Officer
Web address: www.northernindiana.va.gov/
**Control**: Veterans Affairs, Government, federal **Service**: General medical and surgical

**Staffed Beds**: 217

### FRANKFORT—Clinton County

⊞ **INDIANA UNIVERSITY HEALTH FRANKFORT (151316)**, 1300 South Jackson Street, Zip 46041–3313; tel. 765/656–3000, (Nonreporting) **A**1 10 18 **F**3 11 15 18 28 29 30 34 35 40 45 50 57 59 64 68 75 79 81 85 86 90 93 107 110 111 114 119 129 132 133 135 146 148 149 150 154 **S** Indiana University Health, Indianapolis, IN
Primary Contact: Kelly Braverman, President
CFO: Wayne Knight, Chief Financial Officer
CMO: Stephen Tharp, Medical Director
CHR: Krista Wright, Director Human Resources
Web address: www.stvincent.org
**Control**: Other not–for–profit (including NFP Corporation) **Service**: General medical and surgical

**Staffed Beds**: 25 **Admissions**: 390 **Census**: 4 **Outpatient Visits**: 21379 **Births**: 0 **Total Expense ($000)**: 23024 **Payroll Expense ($000)**: 7202 **Personnel**: 103

### FRANKFORT—Marion County

**INDIANA UNIVERSITY HEALTH METHODIST HOSPITAL** See Indiana University Health University Hospital, Indianapolis

**METHODIST HOSPITAL** See Indiana University Health Methodist Hospital

### FRANKFORT—Clinton County

**ST. VINCENT FRANKFORT HOSPITAL** See Indiana University Health Frankfort

### FRANKLIN—Johnson County

★ ○ **JOHNSON MEMORIAL HOSPITAL (150001)**, 1125 West Jefferson Street, Zip 46131–2140, Mailing Address: P.O. Box 549, Zip 46131–0549; tel. 317/736–3300, (Nonreporting) **A**5 10 11 **F**12 13 15 18 20 28 29 30 31 34 35 36 40 44 45 49 50 53 54 55 57 59 62 64 65 68 70 74 75 76 77 78 79 81 82 85 87 90 92 93 95 96 97 102 104 105 107 108 110 111 113 114 115 118 119 129 130 131 132 134 135 144 146 147 148 154 156 **P**8
Primary Contact: Larry Heydon, President and Chief Executive Officer
COO: Steve Wohlford, Chief Operating Officer
CFO: Tim Balasia, Chief Financial Officer
CMO: David Dunkle, Vice President Medical Affairs
CIO: Scott Krodel, Vice President Information Systems
CHR: Judy Ware, Director Human Resources
CNO: Anita M. Keller, R.N., MSN, Chief Nursing Officer
Web address: www.johnsonmemorial.org
**Control**: County, Government, Nonfederal **Service**: General medical and surgical

**Staffed Beds**: 49 **Admissions**: 2011 **Census**: 16 **Outpatient Visits**: 155576 **Births**: 413 **Total Expense ($000)**: 89372 **Payroll Expense ($000)**: 42019 **Personnel**: 674

### GARY—Lake County

⊞ △ **METHODIST HOSPITALS (150002)**, 600 Grant Street, Zip 46402–6099; tel. 219/886–4000, (Includes SOUTHLAKE CAMPUS, Mailing address: 8701 Broadway, Merrillville, Indiana, Zip 46410; tel. 219/738–5500), (Nonreporting) **A**1 2 3 5 7 10 **F**3 8 11 12 13 15 18 20 22 24 26 28 29 30 31 34 35 37 40 43 45 46 47 48 49 50 51 54 55 57 58 59 61 62 64 67 70 72 73 74 75 76 77 78 79 81 82 85 86 87 89 90 91 93 96 98 100 101 102 103 107 108 110 111 114 115 118 119 120 121 123 124 126 130 132 134 135 146 147 148 149 154 156 **P**6
Primary Contact: Matthew Doyle, CPA, President and Chief Executive Officer
CIO: Timothy Diamond, Chief Information Officer
CHR: Alex Horvath, Vice President Human Resources
CNO: James M Renneker, FACHE, MSN, R.N., Vice President and Chief Nursing Officer
Web address: www.methodisthospitals.org
**Control**: Other not–for–profit (including NFP Corporation) **Service**: General medical and surgical

**Staffed Beds**: 494 **Admissions**: 13686 **Census**: 237 **Outpatient Visits**: 289801 **Births**: 1089 **Total Expense ($000)**: 346428 **Payroll Expense ($000)**: 149674 **Personnel**: 1991

**METHODIST HOSPITALS, INC** See Methodist Hospitals

### GOSHEN—Elkhart County

⊞ **GOSHEN HEALTH (150026)**, 200 High Park Avenue, Zip 46526–4899, Mailing Address: P.O. Box 139, Zip 46527–0139; tel. 574/533–2141, (Nonreporting) **A**1 2 10
Primary Contact: Randal Christophel, President and Chief Executive Officer
COO: Robert T Myers, Chief Operating Officer
CMO: Randall Cammenga, M.D., Vice President Medical Affairs
CHR: Alan Weldy, Vice President Human Resources, Compliance and Legal Services
Web address: www.https://goshenhealth.com/Home
**Control**: Other not–for–profit (including NFP Corporation) **Service**: General medical and surgical

**Staffed Beds**: 122

**GOSHEN HOSPITAL** See Goshen Health

**OAKLAWN HOSPITAL** See Oaklawn Psychiatric Center

**OAKLAWN PSYCHIATRIC CENTER (154031)**, 330 Lakeview Drive, Zip 46528–9365, Mailing Address: P.O. Box 809, Zip 46527–0809; tel. 574/533–1234, (Nonreporting) **A**10 **F**5 30 31 68 98 100 104 106 130 143 152 153 154 158
Primary Contact: Laurie N. Nafziger, President and Chief Executive Officer
CFO: Joseph Barkman, Vice President Financial Services
CMO: Daniel Kinsey, M.D., Medical Director
CIO: Jennifer Glick, Manager Clinical Informatics
CHR: Jill Seifer, Vice President Human Resources
CNO: Elaine G Miller, Director of Nursing
Web address: www.oaklawn.org
**Control**: Other not–for–profit (including NFP Corporation) **Service**: Psychiatric

**Staffed Beds**: 16 **Admissions**: 537 **Census**: 12 **Births**: 0 **Total Expense ($000)**: 57774 **Payroll Expense ($000)**: 36105

### GREENCASTLE—Putnam County

○ **PUTNAM COUNTY HOSPITAL (151333)**, 1542 South Bloomington Street, Zip 46135–2297; tel. 765/653–5121, (Nonreporting) **A**2 10 11 18
Primary Contact: Dennis Weatherford, Chief Executive Officer
CFO: Kevin Fowler, Director Finance
Web address: www.pchosp.org/
**Control**: County, Government, Nonfederal **Service**: General medical and surgical

**Staffed Beds**: 25

**IN**

## GREENFIELD—Hancock County

**HANCOCK MEMORIAL HOSPITAL** See Hancock Regional Hospital

★ ○ **HANCOCK REGIONAL HOSPITAL (150037)**, 801 North State Street, Zip 46140–1270, Mailing Address: P.O. Box 827, Zip 46140–0827; tel. 317/462–5544, (Nonreporting) **A**2 10 11 **F**3 13 15 18 20 22 28 29 30 31 32 34 35 36 37 38 40 41 44 45 46 47 48 49 51 53 54 55 56 57 58 59 63 64 65 70 74 75 76 78 79 81 82 83 84 85 86 87 89 92 93 98 100 101 102 103 104 107 108 110 111 114 115 117 119 120 121 123 124 127 129 130 132 134 135 144 145 146 147 149 156 **P**6 8
Primary Contact: Steven V. Long, FACHE, President and Chief Executive Officer
COO: Robert Lawrence Matt, Vice President and Chief Operating Officer
CFO: Rick Edwards, Vice President and Chief Financial Officer
CMO: Michael Fletcher, M.D., Vice President and Chief Medical Officer
CIO: Jon Miller, Director Accounting and Information Services
CHR: Laura L Nichols, Director Human Resources
Web address: www.hancockregional.org
**Control:** County, Government, Nonfederal **Service:** General medical and surgical

**Staffed Beds:** 68 **Admissions:** 3105 **Census:** 33 **Outpatient Visits:** 142197 **Births:** 366 **Total Expense ($000):** 138622 **Payroll Expense ($000):** 50396 **Personnel:** 858

## GREENSBURG—Decatur County

★ ⇑ **DECATUR COUNTY MEMORIAL HOSPITAL (151332)**, 720 North Lincoln Street, Zip 47240–1398; tel. 812/663–1171, (Total facility includes 370 beds in nursing home–type unit) (Nonreporting) **A**10 18 21 **F**3 7 11 13 15 18 28 29 30 31 32 34 35 36 40 44 45 50 51 53 54 57 59 64 65 68 74 75 76 77 78 79 80 81 85 87 89 92 93 96 97 104 107 108 110 111 115 118 119 127 128 129 130 131 132 133 135 143 144 146 147 156 157 **P**6
Primary Contact: Rex McKinney, President and Chief Executive Officer
COO: Eric Stokes, Vice President of Operations
CFO: Jerry Marks, Vice President Finance
CMO: Jennifer Fletcher, Chief of Staff
CHR: Amy Lynn Wickens, Executive Director Human Resources
CNO: Kathy Stephens, Vice President of Patient Care
Web address: www.dcmh.net
**Control:** County, Government, Nonfederal **Service:** General medical and surgical

**Staffed Beds:** 395 **Admissions:** 1688 **Census:** 456 **Outpatient Visits:** 70407 **Births:** 222 **Total Expense ($000):** 73537 **Payroll Expense ($000):** 48956

## GREENWOOD—Johnson County

☐ **VALLE VISTA HEALTH SYSTEM (154024)**, 898 East Main Street, Zip 46143–1400; tel. 317/887–1348, (Nonreporting) **A**1 10 **F**4 5 98 99 105 106 151 152 153 154 **S** Universal Health Services, Inc., King of Prussia, PA
Primary Contact: Sergio Chapman Cianci, Chief Executive Officer
CFO: Tim Sides, Chief Financial Officer
CMO: Jennifer Comer, M.D., Medical Director
CIO: Karen Hayden, Director Health Information Services, Performance Improvement and Risk Management
CHR: Ismael Santos, Director Human Resources
Web address: www.vallevistahospital.com
**Control:** Corporation, Investor–owned (for–profit) **Service:** Psychiatric

**Staffed Beds:** 132 **Admissions:** 4457 **Census:** 87 **Outpatient Visits:** 101539 **Births:** 0 **Personnel:** 220

**VALLE VISTA HOSPITAL** See Valle Vista Health System

## HAMMOND—Lake County

○ △ **FRANCISCAN HEALTH HAMMOND (150004)**, 5454 Hohman Avenue, Zip 46320–1999; tel. 219/932–2300, (Includes SAINT MARGARET MERCY HEALTHCARE CENTERS-NORTH CAMPUS, Mailing address: 5454 Hohman Avenue, Hammond, Indiana, Zip 46320; tel. 219/932–2300), (Nonreporting) **A**3 7 10 11 **S** Franciscan Health, Mishawaka, IN
Primary Contact: Patrick J. Maloney, Chief Executive Officer
CFO: Marc Golan, Chief Financial Officer
Web address: www.https:www.franciscanhealth.org/healthcare-facilities/franciscan-health-hammond-18
**Control:** Church operated, Nongovernment, not–for–profit **Service:** General medical and surgical

**Staffed Beds:** 406

**FRANCISCAN ST. MARGARET HEALTH - HAMMOND** See Franciscan Health Hammond

⊞ **KINDRED HOSPITAL NORTHWEST INDIANA (152012)**, 5454 Hohman Avenue, 5th Floor, Zip 46320–1931; tel. 219/937–9900, (Nonreporting) **A**1 10 **S** Kindred Healthcare, Louisville, KY
Primary Contact: Sohail Azeem, Chief Executive Officer
Web address: www.khnwindiana.com
**Control:** Corporation, Investor–owned (for–profit) **Service:** Acute long–term care hospital

**Staffed Beds:** 70

**SAINT MARGARET HOSP & HLTH CTR** See Saint Margaret Mercy Healthcare Centers-North Campus

**TRIUMPH HOSPITAL NORTHWEST INDIANA** See Kindred Hospital Northwest Indiana

## HARTFORD CITY—Blackford County

**BLACKFORD COMMUNITY HOSPITAL** See Indiana University Health Blackford Hospital

⊞ **INDIANA UNIVERSITY HEALTH BLACKFORD HOSPITAL (151302)**, 410 Pilgrim Boulevard, Zip 47348–1897; tel. 765/348–0300, (Nonreporting) **A**1 10 18 **F**3 11 15 28 29 34 35 40 44 45 50 57 59 64 75 81 85 87 93 107 110 115 119 130 132 133 146 154 157 **S** Indiana University Health, Indianapolis, IN
Primary Contact: David W. Hyatt, FACHE, President - Blackford Hospital and Rural Strategy Indiana University Health
CFO: John Vanator, CPA, Chief Financial Officer
CNO: Rodney Stevens, East Central Region Director of Nursing Practice
Web address: www.iuhealth.org/blackford
**Control:** Other not–for–profit (including NFP Corporation) **Service:** General medical and surgical

**Staffed Beds:** 15 **Admissions:** 395 **Census:** 6 **Outpatient Visits:** 23627 **Births:** 0 **Total Expense ($000):** 18676 **Payroll Expense ($000):** 4608 **Personnel:** 74

## HOBART—Lake County

☐ △ **ST. MARY MEDICAL CENTER (150034)**, 1500 South Lake Park Avenue, Zip 46342–6699; tel. 219/942–0551, (Nonreporting) **A**1 2 7 10 **S** Community Healthcare System, Hammond, IN
Primary Contact: Janice L. Ryba, JD, Chief Executive Officer
CFO: Mary Sudicky, Chief Financial Officer
CIO: Gary Weiner, Vice President Information Technology and Chief Information Officer
CHR: Tony Ferracane, Vice President Human Resources
Web address: www.comhs.org
**Control:** Other not–for–profit (including NFP Corporation) **Service:** General medical and surgical

**Staffed Beds:** 200

## HUNTINGTON—Huntington County

**HUNTINGTON MEMORIAL HOSPITAL** See Parkview Huntington Hospital

⊞ **PARKVIEW HUNTINGTON HOSPITAL (150091)**, 2001 Stults Road, Zip 46750–1291; tel. 260/355–3000, (Nonreporting) **A**1 10 **F**3 7 8 13 15 28 29 30 31 32 34 35 36 38 39 40 44 45 46 50 53 56 57 59 64 68 69 70 75 76 77 78 79 81 85 86 87 93 96 97 107 108 111 119 129 130 131 132 134 135 146 148 154 156 **P**6 **S** Parkview Health, Fort Wayne, IN
Primary Contact: Juli Johnson, MSN, R.N., President
CMO: Jeffrey Brooks, M.D., Chief Medical Officer
CIO: Ron Double, Chief Information Officer
CHR: Dena M Jacquay, Chief Human Resource Officer
CNO: Doug R Selig, MSN, R.N., Vice President of Patient Services
Web address: www.parkview.com
**Control:** Other not–for–profit (including NFP Corporation) **Service:** General medical and surgical

**Staffed Beds:** 36 **Admissions:** 1861 **Census:** 13 **Outpatient Visits:** 51539 **Births:** 324 **Total Expense ($000):** 59303 **Payroll Expense ($000):** 16463 **Personnel:** 247

*Many Facility Codes have changed. Please refer to the AHA Guide Code Chart.*
© 2021 AHA Guide

## INDIANAPOLIS—Hamilton County

☒ **ASCENSION ST. VINCENT HEART CENTER (150153)**, 10580 North Meridian Street, Zip 46290–1028; tel. 317/583–5000, (Nonreporting) **A**1 10 **F**3 17 18 20 22 24 26 28 29 30 35 40 43 44 45 50 58 59 64 65 66 68 81 87 107 111 115 119 129 130 135 149 154 157 **S** Ascension Healthcare, Saint Louis, MO
Primary Contact: Lori Shannon, President
CFO: Becky Jacobson, Vice President Finance
CMO: Don Stogsdill, Chief Medical Officer
CIO: Jeremy Long, Chief Information Officer
Web address: www.bestheartcare.com/
**Control:** Partnership, Investor–owned (for–profit) **Service:** Heart

Staffed Beds: 80 Admissions: 4400 Census: 55 Outpatient Visits: 14565 Births: 0 Total Expense ($000): 111427 Payroll Expense ($000): 26538

## INDIANAPOLIS—Marion County

☒ **ASCENSION ST. VINCENT INDIANAPOLIS HOSPITAL (150084)**, 2001 West 86th Street, Zip 46260–1991, Mailing Address: P.O. Box 40970, Zip 46240–0970; tel. 317/338–2345, (Includes PEYTON MANNING CHILDREN'S HOSPITAL AT ST. VINCENT, Mailing address: 2001 West 86th Street, Indianapolis, Indiana, Zip 46260, P O Box 40970, Zip 46240–0970, tel. 317/415–8111; Hossain Marandi, M.D., FACHE, President and Chief Executive Officer; PEYTON MANNING CHILDREN'S HOSPITAL, Mailing address: 1707 West 86th Street, Indianapolis, Indiana, Zip 46240, P O Box 40407, Zip 46240, tel. 317/415–5500; Hossain Marandi, M.D., FACHE, President and Chief Executive Officer; ST. VINCENT STRESS CENTER, Mailing address: 8401 Harcourt Road, Indianapolis, Indiana, Zip 46260, P O Box 80160, Zip 46280, tel. 317/338–4600; Sheila Mishler, Chief Executive Officer; ST. VINCENT WOMEN'S HOSPITAL, Mailing address: 8111 Township Line Road, Indianapolis, Indiana, Zip 46260–8043; tel. 317/415–8111; Anne Coleman, Administrator; (Nonreporting) **A**1 2 3 5 8 10 13 **F**3 4 5 7 8 9 11 13 15 17 18 19 20 21 22 23 24 25 26 27 28 29 30 31 32 34 35 36 37 38 39 40 41 43 44 45 46 47 48 49 50 51 53 54 55 56 57 58 59 61 62 63 64 65 66 68 70 71 72 73 74 75 76 77 78 79 81 82 83 84 85 86 87 88 89 90 91 92 93 94 95 96 97 98 99 100 101 102 103 104 105 107 108 109 110 111 114 115 117 118 119 120 121 124 126 129 130 131 132 134 135 137 138 141 142 143 146 147 148 149 151 152 153 154 **P**6 **S** Ascension Healthcare, Saint Louis, MO
Primary Contact: Erica Wehrmeister, President Central Region
COO: Erica Wehrmeister, Chief Operating Officer
CFO: Terry Metzger, Vice President, Finance
CIO: Randy Cox, Chief Information Officer
CHR: Audra Pratt, Chief Human Resource Officer
CNO: Mary Myers, R.N., MSN, Chief Nursing Officer
Web address: www.stvincent.org
**Control:** Church operated, Nongovernment, not–for–profit **Service:** General medical and surgical

Staffed Beds: 840 Admissions: 31088 Census: 505 Outpatient Visits: 737176 Births: 2897 Total Expense ($000): 1082296 Payroll Expense ($000): 313065 Personnel: 3844

☒ **ASCENSION ST. VINCENT SETON SPECIALTY HOSPITAL (152020)**, 8050 Township Line Road, Zip 46260–2478; tel. 317/415–8500, (Nonreporting) **A**1 10 **F**1 3 29 30 31 35 44 68 75 85 107 114 119 130 132 148 154 **S** Ascension Healthcare, Saint Louis, MO
Primary Contact: Erica Wehrmeister, President Central Region
CFO: Terry Metzger, Chief Financial Officer
CMO: Alain Broccard, M.D., Chief Medical Officer
Web address: www.stvincent.org/
**Control:** Church operated, Nongovernment, not–for–profit **Service:** Acute long–term care hospital

Staffed Beds: 74 Admissions: 352 Census: 36 Outpatient Visits: 0 Births: 0 Total Expense ($000): 28094 Payroll Expense ($000): 10762 Personnel: 173

**CLARIAN HEALTH PARTNERS** See Indiana University Health University Hospital

**COMMUNITY HOSP SOUTH** See Community Hospital South

☒ **COMMUNITY HOSPITAL EAST (150074)**, 1500 North Ritter Avenue, Zip 46219–3095; tel. 317/355–1411, (Includes COMMUNITY HEART AND VASCULAR HOSPITAL, Mailing address: 8075 North Shadeland Avenue, Indianapolis, Indiana, Zip 46250–2693; tel. 317/621–8000; Kathleen R Krusie, FACHE, President), (Nonreporting) **A**1 2 3 10 13 **F**3 8 11 13 18 20 22 26 28 29 30 31 34 35 36 38 40 44 45 46 47 48 49 50 51 53 56 57 60 61 64 65 70 72 74 75 76 77 78 79 80 81 84 85 87 92 96 107 111 114 115 118 119 120 121 123 124 126 129 130 132 146 147 148 149 154 156 **P**1 5 8 **S** Community Health Network, Indianapolis, IN
Primary Contact: David Kiley, M.D., Senior Vice President, President Indianapolis Region
CNO: Paige Dooley, R.N., MSN, Chief Nursing Executive
Web address: www.ecommunity.com/east
**Control:** Other not–for–profit (including NFP Corporation) **Service:** General medical and surgical

Staffed Beds: 181 Admissions: 18971 Census: 239 Outpatient Visits: 498166 Births: 970 Total Expense ($000): 719260 Payroll Expense ($000): 194587 Personnel: 1194

☒ △ **COMMUNITY HOSPITAL NORTH (150169)**, 7150 Clearvista Drive, Zip 46256–1695, Mailing Address: 7250 Clearvista Drive, Suite 200, Zip 46256–1695; tel. 317/355–2469, (Nonreporting) **A**1 3 5 7 10 **F**3 11 13 29 30 31 34 35 40 41 43 44 45 46 47 48 49 50 56 57 59 61 65 70 72 74 75 76 77 78 79 80 81 82 84 85 87 88 89 96 98 101 103 107 108 111 114 119 126 129 130 131 132 145 146 147 148 **P**1 5 **S** Community Health Network, Indianapolis, IN
Primary Contact: David Kiley, M.D., Indianapolis Region President
CFO: Amy Campbell, Chief Financial Officer
CMO: Wesley Wong, M.D., Acting Vice President Medical and Academic Affairs
CIO: Ron Thieme, Ph.D., Chief Knowledge and Information Officer
CHR: Steve Pearcy, Director Human Resources
Web address: www.ecommunity.com/north
**Control:** Other not–for–profit (including NFP Corporation) **Service:** General medical and surgical

Staffed Beds: 353 Admissions: 17921 Census: 233 Outpatient Visits: 249040 Births: 3768 Personnel: 1214

☒ **COMMUNITY HOSPITAL SOUTH (150128)**, 1402 East County Line Road South, Zip 46227–0963; tel. 317/887–7000, (Nonreporting) **A**1 3 5 10 **F**3 11 12 13 15 20 22 26 28 29 30 31 34 35 40 41 44 45 46 47 48 49 51 53 57 59 60 62 63 64 68 70 72 74 75 76 77 78 79 80 81 82 84 85 86 87 89 92 94 100 107 108 111 118 119 126 130 132 135 146 156 157 **P**1 5 8 **S** Community Health Network, Indianapolis, IN
Primary Contact: David Kiley, M.D., Indianapolis Region President
COO: Nichole Goddard, Chief Operating Officer, South Region
CFO: Leslie Yoder, Executive Director, Finance
CMO: Randy Lee, M.D., Senior Vice President Medical Affairs
CHR: Edie Garriott, Director Human Resources
CNO: Anita Capps, R.N., Chief Nursing Executive
Web address: www.ecommunity.com
**Control:** Other not–for–profit (including NFP Corporation) **Service:** General medical and surgical

Staffed Beds: 171 Admissions: 10060 Census: 102 Births: 1695 Total Expense ($000): 217250 Payroll Expense ($000): 65295 Personnel: 724

**COMMUNITY HSPS OF INDIANAPOLIS** See Community Hospital East

☒ **ESKENAZI HEALTH (150024)**, 720 Eskenazi Avenue, Zip 46202–5166; tel. 317/880–0000, (Nonreporting) **A**1 3 5 7 10 13 14 15 16 18 20 22 25 29 30 31 32 34 35 36 38 39 40 43 44 47 48 49 50 53 54 55 56 57 59 61 62 64 65 66 68 70 71 72 74 75 76 77 78 79 81 82 83 84 85 86 87 93 97 98 100 101 102 103 104 105 106 107 110 111 115 119 130 132 134 135 143 144 145 146 147 148 150 153 156 157
Primary Contact: Lisa E. Harris, M.D., Chief Executive Officer
COO: Neil Johnson, Chief Operating Officer
CFO: Aaron Eichorn, Interim Chief Financial Officer
CMO: David W Crabb, M.D., Chief Medical Officer
CIO: Scott Morris, Vice President Information Systems
CHR: Christia Hicks, Vice President Human Resources
CNO: Lee Ann Blue, MSN, R.N., Chief Nursing Officer and Executive Vice President Patient Care Services
Web address: www.eskenazihealth.edu
**Control:** County, Government, Nonfederal **Service:** General medical and surgical

Staffed Beds: 343 Admissions: 17619 Census: 240 Outpatient Visits: 953299 Births: 2704 Total Expense ($000): 716682 Payroll Expense ($000): 263254 Personnel: 4008

IN

---

**Hospital, Medicare Provider Number, Address, Telephone, Approval, Facility, and Physician Codes, Health Care System**

★ American Hospital Association (AHA) membership
□ The Joint Commission accreditation
○ Healthcare Facilities Accreditation Program
◇ DNV Healthcare Inc. accreditation
⇑ Center for Improvement in Healthcare Quality Accreditation
△ Commission on Accreditation of Rehabilitation Facilities (CARF) accreditation

☐ **FAIRBANKS (150179)**, 8102 Clearvista Parkway, Zip 46256–4698;
tel. 317/849–8222, (Nonreporting) **A**1 3 10
Primary Contact: Barb Elliott, Interim President and Chief Executive Officer
CFO: Barb Elliott, Chief Financial Officer
CMO: Dennis Rhyne, M.D., Acting Medical Director
CIO: Randy Walls, Manager Information Services
CHR: Sharon Baker, Director Support Services
CNO: Jennifer M Horstman, R.N., Chief Nursing Officer and Chief Information
Officer
Web address: www.fairbankscd.org
**Control:** Other not–for–profit (including NFP Corporation) **Service:** Alcoholism and
other chemical dependency

**Staffed Beds:** 86

**FAIRBANKS HOSPITAL** See Fairbanks

**FRANCISCAN HEALTH - INDIANAPOLIS** See Franciscan Health Indianapolis

○ △ **FRANCISCAN HEALTH INDIANAPOLIS (150162)**, 8111 South Emerson
Avenue, Zip 46237–8601; tel. 317/528–5000, (Nonreporting) **A**2 3 5 7 10 11 **S**
Franciscan Health, Mishawaka, IN
Primary Contact: James Callaghan III, M.D., President and Chief Executive Officer
CFO: Keith A. Lauter, Regional Chief Financial Officer
CMO: Christopher Doehring, M.D., Vice President Medical Affairs
CIO: Barbara Coulter, Director Information Systems
CHR: Corey Baute, Vice President Human Resources
CNO: Agnes Therady, MSN, FACHE, Vice President and Chief Nursing Officer
Web address: www.stfrancishospitals.org
**Control:** Church operated, Nongovernment, not–for–profit **Service:** General
medical and surgical

**Staffed Beds:** 485

**INDIANA HEART HOSPITAL** See Community Heart and Vascular Hospital

**INDIANA ORTHOPAEDIC HOSPITAL** See Orthoindy Hospital

⊞ **INDIANA UNIVERSITY HEALTH UNIVERSITY HOSPITAL (150056)**, 550
University Boulevard, Zip 46202–5149, Mailing Address: P.O. Box 1367,
Zip 46206–1367; tel. 317/944–5000, (Includes INDIANA UNIVERSITY HEALTH
METHODIST HOSPITAL, Mailing address: 1300 South Jackson St, Frankfort,
Indiana, Zip 46041, 1701 North Senate Boulevard, Indianapolis, Zip 46202,
tel. 317/962–2000; Ryan Nagy, M.D., President and Chief Medical Officer;
INDIANA UNIVERSITY HEALTH SAXONY HOSPITAL, Mailing address: 13000
East 136th Street, Fishers, Indiana, Zip 46037–9478; tel. 317/678–2000;
Alicia Schulhof, President and Chief Executive Officer; INDIANA UNIVERSITY
HOSPITAL, Mailing address: 550 North University Boulevard, Indianapolis, Indiana,
Zip 46202–5262; tel. 317/274–5000; RILEY HOSPITAL FOR CHILDREN AT
INDIANA UNIVERSITY HEALTH, Mailing address: 702 Barnhill Drive, Indianapolis,
Indiana, Zip 46202–5225, 705 Riley Hospital Dr, Zip 46202, tel. 317/274–5000),
(Nonreporting) **A**1 2 3 5 8 10 **F**3 5 6 7 8 9 11 12 13 15 16 17 18 19 20 21 22
23 24 25 26 27 28 29 30 31 32 33 34 35 36 37 38 39 40 41 43 44 45 46 47
48 49 50 51 52 53 54 55 56 57 58 59 60 61 62 63 64 65 68 69 70 71 72 73
74 75 76 77 78 79 80 81 82 83 84 85 86 87 88 89 90 91 92 93 94 95 96 97
98 99 100 101 102 103 104 105 106 107 108 109 110 111 112 113 114 115
116 117 118 119 120 121 123 124 126 129 130 131 132 134 135 136 137
138 139 140 141 142 144 145 146 147 148 149 150 151 152 153 154 155
156 157 **S** Indiana University Health, Indianapolis, IN
Primary Contact: Ryan Nagy, M.D., President and Chief Medical Officer
Web address: www.iuhealth.org
**Control:** Other not–for–profit (including NFP Corporation) **Service:** General
medical and surgical

**Staffed Beds:** 1296 **Admissions:** 44686 **Census:** 906 **Outpatient
Visits:** 1978276 **Births:** 2749 **Total Expense ($000):** 3323179 **Payroll
Expense ($000):** 1075876 **Personnel:** 14329

**INDIANA UNIVERSITY HOSPITAL** See Indiana University Health University
Hospital, Indianapolis

**INDIANA UNIVERSITY MED CENTER** See Indiana University Hospital

⊞ **KINDRED HOSPITAL INDIANAPOLIS NORTH (152013)**, 8060 Knue Road,
Zip 46250–1976; tel. 317/813–8900, (Nonreporting) **A**1 10 **S** Kindred
Healthcare, Louisville, KY
Primary Contact: Nakia Tremble, Chief Executive Officer
CFO: Chad Watson, Market Controller
CHR: Jeffrey Herdelin, Vice President Human Resources
CNO: Teresa Richardson, Chief Clinical Officer
Web address: www.kindredindynorth.com/
**Control:** Corporation, Investor–owned (for–profit) **Service:** Acute long–term care
hospital

**Staffed Beds:** 45

⊞ **KINDRED HOSPITAL-INDIANAPOLIS (152007)**, 1700 West 10th Street,
Zip 46222–3802; tel. 317/636–4400, (Nonreporting) **A**1 10 **S** Kindred
Healthcare, Louisville, KY
Primary Contact: Brad Klawitter, Chief Executive Officer
COO: Angela Lynne Rotert, Chief Clinical Officer
CFO: William Brenner, Chief Financial Officer
CHR: Joe Housh, District Director Human Resources
Web address: www.kindredhospitalindy.com/
**Control:** Corporation, Investor–owned (for–profit) **Service:** Acute long–term care
hospital

**Staffed Beds:** 59

**LARUE D. CARTER MEMORIAL HOSPITAL (154008)**, 2601 Cold Spring Road,
Zip 46222–2273; tel. 317/941–4000, (Nonreporting) **A**5 10
Primary Contact: Robert Clover, Interim Superintendent
CFO: Michael Logar, Assistant Superintendent
CMO: Beth Pfau, M.D., Chief Medical Officer
CIO: Denton Gross, Director Information Services
CHR: Rebecca Dutton, Director Human Resources
CNO: Todd Rittman, Director of Nursing
**Control:** State, Government, Nonfederal **Service:** Psychiatric

**Staffed Beds:** 148

☐ **NEURODIAGNOSTIC INSTITUTE AND ADVANCED TREATMENT CENTER
(154008)**, 5435 East 16th Street, Zip 46218; tel. 317/941–4000, (Nonreporting)
**A**1
Primary Contact: Robert Clover, Superintendent
CNO: Cynthia Wilson, Director, NDI Advanced Treatment Center, Nursing and BHRA
Unit Services
Web address: www.https://www.in.gov/fssa/dmha/index.htm
**Control:** State, Government, Nonfederal **Service:** Psychiatric

**Staffed Beds:** 318

☐ **NEUROPSYCHIATRIC HOSPITAL OF INDIANAPOLIS (154063)**, 6720
Parkdale Place, Zip 46254–4668; tel. 317/744–9200, (Nonreporting) **A**1 10 **S**
NeuroPsychiatric Hospitals, Mishawaka, IN
Primary Contact: Tracy Davis, Chief Executive Officer
Web address: www.https://www.neuropsychiatrichospitals.net
**Control:** Corporation, Investor–owned (for–profit) **Service:** Psychiatric

**Staffed Beds:** 50

☐ **OPTIONS BEHAVIORAL HEALTH SYSTEM (154057)**, 5602 Caito Drive,
Zip 46226–1346; tel. 317/544–4340, (Nonreporting) **A**1 10 **F**4 98 99 100 102
106 153 **P**5 **S** Acadia Healthcare Company, Inc., Franklin, TN
Primary Contact: Dustin Thiels, Chief Executive Officer
Web address: www.optionsbehavioralhealthsystem.com/
**Control:** State, Government, Nonfederal **Service:** Psychiatric

**Staffed Beds:** 84 **Admissions:** 2457 **Census:** 44 **Births:** 0

○ **ORTHOINDY HOSPITAL (150160)**, 8400 Northwest Boulevard,
Zip 46278–1381; tel. 317/956–1000, (Nonreporting) **A**3 10 11
Primary Contact: Timothy Dicke, M.D., Chief Executive Officer
COO: Stacie Vance, Chief Nursing Officer and
CFO: Anthony Gioia, Chief Financial Officer
CMO: Joseph Randolph, M.D., Chairman Medical Executive Committee
CIO: Paul Frey, Director Information Technology Applications
CHR: Kristy Hensley, Director Human Resources
CNO: Stacie Vance, Chief Nursing Officer and Vice President Operations
Web address: www.orthoindy.com
**Control:** Corporation, Investor–owned (for–profit) **Service:** Orthopedic

**Staffed Beds:** 38

**IN**

*Many Facility Codes have changed. Please refer to the AHA Guide Code Chart.*

☐ △ **REHABILITATION HOSPITAL OF INDIANA (153028)**, 4141 Shore Drive, Zip 46254–2607; tel. 317/329–2000, (Nonreporting) **A**1 3 5 7 10 **F**28 29 30 33 35 54 57 58 64 75 79 86 87 90 91 92 93 96 130 131 132 146 148 **P**5 **S** Indiana University Health, Indianapolis, IN
Primary Contact: Daniel B. Woloszyn, Chief Executive Officer
COO: Monte Spence, Chief Operating Officer
CFO: Marjorie Basey, Chief Financial Officer
CMO: Flora Hammond, M.D., Chief Medical Affairs
CIO: Gary Skinner, Director Information Technology
CHR: Joni Brown, Director Human Resources
CNO: Debra Cordes, Chief Nursing Officer
Web address: www.rhin.com
**Control**: Other not–for–profit (including NFP Corporation) **Service**: Rehabilitation

**Staffed Beds**: 83 **Admissions**: 1348 **Census**: 57 **Outpatient Visits**: 24761 **Births**: 0 **Total Expense ($000)**: 46154 **Payroll Expense ($000)**: 24946 **Personnel**: 361

☒ △ **RICHARD L. ROUDEBUSH VETERANS AFFAIRS MEDICAL CENTER**, 1481 West Tenth Street, Zip 46202–2884; tel. 317/554–0000, (Nonreporting) **A**1 2 3 5 7 8 **F**3 5 18 20 22 24 26 28 29 30 31 33 34 35 36 38 39 40 44 45 46 47 49 50 53 54 56 57 58 59 60 61 62 63 64 65 66 70 71 74 75 77 78 79 80 81 82 83 84 85 86 87 90 91 92 93 94 96 97 98 100 101 102 103 104 105 106 107 108 111 115 117 118 119 120 121 123 124 126 127 129 130 132 135 143 146 147 148 149 152 153 154 156 157 158 **S** Department of Veterans Affairs, Washington, DC
Primary Contact: Laura E. Ruzick, Medical Center Director
COO: Ginny L Creasman, Associate Director
CFO: Colin Lennon, Chief Financial Officer
CMO: Imtiaz A Munshi, M.D., Chief of Staff
CIO: Steve Stoner, Chief Information Officer
CHR: Chari Weddle, Chief Human Resource Management Service
CNO: Patricia Mathis, Associate Director Patient Care Service
Web address: www.indianapolis.va.gov
**Control**: Veterans Affairs, Government, federal **Service**: General medical and surgical

**Staffed Beds**: 197 **Admissions**: 9417 **Census**: 148 **Outpatient Visits**: 736355 **Births**: 0 **Total Expense ($000)**: 586883 **Payroll Expense ($000)**: 255730 **Personnel**: 3143

**RILEY HOSPITAL FOR CHILDREN** See Riley Hospital for Children at Indiana University Health

**RILEY HOSPITAL FOR CHILDREN AT INDIANA UNIVERSITY HEALTH** See Indiana University Health University Hospital, Indianapolis

**SELECT SPECIALTY HOSPITAL-INDIANAPOLIS** See Kindred Hospital Indianapolis North

**ST VINCENT CHILDREN'S HOSPITAL** See Peyton Manning Children's Hospital at St. Vincent

**ST. VINCENT HEART CENTER** See Ascension St. Vincent Heart Center

**ST. VINCENT INDIANAPOLIS HOSPITAL** See Ascension St. Vincent Indianapolis Hospital

**ST. VINCENT PEDIATRIC REHABILITATION CENTER** See Peyton Manning Children's Hospital

**ST. VINCENT SETON SPECIALTY HOSPITAL** See Ascension St. Vincent Seton Specialty Hospital

**VENCOR HOSPITAL-INDIANAPOLIS** See Kindred Hospital-Indianapolis

**WISHARD-ESKENAZI HEALTH** See Eskenazi Health

**WOMEN'S HOSPITAL-INDIANAPOLIS** See St. Vincent Women's Hospital

☒ **MEMORIAL HOSPITAL AND HEALTH CARE CENTER (150115)**, 800 West Ninth Street, Zip 47546–2516; tel. 812/996–2345, (Total facility includes 14 beds in nursing home–type unit) (Nonreporting) **A**1 2 3 5 10 **F**3 5 7 8 11 12 13 15 18 20 22 24 26 28 29 30 31 34 35 36 40 41 43 45 46 47 48 49 50 51 53 54 56 57 59 62 64 66 68 70 74 75 76 77 78 79 81 82 84 85 86 87 89 90 93 97 98 100 101 102 103 104 107 108 110 111 112 113 114 115 116 117 118 119 120 121 126 127 128 129 130 131 132 135 144 146 147 148 149 154 156 **P**6 **S** American Province of Little Company of Mary Sisters, Evergreen Park, IL
Primary Contact: E Kyle. Bennett, President and Chief Executive Officer
CFO: Ted Miller, Vice President and Chief Financial Officer
CMO: Stan Tretter, M.D., Chief Medical Officer
CIO: Mathew P. Gaug, Vice President Information Systems and Chief Information Officer
CHR: Richard Pea, Director Human Resources
CNO: Lori Persohn, R.N., MSN, Vice President, Patient Services and Chief Nursing Officer
Web address: www.mhhcc.org
**Control**: Church operated, Nongovernment, not–for–profit **Service**: General medical and surgical

**Staffed Beds**: 137 **Admissions**: 5473 **Census**: 60 **Outpatient Visits**: 254430 **Births**: 893 **Total Expense ($000)**: 225930 **Payroll Expense ($000)**: 102527 **Personnel**: 1412

☒ **CLARK MEMORIAL HEALTH (150009)**, 1220 Missouri Avenue, Zip 47130–3743, Mailing Address: P.O. Box 69, Zip 47131–0600; tel. 812/282–6631, (Nonreporting) **A**1 2 3 5 10 **S** LifePoint Health, Brentwood, TN
Primary Contact: Martin Padgett, President and Chief Executive Officer
CMO: William Templeton, M.D., IIIMedical Director
CIO: Larry Reverman, Director Information Systems
CHR: Scott Hicks, Vice President
CNO: Kathy Neuner, R.N., Chief Nursing Officer
Web address: www.clarkmemorial.org
**Control**: County, Government, Nonfederal **Service**: General medical and surgical

**Staffed Beds**: 185

**CLARK MEMORIAL HOSPITAL** See Clark Memorial Health

☐ **WELLSTONE REGIONAL HOSPITAL (154051)**, 2700 Vissing Park Road, Zip 47130–5989; tel. 812/284–8000, (Nonreporting) **A**1 10 **F**4 5 98 99 102 103 104 105 152 153 154 **S** Universal Health Services, Inc., King of Prussia, PA
Primary Contact: Greg Stewart, Chief Executive Officer
CFO: Patricia Ellison, Chief Financial Officer
CMO: Asad Ismail, M.D., Medical Director
CIO: Timothy Wise, Director, Information Technology
CHR: Tiffany Pierce, Director Human Resources
CNO: Carrie Dodson, Director of Nursing
Web address: www.wellstonehospital.com
**Control**: Corporation, Investor–owned (for–profit) **Service**: Psychiatric

**Staffed Beds**: 100 **Admissions**: 3370 **Census**: 71 **Outpatient Visits**: 6962 **Births**: 0 **Total Expense ($000)**: 16040 **Payroll Expense ($000)**: 10179

**COMMUNITY HOSP OF NOBLE COUNTY** See Parkview Noble Hospital

☒ **PARKVIEW NOBLE HOSPITAL (150146)**, 401 Sawyer Road, Zip 46755–2568; tel. 260/347–8700, (Nonreporting) **A**1 10 **F**3 7 13 15 28 29 34 35 40 45 46 47 50 54 57 59 64 70 74 75 76 79 81 82 85 87 93 97 107 108 110 111 114 118 119 129 130 132 135 143 145 146 154 156 **P**6 **S** Parkview Health, Fort Wayne, IN
Primary Contact: Gary W. Adkins, President
COO: Gary W Adkins, Chief Executive Officer
CFO: Kem Prince, Manager of Finance
CMO: Gerald Warrener, M.D., Chief Medical Officer
CIO: Ron Double, Chief Information Officer
CHR: Bruce Buttermore, Manager Human Resources
CNO: Catherine Byrd, Vice President Patient Services
Web address: www.parkview.com
**Control**: Other not–for–profit (including NFP Corporation) **Service**: General medical and surgical

**Staffed Beds**: 31 **Admissions**: 1726 **Census**: 13 **Outpatient Visits**: 60498 **Births**: 245 **Total Expense ($000)**: 59350 **Payroll Expense ($000)**: 15253 **Personnel**: 220

**IN**

| Hospital, Medicare Provider Number, Address, Telephone, Approval, Facility, and Physician Codes, Health Care System |
| --- |

★ American Hospital Association (AHA) membership   ○ Healthcare Facilities Accreditation Program   ⇑ Center for Improvement in Healthcare Quality Accreditation
☐ The Joint Commission accreditation   ◇ DNV Healthcare Inc. accreditation   △ Commission on Accreditation of Rehabilitation Facilities (CARF) accreditation

## KNOX—St. Joseph County

☐ **MEDICAL BEHAVIORAL HOSPITAL OF MISHAWAKA (154061)**, 5985 E 200
S, Zip 46534, Mailing Address: 1625 East Jefferson Boulevard, Mishawaka,
Zip 46545–7103; tel. 574/255–1400, (Nonreporting) **A**1 10 **S** NeuroPsychiatric
Hospitals, Mishawaka, IN
Primary Contact: Emily Ryan, Chief Executive Officer
COO: Christy Gilbert, President and Chief Operating Officer
Web address: www.physicianshospitalsystem.net/
**Control**: Partnership, Investor–owned (for–profit) **Service**: Psychiatric

**Staffed Beds**: 30

**RIVERCREST SPECIALTY HOSPITAL** See Medical Behavioral Hospital of
Mishawaka

## KNOX—Starke County

☒ **STARKE HOSPITAL (150102)**, 102 East Culver Road, Zip 46534–2216, Mailing
Address: P.O. Box 339, Zip 46534–0339; tel. 574/772–6231, (Nonreporting)
**A**1 10 **F**3 15 18 29 30 32 34 35 38 40 45 46 49 50 53 57 59 65 68 74 75 77
79 81 85 87 93 94 107 108 110 111 114 115 116 117 119 130 146 149 **S**
Community Health Systems, Inc., Franklin, TN
Primary Contact: Ashley Dickinson, Chief Executive Officer
COO: Jeff Vice, Chief Operating Officer
CFO: Drew Keesbury, Chief Financial Officer
CMO: A N Damodaran, M.D., President Medical Staff
CIO: Ashley Norem, Chief Information Systems
CHR: Doug Jesch, Director Human Resources
CNO: Anetra Jones, R.N., M.P.H., Chief Nursing Officer
Web address: www.https://www.starkehealth.com
**Control**: Corporation, Investor–owned (for–profit) **Service**: General medical and surgical

**Staffed Beds**: 15 **Admissions**: 462 **Census**: 4 **Outpatient Visits**: 26226
**Births**: 0 **Total Expense ($000)**: 14611 **Payroll Expense ($000)**: 6542
**Personnel**: 104

**STARKE HOSPITAL** See Starke Hospital

## KOKOMO—Howard County

☒ **ASCENSION ST. VINCENT KOKOMO (150010)**, 1907 West Sycamore Street,
Zip 46901–4197; tel. 765/452–5611, (Nonreporting) **A**1 10 **F**3 4 5 7 8 13 15 18
20 28 29 30 31 34 35 36 38 40 44 45 49 50 51 53 55 57 59 64 66 68 69 70
73 74 75 76 77 78 79 81 82 85 86 87 90 93 96 98 100 101 102 104 105 107
108 110 111 115 118 119 120 121 123 126 129 130 131 132 135 143 145
146 147 148 149 151 154 155 156 **S** Ascension Healthcare, Saint Louis, MO
Primary Contact: Margaret M. Johnson, President, St. Vincent Northwest Region
CMO: David L Williams, M.D., Chief Medical Officer
CIO: Jeffrey Scott, Chief Information Officer
CHR: Cindy Babb, Executive Director Human Resources and Organizational
Effectiveness
CNO: Kathleen K Peoples, R.N., MS, Vice President of Nursing
Web address: www.stvincent.org/stjoseph
**Control**: Other not–for–profit (including NFP Corporation) **Service**: General
medical and surgical

**Staffed Beds**: 117 **Admissions**: 4847 **Census**: 56 **Outpatient
Visits**: 199550 **Births**: 766 **Total Expense ($000)**: 142157 **Payroll Expense
($000)**: 36243 **Personnel**: 416

☒ **COMMUNITY HOWARD REGIONAL HEALTH (150007)**, 3500 South Lafountain
Street, Zip 46902–3803, Mailing Address: P.O. Box 9011, Zip 46904–9011;
tel. 765/453–0702, (Nonreporting) **A**1 2 10 **F**3 7 8 13 15 17 18 20 22 26 28
29 30 31 34 35 36 37 38 40 45 46 49 50 53 57 59 60 63 64 67 71 73 74 76
77 78 79 81 82 84 85 87 89 92 97 98 100 104 106 107 108 110 111 115
116 117 118 119 121 122 123 124 126 130 131 132 135 148 154 **P**5 **S**
Community Health Network, Indianapolis, IN
Primary Contact: Joseph Hooper, President and Chief Executive Officer
COO: Theodore Brown, Chief Operating Officer
CFO: Theodore Brown, Vice President Financial Services
CIO: Kevin Purvis, Chief Information Officer
CHR: Michael L Williams, FACHE, Vice President Human Resources
CNO: Melodi Greene, R.N., MS, Chief Nursing Officer
Web address: www.howardregional.org
**Control**: Other not–for–profit (including NFP Corporation) **Service**: General
medical and surgical

**Staffed Beds**: 196 **Admissions**: 5182 **Census**: 48 **Outpatient
Visits**: 134756 **Births**: 411 **Total Expense ($000)**: 146671 **Payroll Expense
($000)**: 45713 **Personnel**: 450

**COMMUNITY HOWARD REGIONAL HOSPITAL** See Community Howard Regional
Health

**ST. VINCENT KOKOMO** See Ascension St. Vincent Kokomo

## LA PORTE—Laporte County

**INDIANA UNIVERSITY HEALTH LA PORTE HOSPITAL** See La Porte Hospital

☒ **LA PORTE HOSPITAL (150006)**, 1007 Lincolnway, Zip 46350–3201, Mailing
Address: P.O. Box 250, Zip 46352–0250; tel. 219/326–1234, (Nonreporting) **A**1
2 10 19 **F**3 11 13 15 17 18 20 22 26 28 29 30 31 32 34 35 39 40 44 45 46
47 48 49 50 51 53 54 57 59 60 64 65 68 70 71 74 75 76 77 78 79 81 82 85
86 87 89 91 92 93 96 97 107 108 110 111 114 115 118 119 126 129 130
131 132 135 144 145 146 147 148 149 154 156 **S** Community Health Systems,
Inc., Franklin, TN
Primary Contact: Ashley Dickinson, Chief Executive Officer
CFO: Drew Keesbury, Chief Financial Officer
CNO: Anetra Jones, R.N., M.P.H., Chief Nursing Officer
Web address: www.https://www.laportehealth.com
**Control**: Corporation, Investor–owned (for–profit) **Service**: General medical and surgical

**Staffed Beds**: 91 **Admissions**: 4768 **Census**: 54 **Outpatient Visits**: 101679
**Births**: 601 **Total Expense ($000)**: 133999 **Payroll Expense ($000)**: 39613
**Personnel**: 887

## LAFAYETTE—Tippecanoe County

**CLARIAN ARNETT HOSPITAL** See Indiana University Health Arnett Hospital

**FRANCISCAN HEALTH - LAFAYETTE CENTRAL** See Franciscan Health Lafayette
Central

○ **FRANCISCAN HEALTH LAFAYETTE EAST (150109)**, 1701 South Creasy
Lane, Zip 47905–4972; tel. 765/502–4000, (Includes FRANCISCAN HEALTH
LAFAYETTE CENTRAL, Mailing address: 1501 Hartford Street, Lafayette, Indiana,
Zip 47904–2134; tel. 765/423–6011; Terrance E. Wilson, President and Chief
Executive Officer), (Nonreporting) **A**2 5 10 11 **S** Franciscan Health, Mishawaka, IN
Primary Contact: Terrance E. Wilson, President and Chief Executive Officer
Web address: www.ste.org
**Control**: Other not–for–profit (including NFP Corporation) **Service**: General
medical and surgical

**Staffed Beds**: 187

**FRANCISCAN ST. ELIZABETH HEALTH - LAFAYETTE EAST** See Franciscan
Health Lafayette East

☒ **INDIANA UNIVERSITY HEALTH ARNETT HOSPITAL (150173)**, 5165 McCarty
Lane, Zip 47905–8764, Mailing Address: P.O. Box 5545, Zip 47903–5545;
tel. 765/448–8000, (Nonreporting) **A**1 2 3 5 10 **F**3 8 11 12 13 15 17 18 20 22
24 26 28 29 30 31 34 35 40 43 45 46 49 50 51 54 56 57 59 61 64 65 68 69
70 72 74 75 76 77 78 79 81 82 84 85 87 89 92 93 97 104 107 108 110 111
114 115 116 117 118 119 120 121 126 129 130 131 132 135 144 145 146
147 148 149 150 154 156 **P**6 **S** Indiana University Health, Indianapolis, IN
Primary Contact: Daniel Neufelder, President
CFO: Cara Breidster, Chief Financial Officer
CMO: Jeffrey P Brown, M.D., Chief Medical Officer
CIO: Rusty McGill, System Director Information Technology
CHR: Koreen H Kyhnell, Vice President Human Resources
Web address: www.iuhealth.org
**Control**: Other not–for–profit (including NFP Corporation) **Service**: General
medical and surgical

**Staffed Beds**: 192 **Admissions**: 10364 **Census**: 128 **Outpatient
Visits**: 108923 **Births**: 1595 **Total Expense ($000)**: 459863 **Payroll
Expense ($000)**: 190680 **Personnel**: 1890

☐ **LAFAYETTE REGIONAL REHABILITATION HOSPITAL (153042)**, 950 Park East
Boulevard, Zip 47905–0792; tel. 765/447–4040, (Nonreporting) **A**1 10 **S** Ernest
Health, Inc., Albuquerque, NM
Primary Contact: Herschel Carey, Chief Executive Officer
Web address: www.lrrh.ernesthealth.com
**Control**: Corporation, Investor–owned (for–profit) **Service**: Rehabilitation

**Staffed Beds**: 40

**ST ELIZABETH MED CENTER** See St. Elizabeth Medical Center

☐ **SYCAMORE SPRINGS (154059)**, 833 Park East Boulevard, Zip 47905–0785;
tel. 765/743–4400, (Nonreporting) **A**1 10 **F**4 5 98 100 102 104 105 135 152
153 154 **P**6 **S** Springstone, Louisville, KY
Primary Contact: Denise Sullivan, Chief Executive Officer
CFO: Michael Huth, Chief Financial Officer
CMO: Nizar El Khalili, M.D., Medical Director
CHR: Pam Sichts, Director Human Resources
CNO: Brooke Lavignette, Director of Nursing
Web address: www.sycamorespringshealth.com
**Control**: Corporation, Investor–owned (for–profit) **Service**: Psychiatric

**Staffed Beds**: 48 **Admissions**: 2246 **Census**: 39 **Outpatient Visits**: 0
**Births**: 0 **Total Expense ($000)**: 15008 **Payroll Expense ($000)**: 8069
**Personnel**: 116

IN

*Many Facility Codes have changed. Please refer to the AHA Guide Code Chart.* © 2021 AHA Guide

## LAGRANGE—Lagrange County

**LAGRANGE COMMUNITY HOSPITAL** See Parkview Lagrange Hospital

✠ **PARKVIEW LAGRANGE HOSPITAL (151323)**, 207 North Townline Road, Zip 46761–1325; tel. 260/463–9000, (Nonreporting) **A**1 10 18 **F**3 7 13 15 17 26 29 30 34 35 40 45 50 51 57 59 63 64 70 75 76 79 81 82 83 84 85 86 87 89 90 93 96 107 108 109 110 111 114 118 119 128 130 132 133 143 146 148 154 156 **P**6 **S** Parkview Health, Fort Wayne, IN
Primary Contact: Jordi K. Disler, President
CFO: Vickie Stanski, Financial Manager
CMO: Jeffrey Brookes, M.D., Chief Medical Officer
CIO: Ron Double, Chief Information Technology Officer
CHR: Bruce Buttermore, Director Human Resources
CNO: Jared Beasley, R.N., Vice President Patient Care
Web address: www.parkview.com
**Control**: Other not–for–profit (including NFP Corporation) **Service**: General medical and surgical

**Staffed Beds: 25 Admissions: 1008 Census: 7 Outpatient Visits: 27463
Births: 230 Total Expense ($000): 36947 Payroll Expense ($000): 10453
Personnel: 155**

## LAWRENCEBURG—Dearborn County

**COMMUNITY MENTAL HEALTH CENTER (154011)**, 285 Bielby Road, Zip 47025–1055; tel. 812/537–1302, (Nonreporting) **A**10
Primary Contact: Tom Talbot, Chief Executive Officer
CFO: Georgii Zhirkin, Chief Financial Officer
CMO: Hasan Bakhtier, M.D., Medical Director
CIO: John McKinley, Director, Information Technology
CHR: Kelly Stewart, Director of Human Resources
Web address: www.cmhcinc.org
**Control**: Other not–for–profit (including NFP Corporation) **Service**: Psychiatric

**Staffed Beds: 16**

**DEARBORN COUNTY HOSPITAL** See Highpoint Health

★ ○ **HIGHPOINT HEALTH (150086)**, 600 Wilson Creek Road, Zip 47025–2751; tel. 812/537–1010, (Nonreporting) **A**10 11 **F**3 11 13 15 18 20 26 28 29 30 34 35 37 40 43 44 45 46 47 49 50 57 59 62 63 64 70 75 76 77 79 81 84 85 86 87 92 93 107 108 110 111 115 116 117 118 119 129 130 131 132 146 148 157 **P**7
Primary Contact: Michael W. Schwebler, President and Chief Executive Officer
CMO: Nancy A. Kennedy, M.D., Chief Medical Officer
CIO: Kathy Dickman, Director of Information Systems
CNO: Angela K. Scudder, MSN, R.N., Vice President Patient Care Services
Web address: www.dch.org
**Control**: County, Government, Nonfederal **Service**: General medical and surgical

**Staffed Beds: 60 Admissions: 2933 Census: 25 Outpatient Visits: 129217
Births: 353 Total Expense ($000): 79221 Payroll Expense ($000): 34185
Personnel: 513**

## LEBANON—Boone County

✠ **WITHAM HEALTH SERVICES (150104)**, 2605 North Lebanon Street, Zip 46052–1476, Mailing Address: P.O. Box 1200, Zip 46052–3005; tel. 765/485–8000, (Nonreporting) **A**1 3 10 **F**7 8 13 15 18 20 22 24 28 29 30 34 40 42 44 45 53 54 56 57 59 64 65 69 70 75 76 77 79 81 82 83 85 86 87 93 94 97 98 107 111 116 121 128 129 130 132 135 143 144 146 147 148 156 **P**1
Primary Contact: Raymond V. Ingham, Ph.D., President and Chief Executive Officer
COO: Diane Feder, R.N., FACHE, Senior Vice President and Chief Operating Officer
CFO: George Pogas, CPA, Senior Vice President and Chief Financial Officer
CMO: Anthony Steele, M.D., Chief Medical Officer
CIO: George Pogas, CPA, Senior Vice President and Chief Financial Officer
CHR: Gary A Deater, Vice President Administration, Human Resources and Risk Management
CNO: Diane Feder, R.N., FACHE, Senior Vice President and Chief Operating Officer
Web address: www.witham.org
**Control**: County, Government, Nonfederal **Service**: General medical and surgical

**Staffed Beds: 78 Admissions: 2761 Census: 43 Outpatient Visits: 156699
Births: 491 Total Expense ($000): 161993 Payroll Expense ($000): 65734
Personnel: 512**

**WITHAM MEMORIAL HOSPITAL** See Witham Health Services

## LINTON—Greene County

✠ **GREENE COUNTY GENERAL HOSPITAL (151317)**, 1185 North 1000 West, Zip 47441–5282; tel. 812/847–2281, (Nonreporting) **A**1 10 18 **F**1 3 6 11 13 15 26 27 28 29 31 34 35 39 40 41 44 45 55 56 57 58 59 64 65 66 67 68 70 75 76 77 78 79 81 85 86 87 89 90 91 93 96 97 107 108 110 111 114 119 127 128 130 131 133 135 144 146 147 148 149 154 156
Primary Contact: Brenda Reetz, FACHE, Chief Executive Officer
CFO: April Settles, Chief Financial Officer
CMO: Mike Gamble, M.D., Chief Medical Officer
CIO: Steve Phillips, Information Officer
CHR: Robin M. Rose, Director of Human Resources
CNO: Jill Raines, R.N., Chief of Clinical Quality
Web address: www.greenecountyhospital.com
**Control**: County, Government, Nonfederal **Service**: General medical and surgical

**Staffed Beds: 25 Admissions: 646 Census: 5 Outpatient Visits: 846050
Births: 89 Total Expense ($000): 40292 Payroll Expense ($000): 19846
Personnel: 343**

## LOGANSPORT—Cass County

**FOUR COUNTY COUNSELING CENTER (154035)**, 1015 Michigan Avenue, Zip 46947–1526; tel. 574/722–5151, (Nonreporting) **A**10
Primary Contact: Carrie Cadwell, PsyD, Chief Executive Officer
CFO: Jason Cadwell, Chief Financial Officer
CMO: John Yarling, M.D., Medical Director
CIO: Becky Mulis, Director of Health Information Management Systems
CHR: Steve Curry, Regional Director Human Resources
CNO: Donna Henry, Vice President of Nursing Services
Web address: www.fourcounty.org
**Control**: Other not–for–profit (including NFP Corporation) **Service**: Psychiatric

**Staffed Beds: 15**

★ ○ **LOGANSPORT MEMORIAL HOSPITAL (150072)**, 1101 Michigan Avenue, Zip 46947–1528, Mailing Address: P.O. Box 7013, Zip 46947–7013; tel. 574/753–7541, (Nonreporting) **A**10 11 20 **F**3 11 13 15 28 29 31 34 35 40 44 45 48 50 51 54 57 59 65 68 70 75 76 77 78 79 81 85 86 87 93 97 107 108 110 111 114 119 121 127 129 130 131 132 135 146 147 148 154 156 157 **P**6
Primary Contact: Perry Gay, President and Chief Executive Officer
CFO: Sherri Gehlhausen, Chief Financial Officer
CMO: Kamlesh Kaul, M.D., Chief of Staff
CIO: Dan Hildebrand, Chief Information Officer
CHR: Lynda J Shrock, Vice President Human Resources
CNO: Tara McVay, Chief Nursing Officer
Web address: www.logansportmemorial.org
**Control**: County, Government, Nonfederal **Service**: General medical and surgical

**Staffed Beds: 83 Admissions: 1622 Census: 12 Outpatient Visits: 123451
Births: 517 Total Expense ($000): 90275 Payroll Expense ($000): 35094
Personnel: 518**

□ **LOGANSPORT STATE HOSPITAL**, 1098 South State Road 25, Zip 46947–6723; tel. 574/737–3633, (Nonreporting) **A**1 **F**98 101 106 130
Primary Contact: Robert Clover, Superintendent and Chief Executive Officer
CFO: Misty Moss, Director Business Administration
CMO: Danny Meadows, M.D., Medical Director
CIO: Joe McIntosh, Director Management Information Systems
CHR: Dianne Renner, Director Human Resources
Web address: www.lshonline.org
**Control**: State, Government, Nonfederal **Service**: Psychiatric

**Staffed Beds: 170 Admissions: 141 Census: 139 Outpatient Visits: 0
Personnel: 422**

**MEMORIAL HOSPITAL** See Logansport Memorial Hospital

---

**Hospital, Medicare Provider Number, Address, Telephone, Approval, Facility, and Physician Codes, Health Care System**

| | | |
|---|---|---|
| ★ American Hospital Association (AHA) membership | ○ Healthcare Facilities Accreditation Program | ⇑ Center for Improvement in Healthcare Quality Accreditation |
| □ The Joint Commission accreditation | ◇ DNV Healthcare Inc. accreditation | △ Commission on Accreditation of Rehabilitation Facilities (CARF) accreditation |

IN

## MADISON—Jefferson County

★ ○ **KING'S DAUGHTERS' HEALTH (150069)**, 1373 East State Road 62, Zip 47250–3357, Mailing Address: P.O. Box 447, Zip 47250–0447; tel. 812/801–0800, (Nonreporting) **A**2 10 11 **F**3 7 8 12 13 15 18 28 29 30 31 32 34 35 40 45 48 50 55 56 57 59 62 63 64 65 68 70 74 75 76 77 78 79 81 82 84 85 86 87 91 93 94 97 107 108 110 111 115 119 120 121 123 129 130 131 132 134 135 144 145 146 147 148 149 150 156 **P**6
Primary Contact: Carol Dozier, President and Chief Executive Officer
CFO: John Price, Chief Financial Officer
CIO: Linda Darnell, Director Management Information Systems
CHR: Susan Kay Poling, Director Human Resources
CNO: Jennifer Lynn Liter, Vice President of Inpatient Services
Web address: www.kdhhs.org
**Control**: Other not–for–profit (including NFP Corporation) **Service**: General medical and surgical

**Staffed Beds**: 60 **Admissions**: 2995 **Census**: 29 **Outpatient Visits**: 203746 **Births**: 499 **Total Expense ($000)**: 124364 **Payroll Expense ($000)**: 50827 **Personnel**: 740

**KING'S DAUGHTERS' HOSPITAL AND HEALTH SERVICES** See King's Daughters' Health

☐ **MADISON STATE HOSPITAL (154019)**, 711 Green Road, Zip 47250–2199; tel. 812/265–2611, (Nonreporting) **A**1 10 **F**34 39 50 56 59 61 98 106 130 135 143 154 156
Primary Contact: Alicia Isaacs, Superintendent and Medical Director
CFO: Carolyn Copeland, Business Administrator
CIO: Ric Martin, Information Specialist
Web address: www.in.gov/fssa/msh
**Control**: State, Government, Nonfederal **Service**: Psychiatric

**Staffed Beds**: 120 **Admissions**: 32 **Census**: 110 **Outpatient Visits**: 0 **Births**: 0 **Total Expense ($000)**: 25484 **Payroll Expense ($000)**: 13294

## MARION—Grant County

☐ **GRANT-BLACKFORD MENTAL HEALTH CENTER (154021)**, 505 North Wabash Avenue, Zip 46952–2608; tel. 765/662–3971, (Nonreporting) **A**1 10 **F**5 98 99 100 101 102 103 104 106
Primary Contact: Paul Kuczora, Chief Executive Officer
Web address: www.cornerstone.org/
**Control**: Other not–for–profit (including NFP Corporation) **Service**: Psychiatric

**Staffed Beds**: 16 **Admissions**: 666 **Census**: 6 **Outpatient Visits**: 60773 **Births**: 0

★ ○ **MARION GENERAL HOSPITAL (150011)**, 441 North Wabash Avenue, Zip 46952–2690; tel. 765/660–6000, (Nonreporting) **A**2 10 11 **F**3 7 8 11 13 15 18 20 22 26 28 29 30 31 34 35 40 41 44 45 47 50 54 57 58 59 64 68 70 73 76 77 78 79 81 82 85 86 87 89 90 91 92 93 96 97 107 108 110 111 114 115 117 118 119 129 130 132 135 144 146 147 148 149 154 156 **P**6
Primary Contact: Stephanie Hilton-Siebert, MSN, President and Chief Executive Officer
CMO: Edward L. Keppler, M.D., Chief Medical Officer
CIO: Emmanuel Ndow, Chief Information Officer
CHR: Karen Jones, Administrative Director Human Resources
CNO: Cynthia Futrell, MSN, R.N., Chief Nursing Officer
Web address: www.mgh.net
**Control**: Other not–for–profit (including NFP Corporation) **Service**: General medical and surgical

**Staffed Beds**: 124 **Admissions**: 5114 **Census**: 56 **Outpatient Visits**: 254330 **Births**: 569 **Total Expense ($000)**: 184898 **Payroll Expense ($000)**: 65842 **Personnel**: 1043

**VETERANS AFFAIRS MED CENTER** See Veterans Affairs Northern Indiana Health Care System-Marion Campus

**VETERANS AFFAIRS NORTHERN INDIANA HEALTH CARE SYSTEM-MARION CAMPUS** See Veterans Affairs Northern Indiana Health Care System, Fort Wayne

## MERRILLVILLE—Lake County

**REGIONAL MENTAL HEALTH CENTER (154020)**, 8555 Taft Street, Zip 46410–6123; tel. 219/769–4005, (Nonreporting) **A**10
Primary Contact: William Trowbridge, President and Chief Executive Officer
Web address: www.regionalmentalhealth.org/
**Control**: Corporation, Investor–owned (for–profit) **Service**: Psychiatric

**Staffed Beds**: 16

**SOUTHLAKE CAMPUS** See Methodist Hospitals, Gary

**SOUTHLAKE CAMPUS** See Southlake Campus

**SOUTHLAKE CENTER FOR MENTAL HEALTH** See Regional Mental Health Center

## MICHIGAN CITY—Laporte County

**FRANCISCAN HEALTH - MICHIGAN CITY** See Franciscan Health Michigan City

○ **FRANCISCAN HEALTH MICHIGAN CITY (150015)**, 301 West Homer Street, Zip 46360–4358; tel. 219/879–8511, (Nonreporting) **A**2 10 11 19 **S** Franciscan Health, Mishawaka, IN
Primary Contact: Dean Mazzoni, President and Chief Executive Officer
CFO: Marc Golan, Regional Chief Financial Officer
CIO: Tim Loosemore, Regional Director Information Systems
CHR: John Barrett, Regional Director Human Resources
CNO: Trish Weber, R.N., FACHE, Vice President Operations and Chief Nursing Officer
Web address: www.franciscanalliance.org
**Control**: Church operated, Nongovernment, not–for–profit **Service**: General medical and surgical

**Staffed Beds**: 171

## MISHAWAKA—St. Joseph County

**MISHAWAKA MEDICAL CENTER** See Saint Joseph Health System

✠ **SAINT JOSEPH HEALTH SYSTEM (150012)**, 5215 Holy Cross Parkway, Zip 46545–1469; tel. 574/335–5000, (Nonreporting) **A**1 3 5 10 **S** Trinity Health, Livonia, MI
Primary Contact: Chad Towner, Chief Executive Officer
COO: Christopher J Karam, Chief Operating Officer
CFO: Kevin J Higdon, Chief Financial Officer
CMO: Genevieve Lankowicz, M.D., Chief Medical Officer
CIO: Gary L Miller, Senior Director Information Systems
CHR: Kurt A Meyer, Chief Human Resource Officer
CNO: Kenneth C Hall, R.N., Chief Nursing Officer
Web address: www.sjmed.com
**Control**: Other not–for–profit (including NFP Corporation) **Service**: General medical and surgical

**Staffed Beds**: 300

○ **UNITY MEDICAL & SURGICAL HOSPITAL (150177)**, 4455 Edison Lakes Parkway, Zip 46545–1442; tel. 574/231–6800, (Nonreporting) **A**10 11
Primary Contact: Kelly Macken-Marble, Interim President and Chief Executive Officer
COO: Donald Allen, Chief Operating Officer
CFO: Matthew M Sherwood, Chief Financial Officer
CMO: Viraj Patel, M.D., Chief Medical Officer
CIO: Richard Leighton, Financial Application Analyst
CHR: Emyle Kruyer-Collins, Chief Human Resources Officer
CNO: Sylvia K Coffing, R.N., MSN, Chief Nursing and Compliance Officer
Web address: www.umsh.net
**Control**: Partnership, Investor–owned (for–profit) **Service**: Surgical

**Staffed Beds**: 15

## MONTICELLO—White County

✠ **INDIANA UNIVERSITY HEALTH WHITE MEMORIAL HOSPITAL (151312)**, 720 South Sixth Street, Zip 47960–8182; tel. 574/583–7111, (Nonreporting) **A**1 10 18 **F**3 15 29 30 31 34 35 40 45 50 59 64 75 77 78 79 81 85 93 107 108 110 111 114 119 129 133 135 146 147 148 149 150 **S** Indiana University Health, Indianapolis, IN
Primary Contact: Mary Minier, President
CMO: Adel Khdour, M.D., Chief Medical Officer
CIO: Michelle Baker, Director Information Systems
CHR: JoEllyn Brockmeyer, Director Human Resources
CNO: Robin C Smith, Chief Nursing Officer
Web address: www.iuhealth.org/white-memorial
**Control**: Other not–for–profit (including NFP Corporation) **Service**: General medical and surgical

**Staffed Beds**: 25 **Admissions**: 629 **Census**: 7 **Outpatient Visits**: 41397 **Births**: 0 **Total Expense ($000)**: 30037 **Payroll Expense ($000)**: 8129 **Personnel**: 136

**IU HEALTH WHITE MEMORIAL HOSPITAL** See Indiana University Health White Memorial Hospital

IN

## MOORESVILLE—Morgan County

**FRANCISCAN - MOORESVILLE** See Franciscan Health Mooresville

○ **FRANCISCAN HEALTH MOORESVILLE (150057)**, 1201 Hadley Road, Zip 46158–1789; tel. 317/831–1160, (Nonreporting) **A**3 5 10 11 **S** Franciscan Health, Mishawaka, IN
Primary Contact: Peter J. Murphy, Senior Vice President and Chief Operating Officer
CIO: Barbara Coulter, Director Information Systems
CHR: John Ross, Vice President
CNO: Agnes Therady, MSN, FACHE, Vice President and Chief Nursing Officer
Web address: www.franciscanalliance.org/hospitals/mooresville/Pages/default.aspx
**Control**: Church operated, Nongovernment, not–for–profit **Service**: General medical and surgical

**Staffed Beds:** 115

## MUNCIE—Delaware County

**AMG SPECIALTY HOSPITAL - MUNCIE** See Central Indiana Amg Specialty Hospital

**BALL MEMORIAL HOSPITAL** See Indiana University Health Ball Memorial Hospital

○ **CENTRAL INDIANA AMG SPECIALTY HOSPITAL (152025)**, 2401 West University Avenue, 8th Floor, Zip 47303–3428; tel. 765/751–5253, (Includes AMG SPECIALTY HOSPITAL - CENTRAL INDIANA HANCOCK CAMPUS, Mailing address: 801 N. State Street, 3rd Floor West, Greenfield, Indiana, Zip 46140–1270; tel. 317/477–6789; William Hedge, Chief Executive Officer), (Nonreporting) **A**10 11
Primary Contact: William Hedge, Chief Executive Officer
CNO: Lisa G. Hayes, Chief Clinical Officer
Web address: www.amgmuncie.com/
**Control**: Corporation, Investor–owned (for–profit) **Service**: Acute long–term care hospital

**Staffed Beds:** 41

⊞ **INDIANA UNIVERSITY HEALTH BALL MEMORIAL HOSPITAL (150089)**, 2401 West University Avenue, Zip 47303–3499; tel. 765/747–3111, (Nonreporting) **A**1 2 3 5 10 19 **F**3 11 12 13 15 17 18 20 22 24 26 28 29 30 31 32 34 35 37 39 40 43 45 46 49 50 51 53 54 56 57 58 59 60 64 65 66 69 70 72 73 74 75 76 77 78 79 80 81 82 84 85 86 87 89 90 92 93 94 96 97 98 100 101 102 105 107 108 110 111 114 115 116 117 118 119 120 121 123 124 126 129 130 132 141 142 146 147 148 149 154 156 157 **S** Indiana University Health, Indianapolis, IN
Primary Contact: Jeffrey C. Bird, M.D., President
COO: Lori Luther, CPA, Chief Operating Officer
CFO: John Vanator, CPA, Chief Financial Officer
CMO: Peter Voss, M.D., Chief Medical Officer
CHR: Ann M. McGuire, Regional Vice President Human Resources
CNO: Carla C. Cox, Chief Nursing Officer
Web address: www.iuhealth.org
**Control**: Other not–for–profit (including NFP Corporation) **Service**: General medical and surgical

**Staffed Beds:** 332 **Admissions:** 15846 **Census:** 235 **Outpatient Visits:** 196967 **Births:** 1215 **Total Expense ($000):** 401016 **Payroll Expense ($000):** 112215 **Personnel:** 1831

**MERIDIAN HEALTH SERVICES (154053)**, 240 North Tillotson Avenue, Zip 47304; tel. 765/747–3281, (Nonreporting) **A**10
Primary Contact: Hank A. Milius, Chief Executive Officer
CMO: Sarfraz Khan, Medical Director
Web address: www.meridianhs.org
**Control**: Other not–for–profit (including NFP Corporation) **Service**: Psychiatric

**Staffed Beds:** 20

## MUNSTER—Lake County

□ △ **COMMUNITY HOSPITAL (150125)**, 901 Macarthur Boulevard, Zip 46321–2959; tel. 219/836–1600, (Nonreporting) **A**1 2 5 7 10 **S** Community Healthcare System, Hammond, IN
Primary Contact: Luis F. Molina, Chief Executive Officer and Administrator
CFO: Daniel R. O'Brien, Vice President and Chief Financial Officer
CMO: David Robinson, President Medical and Dental Staff
CIO: Gary Weiner, Vice President Information Technology, Chief Information Officer
CHR: Debbie Brandt, Director Human Resources
CNO: Ronda McKay, R.N., Vice President Patient Care Services, Chief Nursing Officer
Web address: www.comhs.org
**Control**: Other not–for–profit (including NFP Corporation) **Service**: General medical and surgical

**Staffed Beds:** 510

**FRANCISCAN HEALTHCARE - MUNSTER** See Franciscan Healthcare Munster

○ **FRANCISCAN HEALTHCARE MUNSTER (150165)**, 701 Superior Avenue, Zip 46321–4037; tel. 219/924–1300, (Nonreporting) **A**3 10 11 **S** Franciscan Health, Mishawaka, IN
Primary Contact: Patrick J. Maloney, Chief Executive Officer
CFO: Harold E Collins, JD, Chief Financial Officer
CMO: Vijay D Gupta, M.D., President and Chief Executive Officer
CIO: Steven Krause, Manager Information Technology
Web address: www.franciscanphysianshospital.org
**Control**: Partnership, Investor–owned (for–profit) **Service**: General medical and surgical

**Staffed Beds:** 32

## NEW ALBANY—Floyd County

○ **BAPTIST HEALTH FLOYD (150044)**, 1850 State Street, Zip 47150–4997; tel. 812/949–5500, (Nonreporting) **A**2 3 5 10 11 **F**3 8 11 12 13 15 17 18 20 22 24 26 28 29 30 31 32 34 35 36 40 43 44 45 46 47 49 50 53 54 55 57 58 59 62 64 70 74 75 76 77 78 79 80 81 82 84 85 86 87 89 92 93 100 107 108 109 110 111 114 115 116 117 118 119 120 121 123 124 129 130 131 132 135 144 145 146 147 148 149 154 156 157 **P**6 **S** Baptist Health, Louisville, KY
Primary Contact: Mike K. Schroyer, FACHE, MSN, R.N., President
COO: Mark Truman, Vice President of Operations
CIO: Brian Cox, Director Information Systems
CNO: Kelly McMinoway, R.N., Vice President, Nursing
Web address: www.baptisthealth.com/floyd
**Control**: Other not–for–profit (including NFP Corporation) **Service**: General medical and surgical

**Staffed Beds:** 236 **Admissions:** 12645 **Census:** 141 **Outpatient Visits:** 262459 **Births:** 1053 **Total Expense ($000):** 282371 **Payroll Expense ($000):** 95317 **Personnel:** 1657

**FLOYD MEMORIAL HOSPITAL AND HEALTH SERVICES** See Baptist Health Floyd

□ **PHYSICIANS' MEDICAL CENTER (150172)**, 4023 Reas Lane, Zip 47150–2228; tel. 812/206–7660, (Nonreporting) **A**1 3 5 10 **F**3 12 29 45 51 77 79 81 82 85 89 94 107 111 144
Primary Contact: Dennis Medley, Chief Executive Officer and Administrator
COO: Rob Jones, Director of Nursing and Operations
CFO: Dennis Medley, Chief Executive Officer
CMO: Perry Cassady, M.D., Medical Director
CIO: Rob Jones, Director of Nursing and Operations
CHR: Mary Arntz, Manager Business Office and Executive Assistant
CNO: Rob Jones, Director of Nursing and Operations
Web address: www.pmcindiana.com
**Control**: Partnership, Investor–owned (for–profit) **Service**: General medical and surgical

**Staffed Beds:** 19 **Admissions:** 1566 **Census:** 5 **Outpatient Visits:** 25748 **Births:** 0 **Total Expense ($000):** 36516 **Payroll Expense ($000):** 11236

**IN**

---

**Hospital, Medicare Provider Number, Address, Telephone, Approval, Facility, and Physician Codes, Health Care System**

★ American Hospital Association (AHA) membership
□ The Joint Commission accreditation
○ Healthcare Facilities Accreditation Program
◇ DNV Healthcare Inc. accreditation
⇧ Center for Improvement in Healthcare Quality Accreditation
△ Commission on Accreditation of Rehabilitation Facilities (CARF) accreditation

☒ △ **SOUTHERN INDIANA REHABILITATION HOSPITAL (153037)**, 3104 Blackiston Boulevard, Zip 47150–9579; tel. 812/941–8300, (Nonreporting) **A**1 7 10 **S** Vibra Healthcare, Mechanicsburg, PA
Primary Contact: William Boso, Executive Director, Administrator
CFO: Robert Steltenpohl, Vice President
CMO: John C Shaw, M.D., Medical Director
CHR: Lisa Burris, Director Human Resources
CNO: Suzann Byers, Director of Nursing
Web address: www.sirh.org
**Control**: Other not–for–profit (including NFP Corporation) **Service**: Rehabilitation

**Staffed Beds**: 60

### NEW CASTLE—Henry County

★ ○ **HENRY COMMUNITY HEALTH (150030)**, 1000 North 16th Street, Zip 47362–4319, Mailing Address: P.O. Box 490, Zip 47362–0490; tel. 765/521–0890, (Nonreporting) **A**10 11 **F**3 8 13 15 28 29 30 32 34 35 36 40 44 45 46 47 48 49 53 54 57 59 62 63 64 65 66 68 70 75 76 77 79 81 82 85 86 87 89 92 93 96 97 104 107 108 110 111 114 115 118 119 127 129 130 131 132 135 144 146 147 148 149 154 156
Primary Contact: Paul Janssen, President and Chief Executive Officer
COO: Brian K Ring, Chief Operating Officer
CFO: Darin Brown, Chief Financial Officer
CMO: Arun Tewari, M.D., Chief Medical Officer
CIO: Mike Spencer, Chief Information Officer
CHR: Deanna Malott, Director Human Resources
CNO: Shelley Wilson, R.N., Chief Nursing Officer
Web address: www.hcmhcares.org
**Control**: County, Government, Nonfederal **Service**: General medical and surgical

**Staffed Beds**: 60 **Admissions**: 2291 **Census**: 21 **Outpatient Visits**: 106611 **Births**: 324 **Total Expense ($000)**: 138011 **Payroll Expense ($000)**: 57406 **Personnel**: 833

**HENRY COUNTY HOSPITAL** See Henry Community Health

### NEWBURGH—Warrick County

**BRENTWOOD MEADOWS** See Brentwood Springs

☐ **BRENTWOOD SPRINGS (154055)**, 4488 Roslin Road, Zip 47630; tel. 812/858–7200, (Nonreporting) **A**1 10 **S** Springstone, Louisville, KY
Primary Contact: Kim Retzner, Chief Executive Officer
Web address: www.https://brentwoodsprings.com
**Control**: Partnership, Investor–owned (for–profit) **Service**: Psychiatric

**Staffed Beds**: 48

☒ **ENCOMPASS HEALTH DEACONESS REHABILITATION HOSPITAL (153025)**, 9355 Warrick Trail, Zip 47630–0015; tel. 812/476–9983, (Nonreporting) **A**1 10 **F**3 28 29 75 87 90 91 94 95 96 130 132 143 148 149 **S** Encompass Health Corporation, Birmingham, AL
Primary Contact: Blake Bunner, Chief Executive Officer
CFO: Rhonda Ramsey, Controller
CMO: Mohammed Adeel, Medical Director
CHR: Wendy Gumbel, Director of Human Resources
CNO: Trish Draeger, Chief Nursing Officer
Web address: www.healthsouthdeaconess.com
**Control**: Corporation, Investor–owned (for–profit) **Service**: Rehabilitation

**Staffed Beds**: 98 **Admissions**: 2164 **Census**: 78 **Outpatient Visits**: 0 **Births**: 0 **Total Expense ($000)**: 27880 **Payroll Expense ($000)**: 13421 **Personnel**: 261

**HEALTHSOUTH DEACONESS REHABILITATION HOSPITAL** See Encompass Health Deaconess Rehabilitation Hospital

**THE HEART HOSPITAL AT DEACONESS GATEWAY** See Deaconess Gateway Hospital

★ ○ **THE WOMEN'S HOSPITAL (150149)**, 4199 Gateway Boulevard, Zip 47630–8940; tel. 812/842–4200, (Nonreporting) **A**3 10 11 **F**3 13 15 29 30 34 35 36 40 50 53 55 57 59 63 64 65 72 75 76 77 81 84 85 86 87 93 110 119 126 130 132 134 135 147 154 **P**6 **S** Deaconess Health System, Evansville, IN
Primary Contact: Christina M. Ryan, R.N., Chief Executive Officer
CFO: Tina Cady, Controller
CIO: Jenny Skelton, System Integration Manager
CHR: Jerri Sue Traylor, Director Human Resources
CNO: Christina M Ryan, R.N., Chief Executive Officer and Chief Nursing Officer
Web address: www.deaconess.com
**Control**: Partnership, Investor–owned (for–profit) **Service**: Obstetrics and gynecology

**Staffed Beds**: 74 **Admissions**: 3776 **Census**: 49 **Outpatient Visits**: 47967 **Births**: 3171 **Total Expense ($000)**: 95500 **Payroll Expense ($000)**: 42800 **Personnel**: 595

### NOBLESVILLE—Hamilton County

○ △ **RIVERVIEW HEALTH (150059)**, 395 Westfield Road, Zip 46060–1425, Mailing Address: P.O. Box 220, Zip 46061–0220; tel. 317/773–0760, (Nonreporting) **A**5 7 10 11 **F**3 11 13 15 17 18 20 22 26 28 29 30 31 34 35 37 40 42 45 49 50 53 54 56 57 59 60 64 65 70 73 74 75 76 77 78 79 81 82 85 86 87 89 90 92 93 94 96 97 104 107 108 110 111 114 115 118 119 120 121 123 124 126 129 130 131 132 144 146 147 148 149 154
Primary Contact: Seth Warren, President and Chief Executive Officer
COO: Lawrence Christman, Chief Financial Officer and Chief Operating Officer
CFO: Brenda Baker, Chief Financial Officer
CMO: Eric Marcotte, M.D., Chief Medical Officer
CIO: Brant Bucciarelli, Chief Information Officer
CHR: Ann Kuzee, Executive Director Human Resources
CNO: Joyce Wood, Vice President Organizational Improvement and Chief Nursing Officer
Web address: www.riverview.org
**Control**: County, Government, Nonfederal **Service**: General medical and surgical

**Staffed Beds**: 176 **Admissions**: 4673 **Census**: 67 **Outpatient Visits**: 438825 **Births**: 606 **Total Expense ($000)**: 231933 **Payroll Expense ($000)**: 81630 **Personnel**: 1004

**RIVERVIEW HOSPITAL** See Riverview Health

### NORTH VERNON—Jennings County

☒ **ASCENSION ST. VINCENT JENNINGS (151303)**, 301 Henry Street, Zip 47265–1097; tel. 812/352–4200, (Nonreporting) **A**1 10 18 **F**3 29 30 34 35 40 44 45 56 57 59 64 81 85 91 93 107 111 115 119 128 133 146 148 **S** Ascension Healthcare, Saint Louis, MO
Primary Contact: Dana M. Muntz, Chief Executive Officer
CFO: Joseph Kubala, Chief Financial Officer
CMO: Jennifer Stanley, M.D., Chief Medical Officer
CHR: Kathryn Johnson, Manager Human Resources, Marketing and Public Relations
Web address: www.stvincent.org
**Control**: Other not–for–profit (including NFP Corporation) **Service**: General medical and surgical

**Staffed Beds**: 17 **Admissions**: 208 **Census**: 3 **Outpatient Visits**: 45773 **Total Expense ($000)**: 16154 **Payroll Expense ($000)**: 3240 **Personnel**: 57

**ST. VINCENT JENNINGS HOSPITAL** See Ascension St. Vincent Jennings

### PAOLI—Orange County

**BLOOMINGTON HOSPITAL OF ORANGE COUNTY** See Indiana University Health Paoli Hospital

☒ **INDIANA UNIVERSITY HEALTH PAOLI HOSPITAL (151306)**, 642 West Hospital Road, Zip 47454–9672, Mailing Address: P.O. Box 499, Zip 47454–0499; tel. 812/723–2811, (Nonreporting) **A**1 10 18 **F**3 13 15 29 30 35 40 45 50 53 57 59 64 76 77 81 84 85 89 93 107 110 111 114 119 129 132 133 135 146 148 149 150 154 **S** Indiana University Health, Indianapolis, IN
Primary Contact: Larry Bailey, President
COO: Sonya M. Zeller, R.N., Vice President, Chief Operating Officer and Chief Nursing Officer
CMO: Jose Lopez, M.D., Medical Staff President
CNO: Sonya M. Zeller, R.N., Vice President, Chief Operating Officer and Chief Nursing Officer
Web address: www.iuhealth.org/paoli
**Control**: Other not–for–profit (including NFP Corporation) **Service**: General medical and surgical

**Staffed Beds**: 24 **Admissions**: 301 **Census**: 3 **Outpatient Visits**: 31772 **Births**: 100 **Total Expense ($000)**: 25429 **Payroll Expense ($000)**: 7626 **Personnel**: 114

**IN**

## PERU—Miami County

✠ **DUKES MEMORIAL HOSPITAL (151318)**, 275 West 12th Street, Zip 46970–1638; tel. 765/472–8000, (Nonreporting) **A**1 10 18 **F**7 8 15 18 28 29 34 35 40 50 56 57 59 64 68 69 70 75 76 77 81 93 97 107 108 109 110 111 115 119 129 130 133 144 146 147 149 154 **P**5 6 **S** Community Health Systems, Inc., Franklin, TN
Primary Contact: Debra Close, Chief Executive Officer
CFO: Adam Cumbo, Chief Financial Officer
CMO: Neil Stalker, M.D., Chief of Staff
Web address: www.dukesmemorialhosp.com
**Control:** Corporation, Investor–owned (for–profit) **Service:** General medical and surgical

**Staffed Beds:** 25 **Admissions:** 994 **Census:** 9 **Outpatient Visits:** 36651 **Births:** 140 **Total Expense ($000):** 33568 **Payroll Expense ($000):** 13189 **Personnel:** 200

## PLYMOUTH—Marshall County

**BEHAVIORAL HLTHCARE OF INDIANA** See Michiana Behavioral Health Center

☐ **MICHIANA BEHAVIORAL HEALTH CENTER (154047)**, 1800 North Oak Drive, Zip 46563–3492; tel. 574/936–3784, (Nonreporting) **A**1 10 **S** Universal Health Services, Inc., King of Prussia, PA
Primary Contact: Zach Glassburn, Chief Executive Officer
CFO: Jeff Calvin, Chief Financial Officer
CMO: Robert Raster, M.D., Medical Director
CIO: Leslie McLaughlin, Director of Business Development
CHR: Becky Nowicki, Director Human Resources
CNO: Brandi Richard, Chief Nursing Officer
Web address: www.https://michianabehavioralhealth.com
**Control:** Corporation, Investor–owned (for–profit) **Service:** Psychiatric

**Staffed Beds:** 75

✠ **PLYMOUTH MEDICAL CENTER (150076)**, 1915 Lake Avenue, Zip 46563–9366, Mailing Address: P.O. Box 670, Zip 46563–0670; tel. 574/948–4000, (Nonreporting) **A**1 10 **S** Trinity Health, Livonia, MI
Primary Contact: Christopher J. Karam, President
COO: Tamara Awald, Chief Nursing Officer and Chief Operating Officer
CFO: Janice Dunn, Chief Financial Officer
CMO: Stephen Anderson, M.D., Chief Medical Officer
CIO: Gary L Miller, Regional Director Information Systems
CHR: Kurt A Meyer, Chief Human Resources Officer
Web address: www.sjmed.com
**Control:** Other not–for–profit (including NFP Corporation) **Service:** General medical and surgical

**Staffed Beds:** 48

**SAINT JOSEPH REGIONAL MEDICAL CENTER-PLYMOUTH CAMPUS** See Plymouth Medical Center

## PORTLAND—Jay County

✠ **INDIANA UNIVERSITY HEALTH JAY HOSPITAL (151320)**, 500 West Votaw Street, Zip 47371–1322; tel. 260/726–7131, (Nonreporting) **A**1 10 18 **F**3 8 11 13 15 28 29 30 32 34 35 40 45 50 57 59 68 75 76 77 81 85 86 87 89 90 93 98 104 107 108 110 111 114 115 119 129 130 132 133 135 146 148 157 **S** Indiana University Health, Indianapolis, IN
Primary Contact: John Vanator, CPA, Chief Executive Officer
CHR: Linda Guise, Senior Human Resource Consultant
CNO: Rebecca Clark, Chief Nursing Officer
Web address: www.iuhealth.org
**Control:** Other not–for–profit (including NFP Corporation) **Service:** General medical and surgical

**Staffed Beds:** 37 **Admissions:** 931 **Census:** 10 **Outpatient Visits:** 77382 **Births:** 79 **Total Expense ($000):** 39079 **Payroll Expense ($000):** 11571 **Personnel:** 207

**JAY COUNTY HOSPITAL** See Indiana University Health Jay Hospital

## PRINCETON—Gibson County

✠ **GIBSON GENERAL HOSPITAL (151319)**, 1808 Sherman Drive, Zip 47670–9931; tel. 812/385–3401, (Total facility includes 45 beds in nursing home–type unit) (Nonreporting) **A**1 10 18 **F**3 11 15 28 29 31 34 35 38 40 44 45 49 50 57 58 59 62 64 68 70 75 77 81 82 89 93 97 102 107 110 111 115 119 127 128 129 130 132 133 148 **S** Deaconess Health System, Evansville, IN
Primary Contact: Claudia A. Eisenmann, President and Chief Executive Officer
CFO: Jared M. Stimpson, Vice Presdient and Chief Financial Officer
CMO: M. S. Krishna, M.D., Chief of Medical Staff
CIO: Jarad Lear, Interim Director of Information Services
CNO: Lois Morgan, R.N., MSN, Vice President and Chief Nursing Officer
Web address: www.gibsongeneral.com
**Control:** Other not–for–profit (including NFP Corporation) **Service:** General medical and surgical

**Staffed Beds:** 70 **Admissions:** 579 **Census:** 28 **Outpatient Visits:** 35797 **Births:** 0 **Total Expense ($000):** 27768 **Payroll Expense ($000):** 10613 **Personnel:** 269

## RENSSELAER—Jasper County

**FRANCISCAN HEALTH RENSSELAER (151324)**, 1104 East Grace Street, Zip 47978–3296; tel. 219/866–5141, (Nonreporting) **A**10 18 **S** Franciscan Health, Mishawaka, IN
Primary Contact: Carlos Vasquez, Vice President and Chief Operating Officer
CFO: Jeffrey D Webb, CPA, Chief Financial Officer
CIO: Kirby Reed, Director Information Systems
CHR: Deana Brown, Director Administrative Services
CNO: Stacie Klingler, R.N., Vice President of Patient Services
Web address: www.franciscanhealth.org
**Control:** Church operated, Nongovernment, not–for–profit **Service:** General medical and surgical

**Staffed Beds:** 46

**JASPER COUNTY HOSPITAL** See Franciscan Health Rensselaer

## RICHMOND—Wayne County

★ ○ **REID HEALTH (150048)**, 1100 Reid Parkway, Zip 47374–1157; tel. 765/983–3000, (Includes REID HEALTH CARE PAVILION, Mailing address: 450 Erie Avenue, Connersville, Indiana, Zip 47331–3176; tel. 765/827–7890; Craig C. Kinyon, President and Chief Executive Officer), (Nonreporting) **A**2 3 **F**3 4 5 7 8 11 13 15 18 20 22 24 26 28 29 30 31 34 35 37 38 40 42 43 44 45 49 50 51 53 54 55 56 57 58 59 61 63 64 68 69 70 71 74 75 76 77 78 79 81 82 83 84 85 86 87 89 90 91 92 93 95 96 97 98 99 100 101 102 103 104 106 107 108 110 111 114 115 116 117 118 119 120 121 123 124 126 127 129 130 131 132 135 143 144 146 147 148 149 151 154 156 **P**6 8
Primary Contact: Craig C. Kinyon, President and Chief Executive Officer
CFO: Christopher D. Knight, Vice President Finance and Chief Financial Officer
CMO: Thomas Huth, M.D., Vice President Medical Affairs
CIO: Tim Love, Director Information Services
CHR: Scott C Rauch, Vice President Human Resources
CNO: Misti Foust-Cofield, R.N., Vice President and Chief Nursing Officer
Web address: www.reidhealth.org
**Control:** Other not–for–profit (including NFP Corporation) **Service:** General medical and surgical

**Staffed Beds:** 261 **Admissions:** 12546 **Census:** 159 **Outpatient Visits:** 318352 **Births:** 820 **Total Expense ($000):** 512282 **Payroll Expense ($000):** 224367 **Personnel:** 3048

**REID HOSPITAL AND HEALTH CARE SERVICES** See Reid Health

☐ **RICHMOND STATE HOSPITAL (154018)**, 498 NW 18th Street, Zip 47374–2851; tel. 765/966–0511, (Nonreporting) **A**1 10 **F**56 98 103 130 135 146 154 **P**6
Primary Contact: Katrina Norris, Superintendent
CFO: Dave Shelford, Assistant Superintendent
CMO: Donald Graber, M.D., Medical Director
CIO: Robert Boatman, Director Information Technology
CHR: Sarah Witt, Director Human Resources
Web address: www.richmondstatehospital.org
**Control:** State, Government, Nonfederal **Service:** Psychiatric

**Staffed Beds:** 179 **Admissions:** 123 **Census:** 169 **Outpatient Visits:** 0 **Births:** 0 **Total Expense ($000):** 30363 **Payroll Expense ($000):** 14417 **Personnel:** 356

IN

---

**Hospital, Medicare Provider Number, Address, Telephone, Approval, Facility, and Physician Codes, Health Care System**

★ American Hospital Association (AHA) membership
☐ The Joint Commission accreditation
○ Healthcare Facilities Accreditation Program
◇ DNV Healthcare Inc. accreditation
⇑ Center for Improvement in Healthcare Quality Accreditation
△ Commission on Accreditation of Rehabilitation Facilities (CARF) accreditation

## ROCHESTER—Fulton County

★ ○ **WOODLAWN HOSPITAL (151313)**, 1400 East Ninth Street,
Zip 46975–8937; tel. 574/223–3141, (Nonreporting) **A**10 11 18 **F**3 11 13 15 28
29 30 31 34 40 46 56 57 59 65 68 69 70 75 76 77 78 79 81 82 93 94 97 107
108 110 111 115 119 129 130 132 133 135 146 147 148 149
Primary Contact: John L. Alley, Chief Executive Officer
CFO: John Kraft, Chief Financial Officer
Web address: www.woodlawnhospital.com
**Control:** County, Government, Nonfederal **Service:** General medical and surgical

**Staffed Beds:** 25 **Admissions:** 899 **Census:** 9 **Outpatient Visits:** 51829
**Births:** 160 **Total Expense ($000):** 58632 **Payroll Expense ($000):** 25745
**Personnel:** 353

## RUSHVILLE—Rush County

★ **RUSH MEMORIAL HOSPITAL (151304)**, 1300 North Main Street,
Zip 46173–1198; tel. 765/932–4111, (Nonreporting) **A**10 18
Primary Contact: Bradley Smith, President and Chief Executive Officer
COO: Gretchen Smith, Vice President of Operations, Risk and Compliance, and
Chief Operating Officer
CFO: Karen Meyer, Vice President Finance and Chief Financial Officer
CMO: Donald Snyder, M.D., Chief Medical Officer
CIO: Jim Boyer, Vice President Information Technology and Chief Information
Officer
CHR: Brian R Bane, Vice President Human Resources
CNO: Carrie Tressler, Vice President of Nursing and Chief Nursing Officer
Web address: www.rushmemorial.com
**Control:** County, Government, Nonfederal **Service:** General medical and surgical

**Staffed Beds:** 25

## SALEM—Washington County

☒ **ASCENSION ST. VINCENT SALEM (151314)**, 911 North Shelby Street,
Zip 47167–1694; tel. 812/883–5881, (Nonreporting) **A**1 10 18 **F**3 11 15 28 29
30 32 34 40 45 47 49 57 59 75 77 79 81 82 85 93 107 111 114 119 124 129
130 131 132 133 148 154 **S** Ascension Healthcare, Saint Louis, MO
Primary Contact: Dana M. Muntz, Chief Executive Officer
CFO: Joseph Kubala, Director Financial and Support Services
CMO: S E Kemker, M.D., President Medical Staff
CIO: Jeremy Long, Manager Information Systems
CHR: Val Potter, Director Human Resources
Web address: www.stvincent.org/St-Vincent-Salem/Default.aspx
**Control:** Other not–for–profit (including NFP Corporation) **Service:** General
medical and surgical

**Staffed Beds:** 25 **Admissions:** 67 **Census:** 2 **Outpatient Visits:** 34089
**Births:** 0 **Total Expense ($000):** 17164 **Payroll Expense ($000):** 4684
**Personnel:** 71

**ST. VINCENT SALEM HOSPITAL** See Ascension St. Vincent Salem

## SCOTTSBURG—Scott County

☒ **SCOTT MEMORIAL HEALTH (151334)**, 1415 North Gardner Street, Zip 47170,
Mailing Address: Box 430, Zip 47170–0430; tel. 812/752–3456, (Nonreporting)
**A**1 10 18 **S** LifePoint Health, Brentwood, TN
Primary Contact: Martin Padgett, Acting Chief Executive Officer
COO: Scott Edwards, Chief Operating Officer
CFO: Angela Doan, Chief Financial Officer
CNO: Dawn Mays, Chief Nursing Officer
Web address: www.scottmemorial.com
**Control:** County, Government, Nonfederal **Service:** General medical and surgical

**Staffed Beds:** 25

**SCOTT MEMORIAL HOSPITAL** See Scott Memorial Health

## SEYMOUR—Jackson County

**MEMORIAL HOSPITAL** See Schneck Medical Center

☒ **SCHNECK MEDICAL CENTER (150065)**, 411 West Tipton Street,
Zip 47274–2363, Mailing Address: P.O. Box 2349, Zip 47274–5000;
tel. 812/522–2349, (Nonreporting) **A**1 2 10 **F**3 5 12 13 15 18 28 29 30 31 34
35 36 40 45 48 53 56 57 59 62 63 64 65 68 69 70 74 75 76 77 78 79 81 82
84 85 87 89 91 93 97 100 101 104 107 110 111 114 115 119 120 121 123
124 126 129 130 131 132 133 135 144 146 147 148
Primary Contact: Eric Fish, M.D., President and Chief Executive Officer
CFO: Deborah Ridlen, CPA, Vice President Finance and Chief Financial Officer
CMO: Eric Fish, M.D., Vice President of Medical Affairs and Chief Medical Officers
CIO: Craig Rice, Director Information Technology
CHR: Kathy Covert, MSN, Vice President Workforce Development and
Organizational Development
CNO: Amy Pettit, R.N., Vice President Nursing Services and Chief Nursing Officer
Web address: www.schneckmed.org
**Control:** County, Government, Nonfederal **Service:** General medical and surgical

**Staffed Beds:** 84 **Admissions:** 2497 **Census:** 24 **Outpatient Visits:** 335444
**Births:** 741 **Total Expense ($000):** 157163 **Payroll Expense ($000):** 71391
**Personnel:** 947

## SHELBYVILLE—Shelby County

★ ○ **MAJOR HOSPITAL (150097)**, 150 West Washington Street,
Zip 46176–1236, Mailing Address: 2451 Intelliplex Drive, Zip 46176;
tel. 317/392–3211, (Nonreporting) **A**2 10 11
Primary Contact: John M. Horner, President and Chief Executive Officer
CFO: Ralph Mercuri, Vice President and Chief Financial Officer
CMO: Douglas S Carter, M.D., Vice President and Chief Medical Officer
CIO: Carol Huesman, Chief Information Officer
CHR: Nicki Sparling, Manager Human Resources
CNO: Valerie L Miller, MSN, R.N., Director of Nursing
Web address: www.majorhospital.org
**Control:** City–county, Government, Nonfederal **Service:** General medical and surgical

**Staffed Beds:** 52

## SOUTH BEND—St. Joseph County

**DOR-A-LIN OF SOUTH BEND** See Saint Joseph's Care Center Notre Dame

## SOUTH BEND—St Joseph County

**MEMORIAL CHILDREN'S HOSPITAL** See Beacon Children's Hospital

## SOUTH BEND—St. Joseph County

**MEMORIAL HOSPITAL** See Memorial Hospital of South Bend

☒ △ **MEMORIAL HOSPITAL OF SOUTH BEND (150058)**, 615 North Michigan
Street, Zip 46601–1033; tel. 574/647–1000, (Includes BEACON CHILDREN'S
HOSPITAL, Mailing address: 615 North Michigan Street, South Bend, Indiana,
Zip 46601; tel. 574/647–1000), (Nonreporting) **A**1 2 3 5 7 10 **F**3 7 8 12 13 15
17 18 19 20 22 24 26 28 29 30 31 34 35 36 38 40 42 43 45 46 47 49 50 53
55 56 58 59 60 61 64 65 67 68 70 72 73 74 75 76 77 78 79 81 82 84 85 86
87 88 89 90 91 92 93 96 98 99 100 102 103 107 108 110 114 115 116 118
119 120 121 123 124 126 129 130 131 132 135 145 146 147 148 150 154
155 156 **S** Beacon Health System, South Bend, IN
Primary Contact: Larry A. Tracy Jr, FACHE, President
CFO: Jeff Costello, Chief Financial Officer, Beacon Health System
CMO: Cheryl Wibbens, M.D., Vice President Medical Staff Affairs
CIO: Mark Warlick, Chief Information Officer
CHR: Steven M Eller, Chief Human Resources Officer
Web address: www.beaconhealthsystem.org
**Control:** Other not–for–profit (including NFP Corporation) **Service:** General
medical and surgical

**Staffed Beds:** 430 **Admissions:** 19353 **Census:** 283 **Outpatient
Visits:** 192328 **Births:** 2360 **Total Expense ($000):** 473239 **Payroll
Expense ($000):** 165239 **Personnel:** 2784

## SULLIVAN—Sullivan County

**MARY SHERMAN HOSPITAL** See Sullivan County Community Hospital

★ ○ **SULLIVAN COUNTY COMMUNITY HOSPITAL (151327)**, 2200 North Section Street, Zip 47882–7523, Mailing Address: P.O. Box 10, Zip 47882–0010; tel. 812/268–4311, (Nonreporting) **A**10 11 18 **F**3 8 11 13 15 28 29 32 34 35 40 44 45 47 48 50 53 56 57 59 61 62 65 69 70 75 76 77 78 79 81 86 87 93 97 107 110 111 114 116 117 118 119 127 129 130 131 133 146 147 148 154 156 **P**7 **S** QHR Health, Brentwood, TN
Primary Contact: Michelle Franklin, Chief Executive Officer
CFO: Jim Bishop, Chief Financial Officer
CMO: Divyesh Purohit, M.D., Chief of Staff
CIO: Hap Beckes, Director Information Systems
CHR: Denise Hart, Director Human Resources
CNO: Lori Resler, R.N., Chief Nurse
Web address: www.schosp.com
**Control**: County, Government, Nonfederal **Service**: General medical and surgical

**Staffed Beds**: 25 **Admissions**: 591 **Census**: 7 **Outpatient Visits**: 68330 **Births**: 92 **Total Expense ($000)**: 35670 **Payroll Expense ($000)**: 16849 **Personnel**: 312

### TELL CITY—Perry County

★ ○ **PERRY COUNTY MEMORIAL HOSPITAL (151322)**, 8885 State Road 237, Zip 47586–2750; tel. 812/547–7011, (Nonreporting) **A**10 11 18 **F**3 7 11 13 15 17 18 28 29 30 31 34 35 40 41 45 50 53 56 57 59 62 64 65 68 70 76 77 78 79 81 82 85 87 89 107 110 111 115 119 124 127 128 129 130 133 135 144 146 148 154 **S** Alliant Management Services, Louisville, KY
Primary Contact: Brian J. Herwig, President and Chief Executive Officer
CMO: James Rogan, M.D., Chief Medical Officer
CIO: Debbie Kleeman, Director Information Systems
CHR: Marchelle Heslep, Human Resources Director
Web address: www.pchospital.org
**Control**: County, Government, Nonfederal **Service**: General medical and surgical

**Staffed Beds**: 25 **Admissions**: 562 **Census**: 5 **Outpatient Visits**: 62096 **Births**: 47 **Total Expense ($000)**: 42745 **Payroll Expense ($000)**: 14459 **Personnel**: 273

### TERRE HAUTE—Vigo County

**COLUMBIA TERRE HAUTE REG HOSP** See Terre Haute Regional Hospital

**HAMILTON CENTER (154009)**, 620 Eighth Avenue, Zip 47804–2744; tel. 812/231–8323, (Nonreporting) **A**10
Primary Contact: Melvin Burks, Chief Executive Officer
COO: Robb Johnson, Director Operations
CFO: Renee Utley, Chief Financial Officer
CMO: Ahsan Mahmood, M.D., Chief Medical Officer
CIO: Hans Eilbracht, Chief Information Officer
CHR: Margie Anshutz, Chief Development Officer
CNO: Rose Christy, Executive Director of Medical Services
Web address: www.hamiltoncenter.org
**Control**: State, Government, Nonfederal **Service**: Psychiatric

**Staffed Beds**: 16

☐ **HARSHA BEHAVIORAL CENTER (154054)**, 1980 East Woodsmall Drive, Zip 47802–4937; tel. 866/644–8880, (Nonreporting) **A**1 10
Primary Contact: Roopam Harshawat, President and Chief Executive Officer
COO: Holly Near, Chief Administrative Officer
CFO: Holly Near, Chief Administrative Officer
CMO: Paras Harshawat, M.D., Medical Director
CHR: Karen Hunt, Executive Director
CNO: Cindy Dowers, Chief Nursing Officer
Web address: www.harshacenter.com
**Control**: Corporation, Investor–owned (for–profit) **Service**: Psychiatric

**Staffed Beds**: 44

⊞ **TERRE HAUTE REGIONAL HOSPITAL (150046)**, 3901 South Seventh Street, Zip 47802–5709; tel. 812/232–0021, (Nonreporting) **A**1 2 10 **S** HCA Healthcare, Nashville, TN
Primary Contact: Nathan Vooys, Chief Executive Officer
COO: Andrea Gwyn, Chief Operating Officer
CIO: Mike Kuckewich, Director Information Systems
CNO: Angela Ellis, R.N., Chief Nursing Officer
Web address: www.regionalhospital.com
**Control**: Corporation, Investor–owned (for–profit) **Service**: General medical and surgical

**Staffed Beds**: 278

★ ○ **UNION HOSPITAL (150023)**, 1606 North Seventh Street, Zip 47804–2780; tel. 812/238–7000, (Nonreporting) **A**2 3 5 10 11 19 **F**3 8 13 15 18 20 22 24 26 28 29 30 31 34 35 36 40 43 45 46 47 48 49 50 51 53 54 57 59 64 68 70 72 73 74 75 76 77 78 79 81 83 85 86 87 89 90 91 92 93 94 95 96 97 107 108 110 111 112 114 115 116 117 118 119 120 121 123 124 126 127 130 131 132 135 144 146 147 149 157 **P**6
Primary Contact: Steve M. Holman, Chief Executive Officer
CFO: Wayne Hutson, Executive Vice President and Chief Financial Officer
CMO: John Bolinger, M.D., Vice President Medical Affairs
CIO: Kym Pfrank, Senior Vice President and Chief Operating Officer
CHR: Sally Zuel, Vice President Human Resources
Web address: www.uhhg.org
**Control**: Other not–for–profit (including NFP Corporation) **Service**: General medical and surgical

**Staffed Beds**: 233 **Admissions**: 15666 **Census**: 169 **Outpatient Visits**: 443871 **Births**: 1756 **Total Expense ($000)**: 391954 **Payroll Expense ($000)**: 114745 **Personnel**: 1742

### TIPTON—Tipton County

⊞ **INDIANA UNIVERSITY HEALTH TIPTON HOSPITAL (151311)**, 1000 South Main Street, Zip 46072–9799; tel. 765/675–8500, (Nonreporting) **A**1 10 18 **F**3 11 15 18 28 29 30 31 34 35 39 40 57 59 70 75 77 78 79 81 82 84 85 86 87 93 102 107 108 110 111 115 119 129 130 131 132 133 135 146 147 148 154 156 **S** Indiana University Health, Indianapolis, IN
Primary Contact: Michael Harlowe, President and Chief Executive Officer
CFO: Randall C. Yust, Chief Financial Officer NCR
CMO: Larry Marcum, Chief Medical Officer
CHR: Shelley E Huff, Regional Program Manager
CNO: Jo Ellen Scott, R.N., MS, Senior Vice President of Patient Care Services and Chief Nursing Officer
Web address: www.iuhealth.org
**Control**: Other not–for–profit (including NFP Corporation) **Service**: General medical and surgical

**Staffed Beds**: 25 **Admissions**: 634 **Census**: 6 **Outpatient Visits**: 30489 **Births**: 0 **Total Expense ($000)**: 39009 **Payroll Expense ($000)**: 11192 **Personnel**: 174

**TIPTON HOSPITAL** See Indiana University Health Tipton Hospital

### VALPARAISO—Porter County

⊞ **PORTER REGIONAL HOSPITAL (150035)**, 85 East U. S. Highway 6, Zip 46383–8947; tel. 219/983–8300, (Nonreporting) **A**1 10 **S** Community Health Systems, Inc., Franklin, TN
Primary Contact: Sean T. Dardeau, FACHE, Chief Executive Officer
COO: Lauren Hull, Chief Operating Officer
CFO: Jeffrey Daneff, Chief Financial Officer
CMO: Ramireddy K Tummuru, M.D., Chief Medical Officer
CIO: Robert Richardson, Information Technology Administrator
CHR: Angie Hampton, Director Human Resources
CNO: Judy Davidson, R.N., IChief Nursing Officer
Web address: www.porterhealth.com
**Control**: Corporation, Investor–owned (for–profit) **Service**: General medical and surgical

**Staffed Beds**: 276

**PORTER-STARKE SERVICES (154052)**, 601 Wall Street, Zip 46383–2512; tel. 219/531–3500, (Nonreporting) **A**10 **F**5 29 32 34 35 38 39 50 56 57 59 65 98 101 102 104 130 135 153 154 156 157 158
Primary Contact: Matthew J. Burden, President and Chief Executive Officer
CFO: Mary Idstein, Chief Financial Officer
CMO: Anand Popli, Medical Director
Web address: www.porterstarke.org
**Control**: Other not–for–profit (including NFP Corporation) **Service**: Psychiatric

**Staffed Beds**: 16 **Admissions**: 533 **Census**: 6 **Births**: 0 **Total Expense ($000)**: 24609 **Payroll Expense ($000)**: 14134

**PORTER-VALPARAISO HOSPITAL CAMPUS** See Porter Regional Hospital

IN

## VINCENNES—Knox County

☒ △ **GOOD SAMARITAN HOSPITAL (150042)**, 520 South Seventh Street, Zip 47591–1038; tel. 812/882–5220, (Nonreporting) **A**1 2 3 5 7 10 19 **F**3 4 5 8 11 13 15 18 20 22 28 29 30 31 34 35 37 38 40 41 43 44 45 46 47 48 49 53 54 56 57 59 63 64 65 67 70 74 75 76 77 78 79 80 81 84 85 87 89 90 93 96 98 100 101 102 104 105 106 107 108 110 111 115 118 119 120 121 123 127 129 130 131 132 134 135 144 146 147 149 150 153 154 156 157
Primary Contact: Robert D. McLin, President and Chief Executive Officer
COO: Adam Thacker, Chief Operating Officer
CFO: Thomas M Cook, Chief Financial Officer
CMO: Charles C Hedde, M.D., Chief Medical Officer
CIO: Daniel Scott, Director of Information Systems
CHR: Dean Wagoner, Director Human Resources
CNO: Karen S. Haak, R.N., MSN, Chief Nursing Officer
Web address: www.gshvin.org/goodsamaritan
**Control**: County, Government, Nonfederal **Service**: General medical and surgical

**Staffed Beds:** 158 **Admissions:** 6799 **Census:** 83 **Outpatient Visits:** 565136 **Births:** 388 **Total Expense ($000):** 244970 **Payroll Expense ($000):** 102748 **Personnel:** 1593

## WABASH—Wabash County

**PARKVIEW WABASH COUNTY HOSPITAL** See Parkview Wabash Hospital

☒ **PARKVIEW WABASH HOSPITAL (151310)**, 10 John Kissinger Drive, Zip 46992–1648; tel. 260/563–3131, (Nonreporting) **A**1 10 18 **F**3 13 15 28 29 30 31 34 35 40 44 45 46 47 50 56 57 59 62 63 68 69 70 75 76 77 78 79 81 85 93 107 108 110 111 119 129 130 131 132 133 135 146 148 154 156 **P**6 **S** Parkview Health, Fort Wayne, IN
Primary Contact: Marilyn J. Custer-Mitchell, President
CMO: Tod Sider, M.D., Chief of Staff
CNO: Cathy Allyson Wolfe, Vice President Patient Care and Chief Nursing Officer
Web address: www.https://www.parkview.com/locations/parkview-wabash-hospital/parkview-wabash-hospital.
**Control**: Other not–for–profit (including NFP Corporation) **Service**: General medical and surgical

**Staffed Beds:** 18 **Admissions:** 1293 **Census:** 9 **Outpatient Visits:** 36285 **Births:** 79 **Total Expense ($000):** 55078 **Payroll Expense ($000):** 12888 **Personnel:** 170

## WARSAW—Kosciusko County

☒ **KOSCIUSKO COMMUNITY HOSPITAL (150133)**, 2101 East Dubois Drive, Zip 46580–3288; tel. 574/267–3200, (Nonreporting) **A**1 10 19 **F**3 7 8 13 15 18 28 29 31 32 35 40 49 50 51 53 54 56 57 59 64 69 70 74 75 76 77 78 79 81 85 86 90 93 107 108 110 111 114 115 116 117 118 119 120 121 126 129 132 144 146 147 148 154 **S** Community Health Systems, Inc., Franklin, TN
Primary Contact: Jae Dale, Chief Executive Officer
CFO: Douglas J BeMent, Chief Financial Officer
CMO: Patrick Silveus, M.D., Medical Director
CIO: Tammy Lukens, Director Information
CHR: Joe Jarboe, Director Human Resources
CNO: Kim Finch, Chief Nursing Officer
Web address: www.kch.com
**Control**: Corporation, Investor–owned (for–profit) **Service**: General medical and surgical

**Staffed Beds:** 72 **Admissions:** 3063 **Census:** 26 **Outpatient Visits:** 98272 **Births:** 469 **Total Expense ($000):** 84311 **Payroll Expense ($000):** 23215 **Personnel:** 711

★ **OTIS R. BOWEN CENTER FOR HUMAN SERVICES (154014)**, 2621 East Jefferson Street, Zip 46580–3880; tel. 574/267–7169, (Nonreporting) **A**10
Primary Contact: Kurt Carlson, Chief Executive Officer
Web address: www.bowencenter.org
**Control**: Other not–for–profit (including NFP Corporation) **Service**: Psychiatric

**Staffed Beds:** 16

## WASHINGTON—Daviess County

☒ △ **DAVIESS COMMUNITY HOSPITAL (150061)**, 1314 East Walnut Street, Zip 47501–2860, Mailing Address: P.O. Box 760, Zip 47501–0760; tel. 812/254–2760, (Nonreporting) **A**1 7 10 **S** Ascension Healthcare, Saint Louis, MO
Primary Contact: Tracy Conroy, Chief Executive Officer
COO: Keith Miller, Chief Operating Officer
CFO: Amanda Rodewald, Interim Chief Financial Officer
CNO: Nancy Case, Chief Nursing Officer
Web address: www.dchosp.org
**Control**: County, Government, Nonfederal **Service**: General medical and surgical

**Staffed Beds:** 72

**DAVIESS COUNTY HOSPITAL** See Daviess Community Hospital

## WEST LAFAYETTE—Tippecanoe County

☒ **RIVER BEND HOSPITAL (154005)**, 2900 North River Road, Zip 47906–3744; tel. 765/464–0400, (Nonreporting) **A**1 10 **F**98 101 103 130 135 151 154 **P**7
Primary Contact: Stephanie Long, President and Chief Executive Officer
COO: Tom Gillian, Chief Operating Officer
CFO: Jeff Nagy, Chief Financial Officer
CMO: Richard Rahdert, M.D., Medical Director
CIO: Craig Anderson, Director Management Information Systems
CHR: Jan Shaw, Director Personnel
CNO: Megan Gibson, Nurse Manager
Web address: www.nchsi.com/riverbendhospital.cfm
**Control**: State, Government, Nonfederal **Service**: Psychiatric

**Staffed Beds:** 16 **Admissions:** 340 **Census:** 6 **Outpatient Visits:** 0 **Births:** 0 **Total Expense ($000):** 11786 **Payroll Expense ($000):** 3017 **Personnel:** 38

**WABASH VALLEY HOSPITAL** See River Bend Hospital

## WILLIAMSPORT—Warren County

☒ **ASCENSION ST. VINCENT WILLIAMSPORT (151307)**, 412 North Monroe Street, Zip 47993–1049; tel. 765/762–4000, (Nonreporting) **A**1 10 18 **F**3 7 15 29 34 35 40 45 50 57 59 64 75 77 79 81 85 86 87 93 97 107 110 111 114 119 127 131 132 133 135 143 149 156 **P**5 **S** Ascension Healthcare, Saint Louis, MO
Primary Contact: Trina Marlatt, R.N., MSN, Administrator
CFO: Janet Merritt, Chief Financial Officer
Web address: www.stvincent.org
**Control**: Other not–for–profit (including NFP Corporation) **Service**: General medical and surgical

**Staffed Beds:** 16 **Admissions:** 519 **Census:** 6 **Outpatient Visits:** 63338 **Births:** 0 **Total Expense ($000):** 21438 **Payroll Expense ($000):** 7599 **Personnel:** 75

**ST. VINCENT WILLIAMSPORT HOSPITAL** See Ascension St. Vincent Williamsport

## WINAMAC—Pulaski County

★ ○ **PULASKI MEMORIAL HOSPITAL (151305)**, 616 East 13th Street, Zip 46996–1117, Mailing Address: P.O. Box 279, Zip 46996–0279; tel. 574/946–2100, (Nonreporting) **A**10 11 18 **F**3 11 13 15 28 29 30 31 34 35 40 43 45 50 56 57 59 64 65 68 73 75 76 77 78 79 81 85 87 93 96 97 100 107 110 111 115 119 127 128 130 131 132 133 135 146 147 148 153 154 **P**6
Primary Contact: Thomas Barry, Chief Executive Officer
CFO: Gregg Malott, Chief Financial Officer
CMO: Rex Allman, M.D., President Medical Staff
CIO: Jeff Boer, Director Information Technology
CHR: Mark Fenn, Director Human Resources
CNO: Linda Webb, R.N., Chief Nursing Executive
Web address: www.pmhnet.com
**Control**: County, Government, Nonfederal **Service**: General medical and surgical

**Staffed Beds:** 25 **Admissions:** 632 **Census:** 8 **Outpatient Visits:** 27696 **Births:** 85 **Total Expense ($000):** 35911 **Payroll Expense ($000):** 17323 **Personnel:** 276

## WINCHESTER—Randolph County

☒ **ASCENSION ST. VINCENT RANDOLPH (151301)**, 473 Greenville Avenue, Zip 47394–9436; tel. 765/584–0004, (Nonreporting) **A**1 10 18 **F**3 13 15 18 28 29 30 31 35 40 44 45 50 59 64 65 68 73 75 76 77 79 81 85 86 87 93 107 108 110 111 115 119 121 129 133 146 148 149 154 **P**3 4 5 **S** Ascension Healthcare, Saint Louis, MO
Primary Contact: Carla Fouse, Administrator and Chief Nursing Officer
CFO: John Arthur, Chief Financial Officer
CNO: Carla Fouse, Chief Nursing Officer
Web address: www.stvincent.org
**Control**: Other not–for–profit (including NFP Corporation) **Service**: General medical and surgical

**Staffed Beds:** 20 **Admissions:** 444 **Census:** 3 **Outpatient Visits:** 47911 **Births:** 226 **Total Expense ($000):** 24288 **Payroll Expense ($000):** 5369 **Personnel:** 71

**ST. VINCENT RANDOLPH HOSPITAL** See Ascension St. Vincent Randolph

# IOWA

## ALBIA—Monroe County

**MONROE COUNTY HOSPITAL** See Monroe County Hospital and Clinics

★ **MONROE COUNTY HOSPITAL AND CLINICS (161342)**, 6580 165th Street,
Zip 52531–8793; tel. 641/932–2134, (Nonreporting) **A**10 18 **F**7 11 15 28 29 31
34 40 43 47 50 57 59 77 81 89 93 107 110 114 119 127 128 130 132 133
154 **P**6 **S** MercyOne, Clive, IA
Primary Contact: Veronica Fuhs, Chief Executive Officer
Web address: www.mchalbia.com
**Control**: County, Government, Nonfederal **Service**: General medical and surgical

**Staffed Beds**: 25 **Admissions**: 192 **Census**: 3 **Outpatient Visits**: 48408
**Births**: 0 **Total Expense ($000)**: 23464 **Payroll Expense ($000)**: 9681
**Personnel**: 132

## ALGONA—Kossuth County

★ **KOSSUTH REGIONAL HEALTH CENTER (161353)**, 1515 South Phillips Street,
Zip 50511–3649; tel. 515/295–2451, (Nonreporting) **A**10 18 **F**11 13 15 17 28
29 30 32 34 35 36 40 41 43 50 56 57 59 62 63 64 65 68 70 75 76 77 78 81
82 84 86 87 92 93 97 107 110 114 119 127 130 131 132 133 146 147 148
149 154 156 **P**8 **S** Trinity Health, Livonia, MI
Primary Contact: Darlene M. Elbert, R.N., MS, Chief Executive Officer and Chief
Nursing Officer
CFO: Jason Feucht, Chief Financial Officer
CMO: Michael Lampe, M.D., Chief of Staff
CIO: Nancy Erickson, Administrator Information Systems
CHR: Paula Seely, Manager Human Resources
CNO: Darlene M Elbert, R.N., MS, Assistant Administrator and Chief Nursing Officer
Web address: www.krhc.com
**Control**: County, Government, Nonfederal **Service**: General medical and surgical

**Staffed Beds**: 23 **Admissions**: 972 **Census**: 11 **Outpatient Visits**: 32464
**Births**: 140 **Total Expense ($000)**: 35360 **Payroll Expense ($000)**: 11824
**Personnel**: 193

**KOSSUTH RGIONAL HEALTH CENTER** See Kossuth Regional Health Center

## AMES—Story County

★ △ ⇑ **MARY GREELEY MEDICAL CENTER (160030)**, 1111 Duff Avenue,
Zip 50010–5745; tel. 515/239–2011, (Nonreporting) **A**2 7 10 19 21 **F**3 7 11 12
13 15 17 18 20 22 26 28 29 30 31 34 35 36 37 38 40 43 45 46 47 48 49 50
53 55 57 58 59 61 62 63 64 65 69 70 72 74 75 76 77 78 79 81 82 84 85 86
87 89 90 92 93 96 98 100 101 102 104 107 108 110 111 114 115 118 119
120 121 123 124 126 129 130 131 133 135 146 147 148 149 156
Primary Contact: Brian Dieter, President and Chief Executive Officer
CFO: Gary Botine, Vice President, Chief Financial Officer
CIO: Scott Carlson, Director
CHR: Betsy V Schoeller, Director Human Resources and Education
Web address: www.mgmc.org
**Control**: City, Government, Nonfederal **Service**: General medical and surgical

**Staffed Beds**: 190 **Admissions**: 8079 **Census**: 101 **Outpatient
Visits**: 153237 **Births**: 1210 **Total Expense ($000)**: 185981 **Payroll
Expense ($000)**: 67103 **Personnel**: 1097

## ANAMOSA—Jones County

**JONES REGIONAL MEDICAL CENTER** See Unitypoint Health - Jones Regional
Medical Center

★ **UNITYPOINT HEALTH - JONES REGIONAL MEDICAL CENTER (161306)**,
1795 Highway 64 East, Zip 52205–2112; tel. 319/462–6131, (Nonreporting)
**A**10 18 **F**3 7 8 11 15 28 29 30 31 34 35 40 43 45 46 50 53 57 59 65 68 71
75 77 78 79 81 82 83 84 87 90 91 93 96 97 102 104 107 110 111 114 118
119 126 127 128 129 130 131 132 133 135 144 146 147 148 149 154 156
157 **S** UnityPoint Health, West Des Moines, IA
Primary Contact: Eric Briesemeister, Chief Executive Officer
CFO: Rachel Von Behren, Director Financial Services
CMO: Victor Salas, M.D., President Medical Staff
CHR: Donna Condry, Director Human Resources
Web address: www.jonesregional.org
**Control**: Other not–for–profit (including NFP Corporation) **Service**: General
medical and surgical

**Staffed Beds**: 22 **Admissions**: 449 **Census**: 7 **Outpatient Visits**: 156321
**Births**: 0 **Total Expense ($000)**: 35821 **Payroll Expense ($000)**: 18802
**Personnel**: 150

## ATLANTIC—Cass County

★ **CASS COUNTY HEALTH SYSTEM (161376)**, 1501 East Tenth Street,
Zip 50022–1997; tel. 712/243–3250, (Nonreporting) **A**10 18 **F**3 13 15 28 29 31
34 35 40 45 50 57 59 64 65 70 75 76 77 78 79 81 82 85 93 97 98 101 102
107 108 110 111 115 119 124 127 129 130 131 132 133 135 146 147 148
154 156
Primary Contact: Brett Altman, FACHE, Chief Executive Officer
COO: Alison Bruckner, Chief Operating Officer
CFO: Abbey Stangl, Chief Financial Officer
CMO: Todd Bean, Chief Medical Officer
CIO: Jeff Osegard, Chief Information Officer
CHR: Denise Coder, Chief Human Resource Officer
Web address: www.casshealth.org
**Control**: County, Government, Nonfederal **Service**: General medical and surgical

**Staffed Beds**: 29 **Admissions**: 987 **Census**: 11 **Outpatient Visits**: 108249
**Births**: 110 **Total Expense ($000)**: 53882 **Payroll Expense ($000)**: 22261
**Personnel**: 318

**CASS COUNTY MEMORIAL HOSPITAL** See Cass County Health System

## AUDUBON—Audubon County

**AUDUBON COUNTY MEMORIAL HOSPITAL** See Audubon County Memorial
Hospital and Clinics

**AUDUBON COUNTY MEMORIAL HOSPITAL AND CLINICS (161330)**, 515
Pacific Avenue, Zip 50025–1056; tel. 712/563–2611, (Nonreporting) **A**10 18 **F**3
15 28 31 34 40 43 45 53 57 59 64 67 78 79 81 82 85 93 110 119 127 128
133 135
Primary Contact: Suzanne Cooner, MSN, R.N., Chief Executive Officer
CFO: Melinda Alt, Chief Financial Officer
CMO: Jeffrey Maire, M.D., Chief of Staff
CIO: Nathan Moser, Information Technology Engineer
CHR: Kolton E. Hewlett, Senior Director, Administration
CNO: Lisa Paulsen, R.N., Chief Nursing Officer
Web address: www.acmhhosp.org
**Control**: County, Government, Nonfederal **Service**: General medical and surgical

**Staffed Beds**: 25 **Admissions**: 170 **Census**: 2 **Outpatient Visits**: 15482
**Births**: 0 **Total Expense ($000)**: 12781 **Payroll Expense ($000)**: 5846
**Personnel**: 90

**IA**

## BELMOND—Wright County

⇧ **BELMOND MEDICAL CENTER** See Iowa Specialty Hospital-Belmond

★ ⇧ **IOWA SPECIALTY HOSPITAL-BELMOND (161301)**, 403 1st Street SE,
Zip 50421–1201; tel. 641/444–3223, (Nonreporting) **A**10 18 21 **F**7 11 12 15 28
29 32 34 35 40 43 45 46 50 56 57 59 62 63 64 65 67 68 70 75 77 79 81 82
85 87 89 92 93 96 97 100 101 102 104 107 110 119 127 128 129 130 131
132 133 135 146 148 149 150 154 **P**6 **S** Iowa Specialty Hospitals, Clarion, IA
Primary Contact: Amy McDaniel, Chief Executive Officer
CFO: Greg Polzin, Chief Financial Officer
CMO: Charles B Brindle, M.D., Chief Medical Staff
CHR: Holly Martin, Director Human Resource
CNO: Lisa Weatherwax, R.N., Chief Nursing Officer
Web address: www.iowaspecialtyhospital.com
**Control**: City, Government, Nonfederal **Service**: General medical and surgical

**Staffed Beds:** 22 **Admissions:** 459 **Census:** 4 **Outpatient Visits:** 49778
**Births:** 0 **Total Expense ($000):** 29099 **Payroll Expense ($000):** 9520
**Personnel:** 175

## BETTENDORF—Scott County

**TRINITY BETTENDORF** See Unitypoint Health - Trinity Bettendorf

⊞ **UNITYPOINT HEALTH - TRINITY BETTENDORF (160104)**, 4500 Utica Ridge
Road, Zip 52722–1626; tel. 563/742–5000, (Nonreporting) **A**1 10 **F**3 11 13 15
18 20 22 26 29 30 34 35 40 44 45 48 50 57 59 64 68 70 73 74 76 79 81 82
85 86 87 89 93 96 97 107 108 110 114 119 126 130 132 146 147 148 149
150 154 157 **S** UnityPoint Health, West Des Moines, IA
Primary Contact: Robert J. Erickson, President and Chief Executive Officer
COO: Jay Willsher, Chief Operating Officer
CFO: Greg Pagliuzza, Chief Financial Officer
CMO: Paul McLoone, M.D., Chief Medical Officer
CHR: Cara Fuller, Vice President Human Resources
CNO: Jean B Doerge, MS, R.N., Chief Nursing Executive
Web address: www.trinityqc.com
**Control**: Other not–for–profit (including NFP Corporation) **Service**: General
medical and surgical

**Staffed Beds:** 95 **Admissions:** 4532 **Census:** 39 **Outpatient Visits:** 86447
**Births:** 981 **Total Expense ($000):** 83280 **Payroll Expense ($000):** 28544
**Personnel:** 372

## BLOOMFIELD—Davis County

**DAVIS COUNTY HOSPITAL** See Davis County Hospital and Clinics

★ **DAVIS COUNTY HOSPITAL AND CLINICS (161327)**, 509 North Madison
Street, Zip 52537–1271; tel. 641/664–2145, (Nonreporting) **A**10 18 **F**3 7 11 15
28 29 34 35 40 44 45 50 57 59 63 64 65 69 75 79 81 84 85 86 87 97 107
110 111 115 119 127 132 133 135 146 **P**6 **S** MercyOne, Clive, IA
Primary Contact: Veronica Fuhs, Chief Executive Officer
CFO: Kendra Warning, Chief Financial Officer
CMO: Robert Floyd, D.O., Chief Medical Staff
CIO: Kendra Warning, Chief Financial Officer
CHR: Pam Young, Director Human Resources
CNO: Susan Kay Pankey, Chief Nursing Officer
Web address: www.daviscountyhospital.org
**Control**: County, Government, Nonfederal **Service**: General medical and surgical

**Staffed Beds:** 13 **Admissions:** 202 **Census:** 2 **Outpatient Visits:** 46383
**Births:** 0 **Total Expense ($000):** 26077 **Payroll Expense ($000):** 10591
**Personnel:** 182

## BOONE—Boone County

★ **BOONE COUNTY HOSPITAL (161372)**, 1015 Union Street, Zip 50036–4821;
tel. 515/432–3140, (Nonreporting) **A**10 18 **F**2 3 7 11 13 15 28 29 30 31 34 35
40 43 45 50 56 57 59 62 64 65 69 70 75 76 77 78 79 81 82 85 86 87 89 91
93 97 107 110 111 114 119 131 132 133 134 145 146 147 148 156 **P**6 **S**
QHR Health, Brentwood, TN
Primary Contact: Joseph S. Smith, Chief Executive Officer
CFO: Joseph Devin, Chief Financial Officer
CMO: Brian Mehlhaus, M.D., Chief of Staff
CIO: Paul Sliva, Chief Information Officer
CHR: Kim Schwartz, Assistant Administrator Human Resources and Operations
Web address: www.boonehospital.com
**Control**: County, Government, Nonfederal **Service**: General medical and surgical

**Staffed Beds:** 25 **Admissions:** 865 **Census:** 9 **Outpatient Visits:** 134945
**Births:** 131 **Total Expense ($000):** 46825 **Payroll Expense ($000):** 20109
**Personnel:** 354

## BRITT—Hancock County

★ **HANCOCK COUNTY HEALTH SYSTEM (161307)**, 532 First Street NW,
Zip 50423–1227; tel. 641/843–5000, (Nonreporting) **A**10 18 **F**3 15 29 34 35
36 40 43 45 46 50 53 56 57 59 62 64 65 75 77 81 82 85 93 97 100 104 107
110 114 119 129 130 131 132 133 135 146 148 154 156 **P**1 **S** Trinity Health,
Livonia, MI
Primary Contact: Laura Zwiefel, Chief Executive Officer
CFO: Julie Damm, Chief Financial Officer
CMO: Catherine Butler, M.D., Chief Medical Staff
CIO: Julie Damm, Chief Financial Officer
CHR: Denise Jakoubeck, Director Human Resources
Web address: www.trusthchs.com/hancock-county-health-system
**Control**: County, Government, Nonfederal **Service**: General medical and surgical

**Staffed Beds:** 25 **Admissions:** 345 **Census:** 7 **Outpatient Visits:** 22074
**Births:** 0 **Total Expense ($000):** 24709 **Payroll Expense ($000):** 8786
**Personnel:** 182

**HANCOCK COUNTY MEMORIAL HOSPITAL** See Hancock County Health System

## CARROLL—Carroll County

★ **ST. ANTHONY REGIONAL HOSPITAL (160005)**, 311 South Clark Street,
Zip 51401–3038, Mailing Address: P.O. Box 628, Zip 51401–0628;
tel. 712/792–3581, (Total facility includes 79 beds in nursing home–type unit)
(Nonreporting) **A**10 20 **F**6 10 11 13 15 28 29 30 31 34 35 37 38 39 40 43 44
45 46 50 51 56 57 59 60 61 62 63 64 65 67 68 69 70 74 75 76 77 78 79 81
82 84 85 86 87 89 93 97 98 100 101 102 103 104 107 108 110 111 115 118
119 120 121 122 123 125 126 127 129 130 131 132 133 134 135 145 146
147 148 156 **P**6
Primary Contact: Edward H. Smith, President and Chief Executive Officer
CFO: John Munson, Vice President and Chief Financial Officer
CMO: Kyle Ulveling, M.D., Chief of Staff
CIO: Chad Lawson, Chief Information Officer
CHR: Anna Fitzpatrick, Director Human Resources
CNO: Karen Timm, R.N., MSN, Vice President Patient Services
Web address: www.stanthonyhospital.org
**Control**: Church operated, Nongovernment, not–for–profit **Service**: General
medical and surgical

**Staffed Beds:** 155 **Admissions:** 2224 **Census:** 104 **Outpatient
Visits:** 113869 **Births:** 333 **Total Expense ($000):** 83694 **Payroll Expense
($000):** 36277 **Personnel:** 601

## CEDAR FALLS—Black Hawk County

⊞ **MERCYONE CEDAR FALLS MEDICAL CENTER (160040)**, 515 College Street,
Zip 50613–2500; tel. 319/268–3000, (Nonreporting) **A**1 10 **F**3 7 8 11 12 15 29
30 35 40 43 44 46 53 57 59 64 68 70 75 77 79 81 91 93 97 98 103 107 110
111 119 130 131 132 146 **S** Trinity Health, Livonia, MI
Primary Contact: MaryJo Kavalier, Administrator
COO: Ryan Meyer, Vice President Operations
CFO: Timothy Huber, Controller
CMO: Matthew Sojka, M.D., Vice President Medical Affairs
CIO: Marge Ray, Director Information Systems
CHR: Suzanne M. Burt, Director Human Resources
CNO: Kelly Richards, Senior Vice President and Chief Nursing Officer
Web address: www.MercyOne.org
**Control**: Church operated, Nongovernment, not–for–profit **Service**: General
medical and surgical

**Staffed Beds:** 50 **Admissions:** 993 **Census:** 16 **Outpatient Visits:** 42166
**Births:** 0 **Total Expense ($000):** 33867 **Payroll Expense ($000):** 10987
**Personnel:** 166

**SARTORI MEMORIAL HOSPITAL** See Mercyone Cedar Falls Medical Center

**IA**

## CEDAR RAPIDS—Linn County

**MERCY MEDICAL CENTER** See Mercy Medical Center - Cedar Rapids

✠ **MERCY MEDICAL CENTER - CEDAR RAPIDS (160079)**, 701 Tenth Street SE,
Zip 52403–1292; tel. 319/398–6011, (Total facility includes 76 beds in nursing
home–type unit) (Nonreporting) **A**1 2 3 5 10 **F**3 4 5 6 11 12 13 15 18 19 20 22
24 26 28 29 30 31 32 34 35 37 38 40 43 44 45 46 48 49 50 51 54 55 56 57
58 59 60 61 62 63 64 65 67 68 70 72 74 75 76 77 78 79 81 82 84 85 86 87
88 89 90 91 92 93 96 98 99 100 101 102 103 104 107 108 109 110 114 115
117 118 119 120 121 123 124 126 128 130 131 132 134 135 145 146 147
148 149 150 153 154 **P**8
Primary Contact: Timothy L. Charles, President and Chief Executive Officer
CFO: Nathan Van Genderen, Executive Vice President and Chief Financial Officer
CMO: Tim Quinn, M.D., Executive Vice President and Chief of Clinical Operations
and President Mercy Care Management
CIO: Jeff Cash, Senior Vice President and Chief Information Officer
CHR: Doug Jontz, Senior Vice President Human Resources
CNO: Mary Brobst, R.N., MSN, Senior Vice President Patient Care Services and
Chief Nursing Officer
Web address: www.mercycare.org
**Control:** Church operated, Nongovernment, not–for–profit **Service:** General
medical and surgical

**Staffed Beds: 302 Admissions: 10625 Census: 159 Outpatient
Visits: 475592 Births: 811 Total Expense ($000): 337216 Payroll Expense
($000): 131455 Personnel: 1895**

**UNITYPOINT HEALTH - ST. LUKE'S** See Unitypoint Health - St. Luke's Hospital

✠ △ **UNITYPOINT HEALTH - ST. LUKE'S HOSPITAL (160045)**, 1026 'A'
Avenue NE, Zip 52402–3026, Mailing Address: P.O. Box 3026, Zip 52406–3026;
tel. 319/369–7211, (Nonreporting) **A**1 2 3 5 7 10 **F**3 5 11 12 13 15 17 18 19
20 22 24 26 28 29 30 31 32 34 35 36 37 39 40 43 45 46 49 50 55 56 57 59
60 61 63 64 65 68 70 72 74 76 77 78 79 81 82 84 85 86 87 89 90 92 93 95
96 98 99 100 101 103 104 105 107 108 110 115 117 118 119 120 121 123
124 126 130 131 132 134 135 145 146 147 148 149 152 153 154 157 **P**7 **S**
UnityPoint Health, West Des Moines, IA
Primary Contact: Michelle Niermann, President and Chief Executive Officer
COO: Casey Greene, Vice President and Chief Operating Officer
CFO: Michael G. Heinrich, Senior Vice President and Chief Financial Officer
CMO: Dustin Arnold, D.O., Chief Medical Officer
CHR: Susan L Slattery, Director Human Resources
CNO: Carmen Kleinsmith, MSN, R.N., Senior Vice President, Chief Nurse Executive
Web address: www.unitypoint.org
**Control:** Other not–for–profit (including NFP Corporation) **Service:** General
medical and surgical

**Staffed Beds: 349 Admissions: 15396 Census: 199 Outpatient
Visits: 613688 Births: 2357 Total Expense ($000): 363534 Payroll
Expense ($000): 157492 Personnel: 2035**

## CENTERVILLE—Appanoose County

**MERCY MEDICAL CENTER-CENTERVILLE** See Mercyone Centerville Medical
Center

★ **MERCYONE CENTERVILLE MEDICAL CENTER (161377)**, 1 St Joseph's Drive,
Zip 52544–8055; tel. 641/437–4111, (Total facility includes 19 beds in nursing
home–type unit) (Nonreporting) **A**10 18 **F**1 3 4 8 11 12 15 16 17 28 29 30 31 34
40 45 46 50 54 57 59 64 67 70 72 73 75 77 78 80 81 85 86 87 88 89 90 93
97 98 107 110 111 113 115 117 119 127 128 129 130 132 133 135 156 157
**P**6 **S** CommonSpirit Health, Chicago, IL
Primary Contact: Matthew Johnson, President
CHR: Tonya Clawson, Manager Human Resources
CNO: Sherri L Doggett, Vice President Patient Services
Web address: www.mercycenterville.org
**Control:** Church operated, Nongovernment, not–for–profit **Service:** General
medical and surgical

**Staffed Beds: 42 Admissions: 364 Census: 22 Outpatient Visits: 93577
Births: 0 Total Expense ($000): 28847 Payroll Expense ($000): 12288
Personnel: 217**

## CHARITON—Lucas County

★ **LUCAS COUNTY HEALTH CENTER (161341)**, 1200 North Seventh Street,
Zip 50049–1258; tel. 641/774–3000, (Nonreporting) **A**10 18 **F**3 11 15 28 29
30 31 34 40 43 44 45 46 47 50 55 64 66 70 75 81 85 87 93 97 107 110 115
119 127 130 131 132 133 143 145 146 148 156 **S** UnityPoint Health, West Des
Moines, IA
Primary Contact: Jay Christensen, FACHE, Interim Chief Executive Officer
CFO: Jay Christensen, FACHE, Chief Financial Officer
CMO: David Marcowitz, M.D., Chief of Staff
CIO: Terri Black, Network Manager
CHR: Lana Kuball, Director Administrative Services
CNO: JoBeth Lawless, Chief Nursing Officer, Nursing Services and Director
Emergency Management Services
Web address: www.lchcia.com
**Control:** County, Government, Nonfederal **Service:** General medical and surgical

**Staffed Beds: 21 Admissions: 258 Census: 3 Outpatient Visits: 23008
Births: 8 Total Expense ($000): 21250 Payroll Expense ($000): 9607
Personnel: 190**

## CHARLES CITY—Floyd County

**FLOYD COUNTY MEDICAL CENTER (161347)**, 800 Eleventh Street,
Zip 50616–3499; tel. 641/228–6830, (Nonreporting) **A**10 18 **F**11 13 15 28 29
34 35 40 45 57 59 64 75 76 79 81 86 89 91 93 107 115 119 127 130 132
146 148 149 154 156 **S** Mayo Clinic, Rochester, MN
Primary Contact: Rod Nordeng, Administrator
CFO: Ron Timpe, Chief Financial Officer
CHR: Don Nosbisch, Director Human Resources
CNO: Viva Boerschel, Director of Nursing
Web address: www.fcmc.us.com/
**Control:** County, Government, Nonfederal **Service:** General medical and surgical

**Staffed Beds: 25 Admissions: 552 Census: 8 Outpatient Visits: 57673
Births: 63 Total Expense ($000): 29799 Payroll Expense ($000): 12458
Personnel: 196**

**FLOYD COUNTY MEMORIAL HOSPITAL** See Floyd County Medical Center

## CHEROKEE—Cherokee County

☐ **CHEROKEE MENTAL HEALTH INSTITUTE (164002)**, 1251 West Cedar Loop,
Zip 51012–1599; tel. 712/225–2594, (Nonreporting) **A**1 10 **F**29 30 68 75 98 99
100 101 130 135 149
Primary Contact: Chris Tosteberg, Superintendent
CFO: Tony Morris, Business Manager
CHR: Mary Ann Hanson, Director Personnel
Web address: www.dhs.state.ia.us
**Control:** State, Government, Nonfederal **Service:** Psychiatric

**Staffed Beds: 36 Admissions: 287 Census: 33 Outpatient Visits: 57
Births: 0 Total Expense ($000): 15587 Payroll Expense ($000): 8562
Personnel: 160**

**CHEROKEE REGIONAL MED CTR** See Cherokee Regional Medical Center

★ **CHEROKEE REGIONAL MEDICAL CENTER (161362)**, 300 Sioux Valley Drive,
Zip 51012–1205; tel. 712/225–5101, (Nonreporting) **A**10 18 **F**7 11 13 15 17
28 29 34 35 40 43 45 53 56 57 59 62 63 64 65 67 68 69 75 76 77 78 81 84
86 87 89 93 96 97 107 111 114 119 125 127 128 129 130 131 132 133 135
146 147 148 154 156 **P**6 **S** UnityPoint Health, West Des Moines, IA
Primary Contact: Gary W. Jordan, FACHE, Chief Executive Officer
CFO: Joan Bierman, Vice President Finance
CIO: Kevin Naslund, Manager Information Technology
CHR: Theresa Conley, Manager Human Resources
CNO: Christy Syndergaard, Vice President Nursing
Web address: www.cherokeermc.org
**Control:** Other not–for–profit (including NFP Corporation) **Service:** General
medical and surgical

**Staffed Beds: 25 Admissions: 788 Census: 7 Outpatient Visits: 52990
Births: 94 Total Expense ($000): 26292 Payroll Expense ($000): 11173
Personnel: 181**

**MENTAL HEALTH INSTITUTE** See Cherokee Mental Health Institute

---

**Hospital, Medicare Provider Number, Address, Telephone, Approval, Facility, and Physician Codes, Health Care System**

★ American Hospital Association (AHA) membership   ○ Healthcare Facilities Accreditation Program   ⇑ Center for Improvement in Healthcare Quality Accreditation
☐ The Joint Commission accreditation   ◇ DNV Healthcare Inc. accreditation   △ Commission on Accreditation of Rehabilitation Facilities (CARF) accreditation

**IA**

## CLARINDA—Page County

**CLARINDA MUNICIPAL HOSPITAL** See Clarinda Regional Health Center

★ **CLARINDA REGIONAL HEALTH CENTER (161352)**, 220 Essie Davison Drive, Zip 51632–2915, Mailing Address: P.O. Box 217, Zip 51632–0217; tel. 712/542–2176, (Nonreporting) **A**10 18 **F**3 7 8 11 15 18 28 29 31 32 34 35 36 40 43 44 45 50 57 59 64 65 68 69 74 75 77 78 79 81 82 84 85 86 87 89 92 93 97 100 101 104 107 110 111 114 118 119 127 128 129 130 131 132 133 135 143 146 148 149 150 154 155 156 **S** Bryan Health, Lincoln, NE
Primary Contact: Charles Nordyke, Chief Executive Officer
COO: Elaine Otte, Chief Operating Officer
CFO: Milton Trabal, Chief Financial Officer
CMO: Autumn Morales, Chief Medical Staff Officer
CIO: Richard Morgan-Fine, IT Director
CHR: Melissa Walter, Director Human Resources
CNO: Sherrie L Laubenthal, R.N., Chief Nursing Officer
Web address: www.clarindahealth.com
**Control**: City, Government, Nonfederal **Service**: General medical and surgical

**Staffed Beds**: 25 **Admissions**: 496 **Census**: 5 **Outpatient Visits**: 61525
**Births**: 0 **Total Expense ($000)**: 32821 **Payroll Expense ($000)**: 12954
**Personnel**: 224

## CLARION—Wright County

★ ⇑ **IOWA SPECIALTY HOSPITAL-CLARION (161302)**, 1316 South Main Street, Zip 50525–2019; tel. 515/532–2811, (Nonreporting) **A**10 18 21 **F**11 13 15 28 29 31 32 34 35 40 43 45 46 50 56 57 59 63 64 65 68 69 71 75 76 77 79 81 82 85 86 87 93 96 97 102 107 110 111 114 119 125 127 130 131 132 133 134 135 146 147 148 149 154 156 **P**4 6 **S** Iowa Specialty Hospitals, Clarion, IA
Primary Contact: Steven J. Simonin, President and Chief Executive Officer
COO: Kirk Rier, Chief Operating Officer
CFO: Greg Polzin, Chief Financial Officer
CMO: Dennis Colby, M.D., Chief of Staff
CHR: Holly Martin, Human Resources Leader
CNO: Abby Young, Chief Nursing Officer
Web address: www.iowaspecialtyhospital.com
**Control**: City, Government, Nonfederal **Service**: General medical and surgical

**Staffed Beds**: 25 **Admissions**: 1215 **Census**: 8 **Outpatient Visits**: 101846
**Births**: 415 **Total Expense ($000)**: 54212 **Payroll Expense ($000)**: 19033
**Personnel**: 327

⇑ **WRIGHT MEDICAL CENTER** See Iowa Specialty Hospital-Clarion

## CLINTON—Clinton County

**MERCY MEDICAL CENTER-CLINTON** See Mercyone Clinton Medical Center

▣ **MERCYONE CLINTON MEDICAL CENTER (160080)**, 1410 North Fourth Street, Zip 52732–2940; tel. 563/244–5555, (Includes MERCY SERVICES FOR AGING, Mailing address: 600 14th Avenue North, Clinton, Iowa, Zip 52732; tel. 563/244–3888) (Total facility includes 86 beds in nursing home–type unit) **A**1 10 **F**3 11 13 15 18 20 22 28 29 30 31 34 35 36 38 40 44 45 47 49 50 53 56 57 59 60 61 62 63 64 68 70 74 75 76 77 78 79 80 81 82 84 85 87 89 93 98 100 101 102 107 108 110 111 115 118 119 121 123 128 129 130 132 144 146 148 **S** Trinity Health, Livonia, MI
Primary Contact: Amy Berentes, R.N., MSN, Executive Vice President and Chief Operating Officer
CFO: Paul Mangin, Vice President Finance
CHR: Shane Buer, Vice President, Human Resources
CNO: Amy Berentes, R.N., MSN, Vice President Patient Care Services
Web address: www.mercyclinton.com
**Control**: Church operated, Nongovernment, not–for–profit **Service**: General medical and surgical

**Staffed Beds**: 193 **Admissions**: 3255 **Census**: 85 **Outpatient Visits**: 88835
**Births**: 322 **Total Expense ($000)**: 97382 **Payroll Expense ($000)**: 39083
**Personnel**: 624

**SAMARITAN SERVICES FOR AGING** See Mercy Services for Aging

## CLIVE—Polk County

**MERCY REHABILITATION HOSPITAL** See Mercyone Clive Rehabilitation Hospital

☐ **MERCYONE CLIVE REHABILITATION HOSPITAL (163025)**, 1401 Campus Drive, Zip 50325–6500; tel. 515/381–6519, (Nonreporting) **A**1 10 **F**3 29 30 56 90 94 95 96 132 143 148
Primary Contact: Nicole Nigg, Chief Executive Officer
Web address: www.mercydesmoines.org
**Control**: Partnership, Investor–owned (for–profit) **Service**: Rehabilitation

**Staffed Beds**: 50 **Admissions**: 909 **Census**: 29 **Outpatient Visits**: 0
**Births**: 0 **Total Expense ($000)**: 11616 **Payroll Expense ($000)**: 6323
**Personnel**: 138

## CORALVILLE—Johnson County

**IOWA MEDICAL AND CLASSIFICATION CENTER**, 2700 Coral Ridge Avenue, Zip 52241–4708, Mailing Address: 2700 Coral Rigde Avenue, Zip 52241; tel. 319/626–2391, (Nonreporting)
Primary Contact: James McKinney, Warden
Web address: www.oakdaleprison.com/
**Control**: State, Government, Nonfederal **Service**: Psychiatric

**Staffed Beds**: 20

## CORNING—Adams County

**ALEGENT CREIGHTON HEALTH MERCY HOSPITAL** See Chi Health Mercy Corning

★ **CHI HEALTH MERCY CORNING (161304)**, 603 Rosary Drive, Zip 50841–1683; tel. 641/322–3121, (Nonreporting) **A**10 18 **F**3 11 15 28 30 31 34 40 43 46 50 53 56 57 59 64 67 69 74 75 77 78 79 81 85 87 89 90 97 107 110 115 119 127 128 129 130 132 133 135 146 147 148 149 154 156 157 **S** CommonSpirit Health, Chicago, IL
Primary Contact: Lisa Wolfe, President
CMO: Maen Haddadin, M.D., President Medical Staff
CIO: Kenneth Lawonn, Senior Vice President and Chief Information Officer
CHR: Sandra Lammers, Coordinator Human Resources and Finance
Web address: www.alegent.com
**Control**: Church operated, Nongovernment, not–for–profit **Service**: General medical and surgical

**Staffed Beds**: 22 **Admissions**: 268 **Census**: 2 **Outpatient Visits**: 19523
**Births**: 0 **Total Expense ($000)**: 14525 **Payroll Expense ($000)**: 4503
**Personnel**: 72

## CORYDON—Wayne County

★ **WAYNE COUNTY HOSPITAL (161358)**, 417 South East Street, Zip 50060–1860, Mailing Address: P.O. Box 305, Zip 50060–0305; tel. 641/872–2260, (Nonreporting) **A**10 18 **F**7 13 15 28 29 31 34 35 40 43 51 56 57 59 60 64 69 70 75 76 77 78 79 81 85 87 89 91 92 93 97 107 110 115 119 126 127 130 131 133 147 148 149 154 **P**6 **S** MercyOne, Clive, IA
Primary Contact: Daren Relph, Chief Executive Officer
COO: Michael Thomas, Associate Administrator
CFO: Diane Hook, Chief Financial Officer
CMO: Joel Baker, D.O., Chief Medical Officer
CIO: Laurie Ehrich, Chief Communications Officer
CHR: Dave Carlyle, Director Human Resources
CNO: Sheila Mattly, Chief Nursing Officer
Web address: www.waynecountyhospital.org
**Control**: County, Government, Nonfederal **Service**: General medical and surgical

**Staffed Beds**: 25 **Admissions**: 620 **Census**: 6 **Outpatient Visits**: 28332
**Births**: 192 **Total Expense ($000)**: 31673 **Payroll Expense ($000)**: 13509
**Personnel**: 263

**IA**

*Many Facility Codes have changed. Please refer to the AHA Guide Code Chart.*

## COUNCIL BLUFFS—Pottawattamie County

**ALEGENT CREIGHTON HEALTH MERCY HOSPITAL** See Chi Health Mercy Council Bluffs

☒ **CHI HEALTH MERCY COUNCIL BLUFFS (160028)**, 800 Mercy Drive, Zip 51503–3128; tel. 712/328–5000, (Nonreporting) **A**1 2 10 **F**3 5 11 13 15 18 20 22 26 28 29 30 31 34 35 37 40 41 43 45 47 48 49 50 57 59 68 70 72 74 76 77 78 79 81 82 84 85 87 89 91 93 98 99 100 101 102 104 105 107 108 110 111 114 115 119 126 129 130 132 146 147 154 **P**8 **S** CommonSpirit Health, Chicago, IL
Primary Contact: Ann Schumacher, R.N., MSN, FACHE, President
CFO: Jeanette Wojtalewicz, Chief Financial Officer
CMO: Joseph Hoagbin, M.D., Chief Quality Officer
CIO: Thomas Haley, Information Technology Services Site Director
CHR: Nancy Wallace, Senior Vice President Human Resources
Web address: www.chihealth.com/chi-health-mercy-council-bluffs
**Control**: Church operated, Nongovernment, not–for–profit **Service**: General medical and surgical

**Staffed Beds:** 146 **Admissions:** 5720 **Census:** 60 **Outpatient Visits:** 83101 **Births:** 270 **Total Expense ($000):** 91050 **Payroll Expense ($000):** 30211 **Personnel:** 442

**JENNIE EDMUNDSON HOSPITAL** See Methodist Jennie Edmundson Hospital

☒ **METHODIST JENNIE EDMUNDSON HOSPITAL (160047)**, 933 East Pierce Street, Zip 51503–4652, Mailing Address: P.O. Box 2C, Zip 51502–3002; tel. 712/396–6000, (Nonreporting) **A**1 2 3 5 10 **F**3 11 13 15 18 20 22 26 28 29 30 31 34 35 39 40 43 44 45 47 49 50 57 58 59 61 64 68 70 73 74 75 76 78 79 81 82 85 86 87 89 92 93 98 100 101 102 107 108 110 111 115 118 119 120 121 123 124 126 129 130 131 132 135 145 146 147 148 149 **P**6 8 **S** Nebraska Methodist Health System, Inc., Omaha, NE
Primary Contact: Steven P. Baumert, President and Chief Executive Officer
COO: David Burd, Senior Vice President, Operations
CFO: Jeff Francis, Vice President Finance and Chief Financial Officer
CMO: Scott Bomgaars, M.D., Vice President Medical Affairs
CIO: Steven Zuber, Vice President
CHR: Holly Huerter, Vice President Human Resources
CNO: Peggy Helget, R.N., MSN, Vice President Patient Services and Chief Nursing Officer
Web address: www.bestcare.org
**Control**: Other not–for–profit (including NFP Corporation) **Service**: General medical and surgical

**Staffed Beds:** 120 **Admissions:** 6135 **Census:** 67 **Outpatient Visits:** 65556 **Births:** 539 **Total Expense ($000):** 110532 **Payroll Expense ($000):** 43440 **Personnel:** 693

## CRESCO—Howard County

**HOWARD COUNTY HOSPITAL** See Regional Health Services of Howard County

★ **REGIONAL HEALTH SERVICES OF HOWARD COUNTY (161328)**, 235 Eighth Avenue West, Zip 52136–1098; tel. 563/547–2101, (Nonreporting) **A**10 18 **F**3 7 11 13 15 28 29 34 35 36 38 40 41 43 44 45 50 53 56 57 59 62 63 64 65 68 75 76 77 81 82 85 87 89 96 104 107 110 115 119 127 128 130 131 132 133 146 147 148 149 150 154 156 **P**8 **S** Trinity Health, Livonia, MI
Primary Contact: Robin M. Schluter, Chief Executive Officer
CFO: Greg Burkel, Chief Financial Officer
CMO: Paul Jensen, M.D., Chief of Staff
CIO: Greg Burkel, Chief Financial Officer
CHR: Jennalee Pedretti, Vice President Operations
CNO: Carol Kerian-Masters, RN, Chief Nursing Officer
Web address: www.rhshc.com
**Control**: County, Government, Nonfederal **Service**: General medical and surgical

**Staffed Beds:** 19 **Admissions:** 265 **Census:** 3 **Outpatient Visits:** 24489 **Births:** 56 **Total Expense ($000):** 23510 **Payroll Expense ($000):** 8889 **Personnel:** 179

## CRESTON—Union County

⇑ **GREATER COMMUNITY HOSPITAL** See Greater Regional Medical Center

★ ⇑ **GREATER REGIONAL MEDICAL CENTER (161365)**, 1700 West Townline Street Suite 3, Zip 50801–1099; tel. 641/782–7091, (Nonreporting) **A**10 18 21 **F**3 7 8 11 13 15 28 29 31 34 35 40 43 44 45 47 48 50 51 56 57 59 64 65 66 70 75 76 77 78 79 81 82 85 86 93 96 97 102 104 107 108 110 111 115 119 120 121 122 123 124 125 127 128 129 131 132 133 146 147 148 149 156 **S** UnityPoint Health, West Des Moines, IA
Primary Contact: Monte Neitzel, Chief Executive Officer
CFO: Matt McCutchan, Chief Financial Officer
CMO: Steve Reeves, M.D., Chief Medical Staff
CIO: Karla Alford, Chief Information Officer
CHR: Amy Rieck, Human Resources Officer
CNO: Amanda Mohr, Chief Nursing Officer
Web address: www.greaterregional.org
**Control**: County, Government, Nonfederal **Service**: General medical and surgical

**Staffed Beds:** 25 **Admissions:** 982 **Census:** 8 **Outpatient Visits:** 126773 **Births:** 187 **Total Expense ($000):** 62638 **Payroll Expense ($000):** 28041 **Personnel:** 399

## DAVENPORT—Scott County

☒ △ **GENESIS MEDICAL CENTER - DAVENPORT (160033)**, 1227 East Rusholme Street, Zip 52803–2498; tel. 563/421–1000, (Includes GENESIS MEDICAL CENTER-EAST CAMPUS, Mailing address: 1227 East Rusholme Street, Davenport, Iowa, Zip 52803; tel. 563/421–1000; GENESIS MEDICAL CENTER-WEST CAMPUS, Mailing address: 1401 West Central Park, Davenport, Iowa, Zip 52804–1769; tel. 563/421–1000), (Nonreporting) **A**1 2 3 5 7 10 **F**3 7 11 12 13 15 17 18 20 22 24 26 28 29 30 31 34 35 37 38 40 43 44 46 49 50 53 54 57 58 59 63 64 68 70 72 76 77 78 79 81 82 84 85 86 87 89 90 91 92 93 94 96 97 98 99 100 102 107 111 114 115 118 119 120 121 123 124 126 129 130 131 132 135 146 147 148 153 154 156 157 **S** Genesis Health System, Davenport, IA
Primary Contact: Jordan Voigt, President
CFO: Mark G Rogers, Interim Vice President Finance and Chief Financial Officer
CMO: Frank Claudy, M.D., Vice President Medical Staff Affairs
CIO: Robert Frieden, Vice President Information Systems
CHR: Heidi Kahly-McMahon, Interim Vice President Human Resources
Web address: www.genesishealth.com
**Control**: Other not–for–profit (including NFP Corporation) **Service**: General medical and surgical

**Staffed Beds:** 368 **Admissions:** 18018 **Census:** 174 **Outpatient Visits:** 214504 **Births:** 1913 **Total Expense ($000):** 348880 **Payroll Expense ($000):** 90337 **Personnel:** 1400

**GENESIS MEDICAL CENTER, DAVENPORT** See Genesis Medical Center - Davenport

**MERCY HOSPITAL** See Genesis Medical Center-West Campus

☒ **SELECT SPECIALTY HOSPITAL-QUAD CITIES (162001)**, 1111 West Kimberly Road, Zip 52806–5711; tel. 563/468–2000, (Nonreporting) **A**1 10 **F**1 3 29 45 75 85 119 130 148 **S** Select Medical Corporation, Mechanicsburg, PA
Primary Contact: Codie Dillie, Chief Executive Officer
Web address: www.selectmedicalcorp.com
**Control**: Corporation, Investor–owned (for–profit) **Service**: Acute long–term care hospital

**Staffed Beds:** 50 **Admissions:** 324 **Census:** 24 **Outpatient Visits:** 0 **Births:** 0 **Total Expense ($000):** 15490 **Payroll Expense ($000):** 6641 **Personnel:** 105

**ST LUKE'S HOSPITAL** See Genesis Medical Center-East Campus

**IA**

---

**Hospital, Medicare Provider Number, Address, Telephone, Approval, Facility, and Physician Codes, Health Care System**

★ American Hospital Association (AHA) membership
☐ The Joint Commission accreditation
○ Healthcare Facilities Accreditation Program
◇ DNV Healthcare Inc. accreditation
⇑ Center for Improvement in Healthcare Quality Accreditation
△ Commission on Accreditation of Rehabilitation Facilities (CARF) accreditation

## DE WITT—Clinton County

**DEWITT COMMUNITY HOSPITAL** See Genesis Medical Center, Dewitt

✠ **GENESIS MEDICAL CENTER, DEWITT (161313)**, 1118 11th Street, Zip 52742–1296; tel. 563/659–4200, (Total facility includes 75 beds in nursing home–type unit) (Nonreporting) **A**1 10 18 **F**3 7 8 11 15 28 29 34 35 38 40 41 43 44 45 49 50 53 57 59 64 68 69 77 81 82 85 86 87 93 102 107 110 115 119 129 130 132 133 134 146 148 149 **P**6 **S** Genesis Health System, Davenport, IA
Primary Contact: Curt Coleman, FACHE, Critical Access Hospitals President
CMO: Steven Fowler, M.D., President Medical Staff
CHR: Kristin Nicholson, Coordinator Human Resources
CNO: Wanda Haack, MSN, R.N., Chief Nursing Officer
Web address: www.genesishealth.com
**Control**: Other not–for–profit (including NFP Corporation) **Service**: General medical and surgical

| | |
|---|---|
| **Staffed Beds:** 88 **Admissions:** 304 **Census:** 73 **Outpatient Visits:** 20257 **Births:** 0 **Total Expense ($000):** 20911 **Payroll Expense ($000):** 7959 **Personnel:** 91 | |

## DECORAH—Winneshiek County

**WINNESHIEK COUNTY MEM HOSPITAL** See Winneshiek Medical Center

✠ **WINNESHIEK MEDICAL CENTER (161371)**, 901 Montgomery Street, Zip 52101–2325; tel. 563/382–2911, (Nonreporting) **A**1 10 18 **F**3 7 8 11 13 15 28 29 31 34 35 36 38 40 43 44 45 50 56 57 59 61 62 63 64 65 68 69 75 76 77 78 79 81 82 86 87 93 94 97 101 104 107 110 111 115 119 128 129 130 131 132 133 135 144 146 147 148 149 150 153 156 **P**6 **S** Mayo Clinic, Rochester, MN
Primary Contact: Lisa Radtke, Chief Administrative Officer
COO: David Rooney, Administrator Operations
CFO: Lynn Luloff, Chief Financial Officer
CMO: Thomas Marquardt, M.D., Interim Chief Medical Officer
CHR: Laurie Bulman, Director Human Resources
CNO: Kathy Moritz, Chief Nursing Officer
Web address: www.winmedical.org
**Control**: County, Government, Nonfederal **Service**: General medical and surgical

| | |
|---|---|
| **Staffed Beds:** 25 **Admissions:** 847 **Census:** 9 **Outpatient Visits:** 113761 **Births:** 268 **Total Expense ($000):** 62807 **Payroll Expense ($000):** 21616 **Personnel:** 385 | |

## DENISON—Crawford County

★ **CRAWFORD COUNTY MEMORIAL HOSPITAL (161369)**, 100 Medical Parkway, Zip 51442–2299; tel. 712/265–2500, (Nonreporting) **A**10 18 **F**3 7 8 11 13 15 17 28 29 31 34 35 40 45 50 54 56 57 59 64 65 67 68 70 75 76 77 78 79 81 82 85 87 89 93 97 101 104 107 110 111 115 119 127 128 133 135 143 148 156 **P**6
Primary Contact: Erin Muck, Chief Executive Officer
CFO: Rachel Melby, Vice President, Chief Financial Officer
CIO: Angie Anderson, Director Information Technology
CHR: Brad L. Bonner, Executive Director, Human Resources and General Counsel
Web address: www.ccmhia.com
**Control**: County, Government, Nonfederal **Service**: General medical and surgical

| | |
|---|---|
| **Staffed Beds:** 25 **Admissions:** 642 **Census:** 5 **Outpatient Visits:** 47837 **Births:** 122 **Total Expense ($000):** 37443 **Payroll Expense ($000):** 18225 **Personnel:** 272 | |

## DES MOINES—Polk County

**BLANK CHILDREN'S HOSPITAL** See Unitypoint Health - Blank Children's Hospital

✠ **BROADLAWNS MEDICAL CENTER (160101)**, 1801 Hickman Road, Zip 50314–1597; tel. 515/282–2200, (Nonreporting) **A**1 3 5 10 **F**3 5 11 13 15 18 29 30 31 32 34 35 38 39 40 43 44 45 48 50 52 53 56 57 58 59 64 65 66 68 70 74 75 76 77 78 79 81 82 85 86 87 92 93 94 97 98 100 101 102 104 105 106 107 111 114 119 127 129 130 131 132 135 144 146 147 148 153 154 156 **P**6
Primary Contact: Jody J. Jenner, President and Chief Executive Officer
CFO: Karlis Vilums, Chief Financial Officer
CMO: Yogesh Shah, M.D., Chief Medical Officer
CHR: Julie Kilgore, Vice President, Human Resources
CNO: Susan N. Kirstein, R.N., MSN, Chief Nursing Officer
Web address: www.broadlawns.org
**Control**: County, Government, Nonfederal **Service**: General medical and surgical

| | |
|---|---|
| **Staffed Beds:** 135 **Admissions:** 2734 **Census:** 61 **Outpatient Visits:** 237794 **Births:** 475 **Total Expense ($000):** 185647 **Payroll Expense ($000):** 86680 **Personnel:** 1080 | |

**DEPT OF VETERANS AFF MED CTR** See Des Moines Division

**DES MOINES DIVISION** See VA Central Iowa Health Care System, Des Moines

⇑ **IOWA METHODIST MEDICAL CENTER** See Unitypoint Health - Iowa Methodist Medical Center

**JOHN STODDARD CANCER CENTER** See Unity Point Health - John Stoddard Cancer Center

**MERCY MEDICAL CENTER-DES MOINES** See Mercyone Des Moines Medical Center

✠ **MERCYONE DES MOINES MEDICAL CENTER (160083)**, 1111 6th Avenue, Zip 50314–2611; tel. 515/247–3121, (Includes MERCYONE WEST DES MOINES MEDICAL CENTER, Mailing address: 1755 59th Place, West Des Moines, Iowa, Zip 50266–7737; tel. 515/358–8000; Karl Keeler, President), (Nonreporting) **A**1 2 3 5 10 13 **F**3 5 6 7 8 9 11 12 13 15 17 18 19 20 21 22 23 24 25 26 27 28 29 30 31 32 34 35 36 38 39 40 41 43 44 46 48 49 50 53 54 55 56 57 58 59 60 61 62 63 64 65 66 68 70 71 72 73 74 75 76 77 78 79 81 82 84 85 86 87 88 89 91 92 93 94 96 97 98 99 100 101 102 103 104 105 107 108 109 110 111 114 115 116 117 118 119 120 121 123 124 126 129 130 131 132 134 135 138 141 142 143 144 145 146 147 148 149 150 152 153 154 156 157 158 **P**6 **S** CommonSpirit Health, Chicago, IL
Primary Contact: Karl Keeler, President
COO: Linda Goodwin, Chief Operating Officer and Chief Nursing Executive
CFO: Randy Rubin, Senior Vice President and Chief Financial Officer
CIO: James Strother, Site Director Information Technology Systems
CHR: Kevin Elsberry, Senior Vice President Human Resources
CNO: Linda Goodwin, Chief Operating Officer and Chief Nursing Executive
Web address: www.mercydesmoines.org
**Control**: Church operated, Nongovernment, not–for–profit **Service**: General medical and surgical

| | |
|---|---|
| **Staffed Beds:** 696 **Admissions:** 34178 **Census:** 451 **Outpatient Visits:** 281726 **Births:** 0 **Total Expense:** 729148 **Payroll Expense:** 265058 **Personnel:** 4066 | |

✠ **SELECT SPECIALTY HOSPITAL-DES MOINES (162003)**, 1111 6th Avenue, 4th Floor Main, Zip 50314–2610; tel. 515/247–4400, (Nonreporting) **A**1 10 **F**1 29 75 148 **S** Select Medical Corporation, Mechanicsburg, PA
Primary Contact: Brent Hanson, Chief Executive Officer
Web address: www.selectspecialtyhospitals.com
**Control**: Corporation, Investor–owned (for–profit) **Service**: Acute long–term care hospital

| | |
|---|---|
| **Staffed Beds:** 30 **Admissions:** 350 **Census:** 26 **Outpatient Visits:** 0 **Births:** 0 **Total Expense ($000):** 14002 **Payroll Expense ($000):** 6523 **Personnel:** 107 | |

**UNITYPOINT HEALTH - DES MOINES** See Unitypoint Health-Iowa Lutheran Hospital

★ △ ⇑ **UNITYPOINT HEALTH - IOWA METHODIST MEDICAL CENTER (160082)**, 1200 Pleasant Street, Zip 50309–1406; tel. 515/241–6212, (Includes POWELL CONVALESCENT CENTER, Mailing address: 1200 Pleasant, Des Moines, Iowa, Zip 50309; tel. 515/263–5612; UNITY POINT HEALTH - JOHN STODDARD CANCER CENTER, Mailing address: 1221 Pleasant Street, Des Moines, Iowa, Zip 50309–1423; tel. 515/241–6212; UNITYPOINT HEALTH - BLANK CHILDREN'S HOSPITAL, Mailing address: 1200 Pleasant Street, Des Moines, Iowa, Zip 50309–1406; tel. 515/241–5437; Steve R. Stephenson, M.D., President and Chief Operating Officer; UNITYPOINT HEALTH - METHODIST WEST HOSPITAL, Mailing address: 1660 60th Street, West Des Moines, Iowa, Zip 50266–7700; tel. 515/343–1000; David A. Stark, FACHE, President and Chief Executive Officer; UNITYPOINT HEALTH-IOWA LUTHERAN HOSPITAL, Mailing address: 700 East University Avenue, Des Moines, Iowa, Zip 50316–2392; tel. 515/263–5612; David A. Stark, FACHE, President and Chief Executive Officer; YOUNKER MEMORIAL REHABILITATION CENTER, Mailing address: 1200 Pleasant Road, Des Moines, Iowa, Zip 50308; tel. 515/263–5612), (Nonreporting) **A**2 3 5 7 10 21 **F**3 7 8 11 12 13 17 18 20 22 24 26 28 29 30 31 32 34 35 37 39 40 41 43 44 45 46 47 48 49 50 53 54 55 56 57 58 60 61 64 65 68 70 71 72 74 75 76 77 78 79 81 82 84 85 86 87 88 89 90 91 92 93 95 96 97 100 107 108 111 114 115 116 117 118 119 120 121 123 124 126 129 130 131 132 134 135 138 146 147 148 149 154 156 157 **P**6 **S** UnityPoint Health, West Des Moines, IA
Primary Contact: David A. Stark, FACHE, President and Chief Executive Officer
COO: Eric L Lothe, FACHE, Executive Vice President and Chief Operating Officer
CFO: Thomas Mathews, Chief Financial Officer
CMO: Mark Purtle, M.D., Vice President Medical Affairs
CHR: Joyce McDanel, Vice President Human Resources and Education
Web address: www.unitypoint.org
**Control**: Other not–for–profit (including NFP Corporation) **Service**: General medical and surgical

| | |
|---|---|
| **Staffed Beds:** 758 **Admissions:** 35845 **Census:** 516 **Outpatient Visits:** 379399 **Births:** 5496 **Total Expense:** 802626 **Payroll Expense:** 339633 **Personnel:** 5113 | |

⊠ △ **VA CENTRAL IOWA HEALTH CARE SYSTEM**, 3600 30th Street, Zip 50310–5753; tel. 515/699–5999, (Includes DES MOINES DIVISION, Mailing address: 3600 30th Street, Des Moines, Iowa, Zip 50310–5774; tel. 515/699–5999; KNOXVILLE DIVISION, Mailing address: 1515 West Pleasant, Knoxville, Iowa, Zip 50138–3399; tel. 515/842–3101) (Total facility includes 108 beds in nursing home–type unit) **A**1 3 5 7 **F**3 4 5 6 8 11 12 15 18 20 22 24 28 29 30 31 33 34 35 36 37 38 39 40 44 45 46 50 53 54 55 56 57 59 61 62 63 64 65 66 70 71 74 75 77 78 79 81 82 83 84 85 86 87 93 94 96 97 98 100 101 102 104 106 107 108 110 111 114 115 117 118 119 127 128 129 130 132 135 137 138 139 140 141 142 143 144 146 147 148 149 150 154 156 157 **S** Department of Veterans Affairs, Washington, DC
Primary Contact: Gail L. Graham, Director
CMO: Fredrick Bahls, M.D., Chief of Staff
CIO: James Danuser, Chief Information Officer
CHR: Sabrina Owen, Human Resources Officer
Web address: www.centraliowa.va.gov/
**Control**: Veterans Affairs, Government, federal **Service**: General medical and surgical

**Staffed Beds**: 223 **Admissions**: 3357 **Census**: 155 **Outpatient Visits**: 374535 **Births**: 0 **Total Expense ($000)**: 270998 **Payroll Expense ($000)**: 120758 **Personnel**: 1734

**VETERANS AFFAIRS CENTRAL IOWA HEALTH CARE SYSTEM** See VA Central Iowa Health Care System

### DUBUQUE—Dubuque County

**MERCY MEDICAL CENTER-DUBUQUE** See Mercyone Dubuque Medical Center

⊠ △ **MERCYONE DUBUQUE MEDICAL CENTER (160069)**, 250 Mercy Drive, Zip 52001–7360; tel. 563/589–8000, (Total facility includes 40 beds in nursing home–type unit) (Nonreporting) **A**1 7 10 **F**3 4 5 8 11 13 15 18 20 22 24 26 28 29 30 31 32 34 35 36 38 39 40 43 44 49 50 51 53 56 57 58 59 61 62 64 65 67 70 72 74 75 76 77 78 79 80 81 84 85 86 87 89 90 91 93 97 98 99 100 101 102 103 104 107 108 110 111 114 115 117 118 119 126 128 129 130 131 132 134 135 144 146 147 148 149 150 156 **P**8 **S** Trinity Health, Livonia, MI
Primary Contact: Kay Takes, R.N., President
CFO: Robert Shafer, Vice President Finance
CIO: Joe Billmeyer, Director, Information Services
CHR: Kathryn Roberts, Director Human Resources
CNO: Robert Wethal, R.N., Vice President Patient Care Services and Chief Nursing Officer
Web address: www.mercydubuque.com
**Control**: Church operated, Nongovernment, not–for–profit **Service**: General medical and surgical

**Staffed Beds**: 234 **Admissions**: 8591 **Census**: 140 **Outpatient Visits**: 46685 **Births**: 783 **Total Expense ($000)**: 169377 **Payroll Expense ($000)**: 58937 **Personnel**: 1065

**UNITYPOINT HEALTH - FINLEY** See Unitypoint Health - Finley Hospital

⊠ △ **UNITYPOINT HEALTH - FINLEY HOSPITAL (160117)**, 350 North Grandview Avenue, Zip 52001–6393; tel. 563/582–1881, (Nonreporting) **A**1 7 10 **F**3 13 15 18 20 22 28 29 30 31 34 35 40 43 44 50 51 55 56 57 58 59 61 62 64 65 68 70 72 74 75 76 77 78 79 81 82 84 85 86 87 90 91 93 96 98 100 102 103 104 107 108 110 111 114 115 116 117 118 119 120 121 123 124 126 129 130 131 132 135 144 146 147 148 149 153 154 156 **S** UnityPoint Health, West Des Moines, IA
Primary Contact: Chad Wolbers, President and Chief Executive Officer
CMO: Bryan Pechous, M.D., Vice President Medical Affairs
CIO: Tim Loeffelholz, Account Executive Information Technology
CHR: Karla Waldbillig, Director Human Resources
CNO: Mary Peters, Chief Nursing Executive
Web address: www.unitypoint.org
**Control**: Other not–for–profit (including NFP Corporation) **Service**: General medical and surgical

**Staffed Beds**: 112 **Admissions**: 4170 **Census**: 49 **Outpatient Visits**: 140773 **Births**: 676 **Total Expense ($000)**: 118722 **Payroll Expense ($000)**: 52504 **Personnel**: 683

### DYERSVILLE—Dubuque County

**MERCY MEDICAL CENTER-DYERSVILLE** See Mercyone Dyersville Medical Center

★ **MERCYONE DYERSVILLE MEDICAL CENTER (161378)**, 1111 Third Street SW, Zip 52040–1725; tel. 563/875–7101, (Nonreporting) **A**10 18 **F**11 15 34 35 36 39 40 44 50 56 57 59 64 65 75 79 81 85 86 93 107 114 119 130 131 132 133 134 135 146 147 149 156 **P**8 **S** Trinity Health, Livonia, MI
Primary Contact: Kay Takes, R.N., President
CFO: Robert Shafer, Vice President Finance
Web address: www.mercydubuque.com/mercy-dyersville
**Control**: Church operated, Nongovernment, not–for–profit **Service**: General medical and surgical

**Staffed Beds**: 20 **Admissions**: 77 **Census**: 2 **Outpatient Visits**: 3554 **Births**: 0 **Total Expense ($000)**: 5377 **Payroll Expense ($000)**: 2293 **Personnel**: 52

### ELKADER—Clayton County

**CENTRAL COMMUNITY HOSPITAL** See Mercyone Elkader Medical Center

★ **MERCYONE ELKADER MEDICAL CENTER (161319)**, 901 Davidson Street NW, Zip 52043–9015; tel. 563/245–7000, (Nonreporting) **A**10 18 **F**7 11 15 28 29 34 35 40 43 45 50 57 59 64 67 68 75 81 85 87 91 93 102 107 110 114 128 133 146 **S** Trinity Health, Livonia, MI
Primary Contact: Brooke Kensinger, Chief Executive Officer
CFO: Patricia Borel, Chief Financial Officer
CIO: Jonathan Holliday, Manager Information Technology
CHR: Angie Gerndt, Human Resources Manager
CNO: Natalie Shea, Chief Nursing Officer
Web address: www.centralcommunityhospital.com
**Control**: Other not–for–profit (including NFP Corporation) **Service**: General medical and surgical

**Staffed Beds**: 15 **Admissions**: 139 **Census**: 3 **Outpatient Visits**: 15070 **Births**: 0 **Total Expense ($000)**: 8707 **Payroll Expense ($000)**: 3169 **Personnel**: 69

### EMMETSBURG—Palo Alto County

★ **PALO ALTO COUNTY HEALTH SYSTEM (161357)**, 3201 First Street, Zip 50536–2516; tel. 712/852–5500, (Total facility includes 22 beds in nursing home–type unit) (Nonreporting) **A**10 18 **F**3 7 11 13 15 28 29 34 35 37 40 43 45 46 50 57 59 62 63 64 65 67 69 71 75 76 77 81 82 85 87 93 97 100 104 107 110 114 119 127 130 131 132 133 143 146 154 158 **S** Trinity Health, Livonia, MI
Primary Contact: Brett Antczak, Chief Executive Officer
CFO: Collette Johnson, Chief Financial Officer
CMO: Madhan Prabhakaran, M.D., Chief Medical Officer
CHR: Tara Helle, Human Resources Lead
CNO: Sara Travis, Chief Nursing Officer and Assistant Administrator
Web address: www.pachs.com
**Control**: County, Government, Nonfederal **Service**: General medical and surgical

**Staffed Beds**: 47 **Admissions**: 363 **Census**: 27 **Outpatient Visits**: 25233 **Births**: 77 **Total Expense ($000)**: 26613 **Payroll Expense ($000)**: 9675 **Personnel**: 223

**PALO ALTO COUNTY HOSPITAL** See Palo Alto County Health System

### ESTHERVILLE—Emmet County

**AVERA HOLY FAMILY HEALTH** See Avera Holy Family Hospital

★ **AVERA HOLY FAMILY HOSPITAL (161351)**, 826 North Eighth Street, Zip 51334–1598; tel. 712/362–2631, (Nonreporting) **A**10 18 **F**3 11 15 28 29 30 31 34 35 37 40 45 55 57 59 64 65 68 69 70 75 77 78 79 81 85 87 93 97 107 110 111 114 119 130 131 132 133 146 154 156 **P**6 **S** Avera Health, Sioux Falls, SD
Primary Contact: Deborah L. Herzberg, R.N., MS, FACHE, Administrator
CFO: Shannon Adams, Chief Financial Officer
CMO: Anthony Cook, M.D., Chief of Staff
CHR: Janette Jensen, Manager Human Resources
CNO: Cathi Rae Scharnberg, R.N., M.P.H., Vice President Patient Services
Web address: www.avera-holyfamily.org
**Control**: Church operated, Nongovernment, not–for–profit **Service**: General medical and surgical

**Staffed Beds**: 25 **Admissions**: 450 **Census**: 5 **Outpatient Visits**: 32911 **Births**: 1 **Total Expense ($000)**: 24575 **Payroll Expense ($000)**: 10195 **Personnel**: 171

**IA**

---

**Hospital, Medicare Provider Number, Address, Telephone, Approval, Facility, and Physician Codes, Health Care System**

★ American Hospital Association (AHA) membership
☐ The Joint Commission accreditation
◯ Healthcare Facilities Accreditation Program
◇ DNV Healthcare Inc. accreditation
⇑ Center for Improvement in Healthcare Quality Accreditation
△ Commission on Accreditation of Rehabilitation Facilities (CARF) accreditation

## FAIRFIELD—Jefferson County

★ **JEFFERSON COUNTY HEALTH CENTER (161364)**, 2000 S Main,
Zip 52556–9572, Mailing Address: P.O. Box 588, Zip 52556–0010;
tel. 641/472–4111, (Nonreporting) **A**10 18 **F**11 15 28 30 31 34 35 36 40 43 45
50 57 59 67 68 70 75 77 78 79 81 85 89 93 96 102 107 110 111 112 114
115 119 127 128 129 132 133 135 143 144 146 148 156
Primary Contact: Bryan Hunger, Chief Executive Officer
CFO: Larry Peach, Chief Financial Officer
CHR: Nanette Everly, Manager Human Resources and Administrative Assistant
Web address: www.jeffersoncountyhealthcenter.org
**Control**: County, Government, Nonfederal **Service**: General medical and surgical

**Staffed Beds**: 25 **Admissions**: 638 **Census**: 9 **Outpatient Visits**: 130256
**Births**: 0 **Total Expense ($000)**: 48676 **Payroll Expense ($000)**: 17180
**Personnel**: 335

**JEFFERSON COUNTY HOSPITAL** See Jefferson County Health Center

## FORT DODGE—Webster County

⇑ **TRINITY REGIONAL MEDICAL CENTER** See Unitypoint Health - Trinity Regional
Medical Center

★ ⇑ **UNITYPOINT HEALTH - TRINITY REGIONAL MEDICAL CENTER (160016)**,
802 Kenyon Road, Zip 50501–5795; tel. 515/573–3101, (Nonreporting) **A**2 10
21 **F**3 11 13 15 17 18 20 22 26 28 29 30 31 32 34 35 38 40 43 44 45 47 49
50 53 57 59 64 68 70 75 76 77 81 82 84 85 86 87 89 93 96 101 102 104
107 108 110 111 115 118 119 120 121 123 127 129 130 135 146 147 149
150 153 156 **S** UnityPoint Health, West Des Moines, IA
Primary Contact: Leah Glasgo, Chief Executive Officer
COO: Troy Martens, Chief Operating Officer
CFO: Brent Feickert, Chief Financial Officer
CHR: Ted W Vaughn, Director Human Resources
CNO: Debra Shriver, R.N., MSN, Chief Nurse Executive
Web address: www.trmc.org
**Control**: Other not–for–profit (including NFP Corporation) **Service**: General
medical and surgical

**Staffed Beds**: 49 **Admissions**: 3155 **Census**: 31 **Outpatient Visits**: 67055
**Births**: 499 **Total Expense ($000)**: 124501 **Payroll Expense ($000)**: 60712
**Personnel**: 502

## FORT MADISON—Lee County

⊞ **FORT MADISON COMMUNITY HOSPITAL (160122)**, 5445 Avenue
'O', Zip 52627–9611, Mailing Address: P.O. Box 174, Zip 52627–0174;
tel. 319/372–6530, (Data for 273 days) (Nonreporting) **A**1 10 **F**3 11 13 15 28 29
31 34 40 43 45 50 51 53 57 59 62 63 64 67 68 70 74 75 76 77 78 79 81 85
86 87 90 91 93 94 96 97 99 100 101 102 103 104 107 108 110 111 115 117
118 119 128 130 131 132 133 143 144 146 147 148 149 **P**6
Primary Contact: Shelby Burchett, Chief Executive Officer
CFO: Bradley J Kokjohn, Chief Financial Officer
CMO: David Wenger-Keller, M.D., Chief of Staff
CIO: Shane Tapper, Director Management Information Systems
CHR: Vicki Kokjohn, Director Employee Relations
CNO: Shelby Dickens, Director, Patient Care Services
Web address: www.fmchosp.com
**Control**: Other not–for–profit (including NFP Corporation) **Service**: General
medical and surgical

**Staffed Beds**: 50 **Admissions**: 726 **Census**: 7 **Outpatient Visits**: 63025
**Births**: 239 **Total Expense ($000)**: 44936 **Payroll Expense ($000)**: 21795
**Personnel**: 407

## GREENFIELD—Adair County

★ **ADAIR COUNTY HEALTH SYSTEM (161310)**, 609 SE Kent Street,
Zip 50849–9454; tel. 641/743–2123, (Nonreporting) **A**10 18 **F**3 7 8 11 15 18
28 29 32 34 35 40 43 45 50 57 59 64 65 69 75 79 81 82 97 104 107 108
110 115 119 127 128 130 133 143 144 148 149 154 156 **P**6 **S** MercyOne,
Clive, IA
Primary Contact: Marcia Hendricks, FACHE, R.N., Chief Executive Officer
CFO: Heather Shaull, Chief Financial Officer
CMO: Jessica Kennedy, D.O., Chief Medical Officer
CIO: Gary Bateman, Chief Information Technology
CHR: Angie Frankl, Director Human Resources
CNO: Cindy K Peeler, R.N., Chief Nursing Officer
Web address: www.adaircountyhealthsystem.org
**Control**: County, Government, Nonfederal **Service**: General medical and surgical

**Staffed Beds**: 17 **Admissions**: 65 **Census**: 1 **Outpatient Visits**: 8897
**Births**: 0 **Total Expense ($000)**: 14513 **Payroll Expense ($000)**: 5880
**Personnel**: 107

**ADAIR COUNTY MEMORIAL HOSPITAL** See Adair County Health System

## GRINNELL—Poweshiek County

**GRINNELL REGIONAL MEDICAL CENTER** See Unitypoint Health - Grinnell
Regional Medical Center

★ ○ **UNITYPOINT HEALTH - GRINNELL REGIONAL MEDICAL CENTER
(160147)**, 210 Fourth Avenue, Zip 50112–1898; tel. 641/236–7511,
(Nonreporting) **A**10 11 **F**3 11 12 13 15 28 29 30 31 32 34 35 36 38 40 43 44
45 46 47 50 53 54 56 57 59 61 62 63 64 65 66 70 75 76 77 78 81 84 85 86
87 93 97 107 110 111 115 118 119 126 127 130 131 132 133 134 135 144
146 147 148 149 150 154 156 **S** UnityPoint Health, West Des Moines, IA
Primary Contact: Jennifer Havens, Chief Executive Officer
CFO: Kyle M Wilcox, Vice President Finance
CIO: David L Ness, Vice President Operations
CHR: Debra S. Nowachek, Director Human Resources
CNO: Doris Rindels, Vice President Operations
Web address: www.grmc.us
**Control**: Other not–for–profit (including NFP Corporation) **Service**: General
medical and surgical

**Staffed Beds**: 49 **Admissions**: 1176 **Census**: 11 **Outpatient Visits**: 47350
**Births**: 190 **Total Expense ($000)**: 48403 **Payroll Expense ($000)**: 24340
**Personnel**: 305

## GRUNDY CENTER—Grundy County

★ ⇑ **GRUNDY COUNTY MEMORIAL HOSPITAL (161303)**, 201 East 'J' Avenue,
Zip 50638–2096; tel. 319/824–5421, (Nonreporting) **A**10 18 21 **F**3 15 28 29 34
35 40 43 50 57 59 63 64 68 75 78 79 81 82 86 87 93 107 110 111 114 119
128 129 130 131 132 133 135 146 148 154 156 **S** UnityPoint Health, West Des
Moines, IA
Primary Contact: Adam Scherling, President
COO: Ryan Bingman, Director Operations
CFO: Lisa Zinkula, Chief Financial Officer
CMO: Douglas Cooper, M.D., Chief Medical Officer
CIO: Steve Bantz, Manager Information Technology
CHR: Keagan Brunscheon, Manager, Human Resources
CNO: Jody Schipper, Director of Nursing
Web address: www.https://www.unitypoint.org
**Control**: County, Government, Nonfederal **Service**: General medical and surgical

**Staffed Beds**: 25 **Admissions**: 239 **Census**: 2 **Outpatient Visits**: 48532
**Births**: 0 **Total Expense ($000)**: 18822 **Payroll Expense ($000)**: 7571
**Personnel**: 109

## GUTHRIE CENTER—Guthrie County

★ **GUTHRIE COUNTY HOSPITAL (161314)**, 710 North 12th Street,
Zip 50115–1544; tel. 641/332–2201, (Nonreporting) **A**10 18 **F**11 15 18 28 29
34 35 40 43 45 53 56 57 59 64 69 75 79 81 85 93 107 110 114 119 128 130
132 133 143 148 154 156 **P**6 **S** UnityPoint Health, West Des Moines, IA
Primary Contact: Patrick Peters, Chief Executive Officer
CFO: Troy Eller, Chief Financial Officer
CMO: Donald Fillman, M.D., Chief Medical Officer
CIO: Jeff Cobb, Information Technologist
CHR: Kimberly Myers, Director Human Resources
CNO: Gregory Opseth, Chief Nursing Officer
Web address: www.guthriecountyhospital.org
**Control**: County, Government, Nonfederal **Service**: General medical and surgical

**Staffed Beds**: 17 **Admissions**: 349 **Census**: 4 **Outpatient Visits**: 30208
**Births**: 0 **Total Expense ($000)**: 16910 **Payroll Expense ($000)**: 7814
**Personnel**: 103

## GUTTENBERG—Clayton County

**GUTTENBERG MUNICIPAL HOSPITAL** See Guttenberg Municipal Hospital and
Clinics

★ **GUTTENBERG MUNICIPAL HOSPITAL AND CLINICS (161312)**, 200 Main
Street, Zip 52052–9108, Mailing Address: P.O. Box 550, Zip 52052–0550;
tel. 563/252–1121, (Nonreporting) **A**10 18 **F**3 7 11 15 28 34 35 40 43 45 50
57 59 64 68 81 85 89 93 97 102 107 110 111 115 119 126 127 128 130 132
133 154 **P**5 6 **S** MercyOne, Clive, IA
Primary Contact: Tim Ahlers, Chief Executive Officer
COO: Lisa Manson, Director Ambulatory Services
CFO: Jill DeMoss, Finance Manager
CMO: Chris Hugo, M.D., Chief of Staff
CIO: Scott R Pauls, Director Information Technology- HealthNet Connect
CHR: Chelsea Greene, Manager Human Resources
Web address: www.guttenberghospital.org
**Control**: City, Government, Nonfederal **Service**: General medical and surgical

**Staffed Beds**: 20 **Admissions**: 237 **Census**: 3 **Outpatient Visits**: 22152
**Births**: 0 **Total Expense ($000)**: 18961 **Payroll Expense ($000)**: 7693
**Personnel**: 138

*Many Facility Codes have changed. Please refer to the AHA Guide Code Chart.* © 2021 AHA Guide

**HAMBURG—Fremont County**

**GEORGE C GRAPE COMMUNITY HOSPITAL** See George C. Grape Community Hospital

**GEORGE C. GRAPE COMMUNITY HOSPITAL (161324)**, 2959 US Highway 275, Zip 51640–5067; tel. 712/382–1515, (Total facility includes 6 beds in nursing home–type unit) (Nonreporting) **A**10 18 **F**11 15 18 28 31 34 35 40 43 45 50 53 59 62 64 65 68 75 77 78 79 81 82 85 91 93 107 110 115 119 128 129 130 133 135 148
Primary Contact: Michael O'Neal, Chief Executive Officer
CFO: Hilary Christiansen, Chief Financial Officer
CMO: Kelli Woltemath, D.O., Chief Medical Staff
CIO: Craig Wells, Chief Information Officer
CHR: Jackie Wertz, Director Human Resources
CNO: Gloria Mattice, R.N., Director Patient Care
Web address: www.grapehospital.com
**Control:** Other not–for–profit (including NFP Corporation) **Service:** General medical and surgical

| Staffed Beds: 25 | Admissions: 116 | Census: 2 | Outpatient Visits: 16341 |
| Births: 0 | Total Expense ($000): 11145 | Payroll Expense ($000): 4492 |
| Personnel: 94 |

**HAMPTON—Franklin County**

★ **FRANKLIN GENERAL HOSPITAL (161308)**, 1720 Central Avenue East, Suite A, Zip 50441–1867; tel. 641/456–5000, (Total facility includes 52 beds in nursing home–type unit) (Nonreporting) **A**10 18 **F**7 10 11 15 28 30 34 40 43 57 59 63 64 65 67 68 75 77 79 81 82 85 86 89 90 93 103 107 111 115 119 127 128 129 130 131 132 133 135 146 147 148 154 **P**8 **S** Trinity Health, Livonia, MI
Primary Contact: Kim Price, Chief Executive Officer
CFO: Lee Elbert, Chief Financial Officer
CHR: Victoria Kruse, Manager Human Resources
CNO: Ronda Reimer, Chief Nursing Officer and Assistant Administrator
Web address: www.franklingeneral.com
**Control:** County, Government, Nonfederal **Service:** General medical and surgical

| Staffed Beds: 77 | Admissions: 244 | Census: 53 | Outpatient Visits: 28467 |
| Births: 0 | Total Expense ($000): 20581 | Payroll Expense ($000): 6375 |
| Personnel: 134 |

**HARLAN—Shelby County**

★ **MYRTUE MEDICAL CENTER (161374)**, 1213 Garfield Avenue, Zip 51537–2057; tel. 712/755–5161, (Nonreporting) **A**10 18 **F**3 5 11 13 15 28 29 31 32 34 35 38 40 43 45 46 50 53 56 57 59 62 63 64 65 68 75 76 77 78 81 85 87 92 93 97 99 101 102 103 104 107 110 115 119 127 129 130 131 132 133 135 146 148 154 156 157 **P**6 8
Primary Contact: Barry Jacobsen, CPA, Chief Executive Officer
CFO: Kristy Hansen, CPA, Chief Financial Officer
CMO: Sarah M. Devine, M.D., Chief of Staff
CIO: Jeffrey Sundholm, Chief Information Officer
CHR: Jill Mages, Chief Human Resource Officer
CNO: Karen Buman, MSN, Chief Nursing Officer
Web address: www.myrtuemedical.org
**Control:** County, Government, Nonfederal **Service:** General medical and surgical

| Staffed Beds: 25 | Admissions: 822 | Census: 9 | Outpatient Visits: 114747 |
| Births: 59 | Total Expense ($000): 42706 | Payroll Expense ($000): 16663 |
| Personnel: 386 |

**SHELBY COUNTY MYRTUE MEM HOSP** See Myrtue Medical Center

**HAWARDEN—Sioux County**

**HAWARDEN COMMUNITY HOSPITAL** See Hawarden Regional Healthcare

★ **HAWARDEN REGIONAL HEALTHCARE (161311)**, 1111 11th Street, Zip 51023–1999; tel. 712/551–3100, (Nonreporting) **A**10 18 **F**3 11 15 28 29 34 35 40 43 45 53 56 57 59 64 65 68 75 77 81 82 92 93 97 104 107 110 114 119 127 128 129 130 131 132 133 135 144 148 154 156 **P**7 **S** Trinity Health, Livonia, MI
Primary Contact: Jayson Pullman, Chief Executive Officer
CFO: Jessica Hughes, Director Finance
CMO: Dale Nystrom, M.D., Chief Medical Officer, Physician
CHR: Maggie Hofer, Human Resources Representative
Web address: www.hawardenregionalhealthcare.com/
**Control:** City, Government, Nonfederal **Service:** General medical and surgical

| Staffed Beds: 20 | Admissions: 185 | Census: 4 | Outpatient Visits: 23395 |
| Births: 0 | Total Expense ($000): 12060 | Payroll Expense ($000): 3850 |
| Personnel: 69 |

**HUMBOLDT—Humboldt County**

★ **HUMBOLDT COUNTY MEMORIAL HOSPITAL (161334)**, 1000 North 15th Street, Zip 50548–1008; tel. 515/332–4200, (Total facility includes 28 beds in nursing home–type unit) (Nonreporting) **A**10 18 **F**7 10 11 12 14 15 28 29 31 34 35 40 41 43 45 47 50 59 62 63 65 68 75 77 81 82 85 93 102 107 110 114 119 129 130 133 135 156 **S** UnityPoint Health, West Des Moines, IA
Primary Contact: Michelle Sleiter, Chief Executive Officer
CFO: AJ Mason, Chief Financial Officer
CHR: Mary Moritz, Administrator Human Resources
Web address: www.humboldthospital.org
**Control:** County, Government, Nonfederal **Service:** General medical and surgical

| Staffed Beds: 49 | Admissions: 603 | Census: 32 | Outpatient Visits: 67355 |
| Births: 0 | Total Expense ($000): 19677 | Payroll Expense ($000): 10119 |
| Personnel: 210 |

**IDA GROVE—Ida County**

★ **HORN MEMORIAL HOSPITAL (161354)**, 701 East Second Street, Zip 51445–1699; tel. 712/364–3311, (Nonreporting) **A**10 18 **F**11 15 28 29 34 40 45 50 57 59 62 63 64 65 66 68 75 77 79 81 82 85 89 93 97 100 107 108 110 111 115 117 119 127 128 129 130 131 132 133 135 146 147 148 154 156 **P**6
Primary Contact: Glen Winekauf, Chief Executive Officer
CFO: Marcia Fehring, Chief Financial Officer
CIO: Robbie Todd, Director Information Technology
CHR: Lorraine Davis, Vice President Human Resources
CNO: Jo Hayes, Chief Nursing Officer
Web address: www.hornmemorialhospital.org
**Control:** Other not–for–profit (including NFP Corporation) **Service:** General medical and surgical

| Staffed Beds: 20 | Admissions: 392 | Census: 5 | Outpatient Visits: 47464 |
| Births: 0 | Total Expense ($000): 20674 | Payroll Expense ($000): 9172 |
| Personnel: 154 |

**INDEPENDENCE—Buchanan County**

★ **BUCHANAN COUNTY HEALTH CENTER (161335)**, 1600 First Street East, Zip 50644–3155; tel. 319/332–0999, (Total facility includes 39 beds in nursing home–type unit) (Nonreporting) **A**10 18 **F**3 11 15 28 29 32 34 35 40 43 45 50 53 56 57 59 64 65 67 75 77 79 81 82 84 85 86 87 91 93 97 107 110 111 114 119 125 127 128 129 130 131 132 133 135 144 146 148 156 **P**6 **S** UnityPoint Health, West Des Moines, IA
Primary Contact: Steve Robert. Slessor, Chief Executive Officer
CFO: Ben Stevens, Chief Financial Officer
CNO: Rachel Goldenstein, R.N., Chief Nursing Officer
Web address: www.bchealth.info
**Control:** County, Government, Nonfederal **Service:** General medical and surgical

| Staffed Beds: 58 | Admissions: 294 | Census: 40 | Outpatient Visits: 70609 |
| Births: 0 | Total Expense ($000): 33065 | Payroll Expense ($000): 13227 |
| Personnel: 209 |

☐ **INDEPENDENCE MENTAL HEALTH INSTITUTE (164003)**, 2277 Iowa Avenue, Zip 50644–9106; tel. 319/334–2583, (Nonreporting) **A**1 10 **F**59 65 75 98 99 101 102 130 135 143 146 149 **P**6
Primary Contact: Bhasker J. Dave, M.D., Superintendent
CFO: Kevin Jimmerson, Business Manager
CMO: Bhasker J Dave, M.D., Superintendent
Web address: www.https://dhs.iowa.gov/mhds/mental-health/in-patient/mental-health-institutes/independence
**Control:** State, Government, Nonfederal **Service:** Psychiatric

| Staffed Beds: 56 | Admissions: 148 | Census: 55 | Outpatient Visits: 35 |
| Births: 0 | Total Expense ($000): 19794 | Payroll Expense ($000): 11393 |
| Personnel: 189 |

**MENTAL HEALTH INSTITUTE** See Independence Mental Health Institute

**PEOPLE'S MEMORIAL HOSPITAL** See Buchanan County Health Center

---

**Hospital, Medicare Provider Number, Address, Telephone, Approval, Facility, and Physician Codes, Health Care System**

★ American Hospital Association (AHA) membership
☐ The Joint Commission accreditation
○ Healthcare Facilities Accreditation Program
◇ DNV Healthcare Inc. accreditation
⇑ Center for Improvement in Healthcare Quality Accreditation
△ Commission on Accreditation of Rehabilitation Facilities (CARF) accreditation

**IA**

## IOWA CITY—Johnson County

⊞ **IOWA CITY VA HEALTH CARE SYSTEM**, 601 Highway 6 West, Zip 52246–2208; tel. 319/338–0581, (Nonreporting) **A**1 3 5 **F**3 5 7 8 11 12 15 18 20 22 24 29 30 31 33 34 35 36 38 39 40 43 44 45 46 47 50 51 54 56 57 58 59 60 61 62 63 64 65 70 71 74 75 78 79 81 82 83 84 85 86 87 91 92 93 94 97 98 100 101 102 103 104 105 107 108 110 111 114 115 116 117 118 119 129 130 135 138 142 143 146 147 148 149 152 153 154 156 157 **P**6 **S** Department of Veterans Affairs, Washington, DC
Primary Contact: Judith Johnson-Mekota, Director
COO: Kevin Kosek, Associate Director Operations
CFO: Jennifer Ruppert, Chief Financial Officer
CMO: Richard A Charlat, Chief of Staff
CIO: Dwight Schuessler, Chief Information Officer
CHR: Dan Helle, Human Resources Officer
CNO: Dawn Oxley, R.N., Associate Director Patient Care Services and Nurse Executive
Web address: www.iowacity.va.gov/
**Control:** Veterans Affairs, Government, federal **Service:** General medical and surgical

**Staffed Beds:** 77 **Admissions:** 3518 **Census:** 53 **Outpatient Visits:** 585985 **Births:** 0 **Total Expense ($000):** 336222 **Payroll Expense ($000):** 165458 **Personnel:** 2018

**IOWA CITY VETERANS AFFAIRS HEALTH CARE SYSTEM** See Iowa City Va Health Care System

**MERCY IOWA CITY** See Mercyone Iowa City Medical Center

⊞ **MERCYONE IOWA CITY MEDICAL CENTER (160029)**, 500 East Market Street, Zip 52245–2689; tel. 319/339–0300, (Nonreporting) **A**1 10 **F**3 5 8 12 13 15 18 20 22 24 26 28 29 30 31 34 35 38 40 43 44 45 47 48 50 51 54 57 59 62 63 64 65 70 72 73 74 75 76 77 78 79 81 85 86 87 89 97 98 100 101 102 104 105 107 108 110 111 114 115 116 117 119 126 127 129 130 132 135 144 145 146 148 152 156 157 **P**8 **S** MercyOne, Clive, IA
Primary Contact: Sean J. Williams, President and Chief Executive Officer
CFO: Douglas Davenport, Interim Chief Financial Officer
CMO: Martin Izakovic, M.D., Vice President Medical Staff Affairs and Chief Medical Officer
CIO: David Fishbaugher, Chief Medical Information
CHR: Dena M Brockhouse, Director Human Resources
CNO: Cindy L Penney, R.N., Vice President Nursing
Web address: www.mercyiowacity.org
**Control:** Church operated, Nongovernment, not–for–profit **Service:** General medical and surgical

**Staffed Beds:** 223 **Admissions:** 6630 **Census:** 61 **Outpatient Visits:** 95855 **Births:** 1110 **Total Expense ($000):** 156081 **Payroll Expense ($000):** 59491 **Personnel:** 872

**UNIVERSITY HOSPITAL SCHOOL** See Center for Disabilities and Development

**UNIVERSITY OF IOWA CHILDREN'S HOSPITAL** See University of Iowa Stead Family Children's Hospital

⊞ **UNIVERSITY OF IOWA HOSPITALS AND CLINICS (160058)**, 200 Hawkins Drive, Zip 52242–1009; tel. 319/356–1616, (Includes CENTER FOR DISABILITIES AND DEVELOPMENT, Mailing address: 200 Hawkins Drive, Iowa City, Iowa, Zip 52242; tel. 319/356–1347; CHEMICAL DEPENDENCY CENTER, Mailing address: 200 Hawkins Drive, Iowa City, Iowa, Zip 52242–1007; tel. 319/384–8765; STATE PSYCHIATRIC HOSPITAL, Mailing address: 200 Hawkins Drive, Iowa City, Iowa, Zip 52242; tel. 319/356–4658; UNIVERSITY OF IOWA STEAD FAMILY CHILDREN'S HOSPITAL, Mailing address: 200 Hawkins Drive, Iowa City, Iowa, Zip 52242–1009; tel. 888/573–5437), (Nonreporting) **A**1 2 3 5 8 10 **F**3 5 6 7 8 9 11 12 13 14 15 16 17 18 19 20 21 22 23 24 25 26 27 28 29 30 31 32 33 34 35 36 37 38 39 40 41 43 44 45 46 47 48 49 50 51 52 53 54 55 56 57 58 59 60 61 62 63 64 65 66 68 70 72 73 74 75 76 77 78 79 80 81 82 83 84 85 86 87 88 89 90 91 92 93 94 96 97 98 99 100 101 102 103 104 105 107 108 109 110 111 114 115 116 117 118 119 120 121 123 124 126 127 129 130 131 132 135 136 137 138 139 140 141 142 143 144 145 146 147 148 152 153 154 155 156 **P**1
Primary Contact: Suresh Gunasekaran, Chief Executive Officer
COO: Sabi Singh, Chief Operating Officer
CFO: Bradley Haws, Chief Financial Officer
CMO: Theresa Brennan, M.D., Chief Medical Officer
CIO: Lee Carmen, Associate Vice President Health Care Information Systems
CHR: Jana Wessels, Associate Vice President Human Resources
CNO: Cindy Dawson, MSN, R.N., Chief Nursing Executive
Web address: www.uihealthcare.com
**Control:** State, Government, Nonfederal **Service:** General medical and surgical

**Staffed Beds:** 773 **Admissions:** 34113 **Census:** 659 **Outpatient Visits:** 1562362 **Births:** 2433 **Total Expense ($000):** 1749752 **Payroll Expense ($000):** 547276 **Personnel:** 8993

## IOWA FALLS—Hardin County

**ELLSWORTH MUNICIPAL HOSPITAL** See Hansen Family Hospital

★ **HANSEN FAMILY HOSPITAL (161380)**, 920 South Oak, Zip 50126–9506; tel. 641/648–4631, (Nonreporting) **A**10 18 **F**3 11 15 28 29 30 34 40 41 43 45 50 53 57 59 64 65 75 77 81 82 85 86 87 89 93 97 100 102 104 107 110 115 119 128 133 135 146 147 149 156 **P**6 **S** Trinity Health, Livonia, MI
Primary Contact: Douglas E. Morse, Chief Executive Officer and Administrator
CFO: Mike White, Chief Financial Officer
CMO: George Pfaltzgraff, Chief Medical Officer
CHR: Cheri Geitz, Director Human Resources
CNO: Katie Rieks, Chief Nursing Officer
Web address: www.hansenfamilyhospital.com
**Control:** City, Government, Nonfederal **Service:** General medical and surgical

**Staffed Beds:** 21 **Admissions:** 431 **Census:** 6 **Outpatient Visits:** 32387 **Births:** 30 **Total Expense ($000):** 24445 **Payroll Expense ($000):** 8714 **Personnel:** 151

## JEFFERSON—Greene County

★ **GREENE COUNTY MEDICAL CENTER (161325)**, 1000 West Lincolnway, Zip 50129–1645; tel. 515/386–2114, (Total facility includes 60 beds in nursing home–type unit) (Nonreporting) **A**10 18 **F**3 11 15 18 28 29 31 32 34 35 36 40 46 50 55 56 57 59 63 64 65 67 68 75 77 79 81 82 85 89 93 97 101 104 107 110 114 119 125 127 128 130 131 132 133 146 147 149 150 154 156 **S** UnityPoint Health, West Des Moines, IA
Primary Contact: Tracy Warner, Chief Executive Officer
COO: Christa Simons, Chief Operating Officer
CFO: Heather Paris, Chief Administrator Officer and Chief Financial Officer
CMO: Michael Line, Chief Medical Officer
CIO: Roger Overby, Executive Director Information Systems
CHR: Cathy Krieger, Human Resources Director
CNO: Katie Heldt, Chief Nursing Officer
Web address: www.gcmchealth.com
**Control:** County, Government, Nonfederal **Service:** General medical and surgical

**Staffed Beds:** 85 **Admissions:** 431 **Census:** 45 **Outpatient Visits:** 18520 **Births:** 0 **Total Expense ($000):** 29192 **Payroll Expense ($000):** 10623 **Personnel:** 242

## KEOKUK—Lee County

**KEOKUK AREA HOSPITAL** See Unitypoint Health-Keokuk

⊞ **UNITYPOINT HEALTH-KEOKUK (160008)**, 1600 Morgan Street, Zip 52632–3456; tel. 319/524–7150, (Nonreporting) **A**1 10 **F**3 11 15 28 29 34 35 40 43 45 46 57 59 62 64 68 70 81 85 86 87 93 96 107 108 115 118 119 129 132 133 146 148 149 156 **S** UnityPoint Health, West Des Moines, IA
Primary Contact: Vickie Reneau, Administrator and Chief Nursing Executive
CFO: Kris Karre, Director Finance and Accounting
CMO: Neville Crenshaw, D.O., Chief of Staff
CIO: Linda Atterberg, Chief Information Officer
CHR: Lora Taylor, Director Human Resources and Compliance Officer
CNO: Vickie Reneau, Administrator and Chief Nursing Executive
Web address: www.keokukhealthsystems.org
**Control:** Other not–for–profit (including NFP Corporation) **Service:** General medical and surgical

**Staffed Beds:** 42 **Admissions:** 396 **Census:** 3 **Outpatient Visits:** 25915 **Births:** 0 **Total Expense ($000):** 19428 **Payroll Expense ($000):** 7505 **Personnel:** 161

## KEOSAUQUA—Van Buren County

**VAN BUREN COUNTY HOSPITAL (161337)**, 304 Franklin Street, Zip 52565–1164; tel. 319/293–3171, (Nonreporting) **A**10 18 **F**3 7 10 11 13 15 28 29 32 34 35 40 43 45 46 50 56 57 59 64 65 75 81 82 85 89 93 97 102 107 110 115 119 125 127 128 130 132 133 135 146 147 154 156 157 **P**6
Primary Contact: Garen Carpenter, Chief Executive Officer
CFO: Kara McEntee, Chief Financial Officer
CIO: Chris McEntee, Network Specialist
CNO: Rhonda Fellows, R.N., Chief Nursing Officer
Web address: www.vbch.org
**Control:** County, Government, Nonfederal **Service:** General medical and surgical

**Staffed Beds:** 25 **Admissions:** 221 **Census:** 2 **Outpatient Visits:** 16950 **Births:** 18 **Total Expense ($000):** 16318 **Payroll Expense ($000):** 8239 **Personnel:** 150

**VAN BUREN COUNTY MEM HOSPITAL** See Van Buren County Hospital

**IA**

## KNOXVILLE—Marion County

**DEPT OF VETERANS AFF MED CTR** See Knoxville Division

**KNOXVILLE AREA COMMUNITY HOSP** See Knoxville Hospital & Clinics

**KNOXVILLE DIVISION** See VA Central Iowa Health Care System, Des Moines

★ **KNOXVILLE HOSPITAL & CLINICS (161355)**, 1002 South Lincoln Street,
Zip 50138–3155; tel. 641/842–2151, (Nonreporting) **A**10 18 **F**3 8 11 15 28 29
31 34 35 37 40 43 45 47 48 49 50 54 57 59 64 65 75 77 81 85 93 97 107
108 110 111 114 118 119 126 129 130 131 133 135 146 148 154 156 **S**
CommonSpirit Health, Chicago, IL
Primary Contact: Kevin Kincaid, Chief Executive Officer
CFO: Maggie Hamilton-Beyer, Chief Financial Officer
CMO: Brent Hoehns, M.D., Chief of Medical Staff
CIO: Thom Richards, Director Information Technology
CNO: MaryJane Hunt, Chief Clinical Officer
Web address: www.knoxvillehospital.org
**Control**: Other not–for–profit (including NFP Corporation) **Service**: General
medical and surgical

**Staffed Beds: 25 Admissions:** 1112 **Census: 9 Outpatient Visits:** 63405
**Births:** 0 **Total Expense ($000):** 33301 **Payroll Expense ($000):** 13624
**Personnel:** 241

## LAKE CITY—Calhoun County

★ **STEWART MEMORIAL COMMUNITY HOSPITAL (161350)**, 1301 West Main,
Zip 51449–1585; tel. 712/464–3171, (Nonreporting) **A**10 18 **F**11 12 13 15
28 29 30 31 34 40 43 45 50 59 64 65 69 75 76 77 80 81 82 86 93 94 107
110 114 119 127 130 133 135 147 154 156 **P**6 **S** UnityPoint Health, West Des
Moines, IA
Primary Contact: Cynthia L. Carstens, R.N., Chief Executive Officer
CFO: Jim Henkenius, Chief Financial Officer
CHR: Bill Albright, Director Human Resources
Web address: www.stewartmemorial.org
**Control**: Other not–for–profit (including NFP Corporation) **Service**: General
medical and surgical

**Staffed Beds: 25 Admissions:** 361 **Census: 4 Outpatient Visits:** 40556
**Births:** 86 **Total Expense ($000):** 27476 **Payroll Expense ($000):** 14279
**Personnel:** 204

## LE MARS—Plymouth County

★ **FLOYD VALLEY HEALTHCARE (161368)**, 714 Lincoln Street NE,
Zip 51031–3314; tel. 712/546–7871, (Nonreporting) **A**10 18 **F**3 10 11 13 15 28
29 31 32 34 35 40 43 45 50 57 59 62 64 65 68 76 78 79 81 85 86 87 107
110 111 114 119 128 130 132 133 135 146 148 154 156 157 **S** Avera Health,
Sioux Falls, SD
Primary Contact: Dustin Wright, Chief Executive Officer
CFO: Daryl Friedenbach, Director Fiscal Services
CMO: Andrew Geha, D.O., President Medical Staff
CIO: Jacob Jorgensen, Chief Information Officer
CHR: Mary Helen Gibson, Director Human Resources
CNO: Lorrie Mortensen, MSN, R.N., Director, Patient Care
Web address: www.floydvalley.org
**Control**: City, Government, Nonfederal **Service**: General medical and surgical

**Staffed Beds: 25 Admissions:** 578 **Census: 6 Outpatient Visits:** 50130
**Births:** 96 **Total Expense ($000):** 41099 **Payroll Expense ($000):** 14639
**Personnel:** 288

**FLOYD VALLEY HOSPITAL** See Floyd Valley Healthcare

## LEON—Decatur County

★ **DECATUR COUNTY HOSPITAL (161340)**, 1405 NW Church Street,
Zip 50144–1299; tel. 641/446–4871, (Nonreporting) **A**10 18 **F**3 7 11 28 29 31
34 40 41 45 50 56 57 59 64 68 69 71 75 78 79 81 82 85 93 104 107 111
114 117 119 130 133 146 148 149 157 **P**6 **S** MercyOne, Clive, IA
Primary Contact: Mike Johnston, Chief Executive Officer
CFO: Tara Spidle, Chief Financial Officer
CMO: Ed Wehling, Chief Medical Staff
CHR: Jo Beth Smith, Vice President Human Resources
Web address: www.decaturcountyhospital.org
**Control**: County, Government, Nonfederal **Service**: General medical and surgical

**Staffed Beds: 11 Admissions:** 192 **Census: 2 Outpatient Visits:** 15920
**Births:** 0 **Total Expense ($000):** 14865 **Payroll Expense ($000):** 4962
**Personnel:** 92

## MANCHESTER—Delaware County

**DELAWARE COUNTY MEM HOSPITAL** See Regional Medical Center

★ **REGIONAL MEDICAL CENTER (161343)**, 709 West Main Street,
Zip 52057–1526, Mailing Address: P.O. Box 359, Zip 52057–0359;
tel. 563/927–3232, (Nonreporting) **A**10 18 **F**3 7 11 13 15 17 28 29 34 35 36
40 43 44 50 53 57 59 61 62 63 64 65 66 68 70 75 76 77 79 81 82 85 86 89
93 94 97 100 104 107 110 111 114 119 126 127 128 129 130 131 132 133
144 146 148 153 **P**6
Primary Contact: Charlie Button, Chief Executive Officer
COO: Amy Mensen, Chief Operating Officer
CFO: Danette Kramer, Chief Financial Officer
CNO: Heather Ries, Chief Nursing Officer
Web address: www.regmedctr.org
**Control**: County, Government, Nonfederal **Service**: General medical and surgical

**Staffed Beds: 25 Admissions:** 669 **Census: 7 Outpatient Visits:** 177664
**Births:** 175 **Total Expense ($000):** 53677 **Payroll Expense ($000):** 25064
**Personnel:** 386

## MANNING—Carroll County

**MANNING GENERAL HOSPITAL** See Manning Regional Healthcare Center

★ **MANNING REGIONAL HEALTHCARE CENTER (161332)**, 1550 6th Street,
Zip 51455–1093; tel. 712/655–2072, (Nonreporting) **A**10 18 **F**3 4 5 11 15 18
29 31 32 34 35 36 40 45 50 56 57 59 64 68 75 78 79 81 82 83 85 97 107
114 119 128 129 130 131 132 133 148 152 154 157 **P**6 **S** MercyOne, Clive, IA
Primary Contact: Linn Block, R.N., Chief Executive Officer
CFO: Amy McLaughlin, CPA, Chief Financial Officer
CMO: Douglas McLaws, D.O., Chief Medical Officer
CIO: Kim C Jahn, Chief Plant Operations and Chief Information Officer
CHR: Shelli Lorenzen, Chief Human Resources Officer
CNO: Michelle Andersen, R.N., Chief Nursing Officer
Web address: www.mrhcia.com
**Control**: Other not–for–profit (including NFP Corporation) **Service**: General
medical and surgical

**Staffed Beds: 27 Admissions:** 164 **Census: 29 Outpatient Visits:** 8302
**Births:** 0 **Total Expense ($000):** 16874 **Payroll Expense ($000):** 7429
**Personnel:** 185

## MAQUOKETA—Jackson County

**JACKSON COUNTY PUBLIC HOSPITAL** See Jackson County Regional Health
Center

⊞ **JACKSON COUNTY REGIONAL HEALTH CENTER (161329)**, 700 West Grove
Street, Zip 52060–2163; tel. 563/652–2474, (Nonreporting) **A**1 10 18 **F**3 7 11
15 28 34 40 43 45 50 53 64 75 81 82 85 87 93 107 110 114 119 128 129
133 146 148 156 **S** Genesis Health System, Davenport, IA
Primary Contact: Curt Coleman, FACHE, President
CFO: Donna Roeder, Chief Financial Officer
CHR: Shannon Langenberg, Director Human Resources
Web address: www.jcrhc.org
**Control**: County, Government, Nonfederal **Service**: General medical and surgical

**Staffed Beds: 12 Admissions:** 252 **Census: 5 Outpatient Visits:** 17075
**Births:** 0 **Total Expense ($000):** 16478 **Payroll Expense ($000):** 5982
**Personnel:** 123

## MARENGO—Iowa County

★ **COMPASS MEMORIAL HEALTHCARE (161317)**, 300 West May Street,
Zip 52301–1261; tel. 319/642–5543, (Nonreporting) **A**10 18 **F**3 15 28 29 31 34
35 38 40 43 45 50 59 64 65 69 75 77 78 79 81 85 87 93 96 97 107 110 111
115 119 127 129 130 131 132 133 135 145 146 148 149 156 **P**6 **S** UnityPoint
Health, West Des Moines, IA
Primary Contact: Barry Goettsch, FACHE, Chief Executive Officer
COO: Mikaela Gehring, Chief Operating Officer
CFO: Matthew Murphy, Chief Financial Officer
CHR: Lesa Waddell, Director Human Resources
CNO: Teresa Sauerbrei, Chief Nursing Officer
Web address: www.compassmemorial.org
**Control**: City, Government, Nonfederal **Service**: General medical and surgical

**Staffed Beds: 25 Admissions:** 354 **Census: 7 Outpatient Visits:** 20426
**Births:** 0 **Total Expense ($000):** 25833 **Payroll Expense ($000):** 10610
**Personnel:** 161

**MARENGO MEMORIAL HOSPITAL** See Compass Memorial Healthcare

**IA**

---

**Hospital, Medicare Provider Number, Address, Telephone, Approval, Facility, and Physician Codes, Health Care System**

★ American Hospital Association (AHA) membership    ○ Healthcare Facilities Accreditation Program    ⇧ Center for Improvement in Healthcare Quality Accreditation
□ The Joint Commission accreditation    ◇ DNV Healthcare Inc. accreditation    △ Commission on Accreditation of Rehabilitation Facilities (CARF) accreditation

## MARSHALLTOWN—Marshall County

**CENTRAL IOWA HEALTHCARE** See Unitypoint Health - Marshalltown

★ **UNITYPOINT HEALTH - MARSHALLTOWN (160001)**, 3 South Fourth Avenue, Zip 50158–2998; tel. 641/754–5151, (Nonreporting) **A**10 **F**3 7 11 12 15 28 29 30 40 41 43 50 54 56 62 64 68 69 75 77 79 81 83 85 87 89 102 107 108 110 111 114 115 119 127 129 130 132 135 144 146 147 148 149 **P**6 **S** UnityPoint Health, West Des Moines, IA
Primary Contact: Jennifer Friedly, President
COO: Shari King, Interim Vice President of Operations
CMO: Russell Adams, M.D., Chief Medical Officer
CHR: Jill Petermeier, Senior Executive Human Resources
Web address: www.https://marshalltown.unitypoint.org
**Control**: Other not-for-profit (including NFP Corporation) **Service**: General medical and surgical

**Staffed Beds**: 27 **Admissions**: 1391 **Census**: 11 **Outpatient Visits**: 126744
**Births**: 234 **Total Expense ($000)**: 64738 **Payroll Expense ($000)**: 33640
**Personnel**: 371

## MASON CITY—Cerro Gordo County

**MERCY MEDICAL CENTER-NORTH IOWA** See Mercyone North Iowa Medical Center

⊠ **MERCYONE NORTH IOWA MEDICAL CENTER (160064)**, 1000 Fourth Street SW, Zip 50401–2800; tel. 641/428–7000, (Nonreporting) **A**1 3 5 10 13 **F**3 11 12 13 15 18 20 22 24 26 28 29 30 31 34 35 36 37 40 43 45 48 50 55 56 57 58 59 61 62 63 64 65 68 69 70 71 72 74 75 76 77 78 79 81 82 84 85 87 89 90 91 92 93 96 97 98 100 101 102 104 105 107 108 109 110 111 112 114 115 116 117 118 119 120 121 122 123 125 126 127 128 129 130 131 132 135 144 146 147 148 149 153 154 **P**1 6 **S** Trinity Health, Livonia, MI
Primary Contact: Rod G. Schlader, President and Chief Executive Officer
COO: Diane Fischels, Senior Vice President and Chief Operating Officer
CFO: Danette Zook, Chief Financial Officer
CMO: Paul Manternach, M.D., Senior Vice President Physician Integration
CIO: Terry Chartier, Director, Information Systems
CHR: Jackie Luecht, Chief Human Resources Officer
CNO: Kim Chamberlin, Vice President Patient Services and Chief Nursing Officer
Web address: www.mercynorthiowa.com
**Control**: Church operated, Nongovernment, not-for-profit **Service**: General medical and surgical

**Staffed Beds**: 228 **Admissions**: 10764 **Census**: 127 **Outpatient Visits**: 413837 **Births**: 918 **Total Expense ($000)**: 384504 **Payroll Expense ($000)**: 152441 **Personnel**: 2083

## MISSOURI VALLEY—Harrison County

**ALEGENT CREIGHTON HEALTH COMMUNITY MEMORIAL HOSPITAL** See Chi Health Missouri Valley

★ **CHI HEALTH MISSOURI VALLEY (161309)**, 631 North Eighth Street, Zip 51555–1102; tel. 712/642–2784, (Nonreporting) **A**10 18 **F**3 15 18 28 29 30 31 34 35 40 43 44 45 46 47 58 59 60 61 64 71 75 81 93 97 107 110 119 127 129 133 146 154 156 157 **S** CommonSpirit Health, Chicago, IL
Primary Contact: Jonathan Moe, President
CMO: Daniel Richter, M.D., Chief of Staff
CIO: Ravae Smallwood, IS Coordinator
CHR: Heidi Winters, Business Partner Human Resources
CNO: Darcy Behrendt, R.N., Vice President, Patient Care Services
Web address: www.chihealth.com/chi-health-missouri-valley
**Control**: Other not-for-profit (including NFP Corporation) **Service**: General medical and surgical

**Staffed Beds**: 12 **Admissions**: 288 **Census**: 5 **Outpatient Visits**: 29055
**Births**: 0 **Total Expense ($000)**: 18843 **Payroll Expense ($000)**: 6580
**Personnel**: 78

## MOUNT AYR—Ringgold County

**RINGGOLD COUNTY HOSPITAL (161373)**, 504 North Cleveland Street, Zip 50854–2201; tel. 641/464–3226, (Nonreporting) **A**10 18 **F**3 7 15 28 29 31 34 35 36 38 40 43 56 57 59 64 65 81 93 97 119 127 133 148 **P**6 **S** MercyOne, Clive, IA
Primary Contact: Gordon W. Winkler, Administrator and Chief Executive Officer
CFO: Teresa Roberts, Chief Financial Officer
CIO: Beth Kosman, Director Health Information Management
CHR: Mitzi Hymbaugh, Chief Personnel
Web address: www.rchmtayr.org
**Control**: Hospital district or authority, Government, Nonfederal **Service**: General medical and surgical

**Staffed Beds**: 16 **Admissions**: 212 **Census**: 3 **Outpatient Visits**: 37625
**Births**: 0 **Total Expense ($000)**: 20905 **Payroll Expense ($000)**: 8609
**Personnel**: 141

## MOUNT PLEASANT—Henry County

★ **HENRY COUNTY HEALTH CENTER (161356)**, 407 South White Street, Zip 52641–2263; tel. 319/385–3141, (Total facility includes 49 beds in nursing home–type unit) (Nonreporting) **A**10 18 **F**3 7 11 13 15 28 29 31 34 35 40 41 43 45 50 53 54 59 64 68 70 75 78 79 81 82 85 86 87 89 93 97 107 108 110 115 118 119 127 128 129 130 131 132 133 146 147 156 **P**6
Primary Contact: Robb Gardner, Chief Executive Officer
CFO: David Muhs, Chief Financial Officer
CMO: Joel Ryon, M.D., Chief of Staff
CHR: Lynn Humphreys, Director Human Resources
CNO: Jodi Geerts, Chief Nursing Officer
Web address: www.hchc.org
**Control**: County, Government, Nonfederal **Service**: General medical and surgical

**Staffed Beds**: 74 **Admissions**: 519 **Census**: 43 **Outpatient Visits**: 52550
**Births**: 121 **Total Expense ($000)**: 38057 **Payroll Expense ($000)**: 14216
**Personnel**: 299

## MUSCATINE—Muscatine County

**TRINITY MUSCATINE** See Unitypoint Health - Trinity Muscatine

⊠ **UNITYPOINT HEALTH - TRINITY MUSCATINE (160013)**, 1518 Mulberry Avenue, Zip 52761–3499; tel. 563/264–9100, (Nonreporting) **A**1 10 20 **F**5 11 13 15 18 28 29 34 38 40 43 45 50 55 56 57 59 61 64 65 66 68 69 70 75 76 77 81 85 87 97 102 107 108 110 111 114 119 127 129 130 131 134 147 148 149 156 **S** UnityPoint Health, West Des Moines, IA
Primary Contact: Robert J. Erickson, President and Chief Executive Officer
CFO: Katie A Marchik, Vice President, Consolidated Services, UnityPoint Health and Chief Financial Officer, Trinity Regional Health System
CMO: Manasi Nadkarni, M.D., Vice President Medical Affairs
CIO: Sean Liddell, Manager Regional Service Information Technology
CHR: Karla Blaser, Director Human Resources
CNO: Pam Askew, R.N., Vice President Patient Care Services
Web address: www.unitypoint.org/quadcities/trinity-muscatine.aspx
**Control**: Other not-for-profit (including NFP Corporation) **Service**: General medical and surgical

**Staffed Beds**: 45 **Admissions**: 1122 **Census**: 9 **Outpatient Visits**: 87504
**Births**: 231 **Total Expense ($000)**: 43749 **Payroll Expense ($000)**: 14788
**Personnel**: 317

## NEVADA—Story County

⇧ **STORY COUNTY HOSPITAL & LTC** See Story County Medical Center

★ ⇧ **STORY COUNTY MEDICAL CENTER (161333)**, 640 South 19th Street, Zip 50201–2902; tel. 515/382–2111, (Total facility includes 65 beds in nursing home–type unit) (Nonreporting) **A**10 18 21 **F**3 7 11 28 29 32 34 35 36 40 43 50 53 57 59 64 65 75 81 85 87 97 107 114 116 119 127 130 133 146 147 **S** UnityPoint Health, West Des Moines, IA
Primary Contact: Nate Thompson, Chief Executive Officer
CFO: Jane Ramthun, Chief Financial Officer
CMO: Arthur Check, M.D., Chief Medical Officer
CHR: Jessica Lingo, Human Resource Generalist
CNO: Beth Rehbein, Chief Nursing and Quality Officer
Web address: www.storymedical.org
**Control**: County, Government, Nonfederal **Service**: General medical and surgical

**Staffed Beds**: 82 **Admissions**: 228 **Census**: 67 **Outpatient Visits**: 50125
**Births**: 0 **Total Expense ($000)**: 28074 **Payroll Expense ($000)**: 11588
**Personnel**: 227

**IA**

*Many Facility Codes have changed. Please refer to the AHA Guide Code Chart.*

## NEW HAMPTON—Chickasaw County

**MERCY MEDICAL CENTER-NEW HAMPTON** See Mercyone New Hampton Medical Center

★ **MERCYONE NEW HAMPTON MEDICAL CENTER (161331)**, 308 North Maple Avenue, Zip 50659–1142; tel. 641/394–4121, (Nonreporting) **A**10 18 **F**3 11 13 15 28 29 34 35 40 43 45 48 56 57 59 64 65 68 74 76 77 79 81 85 93 97 107 110 119 131 133 146 149 **P**1 **S** Trinity Health, Livonia, MI
Primary Contact: Aaron Flugum, Chief Executive Officer
CFO: Jennifer Rapenske, Manager Financial Services
CMO: Daniel Paul McQuillen, M.D., Chief of Medical Staff
CIO: Terry Chartier, Director, Information Systems
CHR: Jackie Luecht, Director, Human Resources
CNO: Cheryl Kay Haggerty, Chief Nursing Officer, Assistant Chief Executive Officer
Web address: www.mercynewhampton.com
**Control:** Church operated, Nongovernment, not–for–profit **Service:** General medical and surgical

**Staffed Beds:** 11 **Admissions:** 272 **Census:** 3 **Outpatient Visits:** 23202
**Births:** 58 **Total Expense ($000):** 18046 **Payroll Expense ($000):** 6768
**Personnel:** 116

## NEWTON—Jasper County

★ **MERCYONE NEWTON MEDICAL CENTER (160032)**, 204 North Fourth Avenue East, Zip 50208–3100; tel. 641/792–1273, (Nonreporting) **A**10 **F**3 11 13 15 17 28 29 30 31 34 35 40 43 44 45 50 57 59 63 64 70 75 76 77 78 79 81 82 85 89 90 93 96 102 107 108 110 111 115 119 128 129 130 131 132 133 135 145 146 148 149 156 **S** CommonSpirit Health, Chicago, IL
Primary Contact: Laurie A. Conner, FACHE, President
CMO: Holly Melahoures, D.O., Chief Medical Officer
CIO: Heather Wolf, Manager Human Resources, Employee Health, InformationTechnology, Support Servicess
CHR: Heather Wolf, Manager Human Resources, Employee Health, Information Technology, Support Services
CNO: Melissa Doehrmann, Director Patient Care Services
Web address: www.skiffmed.com
**Control:** Other not–for–profit (including NFP Corporation) **Service:** General medical and surgical

**Staffed Beds:** 34 **Admissions:** 842 **Census:** 8 **Outpatient Visits:** 81902
**Births:** 161 **Total Expense ($000):** 34499 **Payroll Expense ($000):** 11159
**Personnel:** 186

**SKIFF MEDICAL CENTER** See Mercyone Newton Medical Center

## OELWEIN—Fayette County

**MERCY HOSPITAL OF FRANCISCAN SISTERS** See Mercyone Oelwein Medical Center

★ **MERCYONE OELWEIN MEDICAL CENTER (161338)**, 201 Eighth Avenue SE, Zip 50662–2447; tel. 319/283–6000, (Total facility includes 37 beds in nursing home–type unit) (Nonreporting) **A**10 18 **F**7 11 15 29 30 34 35 40 57 59 69 75 79 93 97 107 110 111 119 127 128 130 132 133 146 147 **S** Trinity Health, Livonia, MI
Primary Contact: Jill Groth, Site Administrator
CFO: Timothy Huber, Vice President and Chief Financial Officer
CMO: James Lehman, M.D., Vice President Medical Affairs
CNO: Kelly Richards, Senior Vice President and Chief Nursing Officer
Web address: www.wheatoniowa.org
**Control:** Church operated, Nongovernment, not–for–profit **Service:** General medical and surgical

**Staffed Beds:** 56 **Admissions:** 255 **Census:** 36 **Outpatient Visits:** 24536
**Births:** 0 **Total Expense ($000):** 13421 **Payroll Expense ($000):** 5366
**Personnel:** 112

## ONAWA—Monona County

★ **BURGESS HEALTH CENTER (161359)**, 1600 Diamond Street, Zip 51040–1548; tel. 712/423–2311, (Nonreporting) **A**10 18 **F**3 7 11 13 15 28 29 31 32 34 35 40 45 50 53 56 57 59 62 63 64 65 68 75 76 77 78 79 80 81 82 85 93 97 100 101 104 107 110 111 115 119 127 130 132 133 135 146 147 148 149 154 156 **P**6
Primary Contact: Francis G. Tramp, President
CFO: Nancy Carlson, Chief Financial Officer
CMO: John Garred, M.D., SrChief Medical Officer
CIO: Grady Warner, Director of Information Technology
CHR: Erin Brekke, Director Human Resources
CNO: Patty Sandman, Senior Director of Nursing
Web address: www.burgesshc.org
**Control:** Other not–for–profit (including NFP Corporation) **Service:** General medical and surgical

**Staffed Beds:** 25 **Admissions:** 611 **Census:** 7 **Outpatient Visits:** 63396
**Births:** 56 **Total Expense ($000):** 29582 **Payroll Expense ($000):** 13207
**Personnel:** 257

**BURGESS MEMORIAL HOSPITAL** See Burgess Health Center

## ORANGE CITY—Sioux County

★ **ORANGE CITY AREA HEALTH SYSTEM (161360)**, 1000 Lincoln Circle SE, Zip 51041–1862; tel. 712/737–4984, (Total facility includes 89 beds in nursing home–type unit) (Nonreporting) **A**10 18 **F**7 10 11 13 15 18 28 29 31 34 35 40 45 50 53 56 57 59 62 63 64 67 68 70 75 76 77 78 79 81 82 85 86 87 89 93 97 99 100 101 102 103 104 107 110 111 114 117 119 120 125 127 130 131 132 133 146 147 148 154 156 **P**6 **S** Sanford Health, Sioux Falls, SD
Primary Contact: Martin W. Guthmiller, Chief Executive Officer
COO: Daniel P McCarty, Chief Operating Officer
CFO: Dina Baas, Director Financial Services
CMO: Alan Laird, M.D., Chief Medical Officer
CHR: Jason Jauron, Director Human Resources
CNO: Laurie Gebauer, Director Patient Care
Web address: www.ochealthsystem.org
**Control:** City, Government, Nonfederal **Service:** General medical and surgical

**Staffed Beds:** 114 **Admissions:** 944 **Census:** 93 **Outpatient Visits:** 81158
**Births:** 203 **Total Expense ($000):** 52031 **Payroll Expense ($000):** 22563
**Personnel:** 441

**ORANGE CITY HEALTH SYSTEM** See Orange City Area Health System

## OSAGE—Mitchell County

**MITCHELL CNTY REG HLTH CTR** See Mitchell County Regional Health Center

★ **MITCHELL COUNTY REGIONAL HEALTH CENTER (161323)**, 616 North Eighth Street, Zip 50461–1498; tel. 641/732–6000, (Nonreporting) **A**10 18 **F**7 8 11 15 18 28 29 34 35 40 45 50 56 57 59 63 64 65 68 75 77 79 81 82 85 87 93 107 110 114 119 127 129 130 132 133 146 154 156 **P**1 **S** Trinity Health, Livonia, MI
Primary Contact: Shelly Russell, Chief Executive Officer
CFO: Gregory Burkel, Chief Financial Officer
CMO: Jeff Nasstrom, D.O., Chief of Staff
CHR: Angie Konig, Senior Director Human Resources
CNO: Judy Brown, Chief Nursing Officer
Web address: www.mcrhc.com
**Control:** County, Government, Nonfederal **Service:** General medical and surgical

**Staffed Beds:** 25 **Admissions:** 349 **Census:** 4 **Outpatient Visits:** 66492
**Births:** 0 **Total Expense ($000):** 27890 **Payroll Expense ($000):** 9992
**Personnel:** 171

**IA**

---

| **Hospital, Medicare Provider Number, Address, Telephone, Approval, Facility, and Physician Codes, Health Care System** | | |
|---|---|---|
| ★ American Hospital Association (AHA) membership | ○ Healthcare Facilities Accreditation Program | ⇧ Center for Improvement in Healthcare Quality Accreditation |
| ☐ The Joint Commission accreditation | ◇ DNV Healthcare Inc. accreditation | △ Commission on Accreditation of Rehabilitation Facilities (CARF) accreditation |

## OSCEOLA—Clarke County

★ ⇑ **CLARKE COUNTY HOSPITAL (161348)**, 800 South Fillmore Street, Zip 50213–1619; tel. 641/342–2184, (Nonreporting) **A**10 18 21 **F**7 11 15 18 28 29 31 34 35 40 42 44 45 51 57 59 64 67 68 75 77 78 79 81 82 84 89 90 93 94 96 97 107 110 111 115 116 117 118 119 128 130 131 132 133 135 148 154 156 **S** UnityPoint Health, West Des Moines, IA
Primary Contact: Brian G. Evans, FACHE, Chief Executive Officer
CFO: Michael Thilges, Chief Financial Officer
CMO: George Fotiadis, M.D., Chief of Staff
CIO: Dennis Blazek, Chief Information Officer
CHR: Kate Emanuel, Director Human Resources
Web address: www.clarkehosp.org
**Control**: County, Government, Nonfederal **Service**: General medical and surgical

**Staffed Beds:** 25 **Admissions:** 274 **Census:** 7 **Outpatient Visits:** 27955 **Births:** 0 **Total Expense ($000):** 23134 **Payroll Expense ($000):** 7724 **Personnel:** 153

## OSKALOOSA—Mahaska County

**MAHASKA COUNTY HOSPITAL** See Mahaska Health Partnership

⊞ **MAHASKA HEALTH PARTNERSHIP (161379)**, 1229 'C' Avenue East, Zip 52577–4298; tel. 641/672–3100, (Nonreporting) **A**1 10 18 **F**3 7 11 13 15 28 29 34 35 40 43 45 46 48 50 54 57 59 63 64 65 68 70 75 76 77 79 81 82 84 85 87 93 97 101 102 104 107 110 111 115 119 126 129 130 131 133 146 148 149 150 154 156
Primary Contact: Kevin DeRonde, Chief Executive Officer
COO: Erin Baldwin, M.P.H., Chief Operating Officer
CMO: Matt Whitis, Chief Medical Officer
CHR: Sarah S. Dickey, Executive Director, Human Resource People and Culture
Web address: www.mahaskahealth.com
**Control**: County, Government, Nonfederal **Service**: General medical and surgical

**Staffed Beds:** 25 **Admissions:** 1006 **Census:** 13 **Outpatient Visits:** 152464 **Births:** 163 **Total Expense ($000):** 60063 **Payroll Expense ($000):** 29971 **Personnel:** 401

## OTTUMWA—Wapello County

⊞ △ **OTTUMWA REGIONAL HEALTH CENTER (160089)**, 1001 Pennsylvania Avenue, Zip 52501–2186; tel. 641/684–2300, (Nonreporting) **A**1 7 10 **F**3 7 11 13 15 18 20 22 26 28 29 30 34 35 40 41 43 45 46 47 48 50 51 53 54 56 57 59 60 64 73 75 76 77 79 81 82 85 87 89 90 93 96 98 102 103 107 108 110 111 114 115 116 117 118 119 120 121 123 126 129 130 131 132 135 146 147 148 154 **S** LifePoint Health, Brentwood, TN
Primary Contact: Philip J. Noel III, Chief Executive Officer
COO: Dennis Hunger, Chief Operating Officer
CFO: Jason Hotchkiss, CPA, Chief Financial Officer
CMO: Sandro Younadam, M.D., Chief Medical Officer
CIO: Scott Garrett, Director of IS
CHR: Lidia Bryant, Director Human Resources
CNO: Lori Bailey, R.N., Vice President and Chief Nursing Officer
Web address: www.ottumwaregionalhealth.com
**Control**: Corporation, Investor–owned (for–profit) **Service**: General medical and surgical

**Staffed Beds:** 86 **Admissions:** 2890 **Census:** 39 **Outpatient Visits:** 129816 **Births:** 445 **Total Expense ($000):** 73856 **Payroll Expense ($000):** 22550 **Personnel:** 486

## PELLA—Marion County

**PELLA COMMUNITY HOSPITAL** See Pella Regional Health Center

⊞ **PELLA REGIONAL HEALTH CENTER (161367)**, 404 Jefferson Street, Zip 50219–1257; tel. 641/628–3150, (Nonreporting) **A**1 10 18 **F**3 11 12 13 15 18 28 29 30 31 32 34 35 40 43 45 50 51 53 57 59 62 63 64 65 70 74 75 76 77 78 79 81 82 84 85 86 87 93 94 97 102 107 108 110 111 115 119 126 127 129 130 131 132 133 146 147 148 149 154 156 157 **P**6
Primary Contact: Robert D. Kroese, FACHE, Chief Executive Officer
COO: Robert D Kroese, FACHE, Chief Executive Officer
CFO: Bruce Heifner, Chief Financial Officer
CIO: Cristina Thomas, Chief Information Systems
CHR: Ashley Arkema, Director of Human Resources
Web address: www.pellahealth.org
**Control**: Other not–for–profit (including NFP Corporation) **Service**: General medical and surgical

**Staffed Beds:** 25 **Admissions:** 1412 **Census:** 13 **Outpatient Visits:** 169780 **Births:** 605 **Total Expense ($000):** 59897 **Payroll Expense ($000):** 21582 **Personnel:** 488

## PERRY—Dallas County

**DALLAS COUNTY HOSPITAL (161322)**, 610 10th Street, Zip 50220–2221; tel. 515/465–3547, (Nonreporting) **A**10 18 **F**15 18 28 29 30 31 34 35 39 40 41 43 45 47 50 56 57 59 65 66 68 75 77 78 79 81 82 85 87 89 93 107 110 114 119 128 130 132 133 135 146 148 154 156 **S** MercyOne, Clive, IA
Primary Contact: Angela Mortoza, Chief Executive Officer
CFO: Randy Loomis, Chief Financial Officer
CMO: Steven Sohn, M.D., President Medical Staff
CHR: Sherry Smith, Manager Human Resources
CNO: Tonya Summerson, Chief Clinical Officer
Web address: www.dallascohospital.org
**Control**: County, Government, Nonfederal **Service**: General medical and surgical

**Staffed Beds:** 15 **Admissions:** 137 **Census:** 2 **Outpatient Visits:** 21357 **Births:** 0 **Total Expense ($000):** 15436 **Payroll Expense ($000):** 4779 **Personnel:** 110

## POCAHONTAS—Pocahontas County

★ **POCAHONTAS COMMUNITY HOSPITAL (161305)**, 606 NW Seventh Street, Zip 50574–1099; tel. 712/335–3501, (Nonreporting) **A**10 18 **F**7 11 15 28 29 30 31 34 35 40 43 45 50 59 64 67 75 77 78 79 81 82 85 90 93 107 110 115 119 128 129 130 132 133 135 146 148 **S** UnityPoint Health, West Des Moines, IA
Primary Contact: James D. Roetman, President and Chief Executive Officer
CFO: Lynn Raveling, Chief Financial Officer
CNO: Susie Aden, Director of IP Services
Web address: www.pocahontashospital.org
**Control**: City, Government, Nonfederal **Service**: General medical and surgical

**Staffed Beds:** 20 **Admissions:** 241 **Census:** 3 **Outpatient Visits:** 20130 **Births:** 0 **Total Expense ($000):** 11111 **Payroll Expense ($000):** 3806 **Personnel:** 84

## PRIMGHAR—O'brien County

**MERCYONE PRIMGHAR** See Mercyone Primghar Medical Center

★ **MERCYONE PRIMGHAR MEDICAL CENTER (161300)**, 255 North Welch Avenue, Zip 51245–7765, Mailing Address: P.O. Box 528, Zip 51245–0528; tel. 712/957–2300, (Nonreporting) **A**10 18 **F**11 15 28 29 34 35 40 45 53 57 59 64 67 75 77 81 89 107 110 119 127 128 132 133 156 **S** Trinity Health, Livonia, MI
Primary Contact: Misty Dulin, CAH, Director
CFO: Sue E McCauley, Director Finance
CMO: Shailesh Desai, M.D., Chief of Staff
Web address: www.baumharmon.org
**Control**: Hospital district or authority, Government, Nonfederal **Service**: General medical and surgical

**Staffed Beds:** 11 **Admissions:** 66 **Census:** 1 **Outpatient Visits:** 15768 **Births:** 0 **Total Expense ($000):** 7445 **Payroll Expense ($000):** 3697 **Personnel:** 52

## RED OAK—Montgomery County

★ **MONTGOMERY COUNTY MEMORIAL HOSPITAL (161363)**, 2301 Eastern Avenue, Zip 51566–1300, Mailing Address: P.O. Box 498, Zip 51566–0498; tel. 712/623–7000, (Nonreporting) **A**10 18 **F**3 11 12 13 15 28 29 31 34 35 40 44 45 50 53 55 57 59 64 65 68 69 70 71 75 76 77 78 79 81 82 85 86 87 93 107 110 111 114 115 118 119 129 130 132 133 135 146 147 148 154 156
Primary Contact: David E. Abercrombie, Chief Executive Officer
CFO: Rick J Leinen, Chief Financial Officer
CMO: Warren Hayes, Chief of Staff
CIO: Ron Kloewer, Chief Information Officer
CHR: Shayla Jennings, Human Resources Director
CNO: Diane McGrew, Chief Nurse Executive
Web address: www.mcmh.org
**Control**: County, Government, Nonfederal **Service**: General medical and surgical

**Staffed Beds:** 25 **Admissions:** 982 **Census:** 12 **Outpatient Visits:** 46551 **Births:** 56 **Total Expense ($000):** 47020 **Payroll Expense ($000):** 20340 **Personnel:** 305

**IA**

*Many Facility Codes have changed. Please refer to the AHA Guide Code Chart.*
© 2021 AHA Guide

## ROCK RAPIDS—Lyon County

★ **AVERA MERRILL PIONEER HOSPITAL (161321)**, 1100 South 10th Avenue, Zip 51246–2020; tel. 712/472–5400, (Data for 61 days) (Nonreporting) **A**18 **F**3 11 15 28 31 32 34 35 38 40 41 44 45 50 54 57 59 63 64 65 68 75 81 85 86 93 97 100 102 107 110 115 119 127 131 132 133 144 148 154 156 **P**6 **S** Avera Health, Sioux Falls, SD
Primary Contact: Craig Hohn, Chief Executive Officer
Web address: www.https://www.avera.org
**Control**: Other not–for–profit (including NFP Corporation) **Service**: General medical and surgical

**Staffed Beds:** 11 **Admissions:** 9 **Census:** 1 **Outpatient Visits:** 1101
**Births:** 0 **Total Expense ($000):** 2890 **Payroll Expense ($000):** 1801
**Personnel:** 55

## ROCK VALLEY—Sioux County

★ **HEGG HEALTH CENTER AVERA (161336)**, 1202 21st Avenue, Zip 51247–1497; tel. 712/476–8000, (Total facility includes 60 beds in nursing home–type unit) (Nonreporting) **A**10 18 **F**3 13 15 28 29 31 34 35 36 40 41 43 44 45 50 53 57 59 62 64 65 67 68 75 76 77 78 79 81 82 85 89 91 93 96 97 107 110 115 119 128 130 131 132 133 144 146 147 148 154 156 **S** Avera Health, Sioux Falls, SD
Primary Contact: Glenn Zevenbergen, Chief Executive Officer
CFO: Bill Slater, Chief Financial Officer
CMO: Jon Engbers, M.D., President
CHR: Tammy Faber, Director Human Resources
Web address: www.hegghc.org
**Control**: Other not–for–profit (including NFP Corporation) **Service**: General medical and surgical

**Staffed Beds:** 85 **Admissions:** 292 **Census:** 62 **Outpatient Visits:** 35145
**Births:** 72 **Total Expense ($000):** 22329 **Payroll Expense ($000):** 11229
**Personnel:** 179

**HEGG MEMORIAL HEALTH CENTER AVERA** See Hegg Health Center Avera

## SAC CITY—Sac County

★ **LORING HOSPITAL (161370)**, 211 Highland Avenue, Zip 50583–2424; tel. 712/662–7105, (Nonreporting) **A**10 18 **F**3 11 15 28 29 30 31 34 35 40 43 45 50 57 59 64 75 77 81 86 87 93 102 107 110 115 125 130 133 141 146 149 154 156 **S** UnityPoint Health, West Des Moines, IA
Primary Contact: Stacy Johnson, Chief Executive Officer
CFO: Stacy Johnson, Chief Executive Officer
CMO: Les Marczewski, M.D., Chief Medical Officer
CIO: Leah Snyder, Director Health Information Services
CHR: Becky Pontious, Human Resources/Accounting
CNO: Kara Wellington, Chief Clinical Officer
Web address: www.loringhospital.org
**Control**: Other not–for–profit (including NFP Corporation) **Service**: General medical and surgical

**Staffed Beds:** 25 **Admissions:** 242 **Census:** 2 **Outpatient Visits:** 25085
**Births:** 0 **Total Expense ($000):** 13106 **Payroll Expense ($000):** 4450
**Personnel:** 107

## SHELDON—O'brien County

**NORTHWEST IOWA HEALTH CENTER** See Sanford Sheldon Medical Center

★ **SANFORD SHELDON MEDICAL CENTER (161381)**, 118 North Seventh Avenue, Zip 51201–1235, Mailing Address: P.O. Box 250, Zip 51201–0250; tel. 712/324–5041, (Total facility includes 68 beds in nursing home–type unit) (Nonreporting) **A**10 18 **F**3 11 13 15 28 29 30 31 32 34 35 40 43 45 56 57 59 61 62 63 64 65 66 67 75 76 77 78 81 84 85 86 89 93 94 96 97 99 100 101 103 104 107 110 111 114 119 127 130 131 133 135 148 149 154 156 **P**6 **S** Sanford Health, Sioux Falls, SD
Primary Contact: Richard E. Nordahl, Senior Director
CFO: Richard E. Nordahl, Senior Director
CMO: Scott Lichty, M.D., Physician
CIO: Jason Brown, Director Information Systems
CHR: Dianne Wolthuizen, Director Human Resources
CNO: Joni DeKok, Chief Nursing Officer
Web address: www.sanfordsheldon.org
**Control**: Other not–for–profit (including NFP Corporation) **Service**: General medical and surgical

**Staffed Beds:** 93 **Admissions:** 754 **Census:** 63 **Outpatient Visits:** 43649
**Births:** 124 **Total Expense ($000):** 32169 **Payroll Expense ($000):** 15536
**Personnel:** 241

## SHENANDOAH—Page County

★ **SHENANDOAH MEDICAL CENTER (161366)**, 300 Pershing Avenue, Zip 51601–2355; tel. 712/246–1230, (Total facility includes 45 beds in nursing home–type unit) (Nonreporting) **A**10 18 **F**3 13 15 18 28 29 31 34 35 40 41 43 45 50 53 56 57 59 64 65 67 68 69 70 74 75 76 77 78 79 81 83 84 85 87 91 93 104 107 108 110 111 115 117 118 119 127 129 130 131 132 133 135 144 146 147 148 149 154 **P**6
Primary Contact: Matt Sells, Chief Executive Officer
COO: Jonathan Moe, Chief Operating Officer
CFO: Kaley Neal, Chief Financial Officer
CMO: Heather Babe, M.D., Chief of Staff
CIO: Chuck Dougherty, Chief Information Officer
CHR: Keli Royal, Chief Human Resources Officer
CNO: Laura Stofferson, Chief Nursing Officer
Web address: www.smchospital.com/
**Control**: Other not–for–profit (including NFP Corporation) **Service**: General medical and surgical

**Staffed Beds:** 70 **Admissions:** 530 **Census:** 42 **Outpatient Visits:** 203843
**Births:** 98 **Total Expense ($000):** 42247 **Payroll Expense ($000):** 21204
**Personnel:** 271

**SHENANDOAH MEMORIAL HOSPITAL** See Shenandoah Medical Center

## SIBLEY—Osceola County

**OSCEOLA COMMUNITY HOSPITAL DBA OSCEOLA REGIONAL HEALTH CENTER** See Osceola Regional Health Center

★ **OSCEOLA REGIONAL HEALTH CENTER (161345)**, 600 9th Avenue North, Zip 51249–1012, Mailing Address: P.O. Box 258, Zip 51249–0258; tel. 712/754–2574, (Nonreporting) **A**10 18 **F**3 8 9 10 11 12 15 17 18 26 28 29 31 32 34 35 36 40 43 45 46 50 53 56 57 59 61 62 64 65 67 68 70 75 77 78 79 81 82 84 85 86 87 89 107 108 110 114 119 125 128 129 130 131 132 133 135 143 144 145 146 147 148 149 154 156 **P**5 **S** Avera Health, Sioux Falls, SD
Primary Contact: Ben Davis, Chief Executive Officer
CFO: Craig Carstens, Chief Financial Officer
CMO: Gregory J Kosters, D.O., Chief Medical Officer
CHR: Emily VanKekerix, Director Human Resources
CNO: Wendy Marco, R.N., Chief Nursing Officer
Web address: www.osceolacommunityhospital.org
**Control**: Other not–for–profit (including NFP Corporation) **Service**: General medical and surgical

**Staffed Beds:** 25 **Admissions:** 223 **Census:** 3 **Outpatient Visits:** 16745
**Births:** 0 **Total Expense ($000):** 11450 **Payroll Expense ($000):** 3718
**Personnel:** 89

## SIGOURNEY—Keokuk County

**KEOKUK COUNTY HEALTH CENTER (161315)**, 23019 Highway 149, Zip 52591–8341; tel. 641/622–2720, (Nonreporting) **A**10 18 **F**1 2 3 7 11 12 15 28 29 30 34 35 38 40 43 44 45 46 50 56 57 59 64 65 66 67 75 77 82 84 86 87 90 91 93 97 107 110 114 117 127 128 129 130 131 132 133 135 146 147 148 156 **P**5
Primary Contact: Matthew Ives, Chief Executive Officer and Chief Financial Officer
CFO: Matthew Ives, Interim Chief Executive Officer and Chief Financial Officer
Web address: www.kchc.net
**Control**: County, Government, Nonfederal **Service**: General medical and surgical

**Staffed Beds:** 14 **Admissions:** 78 **Census:** 3 **Outpatient Visits:** 22775
**Births:** 0 **Total Expense ($000):** 12856 **Payroll Expense ($000):** 6656
**Personnel:** 107

**IA**

---

Hospital, Medicare Provider Number, Address, Telephone, Approval, Facility, and Physician Codes, Health Care System

★ American Hospital Association (AHA) membership   ◯ Healthcare Facilities Accreditation Program   ⇑ Center for Improvement in Healthcare Quality Accreditation
☐ The Joint Commission accreditation   ◇ DNV Healthcare Inc. accreditation   △ Commission on Accreditation of Rehabilitation Facilities (CARF) accreditation

## SIOUX CENTER—Sioux County

**SIOUX CENTER COMMUNITY HOSPITAL AND HEALTH CENTER AVERA** See Sioux Center Health

★ **SIOUX CENTER HEALTH (161346)**, 1101 9th Street SE, Zip 51250; tel. 712/722–8107, (Total facility includes 69 beds in nursing home–type unit) (Nonreporting) **A**10 18 **F**3 5 8 10 12 13 15 18 26 28 29 30 31 34 35 40 41 43 45 50 56 57 59 62 63 64 65 67 68 74 75 76 77 78 79 80 81 82 84 85 86 87 89 93 96 97 100 101 104 107 108 110 111 114 119 125 128 130 131 132 133 144 146 147 148 149 154 156 157 **P**6 **S** Avera Health, Sioux Falls, SD
Primary Contact: Cory D. Nelson, Administrator
CFO: Kari Timmer, Chief Financial Officer
CHR: Theresa Tucker, Human Resources Officer
Web address: www.siouxcenterhealth.org
**Control**: Other not–for–profit (including NFP Corporation) **Service**: General medical and surgical

**Staffed Beds:** 88 **Admissions:** 530 **Census:** 72 **Outpatient Visits:** 55796 **Births:** 185 **Total Expense ($000):** 44207 **Payroll Expense ($000):** 19121 **Personnel:** 345

## SIOUX CITY—Woodbury County

**MERCY MEDICAL CENTER-SIOUX CITY** See Mercyone Siouxland Medical Center

⊞ **MERCYONE SIOUXLAND MEDICAL CENTER (160153)**, 801 Fifth Street, Zip 51101–1326, Mailing Address: P.O. Box 3168, Zip 51102–3168; tel. 712/279–2010, (Nonreporting) **A**1 3 5 10 19 **F**3 5 8 11 12 13 15 17 18 20 22 24 26 28 29 30 31 32 34 35 37 40 43 44 45 49 50 56 57 59 64 65 68 70 71 74 75 76 77 78 79 81 82 84 85 87 89 90 91 92 93 96 97 98 100 102 107 108 110 111 114 115 118 119 124 126 127 128 129 130 144 145 146 148 149 150 154 156 157 **P**6 8 **S** Trinity Health, Livonia, MI
Primary Contact: Beth Hughes, President
CFO: Hugh DePaulis, Interim Vice President and Chief Financial Officer
CMO: Jerome Pierson, Chief Medical Officer
CIO: Steve Larson, M.D., Director Information Systems
CHR: Julie Anfinson, Director Human Resources
CNO: Tracy Larson, MS, Vice President Patient Care Services and Chief Nursing Officer
Web address: www.mercysiouxcity.com
**Control**: Church operated, Nongovernment, not–for–profit **Service**: General medical and surgical

**Staffed Beds:** 199 **Admissions:** 8839 **Census:** 141 **Outpatient Visits:** 209686 **Births:** 188 **Total Expense ($000):** 208510 **Payroll Expense ($000):** 82892 **Personnel:** 1319

⇑ **UNITYPOINT HEALTH - ST. LUKE'S** See Unitypoint Health - St. Lukes's Sioux City

★ ⇑ **UNITYPOINT HEALTH - ST. LUKES'S SIOUX CITY (160146)**, 2720 Stone Park Boulevard, Zip 51104–3734; tel. 712/279–3500, (Nonreporting) **A**3 5 10 21 **F**3 11 13 15 17 18 20 22 26 28 29 30 31 34 35 39 40 43 45 49 50 51 54 56 57 58 59 60 64 68 70 72 73 74 75 76 77 78 79 81 82 84 85 86 88 89 90 91 92 93 96 97 98 102 104 107 108 111 114 115 118 119 126 129 130 131 132 135 142 143 144 145 146 147 149 154 156 157 **S** UnityPoint Health, West Des Moines, IA
Primary Contact: Lynn Wold, President and Chief Executive Officer
COO: Chad Markham, Chief Operating Officer
CFO: James Gobell, Chief Financial Officer
CIO: James Gobell, Chief Financial Officer
CHR: Tammy Hartnett, Employee Relations Manager
CNO: Priscilla Stokes, MS, R.N., Vice President Patient Care and Hospital Operations
Web address: www.stlukes.org
**Control**: Other not–for–profit (including NFP Corporation) **Service**: General medical and surgical

**Staffed Beds:** 165 **Admissions:** 9280 **Census:** 110 **Outpatient Visits:** 87016 **Births:** 2048 **Total Expense ($000):** 168181 **Payroll Expense ($000):** 72758 **Personnel:** 1199

## SPENCER—Clay County

★ **SPENCER HOSPITAL (160112)**, 1200 First Avenue East, Suite 1, Zip 51301–4342; tel. 712/264–6111, (Nonreporting) **A**10 **F**3 7 8 11 13 15 28 29 30 31 34 35 37 40 43 45 50 53 57 59 60 62 63 64 65 70 75 76 77 78 79 81 82 85 86 87 93 96 98 107 108 109 110 111 115 118 119 120 121 123 126 127 129 130 131 132 133 135 144 146 147 148 149
Primary Contact: William J. Bumgarner, President
CFO: Stacy E Mol, CPA, Director Finance
CMO: Sonia Sather, M.D., President Medical Staff
CIO: Brenda Marie Tiefenthaler, R.N., MSN, Vice President Patient Care and Informatics
CHR: Stephen Deutsch, Vice President Operations and Support
CNO: Brenda Marie Tiefenthaler, R.N., MSN, Vice President Patient Care and Informatics
Web address: www.spencerhospital.org
**Control**: City, Government, Nonfederal **Service**: General medical and surgical

**Staffed Beds:** 64 **Admissions:** 2409 **Census:** 25 **Outpatient Visits:** 123153 **Births:** 250 **Total Expense ($000):** 94138 **Payroll Expense ($000):** 24506 **Personnel:** 417

**SPENCER MUNICIPAL HOSPITAL** See Spencer Hospital

## SPIRIT LAKE—Dickinson County

**DICKINSON COUNTY MEM HOSPITAL** See Lakes Regional Healthcare

★ **LAKES REGIONAL HEALTHCARE (160124)**, 2301 Highway 71 South, Zip 51360–0159; tel. 712/336–1230, (Nonreporting) **A**10 **F**3 7 11 13 15 28 29 30 31 34 35 37 40 41 43 45 50 54 57 59 62 63 64 65 70 75 76 77 78 79 81 85 89 91 93 97 107 110 111 115 119 126 128 129 130 132 133 135 143 146 148 149 152 154 156 **P**5 **S** Avera Health, Sioux Falls, SD
Primary Contact: Jason Harrington, FACHE, President and Chief Executive Officer
CFO: Steve Alger, Senior Vice President and Chief Financial Officer
CMO: Zachary A. Borus, M.D., Medical Chief of Staff
CIO: Derek Larson, Information Technology Network
CHR: Sonja Hamm, Vice President Human and Foundation Resources
CNO: Connie Lange, R.N., Vice President Quality, Inpatient and Community Services
Web address: www.lakeshealth.org
**Control**: County, Government, Nonfederal **Service**: General medical and surgical

**Staffed Beds:** 30 **Admissions:** 1009 **Census:** 8 **Outpatient Visits:** 108035 **Births:** 195 **Total Expense ($000):** 43096 **Payroll Expense ($000):** 13193 **Personnel:** 222

## STORM LAKE—Buena Vista County

**BUENA VISTA COUNTY HOSPITAL** See Buena Vista Regional Medical Center

⊞ **BUENA VISTA REGIONAL MEDICAL CENTER (161375)**, 1525 West Fifth Street, Zip 50588–3027, Mailing Address: P.O. Box 309, Zip 50588–0309; tel. 712/732–4030, (Nonreporting) **A**1 10 18 **F**3 7 8 11 13 15 18 28 29 30 31 34 40 43 45 53 55 56 57 59 63 64 68 70 74 75 76 77 78 79 81 82 84 85 86 87 93 96 98 103 107 108 110 111 115 117 118 119 128 129 130 131 132 133 135 146 147 148 **S** UnityPoint Health, West Des Moines, IA
Primary Contact: Steven Colerick, Chief Executive Officer
CFO: Krista Ketcham, Chief Financial Officer
CMO: Seth Harrer, M.D., Chief of Staff
CIO: Steve Spurlock, Director Information Systems
CHR: Carrie Turnquist, Director Human Resources
CNO: Dawn M Bach, MS, Chief Clinical Officer
Web address: www.bvrmc.org
**Control**: County, Government, Nonfederal **Service**: General medical and surgical

**Staffed Beds:** 35 **Admissions:** 1228 **Census:** 15 **Outpatient Visits:** 66275 **Births:** 325 **Total Expense ($000):** 53368 **Payroll Expense ($000):** 20278 **Personnel:** 359

**IA**

**SUMNER—Bremer County**

★ **COMMUNITY MEMORIAL HOSPITAL (161320)**, 909 West First Street,
Zip 50674–1203, Mailing Address: P.O. Box 148, Zip 50674–0148;
tel. 563/578–3275, (Nonreporting) **A**10 18 **F**3 11 15 28 29 34 40 45 57 59 64
77 81 82 85 86 97 107 110 114 119 128 129 131 133 135 148 149 156 **P**5 6
**S** UnityPoint Health, West Des Moines, IA
Primary Contact: Dawn Everding, President and Chief Financial Officer
CFO: Dawn Everding, President and Chief Financial Officer
CMO: Jeff Roske, D.O., Chief Medical Staff
CHR: Robin Elliott, Personnel Officer
CNO: Lynne Niemann, Director Nurses and Patient Care
Web address: www.cmhsumner.org
**Control**: Other not–for–profit (including NFP Corporation) **Service**: General
medical and surgical

> **Staffed Beds:** 16 **Admissions:** 188 **Census:** 3 **Outpatient Visits:** 38791
> **Births:** 0 **Total Expense ($000):** 14457 **Payroll Expense ($000):** 5095
> **Personnel:** 74

**VINTON—Benton County**

★ **VIRGINIA GAY HOSPITAL (161349)**, 502 North 9th Avenue, Zip 52349–2299;
tel. 319/472–6200, (Total facility includes 40 beds in nursing home–type unit)
(Nonreporting) **A**10 18 **F**3 15 28 29 34 40 43 45 53 57 59 62 63 64 65 75 77
81 85 86 87 91 93 96 97 100 104 107 110 111 114 119 125 127 129 130
131 132 133 143 146 148 149 154 156
Primary Contact: Michele Schoonover, Chief Executive Officer
CFO: Barry Dietsch, Chief Financial Officer
CMO: Brian Meeker, D.O., President Medical Staff
CIO: Sherri Isbell, Chief Information Officer
CHR: Kim Frank, Chief Human Resources Officer
CNO: Tina M Eden, Director of Nursing
Web address: www.myvgh.org
**Control**: Other not–for–profit (including NFP Corporation) **Service**: General
medical and surgical

> **Staffed Beds:** 65 **Admissions:** 356 **Census:** 40 **Outpatient Visits:** 82673
> **Births:** 0 **Total Expense ($000):** 27529 **Payroll Expense ($000):** 13533
> **Personnel:** 246

**WASHINGTON—Washington County**

**WASHINGTON COUNTY HOSPITAL** See Washington County Hospital and Clinics

★ **WASHINGTON COUNTY HOSPITAL AND CLINICS (161344)**, 400 East Polk
Street, Zip 52353–1237, Mailing Address: P.O. Box 909, Zip 52353–0909;
tel. 319/653–5481, (Total facility includes 43 beds in nursing home–type unit)
(Nonreporting) **A**10 18 **F**3 15 18 28 29 40 43 45 50 59 64 67 74 75 81 85 86
92 93 96 97 107 110 111 115 119 127 130 132 133 146 147 148 **P**6
Primary Contact: Todd Patterson, Chief Executive Officer
CFO: Steve Sanders, Chief Financial Officer
CMO: Matt Prihoda, M.D., Chief of Staff
CIO: Makyla Maize, Director Information Services
CHR: Tracy Ousey, Director Human Resources
CNO: Andrea Leyden RNChief Nursing Officer
Web address: www.wchc.org
**Control**: County, Government, Nonfederal **Service**: General medical and surgical

> **Staffed Beds:** 68 **Admissions:** 1043 **Census:** 39 **Outpatient Visits:** 53937
> **Births:** 0 **Total Expense ($000):** 43214 **Payroll Expense ($000):** 18408
> **Personnel:** 290

**WATERLOO—Black Hawk County**

**COVENANT MEDICAL CENTER** See Mercyone Waterloo Medical Center

☒ △ **MERCYONE WATERLOO MEDICAL CENTER (160067)**, 3421 West Ninth
Street, Zip 50702–5401; tel. 319/272–8000, (Nonreporting) **A**1 2 3 5 7 10 **F**3 4
5 7 11 13 15 18 19 20 22 26 28 29 30 31 33 34 35 40 43 44 46 49 50 51 53
56 57 58 59 60 61 62 64 68 70 71 72 74 75 76 77 78 79 81 82 86 87 89 90
93 97 98 99 100 101 102 104 107 108 110 111 114 115 116 118 119 120
126 127 129 130 131 132 135 143 144 146 147 148 152 154 155 **S** Trinity
Health, Livonia, MI
Primary Contact: Jack Dusenbery, President and Chief Executive Officer
COO: Ryan Meyer, Vice President Operations
CFO: Timothy Huber, Controller
CMO: Matthew Sojka, M.D., Vice President, Medical Affairs
CIO: Marge Ray, Director Information Systems
CHR: Suzanne M. Burt, Director Human Resources
CNO: Kelly Richards, Vice President and Chief Nursing Officer
Web address: www.MercyOne.org
**Control**: Church operated, Nongovernment, not–for–profit **Service**: General
medical and surgical

> **Staffed Beds:** 240 **Admissions:** 6840 **Census:** 81 **Outpatient
> Visits:** 646329 **Births:** 1352 **Total Expense ($000):** 302271 **Payroll
> Expense ($000):** 135953 **Personnel:** 1797

☒ △ **UNITYPOINT HEALTH - ALLEN HOSPITAL (160110)**, 1825 Logan Avenue,
Zip 50703–1916; tel. 319/235–3941, (Nonreporting) **A**1 3 5 7 10 **F**3 8 11 13
15 18 20 22 24 26 28 29 30 31 34 35 37 40 43 45 46 48 49 50 51 54 56 57
59 63 64 66 68 70 72 74 75 76 77 78 79 81 82 84 85 86 87 88 90 91 92 93
96 97 98 99 100 101 102 103 104 107 108 110 111 114 115 118 119 126
127 129 130 132 135 146 147 148 149 153 **P**6 **S** UnityPoint Health, West Des
Moines, IA
Primary Contact: Pamela K. Delagardelle, President and Chief Executive Officer
COO: Jennifer Friedly, Chief Operating Officer and Vice President
CFO: Craig Flanagan, Chief Financial Officer
CMO: Timothy Horrigan, M.D., Chief Quality Officer
CIO: Daniel Norman, Regional Service Manager
CHR: Steven Sesterhenn, Vice President
CNO: Mary Hagen, R.N., MSN, VP and Chief Nursing Officer
Web address: www.unitypoint.org/waterloo
**Control**: Other not–for–profit (including NFP Corporation) **Service**: General
medical and surgical

> **Staffed Beds:** 204 **Admissions:** 10213 **Census:** 102 **Outpatient
> Visits:** 572518 **Births:** 1231 **Total Expense ($000):** 270106 **Payroll
> Expense ($000):** 107207 **Personnel:** 1393

**UNITYPOINT HEALTH - WATERLOO** See Unitypoint Health - Allen Hospital

**WAUKON—Allamakee County**

★ **VETERANS MEMORIAL HOSPITAL (161318)**, 40 First Street SE,
Zip 52172–2099; tel. 563/568–3411, (Nonreporting) **A**10 18 **F**7 11 13 15 28 34
36 40 45 57 59 62 64 65 68 75 76 77 79 81 86 93 100 102 107 110 111 115
119 128 131 132 133 144 146 148 149 154 156 **P**6
Primary Contact: Michael F. Coyle, Chief Executive Officer
CFO: Scott Knode, Chief Financial Officer
CHR: Erin Berns, Director Human Resources
Web address: www.https://www.veteransmemorialhospital.com
**Control**: City, Government, Nonfederal **Service**: General medical and surgical

> **Staffed Beds:** 20 **Admissions:** 511 **Census:** 7 **Outpatient Visits:** 43795
> **Births:** 104 **Total Expense ($000):** 19522 **Payroll Expense ($000):** 9457
> **Personnel:** 142

**WAVERLY—Bremer County**

☒ **WAVERLY HEALTH CENTER (161339)**, 312 Ninth Street SW, Zip 50677–2999;
tel. 319/352–4120, (Nonreporting) **A**1 10 18 **F**3 7 8 11 12 13 15 28 29 34 35
36 40 43 45 50 57 59 63 64 75 76 77 81 85 86 97 104 107 110 111 114 119
127 130 132 133 135 144 146 147 156 **P**6
Primary Contact: James Atty, Chief Executive Officer
CFO: Lisa Bennett, Chief Financial Officer
CMO: Clay Dahlquist, M.D., Chief Medical Officer
CIO: Jerry Tiedt, Director Information Systems
CHR: Angie Tye, Director Human Resources
CNO: Joanne Nathem, MSN, R.N., Chief Clinical and Nursing Officer
Web address: www.waverlyhealthcenter.org
**Control**: City, Government, Nonfederal **Service**: General medical and surgical

> **Staffed Beds:** 25 **Admissions:** 861 **Census:** 7 **Outpatient Visits:** 121830
> **Births:** 247 **Total Expense ($000):** 59938 **Payroll Expense ($000):** 26983
> **Personnel:** 340

**WAVERLY MUNICIPAL HOSPITAL** See Waverly Health Center

**IA**

---

**Hospital, Medicare Provider Number, Address, Telephone, Approval, Facility, and Physician Codes, Health Care System**

★ American Hospital Association (AHA) membership  ◯ Healthcare Facilities Accreditation Program  ⇑ Center for Improvement in Healthcare Quality Accreditation
☐ The Joint Commission accreditation  ◇ DNV Healthcare Inc. accreditation  △ Commission on Accreditation of Rehabilitation Facilities (CARF) accreditation

## WEBSTER CITY—Hamilton County

**HAMILTON HOSPITAL** See Van Diest Medical Center

★ **VAN DIEST MEDICAL CENTER (161361)**, 2350 Hospital Drive, Zip 50595–6600, Mailing Address: P.O. Box 430, Zip 50595–0430; tel. 515/832–9400, (Nonreporting) **A**10 18 **F**3 7 8 11 15 28 29 31 36 40 43 45 50 75 77 81 85 89 93 96 97 107 110 111 115 119 127 128 130 133 147 154 157 **S** MercyOne, Clive, IA
Primary Contact: Lisa Carolyn. Ridge, Chief Executive Officer
CFO: Alice Heinrichs, CPA, Chief Financial Officer
CMO: Nicole Ehn, M.D., Chief of Staff
CIO: Erick Schrier, Supervisor Information Technology
CHR: Jodie Harker, Director Human Resources
CNO: Janet Naset-Payne, MS, R.N., Chief Nursing Officer
Web address: www.vandiestmc.org
**Control:** County, Government, Nonfederal **Service:** General medical and surgical

**Staffed Beds: 25 Admissions: 702 Census: 8 Outpatient Visits:** 55543
**Births: 15 Total Expense ($000):** 32959 **Payroll Expense ($000):** 13850
**Personnel:** 219

## WEST BURLINGTON—Des Moines County

**GREAT RIVER HEALTH SYSTEM** See Great River Medical Center

★ △ **GREAT RIVER MEDICAL CENTER (160057)**, 1221 South Gear Avenue, Zip 52655–1681; tel. 319/768–1000, (Total facility includes 160 beds in nursing home–type unit) (Nonreporting) **A**7 10 19 22 **F**3 5 7 11 13 15 18 20 22 28 29 30 31 32 34 35 36 38 40 43 45 48 50 53 57 59 60 62 63 64 68 69 70 73 75 77 78 79 81 82 84 85 86 87 90 91 92 93 96 98 99 100 101 102 103 104 107 108 110 111 114 115 116 117 118 119 120 121 123 128 129 130 131 132 143 146 147 148 154 156 157 **P**6
Primary Contact: Matthew Wenzel, President and Chief Executive Officer
CFO: Jeremy Alexander, Chief Financial Officer
CMO: Michael Jerry McCoy, M.D., Chief Medical Officer
CIO: Levi Nathan Gause, M.D., Chief Information Officer and Vice President Health System Informatics
CHR: James M. Kammerer, Vice President Support Services
CNO: Teresa Colgan, Vice President Nursing
Web address: www.greatrivermedical.org
**Control:** Other not–for–profit (including NFP Corporation) **Service:** General medical and surgical

**Staffed Beds: 291 Admissions: 6272 Census: 215 Outpatient Visits:** 294225 **Births: 526 Total Expense ($000):** 195286 **Payroll Expense ($000):** 75508 **Personnel:** 1517

## WEST DES MOINES—Polk County

**MERCY MEDICAL CENTER - WEST LAKES** See Mercyone West Des Moines Medical Center

**METHODIST WEST HOSPITAL** See Unitypoint Health - Methodist West Hospital

## WEST UNION—Fayette County

★ **GUNDERSEN PALMER LUTHERAN HOSPITAL AND CLINICS (161316)**, 112 Jefferson Street, Zip 52175–1022; tel. 563/422–3811, (Nonreporting) **A**10 18 **F**3 11 13 15 28 29 30 31 32 34 35 36 38 40 43 44 45 50 53 56 57 59 62 63 64 65 68 75 76 77 78 79 81 82 85 86 87 89 91 93 96 100 101 107 110 111 115 119 127 128 129 130 131 132 133 135 146 148 154 156
Primary Contact: Patrice Kuennen, Chief Executive Officer
CFO: Joni Gisleson, Director Finance
CMO: Chaudri Rasool, D.O., Chief of Staff
CIO: Kurt Chicken, Director Support Services
CHR: Cheryl Meyer, Director Human Resources
CNO: Kathy Begalske, Chief Nursing Officer
Web address: www.palmerlutheran.org
**Control:** Other not–for–profit (including NFP Corporation) **Service:** General medical and surgical

**Staffed Beds: 25 Admissions: 257 Census: 5 Outpatient Visits:** 86686
**Births: 66 Total Expense ($000):** 29409 **Payroll Expense ($000):** 9569
**Personnel:** 189

**PALMER LUTHERAN HEALTH CENTER** See Gundersen Palmer Lutheran Hospital and Clinics

## WINTERSET—Madison County

★ **MADISON COUNTY HEALTH CARE SYSTEM (161326)**, 300 West Hutchings Street, Zip 50273–2109; tel. 515/462–2373, (Nonreporting) **A**10 18 **F**3 15 18 28 31 35 37 40 43 45 57 59 64 78 79 81 93 97 107 110 114 119 127 130 131 133 135 144 146 149 156 **P**6 **S** CommonSpirit Health, Chicago, IL
Primary Contact: Marcia Hendricks, FACHE, R.N., Chief Executive Officer
CFO: Rebekah Gillespie, Chief Financial Officer
CMO: Joe Kimball, D.O., Chief of Staff
CIO: Dan VandenBosch, Chief Information Officer
CHR: Jennifer Jackson, Director Human Resources
CNO: Kim Hulbert, R.N., Chief Clinical Officer
Web address: www.madisonhealth.com
**Control:** County, Government, Nonfederal **Service:** General medical and surgical

**Staffed Beds: 12 Admissions: 277 Census: 4 Outpatient Visits:** 64567
**Births: 1 Total Expense ($000):** 23906 **Payroll Expense ($000):** 9001
**Personnel:** 141

**MADISON COUNTY HEALTH CARE SYSTEM (DKA MADISON COUNTY MEMORIAL HOSPITAL)** See Madison County Health Care System

*Many Facility Codes have changed. Please refer to the AHA Guide Code Chart.* © 2021 AHA Guide

# KANSAS

## ABILENE—Dickinson County

★ **MEMORIAL HEALTH SYSTEM (171381)**, 511 NE Tenth Street, Zip 67410–2153; tel. 785/263–2100, (Total facility includes 75 beds in nursing home–type unit) (Nonreporting) **A**10 18 **F**3 11 13 15 18 28 29 34 40 45 53 57 59 62 63 64 68 69 75 76 77 81 82 85 87 89 93 97 98 103 104 107 108 110 111 115 119 127 128 129 130 131 132 133 143 145 146 148 149 154 158 **P**6
Primary Contact: Harold Courtois, Chief Executive Officer
CFO: Elgin Glanzer, Chief Financial Officer
CMO: W L Short, M.D., Chief Medical Officer
CIO: Blaine Cappel, Director Information Systems
CNO: Brenda L. Moffitt, Chief Nursing Officer
Web address: www.mhsks.org
**Control**: Hospital district or authority, Government, Nonfederal **Service**: General medical and surgical

| | |
|---|---|
| **Staffed Beds:** 110 **Admissions:** 807 **Census:** 84 **Outpatient Visits:** 25796 **Births:** 37 **Total Expense ($000):** 39543 **Payroll Expense ($000):** 19246 **Personnel:** 291 | |

**MEMORIAL HOSPITAL** See Memorial Health System

## ANDOVER—Butler County

**KANSAS MEDICAL CENTER (170197)**, 1124 West 21st Street, Zip 67002–5500; tel. 316/300–4000, (Nonreporting) **A**10 **F**3 18 20 22 24 28 29 30 40 42 49 60 64 68 70 75 77 79 81 85 87 93 102 107 108 111 115 117 119 126 130 131 146 148 157
Primary Contact: Badr Idbeis, M.D., Chief Executive Officer
COO: Daryl W Thornton, Chief Operating Officer
CFO: Steven N Hadley, Chief Financial Officer
CMO: G. Whitney Reader, M.D., Chief Medical Officer
CIO: Mike Buffington, Manager Information Technology
CHR: Norm Nevins, Manager Human Resources
CNO: Janet Kaiser, R.N., Chief Nursing Officer
Web address: www.ksmedcenter.com/
**Control**: Corporation, Investor–owned (for–profit) **Service**: General medical and surgical

| | |
|---|---|
| **Staffed Beds:** 58 **Admissions:** 2620 **Census:** 28 **Outpatient Visits:** 13564 **Births:** 0 **Personnel:** 288 | |

## ANTHONY—Harper County

**HOSPITAL DISTRICT 6** See Hospital District 6 - Patterson Health Center

★ **HOSPITAL DISTRICT 6 - PATTERSON HEALTH CENTER (171346)**, 485 N KS Hwy 2, Zip 67003–2526; tel. 620/914–1200, (Nonreporting) **A**10 18
Primary Contact: William Pat. Patton, Chief Executive Officer
CFO: Lori Allen, Chief Financial Officer
CNO: Teresa Tomlin, R.N., Chief Nursing Officer
Web address: www.pattersonhc.org
**Control**: Hospital district or authority, Government, Nonfederal **Service**: General medical and surgical

| | |
|---|---|
| **Staffed Beds:** 25 | |

## ARKANSAS CITY—Cowley County

★ **SOUTH CENTRAL KANSAS MEDICAL CENTER (170150)**, 6401 Patterson Parkway, Zip 67005–5701; tel. 620/442–2500, (Nonreporting) **A**10 20 **F**3 8 11 12 13 15 19 29 30 34 35 39 40 41 45 47 48 50 54 56 57 59 64 68 70 75 76 79 81 82 85 87 93 97 98 100 103 107 108 110 111 115 119 127 130 132 133 135 146 147 148 149 154 156 157
Primary Contact: Jeff Bowman, Chief Executive Officer
CFO: Holly Beaty, Chief Financial Officer
CMO: Kamran Shahzada, M.D., Chief Medical Staff
CHR: Clayton Pappan, Director Human Resources and Marketing
CNO: Patricia Davis, Chief Nursing Officer
Web address: www.sckrmc.org
**Control**: City, Government, Nonfederal **Service**: General medical and surgical

| | |
|---|---|
| **Staffed Beds:** 44 **Admissions:** 860 **Census:** 16 **Outpatient Visits:** 22383 **Births:** 58 **Total Expense ($000):** 18943 **Payroll Expense ($000):** 6751 **Personnel:** 174 | |

**SOUTH CENTRAL KANSAS REGIONAL MEDICAL CENTER** See South Central Kansas Medical Center

## ASHLAND—Clark County

**ASHLAND DISTRICT HOSPITAL** See Ashland Health Center

★ **ASHLAND HEALTH CENTER (171304)**, 709 Oak Street, Zip 67831–0188, Mailing Address: P.O. Box 188, Zip 67831–0188; tel. 620/635–2241, (Nonreporting) **A**10 18 **F**2 30 34 40 53 59 62 64 68 85 87 93 107 127 128 133 143 154 156 **S** Great Plains Health Alliance, Inc., Wichita, KS
Primary Contact: Sandrea Wright, Chief Executive Officer
CFO: Debbie Filson, Chief Financial Officer
CMO: Daniel Shuman, D.O., Chief Medical Officer
CIO: Alan Romans, Director Information Technology
CHR: Debbie Filson, Chief Financial Officer
CNO: Patty Young, R.N., Chief Nursing Officer
Web address: www.ashlandhc.org
**Control**: Hospital district or authority, Government, Nonfederal **Service**: General medical and surgical

| | |
|---|---|
| **Staffed Beds:** 25 **Admissions:** 100 **Census:** 15 **Outpatient Visits:** 4018 **Births:** 0 **Total Expense ($000):** 8610 **Payroll Expense ($000):** 2980 **Personnel:** 62 | |

## ATCHISON—Atchison County

★ ○ **ATCHISON HOSPITAL (171382)**, 800 Raven Hill Drive, Zip 66002–9204; tel. 913/367–2131, (Nonreporting) **A**10 11 18 **F**3 11 13 15 28 29 30 31 34 35 39 40 45 49 50 57 59 62 63 64 65 68 70 75 76 77 79 81 82 85 87 89 92 93 96 97 107 108 110 111 115 118 119 127 129 130 131 132 133 135 144 146 147 148 149
Primary Contact: Jeffery Perry, President and Chief Executive Officer
COO: Sandra Leggett, Chief Operating Officer
CFO: Gary R Foll, Chief Financial Officer
CMO: McGarrett Groth, Chief of Staff
CIO: Terry Davis, Manager Information Systems
CHR: Jill Wenger, Chief Human Resources Officer
Web address: www.atchisonhospital.org
**Control**: Other not–for–profit (including NFP Corporation) **Service**: General medical and surgical

| | |
|---|---|
| **Staffed Beds:** 25 **Admissions:** 864 **Census:** 9 **Outpatient Visits:** 75597 **Births:** 143 **Total Expense ($000):** 41127 **Payroll Expense ($000):** 19078 **Personnel:** 299 | |

---

**KS**

## ATWOOD—Rawlins County

★ **RAWLINS COUNTY HEALTH CENTER (171307)**, 707 Grant Street, Zip 67730–1526, Mailing Address: P.O. Box 47, Zip 67730–0047; tel. 785/626–3211, (Nonreporting) **A**10 18 **F**3 28 29 34 35 40 41 43 45 50 53 59 64 65 66 67 75 81 83 84 85 86 87 93 97 107 115 125 127 128 130 131 132 133 135 147 148 149 154 156
Primary Contact: Ronald R. Robinson, M.D., FACHE, M.P.H., Chief Executive Officer and Chief Medical Officer
COO: Ryan Marvin, Support Services Director
CFO: Heather Prideaux, Chief Financial Officer
CMO: Ronald R. Robinson, M.D., FACHE, M.P.H., Chief Executive Officer and Chief Medical Officer
CIO: Destiny Schroeder, Information Systems Director
CHR: Tara Bowles, Employee Relations Director
Web address: www.rchc.us
**Control**: County, Government, Nonfederal **Service**: General medical and surgical

> **Staffed Beds**: 15 **Admissions**: 230 **Census**: 4 **Outpatient Visits**: 6276
> **Births**: 0 **Total Expense ($000)**: 8351 **Payroll Expense ($000)**: 3566
> **Personnel**: 78

**RAWLINS COUNTY HOSPITAL** See Rawlins County Health Center

## BELLEVILLE—Republic County

★ **REPUBLIC COUNTY HOSPITAL (171361)**, 2420 'G' Street, Zip 66935–2400; tel. 785/527–2254, (Nonreporting) **A**10 18 **F**3 13 15 28 29 30 31 34 35 40 43 45 56 57 59 64 68 75 76 77 79 81 82 85 86 87 89 91 93 94 104 107 108 110 114 119 128 129 130 131 133 148 153 156 **S** Great Plains Health Alliance, Inc., Wichita, KS
Primary Contact: Rita K. Buurman, Interim Chief Executive Officer
CFO: Barry Bottger, Chief Financial Officer
Web address: www.rphospital.org
**Control**: Other not–for–profit (including NFP Corporation) **Service**: General medical and surgical

> **Staffed Beds**: 25 **Admissions**: 692 **Census**: 16 **Outpatient Visits**: 17273
> **Births**: 45 **Total Expense ($000)**: 14371 **Payroll Expense ($000)**: 6208
> **Personnel**: 119

## BELOIT—Mitchell County

**MITCHELL COUNTY HOSPITAL** See Mitchell County Hospital Health Systems

★ **MITCHELL COUNTY HOSPITAL HEALTH SYSTEMS (171375)**, 400 West 8th Street, Zip 67420–1605, Mailing Address: P.O. Box 399, Zip 67420–0399; tel. 785/738–2266, (Total facility includes 40 beds in nursing home–type unit) (Nonreporting) **A**10 18 **F**2 3 11 13 15 28 29 31 34 40 43 45 48 50 56 59 63 64 68 69 70 74 76 77 81 82 84 86 87 93 98 103 107 111 114 119 128 129 130 132 133 148 149
Primary Contact: Jeremy Armstrong, FACHE, Chief Executive Officer
CFO: Eldon Koepke, Chief Financial Officer
CIO: Nate Richards, Director Information Technology
CHR: Phyllis Oetting, Director Human Resources
CNO: Jan Kemmerer, Director of Nursing
Web address: www.mchks.com
**Control**: County, Government, Nonfederal **Service**: General medical and surgical

> **Staffed Beds**: 75 **Admissions**: 1423 **Census**: 56 **Outpatient Visits**: 17000
> **Births**: 94 **Total Expense ($000)**: 26492 **Payroll Expense ($000)**: 11958
> **Personnel**: 267

## BURLINGTON—Coffey County

★ ⇑ **COFFEY COUNTY HOSPITAL (171385)**, 801 North 4th Street, Zip 66839–2602; tel. 620/364–2121, (Total facility includes 30 beds in nursing home–type unit) (Nonreporting) **A**10 18 21 **F**3 7 10 11 13 15 17 29 30 31 34 40 45 57 59 62 64 65 67 68 70 75 76 77 78 79 81 82 85 87 93 107 110 111 114 119 125 127 128 130 133 146 149
Primary Contact: Leonard Hernandez, Chief Executive Officer
CFO: Jim Van Hoet, Chief Financial Officer
CMO: John Shell, M.D., Chief Medical Officer
CIO: Adam Haag, Manager Information Technology
CHR: Theresa Thoele, Director Human Resources
CNO: Melissa Hall, Chief Nursing Officer
Web address: www.coffeyhealth.org
**Control**: County, Government, Nonfederal **Service**: General medical and surgical

> **Staffed Beds**: 55 **Admissions**: 400 **Census**: 28 **Outpatient Visits**: 27341
> **Births**: 70 **Total Expense ($000)**: 25716 **Payroll Expense ($000)**: 14302
> **Personnel**: 200

## CALDWELL—Sumner County

★ **SUMNER COUNTY HOSPITAL DISTRICT 1 (171329)**, 601 South Osage Street, Zip 67022–1654; tel. 620/845–6492, (Nonreporting) **A**10 18 **F**7 11 34 35 40 45 46 50 57 59 64 67 75 81 82 84 87 89 93 107 114 119 128 133 148 **P**5
Primary Contact: Brooke Bollman, Chief Executive Officer and Administrator
CMO: Jim Blunk, D.O., Chief Medical Officer
CIO: Trey Watson, Network Administrator
Web address: www.sumnercountyhospital.org
**Control**: Hospital district or authority, Government, Nonfederal **Service**: General medical and surgical

> **Staffed Beds**: 25 **Admissions**: 142 **Census**: 1 **Outpatient Visits**: 1232
> **Births**: 0 **Total Expense ($000)**: 5296 **Payroll Expense ($000)**: 2286
> **Personnel**: 63

**SUMNER COUNTY HOSPITAL DISTRICT ONE** See Sumner County Hospital District 1

## CHANUTE—Neosho County

⇑ **NEOSHO MEMORIAL REG MED CNTR** See Neosho Memorial Regional Medical Center

★ ⇑ **NEOSHO MEMORIAL REGIONAL MEDICAL CENTER (171380)**, 629 South Plummer, Zip 66720–1928, Mailing Address: P.O. Box 426, Zip 66720–0426; tel. 620/431–4000, (Nonreporting) **A**10 18 21 **F**3 7 13 15 28 29 30 40 43 47 48 50 62 63 64 70 76 79 81 85 107 108 110 111 114 119 126 127 129 130 133 143 146 147 149 154 **P**8 **S** QHR Health, Brentwood, TN
Primary Contact: Dennis Franks, FACHE, Chief Executive Officer
COO: Wendy Brazil, Chief Operating Officer
CFO: Nancy Woodyard, Chief Financial Officer
CMO: Charles Van Houden, M.D., Chief Medical Officer
CIO: Gretchen Keller, Director Health Information
CHR: R C Rowan, Director Human Resources
CNO: Jennifer Newton, R.N., Chief Nursing Officer
Web address: www.nmrmc.com
**Control**: County, Government, Nonfederal **Service**: General medical and surgical

> **Staffed Beds**: 25 **Admissions**: 1432 **Census**: 12 **Outpatient Visits**: 54823
> **Births**: 352 **Total Expense ($000)**: 51527 **Payroll Expense ($000)**: 21266
> **Personnel**: 332

## CLAY CENTER—Clay County

**CLAY COUNTY HOSPITAL** See Clay County Medical Center

★ **CLAY COUNTY MEDICAL CENTER (171371)**, 617 Liberty Street, Zip 67432–1564, Mailing Address: P.O. Box 512, Zip 67432–0512; tel. 785/632–2144, (Nonreporting) **A**10 18 **F**13 15 18 19 28 29 30 31 40 45 50 53 55 57 59 63 64 68 70 74 75 76 77 78 79 81 82 84 85 86 87 89 93 96 97 107 108 111 114 119 127 130 132 133 135 146 148 149
Primary Contact: Austin M. Gillard, Chief Executive Officer
CFO: James Garbarino, Chief Financial Officer
CIO: Chris Wolf, Director Information Technology
CHR: Cindy Rush, Director Human Resources
CNO: Sara Beikman, Director of Nursing
Web address: www.ccmcks.org
**Control**: County, Government, Nonfederal **Service**: General medical and surgical

> **Staffed Beds**: 25 **Admissions**: 805 **Census**: 11 **Outpatient Visits**: 87119
> **Births**: 44 **Total Expense ($000)**: 27437 **Payroll Expense ($000)**: 12117
> **Personnel**: 209

## COFFEYVILLE—Montgomery County

⊞ **COFFEYVILLE REGIONAL MEDICAL CENTER (170145)**, 1400 West Fourth, Zip 67337–3306; tel. 620/251–1200, (Nonreporting) **A**1 10 20 **F**3 7 11 13 15 28 29 30 31 34 40 45 50 51 57 59 62 64 65 66 70 74 76 77 78 79 81 82 85 86 87 93 97 107 108 109 110 111 113 117 119 120 121 123 127 130 131 132 135 146 147 148 154 156 **P**6 8
Primary Contact: Brian Lawrence, Chief Executive Officer
CIO: Kris Penco, Director Information Systems
CHR: Becky McCune, Director Human Resources, Community Relations and Education
CNO: Sarah M Hoy, Chief Nursing Officer
Web address: www.https://www.crmcinc.org
**Control**: Other not–for–profit (including NFP Corporation) **Service**: General medical and surgical

> **Staffed Beds**: 47 **Admissions**: 1329 **Census**: 11 **Outpatient Visits**: 46497
> **Births**: 227 **Total Expense ($000)**: 44681 **Payroll Expense ($000)**: 19531
> **Personnel**: 300

*Many Facility Codes have changed. Please refer to the AHA Guide Code Chart.*  © 2021 AHA Guide

## COLBY—Thomas County

★ **CITIZENS MEDICAL CENTER (171362)**, 100 East College Drive,
Zip 67701–3799; tel. 785/462–7511, (Total facility includes 60 beds in nursing
home–type unit) (Nonreporting) **A**10 18 **F**3 11 12 13 15 28 29 30 31 34 35 40
43 50 53 56 57 59 64 65 67 68 75 76 77 78 81 82 86 87 90 93 97 107 108
110 111 115 119 127 128 130 131 132 133 144 146 147 148 149 154 156
157 **P**6
Primary Contact: Greg Unruh, Chief Executive Officer
CMO: Kelly Gabel, Chief of Staff
CIO: Jacee Dobbs, Chief Information Officer
CHR: Margaret Kummer, Chief Human Resource Officer
CNO: Jenny Niblock, Chief Clinical Officer
Web address: www.cmciks.com
**Control:** Other not–for–profit (including NFP Corporation) **Service:** General
medical and surgical

| | |
|---|---|
| **Staffed Beds:** 85 **Admissions:** 686 **Census:** 59 **Outpatient Visits:** 159001 **Births:** 178 **Total Expense ($000):** 42397 **Payroll Expense ($000):** 20568 **Personnel:** 338 | |

## COLDWATER—Comanche County

★ **COMANCHE COUNTY HOSPITAL (171312)**, 202 South Frisco Street,
Zip 67029–9101, Mailing Address: HC 65, Box 8A, Zip 67029–9500;
tel. 620/582–2144, (Nonreporting) **A**10 18 **F**3 11 30 31 40 43 53 59 61 68 75
78 93 102 107 128 133 156 **S** Great Plains Health Alliance, Inc., Wichita, KS
Primary Contact: Lisa Brooks, Administrator
CMO: Daniel Schowengerdt, M.D., Chief of Staff
CIO: LaNell Wagnon, Director Medical Records
CNO: Sandra Dobrinski, Director of Nursing
Web address: www.gpha.com
**Control:** County, Government, Nonfederal **Service:** General medical and surgical

| | |
|---|---|
| **Staffed Beds:** 12 **Admissions:** 136 **Census:** 2 **Outpatient Visits:** 9046 **Births:** 0 **Total Expense ($000):** 5383 **Payroll Expense ($000):** 2480 **Personnel:** 55 | |

## COLUMBUS—Cherokee County

★ **MERCY HOSPITAL COLUMBUS (171308)**, 220 North Pennsylvania Avenue,
Zip 66725–1110; tel. 620/429–2545, (Nonreporting) **A**10 18 **S** Mercy,
Chesterfield, MO
Primary Contact: Angie Saporito, Administrator
Web address: www.mercy.net/newsroom-mercy-maude-norton-hospital-quick-facts
**Control:** Church operated, Nongovernment, not–for–profit **Service:** General
medical and surgical

| | |
|---|---|
| **Staffed Beds:** 18 | |

**MERCY MAUDE NORTON HOSPITAL** See Mercy Hospital Columbus

## CONCORDIA—Cloud County

★ **CLOUD COUNTY HEALTH CENTER (171349)**, 1100 Highland Drive,
Zip 66901–3923; tel. 785/243–1234, (Nonreporting) **A**10 18 **F**3 11 15 28 31 34
35 40 41 45 56 57 59 64 65 70 74 75 77 79 81 82 85 86 87 89 93 96 97 102
107 108 114 118 119 127 130 133 135 146 148 154 **S** Salina Regional Health
Center, Salina, KS
Primary Contact: David Garnas, Administrator
CFO: Pamela Blochlinger, Acting Vice President Finance
CMO: Justin Poore, D.O., Chief Medical Staff
CIO: Jenny Bergstrom, Project Manager Information Technology
CHR: Dawn Thoman, Vice President Human Resources
CNO: Michelle Metro, Vice President Nursing
Web address: www.cchc.com
**Control:** Other not–for–profit (including NFP Corporation) **Service:** General
medical and surgical

| | |
|---|---|
| **Staffed Beds:** 25 **Admissions:** 364 **Census:** 6 **Outpatient Visits:** 36990 **Births:** 0 **Total Expense ($000):** 14943 **Payroll Expense ($000):** 8091 **Personnel:** 137 | |

**ST JOSEPH HOSPITAL** See Cloud County Health Center

## COUNCIL GROVE—Morris County

★ **MORRIS COUNTY HOSPITAL (171379)**, 600 North Washington Street,
Zip 66846–1422; tel. 620/767–6811, (Nonreporting) **A**10 18 **F**7 11 13 15 18 28
35 40 45 59 64 65 70 76 77 81 82 87 93 94 96 107 110 111 119 130 132
133 146 148 149 156 **P**6
Primary Contact: Kevin Leeper, Chief Executive Officer
CFO: Ron Christenson, Chief Financial Officer
CMO: Lora Siegle, M.D., Chief Medical Officer
CIO: Bill Lauer, Chief Information Officer
CHR: Don Zimmerman, Director Human Resources
CNO: Stephanne Wolf, Chief Nursing Officer
Web address: www.mrcohosp.com
**Control:** County, Government, Nonfederal **Service:** General medical and surgical

| | |
|---|---|
| **Staffed Beds:** 21 **Admissions:** 294 **Census:** 4 **Outpatient Visits:** 13484 **Births:** 11 **Total Expense ($000):** 12894 **Payroll Expense ($000):** 5500 **Personnel:** 102 | |

## DERBY—Sedgwick County

☐ **ROCK REGIONAL HOSPITAL (170402)**, 3251 North Rock Road,
Zip 67037–3850; tel. 316/425–2400, (Data for 251 days) (Nonreporting) **A**1 **F**3
18 20 22 26 40 46 70 74 75 79 81 107 109 111 115 119 130 154
Primary Contact: Teresa Collins, R.N., Interim Chief Executive Officer
Web address: www.https://rockregionalhospitalderby.com
**Control:** Partnership, Investor–owned (for–profit) **Service:** General medical and
surgical

| | |
|---|---|
| **Staffed Beds:** 17 **Admissions:** 609 **Census:** 3 **Outpatient Visits:** 1653 **Births:** 0 **Total Expense ($000):** 27770 **Payroll Expense ($000):** 6250 **Personnel:** 171 | |

## DIGHTON—Lane County

★ **LANE COUNTY HOSPITAL (171303)**, 235 West Vine, Zip 67839–0969, Mailing
Address: P.O. Box 969, Zip 67839–0969; tel. 620/397–5321, (Nonreporting) **A**10
18 **F**40 59 77 93 97 127 128 133 156 **P**6 **S** Great Plains Health Alliance, Inc.,
Wichita, KS
Primary Contact: Marcia Gabel, Chief Financial Officer and Co-Chief Executive
Officer
CFO: Marcia Gabel, Chief Financial Officer
CMO: Paul Chinburg, M.D., Medical Director
CHR: Dina Casey, Human Resources Officer
CNO: Jennifer Whipple, Director Nursing
Web address: www.lanecountyhospital.com/
**Control:** County, Government, Nonfederal **Service:** General medical and surgical

| | |
|---|---|
| **Staffed Beds:** 25 **Admissions:** 60 **Census:** 18 **Outpatient Visits:** 9509 **Births:** 0 **Total Expense ($000):** 5912 **Payroll Expense ($000):** 2632 **Personnel:** 54 | |

## DODGE CITY—Ford County

⊞ **WESTERN PLAINS MEDICAL COMPLEX (170175)**, 3001 Avenue 'A',
Zip 67801–6508, Mailing Address: P.O. Box 1478, Zip 67801–1478;
tel. 620/225–8400, (Nonreporting) **A**1 5 10 20 **F**3 8 11 13 15 18 20 22 24 28
29 30 34 35 40 50 57 60 64 68 70 74 75 76 77 79 81 82 85 88 89 93 107
108 110 111 115 119 130 131 132 133 144 146 149 150 154 **P**6 **S** LifePoint
Health, Brentwood, TN
Primary Contact: Jerry Dooley, Interim Chief Executive Officer
CFO: Ryan Pugh, Chief Financial Officer
CMO: Merrill Conant, M.D., Chief of Staff
CIO: Shawna Culver, Director Information Systems
CHR: Corry Israel, Director Human Resources
CNO: Jay Trevor Fogg, Chief Nursing Officer
Web address: www.westernplainsmc.com
**Control:** Corporation, Investor–owned (for–profit) **Service:** General medical and
surgical

| | |
|---|---|
| **Staffed Beds:** 45 **Admissions:** 1852 **Census:** 13 **Outpatient Visits:** 33448 **Births:** 651 **Total Expense ($000):** 35335 **Payroll Expense ($000):** 12494 **Personnel:** 212 | |

**WESTERN PLAINS REGIONAL HOSP** See Western Plains Medical Complex

---

**Hospital, Medicare Provider Number, Address, Telephone, Approval, Facility, and Physician Codes, Health Care System**

★ American Hospital Association (AHA) membership
☐ The Joint Commission accreditation
○ Healthcare Facilities Accreditation Program
◇ DNV Healthcare Inc. accreditation
⇑ Center for Improvement in Healthcare Quality Accreditation
△ Commission on Accreditation of Rehabilitation Facilities (CARF) accreditation

**KS**

## EL DORADO—Butler County

☒ **SUSAN B. ALLEN MEMORIAL HOSPITAL (170017)**, 720 West Central Avenue, Zip 67042–2112; tel. 316/321–3300, (Nonreporting) **A**1 10 **F**3 11 13 15 28 34 35 40 45 55 57 59 60 62 64 68 69 70 75 76 79 81 85 92 93 96 97 107 108 110 111 115 119 120 121 123 130 133 144 146 148 149 154 155
Primary Contact: Jeff Egbert, Interim Chief Executive Officer
CFO: Gene Kaberline, Chief Financial Officer
CMO: Paige Dodson, M.D., M.P.H., Chief Medical Officer
CHR: D. Gay Kimble, Chief Human Resource Officer
CNO: Cecilia B Goebel, R.N., Chief Nursing Officer
Web address: www.sbamh.com
**Control**: Other not–for–profit (including NFP Corporation) **Service**: General medical and surgical

**Staffed Beds**: 20 **Admissions**: 1296 **Census**: 15 **Outpatient Visits**: 250207 **Births**: 249 **Total Expense ($000)**: 50085 **Payroll Expense ($000)**: 19198 **Personnel**: 283

## ELKHART—Morton County

**MORTON COUNTY HEALTH SYSTEM (170166)**, 445 Hilltop Street, Zip 67950–0937, Mailing Address: P.O. Box 937, Zip 67950–0937; tel. 620/697–2141, (Nonreporting) **A**10 20 **F**3 28 29 34 40 54 56 57 59 64 83 86 87 93 94 96 97 104 107 114 119 127 130 131 132 133 154
Primary Contact: Patrick Custer, Interim Chief Executive Officer
CFO: Michael Soodjinda, Chief Financial Officer
CHR: Sonja May, Director Human Resources
Web address: www.mchswecare.com
**Control**: County, Government, Nonfederal **Service**: General medical and surgical

**Staffed Beds**: 24 **Admissions**: 209 **Census**: 2 **Outpatient Visits**: 8695 **Births**: 0 **Total Expense ($000)**: 753642 **Payroll Expense ($000)**: 4088 **Personnel**: 55

**MORTON COUNTY HOSPITAL** See Morton County Health System

## ELLINWOOD—Barton County

★ **ELLINWOOD DISTRICT HOSPITAL (171301)**, 605 North Main Street, Zip 67526–1440; tel. 620/564–2548, (Nonreporting) **A**10 18 **F**11 40 64 65 93 107 127 128 133 154 156 **S** Great Plains Health Alliance, Inc., Wichita, KS
Primary Contact: Kile Magner, Administrator
CFO: Summer Zink, Chief Financial Officer
CMO: Charlie Joslin, Chief of Staff
CIO: Becky L Burns, Manager Health Information Management
CHR: Chris Robl, Human Resources
CNO: Jill Ritchie, Director of Nursing
Web address: www.ellinwooddistricthospital.org
**Control**: Other not–for–profit (including NFP Corporation) **Service**: General medical and surgical

**Staffed Beds**: 25 **Admissions**: 242 **Census**: 6 **Outpatient Visits**: 13296 **Births**: 0 **Total Expense ($000)**: 7405 **Payroll Expense ($000)**: 3582 **Personnel**: 86

## ELLSWORTH—Ellsworth County

**ELLSWORTH COUNTY HOSPITAL** See Ellsworth County Medical Center

★ **ELLSWORTH COUNTY MEDICAL CENTER (171327)**, 1604 Aylward Street, Zip 67439–0087, Mailing Address: P.O. Box 87, Zip 67439–0087; tel. 785/472–3111, (Nonreporting) **A**10 18 **F**3 11 28 29 34 35 40 45 47 53 57 59 64 67 75 77 83 85 86 87 93 97 107 115 119 127 128 130 133 146 147 148 156 **P**6
Primary Contact: Andrew P. Bair, Chief Executive Officer
CFO: Preston Sauers, Chief Financial Officer
CIO: Lynette Dick, Director of Support Services
CHR: Christa N Bohnen, Director Human Resources
CNO: Amanda Thrasher, Director Nursing
Web address: www.ewmed.com
**Control**: County, Government, Nonfederal **Service**: General medical and surgical

**Staffed Beds**: 19 **Admissions**: 462 **Census**: 5 **Outpatient Visits**: 11932 **Births**: 0 **Total Expense ($000)**: 18242 **Payroll Expense ($000)**: 8759 **Personnel**: 161

## EMPORIA—Lyon County

**NEWMAN MEM CNTY HOSPITAL** See Newman Regional Health

○ **NEWMAN REGIONAL HEALTH (171384)**, 1201 West 12th Avenue, Zip 66801–2597; tel. 620/343–6800, (Nonreporting) **A**10 11 18 **F**3 11 13 15 17 18 20 22 26 28 29 31 39 40 41 43 45 51 53 59 61 63 64 65 68 70 76 77 78 79 81 82 84 85 86 87 89 90 93 96 102 107 108 111 114 118 119 127 129 130 131 132 133 135 144 145 146 147 148 149 156 **P**6
Primary Contact: Robert N. Wright, Chief Executive Officer
CFO: Holly French, Chief Financial Officer
CHR: Tabatha Tafoya, Director Human Resources
CNO: Julia Pyle, R.N., Chief Nursing Officer
Web address: www.newmanrh.org
**Control**: County, Government, Nonfederal **Service**: General medical and surgical

**Staffed Beds**: 35 **Admissions**: 1879 **Census**: 21 **Outpatient Visits**: 55115 **Births**: 376 **Total Expense ($000)**: 73913 **Payroll Expense ($000)**: 31747 **Personnel**: 503

## EUREKA—Greenwood County

**GREENWOOD COUNTY HOSPITAL (171339)**, 100 West 16th Street, Zip 67045–1064; tel. 620/583–7451, (Nonreporting) **A**10 18
Primary Contact: Sandra Dickerson, Chief Executive Officer
CFO: Melody Curnutt, CPA, Chief Financial Officer
CMO: Mark Basham, M.D., Chief Medical Officer
CIO: Jason Clark, Director Information Systems
CHR: Janel M Palmer, Director Human Resources
CNO: Rebecca Randall, Chief Nursing Officer
Web address: www.gwch.org
**Control**: County, Government, Nonfederal **Service**: General medical and surgical

**Staffed Beds**: 25

## FREDONIA—Wilson County

★ **FREDONIA REGIONAL HOSPITAL (171374)**, 1527 Madison Street, Zip 66736–1751, Mailing Address: P.O. Box 579, Zip 66736–0579; tel. 620/378–2121, (Nonreporting) **A**10 18 **F**3 7 11 15 30 40 57 59 81 82 85 91 93 103 107 110 111 115 119 128 133 154 156 **S** Great Plains Health Alliance, Inc., Wichita, KS
Primary Contact: Johnathan Durrett, Chief Executive Officer
CFO: Tracy Row, Manager Business Office
CMO: Jennifer McKenney, M.D., Chief Medical Officer
CIO: Tyler Row, Director Information Technology
CHR: Debbie Marr, Administrative Assistant and Director Human Resources
CNO: Ryan Duft, R.N., Chief Nursing Officer
Web address: www.fredoniaregionalhospital.org
**Control**: City, Government, Nonfederal **Service**: General medical and surgical

**Staffed Beds**: 25 **Admissions**: 316 **Census**: 4 **Outpatient Visits**: 29832 **Births**: 0 **Total Expense ($000)**: 12243 **Payroll Expense ($000)**: 4570 **Personnel**: 108

## GALENA—Cherokee County

⇑ **PREMIER SURGICAL INSTITUTE (170203)**, 1619 West 7th Street, Zip 66739; tel. 620/783–1732, (Nonreporting) **A**10 21
Primary Contact: Travis W. Roderick, Chief Executive Officer
Web address: www.premiersurgicalinstitute.com/
**Control**: City, Government, Nonfederal **Service**: General medical and surgical

**Staffed Beds**: 25

## GARDEN CITY—Finney County

☒ **ST. CATHERINE HOSPITAL (170023)**, 401 East Spruce Street, Zip 67846–5679; tel. 620/272–2561, (Nonreporting) **A**1 10 20 **F**3 8 13 15 18 20 22 29 30 31 34 35 40 45 49 51 57 59 63 64 65 68 69 70 73 74 75 76 77 78 79 81 82 83 84 85 86 87 89 90 91 92 93 94 96 100 102 107 108 109 110 111 112 113 114 115 116 117 118 119 120 121 122 123 124 127 130 131 132 135 144 146 147 148 154 156 **P**5 6 **S** CommonSpirit Health, Chicago, IL
Primary Contact: Christine McSweeney, FACHE, President and Chief Executive Officer
CFO: Amanda Vaughan, Chief Financial Officer
CMO: Matthew C Byrnes, M.D., Chief Medical Officer
CIO: Lance Kellenbarger, Site Director Information Systems
CHR: Kathy E Morrison, Executive Director Human Resources
CNO: Margaret Elizabeth Prewitt, Vice President Patient Services and Chief Nursing Officer
Web address: www.StCatherineHosp.org
**Control**: Church operated, Nongovernment, not–for–profit **Service**: General medical and surgical

**Staffed Beds**: 100 **Admissions**: 4059 **Census**: 45 **Outpatient Visits**: 167114 **Births**: 652 **Total Expense ($000)**: 121814 **Payroll Expense ($000)**: 32073 **Personnel**: 567

*Many Facility Codes have changed. Please refer to the AHA Guide Code Chart.* © 2021 AHA Guide

## GARDNER—Johnson County

**GREAT PLAINS HOSP & HEALTH CTR** See Meadowbrook Rehabilitation Hospital

△ **MEADOWBROOK REHABILITATION HOSPITAL (173033)**, 427 West Main Street, Zip 66030–1183; tel. 913/856–8747, (Nonreporting) **A**7 10
Primary Contact: Kristen Barrett, Chief Executive Officer
CFO: Kelly Taul, Business Manager
CMO: David Edalati, M.D., Medical Director
CHR: Carrie Moore, Director Human Resources
CNO: Lisa Perez, R.N., Director Nursing
Web address: www.recover-care.com
**Control**: Partnership, Investor–owned (for–profit) **Service**: Rehabilitation

| **Staffed Beds**: 96 |
|---|

## GARNETT—Anderson County

★ **ANDERSON COUNTY HOSPITAL (171316)**, 421 South Maple, Zip 66032–1334, Mailing Address: P.O. Box 309, Zip 66032–0309; tel. 785/448–3131, (Total facility includes 30 beds in nursing home–type unit) (Nonreporting) **A**10 18 **F**3 7 11 15 18 29 30 34 35 40 43 44 45 50 56 57 59 64 65 67 68 75 77 79 81 85 86 87 93 96 97 102 107 108 110 115 118 119 127 130 131 133 135 146 148 149 154 **P**6 **S** Saint Luke's Health System, Kansas City, MO
Primary Contact: Rick McKain, Chief Executive Officer
CFO: Vicki L Mills, Chief Financial Officer
CMO: Mackenzie Peterson, M.D., Chief of Staff
CHR: Karen Gillespie, Director Human Resources
CNO: Margo L Williams, R.N., Chief Nursing Officer
Web address: www.saint-lukes.org
**Control**: Other not–for–profit (including NFP Corporation) **Service**: General medical and surgical

| **Staffed Beds**: 42 **Admissions**: 241 **Census**: 32 **Outpatient Visits**: 47538 **Births**: 0 **Total Expense ($000)**: 28776 **Payroll Expense ($000)**: 11720 **Personnel**: 213 |
|---|

## GIRARD—Crawford County

★ **GIRARD MEDICAL CENTER (171376)**, 302 North Hospital Drive, Zip 66743–2000; tel. 620/724–8291, (Nonreporting) **A**10 18 **F**3 6 8 11 12 15 28 29 34 35 40 43 44 45 47 50 51 53 56 57 59 62 64 65 68 70 75 77 79 81 86 87 93 97 98 100 101 103 104 107 114 119 127 128 130 131 132 133 144 146 148 149 154
Primary Contact: Ruth Duling, Chief Executive Officer
CFO: Holly Koch, Chief Financial Officer
CIO: Jeff Barnes, Director Information Technology
CHR: Gregory Sullivan, Manager Human Resources
CNO: Joyce Geier, Director Nursing
Web address: www.girardmedicalcenter.com
**Control**: Hospital district or authority, Government, Nonfederal **Service**: General medical and surgical

| **Staffed Beds**: 35 **Admissions**: 661 **Census**: 12 **Outpatient Visits**: 22493 **Births**: 0 **Total Expense ($000)**: 18954 **Payroll Expense ($000)**: 9573 **Personnel**: 187 |
|---|

**HOSPITAL DISTRICT NUMBER 1 OF CRAWFORD COUNTY** See Girard Medical Center

## GOODLAND—Sherman County

★ **GOODLAND REGIONAL MEDICAL CENTER (171370)**, 220 West Second Street, Zip 67735–1602; tel. 785/890–3625, (Nonreporting) **A**10 18
Primary Contact: Ronald R. Robinson, M.D., FACHE, M.P.H., Chief Executive Officer
CFO: Derick Lorentz, Chief Financial Officer
CMO: Travis Daise, M.D., Chief Medical Officer
CHR: Kim Horineck, Chief Human Resource Officer
Web address: www.goodlandregional.com
**Control**: County, Government, Nonfederal **Service**: General medical and surgical

| **Staffed Beds**: 25 |
|---|

**NORTHWEST KANSAS REG MED CTR** See Goodland Regional Medical Center

## GREAT BEND—Barton County

**GREAT BEND REGIONAL HOSPITAL** See University of Kansas Health System Great Bend Campus

★ **UNIVERSITY OF KANSAS HEALTH SYSTEM GREAT BEND CAMPUS (170191)**, 514 Cleveland Street, Zip 67530–3562; tel. 620/792–8833, (Nonreporting) **A**10 20 22 **S** The University of Kansas Health System, Kansas City, KS
Primary Contact: Jesse Mock, Chief Executive Officer
COO: Adina Gregory, Chief Operating Officer
CFO: Timothy Latimer, Chief Financial Officer
CMO: Randall Hildebrand, M.D., Chief Medical Officer
CHR: Brenda Kaiser, Director Human Resources
CNO: Adina Gregory, Chief Nursing Officer
Web address: www.gbregional.com
**Control**: Hospital district or authority, Government, Nonfederal **Service**: Surgical

| **Staffed Beds**: 33 |
|---|

## GREENSBURG—Kiowa County

★ ⇧ **KIOWA COUNTY MEMORIAL HOSPITAL (171332)**, 721 West Kansas Avenue, Zip 67054–1633; tel. 620/723–3341, (Nonreporting) **A**10 18 21 **F**3 7 34 40 50 53 59 64 68 107 114 127 128 133 149 156 **S** Great Plains Health Alliance, Inc., Wichita, KS
Primary Contact: Mary Sweet, Administrator
CFO: Ron Tucker, Business Office Manager
CMO: Nizar Kibar, M.D., Chief Medical Staff
CIO: Jeremy Steven Hoover, Chief Information Officer
CHR: Cathy McFall, Human Resources Manager
CNO: Vanessa Kirk, Director of Nursing
Web address: www.kcmh.net
**Control**: Other not–for–profit (including NFP Corporation) **Service**: General medical and surgical

| **Staffed Beds**: 15 **Admissions**: 112 **Census**: 7 **Outpatient Visits**: 11716 **Births**: 0 **Total Expense ($000)**: 9265 **Payroll Expense ($000)**: 3575 **Personnel**: 73 |
|---|

## HANOVER—Washington County

★ **HANOVER HOSPITAL (171365)**, 205 South Hanover, Zip 66945–8924, Mailing Address: P.O. Box 38, Zip 66945–0038; tel. 785/337–2214, (Nonreporting) **A**10 18 **F**2 7 28 40 53 64 69 81 107 115 127 133 **P**4
Primary Contact: Brittni Oehmke, Administrator
CFO: Sheryl Adam, Chief Financial Officer
**Control**: Hospital district or authority, Government, Nonfederal **Service**: General medical and surgical

| **Staffed Beds**: 25 **Admissions**: 124 **Census**: 4 **Outpatient Visits**: 3670 **Births**: 0 **Total Expense ($000)**: 6043 **Payroll Expense ($000)**: 2651 **Personnel**: 53 |
|---|

**WASHINGTON CNTY HOSP DIST 1** See Hanover Hospital

## HAYS—Ellis County

★ ⇧ **HAYS MEDICAL CENTER (170013)**, 2220 Canterbury Drive, Zip 67601–2370, Mailing Address: P.O. Box 8100, Zip 67601–8100; tel. 785/623–5000, (Nonreporting) **A**5 10 21 **F**3 11 12 13 15 18 20 22 24 26 28 29 30 31 32 34 35 36 37 38 40 41 43 45 51 53 55 56 57 59 60 63 64 65 66 68 69 70 71 72 73 75 76 77 78 79 80 81 82 84 85 86 87 89 92 93 96 97 107 108 110 111 115 118 119 120 121 123 124 126 127 129 130 131 132 135 144 146 147 148 149 154 156 **P**6 **S** The University of Kansas Health System, Kansas City, KS
Primary Contact: Edward Herrman, R.N., FACHE, President and Chief Executive Officer
COO: Bryce A Young, Chief Operating Officer
CFO: George Harms, Chief Financial Officer
CIO: Scott Rohleder, Chief Information Officer
CHR: Bryce A Young, Chief Operating Officer
CNO: Terry Siek, MSN, R.N., Chief Nursing Officer
Web address: www.haysmed.com
**Control**: Other not–for–profit (including NFP Corporation) **Service**: General medical and surgical

| **Staffed Beds**: 127 **Admissions**: 4890 **Census**: 54 **Outpatient Visits**: 164382 **Births**: 641 **Total Expense ($000)**: 187506 **Payroll Expense ($000)**: 81407 **Personnel**: 1284 |
|---|

---

| Hospital, Medicare Provider Number, Address, Telephone, Approval, Facility, and Physician Codes, Health Care System |
|---|

★ American Hospital Association (AHA) membership
☐ The Joint Commission accreditation
◯ Healthcare Facilities Accreditation Program
◇ DNV Healthcare Inc. accreditation
⇧ Center for Improvement in Healthcare Quality Accreditation
△ Commission on Accreditation of Rehabilitation Facilities (CARF) accreditation

**KS**

## HERINGTON—Dickinson County

★ **HERINGTON MUNICIPAL HOSPITAL (171340)**, 100 East Helen Street,
Zip 67449–1606; tel. 785/258–2207, (Nonreporting) **A**10 18
Primary Contact: Isabel Schmedemann, Chief Executive Officer and Administrator
CFO: Alan Meisinger, Chief Financial Officer
CMO: John Mosier, D.O., Chief of Staff
CHR: Nicole Will, Human Resources Officer
CNO: Roni Baker, Director of Nursing
Web address: www.heringtonhospital.org
**Control**: City, Government, Nonfederal **Service**: General medical and surgical

| Staffed Beds: 25 |
|---|

## HIAWATHA—Brown County

★ **HIAWATHA COMMUNITY HOSPITAL (171341)**, 300 Utah Street,
Zip 66434–2314; tel. 785/742–2131, (Nonreporting) **A**10 18 **F**8 11 13 15 28 29
40 43 45 67 69 70 76 81 82 85 107 111 114 119 127 128 130 133 143 146
149 155 156 **P**6
Primary Contact: John Broberg, Chief Executive Officer
CFO: Jenny Knudson, Controller
CMO: Steffen Shamburg, M.D., Chief of Staff
CIO: Cheryl Wenger, Manager Health Information and Quality Assurance
CHR: Alison Keri, Director Human Resources
CNO: Lisa Thompson, MSN, R.N., Director of Nursing
Web address: www.hch-ks.org
**Control**: Other not–for–profit (including NFP Corporation) **Service**: General
medical and surgical

| Staffed Beds: 25 Admissions: 629 Census: 5 Outpatient Visits: 30987 |
|---|
| Births: 80 Total Expense ($000): 25577 Payroll Expense ($000): 11346 |
| Personnel: 201 |

## HILL CITY—Graham County

★ **GRAHAM COUNTY HOSPITAL (171325)**, 304 West Prout Street,
Zip 67642–1435; tel. 785/421–2121, (Nonreporting) **A**10 18 **F**3 11 34 40 50 53
59 64 67 68 81 82 84 93 107 114 127 128 133 148 149
Primary Contact: Melissa Atkins, CPA, Chief Executive Officer
CHR: Donella Belleau, Director Human Resources
Web address: www.grahamcountyhospital.org
**Control**: County, Government, Nonfederal **Service**: General medical and surgical

| Staffed Beds: 15 Admissions: 321 Census: 5 Outpatient Visits: 7499 |
|---|
| Births: 0 Total Expense ($000): 7908 Payroll Expense ($000): 3797 |
| Personnel: 69 |

## HILLSBORO—Marion County

**HILLSBORO COMMUNITY HOSPITAL (171357)**, 701 South Main Street,
Zip 67063–1553; tel. 620/947–3114, (Nonreporting) **A**10 18 **F**3 29 40 45 50 57
59 64 68 81 82 93 97 104 107 115 119 127 130 131 133 149 154 **P**5 **S** Rural
Community Hospitals of America, Kansas City, MO
Primary Contact: Mark Rooker, Chief Executive Officer
COO: Johna Magnuson, Director Nursing
CIO: Marsha Setzkorn-Meyer, Director Public Relations and Marketing
CHR: Wendy McCarty, Director Human Resources
Web address: www.hchks.com
**Control**: Corporation, Investor–owned (for–profit) **Service**: General medical and
surgical

| Staffed Beds: 15 Admissions: 280 Census: 2 Outpatient Visits: 15488 |
|---|
| Births: 0 Total Expense ($000): 5988 Payroll Expense ($000): 3422 |
| Personnel: 50 |

**HILLSBORO COMMUNITY MEDICAL CENTER** See Hillsboro Community Hospital

## HOISINGTON—Barton County

★ **CLARA BARTON HOSPITAL (171333)**, 250 West Ninth Street,
Zip 67544–1706; tel. 620/653–2114, (Nonreporting) **A**10 18 **F**11 15 28 40 56
57 59 64 77 81 85 92 93 97 107 114 126 127 128 130 133 148 **P**6
Primary Contact: James Blackwell, President and Chief Executive Officer
CMO: Nathan Knackstedt, D.O., Chief of Staff
CHR: John Moshier, Director Human Resources
CNO: Jane Schepmann, Vice President and Chief Nursing Officer
Web address: www.clarabartonhospital.org
**Control**: Other not–for–profit (including NFP Corporation) **Service**: General
medical and surgical

| Staffed Beds: 23 Admissions: 659 Census: 10 Outpatient Visits: 47670 |
|---|
| Births: 0 Total Expense ($000): 25647 Payroll Expense ($000): 12057 |
| Personnel: 212 |

**HOISINGTON LUTHERAN HOSPITAL** See Clara Barton Hospital

## HOLTON—Jackson County

**HOLTON CITY HOSPITAL** See Holton Community Hospital

★ **HOLTON COMMUNITY HOSPITAL (171319)**, 1110 Columbine Drive,
Zip 66436–8824; tel. 785/364–2116, (Nonreporting) **A**10 18 **F**3 11 15 18 28 29
34 40 43 45 50 57 59 62 63 64 65 74 75 77 79 81 82 87 93 97 107 114 119
127 130 131 132 133 135 146 147 148 156 157 **P**3
Primary Contact: Carrie L. Saia, Chief Executive Officer
CFO: Bart Kenton, Chief Financial Officer
CMO: Joel Hutchsin, M.D., Chief Medical Staff
CIO: Holli Peters, Director Health Information Management
CHR: Gretchen Snavely, Director Human Resources
CNO: Mandy Bontrager, Director Nursing
Web address: www.holtonhospital.com
**Control**: Other not–for–profit (including NFP Corporation) **Service**: General
medical and surgical

| Staffed Beds: 12 Admissions: 240 Census: 4 Outpatient Visits: 50545 |
|---|
| Births: 0 Total Expense ($000): 17802 Payroll Expense ($000): 8115 |
| Personnel: 149 |

## HOXIE—Sheridan County

**SHERIDAN COUNTY HEALTH COMPLEX (171347)**, 826 18th Street,
Zip 67740–0167, Mailing Address: P.O. Box 167, Zip 67740–0167;
tel. 785/675–3281, (Total facility includes 32 beds in nursing home–type unit)
(Nonreporting) **A**10 18 **F**3 7 11 29 34 35 40 45 50 53 56 57 59 64 66 67 69 75
81 82 85 87 92 93 97 100 101 107 115 119 125 130 133 135 143 147 148
149 154
Primary Contact: Niceta Farber, Chief Executive Officer
CFO: Michael O'Dell, Chief Financial Officer
CMO: Victor Nemechek, M.D., Chief of Staff and Chief Medical Officer
CHR: Shelby Moss, Human Resource Officer
CNO: Hannah Schoendaler, Chief Nursing Officer
Web address: www.sheridancountyhospital.com
**Control**: County, Government, Nonfederal **Service**: General medical and surgical

| Staffed Beds: 50 Admissions: 156 Census: 30 Outpatient Visits: 7406 |
|---|
| Births: 0 Total Expense ($000): 12666 Payroll Expense ($000): 6653 |
| Personnel: 135 |

**SHERIDAN COUNTY HOSPITAL** See Sheridan County Health Complex

## HUGOTON—Stevens County

**STEVENS COUNTY HOSPITAL (171335)**, 1006 South Jackson Street,
Zip 67951–2858, Mailing Address: P.O. Box 10, Zip 67951–0010;
tel. 620/544–8511, (Total facility includes 77 beds in nursing home–type unit)
(Nonreporting) **A**10 18 **F**3 11 15 28 29 30 40 46 50 57 59 66 67 68 71 81 93
107 119 125 127 128 130 132 133 135 143 146 147 149
Primary Contact: Linda Stalcup, Chief Executive Officer
CMO: Samer Al-hashmi, M.D., Chief Medical Staff
Web address: www.stevenscountyhospital.com/
**Control**: County, Government, Nonfederal **Service**: General medical and surgical

| Staffed Beds: 94 Admissions: 258 Census: 277 Outpatient Visits: 12793 |
|---|
| Births: 0 Total Expense ($000): 17760 Payroll Expense ($000): 8360 |
| Personnel: 162 |

## HUTCHINSON—Reno County

⊞ △ **HUTCHINSON REGIONAL MEDICAL CENTER (170020)**, 1701 East 23rd
Avenue, Zip 67502–1191; tel. 620/665–2000, (Nonreporting) **A**1 7 10 **F**3 7 11
13 18 20 22 24 26 28 29 30 31 34 35 40 43 45 47 48 49 50 51 53 57 60 64
68 70 74 76 77 78 79 81 82 83 85 87 89 90 93 98 102 106 107 108 111 114
115 119 120 121 123 126 128 129 130 143 146 148 154 156
Primary Contact: Ken Johnson, President and Chief Executive Officer
CFO: Cassie Dolen, Vice President Finance and Chief Financial Officer
CMO: Thomas Smith, M.D., Vice President Medical Affairs
CIO: Calvin Wright, Chief Information Officer
CHR: Kevin Chiles, Vice President Human Resources
CNO: Julie R. Ward, MSN, R.N., Vice President Patient Care Services
Web address: www.hutchregional.com
**Control**: Other not–for–profit (including NFP Corporation) **Service**: General
medical and surgical

| Staffed Beds: 146 Admissions: 5580 Census: 58 Outpatient |
|---|
| Visits: 119249 Births: 499 Total Expense ($000): 138974 Payroll Expense |
| ($000): 48386 Personnel: 886 |

*Many Facility Codes have changed. Please refer to the AHA Guide Code Chart.* © 2021 AHA Guide

**PROMISE REGIONAL MEDICAL CENTER-HUTCHINSON** See Hutchinson Regional Medical Center

**SUMMIT SURGICAL (170198)**, 1818 East 23rd Avenue, Zip 67502–1106; tel. 620/663–4800, (Nonreporting) **A**10
Primary Contact: Ann Hentzen Page, M.D., Chief Executive Officer
COO: Nancy Corwin, Chief Operating Officer
CMO: Ann Hentzen Page, M.D., Medical Director
CNO: Nancy Corwin, Chief Nursing Officer
Web address: www.summitks.com
**Control:** Partnership, Investor–owned (for–profit) **Service:** Surgical

| Staffed Beds: 10 |
| --- |

**SUMMIT SURGICAL, LLC** See Summit Surgical

### IOLA—Allen County

**ALLEN COUNTY HOSPITAL** See Allen County Regional Hospital

**ALLEN COUNTY REGIONAL HOSPITAL (171373)**, 3066 N. Kentucky St, Zip 66749, Mailing Address: P.O. Box 540, Zip 66749–0540; tel. 620/365–1000, (Nonreporting) **A**1 10 18 **F**3 11 13 29 30 31 34 35 40 43 45 57 59 62 63 64 65 75 76 77 78 79 81 82 84 85 86 89 92 103 104 107 115 119 127 129 130 133 146 148 149
Primary Contact: Elmore Patterson, Administrator
CFO: Larry Peterson, Chief Financial Officer
CMO: Brian Wolfe, Chief of Staff
CHR: Paula Sell, Director Human Resources
CNO: Patty McGuffin, Chief Nursing Officer
Web address: www.allencountyhospital.com
**Control:** County, Government, Nonfederal **Service:** General medical and surgical

| Staffed Beds: 25 Admissions: 541 Census: 6 Outpatient Visits: 19202 Births: 49 Total Expense ($000): 23750 Payroll Expense ($000): 7941 Personnel: 153 |
| --- |

### JETMORE—Hodgeman County

★ **HODGEMAN COUNTY HEALTH CENTER (171369)**, 809 Bramley Street, Zip 67854–9320, Mailing Address: P.O. Box 310, Zip 67854–0310; tel. 620/357–8361, (Total facility includes 17 beds in nursing home–type unit) (Nonreporting) **A**10 18 **F**3 29 32 33 40 50 53 55 59 64 67 68 81 82 93 97 107 115 125 127 130 133 143 147 148 149 **P**6
Primary Contact: Phil Ginder, Chief Executive Officer
Web address: www.hchconline.org
**Control:** County, Government, Nonfederal **Service:** General medical and surgical

| Staffed Beds: 25 Admissions: 226 Census: 22 Outpatient Visits: 4349 Births: 0 Personnel: 74 |
| --- |

### JOHNSON—Stanton County

**STANTON COUNTY HEALTH CARE FACILITY** See Stanton County Hospital

**STANTON COUNTY HOSPITAL (171343)**, 404 North Chestnut Street, Zip 67855–5001, Mailing Address: P.O. Box 779, Zip 67855–0779; tel. 620/492–6250, (Total facility includes 25 beds in nursing home–type unit) (Nonreporting) **A**10 18 **F**11 13 34 35 40 41 45 50 54 56 57 59 64 68 75 76 81 82 86 87 93 97 107 114 127 130 131 133 143 154
Primary Contact: Jay Tusten, Chief Executive Officer
CMO: Bill Troup, M.D., Chief of Staff
CIO: Marco Medina, Chief Information Officer
CHR: Camille Davidson, Director Human Resources
CNO: Marianne Mills, R.N., Chairperson
Web address: www.stantoncountyhospital.com
**Control:** County, Government, Nonfederal **Service:** General medical and surgical

| Staffed Beds: 40 Admissions: 63 Census: 24 Outpatient Visits: 12434 Births: 15 Total Expense ($000): 9997 Payroll Expense ($000): 4046 Personnel: 87 |
| --- |

### JUNCTION CITY—Geary County

✠ **GEARY COMMUNITY HOSPITAL (170074)**, 1102 St Mary's Road, Zip 66441–4196, Mailing Address: P.O. Box 490, Zip 66441–0490; tel. 785/238–4131, (Nonreporting) **A**1 10 **F**3 8 11 12 13 15 29 30 32 34 35 40 45 50 57 59 64 65 70 75 76 77 79 81 85 86 87 97 107 108 109 110 111 113 115 117 118 119 127 129 130 131 132 133 144 146 148 149 154 156
Primary Contact: Frank Corcoran, R.N., Chief Executive Officer
CFO: Emily Emery Shea, Interim Chief Financial Officer
CMO: Jimmy Jenkins, M.D., Chief Medical Officer
CIO: Kyle Ibarra, Director Information Systems
CHR: Loren Streit, Director Human Resources
Web address: www.https://gearycommunityhospital.org
**Control:** County, Government, Nonfederal **Service:** General medical and surgical

| Staffed Beds: 49 Admissions: 791 Census: 6 Outpatient Visits: 41387 Births: 213 Total Expense ($000): 37451 Payroll Expense ($000): 15143 Personnel: 242 |
| --- |

✠ **IRWIN ARMY COMMUNITY HOSPITAL**, 600 Caisson Hill Road, Zip 66442–7037; tel. 785/239–7000, (Nonreporting) **A**1 3 5 **S** Department of the Army, Office of the Surgeon General, Falls Church, VA
Primary Contact: Colonel Risa Ware, Commander
CMO: Lieutenant ColonelMark S Ochoa, M.D., Deputy Commander, Clinical Services
CIO: David Dougherty, Chief Information Management Officer
CHR: Hope Brunton, Chief Manpower Branch
Web address: www.iach.amedd.army.mil
**Service:** General medical and surgical

| Staffed Beds: 44 |
| --- |

### KANSAS CITY—Wyandotte County

☐ **KVC PRAIRIE RIDGE PSYCHIATRIC HOSPITAL**, 4300 Brenner Drive, Zip 66104–1163; tel. 913/334–0294, (Nonreporting) **A**1 5
Primary Contact: Jason R. Hooper, President and Chief Executive Officer
CMO: Vishal Adma, M.D., Medical Director
Web address: www.kvc.org
**Control:** Other not–for–profit (including NFP Corporation) **Service:** Children's hospital psychiatric

| Staffed Beds: 109 |
| --- |

**KVC PSYCHIATRIC HOSPITAL** See Kvc Prairie Ridge Psychiatric Hospital

☐ **PROVIDENCE MEDICAL CENTER (170146)**, 8929 Parallel Parkway, Zip 66112–1689; tel. 913/596–4000, (Total facility includes 45 beds in nursing home–type unit) (Nonreporting) **A**1 10 **F**3 13 15 17 18 20 22 24 28 29 30 31 34 35 40 41 43 44 45 49 53 56 57 59 64 70 72 74 75 76 77 78 79 81 82 84 85 87 93 97 102 103 107 108 110 111 114 119 120 121 123 124 126 128 129 130 131 132 135 143 146 147 148 149 156 **P**6 **S** Prime Healthcare, Ontario, CA
Primary Contact: Karen Orr, Administrator and Chief Nursing Officer
CFO: David Dulny, Chief Financial Officer
CMO: Sabato Sisillo, M.D., Chief Medical Officer
CIO: Charles Soeken, Director Information Technology
CHR: Brenda Farwell, Director Human Resources
CNO: Karen Orr, Chief Nursing Officer
Web address: www.providencekc.com
**Control:** Individual, Investor–owned (for–profit) **Service:** General medical and surgical

| Staffed Beds: 221 Admissions: 8477 Census: 121 Outpatient Visits: 192276 Births: 376 Total Expense ($000): 145033 Payroll Expense ($000): 60004 Personnel: 787 |
| --- |

**PROVIDENCE-ST MARGARET CENTER** See Providence Medical Center

**SELECT SPECIALTY HOSP - KANSAS** See Select Specialty Hospital-Kansas City, Kansas City

**SELECT SPECIALTY HOSPITAL-KANSAS CITY A**1 10
Web address: www.selectspecialtyhospitals.com

✠ **SELECT SPECIALTY HOSPITAL-KANSAS CITY (172005)**, 1731 North 90th Street, Zip 66112–1515; tel. 913/732–5900, (Nonreporting) **A**1 10 **S** Select Medical Corporation, Mechanicsburg, PA
Primary Contact: Bridgette Hunter, Chief Executive Officer
Web address: www.selectspecialtyhospitals.com
**Control:** Corporation, Investor–owned (for–profit) **Service:** Acute long–term care hospital

| Staffed Beds: 40 |
| --- |

**Hospital, Medicare Provider Number, Address, Telephone, Approval, Facility, and Physician Codes, Health Care System**

★ American Hospital Association (AHA) membership  ○ Healthcare Facilities Accreditation Program  ⇑ Center for Improvement in Healthcare Quality Accreditation
☐ The Joint Commission accreditation  ◇ DNV Healthcare Inc. accreditation  △ Commission on Accreditation of Rehabilitation Facilities (CARF) accreditation

**KS**

© 2021 AHA Guide    *Many Facility Codes have changed. Please refer to the AHA Guide Code Chart.*    Hospitals **A267**

**THE UNIVERSITY OF KANSAS HEALTH SYSTEM** See The University of Kansas Hospital

✠ **THE UNIVERSITY OF KANSAS HOSPITAL (170040)**, 4000 Cambridge Street, MS 3011, Zip 66160–8501; tel. 913/588–5000, (Includes THE UNIVERSITY OF KANSAS HOSPITAL - INDIAN CREEK CAMPUS, Mailing address: 10720 Nall Avenue, Overland Park, Kansas, Zip 66211–1206; tel. 913/754–5000), (Nonreporting) **A**1 2 3 5 8 10 **F**3 5 8 9 11 12 13 15 16 17 18 20 22 24 26 28 29 30 31 32 34 35 36 37 38 39 40 41 43 44 45 46 47 48 49 50 51 52 54 55 56 57 58 59 60 61 64 65 68 70 72 74 75 76 77 78 79 80 81 82 83 84 85 86 87 88 89 90 92 93 96 97 98 99 100 101 102 103 104 105 107 108 110 111 112 114 115 116 117 118 119 120 121 123 124 126 129 130 131 132 135 136 137 138 139 141 142 144 145 146 147 148 149 154 156 157 **P**6 **S** The University of Kansas Health System, Kansas City, KS
Primary Contact: Bob Page, Chief Executive Officer
COO: Tammy Peterman, R.N., MS, Executive Vice President, Chief Operating Officer and Chief Nursing Officer
CFO: Bill Marting, Senior Vice President and Chief Financial Officer
CMO: Lou Wetzel, M.D., Chief of Staff
CIO: Chris Hansen, Senior Vice President and Chief Information Officer
CHR: Alisa Ford, Vice President Human Resources
CNO: Tammy Peterman, R.N., MS, Executive Vice President, Chief Operating Officer and Chief Nursing Officer
Web address: www.kumed.com
**Control**: Hospital district or authority, Government, Nonfederal **Service**: General medical and surgical

**Staffed Beds**: 916 **Admissions**: 43470 **Census**: 672 **Outpatient Visits**: 1692116 **Births**: 2358 **Total Expense ($000)**: 2422298 **Payroll Expense ($000)**: 1063413 **Personnel**: 11715

### KINGMAN—Kingman County

★ **KINGMAN COMMUNITY HOSPITAL (171378)**, 750 Avenue D West, Zip 67068–0376; tel. 620/532–3147, (Nonreporting) **A**10 18 **F**3 11 15 17 18 28 29 31 34 35 40 45 50 54 56 57 59 64 70 75 77 78 81 86 87 89 90 93 97 107 114 119 127 128 129 130 132 133 145 146 148 154 156 **P**6
Primary Contact: Shannan Flach, Chief Executive Officer
CFO: Kent Hudson, Chief Financial Officer
CIO: Jay Gehring, Director Information Systems
CHR: Nancy Stucky, Director Human Resources and Public Relations
CNO: Nita McFarland, Director of Nursing
Web address: www.kchks.com
**Control**: Other not–for–profit (including NFP Corporation) **Service**: General medical and surgical

**Staffed Beds**: 25 **Admissions**: 401 **Census**: 5 **Outpatient Visits**: 20515 **Births**: 0 **Total Expense ($000)**: 11279 **Payroll Expense ($000)**: 5920 **Personnel**: 103

**NINNESCAH VALLEY HEALTH SYSTEM** See Kingman Community Hospital

### KINSLEY—Edwards County

**EDWARDS COUNTY HOSPITAL AND HEALTHCARE CENTER** See Edwards County Medical Center

**EDWARDS COUNTY MEDICAL CENTER (171317)**, 620 West Eighth Street, Zip 67547–2329, Mailing Address: P.O. Box 99, Zip 67547–0099; tel. 620/659–3621, (Nonreporting) **A**10 18
Primary Contact: Jimmie W. Hansel, Ph.D., Chief Executive Officer
CHR: Tammy K Lampe, Director Human Resources
Web address: www.edwardscohospital.com
**Control**: County, Government, Nonfederal **Service**: General medical and surgical

**Staffed Beds**: 22

### KIOWA—Barber County

★ **KIOWA DISTRICT HEALTHCARE (171331)**, 1002 South Fourth Street, Zip 67070–1825, Mailing Address: P.O. Box 184, Zip 67070–0184; tel. 620/825–4131, (Total facility includes 28 beds in nursing home–type unit) (Nonreporting) **A**10 18 **F**2 3 12 34 40 41 45 55 56 57 59 64 65 67 69 81 84 85 87 91 92 93 97 107 114 119 127 128 133 148 150 154 **P**6
Primary Contact: Janell Goodno, Chief Executive Officer
CFO: Robin Lewis, Chief Financial Officer
CMO: Paul Wilhelm, M.D., Chief of Staff
CHR: Tara Girty, Director Human Resources
Web address: www.k-d-h.com
**Control**: Hospital district or authority, Government, Nonfederal **Service**: General medical and surgical

**Staffed Beds**: 39 **Admissions**: 355 **Census**: 24 **Outpatient Visits**: 6618 **Births**: 0 **Total Expense ($000)**: 7680 **Payroll Expense ($000)**: 3065 **Personnel**: 75

**KIOWA DISTRICT HOSPITAL AND MANOR** See Kiowa District Healthcare

### LA CROSSE—Rush County

**RUSH COUNTY HEALTHCARE CENTER** See Rush County Memorial Hospital

★ **RUSH COUNTY MEMORIAL HOSPITAL (171342)**, 801 Locust Street, Zip 67548–9673, Mailing Address: P.O. Box 520, Zip 67548–0520; tel. 785/222–2545, (Total facility includes 18 beds in nursing home–type unit) (Nonreporting) **A**10 18 **F**3 34 40 45 53 59 64 67 77 81 82 93 97 107 115 119 127 128 133 148
Primary Contact: Michael Cooper, Chief Executive Officer
CMO: Robert Ladd, M.D., Medical Director
CHR: Brenda Legleiter, Director Quality and Human Resources
Web address: www.rushcountymemorialhospital.com
**Control**: County, Government, Nonfederal **Service**: General medical and surgical

**Staffed Beds**: 25 **Admissions**: 232 **Census**: 19 **Outpatient Visits**: 17187 **Births**: 0 **Total Expense ($000)**: 6097 **Payroll Expense ($000)**: 2863 **Personnel**: 73

### LAKIN—Kearny County

★ **KEARNY COUNTY HOSPITAL (171313)**, 500 Thorpe Street, Zip 67860–9625; tel. 620/355–7111, (Total facility includes 75 beds in nursing home–type unit) (Nonreporting) **A**3 10 18 **F**2 3 6 10 13 28 29 34 35 40 45 50 56 57 58 59 64 67 68 69 75 76 79 81 82 85 86 87 89 93 97 107 110 111 114 119 125 127 128 130 131 132 133 143 149 156 **P**6
Primary Contact: David Hofmeister, Chief Executive Officer
COO: Shari Campbell, Chief Operating Officer
CFO: Kelly Ann Speckman, Chief Financial Officer
CMO: Arlo Reimer, M.D., Chief of Staff
CIO: Lisa Kay-Garcia, Chief Information Officer
CHR: Laci Williams, Director Human Resources
CNO: Susan D Stingley, Chief Nursing Officer
Web address: www.kearnycountyhospital.com
**Control**: County, Government, Nonfederal **Service**: General medical and surgical

**Staffed Beds**: 100 **Admissions**: 503 **Census**: 72 **Outpatient Visits**: 48131 **Births**: 261 **Total Expense ($000)**: 26541 **Payroll Expense ($000)**: 13643 **Personnel**: 241

### LARNED—Pawnee County

☐ **LARNED STATE HOSPITAL (174006)**, 1301 Kansas Highway 264, Zip 67550; tel. 620/285–2131, (Nonreporting) **A**1 10 **F**3 29 30 38 50 53 57 75 86 87 97 98 100 101 102 103 130 132 135 143 149 154 156 **P**6
Primary Contact: Thomas Kinlen, Superintendent
COO: Steve Spain, Chief Operating Officer
CMO: Sayed Jehan, M.D., Interim Medical Director
CIO: Sid Smith, Director Information Resources
CHR: Kerri Barnard, Director Human Resources
CNO: Holly Hertel, Director Nursing
Web address: www.larnedstatehospital.org
**Control**: State, Government, Nonfederal **Service**: Psychiatric

**Staffed Beds**: 506 **Admissions**: 1420 **Census**: 465 **Outpatient Visits**: 0 **Births**: 0 **Total Expense ($000)**: 66677 **Payroll Expense ($000)**: 32957 **Personnel**: 592

**PAWNEE VALLEY COMMUNITY HOSPITAL** See University of Kansas Health System Pawnee Valley Campus

★ **UNIVERSITY OF KANSAS HEALTH SYSTEM PAWNEE VALLEY CAMPUS (171345)**, 923 Carroll Avenue, Zip 67550–2429; tel. 620/285–3161, (Nonreporting) **A**10 18 **F**3 11 15 28 29 30 34 40 43 45 46 57 68 77 81 82 84 85 86 87 91 93 94 102 107 111 115 127 129 130 131 132 133 135 147 148 149 156 **P**6 **S** The University of Kansas Health System, Kansas City, KS
Primary Contact: Melanie D. Urban, Administrator
COO: Bryce A Young, Chief Operating Officer
CFO: George Harms, Chief Financial Officer
CMO: David Sanger, M.D., Chief Medical Officer
CHR: Bruce Whittington, Vice President Human Resources
Web address: www.pawneevalleyhospital.com
**Control**: County, Government, Nonfederal **Service**: General medical and surgical

**Staffed Beds**: 22 **Admissions**: 176 **Census**: 5 **Outpatient Visits**: 50927 **Births**: 0 **Total Expense ($000)**: 15495 **Payroll Expense ($000)**: 7093 **Personnel**: 132

*Many Facility Codes have changed. Please refer to the AHA Guide Code Chart.*

© 2021 AHA Guide

**KS**

## LAWRENCE—Douglas County

**LAWRENCE MEMORIAL HOSPITAL** See Lmh Health

✠ **LMH HEALTH (170137)**, 325 Maine Street, Zip 66044–1360; tel. 785/505–5000, (Total facility includes 17 beds in nursing home–type unit) (Nonreporting) **A**1 3 5 10 20 **F**3 11 13 15 18 19 20 22 26 28 29 30 31 34 35 38 39 40 43 44 45 49 50 51 54 55 56 57 59 61 64 65 67 69 70 73 74 75 76 77 78 79 81 82 84 85 86 87 89 90 93 94 96 97 100 102 107 110 111 114 115 118 119 120 124 126 128 130 131 132 135 145 146 147 148 154 156 **P**6 7
Primary Contact: Russell W. Johnson, President and Chief Executive Officer
CFO: Joe Pedley, CPA, Vice President and Chief Financial Officer
CIO: Michael Williams, Chief Information Officer
CHR: Colleen Browne, Vice President and Chief People Officer
CNO: Traci Hoopingarner, R.N., Chief Nursing Officer
Web address: www.lmh.org
**Control**: Other not–for–profit (including NFP Corporation) **Service**: General medical and surgical

**Staffed Beds**: 142 **Admissions**: 6727 **Census**: 66 **Outpatient Visits**: 253668 **Births**: 992 **Total Expense ($000)**: 299464 **Payroll Expense ($000)**: 120279 **Personnel**: 1601

## LEAVENWORTH—Leavenworth County

**CUSHING MEMORIAL HOSPITAL** See Saint Luke's Cushing Hospital

**DWIGHT D. EISENHOWER VETERANS AFFAIRS MEDICAL CENTER** See Veterans Affairs Eastern Kansas Health Care System-Dwight D. Eisenhower Veterans Affairs Medical Center

☐ **SAINT JOHN HOSPITAL (170009)**, 3500 South Fourth Street, Zip 66048–5043; tel. 913/680–6000, (Nonreporting) **A**1 10 **F**3 15 18 29 30 34 35 40 44 45 46 50 54 56 57 59 64 68 70 74 75 77 79 82 85 87 93 97 98 100 102 103 107 114 115 119 130 133 146 148 149 154 **P**6 **S** Prime Healthcare, Ontario, CA
Primary Contact: Paula Ellis, Administrator
CFO: David Dulny, Chief Financial Officer
CMO: Sabato Sisillo, M.D., Chief Medical Officer
CIO: Charles Soeken, Director Information Technology
CHR: Brenda Farwell, Director Human Resources
CNO: Jodi Fincher, R.N., Vice President Patient Care Services
Web address: www.providence-health.org/sjh
**Control**: Individual, Investor–owned (for–profit) **Service**: General medical and surgical

**Staffed Beds**: 58 **Admissions**: 1697 **Census**: 30 **Outpatient Visits**: 23897 **Births**: 0 **Total Expense ($000)**: 27942 **Payroll Expense ($000)**: 12666 **Personnel**: 161

✠ **SAINT LUKE'S CUSHING HOSPITAL (170133)**, 711 Marshall Street, Zip 66048–3235; tel. 913/684–1100, (Nonreporting) **A**1 10 **F**3 11 15 28 29 30 34 40 44 50 59 68 81 87 93 94 100 102 107 110 115 119 130 146 154 **S** Saint Luke's Health System, Kansas City, MO
Primary Contact: Adele Ducharme, MSN, R.N., Chief Executive Officer
CFO: Jackie Martin, Chief Financial Officer
CMO: Nicholas Brockert, President
CHR: Donna Kunz, System Director Human Resources
CNO: Karin Sundblom, MSN, R.N., Chief Nursing Officer
Web address: www.https://www.saintlukeskc.org/locations/saint-lukes-cushing-hospital
**Control**: Other not–for–profit (including NFP Corporation) **Service**: General medical and surgical

**Staffed Beds**: 8 **Admissions**: 746 **Census**: 5 **Outpatient Visits**: 37753 **Births**: 73 **Total Expense ($000)**: 43417 **Payroll Expense ($000)**: 12917 **Personnel**: 127

**ST JOHN HOSPITAL** See Saint John Hospital

**VETERANS AFFAIRS EASTERN KANSAS HEALTH CARE SYSTEM-DWIGHT D. EISENHOWER VETERANS AFFAIRS MEDICAL CENTER** See Veterans Affairs Eastern Kansas Health Care System, Topeka

## LEAWOOD—Johnson County

☐ **DOCTOR'S HOSPITAL (170194)**, 4901 College Boulevard, Zip 66211–1602; tel. 913/529–1801, (Nonreporting) **A**1 10
Primary Contact: Phil Harness, Chief Executive Officer
Web address: www.dshospital.net
**Control**: Partnership, Investor–owned (for–profit) **Service**: General medical and surgical

**Staffed Beds**: 9

○ **KANSAS CITY ORTHOPAEDIC INSTITUTE (170188)**, 3651 College Boulevard, Zip 66211–1910; tel. 913/338–4100, (Nonreporting) **A**3 5 10 11 **F**29 77 79 81 82 93 111 **P**5
Primary Contact: Charles E. Rhoades, M.D., Chief Executive Officer
CIO: Jim Leveling, Director Information Technology
CHR: Laura Sinclair, Director Human Resources
Web address: www.kcoi.com
**Control**: Partnership, Investor–owned (for–profit) **Service**: Orthopedic

**Staffed Beds**: 17 **Admissions**: 1123 **Census**: 6 **Outpatient Visits**: 40810 **Births**: 0 **Personnel**: 216

## LENEXA—Johnson County

**MINIMALLY INVASIVE SURGERY CENTER** See Minimally Invasive Surgery Hospital

☐ **MINIMALLY INVASIVE SURGERY HOSPITAL (170199)**, 11217 Lakeview Avenue, Zip 66219–1399; tel. 913/322–7401, (Nonreporting) **A**1 10
Primary Contact: Parajeet Sabharrwal, Chief Executive Officer
Web address: www.mishhospital.com
**Control**: Corporation, Investor–owned (for–profit) **Service**: Surgical

**Staffed Beds**: 9

## LEOTI—Wichita County

★ **WICHITA COUNTY HEALTH CENTER (171306)**, 211 East Earl Street, Zip 67861–9620; tel. 620/375–2233, (Nonreporting) **A**10 18 **S** Great Plains Health Alliance, Inc., Wichita, KS
Primary Contact: Teresa Clark, Chief Executive Officer and Administrator
CFO: Janice Campas, Chief Financial Officer
CMO: Jeffrey Alpert, M.D., Medical Director
CHR: Patti Whalen, Manager Human Resources
Web address: www.wichitacountyhealthcenter.com
**Control**: County, Government, Nonfederal **Service**: General medical and surgical

**Staffed Beds**: 42

**WICHITA COUNTY HOSPITAL** See Wichita County Health Center

## LIBERAL—Seward County

☐ **SOUTHWEST MEDICAL CENTER (170068)**, 315 West 15th Street, Zip 67901–2455, Mailing Address: Box 1340, Zip 67905–1340; tel. 620/624–1651, (Total facility includes 18 beds in nursing home–type unit) (Nonreporting) **A**1 10 **F**3 11 13 15 28 29 31 34 40 45 48 49 57 59 68 70 73 75 76 77 79 81 85 87 89 93 96 98 103 107 108 110 111 114 118 119 128 129 130 131 145 146 147 148 149 154 157
Primary Contact: Robert Whitaker, President and Chief Executive Officer
CHR: Lisa L Mathes, Human Resources Director
CNO: Jo L Harrison, Vice President of Patient Care Services
Web address: www.swmedcenter.com
**Control**: County, Government, Nonfederal **Service**: General medical and surgical

**Staffed Beds**: 101 **Admissions**: 2750 **Census**: 24 **Outpatient Visits**: 60454 **Births**: 909 **Total Expense ($000)**: 66117 **Payroll Expense ($000)**: 28229 **Personnel**: 434

## LINCOLN—Lincoln County

**LINCOLN COUNTY HOSPITAL (171360)**, 624 North Second Street, Zip 67455–1738, Mailing Address: P.O. Box 406, Zip 67455–0406; tel. 785/524–4403, (Nonreporting) **A**10 18 **F**3 11 15 40 68 69 77 93 107 110 111 115 119 127 129 133 154 **P**6
Primary Contact: Tawnya Seitz, Acting Chief Executive Officer
CFO: Tawnya Seitz, Chief Financial Officer
CNO: Christa Haesemeyer, Chief Nursing Officer
Web address: www.lincolncountyhospital.net
**Control**: County, Government, Nonfederal **Service**: General medical and surgical

**Staffed Beds**: 14 **Admissions**: 96 **Census**: 1 **Outpatient Visits**: 4380 **Births**: 0 **Total Expense ($000)**: 8677 **Payroll Expense ($000)**: 3535 **Personnel**: 54

**LINDSBORG—Mcpherson County**

★ **LINDSBORG COMMUNITY HOSPITAL (171358)**, 605 West Lincoln Street,
Zip 67456–2328; tel. 785/227–3308, (Nonreporting) **A**10 18 **F**3 11 12 28 29
36 40 45 46 53 59 64 65 67 81 87 93 97 107 115 119 128 130 133 144 148
154 **S** Salina Regional Health Center, Salina, KS
Primary Contact: Larry VanDerWege, Administrator
CFO: Laraine Gengler, Chief Financial Officer
CIO: Jeremy Snapp, Director Information Systems
CHR: Brad Malm, Director Human Resources and Education
CNO: Beth Hedberg, R.N., Director Nursing
Web address: www.lindsborghospital.org
**Control**: Other not–for–profit (including NFP Corporation) **Service**: General
medical and surgical

> **Staffed Beds**: 12 **Admissions**: 186 **Census**: 4 **Outpatient Visits**: 23190
> **Births**: 0 **Total Expense ($000)**: 12648 **Payroll Expense ($000)**: 5704
> **Personnel**: 99

**LYONS—Rice County**

★ **HOSPITAL DISTRICT NO 1 OF RICE COUNTY (171330)**, 619 South Clark
Street, Zip 67554–3003, Mailing Address: P.O. Box 828, Zip 67554–0828;
tel. 620/257–5173, (Nonreporting) **A**10 18 **F**3 13 28 29 34 40 43 45 59 65 75
77 81 93 107 125 127 133 154
Primary Contact: George M. Stover, Chief Executive Officer
CFO: Terry Pound, Chief Financial Officer
CMO: Kristina Darnauer, M.D., Chief of Staff
CNO: Judy Hogdson, R.N., Chief Nursing Officer
Web address: www.ricecountyhospital.com
**Control**: Hospital district or authority, Government, Nonfederal **Service**: General
medical and surgical

> **Staffed Beds**: 25 **Admissions**: 378 **Census**: 13 **Outpatient Visits**: 42125
> **Births**: 90 **Total Expense ($000)**: 14951 **Payroll Expense ($000)**: 7383
> **Personnel**: 116

**HOSPITAL DISTRICT ONE OF RICE COUNTY** See Hospital District No 1 of Rice
County

**MANHATTAN—Riley County**

**ASCENSION VIA CHRISTI HOSPITAL** See Ascension Via Christi Hospital,
Manhattan

⊠ **ASCENSION VIA CHRISTI HOSPITAL, MANHATTAN (170142)**, 1823 College
Avenue, Zip 66502–3346; tel. 785/776–3322, (Nonreporting) **A**1 10 19 **F**3 11
12 13 15 18 22 28 29 30 31 34 35 37 40 41 44 45 49 50 51 60 67 76 77
79 81 82 83 84 85 86 87 89 90 92 94 95 96 102 104 107 108 109 110 111
115 119 126 129 130 132 133 145 146 147 148 149 154 **P**7 **S** Ascension
Healthcare, Saint Louis, MO
Primary Contact: Robert C. Copple, FACHE, Senior Administrator
CFO: James Fraser, Administrator Finance
CIO: Andy Gagnon, Manager Information Technology
CHR: Renee Reed, Director Human Resources
CNO: Jennifer Goehring, R.N., Assistant Chief Nursing Officer
Web address: www.https://www.viachristi.org/manhattan
**Control**: Other not–for–profit (including NFP Corporation) **Service**: General
medical and surgical

> **Staffed Beds**: 88 **Admissions**: 4070 **Census**: 39 **Outpatient Visits**: 103062
> **Births**: 1026 **Total Expense ($000)**: 86382 **Payroll Expense ($000)**: 26377
> **Personnel**: 365

**MANHATTAN SURGICAL (170190)**, 1829 College Avenue, Zip 66502–3381;
tel. 785/776–5100, (Nonreporting) **A**10
Primary Contact: Christopher R. Stipe, FACHE, Chief Executive Officer
Web address: www.manhattansurgical.com
**Control**: Corporation, Investor–owned (for–profit) **Service**: Surgical

> **Staffed Beds**: 13

**MANHATTAN SURGICAL CENTER** See Manhattan Surgical

**MANKATO—Jewell County**

**JEWELL COUNTY HOSPITAL (171309)**, 100 Crestvue Avenue,
Zip 66956–2407, Mailing Address: P.O. Box 327, Zip 66956–0327;
tel. 785/378–3137, (Nonreporting) **A**10 18 **F**2 3 29 40 50 64 75 77 87 93 107
127 128 130 133 148 156
Primary Contact: Doyle L. McKimmy, FACHE, Chief Executive Officer
COO: Eric Borden, Chief Operating Officer and Chief Financial Officer
CFO: Eric Borden, Chief Operating Officer and Chief Financial Officer
Web address: www.https://www.jewellcohospital.org/
**Control**: County, Government, Nonfederal **Service**: General medical and surgical

> **Staffed Beds**: 25 **Admissions**: 73 **Census**: 18 **Outpatient Visits**: 15540
> **Births**: 0 **Total Expense ($000)**: 5819 **Payroll Expense ($000)**: 3008
> **Personnel**: 59

**MARION—Marion County**

**ST LUKE HOSPITAL** See St. Luke Hospital and Living Center

**ST. LUKE HOSPITAL AND LIVING CENTER (171356)**, 535 South Freeborn,
Zip 66861–1256; tel. 620/382–2177, (Nonreporting) **A**10 18
Primary Contact: Jeremy Ensey, Chief Executive Officer
CFO: Bev Reid, Chief Financial Officer
CMO: Don Hodson, M.D., Chief Medical Officer
CIO: Jeff Methvin, Manager Information Technology
CHR: Sharon Zogelman, Director Human Resources
Web address: www.slhmarion.org
**Control**: Hospital district or authority, Government, Nonfederal **Service**: General
medical and surgical

> **Staffed Beds**: 39

**MARYSVILLE—Marshall County**

★ **COMMUNITY MEMORIAL HEALTHCARE (171363)**, 708 North 18th Street,
Zip 66508–1338; tel. 785/562–2311, (Nonreporting) **A**10 18 **F**3 13 15 28 29 34
35 40 45 47 50 57 59 62 64 69 75 76 81 87 97 107 108 111 114 119 127
128 129 130 131 132 133 135 146
Primary Contact: Curtis R. Hawkinson, Chief Executive Officer
CFO: Daniel Fehr, Chief Financial Officer
CMO: Shane Thoreson, M.D., Chief Medical Officer
CIO: Scott Keller, Director Information Technology
CHR: Jessie Schneider, Director Human Resources
CNO: Diane Luebcke, R.N., Director Nursing
Web address: www.cmhcare.org
**Control**: Other not–for–profit (including NFP Corporation) **Service**: General
medical and surgical

> **Staffed Beds**: 25 **Admissions**: 691 **Census**: 10 **Outpatient Visits**: 28708
> **Births**: 47 **Total Expense ($000)**: 22483 **Payroll Expense ($000)**: 10025
> **Personnel**: 183

**COMMUNITY MEMORIAL HOSPITAL** See Community Memorial Healthcare

**MCPHERSON—McPherson County**

★ **MCPHERSON HOSPITAL (170105)**, 1000 Hospital Drive, Zip 67460–2326;
tel. 620/241–2250, (Nonreporting) **A**10 **F**3 7 11 13 15 28 29 34 35 40 45 50
53 54 59 64 65 70 75 76 77 81 82 85 86 87 97 107 110 114 119 130 133
144 146 147 148 154 156 **P**6
Primary Contact: Terri Gehring, President and Chief Executive Officer
COO: Terri Gehring, Vice President Operations
CFO: George Halama, Vice President Finance
CHR: Cathy Dunham, Vice President Human Resources
CNO: Beth Worden, Director Nursing Services
Web address: www.mcphersonhospital.org
**Control**: Other not–for–profit (including NFP Corporation) **Service**: General
medical and surgical

> **Staffed Beds**: 33 **Admissions**: 772 **Census**: 7 **Outpatient Visits**: 67887
> **Births**: 98 **Total Expense ($000)**: 32240 **Payroll Expense ($000)**: 14699
> **Personnel**: 260

**MEMORIAL HOSPITAL** See Mcpherson Hospital

KS

*Many Facility Codes have changed. Please refer to the AHA Guide Code Chart.*
© 2021 AHA Guide

## MEADE—Meade County

★ **MEADE DISTRICT HOSPITAL (171321)**, 510 East Carthage Street, Zip 67864-6401, Mailing Address: P.O. Box 820, Zip 67864-0820; tel. 620/873-2141, (Total facility includes 45 beds in nursing home–type unit) (Nonreporting) **A**10 18 **F**3 28 29 40 45 53 57 59 62 64 67 79 80 81 82 87 92 93 107 108 110 115 119 127 128 129 130 131 133 143 148 149
Primary Contact: Tara Ramlochan, Chief Executive Officer
CIO: Matt Bobo, Chief Information Officer
Web address: www.meadehospital.com
**Control:** Hospital district or authority, Government, Nonfederal **Service:** General medical and surgical

| | |
|---|---|
| **Staffed Beds:** 65 **Admissions:** 234 **Census:** 36 **Outpatient Visits:** 11281 **Births:** 0 **Total Expense ($000):** 14071 **Payroll Expense ($000):** 7596 **Personnel:** 107 | |

## MEDICINE LODGE—Barber County

**MEDICINE LODGE MEMORIAL HOSPITAL (171334)**, 710 North Walnut Street, Zip 67104-1019; tel. 620/886-3771, (Nonreporting) **A**10 18 **F**3 7 11 40 44 45 56 64 81 93 107 119 127 128 133 148 154 156 **S** Great Plains Health Alliance, Inc., Wichita, KS
Primary Contact: Kevin A. White, Administrator
CFO: Thomas G Lee, Chief Financial Officer
CHR: Johnnie Davis, Director Human Resources
CNO: Kathryn I. Burns, R.N., Director of Nursing
Web address: www.mlmh.net/
**Control:** Hospital district or authority, Government, Nonfederal **Service:** General medical and surgical

| | |
|---|---|
| **Staffed Beds:** 25 **Admissions:** 229 **Census:** 18 **Outpatient Visits:** 16890 **Births:** 0 **Total Expense ($000):** 10795 **Payroll Expense ($000):** 4888 **Personnel:** 87 | |

## MINNEAPOLIS—Ottawa County

★ **OTTAWA COUNTY HEALTH CENTER (171328)**, 215 East Eighth, Zip 67467-1902, Mailing Address: P.O. Box 290, Zip 67467-0290; tel. 785/392-2122, (Total facility includes 5 beds in nursing home–type unit) (Nonreporting) **A**10 18 **F**28 29 34 35 40 53 56 64 67 85 86 93 107 114 128 130 133 143 154 156 **S** Great Plains Health Alliance, Inc., Wichita, KS
Primary Contact: Jody Parks, Administrator
CFO: Cheryl Lanoue, Chief Financial Officer
CIO: Linda Wright, Director Information
CNO: Marlene Gawith, Director of Nursing
Web address: www.ottawacountyhealthcenter.com
**Control:** Other not–for–profit (including NFP Corporation) **Service:** General medical and surgical

| | |
|---|---|
| **Staffed Beds:** 30 **Admissions:** 217 **Census:** 21 **Outpatient Visits:** 6285 **Births:** 0 **Total Expense ($000):** 6835 **Payroll Expense ($000):** 3105 **Personnel:** 75 | |

**OTTAWA COUNTY HOSPITAL** See Ottawa County Health Center

## MINNEOLA—Ford County

★ **MINNEOLA DISTRICT HOSPITAL (171368)**, 212 Main Street, Zip 67865-8511, Mailing Address: P.O. Box 127, Zip 67865-0127; tel. 620/885-4264, (Total facility includes 36 beds in nursing home–type unit) (Nonreporting) **A**10 18 **F**29 40 45 46 56 57 64 65 67 81 83 93 102 107 127 128 130 133 148 156 **S** Great Plains Health Alliance, Inc., Wichita, KS
Primary Contact: Deborah Bruner, Chief Executive Officer and Administrator
CFO: Marion Zirger, Chief Financial Officer
CMO: Tony Luna, M.D., Chief of Staff
CHR: Vena Harris, Director Human Resources
CNO: Amanda Stout, Chief Nursing Officer
Web address: www.minneolahealthcare.com
**Control:** Hospital district or authority, Government, Nonfederal **Service:** General medical and surgical

| | |
|---|---|
| **Staffed Beds:** 50 **Admissions:** 228 **Census:** 28 **Outpatient Visits:** 9394 **Births:** 0 **Total Expense ($000):** 14862 **Payroll Expense ($000):** 6573 **Personnel:** 98 | |

## MOUNDRIDGE—Mcpherson County

**MERCY HOSPITAL** See Mercy Hospital Inc.

★ **MERCY HOSPITAL INC. (170075)**, 218 East Pack Street, Zip 67107-8815, Mailing Address: P.O. Box 180, Zip 67107-0180; tel. 620/345-6391, (Nonreporting) **A**10 **F**29 30 34 35 40 45 50 59 67 77 81 86 87 89 92 93 128 130 133 146 149 154
Primary Contact: Aaron Herbel, Administrator
CFO: Trevor Wiebe, Business Office Manager, Information Technology
CNO: Lorie Friesen, Director of Nursing
Web address: www.https://www.mercyh.org
**Control:** Church operated, Nongovernment, not–for–profit **Service:** General medical and surgical

| | |
|---|---|
| **Staffed Beds:** 14 **Admissions:** 286 **Census:** 4 **Outpatient Visits:** 9165 **Births:** 0 **Total Expense ($000):** 3459 **Payroll Expense ($000):** 1635 **Personnel:** 40 | |

## MULVANE—Sedgwick County

**ASCENSION VIA CHRISTI HOSPITAL ST. FRANCIS** See Ascension Via Christi St. Francis

✠ **ASCENSION VIA CHRISTI ST. FRANCIS (170122)**, 211 N College Ave, Zip 67110, Mailing Address: 929 North St Francis Street, Wichita, Zip 67214-3882; tel. 316/268-5000, (Includes GOOD SHEPHERD CAMPUS, Mailing address: 8901 East Orme, Wichita, Kansas, Zip 67207; tel. 316/858-0333; Kevin Strecker, President; ST. FRANCIS CAMPUS, Mailing address: 929 North St Francis Street, Wichita, Kansas, Zip 67214-3882; tel. 316/268-5000; Kevin Strecker, President; ST. JOSEPH CAMPUS, Mailing address: 3600 East Harry Street, Wichita, Kansas, Zip 67218-3713; tel. 316/685-1111; Robyn Chadwick, President), (Nonreporting) **A**1 3 5 10 13 **F**3 7 11 12 13 15 16 17 18 20 21 22 23 24 26 27 28 29 30 31 32 34 35 38 40 43 44 45 46 48 49 50 51 54 56 57 58 59 60 61 62 64 68 70 72 74 75 76 77 78 79 80 81 82 84 85 86 87 88 89 92 93 97 98 99 100 102 103 104 105 107 108 110 111 114 115 117 118 119 120 121 123 124 126 130 131 132 135 136 141 142 143 146 147 148 153 154 **S** Ascension Healthcare, Saint Louis, MO
Primary Contact: Kevin Strecker, President
CFO: Jeff Seirer, Interim Chief Financial Officer
CMO: Darrell Youngman, D.O., Chief Medical Officer
CIO: Donna Roach, Chief Information Officer
CHR: Judy Espinoza, Chief Human Resources Officer
Web address: www.via-christi.org
**Control:** Church operated, Nongovernment, not–for–profit **Service:** General medical and surgical

| | |
|---|---|
| **Staffed Beds:** 653 **Admissions:** 30160 **Census:** 422 **Outpatient Visits:** 270511 **Births:** 2536 **Total Expense ($000):** 533563 **Payroll Expense ($000):** 157325 **Personnel:** 2587 | |

## NEODESHA—Wilson County

**WILSON COUNTY HOSPITAL** See Wilson Medical Center

★ **WILSON MEDICAL CENTER (171344)**, 2600 Ottawa Road, Zip 66757-1897, Mailing Address: P.O. Box 360, Zip 66757-0360; tel. 620/325-2611, (Nonreporting) **A**10 18 **F**3 11 15 29 32 34 35 36 40 44 45 53 57 59 64 75 77 81 82 85 86 89 90 93 107 110 114 119 127 128 130 133 146 148 149 154 **P**6 **S** QHR Health, Brentwood, TN
Primary Contact: Dennis R. Shelby, Chief Executive Officer
CFO: John Gutschenritter, Chief Financial Officer
CIO: Kevin Myers, Director Information Technology
CHR: Laura L Dean, Director Human Resources
CNO: Temple Monroe, Director Nursing Operations
Web address: www.wilsonmedical.org
**Control:** County, Government, Nonfederal **Service:** General medical and surgical

| | |
|---|---|
| **Staffed Beds:** 15 **Admissions:** 288 **Census:** 8 **Outpatient Visits:** 18434 **Births:** 0 **Total Expense ($000):** 18184 **Payroll Expense ($000):** 7815 **Personnel:** 162 | |

---

**Hospital, Medicare Provider Number, Address, Telephone, Approval, Facility, and Physician Codes, Health Care System**

★ American Hospital Association (AHA) membership
□ The Joint Commission accreditation
○ Healthcare Facilities Accreditation Program
◇ DNV Healthcare Inc. accreditation
⇑ Center for Improvement in Healthcare Quality Accreditation
△ Commission on Accreditation of Rehabilitation Facilities (CARF) accreditation

**KS**

## NESS CITY—Ness County

**NESS COUNTY HOSPITAL** See Ness County Hospital District No 2

★ **NESS COUNTY HOSPITAL DISTRICT NO 2 (171336)**, 312 Custer Street, Zip 67560–1654; tel. 785/798–2291, (Total facility includes 30 beds in nursing home–type unit) (Nonreporting) **A**10 18 **F**7 40 45 59 62 67 81 93 114 125 127 133 154
Primary Contact: Curt Thomas, Administrator
CFO: Debra Frank, Chief Financial Officer
CMO: Mikhail Imseis, M.D., Chief of Staff
CIO: Vicki Howe, Health Information Management
CHR: Shelly McDonald, Chief Human Resources Officer
CNO: Cindy Maier, R.N., Director of Nursing
Web address: www.nchospital.org
**Control**: Hospital district or authority, Government, Nonfederal **Service**: General medical and surgical

**Staffed Beds: 55 Admissions: 217 Census: 37 Outpatient Visits: 13086 Births: 0 Total Expense ($000): 10325 Payroll Expense ($000): 4615 Personnel: 96**

## NEWTON—Harvey County

★ ○ **NEWTON MEDICAL CENTER (170103)**, 600 Medical Center Drive, Zip 67114–8780, Mailing Address: P.O. Box 308, Zip 67114–0308; tel. 316/283–2700, (Nonreporting) **A**3 5 10 11 **F**3 11 13 15 20 22 28 29 30 31 34 35 37 40 45 51 59 62 64 68 70 73 74 75 76 77 79 81 84 85 86 90 93 98 102 103 107 108 110 111 115 118 119 126 130 131 132 133 146 147 148 149 154 156 157 **P**6
Primary Contact: Vallerie L. Gleason, President and Chief Executive Officer
COO: Todd Tangeman, Chief Operating Officer
CFO: Todd Kasitz, Vice President Finance
CIO: Mike Cottle, Chief Information Officer
CHR: Todd Tangeman, Chief Operating Officer and Chief Human Resource Officer
CNO: Heather Porter, Chief Clinical Officer
Web address: www.newtonmedicalcenter.com
**Control**: Other not–for–profit (including NFP Corporation) **Service**: General medical and surgical

**Staffed Beds: 103 Admissions: 2788 Census: 35 Outpatient Visits: 62134 Births: 462 Total Expense ($000): 81067 Payroll Expense ($000): 40396 Personnel: 689**

□ **PRAIRIE VIEW (174016)**, 1901 East First Street, Zip 67114–5010, Mailing Address: P.O. Box 467, Zip 67114–0467; tel. 316/284–6400, (Nonreporting) **A**1 10
Primary Contact: Jessie Kaye, Chief Executive Officer
CFO: Lisa Ramsey, Chief Financial Officer
CMO: Gary Fast, M.D., Medical Director
CIO: Chad Roth, Director Information Services
CHR: Joy Robb, Vice President Human Resources
CNO: Patrick Flaming, R.N., Director Inpatient Operations
Web address: www.prairieview.org
**Control**: Other not–for–profit (including NFP Corporation) **Service**: Psychiatric

**Staffed Beds: 38**

**PRAIRIE VIEW MENTAL HLTH CNTR** See Prairie View

## NORTON—Norton County

★ **NORTON COUNTY HOSPITAL (171348)**, 102 East Holme, Zip 67654–1406, Mailing Address: P.O. Box 250, Zip 67654–0250; tel. 785/877–3351, (Nonreporting) **A**10 18 **F**3 13 15 28 29 30 34 35 40 45 50 59 64 65 67 68 76 77 78 79 81 85 86 87 93 97 107 110 111 112 119 127 128 129 130 131 133 135 154 **P**6
Primary Contact: Gina Frack, Chief Executive Officer
CHR: Shannan Hempler, Director Human Resources
Web address: www.ntcohosp.com
**Control**: County, Government, Nonfederal **Service**: General medical and surgical

**Staffed Beds: 25 Admissions: 243 Census: 3 Outpatient Visits: 17457 Births: 5 Total Expense ($000): 13864 Payroll Expense ($000): 5969 Personnel: 106**

## OAKLEY—Logan County

**LOGAN COUNTY HOSPITAL (171326)**, 211 Cherry Street, Zip 67748–1201; tel. 785/672–3211, (Nonreporting) **A**10 18 **F**28 29 32 34 40 45 53 54 56 57 59 69 71 77 81 91 93 107 114 127 128 130 133 148 154 **P**8
Primary Contact: Meldon L. Snow, Chief Executive Officer
COO: Aimee Zimmerman, R.N., Chief Operations Officer
CFO: Bonnie Hagel, Chief Financial Officer
CMO: Celeste Rains, D.O., Chief of Staff
CIO: Russ Kahle, Chief Information Officer
CHR: Steve Allison, Director Human Resources
CNO: Marcia Kruse, R.N., Director Nursing
Web address: www.logancountyhospital.org
**Control**: County, Government, Nonfederal **Service**: General medical and surgical

**Staffed Beds: 25 Admissions: 93 Census: 1 Outpatient Visits: 7099 Births: 0 Total Expense ($000): 12203 Payroll Expense ($000): 6130**

## OBERLIN—Decatur County

**DECATUR COUNTY HOSPITAL AND CEDAR LIVING CENTER** See Decatur Health Systems

**DECATUR HEALTH SYSTEMS (171352)**, 810 West Columbia Street, Zip 67749–2450, Mailing Address: P.O. Box 268, Zip 67749–0268; tel. 785/475–2208, (Nonreporting) **A**10 18 **F**3 15 34 40 41 45 50 53 56 59 63 64 77 81 82 83 84 85 86 87 89 93 97 102 107 110 114 125 127 128 130 131 133 135 148 149 154 158 **P**6
Primary Contact: Kristopher Matthews, Chief Operating Officer
CFO: Amanda Fortin, Manager Finance
CMO: Elizabeth Sliter, M.D., Chairman Medical Staff
CIO: Natasha Weishapl, Manager Business Office and Human Resources
CHR: Natasha Weishapl, Manager Business Office and Human Resources
Web address: www.decaturhealthsystems.org
**Control**: Other not–for–profit (including NFP Corporation) **Service**: General medical and surgical

**Staffed Beds: 12 Admissions: 111 Census: 1 Outpatient Visits: 7350 Births: 0 Total Expense ($000): 8157 Payroll Expense ($000): 3812 Personnel: 81**

## OLATHE—Johnson County

□ **COTTONWOOD SPRINGS HOSPITAL (174020)**, 13351 South Arapaho Drive, Zip 66062–1520; tel. 913/353–3000, (Nonreporting) **A**1 10 **S** Springstone, Louisville, KY
Primary Contact: Jason Toalson, Chief Executive Officer
Web address: www.cottonwoodsprings.com
**Control**: Corporation, Investor–owned (for–profit) **Service**: Psychiatric

**Staffed Beds: 72**

□ **OLATHE MEDICAL CENTER (170049)**, 20333 West 151st Street, Zip 66061–5350; tel. 913/791–4200, (Nonreporting) **A**1 2 10 **F**3 11 12 13 15 18 20 22 24 26 28 29 30 31 34 35 39 40 45 46 47 48 49 56 57 58 59 61 62 63 64 65 68 70 73 74 75 76 77 78 79 80 81 82 84 85 86 87 89 91 92 93 107 108 110 111 115 116 117 118 119 120 121 123 124 126 129 130 131 132 135 145 146 147 148 149 156
Primary Contact: Stan Holm, President and Chief Executive Officer
COO: John Staton, Senior Vice President Operations
CFO: Tierney Lynn Grasser, Senior Vice President and Chief Financial Officer
CMO: James L Wetzel, M.D., Senior Vice President, Chief Medical Officer
CIO: Randy Rahman, Vice President and Chief Information Officer
CHR: David Klimek, Vice President Human Resources
CNO: Amy J Meglemre, R.N., MSN, Senior Vice President and Chief Nursing Officer
Web address: www.olathehealth.org
**Control**: Other not–for–profit (including NFP Corporation) **Service**: General medical and surgical

**Staffed Beds: 254 Admissions: 10849 Census: 104 Outpatient Visits: 353249 Births: 1352 Personnel: 1435**

## ONAGA—Pottawatomie County

★ **COMMUNITY HEALTHCARE SYSTEM (171354)**, 120 West Eighth Street, Zip 66521–9574; tel. 785/889–4272, (Total facility includes 78 beds in nursing home–type unit) (Nonreporting) **A**10 18 **F**2 3 5 6 10 11 12 13 15 28 29 31 32 34 35 36 40 43 45 50 53 56 57 59 62 64 65 67 74 75 77 78 81 82 84 85 86 87 93 97 99 100 101 102 103 104 105 106 107 110 111 114 119 125 127 128 130 131 132 133 134 135 143 144 145 146 147 148 149 151 152 153 154 156 **P**6
Primary Contact: Todd Willert, Chief Executive Officer
COO: Marcia S Walsh, M.P.H., Chief Operating Officer
CFO: Monica Holthaus, Chief Financial Officer
CMO: Marcus Weiser, D.O., Chief of Staff
CIO: Rod Evans, Chief Information Officer
CHR: Terry D. Bernatis, Director Human Resources
CNO: Rosalind Lewis, R.N., MSN, Director of Ancillary Services
Web address: www.chcsks.org
**Control:** Other not–for–profit (including NFP Corporation) **Service:** General medical and surgical

**Staffed Beds:** 150 **Admissions:** 1008 **Census:** 73 **Outpatient Visits:** 87301 **Births:** 85 **Total Expense ($000):** 37031 **Payroll Expense ($000):** 19975 **Personnel:** 237

**COMMUNITY HLTH CARE SYST INC** See Community Healthcare System

## OSAWATOMIE—Miami County

**OSAWATOMIE STATE HOSPITAL** See Osawatomie State Hospital at Adair Acute Care

**OSAWATOMIE STATE HOSPITAL AT ADAIR ACUTE CARE (174022)**, 500 State Hospital Drive, Zip 66064–1813, Mailing Address: P.O. Box 500, Zip 66064–0500; tel. 913/755–7000, (Nonreporting) **A**10 **F**30 50 86 87 98 100 101 130 135 146 149 156 157 **P**6
Primary Contact: Kristin Feeback, Superintendent
CMO: Maria Gustilo, M.D., Medical Director
CHR: Dezerae Curran, Director Human Resources
Web address: www.srskansas.org/osh/osh-rmhf_info.html
**Control:** State, Government, Nonfederal **Service:** Psychiatric

**Staffed Beds:** 174 **Admissions:** 1357 **Census:** 142 **Outpatient Visits:** 0 **Births:** 0 **Total Expense ($000):** 41056 **Payroll Expense ($000):** 24286 **Personnel:** 425

## OSBORNE—Osborne County

**OSBORNE COUNTY MEMORIAL HOSPITAL (171364)**, 424 West New Hampshire Street, Zip 67473–2314, Mailing Address: P.O. Box 70, Zip 67473–0070; tel. 785/346–2121, (Nonreporting) **A**10 18 **S** Great Plains Health Alliance, Inc., Wichita, KS
Primary Contact: Marianna Harris, Administrator
CFO: Linda Murphy, Chief Financial Officer
CMO: Erin Baxa, M.D., Chief Medical Officer
CNO: Monica Mullender, Director of Nursing
Web address: www.ocmh.org
**Control:** County, Government, Nonfederal **Service:** General medical and surgical

**Staffed Beds:** 25

## OTTAWA—Franklin County

✠ **ADVENTHEALTH OTTAWA (170014)**, 1301 South Main Street, Zip 66067–3598; tel. 785/229–8200, (Nonreporting) **A**1 10 20 **F**3 11 13 15 18 28 29 30 32 34 35 40 41 43 44 45 50 53 56 57 59 64 68 70 75 76 77 79 81 82 85 86 87 89 92 93 94 96 97 107 108 110 111 114 115 118 119 127 129 130 131 132 134 135 144 146 147 148 149 154 156 **P**6 **S** AdventHealth, Altamonte Springs, FL
Primary Contact: Dallas Purkeypile, Chief Executive Officer
Web address: www.ransom.org
**Control:** Church operated, Nongovernment, not–for–profit **Service:** General medical and surgical

**Staffed Beds:** 38 **Admissions:** 1268 **Census:** 10 **Outpatient Visits:** 109548 **Births:** 145 **Total Expense ($000):** 47535 **Payroll Expense ($000):** 20993 **Personnel:** 332

**RANSOM MEMORIAL HOSPITAL** See Adventhealth Ottawa

## OVERLAND PARK—Johnson County

☐ **CHILDREN'S MERCY HOSPITAL KANSAS (173300)**, 5808 West 110th Street, Zip 66211–2504; tel. 913/696–8000, (Nonreporting) **A**1 10 **F**3 7 8 9 12 19 27 29 30 32 35 36 38 40 41 44 45 48 50 55 58 59 62 64 65 68 74 75 79 80 81 87 89 93 100 104 107 111 115 119 129 130 131 132 134 146 148 149 150 154 155 156 157 **P**6
Primary Contact: Paul D. Kempinski, Chief Executive Officer
COO: Jodi Coombs, R.N., Executive Vice President, Chief Operating Officer
CFO: David Cauble, Executive Vice President and Chief Financial Officer
CIO: Chad Mills, Senior Vice President, Chief Information Officer
CHR: Robin Faulk, Senior Vice President, Chief Human Resources Officer
CNO: Cheri Hunt, Senior Vice President Patient Care Services, Chief Nursing Officer
Web address: www.childrens-mercy.org
**Control:** Other not–for–profit (including NFP Corporation) **Service:** Children's general medical and surgical

**Staffed Beds:** 52 **Admissions:** 2590 **Census:** 16 **Outpatient Visits:** 156410 **Births:** 0 **Total Expense ($000):** 100204 **Payroll Expense ($000):** 65014 **Personnel:** 793

**CHILDREN'S MERCY SOUTH** See Children's Mercy Hospital Kansas

**COLUMBIA OVERLAND PARK REG CTR** See Overland Park Regional Medical Center

**HEARTLAND SURGICAL SPECIALTY HOSPITAL** See The University of Kansas Hospital - Indian Creek Campus

☐ **KPC PROMISE HOSPITAL OF OVERLAND PARK (172004)**, 6509 West 103rd Street, Zip 66212–1728; tel. 913/649–3701, (Nonreporting) **A**1 10 **S** KPC Healthcare, Inc., Santa Ana, CA
Primary Contact: Robert Beck, Chief Executive Officer
CFO: William Scott, Chief Financial Officer
CHR: Darren Enochs, Director Human Resources
Web address: www.overlandpark.kpcph.com
**Control:** Corporation, Investor–owned (for–profit) **Service:** Acute long–term care hospital

**Staffed Beds:** 104

✠ **MENORAH MEDICAL CENTER (170182)**, 5721 West 119th Street, Zip 66209–3722; tel. 913/498–6000, (Nonreporting) **A**1 2 3 5 10 **F**3 12 13 15 18 20 22 24 26 28 29 30 31 34 35 38 40 45 46 47 49 55 57 58 59 60 64 65 68 70 72 74 75 76 77 78 79 81 82 84 85 86 87 90 93 100 102 107 108 110 111 114 115 116 117 119 120 121 126 129 130 131 132 135 145 146 148 149 154 **S** HCA Healthcare, Nashville, TN
Primary Contact: Phil Buttell, Chief Executive Officer
CFO: Deborah Gafford, Chief Financial Officer
CMO: James Cheray, M.D., Chief Medical Officer
CIO: Christina McGinnis, Director Information Technology
CHR: Amy Hunt, Director Human Resources
CNO: Kelly Reno, R.N., Chief Nursing Officer
Web address: www.menorahmedicalcenter.com
**Control:** Corporation, Investor–owned (for–profit) **Service:** General medical and surgical

**Staffed Beds:** 158 **Admissions:** 8728 **Census:** 106 **Outpatient Visits:** 70432 **Births:** 381 **Total Expense ($000):** 225219 **Payroll Expense ($000):** 59700 **Personnel:** 918

✠ **OVERLAND PARK REGIONAL MEDICAL CENTER (170176)**, 10500 Quivira Road, Zip 66215–2306, Mailing Address: P.O. Box 15959, Zip 66215–5959; tel. 913/541–5000, (Nonreporting) **A**1 2 3 5 10 **F**3 8 13 15 18 19 20 22 24 26 28 29 30 31 34 35 37 40 41 42 43 45 49 50 52 55 56 57 59 60 61 64 65 67 70 72 73 74 75 76 77 78 79 81 82 83 84 85 86 87 88 91 92 93 107 108 110 111 114 115 119 126 129 130 131 135 144 145 146 147 149 156 **P**6 **S** HCA Healthcare, Nashville, TN
Primary Contact: Matt Sogard, Chief Executive Officer
CFO: Steven R Cleary, Chief Financial Officer
CMO: George D. Stamos, M.D., Chief Medical Officer
CHR: Connie Miller, Vice President Human Resources
Web address: www.oprmc.com
**Control:** Corporation, Investor–owned (for–profit) **Service:** General medical and surgical

**Staffed Beds:** 283 **Admissions:** 12017 **Census:** 156 **Outpatient Visits:** 97315 **Births:** 2821 **Total Expense ($000):** 219101 **Payroll Expense ($000):** 74692 **Personnel:** 904

---

Hospital, Medicare Provider Number, Address, Telephone, Approval, Facility, and Physician Codes, Health Care System

★ American Hospital Association (AHA) membership    ○ Healthcare Facilities Accreditation Program    ⇑ Center for Improvement in Healthcare Quality Accreditation
☐ The Joint Commission accreditation    ◇ DNV Healthcare Inc. accreditation    △ Commission on Accreditation of Rehabilitation Facilities (CARF) accreditation

**KS**

**PROMISE HOSPITAL OF OVERLAND PARK** See Kpc Promise Hospital of Overland Park

⊞ **REHABILITATION HOSPITAL OF OVERLAND PARK (173032)**, 5100 Indian Creek Parkway, Zip 66207–4115; tel. 913/544–1957, (Nonreporting) **A**1 10 **F**3 34 35 56 64 74 75 79 86 87 90 91 93 96 100 131 148 154 **S** Post Acute Medical, LLC, Enola, PA
Primary Contact: John Hughes, Chief Executive Officer
Web address: www.warmsprings.org
**Control:** Partnership, Investor–owned (for–profit) **Service:** Rehabilitation

**Staffed Beds: 45 Admissions: 1209 Census: 38 Outpatient Visits: 3803 Births: 0 Total Expense ($000): 19622 Payroll Expense ($000): 8545 Personnel: 169**

**SAINT LUKE'S SOUTH** See Saint Luke's South Hospital

⊞ **SAINT LUKE'S SOUTH HOSPITAL (170185)**, 12300 Metcalf Avenue, Zip 66213–1324; tel. 913/317–7000, (Includes SAINT LUKE'S COMMUNITY HOSPITAL AT LEAWOOD, Mailing address: 13200 State Line Road, Leawood, Kansas, Zip 66209; tel. 913/222–8380; Bobby Olm-Shipman, Chief Executive Officer), (Nonreporting) **A**1 2 10 **F**3 12 13 15 18 20 22 26 28 29 30 31 34 35 38 39 40 42 44 45 47 48 49 50 54 56 58 59 60 64 65 68 70 73 74 75 76 77 78 79 80 81 82 84 85 86 87 89 90 93 94 95 96 100 102 107 108 110 111 114 115 117 118 119 120 121 123 126 129 130 131 132 135 141 146 147 148 149 154 **S** Saint Luke's Health System, Kansas City, MO
Primary Contact: Bobby Olm-Shipman, Chief Executive Officer
COO: Taylor Warwick, Vice President Operations
CFO: Matt Marino, Chief Financial Officer
CMO: Michael Davenport, D.O., President, Medical Staff
CIO: Deborah Gash, Chief Information Officer
CHR: Carol Ferrara, Director Human Resources
CNO: Julia Woods, MSN, Vice President and Chief Nursing Officer
Web address: www.saintlukeshealthsystem.org/south
**Control:** Church operated, Nongovernment, not–for–profit **Service:** General medical and surgical

**Staffed Beds: 174 Admissions: 6536 Census: 71 Outpatient Visits: 130526 Births: 495 Total Expense ($000): 186807 Payroll Expense ($000): 54128 Personnel: 906**

### PAOLA—Miami County

**MIAMI COUNTY HOSPITAL** See Miami County Medical Center

☐ **MIAMI COUNTY MEDICAL CENTER (170109)**, 2100 Baptiste Drive, Zip 66071–1314, Mailing Address: P.O. Box 365, Zip 66071–0365; tel. 913/294–2327, (Nonreporting) **A**1 10 **F**3 11 15 18 28 34 40 43 57 59 64 68 75 77 78 79 81 82 85 87 93 107 108 110 111 115 119 127 130 131 135 145 146 148 156
Primary Contact: Paul W. Luce, R.N., MSN, Vice President Operations
CFO: Cheryl Sharp, Chief Financial Office
CMO: Christopher Eckland, M.D., Chief Medical Officer
CIO: Randy Rahman, Chief Information Officer
CHR: David Klimek, Chief Human Resources Officer
CNO: Aubree Slayman, Director Patient Services
Web address: www.olathehealth.org
**Control:** Other not–for–profit (including NFP Corporation) **Service:** General medical and surgical

**Staffed Beds: 18 Admissions: 520 Census: 3 Outpatient Visits: 59263 Births: 0 Total Expense ($000): 30392 Payroll Expense ($000): 14526 Personnel: 125**

### PARSONS—Labette County

**LABETTE COUNTY MEDICAL CENTER** See Labette Health

★ ○ **LABETTE HEALTH (170120)**, 1902 South U S Highway 59, Zip 67357–7404; tel. 620/421–4880, (Nonreporting) **A**10 11 **F**3 11 13 15 29 30 34 40 42 43 50 53 59 62 70 74 75 76 77 79 81 86 90 93 97 107 108 110 111 114 119 126 127 129 130 133 143 144 146 147 148 149 154 156 **P**6
Primary Contact: Brian A. Williams, Chief Executive Officer
CFO: Thomas Macaronas, Chief Financial Officer
CHR: Christina Sykes, Director Human Resources
Web address: www.labettehealth.com
**Control:** County, Government, Nonfederal **Service:** General medical and surgical

**Staffed Beds: 56 Admissions: 1789 Census: 17 Outpatient Visits: 98381 Births: 201 Total Expense ($000): 79007 Payroll Expense ($000): 35365 Personnel: 612**

**PARSONS STATE HOSP & TRNG CNTR** See Parsons State Hospital and Training Center

**PARSONS STATE HOSPITAL AND TRAINING CENTER**, 2601 Gabriel Avenue, Zip 67357–2341, Mailing Address: P.O. Box 738, Zip 67357–0738; tel. 620/421–6550, (Nonreporting) **F**35 39 67 75 130 146
Primary Contact: Jerry A. Rea, Ph.D., Superintendent
CFO: John Spare, Accountant
CMO: Rema Menon, M.D., Clinical Director
CIO: Ron Malmstrom, Information Research Specialist
CHR: Tim B Posch, Business Manager and Director Personnel
Web address: www.pshtc.org
**Control:** State, Government, Nonfederal **Service:** Intellectual disabilities

**Staffed Beds: 172 Admissions: 9 Census: 161 Outpatient Visits: 0 Births: 0 Total Expense ($000): 28628 Payroll Expense ($000): 16761 Personnel: 492**

### PHILLIPSBURG—Phillips County

★ **PHILLIPS COUNTY HEALTH SYSTEMS (171353)**, 1150 State Street, Zip 67661–1743, Mailing Address: P.O. Box 607, Zip 67661–0607; tel. 785/543–5226, (Nonreporting) **A**10 18 **F**3 11 15 28 30 40 45 50 59 64 68 75 77 81 86 87 91 107 110 115 117 119 127 130 131 132 133 135 145 146 148 154
Primary Contact: Rex D. Walk, Chief Executive Officer
CFO: Krystal Schwenn, Chief Financial Officer
CMO: Doak Doolittle, M.D., Chief of Staff
CIO: Steven Seems, Director of Information Technology
CHR: Peggy Fabin, Director Human Resources
CNO: Vickie Gibbs, Director Nursing
Web address: www.phillipshospital.org
**Control:** Other not–for–profit (including NFP Corporation) **Service:** General medical and surgical

**Staffed Beds: 25 Admissions: 191 Census: 7 Outpatient Visits: 27282 Births: 0 Total Expense ($000): 12822 Payroll Expense ($000): 5054 Personnel: 111**

**PHILLIPS COUNTY HOSPITAL** See Phillips County Health Systems

### PITTSBURG—Crawford County

⊞ **ASCENSION VIA CHRISTI HOSPITAL (170006)**, 1 Mt. Carmel Way, Zip 66762–7587; tel. 620/231–6100, (Nonreporting) **A**1 10 **F**3 5 11 12 13 15 18 20 22 26 28 29 30 31 34 35 40 42 43 45 46 47 48 50 51 53 54 56 57 58 59 62 64 68 69 70 74 75 76 77 78 79 81 82 84 85 86 89 90 93 104 107 108 109 110 111 112 114 115 116 117 118 119 120 121 122 123 126 129 130 131 132 133 135 143 145 146 147 148 154 156 157 **P**8 **S** Ascension Healthcare, Saint Louis, MO
Primary Contact: Randall R. Cason, FACHE, Senior Administrator
CFO: Mike Joy, Administrator, Finance
CIO: Missy McDown, Director Information Systems
CHR: Laurie Johnson, Director - Human Resources
CNO: Amy Katherine Renn, Interim Administrator, Patient Care and Nursing
Web address: www.viachristi.org/pittsburg
**Control:** Church operated, Nongovernment, not–for–profit **Service:** General medical and surgical

**Staffed Beds: 91 Admissions: 3150 Census: 33 Outpatient Visits: 103167 Births: 577 Total Expense ($000): 92842 Payroll Expense ($000): 32355 Personnel: 458**

**ASCENSION VIA CHRISTI HOSPITAL, PITTSBURG** See Ascension Via Christi Hospital

### PLAINVILLE—Rooks County

**PLAINVILLE RURAL HOSP DIST ONE** See Rooks County Health Center

★ **ROOKS COUNTY HEALTH CENTER (171311)**, 1210 North Washington Street, Zip 67663–1632, Mailing Address: P.O. Box 389, Zip 67663–0389; tel. 785/434–4553, (Nonreporting) **A**10 18 **F**3 13 15 28 29 31 34 35 40 43 45 47 50 57 59 64 67 76 77 79 81 85 86 87 93 96 107 108 110 111 114 119 125 128 130 131 133 135 143 144 146 148 149
Primary Contact: Anthony Thomas, Chief Executive Officer
COO: William D Stahl, Chief Operating Officer
CFO: Frank A Rajewski, Chief Financial Officer
CMO: Lynn Fisher, M.D., Chief of Staff
CHR: Cindi Knipp, Director Human Resources
Web address: www.rookscountyhealthcenter.com
**Control:** Hospital district or authority, Government, Nonfederal **Service:** General medical and surgical

**Staffed Beds: 22 Admissions: 323 Census: 5 Outpatient Visits: 25157 Births: 31 Total Expense ($000): 17185 Payroll Expense ($000): 6719 Personnel: 135**

## PRATT—Pratt County

★ **PRATT REGIONAL MEDICAL CENTER (170027)**, 200 Commodore Street, Zip 67124–2903; tel. 620/672–7451, (Total facility includes 45 beds in nursing home–type unit) (Nonreporting) **A**10 20 **F**3 7 11 13 15 30 31 34 40 45 49 50 56 57 59 61 62 64 68 70 75 76 77 79 81 82 85 86 87 93 107 108 114 118 119 124 126 127 130 131 133 145 146 147 148 155 156
Primary Contact: Susan M. Page, President and Chief Executive Officer
CFO: Vincent Scot Wilczek, Controller
CIO: Vikki Mader, Director Health Information Services
CHR: Kenneth A Brown, Vice President and Chief Human Resource Officer
CNO: Jack L Kennedy, R.N., MS, Vice President and Chief Nursing Officer
Web address: www.prmc.org
**Control**: Other not–for–profit (including NFP Corporation) **Service**: General medical and surgical

**Staffed Beds: 80 Admissions: 1514 Census: 43 Outpatient Visits: 100589 Births: 213 Total Expense ($000): 56242 Payroll Expense ($000): 24184 Personnel: 402**

## QUINTER—Gove County

**GOVE COUNTY HOSPITAL** See Gove County Medical Center

**GOVE COUNTY MEDICAL CENTER (171367)**, 520 West Fifth Street, Zip 67752–0129, Mailing Address: P.O. Box 129, Zip 67752–0129; tel. 785/754–3341, (Total facility includes 42 beds in nursing home–type unit) (Nonreporting) **A**10 18 **F**3 11 13 28 29 34 40 45 57 67 75 81 82 86 93 107 115 119 125 129 133 135 143 148 156
Primary Contact: David Caudill, Chief Executive Officer
CFO: Alan Waites, Chief Financial Officer
CIO: Brad Mullins, Director Information Technology
CHR: Valerie Schneider, Director Human Resources
CNO: Renee Wagoner, R.N., Director of Nursing
Web address: www.govecountymedicalcenter.org
**Control**: County, Government, Nonfederal **Service**: General medical and surgical

**Staffed Beds: 63 Admissions: 474 Census: 45 Outpatient Visits: 10298 Births: 44 Total Expense ($000): 15858 Payroll Expense ($000): 6985 Personnel: 160**

## RANSOM—Ness County

★ **GRISELL MEMORIAL HOSPITAL DISTRICT ONE (171300)**, 210 South Vermont Avenue, Zip 67572–9525; tel. 785/731–2231, (Total facility includes 30 beds in nursing home–type unit) (Nonreporting) **A**10 18 **F**3 40 67 69 85 93 97 127 128 133 156 **P**6 **S** Great Plains Health Alliance, Inc., Wichita, KS
Primary Contact: Rayna Bittel, Co-Chief Executive Officer and Chief Financial Officer
CFO: Rayna Bittel, Chief Financial Officer
CMO: Allen McLain, M.D., Chief of Staff
CNO: Joni Pfaff, Chief Nursing Officer
Web address: www.grisellmemorialhospital.org
**Control**: Hospital district or authority, Government, Nonfederal **Service**: General medical and surgical

**Staffed Beds: 42 Admissions: 53 Census: 25 Outpatient Visits: 3742 Births: 0 Total Expense ($000): 6856 Payroll Expense ($000): 3005 Personnel: 69**

## RUSSELL—Russell County

★ **RUSSELL REGIONAL HOSPITAL (171350)**, 200 South Main Street, Zip 67665–2920; tel. 785/483–3131, (Total facility includes 23 beds in nursing home–type unit) (Nonreporting) **A**10 18 **F**9 11 15 29 34 40 45 46 50 53 57 59 64 65 66 67 68 69 75 77 81 82 85 87 93 97 107 108 109 110 115 119 127 129 130 131 133 135 145 146 147 148 149 154
Primary Contact: Sharon Collins, Chief Executive Officer
CFO: Kevin Kreutzer, Chief Financial Officer
CMO: Tyrel Somers, M.D., Chief Medical Officer
CIO: David Schraeder, Director Information Systems
CNO: Deb Strobel, R.N., Chief Nursing Officer
Web address: www.russellhospital.org
**Control**: Other not–for–profit (including NFP Corporation) **Service**: General medical and surgical

**Staffed Beds: 48 Admissions: 419 Census: 28 Outpatient Visits: 35565 Births: 0 Total Expense ($000): 19097 Payroll Expense ($000): 9684 Personnel: 171**

## SABETHA—Nemaha County

★ **SABETHA COMMUNITY HOSPITAL (171338)**, 14th and Oregon Streets, Zip 66534–0229, Mailing Address: P.O. Box 229, Zip 66534–0229; tel. 785/284–2121, (Nonreporting) **A**10 18 **F**3 11 13 15 28 34 35 40 43 45 50 56 57 59 62 63 64 68 75 76 77 78 79 81 82 84 85 86 93 107 110 114 119 128 130 132 133 146 148 156 **P**6 **S** Great Plains Health Alliance, Inc., Wichita, KS
Primary Contact: Lora Key, Chief Executive Officer
CFO: Lori Lackey, Chief Financial Officer
CMO: James Longabaugh, M.D., Chief Medical Staff
CIO: Garrett Colglazier, Director Health Information Management
CHR: Julie K Holthaus, Director Human Resources
CNO: Rhonda Spellmeier, R.N., Director of Nursing
Web address: www.sabethahospital.com
**Control**: Other not–for–profit (including NFP Corporation) **Service**: General medical and surgical

**Staffed Beds: 25 Admissions: 335 Census: 5 Outpatient Visits: 37434 Births: 27 Total Expense ($000): 13151 Payroll Expense ($000): 6328 Personnel: 110**

## SAINT FRANCIS—Cheyenne County

★ **CHEYENNE COUNTY HOSPITAL (171310)**, 210 West First Street, Zip 67756–3540, Mailing Address: P.O. Box 547, Zip 67756–0547; tel. 785/332–2104, (Nonreporting) **A**10 18 **F**3 8 11 13 28 29 34 40 57 59 64 65 66 68 76 77 81 89 97 107 119 127 128 133 148 156 **S** Great Plains Health Alliance, Inc., Wichita, KS
Primary Contact: Rance Ramsey, Chief Executive Officer
CFO: Heidi Tice, Chief Financial Officer
CMO: Mary Beth Miller, M.D., Chief of Staff
CIO: Carol Sloper, Manager Information Technology
CHR: Sara Wilson, Director Human Resources
CNO: Judith Ann Hodgson, Chief Nursing Officer
Web address: www.cheyennecountyhospital.com
**Control**: Other not–for–profit (including NFP Corporation) **Service**: General medical and surgical

**Staffed Beds: 16 Admissions: 284 Census: 4 Outpatient Visits: 21160 Births: 12 Total Expense ($000): 10572 Payroll Expense ($000): 4133 Personnel: 88**

## SALINA—Saline County

**ASBURY-SALINA REG MEDICAL CTR** See Salina Regional Health Center-Santa Fe Campus

★ ○ **SALINA REGIONAL HEALTH CENTER (170012)**, 400 South Santa Fe Avenue, Zip 67401–4198, Mailing Address: P.O. Box 5080, Zip 67402–5080; tel. 785/452–7000, (Includes SALINA REGIONAL HEALTH CENTER- PENN CAMPUS, Mailing address: 139 North Penn Street, Salina, Kansas, Zip 67401, P O Box 5080, Zip 67402–5080, tel. 913/452–7000; SALINA REGIONAL HEALTH CENTER-SANTA FE CAMPUS, Mailing address: 400 South Santa Fe Avenue, Salina, Kansas, Zip 67401, Box 5080, Zip 67402–5080, tel. 913/452–7000), (Nonreporting) **A**3 5 10 11 20 **F**3 13 15 18 19 20 22 24 28 29 30 31 40 43 45 46 47 48 49 51 53 54 55 57 59 63 64 65 68 70 71 72 73 74 76 77 78 79 81 85 86 87 89 90 98 100 101 102 104 105 107 108 110 111 114 115 116 117 118 119 120 121 122 123 124 126 129 130 143 144 145 146 147 148 149 153 154 **P**6 **S** Salina Regional Health Center, Salina, KS
Primary Contact: Joel Phelps, President and Chief Executive Officer
CFO: Joe Tallon, Vice President Finance
CIO: Larry Barnes, Vice President Information Technology
CHR: David Moody, Vice President Human Resources
Web address: www.srhc.com
**Control**: Other not–for–profit (including NFP Corporation) **Service**: General medical and surgical

**Staffed Beds: 207 Admissions: 8954 Census: 116 Outpatient Visits: 286901 Births: 1107 Total Expense ($000): 263025 Payroll Expense ($000): 109569 Personnel: 1542**

---

**KS**

**SALINA SURGICAL HOSPITAL (170187)**, 401 South Santa Fe Avenue,
Zip 67401–4143, Mailing Address: 401 South Sante Fe Avenue, Zip 67401–4143;
tel. 785/827–0610, (Nonreporting) **A**10 **F**29 45 48 49 51 59 74 79 81 85
89 131
Primary Contact: LuAnn Puvogel, R.N., Chief Executive Officer
CFO: Elizabeth Bishop, Business Office Manager
CMO: Michael Johnson, M.D., Medical Director
CIO: Earl Akers, Supervisor Information Technology
CHR: Elizabeth Bishop, Business Office Manager
CNO: Jolene Glavin, R.N., MSN, Director Nursing
Web address: www.salinasurgical.com/
**Control**: Partnership, Investor–owned (for–profit) **Service**: Surgical

**Staffed Beds**: 16 **Admissions**: 797 **Census**: 5 **Outpatient Visits**: 7915
**Births**: 0 **Total Expense ($000)**: 19100 **Payroll Expense ($000)**: 6504
**Personnel**: 95

**ST JOHN'S REGIONAL HEALTH CTR** See Salina Regional Health Center- Penn
Campus

### SATANTA—Haskell County

**SATANTA DISTRICT HOSPITAL** See Satanta District Hospital and Long Term Care

★ **SATANTA DISTRICT HOSPITAL AND LONG TERM CARE (171324)**, 401
South Cheyenne Street, Zip 67870–0159, Mailing Address: P.O. Box 159,
Zip 67870–0159; tel. 620/649–2761, (Total facility includes 44 beds in nursing
home–type unit) (Nonreporting) **A**10 18 **F**3 11 40 43 45 57 64 67 68 75 81 87
93 104 107 119 127 128 130 133 156 **P**4 **S** Great Plains Health Alliance, Inc.,
Wichita, KS
Primary Contact: Jeremy Clingenpeel, Administrator
CFO: Libby Anderson, Chief Financial Officer
CMO: Virgilio Taduran, M.D., Chief Medical Officer
CIO: Ben Leppke, Chief Information Officer
CHR: Samantha Hett, Manager Human Resources
CNO: Tina Pendergraft, Chief Nursing Officer
Web address: www.satantahospital.org
**Control**: Hospital district or authority, Government, Nonfederal **Service**: General
medical and surgical

**Staffed Beds**: 57 **Admissions**: 126 **Census**: 40 **Outpatient Visits**: 19988
**Births**: 0 **Total Expense ($000)**: 13326 **Payroll Expense ($000)**: 6633
**Personnel**: 137

### SCOTT CITY—Scott County

★ **SCOTT COUNTY HOSPITAL (171372)**, 201 East Albert Avenue,
Zip 67871–1203; tel. 620/872–5811, (Nonreporting) **A**10 18 **F**3 7 11 13 15 28
29 30 32 34 40 41 56 57 59 64 65 68 69 74 75 76 77 81 82 85 87 89 93 97
102 107 108 110 111 114 119 127 128 129 130 131 132 133 135 146 147
148 149 154 156 157 **P**6
Primary Contact: David Mark. Burnett, President and Chief Executive Officer
CMO: Matthew Lightner, M.D., Chief Medical Staff
CHR: Whisper Carson, Manager Human Resource
CNO: Jeri Grove, Chief Nursing Officer
Web address: www.scotthospital.net
**Control**: County, Government, Nonfederal **Service**: General medical and surgical

**Staffed Beds**: 22 **Admissions**: 532 **Census**: 10 **Outpatient Visits**: 30777
**Births**: 42 **Total Expense ($000)**: 21304 **Payroll Expense ($000)**: 11528
**Personnel**: 219

### SEDAN—Chautauqua County

**SEDAN CITY HOSPITAL (171318)**, 300 North Street, Zip 67361–1051, Mailing
Address: P.O. Box 'C', Zip 67361–0427; tel. 620/725–3115, (Nonreporting) **A**10
18 **F**29 34 40 57 64 93 107 119 128 130 133 148
Primary Contact: Michelle Williams, Administrator
CFO: Jennifer Seever, Regional Chief Financial Officer
CMO: James McDermott, M.D., Chief of Staff
**Control**: City, Government, Nonfederal **Service**: General medical and surgical

**Staffed Beds**: 20 **Admissions**: 182 **Census**: 2 **Outpatient Visits**: 9118
**Births**: 0 **Total Expense ($000)**: 4680 **Payroll Expense ($000)**: 2095
**Personnel**: 37

### SENECA—Nemaha County

★ **NEMAHA VALLEY COMMUNITY HOSPITAL (171315)**, 1600 Community Drive,
Zip 66538–9739; tel. 785/336–6181, (Nonreporting) **A**10 18 **F**11 12 13 15 28
34 35 40 50 57 59 64 65 75 76 77 78 79 81 84 85 89 93 107 114 119 127
129 130 131 132 133 135 146 154 156 **P**6
Primary Contact: Kiley Floyd, Chief Executive Officer
CFO: Abbie Thomas, Chief Financial Officer
CMO: Tony Bartkoski, M.D., Chief of Medical Staff
CHR: Ronnette Worthley, Manager Human Resource
CNO: Lynda Cross, R.N., Director of Nurses
Web address: www.nemvch.org
**Control**: Other not–for–profit (including NFP Corporation) **Service**: General
medical and surgical

**Staffed Beds**: 15 **Admissions**: 270 **Census**: 5 **Outpatient Visits**: 19403
**Births**: 58 **Total Expense ($000)**: 17350 **Payroll Expense ($000)**: 8308
**Personnel**: 157

### SHAWNEE MISSION—Johnson County

⊠ **ADVENTHEALTH SHAWNEE MISSION (170104)**, 9100 West 74th
Street, Zip 66204–4004, Mailing Address: Box 2923, Zip 66201–1323;
tel. 913/676–2000, (Nonreporting) **A**1 2 3 5 10 **F**3 4 5 8 11 12 13 15 17 18 20
22 24 26 28 29 30 31 32 34 35 36 40 42 45 46 47 48 49 53 54 55 56 57 58
59 60 61 62 64 65 70 72 74 75 76 77 78 79 80 81 82 83 84 85 86 87 89 93
96 97 98 100 101 102 103 104 105 106 107 108 110 111 114 115 117 118
119 120 121 123 124 126 129 130 131 132 135 141 142 144 145 146 147
148 149 153 154 156 157 **P**6 **S** AdventHealth, Altamonte Springs, FL
Primary Contact: Michael Knecht, President
CFO: Karsten Randolph, Executive Vice President and Chief Financial Officer
CMO: Sherri Martin, M.D., President Medical Staff
CIO: Mike Allen, Director Information Services
CHR: Brad Hoffman, Administrative Director Human Resources
CNO: Sheri Hawkins, Chief Nursing Officer
Web address: www.shawneemission.org
**Control**: Church operated, Nongovernment, not–for–profit **Service**: General
medical and surgical

**Staffed Beds**: 397 **Admissions**: 20227 **Census**: 226 **Outpatient
Visits**: 631496 **Births**: 4773 **Total Expense ($000)**: 477960 **Payroll
Expense ($000)**: 190600 **Personnel**: 2812

⊠ **MID—AMERICA REHABILITATION HOSPITAL (173026)**, 5701 West 110th
Street, Zip 66211–2503, Mailing Address: Overland Park, tel. 913/491–2400,
(Nonreporting) **A**1 10 **F**29 34 36 56 62 68 82 87 90 93 94 95 96 100 130 132
135 148 **S** Encompass Health Corporation, Birmingham, AL
Primary Contact: Tiffany Kiehl, Chief Executive Officer
CFO: Richard Lane, Chief Financial Officer
CMO: Cielo Dehning, M.D., Medical Director
CHR: Elizabeth Gibson, Director Human Resources
CNO: Amy McKay, Chief Nursing Officer
Web address: www.midamericarehabhospital.com
**Control**: Corporation, Investor–owned (for–profit) **Service**: Rehabilitation

**Staffed Beds**: 98 **Admissions**: 1718 **Census**: 57 **Outpatient Visits**: 9625
**Births**: 0 **Total Expense ($000)**: 28218 **Payroll Expense ($000)**: 14835
**Personnel**: 222

**SHAWNEE MISSION MEDICAL CENTER** See Adventhealth Shawnee Mission

### SMITH CENTER—Smith County

★ **SMITH COUNTY MEMORIAL HOSPITAL (171377)**, 921 East Highway 36,
Zip 66967; tel. 785/282–6845, (Nonreporting) **A**10 18 **F**3 13 15 28 29 30 31
34 40 43 45 53 64 65 68 69 75 76 81 85 89 91 93 107 110 114 119 127 128
130 133 135 154 156 **P**6 **S** Great Plains Health Alliance, Inc., Wichita, KS
Primary Contact: Allen Van Driel, Chief Executive Officer
CFO: Avery Aiken, Chief Financial Officer
CIO: Tammy Gaston, Chief Information Officer
CHR: Julie Haresnape, Coordinator Human Resources
CNO: Sarah Ragsdale, Chief Nursing Officer
Web address: www.scmhks.org
**Control**: Other not–for–profit (including NFP Corporation) **Service**: General
medical and surgical

**Staffed Beds**: 16 **Admissions**: 525 **Census**: 5 **Outpatient Visits**: 28620
**Births**: 45 **Total Expense ($000)**: 17960 **Payroll Expense ($000)**: 6445
**Personnel**: 117

## STAFFORD—Stafford County

★ **STAFFORD COUNTY HOSPITAL (171323)**, 502 South Buckeye Street,
Zip 67578–2035, Mailing Address: P.O. Box 190, Zip 67578–0190;
tel. 620/234–5221, (Nonreporting) **A**10 18 **F**3 15 29 35 40 57 59 62 64 67 77
93 107 128 130 133
Primary Contact: Todd Taylor, Chief Executive Officer
Web address: www.staffordcounty.org
**Control**: County, Government, Nonfederal **Service**: General medical and surgical

**Staffed Beds**: 25 **Admissions**: 48 **Census**: 1 **Outpatient Visits**: 41357
**Births**: 0 **Total Expense ($000)**: 8321 **Payroll Expense ($000)**: 249
**Personnel**: 42

**STAFFORD DISTRICT HOSPITAL 4** See Stafford County Hospital

## SYRACUSE—Hamilton County

★ **HAMILTON COUNTY HOSPITAL (171322)**, 700 North Huser Street,
Zip 67878–0948, Mailing Address: P.O. Box 948, Zip 67878–0948;
tel. 620/384–7461, (Nonreporting) **A**10 18 **F**3 34 40 41 57 59 64 75 83 85 86
87 91 93 97 107 111 114 127 130 133 143
Primary Contact: Brandon Bullard, Chief Executive Officer
CMO: Richard Carter, M.D., Chief Medical Director
CNO: Malachi Lones, Chief Nursing Officer
Web address: www.myhch.org
**Control**: County, Government, Nonfederal **Service**: General medical and surgical

**Staffed Beds**: 25 **Admissions**: 54 **Census**: 2 **Outpatient Visits**: 5835
**Births**: 0 **Total Expense ($000)**: 7518 **Payroll Expense ($000)**: 1087
**Personnel**: 44

## TOPEKA—Shawnee County

**COLMERY-O'NEIL VETERANS AFFAIRS MEDICAL CENTER** See Veterans
Affairs Eastern Kansas Health Care System-Colmery-O'Neil Veterans Affairs Medical
Center

**KANSAS NEUROLOGICAL INSTITUTE**, 3107 West 21st Street,
Zip 66604–3298; tel. 785/296–5301, (Nonreporting)
Primary Contact: Brent Widick, Superintendent
CFO: Sara Hoyer, Director Administrative Services
CMO: Mary Gingrich, Director Health Care Services
CIO: Cheryl Fuller, Director Information Resources
CHR: Shawna Mercer, Director Human Resources
Web address: www.kdads.ks.gov/state-hospitals-and-institutions/kansas-
neurological-institute
**Control**: State, Government, Nonfederal **Service**: Intellectual disabilities

**Staffed Beds**: 142

⊞ **KANSAS REHABILITATION HOSPITAL (173025)**, 1504 SW Eighth Avenue,
Zip 66606–1632; tel. 785/235–6600, (Nonreporting) **A**1 10 **F**29 75 86 90 91 95
96 130 132 148 149 **S** Encompass Health Corporation, Birmingham, AL
Primary Contact: William J. Overbey, Chief Executive Officer
CMO: Joseph Sankoorikal, M.D., Chief Medical Staff
CHR: Dina Cox, Director Human Resources
CNO: Carol Swanger, Chief Nursing Officer
Web address: www.kansasrehabhospital.com
**Control**: Corporation, Investor–owned (for–profit) **Service**: Rehabilitation

**Staffed Beds**: 57 **Admissions**: 1192 **Census**: 36 **Outpatient Visits**: 0
**Births**: 0 **Total Expense ($000)**: 16623 **Payroll Expense ($000)**: 7954
**Personnel**: 137

**ST. FRANCIS HEALTH** See University of Kansas Health System St. Francis
Campus

⊞ **STORMONT VAIL HEALTH (170086)**, 1500 SW Tenth Avenue, Zip 66604–1353;
tel. 785/354–6000, (Nonreporting) **A**1 2 10 **F**3 8 11 12 13 15 17 18 19 20 22
24 26 28 29 30 31 34 35 37 40 43 44 45 46 47 49 50 51 54 55 56 57 58 59
60 61 64 65 68 70 71 72 74 75 76 77 78 79 81 82 84 85 86 87 88 89 91 92
93 97 98 99 100 101 102 103 104 105 107 108 110 111 112 114 115 116
117 118 119 120 121 123 126 129 130 131 132 135 143 144 145 146 147
148 149 150 153 154 156 **P**6
Primary Contact: Rob Kenagy, M.D., President and Chief Executive Officer
CFO: Robert Langland, Senior Vice President and Chief Financial Officer
CMO: Kevin Dishman, M.D., Chief Medical Officer
CIO: Judy Corzine, Administrative Director and Chief Information Officer
CHR: Darlene Stone, Chief Experience Officer
CNO: Carol Perry, R.N., Vice President and Chief Nursing Officer
Web address: www.stormontvail.org
**Control**: Other not–for–profit (including NFP Corporation) **Service**: General
medical and surgical

**Staffed Beds**: 390 **Admissions**: 23902 **Census**: 264 **Outpatient**
**Visits**: 148958 **Births**: 1722 **Total Expense ($000)**: 725366 **Payroll**
**Expense ($000)**: 381286 **Personnel**: 4547

**STORMONT-VAIL HEALTHCARE** See Stormont Vail Health

⊞ **UNIVERSITY OF KANSAS HEALTH SYSTEM ST. FRANCIS CAMPUS**
**(170016)**, 1700 SW 7th Street, Zip 66606–1690; tel. 785/295–8000,
(Nonreporting) **A**1 2 3 5 10 **F**8 12 13 15 18 20 22 24 26 28 29 31 34 35 36 37
38 40 44 45 47 48 49 50 51 53 54 56 57 58 59 61 62 64 65 70 71 73 74 75
76 77 78 79 80 81 82 85 86 87 89 90 92 93 95 96 107 108 110 111 115 116
117 118 119 120 121 123 126 127 129 130 131 132 135 146 147 148 149
154 **P**6 **S** Ardent Health Services, Nashville, TN
Primary Contact: Steven Anderson, Chief Executive Officer
CFO: Samuel Moore, Chief Financial Officer
CMO: Jaquelyn Hyland, M.D., Chief Medical Officer
CIO: Jamie Hilliard, Director of Information Technology
CHR: Steve Saffa, Director Human Resources
CNO: Lisa Alexander, Vice President Patient Services and Chief Nursing Officer
Web address: www.stfrancistopeka.org
**Control**: Partnership, Investor–owned (for–profit) **Service**: General medical and
surgical

**Staffed Beds**: 264 **Admissions**: 7750 **Census**: 84 **Outpatient**
**Visits**: 190576 **Births**: 912 **Total Expense ($000)**: 253280 **Payroll Expense**
**($000)**: 95854 **Personnel**: 1349

⊞ **VETERANS AFFAIRS EASTERN KANSAS HEALTH CARE SYSTEM**, 2200 South
West Gage Boulevard, Zip 66622–0002; tel. 785/350–3111, (Includes VETERANS
AFFAIRS EASTERN KANSAS HEALTH CARE SYSTEM-COLMERY-O'NEIL VETERANS
AFFAIRS MEDICAL CENTER, Mailing address: 2200 South West Gage Boulevard,
Topeka, Kansas, Zip 66622–0002; tel. 785/350–3111; VETERANS AFFAIRS
EASTERN KANSAS HEALTH CARE SYSTEM-DWIGHT D. EISENHOWER VETERANS
AFFAIRS MEDICAL CENTER, Mailing address: 4101 South 4th Street Trafficway,
Leavenworth, Kansas, Zip 66048–5055; tel. 913/682–2000), (Nonreporting) **A**1
3 5 **F**1 3 4 5 6 11 18 29 30 31 33 34 35 36 38 39 40 44 45 50 53 54 56 57
58 59 62 63 64 65 66 70 71 74 75 77 78 79 81 82 84 85 86 87 93 94 96
97 98 100 101 103 104 105 106 107 108 111 115 116 117 119 127 128
129 130 132 135 144 146 147 148 149 150 152 153 154 156 157 158 **S**
Department of Veterans Affairs, Washington, DC
Primary Contact: Anthony Rudy. Klopfer, FACHE, Director
COO: John Moon, Associate Director
CMO: Rajeev Trehan, M.D., M.P.H., Chief of Staff
CIO: Joni Davin, Director Information and Business Management Service Line
Web address: www.topeka.va.gov/
**Control**: Veterans Affairs, Government, federal **Service**: Chronic disease

**Staffed Beds**: 130 **Admissions**: 4 **Census**: 1 **Outpatient Visits**: 3300
**Births**: 0 **Personnel**: 1250

**VETERANS AFFAIRS EASTERN KANSAS HEALTH CARE SYSTEM-COLMERY-**
**O'NEIL VETERANS AFFAIRS MEDICAL CENTER** See Veterans Affairs Eastern
Kansas Health Care System, Topeka

## TRIBUNE—Greeley County

★ **GREELEY COUNTY HEALTH SERVICES (171359)**, 506 Third Street,
Zip 67879–9684, Mailing Address: P.O. Box 338, Zip 67879–0338;
tel. 620/376–4221, (Total facility includes 32 beds in nursing home–type unit)
(Nonreporting) **A**10 18 **F**3 28 29 32 34 40 45 50 57 59 64 65 66 69 81 93 97
107 127 133 147 **S** QHR Health, Brentwood, TN
Primary Contact: Trice Watts, Chief Financial Officer and Chief Executive Officer
CFO: Trice Watts, Chief Financial Officer
CMO: Wendel Ellis, D.O., Chief Medical Staff
CIO: Shanon Schneider, Chief Information Officer
CHR: Katelyn Reynolds, Manager Human Resources
CNO: Janie Schmidt, Director of Nursing
Web address: www.mygchs.com
**Control**: Other not–for–profit (including NFP Corporation) **Service**: General medical and surgical

**Staffed Beds**: 50 **Admissions**: 207 **Census**: 29 **Outpatient Visits**: 11747
**Births**: 0 **Total Expense ($000)**: 12287 **Payroll Expense ($000)**: 5948
**Personnel**: 110

**GREELEY COUNTY HOSPITAL** See Greeley County Health Services

## ULYSSES—Grant County

★ **BOB WILSON MEMORIAL GRANT COUNTY HOSPITAL (170110)**, 415 North
Main Street, Zip 67880–2133; tel. 620/356–1266, (Nonreporting) **A**10 20 **F**3
11 13 15 29 30 34 35 40 45 50 57 59 64 68 75 76 79 81 82 85 86 87 91
93 96 97 107 119 127 130 133 146 148 154 157 **P**6 **S** CommonSpirit Health,
Chicago, IL
Primary Contact: Christine McSweeney, FACHE, President and Chief Executive Officer
CFO: Amanda Vaughan, Chief Financial Officer
CIO: Chris Moffet, Director Information Services
CHR: Tammy Oxford, Director Human Resources
Web address: www.bwmgch.com
**Control**: Corporation, Investor–owned (for–profit) **Service**: General medical and surgical

**Staffed Beds**: 26 **Admissions**: 191 **Census**: 2 **Outpatient Visits**: 7486
**Births**: 11 **Total Expense ($000)**: 14879 **Payroll Expense ($000)**: 5126
**Personnel**: 72

## WAKEENEY—Trego County

★ **TREGO COUNTY-LEMKE MEMORIAL HOSPITAL (171355)**, 320 North 13th
Street, Zip 67672–2099; tel. 785/743–2182, (Total facility includes 37 beds in
nursing home–type unit) (Nonreporting) **A**10 18 **F**3 8 10 11 15 28 29 34 40 45
53 57 59 62 64 67 69 71 81 86 89 93 107 110 114 127 128 130 133 143
146 148 154 156 **P**6 **S** Great Plains Health Alliance, Inc., Wichita, KS
Primary Contact: David Augustine, Chief Executive Officer
CFO: ReChelle Horinek, Chief Financial Officer
CMO: Gordon Lang, M.D., Chief of Staff
CHR: Jeff Bieker, Director Human Resource
CNO: Sandy Purinton, Chief Nursing Officer
Web address: www.tclmh.org
**Control**: County, Government, Nonfederal **Service**: General medical and surgical

**Staffed Beds**: 62 **Admissions**: 524 **Census**: 45 **Outpatient Visits**: 25628
**Births**: 0 **Total Expense ($000)**: 17578 **Payroll Expense ($000)**: 8013
**Personnel**: 182

## WAMEGO—Pottawatomie County

**WAMEGO CITY HOSPITAL** See Wamego Health Center

★ **WAMEGO HEALTH CENTER (171337)**, 711 Genn Drive, Zip 66547–1179;
tel. 785/456–2295, (Nonreporting) **A**10 18 **F**3 11 15 28 29 34 40 45 56 59 64
65 75 77 81 93 97 107 114 119 127 130 131 132 133 143 146 147 148 149
Primary Contact: Steve Land, Senior Administrator
COO: Brian Smith, Director of Operations
CFO: Keith Zachariasen, Chief Financial Officer
CMO: Roland Darey, M.D., Medical Director
CIO: Wes Janzen, Chief Information Officer
CHR: Renee Reed, Director Human Resources
CNO: Tresha Flanary, R.N., Chief Clinical Services Officer
Web address: www.https://www.wamegohealthcenter.com
**Control**: Other not–for–profit (including NFP Corporation) **Service**: General medical and surgical

**Staffed Beds**: 18 **Admissions**: 250 **Census**: 5 **Outpatient Visits**: 41969
**Births**: 0 **Total Expense ($000)**: 12712 **Payroll Expense ($000)**: 6100
**Personnel**: 82

## WASHINGTON—Washington County

**WASHINGTON COUNTY HOSPITAL (171351)**, 304 East Third Street,
Zip 66968–2033; tel. 785/325–2211, (Nonreporting) **A**10 18 **F**3 11 13 15 28 29
34 35 40 41 45 64 67 68 69 76 81 83 85 91 93 97 107 110 114 127 133 144
148 149 154 **P**6
Primary Contact: Roxanne Schottel, Chief Executive Officer
CFO: Roxanne Schottel, Chief Executive Officer
CNO: Kelly Otott, R.N., Chief Nursing Officer
Web address: www.washingtoncountyhospital.net
**Control**: County, Government, Nonfederal **Service**: General medical and surgical

**Staffed Beds**: 18 **Admissions**: 306 **Census**: 3 **Outpatient Visits**: 9775
**Births**: 14 **Total Expense ($000)**: 6593 **Payroll Expense ($000)**: 2758
**Personnel**: 47

## WICHITA—Sedgwick County

**AMG SPECIALTY HOSPITAL-WICHITA (172003)**, 8080 East Pawnee Street,
Zip 67207–5475; tel. 316/682–0004, (Nonreporting) **A**10 **S** AMG Integrated
Healthcare Management, Lafayette, LA
Primary Contact: Robert A. Loepp Jr, FACHE, Chief Executive Officer
CFO: Myra Dick, Manager Business Office
CIO: Michelle Bradley, Director Health Information Management
CHR: Adrienne Burkholder, Director Human Resources
Web address: www.amgwichita.com/
**Control**: Corporation, Investor–owned (for–profit) **Service**: Acute long–term care hospital

**Staffed Beds**: 26

⊞ **ASCENSION VIA CHRISTI HOSPITAL ON ST. TERESA (170200)**, 14800 West
St. Teresa, Zip 67235–9602; tel. 316/796–7000, (Nonreporting) **A**1 10 **F**3 8 18
20 22 29 30 34 35 40 45 50 64 68 70 75 78 79 81 85 87 90 92 93 96 107
108 111 114 118 119 130 146 147 148 154 **S** Ascension Healthcare, Saint
Louis, MO
Primary Contact: Laurie Labarca, President
Web address: www.via-christi.org/st-teresa
**Control**: Church operated, Nongovernment, not–for–profit **Service**: General medical and surgical

**Staffed Beds**: 48 **Admissions**: 1566 **Census**: 21 **Outpatient Visits**: 27543
**Births**: 0 **Total Expense ($000)**: 32420 **Payroll Expense ($000)**: 9440
**Personnel**: 137

**ASCENSION VIA CHRISTI HOSPITAL ST. FRANCIS** See St. Francis Campus

⊞ **ASCENSION VIA CHRISTI REHABILITATION HOSPITAL (173028)**, 1151 North
Rock Road, Zip 67206–1262; tel. 316/634–3400, (Nonreporting) **A**1 10 **F**11 29
30 34 35 44 50 54 57 69 64 77 86 87 90 92 93 95 96 119 129 130 131 132
143 146 148 **S** Ascension Healthcare, Saint Louis, MO
Primary Contact: Laurie Labarca, President
CMO: Kevin Rieg, M.D., President Medical Staff
CNO: Cindy Hagerty, Assistant Chief Nurse Officer and Administrator of Operations
Web address: www.via-christi.org
**Control**: Church operated, Nongovernment, not–for–profit **Service**: Rehabilitation

**Staffed Beds**: 21 **Admissions**: 596 **Census**: 18 **Outpatient Visits**: 104540
**Births**: 0 **Total Expense ($000)**: 21312 **Payroll Expense ($000)**: 8827
**Personnel**: 156

**CHILDREN'S CENTER AT WESLEY** See Wesley Children's Hospital

**GALICHIA HEART HOSPITAL** See Wesley Woodlawn Hospital & Er

**HCA WESLEY REHABILITATION HOSP** See Wesley Rehabilitation Hospital

**KANSAS HEART HOSPITAL (170186)**, 3601 North Webb Road,
Zip 67226–8129; tel. 316/630–5000, (Nonreporting) **A**10
Primary Contact: Thomas L. Ashcom, M.D., Ph.D., Chief Executive Officer
COO: Joyce Heismeyer, Chief Operating Officer
CFO: Steve Smith, Chief Financial Officer
CHR: Teresa E Wolfe, Manager Human Resources
CNO: Susan Bradford, Director Nursing
Web address: www.kansasheart.com
**Control**: Corporation, Investor–owned (for–profit) **Service**: Heart

**Staffed Beds**: 54

*Many Facility Codes have changed. Please refer to the AHA Guide Code Chart.* © 2021 AHA Guide

**KANSAS SPINE & SPECIALTY HOSPITAL (170196)**, 3333 North Webb Road, Zip 67226–8123; tel. 316/462–5000, (Nonreporting) **A**10 **F**3 29 79 81 82 85 87 107 111 114 126 149 **P**2
Primary Contact: Thomas M. Schmitt, Chief Executive Officer
CFO: Jennifer Gerken, R.N., Chief Financial Officer
CIO: Michael Knocke, Chief Information Officer
CHR: Angela L. Anderson, Manager Human Resource
CNO: John Coslett, R.N., Chief Nursing Officer
Web address: www.ksspine.com
**Control**: Corporation, Investor–owned (for–profit) **Service**: General medical and surgical

**Staffed Beds**: 36 **Admissions**: 2176 **Census**: 13 **Outpatient Visits**: 11601
**Births**: 0 **Personnel**: 181

**KANSAS SPINE AND SPECIALTY HOSPITAL** See Kansas Spine & Specialty Hospital

○ **KANSAS SURGERY AND RECOVERY CENTER (170183)**, 2770 North Webb Road, Zip 67226–8112; tel. 316/634–0090, (Nonreporting) **A**3 10 11 **F**45 51 64 68 79 81 85 87 93 107 111 114 119 126 130
Primary Contact: Ely Bartal, M.D., Chief Executive Officer
CFO: Ashley Simon, Chief Financial Officer
CMO: Ely Bartal, M.D., Chief Executive Officer and Medical Director
CIO: Jonathan Wells, Supervisor Information Technology
CNO: Becky Bailey, R.N., Director Nursing
Web address: www.ksrc.org
**Control**: Partnership, Investor–owned (for–profit) **Service**: Surgical

**Staffed Beds**: 32 **Admissions**: 2096 **Census**: 12 **Outpatient Visits**: 11789
**Births**: 0 **Total Expense ($000)**: 33305 **Payroll Expense ($000)**: 8594
**Personnel**: 154

**LTAC OF WICHITA** See Amg Specialty Hospital-Wichita

✠ **ROBERT J. DOLE VETERANS AFFAIRS MEDICAL CENTER**, 5500 East Kellogg, Zip 67218–1607; tel. 316/685–2221, (Nonreporting) **A**1 3 5 **S** Department of Veterans Affairs, Washington, DC
Primary Contact: Candace Ifabiyi, Medical Center Director
CFO: Ronald Dreher, Finance Officer
CMO: Kent Murray, M.D., Chief of Staff
CIO: Sharon Williamson, Chief Information Technology
CHR: Nancy Gerstner, Manager Human Resources
Web address: www.wichita.va.gov
**Control**: Veterans Affairs, Government, federal **Service**: General medical and surgical

**Staffed Beds**: 41

✠ **SELECT SPECIALTY HOSPITAL-WICHITA (172007)**, 929 North St Francis Street, Zip 67214–3821; tel. 316/261–8303, (Nonreporting) **A**1 2 3 10 **S** Select Medical Corporation, Mechanicsburg, PA
Primary Contact: Christopher Keith, Chief Executive Officer
CHR: Renee Schaffer, Coordinator Human Resources
CNO: Lindsey Cahoj, Chief Nursing Officer
Web address: www.selectspecialtyhospitals.com/company/locations/wichita.aspx
**Control**: Corporation, Investor–owned (for–profit) **Service**: Acute long–term care hospital

**Staffed Beds**: 48

**VETERANS AFFAIRS MED & REG CTR** See Robert J. Dole Veterans Affairs Medical Center

**VIA CHRISTI BEHAVIORAL HEALTH CENTER** See Good Shepherd Campus

**VIA CHRISTI HOSPITAL ON ST. TERESA** See Ascension Via Christi Hospital on St. Teresa

**VIA CHRISTI REHABILITATION HOSPITAL** See Ascension Via Christi Rehabilitation Hospital

**VIA CHRISTI ST. JOSEPH** See St. Joseph Campus

✠ **WESLEY HEALTHCARE CENTER (170123)**, 550 North Hillside, Zip 67214–4976; tel. 316/962–2000, (Includes WESLEY CHILDREN'S HOSPITAL, Mailing address: 550 North Hillside Street, Wichita, Kansas, Zip 67214–4910; tel. 316/962–2000; WESLEY WOODLAWN HOSPITAL & ER, Mailing address: 2610 North Woodlawn, Wichita, Kansas, Zip 67220; tel. 316/858–2610; Thomas Owings, Chief Executive Officer), (Nonreporting) **A**1 2 3 5 10 **S** HCA Healthcare, Nashville, TN
Primary Contact: Bill Voloch, President and Chief Executive Officer
CFO: Bradley Schultz, Chief Financial Officer
CMO: Francie H Ekengren, M.D., Chief Medical Officer
CIO: Jeffrey Schauf, Director Information Systems
CHR: Jennifer Krier, Vice President Human Resources
Web address: www.wesleymc.com
**Control**: Corporation, Investor–owned (for–profit) **Service**: General medical and surgical

**Staffed Beds**: 859

**WESLEY MEDICAL CENTER** See Wesley Healthcare Center

✠ **WESLEY REHABILITATION HOSPITAL (173027)**, 8338 West 13th Street North, Zip 67212–2984; tel. 316/729–9999, (Nonreporting) **A**1 10 **F**29 34 62 63 64 68 90 91 93 95 96 132 148 **S** Encompass Health Corporation, Birmingham, AL
Primary Contact: Thomas Laughlin, Chief Executive Officer
CFO: Bob Peck, Chief Financial Officer
CIO: Debbie Patterson, Director Health Information Management
CHR: Betty Shuman, Director Human Resources
CNO: Jessika M Workman, Chief Nursing Officer
Web address: www.wesleyrehabhospital.com
**Control**: Corporation, Investor–owned (for–profit) **Service**: Rehabilitation

**Staffed Beds**: 65 **Admissions**: 961 **Census**: 35 **Outpatient Visits**: 8372
**Births**: 0 **Total Expense ($000)**: 17369 **Payroll Expense ($000)**: 8461
**Personnel**: 149

**WINCHESTER—Jefferson County**

★ **F. W. HUSTON MEDICAL CENTER (171314)**, 408 Delaware Street, Zip 66097–4003; tel. 913/774–4340, (Total facility includes 38 beds in nursing home–type unit) (Nonreporting) **A**10 18 **F**3 10 40 56 57 64 67 69 75 77 93 97 104 107 111 125 128 130 133 143 144 **P**8
Primary Contact: LaMont Cook, Administrator
CFO: Jason Johnson, Controller
CMO: William Greiner, M.D., Chief of Staff
CIO: Jason Johnson, Controller
CHR: Melody Keirns, Manager Human Resources
CNO: Heather R Aranda, R.N., MSN, Chief Nursing Officer
Web address: www.jcmhospital.org
**Control**: Other not–for–profit (including NFP Corporation) **Service**: General medical and surgical

**Staffed Beds**: 69 **Admissions**: 59 **Census**: 31 **Outpatient Visits**: 11502
**Births**: 0 **Total Expense ($000)**: 6077 **Payroll Expense ($000)**: 3932
**Personnel**: 71

**JEFFERSON COUNTY MEMORIAL HOSPITAL** See F. W. Huston Medical Center

**WINFIELD—Cowley County**

★ **WILLIAM NEWTON HOSPITAL (171383)**, 1300 East Fifth Street, Zip 67156–2407; tel. 620/221–2300, (Nonreporting) **A**5 10 18 **F**3 8 11 13 15 17 18 28 29 34 35 40 45 50 56 57 59 62 64 65 69 70 75 76 77 79 81 85 89 91 93 94 97 107 108 110 111 115 119 127 130 133 146 148 149 150 156
Primary Contact: J. Ben. Quinton, Administrator
COO: Shona Salzman, Chief Operating Officer
CFO: Brian Barta, Assistant Administrator and Chief Financial Officer
CMO: Bryan Dennett, M.D., Chief of Staff
CIO: Randy Mayo, Director Information Technology
CHR: Cathy McClurg, Director Human Resources
Web address: www.wnmh.org
**Control**: Other not–for–profit (including NFP Corporation) **Service**: General medical and surgical

**Staffed Beds**: 25 **Admissions**: 1331 **Census**: 13 **Outpatient Visits**: 85896
**Births**: 293 **Total Expense ($000)**: 41755 **Payroll Expense ($000)**: 17175
**Personnel**: 333

**WILLIAM NEWTON MEM HOSPITAL** See William Newton Hospital

**KS**

# KENTUCKY

## ALBANY—Clinton County

**CLINTON COUNTY HOSPITAL** See The Medical Center Albany

**THE MEDICAL CENTER ALBANY (180106)**, 723 Burkesville Road, Zip 42602–1654; tel. 606/387–8000, (Nonreporting) **A**10 **S** Med Center Health, Bowling Green, KY
Primary Contact: Laura Belcher, Administrator
CFO: Ronald G. Sowell, FACHE, Executive Vice President, Chief Financial Officer
CIO: Mark Brookman, Chief Information Officer
CHR: Lynn Williams, Vice President, Human Resources
Web address: www.chc.net/services/hospitals/the_medical_center_at_albany.aspx
**Control:** Other not–for–profit (including NFP Corporation) **Service:** General medical and surgical

| **Staffed Beds:** 42 |
|---|

## ASHLAND—Boyd County

☐ **KING'S DAUGHTERS MEDICAL CENTER (180009)**, 2201 Lexington Avenue, Zip 41101–2874, Mailing Address: P.O. Box 151, Zip 41105–0151; tel. 606/408–4000, (Nonreporting) **A**1 2 3 5 10
Primary Contact: Kristie Whitlatch, President
COO: Bob Lucas, Vice President Operations
CFO: Paul L McDowell, Vice President Finance and Chief Financial Officer
CMO: Phil Fioret, M.D., Vice President Medical Affairs
CIO: David Oliver, Director Information Systems
Web address: www.kdmc.com
**Control:** Other not–for–profit (including NFP Corporation) **Service:** General medical and surgical

| **Staffed Beds:** 448 |
|---|

**KING'S DAUGHTERS' MEDICAL CTR** See King's Daughters Medical Center

## BARBOURVILLE—Knox County

⇧ **BARBOURVILLE ARH** See Barbourville ARH Hospital

⇧ **BARBOURVILLE ARH HOSPITAL (181328)**, 80 Hospital Drive, Zip 40906–7363, Mailing Address: P.O. Box 10, Zip 40906–0010; tel. 606/546–4175, (Nonreporting) **A**10 18 21 **F**3 11 15 28 29 30 34 35 39 40 50 57 59 64 70 81 85 87 107 108 110 114 119 127 130 133 146 154
Primary Contact: Charles D. Lovell Jr, FACHE, Chief Executive Officer
CFO: Amanda Ellis, Chief Financial Officer
CMO: Kamran Hasni, M.D., Chief of Medical Staff
CIO: Evan Davis, Director Technology and Environmental Services
CHR: Janet Wilder, Director Human Resources
CNO: Brenda Graham, Chief Nursing Officer
Web address: www.https://www.arh.org/locations/barbourville.aspx
**Control:** Other not–for–profit (including NFP Corporation) **Service:** General medical and surgical

| **Staffed Beds:** 25 **Admissions:** 789 **Census:** 8 **Outpatient Visits:** 44917 **Births:** 0 |
|---|

## BARDSTOWN—Nelson County

⊞ **CHI FLAGET MEMORIAL HOSPITAL (180025)**, 4305 New Shepherdsville Road, Zip 40004–9019; tel. 502/350–5000, (Nonreporting) **A**1 2 3 5 10 **F**3 11 12 13 15 18 29 30 31 34 35 37 40 45 49 55 59 60 62 63 64 70 76 78 79 81 82 84 85 87 91 93 96 107 111 116 117 119 120 128 129 130 132 144 146 147 148 **S** CommonSpirit Health, Chicago, IL
Primary Contact: Jennifer Nolan, President and Chief Executive Officer
CFO: Jim Wentz, Chief Financial Officer
CMO: Mickey Anderson, M.D., Vice President Medical Affairs
CHR: Tanja Oquendo, Chief Human Resources Officer
CNO: Norma Goss, R.N., Chief Nursing Officer
Web address: www.kentuckyonehealth.org/flaget
**Control:** Other not–for–profit (including NFP Corporation) **Service:** General medical and surgical

| **Staffed Beds:** 42 **Admissions:** 2587 **Census:** 27 **Outpatient Visits:** 75232 **Births:** 300 **Total Expense ($000):** 67838 **Payroll Expense ($000):** 17266 **Personnel:** 287 |
|---|

**FLAGET MEMORIAL HOSPITAL** See Chi Flaget Memorial Hospital

## BENTON—Marshall County

**MARSHALL COUNTY HOSPITAL**A1 10 18 **F**3 11 15 18 19 28 29 30 34 35 40 57 59 62 77 79 81 85 90 93 107 108 119 127 130 132 133 135 148 149 **P**6
Primary Contact: , R.N.
CFO: Janice Kelley, Chief Financial Officer
CMO: Edwin Perez, M.D., Chief of Medical Staff
CIO: Dave Cope, Director Information Systems
CHR: Janice Bone, Human Resources
Web address: www.marshallcountyhospital.org

⊞ **MARSHALL COUNTY HOSPITAL (181327)**, 615 Old Symsonia Road, Zip 42025–5042; tel. 270/527–4800, (Nonreporting) **A**1 10 18 **F**3 11 15 18 19 28 29 30 34 35 40 57 59 62 77 79 81 85 90 93 107 108 119 127 130 132 133 135 148 149 **P**6
Primary Contact: David G. Fuqua, Chief Executive Officer
CFO: Janice Kelley, Chief Financial Officer
CMO: Edwin Perez, M.D., Chief of Medical Staff
CIO: Dave Cope, Director Information Systems
CHR: Janice Bone, Human Resources
Web address: www.marshallcountyhospital.org
**Control:** Hospital district or authority, Government, Nonfederal **Service:** General medical and surgical

| **Staffed Beds:** 25 **Admissions:** 587 **Census:** 5 **Outpatient Visits:** 16994 **Births:** 0 **Total Expense ($000):** 22048 **Payroll Expense ($000):** 9069 **Personnel:** 223 |
|---|

## BEREA—Madison County

⊞ **CHI SAINT JOSEPH BEREA (181329)**, 305 Estill Street, Zip 40403–1909; tel. 859/986–3151, (Nonreporting) **A**1 10 18 **F**3 29 40 45 70 77 79 81 82 91 97 107 111 114 119 133 156 **P**4 **S** CommonSpirit Health, Chicago, IL
Primary Contact: Terrence G. Deis, CPA, FACHE, President
CFO: Christy Spitser, Vice President Finance
CMO: Joshua Huffman, M.D., Chief Medical Staff
CHR: Sandra Turqueza, Human Resources Business Partner
CNO: Leslie Adams, Chief Nursing Officer
Web address: www.kentuckyonehealth.org/berea
**Control:** Other not–for–profit (including NFP Corporation) **Service:** General medical and surgical

| **Staffed Beds:** 25 **Admissions:** 707 **Census:** 7 **Outpatient Visits:** 50297 **Births:** 0 **Total Expense ($000):** 24910 **Payroll Expense ($000):** 10222 **Personnel:** 165 |
|---|

**SAINT JOSEPH BEREA** See Chi Saint Joseph Berea

## BOWLING GREEN—Warren County

☐ **COMMONWEALTH REGIONAL SPECIALTY HOSPITAL (182005)**, 250 Park Drive, 6th Floor, Zip 42101–1760, Mailing Address: P.O. Box 90010, Zip 42102–9010; tel. 270/796–6200, (Nonreporting) **A**1 10 **F**1 3 29 30 34 35 50 57 68 85 87 130 135 143 146 148 149 **S** Med Center Health, Bowling Green, KY
Primary Contact: Christa Atkins, Administrator
CFO: Ronald G. Sowell, FACHE, Executive Vice President
CMO: Doug Thomson, M.D., Chief Medical Officer
CIO: Jean Cherry, Executive Vice President
CHR: Lynn Williams, Vice President Human Resources
Web address: www.commonwealthregionalspecialtyhospital.org
**Control:** Other not–for–profit (including NFP Corporation) **Service:** Acute long–term care hospital

| **Staffed Beds:** 28 **Admissions:** 270 **Census:** 15 **Outpatient Visits:** 0 **Births:** 0 **Personnel:** 55 |
|---|

**GREENVIEW REGIONAL HOSPITAL** See Tristar Greenview Regional Hospital

☐ **MEDICAL CENTER AT BOWLING GREEN (180013)**, 250 Park Street, Zip 42101–1795, Mailing Address: P.O. Box 90010, Zip 42102–9010; tel. 270/745–1000, (Nonreporting) **A**1 2 3 10 19 **F**1 3 7 12 13 15 17 18 20 22 24 26 28 29 30 31 34 37 39 40 45 46 48 49 50 51 56 57 58 59 60 62 64 68 70 73 74 75 76 78 79 81 82 84 85 86 87 91 92 93 98 100 102 103 104 107 108 110 111 114 115 116 117 118 119 120 121 122 123 124 126 129 130 132 135 145 146 147 148 149 154 **S** Med Center Health, Bowling Green, KY
Primary Contact: Connie Smith, FACHE, MSN, R.N., Chief Executive Officer
CFO: Ronald G. Sowell, FACHE, Executive Vice President
CIO: Mark Brookman, Chief Information Officer
CHR: Lynn Williams, Vice President Human Resources
CNO: Jill Payne, Executive Vice President and Chief Nursing Officer
Web address: www.themedicalcenter.org
**Control**: Other not–for–profit (including NFP Corporation) **Service**: General medical and surgical

**Staffed Beds: 337 Admissions: 16668 Census: 234 Outpatient Visits: 146019 Births: 2713 Personnel: 2052**

**MEDIPLEX REHABILITATION HOSP** See Southern Kentucky Rehabilitation Hospital

☐ **RIVENDELL BEHAVIORAL HEALTH (184017)**, 1035 Porter Pike, Zip 42103–9581; tel. 270/843–1199, (Nonreporting) **A**1 10 **S** Universal Health Services, Inc., King of Prussia, PA
Primary Contact: Matt Ours, Chief Executive Officer and Managing Director
CFO: Tim Gore, Chief Financial Officer
Web address: www.rivendellbehavioral.com
**Control**: Corporation, Investor–owned (for–profit) **Service**: Psychiatric

**Staffed Beds: 125**

✠ △ **SOUTHERN KENTUCKY REHABILITATION HOSPITAL (183029)**, 1300 Campbell Lane, Zip 42104–4162; tel. 270/594–5980, (Nonreporting) **A**1 7 10 **S** Vibra Healthcare, Mechanicsburg, PA
Primary Contact: Stuart Locke, Chief Executive Officer
COO: Dana Lewis, Director Clinical Services
CMO: Jim Farrage, M.D., Medical Director
CHR: Suzanne Cornett, Director Human Resources
Web address: www.skyrehab.com
**Control**: Corporation, Investor–owned (for–profit) **Service**: Rehabilitation

**Staffed Beds: 60**

**THE MEDICAL CENTER AT BOWLING GREEN** See Medical Center at Bowling Green

✠ **TRISTAR GREENVIEW REGIONAL HOSPITAL (180124)**, 1801 Ashley Circle, Zip 42104–3362; tel. 270/793–1000, (Nonreporting) **A**1 10 19 **S** HCA Healthcare, Nashville, TN
Primary Contact: Michael Sherrod, Chief Executive Officer
COO: Andrew Bedi, Chief Operating Officer
CMO: Wayne Bush, M.D., Chief of Staff
CIO: Cyndi Talley, Director Information Systems
CHR: Judy Fulkerson, Director Human Resources
Web address: www.greenviewhospital.com
**Control**: Corporation, Investor–owned (for–profit) **Service**: General medical and surgical

**Staffed Beds: 211**

## BURKESVILLE—Cumberland County

**CUMBERLAND COUNTY HOSPITAL (181317)**, 299 Glasgow Road, Zip 42717–9696, Mailing Address: P.O. Box 280, Zip 42717–0280; tel. 270/864–2511, (Nonreporting) **A**10 18
Primary Contact: Richard Neikirk, Chief Executive Officer
COO: Steve Burns, Chief Operating Officer
CFO: Rick Capps, Chief Financial Officer
CMO: Christian Konsavage, M.D., Chief of Staff
CHR: Martha Young, Director Human Resources
CNO: Susan S Flowers, MSN, R.N., Chief Nursing Officer
Web address: www.cchospital.org
**Control**: Other not–for–profit (including NFP Corporation) **Service**: General medical and surgical

**Staffed Beds: 25**

## CADIZ—Trigg County

**TRIGG COUNTY HOSPITAL (181304)**, 254 Main Street, Zip 42211–9153, Mailing Address: P.O. Box 312, Zip 42211–0312; tel. 270/522–3215, (Nonreporting) **A**10 18 **F**7 8 15 28 29 30 34 38 40 45 46 48 50 54 57 59 64 65 68 74 77 81 87 90 93 96 97 98 100 101 104 107 111 114 119 127 128 130 133 146 154
Primary Contact: John Sumner, Chief Executive Officer
CMO: Stuart Harris, M.D., Chief of Staff
CHR: Janet James, Director Human Resources
Web address: www.trigghospital.org
**Control**: City–county, Government, Nonfederal **Service**: General medical and surgical

**Staffed Beds: 18 Admissions: 348 Census: 8 Outpatient Visits: 39969 Births: 0 Total Expense ($000): 18245 Payroll Expense ($000): 7019 Personnel: 156**

## CAMPBELLSVILLE—Taylor County

**TAYLOR COUNTY HOSPITAL** See Taylor Regional Hospital

✠ **TAYLOR REGIONAL HOSPITAL (180087)**, 1700 Old Lebanon Road, Zip 42718–9600; tel. 270/465–3561, (Nonreporting) **A**1 2 10 **F**3 8 11 13 15 18 20 28 29 30 31 32 34 35 39 40 41 45 46 48 49 50 51 54 56 57 59 64 65 68 70 74 75 76 77 78 79 81 85 86 87 93 97 107 108 110 111 115 118 119 126 127 129 130 131 132 134 135 141 143 146 147 148 149 150 **P**6 **S** CommonSpirit Health, Chicago, IL
Primary Contact: Jane Wheatley, Chief Executive Officer
CFO: Paul Phillips, Chief Financial Officer
CIO: Christopher Michael Gibbs, Director Information Management Systems
CHR: Andrea Settle, Director Human Resources
CNO: Dana M. Garrett, R.N., Nursing Services Administrator
Web address: www.trhosp.org
**Control**: Hospital district or authority, Government, Nonfederal **Service**: General medical and surgical

**Staffed Beds: 90 Admissions: 2350 Census: 26 Outpatient Visits: 98758 Births: 306 Total Expense ($000): 83486 Payroll Expense ($000): 37317 Personnel: 604**

## CARROLLTON—Carroll County

**CARROLL COUNTY MEMORIAL HOSPITAL (181310)**, 309 11th Street, Zip 41008–1400; tel. 502/732–4321, (Nonreporting) **A**10 18 **S** Alliant Management Services, Louisville, KY
Primary Contact: Harry Hays, Chief Executive Officer
CMO: Winston Yap, M.D., Chief Medical Officer
CHR: Kimberly Adams, Manager Human Resources
CNO: Lisa Penick, R.N., Chief Nursing Officer
Web address: www.ccmhosp.com
**Control**: County, Government, Nonfederal **Service**: General medical and surgical

**Staffed Beds: 25**

**CARROLL COUNTY REG MED CENTER** See Carroll County Memorial Hospital

## COLUMBIA—Adair County

☐ **T.J. HEALTH COLUMBIA (180149)**, 901 Westlake Drive, Zip 42728–1123, Mailing Address: P.O. Box 1269, Zip 42728–6269; tel. 270/384–4753, (Nonreporting) **A**1 10
Primary Contact: Neil Thornbury, Chief Executive Officer
CFO: David R Hayes, Chief Financial Officer
CMO: Charles Giles, M.D., President Medical Staff
CHR: Tonya Grant, Director Human Resources
CNO: Gidgett Warren, Director of Nursing
Web address: www.healthiercolumbia.org/
**Control**: Hospital district or authority, Government, Nonfederal **Service**: General medical and surgical

**Staffed Beds: 32**

**TJ HEALTH COLUMBIA** See T.J. Health Columbia

---

**Hospital, Medicare Provider Number, Address, Telephone, Approval, Facility, and Physician Codes, Health Care System**

★ American Hospital Association (AHA) membership
☐ The Joint Commission accreditation
○ Healthcare Facilities Accreditation Program
◇ DNV Healthcare Inc. accreditation
⇑ Center for Improvement in Healthcare Quality Accreditation
△ Commission on Accreditation of Rehabilitation Facilities (CARF) accreditation

## CORBIN—Whitley County

⇧ **BAPTIST HEALTH CORBIN (180080)**, 1 Trillium Way, Zip 40701–8420; tel. 606/528–1212, (Nonreporting) **A**10 19 21 **S** Baptist Health, Louisville, KY
Primary Contact: Anthony Powers, Interim President and Vice President of Patient Services
CFO: Pamela K. Jones, Executive Director of Finance
CMO: David Worthy, M.D., Vice President and Chief Medical Officer
CIO: Rodney Richardson, Director of Information Technology
CHR: Tim Perry, Executive Director of Human Resources
CNO: Sherrie Mays, MSN, R.N., Vice President and Chief Nursing Officer
Web address: www.baptisthealth.com/corbin
**Control**: Other not–for–profit (including NFP Corporation) **Service**: General medical and surgical

**Staffed Beds:** 273

⇧ **BAPTIST REGIONAL MEDICAL CENTER** See Baptist Health Corbin

★ **CONTINUECARE HOSPITAL AT BAPTIST HEALTH CORBIN (182006)**, 1 Trillium Way, Lower Level, Zip 40701–8727; tel. 606/523–5150, (Nonreporting) **A**10 22 **F**1 3 29 30 34 57 59 85 148 **S** Community Hospital Corporation, Plano, TX
Primary Contact: Tuan Le, Chief Executive Officer
COO: Wilson Weber, Chief Operating Officer
CFO: Lisa Young, CPA, Chief Financial Officer
CMO: Steve Morton, M.D., Chief Medical Officer
CIO: Brian Doerr, Chief Information Officer
CHR: Amie Marcum, Human Resources Coordinator
CNO: Della Rains, Chief Nursing Officer
Web address: www.continuecare.org
**Control**: Other not–for–profit (including NFP Corporation) **Service**: Acute long–term care hospital

**Staffed Beds:** 32 **Admissions:** 225 **Census:** 18 **Outpatient Visits:** 0
**Births:** 0 **Total Expense ($000):** 9028 **Payroll Expense ($000):** 3382
**Personnel:** 75

**CONTINUECARE HOSPITAL AT BAPTIST HEALTH CORBIN** See Continuecare Hospital at Baptist Health Corbin

## COVINGTON—Kenton County

**ST. ELIZABETH MEDICAL CENTER-NORTH** See St. Elizabeth Covington

## CYNTHIANA—Harrison County

⊠ **HARRISON MEMORIAL HOSPITAL (180079)**, 1210 KY Highway 36E, Zip 41031–7498; tel. 859/234–2300, (Nonreporting) **A**1 2 10 **F**3 11 13 15 18 20 22 26 28 29 30 31 34 35 36 39 40 43 44 45 47 49 50 53 57 59 61 64 68 69 70 74 75 76 77 78 79 81 82 85 86 87 89 93 97 107 108 111 115 118 119 129 130 131 132 133 135 144 146 147 148 **P**6
Primary Contact: Sheila Currans, Chief Executive Officer
CFO: David Mellett, Chief Financial Officer
CIO: Martha Sullivan, Chief Information Officer
CHR: Rebecca Jenkins, Director Human Resources Management
CNO: Wendy Reeder, R.N., Chief Nursing Officer
Web address: www.harrisonmemhosp.com
**Control**: Other not–for–profit (including NFP Corporation) **Service**: General medical and surgical

**Staffed Beds:** 34 **Admissions:** 1222 **Census:** 11 **Outpatient Visits:** 81037
**Births:** 200 **Total Expense ($000):** 61372 **Payroll Expense ($000):** 26465
**Personnel:** 380

## DANVILLE—Boyle County

☐ **EPHRAIM MCDOWELL REGIONAL MEDICAL CENTER (180048)**, 217 South Third Street, Zip 40422–1823; tel. 859/239–1000, (Nonreporting) **A**1 2 3 5 10 19 **S** Ephraim McDowell Health, Danville, KY
Primary Contact: Daniel E. McKay, Chief Executive Officer
COO: Burt Piper, Chief Operating Officer
CFO: William R Snapp IIIExecutive Vice President Finance and Chief Financial Officer
CMO: Kryder Van Buskirk IIIMedical Staff President at EMRMC
CIO: Gary Neat, Chief Information Officer
CHR: Libby Mayes, Human Resource Director
Web address: www.emrmc.org
**Control**: Other not–for–profit (including NFP Corporation) **Service**: General medical and surgical

**Staffed Beds:** 159

## EDGEWOOD—Kenton County

⊠ **ENCOMPASS HEALTH REHABILITATION HOSPITAL OF NORTHERN KENTUCKY (183027)**, 201 Medical Village Drive, Zip 41017–3407; tel. 859/341–2044, (Nonreporting) **A**1 10 **S** Encompass Health Corporation, Birmingham, AL
Primary Contact: Jeremy Yates, Chief Executive Officer
CFO: Lisa McGue, Controller
CMO: Neal Moser, M.D., Medical Director
CHR: Bridgette Keith, Director Human Resources
CNO: Terri Ballard, Chief Nursing Officer
Web address: www.healthsouthkentucky.com
**Control**: Partnership, Investor–owned (for–profit) **Service**: Rehabilitation

**Staffed Beds:** 40

**HEALTHSOUTH NORTHERN KENTUCKY REHABILITATION HOSPITAL** See Encompass Health Rehabilitation Hospital of Northern Kentucky

☐ **ST. ELIZABETH EDGEWOOD (180035)**, 1 Medical Village Drive, Zip 41017–3403; tel. 859/301–2000, (Includes ST. ELIZABETH COVINGTON, Mailing address: 1500 James Simpson Jr. Way, Covington, Kentucky, Zip 41014–1585; tel. 859/655–8800), (Nonreporting) **A**1 2 3 5 10 **F**3 8 9 13 14 15 17 18 20 22 24 26 28 29 30 31 34 35 36 37 38 39 40 44 45 46 47 48 49 50 55 57 58 59 60 61 63 64 65 70 71 72 73 74 75 76 77 78 79 80 81 82 83 84 85 86 87 92 93 96 97 101 102 104 107 108 109 110 111 114 115 117 118 119 120 121 123 124 126 129 130 131 132 135 141 145 146 147 148 149 150 153 154 **P**6 8 **S** St. Elizabeth Healthcare, Edgewood, KY
Primary Contact: Garren Colvin, Chief Executive Officer
CMO: Karl Schmitt, M.D., Chief of Staff
CIO: Alex Rodriguez, Vice President and Chief Information Officer
CHR: Martin Oscadal, Vice President Human Resources
Web address: www.stelizabeth.com
**Control**: Church operated, Nongovernment, not–for–profit **Service**: General medical and surgical

**Staffed Beds:** 490 **Admissions:** 27232 **Census:** 329 **Outpatient Visits:** 1369680 **Births:** 4255 **Total Expense ($000):** 827146 **Payroll Expense ($000):** 305545 **Personnel:** 3130

**ST. ELIZABETH HEALTHCARE-EDGEWOOD** See St. Elizabeth Edgewood

## ELIZABETHTOWN—Hardin County

⊠ **ENCOMPASS REHABILITATION HOSPITAL OF LAKEVIEW (183028)**, 134 Heartland Drive, Zip 42701–2778; tel. 270/769–3100, (Nonreporting) **A**1 10 **S** Encompass Health Corporation, Birmingham, AL
Primary Contact: Lori Jarboe, Chief Executive Officer
CFO: Scott Hart, Controller
CMO: Toni Abang, M.D., Medical Director
CHR: Janet Morris, Director Human Resources
Web address: www.healthsouthlakeview.com
**Control**: Corporation, Investor–owned (for–profit) **Service**: Rehabilitation

**Staffed Beds:** 40

☐ **HARDIN MEMORIAL HEALTH (180012)**, 913 North Dixie Avenue, Zip 42701–2503; tel. 270/737–1212, (Total facility includes 15 beds in nursing home–type unit) (Nonreporting) **A**1 2 3 5 10 19 **F**3 8 11 12 13 15 17 18 20 22 24 28 29 30 31 32 34 35 36 37 39 40 44 45 48 49 50 51 52 54 57 58 59 64 68 70 71 72 74 75 76 77 78 79 80 81 82 84 85 86 87 89 93 94 96 98 102 107 110 111 114 115 117 118 119 120 121 124 126 127 128 129 130 131 132 134 135 144 146 147 148 149 154 156 **S** Baptist Health, Louisville, KY
Primary Contact: Dennis B. Johnson, President and Chief Executive Officer
COO: Tom Carrico, Vice President of Operations
CFO: Lennis Thompson IIVice President and Chief Financial Officer
CMO: John Godfrey, M.D., Vice President and Chief Executive Officer
CIO: Trey Hyberger, Director Information Technology
CHR: Myra Covault, Associate Vice President of Human Resources
CNO: Sharon Wright, R.N., Vice President and Chief Nursing Officer
Web address: www.hmh.net
**Control**: County, Government, Nonfederal **Service**: General medical and surgical

**Staffed Beds:** 268 **Admissions:** 13282 **Census:** 156 **Outpatient Visits:** 463268 **Births:** 1661

**HARDIN MEMORIAL HOSPITAL** See Hardin Memorial Health

**HEALTHSOUTH LAKEVIEW REHABILITATION HOSPITAL** See Encompass Rehabilitation Hospital of Lakeview

*Many Facility Codes have changed. Please refer to the AHA Guide Code Chart.*

© 2021 AHA Guide

## ERLANGER—Kenton County

**SUN BEHAVIORAL HEALTH** See Sun Behavioral Kentucky

⊞ **SUN BEHAVIORAL KENTUCKY (184006)**, 820 Dolwick Drive, Zip 41018,
Mailing Address: 3900 Olympic Blvd., Ste 400, Zip 41018; tel. 859/429–5188,
(Nonreporting) **A**1 10
Primary Contact: Brad Lincks, Chief Executive Officer
COO: Carol Parke, Chief Operating Officer, SUN Kentucky
Web address: www.https://www.sunkentucky.com/
**Control**: Corporation, Investor–owned (for–profit) **Service**: Psychiatric

**Staffed Beds**: 197

## FLEMINGSBURG—Fleming County

⊞ **FLEMING COUNTY HOSPITAL (181332)**, 55 Foundation Drive,
Zip 41041–9815, Mailing Address: P.O. Box 388, Zip 41041–0388;
tel. 606/849–5000, (Nonreporting) **A**1 10 18 **S** LifePoint Health, Brentwood, TN
Primary Contact: Brian Springate, Chief Executive Officer
CFO: Theresa Fite, R.N., Chief Financial Officer
CMO: Samuel Gehring, M.D., Chief of Staff
CIO: Don Daugherty, Director Information Systems
CHR: Marsha Mitchell, Director Human Resources
CNO: Lynda Skaggs, Chief Nursing Officer
Web address: www.flemingcountyhospital.org
**Control**: Other not–for–profit (including NFP Corporation) **Service**: General
medical and surgical

**Staffed Beds**: 52

## FLORENCE—Boone County

**GATEWAY REHABILITATION HOSPITA** See Gateway Rehabilitation Hospital

☐ △ **GATEWAY REHABILITATION HOSPITAL (183030)**, 5940 Merchant Street,
Zip 41042–1158; tel. 859/426–2400, (Nonreporting) **A**1 7 10 **S** Vibra Healthcare,
Mechanicsburg, PA
Primary Contact: Frank Schneider, FACHE, Chief Executive Officer
CFO: Margaret Cesarez, Chief Financial Officer
CNO: Jenna Wellbrock, Chief Nursing Officer
Web address: www.gatewayflorence.com/
**Control**: Corporation, Investor–owned (for–profit) **Service**: Rehabilitation

**Staffed Beds**: 40

☐ **ST. ELIZABETH FLORENCE (180045)**, 4900 Houston Road, Zip 41042–4824;
tel. 859/212–5200, (Total facility includes 16 beds in nursing home–type unit)
(Nonreporting) **A**1 10 **F**3 11 12 15 20 28 29 30 31 34 35 38 39 40 44 45 46 47
48 49 50 55 56 57 59 60 61 63 64 65 70 74 75 77 78 79 80 81 82 84 85 86
87 92 93 97 100 101 102 107 108 110 111 115 118 119 126 128 129 130
132 135 141 145 146 147 148 149 150 154 **P**6 8 **S** St. Elizabeth Healthcare,
Edgewood, KY
Primary Contact: Garren Colvin, Chief Executive Officer
COO: Chris Carle, Senior Vice President and Chief Operating Officer
CMO: George Hall, M.D., Vice President Medical Affairs
CIO: Alex Rodriguez, Vice President and Chief Information Officer
CHR: Martin Oscadal, Senior Vice President Human Resources
Web address: www.stelizabeth.com
**Control**: Church operated, Nongovernment, not–for–profit **Service**: General
medical and surgical

**Staffed Beds**: 147 **Admissions**: 9582 **Census**: 110 **Outpatient
Visits**: 188150 **Births**: 0 **Total Expense ($000)**: 159478 **Payroll Expense
($000)**: 65665 **Personnel**: 890

**ST. ELIZABETH HEALTHCARE FLORENCE** See St. Elizabeth Florence

## FORT CAMPBELL—Christian County

⊞ **COLONEL FLORENCE A. BLANCHFIELD ARMY COMMUNITY HOSPITAL**,
650 Joel Drive, Zip 42223–5318; tel. 270/798–8040, (Nonreporting) **A**1 3 5 **S**
Department of the Army, Office of the Surgeon General, Falls Church, VA
Primary Contact: Colonel Patrick T. Birchfield, Commanding Officer
CHR: MajorTravis Burchett, Troop Commander Human Resources
Web address: www.https://blanchfield.amedd.army.mil/
**Service**: General medical and surgical

**Staffed Beds**: 66

## FORT THOMAS—Campbell County

**CARDINAL HILL SPECIALTY HOSPITAL** See Select Specialty Hospital-Northern
Kentucky

⊞ **SELECT SPECIALTY HOSPITAL-NORTHERN KENTUCKY (182004)**, 85 North
Grand Avenue, Zip 41075–1793; tel. 859/572–3880, (Nonreporting) **A**1 10 **S**
Select Medical Corporation, Mechanicsburg, PA
Primary Contact: Mavis Bechtle, MSN, R.N., FACHE, Chief Executive Officer
Web address: www.selectspecialtyhospitals.com
**Control**: Corporation, Investor–owned (for–profit) **Service**: Acute long–term care
hospital

**Staffed Beds**: 33

☐ **ST. ELIZABETH FORT THOMAS (180001)**, 85 North Grand Avenue,
Zip 41075–1796; tel. 859/572–3100, (Includes ST. ELIZABETH FALMOUTH,
Mailing address: 512 South Maple Avenue, Falmouth, Kentucky, Zip 41040–1422;
tel. 859/572–3500; Garren Colvin, Chief Executive Officer) (Total facility includes
21 beds in nursing home–type unit) **A**1 2 10 **F**3 5 9 11 15 18 20 28 29 30 31 34
35 39 40 44 45 47 48 49 50 51 55 56 57 58 59 60 61 63 64 65 70 71 74 75
77 78 79 80 81 82 85 86 87 91 92 93 94 97 100 102 107 108 110 111 115
118 119 120 121 123 126 128 129 130 135 141 146 147 149 150 152 153
154 **P**6 8 **S** St. Elizabeth Healthcare, Edgewood, KY
Primary Contact: Garren Colvin, Chief Executive Officer
COO: Thomas Saalfeld, Senior Vice President and Chief Operating Officer
CMO: George Hall, M.D., Vice President Medical Affairs
CIO: Alex Rodriguez, Vice President and Chief Information Officer
CHR: Martin Oscadal, Senior Vice President Human Resources
Web address: www.stelizabeth.com
**Control**: Church operated, Nongovernment, not–for–profit **Service**: General
medical and surgical

**Staffed Beds**: 137 **Admissions**: 7324 **Census**: 98 **Outpatient
Visits**: 145738 **Births**: 0 **Total Expense ($000)**: 143366 **Payroll Expense
($000)**: 58338 **Personnel**: 681

**ST. ELIZABETH HEALTHCARE FORT THOMAS** See St. Elizabeth Fort Thomas

## FRANKFORT—Franklin County

**COLUMBIA HOSPITAL FRANKFORT** See Frankfort Regional Medical Center

⊞ **FRANKFORT REGIONAL MEDICAL CENTER (180127)**, 299 King's Daughters
Drive, Zip 40601–4186; tel. 502/875–5240, (Nonreporting) **A**1 2 10 19 **S** HCA
Healthcare, Nashville, TN
Primary Contact: Reed Hammond, Chief Executive Officer
CMO: Willis P McKee, M.D., JrChief Medical Officer
CIO: Craig Willard, Director Information Technology and Systems
CHR: Bev Young, Director Human Resources
Web address: www.frankfortregional.com
**Control**: Corporation, Investor–owned (for–profit) **Service**: General medical and
surgical

**Staffed Beds**: 173

## FRANKLIN—Simpson County

☐ **MEDICAL CENTER AT FRANKLIN (181318)**, 1100 Brookhaven Road,
Zip 42134–2746; tel. 270/598–4800, (Nonreporting) **A**1 10 18 **F**3 15 28 29 30
34 35 40 46 50 57 59 64 68 75 77 81 82 86 87 93 107 108 110 111 114 119
127 130 133 135 146 148 149 **S** Med Center Health, Bowling Green, KY
Primary Contact: Annette Runyon, Vice President and Administrator
CFO: Ronald G. Sowell, FACHE, Executive Vice President
CIO: Mark Brookman, Vice President and Chief Information Officer
Web address: www.themedicalcenterfranklin.org
**Control**: Other not–for–profit (including NFP Corporation) **Service**: General
medical and surgical

**Staffed Beds**: 25 **Admissions**: 880 **Census**: 19 **Outpatient Visits**: 20066
**Births**: 0 **Personnel**: 141

**THE MEDICAL CENTER AT FRANKLIN** See Medical Center at Franklin

---

**Hospital, Medicare Provider Number, Address, Telephone, Approval, Facility, and Physician Codes, Health Care System**

★ American Hospital Association (AHA) membership
☐ The Joint Commission accreditation
○ Healthcare Facilities Accreditation Program
◇ DNV Healthcare Inc. accreditation
⇑ Center for Improvement in Healthcare Quality Accreditation
△ Commission on Accreditation of Rehabilitation Facilities (CARF) accreditation

## GEORGETOWN—Scott County

**COLUMBIA HOSPITAL GEORGETOWN** See Georgetown Community Hospital

☒ **GEORGETOWN COMMUNITY HOSPITAL (180101)**, 1140 Lexington Road, Zip 40324–9362; tel. 502/868–1100, (Nonreporting) **A**1 2 10 **S** LifePoint Health, Brentwood, TN
Primary Contact: William Haugh, Administrator
CFO: Patrick C Bolander, Chief Financial Officer
CMO: Brian Allen, M.D., President Medical Staff
CHR: Marrianne Slonina, Director Human Resources
Web address: www.georgetowncommunityhospital.com
**Control:** Corporation, Investor–owned (for–profit) **Service:** General medical and surgical

**Staffed Beds:** 58

## GLASGOW—Barren County

☐ **T. J. SAMSON COMMUNITY HOSPITAL (180017)**, 1301 North Race Street, Zip 42141–3483; tel. 270/651–4444, (Nonreporting) **A**1 2 3 5 10 19
Primary Contact: Neil Thornbury, Chief Executive Officer
COO: Margie Gentry, Controller
CFO: Mei Deng, Chief Financial Officer
CIO: Chad Friend, Director
CHR: LaDonna Rogers, Executive Vice President Human Resources
CNO: Megan Calkins, R.N., Chief Nursing Officer
Web address: www.tjsamson.org
**Control:** Other not–for–profit (including NFP Corporation) **Service:** General medical and surgical

**Staffed Beds:** 114

## GREENSBURG—Green County

**JANE TODD CRAWFORD HOSPITAL (181325)**, 202-206 Milby Street, Zip 42743–1100, Mailing Address: P.O. Box 220, Zip 42743–0220; tel. 270/932–4211, (Nonreporting) **A**10 18
Primary Contact: Rex A. Tungate, Chief Executive Officer
CFO: Richard Hendershot, Chief Financial Officer
CMO: Shane DeSimone, M.D., Chief of Staff
CHR: Mary Ann Quinn, Administrative Assistant
CNO: Roxie Montgomery, Director of Nursing
Web address: www.janetoddhospital.com
**Control:** County, Government, Nonfederal **Service:** General medical and surgical

**Staffed Beds:** 45

**JANE TODD CRAWFORD MEM HOSP** See Jane Todd Crawford Hospital

## GREENVILLE—Muhlenberg County

**MUHLENBERG COMMUNITY HOSPITAL** See Owensboro Health Muhlenberg Community Hospital

☐ **OWENSBORO HEALTH MUHLENBERG COMMUNITY HOSPITAL (180004)**, 440 Hopkinsville Street, Zip 42345–1124, Mailing Address: P.O. Box 387, Zip 42345–0378; tel. 270/338–8000, (Nonreporting) **A**1 10 **S** Owensboro Health, Owensboro, KY
Primary Contact: Ed Heath, FACHE, Chief Executive Officer
CMO: Vincent P Genovese, M.D., President Medical Staff
CIO: Alan Trail, Director Information Systems
CHR: Lisa R Hope, Director Human Resources
CNO: Kathy Mitchell, Chief Nursing Officer
Web address: www.ww.owensborohealth.org/
**Control:** Other not–for–profit (including NFP Corporation) **Service:** General medical and surgical

**Staffed Beds:** 105

## HARDINSBURG—Breckinridge County

☐ **BRECKINRIDGE MEMORIAL HOSPITAL (181319)**, 1011 Old Highway 60, Zip 40143–2597; tel. 270/756–7000, (Nonreporting) **A**1 10 18 **S** Alliant Management Services, Louisville, KY
Primary Contact: Angela Portman, Chief Executive Officer
CFO: Timothy D Crockett, Chief Financial Officer
CMO: Brian O'Donoghue, M.D., Chief Medical Officer
CHR: James Turpin, Human Resources
CNO: Tiffany Kennedy, Chief Nursing Officer
Web address: www.breckinridgehealth.org/
**Control:** Other not–for–profit (including NFP Corporation) **Service:** General medical and surgical

**Staffed Beds:** 43

## HARLAN—Harlan County

⇑ **HARLAN ARH HOSPITAL (180050)**, 81 Ball Park Road, Zip 40831–1792; tel. 606/573–8100, (Nonreporting) **A**2 3 5 10 21 **F**3 11 13 15 18 20 28 29 30 32 34 35 40 43 50 54 57 59 62 64 70 75 76 77 78 79 81 82 85 86 87 89 93 97 98 99 102 103 107 108 111 115 118 119 127 129 130 132 146 147 148 154 **S** Appalachian Regional Healthcare, Inc., Lexington, KY
Primary Contact: Donald R. Fields, Community Chief Executive Officer
CFO: Brad Burkhart, Assistant Administrator
CHR: Sabra Howard, Manager Human Resources
Web address: www.arh.org
**Control:** Other not–for–profit (including NFP Corporation) **Service:** General medical and surgical

**Staffed Beds:** 103 **Admissions:** 4208 **Census:** 50 **Outpatient Visits:** 72409 **Births:** 155

⇑ **HARLAN ARH HOSPITAL** See Harlan Arh Hospital

## HARRODSBURG—Mercer County

☒ **EPHRAIM MCDOWELL JAMES B. HAGGIN MEMORIAL HOSPITAL (181302)**, 464 Linden Avenue, Zip 40330–1862; tel. 859/734–5441, (Nonreporting) **A**1 10 18 **S** Ephraim McDowell Health, Danville, KY
Primary Contact: Lynne Warner Lynn, R.N., Administrator
CFO: Tony Patterson, Chief Financial Officer
Web address: www.hagginhosp.org
**Control:** Other not–for–profit (including NFP Corporation) **Service:** General medical and surgical

**Staffed Beds:** 25

**JAMES B. HAGGIN MEMORIAL HOSPITAL** See Ephraim Mcdowell James B. Haggin Memorial Hospital

## HARTFORD—Ohio County

☒ **OHIO COUNTY HOSPITAL (181323)**, 1211 Main Street, Zip 42347–1619; tel. 270/298–7411, (Nonreporting) **A**1 10 18 **F**3 11 15 18 26 28 29 30 35 36 40 48 49 50 59 63 64 65 74 75 77 79 81 82 84 85 87 92 93 97 107 110 111 115 119 127 129 130 132 133 135 146 147 148 149 154 156 157 **S** QHR Health, Brentwood, TN
Primary Contact: Blaine Pieper, Chief Executive Officer
CFO: John Tichenor, Chief Financial Officer
CMO: Joshua Skibba, Chief Medical Officer
CHR: Sue Wydick, Director Human Resources
CNO: Athena Minor, Chief Nursing Officer
Web address: www.ohiocountyhospital.com
**Control:** Other not–for–profit (including NFP Corporation) **Service:** General medical and surgical

**Staffed Beds:** 30 **Admissions:** 875 **Census:** 9 **Outpatient Visits:** 50541 **Births:** 0 **Total Expense ($000):** 39773 **Payroll Expense ($000):** 20700 **Personnel:** 498

## HAZARD—Perry County

⇑ **ARH REGIONAL MEDICAL CENTER** See Hazard Arh Regional Medical Center

⇑ **HAZARD ARH REGIONAL MEDICAL CENTER (180029)**, 100 Medical Center Drive, Zip 41701–9421; tel. 606/439–6600, (Nonreporting) **A**2 3 5 10 19 21 **S** Appalachian Regional Healthcare, Inc., Lexington, KY
Primary Contact: Dan Stone, Senior Community Chief Executive Officer
CMO: J D Miller, M.D., Chief Medical Officer
CIO: Jeff Brady, Director Information Systems
CHR: Sheila Cornett, Manager Human Resources
Web address: www.arh.org
**Control:** Other not–for–profit (including NFP Corporation) **Service:** General medical and surgical

**Staffed Beds:** 358

**A284** Hospitals

*Many Facility Codes have changed. Please refer to the AHA Guide Code Chart.*

© 2021 AHA Guide

## HENDERSON—Henderson County

**COMMUNITY METHODIST HOSPITAL** See Methodist Hospital

☐ **METHODIST HOSPITAL (180056)**, 1305 North Elm Street, Zip 42420–2775, Mailing Address: P.O. Box 48, Zip 42419–0048; tel. 270/827–7700, (Nonreporting) **A**1 2 10 13 **F**3 11 13 15 18 29 30 31 34 35 36 40 45 46 47 49 50 51 53 54 57 58 59 64 66 68 70 72 74 75 76 77 78 79 81 85 86 87 107 108 110 111 114 115 118 119 127 129 130 131 132 135 146 147 148 149 156
Primary Contact: Linda E. White, Chief Executive Officer
CFO: David Massengale, Vice President and Chief Financial Officer
CMO: John Logan, M.D., Chief Medical Officer
CIO: Randy McCleese, Chief Information Officer
CHR: Ty Kahle, Vice President Human Resources
Web address: www.methodisthospital.net
**Control**: Other not–for–profit (including NFP Corporation) **Service**: General medical and surgical

**Staffed Beds**: 123 **Admissions**: 3365 **Census**: 50 **Outpatient Visits**: 235521 **Births**: 625 **Total Expense ($000)**: 93578 **Payroll Expense ($000)**: 32299 **Personnel**: 843

## HOPKINSVILLE—Christian County

☐ **CUMBERLAND HALL HOSPITAL (184014)**, 270 Walton Way, Zip 42240–6808; tel. 270/886–1919, (Nonreporting) **A**1 10 **S** Universal Health Services, Inc., King of Prussia, PA
Primary Contact: David Melear, Chief Executive Officer
CFO: Mark Wallace, Chief Financial Officer
CMO: Deepak Patel, M.D., Medical Director
CIO: Patricia Gray, Director Health Information Management
CHR: Kelly Hagy, Director Human Resources
CNO: Denise Lyons, Chief Nursing Officer
Web address: www.cumberlandhallhospital.com
**Control**: Corporation, Investor–owned (for–profit) **Service**: Psychiatric

**Staffed Beds**: 97

☐ **JENNIE STUART MEDICAL CENTER (180051)**, 320 West 18th Street, Zip 42240–1965, Mailing Address: P.O. Box 2400, Zip 42241–2400; tel. 270/887–0100, (Nonreporting) **A**1 10 20
Primary Contact: Eric A. Lee, President and Chief Executive Officer
CMO: Casey Covington, M.D., President Elect, Medical Staff
CIO: Jerry Houston, Director Information Systems
CHR: Austin Moss, Vice President Human Resources
Web address: www.jsmc.org
**Control**: Other not–for–profit (including NFP Corporation) **Service**: General medical and surgical

**Staffed Beds**: 139

☐ **WESTERN STATE HOSPITAL (184002)**, Russellville Road, Zip 42240–3017, Mailing Address: P.O. Box 2200, Zip 42241–2200; tel. 270/889–6025, (Nonreporting) **A**1 10 **F**98 100 101 102 103 130 149
Primary Contact: Roger Westfall, Director
CFO: Jessica Cates, Fiscal Manager
CMO: Nayyar Iqbal, M.D., Director Medical Staff
CIO: Valerie Majors, Director Information Services
CHR: James L Hayes, Director Human Resources
CNO: Jill Thomas, Director of Nursing
Web address: www.westernstatehospital.ky.gov
**Control**: State, Government, Nonfederal **Service**: Psychiatric

**Staffed Beds**: 205 **Admissions**: 2134 **Census**: 109 **Outpatient Visits**: 0 **Births**: 0

## HORSE CAVE—Hart County

**MEDICAL CENTER AT CAVERNA** See The Medical Center at Caverna

**THE MEDICAL CENTER AT CAVERNA (181314)**, 1501 South Dixie Street, Zip 42749–1477; tel. 270/786–2191, (Nonreporting) **A**10 18 **S** Med Center Health, Bowling Green, KY
Primary Contact: Alan B. Alexander, FACHE, Vice President and Administrator
CFO: Ronald G. Sowell, FACHE, Executive Vice President and Chief Financial Officer
CIO: Mark Brookman, Vice President, Chief Information Officer
CHR: Lynn Williams, Vice President, Human Resources
CNO: Penny Nole, Director of Patient Care Services
Web address: www.TheMedicalCenterCaverna.org
**Control**: Corporation, Investor–owned (for–profit) **Service**: General medical and surgical

**Staffed Beds**: 25

## HYDEN—Leslie County

⇑ **MARY BRECKINRIDGE ARH HOSPITAL (181316)**, 130 Kate Ireland Drive, Zip 41749–9071, Mailing Address: P.O. Box 447-A, Zip 41749–0717; tel. 606/672–2901, (Nonreporting) **A**10 18 21 **F**2 3 11 15 29 30 32 34 35 40 50 57 59 62 65 68 75 77 81 86 87 93 107 110 115 119 130 132 133 135 146 154 **S** Appalachian Regional Healthcare, Inc., Lexington, KY
Primary Contact: Mallie S. Noble, Administrator
COO: Nathan W Lee, Chief Executive Officer
CFO: Robert Besten, Chief Financial Officer
CMO: Roy Varghese, M.D., Chief of Staff
CIO: Frank Baker, Chief Information Officer
CHR: Beulah Couch, Director Human Resources
Web address: www.frontiernursing.org
**Control**: Other not–for–profit (including NFP Corporation) **Service**: General medical and surgical

**Staffed Beds**: 25 **Admissions**: 351 **Census**: 11 **Outpatient Visits**: 21202 **Births**: 0

⇑ **MARY BRECKINRIDGE HOSPITAL** See Mary Breckinridge Arh Hospital

## IRVINE—Estill County

**MARCUM AND WALLACE MEMORIAL HOSPITAL** See Mercy Health - Marcum and Wallace

**MERCY HEALTH - MARCUM AND WALLACE (181301)**, 60 Mercy Court, Zip 40336–1331; tel. 606/723–2115, (Nonreporting) **A**10 18 **S** Mercy Health, Cincinnati, OH
Primary Contact: Susan Starling, President and Chief Executive Officer
CFO: Lori Witt, Site Finance Director
CMO: Maher Kassis, M.D., Chief Medical Staff
CHR: Dana Stepp, Human Resources Officer
CNO: Trena Stocker, Chief Nursing Executive
Web address: www.marcumandwallace.org
**Control**: Church operated, Nongovernment, not–for–profit **Service**: General medical and surgical

**Staffed Beds**: 25

## JACKSON—Breathitt County

☐ **KENTUCKY RIVER MEDICAL CENTER (180139)**, 540 Jett Drive, Zip 41339–9622; tel. 606/666–6000, (Nonreporting) **A**1 10 20 **S** Quorum Health, Brentwood, TN
Primary Contact: Derek W. Cimala, Chief Executive Officer
CFO: Michael Ackley, Chief Financial Officer
CMO: Eunice Johnson, M.D., Chief Medical Staff
CIO: Diana Tyra, Director Health Information
CHR: Naomi Mitchell, Director Human Resources
Web address: www.kentuckyrivermc.com
**Control**: Corporation, Investor–owned (for–profit) **Service**: General medical and surgical

**Staffed Beds**: 54

## LA GRANGE—Oldham County

☐ **BAPTIST HEALTH LA GRANGE (180138)**, 1025 New Moody Lane, Zip 40031–9154; tel. 502/222–5388, (Nonreporting) **A**1 2 5 10 **S** Baptist Health, Louisville, KY
Primary Contact: Clint Kaho, President
CFO: Jim Morris, Vice President Finance
CMO: Matt McDanald, M.D., Chief Medical Officer
CHR: Kayla Batts, Manager Human Resources
CNO: Nathan Wilson, R.N., Vice President and Chief Nursing Officer
Web address: www.baptisthealthlagrange.com
**Control**: Other not–for–profit (including NFP Corporation) **Service**: General medical and surgical

**Staffed Beds**: 65

**BAPTIST HOSPITAL NORTHEAST** See Baptist Health La Grange

---

**Hospital, Medicare Provider Number, Address, Telephone, Approval, Facility, and Physician Codes, Health Care System**

★ American Hospital Association (AHA) membership
☐ The Joint Commission accreditation
○ Healthcare Facilities Accreditation Program
◇ DNV Healthcare Inc. accreditation
⇑ Center for Improvement in Healthcare Quality Accreditation
△ Commission on Accreditation of Rehabilitation Facilities (CARF) accreditation

## LEBANON—Marion County

**NORTON SPRING VIEW HOSPITAL** See Spring View Hospital

⊞ **SPRING VIEW HOSPITAL (180024)**, 320 Loretto Road, Zip 40033–1300; tel. 270/692–3161, (Nonreporting) **A**1 10 **S** LifePoint Health, Brentwood, TN
Primary Contact: Reba Celsor, Chief Executive Officer
CFO: Denise Thomas, Chief Financial Officer
CIO: Douglas Bland, Manager Information Services
CHR: Ann Dabney, Manager Human Resources
CNO: Linda Hunter, Chief Nursing Officer
Web address: www.springviewhospital.com
**Control:** Corporation, Investor–owned (for–profit) **Service:** General medical and surgical

**Staffed Beds:** 60

## LEITCHFIELD—Grayson County

**GRAYSON COUNTY HOSPITAL** See Twin Lakes Regional Medical Center

☐ **TWIN LAKES REGIONAL MEDICAL CENTER (180070)**, 910 Wallace Avenue, Zip 42754–2414; tel. 270/259–9400, (Nonreporting) **A**1 10 **S** Alliant Management Services, Louisville, KY
Primary Contact: Wayne Meriwether, Chief Executive Officer
COO: Deneace Clemons, Chief Operating Officer
CFO: Scott Arndell, Chief Financial Officer
CIO: Robbie Lindsey, Chief Information Officer
CHR: Kim Rayls, Director Human Resources
CNO: David Logdson, Chief Nursing Officer
Web address: www.tlrmc.com
**Control:** Other not–for–profit (including NFP Corporation) **Service:** General medical and surgical

**Staffed Beds:** 75

## LEXINGTON—Fayette County

☐ **BAPTIST HEALTH LEXINGTON (180103)**, 1740 Nicholasville Road, Zip 40503–1499; tel. 859/260–6100, (Nonreporting) **A**1 2 3 5 10 **F**3 11 12 13 15 17 18 20 22 24 26 28 29 30 31 34 35 36 39 40 44 45 46 47 48 49 54 55 56 57 58 59 60 64 65 68 70 72 74 75 76 77 78 79 81 82 85 86 87 92 93 97 107 108 110 111 114 115 117 118 119 120 121 124 126 129 130 131 132 135 144 146 147 148 154 156 157 **S** Baptist Health, Louisville, KY
Primary Contact: William G. Sisson, FACHE, President
COO: Karen S Hill, R.N., FACHE, Chief Operating Officer and Chief Nursing Officer
CFO: Stephanie Doom, Chief Financial Officer
CMO: James Borders, M.D., Chief Medical Officer
CIO: Lisa Fluty, Director Information Services
CHR: Lynette Walker, R.N., Ph.D., Vice President Human Resources
CNO: Karen S Hill, R.N., FACHE, Chief Operating Officer and Chief Nursing Officer
Web address: www.baptisthealthlexington.com
**Control:** Other not–for–profit (including NFP Corporation) **Service:** General medical and surgical

**Staffed Beds:** 434 **Admissions:** 20445 **Census:** 266 **Outpatient Visits:** 342722 **Births:** 3788 **Total Expense ($000):** 520123 **Payroll Expense ($000):** 147382 **Personnel:** 2440

**CARDINAL HILL HOSPITAL** See Cardinal Hill Rehabilitation Hospital

⊞ **CARDINAL HILL REHABILITATION HOSPITAL (183026)**, 2050 Versailles Road, Zip 40504–1405; tel. 859/254–5701, (Nonreporting) **A**1 3 5 10 **S** Encompass Health Corporation, Birmingham, AL
Primary Contact: Tara Diebling, Chief Executive Officer
CFO: Marty Lautner, Vice President Finance and Chief Financial Officer
CMO: William Lester, M.D., Vice President Medical Affairs
CIO: LouAnn Hyder, Director Information Integrity Management
CHR: Barry K Lindeman, Director Human Resources
CNO: Maureen Couture, Chief Nursing Officer and Vice President Nursing
Web address: www.cardinalhillhealthsouth.com
**Control:** Other not–for–profit (including NFP Corporation) **Service:** Rehabilitation

**Staffed Beds:** 232

**CENTRAL BAPTIST HOSPITAL** See Baptist Health Lexington

**CHARTER RIDGE BEHAVIORAL HLTH** See Ridge Behavioral Health System

⊞ **CHI SAINT JOSEPH EAST (180143)**, 150 North Eagle Creek Drive, Zip 40509–1805; tel. 859/967–5000, (Includes WOMEN'S HOSPITAL SAINT JOSEPH EAST, Mailing address: 170 North Eagle Creek Drive, Lexington, Kentucky, Zip 40509–9087; tel. 859/572–3500), (Nonreporting) **A**1 2 5 10 **F**3 11 12 13 15 18 29 30 31 35 37 40 47 49 50 60 68 70 72 74 75 76 77 78 79 81 82 85 86 93 107 108 111 114 118 119 120 121 122 123 126 129 142 146 147 148 **S** CommonSpirit Health, Chicago, IL
Primary Contact: Jason M. Adams, President
COO: Jason M. Adams, Chief Operating Officer
CFO: Melinda S Evans, Vice President Finance
CIO: Janie Fergus, Director and Chief Information Officer
Web address: www.sjhlex.org
**Control:** Church operated, Nongovernment, not–for–profit **Service:** General medical and surgical

**Staffed Beds:** 150 **Admissions:** 7699 **Census:** 69 **Outpatient Visits:** 164517 **Births:** 2313 **Total Expense ($000):** 196066 **Payroll Expense ($000):** 50326 **Personnel:** 735

⊞ **CHI SAINT JOSEPH HEALTH (180010)**, One St Joseph Drive, Zip 40504–3754; tel. 859/313–1000, (Nonreporting) **A**1 2 3 10 **F**3 8 11 12 15 17 18 19 20 22 24 25 26 27 28 29 30 31 34 35 37 40 41 45 47 49 50 51 54 55 56 57 58 59 64 65 66 68 70 74 77 78 79 81 82 83 84 85 86 87 91 92 93 94 97 107 110 111 114 115 116 117 118 119 120 121 123 126 127 129 130 132 135 144 146 147 148 156 **S** CommonSpirit Health, Chicago, IL
Primary Contact: Bruce J. Tassin, President
COO: Jason M. Adams, Chief Operating Officer
CFO: Melinda S Evans, Vice President Finance
CIO: Janie Fergus, Director and Chief Information Officer
Web address: www.chisaintjosephhealth.org/saint-joseph-hospital-lexington
**Control:** Church operated, Nongovernment, not–for–profit **Service:** General medical and surgical

**Staffed Beds:** 307 **Admissions:** 13909 **Census:** 182 **Outpatient Visits:** 100549 **Births:** 0 **Total Expense ($000):** 269856 **Payroll Expense ($000):** 74275 **Personnel:** 1163

⊞ **CONTINUING CARE HOSPITAL (182002)**, 1 Saint Joseph Drive, Zip 40504–3742; tel. 859/967–5744, (Nonreporting) **A**1 3 10 **S** CommonSpirit Health, Chicago, IL
Primary Contact: Robert C. Desotelle, President and Chief Executive Officer
CMO: Michael Miedler, M.D., Chief Medical Officer
CNO: Regina Masters, R.N., MSN, Director of Nursing
Web address: www.kentuckyonehealth.org
**Control:** Church operated, Nongovernment, not–for–profit **Service:** Acute long–term care hospital

**Staffed Beds:** 23

☐ **EASTERN STATE HOSPITAL (184004)**, 1350 Bull Lea Road, Zip 40511; tel. 859/246–8000, (Nonreporting) **A**1 3 5 10 **F**30 35 98 101 103 130 132 135 143 146 149 150
Primary Contact: Carrie Rudzik, Chief Administrative Officer
CFO: Susan M Griffith, Finance Business Partner Specialist
CMO: Andrew Cooley, M.D., Chief Medical Officer
CIO: Steve Kincaid, Information Technology Manager
CHR: Stephanie DeRossette, Human Resources Business Partner
CNO: Marc Anthony Woods, Assistant Chief Nurse Executive
Web address: www.https://ukhealthcare.uky.edu/
**Control:** State, Government, Nonfederal **Service:** Psychiatric

**Staffed Beds:** 140 **Admissions:** 2425 **Census:** 102 **Outpatient Visits:** 0 **Births:** 0 **Personnel:** 401

**FEDERAL MEDICAL CENTER**, 3301 Leestown Road, Zip 40511–8799; tel. 859/255–6812, (Nonreporting)
Primary Contact: Francisco Quintana, Warden
CFO: Mike Kinsel, Controller
CMO: Michael Growse, M.D., Clinical Director
**Control:** Department of Justice, Government, federal **Service:** Hospital unit of an institution (prison hospital, college infirmary, etc.)

**Staffed Beds:** 22

⊞ △ **LEXINGTON VETERANS AFFAIRS MEDICAL CENTER**, 1101 Veterans Drive, Zip 40502–2235; tel. 859/281–4901, (Nonreporting) **A**1 3 5 7 **S** Department of Veterans Affairs, Washington, DC
Primary Contact: James Belmont, Interim Director
CFO: Patricia Swisshelm, Acting Chief Fiscal Service
CMO: Patricia Breeden, M.D., Chief of Staff
CIO: Jeffrey Sutton, Chief Information Officer
CHR: Laura Faulkner, Chief Human Resource Management Service
CNO: Mary Kelly McCullough, Associate Director Patient Care Services
Web address: www.lexington.va.gov/
**Control:** Veterans Affairs, Government, federal **Service:** General medical and surgical

**Staffed Beds:** 168

*Many Facility Codes have changed. Please refer to the AHA Guide Code Chart.*   © 2021 AHA Guide

**RIDGE BEHAVIORAL HEALTH SYSTEM (184009)**, 3050 Rio Dosa Drive, Zip 40509–1540; tel. 859/269–2325, (Nonreporting) **A**1 3 5 10 **S** Universal Health Services, Inc., King of Prussia, PA
Primary Contact: Nina W. Eisner, Chief Executive Officer and Managing Director
CFO: Richard McDowell, Chief Financial Officer
CMO: Michael Rieser, M.D., Medical Director
CNO: Georgia Swank, Chief Nursing Officer
Web address: www.ridgebhs.com
**Control:** Corporation, Investor–owned (for–profit) **Service:** Psychiatric

**Staffed Beds:** 110

**SAINT JOSEPH EAST** See Chi Saint Joseph East

**SAINT JOSEPH HOSPITAL** See Chi Saint Joseph Health

**SELECT SPECIALTY HOSPITAL-LEXINGTON (182003)**, 310 South Limestone Street, 3rd Floor, Zip 40508–3008; tel. 859/226–7096, (Nonreporting) **A**1 10 **S** Select Medical Corporation, Mechanicsburg, PA
Primary Contact: Kim Pennington, Chief Executive Officer
CMO: Fadi Bacha, M.D., Chief Medical Officer
CHR: Tina Kirkland-Rose, Coordinator Human Resources
CNO: Katie Meredith, Chief Nursing Officer
Web address: www.lexington.selectspecialtyhospitals.com/
**Control:** Corporation, Investor–owned (for–profit) **Service:** Acute long–term care hospital

**Staffed Beds:** 41

**UK HEALTHCARE GOOD SAMARITAN** See UK Healthcare Good Samaritan Hospital

**UNIVERSITY OF KENTUCKY ALBERT B. CHANDLER HOSPITAL (180067)**, 800 Rose Street, Zip 40536–0293; tel. 859/323–5000, (Includes KENTUCKY CHILDREN'S HOSPITAL, Mailing address: N-100 - 800 Rose Street, Lexington, Kentucky, Zip 40536–0293; tel. 859/257–1000; UK HEALTHCARE GOOD SAMARITAN HOSPITAL, Mailing address: 310 South Limestone Street, Lexington, Kentucky, Zip 40508–3008; tel. 859/226–7000), (Nonreporting) **A**1 2 3 5 8 10 **F**3 5 6 7 9 11 12 13 15 16 17 18 19 20 21 22 23 24 25 26 27 28 29 30 31 32 34 35 36 37 38 39 40 41 43 44 45 46 47 48 49 50 52 54 55 56 57 58 59 60 61 64 65 66 68 70 72 73 74 75 76 77 78 79 81 82 84 85 86 87 88 89 91 92 93 94 95 96 97 98 99 100 101 102 103 104 107 110 111 114 115 116 118 119 120 121 123 124 126 127 129 130 131 132 134 135 136 137 138 139 140 141 142 143 145 146 147 148 149 150 154 155 156 157 **P**6
Primary Contact: Mark Newman, M.D., Executive Vice President of Health Affairs
CHR: Kimberly P Wilson, Director Human Resources
Web address: www.ukhealthcare.uky.edu
**Control:** State, Government, Nonfederal **Service:** General medical and surgical

**Staffed Beds:** 943 **Admissions:** 42152 **Census:** 774 **Outpatient Visits:** 2144375 **Births:** 1973 **Total Expense ($000):** 1490177 **Payroll Expense ($000):** 531957 **Personnel:** 8970

**UNIVERSITY OF KENTUCKY HOSPITAL** See University of Kentucky Albert B. Chandler Hospital

**VETERANS AFFAIRS MEDICAL CENTER-LEXINGTON** See Lexington Veterans Affairs Medical Center

**CASEY COUNTY HOSPITAL (181309)**, 187 Wolford Avenue, Zip 42539–3278; tel. 606/787–6275, (Nonreporting) **A**1 10 18
Primary Contact: Rex A. Tungate, Chief Executive Officer
CFO: Richard Hendershot, Chief Financial Officer
CMO: Housam Haddad, M.D., Chief of Staff
CHR: Mary Ann Quinn, Administrative Assistant
CNO: Sue Antle, Director of Nursing
Web address: www.caseycountyhospital.com
**Control:** County, Government, Nonfederal **Service:** General medical and surgical

**Staffed Beds:** 24

**CASEY COUNTY WAR MEM HOSPITAL** See Casey County Hospital

**CHI SAINT JOSEPH LONDON (180011)**, 1001 Saint Joseph Lane, Zip 40741–8345; tel. 606/330–6000, (Nonreporting) **A**1 10 19 **F**3 13 15 20 22 26 28 29 30 31 34 35 40 45 47 49 50 51 57 59 60 61 64 70 74 75 76 78 79 80 81 82 85 87 89 92 93 97 107 108 110 111 114 115 119 127 129 130 131 135 146 147 149 150 156 **S** CommonSpirit Health, Chicago, IL
Primary Contact: Terrence G. Deis, CPA, FACHE, President
CFO: Christy Spitser, Vice President Finance and Business Development
CMO: Shelley Stanko, M.D., Chief Medical Officer
CHR: Sandra Turqueza, Senior Human Resources Business Partner
CNO: Lewis Stephen O'Neal, R.N., MSN, Chief Nursing Officer
Web address: www.saintjosephhealthsystem.org
**Control:** Church operated, Nongovernment, not–for–profit **Service:** General medical and surgical

**Staffed Beds:** 116 **Admissions:** 5901 **Census:** 69 **Outpatient Visits:** 108176 **Births:** 1161 **Total Expense ($000):** 126516 **Payroll Expense ($000):** 38609 **Personnel:** 695

**SAINT JOSEPH LONDON** See Chi Saint Joseph London

**HUMANA HOSPITAL-LOUISA** See Three Rivers Medical Center

**THREE RIVERS MEDICAL CENTER (180128)**, 2485 Highway 644, Zip 41230–9242, Mailing Address: P.O. Box 769, Zip 41230–0769; tel. 606/638–9451, (Nonreporting) **A**1 10 20 **F**3 11 12 15 18 29 35 38 40 45 49 50 51 68 70 75 79 81 84 85 87 93 98 100 104 107 108 111 115 119 129 130 133 146 147 149 150 154 157 **S** Quorum Health, Brentwood, TN
Primary Contact: Greg Kiser, Chief Executive Officer
CFO: Michael Ackley, Chief Financial Officer
CHR: Pat Hart, Director Human Resources
CNO: Cathy Heston, Chief Nursing Officer
Web address: www.threeriversmedicalcenter.com
**Control:** Corporation, Investor–owned (for–profit) **Service:** General medical and surgical

**Staffed Beds:** 90 **Admissions:** 2286 **Census:** 24 **Outpatient Visits:** 50664 **Births:** 0 **Personnel:** 284

**AUDUBON HOSPITAL** See Norton Audubon Hospital

△ **BAPTIST HEALTH LOUISVILLE (180130)**, 4000 Kresge Way, Zip 40207–4676; tel. 502/897–8100, (Nonreporting) **A**1 2 3 5 7 10 **F**3 5 6 8 11 12 13 15 17 18 20 22 24 26 28 29 30 31 34 35 36 37 38 40 44 45 46 47 48 49 50 51 54 56 57 58 59 61 64 70 72 74 75 76 78 79 81 82 83 84 85 86 87 90 91 92 93 98 100 101 102 103 104 105 107 108 110 111 114 115 116 117 118 119 120 121 123 124 126 129 130 135 141 146 147 148 149 153 154 156 157 **P**6 **S** Baptist Health, Louisville, KY
Primary Contact: Larry W. Gray, President
COO: Clint Kaho, Vice President
CFO: Jim Morris, Vice President Finance
CMO: Kenneth Anderson, M.D., Vice President and Chief Medical Officer
CIO: Shari Price, Director Information Services
CHR: Kim Scaglione, Vice President Human Resources
CNO: Karen Newman, Ed.D., MSN, R.N., Vice President and Chief Nursing Officer
Web address: www.baptisthealthlouisville.com
**Control:** Other not–for–profit (including NFP Corporation) **Service:** General medical and surgical

**Staffed Beds:** 500 **Admissions:** 25055 **Census:** 315 **Outpatient Visits:** 431788 **Births:** 3075 **Total Expense ($000):** 516925 **Payroll Expense ($000):** 167205 **Personnel:** 2638

**BAPTIST HOSPITAL EAST** See Baptist Health Louisville

**CARITAS MEDICAL CENTER** See UofI Health - Mary and Elizabeth Hospital

☐ **CENTRAL STATE HOSPITAL (184015)**, 10510 LaGrange Road,
Zip 40223–1228; tel. 502/253–7060, (Nonreporting) **A**1 3 5 10
Primary Contact: Josie Goodman, Hospital Director
CFO: Robert Underhill, Director of Business Services
CMO: Vital Shah, M.D., Associate Director and Chief Medical Officer
CIO: Randy Spicer, Information Technology Supervisor
CHR: Sonya Wheatley, Human Resources Manager
CNO: Jennifer Fowler
**Control**: State, Government, Nonfederal **Service**: Psychiatric

| Staffed Beds: 112 |
|---|

**CHI OUR LADY OF PEACE** See UofI Health - Peace Hospital

**FRAZIER INSTITUTE** See UofI Health - Frazier Rehabilitation Institute

**HUMANA HOSPITAL-UNIVERSITY** See UofI Health - UofI Hospital

**KINDRED HOSPITAL LOUISVILLE AT JEWISH HOSPITAL** See Kindred Hospital-Louisville, Louisville

☒ **KINDRED HOSPITAL-LOUISVILLE (182001)**, 1313 Saint Anthony Place,
Zip 40204–1740; tel. 502/587–7001, (Includes KINDRED HOSPITAL LOUISVILLE
AT JEWISH HOSPITAL, Mailing address: 200 Abraham Flexner Way, 2nd Floor,
Louisville, Kentucky, Zip 40202; tel. 502/587–3999; Tim Phoenix, Chief Executive
Officer), (Nonreporting) **A**1 3 5 10 **S** Kindred Healthcare, Louisville, KY
Primary Contact: Jack Nicholson, Chief Executive Officer
Web address: www.kindredlouisville.com
**Control**: Corporation, Investor–owned (for–profit) **Service**: Acute long–term care
hospital

| Staffed Beds: 117 |
|---|

**KOSAIR CHILDREN'S HOSPITAL** See Norton Children's Hospital

★ **NORTON CHILDREN'S HOSPITAL (189801)**, 231 East Chestnut Street,
Zip 40202–1821; tel. 502/629–6000, (Nonreporting) **A**2 3 5 8 10 **F**3 7 8 11 16
18 19 20 21 22 23 24 25 26 27 28 29 30 31 32 34 35 36 38 39 40 41 42 43
44 45 47 48 49 50 51 54 57 58 59 60 61 64 65 67 68 72 73 74 75 78 79 81
82 84 85 86 87 88 89 91 92 93 96 98 99 101 102 107 108 111 114 115 116
117 119 126 130 131 132 134 136 137 138 144 145 146 148 149 150 154
155 156 **P**6 **S** Norton Healthcare, Louisville, KY
Primary Contact: Emmett Ramser, Chief Administrative Officer
Web address: www.kosairchildrens.com/
**Control**: Other not–for–profit (including NFP Corporation) **Service**: Children's
general medical and surgical

| Staffed Beds: 279 Admissions: 10453 Census: 205 Outpatient |
|---|
| Visits: 129592 Births: 0 Total Expense ($000): 343431 Payroll Expense ($000): 108410 Personnel: 1621 |

**NORTON HEALTHCARE** See Norton Hospital

**NORTON HEALTHCARE PAVILION** See Norton Hospital, Louisville

☒ **NORTON HOSPITAL (180088)**, 200 East Chestnut Street, Zip 40202–1800,
Mailing Address: P.O. Box 35070, Zip 40232–5070; tel. 502/629–8000,
(Includes NORTON AUDUBON HOSPITAL, Mailing address: One Audubon Plaza
Drive, Louisville, Kentucky, Zip 40217–1300, P O Box 17550, Zip 40217–0550,
tel. 502/636–7111; Jon Cooper, Chief Administrative Officer; NORTON
BROWNSBORO HOSPITAL, Mailing address: 4960 Norton Healthcare Boulevard,
Louisville, Kentucky, Zip 40241–2831; tel. 502/446–8000; Andrew Strausbaugh,
Chief Administrative Officer; NORTON HEALTHCARE PAVILION, Mailing address:
315 East Broadway, Louisville, Kentucky, Zip 40202–1703; tel. 502/629–2000;
NORTON WOMEN'S and CHILDREN'S HOSPITAL, Mailing address: 4001 Dutchmans
Lane, Louisville, Kentucky, Zip 40207–4799; tel. 502/893–1000; Charlotte Ipsan,
Chief Administrative Officer), (Nonreporting) **A**1 2 3 5 8 10 **F**3 7 11 12 13 15 17
18 20 22 24 26 28 29 30 31 34 35 36 38 39 40 44 45 46 47 48 49 50 51 53
55 56 57 59 61 64 68 70 72 73 74 75 76 78 79 81 82 83 84 85 86 87 89 91
92 93 95 96 98 100 101 102 107 108 110 111 114 115 116 117 118 119
120 121 123 124 126 129 130 131 132 133 134 135 146 147 148 149 150
154 155 156 157 **P**6 **S** Norton Healthcare, Louisville, KY
Primary Contact: Matthew Ayers, Chief Administrative Officer
CFO: Carl Amorose, Vice President Finance
Web address: www.nortonhealthcare.com/nortonhospital
**Control**: Other not–for–profit (including NFP Corporation) **Service**: General
medical and surgical

| Staffed Beds: 1263 Admissions: 66372 Census: 831 Outpatient |
|---|
| Visits: 572595 Births: 7908 Total Expense ($000): 1165746 Payroll Expense ($000): 363425 Personnel: 5778 |

**NORTON MEDICAL PAVILION** See Norton Healthcare Pavilion

**NORTON SOUTHWEST HOSPITAL** See Norton Brownsboro Hospital

**NORTON WOMEN'S AND KOSAIR CHILDREN'S HOSPITAL** See Norton
Women's and Children's Hospital

☒ **ROBLEY REX VETERANS AFFAIRS MEDICAL CENTER**, 800 Zorn Avenue,
Zip 40206–1499; tel. 502/287–4000, (Nonreporting) **A**1 3 5 **S** Department of
Veterans Affairs, Washington, DC
Primary Contact: Marylee Rothschild, M.D., Chief of Staff
CFO: Barbara Roberts, Chief Financial Officer
CMO: Marylee Rothschild, M.D., Chief of Staff
CIO: Augustine Bittner, Chief Information Officer
CHR: Angela Dutton, Chief Human Resources Management Service
Web address: www.louisville.va.gov
**Control**: Veterans Affairs, Government, federal **Service**: General medical and
surgical

| Staffed Beds: 116 |
|---|

**TEN BROECK DUPONT** See The Brook at Dupont

**TEN BROECK HOSPITAL** See The Brook Hospital - KMI

☐ **THE BROOK AT DUPONT (184007)**, 1405 Browns Lane, Zip 40207–4608;
tel. 502/896–0495, (Nonreporting) **A**1 10 **S** Universal Health Services, Inc., King
of Prussia, PA
Primary Contact: Paul Andrews, Chief Executive Officer
Web address: www.thebrookhospitals.com/
**Control**: Corporation, Investor–owned (for–profit) **Service**: Psychiatric

| Staffed Beds: 88 |
|---|

☐ **THE BROOK HOSPITAL - KMI (184008)**, 8521 Old LaGrange Road,
Zip 40242–3800; tel. 502/426–6380, (Nonreporting) **A**1 3 5 10 **S** Universal
Health Services, Inc., King of Prussia, PA
Primary Contact: Paul Andrews, Chief Executive Officer
COO: Kim Peabody, Chief Operating Officer
CFO: Glenn Brewer, Chief Financial Officer
CMO: Timothy Burke, M.D., Medical Director
CIO: John Ford, Information Technology Director
CHR: Christina Taylor, Director Human Resources
CNO: John Bisig, Chief Nursing Officer
Web address: www.thebrookhospitals.com
**Control**: Corporation, Investor–owned (for–profit) **Service**: Psychiatric

| Staffed Beds: 110 |
|---|

☒ △ **UOFL HEALTH - JEWISH HOSPITAL (180040)**, 200 Abraham Flexner
Way, Zip 40202–1886; tel. 502/587–4011, (Includes UOFL HEALTH - FRAZIER
REHABILITATION INSTITUTE, Mailing address: 220 Abraham Flexner Way, Louisville,
Kentucky, Zip 40202–1887; tel. 502/582–7400; Cathy Spalding, Administrator),
(Nonreporting) **A**1 3 5 7 10 **F**3 8 12 15 17 18 20 22 24 26 28 29 30 34 40 42
44 45 46 47 48 49 50 53 54 56 59 60 64 65 67 68 70 74 75 77 79 81 83 85
87 90 91 92 93 94 95 96 107 108 109 110 111 112 113 114 115 118 119
126 130 131 137 138 139 140 141 142 146 148 149 154 156 157 **S** UofL
Health, Louisville, KY
Primary Contact: John Walsh, FACHE, Chief Administrative Officer
CFO: Ronald Farr, Chief Financial Officer
CMO: James P Ketterhagen, M.D., Senior Vice President and Chief Medical Officer
CIO: Thomas Wittman, Chief Information Officer
CHR: Julie McGregor, Vice President and Chief People Officer
CNO: Cheryl Fugatte, MSN, Vice President and Chief Nursing Officer
Web address: www.https://www.uoflhealth.com/locations/transitional-care-
hospitals/kindred-hospital-louisville-at-jewish-hospital
**Control**: Other not–for–profit (including NFP Corporation) **Service**: General
medical and surgical

| Staffed Beds: 426 Admissions: 15192 Census: 276 Outpatient |
|---|
| Visits: 152351 Births: 0 Total Expense ($000): 429621 Payroll Expense ($000): 130530 Personnel: 2327 |

*Many Facility Codes have changed. Please refer to the AHA Guide Code Chart.*

★ **UOFL HEALTH - MARY AND ELIZABETH HOSPITAL**, 1850 Bluegrass Avenue, Zip 40215–1199; tel. 502/361–6000, (Nonreporting) **A**3 5 10 **F**3 11 12 15 18 20 22 29 30 34 35 40 44 45 47 49 50 53 56 59 60 63 64 68 69 70 74 75 79 81 82 84 85 86 87 107 108 110 111 114 115 118 119 130 132 135 154 156 **S** UofL Health, Louisville, KY
Primary Contact: Melisa Adkins, Chief Executive Officer
COO: Kenneth Johnson, Vice President
CFO: Elaine Hayes, Controller
CMO: Val Slayton, M.D., Vice President Medical Affairs
CHR: Julie McGregor, Director Human Resources
Web address: www.jhsmh.org
**Control**: Other not–for–profit (including NFP Corporation) **Service**: General medical and surgical

**Staffed Beds**: 170 **Admissions**: 7302 **Census**: 83 **Outpatient Visits**: 80252 **Births**: 0 **Total Expense ($000)**: 122309 **Payroll Expense ($000)**: 46909 **Personnel**: 701

★ **UOFL HEALTH - PEACE HOSPITAL**, 2020 Newburg Road, Zip 40205–1879; tel. 502/479–4500, (Nonreporting) **A**5 **F**5 29 30 35 44 50 56 98 99 100 101 104 105 130 132 143 152 153 154 **S** UofL Health, Louisville, KY
Primary Contact: Martha S. Mather, Chief Administrative Officer
CFO: Beckie Kistler, Director of Finance
CHR: Jan Ostbloom, Human Resources Consultant
Web address: www.kentuckyonehealth.org/our-lady-of-peace
**Control**: Other not–for–profit (including NFP Corporation) **Service**: Psychiatric

**Staffed Beds**: 220 **Admissions**: 8565 **Census**: 178 **Outpatient Visits**: 28788 **Births**: 0 **Total Expense ($000)**: 57902 **Payroll Expense ($000)**: 30889 **Personnel**: 599

⊞ **UOFL HEALTH - UOFL HOSPITAL (180141)**, 530 South Jackson Street, Zip 40202–3611; tel. 502/562–3000, (Nonreporting) **A**1 2 3 5 8 10 11 13 15 16 17 18 20 22 24 26 28 29 30 31 34 35 36 37 38 40 43 45 46 47 48 49 50 51 54 56 57 58 59 60 64 66 68 70 71 72 73 74 75 76 77 78 79 80 81 82 84 85 86 87 91 92 93 96 98 100 101 102 103 107 108 109 110 111 112 114 115 116 117 118 119 120 121 123 124 126 130 132 135 136 144 145 146 147 148 149 150 154 156 **P**1
Primary Contact: Thomas Miller, Chief Executive Officer
COO: Kenneth P. Marshall, Chief Operating Officer
CFO: Kirk Strack, Assistant Chief Financial Officer
CMO: Mark P Pfeifer, M.D., Senior Vice President and Chief Medical Officer
CIO: Troy May, Chief Information Officer
CNO: Mary Jane Adams, R.N., MSN, Senior Vice President and Chief Nursing Officer
Web address: www.ulh.org
**Control**: Other not–for–profit (including NFP Corporation) **Service**: General medical and surgical

**Staffed Beds**: 340 **Admissions**: 16467 **Census**: 269 **Outpatient Visits**: 190286 **Births**: 1906 **Total Expense ($000)**: 579545 **Payroll Expense ($000)**: 174169 **Personnel**: 2743

**VENCOR HOSPITAL-LOUISVILLE** See Kindred Hospital-Louisville

**VETERANS AFFAIRS MEDICAL CENTER-LOUISVILLE** See Robley Rex Veterans Affairs Medical Center

### MADISONVILLE—Hopkins County

☐ **BAPTIST HEALTH MADISONVILLE (180093)**, 900 Hospital Drive, Zip 42431–1694; tel. 270/825–5100, (Nonreporting) **A**1 2 3 5 10 **S** Baptist Health, Louisville, KY
Primary Contact: Robert L. Ramey, President
COO: Kevin Moser, Vice President of Operations
CFO: Kim Ashby, Vice President of Finance
CMO: Wayne Lipson, M.D., Chief Physician Executive
CIO: Karla Durham, Director of Information Systems
CHR: Lorie A. Oglesby, Director of Human Resources
CNO: Denise Dunn, R.N., Chief Nursing Officer
Web address: www.baptisthealthmadisonville.com
**Control**: Other not–for–profit (including NFP Corporation) **Service**: General medical and surgical

**Staffed Beds**: 175

★ **CONTINUECARE HOSPITAL AT MADISONVILLE (182009)**, 900 Hospital Drive, 4th Floor, Zip 42431–1644; tel. 270/825–5450, (Nonreporting) **A**10 22 **F**1 3 29 84 **S** Community Hospital Corporation, Plano, TX
Primary Contact: Kenneth F. Graves III, Chief Executive Officer
CNO: Kay Marantette, Chief Nursing Officer
Web address: www.continuecare.org/madisonville/
**Control**: Other not–for–profit (including NFP Corporation) **Service**: Acute long–term care hospital

**Staffed Beds**: 35 **Admissions**: 181 **Census**: 14 **Outpatient Visits**: 0 **Births**: 0 **Total Expense ($000)**: 6549 **Payroll Expense ($000)**: 2330 **Personnel**: 67

**REGIONAL MEDICAL CENTER OF HOPKINS COUNTY** See Baptist Health Madisonville

### MANCHESTER—Clay County

⊞ ○ **ADVENTHEALTH MANCHESTER (180043)**, 210 Marie Langdon Drive, Zip 40962–6388; tel. 606/598–5104, (Nonreporting) **A**1 10 11 **S** AdventHealth, Altamonte Springs, FL
Primary Contact: Chris Self, Chief Executive Officer
CFO: Paul Merklin, Vice President Finance and Chief Financial Officer
CMO: Jeff Newswanger, M.D., Chief Medical Officer
CHR: Joe Skula, Director Human Resources
Web address: www.manchestermemorial.org
**Control**: Church operated, Nongovernment, not–for–profit **Service**: General medical and surgical

**Staffed Beds**: 49

**MANCHESTER MEMORIAL HOSPITAL** See Adventhealth Manchester

### MARION—Crittenden County

**CRITTENDEN COUNTY HOSPITAL (180095)**, 520 West Gum Street, Zip 42064–1516, Mailing Address: P.O. Box 386, Zip 42064–0386; tel. 270/965–5281, (Nonreporting) **A**10 20
Primary Contact: Jonathan Gleason, Chief Executive Officer
COO: Robin Curnel, MSN, Chief Operating Officer and Chief Nursing Officer
CFO: Karen Paris, Controller
CMO: Steven Burkhart, M.D., Chief Medical Officer
CIO: Reese Baker, Director Information Systems
CHR: Jan Gregory, Chief of Human Resources
CNO: Robin Curnel, MSN, Chief Operating Officer and Chief Nursing Officer
Web address: www.crittenden-health.org
**Control**: Other not–for–profit (including NFP Corporation) **Service**: General medical and surgical

**Staffed Beds**: 48

### MARTIN—Floyd County

★ ⇑ **ARH OUR LADY OF THE WAY (181305)**, 11203 Main Street, Zip 41649; tel. 606/285–6400, (Nonreporting) **A**10 18 21 **F**3 15 18 28 35 40 56 81 104 111 114 119 130 **S** Appalachian Regional Healthcare, Inc., Lexington, KY
Primary Contact: Kathy Stumbo, President
CFO: Robert Brock, Vice President Finance
CMO: John Triplett, D.O., President Medical Staff
CIO: Chris Dye, Director Information Systems
Web address: www.saintjosephmartin.org
**Control**: Other not–for–profit (including NFP Corporation) **Service**: General medical and surgical

**Staffed Beds**: 25 **Admissions**: 542 **Census**: 9 **Outpatient Visits**: 26532 **Births**: 0

⇑ **SAINT JOSEPH - MARTIN** See Arh Our Lady of The Way

---

**Hospital, Medicare Provider Number, Address, Telephone, Approval, Facility, and Physician Codes, Health Care System**

★ American Hospital Association (AHA) membership
☐ The Joint Commission accreditation
○ Healthcare Facilities Accreditation Program
◇ DNV Healthcare Inc. accreditation
⇑ Center for Improvement in Healthcare Quality Accreditation
△ Commission on Accreditation of Rehabilitation Facilities (CARF) accreditation

## MAYFIELD—Graves County

⊞ **JACKSON PURCHASE MEDICAL CENTER (180116)**, 1099 Medical Center Circle, Zip 42066–1159; tel. 270/251–4100, (Nonreporting) **A**1 10 19 **S** LifePoint Health, Brentwood, TN
Primary Contact: David Anderson, Chief Executive Officer
CFO: Vicki Parks, Chief Financial Officer
CMO: Rudy Triana, M.D., Chief of Staff
CIO: Randy McDaniel, Information Systems Director
CHR: Tressa B Hargrove, Director Human Resources
CNO: Julia Grove, Chief Nursing Officer
Web address: www.jacksonpurchase.com
**Control**: Corporation, Investor–owned (for–profit) **Service**: General medical and surgical

> **Staffed Beds**: 227

**PINELAKE REGIONAL HOSPITAL** See Jackson Purchase Medical Center

## MAYSVILLE—Mason County

**MEADOVIEW REGIONAL MEDICAL CTR** See Meadowview Regional Medical Center

⊞ **MEADOWVIEW REGIONAL MEDICAL CENTER (180019)**, 989 Medical Park Drive, Zip 41056–8750; tel. 606/759–5311, (Nonreporting) **A**1 10 **S** LifePoint Health, Brentwood, TN
Primary Contact: Joseph G. Koch, Chief Executive Officer
CFO: Clayton Kolodziejczyk, Chief Financial Officer
CMO: Eric Lohman, M.D., Chief of Staff
CHR: Diana Kennedy, Director Human Resources
Web address: www.meadowviewregional.com
**Control**: Corporation, Investor–owned (for–profit) **Service**: General medical and surgical

> **Staffed Beds**: 100

## MCDOWELL—Floyd County

⇑ **MCDOWELL ARH HOSPITAL (181331)**, Route 122, Zip 41647, Mailing Address: P.O. Box 247, Zip 41647–0247; tel. 606/377–3400, (Nonreporting) **A**10 18 21 **F**3 11 15 29 30 34 35 40 50 57 59 62 64 65 75 77 82 86 87 93 97 107 111 115 119 127 130 131 133 146 154 **S** Appalachian Regional Healthcare, Inc., Lexington, KY
Primary Contact: Russell Barker, Community Chief Executive Officer
COO: Russell Barker, Community Chief Executive Officer
CMO: Mary A Hall, Chief Medical Staff
CIO: Jeff Brady, Director Information Systems
CHR: Stephanie Owens, Manager Human Resources
Web address: www.arh.org
**Control**: Other not–for–profit (including NFP Corporation) **Service**: General medical and surgical

> **Staffed Beds**: 25 **Admissions**: 357 **Census**: 5 **Outpatient Visits**: 36004
> **Births**: 0

⇑ **MCDOWELL ARH HOSPITAL** See Mcdowell Arh Hospital

## MIDDLESBORO—Bell County

⇑ **MIDDLESBORO APPALACHIAN REGIONAL HOSPITAL** See Middlesboro Arh Hospital

⇑ **MIDDLESBORO ARH HOSPITAL (180020)**, 3600 West Cumberland Avenue, Zip 40965–2614, Mailing Address: P.O. Box 340, Zip 40965–0340; tel. 606/242–1100, (Nonreporting) **A**10 21 **F**3 11 13 15 17 18 20 28 29 30 31 34 35 39 40 45 46 49 50 57 59 62 64 65 70 75 76 77 78 79 81 85 86 87 89 90 93 97 107 108 110 111 115 118 119 127 129 132 133 146 147 148 154 **S** Appalachian Regional Healthcare, Inc., Lexington, KY
Primary Contact: Michael Slusher, FACHE, Community Chief Executive Officer
CFO: Joseph Horton, Assistant Administrator
CMO: Robert Thomas, M.D., Chief of Staff
CHR: Christopher Thompson, Human Resources Manager
CNO: Vicki Thompson, MSN, Community Chief Nursing Officer
Web address: www.arh.org/middlesboro
**Control**: Other not–for–profit (including NFP Corporation) **Service**: General medical and surgical

> **Staffed Beds**: 46 **Admissions**: 1450 **Census**: 20 **Outpatient Visits**: 64345
> **Births**: 204

## MONTICELLO—Wayne County

○ **WAYNE COUNTY HOSPITAL (181321)**, 166 Hospital Street, Zip 42633–2416; tel. 606/348–9343, (Nonreporting) **A**10 11 18 **F**3 15 29 30 40 47 75 81 107 108 114 119 127 133 135 146
Primary Contact: Joseph Murrell, Chief Executive Officer
CFO: Anne Sawyer, Chief Financial Officer
CMO: David Mayer, Chief of Staff
CIO: Angela Burton, Privacy Officer
CHR: Mollie Dick, Coordinator Human Resources
CNO: Lora Elam, R.N., Chief Nursing Officer
Web address: www.waynehospital.org
**Control**: Other not–for–profit (including NFP Corporation) **Service**: General medical and surgical

> **Staffed Beds**: 25 **Admissions**: 496 **Census**: 9 **Outpatient Visits**: 23767
> **Births**: 0 **Total Expense ($000)**: 15498 **Payroll Expense ($000)**: 6642
> **Personnel**: 160

## MOREHEAD—Rowan County

⊞ **ST. CLAIRE HEALTHCARE (180018)**, 222 Medical Circle, Zip 40351–1179; tel. 606/783–6500, (Nonreporting) **A**1 2 3 5 10 13
Primary Contact: Mark J. Neff, FACHE, President and Chief Executive Officer
CFO: Chris McClurg, Vice President Finance and Chief Financial Officer
CMO: William L Melahn, M.D., Vice President Medical Affairs and Chief Medical Officer
CIO: Randy McCleese, Vice President Information Services and Chief Information Officer
CNO: Lerae Wilson, Vice President Patient Services and Chief Nursing Officer
Web address: www.st-claire.org
**Control**: Church operated, Nongovernment, not–for–profit **Service**: General medical and surgical

> **Staffed Beds**: 133

**ST. CLAIRE REGIONAL MEDICAL CENTER** See St. Claire Healthcare

## MORGANFIELD—Union County

☐ **METHODIST HOSPITAL UNION COUNTY (181306)**, 4604 Highway 60 West, Zip 42437–9570; tel. 270/389–5000, (Nonreporting) **A**1 10 18 **F**3 11 15 29 30 34 36 40 43 45 57 68 75 77 81 85 86 87 93 107 114 119 130 133 135 146 148 149 156
Primary Contact: Benny Nolen, President and Chief Executive Officer
CFO: David Massengale, Chief Financial Officer
CMO: William Clapp, M.D., Chief of Medical Staff
CIO: Randy McCleese, Chief Information Officer
CHR: Ty Kahle, Assistant Vice President Human Resources
CNO: Peggy F Creighton, R.N., Director of Nursing
Web address: www.methodisthospital.net
**Control**: Other not–for–profit (including NFP Corporation) **Service**: General medical and surgical

> **Staffed Beds**: 25 **Admissions**: 564 **Census**: 14 **Outpatient Visits**: 30455
> **Births**: 0 **Total Expense ($000)**: 15812 **Payroll Expense ($000)**: 5437
> **Personnel**: 114

**UNION CNTY METHODIST HOSPITAL** See Methodist Hospital Union County

## MOUNT STERLING—Montgomery County

**GATEWAY REGIONAL HEALTH SYSTEM** See Saint Joseph Mount Sterling

⊞ **SAINT JOSEPH MOUNT STERLING (180064)**, 225 Falcon Drive, Zip 40353–1158, Mailing Address: P.O. Box 7, Zip 40353–0007; tel. 859/497–5000, (Nonreporting) **A**1 10 **F**3 11 13 15 17 28 29 30 34 35 36 37 40 45 46 57 59 64 68 70 74 75 76 77 78 79 81 86 87 93 97 107 111 114 119 129 130 132 133 135 146 147 148 156 **S** CommonSpirit Health, Chicago, IL
Primary Contact: Terrence G. Deis, CPA, FACHE, President
CFO: Amanda Kinman, Director of Finance
CMO: Jeff McGinnis, M.D., President Medical Staff
CIO: Jeff Ryder, Director Information Systems
CHR: Annette Saadat, Human Resources Business Partner
CNO: Cinda Fluke, R.N., Chief Nursing Officer
Web address: www.sjhlex.org
**Control**: Other not–for–profit (including NFP Corporation) **Service**: General medical and surgical

> **Staffed Beds**: 42 **Admissions**: 1715 **Census**: 18 **Outpatient Visits**: 69531
> **Births**: 238 **Total Expense ($000)**: 48008 **Payroll Expense ($000)**: 12782
> **Personnel**: 235

*Many Facility Codes have changed. Please refer to the AHA Guide Code Chart.*

© 2021 AHA Guide

## MOUNT VERNON—Rockcastle County

**ROCKCASTLE HOSPITAL AND RESPIRATORY CARE CENTER** See Rockcastle Regional Hospital and Respiratory Care Center

☒ **ROCKCASTLE REGIONAL HOSPITAL AND RESPIRATORY CARE CENTER (180115)**, 145 Newcomb Avenue, Zip 40456–2728, Mailing Address: P.O. Box 1310, Zip 40456–1310; tel. 606/256–2195, (Nonreporting) **A**1 2 10
Primary Contact: Stephen A. Estes, Chief Executive Officer
CFO: Charles Black JrChief Financial Officer
CMO: Jon A Arvin, M.D., Chief Medical Officer
CIO: Maleigha Amyx, Chief Information Officer
CHR: Carmen Poynter, Director Human Resources
CNO: Tammy Brock, MSN, R.N., Chief Nursing Officer
Web address: www.rockcastleregional.org
**Control**: Other not–for–profit (including NFP Corporation) **Service**: General medical and surgical

**Staffed Beds: 105**

## MURRAY—Calloway County

☒ **MURRAY-CALLOWAY COUNTY HOSPITAL (180027)**, 803 Poplar Street, Zip 42071–2432; tel. 270/762–1100, (Nonreporting) **A**1 2 10 19
Primary Contact: Colonel Jerome Penner, Chief Executive Officer
COO: John R Wilson, Chief Operating Officer
CFO: John Bradford, Chief Financial Officer
CIO: Brian Benedict, Director of Information Technology
CHR: John R Wilson, Vice President, Human Resources
CNO: Jeffrey L Eye, R.N., Vice President Patient Care Services
Web address: www.murrayhospital.org
**Control**: City–county, Government, Nonfederal **Service**: General medical and surgical

**Staffed Beds: 259**

## OWENSBORO—Daviess County

**MERCY HOSPITAL** See Healthpark

☒ △ **OWENSBORO HEALTH REGIONAL HOSPITAL (180038)**, 1201 Pleasant Valley Road, Zip 42303; tel. 270/417–2000, (Includes HEALTHPARK, Mailing address: 1006 Ford Avenue, Owensboro, Kentucky, Zip 42301, P O Box 2839, Zip 42302, tel. 270/688–5433) (Total facility includes 30 beds in nursing home–type unit) **A**1 2 3 5 7 10 **F**3 5 11 13 15 17 18 20 22 24 26 28 29 30 31 32 34 35 40 43 44 45 46 49 53 54 56 57 58 59 61 62 64 65 66 70 72 74 75 76 77 78 79 81 82 83 84 85 86 87 89 90 91 92 93 97 98 100 101 102 103 104 105 107 108 110 111 114 115 116 117 118 119 120 121 123 124 126 127 128 129 130 131 132 135 144 145 146 147 148 149 153 156 **S** Owensboro Health, Owensboro, KY
Primary Contact: Greg Strahan, President and Chief Executive Officer
COO: Deborah K Bostic, Chief Operating Officer
CFO: John Hackbarth, CPA, Senior Vice President Finance and Chief Financial Officer
CMO: Francis DuFrayne, M.D., Chief Medical Officer
CIO: Tim Belec, Chief Information Officer
CHR: Mia Suter, Chief Administration Officer
CNO: Joni Sims, Chief Nursing Officer
Web address: www.owensborohealth.org
**Control**: Other not–for–profit (including NFP Corporation) **Service**: General medical and surgical

**Staffed Beds: 360 Admissions: 16074 Census: 204 Outpatient Visits: 1042264 Births: 2080 Total Expense ($000): 471334 Payroll Expense ($000): 160135 Personnel: 2282**

**OWENSBORO MEDICAL HEALTH SYSTEM** See Owensboro Health Regional Hospital

**RIVERVALLEY BEHAVIORAL HEALTH HOSPITAL (184013)**, 1000 Industrial Drive, Zip 42301–8715; tel. 270/689–6500, (Nonreporting) **A**10 **F**29 32 34 35 38 40 41 50 58 59 64 68 86 98 99 100 101 102 104 130 132 154
Primary Contact: Wanda Figuerora Peralta, President and Chief Executive Officer
COO: Michelle Parks, Administrator
CFO: J Michael Mountain, Chief Financial Officer
CMO: David Harmon, D.O., Vice President Medical Services
CIO: Travis Taggart, Director Information Technology
CHR: Cathryn H Gaddis, Director Human Resources
Web address: www.rvbh.com
**Control**: Other not–for–profit (including NFP Corporation) **Service**: Children's hospital psychiatric

**Staffed Beds: 80 Admissions: 787 Census: 31 Outpatient Visits: 1429 Births: 0 Total Expense ($000): 7558 Payroll Expense ($000): 3098 Personnel: 76**

**VALLEY HOSPITAL** See Rivervalley Behavioral Health Hospital

## PADUCAH—Mccracken County

☐ **BAPTIST HEALTH PADUCAH (180104)**, 2501 Kentucky Avenue, Zip 42003–3200; tel. 270/575–2100, (Nonreporting) **A**1 2 10 19 **F**3 11 12 13 15 17 18 20 22 24 26 28 29 30 31 32 34 35 40 45 46 48 50 51 57 58 59 64 68 70 72 73 74 75 76 77 78 79 81 82 84 85 86 87 89 91 92 93 96 107 108 109 110 111 112 113 114 115 116 117 118 119 120 121 124 126 129 130 131 132 134 135 145 146 147 148 149 154 156 157 **S** Baptist Health, Louisville, KY
Primary Contact: Christopher Roty, President
COO: Bonnie W Schrock, FACHE, Chief Operating Officer
CMO: Bradley W. Housman, M.D., Chief Medical Officer
CIO: Jay Orazine, Director Information Services
CNO: Sharon Freyer, R.N., Chief Nursing Officer
Web address: www.baptisthealthpaducah.com
**Control**: Other not–for–profit (including NFP Corporation) **Service**: General medical and surgical

**Staffed Beds: 188 Admissions: 9872 Census: 105 Outpatient Visits: 168468 Births: 1132 Total Expense ($000): 259509 Payroll Expense ($000): 76099 Personnel: 1235**

## PADUCAH—McCracken County

**CONTINUECARE HOSPITAL** See Continuecare Hospital at Baptist Health Paducah

★ **CONTINUECARE HOSPITAL AT BAPTIST HEALTH PADUCAH (182008)**, 2501 Kentucky Avenue, 5th Floor, Zip 42003–3813; tel. 270/575–2598, (Nonreporting) **A**10 22 **F**1 3 29 34 35 148 154 **S** Community Hospital Corporation, Plano, TX
Primary Contact: Lee Gentry, FACHE, Chief Executive Officer
CNO: Mary Lou Young, Chief Nursing Officer
Web address: www.continuecare.com/paducah//
**Control**: Other not–for–profit (including NFP Corporation) **Service**: Acute long–term care hospital

**Staffed Beds: 37 Admissions: 234 Census: 16 Outpatient Visits: 0 Births: 0 Total Expense ($000): 8113 Payroll Expense ($000): 3793 Personnel: 45**

## PADUCAH—Mccracken County

☐ △ **LOURDES HOSPITAL (180102)**, 1530 Lone Oak Road, Zip 42003–7900, Mailing Address: P.O. Box 7100, Zip 42002–7100; tel. 270/444–2444, (Nonreporting) **A**1 7 10 19 **S** Mercy Health, Cincinnati, OH
Primary Contact: Michael Yungmann, President and Chief Executive Officer
CHR: Kim Lindsey, Chief Human Resources Officer
Web address: www.lourdes-pad.org
**Control**: Church operated, Nongovernment, not–for–profit **Service**: General medical and surgical

**Staffed Beds: 281**

**WESTERN BAPTIST HOSPITAL** See Baptist Health Paducah

---

**Hospital, Medicare Provider Number, Address, Telephone, Approval, Facility, and Physician Codes, Health Care System**

★ American Hospital Association (AHA) membership
☐ The Joint Commission accreditation
○ Healthcare Facilities Accreditation Program
◇ DNV Healthcare Inc. accreditation
⇑ Center for Improvement in Healthcare Quality Accreditation
△ Commission on Accreditation of Rehabilitation Facilities (CARF) accreditation

## PAINTSVILLE—Johnson County

☐ **PAUL B. HALL REGIONAL MEDICAL CENTER (180078)**, 625 James S. Trimble Boulevard, Zip 41240–0000; tel. 606/789–3511, (Nonreporting) **A**1 10 **S** Quorum Health, Brentwood, TN
Primary Contact: Deborah Trimble, R.N., Chief Executive Officer
CFO: Pattie Major, Chief Financial Officer
CMO: F K Belhasen, M.D., Medical Director
CHR: Carla J. Stapleton, Director Human Resources
Web address: www.pbhrmc.com
**Control**: Corporation, Investor–owned (for–profit) **Service**: General medical and surgical

| **Staffed Beds:** 72 |
|---|

## PARIS—Bourbon County

⊠ **BOURBON COMMUNITY HOSPITAL (180046)**, 9 Linville Drive, Zip 40361–2196; tel. 859/987–3600, (Nonreporting) **A**1 10 **S** LifePoint Health, Brentwood, TN
Primary Contact: Matt Smith, Interim Chief Executive Officer
CFO: Michael Snedegar, Chief Financial Officer
CMO: C. Ray Young, M.D., Chief Medical Officer
CIO: Phil Osborne, Director Information Technology
CHR: Roger K Davis, Director Human Resources
Web address: www.bourbonhospital.com
**Control**: Corporation, Investor–owned (for–profit) **Service**: General medical and surgical

| **Staffed Beds:** 58 |
|---|

**BURBON COMMUNITY HOSPITAL** See Bourbon Community Hospital

## PIKEVILLE—Pike County

☐ **PIKEVILLE MEDICAL CENTER (180044)**, 911 Bypass Road, Zip 41501–1689; tel. 606/218–3500, (Nonreporting) **A**1 2 3 5 10 **F**3 11 12 13 15 18 20 22 24 26 28 29 30 31 32 34 35 39 40 43 45 49 50 51 55 57 59 60 61 62 64 65 66 68 69 70 72 74 75 76 77 78 79 81 82 84 85 86 87 89 90 93 95 96 97 107 108 110 111 115 116 117 118 119 121 123 124 126 127 129 130 131 132 135 146 147 148 154 156 **P**6
Primary Contact: Donovan Blackburn, Chief Executive Officer and Vice President of Board of Directors
COO: Kansas Justice, Senior Vice President and Chief Operating Officer
CFO: Michelle Hagy, Senior Vice President and Chief Financial Officer
CMO: Aaron Crum, M.D., Chief Medical Officer, Assistant Chief Executive Officer and Senior Vice President
CIO: Tony Damron, Senior Vice President and Chief Information Officer
CNO: Michelle L. Rainey, Senior Vice President and Chief Nursing Officer
Web address: www.pikevillehospital.org
**Control**: Other not–for–profit (including NFP Corporation) **Service**: General medical and surgical

| **Staffed Beds:** 340 **Admissions:** 14338 **Census:** 233 **Outpatient** **Visits:** 500431 **Births:** 962 **Total Expense ($000):** 540931 **Payroll Expense ($000):** 221360 **Personnel:** 2910 |
|---|

**PIKEVILLE METHODIST HOSPITAL** See Pikeville Medical Center

## PINEVILLE—Bell County

**PINEVILLE COMMUNITY HEALTH CENTER (180021)**, 850 Riverview Avenue, Zip 40977–1452; tel. 606/337–3051, (Nonreporting) **A**10 22
Primary Contact: Terry Nichols, Chief Executive Officer
CFO: Colan Kelly, Chief Financial Officer
CMO: Michael Peterson, M.D., Chief of Staff
CIO: David Hall, Chief Information Officer
CHR: Josh Collett, Director Human Resources
CNO: Dinah Jarvis, Director of Nursing
Web address: www.southeasternkyhealth.com
**Control**: Other not–for–profit (including NFP Corporation) **Service**: General medical and surgical

| **Staffed Beds:** 150 |
|---|

**SOUTHEASTERN KENTUCKY MEDICAL CENTER** See Pineville Community Health Center

## PRESTONSBURG—Floyd County

★ ⇑ **HIGHLANDS ARH REGIONAL MEDICAL CENTER (180005)**, 5000 Kentucky Route 321, Zip 41653–1273; Mailing Address: P.O. Box 668, Zip 41653–0668; tel. 606/886–8511, (Nonreporting) **A**2 10 19 21 **S** Appalachian Regional Healthcare, Inc., Lexington, KY
Primary Contact: Timothy A. Hatfield, Community Chief Executive Officer
COO: Justin Harris, Chief Operating Officer
CIO: Michael Roberts, Chief Technology Officer
CNO: Susan Renee' Ellis, R.N., MSN, Community Chief Nursing Officer
Web address: www.arh.org
**Control**: Other not–for–profit (including NFP Corporation) **Service**: General medical and surgical

| **Staffed Beds:** 139 |
|---|

⇑ **HIGHLANDS REGIONAL MEDICAL CENTER** See Highlands Arh Regional Medical Center

## PRINCETON—Caldwell County

**CALDWELL COUNTY HOSPITAL** See Caldwell Medical Center

★ **CALDWELL MEDICAL CENTER (181322)**, 100 Medical Center Drive, Zip 42445–2430, Mailing Address: P.O. Box 410, Zip 42445–0410; tel. 270/365–0300, (Nonreporting) **A**10 18 **S** QHR Health, Brentwood, TN
Primary Contact: Daniel Odegaard, FACHE, Chief Executive Officer
CFO: Shane Whittington, Chief Financial Officer
CHR: Rhonda Burns, Director Human Resources
CNO: Douglas James, Chief Nursing Officer
Web address: www.caldwellhosp.org
**Control**: Other not–for–profit (including NFP Corporation) **Service**: General medical and surgical

| **Staffed Beds:** 25 |
|---|

## RADCLIFF—Hardin County

☐ **LINCOLN TRAIL BEHAVIORAL HEALTH SYSTEM (184012)**, 3909 South Wilson Road, Zip 40160–8944, Mailing Address: P.O. Box 369, Zip 40159–0369; tel. 270/351–9444, (Nonreporting) **A**1 10 **S** Universal Health Services, Inc., King of Prussia, PA
Primary Contact: Leslie Flechler, Chief Executive Officer
CFO: Debbie Ditto, CPA, Controller
CMO: Muhammad W. Sajid, M.D., Medical Director
CHR: Charlotte C Davis, Director Human Resources
Web address: www.lincolnbehavioral.com
**Control**: Corporation, Investor–owned (for–profit) **Service**: Psychiatric

| **Staffed Beds:** 140 |
|---|

**LINCOLN TRAIL HOSPITAL** See Lincoln Trail Behavioral Health System

## RICHMOND—Madison County

○ **BAPTIST HEALTH RICHMOND (180049)**, 801 Eastern Bypass, Zip 40475–2405, Mailing Address: P.O. Box 1600, Zip 40476–2603; tel. 859/623–3131, (Nonreporting) **A**10 11 19 **S** Baptist Health, Louisville, KY
Primary Contact: Greg Donavan. Gerard, President
CMO: Richard Shelton, M.D., Chief Medical Officer
CIO: Kelly Bonzo, Director
CHR: Joy M Benedict, Director Human Resources
CNO: Melinda Lee Blair, Vice President and Chief Nursing Officer
Web address: www.baptisthealthrichmond.com
**Control**: Other not–for–profit (including NFP Corporation) **Service**: General medical and surgical

| **Staffed Beds:** 60 |
|---|

**PATTIE A. CLAY REGIONAL MEDICAL CENTER** See Baptist Health Richmond

## RUSSELL SPRINGS—Russell County

★ **RUSSELL COUNTY HOSPITAL (181330)**, 153 Dowell Road, Zip 42642–4579, Mailing Address: P.O. Box 1610, Zip 42642–1610; tel. 270/866–4141, (Nonreporting) **A**10 18
Primary Contact: Scott Thompson, Chief Executive Officer
CFO: Janie Landis, Chief Financial Officer
CMO: Jerry D. Westerfield, M.D., Chief of Medical Staff
CIO: Monte Monsanto, Chief Information Systems
CHR: Jennifer Goode, Director Human Resources
CNO: Judy Chenoweth, Chief Nursing Officer
Web address: www.russellcohospital.org
**Control**: County, Government, Nonfederal **Service**: General medical and surgical

| **Staffed Beds:** 25 |
|---|

*Many Facility Codes have changed. Please refer to the AHA Guide Code Chart.*

## RUSSELLVILLE—Logan County

**COLUMBIA LOGAN MEMORIAL HOSP** See Logan Memorial Hospital

⌗ **LOGAN MEMORIAL HOSPITAL (180066)**, 1625 South Nashville Road, Zip 42276–8834, Mailing Address: P.O. Box 10, Zip 42276–0010; tel. 270/726–4011, (Nonreporting) **A**1 10 **S** LifePoint Health, Brentwood, TN
Primary Contact: James Bills, Chief Executive Officer
CFO: Tim Prestridge, Interim Chief Financial Officer
CIO: Randy Compton, Information Technology and System Director
CHR: Susan Renodin Deaton, Human Resources Director
CNO: Deborah Brown, Chief Nursing Officer
Web address: www.loganmemorial.com
**Control**: Corporation, Investor–owned (for–profit) **Service**: General medical and surgical

**Staffed Beds:** 30

## SALEM—Livingston County

**LIVINGSTON COUNTY HOSPITAL** See Livingston Hospital and Healthcare Services

**LIVINGSTON HOSPITAL AND HEALTHCARE SERVICES (181320)**, 131 Hospital Drive, Zip 42078–8043; tel. 270/988–2299, (Nonreporting) **A**10 18
Primary Contact: Elizabeth Snodgrass, Chief Executive Officer
CMO: William Guyette, M.D., President Medical Staff
CIO: Shannan Landreth, Information Systems
CHR: Carla Wiggins, Director Human Resources
CNO: Joanna Stone, Chief Nursing Officer
Web address: www.lhhs.org
**Control**: Other not–for–profit (including NFP Corporation) **Service**: General medical and surgical

**Staffed Beds:** 25

## SCOTTSVILLE—Allen County

**ALLEN COUNTY WAR MEM HOSPITAL** See Medical Center at Scottsville

**MEDICAL CENTER AT SCOTTSVILLE (181324)**, 456 Burnley Road, Zip 42164–6355; tel. 270/622–2800, (Total facility includes 110 beds in nursing home–type unit) (Nonreporting) **A**10 18 **F**3 15 28 29 30 34 35 40 45 50 56 57 59 64 68 75 81 82 85 86 87 93 97 103 104 107 110 111 114 119 127 128 130 132 133 135 143 146 148 149 154 **S** Med Center Health, Bowling Green, KY
Primary Contact: Eric Hagan, R.N., Executive Vice President and Administrator
CFO: Ronald G. Sowell, FACHE, Chief Financial Officer
CIO: Mark Brookman, Chief Information Officer
CHR: Lynn Williams, Vice President Human Resources
Web address: www.themedicalcenterscottsville.org/
**Control**: Other not–for–profit (including NFP Corporation) **Service**: General medical and surgical

**Staffed Beds:** 135 **Admissions:** 709 **Census:** 124 **Outpatient Visits:** 25447 **Births:** 0 **Personnel:** 250

## SHELBYVILLE—Shelby County

**UNITED MEDICAL CTR-SHELBYVILLE** See Uofl Health - Shelbyville Hospital

⌗ **UOFL HEALTH - SHELBYVILLE HOSPITAL (180016)**, 727 Hospital Drive, Zip 40065–1699; tel. 502/647–4000, (Nonreporting) **A**1 10 **F**3 11 15 18 28 29 34 35 40 41 44 45 46 50 57 59 63 64 68 71 75 77 79 80 81 82 85 87 93 94 96 107 108 110 111 115 119 129 131 132 134 135 146 149 154 156 **S** UofL Health, Louisville, KY
Primary Contact: Aaron Garofola, Chief Executive Officer
CFO: Erika McGimsey, Controller
CMO: Tony Perez, M.D., President Medical Staff
CHR: Cindy Stewart Rattray, Director Human Resources
Web address: www.kentuckyonehealth.org/jewish-hospital-shelbyville
**Control**: Other not–for–profit (including NFP Corporation) **Service**: General medical and surgical

**Staffed Beds:** 30 **Admissions:** 380 **Census:** 3 **Outpatient Visits:** 35347 **Births:** 0 **Total Expense ($000):** 26138 **Payroll Expense ($000):** 8640 **Personnel:** 136

## SOMERSET—Pulaski County

**COLUMBIA LAKE CUMBERLAND HOSP** See Lake Cumberland Regional Hospital

⌗ **LAKE CUMBERLAND REGIONAL HOSPITAL (180132)**, 305 Langdon Street, Zip 42503–2750, Mailing Address: P.O. Box 620, Zip 42502–0620; tel. 606/679–7441, (Nonreporting) **A**1 2 3 10 13 **S** LifePoint Health, Brentwood, TN
Primary Contact: Robert Parker, Chief Executive Officer
COO: Elizabeth Jones, Chief Operating Officer
CFO: Steve Sloan, Chief Financial Officer
CMO: Michael Citak, M.D., Chief Medical Officer
CIO: Thomas Gilbert, Director Information Technology Services
CHR: James Hughes, Director Human Resources
CNO: Sheryl Glasscock, Chief Nursing Officer
Web address: www.lakecumberlandhospital.com
**Control**: Corporation, Investor–owned (for–profit) **Service**: General medical and surgical

**Staffed Beds:** 295

## SOUTH WILLIAMSON—Pike County

☐ ⇑ **TUG VALLEY ARH REGIONAL MEDICAL CENTER (180069)**, 260 Hospital Drive, Zip 41503–4072; tel. 606/237–1710, (Total facility includes 35 beds in nursing home–type unit) (Nonreporting) **A**1 10 19 21 **F**3 11 13 15 29 30 34 35 40 43 50 54 57 59 60 62 64 67 70 74 75 76 77 79 81 82 85 86 87 89 93 97 107 108 110 111 115 118 119 127 128 129 130 132 146 147 154 **S** Appalachian Regional Healthcare, Inc., Lexington, KY
Primary Contact: Timothy A. Hatfield, Community Chief Executive Officer
CMO: J D Miller, M.D., Vice President Medical Affairs
CIO: Jeff Brady, Chief Information Officer
Web address: www.arh.org/locations/tug_valley/about_us.aspx
**Control**: Other not–for–profit (including NFP Corporation) **Service**: General medical and surgical

**Staffed Beds:** 123 **Admissions:** 2245 **Census:** 42 **Outpatient Visits:** 53533 **Births:** 100

⇑ **WILLIAMSON ARH HOSPITAL** See Tug Valley Arh Regional Medical Center

## STANFORD—Lincoln County

☐ **EPHRAIM MCDOWELL FORT LOGAN HOSPITAL (181315)**, 110 Metker Trail, Zip 40484–1020; tel. 606/365–4600, (Nonreporting) **A**1 10 18 **S** Ephraim McDowell Health, Danville, KY
Primary Contact: Ina Louise Glass, MSN, Administrator
CFO: William R Snapp IIIVice President and Chief Financial Officer
CMO: James Turpin, Chief of Staff
CIO: Gary Neat, Director Information Systems
CHR: Carl Metz, Vice President
CNO: Ina Louise Glass, MSN, Administrator
Web address: www.fortloganhospital.org
**Control**: Other not–for–profit (including NFP Corporation) **Service**: General medical and surgical

**Staffed Beds:** 25

**FORT LOGAN HOSPITAL** See Ephraim Mcdowell Fort Logan Hospital

## TOMPKINSVILLE—Monroe County

☐ **MONROE COUNTY MEDICAL CENTER (180105)**, 529 Capp Harlan Road, Zip 42167–1840; tel. 270/487–9231, (Nonreporting) **A**1 10 20
Primary Contact: Vicky McFall, Chief Executive Officer
CFO: Rickie F Brown, Chief Financial Officer
CIO: Paul McKiddy, Director Information Technology
CHR: Sue Page, Director Human Resources
Web address: www.mcmccares.com
**Control**: Other not–for–profit (including NFP Corporation) **Service**: General medical and surgical

**Staffed Beds:** 49

---

**Hospital, Medicare Provider Number, Address, Telephone, Approval, Facility, and Physician Codes, Health Care System**

★ American Hospital Association (AHA) membership
☐ The Joint Commission accreditation
○ Healthcare Facilities Accreditation Program
◇ DNV Healthcare Inc. accreditation
⇑ Center for Improvement in Healthcare Quality Accreditation
△ Commission on Accreditation of Rehabilitation Facilities (CARF) accreditation

**KY**

## VERSAILLES—Woodford County

★ **BLUEGRASS COMMUNITY HOSPITAL (181308)**, 360 Amsden Avenue, Zip 40383–1286; tel. 859/873–3111, (Nonreporting) **A**10 18 **S** LifePoint Health, Brentwood, TN
Primary Contact: Tommy Haggard, Chief Executive Officer
CFO: Shellie Shouse, Chief Financial Officer
CMO: Michele Welling, M.D., Chief of Staff
CHR: Marcia Carter, Director Human Resources
CNO: Kathy Russell, R.N., Chief Nursing Officer
Web address: www.bluegrasscommunityhospital.com
**Control**: Other not–for–profit (including NFP Corporation) **Service**: General medical and surgical

Staffed Beds: 16

**WOODFORD HOSPITAL** See Bluegrass Community Hospital

## WEST LIBERTY—Morgan County

⇑ **MORGAN COUNTY APPALACHIAN REGIONAL HOSPITAL** See Morgan County Arh Hospital

⇑ **MORGAN COUNTY ARH HOSPITAL (181307)**, 476 Liberty Road, Zip 41472–2049, Mailing Address: P O Box 579, Zip 41472–0579; tel. 606/743–3186, (Nonreporting) **A**10 18 21 **F**11 15 28 29 30 34 35 40 43 50 56 57 59 62 64 75 82 85 86 87 93 107 110 115 119 129 130 132 133 146 148 154 **S** Appalachian Regional Healthcare, Inc., Lexington, KY
Primary Contact: Stephen M. Gavalchik, FACHE, Community Chief Executive Officer
COO: Paul V Miles, Chief Operating Officer
CMO: J D Miller, M.D., Vice President Medical Affairs
CIO: Jeff Brady, Director Information Systems
CHR: Lisa Redding, Manager Human Resources
Web address: www.arh.org
**Control**: Other not–for–profit (including NFP Corporation) **Service**: General medical and surgical

Staffed Beds: 25 Admissions: 151 Census: 3 Outpatient Visits: 27224 Births: 0

## WHITESBURG—Letcher County

⇑ **WHITESBURG APPALACHIAN REGIONAL HOSPITAL** See Whitesburg Arh Hospital

⇑ **WHITESBURG ARH HOSPITAL (180002)**, 240 Hospital Road, Zip 41858–7627; tel. 606/633–3500, (Nonreporting) **A**3 10 20 21 **F**3 11 13 15 18 20 22 24 26 28 29 30 31 32 34 35 40 43 50 54 57 59 62 64 70 75 76 77 81 82 85 86 87 89 93 97 107 108 110 111 115 118 119 127 129 130 133 146 147 154 **S** Appalachian Regional Healthcare, Inc., Lexington, KY
Primary Contact: Dena C. Sparkman, Community Chief Executive Officer
COO: Paul V Miles, Vice President Administration
CMO: Ricky M Collins, M.D., Chief of Staff
CIO: Brent Styer, Director Information Technology
CHR: Daniel Fitzpatrick, Director Human Resources
Web address: www.arh.org/whitesburg
**Control**: Other not–for–profit (including NFP Corporation) **Service**: General medical and surgical

Staffed Beds: 90 Admissions: 3404 Census: 39 Outpatient Visits: 58118 Births: 445

## WILLIAMSTOWN—Grant County

**ST. ELIZABETH GRANT (181311)**, 238 Barnes Road, Zip 41097–9482; tel. 859/824–8240, (Nonreporting) **A**10 18 **F**3 15 18 26 28 29 30 31 34 35 38 40 44 45 50 57 59 63 64 65 74 75 78 79 84 93 97 107 108 110 111 115 119 128 129 130 131 132 133 135 141 146 148 149 153 154 **P**6 8 **S** St. Elizabeth Healthcare, Edgewood, KY
Primary Contact: Garren Colvin, Chief Executive Officer
Web address: www.stelizabeth.com
**Control**: Church operated, Nongovernment, not–for–profit **Service**: General medical and surgical

Staffed Beds: 24 Admissions: 199 Census: 2 Outpatient Visits: 54996 Births: 0 Total Expense ($000): 28332 Payroll Expense ($000): 9823 Personnel: 102

**ST. ELIZABETH MEDICAL CENTER-GRANT COUNTY** See St. Elizabeth Grant

## WINCHESTER-Clark County

✉ **CLARK REGIONAL MEDICAL CENTER (180092)**, 175 Hospital Drive, Zip 40391–9591; tel. 859/745–3500, (Nonreporting) **A**1 2 10 **S** LifePoint Health, Brentwood, TN
Primary Contact: Aphreikah DuHaney-West, Chief Executive Officer
CFO: Amber Goodpaster, Chief Financial Officer
CMO: Ben McQuaide, M.D., Chief of Staff
CHR: Deidre Bradley, Vice President Human Resources
CNO: Barbara Kinder, R.N., Chief Clinical Officer
Web address: www.clarkregional.org
**Control**: Corporation, Investor–owned (for–profit) **Service**: General medical and surgical

Staffed Beds: 79

# LOUISIANA

## ABBEVILLE—Vermilion Parish

✠ **ABBEVILLE GENERAL HOSPITAL (190034)**, 118 North Hospital Drive, Zip 70510–4077, Mailing Address: P.O. Box 580, Zip 70511–0580; tel. 337/893–5466, (Nonreporting) **A**1 10 **F**3 11 13 15 29 30 31 34 40 45 49 50 54 59 60 64 66 68 70 75 76 79 81 82 85 86 87 89 97 98 103 105 107 108 111 114 119 127 128 130 133 144 146 149 153 154 156 **P**6
Primary Contact: Ray A. Landry, FACHE, Chief Executive Officer
COO: Tom Pigott, Chief Operating Officer
CFO: Troy Hair, Chief Financial Officer
CMO: Weston Miller, M.D., Chief Medical Officer
CIO: Charles W Guidry, Network Development Executive, Director Information Technology
CNO: Heidi Broussard, Chief Nursing Officer
Web address: www.abbgen.net
**Control**: Hospital district or authority, Government, Nonfederal **Service**: General medical and surgical

**Staffed Beds**: 60 **Admissions**: 1901 **Census**: 27 **Outpatient Visits**: 115220
**Births**: 197 **Total Expense ($000)**: 54808 **Payroll Expense ($000)**: 26429
**Personnel**: 448

## ALEXANDRIA—Rapides Parish

⇑ **CENTRAL LOUISIANA SURGICAL HOSPITAL (190298)**, 651 North Bolton Avenue, Zip 71301–7449, Mailing Address: P.O. Box 8646, Zip 71306–1646; tel. 318/443–3511, (Nonreporting) **A**10 21
Primary Contact: Louise Barker, R.N., Chief Executive Officer
CFO: Michael Fuselier, FACHE, CPA, R.N., Chief Financial Officer
CMO: Renick Webb, M.D., Chief Medical Director
CHR: Debbie Norman, Director Human Resources
CNO: Carol Wells, R.N., MSN, Chief Nursing Officer
Web address: www.clshospital.com
**Control**: Corporation, Investor–owned (for–profit) **Service**: Surgical

**Staffed Beds**: 24

☐ **CHRISTUS DUBUIS HOSPITAL OF ALEXANDRIA (192012)**, 3330 Masonic Drive, 4th Floor, Zip 71301–3841; tel. 318/448–4938, (Nonreporting) **A**1 10 **S** LHC Group, Lafayette, LA
Primary Contact: Beth Parsons, R.N., Administrator
CNO: Kimberly Bennett, R.N., Director of Nursing
Web address: www.christusdubuis.org/CHRISTUSDubuisHospitalofAlexandriaLA
**Control**: Church operated, Nongovernment, not–for–profit **Service**: Acute long–term care hospital

**Staffed Beds**: 25

**CHRISTUS ST FRANCES HOSPITAL** See Christus St. Frances Cabrini Hospital

✠ **CHRISTUS ST. FRANCES CABRINI HOSPITAL (190019)**, 3330 Masonic Drive, Zip 71301–3899; tel. 318/487–1122, (Nonreporting) **A**1 2 10 **F**3 11 12 13 15 18 20 22 24 26 28 29 30 31 34 35 40 45 46 49 57 58 59 64 66 70 72 74 75 76 78 79 81 82 84 85 86 87 90 91 93 98 102 104 105 107 108 111 114 115 116 117 118 119 120 121 124 126 129 130 131 132 135 144 146 147 148 149 156 **S** CHRISTUS Health, Irving, TX
Primary Contact: Chris Karam, FACHE, President and Chief Executive Officer, Senior Vice President Group Operations
COO: Lisa R. Lauve, R.N., Regional Chief Nursing Executive and Chief Operating Officer
CFO: Gary Karg, Interim Vice President Finance
CHR: Wendy Chandler, Regional Vice President Human Resources
CNO: Linda Rittermeyer, Chief Nursing Officer
Web address: www.cabrini.org/
**Control**: Church operated, Nongovernment, not–for–profit **Service**: General medical and surgical

**Staffed Beds**: 293 **Admissions**: 12062 **Census**: 185 **Outpatient Visits**: 239062 **Births**: 1098 **Total Expense ($000)**: 247012 **Payroll Expense ($000)**: 79111 **Personnel**: 1210

**COMPASS BEHAVIORAL CENTER OF ALEXANDRIA (194106)**, 6410 Masonic Drve, Zip 71301–2319; tel. 318/442–3163, (Nonreporting) **A**10 F5 98 100 101 103 104 105 130 135 152 153 154 **S** Compass Health, Crowley, LA
Primary Contact: Micah J. Hicks, R.N., Chief Executive Officer, CENLA Regional
CNO: Cheryl Lachney, Director of Nursing
Web address: www.https://www.compasshealthcare.com
**Control**: Corporation, Investor–owned (for–profit) **Service**: Psychiatric

**Staffed Beds**: 36 **Admissions**: 600 **Census**: 17 **Outpatient Visits**: 6200
**Births**: 0 **Total Expense ($000)**: 4272 **Payroll Expense ($000)**: 2119
**Personnel**: 85

**CROSSROADS REGIONAL HOSPITAL** See Longleaf Hospital

**DUBUIS HOSPITAL OF ALEXANDRIA** See Christus Dubuis Hospital of Alexandria

**EMCOMPASS HEALTH REHABILITATION HOSPITAL OF ALEXANDRIA** See Encompass Health Rehabilitation Hospital of Alexandria

✠ **ENCOMPASS HEALTH REHABILITATION HOSPITAL OF ALEXANDRIA (193031)**, 104 North Third Street, Zip 71301–8581; tel. 318/449–1370, (Nonreporting) **A**1 10 **S** Encompass Health Corporation, Birmingham, AL
Primary Contact: David Goodson, Chief Executive Officer
CFO: Linda Wright, Chief Financial Officer
CMO: Vasudeva Dhulipala, M.D., Medical Director
CHR: Suzie Wagner, Director Human Resources
Web address: www.healthsouthalexandria.com
**Control**: Partnership, Investor–owned (for–profit) **Service**: Rehabilitation

**Staffed Beds**: 47

☐ **LONGLEAF HOSPITAL (194022)**, 44 Versailles Boulevard, Zip 71303–3960; tel. 318/445–5111, (Nonreporting) **A**1 10 **F**4 5 29 34 35 38 68 98 100 101 102 103 104 105 130 132 151 152 153 **S** Acadia Healthcare Company, Inc., Franklin, TN
Primary Contact: Claire Hick, Chief Executive Officer
CFO: Robert Jackson, Chief Financial Officer
Web address: www.longleafhospital.com/
**Control**: Corporation, Investor–owned (for–profit) **Service**: Psychiatric

**Staffed Beds**: 129 **Admissions**: 4053 **Census**: 92 **Outpatient Visits**: 3412
**Births**: 0

☐ **OCEANS BEHAVIORAL HOSPITAL OF ALEXANDRIA (194096)**, 2621 North Bolton Avenue, Zip 71303–4506; tel. 318/448–8473, (Nonreporting) **A**1 10 **S** Oceans Healthcare, Plano, TX
Primary Contact: Lee Edge, Administrator
Web address: www.obha.info/
**Control**: Corporation, Investor–owned (for–profit) **Service**: Psychiatric

**Staffed Beds**: 24

✠ **RAPIDES REGIONAL MEDICAL CENTER (190026)**, 211 4th ST, Zip 71301–8421, Mailing Address: 211 Fourth Street, Zip 71301–8421; tel. 318/769–3000, (Nonreporting) **A**1 2 3 5 10 **F**3 11 13 15 17 18 19 20 22 24 26 28 29 30 31 32 34 35 36 38 40 41 43 44 45 46 47 48 49 50 51 54 55 57 59 60 61 64 65 66 68 70 72 74 75 76 77 78 79 81 82 84 85 86 87 88 89 97 107 108 110 111 114 115 118 119 120 121 123 124 126 129 130 131 132 135 144 146 147 148 149 154 156 157 **S** HCA Healthcare, Nashville, TN
Primary Contact: Jason E. Cobb, FACHE, Chief Executive Officer
COO: Vernon Jones, Chief Operating Officer
CFO: Johnny H. Williams, Interim Chief Financial Officer and Director Financial Services
CMO: David Rhodes, M.D., Senior Vice President Medical Affairs and Chief Medical Officer
CHR: Stephen W Scull, Vice President Ethics and Compliance officer
CNO: Barbara J Griffin, MSN, R.N., Chief Nursing Officer
Web address: www.rapidesregional.com
**Control**: Partnership, Investor–owned (for–profit) **Service**: General medical and surgical

**Staffed Beds**: 357 **Admissions**: 14742 **Census**: 221 **Outpatient Visits**: 210863 **Births**: 1659 **Total Expense ($000)**: 246518 **Payroll Expense ($000)**: 86081 **Personnel**: 1431

---

**Hospital, Medicare Provider Number, Address, Telephone, Approval, Facility, and Physician Codes, Health Care System**

★ American Hospital Association (AHA) membership
☐ The Joint Commission accreditation
○ Healthcare Facilities Accreditation Program
◇ DNV Healthcare Inc. accreditation
⇑ Center for Improvement in Healthcare Quality Accreditation
△ Commission on Accreditation of Rehabilitation Facilities (CARF) accreditation

**LA**

☐ **RIVERSIDE HOSPITAL (192043)**, 13 Heyman Lane, Zip 71303–3574;
tel. 318/767–2900, (Nonreporting) **A**1 10
Primary Contact: Wade K. Lester, Chief Executive Officer
COO: Amy Perry Grimes, Chief Operating Officer
CNO: Michael Parham, R.N., Chief Nursing Officer
Web address: www.riversidehospital.net
**Control**: Corporation, Investor–owned (for–profit) **Service**: Acute long–term care hospital

**Staffed Beds:** 27

**RIVERSIDE HOSPITAL OF LOUISIANA** See Riverside Hospital

**AMITE—Tangipahoa Parish**

★ **HOOD MEMORIAL HOSPITAL (191309)**, 301 Walnut Street, Zip 70422–2098;
tel. 985/748–9485, (Nonreporting) **A**10 18
Primary Contact: Michael Whittington, R.N., Chief Executive Officer and Administrator
CFO: Mike Estay, Chief Financial Officer
CMO: Richard Bridges, M.D., Chief of Staff
CIO: Schley Harvin, Information Technology Technician
CHR: Alicia Chatelain, Director Human Resource
CNO: Todd Acosta, R.N., Chief Nursing Officer
Web address: www.hoodmemorial.com
**Control**: Hospital district or authority, Government, Nonfederal **Service**: General medical and surgical

**Staffed Beds:** 25

**ARCADIA—Bienville Parish**

**BIENVILLE MEDICAL CENTER (191320)**, 1175 Pine Street, Suite 200,
Zip 71001–3122; tel. 318/263–4700, (Nonreporting) **A**10 18 **S** Allegiance Health Management, Shreveport, LA
Primary Contact: Kirk Lemoine, Chief Executive Officer
Web address: www.bienvillemedicalcenter.net/
**Control**: Other not–for–profit (including NFP Corporation) **Service**: General medical and surgical

**Staffed Beds:** 21

**BASTROP—Morehouse Parish**

☐ **CYPRESS GROVE BEHAVIORAL HEALTH (194083)**, 4673 Eugene Ware
Boulevard, Zip 71220–1425; tel. 318/281–2448, (Nonreporting) **A**1 10
Primary Contact: Doug Bice, Administrator
COO: Christine Murphy, MS, Chief Operating Officer
CFO: Paul Coburn, Chief Financial Officer
CMO: Tommy Dansby, Chief Medical Officer
CHR: Lindsay Cobb, Director Human Resources
CNO: Shelly Hoard RNDirector of Nursing
**Control**: Corporation, Investor–owned (for–profit) **Service**: Psychiatric

**Staffed Beds:** 60

**LIBERTY HEALTHCARE SYSTEMS** See Cypress Grove Behavioral Health

★ **MOREHOUSE GENERAL HOSPITAL (190116)**, 323 West Walnut Avenue,
Zip 71220–4521, Mailing Address: P.O. Box 1060, Zip 71221–1060;
tel. 318/283–3600, (Nonreporting) **A**10 **S** Community Hospital Corporation, Plano, TX
Primary Contact: Derrick A. Frazier, FACHE, Chief Executive Officer
COO: John Bowie, Chief Operating Officer
CFO: Jason Bonner, Interim Chief Financial, Accounting Analyst
CMO: John Coats, M.D., Chief Medical Staff
CIO: B J Vail, Director Information Systems
CHR: Debbie Spann, Director Human Resources
CNO: Melinda Jones, R.N., Chief Nursing Officer
Web address: www.mghospital.com
**Control**: Hospital district or authority, Government, Nonfederal **Service**: General medical and surgical

**Staffed Beds:** 49

**STERLINGTON REHABILITATION HOSPITAL (193069)**, 370 W Hickory Ave,
Zip 71220–4442, Mailing Address: P.O. Box 627, Sterlington, Zip 71280–0627;
tel. 318/665–9950, (Nonreporting) **A**10 **F**28 34 35 56 59 64 65 66 75 86 90 91
93 96 97 104 127 130 143 147 148 153 154 **P**5
Primary Contact: Catherine M. Waldrop, Administrator
Web address: www.https://sterlingtonrehab.com/
**Control**: Corporation, Investor–owned (for–profit) **Service**: Rehabilitation

**Staffed Beds:** 10 **Admissions:** 257 **Census:** 8 **Outpatient Visits:** 1615
**Births:** 0 **Total Expense ($000):** 10323 **Payroll Expense ($000):** 5520
**Personnel:** 58

**BATON ROUGE—East Baton Rouge Parish**

☐ **APOLLO BEHAVIORAL HEALTH HOSPITAL (194105)**, 9938 Airline Highway,
Zip 70816–8193; tel. 225/663–2881, (Nonreporting) **A**1 **F**5 98 105 153 154
Primary Contact: Gopinath Gopalam, Administrator and Chief Executive Officer
Web address: www.apollo-bhh.com/about-us/
**Control**: Corporation, Investor–owned (for–profit) **Service**: Psychiatric

**Staffed Beds:** 24 **Admissions:** 24 **Census:** 21 **Outpatient Visits:** 0 **Births:** 0
**Total Expense ($000):** 5784 **Payroll Expense ($000):** 3021

☐ **BATON ROUGE BEHAVIORAL HOSPITAL (194107)**, 4040 North Boulevard,
Zip 70806–3829; tel. 225/300–8470, (Nonreporting) **A**1 10 **S** Oglethorpe
Recovery and Behavioral Hospitals, Tampa, FL
Primary Contact: Clay Aguillard, R.N., Administrator
COO: James O'Shea, Chief Operating Officer
CFO: Warren Knight, Chief Financial Officer
CMO: Richard Capiola, M.D., Chief Medical Officer
CNO: Francine Mineau, Chief Nursing Officer
Web address: www.batonrougebehavioral.com
**Control**: Corporation, Investor–owned (for–profit) **Service**: Psychiatric

**Staffed Beds:** 15

**BATON ROUGE GEN HEALTH CENTER** See Baton Rouge General Medical Center-Bluebonnet

⊠ **BATON ROUGE GENERAL MEDICAL CENTER (190065)**, 8585 Picardy
Avenue, Zip 70809–3679; tel. 225/763–4000, (Includes BATON ROUGE GENERAL
MEDICAL CENTER-BLUEBONNET, Mailing address: 8585 Picardy Avenue,
Baton Rouge, Louisiana, Zip 70809–3679, P O Box 84330, Zip 70884–4330,
tel. 225/763–4000; Edgardo J. Tenreiro, FACHE, Chief Executive Officer and Chief
Operating Officer), (Nonreporting) **A**1 2 3 5 10 19 **F**3 7 8 11 12 13 15 16 18 19
20 22 24 26 28 29 30 31 34 35 38 40 44 45 46 47 49 50 51 53 54 56 57 58
59 60 61 64 65 68 70 72 74 75 76 77 78 79 81 82 84 86 87 90 91 93 96 97
98 99 100 101 102 103 104 107 108 110 111 113 114 115 116 117 118 119
120 121 123 124 126 128 129 130 131 132 135 143 144 146 147 148 153
154 156 **S** General Health System, Baton Rouge, LA
Primary Contact: Edgardo J. Tenreiro, FACHE, Chief Executive Officer
COO: Stephen Mumford, Chief Operating Officer
CFO: Kendall Johnson, Chief Financial Officer
CIO: Bennett Cheramie, Vice President Information Technology
CHR: Paul Douglas, Vice President Human Resources
CNO: Monica Nijoka, Chief Nursing Officer
Web address: www.brgeneral.org
**Control**: Other not–for–profit (including NFP Corporation) **Service**: General medical and surgical

**Staffed Beds:** 362 **Admissions:** 15378 **Census:** 219 **Outpatient
Visits:** 274472 **Births:** 807 **Total Expense ($000):** 385323 **Payroll Expense
($000):** 116148 **Personnel:** 2495

☐ **BATON ROUGE REHABILITATION HOSPITAL (193028)**, 8595 United Plaza
Boulevard, Zip 70809–2251; tel. 225/927–0567, (Nonreporting) **A**1 10
Primary Contact: Trisha Guidry, Administrator
CFO: Nicholas Hluchy, Business Analyst, Support Services Manager
CMO: Catalina R. Negulescu, M.D., Medical Officer
CIO: Laura Simon, R.N., MSN, Director Quality Operations and Nursing
CHR: Michelle Smith, Coordinator Human Resources
CNO: Laura Simon, R.N., MSN, Director, Quality Operations and Nursing
Web address: www.brrehab.com
**Control**: Corporation, Investor–owned (for–profit) **Service**: Rehabilitation

**Staffed Beds:** 80

**BEHAVIORAL HOSPITAL OF BATON ROUGE** See Baton Rouge Behavioral Hospital

**BETHESDA REHABILITATION HOSPITAL (193092)**, 7414 Sumrall Drive,
Zip 70812–1240; tel. 225/767–2034, (Nonreporting) **A**10
Primary Contact: Lionel Murphy, Chief Executive Officer
CNO: Yolanda Scales, R.N., Director of Nursing
**Control**: Corporation, Investor–owned (for–profit) **Service**: Rehabilitation

**Staffed Beds:** 18

**HEALTHSOUTH REHABILITATION HOSPITAL OF BATON ROUGE** See Baton
Rouge Rehabilitation Hospital

*Many Facility Codes have changed. Please refer to the AHA Guide Code Chart.*     © 2021 AHA Guide

**KPC PROMISE HOSPITAL OF BATON ROUGE (192004)**, 5130 Mancuso Lane, Zip 70809–3583; tel. 225/490–9600, (Data for 200 days) (Nonreporting) **A**1 **F**1 3 29 38 56 60 65 68 75 77 82 91 94 119 143 148 149 **S** KPC Healthcare, Inc., Santa Ana, CA
Primary Contact: Kiley P. Cedotal, FACHE, Chief Executive Officer
COO: Michael R Sanders, MS, Chief Operating Officer
CFO: Trina Arceneaux, Assistant Chief Financial Officer
CMO: Subhaker Gummadi, M.D., Chief Medical Staff
CIO: Charmaine T Mosby, Area Director Health Information Management
CHR: Marilyn Hamilton, Director Human Resources
CNO: Larrie Arceneaux, Chief Clinical Officer
Web address: www.batonrouge.kpcph.com/
**Control:** Corporation, Investor–owned (for–profit) **Service:** Acute long–term care hospital

**Staffed Beds:** 39 **Admissions:** 303 **Census:** 43 **Outpatient Visits:** 0 **Births:** 0

**LAKEWOOD QUARTERS REHAB HOSP** See Sage Rehabilitation Hospital

**NEUROMEDICAL CENTER REHABILITATION HOSPITAL** See The Neuromedical Center Rehabilitation Hospital

**OCEANS BEHAVIORAL HOSPITAL OF BATON ROUGE (194086)**, 11135 Florida Boulevard, Zip 70815–2013; tel. 225/356–7030, (Nonreporting) **A**1 10 **S** Oceans Healthcare, Plano, TX
Primary Contact: Valerie Dalton, R.N., Administrator
Web address: www.obhbr.info/
**Control:** Corporation, Investor–owned (for–profit) **Service:** Psychiatric

**Staffed Beds:** 20

**OCHSNER MEDICAL CENTER - BATON ROUGE (190202)**, 17000 Medical Center Drive, Zip 70816–3224; tel. 225/752–2470, (Nonreporting) **A**1 3 10 **F**3 11 12 13 15 18 20 22 24 26 28 29 30 31 34 35 36 40 41 42 44 45 46 47 48 49 51 54 57 58 59 60 64 68 70 72 74 75 76 77 78 79 81 82 85 86 87 93 97 102 104 107 108 110 111 114 116 117 119 126 129 130 131 132 135 144 146 147 148 154 **P**6 **S** Ochsner Health, New Orleans, LA
Primary Contact: Eric McMillen, FACHE, Chief Executive Officer
CFO: Stephanie Bushart, Chief Financial Officer
CMO: F Ralph Dauterive, M.D., Vice President Medical Affairs
CHR: Jan Rivers, Director Human Resources
Web address: www.https://www.ochsner.org/locations/ochsner-medical-center-baton-rouge
**Control:** Other not–for–profit (including NFP Corporation) **Service:** General medical and surgical

**Staffed Beds:** 162 **Admissions:** 6795 **Census:** 74 **Outpatient Visits:** 115350 **Births:** 1426 **Total Expense ($000):** 259265 **Payroll Expense ($000):** 83609 **Personnel:** 1127

**OCHSNER MEDICAL CENTER-BATON ROUGE** See Ochsner Medical Center - Baton Rouge

**OUR LADY OF THE LAKE REGIONAL MEDICAL CENTER (190064)**, 5000 Hennessy Boulevard, Zip 70808–4375; tel. 225/765–6565, (Includes OUR LADY OF THE LAKE ASCENSION, Mailing address: 1125 West Highway 30, Gonzales, Louisiana, Zip 70737–5004; tel. 225/647–5000; Scott Wester, President and Chief Executive Officer; OUR LADY OF THE LAKE CHILDREN'S HOSPITAL, Mailing address: 5000 Hennessy Boulevard, Baton Rouge, Louisiana, Zip 70808–4375; tel. 225/765–8886; Trey Dunbar, M.D., President) (Total facility includes 390 beds in nursing home–type unit) **A**1 2 3 5 10 **F**3 8 11 12 14 15 17 18 19 20 21 22 23 24 25 26 27 28 29 30 31 32 34 35 37 38 39 40 41 42 43 44 45 46 47 48 49 50 51 53 54 55 56 57 58 59 60 61 63 64 65 66 70 71 74 75 77 78 79 81 82 83 84 85 86 87 88 89 90 95 96 97 98 99 100 101 102 103 104 105 107 108 110 111 114 115 116 117 118 119 125 126 127 129 130 131 132 134 135 141 142 143 144 145 146 147 148 149 150 153 154 156 158 **P**6 **S** Franciscan Missionaries of Our Lady Health System, Inc., Baton Rouge, LA
Primary Contact: K Scott. Wester, FACHE, President and Chief Executive Officer
COO: Stephanie Manson, Chief Operating Officer
CFO: Lowell Stanton, Chief Financial Officer
CMO: Richard Vath, M.D., Vice President Medical Affairs
CIO: Vindell Washington, M.D., Vice President Performance Excellence and Technology
CHR: Cora Ford, Vice President Human Resources
CNO: Nicole Telhiard, MSN, Chief Nursing Officer
Web address: www.ololrmc.com
**Control:** Church operated, Nongovernment, not–for–profit **Service:** General medical and surgical

**Staffed Beds:** 1122 **Admissions:** 38991 **Census:** 783 **Outpatient Visits:** 2048072 **Births:** 0 **Total Expense ($000):** 1089703 **Payroll Expense ($000):** 279255 **Personnel:** 7064

**PROMISE HOSPITAL BATON ROUGE** See Kpc Promise Hospital of Baton Rouge

**REGIONS BEHAVIORAL HOSPITAL (194115)**, 8416 Cumberland Place, Zip 70806–6543; tel. 225/408–6060, (Nonreporting) **A**1
Primary Contact: Robert Stephen. Richardson Jr, Administrator
COO: Marc Crawford, Chief Operating Officer
CHR: Julia Perry, Director Human Resources
Web address: www.https://www.regionsbh.com/
**Control:** Corporation, Investor–owned (for–profit) **Service:** Psychiatric

**Staffed Beds:** 24

**SAGE REHABILITATION HOSPITAL (193078)**, 8000 Summa Avenue, Zip 70809–3423, Mailing Address: P.O. Box 82681, Zip 70884–2681; tel. 225/819–0703, (Total facility includes 25 beds in nursing home–type unit) (Nonreporting) **A**10 **F**29 75 77 87 90 93 128 130 148 **S** The Carpenter Health Network, Baton Rouge, LA
Primary Contact: Karen Crayton, Administrator
CMO: Christopher Belleau, M.D., Medical Director
CHR: Kathy Ringe, Director Human Resources
CNO: Beth Sibley, Director of Nursing
Web address: www.sage-rehab.org
**Control:** Individual, Investor–owned (for–profit) **Service:** Rehabilitation

**Staffed Beds:** 45 **Admissions:** 688 **Census:** 32 **Outpatient Visits:** 3789 **Births:** 0 **Total Expense ($000):** 10767 **Payroll Expense ($000):** 5672 **Personnel:** 118

**SEASIDE HEALTH SYSTEM** See Seaside Health System - Baton Rouge

**SEASIDE HEALTH SYSTEM - BATON ROUGE (194103)**, 4363 Convention Street, Zip 70806–3906, Mailing Address: 4363 Convention Stret, Zip 70806–3906; tel. 225/238–3043, (Nonreporting) **A**1 10
Primary Contact: Kyle Hyduke, Chief Executive Officer
Web address: www.https://www.seasidehc.com/
**Control:** Partnership, Investor–owned (for–profit) **Service:** Psychiatric

**Staffed Beds:** 24

**SPINE HOSPITAL OF LOUISIANA (FORMALLY THE NEUROMEDICAL CENTER SURGICAL HOSPITAL)** See The Spine Hospital of Louisiana at The Neuromedical Center

**SURGICAL SPECIALTY CENTER OF BATON ROUGE (190251)**, 8080 Bluebonnet Boulevard, Zip 70810–7827; tel. 225/408–8080, (Nonreporting) **A**1 10
Primary Contact: Ann Heine, Chief Executive Officer
CNO: Kari Ulrich, R.N., Chief Nursing Officer, Director Operating Room
Web address: www.sscbr.com
**Control:** Corporation, Investor–owned (for–profit) **Service:** Surgical

**Staffed Beds:** 14

**SURGICAL SPECIALTY CENTRE** See Surgical Specialty Center of Baton Rouge

**THE GENERAL (190316)**, 3600 Florida Street, Suite 2020, Zip 70806–3842; tel. 225/381–6393, (Nonreporting) **S** General Health System, Baton Rouge, LA
Primary Contact: Edgardo J. Tenreiro, FACHE, President and Chief Executive Officer
**Control:** Other not–for–profit (including NFP Corporation) **Service:** General medical and surgical

**Staffed Beds:** 231

**THE NEUROMEDICAL CENTER REHABILITATION HOSPITAL (193090)**, 10101 Park Rowe Avenue, Suite 500, Zip 70810–1685; tel. 225/906–2999, (Nonreporting) **A**10 **S** AMG Integrated Healthcare Management, Lafayette, LA
Primary Contact: Bradley Pevey, Chief Executive Officer
Web address: www.theneuromedicalcenter.com
**Control:** Corporation, Investor–owned (for–profit) **Service:** Rehabilitation

**Staffed Beds:** 23

LA

**THE SPINE HOSPITAL OF LOUISIANA AT THE NEUROMEDICAL CENTER (190266)**, 10105 Park Rowe Circle, Suite 250, Zip 70810–1684; tel. 225/763–9900, (Nonreporting) **A**10
Primary Contact: Robert D. Blair, Chief Executive Officer
CFO: Allison Doherty, Chief Financial Officer
CMO: Greg Fautheree, M.D., Medical Director
CIO: Jeremy Deprato, Director Information Technology
CHR: Kimberly Jones, Director Human Resources
CNO: Kim Pettijohn, R.N., MSN, Chief Nursing Officer
Web address: www.theneuromedicalcenter.com
**Control:** Corporation, Investor–owned (for–profit) **Service:** Surgical

Staffed Beds: 23

⊞ **WOMAN'S HOSPITAL (190128)**, 100 Woman's Way, Zip 70817–5100, Mailing Address: P.O. Box 95009, Zip 70895–9009; tel. 225/927–1300, (Nonreporting) **A**1 2 3 5 10 **F**3 11 12 13 15 29 31 32 34 35 36 38 40 45 50 53 54 55 57 58 59 61 64 65 66 68 70 71 72 75 76 77 78 79 81 83 84 85 86 87 93 107 108 110 111 115 116 117 118 119 120 121 123 126 129 130 131 132 135 146 147 148 149 154 156 **P**6
Primary Contact: Barbara Griffith, M.D., Chief Executive Officer
COO: Stephanie Anderson, Executive Vice President and Chief Operating Officer
CMO: Dore Binder, M.D., Chief Medical Officer
CIO: Paul Kirk, Vice President
CHR: Donna L Bodin, Vice President
CNO: Cheri Barker Johnson, Senior Vice President and Chief Nursing Officer
Web address: www.womans.org
**Control:** Other not–for–profit (including NFP Corporation) **Service:** Obstetrics and gynecology

Staffed Beds: 228 Admissions: 10845 Census: 138 Outpatient
Visits: 158254 Births: 8052 Total Expense ($000): 281962 Payroll
Expense ($000): 133975 Personnel: 1831

**WOMAN'S HOSPITAL FOUNDATION** See Woman's Hospital

### BERNICE—Union Parish

**REEVES MEMORIAL MEDICAL CENTER (191326)**, 409 First Street, Zip 71222–4001, Mailing Address: P.O. Box 697, Zip 71222–0697; tel. 318/285–9066, (Nonreporting) **A**10 18
Primary Contact: David Caston, Chief Executive Officer
COO: Beth Jones, Chief Operating Officer
CFO: Charolette Thompson, Chief Financial Officer
CMO: R Brian Harris, M.D., Chief of Staff
CIO: Scott Dickson, Director Information Technology
CHR: Robin Adams, Director Human Resources
CNO: Beth Jones, Director of Nursing
Web address: www.reevesmemorial.com/
**Control:** Hospital district or authority, Government, Nonfederal **Service:** General medical and surgical

Staffed Beds: 11

**TRI-WARD GENERAL HOSPITAL** See Reeves Memorial Medical Center

### BOGALUSA—Washington Parish

**OUR LADY OF ANGELS HOSPITAL** See Our Lady of The Angels Hospital

⊞ **OUR LADY OF THE ANGELS HOSPITAL (190312)**, 433 Plaza Street, Zip 70427–3793; tel. 985/730–6700, (Includes BOGALUSA COMMUNITY MEDICAL CENTER, Mailing address: 433 Plaza Street, Bogalusa, Louisiana, Zip 70427–3793; tel. 985/730–6700), (Nonreporting) **A**1 3 5 10 **S** Franciscan Missionaries of Our Lady Health System, Inc., Baton Rouge, LA
Primary Contact: Rene J. Ragas, President and Chief Executive Officer, Northshore Market
CFO: Brooke Cummings, Chief Financial Officer
CMO: C. Bryan Miller, M.D., Chief Medical Officer
CIO: Mike Gilly, Chief Information Officer
CHR: Christi Brown, Director Human Resources
CNO: Mark Kellar, R.N., Interim Chief Nursing Officer
Web address: www.oloah.org
**Control:** Church operated, Nongovernment, not–for–profit **Service:** General medical and surgical

Staffed Beds: 57

### BOSSIER CITY—Bossier Parish

**CORNERSTONE HOSPITAL OF BOSSIER CITY** See Cornerstone Hospitals Bossier City

☐ **CORNERSTONE HOSPITALS BOSSIER CITY (192006)**, 4900 Medical Drive, Zip 71112–4521; tel. 318/747–9500, (Nonreporting) **A**1 10 **S** Cornerstone Healthcare Group, Dallas, TX
Primary Contact: Sheri Burnette, R.N., Chief Executive Officer
CMO: James Jackson, M.D., Chief of Staff
CNO: Tamara Grimm, R.N., Chief Clinical Officer and Chief Nursing Officer
Web address: www.chghospitals.com/
**Control:** Corporation, Investor–owned (for–profit) **Service:** Acute long–term care hospital

Staffed Beds: 54

⇑ **PATHWAY REHABILITATION HOSPITAL** See Pathway Rehabilitation Hospital of Bossier

⇑ **PATHWAY REHABILITATION HOSPITAL OF BOSSIER (193094)**, 4900 Medical Drive, Zip 71112–4521; tel. 318/841–5555, (Nonreporting) **A**10 21
Primary Contact: James Manning, Administrator
Web address: www.pathrehab.com
**Control:** Corporation, Investor–owned (for–profit) **Service:** Rehabilitation

Staffed Beds: 24

**PROMISE HOSPITAL OF BOSSIER CITY** See Promise Hospital of Louisiana - Bossier City Campus

**RED RIVER BEHAVIORAL CENTER (194079)**, 2800 Melrose Avenue, Zip 71111–5870; tel. 318/549–2033, (Nonreporting) **A**10 **F**29 38 56 98 100 101 103 130 135 143 154
Primary Contact: Susan Kottenbrook, Administrator
CNO: John Crumpler, R.N., Director of Nursing
Web address: www.redriverbc.com
**Control:** Partnership, Investor–owned (for–profit) **Service:** Psychiatric

Staffed Beds: 20 Admissions: 321 Census: 15 Outpatient Visits: 0
Births: 0

**WILLIS-KNIGHTON BOSSIER HEALTH CENTER** See Wk Bossier Health Center

### BREAUX BRIDGE—St. Martin Parish

**GARY MEMORIAL HOSPITAL** See St. Martin Hospital

**GENESIS BEHAVIORAL HOSPITAL (194089)**, 606 Latiolais Drive, Zip 70517–4231, Mailing Address: PO BOX 159, Zip 70517–0159; tel. 337/442–6084, (Nonreporting) **A**10
Primary Contact: William Arledge, Administrator and Chief Financial Officer
COO: Gretchen Kaltenbach, R.N., Chief Operating Officer
CFO: William Arledge, Administrator and Chief Financial Officer
Web address: www.genesisbh.com/
**Control:** Corporation, Investor–owned (for–profit) **Service:** Psychiatric

Staffed Beds: 18

★ **ST. MARTIN HOSPITAL (191302)**, 210 Champagne Boulevard, Zip 70517–3700, Mailing Address: P.O. Box 357, Zip 70517–0357; tel. 337/332–2178, (Nonreporting) **A**10 18 **F**3 15 18 28 29 30 34 35 40 54 57 59 64 68 75 77 87 91 93 107 110 111 114 119 130 133 146 148 149 154 **S** Lafayette General Health, Lafayette, LA
Primary Contact: Glenn Dailey, Chief Executive Officer
CFO: Shadelle Huval, Director Finance
CHR: Rena B Mouisset, Director Human Resources and Contract Compliance
CNO: Annette Wyble Hatsfelt, R.N., Chief Nursing Officer
Web address: www.stmartinhospital.org
**Control:** Other not–for–profit (including NFP Corporation) **Service:** General medical and surgical

Staffed Beds: 25 Admissions: 465 Census: 13 Outpatient Visits: 192217
Births: 0 Total Expense ($000): 19939 Payroll Expense ($000): 7811
Personnel: 126

*Many Facility Codes have changed. Please refer to the AHA Guide Code Chart.*     © 2021 AHA Guide

## BROUSSARD—Lafayette Parish

☐ **OCEANS BEHAVIORAL HOSPITAL OF BROUSSARD (194073)**, 418 Albertson Parkway, Zip 70518–4971; tel. 337/237–6444, (Nonreporting) **A**1 3 10 **S** Oceans Healthcare, Plano, TX
Primary Contact: Amy Dysart-Credeur, Administrator
Web address: www.obhb.info/
**Control**: Corporation, Investor–owned (for–profit) **Service**: Psychiatric

**Staffed Beds: 38**

## BUNKIE—Avoyelles Parish

**BEACON BEHAVIORAL HOSPITAL (194112)**, 323 Evergreen Street, Zip 71322–1307; tel. 318/346–3143, (Nonreporting) **S** Beacon Health System, South Bend, IN
Primary Contact: Amy Savant, Administrator and Chief Executive Officer
CNO: Charlene Kessler, R.N., Director of Nursing
Web address: www.beaconbh.com
**Control**: Other not–for–profit (including NFP Corporation) **Service**: Psychiatric

**Staffed Beds: 17**

**BUNKIE GENERAL HOSPITAL (191311)**, 427 Evergreen Highway, Zip 71322, Mailing Address: P.O. Box 380, Zip 71322–0380; tel. 318/346–6681, (Nonreporting) **A**10 18
Primary Contact: Linda F. Deville, Chief Executive Officer
CFO: Layla Chase, Interim Chief Financial Officer
CMO: Mohit Srivastava, M.D., Chief of Staff
CIO: Kiland Jackson, Chief Information Officer
CHR: Tina Louise Juneau, Director Human Resources
CNO: Corey Jeansonne, Chief Nursing Officer
Web address: www.bunkiegeneral.com
**Control**: Hospital district or authority, Government, Nonfederal **Service**: General medical and surgical

**Staffed Beds: 18**

## CAMERON—Cameron Parish

**SOUTH CAMERON MEMORIAL HOSPITAL (190307)**, 5360 West Creole Highway, Zip 70631–5127; tel. 337/542–4111, (Includes CALCASIEU OAKS GERIATRIC PSYCHIATRIC HOSPITAL, Mailing address: 2837 Ernest Street, Lake Charles, Louisiana, Zip 70601–8785; tel. 337/439–8111; Erica Williams, Assistant Chief Executive Officer), (Nonreporting) **A**10
Primary Contact: Leslie T. Trahan, Chief Executive Officer
**Control**: Hospital district or authority, Government, Nonfederal **Service**: General medical and surgical

**Staffed Beds: 30**

## CHALMETTE—Saint Bernard Parish

**BERNARD PARISH HOSPITAL** See St. Bernard Parish Hospital

⊞ **ST. BERNARD PARISH HOSPITAL (190308)**, 8000 West Judge Perez Drive, Zip 70043–1668; tel. 504/826–9500, (Nonreporting) **A**1 10 **F**3 15 18 20 22 26 29 34 35 40 44 45 50 53 57 59 64 65 70 77 79 81 82 85 86 87 93 107 108 110 111 115 119 130 135 146 148 154 156 **S** Ochsner Health, New Orleans, LA
Primary Contact: Kimberly Keene, R.N., Chief Executive Officer
CFO: Anthony Bonnecarrere, Controller
CMO: Paul Verrette, M.D., Chief Medical Officer
CIO: Zane Looney, Chief Information Officer
CHR: Melody M O'Connell, Director Human Resources
CNO: Janice Kishner, R.N., FACHE, Chief Clinical Officer
Web address: www.sbph.net
**Control**: Hospital district or authority, Government, Nonfederal **Service**: General medical and surgical

**Staffed Beds: 40 Admissions: 1216 Census: 14 Outpatient Visits: 40196 Births: 0 Total Expense ($000): 48173 Payroll Expense ($000): 6819 Personnel: 276**

## CHURCH POINT—Acadia Parish

**ACADIA-ST. LANDRY HOSPITAL (191319)**, 810 South Broadway Street, Zip 70525–4497; tel. 337/684–5435, (Nonreporting) **A**10 18
Primary Contact: Cindy Walters, Chief Executive Officer
CFO: Tiffany Young, Chief Financial Officer
CMO: Ty Hargroder, M.D., Chief of Staff
CNO: Mona McCall, R.N., Director of Nursing
Web address: www.aslh.org
**Control**: Other not–for–profit (including NFP Corporation) **Service**: General medical and surgical

**Staffed Beds: 25**

## COLUMBIA—Caldwell Parish

**CALDWELL MEMORIAL HOSPITAL (190190)**, 411 Main Street, Zip 71418–6704, Mailing Address: P.O. Box 899, Zip 71418–0899; tel. 318/649–6111, (Nonreporting) **A**10
Primary Contact: Danielle H. Williams, Administrator
COO: Lisa Patrick, Chief Operating Officer
CFO: William H Clark, Chief Financial Officer
Web address: www.https://www.mycaldwellmemorial.com/
**Control**: Other not–for–profit (including NFP Corporation) **Service**: General medical and surgical

**Staffed Beds: 47**

**CITIZENS MEDICAL CENTER (190184)**, 7939 U S Highway 165, Zip 71418–1079, Mailing Address: P.O. Box 1079, Zip 71418–1079; tel. 318/649–6106, (Nonreporting) **A**10
Primary Contact: Steve Barbo, R.N., Chief Executive Officer
Web address: www.citizensmedcenter.com/
**Control**: Hospital district or authority, Government, Nonfederal **Service**: General medical and surgical

**Staffed Beds: 40**

## COUSHATTA—Red River Parish

**CHRISTUS COUSHATTA HEALTH CARE** See Christus Coushatta Health Care Center

⊞ **CHRISTUS COUSHATTA HEALTH CARE CENTER (191312)**, 1635 Marvel Street, Zip 71019–9022, Mailing Address: P.O. Box 589, Zip 71019–0589; tel. 318/932–2000, (Nonreporting) **A**1 10 18 **S** CHRISTUS Health, Irving, TX
Primary Contact: Brandon Hillman, R.N., Administrator
CFO: Bryan Pannagl, Chief Financial Officer
CMO: Jonathan Weisul, M.D., Vice President Medical Affairs and Chief Medical Officer
CIO: Bruce Honea, Director Information Services
CHR: Donnette Craig, Director Human Resources
CNO: Kay Sour, Director of Nursing
Web address: www.christuscoushatta.org
**Control**: Church operated, Nongovernment, not–for–profit **Service**: General medical and surgical

**Staffed Beds: 25**

**SPECIALTY REHABILITATION HOSPITAL** See Specialty Rehabilitation Hospital of Coushatta

**SPECIALTY REHABILITATION HOSPITAL OF COUSHATTA (193080)**, 1110 Ringgold Avenue Suite B, Zip 71019–9073; tel. 318/932–1770, (Nonreporting) **A**10
Primary Contact: Craig Ball, Chief Executive Officer
COO: Charlie Ball, Chief Operating Officer
CFO: Connie Ball, Chief Financial Officer
CMO: Jalal Joudeh, M.D., Chief Medical Officer
CHR: Denise Logan, Director Human Resources
Web address: www.specialtyhealthcare.com
**Control**: Individual, Investor–owned (for–profit) **Service**: Rehabilitation

**Staffed Beds: 12**

---

**Hospital, Medicare Provider Number, Address, Telephone, Approval, Facility, and Physician Codes, Health Care System**

★ American Hospital Association (AHA) membership
☐ The Joint Commission accreditation
○ Healthcare Facilities Accreditation Program
◇ DNV Healthcare Inc. accreditation
⇑ Center for Improvement in Healthcare Quality Accreditation
△ Commission on Accreditation of Rehabilitation Facilities (CARF) accreditation

**LA**

## COVINGTON—St. Tammany Parish

**AMG PHYSICAL REHABILITATION HOSPITAL (193097)**, 5025 Keystone Boulevard, Suite 200, Zip 70433; tel. 985/888–0301, (Nonreporting) **A**10 22 **S** AMG Integrated Healthcare Management, Lafayette, LA
Primary Contact: John Derrick. Landreneau, R.N., Chief Executive Officer
Web address: www.amgcovingtonprh.com/
**Control**: Partnership, Investor–owned (for–profit) **Service**: Rehabilitation

Staffed Beds: 24

⇑ **AVALA (190267)**, 67252 Industry Lane, Zip 70433–8704; tel. 985/809–9888, (Nonreporting) **A**10 21
Primary Contact: Scott Boudreaux, Chief Executive Officer
CFO: Denise Businelle, Chief Financial Officer
CMO: William Preau, M.D., Medical Director
CIO: Skip Federico, Director Information Systems
CHR: Pam Collins, Director Human Resources
Web address: www.fairwaymedical.com
**Control**: Corporation, Investor–owned (for–profit) **Service**: General medical and surgical

Staffed Beds: 21

**COLUMBIA LAKEVIEW REG MED CTR** See Lakeview Regional Medical Center

☐ **COVINGTON BEHAVIORAL HEALTH (194069)**, 201 Greenbrier Boulevard, Zip 70433–7236; tel. 985/893–2970, (Nonreporting) **A**1 10 **S** Acadia Healthcare Company, Inc., Franklin, TN
Primary Contact: Tanmay Mathur, Chief Executive Officer
CFO: Bryan McCauley, Chief Financial Officer
CMO: Jason Coe, M.D., Medical Director
Web address: www.greenbrierhospital.com/
**Control**: Corporation, Investor–owned (for–profit) **Service**: Psychiatric

Staffed Beds: 60

**COVINGTON BEHAVIORIAL HEALTH** See Covington Behavioral Health

⇑ **FAIRWAY MEDICAL SURGICAL HOSPITAL** See Avala

**NORTHSHORE SPECIALTY HOSPITAL** See Pam Specialty Hospital of Covington

✥ **PAM SPECIALTY HOSPITAL OF COVINGTON (192048)**, 20050 Crestwood Boulevard, Zip 70433–5207; tel. 985/875–7525, (Nonreporting) **A**1 10 **F**1 29 64 75 130 143 154 **S** Post Acute Medical, LLC, Enola, PA
Primary Contact: Brian Davis, Chief Executive Officer
COO: John Bauer, Chief Operating Officer
CFO: Karick Stober, Chief Financial Officer
CMO: Adam Burick, M.D., Chief Medical Officer
CIO: Bryan Munchel, Senior Vice President and Chief Information Officer
Web address: www.postacutemedical.com
**Control**: Partnership, Investor–owned (for–profit) **Service**: Acute long–term care hospital

Staffed Beds: 42 **Admissions**: 578 **Census**: 27 **Outpatient Visits**: 2645 **Births**: 0 **Total Expense ($000)**: 15915 **Payroll Expense ($000)**: 6461 **Personnel**: 79

✥ **ST. TAMMANY HEALTH SYSTEM (190045)**, 1202 South Tyler Street, Zip 70433–2330; tel. 985/898–4000, (Nonreporting) **A**1 2 10 **F**3 8 11 12 13 15 17 18 20 22 24 26 28 29 30 31 34 35 37 40 41 42 43 44 45 46 48 49 50 54 55 57 59 62 63 64 65 69 70 72 74 75 76 77 78 79 81 82 84 85 86 87 88 89 92 93 96 97 107 108 109 110 111 114 115 119 124 126 129 130 132 135 146 147 148 149 154 156 **P**6
Primary Contact: Joan M. Coffman, FACHE, President and Chief Executive Officer
COO: Sharon A Toups, Senior Vice President and Chief Operating Officer
CFO: Sandra P Dipietro, Chief Financial Officer
CMO: Robert Capitelli, M.D., Senior Vice President and Chief Medical Officer
CIO: Craig Doyle, Director and Chief Information Officer
CHR: Carolyn Adema, Senior Vice President
CNO: Kerry K. Milton, R.N., Chief Nursing Officer
Web address: www.stph.org
**Control**: Hospital district or authority, Government, Nonfederal **Service**: General medical and surgical

Staffed Beds: 206 **Admissions**: 11784 **Census**: 143 **Outpatient Visits**: 440094 **Births**: 2088 **Total Expense ($000)**: 335403 **Payroll Expense ($000)**: 139735 **Personnel**: 2017

**ST. TAMMANY PARISH HOSPITAL** See St. Tammany Health System

## CROWLEY—Acadia Parish

**ACADIA GENERAL** See Acadia General Hospital

★ **ACADIA GENERAL HOSPITAL (190044)**, 1305 Crowley Rayne Highway, Zip 70526–8202; tel. 337/783–3222, (Nonreporting) **A**10 **S** Lafayette General Health, Lafayette, LA
Primary Contact: Joe J. Mitchell, R.N., FACHE, Chief Executive Officer
CMO: Bahman Sabbaghian, M.D., Chief Medical Officer
CNO: Caroline Marceaux, MSN, R.N., Chief Nursing Officer
Web address: www.acadiageneral.com
**Control**: Other not–for–profit (including NFP Corporation) **Service**: General medical and surgical

Staffed Beds: 140

## CUT OFF—Lafourche Parish

★ ⇑ **LADY OF THE SEA GENERAL HOSPITAL (191325)**, 200 West 134th Place, Zip 70345–4143; tel. 985/632–6401, (Nonreporting) **A**10 18 21 **F**3 15 29 34 35 40 45 50 57 59 60 62 70 81 85 87 107 108 110 111 114 119 127 130 132 133 135 146 148 149
Primary Contact: Karen S. Collins, Chief Executive Officer
COO: Lloyd Guidry, Chief Operating Officer
CFO: Jacquelyn Richoux, Chief Financial Officer
CMO: William Crenshaw, M.D., Chief of Staff
CIO: Bennie Smith, Chief Information Officer
CHR: Bennie Smith, Director Human Resources and Risk Management
CNO: Holly Griffin, R.N., Chief Nursing Officer
Web address: www.losgh.org
**Control**: Hospital district or authority, Government, Nonfederal **Service**: General medical and surgical

Staffed Beds: 25 **Admissions**: 533 **Census**: 6 **Outpatient Visits**: 86005 **Births**: 0 **Total Expense ($000)**: 35339 **Payroll Expense ($000)**: 14161 **Personnel**: 276

## DE RIDDER—Beauregard Parish

✥ **BEAUREGARD HEALTH SYSTEM (190050)**, 600 South Pine Street, Zip 70634–4942, Mailing Address: P.O. Box 730, Zip 70634–0730; tel. 337/462–7100, (Nonreporting) **A**1 10 **F**3 11 13 15 18 20 26 28 29 30 31 34 35 39 40 45 46 50 53 57 64 70 75 76 78 79 81 85 89 91 93 96 107 108 110 111 114 119 127 129 130 131 133 144 148 154 156 **P**6
Primary Contact: William F. Barrow II, Chief Executive Officer
CFO: Darrell L Kingham, CPA, Vice President Finance
CMO: David Jones, M.D., Chief Medical Officer
CIO: Meg Jackson, Director Information Technology
CHR: Kelli C Broocks, Director Human Resources, Public Relations and Physician Recruitment
CNO: Anita Thibodeaux, Chief Nursing Officer
Web address: www.beauregard.org
**Control**: Hospital district or authority, Government, Nonfederal **Service**: General medical and surgical

Staffed Beds: 49 **Admissions**: 1947 **Census**: 20 **Outpatient Visits**: 85709 **Births**: 325 **Total Expense ($000)**: 40412 **Payroll Expense ($000)**: 19720 **Personnel**: 364

**BEAUREGARD MEMORIAL HOSPITAL** See Beauregard Health System

## DELHI—Richland Parish

**RICHLAND PARISH HOSPITAL** See Richland Parish Hospital-Delhi

**RICHLAND PARISH HOSPITAL-DELHI (191323)**, 407 Cincinnati Street, Zip 71232–3007; tel. 318/878–5171, (Nonreporting) **A**10 18
Primary Contact: Michael W. Carroll, Administrator
CFO: Jinger Greer, CPA, Chief Financial Officer
CIO: Barbra Hutchison, Director Medical Records
CHR: Patsy Stout, Director Personnel
Web address: www.delhihospital.com
**Control**: Hospital district or authority, Government, Nonfederal **Service**: General medical and surgical

Staffed Beds: 25

*Many Facility Codes have changed. Please refer to the AHA Guide Code Chart.*   © 2021 AHA Guide

## DENHAM SPRINGS—Livingston Parish

**SAGE SPECIALTY HOSPITAL** See Sage Specialty Hospital (Ltac)

**SAGE SPECIALTY HOSPITAL (LTAC) (192008)**, 8375 Florida Boulevard, Zip 70726–7806; tel. 225/665–2664, (Includes SAGE SPECIALTY HOSPITAL, Mailing address: 8225 Summa Avenue, Building B, Baton Rouge, Louisiana, Zip 70809–3422; tel. 225/208–0300; Pat Mitchell, Chief Executive Officer), (Nonreporting) **A**10 **S** The Carpenter Health Network, Baton Rouge, LA
Primary Contact: Sharon Faulkner, R.N., Administrator
CFO: Jessica McGee, Chief Financial Officer
CMO: Durwin Walker, M.D., Chief Medical Officer
CHR: Kim Hernandez, Chief Human Resources Officer
CNO: Sharon Faulkner, R.N., Chief Nursing Officer
Web address: www.https://www.thecarpenterhealthnetwork.com/locations/sage-specialty-hospital/
**Control:** Individual, Investor–owned (for–profit) **Service:** Acute long–term care hospital

**Staffed Beds:** 117

## DEQUINCY—Calcasieu Parish

**DEQUINCY MEMORIAL HOSPITAL (191307)**, 110 West Fourth Street, Zip 70633–3508, Mailing Address: P.O. Box 1166, Zip 70633–1166; tel. 337/786–1200, (Nonreporting) **A**10 18
Primary Contact: Calvin Green, Interim Chief Executive Officer
CFO: Vicky Kelley, Chief Financial Officer
CMO: Jalal Joudeh, M.D., Chief of Staff
CNO: Darrell Ross, Chief Nursing Officer
Web address: www.dequincymemorial.com/
**Control:** City, Government, Nonfederal **Service:** General medical and surgical

**Staffed Beds:** 19

**DEQUINCY MEMORIAL HOSPITAL** See Dequincy Memorial Hospital

## DERIDDER—Beauregard Parish

**OCEANS BEHAVIORAL HOSPITAL OF DE RIDDER** See Oceans Behavioral Hospital of Deridder

☒ **OCEANS BEHAVIORAL HOSPITAL OF DERIDDER (194081)**, 1420 Blankenship Drive, Zip 70634–4604; tel. 337/460–9472, (Nonreporting) **A**1 10 **S** Oceans Healthcare, Plano, TX
Primary Contact: Stuart Archer, Chief Executive Officer, Oceans Healthcare
Web address: www.obhd.info/
**Control:** Corporation, Investor–owned (for–profit) **Service:** Psychiatric

**Staffed Beds:** 20

## DONALDSONVILLE—Ascension Parish

☒ **PREVOST MEMORIAL HOSPITAL (191308)**, 301 Memorial Drive, Zip 70346–4376; tel. 225/473–7931, (Nonreporting) **A**1 10 18
Primary Contact: Vincent A. Cataldo, Administrator
CFO: Nobie Landry, Chief Financial Officer
CMO: Glenn Schexnayder, M.D., Chief of Staff
CHR: Linda Cataldo, Human Resources Secretary
Web address: www.prevosthospital.net
**Control:** Hospital district or authority, Government, Nonfederal **Service:** General medical and surgical

**Staffed Beds:** 25

## EUNICE—Saint Landry Parish

**EUNICE COMMUNITY MEDICAL CTR** See Acadian Medical Center

## FARMERVILLE—Union Parish

**UNION GENERAL HOSPITAL (191301)**, 901 James Avenue, Zip 71241–2234, Mailing Address: P.O. Box 398, Zip 71241–0398; tel. 318/368–9751, (Nonreporting) **A**10 18 **F**15 29 32 34 35 40 45 50 56 81 93 104 107 110 115 119 127 128 133 134 143 149 153
Primary Contact: Evalyn Ormond, Chief Executive Officer
COO: Dianne Davidson, Chief Operating Officer
CFO: William Adcock, Chief Financial Officer
CHR: Sheri Taylor, Director Human Resources
CNO: Darra Jung, Director of Nursing
Web address: www.uniongen.com
**Control:** Other not–for–profit (including NFP Corporation) **Service:** General medical and surgical

**Staffed Beds:** 15 **Admissions:** 338 **Census:** 5 **Outpatient Visits:** 29788
**Births:** 0 **Total Expense ($000):** 14444 **Payroll Expense ($000):** 5753
**Personnel:** 113

## FERRIDAY—Concordia Parish

**RIVERLAND MEDICAL CENTER (191318)**, 1700 EE Wallace Boulevard North, Zip 71334–2239, Mailing Address: P.O. Box 111, Zip 71334–0111; tel. 318/757–6551, (Nonreporting) **A**10 18 **F**3 15 29 34 35 40 45 57 59 68 70 75 77 81 85 86 87 93 107 110 114 119 127 133 148 153 154 **P**6
Primary Contact: Samuel Ellard, Chief Executive Officer
COO: Nekisha Smith, Chief Operating Officer
CFO: Spencer Holder, Chief Financial Officer
CMO: Carrie Bonomo, M.D., Chief of Staff
CHR: Debra Stephens, Director Personnel
CNO: Shelia James, Director of Nursing
Web address: www.riverlandmedical.com/
**Control:** Hospital district or authority, Government, Nonfederal **Service:** General medical and surgical

**Staffed Beds:** 25 **Admissions:** 835 **Census:** 11 **Outpatient Visits:** 114623
**Births:** 0 **Total Expense ($000):** 17762 **Payroll Expense ($000):** 7680
**Personnel:** 147

## FORT POLK—Vernon Parish

☒ **BAYNE-JONES ARMY COMMUNITY HOSPITAL**, 1585 3rd Street, Building 283, Zip 71459–5102; tel. 337/531–3928, (Nonreporting) **A**1 **S** Department of the Army, Office of the Surgeon General, Falls Church, VA
Primary Contact: Colonel Jody L. Dugai, Commanding Officer
COO: Larry R. Patterson, Deputy Commander Administration
CFO: CaptainDustin Mullins, Chief Resource Management
CIO: MajorWilliam Callahan, Chief Information Management Division
CHR: CaptainDustin Mullins, Chief Human Resources
CNO: ColonelMichael Szymaniak, Deputy Commander for Nursing
Web address: www.https://bjach.polk.amedd.army.mil/
**Service:** General medical and surgical

**Staffed Beds:** 13

## FRANKLIN—St. Mary Parish

☒ **FRANKLIN FOUNDATION HOSPITAL (191310)**, 1097 Northwest Boulevard, Zip 70538–3407, Mailing Address: P.O. Box 577, Zip 70538–0577; tel. 337/828–0760, (Nonreporting) **A**1 10 18 **F**3 11 13 15 18 26 29 34 35 40 45 50 57 58 59 68 70 75 76 77 79 81 85 93 107 110 111 119 130 132 133 135 145 147 148 149 154 **P**6
Primary Contact: Stephanie A. Guidry, Chief Executive Officer
CFO: Ron Bailey, Chief Financial Officer
CMO: Jesus Chua, M.D., Chief of Staff
CIO: John Spradlin, Information Systems Director
CHR: Elmo Vinas, Director Human Resources
CNO: Michelle Skillings, Chief Nursing Officer
Web address: www.franklinfoundation.org
**Control:** Hospital district or authority, Government, Nonfederal **Service:** General medical and surgical

**Staffed Beds:** 22 **Admissions:** 568 **Census:** 9 **Outpatient Visits:** 29615
**Births:** 46 **Total Expense ($000):** 26420 **Payroll Expense ($000):** 12323
**Personnel:** 256

---

**Hospital, Medicare Provider Number, Address, Telephone, Approval, Facility, and Physician Codes, Health Care System**

★ American Hospital Association (AHA) membership
☐ The Joint Commission accreditation
○ Healthcare Facilities Accreditation Program
◇ DNV Healthcare Inc. accreditation
⇑ Center for Improvement in Healthcare Quality Accreditation
△ Commission on Accreditation of Rehabilitation Facilities (CARF) accreditation

**LA**

### FRANKLINTON—Washington Parish

☒ **RIVERSIDE MEDICAL CENTER (191313)**, 1900 Main Street, Zip 70438–3688; tel. 985/839–4431, (Nonreporting) **A**1 10 18
Primary Contact: Peter Sullivan, Chief Executive Officer
CFO: Brandon Anzaldua, Chief Financial Officer
CMO: Chris Foret, M.D., Chief of Staff
CHR: John Seal, Director Human Resources
Web address: www.rmchospital.com
**Control:** Hospital district or authority, Government, Nonfederal **Service:** General medical and surgical

Staffed Beds: 25

### GONZALES—Ascension Parish

**ASCENSION GONZALES REHABILITATION HOSPITAL** See United Medical Rehabilitation Hospital - Gonzales

**BEHAVIORAL HOSPITAL - LUTCHER** See St. James Behavioral Health Hospital

**ST. ELIZABETH HOSPITAL** See Our Lady of The Lake Ascension

☐ **ST. JAMES BEHAVIORAL HEALTH HOSPITAL (194088)**, 3136 South Saint Landry Avenue, Zip 70737–5801; tel. 225/647–7524, (Nonreporting) **A**1 10
Primary Contact: Andrew Hines, Administrator
COO: Wendell Smith, Chief Operating Officer
CFO: Rama Kongara, Chief Financial Officer
CMO: Lance Bullock, M.D., Medical Director
CHR: Dessa Frederick, Manager Human Resources
Web address: www.sjbhh.net
**Control:** Corporation, Investor–owned (for–profit) **Service:** Psychiatric

Staffed Beds: 10

### GREENSBURG—St. Helena Parish

**ST. HELENA PARISH HOSPITAL (191300)**, 16874 Highway 43, Zip 70441–4834; tel. 225/222–6111, (Nonreporting) **A**10 18
Primary Contact: Naveed Awan, FACHE, Chief Executive Officer
CFO: Theresa Brinkhaus, Chief Financial Officer
CMO: Anjanette Varnado, M.D., Chief Medical Officer
CHR: Lorraine L Ballard, Director Human Resources
CNO: Julie Morgan, Director of Nursing
Web address: www.sthelenaparishhospital.com
**Control:** Other not–for–profit (including NFP Corporation) **Service:** General medical and surgical

Staffed Beds: 75

### GRETNA—Jefferson Parish

**MEADOWCREST HOSPITAL** See Ochsner Medical Center - West Bank

**UNITED MEDICAL HEALTHWEST NEW ORLEANS, LLC (193074)**, 3201 Wall Boulevard, Suite B, Zip 70056–7755; tel. 504/433–5551, (Nonreporting) **A**10 **S** United Medical Rehabilitation Hospitals, Gretna, LA
Primary Contact: Kian Marigny, Administrator
CMO: Kenneth Williams, M.D., Medical Director
Web address: www.https://umrhospital.com/locations/new-orleans/
**Control:** Individual, Investor–owned (for–profit) **Service:** Rehabilitation

Staffed Beds: 21

**UNITED MEDICAL REHABILITATION HOSPITAL** See United Medical Healthwest New Orleans, LLC

### HAMMOND—Tangipahoa Parish

⇑ **CYPRESS POINTE SURGICAL HOSPITAL (190303)**, 42570 South Airport Road, Zip 70403–0946; tel. 985/510–6200, (Nonreporting) **A**10 21
Primary Contact: Glenda Dobson, R.N., Chief Executive Officer
COO: Scot Treitler, Chief Operating Officer
CFO: Donna Varnado, Vice President Finance
CNO: Denise Fortenberry, Chief Nursing Officer and Chief Compliance Officer
Web address: www.cpsh.org
**Control:** Corporation, Investor–owned (for–profit) **Service:** Surgical

Staffed Beds: 24

**NORTH OAKS HEALTH SYSTEM** See North Oaks Medical Center

☒ **NORTH OAKS MEDICAL CENTER (190015)**, 15790 Paul Vega, MD, Drive, Zip 70403–1436, Mailing Address: P.O. Box 2668, Zip 70404–2668; tel. 985/345–2700, (Nonreporting) **A**1 10 19 **F**3 12 13 15 18 20 22 24 26 28 29 30 31 32 34 40 43 45 49 50 54 56 57 58 59 63 64 68 70 72 73 74 75 76 77 78 79 81 82 84 85 86 87 89 93 94 96 102 107 108 110 111 114 115 118 119 126 129 130 131 132 135 143 144 146 147 148 149 154 156 **P**6 **S** North Oaks Health System, Hammond, LA
Primary Contact: Michele Kidd. Sutton, FACHE, President and Chief Executive Officer
COO: Michael Watkins, Chief Operating Officer
CFO: Mark Anderson, Chief Financial Officer
CMO: Robert Peltier, M.D., Chief Medical Officer
CIO: Doug Bankston, Director Technical Services
CHR: Jeff Jarreau, Chief Human Resources Officer
CNO: Kirsten S Riney, MSN, R.N., Chief Nursing Officer
Web address: www.northoaks.org
**Control:** Hospital district or authority, Government, Nonfederal **Service:** General medical and surgical

Staffed Beds: 248 Admissions: 10877 Census: 153 Outpatient Visits: 510898 Births: 1130 Total Expense ($000): 322311 Payroll Expense ($000): 170321 Personnel: 1851

☐ △ **NORTH OAKS REHABILITATION HOSPITAL (193044)**, 1900 South Morrison Boulevard, Zip 70403–5742; tel. 985/542–7777, (Nonreporting) **A**1 7 10 **F**29 56 75 86 87 90 130 132 143 154 **S** North Oaks Health System, Hammond, LA
Primary Contact: Mac Barrient, Administrator
CFO: Mark Anderson, Chief Financial Officer
CMO: Robert Peltier, M.D., Senior Vice President, Chief Medical Officer, North Oaks Health System
CIO: Herbert Robinson, M.D., Vice President, Chief Medical Information Officer, North Oaks Health System
CHR: Jeff Jarreau, Senior Vice President, Human Resources, North Oaks Health System
Web address: www.northoaks.org
**Control:** Hospital district or authority, Government, Nonfederal **Service:** Rehabilitation

Staffed Beds: 27 Admissions: 515 Census: 16 Outpatient Visits: 0 Births: 0 Total Expense ($000): 10256 Payroll Expense ($000): 2656 Personnel: 45

☒ **PAM SPECIALTY HOSPITAL OF HAMMOND (192036)**, 42074 Veterans Avenue, Zip 70403–1408; tel. 985/902–8148, (Nonreporting) **A**1 10 **F**1 29 60 75 77 148 149 **S** Post Acute Medical, LLC, Enola, PA
Primary Contact: Nicholas Paul. Mendez, Chief Executive Officer and Director of Nursing
Web address: www.postacutemedical.com/facilities/find-facility/specialty-hospitals/PAM-Specialty-Hospital-Hammond
**Control:** Partnership, Investor–owned (for–profit) **Service:** Acute long–term care hospital

Staffed Beds: 40 Admissions: 518 Census: 26 Outpatient Visits: 0 Births: 0 Total Expense ($000): 13676 Payroll Expense ($000): 5441 Personnel: 131

**POST ACUTE SPECIALTY HOSPITAL OF HAMMOND** See Pam Specialty Hospital of Hammond

**UNITED MEDICAL REHABILITATION HOSPITAL (193079)**, 15717 Belle Drive, Zip 70403–1439; tel. 985/340–5998, (Includes UNITED MEDICAL REHABILITATION HOSPITAL - GONZALES, Mailing address: 333 East Worthy Road, Gonzales, Louisiana, Zip 70737–4234; tel. 225/450–2231; Cyrillia Bonds, R.N., Administrator), (Nonreporting) **A**10 **S** United Medical Rehabilitation Hospitals, Gretna, LA
Primary Contact: Cyrillia Bonds, R.N., Administrator
CFO: Warren Swenson, Chief Financial Officer
CMO: Luis Franco, M.D., Medical Director
CHR: Mark Gros, Director Human Resources
Web address: www.umrhospital.com
**Control:** Corporation, Investor–owned (for–profit) **Service:** Rehabilitation

Staffed Beds: 20

## HOMER—Claiborne Parish

⇑ **CLAIBORNE MEMORIAL MEDICAL CENTER (190114)**, 620 East College Street, Zip 71040–3202; tel. 318/927–2024, (Nonreporting) **A**10 21
Primary Contact: Tina Haynes, Interim Chief Executive Officer
CFO: Amy H. Legendre, Chief Financial Officer
CMO: Mark Haynes, M.D., Chief of Staff
CIO: Angie Costakis, Chief Information Officer
CHR: William Colvin, Human Resources Director
CNO: Kristie M. Copeland, Interim Chief Nursing Officer
Web address: www.claibornemedical.com/
**Control**: City, Government, Nonfederal **Service**: General medical and surgical

**Staffed Beds: 57**

⇑ **HOMER MEMORIAL HOSPITAL** See Claiborne Memorial Medical Center

## HOUMA—Terrebonne Parish

**AMG SPECIALTY HOSPITAL-HOUMA (192037)**, 629 Dunn Street, Zip 70360–4707; tel. 985/274–0001, (Nonreporting) **A**10 22 **S** AMG Integrated Healthcare Management, Lafayette, LA
Primary Contact: Rachel Mayeaux, Chief Executive Officer
Web address: www.amghouma.com/
**Control**: Corporation, Investor–owned (for–profit) **Service**: Acute long–term care hospital

**Staffed Beds: 40**

**COMPASS BEHAVIORAL CENTER OF HOUMA (194109)**, 4701 West Park Avenue, Zip 70364–4426; tel. 985/876–1715, (Nonreporting) **A**10 **F**98 100 101 102 103 104 105 130 135 153 154 **P**5 6 **S** Compass Health, Crowley, LA
Primary Contact: Riane Ortega, Chief Executive Officer
Web address: www.compasshealthcare.com/site83.php
**Control**: Individual, Investor–owned (for–profit) **Service**: Psychiatric

**Staffed Beds: 20 Admissions: 387 Census: 13 Outpatient Visits: 0 Births: 0 Total Expense ($000): 3367 Payroll Expense ($000): 1604 Personnel: 38**

**COMPASS BEHAVIORAL CENTER OF HOUMA, INC.** See Compass Behavioral Center of Houma

⊞ **LEONARD J. CHABERT MEDICAL CENTER (190183)**, 1978 Industrial Boulevard, Zip 70363–7094; tel. 985/873–2200, (Nonreporting) **A**1 3 5 10 **F**3 4 15 18 20 22 24 26 29 31 34 35 38 40 44 45 46 48 49 50 51 56 57 58 59 61 64 66 68 70 74 77 78 79 81 82 84 85 86 87 89 93 97 98 102 107 108 110 111 115 119 130 146 147 148 149 154 156 **S** Ochsner Health, New Orleans, LA
Primary Contact: Timothy J. Allen, FACHE, Chief Executive Officer
COO: Kendrick Duet, Chief Operating Officer
CNO: Jana Semere, Chief Nursing Officer
Web address: www.ochsner.org/locations/leonard_j_chabert_medical_center/
**Control**: State, Government, Nonfederal **Service**: General medical and surgical

**Staffed Beds: 80 Admissions: 2744 Census: 40 Outpatient Visits: 174551 Births: 0 Total Expense ($000): 132697 Payroll Expense ($000): 32475 Personnel: 816**

**PHYSICIANS ALLIANCE HOSPITAL OF HOUMA** See Amg Specialty Hospital-Houma

☐ **PHYSICIANS MEDICAL CENTER (190241)**, 218 Corporate Drive, Zip 70360–2768; tel. 985/853–1390, (Nonreporting) **A**1 10 **F**12 15 29 45 51 65 75 79 81 82 85 87 107 110 115 119 120 124 132
Primary Contact: Andrew Knizley, Chief Executive Officer
Web address: www.physicianshouma.com/
**Control**: Corporation, Investor–owned (for–profit) **Service**: Surgical

**Staffed Beds: 15 Admissions: 364 Census: 2 Outpatient Visits: 9085 Births: 0 Total Expense ($000): 18386 Payroll Expense ($000): 5240 Personnel: 114**

**PHYSICIANS SURG SPEC HOSPITAL** See Physicians Medical Center

**SOUTH LOUISIANA MEDICAL CENTER** See Leonard J. Chabert Medical Center

⊞ △ **TERREBONNE GENERAL MEDICAL CENTER (190008)**, 8166 Main Street, Zip 70360–3498; tel. 985/873–4141, (Total facility includes 8 beds in nursing home–type unit) (Nonreporting) **A**1 2 5 7 10 19 **F**8 11 13 14 15 17 18 20 22 24 26 29 30 31 34 35 40 44 49 50 53 55 57 58 59 64 65 68 70 72 74 75 76 77 78 79 81 84 85 86 87 89 90 91 92 93 96 102 107 108 109 110 111 112 115 116 117 118 119 121 123 124 128 130 131 132 134 135 143 146 147 148 149 157 **P**6
Primary Contact: Phyllis L. Peoples, President and Chief Executive Officer
COO: Diane Yeates, FACHE, Chief Operating Officer
CFO: Meggan Murray, Assistant Vice President Finance
CMO: Frederick Rau, M.D., Chief of Staff
CIO: Jeff Sardella, Director Information Technology
CHR: Mickie Rousseau, Director Human Resources
CNO: Teresita McNabb, FACHE, R.N., Vice President Nursing Services
Web address: www.tgmc.com
**Control**: Hospital district or authority, Government, Nonfederal **Service**: General medical and surgical

**Staffed Beds: 230 Admissions: 7892 Census: 113 Outpatient Visits: 141431 Births: 1581 Total Expense ($000): 197881 Payroll Expense ($000): 73593 Personnel: 1393**

## INDEPENDENCE—Tangipahoa Parish

☐ **LALLIE KEMP MEDICAL CENTER (191321)**, 52579 Highway 51 South, Zip 70443–2231; tel. 985/878–9421, (Nonreporting) **A**1 3 5 10 18
Primary Contact: Rhonda G. Green, R.N., Administrator
COO: Lisa G Bruhl, Chief Operating Officer
CFO: Chad Thompson, Chief Financial Officer
CMO: Kathy Willis, M.D., Medical Director
CIO: Charles Tate, Director Information Technology
CHR: Diane Farnham, Acting Director Human Resources
CNO: Vicki Hirsch, R.N., Director of Nursing
Web address: www.lsuhospitals.org/Hospitals/LK/LK.aspx
**Control**: State, Government, Nonfederal **Service**: General medical and surgical

**Staffed Beds: 24**

**LALLIE KEMP REGIONAL MED CTR** See Lallie Kemp Medical Center

## JACKSON—East Feliciana Parish

**EAST LOUISIANA STATE HOSPITAL** See Eastern Louisiana Mental Health System

☐ **EASTERN LOUISIANA MENTAL HEALTH SYSTEM (194008)**, 4502 Highway 10, Zip 70748, Mailing Address: P.O. Box 498, Zip 70748–0498; tel. 225/634–0100, (Nonreporting) **A**1 3 10 **S** Louisiana State Hospitals, Baton Rouge, LA
Primary Contact: Hampton P. S. Lea, Chief Executive Officer
CFO: Laura Lott, Administrative Director
CMO: John W Thompson, M.D., Chief of Staff
CIO: Deborah Brandon, Director Total Quality Management
CHR: Vikki Riggle, Director Human Resources
CNO: Mary Fontenelle, Executive Nurse Director
Web address: www.new.dhh.louisiana.gov/index.cfm/directory/detail/219
**Control**: State, Government, Nonfederal **Service**: Psychiatric

**Staffed Beds: 473**

**VILLA FELICIANA CHRON DIS HOSP** See Villa Feliciana Medical Complex

**VILLA FELICIANA MEDICAL COMPLEX (190199)**, 5002 Highway 10, Zip 70748–3627, Mailing Address: P.O. Box 438, Zip 70748–0438; tel. 225/634–4017, (Nonreporting) **A**10
Primary Contact: Patrick Eckler, Administrator
CFO: Kim Jelks, Fiscal Officer
CMO: John F Piker, M.D., Medical Director
CIO: Michael James, Information Technology Technical Support Specialist 1
CHR: Sandra Delatte, Director Human Resources
CNO: Linda Williams, Director of Nursing
Web address: www.ldh.la.gov/index.cfm/directory/detail/535
**Control**: State, Government, Nonfederal **Service**: Other specialty treatment

**Staffed Beds: 299**

---

**Hospital, Medicare Provider Number, Address, Telephone, Approval, Facility, and Physician Codes, Health Care System**

★ American Hospital Association (AHA) membership
☐ The Joint Commission accreditation
○ Healthcare Facilities Accreditation Program
◇ DNV Healthcare Inc. accreditation
⇑ Center for Improvement in Healthcare Quality Accreditation
△ Commission on Accreditation of Rehabilitation Facilities (CARF) accreditation

**LA**

## JEFFERSON—Jefferson Parish

✉ **OCHSNER REHABILITATON HOSPITAL WEST CAMPUS (193099)**, 2614 Jefferson Highway, Zip 70121–3828; tel. 504/291–5100, (Nonreporting) **A**1 **F**3 29 34 44 60 68 75 90 96 119 130 132 148 **S** Select Medical Corporation, Mechanicsburg, PA
Primary Contact: Neil Fedders, Interim Chief Executive Officer
CNO: Patrick Faucheaux, R.N., Chief Nursing Officer
Web address: www.https://www.ochsner.org/services/rehabilitation
**Control:** Corporation, Investor–owned (for–profit) **Service:** Rehabilitation

**Staffed Beds:** 42 **Admissions:** 1014 **Census:** 38 **Outpatient Visits:** 0
**Births:** 0

## JENA—La Salle Parish

**LA SALLE GENERAL HOSPITAL** See Lasalle General Hospital

★ **LASALLE GENERAL HOSPITAL (190145)**, 187 Ninth Street, Zip 71342–3901, Mailing Address: P.O. Box 2780, Zip 71342–2780; tel. 318/992–9200, (Nonreporting) **A**3 10 **F**4 7 11 15 18 29 33 34 35 40 53 57 59 62 64 81 93 97 98 100 103 104 107 108 110 111 115 119 127 130 133 149
Primary Contact: Lana B. Francis, Chief Executive Officer
CHR: Allyson Fannin, Human Resources Officer
CNO: Carolyn Francis, R.N., MSN, Director of Nursing
Web address: www.lasallegeneralhospital.com
**Control:** Hospital district or authority, Government, Nonfederal **Service:** General medical and surgical

**Staffed Beds:** 46 **Admissions:** 943 **Census:** 18 **Outpatient Visits:** 66482
**Births:** 0 **Total Expense ($000):** 22983 **Payroll Expense ($000):** 9348
**Personnel:** 208

## JENNINGS—Jefferson Davis Parish

✉ **JENNINGS AMERICAN LEGION HOSPITAL (190053)**, 1634 Elton Road, Zip 70546–3614; tel. 337/616–7000, (Nonreporting) **A**1 10 **F**3 11 15 18 20 28 29 34 40 45 50 64 70 75 76 79 81 107 108 111 115 119 127 130 133 147 149
Primary Contact: Dana D. Williams, Chief Executive Officer
COO: Keith J Simpson, Chief Operating Officer
CIO: Gary Courrege, Chief Information Officer
CHR: Ruth Carnes, Manager Human Resources
CNO: Theresa L Woods, MSN, R.N., FACHE, Chief Nursing Officer
Web address: www.jalh.com
**Control:** Other not–for–profit (including NFP Corporation) **Service:** General medical and surgical

**Staffed Beds:** 49 **Admissions:** 2403 **Census:** 25 **Outpatient Visits:** 39475
**Births:** 569 **Total Expense ($000):** 45365 **Payroll Expense ($000):** 21279
**Personnel:** 432

**JENNINGS SENIOR CARE HOSPITAL (194082)**, 1 Hospital Drive, Suite 201, Zip 70546–3641; tel. 337/824–1558, (Nonreporting) **A**10 **F**98 100 101 104 105 153 **P**5
Primary Contact: Andre' Robichaux, Administrator
Web address: www.https://www.compasshealthcare.com/locations/jennings-senior-care-hospital/
**Control:** Corporation, Investor–owned (for–profit) **Service:** Psychiatric

**Staffed Beds:** 20 **Admissions:** 322 **Census:** 14 **Outpatient Visits:** 0
**Births:** 0 **Total Expense ($000):** 5775 **Payroll Expense ($000):** 2776
**Personnel:** 61

**REHABILITATION HOSPITAL OF JENNINGS (193067)**, 1 Hospital Drive, Suite 101, Zip 70546–3641; tel. 337/821–5353, (Nonreporting) **A**10
Primary Contact: Michael Holland, M.D., Chief Executive Officer
Web address: www.jenningsrehab.com
**Control:** Partnership, Investor–owned (for–profit) **Service:** Rehabilitation

**Staffed Beds:** 16

## JONESBORO—Jackson Parish

★ **JACKSON PARISH HOSPITAL (191317)**, 165 Beech Springs Road, Zip 71251–2059; tel. 318/259–4435, (Nonreporting) **A**10 18
Primary Contact: John Morgan, R.N., Chief Executive Officer
CFO: Bill Stansbury, Chief Financial Officer
CMO: W. James (Jamie) Slusher, M.D., Chief of Staff
CIO: Monie Phillips IIIDirector Clinical Informatics
CHR: Phillip Thomas JrDirector Human Resources
CNO: Christy Wyatt, R.N., Interim Chief Nursing Officer
Web address: www.jacksonparishhospital.com
**Control:** Hospital district or authority, Government, Nonfederal **Service:** General medical and surgical

**Staffed Beds:** 25

## KAPLAN—Vermilion Parish

**ABROM KAPLAN MEMORIAL HOSPITAL (191322)**, 1310 West Seventh Street, Zip 70548–2910; tel. 337/643–8300, (Nonreporting) **A**10 18 **S** Lafayette General Health, Lafayette, LA
Primary Contact: Bryce Quebodeaux, Chief Executive Officer
CFO: Michael G. Johnson, CPA, Chief Financial Officer
CMO: Scott Bergeaux, M.D., Chief Medical Staff
CIO: Michael Cardiff, Systems Supervisor
CHR: Linda Guidry, Human Resources Generalist
CNO: Jennifer Gerard, R.N., Chief Nursing Officer
Web address: www.lafayettegeneral.com
**Control:** Hospital district or authority, Government, Nonfederal **Service:** General medical and surgical

**Staffed Beds:** 35

## KENNER—Jefferson Parish

**KENNER REGIONAL MEDICAL CENTER** See Ochsner Medical Center - Kenner

**LAKE PINES HOSPITAL** See Perimeter Behavioral Hospital of New Orleans

☐ **OCEANS BEHAVIORAL HOSPITAL OF GREATER NEW ORLEANS (194098)**, 716 Village Road, Zip 70065–2751; tel. 504/464–8895, (Includes OCEANS BEHAVIORAL HOSPITAL GREATER NEW ORLEANS - MARRERO, Mailing address: 4500 Wichers Drive, Marrero, Louisiana, Zip 70072–3184; tel. 504/349–1661; Deborah Spiers, Administrator), (Nonreporting) **A**1 10 **S** Oceans Healthcare, Plano, TX
Primary Contact: Deborah Spiers, Administrator
Web address: www.obhgno.info/
**Control:** Corporation, Investor–owned (for–profit) **Service:** Psychiatric

**Staffed Beds:** 30

✉ **OCHSNER MEDICAL CENTER - KENNER (190274)**, 180 West Esplanade Avenue, Zip 70065–6001; tel. 504/468–8600, (Nonreporting) **A**1 3 5 10 **F**3 13 15 18 20 22 29 30 31 34 35 37 38 40 41 42 44 45 46 49 50 51 53 54 56 57 58 59 60 61 64 65 66 68 70 72 74 75 76 77 78 79 81 82 83 84 85 86 87 93 97 102 107 110 114 116 117 120 129 130 131 132 135 146 147 148 154 157 **S** Ochsner Health, New Orleans, LA
Primary Contact: Stephen Robinson Jr, FACHE, Chief Executive Officer
COO: Jeffery H Edge, Chief Operating Officer
CFO: Tara Alleman, Chief Financial Officer
CMO: James Tebbe, M.D., Vice President Medical Affairs
CIO: Dere Krummel, Director Information Systems
Web address: www.https://www.ochsner.org/locations/ochsner-medical-center-kenner/
**Control:** Other not–for–profit (including NFP Corporation) **Service:** General medical and surgical

**Staffed Beds:** 110 **Admissions:** 6414 **Census:** 72 **Outpatient Visits:** 183290 **Births:** 1120 **Total Expense ($000):** 169576 **Payroll Expense ($000):** 57970 **Personnel:** 886

☐ **PERIMETER BEHAVIORAL HOSPITAL OF NEW ORLEANS (194113)**, 3639 Loyola Drive, Zip 70065; tel. 504/305–2700, (Nonreporting) **A**1 **S** Perimeter Healthcare, Alpharetta, GA
Primary Contact: Debbie Tullier, Chief Executive Officer
Web address: www.https://www.lakepineshospital.com/
**Control:** Corporation, Investor–owned (for–profit) **Service:** Psychiatric

**Staffed Beds:** 36

## KENTWOOD—Tangipahoa Parish

**SOUTHEAST REGIONAL MEDICAL CENTER (192040)**, 719 Avenue G, Zip 70444–2601; tel. 985/229–9193, (Nonreporting) **A**10
Primary Contact: Lionel Murphy, Chief Executive Officer
**Control:** Corporation, Investor–owned (for–profit) **Service:** Acute long–term care hospital

**Staffed Beds:** 14

*Many Facility Codes have changed. Please refer to the AHA Guide Code Chart.*

LA

## KINDER—Allen Parish Parish

**ALLEN PARISH COMMUNITY HEALTHCARE (190133)**, 108 Sixth Avenue, Zip 70648-3187, Mailing Address: P.O. Box 1670, Zip 70648-1670; tel. 337/738-2527, (Nonreporting) **A**10
Primary Contact: Jackie Costley. Reviel, R.N., Chief Executive Officer
COO: Terry Willet, Chief Financial Officer
CFO: Stephen Thames, Chief Financial Officer
CMO: Ejiro Ughouwa, M.D., Chief of Staff
CIO: Bill Marcantel, Chief Information Systems
CHR: Amand Lambert, Director Human Resources
CNO: Malissa Reardon, R.N., Interim Chief Nursing Officer
Web address: www.allenparishhospital.com
**Control**: Hospital district or authority, Government, Nonfederal **Service**: General medical and surgical

**Staffed Beds**: 49

**ALLEN PARISH HOSPITAL** See Allen Parish Community Healthcare

## LA PLACE—St. John the Baptist Parish

☐ **RIVER PLACE BEHAVIORAL HEALTH (194114)**, 500 Rue De Sante, Zip 70068-5418; tel. 985/303-2327, (Nonreporting) **A**1 **S** Acadia Healthcare Company, Inc., Franklin, TN
Primary Contact: Jeremy Pitzer, Chief Executive Officer
Web address: www.riverplacebh.com
**Control**: Corporation, Investor-owned (for-profit) **Service**: Psychiatric

**Staffed Beds**: 82

## LACOMBE—St. Tammany Parish

**BEACON BEHAVIORAL HOSPITAL - NORTHSHORE (194080)**, 64026 Highway 434, Suite 300, Zip 70445-5417; tel. 985/882-0226, (Nonreporting) **A**10 **F**29 56 64 98 101 102 103 104 132 153 154
Primary Contact: Danielle Sones, Administrator
Web address: www.magnoliabh.com/
**Control**: Corporation, Investor-owned (for-profit) **Service**: Psychiatric

**Staffed Beds**: 22 **Admissions**: 581 **Census**: 16 **Outpatient Visits**: 0
**Births**: 0 **Total Expense ($000)**: 4073 **Payroll Expense ($000)**: 1627

**BEACON BEHAVIORAL HOSPITAL NORTHSHORE** See Beacon Behavioral Hospital - Northshore

⊞ **NORTHSHORE REHABILITATION HOSPITAL**, 64030 State Highway 434, Zip 70445; tel. 985/218-4660, (Data for 122 days) (Nonreporting) **A**1 **F**29 90 95 96 111 115 119 **S** Select Medical Corporation, Mechanicsburg, PA
Primary Contact: Laurel DuPont, Chief Executive Officer
CNO: Fran E. St. Pierre, R.N., Chief Nursing Officer
Web address: www.northshore-rehab.com
**Control**: Partnership, Investor-owned (for-profit) **Service**: Rehabilitation

**Staffed Beds**: 30 **Admissions**: 173 **Census**: 17 **Outpatient Visits**: 0
**Births**: 0 **Personnel**: 70

## LAFAYETTE—Lafayette Parish

**AMG SPECIALTY HOSPITAL - LAFAYETTE** See Amg Specialty Hospital-Lafayette

**AMG SPECIALTY HOSPITAL-LAFAYETTE (192029)**, 4811 Ambassador Caffery Parkway, 4th Floor, Zip 70508-7265; tel. 337/839-9880, (Nonreporting) **A**10 22 **F**1 29 **S** AMG Integrated Healthcare Management, Lafayette, LA
Primary Contact: April Ebeling, Chief Executive Officer
CFO: Jessica McGee, Chief Financial Officer
CMO: Maximo LaMarche, M.D., Chief Medical Officer
CNO: Mary Bollich, Director of Nurses
Web address: www.amglafayette.com
**Control**: Corporation, Investor-owned (for-profit) **Service**: Acute long-term care hospital

**Staffed Beds**: 18 **Admissions**: 230 **Census**: 15 **Outpatient Visits**: 0
**Births**: 0

★ **COMPASS BEHAVIORAL CENTER OF LAFAYETTE (194085)**, 312 Youngsville Highway, Zip 70508; tel. 337/534-4655, (Nonreporting) **F**98 100 104 105 153 154 **S** Compass Health, Crowley, LA
Primary Contact: Aimee Monaghan, Administrator
Web address: www.compasshealthcare.com
**Control**: Corporation, Investor-owned (for-profit) **Service**: Psychiatric

**Staffed Beds**: 24 **Admissions**: 309 **Census**: 12 **Outpatient Visits**: 9240
**Births**: 0 **Total Expense ($000)**: 5346 **Payroll Expense ($000)**: 2497
**Personnel**: 50

**HEART HOSPITAL OF LAFAYETTE** See Our Lady of Lourdes Heart Hospital

⊞ **LAFAYETTE GENERAL MEDICAL CENTER (190002)**, 1214 Coolidge Boulevard, Zip 70503-2696, Mailing Address: P.O. Box 52009 OCS, Zip 70505-2009; tel. 337/289-7991, (Includes LAFAYETTE BEHAVIORAL HEALTH, Mailing address: 302 Dulles Drive, Lafayette, Louisiana, Zip 70506-3008; tel. 337/289-8595; Sandra Armand, Director; LAFAYETTE GENERAL ORTHOPEDIC HOSPITAL, Mailing address: 2810 Ambassador Caffery Parkway, Lafayette, Louisiana, Zip 70506-5906; tel. 337/981-2949; Jude Fontenot, Administrator; LAFAYETTE GENERAL SURGICAL HOSPITAL, Mailing address: 1000 West Pinhook Road, Suite 100, Lafayette, Louisiana, Zip 70503-2460; tel. 337/289-8095; Kenneth M. LeBaron, R.N., Administrator; LAFAYETTE SURGICAL SPECIALTY HOSPITAL, Mailing address: 1101 Kaliste Saloom Road, Lafayette, Louisiana, Zip 70508-5705; tel. 337/769-4100; Buffy H. Domingue, Chief Executive Officer), (Nonreporting) **A**1 2 3 5 10 **S** Lafayette General Health, Lafayette, LA
Primary Contact: Patrick W. Gandy Jr, CPA, Executive Vice President and Chief Executive Officer
COO: Al J. Patin, R.N., Senior Vice President and Chief Operating Officer
CFO: Kim Hebert, Chief Financial Officer
CMO: Stephen G. Rees, M.D., Vice President Medical Affairs
CIO: Michael Dozier, Vice President, Chief Information Officer
CHR: Sheena Bouquet Ronsonet, Vice President
CNO: Renee D. Delahoussaye, R.N., Vice President, Chief Nursing Officer
Web address: www.lafayettegeneral.com
**Control**: Other not-for-profit (including NFP Corporation) **Service**: General medical and surgical

**Staffed Beds**: 440

**LAFAYETTE GENERAL SOUTHWEST** See Lafayette General Orthopedic Hospital

**LAFAYETTE PHYSICAL REHABILITATION HOSPITAL (193093)**, 307 Polly Lane, Zip 70508-4960; tel. 337/314-1111, (Nonreporting) **A**10 22 **S** AMG Integrated Healthcare Management, Lafayette, LA
Primary Contact: Bruce J. Bartels, Chief Executive Officer
Web address: www.lafayettephysicalrehab.com/
**Control**: Corporation, Investor-owned (for-profit) **Service**: Rehabilitation

**Staffed Beds**: 32

**LOUISIANA EXTENDED CARE HOSPITAL OF LAFAYETTE (192032)**, 2810 Ambassador Caffery Parkway, 6th Floor, Zip 70506-5906; tel. 337/289-8180, (Includes EUNICE EXTENDED CARE HOSPITAL, Mailing address: 3879 Highway 190, Eunice, Louisiana, Zip 70535; tel. 337/546-0024; Kermit C. Simmons, Administrator), (Nonreporting) **A**10 **S** LHC Group, Lafayette, LA
Primary Contact: Kermit C. Simmons, Administrator
CMO: David Ashton Reed, M.D., Chief Medical Officer
CNO: Belinda Trahan, Chief Nursing Officer
Web address: www.lhcgroup.com
**Control**: Other not-for-profit (including NFP Corporation) **Service**: Acute long-term care hospital

**Staffed Beds**: 42

**OASIS REHAB HOSP OF LAFAYETTE** See Louisiana Extended Care Hospital of Lafayette

**OUR LADY OF LOURDES MED CENTER** See Our Lady of Lourdes Regional Medical Center

**LA**

⊞ **OUR LADY OF LOURDES REGIONAL MEDICAL CENTER (190102)**, 4801 Ambassador Caffery Parkway, Zip 70508–6917; tel. 337/470–2000, (Includes OUR LADY OF LOURDES HEART HOSPITAL, Mailing address: 1105 Kaliste Saloom Road, Lafayette, Louisiana, Zip 70508–5705; tel. 337/521–1000; Michelle B. Crain, R.N., MSN, Administrator and Chief Operating Officer; OUR LADY OF LOURDES WOMEN'S and CHILDREN'S HOSPITAL, Mailing address: 4600 Ambassador Caffery Parkway, Lafayette, Louisiana, Zip 70508–6923, P O Box 88030, Zip 70598–8030, tel. 337/521–9100; W. Bryan Lee, FACHE, Chief Executive Officer), (Nonreporting) **A**1 2 5 10 **F**3 8 9 11 12 13 15 16 18 19 20 22 24 26 28 29 30 31 32 34 35 38 39 40 41 42 43 46 48 49 50 51 53 54 55 56 57 58 59 60 61 64 65 66 68 70 72 74 75 76 77 78 79 81 82 84 85 86 87 88 89 90 93 94 96 107 108 110 111 114 115 117 118 119 126 127 129 130 132 134 135 143 144 146 147 148 149 150 154 **P**6 **S** Franciscan Missionaries of Our Lady Health System, Inc., Baton Rouge, LA
Primary Contact: W. Bryan, Lee, FACHE, Chief Executive Officer
COO: Donna F. Landry, Chief Operating Officer
CIO: Ryan J Latiolais, Director Information Systems
CHR: Jennifer Lynch Trahan, Assistant Vice President Human Resources
CNO: Gilbert Glenn Humbert, R.N., JrChief Nursing Officer
Web address: www.lourdesrmc.com
**Control:** Church operated, Nongovernment, not–for–profit **Service:** General medical and surgical

**Staffed Beds:** 296 **Admissions:** 12638 **Census:** 183 **Outpatient Visits:** 125558 **Births:** 549 **Total Expense ($000):** 276932 **Payroll Expense ($000):** 76488 **Personnel:** 2148

⇑ **PARK PLACE SURGERY CENTER** See Park Place Surgical Hospital

⇑ **PARK PLACE SURGICAL HOSPITAL (190255)**, 4811 Ambassador Caffery Parkway, Zip 70508–6917; tel. 337/237–8119, (Nonreporting) **A**10 21
Primary Contact: Brandon Moore, FACHE, Chief Executive Officer
Web address: www.parkplacesurgery.com/
**Control:** Partnership, Investor–owned (for–profit) **Service:** Surgical

**Staffed Beds:** 10

☐ **UNIVERSITY HOSPITAL & CLINICS (190006)**, 2390 West Congress Street, Zip 70506–4298; tel. 337/261–6000, (Nonreporting) **A**1 2 3 5 10 **S** Lafayette General Health, Lafayette, LA
Primary Contact: Katherine D. Hebert, MS, Chief Executive Officer
CMO: James B Falterman, M.D., JrMedical Director
CIO: Michael Dozier, Senior Vice President, Chief Information Officer
CHR: Sheena Bouquet Ronsonet, Vice President Human Resources
CNO: Laurence Marie Vincent, Chief Nursing Officer
Web address: www.lafayettegeneral.com
**Control:** Other not–for–profit (including NFP Corporation) **Service:** General medical and surgical

**Staffed Beds:** 52

**UNIVERSITY HOSPITAL AND CLINICS** See University Hospital & Clinics

**UNIVERSITY MEDICAL CENTER-PSYCHIATRIC UNIT** See Lafayette Behavioral Health

**VERMILION BEHAVIORAL HEALTH SYSTEMS** See Vermilion Behavioral Health Systems - North Campus

☐ **VERMILION BEHAVIORAL HEALTH SYSTEMS - NORTH CAMPUS (194044)**, 2520 North University Avenue, Zip 70507–5306; tel. 337/234–5614, (Includes VERMILION BEHAVIORAL HEALTH SYSTEMS - SOUTH CAMPUS, Mailing address: 1131 Rue De Belier, Lafayette, Louisiana, Zip 70506–6532; tel. 337/991–0571; Stephanie H. Santori, Chief Executive Officer), (Nonreporting) **A**1 10 **S** Acadia Healthcare Company, Inc., Franklin, TN
Primary Contact: Stephanie H. Santori, Chief Executive Officer
CFO: Margot Mokdessi, Interim Chief Financial Officer
CMO: Bob Winston, M.D., Medical Director
CHR: Claire Rowland, Director Human Resources
CNO: Amy LaHood, R.N., Director of Nursing
Web address: www.acadiavermilion.com
**Control:** Corporation, Investor–owned (for–profit) **Service:** Psychiatric

**Staffed Beds:** 78

**VERMILION BEHAVIORAL HEALTH SYSTEMS SOUTH** See Vermilion Behavioral Health Systems - South Campus

**WOMEN'S AND CHILDREN'S HOSPITAL** See Our Lady of Lourdes Women's and Children's Hospital

⇑ **AVAIL HEALTH LAKE CHARLES HOSPITAL**, 3730 Nelson Road, Zip 70605; tel. 337/656–7700, (Nonreporting) **A**21
Primary Contact: Lance Armentor, Chief Executive Officer
**Control:** Other not–for–profit (including NFP Corporation) **Service:** General medical and surgical

**Staffed Beds:** 10

**CHRISTUS LAKE AREA HOSPITAL** See Christus Ochsner Lake Area Hospital

⊞ **CHRISTUS OCHSNER LAKE AREA HOSPITAL (190201)**, 4200 Nelson Road, Zip 70605–4118; tel. 337/474–6370, (Nonreporting) **A**1 10 **F**8 11 12 13 15 29 30 31 32 34 35 40 41 50 55 56 57 58 59 60 61 64 65 68 70 72 73 76 78 79 81 86 87 89 93 97 107 108 110 111 114 115 118 119 126 132 135 146 147 157 **P**8 **S** CHRISTUS Health, Irving, TX
Primary Contact: Kevin Holland, Chief Executive Officer, CHRISTUS Southwestern Louisiana
CFO: Dawn Johnson-Hatcher, Chief Financial Officer
CIO: Aaron Cook, Director Information Services
CHR: Lisa Friday, Director Human Resources
CNO: Robbin Odom, R.N., MSN, Chief Nursing Officer
Web address: www.Lakeareamc.com
**Control:** Church operated, Nongovernment, not–for–profit **Service:** Obstetrics and gynecology

**Staffed Beds:** 88 **Admissions:** 2592 **Census:** 27 **Outpatient Visits:** 74566 **Births:** 1205 **Total Expense ($000):** 65176 **Payroll Expense ($000):** 20743 **Personnel:** 286

⊞ △ **CHRISTUS OCHSNER ST. PATRICK (190027)**, 524 Dr Michael Debakey Drive, Zip 70601–5799, Mailing Address: P.O. Box 3401, Zip 70602–3401; tel. 337/436–2511, (Nonreporting) **A**1 2 7 10 **F**3 11 15 17 18 20 22 24 26 28 29 30 31 32 34 35 37 38 40 44 45 47 48 49 50 56 57 59 61 64 65 70 74 75 78 79 81 84 85 86 87 89 90 93 96 97 98 100 101 102 103 104 105 107 108 110 115 118 119 120 121 122 123 124 126 130 131 132 134 135 146 147 148 153 154 **P**8 **S** CHRISTUS Health, Irving, TX
Primary Contact: Kevin Holland, Chief Executive Officer, CHRISTUS Southwestern Louisiana
CFO: John Shaughnessy, Regional Chief Financial Officer
CMO: Timothy Haman, M.D., Vice President Medical Affairs
CHR: Shelly Aguillard, Vice President Human Resources
CNO: Ginger Disante, Chief Nursing Officer
Web address: www.christusochsner.org
**Control:** Church operated, Nongovernment, not–for–profit **Service:** General medical and surgical

**Staffed Beds:** 160 **Admissions:** 8111 **Census:** 112 **Outpatient Visits:** 100845 **Births:** 0 **Total Expense ($000):** 148048 **Payroll Expense ($000):** 44798 **Personnel:** 727

**CHRISTUS OCHSNER ST. PATRICK HOSPITAL SOUTHWEST LOUISIANA** See Christus Ochsner St. Patrick

**CORNERSTONE HOSPITAL OF SOUTHWEST LOUISIANA** See Cornerstone Hospitals Southwest Louisiana

☐ **CORNERSTONE HOSPITALS SOUTHWEST LOUISIANA (192013)**, 524 Doctor Michael Debakey Drive, Zip 70601–5725; tel. 337/310–6000, (Nonreporting) **A**1 10 **S** Cornerstone Healthcare Group, Dallas, TX
Primary Contact: Jan Turk, Chief Executive Officer
CFO: Amy Bryant, Chief Financial Officer
CNO: Jeffrey Clark, Chief Nursing Officer
Web address: www.chghospitals.com/sulphur/
**Control:** Partnership, Investor–owned (for–profit) **Service:** Acute long–term care hospital

**Staffed Beds:** 30

✠ **LAKE CHARLES MEMORIAL HOSPITAL (190060)**, 1701 Oak Park Boulevard, Zip 70601–8911; tel. 337/494–3000, (Includes LAKE CHARLES MEMORIAL HOSPITAL FOR WOMEN, Mailing address: 1900 West Gauthier Road, Lake Charles, Louisiana, Zip 70605–7170; tel. 337/480–7000; Nancy Coffey, Interim Administrator and Director Emergency Department), (Nonreporting) **A**1 2 3 5 10 19 **F**3 8 11 13 15 17 18 20 22 24 26 28 29 30 31 34 37 40 43 45 49 50 53 54 56 57 58 60 62 64 66 70 72 73 74 75 76 77 78 79 81 82 84 85 86 87 88 89 90 93 98 99 102 103 107 108 110 111 114 115 119 120 121 123 124 126 127 129 130 131 132 144 146 147 148 149 153 156 157 **P**1 6 7
Primary Contact: Larry M. Graham, FACHE, President and Chief Executive Officer
COO: Anna Leah Cazes, Interim Chief Nursing Officer, Senior Vice President, Chief Operating Officer
CFO: Charles P Whitson, CPA, Senior Vice President Finance
CMO: Manley Jordan, M.D., Chief Medical Officer
CIO: Belinda Sommers, Chief Information Officer
CHR: Ginger Consigney, Vice President Human Resources
CNO: Anna Leah Cazes, Interim Chief Nursing Officer, Senior Vice President and Chief Operating Officer
Web address: www.lcmh.com
**Control:** Other not–for–profit (including NFP Corporation) **Service:** General medical and surgical

**Staffed Beds:** 355 **Admissions:** 13890 **Census:** 202 **Outpatient Visits:** 331943 **Births:** 2082 **Total Expense ($000):** 317292 **Payroll Expense ($000):** 104849 **Personnel:** 2481

**OCEANS BEHAVIORAL HOSPITAL OF LAKE CHARLES (194090)**, 4250 5th Avenue, Zip 70607–3900; tel. 337/474–7581, (Nonreporting) **A**10 **S** Oceans Healthcare, Plano, TX
Primary Contact: Emily McDaniel, Administrator
Web address: www.obhlc.info/
**Control:** Corporation, Investor–owned (for–profit) **Service:** Psychiatric

**Staffed Beds:** 40

### LAKE PROVIDENCE—East Carroll Parish

**EAST CARROLL PARISH HOSPITAL (190208)**, 336 North Hood Street, Zip 71254–2140; tel. 318/559–4023, (Nonreporting) **A**10
Primary Contact: LaDonna Englerth, Administrator and Chief Executive Officer
**Control:** Hospital district or authority, Government, Nonfederal **Service:** General medical and surgical

**Staffed Beds:** 11

### LEESVILLE—Vernon Parish

**BYRD MEMORIAL HOSPITAL** See Byrd Regional Hospital

☐ **BYRD REGIONAL HOSPITAL (190164)**, 1020 West Fertitta Boulevard, Zip 71446–4645; tel. 337/239–9041, (Nonreporting) **A**1 10 **S** Allegiance Health Management, Shreveport, LA
Primary Contact: Kevin Quinn, Chief Executive Officer
CFO: Jared Graves, Chief Financial Officer
CMO: Charles Caldwell, M.D., Chief of Staff
CHR: Karolyne Christian, Director Human Resources
Web address: www.byrdregional.com/
**Control:** Corporation, Investor–owned (for–profit) **Service:** General medical and surgical

**Staffed Beds:** 60

☐ **CLEARSKY REHABILITATION HOSPITAL OF LEESVILLE (193086)**, 900 South 6th Street, Zip 71446–4723; tel. 337/392–8118, (Nonreporting) **A**1 10
Primary Contact: Jack M. Causey, Chief Executive Officer
CMO: Gregory D Lord, M.D., Chief Medical Officer
CHR: Melanie Packer, Administrative Assistant, Director of Human Resources
Web address: www.https://www.clearskyhealth.com/Leesville/
**Control:** Corporation, Investor–owned (for–profit) **Service:** Rehabilitation

**Staffed Beds:** 16

☐ **CLEARSKY REHABILITATION HOSPITAL OF ROSEPINE (193050)**, 8088 Hawks Road, Zip 71446–6649; tel. 337/462–8280, (Nonreporting) **A**1 10 **F**3 29 34 90
Primary Contact: Angela Williams, Chief Executive Officer
Web address: www.https://www.clearskyhealth.com/Rosepine/
**Control:** Corporation, Investor–owned (for–profit) **Service:** Rehabilitation

**Staffed Beds:** 36 **Admissions:** 469 **Census:** 16 **Outpatient Visits:** 0 **Births:** 0 **Total Expense ($000):** 4575 **Payroll Expense ($000):** 2201 **Personnel:** 54

**LEESVILLE REHABILITATION HOSPITAL** See Clearsky Rehabilitation Hospital of Leesville

**TRI PARISH REHABILITATION HOSPITAL** See Clearsky Rehabilitation Hospital of Rosepine

### LULING—St. Charles Parish

**SPECIALTY REHABILITATION HOSPITAL** See Premier Rehabilitation

**ST CHARLES HOSPITAL** See St. Charles Parish Hospital

✠ **ST. CHARLES PARISH HOSPITAL (190079)**, 1057 Paul Maillard Road, Zip 70070–4349, Mailing Address: P.O. Box 87, Zip 70070–0087; tel. 985/785–6242, (Nonreporting) **A**1 10 **F**3 7 11 15 18 20 22 28 29 30 31 34 40 45 50 51 59 60 64 68 70 75 78 79 81 82 85 86 87 93 96 97 98 100 102 107 108 110 111 115 119 130 131 135 146 148 154 157 **P**6 **S** Ochsner Health, New Orleans, LA
Primary Contact: Terrell Neal, R.N., Chief Executive Officer
CFO: Peter Torsch, Chief Financial Officer
CMO: Vadakkipalayam N. Devarajan, Chief Medical Staff
CIO: Angela Boudreaux, Director Information Technology
CHR: Karen Ann Judlin, Director Human Resources
Web address: www.https://www.ochsner.org/locations/st-charles-parish-hospital/
**Control:** Hospital district or authority, Government, Nonfederal **Service:** General medical and surgical

**Staffed Beds:** 59 **Admissions:** 1677 **Census:** 25 **Outpatient Visits:** 37281 **Births:** 0 **Total Expense ($000):** 48447 **Payroll Expense ($000):** 9439 **Personnel:** 117

### LUTCHER—St. James Parish

**BEACON BEHAVIORAL HOSPITAL (194102)**, 2471 Louisiana Avenue, Zip 70071–5413; tel. 225/258–6103, (Nonreporting)
Primary Contact: Denise White, Administrator
Web address: www.beaconbh.com
**Control:** Other not–for–profit (including NFP Corporation) **Service:** Psychiatric

**Staffed Beds:** 19

✠ **ST. JAMES PARISH HOSPITAL (191305)**, 1645 Lutcher Avenue, Zip 70071–5150; tel. 225/869–5512, (Nonreporting) **A**1 10 18 **F**3 15 29 34 35 40 45 46 50 51 57 59 64 75 77 80 81 85 93 107 108 110 111 114 119 128 129 130 132 133 144 149 154
Primary Contact: MaryEllen Pratt, FACHE, Chief Executive Officer
CFO: Tracy L George, Chief Financial Officer
CIO: Jeremy Martin, Chief Support Services Officer
CHR: Lisa Faucheux, Director Human Resources
CNO: Rhonda Zeringue, R.N., Chief Nursing Officer
Web address: www.sjph.org
**Control:** Hospital district or authority, Government, Nonfederal **Service:** General medical and surgical

**Staffed Beds:** 25 **Admissions:** 492 **Census:** 8 **Outpatient Visits:** 30483 **Births:** 1 **Total Expense ($000):** 27263 **Payroll Expense ($000):** 12006 **Personnel:** 232

### MAMOU—Evangeline Parish

✠ **SAVOY MEDICAL CENTER (190025)**, 801 Poinciana Avenue, Zip 70554–2298; tel. 337/468–5261, (Nonreporting) **A**1 10 **F**5 15 70 78 81 90 93 98 104 107 119 127 146 152 154 **S** CHRISTUS Health, Irving, TX
Primary Contact: Eugene H. Burge Jr, Chief Executive Officer
COO: Gerald Fuselier, Chief Operating Officer
CMO: Greg Savoy, M.D., Chief Medical Officer
CIO: Daniel Lahaye, Manager
CHR: Annette Thibodeaux, Director Human Resources
Web address: www.savoymedical.com/
**Control:** City, Government, Nonfederal **Service:** General medical and surgical

**Staffed Beds:** 60 **Admissions:** 1617 **Census:** 31 **Outpatient Visits:** 21165 **Births:** 0 **Total Expense ($000):** 23132 **Payroll Expense ($000):** 8225 **Personnel:** 272

---

**Hospital, Medicare Provider Number, Address, Telephone, Approval, Facility, and Physician Codes, Health Care System**

★ American Hospital Association (AHA) membership
☐ The Joint Commission accreditation
○ Healthcare Facilities Accreditation Program
◇ DNV Healthcare Inc. accreditation
⇑ Center for Improvement in Healthcare Quality Accreditation
△ Commission on Accreditation of Rehabilitation Facilities (CARF) accreditation

**LA**

## MANDEVILLE—St. Tammany Parish

☐ **NORTHLAKE BEHAVIORAL HEALTH SYSTEM (194007)**, 23515 Highway 190, Zip 70448–7334; tel. 985/626–6300, (Nonreporting) **A**1 3 10
Primary Contact: Wayne Thompson, Interim Chief Executive Officer and Chief Financial Officer
CFO: Wayne Thompson, Interim Chief Executive Officer and Chief Financial Officer
CMO: Hyon Su Kim, M.D., Medical Director
CIO: Archie Carriere, Information Technology Technician
CHR: Nicole Messa-Gill, Manager Human Resources
CNO: Jo Nell King, Director of Nursing
Web address: www.https://northlakebh.org/
**Control**: State, Government, Nonfederal **Service**: Psychiatric

| Staffed Beds: 122 |
|---|

**NORTHLAKE BEHAVIORAL HOSPITAL SYSTEM** See Northlake Behavioral Health System

## MANSFIELD—De Soto Parish

**DE SOTO GENERAL HOSPITAL** See De Soto Regional Health System

**DE SOTO REGIONAL HEALTH SYSTEM (190118)**, 207 Jefferson Street, Zip 71052–2603, Mailing Address: P.O. Box 1636, Zip 71052–1636; tel. 318/872–4610, (Nonreporting) **A**5 10 20 **S** Willis-Knighton Health System, Shreveport, LA
Primary Contact: Todd Eppler, FACHE, Chief Executive Officer
CFO: Christopher Davis, Vice President, Finance
CMO: Denis Kamberov, M.D., Chief of Staff
CNO: Beth Westerchil, R.N., Chief Nurse Executive
Web address: www.desotoregional.com
**Control**: Other not–for–profit (including NFP Corporation) **Service**: General medical and surgical

| Staffed Beds: 10 |
|---|

## MANY—Sabine Parish

**SABINE MEDICAL CENTER (190218)**, 240 Highland Drive, Zip 71449–3718; tel. 318/256–5691, (Nonreporting) **A**10 20 **S** Allegiance Health Management, Shreveport, LA
Primary Contact: Dale Anderson, Chief Executive Officer
COO: Doug Plummer, Chief Operating Officer
CFO: Frances F Hopkins, Chief Financial Officer
CNO: Karen Ford, Chief Nursing Officer
Web address: www.sabinemedicalcenter.net
**Control**: Individual, Investor–owned (for–profit) **Service**: General medical and surgical

| Staffed Beds: 24 |
|---|

## MARKSVILLE—Avoyelles Parish

**AVOYELLES HOSPITAL (190099)**, 4231 Highway 1192, Zip 71351–4711, Mailing Address: P.O. Box 249, Zip 71351–0249; tel. 318/253–8611, (Includes FREEDOM BEHAVIORAL MARKSVILLE, Mailing address: 426 North Washington Street, Marksville, Louisiana, Zip 71351–2426, P.O. Box 249, Zip 71351–0249, tel. 318/409–0635; Timothey Curry, Chief Executive Officer), (Nonreporting) **A**10 **F**3 15 29 30 34 40 43 45 54 56 57 64 65 70 81 82 85 98 103 107 110 114 119 127 128 130 133 146 149 154
Primary Contact: Timothey Curry, Chief Executive Officer
CFO: Christina White, Financial Manager
CMO: James L. Bordelon, M.D., JrChief of Staff
CIO: Blaine Brouillette, Director Information Technology
CHR: Allison Ferguson, Director Human Resources
CNO: Cindy K. Juneau, Chief Nursing Officer
Web address: www.avoyelleshospital.com
**Control**: Corporation, Investor–owned (for–profit) **Service**: General medical and surgical

| Staffed Beds: 32 Admissions: 1818 Census: 9 Outpatient Visits: 39117 Births: 0 Total Expense ($000): 19432 Payroll Expense ($000): 9763 Personnel: 242 |
|---|

**COMPASS BEHAVIORAL CENTER OF MARKSVILLE**, 137 Dr. Childress Drive, Zip 71351; tel. 318/256–3332, (Data for 98 days) (Nonreporting) **F**98 100 103 104 105 130 153 154 **S** Compass Health, Crowley, LA
Primary Contact: Jaime Lucas, Administrator
Web address: www.https://www.compasshealthcare.com/locations/
**Control**: Corporation, Investor–owned (for–profit) **Service**: Psychiatric

| Staffed Beds: 16 Admissions: 45 Census: 9 Outpatient Visits: 0 Births: 0 |
|---|

**HUMANA HOSPITAL-MARKSVILLE** See Avoyelles Hospital

## MARRERO—Jefferson Parish

**BRIDGEPOINT CONTINUING CARE HOSPITAL (192007)**, 1101 Medical Center Boulevard, 7th Floor, Zip 70072–3147; tel. 504/349–6836, (Nonreporting) **A**10
Primary Contact: Keith Carruth, Market Executive Officer
Web address: www.https://www.bridgepointhealthcare.com/
**Control**: Corporation, Investor–owned (for–profit) **Service**: Acute long–term care hospital

| Staffed Beds: 56 |
|---|

**LOUISIANA CONTINUING CARE HOSPITAL** See Bridgepoint Continuing Care Hospital

☐ △ **WEST JEFFERSON MEDICAL CENTER (190039)**, 1101 Medical Center Boulevard, Zip 70072–3191; tel. 504/347–5511, (Nonreporting) **A**1 3 5 7 10 **F**3 7 8 11 12 13 15 17 18 20 22 24 26 28 29 30 31 34 35 37 38 39 40 41 43 45 46 47 48 49 50 51 53 56 57 59 61 64 65 68 70 72 74 75 76 78 79 81 82 84 85 86 87 90 91 93 96 97 102 107 108 109 110 111 112 114 115 117 118 119 120 121 124 126 127 129 130 132 135 146 147 148 149 154 157 **P**3 6 **S** LCMC Health, New Orleans, LA
Primary Contact: Rob Calhoun, President and Chief Executive Offricer
COO: Eli Smith, Chief Operating Officer
CFO: Jay M Pennisson, Chief Financial Officer
CMO: Robert Chugden, M.D., Chief Medical Officer
CHR: Floyd Riedlinger, Director Human Resources
CNO: Monica Bologna, R.N., Chief Nursing Officer
Web address: www.wjmc.org
**Control**: Other not–for–profit (including NFP Corporation) **Service**: General medical and surgical

| Staffed Beds: 252 Admissions: 9339 Census: 142 Outpatient Visits: 350146 Births: 1084 Total Expense ($000): 293420 Payroll Expense ($000): 96326 Personnel: 1363 |
|---|

## METAIRIE—Jefferson Parish

**DOCTORS HOSP OF JEFFERSON** See Doctors Hospital of Jefferson

☐ △ **EAST JEFFERSON GENERAL HOSPITAL (190146)**, 4200 Houma Boulevard, Zip 70006–2996; tel. 504/503–4000, (Includes DOCTORS HOSPITAL OF JEFFERSON, Mailing address: 4320 Houma Boulevard, Metairie, Louisiana, Zip 70006–2973; tel. 504/849–4000), (Nonreporting) **A**1 2 3 5 7 10 **F**3 7 8 11 13 14 15 17 18 20 22 24 26 28 29 30 31 34 35 36 37 40 44 45 46 47 48 49 50 51 53 54 55 56 57 58 59 64 65 70 72 73 74 75 76 77 78 79 81 82 84 85 86 87 90 91 92 93 96 97 98 102 103 107 108 110 111 114 115 117 118 119 120 121 123 124 126 128 129 130 131 132 135 141 142 145 146 147 148 149 156 **P**6 7
Primary Contact: Gerald L. Parton, FACHE, President and Chief Executive Officer
COO: Paolo Zambito, R.N., Chief Operating Officer
CFO: Robert Riley, Interim Chief Financial Officer
CMO: Raymond P DeCorte, M.D., Chief Medical Officer
CHR: Frank Martinez, Senior Vice President Human Resources
CNO: Ruby Brewer RNSenior Vice President, Chief Nursing and Quality Officer
Web address: www.ejgh.org
**Control**: Hospital district or authority, Government, Nonfederal **Service**: General medical and surgical

| Staffed Beds: 412 Admissions: 12709 Census: 175 Outpatient Visits: 204410 Births: 922 Total Expense ($000): 342495 Payroll Expense ($000): 99066 Personnel: 1846 |
|---|

**LAKESIDE HOSPITAL** See Tulane-Lakeside Hospital

⇑ **OMEGA HOSPITAL (190302)**, 2525 Severn Avenue, Zip 70002–5932; tel. 504/832–4200, (Nonreporting) **A**10 21 **F**107 108 119
Primary Contact: Eric George, M.D., Chief Executive Officer
Web address: www.omegahospital.com
**Control**: Partnership, Investor–owned (for–profit) **Service**: General medical and surgical

| Staffed Beds: 16 Admissions: 102 Census: 1 Outpatient Visits: 1682 Births: 0 |
|---|

⇑ **OMEGA INST OF HEALTH & HOSP** See Omega Hospital

*Many Facility Codes have changed. Please refer to the AHA Guide Code Chart.*

## MINDEN—Webster Parish

☐ **MINDEN MEDICAL CENTER (190144)**, 1 Medical Plaza Place,
Zip 71055–3330, Mailing Address: P.O. Box 5003, Zip 71058–5003;
tel. 318/377–2321, (Nonreporting) **A1** 10 19 **S** Allegiance Health Management,
Shreveport, LA
Primary Contact: James R. Williams, Chief Executive Officer
CMO: G Max Stell, M.D., Medical Director
CIO: Mace Morgan, Director Information Systems
CHR: Mary Winget, Director Human Resources
CNO: Donna Carter, MSN, R.N., Chief Nursing Officer
Web address: www.mindenmedicalcenter.com
**Control:** Corporation, Investor–owned (for–profit) **Service:** General medical and
surgical

**Staffed Beds:** 161

## MONROE—Ouachita Parish

**ALLEGIANCE BEHAVIORAL HEALTH CENTERS** See Allegiance Behavioral Health
Center

**BASTROP REHABILITATION HOSPITAL** See Riverbend Rehabilitation Hospital

⇑ **MONROE SURGICAL HOSPITAL (190245)**, 2408 Broadmoor Boulevard,
Zip 71201–2963; tel. 318/410–0002, (Nonreporting) **A10** 21
Primary Contact: Robyn Hemphill, Chief Executive Officer and Chief Nursing Officer
CNO: Sharon R. Tackett, R.N., Chief Nursing Officer
Web address: www.monroesurgical.com
**Control:** Corporation, Investor–owned (for–profit) **Service:** Surgical

**Staffed Beds:** 10

☐ **OCHSNER LSU HEALTH SHREVEPORT - MONROE MEDICAL CENTER
(190011)**, 4864 Jackson Street, Zip 71202–6497, Mailing Address: P.O. Box
1881, Zip 71210–8005; tel. 318/330–7000, (Nonreporting) **A1** 3 5 10 **S**
University Health System, Shreveport, LA
Primary Contact: Charles D. Daigle, Chief Executive Officer
COO: Jonathan Phillips, Chief Operating Officer
CFO: Dorothy Whittington, Chief Financial Officer
CMO: Michael O'Neal, M.D., Chief Medical Officer
CIO: Todd Walters, Director of UHC Information Technology Services
CHR: Rob Hartmann, Assistant Director Human Resources Management
CNO: Traci S. Jordan, MS, R.N., Chief Nursing Officer
Web address: www.uhsystem.com
**Control:** State, Government, Nonfederal **Service:** General medical and surgical

**Staffed Beds:** 123

**RIVERBEND REHABILITATION HOSPITAL (193058)**, 4310 South Grand Street,
Zip 71202–6322; tel. 318/654–8300, (Nonreporting) **A10 F**29 34 35 59 90 91
96 100 104 105 127 130 143 147 148 153 154 **P**5
Primary Contact: Patrick King, Administrator
CMO: Jeffery Combetta, M.D., Medical Director
CHR: Rhonda Church, Director Human Resources
Web address: www.ldh.la.gov/index.cfm/directory/detail/1772/catid/169
**Control:** Partnership, Investor–owned (for–profit) **Service:** Rehabilitation

**Staffed Beds:** 12 **Admissions:** 216 **Census:** 7 **Outpatient Visits:** 0 **Births:** 0
**Total Expense ($000):** 2920 **Payroll Expense ($000):** 1440 **Personnel:** 33

**SPECIALTY EXTENDED CARE HOSPITAL OF MONROE** See Specialty Hospital

**SPECIALTY HOSPITAL (192016)**, 309 Jackson Street, 7th Floor,
Zip 71201–7407, Mailing Address: P.O. Box 1532, Zip 71210–1532;
tel. 318/966–7045, (Nonreporting) **A10 S** LHC Group, Lafayette, LA
Primary Contact: Cleta Munholland, Administrator
COO: Pamela Chappell, R.N., Assistant Administrator
CNO: Jerry Rogers, R.N., Director Nurses and Infection Control
Web address: www.lhcgroup.com
**Control:** Church operated, Nongovernment, not–for–profit **Service:** Acute long–
term care hospital

**Staffed Beds:** 32

---

⊞ **ST. FRANCIS MEDICAL CENTER (190125)**, 309 Jackson Street,
Zip 71201–7407, Mailing Address: P.O. Box 1901, Zip 71210–1901;
tel. 318/966–4000, (Nonreporting) **A1** 3 10 **F**3 12 13 15 17 18 19 20 21 22 23
24 25 26 27 28 29 30 31 32 34 35 37 39 40 44 45 46 49 50 54 55 56 57 59
64 65 68 69 70 71 72 74 75 76 77 78 79 81 84 85 87 88 90 92 93 96 97 107
108 110 111 114 115 118 119 124 126 128 129 130 131 132 135 146 147
148 154 156 157 **P**8 **S** Franciscan Missionaries of Our Lady Health System, Inc.,
Baton Rouge, LA
Primary Contact: Kristin Wolkart, R.N., President and Chief Executive Officer
CFO: Jeremy Rogers, Chief Financial Officer
CMO: Thomas Gullatt, M.D., Chief Medical Officer
CNO: Kayla Johnson, R.N., Vice President Patient Care Services and Chief Nursing
Officer
Web address: www.stfran.com
**Control:** Church operated, Nongovernment, not–for–profit **Service:** General
medical and surgical

**Staffed Beds:** 384 **Admissions:** 14310 **Census:** 217 **Outpatient
Visits:** 259350 **Births:** 1786 **Total Expense ($000):** 295265 **Payroll
Expense ($000):** 106661 **Personnel:** 1772

**UNIVERSITY HEALTH CONWAY** See Ochsner Lsu Health Shreveport - Monroe
Medical Center

## MORGAN CITY—St. Mary Parish

⊞ **OCHSNER ST. MARY (190014)**, 1125 Marguerite Street, Zip 70380–1855,
Mailing Address: P.O. Box 2308, Zip 70381–2308; tel. 985/384–2200,
(Nonreporting) **A1** 10 20 **S** Ochsner Health, New Orleans, LA
Primary Contact: Anthony Young, Chief Executive Officer
COO: Don Knight, Assistant Administrator and Risk Manager
CFO: Debbie Kyzar, Interim Chief Financial Officer
CMO: Eric Melancon, Chief of Staff
CIO: Rene Bilello, Manager Information System
CHR: Timothy Hebert, Director Human Resources
CNO: Jennifer Wise, Chief Nursing Officer
Web address: www.techeregional.com
**Control:** Corporation, Investor–owned (for–profit) **Service:** General medical and
surgical

**Staffed Beds:** 164

**TECHE REGIONAL MEDICAL CENTER** See Ochsner St. Mary

## NAPOLEONVILLE—Assumption Parish

★ **ASSUMPTION COMMUNITY HOSPITAL (191303)**, 135 Highway 402,
Zip 70390–2217; tel. 985/369–3600, (Nonreporting) **A10** 18 **S** Franciscan
Missionaries of Our Lady Health System, Inc., Baton Rouge, LA
Primary Contact: Christina P. Hockaday, FACHE, Chief Executive Officer
CHR: Letonia Pierre, Coordinator Human Resources
CNO: Donna Mullings, Director of Nursing
Web address: www.https://ololrmc.com
**Control:** Other not–for–profit (including NFP Corporation) **Service:** General
medical and surgical

**Staffed Beds:** 6

**OUR LADY OF THE LAKE** See Assumption Community Hospital

## NATCHITOCHES—Natchitoches Parish

**GENESIS SPECIALTY HOSPITAL** See Louisiana Extended Care Hospital of
Natchitoches

★ **LOUISIANA EXTENDED CARE HOSPITAL OF NATCHITOCHES (192035)**,
501 Keyser Avenue, Zip 71457–6018; tel. 318/354–2044, (Nonreporting) **A10**
**F**1 3 28 29 30 34 50 57 59 68 74 75 85 86 87 91 97 130 148 **S** LHC Group,
Lafayette, LA
Primary Contact: John Rivoire, R.N., MSN, Administrator
Web address: www.https://lhcgroup.com/locations/louisiana-extended-care-
hospital-of-natchitoches/
**Control:** Partnership, Investor–owned (for–profit) **Service:** Acute long–term care
hospital

**Staffed Beds:** 21 **Admissions:** 252 **Census:** 15 **Outpatient Visits:** 0
**Births:** 0 **Personnel:** 46

**NATCHITOCHES PARISH HOSPITAL** See Natchitoches Regional Medical Center

---

**Hospital, Medicare Provider Number, Address, Telephone, Approval, Facility, and Physician Codes, Health Care System**

★ American Hospital Association (AHA) membership  ○ Healthcare Facilities Accreditation Program  ⇑ Center for Improvement in Healthcare Quality Accreditation
☐ The Joint Commission accreditation  ◇ DNV Healthcare Inc. accreditation  △ Commission on Accreditation of Rehabilitation Facilities (CARF) accreditation

**LA**

✠ **NATCHITOCHES REGIONAL MEDICAL CENTER (190007)**, 501 Keyser Avenue, Zip 71457–6036, Mailing Address: P.O. Box 2009, Zip 71457–2009; tel. 318/214–4200, (Nonreporting) **A**1 10 20 **F**3 5 7 8 10 11 13 15 18 28 29 30 31 32 34 35 36 37 38 39 40 41 42 43 45 46 47 50 51 53 54 56 57 58 59 60 61 65 66 69 70 71 74 75 76 77 78 79 81 82 85 86 87 93 94 97 98 100 101 102 103 104 105 106 107 108 109 110 111 112 114 119 120 121 124 125 126 127 129 130 131 132 133 135 143 144 145 146 147 148 152 153 154 156 **S** CHRISTUS Health, Irving, TX
Primary Contact: D. Kirk. Soileau, FACHE, Chief Executive Officer
CFO: Brad McCormick, Chief Financial Officer
CMO: Phyllis Mason, M.D., Chief Medical Officer
CHR: Ernie Scott, Director Human Resources
CNO: Dawna DeBlieux, Vice President Patient Care Services and Chief Nurse Executive
Web address: www.nrmchospital.org
**Control**: Hospital district or authority, Government, Nonfederal **Service**: General medical and surgical

**Staffed Beds:** 91 **Admissions:** 2330 **Census:** 28 **Outpatient Visits:** 98084 **Births:** 495 **Total Expense ($000):** 70143 **Payroll Expense ($000):** 31052 **Personnel:** 741

### NEW IBERIA—Iberia Parish

**IBERIA GENERAL HOSP & MED CTR** See Iberia Medical Center

☐ **IBERIA MEDICAL CENTER (190054)**, 2315 East Main Street, Zip 70560–4031, Mailing Address: P.O. Box 13338, Zip 70562–3338; tel. 337/364–0441, (Nonreporting) **A**1 10 **F**3 11 13 15 18 20 22 28 29 30 31 34 39 40 45 46 47 48 49 50 53 57 64 70 72 74 75 76 78 79 81 85 89 90 93 97 98 103 107 108 110 111 115 127 130 135 146 149 **P**6 **S** HealthTech Management Services, Brentwood, TN
Primary Contact: Dionne Viator, CPA, FACHE, President and Chief Executive Officer
COO: Shane P Myers, Chief Operating Officer
CFO: Amy Langlinias, Chief Financial Officer
CMO: Shawn Baquet, Chief of Staff
CIO: Vance Robinson, Chief Information Officer
CHR: Lori Spann, Director Human Resources
CNO: Sandy Morein, Chief Nursing Officer
Web address: www.iberiamedicalcenter.com
**Control**: Hospital district or authority, Government, Nonfederal **Service**: General medical and surgical

**Staffed Beds:** 137 **Admissions:** 4956 **Census:** 61 **Outpatient Visits:** 117458 **Births:** 343 **Total Expense ($000):** 101587 **Payroll Expense ($000):** 37670 **Personnel:** 682

☐ **IBERIA REHABILITATION HOSPITAL (193096)**, 532 Jefferson Terrace, Zip 70560–4948; tel. 337/364–6923, (Nonreporting) **A**1 10
Primary Contact: Athan J. Olivier III, R.N., MSN, FACHE, Administrator and Chief Executive Officer
Web address: www.iberiarehab.net/
**Control**: Partnership, Investor–owned (for–profit) **Service**: Rehabilitation

**Staffed Beds:** 24

### NEW ORLEANS—Orleans Parish

**BEACON BEHAVIORAL HOSPITAL - NEW ORLEANS (194084)**, 14500 Hayne Boulevard, Suite 200, Zip 70128–1751; tel. 504/210–0460, (Nonreporting) **A**10
Primary Contact: Sean Wendell, CPA, Chief Executive Officer
Web address: www.https://www.beaconbh.com/
**Control**: Corporation, Investor–owned (for–profit) **Service**: Psychiatric

**Staffed Beds:** 24

**BLIANT SPECIALTY HOSPITAL (192030)**, 14500 Hayne Boulevard, Suite 100, Zip 70128–1751; tel. 504/210–3000, (Nonreporting) **A**10
Primary Contact: Juanita Bates. Bonds, M.D., President and Chief Executive Officer
CMO: Ricardo Febry, M.D., Medical Director
CHR: Nicole Wilson, Manager Human Resources
CNO: Collette Jackson, R.N., Director of Clinical Services
Web address: www.bliantspecialtyhospital.com
**Control**: Corporation, Investor–owned (for–profit) **Service**: Acute long–term care hospital

**Staffed Beds:** 73

☐ △ **CHILDREN'S HOSPITAL (193300)**, 200 Henry Clay Avenue, Zip 70118–5720; tel. 504/899–9511, (Includes CHILDREN'S HOSPITAL BEHAVIORAL HEALTH CENTER, Mailing address: 210 State Street, Building 10, New Orleans, Louisiana, Zip 70118–5735; tel. 504/869–7200; John R. Nickens IV, Chief Executive Officer), (Nonreporting) **A**1 2 3 5 7 10 **F**3 7 11 17 19 21 23 25 27 28 29 30 31 32 34 35 38 39 40 41 44 45 46 48 49 50 51 54 55 58 59 60 61 63 64 65 68 71 72 74 75 77 78 79 81 83 84 88 89 90 92 93 94 98 99 100 102 107 111 115 116 117 126 129 130 131 132 136 138 139 146 148 149 150 154 155 157 **S** LCMC Health, New Orleans, LA
Primary Contact: John R. Nickens IV, President and Chief Executive Officer
COO: Jonathan Brouk, Chief Operating Officer
CFO: Courtney Garrett, CPA, Senior Vice President, Chief Financial Officer
CMO: George Bisset, M.D., IIIChief Medical Officer
CIO: Tanya Townsend, Senior Vice President, Chief Information Officer (part of LCMC)
CHR: Wendy L Willis, Vice President Human Resources
CNO: Diane Michel, Senior Vice President, Chief Nursing Officer
Web address: www.chnola.org
**Control**: Other not–for–profit (including NFP Corporation) **Service**: General medical and surgical

**Staffed Beds:** 170 **Admissions:** 7795 **Census:** 139 **Outpatient Visits:** 308636 **Births:** 0 **Total Expense ($000):** 318100 **Payroll Expense ($000):** 123700 **Personnel:** 2163

**COBALT REHABILITATION HOSPITAL OF NEW ORLEANS (193098)**, 3801 Bienville Street, Zip 70119; tel. 504/930–3500, (Nonreporting) **A**10 22
Primary Contact: Scott Tranchina, R.N., MSN, Administrator
**Control**: Partnership, Investor–owned (for–profit) **Service**: Rehabilitation

**Staffed Beds:** 60

☐ **COMMUNITY CARE HOSPITAL (194056)**, 1421 General Taylor Street, Zip 70115–3717; tel. 504/899–2500, (Nonreporting) **A**1 10
Primary Contact: Paul B. Kavanaugh, President and Chief Executive Officer
CNO: Christine Richmond, Director of Nursing
Web address: www.communitycarehospital.com
**Control**: State, Government, Nonfederal **Service**: Psychiatric

**Staffed Beds:** 36

**CURAHEALTH NEW ORLEANS (192009)**, 3801 Bienville Street, 1st Floor, Zip 70119–5251; tel. 504/930–3500, (Includes CURAHEALTH HOSPITAL OF SLIDELL, Mailing address: 1444 Lindberg Drive, Suite 100, Suite 100, Slidell, Louisiana, Zip 70458–8056; tel. 985/607–6300; Kristy Caleyo, MSN, R.N., Market Chief Executive Officer), (Nonreporting) **A**10 **S** Curahealth Hospitals, Garland, TX
Primary Contact: Kristy Caleyo, MSN, R.N., Chief Executive Officer
CFO: Laurie Champagne, Controller
Web address: www.curahealth.com
**Control**: Corporation, Investor–owned (for–profit) **Service**: Acute long–term care hospital

**Staffed Beds:** 80

### NEW ORLEANS—Jefferson Parish

**EXTENDED CARE HOSPITAL** See Ochsner Extended Care Hospital

### NEW ORLEANS—Orleans Parish

**INTERIM LSU PUBLIC HOSPITAL** See University Medical Center

**KINDRED HOSPITAL-NEW ORLEANS** See Curahealth New Orleans

**MEMORIAL MEDICAL CENTER** See Ochsner Baptist Medical Center

☐ **NEW ORLEANS EAST HOSPITAL (190313)**, 5620 Read Boulevard, Zip 70127–3106, Mailing Address: 5620 Read Blvd, Zip 70127–3106; tel. 504/592–6600, (Nonreporting) **A**1 **F**3 11 15 18 20 26 29 30 34 35 38 40 44 45 50 57 58 59 61 63 64 65 68 70 71 74 75 77 79 81 82 85 86 87 91 93 97 107 108 110 111 115 118 119 129 130 131 132 133 134 146 147 148 149 154 156 157 **P**8 **S** LCMC Health, New Orleans, LA
Primary Contact: Takeisha C. Davis, M.D., M.P.H., President and Chief Executive Officer
COO: Dante Green, Assistant Vice President Operations
CFO: Danielle S. Willis, CPA, Interim Chief Financial Officer, Manager Finance
CHR: Brion Stanford, Director Human Resources
CNO: Martha Smith, R.N., Chief Nursing Officer
Web address: www.noehospital.org
**Control**: Hospital district or authority, Government, Nonfederal **Service**: General medical and surgical

**Staffed Beds:** 34 **Admissions:** 1280 **Census:** 13 **Outpatient Visits:** 99333 **Births:** 0 **Total Expense ($000):** 60934 **Payroll Expense ($000):** 21789 **Personnel:** 246

*Many Facility Codes have changed. Please refer to the AHA Guide Code Chart.* © 2021 AHA Guide

**NEW ORLEANS—Jefferson Parish**

**OCHSNER CLINIC FOUNDATION** See Ochsner Medical Center

**OCHSNER EXTENDED CARE HOSPITAL (192015)**, 2614 Jefferson Highway, 2nd Floor, Zip 70121–3828; tel. 504/314–4242, (Nonreporting) **A**10 **S** LHC Group, Lafayette, LA
Primary Contact: Len McDade, Chief Executive Officer
CMO: Jeremiah Newsom, M.D., Medical Director
CNO: Erika Plaisance, Chief Nursing Officer
Web address: www.lhcgroup.com/
**Control:** Corporation, Investor–owned (for–profit) **Service:** Acute long–term care hospital

Staffed Beds: 32

☒ **OCHSNER MEDICAL CENTER (190036)**, 1514 Jefferson Highway, Zip 70121–2429; tel. 504/842–3000, (Includes OCHSNER BAPTIST MEDICAL CENTER, Mailing address: 2700 Napoleon Avenue, New Orleans, Louisiana, Zip 70115–6914; tel. 504/899–9311; Beth Walker, Chief Executive Officer; OCHSNER HOSPITAL FOR ORTHOPEDICS & SPORTS MEDICINE, Mailing address: 1221 South Clearview Parkway, New Orleans, Louisiana, Zip 70121–1011; tel. 504/842–6684; Robert K. Wolterman, Chief Executive Officer; OCHSNER MEDICAL CENTER - WEST BANK, Mailing address: 2500 Belle Chasse Highway, Gretna, Louisiana, Zip 70056–7127; tel. 504/392–3131; Mary Deynoodt, Interim Chief Executive Officer and Chief Operating Officer; OCHSNER MEDICAL CENTER FOR CHILDREN, Mailing address: 1514 Jefferson Highway, New Orleans, Louisiana, Zip 70121–2429; tel. 504/842-3000) (Total facility includes 30 beds in nursing home–type unit) **A**1 2 3 5 8 10 **F**3 4 5 6 7 8 9 11 12 13 14 15 17 18 19 20 21 22 23 24 25 26 27 28 29 30 31 32 34 35 36 37 38 40 41 42 43 44 45 46 47 48 49 50 51 53 54 55 56 57 58 59 60 61 63 64 65 68 70 71 72 73 74 75 76 77 78 79 80 81 82 83 84 85 86 87 88 89 90 91 92 93 94 96 97 98 99 100 101 102 103 104 105 106 107 108 110 111 112 114 115 116 117 118 119 120 121 123 124 126 128 129 130 131 132 134 135 136 137 138 139 140 141 142 145 146 147 148 151 152 153 154 155 **S** Ochsner Health, New Orleans, LA
Primary Contact: Robert K. Wolterman, Chief Executive Officer
CFO: Scott J Posecai, Executive Vice President and Chief Financial Officer
CMO: Patrick J Quinlan, M.D., Chief Executive Officer, Ochsner Clinic Foundation & International Services, Exec. Director Ochsner Center for Community
CIO: Lynn Witherspoon, Vice President and Chief Information Officer
CHR: Joan Mollohan, Vice President Human Resources
Web address: www.ochsner.org
**Control:** Other not–for–profit (including NFP Corporation) **Service:** General medical and surgical

Staffed Beds: 962 Admissions: 42525 Census: 684 Outpatient Visits: 322708 Births: 4793 Total Expense ($000): 1672174 Payroll Expense ($000): 565597 Personnel: 9162

**NEW ORLEANS—Orleans Parish**

**PSYCHIATRIC PAVILION NEW ORLEANS** See Beacon Behavioral Hospital - New Orleans

**NEW ORLEANS—Jefferson Parish**

☐ **RIVER OAKS HOSPITAL (194031)**, 1525 River Oaks Road West, Zip 70123–2162; tel. 504/734–1740, (Includes RIVER OAKS CHILD AND ADOLESCENT HOSPITAL, Mailing address: 1525 River Oaks Road West, New Orleans, Louisiana, Zip 70123–2162; tel. 504/734–1740), (Nonreporting) **A**1 10 **S** Universal Health Services, Inc., King of Prussia, PA
Primary Contact: Chuck Webb, Interim Chief Executive Officer
CFO: Brandon Frazier, Chief Financial Officer
CMO: Lincoln Paine, M.D., Medical Director
CIO: Vincent Chatelain, Director Business Development
CHR: Wanda Hoffmann, Director Human Resources
CNO: Jason Krause, R.N., Director of Nursing
Web address: www.riveroakshospital.com
**Control:** Corporation, Investor–owned (for–profit) **Service:** Psychiatric

Staffed Beds: 126

**RIVER OAKS PSYCH HOSPITAL** See River Oaks Hospital

**NEW ORLEANS—Orleans Parish**

**SEASIDE BEHAVIORAL CENTER** See Seaside Behavioral Center - New Orleans

**SEASIDE BEHAVIORAL CENTER - NEW ORLEANS (194100)**, 4201 Woodland Drive, Zip 70131–7339; tel. 504/393–4223, (Nonreporting) **A**3 10 **F**35 98 100 101 102 103 105 130 143 153
Primary Contact: Mary L. Matamoros, R.N., Administrator
CHR: Sherry May Campbell, Director of Human Resources, Medical Records
CNO: Justin Bernier, R.N., Director of Nursing
Web address: www.seasidehc.com
**Control:** Corporation, Investor–owned (for–profit) **Service:** Psychiatric

Staffed Beds: 49 Admissions: 1728 Census: 41 Outpatient Visits: 0 Births: 0

**ST. CHARLES SURGICAL HOSPITAL (190300)**, 1717 Saint Charles Avenue, Zip 70130–5223; tel. 504/529–6600, (Nonreporting) **A**10 22
Primary Contact: Penny Banks, R.N., Administrator
Web address: www.scsh.com
**Control:** Corporation, Investor–owned (for–profit) **Service:** Surgical

Staffed Beds: 39

**ST. THERESA SPECIALTY HOSPITAL** See Bliant Specialty Hospital

☐ △ **TOURO INFIRMARY (190046)**, 1401 Foucher Street, Zip 70115–3593; tel. 504/897–7011, (Includes TOURO REHABILITATION CENTER, Mailing address: 1401 Foucher Street, New Orleans, Louisiana, Zip 70115–3515; tel. 504/897–8560; Susan E. Andrews, Chief Executive Officer), (Nonreporting) **A**1 2 3 5 7 10 **F**3 8 10 11 13 15 18 20 22 24 26 28 29 30 31 34 35 37 39 40 44 45 46 50 53 54 55 57 58 59 60 61 62 64 68 70 72 74 75 76 77 78 79 81 83 84 85 86 87 90 92 93 96 107 108 109 110 111 114 115 116 117 118 119 120 121 123 124 125 126 130 131 132 135 143 144 146 147 148 149 154 **S** LCMC Health, New Orleans, LA
Primary Contact: Manuel Linares, President and Chief Executive Officer
COO: Stephen Baldwin, Chief Operating Officer
CFO: Bradley Sinclair, Chief Financial Officer
CMO: Christopher Lege, Chief Medical Officer
CIO: Leann Hughes-Mickel, Chief Information Officer
CHR: Cindy Mousa, Director Human Resources
CNO: Patricia A Rosenberg, R.N., MSN, Chief Nursing Officer
Web address: www.touro.com
**Control:** Other not–for–profit (including NFP Corporation) **Service:** General medical and surgical

Staffed Beds: 280 Admissions: 10317 Census: 173 Outpatient Visits: 271755 Births: 3118 Total Expense ($000): 281835 Payroll Expense ($000): 90291

☒ **TULANE HEALTH SYSTEM (190176)**, 1415 Tulane Avenue, Zip 70112–2600; tel. 504/988–5263, (Includes LAKEVIEW REGIONAL MEDICAL CENTER, Mailing address: 95 Judge Tanner Boulevard, Covington, Louisiana, Zip 70433–7507; tel. 985/867–3800; Hiral Patel, M.D., Chief Executive Officer; TULANE-LAKESIDE HOSPITAL, Mailing address: 4700 South I 10 Service Road West, Metairie, Louisiana, Zip 70001–1269; tel. 504/780–4200), (Nonreporting) **A**1 2 3 5 8 10 **F**3 8 12 13 15 17 18 19 20 21 22 23 24 25 26 28 29 30 31 34 35 37 40 43 45 46 47 48 49 50 55 56 59 60 61 64 68 70 72 74 75 76 77 78 79 80 81 82 85 87 88 89 90 91 93 96 97 98 100 102 104 107 108 109 110 111 112 114 115 116 118 119 120 121 123 124 126 130 131 132 135 136 137 138 139 140 141 142 146 147 148 154 156 **S** HCA Healthcare, Nashville, TN
Primary Contact: Robert Lynch, M.D., Chief Executive Officer
COO: Thomas Patrias, FACHE, Chief Operating Officer
CFO: Regina Ramazani, Chief Financial Officer
CMO: John Pigott, M.D., Chief Medical Officer
CIO: Sue Rachuig, Director Information Services
CHR: Leah Grau, Director Human Resources
CNO: Jana S Stonestreet, R.N., Ph.D., Chief Nursing Officer
Web address: www.tuhc.com
**Control:** Partnership, Investor–owned (for–profit) **Service:** General medical and surgical

Staffed Beds: 543 Admissions: 18508 Census: 259 Outpatient Visits: 318170 Births: 2622 Total Expense ($000): 564633 Payroll Expense ($000): 153965 Personnel: 1892

**TULANE MEDICAL CENTER** See Tulane Health System

**LA**

☐ **UNIVERSITY MEDICAL CENTER (190005)**, 2000 Canal Street,
Zip 70112–3018; tel. 504/702–3000, (Nonreporting) **A**1 2 3 5 8 10 **F**3 11 12 15
16 18 20 22 24 26 29 30 31 34 35 39 40 43 45 46 47 49 50 51 55 57 58 59
61 63 64 65 66 70 74 75 77 78 79 81 83 84 85 86 87 92 93 94 97 98 100
102 104 107 108 110 111 112 114 115 116 117 118 119 123 126 129 130
135 141 142 145 146 147 148 149 150 153 154 156 **S** LCMC Health, New
Orleans, LA
Primary Contact: Danny Hardman, FACHE, R.N., Chief Executive Officer
COO: Lisa Miranda, Vice President Operations
CFO: Christine Williams, Chief Financial Officer
CNO: Denise Danna SuffixChief Nursing Officer
Web address: www.umcno.org
**Control**: Other not–for–profit (including NFP Corporation) **Service**: General
medical and surgical

> **Staffed Beds**: 366 **Admissions**: 15463 **Census**: 290 **Outpatient**
> **Visits**: 411390 **Births**: 0 **Total Expense ($000)**: 723074 **Payroll Expense**
> **($000)**: 163851 **Personnel**: 3006

### NEW ROADS—Pointe Coupee Parish

⊞ **POINTE COUPEE GENERAL HOSPITAL (191316)**, 2202 False River Drive,
Zip 70760–2614; tel. 225/638–6331, (Nonreporting) **A**1 10 18 **F**3 29 34 40 75
77 81 107 110 111 119 130 133 146 148 154
Primary Contact: Chad E. Olinde, CPA, Administrator and Chief Executive Officer
CFO: John Cazayoux, Chief Financial Officer
CMO: Paul Rachal, M.D., Chief Medical Officer
CIO: Anthony Sauro, Chief Information Officer
CHR: Lisa Patterson, Director Human Resources
CNO: Valerie Sparks Jarreau, R.N., Chief Nursing Officer
Web address: www.pcgh.org
**Control**: Hospital district or authority, Government, Nonfederal **Service**: General
medical and surgical

> **Staffed Beds**: 23 **Admissions**: 132 **Census**: 1 **Outpatient Visits**: 38379
> **Births**: 0 **Total Expense ($000)**: 18537 **Payroll Expense ($000)**: 7953
> **Personnel**: 176

### OAK GROVE—West Carroll Parish

**WEST CARROLL MEMORIAL HOSPITAL (190081)**, 706 Ross Street,
Zip 71263–9798; tel. 318/428–3237, (Nonreporting) **A**10
Primary Contact: R. Randall. Morris, Administrator
**Control**: Other not–for–profit (including NFP Corporation) **Service**: General
medical and surgical

> **Staffed Beds**: 21

### OAKDALE—Allen Parish

**HUMANA HOSPITAL-OAKDALE** See Oakdale Community Hospital

**OAKDALE COMMUNITY HOSPITAL (190106)**, 130 North Hospital
Drive, Zip 71463–3035, Mailing Address: P.O. Box 629, Zip 71463–0629;
tel. 318/335–3700, (Nonreporting) **A**10
Primary Contact: Gene Amons, R.N., Chief Executive Officer
CFO: Suzette Fatula, Chief Financial Officer
CMO: Tommy Davis, M.D., Chief of Staff
CIO: Monica King, Chief Information Officer
CHR: Becky Johnson, Director Human Resources
CNO: Kendra Wisby, R.N., Chief Nursing Officer
Web address: www.oakdalecommunityhospital.com/
**Control**: Partnership, Investor–owned (for–profit) **Service**: General medical and
surgical

> **Staffed Beds**: 27

### OLLA—Caldwell Parish

**HARDTNER MEDICAL CENTER (191315)**, 1102 North Pine Road,
Zip 71465–4804; tel. 318/495–3131, (Nonreporting) **A**10 18 **F**3 11 12 15 18 28
29 32 33 34 39 40 46 50 57 59 64 65 68 79 81 82 90 93 94 98 100 102 103
104 107 110 111 114 119 127 130 132 133 143 146 147 148 149 154
155 157
Primary Contact: Paul G. Mathews, CPA, Administrator
CIO: Sarah Thompson, Director Health Information Management
CNO: Cherry B Salter, Director of Nursing
Web address: www.hardtnermedical.com
**Control**: Hospital district or authority, Government, Nonfederal **Service**: General
medical and surgical

> **Staffed Beds**: 35 **Admissions**: 813 **Census**: 13 **Outpatient Visits**: 16616
> **Births**: 0 **Total Expense ($000)**: 22464 **Payroll Expense ($000)**: 13429
> **Personnel**: 289

### OPELOUSAS—St. Landry Parish

☐ **OCEANS BEHAVIORAL HOSPITAL OF OPELOUSAS (194095)**, 1310 Heather
Drive, Zip 70570–7714; tel. 337/948–8820, (Nonreporting) **A**1 10 **S** Oceans
Healthcare, Plano, TX
Primary Contact: Katherine Simoneaux, Administrator
CNO: Heather Comeaux, R.N., Director of Nursing
Web address: www.obho.info/
**Control**: Corporation, Investor–owned (for–profit) **Service**: Psychiatric

> **Staffed Beds**: 20

**OPELOUSAS GENERAL HEALTH STSTEM-SOUTH CAMPUS** See Opelousas
General Health System-South Campus

⊞ **OPELOUSAS GENERAL HEALTH SYSTEM (190017)**, 539 East Prudhomme
Street, Zip 70570–6499, Mailing Address: P.O. Box 1389, Zip 70571–1389;
tel. 337/948–3011, (Includes OPELOUSAS GENERAL HEALTH SYSTEM-SOUTH
CAMPUS, Mailing address: 3983 I-49 South Service Road, Opelousas, Louisiana,
Zip 70570–8975; tel. 337/948–2100; Kenneth J. Cochran, R.N., FACHE,
President and Chief Executive Officer), (Nonreporting) **A**1 2 10 19 **F**3 13 15 28
29 31 34 37 40 44 45 48 49 50 57 60 64 68 70 76 77 78 79 80 81 85 87 89
90 91 93 96 97 98 102 103 104 105 107 108 110 111 112 114 115 116 117
119 121 126 129 130 131 132 146 147 148 149 153
Primary Contact: Kenneth J. Cochran, R.N., FACHE, President and Chief Executive
Officer
COO: Bob Hardy, Chief Operating Officer
CFO: James B Juneau, Chief Financial Officer
CMO: Hunt Deblanc, M.D., Chief of Staff
CIO: Jared Lormand, Vice President Information Technology
CHR: Suzanne F Kidder, Human Resources Officer
CNO: Kimberly Probus, Chief Nursing Officer
Web address: www.opelousasgeneral.com
**Control**: Other not–for–profit (including NFP Corporation) **Service**: General
medical and surgical

> **Staffed Beds**: 187 **Admissions**: 7598 **Census**: 88 **Outpatient**
> **Visits**: 159354 **Births**: 966 **Total Expense ($000)**: 150519 **Payroll Expense**
> **($000)**: 53966 **Personnel**: 967

**OPELOUSAS GENERAL HOSPITAL** See Opelousas General Health System

**ST. LANDRY EXTENDED CARE HOSPITAL (192034)**, 539 East Prudhomme
Street, 6th Floor, Zip 70570–6499; tel. 337/948–2251, (Nonreporting) **A**10 **S**
LHC Group, Lafayette, LA
Primary Contact: Biff David, R.N., Administrator
CNO: Shelia B. Johnson, Director of Nursing
Web address: www.lhcgroup.com
**Control**: Corporation, Investor–owned (for–profit) **Service**: Acute long–term care
hospital

> **Staffed Beds**: 41

### PINEVILLE—Rapides Parish

⊞ **ALEXANDRIA VETERANS AFFAIRS HEALTH CARE SYSTEM**, 2495 Shreveport
Highway, 71 N, Zip 71360–4044, Mailing Address: P.O. Box 69004, Alexandria,
Zip 71306–9004; tel. 318/473–0010, (Total facility includes 90 beds in nursing
home–type unit) (Nonreporting) **A**1 3 5 **F**1 5 6 7 8 14 18 29 30 31 33 34 35 36
38 39 44 45 46 48 50 53 54 56 57 59 61 62 63 64 65 66 68 71 75 77 79 81
82 83 84 85 86 87 91 92 93 94 96 97 98 100 101 102 104 105 107 108 109
110 111 112 113 114 115 116 117 118 119 127 128 130 132 133 135 143
144 146 147 148 149 150 153 154 156 157 **S** Department of Veterans Affairs,
Washington, DC
Primary Contact: Peter C. Dancy Jr, FACHE, Director
CFO: Bianca A. Obey, Chief Financial Officer
CMO: Robert Bernard, M.D., Chief of Staff
CIO: Robin McBryde, Chief Information Officer
CHR: Alex Love, Acting Manager Human Resources
CNO: Amy Lesniewski, Associate Director Patient Care Services
Web address: www.alexandria.va.gov/
**Control**: Veterans Affairs, Government, federal **Service**: General medical and
surgical

> **Staffed Beds**: 144 **Admissions**: 1102 **Census**: 84 **Outpatient**
> **Visits**: 330132 **Births**: 0 **Personnel**: 1150

*Many Facility Codes have changed. Please refer to the AHA Guide Code Chart.*

**CENTRAL LOUISIANA STATE HOSPITAL (194025)**, 242 West Shamrock Avenue, Zip 71360–6439, Mailing Address: P.O. Box 5031, Zip 71361–5031; tel. 318/484–6200, (Nonreporting) **A**1 10 **F**29 30 38 50 59 68 74 75 77 86 87 98 100 130 132 135 149 **P**6 **S** Louisiana State Hospitals, Baton Rouge, LA
Primary Contact: Sandra Duck, R.N., MSN, Mental Hospital Administrator 2
COO: Paul Benoit, Associate Administrator
CFO: Tina Darbonne, Chief Financial Officer
CMO: Joel Breving, M.D., Medical Director
CIO: William Haynes, Director Information Technology
CHR: Tom Crout, MS, Director Human Resources
Web address: www.dhh.louisiana.gov/index.cfm/directory/detail/217
**Control**: State, Government, Nonfederal **Service**: Psychiatric

Staffed Beds: 120 Admissions: 19 Census: 116 Outpatient Visits: 0
Births: 0

**VETERANS AFFAIRS MEDICAL CENTER - ALEXANDRIA** See Alexandria Veterans Affairs Health Care System

### PLAQUEMINE—Iberville Parish

**ACCORD REHABILIATION HOSPITAL (193070)**, 59213 Riverwest Drive, Zip 70764–6552; tel. 225/687–8100, (Nonreporting) **A**10
Primary Contact: Julene Mcalister, Administrator
Web address: www.mmoinc.com
**Control**: Other not–for–profit (including NFP Corporation) **Service**: Rehabilitation

Staffed Beds: 8

**MMO REHABILITATION AND WELLNESS CENTER** See Accord Rehabiliation Hospital

### PRAIRIEVILLE—Ascension Parish

**PRAIRIEVILLE FAMILY HOSPITAL**, 37358 Market Place Drive, Zip 70769–3482; tel. 225/755–9765, (Nonreporting)
Primary Contact: John J. McLean, M.D., Chief Executive Officer
COO: Mary-Katherine Moore, Chief Operating Officer
Web address: www.https://prairievillefamilyhospital.com
**Control**: Other not–for–profit (including NFP Corporation) **Service**: General medical and surgical

Staffed Beds: 10

### RACELAND—Lafourche Parish

**OCHSNER ST. ANNE GENERAL HOSPITAL (191324)**, 4608 Highway 1, Zip 70394–2623; tel. 985/537–6841, (Nonreporting) **A**1 10 18 **F**3 4 13 14 15 17 18 29 30 34 35 38 40 44 45 50 51 56 57 59 64 65 68 70 74 75 76 77 81 82 85 86 87 89 90 97 98 102 104 107 110 111 114 119 128 130 133 135 146 147 149 154 156 **S** Ochsner Health, New Orleans, LA
Primary Contact: Timothy J. Allen, FACHE, Chief Executive Officer
COO: Fernis LeBlanc, Chief Operating Officer
CNO: Jana Semere, Chief Nursing Officer
Web address: www.ochsner.org/locations/ochsner-st-anne
**Control**: Other not–for–profit (including NFP Corporation) **Service**: General medical and surgical

Staffed Beds: 35 Admissions: 1945 Census: 18 Outpatient Visits: 79249
Births: 355 Total Expense ($000): 56615 Payroll Expense ($000): 23125
Personnel: 410

**ST ANNE GENERAL HOSPITAL** See Ochsner St. Anne General Hospital

### RAYVILLE—Richland Parish

**RICHARDSON MEDICAL CENTER (190151)**, 254 Highway 3048, Zip 71269–0388, Mailing Address: P.O. Box 388, Zip 71269–0388; tel. 318/728–4181, (Nonreporting) **A**10
Primary Contact: James W. Barrett, Chief Executive Officer
CFO: Mallory Gulley Wells, CPA, Chief Financial Officer
CMO: David Thompson, M.D., Chief of Staff
CHR: Rita Brown, Director Human Resources
CNO: Trey McCleland, R.N., Director of Nursing
Web address: www.richardsonmed.org
**Control**: Hospital district or authority, Government, Nonfederal **Service**: General medical and surgical

Staffed Beds: 38

**RICHLAND PARISH HOSP-RAYVILLE** See Richardson Medical Center

### RUSTON—Lincoln Parish

**ALLEGIANCE BEHAVIORAL HEALTH CENTERS OF MONROE** See Allegiance Behavioral Health Centers of Ruston

**ALLEGIANCE BEHAVIORAL HEALTH CENTERS OF RUSTON (194087)**, 1401 Ezelle Street, Zip 71270–7218; tel. 318/329–2174, (Includes ALLEGIANCE BEHAVIORAL HEALTH CENTER, Mailing address: 4402 Sterlington Road, Monroe, Louisiana, Zip 71203–2338; tel. 318/966–4686; Angie Alexander, Chief Executive Officer; ALLEGIANCE HEALTH CENTER OF RUSTON, Mailing address: 1401 Ezell Street, Ruston, Louisiana, Zip 71270–7218; tel. 318/255–8085; Angie Alexander, Chief Executive Officer)
Primary Contact: Angie Alexander, Chief Executive Officer
Web address: www.ahmgt.com
**Control**: Corporation, Investor–owned (for–profit) **Service**: Psychiatric

Staffed Beds: 38

**LIBERTY HEALTHCARE SYSTEMS** See Serenity Springs Specialty Hospital

**LIFECARE SPECIALTY HOSPITAL OF NORTH LOUISIANA** See Ruston Regional Specialty Hospital

**LINCOLN GENERAL HOSPITAL** See Northern Louisiana Medical Center

**NORTHERN LOUISIANA MEDICAL CENTER (190086)**, 401 East Vaughn Avenue, Zip 71270–5950; tel. 318/254–2100, (Includes GREEN CLINIC SURGICAL HOSPITAL, Mailing address: 1118 Farmerville Street, Ruston, Louisiana, Zip 71270–5914; tel. 318/232–7700; Chad Conner, Administrator), (Nonreporting) **A**1 10 19 **S** Allegiance Health Management, Shreveport, LA
Primary Contact: Keith Newton, Chief Executive Officer
CFO: Michael Lockridge, Chief Financial Officer
CMO: Robin Sharp, M.D., Chief of Staff
CIO: Heather Nolan, Director Information Services
CHR: Tonya Duggan, Director Human Resources
CNO: Hartland Hintze, Chief Nursing Officer
Web address: www.northernlouisianamedicalcenter.com
**Control**: Other not–for–profit (including NFP Corporation) **Service**: General medical and surgical

Staffed Beds: 91

**RUSTON REGIONAL SPECIALTY HOSPITAL (192022)**, 1401 Ezell Street, Zip 71270–7218; tel. 318/251–3126, (Nonreporting) **A**1 10
Primary Contact: Mark J. Rice, Administrator
Web address: www.rustonregional.com/
**Control**: Corporation, Investor–owned (for–profit) **Service**: Acute long–term care hospital

Staffed Beds: 55

**SERENITY SPRINGS SPECIALTY HOSPITAL (194074)**, 1495 Frazier Road, Zip 71270–1632; tel. 318/202–3860, (Nonreporting) **A**10
Primary Contact: Adrian Williams, Chief Executive Officer
Web address: www.serenityhospital.com
**Control**: Corporation, Investor–owned (for–profit) **Service**: Psychiatric

Staffed Beds: 18

### SAINT FRANCISVILLE—West Feliciana Parish

**WEST FELICIANA HOSPITAL (191306)**, 5266 Commerce Street, Zip 70775, Mailing Address: P.O. Box 368, Zip 70775–0368; tel. 225/635–3811, (Nonreporting) **A**1 10 18
Primary Contact: Lee J. Chastant III, Chief Executive Officer
CFO: Linda Harvey, Chief Financial Officer
CHR: Neta F Leake, Administrative Assistant Human Resources
CNO: Angela Noble, Director of Nursing
Web address: www.wfph.org
**Control**: Hospital district or authority, Government, Nonfederal **Service**: General medical and surgical

Staffed Beds: 12

**WEST FELICIANA PARISH HOSPITAL** See West Feliciana Hospital

### SHREVEPORT—Caddo Parish

**BRENTWOOD BEHAVIORAL COMPANY** See Brentwood Hospital

---

**Hospital, Medicare Provider Number, Address, Telephone, Approval, Facility, and Physician Codes, Health Care System**

★ American Hospital Association (AHA) membership ○ Healthcare Facilities Accreditation Program ⇑ Center for Improvement in Healthcare Quality Accreditation
☐ The Joint Commission accreditation ◇ DNV Healthcare Inc. accreditation △ Commission on Accreditation of Rehabilitation Facilities (CARF) accreditation

**LA**

☐ **BRENTWOOD HOSPITAL (194020)**, 1006 Highland Avenue, Zip 71101–4103; tel. 318/678–7500, (Nonreporting) **A**1 3 10 **F**3 4 5 29 35 38 87 98 99 100 101 102 103 104 105 135 151 152 153 154 **S** Universal Health Services, Inc., King of Prussia, PA
Primary Contact: William Weaver, Chief Executive Officer
CFO: Kae Bell, Chief Financial Officer
CMO: ColonelDaniel Feeney, M.D., Medical Director
CHR: Talicia Johnson, Director Human Resources
CNO: Ravon Dominique, Chief Nursing Officer
Web address: www.brentwoodbehavioral.com
**Control**: State, Government, Nonfederal **Service**: Psychiatric

**Staffed Beds:** 238 **Admissions:** 6507 **Census:** 161 **Outpatient Visits:** 17246 **Births:** 0 **Total Expense ($000):** 33795 **Payroll Expense ($000):** 17028 **Personnel:** 407

☒ **CHRISTUS HEALTH SHREVEPORT-BOSSIER (190041)**, 1453 East Bert Kouns Industrial Loop, Zip 71105–6800; tel. 318/681–5000, (Includes CHRISTUS BOSSIER EMERGENCY HOSPITAL, Mailing address: 2531 Viking Drive, Bossier City, Louisiana, Zip 71111; tel. 318/681–7000; Jennifer Varnadore, Administrator; CHRISTUS HIGHLAND MEDICAL CENTER, Mailing address: 1453 East Bert Kouns Industrial Loop, Shreveport, Louisiana, Zip 71105–6050; tel. 318/681–5000; Thomas S. Trawick, M.D., Chief Executive Officer; CHRISTUS IN-PATIENT REHABILITATION CENTER SHREVEPORT-BOSSIER, Mailing address: 1035 Margaret Place, Shreveport, Louisiana, Zip 71101–4315; tel. 318/681–4434; Thomas S. Trawick, M.D., Chief Executive Officer and Chief Medical Officer), (Nonreporting) **A**1 2 3 10 **F**3 11 12 13 15 17 18 20 22 24 26 28 29 30 31 32 34 35 40 42 45 46 47 48 49 50 53 54 55 56 57 58 59 61 64 70 72 73 74 75 76 77 78 79 80 81 82 84 85 86 87 90 93 96 97 102 107 108 110 111 114 115 119 120 121 123 124 126 130 131 132 134 135 146 147 148 149 156 **S** CHRISTUS Health, Irving, TX
Primary Contact: Thomas S. Trawick, M.D., Chief Executive Officer
COO: Joshua Lamb, Vice President Operations
CFO: Bryan Pannagl, Chief Financial Officer
CMO: Richard Michael, M.D., Vice President Medical Affairs
CIO: Mary Merryman, Regional Director Information Management
CHR: Wendy Chandler, Vice President Human Resources
CNO: Ginger Disante, Chief Nursing Executive
Web address: www.christushealthsb.org
**Control**: Church operated, Nongovernment, not–for–profit **Service**: General medical and surgical

**Staffed Beds:** 188 **Admissions:** 8743 **Census:** 109 **Outpatient Visits:** 226687 **Births:** 1056 **Total Expense ($000):** 230535 **Payroll Expense ($000):** 61074 **Personnel:** 911

**CHRISTUS HIGHLAND MEDICAL CENTER** See Christus Health Shreveport-Bossier

**CHRISTUS SCHUMPERT HIGHLAND** See Christus Highland Medical Center

**LIFECARE HOSPITALS OF SHREVEPORT - NORTH CAMPUS** See Pam Specialty Hospital of Shreveport North

**LIFECARE HOSPITALS OF SHREVEPORT-WILLIS KNIGHTON** See Pam Specialty Hospital of Shreveport South

☐ **OCHSNER LSU HEALTH SHREVEPORT - ACADEMIC MEDICAL CENTER (190098)**, 1501 Kings Highway, Zip 71103–4228, Mailing Address: P.O. Box 33932, Zip 71130–3932; tel. 318/675–5000, (Includes CHILDREN'S HOSPITAL OF SHREVEPORT, Mailing address: 1501 Kings Highway, Shreveport, Louisiana, Zip 71103–4228, PO Box 33932, Zip 71130–3932, tel. 318/675–5000), (Nonreporting) **A**1 3 5 10 **S** University Health System, Shreveport, LA
Primary Contact: Charles D. Daigle, Chief Executive Officer
COO: Mark Randolph, Chief Operating Officer
CFO: Harold White, Vice Chancellor
CMO: Kevin Sittig, M.D., Senior Associate Dean and Chief Medical Officer
CIO: Marcus Hobgood, Director Information Services
CHR: David Fuqua, Director Human Resources Management
Web address: www.lsuhscshreveport.edu
**Control**: State, Government, Nonfederal **Service**: General medical and surgical

**Staffed Beds:** 386

**OCHSNER LSU HEALTH SHREVPORT - ACADEMIC MEDICAL CENTER** See Ochsner Lsu Health Shreveport - Academic Medical Center

☒ **OVERTON BROOKS VETERANS AFFAIRS MEDICAL CENTER**, 510 East Stoner Avenue, Zip 71101–4295; tel. 318/221–8411, (Nonreporting) **A**1 3 5 **S** Department of Veterans Affairs, Washington, DC
Primary Contact: Richard Crockett, Director
CFO: Kim Lane, Chief Fiscal Service
CIO: Janey Taylor, Chief Information and Technology
CHR: Michael L Palmier, Chief Human Resources Management
Web address: www.shreveport.va.gov/
**Control**: Veterans Affairs, Government, federal **Service**: General medical and surgical

**Staffed Beds:** 100

☒ **PAM SPECIALTY HOSPITAL OF SHREVEPORT SOUTH (192011)**, 8001 Youree Drive, Zip 71115–2302; tel. 318/212–2200, (Includes PAM SPECIALTY HOSPITAL OF SHREVEPORT NORTH, Mailing address: 2550 Kings Highway, Shreveport, Louisiana, Zip 71103–3922; tel. 318/212–3200; Marc B. Pearce, Chief Executive Officer) (Data for 92 days) **A**1 **F**1 3 148 **S** Post Acute Medical, LLC, Enola, PA
Primary Contact: Marc B. Pearce, Chief Executive Officer
Web address: www.postacutemedical.com
**Control**: Partnership, Investor–owned (for–profit) **Service**: Acute long–term care hospital

**Staffed Beds:** 54 **Admissions:** 201 **Census:** 47 **Outpatient Visits:** 0 **Births:** 0 **Total Expense ($000):** 4973 **Payroll Expense ($000):** 2540 **Personnel:** 138

**PHYSICIANS BEHAVIORAL HOSPITAL (194094)**, 2025 Desoto Street, Zip 71103–4717; tel. 318/550–0520, (Nonreporting) **A**10
Primary Contact: Allison Cooper, Administrator
**Control**: Corporation, Investor–owned (for–profit) **Service**: Psychiatric

**Staffed Beds:** 24

☐ **PROMISE HOSPITAL OF LOUISIANA - SHREVEPORT CAMPUS (192010)**, 1800 Irving Place, Zip 71101–4608; tel. 318/425–4096, (Includes PROMISE HOSPITAL OF LOUISIANA - BOSSIER CITY CAMPUS, Mailing address: 2525 Viking Drive, Bossier City, Louisiana, Zip 71111–2103; tel. 318/841–2525), (Nonreporting) **A**1 3 10
Primary Contact: Rick Stockton, Chief Executive Officer
Web address: www.promise-shreveport.com
**Control**: Corporation, Investor–owned (for–profit) **Service**: Acute long–term care hospital

**Staffed Beds:** 146

**PROMISE SPECIALTY HOSPITAL OF SHREVEPORT** See Promise Hospital of Louisiana - Shreveport Campus

**SHRINERS HOSPITALS FOR CHILDREN, SHREVEPORT** See Shriners Hospitals for Children-Shreveport

☐ **SHRINERS HOSPITALS FOR CHILDREN-SHREVEPORT (193301)**, 3100 Samford Avenue, Zip 71103–4289; tel. 318/222–5704, (Nonreporting) **A**1 3 5 10 **F**3 29 30 34 55 58 59 64 68 77 79 81 85 89 93 119 130 131 146 154 **S** Shriners Hospitals for Children, Tampa, FL
Primary Contact: Garry Kim. Green, FACHE, Administrator
CFO: Clarissa Brown-Smith, Director Fiscal Services
CMO: Cary Mielke, M.D., Chief of Staff
CIO: Michael Lyons, Regional Information Systems Director
CHR: Mehar Sikand, Manager Human Resources
CNO: Kathleen A. Redler, Director Patient Care Services
Web address: www.https://www.shrinershospitalsforchildren.org/shreveport
**Control**: Other not–for–profit (including NFP Corporation) **Service**: Children's orthopedic

**Staffed Beds:** 45 **Admissions:** 386 **Census:** 3 **Outpatient Visits:** 19257 **Births:** 0 **Personnel:** 164

**SPECIALISTS HOSPITAL - SHREVEPORT** See Specialists Hospital Shreveport

**SPECIALISTS HOSPITAL SHREVEPORT (190278)**, 1500 Line Avenue, Zip 71101–4639; tel. 318/213–3800, (Nonreporting) **A**10
Primary Contact: Kandi Moore, R.N., Administrator
COO: Devin Jenkins, Chief Operating Officer
CFO: Misty Cooper, Chief Financial Officer
CMO: Val Irion, M.D., Medical Director
CHR: Crystal Lawson, Director Human Resource
CNO: Mary Virginia Loftus, Chief Nursing Officer
Web address: www.specialistshospitalshreveport.com/
**Control**: Corporation, Investor–owned (for–profit) **Service**: Orthopedic

**Staffed Beds:** 15

*Many Facility Codes have changed. Please refer to the AHA Guide Code Chart.*

© 2021 AHA Guide

**VETERANS AFFAIRS MED CENTER** See Overton Brooks Veterans Affairs Medical Center

**WILLIS-KNIGHT SOUTH** See Willis-Knighton South - The Center for Women's Health

✠ △ **WILLIS-KNIGHTON MEDICAL CENTER (190111)**, 2600 Greenwood Road, Zip 71103–3908, Mailing Address: P.O. Box 32600, Zip 71130–2600; tel. 318/212–4000, (Includes WILLIS-KNIGHTON PIERREMONT HEALTH CENTER, Mailing address: 8001 Youree Drive, Shreveport, Louisiana, Zip 71115; tel. 318/212–3000; WILLIS-KNIGHTON SOUTH - THE CENTER FOR WOMEN'S HEALTH, Mailing address: 2510 Bert Kouns Industrial Loop, Shreveport, Louisiana, Zip 71118; tel. 318/212–5000; WK BOSSIER HEALTH CENTER, Mailing address: 2400 Hospital Drive, Bossier City, Louisiana, Zip 71111–2385; tel. 318/212–7000; Todd Blanchard, Administrator) (Total facility includes 155 beds in nursing home–type unit) **A**1 2 3 5 7 10 **F**3 4 5 7 8 12 13 15 17 18 20 22 24 26 28 29 30 31 32 34 35 39 40 44 46 47 48 49 50 51 52 53 54 55 56 57 58 59 60 62 63 64 65 66 68 70 72 74 75 76 77 78 79 81 82 84 85 86 87 88 89 90 91 92 93 94 96 97 98 100 101 102 104 105 107 108 109 110 111 112 114 115 116 117 118 119 120 121 122 123 124 125 126 127 128 129 130 131 132 133 134 135 138 139 142 143 144 147 148 149 152 153 156 **S** Willis-Knighton Health System, Shreveport, LA
Primary Contact: James K. Elrod, LFACHE, Chief Executive Officer
CMO: Dan Moller, M.D., Chief Medical Officer
CHR: Mike Chandler, Administrator
CNO: Renee McCuller, R.N., MSN, Chief Nursing Officer
Web address: www.wkhs.com
**Control:** Other not–for–profit (including NFP Corporation) **Service:** General medical and surgical

**Staffed Beds:** 758 **Admissions:** 54520 **Census:** 519 **Outpatient Visits:** 776300 **Births:** 2845 **Personnel:** 5918

### SLIDELL—St. Tammany Parish

**CYPRESS POINTE HOSPITAL EAST** See Sterling Surgical Hospital

**NORTHSHORE REGIONAL MEDICAL CENTER** See Ochsner Medical Center - North Shore

✠ **OCHSNER MEDICAL CENTER - NORTH SHORE (190204)**, 100 Medical Center Drive, Zip 70461–5520; tel. 985/649–7070, (Nonreporting) **A**1 10 **F**3 12 15 18 24 29 30 31 32 34 35 38 40 41 45 46 49 50 51 57 59 60 61 68 70 74 75 77 78 79 81 84 85 86 87 91 93 95 96 97 102 107 110 111 114 118 119 126 130 132 135 146 147 148 154 **S** Ochsner Health, New Orleans, LA
Primary Contact: Sandy Badinger, Chief Executive Officer
CFO: Alisha Neal, Chief Financial Officer
CMO: James Newcomb, M.D., Vice President Medical
CHR: Terri Joseph-Taylor, Chief Human Resource Manager
CNO: Cheryl Woods, Chief Nursing Officer
Web address: www.https://www.ochsner.org/locations/ochsner-medical-center-north-shore/
**Control:** Other not–for–profit (including NFP Corporation) **Service:** General medical and surgical

**Staffed Beds:** 145 **Admissions:** 4208 **Census:** 53 **Outpatient Visits:** 96311 **Births:** 0 **Total Expense ($000):** 93732 **Payroll Expense ($000):** 36950 **Personnel:** 622

✠ **SLIDELL MEMORIAL HOSPITAL (190040)**, 1001 Gause Boulevard, Zip 70458–2987; tel. 985/280–2200, (Nonreporting) **A**1 2 3 5 10 **F**3 11 13 15 17 18 20 22 24 26 28 29 30 31 32 34 35 40 45 47 49 54 56 57 59 64 65 70 72 75 76 77 78 79 81 82 83 85 86 87 91 93 96 97 102 107 108 110 111 114 115 116 117 118 119 120 121 124 129 130 132 154 **S** Ochsner Health, New Orleans, LA
Primary Contact: Sandy Badinger, Chief Executive Officer
COO: Holly Sanchez, Chief Operating Officer
CFO: David Grizzard, CPA, Chief Financial Officer
CMO: James Newcomb, M.D., Vice President Medical Affairs
CIO: Holly Sanchez, Chief Information Officer
CNO: Theresa Williams, MSN, Chief Nursing Officer
Web address: www.slidellmemorial.org
**Control:** Hospital district or authority, Government, Nonfederal **Service:** General medical and surgical

**Staffed Beds:** 175 **Admissions:** 7570 **Census:** 89 **Outpatient Visits:** 143487 **Births:** 1129 **Total Expense ($000):** 201458 **Payroll Expense ($000):** 85416 **Personnel:** 1149

**SLIDELL MEMORIAL HSP & MED CTR** See Slidell Memorial Hospital

☐ **SOUTHERN SURGICAL HOSPITAL (190270)**, 1700 Lindberg Drive, Zip 70458–8062; tel. 985/641–0600, (Nonreporting) **A**1 10 **F**3 8 12 17 18 26 29 34 35 37 45 47 51 57 59 60 64 66 68 70 74 75 79 81 82 85 86 87 89 107 111 112 114 119 126 130 131 132 135 143
Primary Contact: Michael J. Pisciotta, Chief Executive Officer
CFO: Michael J Maurin, Chief Financial Officer
CMO: J Gosey, M.D., Medical Director
CIO: Buddy Graves, Chief Information Officer
CHR: Lorrie Alfred, Director Human Resources
Web address: www.sshla.com/
**Control:** Corporation, Investor–owned (for–profit) **Service:** General medical and surgical

**Staffed Beds:** 37 **Admissions:** 1350 **Census:** 12 **Outpatient Visits:** 6200 **Births:** 0 **Total Expense ($000):** 26200 **Payroll Expense ($000):** 8000

**STERLING SURGICAL HOSPITAL (190256)**, 989 Robert Boulevard, Zip 70458–2009; tel. 985/690–8200, (Nonreporting) **A**10
Primary Contact: Michael Lamb, Administrator
Web address: www.sterlingsurgical.net/
**Control:** Corporation, Investor–owned (for–profit) **Service:** Surgical

**Staffed Beds:** 10

### SPRINGHILL—Webster Parish

**COLUMBIA SPRINGHILL MED CTR** See Springhill Medical Center

☐ **SPRINGHILL MEDICAL CENTER (190088)**, 2001 Doctors Drive, Zip 71075–4526, Mailing Address: P.O. Box 920, Zip 71075–0920; tel. 318/539–1000, (Nonreporting) **A**1 10 20 **F**15 29 30 32 34 35 40 41 43 45 50 54 56 57 59 64 66 68 70 78 81 85 86 87 89 91 93 98 101 102 103 107 110 114 119 127 130 133 135 146 148 149 154 157 **S** Willis-Knighton Health System, Shreveport, LA
Primary Contact: Michael G. Patronis, Chief Executive Officer
COO: Dana R. Jones, R.N., MSN, Chief Operating Officer
CFO: Douglas Lahasky, Chief Financial Officer
CMO: Jerry W. Sessions, M.D., Chief Medical Staff
CIO: Brian Griffin, Director Information Services
CHR: Ashley Ortego, Director Human Resources and Marketing
CNO: Kristin B Cole, R.N., Chief Nursing Officer
Web address: www.smccare.com
**Control:** Other not–for–profit (including NFP Corporation) **Service:** General medical and surgical

**Staffed Beds:** 34 **Admissions:** 864 **Census:** 11 **Births:** 0

### SULPHUR—Calcasieu Parish

☐ **WEST CALCASIEU CAMERON HOSPITAL (190013)**, 701 Cypress Street, Zip 70663–5000, Mailing Address: P.O. Box 2509, Zip 70664–2509; tel. 337/527–7034, (Nonreporting) **A**1 10 **F**3 7 8 11 13 15 18 20 22 28 29 30 31 34 35 37 38 39 40 44 45 46 50 53 54 57 59 62 65 68 70 75 76 77 78 79 81 85 86 87 89 91 93 96 97 107 108 110 111 114 115 118 119 127 129 130 132 134 135 141 146 147 148 149 154 156
Primary Contact: Janie D. Fruge, FACHE, Chief Executive Officer
CFO: Jobie James, Chief Financial Officer
CIO: Michael Klenke, Chief Information Security Officer
CHR: Christi Kingsley, Vice President Human Resources
CNO: Brian C. Thompson, R.N., Chief Nursing Officer
Web address: www.https://wcch.com/
**Control:** Hospital district or authority, Government, Nonfederal **Service:** General medical and surgical

**Staffed Beds:** 79 **Admissions:** 2375 **Census:** 23 **Outpatient Visits:** 91606 **Births:** 319 **Total Expense ($000):** 74538 **Payroll Expense ($000):** 32287 **Personnel:** 634

**WEST CALCASIEU-CAMERON HOSP** See West Calcasieu Cameron Hospital

---

Hospital, Medicare Provider Number, Address, Telephone, Approval, Facility, and Physician Codes, Health Care System

★ American Hospital Association (AHA) membership    ○ Healthcare Facilities Accreditation Program    ⇪ Center for Improvement in Healthcare Quality Accreditation
☐ The Joint Commission accreditation    ◇ DNV Healthcare Inc. accreditation    △ Commission on Accreditation of Rehabilitation Facilities (CARF) accreditation

**LA**

### TALLULAH—Madison Parish

**MADISON PARISH HOSPITAL (191314)**, 900 Johnson Street, Zip 71282–4537; tel. 318/574–2374, (Nonreporting) **A**10 18
Primary Contact: Ted Topolewski, Chief Executive Officer
CFO: W Robert Laurents, CPA, Chief Financial Officer
CMO: Donald Perry, M.D., Chief Medical Officer
CIO: Charles Whitaker, Director Information Technology
CHR: Chasity Whitaker, Administrative Assistant
Web address: www.madisonparishhospital.com
**Control:** Other not–for–profit (including NFP Corporation) **Service:** General medical and surgical

| Staffed Beds: 25 |
|---|

### THIBODAUX—Lafourche Parish

**THIBODAUX REGIONAL HEALTH CENTER** See Thibodaux Regional Health System

✉ △ **THIBODAUX REGIONAL HEALTH SYSTEM (190004)**, 602 North Acadia Road, Zip 70301–4847, Mailing Address: P.O. Box 1118, Zip 70302–1118; tel. 985/447–5500, (Nonreporting) **A**1 2 7 10 **F**3 8 11 12 13 15 18 19 20 22 24 28 29 30 31 32 34 37 39 40 46 49 50 53 57 59 62 64 70 73 74 75 76 78 79 81 82 85 86 87 89 90 92 93 96 97 98 103 104 107 108 110 111 115 116 117 119 120 121 123 124 126 127 129 130 131 132 134 135 146 147 148 149 153 154 156 **S** QHR Health, Brentwood, TN
Primary Contact: Greg K. Stock, FACHE, Chief Executive Officer
COO: Eric Degravelle, Vice President Professional Services
CFO: Theunette Antill, Chief Financial Officer
CIO: Bernie Clement, Chief Information Officer
CHR: Casey Peltier, Director Human Resources
CNO: Beth Norris MSN, RN-BVice President Patient Care Services
Web address: www.thibodaux.com
**Control:** Other not–for–profit (including NFP Corporation) **Service:** General medical and surgical

| Staffed Beds: 154 Admissions: 6296 Census: 75 Outpatient Visits: 283879 Births: 1108 Total Expense ($000): 185239 Payroll Expense ($000): 72964 Personnel: 1070 |
|---|

### VIDALIA—Concordia Parish

**PROMISE HOSPITAL OF MISS LOU** See Riverbridge Specialty Hospital, Vidalia

☐ **RIVERBRIDGE SPECIALTY HOSPITAL (192028)**, 209 Front Street, Zip 71373–2837; tel. 318/336–6500, (Nonreporting) **A**1 10 **F**1 29 60 64 93 130 133 143 148
Primary Contact: Michael Harrell, R.N., Chief Executive Officer
COO: Howard B Koslow, President and Chief Executive Officer
CFO: James Hopwood, Chief Financial Officer
CMO: Randy Tillman, M.D., Chief Medical Staff
CIO: Robert Greene, Director Information Technology
CHR: Roxan Houghton, Director Human Resources
CNO: Regetta Woods, Chief Nursing Officer and Chief Clinical Officer
Web address: www.riverbridgela.com
**Control:** Individual, Investor–owned (for–profit) **Service:** Acute long–term care hospital

| Staffed Beds: 40 Admissions: 450 Census: 29 Outpatient Visits: 0 Births: 0 |
|---|

**RIVERBRIDGE SPECIALTY HOSPITAL A**1 10 **F**1 29 60 64 93 130 133 143 148
COO: Howard B Koslow, President and Chief Executive Officer
CFO: James Hopwood, Chief Financial Officer
CMO: Randy Tillman, M.D., Chief Medical Staff
CIO: Robert Greene, Director Information Technology
CHR: Roxan Houghton, Director Human Resources
CNO: Regetta Woods, Chief Nursing Officer and Chief Clinical Officer
Web address: www.riverbridgela.com

### VILLE PLATTE—Evangeline Parish

☐ **MERCY REGIONAL MEDICAL CENTER (190167)**, 800 East Main Street, Zip 70586–4618; tel. 337/363–5684, (Includes ACADIAN MEDICAL CENTER, Mailing address: 3501 Highway 190, Eunice, Louisiana, Zip 70535–5129; tel. 337/580–7500; Kevin Frank, Chief Executive Officer), (Nonreporting) **A**1 10 **S** Allegiance Health Management, Shreveport, LA
Primary Contact: Kristopher Aguillard, Chief Executive Officer
CFO: Michael Fontenot, Regional Chief Financial Officer
CMO: Zebediah Stearns, M.D., Chief of Staff
CIO: Courtney Bieber, Director Information Systems
CHR: Cody Ardoin, Director Human Resources
Web address: www.mercyregionalmedicalcenter.com
**Control:** Corporation, Investor–owned (for–profit) **Service:** General medical and surgical

| Staffed Beds: 109 |
|---|

### VIVIAN—Caddo Parish

**NORTH CADDO MEDICAL CENTER (191304)**, 815 South Pine Street, Zip 71082–3353, Mailing Address: P.O. Box 792, Zip 71082–0792; tel. 318/375–3235, (Nonreporting) **A**3 5 10 18
Primary Contact: David C. Jones, Administrator
CFO: Dakota Robinson, Interim Chief Financial Officer and Controller
CMO: John H Haynes, M.D., JrChief of Medical Staff
Web address: www.ncmcla.com/
**Control:** Hospital district or authority, Government, Nonfederal **Service:** General medical and surgical

| Staffed Beds: 27 |
|---|

**NORTH CADDO MEMORIAL HOSPITAL** See North Caddo Medical Center

### WEST MONROE—Ouachita Parish

**CORNERSTONE HOSPITALS WEST MONROE (192031)**, 6198 Cypress Street, Zip 71291–9010; tel. 318/396–5600, (Nonreporting) **A**10 22 **S** Cornerstone Healthcare Group, Dallas, TX
Primary Contact: Chris Simpson, Chief Executive Officer
CFO: Kurt Schultz, Chief Financial Officer
CMO: Khaled Shafici, M.D., President Medical Staff
CHR: Dan Perkins, Corporate Director Human Resources
Web address: www.chghospitals.com/chwm.html
**Control:** Corporation, Investor–owned (for–profit) **Service:** Acute long–term care hospital

| Staffed Beds: 40 |
|---|

**CORNERSTONE HOSPITAL-WEST MONROE** See Cornerstone Hospitals West Monroe

⇑ **GLENWOOD REGIONAL MEDICAL CENTER (190160)**, 503 McMillan Road, Zip 71291–5327; tel. 318/329–4200, (Includes GLENWOOD SURGERY CENTER, Mailing address: 1275 Glenwood Drive, West Monroe, Louisiana, Zip 71291–5539, 503 McMillan Road, Zip 71291–5327, tel. 318/322–1339; Jeremy M. Tinnerello, MSN, R.N., President), (Nonreporting) **A**10 21 **F**3 8 12 13 15 17 18 20 22 24 26 28 29 30 31 34 35 37 38 40 41 45 46 47 48 49 50 51 54 55 56 57 58 59 60 61 62 63 64 68 70 71 72 74 75 76 78 79 81 82 83 84 85 86 87 90 91 92 93 94 96 97 98 100 101 102 103 104 107 108 110 111 113 114 115 116 117 119 120 121 126 129 130 131 132 134 146 147 148 149 153 154 **S** Steward Health Care System, LLC, Dallas, TX
Primary Contact: Jeremy M. Tinnerello, MSN, R.N., President
COO: Jeremy M. Tinnerello, MSN, R.N., President
CFO: John DeSantis, Interim Chief Financial Officer
CMO: Steve McMahan, M.D., Chief Medical Officer
CIO: Ronnie Maxwell, Director Information Systems
CHR: Jan Walker, Director Human Resources
CNO: Lori Mathieu, MSN, Chief Nursing Officer
Web address: www.https://www.glenwoodregional.org/
**Control:** Corporation, Investor–owned (for–profit) **Service:** General medical and surgical

| Staffed Beds: 278 Admissions: 11250 Census: 142 Outpatient Visits: 62375 Births: 720 Total Expense ($000): 175036 Payroll Expense ($000): 49107 |
|---|

**LOUISIANA EXTENDED CARE HOSPITAL OF WEST MONROE (192055)**, 503 McMillan Road, 3rd Floor, Zip 71291–5327; tel. 318/329–4378, (Nonreporting) **A**10 **S** LHC Group, Lafayette, LA
Primary Contact: Cleta Munholland, Administrator
COO: Pamela Chappell, R.N., Assistant Administrator
CNO: Shelly Nugent, R.N., Director Nurses and Infection Control
**Control:** Corporation, Investor–owned (for–profit) **Service:** Acute long–term care hospital

| Staffed Beds: 18 |
|---|

**LOUISIANA EXTENDED CARE HOSPITAL WEST MONROE** See Louisiana Extended Care Hospital of West Monroe

**OUACHITA COMMUNITY HOSPITAL** See Glenwood Surgery Center

## WINNFIELD—Winn Parish

**HUMANA HOSPITAL-WINN PARISH** See Winn Parish Medical Center

**WINN PARISH MEDICAL CENTER (190090)**, 301 West Boundary Avenue,
Zip 71483–3427, Mailing Address: P.O. Box 152, Zip 71483–0152;
tel. 318/648–3000, (Nonreporting) **A**10
Primary Contact: Kathy Hall, Chief Executive Officer
CFO: Suzette Fatula, Chief Financial Officer
CMO: Eric Dupree, M.D., Chief of Staff
CHR: Ashley S. Files, Director Human Resources, Public Relations and Marketing
Web address: www.winnparishmedical.com
**Control**: Partnership, Investor–owned (for–profit) **Service**: General medical and
surgical

**Staffed Beds: 60**

## WINNSBORO—Franklin Parish

**FRANKLIN MEDICAL CENTER (190140)**, 2106 Loop Road, Zip 71295–3344,
Mailing Address: P.O. Box 1300, Zip 71295–1300; tel. 318/435–9411,
(Nonreporting) **A**5 10
Primary Contact: Blake Kramer, Administrator
CFO: William E Page, CPA, Chief Financial Officer
CMO: Jay Busby, M.D., President Medical Staff
CIO: Judy Ogden, Director Information Technology
Web address: www.fmc-cares.com
**Control**: Hospital district or authority, Government, Nonfederal **Service**: General
medical and surgical

**Staffed Beds: 43**

**FRANKLIN PARISH HOSPITAL** See Franklin Medical Center

## ZACHARY—East Baton Rouge Parish

**AMG SPECIALTY HOSPITAL-ZACHARY (192041)**, 4601 McHugh Road, Building
B, Zip 70791–5348; tel. 225/683–1600, (Nonreporting) **A**10 **S** AMG Integrated
Healthcare Management, Lafayette, LA
Primary Contact: Meagan Falgout, Chief Executive Officer
Web address: www.amgzachary.com/
**Control**: Corporation, Investor–owned (for–profit) **Service**: Acute long–term care
hospital

**Staffed Beds: 16**

**LANE MEMORIAL HOSPITAL** See Lane Regional Medical Center

⊞ **LANE REGIONAL MEDICAL CENTER (190020)**, 6300 Main Street,
Zip 70791–4037; tel. 225/658–4000, (Total facility includes 39 beds in nursing
home–type unit) (Nonreporting) **A**1 10 **F**3 8 11 13 15 20 22 26 29 34 35 36 39
40 45 46 50 54 57 59 62 64 67 70 73 75 76 77 78 79 80 81 85 86 87 90
107 108 110 111 114 115 119 130 132 144 146 148 154 157 **S** QHR Health,
Brentwood, TN
Primary Contact: Larry R. Meese Jr, FACHE, Chief Executive Officer
COO: David S. Beck, Chief Operating Officer
CFO: Will Grant, Interim Chief Financial Officer
CNO: Staci Sullivan, R.N., Chief Nursing Officer
Web address: www.lanermc.org
**Control**: Hospital district or authority, Government, Nonfederal **Service**: General
medical and surgical

**Staffed Beds: 179 Admissions: 3741 Census: 78 Outpatient Visits: 71470
Births: 358 Total Expense ($000): 83283 Payroll Expense ($000): 33259
Personnel: 445**

---

**Hospital, Medicare Provider Number, Address, Telephone, Approval, Facility, and Physician Codes, Health Care System**

★ American Hospital Association (AHA) membership
□ The Joint Commission accreditation
○ Healthcare Facilities Accreditation Program
◇ DNV Healthcare Inc. accreditation
⇑ Center for Improvement in Healthcare Quality Accreditation
△ Commission on Accreditation of Rehabilitation Facilities (CARF) accreditation

# MAINE

**ME**

## AUGUSTA—Kennebec County

**AUGUSTA MENTAL HLTH INSTITUTE** See Riverview Psychiatric Center

✠ **MAINE VETERANS AFFAIRS MEDICAL CENTER**, 1 VA Center,
Zip 04330–6719; tel. 207/623–8411, (Nonreporting) **A**1 3 5 **S** Department of
Veterans Affairs, Washington, DC
Primary Contact: Tracye B. Davis, Medical Center Director
CFO: Daniel Howard, Chief Financial Officer
CMO: Timothy J Richardson, M.D., Chief of Staff
CIO: Richard McNaughton, Chief Information Management Service
CHR: Christine Miller, Chief Human Resources Management Services
Web address: www.maine.va.gov/
**Control:** Veterans Affairs, Government, federal **Service:** General medical and surgical

> **Staffed Beds:** 167

✠ **MAINEGENERAL MEDICAL CENTER (200039)**, 35 Medical Center Parkway,
Zip 4330; tel. 207/626–1000, (Includes MAINEGENERAL MEDICAL CENTER-
AUGUSTA CAMPUS, Mailing address: 35 Medical Center Parkway, Augusta, Maine,
Zip 04330–9988; tel. 207/626–1000; Chuck Hays, President and Chief Executive
Officer), (Nonreporting) **A**1 2 3 10 19 **F**3 4 5 8 11 12 13 15 17 18 20 26 28 29
30 31 34 35 36 40 42 44 45 46 47 48 49 50 51 54 55 56 57 58 59 61 64 65
70 73 74 75 76 77 78 79 81 82 84 85 86 87 89 90 92 93 96 97 98 99 100
101 102 104 107 108 110 115 116 117 118 119 120 121 123 124 126 129
130 131 132 134 135 144 145 146 147 148 149 153 154 156 **P**6 8
Primary Contact: Chuck Hays, President and Chief Executive Officer
COO: Paul Stein, Chief Operating Officer
CFO: Terry Brann, Chief Financial Officer
CMO: Andrew J. Dionne, M.D., Chief Medical Officer
CIO: Daniel Burgess, Chief Information Officer
CHR: Rebecca Lamey, Vice President Human Resources
CNO: Jennifer Riggs, R.N., Chief Nurse Officer
Web address: www.mainegeneral.org
**Control:** Other not–for–profit (including NFP Corporation) **Service:** General
medical and surgical

> **Staffed Beds:** 197 **Admissions:** 10470 **Census:** 160 **Outpatient
> Visits:** 824342 **Births:** 1040 **Total Expense ($000):** 505907 **Payroll
> Expense ($000):** 211624 **Personnel:** 3164

**MAINEGENERAL MEDICAL CENTER-AUGUSTA CAMPUS** See Mainegeneral
Medical Center, Augusta

**MAINEGENERAL MEDICAL CENTER-WATERVILLE CAMPUS** See Mainegeneral
Medical Center

**MID-MAINE GENERAL MEDICAL CTR** See Mainegeneral Medical Center-Augusta Campus

☐ **RIVERVIEW PSYCHIATRIC CENTER (204008)**, 250 Arsenal Street,
Zip 04330–5742; tel. 207/624–3900, (Nonreporting) **A**1 10
Primary Contact: Rodney Bouffard, Superintendent
COO: David Lovejoy, Chief Operations Officer
CFO: Samantha Kavanaugh, Chief Financial Officer
CMO: Brendan Kirby, M.D., Medical Director
CHR: Aimee Rice, Human Resources Manager
CNO: Roland Pushard, Director of Nursing
Web address: www.state.me.us/dhhs/riverview
**Control:** State, Government, Nonfederal **Service:** Psychiatric

> **Staffed Beds:** 92

**VETERANS AFFAIRS MEDICAL CENTER** See Maine Veterans Affairs Medical Center

## BANGOR—Penobscot County

**ACADIA HOSPITAL** See The Acadia Hospital

**BANGOR MENTAL HEALTH INSTITUTE** See Dorothea Dix Psychiatric Center

☐ **DOROTHEA DIX PSYCHIATRIC CENTER (204004)**, 656 State Street,
Zip 04401–5609, Mailing Address: P.O. Box 926, Zip 04402–0926;
tel. 207/941–4000, (Nonreporting) **A**1 10
Primary Contact: Carolyn Dimek, Acting Superintendent
CMO: Michelle Gardner, M.D., Clinical Director
CHR: Tamra Hanson, Human Resource Manager
CNO: Christine Bellatty, Acting Director of Nursing
Web address: www.maine.gov/dhhs/ddpc/index.shtml
**Control:** State, Government, Nonfederal **Service:** Psychiatric

> **Staffed Beds:** 45

**EASTERN MAINE MEDICAL CENTER** See Northern Light Eastern Maine Medical Center

✠ **NORTHERN LIGHT EASTERN MAINE MEDICAL CENTER (200033)**, 489
State Street, Zip 04401–6674, Mailing Address: P.O. Box 404, Zip 04402–0404;
tel. 207/973–7000, (Nonreporting) **A**1 2 3 5 10 13 **F**3 11 12 13 15 17 18 19 20
22 24 26 27 28 29 30 31 32 34 36 37 39 40 43 44 45 46 47 48 49 50 51 53
54 55 56 57 58 59 61 64 70 72 74 75 76 77 78 79 81 82 84 85 86 87 88 89
90 92 93 94 96 97 100 102 107 108 110 111 114 115 117 118 119 120 121
123 124 126 129 130 131 132 145 146 147 148 149 154 156 **P**6 **S** Northern
Light Health, Brewer, ME
Primary Contact: Rand O'Leary, FACHE, President
CMO: James Raczek, M.D., Sr. Vice President of Operations and Chief Medical Officer
CIO: Catherine Bruno, FACHE, Chief Information Officer
CHR: Greg Howat, Vice President Human Resources
Web address: www.https://northernlighthealth.org/Eastern-Maine-Medical-Center
**Control:** Other not-for-profit (including NFP Corporation) **Service:** General
medical and surgical

> **Staffed Beds:** 392 **Admissions:** 20321 **Census:** 316 **Outpatient
> Visits:** 804766 **Births:** 1735 **Total Expense ($000):** 879046 **Payroll
> Expense ($000):** 349795 **Personnel:** 3763

★ ⇑ **ST. JOSEPH HOSPITAL (200001)**, 360 Broadway, Zip 04401–3979, Mailing
Address: P.O. Box 403, Zip 04402–0403; tel. 207/262–1000, (Nonreporting) **A**10
21 **S** Covenant Health, Tewksbury, MA
Primary Contact: Mary Prybylo, Senior Vice President and President
CFO: Michael Hendrix, Chief Financial Officer
CMO: William Wood, M.D., Vice President Medical Affairs
CHR: Paige A Hagerstrom, System Director of Talent Management
CNO: Dianne Swandal, R.N., MSN, Vice President Patient Care
Web address: www.sjhhealth.com
**Control:** Church operated, Nongovernment, not-for-profit **Service:** General
medical and surgical

> **Staffed Beds:** 84

✠ **THE ACADIA HOSPITAL (204006)**, 268 Stillwater Avenue, Zip 04401–3945,
Mailing Address: P.O. Box 422, Zip 04402–0422; tel. 207/973–6100,
(Nonreporting) **A**1 5 10 **F**5 6 29 30 50 56 57 66 68 75 77 87 98 99 100 101
103 104 105 130 132 152 153 154 **S** Northern Light Health, Brewer, ME
Primary Contact: Scott Oxley, President
CFO: Marie Suitter, Chief Financial Officer
CMO: Anthony Ng, M.D., Vice President and Chief Medical Officer
CIO: Jeanne Paradis, Director Information Services
CHR: Paul Bolin, Vice President and Chief Human Resources Officer
CNO: Wayne Steller, Vice President Chief Nursing Officer
Web address: www.acadiahospital.org
**Control:** Other not-for-profit (including NFP Corporation) **Service:** Psychiatric

> **Staffed Beds:** 68 **Admissions:** 1484 **Census:** 61 **Outpatient Visits:** 106209
> **Births:** 0 **Total Expense ($000):** 53902 **Payroll Expense ($000):** 30755
> **Personnel:** 585

## BAR HARBOR—Hancock County

★ **MOUNT DESERT ISLAND HOSPITAL (201304)**, 10 Wayman Lane,
Zip 04609–1625, Mailing Address: P.O. Box 8, Zip 04609–0008; tel. 207/288–5081,
(Nonreporting) **A**10 18 **F**3 5 6 10 11 13 15 28 29 31 34 35 36 39 40 50 54 56 57
59 64 65 70 74 75 76 77 78 79 81 82 84 85 87 91 92 93 97 100 104 107 110
111 115 118 119 125 127 130 131 132 133 135 145 146 147 154
Primary Contact: Arthur J. Blank, President and Chief Executive Officer
COO: Christina Maguire, Senior Vice President, Chief Operating Officer and Chief
Financial Officer
CFO: Christina Maguire, Senior Vice President, Chief Operating Officer and Chief
Financial Officer
CMO: Stuart Davidson, M.D., Chief Medical Officer
CIO: Tom Mockus, Director Information Services
CHR: Sara O'Connell, Director Human Resources
CNO: Karen Mueller, R.N., Chief Nursing Officer
Web address: www.mdihospital.org
**Control:** Other not-for-profit (including NFP Corporation) **Service:** General
medical and surgical

> **Staffed Beds:** 25 **Admissions:** 804 **Census:** 7 **Outpatient Visits:** 6888
> **Births:** 72 **Total Expense ($000):** 61372 **Payroll Expense ($000):** 28911
> **Personnel:** 390

## BELFAST—Waldo County

**WALDO COUNTY GENERAL HOSPITAL (201312)**, 118 Northport Avenue, Zip 04915–6072, Mailing Address: P.O. Box 287, Zip 04915–0287; tel. 207/338–2500, (Nonreporting) **A**5 10 18 **F**3 11 13 15 18 27 29 30 31 34 35 39 40 45 46 55 57 59 62 63 64 70 74 75 76 77 78 79 81 82 83 84 85 87 93 97 102 107 110 111 115 117 119 125 129 130 131 132 133 145 146 147 148 154 156 **P**8 **S** MaineHealth, Portland, ME
Primary Contact: Mark Fourre, President
CFO: Linda Drinkwater, Chief Financial Officer
CMO: Kent Clark, M.D., Chief Medical Affairs and Quality
CIO: David Felton, Manager Information Systems
CHR: Karen Littlefield, Director Human Resources
CNO: Paula Delahanty, Regional Chief Nursing Officer
Web address: www.wcgh.org
**Control:** Other not–for–profit (including NFP Corporation) **Service:** General medical and surgical

**Staffed Beds:** 25 **Admissions:** 1309 **Census:** 17 **Outpatient Visits:** 131311 **Births:** 139 **Total Expense ($000):** 104262 **Payroll Expense ($000):** 47917 **Personnel:** 659

**WALDO COUNTY GENERAL HOSPITAL MAINE HEALTH** See Waldo County General Hospital

## BIDDEFORD—York County

**SOUTHERN MAINE HEALTH CARE - BIDDEFORD MEDICAL CENTER (200019)**, One Medical Center Drive, Zip 04005–9496, Mailing Address: P.O. Box 626, Zip 04005–0626; tel. 207/283–7000, (Includes SOUTHERN MAINE HEALTH CARE - BIDDEFORD MEDICAL CENTER, Mailing address: One Medical Center Drive, Biddeford, Maine, Zip 04005–9496, P.O. Box 626, Zip 04005–0626, tel. 207/283–7000; Edward J McGeachey, President and Chief Executive Officer) (Total facility includes 112 beds in nursing home–type unit) **A**1 2 3 10 **F**8 10 11 12 13 15 18 20 22 26 28 29 30 31 32 33 34 35 40 42 44 45 46 49 50 54 56 57 59 61 64 65 68 70 74 75 76 77 78 79 81 82 84 86 87 89 93 97 98 100 102 104 105 107 108 110 111 115 117 119 128 129 130 131 132 135 144 146 147 148 149 154 156 **P**6
Primary Contact: Nathan Howell, President
COO: Patricia Aprile, Chief Operating Officer
CFO: Norman Belair, Senior Vice President and Chief Financial Officer
CMO: Michael Albaum, M.D., Senior Vice President and Chief Medical Officer
CIO: Ralph Johnson, Chief Information Officer
CHR: Yvonne McAllister, Senior Director Human Resources
CNO: Joanna Salamone, Senior Vice President Clinical Services and Chief Nursing Officer
Web address: www.smhc.org
**Control:** Other not–for–profit (including NFP Corporation) **Service:** General medical and surgical

**Staffed Beds:** 196 **Admissions:** 7139 **Census:** 144 **Outpatient Visits:** 501132 **Births:** 520 **Total Expense ($000):** 302931 **Payroll Expense ($000):** 143109 **Personnel:** 1765

**SOUTHERN MAINE HEALTH CARE - BIDDEFORD MEDICAL CTR** See Southern Maine Health Care - Biddeford Medical Center

**SOUTHERN MAINE HEALTHCARE - BIDDEFORD CAMPUS** See Southern Maine Health Care - Biddeford Medical Center

## BLUE HILL—Hancock County

**BLUE HILL MEMORIAL HOSPITAL** See Northern Light Blue Hill Hospital

**NORTHERN LIGHT BLUE HILL HOSPITAL (201300)**, 57 Water Street, Zip 04614–5231, Mailing Address: P.O. Box 1029, Zip 04614–1029; tel. 207/374–3400, (Nonreporting) **A**10 18 **S** Northern Light Health, Brewer, ME
Primary Contact: John Ronan, President
CFO: Wendy Jones, Interim Chief Financial Officer
CHR: David Wheaton, Director Human Resources
CNO: Kathy Lirakis, R.N., Chief Nursing Officer
Web address: www.bhmh.org
**Control:** Other not–for–profit (including NFP Corporation) **Service:** General medical and surgical

**Staffed Beds:** 23

## BRIDGTON—Cumberland County

★ **BRIDGTON HOSPITAL (201310)**, 10 Hospital Drive, Zip 04009–1148; tel. 207/647–6000, (Nonreporting) **A**10 18 **F**1 3 4 8 11 13 15 18 29 30 31 34 35 40 43 44 45 50 57 59 64 65 67 68 75 76 77 78 79 80 81 85 87 90 91 93 94 96 97 98 107 108 110 114 119 128 130 131 132 133 135 143 144 146 148 **P**8 **S** Central Maine HealthCare, Lewiston, ME
Primary Contact: Peter J. Wright, FACHE, President
COO: Robert Slattery, Vice President of Operations
CMO: Alan Verrill, M.D., President Medical Staff
CHR: Kirk Miklavic, Director Human Resources
Web address: www.bridgtonhospital.org
**Control:** Other not–for–profit (including NFP Corporation) **Service:** General medical and surgical

**Staffed Beds:** 22 **Admissions:** 928 **Census:** 10 **Outpatient Visits:** 82858 **Births:** 41 **Total Expense ($000):** 47363 **Payroll Expense ($000):** 15824 **Personnel:** 242

**NORTHERN CUMBERLAND MEM HOSP** See Bridgton Hospital

## BRUNSWICK—Cumberland County

✠ **MID COAST HOSPITAL (200021)**, 123 Medical Center Drive, Zip 04011–2652; tel. 207/373–6000, (Nonreporting) **A**1 2 3 10 **F**3 5 11 12 13 15 18 20 28 29 30 31 32 34 35 36 40 41 44 45 46 47 48 49 51 53 54 56 57 58 59 61 64 65 66 68 70 74 75 76 77 78 79 81 82 84 85 86 87 89 92 93 97 98 101 102 103 105 107 108 110 111 115 119 129 130 131 132 134 135 144 146 147 148 149 150 152 153 154 156
Primary Contact: Lois N. Skillings, R.N., MSN, FACHE, President and Chief Executive Officer
COO: Philip A Ortolani, Vice President Operations
CFO: Robert N McCue, Vice President Finance
CMO: Scott Mills, M.D., Vice President Medical Staff Administration and Chief Medical Officer
CIO: Gale Stoy, Manager Information Systems
CHR: Coleen M Farrell, Vice President Human Resources
CNO: Deborah MacLeod, MS, R.N., Vice President Nursing and Patient Care Services
Web address: www.midcoasthealth.com
**Control:** Other not–for–profit (including NFP Corporation) **Service:** General medical and surgical

**Staffed Beds:** 93 **Admissions:** 5116 **Census:** 64 **Outpatient Visits:** 252642 **Births:** 585 **Total Expense ($000):** 204159 **Payroll Expense ($000):** 93578 **Personnel:** 1222

## CALAIS—Washington County

★ **CALAIS REGIONAL HOSPITAL (201305)**, 24 Hospital Lane, Zip 04619–1398; tel. 207/454–7521, (Nonreporting) **A**10 18 **F**3 8 11 15 18 28 29 32 34 35 40 45 50 54 57 59 62 64 65 68 75 77 81 82 83 85 87 90 93 97 107 108 110 111 115 119 127 129 130 133 146 149 154 156 157
Primary Contact: Rodney Boula, Chief Executive Officer
CFO: Jennifer Griffey, Vice President of Finance
CIO: Dee Dee Travis, Vice President Community Relations
CNO: Kelly Ball, Vice President of Clinical Operations
Web address: www.calaishospital.com
**Control:** Other not–for–profit (including NFP Corporation) **Service:** General medical and surgical

**Staffed Beds:** 10 **Admissions:** 603 **Census:** 8 **Outpatient Visits:** 34373 **Births:** 0 **Total Expense ($000):** 29122 **Payroll Expense ($000):** 12927 **Personnel:** 285

---

**Hospital, Medicare Provider Number, Address, Telephone, Approval, Facility, and Physician Codes, Health Care System**

★ American Hospital Association (AHA) membership  ○ Healthcare Facilities Accreditation Program  ⇑ Center for Improvement in Healthcare Quality Accreditation
☐ The Joint Commission accreditation  ◇ DNV Healthcare Inc. accreditation  △ Commission on Accreditation of Rehabilitation Facilities (CARF) accreditation

**ME**

## CARIBOU—Aroostook County

✉ **CARY MEDICAL CENTER (200031)**, 163 Van Buren Road, Suite 1, Zip 04736–3567; tel. 207/498–3111, (Total facility includes 9 beds in nursing home–type unit) (Nonreporting) **A**1 10 **F**3 8 11 13 15 28 29 31 32 34 35 36 38 40 43 44 51 53 54 56 57 59 61 64 67 68 70 75 76 77 78 79 81 82 84 85 86 87 89 90 93 97 107 108 111 115 118 119 121 130 131 132 135 144 146 147 148 156 **S** QHR Health, Brentwood, TN
Primary Contact: Kris A. Doody, R.N., Chief Executive Officer
COO: Leslie Anderson, Chief Operating Officer
CFO: Chelsea Lee Desrosiers, Chief Financial Officer
CMO: Regen Gallagher, D.O., Chief Medical Officer
CIO: Dave Silsbee, Chief Information Officer
CHR: Paula A. Parent, Chief Nursing Officer and Director of Human Resources
CNO: Paula A. Parent, Chief Nursing Officer
Web address: www.carymedicalcenter.org
**Control**: City, Government, Nonfederal **Service**: General medical and surgical

**Staffed Beds**: 49 **Admissions**: 1708 **Census**: 32 **Outpatient Visits**: 69178
**Births**: 204 **Total Expense ($000)**: 59296 **Payroll Expense ($000)**: 23068
**Personnel**: 428

## DAMARISCOTTA—Lincoln County

**LINCOLN HEALTH** See Lincolnhealth

★ **LINCOLNHEALTH (201302)**, 35 Miles Street, Zip 04543–4047; tel. 207/563–1234, (Includes LINCOLNHEALTH MILES CAMPUS, Mailing address: 35 Miles Street, Damariscotta, Maine, Zip 04543–4047; tel. 207/563–1234; James W Donovan, President; LINCOLNHEALTH ST. ANDREWS CAMPUS, Mailing address: 6 St Andrews Lane, Boothbay Harbor, Maine, Zip 04538–1732, P O Box 417, Zip 04538–0417, tel. 207/633–2121) (Total facility includes 66 beds in nursing home–type unit) **A**10 18 **F**3 5 10 11 13 15 29 30 32 34 35 40 44 45 50 57 59 64 65 67 70 75 76 78 79 81 84 85 86 87 93 96 97 107 108 110 111 114 115 119 125 127 128 130 132 133 135 144 146 147 148 149 156 **P**6 **S** MaineHealth, Portland, ME
Primary Contact: James W. Donovan, President
COO: Cynthia Wade, R.N., RN, BSNExecutive Vice President and Chief Operating Officer
CFO: Wayne Printy, Chief Financial Officer and Senior Vice President Finance
CIO: David Felton, Regional Chief Information Officer
CHR: Thomas R Girard, Vice President Human Resources
CNO: Christine Anderson, Chief Nursing Officer and Vice President of Patient Care Services
Web address: www.lchcare.org
**Control**: Other not–for–profit (including NFP Corporation) **Service**: General medical and surgical

**Staffed Beds**: 91 **Admissions**: 1847 **Census**: 76 **Outpatient Visits**: 115876
**Births**: 106 **Total Expense ($000)**: 90815 **Payroll Expense ($000)**: 26353
**Personnel**: 530

## DOVER–FOXCROFT—Piscataquis County

★ **MAYO REGIONAL HOSPITAL (201309)**, 897 West Main Street, Zip 04426–1099; tel. 207/564–8401, (Nonreporting) **A**10 18 **F**3 5 7 8 11 13 15 29 30 31 34 35 40 45 50 57 59 64 65 71 75 76 77 78 79 80 81 82 85 86 87 93 96 97 104 107 110 111 114 119 127 129 130 133 134 135 146 147 148 149 153 156 **S** Northern Light Health, Brewer, ME
Primary Contact: Marie E. Vienneau, FACHE, President and Chief Executive Officer
CFO: Nancy Glidden, Chief Financial Officer and Vice President Finance
CMO: Challa Reddy, M.D., President Medical Staff
CHR: James R Godley, Vice President of Human Resources
CNO: Denise Scuderi, Vice President Patient Care Services
Web address: www.mayohospital.com
**Control**: Hospital district or authority, Government, Nonfederal **Service**: General medical and surgical

**Staffed Beds**: 25 **Admissions**: 1203 **Census**: 12 **Outpatient Visits**: 66200
**Births**: 95 **Total Expense ($000)**: 57122 **Payroll Expense ($000)**: 27537
**Personnel**: 409

## ELLSWORTH—Hancock County

✉ **NORTHERN LIGHT MAINE COAST HOSPITAL (200050)**, 50 Union Street, Zip 04605–1599; tel. 207/664–5311, (Nonreporting) **A**1 10 **S** Northern Light Health, Brewer, ME
Primary Contact: John Ronan, President
CFO: Chris Frauenhofer, Chief Financial Officer
CMO: Sheena Whittaker, M.D., Chief Medical Officer
CIO: Scott Burtchell, Director Information Systems
CHR: Noah Lundy, Director of Human Resources
CNO: Kristin Cyr, R.N., MSN, Senior Nursing Executive and Vice President of Patient Care Services
Web address: www.mainehospital.org
**Control**: Other not–for–profit (including NFP Corporation) **Service**: General medical and surgical

**Staffed Beds**: 52

## FARMINGTON—Franklin County

✉ **FRANKLIN MEMORIAL HOSPITAL (200037)**, 111 Franklin Health Commons, Zip 04938–6144; tel. 207/778–6031, (Nonreporting) **A**1 5 10 20 **F**3 5 7 8 11 13 15 28 29 30 31 32 34 40 45 46 50 54 59 61 64 65 70 75 76 77 78 79 81 83 85 86 87 89 93 94 97 101 102 107 108 110 111 115 118 119 130 131 135 143 146 147 149
Primary Contact: Trampas Hutches, President
CFO: Wayne Bennett, Chief Financial Officer
CMO: Michael Rowland, M.D., Vice President Medical Affairs
CIO: Ralph Johnson, Chief Information Officer
CHR: Joline Hart, Vice President Human Resources
Web address: www.mainehealth.org/franklin-community-health-network/locations/franklin-memorial-hospital
**Control**: Other not–for–profit (including NFP Corporation) **Service**: General medical and surgical

**Staffed Beds**: 48 **Admissions**: 1655 **Census**: 17 **Outpatient Visits**: 16736
**Births**: 232 **Total Expense ($000)**: 94585 **Payroll Expense ($000)**: 39555
**Personnel**: 633

## FORT FAIRFIELD—Aroostook County

**COMMUNITY GENERAL HEALTH CENTER** See The Aroostook Medical Center, Presque Isle

**COMMUNITY GENERAL HOSPITAL** See Community General Health Center

## FORT KENT—Aroostook County

✉ **NORTHERN MAINE MEDICAL CENTER (200052)**, 194 East Main Street, Zip 04743–1497; tel. 207/834–3155, (Total facility includes 45 beds in nursing home–type unit) (Nonreporting) **A**1 10 20 **F**3 13 15 29 31 34 40 45 50 54 57 59 62 64 67 68 70 75 76 77 78 79 81 82 85 86 87 89 98 99 100 101 102 103 104 107 108 110 111 115 119 127 128 130 131 132 133 135 146 147 148 156 **P**6
Primary Contact: Peter Sirois, President and Chief Executive Officer
CFO: Cindy Daigle, Chief Financial Officer
CMO: Michael Sullivan, M.D., Chief Medical Officer
CIO: Adam Landry, Director of Information Systems
CHR: Robin Damboise, Director Human Resources
CNO: Alain Bois, R.N., Director of Nursing
Web address: www.nmmc.org
**Control**: Other not–for–profit (including NFP Corporation) **Service**: General medical and surgical

**Staffed Beds**: 81 **Admissions**: 1416 **Census**: 68 **Outpatient Visits**: 50327
**Births**: 44 **Total Expense ($000)**: 58503 **Payroll Expense ($000)**: 31741
**Personnel**: 414

## GREENVILLE—Piscataquis County

**CHARLES A. DEAN MEMORIAL HOSPITAL** See Northern Light Ca Dean Hospital

★ **NORTHERN LIGHT CA DEAN HOSPITAL (201301)**, 364 Pritham Avenue, Zip 04441–1395, Mailing Address: P.O. Box 1129, Zip 04441–1129; tel. 207/695–5200, (Nonreporting) **A**10 18 **F**7 11 28 29 30 34 35 40 45 53 54 56 59 62 64 77 85 93 97 102 104 107 119 127 128 130 133 143 148 154 **S** Northern Light Health, Brewer, ME
Primary Contact: Marie E. Vienneau, FACHE, President
CFO: Edward Olivier, Chief Financial Officer
CMO: Darin Peck, M.D., Chief of Staff
Web address: www.cadean.org
**Control**: Other not–for–profit (including NFP Corporation) **Service**: General medical and surgical

**Staffed Beds**: 25 **Admissions**: 183 **Census**: 17 **Outpatient Visits**: 76998
**Births**: 0 **Total Expense ($000)**: 17900 **Payroll Expense ($000)**: 9139
**Personnel**: 138

*Many Facility Codes have changed. Please refer to the AHA Guide Code Chart.*
© 2021 AHA Guide

## HOULTON—Aroostook County

★ **HOULTON REGIONAL HOSPITAL (201308)**, 20 Hartford Street,
Zip 04730–1891; tel. 207/532–2900, (Nonreporting) **A**10 18 **F**3 11 13 15 28
29 30 34 40 43 45 46 50 59 65 67 75 76 77 79 81 85 93 96 97 107 108 110
114 119 127 129 130 132 133 146 148 149
Primary Contact: Shawn D. Anderson, Chief Executive Officer
CFO: Cynthia Thompson, Chief Financial Officer
CMO: Brian Griffin, Director of Medical Affairs
Web address: www.houlton.net/hrh
**Control:** Other not–for–profit (including NFP Corporation) **Service:** General
medical and surgical

**Staffed Beds:** 25 **Admissions:** 1093 **Census:** 17 **Outpatient Visits:** 90815
**Births:** 112 **Total Expense ($000):** 47568 **Payroll Expense ($000):** 20395
**Personnel:** 308

## LEWISTON—Androscoggin County

✉ △ **CENTRAL MAINE MEDICAL CENTER (200024)**, 300 Main Street,
Zip 04240–7027; tel. 207/795–0111, (Nonreporting) **A**1 2 3 5 7 10 13 19 **F**3 11
12 13 15 18 19 20 22 24 26 28 29 30 31 32 34 35 36 40 41 43 44 45 46 47
48 49 50 51 52 54 55 56 57 58 59 61 64 65 66 67 68 70 71 73 74 75 76 77
78 79 81 82 84 85 86 87 89 90 91 92 93 97 101 104 107 108 110 114 115
118 119 120 121 123 124 129 130 131 132 135 143 146 147 148 149 150
**P**5 8 **S** Central Maine HealthCare, Lewiston, ME
Primary Contact: David Tupponce, M.D., President
CFO: John Whitlock, Chief Financial Officer
CMO: David Lauver, M.D., Chief Division Hospital Based Care
CIO: Denis Tanguay, Chief Information Officer
CHR: Kirk Miklavic, Director, Human Resources
Web address: www.cmmc.org
**Control:** Other not–for–profit (including NFP Corporation) **Service:** General
medical and surgical

**Staffed Beds:** 190 **Admissions:** 9437 **Census:** 124 **Outpatient
Visits:** 357115 **Births:** 567 **Total Expense ($000):** 408086 **Payroll Expense
($000):** 145816 **Personnel:** 1735

⇑ **ST MARY'S GENERAL HOSPITAL** See St. Mary's Regional Medical Center

★ ⇑ **ST. MARY'S REGIONAL MEDICAL CENTER (200034)**, 93 Campus
Avenue, Zip 04240–6030, Mailing Address: P.O. Box 291, Zip 04243–0291;
tel. 207/777–8100, (Nonreporting) **A**2 5 10 21 **S** Covenant Health, Tewksbury, MA
Primary Contact: Steven C. Jorgensen, President
CFO: Michael Hendrix, Chief Financial Officer
CMO: Christopher Bowe, M.D., Chief Medical Officer, Medical Affairs
CIO: Karen Bowling, Chief Information Officer
CHR: Nicole Morin-Scribner, Director Human Resources
CNO: Karen Clark, Vice President Patient Care Services
Web address: www.stmarysmaine.com
**Control:** Other not–for–profit (including NFP Corporation) **Service:** General
medical and surgical

**Staffed Beds:** 350

## LINCOLN—Penobscot County

★ **PENOBSCOT VALLEY HOSPITAL (201303)**, 7 Transalpine Road,
Zip 04457–4222, Mailing Address: P.O. Box 368, Zip 04457–0368;
tel. 207/794–3321, (Nonreporting) **A**10 18
Primary Contact: Crystal Landry, R.N., Chief Executive Officer
CFO: Ann Marie Rush, Chief Financial Officer
CHR: Sarah Loman, Director Human Resources
Web address: www.pvhme.com
**Control:** Other not–for–profit (including NFP Corporation) **Service:** General
medical and surgical

**Staffed Beds:** 25

## MACHIAS—Washington County

★ **DOWN EAST COMMUNITY HOSPITAL (201311)**, 11 Hospital Drive,
Zip 04654–3325; tel. 207/255–3356, (Nonreporting) **A**10 18 **F**3 13 15 28 29 34
35 40 45 57 64 65 75 76 77 79 81 82 83 84 85 89 93 97 107 108 110 111
115 119 127 130 133 146 147 148
Primary Contact: Steve Lail, Chief Executive Officer
CFO: Lynnette Parr, Chief Financial Officer
CMO: Aziz Massaad, M.D., Medical Staff President
CHR: Ernestine O Reisman, Vice President Human Resources
CNO: Stephanie Lakeman Baillargeon, R.N., Chief Nursing Officer
Web address: www.dech.org
**Control:** Other not–for–profit (including NFP Corporation) **Service:** General
medical and surgical

**Staffed Beds:** 25 **Admissions:** 881 **Census:** 9 **Outpatient Visits:** 44972
**Births:** 177 **Total Expense ($000):** 48400 **Payroll Expense ($000):** 20446
**Personnel:** 276

## MARS HILL—Aroostook County

**AROOSTOOK HEALTH CENTER** See The Aroostook Medical Center, Presque Isle

## MILLINOCKET—Penobscot County

★ **MILLINOCKET REGIONAL HOSPITAL (201307)**, 200 Somerset Street,
Zip 04462–1298; tel. 207/723–5161, (Nonreporting) **A**10 18 **F**3 8 11 15 29 31
34 35 40 41 45 50 53 54 56 59 64 65 68 75 77 78 79 80 81 82 85 87 93 96
97 107 108 110 111 114 118 119 127 128 130 131 132 133 135 144 145
148 154 156
Primary Contact: Robert Peterson, Chief Executive Officer
CFO: Catherine LeMay, Vice President Finance
CMO: Daniel Herbert, M.D., Medical Administrative Officer
CHR: Lisa Arsenault, Vice President Human Resources and Compliance
CNO: Mary Tatro EsqChief Nursing Officer
Web address: www.mrhme.org
**Control:** Other not–for–profit (including NFP Corporation) **Service:** General
medical and surgical

**Staffed Beds:** 25 **Admissions:** 520 **Census:** 6 **Outpatient Visits:** 26191
**Births:** 2 **Total Expense ($000):** 31333 **Payroll Expense ($000):** 14817
**Personnel:** 235

## NORWAY—Oxford County

★ **STEPHENS MEMORIAL HOSPITAL (201315)**, 181 Main Street,
Zip 04268–5664; tel. 207/743–5933, (Nonreporting) **A**3 10 18 **F**3 7 13 15 28
29 30 31 34 35 40 43 45 59 61 64 65 68 75 76 78 80 81 84 85 87 89 93 96
97 107 110 111 115 118 119 127 130 132 135 146 147 148 149 154 156 **S**
MaineHealth, Portland, ME
Primary Contact: Timothy A. Churchill, President
CMO: James Eshleman, D.O., President Medical Staff
CHR: Roberta Metivier, Vice President Human Resources and Administrator,
Western Main Nursing Home
Web address: www.https://mainehealth.org
**Control:** Other not–for–profit (including NFP Corporation) **Service:** General
medical and surgical

**Staffed Beds:** 25 **Admissions:** 1316 **Census:** 12 **Outpatient Visits:** 95934
**Births:** 166 **Total Expense ($000):** 76351 **Payroll Expense ($000):** 32329
**Personnel:** 475

---

**Hospital, Medicare Provider Number, Address, Telephone, Approval, Facility, and Physician Codes, Health Care System**

★ American Hospital Association (AHA) membership
☐ The Joint Commission accreditation
○ Healthcare Facilities Accreditation Program
◇ DNV Healthcare Inc. accreditation
⇑ Center for Improvement in Healthcare Quality Accreditation
△ Commission on Accreditation of Rehabilitation Facilities (CARF) accreditation

## PITTSFIELD—Somerset County

✣ **NORTHERN LIGHT SEBASTICOOK VALLEY HOSPITAL (201313)**, 447 North Main Street, Zip 04967–3707; tel. 207/487–4000, (Nonreporting) **A**1 10 18 **F**3 7 11 15 18 28 29 30 32 34 35 40 45 46 50 51 57 59 64 65 70 75 77 78 79 81 87 93 96 97 104 107 108 111 119 127 129 130 132 133 135 143 146 147 148 156 **P**6 **S** Northern Light Health, Brewer, ME
Primary Contact: Terri Vieira, President
COO: Michael Peterson, FACHE, Chief Operating Officer
CFO: Randal Clark, Vice President Finance
CMO: Robert Schlager, M.D., Chief Medical Officer
CIO: Michael Peterson, FACHE, Chief Operating Officer
CHR: Tammy Hatch, Manager
Web address: www.sebasticookvalleyhealth.org
**Control:** Other not–for–profit (including NFP Corporation) **Service:** General medical and surgical

| | |
|---|---|
| **Staffed Beds:** 25 **Admissions:** 631 **Census:** 12 **Outpatient Visits:** 82432 **Births:** 0 **Total Expense ($000):** 39762 **Payroll Expense ($000):** 16329 **Personnel:** 274 | |

**NORTHLIGHT SEBASTICOOK VALLEY HOSPITAL** See Northern Light Sebasticook Valley Hospital

## PORTLAND—Cumberland County

**BRIGHTON CAMPUS-MAINE MED CTR** See Maine Medical Center, Brighton Campus

**HEALTHSOUTH REHAB HOSPITAL** See New England Rehabilitation Hospital of Portland

✣ **MAINE MEDICAL CENTER (200009)**, 22 Bramhall Street, Zip 04102–3175; tel. 207/662–0111, (Includes BARBARA BUSH CHILDREN'S HOSPITAL, Mailing address: 22 Bramhall Street, Portland, Maine, Zip 04102–3134; tel. 207/662–0111; Richard W Petersen, President and Chief Executive Officer; MAINE MEDICAL CENTER, BRIGHTON CAMPUS, Mailing address: 335 Brighton Avenue, Portland, Maine, Zip 04102–9735, P O Box 9735, Zip 04102–9735, tel. 207/879–8000; Richard W Petersen, President and Chief Executive Officer) (Total facility includes 121 beds in nursing home–type unit) **A**1 2 3 5 8 10 **F**1 3 5 6 7 11 12 13 15 16 17 18 19 20 21 22 23 24 25 26 27 28 29 30 31 32 34 35 36 38 40 41 42 43 44 45 46 47 48 49 51 54 55 56 57 58 59 60 61 64 65 66 67 68 70 71 72 73 74 75 76 78 79 80 81 82 84 85 86 87 88 89 91 92 93 94 97 98 99 100 101 102 103 104 105 107 108 110 111 115 116 117 118 119 120 121 123 124 126 128 129 130 131 132 134 135 138 141 144 146 147 148 149 151 153 154 **P**6 8 **S** MaineHealth, Portland, ME
Primary Contact: Richard W. Petersen, President and Chief Executive Officer
COO: Jeff Sanders, Senior Vice President, Chief Operating Officer
CFO: Lou Inzana, Senior Vice President and Chief Financial Officer
CMO: Joel Botler, M.D., Chief Medical Officer
CHR: Judith M West, Senior Vice President Human Resources and Chief Human Resources Officer
CNO: Marjorie Wiggins, Senior Vice President, Chief Nursing Officer
Web address: www.mmc.org
**Control:** Other not–for–profit (including NFP Corporation) **Service:** General medical and surgical

| | |
|---|---|
| **Staffed Beds:** 758 **Admissions:** 30008 **Census:** 580 **Outpatient Visits:** 1100152 **Births:** 2916 **Total Expense ($000):** 1547790 **Payroll Expense ($000):** 657229 **Personnel:** 9147 | |

**MERCY HOSPITAL OF PORTLAND** See Northern Light Mercy Hospital

✣ **NEW ENGLAND REHABILITATION HOSPITAL OF PORTLAND (203025)**, 335 Brighton Avenue, Zip 04102–2363; tel. 207/775–4000, (Nonreporting) **A**1 3 10 **F**3 29 50 90 91 92 93 95 96 132 135 146 148 **S** Encompass Health Corporation, Birmingham, AL
Primary Contact: Jeanine Chesley, Chief Executive Officer
CFO: James Paladino, Controller
CMO: Thomas Morrione, Medical Director
CHR: Mary Cote, Director Human Resources
CNO: Sharon Kuhrt, Chief Nursing Officer
Web address: www.nerhp.org
**Control:** Partnership, Investor–owned (for–profit) **Service:** Rehabilitation

| | |
|---|---|
| **Staffed Beds:** 90 **Admissions:** 1820 **Census:** 63 **Outpatient Visits:** 10258 **Births:** 0 **Total Expense ($000):** 28687 **Payroll Expense ($000):** 15622 **Personnel:** 227 | |

✣ **NORTHERN LIGHT MERCY HOSPITAL (200008)**, 144 State Street, Zip 04101–3795; tel. 207/879–3000, (Nonreporting) **A**1 2 5 10 **F**3 11 13 15 18 20 29 30 31 34 35 36 40 44 45 48 49 50 51 54 55 56 57 58 59 61 64 68 70 73 74 75 76 78 79 81 82 84 86 87 93 96 97 100 102 104 107 108 110 111 114 115 119 130 132 135 143 144 146 147 148 149 154 156 **P**6 **S** Northern Light Health, Brewer, ME
Primary Contact: Charles D. Therrien, President
CFO: Michael Hachey, Senior Vice President and Chief Financial Officer
CIO: Craig Dreher, Chief Information Officer
CHR: Elizabeth B Christensen, Director Human Resources
CNO: Bette Neville, R.N., MSN, Vice President and Chief Nursing Officer
Web address: www.https://northernlighthealth.org/Mercy-Hospital
**Control:** Other not–for–profit (including NFP Corporation) **Service:** General medical and surgical

| | |
|---|---|
| **Staffed Beds:** 104 **Admissions:** 4165 **Census:** 45 **Outpatient Visits:** 346079 **Births:** 649 **Total Expense ($000):** 221939 **Payroll Expense ($000):** 94526 **Personnel:** 1055 | |

**THE BARBARA BUSH CHILDREN'S HOSPITAL** See Barbara Bush Children's Hospital

## PRESQUE ISLE—Aroostook County

**AROOSTOOK MEDICAL CENTER** See The Aroostook Medical Center

✣ **THE AROOSTOOK MEDICAL CENTER (200018)**, 140 Academy Street, Zip 04769–3171, Mailing Address: P.O. Box 151, Zip 04769–0151; tel. 207/768–4000, (Includes AROOSTOOK HEALTH CENTER, Mailing address: 15 Highland Avenue, Mars Hill, Maine, Zip 4758; tel. 207/768–4900; ARTHUR R. GOULD MEMORIAL HOSPITAL, Mailing address: 140 Academy Street, Presque Isle, Maine, Zip 4769, P O Box 151, Zip 4769, tel. 207/768–4000; COMMUNITY GENERAL HEALTH CENTER, Mailing address: 3 Green Street, Fort Fairfield, Maine, Zip 4742; tel. 207/768–4700) (Total facility includes 64 beds in nursing home–type unit) **A**1 10 **F**3 7 8 12 13 15 18 20 28 29 30 31 32 34 35 36 38 40 43 45 51 52 53 54 56 57 59 60 61 64 65 67 70 74 75 76 78 79 81 82 84 85 86 87 89 90 91 93 96 97 104 107 108 110 114 115 116 117 118 119 120 121 123 128 129 130 131 132 133 134 135 143 144 146 147 148 149 150 154 156 **P**6 **S** Northern Light Health, Brewer, ME
Primary Contact: Gregory LaFrancois, President
COO: Jay Reynolds, M.D., Chief Medical Officer and Chief Clinical Officer
CFO: C Bruce Sandstrom, Vice President and Chief Financial Officer
CMO: Jay Reynolds, M.D., Chief Medical Officer and Chief Clinical Officer
CIO: Kyle Johnson, Chief Information Officer
CHR: Joseph Siddiqui, Vice President Human Resources
Web address: www.tamc.org
**Control:** Other not–for–profit (including NFP Corporation) **Service:** General medical and surgical

| | |
|---|---|
| **Staffed Beds:** 114 **Admissions:** 2336 **Census:** 85 **Outpatient Visits:** 270212 **Births:** 180 **Total Expense ($000):** 140548 **Payroll Expense ($000):** 66421 **Personnel:** 820 | |

## ROCKPORT—Knox County

☐ **PEN BAY MEDICAL CENTER (200063)**, 6 Glen Cove Drive, Zip 04856–4240; tel. 207/921–8000, (Total facility includes 70 beds in nursing home–type unit) (Nonreporting) **A**1 3 10 20 **F**3 4 5 13 15 18 28 29 30 31 32 34 35 36 38 40 44 45 46 47 48 49 50 55 56 58 59 64 65 68 69 70 74 75 76 77 78 79 81 82 83 84 85 87 89 91 92 93 94 96 97 98 100 104 107 108 110 111 115 116 117 118 119 130 131 132 135 146 147 148 149 154 156 157 **S** MaineHealth, Portland, ME
Primary Contact: Mark Fourre, President
COO: Eric Waters, Vice President Operations
CFO: Maura Kelly, Vice President Fiscal Services
CMO: Dana L Goldsmith, M.D., Vice President Medical Affairs
CIO: Brooks Betts, Director Information Systems and Chief Information Officer
CHR: Thomas R Girard, Vice President Human Resources
CNO: Paula Delahanty, Regional Chief Nursing Officer
Web address: www.penbayhealthcare.org
**Control:** Other not–for–profit (including NFP Corporation) **Service:** General medical and surgical

| | |
|---|---|
| **Staffed Beds:** 151 **Admissions:** 3425 **Census:** 109 **Outpatient Visits:** 194877 **Births:** 272 **Total Expense ($000):** 167134 **Payroll Expense ($000):** 74210 **Personnel:** 1015 | |

**PENOBSCOT BAY MEDICAL CENTER** See Pen Bay Medical Center

**ME**

*Many Facility Codes have changed. Please refer to the AHA Guide Code Chart.*

## RUMFORD—Oxford County

**RUMFORD COMMUNITY HOSPITAL** See Rumford Hospital

★ **RUMFORD HOSPITAL (201306)**, 420 Franklin Street, Zip 04276–2145;
tel. 207/369–1000, (Nonreporting) **A**3 10 18 **F**1 3 4 8 11 13 15 16 17 18 28 29
30 31 34 35 40 43 44 45 50 53 57 59 64 65 67 68 70 72 73 75 76 77 78 79
80 81 85 87 88 89 90 91 93 94 96 97 98 107 110 114 119 127 128 130 132
133 135 143 144 146 148 **P**8 **S** Central Maine HealthCare, Lewiston, ME
Primary Contact: Peter J. Wright, FACHE, President
CNO: Becky Hall, R.N., Director Nursing
Web address: www.rumfordhospital.org
**Control**: Other not–for–profit (including NFP Corporation) **Service**: General
medical and surgical

| | |
|---|---|
| **Staffed Beds:** 25 **Admissions:** 859 **Census:** 10 **Outpatient Visits:** 67644 **Births:** 96 **Total Expense ($000):** 43040 **Payroll Expense ($000):** 15267 **Personnel:** 213 | |

## SKOWHEGAN—Somerset County

★ **REDINGTON-FAIRVIEW GENERAL HOSPITAL (201314)**, 46 Fairview Avenue,
Zip 4976, Mailing Address: PO Box 468, Zip 04976–0468; tel. 207/474–5121,
(Nonreporting) **A**10 18 **F**3 7 11 13 15 18 28 29 31 34 35 40 45 47 50 53 56 57
59 65 68 70 74 75 76 77 79 81 82 84 85 91 92 93 97 107 108 110 114 115
118 119 130 131 132 133 134 135 146 147 148 149 155 156 **P**6
Primary Contact: Richard Willett, Chief Executive Officer
CFO: Elmer H Doucette, Chief Financial Officer
CMO: Gust Stringos, M.D., Medical Staff Director
CHR: Lisa G. Landry, Human Resources Director
CNO: Sherry L Rogers, MS, R.N., Chief Nursing Officer
Web address: www.rfgh.net
**Control**: Other not–for–profit (including NFP Corporation) **Service**: General
medical and surgical

| | |
|---|---|
| **Staffed Beds:** 25 **Admissions:** 1349 **Census:** 14 **Outpatient Visits:** 133656 **Births:** 128 **Total Expense ($000):** 96579 **Payroll Expense ($000):** 47479 **Personnel:** 632 | |

## WATERVILLE—Kennebec County

**INLAND HOSPITAL** See Northern Light Inland Hospital

★ ○ **NORTHERN LIGHT INLAND HOSPITAL (200041)**, 200 Kennedy Memorial
Drive, Zip 04901–4595; tel. 207/861–3000, (Nonreporting) **A**10 11 **F**3 13 15 18
28 29 30 34 35 40 44 45 46 50 51 56 57 59 64 68 70 74 75 76 77 79 81 82
85 92 93 97 100 102 104 107 108 109 110 111 115 119 127 129 130 132
146 147 148 149 151 154 **P**6 **S** Northern Light Health, Brewer, ME
Primary Contact: Terri Vieira, President
COO: Daniel Booth, Vice President Operations and Chief Human Resources Officer
CFO: Dean Bither, Chief Financial Officer
CMO: Michael Palumbo, D.O., Vice President Medical Affairs and Chief Education
CIO: Kevin Dieterich, Director Information Services
CHR: Daniel Booth, Vice President Operations
Web address: www.inlandhospital.org
**Control**: Other not–for–profit (including NFP Corporation) **Service**: General
medical and surgical

| | |
|---|---|
| **Staffed Beds:** 29 **Admissions:** 1261 **Census:** 11 **Outpatient Visits:** 13649 **Births:** 292 **Total Expense ($000):** 75115 **Payroll Expense ($000):** 28942 **Personnel:** 452 | |

## WESTBROOK—Cumberland County

**JACKSON BROOK INSTITUTE** See Spring Harbor Hospital

☒ **SPRING HARBOR HOSPITAL (204005)**, 123 Andover Road, Zip 04092–3850;
tel. 207/761–2200, (Nonreporting) **A**1 3 10 **F**50 59 68 75 80 87 98 99 100 103
104 130 132 157 **S** MaineHealth, Portland, ME
Primary Contact: Mary Jane Krebs, FACHE, President
CFO: Michael Abbatiello, Chief Financial Officer
CMO: Girard Robinson, M.D., Senior Vice President Medical and Clinical Affairs
CIO: Susan Moulton, Director Health Information Management
CHR: Timothy McNulty, Director Human Resources
Web address: www.springharbor.org
**Control**: Other not–for–profit (including NFP Corporation) **Service**: Psychiatric

| | |
|---|---|
| **Staffed Beds:** 100 **Admissions:** 2159 **Census:** 81 **Outpatient Visits:** 1614 **Births:** 0 **Total Expense ($000):** 41218 **Payroll Expense ($000):** 20963 **Personnel:** 298 | |

## YORK—York County

★ **YORK HOSPITAL (200020)**, 15 Hospital Drive, Zip 03909–1099;
tel. 207/363–4321, (Nonreporting) **A**10
Primary Contact: Jennifer Cutts, M.D., Interim Chief Executive Officer
CFO: Robin LaBonte, Leader Financial Care
CMO: Jennifer Cutts, M.D., Chief Medical Officer
CIO: Robin LaBonte, Leader Financial Care
CHR: Olivia Chayer, Director, Human Resources
Web address: www.yorkhospital.com
**Control**: Other not–for–profit (including NFP Corporation) **Service**: General
medical and surgical

| | |
|---|---|
| **Staffed Beds:** 58 | |

---

**Hospital, Medicare Provider Number, Address, Telephone, Approval, Facility, and Physician Codes, Health Care System**

★ American Hospital Association (AHA) membership    ○ Healthcare Facilities Accreditation Program    ⇑ Center for Improvement in Healthcare Quality Accreditation
□ The Joint Commission accreditation    ◇ DNV Healthcare Inc. accreditation    △ Commission on Accreditation of Rehabilitation Facilities (CARF) accreditation

# MARYLAND

## ANNAPOLIS—Anne Arundel County

**ANNE ARUNDEL MEDICAL CENTER (210023)**, 2001 Medical Parkway, Zip 21401–3019; tel. 443/481–1000, (Total facility includes 40 beds in nursing home–type unit) (Nonreporting) **A**1 2 3 5 10 **F**3 4 5 9 11 12 13 14 15 18 20 22 26 28 29 30 31 32 34 35 37 38 39 40 41 44 45 46 47 49 50 53 54 55 56 57 58 59 60 61 63 64 65 66 68 70 72 74 75 76 77 78 79 81 82 83 84 85 87 89 91 92 93 94 96 97 100 101 102 105 107 108 110 111 114 115 116 117 118 119 120 121 123 124 126 130 131 132 134 135 146 147 148 149 150 152 153 154 156 157 **P**6 7 8
Primary Contact: Sherry B. Perkins, Ph.D., R.N., President
CFO: Robert Reilly, Vice President and Chief Financial Officer
CMO: Mitchell B Schwartz, M.D., Chief Medical Officer
CIO: Barbara Baldwin, Chief Information Officer
CHR: Julie McGovern, Vice President Human Resources
CNO: Barbara S Jacobs, MSN, Vice President, Nursing and Chief Nursing Officer
Web address: www.aahs.org
**Control**: Other not–for–profit (including NFP Corporation) **Service**: General medical and surgical

**Staffed Beds**: 412 **Admissions**: 26752 **Census**: 298 **Outpatient Visits**: 501885 **Births**: 5299 **Total Expense ($000)**: 557932 **Payroll Expense ($000)**: 215316 **Personnel**: 4143

## BALTIMORE—Baltimore County

**BON SECOURS BALTIMORE HEALTH SYSTEM** See Grace Medical Center

**FRANCIS SCOTT KEY MED CENTER** See Johns Hopkins Bayview Medical Center

**GOOD SAMARITAN HOSPITAL OF MARYLAND** See Medstar Good Samaritan Hospital

**GRACE MEDICAL CENTER (210013)**, 2000 West Baltimore Street, Zip 21223–1558; tel. 410/362–3000, (Nonreporting) **A**1 10 **F**3 15 18 20 26 29 30 40 44 49 58 59 60 64 66 70 77 78 79 81 84 85 87 97 98 99 100 101 102 103 104 105 107 108 110 111 115 119 130 143 146 148 153 154 156 158 **S** LifeBridge Health, Baltimore, MD
Primary Contact: Daniel Blum, President
CFO: Patricia Miley, Director of Finance
CMO: Esti Schabelman, Chief Medical Officer
Web address: www.lifebridgehealth.org
**Control**: Church operated, Nongovernment, not–for–profit **Service**: General medical and surgical

**Staffed Beds**: 68 **Admissions**: 3000 **Census**: 50 **Outpatient Visits**: 31973 **Births**: 0 **Total Expense ($000)**: 114972 **Payroll Expense ($000)**: 42532 **Personnel**: 644

**GREATER BALTIMORE MEDICAL CENTER (210044)**, 6701 North Charles Street, Zip 21204–6892; tel. 443/849–2000, (Total facility includes 27 beds in nursing home–type unit) (Nonreporting) **A**1 2 3 5 10 **F**8 11 12 13 18 20 22 26 29 30 31 34 35 38 40 41 44 45 46 47 48 49 50 51 53 55 56 57 58 59 60 61 62 63 64 68 70 72 73 74 75 76 77 78 79 80 81 82 83 84 85 86 87 89 92 93 96 97 102 107 108 114 115 119 120 121 123 124 126 128 129 130 132 135 136 142 145 146 147 148 154 156 157 **P**4
Primary Contact: John B. Chessare, M.D., M.P.H., FACHE, President and Chief Executive Officer
COO: Keith R Poisson, Executive Vice President and Chief Operating Officer
CFO: Eric L Melchior, Executive Vice President and Chief Financial Officer
CMO: John R Saunders, M.D., Senior Vice President Medical Affairs and Chief Medical Officer
CHR: Deloris Simpson-Tuggle, Vice President Human Resources and Organizational Development and Chief Human Resources Officer
CNO: Jody Porter, R.N., Senior Vice President Patient Care Services and Chief Nursing Officer
Web address: www.gbmc.org
**Control**: Other not–for–profit (including NFP Corporation) **Service**: General medical and surgical

**Staffed Beds**: 383 **Admissions**: 17674 **Census**: 188 **Outpatient Visits**: 515434 **Births**: 4090 **Total Expense ($000)**: 524079 **Payroll Expense ($000)**: 277529 **Personnel**: 3746

**JOHNS HOPKINS BAYVIEW MEDICAL CENTER (210029)**, 4940 Eastern Avenue, Zip 21224–2780; tel. 410/550–0100, (Nonreporting) **A**1 3 5 7 8 10 **F**1 2 3 4 5 6 8 9 11 12 13 15 16 17 18 20 22 26 28 29 30 31 32 34 35 36 38 40 41 43 44 45 46 47 48 49 50 51 54 55 56 57 58 59 60 61 64 65 66 68 70 71 72 74 75 76 77 78 79 80 81 82 84 85 86 87 89 90 92 93 96 97 98 99 100 101 102 103 104 107 108 110 111 115 116 117 118 119 120 121 123 126 130 131 132 134 135 141 143 146 147 148 149 152 153 154 157 **P**6 **S** Johns Hopkins Health System, Baltimore, MD
Primary Contact: Richard G. Bennett, M.D., President
CFO: Carl H Francioli, Vice President Finance
CIO: Sandy Reckert, Director Communications and Public Affairs
CHR: Craig R Brodian, Vice President Human Resources
Web address: www.hopkinsbayview.org
**Control**: Other not–for–profit (including NFP Corporation) **Service**: General medical and surgical

**Staffed Beds**: 411 **Admissions**: 19184 **Census**: 315 **Outpatient Visits**: 403303 **Births**: 1330 **Total Expense ($000)**: 585519 **Payroll Expense ($000)**: 199642 **Personnel**: 3936

**JOHNS HOPKINS HOSPITAL (210009)**, 600 North Wolfe Street, Admin 104, Zip 21287–1629; tel. 410/955–5000, (Includes JOHNS HOPKINS CHILDREN'S CENTER, Mailing address: 1800 Orleans Street, Baltimore, Maryland, Zip 21287–0010; tel. 410/955–5000), (Nonreporting) **A**1 2 3 5 7 8 10 **F**3 4 5 6 7 8 9 11 13 14 15 16 17 18 19 20 21 22 23 24 25 26 27 28 29 30 31 32 34 35 36 38 39 40 41 43 44 45 46 47 48 49 50 51 52 54 55 56 57 58 59 60 61 63 64 65 66 68 70 72 74 75 76 77 78 79 80 81 82 83 84 85 86 87 88 89 90 91 92 93 94 95 96 97 98 99 100 101 102 103 104 105 106 107 108 109 110 111 112 113 114 115 116 117 118 119 120 121 123 124 126 129 130 131 132 134 135 136 137 138 139 140 141 142 143 145 146 147 148 149 150 151 152 153 154 155 156 157 **P**6 **S** Johns Hopkins Health System, Baltimore, MD
Primary Contact: Redonda G. Miller, M.D., President
COO: Charles B. Reuland, Sc.D., Executive Vice President and Chief Operatng Officer
CFO: Ronald J Werthman, Senior Vice President Finance, Chief Financial Officer and Treasurer
CIO: Stephanie L Reel, Senior Vice President Information Services
CHR: Bonnie Windsor, Senior Vice President Human Resources
CNO: Deborah Baker, Vice President, Nursing
Web address: www.hopkinsmedicine.org
**Control**: Other not–for–profit (including NFP Corporation) **Service**: General medical and surgical

**Staffed Beds**: 1008 **Admissions**: 41573 **Census**: 863 **Outpatient Visits**: 642117 **Births**: 2396 **Total Expense ($000)**: 2439538 **Payroll Expense ($000)**: 660812 **Personnel**: 10955

**KENNEDY KRIEGER CHILDREN'S HSP** See Kennedy Krieger Institute

**KENNEDY KRIEGER INSTITUTE (213301)**, 707 North Broadway, Zip 21205–1890; tel. 443/923–9200, (Nonreporting) **A**1 3 5 7 10
Primary Contact: Bradley Schlagger, M.D., President and Chief Executive Officer
COO: James M Anders JrAdministrator and Chief Operating Officer
CFO: Michael J Neuman, Vice President Finance
CMO: Michael V Johnston, M.D., Chief Medical Officer and Senior Vice President Medical Programs
CIO: Kenneth Davis, Assistant Vice President Information Systems
CHR: Michael Loughran, Vice President Human Resources
Web address: www.kennedykrieger.org
**Control**: Other not–for–profit (including NFP Corporation) **Service**: Children's other specialty

**Staffed Beds**: 70

**KERNAN ORTHOPAEDICS AND REHABILITATION** See University of Maryland Rehabilitation & Orthopaedic Institute

**KESWICK-HOME FOR INCURABLES** See Keswick Multi-Care Center

*Many Facility Codes have changed. Please refer to the AHA Guide Code Chart.*  © 2021 AHA Guide

**LEVINDALE HEBREW GERIATRIC CENTER AND HOSPITAL** See Levindale Hebrew Hospital and Nursing

☐ △ **LEVINDALE HEBREW HOSPITAL AND NURSING (210064)**, 2434 West Belvedere Avenue, Zip 21215–5267; tel. 410/601–2400, (Nonreporting) **A**1 7 10 **S** LifeBridge Health, Baltimore, MD
Primary Contact: Deborah Graves, R.N., President and Chief Operating Officer
CMO: Susan M Levy, M.D., Vice President Medical Affairs
CIO: Tressa Springmann, Vice President and Chief Information Officer
CHR: Cheryl T. Boyer, Vice President Human Resources
CNO: Candy Hamner, Vice President and Chief Nursing Officer
Web address: www.sinai-balt.com
**Control**: Other not–for–profit (including NFP Corporation) **Service**: Acute long–term care hospital

**Staffed Beds**: 490

**MARYLAND GENERAL HOSPITAL** See University of Maryland Medical Center Midtown Campus

⊞ **MEDSTAR FRANKLIN SQUARE MEDICAL CENTER (210015)**, 9000 Franklin Square Drive, Zip 21237–3901; tel. 443/777–7000, (Nonreporting) **A**1 2 3 5 8 10 **F**3 5 9 11 12 13 15 18 20 22 26 28 29 30 31 32 34 35 36 37 38 39 40 41 44 45 46 47 48 49 50 51 55 56 57 58 59 60 61 63 64 65 66 69 70 71 72 74 75 76 77 78 79 81 82 84 85 86 87 89 92 93 94 97 98 99 100 101 102 103 104 107 108 110 111 114 115 118 119 120 121 123 124 126 129 130 131 132 134 135 145 146 147 148 149 154 **P**1 6 **S** MedStar Health, Columbia, MD
Primary Contact: Stuart M. Levine, M.D., President
CFO: Robert P Lally JrVice President Finance
CMO: Tony Sclama, M.D., Vice President Medical Affairs
CIO: Stephen Mannion, Assistant Vice President Information Systems Customer Service
CNO: Lawrence F Strassner III, Ph.D., FACHE, R.N., MS, Senior Vice President Operations and Chief Nursing Officer
Web address: www.medstarfranklin.org
**Control**: Other not–for–profit (including NFP Corporation) **Service**: General medical and surgical

**Staffed Beds**: 369 **Admissions**: 20266 **Census**: 244 **Outpatient Visits**: 398162 **Births**: 2322 **Total Expense ($000)**: 538272 **Payroll Expense ($000)**: 231662 **Personnel**: 2732

**MEDSTAR FRANKLIN SQUARE MEDICAL CENTER** See Medstar Franklin Square Medical Center

⊞ △ **MEDSTAR GOOD SAMARITAN HOSPITAL (210056)**, 5601 Loch Raven Boulevard, Zip 21239–2995; tel. 443/444–8000, (Nonreporting) **A**1 3 5 7 10 **F**3 5 6 8 9 10 11 15 17 18 28 29 30 31 34 35 38 40 44 45 46 47 48 49 50 51 53 56 57 58 59 60 61 64 65 66 68 69 70 74 75 77 78 79 80 81 82 84 85 86 87 90 91 92 93 95 96 97 100 101 102 104 107 108 110 111 114 115 116 117 118 119 120 121 123 124 129 130 131 132 135 143 145 146 148 149 154 156 **P**1 6 **S** MedStar Health, Columbia, MD
Primary Contact: Bradley Chambers, President and Senior Vice President, MedStar Health
CFO: Deana Stout, Vice President Financial Services
Web address: www.goodsam-md.org
**Control**: Other not–for–profit (including NFP Corporation) **Service**: General medical and surgical

**Staffed Beds**: 199 **Admissions**: 8418 **Census**: 130 **Outpatient Visits**: 226687 **Births**: 0 **Total Expense ($000)**: 262314 **Payroll Expense ($000)**: 116952 **Personnel**: 1492

⊞ **MEDSTAR HARBOR HOSPITAL (210034)**, 3001 South Hanover Street, Zip 21225–1290; tel. 410/350–3200, (Nonreporting) **A**1 3 5 10 **F**3 9 11 13 15 18 29 30 34 35 36 40 43 44 45 46 48 49 50 51 53 54 55 56 57 58 59 60 61 63 64 65 66 68 70 73 74 75 76 77 78 79 81 82 84 85 86 87 89 92 93 94 97 98 100 102 103 104 105 107 108 110 111 114 115 119 129 130 131 132 135 146 147 149 153 154 **P**1 6 **S** MedStar Health, Columbia, MD
Primary Contact: Jill Donaldson, President
CFO: David R Pitman, Vice President Finance
CMO: Allan Birenberg, Vice President Medical Affairs
CIO: Cynthia Tanebaum, Director Information Services
CHR: Karen Evelius, Director Human Resources
CNO: Lenora Addison, Vice President Patient Care and Nursing
Web address: www.harborhospital.org
**Control**: Other not–for–profit (including NFP Corporation) **Service**: General medical and surgical

**Staffed Beds**: 128 **Admissions**: 7362 **Census**: 94 **Outpatient Visits**: 143296 **Births**: 1333 **Total Expense ($000)**: 190215 **Payroll Expense ($000)**: 84714 **Personnel**: 1011

**MEDSTAR HARBOR HOSPITAL** See Medstar Harbor Hospital

⊞ **MEDSTAR UNION MEMORIAL HOSPITAL (210024)**, 201 East University Parkway, Zip 21218–2895; tel. 410/554–2000, (Nonreporting) **A**1 3 5 10 **F**3 9 11 15 17 18 20 22 24 26 28 29 30 34 35 37 38 39 40 43 44 46 50 51 53 54 55 57 58 59 60 61 64 65 66 68 70 74 75 77 78 79 80 81 82 84 85 86 87 91 92 93 94 96 97 100 101 102 104 105 107 108 110 111 114 115 118 119 126 130 131 132 135 141 145 146 149 150 153 154 156 **P**1 6 **S** MedStar Health, Columbia, MD
Primary Contact: Bradley Chambers, President
COO: Neil MacDonald, Vice President, Operations
CFO: Deana Stout, Vice President, Finance
CMO: Stuart Bell, M.D., Vice President, Medical Affairs
CIO: Janet Decker, Assistant Vice President, Information Systems
CHR: Ashley Handwerk, Director, Human Resources
CNO: Karen Owings, MSN, Vice President, Patient Care Services
Web address: www.medstarunionmemorial.org
**Control**: Other not–for–profit (including NFP Corporation) **Service**: General medical and surgical

**Staffed Beds**: 214 **Admissions**: 10726 **Census**: 132 **Outpatient Visits**: 298210 **Births**: 0 **Total Expense ($000)**: 448102 **Payroll Expense ($000)**: 194105 **Personnel**: 1917

**MEDSTAR UNION MEMORIAL HOSPITAL** See Medstar Union Memorial Hospital

⊞ **MERCY MEDICAL CENTER (210008)**, 301 St Paul Place, Zip 21202–2165; tel. 410/332–9000, (Nonreporting) **A**1 2 3 5 10 **F**3 4 11 13 14 15 18 20 29 30 31 34 35 36 37 39 40 41 44 45 46 47 48 49 50 51 55 57 58 59 64 65 66 68 70 72 74 75 76 77 78 79 81 82 84 85 86 87 89 92 93 94 100 102 107 108 110 111 114 115 116 117 118 119 120 121 123 124 126 128 129 130 131 132 135 141 142 143 144 145 146 147 148 149 150 154 156 157 158
Primary Contact: David N. Maine, M.D., President and Chief Executive Officer
COO: Susan D Finlayson, MSN, R.N., Senior Vice President of MMC Operations
CFO: Justin Deibel, Senior Vice President and Chief Financial Officer
CMO: Wilma Rowe, M.D., Senior Vice President Medical Affairs
CIO: Kathleen Perry, Senior Vice President and Chief Information Officer
CHR: Tammy Janus, Senior Vice President Human Resources
CNO: Kim Bushnell, R.N., Vice President, Patient Care Services
Web address: www.mdmercy.com
**Control**: Church operated, Nongovernment, not–for–profit **Service**: General medical and surgical

**Staffed Beds**: 229 **Admissions**: 14175 **Census**: 171 **Outpatient Visits**: 273878 **Births**: 2478 **Total Expense ($000)**: 493863 **Payroll Expense ($000)**: 182520 **Personnel**: 3747

---

**MT. WASHINGTON PEDIATRIC HOSPITAL (213300)**, 1708 West Rogers Avenue, Zip 21209–4545; tel. 410/578–8600, (Nonreporting) **A**1 3 5 7 10 **S** University of Maryland Medical System, Baltimore, MD
Primary Contact: Sheldon J. Stein, President and Chief Executive Officer
CFO: Mary Miller, Vice President Finance and Business Development
CMO: Richard Katz, M.D., Vice President Medical Affairs
CIO: Tim Brady, Director Information Systems
CHR: Thomas J Ellis, Vice President Human Resources
Web address: www.mwph.org
**Control:** Other not–for–profit (including NFP Corporation) **Service:** Children's other specialty

**Staffed Beds:** 61

**SAINT AGNES HEALTHCARE (210011)**, 900 Caton Avenue, Zip 21229–5201; tel. 667/234–6000, (Nonreporting) **A**1 2 3 5 10 **F**3 8 11 12 13 14 15 17 18 20 22 26 28 29 30 31 32 34 35 40 41 44 46 49 50 53 54 55 56 57 58 59 60 61 64 65 68 70 72 74 75 76 77 78 79 81 82 84 85 86 87 88 89 92 93 96 97 100 107 108 110 111 114 115 117 118 119 120 121 123 124 126 129 130 131 132 134 135 144 146 147 148 149 150 154 156 157 **P**6 **S** Ascension Healthcare, Saint Louis, MO
Primary Contact: Edward Lovern, President and Chief Executive Officer
CFO: Scott Furniss, Vice President and Chief Financial Officer
CMO: Nancy Hammond, M.D., Vice President, Chief Medical Officer
CHR: James Bobbitt, Vice President Human Resources, Group Ministry Market
CNO: Yolanda Copeland, R.N., Senior Vice President Patient Care Services and Chief Nursing Officer
Web address: www.stagnes.org
**Control:** Church operated, Nongovernment, not–for–profit **Service:** General medical and surgical

**Staffed Beds:** 367 **Admissions:** 16714 **Census:** 181 **Outpatient Visits:** 505112 **Births:** 1912 **Total Expense ($000):** 409375 **Payroll Expense ($000):** 206907 **Personnel:** 2394

**SAINT AGNES HOSPITAL** See Saint Agnes Healthcare

**SHEPPARD AND ENOCH PRATT HOSPITAL** See Sheppard Pratt Health System

**SHEPPARD PRATT HEALTH SYSTEM (214000)**, 6501 North Charles Street, Zip 21204–6819, Mailing Address: P.O. Box 6815, Zip 21285–6815; tel. 410/938–3000, (Nonreporting) **A**1 3 5 10 **F**4 6 29 30 34 35 36 38 50 56 57 58 59 64 68 75 77 82 86 87 98 99 100 101 103 104 105 106 130 131 132 135 143 144 146 149 150 153 154
Primary Contact: Harsh Trivedi, M.D., President and Chief Executive Officer
CFO: Ray R Dziesinski, Vice President and Chief Financial Officer
CIO: Matthew Knudsen, Director, Information Systems
CHR: Cathy Doughty, Vice President Human Resources
CNO: Ernestine Y. Cosby, Vice President Clinical Services and Chief Nursing Officer
Web address: www.sheppardpratt.org
**Control:** Other not–for–profit (including NFP Corporation) **Service:** Psychiatric

**Staffed Beds:** 338 **Admissions:** 7958 **Census:** 298 **Outpatient Visits:** 83178 **Births:** 0 **Total Expense ($000):** 234768 **Payroll Expense ($000):** 121914 **Personnel:** 2399

**SINAI HOSPITAL OF BALTIMORE (210012)**, 2401 West Belvedere Avenue, Zip 21215–5271; tel. 410/601–9000, (Nonreporting) **A**1 2 3 5 7 10 **F**2 3 5 6 8 9 12 13 15 17 18 19 20 22 24 26 29 30 31 32 34 35 36 37 38 39 40 41 43 44 46 47 49 50 51 52 54 55 56 57 58 59 60 61 63 64 65 66 68 70 72 73 74 75 76 77 78 79 80 81 82 84 85 86 87 88 89 90 91 92 93 94 95 96 97 98 100 101 102 104 107 108 110 111 114 115 116 117 118 119 126 129 130 131 132 134 135 141 142 146 147 148 149 150 154 156 157 **S** LifeBridge Health, Baltimore, MD
Primary Contact: Daniel Blum, President and Chief Operating Officer, Senior Vice President LifeBridge Health
CFO: David Krajewski, Senior Vice President and Chief Financial Officer
CMO: Daniel C Silverman, M.D., Vice President and Chief Medical Officer
CIO: Karen Barker, Vice President and Chief Information Officer
CHR: Cheryl T. Boyer, Vice President Human Resources
CNO: Linda Kosnik, R.N., MSN, Chief Nursing Officer and Vice President, Patient Care Services
Web address: www.lifebridgehealth.org
**Control:** Other not–for–profit (including NFP Corporation) **Service:** General medical and surgical

**Staffed Beds:** 289 **Admissions:** 16445 **Census:** 289 **Outpatient Visits:** 173124 **Births:** 1748 **Total Expense ($000):** 795438 **Payroll Expense ($000):** 281191 **Personnel:** 4234

**SPRING GROVE HOSPITAL CENTER (214018)**, 55 Wade Avenue, Zip 21228–4663; tel. 410/402–6000, (Nonreporting) **A**1 3 5 10
Primary Contact: David S. Helsel, M.D., Chief Executive Officer
CFO: Edward Swartz, Chief Financial Officer
CMO: Kelly Phillips, M.D., M.P.H., Clinical Director and Chief Staff
Web address: www.springgrove.com
**Control:** State, Government, Nonfederal **Service:** Psychiatric

**Staffed Beds:** 377

**UNIV OF MARYLAND MED SYSTEM** See University of Maryland Medical Center

**UNIVERSITY OF MARYLAND MEDICAL CENTER (210002)**, 22 South Greene Street, Zip 21201–1595; tel. 410/328–9199, (Includes UNIVERSITY OF MARYLAND HOSPITAL FOR CHILDREN, Mailing address: 22 South Greene Street, Baltimore, Maryland, Zip 21201–1544; tel. 800/492–5538), (Nonreporting) **A**1 2 3 5 8 10 **F**3 5 6 7 8 9 11 12 13 14 15 17 18 19 20 21 22 23 24 25 26 27 28 29 30 31 32 34 35 36 37 38 39 40 41 43 44 45 46 47 48 49 50 51 52 54 55 56 57 58 59 60 61 64 65 66 68 70 71 72 74 75 76 77 78 79 81 82 85 86 87 88 89 92 93 94 97 98 99 100 101 102 103 104 105 106 107 108 109 110 111 114 115 116 117 118 119 120 121 122 123 124 126 129 130 131 132 134 135 136 137 138 139 140 141 142 143 144 145 146 147 148 149 150 153 154 155 157 **P**6 **S** University of Maryland Medical System, Baltimore, MD
Primary Contact: Mohan Suntha, M.D., President and Chief Executive Officer
CFO: Joseph E Hoffman III Senior Vice President and Chief Financial Officer
CMO: Jonathan Gottlieb, M.D., Senior Vice President and Chief Medical Officer
CIO: Jon P Burns, Chief Information Officer
CHR: R Keith Allen, Senior Vice President Human Resources
CNO: Lisa Rowen, R.N., Senior Vice President and Chief Nursing Officer
Web address: www.umm.edu
**Control:** Other not–for–profit (including NFP Corporation) **Service:** General medical and surgical

**Staffed Beds:** 693 **Admissions:** 25921 **Census:** 617 **Outpatient Visits:** 336145 **Births:** 1862 **Total Expense ($000):** 1639396 **Payroll Expense ($000):** 520403 **Personnel:** 8409

**UNIVERSITY OF MARYLAND MEDICAL CENTER MIDTOWN CAMPUS (210038)**, 827 Linden Avenue, Zip 21201–4606; tel. 410/225–8000, (Nonreporting) **A**1 3 5 10 **F**1 3 5 11 15 18 20 29 30 34 35 40 44 45 49 50 56 57 59 60 61 63 64 65 66 68 70 74 75 77 78 79 81 82 84 87 91 93 94 96 97 98 100 101 102 104 106 107 108 111 114 115 118 119 129 130 143 146 148 149 153 154 156 **P**7 **S** University of Maryland Medical System, Baltimore, MD
Primary Contact: Mohan Suntha, M.D., President and Chief Executive Officer
COO: Donald Ray, Vice President Operations
CFO: Craig Fleischmann, Vice President Finance
CMO: W Eugene Egerton, M.D., Chief Medical Officer
CIO: Jon P Burns, Senior Vice President and Chief Information Officer
CHR: Paula Henderson, Vice President Human Resources
CNO: Lisa Rowen, R.N., Chief Nursing Officer
Web address: www.ummidtown.org/
**Control:** Other not–for–profit (including NFP Corporation) **Service:** General medical and surgical

**Staffed Beds:** 189 **Admissions:** 4405 **Census:** 95 **Outpatient Visits:** 98037 **Births:** 0 **Total Expense ($000):** 229220 **Payroll Expense ($000):** 83360 **Personnel:** 1251

*Many Facility Codes have changed. Please refer to the AHA Guide Code Chart.* © 2021 AHA Guide

△ **UNIVERSITY OF MARYLAND REHABILITATION & ORTHOPAEDIC INSTITUTE (210058)**, 2200 Kernan Drive, Zip 21207–6697; tel. 410/448–2500, (Nonreporting) **A**1 3 5 7 10 **S** University of Maryland Medical System, Baltimore, MD
Primary Contact: Cynthia Kelleher, M.P.H., President and Chief Executive Officer
CFO: W Walter Augustin, CPA, III Vice President Financial Services and Chief Financial Officer
CMO: John P. Straumanis, M.D., Vice President Medical Affairs and Chief Medical Officer
CIO: Linda Hines, Vice President Information Technology and Information Systems
CHR: Paula Henderson, Vice President Human Resources
CNO: Cheryl D Lee, R.N., MSN, Vice President of Patient Care Services and Chief Nursing Officer
Web address: www.umrehabortho.org
**Control**: Other not–for–profit (including NFP Corporation) **Service**: Rehabilitation

**Staffed Beds: 141**

**VETERANS AFFAIRS MARYLAND HEALTH CARE SYSTEM-BALTIMORE DIVISION**, 10 North Greene Street, Zip 21201–1524; tel. 410/605–7001, (Includes VETERANS AFFAIRS MARYLAND HEALTH CARE SYSTEM-PERRY POINT DIVISION, Mailing address: Circle Drive, Perry Point, Maryland, Zip 21902; tel. 410/642–2411; Adam M. Robinson, Director), (Nonreporting) **A**1 2 3 5 **S** Department of Veterans Affairs, Washington, DC
Primary Contact: Adam M. Robinson, Director
CFO: MajorTom Scheffler, Chief Fiscal Officer
CMO: Dorothy Snow, M.D., Chief of Staff
CIO: Sharon Zielinski, Chief Information Resource Officer
CHR: Jeff Craig, Chief Human Resource Management
Web address: www.maryland.va.gov/
**Control**: Veterans Affairs, Government, federal **Service**: General medical and surgical

**Staffed Beds: 727**

**VETERANS AFFAIRS MED CENTER** See Veterans Affairs Maryland Health Care System-Baltimore Division

### BEL AIR—Harford County

**UNIVERSITY OF MARYLAND UPPER CHESAPEAKE MEDICAL CENTER (210049)**, 500 Upper Chesapeake Drive, Zip 21014–4324; tel. 443/643–1000, (Nonreporting) **A**1 2 3 5 10 **F**11 13 15 18 20 22 26 28 29 30 31 34 35 36 38 40 41 45 46 49 50 51 54 57 59 60 64 65 68 70 71 74 75 76 77 78 79 81 82 84 85 86 87 89 92 93 96 107 108 110 111 114 115 118 119 120 121 124 130 132 143 146 147 **S** University of Maryland Medical System, Baltimore, MD
Primary Contact: Lyle Ernest. Sheldon, FACHE, President and Chief Executive Officer
CMO: Peggy Vaughan, M.D., Senior Vice President Medical Affairs
CIO: Rick Casteel, Vice President Management Information Systems and Chief Information Officer
CHR: Toni M Shivery, Vice President Human Resources
Web address: www.uchs.org
**Control**: Other not–for–profit (including NFP Corporation) **Service**: General medical and surgical

**Staffed Beds: 149 Admissions: 10817 Census: 116 Outpatient Visits: 124856 Births: 1334 Total Expense ($000): 260846 Payroll Expense ($000): 108409 Personnel: 1274**

**UPPER CHESAPEAKE MEDICAL CENTER** See University of Maryland Upper Chesapeake Medical Center

### BERLIN—Worcester County

**ATLANTIC GENERAL HOSPITAL (210061)**, 9733 Healthway Drive, Zip 21811–1155; tel. 410/641–1100, (Nonreporting) **A**1 10
Primary Contact: Michael A. Franklin, FACHE, President and Chief Executive Officer
COO: Kim Justice, Vice President Planning and Operations
CFO: Cheryl Nottingham, Chief Financial Officer
CMO: Sally Dowling, M.D., Vice President Medical Affairs
CIO: Jonathan Bauer, Vice President Information Systems and Chief Information Officer
CHR: Jim Brannon, Vice President Human Resources
CNO: Matthew Morris, Vice President Patient Care Services and Chief Nursing Officer
Web address: www.atlanticgeneral.org
**Control**: Other not–for–profit (including NFP Corporation) **Service**: General medical and surgical

**Staffed Beds: 45**

### BETHESDA—Montgomery County

**NATIONAL INSTITUTES OF HEALTH CLINICAL CENTER**, 9000 Rockville Pike, Building 10, Room 6-2551, Zip 20892–1504; tel. 301/496–4000, (Includes CHILDREN'S INN AT NIH, Mailing address: 7 West Drive, Bethesda, Maryland, Zip 20814–1509; tel. 301/496–5672), (Nonreporting) **A**1 3 5 8 **F**3 4 5 14 20 22 26 30 31 36 39 45 53 55 57 58 59 60 61 63 64 65 67 68 70 74 75 77 78 79 80 81 82 83 84 85 86 87 89 91 92 93 94 95 96 98 99 100 101 104 107 108 111 112 114 115 116 117 118 119 120 121 124 126 129 130 132 135 136 141 145 146 148 149 152 156 **S** U. S. Indian Health Service, Rockville, MD
Primary Contact: James K. Gilman, M.D., Chief Executive Officer
COO: CaptainPius Aiyelawo, Chief Operating Officer
CFO: Maria Joyce, Chief Financial Officer
CMO: David K Henderson, M.D., Deputy Director Clinical Care
CIO: Jon W McKeeby, Chief Information Officer
CHR: Bonnie Tuma, Human Resources Team Lead
CNO: Clare Hastings, R.N., Ph.D., Chief Nurse Officer
Web address: www.clinicalcenter.nih.gov
**Control**: Public Health Service other than 47, Government, federal **Service**: Other specialty treatment

**Staffed Beds: 121 Admissions: 4693 Census: 117 Outpatient Visits: 96860 Births: 0 Total Expense ($000): 528528 Payroll Expense ($000): 188652 Personnel: 2014**

**NATIONAL NAVAL MEDICAL CENTER** See Walter Reed National Military Medical Center

**NATLIONAL INSTITUTES OF HEALTH** See National Institutes of Health Clinical Center

**SUBURBAN HOSP HEALTHCARE SYST** See Suburban Hospital

**SUBURBAN HOSPITAL (210022)**, 8600 Old Georgetown Road, Zip 20814–1497; tel. 301/896–3100, (Nonreporting) **A**1 2 3 5 10 **F**3 5 8 11 15 17 18 20 22 24 26 28 29 30 31 34 35 36 37 38 39 40 41 43 44 45 46 49 50 51 53 56 57 58 59 60 64 70 71 74 75 77 78 79 81 82 84 85 87 89 92 93 98 100 101 102 104 105 106 107 108 110 111 114 115 118 119 120 121 123 126 130 132 135 146 148 149 150 152 153 156 157 **S** Johns Hopkins Health System, Baltimore, MD
Primary Contact: Jacky Schultz, MSN, R.N., President
COO: Joseph Linstrom, Vice President Operations
CFO: Marty Basso, Senior Vice President Finance
CMO: Eric D Dobkin, M.D., Vice President Medical Affairs
CIO: Jason Cole, Senior Director, Management Information Systems
CHR: Queenie C. Plater, Vice President, Human Resources National Capital Region Johns Hopkins Medicine
CNO: LeighAnn Sidone, MSN, R.N., Chief Nursing Officer
Web address: www.suburbanhospital.org
**Control**: Other not–for–profit (including NFP Corporation) **Service**: General medical and surgical

**Staffed Beds: 208 Admissions: 13508 Census: 160 Outpatient Visits: 59425 Births: 0 Total Expense ($000): 300567 Payroll Expense ($000): 110022 Personnel: 1539**

**THE CHILDREN'S INN AT NIH** See Children's Inn at Nih

---

**Hospital, Medicare Provider Number, Address, Telephone, Approval, Facility, and Physician Codes, Health Care System**

★ American Hospital Association (AHA) membership
☐ The Joint Commission accreditation
○ Healthcare Facilities Accreditation Program
◇ DNV Healthcare Inc. accreditation
⇧ Center for Improvement in Healthcare Quality Accreditation
△ Commission on Accreditation of Rehabilitation Facilities (CARF) accreditation

⊞ **WALTER REED NATIONAL MILITARY MEDICAL CENTER**, 8901 Wisconsin Avenue, Zip 20889–5600; tel. 301/295–4611, (Nonreporting) **A**1 2 3 5 **F**3 5 8 9 12 13 14 15 18 19 20 22 24 26 28 29 30 31 32 33 34 35 36 37 38 39 40 43 44 45 46 47 48 49 50 51 52 53 54 55 56 57 58 59 60 61 64 65 70 72 74 75 76 77 78 79 80 81 82 83 84 85 86 87 88 89 91 92 93 94 96 97 98 100 101 102 104 107 108 109 110 111 112 113 114 115 116 117 118 119 120 121 122 123 124 126 129 130 131 132 134 135 138 141 143 144 145 146 147 148 149 153 154 156 157 158 **S** Bureau of Medicine and Surgery, Department of the Navy, Falls Church, VA
Primary Contact: Captain Mark A. Kobelja, MC, USN, Director
CFO: CommanderJoseph Pickel, Director Resource Management
CIO: CommanderCayetano Thornton, Chief Information Officer
CHR: CaptainJaime Carroll, Department Head
Web address: www.wrnmmc.capmed.mil/SitePages/home.aspx
**Control**: Department of Defense, Government, federal **Service**: General medical and surgical

**Staffed Beds**: 251 **Admissions**: 13236 **Census**: 149 **Outpatient Visits**: 934930 **Births**: 1185 **Total Expense ($000)**: 836929 **Payroll Expense ($000)**: 348215 **Personnel**: 6650

### CAMBRIDGE—Dorchester County

**DORCHESTER GENERAL HOSPITAL** See University of Maryland Shore Medical Center at Dorchester

☐ **EASTERN SHORE HOSPITAL CENTER (214002)**, 5262 Woods Road, Zip 21613–3796; tel. 410/221–2300, (Nonreporting) **A**1 10
Primary Contact: Randy L. Bradford, Chief Executive Officer
COO: William Webb, Assistant Superintendent
CFO: William Webb, Assistant Superintendent
CMO: Evangeline Garcia, M.D., Clinical Director
CHR: Cassandra Stanley, Director Personnel
CNO: Lisa Hines, Director of Performance Improvement
Web address: www.dhmh.state.md.us/eshc
**Control**: State, Government, Nonfederal **Service**: Psychiatric

**Staffed Beds**: 80

⊞ **UNIVERSITY OF MARYLAND SHORE MEDICAL CENTER AT DORCHESTER**, 300 Byrn Street, Zip 21613–1908; tel. 410/228–5511, (Nonreporting) **A**1 **S** University of Maryland Medical System, Baltimore, MD
Primary Contact: Kenneth D. Kozel, FACHE, President and Chief Executive Officer
COO: Robert A Frank, Senior Vice President Operations
CFO: Joanne A Hahey, Senior Vice President and Chief Financial Officer
CMO: William Huffner, M.D., Vice President Medical Affairs
CIO: Elizabeth Fish, Chief Information Officer
CHR: Susan Coe, Regional Vice President Human Resources
Web address: www.shorehealth.org
**Control**: Other not–for–profit (including NFP Corporation) **Service**: General medical and surgical

**Staffed Beds**: 47

### CHESTERTOWN—Kent County

**CHESTER RIVER HEALTH SYSTEM** See University of Maryland Shore Medical Center at Chestertown

⊞ **UNIVERSITY OF MARYLAND SHORE MEDICAL CENTER AT CHESTERTOWN (210030)**, 100 Brown Street, Zip 21620–1499; tel. 410/778–3300, (Nonreporting) **A**1 10 **S** University of Maryland Medical System, Baltimore, MD
Primary Contact: Kenneth D. Kozel, FACHE, President and Chief Executive Officer
COO: Robert A Frank, Senior Vice President of Operations
CFO: Joanne A Hahey, Vice President Finance and Chief Financial Officer
CMO: William Huffner, M.D., Chief Medical Officer
CIO: Elizabeth Fish, Senior Director Site Executive and Information Technology
CHR: Susan Coe, Vice President Human Resources
CNO: Ruth Ann Jones, Ed.D., MSN, R.N., Senior Vice President, Chief Nursing Officer
Web address: www.umms.org/hospitals/shore-health-system.htm
**Control**: Other not–for–profit (including NFP Corporation) **Service**: General medical and surgical

**Staffed Beds**: 124

### CHEVERLY—Prince George's County

**PRINCE GEORGE'S HOSPITAL CENTER** See University of Maryland Capital Region Health Prince George's Hospital Center

☐ △ **UNIVERSITY OF MARYLAND CAPITAL REGION HEALTH PRINCE GEORGE'S HOSPITAL CENTER (210003)**, 3001 Hospital Drive, Zip 20785–1189; tel. 301/618–2000, (Includes GLADYS SPELLMAN SPECIALTY HOSPITAL AND NURSING CENTER, Mailing address: 3001 Hospital Drive, Sixth Floor, Cheverly, Maryland, Zip 20785–1189; tel. 301/618–6666; Trudy Hall, M.D., Vice President, Medical Affairs; UNIVERSITY OF MARYLAND CAPITAL REGION HEALTH AT LAUREL MEDICAL CENTER, Mailing address: 7300 Van Dusen Road, Laurel, Maryland, Zip 20707–9463; tel. 301/725–4300; Trudy Hall, M.D., Vice President Medical Affairs and Interim Chief Executive Officer), (Nonreporting) **A**1 3 5 7 10 **F**3 8 11 12 13 15 17 18 20 22 24 26 28 29 30 31 34 35 37 38 40 43 44 45 46 49 50 54 57 58 59 60 61 63 64 65 68 70 71 72 74 75 76 77 78 79 81 82 84 85 87 89 91 92 96 97 98 100 101 102 104 105 106 107 108 109 111 112 114 116 117 119 130 132 134 135 136 141 143 146 147 148 149 150 152 153 154 156 157 **S** University of Maryland Medical System, Baltimore, MD
Primary Contact: Nathaniel Richardson Jr, President and Chief Executive Officer
CFO: William Brosius, Chief Financial Officer
CIO: Henry Archibong, Vice President, Information Services and Technology
CHR: Veronica Ford, Vice President Human Resources
CNO: Katie Boston-Leary, Vice President and Chief Nursing Officer, UMPGHC
Web address: www.princegeorgeshospital.org
**Control**: Other not–for–profit (including NFP Corporation) **Service**: General medical and surgical

**Staffed Beds**: 245 **Admissions**: 10291 **Census**: 172 **Outpatient Visits**: 44247 **Births**: 1270 **Total Expense ($000)**: 307427 **Payroll Expense ($000)**: 118862 **Personnel**: 2008

### CLINTON—Prince George's County

⊞ **MEDSTAR SOUTHERN MARYLAND HOSPITAL CENTER (210062)**, 7503 Surratts Road, Zip 20735–3358; tel. 301/868–8000, (Nonreporting) **A**1 2 3 5 10 **F**3 13 15 17 18 20 22 26 28 29 30 31 34 35 37 38 39 40 44 45 46 47 48 49 50 51 57 58 59 60 61 64 65 66 68 70 73 74 75 76 77 78 79 81 82 84 85 86 87 89 93 98 100 101 102 104 105 107 108 110 111 114 115 118 119 120 121 123 126 129 130 132 135 141 143 146 147 148 149 154 156 **S** MedStar Health, Columbia, MD
Primary Contact: Christine R. Wray, President
CFO: Daniel Feeley, Interim Chief Financial Officer
CMO: Yvette Johnson-Threat, Vice President Medical Affairs
CIO: Lou Mavromatis, Vice President Information Technology
CHR: Paul Zeller, Vice President Human Resources
Web address: www.medstarsouthernmaryland.org
**Control**: Other not–for–profit (including NFP Corporation) **Service**: General medical and surgical

**Staffed Beds**: 135 **Admissions**: 10236 **Census**: 132 **Outpatient Visits**: 110549 **Births**: 1231 **Total Expense ($000)**: 229412 **Payroll Expense ($000)**: 94945 **Personnel**: 1030

**SOUTHERN MARYLAND HOSPITAL CENTER** See Medstar Southern Maryland Hospital Center

### COLUMBIA—Howard County

⊞ **HOWARD COUNTY GENERAL HOSPITAL (210048)**, 5755 Cedar Lane, Zip 21044–2999; tel. 410/740–7890, (Nonreporting) **A**1 3 5 10 **F**3 8 11 13 15 18 20 22 26 28 29 30 31 32 34 35 36 39 40 41 44 45 46 47 49 50 51 55 56 57 58 59 60 61 64 65 68 70 72 74 75 76 77 78 79 81 82 84 85 86 87 89 91 92 93 96 98 99 100 101 102 103 107 108 110 111 115 118 119 130 131 132 134 135 146 147 148 149 154 156 **P**6 **S** Johns Hopkins Health System, Baltimore, MD
Primary Contact: Steven C. Snelgrove, President
CFO: Claro M Pio Roda, Dr.PH, Vice President, Finance and Chief Financial Officer
CMO: Mohammed Shafeeq Ahmed, M.D., Vice President of Medical Affairs and Chief Medical Officer
CHR: Jon Oravec, Vice President, Human Resources
CNO: Karen Davis, Chief Nursing Officer and Vice President, Nursing
Web address: www.hcgh.org
**Control**: Other not–for–profit (including NFP Corporation) **Service**: General medical and surgical

**Staffed Beds**: 259 **Admissions**: 14552 **Census**: 162 **Outpatient Visits**: 130626 **Births**: 3079 **Total Expense ($000)**: 265095 **Payroll Expense ($000)**: 98724 **Personnel**: 1453

## CRISFIELD—Somerset County

**MCCREADY FOUNDATION** See Tidalhealth Mccready

## CUMBERLAND—Allegany County

☐ **THOMAS B. FINAN CENTER (214012)**, 10102 Country Club Road SE, Zip 21502–8339, Mailing Address: P.O. Box 1722, Zip 21501–1722; tel. 301/777–2405, (Nonreporting) **A**1 10 **F**10 30 75 86 87 98 130 132 149
Primary Contact: John Cullen, Chief Executive Officer
COO: Craig Alexander, Chief Operating Officer
CFO: Gina Spears, Chief Financial Officer
CMO: David Millis, M.D., Clinical Director
CHR: Chris Loney, Director Personnel
CNO: Gayle Walter, Director of Nursing
Web address: www.dhmh.state.md.us
**Control:** State, Government, Nonfederal **Service:** Psychiatric

**Staffed Beds:** 88 **Admissions:** 99 **Census:** 83 **Outpatient Visits:** 0
**Births:** 0 **Total Expense ($000):** 21241 **Payroll Expense ($000):** 9011
**Personnel:** 198

☒ △ **WESTERN MARYLAND REGIONAL MEDICAL CENTER (210027)**, 12500 Willowbrook Road SE, Zip 21502–6393, Mailing Address: P.O. Box 539, Zip 21501–0539; tel. 240/964–7000, (Total facility includes 88 beds in nursing home–type unit) (Nonreporting) **A**1 2 3 7 10 **F**3 5 11 13 14 15 17 18 20 22 24 26 28 29 30 31 32 34 35 38 40 41 43 44 45 49 50 53 54 56 57 58 59 60 62 63 64 66 68 70 73 74 75 76 77 78 79 80 81 82 84 85 86 87 89 90 93 94 96 97 98 100 101 102 104 107 108 110 111 114 115 116 117 119 120 121 124 126 128 129 130 132 134 135 143 144 145 146 148 150 153 154 156 **P**6
Primary Contact: Barry P. Ronan, President and Chief Executive Officer
COO: Nancy D. Adams, R.N., Senior Vice President and Chief Operating Officer
CFO: Kimberly S. Repac, Senior Vice President and Chief Financial Officer
CMO: Gerald Goldstein, M.D., Senior Vice President and Chief Medical Officer
CIO: William J. Byers, Chief Information Officer
CHR: Jennifer J. Williams, Director, Human Resources
CNO: James M. Karstetter, R.N., IIVice President and Chief Nursing Officer
Web address: www.wmhs.com
**Control:** Other not–for–profit (including NFP Corporation) **Service:** General medical and surgical

**Staffed Beds:** 321 **Admissions:** 11094 **Census:** 215 **Outpatient Visits:** 528839 **Births:** 932 **Total Expense ($000):** 330368 **Payroll Expense ($000):** 126698 **Personnel:** 1956

## EASTON—Talbot County

**MEMORIAL HOSPITAL AT EASTON MARYLAND** See University of Maryland Shore Medical Center at Easton

☒ △ **UNIVERSITY OF MARYLAND SHORE MEDICAL CENTER AT EASTON (210037)**, 219 South Washington Street, Zip 21601–2996; tel. 410/822–1000, (Nonreporting) **A**1 2 7 10 **S** University of Maryland Medical System, Baltimore, MD
Primary Contact: Kenneth D. Kozel, FACHE, President and Chief Executive Officer
COO: Robert A Frank, Senior Vice President of Operations
CFO: Joanne A Hahey, Senior Vice President and Chief Financial Officer
CMO: William Huffner, M.D., Chief Medical Officer
CIO: Elizabeth Fish, Chief Information Officer
CHR: Susan Coe, Regional Vice President Human Resources
CNO: Ruth Ann Jones, Ed.D., MSN, R.N., Senior Vice President, Chief Nursing Officer
Web address: www.shorehealth.org
**Control:** Other not–for–profit (including NFP Corporation) **Service:** General medical and surgical

**Staffed Beds:** 132

## ELKTON—Cecil County

☒ **UNION HOSPITAL (210032)**, 106 Bow Street, Zip 21921–5596; tel. 410/398–4000, (Nonreporting) **A**1 2 10 **F**2 3 11 12 13 15 18 26 29 30 31 34 35 38 40 44 45 46 49 50 51 53 54 57 59 61 64 69 70 74 75 76 77 78 79 81 82 84 85 86 87 89 92 93 97 98 100 102 104 107 108 110 111 114 118 119 129 130 131 132 135 146 147 148 149 154 156
Primary Contact: Richard C. Szumel, M.D., Chief Executive Officer
CFO: Laurie Beyer, Senior Vice President and Chief Financial Officer
CMO: Cydney Teal, M.D., Vice President Medical Affairs
CIO: Anne Lara, Chief Information Officer
CHR: Terrence Lovell, Vice President Human Resources
Web address: www.uhcc.com
**Control:** Other not–for–profit (including NFP Corporation) **Service:** General medical and surgical

**Staffed Beds:** 104 **Admissions:** 4937 **Census:** 54 **Outpatient Visits:** 136676 **Births:** 549 **Total Expense ($000):** 162448 **Payroll Expense ($000):** 72951 **Personnel:** 953

**UNION HOSPITAL OF CECIL COUNTY** See Union Hospital

## FREDERICK—Frederick County

☒ **FREDERICK HEALTH (210005)**, 400 West Seventh Street, Zip 21701–4593; tel. 240/566–3300, (Nonreporting) **A**1 10 **F**3 11 12 13 15 18 20 22 26 28 29 30 31 34 35 37 38 40 41 44 45 46 48 49 50 53 54 56 57 58 59 60 61 62 63 64 68 70 72 74 75 76 77 78 79 81 82 84 85 86 87 89 93 98 100 102 105 107 108 110 111 114 115 117 118 119 120 121 123 124 126 129 130 131 132 135 146 147 148 149 153 154 157 **P**6
Primary Contact: Thomas A. Kleinhanzl, President and Chief Executive Officer
COO: Cheryl Cioffi, R.N., Senior Vice President, Chief Operating Officer and Chief Nursing Officer
CFO: Michelle K Mahan, Senior Vice President and Chief Financial Officer
CMO: Manuel Casiano, M.D., Senior Vice President Medical Affairs
CIO: David Quirke, Vice President Information Services
CNO: Cheryl Cioffi, R.N., Senior Vice President, Chief Operating Officer and Chief Nursing Officer
Web address: www.fmh.org
**Control:** Other not–for–profit (including NFP Corporation) **Service:** General medical and surgical

**Staffed Beds:** 281 **Admissions:** 15796 **Census:** 199 **Outpatient Visits:** 598255 **Births:** 2513 **Total Expense ($000):** 340006 **Payroll Expense ($000):** 131365 **Personnel:** 1937

**FREDERICK REGIONAL HEALTH SYSTEM** See Frederick Health

## GERMANTOWN—Montgomery County

☒ **HOLY CROSS GERMANTOWN HOSPITAL (210065)**, 19801 Observation Drive, Zip 20876–4070; tel. 301/557–6000, (Nonreporting) **A**1 3 10 **F**3 11 12 13 18 26 29 30 35 39 40 45 46 49 50 56 58 59 64 66 68 70 74 75 76 77 78 79 81 84 85 86 87 93 97 98 100 102 107 108 111 115 118 119 126 130 132 146 147 148 149 **S** Trinity Health, Livonia, MI
Primary Contact: Doug Ryder, President
CMO: Blair Eig, M.D., Vice President and Chief Medical Officer, Medical Affairs
CNO: Kimberly Elliott, Chief Nursing Officer
Web address: www.holycrosshealth.org/germantown
**Control:** Church operated, Nongovernment, not–for–profit **Service:** General medical and surgical

**Staffed Beds:** 72 **Admissions:** 5843 **Census:** 58 **Outpatient Visits:** 33294 **Births:** 951 **Total Expense ($000):** 108726 **Payroll Expense ($000):** 37680 **Personnel:** 585

---

**MD**

## GLEN BURNIE—Anne Arundel County

**BALTIMORE WASHINGTON MEDICAL CENTER** See University of Maryland Baltimore Washington Medical Center

✉ **UNIVERSITY OF MARYLAND BALTIMORE WASHINGTON MEDICAL CENTER (210043)**, 301 Hospital Drive, Zip 21061–5899; tel. 410/787–4000, (Nonreporting) **A**1 2 3 5 10 **F**3 11 13 15 18 20 22 26 28 29 30 31 34 35 37 40 41 44 45 46 48 49 50 51 54 55 56 57 58 59 60 61 63 64 65 68 70 74 75 76 77 78 79 81 82 83 84 85 86 87 89 93 98 100 101 102 104 105 107 108 111 114 115 118 119 120 121 123 124 126 130 132 135 146 147 148 149 150 154 156 **P**6 **S** University of Maryland Medical System, Baltimore, MD
Primary Contact: Karen E. Olscamp, President and Chief Executive Officer
COO: Kathleen McCollum, Senior Vice President, Clinical Integration and Chief Operating Officer
CFO: Al Pietsch, CPA, Senior Vice President and Chief Financial Officer
CMO: Neel Vibhakar, M.D., Senior Vice President and Chief Medical Officer
CIO: Jon P Burns, Senior Vice President and Chief Information Officer
CHR: Kathy Poehler, Vice President, Human Resources
CNO: Catherine Whitaker, MSN, R.N., Vice President and Chief Nursing Officer
Web address: www.mybwmc.org
**Control**: Other not–for–profit (including NFP Corporation) **Service**: General medical and surgical

**Staffed Beds**: 272 **Admissions**: 17186 **Census**: 208 **Outpatient Visits**: 123859 **Births**: 1455 **Total Expense ($000)**: 362521 **Payroll Expense ($000)**: 145749 **Personnel**: 2668

## HAGERSTOWN—Washington County

☐ **BROOK LANE HEALTH SERVICES (214003)**, 13121 Brook Lane, Zip 21742–1435, Mailing Address: P.O. Box 1945, Zip 21742–1945; tel. 301/733–0330, (Nonreporting) **A**1 10
Primary Contact: R Lynn. Rushing, Chief Executive Officer
COO: Jason Allen, Chief Operating Officer
CFO: David Schey, Chief Financial Officer
CMO: David Gonzalez, M.D., Medical Director
CIO: Robert Fritz, Chief Information Officer
CHR: Nicole Twigg, Director Human Resources
CNO: Jason Allen, Director Patient Care Services
Web address: www.brooklane.org
**Control**: Other not–for–profit (including NFP Corporation) **Service**: Psychiatric

**Staffed Beds**: 57

**BROOK LANE PSYCHIATRIC CENTER** See Brook Lane Health Services

✉ △ **MERITUS MEDICAL CENTER (210001)**, 11116 Medical Campus Road, Zip 21742–6710; tel. 301/790–8000, (Nonreporting) **A**1 2 3 5 7 10 13 **F**3 5 11 12 13 15 17 18 20 22 26 28 29 30 31 34 35 38 40 43 44 49 51 52 54 55 56 57 58 59 60 61 62 64 65 70 74 75 76 77 78 79 81 82 83 84 85 86 87 89 90 93 94 96 97 98 99 100 101 102 103 104 107 108 110 111 114 115 118 119 120 121 123 130 131 132 135 143 144 145 146 147 148 153 154 155 157 **P**6 8
Primary Contact: Maulik Joshi, President and Chief Executive Officer
CFO: Thomas T. Chan, Chief Financial Officer
CMO: Heather Lorenzo, M.D., Vice President and Chief Medical Officer
CHR: Laura Minteer, Chief Human Resource Officer
CNO: Melanie M Heuston, Chief Nursing Office
Web address: www.meritushealth.com
**Control**: Other not–for–profit (including NFP Corporation) **Service**: General medical and surgical

**Staffed Beds**: 278 **Admissions**: 15784 **Census**: 183 **Outpatient Visits**: 180084 **Births**: 1815 **Total Expense ($000)**: 331754 **Payroll Expense ($000)**: 123429 **Personnel**: 1991

**WASHINGTON COUNTY HEALTH SYSTEM** See Meritus Medical Center

**WESTERN MARYLAND CENTER** See Western Maryland Hospital Center

☐ △ **WESTERN MARYLAND HOSPITAL CENTER (212002)**, 1500 Pennsylvania Avenue, Zip 21742–3194; tel. 301/745–4200, (Nonreporting) **A**1 7 10
Primary Contact: Michael Reyka, Ph.D., Chief Executive Officer
COO: David Davis, Chief Operating Officer
CFO: Kelly Edmonds, Chief Financial Officer
CMO: Monica Stallworth, M.D., Chief of Staff
CIO: Ron Keplinger, Chief Information Officer
CHR: David Davis, Chief Operating Officer
Web address: www.wmhc.us
**Control**: State, Government, Nonfederal **Service**: Acute long–term care hospital

**Staffed Beds**: 120

## HAVRE DE GRACE—Harford County

**HARFORD MEMORIAL HOSPITAL** See University of Maryland Harford Memorial Hospital

✉ **UNIVERSITY OF MARYLAND HARFORD MEMORIAL HOSPITAL (210006)**, 501 South Union Avenue, Zip 21078–3493; tel. 443/843–5000, (Nonreporting) **A**1 10 **F**11 12 15 29 30 31 34 35 36 38 40 46 49 50 51 57 59 60 64 65 66 68 70 71 74 75 77 79 81 82 84 85 86 87 92 93 96 98 102 104 107 108 110 111 114 115 118 119 129 130 132 135 146 148 154 **S** University of Maryland Medical System, Baltimore, MD
Primary Contact: Lyle Ernest. Sheldon, FACHE, President and Chief Executive Officer
CMO: Peggy Vaughan, M.D., Senior Vice President Medical Affairs
CIO: Rick Casteel, Vice President Management Information Systems and Chief Information Officer
CHR: Toni M Shivery, Vice President Human Resources
Web address: www.uchs.org
**Control**: Other not–for–profit (including NFP Corporation) **Service**: General medical and surgical

**Staffed Beds**: 82 **Admissions**: 4159 **Census**: 56 **Outpatient Visits**: 63218 **Births**: 0 **Total Expense ($000)**: 92520 **Payroll Expense ($000)**: 43925 **Personnel**: 548

## JESSUP—Howard County

☐ **CLIFTON T. PERKINS HOSPITAL CENTER**, 8450 Dorsey Run Road, Zip 20794–9486; tel. 410/724–3000, (Nonreporting) **A**1 3 5
Primary Contact: John Robison, Chief Executive Officer
COO: Thomas D Lewis, Chief Operating Officer
CFO: George Parnel, Chief Financial Officer
CMO: Muhammed Ajanah, M.D., Clinical Director
CIO: Chanda Hamilton, Chief Information Officer
CHR: Beverly Stacie, Director Human Resources
Web address: www.dhmh.state.md.us/perkins/
**Control**: State, Government, Nonfederal **Service**: Psychiatric

**Staffed Beds**: 250

## LA PLATA—Charles County

**CIVISTA HEALTH** See University of Maryland Charles Regional Medical Center

✉ **UNIVERSITY OF MARYLAND CHARLES REGIONAL MEDICAL CENTER (210035)**, 5 Garrett Avenue, Zip 20646–5960, Mailing Address: P.O. Box 1070, Zip 20646–1070; tel. 301/609–4000, (Nonreporting) **A**1 10 **F**11 13 28 29 30 31 34 35 38 40 44 45 50 51 56 57 59 61 64 70 74 76 77 78 79 81 82 84 85 86 87 89 92 93 97 100 107 108 111 115 118 119 130 132 135 145 146 148 149 156 **S** University of Maryland Medical System, Baltimore, MD
Primary Contact: Noel A. Cervino, President and Chief Executive Officer
CFO: Albert Zanger, Vice President, Chief Financial Officer
CMO: Joseph Moser, M.D., Chief Medical Officer
CIO: Elizabeth Fish, Information Technology Site Executive
CHR: Stacey M Cook, MS, Vice President, Human Resources
CNO: Dana Levy, Chief Nursing Officer
Web address: www.charlesregional.org
**Control**: Other not–for–profit (including NFP Corporation) **Service**: General medical and surgical

**Staffed Beds**: 108 **Admissions**: 6049 **Census**: 71 **Outpatient Visits**: 71629 **Births**: 712 **Total Expense ($000)**: 121690 **Payroll Expense ($000)**: 47013 **Personnel**: 666

## LANHAM—Prince George's County

**AMI DOCTORS' HOSPITAL** See Doctors Community Hospital

✉ **DOCTORS COMMUNITY HOSPITAL (210051)**, 8118 Good Luck Road, Zip 20706–3574; tel. 301/552–8118, (Nonreporting) **A**1 3 10 **F**3 8 12 15 18 20 26 27 28 29 30 31 34 35 40 44 45 46 47 49 50 51 53 54 57 59 64 70 71 75 77 78 79 81 82 84 85 93 107 108 111 114 115 118 119 123 126 129 130 131 132 135 146 149 154 156
Primary Contact: Paul Grenaldo, President
CFO: Camille Bash, Chief Financial Officer
CMO: Sunil Madan, M.D., Chief Medical Officer and Chief Population Health Officer
CIO: Joyce Hanscome, Chief Information Officer
CHR: Paul Hagens, Vice President Human Resources
Web address: www.dchweb.org
**Control**: Other not–for–profit (including NFP Corporation) **Service**: General medical and surgical

**Staffed Beds**: 190 **Admissions**: 10406 **Census**: 149 **Outpatient Visits**: 61812 **Births**: 0 **Total Expense ($000)**: 169614 **Payroll Expense ($000)**: 86212 **Personnel**: 1390

*Many Facility Codes have changed. Please refer to the AHA Guide Code Chart.*

© 2021 AHA Guide

## LAUREL—Prince George's County

**UNIVERSITY OF MARYLAND CAPITAL REGION HEALTH AT LAUREL REGIONAL MEDICAL CENTER** See University of Maryland Capital Region Health at Laurel Medical Center

## LEONARDTOWN—St. Mary's County

✠ **MEDSTAR ST. MARY'S HOSPITAL (210028)**, 25500 Point Lookout Road, Zip 20650–2015, Mailing Address: PO Box 527, Zip 20650–0527; tel. 301/475–6001, (Nonreporting) **A**1 2 10 **F**3 11 12 13 15 18 28 29 30 31 32 34 35 36 39 40 44 45 48 50 51 53 54 57 59 63 64 65 66 68 70 71 74 75 76 77 78 79 81 82 84 85 86 87 89 93 97 98 100 101 102 103 104 105 107 108 110 111 114 115 116 117 118 119 129 132 134 135 143 146 147 148 149 150 154 156 **P**6 **S** MedStar Health, Columbia, MD
Primary Contact: Christine R. Wray, President
COO: Stephen T. Michaels, M.D., Chief Operating Officer and Chief Medical Officer
CIO: Donald Sirk, Director Information Systems
CNO: Dawn Yeitrakis, Vice President, Nursing
Web address: www.medstarstmarys.org
**Control**: Other not–for–profit (including NFP Corporation) **Service**: General medical and surgical

**Staffed Beds:** 96 **Admissions:** 6354 **Census:** 68 **Outpatient Visits:** 164994 **Births:** 1096 **Total Expense ($000):** 151738 **Payroll Expense ($000):** 62251 **Personnel:** 949

**MEDSTAR ST. MARY'S HOSPITAL** See Medstar St. Mary's Hospital

## OAKLAND—Garrett County

**GARRETT COUNTY MEMORIAL HOSPITAL** See Garrett Regional Medical Center

✠ **GARRETT REGIONAL MEDICAL CENTER (210017)**, 251 North Fourth Street, Zip 21550–1375; tel. 301/533–4000, (Total facility includes 10 beds in nursing home–type unit) (Nonreporting) **A**1 10 **F**3 11 13 28 29 30 31 32 34 35 38 40 45 50 53 56 57 59 64 65 68 70 75 76 77 78 79 81 83 84 85 87 102 104 107 108 114 119 128 130 132 135 141 143 144 146 147 148 149 154 156 **P**6
Primary Contact: Mark G. Boucot, FACHE, President and Chief Executive Officer
CFO: Tracy Lipscomb, CPA, Vice President Financial Services and Chief Financial Officer
CMO: Marjorie Fridkin, M.D., Chief Medical Officer
CIO: Steven Peterson, Chief Information Officer, Vice President of Operations
CHR: Laura M Waters, Vice President Human Resources
CNO: Kendra Thayer, MSN, R.N., Chief Nursing Officer, Vice President Clinical Services
Web address: www.https://www.gcmh.com
**Control**: Other not–for–profit (including NFP Corporation) **Service**: General medical and surgical

**Staffed Beds:** 59 **Admissions:** 2017 **Census:** 25 **Outpatient Visits:** 78086 **Births:** 491 **Total Expense ($000):** 57474 **Payroll Expense ($000):** 24147 **Personnel:** 485

## OLNEY—Montgomery County

✠ **MEDSTAR MONTGOMERY MEDICAL CENTER (210018)**, 18101 Prince Philip Drive, Zip 20832–1512; tel. 301/774–8882, (Nonreporting) **A**1 2 3 5 10 **F**3 4 5 11 12 13 15 18 19 20 26 28 29 30 31 34 35 36 37 38 39 40 41 44 45 46 48 50 51 53 55 56 57 58 59 61 63 64 65 68 70 73 74 75 76 77 78 79 81 82 84 85 86 87 89 92 93 97 98 99 100 101 102 103 104 105 107 108 110 111 114 115 118 119 120 121 123 124 126 129 130 131 132 134 135 146 147 148 149 152 153 154 156 **P**1 6 **S** MedStar Health, Columbia, MD
Primary Contact: Thomas J. Senker, FACHE, President
CFO: David A Havrilla, Chief Financial Officer
CMO: Frederick Finelli, M.D., Vice President Medical Affairs
CIO: Chistiane Brown, Assistant Vice President
CHR: Kevin Mell, Vice President Operations
Web address: www.medstarmontgomery.org
**Control**: Other not–for–profit (including NFP Corporation) **Service**: General medical and surgical

**Staffed Beds:** 98 **Admissions:** 6158 **Census:** 74 **Outpatient Visits:** 74702 **Births:** 521 **Total Expense ($000):** 164867 **Payroll Expense ($000):** 70097 **Personnel:** 824

**MEDSTAR MONTGOMERY MEDICAL CENTER** See Medstar Montgomery Medical Center

## OXEN HILL—Prince George's County

**FORT WASHINGTON HOSPITAL** See Fort Washington Medical Center

✠ **FORT WASHINGTON MEDICAL CENTER (210060)**, 174 Waterfront Street, Suite 225, Zip 20744; tel. 301/292–7000, (Nonreporting) **A**1 10
Primary Contact: Joseph B. Tucker, Interim President and Chief Executive Officer
COO: Al Campbell, Senior Vice President and Chief Operating Officer
CFO: Joseph B Tucker, Senior Vice President and Chief Financial Officer
CMO: Elias Debbas, M.D., President Medical Staff
CIO: Fred Ashby, Director Information Technology
CHR: Alexander Morris, Corporate Director Human Resources
Web address: www.fortwashingtonmc.org
**Control**: Other not–for–profit (including NFP Corporation) **Service**: General medical and surgical

**Staffed Beds:** 37

## PERRY POINT—Cecil County

**VETERANS AFFAIRS MARYLAND HEALTH CARE SYSTEM-PERRY POINT DIVISION** See Veterans Affairs Maryland Health Care System-Baltimore Division, Baltimore

**VETERANS AFFAIRS MED CENTER** See Veterans Affairs Maryland Health Care System-Perry Point Division

## PRINCE FREDERICK—Calvert County

**CALVERT MEMORIAL HOSPITAL** See Calverthealth Medical Center

✠ **CALVERTHEALTH MEDICAL CENTER (210039)**, 100 Hospital Road, Zip 20678–4017; tel. 410/535–4000, (Nonreporting) **A**1 10 **F**3 8 11 18 20 26 28 29 30 31 32 34 35 36 38 39 40 41 43 45 46 47 48 49 50 51 54 56 57 59 61 64 65 66 68 70 71 74 75 76 77 78 79 81 85 86 87 89 93 98 99 100 101 102 104 105 107 108 111 112 114 115 119 124 127 130 132 134 135 146 147 148 149 150 154 156 157 **P**4
Primary Contact: Dean Teague, FACHE, Chief Executive Officer
CFO: Carolyn Heithaus, Chief Financial Officer
CMO: J Michael Brooks, M.D., Chief Medical Officer
CIO: Philip Campbell, Vice President Information Services
CHR: Anthony M. Bladen, Vice President Human Resources
CNO: Diane Couchman, Vice President Patient Care Services and Chief Nursing Executive
Web address: www.calverthealthmedicine.org/
**Control**: Other not–for–profit (including NFP Corporation) **Service**: General medical and surgical

**Staffed Beds:** 71 **Admissions:** 5423 **Census:** 52 **Outpatient Visits:** 117538 **Births:** 590 **Total Expense ($000):** 135516 **Payroll Expense ($000):** 57652 **Personnel:** 952

## RANDALLSTOWN—Baltimore County

☐ **NORTHWEST HOSPITAL (210040)**, 5401 Old Court Road, Zip 21133–5185; tel. 410/521–2200, (Nonreporting) **A**1 2 3 5 10 **F**1 3 8 9 11 12 15 18 28 29 30 31 34 35 38 39 40 44 45 49 51 55 56 58 60 61 63 64 67 68 70 74 75 77 78 79 80 81 82 83 84 85 87 93 94 96 97 98 100 101 102 107 108 110 111 114 115 118 119 126 129 130 131 132 134 143 146 147 148 149 150 154 157 **S** LifeBridge Health, Baltimore, MD
Primary Contact: Craig Carmichael, President and Chief Operating Officer, Senior Vice President, LifeBridge Health
COO: Craig Carmichael, President and Chief Operating Officer, Senior Vice President, LifeBridge Health
CFO: David McCormick, Chief Financial Officer, Northwest Hospital, Assistant Vice President, Finance, LifeBridge Health
CIO: Tressa Springmann, Vice President and Chief Information Officer
CHR: Tracie Oden, Vice President, Human Resources
CNO: Kim Bushnell, R.N., Vice President, Patient Care Services and Chief Nursing Officer, Northwest
Web address: www.lifebridgehealth.org
**Control**: Other not–for–profit (including NFP Corporation) **Service**: General medical and surgical

**Staffed Beds:** 178 **Admissions:** 10316 **Census:** 164 **Outpatient Visits:** 80468 **Births:** 0 **Total Expense ($000):** 246006 **Payroll Expense ($000):** 92389 **Personnel:** 1407

**NORTHWEST HOSPITAL CENTER** See Northwest Hospital

---

**Hospital, Medicare Provider Number, Address, Telephone, Approval, Facility, and Physician Codes, Health Care System**

★ American Hospital Association (AHA) membership
☐ The Joint Commission accreditation
○ Healthcare Facilities Accreditation Program
◇ DNV Healthcare Inc. accreditation
⇑ Center for Improvement in Healthcare Quality Accreditation
△ Commission on Accreditation of Rehabilitation Facilities (CARF) accreditation

**MD**

## ROCKVILLE—Montgomery County

**ADVENTIST BEHAVIORAL HEALTH ROCKVILLE** See Adventist Behavioral Health and Wellness Services

☐ △ **ADVENTIST HEALTHCARE PHYSICAL HEALTH AND REHABILITATION (213029)**, 9909 Medical Center Drive, Zip 20850–6361; tel. 240/864–6000, (Nonreporting) **A**1 7 10 **F**3 28 29 30 34 35 50 53 56 57 58 59 64 68 74 75 77 87 90 93 94 96 130 131 132 146 149 154 **P**6 **S** Adventist HealthCare, Gaithersburg, MD
Primary Contact: Brent Reitz, President
COO: Jason Makaroff, Chief Operating Officer and Associate Vice President
CMO: Terrence P Sheehan, M.D., Medical Director
CHR: Carrie Hibbard, Human Resource Business Partner
CNO: Valerie Summerlin, R.N., MS, Chief Nursing Officer
Web address: www.adventistrehab.com
**Control**: Church operated, Nongovernment, not–for–profit **Service**: Rehabilitation

> **Staffed Beds**: 97 **Admissions**: 1949 **Census**: 77 **Outpatient Visits**: 47595
> **Births**: 0 **Total Expense ($000)**: 47476 **Payroll Expense ($000)**: 27514
> **Personnel**: 364

☐ **ADVENTIST HEALTHCARE SHADY GROVE MEDICAL CENTER (210057)**, 9901 Medical Center Drive, Zip 20850–3395; tel. 240/826–6000, (Includes Adventist Behavioral Health and Wellness Services, Mailing address: 14901 Broschart Road, Rockville, Maryland, Zip 20850–3318; tel. 301/251–4500; John Sackett, President SGMC and Executive Vice President and Chief Operating Officer), (Nonreporting) **A**1 3 5 10 **F**3 5 12 13 15 18 20 22 26 28 29 30 31 35 39 40 41 42 45 46 47 48 50 51 57 60 64 66 68 70 72 74 75 76 77 78 79 81 82 84 85 87 89 98 99 100 101 102 103 104 105 106 107 108 110 111 114 115 116 117 119 120 121 126 130 132 134 135 146 147 148 149 153 156 **P**8 **S** Adventist HealthCare, Gaithersburg, MD
Primary Contact: John Sackett, President SGMC and Executive Vice President and Chief Operating Officer
COO: Eunmee Shim, R.N., MSN, Vice President Operations
CFO: Daniel Cochran, Vice President and Chief Financial Officer
CMO: Kevin Smothers, M.D., Vice President Chief Medical Officer
CIO: christopher Ghion, Vice President and Chief Information Officer
CNO: Joan M Vincent, MSN, MS, R.N., Vice President Patient Care Services and Chief Nurse Executive
Web address: www.adventisthealthcare.com
**Control**: Church operated, Nongovernment, not–for–profit **Service**: General medical and surgical

> **Staffed Beds**: 460 **Admissions**: 19153 **Census**: 282 **Outpatient Visits**: 121033 **Births**: 4062 **Total Expense ($000)**: 423846 **Payroll Expense ($000)**: 161156 **Personnel**: 2210

**ADVENTIST REHABILITATION HOSPITAL OF MARYLAND** See Adventist Healthcare Physical Health and Rehabilitation

**SHADY GROVE ADVENTIST HOSPITAL** See Adventist Healthcare Shady Grove Medical Center

## SALISBURY—Wicomico County

☒ **DEER'S HEAD HOSPITAL CENTER (212003)**, 351 Deer's Head Hospital Road, Zip 21801–3201, Mailing Address: PO Box 2018, Zip 21802–2018; tel. 410/543–4000, (Total facility includes 48 beds in nursing home–type unit) (Nonreporting) **A**1 10 **F**1 3 11 28 29 30 44 50 56 57 59 60 61 65 68 75 77 82 84 85 86 87 90 91 93 94 96 128 130 132 135 146 148 149 156
Primary Contact: Mary Beth Waide, JD, MS, R.N., Chief Executive Officer
COO: Luanne Dashield, Chief Operating Officer
CFO: Kenneth Waller, Fiscal Administrator
CMO: Robert Coker, M.D., Medical Director
CIO: Mac Beattie, Computer Network Specialist
CHR: Andre Harmon, Chief Human Resource Officer
CNO: Cheri Porcelli, MSN, R.N., Chief Nursing Officer
Web address: www.https://health.maryland.gov/deershead/Pages/Home.aspx
**Control**: State, Government, Nonfederal **Service**: Chronic disease

> **Staffed Beds**: 54 **Admissions**: 79 **Census**: 44 **Outpatient Visits**: 7450 **Births**: 0 **Total Expense ($000)**: 23544 **Payroll Expense ($000)**: 9510 **Personnel**: 171

**DEER'S HEAD HOSPITASL CENTER** See Deer's Head Hospital Center

☒ △ **ENCOMPASS HEALTH REHABILITATION HOSPITAL OF SALISBURY (213028)**, 220 Tilghman Road, Zip 21804–1921; tel. 410/546–4600, (Nonreporting) **A**1 7 10 **S** Encompass Health Corporation, Birmingham, AL
Primary Contact: Steven Walas, Chief Executive Officer
CFO: Karen Rounsley, Controller
CHR: Belinda Thompson, Coordinator Human Resources
CNO: Belle Goslee, Chief Nursing Officer
Web address: www.healthsouthchesapeake.com
**Control**: Corporation, Investor–owned (for–profit) **Service**: Rehabilitation

> **Staffed Beds**: 54

**HEALTHSOUTH CHESAPEAKE REHABILITATION HOSPITAL** See Encompass Health Rehabilitation Hospital of Salisbury

**PENINSULA REGIONAL HEALTH SYSTEM** See Tidalhealth Peninsula

☒ **TIDALHEALTH PENINSULA (210019)**, 100 East Carroll Street, Zip 21801–5422; tel. 410/546–6400, (Includes TIDALHEALTH MCCREADY, Mailing address: 201 Hall Highway, Crisfield, Maryland, Zip 21817–1299; tel. 410/968–1200; Kathleen Harrison, Chief Executive Officer), (Nonreporting) **A**1 2 5 10 **F**3 11 12 13 15 17 18 20 22 24 26 28 29 30 31 32 34 35 37 40 43 44 45 46 47 48 49 50 51 53 54 57 58 59 60 61 64 68 70 71 73 74 75 76 77 78 79 81 82 84 85 86 87 89 92 97 98 100 102 104 105 107 108 110 111 114 115 118 119 120 121 123 124 126 130 132 134 135 143 144 145 146 147 148 149 153 154 156 **P**5 8 **S** TidalHealth, Salisbury, MD
Primary Contact: Steven E. Leonard, President and Chief Executive Officer
COO: Cindy Lunsford, Executive Vice President and Chief Operating Officer
CFO: Bruce Ritchie, Vice President of Finance and Chief Financial Officer
CMO: Charles B Silvia, M.D., Chief Medical Officer and Vice President Medical Affairs
CIO: Raymond Adkins, Chief Information Officer
CHR: Scott Peterson, Vice President of People and Organizational Development
CNO: Karen C Poisker, MSN, Vice President Patient Care Services and Chief Nursing Officer
Web address: www.peninsula.org
**Control**: Other not–for–profit (including NFP Corporation) **Service**: General medical and surgical

> **Staffed Beds**: 298 **Admissions**: 15629 **Census**: 186 **Outpatient Visits**: 614901 **Births**: 1871 **Total Expense ($000)**: 461195 **Payroll Expense ($000)**: 189698 **Personnel**: 2736

## SILVER SPRING—Montgomery County

☐ **ADVENTIST HEALTHCARE WHITE OAK MEDICAL CENTER (210016)**, 11890 Healing Way, Zip 20904; tel. 240/637–4000, (Includes ADVENTIST HEALTHCARE WASHINGTON ADVENTIST HOSPITAL, Mailing address: 7600 Carroll Avenue, Takoma Park, Maryland, Zip 20912–6392; tel. 301/891–7600; Erik Wangsness, President), (Nonreporting) **A**1 5 **S** Adventist HealthCare, Gaithersburg, MD
Primary Contact: Anthony Stahl, FACHE, Ph.D., Chief Executive Officer
Web address: www.https://www.adventisthealthcare.com
**Control**: Church operated, Nongovernment, not–for–profit **Service**: General medical and surgical

> **Staffed Beds**: 222

**HOLY CROSS HEALTH** See Holy Cross Hospital

☒ **HOLY CROSS HOSPITAL (210004)**, 1500 Forest Glen Road, Zip 20910–1487; tel. 301/754–7000, (Nonreporting) **A**1 2 3 5 10 **F**3 7 8 11 12 13 15 18 20 29 30 31 40 41 46 49 50 56 58 60 64 66 67 68 69 70 72 74 75 76 77 78 79 81 82 84 85 86 87 89 93 97 100 102 107 108 110 111 115 118 119 120 121 123 124 126 129 130 132 141 146 147 148 149 154 **S** Trinity Health, Livonia, MI
Primary Contact: Louis Damiano, M.D., President
CFO: Anne Gillis, Chief Financial Officer
CMO: Blair Eig, M.D., Senior Vice President Medical Affairs
CIO: Matthew Trimmer, Director Information Services
CHR: J Manuel Ocasio, Vice President Human Resources
CNO: Celia Guarino, R.N., MSN, Vice President and Chief Nursing Officer
Web address: www.holycrosshealth.org
**Control**: Church operated, Nongovernment, not–for–profit **Service**: General medical and surgical

> **Staffed Beds**: 367 **Admissions**: 30125 **Census**: 335 **Outpatient Visits**: 157868 **Births**: 9336 **Total Expense ($000)**: 439449 **Payroll Expense ($000)**: 203799 **Personnel**: 2798

## SILVER SPRING—Prince George's County

**SAINT LUKE INSTITUTE**, 8901 New Hampshire Avenue, Zip 20903–3611; tel. 301/445–7970, (Nonreporting) **F**29 30 54 98 101 104 106 153 154
Primary Contact: David Songy, President and Chief Executive Officer
COO: SisterDanile Lynch, Chief Operating Officer
Web address: www.sli.org
**Control**: Other not–for–profit (including NFP Corporation) **Service**: Psychiatric

> **Staffed Beds**: 52 **Admissions**: 61 **Census**: 1 **Outpatient Visits**: 2021 **Births**: 0 **Total Expense ($000)**: 7913 **Payroll Expense ($000)**: 4605

*Many Facility Codes have changed. Please refer to the AHA Guide Code Chart.*

## SYKESVILLE—Carroll County

☐ **SPRINGFIELD HOSPITAL CENTER (214004)**, 6655 Sykesville Road,
Zip 21784–7966; tel. 410/970–7000, (Nonreporting) **A**1 3 10
Primary Contact: Paula A. Langmead, Chief Executive Officer
COO: Daniel Triplett, Acting Chief Operating Officer
CFO: Keith Hardesty, Chief Financial Officer
CMO: Kim Bright, M.D., Clinical Director
CIO: Denise Maskell, Chief Information Officer
CNO: Gloria Merek, Director of Nursing
Web address: www.dhmh.state.md.us/springfield
**Control**: State, Government, Nonfederal **Service**: Psychiatric

**Staffed Beds:** 220

## TAKOMA PARK—Montgomery County

**WASHINGTON ADVENTIST HOSPITAL** See Adventist Healthcare Washington
Adventist Hospital

## TOWSON—Baltimore County

**ST. JOSEPH MEDICAL CENTER** See University of Maryland St. Joseph Medical
Center

✠ **UNIVERSITY OF MARYLAND ST. JOSEPH MEDICAL CENTER (210007)**,
7601 Osler Drive, Zip 21204–7582; tel. 410/337–1000, (Nonreporting) **A**1 2
3 5 10 **F**3 11 13 15 17 18 20 22 24 26 28 29 30 31 34 35 36 37 40 41 44
45 46 47 48 49 50 54 55 56 57 58 59 60 61 64 65 66 68 70 71 72 74 75
76 77 78 79 81 82 84 85 86 87 91 92 93 97 98 100 101 102 103 104 107
108 114 115 118 119 122 123 124 126 130 131 132 134 135 144
146 147 148 149 153 156 157 **P**8 **S** University of Maryland Medical System,
Baltimore, MD
Primary Contact: Thomas Smyth, President and Chief Executive Officer
CMO: Gail Cunningham, Interim Chief Medical Officer
CIO: Thomas Gronert, Chief Information Officer
CNO: Pamela Jamieson, Vice President Patient Care Services and Chief Nursing
Officer
Web address: www.stjosephtowson.com/home.aspx
**Control**: Other not-for-profit (including NFP Corporation) **Service**: General
medical and surgical

**Staffed Beds:** 287 **Admissions:** 14569 **Census:** 164 **Outpatient
Visits:** 101957 **Births:** 2043 **Total Expense ($000):** 322702 **Payroll
Expense ($000):** 113096 **Personnel:** 1893

## WESTMINSTER—Carroll County

**CARROLL HOSPITAL** See Carroll Hospital Center

✠ **CARROLL HOSPITAL CENTER (210033)**, 200 Memorial Avenue,
Zip 21157–5799; tel. 410/848–3000, (Nonreporting) **A**1 2 3 10 **F**3 7 11 13 15
17 18 19 20 22 26 28 29 30 31 32 34 35 36 38 39 40 44 45 46 49 50 51 54
55 56 57 58 59 61 62 63 64 68 70 74 75 76 77 78 79 81 82 83 84 85 86 87
89 94 96 97 98 99 100 101 102 103 105 107 108 109 110 111 114 115 116
117 119 126 127 129 130 131 132 134 135 143 146 147 148 149 153 154
155 156 157 **P**8 **S** LifeBridge Health, Baltimore, MD
Primary Contact: Garrett W. Hoover, FACHE, President and Chief Operating Officer,
Senior Vice President LifeBridge Health
COO: Garrett W Hoover, FACHE, President and Chief Operating Officer, Senior Vice
President LifeBridge Health
CFO: Kevin Kelbly, Senior Vice President Finance and Corporate Fiscal Affairs
CMO: Mark Olszyk, M.D., Vice President Medical Affairs and Chief Medical Officer
CHR: Holly Phipps Adams, Vice President of Human Resources
CNO: Stephanie Reid, R.N., Vice President of Patient Care Services and Chief
Nursing Officer
Web address: www.carrollhospitalcenter.org
**Control**: Other not-for-profit (including NFP Corporation) **Service**: General
medical and surgical

**Staffed Beds:** 113 **Admissions:** 10591 **Census:** 114 **Outpatient
Visits:** 121971 **Births:** 1036 **Total Expense ($000):** 231617 **Payroll
Expense ($000):** 91290 **Personnel:** 1427

# MASSACHUSETTS

**MA**

### ATHOL—Worcester County

☐ **ATHOL HOSPITAL (221303)**, 2033 Main Street, Zip 01331–3598;
tel. 978/249–3511, (Nonreporting) **A**1 10 18 **F**3 15 18 29 31 34 35 40 45 64
75 77 78 79 81 84 85 87 97 100 107 110 114 119 127 130 132 133 144 146
149 154 **S** Heywood Healthcare, Gardner, MA
Primary Contact: Winfield S. Brown, FACHE, President and Chief Executive Officer
COO: Michael Grimmer, Chief Operating Officer
CFO: Robert Crosby, Chief Financial Officer
CMO: Mohsen Noreldin, M.D., President Medical Staff
CIO: Carol Roosa, Vice President Information Services and Chief Information Officer
CNO: Lucille Songer, Chief Nursing Officer
Web address: www.atholhospital.org
**Control**: Other not-for-profit (including NFP Corporation) **Service**: General
medical and surgical

> **Staffed Beds:** 21 **Admissions:** 490 **Census:** 9 **Outpatient Visits:** 56612
> **Births:** 0 **Total Expense ($000):** 30125 **Payroll Expense ($000):** 8454
> **Personnel:** 137

**ATHOL MEMORIAL HOSPITAL** See Athol Hospital

### ATTLEBORO—Bristol County

☐ **ARBOUR-FULLER HOSPITAL (224021)**, 200 May Street, Zip 02703–5520;
tel. 508/761–8500, (Nonreporting) **A**1 10 **S** Universal Health Services, Inc., King
of Prussia, PA
Primary Contact: Rachel Legend, Chief Executive Officer
CFO: James Rollins, Chief Financial Officer
CMO: Aminadav Zakai, M.D., Medical Director
CHR: Brian Jenkins, Director Human Resources
Web address: www.arbourhealth.com
**Control**: Corporation, Investor-owned (for-profit) **Service**: Psychiatric

> **Staffed Beds:** 46

**FULLER MEMORIAL HOSPITAL** See Arbour-Fuller Hospital

★ ⇑ **STURDY MEMORIAL HOSPITAL (220008)**, 211 Park Street,
Zip 02703–3137, Mailing Address: PO Box 2963, Zip 02703–0963;
tel. 508/222–5200, (Nonreporting) **A**2 10 21 **F**3 13 15 18 28 29 30 31 32 34
35 36 40 44 45 46 47 48 49 50 53 54 57 58 59 64 70 74 75 76 77 78 79 81
82 85 86 87 93 97 100 107 108 109 110 111 115 118 119 129 130 131 132
134 144 146 147 148
Primary Contact: Joseph Casey, Interim President and Chief Executive Officer
CFO: Amy Pfeffer, Chief Financial Officer
CMO: Brian Kelly, M.D., Vice President Medical Affairs and Medical Director
CHR: Cheryl Barrows, Vice President Human Resources
CNO: David Spoor, R.N., Vice President, Patient Care Services and Chief Nursing Officer
Web address: www.sturdymemorial.org
**Control**: Other not-for-profit (including NFP Corporation) **Service**: General
medical and surgical

> **Staffed Beds:** 132 **Admissions:** 7193 **Census:** 78 **Outpatient
> Visits:** 203154 **Births:** 644 **Total Expense ($000):** 198128 **Payroll Expense
> ($000):** 90437 **Personnel:** 1161

### AYER—Middlesex County

**DEACONESS-NASHOBA HOSPITAL** See Nashoba Valley Medical Center

☐ **NASHOBA VALLEY MEDICAL CENTER (220098)**, 200 Groton Road,
Zip 01432–3300; tel. 978/784–9000, (Nonreporting) **A**1 10 **S** Steward Health
Care System, LLC, Dallas, TX
Primary Contact: Korry Dow, President
CFO: Ben Moll, Assistant Chief Financial Officer
CMO: Michael Older, M.D., President Medical Staff
CNO: Cheryl L Bonasoro, MSN, R.N., Vice President of Nursing and Chief Operating
Officer
Web address: www.https://www.nashobamed.org
**Control**: Corporation, Investor-owned (for-profit) **Service**: General medical and
surgical

> **Staffed Beds:** 48

### BEDFORD—Middlesex County

⊞ **BEDFORD VETERANS AFFAIRS MEDICAL CENTER, EDITH NOURSE ROGERS
MEMORIAL VETERANS HOSPITAL**, 200 Springs Road, Zip 01730–1198;
tel. 781/687–2000, (Nonreporting) **A**1 3 5 **F**3 4 5 6 12 18 29 30 34 35 36 38
39 44 53 54 56 57 58 59 62 63 64 65 66 68 74 75 77 82 83 84 86 87 91 92
93 94 97 98 100 101 102 103 104 105 106 119 128 130 132 135 143 144
146 147 148 149 151 152 153 154 156 157 158 **S** Department of Veterans
Affairs, Washington, DC
Primary Contact: Joan Clifford, R.N., FACHE, Medical Center Director and Chief
Executive Officer
COO: Mark Fontaine-Westhart, Associate Director
CFO: Edward Koetting, Chief Financial Officer
CMO: Dan Berlowitz, M.D., M.P.H., Acting Chief of Staff
CHR: Robert Colpitts, Chief Human Resource Service
CNO: Mary Ann Petrillo, R.N., MSN, Acting Associate Director Nursing and Patient
Clinical Services
Web address: www.bedford.va.gov
**Control**: Veterans Affairs, Government, federal **Service**: Psychiatric

> **Staffed Beds:** 300 **Admissions:** 1496 **Census:** 319 **Outpatient
> Visits:** 213860 **Births:** 0 **Total Expense ($000):** 177532 **Payroll Expense
> ($000):** 109540 **Personnel:** 976

**EDITH NOURSE ROGERS MEMORIAL VETERANS HOSPITAL** See Bedford
Veterans Affairs Medical Center, Edith Nourse Rogers Memorial Veterans Hospital

### BELMONT—Middlesex County

⊞ **MCLEAN HOSPITAL (224007)**, 115 Mill Street, Zip 02478–1064;
tel. 617/855–2000, **A**1 3 5 10 **F**4 5 29 30 50 53 56 58 64 68 77
86 98 100 101 103 104 105 106 111 119 130 132 134 146 152 153 157 **P**6
**S** Mass General Brigham, Boston, MA
Primary Contact: Scott L. Rauch, M.D., President and Psychiatrist in Chief
COO: Michele L Gougeon, Executive Vice President and Chief Operating Officer
CFO: David A Lagasse, Senior Vice President Fiscal Affairs
CMO: Joseph Gold, M.D., Chief Medical Officer
CHR: Lisa D. Pratt, Vice President, Human Resources
CNO: Linda Flaherty, R.N., Senior Vice President, Patient Care Services
Web address: www.mcleanhospital.org
**Control**: Other not-for-profit (including NFP Corporation) **Service**: Psychiatric

> **Staffed Beds:** 217 **Admissions:** 5968 **Census:** 200 **Outpatient
> Visits:** 49245 **Births:** 0 **Total Expense ($000):** 251323 **Payroll Expense
> ($000):** 107102 **Personnel:** 1805

### BEVERLY—Essex County

⊞ **BEVERLY HOSPITAL (220033)**, 85 Herrick Street, Zip 01915–1777;
tel. 978/922–3000, (Includes ADDISON GILBERT HOSPITAL, Mailing address:
298 Washington Street, Gloucester, Massachusetts, Zip 01930–4887;
tel. 978/283–4000), (Nonreporting) **A**1 2 3 5 10 **S** Beth Israel Lahey Health,
Boston, MA
Primary Contact: Philip M. Cormier, Chief Executive Officer
COO: Pauline Pike, Chief Operating Officer
CFO: Connie Woodworth, Vice President Finance
CMO: Peter H Short, M.D., Senior Vice President Medical Affairs
CIO: Robert Laramie, Chief Information Officer
CHR: Althea C Lyons, Vice President Human Resources and Development
Web address: www.beverlyhospital.org
**Control**: Other not-for-profit (including NFP Corporation) **Service**: General
medical and surgical

> **Staffed Beds:** 320

### BOSTON—Suffolk County

☐ **ARBOUR HOSPITAL (224013)**, 49 Robinwood Avenue, Zip 02130–2156;
tel. 617/522–4400, (Nonreporting) **A**1 10 **S** Universal Health Services, Inc., King
of Prussia, PA
Primary Contact: Eric Kennedy, Chief Executive Officer
Web address: www.arbourhealth.com
**Control**: Other not-for-profit (including NFP Corporation) **Service**: Psychiatric

> **Staffed Beds:** 118

*Many Facility Codes have changed. Please refer to the AHA Guide Code Chart.*    © 2021 AHA Guide

**BETH ISRAEL DEACONESS MEDICAL CENTER (220086)**, 330 Brookline Avenue, Zip 02215–5491; tel. 617/667–7000, (Nonreporting) **A**1 2 3 5 8 10 **F**3 5 6 9 11 12 13 14 15 17 18 20 22 24 26 28 30 31 34 35 36 37 38 40 43 44 45 46 47 48 49 50 51 52 53 54 55 56 57 58 59 60 61 63 64 65 66 68 70 71 72 73 74 75 76 77 78 79 81 82 84 85 86 87 92 93 97 98 100 101 102 103 104 107 108 109 110 111 112 113 114 115 116 117 118 119 120 121 123 124 126 129 130 131 132 135 136 138 139 141 142 143 144 145 146 147 148 149 150 154 156 157 **P**8 **S** Beth Israel Lahey Health, Boston, MA
Primary Contact: Peter J. Healy, President and Chief Executive Officer
CFO: Steven P Fischer, Chief Financial Officer
CMO: Anthony Weiss, M.D., Chief Medical Officer
CHR: Judi Bieber, Senior Vice President Human Resources
CNO: Marsha L. Maurer, R.N., MS, Chief Nursing Officer Patient Care Services
Web address: www.bidmc.harvard.edu
**Control**: Other not–for–profit (including NFP Corporation) **Service**: General medical and surgical

**Staffed Beds**: 719 **Admissions**: 35398 **Census**: 575 **Outpatient Visits**: 1153180 **Births**: 5354 **Total Expense ($000)**: 1865302 **Payroll Expense ($000)**: 671959 **Personnel**: 8464

**BOSTON CHILDREN'S HOSPITAL (223302)**, 300 Longwood Avenue, Zip 02115–5737; tel. 617/355–6000, (Nonreporting) **A**1 3 5 8 10 **F**3 5 8 11 12 14 18 19 20 21 22 23 24 25 26 27 28 29 30 31 32 34 35 36 37 38 39 40 41 42 43 44 45 46 48 49 50 51 54 55 57 58 59 60 61 62 63 64 67 68 72 74 75 77 78 79 80 81 82 83 84 85 86 87 88 89 92 93 94 97 98 99 100 101 102 104 105 106 107 108 109 111 112 113 114 115 116 117 118 119 120 121 123 124 126 129 130 131 132 134 135 136 137 138 139 140 141 142 143 144 146 147 148 149 150 153 154 156 157 **P**3 5
Primary Contact: Sandra L. Fenwick, M.P.H., Chief Executive Officer
COO: Kevin B Churchwell, M.D., President and Chief Operating Officer
CFO: Douglas M Vanderslice, Senior Vice President and Chief Financial Officer
CIO: Daniel Nigrin, M.D., Vice President Information Services and Chief Information Officer
Web address: www.childrenshospital.org/
**Control**: Other not–for–profit (including NFP Corporation) **Service**: Children's general medical and surgical

**Staffed Beds**: 415 **Admissions**: 13279 **Census**: 335 **Outpatient Visits**: 752412 **Births**: 0 **Total Expense ($000)**: 1800729 **Payroll Expense ($000)**: 642960 **Personnel**: 10634

**BOSTON MEDICAL CENTER (220031)**, 1 Boston Medical Center Place, Zip 02118–2908; tel. 617/638–8000, (Nonreporting) **A**1 2 3 5 8 10 **F**3 5 8 9 12 13 15 17 18 20 22 24 26 28 29 30 34 35 36 38 40 41 43 44 45 46 47 48 49 50 54 55 56 57 58 59 60 61 64 65 66 68 70 72 73 74 75 76 77 78 79 81 82 84 85 86 87 88 89 93 97 99 100 101 102 103 104 107 108 110 111 114 116 117 118 119 120 121 123 124 126 129 130 131 132 134 135 136 138 142 143 144 145 146 147 148 149 150 **P**7
Primary Contact: Kate Walsh, M.P.H., President and Chief Executive Officer
CFO: Ronald E Bartlett, Chief Financial Officer
CMO: Ravin Davidoff, M.D., Chief Medical Officer
CHR: Stephanie Lovell, Vice President and General Counsel
Web address: www.bmc.org
**Control**: Other not–for–profit (including NFP Corporation) **Service**: General medical and surgical

**Staffed Beds**: 399 **Admissions**: 23289 **Census**: 356 **Outpatient Visits**: 998301 **Births**: 2919 **Total Expense ($000)**: 1630310 **Payroll Expense ($000)**: 533382 **Personnel**: 7418

**BRIGHAM AND WOMEN'S FAULKNER HOSPITAL (220119)**, 1153 Centre Street, Zip 02130–3446; tel. 617/983–7000, (Nonreporting) **A**1 3 5 10 **F**3 4 5 12 15 18 28 29 30 34 35 37 38 40 45 46 47 48 49 50 56 57 58 59 61 63 68 70 74 75 77 79 81 82 84 85 87 93 96 97 100 101 102 103 104 105 107 108 110 111 119 126 129 130 132 146 149 150 152 153 154 156 157 **S** Mass General Brigham, Boston, MA
Primary Contact: David O. McCready, President
CFO: Gerard Hadley, Vice President Finance for Brigham & Women's Faulkner Hospital and Vice President Finance and Controller
CMO: Margaret M. Duggan, M.D., Chief Medical Officer
CIO: Catherine Schroeder, Deputy Chief Information Officer
CHR: Laura Barnett, Executive Director, Human Resources
CNO: Cori Loescher, R.N., Chief Nursing Officer and Vice President of Patient Care Services
Web address: www.brighamandwomensfaulkner.org/index.asp
**Control**: Other not–for–profit (including NFP Corporation) **Service**: General medical and surgical

**Staffed Beds**: 171 **Admissions**: 9818 **Census**: 120 **Outpatient Visits**: 228347 **Births**: 0 **Total Expense ($000)**: 266553 **Payroll Expense ($000)**: 111480 **Personnel**: 1379

**BRIGHAM AND WOMEN'S HOSPITAL (220110)**, 75 Francis Street, Zip 02115–6110; tel. 617/732–5500, (Nonreporting) **A**1 3 3 5 8 10 **F**3 5 6 8 9 11 12 13 14 15 16 17 18 20 22 24 28 29 30 31 33 34 35 36 37 38 39 40 43 44 45 46 47 48 49 50 51 52 54 55 56 57 58 59 60 61 64 65 66 68 70 71 72 73 74 75 76 77 78 79 81 82 83 84 85 86 87 92 93 97 100 101 102 104 105 107 108 110 111 112 117 118 119 120 121 123 124 126 129 130 131 132 133 134 135 136 137 138 139 140 141 142 143 144 145 146 147 148 149 150 152 153 154 156 157 **P**6 **S** Mass General Brigham, Boston, MA
Primary Contact: Elizabeth Nabel, M.D., President
COO: Ron Walls, M.D., Executive Vice President and Chief Operating Officer
CFO: Christopher Dunleavy, Senior Vice President Finance and Chief Financial Officer
CMO: Stanley Ashley, M.D., Senior Vice President Medical Affairs and Chief Medical Officer
CIO: Adam Landman, M.D., Chief Information Officer
CHR: Sabrina Williams, Interim Vice President Human Resources
CNO: Madelyn Pearson, R.N., Senior Vice President Patient Care Services and Chief Nursing Officer
Web address: www.brighamandwomens.org
**Control**: Other not–for–profit (including NFP Corporation) **Service**: General medical and surgical

**Staffed Beds**: 822 **Admissions**: 41537 **Census**: 735 **Outpatient Visits**: 1249937 **Births**: 6325 **Total Expense ($000)**: 3024393 **Payroll Expense ($000)**: 875487 **Personnel**: 14327

**CARITAS CARNEY HOSPITAL** See Carney Hospital

**CARNEY HOSPITAL (220017)**, 2100 Dorchester Avenue, Zip 02124–5615; tel. 617/296–4000, (Nonreporting) **A**1 3 5 10 **S** Steward Health Care System, LLC, Dallas, TX
Primary Contact: Tom Sands, Interim Chief Executive Officer
COO: Christian Stroucken, Chief Operating Officer
CFO: David McGrail, Vice President Finance
CMO: Alexander White, Vice President Medical Affairs
CHR: Mary Orlandi, Manager Human Resources
Web address: www.carneyhospital.org
**Control**: Corporation, Investor–owned (for–profit) **Service**: General medical and surgical

**Staffed Beds**: 81

**CHILDREN'S HOSPITAL BOSTON** See Boston Children's Hospital

**DANA-FARBER CANCER INSTITUTE (220162)**, 450 Brookline Avenue, Zip 02215–5418; tel. 617/632–3000, (Nonreporting) **A**1 2 3 5 8 10 **F**3 11 15 29 30 31 32 34 35 36 44 50 54 55 56 57 58 59 66 68 71 75 77 78 82 83 84 85 86 87 99 100 101 104 107 108 110 111 114 115 117 118 119 120 121 123 124 130 132 134 135 136 144 146 147 148 149 150 154 **P**6
Primary Contact: Laurie H. Glimcher, President and Chief Executive Officer
COO: James G. Terwilliger, Executive Vice President and Chief Operating Officer
CFO: Michael L. Reney, Senior Vice President for Finance and Chief Financial Officer
CMO: Craig A. Bunnell, Chief Medical Officer
CIO: Naomi Lenane, Chief Information Officer
CHR: Deborah Hicks, Senior Vice President, Chief People and Culture Officer
CNO: Anne H Gross, Senior Vice President, Patient Care Services and Chief Nursing Officer
Web address: www.dana-farber.org
**Control**: Other not–for–profit (including NFP Corporation) **Service**: Cancer

**Staffed Beds**: 30 **Admissions**: 1614 **Census**: 28 **Outpatient Visits**: 490885 **Births**: 0 **Total Expense ($000)**: 1880775 **Payroll Expense ($000)**: 489572 **Personnel**: 5463

**DR. SOLOMON CARTER FULLER MENTAL HEALTH CENTER (224040)**, 85 East Newton Street, Zip 02118–2340; tel. 617/626–8700, (Nonreporting) **A**3 5 10
Primary Contact: Mary-Louise White, M.D., Chief Operating Officer
Web address: www.https://www.mass.gov/service-details/metro-boston-area
**Control**: State, Government, Nonfederal **Service**: Psychiatric

**Staffed Beds**: 32

**FAULKNER HOSPITAL** See Brigham and Women's Faulkner Hospital

---

Hospital, Medicare Provider Number, Address, Telephone, Approval, Facility, and Physician Codes, Health Care System

★ American Hospital Association (AHA) membership    ○ Healthcare Facilities Accreditation Program    ⇑ Center for Improvement in Healthcare Quality Accreditation
□ The Joint Commission accreditation    ◇ DNV Healthcare Inc. accreditation    △ Commission on Accreditation of Rehabilitation Facilities (CARF) accreditation

✠ **MASSACHUSETTS EYE AND EAR (220075)**, 243 Charles Street, Zip 02114–3002; tel. 617/523–7900, (Nonreporting) **A**1 3 5 10 **F**3 7 8 11 29 30 31 34 35 36 40 41 44 50 54 55 56 57 58 59 64 65 66 68 74 75 77 78 81 82 85 86 87 107 111 114 119 126 129 130 132 141 146 **P**6 **S** Mass General Brigham, Boston, MA
Primary Contact: John R. Fernandez, President and Chief Executive Officer
CFO: CarolAnn Williams, Chief Financial Officer
CIO: Leo Hill, Chief Information Officer
CHR: Martha Pyle Farrell, Vice President Human Resources and General Counsel
Web address: www.masseyeandear.org
**Control:** Other not–for–profit (including NFP Corporation) **Service:** Eye, ear, nose and throat

**Staffed Beds:** 41 **Admissions:** 1175 **Census:** 12 **Outpatient Visits:** 412346
**Births:** 0 **Total Expense ($000):** 289931 **Payroll Expense ($000):** 81528
**Personnel:** 1850

**MASSACHUSETTS EYE AND EAR INFIRMARY** See Massachusetts Eye and Ear

✠ **MASSACHUSETTS GENERAL HOSPITAL (220071)**, 55 Fruit Street, Zip 02114–2696; tel. 617/726–2000, (Includes MASSGENERAL HOSPITAL FOR CHILDREN, Mailing address: 55 Fruit Street, Boston, Massachusetts, Zip 02114–2621; tel. 888/644–3248), (Nonreporting) **A**1 3 5 8 10 **F**3 4 5 6 8 9 11 12 13 14 15 16 17 18 19 20 21 22 23 24 25 26 27 28 29 30 31 32 33 34 35 36 37 38 39 40 41 43 44 45 46 47 48 49 50 51 52 53 54 55 56 57 58 59 60 61 62 63 64 65 66 68 70 71 72 73 74 75 76 77 78 79 80 81 82 84 85 86 87 88 89 91 92 93 94 96 97 98 99 100 101 102 103 104 105 107 108 110 111 112 113 114 115 116 117 118 119 120 121 122 123 124 126 129 131 132 134 135 136 137 138 139 140 141 142 143 144 145 146 147 148 149 150 153 154 156 157 **P**6 7 **S** Mass General Brigham, Boston, MA
Primary Contact: Peter L. Slavin, M.D., President
CFO: Sally Mason Boemer, Senior Vice President Finance
CMO: Britain Nicholson, M.D., Chief Medical Officer
CIO: Keith Jennings, Chief Information Officer
CHR: Jovita Thomas-Williams, Senior Vice President of Human Resources
CNO: Jeanette R Ives Erickson, MS, R.N., Senior Vice President Patient Care and Chief Nurse
Web address: www.massgeneral.org
**Control:** Other not–for–profit (including NFP Corporation) **Service:** General medical and surgical

**Staffed Beds:** 1035 **Admissions:** 50529 **Census:** 873 **Outpatient Visits:** 871771 **Births:** 3826 **Total Expense ($000):** 4060179 **Payroll Expense ($000):** 1151073 **Personnel:** 17852

✠ **NEW ENGLAND BAPTIST HOSPITAL (220088)**, 125 Parker Hill Avenue, Zip 02120–2847; tel. 617/754–5800, (Nonreporting) **A**1 3 5 10 **F**3 8 9 14 18 29 30 34 35 37 44 45 50 53 54 57 58 59 64 65 66 70 74 75 77 79 81 82 86 87 92 93 97 107 108 111 115 119 130 131 141 146 148 157 **S** Beth Israel Lahey Health, Boston, MA
Primary Contact: David Passafaro, Chief Executive Officer
CFO: Thomas Gheringhelli, Senior Vice President, Chief Financial Officer
CHR: Linda Thompson, Senior Vice President, Human Resources and Service Excellence
CNO: Mary Sullivan Smith, R.N., MS, Senior Vice President, Chief Operating Officer and Chief Nursing Officer
Web address: www.nebh.org
**Control:** Other not–for–profit (including NFP Corporation) **Service:** Orthopedic

**Staffed Beds:** 113 **Admissions:** 8186 **Census:** 52 **Outpatient Visits:** 125807 **Births:** 0 **Total Expense ($000):** 231029 **Payroll Expense ($000):** 85255 **Personnel:** 897

☐ **SHRINERS HOSPITALS FOR CHILDREN-BOSTON (223304)**, 51 Blossom Street, Zip 02114–2601; tel. 617/722–3000, (Nonreporting) **A**1 3 5 10 **F**3 16 29 30 32 34 35 36 39 57 58 59 64 68 75 79 81 82 85 87 89 93 94 100 101 104 119 130 132 134 143 146 148 154 158 **S** Shriners Hospitals for Children, Tampa, FL
Primary Contact: Eileen F. Skinner, FACHE, Administrator
CFO: Maria Chung, CPA, Director Fiscal Services
CMO: Matthias B Donelan, M.D., Chief of Staff
CIO: Mary Dolan, Regional Director Information Services and HIPAA Security Official
CHR: John Donlin, Regional Director Human Resources - Boston, Erie, and Springfield
Web address: www.shrinershospitalsforchildren.org/Hospitals/Locations/Boston
**Control:** Other not–for–profit (including NFP Corporation) **Service:** Children's other specialty

**Staffed Beds:** 18 **Admissions:** 119 **Census:** 5 **Outpatient Visits:** 7125
**Births:** 0 **Total Expense ($000):** 40623 **Payroll Expense ($000):** 14153
**Personnel:** 180

**SHRINERS HOSPITALS FOR CHILDREN-BOSTON BURNS HOSPITAL** See Shriners Hospitals for Children-Boston

✠ **TUFTS MEDICAL CENTER (220116)**, 800 Washington Street, Zip 02111–1552; tel. 617/636–5000, (Nonreporting) **A**1 2 3 5 8 10 **F**3 4 5 9 12 13 14 15 17 18 19 20 21 22 23 24 25 26 27 28 29 30 31 32 34 35 36 37 39 40 41 42 43 44 45 46 47 49 50 51 52 55 56 57 58 59 61 64 65 68 70 71 72 74 75 76 77 78 79 81 82 84 85 86 87 88 89 93 97 98 100 102 104 107 108 110 111 114 115 116 117 118 119 120 121 123 124 126 129 130 131 132 134 135 136 137 138 141 143 146 147 148 149 151 154 156 157 **P**5
Primary Contact: Michael Tarnoff, M.D., Interim Chief Executive Officer
CFO: Kristine Hanscom, Chief Financial Officer
CMO: David Fairchild, M.D., Chief Medical Officer
CIO: William Shickolovich, Chief Information Officer
CNO: Therese M. Hudson-Jinks, R.N., MSN, Chief Nursing Officer
Web address: www.tuftsmedicalcenter.org
**Control:** Other not–for–profit (including NFP Corporation) **Service:** General medical and surgical

**Staffed Beds:** 287 **Admissions:** 16341 **Census:** 269 **Outpatient Visits:** 450485 **Births:** 1333 **Total Expense ($000):** 859069 **Payroll Expense ($000):** 335674 **Personnel:** 6645

**TUFTS-NEW ENGLAND MED CENTER** See Tufts Medical Center

**BRADFORD—Essex County**

✠ **WHITTIER REHABILITATION HOSPITAL (222047)**, 145 Ward Hill Avenue, Zip 01835–6928; tel. 978/372–8000, (Nonreporting) **A**1 10 **S** Whittier Health Network, Haverhill, MA
Primary Contact: Alfred J. Arcidi, M.D., Senior Vice President
Web address: www.whittierhealth.com
**Control:** Partnership, Investor–owned (for–profit) **Service:** Acute long–term care hospital

**Staffed Beds:** 60

**BRAINTREE—Norfolk County**

✠ **ENCOMPASS HEALTH REHABILITATION HOSPITAL OF BRAINTREE (223027)**, 250 Pond Street, Zip 02184–5351; tel. 781/348–2500, (Nonreporting) **A**1 5 10 **S** Encompass Health Corporation, Birmingham, AL
Primary Contact: Randy Doherty, CPA, Chief Executive Officer
CFO: Barry Leonard IVice President of Finance
CMO: Arthur Williams, M.D., Medical Director
CHR: Cathryn Wigman, Director Human Resources
CNO: Jinia Drinkwater, R.N., Director Patient Care Services
Web address: www.braintreerehabhospital.com
**Control:** Corporation, Investor–owned (for–profit) **Service:** Rehabilitation

**Staffed Beds:** 187

**HEALTHSOUTHBRAINTREE REHABILITATION HOSPITAL** See Encompass Health Rehabilitation Hospital of Braintree

**BRIDGEWATER—Plymouth County**

**BRIDGEWATER STATE HOSPITAL**, 20 Administration Road, Zip 02324–3201; tel. 508/279–4521, (Nonreporting) **A**3 5
Primary Contact: Daniel Calais Jr, Superintendent
CFO: Diane Wholley, Director Fiscal Services
**Control:** State, Government, Nonfederal **Service:** Psychiatric

**Staffed Beds:** 350

**BRIGHTON—Suffolk County**

**CARITAS ST. ELIZABETH'S MEDICAL CENTER** See St. Elizabeth's Medical Center

✠ **FRANCISCAN CHILDREN'S (223300)**, 30 Warren Street, Zip 02135–3680; tel. 617/254–3800, (Nonreporting) **A**1 3 5 10 **F**1 29 30 34 35 38 39 58 59 64 68 77 81 87 90 91 93 94 98 99 100 101 104 106 130 146 **P**6
Primary Contact: John D. Nash, FACHE, President and Chief Executive Officer
COO: Donna Polselli, Chief Operating Officer
CFO: Alex Denucci, Chief Financial Officer
CMO: Jane E O'Brien, M.D., Medical Director
CIO: Sean McKeon, Director, Information Technology
CHR: Nancy Murphy, Vice President, Human Resources
CNO: Mary Lou Kelleher, R.N., MSN, Vice President, Nursing
Web address: www.franciscanhospital.org
**Control:** Other not–for–profit (including NFP Corporation) **Service:** Children's rehabilitation

**Staffed Beds:** 76 **Admissions:** 778 **Census:** 65 **Outpatient Visits:** 39786
**Births:** 0 **Total Expense ($000):** 64197 **Payroll Expense ($000):** 37470
**Personnel:** 610

**FRANCISCAN HOSPITAL FOR CHILDREN** See Franciscan Children's

*Many Facility Codes have changed. Please refer to the AHA Guide Code Chart.*

© 2021 AHA Guide

**MA**

☐ **ST. ELIZABETH'S MEDICAL CENTER (220036)**, 736 Cambridge Street, Zip 02135–2997; tel. 617/789–3000, (Nonreporting) **A**1 2 3 5 10 **S** Steward Health Care System, LLC, Dallas, TX
Primary Contact: Craig T. Williams, President
CMO: Dicken S.C. Ko, M.D., Vice President of Medical Affairs and Chief Medical Officer
CIO: Joseph Schmitt, Chief Information Officer
CHR: Claudia Henderson, Chief Human Resources
Web address: www.semc.org/
**Control**: Corporation, Investor–owned (for–profit) **Service**: General medical and surgical

**Staffed Beds:** 338

**BROCKTON—Plymouth County**

**BROCKTON HOSPITAL** See Signature Healthcare Brockton Hospital

**BROCKTON VETERANS AFFAIRS MEDICAL CENTER** See Veterans Affairs Boston Healthcare System Brockton Division

**CARDINAL CUSHING GEN HOSPITAL** See Good Samaritan Medical Center - Cushing Campus

**CARITAS GOOD SAMARITAN MEDICAL CENTER** See Good Samaritan Medical Center

☐ **GOOD SAMARITAN MEDICAL CENTER (220111)**, 235 North Pearl Street, Zip 02301–1794; tel. 508/427–3000, (Includes GOOD SAMARITAN MEDICAL CENTER - CUSHING CAMPUS, Mailing address: 235 North Pearl Street, Brockton, Massachusetts, Zip 02401–1794; tel. 508/427–3000), (Nonreporting) **A**1 2 3 5 10 **S** Steward Health Care System, LLC, Dallas, TX
Primary Contact: Harrison Bane, President
COO: Donna Rubinate, R.N., Chief Operating Officer
CFO: Thomas Whalen, Vice President Finance
CMO: Scott Stewart, M.D., Vice President Medical Management
CIO: Lori Caswell, Director Information Technology
CHR: David J Cronin, Regional Vice President Human Resources
Web address: www.goodsamaritanmedical.org
**Control**: Corporation, Investor–owned (for–profit) **Service**: General medical and surgical

**Staffed Beds:** 190

⊞ **SIGNATURE HEALTHCARE BROCKTON HOSPITAL (220052)**, 680 Centre Street, Zip 02302–3395; tel. 508/941–7000, (Nonreporting) **A**1 2 3 10 **F**3 12 13 15 17 18 20 22 28 29 30 31 34 35 38 40 44 45 46 47 48 49 50 51 52 54 57 58 59 61 64 65 68 70 73 74 75 76 77 78 79 81 82 85 86 87 89 93 97 98 100 102 104 107 108 110 111 114 115 116 117 118 119 120 121 123 124 130 131 132 135 144 146 147 148 149 **P**6 8
Primary Contact: Kim Norton. Hollon, FACHE, President and Chief Executive Officer
CFO: Kevin G Murphy, Chief Financial Officer
CIO: Gerald Greeley, Chief Information Officer
CHR: David Fisher, Vice President Human Resources
CNO: Kim Walsh, Chief Nursing Officer
Web address: www.signature-healthcare.org
**Control**: Other not–for–profit (including NFP Corporation) **Service**: General medical and surgical

**Staffed Beds:** 216 **Admissions:** 10367 **Census:** 134 **Outpatient Visits:** 400743 **Births:** 1285 **Total Expense ($000):** 288576 **Payroll Expense ($000):** 123931 **Personnel:** 1410

★ **VETERANS AFFAIRS BOSTON HEALTHCARE SYSTEM BROCKTON DIVISION**, 940 Belmont Street, Zip 02301–5596; tel. 508/583–4500, (Includes VETERANS AFFAIRS MEDICAL CENTER WEST ROXBURY DIVISION, Mailing address: 1400 VFW Parkway, West Roxbury, Massachusetts, Zip 2132, 1400 VVF Parkway, West Roxbury, Boston, Zip 2132, tel. 617/323–7700; William H Kelleher, Director), (Nonreporting) **A**3 **S** Department of Veterans Affairs, Washington, DC
Primary Contact: Vincent Ng, Director
CFO: Joe Costa, Acting Chief Fiscal Officer
Web address: www.boston.va.gov/
**Control**: Veterans Affairs, Government, federal **Service**: General medical and surgical

**Staffed Beds:** 375

**BROOKLINE—Norfolk County**

☐ **ARBOUR H. R. I. HOSPITAL (224018)**, 227 Babcock Street, Zip 02446–6799; tel. 617/731–3200, (Nonreporting) **A**1 10 **F**3 4 5 29 30 34 35 36 38 57 59 61 68 75 77 82 86 87 98 100 101 102 105 119 130 132 135 143 147 149 150 152 153 154 **S** Universal Health Services, Inc., King of Prussia, PA
Primary Contact: Jameson Pinette, Chief Executive Officer
CFO: Diane Airosus, Chief Financial Officer
CMO: Krishnaswamy Gajaraj, M.D., Medical Director
CHR: Katherine McCarthy, Director Human Resources
Web address: www.HRIHospital.com
**Control**: Corporation, Investor–owned (for–profit) **Service**: Psychiatric

**Staffed Beds:** 76 **Admissions:** 2036 **Census:** 59 **Outpatient Visits:** 19887 **Births:** 0 **Total Expense ($000):** 20270 **Payroll Expense ($000):** 10675 **Personnel:** 143

☐ **BOURNEWOOD HEALTH SYSTEMS (224022)**, 300 South Street, Zip 02467–3658; tel. 617/469–0300, (Nonreporting) **A**1 3 5 10
Primary Contact: Marcia Fowler, Chief Executive Officer
CFO: Michael Gale, Chief Financial Officer
CMO: Carmel Heinsohn, M.D., Medical Director
CHR: Paula Berardi, Manager Human Resources
Web address: www.bournewood.com
**Control**: Corporation, Investor–owned (for–profit) **Service**: Psychiatric

**Staffed Beds:** 90

**BOURNEWOOD HOSPITAL** See Bournewood Health Systems

**H R I HOSPITAL** See Arbour H. R. I. Hospital

**BURLINGTON—Middlesex County**

**LAHEY CLINIC HOSPITAL** See Lahey Hospital & Medical Center, Burlington

⊞ **LAHEY HOSPITAL & MEDICAL CENTER, BURLINGTON (220171)**, 41 Mall Road, Zip 01805–0001, Mailing Address: 31 Mall Road, Zip 01805–0001; tel. 781/744–5100, (Includes LAHEY MEDICAL CENTER, PEABODY, Mailing address: 1 Essex Center Drive, Peabody, Massachusetts, Zip 01960–2901; tel. 978/538–4000), (Nonreporting) **A**1 2 3 5 8 10 19 **F**3 6 8 9 11 12 15 17 18 20 22 24 26 28 29 30 31 34 35 36 37 38 40 43 44 45 46 47 48 49 50 51 52 53 54 55 56 57 58 59 60 61 63 64 65 68 70 74 75 77 78 79 81 82 84 85 86 87 91 92 93 96 97 100 101 102 104 108 110 111 114 115 116 117 118 119 120 121 122 123 124 126 129 130 131 132 135 136 138 139 141 142 144 145 146 147 148 149 150 153 154 157 **P**6 **S** Beth Israel Lahey Health, Boston, MA
Primary Contact: David L. Longworth, M.D., Chief Executive Officer
COO: Richard R Bias, Chief Operating Officer
CFO: Timothy P. O'Connor, Executive Vice President and Chief Financial Officer
CMO: Timothy Liesching, M.D., Chief Medical Officer
CIO: Bruce Metz, Ph.D., Senior Vice President and Chief Information Officer
CHR: Elizabeth P. Conrad, Senior Vice President and Chief Human Resource Officer
Web address: www.lahey.org
**Control**: Other not–for–profit (including NFP Corporation) **Service**: General medical and surgical

**Staffed Beds:** 345 **Admissions:** 23936 **Census:** 322 **Outpatient Visits:** 852247 **Births:** 0 **Total Expense ($000):** 976212 **Payroll Expense ($000):** 298711 **Personnel:** 3915

**CAMBRIDGE—Middlesex County**

⊞ **CAMBRIDGE HEALTH ALLIANCE (220011)**, 1493 Cambridge Street, Zip 02139–1099; tel. 617/665–1000, (Includes CAMBRIDGE HOSPITAL, Mailing address: 1493 Cambridge Street, Cambridge, Massachusetts, Zip 02139–1099; tel. 617/498–1000; SOMERVILLE HOSPITAL, Mailing address: 230 Highland Avenue, Somerville, Massachusetts, Zip 2143; tel. 617/666–4400; WHIDDEN MEMORIAL HOSPITAL, Mailing address: 103 Garland Street, Everett, Massachusetts, Zip 02149–5095; tel. 617/389–6270), (Nonreporting) **A**1 2 3 5 8 10
Primary Contact: Assaad Sayah, M.D., Chief Executive Officer
CFO: Jill I Batty, Chief Financial Officer
CMO: Assaad Sayah, M.D., Chief Medical Officer
CIO: Brian Herrick, M.D., Chief Information Officer
CHR: Joy U Curtis, Senior Vice President Human Resources
CNO: Elizabeth Cadigan, R.N., MSN, Senior Vice President Patient Care Services and Chief Nursing Officer
Web address: www.challiance.org
**Control**: Hospital district or authority, Government, Nonfederal **Service**: General medical and surgical

**Staffed Beds:** 274

**CAMBRIDGE PUB HLTH COMMISSION** See Cambridge Health Alliance

**MA**

---

**Hospital, Medicare Provider Number, Address, Telephone, Approval, Facility, and Physician Codes, Health Care System**

★ American Hospital Association (AHA) membership　　○ Healthcare Facilities Accreditation Program　　⇑ Center for Improvement in Healthcare Quality Accreditation
☐ The Joint Commission accreditation　　◇ DNV Healthcare Inc. accreditation　　△ Commission on Accreditation of Rehabilitation Facilities (CARF) accreditation

**MA**

⊞ **MOUNT AUBURN HOSPITAL (220002)**, 330 Mount Auburn Street,
Zip 02138–5597; tel. 617/492–3500, (Nonreporting) **A**1 2 3 5 8 10 **F**3 5 11 12
13 14 15 18 20 22 24 26 28 29 30 31 34 35 36 37 40 45 49 50 51 52 55 56
57 58 59 60 61 62 63 64 65 68 70 73 74 75 76 77 78 79 81 82 86 87 93 97
98 100 101 102 103 104 107 108 110 111 114 115 117 118 119 120 121
123 124 126 129 130 131 132 135 144 145 146 147 154 **P**5 6 7 **S** Beth Israel
Lahey Health, Boston, MA
Primary Contact: Jeanette G. Clough, President and Chief Executive Officer
COO: Nicholas T Dileso, R.N., Chief Operating Officer
CFO: William Sullivan
CIO: Kendall White, Chief Information Officer
CHR: Tom Fabiano, Director Human Resources
CNO: Deborah Baker, Vice President, Patient Care Services
Web address: www.mountauburnhospital.org
**Control**: Other not–for–profit (including NFP Corporation) **Service**: General
medical and surgical

**Staffed Beds**: 205 **Admissions**: 11125 **Census**: 137 **Births**: 2540 **Total
Expense ($000)**: 330868 **Payroll Expense ($000)**: 141283

**SPAULDING HOSPITAL CAMBRIDGE** See Spaulding Hospital for Continuing
Medical Care Cambridge

⊞ **SPAULDING HOSPITAL FOR CONTINUING MEDICAL CARE CAMBRIDGE
(222000)**, 1575 Cambridge Street, Zip 02138–4308; tel. 617/876–4344,
(Nonreporting) **A**1 10 **F**1 3 7 30 31 34 35 36 50 54 57 58 60 64 68 71 74 75
77 78 85 86 87 91 92 93 94 95 96 100 119 129 130 131 132 146 148 149
154 157 **P**6 **S** Mass General Brigham, Boston, MA
Primary Contact: Maureen Banks, President
CFO: Mary Shaughnessy, Vice President Finance
CMO: Jonathon Schwartz, M.D., Chief Medical Officer
CIO: John Campbell, Chief Information Officer
CHR: Jack Carroll, Director Human Resources
Web address: www.spauldingnetwork.org
**Control**: Other not–for–profit (including NFP Corporation) **Service**: Acute long–
term care hospital

**Staffed Beds**: 118 **Admissions**: 1119 **Census**: 112 **Outpatient Visits**: 0
**Births**: 0 **Total Expense ($000)**: 83465 **Payroll Expense ($000)**: 37503
**Personnel**: 473

### CANTON—Norfolk County

**MASSACHUSETTS HOSPITAL SCHOOL** See Pappas Rehabilitation Hospital for
Children

☐ **PAPPAS REHABILITATION HOSPITAL FOR CHILDREN (222025)**, 3
Randolph Street, Zip 02021–2351; tel. 781/828–2440, (Nonreporting) **A**1 10 **S**
Massachusetts Department of Public Health, Boston, MA
Primary Contact: Brian V. Devin, Chief Executive Officer
CFO: Sharon Porter, Chief Financial Officer
CMO: Aruna Sachdev, M.D., Medical Director
CIO: Robert Lima, Director Information Systems
CHR: Trish Scully, Manager Employment Services
Web address: www.mhsf.us/
**Control**: State, Government, Nonfederal **Service**: Children's acute long-term Care

**Staffed Beds**: 80

### CHARLESTOWN—Suffolk County

⊞ △ **SPAULDING REHABILITATION HOSPITAL (223034)**, 300 First Avenue,
Zip 02129–3109; tel. 617/952–5000, (Nonreporting) **A**1 3 5 7 10 **F**3 7 28 29
30 34 35 36 54 57 58 60 64 68 71 74 75 77 82 86 87 90 91 92 93 94 95
96 100 119 130 131 132 146 148 149 154 157 **P**6 **S** Mass General Brigham,
Boston, MA
Primary Contact: David E. Storto, President
COO: Maureen Banks, Chief Operating Officer
CFO: Amy Guay, Chief Financial Officer
CMO: Ross Zafonte, D.O., Chief, Physical Medicine and Rehabilitation and Vice
President Medical Affairs, Research and Education
CIO: John Campbell, Chief Information Officer
CHR: Russell Averna, Vice President Human Resources
CNO: Maureen Banks, Chief Nursing Officer
Web address: www.spauldingrehab.org
**Control**: Other not–for–profit (including NFP Corporation) **Service**: Rehabilitation

**Staffed Beds**: 132 **Admissions**: 2099 **Census**: 124 **Outpatient
Visits**: 376899 **Births**: 0 **Total Expense ($000)**: 171733 **Payroll Expense
($000)**: 75310 **Personnel**: 1077

### CLINTON—Worcester County

**CLINTON HOSPITAL** See Umass Memorial Healthalliance-Clinton Hospital

### CONCORD—Middlesex County

⊞ **EMERSON HOSPITAL (220084)**, 133 Old Road to Nine Acre Corner,
Zip 01742–9120; tel. 978/369–1400, (Nonreporting) **A**1 5 10 **F**3 5 7 8 11 12 13
14 15 17 18 28 29 30 31 32 34 35 36 37 38 40 45 48 49 50 51 54 57 59 60
62 64 65 68 70 73 74 75 76 77 78 79 81 82 85 86 87 89 93 98 100 101 102
103 104 105 107 110 111 114 115 119 128 129 130 131 132 135 144 145
146 148 152 153 156 157 **P**5 8
Primary Contact: Christine C. Schuster, R.N., President and Chief Executive Officer
CFO: Michael Hachey, Senior Vice President and Chief Financial Officer
CMO: Barrett Kitch, M.D., Senior Vice President, Clinical Affairs and Chief Medical
Officer
CIO: Renee Fosberg, Chief Information Officer
CNO: Joyce Welsh, R.N., MS, Vice President of Clinical Services and Chief Nursing
Officer
Web address: www.emersonhospital.org
**Control**: Other not–for–profit (including NFP Corporation) **Service**: General
medical and surgical

**Staffed Beds**: 175 **Admissions**: 7517 **Census**: 100 **Outpatient
Visits**: 299108 **Births**: 1258 **Total Expense ($000)**: 268383 **Payroll
Expense ($000)**: 125424 **Personnel**: 1460

### DARTMOUTH—Bristol County

☐ **SOUTHCOAST BEHAVIORAL HEALTH (224041)**, 581 Faunce Corner Road,
Zip 02747–1242; tel. 888/210–2475, (Nonreporting) **A**1 10 **S** Acadia Healthcare
Company, Inc., Franklin, TN
Primary Contact: Richard Remley, Chief Executive Officer
Web address: www.southcoastbehavioral.com
**Control**: Corporation, Investor–owned (for–profit) **Service**: Psychiatric

**Staffed Beds**: 120

### EAST SANDWICH—Barnstable County

**REHABILITATION HOSPITAL OF THE CAPE AND ISLANDS** See Spaulding
Rehabilitation Hospital Cape Cod

⊞ △ **SPAULDING REHABILITATION HOSPITAL CAPE COD (223032)**, 311
Service Road, Zip 02537–1370; tel. 508/833–4000, (Nonreporting) **A**1 7 10 **F**3
29 30 32 34 35 36 50 60 64 74 75 77 79 82 90 91 92 93 96 130 131 132
135 146 147 148 **S** Mass General Brigham, Boston, MA
Primary Contact: Maureen Banks, President
COO: Stephanie Nadolny, Vice President of Hospital Operations
CFO: Mary Shaughnessy, Vice President Finance
CMO: David Lowell, M.D., Chief Medical Officer
CIO: John Campbell, Chief Information Officer
CHR: Russell Averna, Vice President of Human Resources
Web address: www.spauldingrehab.org
**Control**: Other not–for–profit (including NFP Corporation) **Service**: Rehabilitation

**Staffed Beds**: 60 **Admissions**: 1080 **Census**: 41 **Outpatient Visits**: 133378
**Births**: 0 **Total Expense ($000)**: 45710 **Payroll Expense ($000)**: 22583
**Personnel**: 439

### EVERETT—Middlesex County

**WHIDDEN MEMORIAL HOSPITAL** See Cambridge Health Alliance, Cambridge

### FALL RIVER—Bristol County

**CHARLTON MEMORIAL HOSPITAL** See Southcoast Hospitals Group, Fall River

**DR J CORRIGAN MENTAL HLTH CNTR** See Dr. J. Corrigan Mental Health Center

☐ **DR. J. CORRIGAN MENTAL HEALTH CENTER (224028)**, 49 Hillside Street,
Zip 02720–5266; tel. 508/235–7200, (Nonreporting) **A**1 3 10 **S** Massachusetts
Department of Mental Health, Boston, MA
Primary Contact: Frank O'Reilly, Director
**Control**: State, Government, Nonfederal **Service**: Psychiatric

**Staffed Beds**: 16

*Many Facility Codes have changed. Please refer to the AHA Guide Code Chart.* © 2021 AHA Guide

**SAINT ANNE'S HOSPITAL (220020)**, 795 Middle Street, Zip 02721–1798; tel. 508/674–5741, (Nonreporting) **A**1 2 3 10 **S** Steward Health Care System, LLC, Dallas, TX
Primary Contact: Michael Bushell, President
CMO: John Conlon, M.D., Chief Medical Officer
CIO: Julie Berry, Chief Information Officer
CHR: Sandra Dellicker, Director of Human Resources
CNO: Carole Billington, R.N., MSN, Vice President Operations, Chief Nursing Officer
Web address: www.saintanneshospital.org
**Control**: Corporation, Investor–owned (for–profit) **Service**: General medical and surgical

**Staffed Beds**: 160

**SOUTHCOAST HOSPITALS GROUP (220074)**, 363 Highland Avenue, Zip 02720–3703; tel. 508/679–3131, (Includes CHARLTON MEMORIAL HOSPITAL, Mailing address: 363 Highland Avenue, Fall River, Massachusetts, Zip 02720–3703; tel. 508/679–3131; Keith A Hovan, R.N., President and Chief Executive Officer; ST. LUKE'S HOSPITAL, Mailing address: 101 Page Street, New Bedford, Massachusetts, Zip 2740; tel. 508/997–1515; Keith A Hovan, R.N., President and Chief Executive Officer; TOBEY HOSPITAL, Mailing address: 43 High Street, Wareham, Massachusetts, Zip 2571; tel. 508/295–0880; Keith A Hovan, R.N., President and Chief Executive Officer), (Nonreporting) **A**1 2 5 10 **F**3 11 12 13 15 17 18 20 22 24 26 28 29 30 31 34 35 37 40 41 44 45 46 47 48 49 50 51 54 56 57 58 59 60 61 64 65 68 70 71 73 74 75 76 77 78 79 81 82 84 85 86 87 89 90 91 92 93 96 100 102 107 108 110 111 114 115 116 117 118 119 120 121 123 124 126 130 131 132 134 135 146 147 148 149 157 **P**1 6
Primary Contact: Keith A. Hovan, R.N., President and Chief Executive Officer
COO: Renee Clark, M.D., Executive Vice President and Chief Operating Officer
CFO: Wade Broughman, Chief Financial Officer
CIO: Jim Feen, Senior Vice President and Chief Information Officer
CHR: Lauren De Simon Johnson, Senior Vice President, Chief Human Resources Officer
CNO: Jacqueline G Somerville, R.N., Ph.D., Senior Vice President and Chief Nursing Officer
Web address: www.southcoast.org
**Control**: Other not–for–profit (including NFP Corporation) **Service**: General medical and surgical

**Staffed Beds**: 497 **Admissions**: 34741 **Census**: 426 **Outpatient Visits**: 950071 **Births**: 3352 **Total Expense ($000)**: 821825 **Payroll Expense ($000)**: 351754 **Personnel**: 3648

**ST ANNE'S HOSPITAL** See Saint Anne's Hospital

### FALMOUTH—Barnstable County

**FALMOUTH HOSPITAL (220135)**, 100 Ter Heun Drive, Zip 02540–2599; tel. 508/548–5300, (Nonreporting) **A**1 2 10 **F**3 8 11 13 15 18 28 29 30 34 35 36 38 40 45 50 53 54 58 59 61 64 65 68 70 74 75 76 77 79 81 82 85 86 87 89 93 96 100 101 102 104 107 108 110 111 115 119 120 121 123 124 129 130 131 132 143 144 146 147 148 149 **P**8 **S** Cape Cod Healthcare, Inc., Hyannis, MA
Primary Contact: Lori Jewett, R.N., Chief Executive Officer
CFO: Michael Connors, Senior Vice President and Chief Financial Officer
CMO: Alex Heard, M.D., Chief Medical Officer
CIO: Paul Solverson, Senior Vice President and Chief Information Officer
CHR: Emily Schorer, Vice President, Human Resources
CNO: Mary Johnson, Chief Nursing Officer
Web address: www.capecodhealth.org
**Control**: Other not–for–profit (including NFP Corporation) **Service**: General medical and surgical

**Staffed Beds**: 95 **Admissions**: 5910 **Census**: 61 **Outpatient Visits**: 146057 **Births**: 327 **Total Expense ($000)**: 163016 **Payroll Expense ($000)**: 72369 **Personnel**: 705

### FRAMINGHAM—Middlesex County

**COLUMBIA METROWEST MEDICAL CTR** See Metrowest Medical Center

**FRAMINGTON UNION HOSPITAL** See Framingham Union Hospital

**METROWEST MEDICAL CENTER (220175)**, 115 Lincoln Street, Zip 01702–6342; tel. 508/383–1000, (Includes FRAMINGHAM UNION HOSPITAL, Mailing address: 115 Lincoln Street, Framingham, Massachusetts, Zip 1702; tel. 508/383–1000; LEONARD MORSE HOSPITAL, Mailing address: 67 Union Street, Natick, Massachusetts, Zip 1760; tel. 508/650–7000), (Nonreporting) **A**1 2 3 5 10 **S** TENET Healthcare Corporation, Dallas, TX
Primary Contact: Andrew D. Harding, R.N., Chief Executive Officer
CHR: Rebecca Heffernan, Director Human Resources
CNO: Susan A Mangini, R.N., FACHE, Chief Nursing Officer
Web address: www.mwmc.com
**Control**: Corporation, Investor–owned (for–profit) **Service**: General medical and surgical

**Staffed Beds**: 160

### GARDNER—Worcester County

**HENRY HEYWOOD MEM HOSPITAL** See Heywood Hospital

**HEYWOOD HOSPITAL (220095)**, 242 Green Street, Zip 01440–1373; tel. 978/632–3420, (Nonreporting) **A**1 5 10 **F**3 9 12 13 15 18 28 29 30 31 34 35 40 44 45 46 47 49 50 53 54 56 61 64 68 70 74 75 76 77 78 79 81 82 84 85 87 89 92 97 98 100 103 104 105 107 108 110 111 114 115 118 119 130 131 132 134 145 146 147 149 153 154 **P**8 **S** Heywood Healthcare, Gardner, MA
Primary Contact: Winfield S. Brown, FACHE, President and Chief Executive Officer
CFO: Robert Crosby, Senior Vice President and Chief Financial Officer
CHR: Thomas Cady, Vice President Human Resources
Web address: www.heywood.org
**Control**: Other not–for–profit (including NFP Corporation) **Service**: General medical and surgical

**Staffed Beds**: 119 **Admissions**: 4285 **Census**: 60 **Outpatient Visits**: 236496 **Births**: 391 **Total Expense ($000)**: 139030 **Payroll Expense ($000)**: 56825 **Personnel**: 731

### GEORGETOWN—Essex County

**BALDPATE HOSPITAL (224033)**, 83 Baldpate Road, Zip 01833–2303; tel. 978/352–2131, (Nonreporting) **A**10
Primary Contact: Lucille M. Batal, Administrator
Web address: www.detoxma.com/
**Control**: Corporation, Investor–owned (for–profit) **Service**: Psychiatric

**Staffed Beds**: 59

### GLOUCESTER—Essex County

**ADDISON GILBERT HOSPITAL** See Beverly Hospital, Beverly

### GREAT BARRINGTON—Berkshire County

**FAIRVIEW HOSPITAL (221302)**, 29 Lewis Avenue, Zip 01230–1713; tel. 413/528–0790, (Nonreporting) **A**1 5 10 18 **F**3 11 13 15 18 28 29 32 34 35 36 40 50 54 56 57 59 64 65 68 70 75 76 77 79 81 85 86 87 89 92 93 94 107 108 110 115 119 130 131 132 133 134 145 146 147 148 149 150 154 156 157 **S** Berkshire Health Systems, Inc., Pittsfield, MA
Primary Contact: Eugene A. Dellea, President
COO: Doreen M Sylvia-Hutchinson, Vice President Operations and Chief Nurse Executive
CFO: Anthony Rinaldi, Executive Vice President
CMO: Brian Burke, M.D., President Medical Staff
CHR: Laura Farkas, Director Human Resources
Web address: www.bhs1.org/body_fh.cfm?id=39
**Control**: Other not–for–profit (including NFP Corporation) **Service**: General medical and surgical

**Staffed Beds**: 25 **Admissions**: 839 **Census**: 8 **Outpatient Visits**: 72099 **Births**: 152 **Total Expense ($000)**: 54661 **Payroll Expense ($000)**: 26877

### GREENFIELD—Franklin County

**BAYSTATE FRANKLIN MEDICAL CENTER (220016)**, 164 High Street, Zip 01301–2613; tel. 413/773–0211, (Nonreporting) **A**1 3 5 10 **F**3 11 12 13 14 15 18 19 28 29 30 31 34 35 36 40 45 46 47 48 49 50 51 55 57 58 59 64 68 70 74 75 76 77 78 79 81 82 85 86 87 89 93 98 100 101 104 105 107 108 110 111 114 115 118 119 129 130 131 132 146 147 148 154 157 **S** Baystate Health, Inc., Springfield, MA
Primary Contact: Ronald Bryant, President
CFO: Andrea Nathanson, Director Finance
CMO: Thomas Higgins, M.D., Chief Medical Officer
CHR: Kerry Damon, Director Human Resources
CNO: Deborah A Provost, Chief Nursing Officer
Web address: www.baystatehealth.org
**Control**: Other not–for–profit (including NFP Corporation) **Service**: General medical and surgical

**Staffed Beds**: 89 **Admissions**: 4502 **Census**: 51 **Outpatient Visits**: 116022 **Births**: 474 **Total Expense ($000)**: 104337 **Payroll Expense ($000)**: 38353 **Personnel**: 744

**FRANKLIN MEDICAL CENTER** See Baystate Franklin Medical Center

---

**Hospital, Medicare Provider Number, Address, Telephone, Approval, Facility, and Physician Codes, Health Care System**

★ American Hospital Association (AHA) membership   ○ Healthcare Facilities Accreditation Program   ⇑ Center for Improvement in Healthcare Quality Accreditation
□ The Joint Commission accreditation   ◇ DNV Healthcare Inc. accreditation   △ Commission on Accreditation of Rehabilitation Facilities (CARF) accreditation

## HAVERHILL—Essex County

**HOLY FAMILY HOPSITAL AT MERRIMACK VALLEY** See Holy Family Hospital at Merrimack Valley

**WHITTIER PAVILION (224039)**, 76 Summer Street, Zip 01830–5814; tel. 978/373–8222, (Nonreporting) **A**10 **S** Whittier Health Network, Haverhill, MA
Primary Contact: Alfred J. Arcidi, M.D., Chief Executive Officer
Web address: www.whittierhealth.com
**Control**: Partnership, Investor–owned (for–profit) **Service**: Psychiatric

**Staffed Beds**: 65

**WHITTIER PAVILLION** See Whittier Pavilion

## HOLYOKE—Hampden County

⇧ **HOLYOKE HOSPITAL** See Holyoke Medical Center

⇧ **HOLYOKE MEDICAL CENTER (220024)**, 575 Beech Street, Zip 01040–2223; tel. 413/534–2500, (Nonreporting) **A**2 5 10 **F**3 12 13 14 15 18 26 28 29 30 31 34 35 38 40 46 48 49 50 51 54 55 57 58 59 60 64 65 67 68 70 74 75 76 77 78 79 81 82 85 87 93 96 98 101 102 104 105 107 108 110 111 114 115 118 119 129 130 132 135 143 145 146 147 148 149 157 **P**6 8
Primary Contact: Spiros Hatiras, FACHE, President and Chief Executive Officer
CFO: Michael J Koziol, Chief Financial Officer
CMO: Karen Ferroni, M.D., Medical Director
CIO: Carl Cameron, Director Information Systems
CHR: Mary Kelleher, Vice President Human Resources
CNO: Colleen Desai, Chief Nursing Officer
Web address: www.holyokehealth.com
**Control**: Other not–for–profit (including NFP Corporation) **Service**: General medical and surgical

**Staffed Beds**: 107 **Admissions**: 6278 **Census**: 73 **Outpatient Visits**: 339632 **Births**: 373 **Total Expense ($000)**: 172823 **Payroll Expense ($000)**: 87770 **Personnel**: 1166

## HYANNIS—Barnstable County

⊞ **CAPE COD HOSPITAL (220012)**, 27 Park Street, Zip 02601–5230; tel. 508/771–1800, (Nonreporting) **A**1 2 3 5 10 20 **F**3 11 13 14 15 17 18 20 22 24 26 28 29 30 31 34 35 37 38 40 45 49 50 51 54 57 58 61 64 65 68 70 74 75 76 77 78 79 81 82 85 86 87 89 93 97 98 99 100 101 102 103 104 105 107 108 110 111 114 115 119 120 121 123 124 126 130 131 132 143 144 146 147 148 149 153 **P**8 **S** Cape Cod Healthcare, Inc., Hyannis, MA
Primary Contact: Michael K. Lauf, President and Chief Executive Officer
CFO: Michael Connors, Senior Vice President and Chief Financial Officer
CMO: Donald Guadagnoli, M.D., Chief Medical Officer
CIO: Paul Solverson, Senior Vice President and Chief Information Officer
CHR: Emily Schorer, Senior Vice President Human Resources
CNO: Judith Quinn, Vice President Patient Care Services
Web address: www.capecodhealth.org
**Control**: Other not–for–profit (including NFP Corporation) **Service**: General medical and surgical

**Staffed Beds**: 259 **Admissions**: 16347 **Census**: 196 **Outpatient Visits**: 360998 **Births**: 754 **Total Expense ($000)**: 554373 **Payroll Expense ($000)**: 223633 **Personnel**: 2003

## JAMAICA PLAIN—Suffolk County

☐ **LEMUEL SHATTUCK HOSPITAL (222006)**, 170 Morton Street, Zip 02130–3735; tel. 617/522–8110, (Nonreporting) **A**1 3 5 10 **S** Massachusetts Department of Public Health, Boston, MA
Primary Contact: Rosette Martinez, Acting Chief Executive Officer
CFO: Mike Donovan, Chief Financial Officer
CMO: Kenneth Freedman, M.D., Chief Medical Officer
CIO: Kathryn Noonan, Director Information Management
CHR: Jill Sampson, Director Human Resources
Web address: www.mass.gov/shattuckhospital
**Control**: State, Government, Nonfederal **Service**: Acute long–term care hospital

**Staffed Beds**: 260

## LAWRENCE—Essex County

⊞ **LAWRENCE GENERAL HOSPITAL (220010)**, 1 General Street, Zip 01841–2961, Mailing Address: P.O. Box 189, Zip 01842–0389; tel. 978/683–4000, (Nonreporting) **A**1 3 5 10
Primary Contact: Deborah J. Wilson, Chief Executive Officer
CFO: Felix V. Mercado, Chief Financial Officer
CMO: Pracha Eamranond, M.D., Senior Vice President Population Health and Medical Affairs
CHR: Cynthia Phelan, Vice President Human Resources
CNO: Karen O. Moore, FACHE, Senior Vice President Operations and Chief Nursing Officer
Web address: www.lawrencegeneral.org
**Control**: Other not–for–profit (including NFP Corporation) **Service**: General medical and surgical

**Staffed Beds**: 189

## LEEDS—Hampshire County

**VA CENTRAL WESTERN MASSACHUSETTS HEALTHCARE SYSTEM** See Veterans Affairs Central Western Massachusetts Healthcare System

⊞ **VETERANS AFFAIRS CENTRAL WESTERN MASSACHUSETTS HEALTHCARE SYSTEM**, 421 North Main Street, Zip 01053–9764; tel. 413/582–3000, (Nonreporting) **A**1 3 5 **S** Department of Veterans Affairs, Washington, DC
Primary Contact: John P. Collins, FACHE, Medical Center Director
COO: Joyce Fredrick, Associate Director
CFO: Andrew McMahon, Chief Fiscal Officer
CMO: Neil Nusbaum, M.D., Chief of Staff
CIO: Michael Marley, Chief Information Officer
CHR: Pablo Feliciano, Manager Human Resources
Web address: www.centralwesternmass.va.gov/
**Control**: Veterans Affairs, Government, federal **Service**: Psychiatric

**Staffed Beds**: 117

## LEOMINSTER—Worcester County

⊞ **UMASS MEMORIAL HEALTHALLIANCE-CLINTON HOSPITAL (220001)**, 60 Hospital Road, Zip 01453–2205; tel. 978/466–2000, (Includes UMASS MEMORIAL HEALTHALLIANCE-CLINTON HOSPITAL, Mailing address: 201 Highland Street, Clinton, Massachusetts, Zip 01510–1096; tel. 978/368–3000; Steven P Roach, FACHE, Interim President), (Nonreporting) **A**1 2 3 5 10 **F**3 5 11 13 15 18 28 29 30 31 34 35 36 40 45 47 49 50 51 54 57 58 59 60 62 63 64 68 70 74 75 76 77 78 79 80 81 82 84 85 93 98 103 107 108 110 114 115 118 119 120 121 123 124 130 131 132 135 144 145 146 149 154 156 **S** UMass Memorial Health Care, Inc., Worcester, MA
Primary Contact: Steven P. Roach, FACHE, Interim Chief Executive Officer
COO: Paul MacKinnon, MS, R.N., Chief Operating Officer
CFO: John Bronhard, CPA, IICorporate Vice President, Chief Financial Officer and Treasurer
CMO: Daniel H O'Leary, M.D., Chief Medical Officer
CHR: Julie DeBono, Director, Human Resources
CNO: Judith Thorpe, R.N., MSN, Vice President and Chief Nursing Officer
Web address: www.healthalliance.com
**Control**: Other not–for–profit (including NFP Corporation) **Service**: General medical and surgical

**Staffed Beds**: 152 **Admissions**: 7455 **Census**: 96 **Outpatient Visits**: 226144 **Births**: 572 **Total Expense ($000)**: 210163 **Payroll Expense ($000)**: 74199 **Personnel**: 873

**UMASS MEMORIAL HEALTHALLIANCE-CLINTON HOSPITAL - LEOMINSTER CAMPUS** See Umass Memorial Healthalliance-Clinton Hospital

## LONGMEADOW—Hampden County

**JEWISH HOME FOR THE AGED** See Jewish Nursing Home of Western Massachusetts

## LOWELL—Middlesex County

✠ **LOWELL GENERAL HOSPITAL (220063)**, 295 Varnum Avenue, Zip 01854–2134; tel. 978/937–6000, (Includes LOWELL GENERAL HOSPITAL, SAINTS CAMPUS, Mailing address: 1 Hospital Drive, Lowell, Massachusetts, Zip 01852–1311, 295 Varnum Ave, Zip 01854–2134, tel. 978/458–1411; Normand E. Deschene, FACHE, Chief Executive Officer), (Nonreporting) **A**1 2 3 5 10 **F**3 11 12 13 15 18 20 22 26 28 29 30 31 32 34 35 36 40 41 43 44 45 46 47 48 49 50 51 54 56 57 58 59 60 61 64 65 68 70 73 74 75 76 78 79 81 82 84 85 86 87 89 93 97 100 107 108 110 114 115 118 119 120 121 123 124 126 129 130 131 132 133 134 143 146 147 149 150 156 157 **P**6 8
Primary Contact: Joseph White, FACHE, President and Chief Executive Officer
COO: Amy J Hoey, R.N., MS, Executive Vice President and Chief Operating Officer
CFO: Susan Green, Senior Vice President Finance, Chief Financial Officer
CMO: Arthur Lauretano, M.D., Chief Medical Officer
CIO: Brian Sandager, Chief Information Officer
CHR: Sabrina M Granville, Senior Vice President and Chief Human Resources Officer
CNO: Cecelia Lynch, R.N., MS, Vice President Patient Care Services and Chief Nursing Officer
Web address: www.lowellgeneral.org
**Control**: Other not–for–profit (including NFP Corporation) **Service**: General medical and surgical

**Staffed Beds**: 325 **Admissions**: 18460 **Census**: 211 **Outpatient Visits**: 504056 **Births**: 2149 **Total Expense ($000)**: 458768 **Payroll Expense ($000)**: 188967 **Personnel**: 2753

**SAINTS MEDICAL CENTER** See Lowell General Hospital, Saints Campus

## LUDLOW—Hampden County

✠ **ENCOMPASS HEALTH REHABILITATION HOSPITAL OF WESTERN MASSACHUSETTS (223030)**, 222 State Street, Zip 01056–3437; tel. 413/308–3300, (Nonreporting) **A**1 10 **S** Encompass Health Corporation, Birmingham, AL
Primary Contact: John R. Hunt, Chief Executive Officer
CFO: John Flaherty, Chief Financial Officer
CMO: Adnan Dahdul, M.D., Medical Director
CHR: Mary Mazza, Director Human Resources
CNO: Deborah Santos, R.N., Chief Nursing Officer
Web address: www.healthsouthrehab.org
**Control**: Corporation, Investor–owned (for–profit) **Service**: Rehabilitation

**Staffed Beds**: 53

**HEALTHSOUTH REHABILITATION HOSPITAL OF WESTERN MASSACHUSETTS** See Encompass Health Rehabilitation Hospital of Western Massachusetts

## LYNN—Essex County

**UNION CAMPUS** See North Shore Medical Center, Salem

**UNION HOSPITAL** See Union Campus

## MARLBOROUGH—Middlesex County

✠ **UMASS MEMORIAL–MARLBOROUGH HOSPITAL (220049)**, 157 Union ST, Zip 01752–1297; tel. 508/481–5000, (Nonreporting) **A**1 3 5 10 **F**3 11 15 18 24 28 29 30 34 35 40 45 49 50 51 53 57 63 68 70 77 79 81 82 85 93 98 100 101 105 107 108 115 119 132 146 147 149 154 157 **S** UMass Memorial Health Care, Inc., Worcester, MA
Primary Contact: Steven P. Roach, FACHE, President and Chief Executive Officer
COO: John Kelly, R.N., Chief Nursing Officer and Chief Operating Officer
CFO: Steven McCue, Chief Financial Officer
CMO: Habib Sioufi, M.D., Chief Medical Officer
CHR: Francis Meringolo, Vice President Human Resources
CNO: John Kelly, R.N., Chief Nursing Officer and Chief Operating Officer
Web address: www.marlboroughhospital.org
**Control**: Other not–for–profit (including NFP Corporation) **Service**: General medical and surgical

**Staffed Beds**: 67 **Admissions**: 4134 **Census**: 45 **Outpatient Visits**: 28669 **Births**: 0

**UMASS–MEM MARLBOROUGH HOSP** See Umass Memorial–Marlborough Hospital

## MEDFORD—Middlesex County

**LAWRENCE MEMORIAL HOSPITAL OF MEDFORD** See Melrosewakefield Healthcare, Melrose

## MELROSE—Middlesex County

**HALLMARK HEALTH SYSTEM** See Melrosewakefield Healthcare

✠ **MELROSEWAKEFIELD HEALTHCARE (220070)**, 585 Lebanon Street, Zip 02176–3225; tel. 781/979–3000, (Includes LAWRENCE MEMORIAL HOSPITAL OF MEDFORD, Mailing address: 170 Governors Avenue, Medford, Massachusetts, Zip 02155–1643; tel. 781/306–6000; MELROSE-WAKEFIELD HOSPITAL, Mailing address: 585 Lebanon Street, Melrose, Massachusetts, Zip 2176; tel. 781/979–3000; Michael V Sack, FACHE, Chief Executive Officer), (Nonreporting) **A**1 3 5 10 **F**3 12 13 15 18 20 22 26 28 29 30 34 35 38 40 41 45 46 47 49 50 51 54 55 56 57 58 59 60 61 62 63 64 65 68 70 72 74 75 76 77 78 79 81 82 84 85 86 87 93 97 98 100 101 102 103 104 107 108 110 111 114 115 116 117 118 119 120 121 123 124 126 130 131 132 135 144 146 147 148 149 154 157
Primary Contact: Susan Sandberg, R.N., Chief Executive Officer
CFO: Michael P. Connelly, CPA, FACHE, Executive Vice President and Chief Financial Officer
CMO: Steven P. Sbardella, M.D., FABC, President Clinical Operations and Chief Medical Officer
CHR: David P. Ryan, Vice President Human Resources
CNO: Deborah L Cronin-Waelde, MSN, R.N., Senior Vice President Clinical Operations and Chief Nursing Officer
Web address: www.melrosewakefield.org
**Control**: Other not–for–profit (including NFP Corporation) **Service**: General medical and surgical

**Staffed Beds**: 216 **Admissions**: 8755 **Census**: 126 **Outpatient Visits**: 425428 **Births**: 791 **Total Expense ($000)**: 211452 **Payroll Expense ($000)**: 106143 **Personnel**: 1043

## METHUEN—Essex County

**CARITAS HOLY FAMILY HOSPITAL AND MEDICAL CENTER** See Holy Family Hospital

☐ **HOLY FAMILY HOSPITAL (220080)**, 70 East Street, Zip 01844–4597; tel. 978/687–0151, (Includes HOLY FAMILY HOSPITAL AT MERRIMACK VALLEY, Mailing address: 140 Lincoln Avenue, Haverhill, Massachusetts, Zip 01830–6798; tel. 978/374–2000; Craig A Jesiolowski, FACHE, President), (Nonreporting) **A**1 2 3 10 **S** Steward Health Care System, LLC, Dallas, TX
Primary Contact: Craig A. Jesiolowski, FACHE, President
COO: Martha M McDrury, R.N., Chief Operating Officer and Chief Nursing Officer
CFO: Jeffrey P. Dion, Vice President and Chief Financial Officer
CHR: Patricia Gauron, Director Human Resources
CNO: Martha M McDrury, R.N., Chief Operating Officer and Chief Nursing Officer
Web address: www.stewardhealth.org/Holy-Family-Hospital
**Control**: Corporation, Investor–owned (for–profit) **Service**: General medical and surgical

**Staffed Beds**: 329

## MILFORD—Worcester County

✠ **MILFORD REGIONAL MEDICAL CENTER (220090)**, 14 Prospect Street, Zip 01757–3003; tel. 508/473–1190, (Includes WHITINSVILLE MEDICAL CENTER, Mailing address: 18 Granite Street, Whitinsville, Massachusetts, Zip 1588; tel. 508/234–6311), (Nonreporting) **A**1 2 3 5 10 **F**3 11 12 13 15 18 20 26 28 29 30 31 32 34 35 40 41 45 46 47 48 49 50 51 52 57 59 64 65 68 70 74 75 76 77 79 80 81 84 85 86 87 93 96 107 108 110 115 118 119 126 130 131 132 134 135 145 146 147 148 149 154 156
Primary Contact: Edward Kelly, Chief Executive Officer and President
COO: Peggy Novick, Vice President, Clinical Support and Outpatient Services
CFO: Jeanne Lynskey, Vice President and Chief Financial Officer
CMO: Mary Czymbor, Chief Medical Officer
CIO: Nicole Heim, Chief Information Officer
CHR: Linda Greason, Vice President Human Resources
CNO: Nancy Tomaso, Vice President, Patient Care Services
Web address: www.milfordregional.org
**Control**: Other not–for–profit (including NFP Corporation) **Service**: General medical and surgical

**Staffed Beds**: 149 **Admissions**: 8999 **Census**: 90 **Outpatient Visits**: 425947 **Births**: 849 **Total Expense ($000)**: 218799 **Payroll Expense ($000)**: 102427 **Personnel**: 1751

**MILFORD-WHITINSVILLE REG HOSP** See Milford Regional Medical Center

---

**Hospital, Medicare Provider Number, Address, Telephone, Approval, Facility, and Physician Codes, Health Care System**

★ American Hospital Association (AHA) membership
☐ The Joint Commission accreditation
○ Healthcare Facilities Accreditation Program
◇ DNV Healthcare Inc. accreditation
⇑ Center for Improvement in Healthcare Quality Accreditation
△ Commission on Accreditation of Rehabilitation Facilities (CARF) accreditation

**MA**

## MILTON—Norfolk County

⊞ **BETH ISRAEL DEACONESS HOSPITAL-MILTON (220108)**, 199 Reedsdale
Road, Zip 02186–3926; tel. 617/696–4600, (Nonreporting) **A**1 3 10 **S** Beth Israel
Lahey Health, Boston, MA
Primary Contact: Richard W. Fernandez, President and Chief Executive Officer
CIO: Jean Fernandez, Chief Information Officer
CHR: Kathleen Harrington, Vice President Human Resources
Web address: www.miltonhospital.org
**Control**: Other not–for–profit (including NFP Corporation) **Service**: General
medical and surgical

**Staffed Beds:** 100

**MILTON HOSPITAL** See Beth Israel Deaconess Hospital-Milton

## NANTUCKET—Nantucket County

⊞ **NANTUCKET COTTAGE HOSPITAL (220177)**, 57 Prospect Street,
Zip 02554–2799; tel. 508/825–8100, (Nonreporting) **A**1 10 **F**13 15 29 31 35
40 45 50 57 59 60 64 68 75 76 77 78 79 81 82 84 85 86 87 89 93 97 100
102 107 110 111 115 119 127 130 132 133 147 148 154 **P**5 **S** Mass General
Brigham, Boston, MA
Primary Contact: Gary Shaw, President and Chief Executive Officer
COO: Jim Kelly, Chief Operating Officer
CFO: David J Burke, Director Finance and Chief Financial Officer
CMO: Jock Lawrason, M.D., Chief Medical Officer
CIO: Terry Hughes, Director Information Systems
CHR: Susan Partridge, Director Human Resources
CNO: Bonnie J Kester, R.N., MSN, Vice President Patient Care Services and Chief
Nursing Officer
Web address: www.nantuckethospital.org
**Control**: Other not–for–profit (including NFP Corporation) **Service**: General
medical and surgical

**Staffed Beds:** 14 **Admissions:** 491 **Census:** 5 **Outpatient Visits:** 85281
**Births:** 134 **Total Expense ($000):** 58674 **Payroll Expense ($000):** 28709
**Personnel:** 256

## NATICK—Middlesex County

**LEONARD MORSE HOSPITAL** See Metrowest Medical Center, Framingham

**METROWEST MEDICAL CENTER** See Leonard Morse Hospital

## NEEDHAM—Norfolk County

⊞ **BETH ISRAEL DEACONESS HOSPITAL-NEEDHAM CAMPUS (220083)**, 148
Chestnut Street, Zip 2492; tel. 781/453–3000, (Nonreporting) **A**1 2 3 5 10 **F**1 3
4 15 16 18 29 30 34 35 40 41 45 50 51 59 60 64 65 67 68 69 70 72 73 74
75 77 79 80 81 82 84 85 87 88 89 90 92 93 100 102 107 108 110 111 114
115 118 119 128 129 130 131 144 145 146 148 149 154 **S** Beth Israel Lahey
Health, Boston, MA
Primary Contact: John M. Fogarty, President and Chief Executive Officer
CFO: Brian Smith, Chief Financial Officer
CMO: Peter Ostrow, M.D., President Medical Staff
Web address: www.bidneedham.org/
**Control**: Other not–for–profit (including NFP Corporation) **Service**: General
medical and surgical

**Staffed Beds:** 52 **Admissions:** 2855 **Census:** 29 **Outpatient Visits:** 222855
**Births:** 0 **Total Expense ($000):** 101459 **Payroll Expense ($000):** 41311
**Personnel:** 490

**DEACONESS-GLOVER HOSPITAL CORP** See Beth Israel Deaconess Hospital-
Needham Campus

## NEW BEDFORD—Bristol County

**NEW BEDFORD REHABILITATION HOSPITAL** See Vibra Hospital of Southeastern
Massachusetts

**ST LUKE'S HOSP OF NEW BEDFORD** See St. Luke's Hospital

**ST. LUKE'S HOSPITAL** See Southcoast Hospitals Group, Fall River

⊞ **VIBRA HOSPITAL OF SOUTHEASTERN MASSACHUSETTS (222043)**, 4499
Acushnet Avenue, Zip 02745–4707; tel. 508/995–6900, (Nonreporting) **A**1
10 **F**1 12 28 29 50 56 57 64 74 75 77 79 87 93 94 96 130 135 **P**6 **S** Vibra
Healthcare, Mechanicsburg, PA
Primary Contact: Edward B. Leary, Chief Executive Officer
CFO: Cheryl Perry, Chief Financial Officer
CMO: Albert Loerinc, M.D., Medical Director
CHR: Ilene Mirabella, Director Human Resources
CNO: Emmanuel Berthil, Chief Clinical Officer
Web address: www.newbedfordrehab.com
**Control**: Corporation, Investor–owned (for–profit) **Service**: Acute long–term care
hospital

**Staffed Beds:** 90 **Admissions:** 668 **Census:** 64 **Outpatient Visits:** 1590
**Births:** 0 **Total Expense ($000):** 41351 **Payroll Expense ($000):** 13573
**Personnel:** 140

## NEWBURYPORT—Essex County

⊞ **ANNA JAQUES HOSPITAL (220029)**, 25 Highland Avenue, Zip 01950–3894;
tel. 978/463–1000, (Nonreporting) **A**1 10 **F**3 8 13 14 15 18 20 26 28 29 31 34
37 40 43 45 46 50 59 65 70 75 76 77 78 79 80 81 82 85 89 92 93 98 99 102
105 107 108 110 114 115 118 119 129 130 135 146 148 149 **P**5 8 **S** Beth Israel
Lahey Health, Boston, MA
Primary Contact: Mark L. Goldstein, President and Chief Executive Officer
CMO: Gail Fayre, M.D., Medical Director
CIO: Robert Buchanan, Chief Information Officer
CHR: Stephen Salvo, Vice President Human Resources
CNO: Richard Maki, R.N., Vice President Nursing and Chief Nursing Officer
Web address: www.ajh.org
**Control**: Other not–for–profit (including NFP Corporation) **Service**: General
medical and surgical

**Staffed Beds:** 123 **Admissions:** 6485 **Census:** 80 **Outpatient Visits:** 258902
**Births:** 656 **Total Expense ($000):** 135243 **Payroll Expense ($000):** 57571
**Personnel:** 683

## NEWTON LOWER FALLS—Middlesex County

⊞ **NEWTON-WELLESLEY HOSPITAL (220101)**, 2014 Washington Street,
Zip 02462–1699; tel. 617/243–6000, (Includes MASSGENERAL FOR CHILDREN
AT NEWTON-WELLESLEY HOSPITAL, Mailing address: 2000 Washington Street,
Newton, Massachusetts, Zip 02462–1650; tel. 617/243–6585), (Nonreporting)
**A**1 2 3 5 10 19 **F**3 8 12 13 15 17 18 19 26 28 29 30 31 34 35 36 40 41 45
46 47 49 50 51 52 53 54 55 56 57 58 59 60 64 65 66 68 70 73 74 75 76 77
78 79 81 82 84 85 86 87 89 92 93 97 98 100 101 102 104 107 108 110 111
114 115 117 118 119 126 129 130 131 132 134 135 144 145 146 147 148
149 150 154 156 157 **P**1 6 **S** Mass General Brigham, Boston, MA
Primary Contact: Gregg S. Meyer, M.D., Interim President
CMO: Timothy Foster, Acting Chief Medical Officer
CIO: Beth Downie, Chief Information Officer
CHR: Beth Taylor, Vice President, Human Resources
Web address: www.nwh.org
**Control**: Other not–for–profit (including NFP Corporation) **Service**: General
medical and surgical

**Staffed Beds:** 201 **Admissions:** 15796 **Census:** 164 **Outpatient
Visits:** 561421 **Births:** 3708 **Total Expense ($000):** 573874 **Payroll
Expense ($000):** 210056 **Personnel:** 2698

## NORTHAMPTON—Hampshire County

⊞ **COOLEY DICKINSON HOSPITAL (220015)**, 30 Locust Street, Zip 01060–2093,
Mailing Address: P.O. Box 5001, Zip 01061–5001; tel. 413/582–2000,
(Nonreporting) **A**1 10 19 **F**3 11 13 15 18 20 22 26 28 29 30 31 34 35 36 38 40
46 49 50 51 54 55 57 59 60 61 64 68 70 74 75 76 77 78 79 81 84 85 86 87
89 93 96 98 100 107 108 110 111 115 119 120 121 123 130 131 132 144
146 147 148 149 154 157 **P**6 8 **S** Mass General Brigham, Boston, MA
Primary Contact: Joanne Marqusee, President and Chief Executive Officer
CFO: Laurie Lamoureux, Director of Finance
CMO: Estevan Garcia, M.D., Chief Medical Officer
CIO: Lee Martinez, Chief Information Officer
CHR: Lori A Kerwood, Director Human Resources
Web address: www.cooleydickinson.org
**Control**: Other not–for–profit (including NFP Corporation) **Service**: General
medical and surgical

**Staffed Beds:** 141 **Admissions:** 6634 **Census:** 82 **Outpatient
Visits:** 259066 **Births:** 559 **Total Expense ($000):** 190977 **Payroll Expense
($000):** 76576 **Personnel:** 1530

## NORWOOD—Norfolk County

**CARITAS NORWOOD HOSPITAL** See Norwood Hospital

☐ **NORWOOD HOSPITAL (220126)**, 800 Washington Street, Zip 02062–3487;
tel. 781/769–4000, (Nonreporting) **A**1 2 5 10 **S** Steward Health Care System,
LLC, Dallas, TX
Primary Contact: Salvatore Perla, President
COO: William P Fleming, Chief Operating Officer
CFO: Mark Johnson, Chief Financial Officer
CHR: Kimberly Brosnan, Director Human Resources
Web address: www.norwood-hospital.org
**Control:** Corporation, Investor–owned (for–profit) **Service:** General medical and
surgical

**Staffed Beds:** 188

## OAK BLUFFS—Dukes County

✠ **MARTHA'S VINEYARD HOSPITAL (221300)**, One Hospital Road, Zip 2557,
Mailing Address: P.O. Box 1477, Zip 02557–1477; tel. 508/693–0410, (Total
facility includes 61 beds in nursing home–type unit) (Nonreporting) **A**1 10 18 **F**3
13 15 28 29 30 31 37 39 40 44 45 50 57 59 60 64 68 69 70 75 76 78 79 81
82 85 86 87 89 93 97 107 110 111 113 115 119 128 130 133 135 146 147
154 **S** Mass General Brigham, Boston, MA
Primary Contact: Denise Schepici, M.P.H., Chief Executive Officer and President
CFO: Edward Olivier, Chief Financial Officer
CMO: Pieter Pil, M.D., Chief Medical Staff
CHR: Christine Gould, Director Human Resources
CNO: Carol A Bardwell, R.N., MSN, Chief Nurse Executive
Web address: www.mvhospital.com/
**Control:** Other not–for–profit (including NFP Corporation) **Service:** General
medical and surgical

**Staffed Beds:** 86 **Admissions:** 981 **Census:** 61 **Outpatient Visits:** 144122
**Births:** 149 **Total Expense ($000):** 94458 **Payroll Expense ($000):** 42315
**Personnel:** 376

## PALMER—Hampden County

✠ **BAYSTATE WING HOSPITAL (220030)**, 40 Wright Street, Zip 01069–1138;
tel. 413/283–7651, (Nonreporting) **A**1 5 10 **F**3 5 11 15 18 29 33 34 35 36 38
40 42 44 45 46 49 50 54 56 57 59 61 64 65 68 70 74 75 79 81 82 85 86 87
93 97 98 100 101 103 104 107 108 110 115 119 129 130 132 135 146 147
149 150 154 **P**8 **S** Baystate Health, Inc., Springfield, MA
Primary Contact: Michael Francis. Moran, President and Chief Administrative
Officer
CFO: Keary T Allicon, Vice President Finance and Chief Financial Officer
CMO: David L Maguire, M.D., Vice President Medical Affairs
CIO: Kenneth Riley, Director Information Systems
CHR: Thomas Guilfoil, Director Human Resources
Web address: www.baystatewinghospital.org/
**Control:** Other not–for–profit (including NFP Corporation) **Service:** General
medical and surgical

**Staffed Beds:** 74 **Admissions:** 3427 **Census:** 47 **Outpatient Visits:** 130889
**Births:** 0 **Total Expense ($000):** 92474 **Payroll Expense ($000):** 37611
**Personnel:** 692

**WING MEMORIAL HOSPITAL AND MEDICAL CENTERS** See Baystate Wing
Hospital

## PEMBROKE—Plymouth County

**AMI PEMBROKE HOSPITAL** See Pembroke Hospital

☐ **PEMBROKE HOSPITAL (224027)**, 199 Oak Street, Zip 02359–1953;
tel. 781/829–7000, (Nonreporting) **A**1 **S** Universal Health Services, Inc., King of
Prussia, PA
Primary Contact: Raymond Robinson, Chief Executive Officer
CFO: Diane Airosus, Chief Financial Officer
CMO: Gary Jacobson, M.D., Chief Medical Officer
Web address: www.arbourhealth.com/organizations/pembroke-hospital/
**Control:** Partnership, Investor–owned (for–profit) **Service:** Psychiatric

**Staffed Beds:** 115

## PITTSFIELD—Berkshire County

✠ **BERKSHIRE MEDICAL CENTER (220046)**, 725 North ST, Zip 01201–4124,
Mailing Address: 725 North Street, Zip 01201–4124; tel. 413/447–2000,
(Includes HILLCREST HOSPITAL, Mailing address: 165 Tor Court,
Pittsfield, Massachusetts, Zip 01201–3099, Box 1155, Zip 01202–1155,
tel. 413/443–4761), (Nonreporting) **A**1 2 3 5 10 12 13 **F**3 4 8 12 13 14 15 17
18 20 26 28 29 30 31 32 34 35 37 38 40 42 43 44 45 46 48 49 50 51 53 54
55 56 57 58 59 60 61 62 63 64 65 68 70 71 74 75 76 77 78 79 81 82 83 85
86 87 89 90 92 93 95 96 98 100 101 102 103 104 105 107 108 110 111 112
114 115 116 117 118 119 120 121 122 123 124 126 129 130 131 132 134
135 144 145 146 147 148 149 150 156 157 **P**8 **S** Berkshire Health Systems,
Inc., Pittsfield, MA
Primary Contact: David E. Phelps, President and Chief Executive Officer
CFO: Darlene Rodowicz, Chief Financial Officer
CIO: William Young, Chief Information Officer
CHR: Arthur D Milano, Vice President Human Resources
CNO: Brenda E Cadorette, Chief Nursing Officer
Web address: www.berkshirehealthsystems.org
**Control:** Other not–for–profit (including NFP Corporation) **Service:** General
medical and surgical

**Staffed Beds:** 271 **Admissions:** 14203 **Census:** 185 **Outpatient**
**Visits:** 498164 **Births:** 638 **Total Expense ($000):** 498976 **Payroll Expense**
**($000):** 214561 **Personnel:** 2861

## PLYMOUTH—Plymouth County

✠ **BETH ISRAEL DEACONESS HOSPITAL PLYMOUTH (220060)**, 275 Sandwich
Street, Zip 02360–2196; tel. 508/746–2000, (Nonreporting) **A**1 2 5 10 **F**3 13 15
17 18 20 22 28 29 30 31 33 34 35 36 37 40 44 45 51 57 58 59 61 64 68 70
74 75 76 77 78 79 81 82 85 86 87 93 96 98 100 102 103 104 107 108 109
110 111 115 117 118 119 120 121 123 126 129 130 131 132 134 135 143
146 147 148 149 157 **S** Beth Israel Lahey Health, Boston, MA
Primary Contact: Kevin B. Coughlin, President and Chief Executive Officer
CFO: Jason Radzevich, Vice President Finance
CMO: Tenny Thomas, M.D., Chief Medical Officer
CIO: Ronald Rutherford, Chief Information Officer
CHR: Paul Mancini, Senior Director Human Resources and Labor Relations
CNO: Donna Doherty, R.N., Vice President of Nursing and Chief Nursing Officer
Web address: www.bidplymouth.org
**Control:** Other not–for–profit (including NFP Corporation) **Service:** General
medical and surgical

**Staffed Beds:** 170 **Admissions:** 11496 **Census:** 133 **Outpatient**
**Visits:** 323296 **Births:** 808 **Total Expense ($000):** 280702 **Payroll Expense**
**($000):** 113216 **Personnel:** 1181

**BETH ISRAEL DEACONESS HOSPITAL-PLYMOUTH** See Beth Israel Deaconess
Hospital Plymouth

## POCASSET—Barnstable County

**CAPE COD & ISLAND COMMUNITY MENTAL HEALTH CENTER** See Pocasset
Mental Health Center

☐ **POCASSET MENTAL HEALTH CENTER (224031)**, 830 County Road,
Zip 02559–2110; tel. 508/564–9600, (Nonreporting) **A**1 10
Primary Contact: Naomi Tavares-Silva, Center Director
Web address: www.https://www.mass.gov/locations/pocasset-mental-health-
center
**Control:** State, Government, Nonfederal **Service:** Psychiatric

**Staffed Beds:** 24

## ROCHDALE—Worcester County

**KINDRED HOSPITAL PARK VIEW-CENTRAL MASSACHUSETTS** See Vibra
Hospital of Western Massachusetts-Central Campus

**VIBRA HOSPITAL OF WESTERN MASSACHUSETTS-CENTRAL CAMPUS** See
Vibra Hospital of Western Massachusetts, Springfield

---

**Hospital, Medicare Provider Number, Address, Telephone, Approval, Facility, and Physician Codes, Health Care System**

★ American Hospital Association (AHA) membership ○ Healthcare Facilities Accreditation Program ⇧ Center for Improvement in Healthcare Quality Accreditation
☐ The Joint Commission accreditation ◇ DNV Healthcare Inc. accreditation △ Commission on Accreditation of Rehabilitation Facilities (CARF) accreditation

## ROSLINDALE—Suffolk County

★ △ **HEBREW REHABILITATION CENTER (222007)**, 1200 Centre Street, Zip 02131–1097; tel. 617/363–8000, (Total facility includes 675 beds in nursing home–type unit) (Nonreporting) **A**7 10 **F**1 2 6 10 29 30 35 50 58 59 60 64 65 68 69 75 77 82 83 84 93 97 100 104 119 125 128 130 132 143 146 148 149 158 **P**6
Primary Contact: Mary K. Moscato, FACHE, President
COO: Brian Murphy, Senior Director Admissions and Referral Services
CFO: Lise Paul, Vice President Reimbursement and Network Planning
CMO: Helen Chen, M.D., Chief Medical Officer
CIO: Eric Rogers, Chief Information Officer
CHR: Deborah Lemmerman, Chief People Officer
CNO: Tammy B. Retalic, R.N., MS, Chief Nursing Officer
Web address: www.hebrewseniorlife.org
**Control**: Other not–for–profit (including NFP Corporation) **Service**: Acute long–term care hospital

> **Staffed Beds:** 725 **Admissions:** 1134 **Census:** 651 **Outpatient Visits:** 57843 **Births:** 0 **Total Expense ($000):** 130711 **Payroll Expense ($000):** 80940 **Personnel:** 1153

**HEBREW REHABILITATION CENTER FOR AGED** See Hebrew Rehabilitation Center

## SALEM—Essex County

**NORTH SHORE CHILDREN'S HOSPITAL** See Massgeneral for Children at North Shore Medical Center

⊞ **NORTH SHORE MEDICAL CENTER (220035)**, 81 Highland Avenue, Zip 01970–2714; tel. 978/741–1200, (Includes MASSGENERAL FOR CHILDREN AT NORTH SHORE MEDICAL CENTER, Mailing address: 57 Highland Avenue, Salem, Massachusetts, Zip 01970–6508; tel. 978/745–2100; SALEM CAMPUS, Mailing address: 81 Highland Avenue, Salem, Massachusetts, Zip 1970; tel. 978/741–1200; Robert G Norton, President; UNION CAMPUS, Mailing address: 500 Lynnfield Street, Lynn, Massachusetts, Zip 01904–1487; tel. 781/581–9200; Robert G Norton, President), (Nonreporting) **A**1 3 5 10 **F**5 12 13 15 18 20 22 26 28 29 30 32 34 35 36 38 40 41 43 44 45 46 47 48 49 50 51 55 56 57 59 60 64 68 70 73 74 75 76 77 79 81 82 84 85 86 87 92 98 99 100 101 102 103 104 105 107 108 110 111 114 115 119 126 129 130 132 135 143 145 146 147 148 149 150 152 153 154 156 157 **P**8 **S** Mass General Brigham, Boston, MA
Primary Contact: David J. Roberts, M.D., President
CFO: Sally Mason Boemer, Chief Financial Officer
CMO: Mitchell S Rein, M.D., Chief Medical Officer
CIO: Fran X. Hinckley, Chief Information Officer
CHR: Arthur Bowes, Senior Vice President Human Resources
CNO: Cheryl Bhima Merrill, MSN, R.N., Senior Vice President Patient Care Services and Chief Nursing Officer
Web address: www.nsmc.partners.org/
**Control**: Other not–for–profit (including NFP Corporation) **Service**: General medical and surgical

> **Staffed Beds:** 362 **Admissions:** 17593 **Census:** 240 **Outpatient Visits:** 623728 **Births:** 1161 **Total Expense ($000):** 459689 **Payroll Expense ($000):** 186010 **Personnel:** 2271

**SALEM HOSPITAL** See Salem Campus

**SALEM HOSPITAL** See North Shore Medical Center

## SOMERVILLE—Middlesex County

**SOMERVILLE HOSPITAL** See Cambridge Health Alliance, Cambridge

## SOUTH WEYMOUTH—Norfolk County

⊞ **SOUTH SHORE HOSPITAL (220100)**, 55 Fogg Road, Zip 02190–2432; tel. 781/624–8000, (Nonreporting) **A**1 2 3 5 10 **F**3 7 11 12 13 15 17 18 20 22 24 26 28 29 30 31 32 34 35 37 40 41 43 44 45 46 49 50 51 53 54 55 57 58 59 60 62 63 64 65 68 70 72 73 74 75 76 78 79 81 82 84 85 86 87 89 91 92 93 96 107 108 110 111 114 115 118 119 124 126 129 130 132 134 135 143 146 147 148 149 150 156 **P**1
Primary Contact: Rose Di Pietro, MSN, R.N., Interim Chief Executive Officer
COO: Joseph Cahill, Executive Vice President and Chief Operating Officer
CFO: Michael Cullen, Senior Vice President and Chief Financial Officer
CMO: John Stevenson, M.D., Senior Vice President and Chief Medical Officer
CIO: Del Dixon, Chief Information Officer
CHR: Robert Wheeler, Vice President Human Resources
Web address: www.southshorehospital.org
**Control**: Other not–for–profit (including NFP Corporation) **Service**: General medical and surgical

> **Staffed Beds:** 411 **Admissions:** 27462 **Census:** 315 **Outpatient Visits:** 542017 **Births:** 3061 **Total Expense ($000):** 647310 **Payroll Expense ($000):** 352131 **Personnel:** 3706

## SOUTHBRIDGE—Worcester County

⊞ **HARRINGTON HOSPITAL (220019)**, 100 South Street, Zip 01550–4051; tel. 508/765–9771, (Nonreporting) **A**1 2 5 10
Primary Contact: Edward H. Moore, President and Chief Executive Officer
COO: Kristin Morales, Chief Operating Officer
CFO: Thomas Sullivan, Vice President Fiscal Services
CMO: Arthur Russo, M.D., Director Medical Affairs
CIO: Harry Lemieux, Chief Information Officer
CHR: Christopher Canniff, Executive Director, Human Resources
CNO: Thomas W. Hijeck, R.N., MS, Vice President Nursing Services and Chief Nursing Officer
Web address: www.harringtonhospital.org
**Control**: Other not–for–profit (including NFP Corporation) **Service**: General medical and surgical

> **Staffed Beds:** 130

**HARRINGTON MEMORIAL HOSPITAL** See Harrington Hospital

## SPRINGFIELD—Hampden County

⊞ **BAYSTATE MEDICAL CENTER (220077)**, 759 Chestnut Street, Zip 01199–0001; tel. 413/794–0000, (Includes BAYSTATE CHILDREN'S HOSPITAL, Mailing address: 759 Chestnut Street, Springfield, Massachusetts, Zip 01199–1001; tel. 413/794–0000; Mark A. Keroack, M.D., M.P.H., President and Chief Executive Officer, Baystate Health), (Nonreporting) **A**1 3 5 8 10 19 **F**3 8 12 13 14 15 17 18 19 20 22 24 26 28 29 30 31 32 34 35 37 38 40 41 43 44 45 46 47 48 49 50 51 52 54 55 56 57 58 59 60 61 64 65 66 68 70 72 73 74 75 76 77 78 79 81 82 83 84 85 86 87 88 89 92 93 96 97 98 100 101 102 103 104 105 107 108 110 111 114 115 118 119 120 121 123 124 126 129 130 131 132 135 138 141 143 145 146 147 148 149 154 156 157 **P**8 **S** Baystate Health, Inc., Springfield, MA
Primary Contact: Nancy Shendell-Falik, R.N., President
COO: Tejas Gandhi, Ph.D., Chief Operating Officer
CFO: Dennis Chalke, Senior Vice President, Chief Financial Officer and Treasurer
CMO: Andrew Artenstein, M.D., Chief Physician Executive, Chief Academic Officer and President, Baystate Medical Practices
CIO: Joel L. Vengco, MS, Vice President, Chief Information Officer
CHR: Paula C Squires, Senior Vice President, Chief Human Resources Officer and Chief Human Resources Officer
CNO: Nancy Shendell-Falik, R.N., Senior Vice President, Chief Operating Officer and Chief Nursing Officer
Web address: www.baystatehealth.org/bmc
**Control**: Other not–for–profit (including NFP Corporation) **Service**: General medical and surgical

> **Staffed Beds:** 734 **Admissions:** 38593 **Census:** 577 **Outpatient Visits:** 867135 **Births:** 4058 **Total Expense ($000):** 1270437 **Payroll Expense ($000):** 457735 **Personnel:** 8021

**KINDRED HOSPITAL PARK VIEW** See Vibra Hospital of Western Massachusetts

**MERCY HOSPITAL** See Mercy Medical Center

⊞ △ **MERCY MEDICAL CENTER (220066)**, 271 Carew Street, Zip 01104–2398, Mailing Address: P.O. Box 9012, Zip 01102–9012; tel. 413/748–9000, (Nonreporting) **A**1 2 7 10 **F**3 4 5 8 11 13 15 18 20 26 29 30 31 34 35 40 44 45 46 47 48 49 50 55 56 57 58 59 64 65 66 67 68 70 71 74 75 76 77 78 79 81 82 85 86 87 90 93 96 97 98 99 100 101 103 104 107 108 110 115 118 119 120 121 123 124 126 129 130 132 135 143 146 147 148 154 156 **S** Trinity Health, Livonia, MI
Primary Contact: Deborah Bitsoli, CPA, President
CFO: Thomas W. Robert, Senior Vice President of Finance and Chief Financial Officer
CMO: Robert Roose, M.D., Chief Medical Officer
CIO: Joan Methe, Chief Information Officer
CHR: Leonard F Pansa, Senior Vice President Human Resources and Administrative Services
CNO: Frances Marthone, Chief Nursing Officer
Web address: www.mercycares.com
**Control**: Other not–for–profit (including NFP Corporation) **Service**: General medical and surgical

> **Staffed Beds:** 329 **Admissions:** 16214 **Census:** 228 **Outpatient Visits:** 623744 **Births:** 1041 **Total Expense ($000):** 331522 **Payroll Expense ($000):** 116104 **Personnel:** 1402

**SHRINERS HOSPITALS FOR CHILDREN, SPRINGFIELD** See Shriners Hospitals for Children-Springfield

*Many Facility Codes have changed. Please refer to the AHA Guide Code Chart.*
© 2021 AHA Guide

☐ **SHRINERS HOSPITALS FOR CHILDREN-SPRINGFIELD (223303)**, 516 Carew Street, Zip 01104–2396; tel. 413/787–2000, (Nonreporting) **A**1 3 5 10 **F**29 34 35 37 39 44 50 57 58 64 66 68 75 77 79 81 82 85 86 87 89 90 91 92 93 94 95 96 119 130 131 132 134 143 146 149 154 **P**1 **S** Shriners Hospitals for Children, Tampa, FL
Primary Contact: H Lee. Kirk Jr, FACHE, Administrator
CFO: Richard Fulkerson, Director Fiscal Services
CMO: David M Drvaric, M.D., Chief of Staff
CIO: Eric Kamens, Regional Director Information Systems
CHR: John Donlin, Director Human Resources
CNO: Diane Brunelle, MSN, R.N., Director Patient Care Services and Chief Nursing Officer
Web address: www.shrinershospitalsforchildren.org/Hospitals/Locations/Springfield.aspx
**Control**: Other not–for–profit (including NFP Corporation) **Service**: Children's orthopedic

**Staffed Beds:** 20 **Admissions:** 129 **Census:** 3 **Outpatient Visits:** 15702 **Births:** 0 **Total Expense ($000):** 24586 **Payroll Expense ($000):** 14796 **Personnel:** 183

☒ **VIBRA HOSPITAL OF WESTERN MASSACHUSETTS (222046)**, 1400 State Street, Zip 01109–2550; tel. 413/726–6700, (Includes VIBRA HOSPITAL OF WESTERN MASSACHUSETTS-CENTRAL CAMPUS, Mailing address: 111 Huntoon Memorial Highway, Rochdale, Massachusetts, Zip 1542; tel. 508/892–6000; Scott MacLean, Administrator), (Nonreporting) **A**1 10 **S** Vibra Healthcare, Mechanicsburg, PA
Primary Contact: Edward B. Leary, Interim Chief Executive Officer
CFO: Anna Dyrkacz, Chief Financial Officer
CHR: Donna Ciarefella, Director Human Resources
Web address: www.vhwmass.com
**Control**: Corporation, Investor–owned (for–profit) **Service**: Acute long–term care hospital

**Staffed Beds:** 174

**STOCKBRIDGE—Berkshire County**

☒ **AUSTEN RIGGS CENTER**, 25 Main Street, Zip 1262, Mailing Address: P.O. Box 962, Zip 01262–0962; tel. 413/298–5511, (Nonreporting) **A**1 **F**98 104 106 130
Primary Contact: Eric M. Plakun, M.D., Medical Center Director and Chief Executive Officer
COO: Chauncey Collins, Chief Operating Officer and Chief Financial Officer
CFO: Chauncey Collins, Chief Operating Officer and Chief Financial Officer
CIO: Ave Schwartz, Chief Information Officer
CHR: Bertha Mary Connelley, Director Human Resources
CNO: Barbara Turner, Director of Nursing
Web address: www.austenriggs.net
**Control**: Other not–for–profit (including NFP Corporation) **Service**: Psychiatric

**Staffed Beds:** 69 **Admissions:** 65 **Census:** 46 **Outpatient Visits:** 5810 **Births:** 0 **Total Expense ($000):** 21255 **Payroll Expense ($000):** 12213 **Personnel:** 133

**STOUGHTON—Norfolk County**

**CURAHEALTH HOSPITAL STOUGHTON** See Curahealth Stoughton

☐ **CURAHEALTH STOUGHTON (222002)**, 909 Sumner Street, 1st Floor, Zip 02072–3396; tel. 781/297–8200, (Nonreporting) **A**1 10 **S** Curahealth Hospitals, Garland, TX
Primary Contact: MacGregor Morgan, R.N., Chief Executive Officer
Web address: www.curahealth.com
**Control**: Corporation, Investor–owned (for–profit) **Service**: Acute long–term care hospital

**Staffed Beds:** 111

☐ **NEW ENGLAND SINAI HOSPITAL AND REHABILITATION CENTER (222027)**, 150 York Street, Zip 02072–1881; tel. 781/344–0600, (Nonreporting) **A**1 5 10 **S** Steward Health Care System, LLC, Dallas, TX
Primary Contact: Mary Beth. Urquhart, Interim President, Vice President Patient Care Services and Chief Nursing Officer
CFO: Victoria Lobban, Vice President Finance
CMO: Lawrence S Hotes, M.D., Chief Medical Officer
CIO: Michael West, Manager Systems Account
CHR: Julie Burke, Director Human Resources
CNO: Mary Beth Urquhart, Vice President Patient Care Services and Director of Quality
Web address: www.newenglandsinai.org
**Control**: Other not–for–profit (including NFP Corporation) **Service**: Acute long–term care hospital

**Staffed Beds:** 212

**TAUNTON—Bristol County**

☐ **MORTON HOSPITAL AND MEDICAL CENTER (220073)**, 88 Washington Street, Zip 02780–2465; tel. 508/828–7000, (Nonreporting) **A**1 10 **S** Steward Health Care System, LLC, Dallas, TX
Primary Contact: Heidi Taylor, President
COO: Donna Maher, R.N., Chief Operating Officer
CMO: Charles Thayer, M.D., Chief Medical Officer
CNO: Lisa Coggins, Chief Nursing Officer
Web address: www.mortonhospital.org
**Control**: Other not–for–profit (including NFP Corporation) **Service**: General medical and surgical

**Staffed Beds:** 153

☐ **TAUNTON STATE HOSPITAL (224001)**, 60 Hodges Avenue Extension, Zip 02780–3034, Mailing Address: PO Box 4007, Zip 02780–0997; tel. 508/977–3000, (Nonreporting) **A**1 10 **S** Massachusetts Department of Mental Health, Boston, MA
Primary Contact: Joyce O Connor, Chief Operating Officer
CHR: Trish Scully, Director Human Resources
**Control**: State, Government, Nonfederal **Service**: Psychiatric

**Staffed Beds:** 45

**TEWKSBURY—Middlesex County**

☐ **TEWKSBURY HOSPITAL (222003)**, 365 East Street, Zip 01876–1998; tel. 978/851–7321, (Nonreporting) **A**1 3 10 **S** Massachusetts Department of Public Health, Boston, MA
Primary Contact: Debra Tosti, Chief Executive Officer
CFO: Maureen DiPalma, Chief Financial Officer
CMO: James DeVita, M.D., Chief Medical Officer
CNO: Janice E Bishop, R.N., Chief Nursing Officer
Web address: www.mass.gov
**Control**: State, Government, Nonfederal **Service**: Acute long–term care hospital

**Staffed Beds:** 381

**TURNERS FALLS—Franklin County**

**FARREN MEMORIAL HOSPITAL** See Farren Care Center

**WALTHAM—Middlesex County**

☐ **WALDEN BEHAVIORAL CARE (224038)**, 9 Hope Avenue, Zip 02453–2741; tel. 781/647–6700, (Nonreporting) **A**1 10
Primary Contact: Stuart Koman, Ph.D., President and Chief Executive Officer
COO: Paula Vass, Vice President Clinical Operations
CFO: Lawrence Behan, Vice President Administration and Finance, Chief Financial Officer
CMO: James Greenblatt, M.D., Chief Medical Officer, Vice President Medical Clinical Services
CIO: Lawrence Behan, Vice President Administration and Finance, Chief Financial Officer
CHR: Carol Pender, Assistant Vice President Human Resources
Web address: www.waldenbehavioralcare.com/
**Control**: Other not–for–profit (including NFP Corporation) **Service**: Psychiatric

**Staffed Beds:** 69

**WALDEN PSYCHIATRIC CARE** See Walden Behavioral Care

**WAREHAM—Plymouth County**

**TOBEY HOSPITAL** See Southcoast Hospitals Group, Fall River

**WEST ROXBURY—Suffolk County**

☒ △ **VETERANS AFFAIRS BOSTON HEALTHCARE SYSTEM**, 1400 VFW Parkway, Zip 02132–4927; tel. 617/323–7700, (Nonreporting) **A**1 3 5 7 8 **S** Department of Veterans Affairs, Washington, DC
Primary Contact: Vincent Ng, Director
CFO: Joe Costa, Chief Financial Officer
CMO: Brian Hoffman, M.D., Chief Medical Services
CIO: David M Goodman, Ph.D., Chief Information Officer
CHR: William Warfield, Chief Human Resources Management
Web address: www.boston.va.gov/
**Control**: Veterans Affairs, Government, federal **Service**: General medical and surgical

**Staffed Beds:** 361

MA

---

Hospital, Medicare Provider Number, Address, Telephone, Approval, Facility, and Physician Codes, Health Care System

★ American Hospital Association (AHA) membership ☐ The Joint Commission accreditation   ○ Healthcare Facilities Accreditation Program ◇ DNV Healthcare Inc. accreditation   ⇧ Center for Improvement in Healthcare Quality Accreditation △ Commission on Accreditation of Rehabilitation Facilities (CARF) accreditation

**VETERANS AFFAIRS MED CENTER** See Veterans Affairs Boston Healthcare System

**VETERANS AFFAIRS MEDICAL CENTER** See Veterans Affairs Medical Center West Roxbury Division

**VETERANS AFFAIRS MEDICAL CENTER WEST ROXBURY DIVISION** See Veterans Affairs Boston Healthcare System Brockton Division, Brockton

### WESTBOROUGH—Worcester County

☐ **WESTBOROUGH BEHAVIORAL HEALTHCARE HOSPITAL (224044)**, 300 Friberg Parkway, Zip 01581–3900; tel. 508/329–6112, (Nonreporting) **A**1 **S** Signature Healthcare Services, Corona, CA
Primary Contact: Erika Heckman, Chief Executive Officer
Web address: www.https://www.westboroughbehavioral.com/
**Control:** Corporation, Investor–owned (for–profit) **Service:** Psychiatric

| Staffed Beds: 120 |
|---|

☐ **WHITTIER REHABILITATION HOSPITAL (222048)**, 150 Flanders Road, Zip 01581–1017; tel. 508/871–2000, (Nonreporting) **A**1 10 **S** Whittier Health Network, Haverhill, MA
Primary Contact: Alfred J. Arcidi, M.D., Senior Vice President
Web address: www.whittierhealth.com
**Control:** Partnership, Investor–owned (for–profit) **Service:** Acute long–term care hospital

| Staffed Beds: 60 |
|---|

### WESTFIELD—Hampden County

✠ **BAYSTATE NOBLE HOSPITAL (220065)**, 115 West Silver Street, Zip 01085–3628; tel. 413/568–2811, (Nonreporting) **A**1 5 10 **F**8 14 15 18 28 29 34 35 38 40 45 50 51 53 57 59 65 68 75 79 80 81 85 87 90 93 96 97 98 100 105 107 108 110 111 115 119 130 144 146 147 149 154 156 157 **P**8 **S** Baystate Health, Inc., Springfield, MA
Primary Contact: Ronald Bryant, President
CFO: John Shaver, Chief Financial Officer
CMO: Stanley Strzempko, M.D., Vice President Medical Affairs and Chief Medical Officer
CIO: Steven Cummings, Chief Operating Officer and Chief Information Officer
CHR: Joanne Ollson, Vice President Human Resources
Web address: www.baystatehealth.org/locations/noble-hospital
**Control:** Other not–for–profit (including NFP Corporation) **Service:** General medical and surgical

| Staffed Beds: 85 Admissions: 2648 Census: 43 Outpatient Visits: 115243 Births: 0 Total Expense ($000): 60160 Payroll Expense ($000): 28547 Personnel: 439 |
|---|

**NOBLE HOSPITAL** See Baystate Noble Hospital

☐ **WESTERN MASSACHUSETTS HOSPITAL (222023)**, 91 East Mountain Road, Zip 01085–1801; tel. 413/562–4131, (Nonreporting) **A**1 10 **S** Massachusetts Department of Public Health, Boston, MA
Primary Contact: Valenda M. Liptak, Chief Executive Officer
CMO: Chabilal Neergheen, M.D., Medical Director
CHR: James E Duggan, Director Human Resources
Web address: www.mass.gov/eohhs/gov/departments/dph/programs/western-massachusetts-hospital.html
**Control:** State, Government, Nonfederal **Service:** Acute long–term care hospital

| Staffed Beds: 80 |
|---|

### WHITINSVILLE—Worcester County

**WHITINSVILLE HOSPITAL** See Whitinsville Medical Center

**WHITINSVILLE MEDICAL CENTER** See Milford Regional Medical Center, Milford

### WINCHESTER—Middlesex County

✠ **WINCHESTER HOSPITAL (220105)**, 41 Highland Avenue, Zip 01890–1496; tel. 781/729–9000, (Nonreporting) **A**1 2 3 5 10 **F**3 8 12 13 15 18 26 28 29 30 31 32 34 35 36 38 40 41 44 45 46 49 50 51 54 55 56 57 59 64 70 73 74 75 76 77 78 79 81 82 85 86 87 89 91 92 93 107 108 110 114 115 118 119 120 121 126 129 130 131 132 135 144 145 146 147 148 149 156 **P**8 **S** Beth Israel Lahey Health, Boston, MA
Primary Contact: Richard I. Weiner, M.D., Chief Executive Officer and Chief Medical Officer
COO: Kathy Schuler, R.N., MS, Chief Operating Officer and Chief Nursing Officer
CFO: Matthew Woods, Vice President Finance
CMO: Richard I. Weiner, M.D., Chief Executive Officer and Chief Medical Officer
CHR: Stephanie M Bettinelli, Vice President of Human Resources
CNO: Kathy Schuler, R.N., MS, Chief Operating Officer and Chief Nursing Officer
Web address: www.winchesterhospital.org
**Control:** Other not–for–profit (including NFP Corporation) **Service:** General medical and surgical

| Staffed Beds: 189 Admissions: 12113 Census: 117 Outpatient Visits: 468447 Births: 2336 Total Expense ($000): 280166 Payroll Expense ($000): 106061 Personnel: 1473 |
|---|

### WOBURN—Middlesex County

✠ **ENCOMPASS HEALTH REHABILITATION HOSPITAL OF NEW ENGLAND (223026)**, Two Rehabilitation Way, Zip 01801–6098; tel. 781/935–5050, (Nonreporting) **A**1 3 10 **S** Encompass Health Corporation, Birmingham, AL
Primary Contact: David Coggins, MS, Chief Executive Officer
CFO: Barbara Polizzotti, Controller
CHR: Lauren Healey, Human Resources Director
CNO: Deborah Rich, R.N., Chief Nursing Officer
Web address: www.newenglandrehab.com
**Control:** Corporation, Investor–owned (for–profit) **Service:** Rehabilitation

| Staffed Beds: 210 |
|---|

**HEALTHSOUTH NEW ENGLAND REHABILITATION HOSPITAL** See Encompass Health Rehabilitation Hospital of New England

### WORCESTER—Worcester County

✠ **ADCARE HOSPITAL OF WORCESTER (220062)**, 107 Lincoln Street, Zip 01605–2499; tel. 508/799–9000, (Nonreporting) **A**3 5 10
Primary Contact: David W. Hillis, Chairman and Chief Executive Officer
COO: Jeffrey W Hillis, Chief Operating Officer
CFO: Christine Judycki-Crepeault, Chief Financial Officer
CMO: Ronald F Pike, M.D., Medical Director
CHR: Joan L. Bertrand, Vice President Human Resources
CNO: Judith Richards, Director of Nursing
Web address: www.adcare.com
**Control:** Other not–for–profit (including NFP Corporation) **Service:** Alcoholism and other chemical dependency

| Staffed Beds: 114 |
|---|

✠ **FAIRLAWN REHABILITATION HOSPITAL (223029)**, 189 May Street, Zip 01602–4339; tel. 508/791–6351, (Nonreporting) **A**1 3 5 10 **F**28 29 34 35 57 60 62 64 74 75 77 79 82 90 91 93 94 95 96 130 131 132 154 **S** Encompass Health Corporation, Birmingham, AL
Primary Contact: Anne Roper, Chief Executive Officer
CFO: John Flaherty, Controller
CMO: Debra Twehous, Medical Director
CIO: Jennifer Jozefiak, Information Officer
CHR: Rosalie Lawless, Director Human Resources
CNO: Lisa Perales, Chief Nursing Officer
Web address: www.fairlawnrehab.org
**Control:** Corporation, Investor–owned (for–profit) **Service:** Rehabilitation

| Staffed Beds: 110 Admissions: 2384 Census: 80 Outpatient Visits: 7024 Births: 0 Total Expense ($000): 36484 Payroll Expense ($000): 17834 Personnel: 336 |
|---|

☐ **HOSPITAL FOR BEHAVIORAL MEDICINE (224045)**, 100 Century Drive, Zip 01606–1244; tel. 774/420–3939, (Nonreporting) **A**1
Primary Contact: Michelle Lynn, Chief Executive Officer
Web address: www.https://www.hospitalforbehavioralmedicine.com/
**Control:** Corporation, Investor–owned (for–profit) **Service:** Psychiatric

| Staffed Beds: 120 |
|---|

✠ **SAINT VINCENT HOSPITAL (220176)**, 123 Summer Street, Zip 01608–1216; tel. 508/363–5000, (Nonreporting) **A**1 2 3 5 10 **S** TENET Healthcare Corporation, Dallas, TX
Primary Contact: Carolyn Jackson, Chief Executive Officer
COO: Ava Jo Collins, FACHE, Chief Operating Officer
CFO: Peter D'Elia, Chief Financial Officer
CMO: Douglas Waite, M.D., Chief Medical Officer
CHR: Jan Peters, Vice President Human Resources
CNO: JoAnn Piedrafite, R.N., Chief Nursing Officer
Web address: www.stvincenthospital.com
**Control:** Corporation, Investor–owned (for–profit) **Service:** General medical and surgical

| Staffed Beds: 283 |
|---|

**SAINT VINCENT HOSPITAL AT WORCESTER MEDICAL CENTER** See Saint Vincent Hospital

**UMASS MEMORIAL HEALTH CARE** See Umass Memorial Medical Center

*Many Facility Codes have changed. Please refer to the AHA Guide Code Chart.*

© 2021 AHA Guide

⊞ **UMASS MEMORIAL MEDICAL CENTER (220163)**, 119 Belmont Street, Zip 01605–2982; tel. 508/334–1000, (Includes HAHNEMANN CAMPUS, Mailing address: 281 Lincoln Street, Worcester, Massachusetts, Zip 1605; tel. 508/334–1000; MEMORIAL CAMPUS, Mailing address: 119 Belmont Street, Worcester, Massachusetts, Zip 1605; tel. 508/334–1000; UMASS MEMORIAL CHILDREN'S MEDICAL CENTER, Mailing address: 55 Lake Avenue North, Worcester, Massachusetts, Zip 01655–0002; tel. 508/334–1000; UNIVERSITY CAMPUS, Mailing address: 55 Lake Avenue North, Worcester, Massachusetts, Zip 01655–0002; tel. 508/334–1000), (Nonreporting) **A**1 2 3 5 8 10 19 **F**1 3 4 6 7 8 9 12 13 14 15 16 17 18 19 20 22 24 26 29 30 31 32 38 40 41 43 45 46 47 48 49 50 51 52 55 56 59 60 61 64 65 67 68 70 71 72 73 74 75 76 77 78 79 80 81 82 84 85 86 87 88 89 90 92 97 98 100 101 102 103 104 107 108 110 114 115 118 119 120 121 123 124 126 127 128 130 131 132 135 136 138 139 141 145 146 147 148 149 150 154 156 **P**5 6 **S** UMass Memorial Health Care, Inc., Worcester, MA
Primary Contact: Michael Gustafson, M.D., President
COO: Andrew Sussman, M.D., Chief Operating Officer
CFO: Therese Day, Chief Financial Officer
CMO: Charles E Cavagnaro, M.D., IIIInterim Chief Medical officer
CIO: George Brenkle, Chief Information Officer
CNO: Justin Precourt, Chief Nursing Officer
Web address: www.umassmemorial.org
**Control**: Other not–for–profit (including NFP Corporation) **Service**: General medical and surgical

**Staffed Beds:** 671 **Admissions:** 38214 **Census:** 572 **Outpatient Visits:** 977405 **Births:** 4292 **Total Expense ($000):** 1810065 **Payroll Expense ($000):** 532192 **Personnel:** 7678

**WORCESTER HAHNEMANN HOSPITAL** See Hahnemann Campus

**WORCESTER MEMORIAL HOSPITAL** See Memorial Campus

☐ **WORCESTER RECOVERY CENTER AND HOSPITAL (224032)**, 309 Belmont Street, Zip 01604–1695; tel. 508/368–3300, (Nonreporting) **A**1 3 5 10 **S** Massachusetts Department of Mental Health, Boston, MA
Primary Contact: Anthony Riccitelli, Chief Operating Officer
COO: Anthony Riccitelli, Chief Operating Officer
CIO: Ron Medciros, Director Applied Information Technology
**Control**: State, Government, Nonfederal **Service**: Psychiatric

**Staffed Beds:** 126

**WORCESTER STATE HOSPITAL** See Worcester Recovery Center and Hospital

# MICHIGAN

**MI**

## ADRIAN—Lenawee County

**BIXBY MEDICAL CENTER** See Promedica Bixby Hospital

★ ○ **PROMEDICA BIXBY HOSPITAL (230005)**, 818 Riverside Avenue, Zip 49221–1446; tel. 517/265–0900, (Nonreporting) **A**2 10 11 **F**3 8 11 15 18 19 26 28 29 30 31 34 35 38 39 40 45 48 53 57 59 62 63 64 65 68 70 74 76 77 78 79 81 82 85 87 92 93 97 100 101 102 104 107 108 109 111 114 115 119 121 126 127 130 132 135 146 148 149 154 157 **P**8 **S** ProMedica Health System, Toledo, OH
Primary Contact: Julie Yaroch, President
COO: Gregory Peckham, Associate Vice President, Operations
CFO: Joe Raj, Administrative Director, Finance
CIO: Patrick Heskett, Director, Information Technology
CHR: Kim Langley, Business Partner
Web address: www.promedica.org
**Control**: Other not–for–profit (including NFP Corporation) **Service**: General medical and surgical

**Staffed Beds:** 66 **Admissions:** 3044 **Census:** 25 **Outpatient Visits:** 104392 **Births:** 495 **Total Expense ($000):** 81433 **Payroll Expense ($000):** 24030 **Personnel:** 399

## ALLEGAN—Allegan County

**ALLEGAN GENERAL HOSPITAL** See Ascension Allegan Hospital

★ **ASCENSION ALLEGAN HOSPITAL (231328)**, 555 Linn Street, Zip 49010–1524; tel. 269/673–8424, (Nonreporting) **A**10 18 **F**3 12 15 28 29 31 34 35 40 43 45 47 48 50 59 75 77 78 79 81 82 85 86 87 96 97 99 100 101 104 107 108 110 115 118 119 127 129 130 131 132 135 144 146 149 153 154 156 **P**3 **S** Ascension Healthcare, Saint Louis, MO
Primary Contact: Peter U. Bergmann, President
CMO: Nabil Nouna, M.D., Chief of Staff
CNO: Kathy Chapman, R.N., Chief Clinical Officer and Vice President of Patient Services
Web address: www.aghosp.org
**Control**: Other not–for–profit (including NFP Corporation) **Service**: General medical and surgical

**Staffed Beds:** 25 **Admissions:** 528 **Census:** 5 **Outpatient Visits:** 54876 **Births:** 0 **Total Expense ($000):** 38342 **Payroll Expense ($000):** 13611 **Personnel:** 249

## ALMA—Gratiot County

**GRATIOT MEDICAL CENTER** See Midmichigan Medical Center-Gratiot

☒ △ **MIDMICHIGAN MEDICAL CENTER-GRATIOT (230030)**, 300 East Warwick Drive, Zip 48801–1014; tel. 989/463–1101, (Nonreporting) **A**1 3 5 7 10 **F**3 12 13 15 18 20 28 29 31 34 35 38 40 42 43 45 57 59 61 64 65 68 70 74 75 76 77 78 79 81 82 85 86 87 89 90 92 93 96 98 100 101 102 103 104 105 107 108 110 111 115 117 118 119 127 129 130 132 135 144 146 149 154 156 **S** MidMichigan Health, Midland, MI
Primary Contact: Marita Hattem-Schiffman, President
CFO: Jeff Provenzano, Vice President and Chief Financial Officer
CNO: LeeAnn Chadwick, Chief Nursing Officer
Web address: www.midmichigan.org/gratiot
**Control**: Other not–for–profit (including NFP Corporation) **Service**: General medical and surgical

**Staffed Beds:** 97 **Admissions:** 4542 **Census:** 65 **Outpatient Visits:** 150008 **Births:** 505 **Total Expense ($000):** 127830 **Payroll Expense ($000):** 36996 **Personnel:** 536

## ALPENA—Alpena County

**ALPENA REGIONAL MEDICAL CENTER** See Midmichigan Medical Center - Alpena

☒ **MIDMICHIGAN MEDICAL CENTER - ALPENA (230036)**, 1501 West Chisholm Street, Zip 49707–1401; tel. 989/356–7000, (Nonreporting) **A**1 2 10 **F**3 11 13 15 20 26 28 29 31 34 35 40 43 44 45 46 47 48 49 50 59 60 62 64 65 70 71 73 74 75 76 77 78 79 81 82 85 86 87 90 92 93 96 97 98 100 101 102 103 104 107 110 111 114 115 118 119 129 130 131 132 135 146 147 148 149 154 156 **S** MidMichigan Health, Midland, MI
Primary Contact: Charles H. Sherwin, President
CMO: Thomas Thornton, M.D., Vice President of Medical Affairs
CNO: Debra Pokorzynski, Vice President of Nursing
Web address: www.midmichigan.org
**Control**: Other not–for–profit (including NFP Corporation) **Service**: General medical and surgical

**Staffed Beds:** 125 **Admissions:** 4588 **Census:** 47 **Outpatient Visits:** 132955 **Births:** 374 **Total Expense ($000):** 127924 **Payroll Expense ($000):** 46420 **Personnel:** 739

## ANN ARBOR—Washtenaw County

**C.S. MOTT CHILDREN'S HOSPITAL** See C. S. Mott Children's Hospital

☒ **MICHIGAN MEDICINE (230046)**, 1500 East Medical Center Drive, Zip 48109; tel. 734/936–4000, (Includes C. S. MOTT CHILDREN'S HOSPITAL, Mailing address: 1540 East Hospital Drive, Ann Arbor, Michigan, Zip 48109–5475; tel. 734/936–4000; Luanne M. Thomas Ewald, Chief Operating Officer), (Nonreporting) **A**1 2 3 5 8 10 **F**3 5 6 8 9 11 12 13 15 16 17 18 19 20 21 22 23 24 25 26 27 28 29 30 31 32 34 35 36 37 38 39 40 41 43 44 45 46 47 48 49 50 51 52 53 54 55 56 57 58 59 60 61 62 64 65 66 68 69 70 72 74 75 76 77 78 79 80 81 82 83 84 85 86 87 88 89 90 91 92 93 94 95 96 97 98 99 100 101 102 103 104 107 108 110 111 112 114 115 116 117 118 119 120 121 123 124 126 127 129 130 131 132 134 135 136 137 138 139 140 141 142 145 146 147 148 149 150 151 153 154 156 **P**1
Primary Contact: David Spahlinger, M.D., President
COO: Tony Denton, JD, Senior Vice President and Chief Operating Officer, University of Michigan Health System
CFO: Paul Castillo, Chief Financial Officer
CMO: Jeffrey Desmond, M.D., Chief Medical Officer
CIO: Andrew Rosenberg, M.D., Chief Information Officer
CHR: Deloris Hunt, Chief Human Resources Officer
CNO: Marge Calarco, Chief Nursing Executive
Web address: www.med.umich.edu
**Control**: Other not–for–profit (including NFP Corporation) **Service**: General medical and surgical

**Staffed Beds:** 1004 **Admissions:** 50833 **Census:** 872 **Outpatient Visits:** 3400863 **Births:** 4845 **Total Expense ($000):** 3578408 **Payroll Expense ($000):** 1269350 **Personnel:** 15692

**UNIVERSITY OF MICHIGAN HEALTH SYSTEM** See Michigan Medicine

☒ **VETERANS AFFAIRS ANN ARBOR HEALTHCARE SYSTEM**, 2215 Fuller Road, Zip 48105–2399; tel. 734/769–7100, (Total facility includes 46 beds in nursing home–type unit) (Nonreporting) **A**1 2 3 5 **F**3 5 12 18 20 22 24 26 28 29 30 31 34 35 36 38 39 40 44 45 46 47 48 49 50 54 56 57 58 59 60 61 63 64 65 68 70 71 74 75 77 78 79 81 82 83 84 85 86 87 91 92 93 94 96 97 98 100 101 102 103 104 105 107 108 111 114 115 116 117 118 119 120 121 123 126 128 129 130 132 135 143 144 146 147 148 149 153 154 156 157 158 **P**6 **S** Department of Veterans Affairs, Washington, DC
Primary Contact: Andrew Pacyna, Acting Director
COO: Himanshu Singh, M.D., Associate Director
CFO: Joel Wallinga, Chief Financial Officer
CMO: Eric Young, M.D., Chief of Staff
CIO: Rob Whitehurst, Chief, Office of Information and Technology
CHR: Stephanie Hunter, Chief Human Resources Officer
CNO: Stacey Breedveld, R.N., MSN, Associate Director for Patient Care
Web address: www.annarbor.va.gov
**Control**: Veterans Affairs, Government, federal **Service**: General medical and surgical

**Staffed Beds:** 102 **Admissions:** 5028 **Census:** 77 **Outpatient Visits:** 610652 **Births:** 0 **Total Expense ($000):** 549133 **Payroll Expense ($000):** 224364 **Personnel:** 2722

**VETERANS AFFAIRS MED CENTER** See Veterans Affairs Ann Arbor Healthcare System

*Many Facility Codes have changed. Please refer to the AHA Guide Code Chart.*    © 2021 AHA Guide

## AUBURN HILLS—Oakland County

☐ **HAVENWYCK HOSPITAL (234023)**, 1525 University Drive, Zip 48326–2673;
tel. 248/373–9200, (Nonreporting) **A**1 10 **F**98 99 103 105 106 130 154 **S**
Universal Health Services, Inc., King of Prussia, PA
Primary Contact: Julie Szyska, Chief Executive Officer and Managing Director
CFO: Steve Sacharski, Chief Financial Officer
CMO: Hani Mekhael, M.D., Chief Staff
CHR: Amy Giannosa, Director Human Resources
CNO: Mitzi Sawicki, Director of Nursing
Web address: www.havenwyckhospital.com
**Control**: Corporation, Investor–owned (for–profit) **Service**: Psychiatric

**Staffed Beds**: 243 **Admissions**: 6639 **Census**: 203 **Outpatient Visits**: 4342
**Births**: 0 **Total Expense ($000)**: 51262 **Payroll Expense ($000)**: 20625
**Personnel**: 394

## BAD AXE—Huron County

**HURON MEDICAL CENTER** See Mclaren Thumb Region

★ **MCLAREN THUMB REGION (230118)**, 1100 South Van Dyke Road,
Zip 48413–9615; tel. 989/269–9521, (Nonreporting) **A**10 20 **S** McLaren Health
Care Corporation, Grand Blanc, MI
Primary Contact: Michael Eric. Johnston, President and Chief Executive Officer
CFO: Kevin J Cawley, Interim Chief Financial Officer
CMO: Craig McManaman, M.D., Chief of Staff
CHR: Nancy Bouck, Senior Director of Human Resources
CNO: Jane Christner, Chief Nursing Officer
Web address: www.huronmedicalcenter.org
**Control**: Other not–for–profit (including NFP Corporation) **Service**: General
medical and surgical

**Staffed Beds**: 46

## BATTLE CREEK—Calhoun County

**BATTLE CREEK ADVENTIST HOSP** See Fieldstone Center

☒ **BATTLE CREEK VETERANS AFFAIRS MEDICAL CENTER**, 5500 Armstrong
Road, Zip 49037–7314; tel. 269/966–5600, (Total facility includes 75 beds in
nursing home–type unit) (Nonreporting) **A**1 3 5 **F**3 4 5 7 12 18 29 30 33 34 35
36 38 39 50 53 54 56 57 58 59 61 62 63 64 65 68 74 75 77 82 83 84 86 87
93 94 96 97 98 100 101 102 103 104 106 107 108 111 114 115 119 127
128 130 132 135 143 144 146 147 148 149 153 154 156 157 **S** Department
of Veterans Affairs, Washington, DC
Primary Contact: James Doelling, Executive Director
COO: Edward G. Dornoff, Associate Director
CFO: James M. Rupert, Chief Fiscal Services
CMO: Wilfredo Rodriguez, M.D., Chief of Staff
CIO: Scott Hershberger, Acting Chief Information Management Services
CHR: Palma Simkins, Chief Human Resources Management Services
CNO: Kay Bower, Associate Director for Patient Care Services
Web address: www.battlecreek.va.gov/
**Control**: Veterans Affairs, Government, federal **Service**: Psychiatric

**Staffed Beds**: 242 **Admissions**: 1610 **Census**: 189 **Outpatient
Visits**: 519713 **Births**: 0 **Personnel**: 1739

**BRONSON BATTLE CREEK** See Bronson Battle Creek Hospital

☒ **BRONSON BATTLE CREEK HOSPITAL (230075)**, 300 North Avenue,
Zip 49017–3307; tel. 269/245–8000, (Includes FIELDSTONE CENTER, Mailing
address: 165 North Washington Avenue, Battle Creek, Michigan, Zip 49037;
tel. 269/245–8570; MAIN CAMPUS, Mailing address: 300 North Avenue, Battle
Creek, Michigan, Zip 49017; tel. 616/966–8000), (Nonreporting) **A**1 2 3 5 10 19
**F**3 4 6 9 11 15 18 28 29 30 31 34 35 36 38 40 43 44 45 46 49 50 51 54 55
56 57 58 59 60 61 63 64 65 66 68 70 71 74 75 76 77 78 79 81 82 84 85 86
87 89 97 98 100 101 102 103 104 107 108 110 111 114 115 116 117 118
119 120 121 123 126 129 130 131 132 134 135 143 144 146 147 148 149
154 156 **P**6 **S** Bronson Healthcare Group, Kalamazoo, MI
Primary Contact: Frank J. Sardone, President and Chief Executive Officer
COO: James E. Mckernan, Chief Operating Officer
CMO: Daniel Stewart, M.D., Vice President Medical Affairs
CHR: John Hayden, Senior Vice President and Human Resources Officer
CNO: Susan Watson, MSN, R.N., Vice President
Web address: www.bronsonhealth.com
**Control**: Other not–for–profit (including NFP Corporation) **Service**: General
medical and surgical

**Staffed Beds**: 198 **Admissions**: 7679 **Census**: 92 **Outpatient
Visits**: 479764 **Births**: 768 **Total Expense ($000)**: 257898 **Payroll Expense
($000)**: 132258 **Personnel**: 1501

☒ **SELECT SPECIALTY HOSPITAL-BATTLE CREEK (232035)**, 300 North Avenue,
Zip 49017–3307; tel. 269/245–4675, (Nonreporting) **A**1 10 **S** Select Medical
Corporation, Mechanicsburg, PA
Primary Contact: Robert Mach, Chief Executive Officer
Web address: www.battlecreek.selectspecialtyhospitals.com/
**Control**: Corporation, Investor–owned (for–profit) **Service**: Acute long–term care hospital

**Staffed Beds**: 25

**SELECT SPECIALTY HOSPITAL-KALAMAZOO** See Select Specialty Hospital-
Battle Creek

**VETERANS AFFAIRS MEDICAL CENTER** See Battle Creek Veterans Affairs
Medical Center

## BAY CITY—Bay County

**BAY REGIONAL MEDICAL CENTER** See Mclaren Bay Region

**BAY REGIONAL MEDICAL CENTER-WEST CAMPUS** See Mclaren Bay Region-
West Campus

**BAY SPECIAL CARE HOSPITAL** See Mclaren Bay Special Care

☐ △ **MCLAREN BAY REGION (230041)**, 1900 Columbus Avenue,
Zip 48708–6831; tel. 989/894–3000, (Includes MCLAREN BAY REGION-
WEST CAMPUS, Mailing address: 3250 East Midland Road, Bay City, Michigan,
Zip 48706; tel. 989/667–6750; Monica Baranski, MS, R.N., President),
(Nonreporting) **A**1 3 5 7 10 13 **F**3 7 11 13 15 17 18 20 22 24 26 28 29 30 31
32 34 35 36 38 40 43 44 45 46 47 48 49 50 54 57 58 59 64 65 68 70 73 74
75 76 78 79 81 82 85 86 87 89 90 92 93 96 97 98 100 102 103 105 107 108
110 111 114 115 119 120 121 123 124 126 129 130 131 132 135 141 143
144 146 147 148 149 154 157 **P**8 **S** McLaren Health Care Corporation, Grand
Blanc, MI
Primary Contact: Clarence Sevillian, President and Chief Executive Officer
COO: Mitch Southwick, Chief Operating Officer
CFO: Damon Sorensen, Chief Financial Officer
CMO: Jason White, M.D., Chief Medical Officer
CIO: Ronald Strachan, Chief Information Officer
CHR: Carolyn Potter, Chief Human Resources Officer
CNO: Ellen E Talbott, MSN, R.N., Vice President Patient Care Services
Web address: www.mclaren.org/bayregion
**Control**: Other not–for–profit (including NFP Corporation) **Service**: General
medical and surgical

**Staffed Beds**: 338 **Admissions**: 16151 **Census**: 214 **Outpatient
Visits**: 340966 **Births**: 719 **Total Expense ($000)**: 318608 **Payroll Expense
($000)**: 132753 **Personnel**: 2137

☐ **MCLAREN BAY SPECIAL CARE (232020)**, 3250 East Midland Road, Suite 1,
Zip 48706–2835; tel. 989/667–6851, (Nonreporting) **A**1 10 **F**1 3 29 79 87 96
148 **S** McLaren Health Care Corporation, Grand Blanc, MI
Primary Contact: Monica Baranski, MS, R.N., President
CMO: Janet Sutton, D.O., Medical Director
CIO: Greg Jacobs, Manager
CHR: Carolyn Potter, Vice President Human Resources
Web address: www.mclaren/bayspecialcare
**Control**: Other not–for–profit (including NFP Corporation) **Service**: Acute long–
term care hospital

**Staffed Beds**: 26 **Admissions**: 184 **Census**: 13 **Outpatient Visits**: 0
**Births**: 0 **Total Expense ($000)**: 5330 **Payroll Expense ($000)**: 2432

## BIG RAPIDS—Mecosta County

**MECOSTA COUNTY MEDICAL CENTER** See Spectrum Health Big Rapids Hospital

☒ **SPECTRUM HEALTH BIG RAPIDS HOSPITAL (230093)**, 605 Oak Street,
Zip 49307–2099; tel. 231/796–8691, (Nonreporting) **A**1 10 20 **F**3 13 15 28 29
34 35 40 43 45 50 57 64 65 68 69 70 75 76 77 79 81 85 87 93 97 107 108
110 111 115 118 119 126 127 129 130 131 132 146 147 148 149 154 156
**P**6 **S** Spectrum Health, Grand Rapids, MI
Primary Contact: Andrea M. Leslie, MSN, R.N., President
CFO: Thomas Khoerl, Vice President Finance
CMO: Christopher Skinner, Chief of Staff
CIO: Patrick Whiteside, Manager Information Services
CHR: Melonie Jackson, Human Resource Business Partner
CNO: Caroline A Ring, Chief Nursing Officer
Web address: www.spectrumhealth.org
**Control**: Other not–for–profit (including NFP Corporation) **Service**: General
medical and surgical

**Staffed Beds**: 48 **Admissions**: 2500 **Census**: 18 **Births**: 521 **Total Expense
($000)**: 71808 **Payroll Expense ($000)**: 23893 **Personnel**: 429

---

**Hospital, Medicare Provider Number, Address, Telephone, Approval, Facility, and Physician Codes, Health Care System**

★ American Hospital Association (AHA) membership   ◯ Healthcare Facilities Accreditation Program   ⇑ Center for Improvement in Healthcare Quality Accreditation
☐ The Joint Commission accreditation   ◇ DNV Healthcare Inc. accreditation   △ Commission on Accreditation of Rehabilitation Facilities (CARF) accreditation

## BRIGHTON—Livingston County

★ **ASCENSION BRIGHTON CENTER FOR RECOVERY (230279)**, 12851 Grand River Road, Zip 48116–8506; tel. 810/227–1211, (Nonreporting) **A**10 **F**4 5 30 34 35 36 38 44 57 68 75 82 86 100 101 104 130 132 135 146 149 150 152 153 157 **S** Ascension Healthcare, Saint Louis, MO
Primary Contact: Raymond A. Waller, Director and Administrator
COO: Raymond A. Waller, Director and Administrator
CFO: Marie Allard, Finance Manager
CMO: Ismael David Yanga, M.D., Chief Medical Officer
CIO: Frank Sanzone, Manager Information Technology
CHR: Marney Daugherty, Worklife Services Consultant
CNO: Barbara Shoup, R.N., Chief Nursing Officer
Web address: www.brightonrecovery.org
**Control**: Church operated, Nongovernment, not–for–profit **Service**: Alcoholism and other chemical dependency

| | |
|---|---|
| **Staffed Beds:** 99 **Admissions:** 3238 **Census:** 76 **Outpatient Visits:** 16625 **Births:** 0 **Total Expense ($000):** 16679 **Payroll Expense ($000):** 7281 **Personnel:** 107 | |

**BRIGHTON CENTER FOR RECOVERY** See Ascension Brighton Center for Recovery

## CADILLAC—Wexford County

**MERCY HOSPITAL CADILLAC** See Munson Healthcare Cadillac Hospital

⊞ **MUNSON HEALTHCARE CADILLAC HOSPITAL (230081)**, 400 Hobart Street, Zip 49601–2389; tel. 231/876–7200, (Nonreporting) **A**1 10 20 **F**3 11 13 15 18 28 29 30 31 34 40 44 45 50 51 59 64 68 70 76 77 78 79 81 85 87 93 97 107 111 114 115 116 119 127 129 130 132 146 154 156 157 **P**6 8 **S** Munson Healthcare, Traverse City, MI
Primary Contact: Peter Marinoff Jr, President
COO: Michael Zdrodowski, Vice President of Operations and Ambulatory Services
CFO: Kristin Ellis, Controller
CMO: Joe Santangelo, M.D., Vice President of Medical Affairs
CIO: Randi Terry, Site Director Management Information Systems
CHR: Kelley Whittington-Geppert, Director Human Resources
CNO: Kathryn Bandfield-Keough, Vice President Patient Care Services
Web address: www.mercyhealthcadillac.com/welcome-cadillac
**Control**: Other not–for–profit (including NFP Corporation) **Service**: General medical and surgical

| | |
|---|---|
| **Staffed Beds:** 49 **Admissions:** 2874 **Census:** 25 **Outpatient Visits:** 165869 **Births:** 313 **Total Expense ($000):** 99608 **Payroll Expense ($000):** 39019 **Personnel:** 590 | |

## CARO—Tuscola County

☐ **CARO CENTER (234025)**, 2000 Chambers Road, Zip 48723–9296; tel. 989/673–3191, (Nonreporting) **A**1 10
Primary Contact: Rose Laskowski, R.N., Director
COO: Rose Laskowski, R.N., Director
CFO: Mary Jo Drzewiecki-Burger, Administrative Manager
CMO: William Clark, M.D., Chief Clinical Affairs
CIO: Michele Wills, Registered Health Information Administrator
CHR: Barbara Frank, Human Resource Specialist
**Control**: State, Government, Nonfederal **Service**: Psychiatric

| | |
|---|---|
| **Staffed Beds:** 193 | |

**CARO COMMUNITY HOSPITAL** See Mclaren Caro Region

**CARO REG MENTAL HLTH CENTER** See Caro Center

★ **MCLAREN CARO REGION (231329)**, 401 North Hooper Street, Zip 48723–1476, Mailing Address: P.O. Box 435, Zip 48723–0435; tel. 989/673–3141, (Nonreporting) **A**10 18 **F**3 11 15 29 34 35 37 40 45 50 54 57 59 64 65 75 77 79 81 84 85 87 89 92 93 97 107 108 110 115 119 129 130 135 144 146 149 154 156 **S** McLaren Health Care Corporation, Grand Blanc, MI
Primary Contact: Marc Augsburger, R.N., President and Chief Executive Officer
CFO: Ron Srebinski, Chief Financial Officer
CMO: T Gard Adams, M.D., Chief of Staff
CHR: Allyson Joyce, Vice President Human Resources
CNO: Kelly Whittaker, Vice President Nursing
Web address: www.cch-mi.org
**Control**: Other not–for–profit (including NFP Corporation) **Service**: General medical and surgical

| | |
|---|---|
| **Staffed Beds:** 25 **Admissions:** 78 **Census:** 1 **Outpatient Visits:** 26671 **Births:** 0 **Total Expense ($000):** 16110 **Payroll Expense ($000):** 6358 **Personnel:** 107 | |

## CARSON CITY—Montcalm County

**CARSON HEALTH** See Sparrow Carson Hospital

⊞ **SPARROW CARSON HOSPITAL (230208)**, 406 East Elm Street, Zip 48811–9693, Mailing Address: P.O. Box 879, Zip 48811–0879; tel. 989/584–3131, (Nonreporting) **A**1 3 10 19 **F**3 11 13 15 18 20 30 31 34 35 40 45 46 50 53 57 59 64 65 70 75 78 79 81 82 85 86 87 93 97 107 108 110 111 115 118 119 126 127 129 130 132 146 147 148 156 **P**6 8 **S** Sparrow Health System, Lansing, MI
Primary Contact: William Roeser, Interim President and Chief Executive Officer
CFO: Richard Reid, Vice President Chief Finance Officer
CMO: Robert Seals, D.O., Medical Director
CIO: Richard Terry, Vice President & Chief Information Officer
CHR: Georgette Russell, Vice President of Talent & Organizational Effectiveness
Web address: www.carsoncityhospital.com
**Control**: Other not–for–profit (including NFP Corporation) **Service**: General medical and surgical

| | |
|---|---|
| **Staffed Beds:** 48 **Admissions:** 603 **Census:** 6 **Outpatient Visits:** 80508 **Births:** 0 **Total Expense ($000):** 50861 **Payroll Expense ($000):** 22360 **Personnel:** 437 | |

## CASS CITY—Tuscola County

★ ○ **HILLS & DALES GENERAL HOSPITAL (231316)**, 4675 Hill Street, Zip 48726–1099; tel. 989/872–2121, (Nonreporting) **A**10 11 18 **F**3 11 15 29 32 34 35 40 45 46 51 53 56 57 59 61 64 65 68 74 75 77 79 81 82 86 87 93 97 107 108 109 110 115 118 119 127 129 130 131 132 133 135 144 146 147 149 156
Primary Contact: Jean Anthony, R.N., President and Chief Executive Officer
CFO: Kenneth Baranski, Chief Financial Officer
CMO: Donald Robbins, M.D., JrChief Staff
CNO: Jennifer TerBush, Vice President, Patient Services
Web address: www.hdghmi.org
**Control**: Other not–for–profit (including NFP Corporation) **Service**: General medical and surgical

| | |
|---|---|
| **Staffed Beds:** 25 **Admissions:** 329 **Census:** 3 **Outpatient Visits:** 106696 **Births:** 0 **Total Expense ($000):** 36722 **Payroll Expense ($000):** 17431 **Personnel:** 301 | |

**HILLS AND DALES GENERAL HOSPITAL** See Hills & Dales General Hospital

## CHARLEVOIX—Charlevoix County

**CHARLEVOIX AREA HOSPITAL** See Munson Healthcare Charlevoix Hospital

⊞ **MUNSON HEALTHCARE CHARLEVOIX HOSPITAL (231322)**, 14700 Lake Shore Drive, Zip 49720–1999; tel. 231/547–4024, (Nonreporting) **A**1 10 18 **F**3 11 13 14 15 18 26 28 29 30 31 34 35 38 40 50 55 56 59 64 65 75 76 77 78 79 81 85 87 93 97 100 104 107 108 115 116 117 119 127 129 130 131 132 133 135 144 146 147 149 154 156 **P**5 6 **S** Munson Healthcare, Traverse City, MI
Primary Contact: Joanne Schroeder, President
COO: John Singer IVChief Operating Officer
CFO: Robert Wilcox, Chief Financial Officer
CMO: James Jeakle, Chief Medical Officer
CIO: David Priest, Director Information Systems
CHR: Patty Fitzgerald, Staff Services
CNO: Bernadette Green Cole, R.N., Chief Nursing Officer
Web address: www.cah.org
**Control**: Other not–for–profit (including NFP Corporation) **Service**: General medical and surgical

| | |
|---|---|
| **Staffed Beds:** 25 **Admissions:** 1094 **Census:** 6 **Outpatient Visits:** 94665 **Births:** 170 **Total Expense ($000):** 58788 **Payroll Expense ($000):** 24827 **Personnel:** 363 | |

MI

*Many Facility Codes have changed. Please refer to the AHA Guide Code Chart.* © 2021 AHA Guide

## CHARLOTTE—Eaton County

**HAYES GREEN BEACH MEMORIAL HOSPITAL** See Sparrow Eaton Hospital

☒ **SPARROW EATON HOSPITAL (231327)**, 321 East Harris Street,
Zip 48813–1629; tel. 517/543–1050, (Nonreporting) **A**1 3 10 18 **F**3 7 11 15 18
26 28 29 34 35 36 40 45 46 50 53 59 64 65 69 75 77 79 81 82 85 87 89 92
93 97 107 108 110 111 115 118 119 126 129 130 131 132 143 144 146 147
148 149 154 **P**6 **S** Sparrow Health System, Lansing, MI
Primary Contact: Matthew Rush, FACHE, President and Chief Executive Officer
CFO: Kim Capps, Chief Financial Officer
CMO: Hugh Lindsey, M.D., Chief Medical Officer
CIO: Kevin Neugent, Chief Information Officer
CHR: Mandy Rood, Vice President Human Resources
CNO: Maureen Hillary, Chief Nursing Officer
Web address: www.hgbhealth.com
**Control**: Other not–for–profit (including NFP Corporation) **Service**: General
medical and surgical

**Staffed Beds**: 25 **Admissions**: 645 **Census**: 4 **Outpatient Visits**: 183741
**Births**: 0 **Total Expense ($000)**: 59314 **Payroll Expense ($000)**: 26431
**Personnel**: 371

## CHELSEA—Washtenaw County

**CHELSEA COMMUNITY HOSPITAL** See St. Joseph Mercy Chelsea

☒ **ST. JOSEPH MERCY CHELSEA (230259)**, 775 South Main Street,
Zip 48118–1383; tel. 734/593–6000, (Nonreporting) **A**1 3 5 10 **F**3 5 8 11 15 18
28 29 30 31 34 35 40 45 50 51 56 57 59 64 65 70 74 75 77 78 79 81 82 84
85 86 87 90 91 92 93 97 98 100 101 102 103 104 107 110 111 114 115 119
120 121 129 130 131 132 134 135 146 147 149 154 156 **P**6 **S** Trinity Health,
Livonia, MI
Primary Contact: Nancy Kay. Graebner, President and Chief Executive Officer
CFO: Barb Fielder, Vice President Finance
CMO: Randall T Forsch, M.D., M.P.H., Chief Medical Officer
CHR: Jeremy Stephens, Vice President and Chief Human Resources Officer
CNO: Kathy M. Brubaker, R.N., MSN, Vice President and Chief Nursing Officer
Web address: www.cch.org
**Control**: Church operated, Nongovernment, not–for–profit **Service**: General
medical and surgical

**Staffed Beds**: 96 **Admissions**: 4237 **Census**: 48 **Outpatient Visits**: 309896
**Births**: 0 **Total Expense ($000)**: 172542 **Payroll Expense ($000)**: 69380
**Personnel**: 911

## CLARE—Clare County

☒ **MIDMICHIGAN MEDICAL CENTER-CLARE (230180)**, 703 North McEwan
Street, Zip 48617–1440; tel. 989/802–5000, (Nonreporting) **A**1 10 **F**3 11 15 18
20 28 29 30 34 35 40 43 45 46 50 53 57 58 59 61 64 75 77 79 80 81 85 86 87
93 97 107 108 110 111 115 118 119 127 129 130 135 144 146 148 154 156
157 **S** MidMichigan Health, Midland, MI
Primary Contact: Raymond Stover, President and Chief Executive Officer
CFO: Jeff Provenzano, Vice President and Chief Financial Officer
CMO: David Bremer, D.O., Chief of Staff
CIO: Michael Larson, Vice President Chief Information Officer
CNO: Glenn King, R.N., MSN, Vice President, Chief Nursing Officer
Web address: www.midmichigan.org
**Control**: Other not–for–profit (including NFP Corporation) **Service**: General
medical and surgical

**Staffed Beds**: 49 **Admissions**: 966 **Census**: 7 **Outpatient Visits**: 98519
**Births**: 0 **Total Expense ($000)**: 52361 **Payroll Expense ($000)**: 14527
**Personnel**: 296

**MIDMICHIGAN REG MED CTR-CLARE** See Midmichigan Medical Center-Clare

## CLINTON TOWNSHIP—Macomb County

**HENRY FORD MACOMB HOSPITAL** See Henry Ford Macomb Hospitals

☒ **HENRY FORD MACOMB HOSPITALS (230047)**, 15855 19 Mile Road,
Zip 48038–6324; tel. 586/263–2300, (Includes HENRY FORD MACOMB HOSPITAL
- MOUNT CLEMENS CAMPUS, Mailing address: 215 North Avenue, Mount Clemens,
Michigan, Zip 48043; tel. 586/466–9300; ST. JOSEPH'S MERCY HOSPITAL-WEST,
Mailing address: 15855 19 Mile Road, Clinton Township, Michigan, Zip 48038;
tel. 586/263–2707; ST. JOSEPH'S MERCY-NORTH, Mailing address: 80650 North
Van Dyke, Romeo, Michigan, Zip 48065; tel. 810/798–3551), (Nonreporting) **A**1
2 3 5 10 13 **F**3 4 7 8 11 12 13 15 18 20 22 24 26 28 29 30 31 32 34 35 36
38 40 41 42 43 44 45 46 47 49 50 51 54 56 57 58 59 60 61 62 63 64 65 66
68 69 70 73 74 75 76 77 78 79 81 82 83 84 85 86 87 89 90 92 93 94 95 96
97 98 100 101 102 103 107 108 110 111 112 114 115 116 117 118 119 120
121 123 124 126 129 130 131 132 134 135 144 146 147 148 149 150 154
156 157 **P**6 8 **S** Henry Ford Health System, Detroit, MI
Primary Contact: Barbara W. Rossmann, R.N., President and Chief Executive
Officer
COO: Gary Beaulac, Chief Operating Officer
CFO: Terry Goodbalian, Vice President Finance and Chief Financial Officer
CMO: Charles Kelly, D.O., Vice President Medical Affairs and Chief Medical Officer
CHR: Joel Gibson, Vice President Human Resources
Web address: www.henryfordmacomb.com
**Control**: Other not–for–profit (including NFP Corporation) **Service**: General
medical and surgical

**Staffed Beds**: 415 **Admissions**: 20850 **Census**: 295 **Outpatient
Visits**: 671759 **Births**: 1644 **Total Expense ($000)**: 544247 **Payroll
Expense ($000)**: 195671 **Personnel**: 3034

**ST JOSEPH'S MERCY HOSPITAL** See St. Joseph's Mercy Hospital-West

## COLDWATER—Branch County

**COMMUNITY HEALTH CENTER OF BRANCH COUNTY** See Promedica
Coldwater Regional Hospital

★ **PROMEDICA COLDWATER REGIONAL HOSPITAL (230022)**, 274 East Chicago
Street, Zip 49036–2041; tel. 517/279–5400, (Nonreporting) **A**5 10 13 19 **F**3 8
11 13 15 18 28 29 30 31 32 34 40 45 50 57 59 62 63 64 70 74 75 76 77 78
79 81 85 87 91 92 93 96 97 98 100 101 102 104 106 107 108 110 111 115
119 127 129 130 132 146 154 **P**6 **S** ProMedica Health System, Toledo, OH
Primary Contact: Randy DeGroot, President and Chief Executive Officer
COO: Mary R Rose, R.N., Chief Clinical Officer
CFO: Amy Crouch, Chief Financial Officer
CMO: Joudat Daoud, M.D., Chief of Staff
CIO: Joel Lederman, Director Information Systems
CHR: Amy Jensen, Director Human Resources
CNO: Mary Rose, Chief Nursing Officer
Web address: www.chcbc.com
**Control**: Other not–for–profit (including NFP Corporation) **Service**: General
medical and surgical

**Staffed Beds**: 62 **Admissions**: 2798 **Census**: 30 **Outpatient Visits**: 111647
**Births**: 315 **Total Expense ($000)**: 68252 **Payroll Expense ($000)**: 30528
**Personnel**: 426

## COMMERCE TOWNSHIP—Oakland County

☒ **DMC HURON VALLEY-SINAI HOSPITAL (230277)**, 1 William Carls Drive,
Zip 48382–2201; tel. 248/937–3300, (Nonreporting) **A**1 3 5 10 **F**3 11 12 13 15
18 20 22 26 28 29 30 31 34 35 37 39 40 44 45 46 47 48 49 50 51 53 55 57
58 59 61 64 65 70 73 74 75 76 77 78 79 81 82 85 86 87 89 91 96 107 108
110 111 114 115 116 117 118 119 121 123 124 126 129 130 131 132 141
145 146 147 148 149 150 154 156 **S** TENET Healthcare Corporation, Dallas, TX
Primary Contact: David McEwen, Chief Executive Officer
COO: Samuel Pieh, Chief Operating Officer
CFO: William Lantzy, Chief Financial Officer
CHR: Nicole Williams, Director of Human Resources Operations
CNO: Lori Stallings-Sicard, R.N., Chief Nursing Officer
Web address: www.hvsh.org
**Control**: Corporation, Investor–owned (for-profit) **Service**: General medical and
surgical

**Staffed Beds**: 156 **Admissions**: 7311 **Census**: 70 **Outpatient Visits**: 92212
**Births**: 923 **Total Expense ($000)**: 162500 **Payroll Expense ($000)**: 55556
**Personnel**: 827

**HURON VALLEY-SINAI HOSPITAL** See Dmc Huron Valley-Sinai Hospital

---

**Hospital, Medicare Provider Number, Address, Telephone, Approval, Facility, and Physician Codes, Health Care System**

★ American Hospital Association (AHA) membership    ○ Healthcare Facilities Accreditation Program    ⇑ Center for Improvement in Healthcare Quality Accreditation
□ The Joint Commission accreditation    ◇ DNV Healthcare Inc. accreditation    △ Commission on Accreditation of Rehabilitation Facilities (CARF) accreditation

## DEARBORN—Wayne County

⊞ **BEAUMONT HOSPITAL - DEARBORN (230020)**, 18101 Oakwood Boulevard, Zip 48124–4089, Mailing Address: P.O. Box 2500, Zip 48123–2500; tel. 313/593–7000, (Nonreporting) **A**1 2 3 5 10 19 **F**3 11 12 13 15 18 19 20 22 24 26 28 29 30 31 32 34 35 37 38 39 40 41 43 44 45 46 47 49 50 51 54 55 56 57 58 59 60 61 64 65 68 70 72 74 75 76 77 78 79 81 82 84 85 86 87 89 92 93 96 97 100 102 107 108 110 111 114 115 117 118 119 120 121 123 124 126 129 130 131 132 135 146 147 149 154 **P**6 8 **S** Beaumont Health, Southfield, MI
Primary Contact: David Claeys, FACHE, Chief Executive Officer
COO: Carolyn Wilson, Chief Operating Officer
CFO: Timothy Jodway, Chief Financial Administrator
CMO: Paolo G Marciano, M.D., Chief Medical Officer
CIO: Subra Sripada, Executive Vice President, Chief Transformation Officer and Chief Information Officer
CHR: Sherry Huffman, Administrator Human Resources
CNO: Mary Ellen Kochis, MSN, R.N., Administrator Nursing Operations
Web address: www.beaumont.org
**Control**: Other not–for–profit (including NFP Corporation) **Service**: General medical and surgical

> **Staffed Beds:** 632 **Admissions:** 32930 **Census:** 476 **Outpatient Visits:** 205424 **Births:** 4045 **Total Expense ($000):** 603765 **Payroll Expense ($000):** 226798 **Personnel:** 3624

**BEAUMONT HOSPITAL-DEARBORN** See Beaumont Hospital - Dearborn

## DECKERVILLE—Sanilac County

**DECKERVILLE COMMUNITY HOSPITAL (231311)**, 3559 Pine Street, Zip 48427–7703, Mailing Address: P.O. Box 126, Zip 48427–0126; tel. 810/376–2835, (Nonreporting) **A**10 18
Primary Contact: Angela McConnachie, Chief Executive Officer and Chief Nursing Officer
CFO: Kim Gentner, Chief Financial Officer
CMO: Josh White, Chief Medical Officer
Web address: www.deckervillehosp.org
**Control**: Other not–for–profit (including NFP Corporation) **Service**: General medical and surgical

> **Staffed Beds:** 15

## DETROIT—Wayne County

**ASCENSION ST. JOHN** See Ascension St. John Hospital

⊞ **ASCENSION ST. JOHN HOSPITAL (230165)**, 22101 Moross Road, Zip 48236–2148; tel. 313/343–4000, (Nonreporting) **A**1 2 3 5 8 10 19 **F**3 8 9 11 12 13 15 17 18 20 22 24 26 28 29 30 31 32 34 35 36 37 38 39 40 41 42 43 44 45 46 47 48 49 50 54 55 56 57 58 59 60 61 63 64 65 66 68 70 72 74 75 76 77 78 79 80 81 82 84 85 86 87 88 89 90 91 92 93 95 96 97 98 100 101 102 107 108 110 111 114 115 118 119 120 121 123 124 126 130 131 132 135 138 141 144 146 147 148 149 150 154 156 157 **S** Ascension Healthcare, Saint Louis, MO
Primary Contact: Kevin Grady, M.D., President
COO: Brant Russell, R.N., Chief Operating Officer
CIO: Ralph Tenney, Chief Information Officer
CHR: Joanne E Tuscany, Director Human Resources
Web address: www.stjohnprovidence.org/stjohnhospital/
**Control**: Church operated, Nongovernment, not–for–profit **Service**: General medical and surgical

> **Staffed Beds:** 592 **Admissions:** 27628 **Census:** 382 **Outpatient Visits:** 941610 **Births:** 2936 **Total Expense ($000):** 861184 **Payroll Expense ($000):** 266562 **Personnel:** 2965

**BARBARA KARMANOS CANCER INST** See Karmanos Cancer Center

**BCA STONECREST HOSPITAL** See Stonecrest Center

**CHILDREN'S HOSPITAL OF MICHIGAN** See Dmc - Children's Hospital of Michigan

**DETROIT RECEIVING HOSPITAL/UNIVERSITY HEALTH CENTER** See Dmc - Detroit Receiving Hospital

⊞ △ **DMC - CHILDREN'S HOSPITAL OF MICHIGAN (233300)**, 3901 Beaubien Street, Zip 48201–2119; tel. 313/745–5852, (Nonreporting) **A**1 3 5 7 10 **F**3 7 8 11 16 17 18 19 20 21 22 23 24 25 26 27 29 30 31 32 33 34 40 41 42 43 44 45 46 48 49 50 51 54 55 57 58 60 61 64 65 66 68 72 74 75 77 78 79 80 81 82 84 85 86 87 88 89 90 91 93 96 97 100 107 108 111 114 115 116 117 119 120 121 123 124 126 129 130 131 132 136 137 138 139 141 146 148 149 150 154 156 **S** TENET Healthcare Corporation, Dallas, TX
Primary Contact: Jill Bembas, Executive Assistant
CFO: Lisa Hutchings, Chief Financial Officer
CMO: Rudolph Valentini, M.D., Chief Medical Officer
CHR: Jonita Edwards, Director Human Resources
CNO: Brenda VanWallaghen, Interim Chief Nursing Officer
Web address: www.chmkids.org
**Control**: Corporation, Investor–owned (for–profit) **Service**: Children's general medical and surgical

> **Staffed Beds:** 227 **Admissions:** 11443 **Census:** 155 **Outpatient Visits:** 301789 **Births:** 0 **Total Expense ($000):** 373654 **Payroll Expense ($000):** 137520 **Personnel:** 2173

⊞ **DMC - DETROIT RECEIVING HOSPITAL (230273)**, 4201 Saint Antoine Street, Zip 48201–2153; tel. 313/745–3000, (Nonreporting) **A**1 3 5 10 **F**3 16 17 18 29 30 34 35 38 39 40 41 43 44 49 50 56 57 58 59 60 61 64 65 66 67 70 72 73 74 75 76 77 79 80 81 82 84 85 86 87 88 89 90 93 97 98 99 100 102 103 104 107 114 115 119 129 130 131 132 135 141 144 146 148 149 150 154 **P**6 **S** TENET Healthcare Corporation, Dallas, TX
Primary Contact: Scott Steiner, FACHE, Chief Executive Officer
COO: Tina Wood, Chief Operations Officer
CFO: Bridgett Feagin, Chief Financial Officer
CMO: Patricia Wilkerson-Uddyback, M.D., Chief Medical Officer
CIO: Michael LeRoy, Senior Vice President and Chief Information Officer
Web address: www.dmc.org
**Control**: Corporation, Investor–owned (for–profit) **Service**: General medical and surgical

> **Staffed Beds:** 219 **Admissions:** 11544 **Census:** 201 **Outpatient Visits:** 122507 **Births:** 0 **Total Expense ($000):** 265742 **Payroll Expense ($000):** 89528 **Personnel:** 1199

⊞ △ **DMC - REHABILITATION INSTITUTE OF MICHIGAN (233027)**, 261 Mack Avenue, Zip 48201–2495; tel. 313/745–1203, (Nonreporting) **A**1 3 5 7 10 **F**11 28 29 30 31 34 35 44 50 53 54 58 64 65 75 82 86 87 90 91 92 93 95 96 130 131 132 146 149 154 **S** TENET Healthcare Corporation, Dallas, TX
Primary Contact: Patty Jobbitt, Chief Executive Officer
CFO: Dan Babb, Chief Financial Officer
CMO: Ali Bitar, M.D., Vice President Medical Affairs
CHR: Paul Sturgis, Director Human Resources
CNO: Julia Libcke, R.N., MSN, VP Patient Care Services
Web address: www.rimrehab.org
**Control**: Corporation, Investor–owned (for–profit) **Service**: Rehabilitation

> **Staffed Beds:** 69 **Admissions:** 1310 **Census:** 58 **Outpatient Visits:** 237417 **Births:** 0 **Total Expense ($000):** 70364 **Payroll Expense ($000):** 38351 **Personnel:** 571

⊞ △ **DMC - SINAI-GRACE HOSPITAL (230024)**, 6071 West Outer Drive, Zip 48235–2679; tel. 313/966–3300, (Nonreporting) **A**1 3 5 7 10 12 13 19 **F**3 8 11 13 15 18 20 22 24 26 28 29 30 31 32 34 35 37 38 39 40 43 44 45 49 50 51 53 54 55 57 58 59 60 61 64 65 66 70 72 74 75 76 77 78 79 80 81 82 84 85 86 87 90 93 96 97 98 100 102 104 107 108 110 111 114 115 117 118 119 120 121 123 126 129 130 131 132 134 135 141 146 147 148 149 150 154 **S** TENET Healthcare Corporation, Dallas, TX
Primary Contact: Daniel Jackson, President
COO: Emily Moorhead, Chief Operating Officer
CFO: Jeffery Wright, Chief Financial Officer
CHR: Joi Little, Chief Human Resources Officer
Web address: www.sinaigrace.org
**Control**: Corporation, Investor–owned (for–profit) **Service**: General medical and surgical

> **Staffed Beds:** 267 **Admissions:** 17978 **Census:** 248 **Outpatient Visits:** 197232 **Births:** 1107 **Total Expense ($000):** 339356 **Payroll Expense ($000):** 128163 **Personnel:** 1686

MI

*Many Facility Codes have changed. Please refer to the AHA Guide Code Chart.*
© 2021 AHA Guide

☒ **DMC HARPER UNIVERSITY HOSPITAL (230104)**, 3990 John 'R' Street, Zip 48201–2018; tel. 313/745–8040, (Includes DMC HUTZEL WOMEN'S HOSPITAL, Mailing address: 3980 John R Street, Detroit, Michigan, Zip 48201; tel. 313/745–7555; Scott Steiner, FACHE, Chief Executive Officer), (Nonreporting) **A**1 3 5 10 19 **F**3 8 9 12 13 15 16 17 18 20 22 24 26 28 29 30 31 34 35 37 40 44 45 46 47 50 51 52 55 57 58 59 60 61 64 65 66 70 72 73 74 75 76 77 78 79 80 81 82 84 85 86 87 88 89 90 92 93 97 98 100 107 108 111 115 118 119 126 130 131 132 134 135 138 146 147 148 149 150 154 **P**6 **S** TENET Healthcare Corporation, Dallas, TX
Primary Contact: Scott Steiner, FACHE, Chief Executive Officer
COO: Tina Wood, Chief Operating Officer
CFO: Bridgett Feagin, Chief Financial Officer
CMO: Patricia Wilkerson-Uddyback, M.D., Chief Medical Officer
CIO: Michael LeRoy, Senior Vice President and Chief Information Officer
CNO: Christine Bowen, R.N., Chief Nursing Officer
Web address: www.harperhospital.org
**Control:** Corporation, Investor–owned (for–profit) **Service:** General medical and surgical

**Staffed Beds:** 394 **Admissions:** 18455 **Census:** 259 **Outpatient Visits:** 183179 **Births:** 3618 **Total Expense ($000):** 459576 **Payroll Expense ($000):** 148199 **Personnel:** 1777

**HARPER UNIVERSITY HOSPITAL/HUTZEL WOMEN'S HOSPITAL** See Dmc Harper University Hospital

☒ **HENRY FORD HOSPITAL (230053)**, 2799 West Grand Boulevard, Zip 48202–2608; tel. 313/916–2600, (Nonreporting) **A**1 2 3 5 8 10 19 **F**3 6 8 9 11 12 13 15 17 18 19 20 22 24 26 28 29 30 31 32 33 34 35 36 37 38 39 40 41 42 43 44 45 46 47 48 49 50 51 52 53 54 55 56 57 58 59 60 61 62 63 64 65 66 68 69 70 71 72 73 74 75 76 77 78 79 80 81 82 83 84 85 86 87 91 92 93 96 97 99 100 101 102 103 104 107 108 110 111 112 113 114 115 116 117 118 119 120 121 123 124 126 129 130 131 132 134 135 136 137 138 139 140 141 142 143 144 145 146 147 148 149 150 154 156 **P**6 8 **S** Henry Ford Health System, Detroit, MI
Primary Contact: Veronica Hall, R.N., Interim President and Chief Executive Officer
CFO: Joseph Schmitt IIISenior Vice President Finance and Chief Financial Officer
CIO: Mary Alice Annecharico, System Vice President and Chief Information Officer
CHR: Antonina Ramsey, Senior Vice President and Chief Human Resource Officer
CNO: Gwen Gnam, R.N., MSN, Chief Nursing Officer
Web address: www.henryfordhealth.org
**Control:** Other not–for–profit (including NFP Corporation) **Service:** General medical and surgical

**Staffed Beds:** 747 **Admissions:** 35986 **Census:** 578 **Outpatient Visits:** 3209569 **Births:** 2712 **Total Expense ($000):** 2314289 **Payroll Expense ($000):** 1141104 **Personnel:** 11457

**HUTZEL WOMEN'S HOSPITAL** See Dmc Hutzel Women's Hospital

☒ △ **JOHN D. DINGELL VETERANS AFFAIRS MEDICAL CENTER**, 4646 John 'R' Street, Zip 48201–1932; tel. 313/576–1000, (Total facility includes 40 beds in nursing home–type unit) (Nonreporting) **A**1 2 3 5 7 **F**3 4 5 8 9 11 12 18 20 28 29 30 31 33 34 35 36 37 38 39 40 44 45 46 49 50 53 54 56 57 58 59 60 61 62 63 64 65 66 67 70 74 75 77 78 79 81 82 83 84 85 86 87 90 91 92 93 94 97 98 100 101 102 103 104 105 107 108 111 114 115 118 119 120 121 126 127 128 129 130 132 133 135 143 144 145 146 147 148 149 152 153 154 156 157 158 **S** Department of Veterans Affairs, Washington, DC
Primary Contact: Pamela J. Reeves, M.D., Director
COO: Annette Walker, Associate Director
CFO: Sherry Riedel, Chief Financial Management Service
CMO: Scott Gruber, M.D., Chief of Staff
CIO: Jonathan Small, Chief Operations Information and Technology
CHR: Kathleen Osinski, Chief Human Resources Service
CNO: Belina Brown-Tezera, MSN, Associate Director Patient Care Services
Web address: www.detroit.va.gov/
**Control:** Veterans Affairs, Government, federal **Service:** General medical and surgical

**Staffed Beds:** 209 **Admissions:** 5654 **Census:** 109 **Outpatient Visits:** 502780 **Births:** 0 **Total Expense ($000):** 419988 **Payroll Expense ($000):** 179498 **Personnel:** 2006

☐ **KARMANOS CANCER CENTER (230297)**, 4100 John 'R' Street, Zip 48201–2013; tel. 313/576–8670, (Nonreporting) **A**1 3 5 10 **F**3 8 14 15 29 30 31 34 35 36 39 44 45 46 47 48 49 50 54 55 57 58 59 60 63 64 68 70 74 75 77 78 79 80 81 82 83 84 85 86 87 100 107 109 110 111 114 115 119 120 121 123 124 126 130 132 135 136 146 147 148 149 154 157 **P**4 5
Primary Contact: Gerold Bepler, M.D., Ph.D., President and Chief Executive Officer
CFO: Brian Gamble, Chief Financial Officer
CMO: George Yoo, M.D., Chief Medical Officer
CIO: Scott McCarter, Chief Information Officer
CHR: David Jansen, Vice President Human Resources
Web address: www.karmanos.org
**Control:** Other not–for–profit (including NFP Corporation) **Service:** Cancer

**Staffed Beds:** 83 **Admissions:** 3034 **Census:** 66 **Outpatient Visits:** 125516 **Births:** 0 **Total Expense ($000):** 283341 **Payroll Expense ($000):** 58095 **Personnel:** 1028

**REHABILITATION INSTITUTE OF MICHIGAN** See Dmc - Rehabilitation Institute of Michigan

**SINAI-GRACE HOSPITAL** See Dmc - Sinai-Grace Hospital

☐ **STONECREST CENTER (234038)**, 15000 Gratiot Avenue, Zip 48205–1973; tel. 313/245–0600, (Nonreporting) **A**1 3 10 **F**98 99 100 101 103 130 149 **S** Acadia Healthcare Company, Inc., Franklin, TN
Primary Contact: Steve Savage, Chief Executive Officer
Web address: www.stonecrestcenter.com
**Control:** Corporation, Investor–owned (for–profit) **Service:** Psychiatric

**Staffed Beds:** 162 **Admissions:** 4704 **Census:** 155 **Outpatient Visits:** 0 **Births:** 0 **Total Expense ($000):** 36642 **Payroll Expense ($000):** 15009 **Personnel:** 267

**VETERANS AFFAIRS MED CENTER** See John D. Dingell Veterans Affairs Medical Center

**DOWAGIAC—Cass County**

☒ **ASCENSION BORGESS-LEE HOSPITAL (231315)**, 420 West High Street, Zip 49047–1943; tel. 269/782–8681, (Nonreporting) **A**1 10 18 **F**3 11 15 18 28 29 30 31 34 35 40 41 50 54 59 64 65 68 70 75 77 78 79 81 85 86 87 93 97 100 104 107 108 110 114 119 127 128 130 132 133 135 146 148 149 **P**6 **S** Ascension Healthcare, Saint Louis, MO
Primary Contact: Peter U. Bergmann, President
CIO: James Keller, Chief Information Officer
Web address: www.borgess.com
**Control:** Church operated, Nongovernment, not–for–profit **Service:** General medical and surgical

**Staffed Beds:** 25 **Admissions:** 218 **Census:** 2 **Outpatient Visits:** 60319 **Births:** 0 **Total Expense ($000):** 22041 **Payroll Expense ($000):** 7613 **Personnel:** 126

**BORGESS-LEE MEMORIAL HOSPITAL** See Ascension Borgess-Lee Hospital

**EAST CHINA—St. Clair County**

☒ **ASCENSION RIVER DISTRICT HOSPITAL (230241)**, 4100 River Road, Zip 48054–2909; tel. 810/329–7111, (Nonreporting) **A**1 3 10 **F**3 7 11 13 15 18 29 30 34 35 36 40 43 44 45 49 50 57 59 60 64 65 68 70 75 76 77 79 81 82 85 86 87 92 93 107 108 110 111 115 119 130 141 146 147 149 154 157 **S** Ascension Healthcare, Saint Louis, MO
Primary Contact: Kevin Grady, M.D., President
CMO: H Lee Bacheldor, D.O., Chief Medical Officer
CHR: Dawn Beindit, Labor Relations Partner
Web address: www.stjohnprovidence.org/RiverDistrict/
**Control:** Church operated, Nongovernment, not–for–profit **Service:** General medical and surgical

**Staffed Beds:** 24 **Admissions:** 1151 **Census:** 8 **Outpatient Visits:** 91691 **Births:** 296 **Total Expense ($000):** 38926 **Payroll Expense ($000):** 15042 **Personnel:** 138

**ST. JOHN RIVER DISTRICT HOSPITAL** See Ascension River District Hospital

**MI**

**Hospital, Medicare Provider Number, Address, Telephone, Approval, Facility, and Physician Codes, Health Care System**

★ American Hospital Association (AHA) membership ◯ Healthcare Facilities Accreditation Program ⇑ Center for Improvement in Healthcare Quality Accreditation
☐ The Joint Commission accreditation ◇ DNV Healthcare Inc. accreditation △ Commission on Accreditation of Rehabilitation Facilities (CARF) accreditation

© 2021 AHA Guide     *Many Facility Codes have changed. Please refer to the AHA Guide Code Chart.*     Hospitals **A353**

## EATON RAPIDS—Eaton County

⇑ **EATON RAPIDS COMM HOSPITAL** See Eaton Rapids Medical Center

★ ⇑ **EATON RAPIDS MEDICAL CENTER (231324)**, 1500 South Main Street, Zip 48827–1952, Mailing Address: P.O. Box 130, Zip 48827–0130; tel. 517/663–2671, (Nonreporting) **A**10 18 21 **F**3 11 14 15 18 28 29 34 35 36 40 41 45 50 53 57 59 64 65 66 68 75 77 81 86 87 91 93 94 96 97 107 110 115 119 127 129 130 131 132 133 144 146 148 149
Primary Contact: Timothy Johnson, President and Chief Executive Officer
CFO: Shari Glynn, Vice President Finance and Chief Financial Officer
CMO: Ashok K Gupta, M.D., Chief of Staff
CIO: Mark Rodge, Director Information Systems
CHR: Laurie Field, Director Human Resources
Web address: www.eatonrapidsmedicalcenter.org
**Control**: Other not–for–profit (including NFP Corporation) **Service**: General medical and surgical

**Staffed Beds**: 20 **Admissions**: 430 **Census**: 4 **Outpatient Visits**: 65596 **Births**: 0 **Total Expense ($000)**: 33688 **Payroll Expense ($000)**: 13367 **Personnel**: 234

## ESCANABA—Delta County

**OSF ST. FRANCIS HOSPITAL AND MEDICAL** See OSF St. Francis Hospital and Medical Group

⊞ **OSF ST. FRANCIS HOSPITAL AND MEDICAL GROUP (231337)**, 3401 Ludington Street, Zip 49829–1377; tel. 906/786–3311, (Nonreporting) **A**1 3 10 18 **F**3 11 13 15 18 28 29 30 31 34 35 40 43 44 45 53 57 59 62 63 64 65 66 68 70 75 76 77 78 79 81 82 83 84 85 86 92 93 96 97 107 108 110 111 115 119 127 129 130 131 132 133 144 146 147 148 149 154 **S** OSF Healthcare, Peoria, IL
Primary Contact: David Lord, President
COO: Kelly Jefferson, Vice President, Operations
CFO: Fred Wagner, Chief Financial Officer
CMO: Mark Povich, D.O., Medical Director
CIO: Mark Irving, Manager Management Information Systems
CHR: Elizabeth Zorza, Assistant Administrator
CNO: Joy Hopkins, Vice President Patient Care Services
Web address: www.osfstfrancis.org
**Control**: Church operated, Nongovernment, not–for–profit **Service**: General medical and surgical

**Staffed Beds**: 25 **Admissions**: 1494 **Census**: 10 **Outpatient Visits**: 113593 **Births**: 308 **Total Expense ($000)**: 91800 **Payroll Expense ($000)**: 34913 **Personnel**: 403

## FARMINGTON HILLS—Oakland County

⊞ **BEAUMONT HOSPITAL - FARMINGTON HILLS (230151)**, 28050 Grand River Avenue, Zip 48336–5933; tel. 248/471–8000, (Nonreporting) **A**1 2 3 5 10 12 13 19 **F**3 9 11 13 15 18 20 22 28 29 30 31 32 34 35 36 38 39 40 41 43 44 45 46 47 48 49 50 51 54 56 57 58 59 60 61 64 65 68 70 74 75 76 77 78 79 81 82 84 85 87 89 90 92 93 96 97 98 100 101 102 103 107 110 111 114 115 118 119 120 121 123 124 126 130 131 132 145 146 147 148 149 154 156 **P**1 6 **S** Beaumont Health, Southfield, MI
Primary Contact: Constance O'Malley, President
COO: Carolyn Wilson, R.N., Chief Operating Officer
CFO: Barbara Hrit, Controller
CMO: Michael Rebock, Chief Medical Officer
CIO: Subra Sripada, Executive Vice President, Chief Transportation Officer and Chief Information Officer
CHR: Dalph Watson, Director of Human Resources
CNO: Kim Guesman, R.N., Chief Nursing Officer
Web address: www.beaumont.org
**Control**: Other not–for–profit (including NFP Corporation) **Service**: General medical and surgical

**Staffed Beds**: 307 **Admissions**: 13608 **Census**: 193 **Outpatient Visits**: 205597 **Births**: 760 **Total Expense ($000)**: 353610 **Payroll Expense ($000)**: 105581 **Personnel**: 1820

**BOTSFORD HOSPITAL** See Beaumont Hospital - Farmington Hills

## FERNDALE—Oakland County

⊞ **HENRY FORD KINGSWOOD HOSPITAL (234011)**, 10300 West Eight Mile Road, Zip 48220–2100; tel. 248/398–3200, (Nonreporting) **A**1 10 **F**29 34 35 44 50 57 58 59 68 75 86 87 98 99 101 103 130 134 135 149 154 **P**6 8 **S** Henry Ford Health System, Detroit, MI
Primary Contact: Cathrine Frank, M.D., Chairperson
CMO: Robert Lagrou, D.O., Medical Director
CNO: Cheryl Taylor, R.N., Director of Nursing
Web address: www.henryford.com
**Control**: Other not–for–profit (including NFP Corporation) **Service**: Psychiatric

**Staffed Beds**: 101 **Admissions**: 3426 **Census**: 68 **Outpatient Visits**: 0 **Births**: 0 **Total Expense ($000)**: 26663 **Payroll Expense ($000)**: 15739 **Personnel**: 238

**KINGSWOOD HOSPITAL** See Henry Ford Kingswood Hospital

## FLINT—Genesee County

⊞ **HURLEY MEDICAL CENTER (230132)**, One Hurley Plaza, Zip 48503–5993; tel. 810/262–9000, (Includes HURLEY CHILDREN'S HOSPITAL, Mailing address: 1 Hurley Plaza, Flint, Michigan, Zip 48503–5902; tel. 313/745–7555), (Nonreporting) **A**1 2 3 5 8 10 **F**3 5 11 12 13 15 16 17 18 19 20 22 26 28 29 30 31 32 35 39 40 41 43 45 46 49 50 52 54 55 56 57 58 59 61 64 66 70 72 74 75 76 77 78 79 80 81 82 84 86 87 88 89 90 93 96 97 98 100 101 102 103 104 107 108 110 111 114 115 118 119 120 121 123 124 126 129 130 131 132 135 141 143 144 146 147 148 154 156 **P**6
Primary Contact: Melany Gavulic, President & Chief Executive Officer
COO: Melany Gavulic, Senior Vice President Operations & COO
CFO: Cass Wisniewski, Interim Chief Financial Officer
CMO: Michael Jaggi, D.O., Vice President and Chief Medical Officer
CIO: Gary Townsend, Chief Information Officer
CHR: Beth Brophy, Interim VP for Human Resources
CNO: Teresa Bourque, Sr. Administrator for Nursing/Chief Nurse
Web address: www.hurleymc.com
**Control**: City, Government, Nonfederal **Service**: General medical and surgical

**Staffed Beds**: 418 **Admissions**: 19106 **Census**: 306 **Outpatient Visits**: 494254 **Births**: 2692 **Total Expense ($000)**: 446452 **Payroll Expense ($000)**: 175900 **Personnel**: 2307

☐ **MCLAREN FLINT (230141)**, 401 South Ballenger Highway, Zip 48532–3685; tel. 810/342–2000, (Nonreporting) **A**1 3 5 8 10 **F**3 8 11 12 13 15 17 18 20 22 24 26 28 29 30 31 34 35 36 37 38 39 40 43 44 45 46 47 48 49 50 53 54 55 56 57 58 59 60 61 64 66 68 70 74 75 76 77 78 79 81 82 85 86 87 90 91 93 95 96 97 98 100 101 102 104 105 107 108 110 111 114 115 118 119 120 121 122 123 124 126 130 131 132 135 141 144 145 146 147 148 149 154 **P**8 **S** McLaren Health Care Corporation, Grand Blanc, MI
Primary Contact: Chad M. Grant, President and Chief Executive Officer
COO: Brent Wheeler, Vice President of Operations
CFO: Fred Korte, Chief Financial Officer
CMO: Binesh Patel, M.D., Chief Medical Officer
CIO: Ronald Strachan, Chief Information Officer
CHR: Rachelle Hulett, Vice President Human Resources
CNO: James Williams, Vice President and Chief Nursing Officer
Web address: www.mclaren.org/flint
**Control**: Other not–for–profit (including NFP Corporation) **Service**: General medical and surgical

**Staffed Beds**: 378 **Admissions**: 19272 **Census**: 278 **Outpatient Visits**: 323764 **Births**: 510 **Total Expense ($000)**: 427309 **Payroll Expense ($000)**: 183128 **Personnel**: 2112

**MCLAREN REGIONAL MEDICAL CENTER** See Mclaren Flint

**SELECT SPECIALTY HOSP-FLINT** See Select Specialty Hospital-Flint

⊞ **SELECT SPECIALTY HOSPITAL-FLINT (232012)**, 401 South Ballenger Highway, 5th Floor Central, Zip 48532–3638; tel. 810/342–4545, (Nonreporting) **A**1 10 **S** Select Medical Corporation, Mechanicsburg, PA
Primary Contact: Christina DeBlouw, Chief Executive Officer
CMO: Jitendra P. Katneni, M.D., Medical Director
CHR: Gayle Barthel, Coordinator Human Resources
CNO: Kathleen Gallardo, Chief Nursing Officer
Web address: www.selectspecialtyhospitals.com/company/locations/flint.aspx
**Control**: Corporation, Investor–owned (for–profit) **Service**: Acute long–term care hospital

**Staffed Beds**: 26

*Many Facility Codes have changed. Please refer to the AHA Guide Code Chart.*

© 2021 AHA Guide

## FRANKFORT—Benzie County

★ **PAUL OLIVER MEMORIAL HOSPITAL (231300)**, 224 Park Avenue, Zip 49635–9658; tel. 231/352–2200, (Total facility includes 35 beds in nursing home–type unit) (Nonreporting) **A**10 18 **F**11 15 28 30 34 35 40 45 50 53 57 59 60 64 75 77 81 86 87 93 107 110 111 115 119 129 130 132 133 143 146 148 154 156 157 **P**6 **S** Munson Healthcare, Traverse City, MI
Primary Contact: James Barker, President and Chief Executive Officer
CMO: George Ryckman, D.O., Chief of Staff
CHR: Julie Banktson, Manager Human Resources
Web address: www.munsonhealthcare.org
**Control**: Other not–for–profit (including NFP Corporation) **Service**: General medical and surgical

| | |
|---|---|
| **Staffed Beds:** 43 **Admissions:** 79 **Census:** 32 **Outpatient Visits:** 57039 **Births:** 0 **Total Expense ($000):** 19038 **Payroll Expense ($000):** 7725 **Personnel:** 165 | |

## FREMONT—Newaygo County

**GERBER MEMORIAL HEALTH SERVICES** See Spectrum Health Gerber Memorial

⊞ **SPECTRUM HEALTH GERBER MEMORIAL (231338)**, 212 South Sullivan Avenue, Zip 49412–1548; tel. 231/924–3300, (Nonreporting) **A**1 2 5 10 18 **F**3 11 13 15 28 29 30 31 32 34 35 36 40 43 45 50 53 59 64 70 75 76 77 78 79 81 86 87 93 96 107 108 110 111 115 118 119 126 127 129 130 131 132 135 146 147 156 **S** Spectrum Health, Grand Rapids, MI
Primary Contact: Randall Kelley, FACHE, President
COO: Shelly Johnson, Chief Operating Officer
CFO: John Sella, Controller
CMO: Jordan Sall, Chief of Staff
CIO: Jeremy Vronko, Manager Information Services
CHR: Jill Vasquez, Senior Business Partner
CNO: Meleah Mariani, Chief Nursing Officer
Web address: www.spectrumhealth.org
**Control**: Other not–for–profit (including NFP Corporation) **Service**: General medical and surgical

| | |
|---|---|
| **Staffed Beds:** 25 **Admissions:** 1697 **Census:** 12 **Outpatient Visits:** 120067 **Births:** 390 **Total Expense ($000):** 99505 **Payroll Expense ($000):** 28006 **Personnel:** 548 | |

## GARDEN CITY—Wayne County

★ ○ **GARDEN CITY HOSPITAL (230244)**, 6245 Inkster Road, Zip 48135–4001; tel. 734/421–3300, (Nonreporting) **A**3 5 10 11 12 13 **F**3 11 13 15 17 18 20 22 26 28 29 31 34 35 36 40 43 44 45 46 47 49 50 59 62 64 65 68 70 74 75 76 77 78 79 80 81 85 87 89 90 91 92 93 96 107 109 110 111 112 114 115 119 129 130 132 135 143 146 147 148 149 154 156 157 **P**5 6 **S** Prime Healthcare, Ontario, CA
Primary Contact: Saju George, Chief Executive Officer
CFO: Gina Butcher, Chief Financial Officer
CMO: H. Rex Reuttinger, D.O., Chief Medical Officer, Administration
CIO: Randall Sanborn, Director Information Systems
CHR: Josie Ciccone, Director, Human Resources
Web address: www.gch.org
**Control**: Corporation, Investor–owned (for–profit) **Service**: General medical and surgical

| | |
|---|---|
| **Staffed Beds:** 162 **Admissions:** 8646 **Census:** 93 **Outpatient Visits:** 96569 **Births:** 468 **Total Expense ($000):** 127220 **Payroll Expense ($000):** 51352 **Personnel:** 877 | |

**GARDEN CITY OSTEO HOSPITAL** See Garden City Hospital

## GAYLORD—Otsego County

⊞ **MUNSON HEALTHCARE OTSEGO MEMORIAL HOSPITAL (230133)**, 825 North Center Avenue, Zip 49735–1592; tel. 989/731–2100, (Total facility includes 34 beds in nursing home–type unit) (Nonreporting) **A**1 10 20 **F**3 13 15 28 29 31 32 34 35 36 40 43 44 45 46 49 50 51 54 56 57 59 64 65 70 75 76 77 78 79 81 82 85 86 87 93 96 97 107 108 110 111 115 118 119 124 126 127 128 130 131 132 134 135 144 146 147 148 149 156 **S** Munson Healthcare, Traverse City, MI
Primary Contact: Thomas R. Lemon, Chief Executive Officer
COO: James Flickema, Vice President Market Development
CFO: Robert Courtois, Vice President Finance
CMO: Kevin Smith, D.O., Chief of Staff
CIO: Timothy Hella, Chief Information Officer
CHR: Terra Deming, Director Human Resources
CNO: Diane Fisher, R.N., VP, Patient Care Services
Web address: www.myomh.org
**Control**: Other not–for–profit (including NFP Corporation) **Service**: General medical and surgical

| | |
|---|---|
| **Staffed Beds:** 80 **Admissions:** 2209 **Census:** 46 **Outpatient Visits:** 338691 **Births:** 385 **Total Expense ($000):** 104247 **Payroll Expense ($000):** 52638 **Personnel:** 679 | |

**OTSEGO MEMORIAL HOSPITAL** See Munson Healthcare Otsego Memorial Hospital

## GLADWIN—Gladwin County

⊞ **MIDMICHIGAN MEDICAL CENTER-GLADWIN (231325)**, 515 Quarter Street, Zip 48624–1959; tel. 989/426–9286, (Nonreporting) **A**1 10 18 **S** MidMichigan Health, Midland, MI
Primary Contact: Raymond Stover, President and Chief Executive Officer
CFO: Jeff Provenzano, Vice President and Chief Financial Officer
CMO: Cheryl Loubert, M.D., Chief Medical Staff
CIO: Dan Waltz, Vice President and Chief Information Officer
CNO: Glenn King, R.N., MSN, Vice President and Chief Nursing Officer
Web address: www.midmichigan.org
**Control**: Other not–for–profit (including NFP Corporation) **Service**: General medical and surgical

| | |
|---|---|
| **Staffed Beds:** 25 | |

**MIDMICHIGAN REG CTR-GLADWIN** See Midmichigan Medical Center-Gladwin

## GRAND BLANC—Genesee County

⊞ **ASCENSION GENESYS HOSPITAL (230197)**, One Genesys Parkway, Zip 48439–8066; tel. 810/606–5000, (Total facility includes 12 beds in nursing home–type unit) (Nonreporting) **A**1 3 5 10 12 13 **F**3 11 12 13 18 20 22 24 26 28 29 30 31 34 35 40 43 44 45 46 47 48 49 50 51 58 59 60 61 63 64 68 70 73 74 75 76 77 78 79 81 82 84 85 86 87 89 90 91 92 96 97 102 107 108 111 115 117 118 119 126 128 129 130 132 135 145 146 147 148 149 154 **P**6 8 **S** Ascension Healthcare, Saint Louis, MO
Primary Contact: Chris Palazzolo, President and Chief Executive Officer
COO: Joy Finkenbiner, Vice President, Operations
CFO: Nancy Haywood, Chief Financial Officer
CMO: Charles Husson, Regional Chief Medical Officer
CIO: Daniel Stross, Chief Information Officer
CNO: Julie A Gorczyca, R.N., Chief Nursing Officer
Web address: www.genesys.org
**Control**: Church operated, Nongovernment, not–for–profit **Service**: General medical and surgical

| | |
|---|---|
| **Staffed Beds:** 428 **Admissions:** 20243 **Census:** 257 **Outpatient Visits:** 202014 **Births:** 1439 **Total Expense ($000):** 407260 **Payroll Expense ($000):** 153556 **Personnel:** 2105 | |

**GENESYS REGIONAL MEDICAL CENTER** See Ascension Genesys Hospital

## GRAND HAVEN—Ottawa County

★ ⇑ **NORTH OTTAWA COMMUNITY HOSPITAL (230174)**, 1309 Sheldon Road, Zip 49417–2488; tel. 616/842–3600, (Nonreporting) **A**10 21 **F**3 7 11 12 13 15 29 30 34 35 37 40 45 46 47 50 51 57 59 63 64 65 68 70 74 75 76 77 79 81 83 84 85 86 87 92 107 108 110 115 119 124 126 129 130 132 135 143 144 145 146 147 148 149 154 157 **P**6
Primary Contact: Shelleye Yaklin, President and Chief Executive Officer
CFO: Mark Gross, Vice President Finance and Chief Financial Officer
CMO: Haney Assaad, Vice President Medical Affairs
CHR: Tim F Gengle, Director Human Resources
CNO: Cindy Van Kampen, Chief Nursing Officer
Web address: www.noch.org
**Control**: Other not–for–profit (including NFP Corporation) **Service**: General medical and surgical

| | |
|---|---|
| **Staffed Beds:** 47 **Admissions:** 1383 **Census:** 9 **Outpatient Visits:** 109199 **Births:** 268 **Total Expense ($000):** 56568 **Payroll Expense ($000):** 19363 **Personnel:** 468 | |

## GRAND RAPIDS—Kent County

**BLODGETT MEMORIAL MEDICAL CTR** See Spectrum Health - Blodgett Campus

**FOREST VIEW HOSPITAL** See Forest View Psychiatric Hospital

☐ **FOREST VIEW PSYCHIATRIC HOSPITAL (234030)**, 1055 Medical Park Drive SE, Zip 49546–3607; tel. 616/942–9610, (Nonreporting) **A**1 3 10 **F**87 98 99 100 101 102 103 104 105 130 132 154 **S** Universal Health Services, Inc., King of Prussia, PA
Primary Contact: Jill A. Krause, Chief Executive Officer
COO: Scott Miles, Chief Operating Officer
CFO: Carl Caley, Chief Financial Officer
CMO: James VanHaren, M.D., Medical Director
CHR: Mike Henderson, Human Resources Director
CNO: Jo ell Harris, R.N., Chief Nursing Officer
Web address: www.forestviewhospital.com
**Control**: Corporation, Investor–owned (for–profit) **Service**: Psychiatric

| | |
|---|---|
| **Staffed Beds:** 108 **Admissions:** 3397 **Census:** 93 **Births:** 0 **Total Expense ($000):** 24227 **Payroll Expense ($000):** 11686 **Personnel:** 169 | |

**MI**

---

**Hospital, Medicare Provider Number, Address, Telephone, Approval, Facility, and Physician Codes, Health Care System**

★ American Hospital Association (AHA) membership
☐ The Joint Commission accreditation
○ Healthcare Facilities Accreditation Program
◇ DNV Healthcare Inc. accreditation
⇑ Center for Improvement in Healthcare Quality Accreditation
△ Commission on Accreditation of Rehabilitation Facilities (CARF) accreditation

**GRAND VALLEY NURSING CENTRE** See Grand Valley Health Center

**MARY FREE BED HOSP & REHAB CTR** See Mary Free Bed Rehabilitation Hospital

☒ △ **MARY FREE BED REHABILITATION HOSPITAL (233026)**, 235 Wealthy Street SE, Zip 49503–5247; tel. 616/840–8000, (Nonreporting) **A**1 3 5 7 10 **F**12 28 29 30 34 35 36 44 50 53 54 57 58 59 60 62 63 64 65 66 68 71 74 75 77 78 79 82 84 85 86 87 90 91 92 93 94 95 96 100 119 130 131 132 143 146 147 149 154 157 **P**6
Primary Contact: Kent Riddle, Chief Executive Officer
CFO: Randall DeNeff, Vice President Finance
CMO: Michael Jakubowski, M.D., Chief Medical Officer
CIO: Jeff Burns, Manager of Information Technology
CHR: Karen S. Powell, Vice President, Human Resources
CNO: Ingrid Cheslek, R.N., Chief Nursing Officer
Web address: www.maryfreebed.com
**Control:** Other not–for–profit (including NFP Corporation) **Service:** Rehabilitation

**Staffed Beds:** 119 **Admissions:** 2194 **Census:** 103 **Outpatient Visits:** 155699 **Births:** 0 **Total Expense ($000):** 135830 **Payroll Expense ($000):** 79790 **Personnel:** 1333

☒ **MERCY HEALTH SAINT MARY'S (230059)**, 200 Jefferson Avenue Southeast, Zip 49503–4598, Mailing Address: 200 Jefferson Avenue SE, Zip 49503–4598; tel. 616/685–5000, (Includes MERCY HEALTH ROCKFORD, Mailing address: 6050 Northland Drive NE, Rockford, Michigan, Zip 49341–9244; tel. 616/685–7950), (Nonreporting) **A**1 2 3 10 **F**3 6 12 13 15 18 20 22 26 28 29 30 34 35 36 37 38 39 40 42 43 44 45 46 47 48 49 50 54 55 56 57 58 59 61 64 66 70 72 74 75 76 77 78 79 80 81 84 85 86 87 97 98 100 101 107 108 110 111 114 115 116 117 118 119 120 121 123 124 126 129 130 132 135 138 144 146 147 148 149 154 156 **P**1 **S** Trinity Health, Livonia, MI
Primary Contact: David Baumgartner, M.D., Interim President
COO: Randall J Wagner, Chief Operating Officer
CFO: Steve Eavenson, Vice President Finance
CMO: Matt Biersack, Chief Medical Officer
CIO: Jim Keller, Site Director Information Services
CHR: Thomas L Karel, Vice President Organization and Talent Effectiveness
CNO: Elizabeth A Murphy, R.N., FACHE, Chief Nursing Officer
Web address: www.mercyhealthsaintmarys.org
**Control:** Other not–for–profit (including NFP Corporation) **Service:** General medical and surgical

**Staffed Beds:** 283 **Admissions:** 16492 **Census:** 197 **Outpatient Visits:** 1204046 **Births:** 2029 **Total Expense ($000):** 587400 **Payroll Expense ($000):** 200099 **Personnel:** 3345

**PINE REST CHRISTIAN HLTH** See Pine Rest Christian Mental Health Services

☐ **PINE REST CHRISTIAN MENTAL HEALTH SERVICES (234006)**, 300 68th Street SE, Zip 49548–6927, Mailing Address: P.O. Box 165, Zip 49501–0165; tel. 616/455–5000, (Nonreporting) **A**1 3 10 **F**4 5 6 29 30 32 34 35 38 56 58 59 66 68 75 77 82 86 87 98 99 100 101 102 103 104 105 106 130 132 134 135 146 147 149 150 153 154 158 **P**6
Primary Contact: Mark C. Eastburg, Ph.D., President and Chief Executive Officer
COO: Robert Nykamp, Vice President and Chief Operating Officer
CFO: Paul H Karsten, Vice President Finance and Chief Financial Officer
CMO: Alan Armstrong, M.D., Chief Medical Officer
Web address: www.pinerest.org
**Control:** Other not–for–profit (including NFP Corporation) **Service:** Psychiatric

**Staffed Beds:** 431 **Admissions:** 9409 **Census:** 182 **Outpatient Visits:** 285689 **Births:** 0 **Total Expense ($000):** 153360 **Payroll Expense ($000):** 93000 **Personnel:** 1611

**SAINT MARY'S HEALTH CARE** See Mercy Health Saint Mary's

☒ △ **SELECT SPECIALTY HOSPITAL - SPECTRUM HEALTH (232029)**, 1840 Wealthy Street, Southeast, Zip 49506–2921; tel. 616/774–3800, (Nonreporting) **A**1 3 7 10 **S** Select Medical Corporation, Mechanicsburg, PA
Primary Contact: Jim Aldrich, Chief Executive Officer
Web address: www.https://grandrapids.selectspecialtyhospitals.com
**Control:** Corporation, Investor–owned (for–profit) **Service:** Acute long–term care hospital

**Staffed Beds:** 36

**SPECTRUM HEALTH - BUTTERWORTH** See Spectrum Health

☒ **SPECTRUM HEALTH - BUTTERWORTH HOSPITAL (230038)**, 100 Michigan Street NE, Zip 49503–2560; tel. 616/391–1774, (Includes HELEN DEVOS CHILDREN'S HOSPITAL, Mailing address: 100 Michigan Street NE, Grand Rapids, Michigan, Zip 49503–2560; tel. 616/391–9000; Robert Connors, M.D., President, Helen DeVos Children's Hospital; SPECTRUM HEALTH - BLODGETT CAMPUS, Mailing address: 1840 Wealthy Street SE, Grand Rapids, Michigan, Zip 49506–2921; tel. 616/774–7444; Julie Wolowitz, Vice President, Imaging, Lab & Blodgett Hospital; SPECTRUM HEALTH, Mailing address: 100 Michigan Street NE, Grand Rapids, Michigan, Zip 49503–2551; tel. 616/391–1774; Christina Freese Decker, FACHE, President and Chief Executive Officer), (Nonreporting) **A**1 2 3 5 8 10 19 **F**3 8 9 11 12 13 15 16 17 18 19 20 21 22 23 24 25 26 27 28 29 30 31 32 34 35 36 37 38 40 41 43 44 45 46 47 48 49 50 51 55 56 58 59 60 61 63 64 65 66 68 70 71 72 73 74 75 76 77 78 79 80 81 82 83 84 85 86 87 88 89 90 93 96 97 100 101 102 104 107 108 110 111 112 114 115 117 118 119 120 121 124 126 128 129 130 131 132 134 135 136 137 138 140 145 146 147 148 149 154 156 157 **P**6 **S** Spectrum Health, Grand Rapids, MI
Primary Contact: Daryl Elmouchi, M.D., President, Spectrum Health West Michigan
COO: Brian Brasser, Chief Operating Officer
CFO: Leslie Flake, Senior Vice President, Finance
CMO: Josh Kooistra, M.D., Senior Vice President, Chief Medical Officer
CIO: Jason Joseph, Vice President, Information Services
CHR: Nicole McConnell, Senior Vice President, Human Resources, SHDS
CNO: Shawn Ulreich, MSN, R.N., Vice President Clinical Operations and Chief Nursing Executive
Web address: www.spectrumhealth.org
**Control:** Other not–for–profit (including NFP Corporation) **Service:** General medical and surgical

**Staffed Beds:** 1381 **Admissions:** 62497 **Census:** 894 **Outpatient Visits:** 1458872 **Births:** 7463 **Total Expense ($000):** 2186788 **Payroll Expense ($000):** 579817 **Personnel:** 9130

**SPECTRUM HEALTH - GRAND RAPIDS** See Spectrum Health - Butterworth Hospital

### GRAYLING—Crawford County

**MERCY HOSPITAL GRAYLING** See Munson Healthcare Grayling Hospital

☒ **MUNSON HEALTHCARE GRAYLING HOSPITAL (230058)**, 1100 East Michigan Avenue, Zip 49738–1312; tel. 989/348–5461, (Total facility includes 39 beds in nursing home–type unit) (Nonreporting) **A**1 10 20 **F**3 11 15 28 29 30 32 34 35 36 38 40 44 45 50 51 53 54 56 57 58 59 60 64 65 66 70 75 76 77 78 79 81 85 86 87 93 97 107 108 111 115 119 127 129 130 131 135 146 147 148 154 156 157 **P**8 **S** Munson Healthcare, Traverse City, MI
Primary Contact: Kirsten Korth-White, President
CFO: Lori Shively, Vice President of Finance
CMO: Vince Schultz, M.D., Chief Medical Officer
CNO: Carla Gardner, Director of Nursing
Web address: www.https://www.munsonhealthcare.org
**Control:** Other not–for–profit (including NFP Corporation) **Service:** General medical and surgical

**Staffed Beds:** 110 **Admissions:** 2664 **Census:** 53 **Outpatient Visits:** 139368 **Births:** 305 **Total Expense ($000):** 89703 **Payroll Expense ($000):** 37139 **Personnel:** 568

### GREENVILLE—Montcalm County

☒ **SPECTRUM HEALTH UNITED HOSPITAL (230035)**, 615 South Bower Street, Zip 48838–2614; tel. 616/754–4691, (Includes SPECTRUM HEALTH KELSEY HOSPITAL, Mailing address: 418 Washington Avenue, Lakeview, Michigan, Zip 48850; tel. 989/352–7211; Andrea M. Leslie, MSN, R.N., President) (Total facility includes 70 beds in nursing home–type unit) **A**1 2 3 10 **F**3 8 13 15 18 28 29 30 31 34 35 40 41 43 45 46 47 50 54 57 59 64 65 66 68 70 71 75 76 77 78 79 81 85 87 93 96 97 107 108 110 111 115 119 124 126 127 128 129 130 131 132 133 134 135 146 147 148 149 154 156 157 **P**6 **S** Spectrum Health, Grand Rapids, MI
Primary Contact: Andrea M. Leslie, MSN, R.N., President
COO: Priscilla Mahar, Chief Operating Officer
CFO: Ryan K Johnson, Controller
CMO: Kevin O'Connor, D.O., President, Medical Staff
CIO: David Dutmers, Manager, Information Services
CHR: Jennifer Nelson, Senior Human Resource Business Partner
CNO: Linda Schaltz, MSN, R.N., Chief Nursing Officer
Web address: www.spectrumhealth.org
**Control:** Other not–for–profit (including NFP Corporation) **Service:** General medical and surgical

**Staffed Beds:** 131 **Admissions:** 3322 **Census:** 87 **Outpatient Visits:** 280699 **Births:** 568 **Total Expense ($000):** 116182 **Payroll Expense ($000):** 38099 **Personnel:** 751

**UNITED MEMORIAL HEALTH CENTER** See Spectrum Health United Hospital

**MI**

**MI**

## GROSSE POINTE—Wayne County

☒ **BEAUMONT HOSPITAL - GROSSE POINTE (230089)**, 468 Cadieux Road, Zip 48230–1507; tel. 313/473–1000, (Nonreporting) **A**1 2 3 5 10 **F**3 11 12 13 15 18 20 22 26 28 29 30 31 32 34 35 36 39 40 43 45 46 47 48 49 50 51 53 54 55 57 58 59 60 61 64 65 68 69 70 71 74 75 76 77 78 79 80 81 82 84 85 86 87 91 92 93 96 100 107 108 110 111 114 115 117 118 119 126 129 130 131 132 134 135 145 146 147 148 149 150 154 156 **P**1 6 **S** Beaumont Health, Southfield, MI
Primary Contact: James Lynch, M.D., Interim Chief Executive Officer
COO: Carolyn Wilson, R.N., Chief Operating Officer
CFO: Maria Miller, Controller
CMO: Donna Hoban, M.D., Senior Vice President and Chief Medical Officer
CIO: Subra Sripada, Executive Vice President, Chief Transportation Officer and Chief Information Officer
CHR: Pandora Walker, Director, Human Resources
Web address: www.beaumont.org
**Control**: Other not–for–profit (including NFP Corporation) **Service**: General medical and surgical

**Staffed Beds: 280 Admissions: 12077 Census: 123 Outpatient Visits: 138346 Births: 667 Total Expense ($000): 220314 Payroll Expense ($000): 81557 Personnel: 1450**

**BEAUMONT HOSPITAL GROSSE POINTE** See Beaumont Hospital - Grosse Pointe

☒ **SELECT SPECIALTY HOSPITAL-GROSSE POINTE (232038)**, 468 Cadieux Road, 3 North East, Zip 48230–1507, Mailing Address: 22101 Moross Road, 6th Floor, Detroit, Zip 48236; tel. 313/473–6131, (Nonreporting) **A**1 10 **S** Select Medical Corporation, Mechanicsburg, PA
Primary Contact: Zaahra Butt, Chief Executive Officer
Web address: www.grossepointe.selectspecialtyhospitals.com/
**Control**: Corporation, Investor–owned (for–profit) **Service**: Acute long–term care hospital

**Staffed Beds: 30**

## HANCOCK—Houghton County

**PORTAGE HEALTH** See Up Health System-Portage

☒ **UP HEALTH SYSTEM-PORTAGE (230108)**, 500 Campus Drive, Zip 49930–1569; tel. 906/483–1000, (Total facility includes 60 beds in nursing home–type unit) (Nonreporting) **A**1 10 20 **F**3 8 13 15 28 29 30 31 34 35 40 43 50 53 56 57 59 60 64 65 67 68 70 75 76 77 78 79 81 85 86 87 89 93 94 97 100 102 107 108 110 111 115 119 129 130 131 132 133 144 145 146 148 154 156 157 **P**6 **S** LifePoint Health, Brentwood, TN
Primary Contact: Edward E. Freysinger, Chief Executive Officer
CFO: Steve Bishop, Chief Financial Officer
CMO: Mary Beth Hines, D.O., Chief Medical Officer
CHR: Robbyn Lucier, Director Human Resources
CNO: Debra Young, R.N., MSN, Vice President, Patient Services and Chief Nursing Officer
Web address: www.portagehealth.org
**Control**: Corporation, Investor–owned (for–profit) **Service**: General medical and surgical

**Staffed Beds: 96 Admissions: 1033 Census: 68 Outpatient Visits: 84832 Births: 188 Total Expense ($000): 67179 Payroll Expense ($000): 29977 Personnel: 438**

## HARBOR BEACH—Huron County

**HARBOR BEACH COMMUNITY HOSPITAL (231313)**, 210 South First Street, Zip 48441–1236; tel. 989/479–3201, (Nonreporting) **A**10 18
Primary Contact: Paul Clabuesch, President and Chief Executive Officer
CFO: Jill Wehner, Vice President Financial Services
CMO: Richard Lloyd, D.O., Chief of Staff
CIO: Tami Nickrand, Director Information Technology
CHR: Tina Osantoski, Director Human Resources
CNO: Deb Geiger, Executive Director of Acute Care
Web address: www.hbch.org
**Control**: Other not–for–profit (including NFP Corporation) **Service**: General medical and surgical

**Staffed Beds: 45**

## HASTINGS—Barry County

**PENNOCK HEALTH SERVICES** See Spectrum Health Pennock

☒ **SPECTRUM HEALTH PENNOCK (231339)**, 1009 West Green Street, Zip 49058–1710; tel. 269/945–3451, (Nonreporting) **A**1 10 18 **F**3 11 12 13 15 29 30 31 32 34 35 36 39 40 44 45 50 53 54 56 57 59 64 65 68 70 74 75 76 77 79 81 82 85 86 87 89 91 92 93 96 97 100 107 108 110 111 115 119 125 126 127 130 131 132 135 144 146 147 148 149 **S** Spectrum Health, Grand Rapids, MI
Primary Contact: Angela Ditmar, R.N., President
COO: Carla Wilson-Neil, FACHE, Chief Operating Officer
CFO: Micheal King, Controller
CMO: Douglas Smendik, M.D., Hospital Medical Director
CIO: Teri VanTongeren, Director Information Services
CHR: Sherri Thrasher, Executive Human Resources Partner
CNO: Steve Marzolf, R.N., Chief Nursing Officer
Web address: www.spectrumhealth.org
**Control**: Other not–for–profit (including NFP Corporation) **Service**: General medical and surgical

**Staffed Beds: 25 Admissions: 1927 Census: 12 Births: 280 Total Expense ($000): 77361 Payroll Expense ($000): 24945 Personnel: 434**

## HILLSDALE—Hillsdale County

**HILLSDALE COMMUNITY HEALTH CENTER** See Hillsdale Hospital

★ ○ **HILLSDALE HOSPITAL (230037)**, 168 South Howell Street, Zip 49242–2081; tel. 517/437–4451, (Total facility includes 39 beds in nursing home–type unit) (Nonreporting) **A**5 10 11 19 **F**3 11 12 13 15 28 29 34 35 38 40 45 46 48 49 50 57 59 62 70 74 75 76 78 79 81 82 87 93 97 98 102 105 106 107 110 111 115 119 127 128 130 131 132 135 146 147 148 154 156 **P**8
Primary Contact: Jeremiah J. Hodshire, President and Chief Executive Officer
CFO: Mark Gross, Chief Finance Officer
CMO: Nichole Ellis, Chief Medical Officer
CIO: Sheila Puffenberger, Manager Information Technology
CHR: Stacy Feltz, Manager Human Resource
CNO: Loren Corbin, Chief Nursing Officer
Web address: www.hillsdalehospital.com
**Control**: Other not–for–profit (including NFP Corporation) **Service**: General medical and surgical

**Staffed Beds: 93 Admissions: 2732 Census: 51 Outpatient Visits: 106262 Births: 357 Total Expense ($000): 64635 Payroll Expense ($000): 24099 Personnel: 423**

## HOLLAND—Ottawa County

⇑ **HOLLAND COMMUNITY HOSPITAL** See Holland Hospital

★ ⇑ **HOLLAND HOSPITAL (230072)**, 602 Michigan Avenue, Zip 49423–4999; tel. 616/392–5141, (Nonreporting) **A**10 21
Primary Contact: Dale Sowders, President and Chief Executive Officer
CFO: Terry L Steele, Vice President Finance and Chief Financial Officer
CMO: William Vandervliet, M.D., Vice President Medical Affairs
CIO: Randy J Paruch, Director, Information Systems
CHR: Michael Matthews, Vice President Human Resources
CNO: Patti J VanDort, MSN, R.N., Vice President Nursing/Chief Nursing Officer
Web address: www.hollandhospital.org
**Control**: Other not–for–profit (including NFP Corporation) **Service**: General medical and surgical

**Staffed Beds: 130**

## HOWELL—Livingston County

**MCPHERSON HOSPITAL** See St. Joseph Mercy Livingston Hospital

---

**Hospital, Medicare Provider Number, Address, Telephone, Approval, Facility, and Physician Codes, Health Care System**

★ American Hospital Association (AHA) membership
☐ The Joint Commission accreditation
○ Healthcare Facilities Accreditation Program
◇ DNV Healthcare Inc. accreditation
⇑ Center for Improvement in Healthcare Quality Accreditation
△ Commission on Accreditation of Rehabilitation Facilities (CARF) accreditation

✠ **ST. JOSEPH MERCY LIVINGSTON HOSPITAL (230069)**, 620 Byron Road, Zip 48843–1093; tel. 517/545–6000, (Nonreporting) **A**1 3 5 10 **F**3 8 11 12 15 18 28 29 30 34 35 40 41 45 50 51 54 56 57 59 61 62 63 64 65 66 68 70 74 75 77 78 79 81 82 84 85 86 87 93 97 100 107 108 110 111 115 117 118 119 120 121 123 126 129 130 131 132 134 135 141 145 146 147 148 149 154 156 157 **P**1 **S** Trinity Health, Livonia, MI
Primary Contact: John F. O'Malley, FACHE, President
COO: Robin Damschroder, Chief Operating Officer
CFO: Kathy O'Connor, Vice President Finance and Controller
CMO: Rosalie Tocco-Bradley, Ph.D., M.D., Chief Medical Officer
CIO: Frank Rademacher, Director, Information Systems
CHR: Tonia Schemer, Interim Chief Human Resources
CNO: Joyce Young, Ph.D., R.N., Vice President, Patient Services and Chief Nursing Officer
Web address: www.stjoeslivingston.org/livingston
**Control**: Church operated, Nongovernment, not–for–profit **Service**: General medical and surgical

**Staffed Beds**: 38 **Admissions**: 2767 **Census**: 24 **Outpatient Visits**: 271619
**Births**: 0 **Total Expense ($000)**: 140424 **Payroll Expense ($000)**: 44893
**Personnel**: 546

### IONIA—Ionia County

**IONIA COUNTY MEMORIAL HOSPITAL** See Sparrow Ionia Hospital

✠ **SPARROW IONIA HOSPITAL (231331)**, 3565 South State Road, Zip 48846–1870; tel. 616/523–1400, (Nonreporting) **A**1 10 18 **F**3 12 15 18 29 31 34 35 40 43 45 50 54 57 59 64 65 68 70 75 77 78 79 81 85 93 97 107 108 110 111 115 119 127 129 130 131 146 148 149 156 **P**6 **S** Sparrow Health System, Lansing, MI
Primary Contact: William Roeser, President and Chief Executive Officer
COO: Kevin A Price, Vice President and Chief Operating Officer
CFO: Mark Brisboe, VP and Chief Financial Officer
CMO: Amy Jentz, M.D., Chief of Staff
CIO: Bob Neal, Information Technology
CHR: Debbie Olsen, Human Resource Partner
Web address: www.sparrow.org/sparrowionia
**Control**: Other not–for–profit (including NFP Corporation) **Service**: General medical and surgical

**Staffed Beds**: 22 **Admissions**: 765 **Census**: 6 **Outpatient Visits**: 150606
**Births**: 0 **Total Expense ($000)**: 54024 **Payroll Expense ($000)**: 21720
**Personnel**: 288

### IRON MOUNTAIN—Dickinson County

**DICKINSON CNTY MEM HOSP SYSTEM** See Dickinson County Healthcare System

✠ **DICKINSON COUNTY HEALTHCARE SYSTEM (230055)**, 1721 South Stephenson Avenue, Zip 49801–3637; tel. 906/774–1313, (Nonreporting) **A**1 10 20 **F**3 11 13 15 28 29 30 31 32 34 35 40 45 46 50 53 59 62 64 65 67 70 75 76 77 78 79 81 85 87 91 92 93 96 107 108 110 111 114 115 119 120 121 127 129 130 131 132 133 144 145 146 147 148 149 154 156 157 **P**6
Primary Contact: Charles Nelson, Chief Executive Officer
COO: Peggy Freeman, Chief Physicians Services Officer
CFO: Jerry L. Worden, Chief Financial Officer
CMO: Don Kube, M.D., Chief Medical Officer
CIO: Dean Decremer, Information Systems Manager
CHR: Paula Swartout, Human Resources Manager
CNO: Susan Hadley, MS, Chief Nursing Officer
Web address: www.dchs.org
**Control**: County, Government, Nonfederal **Service**: General medical and surgical

**Staffed Beds**: 49 **Admissions**: 2073 **Census**: 19 **Outpatient Visits**: 218399
**Births**: 356 **Total Expense ($000)**: 98921 **Payroll Expense ($000)**: 39620
**Personnel**: 521

✠ **OSCAR G. JOHNSON VETERANS AFFAIRS MEDICAL CENTER**, 325 East 'H' Street, Zip 49801–4792; tel. 906/774–3300, (Nonreporting) **A**1 **S** Department of Veterans Affairs, Washington, DC
Primary Contact: James W. Rice, Director
Web address: www.ironmountain.va.gov/
**Control**: Veterans Affairs, Government, federal **Service**: General medical and surgical

**Staffed Beds**: 17

**VETERANS AFFAIRS MEDICAL CENTER** See Oscar G. Johnson Veterans Affairs Medical Center

### IRON RIVER—Iron County

**ASPIRUS IRON RIVER HOSPITALS & CLINICS** See Aspirus Iron River Hospitals & Clinics, Inc.

✠ **ASPIRUS IRON RIVER HOSPITALS & CLINICS, INC. (231318)**, 1400 West Ice Lake Road, Zip 49935–9526; tel. 906/265–6121, (Nonreporting) **A**1 10 18 **F**11 15 28 29 31 32 34 35 40 43 48 50 54 56 57 59 63 64 70 75 77 78 79 81 86 87 89 93 97 107 111 115 119 128 130 131 132 133 135 144 145 146 147 148 154 156 **S** Aspirus, Inc., Wausau, WI
Primary Contact: Connie L. Koutouzos, R.N., MSN, Chief Executive Officer
CFO: Glenn E Dobson, Vice President, Finance and Chief Financial Officer
CMO: Nasseem Rizkalla, M.D., Chief Medical Officer
CHR: Carol Bastianello, Director Human Resources
CNO: Nancy Lynn Ponozzo, MSN, R.N., Chief Nursing Officer
Web address: www.aspirus.org
**Control**: Other not–for–profit (including NFP Corporation) **Service**: General medical and surgical

**Staffed Beds**: 12 **Admissions**: 595 **Census**: 5 **Outpatient Visits**: 63151
**Births**: 0 **Total Expense ($000)**: 42089 **Payroll Expense ($000)**: 14808
**Personnel**: 240

### IRONWOOD—Gogebic County

**ASPIRUS IRONWOOD HOSITAL & CLINICS, INC.** See Aspirus Ironwood Hospitals & Clinics, Inc.

✠ **ASPIRUS IRONWOOD HOSPITALS & CLINICS, INC. (231333)**, N10561 Grand View Lane, Zip 49938–9622; tel. 906/932–2525, (Nonreporting) **A**1 5 10 18 **F**3 11 13 15 28 29 31 34 35 40 46 50 57 59 64 65 70 75 76 78 79 81 85 87 89 93 104 107 110 114 115 119 127 130 132 133 135 146 147 148 149 **S** Aspirus, Inc., Wausau, WI
Primary Contact: Paula L. Chermside, Chief Executive Officer
COO: Paula L. Chermside, Chief Executive Officer
CFO: Mick Hagwell, Chief Financial Officer
CMO: Chris Pogliano, M.D., Chief Medical Staff
CHR: Keri Van Epern, Manager Human Resources
CNO: Grace Tousignant, R.N., MSN, Chief Nursing Officer
Web address: www.aspirus.org
**Control**: Other not–for–profit (including NFP Corporation) **Service**: General medical and surgical

**Staffed Beds**: 25 **Admissions**: 909 **Census**: 10 **Outpatient Visits**: 66283
**Births**: 125 **Total Expense ($000)**: 62012 **Payroll Expense ($000)**: 23546
**Personnel**: 78

### ISHPEMING—Marquette County

✠ **UP HEALTH SYSTEM-BELL (231321)**, 901 Lakeshore Drive, Zip 49849–1367; tel. 906/486–4431, (Nonreporting) **A**1 10 18 **F**3 11 13 15 29 30 34 40 50 53 57 59 64 65 68 70 75 76 77 79 81 82 85 87 92 93 96 97 107 108 110 114 119 129 133 135 144 145 146 147 156 **P**6 **S** LifePoint Health, Brentwood, TN
Primary Contact: Mitchell D. Leckelt, Chief Executive Officer
CFO: Teresa J Perry, Chief Financial Officer
CMO: Douglas LaBelle, M.D., Chief Medical Officer
CIO: Mike Brady, Director Information Technology
CHR: Tami Ketchem, Human Resource Director
CNO: Sandra McGovern, Chief Nursing Officer
Web address: www.bellhospital.org
**Control**: Corporation, Investor–owned (for–profit) **Service**: General medical and surgical

**Staffed Beds**: 25 **Admissions**: 950 **Census**: 7 **Outpatient Visits**: 54095
**Births**: 285 **Total Expense ($000)**: 38694 **Payroll Expense ($000)**: 14186
**Personnel**: 274

**UP HEALTH SYSTEM-BELL HOSPITAL** See Up Health System-Bell

### JACKSON—Jackson County

**ALLEGIANCE HEALTH** See Henry Ford Allegiance Health

**CARELINK OF JACKSON** See Henry Ford Allegiance Specialty Hospital

**DUANE L. WATERS HOSPITAL**, 3857 Cooper Street, Zip 49201–7521; tel. 517/780–5600, (Nonreporting)
Primary Contact: Carol Griffes, Administrator
**Control**: State, Government, Nonfederal **Service**: Hospital unit of an institution (prison hospital, college infirmary, etc.)

**Staffed Beds**: 150

*Many Facility Codes have changed. Please refer to the AHA Guide Code Chart.*

**MI**

✠ **HENRY FORD ALLEGIANCE HEALTH (230092)**, 205 North East Avenue, Zip 49201–1753; tel. 517/205–4800, (Nonreporting) **A**1 2 3 5 10 12 13 **F**3 4 5 7 8 9 11 12 13 15 17 18 20 22 24 26 28 29 30 31 34 35 37 38 40 43 44 45 46 47 48 49 50 51 53 56 57 58 59 61 62 63 64 65 68 70 71 73 74 75 76 77 78 79 80 81 82 84 85 87 89 91 92 93 96 97 98 100 101 102 103 104 105 107 108 110 111 115 118 119 120 121 123 126 128 129 130 131 132 135 143 146 147 148 149 152 153 154 **P**6 **S** Henry Ford Health System, Detroit, MI
Primary Contact: Paula R. Autry, FACHE, President and Chief Executive Officer
COO: Ondrea Bates, Senior Vice President, Operations and Continuum of Care
CFO: Kevin Leonard, Vice President, Finance
CMO: Ray King, M.D., Senior Vice President, Medical Affairs and Chief Medical Officer
CIO: Aaron Wootton, Vice President, Health Information Systems and Chief Information Officer
CHR: Patricia Seagram, Vice President Human Resources
CNO: Wendy Boersma, Vice President, Nursing and Chief Nursing Officer
Web address: www.allegiancehealth.org
**Control**: Other not–for–profit (including NFP Corporation) **Service**: General medical and surgical

**Staffed Beds: 404 Admissions: 17926 Census: 226 Outpatient Visits: 885992 Births: 1459 Total Expense ($000): 655905 Payroll Expense ($000): 280043 Personnel: 3818**

✠ **HENRY FORD ALLEGIANCE SPECIALTY HOSPITAL (232036)**, 110 North Elm Avenue, Zip 49202–3595; tel. 517/205–4463, (Nonreporting) **A**1 10 **S** Henry Ford Health System, Detroit, MI
Primary Contact: J Mark. Fall, Chief Executive Officer
COO: Charlotte Hyatt, MSN, R.N., Chief Operating Officer and Chief Nursing Officer
CFO: Dale L Friesen, Chief Financial Officer
CMO: Robert Albertson, M.D., Chief Medical Officer
CNO: Charlotte Hyatt, MSN, R.N., Chief Operating Officer and Chief Nursing Officer
Web address: www.https://www.henryford.com/locations/allegiance-specialty-hospital
**Control**: Other not–for–profit (including NFP Corporation) **Service**: Acute long–term care hospital

**Staffed Beds: 44**

### KALAMAZOO—Kalamazoo County

✠ **ASCENSION BORGESS HOSPITAL (230117)**, 1521 Gull Road, Zip 49048–1640; tel. 269/226–7000, (Includes BORGESS-PIPP HOSPITAL, Mailing address: 411 Naomi Street, Plainwell, Michigan, Zip 49080–1222; tel. 269/685–6811; Donna Cassidy, Administrator), (Nonreporting) **A**1 3 5 10 **F**3 7 8 9 11 12 13 15 17 18 20 22 24 26 28 29 30 31 32 33 34 35 36 37 38 39 40 43 44 45 46 47 49 50 53 54 56 57 58 59 60 61 64 68 70 73 74 75 76 77 78 79 81 82 83 84 85 86 87 90 91 92 93 94 96 97 98 99 100 101 102 103 105 107 108 110 114 118 119 126 127 129 130 131 132 135 144 146 147 148 149 154 156 157 **P**6 8 **S** Ascension Healthcare, Saint Louis, MO
Primary Contact: Peter U. Bergmann, President and Chief Executive Officer
COO: Mark Anthony, Executive Vice President and Chief Operating Officer
CHR: Laura Lentenbrink, Vice President, Human Resources
Web address: www.borgess.com
**Control**: Church operated, Nongovernment, not–for–profit **Service**: General medical and surgical

**Staffed Beds: 308 Admissions: 17029 Census: 219 Outpatient Visits: 352188 Births: 743 Total Expense ($000): 452379 Payroll Expense ($000): 128375 Personnel: 1511**

**BORGESS MEDICAL CENTER** See Ascension Borgess Hospital

✠ **BRONSON METHODIST HOSPITAL (230017)**, 601 John Street, Zip 49007–5346; tel. 269/341–6000, (Includes CHILDREN'S HOSPITAL AT BRONSON, Mailing address: 601 John Street, Kalamazoo, Michigan, Zip 49007–5341; tel. 269/341–7654), (Nonreporting) **A**1 3 5 10 **F**3 8 9 11 12 15 16 17 18 19 20 22 24 26 28 29 30 31 32 34 35 36 37 39 40 41 43 44 45 46 47 48 49 50 51 54 55 56 57 58 59 60 61 63 64 65 66 68 70 71 72 74 75 76 77 78 79 80 81 82 84 85 86 87 88 89 92 93 97 101 102 107 108 110 111 114 115 116 117 118 119 126 129 130 131 132 134 135 141 143 146 147 148 149 154 155 156 157 158 **P**6 **S** Bronson Healthcare Group, Kalamazoo, MI
Primary Contact: Frank J. Sardone, President and Chief Executive Officer
COO: Kenneth L Taft, Executive Vice President and Chief Operating Officer
CMO: Scott Larson, M.D., Vice President Medical Affairs and Chief Medical Officer
CHR: John Hayden, Vice President and Chief Human Resources Officer
CNO: Denise Neely, Vice President and Chief Nursing Officer
Web address: www.bronsonhealth.com
**Control**: Other not–for–profit (including NFP Corporation) **Service**: General medical and surgical

**Staffed Beds: 415 Admissions: 23629 Census: 285 Outpatient Visits: 1179453 Births: 3983 Total Expense ($000): 842917 Payroll Expense ($000): 422004 Personnel: 4117**

☐ **KALAMAZOO PSYCHIATRIC HOSPITAL (234026)**, 1312 Oakland Drive, Zip 49008–1205; tel. 269/337–3000, (Nonreporting) **A**1 10
Primary Contact: Robert Hill, M.D., Hospital Director and Chief Executive Officer
CMO: V.R. Kanaparti, M.D., Director Medical Services
CIO: Brian Bayer, Information Technology Site Leader
CHR: Holly Hiday, Director Human Resources
CNO: Kathleen Millard, Acting Director Nursing
**Control**: State, Government, Nonfederal **Service**: Psychiatric

**Staffed Beds: 203**

**KALAMAZOO REG PSYCHIATRIC HOSP** See Kalamazoo Psychiatric Hospital

**THE CHILDREN'S HOSPITAL AT BRONSON** See Children's Hospital at Bronson

### KALKASKA—Kalkaska County

★ **KALKASKA MEMORIAL HEALTH CENTER (231301)**, 419 South Coral Street, Zip 49646–2503; tel. 231/258–7500, (Total facility includes 104 beds in nursing home–type unit) (Nonreporting) **A**10 18 **F**2 10 15 28 35 40 44 45 50 64 65 66 79 81 84 87 93 97 107 110 111 115 119 125 127 128 129 130 132 134 143 144 146 147 148 154 156 157 **P**6 **S** Munson Healthcare, Traverse City, MI
Primary Contact: Kevin L. Rogols, FACHE, Administrator
CHR: Kimberly Babcock, Administrative Director of Operations
CNO: Christine Bissonette, R.N., Service Line Director for Acute Services
Web address: www.munsonhealthcare.org
**Control**: Hospital district or authority, Government, Nonfederal **Service**: General medical and surgical

**Staffed Beds: 112 Admissions: 325 Census: 99 Outpatient Visits: 73645 Births: 0 Total Expense ($000): 47122 Payroll Expense ($000): 23882 Personnel: 435**

**KALKASKA MEMORIAL HLTH CTR** See Kalkaska Memorial Health Center

### LAKEVIEW—Montcalm County

**SPECTRUM HEALTH KELSEY HOSPITAL** See Spectrum Health United Hospital, Greenville

**SPECTRUM HLTH KELSEY CAMPUS** See Spectrum Health Kelsey Hospital

### L'ANSE—Baraga County

✠ **BARAGA COUNTY MEMORIAL HOSPITAL (231307)**, 18341 U.S. Highway 41, Zip 49946–8024; tel. 906/524–3300, (Nonreporting) **A**1 10 18 **F**3 11 15 28 31 34 35 40 43 45 50 53 57 59 62 63 64 75 77 78 79 81 82 84 85 89 93 107 108 110 115 118 119 127 130 132 133 146 154 156
Primary Contact: Margie Hale, R.N., MSN, Chief Executive Officer
CFO: Gail Jestila-Peltola, Chief Financial Officer
CMO: Sharon Gilliland, Chief of Staff
CIO: Taylor Makela, Director Information Technology
CHR: Janelle E Beeler, Human Resource Manager
CNO: Bonny Cotter, Chief Nursing Officer
Web address: www.bcmh.org
**Control**: County, Government, Nonfederal **Service**: General medical and surgical

**Staffed Beds: 15 Admissions: 396 Census: 5 Outpatient Visits: 22361 Births: 1 Total Expense ($000): 22040 Payroll Expense ($000): 8456 Personnel: 146**

**MI**

---

**Hospital, Medicare Provider Number, Address, Telephone, Approval, Facility, and Physician Codes, Health Care System**

★ American Hospital Association (AHA) membership
☐ The Joint Commission accreditation
○ Healthcare Facilities Accreditation Program
◇ DNV Healthcare Inc. accreditation
⇑ Center for Improvement in Healthcare Quality Accreditation
△ Commission on Accreditation of Rehabilitation Facilities (CARF) accreditation

## LANSING—Ingham County

**INGHAM REGIONAL MEDICAL CENTER** See Mclaren Greater Lansing

**INGHAM REGIONAL MEDICAL CENTER, GREENLAWN CAMPUS** See Mclaren Greater Lansing

**INGHAM REGIONAL ORTHOPEDIC HOSPITAL, PENNSYLVANIA CAMPUS** See Mclaren Orthopedic Hospital

☐ **MCLAREN GREATER LANSING (230167)**, 401 West Greenlawn Avenue, Zip 48910–2819; tel. 517/975–6000, (Includes MCLAREN GREATER LANSING, Mailing address: 401 West Greenlawn Avenue, Lansing, Michigan, Zip 48910–2819; tel. 517/975–6000; MCLAREN ORTHOPEDIC HOSPITAL, Mailing address: 2727 South Pennsylvania Avenue, Lansing, Michigan, Zip 48910–3490; tel. 517/975–6000; Casey Kandow, Interim President and Chief Executive Officer), (Nonreporting) **A**1 3 5 10 13 **S** McLaren Health Care Corporation, Grand Blanc, MI
Primary Contact: Kirk M. Ray, President and Chief Executive Officer
COO: Casey Kandow, Chief Operating Officer
CFO: Dale Thompson, Chief Financial Officer
CMO: Linda Peterson, Vice President Medical Affairs
CHR: Amy Dorr, Vice President Human Resources
Web address: www.mclaren.org
**Control:** Other not–for–profit (including NFP Corporation) **Service:** General medical and surgical

**Staffed Beds:** 321

**SPARROW HEALTH SYSTEM** See Sparrow Hospital

☒ △ **SPARROW HOSPITAL (230230)**, 1215 East Michigan Avenue, Zip 48912–1811; tel. 517/364–1000, (Includes SPARROW CHILDREN'S CENTER, Mailing address: 1215 East Michigan Avenue, Lansing, Michigan, Zip 48912–1811; tel. 517/364–1000), (Nonreporting) **A**1 2 3 5 10 13 **F**3 5 11 12 13 15 17 18 20 22 24 26 28 29 30 31 34 35 36 40 41 43 44 45 46 49 50 51 54 56 57 58 59 60 63 64 65 67 70 72 74 75 76 77 78 79 81 82 84 85 86 87 88 89 90 91 92 93 94 96 97 98 100 101 102 103 104 105 107 108 109 110 111 114 115 116 117 118 119 120 121 123 124 126 129 130 131 132 135 144 146 147 148 149 156 **P**1 6 **S** Sparrow Health System, Lansing, MI
Primary Contact: Mark Brett, Chief Executive Officer
COO: Joseph Ruth, Executive Vice President and Chief Operating Officer
CFO: Paula Reichle, Senior Vice President and Chief Operating Officer
CMO: Brian D. Schroeder, M.D., Senior Vice President and Chief Medical Officer
CIO: Thomas Bres, Senior Vice President and Chief Administrative Officer
CHR: Paul Sturgis, Senior Vice President and Chief Human Resources Officer
CNO: Mary Lou Wesley, R.N., Senior Vice President and Chief Nursing Officer
Web address: www.sparrow.org
**Control:** Other not–for–profit (including NFP Corporation) **Service:** General medical and surgical

**Staffed Beds:** 632 **Admissions:** 32536 **Census:** 463 **Outpatient Visits:** 939180 **Births:** 4068 **Total Expense ($000):** 962955 **Payroll Expense ($000):** 455698 **Personnel:** 5399

**SPARROW REGIONAL CHILDREN'S CENTER** See Sparrow Children's Center

★ ○ **SPARROW SPECIALTY HOSPITAL (232037)**, 8 West Sparrow Hospital Tower, Zip 48912; tel. 517/364–4840, (Nonreporting) **A**10 11 **F**1 3 29 30 60 68 85 100 101 119 130 148 **P**6 **S** Sparrow Health System, Lansing, MI
Primary Contact: Lou Little, President and Chief Executive Officer
CFO: David Przybylski, Controller
CMO: Paul Entler, D.O., Medical Director
CHR: Paul Sturgis, Chief Human Resource Officer
CNO: Tina Gross, MSN, R.N., Chief Nursing Officer
Web address: www.sparrowspecialty.org
**Control:** Other not–for–profit (including NFP Corporation) **Service:** Acute long–term care hospital

**Staffed Beds:** 30 **Admissions:** 342 **Census:** 24 **Outpatient Visits:** 0 **Births:** 0 **Total Expense ($000):** 13733 **Payroll Expense ($000):** 6429 **Personnel:** 96

## LAPEER—Lapeer County

**LAPEER REGIONAL MEDICAL CENTER** See Mclaren Lapeer Region

☐ **MCLAREN LAPEER REGION (230193)**, 1375 North Main Street, Zip 48446–1350; tel. 810/667–5500, (Total facility includes 19 beds in nursing home–type unit) (Nonreporting) **A**1 10 **F**3 12 13 15 18 20 26 28 29 30 31 34 35 40 43 44 45 49 54 56 57 59 61 64 68 70 74 76 77 79 81 82 84 85 86 87 92 93 94 97 98 100 101 102 107 108 110 111 114 115 119 126 128 129 130 131 135 143 144 146 148 149 154 157 **S** McLaren Health Care Corporation, Grand Blanc, MI
Primary Contact: Chris Candela, President and Chief Executive Officer
CFO: Benjamin Brow, Vice President of Finance
CMO: Gary Salem, M.D., Vice President Medical Affairs
CIO: Gayle Consiglio, Chief Information Officer
CHR: Amy Dorr, Vice President Human Resources
Web address: www.lapeerregional.org
**Control:** Other not–for–profit (including NFP Corporation) **Service:** General medical and surgical

**Staffed Beds:** 131 **Admissions:** 6361 **Census:** 85 **Outpatient Visits:** 182378 **Births:** 239 **Total Expense ($000):** 115384 **Payroll Expense ($000):** 54251 **Personnel:** 664

## LAURIUM—Houghton County

**ASPIRUS KEWEENAW HOSPITAL** See Aspirus Keweenaw Hospital, Inc.

☒ **ASPIRUS KEWEENAW HOSPITAL, INC. (231319)**, 205 Osceola Street, Zip 49913–2134; tel. 906/337–6500, (Nonreporting) **A**1 10 18 **F**3 5 8 11 13 15 18 28 29 30 31 34 35 36 40 43 45 52 53 56 57 61 64 65 66 68 70 75 76 77 78 79 81 82 85 87 89 93 97 107 108 110 114 118 119 127 130 131 132 133 135 147 148 149 154 156 **S** Aspirus, Inc., Wausau, WI
Primary Contact: Christine K. Harff, UP Regional President
CFO: Andrew Costic, Vice President of Regional Finance
CMO: Michael Luoma, M.D., Chief of Staff
CHR: Chad Rowe, Human Resource Director
CNO: Grace Tousignant, R.N., MSN, Chief Nursing Officer
Web address: www.aspirus.org
**Control:** Other not–for–profit (including NFP Corporation) **Service:** General medical and surgical

**Staffed Beds:** 25 **Admissions:** 1182 **Census:** 9 **Outpatient Visits:** 50652 **Births:** 185 **Total Expense ($000):** 55466 **Payroll Expense ($000):** 21040 **Personnel:** 306

## LINCOLN PARK—Wayne County

**VIBRA HOSPITAL OF SOUTHEASTERN MICHIGAN** See Vibra Hospital of Southeastern Michigan, LLC

☒ **VIBRA HOSPITAL OF SOUTHEASTERN MICHIGAN, LLC (232019)**, 26400 West Outer Drive, Zip 48146–2088; tel. 313/386–2000, (Nonreporting) **A**1 10 **S** Vibra Healthcare, Mechanicsburg, PA
Primary Contact: Reginald Lee, Chief Executive Officer
COO: Cindy Brassinger, Chief Operating Officer
CFO: Douglas Morris, Chief Financial Officer
CHR: Karen D Gray, Director Human Resources
Web address: www.vhsemichigan.com/
**Control:** Corporation, Investor–owned (for–profit) **Service:** Acute long–term care hospital

**Staffed Beds:** 220

## LIVONIA—Wayne County

**ST MARY HOSPITAL** See St. Mary Mercy Hospital

☒ **ST. MARY MERCY HOSPITAL (230002)**, 36475 Five Mile Road, Zip 48154–1988; tel. 734/655–4800, (Nonreporting) **A**1 2 3 5 10 **F**3 4 5 8 12 13 15 18 20 22 26 28 29 30 31 34 35 38 40 43 44 45 46 47 49 50 51 53 54 55 56 57 58 59 63 64 68 70 74 75 76 77 78 79 81 84 85 87 90 93 97 98 100 101 102 104 107 108 110 111 114 115 116 117 118 119 120 121 126 129 130 131 132 135 143 145 146 147 148 149 153 154 **P**6 **S** Trinity Health, Livonia, MI
Primary Contact: David A. Spivey, President and Chief Executive Officer
CFO: Mike Samyn, Vice President, Finance and Chief Financial Officer
CMO: Matthew Griffin, M.D., Chief Medical Officer
CIO: Janet Yim, Director Information Services
CHR: Kenneth Antczak, Vice President Human Resources
Web address: www.stmarymercy.org
**Control:** Church operated, Nongovernment, not–for–profit **Service:** General medical and surgical

**Staffed Beds:** 304 **Admissions:** 17365 **Census:** 207 **Outpatient Visits:** 287033 **Births:** 706 **Total Expense ($000):** 334942 **Payroll Expense ($000):** 151759 **Personnel:** 2017

MI

*Many Facility Codes have changed. Please refer to the AHA Guide Code Chart.*

© 2021 AHA Guide

MI

## LUDINGTON—Mason County

û **MEMORIAL MEDICAL CENTER OF WEST MICHIGAN** See Spectrum Health Ludington Hospital

★ û **SPECTRUM HEALTH LUDINGTON HOSPITAL (230110)**, One Atkinson Drive, Zip 49431–1906, Mailing Address: PO Box 2408, Grand Rapids, Zip 49501–2408; tel. 231/843–2591, (Nonreporting) **A**10 20 21 **F**3 8 11 13 15 28 29 31 32 34 35 37 38 40 41 43 44 45 49 50 51 53 54 57 59 64 68 70 75 76 77 78 79 81 82 85 86 87 92 93 96 100 102 104 107 108 110 111 114 115 118 119 127 129 130 131 132 135 146 147 148 149 154 156 **P**6 **S** Spectrum Health, Grand Rapids, MI
Primary Contact: Randall Kelley, FACHE, President
CFO: Kerri Nelson, Chief Financial Officer
CMO: Steve Strbich, D.O., Chief of Staff
CIO: Jeremy Vronko, Manager, Information Services
CHR: Jill Vasquez, Manager Human Resources
CNO: Helen Johnson, R.N., MSN, Vice President Patient Services
Web address: www.mmcwm.com
**Control:** Other not–for–profit (including NFP Corporation) **Service:** General medical and surgical

**Staffed Beds:** 30 **Admissions:** 1957 **Census:** 19 **Outpatient Visits:** 118361 **Births:** 307 **Total Expense ($000):** 90992 **Payroll Expense ($000):** 27047 **Personnel:** 559

## MADISON HEIGHTS—Oakland County

**ST. JOHN PROVIDENCE MACOMB-OAKLAND HOSPITAL, OAKLAND CENTER** See St. John Macomb-Oakland Hospital, Madison Heights Campus

## MANISTEE—Manistee County

⊠ **MUNSON HEALTHCARE MANISTEE HOSPITAL (230303)**, 1465 East Parkdale Avenue, Zip 49660–9709; tel. 231/398–1000, (Nonreporting) **A**1 10 20 **F**3 11 15 28 29 31 34 35 39 40 45 48 50 53 54 57 59 64 74 77 78 79 80 81 85 92 93 96 97 107 108 110 111 115 118 119 127 129 131 135 146 147 148 149 **P**6 **S** Munson Healthcare, Traverse City, MI
Primary Contact: James Barker, Chief Executive Officer
COO: Donn J Lemmer, Chief Financial Officer and Chief Operating Officer
CFO: Donn J Lemmer, Chief Financial Officer and Chief Operating Officer
CMO: Marion Fuller, Chief of Staff
CHR: Kim Weckesser, Director Human Resources
CNO: Thomas Kane, R.N., Vice President Patient Services and Chief Nursing Officer
Web address: www.westshoremedcenter.org
**Control:** Other not–for–profit (including NFP Corporation) **Service:** General medical and surgical

**Staffed Beds:** 45 **Admissions:** 1137 **Census:** 9 **Outpatient Visits:** 93291 **Births:** 166 **Total Expense ($000):** 73770 **Payroll Expense ($000):** 26878 **Personnel:** 292

**WEST SHORE MEDICAL CENTER** See Munson Healthcare Manistee Hospital

## MANISTIQUE—Schoolcraft County

★ **SCHOOLCRAFT MEMORIAL HOSPITAL (231303)**, 7870W US Highway 2, Zip 49854–8992; tel. 906/341–3200, (Nonreporting) **A**10 18 **F**3 11 15 18 19 28 29 30 31 32 34 35 40 41 45 50 53 56 57 59 62 63 64 65 68 70 75 77 78 79 81 82 85 90 93 97 100 107 108 110 114 115 118 119 127 129 130 132 133 144 146 147 148 154 156 **P**6
Primary Contact: Robert Crumb, MS, Chief Executive Officer
CMO: John P Galey, M.D., Chief Medical Officer
CIO: Kent La Croix, Chief Information Officer
CHR: Fawn Freeborn, Human Resources Generalist
CNO: Cindy Olli, R.N., Chief Nursing Officer
Web address: www.scmh.org
**Control:** County, Government, Nonfederal **Service:** General medical and surgical

**Staffed Beds:** 12 **Admissions:** 360 **Census:** 3 **Outpatient Visits:** 44713 **Births:** 0 **Total Expense ($000):** 39250 **Payroll Expense ($000):** 19311 **Personnel:** 296

## MARLETTE—Sanilac County

**MARLETTE COMMUNITY HOSPITAL** See Marlette Regional Hospital

○ **MARLETTE REGIONAL HOSPITAL (231330)**, 2770 Main Street, Zip 48453–1141, Mailing Address: P.O. Box 307, Zip 48453–0307; tel. 989/635–4000, (Nonreporting) **A**10 11 18
Primary Contact: Daniel Babcock, Chief Executive Officer
CFO: James L Singles, Chief Financial Officer
CMO: Daniel Kulick, M.D., Chief of Staff
CIO: Paul Gugel, Manager Information Technology
CHR: Connie Kennedy, Director Human Resources
CNO: Hilda Hebberd, R.N., MSN, Senior Director Clinical Services
Web address: www.marletteregionalhospital.org
**Control:** Other not–for–profit (including NFP Corporation) **Service:** General medical and surgical

**Staffed Beds:** 74

## MARQUETTE—Marquette County

**MARQUETTE GENERAL HOSPITAL** See Up Health System-Marquette

⊠ **UP HEALTH SYSTEM-MARQUETTE (230054)**, 580 West College Avenue, Zip 49855–2736; tel. 906/228–9440, (Nonreporting) **A**1 2 3 5 10 **F**3 5 7 12 13 14 15 18 19 20 22 24 26 28 29 30 31 32 34 35 38 40 43 45 46 47 48 49 50 55 56 57 58 59 60 64 65 68 70 72 73 74 75 76 77 78 79 81 82 84 85 86 87 89 90 93 94 98 99 100 101 104 107 108 110 111 115 117 118 119 120 121 123 124 127 129 130 131 132 135 146 147 148 149 154 155 156 157 **P**6 **S** Duke LifePoint Healthcare, Brentwood, TN
Primary Contact: Garfield Atchison, Chief Executive Officer
COO: Steven Salyer, Chief Operating Officer
CFO: Steve Embree, Chief Financial Officer
CMO: Tom Noren, M.D., Chief Medical Officer
CIO: Doug Stacy, Director Information Technology
CHR: Ruth Solinski, Senior Director Human Resources
Web address: www.mgh.org
**Control:** Corporation, Investor–owned (for–profit) **Service:** General medical and surgical

**Staffed Beds:** 211 **Admissions:** 9924 **Census:** 130 **Outpatient Visits:** 265707 **Births:** 498 **Total Expense ($000):** 331755 **Payroll Expense ($000):** 111250 **Personnel:** 1520

## MARSHALL—Calhoun County

★ û **OAKLAWN HOSPITAL (230217)**, 200 North Madison Street, Zip 49068–1199; tel. 269/781–4271, (Nonreporting) **A**10 21
Primary Contact: Gregg M. Beeg, FACHE, Interim President and Chief Executive Officer
COO: Sharon Thomas-Boyd, Chief Operating Officer
CFO: Andrew J. Poole IIIInterim Chief Financial Officer
CNO: Theresa Dawson, MSN, R.N., Chief Nursing Officer
Web address: www.oaklawnhospital.org
**Control:** Other not–for–profit (including NFP Corporation) **Service:** General medical and surgical

**Staffed Beds:** 78

## MIDLAND—Midland County

⊠ **MIDMICHIGAN MEDICAL CENTER-MIDLAND (230222)**, 4000 Wellness Drive, Zip 48670–2000; tel. 989/839–3000, (Nonreporting) **A**1 2 3 5 10 **F**3 7 8 11 12 13 15 17 18 20 22 24 26 28 29 30 31 32 34 35 36 37 38 40 43 45 46 47 48 49 50 51 53 54 56 57 58 59 60 61 62 63 64 65 68 70 71 74 75 76 77 78 79 80 81 82 84 85 86 87 89 91 92 93 94 97 98 100 101 102 104 107 108 109 110 111 114 115 116 117 118 119 120 121 122 123 124 126 127 129 130 131 132 135 143 144 146 147 148 149 154 156 157 **P**5 **S** MidMichigan Health, Midland, MI
Primary Contact: Gregory H. Rogers, President
CFO: Scott D Currie, Vice President and Chief Financial Officer
CMO: Margueritte Kuhn, M.D., Vice President Medical Affairs
CIO: C Harlan Goodrich, Vice President and Chief Information Officer
CNO: Jan Penney, R.N., Vice President and Chief Nursing Officer
Web address: www.midmichigan.org
**Control:** Other not–for–profit (including NFP Corporation) **Service:** General medical and surgical

**Staffed Beds:** 270 **Admissions:** 14548 **Census:** 162 **Outpatient Visits:** 280933 **Births:** 1295 **Total Expense ($000):** 420190 **Payroll Expense ($000):** 123507 **Personnel:** 2047

**MIDMICHIGAN REG MEDICAL CENTER** See Midmichigan Medical Center-Midland

---

Hospital, Medicare Provider Number, Address, Telephone, Approval, Facility, and Physician Codes, Health Care System

★ American Hospital Association (AHA) membership
☐ The Joint Commission accreditation
○ Healthcare Facilities Accreditation Program
◇ DNV Healthcare Inc. accreditation
û Center for Improvement in Healthcare Quality Accreditation
△ Commission on Accreditation of Rehabilitation Facilities (CARF) accreditation

## MONROE—Monroe County

**MERCY MEMORIAL HOSPITAL SYSTEM** See Promedica Monroe Regional Hospital

☒ **PROMEDICA MONROE REGIONAL HOSPITAL (230099)**, 718 North Macomb Street, Zip 48162–7815; tel. 734/240–8400, (Nonreporting) **A**1 2 3 5 10 12 13 **F**3 5 11 13 15 18 20 21 22 28 29 30 31 34 35 36 38 40 41 43 44 45 46 49 50 51 53 54 56 57 59 65 66 69 70 71 74 75 76 77 78 79 81 82 85 86 87 92 93 97 98 100 101 102 104 107 108 109 110 111 113 114 115 116 117 118 119 124 126 129 130 132 135 145 146 147 148 149 150 154 156 **S** ProMedica Health System, Toledo, OH
Primary Contact: Darrin Arquette, President
CNO: Maurine Weis, Vice President Patient Care Services and Chief Nursing Officer
Web address: www.promedica.org
**Control:** Other not–for–profit (including NFP Corporation) **Service:** General medical and surgical

> **Staffed Beds:** 100 **Admissions:** 6151 **Census:** 70 **Outpatient Visits:** 156656 **Births:** 625 **Total Expense ($000):** 139373 **Payroll Expense ($000):** 48871 **Personnel:** 813

## MOUNT CLEMENS—Macomb County

☐ **MCLAREN MACOMB (230227)**, 1000 Harrington Boulevard, Zip 48043–2992; tel. 586/493–8000, (Nonreporting) **A**1 3 5 10 12 13 **F**3 8 11 12 13 14 15 18 19 20 22 24 26 28 29 30 31 34 35 36 37 40 41 43 45 46 47 48 49 50 51 54 55 56 59 62 63 64 65 66 68 70 71 74 75 76 77 78 79 81 82 84 85 87 89 92 93 94 96 100 102 107 110 111 114 115 118 119 120 121 123 124 126 129 130 131 132 135 145 146 147 148 149 154 156 **P**8 **S** McLaren Health Care Corporation, Grand Blanc, MI
Primary Contact: Thomas M. Brisse, President and Chief Executive Officer
COO: Sue Durst, R.N., MS, Vice President Plant Operations
CFO: Brian Baluntanski, Chief Financial Officer
CMO: Dennis J. Cunningham, M.D., Chief Medical Officer
CNO: Julia Libcke, R.N., MSN, Chief Nursing Officer
Web address: www.mclaren.org/macomb/macomb.aspx
**Control:** Other not–for–profit (including NFP Corporation) **Service:** General medical and surgical

> **Staffed Beds:** 288 **Admissions:** 14496 **Census:** 175 **Outpatient Visits:** 170155 **Births:** 976 **Total Expense ($000):** 347860 **Payroll Expense ($000):** 142776 **Personnel:** 1844

**MOUNT CLEMENS REGIONAL MEDICAL CENTER** See Mclaren Macomb

☒ **SELECT SPECIALTY HOSPITAL-MACOMB COUNTY (232023)**, 215 North Avenue, Zip 48043–1700; tel. 586/307–9000, (Nonreporting) **A**1 10 **S** Select Medical Corporation, Mechanicsburg, PA
Primary Contact: Jon P. O'Malley, Chief Executive Officer
CFO: Sharon Ryan, Regional Controller
CMO: Arsenio V Deleon, M.D., Chief Medical Officer
CHR: Katelyn Andre, Human Resource Coordinator
CNO: Lydia Alaszewski, Chief Nursing Officer
Web address: www.macomb.selectspecialtyhospitals.com/
**Control:** Corporation, Investor–owned (for–profit) **Service:** Acute long–term care hospital

> **Staffed Beds:** 36

**ST JOSEPH'S MERCY HOSP-EAST** See Henry Ford Macomb Hospital - Mount Clemens Campus

## MOUNT PLEASANT—Isabella County

**CENTRAL MICHIGAN COMMUNITY HOSPITAL** See Mclaren Central Michigan

☐ **MCLAREN CENTRAL MICHIGAN (230080)**, 1221 South Drive, Zip 48858–3257; tel. 989/772–6700, (Nonreporting) **A**1 10 19 **F**3 11 12 13 15 18 20 22 26 28 29 30 31 34 35 40 44 45 48 49 50 51 54 57 59 62 64 65 68 70 74 75 76 77 78 79 81 82 85 86 87 89 96 97 107 108 110 111 114 117 118 119 120 121 123 124 129 130 131 132 144 145 146 147 148 156 **P**8 **S** McLaren Health Care Corporation, Grand Blanc, MI
Primary Contact: Martin Tursky, President and Chief Executive Officer
CMO: Ashok Vashishta, M.D., Vice President Medical Affairs
CIO: Nicolette Zalud, Customer Site Manager
CHR: Carolyn Potter, Vice President Human Resources
CNO: Sheri Myers, Vice President Patient Care Services
Web address: www.cmch.org
**Control:** Other not–for–profit (including NFP Corporation) **Service:** General medical and surgical

> **Staffed Beds:** 78 **Admissions:** 2679 **Census:** 20 **Outpatient Visits:** 105025 **Births:** 478 **Total Expense ($000):** 87624 **Payroll Expense ($000):** 35352 **Personnel:** 428

## MUNISING—Alger County

☐ **MUNISING MEMORIAL HOSPITAL (231308)**, 1500 Sand Point Road, Zip 49862–1406; tel. 906/387–4110, (Nonreporting) **A**10 18
Primary Contact: Melissa Hall, Chief Executive Officer
CFO: Wendy Rautio, Chief Financial Officer
CMO: Christine Krueger, M.D., Chief of Staff
CNO: Andrea Wills, R.N., Chief Nursing Executive
Web address: www.munisingmemorial.org
**Control:** Other not–for–profit (including NFP Corporation) **Service:** General medical and surgical

> **Staffed Beds:** 11

## MUSKEGON—Muskegon County

**GREAT LAKES SPECIALTY HOSPITAL-MUSKEGON** See Select Specialty Hospital-Muskegon

☒ **MERCY HEALTH HACKLEY CAMPUS (230066)**, 1700 Clinton Street, Zip 49442–5502, Mailing Address: P.O. Box 3302, Zip 49443–3302; tel. 231/726–3511, (Includes MERCY HEALTH, GENERAL CAMPUS, Mailing address: 1700 Oak Avenue, Muskegon, Michigan, Zip 49442; tel. 231/672–3311; Greg Loomis, Interim President and Chief Operating Officer; MERCY HEALTH, MERCY CAMPUS, Mailing address: 1500 East Sherman Boulevard, Muskegon, Michigan, Zip 49444–1849; tel. 231/672–2000; Gary Allore, President), (Nonreporting) **A**1 2 3 5 10 **F**3 7 11 12 13 15 18 20 22 24 26 28 29 30 34 35 36 38 40 43 44 45 46 47 48 49 50 51 54 56 57 59 61 64 68 70 76 77 79 81 82 84 85 86 87 89 90 92 93 96 97 98 104 107 110 111 114 115 118 119 120 121 123 124 129 130 131 132 144 146 147 148 149 153 154 156 **P**1 **S** Trinity Health, Livonia, MI
Primary Contact: Gary Allore, President
CMO: F. Remington Sprague, M.D., Chief Medical Officer
CIO: William Stefl, Director Information Systems
CNO: Kimberly Anne Maguire, Chief Nursing Officer
Web address: www.mercyhealthmuskegon.com
**Control:** Other not–for–profit (including NFP Corporation) **Service:** General medical and surgical

> **Staffed Beds:** 366 **Admissions:** 18989 **Census:** 216 **Outpatient Visits:** 1024825 **Births:** 1049 **Total Expense ($000):** 613559 **Payroll Expense ($000):** 267648 **Personnel:** 3397

**MERCY HEALTH PARTNERS, MERCY CAMPUS** See Mercy Health, Mercy Campus

**MERCY HEALTH PARTNERS-MUSKEGON GENERAL CAMPUS** See Mercy Health, General Campus

**MERCY HEALTH, HACKLEY CAMPUS** See Mercy Health Hackley Campus

☒ **SELECT SPECIALTY HOSPITAL-MUSKEGON (232021)**, 1700 Clinton Street, 3 South, Zip 49442–5502; tel. 231/728–5811, (Nonreporting) **A**1 10 **S** Select Medical Corporation, Mechanicsburg, PA
Primary Contact: Kerry McLane, Chief Executive Officer
Web address: www.greatlakesspecialtyhospital.com
**Control:** Corporation, Investor–owned (for–profit) **Service:** Acute long–term care hospital

> **Staffed Beds:** 31

## NEW BALTIMORE—Macomb County

**HARBOR OAKS HOSPITAL (234021)**, 35031 23 Mile Road, Zip 48047–3649; tel. 586/725–5777, (Nonreporting) **A**10 **S** Acadia Healthcare Company, Inc., Franklin, TN
Primary Contact: Briana Jacob, Chief Executive Officer
CFO: Michael Ferguson, Chief Financial Officer
CMO: James D. Adamo, M.D., Medical Director
CHR: Zena Ridley, Director Human Resources
CNO: Leeann Duncan, Director Patient Care Services
Web address: www.harboroaks.com
**Control:** Corporation, Investor–owned (for–profit) **Service:** Psychiatric

> **Staffed Beds:** 99

**PSYCHIATRIC CENTER OF MICHIGAN** See Harbor Oaks Hospital

*Many Facility Codes have changed. Please refer to the AHA Guide Code Chart.* © 2021 AHA Guide

MI

## NEWBERRY—Luce County

★ ⇑ **HELEN NEWBERRY JOY HOSPITAL (231304)**, 502 West Harrie Street, Zip 49868–1209; tel. 906/293–9200, (Total facility includes 39 beds in nursing home–type unit) (Nonreporting) **A**10 18 21 **F**3 15 28 29 31 34 35 40 43 45 53 57 59 64 65 75 78 79 81 87 93 97 107 108 115 118 119 127 128 129 130 131 132 133 143 144 154
Primary Contact: Hunter Kyle. Nostrant, Chief Executive Officer
CFO: Wendy Rautio, Chief Financial Officer
CMO: Michael Gregory Beaulieu, M.D., Chief Medical Officer
CIO: Howard Bliss, Director of Information Systems
CNO: Joe Johnson, Chief Nursing Officer
Web address: www.hnjh.org
**Control**: County, Government, Nonfederal **Service**: General medical and surgical

**Staffed Beds**: 64 **Admissions**: 346 **Census**: 34 **Outpatient Visits**: 31474 **Births**: 0 **Total Expense ($000)**: 33256 **Payroll Expense ($000)**: 13888 **Personnel**: 253

## NORTHVILLE—Wayne County

☐ **HAWTHORN CENTER**, 18471 Haggerty Road, Zip 48168–9575; tel. 248/735–6771, (Nonreporting) **A**1 3
Primary Contact: George Mellows, Facility Director
CIO: Robert W Bailey, Chief Information Officer
Web address: https://www.michigan.gov
**Control**: State, Government, Nonfederal **Service**: Children's hospital psychiatric

**Staffed Beds**: 69

## NOVI—Oakland County

**PROVIDENCE - PROVIDENCE PARK HOSPITAL, NOVI CAMPUS** See Ascension of Providence Hospital, Southfield Campus, Southfield

**PROVIDENCE PARK HOSPITAL** See Providence - Providence Park Hospital, Novi Campus

## ONTONAGON—Ontonagon County

**ASPIRUS ONTONAGON HOSPITAL** See Aspirus Ontonagon Hospital, Inc.

⊠ **ASPIRUS ONTONAGON HOSPITAL, INC. (231309)**, 601 South Seventh Street, Zip 49953–1459; tel. 906/884–8000, (Total facility includes 46 beds in nursing home–type unit) (Nonreporting) **A**1 5 10 18 **F**3 15 28 29 31 34 35 40 41 43 45 53 56 59 64 65 68 75 77 78 79 81 85 87 93 94 97 107 110 114 119 127 128 131 132 133 147 149 154 156 **P**6 **S** Aspirus, Inc., Wausau, WI
Primary Contact: Dylan Taylor, Chief Administrative Officer
CMO: Richard Chaltry, M.D., Director Medical Staff
CHR: Gina Kasten, Manager Human Resources
Web address: www.aspirus.org
**Control**: Other not–for–profit (including NFP Corporation) **Service**: General medical and surgical

**Staffed Beds**: 56 **Admissions**: 206 **Census**: 41 **Outpatient Visits**: 13431 **Births**: 0 **Total Expense ($000)**: 15560 **Payroll Expense ($000)**: 5805 **Personnel**: 126

## OWOSSO—Shiawassee County

⊠ **MEMORIAL HEALTHCARE (230121)**, 826 West King Street, Zip 48867–2120; tel. 989/723–5211, (Total facility includes 32 beds in nursing home–type unit) (Nonreporting) **A**1 10 **F**3 11 13 15 28 29 30 31 32 34 35 36 38 40 45 50 51 56 57 58 59 62 63 64 65 69 70 74 75 76 77 78 79 81 82 85 87 89 93 97 98 100 101 102 107 108 110 111 115 119 127 128 129 130 131 132 143 144 146 147 148 154 156 **P**6
Primary Contact: Brian Long, FACHE, President and Chief Executive Officer
COO: Tim Susterich, Chief Financial Officer and Chief Operating Officer
CFO: Tim Susterich, Chief Financial Officer and Chief Operating Officer
CMO: Wael Salman, M.D., Vice President Medical Affairs
CIO: Tom Kurtz, Vice President Information Services and Chief Information Officer
CNO: Jim Nemeth, Senior Vice President of Patient Care Services and Chief Nursing Officer
Web address: www.memorialhealthcare.org
**Control**: Other not–for–profit (including NFP Corporation) **Service**: General medical and surgical

**Staffed Beds**: 150 **Admissions**: 3908 **Census**: 74 **Outpatient Visits**: 433312 **Births**: 428 **Total Expense ($000)**: 195501 **Payroll Expense ($000)**: 83799 **Personnel**: 1351

**MEMORIAL HEALTHCARE CENTER** See Memorial Healthcare

## PAW PAW—Van Buren County

⊠ **BRONSON LAKEVIEW HOSPITAL (231332)**, 408 Hazen Street, Zip 49079–1019, Mailing Address: P.O. Box 209, Zip 49079–0209; tel. 269/657–3141, (Nonreporting) **A**1 10 18 **F**3 6 9 11 15 18 29 30 34 35 36 40 44 55 56 57 58 59 63 64 65 66 68 71 74 75 77 79 81 82 84 85 86 87 93 97 98 100 101 102 103 107 108 110 111 114 115 118 119 127 129 130 132 135 143 146 147 148 149 154 156 **P**6 **S** Bronson Healthcare Group, Kalamazoo, MI
Primary Contact: Kirk Richardson, R.N., Senior Vice President, Chief Operating Officer, and Chief Nursing Officer
COO: Kirk Richardson, R.N., Senior Vice President, Chief Operating Officer, and Chief Nursing Officer
CFO: Becky East, CPA, Senior Vice President, Chief Financial Officer
CMO: Matthew Dommer, M.D., Vice President for Medical Affairs
CIO: Ash Goel, Senior Vice President Information Technology and Chief Information/Medical Informatics Officer
CHR: John Hayden, Senior Vice President and Chief Human Resources Officer
CNO: Kirk Richardson, R.N., Senior Vice President, Chief Operating Officer, and Chief Nursing Officer
Web address: www.bronsonhealth.com/lakeview
**Control**: Other not–for–profit (including NFP Corporation) **Service**: General medical and surgical

**Staffed Beds**: 35 **Admissions**: 766 **Census**: 11 **Outpatient Visits**: 117719 **Births**: 0 **Total Expense ($000)**: 53251 **Payroll Expense ($000)**: 27881 **Personnel**: 243

**LAKEVIEW COMMUNITY HOSPITAL** See Bronson Lakeview Hospital

## PETOSKEY—Emmet County

☐ **MCLAREN NORTHERN MICHIGAN (230105)**, 416 Connable Avenue, Zip 49770–2297; tel. 231/487–4000, (Nonreporting) **A**1 10 **F**3 13 15 17 18 20 22 24 26 28 29 30 31 32 34 35 36 38 40 42 44 45 48 49 50 51 53 57 58 59 60 64 68 70 74 75 76 77 78 79 81 82 85 86 87 89 90 91 93 94 96 107 108 110 111 114 115 119 120 121 123 124 127 129 130 132 135 146 148 149 154 156 157 **P**8 **S** McLaren Health Care Corporation, Grand Blanc, MI
Primary Contact: David M. Zechman, FACHE, President and Chief Executive Officer
CFO: David Bellamy, Chief Financial Officer
CMO: Kirk Lufkin, M.D., VPMA
CIO: David Bellamy, Chief Financial Officer
CHR: Gene Kaminski, Vice President Human Resources and Hospitality Services
CNO: Jennifer Woods, R.N., MSN, Chief Nursing Officer
Web address: www.northernhealth.org
**Control**: Other not–for–profit (including NFP Corporation) **Service**: General medical and surgical

**Staffed Beds**: 188 **Admissions**: 9210 **Census**: 101 **Outpatient Visits**: 209379 **Births**: 562 **Total Expense ($000)**: 258001 **Payroll Expense ($000)**: 84936 **Personnel**: 1313

**NORTHERN MICHIGAN REGIONAL HOSPITAL** See Mclaren Northern Michigan

## PIGEON—Huron County

⊠ **SCHEURER HEALTH (231310)**, 170 North Caseville Road, Zip 48755–9781; tel. 989/453–3223, (Total facility includes 19 beds in nursing home–type unit) (Nonreporting) **A**1 10 18 **F**3 7 8 10 11 15 28 29 30 31 32 34 35 37 40 43 44 45 50 53 54 56 57 59 64 65 68 69 75 77 78 79 81 85 86 87 91 93 97 107 108 110 115 118 119 125 127 130 131 132 133 134 144 146 149 156 **P**6
Primary Contact: Terrance Lerash, President and Chief Executive Officer
CFO: Terry Lutz, Chief Financial Officer
CMO: Ross Ramsey, M.D., Chief of Staff
CIO: Carleen Giddings, Information Technology System Leader
CHR: Gregory S. Foy, Risk Manager
CNO: Kendra Kretzschmer, Patient Care System Leader
Web address: www.scheurer.org
**Control**: Other not–for–profit (including NFP Corporation) **Service**: General medical and surgical

**Staffed Beds**: 44 **Admissions**: 316 **Census**: 21 **Outpatient Visits**: 42499 **Births**: 0 **Total Expense ($000)**: 41335 **Payroll Expense ($000)**: 20268 **Personnel**: 360

**SCHEURER HOSPITAL** See Scheurer Health

---

**MI**

## PLAINWELL—Allegan County

**BORGESS-PIPP HEALTH CENTER** See Borgess-Pipp Hospital

## PONTIAC—Oakland County

**DOCTORS' HOSPITAL OF MICHIGAN** See Pontiac General Hospital

☐ **MCLAREN OAKLAND (230207)**, 50 North Perry Street, Zip 48342–2253; tel. 248/338–5000, (Total facility includes 120 beds in nursing home–type unit) (Nonreporting) **A**1 3 5 10 12 **F**3 7 8 11 12 14 15 18 20 24 26 28 29 30 31 32 33 34 35 36 40 42 43 44 45 50 53 54 57 59 62 63 64 65 66 68 70 74 75 77 78 79 81 82 85 90 92 93 94 98 103 107 108 111 114 116 118 119 124 126 128 129 130 132 135 136 137 138 139 140 141 142 143 144 146 148 149 154 **P**8 **S** McLaren Health Care Corporation, Grand Blanc, MI
Primary Contact: Margaret Dimond, Ph.D., President and Chief Executive Officer
COO: Nicholle Mehr, Vice President Operations
CFO: Lynn Marcotte, Chief Financial Officer
CMO: Steven Calkin, D.O., Vice President Medical Affairs
CIO: Kelly Finley, Customer Site Executive
CHR: Dwan Cosby, Manager Human Resources
CNO: Calandra Anderson, Vice President Patient Care and Chief Nursing Officer
Web address: www.mclaren.org/oakland
**Control:** Other not–for–profit (including NFP Corporation) **Service:** General medical and surgical

**Staffed Beds:** 277 **Admissions:** 5782 **Census:** 199 **Outpatient Visits:** 164119 **Births:** 0 **Total Expense ($000):** 205825 **Payroll Expense ($000):** 78827 **Personnel:** 1228

☐ ○ **PIONEER SPECIALTY HOSPITAL (232039)**, 50 North Perry Street, 6th Floor, Zip 48342–2217; tel. 248/338–5430, (Nonreporting) **A**1 11
Primary Contact: Denise Wayne, Chief Executive Officer
Web address: www.pioneerspecialtyhospital.com
**Control:** Individual, Investor–owned (for–profit) **Service:** Acute long–term care hospital

**Staffed Beds:** 30

**POH REGIONAL MEDICAL CENTER** See Mclaren Oakland

**PONTIAC GENERAL HOSPITAL (230013)**, 461 West Huron Street, Zip 48341–1601; tel. 248/857–7200, (Nonreporting) **A**3 10
Primary Contact: Robert Barrow, Chief Executive Officer
COO: Dennis Franks, Vice President Operations
CFO: Dennis Franks, Interim Chief Financial Officer
CMO: Ray Breitenbach, M.D., Chief of Staff
CIO: Albert Sinisi, Director Information Systems
Web address: www.pontiacgeneral.com
**Control:** Other not–for–profit (including NFP Corporation) **Service:** General medical and surgical

**Staffed Beds:** 106

★ **SELECT SPECIALTY HOSPITAL-PONTIAC (232030)**, 44405 Woodward Avenue, 8th Floor, Zip 48341–5023; tel. 248/452–5252, (Nonreporting) **S** Select Medical Corporation, Mechanicsburg, PA
Primary Contact: Peggy Kingston, Chief Executive Officer
CMO: Fadi Salloum, M.D., Medical Director
CNO: Cathy Boyd, Chief Nursing Officer
Web address: www.selectspecialtyhospitals.com/company/locations/pontiac.aspx
**Control:** Corporation, Investor–owned (for–profit) **Service:** Acute long–term care hospital

**Staffed Beds:** 30

**ST JOSEPH MERCY-OAKLAND** See St. Joseph Mercy Oakland

⊞ **ST. JOSEPH MERCY OAKLAND (230029)**, 44405 Woodward Avenue, Zip 48341–5023; tel. 248/858–3000, (Nonreporting) **A**1 2 3 5 10 **F**3 8 11 12 13 15 17 18 20 22 24 26 28 29 30 31 34 35 36 39 40 41 43 44 45 46 48 49 50 53 54 55 56 57 58 59 61 64 65 66 68 70 72 74 75 76 77 78 79 81 82 84 85 86 87 89 90 93 96 97 98 100 102 105 107 108 110 111 114 115 118 119 126 129 130 131 132 135 144 146 147 148 149 150 154 **P**6 7 **S** Trinity Health, Livonia, MI
Primary Contact: Shannon Striebich, Chief Executive Officer
CFO: Michael Gusho, Chief Financial Officer
CMO: Fabian Fregoli, M.D., Chief Medical Officer
CIO: Robert Jones, Director Management Information Systems
CHR: Ane McNeil, Vice President Human Resources
CNO: Douglas R Dascenzo, MSN, R.N., Chief Nursing Officer
Web address: www.stjoesoakland.com
**Control:** Church operated, Nongovernment, not–for–profit **Service:** General medical and surgical

**Staffed Beds:** 396 **Admissions:** 20365 **Census:** 266 **Outpatient Visits:** 380829 **Births:** 1752 **Total Expense ($000):** 460827 **Payroll Expense ($000):** 185429 **Personnel:** 2632

## PORT HURON—St. Clair County

⊞ **LAKE HURON MEDICAL CENTER (230031)**, 2601 Electric Avenue, Zip 48060–6518; tel. 810/985–1500, (Nonreporting) **A**1 10 **F**3 12 15 18 20 28 29 30 31 34 35 40 43 45 46 47 49 50 54 56 57 58 59 64 66 70 74 75 77 78 79 81 82 85 86 87 90 91 93 96 97 107 108 110 114 115 119 120 121 123 126 130 131 132 135 146 147 148 149 154 156 **P**6 8 **S** Prime Healthcare, Ontario, CA
Primary Contact: Jose Kottoor, Chief Executive Officer
COO: Ken Sanger, R.N., Chief Nursing Officer and Chief Operations Officer
CFO: Chris Fulks, Vice President Finance
CMO: Sridhar Reddy, M.D., Chief Medical Officer
CIO: Jefferey Wagner, Director, Information Technology
CHR: Debra A Seifert, Director Human Resources
CNO: Ken Sanger, R.N., Chief Nursing Officer and Chief Operations Officer
Web address: www.https://www.mylakehuron.com
**Control:** Corporation, Investor–owned (for–profit) **Service:** General medical and surgical

**Staffed Beds:** 75 **Admissions:** 3578 **Census:** 41 **Outpatient Visits:** 107656 **Births:** 0 **Total Expense ($000):** 71897 **Payroll Expense ($000):** 26723 **Personnel:** 458

**MARWOOD MANOR** See Marwood Manor Nursing Home

⊞ **MCLAREN PORT HURON (230216)**, 1221 Pine Grove Avenue, Zip 48060–3511; tel. 810/987–5000, (Nonreporting) **A**1 10 **F**3 5 11 12 13 15 17 18 20 22 24 26 28 29 30 31 32 34 35 36 39 40 43 44 45 46 48 49 50 51 54 56 57 58 59 61 64 65 66 68 70 72 74 75 76 77 78 79 81 82 84 85 86 87 89 92 93 94 96 97 98 99 100 101 102 103 104 107 108 110 111 114 115 116 117 118 119 120 121 126 129 130 131 132 134 135 144 145 146 147 148 149 153 154 156 157 **P**6 **S** McLaren Health Care Corporation, Grand Blanc, MI
Primary Contact: Jennifer Montgomery, FACHE, R.N., President and Chief Executive Officer
COO: John Liston, Chief Operating Officer
CFO: Bridget Sholtis, Chief Financial Officer
CMO: Michael W Tawney, D.O., Vice President Medical Affairs
CIO: John McGrath, Chief Information Officer
CHR: Doris A Seidl, Vice President Human Resources
CNO: Christine R Sansom, Chief Nursing Officer
Web address: www.porthuronhospital.org
**Control:** Other not–for–profit (including NFP Corporation) **Service:** General medical and surgical

**Staffed Beds:** 186 **Admissions:** 11911 **Census:** 126 **Outpatient Visits:** 246313 **Births:** 1025 **Total Expense ($000):** 207739 **Payroll Expense ($000):** 77557 **Personnel:** 1227

**PORT HURON HOSPITAL** See Mclaren Port Huron

**ST. JOSEPH MERCY PORT HURON** See Lake Huron Medical Center

## REED CITY—Osceola County

⊞ **SPECTRUM HEALTH REED CITY HOSPITAL (231323)**, 300 North Patterson Road, Zip 49677–8041, Mailing Address: P.O. Box 75, Zip 49677–0075; tel. 231/832–3271, (Total facility includes 50 beds in nursing home–type unit) (Nonreporting) **A**1 10 18 **F**3 15 29 31 34 35 36 40 45 47 50 59 64 65 68 75 77 78 81 86 87 93 97 100 107 110 115 119 127 128 129 130 132 133 146 148 149 154 156 157 **P**6 **S** Spectrum Health, Grand Rapids, MI
Primary Contact: Andrea M. Leslie, MSN, R.N., President
COO: Cathy Rybicki, Chief Operating Officer
CFO: Thomas Knoerl, Vice President Finance
CMO: Thomas Campana, M.D., Chief of Staff
CIO: Brandi Johnson, Site Manager Technology Information Systems
CHR: Kris Miller, Senior Human Resources Business Partner
Web address: www.spectrumhealth.org/reedcity
**Control:** Other not–for–profit (including NFP Corporation) **Service:** General medical and surgical

**Staffed Beds:** 75 **Admissions:** 390 **Census:** 53 **Births:** 0 **Total Expense ($000):** 56829 **Payroll Expense ($000):** 16611 **Personnel:** 260

**SPECTRUM HEALTH-REED CITY** See Spectrum Health Reed City Hospital

*Many Facility Codes have changed. Please refer to the AHA Guide Code Chart.*

© 2021 AHA Guide

## ROCHESTER—Oakland County

✠ **ASCENSION CRITTENTON HOSPITAL MEDICAL CENTER (230254)**, 1101 West University Drive, Zip 48307–1831; tel. 248/652–5000, (Nonreporting) **A**1 3 5 10 **F**3 8 13 15 17 18 20 22 24 25 26 28 29 30 34 35 36 38 40 43 44 46 48 49 50 51 53 54 56 57 58 59 63 64 65 66 68 70 73 74 75 76 77 79 81 82 84 85 86 87 90 93 97 98 100 107 108 110 111 114 115 119 126 129 130 131 132 134 135 143 146 147 148 149 154 156 **S** Ascension Healthcare, Saint Louis, MO
Primary Contact: Chris Palazzolo, President and Chief Executive Officer
COO: Tomasine Marx, Chief Financial Officer and Chief Operating Officer
CFO: Tomasine Marx, Chief Financial Officer and Chief Operating Officer
CMO: Sheryl Wissman, M.D., Chief Medical Officer
CIO: Ralph Tenney, Chief Information Officer
CHR: Ann Vano, Vice President, Human Resources
Web address: www.crittenton.com
**Control**: Other not–for–profit (including NFP Corporation) **Service**: General medical and surgical

**Staffed Beds: 226 Admissions: 9611 Census: 121 Outpatient Visits: 200305 Births: 622 Total Expense ($000): 216345 Payroll Expense ($000): 71536 Personnel: 839**

**CRITTENTON HOSPITAL MEDICAL CENTER** See Ascension Crittenton Hospital Medical Center

## ROMEO—Macomb County

**ST JOSEPH'S-TRI COUNTY HOSP** See St. Joseph's Mercy-North

**ST. JOSEPH'S MERCY-NORTH** See Henry Ford Macomb Hospitals, Clinton Township

## ROYAL OAK—Oakland County

**BEAUMONT HOSP - ROYAL OAK** See Beaumont Hospital - Royal Oak

✠ **BEAUMONT HOSPITAL - ROYAL OAK (230130)**, 3601 West Thirteen Mile Road, Zip 48073–6712; tel. 248/898–5000, (Includes BEAUMONT CHILDREN'S HOSPITAL, Mailing address: 3601 West 13 Mile Road, Royal Oak, Michigan, Zip 48073–6712; tel. 248/898–5000), (Nonreporting) **A**1 2 3 5 8 10 19 **F**3 6 8 11 12 13 15 17 18 19 20 22 24 26 28 29 30 31 32 34 35 36 37 38 39 40 41 43 44 45 46 47 48 49 50 51 54 55 56 57 58 59 60 61 64 65 66 68 70 71 72 74 75 76 77 78 79 80 81 82 83 84 85 86 87 88 89 90 91 92 93 95 96 97 98 100 101 102 104 105 107 108 109 110 111 114 115 117 118 119 120 121 122 123 124 126 129 130 131 132 134 135 138 139 141 142 143 144 145 146 147 148 149 150 154 156 157 **P**1 6 **S** Beaumont Health, Southfield, MI
Primary Contact: Nancy Susick, MSN, President
COO: Debra Guido-Allen, Chief Operating Officer
CFO: John Kerndl, Executive Vice President and Chief Financial Officer
CMO: Leslie Rocher, Senior Vice President and Chief Medical Officer
CIO: Subra Sripada, Executive Vice President, Chief Transportation Officer and Chief Information Officer
CHR: Michael L Dixon, Vice President, Human Resources
CNO: Anne Stewart, Vice President and Chief Nursing Officer
Web address: www.beaumont.org
**Control**: Other not–for–profit (including NFP Corporation) **Service**: General medical and surgical

**Staffed Beds: 1109 Admissions: 57369 Census: 824 Outpatient Visits: 514095 Births: 6986 Total Expense ($000): 1327269 Payroll Expense ($000): 459129 Personnel: 8031**

## SAGINAW—Saginaw County

✠ △ **ALEDA E. LUTZ VETERANS AFFAIRS MEDICAL CENTER**, 1500 Weiss Street, Zip 48602–5298; tel. 989/497–2500, (Total facility includes 81 beds in nursing home–type unit) (Nonreporting) **A**1 3 7 **F**3 5 8 11 12 15 18 29 30 31 34 35 36 38 39 44 45 50 53 54 56 57 58 59 61 63 64 68 74 75 77 78 81 82 83 84 85 86 87 93 94 97 100 101 102 104 107 108 119 127 128 130 131 132 133 135 136 137 138 139 140 141 142 143 144 146 147 148 149 154 156 157 **S** Department of Veterans Affairs, Washington, DC
Primary Contact: Karandeep Sraon, Interim Director
COO: Stephanie Young, Associate Director
CFO: Jeff Drew, Fiscal Officer
CMO: Gregory Movsesian, M.D., Acting Chief of Staff
CIO: Angie Schmus, Chief Information Technology
CHR: Thomas Stredney, Chief Human Resources Management Service
CNO: Penny Holland, Associate Director for Patient Care Services
Web address: www.saginaw.va.gov/
**Control**: Veterans Affairs, Government, federal **Service**: General medical and surgical

**Staffed Beds: 89 Admissions: 906 Census: 33 Outpatient Visits: 427692 Births: 0 Total Expense ($000): 251429 Payroll Expense ($000): 98169 Personnel: 1234**

✠ **ASCENSION ST. MARY'S OF MICHIGAN (230077)**, 800 South Washington Avenue, Zip 48601–2594; tel. 989/907–8000, (Nonreporting) **A**1 2 3 5 10 19 **F**2 3 11 12 15 17 18 20 22 24 26 28 29 30 31 34 35 37 40 41 42 43 45 46 49 50 54 56 57 58 59 64 66 70 74 77 78 79 80 81 85 86 87 92 93 96 97 100 102 107 108 110 111 114 115 118 119 120 121 123 124 126 129 130 131 132 135 144 146 149 154 **P**6 8 **S** Ascension Healthcare, Saint Louis, MO
Primary Contact: Stephanie J. Duggan, M.D., President
CFO: Nancy Haywood, Chief Financial Officer
CMO: Raghu Sarvepalli, M.D., Vice President of Medical Affairs
CIO: Daniel Stross, Chief Information Officer
CHR: Paula Coffee, Director Human Resources
CNO: Bernie Jore, Chief Nursing Officer
Web address: www.stmarysofmichigan.org
**Control**: Church operated, Nongovernment, not–for–profit **Service**: General medical and surgical

**Staffed Beds: 179 Admissions: 9802 Census: 129 Outpatient Visits: 322637 Births: 0 Total Expense ($000): 289284 Payroll Expense ($000): 100841 Personnel: 1072**

★ ○ △ **COVENANT HEALTHCARE (230070)**, 1447 North Harrison Street, Zip 48602–4727; tel. 989/583–0000, (Includes COVENANT MEDICAL CENTER-COOPER, Mailing address: 700 Cooper Avenue, Saginaw, Michigan, Zip 48602–5399; tel. 989/583–0000; Edward Bruff, President and Chief Executive Officer; COVENANT MEDICAL CENTER-HARRISON, Mailing address: 1447 North Harrison Street, Saginaw, Michigan, Zip 48602–4785; tel. 989/583–0000; Edward Bruff, President and Chief Executive Officer; COVENANT MEDICAL CENTER, Mailing address: 515 N. Michigan Avenue, Saginaw, Michigan, Zip 48602–4316; tel. 989/583–6000; Edward Bruff, President and Chief Executive Officer) (Total facility includes 20 beds in nursing home–type unit) **A**2 3 5 7 10 11 **F**3 8 11 12 13 15 17 18 19 20 22 24 25 26 27 28 29 30 31 35 36 40 41 42 43 45 46 47 48 49 50 54 57 58 59 60 61 62 63 64 65 70 72 74 75 76 77 78 79 81 82 83 84 86 87 88 89 90 91 92 93 94 97 107 108 110 111 113 114 115 118 119 120 121 123 124 126 128 129 130 131 132 135 143 144 146 147 148 154 **P**8
Primary Contact: Edward Bruff, President and Chief Executive Officer
COO: Daniel M George, Executive Vice President, Operations
CFO: Kevin Albosta, Vice President, Chief Financial Officer
CMO: John Kosanovich, M.D., Executive Vice President Physician Enterprise and Chief Executive Officer, Covenant Medical Group
CHR: Kevin Birchmeier, Director Human Resources
CNO: Beth Charlton, Vice President Patient Services and Chief Nursing Officer
Web address: www.covenanthealthcare.com
**Control**: Other not–for–profit (including NFP Corporation) **Service**: General medical and surgical

**Staffed Beds: 534 Admissions: 26449 Census: 397 Outpatient Visits: 467754 Births: 2976 Total Expense ($000): 635250 Payroll Expense ($000): 305538 Personnel: 4377**

**COVENANT MEDICAL CENTER** See Covenant Healthcare

**HEALTHSOURCE SAGINAW** See Healthsource Saginaw, Inc.

□ **HEALTHSOURCE SAGINAW, INC. (230275)**, 3340 Hospital Road, Zip 48603–9622; tel. 989/790–7700, (Total facility includes 213 beds in nursing home–type unit) (Nonreporting) **A**1 3 5 10 **F**4 5 64 90 91 93 96 98 99 100 101 103 104 128 130 143 146
Primary Contact: Lisa Lapham, President and Chief Executive Officer
CFO: Glen Chipman, Chief Financial Officer
CMO: Daniel Duffy, D.O., Chief Medical Director
CIO: Greg Sieg, Support Services Executive
CHR: Krystal Hadaway, Director Human Resources
CNO: Susan Graham, R.N., Nurse Executive
Web address: www.healthsourcesaginaw.org
**Control**: Other not–for–profit (including NFP Corporation) **Service**: Psychiatric

**Staffed Beds: 347 Admissions: 4161 Census: 274 Outpatient Visits: 13290 Births: 0 Total Expense ($000): 54467 Payroll Expense ($000): 26439 Personnel: 548**

**MI**

---

**Hospital, Medicare Provider Number, Address, Telephone, Approval, Facility, and Physician Codes, Health Care System**

★ American Hospital Association (AHA) membership ○ Healthcare Facilities Accreditation Program ⇧ Center for Improvement in Healthcare Quality Accreditation
□ The Joint Commission accreditation ◇ DNV Healthcare Inc. accreditation △ Commission on Accreditation of Rehabilitation Facilities (CARF) accreditation

**SAGINAW GENERAL HOSPITAL** See Covenant Medical Center-Harrison

☒ **SELECT SPECIALTY HOSPITAL-SAGINAW (232033)**, 1447 North Harrison Street, 8th Floor, Zip 48602–4785; tel. 989/583–4235, (Nonreporting) **A**1 10 **S** Select Medical Corporation, Mechanicsburg, PA
Primary Contact: Matthew J. Campbell Esq, Chief Executive Officer
CNO: Shannon Sequin, MSN, Chief Nursing Officer
Web address: www.selectspecialtyhospitals.com/company/locations/saginaw.aspx
**Control**: Corporation, Investor–owned (for–profit) **Service**: Acute long–term care hospital

| Staffed Beds: 32 |
|---|

**SELECT SPECIALTY HOSP-SAGINAW** See Select Specialty Hospital-Saginaw

**ST LUKE'S HOSPITAL** See Covenant Medical Center-Cooper

**ST. MARY'S OF MICHIGAN** See Ascension St. Mary's of Michigan

**VETERANS AFFAIRS MED CENTER** See Aleda E. Lutz Veterans Affairs Medical Center

**SAINT IGNACE—Mackinac County**

⇑ **MACKINAC STRAITS HEALTH SYSTEM** See Mackinac Straits Health System, Inc.

★ ⇑ **MACKINAC STRAITS HEALTH SYSTEM, INC. (231306)**, 1140 North State Street, Zip 49781–1048; tel. 906/643–8585, (Total facility includes 48 beds in nursing home–type unit) (Nonreporting) **A**10 18 21 **F**3 8 15 28 29 31 40 42 45 51 54 56 59 64 65 74 75 77 78 79 81 91 93 97 107 110 111 115 119 127 128 130 133 135 146 147 148 154 156
Primary Contact: Karen Cheeseman, Chief Executive Officer
CFO: Ryan Speas, Chief Financial Officer
CMO: Loretta Leja, M.D., Chief of Staff
CHR: Kevin McElroy, Chief Human Resources Officer
Web address: www.mackinacstraitshealth.org
**Control**: Other not–for–profit (including NFP Corporation) **Service**: General medical and surgical

| Staffed Beds: 63 Admissions: 352 Census: 53 Outpatient Visits: 36968 Births: 0 Total Expense ($000): 45011 Payroll Expense ($000): 15650 Personnel: 179 |
|---|

**SAINT JOHNS—Clinton County**

☐ **CEDAR CREEK HOSPITAL OF MICHIGAN (234043)**, 101 W Townsend Road, Zip 48879–9200; tel. 833/837–0923, (Nonreporting) **A**1 **S** Universal Health Services, Inc., King of Prussia, PA
Primary Contact: Scott Miles, Chief Executive Officer
Web address: www.cedarcreekhospital.com
**Control**: Corporation, Investor–owned (for–profit) **Service**: Psychiatric

| Staffed Beds: 54 |
|---|

**CLINTON MEMORIAL HOSPITAL** See Sparrow Clinton Hospital

☒ **SPARROW CLINTON HOSPITAL (231326)**, 805 South Oakland Street, Zip 48879–2253; tel. 989/227–3400, (Nonreporting) **A**1 10 18 **F**3 11 15 18 31 32 34 35 40 43 45 50 53 57 59 64 68 70 75 77 78 79 81 85 93 97 107 108 110 111 115 119 129 130 131 133 146 148 149 156 **P**6 **S** Sparrow Health System, Lansing, MI
Primary Contact: Beth Ann Daugherty, M.P.H., R.N., President
COO: Kevin A Price, Vice President and Chief Operating Officer
CFO: Mark Brisboe, VP and Chief Financial Officer
CMO: Christopher Beal, M.D., Chief of Staff
Web address: www.sparrowclinton.org
**Control**: Other not–for–profit (including NFP Corporation) **Service**: General medical and surgical

| Staffed Beds: 25 Admissions: 844 Census: 8 Outpatient Visits: 94974 Births: 0 Total Expense ($000): 45255 Payroll Expense ($000): 17934 Personnel: 210 |
|---|

**SAINT JOSEPH—Berrien County**

☒ **SPECTRUM HEALTH LAKELAND (230021)**, 1234 Napier Avenue, Zip 49085–2158; tel. 269/983–8300, (Includes LAKELAND HOSPITAL, NILES, Mailing address: 31 North Saint Joseph Avenue, Niles, Michigan, Zip 49120; tel. 269/683–5510; Debra Johnson, R.N., Chief Administrator), (Nonreporting) **A**1 2 3 5 8 10 13 **S** Spectrum Health, Grand Rapids, MI
Primary Contact: Loren Hamel, M.D., President and Chief Executive Officer
CFO: Timothy Calhoun, Vice President Finance and Chief Financial Officer
CMO: Stephen Hempel, M.D., President Medical Staff
CIO: Emily Gallay, Vice President and Chief Information Officer
Web address: www.lakelandhealth.org
**Control**: Other not–for–profit (including NFP Corporation) **Service**: General medical and surgical

| Staffed Beds: 300 |
|---|

**SPECTRUM HEALTH LAKELAND** See Spectrum Health Lakeland

**SALINE—Washtenaw County**

☐ **CENTER FOR FORENSIC PSYCHIATRY (234041)**, 8303 Platt Rd, Zip 48176–9773, Mailing Address: P.O. Box 2060, Ann Arbor, Zip 48106–2060; tel. 734/429–2531, (Nonreporting) **A**1 3 10
Primary Contact: Diane Heisel, Acting Director
Web address: www.michigan.gov
**Control**: County, Government, Nonfederal **Service**: Psychiatric

| Staffed Beds: 210 |
|---|

**SANDUSKY—Sanilac County**

**MCKENZIE HEALTH SYSTEM (231314)**, 120 North Delaware Street, Zip 48471–1087; tel. 810/648–3770, (Nonreporting) **A**10 18
Primary Contact: Steve Barnett, President and Chief Executive Officer
COO: Billi Jo Hennika, Vice President Operations
CFO: Amy Ruedisueli, Vice President of Finance
CMO: James C. Sams, Chief of Staff
CHR: Carrie Krampits, Director Human Resources
CNO: Patricia Schafsnitz, Director of Nursing Services
Web address: www.mckenziehealth.org
**Control**: Other not–for–profit (including NFP Corporation) **Service**: General medical and surgical

| Staffed Beds: 25 |
|---|

**MCKENZIE MEMORIAL HOSPITAL** See Mckenzie Health System

**SAULT SAINTE MARIE—Chippewa County**

⇑ **CHIPPEWA CNTY WAR MEM HOSPITAL** See War Memorial Hospital

★ ⇑ **WAR MEMORIAL HOSPITAL (230239)**, 500 Osborn Boulevard, Zip 49783–1884; tel. 906/635–4460, (Total facility includes 51 beds in nursing home–type unit) (Nonreporting) **A**10 20 21 **F**3 11 12 13 15 18 28 29 30 31 34 35 36 38 40 43 44 50 51 53 54 55 56 57 59 60 61 64 65 66 68 70 75 76 77 78 79 81 82 85 87 92 93 96 97 98 100 101 103 104 106 107 108 110 111 115 119 126 127 128 129 130 131 132 133 135 143 144 146 147 148 154 156 **P**6
Primary Contact: David B. Jahn, President and Chief Executive Officer
COO: Marla Bunker, Vice President Nursing and Chief Operating Officer
CFO: Kevin Kalchik, Chief Financial Officer
CMO: Paula Rechner, M.D., Chief Medical Officer
CIO: Sandy DePlonty, Senior Director Clinical Services
CHR: Susan Sliger, Director Human Resources
CNO: Marla Bunker, Vice President Nursing and Chief Operating Officer
Web address: www.warmemorialhospital.org
**Control**: Other not–for–profit (including NFP Corporation) **Service**: General medical and surgical

| Staffed Beds: 120 Admissions: 2887 Census: 83 Outpatient Visits: 214749 Births: 310 Total Expense ($000): 106996 Payroll Expense ($000): 44986 Personnel: 775 |
|---|

**SHELBY—Oceana County**

**MERCY HEALTH PARTNERS, LAKESHORE CAMPUS** See Mercy Health, Lakeshore Campus

☒ **MERCY HEALTH, LAKESHORE CAMPUS (231320)**, 72 South State Street, Zip 49455–1299; tel. 231/861–2156, (Nonreporting) **A**1 10 18 **F**3 11 15 29 30 34 35 40 43 45 47 50 57 59 68 81 83 84 85 87 89 97 107 110 111 114 119 127 129 131 132 146 **S** Trinity Health, Livonia, MI
Primary Contact: John T. Foss, Vice President, Operations
Web address: www.mercyhealthmuskegon.com
**Control**: Other not–for–profit (including NFP Corporation) **Service**: General medical and surgical

| Staffed Beds: 24 Admissions: 317 Census: 3 Outpatient Visits: 99649 Births: 0 Total Expense ($000): 32351 Payroll Expense ($000): 14159 Personnel: 201 |
|---|

**SHERIDAN—Montcalm County**

○ **SHERIDAN COMMUNITY HOSPITAL (231312)**, 301 North Main Street, Zip 48884–9235, Mailing Address: P.O. Box 279, Zip 48884–0279; tel. 989/291–3261, (Nonreporting) **A**10 11 18 **F**3 4 5 8 11 15 30 34 35 40 45 50 57 59 64 68 75 77 81 84 86 87 93 97 107 110 114 115 119 127 133 144 146 152 **P**6
Primary Contact: Lili Petricevic, Chief Executive Officer
COO: Steve Scott, Chief Operating Officer
CMO: Maria Charlotte Alvarez, M.D., Chief of Staff
CIO: David Bussler, Chief Information Officer
CHR: Sharon Bowers, R.N., Manager of Community, Public and Employee Relations
CNO: Kim Christensen, Interim Chief Nursing Executive
Web address: www.sheridanhospital.com
**Control**: Other not–for–profit (including NFP Corporation) **Service**: General medical and surgical

| Staffed Beds: 12 Admissions: 78 Census: 1 Outpatient Visits: 16963 Births: 0 Total Expense ($000): 12739 Payroll Expense ($000): 5240 Personnel: 105 |
|---|

MI

## SOUTH HAVEN—Van Buren County

☒ **BRONSON SOUTH HAVEN HOSPITAL (230085)**, 955 South Bailey Avenue, Zip 49090–6743; tel. 269/637–5271, (Nonreporting) **A**1 10 **F**3 11 15 18 28 29 30 31 34 35 36 39 40 45 50 53 54 57 59 64 65 68 70 75 77 78 79 82 84 85 86 87 93 97 107 108 110 111 114 115 118 119 127 129 130 131 132 135 144 146 147 148 149 154 156 **P**6 **S** Bronson Healthcare Group, Kalamazoo, MI
Primary Contact: Kirk Richardson, R.N., Vice President, Chief Operating Officer and Chief Nursing Officer
CFO: Mark Gross, Executive Vice President and Chief Financial Officer
CMO: Allan Caudill, M.D., Chief of Staff
CIO: Dennis Sorenson, Supervisor Information Technology
CHR: Kim Wise, Director Human Resources
CNO: Donna Cassidy, Chief Nursing Executive
Web address: www.sh-hs.org
**Control**: Other not–for–profit (including NFP Corporation) **Service**: General medical and surgical

**Staffed Beds:** 49 **Admissions:** 398 **Census:** 3 **Outpatient Visits:** 103944 **Births:** 0 **Total Expense ($000):** 38822 **Payroll Expense ($000):** 20240 **Personnel:** 243

**SOUTH HAVEN HEALTH SYSTEM** See Bronson South Haven Hospital

## SOUTHFIELD—Oakland County

☒ **ASCENSION OF PROVIDENCE HOSPITAL, SOUTHFIELD CAMPUS (230019)**, 16001 West Nine Mile Road, Zip 48075; tel. 248/849–3400, (Includes PROVIDENCE – PROVIDENCE PARK HOSPITAL, NOVI CAMPUS, Mailing address: 47601 Grand River Avebue, Novi, Michigan, Zip 48374–1233; tel. 248/465–4100; Joseph R. Hurshe, President), (Nonreporting) **A**1 2 3 5 10 19 **F**3 9 11 12 13 15 17 18 20 22 24 26 28 29 30 31 34 35 36 37 38 39 40 43 44 45 46 47 48 49 50 51 54 55 56 57 58 59 60 61 63 64 65 66 68 70 72 74 75 76 77 78 79 80 81 82 84 85 86 87 90 91 92 93 96 97 98 100 101 102 107 108 110 111 114 115 118 119 120 121 123 124 126 129 130 131 132 135 141 146 147 148 149 150 154 156 157 **S** Ascension Healthcare, Saint Louis, MO
Primary Contact: Joseph R. Hurshe, President
CFO: Douglas Winner, Chief Financial Officer, Acute Care Operations
CHR: Ann Vano, Vice President Human Resources
Web address: www.https://ascension.org/michigan
**Control**: Church operated, Nongovernment, not–for–profit **Service**: General medical and surgical

**Staffed Beds:** 628 **Admissions:** 31598 **Census:** 390 **Outpatient Visits:** 820057 **Births:** 3336 **Total Expense ($000):** 737363 **Payroll Expense ($000):** 240167 **Personnel:** 2695

**OAKLAND REGIONAL HOSPITAL** See Surgeons Choice Medical Center

**PROVIDENCE-PROVIDENCE PARK HOSPITALS** See Ascension of Providence Hospital, Southfield Campus

☒ **STRAITH HOSPITAL FOR SPECIAL SURGERY (230071)**, 23901 Lahser Road, Zip 48033–6035; tel. 248/357–3360, (Nonreporting) **A**1 10
Primary Contact: Jan Rys, R.N., Chief Executive Officer
CFO: Bradley Bescoe, Chief Financial Officer
CNO: Michelle Holder, Nurse Executive
Web address: www.straith.org/
**Control**: Other not–for–profit (including NFP Corporation) **Service**: Surgical

**Staffed Beds:** 24

○ **SURGEONS CHOICE MEDICAL CENTER (230301)**, 22401 Foster Winter Drive, Zip 48075–3724; tel. 248/423–5100, (Nonreporting) **A**3 10 11
Primary Contact: Steven Craig, Ph.D., Chief Operating Officer and Acting Chief Executive Officer
COO: Steven Craig, Ph.D., Chief Operating Officer and Acting Chief Executive Officer
CMO: John Jack Ryan, M.D., Chief Medical Officer
CIO: William Moncrief, ORH IT Client Executive
CHR: Gordon Meyer, Director Human Resources
CNO: Lola Evans, Director of Nursing
Web address: www.oaklandregionalhospital.com
**Control**: Corporation, Investor–owned (for–profit) **Service**: Surgical

**Staffed Beds:** 71

## STANDISH—Arenac County

☒ **ASCENSION STANDISH HOSPITAL (231305)**, 805 West Cedar Street, Zip 48658–9526; tel. 989/846–4521, (Total facility includes 29 beds in nursing home–type unit) (Nonreporting) **A**1 10 18 **F**2 3 29 30 34 35 40 50 59 64 70 77 84 85 86 87 97 100 102 128 130 132 133 135 146 149 154 **S** Ascension Healthcare, Saint Louis, MO
Primary Contact: Stephanie J. Duggan, M.D., President
CFO: Tony Doud, Controller
CMO: Jaya Sankaran, M.D., Chief of Staff
CIO: Tammy Copes, Director Information Systems
CHR: Renee Reetz, Director Human Resources
Web address: www.stmarysofmichigan.org/standish
**Control**: Church operated, Nongovernment, not–for–profit **Service**: General medical and surgical

**Staffed Beds:** 54 **Admissions:** 743 **Census:** 29 **Births:** 0

**ST. MARY'S OF MICHIGAN STANDISH HOSPITAL** See Ascension Standish Hospital

## STURGIS—St. Joseph County

★ ⇧ **STURGIS HOSPITAL (230096)**, 916 Myrtle Street, Zip 49091–2326; tel. 269/651–7824, (Nonreporting) **A**10 21
Primary Contact: Robert J. Morin, Chief Financial Officer and Chief Operating Officer
COO: Robert J. Morin, Chief Financial Officer and Chief Operating Officer
CFO: Robert J. Morin, Chief Financial Officer and Chief Operating Officer
CMO: James Grannell, Chief Medical Officer
CIO: Rita Denison, Director of Information Systems
CHR: Mary Kay Schultz, Director Human Resources
CNO: Charlotte J Pavilanis, R.N., Vice President of Clinical Services and Chief Nursing Officer
Web address: www.sturgishospital.com
**Control**: Other not–for–profit (including NFP Corporation) **Service**: General medical and surgical

**Staffed Beds:** 49

## TAWAS CITY—Iosco County

☒ **ASCENSION ST. JOSEPH HOSPITAL (230100)**, 200 Hemlock Street, Zip 48763–9237, Mailing Address: P.O. Box 659, Zip 48764–0659; tel. 989/362–3411, (Nonreporting) **A**1 10 20 **F**3 8 13 15 29 30 31 34 35 40 43 45 50 59 65 68 70 75 76 78 79 81 82 93 107 110 111 115 118 119 127 129 130 135 146 147 149 154 156 **S** Ascension Healthcare, Saint Louis, MO
Primary Contact: Stephanie J. Duggan, M.D., President
CFO: Tony Doud, Controller
CIO: Daniel Stross, Chief Information Officer
CHR: Nancy Bodenner, Director Human Resources
Web address: www.sjhsys.org
**Control**: Church operated, Nongovernment, not–for–profit **Service**: General medical and surgical

**Staffed Beds:** 47 **Admissions:** 1503 **Census:** 9 **Outpatient Visits:** 173349 **Births:** 204 **Total Expense ($000):** 52979 **Payroll Expense ($000):** 17882 **Personnel:** 170

**ST. JOSEPH HEALTH SYSTEM** See Ascension St. Joseph Hospital

## TAYLOR—Wayne County

☒ **BEAUMONT HOSPITAL - TAYLOR (230270)**, 10000 Telegraph Road, Zip 48180–3330; tel. 313/295–5000, (Nonreporting) **A**1 3 5 10 **F**3 11 15 29 30 34 35 37 38 39 40 44 46 49 50 56 57 59 61 64 65 68 70 74 75 79 81 82 85 86 87 90 92 93 96 98 100 101 102 104 105 107 108 111 114 117 118 119 126 130 131 132 135 146 148 149 154 **P**6 8 **S** Beaumont Health, Southfield, MI
Primary Contact: Lee Ann Odom, Division President
COO: Carolyn Wilson, R.N., Chief Operating Officer
CFO: Mark Deming, Administrator, Finance and Support
CMO: Kassem Charara, Chief Medical Officer
CIO: Subra Sripada, Exec. Vice President, Chief Transformation Officer and Chief Information Officer
CHR: Karen Krolicki, Director, Human Resources
CNO: Kristine Marie Donahue, Administrator, Clinical Operations
Web address: www.beaumont.org
**Control**: Other not–for–profit (including NFP Corporation) **Service**: General medical and surgical

**Staffed Beds:** 180 **Admissions:** 8310 **Census:** 130 **Outpatient Visits:** 97404 **Births:** 0 **Total Expense ($000):** 152737 **Payroll Expense ($000):** 64879 **Personnel:** 1126

**OAKWOOD HOSPITAL-TAYLOR** See Beaumont Hospital - Taylor

---

**Hospital, Medicare Provider Number, Address, Telephone, Approval, Facility, and Physician Codes, Health Care System**

★ American Hospital Association (AHA) membership
□ The Joint Commission accreditation
○ Healthcare Facilities Accreditation Program
◇ DNV Healthcare Inc. accreditation
⇧ Center for Improvement in Healthcare Quality Accreditation
△ Commission on Accreditation of Rehabilitation Facilities (CARF) accreditation

## TECUMSEH—Lenawee County

**HERRICK MEDICAL CENTER** See Promedica Herrick Hospital

★ ○ **PROMEDICA HERRICK HOSPITAL (231334)**, 500 East Pottawatamie Street, Zip 49286–2018; tel. 517/424–3000, (Nonreporting) **A**10 11 18 **F**8 11 15 18 26 29 34 35 36 39 40 53 57 59 65 68 74 75 77 81 82 87 92 93 96 97 104 107 108 110 114 119 129 130 132 135 146 147 148 149 150 154 156 157 **P**8 **S** ProMedica Health System, Toledo, OH
Primary Contact: Julie Yaroch, President
COO: Gregory Peckham, Associate Vice President, Operations
CFO: Joe Raj, Administrative Director, Finance
CIO: Patrick Heskett, Director, Information Technology
CHR: Kim Langley, Business Partner
Web address: www.promedica.org
**Control**: Other not–for–profit (including NFP Corporation) **Service**: General medical and surgical

**Staffed Beds: 10 Admissions: 75 Census: 1 Outpatient Visits:** 34615 **Births: 0 Total Expense ($000):** 24246 **Payroll Expense ($000):** 5917 **Personnel:** 67

## THREE RIVERS—St. Joseph County

**THREE RIVERS AREA HOSPITAL** See Three Rivers Health

★ ○ **THREE RIVERS HEALTH (230015)**, 701 South Health Parkway, Zip 49093–8352; tel. 269/278–1145, (Nonreporting) **A**10 11 **F**3 4 11 13 15 28 29 31 32 34 40 45 50 53 54 61 62 63 65 70 75 76 77 79 81 82 90 93 96 97 107 108 110 111 115 119 127 129 130 131 132 133 147 148 154 156 **S** QHR Health, Brentwood, TN
Primary Contact: David A. Shannon, Interim Chief Executive Officer
COO: Laurie Herbert, Vice President Operations
CFO: Steve Andrews, Chief Financial Officer
CIO: Dave Parks, Chief Information Officer
Web address: www.threerivershealth.org
**Control**: Other not–for–profit (including NFP Corporation) **Service**: General medical and surgical

**Staffed Beds: 60 Admissions: 1301 Census: 13 Outpatient Visits:** 257181 **Births: 278 Total Expense ($000):** 62992 **Payroll Expense ($000):** 23121 **Personnel:** 433

## TRAVERSE CITY—Grand Traverse County

⊞ **MUNSON MEDICAL CENTER (230097)**, 1105 Sixth Street, Zip 49684–2386; tel. 231/935–5000, (Nonreporting) **A**1 2 3 5 10 13 **F**2 4 10 15 17 28 34 35 39 40 43 44 45 47 48 49 50 53 54 55 56 57 58 59 60 61 62 63 65 68 70 71 72 74 75 76 77 78 79 81 82 84 85 86 87 89 90 92 93 94 96 97 98 100 101 102 103 104 105 107 108 110 111 115 116 117 118 119 120 121 123 124 126 129 130 131 132 134 135 141 142 143 144 145 146 147 148 149 154 156 157 **P**6 **S** Munson Healthcare, Traverse City, MI
Primary Contact: Matt Wille, President and Chief Executive Officer
COO: Derk F. Pronger, Chief Operating Officer
CFO: Mark A Helper, Corporate Vice President and Chief Financial Officer
CMO: Kevin Omilusik, M.D., Chief Medical Officer
CIO: Christopher J Podges, Vice President and Chief Information Officer
CHR: Suzanne K Peters, Vice President Human Resources
Web address: www.munsonhealthcare.org
**Control**: Other not–for–profit (including NFP Corporation) **Service**: General medical and surgical

**Staffed Beds: 442 Admissions: 21441 Census: 272 Outpatient Visits:** 562109 **Births: 1792 Total Expense ($000):** 629616 **Payroll Expense ($000):** 241086 **Personnel:** 3615

## TRENTON—Wayne County

⊞ **BEAUMONT HOSPITAL - TRENTON (230176)**, 5450 Fort Street, Zip 48183–4625; tel. 734/671–3800, (Nonreporting) **A**1 3 5 10 12 13 **F**3 8 11 12 13 15 18 20 22 26 28 29 30 34 35 38 39 40 43 44 45 46 47 49 50 51 56 57 59 60 61 64 65 68 70 74 75 76 78 79 80 81 82 84 85 87 91 92 93 100 102 107 108 110 111 114 115 119 126 130 131 132 135 146 147 148 149 150 154 157 **P**6 8 **S** Beaumont Health, Southfield, MI
Primary Contact: Lee Ann Odom, Interim President
COO: Carolyn Wilson, R.N., Executive Vice President, Chief Operating Officer
CFO: Shawn Beggs, Administrator, Finance
CMO: Jonathan Kaper, Chief Medical Officer
CHR: Michelle Corra, Administrator, Human Resources
CNO: Susan G Schulz, Chief Nursing Officer
Web address: www.beaumont.org
**Control**: Other not–for–profit (including NFP Corporation) **Service**: General medical and surgical

**Staffed Beds: 193 Admissions: 10296 Census: 111 Outpatient Visits:** 92478 **Births: 679 Total Expense ($000):** 181234 **Payroll Expense ($000):** 67062 **Personnel:** 1110

**BEAUMONT HOSPITAL-SOUTHSHORE** See Beaumont Hospital - Trenton

## TROY—Oakland County

⊞ **BEAUMONT HOSPITAL - TROY (230269)**, 44201 Dequindre Road, Zip 48085–1117; tel. 248/964–5000, (Nonreporting) **A**1 2 3 5 10 13 19 **F**3 8 11 12 13 15 17 18 19 20 22 24 26 28 29 30 31 32 34 35 36 37 38 39 40 41 43 44 45 46 47 49 50 53 54 55 58 59 60 61 64 65 66 68 70 71 72 74 75 76 77 78 79 80 81 82 84 85 86 87 89 90 91 92 93 96 97 100 102 107 108 109 110 111 114 115 117 118 119 120 121 123 124 126 129 130 131 132 135 141 142 143 145 146 147 148 149 150 157 **P**6 **S** Beaumont Health, Southfield, MI
Primary Contact: James Lynch, M.D., Interim President
COO: Carolyn Wilson, R.N., Chief Operating Officer
CFO: Mark Leonard, Vice President Finance
CMO: James Lynch, M.D., Senior Vice President and Chief Medical Officer
CIO: Subra Sripada, Executive Vice President, Chief Transportation Officer and Chief Information Officer
CHR: Lisa Ouelette, Director Human Resources
Web address: www.beaumont.org
**Control**: Other not–for–profit (including NFP Corporation) **Service**: General medical and surgical

**Staffed Beds: 520 Admissions: 36537 Census: 435 Outpatient Visits:** 370909 **Births: 3546 Total Expense ($000):** 662299 **Payroll Expense ($000):** 256702 **Personnel:** 4376

**BEAUMONT HOSPITALS - TROY** See Beaumont Hospital - Troy

## TUPELO—Lee County

⊞ △ **NORTH MISSISSIPPI HEALTH SERVICES, INC. (250004)**, 830 South Gloster Street, Zip 38801–4934; tel. 662/377–3136, (Total facility includes 107 beds in nursing home–type unit) (Nonreporting) **A**1 2 3 5 7 8 10 **F**3 4 5 6 7 8 9 11 12 13 15 17 18 20 22 24 26 28 29 30 31 32 34 35 38 40 43 44 45 46 47 48 49 50 51 53 54 55 56 57 58 59 61 62 63 64 65 66 68 70 71 72 73 74 75 76 77 78 79 81 83 84 85 86 87 88 89 90 91 92 93 94 95 96 97 98 100 101 103 104 107 108 109 110 111 112 113 114 115 116 117 118 119 120 121 122 123 124 126 128 129 130 131 132 134 135 146 147 148 152 154 **S** North Mississippi Health Services, Inc., Tupelo, MS
Primary Contact: David C. Wilson, President
CFO: Sharon Nobles, Chief Financial Officer
CMO: Jeremy Blanchard, M.D., Chief Medical Officer
CIO: James Weldon, Chief Information Officer
Web address: www.nmhs.net
**Control**: Other not–for–profit (including NFP Corporation) **Service**: General medical and surgical

**Staffed Beds: 741 Admissions: 25614 Census: 468 Outpatient Visits:** 655958 **Births: 2272 Total Expense ($000):** 703903 **Payroll Expense ($000):** 272702 **Personnel:** 4090

## WARREN—Macomb County

⊞ **ASCENSION MACOMB-OAKLAND HOSPITAL (230195)**, 11800 East 12 Mile Road, Zip 48093–3472; tel. 586/573–5000, (Includes ST. JOHN MACOMB-OAKLAND HOSPITAL, MADISON HEIGHTS CAMPUS, Mailing address: 27351 Dequindre, Madison Heights, Michigan, Zip 48071–3487; tel. 248/967–7000; Terry Hamilton, President; ST. JOHN MACOMB-OAKLAND HOSPITAL, WARREN CAMPUS, Mailing address: 11800 East Twelve Mile Road, Warren, Michigan, Zip 48093–3472; tel. 586/573–5000; Terry Hamilton, President), (Nonreporting) **A**1 2 3 5 10 12 **F**3 11 12 13 15 18 20 22 24 26 28 29 30 31 34 35 36 38 39 40 43 44 45 46 47 48 49 50 51 54 58 59 60 61 63 64 65 66 70 74 75 76 77 78 79 80 81 82 84 85 86 87 90 92 93 96 97 98 100 101 102 105 107 108 110 111 115 118 119 121 123 126 129 130 131 132 135 141 146 147 148 149 150 154 156 157 **P**4 6 8 **S** Ascension Healthcare, Saint Louis, MO
Primary Contact: Gary Druskovich, M.D., President
COO: William Mott, Chief Operating Officer
CFO: Patrick McGuire, Chief Financial Officer, Michigan Market
CMO: Gary L Berg, D.O., Chief Medical Officer
CIO: Ralph Tenney, Chief Information Officer
CHR: Joanne E Tuscany, Senior Director Human Resources
CNO: Kim Ronnisch, Vice President Nursing and Chief Nursing Officer
Web address: www.stjohnprovidence.org/macomb-oakland/
**Control**: Church operated, Nongovernment, not–for–profit **Service**: General medical and surgical

**Staffed Beds: 523 Admissions: 23784 Census: 333 Outpatient Visits:** 436927 **Births: 786 Total Expense ($000):** 402839 **Payroll Expense ($000):** 154388 **Personnel:** 2060

*Many Facility Codes have changed. Please refer to the AHA Guide Code Chart.*

© 2021 AHA Guide

MI

☐ **BEHAVIORAL CENTER OF MICHIGAN (234042)**, 4050 East 12 Mile Road, Zip 48092–2534; tel. 586/261–2266, (Nonreporting) **A**1 10
Primary Contact: Ryan Gunabalan, Chief Executive Officer
COO: Efren Lusterio, Director of Nursing
CFO: Mark Corey, Chief Financial Officer
CMO: Eleanor Medina, M.D., Chief Medical Officer
CIO: Kashmira Khade, Coordinator Non-Clinical Services
CHR: Erin R Youngblood, Chief Human Resources Officer
Web address: www.behavioralcenter.com
**Control**: Corporation, Investor–owned (for–profit) **Service**: Psychiatric

**Staffed Beds: 42**

**JOHN MACOMB-OAKLAND HOSPITAL** See Ascension Macomb-Oakland Hospital

**KERN HOSPITAL & MEDICAL CENTER** See Southeast Michigan Surgical Hospital

☐ **SOUTHEAST MICHIGAN SURGICAL HOSPITAL (230264)**, 21230 Dequindre, Zip 48091–2287; tel. 586/427–1000, (Nonreporting) **A**1 10 **S** National Surgical Healthcare, Chicago, IL
Primary Contact: Barry Cullen, Chief Executive Officer
CMO: Benjamin Paolucci, D.O., Chief of Staff
CHR: Dawn Meiers, Coordinator Medical Staff and Personnel Services
Web address: www.nshinc.com
**Control**: Corporation, Investor–owned (for–profit) **Service**: Surgical

**Staffed Beds: 13**

**ST. JOHN MACOMB-OAKLAND HOSPITAL** See St. John Macomb-Oakland Hospital, Warren Campus

### WATERVLIET—Berrien County

**LAKELAND COMMUNITY HOSPITAL WATERVLIET** See Lakeland Hospital, Watervliet

☒ △ **LAKELAND HOSPITAL, WATERVLIET (230078)**, 400 Medical Park Drive, Zip 49098–9225; tel. 269/463–3111, (Nonreporting) **A**1 7 10 **F**3 11 15 29 30 34 35 38 40 45 50 54 57 59 64 68 75 77 81 86 87 90 93 94 96 97 107 119 127 130 131 132 135 144 146 148 149 154 **S** Spectrum Health, Grand Rapids, MI
Primary Contact: Ray Cruse, Chief Executive Officer
CFO: Timothy Calhoun, Vice President Finance, Chief Financial Officer
CIO: Norma Tirado, Vice President, Human Resources and Health Information Technology
CHR: Norma Tirado, Vice President, Human Resources and Health Information Technology
CNO: Connie Harmon, Director of Nursing
**Control**: Other not–for–profit (including NFP Corporation) **Service**: General medical and surgical

**Staffed Beds: 44 Admissions: 514 Census: 14 Outpatient Visits: 155483 Births: 0 Total Expense ($000): 39497 Payroll Expense ($000): 20590 Personnel: 255**

### WAYNE—Wayne County

**BEAUMONT HOSPITAL - WAYNE** See Beaumont Hospital, Wayne

☒ **BEAUMONT HOSPITAL, WAYNE (230142)**, 33155 Annapolis Street, Zip 48184–2405; tel. 734/467–4000, (Nonreporting) **A**1 3 5 10 **F**3 11 12 13 15 18 20 22 26 28 29 30 31 34 35 38 40 42 43 44 45 46 47 49 50 57 59 60 61 64 65 68 70 74 75 76 77 78 79 81 82 84 85 86 87 91 92 93 96 100 102 107 108 110 111 115 117 118 119 126 130 131 132 134 135 143 146 147 148 149 P6 8 **S** Beaumont Health, Southfield, MI
Primary Contact: Eric W. Widner, FACHE, Division President
COO: Carolyn Wilson, R.N., Chief Operating Officer
CFO: Jacqueline Nash, Controller
CMO: Ashok Jain, M.D., Senior Vice President and Chief Medical Officer
CIO: Subra Sripada, Executive Vice President, Chief Transformation Officer and Chief Information Officer
CHR: Robert L James, Director Human Resources
CNO: Diane L Hartley, Director of Patient Care Services
Web address: www.beaumont.org
**Control**: Other not–for–profit (including NFP Corporation) **Service**: General medical and surgical

**Staffed Beds: 185 Admissions: 8085 Census: 87 Outpatient Visits: 119142 Births: 912 Total Expense ($000): 161353 Payroll Expense ($000): 64483 Personnel: 1068**

### WEST BLOOMFIELD—Oakland County

**HENRY FORD MEDICAL CENTER** See Henry Ford West Bloomfield Hospital

☒ **HENRY FORD WEST BLOOMFIELD HOSPITAL (230302)**, 6777 West Maple Road, Zip 48322–3013; tel. 248/325–1000, (Nonreporting) **A**1 2 3 10 **F**3 6 11 12 13 15 18 20 22 26 28 29 30 31 32 33 34 35 36 37 38 39 40 41 43 44 45 46 47 49 50 51 53 54 55 56 57 58 59 60 61 62 63 64 65 66 70 73 74 75 76 77 78 79 80 81 82 84 85 86 87 89 92 93 96 97 100 101 102 107 108 109 110 111 114 115 117 118 119 120 121 123 124 126 130 131 132 134 135 141 143 146 147 148 149 150 153 154 156 **P**6 8 **S** Henry Ford Health System, Detroit, MI
Primary Contact: Eric Wallis, R.N., President
COO: Karen Harris, R.N., Chief Nursing and Operations Officer
CFO: Terry Goodbalian, Regional Chief Financial Officer
CMO: Betty Chu, M.D., Chief Medical Officer and Vice President of Medical Affairs
CIO: Mary Alice Annecharico, System Vice President and Chief Information Officer
CNO: Karen Harris, R.N., Chief Nursing and Operations Officer
Web address: www.henryford.com
**Control**: Other not–for–profit (including NFP Corporation) **Service**: General medical and surgical

**Staffed Beds: 212 Admissions: 12169 Census: 127 Outpatient Visits: 215125 Births: 2123 Total Expense ($000): 311237 Payroll Expense ($000): 119625 Personnel: 1966**

### WEST BRANCH—Ogemaw County

★ ○ **MIDMICHIGAN MEDICAL CENTER - WEST BRANCH (230095)**, 2463 South M-30, Zip 48661–1199; tel. 989/345–3660, (Nonreporting) **A**10 11 20 **F**3 11 15 17 18 20 28 29 30 34 35 40 50 59 64 75 77 79 81 93 107 111 115 117 119 130 135 146 148 149 154 156 **P**2 **S** MidMichigan Health, Midland, MI
Primary Contact: Robert McGrail, Chief Executive Officer
CFO: Kathy Kohr, Chief Financial Officer
CMO: Mark Weber, M.D., President Medical Staff
CHR: Kent Allen, Director Human Resources
CNO: Nicole Gillette, R.N., Chief Nursing Officer
Web address: www.wbrmc.com
**Control**: Other not–for–profit (including NFP Corporation) **Service**: General medical and surgical

**Staffed Beds: 88 Admissions: 2238 Census: 21 Outpatient Visits: 60845 Births: 0 Total Expense ($000): 54018 Payroll Expense ($000): 16316 Personnel: 307**

**WEST BRANCH REGIONAL MEDICAL CENTER** See Midmichigan Medical Center - West Branch

### WESTLAND—Wayne County

☐ **WALTER P. REUTHER PSYCHIATRIC HOSPITAL (234035)**, 30901 Palmer Road, Zip 48186–5389; tel. 734/367–8400, (Nonreporting) **A**1 10
Primary Contact: Richard T. Young, FACHE, Director
CMO: H. Bandla, M.D., Chief Clinical Affairs
CHR: Deborah Moore, Director Human Resources
Web address: www.mhweb.org/wayne/reuther.htm
**Control**: State, Government, Nonfederal **Service**: Psychiatric

**Staffed Beds: 239**

### WYANDOTTE—Wayne County

**HENRY FORD WYANDOTTE HOSP** See Henry Ford Wyandotte Hospital

---

**Hospital, Medicare Provider Number, Address, Telephone, Approval, Facility, and Physician Codes, Health Care System**

★ American Hospital Association (AHA) membership     ○ Healthcare Facilities Accreditation Program     ⇑ Center for Improvement in Healthcare Quality Accreditation
☐ The Joint Commission accreditation     ◇ DNV Healthcare Inc. accreditation     △ Commission on Accreditation of Rehabilitation Facilities (CARF) accreditation

✠ △ **HENRY FORD WYANDOTTE HOSPITAL (230146)**, 2333 Biddle Avenue, Zip 48192–4668; tel. 734/246–6000, (Nonreporting) **A**1 3 5 7 10 **F**3 8 11 12 13 15 18 20 22 26 28 29 30 31 32 34 35 36 38 40 41 42 43 44 45 46 47 49 50 51 53 54 56 57 58 59 60 61 62 63 64 65 66 68 70 73 74 75 76 77 78 79 80 81 82 84 85 86 87 90 92 93 96 97 98 100 102 107 108 110 111 114 115 116 117 118 119 126 129 130 131 132 135 144 146 147 148 149 154 156 157 **P**6 8 **S** Henry Ford Health System, Detroit, MI
Primary Contact: Peter Karadjoff, Interim President
CFO: Terry Goodbalian, Vice President, Finance and Chief Financial Officer
CMO: Dennis R Lemanski, D.O., Senior Vice President Medical Affairs and Medical Education/CMO
CIO: Mary Alice Annecharico, System Vice President and Chief Information Officer
CNO: Josephine Sclafani Wahl, R.N., MS, FACHE, VP, Patient Care Services & CNO
Web address: www.henryfordhealth.org
**Control**: Other not–for–profit (including NFP Corporation) **Service**: General medical and surgical

**Staffed Beds**: 378 **Admissions**: 14910 **Census**: 195 **Outpatient Visits**: 385698 **Births**: 1559 **Total Expense ($000)**: 329246 **Payroll Expense ($000)**: 136219 **Personnel**: 2080

**SELECT SPEC HOSP-WYANDOTTE** See Select Specialty Hospital-Downriver

✠ **SELECT SPECIALTY HOSPITAL-DOWNRIVER (232031)**, 2333 Biddle Avenue, 8th Floor, Zip 48192–4668; tel. 734/246–5500, (Includes SELECT SPECIALTY HOSPITAL-NORTHWEST DETROIT, Mailing address: 6071 West Outer Drive, Detroit, Michigan, Zip 48235–2624; tel. 313/966–4747; Marilouise Riska, Chief Executive Officer), (Nonreporting) **A**1 10 **S** Select Medical Corporation, Mechanicsburg, PA
Primary Contact: John Ponczocha, Chief Executive Officer
CMO: Roderick Boyer, M.D., Medical Director
CHR: Barb Wierzbicki, Manager Human Resources
CNO: Angela Kudla, MSN, R.N., Chief Nursing Officer
Web address: www.downriver.selectspecialtyhospitals.com/
**Control**: Corporation, Investor–owned (for–profit) **Service**: Acute long–term care hospital

**Staffed Beds**: 35

**WYOMING—Kent County**

★ ○ **METRO HEALTH - UNIVERSITY OF MICHIGAN HEALTH (230236)**, 5900 Byron Center Avenue SW, Zip 49519–9606, Mailing Address: P.O. Box 916, Zip 49509–0916; tel. 616/252–7200, (Nonreporting) **A**3 5 10 11 13 **F**3 12 13 15 18 19 20 22 26 28 29 30 31 34 35 40 43 44 45 48 49 50 54 57 58 59 64 65 66 70 74 75 76 77 78 79 80 81 85 86 87 92 97 107 108 110 111 115 119 126 129 130 131 132 135 144 146 147 148 149 150 154 156 **P**6 8
Primary Contact: Peter Hahn, M.D., President and Chief Executive Officer
CFO: Kris Kurtz, Chief Financial Officer
CIO: Joshua Wilda, Chief Information Officer
CNO: Steve Polega, Chief Nursing Officer
Web address: www.metrohealth.net
**Control**: Other not–for–profit (including NFP Corporation) **Service**: General medical and surgical

**Staffed Beds**: 208 **Admissions**: 9319 **Census**: 106 **Outpatient Visits**: 601619 **Births**: 1737 **Total Expense ($000)**: 472404 **Payroll Expense ($000)**: 195687 **Personnel**: 2632

**METRO HEALTH HOSPITAL** See Metro Health - University of Michigan Health

**YPSILANTI—Washtenaw County**

**ADDISON COMMUNITY HOSPITAL** See Forest Health Medical Center

☐ **FOREST HEALTH MEDICAL CENTER (230144)**, 135 South Prospect Street, Zip 48198–7914; tel. 734/547–4700, (Nonreporting) **A**1 10 **F**12 30 64 74 75 79 81 82 85 111 119 130 132 149
Primary Contact: Trevor J. Dyksterhouse, President
COO: Andrea Walrath, Chief Operating Officer
CFO: David Althoen, Director Financial Planning and Analysis
CMO: Jason Adams, M.D., Medical Staff President
CIO: Andrea Walrath, Chief Operating Officer
CHR: Amy Mohr, Coordinator Human Resources
Web address: www.fhmc-mi.com
**Control**: Corporation, Investor–owned (for–profit) **Service**: General medical and surgical

**Staffed Beds**: 24 **Admissions**: 1160 **Census**: 4 **Outpatient Visits**: 17692 **Births**: 0 **Personnel**: 48

✠ **SELECT SPECIALTY HOSPITAL-ANN ARBOR (232024)**, 5301 East Huron River Drive, 7th Floor, Zip 48197–1051; tel. 734/712–6751, (Nonreporting) **A**1 10 **S** Select Medical Corporation, Mechanicsburg, PA
Primary Contact: Bryan Cutliff, Chief Executive Officer
CMO: Hamid Halimi, M.D., Medical Director
CHR: Cindy Hardick, Human Resources Coordinator
CNO: Tim Varney, R.N., Chief Nursing Officer
Web address: www.annarbor.selectspecialtyhospitals.com/
**Control**: Corporation, Investor–owned (for–profit) **Service**: Acute long–term care hospital

**Staffed Beds**: 36

✠ **ST. JOSEPH MERCY ANN ARBOR (230156)**, 5301 Mcauley Drive, Zip 48197–1051, Mailing Address: P.O. Box 995, Ann Arbor, Zip 48106–0995; tel. 734/712–3456, (Nonreporting) **A**1 2 3 5 10 **F**3 4 5 8 11 12 13 15 17 18 20 22 24 26 28 29 30 31 32 34 35 36 37 38 40 41 43 44 45 46 47 48 49 50 51 53 54 55 56 57 58 59 61 64 65 66 68 70 71 72 73 74 75 76 77 78 79 80 81 82 83 84 85 86 87 89 90 91 92 93 94 95 96 97 98 100 101 102 103 104 105 107 108 109 110 111 114 115 118 119 120 121 123 124 126 129 130 131 132 134 135 141 143 144 146 147 148 149 153 154 156 157 **P**5 6 **S** Trinity Health, Livonia, MI
Primary Contact: Alonzo T. Lewis, Senior Vice President, Operations
CFO: Kathy O'Connor, Vice President Finance
CMO: Rosalie Tocco-Bradley, Ph.D., M.D., Chief Medical Officer
CIO: Frank Rademacher, Senior Director Information Systems
CNO: Joyce Young, Ph.D., R.N., Vice President, Patient Services and Chief Nursing Officer
Web address: www.sjmercyhealth.org
**Control**: Church operated, Nongovernment, not–for–profit **Service**: General medical and surgical

**Staffed Beds**: 509 **Admissions**: 32029 **Census**: 401 **Outpatient Visits**: 1129091 **Births**: 3974 **Total Expense ($000)**: 834418 **Payroll Expense ($000)**: 292909 **Personnel**: 5136

**ST. JOSEPH MERCY HOSPITAL ANN ARBOR** See St. Joseph Mercy Ann Arbor

**ZEELAND—Ottawa County**

✠ **SPECTRUM HEALTH ZEELAND COMMUNITY HOSPITAL (230003)**, 8333 Felch Street, Zip 49464–2608; tel. 616/772–4644, (Nonreporting) **A**1 10 **F**3 12 13 15 18 29 32 34 35 38 39 40 43 44 45 46 47 50 57 59 64 65 68 70 74 75 76 78 79 81 85 86 87 89 91 92 93 107 108 110 111 115 118 119 126 129 130 132 134 135 144 146 147 148 154 **S** Spectrum Health, Grand Rapids, MI
Primary Contact: Ron Lewis, President
CFO: Ryan J. Powers, Vice President Finance
CMO: Ruel R. Lirio, M.D., Clinical Physician Advisor
CIO: Imran Syed, Manager Technology Information Services
CHR: Jennifer F Becksvoort, Senior Human Resource Business Partner
CNO: Jane Czerew, Vice President Clinical Services and Quality
Web address: www.spectrumhealth.org/zeeland
**Control**: Other not–for–profit (including NFP Corporation) **Service**: General medical and surgical

**Staffed Beds**: 55 **Admissions**: 2700 **Census**: 18 **Outpatient Visits**: 146035 **Births**: 732 **Total Expense ($000)**: 62579 **Payroll Expense ($000)**: 19773 **Personnel**: 336

**ZEELAND COMMUNITY HOSPITAL** See Spectrum Health Zeeland Community Hospital

MI

*Many Facility Codes have changed. Please refer to the AHA Guide Code Chart.*

© 2021 AHA Guide

# MINNESOTA

## ADA—Norman County

**ESSENTIA HEALTH ADA** See Essentia Health-Ada

★ **ESSENTIA HEALTH-ADA (241313)**, 201 9th Street West, Zip 56510–1279; tel. 218/784–5000, (Nonreporting) **A**10 18 **F**7 15 28 29 34 35 40 41 45 56 57 59 64 65 77 79 81 82 87 89 93 97 104 107 114 115 127 130 131 133 135 154 156 **S** Essentia Health, Duluth, MN
Primary Contact: Erin Stoltman, Administrator
CMO: Jeff Peterson, M.D., Chief of Staff
CHR: Shayla Hennenberg, Director Human Resources
Web address: www.essentiahealth.org
**Control**: Other not-for-profit (including NFP Corporation) **Service**: General medical and surgical

**Staffed Beds**: 14 **Admissions**: 41 **Census**: 1 **Outpatient Visits**: 8794 **Births**: 0 **Total Expense ($000)**: 9192 **Payroll Expense ($000)**: 4394 **Personnel**: 64

## ADRIAN—Nobles County

**ARNOLD MEMORIAL HOSPITAL** See Arnold Memorial Health Care Center

## AITKIN—Aitkin County

⊠ **RIVERWOOD HEALTHCARE CENTER (241305)**, 200 Bunker Hill Drive, Zip 56431–1865; tel. 218/927–2121, (Nonreporting) **A**1 10 18
Primary Contact: Todd Sandberg, Chief Executive Officer
COO: Cindi Baker, Chief Operating Officer
CFO: Casey R Johnson, Chief Financial Officer
CMO: Mark Heggem, M.D., Chief Medical Officer
CIO: Daryl Kallevig, Chief Information Officer
CHR: Cindi Hills, Director Human Resources
CNO: Kristine Layne, R.N., Chief Nursing Officer
Web address: www.riverwoodhealthcare.org
**Control**: Other not-for-profit (including NFP Corporation) **Service**: General medical and surgical

**Staffed Beds**: 25

**RIVERWOOD HEALTHCARE CENTER** See Riverwood Healthcare Center

## ALBERT LEA—Freeborn County

**MAYO CLINIC HEALTH SYSTEM - ALBERT LEA & AUSTIN** See Mayo Clinic Health System - Albert Lea and Austin

☐ **MAYO CLINIC HEALTH SYSTEM - ALBERT LEA AND AUSTIN (240043)**, 404 West Fountain Street, Zip 56007–2473; tel. 507/373–2384, (Includes MAYO CLINIC HEALTH SYSTEM - ALBERT LEA AND AUSTIN, Mailing address: 1000 First Drive NW, Austin, Minnesota, Zip 55912–2904; tel. 507/433–7351; Brian Whited, M.D., Vice Chair, Mayo Health System), (Nonreporting) **A**1 3 5 10 20 **F**3 5 13 15 18 28 29 30 31 32 34 35 38 40 43 45 46 52 57 59 63 64 65 70 74 75 76 77 78 79 81 82 85 86 87 92 93 97 98 104 106 107 110 111 115 119 129 130 131 132 135 146 147 148 149 154 156 **S** Mayo Clinic, Rochester, MN
Primary Contact: Brian Whited, M.D., Vice Chair, Mayo Health System
CMO: John Grzybowski, M.D., Medical Director
CHR: Monica Fleegel, Director Human Resources
CNO: Lori Routh, R.N., Nurse Administrator
Web address: www.almedcenter.org
**Control**: Other not-for-profit (including NFP Corporation) **Service**: General medical and surgical

**Staffed Beds**: 81 **Admissions**: 4202 **Census**: 45 **Outpatient Visits**: 292426 **Births**: 729 **Personnel**: 1099

## ALEXANDRIA—Sherburne County

**ALEXANDRIA COMM BEHAV HOSPITAL** See Community Behavioral Health Hospital - Alexandria

## ALEXANDRIA—Douglas County

★ ○ **ALOMERE HEALTH (240030)**, 111 17th Avenue East, Zip 56308–3798; tel. 320/762–1511, (Nonreporting) **A**2 10 11 **F**3 8 11 13 15 28 29 30 31 32 34 35 36 40 43 50 57 61 64 65 68 70 76 77 78 79 81 82 85 86 87 89 91 93 97 107 108 111 115 117 118 119 126 129 130 131 132 135 144 146 149 154 157 **P**6
Primary Contact: Carl P. Vaagenes, Chief Executive Officer
CFO: Nate Meyer, Director Finance
CMO: Deborah S. Dittberner, M.D., Chief Medical Officer
CHR: Shelly Gompf, Director Human Resources
Web address: www.dchospital.com
**Control**: County, Government, Nonfederal **Service**: General medical and surgical

**Staffed Beds**: 99 **Admissions**: 3393 **Census**: 28 **Outpatient Visits**: 281054 **Births**: 631 **Total Expense ($000)**: 171593 **Payroll Expense ($000)**: 49318 **Personnel**: 795

## ALEXANDRIA—Sherburne County

☐ **COMMUNITY BEHAVIORAL HEALTH HOSPITAL - ALEXANDRIA (244012)**, 1610 8th Avenue East, Zip 56308–2472; tel. 320/335–6201, (Nonreporting) **A**1 10 **S** Minnesota Department of Human Services, Saint Paul, MN
Primary Contact: Jennifer Westrum, Administrator
CFO: Shirley Jacobson, Chief Financial Officer
Web address: www.health.state.mn.us
**Control**: State, Government, Nonfederal **Service**: Psychiatric

**Staffed Beds**: 16

## ALEXANDRIA—Douglas County

**DOUGLAS COUNTY HOSPITAL** See Alomere Health

## ANNANDALE—Wright County

**ANNANDALE COMM BEHAV HOSPITAL** See Community Behavioral Health Hospital - Annandale

☐ **COMMUNITY BEHAVIORAL HEALTH HOSPITAL - ANNANDALE (244011)**, 400 Annandale Boulevard, Zip 55302–3141; tel. 651/259–3850, (Nonreporting) **A**1 10 **S** Minnesota Department of Human Services, Saint Paul, MN
Primary Contact: James P. Kelly, FACHE, Administrator
CMO: Shabeer A Ahmed, M.D., Clinical Director
CNO: Lennetta M Reynolds, Administrative Supervisor
Web address: www.health.state.mn.us
**Control**: State, Government, Nonfederal **Service**: Psychiatric

**Staffed Beds**: 16

## ANOKA—Anoka County

**ANOKA METRO REGIONAL TREATMENT CENTER (244002)**, 3301 Seventh Avenue, Zip 55303–4516, Mailing Address: 3301 Seventh Avenue North, Zip 55303–4516; tel. 651/431–5000, (Nonreporting) **A**10 **S** Minnesota Department of Human Services, Saint Paul, MN
Primary Contact: Rochelle M. Fischer, Hospital Administrator
Web address: www.health.state.mn.us
**Control**: State, Government, Nonfederal **Service**: Psychiatric

**Staffed Beds**: 200

**ANOKA-METROPOLITAN REGIONAL TREATMENT CENTER** See Anoka Metro Regional Treatment Center

## APPLETON—Swift County

**APPLETON AREA HEALTH SERVICES (241341)**, 30 South Behl Street, Zip 56208–1699; tel. 320/289–2422, (Nonreporting) **A**10 18
Primary Contact: Lori Andreas, Chief Executive Officer and Administrator
CFO: Anne Kells, Interim Chief Financial Officer
Web address: www.appletonareahealth.com
**Control**: City, Government, Nonfederal **Service**: General medical and surgical

**Staffed Beds**: 15

**APPLETON MUNICIPAL HOSPITAL AND NURSING HOME** See Appleton Area Health Services

---

**Hospital, Medicare Provider Number, Address, Telephone, Approval, Facility, and Physician Codes, Health Care System**

★ American Hospital Association (AHA) membership
☐ The Joint Commission accreditation
○ Healthcare Facilities Accreditation Program
◇ DNV Healthcare Inc. accreditation
⇑ Center for Improvement in Healthcare Quality Accreditation
△ Commission on Accreditation of Rehabilitation Facilities (CARF) accreditation

## ARLINGTON—Sibley County

★ ⇑ **RIDGEVIEW SIBLEY MEDICAL CENTER (241311)**, 601 West Chandler Street, Zip 55307–2127; tel. 507/964–2271, (Nonreporting) **A**10 18 21 **F**3 15 28 29 31 34 35 40 43 45 46 57 59 64 65 66 77 78 81 86 87 93 96 97 107 110 115 119 127 128 130 133 135 144 154 **S** Ridgeview Medical Center, Waconia, MN
Primary Contact: Ben Nielsen, Chief Operating Officer
CFO: Darla Anderson, Chief Financial Officer
CMO: Ehtaisham Mohammed, M.D., Chief Medical Officer
CIO: Chris Bulau, Manager Information Technology
CHR: Sara Christiansen, Interim Director Human Resources
CNO: Sandy Domeier, Director Patient Care Services
Web address: www.sibleymedical.org
**Control**: Other not–for–profit (including NFP Corporation) **Service**: General medical and surgical

**Staffed Beds:** 6 **Admissions:** 194 **Census:** 2 **Outpatient Visits:** 25586 **Births:** 0 **Total Expense ($000):** 13794 **Payroll Expense ($000):** 5539 **Personnel:** 95

⇑ **SIBLEY MEDICAL CENTER** See Ridgeview Sibley Medical Center

## AURORA—St. Louis County

**ESSENTIA HEALTH NORTHERN PINES** See Essentia Health Northern Pines Medical Center

★ **ESSENTIA HEALTH NORTHERN PINES MEDICAL CENTER (241340)**, 5211 Highway 110, Zip 55705–1599; tel. 218/229–2211, (Total facility includes 50 beds in nursing home–type unit) (Nonreporting) **A**10 18 **F**3 28 29 34 40 43 50 56 57 59 64 65 75 81 82 85 87 93 96 97 100 102 107 127 128 130 133 135 148 149 154 157 **P**6 **S** Essentia Health, Duluth, MN
Primary Contact: Laura Ackman, Chief Operating Officer and Administrator
CFO: Kevin Boren, Chief Financial Officer
CMO: Michelle Oman, D.O., Chief Medical Officer
CHR: Kim Carlson, Director Human Resources
CNO: Cindy Loe, R.N., Director of Nursing
Web address: www.essentiahealth.org/NorthernPines/FindaClinic/Essentia-HealthNorthern-Pines-36.aspx
**Control**: Other not–for–profit (including NFP Corporation) **Service**: General medical and surgical

**Staffed Beds:** 58 **Admissions:** 170 **Census:** 35 **Outpatient Visits:** 27981 **Births:** 0 **Total Expense ($000):** 11986 **Payroll Expense ($000):** 7647 **Personnel:** 85

## AUSTIN—Mower County

**MAYO CLINIC HEALTH SYSTEM-ALBERT LEA AND AUSTIN** See Mayo Clinic Health System - Albert Lea and Austin

## BAGLEY—Clearwater County

**CLEARWATER HEALTH SERVICES** See Sanford Bagley Medical Center

★ **SANFORD BAGLEY MEDICAL CENTER (241328)**, 203 Fourth Street NW, Zip 56621–8307; tel. 218/694–6501, (Nonreporting) **A**10 18 **F**7 8 28 29 33 34 35 40 50 53 54 57 59 65 68 75 77 81 86 93 96 97 107 115 127 132 133 134 135 146 147 149 157 **P**6 **S** Sanford Health, Sioux Falls, SD
Primary Contact: Robert Belanger, Administrator Director
CMO: Andre Spence, Chief Medical Staff
CNO: Stephanie McKnight, Hospital Nursing Manager
Web address: www.sanfordhealth.org
**Control**: Other not–for–profit (including NFP Corporation) **Service**: General medical and surgical

**Staffed Beds:** 8 **Admissions:** 133 **Census:** 2 **Outpatient Visits:** 7541 **Total Expense ($000):** 11812 **Payroll Expense ($000):** 5821 **Personnel:** 83

## BAUDETTE—Lake of The Woods County

★ **CHI LAKEWOOD HEALTH (241301)**, 600 Main Avenue South, Zip 56623–2855; tel. 218/634–2120, (Nonreporting) **A**10 18 **S** CommonSpirit Health, Chicago, IL
Primary Contact: Jeffry Stampohar, Vice President of Hospital
CFO: Jay Ross, Vice President of Finance
CMO: Justin Quo, Chief of Staff
CIO: Dan Leadbetter, Information Technology Systems Site Lead
CNO: Danielle Abel, Vice President of Patient Care Services
Web address: www.lakewoodhealthcenter.org
**Control**: Church operated, Nongovernment, not–for–profit **Service**: General medical and surgical

**Staffed Beds:** 55

**LAKEWOOD HEALTH CENTER** See Chi Lakewood Health

## BAXTER—Crow Wing County

**BAXTER COMMUNITY BEHAV HOSP** See Community Behavioral Health Hospital - Baxter

⊠ **COMMUNITY BEHAVIORAL HEALTH HOSPITAL - BAXTER (244015)**, 14241 Grand Oaks Drive, Zip 56425–8749; tel. 218/316–3101, (Nonreporting) **A**1 10 **S** Minnesota Department of Human Services, Saint Paul, MN
Primary Contact: Ryan D. Cerney, Administrator
Web address: www.business.explorebrainerdlakes.com/list/member/community-behavioral-health-hospital-baxter-8647
**Control**: State, Government, Nonfederal **Service**: Psychiatric

**Staffed Beds:** 16

## BEMIDJI—Beltrami County

☐ **COMMUNITY BEHAVIORAL HEALTH HOSPITAL - BEMIDJI (244014)**, 800 Bemidji Avenue North, Zip 56601–3054; tel. 218/308–2400, (Nonreporting) **A**1 10 **S** Minnesota Department of Human Services, Saint Paul, MN
Primary Contact: Larry A. Laudon, Administrator
**Control**: State, Government, Nonfederal **Service**: Psychiatric

**Staffed Beds:** 16

**NORTH COUNTRY REGIONAL HOSPITAL** See Sanford Bemidji Medical Center

⊠ **SANFORD BEMIDJI MEDICAL CENTER (240100)**, 1300 Anne Street NW, Zip 56601–5103; tel. 218/751–5430, (Total facility includes 78 beds in nursing home–type unit) (Nonreporting) **A**1 2 10 **F**3 8 11 13 15 17 18 20 22 26 28 29 30 31 32 33 34 35 38 40 41 45 46 49 50 51 53 54 56 57 58 59 60 61 62 63 64 65 68 70 73 74 75 76 77 78 79 81 82 83 84 85 86 87 88 89 90 91 93 94 96 97 101 102 104 107 108 110 111 114 115 118 119 120 121 123 124 126 127 128 129 130 131 132 134 135 144 146 147 148 149 153 154 155 156 157 **P**6 **S** Sanford Health, Sioux Falls, SD
Primary Contact: Susan Jarvis, President
CMO: Daniel DeKrey, M.D., Chief of Staff
CIO: Dan Moffatt, Chief Information Officer
Web address: www.sanfordhealth.org/bemidji
**Control**: Other not–for–profit (including NFP Corporation) **Service**: General medical and surgical

**Staffed Beds:** 196 **Admissions:** 6471 **Census:** 144 **Outpatient Visits:** 282506 **Births:** 887 **Total Expense ($000):** 302543 **Payroll Expense ($000):** 134151 **Personnel:** 1423

## BENSON—Swift County

**SWIFT COUNTY - BENSON HEALTH SERVICES (241365)**, 1815 Wisconsin Avenue, Zip 56215–1653; tel. 320/843–1311, (Nonreporting) **A**10 18
Primary Contact: Dan Enderson, Co-Chief Executive Officer
COO: Dan Enderson, Chief Operating Officer and Chief Financial Officer
CFO: Dan Enderson, Chief Operating Officer and Chief Financial Officer
CMO: Richard Horecka, Chief Medical Officer
Web address: www.scbh.org
**Control**: Hospital district or authority, Government, Nonfederal **Service**: General medical and surgical

**Staffed Beds:** 18

**SWIFT COUNTY-BENSON HOSPITAL** See Swift County - Benson Health Services

## BIGFORK—Itasca County

**BIG FORK VALLEY HOSPITAL** See Bigfork Valley Hospital

★ **BIGFORK VALLEY HOSPITAL (241316)**, 258 Pine Tree Drive, Zip 56628, Mailing Address: P.O. Box 258, Zip 56628–0258; tel. 218/743–3177, (Nonreporting) **A**10 18
Primary Contact: Aaron Saude, Chief Executive Officer
CFO: Christine Lokken, Chief Financial Officer
CMO: Edwin Anderson, M.D., Chief of Staff and Chief Medical Officer
CIO: Amanda Niemala, Director of Information Services
CHR: Angela Kleffman, Director of Ancillary Services
CNO: Nancy Probst, R.N., Chief Nursing Officer
Web address: www.bigforkvalley.org
**Control**: Hospital district or authority, Government, Nonfederal **Service**: General medical and surgical

**Staffed Beds:** 67

## BLUE EARTH—Faribault County

✠ **UNITED HOSPITAL DISTRICT (241369)**, 515 South Moore Street, Zip 56013–2158, Mailing Address: P.O. Box 160, Zip 56013–0160; tel. 507/526–3273, (Nonreporting) **A**1 10 18
Primary Contact: Richard M. Ash, Chief Executive Officer
CFO: Patrick Justin, Chief Financial Officer
CMO: Bob Karp, M.D., Chief Medical Officer
CIO: Mary Hynes, Manager Information Services
CHR: Shanna Gudahl, Manager Human Resources
CNO: Candace Arends, R.N., Chief Nursing Officer
Web address: www.uhd.org
**Control:** Hospital district or authority, Government, Nonfederal **Service:** General medical and surgical

**Staffed Beds:** 25

## BRAINERD—Crow Wing County

**ESSENTIA HEALTH - ST. JOSEPH'S MEDICAL CENTER** See Essentia Health-St. Joseph's Medical Center

✠ **ESSENTIA HEALTH-ST. JOSEPH'S MEDICAL CENTER (240075)**, 523 North Third Street, Zip 56401–3098; tel. 218/829–2861, (Nonreporting) **A**1 2 10 **F**3 4 5 11 13 15 18 20 22 26 28 29 30 31 32 34 35 40 43 45 49 50 51 54 57 59 64 65 70 74 75 76 77 78 81 82 86 87 89 91 93 96 97 98 100 102 105 107 111 118 119 126 130 131 132 135 144 145 146 148 152 154 **P**6 **S** Essentia Health, Duluth, MN
Primary Contact: Adam Rees, President
COO: Mike Larson, Chief Operating Officer
CFO: Dave Pilot, Chief Financial Officer
CMO: Peter Henry, M.D., Chief Medical Officer
CIO: Pam Marlatt, Business Systems Director
CHR: Sarah Carlson, Director Human Resources
CNO: Patricia DeLong, Chief Nursing Officer
Web address: www.essentiahealth.org
**Control:** Church operated, Nongovernment, not–for–profit **Service:** General medical and surgical

**Staffed Beds:** 127 **Admissions:** 4848 **Census:** 51 **Outpatient Visits:** 95317 **Births:** 405 **Total Expense ($000):** 203728 **Payroll Expense ($000):** 96559 **Personnel:** 790

## BRECKENRIDGE—Wilkin County

✠ **CHI ST. FRANCIS HEALTH (241377)**, 2400 St Francis Drive, Zip 56520–1025; tel. 218/643–3000, (Nonreporting) **A**1 10 18 **S** CommonSpirit Health, Chicago, IL
Primary Contact: David A. Nelson, President and Chief Executive Officer
CFO: Joshua Senger, Chief Financial Officer
CHR: Gail Grant, Director Human Resources
CNO: Alice Pesonen-Johnson, Chief Nursing Officer
Web address: www.sfcare.org
**Control:** Church operated, Nongovernment, not–for–profit **Service:** General medical and surgical

**Staffed Beds:** 105

**ST. FRANCIS HEALTHCARE CAMPUS** See Chi St. Francis Health

## BROOKLYN PARK—Hennepin County

**PRAIRIECARE** See Prairiecare - Brooklyn Park

☐ **PRAIRIECARE - BROOKLYN PARK (244016)**, 9400 Zane Avenue North, Zip 55443, Mailing Address: 12915 63rd Avenue North, Maple Grove, Zip 55369–6001; tel. 763/383–5800, (Nonreporting) **A**1 3
Primary Contact: Joel V. Oberstar, M.D., Chief Executive Officer and Chief Medical Officer
Web address: www.prairie-care.com
**Control:** Corporation, Investor–owned (for–profit) **Service:** Psychiatric

**Staffed Beds:** 50

## BUFFALO—Wright County

✠ **BUFFALO HOSPITAL (240076)**, 303 Catlin Street, Zip 55313–1947; tel. 763/682–1212, (Nonreporting) **A**1 10 **F**3 13 15 18 28 29 30 31 32 34 35 36 40 43 44 45 50 53 57 59 64 75 76 77 78 79 80 81 85 86 87 93 107 110 111 114 115 119 129 130 131 132 135 146 148 149 150 154 **S** Allina Health, Minneapolis, MN
Primary Contact: Kelly Spratt, President
COO: Heather Johnson, Director of Finance, Operations and Business Development
CFO: Heather Johnson, Director of Finance, Operations and Business Development
CMO: Corey Martin, M.D., Director Medical Affairs
CIO: Jonathan Cloutier, Manager, Information Services
CHR: Leah Schmoyer, Human Resources Director
CNO: Gretchen A Frederick, R.N., Director Patient Care Services
Web address: www.buffalohospital.org
**Control:** Other not–for–profit (including NFP Corporation) **Service:** General medical and surgical

**Staffed Beds:** 39 **Admissions:** 2215 **Census:** 16 **Outpatient Visits:** 75778 **Births:** 612 **Total Expense ($000):** 72722 **Payroll Expense ($000):** 29615 **Personnel:** 335

**HEALTH ONE BUFFALO HOSPITAL** See Buffalo Hospital

## BURNSVILLE—Dakota County

✠ **FAIRVIEW RIDGES HOSPITAL (240207)**, 201 East Nicollet Boulevard, Zip 55337–5799; tel. 952/892–2000, (Nonreporting) **A**1 2 3 5 10 **F**3 13 15 18 20 22 28 29 30 31 34 35 40 41 43 44 45 46 49 50 53 55 57 59 64 65 68 70 72 74 75 76 77 78 79 81 82 84 85 86 87 89 93 96 107 108 110 111 114 115 116 117 118 119 126 130 132 146 148 149 154 **P**6 **S** M Health Fairview, Minneapolis, MN
Primary Contact: Jeoff Will, Chief Operating Officer, Acute Care Services
COO: Brian A Knapp, Vice President Operations
CFO: Alan Lem, Vice President Finance
CMO: Paul Kettler, M.D., Vice President Medical Affairs
CHR: Michelle LeDell, Director Human Resource
CNO: Julie Sethney, R.N., Vice President Patient Care
Web address: www.fairview.org
**Control:** Other not–for–profit (including NFP Corporation) **Service:** General medical and surgical

**Staffed Beds:** 162 **Admissions:** 11209 **Census:** 116 **Outpatient Visits:** 128923 **Births:** 2251 **Total Expense ($000):** 245228 **Payroll Expense ($000):** 103970 **Personnel:** 1009

## CAMBRIDGE—Isanti County

✠ **CAMBRIDGE MEDICAL CENTER (240020)**, 701 South Dellwood Street, Zip 55008–1920; tel. 763/689–7700, (Nonreporting) **A**1 2 10 **F**5 11 13 14 15 18 28 29 30 31 32 34 35 38 40 43 45 50 55 56 57 59 61 64 65 69 74 75 76 77 78 79 81 82 85 86 87 93 97 98 100 101 102 104 107 108 111 114 115 119 125 129 130 131 132 134 135 144 145 146 147 148 149 154 156 **P**5 6 **S** Allina Health, Minneapolis, MN
Primary Contact: Kelly Spratt, President
CFO: Nancy Treacy, Director Finance
CHR: Diane Rasmussen, Director Human Resources
CNO: Sherri Abrahamson-Baty, Director Patient Care Services
Web address: www.allina.com/ahs/cambridge.nsf
**Control:** Other not–for–profit (including NFP Corporation) **Service:** General medical and surgical

**Staffed Beds:** 57 **Admissions:** 2794 **Census:** 27 **Outpatient Visits:** 81213 **Births:** 269 **Total Expense ($000):** 78944 **Payroll Expense ($000):** 34121 **Personnel:** 608

**CAMBRIDGE MEMORIAL HOSPITAL** See Cambridge Medical Center

---

**Hospital, Medicare Provider Number, Address, Telephone, Approval, Facility, and Physician Codes, Health Care System**

★ American Hospital Association (AHA) membership
☐ The Joint Commission accreditation
○ Healthcare Facilities Accreditation Program
◇ DNV Healthcare Inc. accreditation
⇧ Center for Improvement in Healthcare Quality Accreditation
△ Commission on Accreditation of Rehabilitation Facilities (CARF) accreditation

**MN**

## CANBY—Yellow Medicine County

★ **SANFORD CANBY MEDICAL CENTER (241347)**, 112 St Olaf Avenue South, Zip 56220–1433; tel. 507/223–7277, (Total facility includes 53 beds in nursing home–type unit) (Nonreporting) **A**10 18 **F**3 7 9 10 11 13 15 28 29 31 34 35 39 40 45 46 53 56 59 60 62 64 65 70 71 75 79 81 85 89 92 93 107 110 119 127 128 130 132 133 135 144 149 156 158 **P**6 **S** Sanford Health, Sioux Falls, SD
Primary Contact: Lori Sisk, R.N., Chief Executive Officer
CFO: Allison Nelson, Chief Financial Officer
CMO: Maritza Lopez, M.D., Chief of Staff
CIO: Cheryl L Ferguson, Associate Administrator
Web address: www.sanfordcanby.org
**Control**: Other not–for–profit (including NFP Corporation) **Service**: General medical and surgical

| | |
|---|---|
| **Staffed Beds:** 78 **Admissions:** 199 **Census:** 46 **Outpatient Visits:** 26382 **Births:** 0 **Total Expense ($000):** 22479 **Payroll Expense ($000):** 10547 **Personnel:** 180 | |

**SANFORD MEDICAL CENTER CANBY** See Sanford Canby Medical Center

## CANNON FALLS—Goodhue County

**CANNON FALLS MEDICAL CENTER** See Mayo Clinic Health System in Cannon Falls

☐ **MAYO CLINIC HEALTH SYSTEM IN CANNON FALLS (241346)**, 32021 County Road 24 Boulevard, Zip 55009–1898; tel. 507/263–4221, (Nonreporting) **A**1 10 18 **F**3 15 18 28 29 34 35 40 45 53 57 59 64 65 67 74 75 77 79 81 87 93 97 104 107 111 115 119 130 133 146 149 154 **S** Mayo Clinic, Rochester, MN
Primary Contact: Brian Whited, M.D., Vice Chair Mayo Clinic Health System
Web address: www.mayoclinichealthsystem.org/locations/cannon-falls
**Control**: Other not–for–profit (including NFP Corporation) **Service**: General medical and surgical

| | |
|---|---|
| **Staffed Beds:** 15 **Admissions:** 351 **Census:** 10 **Outpatient Visits:** 23195 **Births:** 0 **Personnel:** 107 | |

## CASS LAKE—Cass County

**U. S. PUBLIC HEALTH SERVICE INDIAN HOSPITAL (241358)**, 425 7th Street North West, Zip 56633; tel. 218/335–3200, (Nonreporting) **A**10 **S** U. S. Indian Health Service, Rockville, MD
Primary Contact: Louis P. Erdrich, Acting Chief Executive Officer
CMO: Antonio Guimaraes, M.D., Clinical Director
CHR: Terrance Lascano, Administrative Officer
CNO: Roberta A Williams, Director of Nursing
Web address: www.ihs.gov
**Control**: PHS, Indian Service, Government, federal **Service**: General medical and surgical

| | |
|---|---|
| **Staffed Beds:** 9 | |

## CLOQUET—Carlton County

**CLOQUET COMMUNITY MEM HOSPITAL** See Community Memorial Hospital

★ **COMMUNITY MEMORIAL HOSPITAL (241364)**, 512 Skyline Boulevard, Zip 55720–1199; tel. 218/879–4641, (Nonreporting) **A**10 18
Primary Contact: Rick Breuer, Chief Executive Officer and Administrator
CFO: Brad Anderson, Chief Financial Officer
CIO: Sam Jacobson, Director Management Information Systems
Web address: www.cloquethospital.com
**Control**: Other not–for–profit (including NFP Corporation) **Service**: General medical and surgical

| | |
|---|---|
| **Staffed Beds:** 69 | |

## COOK—St. Louis County

★ **COOK HOSPITAL & CARE CENTER (241312)**, 10 Fifth Street SE, Zip 55723–9745; tel. 218/666–5945, (Nonreporting) **A**10 18
Primary Contact: Teresa Debevec, Chief Executive Officer and Administrator
COO: Julie Lesemann, Chief Operating Officer and Assistant Administrator
CFO: Kaylee S. Hoard, Chief Financial Officer
Web address: www.cookhospital.org
**Control**: Hospital district or authority, Government, Nonfederal **Service**: General medical and surgical

| | |
|---|---|
| **Staffed Beds:** 42 | |

**COOK HOSPITAL AND CARE CENTER** See Cook Hospital & Care Center

## COON RAPIDS—Anoka County

**HEALTH ONE MERCY HOSPITAL** See Mercy Hospital

⊞ **MERCY HOSPITAL (240115)**, 4050 Coon Rapids Boulevard, Zip 55433–2586; tel. 763/236–6000, (Includes MERCY HOSPITAL-UNITY CAMPUS, Mailing address: 550 Osborne Road NE, Fridley, Minnesota, Zip 55432–2799; tel. 763/236–5000; Sara J. Criger, President), (Nonreporting) **A**1 2 3 5 10 **F**3 4 5 8 11 13 17 18 20 22 24 26 28 29 30 31 34 35 36 37 38 40 43 45 46 49 50 53 55 56 57 59 64 65 68 69 70 74 75 76 77 78 79 81 82 85 86 87 93 96 97 98 100 101 102 103 104 105 107 108 111 114 115 119 126 130 131 132 135 145 146 152 153 154 **S** Allina Health, Minneapolis, MN
Primary Contact: Sara J. Criger, President
COO: Daniel Steffen, Vice President, Operations
CFO: Phillip Krolik, Vice President, Finance
CMO: Ryan Else, M.D., Vice President Medical Affairs
CIO: Susan Heichert, Chief Information Officer
CHR: Jim McGlade, Vice President, Human Resources
CNO: MariBeth Olson, R.N., Vice President Patient Care Services
Web address: www.allinamercy.org
**Control**: Other not–for–profit (including NFP Corporation) **Service**: General medical and surgical

| | |
|---|---|
| **Staffed Beds:** 471 **Admissions:** 32741 **Census:** 357 **Outpatient Visits:** 234218 **Births:** 2964 **Total Expense ($000):** 714326 **Payroll Expense ($000):** 259481 **Personnel:** 2419 | |

## CROOKSTON—Polk County

**GLENMORE FOUNDATION** See Glenmore Recovery Center

⊞ **RIVERVIEW HEALTH (241320)**, 323 South Minnesota Street, Zip 56716–1601; tel. 218/281–9200, (Total facility includes 22 beds in nursing home–type unit) (Nonreporting) **A**1 10 18 **F**2 3 5 6 10 11 12 13 15 18 28 29 34 35 40 43 45 47 50 56 57 59 62 64 65 70 74 75 76 77 79 81 82 85 86 87 89 91 92 93 94 97 107 108 110 111 115 119 127 129 130 131 132 133 135 143 146 147 148 149 154 156 **P**6
Primary Contact: Carrie Michalski, President and Chief Executive Officer
COO: Chris Bruggeman, Chief Operating Officer
CFO: Betty Arvidson, Chief Financial Officer
CMO: Colin Fennell, M.D., Chief Medical Officer
CIO: Nichole Beauchane, Director Information Technology
CHR: Jean Tate, Vice President Human Resources
CNO: April Grunhovd, Vice President of Patient Care Services and Chief Nursing Officer
Web address: www.riverviewhealth.org
**Control**: Other not–for–profit (including NFP Corporation) **Service**: General medical and surgical

| | |
|---|---|
| **Staffed Beds:** 49 **Admissions:** 729 **Census:** 29 **Outpatient Visits:** 45942 **Births:** 68 **Total Expense ($000):** 61263 **Payroll Expense ($000):** 30110 **Personnel:** 330 | |

**RIVERVIEW HEALTHCARE ASSOCIATION** See Riverview Health

## CROSBY—Crow Wing County

**CUYUNA RANGE DISTRICT HOSPITAL** See Cuyuna Regional Medical Center

⊞ **CUYUNA REGIONAL MEDICAL CENTER (241353)**, 320 East Main Street, Zip 56441–1690; tel. 218/546–7000, (Nonreporting) **A**1 2 3 5 10 18
Primary Contact: Kyle Bauer, Chief Executive Officer
COO: Amy Hart, Chief Operating Officer
CFO: Katie Berg, Chief Financial Officer
CMO: Robert Westin, M.D., Chief Medical Officer
CHR: Caity Eggen, Chief Human Resource Officer
CNO: Renee Steffin, Chief Nursing Officer
Web address: www.cuyunamed.org
**Control**: Hospital district or authority, Government, Nonfederal **Service**: General medical and surgical

| | |
|---|---|
| **Staffed Beds:** 142 | |

MN

## DAWSON—Lac Qui Parle County

**JOHNSON MEM HOSPITAL & HOME** See Johnson Memorial Health Services

**JOHNSON MEMORIAL HEALTH SERVICES (241314)**, 1282 Walnut Street, Zip 56232–2333; tel. 320/769–4323, (Total facility includes 56 beds in nursing home–type unit) (Nonreporting) **A**10 18 **F**3 7 8 10 11 12 15 28 31 32 34 40 41 43 45 50 56 57 59 62 64 65 66 69 71 75 77 81 82 93 97 107 110 111 115 119 127 128 129 130 133 135 145 147 148 154 **P**6
Primary Contact: Stacey Lee, CPA, JD, Chief Executive Officer
CFO: Crystal Bothun, Chief Financial Officer
CMO: Erik Shelstad, M.D., Chief of Staff
CIO: Steve Coubal, Manager Information Technology and Systems
CHR: Megan Lynch, Manager Human Resources
Web address: www.jmhsmn.org
**Control**: Hospital district or authority, Government, Nonfederal **Service**: General medical and surgical

**Staffed Beds**: 76 **Admissions**: 240 **Census**: 52 **Outpatient Visits**: 11745 **Births**: 0 **Total Expense ($000)**: 18192 **Payroll Expense ($000)**: 9150 **Personnel**: 151

## DEER RIVER—Itasca County

**DEER RIVER HEALTHCARE CENTER** See Essentia Health-Deer River

★ **ESSENTIA HEALTH-DEER RIVER (241360)**, 115 10th Avenue NE, Zip 56636–8795; tel. 218/246–2900, (Total facility includes 32 beds in nursing home–type unit) (Nonreporting) **A**10 18 **F**3 7 11 12 13 15 28 29 31 34 35 40 45 46 50 56 57 59 62 64 65 69 71 74 75 77 78 79 81 82 85 91 92 93 96 97 107 108 110 115 118 119 125 127 130 131 133 135 143 146 147 148 149 154 156 **S** Essentia Health, Duluth, MN
Primary Contact: Marsha Green, Administrator and Chief Operating Officer
COO: Marsha Green, Administrator and Chief Operating Officer
CMO: David Goodall, M.D., Chief Medical Staff
CHR: Brittany Mohler, Director Human Resources
Web address: www.essentiahealth.org
**Control**: Other not–for–profit (including NFP Corporation) **Service**: General medical and surgical

**Staffed Beds**: 52 **Admissions**: 450 **Census**: 24 **Outpatient Visits**: 45030 **Births**: 61 **Total Expense ($000)**: 33784 **Payroll Expense ($000)**: 14881 **Personnel**: 157

## DETROIT LAKES—Becker County

**ESSENTIA HEALTH ST. MARY'S - DETROIT LAKES (240101)**, 1027 Washington Avenue, Zip 56501–3409; tel. 218/847–5611, (Total facility includes 96 beds in nursing home–type unit) (Nonreporting) **A**1 10 20 **F**10 11 13 15 18 28 29 30 31 34 35 40 41 43 45 56 57 59 62 64 65 70 75 76 77 78 79 81 82 85 87 89 91 93 97 104 107 110 111 114 115 118 119 125 127 128 130 131 132 135 144 146 147 148 149 154 156 **S** Essentia Health, Duluth, MN
Primary Contact: Ryan Hill, Interim Administrator
CFO: Ryan Hill, Senior Financial Advisor
CMO: Rich Vetter, M.D., Associate Chief
CIO: Ken Gilles, Associate Chief Information Officer
CHR: Diane Sundrud, Human Resource Service Partner
CNO: Kay Larson, R.N., Chief Nursing Officer
Web address: www.essentiahealth.org
**Control**: Other not–for–profit (including NFP Corporation) **Service**: General medical and surgical

**Staffed Beds**: 132 **Admissions**: 2426 **Census**: 101 **Outpatient Visits**: 241303 **Births**: 471 **Total Expense ($000)**: 127752 **Payroll Expense ($000)**: 59999 **Personnel**: 649

**ESSENTIA HEALTH ST. MARY'S HOSPITAL - DETROIT LAKES** See Essentia Health St. Mary's - Detroit Lakes

## DULUTH—St. Louis County

△ **ESSENTIA HEALTH DULUTH (240019)**, 502 East Second Street, Zip 55805–1982; tel. 218/727–8762, (Nonreporting) **A**1 3 7 10 **F**3 5 11 12 15 16 29 30 31 32 34 35 49 50 51 52 54 55 56 57 59 61 64 65 70 74 75 77 78 79 81 82 84 85 86 87 90 91 92 93 94 96 97 98 99 100 101 103 104 105 107 108 110 111 114 115 116 117 118 119 120 121 123 124 130 131 132 134 135 141 144 146 147 148 149 151 153 154 157 **P**6 **S** Essentia Health, Duluth, MN
Primary Contact: Bradley Beard, Chief Operating Officer
CFO: Kevin Boren, Chief Financial Officer
CMO: Hugh Renier, M.D., Vice President Medical Affairs
CIO: Dennis Dassenko, Chief Information Officer
CHR: Diane Davidson, Senior Vice President Human Resources
CNO: Sandee Carlson, Director of Nursing
Web address: www.smdcmedicalcenter.org
**Control**: Other not–for–profit (including NFP Corporation) **Service**: General medical and surgical

**Staffed Beds**: 154 **Admissions**: 3307 **Census**: 75 **Outpatient Visits**: 545784 **Births**: 0 **Total Expense ($000)**: 435166 **Payroll Expense ($000)**: 236767 **Personnel**: 1690

**ESSENTIA HEALTH ST. MARY'S MEDICAL CENTER (240002)**, 407 East Third Street, Zip 55805–1984; tel. 218/786–4000, (Includes ST. MARY'S CHILDREN'S HOSPITAL, Mailing address: 407 East Third Street, Duluth, Minnesota, Zip 55805–1950; tel. 218/786–5437), (Nonreporting) **A**1 2 3 5 10 **F**3 11 12 13 17 18 20 22 24 26 28 29 30 34 35 37 38 40 41 43 45 46 47 49 50 57 59 63 65 67 70 72 74 76 78 79 81 83 84 85 86 87 88 89 91 102 107 108 111 115 119 126 129 130 132 135 141 146 149 154 157 **S** Essentia Health, Duluth, MN
Primary Contact: James Garvey, Senior Vice President Hospital Practice, Essentia Health East
CMO: Hugh Renier, M.D., Vice President Medical Affairs
CIO: Tess Jettergren, Director Clinical Informatics
CHR: Glen Porter, Vice President Human Resources
Web address: www.essentiahealth.org/StMarysMedicalCenter/FindaClinic/Essentia-HealthSt-Marys-Medical-Center-46.aspx
**Control**: Other not–for–profit (including NFP Corporation) **Service**: General medical and surgical

**Staffed Beds**: 307 **Admissions**: 18776 **Census**: 242 **Outpatient Visits**: 132569 **Births**: 1210 **Total Expense ($000)**: 426176 **Payroll Expense ($000)**: 166528 **Personnel**: 1804

**SMDC MEDICAL CENTER** See Essentia Health Duluth

★ △ ⇑ **ST. LUKE'S HOSPITAL (240047)**, 915 East First Street, Zip 55805–2193; tel. 218/249–5555, (Nonreporting) **A**2 3 5 7 10 19 21 **F**3 8 9 11 12 15 18 20 22 24 26 28 29 30 31 34 35 39 40 43 45 46 47 48 49 51 53 54 57 58 59 60 61 62 63 64 65 70 74 75 76 77 78 79 81 82 83 84 85 86 87 89 90 91 92 93 97 98 100 102 104 107 108 110 114 115 117 118 119 120 121 123 124 126 129 130 131 132 144 145 146 147 148 149 154 155 156 **P**6 **S** St. Luke's, Duluth, MN
Primary Contact: Kevin J. Nokels, FACHE, President and Chief Executive Officer
CFO: Eric Lohn, Vice President and Chief Financial Officer
CMO: Nicholas Van Deelen, Chief Medical Officer and Vice President, Medical Affairs
CIO: Clark Averill, Director Information Technology
CHR: Marla Halvorson, Director Human Resources
CNO: Susan Hamel, Chief Nursing Officer
Web address: www.slhduluth.com
**Control**: Other not–for–profit (including NFP Corporation) **Service**: General medical and surgical

**Staffed Beds**: 267 **Admissions**: 11480 **Census**: 162 **Outpatient Visits**: 711370 **Births**: 801 **Total Expense ($000)**: 506469 **Payroll Expense ($000)**: 243149 **Personnel**: 2306

**ST. MARY'S MEDICAL CENTER** See Essentia Health St. Mary's Medical Center

## EDINA—Hennepin County

**✠ FAIRVIEW SOUTHDALE HOSPITAL (240078)**, 6401 France Avenue South, Zip 55435–2199; tel. 952/924–5000, (Nonreporting) **A**1 2 3 5 10 **F**3 13 15 17 18 20 22 24 26 28 29 30 31 35 40 43 44 45 46 49 50 51 59 64 65 68 70 71 74 75 76 77 78 79 81 84 85 87 88 92 93 98 100 101 107 108 110 111 114 115 116 117 118 119 121 126 130 132 146 148 149 154 **P**6 **S** M Health Fairview, Minneapolis, MN
Primary Contact: Jeoff Will, Chief Operating Officer, Acute Care Services
COO: Jeoff Will, Chief Operating Officer, Acute Care Services
CFO: Alan Lem, Vice President Finance
CHR: Michelle LeDell, Director Human Resources
Web address: www.fairview.org
**Control**: Other not–for–profit (including NFP Corporation) **Service**: General medical and surgical

**Staffed Beds:** 316 **Admissions:** 18742 **Census:** 213 **Outpatient Visits:** 132758 **Births:** 2994 **Total Expense ($000):** 453868 **Payroll Expense ($000):** 178235 **Personnel:** 1770

## ELBOW LAKE—Grant County

**ELEAH MEDICAL CENTER** See Prairie Ridge Hospital and Health Services

**★ PRAIRIE RIDGE HOSPITAL AND HEALTH SERVICES (241379)**, 1411 Highway 79 East, Zip 56531–4645; tel. 218/685–7300, (Nonreporting) **A**10 18
Primary Contact: Danielle Lesmeister, Chief Executive Officer
CFO: Brett Longtin, Chief Financial Officer
CMO: Phillip Walter Holmes, M.D., Chief of Staff
CHR: Kim Blank, Director Human Resources
CNO: Alycia Athey, Director of Nursing
Web address: www.prairiehealth.org
**Control**: Other not–for–profit (including NFP Corporation) **Service**: General medical and surgical

**Staffed Beds:** 9

## ELY—St. Louis County

**★ ELY-BLOOMENSON COMMUNITY HOSPITAL (241318)**, 328 West Conan Street, Zip 55731–1198; tel. 218/365–3271, (Nonreporting) **A**10 18 **F**3 15 28 31 40 45 53 59 64 81 107 110 119 130 133 148 149
Primary Contact: Patti Banks, Interim Chief Executive Officer
COO: Patti Banks, Chief Operating Officer
CHR: Rochelle Sjoberg, Chief Human Resources Officer
CNO: Rebecca Holmstrom, Chief Nursing Officer
Web address: www.ebch.org
**Control**: Other not–for–profit (including NFP Corporation) **Service**: General medical and surgical

**Staffed Beds:** 21 **Admissions:** 258 **Census:** 2 **Outpatient Visits:** 9435 **Births:** 0

## FAIRMONT—Martin County

**FAIRMONT MEDICAL CENTER-MAYO HEALTH SYSTEM** See Mayo Clinic Health System in Fairmont

**☐ MAYO CLINIC HEALTH SYSTEM IN FAIRMONT (240166)**, 800 Medical Center Drive, Zip 56031–4575; tel. 507/238–8100, (Nonreporting) **A**1 10 20 **F**3 11 12 13 15 18 28 29 30 31 34 35 40 43 45 57 59 64 65 68 74 75 76 77 78 79 80 81 85 86 87 92 93 97 100 101 104 107 108 110 111 115 118 119 129 130 132 133 144 146 148 149 **S** Mayo Clinic, Rochester, MN
Primary Contact: James Hebl, M.D., Regional Vice President
COO: Gayle B Hansen, R.N., Chief Operating Officer
CFO: Brian Suter, Chief Financial Officer
CMO: Rufus Rodriguez, M.D., Medical Director
Web address: www.fairmontmedicalcenter.org
**Control**: Other not–for–profit (including NFP Corporation) **Service**: General medical and surgical

**Staffed Beds:** 23 **Admissions:** 1263 **Census:** 13 **Outpatient Visits:** 81022 **Births:** 205 **Personnel:** 258

## FARIBAULT—Rice County

**✠ DISTRICT ONE HOSPITAL (240071)**, 200 State Avenue, Zip 55021–6345; tel. 507/334–6451, (Nonreporting) **A**1 2 10 **F**3 8 13 15 28 29 31 40 43 45 50 59 64 76 77 78 79 80 81 84 85 87 89 91 93 96 102 110 119 129 130 131 132 146 147 149 154 **S** Allina Health, Minneapolis, MN
Primary Contact: David L. Albrecht, President
COO: Rick Miller, Director, Operations and Finance
CFO: Rick Miller, Chief Financial Officer
CMO: Amy Elliott, M.D., Director Medical Affairs
Web address: www.allinahealth.org/District-One-Hospital/
**Control**: Other not–for–profit (including NFP Corporation) **Service**: General medical and surgical

**Staffed Beds:** 34 **Admissions:** 1371 **Census:** 9 **Outpatient Visits:** 51736 **Births:** 330 **Total Expense ($000):** 50560 **Payroll Expense ($000):** 17829 **Personnel:** 190

**RICE CNTY DISTRICT ONE HOSP** See District One Hospital

## FERGUS FALLS—Otter Tail County

**☐ COMMUNITY BEHAVIORAL HEALTH HOSPITAL - FERGUS FALLS (244013)**, 1801 West Alcott Avenue, Zip 56537–2661, Mailing Address: P.O. Box 478, Zip 56538–0478; tel. 218/332–5001, (Nonreporting) **A**1 10 **S** Minnesota Department of Human Services, Saint Paul, MN
Primary Contact: Brenda Schleske, Administrator
**Control**: State, Government, Nonfederal **Service**: Psychiatric

**Staffed Beds:** 16

**FERGUS FALLS COMM BEHAV HOSP** See Community Behavioral Health Hospital - Fergus Falls

**✠ LAKE REGION HEALTHCARE (240052)**, 712 South Cascade Street, Zip 56537–2900, Mailing Address: P.O. Box 728, Zip 56538–0728; tel. 218/736–8000, (Nonreporting) **A**1 10 20 **F**3 7 10 11 13 15 18 28 29 30 31 32 35 40 42 43 45 46 50 51 53 54 57 58 59 64 65 70 74 75 76 78 79 81 85 86 87 89 90 93 97 98 100 104 107 108 110 111 115 118 119 120 121 123 129 130 131 133 144 146 147 148 149 154 156
Primary Contact: Kent D. Mattson, Chief Executive Officer
CFO: Brett Longtin, Chief Financial Officer
CMO: Greg Smith, Chief Medical Officer
CIO: Wade A Jyrkas, Director Computer Information Systems
CHR: Kim Blank, Director Human Resources
CNO: Lucia E Anderson, Senior Vice President Operations and Chief Nurse Executive
Web address: www.lrhc.org
**Control**: Other not–for–profit (including NFP Corporation) **Service**: General medical and surgical

**Staffed Beds:** 166 **Admissions:** 2204 **Census:** 22 **Outpatient Visits:** 202841 **Births:** 264 **Total Expense ($000):** 133778 **Payroll Expense ($000):** 43764 **Personnel:** 718

**LAKE REGION HEALTHCARE CORPORATION** See Lake Region Healthcare

## FOSSTON—Polk County

**ESSENTIA HEALTH FOSSTON** See Essentia Health-Fosston

**★ ESSENTIA HEALTH-FOSSTON (241357)**, 900 Hilligoss Boulevard SE, Zip 56542–1599; tel. 218/435–1133, (Total facility includes 50 beds in nursing home–type unit) (Nonreporting) **A**10 18 **F**3 7 10 11 13 15 18 28 29 31 34 35 40 43 44 50 56 57 59 62 63 65 68 70 75 76 77 78 79 80 81 82 84 85 87 93 97 104 107 110 114 127 128 129 130 131 132 133 135 146 148 149 154 157 **P**6 **S** Essentia Health, Duluth, MN
Primary Contact: Kevin Gish, Administrator and Vice President
CFO: Kim Bodensteiner, Chief Financial Officer
CHR: Diane Sundrud, Director Human Resources
Web address: www.essentiahealth.org
**Control**: Other not–for–profit (including NFP Corporation) **Service**: General medical and surgical

**Staffed Beds:** 74 **Admissions:** 587 **Census:** 44 **Outpatient Visits:** 57316 **Births:** 72 **Total Expense ($000):** 27814 **Payroll Expense ($000):** 13099 **Personnel:** 213

## FRIDLEY—Anoka County

**UNITY HOSPITAL** See Mercy Hospital-Unity Campus

**MN**

## GLENCOE—Mcleod County

★ **GLENCOE REGIONAL HEALTH (241355)**, 1805 Hennepin Avenue North,
Zip 55336–1416; tel. 320/864–3121, (Total facility includes 108 beds in nursing
home–type unit) (Nonreporting) **A**10 18 **F**3 11 13 15 28 29 31 34 40 43 45 48 50
56 64 68 75 76 77 78 79 81 85 86 87 89 93 97 107 110 111 115 118 119 125
128 130 132 133 135 146 148 149 156 **P**6 **S** HealthPartners, Bloomington, MN
Primary Contact: Patricia Henderson, R.N., Interim Chief Executive Officer
CFO: John C Doidge, Vice President Finance
CMO: Kristine Knudten, M.D., Vice President Medical Affairs
CIO: Ryan Lake, Director Information Technology
CHR: Jill Hatlestad, Vice President Human Resources and Marketing
CNO: Patricia Henderson, R.N., Vice President Nursing and Clinical Services
Web address: www.grhsonline.org
**Control**: Other not–for–profit (including NFP Corporation) **Service**: General
medical and surgical

**Staffed Beds:** 133 **Admissions:** 993 **Census:** 97 **Outpatient Visits:** 29973
**Births:** 163 **Total Expense ($000):** 61671 **Payroll Expense ($000):** 30770
**Personnel:** 424

**GLENCOE REGIONAL HEALTH SERVICES** See Glencoe Regional Health

## GLENWOOD—Pope County

★ **GLACIAL RIDGE HEALTH SYSTEM (241376)**, 10 Fourth Avenue SE,
Zip 56334–1898; tel. 320/634–4521, (Nonreporting) **A**10 18 **F**11 12 13 15 17
28 31 34 35 40 41 43 45 53 59 62 63 64 75 76 77 79 81 93 107 110 111
115 119 127 130 133 146 148 149 154 155
Primary Contact: Kirk A. Stensrud, Chief Executive Officer
CFO: Kyle Chase, Chief Financial Officer
CMO: Gustave Mellgren, M.D., Chief of Staff
CIO: Jeff Ofstedal, Manager Information Technology
CHR: Gordon Paulson, Manager Human Resources
CNO: Lynn Flesner, Director of Nursing
Web address: www.glacialridge.org
**Control**: Hospital district or authority, Government, Nonfederal **Service**: General
medical and surgical

**Staffed Beds:** 22 **Admissions:** 702 **Census:** 8 **Outpatient Visits:** 19118
**Births:** 98 **Total Expense ($000):** 44342 **Payroll Expense ($000):** 21200
**Personnel:** 317

**GLACIAL RIDGE HOSPITAL** See Glacial Ridge Health System

## GOLDEN VALLEY—Hennepin County

**GOLDEN VALLEY HEALTH CENTER** See Regency Hospital of Minneapolis

⊠ **REGENCY HOSPITAL OF MINNEAPOLIS (242005)**, 1300 Hidden Lakes
Parkway, Zip 55422–4286; tel. 763/588–2750, (Nonreporting) **A**1 10 **S** Select
Medical Corporation, Mechanicsburg, PA
Primary Contact: Sean Stricker, Chief Executive Officer
CMO: Alaka Nagaraj, M.D., Medical Director
CNO: Caren Gaytko, Chief Nursing Officer
Web address: www.regencyhospital.com
**Control**: Corporation, Investor–owned (for–profit) **Service**: Acute long–term care
hospital

**Staffed Beds:** 92

## GRACEVILLE—Big Stone County

★ **ESSENTIA HEALTH–GRACEVILLE (241321)**, 115 West Second Street,
Zip 56240–4845, Mailing Address: P.O. Box 157, Zip 56240–0157;
tel. 320/748–7223, (Total facility includes 40 beds in nursing home–type unit)
(Nonreporting) **A**10 18 **F**3 15 28 30 33 34 40 41 43 56 57 59 62 64 65 68 75
77 81 82 85 87 93 97 107 110 115 127 128 133 146 147 148 149 154
156 **P**6 **S** Essentia Health, Duluth, MN
Primary Contact: Julie Rosenberg, Administrator
CMO: Arthur Van Vranken, M.D., Chief Medical Officer
CIO: Brad Tostenson, Chief Information Officer
CHR: Jenny Lee, Human Resources Generalist
CNO: Jill Johnsrud, Director of Nursing
Web address: www.essentiahealth.org/HolyTrinityHospital/FindaClinic/Essentia-
HealthHoly-Trinity-Hospital-96.aspx
**Control**: Other not–for–profit (including NFP Corporation) **Service**: General
medical and surgical

**Staffed Beds:** 55 **Admissions:** 105 **Census:** 35 **Outpatient Visits:** 6448
**Births:** 0 **Total Expense ($000):** 10230 **Payroll Expense ($000):** 4866
**Personnel:** 97

**ESSENTIA HEALTH–HOLY TRINITY HOSPITAL** See Essentia Health-Graceville

## GRAND MARAIS—Cook County

**COOK COUNTY NORTH SHORE HOSPITAL** See North Shore Health

★ **NORTH SHORE HEALTH (241317)**, 515 5th Avenue West, Zip 55604–3017;
tel. 218/387–3040, (Nonreporting) **A**10 18
Primary Contact: Kimber L. Wraalstad, FACHE, Administrator
CFO: Vera Schumann, Director of Finance and Controller
CMO: Milan Schmidt, Medical Director
CIO: Greg Johnson, IT Coordinator
CHR: Michele Starkey, Director Human Resources
CNO: Fred Andrews, Director of Nursing
Web address: www.northshorehealthgm.com
**Control**: Hospital district or authority, Government, Nonfederal **Service**: General
medical and surgical

**Staffed Beds:** 53

## GRAND RAPIDS—Itasca County

⊠ **GRAND ITASCA CLINIC AND HOSPITAL (240064)**, 1601 Golf Course Road,
Zip 55744–8648; tel. 218/326–5000, (Nonreporting) **A**1 10 20 **S** M Health
Fairview, Minneapolis, MN
Primary Contact: Jean MacDonell, President and Chief Executive Officer
CFO: Todd Christensen, Vice President, Finance
CMO: Dan Soular, M.D., Vice President, Medical Affairs
CHR: Katherine Burns-Chistenson, Human Resource Director
CNO: Sandy Lenarz, Chief Nursing Officer
Web address: www.granditasca.org
**Control**: Other not–for–profit (including NFP Corporation) **Service**: General
medical and surgical

**Staffed Beds:** 31

**ITASCA MEDICAL CENTER** See Grand Itasca Clinic and Hospital

## GRANITE FALLS—Yellow Medicine County

★ **AVERA GRANITE FALLS HEALTH CENTER (241343)**, 345 Tenth Avenue,
Zip 56241–1499; tel. 320/564–3111, (Nonreporting) **A**10 18 **S** Avera Health,
Sioux Falls, SD
Primary Contact: Thomas Kooiman, Chief Executive Officer
CFO: Val Hoffman, Chief Financial Officer
CIO: Kris Wilke, Manager Health Information
CHR: Sue Tollefson, Coordinator Payroll Personnel
CNO: Patty Massman, Director of Nursing
Web address: www.granitefallshealthcare.com
**Control**: City, Government, Nonfederal **Service**: General medical and surgical

**Staffed Beds:** 82

**GRANITE FALLS HEALTH** See Avera Granite Falls Health Center

## HALLOCK—Kittson County

★ **KITTSON MEMORIAL HEALTHCARE CENTER (241336)**, 1010 South Birch
Street, Zip 56728–4215, Mailing Address: P.O. Box 700, Zip 56728–0700;
tel. 218/843–3612, (Nonreporting) **A**10 18
Primary Contact: Gabriel Mooney, Chief Executive Officer
CMO: Thomas Lohstreter, M.D., Chief of Staff
CIO: Holly Knutson, Manager Information Technology
CHR: Carlene Cole, Manager Human Resources
CNO: Tawnya Sorenson, Director of Nursing
Web address: www.https://kittsonhc.org
**Control**: Other not–for–profit (including NFP Corporation) **Service**: General
medical and surgical

**Staffed Beds:** 75

**KITTSON MEMORIAL HOSPITAL** See Kittson Memorial Healthcare Center

**MN**

---

**Hospital, Medicare Provider Number, Address, Telephone, Approval, Facility, and Physician Codes, Health Care System**

★ American Hospital Association (AHA) membership ○ Healthcare Facilities Accreditation Program ⇑ Center for Improvement in Healthcare Quality Accreditation
☐ The Joint Commission accreditation ◇ DNV Healthcare Inc. accreditation △ Commission on Accreditation of Rehabilitation Facilities (CARF) accreditation

## HASTINGS—Dakota County

☒ **REGINA HOSPITAL (240059)**, 1175 Nininger Road, Zip 55033–1098; tel. 651/480–4100, (Nonreporting) **A**1 10 **F**3 8 11 13 15 28 29 30 31 34 35 40 43 45 46 50 59 75 76 77 78 79 80 81 82 85 87 93 98 103 107 110 111 114 119 129 130 132 145 146 148 149 154 157 **S** Allina Health, Minneapolis, MN
Primary Contact: Helen J. Strike, R.N., President
CFO: Andy Rolling, Director of Finance
CMO: James Noreen, M.D., Chief Medical Officer
Web address: www.reginamedical.org
**Control**: Other not–for–profit (including NFP Corporation) **Service**: General medical and surgical

**Staffed Beds**: 49 **Admissions**: 1523 **Census**: 21 **Outpatient Visits**: 56459 **Births**: 217 **Total Expense ($000)**: 64655 **Payroll Expense ($000)**: 20810 **Personnel**: 254

**REGINA MEDICAL CENTER** See Regina Hospital

## HENDRICKS—Lincoln County

**HENDRICKS COMMUNITY HOSPITAL** See Hendricks Community Hospital Association

★ **HENDRICKS COMMUNITY HOSPITAL ASSOCIATION (241339)**, 503 East Lincoln Street, Zip 56136–9598, Mailing Address: P.O. Box 106, Zip 56136–0106; tel. 507/275–3134, (Total facility includes 48 beds in nursing home–type unit) (Nonreporting) **A**10 18 **F**2 3 7 11 15 17 28 29 31 34 35 40 50 59 62 63 70 81 89 93 107 125 127 128 130 132 133 146 148 156 158
Primary Contact: Jeffrey Gollaher, Chief Executive Officer
CMO: Tabb McCluskey, M.D., Chief Medical Officer
CHR: Lynn R Olson, Director Human Resources
Web address: www.hendrickshosp.org
**Control**: Other not–for–profit (including NFP Corporation) **Service**: General medical and surgical

**Staffed Beds**: 59 **Admissions**: 152 **Census**: 46 **Outpatient Visits**: 10841 **Births**: 0 **Total Expense ($000)**: 14220 **Payroll Expense ($000)**: 7208 **Personnel**: 122

## HIBBING—St. Louis County

☒ **FAIRVIEW RANGE MEDICAL CENTER (240040)**, 750 East 34th Street, Zip 55746–4600; tel. 218/262–4881, (Nonreporting) **A**1 2 10 **F**3 11 13 15 18 28 29 30 31 32 33 34 35 36 40 43 45 50 54 56 57 58 59 62 63 64 65 68 70 75 76 77 78 79 81 82 83 84 85 87 89 93 97 98 100 102 104 105 107 108 110 111 115 118 119 120 121 123 129 130 131 132 135 143 144 145 146 147 148 149 150 154 **P**5 6 **S** M Health Fairview, Minneapolis, MN
Primary Contact: Patrick Sharp, President and Chief Executive Officer
CFO: Tom Fink, Vice President Regional Finance Officer
CMO: Susan Rudberg, M.D., Chief Medical Officer
CIO: Jessica Valento, Director Information Systems
CHR: Mitchell S Vincent, Vice President Organizational Support
CNO: Sherry Burg, Chief Nursing Officer
Web address: www.range.fairview.org
**Control**: Other not–for–profit (including NFP Corporation) **Service**: General medical and surgical

**Staffed Beds**: 72 **Admissions**: 2489 **Census**: 37 **Outpatient Visits**: 50532 **Births**: 317 **Total Expense ($000)**: 79416 **Payroll Expense ($000)**: 44759 **Personnel**: 813

**RANGE REGIONAL HEALTH SERVICES** See Fairview Range Medical Center

## HUTCHINSON—Mcleod County

**HUTCHINSON AREA HEALTH CARE** See Hutchinson Health

☐ **HUTCHINSON HEALTH (240187)**, 1095 Highway 15 South, Zip 55350–3182; tel. 320/234–5000, (Nonreporting) **A**1 10 20 **S** HealthPartners, Bloomington, MN
Primary Contact: Jim Lyons, President
COO: Glen Kegley, Chief Operating Officer
CFO: Pamela Larson, Division Director Financial Services
CMO: Brian Pollman, Chief Medical Officer
CIO: Tara Nelson, Chief Clinic Officer
CHR: Rebecca Streich, Manager Human Resources and Education Manager
CNO: Susan Karnitz, Chief Nursing Director
Web address: www.hutchhealth.com
**Control**: Other not–for–profit (including NFP Corporation) **Service**: General medical and surgical

**Staffed Beds**: 49

## INTERNATIONAL FALLS—Koochiching County

**INTERNATIONAL FALLS MEM HOSP** See Rainy Lake Medical Center

**RAINY LAKE MEDICAL CENTER (241322)**, 1400 Highway 71, Zip 56649–2189; tel. 218/283–4481, (Nonreporting) **A**10 18 **F**3 13 15 26 27 28 29 30 31 34 35 40 43 44 45 46 49 50 54 56 57 59 64 65 66 68 76 77 78 79 81 82 83 85 87 89 93 97 107 110 111 115 119 127 129 131 132 133 135 143 144 146 147 149 150 154 156 157 **P**6
Primary Contact: Robert Pastor II, R.N., Chief Executive Officer
CFO: Melissa Marcotte, Chief Financial Officer
CIO: Michael Blesi, Director Information Technology
CNO: Donita Ettestad, R.N., MS, Chief Nursing Officer
Web address: www.rainylakemedical.com
**Control**: Other not–for–profit (including NFP Corporation) **Service**: General medical and surgical

**Staffed Beds**: 16 **Admissions**: 514 **Census**: 7 **Outpatient Visits**: 37350 **Births**: 44 **Total Expense ($000)**: 29006 **Payroll Expense ($000)**: 11753 **Personnel**: 158

## JACKSON—Jackson County

**SANFORD JACKSON MED CENTER** See Sanford Jackson Medical Center

★ **SANFORD JACKSON MEDICAL CENTER (241315)**, 1430 North Highway, Zip 56143–1093; tel. 507/847–2420, (Nonreporting) **A**10 18 **F**3 28 29 31 32 34 35 40 41 43 44 49 50 56 57 59 62 64 65 68 77 81 85 86 87 89 91 93 97 101 102 104 107 108 114 125 127 128 130 131 132 133 135 143 149 154 156 **P**6 **S** Sanford Health, Sioux Falls, SD
Primary Contact: Dawn Schnell, Chief Nursing Officer and Interim Senior Director
CFO: Gail Eike, Chief Financial Officer
CMO: SisterMarie Paul Lockerd, M.D., Chief Medical Officer
CNO: Dawn Schnell, Chief Nursing Officer
Web address: www.sanfordjackson.org
**Control**: Other not–for–profit (including NFP Corporation) **Service**: General medical and surgical

**Staffed Beds**: 16 **Admissions**: 100 **Census**: 2 **Outpatient Visits**: 25737 **Births**: 0 **Total Expense ($000)**: 11086 **Payroll Expense ($000)**: 4380 **Personnel**: 41

## LAKE CITY—Goodhue County

**LAKE CITY MEDICAL CENTER-MAYO** See Mayo Clinic Health System in Lake City

☐ **MAYO CLINIC HEALTH SYSTEM IN LAKE CITY (241338)**, 500 West Grant Street, Zip 55041–1143; tel. 651/345–3321, (Total facility includes 90 beds in nursing home–type unit) (Nonreporting) **A**1 10 18 **F**15 28 29 30 34 35 40 45 57 59 64 67 69 75 79 81 87 92 93 97 107 110 111 114 119 128 130 132 133 146 148 149 154 **S** Mayo Clinic, Rochester, MN
Primary Contact: Brian Whited, M.D., President and Chief Executive Officer
Web address: www.lakecitymedicalcenter.org
**Control**: Other not–for–profit (including NFP Corporation) **Service**: General medical and surgical

**Staffed Beds**: 102 **Admissions**: 553 **Census**: 89 **Outpatient Visits**: 23191 **Births**: 0 **Personnel**: 101

## LE SUEUR—Le Sueur County

**RIDGEVIEW LE SEUR MEDICAL CENTER** See Ridgeview Le Sueur Medical Center

★ **RIDGEVIEW LE SUEUR MEDICAL CENTER (241375)**, 621 South Fourth Street, Zip 56058–2298; tel. 507/665–3375, (Total facility includes 40 beds in nursing home–type unit) (Nonreporting) **A**10 18 **F**3 7 15 40 43 45 69 81 87 97 107 115 128 130 133 144 154 **S** Ridgeview Medical Center, Waconia, MN
Primary Contact: Pamela Williams, Regional Vice President
CFO: Patricia Schlegel, Executive Director Finance
CMO: Carolyn Stelter, M.D., Chief of Staff
CHR: Bonnie Barnhardt, Executive Director Human Resources
CNO: Kim Putz, R.N., Director, Nursing Hospital
Web address: www.mvhc.org
**Control**: Other not–for–profit (including NFP Corporation) **Service**: General medical and surgical

**Staffed Beds**: 49 **Admissions**: 156 **Census**: 32 **Outpatient Visits**: 8378 **Births**: 0 **Total Expense ($000)**: 12456 **Payroll Expense ($000)**: 2696 **Personnel**: 108

*Many Facility Codes have changed. Please refer to the AHA Guide Code Chart.*

© 2021 AHA Guide

## LITCHFIELD—Meeker County

**MEEKER COUNTY MEM HOSPITAL** See Meeker Memorial Hospital

**MEEKER MEMORIAL HOSPITAL (241366)**, 612 South Sibley Avenue,
Zip 55355–3398; tel. 320/693–4500, (Nonreporting) **A**10 18
Primary Contact: Kurt Waldbillig, Chief Executive Officer
CFO: Stephen Plaisance, Chief Financial Officer
CMO: Tim Peterson, M.D., Chief of Staff
CIO: Troy Bruning, Director Information Technology
CHR: Cindi Twardy, Manager Human Resources
CNO: Joan Bitz, Chief Nursing Officer
Web address: www.meekermemorial.org
**Control:** County, Government, Nonfederal **Service:** General medical and surgical

**Staffed Beds:** 38

## LITTLE FALLS—Morrison County

✠ **CHI ST. GABRIEL'S HEALTH (241370)**, 815 Second Street SE,
Zip 56345–3596; tel. 320/632–5441, (Nonreporting) **A**1 10 18 **F**4 11 13 14 15
17 18 28 29 30 32 34 35 40 43 45 57 59 62 63 64 65 68 70 75 76 77 78 79
81 84 86 87 89 90 91 92 93 96 97 104 107 110 111 115 116 117 119 127
128 129 130 132 133 135 143 144 146 147 149 154 156 **S** CommonSpirit
Health, Chicago, IL
Primary Contact: Steve Smith, President and Chief Financial Officer
CFO: Steve Smith, President and Chief Financial Officer
CMO: Susan Okoniewski, M.D., Chief of Staff
Web address: www.stgabriels.com
**Control:** Other not–for–profit (including NFP Corporation) **Service:** General medical and surgical

**Staffed Beds:** 25 **Admissions:** 1167 **Census:** 9 **Outpatient Visits:** 34942
**Births:** 127 **Total Expense ($000):** 74327 **Payroll Expense ($000):** 30296
**Personnel:** 394

**ST. GABRIEL'S HOSPITAL** See Chi St. Gabriel's Health

## LONG PRAIRIE—Todd County

★ **CENTRACARE - LONG PRAIRIE (241326)**, 20 Ninth Street SE,
Zip 56347–1404; tel. 320/732–2141, (Nonreporting) **A**5 10 18 **S** CentraCare
Health, Saint Cloud, MN
Primary Contact: Daniel J. Swenson, FACHE, Administrator
CFO: Larry Knutson, Director Finance
CMO: Rene Eldidy, M.D., Chief of Staff
Web address: www.centracare.com
**Control:** Other not–for–profit (including NFP Corporation) **Service:** General medical and surgical

**Staffed Beds:** 20

**CENTRACARE HEALTH-LONG PRAIRIE** See Centracare - Long Prairie

## LUVERNE—Rock County

**SANFORD HOSPITAL LUVERNE** See Sanford Luverne Medical Center

★ **SANFORD LUVERNE MEDICAL CENTER (241371)**, 1600 North Kniss Avenue,
Zip 56156–1067; tel. 507/283–2321, (Nonreporting) **A**10 18 **F**3 4 5 7 8 11 13
15 18 19 28 29 31 32 34 35 40 43 45 56 57 59 63 64 65 67 68 74 75 76 77
78 79 81 82 83 84 85 86 87 90 93 96 97 107 111 114 118 119 128 129 131
132 133 135 146 147 148 149 152 154 156 157 **P**6 **S** Sanford Health, Sioux
Falls, SD
Primary Contact: Tammy Loosbrock, Senior Director
COO: Nancy E Drenth, R.N., Director Ancillary Services
CFO: Stanley Knobloch, Director Fiscal Services
CMO: Judy S Chesley, M.D., Chief of Staff
CNO: Nyla H Sandbulte, R.N., Director of Nursing
Web address: www.sanfordluverne.org
**Control:** Other not–for–profit (including NFP Corporation) **Service:** General medical and surgical

**Staffed Beds:** 25 **Admissions:** 532 **Census:** 6 **Outpatient Visits:** 41557
**Births:** 58 **Total Expense ($000):** 25277 **Payroll Expense ($000):** 11566
**Personnel:** 158

## MADELIA—Watonwan County

✠ **MADELIA COMMUNITY HOSPITAL (241323)**, 121 Drew Avenue SE,
Zip 56062–1899; tel. 507/642–3255, (Nonreporting) **A**1 5 10 18 **F**3 13 15 34
35 40 57 59 62 64 68 69 75 76 77 81 82 84 85 86 93 102 104 107 110 115
119 128 130 132 133 144 145 148 149 154
Primary Contact: Jeff Mengenhausen, Chief Executive Officer
CFO: Donna M Klinkner, Chief Financial Officer
CMO: Todd Gavin, Chief Medical Officer
CIO: Valerie Juhl, Director of Health
CHR: Donna M Klinkner, Chief Financial Officer
CNO: Deidre Hruby, Director of Patient Care
Web address: www.mchospital.org
**Control:** Other not–for–profit (including NFP Corporation) **Service:** General medical and surgical

**Staffed Beds:** 21 **Admissions:** 173 **Census:** 3 **Outpatient Visits:** 11084
**Births:** 0 **Total Expense ($000):** 12471 **Payroll Expense ($000):** 4559
**Personnel:** 104

## MADISON—Lac Qui Parle County

**MADISON HEALTHCARE SERVICES (241372)**, 900 Second Avenue,
Zip 56256–1006; tel. 320/598–7556, (Nonreporting) **A**10 18
Primary Contact: Erik Bjerke, Chief Executive Officer
CFO: Carol Borgerson, Chief Financial Officer
CIO: Jerry Harberts, Information Technologist
CHR: Kelly Johnson, Director Human Resources
Web address: www.mlhmn.org/
**Control:** Other not–for–profit (including NFP Corporation) **Service:** General medical and surgical

**Staffed Beds:** 12

**MADISON HOSPITAL** See Madison Healthcare Services

## MAHNOMEN—Mahnomen County

**MAHNOMEN COUNTY & VILLAGE HOSP** See Mahnomen Health Center

**MAHNOMEN HEALTH CENTER (241300)**, 414 West Jefferson Avenue,
Zip 56557–4912, Mailing Address: P.O. Box 396, Zip 56557–0396;
tel. 218/935–2511, (Nonreporting) **A**10 18 **S** Sanford Health, Sioux Falls, SD
Primary Contact: Dale K. Kruger, Chief Executive Officer
CFO: Mary Pazdernik, Chief Financial Officer
CMO: Anju Gurung, M.D., Chief Medical Officer
CHR: Kristi Stall, Chief Human Resources Officer
Web address: www.mahnomenhealthcenter.com
**Control:** City–county, Government, Nonfederal **Service:** General medical and surgical

**Staffed Beds:** 50

## MANKATO—Blue Earth County

**IMMANUEL ST. JOSEPH'S-MAYO HEALTH SYSTEM** See Mayo Clinic Health
System in Mankato

✠ **MAYO CLINIC HEALTH SYSTEM IN MANKATO (240093)**, 1025 Marsh Street,
Zip 56001–4752; tel. 507/625–4031, (Nonreporting) **A**1 3 5 10 **F**3 9 12 13 15
18 19 20 22 26 28 29 30 31 32 33 34 35 36 37 38 40 41 43 45 53 54 56
57 58 59 60 61 63 64 65 70 73 74 75 76 77 78 79 81 82 83 84 85 87 89
92 93 97 98 100 102 104 107 108 110 111 114 115 118 119 120 121 126
127 129 130 131 132 135 144 146 147 148 149 154 155 156 **S** Mayo Clinic,
Rochester, MN
Primary Contact: James Hebl, M.D., Regional Vice President
CMO: Susan Pearson, M.D., Chief Medical Officer
CIO: Sarah Daniels, Vice President, Information Technology
CHR: Beth Dittbenner, Regional Director, Human Resources
CNO: Laura Evenson, Chief Nursing Officer
Web address: www.mayoclinichealthsystem.org
**Control:** Other not–for–profit (including NFP Corporation) **Service:** General medical and surgical

**Staffed Beds:** 170 **Admissions:** 9661 **Census:** 111 **Outpatient
Visits:** 284567 **Births:** 1401 **Personnel:** 1660

**MN**

---

**Hospital, Medicare Provider Number, Address, Telephone, Approval, Facility, and Physician Codes, Health Care System**

★ American Hospital Association (AHA) membership    ○ Healthcare Facilities Accreditation Program    ⇧ Center for Improvement in Healthcare Quality Accreditation
□ The Joint Commission accreditation    ◇ DNV Healthcare Inc. accreditation    △ Commission on Accreditation of Rehabilitation Facilities (CARF) accreditation

© 2021 AHA Guide     *Many Facility Codes have changed. Please refer to the AHA Guide Code Chart.*     Hospitals **A379**

### MAPLE GROVE—Hennepin County

⇑ **MAPLE GROVE HOSPITAL (240214)**, 9875 Hospital Drive, Zip 55369–4648; tel. 763/581–1000, (Nonreporting) **A**5 10 21 **F**3 13 15 18 29 30 40 43 45 47 50 53 60 68 70 72 76 77 79 81 84 85 89 100 102 107 108 111 115 118 119 126 130 146 148 149 **P**8 **S** North Memorial Health Care, Robbinsdale, MN
Primary Contact: Andrew S. Cochrane, Chief Executive Officer
CMO: Pamela Doorenbos, M.D., Vice President, Medical Affairs
CNO: Wendy Ulferts, Vice President and Chief Nursing Officer
Web address: www.maplegrovehospital.org
**Control:** Other not–for–profit (including NFP Corporation) **Service:** General medical and surgical

**Staffed Beds:** 108 **Admissions:** 9947 **Census:** 87 **Outpatient Visits:** 235129 **Births:** 4681 **Total Expense ($000):** 167333 **Payroll Expense ($000):** 63023 **Personnel:** 850

### MAPLEWOOD—Ramsey County

**HEALTHEAST ST JOHN'S HOSPITAL** See St. John's Hospital

✚ **ST. JOHN'S HOSPITAL (240210)**, 1575 Beam Avenue, Zip 55109–1126; tel. 651/232–7000, (Nonreporting) **A**1 3 5 10 **F**3 5 13 15 18 28 30 31 34 35 36 37 38 40 43 44 45 46 49 50 53 54 55 61 63 64 68 70 72 74 75 76 77 78 79 81 82 84 85 86 87 93 100 102 104 107 108 110 111 114 115 116 117 119 120 121 123 126 130 131 132 135 146 147 148 149 **P**6 **S** M Health Fairview, Minneapolis, MN
Primary Contact: Lia Christiansen, Chief Operating Officer, Acute Care Hospitals
COO: M. Osman Akhtar, Chief Operating Officer
CMO: Mark Welton, M.D., Chief Medical Officer
CIO: Alistar Jacques, Chief Information Officer
CHR: Carolyn Jacobson, Chief Human Resources Officer
CNO: Laura Reed, R.N., Chief Nursing Executive
Web address: www.stjohnshospital-mn.org
**Control:** Other not–for–profit (including NFP Corporation) **Service:** General medical and surgical

**Staffed Beds:** 192 **Admissions:** 11165 **Census:** 105 **Outpatient Visits:** 106654 **Births:** 2130 **Total Expense ($000):** 253572 **Payroll Expense ($000):** 107662 **Personnel:** 1078

### MARSHALL—Lyon County

★ ○ **AVERA MARSHALL REGIONAL MEDICAL CENTER (241359)**, 300 South Bruce Street, Zip 56258–3900; tel. 507/532–9661, (Total facility includes 76 beds in nursing home–type unit) (Nonreporting) **A**10 11 18 **F**3 8 11 12 13 15 17 18 28 29 30 31 33 34 35 40 41 43 45 50 54 56 57 59 60 62 63 64 65 70 75 76 78 79 81 82 84 85 87 89 97 98 101 102 104 107 110 111 115 119 120 121 123 128 129 130 131 132 133 144 146 148 149 156 157 **S** Avera Health, Sioux Falls, SD
Primary Contact: Mary B. Maertens, FACHE, President and Chief Executive Officer
CMO: Steven T. Meister, M.D., Vice President, Ambulatory Services
CHR: Sonya J Kayser, Human Resources Officer
CNO: Dodie Derynck, Chief Nursing Officer
Web address: www.avera.org
**Control:** Church operated, Nongovernment, not–for–profit **Service:** General medical and surgical

**Staffed Beds:** 111 **Admissions:** 2108 **Census:** 91 **Outpatient Visits:** 35096 **Births:** 482 **Total Expense ($000):** 66194 **Payroll Expense ($000):** 26022 **Personnel:** 523

**WEINER MEMORIAL MEDICAL CENTER** See Avera Marshall Regional Medical Center

### MELROSE—Stearns County

★ **CENTRACARE - MELROSE (241330)**, 525 Main Street West, Zip 56352–1043; tel. 320/256–4231, (Nonreporting) **A**5 10 18 **S** CentraCare Health, Saint Cloud, MN
Primary Contact: Gerry Gilbertson, FACHE, Administrator
COO: Gerry Gilbertson, FACHE, Administrator
CFO: Adam Paulson, Director Finance
CMO: Dante Beretta, M.D., Chief of Staff
CIO: Janet Kruzel, Business Office Manager
CHR: Joyce Chan, Chief Human Resources Officer
CNO: Keri Wimmer, R.N., Patient Care Director
Web address: www.centracare.com
**Control:** Other not–for–profit (including NFP Corporation) **Service:** General medical and surgical

**Staffed Beds:** 93

**CENTRACARE HEALTH-MELROSE** See Centracare - Melrose

### MINNEAPOLIS—Hennepin County

✚ △ **ABBOTT NORTHWESTERN HOSPITAL (240057)**, 800 East 28th Street, Zip 55407–3799; tel. 612/863–4000, (Includes PHILLIPS EYE INSTITUTE, Mailing address: 2215 Park Avenue, Minneapolis, Minnesota, Zip 55404–3756; tel. 612/775–8800; Daniel S Conrad, M.D., President; SISTER KENNY REHABILITATION INSTITUTE, Mailing address: 810 East 27th Street, Minneapolis, Minnesota, Zip 55407; tel. 612/874–4000) (Total facility includes 48 beds in nursing home–type unit) **A**1 2 3 5 7 10 **F**3 5 8 12 13 15 17 18 19 20 22 24 26 28 29 30 31 34 35 36 38 39 40 42 43 44 45 46 47 48 49 50 51 52 53 54 55 56 57 58 59 60 61 63 64 65 66 68 70 74 75 76 77 78 79 81 82 83 84 85 86 87 90 91 92 93 95 96 97 98 99 100 101 102 104 105 107 108 109 110 111 112 113 114 115 116 117 118 119 120 121 123 124 126 128 129 130 131 132 135 137 138 141 144 145 146 147 148 149 153 154 157 **S** Allina Health, Minneapolis, MN
Primary Contact: Ann Madden Rice, President
CFO: Brian Weinreis, Vice President Operations and Finance
CMO: Penny Ann Wheeler, M.D., President and Chief Medical Officer
CIO: Susan Heichert, Senior Vice President and Chief Information Officer
CHR: Margaret Butler, Vice President Human Resources
CNO: Mandy Richards, R.N., MSN, System Chief Nursing Officer, Allina Health Vice President of Care
Web address: www.abbottnorthwestern.com
**Control:** Other not–for–profit (including NFP Corporation) **Service:** General medical and surgical

**Staffed Beds:** 697 **Admissions:** 35509 **Census:** 469 **Outpatient Visits:** 534107 **Births:** 4593 **Total Expense ($000):** 1256114 **Payroll Expense ($000):** 532724 **Personnel:** 4461

**ABBOTT-NORTHWESTERN HOSPITAL** See Abbott Northwestern Hospital

**CHILDREN'S HEALTH CARE** See Children's Hospitals and Clinics of Minnesota

✚ **CHILDREN'S HOSPITALS AND CLINICS OF MINNESOTA (243302)**, 2525 Chicago Avenue South, Zip 55404–4518; tel. 612/813–6100, (Includes CHILDREN'S HOSPITALS AND CLINICS OF MINNESOTA, Mailing address: 345 North Smith Avenue, Saint Paul, Minnesota, Zip 55102–2346; tel. 651/220–6000; Robert Bonar Jr, Chief Executive Officer), (Nonreporting) **A**1 3 5 10 **F**3 8 9 17 18 19 20 21 22 23 24 25 26 27 28 29 30 31 32 34 35 36 38 40 41 43 44 45 50 51 54 55 57 58 59 61 62 63 64 65 68 71 72 73 74 75 77 78 79 81 82 84 85 86 87 88 89 92 93 97 100 101 102 104 107 108 111 112 114 115 119 126 129 130 131 132 134 135 136 137 145 146 148 154 156
Primary Contact: Marc Gorelick, M.D., President and Chief Executive Officer
COO: Trevor Sawallish, Senior Vice President Clinical Operations and Chief Operating Officer
CFO: Rebecca Woitalewicz, Chief Financial Officer
CMO: Emily Chapman, Chief Medical Officer
CIO: Jeffrey D Young, Chief Information Officer
CHR: Samantha Hanson, Chief Human Resources Officer
CNO: Roxanne Fernandes, R.N., Chief Nursing Officer
Web address: www.childrensmn.org
**Control:** Other not–for–profit (including NFP Corporation) **Service:** Children's general medical and surgical

**Staffed Beds:** 429 **Admissions:** 14687 **Census:** 276 **Outpatient Visits:** 574464 **Births:** 0 **Total Expense ($000):** 943640 **Payroll Expense ($000):** 439951 **Personnel:** 4145

**FAIRVIEW RIVERSIDE HOSPITAL** See University of Minnesota, Minneapolis

**FAIRVIEW-UNIVERSITY MED CENTER** See University of Minnesota

**HENNEPIN COUNTY MEDICAL CENTER** See Hennepin Healthcare

☐ △ **HENNEPIN HEALTHCARE (240004)**, 701 Park Avenue South, Zip 55415–1829; tel. 612/873–3000, (Includes HCMC DEPARTMENT OF PEDIATRICS, Mailing address: 701 Park Avenue, Minneapolis, Minnesota, Zip 55415–1623; tel. 612/873–2064), (Nonreporting) **A**1 2 3 5 7 8 10 **F**3 5 7 8 12 13 15 16 18 20 22 24 26 28 29 30 31 32 33 34 35 36 38 39 40 41 43 44 45 46 47 48 49 50 51 53 54 55 56 57 58 59 60 61 62 63 64 65 66 68 70 72 74 75 76 77 78 79 81 82 84 85 86 87 88 89 90 92 93 94 96 97 98 99 100 101 102 103 104 105 106 107 108 110 111 112 114 115 117 118 119 120 121 126 129 130 131 132 134 135 136 138 139 140 141 144 145 146 147 148 149 150 153 154 156 157 **P**6
Primary Contact: Jennifer DeCubellis, Chief Executive Officer
COO: Emily Blomberg, Chief Operating Officer
CFO: Derrick O. Hollings, Chief Financial Officer
CMO: Dan Hoody, M.D., Interim Chief Medical Officer
CIO: Nancy Garrett, Chief Analytics and Information Technology Officer
CHR: Walter Chesley, Senior Vice President Human Resources
CNO: Lori J. Brown, R.N., FACHE, Chief Nursing Officer
Web address: www.hcmc.org
**Control:** County, Government, Nonfederal **Service:** General medical and surgical

**Staffed Beds:** 439 **Admissions:** 21812 **Census:** 342 **Outpatient Visits:** 771790 **Births:** 1831 **Total Expense ($000):** 1070696 **Payroll Expense ($000):** 587428 **Personnel:** 5762

☒ △ **MINNEAPOLIS VETERANS AFFAIRS HEALTH CARE SYSTEM**, One
Veterans Drive, Zip 55417–2399; tel. 612/725–7000, (Nonreporting) **A**1 2 3 5 7
8 **S** Department of Veterans Affairs, Washington, DC
Primary Contact: Patrick J. Kelly, FACHE, Director
COO: Kurt Thielen, Associate Director
CFO: LeAnn Stomberg, Chief Financial Officer
CMO: Kent Crossley, M.D., Chief of Staff
CIO: Brian Bornick, Chief Information Officer
CHR: Tom Johnson, Chief Human Resource Officer
CNO: Helen Pearlman, Nurse Executive
Web address: www.minneapolis.va.gov
**Control**: Veterans Affairs, Government, federal **Service**: General medical and surgical

**Staffed Beds: 309**

**SISTER KENNY INSTITUTE** See Sister Kenny Rehabilitation Institute

**SISTER KENNY REHABILITATION INSTITUTE** See Abbott Northwestern Hospital, Minneapolis

**ST. MARY'S HOSPITAL AND REHABILITATION CENTER** See University of Minnesota, Minneapolis

**THE HCMC DEPARTMENT OF PEDIATRICS** See Hcmc Department of Pediatrics

☒ △ **UNIVERSITY OF MINNESOTA (240080)**, 2450 Riverside Avenue,
Zip 55454–1400, Mailing Address: 2520 University Ave SE Ste 201, Zip 55414;
tel. 612/624–8618, (Includes FAIRVIEW RIVERSIDE HOSPITAL, Mailing address:
2312 South Sixth Street, Minneapolis, Minnesota, Zip 55454; tel. 612/371–6300;
ST. MARY'S HOSPITAL AND REHABILITATION CENTER, Mailing address: 2414
South Seventh Street, Minneapolis, Minnesota, Zip 55454; tel. 612/338–2229;
UNIVERSITY OF MINNESOTA HOSPITAL AND CLINIC, Mailing address: 420 SE
Delaware Street, Minneapolis, Minnesota, Zip 55455–0392; tel. 612/626–3000;
UNIVERSITY OF MINNESOTA MASONIC CHILDREN'S HOSPITAL, Mailing
address: 420 Delaware Street, SE, Minneapolis, Minnesota, Zip 55455–0341;
tel. 888/543–7866) (Total facility includes 22 beds in nursing home–type unit) **A**1
2 3 5 7 8 10 **F**3 4 5 11 12 13 15 17 18 19 20 21 22 23 24 25 26 27 28 29 30
31 32 33 34 35 36 37 38 39 40 41 43 44 45 46 47 48 49 50 51 55 56 57 58
59 60 61 64 65 68 70 72 74 75 76 77 78 79 80 81 82 84 85 86 87 88 89 90
91 92 93 94 96 97 98 99 100 101 102 103 104 105 106 107 108 109 110
111 112 113 114 115 116 117 118 119 120 121 123 124 126 128 130 132
134 135 136 137 138 139 140 141 142 145 146 147 148 149 151 153 154
156 **P**6 **S** M Health Fairview, Minneapolis, MN
Primary Contact: John Doherty, Co-President, M Health
CFO: John Doherty, Vice President Finance
CMO: Barbara Gold, M.D., Chief Medical Officer
CHR: Don Moschkau, Senior Director Human Resources
Web address: www.fairview.org
**Control**: Other not–for–profit (including NFP Corporation) **Service**: General medical and surgical

**Staffed Beds: 861 Admissions: 32539 Census: 643 Outpatient
Visits: 418906 Births: 2430 Total Expense ($000): 1737032 Payroll
Expense ($000): 568400 Personnel: 5275**

**UNIVERSITY OF MINNESOTA CHILDREN'S HOSPITAL, FAIRVIEW** See University of Minnesota Masonic Children's Hospital

**UNIVERSITY OF MINNESOTA HOSPITAL AND CLINIC** See University of Minnesota, Minneapolis

**UNIVERSITY OF MN HOSPITAL** See University of Minnesota Hospital and Clinic

**VETERANS AFFAIRS MEDICAL CENTER** See Minneapolis Veterans Affairs Health Care System

### MONTEVIDEO—Chippewa County

★ **CCM HEALTH (241325)**, 824 North 11th Street, Zip 56265–1683;
tel. 320/269–8877, (Nonreporting) **A**10 18
Primary Contact: Brian A. Lovdahl, Chief Executive Officer
CFO: Darlene Boike, Chief Financial Officer
CIO: Jeff Plemel, Director Health Information
CHR: Vonnie Erickson, Human Resource Manager
CNO: Terry Anderson, R.N., Director of Nursing Services
Web address: www.montevideomedical.com
**Control**: City–county, Government, Nonfederal **Service**: General medical and surgical

**Staffed Beds: 25**

**CHIPPEWA COUNTY-MONTEVIDEO HOSPITAL** See Ccm Health

### MONTICELLO—Wright County

★ ⇑ **CENTRACARE - MONTICELLO (241362)**, 1013 Hart Boulevard,
Zip 55362–8230; tel. 763/295–2945, (Total facility includes 89 beds in nursing
home–type unit) (Nonreporting) **A**5 10 18 21 **F**3 13 15 30 31 34 40 43 45 59
64 69 70 76 77 78 79 81 85 87 98 100 103 107 108 110 111 115 116 117
118 119 120 121 128 129 130 133 145 146 148 149 154 156 **S** CentraCare
Health, Saint Cloud, MN
Primary Contact: John Hering, M.D., Administrator
CFO: Jason Weaver, Director Finance
CNO: Lynn Christian, MSN, R.N., Senior Director Acute Care Nursing
Web address: www.centracare.com
**Control**: Other not–for–profit (including NFP Corporation) **Service**: General medical and surgical

**Staffed Beds: 122 Admissions: 1291 Census: 97 Outpatient Visits: 31205
Births: 238 Total Expense ($000): 73304 Payroll Expense ($000): 34861
Personnel: 468**

⇑ **CENTRACARE HEALTH-MONTICELLO** See Centracare - Monticello

### MOOSE LAKE—Carlton County

★ **ESSENTIA HEALTH MOOSE LAKE (241350)**, 4572 County Road 61,
Zip 55767–9405; tel. 218/485–4481, (Nonreporting) **A**10 18 **S** Essentia Health,
Duluth, MN
Primary Contact: Michael Youso, Chief Executive Officer
CHR: Sonya Towle, Director Human Resources
CNO: Donita Korpela, R.N., Director of Patient Care Services
Web address: www.mercymooselake.com
**Control**: Hospital district or authority, Government, Nonfederal **Service**: General medical and surgical

**Staffed Beds: 25**

**MERCY HOSPITAL AND HEALTH CARE CENTER** See Essentia Health Moose Lake

### MORA—Kanabec County

**FIRSTLIGHT HEALTH SYSTEM** See Welia Health

☒ **WELIA HEALTH (241367)**, 301 South Highway 65 South, Zip 55051–1899;
tel. 320/679–1212, (Nonreporting) **A**1 10 18 **F**3 7 11 13 15 28 31 34 35 40 43
51 53 68 70 75 76 77 78 79 81 84 85 87 93 94 97 107 108 110 111 115 119
127 130 131 132 133 135 144 146 147 148 149 154
Primary Contact: Randy Ulseth, Chief Executive Officer
COO: Sandy Zutz-Wiczek, Chief Operating Officer
CFO: Josh Asp, Chief Financial Officer
CMO: Brian Niskanen, Chief Medical Officer
CIO: Becky Gallik, Information Systems Manager
CNO: Diane Bankers, Chief Nursing Officer
Web address: www.https://www.weliahealth.org
**Control**: County, Government, Nonfederal **Service**: General medical and surgical

**Staffed Beds: 25 Admissions: 1163 Census: 9 Outpatient Visits: 161417
Births: 191 Total Expense ($000): 90702 Payroll Expense ($000): 28814
Personnel: 429**

### MORRIS—Stevens County

**STEVENS COMM MEMORIAL HOSPITAL** See Stevens Community Medical Center

★ **STEVENS COMMUNITY MEDICAL CENTER (241363)**, 400 East First Street,
Zip 56267–1408; tel. 320/589–1313, (Nonreporting) **A**10 18 **F**3 11 13 15 28 29
31 34 35 40 43 44 45 50 54 57 59 64 70 75 76 77 79 81 85 86 87 89 97 107
110 111 115 119 127 128 130 131 132 133 135 144 146 148 149 154 **P**6
Primary Contact: John Rau, President and Chief Executive Officer
CFO: Kerrie McEvilly, Vice President Finance
CIO: Kerrie McEvilly, Vice President Finance
CHR: Karla Larson, Director Human Resources
Web address: www.scmcinc.org
**Control**: Other not–for–profit (including NFP Corporation) **Service**: General medical and surgical

**Staffed Beds: 25 Admissions: 592 Census: 5 Outpatient Visits: 77611
Births: 89 Total Expense ($000): 37268 Payroll Expense ($000): 17900
Personnel: 233**

---

**Hospital, Medicare Provider Number, Address, Telephone, Approval, Facility, and Physician Codes, Health Care System**

★ American Hospital Association (AHA) membership ○ Healthcare Facilities Accreditation Program ⇑ Center for Improvement in Healthcare Quality Accreditation
☐ The Joint Commission accreditation ◇ DNV Healthcare Inc. accreditation △ Commission on Accreditation of Rehabilitation Facilities (CARF) accreditation

**MN**

**NEW PRAGUE—Scott County**

☐ **MAYO CLINIC HEALTH SYSTEM IN NEW PRAGUE (241361)**, 301 Second Street NE, Zip 56071–1799; tel. 952/758–4431, (Nonreporting) **A**1 3 10 18 **F**11 13 15 18 28 29 30 31 34 35 36 40 43 45 46 57 59 64 65 68 74 75 76 77 78 79 81 82 85 86 87 92 93 97 107 108 110 111 114 116 117 119 125 128 129 130 131 132 133 144 146 147 148 149 154 156 **S** Mayo Clinic, Rochester, MN
Primary Contact: James Hebl, M.D., Regional Vice President
Web address: www.mayoclinichealthsystem.org/locations/new-prague
**Control:** Other not–for–profit (including NFP Corporation) **Service:** General medical and surgical

**Staffed Beds:** 19 **Admissions:** 676 **Census:** 10 **Outpatient Visits:** 46941 **Births:** 130 **Personnel:** 163

**MAYO CLINIC HEALTH SYSTEM IN PRAGUE** See Mayo Clinic Health System in New Prague

**NEW ULM—Brown County**

✉ **NEW ULM MEDICAL CENTER (241378)**, 1324 Fifth Street North, Zip 56073–1553; tel. 507/217–5000, (Nonreporting) **A**1 3 5 10 18 **F**3 4 5 8 13 15 28 29 31 32 34 35 36 40 42 43 46 50 55 56 57 59 64 65 68 70 74 75 76 77 78 79 81 82 84 85 87 93 94 97 98 100 101 102 104 107 108 110 111 115 119 129 130 131 132 135 144 146 148 149 154 156 **S** Allina Health, Minneapolis, MN
Primary Contact: Toby Freier, President
COO: Carisa Buegler, Director of Operations
CFO: Michael Grand, Director of Finance
CMO: Andrew Reeves, M.D., Director Medical Affairs
CHR: Katie Slette, Director Human Resources
CNO: Jennifer Brehmer, Director Patient Care
Web address: www.newulmmedicalcenter.com
**Control:** Other not–for–profit (including NFP Corporation) **Service:** General medical and surgical

**Staffed Beds:** 44 **Admissions:** 1940 **Census:** 19 **Outpatient Visits:** 119858 **Births:** 278 **Total Expense ($000):** 100881 **Payroll Expense ($000):** 32503 **Personnel:** 410

**SIOUX VALLEY HOSPITAL** See New Ulm Medical Center

**NORTHFIELD—Dakota County**

**NORTHFIELD HOSPITAL** See Northfield Hospital and Clinics

★ **NORTHFIELD HOSPITAL AND CLINICS (240014)**, 2000 North Avenue, Zip 55057–1498; tel. 507/646–1000, (Total facility includes 40 beds in nursing home–type unit) (Nonreporting) **A**10 **F**3 4 7 11 13 15 30 31 40 43 47 48 62 63 64 68 69 70 75 76 77 78 79 81 85 87 89 93 107 110 111 115 119 128 129 130 131 132 133 144 146 149 154 **P**6
Primary Contact: Steve Underdahl, President and Chief Executive Officer
COO: Jerry Ehn, Chief Operating Officer
CFO: Scott D Edin, Vice President, Finance and Chief Financial Officer
CMO: Jeff Meland, M.D., Vice President, Chief Medical Officer
CHR: Jeffrey S. Mutz, Human Resources Director
CNO: Tammy A. Hayes, R.N., MS, Chief Nurse Executive and Long Term Care Administrator
Web address: www.northfieldhospital.org
**Control:** City, Government, Nonfederal **Service:** General medical and surgical

**Staffed Beds:** 77 **Admissions:** 1802 **Census:** 48 **Outpatient Visits:** 147103 **Births:** 505 **Total Expense ($000):** 110712 **Payroll Expense ($000):** 50054 **Personnel:** 565

**OLIVIA—Renville County**

★ **RC HOSPITAL AND CLINICS (241306)**, 100 Healthy Way, Zip 56277–1117; tel. 320/523–1261, (Nonreporting) **A**10 18 **F**3 8 15 17 28 29 34 35 40 41 43 45 46 57 59 63 64 65 68 70 75 76 77 79 81 82 85 86 89 93 94 96 97 107 111 114 119 126 127 129 130 131 132 133 146 148 149 156
Primary Contact: Nathan Blad, Chief Executive Officer
CFO: Nathan Blad, Chief Financial Officer
CIO: Cherry Weigel, Director Health Information Management
Web address: www.rchospital.com
**Control:** County, Government, Nonfederal **Service:** General medical and surgical

**Staffed Beds:** 16 **Admissions:** 334 **Census:** 2 **Outpatient Visits:** 75577 **Births:** 41 **Total Expense ($000):** 29747 **Payroll Expense ($000):** 11587 **Personnel:** 130

**RENVILLE COUNTY HOSPITAL** See RC Hospital and Clinics

**ONAMIA—Mille Lacs County**

★ **MILLE LACS HEALTH SYSTEM (241356)**, 200 North Elm Street, Zip 56359–7901; tel. 320/532–3154, (Total facility includes 57 beds in nursing home–type unit) (Nonreporting) **A**10 18 **F**7 11 15 28 29 31 33 34 40 43 45 50 59 62 63 64 75 77 81 85 93 97 98 103 107 114 115 127 129 130 132 133 135 144 149 156 157
Primary Contact: Bill Nelson, Chief Executive Officer
COO: Kim Kucera, Chief Operating Officer
CFO: John Unzen, Chief Financial Officer
CMO: Thomas H Bracken, M.D., Vice President Medical Affairs
Web address: www.mlhealth.org
**Control:** Other not–for–profit (including NFP Corporation) **Service:** General medical and surgical

**Staffed Beds:** 85 **Admissions:** 890 **Census:** 65 **Outpatient Visits:** 23294 **Births:** 2 **Total Expense ($000):** 43015 **Payroll Expense ($000):** 21972 **Personnel:** 359

**MILLE LACS HOSPITAL** See Mille Lacs Health System

**ORTONVILLE—Big Stone County**

★ **ORTONVILLE AREA HEALTH SERVICES (241342)**, 450 Eastvold Avenue, Zip 56278–1133; tel. 320/839–2502, (Nonreporting) **A**10 18 **S** Sanford Health, Sioux Falls, SD
Primary Contact: David Rogers, Chief Executive Officer
CMO: Stacy Longnecker, Chief of Staff
CIO: Barbara Voecks, Chief Information Officer
CHR: Kim McCrea, Chief Human Resources Officer
CNO: Jennifer Wiik, Chief Nursing Officer
Web address: www.oahs.us
**Control:** City, Government, Nonfederal **Service:** General medical and surgical

**Staffed Beds:** 90

**OWATONNA—Steele County**

**HEALTH ONE OWATONNA HOSPITAL** See Owatonna Hospital

✉ **OWATONNA HOSPITAL (240069)**, 2250 NW 26th Street, Zip 55060–5503; tel. 507/451–3850, (Nonreporting) **A**1 10 **F**11 13 28 29 34 35 40 57 76 77 79 80 81 93 98 100 101 102 107 108 119 129 130 131 145 149 154 **S** Allina Health, Minneapolis, MN
Primary Contact: David L. Albrecht, President
COO: Mark T Gillen, Director of Operations
CFO: Mark T Gillen, Director Finance and Operations
CHR: Sarah Stumme, Director Human Resources
CNO: Anne Draeger, Chief Nursing Officer
Web address: www.owatonnahospital.com
**Control:** Other not–for–profit (including NFP Corporation) **Service:** General medical and surgical

**Staffed Beds:** 42 **Admissions:** 2438 **Census:** 23 **Outpatient Visits:** 39431 **Births:** 466 **Total Expense ($000):** 54822 **Payroll Expense ($000):** 20469 **Personnel:** 227

**PARK RAPIDS—Hubbard County**

✉ **CHI ST. JOSEPH'S HEALTH (241380)**, 600 Pleasant Avenue, Zip 56470–1431; tel. 218/732–3311, (Nonreporting) **A**1 10 18 **S** CommonSpirit Health, Chicago, IL
Primary Contact: Benjamin Koppelman, President
CFO: Jay Ross, Chief Financial Officer
CMO: Kia Parsi, M.D., Chief Medical Officer
CHR: John Tormanen, Director Mission and Human Resources
CNO: Deb Haagenson, R.N., Vice President of Patient Care
Web address: www.sjahs.org
**Control:** Church operated, Nongovernment, not–for–profit **Service:** General medical and surgical

**Staffed Beds:** 25

**ST. JOSEPH'S AREA HEALTH SERVICES** See Chi St. Joseph's Health

**MN**

*Many Facility Codes have changed. Please refer to the AHA Guide Code Chart.*

© 2021 AHA Guide

## PAYNESVILLE—Stearns County

★ **CENTRACARE HEALTH-PAYNESVILLE (241349)**, 200 West 1st Street, Zip 56362–1496; tel. 320/243–3767, (Total facility includes 51 beds in nursing home–type unit) (Nonreporting) **A**5 10 18 **F**2 7 10 11 13 15 28 31 34 40 43 45 50 56 57 64 65 71 76 81 82 85 93 107 110 111 115 119 125 128 130 133 135 145 146 148 149 156 **S** CentraCare Health, Saint Cloud, MN
Primary Contact: Brandon E. Pietsch, Administrator
CFO: Jennifer Holtz, Director Finance
CMO: Timothy Malling, M.D., Chief of Staff
CHR: Paulette Hagen, Human Resources and Administrative Services Director
CNO: Rachel A Walz, Director Patient Care
Web address: www.centracare.com
**Control**: Other not–for–profit (including NFP Corporation) **Service**: General medical and surgical

**Staffed Beds:** 66 **Admissions:** 508 **Census:** 50 **Outpatient Visits:** 40247 **Births:** 67 **Total Expense ($000):** 40324 **Payroll Expense ($000):** 19679 **Personnel:** 242

**PAYNESVILLE AREA HEALTH CARE SYSTEM** See Centracare Health-Paynesville

## PERHAM—Otter Tail County

☒ **PERHAM HEALTH (241373)**, 1000 Coney Street West, Zip 56573–1108; tel. 218/347–4500, (Total facility includes 96 beds in nursing home–type unit) (Nonreporting) **A**1 10 18 **F**2 3 10 13 15 28 29 30 32 33 34 35 36 40 43 45 50 56 57 59 62 64 65 66 69 75 76 77 81 85 86 91 93 97 107 110 111 119 125 128 130 131 132 133 135 144 146 147 148 149 154 156 158 **S** Sanford Health, Sioux Falls, SD
Primary Contact: Chuck Hofius, Chief Executive Officer
CFO: Brad D Wurgler, Chief Financial Officer
CMO: Tim Studer, President Medical Staff
CIO: Jim Rieber, Director Information Systems
CNO: Bonnie Johnson, R.N., Vice President of Patient Services
Web address: www.perhamhealth.org
**Control**: Hospital district or authority, Government, Nonfederal **Service**: General medical and surgical

**Staffed Beds:** 121 **Admissions:** 566 **Census:** 94 **Outpatient Visits:** 405761 **Births:** 156 **Total Expense ($000):** 58330 **Payroll Expense ($000):** 26698 **Personnel:** 271

**PERHAM MEMORIAL HOSPITAL AND HOME** See Perham Health

## PIPESTONE—Pipestone County

★ **PIPESTONE COUNTY MEDICAL CENTER AVERA (241374)**, 916 4th Avenue SW, Zip 56164–1890; tel. 507/825–5811, (Nonreporting) **A**10 18 **S** Avera Health, Sioux Falls, SD
Primary Contact: Bradley D. Burris, Chief Executive Officer
CFO: Dave Keeler, Chief Financial Officer
CHR: Judy Raschke, Director Human Resources
CNO: Jessica Smidt, R.N., Director of Nursing
Web address: www.pcmchealth.org
**Control**: County, Government, Nonfederal **Service**: General medical and surgical

**Staffed Beds:** 18

**PIPESTONE COUNTY MEDICAL CENTER/AVERA HEALTH** See Pipestone County Medical Center Avera

## PRINCETON—Sherburne County

**FAIRVIEW NORTHLAND HEALTH SERV** See Fairview Northland Medical Center

☒ **FAIRVIEW NORTHLAND MEDICAL CENTER (240141)**, 911 Northland Drive, Zip 55371–2173; tel. 763/389–1313, (Nonreporting) **A**1 5 10 **F**3 11 13 15 18 34 35 40 41 43 47 48 50 51 57 59 64 69 70 75 76 77 78 79 81 85 86 87 89 93 94 101 107 110 111 115 119 126 130 131 132 146 148 149 154 **P**6 **S** M Health Fairview, Minneapolis, MN
Primary Contact: Lia Christiansen, Chief Operating Officer, Acute Care Hospitals
CFO: Tim Lynch, Director of Finance
CMO: Greg Schoen, M.D., Regional Medical Director
CNO: Karen Whiley, Vice President Patient Care Services
Web address: www.northland.fairview.org
**Control**: Other not–for–profit (including NFP Corporation) **Service**: General medical and surgical

**Staffed Beds:** 23 **Admissions:** 1488 **Census:** 12 **Outpatient Visits:** 54535 **Births:** 364 **Total Expense ($000):** 71126 **Payroll Expense ($000):** 26884 **Personnel:** 239

## RED LAKE—Beltrami County

☐ **RED LAKE INDIAN HEALTH SERVICE HOSPITAL (240206)**, 24760 Hospital Drive, Zip 56671, Mailing Address: P.O. Box 497, Zip 56671–0497; tel. 218/679–3912, (Nonreporting) **A**1 10 **S** U. S. Indian Health Service, Rockville, MD
Primary Contact: Norine Smith, Chief Executive Officer
CMO: Paul Ditmanson, M.D., Clinical Director
CNO: Mary Ann Cook, R.N., Director of Nursing
Web address: www.rlnnredlakehospital.com/
**Control**: PHS, Indian Service, Government, federal **Service**: General medical and surgical

**Staffed Beds:** 19

**U.S. PUBLIC HEALTH SERVICE INDIAN HOSPITAL** See Red Lake Indian Health Service Hospital

## RED WING—Goodhue County

**FAIRVIEW RED WING MEDICAL CENTER** See Mayo Clinic Health System in Red Wing

☐ **MAYO CLINIC HEALTH SYSTEM IN RED WING (240018)**, 701 Hewitt Boulevard, Zip 55066–2848, Mailing Address: P.O. Box 95, Zip 55066–0095; tel. 651/267–5000, (Nonreporting) **A**1 3 5 10 **F**3 11 13 15 18 28 29 30 31 34 35 36 40 43 45 57 59 63 64 65 74 75 76 77 78 79 81 82 85 86 87 93 94 97 100 104 107 111 115 119 130 131 132 146 147 149 154 **P**6 **S** Mayo Clinic, Rochester, MN
Primary Contact: Brian Whited, M.D., President and Chief Executive Officer
Web address: www.mayoclinichealthsystem.org/locations/red-wing
**Control**: Other not–for–profit (including NFP Corporation) **Service**: General medical and surgical

**Staffed Beds:** 28 **Admissions:** 1763 **Census:** 14 **Outpatient Visits:** 131879 **Births:** 273 **Personnel:** 463

## REDWOOD FALLS—Redwood County

★ **CARRIS HEALTH - REDWOOD (241351)**, 100 Fallwood Road, Zip 56283–1828; tel. 507/637–4500, (Nonreporting) **A**10 18 **S** CentraCare Health, Saint Cloud, MN
Primary Contact: Carnie Allex, Administrator
CFO: Thomas Richard, Director Budget and Revenue Cycle
CIO: Tom Balko, Manager Information Systems
CHR: Jody Rindfleisch, Manager Human Resources
CNO: Dawn Allen, R.N., Chief Clinical Officer
Web address: www.redwoodareahospital.org
**Control**: City, Government, Nonfederal **Service**: General medical and surgical

**Staffed Beds:** 25

**REDWOOD AREA HOSPITAL** See Carris Health - Redwood

## ROBBINSDALE—Hennepin County

⇑ **NORTH MEMORIAL HEALTH** See North Memorial Health Hospital

△ ⇑ **NORTH MEMORIAL HEALTH HOSPITAL (240001)**, 3300 Oakdale Avenue North, Zip 55422–2926; tel. 763/520–5200, (Nonreporting) **A**2 3 5 7 10 21 **F**3 7 11 12 13 15 17 18 20 22 24 26 28 29 30 31 34 35 38 40 43 44 45 46 49 50 53 54 55 56 57 58 59 60 61 63 64 68 70 72 73 74 75 76 77 78 79 80 81 82 84 85 86 87 88 89 90 91 92 93 96 97 98 100 102 103 104 105 107 108 110 111 114 115 117 118 119 124 126 127 129 130 132 135 144 146 147 148 149 150 153 154 155 156 157 158 **P**6 8 **S** North Memorial Health Care, Robbinsdale, MN
Primary Contact: Jeff Wicklander, President
COO: Steve Horstmann, Vice President Operations
CFO: Daniel Fromm, Chief Financial Officer
CMO: Andrew Houlton, M.D., Chief Medical Officer
CIO: Patrick Taffe, Vice President Information Services
CHR: Melissa Smith, Interim Vice President Human Resources
CNO: Kelly Lynn White, Vice President of Patient Care and Chief Nursing Officer
Web address: www.northmemorial.com
**Control**: Other not–for–profit (including NFP Corporation) **Service**: General medical and surgical

**Staffed Beds:** 358 **Admissions:** 18824 **Census:** 240 **Outpatient Visits:** 134252 **Births:** 673 **Total Expense ($000):** 801554 **Payroll Expense ($000):** 376298 **Personnel:** 4312

---

**Hospital, Medicare Provider Number, Address, Telephone, Approval, Facility, and Physician Codes, Health Care System**

★ American Hospital Association (AHA) membership ☐ The Joint Commission accreditation ○ Healthcare Facilities Accreditation Program ◇ DNV Healthcare Inc. accreditation ⇑ Center for Improvement in Healthcare Quality Accreditation △ Commission on Accreditation of Rehabilitation Facilities (CARF) accreditation

**MN**

## ROCHESTER—Olmsted County

☐ **COMMUNITY BEHAVIORAL HEALTH HOSPITAL - ROCHESTER (244017)**, 251 Wood Lake Drive SE, Zip 55904–5530; tel. 507/206–2561, (Nonreporting) **A**1 10 **S** Minnesota Department of Human Services, Saint Paul, MN
Primary Contact: James Pierce, Administrator
CFO: Shirley Jacobson, Chief Financial Officer
CMO: Peter S Millen, Chief Medical Officer MHSATS
CIO: Thomas Baden JrChief Information Officer
CHR: Connie Jones, Director Human Resources
CNO: Pamela R Bajari, R.N., Nurse Executive MHSATS
Web address: www.health.state.mn.us
**Control:** State, Government, Nonfederal **Service:** Psychiatric

**Staffed Beds:** 8

**MAYO CLINIC - SAINT MARYS HOSPITAL** See Mayo Clinic Hospital - Saint Marys Campus

☒ △ **MAYO CLINIC HOSPITAL - ROCHESTER (240010)**, 1216 Second Street SW, Zip 55902–1906; tel. 507/255–5123, (Includes MAYO CLINIC HOSPITAL - METHODIST CAMPUS, Mailing address: 201 West Center Street, Rochester, Minnesota, Zip 55902–3084; tel. 507/266–7890; MAYO CLINIC HOSPITAL - SAINT MARYS CAMPUS, Mailing address: 1216 Second Street SW, Rochester, Minnesota, Zip 55902–1970; tel. 507/255–5123; Kenneth F. Ackerman, FACHE, Chair, Hospital Operation; MAYO EUGENIO LITTA CHILDREN'S HOSPITAL, Mailing address: 200 First Street, SW, Rochester, Minnesota, Zip 55905–0001; tel. 507/255–5123), (Nonreporting) **A**1 2 3 5 7 8 10 20 **F**3 6 7 8 9 11 12 13 14 15 17 18 19 20 21 22 23 24 25 26 27 28 29 30 31 34 35 36 37 38 39 40 41 43 44 45 46 47 48 49 50 51 52 53 54 55 56 57 58 59 60 61 63 64 65 68 70 71 72 74 75 76 77 78 79 80 81 82 84 85 86 87 88 89 90 91 92 93 94 95 96 97 98 99 100 101 102 103 104 105 107 108 110 111 112 114 115 116 117 118 119 120 121 122 123 124 126 130 132 134 135 136 137 138 139 140 141 142 143 145 146 147 148 149 150 153 154 155 157 **P**6 **S** Mayo Clinic, Rochester, MN
Primary Contact: Kenneth F. Ackerman, FACHE, Hospital Administrator
COO: Jeffrey W. Bolton, Chief Administrative Officer
CFO: Kedrick D. Adkins, Chief Financial Officer
CMO: Robert R. Cima, M.D., Medical Director, Hospital Operations
CIO: Christopher J. Ross, Chief Information Technology Officer
CHR: Cathryn H. Fraser, Chief Human Resources Officer
CNO: Pamela O. Johnson, MS, R.N., Chief Nursing Officer
Web address: www.mayoclinic.org
**Control:** Other not–for–profit (including NFP Corporation) **Service:** General medical and surgical

**Staffed Beds:** 1287 **Admissions:** 60624 **Census:** 912 **Outpatient Visits:** 432470 **Births:** 2332 **Personnel:** 33745

⇑ **OLMSTED COMMUNITY HOSPITAL** See Olmsted Medical Center

★ ⇑ **OLMSTED MEDICAL CENTER (240006)**, 1650 Fourth Street SE, Zip 55904–4717, Mailing Address: 210 Ninth Street SE, Zip 55904–6756; tel. 507/288–3443, (Nonreporting) **A**10 21 **F**3 11 12 13 15 18 26 28 29 30 34 35 40 44 45 46 50 53 54 56 57 58 59 64 65 68 70 74 75 76 77 79 81 82 84 85 86 87 92 93 97 99 100 102 104 107 108 110 111 115 119 129 130 131 132 135 146 147 148 149 154 156
Primary Contact: Tim W. Weir, FACHE, Chief Executive Officer
COO: Robert Cunningham, Chief Operations Officer
CFO: Kevin A Higgins, Chief Financial Officer
CMO: Randy Hemann, M.D., Chief Medical Officer
CIO: Tom Ogg, Chief Information Officer
CHR: Tom Hunsberger, Director Human Resources
CNO: Sharon L Schneller, Chief Nursing Officer
Web address: www.olmmed.org
**Control:** Other not–for–profit (including NFP Corporation) **Service:** General medical and surgical

**Staffed Beds:** 41 **Admissions:** 1880 **Census:** 13 **Outpatient Visits:** 334485 **Births:** 949 **Total Expense ($000):** 210756 **Payroll Expense ($000):** 108058 **Personnel:** 937

**ROCHESTER COMM BEHAV HOSPITAL** See Community Behavioral Health Hospital - Rochester

**ROCHESTER METHODIST HOSPITAL** See Mayo Clinic Hospital - Methodist Campus

## ROSEAU—Roseau County

☒ **LIFECARE MEDICAL CENTER (241344)**, 715 Delmore Drive, Zip 56751–1599; tel. 218/463–2500, (Total facility includes 90 beds in nursing home–type unit) (Nonreporting) **A**1 10 18 **F**3 7 10 11 13 15 28 29 30 31 32 34 35 36 40 43 45 53 56 57 59 62 63 64 65 68 75 76 77 81 82 84 85 86 93 104 107 110 111 115 118 119 128 129 130 132 133 135 144 146 147 148 149 156 **P**6
Primary Contact: Keith Okeson, President and Chief Executive Officer
COO: Shannon Carlson, Chief Operating Officer
CFO: Cathy Huss, Chief Financial Officer
CIO: Kevin Schumacher, Director of Information Systems
CHR: Lois Slick, Director of Human Resources
CNO: Nathan Brovold, Chief Nursing Officer
Web address: www.lifecaremedicalcenter.org
**Control:** Other not–for–profit (including NFP Corporation) **Service:** General medical and surgical

**Staffed Beds:** 115 **Admissions:** 652 **Census:** 90 **Outpatient Visits:** 44209 **Births:** 168 **Total Expense ($000):** 47828 **Payroll Expense ($000):** 21700 **Personnel:** 317

**ROSEAU AREA HOSPITAL & HOMES** See Lifecare Medical Center

## SAINT CLOUD—Stearns County

☒ △ **ST. CLOUD HOSPITAL (240036)**, 1406 Sixth Avenue North, Zip 56303–1901; tel. 320/251–2700, (Nonreporting) **A**1 2 3 5 7 10 20 **F**3 5 11 12 13 14 15 17 18 19 20 22 24 26 28 29 30 31 32 34 35 36 37 38 39 40 43 44 45 46 47 48 49 50 51 54 56 57 58 59 60 61 62 63 64 66 68 69 70 72 74 75 76 77 78 79 80 81 82 84 85 86 87 88 89 90 92 93 96 97 98 99 100 101 102 103 104 105 106 107 108 110 111 115 117 118 119 120 121 123 124 126 129 130 131 132 134 135 141 144 145 146 147 148 149 150 151 152 153 156 157 **P**6 **S** CentraCare Health, Saint Cloud, MN
Primary Contact: Craig J. Broman, FACHE, President
COO: Joy Plamann, R.N., Chief Nursing and Operating Officer
CFO: Greg Klugherz, Vice President Corporate Services and Chief Financial Officer
CMO: Mark Matthias, M.D., Vice President of Medical Affairs
CIO: Amy Porwoll, Vice President of Information Systems
CHR: Duane Rasmusson, Vice President Human Resources
CNO: Joy Plamann, R.N., Chief Nursing and Operating Officer
Web address: www.centracare.com
**Control:** Other not–for–profit (including NFP Corporation) **Service:** General medical and surgical

**Staffed Beds:** 477 **Admissions:** 28160 **Census:** 332 **Outpatient Visits:** 523728 **Births:** 2552 **Total Expense ($000):** 821399 **Payroll Expense ($000):** 353483 **Personnel:** 4077

☒ **ST. CLOUD VETERANS AFFAIRS HEALTH CARE SYSTEM**, 4801 Veterans Drive, Zip 56303–2099; tel. 320/252–1670, (Nonreporting) **A**1 3 **S** Department of Veterans Affairs, Washington, DC
Primary Contact: Stephen Black, MS, Health Care System Director
COO: Barry I Bahl, Director
CFO: Joseph Schmitz, Chief Financial Officer
CMO: Susan Markstrom, M.D., Chief of Staff
CIO: Denise Hanson, Information Technology Specialist
CHR: Lisa Rosendahl, Director Human Resources
CNO: Meri Hauge, R.N., MSN, Associate Director of Patient Care Services and Nurse Executive
Web address: www.stcloud.va.gov
**Control:** Veterans Affairs, Government, federal **Service:** Psychiatric

**Staffed Beds:** 388

**VETERANS AFFAIRS MEDICAL CENTER** See St. Cloud Veterans Affairs Health Care System

## SAINT JAMES—Watonwan County

☐ **MAYO CLINIC HEALTH SYSTEM IN SAINT JAMES (241333)**, 1101 Moulton and Parsons Drive, Zip 56081–5550; tel. 507/375–3261, (Nonreporting) **A**1 10 18 **F**3 15 28 30 34 35 40 59 64 65 75 81 85 97 107 110 115 128 130 133 135 146 149 **S** Mayo Clinic, Rochester, MN
Primary Contact: James Hebl, M.D., Regional Vice President
COO: Richard Grace, Chief Administrative Officer
CFO: James Tarasovich, Chief Financial Officer
CMO: Jennifer Langbehn, Medical Director
CHR: Gayle B Hansen, R.N., Chief Integration Officer
Web address: www.mayoclinichealthsystem.org/locations/st-james
**Control:** Other not–for–profit (including NFP Corporation) **Service:** General medical and surgical

**Staffed Beds:** 9 **Admissions:** 260 **Census:** 7 **Outpatient Visits:** 22619 **Births:** 0 **Personnel:** 70

**ST. JAMES MEDICAL CENTER** See Mayo Clinic Health System in Saint James

*Many Facility Codes have changed. Please refer to the AHA Guide Code Chart.*
© 2021 AHA Guide

## SAINT LOUIS PARK—Hennepin County

**METHODIST HOSPITAL** See Park Nicollet Methodist Hospital

☐ **PARK NICOLLET METHODIST HOSPITAL (240053)**, 6500 Excelsior Boulevard, Zip 55426–4702; tel. 952/993–5000, (Nonreporting) **A**1 2 3 5 10 **F**8 11 12 13 15 18 20 22 24 26 28 29 30 31 34 38 40 42 43 44 45 46 47 49 50 51 53 54 55 56 57 58 59 62 63 64 68 71 74 75 77 78 79 81 82 83 84 85 86 87 93 94 97 100 102 107 108 111 114 115 117 119 120 121 123 124 126 129 130 132 144 145 146 147 148 149 154 156 **S** HealthPartners, Bloomington, MN
Primary Contact: Jennifer Myster, President
COO: Michael Kaupa, Executive Vice President and Chief Operating Officer
CFO: Sheila McMillan, Chief Financial Officer
CMO: Steven Connelly, M.D., President and Chief Medical Officer
CIO: Julie Flaschenriem, Chief Information Officer
CHR: Paul Dominski, Vice President Human Resources
Web address: www.parknicollet.com
**Control:** Other not–for–profit (including NFP Corporation) **Service:** General medical and surgical

**Staffed Beds:** 346 **Admissions:** 22863 **Census:** 236 **Births:** 3040 **Total Expense ($000):** 582767 **Payroll Expense ($000):** 253080

## SAINT PAUL—Ramsey County

☒ **BETHESDA HOSPITAL (242004)**, 559 Capitol Boulevard, Zip 55103–2101; tel. 651/232–2000, (Nonreporting) **A**1 5 10 **F**1 3 6 11 29 30 38 44 50 53 56 64 68 74 75 77 82 84 85 86 87 91 93 96 100 104 107 119 130 132 148 156 **P**6 **S** M Health Fairview, Minneapolis, MN
Primary Contact: Jeoff Will, Chief Operating Office, Acute Care Services
COO: Jeoff Will, Chief Operating Officer, Acute Care Services
CMO: Mark Welton, M.D., Chief Medical Officer
CIO: Alistar Jacques, Chief Information Officer
CHR: Carolyn Jacobson, Chief Human Resources Officer
CNO: Laura Reed, R.N., Chief Nursing Executive
Web address: www.healtheast.org
**Control:** Other not–for–profit (including NFP Corporation) **Service:** Acute long–term care hospital

**Staffed Beds:** 114 **Admissions:** 989 **Census:** 81 **Outpatient Visits:** 3801 **Births:** 0 **Total Expense ($000):** 84547 **Payroll Expense ($000):** 45137 **Personnel:** 435

**CHILDREN'S HOSPITAL & CLINICS** See Children's Hospitals and Clinics of Minnesota

**GILLETTE CHILDREN'S SPEC CARE** See Gillette Children's Specialty Healthcare

☐ △ **GILLETTE CHILDREN'S SPECIALTY HEALTHCARE (243300)**, 200 University Avenue East, Zip 55101–2507; tel. 651/291–2848, (Nonreporting) **A**1 3 5 7 10
Primary Contact: Barbara Walczyk-Joers, President and Chief Executive Officer
CFO: Patrick Nolan, Vice President Finance and Chief Financial Officer
CMO: Steven Koop, M.D., Chief Medical Officer, Medical Director
CIO: Timothy Getsay, Chief Information Officer, Vice President of Performance & Information Mgmt
CHR: Kit Brady, Vice President Human Resources, Education and Guest Experience
CNO: Karen Brill, R.N., Chief Nursing Officer, Vice President Care
Web address: www.gillettechildrens.org
**Control:** Other not–for–profit (including NFP Corporation) **Service:** Children's other specialty

**Staffed Beds:** 60

**HEALTHEAST BETHESDA HOSPITAL** See Bethesda Hospital

**HEALTHEAST ST JOSEPH'S HOSP** See St. Joseph's Hospital

☐ △ **REGIONS HOSPITAL (240106)**, 640 Jackson Street, Zip 55101–2595; tel. 651/254–3456, (Nonreporting) **A**1 2 3 5 7 8 10 **S** HealthPartners, Bloomington, MN
Primary Contact: Megan Remark, President and Chief Executive Officer
CFO: Heidi Conrad, Vice President and Chief Financial Officer
CMO: Charles Fazio, Chief Health Officer and Medical Director Health Plan
CIO: Kari Toft, Vice President, Chief Information Officer
CHR: Alicia Gilbert, Vice President
CNO: Chris Boese, Vice President and Chief Nursing Officer
Web address: www.regionshospital.com
**Control:** Other not–for–profit (including NFP Corporation) **Service:** General medical and surgical

**Staffed Beds:** 463

**ST PAUL-RAMSEY MEDICAL CENTER** See Regions Hospital

☒ **ST. JOSEPH'S HOSPITAL (240063)**, 45 West 10th Street, Zip 55102–1053; tel. 651/232–3000, (Nonreporting) **A**1 3 5 10 **F**3 4 5 12 15 17 18 20 22 24 26 28 29 30 35 36 37 38 40 44 45 49 50 53 58 61 63 64 68 70 74 75 77 79 81 84 85 86 87 92 93 96 97 98 100 101 102 103 104 107 108 110 111 114 115 118 119 120 121 124 130 132 146 148 149 152 154 **P**6 **S** M Health Fairview, Minneapolis, MN
Primary Contact: Lia Christiansen, Chief Operating Officer, Acute Care Hospitals
COO: Lia Christiansen, Chief Operating Officer, Acute Care Hospitals
CMO: Kevin C. Garrett, M.D., Medical Executive East Region
CIO: Joanne Sunquist, Chief Information Officer East Region
CHR: Carolyn Jacobson, Chief Human Resource Officer
CNO: Debra J. Hurd, MS, R.N., Vice President and Chief Nursing Officer
Web address: www.healtheast.org
**Control:** Other not–for–profit (including NFP Corporation) **Service:** General medical and surgical

**Staffed Beds:** 239 **Admissions:** 11437 **Census:** 180 **Outpatient Visits:** 45625 **Births:** 0 **Total Expense ($000):** 334736 **Payroll Expense ($000):** 144466 **Personnel:** 1386

☒ △ **UNITED HOSPITAL (240038)**, 333 North Smith Avenue, Zip 55102–2389; tel. 651/241–8000, (Nonreporting) **A**1 2 3 5 7 10 **F**3 8 12 13 15 17 18 20 22 24 26 28 29 30 31 34 35 36 37 40 43 44 45 46 47 48 49 50 51 53 54 56 58 59 60 61 64 65 68 70 74 75 76 77 78 79 80 81 82 83 84 85 86 87 90 91 92 93 95 96 97 98 99 100 102 103 104 105 107 108 110 111 112 113 114 115 118 119 120 121 123 124 126 129 130 132 134 135 146 148 149 153 154 156 157 **P**6 **S** Allina Health, Minneapolis, MN
Primary Contact: Thomas O'Connor, President
CFO: John Bien, Vice President Finance
CMO: Alison Peterson, Vice President Medical Affairs
CIO: Susan Heichert, Senior Vice President
CHR: Jim McGlade, Director Human Resources
CNO: Janet K. Pestle, R.N., MSN, Chief Nursing Officer
Web address: www.allina.com
**Control:** Other not–for–profit (including NFP Corporation) **Service:** General medical and surgical

**Staffed Beds:** 380 **Admissions:** 23791 **Census:** 276 **Outpatient Visits:** 188677 **Births:** 3785 **Total Expense ($000):** 612365 **Payroll Expense ($000):** 233613 **Personnel:** 2125

## SAINT PETER—Nicollet County

★ ⇑ **RIVER'S EDGE HOSPITAL AND CLINIC (241334)**, 1900 North Sunrise Drive, Zip 56082–5376; tel. 507/931–2200, (Nonreporting) **A**10 18 21 **S** QHR Health, Brentwood, TN
Primary Contact: Joseph Stratton, FACHE, Chief Executive Officer
CFO: Lori Zook, Chief Financial Officer
CIO: Kevin Schaefer, Manager Information Services
CHR: Jackie Kimmet, Chief Human Resource Officer
CNO: Paula Meskan, R.N., Chief Nursing Officer
Web address: www.rehc.org
**Control:** City, Government, Nonfederal **Service:** General medical and surgical

**Staffed Beds:** 17

⇑ **ST PETER COMMUNITY HOSPITAL** See River's Edge Hospital and Clinic

## SANDSTONE—Pine County

★ **ESSENTIA HEALTH SANDSTONE (241309)**, 705 Lundorff Drive, Zip 55072–5009; tel. 320/245–2212, (Nonreporting) **A**10 18 **F**3 7 15 28 29 30 31 34 35 40 43 45 59 64 65 75 77 80 81 82 85 87 89 91 92 93 107 110 115 119 129 132 133 135 144 146 148 149 154 156 **P**5 6 **S** Essentia Health, Duluth, MN
Primary Contact: Michael D. Hedrix, Administrator and President
CMO: Sarah Aldredge, M.D., Chief Medical Officer
Web address: www.pinemedicalcenter.org
**Control:** Hospital district or authority, Government, Nonfederal **Service:** General medical and surgical

**Staffed Beds:** 9 **Admissions:** 258 **Census:** 2 **Outpatient Visits:** 13438 **Births:** 0 **Total Expense ($000):** 19635 **Payroll Expense ($000):** 7302 **Personnel:** 87

**PINE MEDICAL CENTER** See Essentia Health Sandstone

**MN**

---

**Hospital, Medicare Provider Number, Address, Telephone, Approval, Facility, and Physician Codes, Health Care System**

★ American Hospital Association (AHA) membership  ○ Healthcare Facilities Accreditation Program  ⇑ Center for Improvement in Healthcare Quality Accreditation
☐ The Joint Commission accreditation  ◇ DNV Healthcare Inc. accreditation  △ Commission on Accreditation of Rehabilitation Facilities (CARF) accreditation

## SAUK CENTRE—Stearns County

★ **CENTRACARE HEALTH-SAUK CENTRE (241368)**, 425 North Elm Street, Zip 56378–1010; tel. 320/352–2221, (Nonreporting) **A**5 10 18 **S** CentraCare Health, Saint Cloud, MN
Primary Contact: Delano Christianson, Administrator
CFO: Delano Christianson, Administrator
Web address: www.centracare.com/hospitals/sauk_centre/index.html
**Control**: City, Government, Nonfederal **Service**: General medical and surgical

**Staffed Beds:** 85

**ST. MICHAEL'S HOSPITAL AND NURSING HOME** See Centracare Health-Sauk Centre

## SHAKOPEE—Scott County

✠ **ST. FRANCIS REGIONAL MEDICAL CENTER (240104)**, 1455 St Francis Avenue, Zip 55379–3380; tel. 952/428–3000, (Nonreporting) **A**1 2 5 10 **F**3 12 13 15 28 29 30 31 34 35 36 38 40 41 43 45 46 50 57 58 59 64 68 75 76 77 78 79 80 81 82 84 86 87 89 93 107 108 110 111 114 117 118 119 124 129 130 131 132 144 146 147 148 149 154 **S** Allina Health, Minneapolis, MN
Primary Contact: Amy L. Jerdee, R.N., President
CFO: Cynthia Vincent, Vice President Finance and Operations
CMO: Monte Johnson, Vice President, Medical Affairs
CIO: Joe Delveaux, Manager Information Services
CHR: Sally Haack, Vice President and Director of Human Resources
CNO: Debora Ryan, R.N., Vice President Patient Care
Web address: www.stfrancis-shakopee.com
**Control**: Other not–for–profit (including NFP Corporation) **Service**: General medical and surgical

**Staffed Beds:** 89 **Admissions:** 6125 **Census:** 48 **Outpatient Visits:** 130785 **Births:** 1069 **Total Expense ($000):** 161966 **Payroll Expense ($000):** 62981 **Personnel:** 629

## SLAYTON—Murray County

★ **MURRAY COUNTY MEDICAL CENTER (241319)**, 2042 Juniper Avenue, Zip 56172–1017; tel. 507/836–6111, (Nonreporting) **A**10 18 **S** Sanford Health, Sioux Falls, SD
Primary Contact: Michael Ladevich, FACHE, Interim Chief Executive Officer
CFO: Renee Logan, Chief Financial Officer
CMO: Joyce Tarbet, M.D., Chief Medical Officer
CIO: Justin Keller, Chief Information Officer
CHR: Nancy Andert, Director Human Resources
Web address: www.murraycountymed.org
**Control**: County, Government, Nonfederal **Service**: General medical and surgical

**Staffed Beds:** 18

**MURRAY COUNTY MEM HOSPITAL** See Murray County Medical Center

## SLEEPY EYE—Brown County

**SLEEPY EYE MEDICAL CENTER (241327)**, 400 Fourth Avenue NW, Zip 56085–1109, Mailing Address: P.O. Box 323, Zip 56085–0323; tel. 507/794–3571, (Nonreporting) **A**10 18
Primary Contact: Kevin Sellheim, Administrator
CHR: Connie Dahlberg, Director Business and Employee
CNO: Karee Schmiesing, Director of Nursing
Web address: www.semedicalcenter.org
**Control**: City, Government, Nonfederal **Service**: General medical and surgical

**Staffed Beds:** 16

**SLEEPY EYE MUNICIPAL HOSPITAL** See Sleepy Eye Medical Center

## SPRING GROVE—Houston County

**TWEETEN LUTHERAN HLTH CARE CTR** See Tweeten Health Services

## STAPLES—Todd County

**GREATER STAPLES HOSPITAL** See Lakewood Health System

**LAKEWOOD HEALTH SYSTEM (241329)**, 49725 County 83, Zip 56479–5280; tel. 218/894–1515, (Nonreporting) **A**10 18
Primary Contact: Tim Rice, President and Chief Executive Officer
CMO: John Halfen, M.D., Medical Director
CHR: Janet Jacobson, Director Human Resources
CNO: Teresa Fisher, Chief Nursing Officer
Web address: www.lakewoodhealthsystem.com
**Control**: Other not–for–profit (including NFP Corporation) **Service**: General medical and surgical

**Staffed Beds:** 135

## STILLWATER—Washington County

☐ **LAKEVIEW HOSPITAL (240066)**, 927 Churchill Street West, Zip 55082–6605; tel. 651/439–5330, (Nonreporting) **A**1 3 5 10 **S** HealthPartners, Bloomington, MN
Primary Contact: Theodore Wegleitner, Chief Executive Officer and President
CFO: Douglas E Johnson, Chief Financial Officer
CMO: Thomas Anderson, Vice President Medical Affairs
CIO: Emad Awwad, Director Care Delivery Sites Information Systems and Technology
CHR: Angy Duchesneau, Senior Director Human Resources
CNO: Robbi Hagelberg, Vice President Nursing Services and Chief Nursing Officer
Web address: www.lakeview.org
**Control**: Other not–for–profit (including NFP Corporation) **Service**: General medical and surgical

**Staffed Beds:** 67

**LAKEVIEW MEMORIAL HOSPITAL** See Lakeview Hospital

## THIEF RIVER FALLS—Pennington County

★ **SANFORD MEDICAL CENTER THIEF RIVER FALLS (241381)**, 3001 Sanford Parkway, Zip 56701–2700; tel. 218/681–4747, (Nonreporting) **A**10 18 **F**3 8 11 13 15 28 29 31 32 33 34 35 39 40 45 53 57 64 65 68 76 78 79 81 82 85 86 87 97 107 110 111 115 119 129 130 131 132 133 135 144 146 147 148 156 **P**6 **S** Sanford Health, Sioux Falls, SD
Primary Contact: Brian J. Carlson, FACHE, Executive Director
COO: Rob Lovejoy, Director, Operations
CMO: Brook Redd, M.D., Chief of Staff
CNO: Janell Hudson, Director, Nursing and Clinical Services
Web address: www.sanfordhealth.org
**Control**: Other not–for–profit (including NFP Corporation) **Service**: General medical and surgical

**Staffed Beds:** 25 **Admissions:** 1367 **Census:** 11 **Outpatient Visits:** 92998 **Births:** 269 **Total Expense ($000):** 65603 **Payroll Expense ($000):** 26527 **Personnel:** 302

**SANFORD THIEF RIVER FALLS BEHAVIORAL HEALTH CENTER (244018)**, 120 LaBree Avenue South, Zip 56701–2819, Mailing Address: 3001 Sanford Parkway, Zip 56701–2819; tel. 218/683–4349, (Nonreporting) **A**10 **F**38 98 100 101 102 104 106 154 **P**6 **S** Sanford Health, Sioux Falls, SD
Primary Contact: Brian J. Carlson, FACHE, Chief Executive Officer
COO: Rob Lovejoy, Chief Operating Officer
Web address: www.sanfordhealth.org/Locations/1766896362
**Control**: Other not–for–profit (including NFP Corporation) **Service**: Psychiatric

**Staffed Beds:** 16 **Admissions:** 550 **Census:** 13 **Outpatient Visits:** 1 **Births:** 0 **Total Expense ($000):** 14011 **Payroll Expense ($000):** 7987 **Personnel:** 91

**SANFORD THIEF RIVER FALLS MEDICAL CENTER** See Sanford Medical Center Thief River Falls

## TRACY—Lyon County

**SANFORD TRACY MED CTR** See Sanford Tracy Medical Center

★ **SANFORD TRACY MEDICAL CENTER (241303)**, 251 Fifth Street East, Zip 56175–1536; tel. 507/629–8400, (Nonreporting) **A**10 18 **F**3 28 29 31 32 34 35 40 41 43 44 49 50 56 57 59 62 64 65 68 77 81 85 86 87 89 91 93 97 101 102 104 107 108 114 125 127 130 131 132 133 135 143 149 154 156 **S** Sanford Health, Sioux Falls, SD
Primary Contact: Stacy Barstad, Chief Executive Officer
CMO: Muhammad Ali, M.D., Chief Medical Officer
CIO: Janet Theisen, Chief Information Officer
CHR: Becky Foster, Employee Relations Specialist
CNO: Jeri Schons, R.N., Chief Nursing Officer
Web address: www.sanfordtracy.org
**Control**: Other not–for–profit (including NFP Corporation) **Service**: General medical and surgical

**Staffed Beds:** 25 **Admissions:** 147 **Census:** 2 **Outpatient Visits:** 17256 **Births:** 0 **Total Expense ($000):** 10132 **Payroll Expense ($000):** 3991 **Personnel:** 67

## TWO HARBORS—Lake County

★ **LAKE VIEW HOSPITAL (241308)**, 325 11th Avenue, Zip 55616–1360; tel. 218/834–7300, (Nonreporting) **A**10 18 **S** St. Luke's, Duluth, MN
Primary Contact: Greg Ruberg, FACHE, President and Chief Executive Officer
CFO: Eric Lohn, Chief Financial Officer
Web address: www.lvmhospital.com
**Control**: Other not–for–profit (including NFP Corporation) **Service**: General medical and surgical

**Staffed Beds:** 25

**LAKE VIEW MEMORIAL HOSPITAL** See Lake View Hospital

MN

## TYLER—Lincoln County

**AVERA TYLER HOSPITAL (241348)**, 240 Willow Street, Zip 56178–1166; tel. 507/247–5521, (Total facility includes 30 beds in nursing home–type unit) (Nonreporting) **A**10 18 **F**7 34 35 40 53 57 59 64 65 81 97 107 108 119 127 128 133 **S** Avera Health, Sioux Falls, SD
Primary Contact: Allen Anderson, Administrator
CNO: Kris Vollmer, Director Patient Care Services
Web address: www.avera.org
**Control**: Church operated, Nongovernment, not–for–profit **Service**: General medical and surgical

**Staffed Beds: 40 Admissions: 160 Census: 28 Outpatient Visits: 6344 Births: 0 Total Expense ($000): 8181 Payroll Expense ($000): 4031 Personnel: 75**

**TYLER HEALTHCARE CENTER AVERA** See Avera Tyler Hospital

## VIRGINIA—St. Louis County

⊞ **ESSENTIA HEALTH-VIRGINIA (240084)**, 901 Ninth Street North, Zip 55792–2398; tel. 218/741–3340, (Nonreporting) **A**1 10 **S** Essentia Health, Duluth, MN
Primary Contact: Sam Stone, Operations Administrator
CFO: Steven Feltman, CPA, Chief Financial Officer
CMO: Michelle Oman, D.O., Chief Medical Officer
Web address: www.essentiahealth.org
**Control**: City, Government, Nonfederal **Service**: General medical and surgical

**Staffed Beds: 144**

**VIRGINIA REGIONAL MEDICAL CENTER** See Essentia Health-Virginia

## WABASHA—Wabasha County

★ **SAINT ELIZABETH'S MEDICAL CENTER (241335)**, 1200 Grant Boulevard West, Zip 55981–1042; tel. 651/565–4531, (Nonreporting) **A**10 18 **S** Ascension Healthcare, Saint Louis, MO
Primary Contact: Thomas Crowley, President and Chief Executive Officer
CFO: John Wolfe, Chief Financial Officer
CMO: Brian E. Kelly, M.D., President Medical Staff
CHR: Jim Root, Vice President Human Resources
CNO: Kathy Lueders, R.N., Director of Nursing-Acute Care
Web address: www.stelizabethswabasha.org
**Control**: Church operated, Nongovernment, not–for–profit **Service**: General medical and surgical

**Staffed Beds: 153**

**ST ELIZABETH HOSPITAL** See Saint Elizabeth's Medical Center

## WACONIA—Carver County

★ ⇑ **RIDGEVIEW MEDICAL CENTER (240056)**, 500 South Maple Street, Zip 55387–1791; tel. 952/442–2191, (Nonreporting) **A**2 10 21 **F**3 7 12 13 15 18 20 22 28 29 30 31 32 34 35 36 38 40 41 42 43 45 46 48 49 54 57 58 59 62 63 64 65 70 73 74 75 76 77 78 79 81 82 84 85 86 87 89 93 96 107 108 110 111 114 115 118 119 126 127 129 130 131 132 135 144 146 147 148 149 156 **P**6 **S** Ridgeview Medical Center, Waconia, MN
Primary Contact: Michael Phelps, President and Chief Executive Officer
CFO: Gordon Gablenz, Vice President Finance
CMO: Alvaro Sanchez, M.D., Chief Medical Officer
CIO: Tamara Korbel, Director Management Information Systems
CHR: Sarah M Hastings, Executive Director
Web address: www.ridgeviewmedical.org
**Control**: Other not–for–profit (including NFP Corporation) **Service**: General medical and surgical

**Staffed Beds: 104 Admissions: 6268 Census: 62 Outpatient Visits: 355194 Births: 1358 Total Expense ($000): 274886 Payroll Expense ($000): 133770 Personnel: 819**

⇑ **WACONIA RIDGEVIEW HOSPITAL** See Ridgeview Medical Center

## WADENA—Wadena County

⊞ **TRI-COUNTY HOSPITAL (241354)**, 415 Jefferson Street North, Zip 56482–1297; tel. 218/631–3510, (Nonreporting) **A**1 10 18
Primary Contact: Joel Beiswenger, Chief Executive Officer
CFO: Kim Aagard, Chief Financial Officer
CMO: John Pate, M.D., Chief Medical Officer
CIO: Bill Blaha, Manager Information Technology
CHR: Bryan Pederson, Human Resources Manager
CNO: Kathy Kleen, Chief Nursing Officer
Web address: www.tchc.org
**Control**: Other not–for–profit (including NFP Corporation) **Service**: General medical and surgical

**Staffed Beds: 25**

## WARREN—Marshall County

★ **NORTH VALLEY HEALTH CENTER (241337)**, 300 West Good Samaritan Drive, Zip 56762; tel. 218/745–4211, (Nonreporting) **A**10 18
Primary Contact: Jon E. Linnell, Chief Executive Officer
CFO: Mitchell Kotrba, Chief Financial Officer
CNO: Sara Marie Kazmierczak, R.N., Director of Nursing
Web address: www.northvalleyhealth.org
**Control**: Other not–for–profit (including NFP Corporation) **Service**: General medical and surgical

**Staffed Beds: 20**

**WARREN COMMUNITY HOSPITAL** See North Valley Health Center

## WASECA—Waseca County

☐ **MAYO CLINIC HEALTH SYSTEM IN WASECA (241345)**, 501 North State Street, Zip 56093–2811; tel. 507/835–1210, (Nonreporting) **A**1 5 10 18 **F**3 11 15 18 28 29 30 34 35 40 43 45 53 57 59 64 65 75 77 79 81 82 85 86 87 93 97 107 110 115 119 128 130 132 133 144 146 148 149 154 156 **S** Mayo Clinic, Rochester, MN
Primary Contact: James Hebl, M.D., Regional Vice President
CMO: Christopher Schimming, M.D., Medical Director
Web address: www.mayoclinichealthsystem.org
**Control**: Other not–for–profit (including NFP Corporation) **Service**: General medical and surgical

**Staffed Beds: 12 Admissions: 275 Census: 7 Outpatient Visits: 27475 Births: 0 Personnel: 87**

**WASECA MEDICAL CENTER** See Mayo Clinic Health System in Waseca

## WESTBROOK—Cottonwood County

★ **SANFORD WESTBROOK MEDICAL CENTER (241302)**, 920 Bell Avenue, Zip 56183–9669, Mailing Address: P.O. Box 188, Zip 56183–0188; tel. 507/274–6121, (Nonreporting) **A**10 18 **F**3 29 31 32 34 35 40 41 43 44 45 50 56 57 59 62 64 65 68 75 77 81 85 86 87 89 91 93 97 101 102 104 107 108 114 125 127 130 131 132 133 135 143 149 154 **P**6 **S** Sanford Health, Sioux Falls, SD
Primary Contact: Stacy Barstad, Chief Executive Officer
COO: Gordon Kopperud, Director Operations
CIO: Janet Theisen, Chief Information Officer
CHR: Becky Foster, Employee Relations Specialist
Web address: www.sanfordwestbrook.org
**Control**: Other not–for–profit (including NFP Corporation) **Service**: General medical and surgical

**Staffed Beds: 8 Admissions: 94 Census: 1 Outpatient Visits: 10534 Births: 0 Total Expense ($000): 7713 Payroll Expense ($000): 2925 Personnel: 36**

**WESTBROOK HEALTH CENTER** See Sanford Westbrook Medical Center

## WHEATON—Traverse County

★ **SANFORD WHEATON MEDICAL CENTER (241304)**, 401 12th Street North, Zip 56296–1099; tel. 320/563–8226, (Nonreporting) **A**10 18 **F**3 7 11 15 18 28 29 30 34 40 43 45 57 59 64 65 81 86 97 107 111 114 119 127 128 133 154 **S** Sanford Health, Sioux Falls, SD
Primary Contact: Chelsie Falk, Senior Director
CFO: Shane Ayres, Chief Financial Officer
CHR: Brenda Petersen, Human Resources
Web address: www.sanfordhealth.org
**Control:** Other not–for–profit (including NFP Corporation) **Service:** General medical and surgical

**Staffed Beds:** 15 **Admissions:** 101 **Census:** 2 **Outpatient Visits:** 14256 **Births:** 0 **Total Expense ($000):** 8061 **Payroll Expense ($000):** 3399 **Personnel:** 46

**WHEATON COMMUNITY HOSPITAL** See Sanford Wheaton Medical Center

## WILLMAR—Kandiyohi County

☐ **CHILD AND ADOLESCENT BEHAVIORAL HEALTH SERVICES (244005)**, 1701 Technology Drive Northeast, Zip 56201–2275; tel. 320/231–5421, (Nonreporting) **A**1 10
Primary Contact: Jacquelyn Sammons, R.N., Supervisor
Web address: www.dhs.state.mn.us
**Control:** County, Government, Nonfederal **Service:** Psychiatric

**Staffed Beds:** 16

⊞ **RICE MEMORIAL HOSPITAL (240088)**, 301 Becker Avenue SW, Zip 56201–3395; tel. 320/235–4543, (Total facility includes 78 beds in nursing home–type unit) (Nonreporting) **A**1 2 10 **F**3 7 8 11 12 13 28 29 30 34 35 39 40 43 45 47 48 49 50 57 59 60 63 64 65 68 70 73 75 76 78 79 81 82 85 86 87 89 90 93 98 100 101 102 103 104 105 107 108 111 115 116 117 118 119 121 126 128 130 132 143 146 148 149 150 153 154 **S** CentraCare Health, Saint Cloud, MN
Primary Contact: Michael Schramm, Chief Executive Officer
CFO: Bill Fenske, Chief Financial Officer
CMO: Kenneth Flowe, M.D., Chief Medical Officer
CIO: Teri Beyer, Chief Information Officer, Quality
Web address: www.ricehospital.com
**Control:** Other not–for–profit (including NFP Corporation) **Service:** General medical and surgical

**Staffed Beds:** 164 **Admissions:** 3547 **Census:** 101 **Outpatient Visits:** 91276 **Births:** 670 **Total Expense ($000):** 122800 **Payroll Expense ($000):** 53037 **Personnel:** 587

## WINDOM—Cottonwood County

★ **WINDOM AREA HEALTH (241332)**, 2150 Hospital Drive, Zip 56101–0339, Mailing Address: P.O. Box 339, Zip 56101–0339; tel. 507/831–2400, (Nonreporting) **A**10 18 **S** Sanford Health, Sioux Falls, SD
Primary Contact: Shelby Medina, Chief Executive Officer
CFO: Kim Armstrong, Chief Financial Officer
CIO: Lori Ling, Information Technician
CHR: Emily Masters, Chief Human Relations Officer
CNO: Kari Witte, Director Patient Care
Web address: www.windomareahospital.com
**Control:** City, Government, Nonfederal **Service:** General medical and surgical

**Staffed Beds:** 18

**WINDOM AREA HOSPITAL** See Windom Area Health

## WINONA—Winona County

**WINONA COMM MEMORIAL HOSPITAL** See Winona Health

★ **WINONA HEALTH (240044)**, 855 Mankato Avenue, Zip 55987–4868, Mailing Address: P.O. Box 5600, Zip 55987–0600; tel. 507/454–3650, (Nonreporting) **A**2 10 20 **F**6 10 11 13 15 28 29 30 31 32 34 35 36 38 40 43 45 50 53 56 57 58 59 60 61 62 63 64 65 70 75 76 77 78 79 81 82 83 84 85 86 87 89 93 96 97 98 100 101 102 104 107 108 110 111 115 116 118 119 127 129 130 131 132 133 135 144 146 147 148 153 154 156
Primary Contact: Rachelle H. Schultz, Ed.D., President and Chief Executive Officer
COO: Robin Hoeg, Chief Operating Officer
CFO: Jan Brosnahan, Chief Financial Officer
CMO: Brett Whyte, M.D., Chief of Medical Staff
CIO: Luke Keninger, Information Technology Client Leader
CHR: Chad Decker, Director Human Resources
Web address: www.winonahealth.org
**Control:** Other not–for–profit (including NFP Corporation) **Service:** General medical and surgical

**Staffed Beds:** 38 **Admissions:** 1741 **Census:** 16 **Outpatient Visits:** 196201 **Births:** 207 **Total Expense ($000):** 111860 **Payroll Expense ($000):** 53981 **Personnel:** 819

## WINSTED—McLeod County

**ST MARY'S HOSPITAL AND HOME** See Health One St Mary's

## WOODBURY—Washington County

**WOODWINDS HEALTH** See Woodwinds Health Campus

⊞ **WOODWINDS HEALTH CAMPUS (240213)**, 1925 Woodwinds Drive, Zip 55125–4445; tel. 651/232–0228, (Nonreporting) **A**1 3 10 **F**3 13 15 28 29 30 31 35 36 37 38 40 43 49 50 59 64 68 70 74 75 76 77 78 79 81 85 86 87 89 93 94 96 97 100 102 107 108 110 111 115 118 119 120 121 124 130 132 146 149 **P**6 **S** M Health Fairview, Minneapolis, MN
Primary Contact: Lia Christiansen, Chief Operating Officer, Acute Care Hospitals
COO: Lia Christiansen, Chief Operating Officer, Acute Care Hospitals
CMO: Kevin C. Garrett, M.D., Medical Executive, East Region
CIO: Joanne Sunquist, Chief Information Officer
CHR: Carolyn Jacobson, Chief Human Resource Officer
CNO: Debra J. Hurd, MS, R.N., Vice President and Chief Nursing Officer
Web address: www.woodwinds.org
**Control:** Other not–for–profit (including NFP Corporation) **Service:** General medical and surgical

**Staffed Beds:** 86 **Admissions:** 7596 **Census:** 55 **Outpatient Visits:** 61318 **Births:** 1641 **Total Expense ($000):** 159883 **Payroll Expense ($000):** 55548 **Personnel:** 584

## WORTHINGTON—Nobles County

**SANFORD MEDICAL CENTER WORTHINGTON** See Sanford Worthington Medical Center

★ **SANFORD WORTHINGTON MEDICAL CENTER (240022)**, 1018 Sixth Avenue, Zip 56187–2202, Mailing Address: P.O. Box 997, Zip 56187–0997; tel. 507/372–2941, (Nonreporting) **A**10 20 **F**3 7 11 13 15 26 27 28 31 34 35 40 43 45 50 57 59 60 62 64 68 69 70 75 76 78 79 81 85 86 93 97 107 110 111 114 116 119 120 121 129 130 131 132 135 144 146 147 148 149 154 **P**6 **S** Sanford Health, Sioux Falls, SD
Primary Contact: Jennifer Weg, MS, R.N., Executive Director
CFO: Linda Wagner, Chief Financial Officer
CMO: Charles Dike, M.D., Chief of Staff
CIO: Brad Klassen, Information Technology Coordinator
CNO: Gwen Post, R.N., Chief Nursing Officer
Web address: www.sanfordhealth.org
**Control:** Other not–for–profit (including NFP Corporation) **Service:** General medical and surgical

**Staffed Beds:** 48 **Admissions:** 1386 **Census:** 8 **Outpatient Visits:** 69139 **Births:** 373 **Total Expense ($000):** 47545 **Payroll Expense ($000):** 20829 **Personnel:** 229

## WYOMING—Chisago County

⊞ **FAIRVIEW LAKES HEALTH SERVICES (240050)**, 5200 Fairview Boulevard, Zip 55092–8013; tel. 651/982–7000, (Nonreporting) **A**1 10 **F**3 11 13 15 18 28 29 30 34 35 40 41 43 45 50 51 57 59 64 65 68 70 75 76 77 81 82 84 85 86 87 89 93 96 100 101 107 110 111 115 119 130 131 132 134 144 146 148 149 154 **P**6 **S** M Health Fairview, Minneapolis, MN
Primary Contact: Lia Christiansen, Chief Operating Officer, Acute Care Hospitals
CFO: Tim Lynch, Director of Finance
CMO: Greg Schoen, M.D., Vice President Medical Affairs
CNO: Karen Whiley, Chief Nursing Officer and Vice President Operations
Web address: www.fairview.org/
**Control:** Other not–for–profit (including NFP Corporation) **Service:** General medical and surgical

**Staffed Beds:** 38 **Admissions:** 2925 **Census:** 23 **Outpatient Visits:** 87058 **Births:** 584 **Total Expense ($000):** 96263 **Payroll Expense ($000):** 40831 **Personnel:** 388

**FAIRVIEW LAKES REGIONAL HEALTH CARE** See Fairview Lakes Health Services

*Many Facility Codes have changed. Please refer to the AHA Guide Code Chart.*
© 2021 AHA Guide

MN

# MISSISSIPPI

## ABERDEEN—Monroe County

⇧ **MONROE REGIONAL HOSPITAL (251302)**, 400 South Chestnut Street, Zip 39730–3335, Mailing Address: P.O. Box 548, Zip 39730–0548; tel. 662/369–2455, (Nonreporting) **A**10 18 21 **F**3 8 10 11 29 35 39 40 45 56 77 81 82 85 86 87 93 96 97 98 100 101 103 104 105 107 112 115 127 130 133 135 143 146
Primary Contact: Christopher Chandler, Chief Executive Officer
CFO: Julie Gieger, Chief Financial Officer
CMO: Kevin Hayes, M.D., Chief of Staff
CHR: Lee Rob, Director Human Resources
**Control**: Corporation, Investor–owned (for–profit) **Service**: General medical and surgical

**Staffed Beds**: 35 **Admissions**: 699 **Census**: 18 **Outpatient Visits**: 13389
**Births**: 0 **Personnel**: 230

⇧ **PIONEER COMMUNITY HOSPITAL OF ABERDEEN** See Monroe Regional Hospital

## ACKERMAN—Choctaw County

⇧ **CHOCTAW COUNTY HOSPITAL** See Choctaw Regional Medical Center

⇧ **CHOCTAW REGIONAL MEDICAL CENTER (251334)**, 8613 Highway 12, Zip 39735–8708; tel. 662/285–6235, (Total facility includes 73 beds in nursing home–type unit) (Nonreporting) **A**10 18 21 **F**3 29 34 40 43 50 57 58 65 87 89 93 104 107 114 119 127 128 130 133 148 **P**4
Primary Contact: Jamie Rodgers, Chief Executive Officer
Web address: www.choctawregional.com
**Control**: County, Government, Nonfederal **Service**: General medical and surgical

**Staffed Beds**: 88 **Admissions**: 510 **Census**: 56 **Outpatient Visits**: 44865
**Births**: 0 **Total Expense ($000)**: 19221 **Payroll Expense ($000)**: 10150
**Personnel**: 291

## AMORY—Monroe County

**GILMORE MEMORIAL HOSPITAL** See North Mississippi Medical Center Gilmore-Amory

⊞ **NORTH MISSISSIPPI MEDICAL CENTER GILMORE-AMORY (250025)**, 1105 Earl Frye Boulevard, Zip 38821–5500, Mailing Address: P.O. Box 459, Zip 38821–0459; tel. 662/256–7111, (Nonreporting) **A**1 10 **F**3 13 15 17 18 29 32 34 35 40 41 43 45 49 50 53 55 57 59 64 65 68 70 72 73 75 76 77 81 85 86 87 88 89 90 107 108 110 111 114 115 119 126 130 135 146 147 **P**8 **S** North Mississippi Health Services, Inc., Tupelo, MS
Primary Contact: Steve Nichols, Chief Executive Officer
CFO: Bert Pickard, Chief Financial Officer
CMO: William Rogers, Chief Medical Officer
CIO: Jeff Wideman, Director Information Systems
CHR: Angie L Weaver, Director Human Resources
Web address: www.gilmorehealth.com
**Control**: Other not–for–profit (including NFP Corporation) **Service**: General medical and surgical

**Staffed Beds**: 95 **Admissions**: 2541 **Census**: 27 **Outpatient Visits**: 48809
**Births**: 596 **Total Expense ($000)**: 38712 **Payroll Expense ($000)**: 13372
**Personnel**: 306

## BATESVILLE—Panola County

**MERIT HEALTH BATESVILLE** See Panola Medical Center

**PANOLA MEDICAL CENTER (250128)**, 303 Medical Center Drive, Zip 38606–8608; tel. 662/563–5611, (Nonreporting) **A**10 **F**3 4 5 11 12 13 15 18 19 28 29 30 32 34 35 38 40 43 45 48 50 56 57 59 64 65 68 70 76 77 81 85 87 89 97 98 100 101 102 103 107 108 114 119 127 129 130 132 146 147
Primary Contact: Wayne D. Thompson, Interim Chief Executive Officer
CMO: Michael R. Hovens, M.D., Chief Medical Officer
CIO: Will Morris, Director Information Technology
CHR: Arthur A Wasek, Director Human Resources
Web address: www.panolamedicalcenter.org/
**Control**: Corporation, Investor–owned (for–profit) **Service**: General medical and surgical

**Staffed Beds**: 106 **Admissions**: 2227 **Census**: 32 **Outpatient Visits**: 18655
**Births**: 261 **Personnel**: 313

## BAY SAINT LOUIS—Hancock County

⊞ **HANCOCK MEDICAL CENTER (250162)**, 149 Drinkwater Boulevard, Zip 39520–1658, Mailing Address: Bay St Louis, tel. 228/467–8600, (Nonreporting) **A**1 10 **F**3 11 12 13 15 18 19 28 29 34 35 39 40 43 45 46 54 57 59 64 65 68 70 74 75 76 77 78 79 81 85 86 87 93 94 97 107 108 110 111 115 118 119 124 127 130 131 146 147 148 **S** Ochsner Health, New Orleans, LA
Primary Contact: Alan Hodges, Chief Executive Officer
CFO: Thomas Ramsey, Chief Financial Officer
CIO: Craig Hodges, Director Information Services
CHR: Cathy Benvenutti, Human Resource Director
CNO: Virginia Kenny, Chief Nursing Officer
Web address: www.ochsner.org/locations/hancock-medical-center
**Control**: Other not–for–profit (including NFP Corporation) **Service**: General medical and surgical

**Staffed Beds**: 102 **Admissions**: 1003 **Census**: 9 **Outpatient Visits**: 54098
**Births**: 190 **Total Expense ($000)**: 45227 **Payroll Expense ($000)**: 21642
**Personnel**: 198

## BAY SPRINGS—Jasper County

★ **JASPER GENERAL HOSPITAL (250018)**, 15 'A' South Sixth Street, Zip 39422–9738, Mailing Address: P.O. Box 527, Zip 39422–0527; tel. 601/764–2101, (Total facility includes 110 beds in nursing home–type unit) (Nonreporting) **A**10 **F**10 55 59 62 64 119 128 130 133
Primary Contact: Eric Jordan, Chief Executive Officer
CFO: Steve Green, Comptroller
CMO: A K Lay, M.D., JrChief Medical Officer
CHR: Beth Gable, Administrative Assistant
CNO: Becky Ulmer, R.N., Director of Nursing
Web address: www.jaspergeneralhospital.com
**Control**: County, Government, Nonfederal **Service**: General medical and surgical

**Staffed Beds**: 126 **Admissions**: 158 **Census**: 114 **Outpatient Visits**: 0
**Births**: 0 **Total Expense ($000)**: 11709 **Payroll Expense ($000)**: 7015
**Personnel**: 178

## BILOXI—Harrison County

**BILOXI REGIONAL MEDICAL CENTER** See Merit Health Biloxi

⊞ **MERIT HEALTH BILOXI (250007)**, 150 Reynoir Street, Zip 39530–4199, Mailing Address: P.O. Box 128, Zip 39533–0128; tel. 228/432–1571, (Nonreporting) **A**1 10 **F**13 15 29 35 40 43 61 70 75 76 77 81 82 86 87 89 90 93 97 107 108 111 116 118 119 130 146 147 **P**8 **S** Community Health Systems, Inc., Franklin, TN
Primary Contact: Tom R. McDougal Jr, FACHE, Chief Executive Officer
CFO: Chad Miller, Chief Financial Officer
CMO: John Nelson, Chief of Staff
CIO: George Bickel, Director, Information Systems
CHR: Angela Thompson, Director of Human Resources
CNO: Rachael Williams, Chief Nursing Officer
Web address: www.merithealthbiloxi.com
**Control**: Corporation, Investor–owned (for–profit) **Service**: General medical and surgical

**Staffed Beds**: 101 **Admissions**: 5471 **Census**: 56 **Outpatient Visits**: 111648 **Births**: 891 **Total Expense ($000)**: 92102 **Payroll Expense ($000)**: 27402 **Personnel**: 535

☐ **OCEANS BEHAVIORAL HOSPITAL BILOXI (254012)**, 180 Debuys Road, Zip 39531–4402; tel. 228/388–0600, (Nonreporting) **A**1 **F**29 75 87 98 99 103 130 **P**1
Primary Contact: Cliff Hermes, Administrator
Web address: www.https://oceanshealthcare.com/biloxi
**Control**: Corporation, Investor–owned (for–profit) **Service**: Psychiatric

**Staffed Beds**: 45 **Admissions**: 746 **Census**: 16 **Outpatient Visits**: 0
**Births**: 0 **Total Expense ($000)**: 8380 **Payroll Expense ($000)**: 2499
**Personnel**: 87

**VA GULF COAST VETERANS HLTH** See Veterans Affairs Gulf Coast Veterans Health Care System

**MS**

✠ **VETERANS AFFAIRS GULF COAST VETERANS HEALTH CARE SYSTEM**, 400 Veterans Avenue, Zip 39531–2410; tel. 228/523–5000, (Nonreporting) **A**1 3 5 **S** Department of Veterans Affairs, Washington, DC
Primary Contact: Bryan C. Matthews, Medical Center Director
COO: Alexander Murray, Interim Associate Director
CFO: John D Williams JrChief Financial Officer
CMO: Kenneth B Simon, M.D., Chief of Staff
CIO: David D Wagner, Chief Information Management Service
CHR: Andrew Roberts, Interim Chief Human Resources Officer
CNO: Deatosha D. Haynes, Interim Associates Director for Patient
Web address: www.biloxi.va.gov/
**Control**: Veterans Affairs, Government, federal **Service**: General medical and surgical

**Staffed Beds: 392**

### BOONEVILLE—Prentiss County

**BAPTIST MEMORIAL HOSPITAL** See Baptist Memorial Hospital-Booneville

✠ **BAPTIST MEMORIAL HOSPITAL-BOONEVILLE (250044)**, 100 Hospital Street, Zip 38829–3359; tel. 662/720–5000, (Nonreporting) **A**1 10 **F**3 15 17 28 29 30 34 35 40 43 56 57 58 63 68 70 74 75 77 81 85 86 87 89 90 93 98 103 107 108 111 115 118 119 130 132 133 145 146 148 153 154 **S** Baptist Memorial Health Care Corporation, Memphis, TN
Primary Contact: James Grantham, Administrator and Chief Executive Officer
CFO: Donavan Leonard, Chief Financial Officer
CMO: Nathan Baldwin, M.D., President Medical Staff
CIO: Linda Chaffin, Director Medical Review
CHR: Shannon Bolen, Director Human Resources
Web address: www.bmhcc.org/booneville
**Control**: Other not–for–profit (including NFP Corporation) **Service**: General medical and surgical

**Staffed Beds: 63 Admissions: 1234 Census: 30 Outpatient Visits: 23418 Births: 0 Total Expense ($000): 19834 Payroll Expense ($000): 8048 Personnel: 161**

### BRANDON—Rankin County

**CROSSGATES RIVER OAKS HOSPITAL** See Merit Health Rankin

✠ **MERIT HEALTH RANKIN (250096)**, 350 Crossgates Boulevard, Zip 39042–2698; tel. 601/825–2811, (Nonreporting) **A**1 5 10 **F**3 15 29 30 34 35 39 40 43 50 57 59 60 64 70 79 81 82 85 87 90 93 97 98 103 104 107 108 110 111 114 119 129 130 146 153 154 **P**5 6 **S** Community Health Systems, Inc., Franklin, TN
Primary Contact: Heather Sistrunk, R.N., Chief Executive Officer
CFO: Christy Wilson, Chief Financial Officer
CMO: Edward Rigdon, M.D., Chief Medical Officer
CIO: Heather Holmes, Director Health Information Systems
CHR: Joy M Hutson, Director Human Resources
CNO: Cynthia Ellis, Chief Nursing Officer
Web address: www.merithealthrankin.com/
**Control**: Corporation, Investor–owned (for–profit) **Service**: General medical and surgical

**Staffed Beds: 134 Admissions: 1727 Census: 27 Outpatient Visits: 42442 Births: 0 Total Expense ($000): 42380 Payroll Expense ($000): 12108 Personnel: 200**

### BROOKHAVEN—Lincoln County

⇧ **KING'S DAUGHTERS HOSPITAL** See King's Daughters Medical Center

★ ⇧ **KING'S DAUGHTERS MEDICAL CENTER (250057)**, 427 Highway 51 North, Zip 39601–2350, Mailing Address: P.O. Box 948, Zip 39602–0948; tel. 601/833–6011, (Nonreporting) **A**10 20 21 **F**3 7 11 13 15 17 29 30 34 35 40 41 45 53 54 57 59 64 65 68 70 73 74 75 76 77 79 80 81 82 86 89 93 96 97 107 108 110 111 114 115 119 126 129 130 131 132 135 146 147 148 149 156 **S** QHR Health, Brentwood, TN
Primary Contact: Alvin Hoover, FACHE, Chief Executive Officer
COO: Thomas Hood, Chief Operating Officer
CMO: Jeffrey Ross, M.D., Chief Medical Officer
CIO: Carl Smith, Chief Information Officer
CHR: Celine H Craig, Chief Human Resources Officer
CNO: Cheri Brooks, R.N., Chief Nursing Officer
Web address: www.kdmc.org
**Control**: Other not–for–profit (including NFP Corporation) **Service**: General medical and surgical

**Staffed Beds: 79 Admissions: 3403 Census: 25 Outpatient Visits: 184362 Births: 717 Total Expense ($000): 88585 Payroll Expense ($000): 37421 Personnel: 612**

### CALHOUN CITY—Calhoun County

★ **BAPTIST MEMORIAL HOSPITAL - CALHOUN (251331)**, 140 Burke-Calhoun City Road, Zip 38916–9690; tel. 662/628–6611, (Total facility includes 120 beds in nursing home–type unit) (Nonreporting) **A**10 18 **F**3 30 40 43 59 64 68 89 107 114 119 127 128 130 133 154 **S** Baptist Memorial Health Care Corporation, Memphis, TN
Primary Contact: Collin Cheek, Administrator
CFO: Kenneth Conley, Chief Financial Officer
CMO: Bruce Longest, M.D., President Medical Staff
Web address: www.baptistonline.org/calhoun/
**Control**: Other not–for–profit (including NFP Corporation) **Service**: General medical and surgical

**Staffed Beds: 145 Admissions: 489 Census: 107 Outpatient Visits: 11156 Births: 0 Total Expense ($000): 12224 Payroll Expense ($000): 4766 Personnel: 208**

**CALHOUN HEALTH SERVICES** See Baptist Memorial Hospital - Calhoun

### CANTON—Madison County

**MADISON RIVER OAKS MEDICAL CENTER** See Merit Health Madison

✠ **MERIT HEALTH MADISON (250038)**, 161 River Oaks Drive, Zip 39046–5375, Mailing Address: PO Box 1607, Zip 39046–5375; tel. 601/855–4000, (Nonreporting) **A**1 3 5 10 **F**3 13 15 18 29 34 35 40 43 50 59 64 68 70 73 76 79 81 82 85 87 89 93 96 108 110 112 114 119 126 129 130 135 146 148 149 154 156 **P**8 **S** Community Health Systems, Inc., Franklin, TN
Primary Contact: Britton Phelps, Chief Executive Officer
CFO: Shea Sutherland, Chief Financial Officer
CMO: Vibha Vig, Chief of Staff
CIO: Rick Hartzog, Chief Information Officer
CHR: Jackie Williams, Director Human Resources
CNO: Tim Lolley, MSN, Chief Nursing Officer
Web address: www.merithealthmadison.com
**Control**: Corporation, Investor–owned (for–profit) **Service**: General medical and surgical

**Staffed Beds: 43 Admissions: 1319 Census: 11 Outpatient Visits: 40441 Births: 453 Personnel: 187**

### CARTHAGE—Leake County

★ **BAPTIST MEDICAL CENTER LEAKE (251315)**, 1100 Highway 16 E, Zip 39051–3809, Mailing Address: P.O. Box 909, Zip 39051–0909; tel. 601/267–1100, (Nonreporting) **A**10 18 **F**29 35 40 43 45 56 59 81 87 107 109 111 114 119 127 130 133 146 148 153 154 **S** Baptist Memorial Health Care Corporation, Memphis, TN
Primary Contact: Daryl W. Weaver, Chief Executive Officer
COO: C Gerald Cotton, Interim Chief Operating Officer
CFO: David Jackson, Chief Financial Officer
CMO: Doug Perry, M.D., Chief of Staff
Web address: www.mbhs.org/locations/baptist-medical-center-leake/
**Control**: Other not–for–profit (including NFP Corporation) **Service**: General medical and surgical

**Staffed Beds: 25 Admissions: 700 Census: 16 Outpatient Visits: 33114 Births: 1 Total Expense ($000): 20858 Payroll Expense ($000): 7704 Personnel: 146**

**LEAKE MEMORIAL HOSPITAL** See Baptist Medical Center Leake

### CENTREVILLE—Wilkinson County

✠ **FIELD MEMORIAL COMMUNITY HOSPITAL (251309)**, 178 Highway 24, Zip 39631–4171; tel. 601/645–5221, (Nonreporting) **A**1 10 18 **F**15 18 29 34 39 40 43 45 57 59 64 75 77 79 81 89 90 93 107 108 110 118 119 127 130 133 148 **P**6
Primary Contact: Chad Netterville, Administrator and Chief Executive Officer
CFO: Bryan N Stevens, Chief Financial Officer
CIO: Locke Wheeles, Information Technology Manager
CHR: Dana McNabb, Human Resources Manager
CNO: Robin Walker, Chief Nursing Officer
Web address: www.fhsms.org
**Control**: County, Government, Nonfederal **Service**: General medical and surgical

**Staffed Beds: 16 Admissions: 436 Census: 9 Outpatient Visits: 11461 Births: 0 Total Expense ($000): 18328 Payroll Expense ($000): 8642 Personnel: 161**

**MS**

## CHARLESTON—Tallahatchie County

⇑ **TALLAHATCHIE GENERAL HOSPITAL (251304)**, 201 South Market, Zip 38921–2236, Mailing Address: P.O. Box 230, Zip 38921–0240; tel. 662/647–5535, (Total facility includes 98 beds in nursing home–type unit) (Nonreporting) **A**10 18 21 **F**29 34 40 43 53 57 64 86 87 93 107 114 127 130 133 143 **P**6
Primary Contact: Jim Blackwood, Chief Executive Officer
CFO: Sammie Bell JrChief Financial Officer
**Control**: County, Government, Nonfederal **Service**: General medical and surgical

**Staffed Beds**: 116 **Admissions**: 650 **Census**: 119 **Births**: 0 **Total Expense ($000)**: 33282 **Payroll Expense ($000)**: 16082 **Personnel**: 222

## CLARKSDALE—Coahoma County

**MERIT HEALTH NORTHWEST MISSISSIPPI** See Northwest Mississippi Medical Center

☐ **NORTHWEST MISSISSIPPI MEDICAL CENTER (250042)**, 1970 Hospital Drive, Zip 38614–7202, Mailing Address: P.O. Box 1218, Zip 38614–1218; tel. 662/627–3211, (Nonreporting) **A**1 10 19 **F**3 13 15 17 18 20 22 28 29 30 31 34 35 40 43 53 57 59 64 70 73 74 76 79 80 81 85 89 93 107 108 110 111 114 115 118 119 126 130 131 132 **P**8 **S** Curae Health, Clinton, TN
Primary Contact: Joel Southern, R.N., MSN, Chief Executive Officer
CFO: Charles H. Hester, CPA, JrChief Financial Officer
CMO: Richard Brownstein, M.D., Chief of Staff
CIO: Adrienne Taylor, Director of Health Information Management
CHR: Devasha Patterson, Director of Human Resources
Web address: www.northwestmsmedicalcenter.org
**Control**: Corporation, Investor–owned (for–profit) **Service**: General medical and surgical

**Staffed Beds**: 181 **Admissions**: 2347 **Census**: 26

## CLEVELAND—Bolivar County

**BOLIVAR COUNTY HOSPITAL** See Bolivar Medical Center

⊞ **BOLIVAR MEDICAL CENTER (250093)**, 901 East Sunflower Road, Zip 38732–2833, Mailing Address: P.O. Box 1380, Zip 38732–1380; tel. 662/846–0061, (Total facility includes 35 beds in nursing home–type unit) (Nonreporting) **A**1 10 20 **F**13 15 29 30 35 39 40 43 70 73 76 81 87 88 89 93 98 103 107 108 111 116 118 119 128 130 133 146 148 **S** LifePoint Health, Brentwood, TN
Primary Contact: Robert L. Marshall Jr, FACHE, Chief Executive Officer
CMO: Mark Blackwood, M.D., Chief of Staff
CIO: Cagri Sapmaz, Information Technology Director
CHR: Ben Bufkin, Human Resource Director
CNO: Joann McCollum, Chief Nursing Officer
Web address: www.bolivarmedical.com
**Control**: Corporation, Investor–owned (for–profit) **Service**: General medical and surgical

**Staffed Beds**: 129 **Admissions**: 3328 **Census**: 67 **Births**: 379 **Total Expense ($000)**: 50177 **Payroll Expense ($000)**: 19353 **Personnel**: 439

## COLLINS—Covington County

★ ⇑ **COVINGTON COUNTY HOSPITAL (251325)**, 701 South Holly Avenue, Zip 39428–3894, Mailing Address: P.O. Box 1149, Zip 39428–1149; tel. 601/765–6711, (Total facility includes 60 beds in nursing home–type unit) (Nonreporting) **A**10 18 21 **F**2 3 7 29 34 35 39 40 43 45 50 54 57 59 60 64 65 66 68 81 89 93 94 98 103 104 105 107 114 119 127 128 130 133 143
Primary Contact: Gregg Gibbes, Chief Executive Officer
CFO: Delilah Hudson, Controller
CMO: Word Johnston, Medical Director
CHR: Beverly K Ponder, Executive Assistant and Human Resources Coordinator
CNO: Martha Lynn Scott, Chief Patient Care Officer
Web address: www.covingtoncountyhospital.com
**Control**: County, Government, Nonfederal **Service**: General medical and surgical

**Staffed Beds**: 95 **Admissions**: 516 **Census**: 69 **Outpatient Visits**: 23136 **Births**: 0 **Total Expense ($000)**: 32018 **Payroll Expense ($000)**: 12815 **Personnel**: 287

## COLUMBIA—Marion County

**MARION GENERAL HOSPITAL (250085)**, 1560 Sumrall Road, Zip 39429–2654, Mailing Address: P.O. Box 630, Zip 39429–0630; tel. 601/736–6303, (Nonreporting) **A**10 **F**3 11 29 32 34 35 39 40 43 57 59 64 65 66 68 70 81 85 87 92 97 107 114 119 127 130 133 146 148 149 154
Primary Contact: Alaina Cedillo, Administrator
CMO: Mark Stevens, M.D., Chief Medical Staff
CIO: Donny Bracey, Director Information Services
CNO: Patricia Reid, Director of Nursing
Web address: www.mgh.net/
**Control**: County, Government, Nonfederal **Service**: General medical and surgical

**Staffed Beds**: 49 **Admissions**: 843 **Census**: 17 **Outpatient Visits**: 28350 **Births**: 0 **Total Expense ($000)**: 12866 **Payroll Expense ($000)**: 5721 **Personnel**: 107

**METHODIST HOSP OF MARION CNTY** See Marion General Hospital

## COLUMBUS—Lowndes County

⊞ **BAPTIST MEMORIAL HOSPITAL-GOLDEN TRIANGLE (250100)**, 2520 Fifth Street North, Zip 39705–2095, Mailing Address: P.O. Box 1307, Zip 39703–1307; tel. 662/244–1000, (Nonreporting) **A**1 3 10 19 **F**3 4 5 11 13 15 17 18 20 22 24 26 28 29 30 31 34 38 39 40 43 45 49 51 57 59 61 64 70 73 75 76 77 79 80 81 84 85 87 88 89 91 93 94 96 98 100 102 104 106 107 108 109 110 111 114 115 116 117 118 119 120 121 123 124 126 128 129 130 132 134 146 147 148 149 153 154 156 157 **P**7 **S** Baptist Memorial Health Care Corporation, Memphis, TN
Primary Contact: Paul Cade, Administrator and Chief Executive Officer
CFO: David Webb, Chief Financial Officer
CMO: John E Reed, M.D., Medical Director
CIO: Sheila Bardwell, Director Information Systems
CHR: Bob McCallister, Director Human Resources
CNO: Mary Ellen Sumrall, Chief Nursing Officer
Web address: www.baptistonline.org/golden-triangle/
**Control**: Other not–for–profit (including NFP Corporation) **Service**: General medical and surgical

**Staffed Beds**: 236 **Admissions**: 9535 **Census**: 124 **Outpatient Visits**: 123632 **Births**: 699 **Total Expense ($000)**: 168066 **Payroll Expense ($000)**: 52557 **Personnel**: 1001

**GOLDEN TRIANGLE REG MED CENTER** See Baptist Memorial Hospital-Golden Triangle

## CORINTH—Alcorn County

**MAGNOLIA HOSPITAL** See Magnolia Regional Health Center

⊞ **MAGNOLIA REGIONAL HEALTH CENTER (250009)**, 611 Alcorn Drive, Zip 38834–9321; tel. 662/293–1000, (Nonreporting) **A**1 3 5 10 19 **F**13 15 17 22 24 29 30 35 39 40 43 51 53 60 62 63 70 75 76 77 78 81 82 86 87 89 93 98 100 101 102 103 107 108 111 116 118 119 127 129 130 131 132 143 146 147 148 **P**7 8 **S** QHR Health, Brentwood, TN
Primary Contact: James M. Hobson, Chief Executive Officer
CMO: Felton Combest, M.D., Vice President Medical Affairs
CIO: David Parker, VP Information Technology
CHR: Regenia Brown, Vice President Human Resources
CNO: Pam B Wallis, MSN, Vice President Nursing Services
Web address: www.mrhc.org
**Control**: City–county, Government, Nonfederal **Service**: General medical and surgical

**Staffed Beds**: 200 **Admissions**: 7811 **Census**: 93 **Outpatient Visits**: 263077 **Births**: 555 **Total Expense ($000)**: 174684 **Payroll Expense ($000)**: 87781 **Personnel**: 1371

## DE KALB—Kemper County

**JOHN C. STENNIS MEMORIAL HOSPITAL (251335)**, 14365 Highway 16 West, Zip 39328–7974; tel. 769/486–1000, (Nonreporting) **A**3 10 18 **F**29 40 43 75 81 107 119 127 128 133 **P**6 **S** Rush Health Systems, Meridian, MS
Primary Contact: Scott Vincent, Chief Executive Officer
Web address: www.johncstennismemorialhospital.com/jcsmh/
**Control**: Other not–for–profit (including NFP Corporation) **Service**: General medical and surgical

**Staffed Beds**: 25 **Admissions**: 314 **Census**: 9 **Outpatient Visits**: 6714 **Births**: 0 **Total Expense ($000)**: 8610 **Payroll Expense ($000)**: 3541 **Personnel**: 86

**MS**

---

## EUPORA—Webster County

✠ **NORTH MISSISSIPPI MEDICAL CENTER-EUPORA (250020)**, 70 Medical Plaza, Zip 39744–4018; tel. 662/258–6221, (Total facility includes 35 beds in nursing home–type unit) (Nonreporting) **A**1 10 20 **F**3 11 15 28 29 30 32 34 35 38 40 43 50 53 57 59 64 65 68 71 74 87 89 90 107 114 119 127 129 130 132 133 135 146 148 149 150 154 156 **S** North Mississippi Health Services, Inc., Tupelo, MS
Primary Contact: Robin Mixon, Administrator
CFO: Adonna Mitchell, Director Fiscal Services
CMO: Charles A. Ozborn, M.D., Chief of Staff
CIO: Helen Reed, Director Health Information
CHR: Lesley Gore, Human Resources Director
Web address: www.nmhs.net/eupora
**Control:** Other not–for–profit (including NFP Corporation) **Service:** General medical and surgical

**Staffed Beds:** 74 **Admissions:** 1628 **Census:** 55 **Outpatient Visits:** 46457 **Births:** 0 **Total Expense ($000):** 23907 **Payroll Expense ($000):** 12092 **Personnel:** 152

**WEBSTER HEALTH SERVICES** See North Mississippi Medical Center-Eupora

## FAYETTE—Jefferson County

★ **JEFFERSON COUNTY HOSPITAL (250060)**, 870 South Main Street, Zip 39069–5695, Mailing Address: P.O. Box 577, Zip 39069–0577; tel. 601/786–3401, (Nonreporting) **A**10 **F**3 40 107 130
Primary Contact: Jana Greene, Chief Executive Officer
CMO: Khar Omolara, M.D., Chief Medical Staff
CHR: Patricia Selmon, Director Public Relations and Chief Human Resources
**Control:** County, Government, Nonfederal **Service:** General medical and surgical

**Staffed Beds:** 30 **Admissions:** 223 **Census:** 6 **Outpatient Visits:** 18627 **Births:** 0 **Total Expense ($000):** 6914 **Payroll Expense ($000):** 3320 **Personnel:** 93

## FLOWOOD—Rankin County

✠ **MERIT HEALTH RIVER OAKS (250138)**, 1030 River Oaks Drive, Zip 39232–9553, Mailing Address: P.O. Box 5100, Jackson, Zip 39296–5100; tel. 601/932–1030, (Nonreporting) **A**1 3 5 10 **F**3 11 12 13 15 18 20 22 29 30 31 34 35 37 39 40 43 45 49 50 51 57 59 64 65 70 72 73 74 76 79 81 82 85 87 89 93 107 108 111 115 119 126 130 144 146 147 149 **S** Community Health Systems, Inc., Franklin, TN
Primary Contact: L Dwayne. Blaylock, Chief Executive Officer
CIO: Pat Jones, Director Information Systems
CHR: Warren Weed, Director Human Resources
CNO: Sherry P Cook, R.N., MSN, Chief Nursing Executive
Web address: www.https://www.merithealthriveroaks.com/
**Control:** Corporation, Investor–owned (for–profit) **Service:** General medical and surgical

**Staffed Beds:** 118 **Admissions:** 4671 **Census:** 47 **Births:** 1474 **Total Expense ($000):** 102814 **Payroll Expense ($000):** 29349 **Personnel:** 553

✠ **MERIT HEALTH WOMAN'S HOSPITAL (250136)**, 1026 North Flowood Drive, Zip 39232–9532, Mailing Address: 1026 North Flowood Drive, Zip 39232; tel. 601/932–1000, (Nonreporting) **A**1 3 5 10 **S** Community Health Systems, Inc., Franklin, TN
Primary Contact: Heather Sistrunk, R.N., Chief Executive Officer
CFO: Nick Renda, Chief Financial Officer
CMO: Ed Barham, M.D., Chief of Staff
CHR: Warren Weed, Director Associate Relations
CNO: Linda Atwood, Chief Nursing Officer
Web address: www.merithealthwomanshospital.com
**Control:** Corporation, Investor–owned (for–profit) **Service:** Obstetrics and gynecology

**Staffed Beds:** 60

**RIVER OAKS HOSPITAL** See Merit Health River Oaks

**WOMAN'S HOSPITAL** See Merit Health Woman's Hospital

## FOREST—Scott County

★ ⇑ **LACKEY MEMORIAL HOSPITAL (251300)**, 330 Broad Street, Zip 39074–3508, Mailing Address: P.O. Box 428, Zip 39074–0428; tel. 601/469–4151, (Total facility includes 20 beds in nursing home–type unit) (Nonreporting) **A**10 18 21 **F**3 8 11 15 18 29 34 35 38 39 40 41 45 50 54 55 56 57 59 64 65 66 68 81 86 87 89 92 97 98 103 104 107 110 111 119 127 128 130 133 **P**6
Primary Contact: Sydney Sawyer, R.N., Chief Executive Officer
CFO: Julie Gieger, Chief Financial Officer
CMO: John Paul Lee, M.D., Chief of Staff
CIO: Eddie Pope, Chief Information Officer
CHR: Donn Paul, Chief Human Resources
Web address: www.lackeymemorialhospital.com
**Control:** Other not–for–profit (including NFP Corporation) **Service:** General medical and surgical

**Staffed Beds:** 55 **Admissions:** 1248 **Census:** 37 **Outpatient Visits:** 15548 **Births:** 0 **Total Expense ($000):** 27378 **Payroll Expense ($000):** 11965 **Personnel:** 257

⇑ **S. E. LACKEY MEMORIAL HOSPITAL** See Lackey Memorial Hospital

## GREENVILLE—Washington County

★ ⇑ **ALLEGIANCE SPECIALTY HOSPITAL OF GREENVILLE (252013)**, 300 South Washington Avenue, 3rd Floor, Zip 38701–4719; tel. 662/332–7344, (Nonreporting) **A**10 21 **F**1 3 29 34 57 130 153 154 **S** Allegiance Health Management, Shreveport, LA
Primary Contact: Vearnail Herzog, Chief Executive Officer
CMO: Parvez Karim, M.D., Chief Medical Officer
CIO: Sharon Scott, Health Information Director
CHR: Sharon Taylor, Human Resources Director
CNO: John Read, Chief Nursing Officer
Web address: www.ahmgt.com
**Control:** Corporation, Investor–owned (for–profit) **Service:** Acute long–term care hospital

**Staffed Beds:** 39 **Admissions:** 350 **Census:** 23 **Outpatient Visits:** 0 **Births:** 0 **Total Expense ($000):** 9828 **Payroll Expense ($000):** 4285 **Personnel:** 104

★ **DELTA REGIONAL MEDICAL CENTER (250082)**, 1400 East Union Street, Zip 38704–5247; tel. 662/378–3783, (Includes THE KING'S DAUGHTERS HOSPITAL, Mailing address: 300 Washington Avenue, Greenville, Mississippi, Zip 38701–3614, P O Box 1857, Zip 38702–1857, tel. 662/378–2020; Scott Christensen, FACHE, Chief Executive Officer), (Nonreporting) **A**3 10 19 **F**3 4 8 11 13 15 18 20 22 28 29 30 31 34 35 39 40 43 45 46 47 50 55 56 57 59 60 62 63 64 65 68 70 72 73 76 78 79 81 85 87 89 90 92 93 96 97 98 100 102 103 104 107 108 109 110 111 114 115 119 127 129 130 131 132 145 146 147 148 149 152 153 154 157 **P**6
Primary Contact: Scott Christensen, FACHE, Chief Executive Officer
CFO: Scott Goodin, Interim Chief Financial Officer
CHR: Chrissy Nicholson, Vice President of Human Resources
CNO: Amy Walker, MSN, Chief Nursing Officer
Web address: www.deltaregional.com
**Control:** County, Government, Nonfederal **Service:** General medical and surgical

**Staffed Beds:** 218 **Admissions:** 6087 **Census:** 88 **Outpatient Visits:** 86853 **Births:** 599 **Personnel:** 699

## GREENWOOD—Leflore County

✠ △ **GREENWOOD LEFLORE HOSPITAL (250099)**, 1401 River Road, Zip 38930–4030, Mailing Address: Drawer 1410, Zip 38935–1410; tel. 662/459–7000, (Nonreporting) **A**1 7 10 19 **F**3 13 15 17 18 20 26 28 29 32 34 35 40 41 43 45 46 47 48 50 53 56 57 58 59 64 65 68 70 74 75 76 79 81 82 85 86 87 89 90 93 96 98 103 107 108 109 110 111 114 117 118 119 120 121 126 127 129 130 132 135 145 146 147 148 149 154 156 **P**6 8
Primary Contact: Dawne Holmes, Interim Chief Executive Officer
CFO: Dawne Holmes, Chief Financial Officer
CMO: Abhash Thakur, M.D., Chief of Staff
CHR: Key Britt, Associate Director
Web address: www.glh.org
**Control:** City–county, Government, Nonfederal **Service:** General medical and surgical

**Staffed Beds:** 208 **Admissions:** 4496 **Census:** 64 **Outpatient Visits:** 144871 **Births:** 461 **Total Expense ($000):** 115942 **Payroll Expense ($000):** 53714 **Personnel:** 785

**MS**

*Many Facility Codes have changed. Please refer to the AHA Guide Code Chart.*

## GRENADA—Grenada County

⇑ **GRENADA LAKE MEDICAL CENTER** See University of Mississippi Medical Center Grenada

★ ⇑ **UNIVERSITY OF MISSISSIPPI MEDICAL CENTER GRENADA (250168)**, 960 Avent Drive, Zip 38901–5230; tel. 662/227–7000, (Nonreporting) **A**10 21 **F**3 11 13 15 17 29 30 32 34 35 39 40 43 44 45 46 50 54 57 59 60 62 64 65 66 70 73 76 77 79 80 81 82 84 85 87 89 90 93 97 107 108 110 111 115 116 118 119 124 127 130 139 143 146 147 148 149 154 156 **P**6 **S** University Hospitals and Health System, Jackson, MS
Primary Contact: Dodie McElmurray, FACHE, Chief Executive Officer
COO: Molly B. Brown, Chief Operating Officer
CFO: Scott Whittemore, Chief Financial Officer
CIO: John Farrish, Health Information Director
CHR: Claudette Hathcock, Administrative Director Human Resources
Web address: www.glmc.net/
**Control:** State, Government, Nonfederal **Service:** General medical and surgical

**Staffed Beds:** 58 **Admissions:** 1860 **Census:** 21 **Outpatient Visits:** 45296 **Births:** 311 **Total Expense ($000):** 51966 **Payroll Expense ($000):** 24959 **Personnel:** 281

## GULFPORT—Harrison County

**COLUMBIA GARDEN PARK HOSPITAL** See Garden Park Medical Center

✠ △ **ENCOMPASS HEALTH REHABILITATION HOSPITAL OF GULFPORT (253027)**, 4500 13th Street, Suite 900, Zip 39501–2515; tel. 228/822–6965, (Nonreporting) **A**1 7 10 **F**29 90 **S** Encompass Health Corporation, Birmingham, AL
Primary Contact: Amber Hester, Chief Executive Officer
Web address: www.healthsouthgulfport.com
**Control:** Corporation, Investor–owned (for–profit) **Service:** Rehabilitation

**Staffed Beds:** 33 **Admissions:** 949 **Census:** 32 **Outpatient Visits:** 0 **Births:** 0 **Total Expense ($000):** 13587 **Payroll Expense ($000):** 7119 **Personnel:** 89

✠ **GARDEN PARK MEDICAL CENTER (250123)**, 15200 Community Road, Zip 39503–3085, Mailing Address: P.O. Box 1240, Zip 39502–1240; tel. 228/575–7000, (Nonreporting) **A**1 10 **F**3 12 13 15 18 29 30 34 35 37 40 43 45 46 47 48 50 51 57 58 59 64 65 68 70 74 76 79 81 83 84 85 86 89 90 98 103 106 107 108 110 111 114 115 126 135 146 147 148 149 150 154 **S** HCA Healthcare, Nashville, TN
Primary Contact: Randy Rogers, FACHE, Chief Executive Officer
COO: Regina Ramazani, Chief Operating Officer
CFO: Regina Ramazani, Chief Financial Officer
CMO: T. Paul Mace, Chief Medical Officer
CIO: Chris Oubre, Information Technology Director
CHR: Michael Pocchiari, Director Human Resources
CNO: Cheryl Thompson, Chief Nursing Officer
Web address: www.gpmedical.com
**Control:** Corporation, Investor–owned (for–profit) **Service:** General medical and surgical

**Staffed Beds:** 68 **Admissions:** 3518 **Census:** 51 **Outpatient Visits:** 59049 **Births:** 420 **Total Expense ($000):** 70294 **Payroll Expense ($000):** 22957 **Personnel:** 370

☐ **GULFPORT BEHAVIORAL HEALTH SYSTEM (254011)**, 11150 Highway 49 North, Zip 39503–4110; tel. 228/831–1700, (Data for 273 days) (Nonreporting) **A**1 10 **F**4 98 99 100 104 **S** Universal Health Services, Inc., King of Prussia, PA
Primary Contact: Michael A. Zieman, FACHE, Administrator
Web address: www.gulfportmemorial.com
**Control:** Corporation, Investor–owned (for–profit) **Service:** Psychiatric

**Staffed Beds:** 89 **Admissions:** 796 **Census:** 16 **Births:** 0 **Total Expense ($000):** 15982 **Payroll Expense ($000):** 5539 **Personnel:** 119

**HEALTHSOUTH REHABILITATION HOSPITAL OF GULFPORT** See Encompass Health Rehabilitation Hospital of Gulfport

**MEMORIAL BEHAVIORAL HEALTH** See Gulfport Behavioral Health System

☐ **MEMORIAL HOSPITAL AT GULFPORT (250019)**, 4500 13th Street, Zip 39501–2569, Mailing Address: P.O. Box 1810, Zip 39502–1810; tel. 228/867–4000, (Nonreporting) **A**1 2 5 10 **F**2 3 11 12 13 15 17 18 20 22 24 28 29 30 31 34 35 40 43 44 45 46 47 48 49 50 53 54 57 59 64 65 68 70 71 72 73 74 76 77 78 79 80 81 82 84 85 87 89 107 108 110 111 114 115 116 117 118 119 120 121 123 124 126 130 132 145 146 148 149 **P**8
Primary Contact: Kent Nicaud, President and Chief Executive Officer
CFO: Mark Wack, Chief Financial Officer
CMO: Larry Couvillon, M.D., Chief Medical Officer
CIO: Gene Thomas, Vice President, Information Systems, Chief Information Officer
CHR: Cathy Wood, Vice President, Human Resources
CNO: Jennifer Dumal, R.N., Chief Operating Officer of Clinical and Chief Nursing Officer
Web address: www.gulfportmemorial.com
**Control:** City–county, Government, Nonfederal **Service:** General medical and surgical

**Staffed Beds:** 281 **Admissions:** 15159 **Census:** 183 **Outpatient Visits:** 763269 **Births:** 1314 **Total Expense ($000):** 550058 **Payroll Expense ($000):** 237416 **Personnel:** 3582

**SELECT SPECIALTY HOSPITAL-GULF COAST** See Select Specialty Hospital-Gulfport

✠ **SELECT SPECIALTY HOSPITAL-GULFPORT (252005)**, 1520 Broad Avenue, Suite 300, Zip 39501–3601; tel. 228/575–7500, (Nonreporting) **A**1 10 **F**1 29 75 82 87 90 **S** Select Medical Corporation, Mechanicsburg, PA
Primary Contact: John O'Keefe, Chief Executive Officer
Web address: www.selectspecialtyhospitals.com/company/locations/gulfcoast.aspx
**Control:** Corporation, Investor–owned (for–profit) **Service:** Acute long–term care hospital

**Staffed Beds:** 61 **Admissions:** 428 **Census:** 32 **Outpatient Visits:** 0 **Births:** 0 **Total Expense ($000):** 20430 **Payroll Expense ($000):** 8785 **Personnel:** 135

## HATTIESBURG—Forrest County

⇑ **FORREST COUNTY GEN HOSPITAL** See Forrest General Hospital

★ △ ⇑ **FORREST GENERAL HOSPITAL (250078)**, 6051 U S Highway 49, Zip 39401–7200, Mailing Address: P.O. Box 16389, Zip 39404–6389; tel. 601/288–7000, (Includes PINE GROVE BEHAVIORAL HEALTH AND ADDICTION SERVICES, Mailing address: 2255 Broadway Drive, Hattiesburg, Mississippi, Zip 39402–3254; tel. 888/574–4673; Debbie F Sanford, R.N., MS, Administrator), (Nonreporting) **A**2 3 5 7 10 19 21 **F**3 4 5 8 12 13 15 17 18 20 22 24 26 28 29 30 31 34 35 37 39 40 43 45 46 47 48 49 53 55 57 58 59 62 63 64 65 68 70 72 73 75 76 77 78 79 81 84 85 86 87 89 90 93 96 97 98 99 100 101 102 103 104 105 106 107 108 111 114 115 118 119 120 121 123 124 126 128 130 132 146 147 149 151 152 154 157 **P**8
Primary Contact: Andy Woodard, President and Chief Executive Officer
COO: Douglas A Jones, Chief Operating Officer
CMO: Steven E Farrell, M.D., Chief Medical Officer
CHR: Troy P Daniels, Chief Human Resources Officer
CNO: Micah Rehm, Chief Nursing Officer
Web address: www.forrestgeneral.com
**Control:** County, Government, Nonfederal **Service:** General medical and surgical

**Staffed Beds:** 545 **Admissions:** 29084 **Census:** 381 **Outpatient Visits:** 155388 **Births:** 2605 **Total Expense ($000):** 460183 **Payroll Expense ($000):** 177861 **Personnel:** 3224

## HATTIESBURG—Lamar County

✠ **MERIT HEALTH WESLEY (250094)**, 5001 Hardy Street, Zip 39402–1308, Mailing Address: P.O. Box 16509, Zip 39404–6509; tel. 601/268–8000, (Nonreporting) **A**1 3 5 10 12 13 19 **F**3 8 11 12 13 15 17 18 20 22 24 26 28 29 30 32 34 35 37 39 40 41 43 45 46 49 53 54 57 58 59 60 61 64 65 70 71 72 73 74 75 76 77 78 79 81 82 85 87 89 90 91 93 96 97 98 103 104 107 108 110 111 114 115 117 118 119 126 128 129 130 132 135 146 148 **S** Community Health Systems, Inc., Franklin, TN
Primary Contact: Matthew Banks, Chief Executive Officer
CFO: Randy Humphrey, Chief Financial Officer
CMO: William Reno, M.D., IIIPresident Medical Staff
CIO: Jesse Folds, Director of Information Technologies
CHR: Terry Trigg, Director Human Resources
Web address: www.wesley.com
**Control:** Corporation, Investor–owned (for–profit) **Service:** General medical and surgical

**Staffed Beds:** 211 **Admissions:** 7604 **Census:** 128 **Outpatient Visits:** 74943 **Births:** 1000 **Personnel:** 820

**WESLEY MEDICAL CENTER** See Merit Health Wesley

---

**Hospital, Medicare Provider Number, Address, Telephone, Approval, Facility, and Physician Codes, Health Care System**

★ American Hospital Association (AHA) membership
☐ The Joint Commission accreditation
○ Healthcare Facilities Accreditation Program
◇ DNV Healthcare Inc. accreditation
⇑ Center for Improvement in Healthcare Quality Accreditation
△ Commission on Accreditation of Rehabilitation Facilities (CARF) accreditation

**MS**

## HAZLEHURST—Copiah County

★ **COPIAH COUNTY MEDICAL CENTER (251327)**, 27190 Highway 28,
Zip 39083–2228, Mailing Address: P.O. Box 889, Zip 39083–0889;
tel. 601/574–7000, (Nonreporting) **A**10 18 **F**3 15 29 30 34 35 39 40 50 51 57
59 64 77 81 93 104 107 110 111 115 119 133 148 149 153 154 156
Primary Contact: Benjamin Lott, Chief Executive Officer
CFO: Bryan N Stevens, Interim Chief Financial Officer
CNO: Alison Mathis, Chief Nursing Officer
Web address: www.myccmc.org/
**Control**: County, Government, Nonfederal **Service**: General medical and surgical

> **Staffed Beds: 25 Admissions: 718 Census: 15 Births: 0 Total Expense
> ($000): 16865 Payroll Expense ($000): 6213 Personnel: 150**

**HARDY WILSON MEMORIAL HOSPITAL** See Copiah County Medical Center

## HOLLY SPRINGS—Marshall County

**ALLIANCE HEALTHCARE SYSTEM (250012)**, 1430 Highway 4 East,
Zip 38635–2140, Mailing Address: P.O. Box 6000, Zip 38634–6000;
tel. 662/252–1212, (Nonreporting) **A**10 20 **F**15 29 35 40 43 57 63 75 87 89 98
103 107 119 127 130 132 133
Primary Contact: Perry E. Williams Sr, Administrator and Chief Executive Officer
COO: Cecelia Bost, Chief Operating Officer
CFO: William F Magee, Chief Financial Officer
CMO: Subbu Rayudu, M.D., Chief of Staff
CIO: Saul Mbenga, Manager Information Technology
CHR: Judy Eggers, Manager Human Resources
Web address: www.alliancehealth.us
**Control**: Corporation, Investor–owned (for–profit) **Service**: General medical and
surgical

> **Staffed Beds: 40 Admissions: 552 Census: 15 Outpatient Visits: 7192
> Births: 0 Total Expense ($000): 11866 Payroll Expense ($000): 4923
> Personnel: 99**

**MARSHALL COUNTY MEDICAL CENTER** See Alliance Healthcare System

## HOUSTON—Chickasaw County

**HOUSTON COMMUNITY HOSPITAL** See Trace Regional Hospital

**TRACE REGIONAL HOSPITAL (250017)**, Highway 8 East, Zip 38851–9396,
Mailing Address: P.O. Box 626, Zip 38851–0626; tel. 662/456–3700, (Nonreporting)
**A**10 **F**15 35 75 90 98 103 107 111 119 127 130 133 135 149 154 **P**6
Primary Contact: Gary L. Staten, Chief Executive Officer
CFO: Pamela W Cook, Chief Financial Officer
CMO: Bill Brohawn, Chief of Staff
CHR: Sherry Craig, Director Human Resources
CNO: Marianne Johnson, Chief Nursing Officer
Web address: www.traceregional.com
**Control**: Corporation, Investor–owned (for–profit) **Service**: General medical and
surgical

> **Staffed Beds: 84 Admissions: 418 Census: 14 Outpatient Visits: 9054
> Births: 0 Total Expense ($000): 10635 Payroll Expense ($000): 6251
> Personnel: 207**

## INDIANOLA—Sunflower County

★ **SOUTH SUNFLOWER COUNTY HOSPITAL (250095)**, 121 East Baker Street,
Zip 38751–2498; tel. 662/635–7201, (Nonreporting) **A**3 10 20 **F**3 8 13 15 34
40 43 50 61 64 65 76 80 81 85 89 107 119 127 133 **P**8
Primary Contact: Courtney Phillips, Chief Executive Officer
COO: Holly H. Sparks, Chief Clinical Officer
CFO: Katie Yates, Chief Financial Officer
CMO: Eric Lessmann, Chief of Staff
CIO: Benjamin Rosenthal, Information Systems Director
CHR: Meredith Taylor, Controller
Web address: www.southsunflower.com
**Control**: County, Government, Nonfederal **Service**: General medical and surgical

> **Staffed Beds: 43 Admissions: 938 Census: 13 Outpatient Visits: 50441
> Births: 177 Total Expense ($000): 17010 Payroll Expense ($000): 6098
> Personnel: 140**

## IUKA—Tishomingo County

**IUKA HOSPITAL** See North Mississippi Medical Center-Iuka

☒ **NORTH MISSISSIPPI MEDICAL CENTER-IUKA (250002)**, 1777 Curtis
Drive, Zip 38852–1001, Mailing Address: P.O. Box 860, Zip 38852–0860;
tel. 662/423–6051, (Nonreporting) **A**1 10 **F**3 15 29 35 40 53 80 82 86 87 89
90 93 107 108 111 114 119 127 129 130 132 133 146 148 **S** North
Mississippi Health Services, Inc., Tupelo, MS
Primary Contact: Fred A. Truesdale Jr, Administrator
CFO: Betty Moore, Business Manager
CMO: Margaret Glynn, M.D., Chief Medical Officer
CIO: Fred A Truesdale Jr Administrator
CHR: Jane Chamblee, Manager Human Resources
Web address: www.nmhs.net
**Control**: Other not–for–profit (including NFP Corporation) **Service**: General
medical and surgical

> **Staffed Beds: 48 Admissions: 839 Census: 12 Outpatient Visits: 20890
> Births: 0 Personnel: 128**

## JACKSON—Hinds County

**BRENTWOOD BEHAVIORAL CARE** See Brentwood Behavioral Healthcare of
Mississippi

☐ **BRENTWOOD BEHAVIORAL HEALTHCARE OF MISSISSIPPI (254007)**, 3531
East Lakeland Drive, Zip 39232–8839; tel. 601/936–2024, (Nonreporting) **A**1 5
10 **F**35 98 99 101 102 104 105 130 153 **S** Universal Health Services, Inc., King
of Prussia, PA
Primary Contact: Michael J. Carney, Chief Executive Officer
Web address: www.brentwoodjackson.com
**Control**: Corporation, Investor–owned (for–profit) **Service**: Psychiatric

> **Staffed Beds: 105 Admissions: 2304 Census: 59 Outpatient Visits: 3714
> Births: 0 Personnel: 216**

**CENTRAL MISSISSIPPI MEDICAL CENTER** See Merit Health Central

☒ **G.V. (SONNY) MONTGOMERY VETERANS AFFAIRS MEDICAL CENTER**, 1500
East Woodrow Wilson Drive, Zip 39216–5199; tel. 601/362–4471, (Nonreporting)
**A**1 3 5 **S** Department of Veterans Affairs, Washington, DC
Primary Contact: David M. Walker, M.D., Medical Center Director
COO: Jed Fillingim, Acting Chief Operating Officer and Associate Director
CFO: Joy Willis, Acting Chief Fiscal Service
CMO: Kent Kirchner, M.D., Chief of Staff
CIO: Robert Wolak, Chief Information Resource Management Service
CHR: Sam Evans, Chief Human Resources Management
Web address: www.jackson.va.gov/
**Control**: Veterans Affairs, Government, federal **Service**: General medical and surgical

> **Staffed Beds: 323**

☒ **MERIT HEALTH CENTRAL (250072)**, 1850 Chadwick Drive, Zip 39204–3479,
Mailing Address: P.O. Box 59001, Zip 39284–9001; tel. 601/376–1000,
(Nonreporting) **A**1 10 **F**3 13 15 16 17 18 20 22 24 26 29 30 31 34 35 37 38 40
43 45 46 49 50 57 59 68 70 72 74 75 76 78 79 81 90 98 100 102 107 108
109 111 114 115 116 117 118 119 122 123 124 126 129 130 134 146 148
154 157 **S** Community Health Systems, Inc., Franklin, TN
Primary Contact: Barry Moss, Chief Executive Officer
COO: Tom Wills, R.N., Chief Operating Officer
CFO: Justin Stroud, Chief Financial Officer
CMO: Greg Oden, Chief Medical Officer
CIO: Tracy Holifield, Director Information Systems
CHR: Sean Jones, Director Human Resources
CNO: Laura Knight, Chief Nursing Officer
Web address: www.merithealthcentral.com/
**Control**: Corporation, Investor–owned (for–profit) **Service**: General medical and surgical

> **Staffed Beds: 230 Admissions: 8714 Census: 150 Births: 634 Total
> Expense ($000): 151229 Payroll Expense ($000): 47667 Personnel: 803**

**METHODIST HOSPITAL & REHAB CTR** See Methodist Rehabilitation Center

☒ △ **METHODIST REHABILITATION CENTER (250152)**, 1350 Woodrow Wilson
Drive, Zip 39216–5198; tel. 601/981–2611, (Total facility includes 60 beds in
nursing home–type unit) (Nonreporting) **A**1 5 7 10 **F**30 34 35 58 64 74 81 82 90
91 92 93 94 95 96 119 130 131 132 146 148
Primary Contact: Mark A. Adams, President and Chief Executive Officer
COO: Joseph M Morette, Executive Vice President
CFO: Gary Armstrong, Executive Vice President
CIO: Gary Armstrong, Executive Vice President
CHR: Steve Hope, Vice President Corporate Services
Web address: www.methodistrehab.org
**Control**: Other not–for–profit (including NFP Corporation) **Service**: Rehabilitation

> **Staffed Beds: 184 Admissions: 1279 Census: 113 Outpatient
> Visits: 61222 Births: 0 Total Expense ($000): 45726 Payroll Expense
> ($000): 25603 Personnel: 627**

*Many Facility Codes have changed. Please refer to the AHA Guide Code Chart.*   © 2021 AHA Guide

MS

**MISSISSIPPI BAPTIST HLTH SYST** See Mississippi Baptist Medical Center

✣ **MISSISSIPPI BAPTIST MEDICAL CENTER (250102)**, 1225 North State Street, Zip 39202–2064; tel. 601/968–1000, (Nonreporting) **A**1 2 3 5 10 **S** Baptist Memorial Health Care Corporation, Memphis, TN
Primary Contact: Bobbie K. Ware, R.N., FACHE, Chief Executive Officer
COO: Bobbie K. Ware, R.N., FACHE, Vice President Patient Care and Chief Nursing Officer
CFO: William Thompson, Chief Financial Officer
CMO: Michael Maples, M.D., Vice President and Chief Medical Officer
CIO: Steve M Stanic, Vice President and Chief Information Officer
CHR: Lee Ann Foreman, Vice President Human Resources
CNO: Bobbie K. Ware, R.N., FACHE, Vice President Patient Care and Chief Nursing Officer
Web address: www.mbhs.org
**Control**: Other not–for–profit (including NFP Corporation) **Service**: General medical and surgical

| Staffed Beds: 638 |
|---|

**MISSISSIPPI HOSPITAL FOR RESTORATIVE CARE** See Select Specialty Hospital - Belhaven

✣ **SELECT SPECIALTY HOSPITAL - BELHAVEN (252003)**, 1225 North State Street, Zip 39202–2097, Mailing Address: P.O. Box 23695, Zip 39225–3695; tel. 601/968–1000, (Nonreporting) **A**1 10 **F**1 3 29 130 **S** Select Medical Corporation, Mechanicsburg, PA
Primary Contact: Robert Shannon. Canard, Chief Executive Officer
CFO: Russell W York, Vice President and Chief Financial Officer
CMO: Holland M Addison, M.D., Medical Director
CIO: Steve M Stanic, Vice President and Chief Information Officer
CHR: Lee Ann Foreman, Vice President Human Resources
Web address: www.https://belhaven.selectspecialtyhospitals.com/
**Control**: Corporation, Investor–owned (for–profit) **Service**: Acute long–term care hospital

| Staffed Beds: 25 Admissions: 319 Census: 24 Outpatient Visits: 0 Births: 0 Total Expense ($000): 13733 Payroll Expense ($000): 6235 Personnel: 118 |
|---|

✣ **SELECT SPECIALTY HOSPITAL-JACKSON (252007)**, 5903 Ridgewood Road, Suite 100, Zip 39211–3700; tel. 601/899–3800, (Nonreporting) **A**1 3 10 **F**1 107 119 **P**7 **S** Select Medical Corporation, Mechanicsburg, PA
Primary Contact: Chandler Ewing, Chief Executive Officer
CFO: Melissa Smith, Controller
CIO: Jacqueline Barnes, Manager Health Information
CHR: Vicki Watson, Manager Human Resources
Web address: www.selectspecialtyhospitals.com/company/locations/jackson.aspx
**Control**: Corporation, Investor–owned (for–profit) **Service**: Acute long–term care hospital

| Staffed Beds: 53 Admissions: 634 Census: 46 Outpatient Visits: 0 Births: 0 Total Expense ($000): 26742 Payroll Expense ($000): 12862 Personnel: 200 |
|---|

**SELECT SPECIALTY HOSP-JACKSON** See Select Specialty Hospital-Jackson

✣ **ST. DOMINIC-JACKSON MEMORIAL HOSPITAL (250048)**, 969 Lakeland Drive, Zip 39216–4606; tel. 601/200–2000, (Nonreporting) **A**1 2 3 5 10 **F**3 4 11 12 13 15 17 18 20 22 24 26 28 29 30 31 34 36 37 38 40 43 46 47 49 50 51 53 58 60 61 64 65 68 70 72 73 74 75 76 77 78 79 80 81 82 84 85 86 87 89 90 92 93 96 97 98 100 101 102 103 107 108 109 110 111 114 115 116 117 118 119 120 121 123 124 126 130 131 146 147 148 154 **P**1 4
Primary Contact: Lester K. Diamond, President
CFO: Sam Scott, Vice President Financial Services
CMO: Eric A McVey, M.D., IIIExecutive Vice President Medical Affairs and Quality
CIO: Keith Van Camp, Vice President Information Services
CHR: Frank Lenior, Vice President Human Resources
Web address: www.stdom.com
**Control**: Church operated, Nongovernment, not–for–profit **Service**: General medical and surgical

| Staffed Beds: 502 Admissions: 38228 Census: 426 Outpatient Visits: 168776 Births: 1638 Total Expense ($000): 495017 Payroll Expense ($000): 205290 Personnel: 2925 |
|---|

**UNIVERSITY HOSPITAL** See University of Mississippi Medical Center

✣ **UNIVERSITY OF MISSISSIPPI MEDICAL CENTER (250001)**, 2500 North State Street, Zip 39216–4505; tel. 601/984–1000, (Includes BLAIR E. BATSON HOSPITAL FOR CHILDREN, Mailing address: 2500 North State State Room W019, Jackson, Mississippi, Zip 39216–4500; tel. 601/984–1000; CHILDREN'S HEALTHCARE OF MISSISSIPPI, Mailing address: 2500 North State Street, Jackson, Mississippi, Zip 39216–4500; tel. 601/984–1000; Guy Giesecke, Chief Executive Officer), (Nonreporting) **A**1 2 3 5 8 10 13 **F**3 6 7 8 9 11 12 13 15 17 18 19 20 21 22 23 24 25 26 27 28 29 30 31 32 34 35 38 39 40 41 43 45 46 47 48 49 50 52 53 54 55 56 57 58 59 60 61 62 64 65 66 68 70 71 72 73 74 76 79 80 81 82 84 85 86 87 88 89 90 92 93 94 97 98 99 100 101 102 103 104 107 108 110 111 112 114 115 116 117 118 119 120 121 123 124 126 129 130 131 132 134 135 136 137 138 139 141 142 143 144 146 148 149 152 154 155 156 **P**6 **S** University Hospitals and Health System, Jackson, MS
Primary Contact: Britt Crewse, Chief Executive Officer
CFO: Dan Janicak, Chief Financial Officer
CMO: William H Cleland, M.D., Chief Medical Officer
CHR: Paula Henderson, Chief Human Resources Officer
Web address: www.umc.edu
**Control**: State, Government, Nonfederal **Service**: General medical and surgical

| Staffed Beds: 697 Admissions: 29688 Census: 580 Outpatient Visits: 623342 Births: 2271 Total Expense ($000): 868075 Payroll Expense ($000): 347284 |
|---|

**VETERANS AFFAIRS MED CENTER** See G.V. (Sonny) Montgomery Veterans Affairs Medical Center

### KEESLER AFB—Harrison County

✣ **U. S. AIR FORCE MEDICAL CENTER KEESLER**, 301 Fisher Street, Room 1A132, Zip 39534–2519; tel. 228/376–2550, (Nonreporting) **A**1 3 5 **S** Department of the Air Force, Washington, DC
Primary Contact: Colonel Thomas Harrell, M.D., Commander
COO: Brigadier GeneralJames Dougherty, Commander
CFO: MajorBrenda Yi, Director Medical Resource Management and Chief Financial Officer
CMO: ColonelJames Gasque, M.D., Chief Hospital Services
CIO: MajorSamuel Silverthorne, Chief Information Officer
CHR: MajorBrenda Yi, Director Medical Resource Management and Chief Financial Officer
Web address: www.keesler.af.mil
**Service**: General medical and surgical

| Staffed Beds: 56 |
|---|

### KOSCIUSKO—Attala County

⇑ **BAPTIST HEALTH SYSTEMS ATTALA** See Baptist Medical Center Attala

★ ⇑ **BAPTIST MEDICAL CENTER ATTALA (251336)**, 220 Highway 12 West, Zip 39090–3208, Mailing Address: P.O. Box 887, Zip 39090–0887; tel. 662/289–4311, (Nonreporting) **A**10 18 21 **F**2 3 8 15 40 45 64 65 81 89 90 93 107 108 110 114 119 127 133 148 153 **S** Baptist Memorial Health Care Corporation, Memphis, TN
Primary Contact: Robert Coleman, Chief Executive Officer
CHR: Stephanie Washington, Human Resources Director
CNO: Allison Schuler, R.N., Chief Nursing Officer
Web address: www.mbhs.org/locations/baptist-medical-center-attala/
**Control**: Other not–for–profit (including NFP Corporation) **Service**: General medical and surgical

| Staffed Beds: 25 Admissions: 467 Census: 9 Births: 0 Personnel: 118 |
|---|

### LAUREL—Jones County

★ ⇑ **SOUTH CENTRAL REGIONAL MEDICAL CENTER (250058)**, 1220 Jefferson Street, Zip 39440–4374, Mailing Address: P.O. Box 607, Zip 39441–0607; tel. 601/426–4000, (Total facility includes 248 beds in nursing home–type unit) (Nonreporting) **A**10 21 **F**3 4 7 12 13 15 17 18 20 26 28 29 30 31 32 34 35 39 40 43 44 45 48 50 51 52 53 57 59 62 63 64 65 68 70 73 74 75 76 77 78 79 81 82 85 86 87 89 90 91 92 93 100 102 104 105 107 108 110 111 115 118 119 126 128 129 130 131 132 134 135 143 144 146 147 148 152 154 157 **P**6
Primary Contact: G Douglas Higginbotham, President and Chief Executive Officer
CFO: Tom Canizaro, Vice President and Chief Financial Officer
CMO: Willus Mark Horne, M.D., Chief Medical Officer
CIO: Dell Blakeney, Vice President and Chief Information Officer
CHR: Janet Staples, Vice President Human Resources
CNO: Beth W Endom, R.N., MSN, Vice President and Chief Nursing Officer
Web address: www.scrmc.com
**Control**: County, Government, Nonfederal **Service**: General medical and surgical

| Staffed Beds: 424 Admissions: 424 Census: 358 Outpatient Visits: 144291 Births: 914 Total Expense ($000): 185855 Payroll Expense ($000): 96973 Personnel: 1811 |
|---|

**MS**

---

**Hospital, Medicare Provider Number, Address, Telephone, Approval, Facility, and Physician Codes, Health Care System**

★ American Hospital Association (AHA) membership ◯ Healthcare Facilities Accreditation Program ⇑ Center for Improvement in Healthcare Quality Accreditation
☐ The Joint Commission accreditation ◇ DNV Healthcare Inc. accreditation △ Commission on Accreditation of Rehabilitation Facilities (CARF) accreditation

## LEAKESVILLE—Greene County

**GREENE COUNTY HOSPITAL (251329)**, 1017 Jackson Avenue,
Zip 39451–9105; tel. 601/394–4139, (Nonreporting) **A**10 18 **F**40 43 107 133
Primary Contact: Richard P. Daughdrill, R.N., Administrator
CFO: Debbie Brannan, Chief Financial Officer
CMO: Jay Pinkerton, M.D., Chief of Staff
CHR: Carla Shows, Payroll Clerk
CNO: Tabatha Pinter, Director of Nursing
Web address: www.georgeregional.com
**Control**: County, Government, Nonfederal **Service**: General medical and surgical

**Staffed Beds**: 7 **Admissions**: 130 **Census**: 4 **Births**: 0 **Total Expense ($000)**: 5050 **Payroll Expense ($000)**: 2269 **Personnel**: 45

## LEXINGTON—Holmes County

**HOLMES COUNTY HOSPITAL AND CLINICS** See University of Mississippi Medical Center Holmes County

⊞ **UNIVERSITY OF MISSISSIPPI MEDICAL CENTER HOLMES COUNTY (251319)**, 239 Bowling Green Road, Zip 39095–5167; tel. 601/496–5200, (Nonreporting) **A**1 10 18 **F**3 15 29 34 40 43 50 56 57 59 64 86 87 89 93 104 107 114 119 127 130 133 146 148 149 153 **P**6 **S** University Hospitals and Health System, Jackson, MS
Primary Contact: Dodie McElmurray, FACHE, Chief Executive Officer
COO: Paige Lawrence, Assistant Administrator
CFO: Scott Whittemore, Chief Financial Officer
CMO: Mark Smothers, M.D., Chief Medical Officer
CIO: Sammuel Townsend, LAN Administrator
CHR: Claudette Hathcock, Human Resources Director
Web address: www.ummchealth.com/holmes/
**Control**: State, Government, Nonfederal **Service**: General medical and surgical

**Staffed Beds**: 25 **Admissions**: 304 **Census**: 7 **Outpatient Visits**: 15315 **Births**: 0 **Total Expense ($000)**: 13550 **Payroll Expense ($000)**: 7140 **Personnel**: 103

## LOUISVILLE—Winston County

**WINSTON CNTY COMM HOSP** See Winston Medical Center

**WINSTON MEDICAL CENTER (250027)**, 562 East Main Street,
Zip 39339–2742, Mailing Address: P.O. Box 967, Zip 39339–0967;
tel. 662/773–6211, (Total facility includes 120 beds in nursing home–type unit)
(Nonreporting) **A**10 20 **F**15 29 34 35 40 43 57 89 98 103 105 107 112 115 119 127 128 130 133 154
Primary Contact: Paul S. Black, Chief Executive Officer
Web address: www.winstonmedical.org
**Control**: Other not–for–profit (including NFP Corporation) **Service**: General medical and surgical

**Staffed Beds**: 144 **Admissions**: 1260 **Census**: 134 **Outpatient Visits**: 25256 **Births**: 0 **Total Expense ($000)**: 19649 **Payroll Expense ($000)**: 7697 **Personnel**: 298

## LUCEDALE—George County

**GEORGE COUNTY HOSPITAL** See George Regional Hospital

**GEORGE REGIONAL HOSPITAL (250036)**, 859 Winter Street, Zip 39452–6603,
Mailing Address: P.O. Box 607, Zip 39452–0607; tel. 601/947–3161, (Nonreporting)
**A**10 20 **F**3 11 13 15 18 30 34 35 40 43 45 47 48 49 53 54 57 59 65 68 70 76 77 81 82 86 87 93 97 107 108 111 119 127 129 130 133 135 146 148 **P**8
Primary Contact: Greg Havard, Chief Executive Officer
CFO: Debbie Brannan, Chief Financial Officer
CMO: Jay Pinkerton, M.D., Chief Medical Officer
CIO: Anthoney Fryfogle, Chief Information Officer
CHR: Carla Shows, Human Resource and Payroll Clerk
CNO: Tabatha Pinter, Director of Nursing
Web address: www.georgeregional.com
**Control**: County, Government, Nonfederal **Service**: General medical and surgical

**Staffed Beds**: 48 **Admissions**: 1027 **Census**: 9 **Outpatient Visits**: 53860 **Births**: 252 **Total Expense ($000)**: 24564 **Payroll Expense ($000)**: 13085 **Personnel**: 261

## MACON—Noxubee County

**NOXUBEE GENERAL HOSPITAL (251307)**, 606 North Jefferson Street,
Zip 39341–2242, Mailing Address: P.O. Box 480, Zip 39341–0480;
tel. 662/726–4231, (Total facility includes 60 beds in nursing home–type unit)
(Nonreporting) **A**10 18 **F**40 89 107 111 127 128 130 133
Primary Contact: Danny H. McKay, Administrator
Web address: www.noxubeecountyms.com/quality-of-life-noxubee-mississipp/
health-care-noxubee-mississippi/
**Control**: County, Government, Nonfederal **Service**: General medical and surgical

**Staffed Beds**: 85 **Admissions**: 514 **Census**: 63 **Outpatient Visits**: 41337 **Births**: 0 **Total Expense ($000)**: 15881 **Payroll Expense ($000)**: 8258 **Personnel**: 135

## MAGEE—Simpson County

**MAGEE GENERAL HOSPITAL (250124)**, 300 Third Avenue SE,
Zip 39111–3698; tel. 601/849–5070, (Nonreporting) **A**10 **F**15 29 35 40 43 81 89 107 108 111 119 129 130 133 146 148
Primary Contact: Gregg Gibbes, Chief Executive Officer
CMO: Kelli Smith, M.D., Chief of Staff
CIO: Kirby Craft, Chief Information Officer
CHR: Steve Beckham, Director Human Resources
CNO: Cindy McIntyre, R.N., Administrative Director Clinical Services
Web address: www.mghosp.org
**Control**: Other not–for–profit (including NFP Corporation) **Service**: General medical and surgical

**Staffed Beds**: 44 **Admissions**: 681 **Census**: 12 **Births**: 0 **Total Expense ($000)**: 14014 **Payroll Expense ($000)**: 5389 **Personnel**: 159

## MAGNOLIA—Pike County

**BEACHAM MEMORIAL HOSPITAL (250049)**, 205 North Cherry Street,
Zip 39652–2819, Mailing Address: P.O. Box 351, Zip 39652–0351;
tel. 601/783–2351, (Nonreporting) **A**10 **F**3 34 35 36 57 59 65 68 98 100 101 103 107 127 130 133 148
Primary Contact: Jason Reed, Chief Executive Officer
CMO: Lucius Lampton, M.D., Medical Director
CHR: Jackie McKenzie, Director Administrative Services
Web address: www.beachammemorial.org
**Control**: Corporation, Investor–owned (for–profit) **Service**: General medical and surgical

**Staffed Beds**: 31 **Admissions**: 1248 **Census**: 24 **Outpatient Visits**: 0 **Births**: 0 **Personnel**: 74

## MCCOMB—Pike County

★ ⇑ **SOUTHWEST MISSISSIPPI REGIONAL MEDICAL CENTER (250097)**,
215 Marion Avenue, Zip 39648–2705, Mailing Address: P.O. Box 1307,
Zip 39649–1307; tel. 601/249–5500, (Nonreporting) **A**10 19 21 **F**3 8 9 11 13 15 17 18 20 22 24 28 29 30 31 34 35 37 39 40 41 43 44 45 46 47 48 49 50 53 55 57 59 64 65 70 72 73 74 75 76 77 79 81 84 85 86 87 93 94 96 107 108 110 111 115 118 119 120 121 127 129 130 131 132 135 145 146 148 149 **P**6 **S** Southwest Health Systems, Mccomb, MS
Primary Contact: Norman M. Price, FACHE, Chief Executive Officer
COO: Richard Williams, Chief Operating Officer
CFO: Charla Rowley, Chief Financial Officer
CMO: Kevin Richardson, M.D., Chief of Staff
CIO: David Hamilton, Chief Information Officer
CHR: Don Haskins, Administrative Director Human Resources
CNO: Michelle Gough MSN, RN-BChief Nursing Officer
Web address: www.smrmc.com
**Control**: Hospital district or authority, Government, Nonfederal **Service**: General medical and surgical

**Staffed Beds**: 143 **Admissions**: 4924 **Census**: 42 **Outpatient Visits**: 97785 **Births**: 584 **Personnel**: 836

## MEADVILLE—Franklin County

**FRANKLIN COUNTY MEMORIAL HOSPITAL (251330)**, 40 Union Church Road, Zip 39653–8336, Mailing Address: P.O. Box 636, Zip 39653–0636;
tel. 601/384–5801, (Nonreporting) **A**10 18 **F**29 39 40 43 56 104 107 119 127 133 148 **P**6
Primary Contact: Mike Boleware, Administrator
Web address: www.fcmh.net
**Control**: County, Government, Nonfederal **Service**: General medical and surgical

**Staffed Beds**: 25 **Admissions**: 323 **Census**: 16 **Outpatient Visits**: 16184 **Births**: 0 **Total Expense ($000)**: 15886 **Payroll Expense ($000)**: 9832 **Personnel**: 189

## MENDENHALL—Simpson County

**SIMPSON GENERAL HOSPITAL (251317)**, 1842 Simpson Highway 149,
Zip 39114–3438; tel. 601/847–2221, (Nonreporting) **A**10 18 **F**3 11 29 30 34 35 40 43 44 54 56 57 59 61 64 65 66 68 81 85 86 87 93 98 100 101 102 103 104 105 107 114 119 127 130 132 133 134 143 146 **P**5
Primary Contact: David Welch, Chief Executive Officer
COO: Al Gary, COO
CFO: Al Gary, COO
CMO: Chip Holbrook, M.D., Chief of Staff
CIO: David Welch, Director Information Technology
CHR: Randall Neely, CEO
CNO: Sharon Burnham, Director of Nursing
Web address: www.simpsongeneralhospital.com
**Control**: Other not–for–profit (including NFP Corporation) **Service**: General medical and surgical

**Staffed Beds**: 35 **Admissions**: 666 **Census**: 16 **Outpatient Visits**: 11485 **Births**: 0 **Personnel**: 151

*Many Facility Codes have changed. Please refer to the AHA Guide Code Chart.*
© 2021 AHA Guide

MS

## MERIDIAN—Lauderdale County

☐ **ALLIANCE HEALTH CENTER (250151)**, 5000 Highway 39 North, Zip 39301–1021; tel. 601/483–6211, (Nonreporting) **A**1 3 10 **F**4 6 35 38 64 86 87 98 99 101 102 103 105 106 135 152 153 154 **P**6 **S** Universal Health Services, Inc., King of Prussia, PA
Primary Contact: Jay Shehi, Chief Executive Officer
CFO: Robert Jackson, Chief Financial Officer
CMO: Terry Jordan, M.D., Chief of Staff
CIO: Brenda Smith, Director Financial Services
CHR: Shrea Johnson, Director Human Resources
Web address: www.alliancehealthcenter.com
**Control:** Corporation, Investor–owned (for–profit) **Service:** Psychiatric

**Staffed Beds:** 154 **Admissions:** 4403 **Census:** 157 **Outpatient Visits:** 0 **Births:** 0
**Total Expense ($000):** 44844 **Payroll Expense ($000):** 12482 **Personnel:** 285

⊞ **ANDERSON REGIONAL HEALTH SYSTEM (250104)**, 2124 14th Street, Zip 39301–4040; tel. 601/553–6000, (Nonreporting) **A**1 2 3 10 19 **F**3 7 11 12 13 15 17 18 20 22 24 26 28 29 30 31 34 35 38 40 41 43 44 45 47 48 49 50 53 54 57 58 59 64 65 68 70 72 73 75 76 77 79 80 81 85 86 87 88 89 90 91 92 93 96 107 110 111 115 116 119 120 121 123 124 126 127 129 130 131 132 135 146 148 149 154 **P**7 8
Primary Contact: John G. Anderson, FACHE, President and Chief Executive Officer
CFO: Steven Brown, Vice President Finance
CMO: Scot Bell, Chief Medical Officer
CHR: Joel Windham, Vice President Human Resources
CNO: Matt Edwards, Vice President Nursing Services and Chief Nursing Officer
Web address: www.andersonregional.org
**Control:** Other not–for–profit (including NFP Corporation) **Service:** General medical and surgical

**Staffed Beds:** 260 **Admissions:** 8872 **Census:** 127 **Outpatient Visits:** 142848 **Births:** 1092 **Total Expense ($000):** 180368 **Payroll Expense ($000):** 58420 **Personnel:** 1088

⊞ △ **ANDERSON REGIONAL HEALTH SYSTEM SOUTH (250081)**, 1102 Constitution Avenue, Zip 39301–4001; tel. 601/553–6000, (Nonreporting) **A**1 7 10 **F**29 35 60 64 65 74 81 82 86 87 90 91 92 96 97 98 103 105 127 130 132 133 146 148 **P**7 8
Primary Contact: Betty Cryer, R.N., Administrator
CFO: Steven Brown, Vice President Finance
CIO: Steve Taylor, Chief Information Officer
CHR: Joel Windham, Vice President Human Resources
Web address: www.andersonregional.org
**Control:** Other not–for–profit (including NFP Corporation) **Service:** General medical and surgical

**Staffed Beds:** 69 **Admissions:** 1378 **Census:** 49 **Outpatient Visits:** 20609 **Births:** 0 **Total Expense ($000):** 19461 **Payroll Expense ($000):** 6232 **Personnel:** 172

**ANDERSON REGIONAL MEDICAL CENTER** See Anderson Regional Health System

**ANDERSON REGIONAL MEDICAL CENTER-SOUTH CAMPUS** See Anderson Regional Health System South

☐ **EAST MISSISSIPPI STATE HOSPITAL**, 1818 College Drive, Zip 39307, Mailing Address: Box 4128, West Station, Zip 39304–4128; tel. 601/482–6186, (Total facility includes 159 beds in nursing home–type unit) (Nonreporting) **A**1 5 **F**29 30 39 60 65 82 86 87 98 103 128 130 135 143 146 148 **S** Mississippi State Department of Mental Health, Jackson, MS
Primary Contact: Charles Carlisle, Director
CFO: Geri Doggett, Director Business
CMO: Gloria Gomez, M.D., Medical Director
CIO: Scotty Taylor, Information Technology Director
CHR: Shearmaine Calaway, Director Human Resources
CNO: Diane Nobles, Nurse Executive
Web address: www.emsh.state.ms.us
**Control:** State, Government, Nonfederal **Service:** Psychiatric

**Staffed Beds:** 267 **Admissions:** 503 **Census:** 255 **Outpatient Visits:** 0 **Births:** 0
**Total Expense ($000):** 52109 **Payroll Expense ($000):** 23271 **Personnel:** 716

**LAUREL WOOD CENTER** See Alliance Health Center

⊞ **REGENCY HOSPITAL OF MERIDIAN (252006)**, 1102 Constitution Avenue, 2nd Floor, Zip 39301–4001; tel. 601/484–7900, (Nonreporting) **A**1 10 **F**1 **S** Select Medical Corporation, Mechanicsburg, PA
Primary Contact: William Heath, Chief Executive Officer
Web address: www.regencyhospital.com
**Control:** Corporation, Investor–owned (for–profit) **Service:** Acute long–term care hospital

**Staffed Beds:** 40 **Admissions:** 235 **Census:** 19 **Outpatient Visits:** 0 **Births:** 0
**Total Expense ($000):** 9629 **Payroll Expense ($000):** 4589 **Personnel:** 80

★ ⇑ **RUSH FOUNDATION HOSPITAL (250069)**, 1314 19th Avenue, Zip 39301–4195; tel. 601/483–0011, (Nonreporting) **A**3 10 19 21 **F**13 15 20 29 35 39 40 43 51 70 72 73 76 77 81 82 86 89 90 93 107 108 118 119 130 131 146 147 148 **P**3 8 **S** Rush Health Systems, Meridian, MS
Primary Contact: Larkin Kennedy, Chief Executive Officer
COO: Jason Payne, Executive Vice President and Chief Operating Officer
CMO: W Scot Bell, M.D., Chief Medical Officer
CIO: Mike Peavy, Chief Information Officer
CHR: Donnie Smith, Director Human Resources
CNO: Casey Bland, Director of Nursing
Web address: www.rushhealthsystems.org/rfh/
**Control:** Other not–for–profit (including NFP Corporation) **Service:** General medical and surgical

**Staffed Beds:** 182 **Admissions:** 5991 **Census:** 66 **Outpatient Visits:** 155343 **Births:** 988 **Personnel:** 709

**SPECIALTY HOSPITAL OF MERIDIAN (252004)**, 1314 19th Avenue, Zip 39301–4116; tel. 601/703–4211, (Nonreporting) **A**3 10 **F**1 3 18 20 34 50 57 59 68 74 78 79 85 87 94 96 112 133 145 148 149 **S** Rush Health Systems, Meridian, MS
Primary Contact: Kawanda Johnson, Vice President
CFO: David Butler, Chief Financial Officer
CMO: John Johnston, Chief Medical Officer
CIO: Mike Peavy, Chief Information Officer
CHR: Scott Vincent, Chief Human Resource Officer
CNO: Ashley Roy, Vice President of Nursing Services
Web address: www.specialtyhospitalofmeridian.com/shm/
**Control:** Other not–for–profit (including NFP Corporation) **Service:** Acute long–term care hospital

**Staffed Beds:** 49 **Admissions:** 559 **Census:** 37 **Outpatient Visits:** 0 **Births:** 0 **Personnel:** 77

## MONTICELLO—Lawrence County

**LAWRENCE COUNTY HOSPITAL (251305)**, Highway 84 East, Zip 39654–0788, Mailing Address: P.O. Box 788, Zip 39654–0788; tel. 601/587–4051, (Nonreporting) **A**10 18 **F**3 18 34 40 43 50 57 59 64 87 107 115 119 127 133 149 153 **P**5 **S** Southwest Health Systems, Mccomb, MS
Primary Contact: Phillip W. Langston, Administrator
CFO: Jennifer Moak, Business Office Manager
Web address: www.smrmc.com
**Control:** County, Government, Nonfederal **Service:** General medical and surgical

**Staffed Beds:** 25 **Admissions:** 437 **Census:** 7 **Outpatient Visits:** 9243 **Births:** 0 **Total Expense ($000):** 11020 **Payroll Expense ($000):** 6148 **Personnel:** 108

## MORTON—Scott County

**SCOTT REGIONAL HOSPITAL (251323)**, 317 Highway 13 South, Zip 39117–3353, Mailing Address: P.O. Box 259, Zip 39117–0259; tel. 601/732–6301, (Nonreporting) **A**10 18 **F**3 30 35 40 43 55 57 77 81 89 93 107 111 112 114 119 127 130 133 **S** Rush Health Systems, Meridian, MS
Primary Contact: Heather Davis, Administrator
CFO: Paul S Black, Chief Financial Officer
CHR: Amy Sugg, Director Human Resources
Web address: www.scottregional.org/srh/
**Control:** Other not–for–profit (including NFP Corporation) **Service:** General medical and surgical

**Staffed Beds:** 25 **Admissions:** 257 **Census:** 10 **Outpatient Visits:** 9930 **Births:** 1 **Total Expense ($000):** 8599 **Payroll Expense ($000):** 3474 **Personnel:** 82

## NATCHEZ—Adams County

⊞ △ **MERIT HEALTH NATCHEZ (250084)**, 54 Seargent 'S' Prentiss Drive, Zip 39120–4726; tel. 601/443–2100, (Nonreporting) **A**1 7 10 20 **F**3 13 15 17 18 26 28 29 35 40 43 45 46 47 60 70 73 74 75 76 77 78 79 81 82 85 86 87 88 89 90 92 93 94 98 103 106 107 108 109 110 111 112 114 115 116 118 119 126 129 130 131 132 134 146 147 156 **P**5 **S** Community Health Systems, Inc., Franklin, TN
Primary Contact: Lance Boyd, Chief Executive Officer
CFO: Charles Mack, Vice President Finance and Chief Financial Officer
CMO: Leslie England, Chief of Staff
CIO: Leslie Makoro, Director Information management Systems
CHR: Jean E Juchnowicz, Director Human Resources
CNO: Lee Hinson, Chief Nursing Officer
Web address: www.natchezregional.com
**Control:** Corporation, Investor–owned (for–profit) **Service:** General medical and surgical

**Staffed Beds:** 136 **Admissions:** 4460 **Census:** 64 **Outpatient Visits:** 52582 **Births:** 737 **Total Expense ($000):** 87308 **Payroll Expense ($000):** 25953 **Personnel:** 420

**NATCHEZ REGIONAL MEDICAL CENTER** See Merit Health Natchez

MS

---

**Hospital, Medicare Provider Number, Address, Telephone, Approval, Facility, and Physician Codes, Health Care System**

★ American Hospital Association (AHA) membership
☐ The Joint Commission accreditation
○ Healthcare Facilities Accreditation Program
◇ DNV Healthcare Inc. accreditation
⇑ Center for Improvement in Healthcare Quality Accreditation
△ Commission on Accreditation of Rehabilitation Facilities (CARF) accreditation

## NEW ALBANY—Union County

⊠ **BAPTIST MEMORIAL HOSPITAL-UNION COUNTY (250006)**, 200 Highway 30 West, Zip 38652–3112; tel. 662/538–7631, (Nonreporting) **A**1 10 **F**3 11 13 15 17 29 30 31 34 35 40 45 51 57 59 64 68 70 75 76 77 78 79 80 81 84 85 86 87 89 90 91 93 96 107 108 110 111 114 115 116 117 118 119 124 130 132 133 135 146 147 148 149 154 156 **P**3 **S** Baptist Memorial Health Care Corporation, Memphis, TN
Primary Contact: James Grantham, Administrator and Chief Executive Officer
CFO: Kim High, Chief Financial Officer
CMO: H F Mason, M.D., Chief Medical Officer
CIO: Missy Coltharp, Director
CHR: Lori Goode, Director Human Resources
CNO: Randy White, Chief Nursing Officer
Web address: www.baptistonline.org/union-county/
**Control**: Other not–for–profit (including NFP Corporation) **Service**: General medical and surgical

| Staffed Beds: 101 Admissions: 2848 Census: 24 Outpatient Visits: 63085 Births: 856 Total Expense ($000): 54214 Payroll Expense ($000): 18395 |

## OCEAN SPRINGS—Jackson County

**OCEAN SPRINGS HOSPITAL** See Singing River Health System, Pascagoula

## OLIVE BRANCH—Desoto County

**CHARTER PARKWOOD HLTH SYSTEM** See Parkwood Behavioral Health System

★ ⇑ **METHODIST HEALTHCARE OLIVE BRANCH HOSPITAL (250167)**, 4250 Bethel Road, Zip 38654–8737; tel. 662/932–9000, (Nonreporting) **A**10 21 **F**3 11 13 15 18 20 22 29 34 35 40 43 44 45 46 47 48 49 50 59 60 64 68 70 71 74 76 78 79 80 81 85 86 87 88 90 91 92 93 96 107 108 109 110 111 112 114 115 119 130 132 135 145 146 147 149 150 154 156 157 **P**8 **S** Methodist Le Bonheur Healthcare, Memphis, TN
Primary Contact: David G. Baytos, President
CFO: Kris Sanders, Chief Financial Officer
CHR: Robin Mathis, Director Human Resources
CNO: Annelise Jensen, Vice President and Chief Nursing Officer
Web address: www.methodisthealth.org/olivebranch
**Control**: Other not–for–profit (including NFP Corporation) **Service**: General medical and surgical

| Staffed Beds: 53 Admissions: 3918 Census: 36 Births: 693 Total Expense ($000): 64910 Payroll Expense ($000): 25684 Personnel: 418 |

⇑ **METHODIST OLIVE BRANCH HOSPITAL** See Methodist Healthcare Olive Branch Hospital

☐ **PARKWOOD BEHAVIORAL HEALTH SYSTEM (254005)**, 8135 Goodman Road, Zip 38654–2103; tel. 662/895–4900, (Total facility includes 40 beds in nursing home–type unit) (Nonreporting) **A**1 10 **F**3 4 5 29 30 34 38 57 59 64 98 99 101 102 103 104 105 106 128 130 151 152 153 154 **P**5 **S** Universal Health Services, Inc., King of Prussia, PA
Primary Contact: Vincent Brummett, Chief Executive Officer
CFO: David Denegri, Chief Financial Officer
CMO: Paul King, M.D., Medical Director
CHR: Julie Dorman, Human Resources Director
CNO: Alicia Plunkett, Chief Nurse Executive
Web address: www.parkwoodbhs.com
**Control**: Corporation, Investor–owned (for–profit) **Service**: Psychiatric

| Staffed Beds: 148 Admissions: 3026 Census: 107 Outpatient Visits: 3649 Births: 0 Total Expense ($000): 17809 Payroll Expense ($000): 8639 Personnel: 162 |

## OXFORD—Lafayette County

**BAPTIST MEM HOSP-NORTH MISS** See Baptist Memorial Hospital-North Mississippi

⊠ △ **BAPTIST MEMORIAL HOSPITAL-NORTH MISSISSIPPI (250034)**, 2301 South Lamar Boulevard, Zip 38655–5373, Mailing Address: P.O. Box 946, Zip 38655–6002; tel. 662/232–8100, (Nonreporting) **A**1 2 7 10 19 **F**3 8 9 11 12 13 15 17 18 20 22 24 26 28 29 30 31 34 35 40 43 45 46 47 48 49 51 54 57 58 59 64 65 70 73 74 76 78 79 81 83 84 85 86 87 90 91 93 96 107 108 110 111 115 116 117 118 119 120 121 123 124 126 129 130 132 146 148 154 **S** Baptist Memorial Health Care Corporation, Memphis, TN
Primary Contact: William C. Henning, Administrator and Chief Executive Officer
CFO: Dana Williams, Chief Financial Officer
CMO: Dennis P Morgan, Chief of Staff
CIO: Linda Britt, Director Information Systems
CHR: Josh Lowery, Director of Human Resources
CNO: Mark Ottens, Chief Nursing Officer
Web address: www.baptistonline.org/north-mississippi/
**Control**: Other not–for–profit (including NFP Corporation) **Service**: General medical and surgical

| Staffed Beds: 184 Admissions: 9890 Census: 105 Outpatient Visits: 100634 Births: 885 Personnel: 925 |

## PASCAGOULA—Jackson County

△ ⇑ **SINGING RIVER HEALTH SYSTEM (250040)**, 2809 Denny Avenue, Zip 39581–5301; tel. 228/809–5000, (Includes OCEAN SPRINGS HOSPITAL, Mailing address: 3109 Bienville Boulevard, Ocean Springs, Mississippi, Zip 39564–4361; tel. 228/818–1111; Heath Thompson, R.N., Administrator; SINGING RIVER HOSPITAL, Mailing address: 2809 Denny Avenue, Pascagoula, Mississippi, Zip 39581–5301; tel. 228/809–5000; Laurin St. Pe', Administrator - Singing River Hospital), (Nonreporting) **A**2 3 7 10 21
Primary Contact: Lee Bond, Chief Executive Officer
CFO: Sandra Albrecht, Interim Chief Financial Officer
CMO: Randy Roth, Chief Medical Officer
CHR: Craig Summerlin, Chief Human Resources Officer
CNO: Susan Russell, Chief Nursing Officer
Web address: www.singingriverhealthsystem.com
**Control**: County, Government, Nonfederal **Service**: General medical and surgical

| Staffed Beds: 361 |

⇑ **SINGING RIVER HOSPITAL SYSTEM** See Singing River Health System

## PHILADELPHIA—Neshoba County

⇑ **CHOCTAW HEALTH CENTER (250127)**, 210 Hospital Circle, Zip 39350–6781; tel. 601/656–2211, (Nonreporting) **A**10 21
Primary Contact: Tina Scott, Acting Health Director
CFO: Myrna Hancock, Director Financial Services
CMO: Juantina Johnson, Chief of Staff
CIO: Raymond Willis, IT Manager
CHR: Anna Denson, Human Resources Specialist
CNO: Regina Isaac, Director of Nursing
Web address: www.choctaw.org
**Control**: Public Health Service other than 47, Government, federal **Service**: General medical and surgical

| Staffed Beds: 26 |

★ ⇑ **NESHOBA COUNTY GENERAL HOSPITAL (250043)**, 1001 Holland Avenue, Zip 39350–2161, Mailing Address: P.O. Box 648, Zip 39350–0648; tel. 601/663–1200, (Total facility includes 160 beds in nursing home–type unit) (Nonreporting) **A**10 20 21 **F**3 6 7 11 15 29 31 32 34 38 40 43 45 54 57 59 64 65 78 81 82 89 90 92 93 96 98 103 104 106 107 108 110 111 115 116 118 119 127 128 129 130 132 133 143 144 146 148 149 153 154
Primary Contact: Lee McCall, Chief Executive Officer
CFO: Scott McNair, Chief Financial Officer
CMO: Heather Cannon, M.D., Medical Director
CHR: Hedda Stewart, Director Human Resources
CNO: Scott Breazeale, Chief Nursing Officer
Web address: www.neshobageneral.com
**Control**: County, Government, Nonfederal **Service**: General medical and surgical

| Staffed Beds: 208 Admissions: 1934 Census: 181 Outpatient Visits: 71111 Births: 0 Total Expense ($000): 39102 Payroll Expense ($000): 19550 Personnel: 504 |

## PICAYUNE—Pearl River County

**CROSBY MEMORIAL HOSPITAL** See Highland Community Hospital

**HIGHLAND COMMUNITY HOSPITAL (250117)**, 130 Highland Parkway, Zip 39466–5574, Mailing Address: P.O. Box 909, Zip 39466–0909; tel. 601/358–9400, (Nonreporting) **A**10 **F**3 11 13 15 18 29 34 40 41 43 44 45 46 50 57 59 64 65 70 75 76 81 85 86 87 89 93 96 102 104 107 108 110 111 114 118 119 127 130 131 132 133 135 146 147 148 154 156
Primary Contact: Bryan K. Maxie, Administrator
CMO: Robert Lopez, Chief Medical Officer
CHR: Cynthia Render-Leach, Director Human Resources
CNO: Kim Varnado, R.N., Chief Nursing Officer
Web address: www.highlandch.com
**Control**: County, Government, Nonfederal **Service**: General medical and surgical

| Staffed Beds: 49 Admissions: 1765 Census: 23 Outpatient Visits: 93658 Births: 279 Total Expense ($000): 39114 Payroll Expense ($000): 15230 Personnel: 261 |

*Many Facility Codes have changed. Please refer to the AHA Guide Code Chart.*

## PONTOTOC—Pontotoc County

☒ **NORTH MISSISSIPPI MEDICAL CENTER-PONTOTOC (251308)**, 176 South Main Street, Zip 38863–3311, Mailing Address: P.O. Box 790, Zip 38863–0790; tel. 662/488–7640, (Total facility includes 44 beds in nursing home–type unit) (Nonreporting) **A**1 10 18 **F**3 11 15 34 35 40 43 57 65 68 82 83 84 86 87 93 104 107 114 119 127 128 130 133 146 **S** North Mississippi Health Services, Inc., Tupelo, MS
Primary Contact: Leslia Carter, Administrator
CFO: M Denise Heard, Director Business Services
CHR: P. Marie Barnes, Director, Human Resources
CNO: Cathy Waldrop, Director, Hospital Nursing Services
Web address: www.nmhs.net
**Control:** Other not–for–profit (including NFP Corporation) **Service:** General medical and surgical

**Staffed Beds:** 69 **Admissions:** 433 **Census:** 59 **Outpatient Visits:** 37555 **Births:** 0 **Personnel:** 235

**NORTH MISSISSIPPI MEDICAL CENTER-PONTOTOC HOSPITAL AND NURSING HOME** See North Mississippi Medical Center-Pontotoc

## POPLARVILLE—Pearl River County

**PEARL RIVER COUNTY HOSPITAL (251333)**, 305 West Moody Street, Zip 39470–7338, Mailing Address: P.O. Box 392, Zip 39470–0392; tel. 601/795–4543, (Nonreporting) **A**10 18 **F**3 35 40 43 64 65 90 93 107 119 127 128 130 133 143 146
Primary Contact: James Williams, Chief Executive Officer
CNO: Lisa Brown, Director of Nursing
Web address: www.prc-med.com/
**Control:** County, Government, Nonfederal **Service:** General medical and surgical

**Staffed Beds:** 18 **Admissions:** 257 **Census:** 9 **Births:** 0 **Total Expense ($000):** 17412 **Payroll Expense ($000):** 10085 **Personnel:** 208

## PORT GIBSON—Claiborne County

★ **CLAIBORNE COUNTY MEDICAL CENTER (251320)**, 123 McComb Avenue, Zip 39150–2915, Mailing Address: P.O. Box 1004, Zip 39150–1004; tel. 601/437–5141, (Nonreporting) **A**10 18 **F**40 43 86 89 98 100 101 103 104 105 106 107 119 130 133 146
Primary Contact: Ada Ratliff, Chief Executive Officer
CFO: Linda Caho-Mooney, Chief Financial Officer
CIO: Ada Ratliff, Chief Information Officer
**Control:** County, Government, Nonfederal **Service:** General medical and surgical

**Staffed Beds:** 22 **Admissions:** 595 **Census:** 14 **Outpatient Visits:** 7360 **Births:** 0 **Total Expense ($000):** 11013 **Payroll Expense ($000):** 4396 **Personnel:** 130

**PATIENT'S CHOICE MEDICAL CENTER OF CLAIBORNE COUNTY** See Claiborne County Medical Center

## PRENTISS—Jefferson Davis County

★ **JEFFERSON DAVIS COMMUNITY HOSPITAL (251326)**, 1102 Rose Street, Zip 39474–5200, Mailing Address: P.O. Box 1288, Zip 39474–1288; tel. 601/792–4276, (Total facility includes 55 beds in nursing home–type unit) (Nonreporting) **A**10 18 **F**3 29 32 34 35 39 40 43 53 57 59 64 65 66 68 87 89 97 104 107 114 119 127 128 130 133 148 149 153 154
Primary Contact: Alaina Cedillo, Administrator
CHR: Diane Daughdrill, Director Human Resources
Web address: www.https://www.forresthealth.org/our-locations/jefferson-davis-community-hospital/
**Control:** County, Government, Nonfederal **Service:** General medical and surgical

**Staffed Beds:** 80 **Admissions:** 228 **Census:** 51 **Outpatient Visits:** 12093 **Births:** 0 **Total Expense ($000):** 11393 **Payroll Expense ($000):** 4700 **Personnel:** 112

**PRENTISS REG HOSP & CARE FACIL** See Jefferson Davis Community Hospital

## PURVIS—Lamar County

☐ **SOUTH MISSISSIPPI STATE HOSPITAL (254008)**, 823 Highway 589, Zip 39475–4194; tel. 601/794–0100, (Nonreporting) **A**1 10 **S** Mississippi State Department of Mental Health, Jackson, MS
Primary Contact: Sabrina Young, Director
CFO: Andy Tucker, Chief Financial Officer
CMO: Allen Harris, M.D., Clinical Director
CIO: Sabrina Young, Administrative Support Director
CHR: Kelly Reid, Human Resources Director
CNO: Pam Brinson, Nurse Executive
Web address: www.smsh.ms.gov/
**Control:** State, Government, Nonfederal **Service:** Psychiatric

**Staffed Beds:** 50

## QUITMAN—Clarke County

**H. C. WATKINS MEMORIAL HOSPITAL (251316)**, 605 South Archusa Avenue, Zip 39355–2331; tel. 601/776–6925, (Nonreporting) **A**10 18 **F**29 34 40 43 57 59 68 89 104 107 114 119 127 129 130 133 153 154 **P**6 **S** Rush Health Systems, Meridian, MS
Primary Contact: Michael Nester, Administrator
CFO: Paul S Black, Controller
CMO: O Wayne Byrd, M.D., Chief of Staff
CIO: Melinda Smith, Chief Information Systems
CHR: Leigh Moore, Administrative Assistant Human Resources
Web address: www.watkinsmemorialhospital.com/hcwmh
**Control:** Other not–for–profit (including NFP Corporation) **Service:** General medical and surgical

**Staffed Beds:** 25 **Admissions:** 336 **Census:** 9 **Outpatient Visits:** 18670 **Births:** 0 **Personnel:** 115

## RALEIGH—Smith County

**PATIENTS CHOICE MEDICAL CENTER OF SMITH COUNTY (250163)**, 347 Magnolia Drive, Zip 39153–6011; tel. 601/782–9997, (Nonreporting) **A**10 **F**98 101 103 104 130 **P**6
Primary Contact: Tim Cockrell, Chief Executive Officer
**Control:** Corporation, Investor–owned (for–profit) **Service:** General medical and surgical

**Staffed Beds:** 20 **Admissions:** 388 **Census:** 14 **Outpatient Visits:** 0 **Births:** 0 **Personnel:** 31

## RICHTON—Perry County

**PERRY COUNTY GENERAL HOSPITAL (251306)**, 206 Bay Avenue, Zip 39476–2941; tel. 601/788–6316, (Nonreporting) **A**10 18 **F**3 34 40 57 59 64 65 93 107 119 127 130 133
Primary Contact: David Paris, Chief Executive Officer
Web address: www.pcghospital.com/
**Control:** Corporation, Investor–owned (for–profit) **Service:** General medical and surgical

**Staffed Beds:** 22 **Admissions:** 109 **Census:** 4 **Outpatient Visits:** 11258 **Births:** 0 **Total Expense ($000):** 4550 **Payroll Expense ($000):** 3174 **Personnel:** 55

## RIPLEY—Tippah County

★ **TIPPAH COUNTY HOSPITAL (251337)**, 1005 City Avenue North, Zip 38663–1414, Mailing Address: P.O. Box 499, Zip 38663–0499; tel. 662/837–9221, (Total facility includes 40 beds in nursing home–type unit) (Nonreporting) **A**10 18 **F**29 40 43 53 81 90 97 107 119 127 128 130 133 **P**1
Primary Contact: Patrick Chapman, Ed.D., Chief Executive Officer
CFO: Stephanie McAlister, Controller
CMO: Troy Cappleman, M.D., Chief of Staff
CHR: Heather Taylor, Human Resources Manager
CNO: Carol Anne Hurt, Chief Nursing Officer
Web address: www.tippahcountyhospital.com/
**Control:** County, Government, Nonfederal **Service:** General medical and surgical

**Staffed Beds:** 65 **Admissions:** 706 **Census:** 45 **Outpatient Visits:** 14949 **Births:** 0 **Total Expense ($000):** 12548 **Payroll Expense ($000):** 4907 **Personnel:** 195

**MS**

---

**Hospital, Medicare Provider Number, Address, Telephone, Approval, Facility, and Physician Codes, Health Care System**

★ American Hospital Association (AHA) membership    ○ Healthcare Facilities Accreditation Program    ⇑ Center for Improvement in Healthcare Quality Accreditation
☐ The Joint Commission accreditation    ◇ DNV Healthcare Inc. accreditation    △ Commission on Accreditation of Rehabilitation Facilities (CARF) accreditation

## ROLLING FORK—Sharkey County

**SHARKEY-ISSAQUENA COMMUNITY HOSPITAL (251338)**, 108 South Fourth Street, Zip 39159–5146, Mailing Address: P.O. Box 339, Zip 39159–0339; tel. 662/873–4395, (Nonreporting) **A**10 18 **F**40 98 103 104 105 107 133
Primary Contact: Jerry Keever, Administrator
**Control**: County, Government, Nonfederal **Service**: General medical and surgical

**Staffed Beds**: 29 **Admissions**: 480 **Census**: 12 **Births**: 0 **Total Expense ($000)**: 12641 **Payroll Expense ($000)**: 5195 **Personnel**: 76

## RULEVILLE—Sunflower County

**NORTH SUNFLOWER CNTY HOSPITAL** See North Sunflower Medical Center

★ **NORTH SUNFLOWER MEDICAL CENTER (251318)**, 840 North Oak Avenue, Zip 38771–3227, Mailing Address: P.O. Box 369, Zip 38771–0369; tel. 662/756–2711, (Total facility includes 60 beds in nursing home–type unit) (Nonreporting) **A**10 18 **F**3 15 18 28 29 30 34 35 39 40 43 44 45 47 50 53 54 56 57 59 63 64 65 74 75 77 81 82 84 85 87 90 92 93 96 97 98 103 104 107 110 111 115 119 127 128 129 130 133 143 145 147 149 153 154
Primary Contact: Billy Marlow, Executive Director and Administrator
COO: Rodney Clark, Chief Operating Officer
CFO: Daniel Ceja, Interim Chief Financial Officer
CMO: Ronald Brent Roberts, M.D., Chief of Medical Staff
CIO: Roger Goss, Chief Information Officer
CHR: Robbie Taylor, Director Human Resources
CNO: Hannah Barrett, Director of Nursing
Web address: www.northsunflower.com
**Control**: County, Government, Nonfederal **Service**: General medical and surgical

**Staffed Beds**: 95 **Admissions**: 1430 **Census**: 92 **Outpatient Visits**: 29836 **Births**: 0 **Total Expense ($000)**: 57684 **Payroll Expense ($000)**: 26196 **Personnel**: 463

## SENATOBIA—Tate County

**NORTH OAK REGIONAL MEDICAL CENTER (250126)**, 401 Getwell Drive, Zip 38668–2213, Mailing Address: P.O. Box 648, Zip 38668–0648; tel. 662/562–3100, (Nonreporting) **A**10
Primary Contact: Philip S. Hanna, Chief Executive Officer
CHR: Olga Burris, Human Resource/Executive Assistant
CNO: Pam Ayers, Chief Nursing Officer
Web address: www.northoakregional.com/
**Control**: Corporation, Investor–owned (for–profit) **Service**: General medical and surgical

**Staffed Beds**: 41

**SENATOBIA COMMUNITY HOSPITAL** See North Oak Regional Medical Center

## SOUTHAVEN—Desoto County

⊞ △ **BAPTIST MEMORIAL HOSPITAL-DESOTO (250141)**, 7601 Southcrest Parkway, Zip 38671–4742; tel. 662/772–4000, (Nonreporting) **A**1 3 7 10 **F**3 8 11 13 15 17 18 20 22 24 26 28 29 30 31 35 40 43 44 45 46 47 48 49 50 57 59 60 68 70 73 74 75 76 77 79 80 81 82 84 85 86 87 90 93 96 107 108 109 110 111 114 115 116 117 118 119 120 121 123 124 126 129 130 131 132 135 143 144 146 147 148 154 156 **P**7 **S** Baptist Memorial Health Care Corporation, Memphis, TN
Primary Contact: Brian Hogan, Chief Executive Officer
CFO: Joe McWherter, Chief Financial Officer
CMO: Joann Wood, M.D., Chief Medical Officer
CHR: Walter Banks, Director Human Resources
Web address: www.baptistonline.org/desoto/
**Control**: Other not–for–profit (including NFP Corporation) **Service**: General medical and surgical

**Staffed Beds**: 229 **Admissions**: 16582 **Census**: 225 **Outpatient Visits**: 130325 **Births**: 1262 **Personnel**: 1544

## STARKVILLE—Oktibbeha County

★ ⇧ **OCH REGIONAL MEDICAL CENTER (250050)**, 400 Hospital Road, Zip 39759–2163, Mailing Address: P.O. Box 1506, Zip 39760–1506; tel. 662/323–4320, (Nonreporting) **A**10 21 **F**3 7 11 13 15 17 28 29 32 34 35 40 41 43 45 47 48 51 53 57 59 61 64 65 70 73 74 75 76 77 79 81 82 87 88 89 90 93 94 97 98 107 108 110 111 114 115 118 119 126 130 131 132 133 135 146 147 149 156 **P**6
Primary Contact: James H. Jackson Jr, Chief Executive Officer
COO: Mike Andrews, Associate Administrator and Chief Operating Officer
CFO: Susan Russell, Chief Financial Officer
CMO: W. Todd Smith, M.D., Chief Medical Officer
CIO: Charles Greene, Chief Information Technology Officer
CHR: Mike Andrews, Associate Administrator and Chief Operating Officer
CNO: Michelle Welander, FACHE, R.N., Chief Nursing Officer
Web address: www.och.org
**Control**: County, Government, Nonfederal **Service**: General medical and surgical

**Staffed Beds**: 96 **Admissions**: 2218 **Census**: 21 **Outpatient Visits**: 231398 **Births**: 964 **Total Expense ($000)**: 71327 **Payroll Expense ($000)**: 35238 **Personnel**: 614

⇧ **OKTIBBEHA COUNTY HOSPITAL** See Och Regional Medical Center

## TUPELO—Lee County

☐ **NORTH MISSISSIPPI STATE HOSPITAL (254009)**, 1937 Briar Ridge Road, Zip 38804–5963; tel. 662/690–4200, (Nonreporting) **A**1 10 **F**3 29 30 34 87 98 101 130 143 146 **S** Mississippi State Department of Mental Health, Jackson, MS
Primary Contact: Paul A. Callens, Ph.D., Director
CFO: Joe Rials, Director Fiscal Services
CMO: Ken Lippincott, M.D., Chief of Staff
CIO: James Wilhite, Director Systems Information
Web address: www.nmsh.state.ms.us
**Control**: State, Government, Nonfederal **Service**: Psychiatric

**Staffed Beds**: 50 **Admissions**: 383 **Census**: 42 **Outpatient Visits**: 0 **Births**: 0 **Personnel**: 102

## TYLERTOWN—Walthall County

★ **WALTHALL COUNTY GENERAL HOSPITAL (251324)**, 100 Hospital Drive, Zip 39667–2099; tel. 601/876–2122, (Nonreporting) **A**10 18 **F**3 34 40 43 57 59 64 65 66 68 81 85 89 92 93 107 111 114 119 127 146 148 149 154
Primary Contact: TaDren Kennedy, Administrator
Web address: www.co.walthall.ms.us/walthall-general-hospital.html
**Control**: County, Government, Nonfederal **Service**: General medical and surgical

**Staffed Beds**: 25 **Admissions**: 181 **Census**: 4 **Outpatient Visits**: 16765 **Births**: 0 **Total Expense ($000)**: 8179 **Payroll Expense ($000)**: 4103 **Personnel**: 89

## UNION—Newton County

**ALLIANCE-LAIRD HOSPITAL** See Laird Hospital

**LAIRD HOSPITAL (251322)**, 25117 Highway 15, Zip 39365–9099; tel. 601/774–8214, (Nonreporting) **A**5 10 18 **F**15 29 35 40 43 81 87 89 93 104 107 111 119 127 130 132 133 146 **S** Rush Health Systems, Meridian, MS
Primary Contact: Thomas G. Bartlett III, Administrator
COO: Morris A Reece, EVP/COO
CFO: Jennifer Flint, Chief Financial Officer
CMO: John Mutziger, M.D., Chief Medical Officer
CIO: Angela Sherrill, Chief Information Officer
CHR: Donnie Smith, Chief Human Resources Officer
CNO: Pam Rigdon, Director Nursing
Web address: www.lairdhospital.com/lh/
**Control**: Other not–for–profit (including NFP Corporation) **Service**: General medical and surgical

**Staffed Beds**: 25 **Admissions**: 693 **Census**: 30 **Outpatient Visits**: 16008 **Births**: 0 **Total Expense ($000)**: 14054 **Payroll Expense ($000)**: 5663 **Personnel**: 262

## VICKSBURG—Warren County

**KPC PROMISE HOSPITAL OF VICKSBURG (252008)**, 1111 North Frontage Road, 2nd Floor, Zip 39180–5102; tel. 601/619–3526, (Data for 108 days) (Nonreporting) **A**10 **F**1 3 11 29 77 148 **S** KPC Healthcare, Inc., Santa Ana, CA
Primary Contact: Kiley P. Cedotal, FACHE, Chief Executive Officer
COO: Dawn Posey, Chief Operating Officer
CFO: Christopher A Stegall, Regional Chief Financial Officer and Chief Operating Officer
CMO: Daniel Edney, M.D., Chief of Staff
CIO: Barbara Whiting, Director Health Information Management
CHR: Debbie Carson, Director Human Resources
Web address: www.vicksburg.kpcph.com/
**Control**: Corporation, Investor–owned (for–profit) **Service**: Acute long–term care hospital

**Staffed Beds**: 27 **Admissions**: 87 **Census**: 25 **Outpatient Visits**: 0 **Births**: 0 **Total Expense ($000)**: 2892 **Payroll Expense ($000)**: 1365 **Personnel**: 50

**KPC PROMISE OF VICKSBURG** See Kpc Promise Hospital of Vicksburg

*Many Facility Codes have changed. Please refer to the AHA Guide Code Chart.* © 2021 AHA Guide

**MS**

✠ **MERIT HEALTH RIVER REGION (250031)**, 2100 Highway 61 North,
Zip 39183–8211, Mailing Address: P.O. Box 590, Zip 39181–0590;
tel. 601/883–5000, (Includes RIVER REGION WEST CAMPUS, Mailing address:
1111 North Frontage Road, Vicksburg, Mississippi, Zip 39180–5102;
tel. 601/883–5000), (Nonreporting) **A**1 10 **F**3 4 11 13 15 17 18 19 20 22 24 28
29 34 35 38 39 40 43 49 50 51 56 59 60 64 68 70 73 75 76 77 78 81 82 87
89 90 93 97 98 99 103 107 108 110 111 115 118 119 126 127 130 131 132
146 147 149 151 **S** Community Health Systems, Inc., Franklin, TN
Primary Contact: Benjamin Richaud, Interim Chief Executive Officer
CFO: John Milazzo, Chief Financial Officer
CMO: W Briggs Hopson, M.D., Clinical Medical Director
CIO: J B White, Director Information Systems
CHR: Hal Harrington, Vice President Human Resources
Web address: www.riverregion.com
**Control**: Corporation, Investor–owned (for–profit) **Service**: General medical and
surgical

**Staffed Beds: 361 Admissions: 7186 Census: 110 Births: 485 Total
Expense ($000): 145249 Payroll Expense ($000): 34240 Personnel: 795**

**RIVER REGION MEDICAL CENTER** See Merit Health River Region

**VICKSBURG MEDICAL CENTER** See River Region West Campus

### WATER VALLEY—Yalobusha County

**YALOBUSHA GENERAL HOSPITAL (250061)**, 630 South Main,
Zip 38965–3468, Mailing Address: P.O. Box 728, Zip 38965–0728;
tel. 662/473–1411, (Total facility includes 122 beds in nursing home–type unit)
(Nonreporting) **A**10 **F**3 7 15 29 32 33 59 65 107 110 114 119 127 128 130
133 143 146 153 154 **P**6
Primary Contact: Terry Varner, Administrator
COO: Ashlee Langdon, Controller
CHR: Katie Rotenberry-Baggett, Administrative Assistant and Human Resources
Web address: www.yalobushageneral.com/
**Control**: County, Government, Nonfederal **Service**: General medical and surgical

**Staffed Beds: 148 Admissions: 927 Census: 125 Births: 0 Total Expense
($000): 25989 Payroll Expense ($000): 15806 Personnel: 213**

### WAYNESBORO—Wayne County

⇑ **WAYNE GENERAL HOSPITAL (250077)**, 950 Matthew Drive, Zip 39367–2590,
Mailing Address: P.O. Box 1249, Zip 39367–1249; tel. 601/735–5151,
(Nonreporting) **A**3 10 20 21 **F**3 7 11 13 15 29 34 40 43 53 59 62 63 64 70 76
81 85 89 93 107 108 115 119 127 130 133 146 148 154
Primary Contact: Kathy Waddell, Administrator
Web address: www.waynegeneralhospital.org
**Control**: County, Government, Nonfederal **Service**: General medical and surgical

**Staffed Beds: 49 Admissions: 1559 Census: 23 Outpatient Visits: 32747
Births: 195 Personnel: 363**

### WEST POINT—Clay County

**CLAY COUNTY MEDICAL CENTER** See North Mississippi Medical Center-West
Point

✠ **NORTH MISSISSIPPI MEDICAL CENTER-WEST POINT (250067)**, 835 Medical
Center Drive, Zip 39773–9320; tel. 662/495–2300, (Nonreporting) **A**1 10 **S**
North Mississippi Health Services, Inc., Tupelo, MS
Primary Contact: Barry L. Keel, Administrator
CFO: Kay Lawler, Business Office Manager
CMO: B Keith Watson, M.D., Chief Medical Staff
CIO: Stacie Griggs, MIS Analyst
CHR: Lauren Hollis, Chief Human Resources Officer
CNO: Pamela White, Chief Nursing Officer
Web address: www.nmhs.net/westpoint
**Control**: Other not–for–profit (including NFP Corporation) **Service**: General
medical and surgical

**Staffed Beds: 49**

### WHITFIELD—Rankin County

✠ **MISSISSIPPI STATE HOSPITAL (254010)**, 3550 Highway 468 West,
Zip 39193–5529, Mailing Address: P.O. Box 157-A, Zip 39193–0157;
tel. 601/351–8000, (Includes WHITFIELD MEDICAL SURGICAL HOSPITAL,
Mailing address: 3550 Highway 468 West, Building 60, Whitfield, Mississippi,
Zip 39193–5529, P O Box 157A, Zip 39193–0157, tel. 601/351–8023),
(Nonreporting) **A**1 3 5 10 **F**3 4 29 30 32 39 68 74 75 86 87 98 99 100 101
104 107 114 119 128 130 143 146 148 149 151 154 **P**1 **S** Mississippi State
Department of Mental Health, Jackson, MS
Primary Contact: James G. Chastain, FACHE, Director
COO: Kelly R Breland, CPA, Director Support Services
CFO: Alicia Harris, Director Fiscal Services
CMO: Duncan Stone, D.D.S., Chief Medical Staff
CIO: Bart Uharriet, Director Information Services
CHR: Katie Storr, Director of Human Resources
CNO: Jackie Yates, R.N., Nurse Executive
Web address: www.msh.state.ms.us
**Control**: State, Government, Nonfederal **Service**: Psychiatric

**Staffed Beds: 349 Admissions: 1837 Census: 294 Outpatient Visits: 1439
Births: 0 Total Expense ($000): 121245 Payroll Expense ($000): 50742
Personnel: 972**

### WIGGINS—Stone County

**STONE COUNTY HOSPITAL (251303)**, 1434 East Central Avenue,
Zip 39577–9602; tel. 601/928–6600, (Nonreporting) **A**10 **F**3 5 7 29 34 35 40
43 46 57 59 64 81 89 97 100 101 103 112 114 115 119 130 133 143
Primary Contact: Lynn Truelove, Chief Executive Officer
Web address: www.schospital.net/
**Control**: City–county, Government, Nonfederal **Service**: General medical and
surgical

**Staffed Beds: 25 Admissions: 351 Census: 13 Outpatient Visits: 12363
Births: 1 Total Expense ($000): 24979 Payroll Expense ($000): 7448
Personnel: 143**

### WINONA—Montgomery County

**TYLER HOLMES MEMORIAL HOSPITAL (251312)**, 409 Tyler Holmes Drive,
Zip 38967–1599; tel. 662/283–4114, (Nonreporting) **A**10 18 **F**3 11 15 29 34 35
40 43 50 57 59 64 68 87 104 107 110 111 115 119 130 133 148 149 153 **P**8
Primary Contact: Sean Johnson, Chief Executive Officer
CFO: Cori Bailey, Accountant
CMO: Eddie Rutherford, Director of Pharmacy
CHR: Becky Corley, Director Human Resources
Web address: www.thmh.org/
**Control**: County, Government, Nonfederal **Service**: General medical and surgical

**Staffed Beds: 25 Admissions: 457 Census: 11 Outpatient Visits: 11741
Births: 0 Total Expense ($000): 13783 Payroll Expense ($000): 6982
Personnel: 134**

### YAZOO CITY—Yazoo County

★ **BAPTIST MEDICAL CENTER YAZOO (251313)**, 823 Grand Avenue,
Zip 39194–3233; tel. 662/746–2261, (Nonreporting) **A**10 18 **F**15 29 40 41 56
64 68 71 74 81 97 107 108 111 114 119 127 133 145 148 149 153 154 **S**
Baptist Memorial Health Care Corporation, Memphis, TN
Primary Contact: Robert Coleman, Chief Executive Officer
COO: Marsha Jones, R.N., Director Nursing
CFO: James L Miller, Chief Financial Officer
CMO: Marion Sigrest, M.D., Chief of Staff
CIO: Benton D Estes, Materials Management
CHR: Stephanie Washington, Director Community Relations and Human Resources
CNO: Marsha Jones, R.N., Director of Nursing
Web address: www.mbhs.org/locations/baptist-medical-center-yazoo/
**Control**: Other not–for–profit (including NFP Corporation) **Service**: General
medical and surgical

**Staffed Beds: 25 Admissions: 563 Census: 11 Outpatient Visits: 24484
Births: 0 Personnel: 108**

**KING'S DAUGHTERS HOSPITAL** See Baptist Medical Center Yazoo

MS

---

**Hospital, Medicare Provider Number, Address, Telephone, Approval, Facility, and Physician Codes, Health Care System**

★ American Hospital Association (AHA) membership    ◯ Healthcare Facilities Accreditation Program    ⇑ Center for Improvement in Healthcare Quality Accreditation
☐ The Joint Commission accreditation    ◇ DNV Healthcare Inc. accreditation    △ Commission on Accreditation of Rehabilitation Facilities (CARF) accreditation

# MISSOURI

## ALBANY—Gentry County

★ **MOSAIC MEDICAL CENTER - ALBANY (261328)**, 705 North College Street, Zip 64402–1433; tel. 660/726–3941, (Nonreporting) **A**10 18 **F**3 11 12 15 18 28 29 32 34 35 39 40 41 44 45 47 50 53 56 57 59 62 64 65 68 74 75 77 79 81 84 85 86 87 89 90 93 97 99 103 104 107 108 110 111 115 119 127 128 130 131 133 135 143 148 149 154 156 **P**6 **S** Mosaic Life Care, Saint Joseph, MO
Primary Contact: Jon D. Doolittle, Regional President
CMO: Angelia Martin, M.D., Chief of Staff
CIO: James Crouch, Vice President Technical Services
CHR: Vickie Cline, Director Human Resources
CNO: Miranda Floyd, R.N., Chief Nursing Officer
Web address: www.northwestmedicalcenter.org
**Control**: Other not–for–profit (including NFP Corporation) **Service**: General medical and surgical

**Staffed Beds**: 25 **Admissions**: 440 **Census**: 6 **Outpatient Visits**: 38728
**Births**: 0 **Total Expense ($000)**: 20228 **Payroll Expense ($000)**: 9274
**Personnel**: 112

**NORTHWEST MEDICAL CENTER** See Mosaic Medical Center - Albany

## APPLETON CITY—St. Clair County

★ **ELLETT MEMORIAL HOSPITAL (261301)**, 610 North Ohio Avenue, Zip 64724–1609, Mailing Address: P.O. Box 6, Zip 64724–0006; tel. 660/476–2111, (Nonreporting) **A**10 18 **F**3 7 11 34 40 45 57 59 64 77 79 90 93 97 107 111 114 119 127 128 129 130 133 143 146 147 154 **P**6
Primary Contact: Laura Smith, Chief Executive Officer
CMO: Richard R Dailey, D.O., President Medical Staff
CIO: Gina Raybourn, Director Health Information
CHR: Cathy Grishow, Director Human Resources
Web address: www.ellettmemorial.com
**Control**: Hospital district or authority, Government, Nonfederal **Service**: General medical and surgical

**Staffed Beds**: 12 **Admissions**: 123 **Census**: 2 **Outpatient Visits**: 8504
**Births**: 0 **Total Expense ($000)**: 10054 **Payroll Expense ($000)**: 3767
**Personnel**: 80

## AURORA—Lawrence County

✠ **MERCY HOSPITAL AURORA (261316)**, 500 Porter Street, Zip 65605–2365; tel. 417/678–2122, (Nonreporting) **A**1 10 18 **F**3 11 13 15 28 29 30 34 35 40 41 45 50 57 59 64 65 75 76 77 81 85 86 87 89 93 94 96 107 108 110 111 114 119 129 132 133 148 149 154 **S** Mercy, Chesterfield, MO
Primary Contact: Nicki Gamet, R.N., Administrator
CFO: Sherry Clouse Day, CPA, Vice President Finance and Regional Chief Financial Officer
CMO: Christie Hurt, M.D., Chief of Staff and Medical Director
CHR: George Roden, Vice President Human Resources
Web address: www.stjohns.com/aboutus/aurora.aspx
**Control**: Church operated, Nongovernment, not–for–profit **Service**: General medical and surgical

**Staffed Beds**: 25 **Admissions**: 553 **Census**: 5 **Outpatient Visits**: 32736
**Births**: 202 **Total Expense ($000)**: 18891 **Payroll Expense ($000)**: 9296
**Personnel**: 151

**ST. JOHN'S HOSPITAL - AURORA** See Mercy Hospital Aurora

## BELTON—Cass County

✠ **BELTON REGIONAL MEDICAL CENTER (260214)**, 17065 South 71 Highway, Zip 64012–4631; tel. 816/348–1200, (Nonreporting) **A**1 2 10 **F**3 15 18 20 29 30 31 34 35 37 40 43 45 57 59 65 68 70 74 75 77 78 79 81 82 85 87 90 93 107 108 110 111 114 115 118 119 129 130 131 132 146 **S** HCA Healthcare, Nashville, TN
Primary Contact: Todd Krass, Chief Executive Officer
CFO: Ronnie Thompson, Chief Financial Officer
CIO: Sarah Richardson, Director Information Systems
CHR: Jessica Sulzen, Director Human Resources
CNO: Heather Palmer, Chief Nursing Officer
Web address: www.beltonregionalmedicalcenter.com
**Control**: Corporation, Investor–owned (for–profit) **Service**: General medical and surgical

**Staffed Beds**: 48 **Admissions**: 3737 **Census**: 33 **Outpatient Visits**: 98048
**Births**: 0 **Total Expense ($000)**: 66375 **Payroll Expense ($000)**: 22141
**Personnel**: 243

**RESEARCH BELTON HOSPITAL** See Belton Regional Medical Center

## BETHANY—Harrison County

★ **HARRISON COUNTY COMMUNITY HOSPITAL (261312)**, 2600 Miller Street, Zip 64424–2701; tel. 660/425–2211, (Nonreporting) **A**10 18 **F**3 11 15 28 29 34 35 40 41 44 45 50 56 57 59 62 64 67 75 77 81 82 87 89 90 92 93 96 97 98 107 108 110 111 115 119 127 128 129 130 131 133 135 143 147 148 149 154 **P**6
Primary Contact: Christina L. Gillespie, Chief Executive Officer
CFO: Lee Ann Miles, Chief Financial Officer
CMO: Terry E. Hall, Chief of Staff
CIO: Will Holt, Director Information Technology
CHR: Cathie Chalfant, Director Human Resources
CNO: Crystal Hicks, R.N., Chief Nursing Officer
Web address: www.hcchospital.org
**Control**: Hospital district or authority, Government, Nonfederal **Service**: General medical and surgical

**Staffed Beds**: 19 **Admissions**: 348 **Census**: 6 **Outpatient Visits**: 62336
**Births**: 0 **Total Expense ($000)**: 24531 **Payroll Expense ($000)**: 10973
**Personnel**: 200

**NOLL MEMORIAL HOSPITAL** See Harrison County Community Hospital

## BLUE SPRINGS—Jackson County

**ST MARY'S HOSP OF BLUE SPRINGS** See St. Mary's Medical Center

☐ **ST. MARY'S MEDICAL CENTER (260193)**, 201 Northwest R D Mize Road, Zip 64014–2518; tel. 816/228–5900, (Nonreporting) **A**1 3 5 10 **F**3 8 15 18 20 22 28 29 30 34 35 40 49 50 53 56 57 59 60 62 63 64 68 70 74 78 79 80 81 82 83 84 85 87 90 93 96 107 108 110 111 113 114 115 119 129 130 131 135 143 145 146 148 154 **S** Prime Healthcare, Ontario, CA
Primary Contact: Drew Grossman, Chief Executive Officer
Web address: www.stmaryskc.com/
**Control**: Corporation, Investor–owned (for–profit) **Service**: General medical and surgical

**Staffed Beds**: 83 **Admissions**: 4886 **Census**: 55 **Outpatient Visits**: 59888
**Births**: 0 **Total Expense ($000)**: 81742 **Payroll Expense ($000)**: 29173
**Personnel**: 460

## BOLIVAR—Polk County

✠ **CITIZENS MEMORIAL HOSPITAL (260195)**, 1500 North Oakland Avenue, Zip 65613–3011; tel. 417/326–6000, (Nonreporting) **A**1 10 20 **F**3 7 11 13 15 18 20 22 26 28 29 31 34 36 40 43 44 50 51 54 56 57 59 64 66 70 74 75 76 77 78 79 80 81 82 85 86 87 89 90 93 94 96 97 98 100 102 103 104 107 108 110 111 115 117 119 126 127 128 129 130 131 132 133 135 146 147 148 149 154 155 156
Primary Contact: Gary D. Fulbright, CPA, Chief Executive Officer
COO: Jeff Miller, Chief Operating Officer
CMO: Ronald A. Evans, M.D., Chief Medical Officer
CIO: Denni McColm, Chief Information Officer
CHR: Jeremy MacLaughlin, Director Human Resources
CNO: Lesa Stock, R.N., Chief Clinical Officer
Web address: www.citizensmemorial.com
**Control**: Hospital district or authority, Government, Nonfederal **Service**: General medical and surgical

**Staffed Beds**: 72 **Admissions**: 3528 **Census**: 35 **Outpatient Visits**: 499416
**Births**: 601 **Total Expense ($000)**: 170413 **Payroll Expense ($000)**: 78554
**Personnel**: 1271

## BONNE TERRE—St. Francois County

★ **PARKLAND HEALTH CENTER-BONNE TERRE (261315)**, 7245 Raider Road, Zip 63628; tel. 573/358–1400, (Nonreporting) **A**10 18 **F**3 11 29 30 31 34 35 40 50 53 57 59 64 75 77 86 90 102 107 119 129 130 143 146 149 154 157 **S** BJC HealthCare, Saint Louis, MO
Primary Contact: Annette D. Schnabel, FACHE, President and Chief Executive Officer
CFO: Cheri L. Goldsmith, Director Financial Services
Web address: www.parklandhealthcenter.org
**Control**: Other not–for–profit (including NFP Corporation) **Service**: General medical and surgical

**Staffed Beds**: 3 **Admissions**: 38 **Census**: 1 **Outpatient Visits**: 21448
**Births**: 0 **Personnel**: 30

**PARKLAND HLYH CTR-BOONE TERRE** See Parkland Health Center-Bonne Terre

*Many Facility Codes have changed. Please refer to the AHA Guide Code Chart.*

© 2021 AHA Guide

**MO**

## BRANSON—Taney County

★ △ ⇧ **COX MEDICAL CENTER BRANSON (260094)**, 525 Branson Landing Boulevard, Zip 65616–2052, Mailing Address: P.O. Box 650, Zip 65615–0650; tel. 417/335–7000, (Nonreporting) **A**7 10 21 **F**3 11 13 15 17 18 20 22 26 28 29 30 31 32 34 35 40 41 45 48 50 53 56 57 59 60 62 64 65 66 68 70 74 75 76 77 78 79 80 81 85 86 87 89 90 98 107 108 110 111 114 117 119 120 121 129 130 131 132 135 144 146 147 148 149 150 154 156 **P**3 6 **S** CoxHealth, Springfield, MO
Primary Contact: William K. Mahoney, FACHE, President and Senior Vice President, Community Hospital Group
CFO: David Strong, Chief Financial Officer/Vice President Finance
CMO: James Duff, M.D., Chief Medical Officer
CHR: Carol Murrow, Vice President Business Development
Web address: www.coxhealth.com
**Control**: Other not–for–profit (including NFP Corporation) **Service**: General medical and surgical

**Staffed Beds:** 126 **Admissions:** 6924 **Census:** 84 **Outpatient Visits:** 194256 **Births:** 541 **Total Expense ($000):** 158850 **Payroll Expense ($000):** 49228 **Personnel:** 1173

⇧ **SKAGGS REGIONAL MEDICAL CENTER** See Cox Medical Center Branson

## BRIDGETON—St. Louis County

**SSM DEPAUL HEALTH CENTER** See Ssm Health Depaul Hospital - St. Louis

⊞ △ **SSM HEALTH DEPAUL HOSPITAL - ST. LOUIS (260104)**, 12303 De Paul Drive, Zip 63044–2512; tel. 314/344–6000, (Total facility includes 52 beds in nursing home–type unit) (Nonreporting) **A**1 2 3 5 7 10 **F**3 4 5 8 11 12 13 15 17 18 20 22 24 26 28 29 30 31 34 35 36 38 40 43 44 45 49 50 51 53 55 56 57 58 59 60 61 64 65 70 73 74 75 76 78 79 81 82 84 85 86 87 89 98 99 100 101 102 104 105 107 108 110 111 114 115 117 118 119 120 121 126 128 129 130 132 135 144 146 147 148 149 153 154 156 **P**6 8 **S** SSM Health, Saint Louis, MO
Primary Contact: Ellis Hawkins, FACHE, President
COO: Kelly Pearce, FACHE, Vice President Operations
CFO: Eileen Lamm, Regional Chief Financial Officer
CMO: Sriram Vissa, M.D., Vice President Medical Affairs
CIO: James Hamner, Regional Information Technology Director
CHR: Rodney Lacy, Leader Human Resources
CNO: Shelly L. Cordum, MSN, R.N., Vice President Nursing and Chief Nursing Officer
Web address: www.ssmdepaul.com
**Control**: Church operated, Nongovernment, not–for–profit **Service**: General medical and surgical

**Staffed Beds:** 523 **Admissions:** 22130 **Census:** 334 **Outpatient Visits:** 248288 **Births:** 1056 **Total Expense ($000):** 433822 **Payroll Expense ($000):** 129558 **Personnel:** 1967

**SSM REHABILITATION HOSPITAL** See Ssm Select Rehabilitation Hospital

## BROOKFIELD—Linn County

**GENERAL JOHN J. PERSHING MEMORIAL HOSPITAL** See Pershing Memorial Hospital

**PERSHING MEMORIAL HOSPITAL (261307)**, 130 East Lockling Avenue, Zip 64628–2337, Mailing Address: P.O. Box 408, Zip 64628–0408; tel. 660/258–2222, (Nonreporting) **A**10 18 **F**11 15 28 29 34 40 57 59 64 75 77 81 85 89 93 97 107 114 119 127 129 130 133 146 149 **P**6
Primary Contact: Phil Hamilton, R.N., Chief Executive Officer
CFO: Gary R Tandy, Chief Financial Officer
CMO: B K Knowles, D.O., Chief of Staff
CIO: Elaine Sutton, Chief Information Officer
CHR: Amy Sayre, Director Human Resources
Web address: www.phsmo.org
**Control**: Other not–for–profit (including NFP Corporation) **Service**: General medical and surgical

**Staffed Beds:** 25 **Admissions:** 200 **Census:** 3 **Outpatient Visits:** 33984 **Births:** 0 **Total Expense ($000):** 17315 **Payroll Expense ($000):** 6980 **Personnel:** 135

## BUTLER—Bates County

★ ⇧ **BATES COUNTY MEMORIAL HOSPITAL (260034)**, 615 West Nursery Street, Zip 64730–1840, Mailing Address: P.O. Box 370, Zip 64730–0370; tel. 660/200–7000, (Nonreporting) **A**5 10 20 21 **F**3 7 11 15 18 28 29 30 31 34 40 45 50 59 64 68 70 77 78 79 81 87 90 93 107 108 109 110 111 115 118 119 127 129 130 132 133 154 **P**6
Primary Contact: Greg Weaver, Interim Chief Executive Officer
COO: Greg Weaver, Chief Operating Officer
CFO: Terri Floyd, Chief Financial Officer
CMO: James Patterson, M.D., Chief of Medical Staff
CIO: Marcia Cook, Director Information Technology
CHR: Melinda R Jackson, Director Human Resources
CNO: Rebecca Tarver, Chief Nursing Officer
Web address: www.bcmhospital.com
**Control**: County, Government, Nonfederal **Service**: General medical and surgical

**Staffed Beds:** 49 **Admissions:** 613 **Census:** 9 **Outpatient Visits:** 76448 **Births:** 0 **Total Expense ($000):** 40163 **Payroll Expense ($000):** 15665 **Personnel:** 277

## CAMERON—Clinton County

**CAMERON COMMUNITY HOSPITAL** See Cameron Regional Medical Center

**CAMERON REGIONAL MEDICAL CENTER (260057)**, 1600 East Evergreen, Zip 64429–2400, Mailing Address: P.O. Box 557, Zip 64429–0557; tel. 816/632–2101, (Nonreporting) **A**3 5 10 **F**3 11 12 13 15 28 29 30 31 34 35 39 46 47 49 56 57 59 61 62 63 64 69 70 74 75 76 77 78 79 81 82 84 85 86 87 89 90 98 100 103 104 107 110 111 115 119 129 130 131 133 143 146 147 148 154
Primary Contact: Joseph F. Abrutz Jr, Administrator
CFO: Rosa Patti, Chief Financial Officer
CIO: Bill Walser, Coordinator Technology
CHR: Pat Bestgen, Manager Human Resources
Web address: www.cameronregional.org
**Control**: Other not–for–profit (including NFP Corporation) **Service**: General medical and surgical

**Staffed Beds:** 58 **Admissions:** 1937 **Census:** 28 **Outpatient Visits:** 320680 **Births:** 101 **Total Expense ($000):** 61309 **Payroll Expense ($000):** 26966 **Personnel:** 392

## CAPE GIRARDEAU—Cape Girardeau County

**LANDMARK HOSPITAL** See Landmark Hospital of Cape Girardeau

**LANDMARK HOSPITAL OF CAPE GIRARDEAU (262015)**, 3255 Independence Street, Zip 63701–4914; tel. 573/335–1091, (Nonreporting) **A**10 22 **F**1 3 29 60 107 111 119 130 148 **S** Landmark Hospitals, Cape Girardeau, MO
Primary Contact: Deborah Sabella, R.N., Chief Executive Officer
COO: Michael L Norman, Executive Vice President and Chief Operating Officer
CFO: Richard H Hogan, CPA, Chief Financial Officer
CMO: William Fritsch, M.D., Medical Director
CIO: Renee Hesselrode, Director Health Information Management
CHR: Angela Kisner, Director Human Resources and Coordinator Medical Staff
Web address: www.landmarkhospitals.com
**Control**: Corporation, Investor–owned (for–profit) **Service**: Acute long–term care hospital

**Staffed Beds:** 30 **Admissions:** 253 **Census:** 20 **Outpatient Visits:** 0 **Births:** 0 **Total Expense ($000):** 12258 **Payroll Expense ($000):** 4130 **Personnel:** 81

**SAINT FRANCIS HEALTHCARE SYSTEM** See Saint Francis Medical Center

⊞ **SAINT FRANCIS MEDICAL CENTER (260183)**, 211 St Francis Drive, Zip 63703–5049; tel. 573/331–3000, (Nonreporting) **A**1 2 5 10 19 **F**3 9 11 12 13 15 17 18 20 22 24 26 28 29 30 31 34 35 40 43 44 45 46 47 48 49 50 51 53 55 56 57 59 60 61 62 63 64 65 70 72 73 74 75 76 77 78 79 80 81 82 83 84 85 86 87 89 90 91 92 93 107 111 115 117 118 119 120 121 123 124 126 129 130 131 132 135 142 144 146 147 148 149
Primary Contact: Maryann Reese, R.N., FACHE, President and Chief Executive Officer
CFO: Tony Balsano, Vice President Finance
CMO: James Schell, M.D., Vice President Medical Affairs
CIO: Edward E Duryee, Director Information Systems
CHR: Teri Kreitzer, Director Human Resources
CNO: Jeannie Fadler, R.N., Vice President Patient Care Services
Web address: www.sfmc.net
**Control**: Church operated, Nongovernment, not–for–profit **Service**: General medical and surgical

**Staffed Beds:** 306 **Admissions:** 10426 **Census:** 130 **Outpatient Visits:** 813672 **Births:** 1024 **Total Expense ($000):** 499918 **Payroll Expense ($000):** 198909 **Personnel:** 2710

**MO**

---

**Hospital, Medicare Provider Number, Address, Telephone, Approval, Facility, and Physician Codes, Health Care System**

★ American Hospital Association (AHA) membership ◯ Healthcare Facilities Accreditation Program ⇧ Center for Improvement in Healthcare Quality Accreditation
☐ The Joint Commission accreditation ◇ DNV Healthcare Inc. accreditation △ Commission on Accreditation of Rehabilitation Facilities (CARF) accreditation

☐ **SOUTHEAST HOSPITAL (260110)**, 1701 Lacey Street, Zip 63701–5230;
tel. 573/334–4822, (Nonreporting) **A**1 5 10 19 **F**3 13 15 17 18 20 22 24 26 28
29 30 31 32 34 35 40 44 47 48 49 50 51 53 54 57 58 59 60 61 62 63 64 65
70 72 73 74 75 76 77 78 79 80 81 82 84 85 86 87 88 89 90 92 93 96 97 107
108 110 111 114 117 118 119 120 121 123 124 126 127 129 130 131 132
135 146 147 148 149 154 156 **S** SoutheastHEALTH, Cape Girardeau, MO
Primary Contact: Kenneth Bateman, CPA, President and Chief Executive Officer
COO: Sylvia Moore, Vice President and Chief Operating Officer
CFO: Bruce Fairbanks, Vice President and Chief Financial Officer
CMO: Matt Shoemaker, D.O., Vice President and Chief Medical Officer
CIO: Mike Dozier, Chief Information Officer
CHR: Lincoln Scott, Vice President Human Resources
CNO: Judy Aslin, MSN, R.N., Vice President and Chief Nursing Officer
Web address: www.sehealth.org/
**Control:** Other not–for–profit (including NFP Corporation) **Service:** General
medical and surgical

**Staffed Beds:** 170 **Admissions:** 7407 **Census:** 99 **Outpatient
Visits:** 477168 **Births:** 736 **Total Expense ($000):** 335258 **Payroll Expense
($000):** 131826 **Personnel:** 1940

**SOUTHEAST MISSOURI HOSPITAL** See Southeast Hospital

## CARROLLTON—Carroll County

★ **CARROLL COUNTY MEMORIAL HOSPITAL (261332)**, 1502 North Jefferson
Street, Zip 64633–1948; tel. 660/542–1695, (Nonreporting) **A**10 18 **F**3 11 15
28 29 30 31 34 35 38 40 45 50 53 56 57 59 62 64 65 68 69 74 75 77 78 79
81 82 85 86 87 90 91 92 93 96 97 103 104 107 108 110 111 115 119 125
127 128 129 130 131 132 133 135 143 146 148 149 153 154
Primary Contact: Jeff A. Tindle, Chief Executive Officer
COO: Tim Braun, Chief Operation Officer
CFO: Amy Ireland, Chief Financial Officer
CMO: Richard Smith, Chief of Staff
CIO: Bill Bollinger, Chief Information Officer
CHR: Michael Schubach, Chief People Officer
CNO: Jeanne Rector, Chief Nursing Officer
Web address: www.carrollcountyhospital.org
**Control:** Other not–for–profit (including NFP Corporation) **Service:** General
medical and surgical

**Staffed Beds:** 25 **Admissions:** 235 **Census:** 5 **Outpatient Visits:** 61632
**Births:** 0 **Total Expense ($000):** 31387 **Payroll Expense ($000):** 10847
**Personnel:** 235

## CARTHAGE—Jasper County

★ **MERCY HOSPITAL CARTHAGE (261338)**, 3125 Dr Russell Smith Way,
Zip 64836–7402; tel. 417/358–8121, (Nonreporting) **A**10 18 **F**3 7 11 15 28 29
30 31 34 35 40 45 50 53 57 59 64 67 68 69 75 79 81 89 98 104 107 108
110 111 115 119 126 127 129 130 131 132 133 135 146 147 154 156 **P**6 **S**
Mercy, Chesterfield, MO
Primary Contact: Scott Watson, Administrator
CFO: Douglas Culver, Chief Financial Officer
CIO: Cheryl Lease-Homeyer, Lead Information Technology Business Partner
CHR: Colette St. Peter, Senior Manager Human Resources
Web address: www.mercy.net
**Control:** Church operated, Nongovernment, not–for–profit **Service:** General
medical and surgical

**Staffed Beds:** 25 **Admissions:** 753 **Census:** 14 **Outpatient Visits:** 108696
**Births:** 0 **Total Expense ($000):** 41003 **Payroll Expense ($000):** 15892
**Personnel:** 246

**MERCY MCCUNE-BROOKS HOSPITAL** See Mercy Hospital Carthage

## CASSVILLE—Barry County

⊠ **MERCY HOSPITAL CASSVILLE (261317)**, 94 Main Street, Zip 65625–1610;
tel. 417/847–6000, (Nonreporting) **A**1 10 18 **F**3 11 15 28 29 30 34 35 40 41
45 50 53 57 59 64 65 68 75 77 81 85 86 87 89 93 94 96 103 107 108 110
111 114 119 132 133 135 148 149 153 154 **S** Mercy, Chesterfield, MO
Primary Contact: Nicki Gamet, R.N., Administrator
CFO: Sherry Clouse Day, CPA, Chief Financial Officer
CMO: Jamie Zengotita, M.D., Chief Medical Staff
CHR: George Roden, Vice President Human Resources
Web address: www.mercy.net/northwestarar/practice/mercy-hospital-cassville
**Control:** Church operated, Nongovernment, not–for–profit **Service:** General
medical and surgical

**Staffed Beds:** 18 **Admissions:** 290 **Census:** 3 **Outpatient Visits:** 33520
**Births:** 0 **Total Expense ($000):** 15592 **Payroll Expense ($000):** 7442
**Personnel:** 104

**ST. JOHN'S HOSPITAL - CASSVILLE** See Mercy Hospital Cassville

## CHESTERFIELD—St. Louis County

**MERCY REHABILITATION HOSPITAL** See Mercy Rehabilitation Hospital St. Louis

☐ △ **MERCY REHABILITATION HOSPITAL ST. LOUIS (263029)**, 14561 North
Outer Forty Road, Zip 63017; tel. 314/881–4000, (Nonreporting) **A**1 7 10 **F**16 29
30 90 130 132 148 **S** Kindred Healthcare, Louisville, KY
Primary Contact: Jerald W. Rumph, Chief Executive Officer
CMO: Siresha Samudrala, M.D., Medical Director
Web address: www.https://www.mercy.net/practice/mercy-rehabilitation-hospital-
st-louis/
**Control:** Partnership, Investor–owned (for–profit) **Service:** Rehabilitation

**Staffed Beds:** 90 **Admissions:** 1929 **Census:** 73 **Outpatient Visits:** 0
**Births:** 0 **Total Expense ($000):** 32936 **Payroll Expense ($000):** 14633
**Personnel:** 196

**ST. LUKE'S DES PERES HOSPITAL** See St. Luke's Hospital

⊠ **ST. LUKE'S HOSPITAL (260179)**, 232 South Woods Mill Road, Zip 63017–3417;
tel. 314/434–1500, (Total facility includes 140 beds in nursing home–type unit)
(Nonreporting) **A**1 2 3 5 10 **F**3 10 11 13 15 17 18 20 22 24 26 28 29 30 31 32
34 35 36 38 39 40 41 44 45 46 49 50 52 53 54 55 56 57 58 59 60 61 62 63
64 65 66 68 69 70 71 73 74 76 77 78 79 81 82 84 85 86 87 89 90 93 97
107 110 111 114 115 116 117 118 119 120 121 123 124 126 128 129 130
131 132 135 141 142 144 145 146 147 148 149 156
Primary Contact: Gary R. Olson, Interim President and Chief Executive Officer
COO: Diane Ray, R.N., FACHE, Senior Vice President and Chief Operating Officer;
Network Chief Nursing Officer
CFO: Scott H. Johnson, Executive Vice President and Chief Financial Officer
CIO: William Meyers, Chief Information Officer
CHR: Janette L. Taaffe, Vice President, Human Resource
CNO: Diane Ray, R.N., FACHE, Senior Vice President and Chief Operating Officer;
Network Chief Nursing Officer
Web address: www.stlukes-stl.com
**Control:** Church operated, Nongovernment, not–for–profit **Service:** General
medical and surgical

**Staffed Beds:** 534 **Admissions:** 15579 **Census:** 275 **Outpatient
Visits:** 1154416 **Births:** 1612 **Total Expense ($000):** 583588 **Payroll
Expense ($000):** 266868 **Personnel:** 3442

⊠ **ST. LUKE'S REHABILITATION HOSPITAL (263030)**, 14709 Olive Boulevard,
Zip 63017–2221; tel. 314/317–5700, (Data for 153 days) (Nonreporting) **A**1 10
**F**3 12 18 28 29 34 50 68 74 75 79 90 96 100 130 132 148 156 **S** Post Acute
Medical, LLC, Enola, PA
Primary Contact: Reagan Simpson, Chief Executive Officer
Web address: www.https://postacutemedical.com/facilities/find-facility/
rehabilitation-hospitals/St-Lukes-Rehabilitation-Hospital
**Control:** Partnership, Investor–owned (for–profit) **Service:** Rehabilitation

**Staffed Beds:** 35 **Admissions:** 327 **Census:** 24 **Outpatient Visits:** 0
**Births:** 0 **Total Expense ($000):** 4693 **Payroll Expense ($000):** 1289
**Personnel:** 56

## CHILLICOTHE—Livingston County

⊠ **HEDRICK MEDICAL CENTER (261321)**, 2799 North Washington Street,
Zip 64601–2902; tel. 660/646–1480, (Nonreporting) **A**1 10 18 **F**3 11 13 15 18
28 29 30 31 34 35 40 43 44 45 50 59 64 68 69 70 74 75 76 77 78 79 81 82
85 86 87 89 90 92 93 96 97 100 102 104 107 108 110 111 115 118 119
127 130 131 133 141 146 147 148 154 **S** Saint Luke's Health System, Kansas
City, MO
Primary Contact: Steven M. Schieber, FACHE, Chief Executive Officer, Critical
Access Region, Saint Luke's Health System
CFO: Janet Buckman, Chief Financial Officer
CHR: Lisa A Hecker, Director Human Resources
CNO: Catherine Hamilton, MSN, Chief Nursing Officer
Web address: www.saintlukeskc.org
**Control:** Church operated, Nongovernment, not–for–profit **Service:** General
medical and surgical

**Staffed Beds:** 25 **Admissions:** 1330 **Census:** 16 **Outpatient Visits:** 111272
**Births:** 318 **Total Expense ($000):** 54329 **Payroll Expense ($000):** 21416
**Personnel:** 310

**MO**

*Many Facility Codes have changed. Please refer to the AHA Guide Code Chart.* © 2021 AHA Guide

## CLINTON—Henry County

✠ **GOLDEN VALLEY MEMORIAL HEALTHCARE (260175)**, 1600 North Second Street, Zip 64735–1192; tel. 660/885–5511, (Nonreporting) **A**1 10 **F**3 7 11 13 15 17 18 28 29 30 31 34 35 40 45 47 48 49 53 57 59 61 62 63 64 68 70 74 75 76 77 78 79 81 85 86 87 89 90 93 96 107 108 111 115 118 127 128 129 130 131 132 133 143 146 147 148 149 155 156
Primary Contact: Craig Thompson, Chief Executive Officer
CFO: Tammy R Nadler, Chief Financial Officer
CIO: Mike Gaul, Director Information Technology
CHR: Greg Shannon, Chief Human Resources Officer
CNO: Lynnette Hayes, Chief Nursing Officer
Web address: www.gvmh.org
**Control**: Hospital district or authority, Government, Nonfederal **Service**: General medical and surgical

**Staffed Beds**: 53 **Admissions**: 2064 **Census**: 18 **Outpatient Visits**: 322072 **Births**: 0 **Total Expense ($000)**: 105083 **Payroll Expense ($000)**: 42994 **Personnel**: 845

**GOLDEN VALLEY MEMORIAL HOSPITAL** See Golden Valley Memorial Healthcare

## COLUMBIA—Boone County

✠ **BOONE HOSPITAL CENTER (260068)**, 1600 East Broadway, Zip 65201–5844; tel. 573/815–8000, (Nonreporting) **A**1 2 3 5 10 **F**3 7 11 12 13 15 17 18 20 22 24 26 28 29 31 34 35 36 40 45 46 47 48 49 50 51 53 54 56 57 58 59 60 61 64 65 68 70 71 72 73 74 75 76 77 78 79 80 81 82 84 85 86 87 90 93 96 107 108 110 111 114 115 117 118 119 126 129 130 131 132 133 135 143 144 145 149 156 **P**1 **S** BJC HealthCare, Saint Louis, MO
Primary Contact: James J. Sinek, FACHE, President
CFO: Randy Morrow, Vice President and Chief Operating Officer
CMO: Jerry Kennett, M.D., Chief Medical Officer
CHR: Michelle Zvanut, Vice President Human Resources
Web address: www.boone.org
**Control**: Other not-for-profit (including NFP Corporation) **Service**: General medical and surgical

**Staffed Beds**: 280 **Admissions**: 13783 **Census**: 165 **Outpatient Visits**: 205832 **Births**: 1610 **Total Expense ($000)**: 331112 **Payroll Expense ($000)**: 91881 **Personnel**: 1438

☐ **CENTERPOINTE HOSPITAL OF COLUMBIA (264032)**, 1201 International Drive, Zip 65202; tel. 573/615–2001, (Nonreporting) **A**1
Primary Contact: James Gallagher, Chief Executive Officer
Web address: www.centerpointehospitalcolumbia.com
**Control**: Corporation, Investor–owned (for–profit) **Service**: Psychiatric

**Staffed Beds**: 72

**CENTERPOINTE HOSPITAL OF COLUMBIA** See Centerpointe Hospital of Columbia

**COLUMBIA REGIONAL HOSPITAL** See Women's and Children's Hospital

**ELLIS FISCHEL CANCER CENTER** See University of Missouri Health Care, Columbia

**ELLIS FISCHEL CANCER CTR** See Ellis Fischel Cancer Center

✠ **HARRY S. TRUMAN MEMORIAL VETERANS HOSPITAL**, 800 Hospital Drive, Zip 65201–5275; tel. 573/814–6000, (Nonreporting) **A**1 3 5 **S** Department of Veterans Affairs, Washington, DC
Primary Contact: Patricia Hall, MSN, Ph.D., R.N., Medical Center Director
COO: Robert G Ritter, FACHE, Associate Director
CFO: Deborah Henderson, Acting Chief Financial Officer
CMO: Lana Zerrer, M.D., Chief of Staff
CIO: Donna Krause, Chief Information Officer
CHR: Jimmy Powell, Manager Human Resources
Web address: www.columbiamo.va.gov
**Control**: Veterans Affairs, Government, federal **Service**: General medical and surgical

**Staffed Beds**: 126

**HOWARD A. RUSK REHABILITATION CENTER** See Rusk Rehabilitation Hospital

**LANDMARK HOSPITAL OF COLUMBIA (263033)**, 604 Old 63 North, Zip 65201–6308; tel. 573/499–6600, (Nonreporting) **A**3 5 10 22 **F**1 3 29 30 70 77 82 84 85 90 130 148 154 **S** Landmark Hospitals, Cape Girardeau, MO
Primary Contact: Nickie Hunt, Chief Executive Officer
Web address: www.landmarkhospitals.com
**Control**: Corporation, Investor–owned (for–profit) **Service**: Acute long–term care hospital

**Staffed Beds**: 23 **Admissions**: 280 **Census**: 17 **Outpatient Visits**: 0 **Births**: 0 **Total Expense ($000)**: 15375 **Payroll Expense ($000)**: 5525 **Personnel**: 58

✠ **RUSK REHABILITATION HOSPITAL (263027)**, 315 Business Loop 70 West, Zip 65203–3248; tel. 573/817–2703, (Nonreporting) **A**1 3 5 10 **F**29 30 90 148 **S** Encompass Health Corporation, Birmingham, AL
Primary Contact: Tom Tisone, Chief Executive Officer
CFO: Jeff Reese, Chief Financial Officer
CMO: Gregory Worsowicz, M.D., Medical Director
CHR: Robin Prater, Director Human Resources
CNO: Lori Mann, R.N., MSN, Chief Nursing Officer
Web address: www.https://www.encompasshealth.com/locations/ruskrehab
**Control**: Hospital district or authority, Government, Nonfederal **Service**: Rehabilitation

**Staffed Beds**: 60 **Admissions**: 1113 **Census**: 41 **Outpatient Visits**: 0 **Births**: 0 **Total Expense ($000)**: 20761 **Payroll Expense ($000)**: 9742 **Personnel**: 122

★ ⇑ **UNIVERSITY OF MISSOURI HEALTH CARE (260141)**, One Hospital Drive, Zip 65212–0001; tel. 573/882–4141, (Includes ELLIS FISCHEL CANCER CENTER, Mailing address: 115 Business Loop 70 West, Columbia, Missouri, Zip 65203; tel. 573/882–5460; WOMEN'S and CHILDREN'S HOSPITAL, Mailing address: 404 Keene Street, Columbia, Missouri, Zip 65201–6626; tel. 573/875–9000; John Hornick, MSN, R.N., Interim Executive Director), (Nonreporting) **A**2 3 5 8 10 21 **F**3 7 9 11 12 13 15 17 18 19 20 22 24 26 28 29 30 31 32 33 34 35 36 37 38 39 40 41 43 44 45 46 47 48 49 50 51 52 53 54 55 56 57 58 59 60 61 64 65 66 68 70 71 72 74 75 76 77 78 79 80 81 82 83 84 85 86 87 88 89 91 92 93 97 98 99 100 101 102 103 104 107 108 110 111 114 115 116 117 118 119 120 121 123 124 126 127 129 130 131 132 134 135 138 141 142 143 144 146 147 148 154 157 **S** University of Missouri Health Care, Columbia, MO
Primary Contact: Jonathan W. Curtright, Chief Executive Officer
CFO: Kevin Necas, Chief Financial Officer
CMO: Stevan Whitt, M.D., Chief Medical Officer
CHR: Sue A. Kopfle, Chief Human Resources Officer
Web address: www.muhealth.org
**Control**: State, Government, Nonfederal **Service**: General medical and surgical

**Staffed Beds**: 603 **Admissions**: 27989 **Census**: 419 **Outpatient Visits**: 1093304 **Births**: 2551 **Total Expense ($000)**: 1023647 **Payroll Expense ($000)**: 319333 **Personnel**: 5827

⇑ **UNIVERSITY OF MISSOURI HOSPITALS AND CLINICS** See University of Missouri Health Care

## DEXTER—Stoddard County

**MISSOURI SOUTHERN HEALTHCARE** See Southeast Health Center of Stoddard County

**SOUTHEAST HEALTH CENTER OF STODDARD COUNTY (260160)**, 1200 North One Mile Road, Zip 63841–1000; tel. 573/624–5566, (Nonreporting) **A**10 **F**11 15 28 29 31 34 39 40 59 62 65 70 75 77 78 81 85 89 90 93 97 98 107 110 111 115 118 119 127 129 130 133 135 146 154 **S** SoutheastHEALTH, Cape Girardeau, MO
Primary Contact: Sue Ann Williams, Chief Executive Officer
Web address: www.sehealth.org
**Control**: Other not–for–profit (including NFP Corporation) **Service**: General medical and surgical

**Staffed Beds**: 36 **Admissions**: 2026 **Census**: 16 **Outpatient Visits**: 107400 **Births**: 0 **Total Expense ($000)**: 36301 **Payroll Expense ($000)**: 13872 **Personnel**: 246

## EL DORADO SPRINGS—Cedar County

**CEDAR COUNTY MEMORIAL HOSPITAL (261323)**, 1401 South Park Street, Zip 64744–2037; tel. 417/876–2511, (Nonreporting) **A**10 18 **F**11 15 18 28 30 34 35 40 45 53 56 57 59 62 64 65 74 77 81 85 89 90 93 102 110 111 114 119 124 127 129 130 133 143 147 148 149 153 **P**6
Primary Contact: Jana Witt, Chief Executive Officer
CFO: Carla Gilbert, Director Finance
CMO: R. John Torontow, M.D., Chief Medical Staff
CIO: Lois Willmore, Supervisor Health Information Management
CHR: Diana Pyle, Director Human Resources and Executive Assistant to Chief Executive Officer
CNO: Drew Alexander, Chief Nursing Officer
Web address: www.cedarcountyhospital.org
**Control**: County, Government, Nonfederal **Service**: General medical and surgical

**Staffed Beds**: 25 **Admissions**: 181 **Census**: 5 **Outpatient Visits**: 16696 **Births**: 0 **Total Expense ($000)**: 13347 **Payroll Expense ($000)**: 4348 **Personnel**: 75

MO

---

**Hospital, Medicare Provider Number, Address, Telephone, Approval, Facility, and Physician Codes, Health Care System**

★ American Hospital Association (AHA) membership
☐ The Joint Commission accreditation
○ Healthcare Facilities Accreditation Program
◇ DNV Healthcare Inc. accreditation
⇑ Center for Improvement in Healthcare Quality Accreditation
△ Commission on Accreditation of Rehabilitation Facilities (CARF) accreditation

## EXCELSIOR SPRINGS—Clay County

★ **EXCELSIOR SPRINGS HOSPITAL (261322)**, 1700 Rainbow Boulevard, Zip 64024–1190; tel. 816/630–6081, (Total facility includes 80 beds in nursing home–type unit) (Nonreporting) **A**10 18 **F**3 11 15 18 19 20 29 31 32 34 35 39 40 45 56 57 59 62 63 64 67 68 70 75 77 78 79 81 82 84 85 86 87 89 90 93 102 103 107 108 110 111 115 116 117 118 119 126 130 133 143 146 154 **P**6
Primary Contact: Kristen DeHart, Chief Executive Officer
CFO: Cameron Meyer, CPA, Chief Financial Officer
CMO: Paul Torres, M.D., Medical Staff President
CHR: Kim Schweizer, Director Human Resources
Web address: www.ESHospital.org
**Control:** City, Government, Nonfederal **Service:** General medical and surgical

**Staffed Beds:** 100 **Admissions:** 305 **Census:** 56 **Outpatient Visits:** 38576 **Births:** 0 **Total Expense ($000):** 30754 **Payroll Expense ($000):** 12769 **Personnel:** 213

**EXCELSIOR SPRINGS MEDICAL CENTER** See Excelsior Springs Hospital

## FAIRFAX—Atchison County

⇑ **COMMUNITY HOSPITAL ASSOCIATION** See Community Hospital-Fairfax

★ ⇑ **COMMUNITY HOSPITAL-FAIRFAX (261303)**, 26136 US Highway 59, Zip 64446–9105, Mailing Address: P.O. Box 107, Zip 64446–0107; tel. 660/686–2211, (Nonreporting) **A**10 18 21 **F**3 11 13 15 18 28 29 30 34 40 45 50 51 59 62 64 75 76 79 81 85 87 89 90 93 96 97 101 103 104 107 110 114 119 127 130 131 132 133 148 149
Primary Contact: Julie L. Jones, Chief Executive Officer
COO: Ann Schlueter, Chief Operating Officer
CFO: Jon Davis, Chief Financial Officer
CMO: Richard Aron Burke, M.D., Chief Medical Officer
CIO: Chris Hedlund, Director Information Systems
Web address: www.fairfaxmed.com
**Control:** Other not–for–profit (including NFP Corporation) **Service:** General medical and surgical

**Staffed Beds:** 18 **Admissions:** 467 **Census:** 6 **Outpatient Visits:** 0 **Births:** 0 **Total Expense ($000):** 20465 **Payroll Expense ($000):** 8542 **Personnel:** 40

## FARMINGTON—St. Francois County

⊞ **PARKLAND HEALTH CENTER - FARMINGTON COMMUNITY (260163)**, 1101 West Liberty Street, Zip 63640–1921; tel. 573/756–6451, (Nonreporting) **A**1 10 20 **F**3 11 13 15 18 28 29 30 34 35 40 45 46 49 50 53 57 59 65 68 69 70 75 76 77 79 81 85 86 87 93 98 102 103 107 108 115 116 118 119 130 141 143 146 147 148 149 154 157 **S** BJC HealthCare, Saint Louis, MO
Primary Contact: Annette D. Schnabel, FACHE, President and Chief Executive Officer
COO: Steven R Marler, Assistant Administrator
CFO: Cheri L. Goldsmith, Director Financial Services
CMO: Scott Kirkley, M.D., BJC Chief Medical Officer Group Liaison
Web address: www.parklandhealthcenter.org
**Control:** Other not–for–profit (including NFP Corporation) **Service:** General medical and surgical

**Staffed Beds:** 102 **Admissions:** 4009 **Census:** 36 **Outpatient Visits:** 102680 **Births:** 502 **Total Expense ($000):** 107994 **Payroll Expense ($000):** 40644 **Personnel:** 474

**PARKLAND HEALTH CENTER - LIBERTY STREET** See Parkland Health Center - Farmington Community

☐ **SOUTHEAST MISSOURI MENTAL HEALTH CENTER (264005)**, 1010 West Columbia Street, Zip 63640–2997; tel. 573/218–6792, (Nonreporting) **A**1 10 **F**4 11 30 39 53 65 75 86 87 97 98 101 103 106 130 132 135 143 146 157
Primary Contact: Julie Inman, Regional Executive Officer
CMO: Jay Englehart, M.D., Medical Director
CHR: Mark Remspecher, Director Human Resources
Web address: www.dmh.missouri.gov/southeast/
**Control:** State, Government, Nonfederal **Service:** Psychiatric

**Staffed Beds:** 348 **Admissions:** 46 **Census:** 325 **Outpatient Visits:** 0 **Births:** 0 **Total Expense ($000):** 74314 **Payroll Expense ($000):** 37766 **Personnel:** 1022

## FENTON—St. Louis County

⊞ **SSM HEALTH ST. CLARE HOSPITAL - FENTON (260081)**, 1015 Bowles Avenue, Zip 63026–2394; tel. 636/496–2000, (Nonreporting) **A**1 3 5 10 **F**3 11 13 15 17 18 20 22 24 28 29 30 31 34 35 40 41 44 45 49 50 51 53 54 56 57 58 59 61 64 70 73 74 75 76 78 79 81 82 84 85 86 87 89 100 102 103 105 107 108 110 111 115 117 119 120 121 129 130 132 135 143 144 146 147 148 154 **P**6 **S** SSM Health, Saint Louis, MO
Primary Contact: Tina Garrison, President
COO: Lee Bernstein, Regional Executive Vice President and Chief Operating Officer
CFO: Hal Holder, Regional Chief Financial Officer-Hospital Operations
CMO: Timothy J Pratt, M.D., Vice President Medical Affairs and Chief Medical Officer
CIO: Michael Paasch, Vice President, Regional Chief Information Officer
CHR: Renee Roach, System Vice President, Human Resources
CNO: Wayne Laramie, Vice President Nursing
Web address: www.ssmstclare.com
**Control:** Church operated, Nongovernment, not–for–profit **Service:** General medical and surgical

**Staffed Beds:** 184 **Admissions:** 9494 **Census:** 108 **Outpatient Visits:** 132264 **Births:** 1120 **Total Expense ($000):** 199608 **Payroll Expense ($000):** 63099 **Personnel:** 902

**SSM ST. CLARE HOSPITAL** See Ssm Health St. Clare Hospital - Fenton

## FESTUS—Jefferson County

**JEFFERSON REGIONAL MEDICAL CENTER** See Mercy Hospital Jefferson

⊞ **MERCY HOSPITAL JEFFERSON (260023)**, 1400 US Highway 61 South, Zip 63028–4100, Mailing Address: P.O. Box 350, Crystal City, Zip 63019–0350; tel. 636/931–1000, (Nonreporting) **A**1 10 **F**3 8 11 12 13 15 18 20 22 28 29 30 31 34 35 40 44 45 46 49 50 51 53 54 57 59 60 62 63 64 68 70 74 75 76 77 78 79 81 82 84 85 86 87 89 90 92 93 96 97 98 100 103 104 107 108 110 111 114 115 117 118 119 129 130 131 132 135 143 144 146 147 148 149 153 154 157 **S** Mercy, Chesterfield, MO
Primary Contact: Eric Ammons, President
COO: Michele C. Meyer, R.N., Vice President of Operations
CMO: Mark Briete, M.D., Vice President Medical Affairs
CIO: Jan Poneta, Director Information Services
CHR: Saundra G Turner, Director Human Resources
Web address: www.mercy.net/crystalcitymo
**Control:** Other not–for–profit (including NFP Corporation) **Service:** General medical and surgical

**Staffed Beds:** 203 **Admissions:** 9848 **Census:** 125 **Outpatient Visits:** 230192 **Births:** 477 **Total Expense ($000):** 180968 **Payroll Expense ($000):** 71539 **Personnel:** 1223

## FORT LEONARD WOOD—Pulaski County

⊞ **GENERAL LEONARD WOOD ARMY COMMUNITY HOSPITAL**, 4430 Missouri Avenue, Zip 65473–8952, Mailing Address: PO Box 4430, Zip 65473–8952; tel. 573/596–0414, (Nonreporting) **A**1 **S** Department of the Army, Office of the Surgeon General, Falls Church, VA
Primary Contact: Colonel Aaron Pitney, Hospital Commander
CFO: MajorMichael Hogan, Chief Resource Management
CMO: Lieutenant ColonelJohn Lowery, M.D., Deputy Commander Clinical Services
CHR: MajorSandra Roper, Chief Human Resources
Web address: www.glwach.amedd.army.mil/
**Service:** General medical and surgical

**Staffed Beds:** 46

## FREDERICKTOWN—Madison County

**MADISON MEDICAL CENTER (261302)**, 611 West Main Street, Zip 63645–1111; tel. 573/783–3341, (Total facility includes 80 beds in nursing home–type unit) (Nonreporting) **A**10 18 **F**6 11 15 18 28 35 45 59 62 64 67 70 77 78 79 81 85 87 92 93 97 103 107 111 119 127 128 130 133 144 146
Primary Contact: Lisa Twidwell, Administrator
CMO: P A George, M.D., Chief of Staff
CHR: Jennifer Penuel, Director Human Resources
Web address: www.madisonmedicalcenter.net
**Control:** County, Government, Nonfederal **Service:** General medical and surgical

**Staffed Beds:** 97 **Admissions:** 402 **Census:** 71 **Outpatient Visits:** 57128 **Births:** 0 **Total Expense ($000):** 19602 **Payroll Expense ($000):** 10147 **Personnel:** 226

**MADISON MEMORIAL HOSPITAL** See Madison Medical Center

**MO**

*Many Facility Codes have changed. Please refer to the AHA Guide Code Chart.*   © 2021 AHA Guide

## FULTON—Callaway County

**CALLAWAY COMMUNITY HOSPITAL** See Fulton Medical Center

**FULTON MEDICAL CENTER (260209)**, 10 South Hospital Drive,
Zip 65251–2510; tel. 573/642–3376, (Nonreporting) **A**5 10 **F**3 11 18 29 30 34
40 50 57 59 64 65 68 75 77 90 93 97 98 102 103 107 111 115 119 127 130
149 154
Primary Contact: David-Paul Cavazos, Interim Chief Executive Officer
Web address: www.fultonmed.com
**Control**: Corporation, Investor–owned (for–profit) **Service**: General medical and
surgical

**Staffed Beds: 37 Admissions: 407 Census: 16 Outpatient Visits: 12560
Births: 0 Total Expense ($000): 16984 Payroll Expense ($000): 4947
Personnel: 122**

☐ **FULTON STATE HOSPITAL (264004)**, 600 East Fifth Street, Zip 65251–1753;
tel. 573/592–4100, (Nonreporting) **A**1 3 5 10 **F**3 4 11 29 30 39 44 50 53 56 57
58 59 75 77 82 86 87 98 100 101 102 103 130 132 135 143 146 149
Primary Contact: Robert Reitz, Ph.D., Chief Executive Officer
COO: Andrew Atkinson, Chief Operating Officer
CFO: Susie Kemp, Chief Financial Officer
CMO: Sanjiv Sethi, M.D., Medical Director
CIO: Keith Jones, Chief Information Officer
CHR: Lori French, Manager Human Resources
CNO: Susan Knoepflein, Chief Nurse Executive
Web address: www.dmh.missouri.gov/fulton
**Control**: State, Government, Nonfederal **Service**: Psychiatric

**Staffed Beds: 399 Admissions: 110 Census: 416 Outpatient Visits: 0
Births: 0 Total Expense ($000): 102595 Payroll Expense ($000): 49752
Personnel: 1230**

## HANNIBAL—Marion County

**HANNIBAL REG HEALTHCARE SYST** See Hannibal Regional Hospital

✠ **HANNIBAL REGIONAL HOSPITAL (260025)**, 6000 Hospital Drive,
Zip 63401–6887, Mailing Address: P.O. Box 551, Zip 63401–0551;
tel. 573/248–1300, (Nonreporting) **A**1 2 10 **F**3 13 15 20 22 26 28 29 31 34 35
40 45 47 49 51 57 59 62 64 68 70 74 75 76 78 79 81 85 86 87 89 90 92 107
108 110 111 115 117 118 119 120 121 123 124 129 130 132 135 148
Primary Contact: C Todd. Ahrens, President and Chief Executive Officer
CFO: Roger J Dix, Vice President Finance
CMO: Bryson McHardy, M.D., President Medical Staff
CIO: Jeff W. Evans, Vice President Information and Technology
CHR: Susan R Wathen, Vice President Human Resources
Web address: www.hannibalhealth.org
**Control**: Other not–for–profit (including NFP Corporation) **Service**: General
medical and surgical

**Staffed Beds: 99 Admissions: 4776 Census: 48 Outpatient Visits: 232632
Births: 605 Total Expense ($000): 185642 Payroll Expense ($000): 77553
Personnel: 856**

## HARRISONVILLE—Cass County

**CASS MEDICAL CENTER** See Cass Regional Medical Center

✠ **CASS REGIONAL MEDICAL CENTER (261324)**, 2800 East Rock Haven Road,
Zip 64701–4411; tel. 816/380–3474, (Nonreporting) **A**1 10 18 **F**3 11 12 15 17
18 28 29 30 31 34 35 40 43 44 45 46 48 50 54 56 57 59 64 65 66 70 74 75
77 78 79 80 81 82 84 85 86 87 90 98 102 103 107 110 111 114 115 119
127 129 130 131 132 133 135 145 146 148 149 154 156 **P**6
Primary Contact: John Christopher. Lang, FACHE, Chief Executive Officer
CFO: Brent Probasco, Chief Financial Officer
CIO: Lester Vohs, Manager Information Systems
CHR: Carla Wallen, Manager Human Resources
CNO: Twila Buckner, R.N., Chief Nursing Officer
Web address: www.cassregional.org
**Control**: County, Government, Nonfederal **Service**: General medical and surgical

**Staffed Beds: 35 Admissions: 974 Census: 14 Outpatient Visits: 107816
Births: 0 Total Expense ($000): 68292 Payroll Expense ($000): 25305
Personnel: 366**

## HAYTI—Pemiscot County

**PEMISCOT MEMORIAL HEALTH SYSTEM (260070)**, 946 East Reed
Street, Zip 63851–1245, Mailing Address: P.O. Box 489, Zip 63851–0489;
tel. 573/359–1372, (Total facility includes 66 beds in nursing home–type
unit) (Nonreporting) **A**10 **F**3 29 30 34 39 40 50 57 59 64 67 68 70 75 81
82 85 87 90 93 97 98 99 103 104 107 119 127 128 130 133 144 149
156 **P**6
Primary Contact: David DeCeault, Chief Executive Officer
CHR: Jackie Powell, Director Human Resources
Web address: www.pemiscot.org/
**Control**: County, Government, Nonfederal **Service**: General medical and surgical

**Staffed Beds: 167 Admissions: 1256 Census: 72 Outpatient Visits: 7928
Births: 0 Total Expense ($000): 32895 Payroll Expense ($000): 13315
Personnel: 343**

**PEMISCOT MEMORIAL HLTH SYSTEMS** See Pemiscot Memorial Health
System

## HERMANN—Gasconade County

**HERMANN AREA DISTRICT HOSPITAL (261314)**, 509 West 18th
Street, Zip 65041–1547, Mailing Address: P.O. Box 470, Zip 65041–0470;
tel. 573/486–2191, (Nonreporting) **A**10 18 **F**3 11 12 15 18 28 29 34 35 40 41
44 45 56 57 59 62 64 67 75 77 78 79 81 85 86 87 89 90 93 96 97 104 107
110 111 114 119 127 128 129 130 133 143 146 **P**6
Primary Contact: Dan McKinney, Administrator
COO: Matt Siebert, Assistant Administrator Ancillary Services
CFO: Christine Lewis, Assistant Administrator, Finance
CMO: Michael Rothermich, M.D., Chief of Staff
CIO: Dee Vaughan, Director Information Technology
CNO: Sue Daller, R.N., Assistant Administrator Nursing
Web address: www.hadh.org
**Control**: Hospital district or authority, Government, Nonfederal **Service**: General
medical and surgical

**Staffed Beds: 24 Admissions: 456 Census: 11 Outpatient Visits: 69504
Births: 0 Total Expense ($000): 17455 Payroll Expense ($000): 8545
Personnel: 156**

## HOUSTON—Texas County

**TEXAS COUNTY MEMORIAL HOSPITAL (260024)**, 1333 South Sam Houston
Boulevard, Zip 65483–2046; tel. 417/967–3311, (Nonreporting) **A**5 10 20 **F**3 7
28 29 34 45 57 59 62 63 64 70 76 81 85 86 89 93 97 110 111 115 119 127
129 130 133 143 148 149
Primary Contact: Wesley E. Murray, Chief Executive Officer
CFO: Linda Pamperien, Chief Financial Officer
CMO: Charles Mueller, M.D., Chief of Staff
CHR: Anita Kuhn, Controller
Web address: www.tcmh.org
**Control**: County, Government, Nonfederal **Service**: General medical and surgical

**Staffed Beds: 47 Admissions: 1135 Census: 11 Outpatient Visits: 104384
Births: 146 Total Expense ($000): 34846 Payroll Expense ($000): 18264
Personnel: 329**

## INDEPENDENCE—Jackson County

✠ **CENTERPOINT MEDICAL CENTER (260095)**, 19600 East 39th Street,
Zip 64057–2301; tel. 816/698–7000, (Nonreporting) **A**1 2 3 5 10 **F**3 8 12 13 15
18 20 22 24 26 28 29 30 31 34 35 38 40 43 46 47 48 49 50 52 54 55 56 57
59 60 64 68 70 72 74 75 76 77 78 79 80 81 82 85 86 87 90 92 93 107 108
110 111 114 115 116 117 118 119 120 121 123 124 126 129 130 131 132
144 145 146 147 148 149 154 **S** HCA Healthcare, Nashville, TN
Primary Contact: Bret Kolman, CPA, FACHE, Chief Executive Officer
CFO: James H Brown, Chief Financial Officer
CMO: Christopher Sullivan, M.D., Chief Medical Officer
CIO: Carl Sifers, Director Information Technology and System Services
CHR: Kyla Stoltz, Vice President Human Resources
CNO: Lynn Barrett, Chief Nursing Officer
Web address: www.centerpointmedical.com
**Control**: Corporation, Investor–owned (for–profit) **Service**: General medical and
surgical

**Staffed Beds: 285 Admissions: 15959 Census: 193 Outpatient
Visits: 160472 Births: 1355 Total Expense ($000): 285309 Payroll
Expense ($000): 87524 Personnel: 1161**

**MO**

## JEFFERSON CITY—Cole County

✠ **CAPITAL REGION MEDICAL CENTER (260047)**, 1125 Madison Street,
Zip 65101–5200, Mailing Address: P.O. Box 1128, Zip 65102–1128;
tel. 573/632–5000, (Nonreporting) **A**1 3 5 10 12 13 **F**3 11 15 17 18 20 22 24
26 28 29 30 31 34 35 36 38 40 45 46 47 48 49 50 51 53 57 58 59 60 61 64 65
68 70 73 74 75 76 77 78 79 80 81 82 85 87 89 90 92 93 96 97 100 107 108
110 111 115 117 118 119 120 121 123 126 129 130 131 132 135 144 146
147 148 149 150 154 **S** University of Missouri Health Care, Columbia, MO
Primary Contact: Gaspare Calvaruso, President
COO: Janet Weckenborg, Vice President Operations
CFO: Tom Luebbering, Vice President Finance
CMO: Mitchell Godbee, Chief of Staff
CIO: Jason Cecil, Vice President, Information
CHR: Sarah Morrow, Vice President Human Resources
Web address: www.crmc.org
**Control**: Other not–for–profit (including NFP Corporation) **Service**: General
medical and surgical

**Staffed Beds: 114 Admissions: 5701 Census: 57 Outpatient
Visits: 457992 Births: 608 Total Expense ($000): 213284 Payroll Expense
($000): 86143 Personnel: 1196**

✠ **SSM HEALTH ST. MARY'S HOSPITAL - JEFFERSON CITY (260011)**, 2505
Mission Drive, Zip 65109; tel. 573/681–3000, (Nonreporting) **A**1 10 19 **F**3 11 13
15 17 18 20 22 24 28 29 30 31 34 40 45 46 47 48 49 50 51 53 57 60 68 70
73 74 75 76 78 79 81 82 84 85 86 87 89 90 98 102 107 108 110 111 115
118 119 120 121 122 123 129 130 131 132 135 146 147 148 149 154 157 **S**
SSM Health, Saint Louis, MO
Primary Contact: Michael A. Baumgartner, President
CFO: James Stratton, Vice President Finance
CMO: Stephen Stewart, M.D., Vice President Medical Affairs
CHR: Susan Mankoski, Vice President Human Resources
CNO: Alice M Chatley, R.N., MSN, Vice President Acute Care Services
Web address: www.lethealingbegin.com
**Control**: Church operated, Nongovernment, not–for–profit **Service**: General
medical and surgical

**Staffed Beds: 92 Admissions: 6578 Census: 66 Outpatient Visits: 234864
Births: 856 Total Expense ($000): 163089 Payroll Expense ($000): 54223
Personnel: 833**

**ST. MARYS HEALTH CENTER** See Ssm Health St. Mary's Hospital - Jefferson City

## JOPLIN—Newton County

★ ○ **FREEMAN HEALTH SYSTEM (260137)**, 1102 West 32nd Street,
Zip 64804–3503; tel. 417/347–1111, (Includes FREEMAN HOSPITAL EAST, Mailing
address: 932 East 34th Street, Joplin, Missouri, Zip 64804–3999, 1102 West 32nd
Street, Zip 64804–3999, tel. 417/347–1111; Paula F Baker, President and Chief
Executive Officer), (Nonreporting) **A**3 5 10 11 13 19 **F**3 7 8 11 12 13 15 17 18 20
22 24 26 28 30 31 34 35 40 43 44 45 46 47 48 49 50 54 56 57 59 60 61 62 64
65 68 70 72 73 74 75 76 77 78 79 81 82 83 84 85 86 87 89 90 92 93 94 96 97
98 100 102 103 107 108 110 111 115 117 119 120 121 124 129 130 131 132
144 145 146 147 148 156 **P**1 6 **S** Freeman Health System, Joplin, MO
Primary Contact: Paula F. Baker, President and Chief Executive Officer
CFO: Steve W Graddy, Chief Financial Officer
CMO: Saba Habis, M.D., Chief Medical Officer
CIO: Skip Rollins, Chief Information Officer
CHR: Mary Frerer, Chief Human Resources Officer
CNO: Jeffrey Carrier, R.N., MS, FACHE, Chief Clinical Officer
Web address: www.freemanhealth.com
**Control**: Other not–for–profit (including NFP Corporation) **Service**: General
medical and surgical

**Staffed Beds: 380 Admissions: 18099 Census: 247 Outpatient
Visits: 637224 Births: 1975 Total Expense ($000): 511510 Payroll
Expense ($000): 237544 Personnel: 3281**

**FREEMAN HOSPITAL WEST** See Freeman Health System

**LANDMARK HOSP OF JOPLIN** See Landmark Hospital of Joplin

**LANDMARK HOSPITAL OF JOPLIN (262016)**, 2040 West 32nd Street,
Zip 64804–3512; tel. 417/627–1300, (Nonreporting) **A**10 22 **F**1 3 29 60 65 75
77 90 119 130 148 154 **S** Landmark Hospitals, Cape Girardeau, MO
Primary Contact: Suzann Gomillion, Interim Chief Executive Officer
CMO: Jack Rhoads, M.D., Medical Director
CHR: Janice Nordstrom, Director Human Resources
CNO: Stephanie Slater-Nesuold, Director of Nursing
Web address: www.landmarkhospitals.com
**Control**: Corporation, Investor–owned (for–profit) **Service**: Acute long–term care
hospital

**Staffed Beds: 28 Admissions: 290 Census: 18 Outpatient Visits: 0
Births: 0 Total Expense ($000): 12137 Payroll Expense ($000): 5105
Personnel: 95**

✠ **MERCY HOSPITAL JOPLIN (260001)**, 100 Mercy Way, Zip 64804–1626;
tel. 417/781–2727, (Includes ST. JOHN'S REHABILITATION CENTER, Mailing address:
2727 McClelland Boulevard, Joplin, Missouri, Zip 64804; tel. 417/659–6716),
(Nonreporting) **A**1 2 10 19 **F**3 5 7 11 12 13 14 15 17 18 19 20 22 24 26 28 29
30 31 34 35 38 39 40 43 44 45 46 47 48 49 51 54 57 58 59 60 61 64 65 66 68
70 72 73 74 75 76 77 78 79 81 83 85 86 87 89 93 94 97 98 99 100 101 102
104 107 108 110 111 114 115 119 120 121 123 124 126 127 129 130 131
132 135 144 146 147 148 154 156 **P**6 **S** Mercy, Chesterfield, MO
Primary Contact: Jeremy Drinkwitz, President and Chief Executive Officer
CHR: Timothy Murphy, Vice President Human Resources
CNO: Kelli Bigando, Chief Nursing Officer
Web address: www.mercy.net/joplinmo
**Control**: Church operated, Nongovernment, not–for–profit **Service**: General
medical and surgical

**Staffed Beds: 237 Admissions: 12945 Census: 156 Outpatient
Visits: 298064 Births: 1170 Total Expense ($000): 240220 Payroll
Expense ($000): 88042 Personnel: 1348**

**OAK HILL HOSPITAL** See Freeman Hospital East

**ST. JOHN'S REGIONAL MEDICAL CENTER** See Mercy Hospital Joplin

## KANSAS CITY—Jackson County

☐ **CENTER FOR BEHAVIORAL MEDICINE (264008)**, 1000 East 24th Street,
Zip 64108–2776; tel. 816/512–7000, (Total facility includes 25 beds in nursing
home–type unit) (Nonreporting) **A**1 3 5 10 **F**4 53 86 87 98 106
Primary Contact: Denise Norbury, MS, R.N., Regional Chief Executive Officer
COO: Megan Roedel, Chief Operating Officer
CFO: Tyler Rinehart, Chief Financial Officer
CMO: Maheshkumar Patel, M.D., Medical Director
CIO: Robert Curren, Director Information Technology
CHR: Silva Ward, Director Human Resources
CNO: John Tucker, Chief Nursing Executive
Web address: www.dmhonline.dmh.state.mo.us
**Control**: State, Government, Nonfederal **Service**: Psychiatric

**Staffed Beds: 90 Admissions: 68 Census: 82 Outpatient Visits: 0
Births: 0 Total Expense ($000): 25234 Payroll Expense ($000): 13692
Personnel: 234**

✠ △ **CHILDREN'S MERCY HOSPITAL KANSAS CITY (263302)**, 2401 Gillham
Road, Zip 64108–4619; tel. 816/234–3000, (Nonreporting) **A**1 3 5 7 8 10 **F**3 7
8 9 11 12 16 19 20 21 22 23 24 25 26 27 29 30 31 32 34 35 36 38 39 40 41
43 44 48 50 54 55 57 58 59 60 61 62 64 65 68 72 73 74 75 77 78 79 81 82
84 85 86 87 88 89 90 91 92 93 94 96 97 100 101 104 107 108 111 115 117
118 119 130 131 132 134 136 137 138 139 141 142 144 146 148 149 150
154 155 156 157
Primary Contact: Paul D. Kempinski, Chief Executive Officer
COO: Jo W. Stueve, Executive Vice President and Co-Chief Operating Officer
CFO: David Cauble, Executive Vice President and Chief Financial Officer
CMO: Charles Roberts, M.D., Executive Vice President and Executive Medical
Director
CIO: David Chou, Vice President, Chief Information and Digital Officer
CNO: Cheri Hunt, Vice President Patient Care Services and Chief Nursing Officer
Web address: www.childrensmercy.org
**Control**: Other not–for–profit (including NFP Corporation) **Service**: Children's
general medical and surgical

**Staffed Beds: 314 Admissions: 13438 Census: 238 Outpatient
Visits: 452376 Births: 159 Total Expense ($000): 1294439 Payroll
Expense ($000): 599972 Personnel: 6256**

**CHILDREN'S MERCY KANSAS CITY** See Children's Mercy Hospital Kansas City

**CRITTENTON CHILDREN'S CENTER** See Saint Luke's Hospital of Kansas City
Crittenton Children's Center

✠ **KANSAS CITY VETERANS AFFAIRS MEDICAL CENTER**, 4801 East Linwood
Boulevard, Zip 64128–2226; tel. 816/861–4700, (Nonreporting) **A**1 2 3 5 **S**
Department of Veterans Affairs, Washington, DC
Primary Contact: David Isaacks, Medical Center Director
CFO: Bryan Bieri, Manager Finance
CMO: Ahmad Batrash, Chief of Staff
CIO: Eddie Johnson, Chief Information Technology Officer
CHR: Kathi Nippert, Acting Chief Human Resources Officer
Web address: www.kansascity.va.gov/
**Control**: Veterans Affairs, Government, federal **Service**: General medical and
surgical

**Staffed Beds: 157**

MO

*Many Facility Codes have changed. Please refer to the AHA Guide Code Chart.*    © 2021 AHA Guide

✠ **KINDRED HOSPITAL NORTHLAND (262018)**, 500 Northwest 68th Street, Zip 64118–2455; tel. 816/420–6300, (Nonreporting) **A**1 10 **S** Kindred Healthcare, Louisville, KY
Primary Contact: Laura Inge, MSN, R.N., Chief Executive Officer
CFO: Brett Stevenson, Controller
CMO: Sean R Muldoon, M.D., Senior Vice President and Chief Medical Officer-Kindred Healthcare, Hospital Division
Web address: www.khnorthland.com
**Control**: Corporation, Investor–owned (for–profit) **Service**: Acute long–term care hospital

**Staffed Beds: 35**

**NORTHLAND LTAC HOSPITAL** See Kindred Hospital Northland

✠ **RESEARCH MEDICAL CENTER (260027)**, 2316 East Meyer Boulevard, Zip 64132–1136; tel. 816/276–4000, (Includes RESEARCH PSYCHIATRIC CENTER, Mailing address: 2323 East 63rd Street, Kansas City, Missouri, Zip 64130–3462; tel. 816/444–8161; Shannon Griggs, Interim Chief Executive Officer) (Nonreporting) **A**1 3 5 10 **F**3 8 11 13 15 16 17 18 20 22 24 26 28 29 30 31 34 35 36 38 39 40 42 43 45 46 47 49 50 52 53 54 55 56 57 58 59 61 64 65 68 70 72 73 74 75 76 77 78 79 80 81 82 84 85 86 87 90 93 96 97 98 99 100 101 102 103 104 105 107 108 110 111 112 114 115 116 117 118 119 120 121 123 124 126 130 131 132 134 136 138 141 143 144 145 146 147 148 149 153 154 156 **P**6 **S** HCA Healthcare, Nashville, TN
Primary Contact: Ashley McClellan, FACHE, Chief Executive Officer
COO: Eric Becker, Chief Operating Officer
CFO: Susan Shreeve, Chief Financial Officer
CMO: James Bower, M.D., Chief Medical Officer
CIO: Shawn Kegley, Director Information Services
CHR: Charlotte O'Neal, Vice President Human Resources
Web address: www.researchmedicalcenter.com
**Control**: Corporation, Investor–owned (for–profit) **Service**: General medical and surgical

**Staffed Beds: 489 Admissions: 20289 Census: 318 Outpatient Visits: 162560 Births: 1064 Total Expense ($000): 542429 Payroll Expense ($000): 143357 Personnel: 1970**

**S JOSEPH MEDICAL CENTER** See St. Joseph Medical Center

✠ **SAINT LUKE'S HOSPITAL OF KANSAS CITY (260138)**, 4401 Wornall Road, Zip 64111–3220; tel. 816/932–3800, (Includes SAINT LUKE'S HOSPITAL OF KANSAS CITY CRITTENTON CHILDREN'S CENTER, Mailing address: 10918 Elm Avenue, Kansas City, Missouri, Zip 64134–4108; tel. 816/765–6600; Jerrie Jacobs-Kenner, President), (Nonreporting) **A**1 2 3 5 8 10 **F**3 5 6 8 9 11 12 13 15 17 18 20 22 24 26 28 29 30 31 32 34 35 36 37 38 39 40 43 44 45 46 47 49 50 55 56 57 58 59 60 61 64 65 66 68 70 72 73 74 75 76 77 78 79 80 81 82 84 85 86 87 89 90 91 92 93 94 95 96 97 98 99 100 101 102 103 104 106 107 108 110 111 114 115 116 117 118 119 120 121 123 124 126 129 130 131 132 134 135 137 138 139 141 145 146 147 148 149 150 151 153 155 158 **S** Saint Luke's Health System, Kansas City, MO
Primary Contact: Jani L. Johnson, R.N., MSN, Chief Executive Officer
COO: Brad Simmons, Chief Operating Officer
CFO: Amy Nachtigal, Chief Financial Officer
CMO: Peter Holt, M.D., Director Medical Affairs
CIO: Deborah Gash, Chief Information Officer
CHR: Doris Rogers, Vice President Human Resources
CNO: Debra Wilson, MSN, Vice President and Chief Nursing Officer
Web address: www.saint-lukes.org
**Control**: Church operated, Nongovernment, not–for–profit **Service**: General medical and surgical

**Staffed Beds: 482 Admissions: 23205 Census: 374 Outpatient Visits: 300960 Births: 2280 Total Expense ($000): 852698 Payroll Expense ($000): 223133 Personnel: 3334**

✠ **SAINT LUKE'S NORTH HOSPITAL - BARRY ROAD (260062)**, 5830 NW Barry Road, Zip 64154–2778; tel. 816/891–6000, (Includes SAINT LUKE'S NORTH HOSPITAL-SMITHVILLE CAMPUS, Mailing address: 601 South 169 Highway, Smithville, Missouri, Zip 64089–9317; tel. 816/532–3700; Adele Ducharme, MSN, R.N., Chief Executive Officer), (Nonreporting) **A**1 2 10 **F**3 11 12 13 15 18 20 22 26 28 29 30 31 34 35 38 40 44 45 46 49 50 53 56 58 59 60 61 64 68 69 70 73 74 75 76 77 78 79 80 81 82 84 85 86 87 89 90 91 92 93 96 98 100 101 102 107 108 110 111 114 115 116 117 118 119 129 130 131 132 135 141 143 146 147 148 149 154 **S** Saint Luke's Health System, Kansas City, MO
Primary Contact: Adele Ducharme, MSN, R.N., Chief Executive Officer
CFO: Julie Murphy, Chief Financial Officer
CMO: Leonardo J Lozada, M.D., Chief Physician Executive
CIO: LaDonna Seger, Director Information Services
CHR: Donna Kunz, System Director Human Resources
CNO: Amy Brummer, MSN, Chief Nursing Officer
Web address: www.saint-lukes.org
**Control**: Church operated, Nongovernment, not–for–profit **Service**: General medical and surgical

**Staffed Beds: 139 Admissions: 7267 Census: 84 Outpatient Visits: 96640 Births: 180 Total Expense ($000): 153559 Payroll Expense ($000): 50141 Personnel: 697**

**SAINT LUKE'S NORTHLAND HOSPITAL - BARRY ROAD** See Saint Luke's North Hospital - Barry Road

☐ **SIGNATURE PSYCHIATRIC HOSPITAL (264030)**, 2900 Clay Edwards Drive, Zip 64116–3235; tel. 816/691–5101, (Nonreporting) **A**1
Primary Contact: Lisa St. Aubyn, Chief Executive Officer
CFO: Robert Jackson, Chief Financial Officer
CMO: Azfar Malik, M.D., Chief Medical Officer
CIO: Tariq Nazir, Interim Director Information Technology
CHR: Maria Griffith, Director Human Resources
Web address: www.sphkc.net
**Control**: Corporation, Investor–owned (for–profit) **Service**: Psychiatric

**Staffed Beds: 24**

**ST LUKE'S HOSPITAL** See Saint Luke's Hospital of Kansas City

☐ **ST. JOSEPH MEDICAL CENTER (260085)**, 1000 Carondelet Drive, Zip 64114–4673; tel. 816/942–4400, (Nonreporting) **A**1 10 **F**3 11 12 15 17 18 20 22 24 26 28 29 30 31 34 35 40 45 48 49 50 53 56 57 59 60 64 68 70 74 75 77 78 79 80 81 82 84 85 90 93 98 102 103 107 108 109 110 111 114 115 119 129 130 132 135 145 146 148 149 156 **S** Prime Healthcare, Ontario, CA
Primary Contact: Jodi Fincher, R.N., Administrator
CFO: Debra Cartwright, Chief Financial Officer
CMO: Tommy Ko, M.D., Chief Medical Officer
CIO: Cheryl Johnson, Regional Chief Information Officer
CHR: Donna Sumner, Director, Human Resources and Organizational Development
CNO: Greg Simpson, Chief Nursing Officer
Web address: www.stjosephkc.com/
**Control**: Individual, Investor–owned (for–profit) **Service**: General medical and surgical

**Staffed Beds: 179 Admissions: 6113 Census: 83 Outpatient Visits: 79856 Births: 0 Total Expense ($000): 149138 Payroll Expense ($000): 47075 Personnel: 682**

**TRUMAN MEDICAL CENTER** See Truman Medical Center-Hospital Hill

**TRUMAN MEDICAL CENTER-EAST** See Truman Medical Center-Lakewood

**MO**

**MO**

⌖ **TRUMAN MEDICAL CENTER-HOSPITAL HILL (260048)**, 2301 Holmes Street, Zip 64108–2640; tel. 816/404–1000, (Nonreporting) **A**1 2 3 5 8 10 **F**3 4 5 8 11 12 13 14 15 17 18 19 20 22 29 30 31 34 35 36 38 39 40 41 43 44 45 46 48 49 50 52 53 54 55 57 58 59 61 64 65 66 68 70 71 72 73 74 75 76 77 78 79 81 82 84 85 86 87 90 92 93 94 97 98 99 100 101 102 104 106 107 108 110 111 114 115 119 129 130 131 132 134 135 142 143 146 147 148 149 150 154 156 157 158 **S** Truman Medical Centers, Kansas City, MO
Primary Contact: Charlie Shields, President and Chief Executive Officer
CFO: Allen Johnson, Chief Financial Officer
CMO: Mark Steele, M.D., Chief Medical Officer
CIO: Mitzi Cardenas, Chief Administrative Officer
CHR: Ruth Pullins, Chief Human Resources Officer
CNO: Amy Peters, R.N., Chief Nursing Officer
Web address: www.trumed.org
**Control**: Other not–for–profit (including NFP Corporation) **Service**: General medical and surgical

**Staffed Beds**: 249 **Admissions**: 12775 **Census**: 193 **Outpatient Visits**: 495608 **Births**: 1748 **Total Expense ($000)**: 478260 **Payroll Expense ($000)**: 154221 **Personnel**: 2799

⌖ **TRUMAN MEDICAL CENTER-LAKEWOOD (260102)**, 7900 Lee's Summit Road, Zip 64139–1236; tel. 816/404–7000, (Total facility includes 188 beds in nursing home–type unit) (Nonreporting) **A**1 3 5 10 **F**3 4 6 11 13 15 18 29 30 32 34 35 36 38 39 40 44 45 50 56 57 58 59 64 65 66 67 68 70 71 72 74 75 76 77 78 79 81 84 85 86 87 89 90 93 94 96 97 98 99 100 101 102 103 104 107 111 115 119 126 128 130 131 132 134 135 143 146 147 148 149 150 154 157 **S** Truman Medical Centers, Kansas City, MO
Primary Contact: Charlie Shields, Chief Executive Officer
COO: Lynette Wheeler, MSN, Chief Operating Officer
CFO: Allen Johnson, Chief Financial Officer
CMO: Mark Steele, M.D., Chief Medical Officer
CIO: Mitzi Cardenas, Chief Administrative Officer
CHR: Ruth Pullins, Chief Human Resources Officer
CNO: Amy Peters, R.N., Chief Nursing Officer
Web address: www.trumed.org
**Control**: Other not–for–profit (including NFP Corporation) **Service**: General medical and surgical

**Staffed Beds**: 298 **Admissions**: 4433 **Census**: 226 **Outpatient Visits**: 443480 **Births**: 1573 **Total Expense ($000)**: 180631 **Payroll Expense ($000)**: 66230 **Personnel**: 981

**VETERANS AFFAIRS MEDICAL CENTER** See Kansas City Veterans Affairs Medical Center

**WESTERN MISSOURI MENTAL HEALTH CENTER** See Center for Behavioral Medicine

### KIRKSVILLE—Adair County

**KIRKSVILLE OSTEO MED CENTER** See Northeast Regional Medical Center

★ ○ **NORTHEAST REGIONAL MEDICAL CENTER (260022)**, 315 South Osteopathy Street, Zip 63501–6401, Mailing Address: P.O. Box C8502, Zip 63501–8599; tel. 660/785–1000, (Nonreporting) **A**3 5 10 11 12 13 **F**3 13 15 17 18 20 22 24 26 28 29 34 39 43 45 46 48 49 50 57 59 60 64 68 70 74 75 76 77 79 81 84 85 86 87 89 90 107 108 110 111 115 119 127 128 129 131 133 135 147 148 149 154 **S** Community Health Systems, Inc., Franklin, TN
Primary Contact: Ranee C. Brayton, FACHE, MSN, R.N., Chief Executive Officer
CFO: Carol Cross, CPA, Chief Financial Officer
CMO: Benjamin Schrant, M.D., Chief of Staff
CIO: Chad Tatro, Supervisor Information Systems
CHR: Jim Bergman, Director Human Resources
CNO: Peggy Parks, R.N., Chief Nursing Officer
Web address: www.nermc.com
**Control**: Corporation, Investor–owned (for–profit) **Service**: General medical and surgical

**Staffed Beds**: 50 **Admissions**: 2306 **Census**: 25 **Outpatient Visits**: 50816 **Births**: 533 **Total Expense ($000)**: 39644 **Payroll Expense ($000)**: 16801 **Personnel**: 369

### LAKE SAINT LOUIS—St. Charles County

⌖ **SSM HEALTH ST. JOSEPH HOSPITAL - LAKE SAINT LOUIS (260200)**, 100 Medical Plaza, Zip 63367–1366; tel. 636/625–5200, (Nonreporting) **A**1 2 10 **F**3 11 13 15 17 18 20 22 28 29 30 31 34 35 36 38 40 41 43 44 46 49 50 51 53 54 55 56 57 59 60 61 64 68 70 73 74 75 76 78 79 81 82 84 85 86 87 89 102 107 108 110 111 115 117 119 129 130 132 135 145 146 147 148 149 157 **P**6 8 **S** SSM Health, Saint Louis, MO
Primary Contact: Lisle Wescott, President
COO: Lee Bernstein, Regional Executive Vice President of Hospital and Chief Operating Officer
CFO: Hal Holder, Regional Chief Financial Officer
CMO: Michael Handler, M.D., Vice President Medical Affairs and Chief Medical Officer
CIO: Sharon Gardner, Manager Information Systems
CHR: Renee Roach, System Vice President
Web address: www.ssmstjoseph.com
**Control**: Church operated, Nongovernment, not–for–profit **Service**: General medical and surgical

**Staffed Beds**: 212 **Admissions**: 9108 **Census**: 96 **Outpatient Visits**: 182320 **Births**: 968 **Total Expense ($000)**: 177355 **Payroll Expense ($000)**: 63000 **Personnel**: 893

**SSM ST. JOSEPH HOSPITAL WEST** See Ssm Health St. Joseph Hospital - Lake Saint Louis

### LAMAR—Barton County

⇑ **BARTON COUNTY MEMORIAL HOSPITAL** See Cox Barton County Memorial Hospital

⇑ **COX BARTON COUNTY MEMORIAL HOSPITAL (261325)**, 29 NW First Lane, Zip 64759–8105; tel. 417/681–5100, (Nonreporting) **A**10 18 21 **F**3 11 15 18 28 30 34 35 40 44 45 50 57 59 64 68 74 75 77 79 81 84 85 86 87 89 90 92 93 97 107 108 110 111 114 119 127 128 129 130 132 133 135 146 148 149 154 156 **P**6 **S** CoxHealth, Springfield, MO
Primary Contact: Christopher B. Wyatt, President
CIO: Brad Butler, Network Administrator
CNO: Marlys Buckner, Chief Nursing Officer
Web address: www.bcmh.net
**Control**: Other not–for–profit (including NFP Corporation) **Service**: General medical and surgical

**Staffed Beds**: 25 **Admissions**: 517 **Census**: 6 **Outpatient Visits**: 35288 **Births**: 0 **Total Expense ($000)**: 22375 **Payroll Expense ($000)**: 11138 **Personnel**: 175

### LEBANON—Laclede County

⌖ **MERCY HOSPITAL LEBANON (260059)**, 100 Hospital Drive, Zip 65536–9210; tel. 417/533–6100, (Nonreporting) **A**1 10 20 **F**3 11 13 15 28 29 30 31 35 36 40 45 47 50 51 57 59 64 65 68 70 71 74 75 76 77 78 79 81 82 83 85 86 87 89 90 93 94 102 107 108 110 111 114 119 129 130 131 132 135 146 147 148 149 156 **S** Mercy, Chesterfield, MO
Primary Contact: Nicki Gamet, R.N., Administrator
CFO: Douglas M Hoban, Vice President and Chief Financial Officer
CNO: Judy O'Connor-Snyder, R.N., Chief Nursing Officer
Web address: www.mercy.net/practice/mercy-hospital-lebanon
**Control**: Church operated, Nongovernment, not–for–profit **Service**: General medical and surgical

**Staffed Beds**: 58 **Admissions**: 2080 **Census**: 16 **Outpatient Visits**: 130128 **Births**: 277 **Total Expense ($000)**: 71258 **Payroll Expense ($000)**: 27798 **Personnel**: 352

**ST. JOHN'S HOSPITAL - LEBANON** See Mercy Hospital Lebanon

### LEE'S SUMMIT—Jackson County

**LEE'S SUMMIT HOSPITAL** See Lee's Summit Medical Center

⌖ **LEE'S SUMMIT MEDICAL CENTER (260190)**, 2100 SE Blue Parkway, Zip 64063–1007; tel. 816/282–5000, (Nonreporting) **A**1 3 5 10 **F**3 12 15 18 20 22 29 30 31 34 40 45 48 49 57 59 64 65 69 70 74 75 77 78 79 80 81 82 84 85 87 93 96 107 110 111 114 115 119 126 129 130 131 145 146 148 149 154 **P**7 **S** HCA Healthcare, Nashville, TN
Primary Contact: John McDonald, Chief Executive Officer
COO: Patrick Kueny, Chief Operating Officer
CFO: John Heurtin, Chief Financial Officer
CIO: Andrew Beechy, Manager Information Technology Systems
CHR: Linda Duncan, Director Human Resources
CNO: Paige Baker, MSN, R.N., Chief Nursing Officer
Web address: www.leessummitmedicalcenter.com
**Control**: Corporation, Investor–owned (for–profit) **Service**: General medical and surgical

**Staffed Beds**: 80 **Admissions**: 4599 **Census**: 46 **Outpatient Visits**: 106168 **Births**: 0 **Total Expense ($000)**: 104591 **Payroll Expense ($000)**: 30525 **Personnel**: 342

*Many Facility Codes have changed. Please refer to the AHA Guide Code Chart.* © 2021 AHA Guide

**SAINT LUKE'S EAST HOSPITAL (260216)**, 100 NE Saint Luke's Boulevard, Zip 64086–6000; tel. 816/347–5000, (Nonreporting) **A**1 10 **F**3 12 13 15 18 20 22 26 28 29 30 31 34 35 38 40 44 45 46 47 49 50 51 56 57 58 59 60 61 64 65 70 72 73 74 75 76 77 78 79 80 81 82 84 85 86 87 89 90 91 92 93 94 96 100 102 103 107 108 110 111 114 115 117 118 119 120 121 123 126 129 130 131 132 135 141 145 146 147 148 149 154 **S** Saint Luke's Health System, Kansas City, MO
Primary Contact: Bobby Olm-Shipman, Chief Executive Officer
CFO: Joseph P Stasi, Chief Financial Officer
CHR: John Clabaugh, Director Human Resources
CNO: Gloria Solis, R.N., MSN, Chief Nursing Officer
Web address: www.saintlukeskc.org
**Control**: Church operated, Nongovernment, not–for–profit **Service**: General medical and surgical

Staffed Beds: **203** Admissions: **13952** Census: **148** Outpatient Visits: **160608** Births: **1843** Total Expense ($000): **266436** Payroll Expense ($000): **77441** Personnel: **1044**

**SAINT LUKE'S EAST-LEE'S SUMMIT** See Saint Luke's East Hospital

### LEXINGTON—Lafayette County

**LAFAYETTE REGIONAL HEALTH CENTER (261320)**, 1500 State Street, Zip 64067–1107; tel. 660/259–2203, (Nonreporting) **A**1 10 18 **F**11 15 29 31 40 68 70 75 78 79 81 85 93 107 110 111 114 116 119 127 129 130 133 147 149 156 **P**6 **S** HCA Healthcare, Nashville, TN
Primary Contact: Darrel Box, Chief Executive Officer
COO: Daniel Astleford, Vice President Operations
CFO: Teri James, Chief Financial Officer
CIO: Keith Richcreek, Manager Technical Services
CHR: Stephen Davidson, Director Human Resources
CNO: Kim Leakey, R.N., Chief Nursing Officer
Web address: www.lafayetteregionalhealthcenter.com
**Control**: Corporation, Investor–owned (for–profit) **Service**: General medical and surgical

Staffed Beds: **25** Admissions: **806** Census: **7** Outpatient Visits: **65632** Births: **0** Total Expense ($000): **30654** Payroll Expense ($000): **9713** Personnel: **178**

**LAFAYETTE REGIONAL HEALTH CNTR** See Lafayette Regional Health Center

### LIBERTY—Clay County

**LIBERTY HOSPITAL (260177)**, 2525 Glenn Hendren Dive, Zip 64068–9600, Mailing Address: P.O. Box 1002, Zip 64069–1002; tel. 816/781–7200, (Nonreporting) **A**1 2 10 **F**3 8 11 13 15 17 18 20 22 24 26 28 29 30 31 34 35 37 40 43 45 46 47 48 49 59 61 62 63 64 65 69 70 73 74 75 76 77 78 79 80 81 82 83 84 85 86 87 90 92 93 96 97 107 108 110 111 114 115 117 118 119 126 129 130 131 132 144 147 148 149 154 156
Primary Contact: David Feess, CPA, President and Chief Executive Officer
CFO: Dan Williams, Vice President Finance and Support
CMO: Robert Haas, M.D., Chief Medical Officer
CIO: Paul Klehn, Chief Information Technology Officer
CHR: Nancy E Cattell, Vice President Human Resources
Web address: www.Libertyhospital.org
**Control**: Hospital district or authority, Government, Nonfederal **Service**: General medical and surgical

Staffed Beds: **171** Admissions: **7807** Census: **84** Outpatient Visits: **339024** Births: **1455** Total Expense ($000): **237304** Payroll Expense ($000): **114322** Personnel: **1611**

### LOUISIANA—Pike County

**PIKE COUNTY MEMORIAL HOSPITAL (261333)**, 2305 Georgia Street, Zip 63353–2559; tel. 573/754–5531, (Nonreporting) **A**1 10 18 **F**3 7 11 15 18 28 29 30 34 35 40 45 50 53 54 56 57 59 64 65 68 74 75 77 79 81 85 86 87 89 90 93 97 100 107 110 115 127 130 131 132 133 147 148 149 156
Primary Contact: Tylie Mills, R.N., Chief Executive Officer
CFO: Ann Tran, Chief Financial Officer
CIO: Jeremy Gruen, Director Information Systems
CHR: Layne Ebers, Director Human Resources and Marketing
CNO: Dolly Giles, Chief Nursing Officer
Web address: www.pcmh-mo.org
**Control**: County, Government, Nonfederal **Service**: General medical and surgical

Staffed Beds: **25** Admissions: **304** Census: **4** Outpatient Visits: **42720** Births: **0** Total Expense ($000): **19169** Payroll Expense ($000): **9387** Personnel: **191**

### MACON—Macon County

**SAMARITAN HOSPITAL (261313)**, 1205 North Missouri Street, Zip 63552–2095; tel. 660/385–8700, (Nonreporting) **A**10 18 **F**3 7 8 9 11 28 29 34 35 40 45 46 53 56 57 59 63 64 65 68 75 77 79 81 82 84 85 86 87 89 90 93 94 107 111 115 119 127 128 129 130 133 146 148 154 **P**6
Primary Contact: Bernard A. Orman Jr, FACHE, Chief Executive Officer
CFO: Susan Spencer, Chief Financial Officer
CHR: Suzanne Britt, Director Human Resources
Web address: www.samaritanhospital.net
**Control**: County, Government, Nonfederal **Service**: General medical and surgical

Staffed Beds: **25** Admissions: **794** Census: **14** Outpatient Visits: **60616** Births: **0** Total Expense ($000): **26963** Payroll Expense ($000): **9566** Personnel: **195**

**SAMARITAN MEMORIAL HOSPITAL** See Samaritan Hospital

### MARSHALL—Saline County

★ **FITZGIBBON HOSPITAL (260142)**, 2305 South 65 Highway, Zip 65340–0250, Mailing Address: P.O. Box 250, Zip 65340–0250; tel. 660/886–7431, (Nonreporting) **A**10 20 **F**3 11 13 15 30 31 33 34 35 40 45 56 57 59 62 63 64 65 68 70 74 75 76 77 78 79 81 85 87 89 90 93 98 103 104 107 108 110 111 119 120 121 127 128 130 131 132 133 146 147 148
Primary Contact: Angela P. Littrell, CPA, President and Chief Executive Officer
CMO: Darin L. Haug, D.O., Chief Medical Officer
CIO: Tom Jones, Chief Information Officer
CHR: Jessica Henderson, Manager Human Resources
CNO: Angela Igo, MSN, R.N., Chief Nursing Officer
Web address: www.fitzgibbon.org
**Control**: Other not–for–profit (including NFP Corporation) **Service**: General medical and surgical

Staffed Beds: **52** Admissions: **1961** Census: **16** Outpatient Visits: **96880** Births: **215** Total Expense ($000): **56876** Payroll Expense ($000): **24451** Personnel: **444**

**JOHN FITZGIBBON MEM HOSPITAL** See Fitzgibbon Hospital

### MARYLAND HEIGHTS—St. Louis County

**RANKEN JORDAN - A PEDIATRIC SPECIALTY HOSPITAL** See Ranken Jordan Pediatric Bridge Hospital

★ **RANKEN JORDAN PEDIATRIC BRIDGE HOSPITAL (263303)**, 11365 Dorsett Road, Zip 63043–3411; tel. 314/872–6400, (Nonreporting) **A**3 5 10 **F**1 3 12 16 29 30 32 34 35 44 50 53 64 75 77 80 86 87 89 90 91 92 93 94 96 99 146 148 149
Primary Contact: Brett Moorehouse, FACHE, Chief Executive Officer
CFO: Kenneth Marx, Chief Financial Officer
CMO: Nicholas Holekamp, M.D., Chief Medical Officer
CHR: Erin Bachelier, Human Resource Administrator
Web address: www.rankenjordan.org
**Control**: Other not–for–profit (including NFP Corporation) **Service**: Children's rehabilitation

Staffed Beds: **60** Admissions: **262** Census: **37** Outpatient Visits: **5272** Births: **0** Total Expense ($000): **38293** Payroll Expense ($000): **20579** Personnel: **359**

### MARYVILLE—Nodaway County

**MOSAIC MEDICAL CENTER - MARYVILLE (260050)**, 2016 South Main Street, Zip 64468–2655; tel. 660/562–2600, (Data for 91 days) (Nonreporting) **A**1 10 20 **F**3 11 13 15 18 28 29 30 31 34 35 38 40 45 57 59 64 65 68 70 75 76 77 78 79 81 82 84 85 86 89 90 93 96 97 98 99 102 103 104 107 111 115 116 117 118 119 127 128 130 131 132 133 135 146 149 154 **S** Mosaic Life Care, Saint Joseph, MO
Primary Contact: Nate Blackford, President
COO: Frank Grispino, Vice President Operations
CFO: Jocelyn Skidmore, Director Finance
CMO: Shirley Harris, M.D., President Medical Staff
CIO: Dave Lewis, Director Information Services
CHR: Krista Barcus, Human Resources Leader
CNO: Debbie Hoffman, Vice President Patient Services
Web address: www.mymosaiclifecare.org
**Control**: Other not–for–profit (including NFP Corporation) **Service**: General medical and surgical

Staffed Beds: **50** Admissions: **359** Census: **15** Outpatient Visits: **28064** Births: **60** Total Expense ($000): **14910** Payroll Expense ($000): **7445** Personnel: **409**

**SSM HEALTH ST. FRANCIS HOSPITAL - MARYVILLE** See Mosaic Medical Center - Maryville

MO

---

**Hospital, Medicare Provider Number, Address, Telephone, Approval, Facility, and Physician Codes, Health Care System**

★ American Hospital Association (AHA) membership
☐ The Joint Commission accreditation
○ Healthcare Facilities Accreditation Program
◇ DNV Healthcare Inc. accreditation
⇑ Center for Improvement in Healthcare Quality Accreditation
△ Commission on Accreditation of Rehabilitation Facilities (CARF) accreditation

## MEMPHIS—Scotland County

★ **SCOTLAND COUNTY HOSPITAL (261310)**, 450 Sigler Avenue,
Zip 63555–1726, Mailing Address: 450 E Sigler Avenue, Zip 63555–1726;
tel. 660/465–8511, (Nonreporting) **A**10 18
Primary Contact: Randy Tobler, M.D., Chief Executive Officer
CFO: Sheryl Templeton, Chief Financial Officer
CMO: Randy Tobler, M.D., Chief Medical Officer
CIO: Ken McMinn, Director Information Technology
CHR: Missy Smith, Coordinator Human Resources
CNO: Carla Cook, Director of Nursing
Web address: www.scotlandcountyhospital.com
**Control:** Hospital district or authority, Government, Nonfederal **Service:** General
medical and surgical

| Staffed Beds: 25 |
|---|

SCOTLAND COUNTY MEMORIAL HOSPITAL See Scotland County Hospital

## MEXICO—Audrain County

AUDRAIN MEDICAL CENTER See Ssm Health St. Mary's Hospital - Audrain

✠ **SSM HEALTH ST. MARY'S HOSPITAL - AUDRAIN (260064)**, 620 East Monroe
Street, Zip 65265–2919; tel. 573/582–5000, (Nonreporting) **A**1 2 10 **F**3 11 15
18 20 22 26 28 29 30 31 34 40 45 54 57 59 64 70 75 77 78 79 81 82 85 87
90 93 98 103 107 110 111 115 118 119 121 123 127 129 130 132 144 146
147 149 **S** SSM Health, Saint Louis, MO
Primary Contact: Michael A. Baumgartner, President
CFO: James Stratton, Regional Vice President Finance
CMO: Diane Jacobi, Chief of Staff
CIO: Dawn Evans, Manager Information Technology
CHR: Christy Smiley, Leader Human Resources
CNO: Romida Sison-Martinez, MBA, R.N., Vice President Nursing
Web address: www.https://www.ssmhealth.com
**Control:** Church operated, Nongovernment, not–for–profit **Service:** General
medical and surgical

| Staffed Beds: 49 Admissions: 1293 Census: 19 Outpatient Visits: 125776 |
|---|
| Births: 26 Total Expense ($000): 64458 Payroll Expense ($000): 19902 |
| Personnel: 275 |

## MILAN—Sullivan County

★ **SULLIVAN COUNTY MEMORIAL HOSPITAL (261306)**, 630 West Third Street,
Zip 63556–1076; tel. 660/265–4212, (Nonreporting) **A**10 18 **F**28 29 32 33 34
40 57 59 65 67 68 77 81 93 97 107 111 114 119 127 128 130 133 147 148
149 154 **P**5 6
Primary Contact: Tony Keene, Chief Executive Officer
COO: Amy J Michael, Chief Operating Officer
CMO: Dale Essmyer, M.D., Chief of Staff
CIO: Vern Johnson, Director Information Technology
CHR: Rae A. Ashby, Director Human Resources
CNO: Tina Sears, Director Patient Care Services
Web address: www.scmhospital.org
**Control:** County, Government, Nonfederal **Service:** General medical and surgical

| Staffed Beds: 25 Admissions: 202 Census: 9 Outpatient Visits: 21064 |
|---|
| Births: 0 Total Expense ($000): 8874 Payroll Expense ($000): 3811 |
| Personnel: 90 |

## MOBERLY—Randolph County

✠ **MOBERLY REGIONAL MEDICAL CENTER (260074)**, 1515 Union Avenue,
Zip 65270–9449; tel. 660/263–8400, (Nonreporting) **A**1 3 5 10 20 **F**3 18 20 22 26
28 29 30 34 35 38 40 44 45 46 50 51 53 56 57 59 64 70 74 75 77 79 81 85 86
87 89 90 93 96 97 98 100 103 107 108 111 115 119 126 127 128 130 131 133
135 141 146 148 149 154 **P**5 **S** Community Health Systems, Inc., Franklin, TN
Primary Contact: Brent Parsons, Chief Executive Officer
COO: Tracey Matheis, Chief Operating Officer
CFO: Tracey Matheis, Chief Financial Officer
CMO: Heather Gessling, M.D., Chief Medical Officer
CHR: Michael Turner, Director Human Resources
CNO: Patsy Lewellen, Interim Chief Nursing Officer
Web address: www.https://www.moberlyregionalmedicalcenter.com
**Control:** Corporation, Investor–owned (for–profit) **Service:** General medical and surgical

| Staffed Beds: 99 Admissions: 1293 Census: 20 Outpatient Visits: 47144 |
|---|
| Births: 0 Total Expense ($000): 43669 Payroll Expense ($000): 13398 |
| Personnel: 258 |

MOBERLY REGIONAL MEDICAL CNTR See Moberly Regional Medical Center

## MONETT—Barry County

⇧ COX MONETT See Cox Monett Hospital

⇧ **COX MONETT HOSPITAL (261329)**, 801 North Lincoln Avenue,
Zip 65708–1641; tel. 417/235–3144, (Nonreporting) **A**10 18 21 **F**3 11 13 15
18 28 29 30 32 34 35 40 45 50 56 57 59 64 68 69 76 77 81 85 89 90 93
107 111 114 119 127 128 129 130 131 133 135 144 146 147 148 154 **P**6 **S**
CoxHealth, Springfield, MO
Primary Contact: Darren Bass, President
CFO: Josh Powell, Facility Controller
CMO: Frank Romero, M.D., Vice President Medical Affairs and Chief Medical Officer
CHR: Debra Isenmann, Human Resources Generalist
CNO: Bev Eli, Chief Nursing Officer
Web address: www.coxhealth.com
**Control:** Other not–for–profit (including NFP Corporation) **Service:** General
medical and surgical

| Staffed Beds: 25 Admissions: 868 Census: 8 Outpatient Visits: 115352 |
|---|
| Births: 283 Total Expense ($000): 43408 Payroll Expense ($000): 21141 |
| Personnel: 322 |

## MOUNTAIN VIEW—Howell County

✠ **MERCY ST. FRANCIS HOSPITAL (261335)**, 100 West Highway 60,
Zip 65548–7125; tel. 417/934–7000, (Nonreporting) **A**1 10 18 **F**3 11 15 28 29
30 34 45 50 57 59 64 65 75 77 81 85 89 93 107 110 111 114 119 129 131
132 133 148 154 **S** Mercy, Chesterfield, MO
Primary Contact: Cynthia Weatherford, R.N., Administrator and Director of Nursing
CFO: Sherry Clouse Day, CPA, Chief Financial Officer
CMO: Barry Spoon, M.D., Chief of Staff
CHR: Tracy Smith, Director Human Resources
Web address: www.stjohns.com/aboutus/stfrancis.aspx
**Control:** Church operated, Nongovernment, not–for–profit **Service:** General
medical and surgical

| Staffed Beds: 20 Admissions: 265 Census: 3 Outpatient Visits: 23784 |
|---|
| Births: 0 Total Expense ($000): 14084 Payroll Expense ($000): 6845 |
| Personnel: 92 |

ST. JOHN'S ST. FRANCIS HOSPITAL See Mercy St. Francis Hospital

## NEOSHO—Newton County

★ **FREEMAN NEOSHO HOSPITAL (261331)**, 113 West Hickory Street,
Zip 64850–1705; tel. 417/455–4352, (Nonreporting) **A**10 18 **F**3 11 15 28 30 34
35 40 44 45 47 50 56 57 59 64 68 70 75 77 79 81 84 85 86 87 90 93 97 107
110 111 114 119 127 130 131 132 133 **S** Freeman Health System, Joplin, MO
Primary Contact: Renee Denton, Chief Operating Officer
CFO: Steve W Graddy, Chief Financial Officer
CMO: Rodney McFarland, M.D., Medical Director
CIO: Sue Annesser, Director Information Systems
CHR: Mary Frerer, Chief Human Resources Officer
Web address: www.freemanhealth.com
**Control:** Other not–for–profit (including NFP Corporation) **Service:** General
medical and surgical

| Staffed Beds: 25 Admissions: 874 Census: 9 Outpatient Visits: 75840 |
|---|
| Births: 0 Total Expense ($000): 25657 Payroll Expense ($000): 11770 |
| Personnel: 177 |

SALE HOSPITAL See Freeman Neosho Hospital

## NEVADA—Vernon County

☐ **HEARTLAND BEHAVIORAL HEALTH SERVICES**, 1500 West Ashland Street,
Zip 64772–1710; tel. 417/667–2666, (Nonreporting) **A**1 3 **F**98 99 101 **S**
Universal Health Services, Inc., King of Prussia, PA
Primary Contact: Alyson Wysong-Harder, Chief Executive Officer
CFO: Wendy Duvall, Chief Financial Officer
CMO: Ahmad Tarar, M.D., Medical Director
CHR: Carri Compton, Administrative Officer
CNO: Amanda Sloniker, Director of Nursing
Web address: www.heartlandbehavioral.com
**Control:** Corporation, Investor–owned (for–profit) **Service:** Psychiatric

| Staffed Beds: 69 Admissions: 2152 Census: 41 Outpatient Visits: 0 |
|---|
| Births: 0 Total Expense ($000): 16297 Payroll Expense ($000): 8446 |
| Personnel: 152 |

HEARTLAND HOSPITAL See Heartland Behavioral Health Services

NEVADA CITY HOSPITAL See Nevada Regional Medical Center

**MO**

*Many Facility Codes have changed. Please refer to the AHA Guide Code Chart.*

**NEVADA REGIONAL MEDICAL CENTER (260061)**, 800 South Ash Street, Zip 64772–3223; tel. 417/667–3355, (Nonreporting) **A**1o 22 **F**3 11 13 14 15 18 26 27 28 29 30 31 32 34 35 40 45 50 54 57 59 64 65 66 70 73 74 75 76 77 78 79 81 82 84 85 86 87 89 90 91 93 94 96 98 99 101 102 103 104 107 108 110 111 115 119 127 129 130 131 132 133 135 143 144 146 147 148 **S** Freeman Health System, Joplin, MO
Primary Contact: Steve Branstetter, Chief Executive Officer
CMO: Warren Lovinger, M.D., Chief Medical Officer
CIO: Marci Hardin, Manager Information Technology
CHR: Heather Brockmeyer, Human Resource Administrative Officer
CNO: Cory Vokoun, Chief Nursing Officer
Web address: www.nrmchealth.com
**Control**: City, Government, Nonfederal **Service**: General medical and surgical

**Staffed Beds:** 71 **Admissions:** 2217 **Census:** 25 **Outpatient Visits:** 64768 **Births:** 0 **Total Expense ($000):** 38688 **Payroll Expense ($000):** 15291 **Personnel:** 260

### NORTH KANSAS CITY—Clay County

☒ **NORTH KANSAS CITY HOSPITAL (260096)**, 2800 Clay Edwards Drive, Zip 64116–3220; tel. 816/691–2000, (Nonreporting) **A**1 2 3 5 10 **F**3 11 12 13 15 17 18 20 22 24 26 28 29 30 31 34 35 37 40 43 44 45 46 47 48 49 50 51 53 54 57 58 59 60 62 64 70 72 73 74 75 76 77 78 79 80 81 82 83 84 85 86 87 89 90 93 96 100 107 108 110 111 114 115 116 117 118 119 120 121 123 124 126 129 130 132 135 146 147 148 149 154
Primary Contact: Stephen Reintjes Sr, M.D., President and Chief Medical Officer
COO: Kerri Jenkins, Senior Vice President and Chief Operating Officer
CFO: Henry Seybold, Senior Vice President and Chief Financial Officer
CMO: James Stewart, Chief Medical Officer
CIO: Kristen Guillaume, Vice President and Chief Information Officer
CHR: Dawn Bryant, Vice President Human Resources
CNO: Sarah G Oakley, R.N., MSN, Vice President Nursing
Web address: www.nkch.org
**Control**: City, Government, Nonfederal **Service**: General medical and surgical

**Staffed Beds:** 411 **Admissions:** 20378 **Census:** 264 **Outpatient Visits:** 313496 **Births:** 1938 **Total Expense ($000):** 507610 **Payroll Expense ($000):** 181074 **Personnel:** 2801

### O'FALLON—St. Charles County

**PROGRESS WEST HEALTHCARE CENTER** See Progress West Hospital

☒ **PROGRESS WEST HOSPITAL (260219)**, Two Progress Point Parkway, Zip 63368–2208; tel. 636/344–1000, (Nonreporting) **A**1 5 10 **F**3 13 15 18 20 22 26 29 30 34 35 40 41 45 49 51 57 59 60 70 73 74 75 76 77 79 81 85 86 87 89 107 108 110 111 115 118 119 130 135 146 148 149 154 **S** BJC HealthCare, Saint Louis, MO
Primary Contact: Chris Watts, President
CFO: Glen Schwaegel, Chief Financial Officer
CMO: Dane Glueck, M.D., Chief of Staff
CHR: Michael J Miller, Director Human Resources
Web address: www.progresswest.org
**Control**: Other not–for–profit (including NFP Corporation) **Service**: General medical and surgical

**Staffed Beds:** 74 **Admissions:** 3726 **Census:** 32 **Outpatient Visits:** 61464 **Births:** 872 **Total Expense ($000):** 86232 **Payroll Expense ($000):** 31748 **Personnel:** 369

### OSAGE BEACH—Camden County

☒ **LAKE REGIONAL HEALTH SYSTEM (260186)**, 54 Hospital Drive, Zip 65065–3050; tel. 573/348–8000, (Total facility includes 16 beds in nursing home–type unit) (Nonreporting) **A**1 2 10 **F**3 11 12 13 15 17 18 20 22 24 28 29 30 31 32 34 35 38 39 40 43 44 45 46 48 49 50 51 53 57 59 60 62 63 64 65 68 70 73 74 75 76 77 78 79 81 82 84 85 86 87 89 93 96 107 108 111 114 115 118 119 120 121 122 123 124 126 127 128 129 130 131 132 135 145 146 148 149 150 154 **P**6
Primary Contact: Dane W. Henry, FACHE, Chief Executive Officer
COO: Kevin G McRoberts, FACHE, Senior Vice President of Operations
CFO: David Halsell, Senior Vice President and Chief Financial Officer
CMO: Harbaksh Sangha, M.D., Chief Medical Officer
CIO: Patrick Neece, Chief Information Officer
CHR: Tom Williams, Vice President Human Resources
CNO: Melissa Hunter, Chief Nursing Officer
Web address: www.lakeregional.com
**Control**: Other not–for–profit (including NFP Corporation) **Service**: General medical and surgical

**Staffed Beds:** 116 **Admissions:** 4913 **Census:** 50 **Outpatient Visits:** 632424 **Births:** 657 **Total Expense ($000):** 201288 **Payroll Expense ($000):** 82876 **Personnel:** 1248

**LAKE REGIONAL HOSPITAL** See Lake Regional Health System

☒ **OSAGE BEACH CENTER FOR COGNITIVE DISORDERS (264031)**, 840 Passover Road, Zip 65065; tel. 573/302–0319, (Nonreporting) **A**1 10 **F**50 56 68 74 75 86 87 98 101 103 149
Primary Contact: Tom Flanagan, Chief Executive Officer
CNO: Lorri Steffen, Director of Nursing
Web address: www.osagebeachccd.com
**Control**: Partnership, Investor–owned (for–profit) **Service**: Psychiatric

**Staffed Beds:** 14 **Admissions:** 644 **Census:** 11 **Outpatient Visits:** 0 **Births:** 0 **Total Expense ($000):** 4754 **Payroll Expense ($000):** 2502 **Personnel:** 40

### PERRYVILLE—Perry County

☒ **PERRY COUNTY MEMORIAL HOSPITAL (261311)**, 434 North West Street, Zip 63775–1398; tel. 573/547–2536, (Nonreporting) **A**1 10 18 **F**3 7 8 11 13 15 28 29 30 31 34 35 40 44 45 49 51 53 54 56 57 59 62 64 66 68 75 76 77 78 79 81 85 87 89 90 92 93 97 100 101 102 103 104 107 111 115 117 119 129 130 131 132 133 135 144 145 146 147 148 154 155 156
Primary Contact: Patrick E. Carron, FACHE, President and Chief Executive Officer
CFO: Randall Wolf, Vice President Finance
CMO: Michael Steele, M.D., Chief of Staff
CIO: Ron Heuring, Director Information Systems
CHR: Christopher Wibbenmeyer, Director Human Resources
Web address: www.pchmo.org
**Control**: Other not–for–profit (including NFP Corporation) **Service**: General medical and surgical

**Staffed Beds:** 25 **Admissions:** 1617 **Census:** 16 **Outpatient Visits:** 52152 **Births:** 136 **Total Expense ($000):** 45845 **Payroll Expense ($000):** 17408 **Personnel:** 332

### PILOT KNOB—Iron County

**IRON COUNTY HOSPITAL** See Iron County Medical Center

**IRON COUNTY MEDICAL CENTER (261336)**, 301 North Highway 21, Zip 63663–0548, Mailing Address: P.O. Box 548, Zip 63663–0548; tel. 573/546–1260, (Nonreporting) **A**10 18
Primary Contact: Joshua Gilmore, Chief Executive Officer
CNO: Cindy Sadler, Chief Nursing Officer
Web address: www.icmedcenter.org/
**Control**: Hospital district or authority, Government, Nonfederal **Service**: General medical and surgical

**Staffed Beds:** 15

### POPLAR BLUFF—Butler County

**JOHN J PERSHING VA MED CNTR** See John J. Pershing Veterans Affairs Medical Center

☒ **JOHN J. PERSHING VETERANS AFFAIRS MEDICAL CENTER**, 1500 North Westwood Boulevard, Zip 63901–3318; tel. 573/686–4151, (Total facility includes 25 beds in nursing home–type unit) (Nonreporting) **A**1 **F**3 5 10 11 15 29 30 33 34 35 36 38 39 45 53 54 56 57 59 62 63 64 65 75 77 79 82 83 84 86 87 90 93 94 97 107 111 119 127 128 130 132 135 143 144 146 147 149 154 156 **S** Department of Veterans Affairs, Washington, DC
Primary Contact: Paul Hopkins, Interim Medical Director
COO: Seth Barlage, Associate Medical Center Director
CFO: Kristy Williams, Manager Finance
CMO: Vijayachandran Nair, M.D., Chief of Staff
CIO: Michael Gustin, Information Technology
CHR: Genise Denton, Manager Human Resources
CNO: Chandra Miller, Director of Nursing
Web address: www.poplarbluff.va.gov
**Control**: Veterans Affairs, Government, federal **Service**: General medical and surgical

**Staffed Beds:** 35 **Admissions:** 629 **Census:** 27 **Outpatient Visits:** 168584 **Births:** 0 **Total Expense ($000):** 197857 **Payroll Expense ($000):** 54053 **Personnel:** 409

MO

---

**Hospital, Medicare Provider Number, Address, Telephone, Approval, Facility, and Physician Codes, Health Care System**

★ American Hospital Association (AHA) membership ○ Healthcare Facilities Accreditation Program ⇑ Center for Improvement in Healthcare Quality Accreditation
☐ The Joint Commission accreditation ◇ DNV Healthcare Inc. accreditation △ Commission on Accreditation of Rehabilitation Facilities (CARF) accreditation

⊞ **POPLAR BLUFF REGIONAL MEDICAL CENTER (260119)**, 3100 Oak Grove Road, Zip 63901, Mailing Address: P.O. Box 88, Zip 63902–0088; tel. 573/776–2000, (Nonreporting) **A**1 2 10 **F**3 17 29 30 31 34 35 45 46 49 50 51 54 56 57 59 60 64 65 68 70 73 74 75 76 77 78 79 80 81 85 87 89 90 98 102 107 108 111 114 117 118 119 120 121 126 127 129 130 131 132 146 148 154 **S** Community Health Systems, Inc., Franklin, TN
Primary Contact: Bryan S. Bateman, Chief Executive Officer
COO: Christian Jones, Chief Operating Officer
CFO: Jeff Kurcab, Chief Financial Officer
CIO: Jamie Chitester, Director Information Systems
CHR: Denise Rushin, Director Human Resources
CNO: Timothy O'Neal, Chief Nursing Officer
Web address: www.poplarbluffregional.com
**Control:** Individual, Investor–owned (for-profit) **Service:** General medical and surgical

> **Staffed Beds:** 255 **Admissions:** 11237 **Census:** 126 **Outpatient Visits:** 91960 **Births:** 1522 **Total Expense ($000):** 201953 **Payroll Expense ($000):** 47214 **Personnel:** 1045

**THREE RIVERS HEALTHCARE** See Poplar Bluff Regional Medical Center

### POTOSI—Washington County

**WASHINGTON COUNTY MEMORIAL HOSPITAL (261308)**, 300 Health Way, Zip 63664–1420; tel. 573/438–5451, (Nonreporting) **A**10 18 **F**3 5 15 28 29 30 33 34 35 40 45 47 51 57 59 64 65 68 81 82 85 87 90 93 97 98 104 107 108 110 111 115 119 127 129 130 133 135 143 144 145 146 148 154
Primary Contact: Michele C. Meyer, R.N., Chief Executive Officer
CFO: Debra Pratt, Chief Financial Officer
CMO: Jonathan Borchers, M.D., Chief Medical Officer
CIO: Jim Smith, Director Information Systems
CHR: Christy Aubuchon, Director Personnel
CNO: Beverly Williams, R.N., Chief Nursing Officer
Web address: www.wcmhosp.org
**Control:** County, Government, Nonfederal **Service:** General medical and surgical

> **Staffed Beds:** 25 **Admissions:** 792 **Census:** 11 **Outpatient Visits:** 54064 **Births:** 0 **Total Expense ($000):** 22349 **Payroll Expense ($000):** 9659 **Personnel:** 221

### RICHMOND—Ray County

★ **RAY COUNTY MEMORIAL HOSPITAL (261327)**, 904 Wollard Boulevard, Zip 64085–2229; tel. 816/470–5432, (Nonreporting) **A**10 18 **F**3 11 15 28 29 30 31 45 57 62 64 75 78 79 81 85 87 93 104 107 108 110 111 115 117 119 130 133 146 154
Primary Contact: Earl Nielsen. Sheehy, FACHE, Chief Executive Officer
CFO: Donald Harr, Controller
CHR: Donna Strain, Director Human Resources
Web address: www.raycountyhospital.com
**Control:** County, Government, Nonfederal **Service:** General medical and surgical

> **Staffed Beds:** 25 **Admissions:** 553 **Census:** 9 **Outpatient Visits:** 14048 **Births:** 0 **Total Expense ($000):** 26811 **Payroll Expense ($000):** 11635 **Personnel:** 215

### RICHMOND HEIGHTS—St. Louis County

**SSM SELECT REHABILITATION HOSPITAL** See Ssm Select Rehabilitation Hospital

⊞ △ **SSM SELECT REHABILITATION HOSPITAL (263031)**, 1027 Bellevue Avenue, 3rd Floor, Zip 63117–1851, Mailing Address: 1027 Bellevue Avenue, Zip 63117–1851; tel. 314/768–5300, (Includes SSM HEALTH REHABILITATION HOSPITAL - LAKE SAINT LOUIS, Mailing address: 100 Medical Plaza, Fifth Floor, Lake Saint Louis, Missouri, Zip 63367–1366; tel. 636/755–6500; John Grubbs, Chief Operating Officer; SSM SELECT REHABILITATION HOSPITAL, Mailing address: 12380 De Paul Drive, Bridgeton, Missouri, Zip 63044–2511; tel. 314/447–9700; Robert Pritts, Chief Executive Officer), (Nonreporting) **A**1 7 10 **S** Select Medical Corporation, Mechanicsburg, PA
Primary Contact: Brenda Hughes, Chief Operating Officer
Web address: www.ssm-select.com
**Control:** Corporation, Investor–owned (for-profit) **Service:** Rehabilitation

> **Staffed Beds:** 125

### ROLLA—Phelps County

**PHELPS COUNTY REGIONAL MEDICAL CENTER** See Phelps Health

⊞ △ **PHELPS HEALTH (260017)**, 1000 West Tenth Street, Zip 65401–2905; tel. 573/458–8899, (Total facility includes 18 beds in nursing home–type unit) (Nonreporting) **A**1 2 7 10 **F**3 7 8 11 13 15 17 18 20 22 26 28 29 30 31 34 35 39 40 45 47 49 50 51 54 56 57 59 60 62 63 64 68 70 73 74 75 76 77 78 79 81 82 84 85 86 87 89 90 93 94 96 98 100 102 107 108 110 111 114 115 117 118 119 120 121 123 126 127 128 129 132 135 143 146 147 148 149 154 155 **P**6
Primary Contact: Edward Clayton, Chief Executive Officer
COO: Jason Shenefield, Senior Vice President and Chief Operating Officer
CFO: Jana Cook, Vice President and Chief Financial Officer
CMO: Donald James, D.O., Senior Vice President and Chief Medical Officer
CIO: Jeff McKune, Chief Health Informatics Officer
CHR: Frank A. Lazzaro IllChief Human Resources Officer
CNO: Keri S. Brookshire-Heavin, Senior Vice President and Chief Nursing Officer
Web address: www.pcrmc.com
**Control:** County, Government, Nonfederal **Service:** General medical and surgical

> **Staffed Beds:** 176 **Admissions:** 6895 **Census:** 88 **Outpatient Visits:** 568088 **Births:** 795 **Total Expense ($000):** 268747 **Payroll Expense ($000):** 118010 **Personnel:** 1697

### SAINT CHARLES—St. Charles County

⊞ **CENTERPOINTE HOSPITAL (264012)**, 4801 Weldon Spring Parkway, Zip 63304–9101; tel. 636/441–7300, (Nonreporting) **A**1 10 **F**4 5 34 35 38 40 44 54 80 87 98 99 100 101 102 103 104 105 106 143 152 153
Primary Contact: Scott Williams, Chief Executive Officer
CFO: Tom Croffut, Chief Financial Officer
CMO: Azfar Malik, M.D., Chief Medical Officer
CIO: Jennifer Bourn, Director, Health Information Services and Medical Staff Services
CHR: Kelli White, Director, Human Resources
Web address: www.centerpointehospital.com
**Control:** Corporation, Investor–owned (for-profit) **Service:** Psychiatric

> **Staffed Beds:** 150 **Admissions:** 4443 **Census:** 107 **Outpatient Visits:** 0 **Births:** 0 **Total Expense ($000):** 36857 **Payroll Expense ($000):** 19977 **Personnel:** 250

### SAINT CHARLES—Saint Charles County

⊞ **SELECT SPECIALTY HOSPITAL-ST. LOUIS (262013)**, 300 First Capitol Drive, Unit 1, Zip 63301–2844; tel. 636/947–5010, (Includes SELECT SPECIALTY HOSPITAL - TOWN AND COUNTRY, Mailing address: 3015 North Ballas Road, Fifth Floor, St. Louis, Missouri, Zip 63131–2329; tel. 314/996–6500; Marie T Droege, Chief Executive Officer), (Nonreporting) **A**1 10 **F**1 29 74 75 148 **S** Select Medical Corporation, Mechanicsburg, PA
Primary Contact: Bruce Eady, Chief Executive Officer
Web address: www.selectspecialtyhospitals.com/company/locations/stlouis.aspx
**Control:** Corporation, Investor–owned (for-profit) **Service:** Acute long–term care hospital

> **Staffed Beds:** 33 **Admissions:** 288 **Census:** 23 **Outpatient Visits:** 0 **Births:** 0 **Total Expense ($000):** 16081 **Payroll Expense ($000):** 7541 **Personnel:** 77

### SAINT CHARLES—St. Charles County

**SPIRIT OF ST LOUIS HOSPITAL** See Centerpointe Hospital

⊞ **SSM HEALTH ST. JOSEPH - ST. CHARLES (260005)**, 300 First Capitol Drive, Zip 63301–2844; tel. 636/947–5000, (Includes SSM HEALTH ST. JOSEPH - WENTZVILLE, Mailing address: 500 Medical Drive, Wentzville, Missouri, Zip 63385–3421; tel. 636/327–1000; Lisle Wescott, President), (Nonreporting) **A**1 2 3 10 **F**3 4 5 11 13 15 17 18 20 22 24 26 28 29 30 31 34 35 38 40 41 42 43 44 45 46 49 50 53 54 55 56 57 58 59 60 64 67 68 70 73 74 75 76 78 79 81 82 84 85 86 87 90 96 97 98 99 100 101 102 103 104 105 107 108 109 110 111 114 118 119 120 121 129 130 132 135 144 146 147 148 152 153 154 **P**6 8 **S** SSM Health, Saint Louis, MO
Primary Contact: Lisle Wescott, President
COO: Michael E. Bowers, Regional Executive Vice President and Chief Operating Officer
CFO: Karen Rewerts, System Vice President Finance
CMO: Douglas Barton, M.D., Chief Medical Officer
CIO: Margaret Feilner, Director Information Services
CHR: Debbie G Walkenhorst, System Vice President Talent Management
Web address: www.ssmhealth.com
**Control:** Church operated, Nongovernment, not–for–profit **Service:** General medical and surgical

> **Staffed Beds:** 341 **Admissions:** 11798 **Census:** 168 **Outpatient Visits:** 196320 **Births:** 542 **Total Expense ($000):** 256107 **Payroll Expense ($000):** 87300 **Personnel:** 1145

**SSM ST. JOSEPH HEALTH CENTER** See Ssm Health St. Joseph - St. Charles

*Many Facility Codes have changed. Please refer to the AHA Guide Code Chart.* © 2021 AHA Guide

MO

## SAINT JOSEPH—Buchanan County

**HEARTLAND LONG TERM ACUTE CARE HOSPITAL** See Long-Term Acute Care Hospital, Mosaic Life Care at St. Joseph

★ **LONG-TERM ACUTE CARE HOSPITAL, MOSAIC LIFE CARE AT ST. JOSEPH (262019)**, 5325 Faraon Street, Zip 64506–3488; tel. 816/271–6000, (Nonreporting) **A**10 **F**1 3 29 85 130 148 149 150 **S** Mosaic Life Care, Saint Joseph, MO
Primary Contact: Dana Anderson, R.N., Administrator
CNO: Douglas Schmitz, Director of Nursing
Web address: www.https://www.mymosaiclifecare.org/General/Long-Term-Acute-Care-Hospital/
**Control:** Other not–for–profit (including NFP Corporation) **Service:** Acute long–term care hospital

**Staffed Beds:** 41 **Admissions:** 214 **Census:** 19 **Outpatient Visits:** 0 **Births:** 0 **Total Expense ($000):** 11048 **Payroll Expense ($000):** 3353 **Personnel:** 47

**MOSAIC LIFE CARE** See Mosaic Life Care at St. Joseph - Medical Center

✠ **MOSAIC LIFE CARE AT ST. JOSEPH - MEDICAL CENTER (260006)**, 5325 Faraon Street, Zip 64506–3488; tel. 816/271–6000, (Nonreporting) **A**1 2 10 20 **F**3 9 11 12 13 15 17 18 20 22 24 26 28 29 30 31 32 33 34 35 36 39 40 43 45 46 47 48 49 50 51 53 54 56 57 58 59 61 62 63 64 65 70 73 74 75 76 78 79 80 81 82 84 85 86 87 89 90 92 93 94 96 97 98 100 101 102 103 104 107 108 110 111 114 115 118 119 120 121 123 124 129 130 131 132 134 135 143 144 145 146 147 148 149 150 154 **P**6 **S** Mosaic Life Care, Saint Joseph, MO
Primary Contact: Samuel Mark. Laney, M.D., Chief Executive Officer
COO: Curt Kretzinger, Chief Operating Officer
CFO: Dwain Stilson, Chief Financial Officer
CMO: Davin Turner, D.O., President and Chief Medical Officer
CIO: Brennan Lehman, Chief Information Officer
CHR: Michael Pulido, Chief Administrative Officer
Web address: www.https://www.mymlc.com
**Control:** Other not–for–profit (including NFP Corporation) **Service:** General medical and surgical

**Staffed Beds:** 352 **Admissions:** 16648 **Census:** 204 **Outpatient Visits:** 1010384 **Births:** 1463 **Total Expense ($000):** 644401 **Payroll Expense ($000):** 277247 **Personnel:** 3580

☐ **NORTHWEST MISSOURI PSYCHIATRIC REHABILITATION CENTER (264007)**, 3505 Frederick Avenue, Zip 64506–2914; tel. 816/387–2300, (Nonreporting) **A**1 3 5 10 **F**4 29 30 65 68 75 77 86 87 97 98 101 102 103 130 132 135 143 **P**6
Primary Contact: Denise Norbury, MS, R.N., Regional Executive Officer
COO: Mary Attebury, Chief Operating Officer
CFO: Randy Riley, Fiscal and Administrative Manager
CMO: James B Reynolds, M.D., Medical Director
CIO: Robert Curren, Western Region Chief Information Technology Officer
CHR: Mary Blakey Gorman, Director Human Resources
CNO: Pam Nold, Chief Nurse Executive
Web address: www.https://dmh.mo.gov
**Control:** State, Government, Nonfederal **Service:** Psychiatric

**Staffed Beds:** 108 **Admissions:** 56 **Census:** 107 **Outpatient Visits:** 0 **Births:** 0 **Total Expense ($000):** 23127 **Payroll Expense ($000):** 11971 **Personnel:** 282

## SAINT LOUIS—St. Louis City County

**BARNES HOSPITAL** See Barnes-Jewish Hospital

## SAINT LOUIS—St. Louis County

**BARNES WEST COUNTY HOSPITAL** See Barnes-Jewish West County Hospital

## SAINT LOUIS—St. Louis City County

✠ **BARNES-JEWISH HOSPITAL (260032)**, 1 Barnes-Jewish Hospital Plaza, Zip 63110–1003; tel. 314/747–3000, (Includes BARNES-JEWISH HOSPITAL PSYCHIATRIC SUPPORT CENTER, Mailing address: 5355 Delmar Boulevard, Saint Louis, Missouri, Zip 63112–3146; tel. 314/286–1700; John M Eiler, Ph.D., Administrative Director) (Total facility includes 120 beds in nursing home–type unit) **A**1 2 3 5 8 10 **F**3 4 5 6 8 9 11 12 13 15 16 17 18 20 22 24 26 28 29 30 31 34 35 36 37 38 39 40 43 44 45 46 47 48 49 50 51 52 53 54 55 56 57 58 59 60 61 63 64 65 66 68 70 71 73 74 75 76 77 78 79 80 81 82 84 85 86 87 89 90 91 92 93 94 96 97 98 100 101 102 103 104 107 108 109 110 111 112 114 115 116 117 118 119 120 121 122 123 124 126 128 129 130 131 132 134 135 136 137 138 139 140 141 142 143 145 146 147 148 149 150 154 156 157 158 **S** BJC HealthCare, Saint Louis, MO
Primary Contact: John Lynch, M.D., President
CFO: Mark Krieger, Vice President and Chief Financial Officer
CHR: Betsy Rodriguez, Vice President Human Resources
Web address: www.barnesjewish.org
**Control:** Other not–for–profit (including NFP Corporation) **Service:** General medical and surgical

**Staffed Beds:** 1395 **Admissions:** 56888 **Census:** 1037 **Outpatient Visits:** 695072 **Births:** 3631 **Total Expense ($000):** 2238941 **Payroll Expense ($000):** 736819 **Personnel:** 12000

## SAINT LOUIS—St. Louis County

✠ **BARNES-JEWISH WEST COUNTY HOSPITAL (260162)**, 12634 Olive Boulevard, Zip 63141–6337; tel. 314/996–8000, (Nonreporting) **A**1 3 5 10 **F**3 12 15 29 34 35 40 45 46 47 49 50 51 57 59 60 64 65 70 74 75 77 78 79 81 82 85 90 93 107 110 111 114 115 119 120 121 123 126 129 130 131 145 146 148 149 154 **S** BJC HealthCare, Saint Louis, MO
Primary Contact: Ann Abad, President
CFO: Diane M Glen, Assistant Administrator
CMO: Sam B Bhayani, M.D., Chief Medical Officer
CNO: Yoany Finetti, R.N., Vice President Patient Care Services Chief Nurse Officer
Web address: www.barnesjewishwestcounty.org
**Control:** Other not–for–profit (including NFP Corporation) **Service:** General medical and surgical

**Staffed Beds:** 68 **Admissions:** 3179 **Census:** 18 **Outpatient Visits:** 183000 **Births:** 0 **Total Expense ($000):** 137648 **Payroll Expense ($000):** 45993 **Personnel:** 532

✠ **CHRISTIAN HOSPITAL (260180)**, 11133 Dunn Road, Zip 63136–6119; tel. 314/653–5000, (Nonreporting) **A**1 3 10 **F**4 5 7 11 15 17 18 20 22 24 26 28 29 30 34 35 36 38 40 42 44 45 46 47 49 50 51 53 56 57 58 59 60 63 64 65 68 69 70 71 74 75 77 78 79 80 81 82 83 84 85 86 87 90 92 93 94 96 102 103 104 105 107 108 109 110 111 112 113 114 115 116 117 118 119 120 121 123 126 129 130 132 135 143 146 147 148 149 152 153 154 **P**6 **S** BJC HealthCare, Saint Louis, MO
Primary Contact: Rick Stevens, President
COO: Douglas Black, Vice President of Operations
CMO: Sebastian Rueckert, M.D., Chief Medical Officer
CIO: Michael Kelly, Vice President
CHR: Bryan Hartwick, Vice President Human Resources
CNO: Jennifer Cordia, Vice President and Chief Nursing Executive
Web address: www.christianhospital.org
**Control:** Other not–for–profit (including NFP Corporation) **Service:** General medical and surgical

**Staffed Beds:** 233 **Admissions:** 13304 **Census:** 184 **Outpatient Visits:** 300112 **Births:** 0 **Total Expense ($000):** 320303 **Payroll Expense ($000):** 125068 **Personnel:** 1656

**CHRISTIAN HOSPITAL NE-NW** See Christian Hospital

**DES PERES HOSPITAL** See St. Luke's Des Peres Hospital

☐ **HAWTHORN CHILDREN PSYCHIATRIC HOSPITAL (264028)**, 1901 Pennsylvania, Zip 63133–1325, Mailing Address: 1901 Pennsylvania Avenue, Zip 63133–1325; tel. 314/512–7800, (Nonreporting) **A**1 3 5 10 **F**98 99 106 **P**6
Primary Contact: Laurent D. Javois, Regional Executive Officer
COO: Marcia F Ford, Chief Operating Officer
CFO: James D Martin, Chief Financial Officer
CMO: Joshua Calhoun, M.D., Medical Director
CHR: Michael McFarlane, Director Human Resource
CNO: Melody Chilese, Chief Nurse Executive
Web address: www.dmh.missouri.gov/hcph/
**Control:** State, Government, Nonfederal **Service:** Children's hospital psychiatric

**Staffed Beds:** 52 **Admissions:** 74 **Census:** 29 **Outpatient Visits:** 0 **Births:** 0 **Total Expense ($000):** 14902 **Payroll Expense ($000):** 8412 **Personnel:** 211

**HAWTHORNE CHILD PSYCH HOSPITAL** See Hawthorn Children Psychiatric Hospital

**KINDRED HOSPITAL ST. LOUIS-ST. ANTHONY'S** See Kindred Hospital St. Louis South

**MO**

---

**Hospital, Medicare Provider Number, Address, Telephone, Approval, Facility, and Physician Codes, Health Care System**

★ American Hospital Association (AHA) membership
☐ The Joint Commission accreditation
○ Healthcare Facilities Accreditation Program
◇ DNV Healthcare Inc. accreditation
⇑ Center for Improvement in Healthcare Quality Accreditation
△ Commission on Accreditation of Rehabilitation Facilities (CARF) accreditation

## SAINT LOUIS—St. Louis City County

⊞ **KINDRED HOSPITAL-ST. LOUIS (262010)**, 4930 Lindell Boulevard, Zip 63108–1510; tel. 314/361–8700, (Includes KINDRED HOSPITAL ST. LOUIS SOUTH, Mailing address: 10018 Kennerly Road, 3rd Floor, Saint Louis, Missouri, Zip 63128; tel. 314/525–8100; Angela Green, Chief Executive Officer), (Nonreporting) **A**1 10 **F**1 29 60 107 111 148 **S** Kindred Healthcare, Louisville, KY
Primary Contact: Kevin L. Shrake, Chief Executive Officer
COO: Dakota Redd, R.N., Chief Clinical Officer
CFO: Maureen Roach, Senior Chief Financial Officer
CMO: Michael Holtzman, M.D., Medical Director
CIO: Thomas C Christman, Director Plant Operations
CHR: Cindy Sander, Coordinator Human Resources
Web address: www.kindredstlouis.com/
**Control**: Corporation, Investor–owned (for–profit) **Service**: Acute long–term care hospital

**Staffed Beds**: 98 **Admissions**: 607 **Census**: 42 **Outpatient Visits**: 0 **Births**: 0 **Total Expense ($000)**: 29819 **Payroll Expense ($000)**: 12476 **Personnel**: 179

## SAINT LOUIS—St. Louis (City) County

**LUTHERAN MEDICAL CENTER** See Southpointe Hospital

## SAINT LOUIS—St. Louis City County

**MALCOLM BLISS MENTAL HLTH CTR** See Metropolitan St. Louis Psychiatric Center

## SAINT LOUIS—St. Louis County

⊞ △ **MERCY HOSPITAL SOUTH (260077)**, 10010 Kennerly Road, Zip 63128–2106; tel. 314/525–1000, (Nonreporting) **A**1 2 7 10 **F**3 4 5 11 12 13 15 17 18 20 22 24 26 28 29 30 31 35 36 38 40 41 43 47 48 49 50 53 54 63 65 68 69 70 73 74 75 76 77 78 79 80 81 82 84 85 86 87 89 90 91 92 93 96 97 98 99 100 101 102 103 104 107 108 109 110 111 114 115 116 117 118 119 120 121 123 124 126 129 130 132 135 143 144 146 147 148 149 153 **S** Mercy, Chesterfield, MO
Primary Contact: Sean Hogan, FACHE, President
COO: Bill Hoefer, Chief Operating Officer
Web address: www.stanthonysmedcenter.com
**Control**: Other not–for–profit (including NFP Corporation) **Service**: General medical and surgical

**Staffed Beds**: 538 **Admissions**: 20711 **Census**: 361 **Outpatient Visits**: 510936 **Births**: 798 **Total Expense ($000)**: 466010 **Payroll Expense ($000)**: 217515 **Personnel**: 2647

⊞ **MERCY HOSPITAL ST. LOUIS (260020)**, 615 South New Ballas Road, Zip 63141–8277; tel. 314/251–6000, (Includes MERCY CHILDREN'S HOSPITAL ST. LOUIS, Mailing address: 615 South New Ballas Road, Saint Louis, Zip 63141–8221; tel. 314/251–6000), (Nonreporting) **A**1 2 3 5 10 **F**3 4 5 8 11 12 13 14 15 16 17 18 19 20 22 24 25 26 27 28 29 30 31 32 33 34 35 36 38 39 40 41 43 45 46 47 48 49 50 51 52 53 54 55 56 57 58 59 60 61 64 66 68 69 70 71 72 73 74 75 76 77 78 79 80 81 82 84 85 86 87 88 89 90 92 93 94 96 98 99 100 101 102 103 104 105 106 107 108 110 111 114 115 116 117 118 119 120 121 123 124 126 129 130 131 132 134 135 143 144 146 147 148 149 153 154 156 157 **S** Mercy, Chesterfield, MO
Primary Contact: Stephen Mackin, President
CFO: Cheryl Matejka, Chief Financial Officer
CMO: Paul Hintze, M.D., Vice President Medical Affairs
CIO: Eugene Roth, Vice President Information Services
CHR: Rocky Ruello, Vice President Human Resources
Web address: www.mercy.net/stlouismo
**Control**: Other not–for–profit (including NFP Corporation) **Service**: General medical and surgical

**Staffed Beds**: 783 **Admissions**: 41125 **Census**: 598 **Outpatient Visits**: 1225912 **Births**: 8647 **Total Expense ($000)**: 950342 **Payroll Expense ($000)**: 348691 **Personnel**: 5482

## SAINT LOUIS—St. Louis City County

☐ **METROPOLITAN ST. LOUIS PSYCHIATRIC CENTER (264025)**, 5351 Delmar, Zip 63112–3198; tel. 314/877–0501, (Nonreporting) **A**1 3 10 **F**11 30 57 98 104 130 146 149
Primary Contact: Laurent D. Javois, Regional Executive Officer
COO: Michael Bruce Anderson, Ph.D., Chief Operating Officer
CFO: James D Martin, Chief Financial Officer
CMO: Davinder Hayreh, M.D., Medical Director
CHR: Michael McFarlane, Director Human Resources
CNO: Sarah Jones, Chief Nurse Executive
Web address: www.dmh.missouri.gov/mpc
**Control**: State, Government, Nonfederal **Service**: Psychiatric

**Staffed Beds**: 50 **Admissions**: 94 **Census**: 49 **Outpatient Visits**: 0 **Births**: 0 **Total Expense ($000)**: 14894 **Payroll Expense ($000)**: 7241 **Personnel**: 191

## SAINT LOUIS—St. Louis County

⊞ **MISSOURI BAPTIST MEDICAL CENTER (260108)**, 3015 North Ballas Road, Zip 63131–2329; tel. 314/996–5000, (Nonreporting) **A**1 2 3 5 10 **F**3 11 13 14 15 17 18 19 20 22 24 26 28 29 30 31 34 35 36 40 41 45 46 48 49 50 51 52 54 55 56 57 58 59 60 63 64 65 68 70 71 72 73 74 75 76 77 78 79 81 82 83 84 85 87 89 90 92 93 94 96 97 100 102 107 108 110 111 114 115 116 117 118 119 120 121 123 124 126 130 132 145 146 147 148 149 154 157 **P**6 **S** BJC HealthCare, Saint Louis, MO
Primary Contact: John Antes, President
COO: Michael Kelly, Vice President Operations
CFO: Amy Desart, Vice President, Chief Financial Officer
CMO: Mitchell Botney, M.D., Vice President Medical Affairs and Chief Medical Officer
CIO: Tracie Jones, Director Information Services
CHR: Cyndy Donato, Vice President, Human Resources
Web address: www.missouribaptist.org
**Control**: Other not–for–profit (including NFP Corporation) **Service**: General medical and surgical

**Staffed Beds**: 449 **Admissions**: 22606 **Census**: 277 **Outpatient Visits**: 383968 **Births**: 3842 **Total Expense ($000)**: 615477 **Payroll Expense ($000)**: 189399 **Personnel**: 2285

**MISSOURI BAPTIST MEDICAL CNTR** See Missouri Baptist Medical Center

## SAINT LOUIS—St. Louis City County

**REHAB INSTTITUTE OF ST LOUIS** See The Rehabilitation Institute of St. Louis

**SAINT LOUIS UNIVERSITY HOSPITAL** See Ssm Health Saint Louis University Hospital

## SAINT LOUIS—St. Louis County

**SHRINERS HOSPITALS FOR CHILDREN, ST. LOUIS** See Shriners Hospitals for Children-St. Louis

☐ **SHRINERS HOSPITALS FOR CHILDREN-ST. LOUIS (263304)**, 4400 Clayton Avenue, Zip 63110–1624; tel. 314/432–3600, (Nonreporting) **A**1 3 5 10 **F**3 29 58 64 74 75 79 81 85 86 87 89 93 94 130 131 143 146 154 **S** Shriners Hospitals for Children, Tampa, FL
Primary Contact: Mark Venable, Interim Administrator
CFO: Sandra K. Lawson, Interim Director Fiscal Services
CMO: Perry L Schoenecker, M.D., Chief of Staff
CIO: Jeanne Hall, Director Information Systems
CHR: Mark Venable, Director Human Resources
Web address: www.https://www.shrinershospitalsforchildren.org
**Control**: Other not–for–profit (including NFP Corporation) **Service**: Children's orthopedic

**Staffed Beds**: 12 **Admissions**: 291 **Census**: 3 **Outpatient Visits**: 9512 **Births**: 0 **Total Expense ($000)**: 27207 **Payroll Expense ($000)**: 8527 **Personnel**: 139

## SAINT LOUIS—St. Louis City County

★ **SSM CARDINAL GLENNON CHILDREN'S HOSPITAL (269807)**, 1465 South Grand Boulevard, Zip 63104–1095; tel. 314/577–5600, (Nonreporting) **A**3 5 10 **F**3 11 12 19 21 23 25 27 29 30 31 32 34 35 38 39 40 41 43 44 45 46 47 48 49 50 51 54 55 57 59 60 61 64 66 68 72 73 74 75 77 78 79 80 81 82 84 85 86 87 88 89 90 93 94 97 99 100 101 102 104 107 108 111 115 118 119 124 127 129 130 131 132 134 136 137 138 139 141 142 144 146 148 150 154 156 **P**6 8 **S** SSM Health, Saint Louis, MO
Primary Contact: Steven Burghart, President
CFO: Karen Rewerts, System Vice President of Finance
CMO: John Peter, M.D., Vice President Medical Affairs
CIO: Michael Paasch, Regional Vice President and Chief Information Officer
CHR: Debbie G Walkenhorst, Network Vice President
Web address: www.cardinalglennon.com
**Control**: Church operated, Nongovernment, not–for–profit **Service**: Children's general medical and surgical

**Staffed Beds**: 176 **Admissions**: 7569 **Census**: 131 **Outpatient Visits**: 247208 **Births**: 0 **Total Expense ($000)**: 352701 **Payroll Expense ($000)**: 107651 **Personnel**: 1533

**SSM CARDINAL GLENNON CHILDREN'S MEDICAL CENTER** See Ssm Cardinal Glennon Children's Hospital

*Many Facility Codes have changed. Please refer to the AHA Guide Code Chart.* © 2021 AHA Guide

MO

✠ **SSM HEALTH SAINT LOUIS UNIVERSITY HOSPITAL (260105)**, 1201 South Grand Boulevard, Zip 63104–1016, Mailing Address: P.O. Box 15250, Zip 63110–0250; tel. 314/577–8000, (Includes SSM HEALTH SAINT LOUIS UNIVERSITY HOSPITAL-SOUTH, Mailing address: 1755 South Grand Boulevard, Saint Louis, Missouri, Zip 63104–1540; tel. 314/577–6027; Raymond Alvey, Chief Financial Officer), (Nonreporting) **A**1 2 3 5 8 10 **F**3 4 6 7 8 9 11 14 15 17 18 20 22 24 26 28 29 30 31 34 35 36 37 38 39 40 43 44 45 46 47 48 49 50 51 55 56 57 58 59 60 61 63 64 65 68 70 74 75 77 78 79 81 82 84 85 86 87 90 91 92 93 94 96 97 98 100 101 102 104 107 108 110 111 112 113 114 115 116 117 118 119 121 123 124 126 129 130 131 132 135 136 138 139 141 142 146 147 148 149 150 156 157 **P**8 **S** SSM Health, Saint Louis, MO
Primary Contact: Steven M. Scott, President
COO: Gretchen Leiterman, Chief Operating Officer
CFO: Raymond Alvey, Chief Financial Officer
CMO: Matthew Broom, Vice President of Medical Affairs and Chief Medical Officer
CIO: Patrick Brennan, Director Information System Technology
Web address: www.https://www.ssmhealth.com
**Control:** Church operated, Nongovernment, not–for–profit **Service:** General medical and surgical

**Staffed Beds:** 356 **Admissions:** 14733 **Census:** 281 **Outpatient Visits:** 178920 **Births:** 0 **Total Expense ($000):** 605867 **Payroll Expense ($000):** 151686 **Personnel:** 1819

**SSM HEALTH SAINT LOUIS UNIVERSITY HOSPITAL - SOUTH CAMPUS** See Ssm Health Saint Louis University Hospital-South

### SAINT LOUIS—St. Louis County

✠ **SSM HEALTH ST. MARY'S HOSPITAL - ST. LOUIS (260091)**, 6420 Clayton Road, Zip 63117–1811; tel. 314/768–8000, (Nonreporting) **A**1 2 3 5 **F**3 4 5 13 15 18 20 22 26 28 29 30 31 34 35 37 38 40 44 45 46 48 49 50 51 52 55 56 57 58 59 60 61 64 66 70 72 73 74 75 76 78 79 81 82 84 85 86 87 97 98 100 101 102 103 104 107 108 110 111 115 119 120 121 126 129 130 132 135 143 144 146 147 148 149 153 154 156 **P**6 8 **S** SSM Health, Saint Louis, MO
Primary Contact: Travis Capers, FACHE, President
CFO: Karen Rewerts, System Vice President of Finance
CMO: Stephen Kelly, M.D., Chief Medical Officer
CIO: Michael Paasch, Regional Chief Information Officer
Web address: www.stmarys-stlouis.com
**Control:** Church operated, Nongovernment, not–for–profit **Service:** General medical and surgical

**Staffed Beds:** 394 **Admissions:** 15941 **Census:** 233 **Outpatient Visits:** 231712 **Births:** 3186 **Total Expense ($000):** 389696 **Payroll Expense ($000):** 115560 **Personnel:** 1677

**SSM ST. MARY'S HEALTH CENTER** See Ssm Health St. Mary's Hospital - St. Louis

### SAINT LOUIS—St. Louis City County

**ST LOUIS STATE PSYCH REHAB CTR** See St. Louis Psychiatric Rehabilitation Center

**ST. ALEXIUS HOSPITAL** See St. Alexius Hospital - Broadway Campus

☐ **ST. ALEXIUS HOSPITAL - BROADWAY CAMPUS (260210)**, 3933 South Broadway, Zip 63118–4601; tel. 314/865–7000, (Includes SOUTHPOINTE HOSPITAL, Mailing address: 2639 Miami Street, Saint Louis, Missouri, Zip 63118–3929; tel. 314/772–1456), (Nonreporting) **A**1 3 5 10 **F**3 11 12 20 29 34 35 38 39 40 43 45 50 51 56 57 59 64 65 70 74 77 79 81 85 86 87 98 102 103 107 108 118 119 130 135 143 146 148 149
Primary Contact: Sonny Saggar, M.D., Chief Executive Officer
CMO: Russell Kraeger, M.D., Chief Medical Officer
CNO: Thomas Saggio, Chief Nursing Officer
Web address: www.stalexiushospital.com
**Control:** Corporation, Investor–owned (for–profit) **Service:** General medical and surgical

**Staffed Beds:** 190 **Admissions:** 2467 **Census:** 60 **Outpatient Visits:** 26328 **Births:** 0 **Total Expense ($000):** 51204 **Payroll Expense ($000):** 28028 **Personnel:** 415

### SAINT LOUIS—St. Louis County

**ST. ANTHONY'S MERCY** See Mercy Hospital South

### SAINT LOUIS—Saint Louis County

**ST. JOHN'S MERCY CHILDREN'S HOSPITAL** See Mercy Children's Hospital St. Louis

### SAINT LOUIS—St. Louis County

**ST. JOHN'S MERCY MEDICAL CENTER** See Mercy Hospital St. Louis

### SAINT LOUIS—St. Louis City County

✠ △ **ST. LOUIS CHILDREN'S HOSPITAL (263301)**, One Children's Place, Zip 63110–1002; tel. 314/454–6000, (Nonreporting) **A**1 3 5 7 8 10 **F**3 7 8 11 16 17 19 20 21 22 23 24 25 26 27 29 30 31 32 34 35 38 39 40 41 43 44 45 46 47 48 49 50 51 54 57 58 59 60 61 62 63 64 65 68 71 72 73 74 75 77 78 79 81 82 83 84 85 86 87 88 89 90 91 92 93 95 96 98 99 100 101 102 104 107 108 109 111 114 115 118 119 126 129 130 131 132 134 136 137 138 139 140 141 142 143 144 145 146 148 149 150 154 155 **S** BJC HealthCare, Saint Louis, MO
Primary Contact: Trisha Lollo, President
CFO: Michele McKee, Vice President and Chief Financial Officer
CMO: F Sessions Cole, M.D., Chief Medical Officer
CNO: Peggy Gordin, Vice President, Patient Care Services and Chief Nursing Officer
Web address: www.stlouischildrens.org
**Control:** Other not–for–profit (including NFP Corporation) **Service:** Children's general medical and surgical

**Staffed Beds:** 344 **Admissions:** 10916 **Census:** 262 **Outpatient Visits:** 417040 **Births:** 0 **Total Expense ($000):** 718296 **Payroll Expense ($000):** 251687 **Personnel:** 3074

☐ **ST. LOUIS PSYCHIATRIC REHABILITATION CENTER (264010)**, 5300 Arsenal Street, Zip 63139–1463; tel. 314/877–6501, (Nonreporting) **A**1 10 **F**11 30 39 65 68 75 86 87 98 100 101 106 130 143 146 157
Primary Contact: Laurent D. Javois, Chief Executive Officer
COO: Felix T Vincenz, Chief Operating Officer
CFO: James D Martin, Chief Financial Officer
CMO: Roy Wilson, M.D., Medical Director
CHR: Michael McFarlane, Chief Human Resource Officer
CNO: Deborah Mokry, Chief Nurse Executive
Web address: www.dmh.missouri.gov
**Control:** State, Government, Nonfederal **Service:** Psychiatric

**Staffed Beds:** 180 **Admissions:** 42 **Census:** 178 **Outpatient Visits:** 0 **Births:** 0 **Total Expense ($000):** 36859 **Payroll Expense ($000):** 18718 **Personnel:** 509

**ST. LOUIS REGIONAL PSYCHIATRIC STABILIZATION CENTER** See Barnes-Jewish Hospital Psychiatric Support Center

### SAINT LOUIS—St. Louis County

✠ **ST. LUKE'S DES PERES HOSPITAL (260176)**, 2345 Dougherty Ferry Road, Zip 63122–3313; tel. 314/966–9100, (Nonreporting) **A**1 3 5 10 12 13 **F**3 12 15 18 20 22 29 30 34 35 36 40 44 45 47 49 50 58 59 60 64 68 70 75 77 79 81 85 86 87 93 107 108 110 111 115 119 130 132 146 149
Primary Contact: David E. Loving, FACHE, Chief Executive Officer
CFO: Steven Downs, Chief Financial Officer
CIO: Mary Estes, Director Information Systems
CHR: Kathaleen Clutts, Chief Human Resources Officer
CNO: Mary Ann Hampton, MSN, R.N., Chief Nursing Officer
Web address: www.despereshospital.com
**Control:** Church operated, Nongovernment, not–for–profit **Service:** General medical and surgical

**Staffed Beds:** 88 **Admissions:** 3255 **Census:** 26 **Outpatient Visits:** 18304 **Births:** 0 **Total Expense ($000):** 96738 **Payroll Expense ($000):** 30098 **Personnel:** 458

### SAINT LOUIS—St. Louis City County

✠ △ **THE REHABILITATION INSTITUTE OF ST. LOUIS (263028)**, 4455 Duncan Avenue, Zip 63110–1111; tel. 314/658–3800, (Nonreporting) **A**1 3 5 7 10 **F**29 34 40 44 56 58 60 64 68 74 75 79 87 90 91 93 94 100 130 132 143 148 149 150 **S** Encompass Health Corporation, Birmingham, AL
Primary Contact: Mark Dwyer, FACHE, Chief Executive Officer
CMO: David Carr, M.D., Physician Medical Director
CHR: Heather Savage, Director Human Resources
CNO: Angelina Sherman, R.N., MSN, Chief Nursing Officer
Web address: www.rehabinstitutestl.com
**Control:** Partnership, Investor–owned (for–profit) **Service:** Rehabilitation

**Staffed Beds:** 131 **Admissions:** 2522 **Census:** 100 **Outpatient Visits:** 10728 **Births:** 0 **Total Expense ($000):** 46814 **Payroll Expense ($000):** 23596 **Personnel:** 312

**VENCOR HOSPITAL-ST LOUIS** See Kindred Hospital-St. Louis

**VETERANS AFFAIRS MEDICAL CENTER** See Veterans Affairs St. Louis Health Care System

**MO**

---

| Hospital, Medicare Provider Number, Address, Telephone, Approval, Facility, and Physician Codes, Health Care System |
|---|

★ American Hospital Association (AHA) membership   ◯ Healthcare Facilities Accreditation Program   ⇧ Center for Improvement in Healthcare Quality Accreditation
☐ The Joint Commission accreditation   ◇ DNV Healthcare Inc. accreditation   △ Commission on Accreditation of Rehabilitation Facilities (CARF) accreditation

⊠ △ **VETERANS AFFAIRS ST. LOUIS HEALTH CARE SYSTEM**, 915 North Grand Boulevard, Zip 63106–1621; tel. 314/652–4100, (Nonreporting) **A**1 3 5 7 **S** Department of Veterans Affairs, Washington, DC
Primary Contact: Keith D. Repko, Director
CFO: Karen Westerheide, Chief Financial Officer
CIO: Steve Warmbold, Director Information Management Service Line
CHR: Marie Lewis, Human Resources Liaison
CNO: Richard Holt, R.N., Associate Director Patient Care Services
Web address: www.stlouis.va.gov/
**Control**: Veterans Affairs, Government, federal **Service**: General medical and surgical

**Staffed Beds:** 356

### SAINT PETERS—St. Charles County

**BARNES ST PETERS HOSPITAL** See Barnes-Jewish St. Peters Hospital

⊠ **BARNES-JEWISH ST. PETERS HOSPITAL (260191)**, 10 Hospital Drive, Zip 63376–1659; tel. 636/916–9000, (Nonreporting) **A**1 3 5 10 **F**3 11 15 18 20 22 26 28 29 30 31 34 35 40 45 46 49 51 57 59 60 64 70 74 75 77 78 79 81 85 86 93 107 108 110 111 115 117 118 119 120 121 123 129 130 132 135 146 147 148 149 156 **S** BJC HealthCare, Saint Louis, MO
Primary Contact: Chris Watts, President
CFO: Glen Schwaegel, Vice President and Chief Financial Officer
CMO: Feliipe Orellana, Chief Medical Officer
CIO: Cindy Gross, Director of Finance
CHR: Michael J Miller, Director Human Resources
CNO: Lauren Beckmann, Vice President Patient Services and Chief Nursing Officer
Web address: www.bjsph.org/
**Control**: Other not–for–profit (including NFP Corporation) **Service**: General medical and surgical

**Staffed Beds:** 102 **Admissions:** 5752 **Census:** 61 **Outpatient Visits:** 124864 **Births:** 0 **Total Expense ($000):** 130835 **Payroll Expense ($000):** 45093 **Personnel:** 562

### SALEM—Dent County

★ **SALEM MEMORIAL DISTRICT HOSPITAL (261318)**, 35629 Highway 72, Zip 65560–7217, Mailing Address: P.O. Box 774, Zip 65560–0774; tel. 573/729–6626, (Total facility includes 18 beds in nursing home–type unit) (Nonreporting) **A**10 18 **F**3 7 11 15 30 34 40 41 57 60 67 75 81 85 87 89 107 119 127 128 130 131 133 149
Primary Contact: Kasey Lucas, Chief Executive Officer, Hospital Administrator
CFO: Becky Cunningham, Controller
CMO: John Demorlis, M.D., Chief Medical Staff
CHR: Jodie Gorman, Director Human Resources
Web address: www.smdh.net
**Control**: Hospital district or authority, Government, Nonfederal **Service**: General medical and surgical

**Staffed Beds:** 43 **Admissions:** 790 **Census:** 28 **Outpatient Visits:** 38080 **Births:** 0 **Total Expense ($000):** 25834 **Payroll Expense ($000):** 11424 **Personnel:** 215

### SEDALIA—Pettis County

⊠ **BOTHWELL REGIONAL HEALTH CENTER (260009)**, 601 East 14th Street, Zip 65301–5972, Mailing Address: P.O. Box 1706, Zip 65302–1706; tel. 660/826–8833, (Total facility includes 10 beds in nursing home–type unit) (Nonreporting) **A**1 10 **F**3 9 11 13 14 15 18 20 22 28 29 30 31 34 35 39 51 54 56 57 59 60 64 65 68 70 73 74 75 76 77 78 79 80 81 82 84 85 86 87 89 92 93 107 108 110 111 114 115 116 117 118 119 120 121 123 124 127 128 129 130 131 132 135 146 147 148
Primary Contact: Lori Wightman, R.N., FACHE, Chief Executive Officer
COO: Thomas Bailey, Chief Operating Officer
CMO: Philip Fracica, M.D., Chief Medical Officer
CIO: Tom Fairfax, Director Information Systems
CHR: Deb Clemmer, Vice President Human Resources
CNO: Regina W Crow, Chief Nursing Officer
Web address: www.brhc.org
**Control**: City, Government, Nonfederal **Service**: General medical and surgical

**Staffed Beds:** 137 **Admissions:** 3881 **Census:** 50 **Outpatient Visits:** 174328 **Births:** 510 **Total Expense ($000):** 123636 **Payroll Expense ($000):** 49075 **Personnel:** 856

### SIKESTON—Scott County

☐ **MISSOURI DELTA MEDICAL CENTER (260113)**, 1008 North Main Street, Zip 63801–5044; tel. 573/471–1600, (Nonreporting) **A**1 5 10 **F**3 5 11 13 15 18 28 29 30 31 34 35 37 40 45 50 51 53 54 56 57 59 60 62 63 64 68 70 74 75 76 77 78 79 81 82 84 85 86 87 89 90 93 97 98 103 104 107 108 110 111 115 116 117 118 119 126 127 129 130 131 132 144 146 147 148 149
Primary Contact: Jason Schrumpf, President
CFO: Greg Carda, Vice President Finance
Web address: www.missouridelta.com
**Control**: Other not–for–profit (including NFP Corporation) **Service**: General medical and surgical

**Staffed Beds:** 108 **Admissions:** 4009 **Census:** 53 **Outpatient Visits:** 238856 **Births:** 451 **Total Expense ($000):** 107155 **Payroll Expense ($000):** 45572 **Personnel:** 821

### SMITHVILLE—Clay County

**SAINT LUKE'S NORTHLAND HOSPITAL-SMITHVILLE CAMPUS** See Saint Luke's North Hospital-Smithville Campus

### SPRINGFIELD—Greene County

★ △ ⇑ **COX MEDICAL CENTERS (260040)**, 1423 North Jefferson Street, Zip 65802–1988; tel. 417/269–3000, (Includes COX MEDICAL CENTER NORTH, Mailing address: 1423 North Jefferson Avenue, Springfield, Missouri, Zip 65802; tel. 417/269–3000; COX MEDICAL CENTER SOUTH, Mailing address: 3801 South National Avenue, Springfield, Missouri, Zip 65807; tel. 417/269–6000), (Nonreporting) **A**3 5 7 10 21 **F**3 4 5 7 11 12 13 15 17 18 19 20 22 24 26 28 29 30 31 32 34 35 38 39 40 41 42 43 44 45 46 47 49 50 51 52 53 54 55 56 57 58 59 60 61 62 64 65 68 69 70 71 72 74 75 76 77 78 79 80 81 82 84 85 86 87 88 89 90 92 93 94 96 97 98 99 100 101 102 103 104 107 108 110 111 114 115 116 117 118 119 120 121 124 126 128 129 130 131 132 134 135 143 144 146 147 148 149 150 152 154 155 156 **P**3 6 **S** CoxHealth, Springfield, MO
Primary Contact: Steven D. Edwards, President and Chief Executive Officer
CFO: Jacob McWay, Senior Vice President and Chief Financial Officer
CMO: Frank Romero, M.D., Chief Medical Officer
CIO: Bruce Robison, Vice President and Chief Information Officer
CHR: John Hursh, Vice President Human Resources
CNO: Karen Kramer, R.N., Senior Vice President, Chief Hospital Officer and System Chief Nursing Officer
Web address: www.coxhealth.com
**Control**: Other not–for–profit (including NFP Corporation) **Service**: General medical and surgical

**Staffed Beds:** 673 **Admissions:** 34376 **Census:** 500 **Outpatient Visits:** 1950512 **Births:** 3539 **Total Expense ($000):** 1155873 **Payroll Expense ($000):** 387267 **Personnel:** 8812

☐ **LAKELAND BEHAVIORAL HEALTH SYSTEM (264024)**, 440 South Market Street, Zip 65806–2026; tel. 417/865–5581, (Nonreporting) **A**1 10 **F**98 99 103 106 130 135 149 **P**6 **S** Acadia Healthcare Company, Inc., Franklin, TN
Primary Contact: Nathan Duncan, Chief Executive Officer
COO: Randy Fox, Director Performance Improvement and Risk Management
CFO: Rick Crump, Chief Financial Officer
CMO: Richard Aiken, M.D., Medical Director
CIO: Brad Strothkamp, Chief Information Systems
CHR: Dave England, Director Human Resources
Web address: www.lakeland-hospital.com
**Control**: Corporation, Investor–owned (for–profit) **Service**: Psychiatric

**Staffed Beds:** 206 **Admissions:** 2791 **Census:** 161 **Outpatient Visits:** 0 **Births:** 0 **Total Expense ($000):** 24618 **Payroll Expense ($000):** 14848 **Personnel:** 347

**LAKELAND REGIONAL HOSPITAL** See Lakeland Behavioral Health System

**LESTER E. COX MEDICAL CENTER NORTH** See Cox Medical Center North

**LESTER E. COX MEDICAL CENTER SOUTH** See Cox Medical Center South

⇑ **LESTER E. COX MEDICAL CENTERS** See Cox Medical Centers

*Many Facility Codes have changed. Please refer to the AHA Guide Code Chart.*
© 2021 AHA Guide

MO

✠ **MERCY HOSPITAL SPRINGFIELD (260065)**, 1235 East Cherokee Street, Zip 65804–2263; tel. 417/820–2000, (Includes MERCY CHILDREN'S HOSPITAL SPRINGFIELD, Mailing address: 1235 East Cherokee Street, Springfield, Missouri, Zip 65804–2203; tel. 417/820–2000; MERCY ORTHOPEDIC HOSPITAL SPRINGFIELD, Mailing address: 3050 East Riverbluff Boulevard, Ozark, Missouri, Zip 65721; tel. 417/820–5611; Robert Steele, M.D., President), (Nonreporting) **A**1 3 5 10 **F**3 4 5 7 9 11 12 13 15 16 17 18 20 22 24 26 28 29 30 31 32 34 35 37 38 39 40 41 43 44 45 46 47 48 49 50 51 54 55 56 57 58 59 60 61 62 63 64 65 66 67 68 70 71 72 73 74 75 76 77 78 79 81 82 84 85 86 87 88 89 90 91 92 93 94 96 97 98 107 111 114 115 117 118 119 120 121 123 124 126 129 130 131 132 135 143 146 147 148 149 155 156 157 **S** Mercy, Chesterfield, MO
Primary Contact: Brent Hubbard, FACHE, President and Chief Operating Officer
COO: Brent Hubbard, FACHE, Chief Operating Officer
CFO: Scott Reynolds, Vice President Finance
CMO: Allan Allphin, M.D., Chief of Staff
CIO: Lori Sturgill, Vice President Business Partnership
CHR: Tanya Maricn, Interim Vice President Human Resources
Web address: www.mercy.net/springfieldmo
**Control:** Church operated, Nongovernment, not–for–profit **Service:** General medical and surgical

**Staffed Beds:** 665 **Admissions:** 36539 **Census:** 487 **Outpatient Visits:** 558112 **Births:** 3026 **Total Expense ($000):** 962635 **Payroll Expense ($000):** 354244 **Personnel:** 7484

☐ △ **MERCY REHABILITION HOSPITAL SPRINGFIELD (263032)**, 5904 South Southwood Road, Zip 65804–5234; tel. 417/227–9000, (Nonreporting) **A**1 7 10 **F**3 29 30 90 95 96 130 132 148
Primary Contact: Brent Yates, Chief Executive Officer
CFO: Melissa Campbell, Chief Financial Officer and Controller
CMO: Hollis Bell, M.D., EsqMedical Director
CHR: Melissa Mooney, Director Human Resources
CNO: Paul Moore, R.N., Chief Clinical Officer
Web address: www.mercy.net
**Control:** Partnership, Investor–owned (for–profit) **Service:** Rehabilitation

**Staffed Beds:** 60 **Admissions:** 1347 **Census:** 43 **Outpatient Visits:** 0 **Births:** 0 **Total Expense ($000):** 17074 **Payroll Expense ($000):** 7831 **Personnel:** 184

☐ **PERIMETER BEHAVIORAL HOSPITAL OF SPRINGFIELD (264033)**, 2828 North National Avenue, Zip 65803–4306; tel. 417/799–7474, (Nonreporting) **A**1 **F**98 99 **S** Perimeter Healthcare, Alpharetta, GA
Primary Contact: Lynn Lemke, Chief Executive Officer
Web address: www.perimeterhealthcare.com
**Control:** Corporation, Investor–owned (for–profit) **Service:** Psychiatric

**Staffed Beds:** 32 **Admissions:** 544 **Census:** 10 **Outpatient Visits:** 0 **Births:** 0 **Personnel:** 57

**PERIMETER BEHAVIORAL HOSPTIAL OF SPRINGFIELD** See Perimeter Behavioral Hospital of Springfield

✠ **SELECT SPECIALTY HOSPITAL-SPRINGFIELD (262017)**, 1630 East Primrose Street, Zip 65804–7929; tel. 417/885–4700, (Nonreporting) **A**1 10 **F**1 3 29 45 85 107 114 148 **S** Select Medical Corporation, Mechanicsburg, PA
Primary Contact: Steve Patterson, Chief Executive Officer
CHR: Tonya Eddington, Coordinator Human Resources
Web address: www.selectspecialtyhospitals.com/company/locations/springfield.aspx
**Control:** Corporation, Investor–owned (for–profit) **Service:** Acute long–term care hospital

**Staffed Beds:** 44 **Admissions:** 464 **Census:** 35 **Outpatient Visits:** 0 **Births:** 0 **Total Expense ($000):** 22174 **Payroll Expense ($000):** 9879 **Personnel:** 116

**ST. JOHN'S CHILDREN'S HOSPITAL** See Mercy Children's Hospital Springfield

**ST. JOHN'S HOSPITAL** See Mercy Hospital Springfield

---

**STE GENEVIEVE—Ste. Genevieve County**

★ **STE. GENEVIEVE COUNTY MEMORIAL HOSPITAL (261330)**, 800 Ste Genevieve Drive, Zip 63670–1434; tel. 573/883–2751, (Nonreporting) **A**10 18 **F**3 11 13 14 15 18 28 29 31 34 35 40 57 110 111 115 119 124 127 129 130 131 132 133 135 145 146 147 148 154 156 **P**3
Primary Contact: Steve Pautler, Ph.D., Chief Executive Officer
CFO: Susan Eckenfels, Chief Financial Officer
CMO: Joseph Sharlow, M.D., Chief of Staff
CHR: Sarah Jo Kelley, Executive Director of Human Resources and Support Services
CNO: Rita Brumfield, R.N., MSN, Chief Nursing Officer
Web address: www.stegenevievehospital.org
**Control:** County, Government, Nonfederal **Service:** General medical and surgical

**Staffed Beds:** 25 **Admissions:** 941 **Census:** 11 **Outpatient Visits:** 122960 **Births:** 199 **Total Expense ($000):** 50952 **Payroll Expense ($000):** 21836 **Personnel:** 365

---

**SULLIVAN—Crawford County**

**MISSOURI BAPT HOSP-SULLIVAN** See Missouri Baptist Sullivan Hospital

★ **MISSOURI BAPTIST SULLIVAN HOSPITAL (261337)**, 751 Sappington Bridge Road, Zip 63080–2354; tel. 573/468–4186, (Nonreporting) **A**10 18 **F**3 4 11 12 13 15 28 29 30 31 34 35 40 50 53 56 57 59 63 64 65 70 75 76 77 78 79 81 82 83 84 85 86 87 89 90 93 97 98 102 103 104 107 111 115 119 127 129 130 131 132 133 146 148 152 154 **S** BJC HealthCare, Saint Louis, MO
Primary Contact: Tony Schwarm, FACHE, President
CFO: Angela Wilks, Finance Director
CMO: Alison Baker, M.D., Chief of Staff
CHR: Kathleen Reed, Manager Human Resources
CNO: Carmen J. Bartolotta, R.N., Vice President, Patient Care Services and Chief Nursing Officer
Web address: www.missouribaptistsullivan.org
**Control:** Other not–for–profit (including NFP Corporation) **Service:** General medical and surgical

**Staffed Beds:** 35 **Admissions:** 2095 **Census:** 22 **Outpatient Visits:** 107920 **Births:** 238 **Total Expense ($000):** 58100 **Payroll Expense ($000):** 22466 **Personnel:** 358

---

**TRENTON—Grundy County**

★ **WRIGHT MEMORIAL HOSPITAL (261309)**, 191 Iowa Boulevard, Zip 64683–8343; tel. 660/358–5700, (Nonreporting) **A**10 18 **F**3 11 15 18 28 29 30 31 34 35 40 44 45 50 59 64 68 74 75 77 78 79 81 82 85 86 87 89 90 93 97 102 104 107 108 110 111 115 119 127 129 130 133 141 146 148 154 **S** Saint Luke's Health System, Kansas City, MO
Primary Contact: Steven M. Schieber, FACHE, Interim Chief Executive Officer
CFO: Leslie Reed, Chief Financial Officer
CMO: Gerald C Zabielski, M.D., Chief Medical Staff
CHR: Jenny Donovan, Director Human Resources
Web address: www.saintlukeshealthsystem.org
**Control:** Church operated, Nongovernment, not–for–profit **Service:** General medical and surgical

**Staffed Beds:** 15 **Admissions:** 436 **Census:** 7 **Outpatient Visits:** 65320 **Births:** 0 **Total Expense ($000):** 32036 **Payroll Expense ($000):** 11000 **Personnel:** 162

---

**TROY—Lincoln County**

**LINCOLN COUNTY MEDICAL CENTER** See Mercy Hospital Lincoln

✠ **MERCY HOSPITAL LINCOLN (261319)**, 1000 East Cherry Street, Zip 63379–1513; tel. 636/528–8551, (Nonreporting) **A**1 10 18 **F**3 11 15 18 28 29 30 34 35 40 44 45 50 51 57 59 63 64 65 68 70 75 77 79 81 85 86 87 90 93 104 107 110 111 113 114 119 127 128 129 130 131 133 135 144 146 149 154 156 157 **S** Mercy, Chesterfield, MO
Primary Contact: Anthony Rothermich, Administrator
CFO: Mark Thorn, FACHE, Executive Director, Finance
CIO: Travis Boyd, Manager, Information Technology
CHR: Mary Kay Kunza, Manager Human Resources
Web address: www.mercy.net
**Control:** Other not–for–profit (including NFP Corporation) **Service:** General medical and surgical

**Staffed Beds:** 9 **Admissions:** 668 **Census:** 9 **Outpatient Visits:** 118264 **Births:** 0 **Total Expense ($000):** 34699 **Payroll Expense ($000):** 17674 **Personnel:** 241

**MO**

---

## UNIONVILLE—Putnam County

★ **PUTNAM COUNTY MEMORIAL HOSPITAL (261305)**, 1926 Oak Street, Zip 63565–1180, Mailing Address: P.O. Box 389, Zip 63565–0389; tel. 660/947–2411, (Nonreporting) **A**10 18 **F**3 4 5 15 29 32 34 35 39 50 57 59 64 75 77 82 85 90 93 97 98 99 102 103 107 110 111 115 119 127 128 130 133 135 147 148 149 152 154 156 **P**3 5 6
Primary Contact: Gayle Pickens, Chief Executive Officer
COO: Jerry Cummings, Chief Operating Officer
CMO: Dawn Ann Fairley, M.D., Chief of Staff
CHR: Debbie Douglas, Director Human Resources
CNO: Nathan Baughman, Chief Nursing Officer
Web address: www.pcmhosp.com
**Control:** County, Government, Nonfederal **Service:** General medical and surgical

**Staffed Beds:** 15 **Admissions:** 245 **Census:** 4 **Outpatient Visits:** 9928 **Births:** 0 **Total Expense ($000):** 8659 **Payroll Expense ($000):** 4193 **Personnel:** 81

## WARRENSBURG—Johnson County

☐ **WESTERN MISSOURI MEDICAL CENTER (260097)**, 403 Burkarth Road, Zip 64093–3101; tel. 660/747–2500, (Nonreporting) **A**1 10 20 **F**3 8 11 13 15 17 18 28 29 30 31 32 34 35 40 43 45 47 56 57 59 60 61 64 65 68 70 74 75 76 77 78 79 81 82 85 89 90 93 97 98 102 103 107 108 110 111 115 117 118 119 127 129 130 131 132 133 135 144 146 147 148 154 156
Primary Contact: Darinda Reberry, MSN, R.N., President and Chief Executive Officer
CFO: Dean Ohmart, Vice President Financial Services and Chief Financial Officer
CIO: Bill Ladd, Director Information Services
CHR: Dennis Long, Director Human Resources
CNO: Jennifer Koepke, R.N., Vice President of Patient Care Services and Chief Nursing Officer
Web address: www.wmmc.com
**Control:** County, Government, Nonfederal **Service:** General medical and surgical

**Staffed Beds:** 57 **Admissions:** 3062 **Census:** 26 **Outpatient Visits:** 148656 **Births:** 652 **Total Expense ($000):** 91704 **Payroll Expense ($000):** 37634 **Personnel:** 577

## WASHINGTON—Franklin County

⊞ **MERCY HOSPITAL WASHINGTON (260052)**, 901 East Fifth Street, Zip 63090–3127; tel. 636/239–8000, (Nonreporting) **A**1 10 **F**3 5 8 11 12 13 14 15 17 18 20 22 26 28 29 30 31 32 34 35 39 40 43 44 46 48 49 50 51 52 53 54 56 57 58 59 61 64 66 68 69 70 73 74 75 76 77 78 79 80 81 82 84 85 86 87 89 92 93 94 96 97 99 100 101 104 107 108 110 111 114 116 117 118 119 120 121 123 127 129 130 131 132 134 135 143 144 146 147 148 149 154 156 157 **S** Mercy, Chesterfield, MO
Primary Contact: Eric J. Eoloff, President
COO: Joan Frost, R.N., Chief Operating Officer
CFO: Cheryl Matejka, Chief Financial Officer
CMO: Thomas Riechers, M.D., Chief Medical Staff
CIO: Michael McCreary, Chief of Services
CHR: Barbara Grayson, Vice President Human Resources
CNO: Anna Landon, Chief Nursing Officer
Web address: www.mercy.net
**Control:** Other not–for–profit (including NFP Corporation) **Service:** General medical and surgical

**Staffed Beds:** 71 **Admissions:** 6710 **Census:** 57 **Outpatient Visits:** 370712 **Births:** 848 **Total Expense ($000):** 175723 **Payroll Expense ($000):** 65465 **Personnel:** 927

**ST. JOHN'S MERCY HOSPITAL** See Mercy Hospital Washington

## WENTZVILLE—St. Charles County

**SSM HEALTH ST. JOSEPH - WENTZVILLE** See Ssm Health St. Joseph - St. Charles, Saint Charles

**SSM ST. JOSEPH - WENTZVILLE** See Ssm Health St. Joseph - Wentzville

## WEST PLAINS—Howell County

⊞ **OZARKS MEDICAL CENTER (260078)**, 1100 Kentucky Avenue, Zip 65775–2029, Mailing Address: P.O. Box 1100, Zip 65775–1100; tel. 417/256–9111, (Nonreporting) **A**1 5 10 **F**2 3 5 11 12 13 15 17 18 20 22 24 28 29 30 31 34 38 40 44 45 49 50 57 59 61 62 63 64 68 70 74 75 76 77 78 79 81 82 83 84 85 86 87 89 90 91 93 94 98 99 100 101 102 103 104 107 108 110 111 115 118 119 120 121 127 129 130 131 132 135 144 145 146 147 148 154 **P**8
Primary Contact: Thomas W. Keller, President and Chief Executive Officer
COO: Kurt Abbey, Chief Nursing Officer and Chief Operating Officer
CFO: Timothy Pollard, Interim Chief Financial Officer
CIO: Timothy J. Temple, Executive Director Information Technology
CHR: Connie Schott, Vice President, Human Resources
CNO: Kurt Abbey, Chief Nursing Officer and Chief Operating Officer
Web address: www.ozarksmedicalcenter.com
**Control:** Other not–for–profit (including NFP Corporation) **Service:** General medical and surgical

**Staffed Beds:** 103 **Admissions:** 5604 **Census:** 52 **Outpatient Visits:** 577144 **Births:** 657 **Total Expense ($000):** 172388 **Payroll Expense ($000):** 76553 **Personnel:** 1176

## WINDSOR—Henry County

**OAKWOOD HOSPITAL** See Royal Oaks Hospital

☐ **ROYAL OAKS HOSPITAL (264020)**, 307 North Main, Zip 65360–1449; tel. 660/647–2182, (Nonreporting) **A**1 3 5 10 **F**98 99 103 135 154 **P**6
Primary Contact: Alan W. Greiman, Chief Executive Officer and President
CFO: Jake Matthew Krafve, Chief Financial Officer
CMO: Syed Arshad Husain, M.D., Executive Vice President and Chief Medical Officer
CIO: Richard Colvert, Chief Information Officer
CHR: Diane Coletta, Vice President Human Resources
CNO: Saundra Overton, R.N., Chief Nursing Officer
Web address: www.compasshealthnetwork.org
**Control:** Other not–for–profit (including NFP Corporation) **Service:** Psychiatric

**Staffed Beds:** 54 **Admissions:** 1520 **Census:** 38 **Outpatient Visits:** 0 **Births:** 0 **Total Expense ($000):** 20571 **Payroll Expense ($000):** 12205 **Personnel:** 123

**MO**

*Many Facility Codes have changed. Please refer to the AHA Guide Code Chart.*
© 2021 AHA Guide

# MONTANA

## ANACONDA—Deer Lodge County

★ **COMMUNITY HOSPITAL OF ANACONDA (271335)**, 401 West Pennsylvania Street, Zip 59711; tel. 406/563–8500, (Total facility includes 32 beds in nursing home–type unit) (Nonreporting) **A**10 18 **F**3 11 13 15 29 30 31 34 35 40 43 45 50 54 57 59 62 63 64 70 74 75 76 77 78 79 81 82 87 89 93 97 99 104 107 111 114 116 119 128 130 133 135 143 144 146 148 156 **P**6
Primary Contact: Jo Ellen Villa, R.N., Chief Executive Officer
CFO: Meg Hickey-Boynton, Chief Financial Officer
CMO: Freddy Bartoletti, M.D., Chief of Staff
CHR: Meg Hickey-Boynton, Director Human Resources and Marketing
CNO: Jamie Johnson, R.N., Vice President Nursing
Web address: www.communityhospitalofanaconda.org
**Control:** Other not–for–profit (including NFP Corporation) **Service:** General medical and surgical

**Staffed Beds:** 57 **Admissions:** 1241 **Census:** 40 **Outpatient Visits:** 74958 **Births:** 158 **Total Expense ($000):** 67628 **Payroll Expense ($000):** 31006 **Personnel:** 375

## BAKER—Fallon County

**FALLON MEDICAL COMPLEX (271301)**, 202 South 4th Street West, Zip 59313–9156, Mailing Address: P.O. Box 820, Zip 59313–0820; tel. 406/778–3331, (Nonreporting) **A**10 18 **F**11 15 32 34 40 56 57 59 62 64 65 66 68 69 75 93 97 107 110 114 119 127 130 133 146 148 149 **P**6
Primary Contact: David Espeland, Chief Executive Officer
CFO: Selena Nelson, Chief Financial Officer
CMO: Darryl Espeland, D.O., Chief Medical Staff
CIO: Susan Stevens, Information Technology Specialist
CHR: Theresa Myers, Personnel Director
CNO: Susan Lunde, R.N., Director of Nursing
Web address: www.fallonmedical.org
**Control:** Other not–for–profit (including NFP Corporation) **Service:** General medical and surgical

**Staffed Beds:** 25 **Admissions:** 159 **Census:** 15 **Outpatient Visits:** 18167 **Births:** 0 **Total Expense ($000):** 10551 **Payroll Expense ($000):** 3635 **Personnel:** 90

## BIG SANDY—Chouteau County

★ **BIG SANDY MEDICAL CENTER (271311)**, 166 Montana Avenue East, Zip 59520–8474, Mailing Address: P.O. Box 530, Zip 59520–0530; tel. 406/378–2188, (Total facility includes 22 beds in nursing home–type unit) (Nonreporting) **A**10 18 **F**40 64 93 127 128 133 154
Primary Contact: Leah Griffith, Chief Executive Officer
CFO: Nora Grubb, Chief Financial Officer
Web address: www.bsmc.org
**Control:** Other not–for–profit (including NFP Corporation) **Service:** General medical and surgical

**Staffed Beds:** 30 **Admissions:** 56 **Census:** 15 **Outpatient Visits:** 2203 **Births:** 0 **Total Expense ($000):** 3060 **Payroll Expense ($000):** 1432 **Personnel:** 39

## BIG SKY—Gallatin County

⇑ **BIG SKY MEDICAL CENTER (271389)**, 334 Town Center Avenue, Suite 161529, Zip 59716, Mailing Address: P.O. Box 161529, Zip 59716–1529; tel. 406/995–6995, (Nonreporting) **A**10 18 21 **F**3 34 35 40 57 97 107 111 115 **P**6
Primary Contact: Taylor Rose, Administrator
Web address: www.https://www.bigskymedicalcenter.org/
**Control:** Other not–for–profit (including NFP Corporation) **Service:** General medical and surgical

**Staffed Beds:** 4 **Admissions:** 34 **Census:** 1 **Outpatient Visits:** 18630 **Births:** 0 **Total Expense ($000):** 11676 **Payroll Expense ($000):** 3039 **Personnel:** 40

⇑ **BOZEMAN HEALTH BIG SKY MEDICAL CENTER** See Big Sky Medical Center

## BIG TIMBER—Sweet Grass County

★ **PIONEER MEDICAL CENTER (271313)**, 301 West Seventh Avenue, Zip 59011–7893, Mailing Address: P.O. Box 1228, Zip 59011–1228; tel. 406/932–4603, (Nonreporting) **A**10 18 **F**2 3 7 10 11 12 28 29 30 34 35 40 41 45 56 57 59 63 64 65 66 67 68 75 77 82 87 93 97 100 101 102 104 107 114 119 127 128 130 131 132 133 134 135 143 146 148 149 154 156
Primary Contact: Bradley C. Howell, Chief Executive Officer
CFO: Kyle Gee, Chief Financial Officer
CMO: Benjamin P Bullington, M.D., Chief of Staff
CHR: Miki Gregorich, Director Human Resources
CNO: Randi Pike, Director of Nursing
Web address: www.pmcmt.org/
**Control:** Other not–for–profit (including NFP Corporation) **Service:** General medical and surgical

**Staffed Beds:** 25 **Admissions:** 79 **Census:** 1 **Outpatient Visits:** 16521 **Births:** 0

## BILLINGS—Yellowstone County

☐ **ADVANCED CARE HOSPITAL OF MONTANA (272001)**, 3528 Gabel Road, Zip 59102–7307; tel. 406/373–8000, (Nonreporting) **A**1 10 **S** Ernest Health, Inc., Albuquerque, NM
Primary Contact: Judi Powers, Chief Executive Officer
Web address: www.achm.ernesthealth.com
**Control:** Corporation, Investor–owned (for–profit) **Service:** Acute long–term care hospital

**Staffed Beds:** 40

⊞ **BILLINGS CLINIC (270004)**, 2800 10th Avenue North, Zip 59101–0703, Mailing Address: P.O. Box 37000, Zip 59107–7000; tel. 406/657–4000, (Nonreporting) **A**1 2 3 5 8 10 19 **F**3 8 9 11 12 13 15 17 18 19 20 22 24 26 27 28 29 30 31 32 34 35 36 38 40 41 43 44 45 46 47 48 49 50 51 52 54 55 56 57 58 59 60 61 62 64 65 66 68 70 72 74 75 76 77 78 79 80 81 82 84 85 86 87 89 91 92 93 97 98 99 100 101 102 103 104 105 107 108 110 111 114 115 116 117 118 119 120 121 124 126 129 130 131 132 134 135 136 146 147 148 154 155 156 **P**6
Primary Contact: Scott J. Ellner, D.O., M.P.H., FACS, Chief Executive Officer
COO: Mary Albers, Chief Operating Officer
CFO: Connie F Prewitt, Chief Financial Officer
CMO: Toni Green-Cheatwood, M.D., Chief Medical Offider
CIO: Chris E Stevens, Chief Information Officer
CHR: Karla Stauffer, Vice President People Resources
CNO: Lu Byrd, R.N., MSN, Vice President Hospital Operations and Chief Nursing Officer
Web address: www.billingsclinic.com
**Control:** Other not–for–profit (including NFP Corporation) **Service:** General medical and surgical

**Staffed Beds:** 291 **Admissions:** 15850 **Census:** 210 **Outpatient Visits:** 888631 **Births:** 1186 **Total Expense ($000):** 705016 **Payroll Expense ($000):** 348164 **Personnel:** 3891

**DEACONESS BILLINGS CLINIC** See Billings Clinic

**SAINT VINCENT HOSPITAL** See St. Vincent Healthcare

⊞ **ST. VINCENT HEALTHCARE (270049)**, 1233 North 30th Street, Zip 59101–0165, Mailing Address: P.O. Box 35200, Zip 59107–5200; tel. 406/237–7000, (Nonreporting) **A**1 2 3 5 10 **F**7 9 11 12 13 15 18 19 20 22 24 26 28 29 30 31 32 34 35 36 37 38 39 40 41 43 44 46 47 49 50 51 56 57 58 59 60 61 64 68 70 71 72 74 75 76 77 78 79 81 82 84 85 86 87 88 89 90 92 93 97 100 101 107 108 110 111 114 115 116 117 118 119 120 121 123 124 126 129 130 131 132 134 135 143 144 145 146 147 148 149 154 155 **P**6 **S** SCL Health, Broomfield, CO
Primary Contact: Steve Loveless, Montana Region President
CFO: Pam Palagi, Montana Region Chief Financial Officer
CMO: Michael Bush, M.D., Chief Medical Officer
CIO: Al Rooney, Director Information Systems
CHR: James Ritchey, Montana Region, Vice President Human Resources
CNO: BJ Gilmore, Chief Nursing Officer
Web address: www.https://www.sclhealth.org
**Control:** Other not–for–profit (including NFP Corporation) **Service:** General medical and surgical

**Staffed Beds:** 263 **Admissions:** 12184 **Census:** 155 **Outpatient Visits:** 152226 **Births:** 1464 **Total Expense ($000):** 420123 **Payroll Expense ($000):** 117926 **Personnel:** 1439

MT

---

**Hospital, Medicare Provider Number, Address, Telephone, Approval, Facility, and Physician Codes, Health Care System**

★ American Hospital Association (AHA) membership
☐ The Joint Commission accreditation
○ Healthcare Facilities Accreditation Program
◇ DNV Healthcare Inc. accreditation
⇑ Center for Improvement in Healthcare Quality Accreditation
△ Commission on Accreditation of Rehabilitation Facilities (CARF) accreditation

☐ **THE REHABILITATION HOSPITAL OF MONTANA (273025)**, 3572 Hesper Road, Zip 59102–6891; tel. 406/413–6200, (Nonreporting) **A**1 **S** Kindred Healthcare, Louisville, KY
Primary Contact: Julie Hauk, Chief Executive Officer
Web address: www.https://www.rehabhospitalofmontana.com/
**Control**: Partnership, Investor–owned (for–profit) **Service**: Rehabilitation

**Staffed Beds: 34**

### BOZEMAN—Gallatin County

★ ⇑ **BOZEMAN HEALTH (270057)**, 915 Highland Boulevard, Zip 59715–6902; tel. 406/585–5000, (Nonreporting) **A**2 10 20 21 **F**3 8 10 13 18 20 22 28 29 30 31 32 34 35 36 37 40 43 45 46 48 49 50 51 54 56 57 58 59 61 64 65 70 71 74 75 76 77 78 79 81 82 83 84 85 86 87 92 93 96 97 100 107 108 111 119 120 121 123 126 129 130 131 132 135 146 147 148 149 154 156 157 **P**6 7
Primary Contact: Kathryn Bertany, M.D., President
CIO: Brad Ludford, Chief Financial Officer
Web address: www.bozemandeaconess.org
**Control**: Other not–for–profit (including NFP Corporation) **Service**: General medical and surgical

**Staffed Beds: 83 Admissions: 5959 Census: 56 Outpatient Visits: 492727 Births: 1151 Total Expense ($000): 315219 Payroll Expense ($000): 77216 Personnel: 1280**

⇑ **BOZEMAN HEALTH DEACONESS HOSPITAL** See Bozeman Health

### BUTTE—Silver Bow County

**ST JAMES COMMUNITY HOSPITAL** See St. James Healthcare

⊞ **ST. JAMES HEALTHCARE (270017)**, 400 South Clark Street, Zip 59701–2328; tel. 406/723–2500, (Nonreporting) **A**1 10 **F**3 11 13 15 18 20 22 28 29 30 31 34 35 40 43 45 47 48 50 51 53 56 57 59 64 65 68 70 71 72 75 76 77 78 79 81 82 85 86 87 89 93 97 107 108 110 111 114 115 117 118 119 120 121 123 124 126 127 130 131 132 135 146 147 148 149 156 157 **P**6 **S** SCL Health, Broomfield, CO
Primary Contact: Jay Doyle, President and Chief Executive Officer
CFO: David Brain, Interim Vice President Finance
CMO: Dennis Salisbury, M.D., Vice President for Medical Affairs
CHR: Trisha Palmer, Director
CNO: Mary Winters, Interim Chief Nursing Officer
Web address: www.stjameshealthcare.org
**Control**: Other not–for–profit (including NFP Corporation) **Service**: General medical and surgical

**Staffed Beds: 73 Admissions: 3394 Census: 41 Outpatient Visits: 56688 Births: 250 Total Expense ($000): 116585 Payroll Expense ($000): 37464 Personnel: 459**

### CHESTER—Liberty County

**LIBERTY COUNTY HOSPITAL** See Liberty Medical Center

★ **LIBERTY MEDICAL CENTER (271334)**, 315 West Madison Avenue, Zip 59522, Mailing Address: P.O. Box 705, Zip 59522–0705; tel. 406/759–5181, (Nonreporting) **A**10 18 **F**2 3 10 11 34 35 40 43 45 56 59 64 67 86 87 93 97 107 114 119 127 128 130 133 154 **P**6
Primary Contact: Matthew Waller, Chief Executive Officer
CMO: Gladys Young, M.D., Chief of Staff
CHR: Bev Halter, Director Human Resources and Payroll
CNO: Shirley Morkrid, Chief Nursing Officer
Web address: www.lchnh.org
**Control**: Other not–for–profit (including NFP Corporation) **Service**: General medical and surgical

**Staffed Beds: 25 Admissions: 48 Census: 1 Outpatient Visits: 10052 Births: 0 Total Expense ($000): 6447 Payroll Expense ($000): 2786 Personnel: 79**

### CHOTEAU—Teton County

**BENEFIS TETON MEDICAL CENTER (271307)**, 915 4th Street North West, Zip 59422–9123; tel. 406/466–5763, (Nonreporting) **A**10 18 **F**2 34 35 40 41 43 53 56 57 59 64 68 93 97 102 104 107 127 133 154 **P**6 **S** Benefis Health System, Great Falls, MT
Primary Contact: Louie King, Chief Executive Officer
Web address: www.tetonmedicalcenter.net
**Control**: Other not–for–profit (including NFP Corporation) **Service**: General medical and surgical

**Staffed Beds: 25 Admissions: 85 Census: 22 Outpatient Visits: 9311 Births: 0 Total Expense ($000): 6810 Payroll Expense ($000): 3146 Personnel: 64**

**TETON MEDICAL CENTER** See Benefis Teton Medical Center

### CIRCLE—McCone County

★ **MCCONE COUNTY HEALTH CENTER (271305)**, 605 Sullivan Avenue, Zip 59215, Mailing Address: P.O. Box 48, Zip 59215–0048; tel. 406/485–3381, (Nonreporting) **A**10 18 **F**2 3 11 34 40 41 57 58 65 69 86 87 93 133 135 143 146 149 154
Primary Contact: Nancy Rosaaen, Chief Executive Officer
CFO: Nancy Rosaaen, Chief Executive Officer
CHR: Jacque Gardner, Administrative Assistant, Clinic Manager, Co-Chief Financial Officer and Chief Human Resources
Web address: www.mcconehealth.org/
**Control**: County, Government, Nonfederal **Service**: General medical and surgical

**Staffed Beds: 25 Admissions: 32 Census: 16 Outpatient Visits: 603 Total Expense ($000): 3865 Payroll Expense ($000): 1588 Personnel: 38**

**MCCONE COUNTY MAF** See Mccone County Health Center

### COLUMBUS—Stillwater County

★ **STILLWATER BILLINGS CLINIC (271330)**, 44 West Fourth Avenue North, Zip 59019–0959, Mailing Address: P.O. Box 959, Zip 59019–0959; tel. 406/322–5316, (Nonreporting) **A**10 18 **F**3 15 28 32 34 35 40 43 45 59 62 64 65 68 77 93 107 110 115 127 133 144 148 154 156
Primary Contact: David Ryerse, Chief Executive Officer
Web address: www.billingsclinic.com
**Control**: Other not–for–profit (including NFP Corporation) **Service**: General medical and surgical

**Staffed Beds: 10 Admissions: 205 Census: 4 Outpatient Visits: 14006 Births: 0 Total Expense ($000): 11200 Payroll Expense ($000): 5564 Personnel: 79**

**STILLWATER COMMUNITY HOSPITAL** See Stillwater Billings Clinic

### CONRAD—Pondera County

**PONDERA MEDICAL CENTER (271324)**, 805 Sunset Boulevard, Zip 59425–1717, Mailing Address: P.O. Box 668, Zip 59425–0668; tel. 406/271–3211, (Nonreporting) **A**10 18
Primary Contact: Bill O'Leary, Chief Executive Officer
CFO: Brigid Burke, Chief Financial Officer
CMO: Jay Taylor, M.D., Chief of Medical Staff
CIO: Sean Kavanagh, Director Information Technology
CHR: Patrick Johnson, Director Human Resources
CNO: Laura Erickson, R.N., Chief Nursing Officer
Web address: www.ponderamedical.org
**Control**: Other not–for–profit (including NFP Corporation) **Service**: General medical and surgical

**Staffed Beds: 79**

### CROW AGENCY—Big Horn County

☐ **CROW/NORTHERN CHEYENNE HOSPITAL (271339)**, 10110 South 7650 East, Zip 59022–0009, Mailing Address: P.O. Box 9, Zip 59022–0009; tel. 406/638–2626, (Nonreporting) **A**1 10 18 **S** U. S. Indian Health Service, Rockville, MD
Primary Contact: Darren Crowe, Chief Executive Officer
CMO: Jim Upchurch, M.D., Chief Medical Officer
CIO: Melanie Falls Down, Site Manager
Web address: www.https://www.ihs.gov/billings/healthcarefacilities/crow/
**Control**: PHS, Indian Service, Government, federal **Service**: General medical and surgical

**Staffed Beds: 24**

**CROW/NORTHERN CHEYENNE INDIAN HOSPITAL** See Crow/Northern Cheyenne Hospital

### CULBERTSON—Roosevelt County

★ **ROOSEVELT MEDICAL CENTER (271308)**, 818 Second Avenue East, Zip 59218, Mailing Address: P.O. Box 419, Zip 59218–0419; tel. 406/787–6401, (Total facility includes 27 beds in nursing home–type unit) (Nonreporting) **A**10 18 **F**2 3 7 15 34 35 40 43 56 57 59 65 69 77 86 93 97 107 127 128 133 143 146 147 154 156 **P**6
Primary Contact: Audrey Stromberg, Administrator
CFO: Jennifer Kessner, Financial Director
CMO: Don Helland, M.D., Chief Medical Officer
CIO: Brian Fordyce, Director Information Technology
CHR: Elizabeth Raaum, Manger Business Office
CNO: Jessica Schmitz, Director of Nursing
Web address: www.roosmem.org
**Control**: Other not–for–profit (including NFP Corporation) **Service**: General medical and surgical

**Staffed Beds: 33 Admissions: 80 Census: 22 Outpatient Visits: 9345 Births: 0 Total Expense ($000): 5938 Payroll Expense ($000): 3128 Personnel: 48**

**ROOSEVELT MEMORIAL MEDICAL CTR** See Roosevelt Medical Center

*Many Facility Codes have changed. Please refer to the AHA Guide Code Chart.*

**MT**

**CUT BANK—Glacier County**

**GLACIER COUNTY MEDICAL CENTER** See Northern Rockies Medical Center

★ **NORTHERN ROCKIES MEDICAL CENTER (271337)**, 802 Second Street SE, Zip 59427–3329; tel. 406/873–2251, (Nonreporting) **A**10 18 **F**34 40 43 45 57 59 64 65 77 81 83 84 93 97 107 119 127 128 133 154 **P**1 **S** QHR Health, Brentwood, TN
Primary Contact: Cherie Taylor, Chief Executive Officer
CFO: Treasure Berkram, Chief Financial Officer
CMO: Robert Clary, M.D., Medical Director
CHR: Ashley Kimmet, Human Resources
CNO: Susie Beals, Chief Nursing Officer
Web address: www.nrmcinc.org
**Control**: Other not–for–profit (including NFP Corporation) **Service**: General medical and surgical

**Staffed Beds**: 29 **Admissions**: 124 **Census**: 1 **Outpatient Visits**: 10420 **Births**: 29 **Total Expense ($000)**: 8971 **Payroll Expense ($000)**: 5295 **Personnel**: 63

**DEER LODGE—Powell County**

**DEER LODGE MEDICAL CENTER (271314)**, 1100 Hollenbeck Lane, Zip 59722–2317; tel. 406/846–2212, (Nonreporting) **A**10 18 **F**8 11 15 18 28 32 33 34 35 40 43 45 50 55 56 57 59 64 65 79 81 82 84 85 86 87 90 91 93 97 107 108 110 119 127 133 147 148 154 156 **P**6
Primary Contact: Tony Pfaff, Chief Executive Officer
CFO: Jaena Richards, Chief Financial Officer
CMO: Michelle Corbin, M.D., Chief of Staff
CIO: Chris Foster, Director Health Information Management
Web address: www.dlmed.org
**Control**: Corporation, Investor–owned (for–profit) **Service**: General medical and surgical

**Staffed Beds**: 16 **Admissions**: 228 **Census**: 3 **Outpatient Visits**: 10151 **Births**: 0 **Total Expense ($000)**: 14508 **Payroll Expense ($000)**: 6736 **Personnel**: 125

**POWELL COUNTY MEDICAL CENTER** See Deer Lodge Medical Center

**DILLON—Beaverhead County**

★ **BARRETT HOSPITAL & HEALTHCARE (271318)**, 600 Mt Highway 91 South, Zip 59725–7379; tel. 406/683–3000, (Nonreporting) **A**5 10 18 **F**3 13 15 28 29 31 34 40 45 50 52 55 57 59 62 63 64 65 69 75 76 77 79 80 81 83 84 85 87 89 93 96 97 107 110 111 115 119 129 130 131 132 133 135 146 148 154 156 **S** HealthTech Management Services, Brentwood, TN
Primary Contact: Ken Westman, Chief Executive Officer
CFO: Dick Achter, Chief Financial Officer
CMO: Carol Kennedy, Chief Clinical Officer
CIO: Dick Achter, Chief Financial Officer
CHR: Geoff Roach, Director Human Resources
Web address: www.barretthospital.org
**Control**: Other not–for–profit (including NFP Corporation) **Service**: General medical and surgical

**Staffed Beds**: 18 **Admissions**: 528 **Census**: 5 **Outpatient Visits**: 30463 **Births**: 80 **Total Expense ($000)**: 34908 **Payroll Expense ($000)**: 16237 **Personnel**: 210

**BARRETT MEMORIAL HOSPITAL** See Barrett Hospital & Healthcare

**EKALAKA—Carter County**

**DAHL MEMORIAL HEALTHCARE ASSOCIATION (271302)**, 215 Sandy Street, Zip 59324, Mailing Address: P.O. Box 46, Zip 59324–0046; tel. 406/775–8730, (Nonreporting) **A**10 18
Primary Contact: Ryan Tooke, Chief Executive Officer
CFO: Nadine Elmore, Chief Executive Officer
CMO: Darryl Espeland, D.O., Medical Director
CIO: Davie Ann Barrere, Coordinator Information Technology
CHR: Melissa Matthews, Director Human Resources
CNO: Patricia Rogers, Director of Nursing
Web address: www.dahlmemorial.com
**Control**: Other not–for–profit (including NFP Corporation) **Service**: General medical and surgical

**Staffed Beds**: 25

**DAHL MEMORIAL MAF** See Dahl Memorial Healthcare Association

**ENNIS—Madison County**

**MADISON VALLEY HOSPITAL** See Madison Valley Medical Center

**MADISON VALLEY MEDICAL CENTER (271329)**, 305 North Main Street, Zip 59729–8001; tel. 406/682–4222, (Nonreporting) **A**10 18 **F**11 18 28 29 32 34 35 38 40 45 46 50 53 55 56 57 59 64 65 68 69 71 75 77 78 79 82 84 87 92 93 94 97 100 102 107 114 119 127 128 130 131 132 133 135 144 148 154 156
Primary Contact: Allen Rohrback, Chief Executive Officer
CMO: Cindy Sharp, M.D., Chief Medical Officer
CIO: Bo Nix, Chief Information Officer
Web address: www.mvmedcenter.org
**Control**: Other not–for–profit (including NFP Corporation) **Service**: General medical and surgical

**Staffed Beds**: 10 **Admissions**: 187 **Census**: 3 **Outpatient Visits**: 6197 **Total Expense ($000)**: 9414 **Payroll Expense ($000)**: 4454

**FORSYTH—Rosebud County**

★ **ROSEBUD HEALTH CARE CENTER (271327)**, 383 North 17th Avenue, Zip 59327–0268, Mailing Address: P.O. Box 268, Zip 59327–0268; tel. 406/346–2161, (Nonreporting) **A**10 18
Primary Contact: Mindy Price, R.N., Chief Executive Officer
CMO: William Anderson, Medical Director
CHR: Dee Raymond, Director Human Resources
CNO: Jeanne Maciag, Director of Nursing
Web address: www.rosebudhealthcare.com/
**Control**: Other not–for–profit (including NFP Corporation) **Service**: General medical and surgical

**Staffed Beds**: 55

**FORT BENTON—Chouteau County**

**CHOUTEAU CNTY DIST HOSPITAL** See Missouri River Medical Center

**MISSOURI RIVER MEDICAL CENTER (271304)**, 1501 St Charles Street, Zip 59442–0249, Mailing Address: P.O. Box 249, Zip 59442–0249; tel. 406/622–3331, (Nonreporting) **A**10 18 **F**1 2 40 41 50 59 65 84 90 97 107 127 130 133 135 143 148 154 **S** Benefis Health System, Great Falls, MT
Primary Contact: Louie King, President, Harry Bold Nursing Home Administrator
CMO: Jace Bird, M.D., Chief Medical Officer
CIO: Bryan Cartwright, Chief Information Technology Officer
CHR: Carolyn Johnsrud, Manager Human Resources
CNO: Janice Woodhouse, Director of Nursing
Web address: www.mrmcfb.org
**Control**: Hospital district or authority, Government, Nonfederal **Service**: Acute long–term care hospital

**Staffed Beds**: 25 **Admissions**: 34 **Census**: 2 **Outpatient Visits**: 13170 **Births**: 0 **Total Expense ($000)**: 5611 **Payroll Expense ($000)**: 2823 **Personnel**: 57

**FORT HARRISON—Lewis and Clark County**

**VA MONTANA HEALTHCARE SYSTEM** See Veterans Affairs Montana Health Care System

⊞ **VETERANS AFFAIRS MONTANA HEALTH CARE SYSTEM**, 3687 Veterans Drive, Zip 59636–9703, Mailing Address: P.O. Box 1500, Zip 59636–1500; tel. 406/442–6410, (Nonreporting) **A**1 **S** Department of Veterans Affairs, Washington, DC
Primary Contact: Judy A. Hayman, Ph.D., Director
CFO: Brian Gustafson, Chief Financial Officer
CMO: Kurt Werner, M.D., Chief of Staff
CIO: Paul Gauthier, Chief Information Resources Management
CHR: Aggie Hamilton, Chief Human Resources
Web address: www.montana.va.gov/
**Control**: Veterans Affairs, Government, federal **Service**: General medical and surgical

**Staffed Beds**: 94

**MT**

Hospital, Medicare Provider Number, Address, Telephone, Approval, Facility, and Physician Codes, Health Care System

★ American Hospital Association (AHA) membership ○ Healthcare Facilities Accreditation Program ⇑ Center for Improvement in Healthcare Quality Accreditation
□ The Joint Commission accreditation ◇ DNV Healthcare Inc. accreditation △ Commission on Accreditation of Rehabilitation Facilities (CARF) accreditation

## GLASGOW—Valley County

⊞ **FRANCES MAHON DEACONESS HOSPITAL (271316)**, 621 Third Street South,
Zip 59230–2699; tel. 406/228–3500, (Nonreporting) **A**1 10 18 **F**3 7 13 15 28
29 31 34 35 40 43 53 56 57 59 61 64 70 75 76 78 79 81 82 86 87 89 93 100
102 107 108 110 111 115 118 119 127 128 130 131 133 145 149 154 **P**6
Primary Contact: Randall G. Holom, Chief Executive Officer
COO: Ellen Guttenberg, Chief Operating Officer
CFO: Cami Kalinski, Director Financial Services
CMO: Kevin Ross, M.D., Chief of Medical Staff
CIO: David L Nixdorf, Director Support Services
CHR: Ben Thoeny, Director Human Resources
CNO: Brenda Koessl, R.N., Director of Nursing Services
Web address: www.fmdh.org
**Control**: Other not–for–profit (including NFP Corporation) **Service**: General
medical and surgical

| **Staffed Beds:** 25 **Admissions:** 498 **Census:** 4 **Outpatient Visits:** 32755 **Births:** 116 **Total Expense ($000):** 27603 **Payroll Expense ($000):** 12811 **Personnel:** 172 |
| --- |

## GLENDIVE—Dawson County

★ **GLENDIVE MEDICAL CENTER (271332)**, 202 Prospect Drive,
Zip 59330–1999; tel. 406/345–3306, (Nonreporting) **A**10 18
Primary Contact: Parker Powell, Chief Executive Officer
CFO: Barbara Markham, Chief Financial Officer
CMO: Joseph M Leal, M.D., JrChief of Staff
CIO: Barbara Markham, Chief Financial Officer
CHR: Joetta J Pearcy, Director, Human Resources
Web address: www.gmc.org
**Control**: Other not–for–profit (including NFP Corporation) **Service**: General
medical and surgical

| **Staffed Beds:** 88 |
| --- |

## GREAT FALLS—Cascade County

**BENEFIS HEALTH CARE-EAST CAMP** See Benefis Health Care-East Campus

**BENEFIS HEALTH CARE-WEST CAMP** See Benefis Health Care-West Campus

△ **BENEFIS HEALTH SYSTEM (270012)**, 1101 26th Street South,
Zip 59405–5104; tel. 406/455–5000, (Includes BENEFIS HEALTH CARE-EAST
CAMPUS, Mailing address: 1101 26th Street, Great Falls, Montana, Zip 59405;
tel. 406/455–5000; BENEFIS HEALTH CARE-WEST CAMPUS, Mailing address:
500 15th Avenue South, Great Falls, Montana, Zip 59405; tel. 406/455–5000)
(Total facility includes 217 beds in nursing home–type unit) **A**2 5 7 10 20 **F**3 4 5
6 8 9 10 11 12 13 15 18 20 22 24 26 28 29 30 31 34 35 36 37 38 40 43 45
46 47 48 49 50 52 53 54 55 56 57 58 59 61 62 63 64 65 70 71 72 73 74 75
76 77 78 79 81 82 83 84 85 86 87 88 89 90 91 92 93 95 96 97 98 100 101
102 104 105 107 108 110 111 114 115 117 119 120 121 123 124 126 127
128 130 131 132 133 135 143 144 146 147 148 149 152 154 155 158 **P**8 **S**
Benefis Health System, Great Falls, MT
Primary Contact: John H. Goodnow, Chief Executive Officer
CFO: Forrest Ehlinger, System Chief Financial Officer
CMO: Gregory Tierney, M.D., President, BMG AND BHS Chief Medical Officer
CIO: Mark Simon, System Chief Information Officer
CNO: Rayn Ginnaty, Vice President Nursing
Web address: www.benefis.org
**Control**: Other not–for–profit (including NFP Corporation) **Service**: General
medical and surgical

| **Staffed Beds:** 502 **Admissions:** 11611 **Census:** 379 **Outpatient Visits:** 563019 **Births:** 1350 **Total Expense ($000):** 454606 **Payroll Expense ($000):** 212213 **Personnel:** 2660 |
| --- |

**BENEFIS HOSPITALS** See Benefis Health System

**GREAT FALLS CLINIC HOSPITAL (270086)**, 3010 15th Avenue South,
Zip 59405–5240, Mailing Address: 3010 15th Street South, Zip 59405–5240;
tel. 406/216–8000, (Nonreporting) **A**10 **F**3 15 18 24 26 27 29 30 31 34 35 38
40 41 44 45 46 47 51 58 59 64 65 68 74 75 77 78 79 81 82 85 86 87 91 92
93 94 107 108 110 111 114 115 119 120 121 123 124 126 130 135 144 146
148 149 156
Primary Contact: Vicki Newmiller, Chief Executive Officer
CFO: Cheryl Cornwell, Chief Financial Officer
CMO: Nicholas Bonfilio, M.D., Chief of Staff
Web address: www.gfclinic.com/location/great-falls-clinic-hospital/
**Control**: Corporation, Investor–owned (for–profit) **Service**: General medical and
surgical

| **Staffed Beds:** 20 **Admissions:** 1347 **Census:** 11 **Outpatient Visits:** 91533 **Births:** 0 **Total Expense ($000):** 64853 **Payroll Expense ($000):** 18522 **Personnel:** 332 |
| --- |

**GREAT FALLS CLINIC MEDICAL CENTER** See Great Falls Clinic Hospital

## HAMILTON—Ravalli County

★ **MARCUS DALY MEMORIAL HOSPITAL (271340)**, 1200 Westwood Drive,
Zip 59840–2345; tel. 406/363–2211, (Nonreporting) **A**10 18 **F**3 7 8 11 13 15
18 27 28 29 30 34 35 40 43 45 50 54 56 57 59 62 63 64 65 68 70 74 75 76
77 79 81 82 83 84 89 91 92 93 97 102 107 110 111 114 115 119 120 126
127 129 130 131 132 133 135 144 145 146 147 148 154
Primary Contact: John Bishop, Chief Executive Officer
CMO: John Moreland, M.D., Chief Medical Officer
CIO: Brad Kowalski, Director Information Technology
CHR: Debbie M Morris, Director Human Resources
CNO: Kathy Padilla, Chief Nursing Officer
Web address: www.mdmh.org
**Control**: Other not–for–profit (including NFP Corporation) **Service**: General
medical and surgical

| **Staffed Beds:** 25 **Admissions:** 1612 **Census:** 11 **Births:** 131 **Total Expense ($000):** 68966 **Payroll Expense ($000):** 37971 |
| --- |

## HARDIN—Big Horn County

★ **BIG HORN COUNTY MEMORIAL HOSPITAL (271338)**, 17 North Miles Avenue,
Zip 59034–2323; tel. 406/665–2310, (Total facility includes 36 beds in nursing
home–type unit) (Nonreporting) **A**10 18 **F**3 10 15 29 34 40 41 43 45 59 64 67
81 89 90 93 107 110 111 114 119 125 128 130 133 143 146 149 154 158
Primary Contact: Kristi Gatrell, Chief Executive Officer
CFO: Roxie Cain, Chief Financial Officer
CNO: Kirsten Willoughby, Director of Nursing
**Control**: Other not–for–profit (including NFP Corporation) **Service**: General
medical and surgical

| **Staffed Beds:** 61 **Admissions:** 191 **Census:** 38 **Outpatient Visits:** 8063 **Births:** 5 **Total Expense ($000):** 16679 **Payroll Expense ($000):** 7793 **Personnel:** 163 |
| --- |

**BIG HORN HOSPITAL ASSOCIAITON** See Big Horn County Memorial Hospital

## HARLEM—Blaine County

☐ **FORT BELKNAP SERVICE UNIT (271315)**, 669 Agency Main Street,
Zip 59526–9455; tel. 406/353–3100, (Nonreporting) **A**1 10 18 **S** U. S. Indian
Health Service, Rockville, MD
Primary Contact: Gregory Smith, M.D., Chief Executive Officer
CMO: Ethel L Moore, M.D., Director of Medical Affairs
CIO: Mikki Grant, Chief Information Officer
CHR: Charlotte Lamebull, Administrative Officer
CNO: Diana Hunter, Director of Nursing
Web address: www.ihs.gov
**Control**: PHS, Indian Service, Government, federal **Service**: General medical and
surgical

| **Staffed Beds:** 6 |
| --- |

**FORT BELKNAP U. S. PUBLIC HEALTH SERVICE INDIAN HOSPITAL** See Fort
Belknap Service Unit

## HARLOWTON—Wheatland County

★ **WHEATLAND MEMORIAL HEALTHCARE (271321)**, 530 Third Street
North West, Zip 59036, Mailing Address: P.O. Box 287, Zip 59036–0287;
tel. 406/632–4351, (Nonreporting) **A**10 18
Primary Contact: Rick Poss, Interim Chief Executive Officer
CFO: Doug Lewis, Chief Financial Officer
CMO: Kathy Jutila, M.D., Chief of Staff
CIO: Ray Hetherington, Network Administrator
CHR: Peggy Hiner, Director Human Resources
CNO: Lauri Ann Cooney, Director Nursing
Web address: www.wheatlandmemorial.org
**Control**: Other not–for–profit (including NFP Corporation) **Service**: General
medical and surgical

| **Staffed Beds:** 25 |
| --- |

**WHEATLAND MEMORIAL HOSPITAL** See Wheatland Memorial Healthcare

*Many Facility Codes have changed. Please refer to the AHA Guide Code Chart.*
© 2021 AHA Guide

## HAVRE—Hill County

★ **NORTHERN MONTANA HEALTH CARE (270032)**, 30 13th Street,
Zip 59501–5222, Mailing Address: P.O. Box 1231, Zip 59501–1231;
tel. 406/265–2211, (Total facility includes 115 beds in nursing home–type unit)
(Nonreporting) **A**10 20 **F**2 5 10 11 13 15 28 29 34 35 36 38 40 43 45 53 56
57 59 60 63 64 68 70 75 76 77 78 79 81 82 84 85 89 93 97 99 101 102 103
104 107 108 110 111 115 118 119 127 128 129 130 132 133 135 146 148
153 154 156 **P**6
Primary Contact: David Henry, President and Chief Executive Officer
CFO: Kim Lucke, Vice President Finance
CNO: Eric Koch, Chief Nursing Officer
Web address: www.nmhcare.org
**Control:** Other not–for–profit (including NFP Corporation) **Service:** General
medical and surgical

> **Staffed Beds: 142 Admissions: 1332 Census: 95 Outpatient Visits: 90413**
> **Births: 329 Total Expense ($000): 62598 Payroll Expense ($000): 32306**
> **Personnel: 521**

**NORTHERN MONTANA HOSPITAL** See Northern Montana Health Care

## HELENA—Lewis AND Clark County

⌧ **SHODAIR CHILDREN'S HOSPITAL (274004)**, 2755 Colonial Drive,
Zip 59601–4926, Mailing Address: P.O. Box 5539, Zip 59604–5539;
tel. 406/444–7500, (Nonreporting) **A**1 10 **F**55 98 99 101 104 106 130 149 154
**P**6
Primary Contact: Craig E. Aasved, Chief Executive Officer
CFO: Ron Wiens, Chief Financial Officer
CMO: Heather Zaluski, M.D., President Medical Staff
CIO: Judy Jackson, Director Health Information Management and Privacy Officer
CNO: Christine Bates, Chief Nursing Officer
Web address: www.shodair.org
**Control:** Other not–for–profit (including NFP Corporation) **Service:** Children's
hospital psychiatric

> **Staffed Beds: 74 Admissions: 1270 Census: 65 Outpatient Visits: 2399**
> **Births: 0 Total Expense ($000): 26596 Payroll Expense ($000): 16941**
> **Personnel: 336**

⇑ **ST PETER'S COMMUNITY HOSPITAL** See St. Peter's Hospital

★ ⇑ **ST. PETER'S HOSPITAL (270003)**, 2475 Broadway, Zip 59601–4928;
tel. 406/442–2480, (Nonreporting) **A**10 20 21 **F**3 7 11 13 15 18 22 26 28 29
30 31 34 35 40 43 44 45 46 49 50 51 54 56 57 59 60 62 63 64 68 70 76 77
78 79 81 82 84 87 89 93 97 98 100 103 104 107 108 110 111 114 115 116
117 118 119 120 121 122 123 124 129 130 135 144 146 148 153 154 156
Primary Contact: Wade C. Johnson, MS, FACHE, Chief Executive Officer
CFO: John Green, Vice President Finance
CMO: Shelly Harkins, M.D., Chief Medical Officer
CHR: Karla Smith, Director Human Resources
CNO: Cheryl Hunt EsqChief Nursing Officer
Web address: www.stpetes.org
**Control:** Other not–for–profit (including NFP Corporation) **Service:** General
medical and surgical

> **Staffed Beds: 123 Admissions: 5483 Census: 59**

## JORDAN—Garfield County

**GARFIELD COUNTY HEALTH CENTER (271310)**, 332 Leavitt Avenue,
Zip 59337, Mailing Address: P.O. Box 389, Zip 59337–0389; tel. 406/557–2500,
(Nonreporting) **A**10 18
Primary Contact: Jay Pottenger, Chief Executive Officer
CFO: Charlotte Herbold, Manager Business Officer
CMO: David M. Kidder, D.O., Chief Medical Officer
CIO: Charlotte Herbold, Manager Business Officer
CNO: Sarah Nordlund, Director of Nursing
Web address: www.garfieldco.us/garfield-county-health-center.html
**Control:** County, Government, Nonfederal **Service:** General medical and surgical

> **Staffed Beds: 32**

## KALISPELL—Flathead County

**GLACIER VIEW HOSPITAL** See Pathways Treatment Center

**HEALTHCENTER NORTHWEST** See The Healthcenter

★ **KALISPELL REGIONAL HEALTHCARE (270051)**, 310 Sunnyview Lane,
Zip 59901–3129; tel. 406/752–5111, (Includes PATHWAYS TREATMENT
CENTER, Mailing address: 200 Heritage Way, Kalispell, Montana, Zip 59901;
tel. 406/756–3950), (Nonreporting) **A**2 3 5 10 **F**3 4 5 7 8 13 15 18 19 20 22
24 26 28 29 30 31 34 35 36 40 43 45 46 49 50 56 57 58 59 62 63 64 70 71
72 74 75 76 77 78 79 81 83 84 85 86 87 88 89 93 97 98 99 100 101 102
103 104 105 107 114 115 118 119 120 121 123 126 129 130 131 132 143
144 145 146 147 148 149 151 152 153 154 155 156 157 **P**6 **S** QHR Health,
Brentwood, TN
Primary Contact: Craig Lambrecht, M.D., President and Chief Executive Officer
COO: Ted W Hirsch, Senior Executive Director
CFO: Tracey Talley, Chief Financial and Information Officer
CHR: Deb Wilson, Director Human Resources
**Control:** Other not–for–profit (including NFP Corporation) **Service:** General
medical and surgical

> **Staffed Beds: 178 Admissions: 8628 Census: 109 Births: 650**
> **Total Expense ($000): 411386 Payroll Expense ($000): 192452**
> **Personnel: 2404**

**KALISPELL REGIONAL MEDICAL CENTER** See Kalispell Regional Healthcare

△ **THE HEALTHCENTER (270087)**, 320 Sunnyview Lane, Zip 59901–3129;
tel. 406/751–7550, (Nonreporting) **A**7 10 **F**3 8 15 33 36 45 46 47 48 49 51 59
64 71 81 82 85 87 90 91 95 96 107 110 111 112 114 115 117 119 124 126
145 147 149 **P**6 **S** QHR Health, Brentwood, TN
Primary Contact: Tate J. Kreitinger, Chief Executive Officer
CFO: Craig Boyer, Chief Financial Officer
CHR: Kathy Welsh, Director of Human Resources
CNO: Heidi Sturm, Executive Director of Nursing
Web address: www.krmc.org
**Control:** Corporation, Investor–owned (for–profit) **Service:** General medical and surgical

> **Staffed Beds: 27 Admissions: 778 Census: 10 Outpatient Visits: 81621**
> **Births: 0 Total Expense ($000): 68464 Payroll Expense ($000): 18101**
> **Personnel: 242**

## LEWISTOWN—Fergus County

**CENTRAL MONTANA MED CTR** See Central Montana Medical Center

★ **CENTRAL MONTANA MEDICAL CENTER (271345)**, 408 Wendell Avenue,
Zip 59457–2261; tel. 406/535–7711, (Nonreporting) **A**10 18 **F**3 7 11 13 15 28
29 31 34 35 40 43 45 50 53 59 62 63 64 65 75 76 77 81 84 85 89 91 92 93
97 107 108 110 111 115 119 129 130 131 132 133 148 154 156 **P**6
Primary Contact: Laura Bennett, Chief Executive Officer
CFO: Alan Aldrich, Chief Financial Officer
CHR: Torie A Lynch, Manager Human Resources
CNO: Karen White, Chief Nursing Officer
Web address: www.cmmccares.com
**Control:** Other not–for–profit (including NFP Corporation) **Service:** General
medical and surgical

> **Staffed Beds: 25 Admissions: 702 Census: 8 Births: 71 Total Expense**
> **($000): 35817 Payroll Expense ($000): 17868 Personnel: 273**

## LIBBY—Lincoln County

★ **CABINET PEAKS MEDICAL CENTER (271320)**, 209 Health Park Drive,
Zip 59923–2130; tel. 406/283–7000, (Nonreporting) **A**5 10 18 **F**1 3 11 13 15
17 28 29 30 31 34 35 40 45 50 54 56 57 59 64 70 75 76 77 79 81 84 85 86
87 89 93 97 102 107 110 111 115 119 128 129 130 131 132 133 135 146
147 148 154 156 **P**6 **S** QHR Health, Brentwood, TN
Primary Contact: Bruce Whitfield, CPA, Chief Executive Officer and Chief Financial
Officer
CFO: Bruce Whitfield, CPA, Chief Executive Officer and Chief Financial Officer
CMO: Jay Maloney, M.D., Chief of Staff
Web address: www.sjlh.com
**Control:** Other not–for–profit (including NFP Corporation) **Service:** General
medical and surgical

> **Staffed Beds: 25 Admissions: 732 Census: 5 Outpatient Visits: 46050**
> **Births: 98 Total Expense ($000): 35301 Payroll Expense ($000): 14951**
> **Personnel: 227**

**ST. JOHN'S LUTHERAN HOSPITAL** See Cabinet Peaks Medical Center

**MT**

---

Hospital, Medicare Provider Number, Address, Telephone, Approval, Facility, and Physician Codes, Health Care System

★ American Hospital Association (AHA) membership  ○ Healthcare Facilities Accreditation Program  ⇑ Center for Improvement in Healthcare Quality Accreditation
□ The Joint Commission accreditation  ◇ DNV Healthcare Inc. accreditation  △ Commission on Accreditation of Rehabilitation Facilities (CARF) accreditation

## LIVINGSTON—Park County

★ **LIVINGSTON HEALTHCARE (271317)**, 320 Alpenglow Lane, Zip 59047–8506; tel. 406/222–3541, (Nonreporting) **A**5 10 18 **F**3 11 13 15 28 29 30 31 34 35 38 40 41 43 45 46 50 55 56 57 59 62 63 64 65 66 67 70 75 76 77 78 79 81 84 85 86 87 89 93 97 100 101 104 107 108 110 111 115 119 124 127 128 129 130 131 132 133 144 146 147 148 149 150 154 156 **P**6
Primary Contact: Deb Anczak, Interim Chief Executive Officer
CFO: Ryan Speas, Director Finance
CMO: D. Scott Coleman, M.D., Medical Director
CIO: Jody Duran, Manager Information Systems
CHR: Vicki Axtell, Director Human Resources
CNO: Dave Noble, Director of Nursing
Web address: www.livingstonhealthcare.org
**Control:** Other not–for–profit (including NFP Corporation) **Service:** General medical and surgical

**Staffed Beds:** 25 **Admissions:** 1209 **Census:** 12 **Outpatient Visits:** 35643 **Births:** 124 **Total Expense ($000):** 51460 **Payroll Expense ($000):** 23110 **Personnel:** 378

**LIVINGSTON MEMORIAL HOSPITAL** See Livingston Healthcare

## MALTA—Phillips County

★ **PHILLIPS COUNTY HOSPITAL (271312)**, 311 South 8th Avenue East, Zip 59538–0640, Mailing Address: P.O. Box 640, Zip 59538–0640; tel. 406/654–1100, (Nonreporting) **A**10 18 **F**3 29 31 34 40 41 56 57 59 62 66 68 82 84 90 93 107 115 119 127 130 132 133 154 156 **P**4
Primary Contact: Scott A. Duke, Interim Chief Executive Officer
CFO: Stephanie Denham, Chief Financial Officer and Human Resources Officer
CMO: Ed Medina, M.D., Medical Director
CHR: Stephanie Denham, Chief Financial Officer and Human Resources Officer
CNO: Lonna Crowder, Director of Nursing
Web address: www.pchospital.us/
**Control:** Other not–for–profit (including NFP Corporation) **Service:** General medical and surgical

**Staffed Beds:** 6 **Admissions:** 180 **Census:** 1 **Outpatient Visits:** 6391 **Births:** 0 **Total Expense ($000):** 6727 **Payroll Expense ($000):** 3404 **Personnel:** 63

**PHILLIPS COUNTY MEDICAL CENTER** See Phillips County Hospital

## MILES CITY—Custer County

**HOLY ROSARY HEALTH CENTER** See Holy Rosary Healthcare

⊞ **HOLY ROSARY HEALTHCARE (271347)**, 2600 Wilson Street, Zip 59301–5094; tel. 406/233–2600, (Total facility includes 64 beds in nursing home–type unit) (Nonreporting) **A**1 10 18 **F**3 13 15 26 27 28 29 30 31 32 34 35 40 43 47 50 56 59 63 64 65 68 70 75 76 77 78 79 81 84 85 87 89 93 94 97 107 108 110 111 115 119 127 128 130 131 132 133 135 146 147 149 154 156 157 **P**6 **S** SCL Health, Broomfield, CO
Primary Contact: Karen Costello, President
CFO: Travis Scheving, Chief Financial Officer
CMO: Michael Bush, M.D., Chief Medical Officer
CHR: Cathy Rodenbaugh, Director Human Resources
CNO: Lisa Sanford, VP Patient Care/CNO
Web address: www.holyrosaryhealthcare.org
**Control:** Other not–for–profit (including NFP Corporation) **Service:** General medical and surgical

**Staffed Beds:** 89 **Admissions:** 1264 **Census:** 62 **Outpatient Visits:** 32338 **Births:** 201 **Total Expense ($000):** 46861 **Payroll Expense ($000):** 15976 **Personnel:** 216

## MISSOULA—Missoula County

⊞ △ **COMMUNITY MEDICAL CENTER (270023)**, 2827 Fort Missoula Road, Zip 59804–7408; tel. 406/728–4100, (Nonreporting) **A**1 2 3 5 7 10 19 **F**3 11 13 15 17 18 20 22 26 28 29 30 31 34 35 37 40 43 46 47 48 49 51 54 55 57 59 63 64 65 68 70 72 74 75 76 78 79 81 82 83 84 85 87 88 89 90 91 92 93 94 96 97 106 107 108 110 111 114 115 116 117 118 119 120 121 123 124 126 130 132 134 135 141 143 144 145 146 147 148 149 154 156 **P**6 7 **S** LifePoint Health, Brentwood, TN
Primary Contact: Dean French, M.D., Chief Executive Officer
CMO: David Lechner, M.D., Chief Medical Officer and Vice President Innovation
CNO: Jan Perry, R.N., Vice President Patient Care Services
Web address: www.communitymed.org
**Control:** Corporation, Investor–owned (for–profit) **Service:** General medical and surgical

**Staffed Beds:** 135 **Admissions:** 4940 **Census:** 63 **Outpatient Visits:** 131591 **Births:** 995 **Total Expense ($000):** 177992 **Payroll Expense ($000):** 64635 **Personnel:** 1015

⊞ **PROVIDENCE ST. PATRICK HOSPITAL (270014)**, 500 West Broadway, Zip 59802–4096, Mailing Address: P.O. Box 4587, Zip 59806–4587; tel. 406/543–7271, (Nonreporting) **A**1 2 3 5 10 19 **F**3 11 12 13 15 18 20 22 24 26 28 29 30 31 34 35 38 40 43 50 51 53 54 57 58 59 60 61 64 65 68 70 72 74 75 76 77 78 79 81 82 84 85 86 87 89 92 93 97 98 99 100 101 102 103 104 105 107 108 110 111 115 117 118 119 120 121 123 124 126 127 129 130 132 141 144 146 148 149 154 156 157 **P**2 **S** Providence St. Joseph Health, Renton, WA
Primary Contact: Joyce Dombrouski, R.N., Chief Executive Officer
CFO: Kirk Bodlovic, WMSA Chief Financial Officer
CHR: Karyn Trainor, Director Human Resources
CNO: Carol Bensen, MSN, R.N., Chief Nursing Officer
Web address: www.https://montana.providence.org/locations-directory/s/st-patrick-hospital
**Control:** Church operated, Nongovernment, not–for–profit **Service:** General medical and surgical

**Staffed Beds:** 200 **Admissions:** 10849 **Census:** 130 **Outpatient Visits:** 343057 **Births:** 494 **Total Expense ($000):** 254372 **Payroll Expense ($000):** 81104 **Personnel:** 1256

**ST. PATRICK HOSPITAL** See Providence St. Patrick Hospital

## PHILIPSBURG—Granite County

★ **GRANITE COUNTY MEDICAL CENTER (271303)**, 310 Sansome Street, Zip 59858–0729, Mailing Address: P.O. Box 729, Zip 59858–0729; tel. 406/859–3271, (Nonreporting) **A**10 18 **S** Providence St. Joseph Health, Renton, WA
Primary Contact: Maria Stoppler, Chief Executive Officer
CFO: Susan Ossello, Chief Financial Officer
CMO: John Moore, M.D., Medical Director
Web address: www.gcmedcenter.org/
**Control:** County, Government, Nonfederal **Service:** General medical and surgical

**Staffed Beds:** 25

**GRANITE COUNTY MEM HOSPITAL** See Granite County Medical Center

## PLAINS—Sanders County

★ **CLARK FORK VALLEY HOSPITAL (271323)**, 10 Kruger Road, Zip 59859, Mailing Address: P.O. Box 768, Zip 59859–0768; tel. 406/826–4800, (Total facility includes 28 beds in nursing home–type unit) (Nonreporting) **A**10 18 **F**3 11 13 15 28 29 30 32 34 35 36 40 43 44 45 50 57 58 59 62 63 64 65 70 75 76 77 79 81 82 83 84 85 86 87 89 91 93 97 107 110 114 115 118 119 127 128 129 130 132 133 135 143 146 147 148 149 154 156 **P**3 6
Primary Contact: Gregory S. Hanson, M.D., Chief Executive Officer
CFO: Carla A Neiman, Chief Financial Officer
CMO: Ronald Black, M.D., Chief Medical Officer
CIO: Carla A Neiman, Chief Financial Officer
CHR: Barry Fowler, Director Human and System Resources
CNO: Lisa Eberhardt, Chief Nursing Officer
Web address: www.cfvh.org
**Control:** Other not–for–profit (including NFP Corporation) **Service:** General medical and surgical

**Staffed Beds:** 44 **Admissions:** 879 **Census:** 32 **Outpatient Visits:** 35874 **Births:** 19 **Total Expense ($000):** 25057 **Payroll Expense ($000):** 10461 **Personnel:** 212

## PLENTYWOOD—Sheridan County

**SHERIDAN MEMORIAL HOSPITAL (271322)**, 440 West Laurel Avenue, Zip 59254–1596; tel. 406/765–3700, (Nonreporting) **A**10 18
Primary Contact: Gregory L. Maurer, Chief Executive Officer
CHR: Roxy Kleppen, Director Human Resource
Web address: www.sheridanmemorial.net/
**Control:** Other not–for–profit (including NFP Corporation) **Service:** General medical and surgical

**Staffed Beds:** 97

**MT**

*Many Facility Codes have changed. Please refer to the AHA Guide Code Chart.* © 2021 AHA Guide

## POLSON—Lake County

✠ **PROVIDENCE ST. JOSEPH MEDICAL CENTER (271343)**, 6 Thirteenth Avenue East, Zip 59860–5315, Mailing Address: P.O. Box 1010, Zip 59860–1010; tel. 406/883–5377, (Nonreporting) **A**1 10 18 **F**3 10 13 15 28 29 30 31 34 35 40 43 45 50 57 59 64 68 75 76 77 79 81 82 85 87 89 93 97 107 110 111 115 119 125 127 129 130 131 133 146 147 148 149 154 **P**6 **S** Providence St. Joseph Health, Renton, WA
Primary Contact: Devin Huntley, Chief Operating Officer
COO: Devin Huntley, Chief Operating Officer
CFO: Kirk Bodlovic, Vice President and Chief Financial Officer
CMO: Kelly Bagnell, M.D., Chief of Staff
Web address: www.saintjoes.org
**Control**: Church operated, Nongovernment, not–for–profit **Service**: General medical and surgical

**Staffed Beds:** 22 **Admissions:** 610 **Census:** 6 **Outpatient Visits:** 93743
**Births:** 111 **Total Expense ($000):** 33092 **Payroll Expense ($000):** 17828
**Personnel:** 211

**ST. JOSEPH HOSPITAL** See Providence St. Joseph Medical Center

## POPLAR—Richland County

**COMMUNITY HOSPITAL** See Poplar Community Hospital

★ **POPLAR COMMUNITY HOSPITAL (271300)**, 211 H Street, Zip 59255–9519, Mailing Address: P.O. Box 38, Zip 59255–0038; tel. 406/768–6100, (Nonreporting) **A**10 18 **F**3 7 31 40 43 50 57 59 75 87 97 101 102 104 107 115 127 130 133 143 147 **P**3
Primary Contact: Margaret B. Norgaard, Chief Executive Officer
CHR: Annie Block, Director Human Resources
Web address: www.nemhs.net
**Control**: Other not–for–profit (including NFP Corporation) **Service**: General medical and surgical

**Staffed Beds:** 20 **Admissions:** 148 **Census:** 5 **Outpatient Visits:** 6898
**Births:** 4 **Total Expense ($000):** 8860 **Payroll Expense ($000):** 3652
**Personnel:** 85

## RED LODGE—Carbon County

★ **BEARTOOTH BILLINGS CLINIC (271326)**, 2525 North Broadway Avenue, Zip 59068–9222, Mailing Address: P.O. Box 590, Zip 59068–0590; tel. 406/446–2345, (Nonreporting) **A**10 18 **F**3 11 15 18 28 29 34 35 40 43 44 45 50 56 57 59 62 63 64 65 68 75 77 81 84 85 86 87 91 93 94 96 97 107 110 114 119 130 131 133 135 146 147 148 149 154 156 **P**6
Primary Contact: Kelley Evans, Chief Administrative Officer
CFO: Kyle Gee, Chief Financial Officer
CMO: William George, M.D., Chief of Staff
CHR: Katie Nordstrom, Director Human Resources
CNO: Bridgett Chartier, Director of Nursing
Web address: www.beartoothbillingsclinic.org
**Control**: Other not–for–profit (including NFP Corporation) **Service**: General medical and surgical

**Staffed Beds:** 10 **Admissions:** 171 **Census:** 1 **Outpatient Visits:** 64212
**Births:** 0 **Total Expense ($000):** 15065 **Payroll Expense ($000):** 5631
**Personnel:** 109

**BEARTOOTH HOSPITAL AND HEALTH CENTER** See Beartooth Billings Clinic

## RONAN—Lake County

★ **ST. LUKE COMMUNITY HEALTHCARE (271325)**, 107 Sixth Avenue SW, Zip 59864–2634; tel. 406/676–4441, (Total facility includes 75 beds in nursing home–type unit) (Nonreporting) **A**10 18 **F**2 13 15 28 29 31 34 40 43 45 53 54 56 57 59 61 64 65 68 75 76 78 79 81 85 93 97 107 108 110 111 115 119 127 128 129 130 131 132 135 144 145 147 154 **P**6
Primary Contact: Steve J. Todd, Chief Executive Officer
COO: Sarah Teaff, Chief Operating Officer
CFO: Paul Soukup, Chief Financial Officer
CMO: Edred T. Vizcarra, M.D., Chief of Staff
CHR: Theresa L. Jones, Manager Human Resources
CNO: Leah Emerson, Director of Nursing
Web address: www.stlukehealthcare.org
**Control**: Other not–for–profit (including NFP Corporation) **Service**: General medical and surgical

**Staffed Beds:** 100 **Admissions:** 972 **Census:** 52 **Outpatient Visits:** 73340
**Births:** 113 **Total Expense ($000):** 41039 **Payroll Expense ($000):** 22269
**Personnel:** 349

**ST. LUKE COMMUNITY HOSPITAL** See St. Luke Community Healthcare

## ROUNDUP—Musselshell County

★ **ROUNDUP MEMORIAL HEALTHCARE (271346)**, 1202 Third Street West, Zip 59072–1816, Mailing Address: P.O. Box 40, Zip 59072–0040; tel. 406/323–2301, (Nonreporting) **A**10 18
Primary Contact: Holly Wolff, Chief Executive Officer
CFO: Kyle Gee, Regional Vice President Financial Operations
CMO: Mark Ward, M.D., Chief of Staff
CNO: Emily Shoup, Director Nursing Services
Web address: www.rmhmt.org/
**Control**: Other not–for–profit (including NFP Corporation) **Service**: General medical and surgical

**Staffed Beds:** 25

**ROUNDUP MEMORIAL HOSPITAL** See Roundup Memorial Healthcare

## SAINT MARY—Glacier County

**BLACKFEET COMMUNITY HOSPITAL (270074)**, 760 New Hospital Circle, Zip 59417–0760, Mailing Address: P.O. Box 760, Browning, Zip 59417–0760; tel. 406/338–6100, (Nonreporting) **A**10 **S** U. S. Indian Health Service, Rockville, MD
Primary Contact: Garland Stiffarm, Chief Executive Officer
CFO: Cleo Main, Finance Officer
CMO: Neil Sun Rhodes, M.D., Chief Medical Officer
CNO: Susan Head, Director Nursing Services
Web address: www.ihs.gov
**Control**: PHS, Indian Service, Government, federal **Service**: General medical and surgical

**Staffed Beds:** 25

**U. S. PUBLIC HEALTH SERVICE BLACKFEET COMMUNITY HOSPITAL** See Blackfeet Community Hospital

## SCOBEY—Daniels County

**DANIELS MEMORIAL HEALTHCARE CENTER (271342)**, 105 Fifth Avenue East, Zip 59263, Mailing Address: P.O. Box 400, Zip 59263–0400; tel. 406/487–2296, (Nonreporting) **A**10 18 **F**2 11 29 40 44 50 56 59 64 65 67 69 85 91 93 97 107 114 119 127 133 143 146 148 **P**6
Primary Contact: Eric Connell, Chief Executive Officer
CMO: Don Sawdey, M.D., Medical Director
CHR: Edith Huda, Director Human Resources
CNO: Kathy Ware, Director of Nursing
Web address: www.danielsmemorialhealthcare.org
**Control**: Other not–for–profit (including NFP Corporation) **Service**: General medical and surgical

**Staffed Beds:** 25 **Admissions:** 69 **Census:** 19 **Outpatient Visits:** 558
**Births:** 0 **Total Expense ($000):** 7991 **Payroll Expense ($000):** 3908

**DANIELS MEMORIAL HOSPITAL** See Daniels Memorial Healthcare Center

## SHELBY—Toole County

★ **MARIAS MEDICAL CENTER (271328)**, 640 Park Drive, Zip 59474–1663, Mailing Address: P.O. Box 915, Zip 59474–0915; tel. 406/434–3200, (Nonreporting) **A**10 18 **F**3 11 13 15 17 28 29 34 40 41 53 56 57 59 65 70 76 77 81 83 85 87 89 93 102 107 110 114 119 129 130 133 146 154
Primary Contact: Ward C. VanWichen, Chief Executive Officer
CFO: Melissa Ostberg, Chief Financial Officer
CMO: Melanie Hardy, D.O., Chief of Staff
CIO: Jayce Yarn, Director Information Technology
CHR: Cindy Lamb, Director Human Resources
CNO: Tamra Fender, Chief Nursing Officer
Web address: www.mmcmt.org
**Control**: County, Government, Nonfederal **Service**: General medical and surgical

**Staffed Beds:** 21 **Admissions:** 221 **Census:** 3 **Births:** 32 **Total Expense ($000):** 12195 **Payroll Expense ($000):** 3876 **Personnel:** 78

**TOOLE COUNTY HOSP & NRSG HOME** See Marias Medical Center

## SHERIDAN—Madison County

**RUBY VALLEY HOSPITAL** See Ruby Valley Medical Center

**Hospital, Medicare Provider Number, Address, Telephone, Approval, Facility, and Physician Codes, Health Care System**
★ American Hospital Association (AHA) membership
□ The Joint Commission accreditation
○ Healthcare Facilities Accreditation Program
◇ DNV Healthcare Inc. accreditation
⇑ Center for Improvement in Healthcare Quality Accreditation
△ Commission on Accreditation of Rehabilitation Facilities (CARF) accreditation

MT

**RUBY VALLEY MEDICAL CENTER (271319)**, 220 East Crofoot Street, Zip 59749–7714, Mailing Address: P.O. Box 336, Zip 59749–0336; tel. 406/842–5453, (Nonreporting) **A**10 18 **F**3 7 29 33 34 35 38 40 43 55 56 57 65 66 81 82 86 87 93 97 100 104 107 114 127 133 135 147 148 149 154 **P**6
Primary Contact: Landon Dybdal, Chief Executive Officer
CFO: Dennis Holschbach, Chief Financial Officer
CMO: Roman Hendrickson, M.D., Medical Director
CHR: Jenny Rohrback, Director Human Resource
CNO: Brenda Green, Director of Nursing
Web address: www.rubyvalleyhospital.com/
**Control**: Hospital district or authority, Government, Nonfederal **Service**: General medical and surgical

**Staffed Beds**: 5 **Admissions**: 134 **Census**: 1 **Outpatient Visits**: 3185 **Births**: 0 **Total Expense ($000)**: 8426 **Payroll Expense ($000)**: 4246 **Personnel**: 74

### SIDNEY—Richland County

**COMMUNITY MEMORIAL HOSPITAL** See Sidney Health Center

★ **SIDNEY HEALTH CENTER (271344)**, 216 14th Avenue SW, Zip 59270–3586; tel. 406/488–2100, (Total facility includes 56 beds in nursing home–type unit) (Nonreporting) **A**10 18 **F**2 3 7 11 13 15 17 28 29 30 31 34 35 36 40 41 45 50 55 56 57 58 59 62 63 64 67 70 75 76 77 78 79 81 82 84 85 86 87 89 90 93 96 97 107 108 110 111 115 119 120 121 122 123 124 127 128 129 130 131 132 133 135 144 145 146 147 148 149 154 156 **P**6
Primary Contact: Jennifer Doty, Chief Executive Officer
CFO: Tina Montgomery, Chief Financial Officer
CMO: Rajohn Karanjai, M.D., Chief Medical Officer
CIO: Brian Fay, Director Information Systems
CHR: Lisa Aisenbrey, Administrator Human Resources and Support Services
Web address: www.sidneyhealth.org
**Control**: Other not–for–profit (including NFP Corporation) **Service**: General medical and surgical

**Staffed Beds**: 81 **Admissions**: 1444 **Census**: 61 **Outpatient Visits**: 50091 **Births**: 208 **Total Expense ($000)**: 69842 **Payroll Expense ($000)**: 27131 **Personnel**: 423

### SUPERIOR—Mineral County

**MINERAL COMMUNITY HOSPITAL (271331)**, 1208 6th Avenue East, Zip 59872–9618; tel. 406/822–4841, (Nonreporting) **A**10 18 **F**34 40 45 48 59 64 69 75 81 93 97 102 107 110 115 133 154
Primary Contact: Steve McNeece, Interim Chief Executive Officer
CFO: Cliff Case, Chief Financial Officer
CMO: Roger Pafford, M.D., Medical Director
CHR: Stacy Conrow-Ververis, Director Human Resources
CNO: Jenifer Mitchell, R.N., Director of Nursing Services
Web address: www.mineralcommunityhospital.com/
**Control**: Other not–for–profit (including NFP Corporation) **Service**: General medical and surgical

**Staffed Beds**: 24 **Admissions**: 143 **Census**: 16 **Outpatient Visits**: 7454 **Births**: 0 **Total Expense ($000)**: 7286 **Payroll Expense ($000)**: 3402 **Personnel**: 82

**MINERAL COUNTY HOSPITAL** See Mineral Community Hospital

### TERRY—Prairie County

**PRAIRIE COMMUNITY HEALTH CENTER** See Prairie Community Hospital

★ **PRAIRIE COMMUNITY HOSPITAL (271309)**, 312 South Adams Avenue, Zip 59349–0156, Mailing Address: P.O. Box 156, Zip 59349–0156; tel. 406/635–5511, (Nonreporting) **A**10 18 **F**2 34 40 41 57 59 64 65 67 93 127 128 133 135 146 148 154 **P**6
Primary Contact: Burt Keltner, Administrator
CFO: Laurie Chandler, Financial Officer
CIO: Laurie Chandler, Chairman
CNO: Susan Morgan, Director of Nursing Services
Web address: www.prairiecommunityhospital.org/
**Control**: Hospital district or authority, Government, Nonfederal **Service**: General medical and surgical

**Staffed Beds**: 22 **Admissions**: 14 **Census**: 1 **Outpatient Visits**: 3749 **Total Expense ($000)**: 3280 **Payroll Expense ($000)**: 1623 **Personnel**: 38

### TOWNSEND—Broadwater County

**BROADWATER HEALTH CENTER (271333)**, 110 North Oak Street, Zip 59644–2306; tel. 406/266–3186, (Nonreporting) **A**10 18 **F**3 7 9 15 29 32 34 40 41 42 43 50 53 54 55 57 59 64 66 71 75 77 79 87 91 93 97 107 111 130 131 133 135 143 144 146 147 148
Primary Contact: Kyle Hopstad, Chief Executive Officer
CFO: Jennifer Clowes, Chief Financial Officer
CMO: Carol Bridges, M.D., Medical Director
CHR: April Campbell, Director Human Resources
CNO: Fran Wright, Director of Nursing
Web address: www.broadwaterhealthcenter.com
**Control**: Other not–for–profit (including NFP Corporation) **Service**: General medical and surgical

**Staffed Beds**: 25 **Admissions**: 8 **Census**: 1 **Births**: 0

### WARM SPRINGS—Deer Lodge County

**MONTANA STATE HOSPITAL (274086)**, 100 Garnet Way, Zip 59756–9705, Mailing Address: P.O. Box 300, tel. 406/693–7000, (Nonreporting) **A**10
Primary Contact: Kyle Fouts, Interim Administrator
CFO: Tracey Thun, Director Business and Support Services
CMO: Thomas Gray, M.D., Medical Director
CIO: Melinda Bridgewater, Director, Information Services
CHR: Todd Thun, Director Human Resources
CNO: Dave Olson, Director of Nursing
Web address: www.msh.mt.gov
**Control**: State, Government, Nonfederal **Service**: Psychiatric

**Staffed Beds**: 270

### WHITE SULPHUR SPRINGS—Meagher County

**MOUNTAINVIEW MEDICAL CENTER (271306)**, 16 West Main Street, Zip 59645–9036, Mailing Address: P.O. Box 'Q', Zip 59645–0817; tel. 406/547–3321, (Nonreporting) **A**10 18 **F**3 14 29 30 33 34 35 40 41 43 50 55 56 57 59 63 64 65 70 75 77 82 84 86 87 90 91 93 97 100 102 104 106 107 114 119 130 133 135 147 148 154
Primary Contact: Rob Brandt, Chief Executive Officer
Web address: www.mvmc.org
**Control**: Other not–for–profit (including NFP Corporation) **Service**: General medical and surgical

**Staffed Beds**: 25 **Admissions**: 44 **Census**: 1 **Outpatient Visits**: 4241 **Births**: 0 **Total Expense ($000)**: 5606 **Payroll Expense ($000)**: 3717

**MOUNTAINVIEW MEMORIAL HOSPITAL** See Mountainview Medical Center

### WHITEFISH—Flathead County

★ **NORTH VALLEY HOSPITAL (271336)**, 1600 Hospital Way, Zip 59937–7849; tel. 406/863–3500, (Nonreporting) **A**10 18 **F**3 11 13 15 28 29 30 31 34 35 37 40 43 50 51 54 56 59 64 65 68 70 75 76 79 81 85 86 87 97 104 107 110 111 114 119 126 127 129 131 132 133 135 144 146 148 156 **P**6 **S** QHR Health, Brentwood, TN
Primary Contact: Kevin Abel, Chief Executive Officer
COO: Christina Bogers, Chief Clinical Officer
CFO: David Richhart, Chief Financial Officer
CMO: Jason Cohen, M.D., Chief Medical Officer
CIO: Michael Barnes, Chief Information Officer
CHR: Joseph Schmier, Interim Director Human Resources
Web address: www.nvhosp.org
**Control**: Other not–for–profit (including NFP Corporation) **Service**: General medical and surgical

**Staffed Beds**: 25 **Admissions**: 1657 **Census**: 13 **Outpatient Visits**: 91462 **Births**: 546 **Total Expense ($000)**: 64620 **Payroll Expense ($000)**: 25743 **Personnel**: 368

### WOLF POINT—Roosevelt County

★ **TRINITY HOSPITAL (271341)**, 315 Knapp Street, Zip 59201–1826; tel. 406/653–6500, (Total facility includes 60 beds in nursing home–type unit) (Nonreporting) **A**10 18 **F**2 3 6 7 8 13 15 29 31 32 34 40 43 45 50 56 57 59 64 70 75 76 78 81 92 93 104 110 119 120 125 127 128 130 133 143 145 154 **P**5
Primary Contact: Margaret B. Norgaard, Chief Executive Officer
Web address: www.nemhs.net
**Control**: Other not–for–profit (including NFP Corporation) **Service**: General medical and surgical

**Staffed Beds**: 82 **Admissions**: 337 **Census**: 50 **Outpatient Visits**: 12158 **Births**: 83 **Total Expense ($000)**: 19375 **Payroll Expense ($000)**: 8981 **Personnel**: 189

MT

# NEBRASKA

## AINSWORTH—Brown County

**BROWN COUNTY HOSPITAL (281325)**, 945 East Zero Street,
Zip 69210–1547; tel. 402/387–2800, (Nonreporting) **A**10 18
Primary Contact: John W. Werner, Chief Executive Officer
CMO: Melvin Campbell, M.D., Medical Staff Chairman
CIO: Mike Depko, Director Information Technology
CHR: Lisa Fischer, Director Human Resources
CNO: Brandy Bussinger, Director of Nursing
Web address: www.browncountyhospital.org
**Control:** County, Government, Nonfederal **Service:** General medical and surgical

| Staffed Beds: 18 |
|---|

## ALBION—Boone County

**BOONE COUNTY COMM HOSPITAL** See Boone County Health Center

★ **BOONE COUNTY HEALTH CENTER (281334)**, 723 West Fairview
Street, Zip 68620–1725, Mailing Address: P.O. Box 151, Zip 68620–0151;
tel. 402/395–2191, (Nonreporting) **A**3 5 10 18
Primary Contact: Tanya Sharp, President and Chief Executive Officer
CFO: Rita Liss, Vice President Fiscal Services and Chief Financial Officer
CMO: Lynette Kramer, M.D., Chief Medical Officer
CIO: Larry Zoucha, Chief Information Officer
CHR: Jennifer Beierman, Director Human Resources
CNO: Cindy Lesiak, Vice President Patient Care Services and Director of Nursing
Web address: www.boonecohealth.org
**Control:** County, Government, Nonfederal **Service:** General medical and surgical

| Staffed Beds: 25 |
|---|

## ALLIANCE—Box Butte County

⊞ **BOX BUTTE GENERAL HOSPITAL (281360)**, 2101 Box Butte Avenue,
Zip 69301–4445, Mailing Address: P.O. Box 810, Zip 69301–0810;
tel. 308/762–6660, (Nonreporting) **A**1 10 18 **F**3 5 11 13 15 28 29 32 34 35 36
38 40 43 47 48 50 51 53 57 59 60 64 68 69 75 77 78 79 81 82 85 86 87 92
93 97 100 101 104 107 108 111 114 116 118 119 127 129 130 131 132 133
134 135 146 148 154 156
Primary Contact: Lori Mazanec, Chief Executive Officer
COO: Jim Bargen, Chief Operating Officer
CFO: Luke Senden, Chief Financial Officer
CHR: Lisa L Hillyer, Human Resources Manager
CNO: Carolyn Jones, R.N., MSN, Chief Nursing Officer
Web address: www.bbgh.org
**Control:** County, Government, Nonfederal **Service:** General medical and surgical

| Staffed Beds: 25 Admissions: 663 Census: 8 Outpatient Visits: 48456 |
|---|
| Births: 38 Total Expense ($000): 46477 Payroll Expense ($000): 16447 |
| Personnel: 281 |

## ALMA—Harlan County

★ **HARLAN COUNTY HEALTH SYSTEM (281300)**, 717 North Brown
Street, Zip 68920–2132, Mailing Address: P.O. Box 836, Zip 68920–0836;
tel. 308/928–2151, (Nonreporting) **A**10 18 **F**1 3 4 11 15 16 17 29 31 40 45 50
57 59 64 67 70 72 73 80 81 85 88 89 90 93 97 98 107 110 114 119 127 128
130 133 135 146 156 **P**6 **S** Great Plains Health Alliance, Inc., Wichita, KS
Primary Contact: Mark A. Miller, FACHE, Chief Executive Officer
CFO: Heidi Cushing, Chief Financial Officer
CMO: Cameron Knackstedt, D.O., Chief Medical Staff
CIO: Michael Andrews, Coordinator Information Systems
CHR: Ana Schluntz, Director of Human Resources
CNO: Shawn Horton, Chief Nursing Officer
Web address: www.harlancountyhealth.com
**Control:** County, Government, Nonfederal **Service:** General medical and surgical

| Staffed Beds: 19 Admissions: 125 Census: 2 Outpatient Visits: 18370 |
|---|
| Births: 0 Total Expense ($000): 9882 Payroll Expense ($000): 3992 |
| Personnel: 70 |

**HARLAN COUNTY HOSPITAL** See Harlan County Health System

## ATKINSON—Holt County

**WEST HOLT MEDICAL SERVICES (281343)**, 406 West Neely Street,
Zip 68713–4801; tel. 402/925–2811, (Nonreporting) **A**10 18 **S** Faith Regional
Health Services, Norfolk, NE
Primary Contact: Ashley Rivera, Chief Executive Officer
CFO: Jeremy Bauer, Director of Finance
CMO: John Tubbs, M.D., Chief of Staff
CIO: Mark Johnson, Chief Information Officer
CHR: Margaret Linse, Administrative Secretary and Director Human Resources
CNO: Jennifer Rystrom, R.N., Chief Nursing Officer
Web address: www.westholtmed.org
**Control:** Other not–for–profit (including NFP Corporation) **Service:** General medical and surgical

| Staffed Beds: 17 |
|---|

**WEST HOLT MEMORIAL HOSPITAL** See West Holt Medical Services

## AUBURN—Nemaha County

★ ⇑ **NEMAHA COUNTY HOSPITAL (281324)**, 2022 13th Street,
Zip 68305–1799; tel. 402/274–4366, (Nonreporting) **A**10 18 21 **F**3 12 15 28 29
30 31 34 35 40 43 62 64 68 74 75 77 78 79 81 85 86 87 93 94 107 110 111
114 117 119 128 129 130 131 133 135 141 148 149 154 156
Primary Contact: Marty Fattig, Chief Executive Officer
COO: Kermit Moore, R.N., Chief Operating Officer and Chief Nursing Officer
CFO: Stacy Taylor, Chief Financial Officer
CIO: Kathy McNaughton, Chief Information Officer
CHR: Susan Shupp, Chief Human Resources Officer
Web address: www.nchnet.org
**Control:** County, Government, Nonfederal **Service:** General medical and surgical

| Staffed Beds: 16 Admissions: 161 Census: 2 Outpatient Visits: 21384 |
|---|
| Births: 0 Total Expense ($000): 10890 Payroll Expense ($000): 5388 |
| Personnel: 88 |

## AURORA—Hamilton County

★ **MEMORIAL COMMUNITY HEALTH (281320)**, 1423 Seventh Street,
Zip 68818–1197; tel. 402/694–3171, (Total facility includes 47 beds in nursing
home–type unit) (Nonreporting) **A**10 18 **F**10 11 13 15 28 29 31 34 35 40 41 43
45 50 51 57 59 64 65 67 75 76 77 78 79 81 82 85 86 87 93 94 97 107 108
110 114 119 130 131 132 133 146 154 156
Primary Contact: Diane R. Keller, Chief Executive Officer
CFO: Phil Fendt, Chief Financial Officer
CMO: Jeff Muilenburg, Chief of Staff
CIO: Brad Tiede, Director Information Systems
CHR: Laura Teichmeier, Director Human Resources
CNO: Lindy Mosel, Director of Nursing
Web address: www.memorialcommunityhealth.org
**Control:** Other not–for–profit (including NFP Corporation) **Service:** General medical and surgical

| Staffed Beds: 63 Admissions: 355 Census: 45 Outpatient Visits: 25813 |
|---|
| Births: 29 Total Expense ($000): 24311 Payroll Expense ($000): 12178 |
| Personnel: 219 |

**MEMORIAL HOSPITAL** See Memorial Community Health

## BASSETT—Rock County

**ROCK COUNTY HOSPITAL (281333)**, 102 East South Street, Zip 68714–5508;
tel. 402/684–3366, (Total facility includes 30 beds in nursing home–type unit)
(Nonreporting) **A**10 18 **F**7 11 15 28 40 53 62 81 84 107 110 119 127 128 133 154
Primary Contact: Stacey A. Knox, Administrator
CMO: John Tubbs, M.D., Chief of Staff
CIO: Cal Alder, Director Information Technology
CHR: Jackie Carpenter, Office Manager
CNO: Katie Ogier, Director of Nursing
Web address: www.rockcountyhospital.com
**Control:** County, Government, Nonfederal **Service:** General medical and surgical

| Staffed Beds: 54 Admissions: 131 Census: 25 Outpatient Visits: 5482 |
|---|
| Births: 0 Total Expense ($000): 12238 Payroll Expense ($000): 4487 |
| Personnel: 91 |

**NE**

---

**Hospital, Medicare Provider Number, Address, Telephone, Approval, Facility, and Physician Codes, Health Care System**

★ American Hospital Association (AHA) membership
□ The Joint Commission accreditation
○ Healthcare Facilities Accreditation Program
◇ DNV Healthcare Inc. accreditation
⇑ Center for Improvement in Healthcare Quality Accreditation
△ Commission on Accreditation of Rehabilitation Facilities (CARF) accreditation

## BEATRICE—Gage County

**BEATRICE COMM HOSP & HLTH CNTR** See Beatrice Community Hospital and Health Center

★ **BEATRICE COMMUNITY HOSPITAL AND HEALTH CENTER (281364)**, 4800 Hospital Parkway, Zip 68310–6906, Mailing Address: P.O. Box 278, Zip 68310–0278; tel. 402/228–3344, (Nonreporting) **A**10 18 **F**3 13 15 28 29 30 31 34 35 40 45 57 62 63 64 65 68 69 70 75 76 78 79 81 82 84 85 87 93 104 107 108 110 111 114 119 127 129 130 131 132 133 135 144 146 147 148 149 156
Primary Contact: Richard Haraldson, CPA, FACHE, Chief Executive Officer
CFO: Chad Jurgens, Senior Executive, Financial Services
CMO: Steven Paulmeyer, M.D., Senior Executive, Medical Services
CHR: Kathryn G. Humble, Senior Executive, Human Resource Services
CNO: Tasha N. Hesman, R.N., Senior Executive, Patient Care Services
Web address: www.beatricecommunityhospital.com
**Control:** Other not–for–profit (including NFP Corporation) **Service:** General medical and surgical

**Staffed Beds:** 25 **Admissions:** 1195 **Census:** 11 **Outpatient Visits:** 213599
**Births:** 217 **Total Expense ($000):** 82357 **Payroll Expense ($000):** 37587
**Personnel:** 480

## BELLEVUE—Sarpy County

**BELLEVUE MEDICAL CENTER** See Nebraska Medicine - Bellevue

☐ **NEBRASKA MEDICINE - BELLEVUE (280132)**, 2500 Bellevue Medical Center Drive, Zip 68123–1591; tel. 402/763–3000, (Nonreporting) **A**1 3 5 10 **F**3 13 15 18 20 22 28 29 30 31 34 35 40 41 44 45 47 48 49 50 51 53 55 57 58 59 60 63 64 65 68 70 74 75 76 77 78 79 81 82 84 85 86 87 91 92 93 96 97 107 108 110 111 114 119 130 131 132 135 141 143 145 146 147 148 149 150 154 **P**6 8
Primary Contact: Suzanne Langan. Nuss, Ph.D., R.N., Vice President of Operations and Chief Nursing Officer
CFO: Stephanie Daubert, Chief Financial Officer
CMO: Jeffrey D. Akerson, M.D., Chief Medical Officer
CIO: Brian Lancaster, Executive Director Information Management
CNO: Ray D. Dial, Director of Nursing
Web address: www.nebraskamed.com
**Control:** Other not–for–profit (including NFP Corporation) **Service:** General medical and surgical

**Staffed Beds:** 69 **Admissions:** 4759 **Census:** 44 **Outpatient Visits:** 126105
**Births:** 463 **Total Expense ($000):** 70046 **Payroll Expense ($000):** 29822
**Personnel:** 409

## BENKELMAN—Dundy County

**DUNDY COUNTY HEALTH SYSTEM** See Dundy County Hospital

★ **DUNDY COUNTY HOSPITAL (281340)**, 1313 North Cheyenne Street, Zip 69021–3074, Mailing Address: P.O. Box 626, Zip 69021–0626; tel. 308/423–2204, (Nonreporting) **A**10 18 **F**3 15 28 29 31 32 33 34 40 43 50 56 57 59 62 64 65 68 78 79 81 82 87 93 97 107 110 115 119 127 130 131 133 154
Primary Contact: Rita A. Jones, Chief Executive Officer
COO: Wendy Elkins, Director Operations
CFO: Renee Fink, CPA, Chief Financial Officer
CMO: Jose Garcia, M.D., Chief Medical Staff
CIO: David Craw, Coordinator Information Technology
CHR: Sandy Noffsinger, Executive Assistant, Risk Manager and Director Marketing
CNO: Laken Vrbas, R.N., Director of Nursing
Web address: www.dchbenkelman.com
**Control:** County, Government, Nonfederal **Service:** General medical and surgical

**Staffed Beds:** 14 **Admissions:** 100 **Census:** 1 **Outpatient Visits:** 9330
**Births:** 0 **Total Expense ($000):** 9338 **Payroll Expense ($000):** 4043
**Personnel:** 71

## BLAIR—Washington County

**MEMORIAL COMMUNITY HOSPITAL** See Memorial Community Hospital and Health System

★ **MEMORIAL COMMUNITY HOSPITAL AND HEALTH SYSTEM (281359)**, 810 North 22nd Street, Zip 68008–1199, Mailing Address: P.O. Box 250, Zip 68008–0250; tel. 402/426–2182, (Nonreporting) **A**10 18
Primary Contact: Manuela Wolf, FACHE, R.N., President and Chief Executive Officer
CFO: Jennifer Newby, Operations Director Support Services and Finance
CMO: Sandra Baumberger, M.D., President Medical Staff
CHR: Kristine Nielsen, Manager Human Resources
CNO: Christinia Jepsen, R.N., Chief Nursing Executive
Web address: www.mchhs.org
**Control:** Other not–for–profit (including NFP Corporation) **Service:** General medical and surgical

**Staffed Beds:** 10

## BRIDGEPORT—Morrill County

**MORRILL COUNTY COMMUNITY HOSPITAL (281318)**, 1313 'S' Street, Zip 69336–0579; tel. 308/262–1616, (Nonreporting) **A**10 18
Primary Contact: Robin Stuart, Chief Executive Officer
CFO: Connie Christensen, Chief Financial Officer
CMO: John Post, M.D., Medical Director
CIO: Lori Shengle, Director Information Technology
CHR: Rhea Basa, Director Human Resources
CNO: Sylvia Marie Lichius, R.N., Chief Nursing Officer
Web address: www.morrillcountyhospital.com
**Control:** County, Government, Nonfederal **Service:** General medical and surgical

**Staffed Beds:** 6

## BROKEN BOW—Custer County

★ **JENNIE M. MELHAM MEMORIAL MEDICAL CENTER (281365)**, 145 Memorial Drive, Zip 68822–1378, Mailing Address: P.O. Box 250, Zip 68822–0250; tel. 308/872–4100, (Nonreporting) **A**10 18 **F**3 13 15 18 28 29 31 34 35 40 41 43 44 50 53 56 57 59 64 76 81 85 86 87 89 92 107 110 114 115 119 125 128 129 130 133 148 154 156
Primary Contact: Veronica Schmidt, President and Chief Executive Officer
CFO: Tim Schuckman, Chief Financial Officer
CIO: Tim Schuckman, Chief Financial Officer
CHR: Teri Sell, Payroll and Personnel Coordinator
CNO: Shelly Amsberry, Director of Nursing
Web address: www.https://www.melham.org
**Control:** Other not–for–profit (including NFP Corporation) **Service:** General medical and surgical

**Staffed Beds:** 12 **Admissions:** 250 **Census:** 2 **Outpatient Visits:** 25000
**Births:** 8

## CALLAWAY—Custer County

★ **CALLAWAY DISTRICT HOSPITAL (281335)**, 211 East Kimball, Zip 68825–2589, Mailing Address: P.O. Box 100, Zip 68825–0100; tel. 308/836–2228, (Nonreporting) **A**10 18
Primary Contact: Brett Eggleston, Chief Executive Officer
CFO: Caleb Kelly Poore, Chief Financial Officer
CHR: Toni French, Manager Human Resources
Web address: www.callawayhospital.org
**Control:** Hospital district or authority, Government, Nonfederal **Service:** General medical and surgical

**Staffed Beds:** 12

## CAMBRIDGE—Furnas County

**CAMBRIDGE MEMOtRIAL HOSPITAL** See Tri Valley Health System

★ **TRI VALLEY HEALTH SYSTEM (281348)**, 1305 West Highway 6 and 34, Zip 69022–0488, Mailing Address: P.O. Box 488, Zip 69022–0488; tel. 308/697–3329, (Nonreporting) **A**10 18
Primary Contact: Jessica Marie. Fisher, Chief Executive Officer
COO: Keith Luedders, Chief Operations Officer
CFO: Diana Swindler, Chief Financial Officer
CMO: Shiuvaun Jaeger, M.D., Chief of Staff
CIO: Ciprian Galarneau, Director Information Systems
CHR: Tammy Claussen, Chief Human Resource Officer
CNO: Clay Jordan, Interim Chief Nursing Officer
Web address: www.trivalleyhealth.com
**Control:** Other not–for–profit (including NFP Corporation) **Service:** General medical and surgical

**Staffed Beds:** 52

## CENTRAL CITY—Merrick County

**LITZENBERG MEMORIAL COUNTY HOSPITAL** See Merrick Medical Center

★ **MERRICK MEDICAL CENTER (281328)**, 1715 26th Street, Zip 68826–9620; tel. 308/946–3015, (Nonreporting) **A**10 18 **S** Bryan Health, Lincoln, NE
Primary Contact: Patrick Avila, President and Chief Executive Officer
CHR: Shauna Graham, Director of Professional Services Human Resources, Marketing Foundation
Web address: www.https://www.bryanhealth.com
**Control:** County, Government, Nonfederal **Service:** General medical and surgical

**Staffed Beds:** 65

**NE**

*Many Facility Codes have changed. Please refer to the AHA Guide Code Chart.*

## CHADRON—Dawes County

★ **CHADRON COMMUNITY HOSPITAL AND HEALTH SERVICES (281341)**, 825 Centennial Drive, Zip 69337–9400; tel. 308/432–5586, (Nonreporting) **A**10 18
Primary Contact: Jeffrey Dewayne. Shelton, Chief Executive Officer
CFO: Russ Bohnenkamp, Chief Financial Officer
CMO: Ed Pelton, Chief of Staff
CHR: Ellen Krueger, Director Human Resources
CNO: Alisha Obando, Director of Nursing
Web address: www.chadronhosp.com
**Control**: Other not–for–profit (including NFP Corporation) **Service**: General medical and surgical

**Staffed Beds:** 25

## COLUMBUS—Platte County

⊞ **COLUMBUS COMMUNITY HOSPITAL (280111)**, 4600 38th Street, Zip 68601–1664, Mailing Address: P.O. Box 1800, Zip 68602–1800; tel. 402/564–7118, (Nonreporting) **A**1 10 20
Primary Contact: Michael T. Hansen, FACHE, President and Chief Executive Officer
COO: James P Goulet, Vice President Operations
CFO: Chad Van Cleave, Chief Financial Officer
CMO: Mark Howerter, M.D., President Medical Staff
CIO: Cheryl Tira, Director Information Systems
CHR: Scott E Messersmith, Director Human Resources
CNO: Linda K Walline, R.N., Ph.D., MSN, Vice President Nursing
Web address: www.columbushosp.org
**Control**: Other not–for–profit (including NFP Corporation) **Service**: General medical and surgical

**Staffed Beds:** 51

## COZAD—Dawson County

★ **COZAD COMMUNITY HEALTH SYSTEM (281327)**, 300 East 12th Street, Zip 69130–1505, Mailing Address: P.O. Box 108, Zip 69130–0108; tel. 308/784–2261, (Nonreporting) **A**5 10 18 **F**3 10 13 15 28 30 31 34 35 40 43 50 53 57 59 62 63 68 70 75 76 77 81 84 86 87 93 94 97 107 114 119 127 128 129 130 131 132 133 135 146 148 149 154 157 **P**6
Primary Contact: Danielle Gearhart, FACHE, Chief Executive Officer
Web address: www.cozadhealthcare.com
**Control**: Hospital district or authority, Government, Nonfederal **Service**: General medical and surgical

**Staffed Beds:** 20 **Admissions:** 241 **Census:** 3 **Outpatient Visits:** 10127 **Births:** 16 **Total Expense ($000):** 16381 **Payroll Expense ($000):** 7929 **Personnel:** 156

**COZAD COMMUNITY HOSPITAL** See Cozad Community Health System

## CREIGHTON—Knox County

★ **AVERA CREIGHTON HOSPITAL (281331)**, 1503 Main Street, Zip 68729–3007, Mailing Address: P.O. Box 186, Zip 68729–0186; tel. 402/358–5700, (Total facility includes 47 beds in nursing home–type unit) (Nonreporting) **A**10 18 **F**15 18 28 29 34 35 40 41 43 45 47 50 53 56 59 65 67 77 79 81 82 89 93 94 97 100 104 107 108 110 115 127 128 129 131 133 143 146 149 154 **S** Avera Health, Sioux Falls, SD
Primary Contact: Todd Consbruck, Chief Executive Officer
CHR: Jane E. Miller, Director Human Resources
CNO: Jean M. Henes, MSN, R.N., Director of Nursing
Web address: www.avera.org/creighton/
**Control**: Other not–for–profit (including NFP Corporation) **Service**: General medical and surgical

**Staffed Beds:** 70 **Admissions:** 202 **Census:** 48 **Outpatient Visits:** 12802 **Total Expense ($000):** 15599 **Payroll Expense ($000):** 7867 **Personnel:** 92

**CREIGHTON AREA HEALTH SERVICES** See Avera Creighton Hospital

## CRETE—Saline County

★ **CRETE AREA MEDICAL CENTER (281354)**, 2910 Betten Drive, Zip 68333–3084, Mailing Address: P.O. Box 220, Zip 68333–0220; tel. 402/826–2102, (Nonreporting) **A**10 18 **F**13 15 28 29 31 34 40 43 45 57 59 64 65 68 78 79 81 93 97 107 111 114 117 119 127 129 130 131 133 143 146 147 148 154 156 **S** Bryan Health, Lincoln, NE
Primary Contact: Stephanie Boldt, President and Chief Executive Officer
CFO: Julie Lacy, Chief Financial Officer
CMO: Russell Ebke, M.D., Chief of Staff
CIO: Drew Kotil, Director Information Technology
CHR: Bobbie Wilson, Director Human Resources
CNO: April R. Gaines, Chief Nursing Officer
Web address: www.creteareamedicalcenter.com
**Control**: Other not–for–profit (including NFP Corporation) **Service**: General medical and surgical

**Staffed Beds:** 24 **Admissions:** 256 **Census:** 2 **Outpatient Visits:** 107494 **Births:** 74

**CRETE MUNICIPAL HOSPITAL** See Crete Area Medical Center

## DAVID CITY—Butler County

★ **BUTLER COUNTY HEALTH CARE CENTER (281332)**, 372 South Ninth Street, Zip 68632–2116; tel. 402/367–1200, (Nonreporting) **A**10 18
Primary Contact: Donald T. Naiberk, Administrator and Chief Executive Officer
CFO: Jodi Prochaska, Chief Financial Officer
CMO: Victor Thoendel, M.D., Chief Medical Officer
CIO: Cindy Neesen, Director of Information Technology
CHR: Andra Vandenberg, Director Human Resources
CNO: Sue M Birkel, R.N., Director of Nursing
Web address: www.bchccnet.org
**Control**: County, Government, Nonfederal **Service**: General medical and surgical

**Staffed Beds:** 20

**BUTLER COUNTY HEALTH CARE CNTR** See Butler County Health Care Center

## ELKHORN—Douglas County

**METHODIST WOMEN'S HOSPITAL** See Nebraska Methodist Hospital, Omaha

## FAIRBURY—Jefferson County

★ **JEFFERSON COMMUNITY HEALTH AND LIFE (281319)**, 2200 'H' Street, Zip 68352–1119, Mailing Address: P.O. Box 277, Zip 68352–0277; tel. 402/729–3351, (Total facility includes 40 beds in nursing home–type unit) (Nonreporting) **A**10 18 **F**2 3 15 28 29 30 31 34 35 40 45 50 53 57 59 62 64 75 77 78 79 81 85 86 87 93 107 110 114 119 127 128 130 131 132 133 135 146 149 154 156
Primary Contact: Burke Kline, Chief Executive Officer
CFO: Chance Klasek, CPA, Chief Financial Officer
CIO: Dennis Ahl, Director Information Technology
CHR: Sandra A. Bauer, Director Human Resources
CNO: Erin L. Starr, Chief Nursing Officer
Web address: www.jchealthandlife.org
**Control**: Other not–for–profit (including NFP Corporation) **Service**: General medical and surgical

**Staffed Beds:** 57 **Admissions:** 258 **Census:** 38 **Outpatient Visits:** 28152 **Births:** 0 **Total Expense ($000):** 22122 **Payroll Expense ($000):** 10613 **Personnel:** 200

**JEFFERSON COMMUNITY HEALTH CENTER** See Jefferson Community Health and Life

**NE**

---

## FALLS CITY—Richardson County

**COMMUNITY MEDICAL CENTER** See Community Medical Center, Inc.

★ **COMMUNITY MEDICAL CENTER, INC. (281352)**, 3307 Barada Street,
Zip 68355–2470, Mailing Address: P.O. Box 399, Zip 68355–0399;
tel. 402/245–2428, (Nonreporting) **A**10 18 **F**3 13 15 28 31 34 35 40 43 45 59
75 76 78 79 81 82 85 93 97 107 111 114 119 127 130 133 135 154
Primary Contact: Ryan C. Larsen, FACHE, Chief Executive Officer
CFO: Scott Sawyer, Chief Financial Officer
CMO: Daniel Samani, M.D.
CIO: Joe Buckminster, Manager Information Technology
CHR: Shannon Weinmann, Director Human Resources
CNO: Ivy Campbell, Director of Nursing
Web address: www.cmcfc.org
**Control:** Other not–for–profit (including NFP Corporation) **Service:** General
medical and surgical

**Staffed Beds:** 24 **Admissions:** 701 **Census:** 7 **Outpatient Visits:** 23560
**Births:** 39 **Total Expense ($000):** 27247 **Payroll Expense ($000):** 9373
**Personnel:** 171

## FRANKLIN—Franklin County

★ **FRANKLIN COUNTY MEMORIAL HOSPITAL (281311)**, 1406 'Q' Street,
Zip 68939–0315, Mailing Address: 1406 Q Street, Zip 68939–0315;
tel. 308/425–6221, (Nonreporting) **A**10 18
Primary Contact: Theresa Rizzo, Administrator
CFO: Amy Kahrs, Director of Finance
CMO: Linda Mazour, M.D., President
CIO: Cathy Webber, Director of Health Information Management
CNO: Kari Yelken, R.N., Director of Nursing
Web address: www.fcmh.com
**Control:** County, Government, Nonfederal **Service:** General medical and surgical

**Staffed Beds:** 14

## FREMONT—Dodge County

**FREMONT HEALTH** See Methodist Fremont Health

⊞ **METHODIST FREMONT HEALTH (280077)**, 450 East 23rd Street,
Zip 68025–2387; tel. 402/721–1610, (Total facility includes 106 beds in nursing
home–type unit) (Nonreporting) **A**1 2 3 5 10 20 **F**3 8 13 15 17 18 20 22 26 28
29 30 31 34 35 37 40 44 45 57 59 62 63 64 68 70 75 76 77 78 81 85 86 87
89 93 98 100 103 104 107 108 110 111 114 119 120 121 123 124 126 128
129 130 131 132 135 143 144 146 156 **P**6 8 **S** Nebraska Methodist Health
System, Inc., Omaha, NE
Primary Contact: Brett M. Richmond, President and Chief Executive Officer
CFO: Jeff Francis, Vice President, Chief Financial Officer
CIO: Kent Sona, Vice President, Chief Information Officer
CHR: Bethany Childers, Director Human Resources
CNO: Melinda Johanna Kentfield, R.N., Chief Nursing Officer
Web address: www.fremonthealth.com
**Control:** Other not–for–profit (including NFP Corporation) **Service:** General
medical and surgical

**Staffed Beds:** 181 **Admissions:** 3129 **Census:** 124 **Outpatient
Visits:** 88294 **Births:** 288 **Total Expense ($000):** 111522 **Payroll Expense
($000):** 53023 **Personnel:** 583

## FRIEND—Saline County

**FRIEND COMMUNITY HEALTHCARE SYSTEM (281330)**, 905 Second Street,
Zip 68359–1133; tel. 402/947–2541, (Nonreporting) **A**10 18
Primary Contact: John W. Wilson, Chief Executive Officer
CFO: Mackenzie Svarc, Finance Director
CMO: Roger Meyer, M.D., Chief of Staff
CHR: Shyanne Scholl, Interim Human Resources Director
CNO: Dayna Pulver, Director of Nursing
Web address: www.friendmed.org/
**Control:** City, Government, Nonfederal **Service:** General medical and surgical

**Staffed Beds:** 63

**WARREN MEMORIAL HOSPITAL** See Friend Community Healthcare System

## GENEVA—Fillmore County

★ **FILLMORE COUNTY HOSPITAL (281301)**, 1900 'F' Street, Zip 68361–1325,
Mailing Address: P.O. Box 193, Zip 68361–0193; tel. 402/759–3167,
(Nonreporting) **A**10 18 **F**7 11 13 15 18 28 29 31 34 37 38 40 41 45 46 47 48
49 50 56 57 59 64 67 68 74 75 76 77 78 79 81 82 85 87 92 93 94 98 101
102 103 104 107 110 111 115 119 126 128 130 131 132 133 143 148 149
153 154 **P**6
Primary Contact: Christopher Nichols, Chief Executive Officer
COO: Debbie Domann, Director of Operations
CFO: Jeanne Ackland, Director of Finance
CMO: Jason Bespalec, M.D., Chief of Staff
CIO: Tyler Gewecke, Information Technology Technician
CHR: Abby Tuberville, Human Resource Manager
Web address: www.fhsofgeneva.org
**Control:** County, Government, Nonfederal **Service:** General medical and surgical

**Staffed Beds:** 30 **Admissions:** 523 **Census:** 10 **Outpatient Visits:** 25115
**Births:** 31 **Total Expense ($000):** 21086 **Payroll Expense ($000):** 8449
**Personnel:** 150

## GENOA—Nance County

**GENOA COMMUNITY HOSPITAL** See Genoa Medical Facilities

**GENOA MEDICAL FACILITIES (281312)**, 706 Ewing Avenue, Zip 68640–3035,
Mailing Address: P.O. Box 310, Zip 68640–0310; tel. 402/993–2283,
(Nonreporting) **A**10 18 **S** Faith Regional Health Services, Norfolk, NE
Primary Contact: Amanda Roebuck, Chief Executive Officer
CFO: Angie Sutton, Chief Financial Officer
CMO: Brian Buhlke, M.D., Medical Director
CHR: Brianna Molt, Human Resources Director
Web address: www.genoamedical.org/
**Control:** City–county, Government, Nonfederal **Service:** General medical and
surgical

**Staffed Beds:** 58

## GORDON—Sheridan County

**GORDON MEMORIAL HEALTH SERVICES (281358)**, 300 East Eighth Street,
Zip 69343–1123; tel. 308/282–0401, (Nonreporting) **A**10 18
Primary Contact: Doris Brown, Chief Executive Officer
CMO: Christopher P. Costa, M.D., Chief of Staff
CIO: Ray Waldron, Director Information Technology
CNO: Megan Heath, Chief Nursing Officer
Web address: www.gordonmemorial.org
**Control:** Hospital district or authority, Government, Nonfederal **Service:** General
medical and surgical

**Staffed Beds:** 25

**GORDON MEMORIAL HOSPITAL** See Gordon Memorial Health Services

## GOTHENBURG—Dawson County

★ **GOTHENBURG HEALTH (281313)**, 910 20th Street, Zip 69138–1237, Mailing
Address: P.O. Box 469, Zip 69138–0469; tel. 308/537–3661, (Nonreporting)
**A**10 18
Primary Contact: Mick Brant, FACHE, Chief Executive Officer
CFO: Michael Pracheil, Chief Financial Officer
CMO: Carol Shackleton, M.D., Medical Director
CIO: Tinna Therrien, R.N., Chief Information Officer and Senior Director Ancillary
Services
CHR: Jim Imler, Director Human Resources
CNO: Susan Moore, MS, R.N., Chief Nursing Officer
Web address: www.gothenburghealth.org
**Control:** Hospital district or authority, Government, Nonfederal **Service:** General
medical and surgical

**Staffed Beds:** 12

**GOTHENBURG MEMORIAL HOSPITAL** See Gothenburg Health

*Many Facility Codes have changed. Please refer to the AHA Guide Code Chart.*

NE

## GRAND ISLAND—Hall County

✠ **CHI HEALTH SAINT FRANCIS (280023)**, 2620 West Faidley Avenue, Zip 68803–4297, Mailing Address: P.O. Box 9804, Zip 68802–9804; tel. 308/384–4600, (Includes ST. FRANCIS MEDICAL PLAZA, Mailing address: 2116 West Faidley Avenue, Grand Island, Nebraska, Zip 68803, P O Box 9804, Zip 68802, tel. 308/384–4600), (Nonreporting) **A**1 2 3 5 10 19 **F**3 5 11 12 13 15 18 19 20 22 28 30 31 34 35 40 43 45 47 50 51 53 59 60 62 63 64 65 67 68 70 73 74 75 76 77 78 79 80 81 82 84 85 91 97 104 110 121 123 128 129 130 132 135 145 146 148 152 **P**8 **S** CommonSpirit Health, Chicago, IL
Primary Contact: Edward J. Hannon, FACHE, President
CFO: Lisa Webb, Vice President Operational Finance
CMO: Shu-Ming Wang, MD, Vice President Medical Affairs
CHR: Nancy Wallace, Vice President Human Resources, CHI Health
CNO: Beth Bartlett, MSN, R.N., Vice President Nursing
Web address: www.saintfrancisgi.org
**Control**: Church operated, Nongovernment, not–for–profit **Service**: General medical and surgical

**Staffed Beds**: 165 **Admissions**: 5901 **Census**: 84 **Outpatient Visits**: 80610
**Births**: 797 **Total Expense ($000)**: 147703 **Payroll Expense ($000)**: 36266
**Personnel**: 576

**SAINT FRANCIS MEDICAL CENTER** See Chi Health Saint Francis

**SAINT FRANCIS MEMORIAL HEALTH CENTER** See St. Francis Medical Plaza

## GRANT—Perkins County

**PERKINS COUNTY COMM HOSPITAL** See Perkins County Health Services

★ **PERKINS COUNTY HEALTH SERVICES (281356)**, 900 Lincoln Avenue, Zip 69140–3095; tel. 308/352–7200, (Nonreporting) **A**10 18
Primary Contact: Neil A. Hilton, FACHE, President and Chief Executive Officer
CMO: Ruth Demmel, M.D., Chief Medical Officer
CIO: Jennifer Baumgartner, Chief Information Officer
CHR: Julie Bevard, Vice President Human Resources
CNO: Dana McArtor, R.N., Director of Nursing
Web address: www.pchsgrant.com
**Control**: Hospital district or authority, Government, Nonfederal **Service**: General medical and surgical

**Staffed Beds**: 20

## HASTINGS—Adams County

✠ **MARY LANNING HEALTHCARE (280032)**, 715 North St Joseph Avenue, Zip 68901–4497; tel. 402/463–4521, (Nonreporting) **A**1 2 3 5 10
Primary Contact: Eric A. Barber, President and Chief Executive Officer
COO: Mark Callahan, Chief Operating Officer
CFO: Shawn A Nordby, Chief Financial Officer
CMO: Abel Luksan, M.D., Chief Medical Officer
CIO: Lisa Nonneman, Director Information Technology Services
CHR: Bruce E Cutright, MS, Vice President Human Resources
CNO: Ronda S Ehly, R.N., Chief Nursing Officer
Web address: www.marylanning.org
**Control**: Other not–for–profit (including NFP Corporation) **Service**: General medical and surgical

**Staffed Beds**: 148

**MARY LANNING MEMORIAL HOSPITAL** See Mary Lanning Healthcare

## HEBRON—Thayer County

★ **THAYER COUNTY HEALTH SERVICES (281304)**, 120 Park Avenue, Zip 68370–2019, Mailing Address: P.O. Box 49, Zip 68370–0049; tel. 402/768–6041, (Nonreporting) **A**10 18
Primary Contact: Paul Edwards, President and Chief Executive Officer
CFO: Doug Wismer, Chief Financial Officer
CMO: Leann Heinrichs, M.D., Chief of Staff
CIO: Rich Neyenhouse, Director Information Technology
CHR: Tamara Brose, Director Human Resources
CNO: Jamie Koch, R.N., Chief Nursing Officer
Web address: www.thayercountyhealth.com
**Control**: County, Government, Nonfederal **Service**: General medical and surgical

**Staffed Beds**: 19

**THAYER COUNTY MEM HOSPITAL** See Thayer County Health Services

## HENDERSON—York County

**HENDERSON COMMUNITY HOSPITAL** See Henderson Health Care Services

**HENDERSON HEALTH CARE SERVICES (281308)**, 1621 Front Street, Zip 68371–8902; tel. 402/723–4512, (Nonreporting) **A**10 18
Primary Contact: Cheryl Brown, Chief Executive Officer
CMO: James M Ohrt, M.D., Director Medical Staff
CHR: Lynette Friesen, Manager Human Resources
CNO: Carrie Peterson, Director of Nursing
Web address: www.hendersonhealthcare.org/getpage.php?name=message
**Control**: Other not–for–profit (including NFP Corporation) **Service**: General medical and surgical

**Staffed Beds**: 56

## HOLDREGE—Phelps County

★ ⇑ **PHELPS MEMORIAL HEALTH CENTER (281362)**, 1215 Tibbals Street, Zip 68949–1255; tel. 308/995–2211, (Nonreporting) **A**10 18 21 **S** QHR Health, Brentwood, TN
Primary Contact: Mark Harrel, Chief Executive Officer
CFO: Loren D Schroder, Chief Financial Officer
CMO: Stuart Embury, M.D., Chief Medical Officer
CIO: Leora Smith, Information System and Health Information Management Team Leader
CHR: Cindy Jackson, Director Human Resources
Web address: www.phelpsmemorial.com
**Control**: Other not–for–profit (including NFP Corporation) **Service**: General medical and surgical

**Staffed Beds**: 25

## IMPERIAL—Chase County

★ **CHASE COUNTY COMMUNITY HOSPITAL (281351)**, 600 West 12th Street, Zip 69033–3130, Mailing Address: P.O. Box 819, Zip 69033–0819; tel. 308/882–7111, (Nonreporting) **A**10 18
Primary Contact: Abigail Cyboron, Chief Executive Officer
CMO: Jonathan Richman, M.D., Chief of Staff
CIO: Jen Harris, Director Health Information Management
CHR: Julie Sharp, Supervisor Human Resources
CNO: Kathy Geier, Director of Nursing
Web address: www.chasecountyhospital.com
**Control**: County, Government, Nonfederal **Service**: General medical and surgical

**Staffed Beds**: 20

## KEARNEY—Buffalo County

✠ **CHI HEALTH GOOD SAMARITAN (280009)**, 10 East 31st Street, Zip 68847–2926, Mailing Address: P.O. Box 1990, Zip 68848–1990; tel. 308/865–7100, (Includes RICHARD H. YOUNG BEHAVIORAL HEALTH CENTER, Mailing address: 1755 Prairie View Place, Kearney, Nebraska, Zip 68848, P O Box 1750, Zip 68848–1705, tel. 308/865–2000; Lacey Witt, Director), (Nonreporting) **A**1 2 3 5 10 19 **F**3 7 11 13 15 18 20 22 24 28 29 30 31 34 35 37 40 41 43 45 46 49 50 51 53 54 55 56 57 58 59 60 62 67 68 70 72 74 75 76 77 78 79 81 82 84 85 89 90 91 93 97 100 101 102 104 107 108 110 111 112 113 114 115 117 119 124 126 129 130 131 132 134 135 146 148 149 150 154 155 **P**8 **S** CommonSpirit Health, Chicago, IL
Primary Contact: Michael H. Schnieders, FACHE, President
CFO: Lisa Webb, Vice President for Operational Finance
CMO: Dennis Edwards, M.D., Vice President Medical Affairs
CIO: Katie Gartner, Director Health Information Management
CHR: Aaron Austin, Division Vice President, Human Resources
CNO: Kimber Bonner, R.N., Vice President Patient Care Services
Web address: www.chihealthgoodsamaritan.org
**Control**: Church operated, Nongovernment, not–for–profit **Service**: General medical and surgical

**Staffed Beds**: 218 **Admissions**: 6848 **Census**: 94 **Outpatient Visits**: 53923
**Births**: 410 **Total Expense ($000)**: 162757 **Payroll Expense ($000)**: 45194
**Personnel**: 659

**GOOD SAMARITAN HOSPITAL** See Chi Health Good Samaritan

**NE**

---

**Hospital, Medicare Provider Number, Address, Telephone, Approval, Facility, and Physician Codes, Health Care System**

★ American Hospital Association (AHA) membership
☐ The Joint Commission accreditation
○ Healthcare Facilities Accreditation Program
◇ DNV Healthcare Inc. accreditation
⇑ Center for Improvement in Healthcare Quality Accreditation
△ Commission on Accreditation of Rehabilitation Facilities (CARF) accreditation

★ ○ **KEARNEY REGIONAL MEDICAL CENTER (280134)**, 804 22nd Avenue, Zip 68845–2206; tel. 855/404–5762, (Nonreporting) **A**10 11
Primary Contact: William Calhoun, FACHE, Chief Executive Officer
COO: John Lanning, Chief Operating Officer
CFO: Steve Regier, Chief Financial Officer
CIO: Travis Gregg, Chief Strategy Officer
CHR: Steve Beck, MS, Chief Human Resource Officer
CNO: Adrienne Carney, R.N., Director Nursing and Surgical Services
Web address: www.kearneyregional.com
**Control:** Partnership, Investor–owned (for–profit) **Service:** General medical and surgical

**Staffed Beds:** 92

**RICHARD H. YOUNG HOSPITAL** See Richard H. Young Behavioral Health Center

### KIMBALL—Kimball County

**KIMBALL COUNTY HOSPITAL** See Kimball Health Services

★ **KIMBALL HEALTH SERVICES (281305)**, 505 South Burg Street, Zip 69145–1398; tel. 308/235–1952, (Nonreporting) **A**10 18
Primary Contact: Ken Hunter, R.N., Chief Executive Officer
CFO: Cassie Gasseling, Chief Financial Officer
CMO: James Plate, M.D., Chief of Staff
CIO: Charles Walker, Director Information Technology
CHR: Jim Imler, Director Human Resources
CNO: Richard Harriger, Director of Emergency Services
Web address: www.kimballhealth.org
**Control:** County, Government, Nonfederal **Service:** General medical and surgical

**Staffed Beds:** 10

### LEXINGTON—Dawson County

★ ⇑ **LEXINGTON REGIONAL HEALTH CENTER (281361)**, 1201 North Erie Street, Zip 68850–1560, Mailing Address: P.O. Box 980, Zip 68850–0980; tel. 308/324–5651, (Nonreporting) **A**3 5 10 18 21
Primary Contact: Leslie Marsh, MSN, Chief Executive Officer
COO: Jim Hain, Chief Operating Officer
CFO: Wade Eschenbrenner, Chief Financial Officer
CMO: Francisca Acosta-Carlson, M.D., Chief of Staff
CIO: Robb Hanna, Executive Director Information Technology
CHR: Jill Denker, Executive Director Human Resources
CNO: Nicole Thorell, R.N., MSN, Chief Nursing Officer
Web address: www.lexingtonregional.org
**Control:** Hospital district or authority, Government, Nonfederal **Service:** General medical and surgical

**Staffed Beds:** 25

⇑ **TRI-COUNTY AREA HOSPITAL** See Lexington Regional Health Center

### LINCOLN—Lancaster County

⊞ △ **BRYAN MEDICAL CENTER (280003)**, 1600 South 48th Street, Zip 68506–1299; tel. 402/481–1111, (Includes BRYAN MEDICAL CENTER-EAST, Mailing address: 1600 South 48th Street, Lincoln, Nebraska, Zip 68506–1299; tel. 402/481–1111; John T. Woodrich, President and Chief Executive Officer, Executive Vice President Bryan Health; BRYAN MEDICAL CENTER-WEST, Mailing address: 2300 South 16th Street, Lincoln, Nebraska, Zip 68502–3781; tel. 402/475–1011; John T. Woodrich, President and Chief Executive Officer, Executive Vice President Bryan Health), (Nonreporting) **A**1 2 3 5 7 10 **F**3 4 5 12 13 15 17 18 19 20 22 24 26 28 29 30 31 34 35 37 38 39 40 43 45 46 47 48 49 50 54 56 57 58 59 61 64 70 71 72 74 75 76 77 78 79 81 82 84 85 86 87 89 90 92 93 96 98 99 100 101 102 103 104 105 107 108 110 111 114 115 116 117 118 119 121 123 126 129 130 131 132 135 145 146 147 148 149 151 152 153 156 **S** Bryan Health, Lincoln, NE
Primary Contact: John T. Woodrich, President and Chief Executive Officer, Executive Vice President Bryan Health
CMO: John Trapp, Vice President Medical Affairs
CIO: George Carr, Chief Information Officer
CNO: Lisa M Vail, R.N., Chief Nursing Officer and Vice President Patient Care Services
Web address: www.bryanhealth.com
**Control:** Other not–for–profit (including NFP Corporation) **Service:** General medical and surgical

**Staffed Beds:** 546 **Admissions:** 29424 **Census:** 387 **Outpatient Visits:** 275482 **Births:** 3383 **Total Expense ($000):** 597459 **Payroll Expense ($000):** 222290 **Personnel:** 3282

**BRYANLGH MEDICAL CENTER** See Bryan Medical Center

**BRYANLGH MEDICAL CENTER-EAST** See Bryan Medical Center-East

**BRYANLGH MEDICAL CENTER-WEST** See Bryan Medical Center-West

★ **CHI HEALTH NEBRASKA HEART (280128)**, 7500 South 91st Street, Zip 68526–9437; tel. 402/327–2700, (Nonreporting) **A**10 **F**17 18 20 22 24 26 29 30 34 45 57 58 59 64 81 107 115 119 130 **P**8 **S** CommonSpirit Health, Chicago, IL
Primary Contact: Derek Vance, FACHE, President
Web address: www.CHIhealthNebraskaHeart.com
**Control:** Church operated, Nongovernment, not–for–profit **Service:** Heart

**Staffed Beds:** 54 **Admissions:** 1792 **Census:** 17 **Outpatient Visits:** 9681 **Births:** 0 **Total Expense ($000):** 58308 **Payroll Expense ($000):** 14750 **Personnel:** 190

⊞ **CHI HEALTH ST ELIZABETH (280020)**, 555 South 70th Street, Zip 68510–2494; tel. 402/219–8000, (Nonreporting) **A**1 2 3 5 10 **F**3 8 11 12 13 15 16 29 30 31 34 35 37 39 40 44 45 46 47 48 49 50 51 53 55 58 59 60 61 64 65 68 70 72 74 75 76 78 79 80 81 84 85 86 87 89 92 100 107 108 110 111 114 115 116 117 118 119 120 121 123 124 126 129 130 131 132 144 145 146 147 148 154 **P**8 **S** CommonSpirit Health, Chicago, IL
Primary Contact: Derek Vance, FACHE, President
CFO: Tyler DeJong, Vice President, Operational Finance
CMO: Michael Ferris, M.D., Chief Medical Officer
CIO: Richard Bohaty, Director Information Technology
CHR: Nancy Wallace, Senior Vice President, Chief Human Resources Officer
CNO: Elizabeth A Raetz, R.N., MSN, Vice President Nursing and Chief Nursing Officer
Web address: www.saintelizabethonline.com
**Control:** Church operated, Nongovernment, not–for–profit **Service:** General medical and surgical

**Staffed Beds:** 235 **Admissions:** 6640 **Census:** 83 **Outpatient Visits:** 81002 **Births:** 1177 **Total Expense ($000):** 179379 **Payroll Expense ($000):** 47331 **Personnel:** 677

**LINCOLN DIVISION** See Veterans Affairs Nebraska-Western Iowa Health Care System - Lincoln, Lincoln

☐ **LINCOLN REGIONAL CENTER (284003)**, West Prospector Place and South Folsom, Zip 68522–2299, Mailing Address: P.O. Box 94949, Zip 68509–4949; tel. 402/471–4444, (Nonreporting) **A**1 10
Primary Contact: Mark LaBouchardiere, Interim Facility Administrator
COO: Stacey Werth-Sweeney, Facility Operating Officer
CFO: Randy Willey, Business Manager
CMO: Vijay Dewan, M.D., Clinical Director
CHR: Scott Rasmussen, Director Human Resources
Web address: www.hhs.state.ne.us/beh/rc
**Control:** State, Government, Nonfederal **Service:** Psychiatric

**Staffed Beds:** 244

**LINCOLN SURGICAL HOSPITAL (280127)**, 1710 South 70th Street, Suite 200, Zip 68506–1677; tel. 402/484–9090, (Nonreporting) **A**10
Primary Contact: Robb Linafelter, Chief Executive Officer
Web address: www.lincolnsurgery.com
**Control:** Corporation, Investor–owned (for–profit) **Service:** Surgical

**Staffed Beds:** 7

**MADONNA CENTERS** See Madonna Rehabilitation Hospital

△ **MADONNA REHABILITATION HOSPITAL (283025)**, 5401 South Street, Zip 68506–2134; tel. 402/489–7102, (Nonreporting) **A**3 5 7 10
Primary Contact: Paul Dongilli Jr, Ph.D., FACHE, President and Chief Executive Officer
CFO: Victor J Witkowicz, Senior Vice President and Chief Financial Officer
CMO: Thomas Stadler, M.D., Vice President Medical Affairs and Chief Medical Officer
CIO: David Rolfe, Chief Information Officer
CHR: Lou Ann Manske, Vice President Human Resources
Web address: www.madonna.org
**Control:** Other not–for–profit (including NFP Corporation) **Service:** Rehabilitation

**Staffed Beds:** 308

**MADONNA REHABILITATION HOSPITAL (282000)**, 5401 South Street, Zip 68506–2150; tel. 402/413–3000, (Nonreporting) **A**3 5 10
Primary Contact: Paul Dongilli Jr, Ph.D., FACHE, President and Chief Executive Officer
Web address: www.madonna.org/
**Control:** Other not–for–profit (including NFP Corporation) **Service:** Acute long–term care hospital

**Staffed Beds:** 300

**NEBRASKA HEART HOSPITAL** See Chi Health Nebraska Heart

*Many Facility Codes have changed. Please refer to the AHA Guide Code Chart.*

**NE**

**NEBRASKA PENAL AND CORRECTIONAL HOSPITAL**, 14th and Pioneer Streets, Zip 68501, Mailing Address: P.O. Box 94661, Zip 94661; tel. 402/471–3161, (Nonreporting)
Primary Contact: Randy T. Kohl, M.D., Deputy Director, Health Services
Web address: www.corrections.nebraska.gov
**Control:** State, Government, Nonfederal **Service:** Hospital unit of an institution (prison hospital, college infirmary, etc.)

Staffed Beds: 12

**SAINT ELIZABETH REGIONAL MEDICAL CENTER** See Chi Health St Elizabeth

☒ **SELECT SPECIALTY HOSPITAL - LINCOLN (282002)**, 2300 South 16th Street, 7th Floor, Zip 68502–3704; tel. 402/483–8444, (Nonreporting) **A**1 10 **S** Select Medical Corporation, Mechanicsburg, PA
Primary Contact: Connie K. Siffring, Chief Executive Officer
CHR: Bob Dorsey, Human Resources Coordinator
CNO: Trisha Smolik, R.N., MSN, Chief Nursing Officer
Web address: www.selectmedical.com
**Control:** Corporation, Investor–owned (for–profit) **Service:** Acute long–term care hospital

Staffed Beds: 24

**VETERANS AFFAIRS MED CENTER** See Lincoln Division

**VETERANS AFFAIRS NEBRASKA-WESTERN IOWA HEALTH CARE SYSTEM**
See Veterans Affairs Nebraska-Western Iowa Health Care System - Lincoln

★ **VETERANS AFFAIRS NEBRASKA-WESTERN IOWA HEALTH CARE SYSTEM - LINCOLN**, 600 South 70th Street, Zip 68510–2493; tel. 402/489–3802, (Includes LINCOLN DIVISION, Mailing address: 600 South 70th Street, Lincoln, Nebraska, Zip 68510–2493; tel. 402/489–3802) **S** Department of Veterans Affairs, Washington, DC
Primary Contact: Don Burman, Director
CIO: David Daiker, Chief Information Resource Management
CHR: Dave Peters, Chief Human Resources Officer
Web address: www.nebraska.va.gov/
**Control:** Veterans Affairs, Government, federal **Service:** General medical and surgical

Staffed Beds: 132

**LYNCH—Boyd County**

**NIOBRARA VALLEY HOSPITAL (281303)**, 401 South Fifth Street, Zip 68746–0118, Mailing Address: P.O. Box 118, Zip 68746–0118; tel. 402/569–2451, (Nonreporting) **A**10 18 **S** Faith Regional Health Services, Norfolk, NE
Primary Contact: Kelly Kalkowski, Chief Executive Officer
CFO: Martha Nelson, Chief Financial Officer
CMO: James Keil, M.D., Chief Medical Officer
CHR: Trudy Nelson, Chief Human Resource Officer
CNO: Debra Dawn Hanzlik, R.N., Director of Nursing
Web address: www.nvhcares.org
**Control:** Other not–for–profit (including NFP Corporation) **Service:** General medical and surgical

Staffed Beds: 20

**MCCOOK—Red Willow County**

★ ⇑ **COMMUNITY HOSPITAL (281363)**, 1301 East 'H' Street, Zip 69001–1328, Mailing Address: P.O. Box 1328, Zip 69001–1328; tel. 308/344–2650, (Nonreporting) **A**3 5 10 18 21
Primary Contact: Troy Bruntz, CPA, President and Chief Executive Officer
CFO: Sean Wolfe, Vice President Finance and Chief Financial Officer
CMO: Jason Blomstedt, Chief of Staff
CIO: Lori Beeby, Director Information Systems
CHR: Leanne R Miller, Director Human Resources
Web address: www.chmccook.org
**Control:** Other not–for–profit (including NFP Corporation) **Service:** General medical and surgical

Staffed Beds: 25

**MINDEN—Kearney County**

**KEARNEY COUNTY COMM HOSPITAL** See Kearney County Health Services

**KEARNEY COUNTY HEALTH SERVICES (281306)**, 727 East First Street, Zip 68959–1705; tel. 308/832–3400, (Nonreporting) **A**10 18
Primary Contact: Luke David. Poore, Chief Executive Officer
CFO: Gavin Blum, Chief Financial Officer
CMO: Douglas Althouse, Chief Medical Staff
CHR: Rebecca L Cooke, Director Human Resources
CNO: Kendra Brown, MSN, R.N., Chief Nursing Officer
Web address: www.kchs.org
**Control:** County, Government, Nonfederal **Service:** General medical and surgical

Staffed Beds: 44

**NEBRASKA CITY—Otoe County**

★ **CHI HEALTH ST. MARY'S (281342)**, 1301 Grundman Boulevard, Zip 68410; tel. 402/873–3321, (Nonreporting) **A**10 18 **F**3 13 15 18 28 29 31 34 35 40 43 44 45 57 59 64 66 68 69 74 75 76 77 78 79 81 82 85 87 97 107 108 110 111 115 118 119 127 129 130 132 133 146 147 148 150 154 156 **S** CommonSpirit Health, Chicago, IL
Primary Contact: Daniel DeFreece, M.D., Interim President
CFO: Tim H. Schnack, Vice President Operations Finance
CMO: Jonathan Stelling, M.D., Vice President Medical Affairs
CNO: Brenda Jean Sebek, R.N., Administrator
Web address: www.chihealthstmarys.com
**Control:** Church operated, Nongovernment, not–for–profit **Service:** General medical and surgical

Staffed Beds: 18 Admissions: 318 Census: 3 Outpatient Visits: 37007 Births: 105 Total Expense ($000): 24768 Payroll Expense ($000): 7461 Personnel: 95

**ST. MARY'S COMMUNITY HOSPITAL** See Chi Health St. Mary's

**NELIGH—Antelope County**

★ **ANTELOPE MEMORIAL HOSPITAL (281326)**, 102 West 9th Street, Zip 68756–1114, Mailing Address: P.O. Box 229, Zip 68756–0229; tel. 402/887–4151, (Nonreporting) **A**10 18
Primary Contact: Diane Carlin, FACHE, Chief Executive Officer
CFO: Martha Nelson, Chief Financial Officer
CMO: Roger Rudloff, M.D., President Medical Staff
CIO: Kevin Trease, Chief Information Officer
CHR: Megan Becklun, Director Human Resources
CNO: Merry Sprout, R.N., Chief Nursing Officer
Web address: www.amhne.org/
**Control:** Other not–for–profit (including NFP Corporation) **Service:** General medical and surgical

Staffed Beds: 23

**NORFOLK—Madison County**

☒ **FAITH REGIONAL HEALTH SERVICES (280125)**, 2700 West Norfolk Avenue, Zip 68701–4438, Mailing Address: P.O. Box 869, Zip 68702–0869; tel. 402/371–4880, (Includes EAST CAMPUS, Mailing address: 1500 Koenigstein Avenue, Norfolk, Nebraska, Zip 68701; tel. 402/371–3402; WEST CAMPUS, Mailing address: 2700 Norfolk Avenue, Norfolk, Nebraska, Zip 68701, P O Box 869, Zip 68702–0869; tel. 402/371–4880) (Total facility includes 63 beds in nursing home–type unit) **A**1 2 3 5 10 20 **F**3 8 10 11 13 15 17 18 20 22 24 26 28 29 30 31 34 35 40 41 43 44 45 46 47 49 50 53 57 58 59 61 62 63 64 67 70 71 73 74 75 76 77 78 79 80 81 82 84 85 86 87 89 90 91 92 93 96 98 100 101 102 107 108 110 111 114 115 119 120 121 123 128 129 130 131 132 135 141 144 146 147 149 154 157 **P**6 8 **S** Faith Regional Health Services, Norfolk, NE
Primary Contact: Kelly Driscoll, R.N., FACHE, President and Chief Executive Officer
CFO: Johnathan Wilker, Vice President Finance and Chief Financial Officer
CMO: Dean O French, M.D., Chief of Staff
CIO: Brian Sterud, Chief Information Officer
CHR: Janet M Pinkelman, Director Human Resources
Web address: www.frhs.org
**Control:** Other not–for–profit (including NFP Corporation) **Service:** General medical and surgical

Staffed Beds: 147 Admissions: 4949 Census: 195 Outpatient Visits: 65284 Births: 819 Total Expense ($000): 158768 Payroll Expense ($000): 55527 Personnel: 1210

NE

## NORTH PLATTE—Lincoln County

✠ **GREAT PLAINS HEALTH (280065)**, 601 West Leota Street, Zip 69101–6598, Mailing Address: P.O. Box 1167, Zip 69103–1167; tel. 308/568–8000, (Nonreporting) **A**1 2 3 5 10 **F**3 11 12 13 15 17 18 20 22 28 29 30 31 34 35 40 41 43 45 46 48 50 51 54 55 57 58 59 60 62 63 64 65 68 70 72 73 74 75 76 78 79 81 82 84 85 86 87 89 93 94 96 97 98 100 102 107 108 109 110 111 115 116 117 118 119 120 121 122 123 124 129 130 131 135 143 145 146 147 148 154 156 157 158 **P**8
Primary Contact: Melvin McNea, Chief Executive Officer
COO: Ivan Mitchell, Chief Operating Officer
CFO: Krystal Claymore, Chief Financial Officer
CIO: Brandon Kelliher, Chief Information Officer
CHR: Jayne Johnson, Director Human Resources
CNO: Tamara Martin-Linnard, R.N., Chief Clinical Officer
Web address: www.gphealth.org
**Control**: Other not-for-profit (including NFP Corporation) **Service**: General medical and surgical

**Staffed Beds**: 116 **Admissions**: 5679 **Census**: 59 **Outpatient Visits**: 177274 **Births**: 565 **Total Expense ($000)**: 216364 **Payroll Expense ($000)**: 85846 **Personnel**: 1023

**GREAT PLAINS REGIONAL MEDICAL CENTER** See Great Plains Health

## OAKLAND—Burt County

★ **MERCYONE OAKLAND MEDICAL CENTER (281321)**, 601 East Second Street, Zip 68045–1499; tel. 402/685–5601, (Nonreporting) **A**10 18 **S** Trinity Health, Livonia, MI
Primary Contact: Rita Going, Director of Critical Access Hospitals
CFO: Terri Mentink, Chief Financial Officer
CMO: Tracie Martin, M.D., Chief Medical Officer
CNO: Jayma Brown, R.N., Director of Nursing
Web address: www.oaklandhospital.org
**Control**: Church operated, Nongovernment, not-for-profit **Service**: General medical and surgical

**Staffed Beds**: 18

**OAKLAND MERCY HOSPITAL** See Mercyone Oakland Medical Center

## OGALLALA—Keith County

✠ **OGALLALA COMMUNITY HOSPITAL (281355)**, 2601 North Spruce Street, Zip 69153–2465; tel. 308/284–4011, (Nonreporting) **A**1 10 18 **F**3 13 15 29 31 34 40 43 45 59 65 68 75 76 77 79 81 85 87 93 97 107 110 111 115 119 127 128 130 132 133 148 149 154 **P**8 **S** Banner Health, Phoenix, AZ
Primary Contact: Timothy Gullingsrud, Chief Executive Officer
CFO: Dena Klockman, Chief Financial Officer
CMO: Gabriel Godina, M.D., Chief of Staff
CHR: Gracie Ramos, Chief Human Resources Officer
CNO: Linda Baldwin, Chief Nursing Officer
Web address: www.https://www.bannerhealth.com/locations/ogallala/ogallala-community-hospital
**Control**: Other not-for-profit (including NFP Corporation) **Service**: General medical and surgical

**Staffed Beds**: 18 **Admissions**: 276 **Census**: 2 **Outpatient Visits**: 32818 **Births**: 52 **Total Expense ($000)**: 22614 **Payroll Expense ($000)**: 9159 **Personnel**: 123

## OMAHA—Douglas County

**ALEGENT CREIGHTON HEALTH IMMANUEL MEDICAL CENTER** See Chi Health Immanuel

**ALEGENT CREIGHTON HEALTH LAKESIDE HOSPITAL** See Chi Health Lakeside

☐ **BOYS TOWN NATIONAL RESEARCH HOSPITAL (283300)**, 555 North 30th Street, Zip 68131–2198; tel. 531/355–6510, (Nonreporting) **A**1 3 5 10
Primary Contact: Edward M. Kolb, M.D., Director
CFO: Anna McCaslin, Director Finance
CMO: Edward M. Kolb, M.D., Medical Director
CNO: Lori S. Umberger, Chief Nursing Officer
Web address: www.boystownhospital.org
**Control**: Other not-for-profit (including NFP Corporation) **Service**: Children's general medical and surgical

**Staffed Beds**: 141

**BOYS TOWN NATL INST FOR CHILD** See Boys Town National Research Hospital

**CHI HEALTH BERGAN MERCY** See Chi Health Creighton University Medical Center - Bergan Mercy

✠ **CHI HEALTH CREIGHTON UNIVERSITY MEDICAL CENTER - BERGAN MERCY (280060)**, 7500 Mercy Road, Zip 68124–2319; tel. 402/398–6060, (Includes LASTING HOPE RECOVERY CENTER, Mailing address: 415 South 25th Avenue, Omaha, Nebraska, Zip 68131; tel. 402/717–5300; Robin Conyers, Administrator), (Nonreporting) **A**1 2 3 5 8 10 **F**3 8 11 13 15 17 18 20 22 23 24 26 28 29 30 31 34 35 37 38 40 42 43 44 45 46 47 48 49 50 51 53 54 55 56 57 58 59 60 61 64 65 68 70 72 74 75 76 77 78 79 81 82 83 84 85 86 87 89 92 93 96 97 98 100 101 102 104 107 108 109 110 111 114 115 116 117 118 119 120 121 123 124 126 130 131 132 134 145 146 147 148 149 150 154 156 **P**8 **S** CommonSpirit Health, Chicago, IL
Primary Contact: Jayleen Casano, Ph.D., FACHE, President
COO: Todd Defreece, Vice President Operations
CFO: Tim H. Schnack, Vice President Financial Services
CMO: Devin Fox, M.D., Vice President Medical Operations
CIO: Anna M. Turman, Division Vice President, Chief Information Officer
CHR: Aaron Austin, Division Vice President Human Resources Administration
CNO: Kelli J. Saucerman-Howard, Vice President Patient Care Services
Web address: www.chihealth.com/chi-health-bergan-mercy
**Control**: Church operated, Nongovernment, not-for-profit **Service**: General medical and surgical

**Staffed Beds**: 385 **Admissions**: 16781 **Census**: 234 **Outpatient Visits**: 163862 **Births**: 3920 **Total Expense ($000)**: 444342 **Payroll Expense ($000)**: 111071 **Personnel**: 1581

★ △ **CHI HEALTH IMMANUEL (280081)**, 6901 North 72nd Street, Zip 68122–1799; tel. 402/572–2121, (Nonreporting) **A**2 3 5 7 10 **F**3 5 11 12 13 15 17 18 20 22 26 28 29 30 31 32 34 35 36 37 38 40 43 45 46 49 50 51 53 55 56 57 58 59 64 65 67 68 70 74 75 76 77 78 79 81 82 84 85 86 87 90 91 92 93 94 95 96 97 98 99 100 101 102 103 104 105 106 107 108 110 111 114 115 117 118 119 120 121 124 126 129 130 131 132 136 141 142 146 147 149 153 154 157 **P**8 **S** CommonSpirit Health, Chicago, IL
Primary Contact: Ann Schumacher, R.N., MSN, FACHE, President
CFO: Tim H. Schnack, Chief Financial Officer
CMO: Joseph Hoagbin, M.D., Chief Medical Officer
CHR: Nancy Wallace, Vice President Human Resources
Web address: www.alegent.com/immanuel
**Control**: Church operated, Nongovernment, not-for-profit **Service**: General medical and surgical

**Staffed Beds**: 269 **Admissions**: 10227 **Census**: 172 **Outpatient Visits**: 119497 **Births**: 699 **Total Expense ($000)**: 170108 **Payroll Expense ($000)**: 57422 **Personnel**: 910

✠ **CHI HEALTH LAKESIDE (280130)**, 6901 N 72nd St, Zip 68122, Mailing Address: 16901 Lakeside Hills Court, Zip 68130–2318; tel. 402/717–8000, (Nonreporting) **A**1 2 3 10 **F**3 13 15 18 20 22 26 28 29 30 31 34 35 36 40 45 46 49 50 53 55 59 60 62 63 64 68 69 70 72 74 75 76 77 78 79 81 82 83 84 85 87 93 97 100 107 108 110 111 114 115 116 117 119 120 124 126 129 130 131 132 135 143 146 147 148 149 154 157 **P**8 **S** CommonSpirit Health, Chicago, IL
Primary Contact: Kevin Miller, President
COO: Kathy Bressler, Division Senior Vice President and Chief Operating Officer
CFO: Nick O'Tool, Vice President Operational Finance
CMO: Patricia Murdock-Langan, M.D., Chief Medical Officer
CIO: Thomas Haley, Information Technology Systems Site Director
CHR: Nancy Wallace, Division Senior Vice President, Chief Human Resource Officer
CNO: Linda K. Chase, Ph.D., R.N., Division Senior Vice President and Chief Nursing Officer
Web address: www.CHIhealth.com
**Control**: Church operated, Nongovernment, not-for-profit **Service**: General medical and surgical

**Staffed Beds**: 137 **Admissions**: 5705 **Census**: 60 **Outpatient Visits**: 102095 **Births**: 890 **Total Expense ($000)**: 121875 **Payroll Expense ($000)**: 37251 **Personnel**: 540

**NE**

*Many Facility Codes have changed. Please refer to the AHA Guide Code Chart.*
© 2021 AHA Guide

✠ **CHILDREN'S HOSPITAL AND MEDICAL CENTER (283301)**, 8200 Dodge St, Zip 68114–4113; tel. 402/955–5400, (Nonreporting) **A**1 3 5 8 10 **F**3 7 8 11 12 13 17 19 21 23 25 27 29 30 31 32 34 35 40 41 43 45 46 47 48 49 50 53 54 55 58 59 60 62 64 65 68 71 72 74 75 76 77 78 79 81 82 84 85 87 88 89 92 93 97 104 107 108 111 115 119 129 130 131 132 137 144 145 146 148 149 154 155 156 **P**6
Primary Contact: Chanda Chacon, President and Chief Executive Officer
COO: Kathy L English, R.N., MSN, Executive Vice President and Chief Operating Officer
CFO: Amy Hatcher, Executive Vice President and Chief Financial Officer
CMO: Christopher Maloney, M.D., Senior Vice President, Medical Affairs and Chief Medical Officer
CIO: Jerry Vuchak, Senior Vice President, Chief Information Officer
CHR: Janel Allen, Senior Vice President and Chief Human Resources Officer
CNO: Kathy L English, R.N., MSN, Executive Vice President and Chief Nursing Officer
Web address: www.childrensomaha.org
**Control**: Other not–for–profit (including NFP Corporation) **Service**: Children's general medical and surgical

**Staffed Beds**: 136 **Admissions**: 4319 **Census**: 101 **Outpatient Visits**: 443684 **Births**: 1 **Total Expense ($000)**: 461735 **Payroll Expense ($000)**: 214689 **Personnel**: 2711

**CHILDREN'S MEMORIAL HOSPITAL** See Children's Hospital and Medical Center

★ ○ **DOUGLAS COUNTY COMMUNITY MENTAL HEALTH CENTER (284009)**, 4102 Woolworth Avenue, Zip 68105–1899; tel. 402/444–7449, (Nonreporting) **A**3 5 10 11
Primary Contact: Sherry L. Glasnapp, Director
CFO: DeDe Will, Director Finance
CMO: Sidney A. Kauzlarich, M.D., Medical Director
CIO: Dianne Wallace, County Information Manager
CHR: Karen Buche, Chief Human Resource Officer
CNO: Marti Christensen, Director of Psychiatric Nursing
Web address: www.co.douglas.ne.us
**Control**: County, Government, Nonfederal **Service**: Psychiatric

**Staffed Beds**: 16

**DOUGLAS COUNTY HOSPITAL** See Douglas County Community Mental Health Center

△ **MADONNA REHABILITATION HOSPITAL (283026)**, 17500 Burke Street, Zip 68118–2244; tel. 844/403–3131, (Nonreporting) **A**3 5 7 10
Primary Contact: Paul Dongilli Jr, Ph.D., FACHE, President and Chief Executive Officer
CFO: Michael Hedderman, Vice President and Chief Financial Officer
CIO: Robert Heydon, Chief Information Officer
Web address: www.https://www.madonna.org
**Control**: Other not–for–profit (including NFP Corporation) **Service**: Rehabilitation

**Staffed Beds**: 57

**MADONNA REHABILITATION SPECIALTY HOSPITAL (282003)**, 17500 Burke Street, Zip 68118–2244; tel. 844/403–3131, (Nonreporting) **A**5 10
Primary Contact: Paul Dongilli Jr, Ph.D., FACHE, President and Chief Executive Officer
Web address: www.https://www.madonna.org
**Control**: Other not–for–profit (including NFP Corporation) **Service**: Acute long–term care hospital

**Staffed Beds**: 48

**MERCY CARE CENTER** See Alegent Health Mercy Care Center

**METHODIST HOSPITAL** See Nebraska Methodist Hospital

**MIDWEST SURGICAL HOSPITAL (280131)**, 7915 Farnam Drive, Zip 68114–4504; tel. 402/399–1900, (Nonreporting) **A**3 10 22
Primary Contact: Charles Livingston, Chief Executive Officer
Web address: www.mwsurgicalhospital.com
**Control**: Corporation, Investor–owned (for–profit) **Service**: Surgical

**Staffed Beds**: 19

**NEBRASKA MEDICINE** See Nebraska Medicine - Nebraska Medical Center

✠ **NEBRASKA MEDICINE - NEBRASKA MEDICAL CENTER (280013)**, 987400 Nebraska Medical Center, Zip 68198–7400; tel. 402/552–2000, (Nonreporting) **A**1 2 3 5 8 10 **F**3 5 6 8 9 11 12 13 15 17 18 20 22 24 26 28 29 30 31 32 34 35 36 37 38 39 40 41 43 44 45 46 47 48 49 50 51 53 54 55 56 57 58 59 60 61 62 63 64 65 66 68 70 71 72 74 75 76 77 78 79 80 81 82 84 85 86 87 88 89 91 92 93 94 96 97 98 100 102 104 107 108 110 111 113 114 115 116 117 118 119 120 121 123 124 126 127 129 130 131 132 134 135 136 137 138 139 140 141 142 143 144 145 146 147 148 149 150 154 156 **P**5 6 8
Primary Contact: James Linder, M.D., Chief Executive Officer
COO: Dennis Bierle, Chief Operating Officer
CFO: Stephanie Daubert, Chief Financial Officer
CMO: Harris Frankel, M.D., Interim Chief Medical Officer
CIO: Michael A Ash, Chief Transformation Officer
CHR: Frank Venuto, Chief Human Capital Officer
CNO: Suzanne Langan Nuss, Ph.D., R.N., Chief Nursing Officer
Web address: www.nebraskamed.com
**Control**: Other not–for–profit (including NFP Corporation) **Service**: General medical and surgical

**Staffed Beds**: 623 **Admissions**: 28920 **Census**: 475 **Outpatient Visits**: 1092806 **Births**: 1663 **Total Expense ($000)**: 1531781 **Payroll Expense ($000)**: 667402 **Personnel**: 7458

✠ △ **NEBRASKA METHODIST HOSPITAL (280040)**, 8303 Dodge Street, Zip 68114–4199; tel. 402/354–4000, (Includes METHODIST WOMEN'S HOSPITAL, Mailing address: 707 North 190th Plaza, Elkhorn, Nebraska, Zip 68022–3974; tel. 402/815–4000; Josie Abboud, R.N., FACHE, President and Chief Executive Officer), (Nonreporting) **A**1 2 3 5 7 10 **F**3 11 12 13 15 18 20 22 24 26 28 29 30 31 34 35 40 45 46 47 48 49 50 51 52 54 55 57 58 59 64 65 66 68 70 71 72 74 75 76 77 78 79 80 81 82 83 84 85 86 87 90 91 92 93 96 100 101 102 104 107 108 110 111 114 115 116 117 118 119 120 121 123 124 126 127 129 130 132 135 142 143 146 147 148 154 156 157 **P**6 8 **S** Nebraska Methodist Health System, Inc., Omaha, NE
Primary Contact: Josie Abboud, R.N., FACHE, President and Chief Executive Officer
CFO: Linda K Burt, Corporate Vice President Finance
CMO: William Shiffermiller, M.D., Vice President Medical Affairs
CHR: Holly Huerter, Vice President Human Resources
CNO: Teri Tipton Bruening, MSN, Chief Nursing Officer and Vice President Patient Care Services
Web address: www.bestcare.org
**Control**: Other not–for–profit (including NFP Corporation) **Service**: General medical and surgical

**Staffed Beds**: 390 **Admissions**: 19274 **Census**: 277 **Outpatient Visits**: 205680 **Births**: 4919 **Total Expense ($000)**: 515113 **Payroll Expense ($000)**: 191832 **Personnel**: 2832

**NEBRASKA ORTHOPAEDIC HOSPITAL** See Orthonebraska Hospital

✠ **NEBRASKA SPINE HOSPITAL (280133)**, 6901 North 72nd Street, Suite 20300, Zip 68122–1755, Mailing Address: 6901 North 72nd Street, Zip 68122–1709; tel. 402/572–3000, (Nonreporting) **A**1 10
Primary Contact: Christopher M. Palumbo, Chief Executive Officer
Web address: www.nebraskaspinehospital.com
**Control**: Partnership, Investor–owned (for–profit) **Service**: Orthopedic

**Staffed Beds**: 34

□ **ORTHONEBRASKA HOSPITAL (280129)**, 2808 South 143rd Plaza, Zip 68144–5611; tel. 402/609–1600, (Nonreporting) **A**1 10
Primary Contact: Levi Scheppers, Chief Executive Officer
COO: Mark E Longacre, FACHE, Chief Operating Officer
CMO: Ian Crabb, M.D., Chief Medical Officer
CIO: Tim Pugsley, Chief Information Officer
CHR: Lori L Thompson, Manager Human Resources
Web address: www.neorthohospital.com
**Control**: Partnership, Investor–owned (for–profit) **Service**: Orthopedic

**Staffed Beds**: 24

**NE**

**Hospital, Medicare Provider Number, Address, Telephone, Approval, Facility, and Physician Codes, Health Care System**

★ American Hospital Association (AHA) membership    ○ Healthcare Facilities Accreditation Program    ⇑ Center for Improvement in Healthcare Quality Accreditation
□ The Joint Commission accreditation    ◇ DNV Healthcare Inc. accreditation    △ Commission on Accreditation of Rehabilitation Facilities (CARF) accreditation

© 2021 AHA Guide    *Many Facility Codes have changed. Please refer to the AHA Guide Code Chart.*    Hospitals **A437**

✉ **SELECT SPECIALTY HOSPITAL-OMAHA (282001)**, 1870 South 75th Street,
Zip 68124–1700; tel. 402/361–5700, (Nonreporting) **A**1 10 **S** Select Medical
Corporation, Mechanicsburg, PA
Primary Contact: Kerry McLane, Interim Chief Executive Officer
COO: Joel White, Chief Operating Officer
CMO: Guillermo Huerta, M.D., Chief Medical Officer
CHR: Laurna Hoss, Human Resource Coordinator
CNO: Amanda Wellman, MSN, R.N., Chief Nursing Officer
Web address: www.https://omaha.selectspecialtyhospitals.com
**Control**: Corporation, Investor–owned (for–profit) **Service**: Acute long–term care
hospital

**Staffed Beds**: 52

**VETERANS AFFAIRS - WESTERN IOWA HEALTHCARE SYSTEM** See Veterans
Affairs Nebraska-Western Iowa Health Care System

✉ **VETERANS AFFAIRS NEBRASKA-WESTERN IOWA HEALTH CARE SYSTEM**,
4101 Woolworth Avenue, Zip 68105–1873; tel. 402/346–8800, (Nonreporting)
**A**1 2 3 5 **S** Department of Veterans Affairs, Washington, DC
Primary Contact: Don Burman, Director
COO: Denise Harrison, Associate Director
CFO: Kirk Kay, Chief Financial Officer
CMO: Grace Stringfellow, M.D., Chief of Staff
CIO: Jennifer Rosenbalm, Manager Business Office
CHR: Cheryl M DeWispelare, Chief Human Resources Officer
CNO: Eileen M Kingston, R.N., Nurse Executive, Associate Director Patient Care
Web address: www.nebraska.va.gov/
**Control**: Veterans Affairs, Government, federal **Service**: General medical and surgical

**Staffed Beds**: 137

### O'NEILL—Holt County

**AVERA ANTHONY'S HOSPITAL** See Avera St. Anthony's Hospital

★ **AVERA ST. ANTHONY'S HOSPITAL (281329)**, 300 North Second Street,
Zip 68763–1514, Mailing Address: P.O. Box 270, Oneill, Zip 68763–0270;
tel. 402/336–2611, (Nonreporting) **A**10 18 **S** Avera Health, Sioux Falls, SD
Primary Contact: Todd Consbruck, President and Chief Executive Officer
CFO: Michael Garman, Chief Financial Officer
CIO: Michael Garman, Chief Financial Officer
CHR: Kathryn Benson, Human Resources Partner
Web address: www.avera.org/st-anthonys
**Control**: Church operated, Nongovernment, not–for–profit **Service**: General
medical and surgical

**Staffed Beds**: 25

### ORD—Valley County

★ **VALLEY COUNTY HEALTH SYSTEM (281353)**, 2707 L Street,
Zip 68862–1275; tel. 308/728–4200, (Nonreporting) **A**10 18 **F**3 7 15 28 29 31
34 35 40 41 43 45 46 50 56 57 59 62 63 64 65 68 74 75 77 78 79 81 82 84
87 90 93 94 97 103 107 110 111 119 127 128 129 130 131 132 133 148
154 156
Primary Contact: Nancy Glaubke, Chief Executive Officer
CFO: Ashley Woodward, Director Financial Services
CMO: Jennifer Bengston, M.D., Chief Medical Officer
CIO: Shane Molacek, Chief Information Officer
CHR: Danielle Proskocil, Director Human Resources
CNO: Vicki Bredthauer, R.N., Director of Nursing
Web address: www.valleycountyhealthsystem.org
**Control**: County, Government, Nonfederal **Service**: General medical and surgical

**Staffed Beds**: 16 **Admissions**: 244 **Census**: 4 **Outpatient Visits**: 25000
**Births**: 0 **Total Expense ($000)**: 21237 **Payroll Expense ($000)**: 9433
**Personnel**: 178

**VALLEY COUNTY HOSPITAL** See Valley County Health System

### OSCEOLA—Polk County

**ANNIE JEFFREY MEM CNTY HOSP** See Annie Jeffrey Memorial County Health Center

**ANNIE JEFFREY MEMORIAL COUNTY HEALTH CENTER (281314)**, 531
Beebe Street, Zip 68651–5537, Mailing Address: P.O. Box 428, Zip 68651–0428;
tel. 402/747–2031, (Nonreporting) **A**10 18
Primary Contact: Joseph W. Lohrman, Chief Executive Officer
CFO: Joseph W Lohrman, Chief Executive Officer
CMO: David Jameson, M.D., Chief of Staff
CIO: Frank Vrba, Chief Information Officer
CHR: Sue Leif, R.N., Director Human Resources
Web address: www.ajhc.org
**Control**: County, Government, Nonfederal **Service**: General medical and surgical

**Staffed Beds**: 16

### OSHKOSH—Garden County

**GARDEN COUNTY HEALTH SERVICES** See Regional West Garden County

★ **REGIONAL WEST GARDEN COUNTY (281310)**, 1100 West Second Street,
Zip 69154–6152; tel. 308/772–3283, (Nonreporting) **A**10 18
Primary Contact: Allen J. Gamble, Interim Chief Executive Officer
CFO: Jennifer Moffat, Staff Accountant
CMO: Steve Boyer, M.D., Chief Medical Officer
CHR: Ricca Sanford, Director Human Resources
CNO: Trish Davison, R.N., Chief Nursing Officer
Web address: www.gchealth.org
**Control**: County, Government, Nonfederal **Service**: General medical and surgical

**Staffed Beds**: 10

### OSMOND—Pierce County

★ **OSMOND GENERAL HOSPITAL (281347)**, 402 North Maple Street,
Zip 68765–5726, Mailing Address: P.O. Box 429, Zip 68765–0429;
tel. 402/748–3393, (Nonreporting) **A**10 18 **F**3 28 34 40 57 59 64 67 69 81 90
97 107 115 127 128 133 143
Primary Contact: Lon Knievel, Chief Executive Officer
CFO: Jodi Aschoff, Chief Financial Officer
CMO: David Mwebe, M.D., Chief of Staff
CNO: Kristen Colsden, Director of Nursing
Web address: www.osmondhospital.com
**Control**: Other not–for–profit (including NFP Corporation) **Service**: General
medical and surgical

**Staffed Beds**: 20 **Admissions**: 156 **Census**: 2 **Outpatient Visits**: 56992
**Births**: 0 **Total Expense ($000)**: 7741 **Payroll Expense ($000)**: 3037
**Personnel**: 58

### PAPILLION—Sarpy County

**ALEGENT CREIGHTON HEALTH MIDLANDS HOSPITAL** See Chi Health
Midlands

✉ **CHI HEALTH MIDLANDS (280105)**, 11111 South 84th Street, Zip 68046–4122;
tel. 402/593–3000, (Nonreporting) **A**1 2 3 5 10 **F**3 8 11 15 18 26 28 29 30 34
35 36 40 43 44 45 46 47 48 49 50 51 53 56 57 59 61 62 63 64 65 68 77
78 79 81 82 84 85 86 87 93 97 100 107 108 110 111 114 115 117 118 119
120 124 129 130 131 132 135 143 144 146 147 149 154 **P**8 **S** CommonSpirit
Health, Chicago, IL
Primary Contact: Kevin Miller, President
CFO: Tyler DeJong, Vice President, Operational Finance
CMO: Patricia Murdock-Langan, M.D., Chief Medical Officer
CIO: Thomas Haley, Information Technology Systems Site Director
CHR: Nancy Wallace, Division Senior Vice President, Chief Human Resource Officer
CNO: Brenda Bergman-Evans, Chief Nursing Officer
Web address: www.CHIhealth.com
**Control**: Church operated, Nongovernment, not–for–profit **Service**: General
medical and surgical

**Staffed Beds**: 28 **Admissions**: 626 **Census**: 5 **Outpatient Visits**: 42657
**Births**: 0 **Total Expense ($000)**: 35146 **Payroll Expense ($000)**: 9718
**Personnel**: 167

### PAWNEE CITY—Pawnee County

**PAWNEE COUNTY MEMORIAL HOSPITAL** See Pawnee County Memorial
Hospital and Rural Health Clinic

★ **PAWNEE COUNTY MEMORIAL HOSPITAL AND RURAL HEALTH CLINIC
(281302)**, 600 'I' Street, Zip 68420–3001, Mailing Address: P.O. Box 433,
Zip 68420–0433; tel. 402/852–2231, (Nonreporting) **A**10 18
Primary Contact: Ruth M. Stephens, MSN, R.N., Chief Executive Officer
CFO: Dawn Friesel, Director of Finance
CHR: Jennifer Bartels, Director Human Resources
CNO: Kelly Findlay, Director of Nurses
Web address: www.pawneehospital.com
**Control**: County, Government, Nonfederal **Service**: General medical and surgical

**Staffed Beds**: 11

*Many Facility Codes have changed. Please refer to the AHA Guide Code Chart.*   © 2021 AHA Guide

**NE**

## PENDER—Thurston County

★ **PENDER COMMUNITY HOSPITAL (281349)**, 100 Hospital Drive,
Zip 68047–0100, Mailing Address: P.O. Box 100, Zip 68047–0100;
tel. 402/385–3083, (Nonreporting) **A**10 18 **S** Trinity Health, Livonia, MI
Primary Contact: Melissa Kelly, Chief Executive Officer and Chief Financial Officer
CFO: Melissa Kelly, Chief Executive Officer and Chief Financial Officer
CMO: Matt Timm, M.D., Medical Director
CIO: Teresa Heise, Coordinator Management Information Systems
CHR: Nancy Suhr, Manager Human Resources
CNO: Katie Peterson, R.N., Chief Nursing Officer
Web address: www.pendercommunityhospital.com
**Control:** Hospital district or authority, Government, Nonfederal **Service:** General
medical and surgical

**Staffed Beds:** 61

## PLAINVIEW—Pierce County

**ALEGENT CREIGHTON HEALTH PLAINVIEW HOSPITAL** See Chi Health
Plainview

★ **CHI HEALTH PLAINVIEW (281346)**, 704 North Third Street, Zip 68769–2047,
Mailing Address: P.O. Box 489, Zip 68769–0489; tel. 402/582–4245,
(Nonreporting) **A**10 18 **S** CommonSpirit Health, Chicago, IL
Primary Contact: Gregory Beckmann, Regional President
CFO: Tim H. Schnack, Chief Financial Officer
CMO: Steve Peterson, M.D., Chief of Staff
CHR: Diane Blair, Human Resources and Admissions
CNO: Debra K Rutledge, R.N., Vice President Nursing Services
Web address: www.alegentcreighton.com/plainview-hospital
**Control:** Church operated, Nongovernment, not–for–profit **Service:** General
medical and surgical

**Staffed Beds:** 15

## RED CLOUD—Webster County

**WEBSTER COUNTY COMMUNITY HOSPITAL (281316)**, Sixth Avenue
and Franklin Street, Zip 68970–0465, Mailing Address: P.O. Box 465,
Zip 68970–0465; tel. 402/746–5600, (Nonreporting) **A**10 18
Primary Contact: Mirya Hallock, Administrator
CFO: Marcia Olson, Business Office Manager
CMO: Amy Springer, Medical Director
CHR: Marcia Olson, Business Office Manager
CNO: Candace Peters, R.N., Director of Nursing
Web address: www.websterhospital.org
**Control:** County, Government, Nonfederal **Service:** General medical and surgical

**Staffed Beds:** 13

## SAINT PAUL—Howard County

**HOWARD COUNTY COMMUNITY HOSPITAL** See Howard County Medical Center

★ **HOWARD COUNTY MEDICAL CENTER (281338)**, 1113 Sherman
Street, Zip 68873–1546, Mailing Address: P.O. Box 406, Zip 68873–0406;
tel. 308/754–4421, (Nonreporting) **A**3 10 18 **F**13 15 28 29 31 34 40 43 50 53
56 57 59 64 75 76 77 81 84 93 97 107 110 111 114 119 127 128 129 130
132 133 135 146 147 148 154 156 157
Primary Contact: Arlan D. Johnson, Chief Executive Officer
COO: Jillyn Klein, Chief Operating Officer
CFO: Morgan Meyer, Chief Financial Officer
CMO: Angela Brennan, M.D., Chief of Staff
CIO: Cheryl Watson, Chief Information Officer
CHR: Leslie Belzer, Director Human Resources
CNO: Janelle Morgan, Interim Director of Nursing
Web address: www.hcmc.us.com
**Control:** County, Government, Nonfederal **Service:** General medical and surgical

**Staffed Beds:** 16 **Admissions:** 239 **Census:** 2 **Outpatient Visits:** 23187
**Births:** 21 **Total Expense ($000):** 17451 **Payroll Expense ($000):** 7705
**Personnel:** 169

## SCHUYLER—Colfax County

**ALEGENT CREIGHTON HEALTH-MEMORIAL HOSPITAL, SCHUYLER** See Chi
Health Schuyler

★ **CHI HEALTH SCHUYLER (281323)**, 104 West 17th Street, Zip 68661–1304;
tel. 402/352–2441, (Nonreporting) **A**10 18 **S** CommonSpirit Health, Chicago, IL
Primary Contact: Connie Peters, R.N., President
CFO: Tim H. Schnack, Chief Financial Officer
CIO: Kenneth Lawonn, Senior Vice President and Chief Information Officer
CHR: Nancy Wallace, Vice President Human Resources
Web address: www.alegent.org
**Control:** Church operated, Nongovernment, not–for–profit **Service:** General
medical and surgical

**Staffed Beds:** 25

## SCOTTSBLUFF—Scotts Bluff County

⊠ △ **REGIONAL WEST MEDICAL CENTER (280061)**, 4021 Avenue 'B',
Zip 69361–4695; tel. 308/635–3711, (Nonreporting) **A**1 2 3 5 7 10
Primary Contact: John Mentgen, FACHE, President and Chief Executive Officer
CFO: Michael F Ickowski, Vice President and Chief Financial Officer
CMO: Lisa Scheppers, Chief Medical Officer
CIO: Montie Hodge, Vice President Information Technology and Chief Information
Officer
CHR: Brenda J Forge, Vice President, Human Resources
CNO: Connie Rupp, MSN, R.N., Executive Vice President and Chief Nursing Officer
Web address: www.rwhs.org
**Control:** Other not–for–profit (including NFP Corporation) **Service:** General
medical and surgical

**Staffed Beds:** 122

## SEWARD—Seward County

**MEMORIAL HEALTH CARE SYSTEM** See Memorial Health Care Systems

★ **MEMORIAL HEALTH CARE SYSTEMS (281339)**, 300 North Columbia Avenue,
Zip 68434–2228; tel. 402/643–2971, (Nonreporting) **A**10 18
Primary Contact: Roger J. Reamer, Chief Executive Officer
CFO: Greg Jerger, Chief Financial Officer
CMO: James Plasek, M.D., Chief of Staff
CIO: Mark Criner, Director Information Technology
CHR: Corey Mann, Director Human Resources
Web address: www.mhcs.us
**Control:** Other not–for–profit (including NFP Corporation) **Service:** General
medical and surgical

**Staffed Beds:** 24

## SIDNEY—Cheyenne County

**MEMORIAL HEALTH CENTER** See Sidney Regional Medical Center

★ **SIDNEY REGIONAL MEDICAL CENTER (281357)**, 1000 Pole Creek Crossing,
Zip 69162–1799; tel. 308/254–5825, (Total facility includes 63 beds in nursing
home–type unit) (Nonreporting) **A**10 18 **F**10 11 12 13 15 18 26 27 28 29 30 31
32 34 35 40 41 45 46 47 48 50 56 57 59 62 63 64 65 68 70 74 75 76 77 78
79 81 82 85 86 87 89 91 92 93 94 97 107 111 115 119 127 129 130 131
132 133 135 143 144 148 154 156 157 **P**6
Primary Contact: Jason Petik, Chief Executive Officer
CMO: Mandy Shaw, M.D., Chief of Staff
CIO: Jennifer Brockhaus, Chief Information Officer
CHR: Catherine T Arterburn, R.N., Vice President Human Resources
CNO: Julie A Slagle, R.N., MSN, Vice President Patient Care Services
Web address: www.sidneyrmc.com
**Control:** Other not–for–profit (including NFP Corporation) **Service:** General
medical and surgical

**Staffed Beds:** 88 **Admissions:** 575 **Census:** 57 **Outpatient Visits:** 40660
**Births:** 70 **Total Expense ($000):** 57271 **Payroll Expense ($000):** 24742
**Personnel:** 357

**NE**

**Hospital, Medicare Provider Number, Address, Telephone, Approval, Facility, and Physician Codes, Health Care System**

★ American Hospital Association (AHA) membership  ○ Healthcare Facilities Accreditation Program  ⇑ Center for Improvement in Healthcare Quality Accreditation
□ The Joint Commission accreditation  ◇ DNV Healthcare Inc. accreditation  △ Commission on Accreditation of Rehabilitation Facilities (CARF) accreditation

© 2021 AHA Guide  *Many Facility Codes have changed. Please refer to the AHA Guide Code Chart.*  Hospitals **A439**

## SUPERIOR—Nuckolls County

**BRODSTONE MEM HOSP** See Brodstone Memorial Hospital

★ **BRODSTONE MEMORIAL HOSPITAL (281315)**, 520 East Tenth Street,
Zip 68978–1225, Mailing Address: P.O. Box 187, Zip 68978–0187;
tel. 402/879–3281, (Nonreporting) **A**10 18 **F**8 11 13 15 17 28 29 30 34 35 40
41 45 50 57 59 64 65 70 74 75 76 77 79 81 82 85 86 87 89 93 94 97 100 107
110 111 115 116 119 127 129 130 131 132 133 135 143 146 148 154 156
Primary Contact: Treg Vyzourek, Chief Executive Officer
COO: Dena C Alvarez, R.N., COO & Chief Compliance Officer
CFO: Sandy Borden, Chief Financial Officer
CMO: Timothy Blecha, M.D., Medical Director
CIO: Tim Hiatt, Chief Information Officer
CHR: Beth A Schlichtman, Chief Human Resources Officer
CNO: Kori Field, Director of Nursing
Web address: www.brodstonehospital.org
**Control:** Other not–for–profit (including NFP Corporation) **Service:** General
medical and surgical

**Staffed Beds:** 25 **Admissions:** 434 **Census:** 5 **Outpatient Visits:** 18000
**Births:** 25 **Total Expense ($000):** 24325 **Payroll Expense ($000):** 10807
**Personnel:** 183

## SYRACUSE—Otoe County

**COMMUNITY MEMORIAL HOSPITAL** See Syracuse Area Health

★ **SYRACUSE AREA HEALTH (281309)**, 2731 Healthcare Drive, Zip 68446,
Mailing Address: P.O. Box N, Zip 68446–0518; tel. 402/269–2011, (Nonreporting)
**A**10 18 **F**3 8 11 15 28 29 34 35 37 40 41 43 45 47 48 50 53 57 59 65 74 75
77 78 79 81 82 85 87 89 91 92 93 94 96 97 107 110 115 119 126 127 128
129 130 131 133 146 148 154 156 157
Primary Contact: Michael Harvey, FACHE, President and Chief Executive Officer
CFO: Karrie Beach, Vice President Finance
CMO: James Steckelberg, M.D., Chief Medical Staff
CIO: Matthew Steinblock, Director Information Systems
CHR: Nancy R. Brack, Vice President Human Resources
CNO: Derek Greenwald, Chief Nursing Officer
Web address: www.syracuseareahealth.com
**Control:** Hospital district or authority, Government, Nonfederal **Service:** General
medical and surgical

**Staffed Beds:** 10 **Admissions:** 174 **Census:** 1 **Outpatient Visits:** 13794 **Births:** 0
**Total Expense ($000):** 21883 **Payroll Expense ($000):** 9040 **Personnel:** 137

## TECUMSEH—Johnson County

★ **JOHNSON COUNTY HOSPITAL (281350)**, 202 High Street, Zip 68450–2443,
Mailing Address: P.O. Box 599, Zip 68450–0599; tel. 402/335–3361,
(Nonreporting) **A**10 18 **F**3 8 15 18 28 31 34 35 36 40 43 45 47 56 57 59 62
64 65 68 75 77 78 79 81 82 89 91 93 97 107 114 115 119 127 128 129 130
133 135 144 147 148 154 156 **P**6
Primary Contact: Mary Kent, Administrator
CMO: Benjamin Biehl, M.D., Chief Medical Officer
CIO: Joseph Randall Stollar, Chief Information Officer
CHR: Susan Hessheimer, Director Human Resources
CNO: Matthew Snyder, R.N., Director of Nursing
Web address: www.jchosp.com
**Control:** County, Government, Nonfederal **Service:** General medical and surgical

**Staffed Beds:** 18 **Admissions:** 153 **Census:** 1 **Outpatient Visits:** 17761
**Births:** 0 **Total Expense ($000):** 16039 **Payroll Expense ($000):** 7241
**Personnel:** 108

## VALENTINE—Cherry County

★ **CHERRY COUNTY HOSPITAL (281344)**, 510 North Green Street,
Zip 69201–1932; tel. 402/376–2525, (Nonreporting) **A**10 18
Primary Contact: Kyle Kellum, Chief Executive Officer
CFO: Peggy Snell, Chief Finance Officer
CNO: Kathryn Renning, Director of Nursing
Web address: www.cherrycountyhospital.org
**Control:** County, Government, Nonfederal **Service:** General medical and surgical

**Staffed Beds:** 25

## WAHOO—Saunders County

**SAUNDERS COUNTY HLTH SERVICES** See Saunders Medical Center

★ **SAUNDERS MEDICAL CENTER (281307)**, 1760 County Road J,
Zip 68066–4152; tel. 402/443–4191, (Nonreporting) **A**10 18 **S** Bryan Health,
Lincoln, NE
Primary Contact: Julie A. Rezac, R.N., Chief Executive Officer
CFO: Chase Manstedt, Chief Financial Officer
CMO: Andrew Opp, M.D., Medical Chief of Staff
CIO: Carrie Stephens, Director Information Technology
CNO: Destiny Bader, Director of Nursing
Web address: www.saundersmedicalcenter.com
**Control:** County, Government, Nonfederal **Service:** General medical and surgical

**Staffed Beds:** 16

## WAYNE—Wayne County

★ **PROVIDENCE MEDICAL CENTER (281345)**, 1200 Providence Road,
Zip 68787–1299; tel. 402/375–3800, (Nonreporting) **A**10 18 **F**3 7 13 15 28 29
30 31 34 35 36 40 50 53 57 59 62 63 64 68 75 76 81 82 84 85 93 107 110
111 115 119 128 130 132 133 135 154
Primary Contact: James Frank, CPA, Chief Executive Officer
COO: Kristine A Giese, Chief Operating Officer
CFO: Kim Hixson, Vice President of Financial Officer and Chief Financial Officer
CNO: Nicole Haglund, Vice President of Nursing Services
Web address: www.providencemedical.com
**Control:** Other not–for–profit (including NFP Corporation) **Service:** General
medical and surgical

**Staffed Beds:** 21 **Admissions:** 366 **Census:** 4 **Outpatient Visits:** 14861
**Births:** 62 **Total Expense ($000):** 23035 **Payroll Expense ($000):** 9047
**Personnel:** 177

## WEST POINT—Cuming County

★ **ST. FRANCIS MEMORIAL HOSPITAL (281322)**, 430 North Monitor Street,
Zip 68788–1555; tel. 402/372–2404, (Nonreporting) **A**10 18 **S** Franciscan
Sisters of Christian Charity Sponsored Ministries, Inc., Manitowoc, WI
Primary Contact: David J. Ameen, Interim President and Chief Executive Officer
CFO: Alisa A. Brunsing, Chief Financial Officer
CMO: Thomas W. Cohee, M.D., Chief of Staff
CIO: Matt Sabus, Chief Information Officer
CHR: Terri Ridder, Director Human Resources
CNO: Dara Schlecht, Chief Nursing Officer
Web address: www.fcswp.org
**Control:** Church operated, Nongovernment, not–for–profit **Service:** General
medical and surgical

**Staffed Beds:** 88

## WINNEBAGO—Thurston County

**TWELVE CLANS UNITY HOSPITAL (280119)**, Highway 7577, Zip 68071;
tel. 402/878–2231, (Nonreporting) **A**10
Primary Contact: Danelle Smith, Chief Executive Officer
CFO: Audrey Parker, Budget Analyst
**Control:** PHS, Indian Service, Government, federal **Service:** General medical and
surgical

**Staffed Beds:** 30

**U. S. PUBLIC HEALTH SERVICE INDIAN HOSPITAL** See Twelve Clans Unity
Hospital

## YORK—York County

★ **YORK GENERAL (281336)**, 2222 North Lincoln Avenue, Zip 68467–1095;
tel. 402/362–6671, (Nonreporting) **A**10 18
Primary Contact: James P. Ulrich Jr, Chief Executive Officer
COO: Jenny Obermier, Senior Vice President, Chief Operating Officer and Chief
Nursing Officer
CFO: Bob McQuistan, Vice President Finance
CMO: Patrick Hotovy, M.D., Chief of Staff
CIO: Chris Kraft, Director Information Systems
CHR: Cathy Norquest, Director Human Resources
CNO: Jenny Obermier, Senior Vice President, Chief Operating Officer and Chief
Nursing Officer
Web address: www.yorkgeneral.org
**Control:** Other not–for–profit (including NFP Corporation) **Service:** General
medical and surgical

**Staffed Beds:** 154

**YORK GENERAL HOSPITAL** See York General

**NE**

# NEVADA

## BATTLE MOUNTAIN—Lander County

**BATTLE MOUNTAIN GENERAL HOSPITAL (291303)**, 535 South Humboldt Street, Zip 89820–1988; tel. 775/635–2550, (Nonreporting) **A**10 18
Primary Contact: Jason Bleak, Chief Executive Officer
CFO: Cindy Fagg, Fiscal Officer
CMO: Mark S. Meyers, M.D., Chief of Staff
CIO: Terry Dunn, Director Information Technology
CHR: Lori Sherbondy, Director Human Resources
CNO: Kelley Price, R.N., Chief Nursing Officer
Web address: www.bmgh.org
**Control:** Hospital district or authority, Government, Nonfederal **Service:** General medical and surgical

| Staffed Beds: 7 |
|---|

## BOULDER CITY—Clark County

**BOULDER CITY HOSPITAL (291309)**, 901 Adams Boulevard, Zip 89005–2213; tel. 702/293–4111, (Nonreporting) **A**10 18
Primary Contact: Thomas Maher, Chief Executive Officer and Administrator
COO: Rae Cummings, Chief Operating Officer
CFO: Douglas Lewis, Chief Financial Officer
CMO: Craig Jorgenson, M.D., Chief of Staff
CHR: Belinda McGraw, Director Human Resources
CNO: Andre Pastian, R.N., MSN, Chief Nursing Officer
Web address: www.bouldercityhospital.org
**Control:** Other not–for–profit (including NFP Corporation) **Service:** General medical and surgical

| Staffed Beds: 82 |
|---|

## CALIENTE—Lincoln County

**GROVER C. DILS MEDICAL CENTER (291312)**, 700 North Spring Street, Zip 89008, Mailing Address: P.O. Box 1010, Zip 89008–1010; tel. 775/726–3171, (Nonreporting) **A**10 18
Primary Contact: Melissa S. Rowe, Chief Executive Officer
CFO: Sherlyn Fackrell, Finance Controller
CMO: R William Katschke, M.D., JrMedical Director
CHR: Rozanne Mangum, Administrative Assistant and Director Human Resources
Web address: www.gcdmc.org
**Control:** Other not–for–profit (including NFP Corporation) **Service:** Other specialty treatment

| Staffed Beds: 20 |
|---|

## CARSON CITY—Carson City County

**CARSON TAHOE CONTINUING CARE HOSPITAL (292008)**, 775 Fleischmann Way, 2nd Floor, Zip 89703–2995; tel. 775/445–7795, (Nonreporting) **A**10 22 **F**1 3 29 68 85 130 148
Primary Contact: Cynthia Parker, R.N., Administrator and Director of Nursing
COO: Michelle L Joy, FACHE, Vice President, Chief Operating Officer
CFO: Ann Beck, Vice President and Chief Financial Officer
CMO: Jose Aguirre, M.D., Medical Director
CHR: Larry Fagerhaug
CNO: Cynthia Parker, R.N., Administrator and Director of Nursing
Web address: www.carsontahoe.com
**Control:** Other not–for–profit (including NFP Corporation) **Service:** Acute long–term care hospital

| Staffed Beds: 29 Admissions: 171 Census: 13 Outpatient Visits: 0 Births: 0 Total Expense ($000): 9052 Payroll Expense ($000): 3289 Personnel: 48 |
|---|

★ **CARSON TAHOE HEALTH (290019)**, 1600 Medical Parkway, Zip 89703–4625, Mailing Address: P.O. Box 2168, Zip 89702–2168; tel. 775/445–8672, (Includes SIERRA SURGERY HOSPITAL, Mailing address: 1400 Medical Parkway, Carson City, Nevada, Zip 89703–4624; tel. 775/883–1700; Ken Doran, Interim Chief Operating Officer), (Nonreporting) **A**2 3 10 22 **F**3 4 5 8 11 12 13 15 17 18 20 22 24 26 28 29 30 31 34 35 38 40 42 45 46 47 49 50 51 54 56 57 59 64 65 68 70 74 75 76 77 78 79 81 82 84 85 86 87 89 93 96 98 100 101 102 103 104 105 107 108 110 111 115 116 117 118 119 126 130 132 135 144 146 147 148 149 152 153 154 156 **P**6
Primary Contact: Alan H. Garrett, Chief Executive Officer
COO: Michelle L Joy, FACHE, Chief Operating Officer
CFO: Ann Beck, Vice President Finance
CMO: Jeffrey Sanders, M.D., Chief of Staff
CHR: Jim Lewandowski, Interim Director of Human Resources
CNO: Anna Anders, R.N., MSN, Vice President and Chief Nursing Officer
Web address: www.carsontahoe.com
**Control:** Other not–for–profit (including NFP Corporation) **Service:** General medical and surgical

| Staffed Beds: 211 Admissions: 12326 Census: 153 Outpatient Visits: 375347 Births: 1011 Total Expense ($000): 281499 Payroll Expense ($000): 94474 Personnel: 1580 |
|---|

**CARSON TAHOE REGIONAL HEALTHCARE** See Carson Tahoe Health

**CONTINUECARE HOSPITAL OF CARSON TAHOE** See Carson Tahoe Continuing Care Hospital

## ELKO—Elko County

**ELKO GENERAL HOSPITAL** See Northeastern Nevada Regional Hospital

⊠ **NORTHEASTERN NEVADA REGIONAL HOSPITAL (290008)**, 2001 Errecart Boulevard, Zip 89801–8333; tel. 775/738–5151, (Nonreporting) **A**1 3 10 20 **F**3 11 13 15 18 20 22 28 29 30 31 34 38 40 41 45 46 50 51 57 59 60 68 70 75 76 77 79 81 85 93 102 107 108 111 115 119 129 148 154 155 **S** LifePoint Health, Brentwood, TN
Primary Contact: Steve Simpson, Chief Executive Officer
CFO: Grant Trollope, Chief Financial Officer
CIO: Jeff Morgan, Director Information Systems
CHR: Laura Elliott, Director Human Resources
Web address: www.nnrhospital.com
**Control:** Corporation, Investor–owned (for–profit) **Service:** General medical and surgical

| Staffed Beds: 75 Admissions: 1809 Census: 12 Outpatient Visits: 46137 Births: 437 Total Expense ($000): 56679 Payroll Expense ($000): 20591 Personnel: 267 |
|---|

## ELY—White Pine County

⊠ **WILLIAM BEE RIRIE HOSPITAL (291302)**, 1500 Avenue 'H', Zip 89301–2699; tel. 775/289–3001, (Nonreporting) **A**1 10 18
Primary Contact: Matthew Walker, Chief Executive Officer and Administrator
CMO: G N Christensen, M.D., Chief Medical Officer
CIO: Destin Brandis, Chief Information Officer
CHR: Vicki Pereace, Manager Human Resources
Web address: www.wbrhely.org/getpage.php?name=index
**Control:** Hospital district or authority, Government, Nonfederal **Service:** General medical and surgical

| Staffed Beds: 25 |
|---|

NV

## FALLON—Churchill County

⊞ **BANNER CHURCHILL COMMUNITY HOSPITAL (291313)**, 801 East Williams Avenue, Zip 89406–3052; tel. 775/423–3151, (Nonreporting) **A**1 10 18 **F**3 7 11 13 15 29 31 34 35 40 41 45 47 50 59 64 65 68 70 75 76 79 81 85 86 87 89 93 97 107 110 111 115 119 127 129 130 146 149 154 **P**8 **S** Banner Health, Phoenix, AZ
Primary Contact: Robert H. Carnahan II, R.N., Chief Executive Officer
CFO: Steve Fraker, Chief Financial Officer
CMO: Tedd McDonald, M.D., Chief Medical Officer
CHR: Darlene Hanefeld, Chief Human Resources Officer
Web address: www.bannerhealth.com/churchill
**Control**: Other not-for-profit (including NFP Corporation) **Service**: General medical and surgical

**Staffed Beds: 25 Admissions: 1466 Census: 13 Outpatient Visits: 74908 Births: 320 Total Expense ($000): 53257 Payroll Expense ($000): 24513 Personnel: 347**

**CHURCHILL COMMUNITY HOSPITAL** See Banner Churchill Community Hospital

## GARDNERVILLE—Douglas County

★ **CARSON VALLEY MEDICAL CENTER (291306)**, 1107 Hwy 395, Zip 89410, Mailing Address: 1107 Highway 395, Zip 89410; tel. 775/782–1500, (Nonreporting) **A**3 10 18 **F**3 15 26 29 30 31 34 35 38 39 40 45 50 54 56 57 59 61 64 65 66 70 74 75 79 81 82 85 87 93 97 100 104 107 108 110 111 114 119 127 128 129 130 131 132 133 144 146 147 148 149 153 154 156 157 **S** Renown Health, Reno, NV
Primary Contact: Jeffrey Prater, Chief Executive Officer
COO: Shannon Albert, Chief Operating Officer
CFO: Colleen Reid, Chief Financial Officer
CMO: Evan Easley, M.D., Chief Medical Officer
CIO: Jason Roberts, Director Information System
CHR: Lisa Tremaine, Manager Human Resources
CNO: Kathy Cocking, R.N., Director of Clinical Services
Web address: www.cvmchospital.org
**Control**: Other not-for-profit (including NFP Corporation) **Service**: General medical and surgical

**Staffed Beds: 23 Admissions: 1170 Census: 12 Births: 0**

## HAWTHORNE—Mineral County

**MOUNT GRANT GENERAL HOSPITAL (291300)**, First and 'A' Street, Zip 89415, Mailing Address: P.O. Box 1510, Zip 89415–1510; tel. 775/945–2461, (Nonreporting) **A**10 18
Primary Contact: Hugh Qualls, Administrator
Web address: www.mgghnv.org/
**Control**: Other not-for-profit (including NFP Corporation) **Service**: General medical and surgical

**Staffed Beds: 35**

## HENDERSON—Clark County

⊞ **DIGNITY HEALTH REHABILITATION HOSPITAL (293035)**, 2930 Siena Heights Drive, Zip 89052; tel. 725/726–2000, (Nonreporting) **A**1 **S** Select Medical Corporation, Mechanicsburg, PA
Primary Contact: Linda Tautz, Chief Executive Officer
Web address: www.https://www.dignityhealthrehab.com
**Control**: Corporation, Investor-owned (for-profit) **Service**: Rehabilitation

**Staffed Beds: 60**

⊞ **ENCOMPASS HEALTH REHABILITATION HOSPITAL OF HENDERSON (293032)**, 10301 Jeffreys Street, Zip 89052–3922; tel. 702/939–9400, (Nonreporting) **A**1 10 **S** Encompass Health Corporation, Birmingham, AL
Primary Contact: Michael Ward, Chief Executive Officer
CFO: Robert Bollard, Chief Financial Officer
Web address: www.hendersonrehabhospital.com
**Control**: Corporation, Investor-owned (for-profit) **Service**: Rehabilitation

**Staffed Beds: 90**

**HEALTHSOUTH REHABILITATION HOSPITAL - HENDERSON** See Encompass Health Rehabilitation Hospital of Henderson

☐ **HENDERSON HOSPITAL (290057)**, 1050 West Galleria Drive, Zip 89011; tel. 702/963–7000, (Nonreporting) **A**1 3 10 **S** Universal Health Services, Inc., King of Prussia, PA
Primary Contact: Samuel Kaufman, Chief Executive Officer
COO: Ryan Tingey, Chief Operating Officer
CNO: Tina Coker, MSN, Chief Nursing Officer
Web address: www.hendersonhospital.com/
**Control**: Corporation, Investor-owned (for-profit) **Service**: General medical and surgical

**Staffed Beds: 145**

★ **KINDRED HOSPITAL LAS VEGAS-SAHARA (292002)**, 102 East Mead Parkway, 3rd Floor, Zip 89015; tel. 702/871–1418, (Includes KINDRED HOSPITAL-FLAMINGO, Mailing address: 2250 East Flamingo Road, Las Vegas, Nevada, Zip 89119; tel. 702/871–1418), (Nonreporting) **A**10 **S** Kindred Healthcare, Louisville, KY
Primary Contact: Bud Schawl, Chief Executive Officer
CFO: William Lysaght, Chief Financial Officer
CMO: Paul Stewart, M.D., Medical Director
CHR: Jim Sturgeon, Area Director Human Resources
Web address: www.kindredhospitallvs.com/
**Control**: Corporation, Investor-owned (for-profit) **Service**: Acute long-term care hospital

**Staffed Beds: 238**

**KINDRED HOSPITAL-LAS VEGAS** See Kindred Hospital Las Vegas-Sahara

**SEVEN HILLS BEHAVIORAL INSTITUTE** See Seven Hills Hospital

**SEVEN HILLS HOSPITAL (294012)**, 3021 West Horizon Ridge Parkway, Zip 89052–3990; tel. 702/646–5000, (Nonreporting) **A**3 10 **S** Acadia Healthcare Company, Inc., Franklin, TN
Primary Contact: Naomi Jones, Chief Executive Officer
CFO: Chantel Hughes, Chief Financial Officer
CMO: Jonathan Wirjo, M.D., Medical Director
CIO: Jessica Raub, Director Health Information Management
CHR: Teresa Sulit, Director of Human Resources
CNO: Rustin Park, Director of Nursing
Web address: www.sevenhillsbi.com
**Control**: Corporation, Investor-owned (for-profit) **Service**: Psychiatric

**Staffed Beds: 134**

⊞ **ST. ROSE DOMINICAN HOSPITALS - ROSE DE LIMA CAMPUS (290012)**, 102 East Lake Mead Parkway, Zip 89015–5524; tel. 702/616–5000, (Nonreporting) **A**1 10 **F**3 8 15 18 20 29 30 31 32 34 35 38 40 44 45 49 50 57 59 61 62 64 65 68 70 74 75 77 78 79 80 82 84 85 86 87 90 91 95 96 102 107 110 111 115 119 130 131 132 135 143 146 147 148 149 **S** CommonSpirit Health, Chicago, IL
Primary Contact: Tom Burns, Chief Operating Officer and Chief Nurse Executive
COO: Teressa Conley, Vice President and Chief Operating Officer
CFO: Kevin Walters, Chief Financial Officer
CMO: Stephen K Jones, M.D., Vice President Medical Staff Affairs
Web address: www.strosehospitals.org
**Control**: Church operated, Nongovernment, not-for-profit **Service**: General medical and surgical

**Staffed Beds: 10 Admissions: 1143 Census: 16 Outpatient Visits: 26216 Births: 0 Total Expense ($000): 74486 Payroll Expense ($000): 31662 Personnel: 121**

⊞ **ST. ROSE DOMINICAN HOSPITALS - SIENA CAMPUS (290045)**, 3001 St Rose Parkway, Zip 89052; tel. 702/616–5000, (Nonreporting) **A**1 3 5 10 **F**3 7 8 12 13 15 17 18 19 20 22 24 26 28 29 30 31 32 34 35 37 38 40 41 42 43 44 45 46 47 48 49 50 51 57 59 61 63 64 68 70 72 74 75 76 78 79 80 81 82 84 85 87 88 89 93 102 107 108 110 111 115 116 117 119 126 130 131 132 135 146 147 148 149 154 156 **S** CommonSpirit Health, Chicago, IL
Primary Contact: Lawrence Barnard, President and Chief Executive Officer
COO: Ryan Christensen, Chief Operatng Officer
CFO: Brian Kleven, Chief Financial Officer
CMO: G. Rodney Buzzas, M.D., Chief Medical Officer
CIO: Russ Patterson, Director Information Technology
CHR: Linda Gerstenberger, Vice President Human Resources
CNO: Beth Carlson, R.N., Chief Nurse Executive
Web address: www.strosehospitals.com
**Control**: Church operated, Nongovernment, not-for-profit **Service**: General medical and surgical

**Staffed Beds: 326 Admissions: 20041 Census: 261 Outpatient Visits: 93249 Births: 3281 Total Expense ($000): 472759 Payroll Expense ($000): 184702 Personnel: 1839**

## INCLINE VILLAGE—Washoe County

★ ○ **INCLINE VILLAGE COMMUNITY HOSPITAL (291301)**, 880 Alder Avenue, Zip 89451–8335; tel. 775/833–4100, (Nonreporting) **A**5 10 11 18 **S** Tahoe Forest Health System, Truckee, CA
Primary Contact: Judy Newland, R.N., Chief Nursing Officer
CFO: Crystal Betts, Chief Financial Officer
CIO: Mark Griffiths, Director Management Information Systems
CHR: Jayne O'Flanagan, Director Human Resources
Web address: www.tfhd.com
**Control**: Hospital district or authority, Government, Nonfederal **Service**: General medical and surgical

**Staffed Beds: 6**

**LAKESIDE COMMUNITY HOSPITAL** See Incline Village Community Hospital

*Many Facility Codes have changed. Please refer to the AHA Guide Code Chart.*   © 2021 AHA Guide

## LAS VEGAS—Clark County

**AMG SPECIALTY HOSPITAL** See Amg Specialty Hospital - Las Vegas

**AMG SPECIALTY HOSPITAL - LAS VEGAS (292007)**, 4015 Mcleod Drive, Zip 89121–4305; tel. 702/433–2200, (Nonreporting) **A**10 22 **S** AMG Integrated Healthcare Management, Lafayette, LA
Primary Contact: Phyllis Mauro, Chief Executive Officer
CMO: Anthony Pollard, D.O., Chief Medical Officer
Web address: www.amgihm.com/locations/#map_top
**Control:** Partnership, Investor–owned (for–profit) **Service:** Acute long–term care hospital

**Staffed Beds:** 24

**BHC MONTEVISTA HOSPITAL** See Montevista Hospital

**CENTENNIAL HILLS HOSPITAL MEDICAL CENTER (290054)**, 6900 North Durango Drive, Zip 89149–4409; tel. 702/835–9700, (Nonreporting) **A**1 3 10 **S** Universal Health Services, Inc., King of Prussia, PA
Primary Contact: Sajit Pullarkat, Chief Executive Officer and Managing Director
Web address: www.centennialhillshospital.com
**Control:** Corporation, Investor–owned (for–profit) **Service:** General medical and surgical

**Staffed Beds:** 165

**COLUMBIA SUNRISE HOSPITAL** See Sunrise Hospital and Medical Center

**COMPLEX CARE HOSPITAL AT TENAYA** See Pam Specialty Hospital of Las Vegas

**DESERT PARKWAY BEHAVIORAL HEALTHCARE HOSPITAL (294013)**, 3247 South Maryland Parkway, Zip 89109–2412; tel. 702/776–3500, (Nonreporting) **A**1 10 **F**4 5 64 93 98 99 100 101 102 103 104 105 130 132 134 151 152 153 154 **S** Signature Healthcare Services, Corona, CA
Primary Contact: Allison Zednicek, Chief Executive Officer
Web address: www.https://www.desertparkway.com/
**Control:** Hospital district or authority, Government, Nonfederal **Service:** Psychiatric

**Staffed Beds:** 152 **Admissions:** 4910 **Census:** 94 **Outpatient Visits:** 0
**Births:** 0

**DESERT SPRINGS HOSPITAL** See Desert Springs Hospital Medical Center

**DESERT SPRINGS HOSPITAL MEDICAL CENTER (290022)**, 2075 East Flamingo Road, Zip 89119–5121; tel. 702/733–8800, (Nonreporting) **A**1 3 10 **S** Universal Health Services, Inc., King of Prussia, PA
Primary Contact: Christopher Loftus, Chief Executive Officer
CFO: George Wiley, Chief Financial Officer
CMO: Golam Choudhury, Chief of Staff
CIO: Alan Woratschek, System Director of Information Services
CNO: Elena McNutt, Chief Nursing Officer
Web address: www.desertspringshospital.com
**Control:** Corporation, Investor–owned (for–profit) **Service:** General medical and surgical

**Staffed Beds:** 293

**DESERT WILLOW TREATMENT CENTER**, 6171 West Charleston Boulevard, Zip 89146–1126; tel. 702/486–8900, (Nonreporting) **A**3 5 **F**29 98 99 106 **P**6
Primary Contact: Jacqueline Wade, Ph.D., Director
Web address: www.dcfs.nv.gov/
**Control:** State, Government, Nonfederal **Service:** Children's hospital psychiatric

**Staffed Beds:** 20 **Admissions:** 142 **Census:** 15 **Outpatient Visits:** 0
**Births:** 0

**ENCOMPASS HEALTH REHABILITATION HOSPITAL OF DESERT CANYON (293033)**, 9175 West Oquendo Road, Zip 89148–1234; tel. 702/252–7342, (Nonreporting) **A**1 5 10 **S** Encompass Health Corporation, Birmingham, AL
Primary Contact: Peggy Nelson, Chief Executive Officer
CMO: Bevins Chue, M.D., Medical Director
CNO: Timothy Murphy, R.N., Chief Nursing Officer
Web address: www.healthsouthdesertcanyon.com
**Control:** Corporation, Investor–owned (for–profit) **Service:** Rehabilitation

**Staffed Beds:** 50

**ENCOMPASS HEALTH REHABILITATION HOSPITAL OF LAS VEGAS (293026)**, 1250 South Valley View Boulevard, Zip 89102–1861; tel. 702/877–8898, (Nonreporting) **A**1 10 **S** Encompass Health Corporation, Birmingham, AL
Primary Contact: Tij Von Nieda, Chief Executive Officer
CFO: Raymond Hardy, Controller
CMO: John D. Reneau, Medical Director
CHR: Cheryl Ballew, Human Resources Director
CNO: Susan Ramirez, Chief Nursing Officer
Web address: www.healthsouthlasvegas.com
**Control:** Corporation, Investor–owned (for–profit) **Service:** Rehabilitation

**Staffed Beds:** 79

**HARMON MEDICAL AND REHABILITATION HOSPITAL (290042)**, 2170 East Harmon Avenue, Zip 89119–7840; tel. 702/794–0100, (Nonreporting) **A**5 10 **S** Fundamental Long Term Care Holdings, LLC, Sparks Glencoe, MD
Primary Contact: Bonnie Essex. Hillegass, Chief Executive Officer
**Control:** Corporation, Investor–owned (for–profit) **Service:** Rehabilitation

**Staffed Beds:** 118

**HEALTHSOUTH DESERT CANYON REHABILITATION HOSPITAL** See Encompass Health Rehabilitation Hospital of Desert Canyon

**HEALTHSOUTH REHABILITATION HOSPITAL-LAS VEGAS** See Encompass Health Rehabilitation Hospital of Las Vegas

**HORIZON SPECIALTY HOSPITAL (292003)**, 640 Desert Lane, Zip 89106–4207; tel. 702/382–3155, (Nonreporting) **A**1 10 **S** Fundamental Long Term Care Holdings, LLC, Sparks Glencoe, MD
Primary Contact: Darrin Cook, Chief Executive Officer and Administrator
CFO: Darnell Bennett, Director Finance
CMO: Syed Rahman, M.D., Chief of Staff
CIO: Azena Ansi, Manager Health Information Management
CHR: Melvin Layugan, Director Human Resources
Web address: www.horizonspecialtyhosp.com/
**Control:** Corporation, Investor–owned (for–profit) **Service:** Acute long–term care hospital

**Staffed Beds:** 49

**MONTEVISTA HOSPITAL (294009)**, 5900 West Rochelle Avenue, Zip 89103–3327; tel. 702/364–1111, (Includes RED ROCK BEHAVIORAL HOSPITAL, Mailing address: 5900 West Rochelle Avenue, Las Vegas, Nevada, Zip 89103–3304, 5900 W Rochelle Ave, Zip 89103–3304, tel. 702/214–8099; Richard Failla, Chief Executive Officer), (Nonreporting) **A**1 3 10 **S** Strategic Behavioral Health, LLC, Memphis, TN
Primary Contact: Steve McCabe, Chief Executive Officer
CMO: William Bauer, M.D., Medical Director
CHR: Carol Nelson, Director Human Resources
Web address: www.montevistahospital.com
**Control:** Corporation, Investor–owned (for–profit) **Service:** Psychiatric

**Staffed Beds:** 202

**MOUNTAIN'S EDGE HOSPITAL** See Orthopedic Specialty Hospital of Nevada

**MOUNTAINVIEW HOSPITAL** See Mountainview Hospital

**MOUNTAINVIEW HOSPITAL (290039)**, 3100 North Tenaya Way, Zip 89128–0436; tel. 702/255–5000, (Nonreporting) **A**1 3 5 10 **S** HCA Healthcare, Nashville, TN
Primary Contact: Jeremy Bradshaw, Chief Executive Officer
CFO: Lana Arad, Chief Financial Officer
CMO: Jack Collier, M.D., Chief of Staff
CHR: Robert Nettles, Director Human Resources
CNO: Natalie Ransom, Chief Nursing Officer
Web address: www.mountainview-hospital.com
**Control:** Corporation, Investor–owned (for–profit) **Service:** General medical and surgical

**Staffed Beds:** 407

**ORTHOPEDIC SPECIALTY HOSPITAL OF NEVADA (290056)**, 8656 West Patrick Lane, Zip 89148–5043; tel. 702/777–7100, (Nonreporting) **A**1 10 **F**29 37 38 50 70 75 79 81 87 96 107 115 119 130 132 135 148
Primary Contact: Melissa War, Chief Nursing Officer
Web address: www.mountainsedgehospital.com/
**Control:** Corporation, Investor–owned (for–profit) **Service:** General medical and surgical

**Staffed Beds:** 130 **Admissions:** 1261 **Census:** 20 **Outpatient Visits:** 35
**Births:** 0 **Total Expense ($000):** 24129 **Payroll Expense ($000):** 7307

NV

**Hospital, Medicare Provider Number, Address, Telephone, Approval, Facility, and Physician Codes, Health Care System**

★ American Hospital Association (AHA) membership
☐ The Joint Commission accreditation
○ Healthcare Facilities Accreditation Program
◇ DNV Healthcare Inc. accreditation
⇑ Center for Improvement in Healthcare Quality Accreditation
△ Commission on Accreditation of Rehabilitation Facilities (CARF) accreditation

✠ **PAM REHABILITATION HOSPITAL OF CENTENNIAL HILLS (293034)**, 6166 North Durango Drive, Zip 89149; tel. 725/223–4100, (Nonreporting) **A**1 10 **S** Post Acute Medical, LLC, Enola, PA
Primary Contact: Samantha Billig, Chief Executive Officer
Web address: www.postacutemedical.com/facilities/find-facility/rehabilitation-hospitals/pam-rehabilitation-hospital-centennial-hills
**Control:** Partnership, Investor–owned (for–profit) **Service:** Rehabilitation

**Staffed Beds:** 44

✠ **PAM SPECIALTY HOSPITAL OF LAS VEGAS (292006)**, 2500 North Tenaya, Zip 89128–0482; tel. 702/562–2021, (Data for 92 days) (Nonreporting) **A**1 3 10 **F**1 3 29 96 107 119 148 **S** Post Acute Medical, LLC, Enola, PA
Primary Contact: Ryan Keele, Chief Executive Officer
CFO: Anna Rich, Chief Financial Officer
CMO: C Dean Milne, D.O., Medical Director
CNO: Robin Wolf, Chief Nursing Officer
Web address: www.https://postacutemedical.com/
**Control:** Partnership, Investor–owned (for–profit) **Service:** Acute long–term care hospital

**Staffed Beds:** 70 **Admissions:** 133 **Census:** 54 **Outpatient Visits:** 0 **Births:** 0

☐ **SANA BEHAVIORAL HOSPITAL (294014)**, 5975 West Twain Avenue, Zip 89103–1237; tel. 725/605–0310, (Nonreporting) **A**1
Primary Contact: Wendy Wood, Chief Executive Officer
Web address: www.https://sanabehavioralhospital.com/
**Control:** Corporation, Investor–owned (for–profit) **Service:** Psychiatric

**Staffed Beds:** 19

✠ **SOUTHERN HILLS HOSPITAL AND MEDICAL CENTER (290047)**, 9300 West Sunset Road, Zip 89148–4844; tel. 702/880–2100, (Nonreporting) **A**1 3 10 **S** HCA Healthcare, Nashville, TN
Primary Contact: Alexis Mussi, Chief Executive Officer
COO: Cullen Brown, Chief Operating Officer
CFO: Jennifer Le, Chief Financial Officer
CMO: Joseph C. Corcoran, D.O., Division Chief Medical Officer
CIO: Gary Sharp, Director Information Technology
CHR: Jennifer McDonnell, Director, Human Resources
CNO: Kelli Wray, Assistant Chief Nursing Officer
Web address: www.southernhillshospital.com
**Control:** Corporation, Investor–owned (for–profit) **Service:** General medical and surgical

**Staffed Beds:** 252

☐ **SOUTHERN NEVADA ADULT MENTAL HEALTH SERVICES (294002)**, 6161 West Charleston Boulevard, Zip 89146–1126; tel. 702/486–6000, (Nonreporting) **A**1 3 5 10 **F**38 50 59 75 86 87 98 104 106 127 130 132 135 146 149 153 154 158
Primary Contact: Chelsea Szklany, Hospital Administrator
Web address: www.mhds.state.nv.us
**Control:** State, Government, Nonfederal **Service:** Psychiatric

**Staffed Beds:** 274 **Admissions:** 2014 **Census:** 227 **Outpatient Visits:** 8050 **Births:** 0 **Total Expense ($000):** 90238 **Payroll Expense ($000):** 43984 **Personnel:** 802

☐ **SPRING MOUNTAIN SAHARA (294010)**, 5460 West Sahara, Zip 89146–3307; tel. 702/216–8900, (Nonreporting) **A**1 10 **F**29 56 98 103 130 149 153 **S** Universal Health Services, Inc., King of Prussia, PA
Primary Contact: Troy Mire, Chief Executive Officer
Web address: www.springmountainsahara.com
**Control:** Corporation, Investor–owned (for–profit) **Service:** Psychiatric

**Staffed Beds:** 30 **Admissions:** 851 **Census:** 22 **Outpatient Visits:** 2882 **Births:** 0 **Total Expense ($000):** 6625 **Payroll Expense ($000):** 3240 **Personnel:** 53

☐ **SPRING MOUNTAIN TREATMENT CENTER (294011)**, 7000 West Spring Mountain Road, Zip 89117–3816; tel. 702/873–2400, (Nonreporting) **A**1 10 **F**29 98 130 143 149 153 **S** Universal Health Services, Inc., King of Prussia, PA
Primary Contact: Troy Mire, Chief Executive Officer and Managing Director
CFO: Sherilene DeLeon, Chief Financial Officer
CMO: Jerome Nwokike, M.D., Medical Director
CNO: Norma Ferris, R.N., MS, Chief Nursing Officer
Web address: www.springmountaintreatmentcenter.com/
**Control:** Corporation, Investor–owned (for–profit) **Service:** Psychiatric

**Staffed Beds:** 110 **Admissions:** 4961 **Census:** 81 **Outpatient Visits:** 821 **Births:** 0 **Total Expense ($000):** 20978 **Payroll Expense ($000):** 9610 **Personnel:** 162

☐ **SPRING VALLEY HOSPITAL MEDICAL CENTER (290046)**, 5400 South Rainbow Boulevard, Zip 89118–1859; tel. 702/853–3000, (Nonreporting) **A**1 3 10 **S** Universal Health Services, Inc., King of Prussia, PA
Primary Contact: Leonard Freehof, Chief Executive Officer and Managing Director
COO: Matthew Wheelus, Chief Operating Officer
CFO: Carl Caley, Chief Financial Officer
CMO: S. Daniel, M.D., Chief Medical Officer
CHR: Angelique Ford, Administrator Human Resources
CNO: Margaret Covelli, R.N., Chief Nursing Officer
Web address: www.springvalleyhospital.com
**Control:** Corporation, Investor–owned (for–profit) **Service:** General medical and surgical

**Staffed Beds:** 169

**ST. ROSE DOMINICAN HOSPITALS - SAN MARTIN CAMPUS** See St. Rose Dominican Hospitals - San Martin Campus

✠ **ST. ROSE DOMINICAN HOSPITALS - SAN MARTIN CAMPUS (290053)**, 8280 West Warm Springs Road, Zip 89113–3612; tel. 702/492–8000, (Nonreporting) **A**1 5 10 **F**3 8 13 15 18 20 22 24 26 28 29 30 31 35 38 40 44 45 47 49 50 57 59 61 64 68 70 72 74 75 76 77 78 79 80 81 85 86 87 93 102 107 108 110 111 115 119 126 130 131 132 135 146 148 149 154 **S** CommonSpirit Health, Chicago, IL
Primary Contact: Kimberly Shaw, President and Chief Executive Officer
CFO: Dev Ramsamy, Chief Financial Officer
CMO: Robert Pretzlaff, M.D., Chief Medical Officer
CIO: Russ Patterson, Site Manager Information Technology
CHR: Linda Gerstenberger, Vice President Human Resources
CNO: Katherine Raymond, Chief Nursing Officer
Web address: www.strosehospitals.org
**Control:** Church operated, Nongovernment, not–for–profit **Service:** General medical and surgical

**Staffed Beds:** 147 **Admissions:** 7647 **Census:** 87 **Outpatient Visits:** 34491 **Births:** 1122 **Total Expense ($000):** 195415 **Payroll Expense ($000):** 69495 **Personnel:** 657

☐ **SUMMERLIN HOSPITAL MEDICAL CENTER (290041)**, 657 Town Center Drive, Zip 89144–6367; tel. 702/233–7000, (Nonreporting) **A**1 3 10 **S** Universal Health Services, Inc., King of Prussia, PA
Primary Contact: Robert S. Freymuller, Chief Executive Officer
Web address: www.summerlinhospital.com
**Control:** Corporation, Investor–owned (for–profit) **Service:** General medical and surgical

**Staffed Beds:** 148

**SUMMERLIN MEDICAL CENTER** See Summerlin Hospital Medical Center

✠ △ **SUNRISE HOSPITAL AND MEDICAL CENTER (290003)**, 3186 South Maryland Parkway, Zip 89109–2306, Mailing Address: P.O. Box 98530, Zip 89193; tel. 702/731–8000, (Nonreporting) **A**1 2 3 5 7 10 **S** HCA Healthcare, Nashville, TN
Primary Contact: Todd Sklamberg, President
COO: Mark J. Amox, Chief Operating Officer
CMO: Katherine Keeley, M.D., Chief of Staff
CIO: Alan Burt, Director Information Services
CNO: Cynthia J Johnson, R.N., Chief Nurse Officer
Web address: www.sunrisehospital.com
**Control:** Corporation, Investor–owned (for–profit) **Service:** General medical and surgical

**Staffed Beds:** 762

**UNIV MED CTR** See University Medical Center

✠ **UNIVERSITY MEDICAL CENTER (290007)**, 1800 West Charleston Boulevard, Zip 89102–2386; tel. 702/383–2000, (Includes CHILDREN'S HOSPITAL OF NEVADA AT UMC, Mailing address: 800 Hope Place, Las Vegas, Nevada, Zip 89106; tel. 702/383–2000), (Nonreporting) **A**1 2 3 5 10 **F**3 8 13 15 16 17 18 20 22 24 26 28 29 31 34 35 36 37 40 41 43 45 46 47 48 49 50 57 58 59 60 61 65 68 70 72 73 74 75 76 77 78 79 80 81 83 84 85 86 87 88 89 91 93 97 102 107 111 115 119 126 130 131 132 135 136 138 141 142 144 146 148 149 154 **P**5 6
Primary Contact: Mason VanHouweling, Chief Executive Officer
COO: Anthony Marinello, Chief Operating Officer
CFO: Jennifer Wakem, Chief Financial Officer
CIO: Lonnie Richardson, Chief Information Officer
CHR: Kurt Houser, Chief Human Resources Officer
CNO: Debra Fox, Chief Nursing Officer
Web address: www.umcsn.com
**Control:** County, Government, Nonfederal **Service:** General medical and surgical

**Staffed Beds:** 498 **Admissions:** 24228 **Census:** 354 **Outpatient Visits:** 453490 **Births:** 1762 **Total Expense ($000):** 686332 **Payroll Expense ($000):** 285628 **Personnel:** 3597

**NV**

*Many Facility Codes have changed. Please refer to the AHA Guide Code Chart.*
© 2021 AHA Guide

☐ **VALLEY HOSPITAL MEDICAL CENTER (290021)**, 620 Shadow Lane,
Zip 89106–4119; tel. 702/388–4000, (Nonreporting) **A**1 3 5 10 12 13 **S**
Universal Health Services, Inc., King of Prussia, PA
Primary Contact: Claude Wise, Chief Executive Officer
CFO: Betsy A Sponsler, Chief Financial Officer
CMO: Dost Wattoo, M.D., Chief of Staff
CIO: Tom Schoenig, Regional Director Information Services
CHR: Dana Thorne, Administrator Human Resources
Web address: www.valleyhospital.net
**Control**: Corporation, Investor–owned (for–profit) **Service**: General medical and
surgical

**Staffed Beds: 365**

**VANCE JOHNSON RECOVERY CENTER**, 2651 Westwood Drive,
Zip 89109–1117; tel. 888/828–2623, (Nonreporting) **S** Oglethorpe Recovery and
Behavioral Hospitals, Tampa, FL
Primary Contact: Dan Mager, Administrator
Web address: www.https://www.oglethorpeinc.com/vance-johnson-recovery-
center/
**Control**: Corporation, Investor–owned (for–profit) **Service**: Psychiatric

**Staffed Beds: 44**

**VEGAS VALLEY REHABILITATION HOSPITAL** See Southern Nevada Medical and
Rehabilitation Center

### LOVELOCK—Pershing County

★ **PERSHING GENERAL HOSPITAL (291304)**, 855 Sixth Street, Zip 89419,
Mailing Address: P.O. Box 661, Zip 89419–0661; tel. 775/273–2621,
(Nonreporting) **A**10 18
Primary Contact: Cynthia Hixenbaugh, Chief Executive Officer
CFO: Marjorie Skinner, Director Finance
CMO: Yousri Gadallah, M.D., Chief Medical Officer
CIO: Jim Weeldreyer, Manager Information Technology
Web address: www.pershinghospital.org
**Control**: Hospital district or authority, Government, Nonfederal **Service**: General
medical and surgical

**Staffed Beds: 38**

### MESQUITE—Clark County

☐ **MESA VIEW REGIONAL HOSPITAL (291307)**, 1299 Bertha Howe Avenue,
Zip 89027–7500; tel. 702/346–8040, (Nonreporting) **A**1 10 18 **S** Quorum Health,
Brentwood, TN
Primary Contact: Ned Hill, Chief Executive Officer
CFO: Mitchell Fransen, Chief Financial Officer
CHR: Steve Siegrist, Director of Human Resources
CNO: Leslie Woodson, Chief Nursing Officer
Web address: www.mesaviewhospital.com
**Control**: Corporation, Investor–owned (for–profit) **Service**: General medical and
surgical

**Staffed Beds: 25**

### NELLIS AFB—Clark County

⊠ **MIKE O'CALLAGHAN FEDERAL HOSPITAL**, 4700 Las Vegas Boulevard North,
Suite 2419, Zip 89191–6600; tel. 702/653–2000, (Nonreporting) **A**1 3 5 **S**
Department of the Air Force, Washington, DC
Primary Contact: Colonel Christian Benjamin, USAF, MC, Commander
COO: ColonelLinnes L Chester, USAF, MSC, Administrator
CFO: MajorKari Turkal-Barrett, Flight Commander Resource Management Officer
CMO: Lieutenant ColonelMarkham Brown, M.D., Chief Medical Staff
CIO: MajorKevin Seeley, Chief Information Officer
Web address: www.nellis.af.mil/
**Service**: General medical and surgical

**Staffed Beds: 46**

**NELLIS FEDERAL HOSPITAL** See Mike O'Callaghan Federal Hospital

### NORTH LAS VEGAS—Clark County

⇑ **LAKE MEAD HOSP MEDICAL CTR** See North Vista Hospital

⇑ **NORTH VISTA HOSPITAL (290005)**, 1409 East Lake Mead Boulevard,
Zip 89030–7197; tel. 702/649–7711, (Nonreporting) **A**10 21 **S** Prime Healthcare,
Ontario, CA
Primary Contact: Vincenzo Variale, Chief Executive Officer
CFO: Peter S Miller, Chief Financial Officer
CHR: Abayomi Fibiyi, Chief Human Resources Officer
Web address: www.northvistahospital.com
**Control**: Corporation, Investor–owned (for–profit) **Service**: General medical and
surgical

**Staffed Beds: 177**

**VA SOUTHERN NEVADA HEALTCARE** See Veterans Affairs Southern Nevada
Healthcare System

⊠ **VETERANS AFFAIRS SOUTHERN NEVADA HEALTHCARE SYSTEM**, 6900
North Pecos Road, Zip 89086–4400; tel. 702/791–9000, (Nonreporting) **A**1 3 5
**S** Department of Veterans Affairs, Washington, DC
Primary Contact: William J. Caron, Chief Executive Officer
CFO: Richard O Hays, Chief Fiscal Service
CMO: Ramanujam Komanduri, M.D., Chief of Staff
Web address: www.lasvegas.va.gov/
**Control**: Veterans Affairs, Government, federal **Service**: General medical and
surgical

**Staffed Beds: 90**

### PAHRUMP—Nye County

★ **DESERT VIEW HOSPITAL (291311)**, 360 South Lola Lane, Zip 89048–0884;
tel. 775/751–7500, (Nonreporting) **A**3 10 18 **F**3 15 29 34 37 40 45 46 56 57
59 81 85 107 108 110 111 114 119 133 148 154 **S** Universal Health Services,
Inc., King of Prussia, PA
Primary Contact: Susan Davila, Chief Executive Officer
CFO: Ryan Eggleston, Chief Financial Officer
CMO: Fredric Siegel, M.D., Chief of Staff
CIO: Chad Andres, Chief Information Officer
CHR: Lisa Doty, Manager Human Resources
CNO: Markeeta Araujo, Chief Nursing Officer
Web address: www.desertviewhospital.com
**Control**: Corporation, Investor–owned (for–profit) **Service**: General medical and
surgical

**Staffed Beds: 25 Admissions: 1687 Census: 13 Outpatient Visits: 53117
Births: 0 Total Expense ($000): 32473 Payroll Expense ($000): 12434
Personnel: 203**

**DESERT VIEW REGIONAL MEDICAL CENTER** See Desert View Hospital

### RENO—Washoe County

**BHC WEST HILLS HOSPITAL** See West Hills Hospital

**IOANNIS A LOUGARIS VA MED CTR** See Veterans Affairs Sierra Nevada Health
Care System

☐ **RENO BEHAVIORAL HEALTHCARE HOSPITAL (294015)**, 6940 Sierra
Center Parkway, Zip 89511; tel. 877/787–8518, (Nonreporting) **A**1 **S** Signature
Healthcare Services, Corona, CA
Primary Contact: Steve Shell, Chief Executive Officer
Web address: www.renobehavioral.com
**Control**: Corporation, Investor–owned (for–profit) **Service**: Psychiatric

**Staffed Beds: 124**

**NV**

**Hospital, Medicare Provider Number, Address, Telephone, Approval, Facility, and Physician Codes, Health Care System**

★ American Hospital Association (AHA) membership    ○ Healthcare Facilities Accreditation Program    ⇑ Center for Improvement in Healthcare Quality Accreditation
☐ The Joint Commission accreditation    ◇ DNV Healthcare Inc. accreditation    △ Commission on Accreditation of Rehabilitation Facilities (CARF) accreditation

© 2021 AHA Guide    *Many Facility Codes have changed. Please refer to the AHA Guide Code Chart.*    Hospitals **A445**

✠ **RENOWN REGIONAL MEDICAL CENTER (290001)**, 1155 Mill Street, Zip 89502–1576; tel. 775/982–4100, (Includes RENOWN CHILDREN'S HOSPITAL, Mailing address: 1155 Mill Street, Reno, Nevada, Zip 89502–1576, 1155 Mill Street - N11, Zip 89502–1576, tel. 775/982–4100; Larry Duncan, Vice President and Administrator Children's Hospital), (Nonreporting) **A**1 2 3 5 8 10 **F**3 5 11 13 15 17 18 19 20 21 22 23 24 25 26 27 29 30 31 32 34 35 40 41 43 44 45 46 48 49 54 56 57 58 59 61 62 63 65 66 68 70 72 73 74 75 76 77 78 79 80 81 84 85 86 87 88 89 92 100 101 102 107 108 111 114 115 118 119 120 121 123 124 126 130 132 135 146 148 149 **S** Renown Health, Reno, NV
Primary Contact: Erik Olson, Chief Executive Officer
COO: Dawn Ahner, Chief Operating Officer Acute Services
CFO: Katie Kucera, interim Chief Financial Officer Acute Services
CMO: Paul Sierzenski, M.D., Chief Medical Officer Acute Services
CIO: Ronald Fuschillo, Chief Information Officer
CHR: Michelle Sanchez-Bickley, Chief Human Resources Officer
CNO: Jennifer Richards, Ph.D., R.N., Chief Nursing Officer Acute Services
Web address: www.renown.org
**Control**: Other not–for–profit (including NFP Corporation) **Service**: General medical and surgical

**Staffed Beds**: 667 **Admissions**: 32215 **Census**: 495 **Outpatient Visits**: 613349 **Births**: 4527 **Total Expense ($000)**: 745584 **Payroll Expense ($000)**: 268273 **Personnel**: 4575

★ △ **RENOWN REHABILITATION HOSPITAL**, 1495 Mill Street, Zip 89502–1479; tel. 775/982–3500, (Nonreporting) **A**7 **F**29 54 77 82 90 93 95 96 148 149 **S** Renown Health, Reno, NV
Primary Contact: Chris Nicholas, Vice President and Administrator
COO: Dawn Ahner, Chief Operating Officer Acute Services
CFO: Ann Beck, Chief Financial Officer
CMO: Paul Sierzenski, M.D., Chief Medical Officer Acute Services
CIO: Ronald Fuschillo, Chief Information Officer
CHR: Michelle Sanchez-Bickley, Vice President Human Resources
CNO: Jennifer Richards, Ph.D., R.N., Chief Nursing Officer
Web address: www.renown.org
**Control**: Other not–for–profit (including NFP Corporation) **Service**: Rehabilitation

**Staffed Beds**: 62 **Admissions**: 824 **Census**: 32 **Outpatient Visits**: 29168 **Births**: 0 **Total Expense ($000)**: 23660 **Payroll Expense ($000)**: 12770 **Personnel**: 342

✠ **RENOWN SOUTH MEADOWS MEDICAL CENTER (290049)**, 10101 Double 'R' Boulevard, Zip 89521–5931; tel. 775/982–7000, (Nonreporting) **A**1 10 **F**10 12 28 29 30 35 38 40 44 46 68 70 74 75 79 81 82 85 87 92 93 97 107 108 111 119 130 131 146 157 **S** Renown Health, Reno, NV
Primary Contact: Chris Nicholas, Vice President and Administrator
COO: Dawn Ahner, Chief Operating Officer Acute Services
CFO: Ann Beck, Chief Financial Officer
CMO: Paul Sierzenski, M.D., Chief Medical Officer Acute Services
CIO: Ronald Fuschillo, Chief Information Officer
CHR: Michelle Sanchez-Bickley, Vice President Human Resources
CNO: Jennifer Richards, Ph.D., R.N., Chief Nursing Officer
Web address: www.renown.org
**Control**: Other not–for–profit (including NFP Corporation) **Service**: General medical and surgical

**Staffed Beds**: 76 **Admissions**: 4388 **Census**: 37 **Outpatient Visits**: 74678 **Births**: 0 **Total Expense ($000)**: 93503 **Payroll Expense ($000)**: 30374 **Personnel**: 381

**RIVERSIDE HOSP - SKILLED CARE** See Riverside Hospital Skilled Care

☐ **SAINT MARY'S REGIONAL MEDICAL CENTER (290009)**, 235 West Sixth Street, Zip 89503–4548; tel. 775/770–3000, (Nonreporting) **A**1 2 3 5 10 **F**13 15 17 18 20 22 24 26 28 29 30 31 34 40 41 44 50 54 57 58 60 64 65 68 70 72 74 75 76 77 78 79 81 82 84 85 86 89 93 98 100 103 107 110 111 114 115 117 118 119 120 121 123 124 126 130 132 143 146 148 149 154 **S** Prime Healthcare, Ontario, CA
Primary Contact: Tiffany Coury, Chief Executive Officer
CFO: John R Deakyne, Chief Financial Officer
CIO: Cindy Mullins, Director Information Technology
CHR: David Milovich, Vice President Human Resources
Web address: www.https://www.saintmarysreno.com/
**Control**: Corporation, Investor–owned (for–profit) **Service**: General medical and surgical

**Staffed Beds**: 305 **Admissions**: 13772 **Census**: 176 **Outpatient Visits**: 139611 **Total Expense ($000)**: 268174 **Payroll Expense ($000)**: 93333

**ST MARY'S REGIONAL MED CENTER** See Saint Mary's Regional Medical Center

☐ **VETERANS AFFAIRS SIERRA NEVADA HEALTH CARE SYSTEM**, 975 Kirman Avenue, Zip 89502–0993; tel. 775/786–7200, (Nonreporting) **A**1 3 5 **S** Department of Veterans Affairs, Washington, DC
Primary Contact: Lisa M. Howard, Director
COO: Lisa M Howard, Associate Director
CFO: Kelly Manson, Chief Financial Officer
CMO: Steven Brilliant, M.D., Chief of Staff
CIO: Jack Smith, Acting Chief Information Resources Management Service
CHR: Debbie Jenkins, Chief Human Resources Management Service
Web address: www.reno.va.gov/
**Control**: Veterans Affairs, Government, federal **Service**: General medical and surgical

**Staffed Beds**: 124

**WASHOE MED CTR REHAB HOSPITAL** See Renown Rehabilitation Hospital

**WASHOE MEDICAL CENTER** See Renown South Meadows Medical Center

**WASHOE MEDICAL CENTER** See Renown Regional Medical Center

☐ **WEST HILLS HOSPITAL (294003)**, 1240 East Ninth Street, Zip 89512–2964; tel. 775/323–0478, (Nonreporting) **A**1 3 10 **S** Universal Health Services, Inc., King of Prussia, PA
Primary Contact: Char Buehrle, Interim Chief Executive Officer
CMO: Philip Rich, M.D., Chief Medical Officer
CHR: Don Gay, Director Human Resources
Web address: www.westhillshospital.net
**Control**: Corporation, Investor–owned (for–profit) **Service**: Psychiatric

**Staffed Beds**: 190

**WILLOW SPRINGS CENTER**, 690 Edison Way, Zip 89502–4135; tel. 775/858–3303, (Nonreporting) **A**3 5 **F**98 99 106
Primary Contact: Andrew Herod, Chief Executive Officer
CFO: Chris Farley, Chief Financial Officer
CMO: Dana Arlien, M.D., Chief Medical Officer
CIO: Wallace Marsh, Director of Information Technology
CHR: Kristine Anglin, Human Resources Manager
CNO: Laurie MacAffee, Director of Nursing
Web address: www.willowspringscenter.com
**Control**: Corporation, Investor–owned (for–profit) **Service**: Children's hospital psychiatric

**Staffed Beds**: 116 **Admissions**: 351 **Census**: 71 **Outpatient Visits**: 159 **Births**: 0 **Total Expense ($000)**: 15961 **Payroll Expense ($000)**: 8408 **Personnel**: 162

**WILLOW SPRINGS RES TREATMENT** See Willow Springs Center

**SPARKS—Washoe County**

**NEVADA MENTAL HEALTH INSTITUTE** See Northern Nevada Adult Mental Health Services

☐ **NORTHERN NEVADA ADULT MENTAL HEALTH SERVICES (294000)**, 480 Galletti Way, Zip 89431–5564; tel. 775/688–2001, (Nonreporting) **A**1 3 5 10
Primary Contact: Cody Phinney, Administrator
CFO: Elizabeth O'Brien, Chief Financial Officer
CIO: Lois Repass, Quality Assurance Specialist and Coordinator Performance Improvement
Web address: www.mhds.state.nv.us/
**Control**: State, Government, Nonfederal **Service**: Psychiatric

**Staffed Beds**: 30

☐ ○ **NORTHERN NEVADA MEDICAL CENTER (290032)**, 2375 East Prater Way, Zip 89434–9641; tel. 775/331–7000, (Nonreporting) **A**1 10 11 **S** Universal Health Services, Inc., King of Prussia, PA
Primary Contact: Alan C. Olive, Chief Executive Officer
CFO: Ryan Heit, Chief Financial Officer
CHR: Patricia Downs, Director Human Resources
CNO: Carla Adams, Chief Nursing Officer
Web address: www.nnmc.com
**Control**: Corporation, Investor–owned (for–profit) **Service**: General medical and surgical

**Staffed Beds**: 108

⊞ **PAM SPECIALTY HOSPITAL OF SPARKS (292004)**, 2375 East Prater Way, Zip 89434–9641; tel. 775/355–5600, (Includes TAHOE PACIFIC HOSPITALS - WEST, Mailing address: 235 West Sixth Street, 5th Floor, Reno, Nevada, Zip 89503–4548; tel. 775/982–4100; TAHOE PACIFIC HOSPITALS, Mailing address: 10101 Double R Boulevard, Reno, Nevada, Zip 89521–5931; tel. 775/331–1044) (Data for 92 days)**A1** 10 **F1** 12 29 74 79 120 148 154 **S** Post Acute Medical, LLC, Enola, PA
Primary Contact: Gary Brooks, Chief Executive Officer
COO: Gary Brooks, Chief Operating Officer
Web address: www.https://postacutemedical.com/
**Control:** Partnership, Investor–owned (for–profit) **Service:** Acute long–term care hospital

**Staffed Beds:** 21 **Admissions:** 70 **Census:** 20 **Outpatient Visits:** 0 **Births:** 0
**Total Expense ($000):** 3163 **Payroll Expense ($000):** 1485 **Personnel:** 94

**SPARKS FAMILY HOSPITAL** See Northern Nevada Medical Center

**TAHOE PACIFIC HOSPITALS** See Pam Specialty Hospital of Sparks

## WINNEMUCCA—Humboldt County

★ **HUMBOLDT GENERAL HOSPITAL (291308)**, 118 East Haskell Street, Zip 89445–3299; tel. 775/623–5222, (Nonreporting) **A3** 5 10 18
Primary Contact: Karen S. Cole, MS, FACHE, Interim Chief Executive Officer
CFO: Sandi Lehman, Chief Financial Officer
CMO: Brad Granath, M.D., Chief of Staff
CHR: Rose Marie Green, Director Human Resources
CNO: Darlene Bryan, R.N., Chief Nursing Officer
Web address: www.hghospital.org
**Control:** Hospital district or authority, Government, Nonfederal **Service:** General medical and surgical

**Staffed Beds:** 67

## YERINGTON—Lyon County

**SOUTH LYON MED CENTER** See South Lyon Medical Center

**SOUTH LYON MEDICAL CENTER (291314)**, 213 South Whitacre, Zip 89447–2561, Mailing Address: P.O. Box 940, Zip 89447–0940; tel. 775/463–2301, (Nonreporting) **A10** 18
Primary Contact: Toni A. Inserra, Interim Administrator
Web address: www.southlyonmedicalcenter.org
**Control:** Other not–for–profit (including NFP Corporation) **Service:** General medical and surgical

**Staffed Beds:** 63

**NV**

Hospital, Medicare Provider Number, Address, Telephone, Approval, Facility, and Physician Codes, Health Care System

★ American Hospital Association (AHA) membership  ○ Healthcare Facilities Accreditation Program  ⇑ Center for Improvement in Healthcare Quality Accreditation
□ The Joint Commission accreditation  ○ DNV Healthcare Inc. accreditation  △ Commission on Accreditation of Rehabilitation Facilities (CARF) accreditation

© 2021 AHA Guide    *Many Facility Codes have changed. Please refer to the AHA Guide Code Chart.*    Hospitals  **A447**

# NEW HAMPSHIRE

## BERLIN—Coos County

★ **ANDROSCOGGIN VALLEY HOSPITAL (301310)**, 59 Page Hill Road, Zip 03570–3531; tel. 603/752–2200, (Nonreporting) **A**10 18 **F**3 8 11 12 13 15 17 28 29 30 34 40 41 45 47 57 59 61 64 67 68 70 74 75 76 77 79 81 82 85 89 92 93 102 107 108 110 115 119 128 129 130 131 132 133 146 147 149 156 **P**6 **S** QHR Health, Brentwood, TN
Primary Contact: Michael Peterson, FACHE, President
CFO: Jeremy Roberge, Director Reimbursement
CMO: Keith M Shute, M.D., Senior Vice President Medical Affairs and Clinical Services
CIO: Linda M Laperle, Vice President Administrative Services
CHR: James A Wheeler, Vice President Human Relations and Community Development
Web address: www.avhnh.com
**Control**: Other not–for–profit (including NFP Corporation) **Service**: General medical and surgical

**Staffed Beds**: 25 **Admissions**: 1125 **Census**: 12 **Outpatient Visits**: 73565
**Births**: 84 **Total Expense ($000)**: 59372 **Payroll Expense ($000)**: 25365
**Personnel**: 315

## CLAREMONT—Sullivan County

★ **VALLEY REGIONAL HOSPITAL (301308)**, 243 Elm Street, Zip 03743–4921; tel. 603/542–7771, (Nonreporting) **A**10 18 **F**3 11 14 15 28 29 31 34 35 38 40 43 45 49 50 54 57 59 64 68 75 77 79 81 83 84 85 87 93 97 107 110 114 118 119 130 131 132 133 135 144 146 147 149 154 156 157 **P**6
Primary Contact: Deanna S. Howard, Interim President and Chief Executive Officer
CFO: Jean Shaw, Chief Financial Officer
CMO: Oliver Herfort, M.D., Chief Medical Officer
CIO: Patricia Witthaus, Director Information Services
CHR: Cheryl Cavanaugh, Senior Director Human Resources
Web address: www.vrh.org
**Control**: Other not–for–profit (including NFP Corporation) **Service**: General medical and surgical

**Staffed Beds**: 25 **Admissions**: 653 **Census**: 10 **Outpatient Visits**: 76590
**Births**: 0 **Total Expense ($000)**: 44130 **Payroll Expense ($000)**: 18795
**Personnel**: 287

## COLEBROOK—Coos County

★ **UPPER CONNECTICUT VALLEY HOSPITAL (301300)**, 181 Corliss Lane, Zip 03576–3207; tel. 603/237–4971, (Nonreporting) **A**10 18 **S** QHR Health, Brentwood, TN
Primary Contact: Scott Colby, President and Chief Executive Officer
CFO: Celeste Pitts, Chief Financial Officer
CMO: Edward Laverty, Chief Medical Officer
CIO: Heather Pollard-Leighton, Director of Administrative Services
CHR: Heidi L Saari, Director, Human Resources
CNO: Lindsay Lea, Chief Nursing Officer
Web address: www.ucvh.org
**Control**: Other not–for–profit (including NFP Corporation) **Service**: General medical and surgical

**Staffed Beds**: 12

## CONCORD—Merrimack County

★ ⇑ **CONCORD HOSPITAL (300001)**, 250 Pleasant Street, Zip 03301–2598; tel. 603/225–2711, (Nonreporting) **A**2 3 5 10 21 **F**3 8 13 14 15 17 18 20 22 24 26 28 29 30 31 34 35 37 38 39 40 43 44 45 46 47 49 50 51 54 55 56 57 58 59 61 64 65 66 68 70 71 73 74 75 76 77 78 79 80 81 82 83 84 85 86 87 89 92 93 97 98 100 101 102 104 105 107 108 110 111 114 115 116 117 118 119 120 121 123 124 126 129 130 132 134 135 144 145 146 147 148 149 150 152 153 154 156 157 **P**6
Primary Contact: Robert P. Steigmeyer, President and Chief Executive Officer
COO: Timothy P. Jones, Chief Operating Officer
CFO: Bruce R. Burns, Chief Financial Officer
CMO: David F. Green, M.D., Chief Medical Officer
CIO: Deane Morrison, Chief Information Officer
CHR: Robin A. Moore, Chief Human Resources Officer
Web address: www.concordhospital.org
**Control**: Other not–for–profit (including NFP Corporation) **Service**: General medical and surgical

**Staffed Beds**: 245 **Admissions**: 12731 **Census**: 154 **Outpatient Visits**: 523456 **Births**: 1317 **Total Expense ($000)**: 507799 **Payroll Expense ($000)**: 248389 **Personnel**: 3208

---

⊞ **ENCOMPASS HEALTH REHABILITATION HOSPITAL OF CONCORD (303027)**, 254 Pleasant Street, Zip 03301–2508; tel. 603/226–9800, (Nonreporting) **A**1 10 **F**28 29 34 35 50 56 64 74 78 79 82 86 87 90 91 93 95 96 130 132 135 148 149 **S** Encompass Health Corporation, Birmingham, AL
Primary Contact: Diana Lachapelle, CPA, Chief Executive Officer
CMO: Muhammad Salmanullah, Chief Medical Director
CHR: Myra Nixon, Director Human Resources
CNO: Joseph Adamski, Chief Nursing Officer
Web address: www.healthsouthrehabconcordnh.com
**Control**: Corporation, Investor–owned (for–profit) **Service**: Rehabilitation

**Staffed Beds**: 50 **Admissions**: 1196 **Census**: 42 **Outpatient Visits**: 4734
**Births**: 0 **Total Expense ($000)**: 17161 **Payroll Expense ($000)**: 10139
**Personnel**: 150

**HEALTHSOUTH REHABILITATION HOSPITAL** See Encompass Health Rehabilitation Hospital of Concord

☐ **NEW HAMPSHIRE HOSPITAL (304000)**, 36 Clinton Street, Zip 03301–2359; tel. 603/271–5300, (Nonreporting) **A**1 3 5 10 **F**3 29 30 32 35 44 50 53 56 57 58 59 65 74 75 86 87 91 98 99 101 102 103 130 132 135 146 149
Primary Contact: Heather Moquin, Chief Executive Officer
COO: Geoffrey C Souther, Chief Operating Officer
CFO: Jamie Dall, Chief Financial Officer
CIO: David Levesque, Director, Information Systems
CHR: Mark Bussiere, Administrator Human Resources
CNO: Roberta A Vitale-Nolen, Administrator, Patient Care Services
Web address: www.dhhs.nh.gov/dcbcs/nhh/
**Control**: State, Government, Nonfederal **Service**: Psychiatric

**Staffed Beds**: 168 **Admissions**: 1185 **Census**: 159 **Outpatient Visits**: 0
**Births**: 0 **Total Expense ($000)**: 75182 **Payroll Expense ($000)**: 33575
**Personnel**: 616

## DERRY—Rockingham County

**HCA PARKLAND MEDICAL CENTER** See Parkland Medical Center

⊞ **PARKLAND MEDICAL CENTER (300017)**, One Parkland Drive, Zip 03038–2750; tel. 603/432–1500, (Nonreporting) **A**1 2 10 **S** HCA Healthcare, Nashville, TN
Primary Contact: John Skevington, Chief Executive Officer
CFO: Jacob Wisemann, Chief Financial Officer
CMO: Edward Yourtee, M.D., Chief Medical Officer
CIO: Brad George, Director Information Systems
CHR: Molly Lahti, Director Human Resources
CNO: Eileen Keefe, Chief Nursing Officer
Web address: www.parklandmedicalcenter.com
**Control**: Corporation, Investor–owned (for–profit) **Service**: General medical and surgical

**Staffed Beds**: 86

## DOVER—Strafford County

⊞ **WENTWORTH-DOUGLASS HOSPITAL (300018)**, 789 Central Avenue, Zip 3820; tel. 603/742–5252, (Nonreporting) **A**1 2 10 **F**3 5 8 12 13 17 18 19 20 22 26 28 29 30 31 32 34 35 36 38 39 40 41 43 44 45 46 47 48 49 50 51 52 53 54 55 57 58 59 61 63 64 65 68 70 73 74 75 76 77 78 79 81 82 84 85 86 87 89 91 92 93 94 96 97 100 101 102 104 107 108 111 114 115 118 119 120 121 123 124 126 129 130 131 132 134 135 143 144 145 146 147 148 149 154 156 **P**6 8 **S** Mass General Brigham, Boston, MA
Primary Contact: Gregory J. Walker, Chief Executive Officer
COO: Jeffrey B Hughes, Chief Operating Officer
CFO: Peter Walcek, Vice President Finance
CMO: Paul Cass, D.O., Chief Medical & Clinical Integration Officer
CIO: Jeffrey Pollock, Chief Information Officer
CHR: Erin J Flanigan, Vice President Human Resources
CNO: Sheila Woolley, R.N., M.P.H., Vice President, Patient Care Services
Web address: www.wdhospital.com
**Control**: Other not–for–profit (including NFP Corporation) **Service**: General medical and surgical

**Staffed Beds**: 142 **Admissions**: 8265 **Census**: 89 **Outpatient Visits**: 343487 **Births**: 1306 **Total Expense ($000)**: 330530 **Payroll Expense ($000)**: 137080 **Personnel**: 2563

*Many Facility Codes have changed. Please refer to the AHA Guide Code Chart.*
© 2021 AHA Guide

## EXETER—Rockingham County

★ ⇑ **EXETER HOSPITAL (300023)**, 5 Alumni Drive, Zip 03833–2128; tel. 603/778–7311, (Nonreporting) **A**2 5 10 21 **F**3 8 13 14 15 18 20 22 26 28 29 30 31 34 35 37 38 40 43 44 45 46 47 48 49 50 51 52 54 55 57 58 59 64 70 74 75 76 77 78 79 80 81 84 85 86 87 89 93 107 108 110 111 114 115 117 118 119 120 121 123 124 126 129 130 131 132 135 143 144 145 146 147 148 149 156
Primary Contact: Kevin J. Callahan, President and Chief Executive Officer
CFO: Kevin J O'Leary, Senior Vice President and Chief Financial Officer
CMO: Richard Hollister, President of Medical Staff
CIO: David Briden, Chief Information Officer
CHR: Christopher M Callahan, Vice President Human Resources
CNO: Susan Burns-Tisdale, Senior Vice President Clinical Operations, Interim CNO
Web address: www.ehr.org
**Control**: Other not–for–profit (including NFP Corporation) **Service**: General medical and surgical

**Staffed Beds**: 99 **Admissions**: 5362 **Census**: 57 **Outpatient Visits**: 219204
**Births**: 548 **Total Expense ($000)**: 240448 **Payroll Expense ($000)**: 86561
**Personnel**: 1082

## FRANKLIN—Merrimack County

★ ⇑ **FRANKLIN REGIONAL HOSPITAL (301306)**, 15 Aiken Avenue, Zip 03235–1299; tel. 603/934–2060, (Nonreporting) **A**10 18 21 **F**3 5 11 15 18 29 30 32 34 35 40 44 50 59 61 64 65 68 74 75 77 79 84 85 87 93 97 98 100 101 102 107 110 119 127 130 132 133 135 146 147 148 149 154 156 157 **P**4 **S** LRGHealthcare, Laconia, NH
Primary Contact: Kevin Donovan, FACHE, President and Chief Executive Officer
CFO: Henry D Lipman, Senior Vice President, Financial Strategy and External Relations
CMO: Peter Doane, M.D., Chief Medical Officer
CIO: Kevin Irish, Chief Information Officer
CHR: Cass Walker, Vice President Administrative & Support Services
CNO: Patti Strohla, R.N., Chief Nursing Officer
Web address: www.lrgh.org
**Control**: Other not–for–profit (including NFP Corporation) **Service**: General medical and surgical

**Staffed Beds**: 31 **Admissions**: 834 **Census**: 10 **Outpatient Visits**: 62681
**Births**: 0 **Total Expense ($000)**: 21487 **Payroll Expense ($000)**: 9859
**Personnel**: 128

## HAMPSTEAD—Rockingham County

☐ **HAMPSTEAD HOSPITAL (304001)**, 218 East Road, Zip 03841–2305; tel. 603/329–5311, (Nonreporting) **A**1 10
Primary Contact: Phillip J. Kubiak, President
COO: Cynthia A Gove, Chief Operating Officer
CFO: Cherie Clough-Berry, Vice President, Finance
CMO: Michael Knight, M.D., Medical Director
CIO: Sandra J Lucia, Director Health Information and Corporate Compliance Officer
CHR: Lisa M Ryan, Coordinator Human Resources
CNO: Julie D'Apollo, R.N., Director of Nursing
Web address: www.hampsteadhospital.com
**Control**: Corporation, Investor–owned (for–profit) **Service**: Psychiatric

**Staffed Beds**: 60

## KEENE—Cheshire County

⊞ **CHESHIRE MEDICAL CENTER (300019)**, 580 Court Street, Zip 03431–1718; tel. 603/354–5400, (Nonreporting) **A**1 3 5 10 **F**3 5 13 15 18 28 29 30 31 34 35 36 38 40 41 44 45 46 49 50 54 55 56 57 58 59 64 65 68 70 74 75 76 77 78 79 80 81 82 84 85 86 87 89 90 91 92 93 96 97 100 104 107 108 110 111 115 118 119 120 121 123 130 131 132 133 135 144 146 147 148 149 154 156
Primary Contact: Don Caruso, M.D., Chief Executive Officer and President
CMO: Don Caruso, M.D., Chief Medical Officer
CIO: Peter Malloy, Chief Information Officer
CHR: Julie Green, Vice President Human Resources
CNO: Cynthia Coughlin, MS, R.N., Chief Nursing Officer
Web address: www.cheshire-med.com
**Control**: Other not–for–profit (including NFP Corporation) **Service**: General medical and surgical

**Staffed Beds**: 94 **Admissions**: 4540 **Census**: 61 **Outpatient Visits**: 435752
**Births**: 390 **Total Expense ($000)**: 218768 **Payroll Expense ($000)**: 107706 **Personnel**: 1283

## LACONIA—Belknap County

★ ⇑ **LAKES REGION GENERAL HOSPITAL (300005)**, 80 Highland Street, Zip 03246–3298; tel. 603/524–3211, (Nonreporting) **A**10 21 **F**3 5 8 11 12 15 28 29 30 31 32 33 34 35 37 39 40 44 45 47 49 50 53 54 56 59 61 64 65 68 70 74 75 77 78 79 81 84 85 87 93 94 97 98 100 102 103 107 108 110 115 118 119 126 129 130 131 132 133 135 146 147 148 149 154 156 157 **S** LRGHealthcare, Laconia, NH
Primary Contact: Kevin Donovan, FACHE, President and Chief Executive Officer
CMO: Peter Doane, M.D., Chief Medical Officer
CIO: Kevin Irish, Chief Information Officer
CHR: Cass Walker, Vice President Administrative & Support Services
Web address: www.lrgh.org
**Control**: Other not–for–profit (including NFP Corporation) **Service**: General medical and surgical

**Staffed Beds**: 82 **Admissions**: 3618 **Census**: 42 **Outpatient Visits**: 301844
**Births**: 0 **Total Expense ($000)**: 204725 **Payroll Expense ($000)**: 83680
**Personnel**: 960

## LANCASTER—Coos County

★ **WEEKS MEDICAL CENTER (301303)**, 173 Middle Street, Zip 03584–3508; tel. 603/788–4911, (Nonreporting) **A**10 18 **S** QHR Health, Brentwood, TN
Primary Contact: Michael Lee, President
CMO: Lars Nielson, M.D., Chief Medical Officer
CIO: Darrell Bodnar, Director Information
CHR: Linda Rexford, Director Human Resources
CNO: Donna Walker, Chief Nurse Executive
Web address: www.weeksmedical.org
**Control**: Other not–for–profit (including NFP Corporation) **Service**: General medical and surgical

**Staffed Beds**: 25

**WEEKS MEDICAL HOSPITAL** See Weeks Medical Center

## LEBANON—Grafton County

★ **ALICE PECK DAY MEMORIAL HOSPITAL (301305)**, 10 Alice Peck Day Drive, Zip 03766–2650; tel. 603/448–3121, (Nonreporting) **A**5 10 18 **F**3 10 15 29 34 35 36 39 40 41 45 50 54 56 57 59 64 65 75 77 79 81 82 85 92 93 97 107 110 111 112 115 119 125 128 129 130 133 135 146 147 148 154 **P**6
Primary Contact: Susan E. Mooney, M.D., MS, President and Chief Executive Officer
CFO: Evalie M Crosby, CPA, Vice President Finance and Chief Financial Officer
CMO: Michael T. Lynch, M.D., Chief Medical Officer
CIO: Kristin Kneisel, Interim Director, Information Services
CNO: Barbra Brown, MS, R.N., Interim Chief Nursing Officer and Vice President of Nursing
Web address: www.alicepeckday.org
**Control**: Other not–for–profit (including NFP Corporation) **Service**: General medical and surgical

**Staffed Beds**: 23 **Admissions**: 851 **Census**: 5 **Outpatient Visits**: 117737
**Births**: 0 **Total Expense ($000)**: 74229 **Payroll Expense ($000)**: 37297
**Personnel**: 401

**CHILDREN'S HOSPITAL AT DARTMOUTH** See Children's Hospital at Dartmouth-Hitchcock

⊞ **DARTMOUTH-HITCHCOCK MEDICAL CENTER (300003)**, One Medical Center Drive, Zip 03756–0001; tel. 603/650–5000, (Includes CHILDREN'S HOSPITAL AT DARTMOUTH-HITCHCOCK, Mailing address: One Medical Center Drive, Lebanon, New Hampshire, Zip 3756; tel. 603/650–5000), (Nonreporting) **A**1 3 5 8 10 **F**3 5 6 7 8 9 11 12 13 14 15 17 18 19 20 21 22 23 24 25 26 27 28 29 30 31 32 33 34 35 36 37 38 39 40 41 43 44 45 46 47 48 49 50 51 52 53 54 55 56 57 58 59 60 61 63 64 65 66 68 70 71 72 74 75 76 77 78 79 80 81 82 83 84 85 86 87 88 89 91 92 93 94 96 97 98 99 100 101 102 103 104 107 108 110 111 112 114 115 116 117 118 119 120 121 123 124 126 129 130 131 132 134 135 136 138 141 142 143 145 146 147 148 149 150 153 154 155 156 157 **P**6
Primary Contact: Joanne M. Conroy, M.D., President and Chief Executive Officer
COO: Patrick Jordan IIIChief Operating Officer
CFO: Daniel Jantzen, Chief Financial Officer
CMO: Alexander de Neshera, M.D., Chief Medical Officer
CHR: Aimee M. Giglio, Chief Human Resources Officer
CNO: Susan A Reeves, Chief Nursing Executive
Web address: www.hitchcock.org
**Control**: Other not–for–profit (including NFP Corporation) **Service**: General medical and surgical

**Staffed Beds**: 416 **Admissions**: 19466 **Census**: 329 **Outpatient Visits**: 1096616 **Births**: 1382 **Total Expense ($000)**: 1549833 **Payroll Expense ($000)**: 679955 **Personnel**: 7164

**MARY HITCHCOCK MEM HOSPITAL** See Dartmouth-Hitchcock Medical Center

**NH**

---

Hospital, Medicare Provider Number, Address, Telephone, Approval, Facility, and Physician Codes, Health Care System

★ American Hospital Association (AHA) membership   ○ Healthcare Facilities Accreditation Program   ⇑ Center for Improvement in Healthcare Quality Accreditation
☐ The Joint Commission accreditation   ◇ DNV Healthcare Inc. accreditation   △ Commission on Accreditation of Rehabilitation Facilities (CARF) accreditation

**LITTLETON—Grafton County**

★ **LITTLETON REGIONAL HEALTHCARE (301302)**, 600 Saint Johnsbury Road, Zip 03561–3442; tel. 603/444–9000, (Nonreporting) **A**5 10 18 **F**3 11 13 15 18 26 28 29 31 32 34 35 36 38 40 44 45 50 56 57 59 64 65 70 74 75 76 77 78 79 81 82 84 85 86 87 89 92 93 96 97 107 108 110 111 114 115 118 119 127 129 130 131 133 143 146 147 148 154 **S** QHR Health, Brentwood, TN
Primary Contact: Robert Nutter, President and Chief Executive Officer
CFO: Jeffrey C. Hebert, Vice President Finance, Chief Financial Officer
CIO: Scott Vachon, Director Information Technology
CHR: Georgene Novak, Director Human Resources
Web address: www.littletonhospital.org
**Control**: Other not–for–profit (including NFP Corporation) **Service**: General medical and surgical

**Staffed Beds**: 25 **Admissions**: 1610 **Census**: 14 **Outpatient Visits**: 60831 **Births**: 316 **Total Expense ($000)**: 99171 **Payroll Expense ($000)**: 43537 **Personnel**: 415

**LITTLETON REGIONAL HOSPITAL** See Littleton Regional Healthcare

**MANCHESTER—Hillsborough County**

⊞ **CATHOLIC MEDICAL CENTER (300034)**, 100 McGregor Street, Zip 03102–3770; tel. 603/668–3545, (Nonreporting) **A**1 2 3 5 10 **F**3 5 9 12 13 15 18 20 22 24 26 28 29 30 31 34 35 36 37 38 39 40 41 43 44 45 46 47 48 49 50 51 52 53 54 57 58 59 60 64 65 66 68 70 71 73 74 75 76 77 78 79 80 81 82 84 85 86 87 90 92 93 94 97 100 102 104 107 110 111 114 115 118 119 126 129 130 131 132 135 143 144 145 146 147 148 149 154 156
Primary Contact: Joseph Pepe, M.D., President and Chief Executive Officer
COO: Alexander J. Walker, Executive Vice President Operations and Strategic Development
CFO: Edward L Dudley IIIExecutive Vice President and Chief Financial Officer
CMO: William H. Goodman, Vice President Medical Affairs, Chief Medical Officer
CIO: Thomas Della Flora, Vice President and Chief Information Officer
CHR: Merryll Rosenfeld, Vice President, Human Resources
CNO: Robert A Duhaime, R.N., Senior Vice President Clinical Operations and Chief Nursing Officer
Web address: www.catholicmedicalcenter.org
**Control**: Other not–for–profit (including NFP Corporation) **Service**: General medical and surgical

**Staffed Beds**: 261 **Admissions**: 12510 **Census**: 184 **Outpatient Visits**: 516127 **Births**: 1127 **Total Expense ($000)**: 430619 **Payroll Expense ($000)**: 186044 **Personnel**: 2064

△ ⇑ **ELLIOT HOSPITAL (300012)**, One Elliot Way, Zip 03103–3502; tel. 603/669–5300, (Nonreporting) **A**2 3 5 7 10 21 **F**3 5 8 9 11 12 13 15 18 20 22 26 28 29 30 31 32 34 35 36 37 38 39 40 41 43 44 45 46 47 48 49 50 51 53 54 55 56 57 59 62 64 65 68 70 72 74 75 76 77 78 79 81 82 83 84 85 86 87 89 91 93 97 98 100 101 102 103 104 105 107 108 110 111 114 115 118 119 120 121 123 124 126 129 130 131 132 134 135 144 146 147 148 149 154 156 **P**6 **S** SolutioNHealth, Manchester, NH
Primary Contact: Greg Baxter, M.D., President
COO: Joseph Tate Curti, Chief Operating Officer
CFO: Richard Elwell, Senior Vice President and Chief Financial Officer
CMO: Greg Baxter, M.D., Senior Vice President Medical Affairs and Chief Medical Officer
CIO: Denise Purington, Vice President and Chief Information Officer
CHR: Catherine Bardier, Vice President, Human Resources
CNO: Martha Leighton, Senior Vice President and Chief Nursing Officer
Web address: www.elliothospital.org
**Control**: Other not–for–profit (including NFP Corporation) **Service**: General medical and surgical

**Staffed Beds**: 268 **Admissions**: 13683 **Census**: 191 **Outpatient Visits**: 519996 **Births**: 1665 **Total Expense ($000)**: 429179 **Payroll Expense ($000)**: 158168 **Personnel**: 3460

★ **MANCHESTER VETERANS AFFAIRS MEDICAL CENTER**, 718 Smyth Road, Zip 03104–4098; tel. 603/624–4366, (Nonreporting) **A**5 **S** Department of Veterans Affairs, Washington, DC
Primary Contact: Alfred Montoya, Director
COO: Richard T Rose, Associate Director
CFO: Frank Ryan, Chief Financial Officer
CMO: Andrew Breuder, M.D., Chief of Staff
CIO: John Foote, Chief Information Officer
CHR: Mary Ellen Kenney, Chief Human Services
Web address: www.manchester.va.gov/
**Control**: Veterans Affairs, Government, federal **Service**: Rehabilitation

**Staffed Beds**: 41

**VETERANS AFFAIRS MEDICAL CENTER** See Manchester Veterans Affairs Medical Center

**NASHUA—Hillsborough County**

★ △ ⇑ **SOUTHERN NEW HAMPSHIRE MEDICAL CENTER (300020)**, 8 Prospect Street, Zip 03060–3925, Mailing Address: P.O. Box 2014, Zip 03061–2014; tel. 603/577–2000, (Data for 273 days) (Nonreporting) **A**2 3 5 7 10 21 **F**3 11 13 15 18 20 22 26 28 29 30 31 34 35 40 43 45 49 50 51 52 57 59 61 65 68 70 72 74 75 76 77 78 79 81 84 85 86 87 89 93 96 98 100 102 104 105 107 110 111 115 118 119 126 129 130 131 132 135 143 146 147 148 149 150 153 154 156 **P**6 **S** SolutioNHealth, Manchester, NH
Primary Contact: Michael S. Rose, President and Chief Executive Officer
COO: Tate Curti, Senior Vice President and Chief Operating Officer
CFO: Paul Trainor, Senior Vice President Finance and Chief Financial Officer
CMO: Timothy Scherer, M.D., Chief Medical Officer
CIO: Andrew Watt, M.D., Vice President, Information Technology & Services, Chief Information Officer, Chief Medical Information Officer
CHR: Jacqueline Woolley, Vice President Human Resources
CNO: Cheryl Gagne lVice President Patient Care Services and Chief Nursing Officer
Web address: www.snhhs.org
**Control**: Other not–for–profit (including NFP Corporation) **Service**: General medical and surgical

**Staffed Beds**: 163 **Admissions**: 6548 **Census**: 108 **Outpatient Visits**: 182964 **Births**: 929 **Total Expense ($000)**: 121030 **Payroll Expense ($000)**: 79293 **Personnel**: 1566

⇑ **SOUTHERN NH REGIONAL MED CTR** See Southern New Hampshire Medical Center

⇑ **ST JOSEPH HEALTHCARE** See St. Joseph Hospital

★ ⇑ **ST. JOSEPH HOSPITAL (300011)**, 172 Kinsley Street, Zip 03060–3648; tel. 603/882–3000, (Nonreporting) **A**2 10 21 **F**3 13 15 18 20 22 28 29 30 31 32 35 36 37 40 43 44 45 46 47 48 49 50 51 54 55 57 59 61 64 65 68 70 71 74 75 76 77 78 79 81 82 83 84 85 86 87 89 90 91 92 93 94 96 97 102 107 108 109 110 111 115 118 119 126 129 130 131 132 144 146 147 148 149 154 157 **P**6 **S** Covenant Health, Tewksbury, MA
Primary Contact: John A. Jurczyk, FACHE, Senior Vice President and President
CFO: Richard Plamondon, Vice President Finance and Chief Financial Officer
CIO: Keith A Choinka, Vice President Information Systems and Chief Information Officer
CHR: Jacqueline Woolley, Vice President Human Resources
Web address: www.stjosephhospital.com
**Control**: Church operated, Nongovernment, not–for–profit **Service**: General medical and surgical

**Staffed Beds**: 135 **Admissions**: 4481 **Census**: 66 **Outpatient Visits**: 161050 **Births**: 362 **Total Expense ($000)**: 225776 **Payroll Expense ($000)**: 91949 **Personnel**: 1177

**NEW LONDON—Merrimack County**

★ **NEW LONDON HOSPITAL (301304)**, 273 County Road, Zip 03257–5736; tel. 603/526–2911, (Data for 273 days) (Nonreporting) **A**3 5 10 18 **F**3 11 13 15 18 20 22 26 28 29 30 31 34 35 40 43 45 49 50 51 52 57 59 61 65 68 70 72 74 75 76 77 78 79 81 84 85 86 87 89 93 96 98 100 102 104 105 107 110 111 115 118 119 126 129 130 131 132 135 143 146 147 148 149 150 153 154 156 **P**6
Primary Contact: Martin Thomas. Manion, Chief Executive Officer
CFO: Lisa Cohen, Chief Financial Officer
CMO: Gregory Curtis, M.D., Chief Medical Officer
CIO: David Foss, Chief Information Officer
CHR: Shari Bostwick, Director Human Resources
CNO: Sally K Patton, R.N., MS, Chief Nursing Officer
Web address: www.newlondonhospital.org
**Control**: Other not–for–profit (including NFP Corporation) **Service**: General medical and surgical

**Staffed Beds**: 163 **Admissions**: 6548 **Census**: 108 **Outpatient Visits**: 182964 **Births**: 929 **Total Expense ($000)**: 121030 **Payroll Expense ($000)**: 79293 **Personnel**: 1566

*Many Facility Codes have changed. Please refer to the AHA Guide Code Chart.*
© 2021 AHA Guide

## NORTH CONWAY—Carroll County

★ **MEMORIAL HOSPITAL (301307)**, 3073 White Mountain Highway, Zip 03860–7101; tel. 603/356–5461, (Total facility includes 45 beds in nursing home–type unit) (Nonreporting) **A**5 10 18 **F**3 13 15 28 29 31 32 34 35 36 40 41 44 45 57 59 64 67 68 70 75 76 77 78 79 81 85 86 87 90 93 94 96 97 100 101 104 107 110 115 119 127 128 130 132 133 146 147 148 154 156 **P**6 **S** MaineHealth, Portland, ME
Primary Contact: Arthur Mathisen, FACHE, President
CFO: Diana J. McLaughlin, Chief Financial Officer
CMO: Ray Rabideau, M.D., Senior Vice President and Chief Medical Officer
CIO: Curtis Kerbs, Regional Chief Information Officer
CHR: Melanie Sleime, Director Human Resources
CNO: Kristine Dascoulias, Chief Nursing Officer
Web address: www.memorialhospitalnh.org
**Control**: Other not–for–profit (including NFP Corporation) **Service**: General medical and surgical

**Staffed Beds**: 70 **Admissions**: 1268 **Census**: 51 **Outpatient Visits**: 55681 **Births**: 209 **Total Expense ($000)**: 77730 **Payroll Expense ($000)**: 30594 **Personnel**: 348

## PETERBOROUGH—Hillsborough County

★ **MONADNOCK COMMUNITY HOSPITAL (301309)**, 452 Old Street Road, Zip 03458–1295; tel. 603/924–7191, (Nonreporting) **A**5 10 18 **F**3 11 13 15 28 29 31 34 35 36 38 40 41 44 50 53 59 64 65 70 75 76 77 78 79 81 82 85 86 87 90 91 92 93 96 97 98 99 100 101 102 103 104 107 108 110 114 118 119 124 127 128 130 131 132 133 134 135 146 147 148 149 154 156 **P**6
Primary Contact: Cynthia McGuire, FACHE, President and Chief Executive Officer
CFO: Richard Scheinblum, Chief Financial Officer
CMO: Michael Lindberg, M.D., Chief Medical Officer
CIO: Peter A Johnson, Interim Chief Information Officer
CHR: John Sansone, Vice President, Human Resources
CNO: Vicki Loughery, R.N., MS, Chief Nursing Officer
Web address: www.monadnockhospital.org
**Control**: Other not–for–profit (including NFP Corporation) **Service**: General medical and surgical

**Staffed Beds**: 25 **Admissions**: 1373 **Census**: 11 **Outpatient Visits**: 82602 **Births**: 301 **Total Expense ($000)**: 91541 **Payroll Expense ($000)**: 36577 **Personnel**: 436

## PLYMOUTH—Grafton County

★ **SPEARE MEMORIAL HOSPITAL (301311)**, 16 Hospital Road, Zip 03264–1199; tel. 603/536–1120, (Nonreporting) **A**5 10 18 **F**3 13 15 28 29 30 31 32 34 35 40 45 47 50 53 54 57 59 64 65 70 75 76 77 79 81 83 84 85 87 89 93 97 107 110 111 113 114 119 127 130 131 132 133 146 147 148 154 156 **P**8
Primary Contact: Michelle McEwen, President and Chief Executive Officer
CFO: Travis Boucher, Chief Financial Officer
CMO: Joseph Ebner, M.D., Chief Medical Officer
CHR: Laurie Bolognani, Human Resources Officer
CNO: Kristine Hering, R.N., Chief Nursing Officer
Web address: www.spearehospital.com
**Control**: Other not–for–profit (including NFP Corporation) **Service**: General medical and surgical

**Staffed Beds**: 25 **Admissions**: 1224 **Census**: 11 **Outpatient Visits**: 14647 **Births**: 155 **Total Expense ($000)**: 64007 **Payroll Expense ($000)**: 26142 **Personnel**: 337

## PORTSMOUTH—Rockingham County

**PORTSMOUTH REGIONAL HOSP** See Portsmouth Regional Hospital

⊞ **PORTSMOUTH REGIONAL HOSPITAL (300029)**, 333 Borthwick Avenue, Zip 03801–7128; tel. 603/436–5110, (Nonreporting) **A**1 2 3 10 **S** HCA Healthcare, Nashville, TN
Primary Contact: Dean Carucci, Chief Executive Officer
COO: Matthew Larkin, Chief Operating Officer
CFO: Richard Senger, Chief Financial Officer
CMO: Tim Pike, M.D., Chief Medical Officer
CIO: Ed Sovetskhy, Director Information Services
CHR: Jackie Brayton, Vice President Human Resources
Web address: www.portsmouthhospital.com
**Control**: Corporation, Investor–owned (for–profit) **Service**: General medical and surgical

**Staffed Beds**: 220

## ROCHESTER—Strafford County

★ **FRISBIE MEMORIAL HOSPITAL (300014)**, 11 Whitehall Road, Zip 03867–3297; tel. 603/332–5211, (Nonreporting) **A**10 **S** HCA Healthcare, Nashville, TN
Primary Contact: Jeff Scionti, Chief Executive Officer
CFO: Robert K. Cochrane, Vice President Finance and Chief Financial Officer
CMO: Trevor Eide, M.D., Chief Medical Officer
CNO: John L Levitow JrVice President Patient Care Services and Chief Nursing Officer
Web address: www.frisbiehospital.com
**Control**: Corporation, Investor–owned (for–profit) **Service**: General medical and surgical

**Staffed Beds**: 96

## SALEM—Rockingham County

☐ △ **NORTHEAST REHABILITATION HOSPITAL (303026)**, 70 Butler Street, Zip 03079–3925; tel. 603/893–2900, (Nonreporting) **A**1 7 10 **F**28 29 62 64 68 69 74 75 77 82 87 90 93 96 131 133 147 148 149 154 157
Primary Contact: John F. Prochilo Jr, Chief Executive Officer
CFO: Charles D. Champagne, Chief Financial Officer
CMO: A Deniz Ozel, M.D., Chief Medical Officer
CHR: Shirley G Lussier, Vice President Human Resources
CNO: Helene Thibodeau, R.N., MSN, Vice President Patient Care Services
Web address: www.northeastrehab.com
**Control**: Corporation, Investor–owned (for–profit) **Service**: Rehabilitation

**Staffed Beds**: 135 **Admissions**: 3486 **Census**: 115 **Outpatient Visits**: 152000 **Births**: 0 **Total Expense ($000)**: 94658 **Payroll Expense ($000)**: 54944 **Personnel**: 781

## WOLFEBORO—Carroll County

★ **HUGGINS HOSPITAL (301312)**, 240 South Main Street, Zip 03894–4455, Mailing Address: P.O. Box 912, Zip 03894–0912; tel. 603/569–7500, (Nonreporting) **A**10 18 **F**2 3 10 15 28 29 34 35 36 40 45 50 53 57 59 64 65 68 70 75 79 81 85 86 87 93 96 97 107 108 110 115 119 130 131 132 133 135 146 147 148 149 156 **P**6
Primary Contact: Jeremy Roberge, President and Chief Executive Officer
CFO: Jeremy Roberge, Chief Financial Officer
CMO: John Boornazian, M.D., Chief Medical Officer
CIO: Pam McGovern, Director Technology
CHR: Laura Stauss, Director of Human Resources
Web address: www.hugginshospital.org
**Control**: Other not–for–profit (including NFP Corporation) **Service**: General medical and surgical

**Staffed Beds**: 25 **Admissions**: 877 **Census**: 11 **Outpatient Visits**: 72195 **Births**: 0 **Total Expense ($000)**: 65088 **Payroll Expense ($000)**: 29904 **Personnel**: 437

## WOODSVILLE—Grafton County

★ **COTTAGE HOSPITAL (301301)**, 90 Swiftwater Road, Zip 03785–1421, Mailing Address: P.O. Box 2001, Zip 03785–2001; tel. 603/747–9000, (Nonreporting) **A**5 10 18 **F**3 8 11 15 28 29 34 40 43 44 45 46 50 54 56 57 59 64 67 70 75 77 79 81 89 97 98 100 103 104 107 110 114 119 127 128 130 132 133 146 147 148 156
Primary Contact: Maria Ryan, Ph.D., Chief Executive Officer
COO: Lori Hughes, R.N., MSN, Chief Nursing Officer, Vice President Operations and Patient Care Services
CFO: Steven L Plant, Chief Financial Officer
CIO: Rick Fredrick, Director Information Technology
CNO: Lori Hughes, R.N., MSN, Chief Nursing Officer, Vice President Operations & Patient Care Services
Web address: www.cottagehospital.org
**Control**: Other not–for–profit (including NFP Corporation) **Service**: General medical and surgical

**Staffed Beds**: 35 **Admissions**: 886 **Census**: 20 **Outpatient Visits**: 32893 **Births**: 0 **Total Expense ($000)**: 34213 **Payroll Expense ($000)**: 16900 **Personnel**: 303

**NH**

---

**Hospital, Medicare Provider Number, Address, Telephone, Approval, Facility, and Physician Codes, Health Care System**

★ American Hospital Association (AHA) membership  ○ Healthcare Facilities Accreditation Program  ⇧ Center for Improvement in Healthcare Quality Accreditation
☐ The Joint Commission accreditation  ◇ DNV Healthcare Inc. accreditation  △ Commission on Accreditation of Rehabilitation Facilities (CARF) accreditation

# NEW JERSEY

## ATLANTIC CITY—Atlantic County

★ ⸸ **ACUITY SPECIALTY HOSPITAL OF NEW JERSEY (312023)**, 1925 Pacific Avenue, 7th Floor, Zip 08401–6713; tel. 609/441–2122, (Nonreporting) **A**10 21 **S** AcuityHealthcare, LP, Charlotte, NC
Primary Contact: Kathleen Kerstetter, MSN, R.N., Chief Executive Officer
CFO: Cheryl Lambert, Chief Financial Officer
CHR: Maria Ciro, Director Human Resources
Web address: www.acuityhealthcare.net
**Control:** Corporation, Investor–owned (for–profit) **Service:** Acute long–term care hospital

**Staffed Beds:** 30

⊠ **ATLANTICARE REGIONAL MEDICAL CENTER (310064)**, 1925 Pacific Avenue, Zip 08401–6713; tel. 609/441–8994, (Includes ATLANTICARE REGIONAL MEDICAL CENTER-MAINLAND DIVISION, Mailing address: Jimmie Leeds Road, Pomona, New Jersey, Zip 8240, 65 West Jimmie Leeds Road, Zip 8240, tel. 609/652–1000; Lori Herdon, President and Chief Executive Officer), (Nonreporting) **A**1 2 3 5 10 **F**3 7 11 12 13 17 18 20 22 24 26 28 29 30 31 34 35 36 37 40 41 42 43 44 45 46 47 48 49 50 54 55 58 61 64 66 68 70 71 72 73 74 75 76 77 78 79 81 82 83 84 85 86 87 97 98 100 102 104 105 107 108 110 111 114 115 116 117 118 119 120 121 123 124 126 130 132 135 143 146 147 148 149 150 153 154 155 156 157 **P**6 **S** Geisinger, Danville, PA
Primary Contact: Lori S. Herndon, R.N., President and Chief Executive Officer
CFO: Walter Greiner, Chief Financial Officer
CMO: Marilouise Vendetti, M.D., Chief Medical Officer
CIO: Christopher A Scanzera, Vice President and Chief Information Officer
CHR: Richard Lovering, Corporate Vice President Human Resources and Organizational Development
Web address: www.atlanticare.org
**Control:** Other not–for–profit (including NFP Corporation) **Service:** General medical and surgical

**Staffed Beds:** 540 **Admissions:** 29217 **Census:** 359 **Outpatient Visits:** 305207 **Births:** 951 **Total Expense ($000):** 704106 **Payroll Expense ($000):** 255712 **Personnel:** 3212

**ATLANTICARE REGIONAL MEDICAL CENTER** See Atlanticare Regional Medical Center

## BAYONNE—Hudson County

**BAYONNE MEDICAL CENTER** See Carepoint Health Bayonne Medical Center

☐ **CAREPOINT HEALTH BAYONNE MEDICAL CENTER (310025)**, 29th Street & Avenue E, Zip 07002–4699, Mailing Address: 29 East 29 Street, Zip 07002–4699; tel. 201/858–5000, (Nonreporting) **A**1 2 3 10 12 13 **S** CarePoint Health, Jersey City, NJ
Primary Contact: Vijayant Singh, M.D., Chief Hospital Executive
CFO: Gary Bryant, Chief Financial Officer
CIO: Joel Taylor, Chief Information Officer
CHR: Jennifer Dobin, Executive Vice President Human Resources
Web address: www.carepointhealth.org
**Control:** Corporation, Investor–owned (for–profit) **Service:** General medical and surgical

**Staffed Beds:** 178

## BELLE MEAD—Somerset County

**CARRIER CLINIC** See Hackensack Meridian Health Carrier Clinic

⊠ **HACKENSACK MERIDIAN HEALTH CARRIER CLINIC (314012)**, 252 County Route 601, Zip 08502–0147, Mailing Address: P.O. Box 147, Zip 08502–0147; tel. 908/281–1000, (Nonreporting) **A**1 5 10 **F**4 5 29 30 38 75 98 99 100 101 102 103 104 106 130 132 149 151 154 **S** Hackensack Meridian Health, Edison, NJ
Primary Contact: Donald J. Parker, President
CFO: Randolph Jacobson, Chief Financial Officer
CMO: Umesh Mehta, M.D., Chief Medical Officer
CIO: Peter Schwartz, Director Information Systems
CHR: Patricia Toole, Chief Hospital Executive
CNO: Shaun Sweeney, R.N., Vice President Patient Care Services
Web address: www.carrierclinic.org
**Control:** Other not–for–profit (including NFP Corporation) **Service:** Psychiatric

**Staffed Beds:** 330 **Admissions:** 6360 **Census:** 264 **Outpatient Visits:** 2859 **Births:** 0 **Total Expense ($000):** 78118 **Payroll Expense ($000):** 49768 **Personnel:** 831

## BELLEVILLE—Essex County

**CLARA MAASS HEALTH SYSTEM** See Clara Maass Medical Center

⊠ **CLARA MAASS MEDICAL CENTER (310009)**, One Clara Maass Drive, Zip 07109–3557; tel. 973/450–2000, (Nonreporting) **A**1 3 10 **F**1 3 8 11 12 13 15 18 19 20 22 26 28 29 30 31 34 35 36 38 39 40 41 46 47 49 50 51 53 55 56 57 58 59 60 61 63 64 65 66 68 70 71 73 74 75 76 77 78 79 81 82 83 84 85 86 87 89 92 93 94 98 100 101 102 103 107 108 110 114 115 119 120 121 123 126 129 130 131 132 135 143 146 147 148 149 154 156 157 **P**6 **S** RWJBarnabas Health, West Orange, NJ
Primary Contact: Mary Ellen Clyne, Ph.D., President and Chief Executive Officer
COO: Jeffrey J. Holt, Chief Operating Officer
CMO: Frank Mazzarella, M.D., Chief Medical Officer
CIO: Michael McTigue, Chief Information Officer
CHR: Jim Rolek, Chief Human Resources Officer, Vice President
CNO: Bonnie Geissler, R.N., Chief Nursing Officer, Vice President Patient Care Services
Web address: www.barnabashealth.org/hospitals/clara_maass/index.html
**Control:** Other not–for–profit (including NFP Corporation) **Service:** General medical and surgical

**Staffed Beds:** 352 **Admissions:** 13563 **Census:** 220 **Outpatient Visits:** 121082 **Births:** 1652 **Total Expense ($000):** 281821 **Payroll Expense ($000):** 116912 **Personnel:** 1310

## BERKELEY HEIGHTS—Union County

**CORNERSTONE BEHAVIORAL HEALTH HOSPITAL OF UNION COUNTY (314027)**, 40 Watchung Way, Zip 07922–2600; tel. 908/790–5300, (Nonreporting) **A**10
Primary Contact: John Bamberger, Administrator
**Control:** County, Government, Nonfederal **Service:** Psychiatric

**Staffed Beds:** 44

**RUNNELLS SPECIALIZED HOSPITAL OF UNION COUNTY** See Runnells Center for Rehabilitation and Healthcare

## BLACKWOOD—Camden County

☐ **NORTHBROOK BEHAVIORAL HEALTH HOSPITAL (314018)**, 425 Woodbury Turnersville Road, Zip 08012–2960; tel. 856/374–6500, (Nonreporting) **A**1 10 **S** Oceans Healthcare, Plano, TX
Primary Contact: Avi Feigenbaum, Chief Executive Officer
Web address: www.northbrookbhh.com
**Control:** Corporation, Investor–owned (for–profit) **Service:** Psychiatric

**Staffed Beds:** 153

## BOONTON TOWNSHIP—Morris County

**SAINT CLARE'S HOSPITAL/BOONTON TOWNSHIP** See Saint Clare's Denville Hospital, Denville

**ST CLARE'S HOSPITAL/BOONTON** See Saint Clare's Hospital/Boonton Township

## BRICK—Ocean County

⊠ △ **HACKENSACK MERIDIAN HEALTH SHORE REHABILITATION INSTITUTE (313033)**, 425 Jack Martin Boulevard, Zip 08724–7732; tel. 732/836–4500, (Nonreporting) **A**1 5 7 10 **F**29 36 50 75 90 91 93 94 95 96 130 132 148 149 **S** Hackensack Meridian Health, Edison, NJ
Primary Contact: Kerri Fitzgerald, Executive Director
CFO: Richard C. Smith, Senior Vice President Finance
CMO: Lisa Luciano, D.O., Medical Director
CNO: Maria Clohsey, Director of Nursing
Web address: www.shorerehabilitationinstitute.com
**Control:** Other not–for–profit (including NFP Corporation) **Service:** Rehabilitation

**Staffed Beds:** 40 **Admissions:** 836 **Census:** 31 **Outpatient Visits:** 15931 **Births:** 0 **Total Expense ($000):** 17986 **Payroll Expense ($000):** 10264 **Personnel:** 142

**SHORE REHABILITATION INSTITUTE** See Hackensack Meridian Health Shore Rehabilitation Institute

**NJ**

*Many Facility Codes have changed. Please refer to the AHA Guide Code Chart.*

© 2021 AHA Guide

## BRICK TOWNSHIP—Ocean County

☒ **HACKENSACK MERIDIAN HEALTH OCEAN MEDICAL CENTER (310052)**, 425 Jack Martin Boulevard, Zip 08724–7732; tel. 732/840–2200, (Nonreporting) **A**1 3 5 10 **F**3 5 11 12 13 15 18 22 28 29 30 31 32 34 35 36 38 40 41 42 43 44 45 46 47 48 49 50 54 55 56 57 58 59 60 61 63 64 65 66 68 70 71 74 75 76 77 78 79 81 82 84 85 86 87 90 91 92 93 94 95 96 97 100 101 102 104 107 108 109 110 111 114 115 116 117 118 119 120 121 123 124 126 129 130 131 132 134 135 141 143 144 146 147 148 149 153 154 **S** Hackensack Meridian Health, Edison, NJ
Primary Contact: Jason Kreitner, FACHE, Chief Hospital Executive
COO: Regina Foley, R.N., FACHE, Vice President Nursing and Operations
CFO: Robert Palermo, Vice President Finance
CMO: James Clarke, M.D., Vice President Medical Affairs and Clinical Effectiveness
CIO: Rebecca Weber, Senior Vice President and Chief Information Officer
CHR: Sherrie String, Senior Vice President Human Resources
Web address: www.meridianhealth.com
**Control**: Other not–for–profit (including NFP Corporation) **Service**: General medical and surgical

**Staffed Beds: 308 Admissions: 28981 Census: 207 Outpatient Visits: 176569 Births: 780 Total Expense ($000): 364078 Payroll Expense ($000): 154919 Personnel: 1769**

**OCEAN MEDICAL CENTER** See Hackensack Meridian Health Ocean Medical Center

## BRIDGETON—Cumberland County

**BRIDGETON HEALTH CENTER** See Inspira Medical Center-Vineland, Vineland

**BRIDGETON HOSPITAL** See Bridgeton Health Center

## BROWNS MILLS—Burlington County

⇧ **DEBORAH HEART AND LUNG CENTER (310031)**, 200 Trenton Road, Zip 08015–1705; tel. 609/893–6611, (Nonreporting) **A**3 5 10 13 21
Primary Contact: Joseph Chirichella, President and Chief Executive Officer
COO: Joseph Manni, Executive Vice President and Chief Operating Officer
CFO: R. Grant Leidy, Chief Financial Officer
CMO: Lynn McGrath, M.D., Vice President Medical Affairs
CIO: Richard Temple, Chief Information Officer
CHR: Marion Stamopoulos, Vice President Human Resources
CNO: Rita Zenna, R.N., Vice President Patient Care Services
Web address: www.deborah.org
**Control**: Other not–for–profit (including NFP Corporation) **Service**: Other specialty treatment

**Staffed Beds: 89**

## CAMDEN—Camden County

**COOPER HEALTH SYSTEM** See Cooper University Health Care

☐ **COOPER UNIVERSITY HEALTH CARE (310014)**, One Cooper Plaza, Zip 08103–1489; tel. 856/342–2000, (Includes CHILDEN'S REGIONAL HOSPITAL AT COOPER, Mailing address: Three Cooper Plaza, Camden, New Jersey, Zip 8103; tel. 800/826–6737), (Nonreporting) **A**1 2 3 5 8 10 13 **F**3 5 7 8 9 11 12 13 15 17 18 19 20 22 24 26 29 30 31 32 34 35 36 37 38 39 40 41 43 44 45 46 47 48 49 51 52 54 55 56 57 58 59 60 61 63 64 65 66 68 70 72 73 74 75 76 77 78 79 80 81 82 84 85 86 87 88 89 92 93 96 97 98 100 101 102 104 107 108 110 111 114 115 117 119 120 121 123 124 126 130 131 132 135 144 146 147 148 149 150 153 154 155 157 **P**6
Primary Contact: Anthony J. Mazzarelli, JD, M.D., Co-President and Chief Executive Officer
CFO: Douglas E. Shirley, Senior Executive Vice President and Chief Financial Officer
CHR: Elizabeth Green, Chief Human Resources Officer
Web address: www.cooperhealth.org
**Control**: Other not–for–profit (including NFP Corporation) **Service**: General medical and surgical

**Staffed Beds: 594 Admissions: 29682 Census: 462 Outpatient Visits: 383579 Births: 2030 Total Expense ($000): 1054009 Payroll Expense ($000): 360504 Personnel: 7103**

**OUR LADY OF LOURDES MEDICAL CENTER** See Virtua Our Lady of Lourdes Hospital

**THE CHILDEN'S REGIONAL HOSPITAL AT COOPER** See Childen's Regional Hospital at Cooper

☒ **VIRTUA OUR LADY OF LOURDES HOSPITAL (310029)**, 1600 Haddon Avenue, Zip 08103–3117; tel. 856/757–3500, (Nonreporting) **A**1 2 3 10 **F**3 7 11 12 13 15 17 18 20 22 24 26 28 29 30 31 32 34 35 36 37 38 40 44 46 47 49 50 55 56 57 58 59 60 61 64 65 66 68 70 73 74 75 76 78 79 81 82 84 85 86 87 90 95 96 107 108 110 111 114 115 118 119 126 130 132 134 135 138 139 142 146 147 148 149 **P**1 **S** Virtua Health, Marlton, NJ
Primary Contact: Mark Nessel, Senior Vice President and Chief Operating Officer
COO: Mark Nessel, Senior Vice President and Chief Operating Officer
CFO: Michael Hammond, Chief Financial Officer
CMO: Alan R Pope, M.D., Chief Medical Officer
CIO: Maureen Hetu, Chief Information Officer
CHR: Jennifer L Moughan, Chief Human Resources Officer
CNO: Audrey Jadczak, R.N., FACHE, Vice President Chief Nursing Officer
Web address: www.https://www.lourdesnet.org/locations/hospitals/our-lady-of-lourdes-medical-center/
**Control**: Other not–for–profit (including NFP Corporation) **Service**: General medical and surgical

**Staffed Beds: 340 Admissions: 11706 Census: 171 Outpatient Visits: 137636 Births: 831 Total Expense ($000): 458002 Payroll Expense ($000): 109773 Personnel: 1277**

## CAPE MAY COURT HOUSE—Cape May County

☒ **CAPE REGIONAL HEALTH SYSTEM (310011)**, Two Stone Harbor Boulevard, Zip 08210–9990; tel. 609/463–2000, (Nonreporting) **A**1 2 10 **F**3 8 11 12 13 15 18 20 28 29 30 31 34 35 40 44 45 46 49 50 57 59 64 70 74 75 76 77 78 79 81 82 85 86 87 89 93 97 107 111 114 118 119 120 121 123 124 129 130 132 135 143 146 149 156
Primary Contact: Joanne Carrocino, FACHE, President and Chief Executive Officer
CFO: Mark Gill, Vice President Finance and Chief Financial Officer
CMO: Andrea C.S. McCoy, M.D., Chief Medical Officer
CIO: Richard Wheatley, Chief Information Officer
CHR: Byron Hunter, Vice President Human Resources
CNO: Rosemary Dunn, R.N., Chief Nursing Officer
Web address: www.caperegional.com
**Control**: Other not–for–profit (including NFP Corporation) **Service**: General medical and surgical

**Staffed Beds: 178 Admissions: 5827 Census: 76 Outpatient Visits: 216555 Births: 314 Total Expense ($000): 123566 Payroll Expense ($000): 53646 Personnel: 983**

**CAPE REGIONAL MEDICAL CENTER** See Cape Regional Health System

## CEDAR GROVE—Essex County

☐ **ESSEX COUNTY HOSPITAL CENTER (314020)**, 204 Grove Avenue, Zip 07009–1436; tel. 973/571–2800, (Nonreporting) **A**1 10
Primary Contact: Frank J. Del Gaudio, Department and Hospital Center Director
CFO: Jacqueline Campoverde, Business Manager
CMO: Bolivar Pascual, M.D., Medical Director
CIO: Vijay Prakash, Information Technology Officer
CHR: Marlon Brown, Human Resources
CNO: Fern Papalia, Director of Nursing
Web address: www.essexcountynj.org
**Control**: County, Government, Nonfederal **Service**: Psychiatric

**Staffed Beds: 180**

## CHESTER—Morris County

**KESSLER INSTITUTE FOR REHABILITATION** See Kessler Institute for Rehabilitation, West Orange

**WELKIND FACILITY** See Kessler Institute for Rehabilitation

## CRANFORD—Union County

**CRANFORD HEALTH AND EC CENTER** See Cranford Health and Extended Care Center

---

**Hospital, Medicare Provider Number, Address, Telephone, Approval, Facility, and Physician Codes, Health Care System**

★ American Hospital Association (AHA) membership
☐ The Joint Commission accreditation
○ Healthcare Facilities Accreditation Program
◇ DNV Healthcare Inc. accreditation
⇧ Center for Improvement in Healthcare Quality Accreditation
△ Commission on Accreditation of Rehabilitation Facilities (CARF) accreditation

**NJ**

## DENVILLE—Morris County

☐ **SAINT CLARE'S DENVILLE HOSPITAL (310050)**, 25 Pocono Road, Zip 07834–2954; tel. 973/625–6000, (Includes SAINT CLARE'S HOSPITAL/ BOONTON TOWNSHIP, Mailing address: 130 Powerville Road, Boonton Township, New Jersey, Zip 7005; tel. 973/316–1800; Brian Finestein, Chief Executive Officer; SAINT CLARE'S HOSPITAL/DENVILLE, Mailing address: 25 Pocono Road, Denville, New Jersey, Zip 7834; tel. 973/625–6000; SAINT CLARE'S HOSPITAL/ DOVER, Mailing address: 400 West Blackwell Street, Dover, New Jersey, Zip 07801–3311; tel. 973/989–3000; Brian Finestein, Chief Executive Officer), (Nonreporting) **A**1 2 3 10 **S** Prime Healthcare, Ontario, CA
Primary Contact: Brian Finestein, Chief Executive Officer
CFO: Thomas G. Scott, CPA, Chief Financial Officer
CMO: Neil Udani, M.D., Chief Medical Officer
CIO: Tero Caamano, Director Information Technology
CHR: Karen Sosnowski, Director, Human Resources
CNO: Jan Bednar, R.N., MS, Chief Nursing Officer
Web address: www.saintclares.org
**Control**: Church operated, Nongovernment, not–for–profit **Service**: General medical and surgical

**Staffed Beds**: 412

**SAINT CLARE'S HEALTH SYSTEM** See Saint Clare's Denville Hospital

**SAINT CLARE'S HOSPITAL/DENVILLE** See Saint Clare's Denville Hospital, Denville

**ST CLARE'S HOSPITAL/DENVILLE** See Saint Clare's Hospital/Denville

## DOVER—Morris County

☒ **KINDRED HOSPITAL-NEW JERSEY MORRIS COUNTY (312020)**, 400 West Blackwell Street, Zip 07801–2525; tel. 973/537–3818, (Includes KINDRED HOSPITAL NEW JERSEY - RAHWAY, Mailing address: 865 Stone Street, Rahway, New Jersey, Zip 7065; tel. 732/669–8200; Patrick J O'Connor, Chief Executive Officer; KINDRED HOSPITAL NEW JERSEY - WAYNE, Mailing address: 224 Hamburg Turnpike, Wayne, New Jersey, Zip 7470; tel. 973/636–7200; Alice M O'Connor, Chief Executive Officer), (Nonreporting) **A**1 10 **S** Kindred Healthcare, Louisville, KY
Primary Contact: Tarra Washington, Chief Executive Officer
CFO: Stephen D. Farber, Chief Financial Officer
CMO: Sean R Muldoon, M.D., Chief Medical Officer
Web address: www.khmorriscounty.com/
**Control**: Corporation, Investor–owned (for–profit) **Service**: Acute long–term care hospital

**Staffed Beds**: 117

**ST. CLARE'S HOSPITAL/DOVER** See Saint Clare's Hospital/Dover

## EAST ORANGE—Essex County

☐ **EAST ORANGE GENERAL HOSPITAL (310083)**, 300 Central Avenue, Zip 07018–2897; tel. 973/672–8400, (Nonreporting) **A**1 10 **F**3 12 15 17 18 28 29 30 34 35 38 40 44 45 48 49 50 51 53 57 59 60 64 65 66 70 74 75 77 79 81 82 84 85 86 87 92 93 94 97 98 100 101 104 107 108 110 111 114 119 130 132 135 143 147 149 150 156 157 158 **P**5 **S** Prospect Medical Holdings, Los Angeles, CA
Primary Contact: Paige Dworak, FACHE, Chief Executive Officer
CMO: Valentine Burroughs, M.D., Chief Medical Officer
CIO: Thomas Ciccarelli, Chief Information Officer
CHR: Chester Banks, Director Human Resources
Web address: www.evh.org
**Control**: Corporation, Investor–owned (for–profit) **Service**: General medical and surgical

**Staffed Beds**: 143 **Admissions**: 5833 **Census**: 96 **Outpatient Visits**: 55214 **Births**: 0 **Total Expense ($000)**: 112212 **Payroll Expense ($000)**: 46273 **Personnel**: 740

**VETERANS ADM MEDICAL CENTER** See East Orange Division

☒ **VETERANS AFFAIRS NEW JERSEY HEALTH CARE SYSTEM**, 385 Tremont Avenue, Zip 07018–1095; tel. 973/676–1000, (Includes EAST ORANGE DIVISION, Mailing address: 385 Tremont Avenue, East Orange, New Jersey, Zip 07018–1095; tel. 973/676–1000; LYONS DIVISION, Mailing address: 151 Knollcroft Road, Lyons, New Jersey, Zip 07939–9998; tel. 908/647–0180), (Nonreporting) **A**1 2 3 5 **S** Department of Veterans Affairs, Washington, DC
Primary Contact: John Griffith, R.N., Associate Director
CFO: Tyrone Taylor, Chief Financial Officer
CMO: Steven L Lieberman, M.D., Chief of Staff
CIO: Kamesha Scarlett, Chief Information Resource Management
CHR: Nancy Hamilton, Chief Human and Learning Resources
CNO: Patrick J Troy, R.N., MSN, Associate Director Patient Care Services
Web address: www.newjersey.va.gov/
**Control**: Veterans Affairs, Government, federal **Service**: General medical and surgical

**Staffed Beds**: 429

## EDISON—Middlesex County

☒ **HACKENSACK MERIDIAN HEALTH JFK MEDICAL CENTER (310108)**, 65 James Street, Zip 8818; tel. 732/321–7000, (Nonreporting) **A**1 2 3 5 10 **F**2 3 5 6 7 8 11 12 13 14 15 18 20 22 26 28 29 30 31 34 35 36 37 38 39 40 41 42 44 45 47 49 50 51 53 54 56 57 58 59 60 61 63 64 66 68 69 70 71 73 74 75 76 77 78 79 80 81 82 84 85 86 87 89 90 91 92 93 94 96 97 100 101 102 104 107 108 109 110 111 113 114 115 116 117 118 119 120 121 123 124 126 129 130 131 132 135 141 143 144 145 146 147 148 149 153 154 156 **S** Hackensack Meridian Health, Edison, NJ
Primary Contact: Amie D. Thornton, Chief Hospital Executive
COO: Scott Gebhard, Executive VP and Chief Operating Officer
CFO: Richard C. Smith, Senior Vice President and Chief Financial Officer
CMO: William F. Oser, M.D., Senior Vice President and Chief Medical Officer
CIO: Indranil Ganguly, Vice President and Chief Information Officer
CHR: Shirley Higgins Bowers, Senior Vice President Human Resources
CNO: James Lindquist, Chief Nursing Officer
Web address: www.jfkmc.org
**Control**: Other not–for–profit (including NFP Corporation) **Service**: General medical and surgical

**Staffed Beds**: 360 **Admissions**: 39055 **Census**: 256 **Outpatient Visits**: 270923 **Births**: 2130 **Total Expense ($000)**: 514117 **Payroll Expense ($000)**: 224109 **Personnel**: 3147

**JFK JOHNSON REHABILITATION INSTITUTE** See Jfk Johnson Rehabilitation Institute at Hackensack Meridian Health

★ △ **JFK JOHNSON REHABILITATION INSTITUTE AT HACKENSACK MERIDIAN HEALTH**, 65 James Street, Zip 8818; tel. 732/321–7050, (Nonreporting) **A**5 7 **F**3 9 28 29 30 35 36 44 50 53 54 64 82 87 90 91 92 93 94 96 130 131 132 143 149 150 157 **S** Hackensack Meridian Health, Edison, NJ
Primary Contact: Anthony Cuzzola, Vice President Operations
COO: Scott Gebhard, Chief Operating Officer
CFO: Richard C. Smith, Chief Financial Officer
CMO: William F. Oser, M.D., Chief Medical Officer
CIO: Neal Ganguly, Chief Information Officer
CNO: James Lindquist, Chief Nursing Officer
Web address: www.njrehab.org
**Control**: Other not–for–profit (including NFP Corporation) **Service**: Rehabilitation

**Staffed Beds**: 94 **Admissions**: 1842 **Census**: 71 **Outpatient Visits**: 208089 **Births**: 0 **Total Expense ($000)**: 84649 **Payroll Expense ($000)**: 54052 **Personnel**: 648

**JFK MEDICAL CENTER** See Hackensack Meridian Health Jfk Medical Center

**ROOSEVELT HOSPITAL** See Roosevelt Care Center

## ELIZABETH—Union County

**CARE ONE AT TRINITAS REGIONAL MEDICAL CENTER** See Careone at Trinitas Regional Medical Center

**CAREONE AT TRINITAS REGIONAL MEDICAL CENTER (312018)**, 225 Williamson Street, Zip 07202–3625; tel. 908/994–5288, (Nonreporting) **A**10
Primary Contact: Sharon Bready, R.N., Chief Executive Officer
Web address: www.care-one.com/locations/ltach-careone-at-trinitas-regional-medical-center/
**Control**: Other not–for–profit (including NFP Corporation) **Service**: Acute long–term care hospital

**Staffed Beds**: 25

**TRINITAS HOSPITAL - JERSEY STREET CAMPUS** See Trinitas Hospital

**TRINITAS HOSPITAL - NEW POINT CAMPUS** See Trinitas Regional Medical Center - New Point Campus

**TRINITAS HOSPITAL-WILLIAMSON STREET CAMPUS** See Trinitas Regional Medical Center

*Many Facility Codes have changed. Please refer to the AHA Guide Code Chart.*   © 2021 AHA Guide

✠ **TRINITAS REGIONAL MEDICAL CENTER (310027)**, 225 Williamson Street, Zip 07202–3625; tel. 908/994–5000, (Includes TRINITAS HOSPITAL, Mailing address: 225 Williamson Street, Elizabeth, New Jersey, Zip 7207; tel. 908/994–5000; Gary S Horan, FACHE, President and Chief Executive Officer; TRINITAS REGIONAL MEDICAL CENTER - NEW POINT CAMPUS, Mailing address: 655 East Jersey Street, Elizabeth, New Jersey, Zip 7206; tel. 908/994–5000; Gary S Horan, FACHE, President and Chief Executive Officer) (Total facility includes 124 beds in nursing home–type unit) **A**1 2 3 5 10 **F**3 5 7 8 11 13 15 17 18 20 22 28 29 30 31 32 34 35 36 38 40 44 45 46 48 49 53 55 56 57 58 59 60 61 64 65 66 68 70 73 74 75 76 77 79 81 82 84 85 86 87 91 93 97 98 99 100 101 102 103 104 105 106 107 108 110 111 115 117 118 119 120 121 123 126 128 129 130 132 134 135 141 143 146 147 148 149 153 154 157 **P**6
Primary Contact: Gary S. Horan, FACHE, President and Chief Executive Officer
CFO: Karen Lumpp, Senior Vice President and Chief Financial Officer
CMO: William McHugh, M.D., Medical Director and Chief Medical Officer
CIO: Judy Comitto, Vice President Information Services and Chief Information Officer
CHR: Glenn Nacion, Vice President Human Resources
CNO: Mary McTigue, Vice President Patient Care Services and Chief Nursing Officer
Web address: www.trinitasrmc.com
**Control**: Other not–for–profit (including NFP Corporation) **Service**: General medical and surgical

**Staffed Beds**: 464 **Admissions**: 11094 **Census**: 335 **Outpatient Visits**: 429950 **Births**: 1387 **Total Expense ($000)**: 302442 **Payroll Expense ($000)**: 142480 **Personnel**: 2266

### ELMER—Salem County

★ ⇑ **INSPIRA MEDICAL CENTER-ELMER (310069)**, 501 West Front Street, Zip 08318–2101; tel. 856/363–1000, (Includes INSPIRA MEDICAL CENTER MULLICA HILL, Mailing address: 700 Mullica Hill Road, Mullica Hill, New Jersey, Zip 08062–4413; tel. 856/508–1000; Amy B. Mansue, President and Chief Executive Officer), (Nonreporting) **A**3 10 21 **F**3 7 8 11 12 13 15 18 28 29 30 34 37 38 40 42 44 50 57 59 64 68 70 74 75 76 77 78 79 81 82 85 86 87 93 107 108 110 111 114 115 116 117 118 119 120 121 123 124 126 130 131 132 134 146 147 148 154 **P**1 **S** Inspira Health Network, Mullica Hill, NJ
Primary Contact: Amy B. Mansue, President and Chief Executive Officer
COO: David Yhlen, Chief Operating Officer
CFO: Thomas Baldosaro, Chief Financial Officer
CMO: Steven C Linn, M.D., Chief Medical Officer
CIO: Thomas Pacek, Vice President Information Systems and Chief Information Officer
CHR: Erich Florentine, Chief People Officer
CNO: Elizabeth Sheridan, Chief Operating Officer and Chief Nursing Executive
Web address: www.inspirahealthnetwork.org/?id=5281&sid=1
**Control**: Other not–for–profit (including NFP Corporation) **Service**: General medical and surgical

**Staffed Beds**: 97 **Admissions**: 3081 **Census**: 34 **Outpatient Visits**: 56946 **Births**: 312 **Total Expense ($000)**: 74671 **Payroll Expense ($000)**: 33102 **Personnel**: 302

⇑ **SOUTH JERSEY HEALTHCARE - ELMER HOSPITAL** See Inspira Medical Center-Elmer

### ENGLEWOOD—Bergen County

✠ **ENGLEWOOD HEALTH (310045)**, 350 Engle Street, Zip 07631–1898; tel. 201/894–3000, (Nonreporting) **A**1 2 3 5 10 **F**3 5 6 7 8 9 11 12 13 15 17 18 19 20 22 24 26 28 29 30 31 32 34 35 36 37 38 39 40 41 44 45 46 47 48 49 50 51 53 54 55 56 57 58 59 60 61 62 63 64 65 68 70 71 72 73 74 75 76 77 78 79 80 81 82 83 84 85 86 87 89 91 92 93 94 96 97 98 100 101 102 103 104 107 108 110 111 114 115 116 117 118 119 120 121 123 124 126 129 130 131 132 133 134 135 141 143 144 145 146 147 148 149 150 153 154 156 157 **P**3 6
Primary Contact: Warren Geller, President and Chief Executive Officer
COO: Helene Wolk, Senior Vice President Operations and Chief Operating Officer
CFO: Anthony T Orlando, Senior Vice President Finance
CIO: Ravikanth Koganti, Vice President Information Technology
CHR: Patricia Wilson, Senior Vice President Human Resources
CNO: Kathleen A. Kaminsky, R.N., Senior Vice President Patient Care Services
Web address: www.englewoodhealth.org
**Control**: Other not–for–profit (including NFP Corporation) **Service**: General medical and surgical

**Staffed Beds**: 295 **Admissions**: 15815 **Census**: 203 **Outpatient Visits**: 1490385 **Births**: 2772 **Total Expense ($000)**: 725235 **Payroll Expense ($000)**: 174716 **Personnel**: 3085

**ENGLEWOOD HOSPITAL AND MEDICAL CENTER** See Englewood Health

### FLEMINGTON—Hunterdon County

✠ **HUNTERDON HEALTHCARE (310005)**, 2100 Wescott Drive, Zip 08822–4604; tel. 908/788–6100, (Nonreporting) **A**1 2 3 5 10 13 **F**3 4 5 8 11 12 13 14 15 17 18 20 22 29 30 31 33 38 40 45 48 49 53 54 55 56 57 58 59 60 61 62 63 65 68 70 71 73 74 75 76 77 78 79 81 82 83 84 85 86 87 89 91 92 93 94 97 98 99 100 101 102 103 104 105 106 107 108 110 114 115 118 119 121 123 126 129 130 131 132 134 135 144 146 147 148 149 150 151 152 153 154 157
Primary Contact: Patrick J. Gavin, M.P.H., President and Chief Executive Officer
COO: Lawrence N Grand, MS, R.N., Chief Operating Officer
CFO: Gail Kosyla, Chief Financial Officer and Senior Vice President Strategy
CMO: Robert Coates, M.D., Vice President, Medical Affairs
CIO: Daniel Morreale, Chief Information Officer
CHR: Violet Kocsis, Chief Human Resources Officer
CNO: Patricia Steingall, MS, R.N., R.N., MS, Vice President, Patient Care Services
Web address: www.hunterdonhealthcare.org
**Control**: Other not–for–profit (including NFP Corporation) **Service**: General medical and surgical

**Staffed Beds**: 184 **Admissions**: 8961 **Census**: 104 **Outpatient Visits**: 733364 **Births**: 1046 **Total Expense ($000)**: 346039 **Payroll Expense ($000)**: 165120 **Personnel**: 2248

**HUNTERDON MEDICAL CENTER** See Hunterdon Healthcare

### FREEHOLD—Monmouth County

✠ **CENTRASTATE HEALTHCARE SYSTEM (310111)**, 901 West Main Street, Zip 07728–2549; tel. 732/431–2000, (Nonreporting) **A**1 2 3 5 10 **F**3 11 12.13 15 18 19 20 28 29 30 31 32 34 35 36 37 38 40 41 45 46 47 49 56 57 58 59 61 64 65 66 70 73 74 75 76 77 78 79 81 82 84 86 87 89 92 93 97 98 100 101 102 107 108 110 114 118 119 120 121 123 124 126 129 130 131 132 134 135 146 147 148 149 154 156 **P**1 6
Primary Contact: John Gribbin, FACHE, President and Chief Executive Officer
COO: Thomas W. Scott, Senior Vice President and Chief Operating Officer
CFO: John Dellocono, Senior Vice President and Chief Financial Officer
CMO: Jack H Dworkin, M.D., Vice President Medical Affairs and Chief Medical Officer
CIO: John Ulett, Vice President and Chief Information Officer
CHR: Fran Keane, Vice President Human Resources
CNO: Linda W Geisler, R.N., FACHE, Vice President Patient Services
Web address: www.centrastate.com
**Control**: Other not–for–profit (including NFP Corporation) **Service**: General medical and surgical

**Staffed Beds**: 259 **Admissions**: 12189 **Census**: 159 **Outpatient Visits**: 239861 **Births**: 664 **Total Expense ($000)**: 293913 **Payroll Expense ($000)**: 115709 **Personnel**: 1492

**CENTRASTATE MEDICAL CENTER** See Centrastate Healthcare System

### HACKENSACK—Bergen County

✠ **HACKENSACK MERIDIAN HEALTH HACKENSACK UNIVERSITY MEDICAL CENTER (310001)**, 30 Prospect Avenue, Zip 07601–1914; tel. 201/996–2000, (Includes THE JOSEPH M. SANZARI CHILDREN'S HOSPITAL, Mailing address: 30 Prospect Avenue, Hackensack, New Jersey, Zip 07601–1914; tel. 201/996–2000), (Nonreporting) **A**1 2 3 5 8 10 **F**2 3 5 6 7 8 9 11 12 13 14 15 17 18 19 20 22 24 26 28 29 30 31 32 33 34 35 36 37 38 39 40 41 43 44 45 46 47 48 49 50 51 52 53 54 55 56 57 58 59 60 61 63 64 65 66 68 69 70 71 72 73 74 75 76 77 78 79 81 82 84 85 86 87 88 89 91 92 93 94 96 97 98 99 100 101 102 103 104 107 108 109 110 111 112 113 114 115 116 117 118 119 120 121 123 124 126 129 130 131 132 134 135 136 138 141 142 143 145 146 147 148 149 150 153 154 155 156 157 158 **S** Hackensack Meridian Health, Edison, NJ
Primary Contact: Mark Sparta, President
CFO: Robert Glenning, Executive Vice President Finance and Chief Financial Officer
CMO: Peter A Gross, M.D., Senior Vice President and Chief Medical Officer
CHR: Nancy R Corcoran, Senior Vice President Human Resources and Quality Service
Web address: www.hackensackumc.org
**Control**: Other not–for–profit (including NFP Corporation) **Service**: General medical and surgical

**Staffed Beds**: 748 **Admissions**: 74210 **Census**: 617 **Outpatient Visits**: 511060 **Births**: 5610 **Total Expense ($000)**: 1732290 **Payroll Expense ($000)**: 623282 **Personnel**: 8333

**HACKENSACK UNIVERSITY MEDICAL CENTER** See Hackensack Meridian Health Hackensack University Medical Center

**NJ**

## HACKETTSTOWN—Warren County

✠ **HACKETTSTOWN MEDICAL CENTER (310115)**, 651 Willow Grove Street, Zip 07840–1799; tel. 908/852–5100, (Nonreporting) **A**1 10 **F**3 5 11 12 15 18 28 29 30 31 34 35 36 38 40 41 44 45 47 49 50 53 56 57 59 60 63 64 65 68 70 74 75 77 78 79 81 82 84 85 86 87 93 94 100 101 102 104 107 108 110 111 114 116 117 118 119 120 129 130 132 135 141 146 148 149 154 156 **P**3 6 **S** Atlantic Health System, Morristown, NJ
Primary Contact: Robert H. Adams, President, Western Region
COO: Donna Watridge, R.N., Director of Operations
CFO: Robert Peterson, CPA, Chief Financial Officer
CMO: Paul Owens, M.D., Chief Medical Officer
CIO: Dorothy Cox, Manager Information Systems
CHR: Kimberly McGovern, Manager Human Resources
CNO: Donna Watridge, R.N., Chief Nursing Officer
Web address: www.atlantichealth.org
**Control**: Other not–for–profit (including NFP Corporation) **Service**: General medical and surgical

**Staffed Beds**: 61 **Admissions**: 3601 **Census**: 41 **Outpatient Visits**: 58909 **Births**: 0 **Total Expense ($000)**: 114833 **Payroll Expense ($000)**: 50553 **Personnel**: 599

**HACKETTSTOWN REGIONAL MEDICAL CENTER** See Hackettstown Medical Center

## HAMILTON—Mercer County

**HAMILTON HOSPITAL** See Robert Wood Johnson University Hospital at Hamilton

✠ **ROBERT WOOD JOHNSON UNIVERSITY HOSPITAL AT HAMILTON (310110)**, One Hamilton Health Place, Zip 08690–3599; tel. 609/586–7900, (Nonreporting) **A**1 2 5 10 **F**3 11 12 15 18 20 22 26 28 29 30 31 32 34 35 36 37 40 41 45 46 47 48 49 50 51 54 55 56 57 58 59 64 65 66 68 69 70 74 75 77 78 79 81 82 84 85 86 87 90 92 93 94 95 96 97 100 107 108 110 111 114 115 116 117 119 121 124 126 129 130 131 132 134 135 143 144 145 146 147 148 149 150 154 156 **P**6 **S** RWJBarnabas Health, West Orange, NJ
Primary Contact: Richard Freeman, President and Chief Executive Officer
COO: Barbara H Smith, Senior Vice President & Chief Operating Officer
CMO: Ronald Ryder, D.O., President of the Medical Staff
CIO: L. Gill Gottle, Senior Vice President and Chief Financial Officer
CNO: Lisa Breza, R.N., Vice President and Chief Nursing Officer
Web address: www.rwjhamilton.org
**Control**: Other not–for–profit (including NFP Corporation) **Service**: General medical and surgical

**Staffed Beds**: 164 **Admissions**: 6942 **Census**: 100 **Outpatient Visits**: 143518 **Births**: 0 **Total Expense ($000)**: 197506 **Payroll Expense ($000)**: 68625 **Personnel**: 949

## HAMMONTON—Camden County

☐ **ANCORA PSYCHIATRIC HOSPITAL (314005)**, 301 Spring Garden Road, Zip 08037–9699; tel. 609/561–1700, (Nonreporting) **A**1 3 10 **F**29 30 39 44 50 56 59 68 75 77 86 87 97 98 101 103 105 106 130 132 135 143 148 149 154 156 **S** Division of Mental Health and Addiction Services, Department of Human Services, State of New Jersey, Trenton, NJ
Primary Contact: Joseph Canale, Acting Chief Executive Officer
CFO: John Holmes, Business Manager
CIO: Charlene Ruberti, Director Information Technology Development
CHR: Alfred Filipini, Manager Human Resources
Web address: www.https://www.state.nj.us/humanservices/dmhas/resources/services/treatment/aph.html
**Control**: State, Government, Nonfederal **Service**: Psychiatric

**Staffed Beds**: 465 **Admissions**: 567 **Census**: 402 **Outpatient Visits**: 1080 **Births**: 0 **Total Expense ($000)**: 13900 **Personnel**: 1506

## HOBOKEN—Hudson County

☐ **CAREPOINT HEALTH HOBOKEN UNIVERSITY MEDICAL CENTER (310040)**, 308 Willow Avenue, Zip 07030–3889; tel. 201/418–1000, (Nonreporting) **A**1 3 5 10 **S** CarePoint Health, Jersey City, NJ
Primary Contact: Ann P. Logan, R.N., Ph.D., Chief Hospital Executive
COO: Ann P. Logan, R.N., Ph.D., Chief Hospital Executive
CMO: Meika Roberson, M.D., Chief Medical Officer
CIO: Joel Taylor, Chief Information Officer
CHR: Roberto Gonzalez, Executive Director Human Resources
CNO: Neena S. Philip, R.N., Vice President of Patient Care Services and Chief Nursing Officer
Web address: www.hobokenumc.com
**Control**: Corporation, Investor–owned (for–profit) **Service**: General medical and surgical

**Staffed Beds**: 228

**HOBOKEN UNIVERSITY MEDICAL CENTER** See Carepoint Health Hoboken University Medical Center

## HOLMDEL—Monmouth County

**BAYSHORE COMMUNITY HOSPITAL** See Hackensack Meridian Health Bayshore Community Hospital

✠ **HACKENSACK MERIDIAN HEALTH BAYSHORE COMMUNITY HOSPITAL (310112)**, 727 North Beers Street, Zip 07733–1598; tel. 732/739–5900, (Nonreporting) **A**1 2 5 10 **F**3 11 12 15 18 20 22 28 29 30 32 34 35 36 38 39 40 41 44 45 46 49 50 51 54 55 56 57 58 59 60 61 63 64 65 66 68 69 70 71 74 75 77 78 79 81 82 84 85 86 87 92 93 94 96 97 100 101 102 108 110 111 114 116 117 118 119 126 129 130 131 132 134 135 141 144 146 147 148 149 150 154 **S** Hackensack Meridian Health, Edison, NJ
Primary Contact: Frank Citara, Chief Hospital Executive
CFO: Joseph M Lemaire, Executive Vice President Finance and Partner Company Operations
CMO: Ian Leber, M.D., Chief Medical Officer
CIO: Rebecca Weber, Senior Vice President and Chief Information Officer
CHR: Sherrie String, Senior Vice President Human Resources
CNO: Linda Walsh, R.N., MSN, Vice President Chief Nursing Executive
Web address: www.bchs.com
**Control**: Other not–for–profit (including NFP Corporation) **Service**: General medical and surgical

**Staffed Beds**: 160 **Admissions**: 16999 **Census**: 116 **Outpatient Visits**: 83156 **Births**: 0 **Total Expense ($000)**: 164339 **Payroll Expense ($000)**: 77738 **Personnel**: 847

## JERSEY CITY—Hudson County

☐ **CAREPOINT HEALTH CHRIST HOSPITAL (310016)**, 176 Palisade Avenue, Zip 07306–1196, Mailing Address: 176 Palisades Avenue, Zip 07306–1196; tel. 201/795–8200, (Nonreporting) **A**1 3 10 12 13 **S** CarePoint Health, Jersey City, NJ
Primary Contact: Marie Theresa Duffy, Chief Hospital Executive
COO: Marie Theresa Duffy, Chief Operating Officer
CFO: Gary Bryant, Executive Vice President and Chief Financial Officer
CHR: Josiane Deroncerey, Director Human Resources
CNO: Denise Cimmino, MSN, R.N., Assistant Vice President, Nursing and Patient Care Services
Web address: www.carepointhealth.org
**Control**: Other not–for–profit (including NFP Corporation) **Service**: General medical and surgical

**Staffed Beds**: 376

**CAREPOINT HEALTH -CHRIST HOSPITAL** See Carepoint Health Christ Hospital

★ ⇑ **JERSEY CITY MEDICAL CENTER (310074)**, 355 Grand Street, Zip 07302–4321; tel. 201/915–2000, (Nonreporting) **A**3 5 10 13 21 **F**3 5 7 8 11 13 15 17 18 20 22 24 26 29 30 31 34 35 38 39 40 41 42 43 45 46 47 48 49 50 54 55 56 57 59 60 61 64 65 66 68 70 71 72 73 74 75 76 77 78 79 81 84 85 87 89 91 92 93 96 97 98 100 101 102 104 105 107 108 110 111 112 114 115 119 126 130 132 143 146 147 148 149 153 154 156 157 158 **P**3 6 **S** RWJBarnabas Health, West Orange, NJ
Primary Contact: Michael Prilutsky, President and Chief Executive Officer
CFO: Paul R Goldberg, Chief Financial Officer
CMO: Kenneth Garay, M.D., Chief Medical Officer
CIO: Stephen Li, Vice President Management Information Systems
CHR: Mary Cataudella, Corporate Director Human Resources
CNO: Joanne Reich, R.N., Chief Nursing Officer
Web address: www.barnabashealth.org/Jersey-City-Medical-Center.aspx
**Control**: Other not–for–profit (including NFP Corporation) **Service**: General medical and surgical

**Staffed Beds**: 332 **Admissions**: 13990 **Census**: 207 **Outpatient Visits**: 249482 **Births**: 1957 **Total Expense ($000)**: 395393 **Payroll Expense ($000)**: 159357 **Personnel**: 2352

⇑ **LIBERTYHEALTH-JERSEY CITY MEDICAL CENTER** See Jersey City Medical Center

*Many Facility Codes have changed. Please refer to the AHA Guide Code Chart.*

## LAKEWOOD—Ocean County

**MONMOUTH MEDICAL CENTER - SOUTHERN CAMPUS** See Monmouth Medical Center, Southern Campus

☒ **MONMOUTH MEDICAL CENTER, SOUTHERN CAMPUS (310084)**, 600 River Avenue, Zip 08701–5237; tel. 732/363–1900, (Nonreporting) **A**1 2 10 **F**3 11 12 15 18 28 29 30 31 34 35 36 38 40 41 44 49 50 51 56 57 58 59 60 61 64 65 66 68 70 74 75 77 78 79 81 82 84 85 86 87 92 93 97 98 100 101 102 103 104 107 108 110 111 114 115 116 117 119 130 131 132 135 143 146 148 149 154 156 157 **P**6 **S** RWJBarnabas Health, West Orange, NJ
Primary Contact: Eric Carney, Chief Executive Officer
COO: Jonathan Tango, Vice President, Operations
CFO: Nikolas Alexiades, Chief Financial Officer
CMO: Rajesh Mohan, M.D., Chief Medical Officer
CIO: Ray Duarte, Director, Information Technology and Services
CHR: Richard Kiernan, Regional Chief Human Resources Officer
CNO: Judy Colorado, R.N., Chief Nursing Officer
Web address: www.rwjbarnabashealth.org/monmouth-medical-center-southern-campus.aspx
**Control**: Other not–for–profit (including NFP Corporation) **Service**: General medical and surgical

**Staffed Beds**: 124 **Admissions**: 5883 **Census**: 101 **Outpatient Visits**: 81435 **Births**: 0 **Total Expense ($000)**: 128654 **Payroll Expense ($000)**: 51080 **Personnel**: 623

**SPECIALTY HOSPITAL AT KIMBALL** See Specialty Hospital of Central Jersey

☐ **SPECIALTY HOSPITAL OF CENTRAL JERSEY (312017)**, 600 River Avenue, 4 and 5 West, Zip 08701–5237; tel. 732/942–3588, (Nonreporting) **A**1 10
Primary Contact: Violeta Peters, R.N., Chief Executive Officer and Interim Center Director
CFO: Kristin Prentiss, Chief Financial Officer
CMO: Howard Lebowitz, M.D., Chief Medical Officer
CHR: Mary Pat Napolitano, Director Human Resources
CNO: Judy Boccellato, R.N., MSN, Chief Nursing Officer
Web address: www.acutecarehs.com
**Control**: Corporation, Investor–owned (for–profit) **Service**: Acute long–term care hospital

**Staffed Beds**: 50

## LAWRENCEVILLE—Mercer County

☒ **ST. LAWRENCE REHABILITATION CENTER (313027)**, 2381 Lawrenceville Road, Zip 08648–2025; tel. 609/896–9500, (Total facility includes 56 beds in nursing home–type unit) (Nonreporting) **A**1 10 **F**34 57 64 90 91 93 96 108 119 128 130 132 134 143 146 148 149
Primary Contact: Darlene S. Hanley, R.N., FACHE, President and Chief Executive Officer
COO: Shirley Pukala, R.N., Assistant Administrator Operations
CFO: Thomas W Boyle, Chief Financial Officer
CMO: Kevin McGuigan, M.D., Medical Director
CIO: Joseph Castronuevo, Director Information Management
CHR: John Levi, Director Human Resources
CNO: Hsiu-chin Brix, R.N., Director of Nursing
Web address: www.slrc.org
**Control**: Church operated, Nongovernment, not–for–profit **Service**: Rehabilitation

**Staffed Beds**: 116 **Admissions**: 1874 **Census**: 81 **Outpatient Visits**: 22577 **Births**: 0 **Total Expense ($000)**: 32109 **Payroll Expense ($000)**: 18910 **Personnel**: 291

## LIVINGSTON—Essex County

☒ **SAINT BARNABAS MEDICAL CENTER (310076)**, 94 Old Short Hills Rd, Zip 07039–5672; tel. 973/322–5000, (Nonreporting) **A**1 2 3 5 8 10 13 **F**3 7 8 11 12 13 16 17 18 19 20 22 24 28 29 30 31 32 34 35 36 37 38 39 40 41 44 45 46 47 48 49 50 53 54 55 56 57 58 59 60 61 63 64 65 66 68 69 70 71 72 73 74 75 76 77 78 79 81 82 84 85 86 87 88 89 91 92 93 94 96 97 100 101 102 107 108 111 114 115 118 119 120 121 123 124 126 129 130 131 132 134 135 138 141 142 143 144 146 147 148 149 150 154 156 157 **P**3 6 **S** RWJBarnabas Health, West Orange, NJ
Primary Contact: Stephen P. Zieniewicz, FACHE, President and Chief Executive Officer
COO: Patrick Ahearn, Chief Operating Officer and Senior Vice President
CFO: Richard Davis, Chief Financial Officer
CMO: Gregory Rokosz, D.O., Senior Vice President Medical and Academic Affairs
CIO: Michael McTigue, Chief Information Officer
CHR: Arnold D Manzo, Vice President Human Resources
CNO: Maggie Lundberg, R.N., Chief Nursing Officer
Web address: www.barnabashealth.org/hospitals/saint_barnabas/index.html
**Control**: Other not–for–profit (including NFP Corporation) **Service**: General medical and surgical

**Staffed Beds**: 561 **Admissions**: 28634 **Census**: 427 **Outpatient Visits**: 343137 **Births**: 5957 **Total Expense ($000)**: 865197 **Payroll Expense ($000)**: 292322 **Personnel**: 3713

**ST BARNABAS MEDICAL CENTER** See Saint Barnabas Medical Center

## LONG BRANCH—Monmouth County

**MONMOUTH MEDICAL CENTER** See Monmouth Medical Center, Long Branch Campus

☒ **MONMOUTH MEDICAL CENTER, LONG BRANCH CAMPUS (310075)**, 300 Second Avenue, Zip 07740–6303; tel. 732/222–5200, (Includes CHILDREN'S HOSPITAL AT MONMOUTH MEDICAL CENTER, Mailing address: 300 Second Avenue, Long Branch, New Jersey, Zip 07740–6303; tel. 732/222–5200), (Nonreporting) **A**1 2 3 5 8 10 **F**3 9 11 12 13 15 18 20 22 28 29 30 31 34 35 37 38 39 40 41 43 44 45 46 47 48 49 50 51 54 55 56 57 58 59 60 61 63 64 66 68 70 72 73 74 75 76 77 78 79 81 82 84 85 86 87 88 89 96 97 98 99 100 101 102 104 105 107 108 109 110 111 114 115 117 118 119 120 121 123 124 126 129 130 132 135 141 143 145 146 147 148 149 153 154 156 157 **P**3 6 **S** RWJBarnabas Health, West Orange, NJ
Primary Contact: Eric Carney, Chief Executive Officer
CMO: Eric Burkett, M.D., Vice President Medical Affairs
CIO: Chris Butler, Chief Information Officer
CHR: Richard Kiernan, Vice President Human Resources
CNO: Diann Johnston, R.N., MSN, Vice President of Patient Care Services
Web address: www.barnabashealth.org/hospitals/monmouth_medical/index.html
**Control**: Other not–for–profit (including NFP Corporation) **Service**: General medical and surgical

**Staffed Beds**: 276 **Admissions**: 17935 **Census**: 205 **Outpatient Visits**: 216130 **Births**: 5797 **Total Expense ($000)**: 394191 **Payroll Expense ($000)**: 152652 **Personnel**: 2059

**THE CHILDREN'S HOSPITAL AT MONMOUTH MEDICAL CENTER** See Children's Hospital at Monmouth Medical Center

## LYONS—Somerset County

**LYONS DIVISION** See Veterans Affairs New Jersey Health Care System, East Orange

**VETERANS AFFAIRS NEW JERSEY HEALTH CARE SYSTEM** See Lyons Division

**NJ**

## MANAHAWKIN—Ocean County

⊞ **HACKENSACK MERIDIAN HEALTH SOUTHERN OCEAN MEDICAL CENTER (310113)**, 1140 Route 72 West, Zip 08050–2499; tel. 609/597–6011, (Nonreporting) **A**1 2 5 10 **F**3 11 12 13 15 18 20 28 29 30 31 32 34 35 36 38 39 44 45 46 48 49 50 51 54 55 56 57 58 59 60 61 63 64 65 66 68 70 71 74 75 76 77 78 79 81 82 84 85 86 87 92 93 94 96 97 100 101 102 107 108 110 111 114 115 119 120 121 123 128 129 130 131 132 134 135 144 145 146 147 148 149 154 156 **S** Hackensack Meridian Health, Edison, NJ
Primary Contact: Michele Morrison, R.N., M.P.H., Chief Hospital Executive
CFO: Joseph M Lemaire, Executive Vice President
CMO: Theodore Zaleski, M.D., Vice President Clinical Effectiveness
CIO: Rebecca Weber, Senior Vice President and Chief Information Officer
CHR: Susan Tillman-Taylor, Manager Human Resources
CNO: Donna Ciufo, R.N., Vice President and Chief Nurse Executive
Web address: www.soch.com
**Control**: Other not–for–profit (including NFP Corporation) **Service**: General medical and surgical

**Staffed Beds: 156 Admissions: 16126 Census: 97 Outpatient Visits: 100466 Births: 328 Total Expense ($000): 197669 Payroll Expense ($000): 79967 Personnel: 841**

**SOUTHERN OCEAN MEDICAL CENTER** See Hackensack Meridian Health Southern Ocean Medical Center

## MARLTON—Burlington County

⊞ △ **KESSLER MARLTON REHABILITATION (313032)**, 92 Brick Road, Zip 08053–2177; tel. 856/988–8778, (Nonreporting) **A**1 7 10 **F**3 29 85 90 130 132 157 **P**8 **S** Select Medical Corporation, Mechanicsburg, PA
Primary Contact: Phyllis J. Schlichtmann, R.N., Chief Executive Officer
CFO: Stuart Moss, Chief Financial Officer
CMO: Kenneth Wu, M.D., Medical Director
CHR: Joanne Cernava, Director Human Resources
CNO: Chris Kreeley, Director Nursing
Web address: www.marltonrehab.com
**Control**: Corporation, Investor–owned (for–profit) **Service**: Rehabilitation

**Staffed Beds: 61 Admissions: 1496 Census: 53 Outpatient Visits: 12982 Births: 0 Personnel: 193**

**MARLTON REHABILITATION HOSPITAL** See Kessler Marlton Rehabilitation

⊞ **VIRTUA MARLTON**, 90 Brick Road, Zip 08053–2177; tel. 856/355–6000, (Nonreporting) **A**1 2 3 5 **F**3 12 18 20 22 29 30 31 40 45 46 47 49 56 60 64 70 75 77 78 79 81 82 84 85 87 91 92 107 108 111 114 115 118 119 130 141 146 149 157 **P**1 **S** Virtua Health, Marlton, NJ
Primary Contact: Dennis W. Pullin, FACHE, President and Chief Executive Officer
COO: Lisa Ferraro, Senior Vice President and Chief Operating Officer
CFO: Robert Segin, Executive Vice President & Chief Financial Officer
CMO: John Matsinger, D.O., Chief Medical Officer
CIO: Thomas Gordon, Chief Information Officer
CHR: Rhonda R Jordan, Chief Human Resources Officer
Web address: www.virtua.org
**Control**: Other not–for–profit (including NFP Corporation) **Service**: General medical and surgical

**Staffed Beds: 185 Admissions: 7632 Census: 100 Outpatient Visits: 42107 Births: 0 Total Expense ($000): 142103 Payroll Expense ($000): 47156 Personnel: 590**

**VIRTUA WEST JERSEY HOSPITAL-MARLTON** See Virtua Marlton

☐ **WEISMAN CHILDREN'S REHABILITATION HOSPITAL (313302)**, 92 Brick Road 3rd Floor, Zip 08053–2177; tel. 856/489–4520, (Nonreporting) **A**1 10
Primary Contact: Kathy Hall-Olsen, Administrator
CMO: Connie Domingo, M.D., Medical Director
CIO: Darren Pedersen, Coordinator Information Technology
CHR: Jill Koerner, Manager Employee Relations
CNO: Daniel William Pfeffer, Chief Nurse Executive
Web address: www.weismanchildrens.com
**Control**: Corporation, Investor–owned (for–profit) **Service**: Children's rehabilitation

**Staffed Beds: 24**

## MONTCLAIR—Essex County

⊞ **HACKENSACK MERIDIAN HEALTH MOUNTAINSIDE MEDICAL CENTER (310054)**, 1 Bay Avenue, Zip 07042–4898; tel. 973/429–6000, (Nonreporting) **A**1 2 3 5 10 **F**3 12 13 15 18 20 28 29 30 31 32 34 35 38 39 40 44 45 46 47 48 49 50 51 52 54 55 56 57 58 59 60 64 66 68 74 75 77 78 79 81 82 84 85 86 87 93 94 96 97 100 101 102 103 104 105 107 108 110 111 114 115 116 117 118 119 121 124 126 129 130 131 132 135 141 146 147 148 149 153 157 **P**5 **S** Ardent Health Services, Nashville, TN
Primary Contact: Tim O'Brien, Chief Executive Officer
CFO: Al Aboud, CPA, Chief Financial Officer
CMO: Valerie Alluson, M.D., Chief Medical Officer
CIO: Max Siu, Chief Information Officer
CNO: Debbie Regen, R.N., Chief Nursing Officer
Web address: www.mountainsidenow.com
**Control**: Partnership, Investor–owned (for–profit) **Service**: General medical and surgical

**Staffed Beds: 202 Admissions: 10211 Census: 135 Outpatient Visits: 104055 Births: 904 Total Expense ($000): 210003 Payroll Expense ($000): 90212 Personnel: 1077**

**HACKENSACK UNIVERSITY MEDICAL CENTER MOUNTAINSIDE** See Hackensack Meridian Health Mountainside Medical Center

## MORRIS PLAINS—Morris County

☐ **GREYSTONE PARK PSYCHIATRIC HOSPITAL (314016)**, 59 Koch Avenue, Zip 07950–4400; tel. 973/538–1800, (Nonreporting) **A**1 3 10 **S** Division of Mental Health and Addiction Services, Department of Human Services, State of New Jersey, Trenton, NJ
Primary Contact: Tomika Carter, Chief Executive Officer
COO: Stacey Provenzano, Chief Operating Officer
CFO: Jack Frey, Acting Business Manager
CMO: Cherry Monroy-Miller, M.D., Acting Medical Director
CIO: David Saleem, Director Information Technology
CHR: James Frey JrActing Manager Human Resources
Web address: www.https://www.state.nj.us/humanservices/dmhas/resources/services/treatment/gpph.html
**Control**: State, Government, Nonfederal **Service**: Psychiatric

**Staffed Beds: 468**

## MORRISTOWN—Morris County

⊞ **MORRISTOWN MEDICAL CENTER (310015)**, 100 Madison Avenue, Zip 07960–6136; tel. 973/971–5000, (Includes GORYEB CHILDREN'S HOSPITAL, Mailing address: 100 Madison Avenue, Morristown, New Jersey, Zip 07960–6136; tel. 973/971–5000), (Nonreporting) **A**1 2 3 5 8 10 **F**3 5 6 8 9 11 12 13 15 17 18 19 20 22 24 26 28 29 30 31 32 33 34 35 36 37 38 39 40 41 43 44 45 46 47 48 49 50 51 53 54 55 56 57 58 59 61 64 65 66 68 70 72 73 74 75 76 77 78 79 81 82 83 84 85 86 87 88 89 90 91 92 93 94 96 97 98 100 101 102 103 104 107 108 110 111 115 117 118 119 120 121 123 124 126 129 130 131 132 134 135 141 143 144 145 146 147 148 149 150 153 154 156 157 **P**3 6 **S** Atlantic Health System, Morristown, NJ
Primary Contact: Trish O'Keefe, Ph.D., R.N., President
CFO: Joseph D'Auria, Director Finance
CNO: Carol S. Jones, MSN, R.N., Interim Chief Nursing Officer
Web address: www.atlantichealth.org/Morristown/
**Control**: Other not–for–profit (including NFP Corporation) **Service**: General medical and surgical

**Staffed Beds: 737 Admissions: 38314 Census: 522 Outpatient Visits: 625285 Births: 4600 Total Expense ($000): 1546943 Payroll Expense ($000): 627380 Personnel: 6332**

**MORRISTOWN MEMORIAL HOSPITAL** See Morristown Medical Center

## MOUNT HOLLY—Burlington County

⊞ **VIRTUA MEMORIAL (310057)**, 175 Madison Avenue, Zip 08060–2099; tel. 609/267–0700, (Nonreporting) **A**1 3 5 10 **F**3 11 12 13 15 18 20 28 29 30 31 40 41 45 46 48 60 64 70 73 74 75 76 77 78 79 81 84 85 86 87 89 92 95 96 98 100 102 107 108 110 111 114 115 119 120 121 123 126 129 130 146 149 154 **P**1 **S** Virtua Health, Marlton, NJ
Primary Contact: Dennis W. Pullin, FACHE, President and Chief Executive Officer
COO: John Kirby, Senior Vice President and Chief Financial Officer
CFO: Robert Segin, Chief Financial Officer
CMO: James P Dwyer, D.O., Executive Vice President and Chief Medical Officer
CHR: E D Dunn, Vice President Human Resources
Web address: www.virtua.org
**Control**: Other not–for–profit (including NFP Corporation) **Service**: General medical and surgical

**Staffed Beds: 334 Admissions: 16188 Census: 200 Outpatient Visits: 148510 Births: 2133 Total Expense ($000): 323459 Payroll Expense ($000): 100755 Personnel: 1301**

**VIRTUA MEMORIAL HOSPITAL BURLINGTON COUNTY** See Virtua Memorial

*Many Facility Codes have changed. Please refer to the AHA Guide Code Chart.*

© 2021 AHA Guide

## NEPTUNE—Monmouth County

☒ **HACKENSACK MERIDIAN HEALTH JERSEY SHORE UNIVERSITY MEDICAL CENTER (310073)**, 1945 Route 33, Zip 07754–0397; tel. 732/775–5500, (Includes K. HOVNANIAN CHILDREN'S HOSPITAL, Mailing address: 1945 State Route 33, Neptune, New Jersey, Zip 07753–4859; tel. 800/560–9990), (Nonreporting) **A**1 2 3 5 8 10 **F**3 5 6 9 11 12 15 17 18 19 20 22 24 26 28 29 30 31 32 34 35 36 37 38 39 40 41 43 44 45 46 47 48 49 50 51 52 54 55 56 57 58 59 60 61 63 64 65 66 68 70 71 72 73 74 75 76 77 78 79 81 82 85 86 87 88 89 92 93 94 96 97 98 99 100 101 102 103 104 105 107 108 111 114 115 116 117 118 119 120 121 123 124 126 129 130 131 132 134 135 141 144 145 146 147 148 149 150 152 153 154 156 157 **S** Hackensack Meridian Health, Edison, NJ
Primary Contact: Vito Buccellato, Chief Hospital Executive
COO: Robert H Adams, Vice President Operations
CMO: David Kountz, M.D., Senior Vice President Medical Affairs
CIO: Rebecca Weber, Senior Vice President and Chief Information Officer
Web address: www.meridianhealth.com
**Control**: Other not–for–profit (including NFP Corporation) **Service**: General medical and surgical

**Staffed Beds**: 588 **Admissions**: 58620 **Census**: 407 **Outpatient Visits**: 254645 **Births**: 2852 **Total Expense ($000)**: 872186 **Payroll Expense ($000)**: 341365 **Personnel**: 3616

**JERSEY SHORE UNIVERSITY MEDICAL CENTER** See Hackensack Meridian Health Jersey Shore University Medical Center

## NEW BRUNSWICK—Middlesex County

☐ **CHILDREN'S SPECIALIZED HOSPITAL (313300)**, 200 Somerset Street, Zip 08901–1942; tel. 732/258–7000, (Includes CHILDREN'S SPECIALIZED HOSPITAL, Mailing address: 200 Somerset Street, New Brunswick, New Jersey, Zip 08901–1942; tel. 732/258–7134; Warren E. Moore, FACHE, President and Chief Executive Officer) (Total facility includes 72 beds in nursing home–type unit) **A**1 3 5 10 **F**29 32 35 54 64 65 74 75 82 90 91 93 94 97 104 130 131 132 146 154 **S** RWJBarnabas Health, West Orange, NJ
Primary Contact: Warren E. Moore, FACHE, President and Chief Executive Officer
COO: Charles Chianese, Vice President, Chief Operating Officer
CFO: Joseph J Dobosh JrVice President and Chief Financial Officer
CMO: Christopher Haines, D.O., Vice President and Chief Medical Officer
CHR: William Dwyer, Vice President and Chief Human Resources Officer
CNO: Bonnie Baloga-Altieri, Ph.D., R.N., Vice President Patient Care Services and Chief Nursing Officer
Web address: www.childrens-specialized.org
**Control**: Other not–for–profit (including NFP Corporation) **Service**: Children's rehabilitation

**Staffed Beds**: 140 **Admissions**: 625 **Census**: 121 **Outpatient Visits**: 230381 **Births**: 0 **Total Expense ($000)**: 151622 **Payroll Expense ($000)**: 90625 **Personnel**: 1175

**CHILDREN'S SPECIALIZED HOSPITAL-PSE&G** See Children's Specialized Hospital

☒ **ROBERT WOOD JOHNSON UNIVERSITY HOSPITAL (310038)**, 1 Robert Wood Johnson Place, Zip 08901–1928; tel. 732/828–3000, (Includes BRISTOL-MYERS SQUIBB CHILDREN'S HOSPITAL, Mailing address: One Robert Wood Johnson Place, New Brunswick, New Jersey, Zip 8901, P.O. Box 2601, Zip 08903–2601, tel. 732/828–3000), (Nonreporting) **A**1 2 3 5 8 10 **F**3 6 7 8 9 11 12 13 14 17 18 19 20 22 24 26 28 29 30 31 32 34 35 37 38 39 40 41 43 44 45 46 47 48 49 50 51 52 53 54 55 56 57 58 59 60 61 62 63 64 65 66 68 70 71 72 73 74 75 76 77 78 79 81 82 84 85 86 87 88 89 91 92 93 94 96 97 100 101 102 104 107 108 109 110 111 114 115 116 117 118 119 120 121 122 123 124 126 130 131 132 134 135 136 137 138 141 142 143 144 145 146 147 148 149 150 154 155 156 157 **P**5 6 **S** RWJBarnabas Health, West Orange, NJ
Primary Contact: John J. Gantner, President and Chief Executive Officer
CFO: Brian M Reilly, Chief Financial Officer
CMO: Joshua M Bershad, M.D., Senior Vice President Medical Affairs and Chief Medical Officer
CIO: Robert G Irwin, Vice President Information Systems
CHR: Martin S Everhart, Senior Vice President Human Resources
CNO: Lori Colineri, R.N., Senior Vice President Nursing and Chief Nursing Officer
Web address: www.rwjuh.edu
**Control**: Other not–for–profit (including NFP Corporation) **Service**: General medical and surgical

**Staffed Beds**: 619 **Admissions**: 28998 **Census**: 487 **Outpatient Visits**: 230202 **Births**: 2672 **Total Expense ($000)**: 1135383 **Payroll Expense ($000)**: 387660 **Personnel**: 4947

☒ **SAINT PETER'S UNIVERSITY HOSPITAL (310070)**, 254 Easton Avenue, Zip 08901–1780; tel. 732/745–8600, (Includes THE CHILDREN'S HOSPITAL AT SAINT PETER'S UNIVERSITY, Mailing address: 254 Easton Avenue, New Brunswick, New Jersey, Zip 08901–1766; tel. 732/565–5437), (Nonreporting) **A**1 2 3 5 8 10 **F**3 12 13 15 18 19 20 22 26 27 29 30 31 32 34 35 37 38 39 40 41 44 45 46 47 49 50 51 54 55 56 57 58 59 60 61 63 64 65 66 67 68 70 71 72 73 74 75 76 77 78 79 81 82 83 84 85 86 87 88 89 91 92 93 94 96 97 100 101 102 104 105 107 108 110 111 113 114 115 118 119 120 121 123 124 126 129 130 131 132 134 135 143 145 146 147 148 149 150 153 154 156 157 **P**6
Primary Contact: Leslie D. Hirsch, FACHE, President and Chief Executive Officer
CFO: Garrick J Stoldt, Vice President and Chief Financial Officer
CHR: Susan Ballestero, Vice President and Chief Human Resources Officer
CNO: Elizabeth Wise, R.N., MS, Chief Nursing Officer and Vice President, Patient Care Services
Web address: www.saintpetersuh.com
**Control**: Church operated, Nongovernment, not–for–profit **Service**: General medical and surgical

**Staffed Beds**: 353 **Admissions**: 19446 **Census**: 225 **Outpatient Visits**: 279331 **Births**: 5178 **Total Expense ($000)**: 467013 **Payroll Expense ($000)**: 225076 **Personnel**: 2343

**ST PETER'S UNIVERSITY HOSPITAL** See Saint Peter's University Hospital

**THE BRISTOL-MYERS SQUIBB CHILDREN'S HOSPITAL** See Bristol-Myers Squibb Children's Hospital

## NEW LISBON—Burlington County

**BUTTONWOOD HOSPITAL OF BURLINGTON** See Aspen Hills Healthcare Center

## NEWARK—Essex County

⇑ **COLUMBUS HOSPITAL LTACH (312024)**, 495 North Thirteenth Street, Zip 07107–1317; tel. 973/587–7777, (Nonreporting) **A**10 21
Primary Contact: Peter Callaghan, President and Chief Executive Officer
CFO: Alexey Gololobov, Chief Financial Officer
CHR: Patrice Ricciardi, Director Human Resources
CNO: Arthur Kharonov, Vice President Nursing
Web address: www.columbusltach.org
**Control**: Corporation, Investor–owned (for–profit) **Service**: Acute long–term care hospital

**Staffed Beds**: 63

☒ **NEWARK BETH ISRAEL MEDICAL CENTER (310002)**, 201 Lyons Avenue at Osborne Terrace, Zip 07112–2027; tel. 973/926–7000, (Includes CHILDREN'S HOSPITAL OF NEW JERSEY, Mailing address: 201 Lyons Avenue, Newark, New Jersey, Zip 07112–2027; tel. 973/926–7000; Darrell K. Terry Sr, M.P.H., FACHE, President and Chief Executive Officer), (Nonreporting) **A**1 2 3 5 8 10 12 13 **F**3 12 15 17 18 19 20 21 22 23 24 25 26 27 28 29 30 31 32 34 35 38 39 40 41 44 45 46 47 48 49 50 51 53 55 56 57 58 59 60 61 64 65 66 68 70 71 72 74 75 76 77 78 79 81 82 84 85 86 87 88 89 91 92 93 94 97 98 99 100 101 102 104 107 108 109 110 111 114 115 117 118 119 120 121 123 126 129 130 131 132 135 137 140 141 143 145 146 147 148 149 153 156 157 **P**3 6 **S** RWJBarnabas Health, West Orange, NJ
Primary Contact: Darrell K. Terry Sr, M.P.H., FACHE, President and Chief Executive Officer
CFO: Douglas A Zehner, Chief Financial Officer
CMO: Jeremias Murillo, M.D., Chief Medical Officer
CHR: Zach Lipner, Vice President Human Resources
CNO: Mary Fuhro, Chief Nursing Officer
Web address: www.barnabashealth.org/hospitals/newark_beth_israel/index.html
**Control**: Other not–for–profit (including NFP Corporation) **Service**: General medical and surgical

**Staffed Beds**: 376 **Admissions**: 20585 **Census**: 370 **Outpatient Visits**: 303446 **Births**: 2892 **Total Expense ($000)**: 653926 **Payroll Expense ($000)**: 288152 **Personnel**: 3187

**NJ**

---

**Hospital, Medicare Provider Number, Address, Telephone, Approval, Facility, and Physician Codes, Health Care System**

★ American Hospital Association (AHA) membership
☐ The Joint Commission accreditation
○ Healthcare Facilities Accreditation Program
◇ DNV Healthcare Inc. accreditation
⇑ Center for Improvement in Healthcare Quality Accreditation
△ Commission on Accreditation of Rehabilitation Facilities (CARF) accreditation

☐ **SAINT MICHAEL'S MEDICAL CENTER (310096)**, 111 Central Avenue, Zip 07102–1909; tel. 973/877–5000, (Nonreporting) **A**1 3 5 10 13 **F**3 5 15 17 18 20 22 24 26 29 30 31 34 37 40 45 47 49 50 57 58 59 61 64 66 68 70 71 74 75 77 78 79 81 85 87 97 98 100 107 108 109 110 111 114 115 119 121 122 123 126 129 130 132 143 147 148 149 154 **S** Prime Healthcare, Ontario, CA
Primary Contact: Alan Sickles, M.D., Chief Executive Officer
COO: Dennis Pettigrew, Chief Operating Officer
CFO: Carolyn Allen, Chief Financial Officer
CMO: Claudia Komer, M.D., Chief Medical Officer
CIO: Tom Addington, Chief Information Officer
CHR: Dennis W. Sparks, Vice President Human Resources
CNO: Nancy Bisco-Flora, Chief Nursing Officer
Web address: www.https://www.smmcnj.com/
**Control:** Corporation, Investor–owned (for–profit) **Service:** General medical and surgical

> **Staffed Beds:** 147 **Admissions:** 7949 **Census:** 87 **Outpatient Visits:** 93612 **Births:** 0 **Total Expense ($000):** 171770 **Payroll Expense ($000):** 77910 **Personnel:** 946

☒ **UNIVERSITY HOSPITAL (310119)**, 150 Bergen Street, Zip 07103–2496; tel. 973/972–4300, (Nonreporting) **A**1 2 3 5 8 10
Primary Contact: Shereef Elnahal, M.D., President and Chief Executive Officer
COO: Nancy Hamstra, Chief Operating Officer
CFO: Thomas M Daly, CPA, Chief Financial Officer
CMO: William Holubek, M.D., Chief Medical Officer
CIO: Richard Tunnell, Chief Information Officer
CHR: Gerard Garcia, Chief Human Resource Officer
CNO: Carl Kirton, Ph.D., Chief Nursing Officer
Web address: www.uhnj.org
**Control:** State, Government, Nonfederal **Service:** General medical and surgical

> **Staffed Beds:** 519

**UNIVERSITY OF MEDICINE AND DENTISTRY OF NEW JERSEY-UNIVERSITY HOSPITAL** See University Hospital

### NEWTON—Sussex County

☒ **NEWTON MEDICAL CENTER (310028)**, 175 High Street, Zip 07860–1004; tel. 973/383–2121, (Nonreporting) **A**1 2 10 **F**3 5 8 11 12 13 15 18 19 20 28 29 30 31 32 34 35 36 38 40 41 44 45 47 49 50 52 53 54 56 57 59 60 64 65 68 69 70 73 74 75 76 77 78 79 81 82 84 85 86 87 91 92 93 94 96 98 100 101 102 104 105 106 107 108 110 111 114 115 118 119 130 132 134 135 141 146 148 149 153 154 156 **P**3 6 **S** Atlantic Health System, Morristown, NJ
Primary Contact: Robert H. Adams, President, Western Region
CFO: Kevin Lenahan, Director Corporate Accounting, Budgets, Grants and Reimbursements
CMO: David Lazarus, M.D., Medical Director Clinical Affairs
CIO: Linda Reed, Vice President Information Systems and Chief Information Officer
CHR: Andrew L Kovach, Vice President Human Resources and Chief Administrative Officer
Web address: www.atlantichealth.org/newton/
**Control:** Other not–for–profit (including NFP Corporation) **Service:** General medical and surgical

> **Staffed Beds:** 148 **Admissions:** 8560 **Census:** 108 **Outpatient Visits:** 94334 **Births:** 500 **Total Expense ($000):** 186670 **Payroll Expense ($000):** 88403 **Personnel:** 1055

**NEWTON MEMORIAL HOSPITAL** See Newton Medical Center

### NORTH BERGEN—Hudson County

☒ **HACKENSACK MERIDIAN HEALTH PALISADES MEDICAL CENTER (310003)**, 7600 River Road, Zip 07047–6217; tel. 201/854–5000, (Nonreporting) **A**1 3 5 10 12 13 **F**3 7 11 12 13 15 18 20 28 29 30 31 34 35 38 40 44 45 46 49 50 56 57 59 60 63 64 65 68 70 72 74 75 76 77 78 79 81 82 84 85 86 87 89 92 93 94 97 100 101 102 104 107 108 110 111 115 119 129 130 132 141 143 146 147 148 149 154 **S** Hackensack Meridian Health, Edison, NJ
Primary Contact: Anthony Passannante Jr, M.D., FACC, President and Chief Hospital Executive
COO: David J Berkowitz, Vice President and Chief Operating Officer
CFO: John Calandriello, Vice President and Chief Financial Officer
CMO: Suresh Raina, M.D., Vice President Medical Staff and Chief Medical Officer
CIO: Albert Porco, Director Management Information Systems
CNO: Ruben D Fernandez, R.N., Vice President and Chief Nursing Officer
Web address: www.palisadesmedical.org
**Control:** Other not–for–profit (including NFP Corporation) **Service:** General medical and surgical

> **Staffed Beds:** 152 **Admissions:** 14859 **Census:** 89 **Outpatient Visits:** 98835 **Births:** 1170 **Total Expense ($000):** 204615 **Payroll Expense ($000):** 95542 **Personnel:** 1072

**HACKENSACKUMC PALISADES** See Hackensack Meridian Health Palisades Medical Center

### PARAMUS—Bergen County

☒ **BERGEN NEW BRIDGE MEDICAL CENTER (310058)**, 230 East Ridgewood Avenue, Zip 07652–4142; tel. 201/967–4000, (Nonreporting) **A**1 3 10
Primary Contact: Deborah D. Visconi, President and Chief Executive Officer
COO: Susan Mendelowitz, R.N., FACHE, Executive Vice President and Chief Operating Officer
CFO: Connie Magdangal, Executive Vice President and Chief Financial Officer
CMO: Robert M Harris, M.D., President Medical and Dental Staff
CIO: Ronald Li, Vice President Management Information Systems
CHR: Guy Mennonna, Senior Vice President Human Resources
Web address: www.bergenregional.com
**Control:** County, Government, Nonfederal **Service:** Psychiatric

> **Staffed Beds:** 1020

**NEW BRIDGE MEDICAL CENTER** See Bergen New Bridge Medical Center

### PASSAIC—Passaic County

☐ **ST. MARY'S GENERAL HOSPITAL (310006)**, 350 Boulevard, Zip 07055–2840; tel. 973/365–4300, (Nonreporting) **A**1 3 10 **S** Prime Healthcare, Ontario, CA
Primary Contact: Edward Condit, President and Chief Executive Officer
CFO: Nicholas Lanza, Controller
CMO: Ronald Poblete, M.D., President Medical and Dental Staff
CHR: Cathy Lynch-Kilic, Vice President Human Resources
Web address: www.smh-passaic.org
**Control:** Other not–for–profit (including NFP Corporation) **Service:** General medical and surgical

> **Staffed Beds:** 287

**ST. MARY'S HOSPITAL** See St. Mary's General Hospital

### PATERSON—Passaic County

⇑ **ST. JOSEPH'S HEALTHCARE SYSTEM** See St. Joseph's University Medical Center

★ ⇑ **ST. JOSEPH'S UNIVERSITY MEDICAL CENTER (310019)**, 703 Main Street, Zip 07503–2691; tel. 973/754–2000, (Includes ST. JOSEPH'S CHILDREN'S HOSPITAL, Mailing address: 703 Main Street, Paterson, New Jersey, Zip 07503–2621; tel. 973/754–2500; Kevin J. Slavin, FACHE, President and Chief Executive Officer; ST. JOSEPH'S WAYNE HOSPITAL, Mailing address: 224 Hamburg Turnpike, Wayne, New Jersey, Zip 07470–2100; tel. 973/942–6900; Daniel B Kline, Vice President, Site Administrator) (Total facility includes 151 beds in nursing home–type unit) **A**2 3 5 10 13 21 **F**3 8 11 12 13 15 17 18 19 20 21 22 23 24 25 26 27 28 29 30 31 32 34 35 36 37 38 39 40 41 43 44 45 46 47 48 49 50 51 54 55 56 57 58 59 60 61 62 63 64 65 66 68 70 72 73 74 75 76 77 78 79 81 82 84 85 86 87 88 90 92 93 94 96 97 98 100 101 102 104 105 106 107 108 110 111 114 115 116 117 118 119 121 123 126 128 129 130 131 132 133 134 135 141 146 147 148 149 150 153 154 156 157 158
Primary Contact: Kevin J. Slavin, FACHE, President and Chief Executive Officer
COO: Lisa Brady, Senior Vice President and Chief Operating Officer
CFO: David Alexander, Senior Vice President and Chief Financial Officer
CMO: James Labagnara, M.D., Vice President Medical Affairs
CIO: Linda Reed, Vice President and Chief Information Officer
CHR: John P Bruno, Senior Vice President Human Resources
CNO: Judy Padula, MSN, R.N., Vice President Patient Care Services and Chief Nursing Officer
Web address: www.stjosephshealth.org
**Control:** Church operated, Nongovernment, not–for–profit **Service:** General medical and surgical

> **Staffed Beds:** 1031 **Admissions:** 28347 **Census:** 610 **Outpatient Visits:** 391534 **Births:** 3231 **Total Expense ($000):** 815724 **Payroll Expense ($000):** 414130 **Personnel:** 4421

### PEAPACK—Somerset County

☐ **MATHENY MEDICAL AND EDUCATIONAL CENTER (312014)**, 65 Highland Avenue, Zip 7977, Mailing Address: P.O. Box 339, Zip 07977–0339; tel. 908/234–0011, (Nonreporting) **A**1 10
Primary Contact: Kendell R. Sprott, M.D., JD, President and Chief Executive Officer
COO: Christopher King, Director Operations and Administrative Services
CFO: Wayne Guberman, Director Finance
CMO: Gary E Eddey, M.D., Medical Director
CIO: Ron Daniel, Manager Information Systems
CHR: Nancy Petrillo, Director Human Resources
Web address: www.matheny.org
**Control:** Other not–for–profit (including NFP Corporation) **Service:** Acute long–term care hospital

> **Staffed Beds:** 101

**MATHENY SCHOOL AND HOSPITAL** See Matheny Medical and Educational Center

## PENNINGTON—Mercer County

⇑ **CAPITAL HEALTH - MERCER CAMPUS** See Capital Health Medical Center-Hopewell

★ ⇑ **CAPITAL HEALTH MEDICAL CENTER-HOPEWELL (310044)**, 1 Capital Way, Zip 08534–2520; tel. 609/303–4000, (Nonreporting) **A**2 10 21 **F**3 8 11 12 13 15 18 20 22 28 29 30 31 32 34 35 36 40 41 44 45 46 47 48 49 50 51 52 55 57 58 59 60 61 64 65 68 70 72 73 74 75 76 78 79 81 82 84 85 86 87 89 93 96 97 107 108 109 110 111 112 114 115 117 118 119 120 121 123 124 126 130 132 135 143 145 146 147 148 154 156 **S** Capital Health, Trenton, NJ
Primary Contact: Al Maghazehe, Ph.D., FACHE, President and Chief Executive Officer
CFO: Shane Fleming, Chief Financial Officer
CMO: Eugene McMahon, Senior Vice President and Chief Medical Officer
CIO: Eugene Grochala, Vice President Information Systems
CHR: Scott Clemmensen, Vice President Human Resources and Leadership Enhancement
CNO: Deborah Mican, R.N., Chief Nursing Officer
Web address: www.capitalhealth.org
**Control:** Other not–for–profit (including NFP Corporation) **Service:** General medical and surgical

**Staffed Beds:** 171 **Admissions:** 14938 **Census:** 177 **Outpatient Visits:** 198182 **Births:** 3398 **Personnel:** 1775

## PERTH AMBOY—Middlesex County

✉ **HACKENSACK MERIDIAN HEALTH RARITAN BAY MEDICAL CENTER (310039)**, 530 New Brunswick Avenue, Zip 08861–3654; tel. 732/442–3700, (Includes OLD BRIDGE DIVISION, Mailing address: One Hospital Plaza, Old Bridge, New Jersey, Zip 8857; tel. 732/360–1000; PERTH AMBOY DIVISION, Mailing address: 530 New Brunswick Avenue, Perth Amboy, New Jersey, Zip 08861–3685; tel. 732/442–3700), (Nonreporting) **A**1 3 5 10 **F**3 4 12 13 15 18 20 22 29 30 31 32 34 35 36 38 40 44 45 46 47 48 49 50 51 54 57 59 60 61 63 64 66 68 70 72 74 75 76 77 78 79 80 81 82 84 85 86 87 89 91 92 93 94 96 97 98 99 100 101 102 103 104 107 108 110 111 114 115 117 119 126 129 130 131 132 135 141 143 146 147 148 149 154 156 157 **S** Hackensack Meridian Health, Edison, NJ
Primary Contact: Thomas Shanahan, CPA, Chief Operating Officer
COO: Thomas Shanahan, CPA, Chief Operating Officer
CFO: Thomas Shanahan, CPA, Chief Financial Officer and Senior Vice President
CMO: Louis Brusco, M.D., Chief Medical Officer
CHR: Vincent Costantino, Vice President Operations and Human Resources
Web address: www.rbmc.org
**Control:** Other not–for–profit (including NFP Corporation) **Service:** General medical and surgical

**Staffed Beds:** 282 **Admissions:** 24206 **Census:** 161 **Outpatient Visits:** 126587 **Births:** 995 **Total Expense ($000):** 246772 **Payroll Expense ($000):** 124229 **Personnel:** 1472

**RARITAN BAY MEDICAL CENTER** See Hackensack Meridian Health Raritan Bay Medical Center

## PHILLIPSBURG—Warren County

☐ **ST. LUKE'S HOSPITAL - WARREN CAMPUS (310060)**, 185 Roseberry Street, Zip 08865–1690; tel. 908/847–6700, (Nonreporting) **A**1 3 5 10 13 **F**3 8 11 12 15 18 20 28 29 30 31 34 35 39 40 44 45 47 48 49 50 51 53 54 59 60 61 64 65 66 70 74 75 77 78 79 81 82 85 86 87 89 91 92 93 97 100 101 102 104 107 108 110 111 115 118 119 124 129 130 131 132 134 146 147 148 149 154 **S** St. Luke's University Health Network, Bethlehem, PA
Primary Contact: Scott R. Wolfe, CPA, President
COO: Alice Wilson, FACHE, Vice President Administration
CMO: Edward Gilkey, M.D., Vice President Medical Affairs
CHR: Morgan G Mahl, Director Human Resources
CNO: Gail Newton, R.N., MSN, Vice President Patient Care Services
Web address: www.slhn.org
**Control:** Other not–for–profit (including NFP Corporation) **Service:** General medical and surgical

**Staffed Beds:** 92 **Admissions:** 4077 **Census:** 51 **Outpatient Visits:** 101531 **Births:** 0 **Total Expense ($000):** 109329 **Payroll Expense ($000):** 45918 **Personnel:** 529

**WARREN HOSPITAL** See St. Luke's Hospital - Warren Campus

## PISCATAWAY—Middlesex County

**RUTGERS UNIVERSITY BEHAVIORAL HEALTHCARE (314011)**, 671 Hoes Lane West, Zip 08854–8021; tel. 732/235–5900, (Nonreporting) **A**3 5 10
Primary Contact: Frank A. Ghinassi, Ph.D., President and Chief Executive Officer
COO: Rosemarie Rosati, Chief Operating Officer
CFO: Alan Weinkrantz, Chief Financial Officer, Finance
CMO: Theresa Miskimen, M.D., Vice President Medical Services
CIO: Adam Levinson, Associate Director, Information Services
CNO: Michele A Miller, R.N., MSN, Vice President, Acute and Nursing Services
Web address: www.ubhc.rutgers.edu
**Control:** State, Government, Nonfederal **Service:** Psychiatric

**Staffed Beds:** 48

**UNIVERSITY BEHAVIORAL HEALTHCARE** See Rutgers University Behavioral Healthcare

## PLAINSBORO—Middlesex County

✉ △ **PENN MEDICINE PRINCETON MEDICAL CENTER (310010)**, One Plainsboro Road, Zip 08536–1913; tel. 609/853–7100, (Nonreporting) **A**1 2 3 5 7 10 **F**3 4 5 8 11 12 13 14 15 18 19 20 22 26 28 29 30 31 34 35 36 37 38 39 40 41 45 46 47 48 49 50 51 53 54 55 56 57 58 59 60 61 62 63 64 65 66 68 70 72 73 74 75 76 77 78 79 81 82 84 85 86 87 89 90 91 92 93 96 97 98 100 101 102 103 104 105 107 108 110 111 114 115 116 117 118 119 120 121 123 124 126 129 130 131 132 134 135 143 144 145 146 147 148 149 150 153 154 155 156 **P**6 **S** University of Pennsylvania Health System, Philadelphia, PA
Primary Contact: Barry S. Rabner, President and Chief Executive Officer, Princeton Healthcare System
COO: James Demetriades, Vice President, Operations
CMO: Donald Denny, M.D., Senior Vice President, Medical Affairs
CIO: Anne Searle, Chief Information Officer
CHR: Marcia M Telthorster, M.Ed, Vice President Human Resources
CNO: Barbara Christiano, Vice President, Patient Care Services and Chief Nursing Officer
Web address: www.princetonhcs.org
**Control:** Other not–for–profit (including NFP Corporation) **Service:** General medical and surgical

**Staffed Beds:** 355 **Admissions:** 18183 **Census:** 273 **Outpatient Visits:** 371654 **Births:** 2124 **Total Expense ($000):** 449891 **Payroll Expense ($000):** 169615 **Personnel:** 2590

**PENN MEDICINE PRINCETON MEDICAL CENTER**A1 2 3 5 7 10 **F**3 4 5 8 11 12 13 14 15 18 19 20 22 26 28 29 30 31 34 35 36 37 38 39 40 41 45 46 47 48 49 50 51 53 54 55 56 57 58 59 60 61 62 63 64 65 66 68 70 72 73 74 75 76 77 78 79 81 82 84 85 86 87 89 90 91 92 93 96 97 98 100 101 102 103 104 105 107 108 110 111 114 115 116 117 118 119 120 121 123 124 126 129 130 131 132 134 135 143 144 145 146 147 148 149 150 153 154 155 156 **P**6
COO: James Demetriades, Vice President, Operations
CMO: Donald Denny, M.D., Senior Vice President, Medical Affairs
CIO: Anne Searle, Chief Information Officer
CHR: Marcia M Telthorster, M.Ed, Vice President Human Resources
CNO: Barbara Christiano, Vice President, Patient Care Services and Chief Nursing Officer
Web address: www.princetonhcs.org
**UNIVERSITY MEDICAL CENTER OF PRINCETON AT PLAINSBORO** See Penn Medicine Princeton Medical Center, Plainsboro

## POMONA—Atlantic County

**ATLANTIC CITY MEDICAL CENTER-MAINLAND DIVISION** See Atlanticare Regional Medical Center-Mainland Division

**ATLANTICARE REGIONAL MEDICAL CENTER-MAINLAND DIVISION** See Atlanticare Regional Medical Center, Atlantic City

✉ △ **BACHARACH INSTITUTE FOR REHABILITATION (313030)**, 61 West Jimmie Leeds Road, Zip 08240–9102, Mailing Address: P.O. Box 723, Zip 08240–0723; tel. 609/652–7000, (Nonreporting) **A**1 7 10
Primary Contact: Richard J. Kathrins, Ph.D., President and Chief Executive Officer
CFO: Jeanne Vuksta, Chief Financial Officer
CMO: Craig Anmuth, M.D., Medical Director
CIO: Jeff Rees, Director Information Systems
CHR: Diane S Croshaw, Vice President Human Resources
Web address: www.bacharach.org
**Control:** Other not–for–profit (including NFP Corporation) **Service:** Rehabilitation

**Staffed Beds:** 80

**BACHARACH REHAB HOSPITAL** See Bacharach Institute for Rehabilitation

---

| Hospital, Medicare Provider Number, Address, Telephone, Approval, Facility, and Physician Codes, Health Care System | | |
|---|---|---|
| ★ American Hospital Association (AHA) membership | ○ Healthcare Facilities Accreditation Program | ⇑ Center for Improvement in Healthcare Quality Accreditation |
| ☐ The Joint Commission accreditation | ◇ DNV Healthcare Inc. accreditation | △ Commission on Accreditation of Rehabilitation Facilities (CARF) accreditation |

## POMPTON PLAINS—Morris County

**CHILTON HOSPITAL** See Chilton Medical Center

☒ **CHILTON MEDICAL CENTER (310017)**, 97 West Parkway, Zip 07444–1696;
tel. 973/831–5000, (Nonreporting) **A**1 2 10 **F**3 9 11 12 13 15 18 20 22 26 28
29 30 31 32 34 35 36 38 39 40 41 44 45 46 47 49 50 53 54 55 56 57 58 59
60 61 64 65 66 68 70 73 74 75 76 77 78 79 81 82 84 85 86 87 89 93 96 97
100 101 102 104 107 108 110 111 114 115 116 118 119 120 121 123 124
126 129 130 131 132 134 135 141 143 146 147 148 149 150 154 156 **P**3 6
**S** Atlantic Health System, Morristown, NJ
Primary Contact: Stephanie L. Schwartz, FACHE, Vice President AHS and President
CMC
CFO: Michael Richetti, Chief Financial Officer
CMO: Charles Ross, M.D., Vice President Medical Affairs
CIO: Karen S Smith, Director Information Services
CHR: Julia McGovern, Vice President Human Resources
Web address: www.chiltonmemorial.org
**Control:** Other not–for–profit (including NFP Corporation) **Service:** General
medical and surgical

**Staffed Beds:** 133 **Admissions:** 8054 **Census:** 104 **Outpatient**
**Visits:** 114370 **Births:** 534 **Total Expense ($000):** 199636 **Payroll Expense**
**($000):** 92446 **Personnel:** 1069

## RAHWAY—Union County

**KINDRED HOSPITAL NEW JERSEY - RAHWAY** See Kindred Hospital-New Jersey
Morris County, Dover

**ROBERT W JOHNSON UNIV HOSP** See Robert Wood Johnson University Hospital
Rahway

☒ **ROBERT WOOD JOHNSON UNIVERSITY HOSPITAL RAHWAY (310024)**, 865
Stone Street, Zip 07065–2797; tel. 732/381–4200, (Nonreporting) **A**1 10 **F**3 11
12 15 17 20 28 29 30 31 34 35 38 40 45 46 47 48 49 50 51 53 56 57 59 60
64 65 66 68 70 74 75 77 78 79 81 86 87 92 93 97 100 101 102 107 108 110
111 114 116 117 118 119 129 130 132 143 146 147 148 149 154 156 **P**6 **S**
RWJBarnabas Health, West Orange, NJ
Primary Contact: Kirk C. Tice, President and Chief Executive Officer
CFO: Peter Bihuniak, Vice President Finance
CMO: Juan Baez, M.D., President Medical Staff
CIO: Denine Izzi, Senior Director Information Technology
CHR: Barbara M Mullery CHHR, Vice President Administration
CNO: Ann Marie Shears, Vice President Patient Care Services
Web address: www.rwjuhr.com
**Control:** Other not–for–profit (including NFP Corporation) **Service:** General
medical and surgical

**Staffed Beds:** 93 **Admissions:** 5073 **Census:** 70 **Outpatient Visits:** 92659
**Births:** 0 **Total Expense ($000):** 117567 **Payroll Expense ($000):** 49190
**Personnel:** 680

## RED BANK—Monmouth County

☒ △ **HACKENSACK MERIDIAN HEALTH RIVERVIEW MEDICAL CENTER**
**(310034)**, 1 Riverview Plaza, Zip 07701–1864; tel. 732/741–2700,
(Nonreporting) **A**1 2 5 7 10 **F**3 5 9 11 13 15 18 20 22 28 29 30 31 32 34 35
36 37 38 39 40 41 44 45 46 47 49 50 51 54 55 56 57 58 59 60 61 63 64 65
66 68 70 71 72 74 75 76 77 78 79 81 82 84 85 86 87 90 91 92 93 94 96 97
98 99 100 101 102 103 104 105 107 108 110 111 114 115 116 117 118 119
120 121 123 124 126 130 131 134 135 141 144 145 146 147 148 149 150
152 153 154 157 **S** Hackensack Meridian Health, Edison, NJ
Primary Contact: M. Todd. Way, President, Central Region
CFO: Joseph M Lemaire, Executive Vice President Finance
CMO: Joseph Reichman, M.D., Vice President Medical Affairs and Clinical
Effectiveness
CIO: Rebecca Weber, Senior Vice President Information Technology
CHR: Sherrie String, Senior Vice President Human Resources
CNO: Rebecca Graboso, Vice President and Chief Nurse Executive
Web address: www.riverviewmedicalcenter.com
**Control:** Other not–for–profit (including NFP Corporation) **Service:** General
medical and surgical

**Staffed Beds:** 300 **Admissions:** 25482 **Census:** 166 **Outpatient**
**Visits:** 127809 **Births:** 1253 **Total Expense ($000):** 292883 **Payroll**
**Expense ($000):** 128257 **Personnel:** 1550

**RIVERVIEW MEDICAL CENTER** See Hackensack Meridian Health Riverview
Medical Center

## RIDGEWOOD—Bergen County

☒ **VALLEY HOSPITAL (310012)**, 223 North Van Dien Avenue, Zip 07450–2726;
tel. 201/447–8000, (Nonreporting) **A**1 2 10 **F**3 7 8 11 12 13 15 17 18 19 20 22
24 26 28 29 30 31 32 34 35 36 37 38 40 41 44 45 46 47 48 49 50 51 52 53
54 55 56 57 58 59 60 61 64 65 66 68 69 70 71 72 73 74 75 76 77 78 79 80
81 82 83 84 85 86 87 88 89 91 92 93 94 96 97 100 101 102 107 108 110
111 115 117 118 119 120 121 123 124 126 129 130 131 132 134 135 141
143 145 146 147 148 149 150 156
Primary Contact: Audrey Meyers, FACHE, President and Chief Executive Officer
COO: Peter Diestel, Senior Vice President and Chief Operating Officer
CFO: Richard Keenan, Senior Vice President Finance and Chief Financial Officer
CMO: Joseph Yallowitz, M.D., Vice President and Chief Medical Officer
CIO: Eric R Carey, Vice President Information Systems and Chief Information Officer
CHR: Jose Balderrama, Vice President Human Resources
CNO: Ann Marie Leichman, MSN, R.N., EsqSenior Vice President Patient Care
Services and Chief Nursing Officer
Web address: www.valleyhealth.com
**Control:** Other not–for–profit (including NFP Corporation) **Service:** General
medical and surgical

**Staffed Beds:** 446 **Admissions:** 28723 **Census:** 304 **Outpatient**
**Visits:** 326027 **Births:** 3510 **Total Expense ($000):** 694795 **Payroll**
**Expense ($000):** 264961 **Personnel:** 3591

## ROCHELLE PARK—Bergen County

**SELECT SPECIALTY HOSPITAL-BELLEVILLE** See Select Specialty Hospital-
Northeast New Jersey

☒ **SELECT SPECIALTY HOSPITAL-NORTHEAST NEW JERSEY (312019)**, 96
Parkway, Zip 07662–4200; tel. 201/221–2352, (Nonreporting) **A**1 10 **S** Select
Medical Corporation, Mechanicsburg, PA
Primary Contact: David Key, Division President
Web address: www.northeastnewjersey.selectspecialtyhospitals.com/about/
**Control:** Corporation, Investor–owned (for–profit) **Service:** Acute long–term care
hospital

**Staffed Beds:** 62

## SADDLE BROOK—Bergen County

**KESSLER INSTITUTE FOR REHABILITATION** See Kessler Institute for
Rehabilitation, West Orange

## SALEM—Salem County

**MEMORIAL HOSPITAL OF SALEM COUNTY** See Salem Medical Center

☒ **SALEM MEDICAL CENTER (310091)**, 310 Woodstown Road, Zip 08079–2080;
tel. 856/935–1000, (Nonreporting) **A**1 10 **F**1 3 16 17 67 70 72 73 81 88 128
Primary Contact: Tammy Torres, R.N., MSN, Chief Executive Officer
CFO: Vincent Riccitelli, Chief Financial Officer
CIO: Brian McCarthy, Director Information Systems
CHR: Victoria A. Bates, Director Human Resources
Web address: www.https://www.smc.health/
**Control:** Other not–for–profit (including NFP Corporation) **Service:** General
medical and surgical

**Staffed Beds:** 126 **Admissions:** 2477 **Census:** 25 **Outpatient Visits:** 37522
**Births:** 0 **Total Expense ($000):** 54161 **Payroll Expense ($000):** 17147
**Personnel:** 330

## SECAUCUS—Hudson County

☐ **HUDSON COUNTY MEADOWVIEW PSYCHIATRIC HOSPITAL (314024)**, 595
County Avenue, Zip 07094–2605; tel. 201/369–5252, (Nonreporting) **A**1 10 **F**34
50 57 65 68 75 87 98 101 103 130 132 135 143 149 **P**6
Primary Contact: Joanne Reilly, Administrator
Web address: www.hudsoncountynj.org
**Control:** County, Government, Nonfederal **Service:** Psychiatric

**Staffed Beds:** 84 **Admissions:** 158 **Census:** 78 **Outpatient Visits:** 0 **Births:** 0
**Total Expense ($000):** 33007 **Payroll Expense ($000):** 12132 **Personnel:** 167

**NJ**

*Many Facility Codes have changed. Please refer to the AHA Guide Code Chart.*
© 2021 AHA Guide

⇑ **HUDSON REGIONAL HOSPITAL (310118)**, 55 Meadowlands Parkway, Zip 07094–2977; tel. 201/392–3100, (Nonreporting) **A**5 10 21 **F**7 15 18 29 33 35 39 40 46 49 70 73 76 79 81 87 89 107 110 111 114 126 129 130 131 154
Primary Contact: Nizar Kifaieh, M.D., President and Chief Executive Officer
COO: Lynn McVey, Chief Operating Officer
CMO: Michael Sciarra, M.D., Chief Medical Officer
CHR: Elizabeth Garrity, Director Human Resources
CNO: Felicia Karsos, R.N., Chief Nursing Officer
Web address: www.hudsonregionalhospital.com/
**Control**: State, Government, Nonfederal **Service**: General medical and surgical

**Staffed Beds:** 104 **Admissions:** 2388 **Census:** 28 **Outpatient Visits:** 27479 **Births:** 435 **Total Expense ($000):** 92250 **Payroll Expense ($000):** 30679 **Personnel:** 566

⇑ **MEADOWLANDS HOSPITAL MEDICAL CENTER** See Hudson Regional Hospital

### SOMERS POINT—Atlantic County

☐ **SHORE MEDICAL CENTER (310047)**, 100 Medical Center Way, Zip 8244; tel. 609/653–3500, (Nonreporting) **A**1 2 10
Primary Contact: Ronald W. Johnson, FACHE, President and Chief Executive Officer
COO: Linda S Kenwood, R.N., MSN, Chief Nursing Officer and Chief Operating Officer
CFO: James T Foley, CPA, Vice President and Chief Financial Officer
CMO: Jeanne M Rowe, M.D., Chief Medical Officer
CIO: Fred Banner, Chief Information Officer
CHR: Alan L Beatty, Vice President Human Resources
CNO: Linda S Kenwood, R.N., MSN, Chief Nursing Officer and Chief Operating Officer
Web address: www.shoremedicalcenter.org
**Control**: Other not–for–profit (including NFP Corporation) **Service**: General medical and surgical

**Staffed Beds:** 198

**SHORE MEMORIAL HOSPITAL** See Shore Medical Center

### SOMERVILLE—Somerset County

⊞ **ROBERT WOOD JOHNSON UNIVERSITY HOSPITAL SOMERSET (310048)**, 110 Rehill Avenue, Zip 08876–2598; tel. 908/685–2200, (Nonreporting) **A**1 2 3 5 10 **F**3 5 7 8 9 11 12 13 14 15 18 20 22 26 28 29 30 31 34 35 36 38 40 44 45 46 47 48 49 50 51 52 53 55 56 57 58 59 61 62 63 65 66 68 70 73 74 75 76 77 78 79 81 82 84 85 86 87 92 93 97 98 100 101 102 104 105 107 108 109 110 111 114 115 116 117 118 119 120 121 123 124 126 129 130 131 132 134 135 143 144 145 146 149 150 152 153 154 156 **P**6 **S** RWJBarnabas Health, West Orange, NJ
Primary Contact: Anthony V. Cava, MS, FACHE, President and Chief Executive Officer
COO: Patrick Delaney, Vice President, Operations
CMO: Salvatore Moffa, M.D., Vice President, Medical Affairs and Chief Medical Officer
CIO: Jordan Ruch, Vice President and Chief Information Officer
CHR: Anastasia Jacobs, Chief Human Resources Officer
CNO: Lynn Kearney, Vice President Nursing
Web address: www.rwjbh.org
**Control**: Other not–for–profit (including NFP Corporation) **Service**: General medical and surgical

**Staffed Beds:** 297 **Admissions:** 13090 **Census:** 174 **Outpatient Visits:** 182518 **Births:** 777 **Total Expense ($000):** 283259 **Payroll Expense ($000):** 121000 **Personnel:** 1711

**SOMERSET MEDICAL CENTER** See Robert Wood Johnson University Hospital Somerset

### STRATFORD—Camden County

**JEFFERSON STRATFORD HOSPITAL** See Jefferson Stratford Hospital, Stratford

⊞ **JEFFERSON STRATFORD HOSPITAL (310086)**, 18 East Laurel Road, Zip 08084–1327; tel. 856/346–6000, (Includes JEFFERSON STRATFORD HOSPITAL, Mailing address: 18 East Laurel Road, Stratford, New Jersey, Zip 8084; tel. 609/346–6000; Brian Sweeney, President and Chief Operating Officer; JEFFERSON WASHINGTON TOWNSHIP HOSPITAL, Mailing address: 435 Hurffville-Cross Keys Road, Turnersville, New Jersey, Zip 8012; tel. 856/582–2500; John W Graham, FACHE, Chief Administrative Officer) (Total facility includes 190 beds in nursing home–type unit) **A**1 2 3 5 10 12 **F**3 4 5 7 8 11 12 13 15 18 20 22 24 29 30 31 32 34 35 38 39 40 41 44 45 46 49 50 51 53 54 55 56 57 59 60 61 62 63 64 65 66 70 72 73 74 75 76 77 78 79 81 82 84 85 86 87 89 92 93 97 98 99 100 101 102 103 104 105 107 108 110 111 114 115 116 119 120 121 123 124 126 128 129 130 131 132 134 143 144 146 147 148 149 152 154 155 156 157 **P**6 **S** Jefferson Health, Philadelphia, PA
Primary Contact: Brian Sweeney, President and Chief Operating Officer
CFO: Glenn Zirbser, Senior Vice President Finance and Chief Financial Officer
CMO: David Condoluci, M.D., Senior Vice President and Chief Medical Officer
CIO: Thomas Balcavage, Vice President Chief Patient Safety and Quality Officer
CHR: Anneliese McMenamin, Senior Vice President Information Technology and Program Services
CNO: Helene M Burns, R.N., Senior Vice President and Chief Nursing Officer
Web address: www.kennedyhealth.org
**Control**: Other not–for–profit (including NFP Corporation) **Service**: General medical and surgical

**Staffed Beds:** 716 **Admissions:** 25578 **Census:** 492 **Outpatient Visits:** 413584 **Births:** 982 **Total Expense ($000):** 560539 **Payroll Expense ($000):** 233049 **Personnel:** 4202

**KENNEDY HEALTH SYSTEM** See Jefferson Stratford Hospital

**KENNEDY UNIVERSITY HOSPITAL - STRATFORD** See Jefferson Stratford Hospital

### SUMMIT—Union County

**OVERLOOK HOSPITAL** See Overlook Medical Center

⊞ **OVERLOOK MEDICAL CENTER (310051)**, 99 Beauvoir Avenue, Zip 07901–3533; tel. 908/522–2000, (Nonreporting) **A**1 2 3 5 8 10 **F**3 5 6 8 9 11 12 13 15 17 18 19 20 22 28 29 30 31 32 34 35 36 37 38 39 40 41 42 44 45 46 47 48 49 50 51 52 53 54 55 56 57 58 59 60 61 64 65 66 68 69 70 71 72 74 75 76 77 78 79 81 82 84 85 86 87 89 91 92 93 94 95 96 97 98 100 101 102 103 104 105 107 108 110 111 113 115 117 118 119 120 121 123 124 126 130 131 132 134 135 141 143 145 146 147 148 149 150 152 153 154 156 157 **P**3 6 **S** Atlantic Health System, Morristown, NJ
Primary Contact: Alan R. Lieber, President, Overlook Medical Center, Vice President, Atlantic Health System
CFO: Kevin Lenahan, Vice President Finance and Chief Financial Officer
CMO: John R Audett, M.D., Medical Director Clinical Affairs
CIO: Elizabeth Lindsay-Wood, Interim Chief Information Officer
CNO: Mary Patricia Sullivan, R.N., MSN, Chief Nursing Officer
Web address: www.atlantichealth.org/Overlook
**Control**: Other not–for–profit (including NFP Corporation) **Service**: General medical and surgical

**Staffed Beds:** 384 **Admissions:** 21892 **Census:** 270 **Outpatient Visits:** 278465 **Births:** 2612 **Total Expense ($000):** 805420 **Payroll Expense ($000):** 356331 **Personnel:** 3734

**SUMMIT HOSPITAL** See Summit Oaks Hospital

☐ **SUMMIT OAKS HOSPITAL (314001)**, 19 Prospect Street, Zip 07901–2530; tel. 908/522–7000, (Nonreporting) **A**1 10 **F**4 5 98 99 100 105 152 153 154 **S** Universal Health Services, Inc., King of Prussia, PA
Primary Contact: Ross Friedman, Chief Executive Officer
Web address: www.summitoakshospital.com/
**Control**: Corporation, Investor–owned (for–profit) **Service**: Psychiatric

**Staffed Beds:** 122 **Admissions:** 3558 **Census:** 108 **Outpatient Visits:** 10744 **Births:** 0 **Total Expense ($000):** 24931 **Payroll Expense ($000):** 14309 **Personnel:** 201

**NJ**

---

**Hospital, Medicare Provider Number, Address, Telephone, Approval, Facility, and Physician Codes, Health Care System**

★ American Hospital Association (AHA) membership   ○ Healthcare Facilities Accreditation Program   ⇑ Center for Improvement in Healthcare Quality Accreditation
☐ The Joint Commission accreditation   ◇ DNV Healthcare Inc. accreditation   △ Commission on Accreditation of Rehabilitation Facilities (CARF) accreditation

© 2021 AHA Guide   *Many Facility Codes have changed. Please refer to the AHA Guide Code Chart.*   Hospitals **A463**

## TEANECK—Bergen County

**HOLY NAME HOSPITAL** See Holy Name Medical Center

✉ **HOLY NAME MEDICAL CENTER (310008)**, 718 Teaneck Road,
Zip 07666–4281; tel. 201/833–3000, (Nonreporting) **A**1 2 3 10 **F**2 3 7 11 12 13
15 18 20 22 28 29 30 31 32 34 35 36 37 38 39 40 44 45 46 47 48 49 50 51
53 54 55 56 57 58 59 60 62 63 64 65 66 68 70 71 73 74 75 76 77 78 79 80
81 82 83 84 85 86 87 89 91 92 93 94 96 97 98 100 101 102 103 107 108
110 111 114 115 116 117 118 119 120 121 123 124 126 129 130 131 132
133 135 143 144 145 146 147 148 149 154 156 **P**4 7
Primary Contact: Michael Maron, President and Chief Executive Officer
CFO: Ryan Kennedy, Chief Financial Officer
CMO: Adam D Jarrett, M.D., Executive Vice President and Chief Medical Officer
CIO: Michael Skvarenina, Assistant Vice President Information Systems
CHR: April Rodgers, Vice President, Human Resources
CNO: Sheryl A Slonim, Executive Vice President and Chief Nursing Officer
Web address: www.holyname.org
**Control**: Other not–for–profit (including NFP Corporation) **Service**: General
medical and surgical

**Staffed Beds:** 318 **Admissions:** 19984 **Census:** 202 **Outpatient
Visits:** 387532 **Births:** 1549 **Total Expense ($000):** 399074 **Payroll
Expense ($000):** 164596 **Personnel:** 2278

## TINTON FALLS—Monmouth County

✉ **ENCOMPASS HEALTH REHABILITATION HOSPITAL OF TINTON FALLS
(313035)**, 2 Centre Plaza, Zip 07724–9744; tel. 732/460–5320, (Nonreporting)
**A**1 10 **S** Encompass Health Corporation, Birmingham, AL
Primary Contact: Beth Lynch, MS, Chief Executive Officer
CFO: Lynne Traister, Controller
CMO: Todd Cooperman, M.D., Medical Director
CHR: Anita Saum, Director Human Resources
Web address: www.rehabnjtintonfalls.com/
**Control**: Corporation, Investor–owned (for–profit) **Service**: Rehabilitation

**Staffed Beds:** 60

**HEALTHSOUTH REHABILITATION HOSPITAL OF TINTON FALLS** See
Encompass Health Rehabilitation Hospital of Tinton Falls

## TOMS RIVER—Ocean County

**COMM KIMBALL HLTH CARE SYSTEM** See Community Medical Center

✉ **COMMUNITY MEDICAL CENTER (310041)**, 99 Route 37 West,
Zip 08755–6423; tel. 732/557–8000, (Nonreporting) **A**1 2 3 5 10 **F**3 11 12 13
15 18 20 22 26 28 29 30 31 32 34 35 36 37 40 41 43 44 49 50 54 55
56 57 58 59 60 61 63 64 68 70 73 74 75 76 77 78 79 81 82 83 84 85 86 87
89 93 96 97 100 102 107 108 109 110 111 114 115 118 119 120 121 123
124 126 129 130 131 132 133 134 135 143 146 147 148 149 154 156 157
**P**3 6 **S** RWJBarnabas Health, West Orange, NJ
Primary Contact: Patrick Ahearn, Chief Executive Officer
CFO: Christopher Reidy, Site Financial Officer
CMO: Meika Neblett, M.D., Chief Medical Officer
CIO: Shaun Fitzsimmons, Director Information Technology Services
CHR: Vanessa Smith, Chief Human Resources Officer
CNO: Donna Bonacorso, R.N., Chief Nursing Officer
Web address: www.https://www.rwjbh.org/community-medical-center/
**Control**: Other not–for–profit (including NFP Corporation) **Service**: General
medical and surgical

**Staffed Beds:** 306 **Admissions:** 20005 **Census:** 290 **Outpatient
Visits:** 240351 **Births:** 2013 **Total Expense ($000):** 378393 **Payroll
Expense ($000):** 142367 **Personnel:** 2182

✉ **ENCOMPASS HEALTH REHABILITATION HOSPITAL OF TOMS RIVER
(313029)**, 14 Hospital Drive, Zip 08755–6470; tel. 732/244–3100,
(Nonreporting) **A**1 10 **S** Encompass Health Corporation, Birmingham, AL
Primary Contact: Patricia Ostaszewski, MS, Chief Executive Officer
COO: Patricia Ostaszewski, MS, Chief Executive Officer
CFO: Janet Turso, Controller
CMO: Carol Sonatore, D.O., Medical Director
CIO: Coleen Rossi, Director Quality Services
CHR: Lori Munyan, Director, Human Resources
CNO: Susan Castor, Chief Nursing Officer
Web address: www.rehabnjtomsriver.com/
**Control**: Corporation, Investor–owned (for–profit) **Service**: Rehabilitation

**Staffed Beds:** 92

**HEALTHSOUTH REHABILITATION HOSPITAL OF TOMS RIVER** See Encompass
Health Rehabilitation Hospital of Toms River

✉ **RWJBARNABAS HEALTH BEHAVIORAL HEALTH CENTER (314022)**, 1691
Highway 9, Zip 8754; tel. 732/914–1688, (Nonreporting) **A**1 10 **F**35 68 98 100
101 103 104 153 **S** RWJBarnabas Health, West Orange, NJ
Primary Contact: Deanna Sperling, R.N., President and Chief Executive Officer
Web address: www.https://www.rwjbh.org/our-locations/behavioral-health-center/
barnabas-health-behavioral-health-center/
**Control**: Other not–for–profit (including NFP Corporation) **Service**: Psychiatric

**Staffed Beds:** 40 **Admissions:** 1329 **Census:** 32 **Outpatient Visits:** 5315
**Births:** 0 **Total Expense ($000):** 10833 **Payroll Expense ($000):** 5816
**Personnel:** 428

**RWJBARNABAS HEALTH BEHAVIORAL HEALTH CENTER AND NETWORK** See
Rwjbarnabas Health Behavioral Health Center

## TRENTON—Mercer County

⇧ **CAPITAL HEALTH - FULD CAMPUS** See Capital Health Regional Medical Center

★ ⇧ **CAPITAL HEALTH REGIONAL MEDICAL CENTER (310092)**, 750 Brunswick
Avenue, Zip 08638–4143; tel. 609/394–6000, (Nonreporting) **A**3 5 10 21 **F**3 7
15 18 29 30 34 35 40 43 44 45 46 47 48 50 54 57 58 59 60 61 64 65 66 68
70 74 75 78 79 81 82 84 85 87 89 93 96 97 98 100 101 102 104 107 108
109 111 112 114 115 118 119 129 130 132 135 143 145 146 147 148 154
156 **S** Capital Health, Trenton, NJ
Primary Contact: Al Maghazehe, Ph.D., FACHE, President and Chief Executive Officer
CFO: Shane Fleming, Chief Financial Officer
CMO: Eugene McMahon, Senior Vice President and Chief Medical Officer
CIO: Eugene Grochala, Vice President Information Systems
CHR: Scott Clemmensen, Vice President Human Resources and Leadership
Enhancement
CNO: Gina Mumolie, Senior Vice President Hospital Administration
Web address: www.capitalhealth.org
**Control**: Other not–for–profit (including NFP Corporation) **Service**: General
medical and surgical

**Staffed Beds:** 168 **Admissions:** 7327 **Census:** 129 **Outpatient
Visits:** 157183 **Births:** 0 **Personnel:** 1494

✉ **ST. FRANCIS MEDICAL CENTER (310021)**, 601 Hamilton Avenue,
Zip 08629–1986; tel. 609/599–5000, (Nonreporting) **A**1 3 10 **F**2 3 10 11 12 15
17 18 20 22 24 26 29 30 31 34 35 40 43 45 46 50 56 57 58 59 60 61 62 64
65 66 70 74 77 78 79 81 82 84 85 86 87 92 93 98 100 101 102 104 107 108
110 111 114 115 118 119 121 123 124 126 129 130 132 135 143 144 146
147 148 149 154 156 157 **S** Trinity Health, Livonia, MI
Primary Contact: Daniel P. Moen, President
CFO: Mark Kelly, Vice President Finance
CMO: C. James Romano, M.D., Chief Medical Officer
CIO: Michael Yulich, Director Information Technology
CHR: Rebecca Capuano, Director Human Resources
Web address: www.stfrancismedical.org/
**Control**: Church operated, Nongovernment, not–for–profit **Service**: General
medical and surgical

**Staffed Beds:** 142 **Admissions:** 4036 **Census:** 64 **Outpatient Visits:** 83173
**Births:** 0 **Total Expense ($000):** 137812 **Payroll Expense ($000):** 53206
**Personnel:** 751

☐ **TRENTON PSYCHIATRIC HOSPITAL (314013)**, Route 29 and Sullivan
Way, Zip 08628–3425, Mailing Address: P.O. Box 7500, West Trenton,
Zip 08628–0500; tel. 609/633–1500, (Nonreporting) **A**1 3 10 **S** Division of
Mental Health and Addiction Services, Department of Human Services, State of
New Jersey, Trenton, NJ
Primary Contact: Robyn Caporoso, Chief Executive Officer
CFO: Joseph Canale, Business Manager
CMO: Lawrence Rossi, M.D., Clinical Director
CIO: Scott Eustace, Director Health Information Technology
CHR: Marybeth Longo, Manager Human Resources
CNO: Colleen Birkhofer, Chief Nursing Officer
Web address: www.state.nj.us/humanservices/dmhs/oshm/tph/
**Control**: State, Government, Nonfederal **Service**: Psychiatric

**Staffed Beds:** 431

## TURNERSVILLE—Camden County

**JEFFERSON WASHINGTON TOWNSHIP HOSPITAL** See Jefferson Stratford
Hospital, Stratford

**KENNEDY UNIVERSITY HOSPITAL - WASHINGTON TOWNSHIP** See Jefferson
Washington Township Hospital

*Many Facility Codes have changed. Please refer to the AHA Guide Code Chart.*        © 2021 AHA Guide

## VINELAND—Cumberland County

☒ **ENCOMPASS HEALTH REHABILITATION HOSPITAL OF VINELAND (313036)**, 1237 West Sherman Avenue, Zip 08360–6920; tel. 856/696–7100, (Nonreporting) **A**1 10 **F**29 30 65 75 90 130 132 148 149 **S** Encompass Health Corporation, Birmingham, AL
Primary Contact: Monica B. Titus, R.N., Chief Executive Officer
CHR: Dawn Pearson, Director Human Resources
Web address: www.healthsouthvineland.com
**Control:** Corporation, Investor–owned (for–profit) **Service:** Rehabilitation

**Staffed Beds:** 41 **Admissions:** 1017 **Census:** 37 **Outpatient Visits:** 0
**Births:** 0 **Total Expense ($000):** 15312 **Payroll Expense ($000):** 8266
**Personnel:** 101

**HEALTHSOUTH REHABILITATION HOSPITAL OF VINELAND** See Encompass Health Rehabilitation Hospital of Vineland

★ ⇑ **INSPIRA MEDICAL CENTER-VINELAND (310032)**, 1505 West Sherman Avenue, Zip 08360–6912; tel. 856/641–8000, (Includes BRIDGETON HEALTH CENTER, Mailing address: 333 Irving Avenue, Bridgeton, New Jersey, Zip 08302–2100; tel. 856/575–4500), (Nonreporting) **A**2 3 5 10 12 13 21 **F**3 4 7 8 11 12 13 15 17 18 20 22 25 29 30 34 35 37 38 40 41 42 44 49 50 54 57 59 64 68 70 72 73 74 75 76 77 78 79 81 82 85 86 87 89 93 98 99 100 104 105 107 108 110 111 114 115 116 117 118 119 120 121 123 124 126 130 131 132 134 144 146 147 148 153 154 **P**8 **S** Inspira Health Network, Mullica Hill, NJ
Primary Contact: Amy B. Mansue, President and Chief Executive Officer
COO: Elizabeth Sheridan, Chief Operating Officer and Chief Nursing Executive
CFO: Thomas Baldosaro, Chief Financial Officer
CMO: Steven C Linn, M.D., Chief Medical Officer
CIO: Thomas Pacek, Vice President Information Systems and Chief Information Officer
CHR: Erich Florentine, Chief People Officer
CNO: Elizabeth Sheridan, Chief Operating Officer and Chief Nursing Executive
Web address: www.inspirahealthnetwork.org/?id=5280&sid=1
**Control:** Other not–for–profit (including NFP Corporation) **Service:** General medical and surgical

**Staffed Beds:** 345 **Admissions:** 17922 **Census:** 248 **Outpatient Visits:** 282199 **Births:** 1891 **Total Expense ($000):** 395256 **Payroll Expense ($000):** 169083 **Personnel:** 1740

⇑ **SOUTH JERSEY HEALTHCARE - REGIONAL MEDICAL CENTER** See Inspira Medical Center-Vineland

## VOORHEES—Camden County

☒ **VIRTUA VOORHEES (310022)**, 100 Bowman Drive, Zip 08043–9612; tel. 856/325–3000, (Includes VOORHEES PEDIATRIC FACILITY, Mailing address: 1304 Laurel Oak Road, Voorhees, New Jersey, Zip 08043–4310; tel. 888/873–5437), (Nonreporting) **A**1 3 5 10 **F**3 11 13 15 28 29 30 31 34 37 39 40 41 45 46 48 49 50 55 64 68 70 72 73 74 75 76 78 79 81 84 85 87 88 89 92 93 107 108 111 115 116 117 119 126 129 130 132 146 147 148 149 157 **P**1 **S** Virtua Health, Marlton, NJ
Primary Contact: Dennis W. Pullin, FACHE, President and Chief Executive Officer
COO: Paul E Minnick, R.N., MSN, Senior Vice President and Chief Operating Officer
CFO: Robert Rosvold, Director Finance
CMO: James P Dwyer, D.O., Executive Vice President and Chief Medical Officer
CIO: Alfred Campanella, Chief Information Officer
Web address: www.virtua.org
**Control:** Other not–for–profit (including NFP Corporation) **Service:** General medical and surgical

**Staffed Beds:** 402 **Admissions:** 22717 **Census:** 267 **Outpatient Visits:** 259309 **Births:** 4805 **Total Expense ($000):** 583367 **Payroll Expense ($000):** 172042 **Personnel:** 2020

**VIRTUA WEST JERSEY HOSPITAL-VOORHEES** See Virtua Voorhees

## WAYNE—Passaic County

**KINDRED HOSPITAL NEW JERSEY - WAYNE** See Kindred Hospital-New Jersey Morris County, Dover

**WAYNE GENERAL HOSPITAL** See St. Joseph's Wayne Hospital

## WEST ORANGE—Essex County

**GROTTA CENTER FOR SENIOR CARE** See Summit Ridge Nursing and Rehabilitation Center

☒ △ **KESSLER INSTITUTE FOR REHABILITATION (313025)**, 1199 Pleasant Valley Way, Zip 07052–1424; tel. 973/731–3600, (Includes KESSLER INSTITUTE FOR REHABILITATION, Mailing address: 1199 Pleasant Valley Way, West Orange, New Jersey, Zip 07052–1424; tel. 973/731–3600; Bonnie A. Evans, Chief Executive Officer; KESSLER INSTITUTE FOR REHABILITATION, Mailing address: 201 Pleasant Hill Road, Chester, New Jersey, Zip 07930–2141; tel. 973/252–6300; Sue Kida, Chief Executive Officer; KESSLER INSTITUTE FOR REHABILITATION, Mailing address: 300 Market Street, Saddle Brook, New Jersey, Zip 07663–5309; tel. 201/368–6000; Philip J Driscoll Jr, Chief Executive Officer), (Nonreporting) **A**1 3 5 7 10 **F**3 29 34 57 58 74 75 78 79 82 86 87 90 91 92 93 94 95 96 119 130 131 132 146 148 149 **S** Select Medical Corporation, Mechanicsburg, PA
Primary Contact: Bonnie A. Evans, Chief Executive Officer
CMO: Bruce M Gans, M.D., Executive Vice President and Chief Medical Officer
CHR: Ken Caldera, Director Human Resources
Web address: www.kessler-rehab.com
**Control:** Corporation, Investor–owned (for–profit) **Service:** Rehabilitation

**Staffed Beds:** 336 **Admissions:** 5739 **Census:** 265 **Outpatient Visits:** 107328 **Births:** 0 **Personnel:** 1085

**KESSLER INSTITUTE FOR REHABILITATION** See Kessler Institute for Rehabilitation, West Orange

## WESTAMPTON—Burlington County

☐ **HAMPTON BEHAVIORAL HEALTH CENTER (314021)**, 650 Rancocas Road, Zip 08060–5613; tel. 609/267–7000, (Nonreporting) **A**1 3 10 **F**30 35 98 99 100 103 104 105 130 132 143 149 153 **P**6 **S** Universal Health Services, Inc., King of Prussia, PA
Primary Contact: Craig Hilton, Chief Executive Officer and Managing Director
COO: Joanne Wijaya, MSN, R.N., Chief Operating Officer and Risk Manager
CFO: Melissa Zinni, Chief Financial Officer
CMO: Anusuya Balasundaram, M.D., Medical Director
CHR: Lori DeCelis, Director Human Resources
CNO: Kathleena Cohen, MSN, R.N., Director of Nursing
Web address: www.hamptonhospital.com
**Control:** Corporation, Investor–owned (for–profit) **Service:** Psychiatric

**Staffed Beds:** 120 **Admissions:** 2525 **Census:** 103 **Outpatient Visits:** 18878 **Births:** 0 **Total Expense ($000):** 30200 **Payroll Expense ($000):** 17528 **Personnel:** 254

**HAMPTON HOSPITAL** See Hampton Behavioral Health Center

## WESTWOOD—Bergen County

**CARE ONE AT HACKENSACK UNIVERSITY MEDICAL CENTER AT PASCACK VALLEY** See Careone at Hackensack University Medical Center at Pascack Valley

**CAREONE AT HACKENSACK UNIVERSITY MEDICAL CENTER AT PASCACK VALLEY**, 250 Old Hook Road, Zip 07675–3123, Mailing Address: 250 Old Hook Road, 4 Central, Zip 07675–3123; tel. 201/781–1555, (Nonreporting)
Primary Contact: Sharon Bready, R.N., Chief Executive Officer
Web address: www.care-one.com/locations/ltach-careone-at-hackensack-university-medical-center-pascack-valley/
**Control:** Other not–for–profit (including NFP Corporation) **Service:** Acute long–term care hospital

**Staffed Beds:** 25

☒ **HACKENSACK MERIDIAN HEALTH PASCACK VALLEY MEDICAL CENTER (310130)**, 250 Old Hook Road, Zip 07675–3123; tel. 201/383–1035, (Nonreporting) **A**1 5 10 **F**3 12 13 15 18 20 28 29 30 34 35 37 40 44 45 46 47 49 50 51 57 59 60 64 68 70 73 74 75 76 77 78 79 81 82 85 87 93 107 108 110 111 115 119 126 129 130 135 141 146 147 148 149 154 156 157 **S** Ardent Health Services, Nashville, TN
Primary Contact: Emily L. Holliman, Chief Executive Officer
COO: Colleen Smorra, Assistant Administrator
CFO: Jason Pritchard, Chief Financial Officer
CMO: George Lin, M.D., Physician Advisor
CIO: Anthony Teri, Director Information Technology
CNO: Susan Giordano, Chief Nursing Officer
Web address: www.hackensackumcpv.com/
**Control:** Partnership, Investor–owned (for–profit) **Service:** General medical and surgical

**Staffed Beds:** 128 **Admissions:** 4752 **Census:** 45 **Outpatient Visits:** 34249 **Births:** 1195 **Total Expense ($000):** 115304 **Payroll Expense ($000):** 37559 **Personnel:** 498

**NJ**

---

**Hospital, Medicare Provider Number, Address, Telephone, Approval, Facility, and Physician Codes, Health Care System**

★ American Hospital Association (AHA) membership
☐ The Joint Commission accreditation
○ Healthcare Facilities Accreditation Program
◇ DNV Healthcare Inc. accreditation
⇑ Center for Improvement in Healthcare Quality Accreditation
△ Commission on Accreditation of Rehabilitation Facilities (CARF) accreditation

**PASCACK VALLEY MEDICAL CENTER** See Hackensack Meridian Health Pascack Valley Medical Center

## WILLINGBORO—Burlington County

✦ **ACUITY SPECIALTY HOSPITAL OF SOUTHERN NEW JERSEY (312022)**, 218 A Sunset Road, Zip 08046–1110, Mailing Address: 220 Sunset Road, Zip 08046–1110; tel. 609/835–3650, (Nonreporting) **A**1 10 **S** AcuityHealthcare, LP, Charlotte, NC
Primary Contact: Garrett Arneson, FACHE, R.N., Chief Executive Officer
CMO: Edward G. Hamaty, D.O., Chief Medical Officer
CHR: Lisa M Sinnott, Director Human Resources
CNO: Eddie Perez, R.N., Chief Clinical Officer/Chief Nurse Executive
Web address: www.willingboro.acuityhealthcare.net
**Control**: Corporation, Investor–owned (for–profit) **Service**: Acute long–term care hospital

**Staffed Beds**: 53

**LOURDES MEDICAL CENTER OF BURLINGTON COUNTY** See Virtua Willingboro Hospital

**LOURDES SPECIALTY HOSPITAL OF SOUTHERN NEW JERSEY** See Acuity Specialty Hospital of Southern New Jersey

✦ **VIRTUA WILLINGBORO HOSPITAL (310061)**, 218-A Sunset Road, Zip 08046–1162; tel. 609/835–2900, (Nonreporting) **A**1 2 3 10 **F**3 7 11 12 15 17 18 29 30 31 34 35 36 38 40 42 44 45 46 47 49 50 55 56 57 59 60 61 64 66 68 70 74 75 78 79 81 82 85 86 87 93 98 100 103 107 108 109 110 111 114 118 119 121 129 130 131 132 135 146 147 148 149 **P**1 **S** Virtua Health, Marlton, NJ
Primary Contact: Mark Nessel, Executive Vice President and Chief Operating Officer
CFO: Michael Hammond, Chief Financial Officer
CMO: Alan R Pope, M.D., Vice President, Medical Affairs
CIO: Mike Elfert, Director Information Services
CNO: Audrey Jadczak, R.N., FACHE, Vice President/Chief Nursing Officer
Web address: www.https://www.lourdesnet.org/locations/hospitals/lourdes-medical-center-of-burlington-county/
**Control**: Other not–for–profit (including NFP Corporation) **Service**: General medical and surgical

**Staffed Beds**: 169 **Admissions**: 5876 **Census**: 92 **Outpatient Visits**: 85636 **Births**: 0 **Total Expense ($000)**: 131245 **Payroll Expense ($000)**: 46017 **Personnel**: 532

## WOODBURY—Gloucester County

★ ⚕ **INSPIRA MEDICAL CENTER-WOODBURY (310081)**, 509 North Broad Street, Zip 08096–1697; tel. 856/845–0100, (Data for 348 days) (Nonreporting) **A**3 5 10 21 **F**3 5 11 12 13 15 18 20 22 24 26 28 29 30 31 34 37 40 41 42 45 46 47 48 49 56 57 58 59 64 66 70 73 74 75 76 78 79 81 84 85 86 87 89 91 92 93 94 96 97 98 100 101 102 104 105 107 110 111 114 115 118 119 126 129 130 132 135 144 146 147 148 149 152 153 154 156 **P**8 **S** Inspira Health Network, Mullica Hill, NJ
Primary Contact: Amy B. Mansue, President and Chief Executive Officer
COO: Patrick B Nolan, Chief Operating Officer
CIO: Robert Mizia, Director Information Systems and Chief Information Officer
CHR: Robert Manestrina, Vice President Human Resources
CNO: Gina Mumolie, Senior Vice President and Chief Nurse Executive
Web address: www.inspirahealthnetwork.org/?id=5282&sid=1
**Control**: Other not–for–profit (including NFP Corporation) **Service**: General medical and surgical

**Staffed Beds**: 311 **Admissions**: 8602 **Census**: 120 **Outpatient Visits**: 167474 **Births**: 847 **Total Expense ($000)**: 215841 **Payroll Expense ($000)**: 96848 **Personnel**: 1126

⚕ **UNDERWOOD-MEMORIAL HOSPITAL** See Inspira Medical Center-Woodbury

## WYCKOFF—Bergen County

✦ **CHRISTIAN HEALTH CARE CENTER (314019)**, 301 Sicomac Avenue, Zip 07481–2194; tel. 201/848–5200, (Total facility includes 298 beds in nursing home–type unit) (Nonreporting) **A**1 10 **F**30 34 35 56 57 58 69 84 87 98 99 101 103 104 105 128 130 132 143 146 153 154
Primary Contact: Douglas A. Struyk, CPA, President and Chief Executive Officer
COO: Steve Dumke, FACHE, Executive Vice President and Chief Operating Officer
CFO: Kevin Stagg, Executive Vice President Finance and Chief Financial Officer
CMO: Allen M. Khademi, M.D., Vice President Medical Affairs
CIO: Ed Rizgallah, Vice President Information Services and Chief Information Officer
CHR: Bob Zierold, Senior Vice President, Chief Human Resources Officer
CNO: Rebecca Dauerman, R.N., Vice President, Administrator Mental Health Services and Chief Nursing Officer
Web address: www.chccnj.org
**Control**: Other not–for–profit (including NFP Corporation) **Service**: Psychiatric

**Staffed Beds**: 451 **Admissions**: 2164 **Census**: 415 **Outpatient Visits**: 58725 **Births**: 0 **Total Expense ($000)**: 80679 **Payroll Expense ($000)**: 44958 **Personnel**: 705

**RAMAPO RIDGE PSYCHIATRIC HOSP** See Christian Health Care Center

*Many Facility Codes have changed. Please refer to the AHA Guide Code Chart.*

**NJ**

# NEW MEXICO

## ACOMA—Bergen County

☐ **ACOMA-CANONCITO-LAGUNA HOSPITAL (320070)**, 80B Veterans Boulevard, Zip 87034, Mailing Address: P.O. Box 130, San Fidel, Zip 87049–0130; tel. 505/552–5300, (Nonreporting) **A1** 10 **S** U. S. Indian Health Service, Rockville, MD
Primary Contact: Melody Price-Yonts, Chief Executive Officer
Web address: www.ihs.gov/albuquerque/index.cfm?module=dsp_abq_acoma_canoncito_laguna
**Control**: PHS, Indian Service, Government, federal **Service**: General medical and surgical

**Staffed Beds**: 6

## ALAMOGORDO—Otero County

⇑ **GERALD CHAMPION MEM HOSPITAL** See Gerald Champion Regional Medical Center

★ △ ⇑ **GERALD CHAMPION REGIONAL MEDICAL CENTER (320004)**, 2669 North Scenic Drive, Zip 88310–8799; tel. 575/439–6100, (Nonreporting) **A3** 5 7 10 13 20 21 **F3** 8 11 12 13 18 20 22 26 28 29 30 31 34 35 37 38 40 43 44 45 50 51 57 59 64 70 74 75 76 77 78 79 81 82 85 86 87 90 91 96 97 98 100 101 102 103 104 105 107 108 111 114 115 117 119 120 121 123 129 130 131 132 144 145 146 147 148 149 153 156 **P8**
Primary Contact: Robert J. Heckert Jr, Chief Executive Officer
CFO: Bashar Naser, Chief Financial Officer
CMO: Lee Saltzgaber, Chief Medical Officer
CIO: Ana Castro, Director Information Technology
CHR: Karen O'Brien, Director Human Resources
CNO: Robert Eldon Middleton, MSN, R.N., IIIVice President Ancillary Services, Chief Administrative Officer andChief Construction Executive
Web address: www.gcrmc.org
**Control**: Other not–for–profit (including NFP Corporation) **Service**: General medical and surgical

**Staffed Beds**: 98 **Admissions**: 4053 **Census**: 53 **Outpatient Visits**: 86795
**Births**: 533 **Total Expense ($000)**: 157249 **Payroll Expense ($000)**: 59854
**Personnel**: 884

## ALBUQUERQUE—Bernalillo County

**AMG SPECIALTY HOSPITAL-ALBUQUERQUE (322003)**, 5400 Gibson Boulevard SE, 3rd Floor, Zip 87108–4729, Mailing Address: 5400 Gibson Boulevad SE, 3rd Floor, Zip 87108–4729; tel. 505/842–5550, (Nonreporting) **A10** 22 **S** AMG Integrated Healthcare Management, Lafayette, LA
Primary Contact: Kendra Camp, R.N., Chief Executive Officer
CMO: Jeffrey Ross, M.D., Medical Director
CHR: Robin Stendel-Freels, Coordinator Human Resources
Web address: www.amgalbuquerque.com/
**Control**: Partnership, Investor–owned (for–profit) **Service**: Acute long–term care hospital

**Staffed Beds**: 24

⊞ **ENCOMPASS HEALTH REHABILITATION HOSPITAL OF ALBUQUERQUE (323027)**, 7000 Jefferson Street NE, Zip 87109–4313; tel. 505/344–9478, (Nonreporting) **A1** 10 **F**28 29 34 35 56 57 59 60 62 64 74 75 77 79 90 91 93 94 95 96 130 132 143 148 **S** Encompass Health Corporation, Birmingham, AL
Primary Contact: Rachelle Spencer, Chief Executive Officer
CFO: Michelle Martinez, Controller
CMO: Joseph Michael Long, M.D., Medical Director
CHR: Kristen Hernandez, Director Human Resources
CNO: Susan Blanchard, R.N., Chief Nursing Officer
Web address: www.encompasshealth.com/albuquerquerehab
**Control**: Corporation, Investor–owned (for–profit) **Service**: Rehabilitation

**Staffed Beds**: 87 **Admissions**: 1789 **Census**: 62 **Births**: 0

☐ **HAVEN BEHAVIORAL SENIOR CARE OF ALBUQUERQUE (324013)**, 5400 Gibson Boulevard SE, 4th Floor, Box #8, Zip 87108–4729; tel. 505/254–4502, (Nonreporting) **A1** 10
Primary Contact: Jennifer Barut, Chief Executive Officer
Web address: www.https://albuquerque.havenbehavioral.com/
**Control**: Corporation, Investor–owned (for–profit) **Service**: Psychiatric

**Staffed Beds**: 32

**HEALTHSOUTH REHABILITATION HOSPITAL OF NEW MEXICO** See Encompass Health Rehabilitation Hospital of Albuquerque

**KASEMAN PRESBYTERIAN HOSPITAL** See Presbyterian Kaseman Hospital

⊞ **KINDRED HOSPITAL-ALBUQUERQUE (322002)**, 700 High Street NE, Zip 87102–2565; tel. 505/242–4444, (Nonreporting) **A1** 10 **S** Kindred Healthcare, Louisville, KY
Primary Contact: Larry Rodgers, Chief Executive Officer
CFO: Sheila Bova, Chief Financial Officer
CMO: Jon Marinaro, M.D., Chief Medical Officer
CHR: Donald Whitney, Director Human Resources
CNO: Diane Nelson, R.N., Chief Nursing Officer
Web address: www.kindredalbuquerque.com/
**Control**: Corporation, Investor–owned (for–profit) **Service**: Acute long–term care hospital

**Staffed Beds**: 61

★ ⇑ **LOVELACE MEDICAL CENTER (320009)**, 601 Martin Luther King Avenue NE, Zip 87102–3619; tel. 505/727–8000, (Includes HEART HOSPITAL OF NEW MEXICO, Mailing address: 504 Elm Street, Albuquerque, New Mexico, Zip 87102; tel. 505/724–2000; Denzil Ross, Administrator), (Nonreporting) **A3** 5 10 21 **F3** 17 18 20 22 24 26 28 29 30 31 34 35 36 38 40 45 46 49 50 51 56 57 58 59 60 64 65 68 70 74 75 77 78 79 81 82 85 87 89 98 100 105 107 108 109 111 114 115 117 118 119 120 121 124 126 130 132 146 148 149 154 157 **S** Ardent Health Services, Nashville, TN
Primary Contact: Denzil Ross, Interim Chief Executive Officer
COO: Denzil Ross, Chief Operating Officer
CHR: Helen V Nielsen, Director Human Resources
CNO: Nancye Cole, MS, R.N., FACHE, Chief Nursing Officer
Web address: www.https://lovelace.com/location/lovelace-medical-center
**Control**: Corporation, Investor–owned (for–profit) **Service**: General medical and surgical

**Staffed Beds**: 247 **Admissions**: 13780 **Census**: 187 **Births**: 0

⇑ **LOVELACE MEDICAL CENTER-DOWNTOWN** See Lovelace Medical Center

**LOVELACE REHABILITATION HOSPITAL** See Lovelace Unm Rehabilitation Hospital

★ △ **LOVELACE UNM REHABILITATION HOSPITAL (323028)**, 505 Elm Street NE, Zip 87102–2500; tel. 505/727–4700, (Nonreporting) **A7** 10 **F3** 29 30 90 143 148 **S** Ardent Health Services, Nashville, TN
Primary Contact: Derrick Jones, Chief Executive Officer
CFO: Andrea Solin, Chief Financial Officer
CHR: Helen V Nielsen, Director Human Resources
CNO: Cynthia Rankin, Chief Nursing Officer
Web address: www.lovelace.com
**Control**: Corporation, Investor–owned (for–profit) **Service**: Rehabilitation

**Staffed Beds**: 52 **Admissions**: 1163 **Census**: 39 **Births**: 0

★ ⇑ **LOVELACE WESTSIDE HOSPITAL (320074)**, 10501 Golf Course Road NW, Zip 87114–5000; tel. 505/727–8000, (Nonreporting) **A10** 21 **F3** 12 13 15 29 30 34 39 40 41 49 51 57 59 68 70 75 76 79 81 85 93 107 110 111 115 119 130 133 135 146 148 **S** Ardent Health Services, Nashville, TN
Primary Contact: Amy Blasing, Chief Executive Officer
CFO: Andrea Solin, Chief Financial Officer
CNO: Brenda Holley, Chief Nursing Officer
Web address: www.lovelace.com/albuquerque-hospital/lovelace-westside-hospital#.UDZ1t6Dhf48
**Control**: Corporation, Investor–owned (for–profit) **Service**: General medical and surgical

**Staffed Beds**: 80 **Admissions**: 3639 **Census**: 29

**NM**

---

<table>
<tr><td colspan="3">**Hospital, Medicare Provider Number, Address, Telephone, Approval, Facility, and Physician Codes, Health Care System**</td></tr>
<tr><td>★ American Hospital Association (AHA) membership</td><td>○ Healthcare Facilities Accreditation Program</td><td>⇑ Center for Improvement in Healthcare Quality Accreditation</td></tr>
<tr><td>☐ The Joint Commission accreditation</td><td>◇ DNV Healthcare Inc. accreditation</td><td>△ Commission on Accreditation of Rehabilitation Facilities (CARF) accreditation</td></tr>
</table>

★ ⇑ **LOVELACE WOMEN'S HOSPITAL (320017)**, 4701 Montgomery Boulevard NE, Zip 87109–1251; tel. 505/727–7800, (Nonreporting) **A**3 10 21 **F**8 11 15 34 35 42 43 46 49 57 59 64 70 72 73 76 78 79 81 85 91 93 107 108 110 111 114 115 116 117 119 126 130 132 146 147 **S** Ardent Health Services, Nashville, TN
Primary Contact: Sheri Milone, Chief Executive Officer and Administrator
COO: Janelle Raborn, Chief Operating Officer
CFO: Joseph Sereno, Chief Financial Officer
CHR: Carol Shelton, Director Human Resources
Web address: www.lovelace.com/albuquerque-hospital/lovelace-womens-hospital#.
UDZ17KDhf48
**Control:** Corporation, Investor–owned (for–profit) **Service:** General medical and surgical

**Staffed Beds:** 78 **Admissions:** 6090 **Census:** 55

☒ △ **NEW MEXICO VETERANS AFFAIRS HEALTH CARE SYSTEM - RAYMOND G. MURPHY MEDICAL CENTER**, 1501 San Pedro SE, Zip 87108–5153; tel. 505/265–1711, (Nonreporting) **A**1 2 3 5 7 8 **S** Department of Veterans Affairs, Washington, DC
Primary Contact: Andrew Welch, Director
CFO: Michael McNeill, Chief Financial Management
CMO: Meghan Gerety, M.D., Chief of Staff
CIO: Ronald Ferrell, Chief Information Officer
CHR: Melvin Hooker, Chief Human Resources
Web address: www.albuquerque.va.gov/
**Control:** Veterans Affairs, Government, federal **Service:** General medical and surgical

**Staffed Beds:** 203

**PRESBYTERIAN HEALTHCARE SERVS** See Presbyterian Hospital

☒ **PRESBYTERIAN HOSPITAL (320021)**, 1100 Central Avenue SE, Zip 87106–4934, Mailing Address: P.O. Box 26666, Zip 87125–6666; tel. 505/841–1234, (Includes PRESBYTERIAN KASEMAN HOSPITAL, Mailing address: 8300 Constitution Avenue NE, Albuquerque, New Mexico, Zip 87110–7624, P O Box 26666, Zip 87125–6666, tel. 505/291–2000; Doyle Boykin, R.N., MSN, Administrator; PRESBYTERIAN RUST MEDICAL CENTER, Mailing address: 2400 Unser Boulevard SE, Rio Rancho, New Mexico, Zip 87124–4740; tel. 505/253–7878; Jeff McBee, Administrator), (Nonreporting) **A**1 2 3 5 10 **F**3 7 8 11 12 13 17 18 19 20 21 22 23 24 25 26 27 28 29 30 31 32 34 35 38 40 42 45 46 47 48 49 50 51 53 55 56 57 58 59 61 62 63 64 65 68 70 72 74 75 76 77 78 79 80 81 82 84 85 86 87 88 89 91 92 93 96 97 98 99 100 101 102 104 107 108 111 112 114 115 116 117 118 119 120 121 126 129 130 131 132 135 138 142 144 146 147 148 149 153 154 **S** Presbyterian Healthcare Services, Albuquerque, NM
Primary Contact: Devon Hyde, Vice President, Chief Administrative Officer
CFO: Dale Maxwell, Executive Vice President and Chief Financial Officer
CMO: Jayne McCormick, M.D., Chief Medical Officer CDS
CIO: Lee Marley, VP/Information Services Chief Application Officer
CHR: Lee Patchell, Lead Human Resources Business Partner
CNO: Ann L Wright, R.N., MSN, Assistant Central Delivery System CNO
Web address: www.phs.org
**Control:** Other not–for–profit (including NFP Corporation) **Service:** General medical and surgical

**Staffed Beds:** 643 **Admissions:** 49131 **Census:** 617 **Outpatient Visits:** 486086 **Births:** 4242 **Total Expense ($000):** 1604464 **Payroll Expense ($000):** 570218 **Personnel:** 6336

**SPECIALTY HOSPITAL OF ALBUQUERQUE** See Amg Specialty Hospital-Albuquerque

**TURQUOISE LODGE** See Turquoise Lodge Hospital

**TURQUOISE LODGE HOSPITAL**, 5901 Zuni Road SE, Zip 87108–3073; tel. 505/841–8978, (Nonreporting) **F**4 5 151 152 154
Primary Contact: Shauna Hartley, Administrator
CFO: Juliette Aragon, Finance Director
CIO: Eric Gurule, Chief Information Officer
CHR: Mario Lechuga, Director Human Resources
CNO: Debra Jane Green, R.N., Director of Nursing
Web address: www.health.state.nm.us
**Control:** State, Government, Nonfederal **Service:** Alcoholism and other chemical dependency

**Staffed Beds:** 40 **Admissions:** 1188 **Census:** 25 **Births:** 0 **Personnel:** 74

**UNIV OF NEW MEXICO HOSPITAL** See Mental Health Center

**UNIVERSITY HOSPITAL** See University of New Mexico Hospitals

☒ **UNIVERSITY OF NEW MEXICO HOSPITALS (320001)**, 2211 Lomas Boulevard NE, Zip 87106–2745; tel. 505/272–2111, (Includes CARRIE TINGLEY HOSPITAL, Mailing address: 1127 University Boulevard NE, Albuquerque, New Mexico, Zip 87102–1715; tel. 505/272–5200; Doris Tinagero, Executive Director; MENTAL HEALTH CENTER, Mailing address: 2600 Marble NE, Albuquerque, New Mexico, Zip 87131–2600; tel. 505/272–2800; UNIVERSITY OF NEW MEXICO CHILDREN'S PSYCHIATRIC HOSPITAL, Mailing address: 1001 Yale Boulevard NE, Albuquerque, New Mexico, Zip 87131–3830; tel. 505/272–2890; UNM CHILDREN'S HOSPITAL, Mailing address: 2211 Lomas Boulevard, NE, 3rd Floor of UNM Hospital, Albuquerque, New Mexico, Zip 87106–2745; tel. 505/272–2111), (Nonreporting) **A**1 2 3 5 8 10 19 **F**3 8 9 11 13 15 16 17 18 19 20 21 22 23 24 25 26 27 28 29 30 31 32 34 35 38 40 41 43 44 45 46 47 48 49 50 51 54 56 57 59 60 61 62 63 64 65 68 70 72 73 74 75 76 77 78 79 81 82 84 85 86 87 88 89 92 93 94 95 96 97 107 108 110 111 113 114 115 116 117 118 119 126 129 130 131 132 135 136 138 144 146 147 148 155 156 **S** University of New Mexico Hospitals, Albuquerque, NM
Primary Contact: Kathleen R. Becker, M.P.H., JD, Chief Executive Officer
CFO: Ella Watt, Chief Financial Officer
CMO: Irene Agostini, M.D., Chief Medical Officer
CIO: Dawn Harrington, Chief Information Officer
CHR: Sara Frasch, Chief Human Resource Officer
Web address: www.unm.edu
**Control:** State, Government, Nonfederal **Service:** General medical and surgical

**Staffed Beds:** 537 **Admissions:** 32111 **Census:** 412 **Outpatient Visits:** 665505 **Births:** 2892 **Total Expense ($000):** 1115713 **Payroll Expense ($000):** 397054 **Personnel:** 6243

**UNM CHILDREN'S PSYCH HOSPITAL** See University of New Mexico Children's Psychiatric Hospital

**VENCOR HOSPITAL - ALBUQUERQUE** See Kindred Hospital-Albuquerque

**VETERANS AFFAIRS MEDICAL CENTER** See New Mexico Veterans Affairs Health Care System - Raymond G. Murphy Medical Center

⇑ **WEST MESA MEDICAL CENTER** See Lovelace Westside Hospital

⇑ **WOMEN'S HOSPITAL** See Lovelace Women's Hospital

**ARTESIA—Eddy County**

★ ⇑ **ARTESIA GENERAL HOSPITAL (320030)**, 702 North 13th Street, Zip 88210–1199; tel. 575/748–3333, (Nonreporting) **A**10 20 21
Primary Contact: Joe Salgado, M.D., Interim Chief Executive Officer
CFO: Carl Hollingsworth, Chief Financial Officer
CMO: Joe Salgado, M.D., Chief of Staff
CHR: Bruce Hinshaw, Director Human Resources
CNO: Wendi Hulett, Chief Nursing Officer
Web address: www.artesiageneral.com
**Control:** Other not–for–profit (including NFP Corporation) **Service:** General medical and surgical

**Staffed Beds:** 30

**CARLSBAD—Eddy County**

☒ **CARLSBAD MEDICAL CENTER (320063)**, 2430 West Pierce Street, Zip 88220–3597; tel. 575/887–4100, (Nonreporting) **A**1 10 **F**3 11 13 15 18 20 22 28 29 30 34 35 40 41 43 45 46 47 50 51 54 57 59 64 65 66 70 76 77 78 79 81 82 83 85 86 87 90 91 92 93 107 108 110 111 115 119 120 121 122 123 129 133 135 144 146 147 148 149 **P**6 **S** Community Health Systems, Inc., Franklin, TN
Primary Contact: Dan Springer, Interim Chief Executive Officer
CFO: Craig Morse, Chief Financial Officer
CIO: Thomas Motejzik, Director Information Systems
CNO: Connie Shofner, Chief Nursing Officer
Web address: www.carlsbadmedicalcenter.com
**Control:** Corporation, Investor–owned (for–profit) **Service:** General medical and surgical

**Staffed Beds:** 66 **Admissions:** 2187 **Census:** 26 **Outpatient Visits:** 67122 **Births:** 356 **Total Expense ($000):** 63279 **Payroll Expense ($000):** 17752 **Personnel:** 355

**COLUMBIA MED CTR OF CARLSBAD** See Carlsbad Medical Center

**CLAYTON—Union County**

★ **UNION COUNTY GENERAL HOSPITAL (321304)**, 300 Wilson Street, Zip 88415–3304, Mailing Address: P.O. Box 489, Zip 88415–0489; tel. 575/374–2585, (Nonreporting) **A**10 18 **F**3 29 32 34 35 40 43 45 50 56 57 59 64 65 66 68 74 75 81 82 83 84 85 87 89 107 108 114 119 127 130 133 154 157 **P**6 **S** Community Hospital Corporation, Plano, TX
Primary Contact: Tammie Stump, R.N., Chief Executive Officer
CFO: Alexander B Altman IIIChief Financial Officer
CMO: Daniel Radunsky, M.D., Medical Staff President
CIO: Kelsey Lawrence, Manager Information Technology
CHR: Jill Swagerty, Director Human Resources
CNO: Stacye Bradley, R.N., Chief Nursing Officer
Web address: www.ucgh.net/
**Control:** County, Government, Nonfederal **Service:** General medical and surgical

**Staffed Beds:** 25 **Admissions:** 132 **Census:** 1

**NM**

*Many Facility Codes have changed. Please refer to the AHA Guide Code Chart.*
© 2021 AHA Guide

## CLOVIS—Curry County

✠ **PLAINS REGIONAL MEDICAL CENTER (320022)**, 2100 North Doctor Martin Luther King Boulevard, Zip 88101–9412, Mailing Address: P.O. Box 1688, Zip 88102–1688; tel. 575/769–2141, (Nonreporting) **A**1 10 **F**3 11 13 15 18 20 28 29 30 31 35 39 40 45 47 48 50 51 56 57 61 62 63 64 65 68 69 70 75 76 77 78 79 80 81 84 85 87 89 93 97 107 108 110 111 112 114 115 116 119 120 121 123 129 130 135 146 148 149 150 154 **P**6 **S** Presbyterian Healthcare Services, Albuquerque, NM
Primary Contact: Jorge Cruz, Interim Chief Executive Officer
CMO: Brian Willmon, M.D., Medical Director
CHR: Cindy Duncan, Manager Human Resources
CNO: Terri A Marney, R.N., Director of Nursing
Web address: www.phs.org
**Control**: Other not–for–profit (including NFP Corporation) **Service**: General medical and surgical

**Staffed Beds**: 81 **Admissions**: 4875 **Census**: 40 **Outpatient Visits**: 123909 **Births**: 1089 **Total Expense ($000)**: 104285 **Payroll Expense ($000)**: 38239 **Personnel**: 551

## CROWNPOINT—McKinley County

**U. S. PUBLIC HEALTH SERVICE INDIAN HOSPITAL (320062)**, Route 9 and State Road 371, Zip 87313, Mailing Address: P.O. Box 358, Zip 87313–0358; tel. 505/786–5291, (Nonreporting) **A**10 **S** U. S. Indian Health Service, Rockville, MD
Primary Contact: Anslem Roanhorse, Chief Executive Officer
CFO: Darlene Kirk, Manager Finance
CMO: John Johnson, M.D., Clinical Director
CIO: Jimmy Burbank, Chief Information Officer
CHR: Christina Bitsilly, Human Resource Specialist
CNO: Alex Daniels, Chief Nurse Executive
Web address: www.ihs.gov
**Control**: PHS, Indian Service, Government, federal **Service**: General medical and surgical

**Staffed Beds**: 12

## DEMING—Luna County

☐ **MIMBRES MEMORIAL HOSPITAL (321309)**, 900 West Ash Street, Zip 88030–4098, Mailing Address: P.O. Box 710, Zip 88031–0710; tel. 575/546–5800, (Nonreporting) **A**1 10 18 **S** Quorum Health, Brentwood, TN
Primary Contact: Gary R. Poquette, FACHE, Chief Executive Officer
CFO: Trisha Smith, Chief Financial Officer
CHR: Johanna Gramer, Director Human Resources
CNO: Joy Harrell, R.N., Chief Nursing Officer
Web address: www.mimbresmemorial.com
**Control**: Corporation, Investor–owned (for–profit) **Service**: General medical and surgical

**Staffed Beds**: 25

## ESPANOLA—Rio Arriba County

**ESPANOLA HOSPITAL** See Presbyterian Espanola Hospital

✠ **PRESBYTERIAN ESPANOLA HOSPITAL (320011)**, 1010 Spruce Street, Zip 87532–2746; tel. 505/753–7111, (Nonreporting) **A**1 10 20 **F**3 7 8 11 13 15 18 29 30 34 35 40 45 50 53 56 57 59 62 64 68 70 76 79 81 85 89 93 97 107 108 110 115 119 129 130 146 151 **P**6 **S** Presbyterian Healthcare Services, Albuquerque, NM
Primary Contact: Brenda Romero, Hospital Chief
CFO: Lupe Lucero, Manager Business Office
CMO: Fernando Bayardo, M.D., Chief Medical Officer
CHR: Joshua Griffith, Manager Human Resources
CNO: Nancy Santiesteban, Director Patient Care Services
Web address: www.phs.org
**Control**: Other not–for–profit (including NFP Corporation) **Service**: General medical and surgical

**Staffed Beds**: 46 **Admissions**: 2483 **Census**: 23 **Outpatient Visits**: 82381 **Births**: 342 **Total Expense ($000)**: 73482 **Payroll Expense ($000)**: 31339 **Personnel**: 373

## FARMINGTON—San Juan County

**LIFECOURSE REHABILITATION HOSP** See San Juan Regional Medical Center Rehabilitation Hospital

★ ⇑ **SAN JUAN REGIONAL MEDICAL CENTER (320005)**, 801 West Maple Street, Zip 87401–5630; tel. 505/609–2000, (Includes SAN JUAN REGIONAL MEDICAL CENTER REHABILITATION HOSPITAL, Mailing address: 525 South Schwartz Avenue, Farmington, New Mexico, Zip 87401–5955; tel. 505/609–2625; Jeff A. Bourgeois, President and Chief Executive Officer), (Nonreporting) **A**10 21 **F**3 7 8 11 13 15 18 20 22 26 28 29 30 31 32 34 35 39 40 43 45 46 47 48 49 50 53 54 57 59 60 61 64 65 68 70 74 75 76 77 78 79 81 82 85 86 87 89 90 92 93 96 97 98 100 102 104 107 108 110 111 112 114 115 117 119 121 130 132 135 143 144 146 147 148 154 155 156 **P**5 6 7
Primary Contact: Jeff A. Bourgeois, President and Chief Executive Officer
COO: John Buffington, Chief Operating Officer
CFO: Karen Miller, Chief Financial Officer
CMO: Melania Yeats, M.D., Chief Medical Officer
CIO: Sheri Rawlings, Chief Information Officer
CHR: Elizabeth Volkerding, Director Workforce Excellence
CNO: Suzanne E Smith, R.N., MSN, Chief Nursing Officer
Web address: www.sanjuanregional.com
**Control**: Other not–for–profit (including NFP Corporation) **Service**: General medical and surgical

**Staffed Beds**: 198 **Admissions**: 9467 **Census**: 101 **Outpatient Visits**: 712385 **Births**: 1026 **Total Expense ($000)**: 306563 **Payroll Expense ($000)**: 141934 **Personnel**: 1484

⇑ **SAN JUAN REGIONAL MEDICAL CNTR** See San Juan Regional Medical Center

## GALLUP—Mckinley County

✠ **GALLUP INDIAN MEDICAL CENTER (320061)**, 516 East Nizhoni Boulevard, Zip 87301–5748, Mailing Address: P.O. Box 1337, Zip 87301; tel. 505/722–1000, (Nonreporting) **A**1 5 10 **S** U. S. Indian Health Service, Rockville, MD
Primary Contact: Sayeeda Hyder, Acting Chief Executive Officer
CFO: Agnes Kee, Financial Manager
CMO: Douglas G Peter, M.D., Chief Medical Officer
CIO: Adrian C Haven, Site Manager
CHR: Karen Lee, Director Human Resources
CNO: Selva Thompson, R.N., Chief Nurse Executive
Web address: www.https://www.ihs.gov/navajo/healthcarefacilities/gallup/
**Control**: PHS, Indian Service, Government, federal **Service**: General medical and surgical

**Staffed Beds**: 57

## GALLUP—McKinley County

★ ⇑ **REHOBOTH MCKINLEY CHRISTIAN HEALTH CARE SERVICES (320038)**, 1901 Red Rock Drive, Zip 87301–5683; tel. 505/863–7000, (Nonreporting) **A**5 10 20 21
Primary Contact: Donald R. Smithburg, Interim Chief Executive Officer
COO: William Kiefer, Chief Operating Officer
CFO: Mary Bevier, Chief Financial Officer
CIO: Randy Myers, Chief Information Officer
CHR: Ronnye Etcitty, Director Human Resources
CNO: Bill Norton, Chief Nursing Officer
Web address: www.rmch.org
**Control**: Other not–for–profit (including NFP Corporation) **Service**: General medical and surgical

**Staffed Beds**: 62

⇑ **REHOBOTH MCKINLEY HOSPITAL** See Rehoboth Mckinley Christian Health Care Services

## GRANTS—Cibola County

✠ **CIBOLA GENERAL HOSPITAL (321308)**, 1016 East Roosevelt Avenue, Zip 87020–2118; tel. 505/287–4446, (Nonreporting) **A**1 10 18 **F**3 13 15 29 30 34 40 45 46 50 56 57 59 64 65 66 68 70 75 76 77 81 85 93 97 107 110 115 119 129 130 133 135 147 148 **S** QHR Health, Brentwood, TN
Primary Contact: Thomas Whelan, Chief Executive Officer
CFO: Ed Brown, Chief Financial Officer
CMO: Janice Shipley, M.D., Chief Medical Officer
CIO: Rick Smith, Director Information Services
CHR: Sheila Cox, Director Human Resources
CNO: Glenna Losito, R.N., MSN, Chief Nursing Officer
Web address: www.cibolahospital.com
**Control**: Other not–for–profit (including NFP Corporation) **Service**: General medical and surgical

**Staffed Beds**: 25 **Admissions**: 905 **Census**: 7

**NM**

---

**Hospital, Medicare Provider Number, Address, Telephone, Approval, Facility, and Physician Codes, Health Care System**

★ American Hospital Association (AHA) membership
☐ The Joint Commission accreditation
○ Healthcare Facilities Accreditation Program
◇ DNV Healthcare Inc. accreditation
⇑ Center for Improvement in Healthcare Quality Accreditation
△ Commission on Accreditation of Rehabilitation Facilities (CARF) accreditation

## HOBBS—Lea County

**LEA REGIONAL HOSPITAL** See Lea Regional Medical Center

✠ **LEA REGIONAL MEDICAL CENTER (320065)**, 5419 North Lovington Highway, Zip 88240–9125, Mailing Address: P.O. Box 3000, Zip 88241–9501; tel. 575/492–5000, (Nonreporting) **A**1 10 **F**3 8 11 13 15 29 30 34 35 37 40 44 45 50 54 57 59 60 64 65 68 70 75 76 77 79 80 81 86 87 89 91 93 100 102 107 108 110 111 112 128 130 131 133 135 146 147 148 154 **S** Community Health Systems, Inc., Franklin, TN
Primary Contact: Dan Springer, Chief Executive Officer
CFO: Jorge Latibeaudiere, Chief Financial Officer
CMO: Chris Driskill, M.D., Chief of Staff
CIO: Terrance J. Purcell, Director Information Services
CHR: Laurie Russell, Director Human Resources
CNO: Eric Simmermon, Chief Nursing Officer
Web address: www.learegionalmedical.com
**Control:** Corporation, Investor–owned (for–profit) **Service:** General medical and surgical

**Staffed Beds:** 84 **Admissions:** 2107 **Census:** 15 **Outpatient Visits:** 45434 **Births:** 466 **Total Expense ($000):** 46957 **Payroll Expense ($000):** 11654 **Personnel:** 204

## LAS CRUCES—Dona Ana County

☐ **ADVANCED CARE HOSPITAL OF SOUTHERN NEW MEXICO (322004)**, 4451 East Lohman Avenue, Zip 88011–8267; tel. 575/521–6600, (Nonreporting) **A**1 10 **S** Ernest Health, Inc., Albuquerque, NM
Primary Contact: Claudia Saiz, Chief Executive Officer
Web address: www.achsnm.ernesthealth.com
**Control:** Corporation, Investor–owned (for–profit) **Service:** Acute long–term care hospital

**Staffed Beds:** 40

**BHC MESILLA VALLEY HOSPITAL** See Mesilla Valley Hospital

**MEMORIAL GENERAL HOSPITAL** See Memorial Medical Center

✠ **MEMORIAL MEDICAL CENTER (320018)**, 2450 South Telshor Boulevard, Zip 88011–5076; tel. 575/522–8641, (Nonreporting) **A**1 2 3 5 10 **F**3 8 11 12 13 15 17 18 20 22 24 28 29 30 31 34 35 40 45 49 50 51 54 57 60 64 65 66 68 70 72 73 74 75 76 78 79 81 84 85 88 89 98 102 107 108 109 110 111 114 115 118 119 120 121 123 144 146 147 148 149 **S** LifePoint Health, Brentwood, TN
Primary Contact: John Harris, Chief Executive Officer
COO: Steven T Ruwoldt, Chief Operating Officer
CFO: Raymond Grenier, Chief Financial Officer
CMO: Bruce San Filippo, M.D., Chief Medical Officer
CHR: Laura Pierce, Director Human Resources
CNO: Caryn Iverson, MSN, Chief Nursing Officer
Web address: www.mmclc.org
**Control:** Corporation, Investor–owned (for–profit) **Service:** General medical and surgical

**Staffed Beds:** 173 **Admissions:** 10249 **Census:** 111 **Outpatient Visits:** 129166 **Births:** 1247 **Total Expense ($000):** 252517 **Payroll Expense ($000):** 93289 **Personnel:** 1290

✠ **MESILLA VALLEY HOSPITAL (324010)**, 3751 Del Rey Boulevard, Zip 88012–8526; tel. 575/382–3500, (Nonreporting) **A**1 10 **S** Universal Health Services, Inc., King of Prussia, PA
Primary Contact: Anna Laliotis, Chief Executive Officer
CFO: Dana McRimmon, Chief Financial Officer
CMO: Arthur L. Ramirez, M.D., Medical Director
CIO: Rebecca Mumpower, Director Marketing
CHR: Linda Moya, Director Human Resources
CNO: Veronica Hughes, Chief Nursing Officer
Web address: www.mesillavalleyhospital.com
**Control:** Corporation, Investor–owned (for–profit) **Service:** Psychiatric

**Staffed Beds:** 105

**MOUNTAIN VIEW REGIONAL MED CTR** See Mountainview Regional Medical Center

✠ **MOUNTAINVIEW REGIONAL MEDICAL CENTER (320085)**, 4311 East Lohman Avenue, Zip 88011–8255; tel. 575/556–7600, (Nonreporting) **A**1 3 5 10 12 13 **S** Community Health Systems, Inc., Franklin, TN
Primary Contact: Derrick Cuenca, Chief Executive Officer
CIO: Donald Harlow, Director of Information Services
CHR: Delilah Doss, Director, Human Resources
CNO: Gayle Nash, R.N., M.P.H., Chief Nursing Officer
Web address: www.mountainviewregional.com
**Control:** Corporation, Investor–owned (for–profit) **Service:** General medical and surgical

**Staffed Beds:** 142

✠ **REHABILITATION HOSPITAL OF SOUTHERN NEW MEXICO (323032)**, 4441 East Lohman Avenue, Zip 88011–8267; tel. 575/521–6400, (Nonreporting) **A**1 10 **S** Ernest Health, Inc., Albuquerque, NM
Primary Contact: Sabrina Martin, Chief Executive Officer
CFO: Elizabeth Striplin, Chief Financial Officer
CMO: Kimberly Encapera, M.D., Medical Director
CHR: Yolanda Mendoza, Director Human Resources
CNO: Carole Carson, Director of Nursing Operations
Web address: www.rhsnm.ernesthealth.com
**Control:** Corporation, Investor–owned (for–profit) **Service:** Rehabilitation

**Staffed Beds:** 40

## LAS VEGAS—San Miguel County

☐ **ALTA VISTA REGIONAL HOSPITAL (320003)**, 104 Legion Drive, Zip 87701–4804; tel. 505/426–3500, (Nonreporting) **A**1 10 20 **S** Quorum Health, Brentwood, TN
Primary Contact: Caleb F. O'Rear, Chief Executive Officer
CMO: Nancy Wright, M.D., Chief Medical Staff
CIO: Laird Thornton, Director Information Systems
CHR: Michael Freeman, Director Human Resources
CNO: Rhonda Clark, Interim Chief Nursing Officer
Web address: www.altavistaregionalhospital.com
**Control:** Corporation, Investor–owned (for–profit) **Service:** General medical and surgical

**Staffed Beds:** 54

**LAS VEGAS MEDICAL CENTER** See New Mexico Behavioral Health Institute at Las Vegas

☐ **NEW MEXICO BEHAVIORAL HEALTH INSTITUTE AT LAS VEGAS**, 3695 Hot Springs Boulevard, Zip 87701–9549; tel. 505/454–2100, (Nonreporting) **A**1
Primary Contact: Frances Tweed, R.N., Executive Director and Administrator
COO: Charles Jaramillo, Chief Operating Officer
CFO: Darlene Martinez, Director Finance
CMO: Daniel Collins, M.D., Clinical Director
CNO: Mabel Arguello-Vasquez, R.N., Executive Nurse Administrator
Web address: www.nmbhi.org
**Control:** State, Government, Nonfederal **Service:** Psychiatric

**Staffed Beds:** 257

**NORTHEASTERN REGIONAL HOSPITAL** See Alta Vista Regional Hospital

## LOS ALAMOS—Los Alamos County

✠ **LOS ALAMOS MEDICAL CENTER (320033)**, 3917 West Road, Zip 87544–2293; tel. 505/661–9500, (Nonreporting) **A**1 10 20 **F**3 8 11 13 15 28 29 31 34 35 40 45 46 49 50 57 59 64 68 70 73 75 76 78 81 85 87 90 93 107 108 110 111 114 119 123 129 130 147 149 **S** LifePoint Health, Brentwood, TN
Primary Contact: John Whiteside, Chief Executive Officer
CFO: Steve Weingart, Chief Financial Officer
CMO: Barbara Van Eeckhout, M.D., Chief of Staff
CIO: Kevin Vigil, Director Information Systems
CHR: Jacqueline Carroll, Director Human Resources
Web address: www.losalamosmedicalcenter.com
**Control:** Corporation, Investor–owned (for–profit) **Service:** General medical and surgical

**Staffed Beds:** 24 **Admissions:** 619 **Census:** 6 **Outpatient Visits:** 47174 **Births:** 87 **Total Expense ($000):** 40575 **Payroll Expense ($000):** 12377

## LOVINGTON—Lea County

⇑ **NOR-LEA GENERAL HOSPITAL** See Nor-Lea Hospital District

★ ⇑ **NOR-LEA HOSPITAL DISTRICT (321305)**, 1600 North Main Avenue, Zip 88260–2871; tel. 575/396–6611, (Nonreporting) **A**10 18 21 **F**3 8 9 15 18 26 28 29 30 31 32 34 35 39 40 43 45 46 49 50 54 57 59 64 65 66 68 69 74 75 77 78 81 82 89 92 93 97 100 101 102 104 107 108 110 111 115 119 127 129 130 132 133 135 146 147 148 149 154
Primary Contact: David B. Shaw, Chief Executive Officer and Administrator
COO: Dan Hamilton, Chief Operating Officer
CFO: Allyson Roberts, CPA, Chief Financial Officer
CMO: Ronald Hopkins, D.O., Chief of Staff
CIO: Brent Kelley, Director Information Technology
CHR: Angela Carrejo, Director Human Resources
CNO: Marcia Patterson, MSN, R.N., Chief Nursing Officer
Web address: www.norlea.org/
**Control:** Hospital district or authority, Government, Nonfederal **Service:** General medical and surgical

**Staffed Beds:** 25 **Admissions:** 441 **Census:** 3 **Outpatient Visits:** 165948 **Births:** 0 **Total Expense ($000):** 83799 **Payroll Expense ($000):** 36821

**NM**

*Many Facility Codes have changed. Please refer to the AHA Guide Code Chart.* © 2021 AHA Guide

## MESCALERO—Otero County

☐ **MESCALERO PUBLIC HEALTH SERVICE INDIAN HOSPITAL (320058)**, 318 Abalone Loop, Zip 88340, Mailing Address: Box 210, Zip 88340–0210; tel. 505/464–3801, (Nonreporting) **A**1 10 **S** U. S. Indian Health Service, Rockville, MD
Primary Contact: Dorlynn Simmons, Chief Executive Officer
CFO: Rainey Enjady, Administrative Officer
CIO: Kathy Murphy, Site Manager
Web address: www.ihs.gov
**Control**: PHS, Indian Service, Government, federal **Service**: General medical and surgical

| **Staffed Beds**: 13 |
|---|

**PHS INDIAN HOSPITAL** See Mescalero Public Health Service Indian Hospital

## PORTALES—Roosevelt County

**ROOSEVELT GENERAL HOSPITAL** See Plains Regional Medical Center-Portales

★ ⇑ **ROOSEVELT GENERAL HOSPITAL (320084)**, 42121 U S Highway 70, Zip 88130, Mailing Address: P.O. Box 868, Zip 88130–0868; tel. 575/359–1800, (Nonreporting) **A**10 21 **F**3 8 15 28 29 34 40 45 50 57 59 64 65 70 75 77 81 82 86 91 92 93 97 104 107 110 111 115 119 127 130 135 146 149 154 **P**6
Primary Contact: Kaye Green, FACHE, Chief Executive Officer
CFO: Eva Steven, Chief Financial Officer
CMO: Les Donaldson, M.D., Chief of Staff
CHR: Cindy Duncan, Director Human Resources
Web address: www.myrgh.org
**Control**: Hospital district or authority, Government, Nonfederal **Service**: General medical and surgical

| **Staffed Beds**: 24 **Admissions**: 351 **Census**: 3 **Outpatient Visits**: 67384 **Births**: 0 **Total Expense ($000)**: 31326 **Payroll Expense ($000)**: 16554 **Personnel**: 213 |
|---|

## RATON—Colfax County

★ **MINERS' COLFAX MEDICAL CENTER (321307)**, 200 Hospital Drive, Zip 87740–2099; tel. 575/445–7700, (Includes MINERS' COLFAX MEDICAL CENTER, Mailing address: 203 Hospital Drive, Raton, New Mexico, Zip 87740, Box 1067, Zip 87740, tel. 575/445–3661; Bo Beames, Chief Executive Officer), (Nonreporting) **A**10 18
Primary Contact: Bo Beames, Interim Chief Executive Officer
CFO: Albino Martinez, Director Budget and Finance
CIO: Richard Laner JrManager Information Systems
CHR: Jamie Johnson, Director Human Resources
Web address: www.minershosp.com
**Control**: County, Government, Nonfederal **Service**: General medical and surgical

| **Staffed Beds**: 25 |
|---|

**MINERS' HOSPITAL OF NEW MEXICO** See Miners' Colfax Medical Center

## RIO RANCHO—Sandoval County

**UNM SANDOVAL REGIONAL MEDICAL CENTER** See Unm Sandoval Regional Medical Center, Inc.

☐ **UNM SANDOVAL REGIONAL MEDICAL CENTER, INC. (320089)**, 3001 Broadmoor Boulevard NE, Zip 87131; tel. 505/994–7000, (Nonreporting) **A**1 3 5 10 **F**3 18 29 30 34 35 40 45 46 47 48 49 50 57 59 70 74 79 81 87 93 94 97 100 107 108 110 111 114 115 119 126 129 130 131 143 146 148 154 **S** University of New Mexico Hospitals, Albuquerque, NM
Primary Contact: Jamie A. Silva-Steele, FACHE, R.N., President and Chief Executive Officer
COO: Pamela Demarest, MSN, R.N., Chief Operating Officer
CFO: Darlene Fernandez, Chief Financial Officer
CMO: Robb McLean, M.D., Chief Medical Officer
CHR: Bernadette Maki, Director Human Resources
CNO: Pamela Demarest, MSN, R.N., Chief Nursing Officer
Web address: www.hsc.unm.edu/health/locations/sandoval-regional-medical-center.html
**Control**: Other not–for–profit (including NFP Corporation) **Service**: General medical and surgical

| **Staffed Beds**: 60 **Admissions**: 2950 **Census**: 33 **Outpatient Visits**: 48257 **Births**: 0 **Total Expense ($000)**: 86224 **Payroll Expense ($000)**: 33389 **Personnel**: 505 |
|---|

## ROSWELL—Chaves County

⊞ **EASTERN NEW MEXICO MEDICAL CENTER (320006)**, 405 West Country Club Road, Zip 88201–5209; tel. 575/622–8170, (Nonreporting) **A**1 10 19 **S** Community Health Systems, Inc., Franklin, TN
Primary Contact: Warren Yehl, Chief Executive Officer
CFO: Leanne Hacker, Chief Financial Officer
CMO: Richard Pinon, Chief Medical Officer
CIO: Deepak Surl, Chief Information Officer
CHR: Sheila Nunez, Director Human Resources
CNO: Kathy Williams, Chief Nursing Officer
Web address: www.enmmc.com
**Control**: Corporation, Investor–owned (for–profit) **Service**: General medical and surgical

| **Staffed Beds**: 149 |
|---|

⇑ **LOVELACE REGIONAL HOSPITAL** See Lovelace Regional Hospital - Roswell

★ ⇑ **LOVELACE REGIONAL HOSPITAL - ROSWELL (320086)**, 117 East 19th Street, Zip 88201–5151; tel. 575/627–7000, (Nonreporting) **A**10 21 **F**3 13 17 18 22 29 34 40 45 57 59 70 76 79 81 82 85 89 90 91 93 111 119 130 146 147 **S** Ardent Health Services, Nashville, TN
Primary Contact: Buddy Daniels, Chief Executive Officer
CFO: Veronica Galaviz, Chief Financial Officer
CNO: Rhonda Rauch, Chief Nursing Officer
Web address: www.lovelace.com
**Control**: Corporation, Investor–owned (for–profit) **Service**: General medical and surgical

| **Staffed Beds**: 26 **Admissions**: 2012 **Census**: 15 **Outpatient Visits**: 32196 **Births**: 929 **Total Expense ($000)**: 38767 **Personnel**: 182 |
|---|

**NEW MEXICO REHAB CTR** See New Mexico Rehabilitation Center

☐ **NEW MEXICO REHABILITATION CENTER (323026)**, 72 Gail Harris Street, Zip 88203–8116; tel. 575/347–3400, (Includes PECOS VALLEY LODGE, Mailing address: 31 Gail Harris Avenue, Roswell, New Mexico, Zip 88201; tel. 505/347–5491), (Nonreporting) **A**1 10
Primary Contact: Jose Gurrola, Administrator
CFO: Curtis Gant, Chief Financial Officer
CMO: Thomas Massaro, M.D., Chief Medical Officer
CIO: Dennis Hoefs, Manager Information Technology
CHR: Cynthia Trujillo, Director Human Resources
**Control**: State, Government, Nonfederal **Service**: Rehabilitation

| **Staffed Beds**: 41 |
|---|

## RUIDOSO—Lincoln County

⊞ **LINCOLN COUNTY MEDICAL CENTER (321306)**, 211 Sudderth Drive, Zip 88345–6043, Mailing Address: P.O. Box 8000, Zip 88355–8000; tel. 575/257–8200, (Nonreporting) **A**1 10 18 **F**3 7 11 13 15 18 29 34 35 39 40 45 46 48 50 53 56 57 59 64 65 68 70 76 77 79 81 85 87 91 93 97 107 110 111 115 119 127 130 131 132 135 144 146 148 **S** Presbyterian Healthcare Services, Albuquerque, NM
Primary Contact: Todd Oberheu, Administrator
CFO: Dudley McCauley, Controller
CMO: Gary Jackson, D.O., Medical Director
CHR: Susanne Johnston, Manager Human Resources
Web address: www.phs.org
**Control**: Other not–for–profit (including NFP Corporation) **Service**: General medical and surgical

| **Staffed Beds**: 25 **Admissions**: 1360 **Census**: 12 **Outpatient Visits**: 51579 **Births**: 241 **Total Expense ($000)**: 46500 **Payroll Expense ($000)**: 21772 **Personnel**: 293 |
|---|

**NM**

---

**Hospital, Medicare Provider Number, Address, Telephone, Approval, Facility, and Physician Codes, Health Care System**

★ American Hospital Association (AHA) membership
☐ The Joint Commission accreditation
○ Healthcare Facilities Accreditation Program
◇ DNV Healthcare Inc. accreditation
⇑ Center for Improvement in Healthcare Quality Accreditation
△ Commission on Accreditation of Rehabilitation Facilities (CARF) accreditation

## SANTA FE—Santa Fe County

✠ △ **CHRISTUS ST. VINCENT REGIONAL MEDICAL CENTER (320002)**, 455 Saint Michaels Drive, Zip 87505–7601, Mailing Address: P.O. Box 2107, Zip 87505; tel. 505/983–3361, (Includes CHRISTUS ST. VINCENT PHYSICIANS MEDICAL CENTER, Mailing address: 2990 Rodeo Park Drive East, Santa Fe, New Mexico, Zip 87505; tel. 505/428–5400; J. Alex Valdez, JD, President and Chief Executive Officer), (Nonreporting) **A**1 3 5 7 10 20 **F**8 12 13 15 17 18 19 20 21 22 24 26 28 29 30 31 32 34 35 36 37 38 39 40 41 42 43 45 46 47 48 49 50 51 53 54 56 57 64 65 66 68 70 73 74 75 76 77 78 79 81 82 83 84 85 86 87 88 90 91 92 93 97 98 100 101 102 104 107 108 109 110 111 112 113 114 115 119 120 121 122 124 126 129 130 131 132 135 143 144 146 147 148 149 150 154 **S** CHRISTUS Health, Irving, TX
Primary Contact: Lillian Montoya, President and Chief Executive Officer
COO: Hope Wade, Chief Operating Officer
CMO: John C Beeson, M.D., Chief Medical Officer
CIO: Ron Dekeyzer, Regional Director Information Systems
CHR: Pearl Mohnkern, Vice President and Director Human Resources
Web address: www.stvin.org
**Control:** Other not–for–profit (including NFP Corporation) **Service:** General medical and surgical

**Staffed Beds:** 219 **Admissions:** 11349 **Census:** 136 **Outpatient Visits:** 192935 **Births:** 1066 **Total Expense ($000):** 430385 **Payroll Expense ($000):** 167268 **Personnel:** 2043

**CHRISTUS ST. VINCENT REGIONAL MEDICAL CENTER** See Christus St. Vincent Regional Medical Center

☐ **PHS SANTA FE INDIAN HOSPITAL (320057)**, 1700 Cerrillos Road, Zip 87505–3554; tel. 505/988–9821, (Nonreporting) **A**1 5 10 **S** U. S. Indian Health Service, Rockville, MD
Primary Contact: Leslie Dye, Chief Executive Officer
CMO: Bret Smoker, M.D., Clinical Director
CIO: Vernita Jones, Site Manager
**Control:** PHS, Indian Service, Government, federal **Service:** General medical and surgical

**Staffed Beds:** 4

**PHYSICIANS MEDICAL CENTER OF SANTA FE HOSPITAL** See Christus St. Vincent Physicians Medical Center

☐ **PRESBYTERIAN SANTA FE MEDICAL CENTER (320090)**, 4801 Beckner Road, Zip 87507; tel. 505/772–1234, (Nonreporting) **A**1 **F**3 11 13 18 19 28 29 30 35 40 44 45 50 59 64 68 74 75 76 77 79 81 87 92 93 97 100 104 107 108 110 111 115 119 130 144 146 147 154 **P**6 **S** Presbyterian Healthcare Services, Albuquerque, NM
Primary Contact: Jon Wade, Chief Executive Officer
Web address: www.https://santa-fe-medical-center.phs.org/Pages/default.aspx
**Control:** Other not–for–profit (including NFP Corporation) **Service:** General medical and surgical

**Staffed Beds:** 24 **Admissions:** 2241 **Census:** 17 **Outpatient Visits:** 47045 **Births:** 285 **Total Expense ($000):** 86299 **Payroll Expense ($000):** 36418 **Personnel:** 472

**SANTA FE USPHS-IHS HOSPITAL** See PHS Santa Fe Indian Hospital

## SANTA ROSA—Guadalupe County

★ **GUADALUPE COUNTY HOSPITAL (320067)**, 117 Camino de Vida, Zip 88435–2267; tel. 575/472–3417, (Nonreporting) **A**10 20 **F**34 35 40 57 59 68 82 107 114 119 148 154
Primary Contact: Christina Campos, Administrator
CFO: Bret Goebel, Chief Financial Officer
CMO: Randal Brown, M.D., Chief of Medical Staff
CIO: Emilio Campos, Department Head Information Technology
CHR: Colleen Gallegos, Director Human Resources
CNO: Mandelyn Cordova, R.N., Director of Nurses
Web address: www.gchnm.org
**Control:** County, Government, Nonfederal **Service:** General medical and surgical

**Staffed Beds:** 10 **Admissions:** 212 **Census:** 2 **Outpatient Visits:** 8209 **Births:** 3

## SANTA TERESA—Dona Ana County

☐ **PEAK BEHAVIORAL HEALTH SERVICES (324012)**, 5065 McNutt Road, Zip 88008–9442; tel. 575/589–3000, (Nonreporting) **A**1 10 **S** Strategic Behavioral Health, LLC, Memphis, TN
Primary Contact: Sandra Emanuel, Chief Executive Officer
COO: Doug Ginn, Executive Vice President Operations
CFO: Espie Herrara, Chief Financial Officer
CHR: Norma Oaxaca, Director Human Resources
Web address: www.peakbehavioral.com/
**Control:** Corporation, Investor–owned (for–profit) **Service:** Psychiatric

**Staffed Beds:** 120

**PEAK PSYCHIACTRIC HOSPITAL** See Peak Behavioral Health Services

## SHIPROCK—San Juan County

✠ **NORTHERN NAVAJO MEDICAL CENTER (320059)**, Highway 491 North, Zip 87420–0160, Mailing Address: P.O. Box 160, Zip 87420–0160; tel. 505/368–6001, (Nonreporting) **A**1 10 **S** U. S. Indian Health Service, Rockville, MD
Primary Contact: Fannessa Comer, Chief Executive Officer
CFO: Shawn Morgan, Finance Officer
CMO: Ira Salom, M.D., Clinical Director
CIO: Roland Chapman, Chief Information Officer
CHR: Gloria Redhorse-Charley, Director Human Resources
CNO: Lavenia Diswood, R.N., Chief Nurse Executive
Web address: www.ihs.gov/
**Control:** PHS, Indian Service, Government, federal **Service:** General medical and surgical

**Staffed Beds:** 68

**SHIPROCK INDIAN HOSPITAL** See Northern Navajo Medical Center

## SILVER CITY—Grant County

☐ **GILA REGIONAL MEDICAL CENTER (320016)**, 1313 East 32nd Street, Zip 88061–7251; tel. 575/538–4000, (Nonreporting) **A**1 3 10 20 **F**3 7 8 11 13 15 18 29 30 31 35 40 45 50 51 53 54 64 68 70 75 76 78 79 81 85 87 89 93 98 100 102 107 108 110 111 115 119 120 121 123 129 130 132 146 149 157
Primary Contact: Richard W. Stokes Jr, CPA, Interim Chief Executive Officer
CFO: Richard W Stokes, CPA, JrChief Financial Officer
CIO: David Furnas, Chief Information Officer
CHR: Barbara Barela, Director Human Resources
CNO: Patricia Sheyka, Chief Nursing Officer
Web address: www.grmc.org
**Control:** County, Government, Nonfederal **Service:** General medical and surgical

**Staffed Beds:** 47 **Admissions:** 1807 **Census:** 17 **Outpatient Visits:** 57771 **Births:** 284 **Total Expense ($000):** 74922 **Payroll Expense ($000):** 28147 **Personnel:** 575

**GILA REGIONAL MEDICAL CTR** See Gila Regional Medical Center

## SOCORRO—Socorro County

✠ **SOCORRO GENERAL HOSPITAL (321301)**, 1202 Highway 60 West, Zip 87801–3914, Mailing Address: P.O. Box 1009, Zip 87801–1009; tel. 575/835–1140, (Nonreporting) **A**1 10 18 **F**3 13 40 62 63 64 76 81 107 115 119 130 132 133 134 135 146 147 **S** Presbyterian Healthcare Services, Albuquerque, NM
Primary Contact: Veronica Pound, R.N., Administrator
CFO: Scott Shannon, Director Finance
CMO: Darla Bejnar, M.D., Chief Medical Officer
CHR: Pam Miller-Balfour, Director Human Resources
CNO: Veronica Pound, R.N., Interim Administrator and Director of Patient Care
Web address: www.phs.org
**Control:** Other not–for–profit (including NFP Corporation) **Service:** General medical and surgical

**Staffed Beds:** 24 **Admissions:** 553 **Census:** 6 **Outpatient Visits:** 31483 **Births:** 134 **Total Expense ($000):** 29018 **Payroll Expense ($000):** 14509 **Personnel:** 164

**NM**

*Many Facility Codes have changed. Please refer to the AHA Guide Code Chart.* © 2021 AHA Guide

## TAOS—Taos County

★ ⥿ **HOLY CROSS HOSPITAL (321310)**, 1397 Weimer Road, Zip 87571–6253; tel. 575/758–8883, (Nonreporting) **A**3 10 18 21 **F**3 11 13 15 18 29 30 32 34 35 40 45 46 50 59 64 68 75 76 77 79 80 81 85 86 87 91 93 97 100 102 107 110 114 115 118 119 130 132 133 145 146 147 148 149 156 **P**8 **S** QHR Health, Brentwood, TN
Primary Contact: William D. Patten Jr, Chief Executive Officer
CFO: Steve Rozenboom, Chief Financial Officer
CHR: Judy Marshall, Director Human Resources
CNO: Denise Clark, Chief Nursing Officer
Web address: www.taoshospital.org
**Control**: Other not–for–profit (including NFP Corporation) **Service**: General medical and surgical

**Staffed Beds**: 25 **Admissions**: 1365 **Census**: 13 **Outpatient Visits**: 60260 **Births**: 154 **Total Expense ($000)**: 64050 **Payroll Expense ($000)**: 27341 **Personnel**: 368

## TRUTH OR CONSEQUENCES—Sierra County

**SIERRA REGIONAL HOSPITAL** See Sierra Vista Hospital

★ **SIERRA VISTA HOSPITAL (321300)**, 800 East Ninth Avenue, Zip 87901–1961; tel. 575/894–2111, (Nonreporting) **A**10 18 **F**7 11 15 16 30 34 40 54 57 59 65 67 93 99 102 104 107 110 127 128 130 133 **S** QHR Health, Brentwood, TN
Primary Contact: David Faulkner, Interim Chief Executive Officer
CFO: Bret Gobel, Chief Financial Officer
CMO: James F Malcolmson, M.D., Chief of Staff
CIO: Dan Morrell, Manager Information Systems
CHR: Mindee Holguin, Manager Human Resources
CNO: Palmer Greene, R.N., Chief Nursing Officer
Web address: www.svhnm.org
**Control**: City–county, Government, Nonfederal **Service**: General medical and surgical

**Staffed Beds**: 15 **Admissions**: 330 **Census**: 3

## TUCUMCARI—Quay County

★ **DR. DAN C. TRIGG MEMORIAL HOSPITAL (321302)**, 301 East Miel De Luna Avenue, Zip 88401–3810, Mailing Address: P.O. Box 608, Zip 88401–0608; tel. 575/461–7000, (Nonreporting) **A**10 18 **F**11 15 29 35 40 59 62 63 64 65 68 87 97 107 110 114 119 130 133 135 146 148 154 **S** Presbyterian Healthcare Services, Albuquerque, NM
Primary Contact: Vickie Gutierrez, Chief Executive
CMO: Darrell Willis, M.D., Chief of Staff
CNO: Vickie Gutierrez, Director of Patient Care
Web address: www.phs.org
**Control**: Other not–for–profit (including NFP Corporation) **Service**: General medical and surgical

**Staffed Beds**: 4 **Admissions**: 178 **Census**: 3 **Outpatient Visits**: 15232 **Births**: 0 **Total Expense ($000)**: 14982 **Payroll Expense ($000)**: 4842 **Personnel**: 76

## ZUNI—McKinley County

☐ **U. S. PUBLIC HEALTH SERVICE INDIAN HOSPITAL (320060)**, Route 301 North B Street, Zip 87327, Mailing Address: P.O. Box 467, Zip 87327–0467; tel. 505/782–4431, (Nonreporting) **A**1 10 **S** U. S. Indian Health Service, Rockville, MD
Primary Contact: Jean Othole, Chief Executive Officer
CFO: Clyde Yatsattie, Administrative Officer
CMO: David Kessler, M.D., Clinical Director
CHR: Cynthia Tsalate, Human Resource Specialist
Web address: www.ihs.gov
**Control**: PHS, Indian Service, Government, federal **Service**: General medical and surgical

**Staffed Beds**: 32

**NM**

# NEW YORK

## ALBANY—Albany County

☐ **ALBANY MEDICAL CENTER (330013)**, 43 New Scotland Avenue, Zip 12208–3478; tel. 518/262–3125, (Includes ALBANY MEDICAL CENTER SOUTH-CLINICAL CAMPUS, Mailing address: 25 Hackett Boulevard, Albany, New York, Zip 12208–3499; tel. 518/242–1200; Timothy W Duffy, General Director), (Nonreporting) **A**1 2 3 5 8 10 **F**3 6 7 8 11 12 13 15 17 18 19 20 21 22 23 24 25 26 27 28 29 30 31 32 34 35 38 39 40 41 43 44 45 46 47 49 50 51 52 53 54 55 56 57 58 59 60 61 64 65 68 70 72 73 74 75 76 77 78 79 81 82 84 85 86 87 88 89 90 92 93 96 97 98 100 102 103 104 105 107 108 109 110 111 114 115 116 117 118 119 120 121 122 123 124 126 130 131 132 135 138 142 145 146 148 154 155 156
Primary Contact: Dennis McKenna, M.D., President and Chief Executive Officer
COO: Bernadette R Pedlow, Senior Vice President Business and Chief Operating Officer
CFO: Frances Spreer-Albert, Chief Financial Officer and Executive Vice President
CMO: Dennis McKenna, M.D., Interim Vice President Medical Affairs
CIO: George Hickman, Executive Vice President and Chief Information Officer
Web address: www.amc.edu
**Control:** Other not–for–profit (including NFP Corporation) **Service:** General medical and surgical

> **Staffed Beds:** 786 **Admissions:** 39978 **Census:** 625 **Outpatient Visits:** 593767 **Births:** 2113 **Total Expense ($000):** 1107826 **Payroll Expense ($000):** 347594 **Personnel:** 6463

✠ **ALBANY STRATTON VETERANS AFFAIRS MEDICAL CENTER**, 113 Holland Avenue, Zip 12208–3473; tel. 518/626–5000, (Nonreporting) **A**1 2 3 5 8 **S** Department of Veterans Affairs, Washington, DC
Primary Contact: Darlene DeLancey, Interim Director
CFO: Gerard Scorzelli, Chief Financial Officer
CMO: Lourdes Irizarry, M.D., Chief of Staff
CIO: Ron Diaz, Manager Operations
CHR: Kenneth Kio, Manager Human Resources
CNO: Deborah Spath, R.N., MSN, Associate Director Patient and Nurses Services
Web address: www.albany.va.gov/
**Control:** Veterans Affairs, Government, federal **Service:** General medical and surgical

> **Staffed Beds:** 121

☐ **CAPITAL DISTRICT PSYCHIATRIC CENTER (334046)**, 75 New Scotland Avenue, Zip 12208–3474; tel. 518/549–6000, (Nonreporting) **A**1 3 5 10 **S** New York State Office of Mental Health, Albany, NY
Primary Contact: William Dickson, Executive Director
COO: Catherine McGregor, Deputy Director Facility and Administrative Services
CMO: Kren K Shriver, M.D., Clinical Director
CNO: Charlene Puorto, Chief Nursing Officer
Web address: www.omh.ny.gov/omhweb/facilities/cdpc/facility.htm
**Control:** State, Government, Nonfederal **Service:** Psychiatric

> **Staffed Beds:** 200

**CHILD'S HOSPITAL** See Albany Medical Center South-Clinical Campus

**MEMORIAL HOSPITAL** See Samaritan Hospital - Albany Memorial Campus

✠ **ST. PETER'S HOSPITAL (330057)**, 315 South Manning Boulevard, Zip 12208–1789; tel. 518/525–1550, (Nonreporting) **A**1 2 3 5 10 **F**3 4 5 8 11 12 13 15 17 18 19 20 22 24 26 27 28 29 30 31 34 35 36 37 38 39 40 44 45 46 47 48 49 50 51 53 54 55 56 57 59 60 61 63 64 65 66 68 70 71 72 73 74 75 76 77 78 79 80 81 84 85 86 87 89 92 93 97 100 107 108 109 110 111 114 115 116 117 118 119 120 121 123 124 126 129 130 132 133 135 143 145 146 147 148 152 156 **P**6 **S** Trinity Health, Livonia, MI
Primary Contact: Michael S. Finegan, President, Acute Care
CFO: Lori Santos, Chief Financial Officer
CMO: Robert Cella, M.D., Chief Medical Officer
CHR: Judy Gray, Vice President Human Resources
CNO: Jane O'Rourke, R.N., Chief Nursing Officer, Vice President Operations
Web address: www.https://www.sphp.com/location/st-peters-hospital
**Control:** Other not–for–profit (including NFP Corporation) **Service:** General medical and surgical

> **Staffed Beds:** 442 **Admissions:** 29638 **Census:** 368 **Outpatient Visits:** 502628 **Births:** 3022 **Total Expense ($000):** 590333 **Payroll Expense ($000):** 209824 **Personnel:** 3299

**VETERANS AFFAIRS MEDICAL CENTER** See Albany Stratton Veterans Affairs Medical Center

## ALEXANDRIA BAY—Jefferson County

**E J NOBLE HOSPITAL SAMARITAN** See River Hospital

**RIVER HOSPITAL (331309)**, 4 Fuller Street, Zip 13607–1316; tel. 315/482–2511, (Nonreporting) **A**10 18
Primary Contact: Emily Mastaler, Chief Executive Officer
COO: William Connor, Assistant Administrator and Director Human Resources
CFO: Traci Mintonye, Chief Financial Officer
CMO: Prasad Yitta, M.D., Medical Director
CIO: John Smithers, Network Specialist
CHR: William Connor, Assistant Administrator and Director Human Resources
CNO: Ann Narrow, Director of Nursing
Web address: www.riverhospital.org
**Control:** Other not–for–profit (including NFP Corporation) **Service:** General medical and surgical

> **Staffed Beds:** 11

## AMITYVILLE—Suffolk County

**BRUNSWICK HOUSE ALCOHOLISM TREATMENT CENTER** See Brunswick Psych Center

☐ **BRUNSWICK PSYCH CENTER (334026)**, 81 Louden Avenue, Zip 11701–2736; tel. 631/789–7421, (Nonreporting) **A**1 10
Primary Contact: Amarjit Singh, M.D., President and Chief Executive Officer
**Control:** Corporation, Investor–owned (for–profit) **Service:** Psychiatric

> **Staffed Beds:** 124

✠ **SOUTH OAKS HOSPITAL (334027)**, 400 Sunrise Highway, Zip 11701–2508; tel. 631/264–4000, (Nonreporting) **A**1 3 10 **F**4 5 53 68 98 99 101 102 103 104 105 135 153 154 **S** Northwell Health, New Hyde Park, NY
Primary Contact: Carolyn Sweetapple, Ph.D., R.N., CPA, Executive Director
CMO: Tina Walch, M.D., Medical Director
CHR: Irene Calvin, Vice President Human Resources
Web address: www.longislandhome.org
**Control:** Other not–for–profit (including NFP Corporation) **Service:** Psychiatric

> **Staffed Beds:** 202 **Admissions:** 5386 **Census:** 173 **Outpatient Visits:** 104567 **Births:** 0 **Total Expense ($000):** 106497 **Payroll Expense ($000):** 62392 **Personnel:** 814

## AMSTERDAM—Montgomery County

✠ **ST. MARY'S HEALTHCARE (330047)**, 427 Guy Park Avenue, Zip 12010–1054; tel. 518/842–1900, (Includes ST. MARY'S HEALTHCARE, Mailing address: 427 Guy Park Avenue, Amsterdam, New York, Zip 12010–1054; tel. 518/842–1900; Scott Bruce, President) (Total facility includes 160 beds in nursing home–type unit) **A**1 10 **F**2 3 4 5 8 11 13 15 17 28 29 30 31 34 35 36 38 40 45 46 49 50 51 54 56 57 59 60 61 65 66 68 70 71 74 75 76 77 78 79 81 83 84 85 86 87 90 93 94 96 97 98 99 100 101 102 103 104 107 108 110 111 115 118 119 126 127 128 130 131 132 135 144 145 146 147 149 150 154 156 **S** Ascension Healthcare, Saint Louis, MO
Primary Contact: Scott Bruce, President
CFO: Rick Henze, Chief Financial Officer
CMO: William Mayer, M.D., Vice President Medical Staff Services
CHR: Albert Turo, Vice President Human Resources
CNO: Michele M Walsh, Chief Nursing Officer
Web address: www.smha.org
**Control:** Other not–for–profit (including NFP Corporation) **Service:** General medical and surgical

> **Staffed Beds:** 290 **Admissions:** 5549 **Census:** 227 **Outpatient Visits:** 431285 **Births:** 422 **Total Expense ($000):** 175365 **Payroll Expense ($000):** 87534 **Personnel:** 1355

**ST. MARY'S HEALTHCARE** See St. Mary's Healthcare, Amsterdam

**ST. MARY'S HOSPITAL** See St. Mary's Healthcare

**ST. MARY'S HOSPITAL AMSTERDAM** See St. Mary's Healthcare

**NY**

*Many Facility Codes have changed. Please refer to the AHA Guide Code Chart.* © 2021 AHA Guide

## AUBURN—Cayuga County

⊞ **AUBURN COMMUNITY HOSPITAL (330235)**, 17 Lansing Street,
Zip 13021–1943; tel. 315/255–7011, (Total facility includes 80 beds in nursing
home–type unit) (Nonreporting) **A**1 10 20 **F**3 8 11 12 13 15 17 18 26 28 29 30
31 34 35 40 44 45 50 51 53 54 57 59 60 64 68 70 74 76 77 78 79 81 82 85
86 87 89 92 93 94 97 98 102 104 107 108 110 111 115 118 119 128 129
130 132 144 146 147 148 149 152 154 **P**5
Primary Contact: Scott A. Berlucchi, FACHE, President and Chief Executive Officer
CFO: Jason Lesch, Chief Financial Officer
CMO: John A. Riccio, M.D., Chief Medical Officer
CIO: Chris Ryan, Chief Information Officer
CHR: Linda Daly, Vice President Human Resources
CNO: Tammy Sunderlin, Director of Nursing
Web address: www.auburnhospital.org
**Control:** Other not–for–profit (including NFP Corporation) **Service:** General
medical and surgical

**Staffed Beds:** 179 **Admissions:** 4846 **Census:** 128 **Outpatient
Visits:** 147281 **Births:** 381 **Total Expense ($000):** 140885 **Payroll Expense
($000):** 68283 **Personnel:** 617

**AUBURN MEMORIAL HOSPITAL** See Auburn Community Hospital

## BATAVIA—Genesee County

**GENESEE MEMORIAL HOSPITAL** See United Memorial Medical Center-North Street

**ST JEROME HOSPITAL** See United Memorial Medical Center-Bank Street

⊞ **UNITED MEMORIAL MEDICAL CENTER (330073)**, 127 North Street,
Zip 14020–1631; tel. 585/343–6030, (Includes UNITED MEMORIAL MEDICAL
CENTER-BANK STREET, Mailing address: 16 Bank Street, Batavia, New York,
Zip 14020–2260; tel. 585/343–6030; UNITED MEMORIAL MEDICAL CENTER-
NORTH STREET, Mailing address: 127 North Street, Batavia, New York,
Zip 14020–1697; tel. 585/343–6030), (Nonreporting) **A**1 3 5 10 13 **F**3 4 8 13
15 17 18 28 29 30 31 34 35 40 49 50 54 57 59 64 65 68 70 75 76 77 78
79 81 82 84 85 86 87 89 93 97 107 111 114 115 119 120 121 122 127 129
130 131 132 135 144 146 147 148 149 154 156 157 **P**5 **S** Rochester Regional
Health, Rochester, NY
Primary Contact: Daniel P. Ireland, FACHE, President
CFO: Robert Chiavetta, Vice President Finance
CMO: Tara L Gellasch, Chief Medical Officer
CIO: Chad Caccamise, Director Information Services
CHR: Eileen Herkimer, Director Human Resources
CNO: Marilyn Almeter, Chief Nursing Officer
Web address: www.ummc.org
**Control:** Other not–for–profit (including NFP Corporation) **Service:** General
medical and surgical

**Staffed Beds:** 133 **Admissions:** 4382 **Census:** 53 **Outpatient
Visits:** 239862 **Births:** 536 **Total Expense ($000):** 107959 **Payroll Expense
($000):** 45199 **Personnel:** 736

**VETERANS AFFAIRS MED CENTER** See Veterans Affairs Western New York
Healthcare System-Batavia Division

★ **VETERANS AFFAIRS WESTERN NEW YORK HEALTHCARE SYSTEM-BATAVIA
DIVISION**, 222 Richmond Avenue, Zip 14020–1288; tel. 585/297–1000,
(Nonreporting) **S** Department of Veterans Affairs, Washington, DC
Primary Contact: Michael J. Swartz, FACHE, Interim Director
Web address: www.buffalo.va.gov/batavia.asp
**Control:** Veterans Affairs, Government, federal **Service:** General medical and
surgical

**Staffed Beds:** 128

## BATH—Steuben County

⊞ **BATH VETERANS AFFAIRS MEDICAL CENTER**, 76 Veterans Avenue,
Zip 14810–0842; tel. 607/664–4000, (Nonreporting) **A**1 **S** Department of
Veterans Affairs, Washington, DC
Primary Contact: Kenneth P. Piazza, Medical Center Director
CFO: Jill Haynes, Financial Coach
CMO: Robert Babcock, M.D., Interim Chief of Staff
CHR: Susan DeSalvo, Manager Human Resources
Web address: www.bath.va.gov
**Control:** Veterans Affairs, Government, federal **Service:** General medical and surgical

**Staffed Beds:** 274

⊞ **IRA DAVENPORT MEMORIAL HOSPITAL (330144)**, 7571 State Route 54,
Zip 14810–9590; tel. 607/776–8500, (Total facility includes 120 beds in nursing
home–type unit) (Nonreporting) **A**1 10 **F**2 3 11 15 18 28 29 34 40 45 50 57 64
68 74 77 79 81 85 91 93 107 111 114 119 128 130 133 143 146 154 **S** Arnot
Health, Elmira, NY
Primary Contact: Elizabeth Weir, MSN, R.N., Site Administrator and Vice President
of Nursing
CFO: Ronald J Kintz, Chief Financial Officer
CMO: Dennis O'Connor, M.D., Medical Director
CIO: Gregg Martin, Chief Information Officer
CHR: Dave Stanbro, Director Human Resources
CNO: Linda Donley, Vice President Operations
Web address: www.arnothealth.org
**Control:** Other not–for–profit (including NFP Corporation) **Service:** General
medical and surgical

**Staffed Beds:** 135 **Admissions:** 439 **Census:** 108 **Outpatient Visits:** 41965
**Births:** 0 **Total Expense ($000):** 24357 **Payroll Expense ($000):** 9992
**Personnel:** 222

**VETERANS AFFAIRS MEDICAL CENTER** See Bath Veterans Affairs Medical Center

## BAY SHORE—Suffolk County

⊞ △ **SOUTHSIDE HOSPITAL (330043)**, 301 East Main Street, Zip 11706–8458;
tel. 631/968–3000, (Nonreporting) **A**1 2 3 5 7 10 **F**3 5 8 11 12 13 15 17 18 20 22
24 26 28 29 30 31 32 34 35 36 38 40 41 43 44 45 46 49 50 51 54 56 57 58 59
60 61 62 63 64 65 66 68 70 73 74 75 76 77 78 79 80 81 82 84 85 86 87 89 92
93 95 96 97 100 101 102 107 108 111 115 119 126 129 130 131 132 134 135
145 146 147 148 149 152 154 157 **S** Northwell Health, New Hyde Park, NY
Primary Contact: Donna Moravick, R.N., MSN, Executive Director
CFO: Michele Cusack, Senior Vice President and Chief Financial Officer
CMO: Jay Enden, M.D., Medical Director
CHR: Anne J Barrett, Associate Executive Director Human Resources
Web address: www.https://www.northwell.edu/find-care/locations/southside-hospital
**Control:** Other not–for–profit (including NFP Corporation) **Service:** General
medical and surgical

**Staffed Beds:** 305 **Admissions:** 21958 **Census:** 270 **Outpatient
Visits:** 153179 **Births:** 2458 **Total Expense ($000):** 707947 **Payroll
Expense ($000):** 353933 **Personnel:** 3147

## BETHPAGE—Nassau County

**NEW ISLAND HOSPITAL** See St. Joseph Hospital

☐ **ST. JOSEPH HOSPITAL (330332)**, 4295 Hempstead Turnpike, Zip 11714–5769;
tel. 516/579–6000, (Nonreporting) **A**1 5 10 **F**3 8 15 18 29 30 31 34 35 39 40
45 46 47 49 50 51 56 57 59 60 63 64 65 68 70 74 75 78 79 80 81 82 84 85
86 87 93 107 108 110 111 114 115 119 129 130 131 132 141 146 148 149
154 156 **S** Catholic Health Services of Long Island, Rockville Centre, NY
Primary Contact: Peter Scaminaci, President
CFO: John Morahan, Vice President Finance
CMO: Howard Sussman, M.D., Chief Medical Officer
CHR: Peter Chiacchiaro, Vice President Human Resources
CNO: Barbara Gibbons, Vice President Patient Care Services
Web address: www.stjosephhospital.chsli.org/
**Control:** Church operated, Nongovernment, not–for–profit **Service:** General
medical and surgical

**Staffed Beds:** 128 **Admissions:** 6149 **Census:** 81 **Outpatient Visits:** 42626
**Births:** 0 **Total Expense ($000):** 134675 **Payroll Expense ($000):** 51684
**Personnel:** 669

## BINGHAMTON—Broome County

**BINGHAMTON GENERAL HOSPITAL** See United Health Services Hospitals-
Binghamton, Binghamton

**BINGHAMTON PSYCHIATRIC CENTER** See Greater Binghamton Health Center

☐ **GREATER BINGHAMTON HEALTH CENTER (334012)**, 425 Robinson Street,
Zip 13904–1735; tel. 607/724–1391, (Nonreporting) **A**1 3 10 **F**29 30 50 54 59
65 66 68 86 98 99 100 101 103 104 106 130 132 135 143 146 149 153 **S**
New York State Office of Mental Health, Albany, NY
Primary Contact: David Peppel, Executive Director
CFO: Cherry Randall, Business Officer
CHR: Renee O'Brien, Director Human Resources
Web address: www.omh.ny.gov/omhweb/facilities/bipc/facility.htm
**Control:** State, Government, Nonfederal **Service:** Psychiatric

**Staffed Beds:** 86 **Admissions:** 277 **Census:** 69 **Outpatient Visits:** 39000
**Births:** 0 **Personnel:** 393

**NY**

---

**Hospital, Medicare Provider Number, Address, Telephone, Approval, Facility, and Physician Codes, Health Care System**

★ American Hospital Association (AHA) membership    ◯ Healthcare Facilities Accreditation Program    ⇑ Center for Improvement in Healthcare Quality Accreditation
☐ The Joint Commission accreditation    ◇ DNV Healthcare Inc. accreditation    △ Commission on Accreditation of Rehabilitation Facilities (CARF) accreditation

**OUR LADY OF LOURDES MEMORIAL HOSPITAL** See Our Lady of Lourdes Memorial Hospital, Inc.

⊠ **OUR LADY OF LOURDES MEMORIAL HOSPITAL, INC. (330011)**, 169 Riverside Drive, Zip 13905–4246; tel. 607/798–5111, (Nonreporting) **A**1 2 3 5 10 13 19 **F**3 11 12 13 15 18 19 28 29 30 31 32 33 34 35 36 39 40 44 45 46 47 49 50 51 53 54 56 57 59 60 62 63 64 65 66 68 70 71 74 75 76 77 78 79 81 84 85 86 87 89 93 97 100 101 104 107 108 110 111 114 115 118 119 120 121 123 124 126 127 129 130 131 132 134 135 143 144 145 146 147 148 149 154 156 157 **P**6 **S** Ascension Healthcare, Saint Louis, MO
Primary Contact: Kathryn Connerton, President and Chief Executive Officer
CFO: Sean Mills, Chief Financial Officer
CMO: Richard Blansky, M.D., Chief Medical Officer
CIO: Thomas Ellerson, Chief Information Officer
CHR: Mary Hughs, Chief Human Resources Officer
Web address: www.lourdes.com
**Control**: Church operated, Nongovernment, not–for–profit **Service**: General medical and surgical

| |
|---|
| **Staffed Beds:** 154 **Admissions:** 10010 **Census:** 112 **Outpatient Visits:** 1695993 **Births:** 921 **Total Expense ($000):** 388685 **Payroll Expense ($000):** 162418 **Personnel:** 2240 |

**UNITED HEALTH SERVICES** See United Health Services Hospitals-Binghamton

☐ **UNITED HEALTH SERVICES HOSPITALS-BINGHAMTON (330394)**, 10-42 Mitchell Avenue, Zip 13903–1678; tel. 607/763–6000, (Includes BINGHAMTON GENERAL HOSPITAL, Mailing address: 10-42 Mitchell Avenue, Binghamton, New York, Zip 13903; tel. 607/762–2200; John M. Carrigg, President and Chief Executive Officer; WILSON MEMORIAL REGIONAL MEDICAL CENTER, Mailing address: 33-57 Harrison Street, Johnson City, New York, Zip 13790; tel. 607/763–6000; John M. Carrigg, President and Chief Executive Officer), (Nonreporting) **A**1 3 8 10 **S** United Health Services, Binghamton, NY
Primary Contact: John M. Carrigg, President and Chief Executive Officer
COO: John M. Carrigg, Executive Vice President and Chief Operating Officer
CFO: David MacDougall, Chief Financial Officer
CMO: Rajesh J Dave', M.D., Executive Vice President and Chief Medical Officer
CIO: Susan Carman, Chief Information Officer
CNO: E. Kay Boland, R.N., MS, Vice President and Chief Nursing Officer
Web address: www.uhs.net
**Control**: Other not–for–profit (including NFP Corporation) **Service**: General medical and surgical

| |
|---|
| **Staffed Beds:** 464 |

### BRENTWOOD—Suffolk County

☐ **PILGRIM PSYCHIATRIC CENTER (334013)**, 998 Crooked Hill Road, Zip 11717–1019; tel. 631/761–3500, (Nonreporting) **A**1 5 10 **S** New York State Office of Mental Health, Albany, NY
Primary Contact: Kathy O'Keefe, Executive Director
Web address: www.omh.ny.gov/omhweb/facilities/pgpc/facility.htm
**Control**: State, Government, Nonfederal **Service**: Psychiatric

| |
|---|
| **Staffed Beds:** 569 |

### BRONX—Bronx County

**BETH ABRAHAM HOSPITAL** See Beth Abraham Health Services

**BRONX HEALTH CARE SYSTEM** See Bronxcare Health System

☐ **BRONX PSYCHIATRIC CENTER (334053)**, 1500 Waters Place, Zip 10461–2796; tel. 718/931–0600, (Nonreporting) **A**1 3 5 10 **F**29 30 34 35 38 39 44 50 53 54 57 58 59 65 71 74 75 77 86 87 96 97 98 100 101 102 104 106 130 132 135 143 146 147 149 153 154 156 157 **S** New York State Office of Mental Health, Albany, NY
Primary Contact: Precious Stepney, Executive Director
CFO: Robert Erway, Director for Administration
Web address: www.omh.ny.gov
**Control**: State, Government, Nonfederal **Service**: Psychiatric

| |
|---|
| **Staffed Beds:** 156 **Admissions:** 99 **Census:** 155 **Births:** 0 **Personnel:** 563 |

⊠ **BRONXCARE HEALTH SYSTEM (330009)**, 1276 Fulton Avenue, Zip 10456–3499; tel. 718/590–1800, (Includes BRONX-LEBANON SPECIAL CARE CENTER, Mailing address: 1265 Fulton Avenue, Bronx, New York, Zip 10465; tel. 718/579–7000; Octavio Marin, Vice President Long Term Care and Ambulatory Care Services; CONCOURSE DIVISION, Mailing address: 1650 Grand Concourse, Bronx, New York, Zip 10457, 1276 Fulton Ave, Zip 10456–3402, tel. 718/590–1800; Miguel A Fuentes Jr, President and Chief Executive Officer; FULTON DIVISION, Mailing address: 1276 Fulton Avenue, Bronx, New York, Zip 10456, 1650 Grand Concourse, Zip 10457–7606, tel. 718/590–1800; Miguel A Fuentes Jr, President and Chief Executive Officer; HIGHBRIDGE WOODYCREST CENTER, Mailing address: 936 Woodycrest Avenue, Bronx, New York, Zip 10452; tel. 718/579–8875; Leonardo Vicent III, Executive Director) (Total facility includes 240 beds in nursing home–type unit) **A**1 3 5 10 **F**3 4 5 6 7 8 11 12 13 15 17 18 19 20 21 22 23 27 28 29 30 31 32 34 35 36 37 38 39 40 41 42 43 44 45 46 47 48 49 50 51 52 54 55 56 57 58 59 60 61 64 65 66 68 70 71 72 73 74 75 76 77 78 79 81 82 83 84 85 86 87 88 89 91 92 93 95 96 97 98 99 100 101 102 103 104 105 106 107 108 110 111 114 115 118 119 126 128 129 130 131 132 133 134 135 143 144 146 147 148 149 151 152 153 154 156 157
Primary Contact: Miguel A. Fuentes Jr, President and Chief Executive Officer
CFO: Victor DeMarco, Chief Financial Officer
CMO: Milton A Gumbs, M.D., Vice President and Medical Director
CIO: Ivan Durbak, Chief Information Officer
CHR: Selena Griffin-Mahon, Assistant Vice President Human Resources
CNO: Patricia Cahill, Vice President, Patient Care Services and Chief Nursing Officer
Web address: www.bronxcare.org
**Control**: Other not–for–profit (including NFP Corporation) **Service**: General medical and surgical

| |
|---|
| **Staffed Beds:** 859 **Admissions:** 29651 **Census:** 690 **Outpatient Visits:** 1092724 **Births:** 1880 **Total Expense ($000):** 860685 **Payroll Expense ($000):** 418607 **Personnel:** 4173 |

⊠ **CALVARY HOSPITAL (332006)**, 1740 Eastchester Road, Zip 10461–2392; tel. 718/863–6900, (Nonreporting) **A**1 3 5 10 **F**1 29 30 35 39 62 63 64 68 74 78 82 84 87 119 121 130 132 134 146 148 149 **P**6
Primary Contact: Frank A. Calamari, President and Chief Executive Officer
COO: Richard J Kutilek, Chief Operating Officer
CFO: Andrew Greco, Chief Financial Officer
CMO: Michael J Brescia, M.D., Executive Medical Director
CIO: Patrick Martin, Director Information Systems
CHR: Michael T Troncone, Chief Human Resources Officer
CNO: Margaret Pelkowski, R.N., Vice President Patient Care Services
Web address: www.calvaryhospital.org
**Control**: Church operated, Nongovernment, not–for–profit **Service**: Other specialty treatment

| |
|---|
| **Staffed Beds:** 225 **Admissions:** 2839 **Census:** 213 **Outpatient Visits:** 94221 **Births:** 0 **Total Expense ($000):** 131857 **Payroll Expense ($000):** 68732 **Personnel:** 1044 |

**CONCOURSE DIVISION** See Bronxcare Health System, Bronx

**CONCOURSE NURSING HOME** See Concourse Regabilitation and Nursing Center

**EINSTEIN-WEILER HOSPITAL** See Jack D Weiler Hospital of Albert Einstein College of Medicine

**FULTON DIVISION** See Bronxcare Health System, Bronx

**HEBREW HOME FOR AGED-RIVERDALE** See Hebrew Home for The Aged at Riverdale

**HEBREW HOSP FOR CHRONIC SICK** See Hebrew Hospital Home, Inc.

**JACK D WEILER HOSPITAL OF ALBERT EINSTEIN COLLEGE OF MEDICINE** See Montefiore Medical Center, Bronx

**JACOBI MEDICAL CENTER** See NYC Health + Hospitals / Jacobi

⊠ △ **JAMES J. PETERS VETERANS AFFAIRS MEDICAL CENTER**, 130 West Kingsbridge Road, Zip 10468–3904; tel. 718/584–9000, (Nonreporting) **A**1 2 3 5 7 8 **S** Department of Veterans Affairs, Washington, DC
Primary Contact: Margaret B. Caplan, Director
CFO: Gregory Angelo, Chief Fiscal Program
CIO: Linda Bund, Chief Information Officer and Director Education
CNO: Kathleen Capitulo, Ph.D., R.N., Chief Nurse Executive
Web address: www.bronx.va.gov/
**Control**: Veterans Affairs, Government, federal **Service**: General medical and surgical

| |
|---|
| **Staffed Beds:** 378 |

*Many Facility Codes have changed. Please refer to the AHA Guide Code Chart.* © 2021 AHA Guide

**LINCOLN MEDICAL AND MENTAL HEALTH CENTER** See NYC Health + Hospitals / Lincoln

✠ **MONTEFIORE MEDICAL CENTER (330059)**, 111 East 210th Street, Zip 10467–2401; tel. 718/920–4321, (Includes CHILDREN'S HOSPITAL OF MONTEFIORE, Mailing address: 3415 Bainbridge Avenue, Bronx, New York, Zip 10467–2403; tel. 718/741–2426; JACK D WEILER HOSPITAL OF ALBERT EINSTEIN COLLEGE OF MEDICINE, Mailing address: 1825 Eastchester Road, Bronx, New York, Zip 10461–2373; tel. 718/904–2000; MONTEFIORE MEDICAL CENTER - NORTH DIVISION, Mailing address: 600 East 233rd Street, Bronx, New York, Zip 10466–2697; tel. 718/920–9000), (Nonreporting) **A**1 2 3 5 8 10 19 **F**3 5 6 7 8 9 12 13 14 15 17 18 19 20 21 22 23 24 25 26 27 28 29 30 31 32 34 35 36 37 38 39 40 41 42 43 44 45 46 47 48 49 50 51 52 54 55 56 57 58 59 60 61 62 63 64 65 66 68 70 71 72 73 74 75 76 77 78 79 80 81 82 83 84 85 86 87 88 89 90 91 92 93 94 96 97 98 99 100 102 103 104 107 108 110 111 114 115 116 117 118 119 120 121 124 126 129 130 131 132 134 135 136 137 138 139 140 141 142 143 144 145 146 147 148 149 150 153 154 156 157 **S** Montefiore Health System, Bronx, NY
Primary Contact: Philip O. Ozuah, M.D., Ph.D., Chief Executive Officer
CFO: Colleen M Blye, Executive Vice President and Chief Financial Officer
CMO: Gary Kalkut, M.D., Senior Vice President and Chief Medical Officer
CIO: Jack Wolf, Vice President Information Systems
Web address: www.montefiore.org
**Control**: Other not–for–profit (including NFP Corporation) **Service**: General medical and surgical

**Staffed Beds: 1545 Admissions: 88096 Census: 1419 Outpatient Visits: 2766093 Births: 5115 Total Expense ($000): 4153294 Payroll Expense ($000): 1956131 Personnel: 21856**

**NORTH CENTRAL BRONX HOSPITAL** See NYC Health + Hospitals / North Central Bronx

✠ **NYC HEALTH + HOSPITALS / JACOBI (330127)**, 1400 Pelham Parkway South, Zip 10461–1197; tel. 718/918–5000, (Nonreporting) **A**1 3 5 10 **F**3 4 5 8 11 12 13 15 18 20 26 29 30 31 32 34 35 38 39 40 41 43 44 45 46 47 49 50 51 52 53 55 56 57 58 59 60 61 64 65 66 68 70 73 74 75 76 77 78 79 81 82 84 85 86 87 89 90 92 93 94 96 97 98 100 101 102 104 107 108 110 111 114 115 116 117 118 119 130 131 132 134 135 141 144 146 147 148 149 150 154 156 157 **P**6 **S** NYC Health + Hospitals, New York, NY
Primary Contact: Christopher Mastromanno, Chief Executive Officer
COO: Jordana Bailey, Chief Operating Officer
CFO: Ellen Barlis, Chief Financial Officer
CMO: Michael Zinaman, M.D., Acting Chief Medical Officer
CIO: Md Alam, Chief Information Officer
CHR: Jamie Grecco, Chief Human Resource Executive
CNO: Suzanne Pennacchio, MSN, R.N., Chief Nursing Officer
Web address: www.nyc.gov/html/hhc/jacobi/home.html
**Control**: City, Government, Nonfederal **Service**: General medical and surgical

**Staffed Beds: 388 Admissions: 18657 Census: 353 Outpatient Visits: 402413 Births: 1842 Total Expense ($000): 791750 Payroll Expense ($000): 268869 Personnel: 2860**

✠ **NYC HEALTH + HOSPITALS / LINCOLN (330080)**, 234 East 149th Street, Zip 10451–5504, Mailing address: 234 East 149th Street, Room 923, Zip 10451–5504; tel. 718/579–5700, (Nonreporting) **A**1 2 5 10 **F**3 5 8 13 15 18 19 29 30 31 32 34 35 38 39 40 41 43 45 46 49 50 51 55 56 57 58 59 60 61 64 65 66 68 70 71 72 73 74 75 76 77 78 79 81 82 84 85 87 88 89 92 93 97 98 100 102 103 104 107 108 110 111 115 119 120 121 123 130 132 134 135 146 147 148 149 150 156 **S** NYC Health + Hospitals, New York, NY
Primary Contact: Milton Nunez, Executive Director
CFO: Caswell Samms, Network Chief Financial Officer
CMO: Anita Soni, M.D., Chief Medical Officer
CIO: James Carr, Chief Information Officer
CHR: Jeannith Michelen, Senior Associate Executive Director
Web address: www.nyc.gov/html/hhc/lincoln/
**Control**: City, Government, Nonfederal **Service**: General medical and surgical

**Staffed Beds: 362 Admissions: 17563 Census: 254 Outpatient Visits: 439940 Births: 1547 Total Expense ($000): 700600 Payroll Expense ($000): 240116 Personnel: 3048**

✠ **NYC HEALTH + HOSPITALS / NORTH CENTRAL BRONX (330385)**, 3424 Kossuth Avenue, Zip 10467–2489; tel. 718/519–3500, (Nonreporting) **A**1 3 5 10 **F**3 5 8 11 12 13 15 18 28 29 30 32 34 35 38 39 40 41 43 44 45 46 48 50 51 55 56 57 58 59 60 61 64 65 66 68 70 73 74 75 76 77 79 81 82 84 85 87 92 93 94 96 97 98 100 101 102 103 104 107 108 110 111 115 119 130 131 132 135 146 147 148 152 154 **P**6 **S** NYC Health + Hospitals, New York, NY
Primary Contact: Cristina Contreras, Executive Director
COO: Sheldon McLeod, Chief Operating Officer
CMO: Joseph Skarzynski, M.D., Medical Director
CIO: Diane Carr, Chief Information Officer
CNO: Elizabeth Gerdts, Chief Nursing Officer
Web address: www.nyc.gov/html/hhc/ncbh/html/home/home.shtml
**Control**: City, Government, Nonfederal **Service**: General medical and surgical

**Staffed Beds: 142 Admissions: 6436 Census: 112 Outpatient Visits: 205674 Births: 986 Total Expense ($000): 226045 Payroll Expense ($000): 85090 Personnel: 1021**

**OUR LADY OF MERCY MED CENTER** See Montefiore Medical Center - North Division

✠ **ST. BARNABAS HOSPITAL (330399)**, 4422 Third Avenue, Zip 10457–2545; tel. 718/960–9000, (Nonreporting) **A**1 3 5 10 12 13 19 **F**3 4 5 11 12 13 15 18 19 20 22 26 29 30 31 32 34 35 36 38 39 40 41 43 44 45 46 47 49 50 51 54 55 56 57 58 59 60 61 64 65 66 68 70 71 72 74 75 76 77 78 79 81 82 83 84 85 86 87 89 91 92 93 94 97 98 100 101 102 104 107 108 109 110 111 114 115 117 119 123 129 130 131 132 134 135 143 146 147 148 149 150 156 157 **P**6
Primary Contact: David A. Perlstein, M.D., President and Chief Executive Officer
COO: Len Walsh, Executive Vice President and Chief Operating Officer
CFO: Todd Gorlewski, Senior Vice President and Chief Financial Officer
CIO: Jitendra Barmecha, M.D., M.P.H., Senior Vice President and Chief Information Officer
CHR: Marc Wolf, Assistant Vice President Human Resources
CNO: Denise Richardson, R.N., MSN, Senior Vice President and Chief Nursing Officer
Web address: www.sbhny.org
**Control**: Other not–for–profit (including NFP Corporation) **Service**: General medical and surgical

**Staffed Beds: 422 Admissions: 14421 Census: 220 Outpatient Visits: 529772 Births: 866 Total Expense ($000): 473761 Payroll Expense ($000): 210847 Personnel: 2472**

**THE CHILDREN'S HOSPITAL OF MONTEFIORE** See Children's Hospital of Montefiore

**VETERANS AFFAIRS MEDICAL CENTER** See James J. Peters Veterans Affairs Medical Center

### BRONXVILLE—Westchester County

**LAWRENCE HOSPITAL CENTER** See New York-Presbyterian/Lawrence Hospital

### BROOKLYN—Kings County

**BETH ISRAEL MEDICAL CENTER-KINGS HIGHWAY DIVISION** See Mount Sinai Beth Israel Brooklyn

**BROOKLYN HOSP-CALEDONIAN HOSP** See Brooklyn Hospital Center

☐ **BROOKLYN HOSPITAL CENTER (330056)**, 121 DeKalb Avenue, Zip 11201–5425; tel. 718/250–8000, (Nonreporting) **A**1 3 5 10
Primary Contact: Gary G. Terrinoni, President and Chief Executive Officer
COO: John Gupta, Executive Vice President and Chief Operating Officer
CIO: Irene Farrelly, Vice President and Chief Information Officer
CHR: Ira Warm, Senior Vice President Human Resources
Web address: www.tbh.org
**Control**: Other not–for–profit (including NFP Corporation) **Service**: General medical and surgical

**Staffed Beds: 297**

**CONEY ISLAND HOSPITAL** See NYC Health + Hospitals / Coney Island

**HOLY FAMILY HOME FOR THE AGED** See Holy Family Home

**NY**

☐ **INTERFAITH MEDICAL CENTER (330397)**, 1545 Atlantic Avenue, Zip 11213–1122; tel. 718/613–4000, (Nonreporting) **A**1 3 5 10 **F**3 4 5 8 15 18 19 20 29 30 34 35 38 39 40 41 44 45 50 54 56 57 58 59 60 61 64 65 66 68 70 74 75 77 78 79 81 84 85 87 89 93 94 97 98 100 101 102 104 107 108 109 110 111 114 115 119 130 132 134 135 146 147 148 149 150 154 155 156 157 158
Primary Contact: LaRay Brown, President and Chief Executive Officer
CMO: Jochanan Weisenfreund, M.D., Senior Vice President Academic and Medical Affairs
CIO: Mark Lederman, Chief Information Officer
CHR: Venra Mathurin, Vice President Human Resources
Web address: www.interfaithmedical.com
**Control:** Other not–for–profit (including NFP Corporation) **Service:** General medical and surgical

**Staffed Beds:** 243 **Admissions:** 8748 **Census:** 193 **Outpatient Visits:** 157260 **Births:** 0 **Total Expense ($000):** 245828 **Payroll Expense ($000):** 125389 **Personnel:** 1507

**KINGS COUNTY HOSPITAL CENTER** See NYC Health + Hospitals / Kings County

☐ **KINGSBORO PSYCHIATRIC CENTER (334063)**, 681 Clarkson Avenue, Zip 11203–2125; tel. 718/221–7395, (Nonreporting) **A**1 3 5 10 **S** New York State Office of Mental Health, Albany, NY
Primary Contact: Deborah Parchment, Executive Director
CFO: Yinusa Awolowo, Business Officer
CMO: Jeffery Lucey, M.D., Clinical Director
CIO: George Gavora, Director Program Evaluation
CHR: Vera Thompson, Director Human Resources
CNO: Deborah Denigris, Chief Nursing Officer
Web address: www.omh.ny.gov/omhweb/facilities/kbpc/facility/htm
**Control:** State, Government, Nonfederal **Service:** Psychiatric

**Staffed Beds:** 290

☐ △ **KINGSBROOK JEWISH MEDICAL CENTER (330201)**, 585 Schenectady Avenue, Zip 11203–1891; tel. 718/604–5000, (Total facility includes 438 beds in nursing home–type unit) (Nonreporting) **A**1 3 5 7 10 **F**3 8 14 15 17 18 28 29 30 31 34 35 39 40 45 46 48 49 50 54 57 59 60 61 64 65 68 70 74 75 77 78 79 80 81 82 84 85 87 90 91 92 93 96 97 98 100 101 103 104 107 108 110 111 115 119 128 130 131 132 135 146 147 148 149 154 156 **P**6
Primary Contact: Paul Rosenfeld, Acting Chief Executive Officer
COO: Paul Rosenfeld, Chief Operating Officer
CFO: John Schmitt, Senior Vice President and Chief Financial Officer
CMO: Sibte Burney, M.D., Senior Vice President Medical Affairs and Chief Medical Officer
CIO: Daniel Morreale, Vice President and Chief Information Officer
CHR: John McKeon, Vice President Human Resources
CNO: Jane Lederer, R.N., Ed.D., Vice President and Chief Nursing Officer
Web address: www.kingsbrook.org
**Control:** Other not–for–profit (including NFP Corporation) **Service:** General medical and surgical

**Staffed Beds:** 647 **Admissions:** 8628 **Census:** 637 **Outpatient Visits:** 120138 **Births:** 0 **Total Expense ($000):** 313756 **Payroll Expense ($000):** 154462 **Personnel:** 1374

**KINGSBROOK JEWISH MEDICAL CNTR** See Kingsbrook Jewish Medical Center

✠ **MAIMONIDES MEDICAL CENTER (330194)**, 4802 Tenth Avenue, Zip 11219–2916; tel. 718/283–6000, (Includes MAIMONIDES INFANTS AND CHILDREN'S HOSPITAL OF BROOKLYN, Mailing address: 4802 Tenth Avenue, Brooklyn, New York, Zip 11219–2916; tel. 718/283–6000), (Nonreporting) **A**1 2 3 5 8 10 13 **F**3 7 8 9 11 12 13 14 15 17 18 19 20 22 24 26 28 29 30 31 32 34 35 37 38 39 40 41 43 44 45 46 47 48 49 50 51 52 54 55 56 57 58 59 60 61 64 65 66 68 70 72 73 74 75 76 77 78 79 81 82 84 85 86 87 88 89 91 92 93 96 97 98 99 100 101 102 103 104 107 108 110 111 114 115 117 118 119 120 121 123 124 126 129 130 131 132 135 144 145 146 147 148 149 150 154 156 **P**5 6
Primary Contact: Kenneth Gibbs, President and Chief Executive Officer
COO: Mark McDougle, Executive Vice President and Chief Operating Officer
CFO: Robert Naldi, Chief Financial Officer
CMO: Samuel Kopel, M.D., Medical Director
CIO: Walter Fahey, Chief Information Officer
Web address: www.maimonidesmed.org/
**Control:** Other not–for–profit (including NFP Corporation) **Service:** General medical and surgical

**Staffed Beds:** 610 **Admissions:** 35654 **Census:** 545 **Outpatient Visits:** 541974 **Births:** 7827 **Total Expense ($000):** 1366786 **Payroll Expense ($000):** 650575 **Personnel:** 5851

**NEW YORK COMM HOSP OF BROOKLYN** See New York Community Hospital

☐ **NEW YORK COMMUNITY HOSPITAL (330019)**, 2525 Kings Highway, Zip 11229–1705; tel. 718/692–5300, (Nonreporting) **A**1 3 10
Primary Contact: Barry Stern, President and Chief Executive Officer
COO: Una E Morrissey, R.N., MSN, Senior Vice President Operations, Chief Operating Officer and Chief Nursing Officer
CFO: Leonardo Tamburello, Chief Financial Officer
CMO: Herbert Rader, M.D., Advisor for Medical Affairs
CIO: Edward B. Stolyar, D.O., Divisional Chief Informational Officer
CHR: Raquel Collado, Vice President Human Resources
CNO: Una E Morrissey, R.N., MSN, Senior Vice President Operations, Chief Operating Officer and Chief Nursing Officer
Web address: www.nych.com
**Control:** Other not–for–profit (including NFP Corporation) **Service:** General medical and surgical

**Staffed Beds:** 134

**NEW YORK METHODIST HOSPITAL** See Newyork-Presbyterian Brooklyn Methodist Hospital

✠ △ **NEWYORK-PRESBYTERIAN BROOKLYN METHODIST HOSPITAL (330236)**, 506 Sixth Street, Zip 11215–3609; tel. 718/780–3000, (Nonreporting) **A**1 2 3 5 7 8 10 **F**3 6 7 9 11 12 13 15 17 18 19 20 22 24 26 29 30 31 32 34 35 36 39 40 43 44 45 46 47 48 49 50 51 52 54 55 56 57 58 59 61 64 65 66 68 70 71 72 73 74 75 76 77 78 79 81 82 84 85 87 88 89 90 91 92 93 95 96 97 98 100 102 103 107 108 109 110 111 112 114 115 118 119 120 121 123 124 126 129 130 131 132 145 146 147 148 149 154 156 **S** NewYork-Presbyterian, New York, NY
Primary Contact: Robert Guimento, President
CFO: Michael Fagan, Senior Vice President Finance
CMO: Steven Silber, M.D., Senior Vice President Medical Affairs
CHR: Rick Pogue, Vice President, Human Resources
CNO: Ernesto Perez-Mir, Vice President, Chief Nursing Officer
Web address: www.nym.org
**Control:** Other not–for–profit (including NFP Corporation) **Service:** General medical and surgical

**Staffed Beds:** 591 **Admissions:** 32225 **Census:** 494 **Outpatient Visits:** 561744 **Births:** 5079 **Total Expense ($000):** 1001507 **Payroll Expense ($000):** 496428 **Personnel:** 4139

✠ **NYC HEALTH + HOSPITALS / CONEY ISLAND (330196)**, 2601 Ocean Parkway, Zip 11235–7795; tel. 718/616–3000, (Nonreporting) **A**1 3 5 10 12 13 **F**3 4 5 13 15 17 18 20 29 30 31 34 39 40 41 44 45 49 50 51 54 55 56 57 58 59 60 61 64 65 66 68 70 72 73 74 75 76 77 78 79 81 82 83 84 85 87 89 90 91 92 93 94 96 97 98 100 102 104 107 108 110 111 114 115 118 119 130 132 135 146 147 148 149 150 151 **P**6 **S** NYC Health + Hospitals, New York, NY
Primary Contact: Svetlana Lipyanskaya, Chief Executive Officer
COO: Mei Kong, Chief Operating Officer
CMO: Wehbeh Wehbeh, M.D., Chief Medical Officer
CIO: Robert Kee, Chief Information Officer
CHR: Andrew Campbell, Associate Executive Director
CNO: Patricia Ruiz, R.N., Chief Nursing Officer
Web address: www.https://www.nychealthandhospitals.org/ConeyIsland/
**Control:** City, Government, Nonfederal **Service:** General medical and surgical

**Staffed Beds:** 371 **Admissions:** 13346 **Census:** 290 **Outpatient Visits:** 218577 **Births:** 1106 **Total Expense ($000):** 507961 **Payroll Expense ($000):** 189729 **Personnel:** 2394

✠ **NYC HEALTH + HOSPITALS / KINGS COUNTY (330202)**, 451 Clarkson Avenue, Zip 11203–2054; tel. 718/245–3131, (Nonreporting) **A**1 3 5 10 **F**3 4 5 8 9 11 12 13 15 17 18 19 20 26 28 29 30 31 32 34 35 38 39 40 41 43 45 46 47 49 50 51 52 53 56 57 58 59 60 61 64 65 66 68 69 70 71 72 73 74 75 76 77 78 79 81 82 84 85 86 87 88 89 90 91 92 93 94 97 98 99 100 101 102 103 104 105 107 108 110 111 114 115 116 119 120 121 123 126 129 130 131 132 134 135 142 143 144 145 146 147 148 149 153 154 156 157 **P**6 **S** NYC Health + Hospitals, New York, NY
Primary Contact: Sheldon Mcleod, Chief Executive Officer
CNO: Opal Sinclair-Chung, R.N., MS, Chief Nursing Officer, Deputy Executive Director
Web address: www.nyc.gov/html/hhc/kchc/html/home/home.shtml
**Control:** City, Government, Nonfederal **Service:** General medical and surgical

**Staffed Beds:** 544 **Admissions:** 20271 **Census:** 429 **Outpatient Visits:** 627209 **Births:** 1679 **Total Expense ($000):** 959247 **Payroll Expense ($000):** 402766 **Personnel:** 4570

✠ **NYC HEALTH + HOSPITALS / WOODHULL (330396)**, 760 Broadway, Zip 11206–5383; tel. 718/963–8000, (Nonreporting) **A**1 3 5 10 **F**3 4 5 11 13 15 18 19 29 30 31 32 34 35 36 37 38 39 40 41 43 44 45 46 49 50 52 55 56 57 58 59 60 61 64 65 66 68 70 71 72 73 74 75 76 77 78 79 81 82 84 85 86 87 89 92 93 94 97 98 102 104 106 107 108 110 111 115 118 119 130 132 134 135 141 144 146 147 149 154 156 **P**6 **S** NYC Health + Hospitals, New York, NY
Primary Contact: Gregory Calliste, Ph.D., FACHE, Chief Executive Officer
CFO: Erika Soiman, CPA, Chief Financial Officer
CMO: Edward Fishkin, M.D., Medical Director
CHR: Irma Suarez, Deputy Executive Director
CNO: Angela Imelda Edwards, R.N., Chief Nurse Executive
Web address: www.https://www.nychealthandhospitals.org/Woodhull/
**Control**: City–county, Government, Nonfederal **Service**: General medical and surgical

**Staffed Beds:** 274 **Admissions:** 9760 **Census:** 215 **Outpatient Visits:** 394788 **Births:** 1412 **Total Expense ($000):** 476001 **Payroll Expense ($000):** 173800 **Personnel:** 2180

**NYU LUTHERAN (NYU HOSPITALS CENTER)** See NYU Langone Hospital-Brooklyn

**ST JOHN'S EPISCOPAL HOME** See St John's Episcopal Homes for The Aged & Blind

✠ **SUNY DOWNSTATE-UNIVERSITY HOSPITAL OF BROOKLYN (330350)**, 450 Clarkson Avenue, Zip 11203–2012, Mailing Address: 450 Clarkson Avenue, MSC#75, Zip 11203–2012; tel. 718/270–1000, (Nonreporting) **A**1 3 5 8 10 **F**8 13 14 15 17 18 19 20 22 24 26 29 30 31 34 35 36 38 40 41 42 44 45 46 47 48 49 50 51 54 55 56 57 58 59 60 61 64 65 66 68 70 72 73 74 75 76 77 78 79 80 81 82 84 86 87 88 89 90 92 93 94 95 96 97 104 107 108 110 111 114 115 118 119 126 130 131 138 143 144 146 147 149 150 154 156 **P**6 Primary Contact: Wayne J. Riley, M.D., M.P.H., President
COO: Patricia A Winston, FACHE, MS, R.N., Vice President, Chief Administrative Officer and Chief Operating Officer
CFO: Richard B. Miller, Ph.D., Vice President Hospital Affairs and Chief Financial Officer
CMO: Michael Lucchesi, M.D., Chief Medical Officer; Chair, Emergency Medicine
CIO: Dilip Nath, Sc.D., Associate Chief Information Officer
CHR: Maria Silas, Manager Human Resources
CNO: Margaret G. Jackson, R.N., Vice President Patient Care Services and Chief Nursing Officer
Web address: www.downstate.edu
**Control**: State, Government, Nonfederal **Service**: General medical and surgical

**Staffed Beds:** 323 **Admissions:** 9560 **Census:** 173 **Outpatient Visits:** 259229 **Births:** 861 **Total Expense ($000):** 527594 **Payroll Expense ($000):** 256262 **Personnel:** 2615

**VETERANS ADMINISTRATION NEW YORK HARBOR HEALTHCARE SYSTEM** See Veterans Affairs New York Harbor Healthcare System

✠ **VETERANS AFFAIRS NEW YORK HARBOR HEALTHCARE SYSTEM**, 800 Poly Place, Zip 11209–7104; tel. 718/630–3500, (Includes VETERANS AFFAIRS NEW YORK HARBOR HEALTHCARE SYSTEM - MANHATTAN CAMPUS, Mailing address: 423 East 23rd Street, New York, New York, Zip 10010–5050; tel. 212/686–7500; Martina A Parauda, Director), (Nonreporting) **A**1 2 3 5 **S** Department of Veterans Affairs, Washington, DC
Primary Contact: Martina A. Parauda, Director
COO: Jodie A. Jackson, Associate Director
CFO: Andre Chance, Chief Financial Officer
CMO: Patrick C. Malloy, M.D., Chief of Staff
CIO: Luis Barrios, Chief Information Officer
CHR: Kevin Grundig, Chief Human Resource Officer
CNO: Cynthia A. Caroselli, R.N., Ph.D., Chief Nursing Officer
Web address: www.nyharbor.va.gov
**Control**: Veterans Affairs, Government, federal **Service**: General medical and surgical

**Staffed Beds:** 522

**WOODHULL MEDICAL AND MENTAL HEALTH CENTER** See NYC Health + Hospitals / Woodhull

**WYCKOFF HEIGHTS HOSPITAL** See Wyckoff Heights Medical Center

☐ **WYCKOFF HEIGHTS MEDICAL CENTER (330221)**, 374 Stockholm Street, Zip 11237–4006; tel. 718/963–7272, (Nonreporting) **A**1 3 5 10 13 **F**3 7 12 13 15 18 20 26 29 30 31 32 34 35 39 40 41 44 49 50 55 56 57 59 60 61 64 70 71 72 74 75 76 78 79 81 82 84 85 87 89 92 93 94 97 100 107 108 110 111 114 115 119 120 121 123 124 130 141 146 147 148 149 150 154 156 **P**1 4 5 7 8
Primary Contact: Ramon J. Rodriguez, President and Chief Executive Officer
COO: David Rock, Executive Vice President and Chief Operating Officer
CFO: Frank A Vutrano, Chief Financial Officer
CMO: Gustavo Del Toro, M.D., Chief Medical Officer
CIO: Jebashini Jesurasa, Vice President, Chief Information Technology Officer
CHR: Margaret E Cornelius, Vice President Human Resources
CNO: Catherine A Gallogly-Simon, R.N., MS, Chief Nursing Officer
Web address: www.wyckoffhospital.org
**Control**: Other not–for–profit (including NFP Corporation) **Service**: General medical and surgical

**Staffed Beds:** 223 **Admissions:** 13086 **Census:** 149 **Outpatient Visits:** 279956 **Births:** 1066 **Total Expense ($000):** 360125 **Payroll Expense ($000):** 177210 **Personnel:** 1837

## BUFFALO—Erie County

**BRYLIN HOSPITALS (334022)**, 1263 Delaware Avenue, Zip 14209–2402; tel. 716/886–8200, (Nonreporting) **A**10
Primary Contact: Eric D. Pleskow, President and Chief Executive Officer
CFO: E Paul Hettich, Chief Financial Officer
CMO: Maria Cartagena, M.D., Chief Medical Officer
CIO: Pawel Wieczorek, Director Information Technology
CHR: Pamela Nicastro, Director Human Resources
Web address: www.brylin.com
**Control**: Corporation, Investor–owned (for–profit) **Service**: Psychiatric

**Staffed Beds:** 88

**BRYLIN HOSPITALS** See Brylin Hospitals

☐ **BUFFALO PSYCHIATRIC CENTER (334052)**, 400 Forest Avenue, Zip 14213–1298; tel. 716/885–2261, (Nonreporting) **A**1 3 5 10 **S** New York State Office of Mental Health, Albany, NY
Primary Contact: Beatrix Souza, Chief Executive Officer
COO: Celia Spacone, M.D., Director Operations
CFO: Pamela Esposito, Director Administration
CMO: Jeffery Grace, M.D., Clinical Director
CIO: Anne Buchheit, Coordinator Mental Health Local Information Systems
CHR: Charles Siewert, Director Human Resources
CNO: Susan Fallis, Chief Nursing Officer
Web address: www.omh.ny.gov
**Control**: State, Government, Nonfederal **Service**: Psychiatric

**Staffed Beds:** 240

**CHILDREN'S HOSPITAL** See Women and Children's Hospital

✠ △ **ERIE COUNTY MEDICAL CENTER (330219)**, 462 Grider Street, Zip 14215–3098; tel. 716/898–3000, (Total facility includes 390 beds in nursing home–type unit) (Nonreporting) **A**1 3 5 7 10 **F**2 3 4 5 12 16 18 20 29 30 31 33 34 35 38 39 40 43 45 49 50 53 54 56 57 58 59 60 61 64 65 66 70 71 74 75 77 78 79 81 82 83 84 85 87 90 91 93 94 96 97 98 99 100 101 102 103 104 105 107 111 115 119 128 130 131 132 135 138 146 148 149 151 154 156 **P**6
Primary Contact: Thomas J. Quatroche Jr, President and Chief Executive Officer
COO: Andrew L Davis JrChief Operating Officer
CFO: Michael Sammarco, M.D., Chief Financial Officer
CMO: Brian Murray, M.D., Medical Director
CIO: Leslie Feidt, Chief Information Officer
CHR: Kathleen O'Hara, Vice President Human Resources
CNO: Karen Ziemianski, R.N., MS, Senior Vice President Nursing
Web address: www.ecmc.edu
**Control**: Hospital district or authority, Government, Nonfederal **Service**: General medical and surgical

**Staffed Beds:** 922 **Admissions:** 20875 **Census:** 806 **Outpatient Visits:** 366483 **Births:** 0 **Total Expense ($000):** 749482 **Payroll Expense ($000):** 259322 **Personnel:** 3122

**NY**

⇑ **KALEIDA HEALTH (330005)**, 100 High Street, Zip 14203–1154; tel. 716/859–5600, (Includes DE GRAFF MEMORIAL HOSPITAL, Mailing address: 445 Tremont Street, North Tonawanda, New York, Zip 14120–0750, P O Box 0750, Zip 14120–0750, tel. 716/694–4500; Darcy Craven, President; MILLARD FILLMORE SUBURBAN HOSPITAL, Mailing address: 1540 Maple Road, Williamsville, New York, Zip 14221; tel. 716/688–3100; Darcy Craven, President; WOMEN AND CHILDREN'S HOSPITAL, Mailing address: 219 Bryant Street, Buffalo, New York, Zip 14222–2099; tel. 716/878–7000; Cheryl Klass, President) (Total facility includes 380 beds in nursing home–type unit) **A**3 5 10 21 **F**1 2 3 6 8 9 11 12 13 15 17 18 19 20 21 22 24 28 29 30 31 32 34 35 36 37 38 39 40 41 43 44 45 46 47 48 49 50 51 54 55 56 57 58 59 60 61 62 63 64 65 66 67 68 70 71 72 73 74 75 76 77 78 79 80 81 82 83 84 85 86 87 88 89 90 91 92 93 94 96 97 99 100 101 102 103 104 107 108 109 110 111 114 115 118 119 120 124 126 128 130 131 132 134 135 136 143 146 147 148 149 154 156
Primary Contact: Jody Lomeo, Chief Executive Officer
COO: Donald Boyd, Executive Vice President and Chief Operating Officer
CFO: Joseph Kessler, Executive Vice President and Chief Financial Officer
CMO: Margaret Paroski, M.D., Executive Vice President and Chief Medical Officer
CIO: Robert Diamond, Senior Vice President and Chief Operating Officer
Web address: www.kaleidahealth.org
**Control**: Other not–for–profit (including NFP Corporation) **Service**: General medical and surgical

**Staffed Beds**: 1409 **Admissions**: 50085 **Census**: 1090 **Outpatient Visits**: 307656 **Births**: 6008 **Total Expense ($000)**: 1463847 **Payroll Expense ($000)**: 629059 **Personnel**: 7877

⇑ **KALEIDA HEALTH** See Kaleida Health

⊞ **MERCY HOSPITAL (330279)**, 565 Abbott Road, Zip 14220–2095; tel. 716/826–7000, (Total facility includes 84 beds in nursing home–type unit) (Nonreporting) **A**1 3 5 10 **F**3 13 15 17 18 20 22 24 26 28 29 30 34 35 38 39 40 41 42 44 45 48 49 50 53 54 56 57 58 59 60 63 64 65 66 68 70 72 74 75 76 77 79 81 84 85 87 90 92 93 95 97 100 107 108 110 111 114 115 118 119 124 126 128 129 130 131 132 141 146 147 148 149 154 156 **P**5 6 **S** Catholic Health System, Buffalo, NY
Primary Contact: Eddie Bratko, President
CFO: James H Dunlop, CPA, JrSenior Vice President Finance and Chief Financial Officer
CMO: Timothy Gabryel, M.D., Vice President Medical Affairs and Medical Director
CIO: Michael Galang, M.D., Chief Information Officer
CHR: Joseph A Scrivo JrDirector Human Resources
CNO: Shari McDonald, Vice President Patient Care Services
Web address: www.chsbuffalo.org
**Control**: Church operated, Nongovernment, not–for–profit **Service**: General medical and surgical

**Staffed Beds**: 436 **Admissions**: 18048 **Census**: 318 **Outpatient Visits**: 274568 **Births**: 2078 **Total Expense ($000)**: 443022 **Payroll Expense ($000)**: 187452 **Personnel**: 2135

**NAZARETH NURSING HOME** See Nazareth Home

**ROSWELL PARK CANCER INSTITUTE** See Roswell Park Comprehensive Cancer Center

☐ **ROSWELL PARK COMPREHENSIVE CANCER CENTER (330354)**, Elm and Carlton Streets, Zip 14263–0001; tel. 716/845–2300, (Nonreporting) **A**1 2 3 5 10 **F**3 14 15 29 30 31 32 34 35 36 38 39 44 45 46 47 49 50 54 55 57 58 59 63 64 66 67 70 74 75 77 78 79 80 81 82 84 85 86 87 90 92 93 94 96 98 107 108 110 111 112 114 115 116 117 118 119 120 121 123 124 126 130 132 134 135 136 141 145 146 147 148 149 157 **P**6
Primary Contact: Candace Johnson, Ph.D., President and Chief Executive Officer
COO: Shirley Johnson, Chief Clinical Operations Officer
CFO: Gregory McDonald, Vice President Finance and Chief Financial Officer
CMO: Boris Kuvshinoff, M.D., IIChief Medical Officer
CIO: Thomas Furlani, M.D., Chief Information Officer
CHR: Errol A. Douglas, MS, Vice President, Human Resources
CNO: Pamela D. Giesie, R.N., Chief Nursing Officer
Web address: www.roswellpark.org
**Control**: Hospital district or authority, Government, Nonfederal **Service**: Cancer

**Staffed Beds**: 133 **Admissions**: 5306 **Census**: 112 **Outpatient Visits**: 263698 **Births**: 0 **Total Expense ($000)**: 713014 **Payroll Expense ($000)**: 226664 **Personnel**: 3327

⊞ **SISTERS OF CHARITY HOSPITAL OF BUFFALO (330078)**, 2157 Main Street, Zip 14214–2692; tel. 716/862–1000, (Includes ELIZABETH SETON CHILDREN'S CENTER, Mailing address: 300 Corporate Boulevard South, Yonkers, New York, Zip 10701–6862; tel. 914/294–6300; ST. JOSEPH HOSPITAL, Mailing address: 2605 Harlem Road, Cheektowaga, New York, Zip 14225–4097; tel. 716/891–2400) (Total facility includes 80 beds in nursing home–type unit) **A**1 3 5 10 13 **F**2 3 5 11 12 13 15 18 28 29 30 31 32 34 35 36 37 38 40 41 44 45 46 47 49 50 53 54 55 57 58 59 60 64 65 66 68 70 72 73 74 75 76 77 78 79 81 82 84 85 87 92 93 97 100 107 108 110 111 114 115 118 119 126 128 129 130 131 132 141 146 147 148 149 154 156 **P**5 6 **S** Catholic Health System, Buffalo, NY
Primary Contact: Martin W. Boryszak, President
COO: John Sperrazza, Chief Operating Officer
CFO: James H Dunlop, CPA, JrChief Financial Officer
CMO: Nady Shehata, M.D., Vice President Medical Affairs
CIO: Michael Galang, M.D., Chief Information Officer
CHR: David DeLorenzo, Senior Director Human Resources
Web address: www.chsbuffalo.org
**Control**: Church operated, Nongovernment, not–for–profit **Service**: General medical and surgical

**Staffed Beds**: 388 **Admissions**: 13550 **Census**: 242 **Outpatient Visits**: 832247 **Births**: 3326 **Total Expense ($000)**: 344833 **Payroll Expense ($000)**: 156626 **Personnel**: 1889

**ST FRANCIS HOSPITAL OF BUFFALO** See St. Francis of Buffalo

**VETERANS AFFAIRS MED CENTER** See Veterans Affairs Western New York Healthcare System-Buffalo Division

⊞ **VETERANS AFFAIRS WESTERN NEW YORK HEALTHCARE SYSTEM-BUFFALO DIVISION**, 3495 Bailey Avenue, Zip 14215–1129; tel. 716/834–9200, (Nonreporting) **A**1 3 5 **S** Department of Veterans Affairs, Washington, DC
Primary Contact: Brian G. Stiller, Director Medical Center
CFO: Susan Gage, Financial Manager
CMO: Ali El-Solh, M.D., Interim Chief of Staff
CIO: Margaret Senker, Chief Information Officer
Web address: www.buffalo.va.gov/index.asp
**Control**: Veterans Affairs, Government, federal **Service**: General medical and surgical

**Staffed Beds**: 113

**WOMEN AND CHILDREN'S HOSPITAL** See Kaleida Health, Buffalo

### CALLICOON—Sullivan County

★ ⇑ **GARNETT HEALTH MEDICAL CENTER - CATSKILLS (331303)**, 8881 Route 97, Zip 12723; tel. 845/887–5530, (Nonreporting) **A**10 18 21 **F**3 11 15 29 30 34 35 40 50 57 59 64 75 85 93 97 107 130 132 133 146 149 **S** Garnett Health, Middletown, NY
Primary Contact: Rolland Bojo, R.N., Administrator
Web address: www.crmcny.org
**Control**: Other not–for–profit (including NFP Corporation) **Service**: General medical and surgical

**Staffed Beds**: 15 **Admissions**: 98 **Census**: 3 **Outpatient Visits**: 17314 **Births**: 0 **Total Expense ($000)**: 5741 **Payroll Expense ($000)**: 2973 **Personnel**: 33

⇑ **GROVER M. HERMANN HOSPITAL** See Garnett Health Medical Center - Catskills

### CANANDAIGUA—Ontario County

★ **CANANDAIGUA VETERANS AFFAIRS MEDICAL CENTER**, 400 Fort Hill Avenue, Zip 14424–1159; tel. 585/394–2000, (Nonreporting) **A**3 5 **S** Department of Veterans Affairs, Washington, DC
Primary Contact: Bruce Tucker, Director
CIO: Bob Corrado, Chief Information Officer
Web address: www.canandaigua.va.gov/
**Control**: Veterans Affairs, Government, federal **Service**: Psychiatric

**Staffed Beds**: 196

NY

**⊠ F. F. THOMPSON HOSPITAL (330074)**, 350 Parrish Street, Zip 14424–1731;
tel. 585/396–6000, (Nonreporting) **A**1 3 5 10 **S** University of Rochester Medical
Center, Rochester, NY
Primary Contact: Michael Stapleton, President and Chief Executive Officer
COO: Kurt Koczent, Executive Vice President and Chief Operating Officer
CFO: Mark Prunoske, Chief Financial Officer and Senior Vice President Finance
CMO: David Baum, M.D., Senior Vice President Medical Services
CHR: Jennifer DeVault, Vice President Associate Services
CNO: Hazel Robertshaw, R.N., Ph.D., Chief Nursing Officer, Vice President Patient Services
Web address: www.thompsonhealth.com
**Control**: Other not–for–profit (including NFP Corporation) **Service**: General
medical and surgical

Staffed Beds: 291

**THOMPSON HEALTH** See F. F. Thompson Hospital

**VETERANS AFFAIRS MEDICAL CENTER** See Canandaigua Veterans Affairs
Medical Center

### CARMEL—Putnam County

**ARMS ACRES**, 75 Seminary Hill Road, Zip 10512–1921; tel. 845/225–3400,
(Nonreporting)
Primary Contact: Patrice Wallace-Moore, Chief Executive Officer and Executive Director
CFO: Jason Burczeuski, Controller
CMO: Fred Hesse, M.D., Medical Director
CIO: Dolores Watson, Director Health Information Management
CHR: Kim Halpin, Director Human Resources
CNO: Barbara Klein, R.N., Director of Nursing
Web address: www.armsacres.com
**Control**: Corporation, Investor–owned (for–profit) **Service**: Alcoholism and other
chemical dependency

Staffed Beds: 183

**☐ PUTNAM HOSPITAL CENTER (330273)**, 670 Stoneleigh Avenue,
Zip 10512–3997; tel. 845/279–5711, (Data for 273 days) (Nonreporting) **A**1 2
3 10 **F**3 8 11 12 13 15 18 28 29 30 31 34 35 36 37 38 40 45 46 49 50 54
55 56 57 59 61 64 65 68 70 74 75 76 77 78 79 81 82 83 84 85 87 89 91 92
93 94 98 100 101 102 104 105 107 108 110 111 114 118 119 120 121 126
129 130 131 132 135 146 147 149 154 156 157 **S** Health Quest Systems, Inc.,
LaGrangeville, NY
Primary Contact: Mark Hirko, M.D., President
CFO: Joseph Hart, Director Finance and Support Services
CNO: Luanne Convery, Vice President Patient Care Services
Web address: www.healthquest.org/carmel/putnam-hospital-center.aspx
**Control**: Other not–for–profit (including NFP Corporation) **Service**: General
medical and surgical

Staffed Beds: 140 Admissions: 4295 Census: 62 Outpatient
Visits: 177739 Births: 301 Total Expense ($000): 120835 Payroll Expense
($000): 47026 Personnel: 623

### CARTHAGE—Jefferson County

**⊠ CARTHAGE AREA HOSPITAL (331318)**, 1001 West Street, Zip 13619–9703;
tel. 315/493–1000, (Nonreporting) **A**1 10 18 **F**3 13 34 38 39 40 41 45 46 50 51 54
55 57 59 62 64 65 68 74 75 76 77 79 81 86 87 89 92 93 97 100 101 102 104
107 108 111 116 119 127 129 130 133 135 146 147 148 149 150 153 154 156
Primary Contact: Richard Duvall, Chief Executive Officer
COO: Natalie Burnham, Chief Operating Officer
CFO: Rob Bloom, Chief Financial Officer
CMO: Michael Gordon, M.D., Chief Medical Officer
CIO: John Cranker, Chief Information Officer
CHR: Diana Chamberlain, Director Human Resources
CNO: Steven Olson, Administrator Patient Care Services
Web address: www.carthagehospital.com
**Control**: Other not–for–profit (including NFP Corporation) **Service**: General
medical and surgical

Staffed Beds: 25 Admissions: 1123 Census: 13 Outpatient Visits: 139162
Births: 335 Total Expense ($000): 53709 Payroll Expense ($000): 28387
Personnel: 495

### CATSKILL—Greene County

**COLUMBIA-GREENE LONG TERM CARE** See Kaaterskill Care

### CLIFTON SPRINGS—Ontario County

**★ ⇧ CLIFTON SPRINGS HOSPITAL AND CLINIC (330265)**, 2 Coulter Road,
Zip 14432–1189; tel. 315/462–9561, (Total facility includes 108 beds in nursing
home–type unit) (Nonreporting) **A**10 21 **F**3 4 5 11 15 28 29 30 31 32 34 36 38
39 40 44 45 48 49 50 51 54 56 57 59 60 64 68 70 71 75 77 78 79 81 82 85
87 90 93 96 97 98 99 100 101 102 103 104 107 108 110 111 114 116 117
118 119 120 121 123 128 130 132 141 146 147 148 149 150 151 154 156
**P**5 6 **S** Rochester Regional Health, Rochester, NY
Primary Contact: Dustin Riccio, M.D., President
CFO: Sharon Kelley, Chief Financial Officer
CIO: Joel Majauskas, Chief Information Officer
CHR: Kathy Babb, Manager Human Resources
CNO: Donna P Smith, R.N., Vice President Chief Operating Officer and Chief
Nursing Officer
Web address: www.cliftonspringshospital.org
**Control**: Other not–for–profit (including NFP Corporation) **Service**: General
medical and surgical

Staffed Beds: 179 Admissions: 2678 Census: 156 Outpatient
Visits: 122915 Births: 0 Total Expense ($000): 70955 Payroll Expense
($000): 36371 Personnel: 508

### COBLESKILL—Schoharie County

**BASSETT HOSP OF SCHOHARIE CNTY** See Cobleskill Regional Hospital

**⊠ COBLESKILL REGIONAL HOSPITAL (331320)**, 178 Grandview Drive,
Zip 12043–5144; tel. 518/254–3456, (Nonreporting) **A**1 10 18 20 **S** Bassett
Healthcare Network, Cooperstown, NY
Primary Contact: Eric H. Stein, FACHE, President
CFO: James Vielkind, Chief Financial Officer
CMO: Roy Korn, M.D., Medical Director
CIO: Bridgette West, Director Patient Access Services
CNO: Susan Oakes Ferrucci, MS, Vice President Patient Services and Chief Nursing
Officer
Web address: www.bassett.org
**Control**: Other not–for–profit (including NFP Corporation) **Service**: General
medical and surgical

Staffed Beds: 40

### COOPERSTOWN—Otsego County

**⊠ BASSETT MEDICAL CENTER (330136)**, One Atwell Road, Zip 13326–1394;
tel. 607/547–3456, (Nonreporting) **A**1 2 3 5 8 10 **S** Bassett Healthcare Network,
Cooperstown, NY
Primary Contact: William W. LeCates, M.D., President
COO: Ronette Wiley, R.N., Executive Vice President and Chief Operating Officer
CFO: Paul G. Swinko JrCorporate Vice President and Chief Financial Officer
CMO: William W. LeCates, M.D., Vice President Medical Affairs and Medical Director
CIO: Amelia Marley, Chief Information Officer
CHR: Sara Z Albright, Vice President Human Resources
CNO: Donna DeGarmo Anderson, R.N., MSN, Vice President Clinical Support and
Chief Nursing Officer
Web address: www.bassett.org
**Control**: Other not–for–profit (including NFP Corporation) **Service**: General
medical and surgical

Staffed Beds: 152

**MARY IMOGENE BASSETT HOSPITAL** See Bassett Medical Center

### CORNING—Steuben County

**CORNING HOSPITAL** See Guthrie Corning Hospital

**⊠ GUTHRIE CORNING HOSPITAL (330277)**, One Guthrie Drive, Zip 14830–3696;
tel. 607/937–7200, (Nonreporting) **A**1 3 10 **F**8 11 13 15 18 20 22 24 26 28 29
30 31 34 37 38 40 45 46 47 48 49 50 51 53 57 59 64 68 70 76 77 78 79 81
85 86 87 91 93 107 108 110 111 112 114 115 116 117 118 119 120 121
123 126 129 130 131 146 148 156 **S** Guthrie Clinic, Sayre, PA
Primary Contact: Paul VerValin, Interim Chief Executive Officer
CFO: Francis M Macafee, Vice President Finance and Chief Financial Officer
CMO: Chris Wentzel, M.D., Interim Medical Director
CHR: Laura Manning, Administrative Director
CNO: Deb Raupers, MSN, R.N., Chief Nursing Officer
Web address: www.corninghospital.com
**Control**: Other not–for–profit (including NFP Corporation) **Service**: General
medical and surgical

Staffed Beds: 65 Admissions: 4560 Census: 40 Outpatient Visits: 153050
Births: 522 Total Expense ($000): 113232 Payroll Expense ($000): 32325
Personnel: 653

**NY**

## CORNWALL—Orange County

**CORNWALL HOSPITAL** See St. Luke's Cornwall Hospital - Cornwall Campus

**ST. LUKE'S CORNWALL HOSPITAL - CORNWALL CAMPUS** See Montefiore St. Luke's Cornwall, Newburgh

## CORTLAND—Cortland County

**CORTLAND REGIONAL MEDICAL CENTER** See Guthrie Cortland Regional Medical Center

☒ **GUTHRIE CORTLAND REGIONAL MEDICAL CENTER (330175)**, 134 Homer Avenue, Zip 13045–1206; tel. 607/756–3500, (Total facility includes 82 beds in nursing home–type unit) (Nonreporting) **A**1 10 20 **F**2 3 8 11 13 15 18 28 29 30 31 34 35 38 40 44 45 49 50 51 54 56 57 59 62 64 70 75 76 77 78 79 81 85 86 87 91 93 96 98 100 102 103 107 108 110 111 118 119 128 130 131 132 133 135 146 147 148 149 150 154 156
Primary Contact: Jennifer Yartym, President
COO: Tracy Gates, Vice President Operations and Chief Operating Officer
CFO: Denise Wrinn, Vice President Finance and Chief Financial Officer
CMO: Russell Firman, M.D., Chief Medical Officer
CIO: Robert J Duthe, Director Information Systems and Chief Information Officer
CNO: Mary Wright, Vice President Nursing Services and Chief Nursing Officer
Web address: www.cortlandregional.org
**Control:** Other not–for–profit (including NFP Corporation) **Service:** General medical and surgical

**Staffed Beds:** 149 **Admissions:** 3971 **Census:** 111 **Outpatient Visits:** 113862 **Births:** 325 **Total Expense ($000):** 95381 **Payroll Expense ($000):** 40315 **Personnel:** 653

## CORTLANDT MANOR—Westchester County

**HUDSON VALLEY HOSPITAL CENTER** See New York-Presbyterian/Hudson Valley Hospital

☒ **NEW YORK-PRESBYTERIAN/HUDSON VALLEY HOSPITAL (330267)**, 1980 Crompond Road, Zip 10567–4182; tel. 914/737–9000, (Nonreporting) **A**1 10 **F**3 8 11 12 13 15 18 28 29 30 31 34 35 36 37 40 41 45 46 47 49 53 54 56 57 59 64 70 73 74 75 76 77 78 79 81 82 84 85 87 89 93 94 102 107 108 110 111 114 115 116 117 119 120 124 129 130 131 132 145 146 147 148 149 154 156 **S** NewYork-Presbyterian, New York, NY
Primary Contact: Stacey Petrower, President
COO: Deborah Neuendorf, Vice President Administration
CFO: Mark Webster, Vice President Finance
CMO: William Higgins, M.D., Vice President Medical Affairs
CIO: Bud Sorbello, Director Management Information Systems
CHR: Jeane L Costella, Vice President
CNO: Kathleen Webster, R.N., MSN, Vice President Patient Services
Web address: www.hvhc.org
**Control:** Other not–for–profit (including NFP Corporation) **Service:** General medical and surgical

**Staffed Beds:** 116 **Admissions:** 7845 **Census:** 86 **Outpatient Visits:** 162515 **Births:** 656 **Total Expense ($000):** 234099 **Payroll Expense ($000):** 95125 **Personnel:** 1009

## CUBA—Allegany County

**CUBA MEMORIAL HOSPITAL (331301)**, 140 West Main Street, Zip 14727–1398; tel. 585/968–2000, (Nonreporting) **A**10 18
Primary Contact: Norma Kerling, Interim Chief Executive Officer and Chief Clinical Officer
CFO: Jack Ormond, Chief Financial Officer
Web address: www.cubamemorialhospital.com
**Control:** Other not–for–profit (including NFP Corporation) **Service:** General medical and surgical

**Staffed Beds:** 81

## DANSVILLE—Livingston County

☒ **NICHOLAS H. NOYES MEMORIAL HOSPITAL (330238)**, 111 Clara Barton Street, Zip 14437–9503; tel. 585/335–6001, (Nonreporting) **A**1 10 **S** University of Rochester Medical Center, Rochester, NY
Primary Contact: Amy Pollard, R.N., President and Chief Executive Officer
CFO: Jay T. Maslyn, Chief Financial Officer
CMO: Douglas Mayhle, M.D., Medical Director
CIO: John Dorak, Director, Information Systems
CHR: Cassie Weitzel, Director, Human Resources
CNO: Tamara West, R.N., MSN, Vice President Patient Care
Web address: www.noyes-health.org
**Control:** Other not–for–profit (including NFP Corporation) **Service:** General medical and surgical

**Staffed Beds:** 40

## DELHI—Delaware County

☒ **O'CONNOR HOSPITAL (331305)**, 460 Andes Road, State Route 28, Zip 13753–7407; tel. 607/746–0300, (Nonreporting) **A**1 10 18 **S** Bassett Healthcare Network, Cooperstown, NY
Primary Contact: Scott Bonderoff, President
CFO: Sue E. Andrews, Chief Financial Officer
CMO: Peter L Sosnow, Medical Director
CHR: Barbara Green, Director Human Resources
CNO: Debra Neale, R.N., Chief Nursing Officer
Web address: www.https://www.bassett.org/locations/oconnor-hospital
**Control:** Other not–for–profit (including NFP Corporation) **Service:** General medical and surgical

**Staffed Beds:** 16

**O'CONNOR HOSPITAL DIVISION** See O'Connor Hospital

## DIX HILLS—Suffolk County

☐ **SAGAMORE CHILDREN'S PSYCHIATRIC CENTER (334064)**, 197 Half Hollow Road, Zip 11746–5861; tel. 631/370–1700, (Nonreporting) **A**1 10 **S** New York State Office of Mental Health, Albany, NY
Primary Contact: Kathy O'Keefe, Interim Executive Director
COO: Cathy Stein, Chief Inpatient Services
CFO: Jane Alexander, Director Facility Administrative Services
CIO: Bryan Doherty, Management Information Technology Services I
CHR: Nancy Angell, Associate Administrator Personnel
CNO: Sandra King, Chief Nursing Officer
Web address: www.omh.ny.gov
**Control:** State, Government, Nonfederal **Service:** Children's hospital psychiatric

**Staffed Beds:** 54

## DOBBS FERRY—Westchester County

**COMMUNITY HOSPITAL AT DOBBS FERRY** See St. John's Riverside Hospital - Dobbs Ferry Pavilion

## DUNKIRK—Chautauqua County

⇑ **BROOKS MEMORIAL HOSPITAL (330229)**, 529 Central Avenue, Zip 14048–2599; tel. 716/366–1111, (Nonreporting) **A**10 21 **F**3 4 5 11 13 15 18 28 29 34 35 40 41 42 45 50 54 57 59 62 64 68 70 76 79 81 84 85 86 87 93 96 97 98 102 104 106 107 108 110 111 115 119 130 131 144 146 147 149
Primary Contact: Mary E. LaRowe, FACHE, President and Chief Executive Officer
CFO: Jeffrey H. Morgan, Vice President Finance and Chief Financial Officer
CIO: Kevin Kimball, Director Information Technology
CHR: Tracie Luther, Director Employee and Labor Relations
CNO: Jodi Witherell, Vice President Patient Care and Quality
Web address: www.brookshospital.org
**Control:** Other not–for–profit (including NFP Corporation) **Service:** General medical and surgical

**Staffed Beds:** 85 **Admissions:** 2581 **Census:** 41 **Outpatient Visits:** 249623 **Births:** 266 **Personnel:** 465

*Many Facility Codes have changed. Please refer to the AHA Guide Code Chart.*

© 2021 AHA Guide

NY

## EAST MEADOW—Nassau County

**NASSAU COUNTY MEDICAL CENTER** See Nassau University Medical Center

✠ **NASSAU UNIVERSITY MEDICAL CENTER (330027)**, 2201 Hempstead Turnpike, Zip 11554–1859; tel. 516/572–0123, (Nonreporting) **A**1 3 5 10 12 13
Primary Contact: Anthony Boutin, M.D., Interim President and Chief Executive Officer
COO: Donald L Ashkenase, Executive Vice President and Chief Operating Officer
CFO: John P Maher, Executive Vice President and Chief Financial Officer
CMO: Anthony Boutin, M.D., Chief Medical Officer
CIO: Farooq Ajmal, Vice President and Chief Information Officer
CHR: Maureen Roarty, Executive Vice President Human Resources
CNO: Kathy Skarka, MSN, R.N., Executive Vice President Patient Care Services
Web address: www.nuhealth.net
**Control**: Hospital district or authority, Government, Nonfederal **Service**: General medical and surgical

**Staffed Beds**: 481

## ELIZABETHTOWN—Essex County

**ELIZABETHTOWN COMMUNITY HOSPITAL** See The University of Vermont Health Network Elizabethtown Community Hospital

✠ **THE UNIVERSITY OF VERMONT HEALTH NETWORK ELIZABETHTOWN COMMUNITY HOSPITAL (331302)**, 75 Park Street, Zip 12932, Mailing Address: P.O. Box 277, Zip 12932–0277; tel. 518/873–6377, (Includes MOSES LUDINGTON HOSPITAL, Mailing address: 1019 Wicker Street, Ticonderoga, New York, Zip 12883–1097; tel. 518/585–2831; John R Remillard, President and Chief Executive Officer), (Nonreporting) **A**1 10 18
Primary Contact: John R. Remillard, President
COO: Matthew Nolan, Chief Operating Officer
CFO: Alan Chardavoyne, Chief Financial Officer
CMO: Rob DeMuro, M.D., Chief Medical Officer
CIO: Darrin Goodrow, Chief Information Officer
CHR: Michelle Meachem, Director Human Resources
CNO: Julie Tromblee, R.N., Chief Nursing Officer
Web address: www.ech.org
**Control**: Other not–for–profit (including NFP Corporation) **Service**: General medical and surgical

**Staffed Beds**: 40

## ELLENVILLE—Ulster County

**ELLENVILLE COMMUNITY HOSPITAL** See Ellenville Regional Hospital

★ **ELLENVILLE REGIONAL HOSPITAL (331310)**, 10 Healthy Way, Zip 12428–5612; tel. 845/647–6400, (Nonreporting) **A**10 18 **F**3 5 11 15 28 29 30 32 34 35 36 38 40 41 45 46 47 48 50 57 59 63 64 68 75 77 79 81 85 87 93 94 107 108 110 111 115 119 132 133 135 146 147 148 149 152 156
Primary Contact: Steven L. Kelley, President and Chief Executive Officer
CFO: Robert Rue, Chief Financial Officer
CMO: Walter Sperling, M.D., Medical Director
CHR: Deborah Briggs, Vice President Human Resources, Marketing, Volunteer Services and Community Relations
CNO: Ann Marie Guntlow, Chief Nursing Officer
Web address: www.ellenvilleregional.org
**Control**: Other not–for–profit (including NFP Corporation) **Service**: General medical and surgical

**Staffed Beds**: 25 **Admissions**: 359 **Census**: 11 **Outpatient Visits**: 30614 **Births**: 2 **Total Expense ($000)**: 19693 **Payroll Expense ($000)**: 10033 **Personnel**: 183

## ELMHURST—Queens County

**ELMHURST HOSPITAL CENTER** See NYC Health + Hospitals / Elmhurst

✠ **NYC HEALTH + HOSPITALS / ELMHURST (330128)**, 79-01 Broadway, Zip 11373–1329; tel. 718/334–4000, (Nonreporting) **A**1 2 3 5 10 **F**2 3 5 8 9 11 13 14 15 17 18 19 20 22 26 29 30 31 34 35 37 38 39 40 41 43 45 46 49 50 51 52 53 54 55 56 57 58 59 60 61 64 65 66 68 70 71 72 73 74 75 76 77 78 79 80 81 82 83 84 85 86 87 89 90 91 92 93 94 96 97 98 99 100 101 102 104 105 107 108 109 110 111 115 118 119 121 123 124 126 130 132 135 141 143 144 145 146 147 148 149 150 152 153 154 156 157 **S** NYC Health + Hospitals, New York, NY
Primary Contact: Israel Rocha Jr, Chief Executive Officer
COO: Wayne Zimmermann, Chief Operating Officer
CFO: David Guzman, Chief Financial Officer
CMO: Jasmin Moshirpur, M.D., Dean and Medical Director
CIO: Jeannith Michelen, Chief Implementation Officer
CHR: Peter Maris, Director Human Resources
CNO: Joann Bernadette Gull, Chief Nursing Officer
Web address: www.nyc.gov/html/hhc/ehc/html/home/home.shtml
**Control**: City, Government, Nonfederal **Service**: General medical and surgical

**Staffed Beds**: 508 **Admissions**: 18425 **Census**: 405 **Outpatient Visits**: 618510 **Births**: 2274 **Total Expense ($000)**: 748052 **Payroll Expense ($000)**: 255950 **Personnel**: 3154

## ELMIRA—Chemung County

☐ **ARNOT OGDEN MEDICAL CENTER (330090)**, 600 Roe Avenue, Zip 14905–1629; tel. 607/737–4100, (Includes ARNOT MEDICAL CENTER - ST. JOSEPH'S CAMPUS, Mailing address: 555 St. Joseph's Boulevard, Elmira, New York, Zip 14901–3223; tel. 607/733–6541; Jonathan I Lawrence, President and Chief Executive Officer), (Nonreporting) **A**1 3 5 10 12 13 **S** Arnot Health, Elmira, NY
Primary Contact: Jonathan I. Lawrence, President and Chief Executive Officer
CFO: Ronald J Kintz, Vice President and Treasurer
CMO: Kenneth Herzl-Betz, M.D., Chief Medical Officer
CIO: Gregg Martin, Chief Information Officer
CHR: Dave Stanbro, Director Human Resources
CNO: Sandra Mac™ McCarthy, Chief Nursing Officer
Web address: www.arnothealth.org
**Control**: Other not–for–profit (including NFP Corporation) **Service**: General medical and surgical

**Staffed Beds**: 266

**ARNOT-OGDEN MEDICAL HOSPITAL** See Arnot Ogden Medical Center

☐ **ELMIRA PSYCHIATRIC CENTER (334045)**, 100 Washington Street, Zip 14901–2898; tel. 607/737–4739, (Nonreporting) **A**1 3 10 **F**29 30 35 38 39 54 57 59 62 68 71 77 87 98 99 100 101 103 104 153 154 157 158 **S** New York State Office of Mental Health, Albany, NY
Primary Contact: David Peppel, Executive Director
COO: Karen Patterson, Deputy Director Operations
CFO: J. Paul Bedzyk, Deputy Director Administration
CMO: Kurt Hahn, M.D., Acting Clinical Director
CIO: Jeremy Newcomer, Director Information Services
CHR: Patricia Santulli, Director Human Resources
CNO: Pam Seeley, Chief Nursing Officer
Web address: www.omh.ny.gov/omhweb/facilities/elpc/facility.htm
**Control**: State, Government, Nonfederal **Service**: Psychiatric

**Staffed Beds**: 61 **Admissions**: 197 **Census**: 55 **Outpatient Visits**: 0 **Births**: 0 **Personnel**: 362

## FAR ROCKAWAY—Queens County

☐ **ST. JOHN'S EPISCOPAL HOSPITAL (330395)**, 327 Beach 19th Street, Zip 11691–4423; tel. 718/869–7000, (Nonreporting) **A**1 3 5 10 12 13 19 **F**3 13 15 17 18 19 29 30 31 32 34 35 38 40 41 45 49 50 54 55 56 57 59 60 61 64 65 68 70 73 74 75 76 77 78 79 81 82 84 85 87 92 93 97 98 100 101 102 103 104 107 108 110 111 114 119 130 132 134 135 141 146 148 149 153 156
Primary Contact: Gerard W. Walsh, Chief Executive Officer
COO: Patrick L Sullivan, Chief Operating Officer
CFO: Kathleen Garcia, Controller
CMO: Raymond Pastore, M.D., Chief Medical Officer
CIO: Michael J Piro, Chief Information Officer
CHR: Roger Franco, Director Human Resources
Web address: www.ehs.org
**Control**: State, Government, Nonfederal **Service**: General medical and surgical

**Staffed Beds**: 213 **Admissions**: 7228 **Census**: 144 **Outpatient Visits**: 122340 **Births**: 582 **Total Expense ($000)**: 267213 **Payroll Expense ($000)**: 135730 **Personnel**: 1246

**NY**

---

**Hospital, Medicare Provider Number, Address, Telephone, Approval, Facility, and Physician Codes, Health Care System**

★ American Hospital Association (AHA) membership
☐ The Joint Commission accreditation
○ Healthcare Facilities Accreditation Program
◇ DNV Healthcare Inc. accreditation
⇧ Center for Improvement in Healthcare Quality Accreditation
△ Commission on Accreditation of Rehabilitation Facilities (CARF) accreditation

## FLUSHING—Queens County

**FLUSHING HOSP MEDICAL CENTER** See Flushing Hospital Medical Center

⊞ **FLUSHING HOSPITAL MEDICAL CENTER (330193)**, 4500 Parsons Boulevard, Zip 11355–2205; tel. 718/670–5000, (Nonreporting) **A**1 3 5 10 **F**3 4 5 7 8 12 13 15 17 18 19 26 27 29 30 31 32 34 35 36 39 40 41 45 49 50 51 55 56 57 59 60 61 63 64 65 68 70 71 72 73 74 75 76 77 78 79 81 82 84 85 87 89 91 92 93 97 98 100 101 104 107 110 111 114 119 126 128 130 132 135 146 147 148 149 150 154 156 **P**5 **S** MediSys Health Network, Jamaica, NY
Primary Contact: Bruce J. Flanz, President and Chief Executive Officer
COO: Robert V Levine, Executive Vice President and Chief Operating Officer
CFO: Mounir F Doss, Executive Vice President and Chief Financial Officer
CIO: Tony Gatto, Director Management Information Systems
Web address: www.flushinghospital.org
**Control**: Other not–for–profit (including NFP Corporation) **Service**: General medical and surgical

**Staffed Beds: 299 Admissions: 13629 Census: 179 Outpatient Visits: 171187 Births: 2565 Total Expense ($000): 807936 Payroll Expense ($000): 133753 Personnel: 1728**

⊞ **NEW YORK-PRESBYTERIAN QUEENS (330055)**, 56-45 Main Street, Zip 11355–5045; tel. 718/670–1231, (Nonreporting) **A**1 2 3 5 10 19 **F**3 11 12 13 15 17 18 19 20 22 24 26 28 29 30 31 32 34 35 37 39 40 41 43 44 45 46 47 48 49 50 51 54 55 56 57 58 59 60 61 64 65 66 68 70 72 73 74 75 76 77 78 79 80 81 82 84 85 87 89 91 92 93 96 97 100 101 107 108 110 111 114 115 118 119 120 121 123 124 126 130 131 141 145 146 147 148 149 154 **S** NewYork-Presbyterian, New York, NY
Primary Contact: Jaclyn Mucaria, President
COO: Robert Blenderman, Senior Vice President and Chief Operating Officer
CFO: Kevin J Ward, Vice President and Chief Financial Officer
CMO: Amir Jaffer, M.D., Senior Vice President Medical Affairs
CIO: Mark Greaker, Chief Information Officer
CHR: Lorraine Orlando, Vice President Human Resources
CNO: Alan M. Levin, MSN, R.N., Chief Nursing Officer
Web address: www.nyhq.org
**Control**: Other not–for–profit (including NFP Corporation) **Service**: General medical and surgical

**Staffed Beds: 510 Admissions: 30882 Census: 434 Outpatient Visits: 513395 Births: 3674 Total Expense ($000): 971969 Payroll Expense ($000): 466582 Personnel: 3926**

**NEW YORK-PRESBYTERIAN/QUEENS** See New York-Presbyterian Queens

## FOREST HILLS—Queens County

**FOREST HILLS HOSPITAL** See Long Island Jewish Forest Hills

## FRESH MEADOWS—Queens County

**CORNERSTONE OF MEDICAL ARTS CENTER HOSPITAL**, 159-05 Union Turnpike, Zip 11366–1950; tel. 212/755–0200, (Nonreporting)
Primary Contact: Thomas C. Puzo, President and Chief Executive Officer
CFO: Jeff OniFather, Chief Financial Officer
CMO: Sami Kaddouri, M.D., Medical Director
CHR: Gloria Burtch, Director Human Resources
Web address: www.cornerstoneny.com
**Control**: Corporation, Investor–owned (for–profit) **Service**: Alcoholism and other chemical dependency

**Staffed Beds: 162**

**MEDICAL ARTS CENTER HOSPITAL** See Cornerstone of Medical Arts Center Hospital

## GENEVA—Ontario County

**FINGER LAKES HOSPITAL** See Geneva General Hospital

⊞ **GENEVA GENERAL HOSPITAL (330058)**, 196 North Street, Zip 14456–1694; tel. 315/787–4000, (Nonreporting) **A**1 3 10 **S** Finger Lakes Health, Geneva, NY
Primary Contact: Jose Acevedo, M.D., President and Chief Executive Officer
CFO: Pamela Johnson, Treasurer and Chief Financial Officer
CMO: Jason Feinberg, M.D., Vice President Medical Affairs and Chief Medical Officer
CIO: Guy W Mosher IIIManager Information Systems
CHR: Patrick R Boyle, Vice President Human Resources
CNO: Ardelle Bigos, Vice President Nursing
Web address: www.flhealth.org
**Control**: Other not–for–profit (including NFP Corporation) **Service**: General medical and surgical

**Staffed Beds: 132**

## GLEN COVE—Nassau County

⊞ **GLEN COVE HOSPITAL (330181)**, 101 St Andrews Lane, Zip 11542–2254; tel. 516/674–7300, (Nonreporting) **A**1 3 5 10 **F**3 5 8 9 11 15 17 18 28 29 30 32 33 34 35 36 38 39 40 43 45 46 47 48 49 50 51 54 55 56 57 58 59 60 61 63 64 65 66 68 69 70 74 75 77 78 81 84 85 86 87 90 91 92 93 94 95 96 97 100 102 104 107 110 111 115 118 119 121 130 131 132 135 143 146 147 149 152 154 156 **S** Northwell Health, New Hyde Park, NY
Primary Contact: Kerri Scanlon, MSN, Executive Director
COO: Michele Frankel, Associate Executive Director Finance
CFO: Michele Frankel, Associate Executive Director Finance
Web address: www.northshorelij.com
**Control**: Other not–for–profit (including NFP Corporation) **Service**: General medical and surgical

**Staffed Beds: 119 Admissions: 4692 Census: 98 Outpatient Visits: 74323 Births: 0 Total Expense ($000): 151609 Payroll Expense ($000): 85263 Personnel: 806**

**NORTH SHORE UNIV HSP GLEN COVE** See Glen Cove Hospital

## GLEN OAKS—Queens County

**LI JEWISH-HILLSIDE MED CENTER** See Zucker Hillside Hospital

**ZUCKER HILLSIDE HOSPITAL** See Long Island Jewish Medical Center, New Hyde Park

## GLENS FALLS—Warren County

★ ⇑ **GLENS FALLS HOSPITAL (330191)**, 100 Park Street, Zip 12801–4413; tel. 518/926–1000, (Nonreporting) **A**2 5 10 19 21 **F**3 5 6 8 11 13 15 17 18 20 22 26 28 29 30 31 32 34 35 36 37 38 40 41 43 44 45 46 47 49 50 53 54 55 57 59 62 64 68 70 71 73 74 75 76 77 78 79 81 82 84 85 86 87 89 92 93 96 97 98 100 102 104 107 108 110 111 114 115 118 119 120 121 123 124 126 127 129 130 131 132 135 144 145 146 148 **P**6
Primary Contact: Dianne Shugrue, President and Chief Executive Officer
COO: Paul Scimeca, Senior Vice President Operations and Chief Operating Officer
CFO: Mitchell Amado, Senior Vice President Finance and Chief Financial Officer
CMO: Howard P Fritz, M.D., Vice President, Medical Affairs and Chief Medical Officer
CNO: Donna Kirker, R.N., MS, Vice President Patient Services and Chief Nursing Officer
Web address: www.glensfallshospital.org
**Control**: Other not–for–profit (including NFP Corporation) **Service**: General medical and surgical

**Staffed Beds: 334 Admissions: 10692 Census: 128 Outpatient Visits: 737577 Births: 1202 Total Expense ($000): 351173 Payroll Expense ($000): 153379 Personnel: 1987**

## GLENVILLE—Schenectady County

**CONIFER PARK**, 79 Glenridge Road, Zip 12302–4523; tel. 518/399–6446, (Nonreporting)
Primary Contact: Jeanne Gluchowski, Executive Director
COO: Jeanne Gluchowski, Executive Director
CFO: Jason Burczeuski, Controller
CMO: John Melbourne, M.D., Medical Director
CIO: Amy Kentera, Chief Information Officer
CHR: Maureen Fowler, Director Human Resources
Web address: www.coniferpark.com/
**Control**: Corporation, Investor–owned (for–profit) **Service**: Alcoholism and other chemical dependency

**Staffed Beds: 225**

**NY**

*Many Facility Codes have changed. Please refer to the AHA Guide Code Chart.* © 2021 AHA Guide

## GLOVERSVILLE—Fulton County

★ ⇧ **NATHAN LITTAUER HOSPITAL AND NURSING HOME (330276)**, 99 East State Street, Zip 12078–1203; tel. 518/725–8621, (Total facility includes 84 beds in nursing home–type unit) (Nonreporting) **A**10 21 **F**3 8 11 13 15 18 28 29 30 31 32 34 35 36 37 40 45 50 53 54 57 59 61 64 65 70 74 75 76 77 78 79 81 82 85 86 87 89 93 96 97 107 108 110 115 118 119 128 129 130 131 132 135 144 145 146 147 149 154 156 **P**6
Primary Contact: Laurence E. Kelly, President and Chief Executive Officer
CMO: Frederick Goldberg, M.D., Vice President Medical Affairs and Chief Medical Officer
CIO: Martin Brown, Vice President Information Services and Chief Information Officer
CHR: Lana Wydra, Vice President Human Resources
CNO: Stephanie Fishel, Vice President Patient Care Services and Chief Nursing Officer
Web address: www.nlh.org
**Control:** Other not–for–profit (including NFP Corporation) **Service:** General medical and surgical

**Staffed Beds:** 137 **Admissions:** 2567 **Census:** 101 **Outpatient Visits:** 257438 **Births:** 397 **Total Expense ($000):** 109967 **Payroll Expense ($000):** 55804 **Personnel:** 817

## GOUVERNEUR—St. Lawrence County

⇧ **EDWARD JOHN NOBLE HOSPITAL OF GOUVERNEUR** See Gouverneur Hospital

★ ⇧ **GOUVERNEUR HOSPITAL (331315)**, 77 West Barney Street, Zip 13642–1040; tel. 315/287–1000, (Nonreporting) **A**10 18 21 **F**3 4 5 11 15 29 34 35 39 40 44 45 46 57 59 64 68 75 77 81 85 87 89 90 93 97 100 107 110 111 115 116 119 127 129 130 132 133 146 147 149 154 **P**7 **S** St. Lawrence Health System, Potsdam, NY
Primary Contact: Eric R. Burch, Chief Executive Officer
CFO: Richard T Lang, Chief Financial Officer
CMO: George Dodds, M.D., Medical Director
CNO: Jennifer Shaver, Director of Nursing
Web address: www.gvnrhospital.org
**Control:** Other not–for–profit (including NFP Corporation) **Service:** General medical and surgical

**Staffed Beds:** 25 **Admissions:** 904 **Census:** 15 **Outpatient Visits:** 40138 **Births:** 0 **Total Expense ($000):** 24223 **Payroll Expense ($000):** 10686 **Personnel:** 188

## GREENPORT—Suffolk County

**EASTERN LONG ISLAND HOSPITAL** See Stony Brook Eastern Long Island Hospital

## HAMILTON—Madison County

⊞ **COMMUNITY MEMORIAL HOSPITAL (331316)**, 150 Broad Street, Zip 13346–9518; tel. 315/824–1100, (Nonreporting) **A**1 10 18
Primary Contact: Sean Fadale, President and Chief Executive Officer
CFO: Christopher W Graham, Chief Financial Officer
CMO: Robert Delorme, Vice President Medical Affairs
CHR: Jennifer Montana, Manager Human Resources
CNO: Denise Hummer, R.N., Vice President Administrative Services
Web address: www.communitymemorial.org
**Control:** Other not–for–profit (including NFP Corporation) **Service:** General medical and surgical

**Staffed Beds:** 25

## HARRIS—Sullivan County

⇧ **CATSKILL REGIONAL MEDICAL CENTER** See Garnet Health Medical Center - Catskills

★ ⇧ **GARNET HEALTH MEDICAL CENTER - CATSKILLS (330386)**, 68 Harris Bushville Road, Zip 12742–5030, Mailing Address: P.O. Box 800, Zip 12742–0800; tel. 845/794–3300, (Total facility includes 64 beds in nursing home–type unit) (Nonreporting) **A**2 10 21 **F**2 3 13 15 17 18 28 29 30 31 32 34 35 40 45 57 59 64 66 70 74 75 76 77 78 79 81 85 87 89 93 97 98 100 102 104 107 108 110 111 115 119 127 128 130 132 133 135 144 146 147 148 149 153 154 **S** Garnet Health, Middletown, NY
Primary Contact: Jonathan Schiller, Chief Executive Officer
CFO: Rick Caprico, Chief Financial Officer
CMO: Gerard Galarneau, M.D., Regional Chief Medical Officer
CNO: Rolland Bojo, R.N., Chief Nursing Officer, Administrator Patient Care and Services
Web address: www.crmcny.org
**Control:** Other not–for–profit (including NFP Corporation) **Service:** General medical and surgical

**Staffed Beds:** 125 **Admissions:** 4292 **Census:** 112 **Outpatient Visits:** 95152 **Births:** 610 **Total Expense ($000):** 99144 **Payroll Expense ($000):** 38970 **Personnel:** 632

## HORNELL—Steuben County

⊞ **ST. JAMES HOSPITAL (330151)**, 7329 Seneca Road North, Zip 14843; tel. 607/247–2200, (Nonreporting) **A**1 10 20 **S** University of Rochester Medical Center, Rochester, NY
Primary Contact: Bryan J. O'Donovan, President and Chief Executive Officer
CMO: John Carroll, M.D., Chief Medical Officer
CIO: Jason Soles, Manager Information Systems
CHR: Jennifer Spike, Director Human Resources
CNO: Kathleen Brodbeck MSN, RN-BChief Nursing Officer
Web address: www.stjamesmercy.org
**Control:** Other not–for–profit (including NFP Corporation) **Service:** General medical and surgical

**Staffed Beds:** 127

**ST. JAMES MERCY HOSPITAL** See St. James Hospital

## HUDSON—Columbia County

★ **COLUMBIA MEMORIAL HOSPITAL (330094)**, 71 Prospect Avenue, Zip 12534–2907; tel. 518/828–7601, (Nonreporting) **A**10 19
Primary Contact: Jay P. Cahalan, President and Chief Executive Officer
COO: Dorothy M. Urschel, Chief Operating Officer
CFO: Bryan Mahoney, Chief Financial Officer
CMO: Lawrence Perl, M.D., Chief Medical Officer
CIO: Bonnie Ratliff, Chief Information Officer
CNO: Mary Ellen Plass, MS, R.N., Senior Vice President and Chief Nursing Officer
Web address: www.columbiamemorialhealth.org
**Control:** Other not–for–profit (including NFP Corporation) **Service:** General medical and surgical

**Staffed Beds:** 192

**COLUMBIA-GREENE MEDICAL CENTER** See Columbia Memorial Hospital

## HUNTINGTON—Suffolk County

⊞ **HUNTINGTON HOSPITAL (330045)**, 270 Park Avenue, Zip 11743–2799; tel. 631/351–2000, (Nonreporting) **A**1 2 3 10 **F**3 8 11 12 13 17 18 20 22 26 29 30 31 32 34 35 36 37 38 40 41 43 44 45 46 47 48 49 50 51 54 55 56 57 58 59 60 61 63 64 65 66 68 69 70 73 74 75 76 78 79 81 82 84 85 86 87 89 97 98 100 101 102 103 104 107 108 110 111 115 118 119 126 130 132 146 147 148 149 150 154 **S** Northwell Health, New Hyde Park, NY
Primary Contact: Nick Fitterman, M.D., Executive Director
CMO: Michael Grosso, M.D., Senior Vice President Medical Affairs
CIO: David Lombardi, Site Chief Information Officer
CHR: Lisa Khavkin, Vice President Human Resources
CNO: Susan Knoepffler, R.N., Vice President Nursing
Web address: www.https://huntington.northwell.edu
**Control:** Other not–for–profit (including NFP Corporation) **Service:** General medical and surgical

**Staffed Beds:** 280 **Admissions:** 17034 **Census:** 209 **Outpatient Visits:** 80543 **Births:** 1431 **Total Expense ($000):** 481056 **Payroll Expense ($000):** 238123 **Personnel:** 2038

## ITHACA—Tompkins County

⊞ **CAYUGA MEDICAL CENTER AT ITHACA (330307)**, 101 Dates Drive, Zip 14850–1342; tel. 607/274–4011, (Nonreporting) **A**1 2 3 5 10 20 **S** Cayuga Health System, Ithaca, NY
Primary Contact: Martin Stallone, M.D., President and Chief Executive Officer
CFO: John Collett, Vice President and Chief Financial Officer
CMO: David M Evelyn, M.D., Vice President Medical Affairs
CIO: Brett Mello, Chief Information Officer
CHR: Brian Forrest, Vice President Human Resources
CNO: Deb Raupers, MSN, R.N., Vice President Patient Services and Chief Nursing Officer
Web address: www.cayugamed.org
**Control:** Other not–for–profit (including NFP Corporation) **Service:** General medical and surgical

**Staffed Beds:** 193

**CAYUGAMEDICAL CENTER** See Cayuga Medical Center at Ithaca

NY

## JAMAICA—Queens County

☐ **CREEDMOOR PSYCHIATRIC CENTER (334004)**, 79-25 Winchester Boulevard, Zip 11427–2128; tel. 718/264–3600, (Nonreporting) **A**1 3 10 **S** New York State Office of Mental Health, Albany, NY
Primary Contact: Ann Marie. Barbarotta, Executive Director
CFO: Viodelda Ho-Shing, Deputy Director Administration
CIO: Ed Yunusov, Chief Information Officer
CHR: Adrienne Jones, Director Human Resources
CNO: Marie S Jean-Louis, R.N., Chief Nursing Officer
Web address: www.omh.ny.gov
**Control:** State, Government, Nonfederal **Service:** Psychiatric

Staffed Beds: 322

**JAMAICA HOSPITAL** See Jamaica Hospital Medical Center

⊞ **JAMAICA HOSPITAL MEDICAL CENTER (330014)**, 8900 Van Wyck Expressway, Zip 11418–2832; tel. 718/206–6000, (Nonreporting) **A**1 3 5 10 13 **S** MediSys Health Network, Jamaica, NY
Primary Contact: Bruce J. Flanz, President and Chief Executive Officer
COO: William Lynch, Executive Vice President and Chief Operating Officer
CFO: Mounir F Doss, Executive Vice President and Chief Financial Officer
CMO: Antonietta Morisco, M.D., Medical Director, Chairman Anesthesiology
CIO: Sami Boshut, Chief Information Officer
CHR: Trina Cornet, JD, Vice President Human Resources
CNO: Kathleen Scher, Ed.D., R.N., Chief Nursing Officer
Web address: www.Jamaicahospital.org
**Control:** Other not–for–profit (including NFP Corporation) **Service:** General medical and surgical

Staffed Beds: 632

**MARGARET TIETZ CNTR FOR NRSG** See Margaret Tietz Center for Nursing

☐ **NEW YORK CITY CHILDREN'S CENTER**, 74-03 Commonwealth Boulevard, Zip 11426–1890; tel. 718/264–4506, (Includes BRONX CHILDREN'S PSYCHIATRIC CENTER, Mailing address: 1000 Waters Place, Bronx, New York, Zip 10461–2799; tel. 718/239–3600; BROOKLYN CHILDREN'S PSYCHIATRIC CENTER, Mailing address: 1819 Bergen Street, Brooklyn, New York, Zip 11233–4513; tel. 718/221–4500), (Nonreporting) **A**1 3 **S** New York State Office of Mental Health, Albany, NY
Primary Contact: Kanika Jefferies, Executive Director
CMO: David M Rube, M.D., Clinical Director
CIO: Ed Yunusov, Coordinator Facility Information Center
Web address: www.omh.ny.gov/omhweb/facilities/nyccc/
**Control:** State, Government, Nonfederal **Service:** Children's hospital psychiatric

Staffed Beds: 102

⊞ **NYC HEALTH + HOSPITALS / QUEENS (330231)**, 82-68 164th Street, Zip 11432–1104; tel. 718/883–3000, (Nonreporting) **A**1 2 3 5 10 **F**3 5 8 9 11 13 15 18 19 28 29 30 31 32 34 35 38 39 40 41 45 46 47 49 50 52 53 54 55 56 58 59 60 61 64 65 66 68 70 71 72 73 74 75 76 77 78 79 81 82 84 85 86 87 93 94 97 98 100 101 102 104 105 107 108 110 111 114 115 116 117 118 119 120 121 123 124 129 130 132 141 143 144 146 147 148 149 152 153 154 156 **S** NYC Health + Hospitals, New York, NY
Primary Contact: Israel Rocha Jr, Chief Executive Officer
COO: Dean Milhaltses, Chief Operating Officer
CFO: Brian Stacey, Chief Financial Officer
CMO: Jasmin Moshirpur, M.D., Chief Medical Officer
CIO: Vincent Smith, Chief Information Officer
CHR: Jeannith Michelen, Senior Associate Executive Director
CNO: Joan Gabriele, Deputy Executive Director
Web address: www.nyc.gov/html/hhc/qhc/html/home/home.shtml
**Control:** City, Government, Nonfederal **Service:** General medical and surgical

Staffed Beds: 253 Admissions: 12515 Census: 202 Outpatient Visits: 507862 Births: 1433 Total Expense ($000): 498829 Payroll Expense ($000): 158376 Personnel: 2418

**QUEENS CHILDREN'S PSYCHIATRIC CENTER** See New York City Children's Center

**QUEENS HOSPITAL CENTER** See NYC Health + Hospitals / Queens

**ST. ALBANS PRIMARY AND EXTENDED CARE CENTER** See Veterans Affairs New York Harbor Healthcare System - St. Albans Community Living Center

## JAMESTOWN—Chautauqua County

⊞ **UPMC CHAUTAUQUA (330239)**, 207 Foote Avenue, Zip 14701–7077, Mailing Address: P.O. Box 840, Zip 14702–0840; tel. 716/487–0141, (Nonreporting) **A**1 10 **F**3 4 5 11 12 13 15 18 20 28 29 34 35 40 44 45 50 57 59 64 70 74 75 76 77 78 79 80 81 82 84 87 89 93 96 98 99 100 102 104 107 108 109 110 115 119 120 124 126 129 130 131 132 135 146 147 148 149 155 156 157 **P**5 **S** UPMC, Pittsburgh, PA
Primary Contact: Brian Durniok, President
CFO: Bradley Dinger, Chief Financial Officer
CMO: Marlene Garone, M.D., Vice President Medical Affairs and Medical Director
CIO: Keith Robison, Chief Information Officer
CHR: Karen Bohall, Director Human Resources
Web address: www.wcahospital.org
**Control:** Other not–for–profit (including NFP Corporation) **Service:** General medical and surgical

Staffed Beds: 111 Admissions: 6740 Census: 98 Outpatient Visits: 202047 Births: 659 Total Expense ($000): 124284 Payroll Expense ($000): 43469 Personnel: 1025

**UPMC CHAUTAUQUA WCA** See UPMC Chautauqua

## JOHNSON CITY—Broome County

**WILSON MEMORIAL REG MED CTR** See Wilson Memorial Regional Medical Center

**WILSON MEMORIAL REGIONAL MEDICAL CENTER** See United Health Services Hospitals-Binghamton, Binghamton

## KATONAH—Westchester County

☐ **FOUR WINDS HOSPITAL (334002)**, 800 Cross River Road, Zip 10536–3549; tel. 914/763–8151, (Nonreporting) **A**1 10
Primary Contact: Martin A. Buccolo, Ph.D., Chief Executive Officer
COO: Moira Morrissey, Chief Operating Officer and General Counsel
CFO: Barry S Weinstein, Chief Financial Officer
CMO: Jonathan Bauman, M.D., Chief Medical Officer
CIO: Barry S Weinstein, Chief Financial Officer
CHR: Susan Cusano, Director Human Resources
Web address: www.fourwindshospital.com
**Control:** Partnership, Investor–owned (for–profit) **Service:** Psychiatric

Staffed Beds: 181

## KENMORE—Erie County

**CATHERINE MCAULEY MANOR** See Mcauley Residence

⊞ **KENMORE MERCY HOSPITAL (330102)**, 2950 Elmwood Avenue, Zip 14217–1390; tel. 716/447–6100, (Total facility includes 160 beds in nursing home–type unit) (Nonreporting) **A**1 3 10 **F**3 11 15 18 29 30 31 34 35 37 38 40 41 44 45 49 50 53 54 57 58 59 63 64 65 66 68 70 74 75 77 79 81 84 85 87 90 92 93 97 100 107 108 110 111 115 117 118 126 128 129 130 131 132 141 146 147 148 149 154 156 **P**5 6 **S** Catholic Health System, Buffalo, NY
Primary Contact: Walter Ludwig, President
CFO: James H Dunlop, CPA, JrExecutive Vice President and Chief Financial Officer
CMO: James Fitzpatrick, M.D., Vice President Medical Affairs
CHR: Laura Cianflone, Director Human Resources
Web address: www.chsbuffalo.org
**Control:** Church operated, Nongovernment, not–for–profit **Service:** General medical and surgical

Staffed Beds: 325 Admissions: 8428 Census: 223 Outpatient Visits: 116847 Births: 0 Total Expense ($000): 176792 Payroll Expense ($000): 75782 Personnel: 979

## KINGSTON—Ulster County

⇑ **BENEDICTINE HOSPITAL** See Health Alliance Hospital - Mary's Avenue Campus

⇑ **HEALTH ALLIANCE HOSPITAL - BROADWAY CAMPUS (330004)**, 396 Broadway, Zip 12401–4692; tel. 845/331–3131, (Nonreporting) **A**3 10 19 21 **S** WMCHealth, Valhalla, NY
Primary Contact: Michael Doyle, M.D., Executive Director and Chief Medical Officer
COO: Robert Seidman, Chief Operating Officer
CFO: Steven J Haas, Chief Financial Officer
CMO: Frank Ehrlich, M.D., Chief Medical Officer
CIO: John Finch, Vice President Information Services
CHR: Greg M Howard, Director Human Resource
Web address: www.hahv.org
**Control:** Other not–for–profit (including NFP Corporation) **Service:** General medical and surgical

Staffed Beds: 150

*Many Facility Codes have changed. Please refer to the AHA Guide Code Chart.*

⇑ **HEALTH ALLIANCE HOSPITAL - MARY'S AVENUE CAMPUS (330224)**, 105 Marys Avenue, Zip 12401–5894; tel. 845/338–2500, (Nonreporting) **A**2 10 19 21 **S** WMCHealth, Valhalla, NY
Primary Contact: Michael Doyle, M.D., Executive Director and Chief Medical Officer
COO: Robert Seidman, Chief Operating Officer
CFO: Steven J Haas, Chief Financial Officer
CMO: Frank Ehrlich, M.D., Chief Medical Officer
CIO: John Finch, Chief Information and Community Officer
CHR: Greg M Howard, Vice President Human Resources
Web address: www.hahv.org
**Control:** Other not–for–profit (including NFP Corporation) **Service:** General medical and surgical

| Staffed Beds: 105 |
|---|

⇑ **KINGSTON HOSPITAL** See Health Alliance Hospital - Broadway Campus

---

**LEWISTON—Niagara County**

⊞ **MOUNT ST. MARY'S HOSPITAL AND HEALTH CENTER (330188)**, 5300 Military Road, Zip 14092–1903; tel. 716/297–4800, (Nonreporting) **A**1 10 **F**3 4 5 11 13 15 18 28 29 30 34 35 38 40 41 44 45 49 50 51 53 54 56 57 58 59 60 64 65 66 68 70 74 75 76 77 79 81 84 85 86 87 92 93 97 100 104 107 108 110 111 114 115 118 119 124 130 131 132 141 143 146 147 148 149 154 156 **P**5 6 **S** Catholic Health System, Buffalo, NY
Primary Contact: Charles J. Urlaub, President and Chief Executive Offricer
CNO: Jessica Visser, R.N., Vice President Patient Care Services and Chief Nursing Officer
Web address: www.msmh.org
**Control:** Church operated, Nongovernment, not–for–profit **Service:** General medical and surgical

| Staffed Beds: 164 Admissions: 3702 Census: 88 Outpatient Visits: 172792 Births: 354 Total Expense ($000): 107001 Payroll Expense ($000): 55735 Personnel: 633 |
|---|

---

**LITTLE FALLS—Herkimer County**

⊞ **LITTLE FALLS HOSPITAL (331311)**, 140 Burwell Street, Zip 13365–1725; tel. 315/823–1000, (Nonreporting) **A**1 10 18 **S** Bassett Healthcare Network, Cooperstown, NY
Primary Contact: Michael L. Ogden, President and Chief Executive Officer
CFO: James Vielkind, Chief Financial Officer
CMO: Louis Oceguera, M.D., Medical Director
CIO: Duane Merry, Chief Information Officer
CHR: Christine Pirri, Vice President Human Resources
CNO: Heidi Camardello, Vice President Patient Care Services and Chief Nursing Officer
Web address: www.bassett.org
**Control:** Other not–for–profit (including NFP Corporation) **Service:** General medical and surgical

| Staffed Beds: 25 |
|---|

---

**LOCKPORT—Niagara County**

⇑ **EASTERN NIAGARA HEALTH SYSTEM** See Eastern Niagara Hospital

★ ⇑ **EASTERN NIAGARA HOSPITAL (330163)**, 521 East Avenue, Zip 14094–3299; tel. 716/514–5700, (Includes EASTERN NIAGARA HOSPITAL LOCKPORT, Mailing address: 521 East Avenue, Lockport, New York, Zip 14094–3299; tel. 716/514–5700), (Nonreporting) **A**10 13 21 **F**3 4 8 15 18 19 28 29 30 31 34 40 45 46 47 48 49 50 51 54 57 59 60 63 65 68 70 74 75 77 79 81 82 83 84 85 87 89 93 94 97 98 100 102 107 108 110 111 115 119 126 130 144 146
Primary Contact: Anne E. McCaffrey, President and Chief Executive Officer
CMO: Bruce J Cusenz, M.D., Medical Director
CHR: Joseph Farrauto, Director Human Resources
CNO: Mary Beth Campo, MS, R.N., Director of Nursing
Web address: www.enhs.org
**Control:** Other not–for–profit (including NFP Corporation) **Service:** General medical and surgical

| Staffed Beds: 113 Admissions: 3307 Census: 62 Outpatient Visits: 96469 Births: 127 Total Expense ($000): 64928 Payroll Expense ($000): 27730 Personnel: 386 |
|---|

**LOCKPORT MEMORIAL HOSPITAL** See Eastern Niagara Hospital Lockport

---

**LONG ISLAND CITY—Queens County**

**MOUNT SINAI HOSPITAL OF QUEENS** See Mount Sinai Queens

---

**LOWVILLE—Lewis County**

⊞ **LEWIS COUNTY GENERAL HOSPITAL (331317)**, 7785 North State Street, Zip 13367–1297; tel. 315/376–5200, (Total facility includes 160 beds in nursing home–type unit) (Nonreporting) **A**1 10 18 **F**2 3 11 13 15 29 30 34 35 36 40 45 50 56 57 59 62 63 70 75 76 77 79 81 82 93 96 97 107 110 111 115 119 127 128 129 130 132 133 141 143 145 146 147 154
Primary Contact: Gerald Cayer, Chief Executive Officer
COO: Michele Prince, Chief Operating Officer
CFO: Jeffrey Hellinger, Chief Financial Officer
CMO: Sean Patrick Harney, Chief Medical Officer, Employed Provider Clinics
CIO: Rob Uttendorfsky, Director Information Management
CHR: Jessica Skiff, Director Human Resources
CNO: Neva Bossard, Chief Nursing Officer
Web address: www.lcgh.net
**Control:** County, Government, Nonfederal **Service:** General medical and surgical

| Staffed Beds: 185 Admissions: 1476 Census: 157 Outpatient Visits: 162530 Births: 201 Total Expense ($000): 82155 Payroll Expense ($000): 31562 Personnel: 540 |
|---|

---

**MALONE—Franklin County**

**ALICE HYDE MEDICAL CENTER** See The University of Vermont Health Network - Alice Hyde Medical Center

⊞ **THE UNIVERSITY OF VERMONT HEALTH NETWORK - ALICE HYDE MEDICAL CENTER (330084)**, 133 Park Street, Zip 12953–1243, Mailing Address: P.O. Box 729, Zip 12953–0729; tel. 518/483–3000, (Total facility includes 165 beds in nursing home–type unit) (Nonreporting) **A**1 10 20 **F**3 10 11 13 15 17 18 28 29 31 34 35 39 40 45 57 59 64 67 70 75 76 77 78 79 81 82 84 85 86 87 90 92 93 96 97 107 108 110 111 115 117 119 121 127 128 129 130 131 132 135 141 146 147 149 154 156 **P**8
Primary Contact: Michelle LeBeau, President
COO: Matthew Jones, Chief Operating Officer and Senior Vice President
CFO: Christopher Hickey, Chief Financial Officer and Senior Vice President
CMO: Kent Hall, M.D., Chief Medical Officer
CIO: Justin Miller, Chief Information Officer and Associate Vice President
CHR: Emily Campbell, Assistant Vice President People and Patient Experience
CNO: Tammy Reynolds, Assistant Vice President, Nursing Operations
Web address: www.UVMHealth.org/AHMC
**Control:** Other not–for–profit (including NFP Corporation) **Service:** General medical and surgical

| Staffed Beds: 206 Admissions: 1655 Census: 173 Outpatient Visits: 203483 Births: 261 Total Expense ($000): 93743 Payroll Expense ($000): 46526 Personnel: 675 |
|---|

---

**MANHASSET—Nassau County**

**MANHASSET AMBULATORY CARE CTR** See Manhasset Ambulatory Care Pavilion

⊞ **NORTH SHORE UNIVERSITY HOSPITAL (330106)**, 300 Community Drive, Zip 11030–3816; tel. 516/562–0100, (Includes SYOSSET HOSPITAL, Mailing address: 221 Jericho Turnpike, Syosset, New York, Zip 11791–4515; tel. 516/496–6500; Michael Fener, Executive Director), (Nonreporting) **A**1 2 3 5 8 10 **F**3 5 6 7 8 9 11 12 13 15 17 18 20 22 24 26 28 29 30 31 34 35 36 37 38 39 40 41 43 44 45 46 47 48 49 50 51 52 53 54 55 56 57 58 59 60 61 62 63 64 65 66 68 69 70 71 72 73 74 75 76 77 78 79 80 81 82 83 84 85 86 87 91 92 93 94 96 97 98 100 101 102 104 107 108 110 111 112 114 115 117 118 119 126 129 130 131 132 134 135 136 137 138 139 141 142 143 144 145 146 147 148 149 150 152 154 156 157 **S** Northwell Health, New Hyde Park, NY
Primary Contact: Alessandro Bellucci, M.D., Executive Director
CFO: Frank Rizzo, Chief Financial Officer, Central Region
CMO: Michael Gitman, M.D., Medical Director
CIO: Nympha Meindel, R.N., Chief Information Officer
CHR: Debra Bierman, Associate Executive Director Human Resources
CNO: Irene Macyk, R.N., MS, Ph.D., Chief Nursing Officer
Web address: www.https://www.northwell.edu/find-care/locations/north-shore-university-hospital
**Control:** Other not–for–profit (including NFP Corporation) **Service:** General medical and surgical

| Staffed Beds: 831 Admissions: 52012 Census: 810 Outpatient Visits: 1137212 Births: 6519 Total Expense ($000): 2970642 Payroll Expense ($000): 1500108 Personnel: 13742 |
|---|

**NY**

---

**Hospital, Medicare Provider Number, Address, Telephone, Approval, Facility, and Physician Codes, Health Care System**

★ American Hospital Association (AHA) membership
☐ The Joint Commission accreditation
○ Healthcare Facilities Accreditation Program
◇ DNV Healthcare Inc. accreditation
⇑ Center for Improvement in Healthcare Quality Accreditation
△ Commission on Accreditation of Rehabilitation Facilities (CARF) accreditation

## MARCY—Oneida County

☐ **CENTRAL NEW YORK PSYCHIATRIC CENTER**, 9005 Old River Road,
Zip 13403–3000, Mailing Address: P.O. Box 300, Zip 13403–0300;
tel. 315/765–3600, (Nonreporting) **A**1 3 **S** New York State Office of Mental
Health, Albany, NY
Primary Contact: Maureen Bosco, Executive Director
Web address: www.omh.ny.gov
**Control:** State, Government, Nonfederal **Service:** Psychiatric

**Staffed Beds:** 226

## MARGARETVILLE—Delaware County

⇑ **MARGARETVILLE HOSPITAL (331304)**, 42084 State Highway 28,
Zip 12455–2820; tel. 845/586–2631, (Nonreporting) **A**10 18 21 **S** WMCHealth,
Valhalla, NY
Primary Contact: Mark Pohar, Executive Director
CHR: Linda Mead, Director Human Resources
Web address: www.margaretvillehospital.org
**Control:** Other not–for–profit (including NFP Corporation) **Service:** General
medical and surgical

**Staffed Beds:** 15

⇑ **MARGARETVILLE MEM HOSPITAL** See Margaretville Hospital

## MASSENA—St. Lawrence County

⊞ **MASSENA HOSPITAL, INC. (330223)**, One Hospital Drive, Zip 13662–1097;
tel. 315/764–1711, (Nonreporting) **A**1 10 20 **S** St. Lawrence Health System,
Potsdam, NY
Primary Contact: David Bender, Chief Executive Officer
CFO: Patrick M. Facteau, Chief Financial Officer
CMO: Nimesh Desai, M.D., Medical Director
CHR: Jonnie Dorothy, Senior Director Human Resources
CNO: Ralene North, Chief Nurse Executive
Web address: www.massenahospital.org
**Control:** City, Government, Nonfederal **Service:** General medical and surgical

**Staffed Beds:** 50

**MASSENA MEMORIAL HOSPITAL** See Massena Hospital, Inc.

## MEDINA—Orleans County

⇑ **MEDINA MEMORIAL HOSPITAL** See Orleans Community Health

⇑ **ORLEANS COMMUNITY HEALTH (331319)**, 200 Ohio Street, Zip 14103–1095;
tel. 585/798–2000, (Total facility includes 30 beds in nursing home–type unit)
(Nonreporting) **A**10 18 21 **F**3 8 29 34 35 40 45 48 54 57 59 60 68 75 77 81 96
107 108 110 111 115 119 128 130 132 133 148 156
Primary Contact: Marc Shurtz, Interim Chief Executive Officer and Chief Financial Officer
CMO: Dale Sponaugle, M.D., Medical Staff President
CHR: Mary Williams, Director Human Resources
CNO: Paula Dresser, Chief Nursing Officer
Web address: www.medinamemorial.org
**Control:** State, Government, Nonfederal **Service:** General medical and surgical

**Staffed Beds:** 55 **Admissions:** 553 **Census:** 39 **Outpatient Visits:** 34183
**Births:** 0 **Personnel:** 199

## MIDDLETOWN—Orange County

★ △ ⇑ **GARNET HEALTH MEDICAL CENTER - CATSKILLS (330126)**, 707
East Main Street, Zip 10940–2650; tel. 845/333–1000, (Nonreporting) **A**2 3 5
7 10 12 13 21 **F**3 5 8 11 12 13 15 17 18 20 22 26 28 29 30 31 34 35 36 40
41 43 45 46 47 48 49 50 51 54 55 58 59 63 64 66 70 72 74 75 76 77 78 79
81 82 84 85 86 87 89 90 91 93 96 97 98 100 101 102 104 107 108 110 111
114 115 116 117 119 120 121 122 123 124 126 129 130 132 135 144 146
148 149 156 **S** Garnet Health, Middletown, NY
Primary Contact: Brian Tew, Chief Executive Officer
COO: Timothy P Selz, Vice President
CFO: Mitch Amodo, Vice President and Chief Financial Officer
CMO: James Oxley, D.O., Vice President Medical Affairs
CHR: Deborah Carr, Vice President Human Resources
Web address: www.ormc.org
**Control:** Other not–for–profit (including NFP Corporation) **Service:** General
medical and surgical

**Staffed Beds:** 340 **Admissions:** 21040 **Census:** 298 **Outpatient
Visits:** 262209 **Births:** 2024 **Total Expense ($000):** 528448 **Payroll
Expense ($000):** 200133 **Personnel:** 2595

⇑ **ORANGE REGIONAL MEDICAL CENTER** See Garnet Health Medical Center -
Catskills

## MINEOLA—Nassau County

**CHILDREN'S MEDICAL CENTER AT WINTHROP UNIVERSITY HOSPITAL** See
Children's Medical Center

**WINTHROP-UNIVERSITY HOSPITAL** See NYU Winthrop Hospital

## MONTOUR FALLS—Schuyler County

⊞ **SCHUYLER HOSPITAL (331313)**, 220 Steuben Street, Zip 14865–9709;
tel. 607/535–7121, (Total facility includes 120 beds in nursing home–type unit)
(Nonreporting) **A**1 3 10 18 **F**3 11 14 15 29 30 34 35 40 50 59 64 70 74 75 77
81 82 85 87 91 92 93 94 97 107 110 111 114 119 128 129 130 133 135 146
149 **P**6 **S** Cayuga Health System, Ithaca, NY
Primary Contact: Rebecca Gould, President and Chief Financial Officer
CFO: Rebecca Gould, President and Chief Financial Officer
CMO: Michael Eisman, M.D., Medical Director
Web address: www.schuylerhospital.org
**Control:** Other not–for–profit (including NFP Corporation) **Service:** General
medical and surgical

**Staffed Beds:** 145 **Admissions:** 765 **Census:** 125 **Outpatient Visits:** 68682
**Births:** 0 **Total Expense ($000):** 34507 **Payroll Expense ($000):** 19430
**Personnel:** 344

## MONTROSE—Westchester County

⊞ **VETERANS AFFAIRS HUDSON VALLEY HEALTH CARE SYSTEM**, 2094 Albany
Post Road, Zip 10548–1454, Mailing Address: P.O. Box 100, Zip 10548–0100;
tel. 914/737–4400, (Includes VETERAN AFFAIRS HUDSON VALLEY HEALTH
CARE SYSTEM-CASTLE POINT CAMPUS, Mailing address: 41 Castle Point Road,
Wappingers, New York, Zip 12590; tel. 914/831–2000; VETERANS AFFAIRS
HUDSON VALLEY HEALTH CARE SYSTEM-MONTROSE CAMPUS, Mailing address:
2094 Albany Post Road, Montrose, New York, Zip 10548; tel. 914/737–4400)
(Total facility includes 121 beds in nursing home–type unit) **A**1 5 **F**3 4 5 7 8 12 18
29 30 31 34 35 36 38 39 44 45 46 47 48 49 53 54 56 57 58 59 61 63 65 66
71 74 75 77 78 79 82 83 84 86 87 90 93 94 97 98 100 101 103 104 106 107
108 111 115 118 119 127 128 129 130 132 135 143 144 146 147 148 149
153 154 156 157 **S** Department of Veterans Affairs, Washington, DC
Primary Contact: Dawn M. Schaal, Interim Director
COO: John M Grady, Associate Director
CFO: John Walsh, Chief Fiscal Services
CMO: Joanne J Malina, M.D., Chief of Staff
CIO: Thomas Rooney, Chief Information Resource Management
CHR: Dardanella Russell, Chief Human Resources Management Service
Web address: www.hudsonvalley.va.gov/
**Control:** Veterans Affairs, Government, federal **Service:** Psychiatric

**Staffed Beds:** 270 **Admissions:** 1476 **Census:** 207 **Outpatient
Visits:** 361474 **Births:** 0 **Total Expense ($000):** 265574 **Payroll Expense
($000):** 126600 **Personnel:** 1349

**VETERANS AFFAIRS HUDSON VALLEY HEALTH CARE SYSTEM-F.D.
ROOSEVELT HOSPITAL** See Veterans Affairs Hudson Valley Health Care System

**VETERANS AFFAIRS HUDSON VALLEY HEALTH CARE SYSTEM-MONTROSE
DIVISION** See Veterans Affairs Hudson Valley Health Care System-Montrose Campus

## MOUNT KISCO—Westchester County

**NORTHERN WESTCHESTER HOSP CTR** See Northern Westchester Hospital

⊞ **NORTHERN WESTCHESTER HOSPITAL (330162)**, 400 East Main Street,
Zip 10549–3477, Mailing Address: 400 East Main Street, G-02, Zip 10549–3477;
tel. 914/666–1200, (Nonreporting) **A**1 2 10 **F**3 7 8 12 13 15 17 18 20 28 29 30
31 34 35 36 37 40 46 47 48 49 50 51 54 55 57 59 60 61 64 65 68 70 72 73
74 75 76 78 79 81 82 84 85 86 87 89 91 92 93 97 98 100 101 102 107 108
109 110 111 114 115 118 119 120 121 123 124 126 129 130 131 132 135
146 147 148 154 **S** Northwell Health, New Hyde Park, NY
Primary Contact: Derek Anderson, Executive Director
CFO: John Partenza, Vice President and Treasurer
CMO: Marla Koroly, M.D., Chief Medical Officer and Senior Vice President Medical Affairs
CIO: Sue Prince, Director Information Systems
CNO: Lauraine Szekely, R.N., Senior Vice President, Patient Care
Web address: www.nwhc.net
**Control:** Other not–for–profit (including NFP Corporation) **Service:** General
medical and surgical

**Staffed Beds:** 195 **Admissions:** 9106 **Census:** 105 **Outpatient
Visits:** 127914 **Births:** 1622 **Total Expense ($000):** 283910 **Payroll
Expense ($000):** 140040 **Personnel:** 1424

NY

## MOUNT VERNON—Westchester County

☐ **MONTEFIORE MOUNT VERNON (330086)**, 12 North Seventh Avenue, Zip 10550–2098; tel. 914/664–8000, (Nonreporting) **A**1 3 10 **F**3 14 15 18 29 30 31 34 35 40 45 50 59 60 61 64 65 66 68 70 74 75 77 78 79 81 84 85 86 87 92 93 97 98 100 102 104 107 110 111 114 119 130 146 147 148 156 **P**5 6 **S** Montefiore Health System, Bronx, NY
Primary Contact: Jaccel Kouns, R.N., MS, Vice President and Executive Director
CFO: Albert M Farina, Chief Financial Officer
CMO: Gary Ishkanian, M.D., Vice President Medical Affairs
CIO: Barbara Cooke, Director Health Information Systems
CHR: Dennis H Ashley, Vice President Human Resources
Web address: www.montefiorehealthsystem.org/landing.cfm?id=17
**Control**: Other not–for–profit (including NFP Corporation) **Service**: General medical and surgical

**Staffed Beds**: 60 **Admissions**: 3267 **Census**: 53 **Outpatient Visits**: 137903 **Births**: 0 **Total Expense ($000)**: 97278 **Payroll Expense ($000)**: 41378 **Personnel**: 472

**MOUNT VERNON HOSPITAL** See Montefiore Mount Vernon

## NEW HAMPTON—Orange County

☐ **MID-HUDSON FORENSIC PSYCHIATRIC CENTER (334061)**, Route 17M, Zip 10958, Mailing Address: P.O. Box 158, Zip 10958–0158; tel. 845/374–8700, (Nonreporting) **A**1 3 10 **F**39 87 98 130 135 149 **S** New York State Office of Mental Health, Albany, NY
Primary Contact: Kristin Orlando, Chief Executive Officer
Web address: www.omh.ny.gov
**Control**: State, Government, Nonfederal **Service**: Psychiatric

**Staffed Beds**: 285 **Admissions**: 309 **Census**: 283 **Outpatient Visits**: 0 **Births**: 0 **Total Expense ($000)**: 99249 **Payroll Expense ($000)**: 49280 **Personnel**: 572

**MID-HUDSON PSYCHIATRIC CENTER** See Mid-Hudson Forensic Psychiatric Center

## NEW HYDE PARK—Queens County

☒ **LONG ISLAND JEWISH MEDICAL CENTER (330195)**, 270-05 76th Avenue, Zip 11040–1496; tel. 718/470–7000, (Includes LONG ISLAND JEWISH FOREST HILLS, Mailing address: 102-01 66th Road, Forest Hills, New York, Zip 11375–2029; tel. 718/830–4000; Susan Browning, Executive Director; LONG ISLAND JEWISH VALLEY STREAM, Mailing address: 900 Franklin Avenue, Valley Stream, New York, Zip 11580–2190; tel. 516/256–6000; Stephen Bello, Executive Director; MANHASSET AMBULATORY CARE PAVILION, Mailing address: 1554 Northern Boulevard, Manhasset, New York, Zip 11030; tel. 516/365–2070; STEVEN AND ALEXANDRA COHEN CHILDREN'S MEDICAL CENTER OF NEW YORK, Mailing address: 270-05 76th Avenue, New Hyde Park, New York, Zip 11040; tel. 718/470–3000; ZUCKER HILLSIDE HOSPITAL, Mailing address: 75-59 263rd Street, Glen Oaks, New York, Zip 11004; tel. 718/470–8000) (Total facility includes 120 beds in nursing home–type unit) **A**1 2 3 5 8 10 **F**2 3 4 5 6 7 8 9 11 12 13 14 15 17 18 19 20 21 22 23 24 25 26 27 28 29 30 31 32 34 35 37 38 39 40 41 43 44 45 46 47 48 49 50 51 52 53 54 55 56 57 58 59 60 61 62 63 64 65 66 67 68 70 71 72 73 74 75 76 77 78 79 80 81 82 84 85 86 87 88 89 92 93 97 98 99 100 101 102 103 104 105 107 108 109 110 111 114 115 116 117 118 119 120 121 123 124 126 128 129 130 131 132 134 135 136 138 141 142 143 144 145 146 147 148 149 151 152 153 154 158 **P**5 6 **S** Northwell Health, New Hyde Park, NY
Primary Contact: Michael Goldberg, Executive Director
CIO: John Bosco, Senior Vice President and Chief Information Officer
CHR: Ronald W Stone, Regional Chief Human Resource Officer
CNO: Marybeth McManus, Chief Nursing Officer
Web address: www.lij.edu
**Control**: Other not–for–profit (including NFP Corporation) **Service**: General medical and surgical

**Staffed Beds**: 1522 **Admissions**: 82844 **Census**: 1339 **Outpatient Visits**: 1076023 **Births**: 10171 **Total Expense ($000)**: 3104113 **Payroll Expense ($000)**: 1529603 **Personnel**: 14978

**NORTH SHORE LONG ISLAND MED CT** See Long Island Jewish Medical Center

## NEW HYDE PARK—Nassau County

**SCHNEIDER CHILDREN'S HOSPITAL** See Steven and Alexandra Cohen Children's Medical Center of New York

**STEVEN AND ALEXANDRA COHEN CHILDREN'S MEDICAL CENTER OF NEW YORK** See Long Island Jewish Medical Center, New Hyde Park

## NEW ROCHELLE—Westchester County

☒ **MONTEFIORE NEW ROCHELLE (330184)**, 16 Guion Place, Zip 10801–5502; tel. 914/365–5000, (Total facility includes 150 beds in nursing home–type unit) (Nonreporting) **A**1 2 3 5 10 19 **F**3 12 13 14 15 18 28 29 30 31 32 34 35 37 40 45 50 55 59 64 65 66 68 70 72 74 75 76 77 78 79 81 82 84 85 86 87 90 92 93 97 100 107 108 110 114 119 128 130 135 146 156 **S** Montefiore Health System, Bronx, NY
Primary Contact: Anthony Alfano, Vice President Executive Director
CMO: Richard Barone, M.D., Medical Director
CHR: Susan Cohen, Director Human Resources
CNO: Danielle Kennedy EsqDirector of Nursing
Web address: www.montefiorehealthsystem.org
**Control**: Other not–for–profit (including NFP Corporation) **Service**: General medical and surgical

**Staffed Beds**: 237 **Admissions**: 6688 **Census**: 220 **Outpatient Visits**: 84039 **Births**: 798 **Total Expense ($000)**: 214024 **Payroll Expense ($000)**: 94107 **Personnel**: 1017

**SOUND SHORE MEDICAL CENTER OF WESTCHESTER** See Montefiore New Rochelle

**UNITED HOME** See United Hebrew Geriatric Center

## NEW YORK—Kings County

☐ **BROOKDALE HOSPITAL MEDICAL CENTER (330233)**, 125 Worth Street, 4th Fl Ste 418, Zip 10013, Mailing Address: One Brookdale Plaza, Brooklyn, Zip 11212–3139; tel. 718/240–5000, (Nonreporting) **A**1 3 5 10
Primary Contact: Dominick Stanzione, President and Chief Executive Officer
CFO: James Porter, Chief Financial Officer
CIO: David Reitzel, Chief Information Officer
CHR: Margaret M Brubaker, Senior Vice President Human Resources
Web address: www.brookdalehospital.org
**Control**: Other not–for–profit (including NFP Corporation) **Service**: General medical and surgical

**Staffed Beds**: 789

## NEW YORK (Includes all hospitals located within the five boroughs)
**BRONX**—Bronx County (Mailing Address – Bronx)
**BROOKLYN**—Kings County (Mailing Address – Brooklyn)
**MANHATTAN**—New York County (Mailing Address – New York)
**QUEENS**—Queens County (Mailing Addresses – Bellerose, Elmhurst, Far Rockaway, Flushing, Forest Hills, Glen Oaks, Holliswood, Jackson Heights, Jamaica, Little Neck, Long Island City, New Hyde Park, and Queens Village)
**RICHMOND VALLEY**—Richmond County (Mailing Address – Staten Island)

## NEW YORK—New York County

**BETH ISRAEL MEDICAL CENTER** See Mount Sinai Beth Israel

**CHILDREN'S HOSP OF NEW YORK** See Morgan Stanley Children's Hospital of New York-Presbyterian

**COLER MEMORIAL HOSPITAL** See Coler Rehabilitation and Nursing Care Center

**COLUMBIA PRESBYTERIAN MED CTR** See New York-Presbyterian/Columbia University Medical Center

**GOLDWATER MEMORIAL HOSPITAL** See Henry J. Carter Specialty Hospital & Nursing Facility

**GOUVERNEUR HOSPITAL** See NYC Health + Hospitals / Gouverneur

NY

☐ **GRACIE SQUARE HOSPITAL (334048)**, 420 East 76th Street, Zip 10021–3396;
tel. 212/988–4400, (Nonreporting) **A**1 10
Primary Contact: David Wyman, President and Chief Executive Officer
Web address: www.nygsh.org
**Control**: Other not–for–profit (including NFP Corporation) **Service**: Psychiatric

**Staffed Beds**: 157

**HARLEM HOSPITAL CENTER** See NYC Health + Hospitals / Harlem

**HENRY J. CARTER SPECIALTY HOSPITAL & NURSING FACILITY** See NYC
Health + Hospitals / Henry J Carter Specialty Hospital and Medical Center, New York

⊞ **HOSPITAL FOR SPECIAL SURGERY (330270)**, 535 East 70th Street,
Zip 10021–4898, Mailing Address: 535 East 70th Street, Belaire 10-08,
Zip 10021–4898; tel. 212/606–1000, (Nonreporting) **A**1 3 5 8 10 19 **F**3 8 9 12
29 30 32 33 34 35 36 37 38 43 44 50 53 54 56 57 58 59 64 66 68 70 74 75
77 79 80 81 82 84 85 86 87 89 91 92 93 94 97 100 107 109 111 114 115 116
117 119 121 123 126 130 131 132 134 141 142 143 146 147 148 149 154 **P**8
Primary Contact: Louis A. Shapiro, President and Chief Executive Officer
COO: Lisa Goldstein, Executive Vice President and Chief Operating Officer
CFO: Stacey Malakoff, Executive Vice President and Chief Financial Officer
CMO: Todd Albert, M.D., Surgeon-in-Chief and Medical Director
CIO: Jamie Nelson, Vice President and Chief Information Officer
CHR: Bruce Slawitsky, Vice President Human Resources
CNO: Stephanie J Goldberg, MSN, R.N., Senior Vice President and Chief Nursing Officer
Web address: www.hss.edu
**Control**: Other not–for–profit (including NFP Corporation) **Service**: Orthopedic

**Staffed Beds**: 205 **Admissions**: 15925 **Census**: 128 **Outpatient
Visits**: 536500 **Births**: 0 **Total Expense ($000)**: 1218833 **Payroll Expense
($000)**: 578600 **Personnel**: 5380

☐ **KIRBY FORENSIC PSYCHIATRIC CENTER (334060)**, 600 East 125th Street,
Zip 10035–6000; tel. 646/672–5800, (Nonreporting) **A**1 3 5 10 **S** New York
State Office of Mental Health, Albany, NY
Primary Contact: Vincent Miccoli, Executive Director
Web address: www.https://www.omh.ny.gov/omhweb/facilities/krpc/
**Control**: Other not–for–profit (including NFP Corporation) **Service**: Psychiatric

**Staffed Beds**: 193

⊞ **LENOX HILL HOSPITAL (330119)**, 100 East 77th Street, Zip 10075–1850;
tel. 212/434–2000, (Includes MANHATTAN EYE, EAR AND THROAT HOSPITAL,
Mailing address: 210 East 64th Street, New York, New York, Zip 10021–9885;
tel. 212/838–9200; Philip P Rosenthal, Executive Director), (Nonreporting) **A**1 3
5 8 10 19 **F**3 7 8 9 11 12 13 14 15 17 18 20 22 24 26 29 30 31 32 34 35 36
37 39 40 42 44 45 46 47 48 49 50 51 52 54 55 56 57 58 59 60 61 62 64 65
66 68 70 72 73 74 75 76 77 78 79 81 82 84 85 86 87 89 91 92 93 94 97 98
100 101 102 103 104 107 108 110 111 114 115 116 117 118 119 120 121
123 124 126 129 130 131 132 135 141 143 146 147 148 149 150 154 **S**
Northwell Health, New Hyde Park, NY
Primary Contact: Jill Kalman, M.D., Executive Director
CIO: Beth Dituro, Divisional Chief Information Officer
Web address: www.lenoxhillhospital.org
**Control**: Other not–for–profit (including NFP Corporation) **Service**: General
medical and surgical

**Staffed Beds**: 414 **Admissions**: 30986 **Census**: 348 **Outpatient
Visits**: 265560 **Births**: 4368 **Total Expense ($000)**: 1479159 **Payroll
Expense ($000)**: 759376 **Personnel**: 6157

**MANHATTAN EET HOSPITAL** See Manhattan Eye, Ear and Throat Hospital

**MANHATTAN PSYCH CENTER** See Manhattan Psychiatric Center-Ward'S Island

☐ **MANHATTAN PSYCHIATRIC CENTER-WARD'S ISLAND (334054)**, 600 East
125th Street, Zip 10035–6000; tel. 646/672–6767, (Nonreporting) **A**1 3 5 10 **S**
New York State Office of Mental Health, Albany, NY
Primary Contact: Vincent Miccoli, Executive Director
Web address: www.omh.ny.gov
**Control**: State, Government, Nonfederal **Service**: Psychiatric

**Staffed Beds**: 745

**MEMORIAL HOSPITAL FOR CANCER** See Memorial Sloan-Kettering Cancer Center

⊞ **MEMORIAL SLOAN-KETTERING CANCER CENTER (330154)**, 1275 York
Avenue, Zip 10065–6007; tel. 212/639–2000, (Nonreporting) **A**1 2 3 5 8 10 **F**3
8 11 14 15 29 31 32 34 35 36 37 39 44 45 46 47 48 49 50 54 55 56 57 58
59 60 61 64 66 68 70 74 75 77 78 79 81 82 84 85 86 87 88 89 92 93 94 96
98 99 100 103 104 107 108 110 111 112 114 115 117 118 119 120 121 123
124 126 130 132 135 136 142 143 144 145 146 147 148 149 154 157 **P**6
Primary Contact: Craig B. Thompson, M.D., President and Chief Executive Officer
COO: Ned Groves, Executive Vice President and Administrator
CFO: Michael Gutnick, Executive Vice President and Chief Financial Officer
CMO: Lisa DeAngelis, M.D., Acting Physician-in-Chief
CIO: Patricia Skarulis, Senior Vice President and Chief Information Systems Officer
CHR: Kerry Bessey, Senior Vice President and Chief Human Resources Officer
CNO: Elizabeth Nelkin McCormick, MSN, R.N., Senior Vice President and Chief
Nursing Officer
Web address: www.mskcc.org
**Control**: Other not–for–profit (including NFP Corporation) **Service**: Cancer

**Staffed Beds**: 498 **Admissions**: 25573 **Census**: 476 **Outpatient
Visits**: 2040051 **Births**: 0 **Total Expense ($000)**: 4388006 **Payroll Expense
($000)**: 1665142 **Personnel**: 20102

**METROPOLITAN HOSPITAL CENTER** See NYC Health + Hospitals / Metropolitan

**MORGAN STANLEY CHILDREN'S HOSPITAL OF NEW YORK-PRESBYTERIAN**
See New York-Presbyterian Hospital, New York

⊞ **MOUNT SINAI BETH ISRAEL (330169)**, First Avenue and 16th Street,
Zip 10003–3803; tel. 212/420–2000, (Includes MOUNT SINAI BETH ISRAEL
BROOKLYN, Mailing address: 3201 Kings Highway, Brooklyn, New York, Zip 11234;
tel. 718/252–3000; Lin H Mo, M.P.H., President), (Nonreporting) **A**1 2 3 5 8 10 19 **F**3 4
5 7 8 11 12 15 18 19 20 22 26 29 30 31 34 35 36 38 39 40 41 44 45 46 47 48
49 50 51 53 54 55 56 57 58 59 60 61 63 64 65 66 68 70 71 74 75 77 78 79 81
82 83 84 85 86 87 92 93 94 97 98 100 101 102 103 104 107 108 110 111 114
115 117 118 119 120 121 123 124 126 130 131 132 134 135 141 143 144 145
146 147 148 149 150 154 156 157 **P**5 **S** Mount Sinai Health System, New York, NY
Primary Contact: Jeremy Boal, M.D., President
COO: Kevin Molloy, Senior Vice President and Chief Operating Officer
CFO: Donald Scanlon, Chief Corporate Services, Mount Sinai Health System
CIO: Kumar Chatani, Senior Vice President and Chief Information Officer Mount
Sinai Health System
CHR: Jane Maksoud, R.N., Senior Vice President Human Resources and Labor
Relations, Mount Sinai Health System
CNO: Mary Walsh, R.N., MSN, Vice President Patient Care Services and Chief
Nursing Officer
Web address: www.bethisraelny.org
**Control**: Other not–for–profit (including NFP Corporation) **Service**: General
medical and surgical

**Staffed Beds**: 510 **Admissions**: 23479 **Census**: 401 **Outpatient
Visits**: 413440 **Births**: 0 **Total Expense ($000)**: 1023953 **Payroll Expense
($000)**: 379751 **Personnel**: 5425

**MOUNT SINAI MEDICAL CENTER** See The Mount Sinai Hospital

⊞ **MOUNT SINAI MORNINGSIDE (330046)**, 1111 Amsterdam Avenue,
Zip 10025–1716; tel. 212/523–4000, (Includes MOUNT SINAI WEST HOSPITAL,
Mailing address: 1000 Tenth Avenue, New York, New York, Zip 10019;
tel. 212/523–4000; Evan Flatow, M.D., President), (Nonreporting) **A**1 2 3 5 8 10
19 **F**3 4 5 7 8 9 11 12 13 15 17 18 20 22 24 26 29 30 31 32 34 35 36 37 38
39 40 41 43 44 45 46 47 48 49 50 51 52 55 56 57 58 59 60 61 63 64 65 66
68 70 71 72 73 74 75 76 77 78 79 81 82 84 85 86 87 90 96 97 98 99 100
101 102 103 104 107 108 110 111 112 114 115 117 118 119 120 121 123
124 126 129 130 131 132 134 135 141 143 145 146 147 148 149 150 153
154 156 157 **S** Mount Sinai Health System, New York, NY
Primary Contact: Arthur A. Gianelli, M.P.H., President
COO: Kevin Molloy, Senior Vice President and Chief Operating Officer
CFO: Donald Scanlon, Chief Corporate Services, Mount Sinai Health System
CIO: Kumar Chatani, Chief Information Officer, Mount Sinai Health System
CHR: Jane Maksoud, R.N., Senior Vice President Human Resources and Labor
Relations, Mount Sinai Health System
CNO: Mary Walsh, R.N., MSN, Vice President Patient Care Services and Chief
Nursing Officer
Web address: www.https://www.mountsinai.org/locations/morningside
**Control**: Other not–for–profit (including NFP Corporation) **Service**: General
medical and surgical

**Staffed Beds**: 749 **Admissions**: 37762 **Census**: 582 **Outpatient
Visits**: 453367 **Births**: 5179 **Total Expense ($000)**: 1349546 **Payroll
Expense ($000)**: 536774 **Personnel**: 6231

**MOUNT SINAI ROOSEVELT HOSPITAL** See Mount Sinai West Hospital

**MOUNT SINAI WEST HOSPITAL** See Mount Sinai Morningside, New York

**NEW YORK DOWNTOWN HOSPITAL** See New York Presbyterian Lower
Manhattan Hospital

**NEW YORK EYE AND EAR INFIRMARY** See New York Eye and Ear Infirmary of
Mount Sinai

*Many Facility Codes have changed. Please refer to the AHA Guide Code Chart.* © 2021 AHA Guide

☒ **NEW YORK EYE AND EAR INFIRMARY OF MOUNT SINAI (330100)**, 310 East
14th Street, Zip 10003–4201; tel. 212/979–4000, (Nonreporting) **A**1 3 5 8 10
**F**3 8 29 30 34 35 44 50 57 58 59 64 66 68 75 81 82 87 107 115 119 129
130 141 143 146 149 157 **S** Mount Sinai Health System, New York, NY
Primary Contact: James C. Tsai, M.D., President
CFO: Donald Scanlon, Chief Corporate Services, Mount Sinai Health System
CIO: Kumar Chatani, Chief Information Officer, Mount Sinai Health System
CHR: Jane Maksoud, R.N., Senior Vice President Human Resources and Labor
Relations, Mount Sinai Health System
Web address: www.nyee.edu
**Control**: Other not–for–profit (including NFP Corporation) **Service**: Eye, ear, nose
and throat

**Staffed Beds: 17 Admissions: 470 Census: 3 Outpatient Visits: 156263
Births: 0 Total Expense ($000): 146630 Payroll Expense ($000): 59608
Personnel: 684**

**NEW YORK FOUNDLING HOSPITAL** See New York Foundling

☐ **NEW YORK STATE PSYCHIATRIC INSTITUTE (334009)**, 1051 Riverside Drive,
Zip 10032–1007; tel. 646/774–5000, (Nonreporting) **A**1 3 5 10 **S** New York
State Office of Mental Health, Albany, NY
Primary Contact: Jeffrey A. Lieberman, M.D., Executive Director
COO: Janelle Dierkens, Chief Administration Officer
CFO: Jonathan Segal, Chief Financial Officer
CMO: David Lowenthal, M.D., Clinical Director
CIO: Joseph Grun, Chief Information Officer
CHR: Rebecca Dechabert, Acting Director Personnel
Web address: www.nyspi.org
**Control**: State, Government, Nonfederal **Service**: Psychiatric

**Staffed Beds: 58**

**NEW YORK WEILL CORNELL MED CTR** See New York-Presbyterian Hospital/
Weill Cornell Medical Center

☒ △ **NEW YORK-PRESBYTERIAN HOSPITAL (330101)**, 525 East 68th Street,
Zip 10065–4870; tel. 212/746–5454, (Includes MORGAN STANLEY CHILDREN'S
HOSPITAL OF NEW YORK-PRESBYTERIAN, Mailing address: 3959 Broadway, New
York, New York, Zip 10032–3784; tel. 212/305–2500; NEW YORK PRESBYTERIAN
LOWER MANHATTAN HOSPITAL, Mailing address: 170 William Street, New York,
New York, Zip 10038–2649; tel. 212/312–5000; Robert E Kelly, M.D., President;
NEW YORK-PRESBYTERIAN HOSPITAL, WESTCHESTER DIVISION, Mailing address:
21 Bloomingdale Road, White Plains, New York, Zip 10605; tel. 914/682–9100;
NEW YORK-PRESBYTERIAN HOSPITAL/WEILL CORNELL MEDICAL CENTER,
Mailing address: 525 East 68th Street, New York, New York, Zip 10021–4885;
tel. 212/746–5454; NEW YORK-PRESBYTERIAN/COLUMBIA UNIVERSITY MEDICAL
CENTER, Mailing address: 161 Fort Washington Avenue, New York, New York,
Zip 10032; tel. 212/305–2500; NEW YORK-PRESBYTERIAN/LAWRENCE HOSPITAL,
Mailing address: 55 Palmer Avenue, Bronxville, New York, Zip 10708–3403;
tel. 914/787–1000; Michael Fosina, M.P.H., FACHE, President; PAYNE WHITNEY
PSYCHIATRIC CLINIC, Mailing address: 525 East 68th Street, New York, New
York, Zip 10021; tel. 212/746–3800; PHYLLIS AND DAVID KOMANSKY CENTER
FOR CHILDREN'S HEALTH, Mailing address: 525 East 68th Street, New York,
New York, Zip 10065–4870; tel. 212/746–5454; THE ALLEN PAVILION, Mailing
address: 5141 Broadway, New York, New York, Zip 10032; tel. 212/932–5000),
(Nonreporting) **A**1 2 3 5 7 8 9 10 **F**3 4 5 6 7 8 11 12 13 14 15 16 17 18 19 20
21 22 23 24 25 26 27 28 29 30 31 32 34 35 36 37 38 39 40 41 42 43 44 45
46 47 48 49 50 51 52 53 54 55 56 57 58 59 60 61 62 63 64 65 66 68 69 70
71 72 73 74 75 76 77 78 79 80 81 82 83 84 85 86 87 88 89 90 91 92 93 94
96 97 98 99 100 101 102 103 104 105 106 107 108 110 111 112 114 115
116 117 118 119 120 121 123 124 126 129 130 131 132 133 134 135 136
137 138 139 140 141 142 143 144 145 146 147 148 149 150 153 154 156
157 **S** NewYork-Presbyterian, New York, NY
Primary Contact: Steven J. Corwin, M.D., President and Chief Executive Officer
COO: Laura Forese, M.D., M.P.H., Executive Assistant to the Chief Operating Officer
CFO: Phyllis R Lantos, Executive Vice President, Corporate Chief Financial Officer
and Treasurer
CMO: Laura Forese, M.D., M.P.H., Executive Vice President and Chief Medical Officer
CIO: Aurelia Boyer, Senior Vice President and Chief Information Officer
CHR: G Thomas Ferguson, Senior Vice President and Chief Human Resources Officer
CNO: Rosemary Ventura, R.N., Chief Nursing Informatics Officer
Web address: www.nyp.org
**Control**: Other not–for–profit (including NFP Corporation) **Service**: General
medical and surgical

**Staffed Beds: 2592 Admissions: 122030 Census: 2124 Outpatient
Visits: 2571605 Births: 16978 Total Expense ($000): 6437131 Payroll
Expense ($000): 3130235 Personnel: 28010**

**NYC HEALTH & HOSPITALS / BELLEVUE** See NYC Health + Hospitals /
Bellevue

☒ **NYC HEALTH + HOSPITALS / BELLEVUE (330204)**, 462 First Avenue,
Zip 10016–9198; tel. 212/562–4141, (Nonreporting) **A**1 3 5 10 **F**3 4 5 11 12 13
15 17 18 19 20 22 24 26 28 29 30 31 34 35 36 37 38 39 40 41 43 45 46 47
48 49 50 52 53 55 56 57 58 59 61 64 65 66 68 70 71 72 73 74 75 76 77 78
79 81 82 83 84 85 86 87 88 89 90 91 92 93 94 96 97 98 99 100 101 102 103
104 105 107 108 110 111 114 115 117 118 119 126 127 130 132 134 135
143 144 146 147 148 149 153 154 156 **S** NYC Health + Hospitals, New York, NY
Primary Contact: William Hicks, Chief Executive Officer
COO: Michael Rawlings, Interim Chief Operating Officer
CFO: Rebecca J Fischer, Chief Financial Officer
CMO: Nathan Link, M.D., Medical Director
CIO: James Carr, Chief Information Officer
CNO: Kim K Mendez, Ed.D., R.N., Chief Nurse Officer
Web address: www.nyc.gov/bellevue
**Control**: City, Government, Nonfederal **Service**: General medical and surgical

**Staffed Beds: 682 Admissions: 24977 Census: 560 Outpatient
Visits: 526385 Births: 1297 Total Expense ($000): 1085002 Payroll
Expense ($000): 364327 Personnel: 4660**

**NYC HEALTH + HOSPITALS / CARTER** See NYC Health + Hospitals / Henry J
Carter Specialty Hospital and Medical Center

☒ **NYC HEALTH + HOSPITALS / HARLEM (330240)**, 506 Lenox Avenue,
Zip 10037–1802; tel. 212/939–1000, (Nonreporting) **A**1 3 5 10-**F**3 4 5 8 11 12
13 15 16 17 18 19 29 30 32 34 35 38 39 40 41 43 44 45 46 47 48 49 50 52
53 55 57 58 59 60 61 64 65 68 70 72 74 75 76 77 78 79 81 82 84 85 86 87 88
89 90 93 94 96 97 98 100 102 104 107 108 110 111 114 115 118 119 130
132 134 135 141 144 146 147 148 149 154 156 **S** NYC Health + Hospitals,
New York, NY
Primary Contact: Ebone' Carrington, Chief Executive Officer and Chief Operating
Officer
COO: Ebone' Carrington, Chief Executive Officer and Chief Operating Officer
Web address: www.nyc.gov/html/hhc/harlem
**Control**: City, Government, Nonfederal **Service**: General medical and surgical

**Staffed Beds: 245 Admissions: 9999 Census: 196 Outpatient
Visits: 282362 Births: 793 Total Expense ($000): 512802 Payroll Expense
($000): 170498 Personnel: 2214**

☒ **NYC HEALTH + HOSPITALS / HENRY J CARTER SPECIALTY HOSPITAL
AND MEDICAL CENTER (332008)**, 1752 Park Avenue, Zip 10035;
tel. 646/686–0000, (Includes COLER REHABILITATION AND NURSING CARE
CENTER, Mailing address: 900 Main Street, Roosevelt Island, New York, New York,
Zip 10044; tel. 212/848–6300; Robert K. Hughes, Chief Executive Officer; HENRY
J. CARTER SPECIALTY HOSPITAL & NURSING FACILITY, Mailing address: 1752 Park
Avenue, New York, New York, Zip 10035; tel. 646/686–0000; Floyd R Long, Chief
Executive Officer) (Total facility includes 164 beds in nursing home–type unit) **A**1
3 10 **F**1 3 11 28 29 30 39 56 58 68 74 75 77 79 84 85 87 100 107 114 119
128 130 132 135 146 148 149 **S** NYC Health + Hospitals, New York, NY
Primary Contact: Floyd R. Long, Executive Director
CFO: Manuela Brito, Chief Financial Officer Post Acute Care
CMO: Vasudeva Raju, M.D., SuffixChief, Long Term Acute Care Medicine
CIO: Steve ONeill, Chief Information Officer
CHR: Jamie Grecco, Director Human Resources Post Acute
CNO: Stanlee Richards, R.N., MS, Chief Nurse Executive
Web address: www.nychealthandhospitals.org/Carter
**Control**: City, Government, Nonfederal **Service**: Acute long–term care hospital

**Staffed Beds: 365 Admissions: 413 Census: 218 Outpatient Visits: 0
Births: 0 Total Expense ($000): 129417 Payroll Expense ($000): 52476
Personnel: 700**

☒ **NYC HEALTH + HOSPITALS / METROPOLITAN (330199)**, 1901 First Avenue,
Zip 10029–7404; tel. 212/423–6262, (Nonreporting) **A**1 3 5 10 **F**3 4 8 11 13 15 17
18 29 30 31 32 34 35 38 39 40 41 44 45 47 48 50 51 52 53 55 56 57 58 59
60 61 64 65 66 68 70 71 72 73 74 75 76 77 78 79 81 82 84 85 86 87 89 90 92
93 94 96 97 98 99 100 101 102 104 107 108 110 111 114 119 130 131 132 134
135 144 146 147 148 149 153 156 157 **S** NYC Health + Hospitals, New York, NY
Primary Contact: Christopher Roker, Chief Executive Officer
COO: William Norberto Wang, M.D., Chief Operating Officer
CFO: Edie Coleman, Chief Financial Officer
CMO: John T Pellicone, M.D., Chief Medical Officer
CIO: Md Alam, Chief Information Officer
CHR: April Alexander, Director Human Resources
CNO: Noreen Brennan, Chief Nursing Officer
Web address: www.nyc.gov/html/hhc/html/home/home.shtml
**Control**: City, Government, Nonfederal **Service**: General medical and surgical

**Staffed Beds: 281 Admissions: 8023 Census: 167 Outpatient
Visits: 362573 Births: 924 Total Expense ($000): 384463 Payroll Expense
($000): 144379 Personnel: 1988**

---

**Hospital, Medicare Provider Number, Address, Telephone, Approval, Facility, and Physician Codes, Health Care System**

★ American Hospital Association (AHA) membership    ○ Healthcare Facilities Accreditation Program    ⇑ Center for Improvement in Healthcare Quality Accreditation
☐ The Joint Commission accreditation    ◇ DNV Healthcare Inc. accreditation    △ Commission on Accreditation of Rehabilitation Facilities (CARF) accreditation

**NYU CHILDREN'S HOSPITAL** See Hassenfeld Childrens Hospital of New York at NYU Langone Medical Center

☒ △ **NYU LANGONE HOSPITALS (330214)**, 550 First Avenue, Zip 10016–6402; tel. 212/263–7300, (Includes HASSENFELD CHILDRENS HOSPITAL OF NEW YORK AT NYU LANGONE MEDICAL CENTER, Mailing address: 550 First Avenue, New York, New York, Zip 10016–6401; tel. 212/263–7300; NYU LANGONE HOSPITAL-BROOKLYN, Mailing address: 150 55th Street, Brooklyn, New York, Zip 11220–2559; tel. 718/630–7000; Bret Rudy, M.D., Executive Director and Senior Vice President; NYU LANGONE ORTHOPEDIC HOSPITAL, Mailing address: 301 East 17th Street, New York, New York, Zip 10003–3890; tel. 212/598–6000; David A Dibner, FACHE, Senior Vice President Hospital Operations and Musculoskeletal Strategic Areas; NYU WINTHROP HOSPITAL, Mailing address: 259 First Street, Mineola, New York, Zip 11501–3957; tel. 516/663–0333; John F Collins, President and Chief Executive Officer; RUSK INSTITUTE AT NYU-HJD, Mailing address: 301 E 17th ST, New York, New York, Zip 10003–3804; tel. 212/598–6000; David A Dibner, FACHE, Senior Vice President Hospital Operations and Musculoskeletal Strategic Areas), (Nonreporting) **A**1 2 3 5 7 8 10 13 **F**3 5 6 7 8 9 11 12 13 15 17 18 19 20 21 22 23 24 25 26 27 28 29 30 31 32 33 34 35 36 37 38 39 40 41 42 43 44 45 46 47 48 49 50 51 52 53 54 55 56 57 58 59 60 61 62 64 65 66 68 70 72 73 74 75 76 77 78 79 81 82 84 85 86 87 88 89 90 91 92 93 94 95 96 97 98 100 101 102 103 104 107 108 110 111 112 113 114 115 116 117 118 119 120 121 123 124 126 129 130 131 132 134 135 136 137 138 139 140 141 142 143 144 145 146 147 148 149 150 153 154 156 157 **P**5 6
Primary Contact: Robert I. Grossman, M.D., Chief Executive Officer
COO: Robert J. Cerfolio, M.D., Chief Operating Officer
CFO: Daniel J. Widawsky, Chief Financial Officer
CMO: Fritz Francois, M.D., Chief Medical Officer
CIO: Nader Mherabi, Senior Vice President and Vice Dean, Chief Information Officer
CHR: Nancy Sanchez, Senior Vice President and Vice Dean Human Resources
Web address: www.nyumedicalcenter.org
**Control:** Other not–for–profit (including NFP Corporation) **Service:** General medical and surgical

**Staffed Beds:** 1689 **Admissions:** 97793 **Census:** 1345 **Outpatient Visits:** 2200779 **Births:** 14926 **Total Expense ($000):** 6554748 **Payroll Expense ($000):** 2159640 **Personnel:** 23818

**NYU LANGONE MEDICAL CENTER** See NYU Langone Hospitals

**NYU LANGONE MEDICAL CENTER'S HOSPITAL FOR JOINT DISEASES** See NYU Langone Orthopedic Hospital

**PAYNE WHITNEY PSYCHIATRIC CLINIC** See New York-Presbyterian Hospital, New York

☐ **ROCKEFELLER UNIVERSITY HOSPITAL (330387)**, 1230 York Avenue, Zip 10065–6399; tel. 212/327–8000, (Nonreporting) **A**1 10
Primary Contact: James G. Krueger, M.D., Ph.D., Chief Executive Officer
CMO: Barbara O'Sullivan, M.D., M.P.H., Medical Director
Web address: www.rucares.org
**Control:** Other not–for–profit (including NFP Corporation) **Service:** Other specialty treatment

**Staffed Beds:** 17

**RUSK INSTITUTE** See Rusk Institute at Nyu-Hjd

**TERENCE CARDINAL COOKE HEALTH CARE CENTER (332022)**, 1249 Fifth Avenue, Zip 10029–4413; tel. 212/360–1000, (Nonreporting) **A**5 10
Primary Contact: Mitch Marsh, Interim Executive Director
COO: Neil Pollack, Senior Administrator
CFO: Ann Marie Covone, Senior Vice President and Chief Financial Officer
CMO: Anthony Lechich, M.D., Chief Medical Officer
CIO: Mitze Amoroso, Chief Information Officer
CHR: Hugo A Pizarro, Vice President Human Resources
CNO: Monica McGibbon, Chief Nursing Officer
Web address: www.tcchcc.org/
**Control:** Church operated, Nongovernment, not–for–profit **Service:** Acute long–term care hospital

**Staffed Beds:** 28

**THE ALLEN PAVILION** See New York-Presbyterian Hospital, New York

☒ △ **THE MOUNT SINAI HOSPITAL (330024)**, One Gustave L Levy Place, Zip 10029–0310; tel. 212/241–6500, (Includes KRAVIS CHILDREN'S HOSPITAL, Mailing address: 1184 Fifth Avenue, New York, New York, Zip 10029–6503, One Gustave L Levy Place, Zip 10029–0312, tel. 212/241–9500; MOUNT SINAI QUEENS, Mailing address: 25-10 30th Avenue, Long Island City, New York, Zip 11102–2448; tel. 718/932–1000; Caryn A Schwab, Executive Director), (Nonreporting) **A**1 2 3 5 7 8 10 **F**3 4 6 7 8 9 11 12 13 14 15 17 18 19 20 21 22 23 24 25 26 27 28 29 30 31 32 33 34 35 36 37 38 39 40 41 43 44 45 46 47 48 49 50 51 52 54 55 56 57 58 59 60 61 62 63 64 65 66 68 70 71 72 73 74 75 76 77 78 79 80 81 82 83 84 85 86 87 88 89 90 91 92 93 94 95 96 97 98 99 100 101 102 103 104 105 107 108 110 111 114 115 117 118 119 120 121 123 124 126 129 130 131 132 134 135 136 137 138 139 141 142 143 144 145 146 147 148 149 150 153 154 156 157 **P**5 **S** Mount Sinai Health System, New York, NY
Primary Contact: David L. Reich, M.D., President and Chief Operating Officer
COO: David L Reich, M.D., President and Chief Operating Officer
CFO: Donald Scanlon, Chief Financial Officer
CMO: Vicki L. LoPachin, M.D., Chief Medical Officer
CIO: Kumar Chatani, Senior Vice President and Chief Information Officer Mount Sinai Health System
CHR: Jane Maksoud, R.N., Senior Vice President Human Resources and Labor Relations
Web address: www.mountsinai.org
**Control:** Other not–for–profit (including NFP Corporation) **Service:** General medical and surgical

**Staffed Beds:** 1198 **Admissions:** 59951 **Census:** 1022 **Outpatient Visits:** 1113035 **Births:** 8082 **Total Expense ($000):** 2896692 **Payroll Expense ($000):** 1139068 **Personnel:** 11694

**VETERANS AFFAIRS NY HARBOR HEALTHCARE SYSTEM - MANHATTAN CAMPUS** See Veterans Affairs New York Harbor Healthcare System - Manhattan Campus

**NEWARK—Wayne County**

☒ **NEWARK-WAYNE COMMUNITY HOSPITAL (330030)**, 1200 Driving Park Avenue, Zip 14513–1057, Mailing Address: P.O. Box 111, Zip 14513–0111; tel. 315/332–2022, (Total facility includes 180 beds in nursing home–type unit) (Nonreporting) **A**1 10 **F**2 3 5 6 11 12 13 15 28 29 30 34 35 38 40 44 45 46 50 51 54 56 57 59 64 68 70 75 76 77 78 80 81 85 86 87 90 93 96 97 98 100 101 102 103 107 108 110 111 115 119 126 127 128 130 131 132 135 141 146 147 148 149 150 154 156 **P**5 6 **S** Rochester Regional Health, Rochester, NY
Primary Contact: Dustin Riccio, M.D., President Eastern Region
CFO: Tom Crilly, Executive Vice President, Chief Financial Officer, Rochester Regional Health
CMO: Robert Mayo, M.D., Executive Vice President, Chief Medical Officer, Rochester Regional Health
CIO: John Glynn, Executive Vice President, Chief Information Officer, Rochester Regional Health
CHR: Janine Schue, Executive Vice President, Chief Human Resources Officer, Rochester Regional Health
CNO: Theresa Glessner, Chief Nursing Officer, Eastern Region
Web address: www.rochesterregional.org
**Control:** Other not–for–profit (including NFP Corporation) **Service:** General medical and surgical

**Staffed Beds:** 289 **Admissions:** 6675 **Census:** 228 **Outpatient Visits:** 95491 **Births:** 656 **Total Expense ($000):** 105439 **Payroll Expense ($000):** 56927 **Personnel:** 738

**VIA HLTH WAYNE-NEWARK COMM HSP** See Newark-Wayne Community Hospital

**NEWBURGH—Orange County**

☒ **MONTEFIORE ST. LUKE'S CORNWALL (330264)**, 70 Dubois Street, Zip 12550–4851; tel. 845/561–4400, (Includes ST. LUKE'S CORNWALL HOSPITAL - CORNWALL CAMPUS, Mailing address: 19 Laurel Avenue, Cornwall, New York, Zip 12518–1499; tel. 845/534–7711; ST. LUKE'S CORNWALL HOSPITAL - NEWBURGH CAMPUS, Mailing address: 70 Dubois Street, Newburgh, New York, Zip 12550–4898; tel. 845/561–4400; Joan Cusack-McGuirk, President and Chief Executive Officer), (Nonreporting) **A**1 2 5 10 **F**3 11 12 13 15 18 20 22 26 28 29 31 34 35 37 40 43 46 49 51 54 57 59 60 61 64 70 72 74 75 76 77 78 79 81 82 84 85 86 87 89 93 100 102 107 108 110 114 115 118 119 120 121 123 124 126 129 130 131 132 146 147 149 154 156 **S** Montefiore Health System, Bronx, NY
Primary Contact: Joan Cusack-McGuirk, President and Chief Executive Officer
CFO: Thomas Gibney, Senior Vice President and Chief Financial Officer
CMO: Christine Jelalian, M.D., Medical Director
CIO: Dwayne Simmons, Interim Chief Information Officer
CHR: Daniel Bengyak, Vice President, Administrative Services
CNO: Margaret Deyo-Allers, Vice President, Chief Nursing Officer
Web address: www.stlukescornwallhospital.org
**Control:** Other not–for–profit (including NFP Corporation) **Service:** General medical and surgical

**Staffed Beds:** 128 **Admissions:** 10393 **Census:** 122 **Outpatient Visits:** 161348 **Births:** 912 **Total Expense ($000):** 228266 **Payroll Expense ($000):** 79001

**ST. LUKE'S CORNWALL HOSPITAL** See Montefiore St. Luke's Cornwall

**ST. LUKE'S HOSPITAL** See St. Luke's Cornwall Hospital - Newburgh Campus

NY

*Many Facility Codes have changed. Please refer to the AHA Guide Code Chart.*    © 2021 AHA Guide

## NIAGARA FALLS—Niagara County

**NIAGARA FALLS MEM MED CNTR** See Niagara Falls Memorial Medical Center

○ **NIAGARA FALLS MEMORIAL MEDICAL CENTER (330065)**, 621 Tenth Street, Zip 14301–1813, Mailing Address: P.O. Box 708, Zip 14302–0708; tel. 716/278–4000, (Nonreporting) **A**3 5 10 11 13
Primary Contact: Joseph A. Ruffolo, President and Chief Executive Officer
CMO: Fatma Patel, M.D., Vice President Medical Affairs
CIO: Diane Martin-Pratt, Director Information Systems
Web address: www.nfmmc.org
**Control**: Other not–for–profit (including NFP Corporation) **Service**: General medical and surgical

| Staffed Beds: 288 |
|---|

## NORTH TONAWANDA—Niagara County

**DE GRAFF MEMORIAL HOSPITAL** See Kaleida Health, Buffalo

## NORTHPORT—Suffolk County

⊞ **NORTHPORT VETERANS AFFAIRS MEDICAL CENTER**, 79 Middleville Road, Zip 11768–2200; tel. 631/261–4400, (Nonreporting) **A**1 2 3 5 **S** Department of Veterans Affairs, Washington, DC
Primary Contact: Antonio Sanchez, M.D., Executive Director
COO: Michael McCully, Chief Operating Officer
CFO: Mary Pat Hessman, Chief Fiscal
CIO: Robert Ziskin, Chief Information Officer
CHR: Wilmino Sainbert, Chief Human Resources Management Service
Web address: www.northport.va.gov/index.asp
**Control**: Veterans Affairs, Government, federal **Service**: General medical and surgical

| Staffed Beds: 254 |
|---|

**VETERANS AFFAIRS MEDICAL CENTER** See Northport Veterans Affairs Medical Center

## NORWICH—Chenango County

**CHENANGO MEMORIAL HOSPITAL** See UHS Chenango Memorial Hospital

★ ○ **UHS CHENANGO MEMORIAL HOSPITAL (330033)**, 179 North Broad Street, Zip 13815–1097; tel. 607/337–4111, (Total facility includes 80 beds in nursing home–type unit) (Nonreporting) **A**10 11 20 **F**3 8 11 13 15 17 18 28 29 32 34 35 38 40 45 47 50 54 56 57 59 61 64 65 68 70 75 76 77 79 81 82 85 86 87 89 93 97 107 108 110 111 115 119 127 128 130 132 133 146 147 148 156 **P**6 **S** United Health Services, Binghamton, NY
Primary Contact: Drake M. Lamen, M.D., President and Chief Executive Officer
COO: Christina A Kisacky, Vice President, Operations
CFO: Peggy Swartwood, Assistant Vice President, Finance and Controller
CIO: Richard Stone, Manager, Technical Services
CHR: Anne L English, Director Human Resources
CNO: David Finney, R.N., Vice President Nursing
Web address: www.https://www.nyuhs.org/locations/uhs-chenango-memorial-hospital/
**Control**: Other not–for–profit (including NFP Corporation) **Service**: General medical and surgical

| Staffed Beds: 138 Admissions: 1246 Census: 65 Outpatient Visits: 253466 Births: 231 Total Expense ($000): 68799 Payroll Expense ($000): 20397 Personnel: 327 |
|---|

## NYACK—Rockland County

☐ **MONTEFIORE NYACK HOSPITAL (330104)**, 160 North Midland Avenue, Zip 10960–1998; tel. 845/348–2000, (Nonreporting) **A**1 2 10 **S** Montefiore Health System, Bronx, NY
Primary Contact: Mark Geller, M.D., President and Chief Executive Officer
COO: Michael Novak, Vice President and Chief Operating Officer
CFO: John Burke, Chief Financial Officer
CMO: Anthony Matejicka, D.O., M.P.H., Vice President, Chief Medical Officer
CHR: Mary K Shinick, Vice President Human Resources
CNO: Kathleen Lunney, MS, R.N., Vice President Patient Care Services and Chief Nursing Officer
Web address: www.https://www.montefiorenyack.org/
**Control**: Other not–for–profit (including NFP Corporation) **Service**: General medical and surgical

| Staffed Beds: 245 |
|---|

## OCEANSIDE—Nassau County

⊞ **MOUNT SINAI SOUTH NASSAU (330198)**, One Healthy Way, Zip 11572–1551; tel. 516/632–3000, (Total facility includes 20 beds in nursing home–type unit) (Nonreporting) **A**1 2 3 5 10 12 13 **F**3 5 7 8 11 12 13 15 17 18 19 20 22 26 28 29 30 31 32 34 35 36 37 38 40 42 43 44 45 46 47 49 50 54 55 56 57 58 59 60 61 62 64 65 66 68 70 73 74 75 76 77 78 79 81 82 83 84 85 86 87 89 91 92 93 97 98 100 101 102 103 104 105 107 108 110 111 114 115 117 118 119 120 121 123 124 126 128 129 130 131 132 135 145 146 147 148 149 153 154 156 157 **P**1 5 7
Primary Contact: Richard J. Murphy, President and Chief Executive Officer
COO: William E. Allison, Senior Vice President and Chief Operating Officer, Administration
CFO: Mark A. Bogen, CPA, Senior Vice President, Finance
CMO: Adhi Sharma, M.D., Senior Vice President, Medical Affairs and Chief Medical Officer
CIO: Noah Caldwell, Vice President and Chief Information Officer
CHR: Paul D. Giordano, Senior Vice President, Human Resources
CNO: Stacey A Conklin, Chief Nursing Officer
Web address: www.southnassau.org
**Control**: Other not–for–profit (including NFP Corporation) **Service**: General medical and surgical

| Staffed Beds: 363 Admissions: 19902 Census: 312 Outpatient Visits: 357188 Births: 2201 Total Expense ($000): 607547 Payroll Expense ($000): 291365 Personnel: 3019 |
|---|

## OGDENSBURG—St. Lawrence County

★ ⇑ **CLAXTON-HEPBURN MEDICAL CENTER (330211)**, 214 King Street, Zip 13669–1142; tel. 315/393–3600, (Nonreporting) **A**2 10 20 21
Primary Contact: Richard Duvall, President and Chief Executive Officer
COO: Brandon Bowline, Chief Operating Officer
CIO: James Flood, Director Information Systems
CHR: Lou-Ann McNally, Executive Director Human Resources and Staff Development
CNO: David Ferris, Chief Nursing Officer and Vice President Patient Care Services
Web address: www.claxtonhepburn.org
**Control**: Other not–for–profit (including NFP Corporation) **Service**: General medical and surgical

| Staffed Beds: 97 |
|---|

⇑ **HEPBURN MEDICAL CENTER** See Claxton-Hepburn Medical Center

☐ **ST. LAWRENCE PSYCHIATRIC CENTER (334003)**, 1 Chimney Point Drive, Zip 13669–2291; tel. 315/541–2001, (Nonreporting) **A**1 3 10 **S** New York State Office of Mental Health, Albany, NY
Primary Contact: Timothy Farrell, Executive Director
CMO: Harishankar Sanghi, M.D., Clinical Director
CHR: Rosie Turnbull, Director Human Resources
Web address: www.omh.ny.gov/omhweb/facilities/slpc/facility.htm
**Control**: State, Government, Nonfederal **Service**: Psychiatric

| Staffed Beds: 146 |
|---|

**NY**

---

## OLEAN—Cattaraugus County

☒ **OLEAN GENERAL HOSPITAL (330103)**, 515 Main Street, Zip 14760–1513; tel. 716/373–2600, (Includes BRADFORD REGIONAL MEDICAL CENTER, Mailing address: 116 Interstate Parkway, Bradford, Pennsylvania, Zip 16701–1036; tel. 814/368–4143; Jeff S. Zewe, R.N., President and Chief Executive Officer) (Total facility includes 95 beds in nursing home–type unit) **A**1 3 5 10 19 **F**3 5 8 11 13 15 18 28 29 30 34 35 38 39 40 45 46 47 48 49 50 51 53 54 56 57 58 59 60 61 62 64 65 69 70 71 74 75 76 77 78 79 81 82 83 84 85 86 87 89 91 92 93 94 96 97 98 100 101 102 105 107 108 109 110 111 114 115 118 119 120 121 123 127 128 129 130 131 132 133 134 135 143 145 146 147 148 149 156 **P**5 8 **S** Upper Allegheny Health System, Olean, NY
Primary Contact: Jeff S. Zewe, R.N., Chief Executive Officer
COO: Richard G Braun, CPA, JrChief Operating Officer
CMO: William Mills, M.D., Senior Vice President Quality and Professional Affairs
CIO: Jason Yaworsky, Senior Vice President Information Systems and Chief Information Officer
CHR: Timothy M McNamara, Senior Vice President Human Resources
Web address: www.ogh.org
**Control:** Other not–for–profit (including NFP Corporation) **Service:** General medical and surgical

**Staffed Beds:** 388 **Admissions:** 9961 **Census:** 209 **Outpatient Visits:** 558635 **Births:** 810 **Total Expense ($000):** 190275 **Payroll Expense ($000):** 72869 **Personnel:** 1096

## ONEIDA—Madison County

☒ **ONEIDA HEALTHCARE (330115)**, 321 Genesee Street, Zip 13421–2611; tel. 315/363–6000, (Total facility includes 160 beds in nursing home–type unit) (Nonreporting) **A**1 10 **F**3 11 13 15 18 29 30 31 34 35 40 45 46 49 50 54 57 59 64 65 68 70 74 75 76 77 78 79 81 85 86 87 89 92 93 97 107 108 110 111 115 117 118 119 126 128 129 130 135 146 148 149 **P**8
Primary Contact: Gene Morreale, President and Chief Executive Officer
COO: Mary Parry, Vice President Operations and Chief Operating Officer
CFO: Jeremiah Sweet, Chief Financial Officer
CMO: Ofrona Reid, M.D., Chief Medical Officer
CIO: Mohammed J. Mere, Chief Information Officer
CHR: Michael Fifield, Vice President Human Resources
CNO: Jacqueline Dawe, R.N., Chief Nursing Officer
Web address: www.oneidahealth.org
**Control:** Other not–for–profit (including NFP Corporation) **Service:** General medical and surgical

**Staffed Beds:** 231 **Admissions:** 2660 **Census:** 169 **Outpatient Visits:** 263685 **Births:** 527 **Total Expense ($000):** 111478 **Payroll Expense ($000):** 53795 **Personnel:** 912

**ONEIDA HEALTHCARE CENTER** See Oneida Healthcare

## ONEONTA—Otsego County

★ ⇑ **AURELIA OSBORN FOX MEMORIAL HOSPITAL (330085)**, 1 Norton Avenue, Zip 13820–2629; tel. 607/432–2000, (Total facility includes 131 beds in nursing home–type unit) (Nonreporting) **A**10 21 **F**2 3 11 15 18 26 28 29 30 34 35 37 39 40 42 45 51 53 54 56 57 59 64 65 68 75 77 81 85 86 87 93 96 97 104 107 108 110 111 115 118 119 120 121 123 128 129 130 135 146 147 154 **S** Bassett Healthcare Network, Cooperstown, NY
Primary Contact: Jeff Joyner, President
COO: Gary Smith, Chief Operating Officer
CFO: Mark J. Wright, Chief Financial Officer
CMO: Reginald Q. Knight, Chief Medical Officer
CHR: Jennie Gliha, Chief Human Resource Officer
CNO: Joan MacDonald, R.N., MSN, Chief Nursing Officer, Vice President Nursing Services
Web address: www.bassett.org/ao-fox-hospital/
**Control:** Other not–for–profit (including NFP Corporation) **Service:** General medical and surgical

**Staffed Beds:** 184 **Admissions:** 2482 **Census:** 148 **Outpatient Visits:** 177909 **Births:** 0 **Total Expense ($000):** 83941 **Payroll Expense ($000):** 31468 **Personnel:** 487

⇑ **AURELIA OXBORN FOX MEM HOSP** See Aurelia Osborn Fox Memorial Hospital

## ORANGEBURG—Rockland County

**ROCKLAND CHILDREN'S PSYCH CNTR** See Rockland Children's Psychiatric Center

☐ **ROCKLAND CHILDREN'S PSYCHIATRIC CENTER (334066)**, 599 Convent Road, Zip 10962–1162; tel. 845/359–7400, (Nonreporting) **A**1 3 5 10 **S** New York State Office of Mental Health, Albany, NY
Primary Contact: Renee Rivera, Executive Director
COO: Kenneth Perrotte, Director Operations
CFO: Peter Gorey, Administrative Coordinator
CMO: Sadhana Sardana, M.D., Clinical Director
CIO: Mary Pivonka, Director Quality Management
Web address: www.omh.ny.gov/
**Control:** State, Government, Nonfederal **Service:** Children's hospital psychiatric

**Staffed Beds:** 54

☐ **ROCKLAND PSYCHIATRIC CENTER (334015)**, 140 Old Orangeburg Road, Zip 10962–1157; tel. 845/359–1000, (Nonreporting) **A**1 3 5 10 **S** New York State Office of Mental Health, Albany, NY
Primary Contact: Janet J. Monroe, R.N., Executive Director
Web address: www.omh.ny.gov/
**Control:** State, Government, Nonfederal **Service:** Psychiatric

**Staffed Beds:** 525

## ORCHARD PARK—Erie County

**ORCHARD PARK NURSING HOME** See Father Baker Manor

## OSSINING—Westchester County

**OSSINING CORRECTIONAL FACILITIES HOSPITAL**, 354 Hunter Street, Zip 10562–5498; tel. 914/941–0108, (Nonreporting) **A**3
Primary Contact: Riza Ferdous, Health Services Director
**Control:** State, Government, Nonfederal **Service:** Hospital unit of an institution (prison hospital, college infirmary, etc.)

**Staffed Beds:** 25

## OSWEGO—Oswego County

☒ **OSWEGO HOSPITAL (330218)**, 110 West Sixth Street, Zip 13126–2507; tel. 315/349–5511, (Nonreporting) **A**1 3 10 20 **F**3 8 11 12 13 15 18 29 34 38 40 41 45 49 50 51 57 59 62 70 75 76 77 79 81 85 86 87 89 93 97 98 100 101 102 104 107 108 110 111 114 115 118 119 130 131 132 135 144 146 156
Primary Contact: Michael Harlovic, R.N., President and Chief Executive Officer
COO: Michael Backus, Executive Vice President and Chief Operating Officer
CFO: Eric Campbell, Chief Financial Officer
CMO: Renato Mandanas, M.D., Chief Medical Officer
CIO: Barry W. Ryle, Chief Information Officer
CHR: James E Marco JrInterim Vice President, Human Resources
CNO: Valerie Favata, R.N., MS, Chief Nursing Officer
Web address: www.oswegohealth.org
**Control:** Other not–for–profit (including NFP Corporation) **Service:** General medical and surgical

**Staffed Beds:** 99 **Admissions:** 4383 **Census:** 54 **Outpatient Visits:** 309903 **Births:** 501 **Personnel:** 975

## PATCHOGUE—Suffolk County

⇑ **BROOKHAVEN MEMORIAL HOSPITAL MEDICAL CENTER** See Long Island Community Hospital

★ ⇑ **LONG ISLAND COMMUNITY HOSPITAL (330141)**, 101 Hospital Road, Zip 11772–4897; tel. 631/654–7100, (Nonreporting) **A**3 5 10 13 21
Primary Contact: Richard T. Margulis, President and Chief Executive Officer
COO: Ron Stephenson, Chief Operating Officer
CFO: Brenda Farrell, Vice President Finance
CMO: Nejat Zeyneloglu, Vice President and Chief Quality Medical Officer
CIO: Joseph Wood, Vice President and Chief Information Officer
CNO: Debra Grimm, MS, R.N., Vice President and Chief Nursing Officer
Web address: www.bmhmc.org
**Control:** Other not–for–profit (including NFP Corporation) **Service:** General medical and surgical

**Staffed Beds:** 247

**NY**

*Many Facility Codes have changed. Please refer to the AHA Guide Code Chart.*     © 2021 AHA Guide

## PENN YAN—Yates County

**SOLDIERS AND SAILORS MEMORIAL HOSPITAL (331314)**, 418 North Main Street, Zip 14527–1085; tel. 315/531–2000, (Nonreporting) **A**10 18 **S** Finger Lakes Health, Geneva, NY
Primary Contact: Jose Acevedo, M.D., President and Chief Executive Officer
COO: Lina Brennan, Site Administrator
CFO: Pamela Johnson, Treasurer and Chief Financial Officer
CMO: Jason Feinberg, M.D., Vice President Medical Affairs and Chief Medical Officer
CIO: Guy W Mosher IIIManager Information Systems
CHR: Patrick R Boyle, Vice President Human Resources
Web address: www.flhealth.org
**Control**: Other not–for–profit (including NFP Corporation) **Service**: General medical and surgical

**Staffed Beds:** 186

## PLAINVIEW—Nassau County

**NORTH SHORE UNIVERSITY HOSPITAL AT PLAINVIEW** See Plainview Hospital

**PLAINVIEW HOSPITAL (330331)**, 888 Old Country Road, Zip 11803–4978; tel. 516/719–3000, (Nonreporting) **A**1 3 5 10 12 13 **F**3 8 15 17 18 29 30 31 34 35 36 38 40 43 44 45 46 49 50 51 57 58 59 60 63 64 65 68 69 70 71 74 75 78 79 81 84 85 86 87 97 100 101 102 107 108 110 111 114 115 119 130 132 135 146 148 154 157 **S** Northwell Health, New Hyde Park, NY
Primary Contact: Michael Fener, Executive Director
CMO: Alan Mensch, M.D., Senior Vice President Medical Affairs
Web address: www.https://www.planview.com/
**Control**: Other not–for–profit (including NFP Corporation) **Service**: General medical and surgical

**Staffed Beds:** 156 **Admissions:** 8393 **Census:** 105 **Outpatient Visits:** 60399 **Births:** 0 **Total Expense ($000):** 238026 **Payroll Expense ($000):** 119928 **Personnel:** 1236

## PLATTSBURGH—Clinton County

**THE UNIVERSITY OF VERMONT HEALTH NETWORK CHAMPLAIN VALLEY PHYSICIANS HOSPITAL MEDICAL CENTER** See The University of Vermont Health Network-Champlain Valley Physicians Hospital

**THE UNIVERSITY OF VERMONT HEALTH NETWORK-CHAMPLAIN VALLEY PHYSICIANS HOSPITAL (330250)**, 75 Beekman Street, Zip 12901–1438; tel. 518/561–2000, (Total facility includes 35 beds in nursing home–type unit) (Nonreporting) **A**1 2 3 5 10 **F**1 3 7 8 13 14 15 17 18 20 22 26 28 29 30 31 34 35 36 37 38 40 41 43 45 46 47 48 49 50 51 53 54 57 59 60 64 65 68 70 75 76 77 78 79 81 82 84 85 86 87 89 90 91 92 93 97 98 99 100 101 102 107 108 109 110 111 112 113 114 115 116 117 118 119 121 122 123 124 126 128 129 130 131 132 135 144 146 147 148 149 154 156 157 **P**6
Primary Contact: Michelle LeBeau, President and Chief Operating Officer
COO: Michelle LeBeau, President and Chief Operating Officer
CFO: Joyce Rafferty, Vice President Finance
CMO: Kent Hall, M.D., Vice President and Chief Medical Officer
CIO: Wouter Rietsema, M.D., Chief Quality and Information Officer
CHR: Dean Civitello, Vice President, Human Resources, Public Relations and Development
Web address: www.https://profiles.health.ny.gov/hospital/view/103048
**Control**: Other not–for–profit (including NFP Corporation) **Service**: General medical and surgical

**Staffed Beds:** 264 **Admissions:** 8744 **Census:** 136 **Outpatient Visits:** 298139 **Births:** 760 **Total Expense ($000):** 365131 **Payroll Expense ($000):** 187995 **Personnel:** 2050

## PORT JEFFERSON—Suffolk County

**MATHER HOSPITAL (330185)**, 75 North Country Road, Zip 11777–2190; tel. 631/473–1320, (Nonreporting) **A**1 2 3 5 10 **F**5 8 11 12 14 15 17 18 29 31 34 35 36 37 38 40 44 45 46 49 51 55 56 57 59 60 64 65 69 70 74 75 77 78 79 81 82 84 85 86 87 93 98 99 100 101 102 103 104 105 107 108 110 111 114 115 118 119 124 126 129 130 132 146 147 148 152 **S** Northwell Health, New Hyde Park, NY
Primary Contact: Kenneth D. Roberts, President
COO: Kevin J Murray, Senior Vice President
CFO: Joseph Wisnoski, Chief Financial Officer
CMO: Joan Faro, M.D., Chief Medical Officer
CIO: Thomas Heiman, Vice President Information Services and Chief Information Officer
CHR: Diane Marotta, Vice President Human Resources
CNO: Marie Mulligan, R.N., MSN, Vice President Nursing
Web address: www.matherhospital.com
**Control**: Other not–for–profit (including NFP Corporation) **Service**: General medical and surgical

**Staffed Beds:** 248 **Admissions:** 11051 **Census:** 182 **Outpatient Visits:** 176828 **Births:** 0 **Total Expense ($000):** 380330 **Payroll Expense ($000):** 180714 **Personnel:** 2298

**ST CHARLES HOSP & REHAB CENTER** See St. Charles Hospital

△ **ST. CHARLES HOSPITAL (330246)**, 200 Belle Terre Road, Zip 11777–1928; tel. 631/474–6000, (Nonreporting) **A**1 2 3 5 7 10 **F**3 4 5 8 11 12 13 15 17 28 29 30 31 32 34 35 37 39 40 41 44 45 46 47 48 49 50 54 57 58 59 64 65 66 68 70 72 73 74 75 76 77 78 79 80 81 82 84 85 86 87 89 90 91 92 93 95 96 97 107 108 110 111 114 115 119 126 129 130 131 132 134 135 141 142 146 148 149 151 153 157 **P**5 6 **S** Catholic Health Services of Long Island, Rockville Centre, NY
Primary Contact: James O'Connor, President
COO: Ronald Weingartner, Vice President Administration
CFO: Kathleen Vasil, Vice President Finance
CMO: Michael Sauter, M.D., Chief Medical Officer
CIO: Felix Pabon-Ramirez, Chief Information Officer
CNO: Nicolette Fiore-Lopez, R.N., Chief Nursing Officer
Web address: www.stcharleshospital.chsli.org
**Control**: Church operated, Nongovernment, not–for–profit **Service**: General medical and surgical

**Staffed Beds:** 243 **Admissions:** 10491 **Census:** 166 **Outpatient Visits:** 23979 **Births:** 1112 **Total Expense ($000):** 239601 **Payroll Expense ($000):** 94504 **Personnel:** 1130

## PORT JERVIS—Orange County

**BON SECOURS COMMUNITY HOSPITAL (330135)**, 160 East Main Street, Zip 12771–2245, Mailing Address: P.O. Box 1014, Zip 12771–0268; tel. 845/858–7000, (Nonreporting) **A**1 10 **S** WMCHealth, Valhalla, NY
Primary Contact: Mary Leahy, M.D., Chief Executive Officer
COO: Gaynor Rosenstein, Vice President Operations
CHR: Kim Hirkaler, Director Human Resources
Web address: www.bonsecourscommunityhosp.org
**Control**: Church operated, Nongovernment, not–for–profit **Service**: General medical and surgical

**Staffed Beds:** 143

**MERCY COMMUNITY HOSPITAL** See Bon Secours Community Hospital

## POTSDAM—St. Lawrence County

★ ⇑ **CANTON-POTSDAM HOSPITAL (330197)**, 50 Leroy Street, Zip 13676–1799; tel. 315/265–3300, (Nonreporting) **A**10 20 21 **S** St. Lawrence Health System, Potsdam, NY
Primary Contact: David B. Acker, FACHE, President and Chief Executive Officer
COO: Eric Burch, Chief Operating Officer
CFO: Richard Jacobs, Vice President Finance and Chief Financial Officer
CMO: Robert T Rogers, M.D., IIMedical Director
CIO: Lyndon Allen, Director Information Systems
CHR: Michael Katz, Vice President Human Resources
CNO: Jan Carroll, MSN, M.P.H., R.N., Chief Nursing Officer
Web address: www.cphospital.org
**Control**: Other not–for–profit (including NFP Corporation) **Service**: General medical and surgical

**Staffed Beds:** 87

## POUGHKEEPSIE—Dutchess County

**SAINT FRANCIS HOSPITAL AND HEALTH CENTERS** See Midhudson Regional Hospital of Westchester Medical Center

**VASSAR BROTHERS HOSPITAL** See Vassar Brothers Medical Center

□ **VASSAR BROTHERS MEDICAL CENTER (330023)**, 45 Reade Place, Zip 12601–3947; tel. 845/454–8500, (Data for 273 days) (Nonreporting) **A**1 2 3 10 **F**3 8 11 13 15 17 18 20 22 24 26 28 29 30 31 34 35 36 37 40 43 44 45 46 47 48 49 50 51 54 55 57 58 59 60 68 70 72 73 74 75 76 77 78 79 81 82 84 85 86 87 89 92 93 97 100 107 108 109 110 111 114 115 117 118 119 120 121 123 124 126 129 130 131 132 135 146 147 148 149 154 156 157 **S** Health Quest Systems, Inc., LaGrangeville, NY
Primary Contact: Peter Kelly, President
COO: Cindy Czaplinski, MSN, R.N., Vice President Operations
CFO: Antonio Perugino, Vice President Finance, Hospitals
CMO: William V. Begg, M.D., IIIVice President Medical Affairs
CNO: Lore Bogolin, MSN, R.N., Vice President Patient Care Services and Chief Nursing Officer
Web address: www.https://patients.healthquest.org/locations/vassar-brothers-medical-center/
**Control**: Other not–for–profit (including NFP Corporation) **Service**: General medical and surgical

**Staffed Beds:** 365 **Admissions:** 16104 **Census:** 283 **Outpatient Visits:** 357911 **Births:** 1995 **Total Expense ($000):** 460647 **Payroll Expense ($000):** 171596 **Personnel:** 1996

**NY**

---

**Hospital, Medicare Provider Number, Address, Telephone, Approval, Facility, and Physician Codes, Health Care System**

★ American Hospital Association (AHA) membership    ○ Healthcare Facilities Accreditation Program    ⇑ Center for Improvement in Healthcare Quality Accreditation
□ The Joint Commission accreditation    ◇ DNV Healthcare Inc. accreditation    △ Commission on Accreditation of Rehabilitation Facilities (CARF) accreditation

## RHINEBECK—Dutchess County

☐ △ **NORTHERN DUTCHESS HOSPITAL (330049)**, 6511 Springbrook Avenue, Zip 12572–3709, Mailing Address: P.O. Box 5002, Zip 12572–5002; tel. 845/876–3001, (Data for 273 days) (Nonreporting) **A**1 3 7 10 **F**3 11 12 13 15 18 28 29 30 31 34 35 36 37 40 44 45 47 48 49 50 53 54 56 57 64 65 68 70 74 75 76 77 78 79 81 82 84 85 87 90 93 100 107 108 110 111 115 118 119 125 126 129 130 132 135 146 147 148 149 154 156 157 158 **S** Health Quest Systems, Inc., LaGrangeville, NY
Primary Contact: Denise George, R.N., President
CMO: John Sabia, M.D., Vice President Medical Affairs
Web address: www.health-quest.org/home_nd.cfm?id=9
**Control:** Other not–for–profit (including NFP Corporation) **Service:** General medical and surgical

**Staffed Beds:** 84 **Admissions:** 3952 **Census:** 58 **Outpatient Visits:** 135267 **Births:** 636 **Total Expense ($000):** 96942 **Payroll Expense ($000):** 37875 **Personnel:** 582

## RIVERHEAD—Suffolk County

**CENTRAL SUFFOLK HOSPITAL** See Peconic Bay Medical Center

✠ **PECONIC BAY MEDICAL CENTER (330107)**, 1300 Roanoke Avenue, Zip 11901–2031; tel. 631/548–6000, (Total facility includes 60 beds in nursing home–type unit) (Nonreporting) **A**1 3 5 10 12 13 **F**3 5 7 11 12 13 15 18 20 22 26 28 29 30 31 33 34 35 37 40 41 43 44 45 46 47 48 49 50 51 52 62 64 67 68 70 74 75 76 77 78 79 80 81 82 83 84 85 86 87 93 96 100 102 107 108 110 111 115 118 119 126 128 130 131 132 143 144 146 147 148 149 152 154 157 **S** Northwell Health, New Hyde Park, NY
Primary Contact: Andrew J. Mitchell, President and Chief Executive Officer
COO: Ronald McManus, Senior Vice President Clinical Services and Business Entities
CFO: Michael F. O'Donnell, CPA, Chief Financial Officer
CIO: Arthur Crowe, Director Information Systems
CHR: Monica Chestnut-Rauls, Vice President Human Resources
CNO: Amy E Loeb, Ed.D., R.N., Chief Nursing Officer
Web address: www.pbmchealth.org
**Control:** Other not–for–profit (including NFP Corporation) **Service:** General medical and surgical

**Staffed Beds:** 170 **Admissions:** 9244 **Census:** 156 **Outpatient Visits:** 297040 **Births:** 389 **Total Expense ($000):** 218210 **Payroll Expense ($000):** 99233 **Personnel:** 1146

## ROCHESTER—Monroe County

✠ **HIGHLAND HOSPITAL (330164)**, 1000 South Avenue, Zip 14620–2733; tel. 585/473–2200, (Nonreporting) **A**1 3 5 10 19 **F**3 12 13 15 18 26 29 30 34 35 36 37 40 44 45 46 47 49 50 54 55 58 59 60 63 64 66 68 70 74 75 76 77 78 79 81 83 84 85 86 87 91 93 97 100 107 108 110 114 115 118 119 120 121 122 123 126 130 132 135 141 145 146 147 148 149 154 156 **P**6 **S** University of Rochester Medical Center, Rochester, NY
Primary Contact: Steven I. Goldstein, President and Chief Executive Officer
COO: Cindy Becker, Vice President and Chief Operating Officer
CFO: Carrie Fuller Spencer, Chief Financial Officer
CMO: Raymond Mayewski, M.D., Chief Medical Officer
CIO: Tom Barnett, Chief Information Officer
CHR: Amy S. Galiana, Chief Human Resource Officer
Web address: www.https://www.urmc.rochester.edu/highland
**Control:** Other not–for–profit (including NFP Corporation) **Service:** General medical and surgical

**Staffed Beds:** 261 **Admissions:** 17250 **Census:** 223 **Outpatient Visits:** 507489 **Births:** 2972 **Total Expense ($000):** 398279 **Payroll Expense ($000):** 191455 **Personnel:** 2533

**HIGHLAND HOSPITAL OF ROCHESTER** See Highland Hospital

✠ **ROCHESTER GENERAL HOSPITAL (330125)**, 1425 Portland Avenue, Zip 14621–3099; tel. 585/922–4000, (Nonreporting) **A**1 2 3 5 10 **F**3 5 8 9 11 12 13 15 17 18 20 22 24 26 29 30 31 32 34 35 38 39 40 41 44 45 47 49 50 51 54 55 56 57 58 59 60 61 63 64 65 66 68 70 71 73 74 75 76 77 78 79 80 81 82 84 85 86 87 89 92 93 96 97 98 100 101 102 103 104 107 108 110 111 114 115 116 117 118 119 120 121 123 124 126 127 129 130 131 132 134 135 141 144 145 146 147 148 149 150 154 156 157 158 **P**5 6 **S** Rochester Regional Health, Rochester, NY
Primary Contact: Kevin John. Casey, President
CMO: Robert Mayo, M.D., Chief Medical Officer
CIO: John Glynn, Chief Information Officer
CHR: Janine Schue, Senior Vice President Human Resources
CNO: Cheryl Sheridan, R.N., Senior Vice President Patient Care Services
Web address: www.https://www.rochesterregional.org/
**Control:** Other not–for–profit (including NFP Corporation) **Service:** General medical and surgical

**Staffed Beds:** 528 **Admissions:** 30722 **Census:** 420 **Outpatient Visits:** 2117122 **Births:** 2089 **Total Expense ($000):** 1120266 **Payroll Expense ($000):** 548229 **Personnel:** 7105

☐ **ROCHESTER PSYCHIATRIC CENTER (334020)**, 1111 Elmwood Avenue, Zip 14620–3005; tel. 585/241–1200, (Nonreporting) **A**1 3 5 10 **S** New York State Office of Mental Health, Albany, NY
Primary Contact: Philip Griffin, Director of Operations
COO: Joseph Coffey, Director Facility Administration
CFO: Rosanne Minnis, Business Officer
CMO: Laurence Guttmacher, M.D., Clinical Director
CIO: Lori Hintz, Coordinator Information Systems
CHR: Colomba Misseritti, Director Human Resources
CNO: Christopher Kirisits, Chief Nursing Officer
Web address: www.omh.ny.gov/omhweb/facilities/ropc/facility.htm
**Control:** State, Government, Nonfederal **Service:** Psychiatric

**Staffed Beds:** 180

✠ △ **STRONG MEMORIAL HOSPITAL OF THE UNIVERSITY OF ROCHESTER (330285)**, 601 Elmwood Avenue, Zip 14642–0002, Mailing Address: 601 Elmwood Avenue, Box 612, Zip 14642–0002; tel. 585/275–2100, (Includes GOLISANO CHILDREN'S HOSPITAL, Mailing address: 601 Elmwood Avenue, Rochester, New York, Zip 14610; tel. 585/275–2182), (Nonreporting) **A**1 2 3 5 7 8 10 19 **F**3 5 6 8 9 11 12 13 14 15 16 17 18 19 20 21 22 23 24 25 26 27 28 29 30 31 32 33 34 35 36 38 39 40 41 42 43 44 45 46 47 48 49 50 51 52 53 54 55 56 57 58 59 60 61 63 64 65 66 68 70 71 72 73 74 75 76 77 78 79 80 81 82 83 84 85 86 87 88 89 90 91 92 93 94 95 96 97 98 99 100 101 102 103 104 105 107 108 110 111 114 115 116 117 118 119 120 121 123 124 126 127 129 130 131 132 133 134 135 136 137 138 139 141 142 143 144 145 146 147 148 149 150 152 153 154 156 157 **P**6 **S** University of Rochester Medical Center, Rochester, NY
Primary Contact: Steven I. Goldstein, President and Chief Executive Officer
COO: Kathleen M Parrinello, Ph.D., Chief Operating Officer
CFO: David L. Kirshner, Chief Financial Officer
CMO: Raymond Mayewski, M.D., Chief Medical Officer
CIO: D Jerome Powell, M.D., Chief Information Officer
CHR: Charles J Murphy, Associate Vice President Human Resources
Web address: www.urmc.rochester.edu
**Control:** Other not–for–profit (including NFP Corporation) **Service:** General medical and surgical

**Staffed Beds:** 878 **Admissions:** 40016 **Census:** 802 **Outpatient Visits:** 1731775 **Births:** 2312 **Total Expense ($000):** 2122624 **Payroll Expense ($000):** 789060 **Personnel:** 12415

✠ △ **UNITY HOSPITAL (330226)**, 1555 Long Pond Road, Zip 14626–4182; tel. 585/723–7000, (Total facility includes 120 beds in nursing home–type unit) (Nonreporting) **A**1 3 5 7 10 **F**3 4 5 11 12 13 15 18 20 22 26 28 29 30 31 33 34 35 38 39 40 44 45 46 47 48 49 50 52 55 56 57 59 60 61 63 64 65 66 68 70 71 73 74 75 76 77 78 79 80 81 82 84 85 86 87 90 91 92 93 96 97 98 100 101 102 103 104 107 108 114 118 119 121 126 128 129 130 131 132 134 135 141 144 146 147 148 149 150 151 156 157 158 **P**5 6 **S** Rochester Regional Health, Rochester, NY
Primary Contact: Douglas Stewart, PsyD, President
COO: Stewart C Putnam, Executive Vice President and Chief Operating Officer
CFO: Tom Crilly, Executive Vice President and Chief Financial Officer
CMO: James Haley, M.D., Senior Vice President and Chief Medical Officer
CIO: John Glynn, Senior Vice President and Chief Information Officer
CHR: Maryalice Keller, Vice President Brand and Talent Management
CNO: Jane McCormack, R.N., MSN, Vice President, Chief Nursing Officer and Nursing and Patient Care Services
Web address: www.unityhealth.org
**Control:** Other not–for–profit (including NFP Corporation) **Service:** General medical and surgical

**Staffed Beds:** 451 **Admissions:** 19077 **Census:** 427 **Outpatient Visits:** 898192 **Births:** 1555 **Total Expense ($000):** 509293 **Payroll Expense ($000):** 260582 **Personnel:** 4048

**UNITY HOSPITAL** See Unity Hospital

NY

## ROCKVILLE CENTRE—Nassau County

**MERCY HOSPITAL** See Mercy Medical Center

☐ **MERCY MEDICAL CENTER (330259)**, 1000 North Village Avenue, Zip 11570–1000; tel. 516/705–2525, (Nonreporting) **A**1 2 3 5 10 13 **F**3 5 8 11 12 13 15 18 20 26 29 30 31 34 35 38 40 45 46 48 49 50 51 56 57 59 60 61 64 68 70 72 74 75 76 77 78 79 81 82 84 85 87 90 93 96 97 98 100 101 102 104 105 107 108 110 111 115 119 130 132 143 146 147 148 149 152 153 154 **S** Catholic Health Services of Long Island, Rockville Centre, NY
Primary Contact: Peter Scaminaci, President
CFO: William C Armstrong, Senior Vice President and Chief Financial Officer
CMO: John Reilly, M.D., Vice President Medical Affairs and Chief Medical Officer
CIO: Marcy Dunn, Vice President Information Services and Chief Information Officer
CHR: Allison Cianciotto Croyle, Vice President of Human Resources
CNO: Beth Vlahavas, R.N., MSN, Vice President Patient Care Services and Chief Nursing Officer
Web address: www.mercymedicalcenter.chsli.org
**Control**: Church operated, Nongovernment, not–for–profit **Service**: General medical and surgical

**Staffed Beds**: 196 **Admissions**: 10684 **Census**: 186 **Outpatient Visits**: 115162 **Births**: 860 **Total Expense ($000)**: 253592 **Payroll Expense ($000)**: 102815 **Personnel**: 1215

## ROME—Oneida County

**ROME HOSP AND MURPHY MEM HOSP** See Rome Memorial Hospital

★ ○ **ROME MEMORIAL HOSPITAL (330215)**, 1500 North James Street, Zip 13440–2844; tel. 315/338–7000, (Total facility includes 82 beds in nursing home–type unit) (Nonreporting) **A**5 10 11 **F**3 5 8 13 15 18 26 29 30 34 35 37 38 40 45 49 50 51 54 55 56 57 59 64 70 74 75 76 77 78 79 80 81 82 85 87 89 90 93 97 98 102 103 107 108 109 110 111 112 113 114 115 116 117 119 120 121 122 123 124 127 128 129 130 132 135 144 146 147 148 149 154 157
Primary Contact: Mark Murphy, Interim President and Chief Executive Officer
CFO: Dewey R Rowlands, Vice President and Chief Financial Officer
CMO: Andrew Bushnell, M.D., Interim Chief Medical Officer
CIO: Mark Rowan, Interim Chief Information Officer
CHR: Regina Chambers, Vice President Human Resource
CNO: Amy Carissimo-Harris, Chief Nursing Officer
Web address: www.romehospital.org
**Control**: Other not–for–profit (including NFP Corporation) **Service**: General medical and surgical

**Staffed Beds**: 203 **Admissions**: 4146 **Census**: 111 **Outpatient Visits**: 155406 **Births**: 503 **Total Expense ($000)**: 88762 **Payroll Expense ($000)**: 40160 **Personnel**: 712

## ROSLYN—Nassau County

**ST. FRANCIS HOSPITAL** See St. Francis Hospital, The Heart Center

☒ **ST. FRANCIS HOSPITAL, THE HEART CENTER (330182)**, 100 Port Washington Boulevard, Zip 11576–1353; tel. 516/562–6000, (Nonreporting) **A**1 3 5 10 **F**3 7 8 11 12 14 15 17 18 19 20 21 22 23 24 26 27 28 29 30 31 34 36 37 38 39 40 44 45 46 47 49 50 51 53 54 55 56 57 58 59 60 61 62 63 64 65 66 68 70 71 74 75 77 78 79 81 82 83 84 85 86 87 93 97 100 102 107 108 109 110 111 114 115 116 117 118 119 120 121 123 126 130 131 132 135 141 146 147 148 149 154 156 **P**5 6 **S** Catholic Health Services of Long Island, Rockville Centre, NY
Primary Contact: Charles Lucore, M.D., President
CFO: William C Armstrong, Vice President and Chief Financial Officer
CMO: Jack Soterakis, M.D., Executive Vice President Medical Affairs
CIO: Marcy Dunn, Vice President Information Services and Chief Information Officer
CHR: Barbara Fierro, Director, Human Resources
CNO: Ann S Cella, R.N., Senior Vice President, Patient Care Services
Web address: www.stfrancisheartcenter.com/index.html
**Control**: Church operated, Nongovernment, not–for–profit **Service**: General medical and surgical

**Staffed Beds**: 320 **Admissions**: 20499 **Census**: 277 **Outpatient Visits**: 247275 **Births**: 0 **Total Expense ($000)**: 714397 **Payroll Expense ($000)**: 286352 **Personnel**: 3002

## SARANAC LAKE—Franklin County

★ ○ **ADIRONDACK HEALTH (330079)**, 2233 State Route 86, Zip 12983–5644, Mailing Address: P.O. Box 471, Zip 12983–0471; tel. 518/891–4141, (Total facility includes 60 beds in nursing home–type unit) (Nonreporting) **A**10 11 **F**3 8 9 12 13 15 18 28 29 30 31 34 35 37 38 39 40 41 42 43 45 46 49 50 53 54 56 57 59 60 64 70 71 74 75 76 77 78 79 81 82 84 85 86 89 90 92 93 94 97 98 102 103 104 107 108 110 111 114 116 119 127 128 129 130 131 132 135 146 147 148 153 154 156 **P**6 **S** QHR Health, Brentwood, TN
Primary Contact: Sylvia Getman, President and Chief Executive Officer
COO: Patti Hammond, Chief Operating Officer
CFO: Tristan Glanville, Chief Financial Officer
CMO: Joahd Toure', M.D., Chief Medical Officer
CHR: Michael D Lee, Chief Human Resources Officer
CNO: Linda McClarigan, R.N., Chief Nursing Officer
Web address: www.adirondackhealth.org
**Control**: Other not–for–profit (including NFP Corporation) **Service**: General medical and surgical

**Staffed Beds**: 120 **Admissions**: 2509 **Census**: 84 **Outpatient Visits**: 160510 **Births**: 186 **Total Expense ($000)**: 121925 **Payroll Expense ($000)**: 56945 **Personnel**: 1167

**ADIRONDACK MEDICAL CENTER** See Adirondack Health

## SARATOGA SPRINGS—Saratoga County

☐ **FOUR WINDS HOSPITAL (334049)**, 30 Crescent Avenue, Zip 12866–5142; tel. 518/584–3600, (Nonreporting) **A**1 10 **F**30 35 99 100 101 103 104 105 153
Primary Contact: Samuel A. Bastien IV, Ph.D., Chief Executive Officer
CFO: Juanita Wheeler-Moore, Director Financial Services
CMO: Kevin P. Martin, M.D., Chief Medical Officer
CIO: Susan Snowdon, Director Information Technology
CHR: Susan M Kirchner, Director Human Resources
CNO: James Colamaria, Director of Nursing
Web address: www.fourwindshospital.com
**Control**: Individual, Investor–owned (for–profit) **Service**: Psychiatric

**Staffed Beds**: 88 **Admissions**: 2510 **Census**: 85 **Outpatient Visits**: 18527 **Births**: 0

☒ **SARATOGA HOSPITAL (330222)**, 211 Church Street, Zip 12866–1003; tel. 518/587–3222, (Nonreporting) **A**1 2 3 10 **F**3 5 8 11 12 13 15 17 18 20 22 26 28 29 30 31 34 35 36 38 39 40 45 46 47 48 49 50 51 53 54 55 56 57 59 60 63 64 65 66 70 74 75 76 77 78 79 81 82 84 85 86 87 92 93 96 97 98 100 101 102 104 107 108 110 111 114 115 116 117 119 120 121 123 126 129 130 131 132 135 144 145 146 147 148 149 157 **P**6
Primary Contact: Angelo G. Calbone, President and Chief Executive Officer
CFO: Gary Foster, Vice President and Chief Financial Officer
CMO: Richard Falivena, D.O., M.P.H., Vice President and Chief Medical Officer
CIO: John Mangona, Vice President, Chief Information Officer and Compliance Officer
CHR: Jeffrey M. Methven, Vice President Ambulatory Services and Chief Human Resources Officer
CNO: Mary Jo LaPosta, Ph.D., R.N., Senior Vice President Patient Care and Organizational Excellence
Web address: www.saratogahospital.org
**Control**: Other not–for–profit (including NFP Corporation) **Service**: General medical and surgical

**Staffed Beds**: 171 **Admissions**: 10938 **Census**: 147 **Outpatient Visits**: 546962 **Births**: 697 **Total Expense ($000)**: 383607 **Payroll Expense ($000)**: 194164 **Personnel**: 2711

**NY**

---

**Hospital, Medicare Provider Number, Address, Telephone, Approval, Facility, and Physician Codes, Health Care System**

★ American Hospital Association (AHA) membership
☐ The Joint Commission accreditation
○ Healthcare Facilities Accreditation Program
◇ DNV Healthcare Inc. accreditation
⇑ Center for Improvement in Healthcare Quality Accreditation
△ Commission on Accreditation of Rehabilitation Facilities (CARF) accreditation

## SCHENECTADY—Schenectady County

**BELLEVUE WOMAN'S HOSPITAL** See Bellevue Woman's Care Center

☒ **ELLIS HOSPITAL (330153)**, 1101 Nott Street, Zip 12308–2425;
tel. 518/243–4000, (Includes BELLEVUE WOMAN'S CARE CENTER, Mailing
address: 2210 Troy Road, Schenectady, New York, Zip 12309–4797;
tel. 518/346–9400; ELLIS HOSPITAL HEALTH CENTER, Mailing address: 600
McClellan Street, Schenectady, New York, Zip 12304–1090; tel. 518/382–2000)
(Total facility includes 82 beds in nursing home–type unit) **A**1 3 5 10 13 **F**8 11 12
13 15 17 18 20 22 24 26 28 29 30 31 34 35 38 39 40 44 45 46 47 48 49 50
51 54 59 60 61 62 64 65 68 70 72 74 75 76 77 78 79 81 82 84 85 87 89 93
97 98 100 102 103 104 105 107 108 109 110 111 112 113 114 115 116 119
120 121 126 128 129 130 131 132 133 135 143 144 147 148 156
Primary Contact: Paul A. Milton, President and Chief Executive Officer
COO: Paul A Milton, Executive Vice President and Chief Operating Officer
CFO: Marc Mesick, Vice President and Chief Financial Officer
CMO: David Liebers, M.D., Chief Medical Officer and Vice President Medical Affairs
CIO: Ron McKinnon, Chief Information Officer
CHR: Joseph Giansante, Vice President Human Resources
Web address: www.ellismedicine.org
**Control:** Other not–for–profit (including NFP Corporation) **Service:** General
medical and surgical

**Staffed Beds:** 541 **Admissions:** 16108 **Census:** 322 **Outpatient
Visits:** 537650 **Births:** 2113 **Total Expense ($000):** 446872 **Payroll
Expense ($000):** 225067 **Personnel:** 2939

**ELLIS HOSPITAL HEALTH CENTER** See Ellis Hospital, Schenectady

**ELLIS HOSPITAL MCCLELLAN CAMPUS** See Ellis Hospital Health Center

**SUNNYVIEW HOSP & REHAB CENTER** See Sunnyview Rehabilitation Hospital

☒ △ **SUNNYVIEW REHABILITATION HOSPITAL (330406)**, 1270 Belmont
Avenue, Zip 12308–2104; tel. 518/382–4500, (Nonreporting) **A**1 3 7 10 **F**3 9 11
28 29 30 34 35 36 38 39 44 50 53 56 57 58 59 60 64 68 74 77 79 82 86 87
90 91 92 93 94 95 96 100 119 130 131 132 135 146 148 149 154 156 157
**P**6 **S** Trinity Health, Livonia, MI
Primary Contact: Edward Eisenman, Chief Executive Officer
CFO: Kristin Signor, Director Finance
CMO: Lynne T Nicolson, M.D., Medical Director
CIO: Patrick Clark, Manager Information Technology
CHR: Meghan Glowa, Director Human Resources
Web address: www.sunnyview.org
**Control:** Other not–for–profit (including NFP Corporation) **Service:** Rehabilitation

**Staffed Beds:** 115 **Admissions:** 2329 **Census:** 89 **Outpatient Visits:** 92346
**Births:** 0 **Total Expense ($000):** 57479 **Payroll Expense ($000):** 31991
**Personnel:** 579

## SLEEPY HOLLOW—Westchester County

☒ **PHELPS MEMORIAL HOSPITAL CENTER (330261)**, 701 North Broadway,
Zip 10591–1020; tel. 914/366–3000, (Nonreporting) **A**1 2 3 5 10 **F**3 4 5 8 9 11
12 13 15 17 18 28 29 30 31 34 35 36 39 40 41 45 46 47 48 49 50 51 53 55
56 57 59 60 61 64 65 68 70 74 75 76 77 78 79 81 82 84 85 86 87 89 90 91
92 93 94 96 97 98 100 101 102 104 105 106 107 108 110 111 114 115 118
119 120 121 124 126 129 130 131 132 135 143 145 146 147 148 149 152
153 154 156 158 **S** Northwell Health, New Hyde Park, NY
Primary Contact: Eileen Egan Esq, Executive Director
CFO: Vincent DeSantis, Vice President Finance
CNO: Mary McDermott, MSN, MS, R.N., Senior Vice President Patient Care
Services and Chief Nursing Officer
Web address: www.phelpshospital.org
**Control:** Other not–for–profit (including NFP Corporation) **Service:** General
medical and surgical

**Staffed Beds:** 153 **Admissions:** 7734 **Census:** 135 **Outpatient
Visits:** 186338 **Births:** 952 **Total Expense ($000):** 284088 **Payroll Expense
($000):** 155684 **Personnel:** 1735

## SMITHTOWN—Suffolk County

**ST JOHN'S EPISCOPAL HOSPITAL** See St. Catherine of Siena Medical Center

☐ **ST. CATHERINE OF SIENA MEDICAL CENTER (330401)**, 50 Route 25-A,
Zip 11787–1348; tel. 631/862–3000, (Total facility includes 240 beds in nursing
home–type unit) (Nonreporting) **A**1 5 10 **F**3 13 15 17 18 20 22 26 29 30 31 34
35 40 45 49 57 59 60 70 72 74 75 76 78 79 81 84 85 87 98 100 102 107
108 110 111 114 115 119 126 128 129 130 132 146 147 148 149 154 **S**
Catholic Health Services of Long Island, Rockville Centre, NY
Primary Contact: James O'Connor, Chief Administrative Officer
COO: Michael Silverman, Chief Operating Officer
CFO: John Pohlman, Vice President Finance and Administration
CMO: Jason Golbin, M.D., Chief Medical Officer
CNO: Mary Jane Finnegan, Chief Nursing Officer
Web address: www.stcatherines.chsli.org/
**Control:** Church operated, Nongovernment, not–for–profit **Service:** General
medical and surgical

**Staffed Beds:** 521 **Admissions:** 13497 **Census:** 394 **Outpatient
Visits:** 35543 **Births:** 469 **Total Expense ($000):** 275612 **Payroll Expense
($000):** 118832 **Personnel:** 1466

## SPRINGVILLE—Erie County

**BERTRAND CHAFFEE HOSPITAL (330111)**, 224 East Main Street,
Zip 14141–1497; tel. 716/592–2871, (Nonreporting) **A**10
Primary Contact: Nils Gunnersen, Administrator
CMO: J Matthew Baker, M.D., President Medical Staff
CHR: Mary Beth Brown, Director Human Resources
Web address: www.chaffeehospitalandhome.com
**Control:** Other not–for–profit (including NFP Corporation) **Service:** General
medical and surgical

**Staffed Beds:** 24

## STAR LAKE—St. Lawrence County

★ **CLIFTON-FINE HOSPITAL (331307)**, 1014 Oswegatchie Trail, Zip 13690–3143;
tel. 315/848–3351, (Nonreporting) **A**10 18
Primary Contact: Dierdra Sorrell, R.N., MSN, Chief Executive Officer
COO: Cathy Rice, Director Support Services
CFO: Heather Cockayne, Chief Financial Officer
CMO: David Welch, M.D., Medical Director
CIO: Joe Deeter, MS, Director Information Systems
CNO: John Schaffer, R.N., Director of Nursing
Web address: www.cliftonfinehospital.org
**Control:** Other not–for–profit (including NFP Corporation) **Service:** General
medical and surgical

**Staffed Beds:** 20

## STATEN ISLAND—Richmond County

**COMM HLTH SYSTEM STATE ISLAND** See Staten Island University Hospital

☒ **RICHMOND UNIVERSITY MEDICAL CENTER (330028)**, 355 Bard Avenue,
Zip 10310–1664; tel. 718/818–1234, (Nonreporting) **A**1 2 3 5 10 **F**3 4 5 7 11
12 13 15 17 18 20 22 26 28 29 30 31 34 35 38 40 41 43 45 46 47 48 49 51
54 55 56 57 58 59 61 64 65 66 67 68 70 71 72 73 74 75 76 77 78 79 80 81
82 84 85 87 88 89 92 93 94 97 98 99 100 101 102 104 105 107 108 111
114 115 117 118 119 120 121 126 129 130 131 132 134 135 146 147 148
149 150 153 154 156
Primary Contact: Daniel J. Messina, Ph.D., FACHE, President and Chief Executive
Officer
CMO: Edward Arsura, M.D., Chief Medical Officer
CHR: Patricia Caldari, Vice President
Web address: www.rumcsi.org
**Control:** Other not–for–profit (including NFP Corporation) **Service:** General
medical and surgical

**Staffed Beds:** 448 **Admissions:** 11701 **Census:** 177 **Outpatient
Visits:** 259305 **Births:** 2973 **Total Expense ($000):** 395063 **Payroll
Expense ($000):** 202145 **Personnel:** 2287

**SEA VIEW HOSPITAL REHABILITATION CENTER AND HOME** See NYC Health
+ Hospitals / Sea View

☐ **SOUTH BEACH PSYCHIATRIC CENTER (334043)**, 777 Seaview Avenue,
Zip 10305–3409; tel. 718/667–2300, (Nonreporting) **A**1 3 10 **S** New York State
Office of Mental Health, Albany, NY
Primary Contact: Doreen Piazza, Acting Executive Director
CHR: George Bouquio, Director Human Resources
Web address: www.omh.ny.gov/omhweb/facilities/sbpc/facility.htm
**Control:** State, Government, Nonfederal **Service:** Psychiatric

**Staffed Beds:** 340

**ST VINCENT'S HOSPITAL** See Richmond University Medical Center

*Many Facility Codes have changed. Please refer to the AHA Guide Code Chart.* © 2021 AHA Guide

☒ △ **STATEN ISLAND UNIVERSITY HOSPITAL (330160)**, 475 Seaview Avenue, Zip 10305–3436; tel. 718/226–9000, (Nonreporting) **A**1 2 3 5 7 8 10 **F**3 4 5 7 8 11 12 13 14 15 16 17 18 19 20 22 24 26 28 29 30 31 32 34 35 38 39 40 41 43 44 45 46 47 48 49 50 51 52 54 55 56 57 58 59 60 61 63 64 65 66 68 70 71 72 73 74 75 76 77 78 79 81 82 84 85 86 87 88 89 90 92 93 94 95 96 97 98 100 101 102 104 105 107 108 110 111 114 115 116 117 118 119 120 121 123 124 126 129 130 131 132 134 135 145 146 147 148 152 153 154 **S** Northwell Health, New Hyde Park, NY
Primary Contact: Brahim Ardolic, M.D., Chief Executive Officer
CFO: Thomas Reca SrDeputy Executive Director and Chief Financial Officer
CMO: Theodore Maniatis, M.D., Medical Director
CIO: Kathy Kania, Associate Executive Director and Chief Information Officer
CHR: Margaret DiAlto, Regional Chief Human Resource Officer
CNO: Terry Pando, R.N., Associate Executive Director and Chief Nursing Officer
Web address: www.siuh.edu
**Control**: Other not–for–profit (including NFP Corporation) **Service**: General medical and surgical

**Staffed Beds**: 627 **Admissions**: 39285 **Census**: 578 **Outpatient Visits**: 947725 **Births**: 2717 **Total Expense ($000)**: 1045525 **Payroll Expense ($000)**: 538386 **Personnel**: 5877

### STONY BROOK—Suffolk County

**STONY' BROOK CHILDREN'S HOSPITAL** See Stony Brook Children's Hospital

☒ **STONY BROOK UNIVERSITY HOSPITAL (330393)**, 101 Nicolls Road, Zip 11794–8410; tel. 631/444–1077, (Includes STONY BROOK CHILDREN'S HOSPITAL, Mailing address: 100 Nicolls Road, Stony Brook, New York, Zip 11794–0001; tel. 631/444–4000; STONY BROOK EASTERN LONG ISLAND HOSPITAL, Mailing address: 201 Manor Place, Greenport, New York, Zip 11944–1298; tel. 631/477–1000; Paul J. Connor III, Chief Administrative Officer; STONY BROOK SOUTHAMPTON HOSPITAL, Mailing address: 240 Meeting House Lane, Southampton, New York, Zip 11968–5090; Robert S Chaloner, Chief Administrative Officer), (Nonreporting) **A**1 2 3 5 8 10 **F**3 4 5 6 7 8 9 11 12 13 14 15 16 17 18 19 20 22 24 26 28 29 30 31 32 34 35 36 37 38 39 40 41 43 44 45 46 47 48 49 50 51 52 53 54 55 56 57 58 59 60 61 62 63 64 65 66 70 71 72 73 74 75 76 77 78 79 80 81 82 83 84 85 86 87 88 89 91 92 93 96 97 98 99 100 101 102 103 104 107 108 110 111 114 115 116 117 118 119 120 121 122 123 124 126 129 130 131 132 134 135 136 138 141 143 144 145 146 147 148 149 150 154 156 157 158 **P**1 6
Primary Contact: Carol Gomes, FACHE, Chief Executive Officer and Chief Operating Officer
COO: Carol Gomes, FACHE, Chief Executive Officer and Chief Operating Officer
CFO: Gary E Bie, CPA, Chief Financial Officer
CMO: Mark Sands, M.D., Chief Medical Officer
CIO: Jim Murry, Chief Information Officer
CHR: Luis de Onis, Interim Chief Human Resources Officer
CNO: Mary Ann T Donohue, Ph.D., R.N., Chief Patient Care Services Officer
Web address: www.https://www.stonybrookmedicine.edu/sbuh
**Control**: State, Government, Nonfederal **Service**: General medical and surgical

**Staffed Beds**: 767 **Admissions**: 39431 **Census**: 650 **Outpatient Visits**: 585464 **Births**: 4729 **Total Expense ($000)**: 1761401 **Payroll Expense ($000)**: 707405 **Personnel**: 7934

**STONY BROOK UNIVERSITY MEDICAL CENTER** See Stony Brook University Hospital

### SUFFERN—Rockland County

**GOOD SAMARITAN HOSPITAL** See Good Samaritan Regional Medical Center

☒ **GOOD SAMARITAN REGIONAL MEDICAL CENTER (330158)**, 255 Lafayette Avenue, Zip 10901–4869; tel. 845/368–5000, (Nonreporting) **A**1 2 5 10 **S** WMCHealth, Valhalla, NY
Primary Contact: Mary Leahy, M.D., Chief Executive Officer
COO: Gerry Durney, Chief Operating Officer
CMO: Rodney W Williams, M.D., JD, MS, Vice President Medical Affairs
CIO: Deborah K Marshall, Vice President Public Relations
CHR: Pamela Tarulli, Senior Vice President Human Resources
Web address: www.goodsamhosp.org
**Control**: Church operated, Nongovernment, not–for–profit **Service**: General medical and surgical

**Staffed Beds**: 308

### SYOSSET—Nassau County

**NORTH SHORE UNIVERSITY HOSPITAL AT SYOSSET** See Syosset Hospital

### SYRACUSE—Onondaga County

**COMMUNITY-GENERAL HOSPITAL OF GREATER SYRACUSE** See Upstate University Hospital at Community General

★ ⇑ **CROUSE HEALTH (330203)**, 736 Irving Avenue, Zip 13210–1690; tel. 315/470–7375, (Nonreporting) **A**3 5 10 21 **F**3 4 5 8 11 12 13 15 18 19 20 21 22 23 26 27 29 31 34 35 36 37 40 49 50 53 58 59 60 64 66 68 70 72 73 74 75 76 77 78 79 81 83 84 86 87 89 91 93 96 107 108 110 112 114 115 116 117 118 119 126 129 130 131 132 135 144 145 146 147 148 149 150 157
Primary Contact: Kimberly Boynton, President and Chief Executive Officer
CFO: Kevin Randall, Chief Financial Officer
CMO: Seth Kronenberg, M.D., Chief Medical Officer
CIO: Kim Rose, Chief Information Technology
CHR: John Bergemann, Director Human Resources
CNO: Betty O'Connor, Chief Nursing Officer
Web address: www.crouse.org
**Control**: Other not–for–profit (including NFP Corporation) **Service**: General medical and surgical

**Staffed Beds**: 487 **Admissions**: 18714 **Census**: 299 **Outpatient Visits**: 452264 **Births**: 3785 **Total Expense ($000)**: 433415 **Payroll Expense ($000)**: 183715 **Personnel**: 2143

⇑ **CROUSE HOSPITAL** See Crouse Health

**RICHARD H HUTCHINGS PSYCH CNTR** See Richard H. Hutchings Psychiatric Center

☐ **RICHARD H. HUTCHINGS PSYCHIATRIC CENTER (334001)**, 620 Madison Street, Zip 13210–2319; tel. 315/426–3632, (Nonreporting) **A**1 3 5 10 **S** New York State Office of Mental Health, Albany, NY
Primary Contact: Colleen A. Sawyer, R.N., MSN, Executive Director
CFO: Robert Stapleton, Director Administration
CMO: Mark Cattalani, M.D., Clinical Director
CIO: Neil Nemi, Administrator Facility Information Center
CHR: Katherine Herron, Director Human Resources
Web address: www.omh.ny.gov
**Control**: State, Government, Nonfederal **Service**: Psychiatric

**Staffed Beds**: 131

⇑ **ST JOSEPH'S HOSPITAL HLTH CNTR** See St. Joseph's Hospital Health Center

★ ⇑ **ST. JOSEPH'S HOSPITAL HEALTH CENTER (330140)**, 301 Prospect Avenue, Zip 13203–1807; tel. 315/448–5111, (Nonreporting) **A**3 5 10 21 **F**3 8 11 12 13 14 15 17 18 20 22 24 26 28 29 30 31 34 35 37 38 39 40 46 47 48 49 50 51 54 57 58 59 60 61 62 64 65 66 68 70 72 73 74 75 76 77 78 79 81 82 83 84 85 87 90 92 93 94 97 98 100 101 102 103 104 106 107 108 110 111 114 115 118 119 126 129 130 131 132 135 144 146 147 148 149 154 **S** Trinity Health, Livonia, MI
Primary Contact: Leslie Paul. Luke, President and Chief Executive Officer
COO: Janet L. Ready, Chief Operating Officer
CFO: Meredith Price, Vice President Fiscal Services and Chief Financial Officer
CMO: Joseph W Spinale, D.O., Chief Medical Officer
CIO: Charles Fennell, Vice President Information Management
CHR: Erika Duncan, Vice President Human Resources
CNO: AnneMarie Czyz, R.N., Ed.D., Chief Operating Officer and Chief Nursing Officer
Web address: www.sjhsyr.org
**Control**: Other not–for–profit (including NFP Corporation) **Service**: General medical and surgical

**Staffed Beds**: 451 **Admissions**: 26226 **Census**: 317 **Outpatient Visits**: 516896 **Births**: 1877 **Total Expense ($000)**: 589944 **Payroll Expense ($000)**: 241726 **Personnel**: 3726

---

**Hospital, Medicare Provider Number, Address, Telephone, Approval, Facility, and Physician Codes, Health Care System**

★ American Hospital Association (AHA) membership
☐ The Joint Commission accreditation
○ Healthcare Facilities Accreditation Program
◇ DNV Healthcare Inc. accreditation
⇑ Center for Improvement in Healthcare Quality Accreditation
△ Commission on Accreditation of Rehabilitation Facilities (CARF) accreditation

**NY**

☒ △ **SYRACUSE VETERANS AFFAIRS MEDICAL CENTER**, 800 Irving Avenue, Zip 13210–2716; tel. 315/425–4400, (Nonreporting) **A**1 3 5 7 **F**1 2 3 4 5 8 12 18 20 22 26 28 30 31 33 34 35 36 38 39 40 45 46 47 49 50 53 54 56 57 58 59 60 61 62 63 64 65 67 70 71 74 75 77 78 79 81 82 84 85 86 87 90 91 92 94 95 97 98 100 101 104 105 106 107 108 111 126 128 132 135 146 147 148 152 153 154 156 157 **S** Department of Veterans Affairs, Washington, DC
Primary Contact: Christopher M. Frani, Interim Director
CFO: Deborah Angell, Chief Financial Officer
CMO: Syed Asif Ali, M.D., Chief of Staff
CIO: James Stenson, Chief Information Officer
CHR: Mark Antinelli, Manager Human Resources
CNO: Cheryl Czajkowski, Associate Director Patient and Nursing Services
Web address: www.syracuse.va.gov/
**Control:** Veterans Affairs, Government, federal **Service:** General medical and surgical

**Staffed Beds: 160 Admissions: 5017 Census: 125 Outpatient Visits: 575491 Births: 0 Total Expense ($000): 353334 Payroll Expense ($000): 204370 Personnel: 1857**

⇑ **UPSTATE MEDICAL UNIVERSITY** See Upstate University Hospital

★ ⇑ **UPSTATE UNIVERSITY HOSPITAL (330241)**, 750 East Adams Street, Zip 13210–2342; tel. 315/464–5540, (Includes GOLISANO CHILDREN'S HOSPITAL, Mailing address: 750 East Adams Street, Syracuse, New York, Zip 13210–2342; tel. 315/464–4570; UPSTATE UNIVERSITY HOSPITAL AT COMMUNITY GENERAL, Mailing address: 4900 Broad Road, Syracuse, New York, Zip 13215–2293; tel. 315/492–5011; Robert J. Corona Jr., Chief Executive Officer), (Nonreporting) **A**2 3 5 8 10 21 **F**3 5 6 9 12 13 15 16 17 18 19 20 22 24 25 26 28 29 30 31 33 34 35 36 37 38 39 40 41 43 44 45 46 47 48 49 50 51 52 53 54 55 56 57 58 59 61 64 65 66 68 70 71 74 76 78 79 81 82 84 85 86 87 88 89 90 92 93 95 96 97 98 100 101 102 104 107 108 109 110 111 112 114 115 118 119 120 121 123 124 126 128 129 130 131 132 135 136 138 141 142 145 146 147 148 149 150 154 156 157 **P**4
Primary Contact: Robert J. Corona Jr., Chief Executive Officer
CFO: Stuart M. Wright, CPA, Chief Financial Officer
CMO: Amy Tucker, M.D., Chief Medical Officer
CIO: Mark Zeman, Chief Information Officer
CHR: Eric Frost, Associate Vice President Human Resources
CNO: Nancy E. Page, MS, R.N., Chief Nursing Officer
Web address: www.upstate.edu/hospital
**Control:** State, Government, Nonfederal **Service:** General medical and surgical

**Staffed Beds: 650 Admissions: 34861 Census: 520 Outpatient Visits: 879551 Births: 1062 Total Expense ($000): 1227732 Payroll Expense ($000): 414835 Personnel: 5835**

**VETERANS AFFAIRS MEDICAL CENTER** See Syracuse Veterans Affairs Medical Center

**TROY—Rensselaer County**

**BURDETT BIRTH CENTER (330409)**, 2215 Burdett Avenue, Suite 200, Zip 12180–2466; tel. 518/271–3393, (Nonreporting) **A**10 **S** Trinity Health, Livonia, MI
Primary Contact: JoAnn Lionarons, Director
Web address: www.burdettbirthcenter.org/
**Control:** Church operated, Nongovernment, not–for–profit **Service:** Obstetrics and gynecology

**Staffed Beds: 15**

**SAMARITAN HOSPITAL** See Samaritan Hospital - Main Campus

★ **SAMARITAN HOSPITAL - MAIN CAMPUS (330180)**, 2215 Burdett Avenue, Zip 12180–2475; tel. 518/271–3300, (Includes SAMARITAN HOSPITAL - ALBANY MEMORIAL CAMPUS, Mailing address: 600 Northern Boulevard, Albany, New York, Zip 12204–1083; tel. 518/471–3221; Michael S. Finegan, President, Acute Care; SAMARITAN HOSPITAL - ST. MARY'S CAMPUS, Mailing address: 1300 Massachusetts Avenue, Troy, New York, Zip 12180–1695; tel. 518/268–5000; Michael S. Finegan, President, Acute Care), (Nonreporting) **A**5 10 19 **F**3 4 8 11 12 15 17 18 20 22 26 28 29 30 31 32 34 35 36 38 40 44 45 46 47 48 49 50 51 55 56 57 59 60 63 64 65 66 68 70 74 75 77 78 79 80 81 84 85 87 93 94 97 98 100 101 102 103 104 107 108 109 111 114 119 120 121 123 126 130 132 135 145 146 147 148 149 150 153 154 **P**6 **S** Trinity Health, Livonia, MI
Primary Contact: Michael S. Finegan, President, Acute Care
CFO: Daniel A Kochie, CPA, Chief Financial Officer
CMO: Daniel C Silverman, M.D., Chief Medical Officer, Acute Care Troy
CIO: Karen LeBlanc, Director, Applications
CNO: Jacqueline Priore, Chief Nursing Officer
Web address: www.sphp.com/sam
**Control:** Other not–for–profit (including NFP Corporation) **Service:** General medical and surgical

**Staffed Beds: 265 Admissions: 11107 Census: 173 Outpatient Visits: 647478 Births: 0 Total Expense ($000): 376146 Payroll Expense ($000): 161906 Personnel: 1894**

**SETON HEALTH ST. MARY'S HOSPITAL** See Samaritan Hospital - St. Mary's Campus

**SETON HLTH SYST-ST MARY'S** See Seton Health System-St. Mary's Hospital

**UTICA—Oneida County**

★ △ ⇑ **FAXTON ST. LUKE'S HEALTHCARE (330044)**, 1656 Champlin Avenue, Zip 13502–4830, Mailing Address: P.O. Box 479, Zip 13503–0479; tel. 315/624–6000, (Includes FAXTON CAMPUS, Mailing address: 1676 Sunset Avenue, Utica, New York, Zip 13502–5475; tel. 315/624–6000; ST. LUKE'S CAMPUS, Mailing address: 1656 Champlin Avenue, Utica, New York, Zip 13502–4830, P O Box 479, Zip 13503–0479, tel. 315/624–6000), (Nonreporting) **A**2 3 7 10 21 **F**2 3 8 11 12 13 15 28 29 30 31 34 35 36 39 40 45 46 47 48 49 50 51 54 56 57 58 59 60 62 64 65 66 68 70 73 74 75 76 77 78 79 80 81 84 85 86 87 89 90 92 93 97 98 100 101 102 104 107 108 110 114 115 119 120 121 123 124 127 130 131 132 135 143 144 146 147 149 150 154 156 **P**6
Primary Contact: Darlene Stromstad, FACHE, President and Chief Executive Officer
COO: Robert Scholefield, MS, R.N., Executive Vice President and Chief Operating Officer
CFO: Louis Aiello, Senior Vice President and Chief Financial Officer
CMO: Michael F Trevisani, M.D., Senior Vice President and Chief Medical Officer
CIO: John Lynch, Vice President and Chief Information Officer
CHR: Jack Davis, Vice President Human Resources
CNO: Linda McCormack-Miller, Chief Nursing Officer
Web address: www.mvhealthsystem.org
**Control:** Other not–for–profit (including NFP Corporation) **Service:** General medical and surgical

**Staffed Beds: 278 Admissions: 12760 Census: 179 Outpatient Visits: 349045 Births: 1761 Total Expense ($000): 310273 Payroll Expense ($000): 152951 Personnel: 2236**

**FAXTON-ST LUKE'S HEALTHCARE** See Faxton Campus

⇑ **FAXTON-ST. LUKE'S HEALTHCARE** See Faxton St. Luke's Healthcare

☐ **MOHAWK VALLEY PSYCHIATRIC CENTER (334021)**, 1400 Noyes Street, Zip 13502–3854; tel. 315/738–3800, (Nonreporting) **A**1 10 **S** New York State Office of Mental Health, Albany, NY
Primary Contact: Colleen A. Sawyer, R.N., MSN, Executive Director
Web address: www.omh.ny.gov/omhweb/facilities/mvpc/facility.htm
**Control:** State, Government, Nonfederal **Service:** Psychiatric

**Staffed Beds: 614**

⇑ **ST ELIZABETH HOSPITAL** See St. Elizabeth Medical Center

**ST LUKE'S MEM HOSPITAL CENTER** See St. Luke's Campus

★ ⇑ **ST. ELIZABETH MEDICAL CENTER (330245)**, 2209 Genesee Street, Zip 13501–5999; tel. 315/798–8100, (Nonreporting) **A**3 5 10 13 21 **F**3 11 15 17 18 20 22 24 26 29 30 32 34 35 36 37 38 40 43 45 50 54 57 58 59 61 64 65 66 68 70 74 75 77 79 80 81 84 85 87 89 90 97 98 100 101 102 104 107 108 110 114 115 118 119 126 127 129 130 132 135 146 147 148 149 150 **P**6
Primary Contact: Darlene Stromstad, FACHE, President and Chief Executive Officer
CFO: Louis Aiello, Chief Financial Officer
CMO: Albert D'Accurzio, M.D., Medical Director
CIO: Robert Gillette, Chief Information Officer
CNO: Varinya Sheppard, R.N., Chief Nursing Officer
Web address: www.stemc.org
**Control:** Church operated, Nongovernment, not–for–profit **Service:** General medical and surgical

**Staffed Beds: 181 Admissions: 10090 Census: 153 Outpatient Visits: 429253 Births: 0 Total Expense ($000): 217291 Payroll Expense ($000): 106640 Personnel: 1709**

**ST. LUKE'S CAMPUS** See Faxton St. Luke's Healthcare, Utica

**VALHALLA—Westchester County**

☒ **BLYTHEDALE CHILDREN'S HOSPITAL (333301)**, 95 Bradhurst Avenue, Zip 10595–1697; tel. 914/592–7555, (Nonreporting) **A**1 3 10
Primary Contact: Larry L. Levine, President and Chief Executive Officer
COO: Maureen Desimone, Chief Operating Officer
CFO: John Canning, Chief Financial Officer
CMO: Joelle Mast, Ph.D., M.D., Chief Medical Officer
CHR: Ronald Gallo, Director Human Resources
Web address: www.blythedale.org
**Control:** Other not–for–profit (including NFP Corporation) **Service:** Children's rehabilitation

**Staffed Beds: 92**

⇑ **WESTCHESTER COUNTY MED CENTER** See Westchester Medical Center

**NY**

*Many Facility Codes have changed. Please refer to the AHA Guide Code Chart.* © 2021 AHA Guide

⇑ **WESTCHESTER MEDICAL CENTER (330234)**, 100 Woods Road, Zip 10595–1530; tel. 914/493–7000, (Includes MARIA FARERI CHILDREN'S HOSPITAL, Mailing address: 100 Woods Road, Valhalla, New York, Zip 10595–1652; tel. 866/962–7337; MIDHUDSON REGIONAL HOSPITAL OF WESTCHESTER MEDICAL CENTER, Mailing address: 241 North Road, Poughkeepsie, New York, Zip 12601–1154; tel. 845/483–5000; Paul S Hochenberg, Executive Director), (Nonreporting) **A**2 3 5 8 10 21 **F**3 4 5 8 12 13 14 15 16 17 18 19 20 21 22 23 24 25 26 27 28 29 30 31 32 34 35 36 37 38 39 40 41 43 44 45 46 47 48 49 50 51 52 54 55 56 57 58 59 60 61 62 64 65 66 68 70 71 72 73 74 75 76 77 78 79 80 81 82 84 85 86 87 88 89 90 91 92 93 94 97 98 99 100 101 102 103 104 107 108 110 111 114 115 116 117 118 119 120 121 123 124 126 129 130 131 132 134 135 136 137 138 139 141 142 145 146 147 148 149 151 154 156 157 **P**6 **S** WMCHealth, Valhalla, NY
Primary Contact: Michael D. Israel, President and Chief Executive Officer
COO: Gary F Brudnicki, Senior Executive Vice President, Chief Operating Officer and Chief Financial Officer
CFO: Gary F Brudnicki, Senior Executive Vice President, Chief Operating Officer and Chief Financial Officer
CMO: Renee Garrick, M.D., Executive Medical Director
CIO: John Moustakakis, Senior Vice President Information Systems and Chief Information Officer
CHR: Jordy Rabinowitz, Senior Vice President Human Resources Operations
CNO: Paula Fessler, MSN, R.N., Chief Nursing Executive
Web address: www.wmchealth.org
**Control:** Hospital district or authority, Government, Nonfederal **Service:** General medical and surgical

**Staffed Beds: 872 Admissions:** 27779 **Census:** 657 **Outpatient Visits:** 269235 **Births:** 904 **Total Expense ($000):** 1323264 **Payroll Expense ($000):** 326866 **Personnel:** 5277

**VALLEY STREAM—Nassau County**

**FRANKLIN HOSPITAL** See Long Island Jewish Valley Stream

**WALTON—Delaware County**

**DELAWARE VALLEY HOSPITAL** See UHS Delaware Valley Hospital

**UHS DELAWARE VALLEY HOSPITAL (331312)**, 1 Titus Place, Zip 13856–1498; tel. 607/865–2100, (Nonreporting) **A**10 18 **F**3 4 5 11 15 18 28 29 30 34 35 40 45 50 57 59 64 75 77 82 85 87 93 97 107 110 115 119 130 131 133 146 147 148 154 **S** United Health Services, Binghamton, NY
Primary Contact: Paul Summers, President and Chief Executive Officer
CFO: Paul Summers, Interim Chief Financial Officer
CMO: John Giannone, M.D., Delaware Valley Hospital Medical Director
CHR: Cynthia Gardepe, Director, Human Resources
CNO: Victoria Conkling, Vice President, Patient Services and Chief Nursing Officer
Web address: www.uhs.net/locations/
**Control:** Other not–for–profit (including NFP Corporation) **Service:** General medical and surgical

**Staffed Beds:** 25 **Admissions:** 375 **Census:** 11 **Outpatient Visits:** 173538 **Births:** 0 **Total Expense ($000):** 24121 **Payroll Expense ($000):** 7995 **Personnel:** 162

**WAPPINGERS—Dutchess County**

**VETERAN AFFAIRS HUDSON VALLEY HEALTH CARE SYSTEM-CASTLE POINT CAMPUS** See Veterans Affairs Hudson Valley Health Care System, Montrose

**VETERAN AFFAIRS HUDSON VALLEY HEALTH CARE SYSTEM-CASTLE POINT DIVISION** See Veteran Affairs Hudson Valley Health Care System-Castle Point Campus

**WARSAW—Wyoming County**

☐ **WYOMING COUNTY COMMUNITY HOSPITAL (330008)**, 400 North Main Street, Zip 14569–1025; tel. 585/786–2233, (Nonreporting) **A**1 10 20
Primary Contact: Joseph L. McTernan, Chief Executive Officer
COO: Michael Corcimiglia, Chief Operating Officer
CFO: Amy Chase, Chief Financial Officer
CMO: Mandip Panesar, M.D., Medical Director
CIO: Dan Flint, Director Healthcare Information Systems
CHR: Daniel Farberman, Director Human Resource
CNO: Connie Almeter, Chief Nursing Officer
Web address: www.wcchs.net
**Control:** County, Government, Nonfederal **Service:** General medical and surgical

**Staffed Beds:** 75

**WARWICK—Orange County**

⌗ **ST. ANTHONY COMMUNITY HOSPITAL (330205)**, 15 Maple Avenue, Zip 10990–1028; tel. 845/986–2276, (Nonreporting) **A**1 10 **S** WMCHealth, Valhalla, NY
Primary Contact: Mary Leahy, M.D., Chief Executive Officer
Web address: www.stanthonycommunityhosp.org
**Control:** Church operated, Nongovernment, not–for–profit **Service:** General medical and surgical

**Staffed Beds:** 60

**WATERTOWN—Jefferson County**

**GOOD SAMARITAN HOSPITAL** See Samaritan Medical Center

⌗ **SAMARITAN MEDICAL CENTER (330157)**, 830 Washington Street, Zip 13601–4034; tel. 315/785–4000, (Nonreporting) **A**1 3 5 10 12 13 20 **F**3 5 8 13 15 18 28 29 30 31 35 40 47 49 50 51 57 60 62 64 68 70 73 75 76 77 78 81 82 87 89 90 93 94 97 98 100 102 104 107 108 111 114 115 116 119 120 121 126 129 130 135 144 146 147 148 154
Primary Contact: Thomas H. Carman, President and Chief Executive Officer
CFO: Sean Mills, Chief Financial Officer
CMO: Mario Victoria, M.D., Vice President, Medical Affairs
CIO: M Andrew Short, Vice President Information Services
CHR: Thomas Shatraw, Director Human Resources
CNO: Kimberly Thibert, R.N., MSN, Vice President Patient Care Services and Chief Nursing Officer
Web address: www.samaritanhealth.com
**Control:** Other not–for–profit (including NFP Corporation) **Service:** General medical and surgical

**Staffed Beds:** 195 **Admissions:** 8569 **Census:** 121 **Outpatient Visits:** 315499 **Births:** 1495 **Total Expense ($000):** 257917 **Payroll Expense ($000):** 108829 **Personnel:** 1835

**WELLSVILLE—Allegany County**

⌗ **JONES MEMORIAL HOSPITAL (330096)**, 191 North Main Street, Zip 14895–1150, Mailing Address: P.O. Box 72, Zip 14895–0072; tel. 585/593–1100, (Nonreporting) **A**1 10 20 **F**3 8 11 13 15 17 28 29 30 31 34 35 36 40 43 50 57 59 61 64 68 70 75 76 77 78 79 81 85 93 97 107 110 114 119 129 131 132 133 146 147 149 156 157 **S** University of Rochester Medical Center, Rochester, NY
Primary Contact: Eva Benedict, R.N., President and Chief Executive Officer
CFO: James Helms, Vice President Finance and Chief Financial Officer
CMO: Kevin McCormick, M.D., Associate Medical Director
CIO: James Helms, Vice President Finance and Chief Financial Officer
CHR: Carrie Walker, Executive Director Human Resources
CNO: Donna Bliven, Vice President Patient Care Services and Chief Nursing Officer
Web address: www.jmhny.org
**Control:** Other not–for–profit (including NFP Corporation) **Service:** General medical and surgical

**Staffed Beds:** 33 **Admissions:** 1788 **Census:** 18 **Outpatient Visits:** 151037 **Births:** 427 **Total Expense ($000):** 45031 **Payroll Expense ($000):** 20780 **Personnel:** 378

**WEST HAVERSTRAW—Rockland County**

☐ △ **HELEN HAYES HOSPITAL (330405)**, Route 9W, Zip 10993–1127; tel. 845/786–4000, (Nonreporting) **A**1 3 5 7 10
Primary Contact: Edmund Coletti, Chief Executive Officer
COO: Kathleen Martucci, Chief Operating Officer
CFO: Lori A. Meszler, Chief Financial Officer
CIO: Virgil Ennis, Chief Information Officer
CHR: Patrick J. Ryan, Chief Human Resources Officer
Web address: www.helenhayeshospital.org
**Control:** State, Government, Nonfederal **Service:** Rehabilitation

**Staffed Beds:** 155

**NY**

---

**Hospital, Medicare Provider Number, Address, Telephone, Approval, Facility, and Physician Codes, Health Care System**

★ American Hospital Association (AHA) membership
☐ The Joint Commission accreditation
○ Healthcare Facilities Accreditation Program
◇ DNV Healthcare Inc. accreditation
⇑ Center for Improvement in Healthcare Quality Accreditation
△ Commission on Accreditation of Rehabilitation Facilities (CARF) accreditation

## WEST ISLIP—Suffolk County

**GOOD SAMARITAN HOSPITAL** See Good Samaritan Hospital Medical Center

**GOOD SAMARITAN HOSPITAL MEDICAL CENTER (330286)**, 1000 Montauk Highway, Zip 11795–4927; tel. 631/376–3000, (Total facility includes 100 beds in nursing home–type unit) (Nonreporting) **A**1 2 3 5 10 13 **F**3 8 11 12 13 15 17 18 20 22 24 26 28 29 30 31 32 34 35 40 41 43 45 46 47 48 49 50 51 54 55 56 57 58 59 64 65 66 68 70 72 73 74 75 76 77 78 79 80 81 82 84 85 86 87 88 89 93 94 99 100 102 103 107 108 110 111 115 117 119 120 121 123 124 126 128 129 130 131 132 146 147 149 154 **S** Catholic Health Services of Long Island, Rockville Centre, NY
Primary Contact: Ruth E Hennessey, President
CFO: Dan Macksood, Regional Senior Vice President and Chief Financial Officer
CMO: Jerome Weiner, M.D., Senior Vice President Medical Affairs
CIO: Marcy Dunn, Vice President Information Services and Chief Information Officer
CHR: Lori Spina, Vice President Human Resources
Web address: www.good-samaritan-hospital.org
**Control**: Church operated, Nongovernment, not–for–profit **Service**: General medical and surgical

**Staffed Beds: 471 Admissions: 24145 Census: 418 Outpatient Visits: 233113 Births: 2656 Total Expense ($000): 774780 Payroll Expense ($000): 335716 Personnel: 2946**

## WEST POINT—Orange County

**KELLER ARMY COMMUNITY HOSPITAL**, 900 Washington Road, Zip 10996–1197, Mailing Address: U S Military Academy, Building 900, Zip 10996–1197; tel. 845/938–5169, (Nonreporting) **A**1 3 5 **F**3 5 7 8 15 29 34 36 38 39 40 45 50 54 57 58 59 61 64 65 68 75 77 79 81 82 87 93 97 100 101 102 104 107 110 111 115 119 130 131 135 146 147 149 154 156 **S** Department of the Army, Office of the Surgeon General, Falls Church, VA
Primary Contact: Colonel Amy L. Jackson, Commander
CIO: Patrick McGuinness, Chief Information Management
CHR: Margaret Greco, Chief Human Resources
Web address: www.https://kach.amedd.army.mil/
**Control**: Department of Defense, Government, federal **Service**: General medical and surgical

**Staffed Beds: 12 Admissions: 571 Census: 3 Outpatient Visits: 152704 Births: 0 Total Expense ($000): 61958 Payroll Expense ($000): 26791 Personnel: 589**

## WEST SENECA—Erie County

**WESTERN NEW YORK CHILDREN'S PSYCHIATRIC CENTER (334065)**, 1010 East and West Road, Zip 14224–3602; tel. 716/677–7000, (Nonreporting) **A**1 3 5 10 **S** New York State Office of Mental Health, Albany, NY
Primary Contact: Kathe Hayes, Executive Director
COO: David Privett, Deputy Director
CMO: Patrick Stein, M.D., Clinical Director
CIO: Dan Hrubiak, Associate Computer Program Analyst
CHR: Charles Siewert, Director Human Resources
Web address: www.omh.ny.gov
**Control**: State, Government, Nonfederal **Service**: Children's hospital psychiatric

**Staffed Beds: 46**

## WESTFIELD—Chautauqua County

★ **WESTFIELD MEMORIAL HOSPITAL (330166)**, 189 East Main Street, Zip 14787–1195; tel. 716/326–4921, (Nonreporting) **A**10 **F**3 11 15 18 28 29 34 35 40 44 45 50 57 59 64 79 81 85 87 93 107 108 110 115 118 119 146 147 148 156 157 **S** Allegheny Health Network, Pittsburgh, PA
Primary Contact: Karen Surkala, President
COO: Patricia Ballman, Director
CFO: Tina Gowen, System Controller
CMO: Russell Elwell, M.D., Medical Director
CIO: Cindy Harper, Manager Patient Data
Web address: www.https://www.ahn.org/locations/westfield-memorial-hospital
**Control**: Other not–for–profit (including NFP Corporation) **Service**: General medical and surgical

**Staffed Beds: 4 Admissions: 88 Census: 1 Outpatient Visits: 23518 Births: 0 Total Expense ($000): 11252 Payroll Expense ($000): 4683 Personnel: 72**

## WHITE PLAINS—Westchester County

**BURKE REHABILITATION CENTER** See Burke Rehabilitation Hospital

△ **BURKE REHABILITATION HOSPITAL (333030)**, 785 Mamaroneck Avenue, Zip 10605–2523; tel. 914/597–2500, (Nonreporting) **A**1 3 5 7 10 **F**11 28 29 30 34 35 53 54 57 58 59 74 75 77 87 90 92 93 94 95 96 100 104 130 131 132 146 148 149 **S** Montefiore Health System, Bronx, NY
Primary Contact: Jeffrey Menkes, President and Chief Executive Officer
COO: Brian M Swift, Senior Administrator Plant Operations
CFO: John Stewart, Director Finance
CIO: Cathy Dwyer, Senior Administrator Information Systems
CHR: Annette Bucci, Vice President Human Resources
CNO: Marie Spencer, Chief Nursing Officer and Senior Administrator
Web address: www.burke.org
**Control**: Other not–for–profit (including NFP Corporation) **Service**: Rehabilitation

**Staffed Beds: 150 Admissions: 2894 Census: 131 Outpatient Visits: 144283 Births: 0 Total Expense ($000): 95929 Payroll Expense ($000): 55608 Personnel: 736**

**NEW YORK-PRESBYTERIAN HOSPITAL, WESTCHESTER DIVISION** See New York-Presbyterian Hospital, New York

**WHITE PLAINS HOSPITAL CENTER (330304)**, 41 East Post Road, Zip 10601–4699; tel. 914/681–0600, (Nonreporting) **A**1 2 3 10 19 **F**3 7 8 9 11 12 13 15 17 18 19 20 22 26 29 30 31 32 34 35 36 37 38 39 40 41 42 44 45 46 47 49 50 51 53 54 55 56 57 58 59 60 61 63 64 65 66 68 70 72 73 74 75 76 77 78 79 81 82 84 85 86 87 89 92 93 96 97 100 101 102 107 108 110 111 114 115 117 118 119 120 121 123 124 126 129 130 131 132 134 135 144 145 146 147 148 149 150 154 156 157 **P**6 **S** Montefiore Health System, Bronx, NY
Primary Contact: Susan Fox, President and Chief Executive Officer
COO: Edward F Leonard, Executive Vice President and Chief Operating Officer
CFO: Joseph Guarracino, Senior Vice President and Chief Financial Officer
CMO: Michael Palumbo, M.D., Executive Vice President and Medical Director
CIO: Rick McCarthy, Chief Information Officer
CHR: John Sanchez, Vice President Human Resources
CNO: Leigh McMahon, MS, R.N., Senior Vice President Patient Care Services and Chief Nursing Officer
Web address: www.wphospital.org
**Control**: Other not–for–profit (including NFP Corporation) **Service**: General medical and surgical

**Staffed Beds: 292 Admissions: 20300 Census: 238 Outpatient Visits: 401301 Births: 1993 Total Expense ($000): 758814 Payroll Expense ($000): 376037 Personnel: 3365**

**WHITE PLAINS HOSPITAL CTR** See White Plains Hospital Center

## WILLIAMSVILLE—Erie County

**MILLARD FILLMORE SUBURBAN HOSPITAL** See Kaleida Health, Buffalo

**ST FRANCIS HOME** See St. Francis of Williamsville

## YONKERS—Westchester County

**ANDRUS PAVILION** See St. John's Riverside Hospital, Yonkers

**ELIZABETH SETON PEDIATRIC CENTER** See Elizabeth Seton Children's Center

**SAINT JOSEPH'S MEDICAL CENTER (330006)**, 127 South Broadway, Zip 10701–4006; tel. 914/378–7000, (Nonreporting) **A**1 3 5 10 **F**3 4 5 8 10 11 15 18 28 29 34 38 39 40 45 46 50 54 56 57 58 59 60 61 62 64 65 68 70 74 75 77 78 79 81 82 85 87 89 91 93 94 97 98 99 100 101 102 103 104 105 106 107 108 110 111 115 118 119 125 128 129 130 131 132 134 135 143 144 146 147 148 149 150 152 153 154 156 157 158 **P**5
Primary Contact: Michael J. Spicer, President and Chief Executive Officer
COO: Frances Casola, Senior Vice President Operations
CFO: Frank Hagan, Senior Vice President Finance
CMO: James Neuendorf, M.D., Medical Director
CIO: Deborah Di Bernardo, Chief Information Officer
CHR: Dean Civitello, Vice President Human Resources
CNO: Margaret M Cusumano, R.N., MSN, Vice President Patient Care Services and Chief Nursing Officer
Web address: www.saintjosephs.org
**Control**: Other not–for–profit (including NFP Corporation) **Service**: General medical and surgical

**Staffed Beds: 473 Admissions: 7037 Census: 209 Outpatient Visits: 870579 Births: 0 Total Expense ($000): 243833 Payroll Expense ($000): 117244 Personnel: 1672**

**ST JOHN'S RIVERSIDE HOSPTIAL** See St. John's Riverside Hospital

☐ **ST. JOHN'S RIVERSIDE HOSPITAL (330208)**, 967 North Broadway, Zip 10701–1399; tel. 914/964–4444, (Includes ANDRUS PAVILION, Mailing address: 967 North Broadway, Yonkers, New York, Zip 10701–1399; tel. 914/964–4444; ST. JOHN'S RIVERSIDE HOSPITAL - PARK CARE PAVILION, Mailing address: Two Park Avenue, Yonkers, New York, Zip 10703–3497; tel. 914/964–7300; ST. JOHN'S RIVERSIDE HOSPITAL - DOBBS FERRY PAVILION, Mailing address: 128 Ashford Avenue, Dobbs Ferry, New York, Zip 10522–1896; tel. 914/693–0700), (Nonreporting) **A**1 2 3 10 19 **F**4 5 8 11 12 13 15 18 29 30 31 34 35 36 37 40 41 45 49 50 51 55 56 57 59 60 61 64 68 70 72 74 76 77 78 79 81 82 83 84 85 93 97 107 108 110 111 114 115 118 119 124 126 129 130 131 132 135 141 142 143 146 147 148 149 152 154
Primary Contact: Ronald J. Corti, President and Chief Executive Officer
COO: Lynn M. Nelson, R.N., R.N., Chief Nursing Officer and Chief Operating Officer
CFO: Dennis M. Keane, Vice President Finance and Chief Financial Officer
CMO: Paul Antonecchia, M.D., Vice President Medical Affairs and Chief Medical Officer
CIO: Peter Weidner, Director Information Technology
CHR: Marc Leff, Vice President Human Resources
CNO: Lynn M. Nelson, R.N., R.N., Chief Nursing Officer and Chief Operating Officer
Web address: www.riversidehealth.org
**Control**: Other not–for–profit (including NFP Corporation) **Service**: General medical and surgical

**Staffed Beds**: 376 **Admissions**: 18654 **Census**: 255 **Outpatient Visits**: 232031 **Births**: 1214 **Total Expense ($000)**: 286874 **Payroll Expense ($000)**: 124633 **Personnel**: 1564

**ST. JOSEPH'S MEDICAL CENTER** See Saint Joseph's Medical Center

**YONKERS GENERAL HOSPITAL** See St. John's Riverside Hospital - Park Care Pavilion

NY

# NORTH CAROLINA

### AHOSKIE—Hertford County

**ROANOKE-CHOWAN HOSPITAL** See Vidant Roanoke-Chowan Hospital

⊞ **VIDANT ROANOKE-CHOWAN HOSPITAL (340099)**, 500 South Academy Street, Zip 27910–3261, Mailing Address: P.O. Box 1385, Zip 27910–1385; tel. 252/209–3000, (Nonreporting) **A**1 10 20 **F**3 11 13 15 29 30 31 34 35 40 43 44 45 56 57 59 64 68 70 75 76 77 78 79 81 82 85 86 87 89 92 93 98 100 101 102 103 107 108 110 111 114 118 119 120 121 123 129 130 132 146 148 149 154 156 **S** Vidant Health, Greenville, NC
Primary Contact: Judy Bruno, President
CFO: Jon Graham, Chief Finance Officer
CMO: David Lingle, Directors Council Chairman and Chief of Staff
CHR: Debbie Sisler, Director, Human Resource
Web address: www.vidanthealth.com
**Control:** Other not–for–profit (including NFP Corporation) **Service:** General medical and surgical

> **Staffed Beds:** 110 **Admissions:** 4860 **Census:** 58 **Outpatient Visits:** 66303 **Births:** 308 **Total Expense ($000):** 78169 **Payroll Expense ($000):** 28152 **Personnel:** 565

### ALBEMARLE—Stanly County

⊞ **ATRIUM HEALTH STANLY (340119)**, 301 Yadkin Street, Zip 28001–3441, Mailing Address: P.O. Box 1489, Zip 28002–1489; tel. 704/984–4000, (Nonreporting) **A**1 2 10 **S** Atrium Health, Charlotte, NC
Primary Contact: Brian Freeman, President
CFO: Nick Samilo, Vice President Fiscal Services and Chief Financial Officer
CMO: Paul D'Amico, M.D., Chief of Staff
CNO: Judy Doran, Vice President of Hospital Services and Chief Nurse Executive
Web address: www.stanly.org
**Control:** Other not–for–profit (including NFP Corporation) **Service:** General medical and surgical

> **Staffed Beds:** 109

**CAROLINAS HEALTHCARE SYSTEM STANLY** See Atrium Health Stanly

### ASHEBORO—Randolph County

⊞ **RANDOLPH HOSPITAL (340123)**, 364 White Oak Street, Zip 27203–5400, Mailing Address: P.O. Box 1048, Zip 27204–1048; tel. 336/625–5151, (Nonreporting) **A**1 10 19 **F**3 8 13 15 18 28 29 30 31 34 35 40 45 49 53 56 57 58 59 62 64 68 70 75 76 77 79 80 81 85 86 87 91 92 93 94 96 97 107 110 111 114 115 118 119 120 121 123 130 131 132 135 143 146 148 **P**6
Primary Contact: Angela P. Orth, Executive Officer
CMO: Charles West, M.D., Chief Medical Officer
CIO: Angela Burgess, Chief Information Officer
Web address: www.randolphhospital.org
**Control:** Other not–for–profit (including NFP Corporation) **Service:** General medical and surgical

> **Staffed Beds:** 70 **Admissions:** 4671 **Census:** 39 **Outpatient Visits:** 57595 **Births:** 708 **Total Expense ($000):** 90550 **Payroll Expense ($000):** 37081 **Personnel:** 767

### ASHEVILLE—Buncombe County

⊞ **ASHEVILLE SPECIALTY HOSPITAL (342017)**, 428 Biltmore Avenue, 4th Floor, Zip 28801–4502; tel. 828/213–5400, (Nonreporting) **A**1 3 10 **S** HCA Healthcare, Nashville, TN
Primary Contact: Julie A. Dikos, President and Chief Executive Officer
CFO: Gregg Dixon, Chief Financial Officer
CMO: Ronnie Jacobs, M.D., Chief Medical Officer
CIO: Megan Serzan, Director of Quality, Compliance, Risk & Safety
CNO: Josephine Picker, MSN, R.N., Director of Nursing
Web address: www.missionhospitals.org/acute-care
**Control:** Partnership, Investor–owned (for–profit) **Service:** Acute long–term care hospital

> **Staffed Beds:** 34

⊞ △ **CAREPARTNERS HEALTH SERVICES (343025)**, 68 Sweeten Creek Road, Zip 28803–2318, Mailing Address: P.O. Box 15025, Zip 28813–0025; tel. 828/277–4800, (Nonreporting) **A**1 3 7 10 **S** HCA Healthcare, Nashville, TN
Primary Contact: Tracy Buchanan, Chief Executive Officer and President
CFO: Gregg Dixon, Chief Financial Officer
CMO: Michael Parmer, Chief Medical Officer
CIO: Jennifer Scott, Director of Informatics
CHR: Katy Pless, Director of Human Resources
CNO: Cathleen Adams, Chief Nursing Officer
Web address: www.carepartners.org
**Control:** Other not–for–profit (including NFP Corporation) **Service:** Rehabilitation

> **Staffed Beds:** 80

**CAREPARTNERS REHABILITATION HOSPITAL** See Carepartners Health Services

⊞ **CHARLES GEORGE VETERANS AFFAIRS MEDICAL CENTER**, 1100 Tunnel Road, Zip 28805–2087; tel. 828/298–7911, (Total facility includes 73 beds in nursing home–type unit) (Nonreporting) **A**1 3 5 **F**3 4 5 12 18 20 22 24 26 28 29 30 31 33 34 35 36 38 39 40 45 49 50 54 56 57 58 59 61 63 64 65 68 70 74 75 77 78 79 80 81 82 83 84 85 86 87 91 92 93 94 97 98 100 101 102 104 107 108 111 114 115 119 128 129 130 132 135 143 145 146 147 148 149 151 153 154 156 157 158 **P**6 **S** Department of Veterans Affairs, Washington, DC
Primary Contact: Cynthia Breyfogle, FACHE, Director
CFO: Margaret Wilkes, Chief Fiscal Officer
CIO: Carla McLendon, Director Information Resource Management Services
CHR: James Sitlinger, Chief Human Resources Management
CNO: David Przestrzelski, Associate Director, Patient Care Services and Chief Nursing Executive
Web address: www.asheville.va.gov/
**Control:** Veterans Affairs, Government, federal **Service:** General medical and surgical

> **Staffed Beds:** 190 **Admissions:** 4961 **Census:** 140 **Outpatient Visits:** 583284 **Births:** 0 **Total Expense ($000):** 353343 **Payroll Expense ($000):** 178329 **Personnel:** 2137

**MEMORIAL MISSION HOSPITAL** See Mission Hospital

⊞ **MISSION HOSPITAL (340002)**, 509 Biltmore Avenue, Zip 28801–4690; tel. 828/213–1111, (Includes MISSION CHILDREN'S HOSPITAL, Mailing address: 509 Biltmore Avenue, Asheville, North Carolina, Zip 28801–4601; tel. 828/213–1111; MISSION HOSPITAL - ST. JOSEPH'S CAMPUS, Mailing address: 428 Biltmore Avenue, Asheville, North Carolina, Zip 28801–9839; tel. 828/213–1111; MISSION HOSPITAL, Mailing address: 509 Biltmore Avenue, Asheville, North Carolina, Zip 28801–4690; tel. 828/213–1111; Chad Patrick, Chief Executive Officer), (Nonreporting) **A**1 2 3 5 10 19 **S** HCA Healthcare, Nashville, TN
Primary Contact: Chad Patrick, Chief Executive Officer
CFO: Paul L McDowell, Deputy Chief Financial Officer
CMO: William Hathaway, M.D., Chief Medical Officer
CIO: Jon Brown, Chief Information Officer
CHR: Sheila M Meadows, Chief Human Resources Officer
CNO: Karen M Olsen, R.N., Chief Nursing Officer
Web address: www.mission-health.org
**Control:** Other not–for–profit (including NFP Corporation) **Service:** General medical and surgical

> **Staffed Beds:** 815

**MISSION HOSPITALS** See Mission Hospital

**ST. JOSEPH'S HOSPITAL** See Mission Hospital - St. Joseph's Campus

**VETERANS AFFAIRS MEDICAL CENTER** See Charles George Veterans Affairs Medical Center

## BERMUDA RUN—Davie County

**WAKE FOREST BAPTIST HEALTH-DAVIE HOSPITAL** See Wake Forest Baptist Health-Davie Medical Center

✠ **WAKE FOREST BAPTIST HEALTH-DAVIE MEDICAL CENTER (340187)**, 329 NC Highway 801 North, Zip 27006; tel. 336/998-1300, (Nonreporting) **A**1 5 10 **F**3 15 18 28 29 30 34 35 40 45 50 56 57 59 64 68 74 75 77 79 81 85 87 93 102 107 110 111 115 119 129 130 131 146 154 **S** Wake Forest Baptist Health, Winston-Salem, NC
Primary Contact: Chad J. Brown, M.P.H., FACHE, President
CFO: Danny Squires, Chief Financial Officer
CMO: Bret Nicks, M.D., Chief Medical Officer and Chief of Staff
CIO: William Showalter, Senior Vice President and Chief Information Officer, Information Technology Services
CHR: Jennifer Bandy, Human Resource Business Partner
CNO: Susan T. Bachmeier, MSN, R.N., Chief Nursing Officer
Web address: www.wakehealth.edu/Davie-Medical-Center
**Control**: Other not-for-profit (including NFP Corporation) **Service**: General medical and surgical

**Staffed Beds**: 25 **Admissions**: 1694 **Census**: 10 **Outpatient Visits**: 79563
**Births**: 0 **Total Expense ($000)**: 62866 **Payroll Expense ($000)**: 21323
**Personnel**: 285

## BLACK MOUNTAIN—Buncombe County

**JULIAN F. KEITH ALCOHOL AND DRUG ABUSE TREATMENT CENTER (344023)**, 201 Tabernacle Road, Zip 28711-2599; tel. 828/669-3400, (Nonreporting) **A**3 10
Primary Contact: Erin Bowman, Director
CFO: Jackie Maurer, Fiscal Officer
CMO: Anthony Burnett, M.D., Medical Director
CHR: Faye Hamlin, Manager Human Resources
Web address: www.ncdhhs.gov/divisions/dsohf/julian-f-keith-alcohol-and-drug-abuse-treatment-center
**Control**: State, Government, Nonfederal **Service**: Alcoholism and other chemical dependency

**Staffed Beds**: 80

**JULIAN K KEITH ALCOHOL CENTER** See Julian F. Keith Alcohol and Drug Abuse Treatment Center

## BLOWING ROCK—Watauga County

**BLOWING ROCK HOSPITAL** See Blowing Rock Rehabilitation & Davant Extended Care Center

## BOLIVIA—Brunswick County

**BRUNSWICK NOVANT MEDICAL CENTER** See Novant Health Brunswick Medical Center

✠ **NOVANT HEALTH BRUNSWICK MEDICAL CENTER (340158)**, 240 Hospital Drive NE, Zip 28422-8346; tel. 910/721-1000, (Nonreporting) **A**1 10 **S** Novant Health, Winston Salem, NC
Primary Contact: Shelbourn Stevens, President and Chief Operating Officer
CFO: Fred M Hargett, Executive Vice President and Chief Financial Officer
CMO: Thomas Zweng, Executive Vice President and Chief Medical Officer
CIO: David B Garrett, Senior Vice President and Chief Information Officer
CNO: Lorna J Ward, MSN, R.N., Chief Nursing Officer
Web address: www.https://www.novanthealth.org
**Control**: Other not-for-profit (including NFP Corporation) **Service**: General medical and surgical

**Staffed Beds**: 54

## BOONE—Watauga County

**WATAUGA COUNTY HOSPITAL** See Watauga Medical Center

✠ **WATAUGA MEDICAL CENTER (340051)**, 336 Deerfield Road, Zip 28607-5008, Mailing Address: P.O. Box 2600, Zip 28607-2600; tel. 828/262-4100, (Nonreporting) **A**1 2 3 10 **F**3 5 13 15 17 18 20 22 26 28 29 30 31 32 34 35 38 40 44 45 46 47 48 49 50 53 54 57 59 64 70 73 75 76 77 78 81 82 84 85 86 87 91 92 93 96 107 108 110 111 114 115 118 119 120 121 122 123 124 126 129 130 131 132 135 144 145 146 147 148 149 154 156 **S** Appalachian Regional Healthcare System, Boone, NC
Primary Contact: Charles Mantooth, President and Chief Executive Officer
CFO: Kevin B May, Chief Financial Officer
CMO: Herman A Godwin, M.D., JrSenior Vice President and Medical Director
CIO: Mike Quinto, Chief Information Officer
CHR: Amy J. Crabbe, Senior Vice President Human Resources
Web address: www.https://apprhs.org/contact-us
**Control**: Other not-for-profit (including NFP Corporation) **Service**: General medical and surgical

**Staffed Beds**: 99 **Admissions**: 4336 **Census**: 41 **Outpatient Visits**: 134032
**Births**: 537 **Total Expense ($000)**: 131355 **Payroll Expense ($000)**: 42934
**Personnel**: 687

## BREVARD—Transylvania County

**TRANSYLVANIA COMM HOSPITAL** See Transylvania Regional Hospital

✠ **TRANSYLVANIA REGIONAL HOSPITAL (341319)**, 260 Hospital Drive, Zip 28712-3378; tel. 828/884-9111, (Nonreporting) **A**1 10 18 **S** HCA Healthcare, Nashville, TN
Primary Contact: Michele Pilon, President and Chief Nursing Officer
CFO: Theresa M Parker, Regional Finance Director
CMO: Mark Lemel, Chief of Staff
CIO: Ed Coye, Director Information Technology
CHR: Susan Stevens, Human Resources Strategic Business Partner
CNO: Melina Arrowood, Interim President and Chief Nursing Officer
Web address: www.trhospital.org
**Control**: Other not-for-profit (including NFP Corporation) **Service**: General medical and surgical

**Staffed Beds**: 102

## BRYSON CITY—Swain County

★ **SWAIN COMMUNITY HOSPITAL (341305)**, 45 Plateau Street, Zip 28713-4200; tel. 828/488-2155, (Nonreporting) **A**10 18 **S** Duke LifePoint Healthcare, Brentwood, TN
Primary Contact: Steve Heatherly, Chief Executive Officer
CMO: David Zimmerman, M.D., Chief of Staff
Web address: www.https://www.myswaincommunity.com
**Control**: Other not-for-profit (including NFP Corporation) **Service**: General medical and surgical

**Staffed Beds**: 25

**SWAIN COUNTY HOSPITAL** See Swain Community Hospital

## BURGAW—Pender County

★ ⇑ **PENDER MEMORIAL HOSPITAL (341307)**, 507 East Freemont Street, Zip 28425-5131; tel. 910/259-5451, (Total facility includes 43 beds in nursing home-type unit) (Nonreporting) **A**10 18 21 **F**3 11 15 29 34 35 40 45 54 56 57 59 62 64 81 85 87 93 96 107 110 114 119 128 130 133 143 146 148 149 **S** New Hanover Regional Medical Center, Wilmington, NC
Primary Contact: Ruth Glaser, President
CFO: Morrison Hall, Chief Financial Officer
CMO: Heather Davis, M.D., Chief of Staff
CIO: Ashley Hernandez, Chief Information Technology Officer
CHR: Lori McKoy, Business Partner
CNO: Cynthia Faulkner, R.N., Chief Nursing Executive
Web address: www.pendermemorial.org
**Control**: County, Government, Nonfederal **Service**: General medical and surgical

**Staffed Beds**: 64 **Admissions**: 353 **Census**: 39 **Outpatient Visits**: 44996
**Births**: 1 **Total Expense ($000)**: 27535 **Payroll Expense ($000)**: 7986
**Personnel**: 248

## BURLINGTON—Alamance County

**ALAMANCE HEALTH SERVICES** See Alamance Regional Medical Center

---

**Hospital, Medicare Provider Number, Address, Telephone, Approval, Facility, and Physician Codes, Health Care System**

★ American Hospital Association (AHA) membership
☐ The Joint Commission accreditation
○ Healthcare Facilities Accreditation Program
◇ DNV Healthcare Inc. accreditation
⇑ Center for Improvement in Healthcare Quality Accreditation
△ Commission on Accreditation of Rehabilitation Facilities (CARF) accreditation

**NC**

☒ **ALAMANCE REGIONAL MEDICAL CENTER (340070)**, 1240 Huffman Mill Road, Zip 27215–8700, Mailing Address: P.O. Box 202, Zip 27216–0202; tel. 336/538–7000, (Total facility includes 129 beds in nursing home–type unit) (Nonreporting) **A**1 10 **F**1 3 8 9 12 13 15 18 20 22 24 26 28 29 30 31 32 34 35 36 38 39 40 44 45 46 47 49 50 53 54 56 57 58 59 60 64 66 68 70 73 74 75 76 77 78 79 81 82 84 85 86 87 89 91 93 94 96 97 98 100 101 102 103 107 108 110 111 115 117 118 119 120 121 123 126 128 130 131 132 135 144 145 146 147 148 154 156 **P**8 **S** Cone Health, Greensboro, NC
Primary Contact: Vicki Moran, Interim President
CFO: Rex Street, Senior Vice President and Chief Financial Officer
CMO: Andrew Lamb, M.D., Chief of Staff
CIO: Terri Andrews, Director Information Technology
Web address: www.armc.com
**Control:** Other not–for–profit (including NFP Corporation) **Service:** General medical and surgical

> **Staffed Beds:** 329 **Admissions:** 12291 **Census:** 180 **Outpatient Visits:** 317772 **Births:** 1253 **Total Expense ($000):** 298784 **Payroll Expense ($000):** 81786 **Personnel:** 1178

### BURNSVILLE—Yancey County

**YANCEY COMMUNITY MEDICAL CENTER** See Blue Ridge Medical Center - Yancey Campus

### BUTNER—Granville County

☐ **CENTRAL REGIONAL HOSPITAL (344004)**, 300 Veazey Road, Zip 27509–1668; tel. 919/764–2000, (Nonreporting) **A**1 3 5 10 **F**3 30 39 40 41 50 53 56 57 59 61 65 68 74 75 77 86 87 91 96 97 98 99 103 119 130 132 135 143 146 149 154 157
Primary Contact: Walter Edwin. Beal, Chief Executive Officer
COO: Cliff Hood, Chief Operating Officer
CFO: Pamela Richardson, Business Manager
CMO: Alan Cook, Chief Medical Officer
CIO: Joe Thurber, Director Information Technology
CHR: Kathleen Tardif, Director of Human Resources
CNO: Diana Holmes, Chief Nursing Officer
**Control:** State, Government, Nonfederal **Service:** Psychiatric

> **Staffed Beds:** 398 **Admissions:** 791 **Census:** 361 **Outpatient Visits:** 0 **Births:** 0 **Total Expense ($000):** 216526 **Payroll Expense ($000):** 96818 **Personnel:** 1690

### CAMP LEJEUNE—Onslow County

**NAVAL HOSPITAL** See Naval Hospital Camp Lejeune

☒ **NAVAL HOSPITAL CAMP LEJEUNE**, 100 Brewster Boulevard, Zip 28547–2538, Mailing Address: P.O. Box 10100, Zip 28547–0100; tel. 910/450–4300, (Nonreporting) **A**1 3 5 **S** Bureau of Medicine and Surgery, Department of the Navy, Falls Church, VA
Primary Contact: Captain Rick Freedman, Commanding Officer
Web address: www.med.navy.mil/sites/nhcl/Pages/default.aspx
**Service:** General medical and surgical

> **Staffed Beds:** 117

### CARY—Wake County

☒ **WAKEMED CARY HOSPITAL (340173)**, 1900 Kildaire Farm Road, Zip 27518–6616; tel. 919/350–8000, (Nonreporting) **A**1 10 **F**3 7 11 12 13 15 18 20 22 24 26 28 29 30 31 32 34 35 36 37 38 40 42 43 44 45 46 48 49 50 53 54 56 57 58 59 60 61 64 65 66 68 70 73 74 75 76 77 78 79 81 82 85 86 87 92 100 101 102 107 108 110 111 114 115 118 119 126 129 130 132 144 146 147 149 150 154 156 **S** WakeMed Health & Hospitals, Raleigh, NC
Primary Contact: Donald R. Gintzig, President and Chief Executive Officer
COO: Denise Wilder Warren, R.N., Executive Vice President and Chief Operating Officer
CMO: West Paul, M.D., Ph.D., Senior Vice President, Chief Quality and Medical Staff Officer
CIO: Denton Arledge, Vice President and Chief Information Officer
CHR: Jeanene R Martin, M.P.H., Senior Vice President Human Resources and Chief People Officer
CNO: Cindy Boily, MSN, R.N., Senior Vice President and Chief Nursing Officer
Web address: www.wakemed.org
**Control:** Other not–for–profit (including NFP Corporation) **Service:** General medical and surgical

> **Staffed Beds:** 178 **Admissions:** 13095 **Census:** 134 **Outpatient Visits:** 260122 **Births:** 2564 **Total Expense ($000):** 227397 **Payroll Expense ($000):** 76763 **Personnel:** 1050

**WESTERN WAKE MED CENTER** See Wakemed Cary Hospital

### CHAPEL HILL—Orange County

**NORTH CAROLINA MEM HOSPITAL** See University of North Carolina Hospitals

☒ △ **UNIVERSITY OF NORTH CAROLINA HOSPITALS (340061)**, 101 Manning Drive, Zip 27514–4220; tel. 984/974–1000, (Includes N.C. WOMEN'S HOSPITAL, Mailing address: 101 Manning Drive, Chapel Hill, North Carolina, Zip 27514–4220; tel. 984/974–1000; Gary L Park, President; NORTH CAROLINA CHILDREN'S HOSPITAL, Mailing address: 101 Manning Drive, Chapel Hill, North Carolina, Zip 27514–4220; tel. 984/974–1000; UNC HEALTH CARE HILLSBOROUGH CAMPUS, Mailing address: 430 Waterstone Drive, Hillsborough, North Carolina, Zip 27278–9078; tel. 984/215–2000; Gary L Park, Chief Executive Officer; UNC LINEBERGER COMPREHENSIVE CANCER CENTER, Mailing address: 450 West Drive, Chapel Hill, North Carolina, Zip 27599–5020; tel. 919/966–3036), (Nonreporting) **A**1 2 3 5 7 8 10 **F**3 5 7 8 9 11 12 13 14 15 16 17 18 19 20 21 22 23 24 25 26 27 28 29 30 31 32 34 35 36 38 39 40 41 43 44 45 46 47 48 49 50 51 52 53 54 55 56 57 58 59 60 61 62 63 64 65 66 68 70 72 73 74 75 76 77 78 79 80 81 82 83 84 85 86 87 88 89 90 92 93 94 97 98 99 100 101 102 103 104 106 107 108 110 111 114 115 116 117 118 119 120 121 123 124 126 129 130 131 132 134 135 136 137 138 139 140 141 142 143 144 145 146 147 148 149 150 154 155 156 157 **S** UNC Health Care, Chapel Hill, NC
Primary Contact: Gary L. Park, President
CFO: Christopher Ellington, Executive Vice President and Chief Financial Officer
CMO: Tony Lindsey, M.D., Chief of Staff
CIO: Tracy Parham
CHR: Scott Doak, System Vice President, Human Resources
CNO: Catherine Madigan, Chief Nursing Executive
Web address: www.unchealthcare.org
**Control:** State, Government, Nonfederal **Service:** General medical and surgical

> **Staffed Beds:** 951 **Admissions:** 41320 **Census:** 802 **Outpatient Visits:** 1608595 **Births:** 4157 **Total Expense ($000):** 1796829 **Payroll Expense ($000):** 616375 **Personnel:** 10496

### CHARLOTTE—Mecklenburg County

☒ △ ⇑ **ATRIUM HEALTH PINEVILLE (340098)**, 10628 Park Road, Zip 28210–8407; tel. 704/667–1000, (Nonreporting) **A**1 2 3 7 10 21 **F**3 13 17 18 20 22 24 26 28 29 30 31 40 42 45 49 50 64 68 70 73 74 75 76 77 78 79 81 82 84 85 86 87 90 91 92 93 100 107 108 111 114 115 119 120 121 123 126 129 130 132 135 146 147 148 149 154 157 **S** Atrium Health, Charlotte, NC
Primary Contact: Alicia Campbell, Vice President, Facility Executive
Web address: www.carolinashealthcare.org/pineville
**Control:** Hospital district or authority, Government, Nonfederal **Service:** General medical and surgical

> **Staffed Beds:** 250 **Admissions:** 17496 **Census:** 226 **Outpatient Visits:** 160047 **Births:** 2246 **Total Expense ($000):** 308582 **Payroll Expense ($000):** 101160 **Personnel:** 1647

☒ **ATRIUM HEALTH UNIVERSITY CITY (340166)**, 8800 North Tryon Street, Zip 28262–3300, Mailing Address: P.O. Box 560727, Zip 28256–0727; tel. 704/863–6000, (Nonreporting) **A**1 2 3 10 **S** Atrium Health, Charlotte, NC
Primary Contact: William H. Leonard, President
CFO: Greg A Gombar, Chief Financial Officer
CIO: John Knox, Senior Vice President and Chief Information Officer
Web address: www.carolinashealthcare.org/university
**Control:** Hospital district or authority, Government, Nonfederal **Service:** General medical and surgical

> **Staffed Beds:** 100

☒ **ATRIUM HEALTH'S CAROLINAS MEDICAL CENTER (340113)**, 1000 Blythe Boulevard, Zip 28203–5871, Mailing Address: P.O. Box 32861, Zip 28232–2861; tel. 704/355–2000, (Includes CAROLINAS MEDICAL CENTER-MERCY, Mailing address: 2001 Vail Avenue, Charlotte, North Carolina, Zip 28207–1289; tel. 704/304–5000; Scott Jones, Vice President and Facility Executive; LEVINE CHILDREN'S HOSPITAL, Mailing address: 1000 Blythe Boulevard, Charlotte, North Carolina, Zip 28203; tel. 704/381–2000), (Nonreporting) **A**1 2 3 5 10 **F**3 4 6 8 13 15 17 18 19 20 21 22 23 24 25 26 27 28 29 30 31 32 34 35 36 37 38 39 40 41 42 43 44 45 46 47 48 49 50 52 54 55 56 57 58 59 60 61 62 64 65 66 68 70 71 72 73 74 75 76 77 78 79 80 81 82 84 85 86 87 88 89 90 93 96 97 98 99 100 101 102 103 104 105 107 108 111 112 114 115 117 118 119 120 121 123 124 126 130 132 134 135 136 137 138 139 141 142 145 146 147 148 151 153 154 156 **S** Atrium Health, Charlotte, NC
Primary Contact: Eugene A. Woods, FACHE, President and Chief Executive Officer
CFO: Anthony C DeFurio, Executive Vice President Chief Financial Officer
CMO: Roger A Ray, M.D., Executive Vice President and Chief Medical Officer
CHR: Jim Dunn, Ph.D., Chief Human Resource Officer
Web address: www.carolinashealthcare.org/cmc
**Control:** Hospital district or authority, Government, Nonfederal **Service:** General medical and surgical

> **Staffed Beds:** 1287 **Admissions:** 61016 **Census:** 1043 **Outpatient Visits:** 1102640 **Births:** 6315 **Total Expense ($000):** 2062714 **Payroll Expense ($000):** 573244 **Personnel:** 10043

*Many Facility Codes have changed. Please refer to the AHA Guide Code Chart.*
© 2021 AHA Guide

✏ △ **ATRIUM HEALTH'S CAROLINAS REHABILITATION (343026)**, 1100 Blythe Boulevard, Zip 28203–5864; tel. 704/355–4300, (Nonreporting) **A**1 3 7 10 **F**3 29 30 34 35 36 50 53 54 56 57 58 59 60 64 68 74 75 78 79 82 84 86 87 90 91 92 93 94 95 96 119 129 130 131 132 143 144 146 147 148 149 154 157 **P**1 **S** Atrium Health, Charlotte, NC
Primary Contact: Robert G. Larrison Jr, President
CFO: William Hopkins, Director Finance
CMO: William Bockenek, M.D., Chief Medical Officer
CHR: Deonca Leach, Director, Human Resources
CNO: Susan Chase, Vice President
Web address: www.carolinashealthcare.org/rehabilitation
**Control**: Other not–for–profit (including NFP Corporation) **Service**: Rehabilitation

**Staffed Beds: 150 Admissions: 2769 Census: 117 Outpatient Visits: 81522 Births: 0 Total Expense ($000): 100195 Payroll Expense ($000): 39808 Personnel: 712**

✏ **CAROLINAS CONTINUECARE HOSPITAL AT PINEVILLE (342015)**, 10648 Park Road, Zip 28210; tel. 704/667–8050, (Nonreporting) **A**1 10 22 **F**1 3 18 20 29 34 35 45 46 59 65 68 74 75 77 82 85 91 96 130 148 154 **S** Community Hospital Corporation, Plano, TX
Primary Contact: Derek Murzyn, Market Chief Executive Officer
CFO: Joanne Tyo, Chief Financial Officer
CMO: Joseph Lang, M.D., Chief of Staff
CHR: Doug Gallagher, Director Human Resources
CNO: Teshia Davis, Chief Clinical Officer
Web address: www.continuecare.org/pineville/
**Control**: Other not–for–profit (including NFP Corporation) **Service**: Acute long–term care hospital

**Staffed Beds: 40 Admissions: 329 Census: 26 Outpatient Visits: 0 Births: 0 Total Expense ($000): 13703 Payroll Expense ($000): 5875 Personnel: 111**

**CAROLINAS CONTINUECARE HOSPITAL AT PINEVILLE** See Carolinas Continuecare Hospital at Pineville

★ **CAROLINAS CONTINUECARE HOSPITAL AT UNIVERSITY (342021)**, 8800 North Tryon Street, Zip 28262–3300; tel. 704/863–8300, (Nonreporting) **A**10 22 **F**1 3 18 20 29 34 35 45 46 59 65 68 74 75 77 82 84 85 91 96 148 154 **S** Community Hospital Corporation, Plano, TX
Primary Contact: Derek Murzyn, Chief Executive Officer
Web address: www.continuecare.org/charlotte//
**Control**: Other not–for–profit (including NFP Corporation) **Service**: Acute long–term care hospital

**Staffed Beds: 35 Admissions: 233 Census: 16 Outpatient Visits: 0 Births: 0 Total Expense ($000): 8502 Payroll Expense ($000): 4104 Personnel: 49**

⇑ **CAROLINAS HEALTHCARE SYSTEM PINEVILLE** See Atrium Health Pineville

**CAROLINAS HEALTHCARE SYSTEM UNIVERSITY** See Atrium Health University City

**CAROLINAS MED CENTER-PINEVILLE** See Carolinas Medical Center-Mercy

**CAROLINAS MEDICAL CENTER** See Atrium Health's Carolinas Medical Center

**CAROLINAS REHABILITATION** See Atrium Health's Carolinas Rehabilitation

★ **NOVANT HEALTH CHARLOTTE ORTHOPAEDIC HOSPITAL (340153)**, 1901 Randolph Road, Zip 28207–1195; tel. 704/316–2000, (Nonreporting) **S** Novant Health, Winston Salem, NC
Primary Contact: Jamie Feinour, Interim President
CFO: Fred M Hargett, Executive Vice President and Chief Financial Officer
CMO: Thomas Zweng, Executive Vice President and Chief Medical Officer
CIO: David B Garrett, Senior Vice President and Chief Information Officer
CNO: Kelli S Sadler Bell, R.N., Vice President, Chief Nursing Officer
Web address: www.novanthealth.org
**Control**: Other not–for–profit (including NFP Corporation) **Service**: Orthopedic

**Staffed Beds: 15**

☐ **NOVANT HEALTH MINT HILL MEDICAL CENTER (340190)**, 8201 Healthcare Loop, Zip 28215–7072; tel. 980/302–1000, (Nonreporting) **A**1 **S** Novant Health, Winston Salem, NC
Primary Contact: Joy Greear, President
Web address: www.https://www.novanthealth.org
**Control**: Other not–for–profit (including NFP Corporation) **Service**: General medical and surgical

**Staffed Beds: 36**

✏ **NOVANT HEALTH PRESBYTERIAN MEDICAL CENTER (340053)**, 200 Hawthorne Lane, Zip 28204–2528, Mailing Address: P.O. Box 33549, Zip 28233–3549; tel. 704/384–4000, (Includes PRESBYTERIAN HEMBY CHILDREN'S HOSPITAL, Mailing address: 200 Hawthorne Lane, Charlotte, North Carolina, Zip 28204–2515; tel. 704/384–5134), (Nonreporting) **A**1 2 3 10 **S** Novant Health, Winston Salem, NC
Primary Contact: Paula Vincent, MSN, President and Chief Operating Officer
CFO: Fred M Hargett, Executive Vice President and Chief Financial Officer
CMO: Thomas Zweng, Executive Vice President and Chief Medical Officer
CIO: David B Garrett, Senior Vice President Information Technology
CNO: Kelli S Sadler Bell, R.N., Vice President, Chief Nursing Officer
Web address: www.novanthealth.org
**Control**: Other not–for–profit (including NFP Corporation) **Service**: General medical and surgical

**Staffed Beds: 440**

**PRESBYTERIAN HOSPITAL** See Novant Health Presbyterian Medical Center

**PRESBYTERIAN-ORTHOPAEDIC HOSPITAL** See Novant Health Charlotte Orthopaedic Hospital

**CHEROKEE—Swain County**

✏ **CHEROKEE INDIAN HOSPITAL (340156)**, 1 Hospital Road, Zip 28719; tel. 828/497–9163, (Nonreporting) **A**1 3 10
Primary Contact: Casey Cooper, Chief Executive Officer
COO: Beth Greene, Chief Operating Officer
CFO: Chrissy Arch, Chief Financial Officer
CMO: Michael E Toedt, M.D., Director Clinical Services
CIO: Anthony Taylor, Manager Information Technology
Web address: www.cherokeehospital.org
**Control**: Other not–for–profit (including NFP Corporation) **Service**: General medical and surgical

**Staffed Beds: 15**

**CHEROKEE INDIAN HOSPITAL AUTHORITY** See Cherokee Indian Hospital

**CLINTON—Sampson County**

**SAMPSON COUNTY MEM HOSPITAL** See Sampson Regional Medical Center

✏ **SAMPSON REGIONAL MEDICAL CENTER (340024)**, 607 Beaman Street, Zip 28328–2697, Mailing Address: P.O. Box 260, Zip 28329–0260; tel. 910/592–8511, (Nonreporting) **A**1 3 5 10 12 13
Primary Contact: Shawn Howerton, M.D., Chief Executive Officer and President, Medical Staff
COO: Geraldine H Shipp, Director of Risk Management
CFO: Jerry Heinzman, Senior Vice President and Chief Financial Officer
CMO: Shawn Howerton, M.D., Chief Executive Officer and President, Medical Staff
CIO: Kelly Lucas, Chief Information Officer
CHR: Michael W. Gilpin, Vice President Human Resources
Web address: www.sampsonrmc.com
**Control**: County, Government, Nonfederal **Service**: General medical and surgical

**Staffed Beds: 83**

**CLYDE—Haywood County**

✏ **HAYWOOD REGIONAL MEDICAL CENTER (340184)**, 262 Leroy George Drive, Zip 28721–7430; tel. 828/456–7311, (Nonreporting) **A**1 3 10 **S** Duke LifePoint Healthcare, Brentwood, TN
Primary Contact: Chris Fensterle, Interim Chief Executive Officer
COO: Teresa Reynolds, Chief Operating Officer
CFO: Rose Coyne, Interim CFO
CMO: Tyson Smith, M.D., Chief Medical Officer
CIO: Greg Copen, Chief Information Officer
CHR: Janet Millsaps, Vice President Human Resources
Web address: www.haymed.org
**Control**: Hospital district or authority, Government, Nonfederal **Service**: General medical and surgical

**Staffed Beds: 146**

**MEDWEST - HAYWOOD** See Haywood Regional Medical Center

## COLUMBUS—Polk County

⊞ **ST. LUKE'S HOSPITAL (341322)**, 101 Hospital Drive, Zip 28722–6418; tel. 828/894–3311, (Nonreporting) **A**1 10 18 **F**11 15 29 30 31 34 35 40 45 57 59 64 70 75 77 78 79 81 82 85 87 93 98 103 107 108 110 115 119 127 130 133 135 146 148 149 153 154 156 **S** Atrium Health, Charlotte, NC
Primary Contact: Michelle Fortune, R.N., Chief Executive Officer
CFO: Elizabeth Presnell, Assistant Vice President of Finance
CMO: James Holleman, M.D., Chief of Staff
CIO: Nick Whichard, Chief Information Officer
CHR: Amy Norville, Vice President Support Services
CNO: Katherine Hefner, MSN, Chief Nursing Officer
Web address: www.saintlukeshospital.com
**Control**: Other not–for–profit (including NFP Corporation) **Service**: General medical and surgical

**Staffed Beds**: 35 **Admissions**: 1582 **Census**: 21 **Outpatient Visits**: 23166 **Births**: 0 **Total Expense ($000)**: 35450 **Payroll Expense ($000)**: 14521 **Personnel**: 303

## CONCORD—Cabarrus County

⊞ **ATRIUM HEALTH CABARRUS (340001)**, 920 Church Street North, Zip 28025–2983; tel. 704/403–3000, (Nonreporting) **A**1 2 3 10 **F**3 5 6 8 9 11 12 13 15 17 18 20 22 24 26 28 29 30 32 34 35 36 38 40 42 43 44 45 46 47 48 49 50 53 54 55 56 57 58 59 60 61 64 65 68 70 71 72 73 74 75 76 78 79 81 82 84 85 86 87 88 89 92 93 94 97 98 100 102 103 104 107 110 111 114 115 117 118 119 120 121 123 124 126 130 131 132 135 145 146 147 148 149 150 154 156 **S** Atrium Health, Charlotte, NC
Primary Contact: Asha Rodriguez, Vice President and Facility Executive
COO: Bill Hubbard, Vice President, Operations
CFO: Rodney Ball, Vice President Finance
CMO: Dan Hagler, M.D., Vice President and Chief Medical Officer
CIO: Lisa Sykes, Manager, Information Services
CHR: Lesley Chambless, Assistant Vice President Workforce Relations
CNO: Kate Grew, MSN, R.N., Vice President/Chief Nurse Executive
Web address: www.carolinashealthcare.org/northeast
**Control**: Hospital district or authority, Government, Nonfederal **Service**: General medical and surgical

**Staffed Beds**: 455 **Admissions**: 24187 **Census**: 320 **Outpatient Visits**: 308369 **Births**: 2754 **Total Expense ($000)**: 485817 **Payroll Expense ($000)**: 170224 **Personnel**: 2787

**CAROLINAS HEALTHCARE SYSTEM NORTHEAST** See Atrium Health Cabarrus

## DANBURY—Stokes County

★ ⇑ **LIFEBRITE COMMUNITY HOSPITAL OF STOKES (341317)**, 1570 NC 8 & 89 Highway North, Zip 27016, Mailing Address: P.O. Box 10, Zip 27016–0010; tel. 336/593–2831, (Nonreporting) **A**10 18 21 **S** LifeBrite Hospital Group, LLC, Lilburn, GA
Primary Contact: Pamela P. Tillman, Administrator
COO: Samantha Freeman-Brown, Assistant Administrator, Respiratory Director
CFO: Warren S. Binderman, Chief Financial Officer
CMO: Kirk S. Sanders, M.D., Chief of Staff
CIO: Ada Ashley, HIM Director
CHR: Shannon Manring, Director Human Resources
CNO: Pamela P. Tillman, Administrator
Web address: www.lifebritestokes.com
**Control**: Corporation, Investor–owned (for–profit) **Service**: General medical and surgical

**Staffed Beds**: 65

⇑ **PIONEER COMMUNITY HOSPITAL OF STOKES** See Lifebrite Community Hospital of Stokes

## DUNN—Harnett County

☐ **HARNETT HEALTH SYSTEM (340071)**, 800 Tilghman Drive, Zip 28334–5599, Mailing Address: P.O. Box 1706, Zip 28335–1706; tel. 910/892–1000, (Includes CENTRAL HARTNETT HOSPITAL, Mailing address: 215 Brightwater Drive, Lillington, North Carolina, Zip 27546; tel. 910/892–1000), (Nonreporting) **A**1 3 5 10 12 13 **S** Cape Fear Valley Health System, Fayetteville, NC
Primary Contact: Kevin Jackson, Interim Chief Executive Officer
COO: Kenneth E Bryan, FACHE, President and Chief Executive Officer
CFO: Lynn Lambert, Chief Financial Officer
CIO: Tim Krieger, Director Information Systems
CHR: Sondra Davis, Vice President Human Resources & System Development
CNO: Vicki Allen, R.N., MS, Vice President Patient Care Services and Chief Nursing Officer
Web address: www.myharnetthealth.org/
**Control**: Other not–for–profit (including NFP Corporation) **Service**: General medical and surgical

**Staffed Beds**: 105

**HARTNETT HEALTH SYSTEM** See Harnett Health System

## DURHAM—Durham County

⊞ **DUKE REGIONAL HOSPITAL (340155)**, 3643 North Roxboro Street, Zip 27704–2763; tel. 919/470–4000, (Nonreporting) **A**1 3 5 10 **F**3 8 11 12 13 15 17 18 20 22 24 26 29 30 31 34 35 40 44 45 47 50 51 57 58 59 60 64 66 68 70 73 74 75 76 77 78 79 80 81 82 84 85 86 87 90 96 98 100 101 102 107 108 110 111 115 118 119 120 121 123 124 126 130 131 132 135 146 147 148 149 154 **P**6 **S** Duke University Health System, Durham, NC
Primary Contact: Kathleen B. Galbraith, FACHE, President
COO: A. Mitch Babb, Vice President, Operations
CFO: Jonathan B Hoy, Chief Financial Officer
CMO: Adia K. Ross, Chief Medical Officer
CIO: Terry Mears, Director Information Systems
CHR: Dexter Nolley, Chief Human Resources Officer
CNO: Victoria K Orto, R.N., Chief Nursing and Patient Care Services Officer
Web address: www.dukehealth.org
**Control**: Other not–for–profit (including NFP Corporation) **Service**: General medical and surgical

**Staffed Beds**: 227 **Admissions**: 17291 **Census**: 227 **Outpatient Visits**: 195900 **Births**: 2309 **Total Expense ($000)**: 381037 **Payroll Expense ($000)**: 165372 **Personnel**: 2221

⊞ **DUKE UNIVERSITY HOSPITAL (340030)**, 2301 Erwin Road, Zip 27705–4699, Mailing Address: P.O. Box 3814, Zip 27710–3708; tel. 919/684–8111, (Includes DUKE CHILDREN'S HOSPITAL & HEALTH CENTER, Mailing address: 2301 Erwin Road, Durham, North Carolina, Zip 27710–0001, PO Box 3708, Zip 27702, tel. 919/684–8111), (Nonreporting) **A**1 2 3 5 8 10 **F**3 6 7 9 11 12 13 15 17 18 19 20 21 22 23 24 25 26 27 28 29 30 31 32 34 35 36 37 39 40 41 43 44 45 46 47 48 49 50 53 54 55 56 57 58 59 60 61 64 65 68 70 72 73 74 75 76 77 78 79 80 81 82 84 85 86 87 88 89 91 92 93 94 96 97 98 99 100 101 102 103 104 107 108 110 111 112 114 115 116 117 118 119 120 121 123 124 126 129 130 131 132 135 136 137 138 139 140 141 142 145 146 147 148 149 154 155 156 **P**1 6 **S** Duke University Health System, Durham, NC
Primary Contact: Thomas Owens, M.D., President
CFO: Sabrina Olsen, Chief Financial Officer
CMO: Lisa C Pickett, M.D., Chief Medical Officer
CIO: Jeffrey Ferranti, M.D., Chief Information Officer
CHR: Deborah Page, Chief Human Resources Officer
CNO: Mary Ann Fuchs, R.N., Vice President Patient Care and System Chief Nurse Executive
Web address: www.dukehealth.org
**Control**: Other not–for–profit (including NFP Corporation) **Service**: General medical and surgical

**Staffed Beds**: 974 **Admissions**: 43881 **Census**: 845 **Outpatient Visits**: 1129738 **Births**: 3553 **Total Expense ($000)**: 2370045 **Payroll Expense ($000)**: 666086 **Personnel**: 11821

**DUKE UNIVERSITY MEDICAL CENTER** See Duke University Hospital

**DURHAM REGIONAL HOSPITAL** See Duke Regional Hospital

✠ **DURHAM VETERANS AFFAIRS MEDICAL CENTER**, 508 Fulton Street, Zip 27705–3897; tel. 919/286–0411, (Nonreporting) **A**1 3 5 **S** Department of Veterans Affairs, Washington, DC
Primary Contact: Paul Crews, Director
COO: Sara Haigh, Associate Director
CFO: David Kuboushek, Chief, Fiscal Service
CMO: John D Shelburne, M.D., Chief of Staff
CIO: Toby Dickerson, Chief Information Resources Management Services
CHR: Jerry Freeman, Chief, Human Resources Management Services
Web address: www.durham.va.gov/
**Control**: Veterans Affairs, Government, federal **Service**: General medical and surgical

**Staffed Beds**: 251

☐ **NORTH CAROLINA SPECIALTY HOSPITAL (340049)**, 3916 Ben Franklin Boulevard, Zip 27704–2383, Mailing Address: PO Box 15819, Zip 27704–2383; tel. 919/956–9300, (Nonreporting) **A**1 10 **F**3 29 30 51 64 70 79 81 82 85 86 87 89 107 119 126 130 131 148 154 **S** National Surgical Healthcare, Chicago, IL
Primary Contact: Randi L. Shults, Chief Executive Officer
CFO: Bill Wilson, Chief Financial Officer
CMO: David Musante, M.D., Medical Director
CHR: Sarah Bohlin, Human Resources Director
CNO: John Medlin, Chief Nursing Officer
Web address: www.ncspecialty.com
**Control**: Partnership, Investor–owned (for–profit) **Service**: Surgical

**Staffed Beds**: 18 **Admissions**: 1608 **Census**: 8 **Outpatient Visits**: 7700 **Births**: 0 **Total Expense ($000)**: 42436 **Payroll Expense ($000)**: 13048 **Personnel**: 227

✠ **SELECT SPECIALTY HOSPITAL-DURHAM (342018)**, 3643 North Roxboro Road, 6th Floor, Zip 27704–2702; tel. 919/470–9159, (Nonreporting) **A**1 10 **S** Select Medical Corporation, Mechanicsburg, PA
Primary Contact: Jennifer Rawley, PharmD, Chief Executive Officer
CHR: Michael Stinson, Human Resources Coordinator
CNO: Cole Oren, R.N., Chief Nursing Officer
Web address: www.selectspecialtyhospitals.com/company/locations/durham.aspx
**Control**: Corporation, Investor–owned (for–profit) **Service**: Acute long–term care hospital

**Staffed Beds**: 30

**VERITAS COLLABORATIVE**, 4024 Stirrup Creek Drive, Zip 27703–9464; tel. 919/908–9730, (Nonreporting) **S** Veritas Collaborative, Durham, NC
Primary Contact: Sara Hofmeier, Executive Director
Web address: www.https://veritascollaborative.com
**Control**: Partnership, Investor–owned (for–profit) **Service**: Psychiatric

**Staffed Beds**: 40

**VERITAS COLLABORATIVE**, 615 Douglas Street, Suite 500, Zip 27705–6616; tel. 919/908–9730, (Nonreporting) **S** Veritas Collaborative, Durham, NC
Primary Contact: Becca Eckstein, Executive Director
Web address: www.https://veritascollaborative.com
**Control**: Partnership, Investor–owned (for–profit) **Service**: Psychiatric

**Staffed Beds**: 25

**VETERANS AFFAIRS MED CENTER** See Durham Veterans Affairs Medical Center

⇑ **MOREHEAD MEMORIAL HOSPITAL** See UNC Rockingham Health Care

★ ⇑ **UNC ROCKINGHAM HEALTH CARE (340060)**, 117 East King's Highway, Zip 27288–5201; tel. 336/623–9711, (Total facility includes 121 beds in nursing home–type unit) (Nonreporting) **A**10 21 **F**3 11 13 15 26 29 30 34 35 40 45 47 48 49 50 57 59 64 68 70 74 76 77 81 85 87 89 90 93 107 108 110 111 114 118 119 128 129 130 132 143 144 146 147 148 154 **S** UNC Health Care, Chapel Hill, NC
Primary Contact: Steven E. Eblin, Interim President and Chief Executive Officer
CFO: LaTonya Brown, Interim Chief Operating Officer and Chief Financial Officer
CIO: Wade Williams, Chief Information Officer
CHR: Janine Eanes, Senior Human Resources Business Partner
CNO: JoAnn P. Smith, R.N., Chief Nursing Officer, and Vice President Patient Care Services
Web address: www.uncrockingham.org
**Control**: Other not–for–profit (including NFP Corporation) **Service**: General medical and surgical

**Staffed Beds**: 188 **Admissions**: 3220 **Census**: 129 **Outpatient Visits**: 68587 **Births**: 432 **Total Expense ($000)**: 62654 **Payroll Expense ($000)**: 24901 **Personnel**: 356

**CHOWAN HOSPITAL** See Vidant Chowan Hospital

✠ **VIDANT CHOWAN HOSPITAL (341318)**, 211 Virginia Road, Zip 27932–9668, Mailing Address: P.O. Box 629, Zip 27932–0629; tel. 252/482–8451, (Nonreporting) **A**1 3 10 18 **F**3 11 13 15 28 29 30 31 34 35 40 45 46 57 59 64 70 74 75 76 77 78 79 81 82 84 85 93 107 108 110 111 114 119 130 132 135 146 147 148 156 **S** Vidant Health, Greenville, NC
Primary Contact: Brian Harvill, President
CMO: William Hope IVChief of Medical Staff
CIO: Brian White, Director Strategic Operations
CHR: Nicole Spell, Director Human Resources
CNO: Cindy Coker, Vice President, Patient Care Services
Web address: www.vidanthealth.com
**Control**: Other not–for–profit (including NFP Corporation) **Service**: General medical and surgical

**Staffed Beds**: 19 **Admissions**: 1538 **Census**: 14 **Outpatient Visits**: 38773 **Births**: 343 **Total Expense ($000)**: 46230 **Payroll Expense ($000)**: 15963 **Personnel**: 299

⇑ **ALBEMARLE HEALTH** See Sentara Albemarle Medical Center

★ ⇑ **SENTARA ALBEMARLE MEDICAL CENTER (340109)**, 1144 North Road Street, Zip 27909–3473, Mailing Address: P.O. Box 1587, Zip 27906–1587; tel. 252/335–0531, (Nonreporting) **A**10 21 **F**3 11 13 15 18 20 22 28 29 30 34 35 36 37 38 39 40 41 44 45 46 47 48 49 50 51 56 57 58 59 60 61 63 64 65 68 70 74 75 76 77 78 79 81 84 85 86 87 91 92 93 94 96 97 102 107 108 110 111 114 118 119 121 130 131 132 135 141 146 147 148 149 154 **S** Sentara Healthcare, Norfolk, VA
Primary Contact: Phillip E. Jackson, President
CFO: Craig Lewis, Chief Financial Officer
CMO: Charles Nicholson, Vice President, Medical Affairs
CHR: Deborah Ferguson, Director, Human Resources
CNO: Jaime Carroll, R.N., Vice President Nursing
Web address: www.albemarlehealth.org
**Control**: Other not–for–profit (including NFP Corporation) **Service**: General medical and surgical

**Staffed Beds**: 109 **Admissions**: 4709 **Census**: 49 **Outpatient Visits**: 260928 **Births**: 390 **Total Expense ($000)**: 111303 **Payroll Expense ($000)**: 41622 **Personnel**: 707

**BLADEN COUNTY HOSPITAL** See Cape Fear Valley - Bladen County Hospital

✠ **CAPE FEAR VALLEY - BLADEN COUNTY HOSPITAL (341315)**, 501 South Poplar Street, Zip 28337–9375, Mailing Address: P.O. Box 398, Zip 28337–0398; tel. 910/862–5100, (Nonreporting) **A**1 10 18 **S** Cape Fear Valley Health System, Fayetteville, NC
Primary Contact: Stephen Fife, Interim Chief Executive Officer
CFO: Stephen Fife, Chief Financial Officer
CIO: Craig Kellum, Director Management Information Systems
CHR: Brenda E. Hubbard, Corporate Director, Human Resources
CNO: Traci R. Preston, Director of Nursing
Web address: www.bchn.org
**Control**: County, Government, Nonfederal **Service**: General medical and surgical

**Staffed Beds**: 25

✠ **HUGH CHATHAM MEMORIAL HOSPITAL (340097)**, 180 Parkwood Drive, Zip 28621–2430, Mailing Address: P.O. Box 560, Zip 28621–0560; tel. 336/527–7000, (Nonreporting) **A**1 10 **F**3 11 13 15 28 29 30 34 40 45 49 53 57 59 62 64 70 74 75 76 77 79 81 85 87 93 96 107 108 110 111 118 119 120 121 125 127 130 131 132 133 135 144 146 147 148 149 154 **P**6
Primary Contact: Paul Hammes, Chief Executive Officer
COO: Mary Blackburn, Vice President Operations and Chief Practice Officer
CFO: Donald E Trippel, Chief Financial Officer
CMO: Dominick Carbone, M.D., Chief of Staff
CIO: Lee Powe, Director Management Information Systems
CHR: Kathy Poteate, Human Resources Manager
CNO: Paula Moore, R.N., Chief Clinical Officer
Web address: www.hughchatham.org
**Control**: Other not–for–profit (including NFP Corporation) **Service**: General medical and surgical

**Staffed Beds**: 35 **Admissions**: 3757 **Census**: 34 **Outpatient Visits**: 71055 **Births**: 573 **Total Expense ($000)**: 67496 **Payroll Expense ($000)**: 24916 **Personnel**: 481

---

**Hospital, Medicare Provider Number, Address, Telephone, Approval, Facility, and Physician Codes, Health Care System**

★ American Hospital Association (AHA) membership
☐ The Joint Commission accreditation
○ Healthcare Facilities Accreditation Program
◇ DNV Healthcare Inc. accreditation
⇑ Center for Improvement in Healthcare Quality Accreditation
△ Commission on Accreditation of Rehabilitation Facilities (CARF) accreditation

**NC**

## FAYETTEVILLE—Cumberland County

**CAPE FEAR VALLEY HEALTH SYSTEM** See Cape Fear Valley Medical Center

⊞ △ **CAPE FEAR VALLEY MEDICAL CENTER (340028)**, 1638 Owen Drive, Zip 28304–3431, Mailing Address: P.O. Box 2000, Zip 28302–2000; tel. 910/615–4000, (Includes BEHAVIORAL HEALTH CARE OF CAPE FEAR VALLEY HEALTH SYSTEM, Mailing address: 711 Executive Place, Fayetteville, North Carolina, Zip 28301; tel. 910/615–3700; CAPE FEAR VALLEY REHABILITATION CENTER, Mailing address: 1638 Owen Drive, Fayetteville, North Carolina, Zip 28304; tel. 910/615–4000), (Nonreporting) **A**1 2 3 5 7 8 10 12 13 19 **F**3 4 5 7 12 13 14 15 17 18 20 22 24 26 28 29 30 31 34 35 38 39 40 41 43 44 45 46 47 48 49 53 54 55 56 57 58 59 60 61 64 65 68 70 72 73 74 75 76 77 78 79 81 82 84 85 86 87 88 89 90 91 92 93 96 97 98 100 101 102 104 107 108 109 110 111 114 115 116 117 118 119 120 121 122 123 124 126 127 129 130 132 135 143 144 146 147 148 149 150 153 154 155 156 **S** Cape Fear Valley Health System, Fayetteville, NC
Primary Contact: Michael Nagowski, Chief Executive Officer
COO: Daniel R Weatherly, Chief Operating Officer
CFO: Sandra Williams, Chief Financial Officer
CMO: Samuel A Fleishman, M.D., Chief Medical Officer
CIO: Phillip E. Wood JrChief Information Officer
CNO: Deborah Marshburn, Chief Nursing Executive
Web address: www.capefearvalley.com
**Control:** Other not–for–profit (including NFP Corporation) **Service:** General medical and surgical

**Staffed Beds:** 620 **Admissions:** 35368 **Census:** 464 **Outpatient Visits:** 266947 **Births:** 4671 **Total Expense ($000):** 739915 **Payroll Expense ($000):** 374254 **Personnel:** 5013

**CUMBERLAND HOSPITAL** See Behavioral Health Care of Cape Fear Valley Health System

⊞ **FAYETTEVILLE VETERANS AFFAIRS MEDICAL CENTER**, 2300 Ramsey Street, Zip 28301–3899; tel. 910/488–2120, (Nonreporting) **A**1 3 5 **S** Department of Veterans Affairs, Washington, DC
Primary Contact: Webster Carl. Bazemore, M.D., Interim Medical Director
COO: James Galkowski, Associate Director for Operations
CFO: Patrick Bullard, Chief Financial Officer
CMO: Greg Antoine, M.D., Chief of Staff
CIO: Kenneth Williams, Chief Information Officer
CHR: Joseph Whaley, Chief, Human Resources Management Service
CNO: Joyce Alexander-Hines, R.N., MSN, Associate Director, Patient Care Services
Web address: www.fayettevillenc.va.gov
**Control:** Veterans Affairs, Government, federal **Service:** General medical and surgical

**Staffed Beds:** 58

**HIGHSMITH-RAINEY MEMORIAL HOSPITAL** See Highsmith-Rainey Specialty Hospital

☐ **HIGHSMITH-RAINEY SPECIALTY HOSPITAL (342014)**, 150 Robeson Street, Zip 28301–5570; tel. 910/615–1000, (Nonreporting) **A**1 10 **F**1 3 11 29 30 35 39 50 51 58 68 70 81 85 107 114 119 130 144 146 148 149 150 **P**6 **S** Cape Fear Valley Health System, Fayetteville, NC
Primary Contact: Kevin Jackson, On Site Administrator
Web address: www.capefearvalley.com
**Control:** Other not–for–profit (including NFP Corporation) **Service:** Acute long–term care hospital

**Staffed Beds:** 66 **Admissions:** 283 **Census:** 55 **Outpatient Visits:** 27602 **Births:** 0 **Total Expense ($000):** 29933 **Payroll Expense ($000):** 17695 **Personnel:** 297

**SOUTHEASTERN REGIONAL REHABILITATION CENTER** See Cape Fear Valley Rehabilitation Center

**VETERANS AFFAIRS MEDICAL CENTER** See Fayetteville Veterans Affairs Medical Center

## FORT BRAGG—Cumberland County

**WOMACK ARMY COMMUNITY HOSPITAL** See Womack Army Medical Center

⊞ **WOMACK ARMY MEDICAL CENTER**, 2817 Reilly Road, Zip 28310–7302; tel. 910/907–6000, (Nonreporting) **A**1 3 5 **S** Department of the Army, Office of the Surgeon General, Falls Church, VA
Primary Contact: Colonel Lance C. Raney, Commander
CIO: Mary Peters, Chief Information Officer
Web address: www.wamc.amedd.army.mil/
**Service:** General medical and surgical

**Staffed Beds:** 156

## FRANKLIN—Macon County

**ANGEL COMMUNITY HOSPITAL** See Angel Medical Center

⊞ **ANGEL MEDICAL CENTER (341326)**, 120 Riverview Street, Zip 28734–2612, Mailing Address: P.O. Box 1209, Zip 28744–0569; tel. 828/524–8411, (Nonreporting) **A**1 3 10 18 **S** HCA Healthcare, Nashville, TN
Primary Contact: Karen S. Gorby, R.N., MSN, FACHE, Chief Executive Officer and Chief Nursing Officer
COO: Martin Wadewitz, Chief Operations Officer/ Vice President, Operations
CFO: George Kimbro, Vice President Finance
CIO: Ed Coye, Director Information Technology Mission Health System Hospitals
CHR: Teresa Mallonee, Director Human Resources
Web address: www.angelmed.org
**Control:** Hospital district or authority, Government, Nonfederal **Service:** General medical and surgical

**Staffed Beds:** 59

## GARNER—Wake County

☐ **STRATEGIC BEHAVIORAL HEALTH - RALEIGH (344028)**, 3200 Waterfield Drive, Zip 27529–7727; tel. 919/800–4400, (Nonreporting) **A**1 10 **S** Strategic Behavioral Health, LLC, Memphis, TN
Primary Contact: Matt Doyle, Chief Executive Officer
CMO: Karen Miles, M.D., Medical Director
CHR: Christina Meeker, Director Human Resources
CNO: Shawanna Royal, R.N., Director Nursing
Web address: www.sbcraleigh.com/
**Control:** Corporation, Investor–owned (for–profit) **Service:** Children's hospital psychiatric

**Staffed Beds:** 50

## GASTONIA—Gaston County

⊞ **CAROMONT REGIONAL MEDICAL CENTER (340032)**, 2525 Court Drive, Zip 28054–2140, Mailing Address: P.O. Box 1747, Zip 28053–1747; tel. 704/834–2000, (Nonreporting) **A**1 2 10
Primary Contact: Chris Peek, Chief Executive Officer
COO: Kathleen Besson, Executive Vice President and Chief Operating Officer
CFO: David O'Connor, Executive Vice President and Chief Financial Officer
CMO: Todd Davis, M.D., Executive Vice President, Chief Medical Officer
CIO: Robin Lynn Lang, Vice President, Chief Information Officer
CHR: Joel Riddle, Senior Director Human Resources
CNO: Scott E. Wells, MSN, R.N., Vice President Patient Care Services
Web address: www.caromonthealth.org
**Control:** Other not–for–profit (including NFP Corporation) **Service:** General medical and surgical

**Staffed Beds:** 423

**CAROMONT REGIONAL MEDICAL CENTER** See Caromont Regional Medical Center

## GOLDSBORO—Wayne County

☐ **CHERRY HOSPITAL (344026)**, 1401 West Ash Street, Zip 27530–1057; tel. 919/947–7000, (Nonreporting) **A**1 3 10 **F**30 39 98 103 106 119 130 143 146 149
Primary Contact: J. Luckey. Welsh Jr, Chief Executive Officer
CFO: Susie Sherrod Sanders, Chief Financial Officer
CMO: Jim Mayo, M.D., Clinical Director
CIO: Mike Letchworth, Manager Information Systems
CHR: Carol Thornton, Director Human Resources
CNO: Debbie Wall, Chief Nursing Officer
Web address: www.cherryhospital.org
**Control:** State, Government, Nonfederal **Service:** Psychiatric

**Staffed Beds:** 243 **Admissions:** 892 **Census:** 227 **Outpatient Visits:** 0 **Births:** 0 **Total Expense ($000):** 112052 **Payroll Expense ($000):** 65467 **Personnel:** 1166

**NC**

*Many Facility Codes have changed. Please refer to the AHA Guide Code Chart.*

**WAYNE MEMORIAL HOSPITAL** See Wayne UNC Health Care

☒ **WAYNE UNC HEALTH CARE (340010)**, 2700 Wayne Memorial Drive, Zip 27534–9494, Mailing Address: P.O. Box 8001, Zip 27533–8001; tel. 919/736–1110, (Nonreporting) **A**1 5 10 **F**3 8 13 15 18 20 22 28 29 30 31 34 35 39 40 45 47 49 50 57 58 59 60 64 66 68 70 73 74 75 76 77 78 79 80 81 85 86 87 89 92 93 96 98 100 101 102 107 108 110 111 114 118 119 126 129 130 132 145 146 147 148 156 **S** UNC Health Care, Chapel Hill, NC
Primary Contact: Janie Jaberg, FACHE, President and Chief Executive Officer
COO: Thomas A Bradshaw, Vice President Operations
CFO: Rebecca W Craig, Vice President and Chief Financial Officer
CIO: Lori Cole, Director Information Technology
Web address: www.waynehealth.org
**Control**: Other not–for–profit (including NFP Corporation) **Service**: General medical and surgical

**Staffed Beds**: 274 **Admissions**: 10392 **Census**: 129 **Outpatient Visits**: 234322 **Births**: 1323 **Total Expense ($000)**: 251341 **Payroll Expense ($000)**: 101898 **Personnel**: 1512

## GREENSBORO—Guilford County

**CHARTER GREENSBORO HEALTH SYST** See Behavioral Health Center

**CONE HEALTH** See Moses H. Cone Memorial Hospital

**GREENSBORO HOSPITAL** See Women's Hospital of Greensboro

☒ **KINDRED HOSPITAL-GREENSBORO (342012)**, 2401 Southside Boulevard, Zip 27406–3311; tel. 336/271–2800, (Nonreporting) **A**1 10 **S** Kindred Healthcare, Louisville, KY
Primary Contact: Mary-Lyn Baldauf, Chief Executive Officer
CFO: Anthony Grate, Controller
CMO: Saad Amin, Medical Director Hospital
CIO: Little Shuford, Health Information Manager
CNO: Anne Correll, Chief Clinical Officer
Web address: www.khgreensboro.com
**Control**: Corporation, Investor–owned (for–profit) **Service**: Acute long–term care hospital

**Staffed Beds**: 101

☒ △ **MOSES H. CONE MEMORIAL HOSPITAL (340091)**, 1200 North Elm Street, Zip 27401–1020; tel. 336/832–7000, (Includes ANNIE PENN HOSPITAL, Mailing address: 618 South Main Street, Reidsville, North Carolina, Zip 27320–5094; tel. 336/951–4000; Cynthia B Farrand, President; BEHAVIORAL HEALTH CENTER, Mailing address: 700 Walter Reed Drive, Greensboro, North Carolina, Zip 27403–1129; tel. 336/832–9600; Debbie Cunningham, R.N., Senior Vice President, Cone Health and President, Maternal, Child and Behavioral Health Services; CONE HEALTH, Mailing address: 1200 North Elm Street, Greensboro, North Carolina, Zip 27401; tel. 336/832–7000; Judith A Schanel, R.N., MSN, FACHE, Chief Operating Officer; WESLEY LONG COMMUNITY HOSPITAL, Mailing address: 501 North Elam Avenue, Greensboro, North Carolina, Zip 27403; tel. 336/832–1000; Paul A Jeffrey, President; WOMEN'S HOSPITAL OF GREENSBORO, Mailing address: 801 Green Valley Road, Greensboro, North Carolina, Zip 27408; tel. 336/832–6500; Debbie Cunningham, R.N., President) (Total facility includes 92 beds in nursing home–type unit) **A**1 3 5 7 10 19 **F**3 5 7 8 12 13 15 17 18 19 20 22 24 26 28 29 30 31 32 34 35 36 37 39 40 41 43 44 45 46 47 49 50 54 55 56 57 58 59 60 61 63 64 66 68 70 72 74 75 76 77 78 79 81 82 83 84 85 86 87 88 89 90 92 93 95 96 97 98 99 100 101 102 103 104 105 107 108 110 111 114 115 117 118 119 120 121 123 124 126 127 128 129 130 131 132 134 135 144 145 146 147 148 149 152 153 154 156 **S** Cone Health, Greensboro, NC
Primary Contact: Preston W. Hammock, President
CFO: Jeffrey Jones, Chief Financial Officer
CMO: William Bowman, M.D., Vice President Medical Affairs
CIO: Steve Horsley, Vice President and Chief Information Officer
CHR: Noel F Burt, Ph.D., Chief Human Resources Officer
CNO: Ann Marie Madden, MS, R.N., Vice President of Patient Care Services and Chief Nursing Officer
Web address: www.conehealth.com/locations/moses-cone-hospital/
**Control**: Other not–for–profit (including NFP Corporation) **Service**: General medical and surgical

**Staffed Beds**: 910 **Admissions**: 48276 **Census**: 589 **Outpatient Visits**: 797276 **Births**: 6003 **Total Expense ($000)**: 1302410 **Payroll Expense ($000)**: 469626 **Personnel**: 10079

**MOSES H. CONE MEMORIAL HOSPITAL** See Cone Health

☒ **SELECT SPECIALTY HOSPITAL-GREENSBORO (342020)**, 1200 North Elm Street, 5th Floor, Zip 27401–1004; tel. 336/832–8571, (Nonreporting) **A**1 10 **S** Select Medical Corporation, Mechanicsburg, PA
Primary Contact: Deana Knight, Chief Executive Officer
CHR: Karen Tracey, Chief Human Resources
CNO: Robin Clark, Chief Nursing Officer
Web address: www.selectspecialtyhospitals.com/company/locations/greensboro.aspx
**Control**: Corporation, Investor–owned (for–profit) **Service**: Acute long–term care hospital

**Staffed Beds**: 30

**VENCOR HOSPITAL-GREENSBORO** See Kindred Hospital-Greensboro

## GREENVILLE—Pitt County

**PITT COUNTY MEMORIAL HOSPITAL** See Vidant Medical Center

☒ △ **VIDANT MEDICAL CENTER (340040)**, 2100 Stantonsburg Road, Zip 27834–2818, Mailing Address: P.O. Box 6028, Zip 27835–6028; tel. 252/847–4100, (Includes JAMES AND CONNIE MAYNARD CHILDREN'S HOSPITAL, Mailing address: 2101 Stantonsburg Road, Greenville, North Carolina, Zip 27834–2817; tel. 252/847–5712; UNIVERSITY HEALTH SYSTEMS CHILDREN'S HOSPITAL, Mailing address: 2100 Stantonsburg Road, Greenville, North Carolina, Zip 27834–2818, PO Box 6028, Zip 27835–6028, tel. 252/847–4100), (Nonreporting) **A**1 2 3 5 7 8 10 **S** Vidant Health, Greenville, NC
Primary Contact: William Brian. Floyd, President
CFO: David S Hughes, Chief Financial Officer
CMO: Paul Shackelford, M.D., Chief Medical Officer
CHR: Tyree Walker, Chief Human Resources Officer
CNO: Linda D Hofler, Ph.D., R.N., FACHE, Senior Vice President, Nurse Executive
Web address: www.https://www.vidanthealth.com/
**Control**: Other not–for–profit (including NFP Corporation) **Service**: General medical and surgical

**Staffed Beds**: 974

**W B JONES ALCOHOLIC REHAB CTR** See Walter B. Jones Alcohol and Drug Abuse Treatment Center

☐ **WALTER B. JONES ALCOHOL AND DRUG ABUSE TREATMENT CENTER (344033)**, 2577 West Fifth Street, Zip 27834–7813; tel. 252/830–3426, (Nonreporting) **A**1
Primary Contact: Ben Gregory, Chief Executive Officer
CFO: Roy Carlton, Chief Financial Officer
CMO: Sonya Longest, M.D., Chief Medical Officer
CIO: Jed Hayn, Chief Information Officer
CHR: Amy Marion, Chief Human Resource Officer
CNO: Linda Roy, R.N., Chief Nursing Officer
Web address: www.ncdhhs.gov
**Control**: State, Government, Nonfederal **Service**: Alcoholism and other chemical dependency

**Staffed Beds**: 80

## HENDERSON—Vance County

**MARIA PARHAM HOSPITAL** See Maria Parham Medical Center

☒ **MARIA PARHAM MEDICAL CENTER (340132)**, 566 Ruin Creek Road, Zip 27536–2927; tel. 252/438–4143, (Nonreporting) **A**1 2 3 5 10 **F**3 11 13 15 18 20 22 28 29 30 31 34 39 40 42 43 44 45 46 48 49 50 54 57 59 60 64 70 74 75 76 77 78 79 80 81 82 85 86 87 90 91 92 93 94 96 97 98 100 102 103 105 107 108 110 111 114 118 119 120 121 123 129 130 131 132 135 146 147 148 149 154 157 **P**6 **S** Duke LifePoint Healthcare, Brentwood, TN
Primary Contact: Bert Beard, Chief Executive Officer
CFO: Jim Chatman, Chief Financial Officer
CIO: Randy Williams, Director Management Information Systems
Web address: www.mariaparham.com
**Control**: Partnership, Investor–owned (for–profit) **Service**: General medical and surgical

**Staffed Beds**: 115 **Admissions**: 4829 **Census**: 57 **Outpatient Visits**: 151448 **Births**: 471 **Total Expense ($000)**: 122935 **Payroll Expense ($000)**: 40304 **Personnel**: 614

## HENDERSONVILLE—Henderson County

✉ ○ **ADVENTHEALTH HENDERSONVILLE (340023)**, 100 Hospital Drive, Zip 28792–5272; tel. 828/684–8501, (Nonreporting) **A**1 2 3 10 11 19 **F**3 11 13 15 18 26 28 29 30 31 34 35 40 50 54 59 62 64 65 68 70 74 75 76 77 78 79 80 81 85 87 93 97 98 100 101 102 103 104 105 107 108 110 111 115 118 119 126 129 130 131 142 144 146 147 148 153 154 **P**6 **S** AdventHealth, Altamonte Springs, FL
Primary Contact: Cory Reeves, President and Chief Executive Officer
COO: Scott Miller, Vice President and Chief Operating Officer
CFO: Ella Stenstrom, Vice President and Chief Financial Officer
CMO: Teresa Herbert, M.D., Chief Medical Officer
CIO: Lee Strickland, Regional Director Information Technology
CHR: Sharon J Campbell, Director, Human Resources
CNO: Roland Eugene Joy JrVice President and Chief Nursing Officer
Web address: www.adventhealth.com/hospital/adventhealth-hendersonville
**Control**: Other not–for–profit (including NFP Corporation) **Service**: General medical and surgical

**Staffed Beds:** 86 **Admissions:** 3989 **Census:** 42 **Outpatient Visits:** 387984 **Births:** 611 **Total Expense ($000):** 194374 **Payroll Expense ($000):** 75463 **Personnel:** 1036

★ ⇑ **MARGARET R. PARDEE MEMORIAL HOSPITAL (340017)**, 800 North Justice Street, Zip 28791–3410; tel. 828/696–1000, (Nonreporting) **A**2 3 10 21 **F**3 4 11 12 13 15 18 20 22 26 28 29 30 31 34 35 36 37 38 39 40 44 45 46 47 48 49 50 54 56 57 58 59 62 63 64 65 68 70 73 74 75 76 77 78 79 81 82 85 86 87 89 92 93 94 97 98 100 101 102 107 108 110 111 114 115 118 119 120 121 123 129 130 131 132 135 143 144 145 146 147 148 149 150 154 156 157 **P**6 **S** UNC Health Care, Chapel Hill, NC
Primary Contact: James M. Kirby II, President and Chief Executive Officer
CFO: Andrew R. Wampler, Chief Financial Officer
CMO: Robert Kiskaddon, M.D., Chief Medical Officer
Web address: www.pardeehospital.org
**Control**: County, Government, Nonfederal **Service**: General medical and surgical

**Staffed Beds:** 158 **Admissions:** 8442 **Census:** 87 **Outpatient Visits:** 533071 **Births:** 336 **Total Expense ($000):** 243837 **Payroll Expense ($000):** 87599 **Personnel:** 1320

**PARK RIDGE HEALTH** See Adventhealth Hendersonville

## HICKORY—Catawba County

**CATAWBA MEMORIAL HOSPITAL** See Catawba Valley Medical Center

✉ △ **CATAWBA VALLEY MEDICAL CENTER (340143)**, 810 Fairgrove Church Road SE, Zip 28602–9643; tel. 828/326–3000, (Nonreporting) **A**1 2 7 10 **F**3 11 12 13 15 18 20 22 26 28 29 30 31 34 35 37 39 40 44 45 49 50 51 53 54 56 57 58 59 61 64 65 68 70 71 72 74 75 76 77 78 79 81 84 85 86 87 89 90 91 92 93 96 97 98 100 101 102 103 104 107 108 109 110 111 114 115 117 118 119 120 121 122 123 124 126 129 130 131 132 135 143 144 145 146 147 148 149 154 156 **P**8
Primary Contact: Edward L. Beard, R.N., President and Chief Executive Officer
CFO: Kimberly Crews, Vice President and Chief Financial Officer
CMO: Andrew Chesson, Chief Medical Officer
CIO: Tim Blanchat, Chief Information Officer
CHR: Phyllis M. Johnston, Vice President
Web address: www.catawbavalleymc.org
**Control**: County, Government, Nonfederal **Service**: General medical and surgical

**Staffed Beds:** 248 **Admissions:** 11986 **Census:** 141 **Outpatient Visits:** 521397 **Births:** 2142 **Total Expense ($000):** 293304 **Payroll Expense ($000):** 130396 **Personnel:** 1776

**FRYE REGIONAL MED CENTER** See Frye Regional Medical Center

✉ **FRYE REGIONAL MEDICAL CENTER (340116)**, 420 North Center Street, Zip 28601–5049, Mailing Address: 1950 11th Street Crt. NW, Zip 28601; tel. 828/315–5000, (Includes FRYE REGIONAL MEDICAL CENTER-SOUTH CAMPUS, Mailing address: One Third Avenue NW, Hickory, North Carolina, Zip 28601, 420 North Center St., Zip 28603, tel. 828/315–5777), (Nonreporting) **A**1 2 10 19 **S** Duke LifePoint Healthcare, Brentwood, TN
Primary Contact: Rod Harkleroad, R.N., Chief Executive Officer
CFO: Jamey Stoner, Chief Financial Officer
CNO: Michelle Dickerson, Chief Nursing Officer
Web address: www.fryemedctr.com
**Control**: Corporation, Investor–owned (for–profit) **Service**: General medical and surgical

**Staffed Beds:** 271

**TEN BROECK HOSPITAL** See Frye Regional Medical Center-South Campus

## HIGH POINT—Guilford County

✉ △ **HIGH POINT MEDICAL CENTER (340004)**, 601 North Elm Street, Zip 27262–4398, Mailing Address: P.O. Box HP-5, Zip 27261–1899; tel. 336/878–6000, (Nonreporting) **A**1 5 7 10 19 **F**3 4 8 12 13 15 17 18 20 22 24 26 28 29 30 31 32 34 35 36 38 39 40 44 45 47 48 49 50 53 54 55 57 58 59 60 61 66 67 68 70 73 74 75 76 77 78 79 81 82 84 85 86 87 89 90 91 92 93 96 98 100 101 102 104 107 108 109 110 111 114 115 116 117 118 119 120 121 123 124 126 130 131 132 135 145 146 147 148 149 154 **S** Wake Forest Baptist Health, Winston-Salem, NC
Primary Contact: James Hoekstra, M.D., President
COO: Gregory W Taylor, M.D., Vice President and Chief Operating Officer
CMO: L Dale Williams, M.D., Vice President and Chief Medical Director
CIO: Nancy Waters, Interim Chief Information Officer
CHR: Katherine Burns, Vice President Human Resources
CNO: Tammi Erving-Mengel, R.N., MSN, Vice President, Chief Nursing Officer
Web address: www.highpointregional.com
**Control**: Other not–for–profit (including NFP Corporation) **Service**: General medical and surgical

**Staffed Beds:** 317 **Admissions:** 13492 **Census:** 166 **Outpatient Visits:** 152044 **Births:** 1216 **Total Expense ($000):** 241990 **Payroll Expense ($000):** 92861 **Personnel:** 1800

**HIGH POINT REGIONAL HEALTH SYSTEM** See High Point Medical Center

## HIGHLANDS—Macon County

✉ **HIGHLANDS-CASHIERS HOSPITAL (341316)**, 190 Hospital Drive, Zip 28741–7600, Mailing Address: P O Drawer 190, Zip 28741–0190; tel. 828/526–1200, (Nonreporting) **A**1 10 18 **S** HCA Healthcare, Nashville, TN
Primary Contact: Jacqueline Medland, MS, Ph.D., President and Chief Nursing Officer
CFO: Lena Cochran, Director of Finance
CHR: Ruby Rowland, Strategic Partner
CNO: Cindy Pierson, Interim Chief Nursing Officer
Web address: www.hchospital.org
**Control**: Other not–for–profit (including NFP Corporation) **Service**: General medical and surgical

**Staffed Beds:** 104

## HUNTERSVILLE—Mecklenburg County

✉ **NOVANT HEALTH HUNTERSVILLE MEDICAL CENTER (340183)**, 10030 Gilead Road, Zip 28078–7545, Mailing Address: P.O. Box 3508, Zip 28070–3508; tel. 704/316–4000, (Nonreporting) **A**1 2 3 5 10 **S** Novant Health, Winston Salem, NC
Primary Contact: Mike Riley, President and Chief Operating Officer
CFO: Fred M Hargett, Executive Vice President and Chief Financial Officer
CMO: Thomas Zweng, Executive Vice President and Chief Medical Officer
CIO: David B Garrett, Senior Vice President and Chief Information Officer
CNO: Katrina King, R.N., Senior Director, Nursing
Web address: www.novanthealth.org
**Control**: Other not–for–profit (including NFP Corporation) **Service**: General medical and surgical

**Staffed Beds:** 91

**PRESBYTERIAN HOSPITAL HUNTERSVILLE** See Novant Health Huntersville Medical Center

## JACKSONVILLE—Onslow County

**BRYNN MARR BEHAVIORAL SYSTEM** See Brynn Marr Hospital

☐ **BRYNN MARR HOSPITAL (344016)**, 192 Village Drive, Zip 28546–7299; tel. 910/577–1400, (Nonreporting) **A**1 10 **S** Universal Health Services, Inc., King of Prussia, PA
Primary Contact: Allison Davenport, Chief Executive Officer
CFO: David Warmerdam, Chief Financial Officer
CMO: Ashraf Mikhail, M.D., Medical Director
CHR: Jennifer Gier, Director Human Resources
CNO: Sheila Maraan, Director of Nursing
Web address: www.brynnmarr.org
**Control**: Corporation, Investor–owned (for–profit) **Service**: Psychiatric

**Staffed Beds:** 99

**NC**

*Many Facility Codes have changed. Please refer to the AHA Guide Code Chart.*
© 2021 AHA Guide

✠ **ONSLOW MEMORIAL HOSPITAL (340042)**, 317 Western Boulevard, Zip 28546–6379, Mailing Address: P.O. Box 1358, Zip 28541–1358; tel. 910/577–2345, (Nonreporting) **A**1 2 10 20 **F**3 8 11 13 15 18 19 20 28 29 31 34 35 40 45 46 47 48 49 54 57 59 60 64 68 70 72 73 75 76 77 79 81 82 84 85 86 87 89 93 96 107 108 110 111 114 115 117 118 119 126 131 132 135 146 147 148 154 **P**7 **S** UNC Health Care, Chapel Hill, NC
Primary Contact: Penney Burlingame Deal, FACHE, R.N., Chief Executive Officer
CMO: Scott Johnston, Chief of Staff
CIO: Rob Lowe, Director, Healthcare Information Management
CHR: Taylor Flowers, Senior Vice President Human Resources
CNO: Regina Lanier, MSN, R.N., Senior Vice President and Chief Nursing Officer
Web address: www.onslow.org
**Control**: Hospital district or authority, Government, Nonfederal **Service**: General medical and surgical

**Staffed Beds**: 149 **Admissions**: 6525 **Census**: 79 **Outpatient Visits**: 130901 **Births**: 1351 **Total Expense ($000)**: 142581 **Payroll Expense ($000)**: 49783 **Personnel**: 848

### JEFFERSON—Ashe County

✠ **ASHE MEMORIAL HOSPITAL (341325)**, 200 Hospital Avenue, Zip 28640–9244; tel. 336/846–7101, (Nonreporting) **A**1 10 18 **S** Novant Health, Winston Salem, NC
Primary Contact: Laura Lambeth, Chief Executive Officer
COO: Joe Thore, Chief Operating Officer
CFO: Charles Wright, Chief Financial Officer
CMO: Jayne Leonard, M.D., Family Medicine
CIO: William Baldwin, Chief Information Officer
CHR: Lana Smith, Human Resources Director
CNO: Sara Houser, Chief Nursing Officer
Web address: www.ashememorial.org
**Control**: Other not–for–profit (including NFP Corporation) **Service**: General medical and surgical

**Staffed Beds**: 25

### KENANSVILLE—Duplin County

**DUPLIN GENERAL HOSPITAL** See Vidant Duplin Hospital

✠ **VIDANT DUPLIN HOSPITAL (340120)**, 401 North Main Street, Zip 28349–8801, Mailing Address: P.O. Box 278, Zip 28349–0278; tel. 910/296–0941, (Nonreporting) **A**1 10 **F**3 11 13 15 18 19 29 30 31 34 35 39 40 45 56 57 59 64 68 70 75 76 77 78 79 81 91 93 98 101 102 103 107 108 110 111 115 116 119 129 130 131 132 135 146 147 154 **S** Vidant Health, Greenville, NC
Primary Contact: Jeffery Dial, Interim President
COO: Matthew Gitzinger, Director of Operations
CFO: Lucinda Crawford, Vice President Financial Services
CMO: Dyrek Miller, M.D., Chief Medical Staff
CIO: Lucinda Crawford, Vice President Financial Services
CHR: Pansy Chase, Director Human Resources
CNO: Sue O. Taylor, Vice President Nursing
Web address: www.vidanthealth.com
**Control**: Other not–for–profit (including NFP Corporation) **Service**: General medical and surgical

**Staffed Beds**: 47 **Admissions**: 3559 **Census**: 48 **Outpatient Visits**: 56135 **Births**: 417 **Total Expense ($000)**: 54266 **Payroll Expense ($000)**: 22096 **Personnel**: 453

### KINGS MOUNTAIN—Cleveland County

**CAROLINAS HEALTHCARE SYSTEM KINGS MOUNTAIN** See Atrium Health Kings Mountain

### KINSTON—Lenoir County

**LENOIR MEMORIAL HOSPITAL** See UNC Lenoir Healthcare

✠ **UNC LENOIR HEALTHCARE (340027)**, 100 Airport Road, Zip 28501–1634, Mailing Address: P.O. Box 1678, Zip 28503–1678; tel. 252/522–7000, (Nonreporting) **A**1 10 **F**3 8 11 12 13 18 20 22 28 29 30 31 34 35 38 40 43 45 47 48 49 50 53 56 57 59 60 61 64 65 68 70 74 75 76 77 78 79 81 85 86 87 89 90 93 102 107 108 111 115 118 119 120 121 123 129 130 132 134 135 143 145 146 147 148 154 156 **S** UNC Health Care, Chapel Hill, NC
Primary Contact: Robert A. Enders Jr, President and Chief Executive Officer
CFO: Jeffrey A. Wakefield, CPA, Vice President and Chief Financial Officer
CMO: Claire Paris, M.D., Vice President and Chief Medical Officer
CIO: Karl Vanderstouw, Vice President and Chief Information Officer
CHR: Jim Dobbins, Vice President and Chief Human Resources Officer
CNO: Shirley S. Harkey, M.D., R.N., FACHE, Interim Vice President and Chief Nursing Officer
Web address: www.lenoirmemorial.org
**Control**: Other not–for–profit (including NFP Corporation) **Service**: General medical and surgical

**Staffed Beds**: 176 **Admissions**: 5587 **Census**: 70 **Outpatient Visits**: 95261 **Births**: 380 **Total Expense ($000)**: 106055 **Payroll Expense ($000)**: 44740 **Personnel**: 779

### LAURINBURG—Scotland County

✠ **SCOTLAND HEALTH CARE SYSTEM (340008)**, 500 Lauchwood Drive, Zip 28352–5599; tel. 910/291–7000, (Nonreporting) **A**1 2 3 5 10 **F**3 11 13 15 18 28 29 31 34 37 40 45 54 57 59 63 64 70 71 73 74 75 76 77 78 79 81 83 84 85 86 87 89 90 92 93 96 97 107 110 111 114 115 119 120 121 123 126 127 130 132 135 144 145 146 147 148 149 156 **S** Atrium Health, Charlotte, NC
Primary Contact: Gregory C. Wood, President and Chief Executive Officer
COO: David Pope, Senior Vice President, Operations
CFO: Matthew Pracht, Vice President Finance
CMO: Cheryl Davis, M.D., Chief Medical Officer
CIO: Chip Reklis, Director Information Systems
CHR: Ann Locklear, Vice President, Human Resources
CNO: Kim Hammonds, R.N., Chief Nursing Officer
Web address: www.scotlandhealth.org
**Control**: Other not–for–profit (including NFP Corporation) **Service**: General medical and surgical

**Staffed Beds**: 104 **Admissions**: 5673 **Census**: 55 **Outpatient Visits**: 67087 **Births**: 730 **Total Expense ($000)**: 168450 **Payroll Expense ($000)**: 58187 **Personnel**: 1013

**SCOTLAND MEMORIAL HOSPITAL** See Scotland Health Care System

### LELAND—Brunswick County

☐ **STRATEGIC BEHAVIORAL HEALTH - WILMINGTON (344030)**, 2050 Mercantile Drive, Zip 28451–4053; tel. 910/371–2500, (Nonreporting) **A**1 10 **S** Strategic Behavioral Health, LLC, Memphis, TN
Primary Contact: Steve McCabe, Chief Executive Officer
CHR: Kelly Pace, Director Human Resource
CNO: Brooke Cook, Director of Nursing
Web address: www.sbcwilmington.com/
**Control**: Corporation, Investor–owned (for–profit) **Service**: Children's hospital psychiatric

**Staffed Beds**: 112

### LENOIR—Caldwell County

**CALDWELL MEMORIAL HOSPITAL** See Caldwell UNC Health Care

✠ **CALDWELL UNC HEALTH CARE (340041)**, 321 Mulberry Street SW, Zip 28645–5720, Mailing Address: P.O. Box 1890, Zip 28645–1890; tel. 828/757–5100, (Nonreporting) **A**1 10 **F**3 8 11 13 15 18 20 22 29 30 31 34 35 37 40 45 46 48 49 50 53 54 55 57 59 64 65 70 75 76 77 78 79 81 82 85 86 87 93 97 107 108 109 110 111 114 119 120 121 122 123 129 132 135 145 146 147 148 149 154 156 **P**6 **S** UNC Health Care, Chapel Hill, NC
Primary Contact: Laura J. Easton, President and Chief Executive Officer
COO: Rebecca T Smith, Chief Operating Officer and Chief Nursing Officer
CFO: Michael L. Bunch, Chief Financial Officer
CMO: David Lowry, M.D., Chief Medical Officer
CIO: Deborah Purcell, Director of Information Technology
CHR: Laura J Easton, President and Chief Executive Officer
CNO: Rebecca T Smith, Chief Operating Officer and Chief Nursing Officer
Web address: www.caldwellmemorial.org
**Control**: Other not–for–profit (including NFP Corporation) **Service**: General medical and surgical

**Staffed Beds**: 82 **Admissions**: 3882 **Census**: 54 **Outpatient Visits**: 101967 **Births**: 351 **Total Expense ($000)**: 127180 **Payroll Expense ($000)**: 56581 **Personnel**: 807

## LEXINGTON—Davidson County

**LEXINGTON MEMORIAL HOSPITAL** See Wake Forest Baptist Health-Lexington Medical Center

**WAKE FOREST BAPTIST HEALTH-LEXINGTON MEDICAL CENTER (340096)**, 250 Hospital Drive, Zip 27292–6728, Mailing Address: P.O. Box 1817, Zip 27293–1817; tel. 336/248–5161, (Nonreporting) **A**1 3 5 10 **F**3 13 15 18 28 29 30 31 34 35 39 40 45 46 50 57 58 59 61 64 65 68 70 74 75 76 78 79 81 82 85 87 89 91 92 93 97 102 107 108 110 111 115 119 120 121 123 129 130 131 146 147 148 154 156 **S** Wake Forest Baptist Health, Winston-Salem, NC
Primary Contact: William B. James, FACHE, President
CFO: Danny Squires, Assistant Vice President and Chief Financial Officer Network Hospital
CMO: Raghava Nagaraj, M.D., Chief Medical Officer
CIO: Will Showalter, Senior Vice President and Chief information Officer
CHR: Lilicia Bailey, Senior Vice President and Chief People Officer
CNO: Clyde A. Bristow, R.N., IIIChief Nursing Officer, Network Hospital
Web address: www.lexington.wakehealth.edu
**Control:** Other not–for–profit (including NFP Corporation) **Service:** General medical and surgical

**Staffed Beds:** 77 **Admissions:** 3622 **Census:** 33 **Outpatient Visits:** 117348 **Births:** 324 **Total Expense ($000):** 91665 **Payroll Expense ($000):** 38361 **Personnel:** 521

## LINCOLNTON—Lincoln County

**ATRIUM HEALTH LINCOLN (340145)**, 433 McAlister Road, Zip 28092–4147, Mailing Address: PO Box 677, Zip 28093–0677; tel. 980/212–2000, (Nonreporting) **A**1 10 **F**3 8 13 15 18 28 29 30 31 34 35 39 40 44 45 50 51 57 59 64 70 73 74 75 76 77 78 79 81 82 84 85 87 91 93 94 96 107 108 111 114 115 118 119 129 130 131 132 146 148 149 150 154 156 **S** Atrium Health, Charlotte, NC
Primary Contact: Teresa C. Watson, Vice President, Facility Executive
CFO: Jarrett L Morris, Controller
CMO: Vineet Goel, Chief Medical Officer
CIO: Jarrett L Morris, Controller and Chief Information Officer
CHR: Lesley Chambless, Assistant Vice President Human Resources
CNO: Elaine S Haynes, R.N., MSN, Vice President Patient Services and Chief Nursing Executive
Web address: www.carolinashealthcare.org/lincoln
**Control:** Hospital district or authority, Government, Nonfederal **Service:** General medical and surgical

**Staffed Beds:** 101 **Admissions:** 4778 **Census:** 53 **Outpatient Visits:** 93029 **Births:** 534 **Total Expense ($000):** 103061 **Payroll Expense ($000):** 34580 **Personnel:** 608

**CAROLINAS HEALTHCARE SYSTEM LINCOLN** See Atrium Health Lincoln

## LUMBERTON—Robeson County

★ ⇧ **SOUTHEASTERN HEALTH (340050)**, 300 West 27th Street, Zip 28358–3075, Mailing Address: P.O. Box 1408, Zip 28359–1408; tel. 910/671–5000, (Nonreporting) **A**2 3 5 10 12 13 21
Primary Contact: Joann Anderson, President and Chief Executive Officer
CFO: C Thomas Johnson IIIVice President Finance and Chief Financial Officer
CMO: Barry Williamson, President Medical Staff
CIO: Eric Harper, Chief Information Officer
CHR: Susan Hayes, Director Human Resources
CNO: Renae Taylor, Chief Nursing Officer
Web address: www.srmc.org
**Control:** Other not–for–profit (including NFP Corporation) **Service:** General medical and surgical

**Staffed Beds:** 385

⇧ **SOUTHEASTERN REGIONAL MEDICAL CENTER** See Southeastern Health

## MARION—Mcdowell County

**MCDOWELL HOSPITAL (340087)**, 430 Rankin Drive, Zip 28752–6568, Mailing Address: P.O. Box 730, Zip 28752–0730; tel. 828/659–5000, (Nonreporting) **A**1 3 10 **S** HCA Healthcare, Nashville, TN
Primary Contact: Carol C. Wolfenbarger, FACHE, MSN, President
CFO: Clint Stewart, Regional Director of Finance East
CMO: Rex Henderson, M.D., Chief of Staff
CIO: Pam Blevins, R.N., Director Information Technology Member Hospitals Mission
CHR: Tonya Revels, Senior Strategic Business Partner
CNO: Kathy Hefner, Chief Nursing Officer
Web address: www.mission-health.org
**Control:** Other not–for–profit (including NFP Corporation) **Service:** General medical and surgical

**Staffed Beds:** 65

## MATTHEWS—Mecklenburg County

**NOVANT HEALTH MATTHEWS MEDICAL CENTER (340171)**, 1500 Matthews Township Parkway, Zip 28105–4656; tel. 704/384–6500, (Nonreporting) **A**1 2 10 **S** Novant Health, Winston Salem, NC
Primary Contact: Jason Bernd, President and Chief Operating Officer
CFO: Fred M Hargett, Executive Vice President and Chief Financial Officer
CMO: Thomas Zweng, Executive Vice President and Chief Medical Officer
CIO: David B Garrett, Senior Vice President and Chief Information Officer
CNO: Tracy B Forster, R.N., Senior Director of Nursing
Web address: www.https://www.novanthealth.org
**Control:** Other not–for–profit (including NFP Corporation) **Service:** General medical and surgical

**Staffed Beds:** 117

**PRESBYTERIAN HOSPITAL MATTHEWS** See Novant Health Matthews Medical Center

## MONROE—Union County

**ATRIUM HEALTH UNION (340130)**, 600 Hospital Drive, Zip 28112–6000, Mailing Address: P.O. Box 5003, Zip 28111–5003; tel. 980/993–3100, (Total facility includes 70 beds in nursing home–type unit) (Nonreporting) **A**1 2 3 10 **F**3 8 13 18 20 22 26 27 28 29 30 31 34 35 39 40 42 45 49 53 56 57 59 60 64 66 68 70 72 74 75 76 77 78 79 81 82 84 86 87 89 93 97 102 107 108 111 114 117 118 119 120 121 123 126 128 129 130 131 132 135 143 146 147 148 154 156 157 **S** Atrium Health, Charlotte, NC
Primary Contact: Denise White, MSN, Vice President, Facility Executive
COO: Dave Anderson, FACHE, Vice President Administration
CFO: John G Moore, Vice President and Chief Financial Officer
CMO: Craig M Slater, M.D., Chief Medical Officer
CIO: Lisa Sykes, Director Information Services
CHR: Rhonda McFarland, Director Human Resources
CNO: Denise White, MSN, Chief Nurse Executive and Vice President Facility Executive
Web address: www.carolinashealthcare.org/union
**Control:** Hospital district or authority, Government, Nonfederal **Service:** General medical and surgical

**Staffed Beds:** 219 **Admissions:** 9350 **Census:** 161 **Outpatient Visits:** 198719 **Births:** 959 **Total Expense ($000):** 202632 **Payroll Expense ($000):** 65431 **Personnel:** 1113

**CAROLINAS HEALTHCARE SYSTEM UNION** See Atrium Health Union

## MOORESVILLE—Iredell County

**LAKE NORMAN REGIONAL MEDICAL CENTER (340129)**, 171 Fairview Road, Zip 28117–9500, Mailing Address: P.O. Box 3250, Zip 28117–3250; tel. 704/660–4000, (Nonreporting) **A**1 10 19 **S** Community Health Systems, Inc., Franklin, TN
Primary Contact: Stephen L. Midkiff, Chief Executive Officer
CFO: Claire Polk, Chief Financial Officer
CHR: Stephanie Williams, Market Director Human Resources
CNO: Marie Marks, Chief Nursing Officer
Web address: www.lnrmc.com
**Control:** Corporation, Investor–owned (for–profit) **Service:** General medical and surgical

**Staffed Beds:** 123

## MOREHEAD CITY—Carteret County

**CARTERET HEALTH CARE (340142)**, 3500 Arendell Street, Zip 28557–2901, Mailing Address: P.O. Box 1619, Zip 28557–1619; tel. 252/499–6000, (Nonreporting) **A**1 2 10 **F**3 7 11 12 13 15 18 20 22 28 29 30 31 34 35 37 40 45 46 54 57 59 62 63 64 65 68 70 74 75 76 77 78 79 81 82 84 85 86 87 89 91 93 97 107 108 110 111 114 115 118 119 120 121 123 129 130 132 135 143 145 146 148 154 156
Primary Contact: Harvey Case, President
CFO: Joanie King, Chief Financial Officer
CMO: Donald Pocock, Vice-President Medical Affairs
CIO: Kyle Marek, Vice President General Services and Chief Information Officer
CHR: Elizabeth Beswick, Vice President Human Resources and Public Relations
Web address: www.carterethealth.org
**Control:** County, Government, Nonfederal **Service:** General medical and surgical

**Staffed Beds:** 104 **Admissions:** 5957 **Census:** 66 **Outpatient Visits:** 183959 **Births:** 783 **Total Expense ($000):** 150621 **Payroll Expense ($000):** 59755 **Personnel:** 934

*Many Facility Codes have changed. Please refer to the AHA Guide Code Chart.*   © 2021 AHA Guide

## MORGANTON—Burke County

☐ **BROUGHTON HOSPITAL (344025)**, 1000 South Sterling Street,
Zip 28655–3999; tel. 828/433–2111, (Nonreporting) **A**1 3 10
Primary Contact: Vivian Streater, Co-Acting Chief Executive Officer
CFO: Bea Tullis, Chief Financial Officer and Budget Officer
CMO: George Krebs, M.D., Chief Medical Officer
CIO: Darin Kiracofe, Director Information Resource Management
CHR: Jean Buchanan, Director Human Resources
CNO: Vivian Streater, Chief Nursing Officer and Co-Acting Chief Executive Officer
Web address: www.ncdhhs.gov/dsohf/broughton
**Control**: State, Government, Nonfederal **Service**: Psychiatric

| Staffed Beds: 297 |
|---|

**CAROLINAS HEALTHCARE SYSTEM - BLUE RIDGE MORGANTON** See
Carolinas Healthcare System Blue Ridge

⊞ **CAROLINAS HEALTHCARE SYSTEM BLUE RIDGE (340075)**, 2201 South
Sterling Street, Zip 28655–4058; tel. 828/580–5000, (Includes CAROLINAS
HEALTHCARE SYSTEM - BLUE RIDGE - MORGANTON, Mailing address: 2201 South
Sterling Street, Morganton, North Carolina, Zip 28655–4058; tel. 828/580–5000;
Kathy C. Bailey, President and Chief Executive Officer; CAROLINAS HEALTHCARE
SYSTEM - BLUE RIDGE - VALDESE CAMPUS, Mailing address: 720 Malcolm
Boulevard, Valdese, North Carolina, Zip 28690–2872, P O Box 700,
Zip 28690–0700, tel. 828/580–5000; Kathy C. Bailey, President and Chief
Executive Officer), (Nonreporting) **A**1 2 3 5 10 13 **F**3 8 13 15 18 20 22 28 29 30
31 34 35 40 45 49 50 53 54 56 57 59 64 68 69 70 71 72 74 76 77 78 81 82
85 86 87 91 93 96 97 98 100 107 110 111 114 115 118 119 120 121 122
123 126 129 130 131 132 134 135 142 144 146 147 148 149 150 154 **P**6 7
**S** Atrium Health, Charlotte, NC
Primary Contact: Kathy C. Bailey, President and Chief Executive Officer
COO: Jonathan Mercer, FACHE, Senior Vice President, Chief Operating Officer
CFO: Robert G. Fritts, Chief Financial Officer and Senior Vice President
CMO: Anthony Frank, M.D., Senior Vice President and Chief Medical Officer
CHR: Lorinnsa Bridges-Kee, Vice President Human Resources
CNO: Barry Nelson, MSN, Vice President Nursing, Chief Nurse Executive
Web address: www.blueridgehealth.org
**Control**: Other not–for–profit (including NFP Corporation) **Service**: General
medical and surgical

| Staffed Beds: 156 Admissions: 6685 Census: 91 Outpatient Visits: 177696 Births: 860 Total Expense ($000): 205945 Payroll Expense ($000): 70440 Personnel: 1525 |
|---|

**GRACE HOSPITAL** See Carolinas Healthcare System - Blue Ridge - Morganton

## MOUNT AIRY—Surry County

**NORTHERN HOSPITAL OF SURRY COUNTY** See Northern Regional Hospital

⊞ **NORTHERN REGIONAL HOSPITAL (340003)**, 830 Rockford Street,
Zip 27030–5365, Mailing Address: P.O. Box 1101, Zip 27030–1101;
tel. 336/719–7000, (Total facility includes 33 beds in nursing home–type unit)
(Nonreporting) **A**1 10 **F**3 5 11 12 13 15 18 28 29 30 31 34 35 40 45 50 53 54
55 56 57 59 64 65 67 70 75 76 77 79 80 81 82 85 86 87 89 97 107 108 110
111 114 115 118 119 128 130 131 132 133 135 145 146 147 148 149 **P**6
Primary Contact: Chris A. Lumsden, President and Chief Executive Officer
CFO: Andrea Hickling, Vice President of Finance and Chief Financial Officer
CMO: Druery DeVore, Chief of Medical Staff
CIO: Rodney Bond, Director of Information Technology
CHR: Julia Nelson, Vice President of Human Resources
CNO: Robin Hodgin, R.N., Vice President of Patient Services and Chief Nursing Officer
Web address: www.northernhospital.com
**Control**: Hospital district or authority, Government, Nonfederal **Service**: General
medical and surgical

| Staffed Beds: 108 Admissions: 4432 Census: 71 Outpatient Visits: 126588 Births: 330 Total Expense ($000): 98293 Payroll Expense ($000): 44991 Personnel: 869 |
|---|

## MURPHY—Cherokee County

⇑ **ERLANGER MURPHY MEDICAL CENTER** See Erlanger Western Carolina
Hospital

⇑ **ERLANGER WESTERN CAROLINA HOSPITAL (341328)**, 3990 U S Highway 64
East Alt, Zip 28906–7917; tel. 828/837–8161, (Nonreporting) **A**10 18 21 **F**3 11
13 14 15 28 29 30 31 34 35 40 45 48 49 50 53 64 68 70 76 77 79 81 84 85
87 93 96 102 107 110 111 114 115 119 127 130 133 144 146 147 148 157
**P**6 **S** Erlanger Health System, Chattanooga, TN
Primary Contact: Mark E. Kimball, Chief Executive Officer
COO: Toni Lovingood, Chief Operating Officer
CFO: Steve Gilgen, Chief Financial Officer
CMO: Jeffrey H Martin, M.D., Chief of Staff
CIO: Connie Stalcup, Manager Information Systems
CHR: Russ Paine, Human Resources Officer
CNO: Teresa Bowleg, R.N., Chief Nursing Officer
Web address: www.https://www.erlanger.org
**Control**: Hospital district or authority, Government, Nonfederal **Service**: General
medical and surgical

| Staffed Beds: 25 Admissions: 1742 Census: 17 Outpatient Visits: 268298 Births: 124 Total Expense ($000): 55435 Payroll Expense ($000): 26582 Personnel: 406 |
|---|

## NAGS HEAD—Dare County

⊞ **THE OUTER BANKS HOSPITAL (341324)**, 4800 South Croatan Highway,
Zip 27959–9704; tel. 252/449–4500, (Nonreporting) **A**1 2 10 18 **S** Vidant Health,
Greenville, NC
Primary Contact: Ronald A. Sloan, FACHE, President
CFO: Todd Warlitner, Vice President Business Operations
CMO: Roger Lever, M.D., President Medical Staff
CHR: Mary Kelley, Director Human Resources
CNO: Marcia Bryant, R.N., Vice President, Clinical Operations
Web address: www.theouterbankshospital.com
**Control**: Other not–for–profit (including NFP Corporation) **Service**: General
medical and surgical

| Staffed Beds: 21 |
|---|

## NEW BERN—Craven County

⊞ △ **CAROLINAEAST HEALTH SYSTEM (340131)**, 2000 Neuse Boulevard,
Zip 28560–3499, Mailing Address: P.O. Box 12157, Zip 28561–2157;
tel. 252/633–8111, (Nonreporting) **A**1 2 7 10 **F**3 7 11 13 15 17 18 20 22 24 26
28 29 30 31 34 35 36 39 40 45 46 47 48 49 53 54 57 58 59 62 64 67 70 74
75 76 77 78 79 81 84 85 86 87 89 90 91 92 93 94 96 98 100 101 102 104
107 108 110 111 114 115 117 118 119 120 121 123 126 130 132 135 141
142 143 146 147 148 149
Primary Contact: G Raymond. Leggett III, President and Chief Executive Officer
CFO: Tammy M. Sherron, Vice President Finance
CMO: Ronald B May, M.D., Vice President Medical Affairs
CIO: Ronald B May, M.D., Vice President Medical Affairs
CHR: Bruce A Martin, Vice President Human Resources
CNO: Rosanne Leahy, Vice President Nursing Services
Web address: www.carolinaeasthealth.com
**Control**: Hospital district or authority, Government, Nonfederal **Service**: General
medical and surgical

| Staffed Beds: 215 Admissions: 13995 Census: 187 Outpatient Visits: 163946 Births: 980 Total Expense ($000): 293140 Payroll Expense ($000): 106706 Personnel: 1722 |
|---|

**CAROLINAEAST MEDICAL CENTER** See Carolinaeast Health System

## NEWLAND—Avery County

**CHARLES A. CANNON JR. MEMORIAL HOSPITAL** See Charles A. Cannon
Memorial Hospital

⊞ **CHARLES A. CANNON MEMORIAL HOSPITAL (341323)**, 434 Hospital
Drive, Zip 28646, Mailing Address: P.O. Box 767, Linville, Zip 28646–0767;
tel. 828/737–7000, (Nonreporting) **A**1 10 18 **S** Appalachian Regional Healthcare
System, Boone, NC
Primary Contact: Carmen Lacey, MSN, R.N., President
CFO: Kevin B May, System Director Finance
CMO: Thomas M Haizlip, M.D., JrChief of Staff
CIO: Nathan White, Chief Information Officer
CHR: Amy J. Crabbe, Vice President People Services
CNO: Carmen Lacey, MSN, R.N., President and Director of Patient Care Services
Web address: www.https://apprhs.org/locations/cannon-memorial-hospital
**Control**: Other not–for–profit (including NFP Corporation) **Service**: General
medical and surgical

| Staffed Beds: 35 |
|---|

**NC**

## NORTH WILKESBORO—Wilkes County

✠ **WAKE FOREST BAPTIST HEALTH - WILKES MEDICAL CENTER (340064)**, 1370 West 'D' Street, Zip 28659–3506, Mailing Address: P.O. Box 609, Zip 28659–0609; tel. 336/651–8100, (Total facility includes 10 beds in nursing home–type unit) (Nonreporting) **A**1 3 10 **F**3 11 13 15 18 28 29 30 34 35 40 45 49 57 59 60 64 67 68 70 74 76 77 79 81 85 87 92 93 107 108 110 111 114 115 119 124 128 129 130 131 146 148 149 154 **S** Wake Forest Baptist Health, Winston-Salem, NC
Primary Contact: Chad J. Brown, M.P.H., FACHE, President
CFO: Barry Wald, Chief Financial Officer
CMO: Richard Barber, M.D., Chief Medical Officer
CIO: William Hofman, Manager Information Technology
CHR: Vanya Baker, Director
CNO: Sandy Sheppard, Vice President Patient Services
Web address: www.wilkesregional.com/
**Control:** Other not–for–profit (including NFP Corporation) **Service:** General medical and surgical

**Staffed Beds:** 80 **Admissions:** 3246 **Census:** 33 **Outpatient Visits:** 72738 **Births:** 322 **Total Expense ($000):** 76274 **Payroll Expense ($000):** 35309 **Personnel:** 552

**WILKES REGIONAL MEDICAL CENTER** See Wake Forest Baptist Health - Wilkes Medical Center

## OXFORD—Granville County

✠ **GRANVILLE HEALTH SYSTEM (340127)**, 1010 College Street, Zip 27565–2507, Mailing Address: P.O. Box 947, Zip 27565–0947; tel. 919/690–3000, (Total facility includes 80 beds in nursing home–type unit) (Nonreporting) **A**1 3 10 **F**2 3 7 11 13 15 18 19 29 30 34 35 38 39 40 45 50 54 55 56 57 59 64 66 70 75 76 77 79 81 82 85 86 93 100 101 104 107 108 110 111 114 115 118 119 124 127 128 129 130 132 133 143 144 146 147 148
Primary Contact: John Snow, Chief Executive Officer
COO: Cristina Rigsbee Carroll, Chief Operating Officer
CFO: Jeffery Armstrong, CPA, Chief Financial Officer
CMO: Richard Pacca, M.D., Chief of Staff
CIO: Geoff Tanthorey, Director, information Systems
CHR: Scott Thomas, Administrative Director Human Resources and Communications
CNO: Bill Hughes, Chief Nursing Officer
Web address: www.ghshospital.org
**Control:** County, Government, Nonfederal **Service:** General medical and surgical

**Staffed Beds:** 142 **Admissions:** 2130 **Census:** 83 **Outpatient Visits:** 64774 **Births:** 260 **Total Expense ($000):** 67188 **Payroll Expense ($000):** 28062 **Personnel:** 567

**GRANVILLE MEDICAL CENTER** See Granville Health System

## PINEHURST—Moore County

**FIRSTHEALTH MOORE REG HOSP** See Firsthealth Moore Regional Hospital

✠ △ **FIRSTHEALTH MOORE REGIONAL HOSPITAL (340115)**, 155 Memorial Drive, Zip 28374–8710, Mailing Address: P.O. Box 3000, Zip 28374–3000; tel. 910/715–1000, (Includes FIRSTHEALTH MOORE REGIONAL HOSPITAL - HOKE, Mailing address: 6408 Fayetteville Road, Raeford, North Carolina, Zip 28376–7977; tel. 910/878–6000; Susan R Beaty, R.N., Administrator; FIRSTHEALTH MOORE REGIONAL HOSPITAL - RICHMOND, Mailing address: 925 Long Drive, Rockingham, North Carolina, Zip 28379–4835; tel. 910/417–3000; John J Jackson, President), (Nonreporting) **A**1 2 5 7 10 19 **S** FirstHealth of the Carolinas, Pinehurst, NC
Primary Contact: Mickey W. Foster, Chief Executive Officer
COO: Brian Canfield, Chief Operating Officer
CFO: Lynn S DeJaco, Chief Financial Officer
CMO: John F Krahnert, M.D., Chief Medical Officer
CIO: David B Dillehunt, Chief Information Officer
CHR: Daniel F Biediger, Vice President Human Resources
CNO: Karen Robeano, R.N., Chief Nursing Officer and Vice President Patient Care Services
Web address: www.firsthealth.org
**Control:** Other not–for–profit (including NFP Corporation) **Service:** General medical and surgical

**Staffed Beds:** 376

## PLYMOUTH—Washington County

**WASHINGTON COUNTY HOSPITAL (341314)**, 958 U S Highway 64 East, Zip 27962–9591, Mailing Address: PO Box 707, Zip 27962–9591; tel. 252/793–4135, (Nonreporting) **A**10 18 **S** Rural Community Hospitals of America, Kansas City, MO
Primary Contact: Melanie A. Perry, Chief Executive Officer
CMO: Robert Venable, M.D., Chief Medical Staff
CIO: Christina Craft, Director Information Systems
CNO: Kimberly Manning, Chief Nursing Officer
**Control:** County, Government, Nonfederal **Service:** General medical and surgical

**Staffed Beds:** 25

## RAEFORD—Hoke County

✠ **HOKE HOSPITAL (340188)**, 210 Medical Pavilion Drive, Zip 28376–9111; tel. 910/904–8000, (Nonreporting) **A**1 10 **S** Cape Fear Valley Health System, Fayetteville, NC
Primary Contact: Roxie Cannon. Wells, M.D., President
Web address: www.capefearvalley.com
**Control:** County, Government, Nonfederal **Service:** General medical and surgical

**Staffed Beds:** 41

## RALEIGH—Wake County

**CENTRAL PRISON HOSPITAL**, 1300 Western Boulevard, Zip 27606–2148; tel. 919/743–2440, (Nonreporting) **A**3
Primary Contact: Dean Doering, Chief Executive Officer
CMO: Olushola Metiko, M.D., Medical Director
CHR: Bruce McKinney, Business Officer, Administrative Services
CNO: Cindy J McLean, R.N., MSN, Director of Nursing
Web address: www.https://www.ncdps.gov/index2.cfm ?a=000003,002240,002381,002252
**Control:** State, Government, Nonfederal **Service:** Hospital unit of an institution (prison hospital, college infirmary, etc.)

**Staffed Beds:** 230

**DUKE HEALTH RALEIGH HOSPITAL** See Duke Raleigh Hospital

✠ **DUKE RALEIGH HOSPITAL (340073)**, 3400 Wake Forest Road, Zip 27609–7373; tel. 919/954–3000, (Nonreporting) **A**1 2 3 5 10 **F**3 11 12 15 18 20 22 24 26 29 30 31 34 35 36 37 39 40 44 45 46 47 49 50 51 55 57 58 59 60 64 68 70 74 75 77 78 79 80 81 82 84 85 86 87 92 93 94 96 100 102 103 107 108 110 111 114 115 117 118 119 120 121 123 124 126 129 130 131 132 135 142 146 147 148 149 154 **P**6 **S** Duke University Health System, Durham, NC
Primary Contact: Leigh Bleecker, Interim President
COO: Brian Sloan, Chief Operating Officer
CFO: Leigh Bleecker, Chief Financial Officer
CMO: Michael Spiritos, Chief Medical Officer
CHR: Alyson Gordon, Chief Human Resources Officer
Web address: www.dukeraleighhospital.org
**Control:** Other not–for–profit (including NFP Corporation) **Service:** General medical and surgical

**Staffed Beds:** 181 **Admissions:** 9627 **Census:** 133 **Outpatient Visits:** 276174 **Births:** 1 **Total Expense ($000):** 470117 **Payroll Expense ($000):** 118434 **Personnel:** 1937

☐ **HOLLY HILL HOSPITAL (344014)**, 3019 Falstaff Road, Zip 27610–1812; tel. 919/250–7000, (Nonreporting) **A**1 10 **F**4 98 105 153 **P**5 6 **S** Universal Health Services, Inc., King of Prussia, PA
Primary Contact: Kevin Poitinger, Chief Executive Officer and Managing Director
COO: Jessica Knudsen, Chief Operating Officer and Director Performance Improvement and Risk Management
CFO: Ron Howard, Chief Financial Officer
CMO: Thomas Cornwall, M.D., Medical Director
CHR: Ebuni McFall-Roberts, Director Human Resources
CNO: Michael Hartley, MS, Chief Nursing Officer
Web address: www.hollyhillhospital.com
**Control:** Corporation, Investor–owned (for–profit) **Service:** Psychiatric

**Staffed Beds:** 285 **Admissions:** 9510 **Census:** 232 **Outpatient Visits:** 5900 **Births:** 0 **Total Expense ($000):** 52164 **Payroll Expense ($000):** 21672 **Personnel:** 453

**HOLLY HILL/ CHARTER BEHAVIORAL** See Holly Hill Hospital

**LARRY B. ZIEVERINK, SR. ALCOHOLISM TREATMENT CENTER**, 3000 Falstaff Road, Zip 27610–1897; tel. 919/250–1500, (Nonreporting)
Primary Contact: Martin D. Woodward, Director Acute Care Services
COO: Martin D Woodward, Director Acute Care Services
CFO: Paul Gross, Human Services and Finance Officer
CMO: Enrique Lopez, M.D., Medical Director
CIO: Wil A Glenn, Director Communications
Web address: www.wakegov.com/county/family/atc
**Control:** County, Government, Nonfederal **Service:** Alcoholism and other chemical dependency

**Staffed Beds:** 34

☐ **TRIANGLE SPRINGS HOSPITAL (344032)**, 10901 World Trade Boulevard, Zip 27617–4203; tel. 919/372–4408, (Nonreporting) **A**1 **F**4 5 38 98 104 105 151 152 153 154 **S** Springstone, Louisville, KY
Primary Contact: Amanda Johanson, Chief Executive Officer
Web address: www.https://www.trianglesprings.com
**Control:** Individual, Investor–owned (for–profit) **Service:** Psychiatric

**Staffed Beds:** 77 **Admissions:** 2546 **Census:** 51 **Outpatient Visits:** 7130 **Births:** 0 **Total Expense ($000):** 15768

**NC**

*Many Facility Codes have changed. Please refer to the AHA Guide Code Chart.* © 2021 AHA Guide

✠ **UNC REX HEALTH CARE (340114)**, 4420 Lake Boone Trail, Zip 27607–6599; tel. 919/784–3100, (Total facility includes 227 beds in nursing home–type unit) (Nonreporting) **A**1 2 3 5 10 **F**3 7 8 11 12 13 15 17 18 20 22 24 26 28 29 30 31 34 35 36 40 44 45 46 47 48 49 50 53 54 55 56 57 58 59 60 62 64 65 66 68 70 71 72 73 74 75 76 77 78 79 81 82 84 85 86 87 89 92 93 96 100 102 107 108 110 111 114 115 116 117 118 119 120 121 123 126 128 129 130 131 132 135 142 143 144 145 146 147 148 149 154 156 157 **P**6 **S** UNC Health Care, Chapel Hill, NC
Primary Contact: Ernest L. Bovio Jr, President
CFO: Andrew Zukowski, Chief Financial Officer
CMO: Linda H. Butler, M.D., Chief Medical Officer
CIO: Tracy Parham, Health Care System Chief Information Officer
CHR: Scott Doak, Vice President, Human Resources
CNO: ColonelJoel Ray, MSN, Vice President and Chief Nursing Officer
Web address: www.rexhealth.com
**Control**: Other not–for–profit (including NFP Corporation) **Service**: General medical and surgical

**Staffed Beds: 666 Admissions: 30540 Census: 523 Outpatient Visits: 1399701 Births: 4726 Total Expense ($000): 1116526 Payroll Expense ($000): 437273 Personnel: 5502**

**UNC REX HEALTHCARE** See UNC Rex Health Care

**WAKE CNTY ALCOHOLISM TREAT CTR** See Larry B. Zieverink, Sr. Alcoholism Treatment Center

**WAKEMED NEW BERN CAMPUS** See Wakemed Raleigh Campus

**WAKEMED NORTH FAMILY HEALTH & WOMEN'S HOSPITAL** See Wakemed North Family Health and Women's Hospital

✠ △ **WAKEMED RALEIGH CAMPUS (340069)**, 3000 New Bern Avenue, Zip 27610–1295; tel. 919/350–8000, (Includes WAKEMED NORTH FAMILY HEALTH AND WOMEN'S HOSPITAL, Mailing address: 10000 Falls of Neuse Road, Raleigh, North Carolina, Zip 27614–7838; tel. 919/350–8000; Thomas J Gough, Senior Vice President, Administrator Community Hospitals), (Nonreporting) **A**1 3 5 7 10 **F**3 5 11 12 13 15 17 18 19 20 22 24 26 27 28 29 30 31 32 34 35 36 37 38 40 41 42 43 44 45 46 48 49 50 53 54 56 57 58 59 60 61 62 64 65 66 68 70 71 72 73 74 75 76 77 78 79 80 81 82 85 86 87 88 89 90 91 92 93 94 95 96 97 100 101 102 107 108 110 111 114 115 118 119 126 129 130 131 132 135 143 144 145 146 147 148 149 150 154 156 **S** WakeMed Health & Hospitals, Raleigh, NC
Primary Contact: Donald R. Gintzig, President and Chief Executive Officer
COO: Denise Wilder Warren, R.N., Executive Vice President and Chief Operating Officer
CMO: West Paul, M.D., Ph.D., Senior Vice President and Chief Quality and Medical Staff Officer
CIO: Peter Marks, Vice President & Chief Information Officer
CHR: Jeanene R Martin, M.P.H., Senior Vice President Human Resources
CNO: Cindy Boily, MSN, R.N., Senior Vice President and Chief Nursing Officer
Web address: www.wakemed.org
**Control**: Other not–for–profit (including NFP Corporation) **Service**: General medical and surgical

**Staffed Beds: 695 Admissions: 35242 Census: 535 Outpatient Visits: 1599597 Births: 6093 Total Expense ($000): 1149445 Payroll Expense ($000): 641819 Personnel: 7272**

**REIDSVILLE—Rockingham County**

**ANNIE PENN HOSPITAL** See Moses H. Cone Memorial Hospital, Greensboro

**ANNIE PENN MEMORIAL HOSPITAL** See Annie Penn Hospital

**ROANOKE RAPIDS—Halifax County**

**HALIFAX REGIONAL MEDICAL CENTER** See Vidant North Hospital

✠ **VIDANT NORTH HOSPITAL (340151)**, 250 Smith Church Road, Zip 27870–4914, Mailing Address: P.O. Box 1089, Zip 27870–1089; tel. 252/535–8011, (Nonreporting) **A**1 10 20 **S** Vidant Health, Greenville, NC
Primary Contact: William Mahone, President
CFO: Sherry Jensen, Vice President, Financial Services
CIO: Robert Gordon, Manager, Information Services
CHR: Thomas Mastroianni, Director, Human Resources
CNO: Jason Harrell, MSN, R.N., Vice President, Patient Care Services
Web address: www.https://halifaxregional.org
**Control**: Other not–for–profit (including NFP Corporation) **Service**: General medical and surgical

**Staffed Beds: 142**

**ROCKINGHAM—Richmond County**

**FIRSTHEALTH RICHMOND MEMORIAL HOSPITAL** See Firsthealth Moore Regional Hospital - Richmond

**ROCKY MOUNT—Nash County**

**LIFECARE HOSPITALS OF NORTH CAROLINA** See Pam Specialty Hospital of Rocky Mount

**NASH HEALTH CARE SYSTEMS** See Nash UNC Health Care

✠ △ **NASH UNC HEALTH CARE (340147)**, 2460 Curtis Ellis Drive, Zip 27804–2237; tel. 252/962–8000, (Nonreporting) **A**1 2 7 10 **F**3 4 8 11 12 13 15 18 20 22 28 29 30 31 34 35 38 40 41 44 45 48 49 50 54 55 57 59 60 63 64 70 73 74 75 76 77 78 79 81 82 84 85 86 87 90 93 96 98 100 101 102 107 108 110 111 114 115 117 118 119 120 121 123 126 127 129 130 131 132 135 146 147 148 **S** UNC Health Care, Chapel Hill, NC
Primary Contact: L. Lee. Isley, FACHE, Ph.D., President and Chief Executive Officer
COO: Crystal Hayden, FACHE, R.N., Executive Vice President, Chief Operating Officer and Chief Nursing Officer
CFO: Shawn Hartley, Chief Financial Officer
CMO: Anne Shriner, M.D., Senior Vice President, Chief Medical Officer
CHR: Katie Davison, Vice President, Human Resources
CNO: Crystal Hayden, FACHE, R.N., Executive Vice President, Chief Operating Officer and Chief Nursing Officer
Web address: www.nhcs.org
**Control**: Hospital district or authority, Government, Nonfederal **Service**: General medical and surgical

**Staffed Beds: 249 Admissions: 11817 Census: 160 Outpatient Visits: 106379 Births: 992 Total Expense ($000): 244190 Payroll Expense ($000): 104915 Personnel: 1576**

✠ **PAM SPECIALTY HOSPITAL OF ROCKY MOUNT (342013)**, 1051 Noell Lane, Zip 27804–1761; tel. 252/451–2300, (Data for 92 days) (Nonreporting) **A**1 10 **F**1 3 29 30 77 91 148 **S** Post Acute Medical, LLC, Enola, PA
Primary Contact: Robyn Perkerson, R.N., Administrator
COO: Robyn Perkerson, R.N., Administrator
CMO: Daniel Crocker, M.D., Chief Medical Officer
CHR: Vicky Goode, Director Human Resources
Web address: www.lifecare-hospitals.com
**Control**: Corporation, Investor–owned (for–profit) **Service**: Acute long–term care hospital

**Staffed Beds: 43 Admissions: 498 Census: 39 Outpatient Visits: 0 Births: 0 Total Expense ($000): 4974 Payroll Expense ($000): 2284 Personnel: 190**

**ROXBORO—Person County**

**PERSON COUNTY MEM HOSPITAL** See Person Memorial Hospital

✠ **PERSON MEMORIAL HOSPITAL (340159)**, 615 Ridge Road, Zip 27573–4629; tel. 336/599–2121, (Total facility includes 60 beds in nursing home–type unit) (Nonreporting) **A**1 10 **F**3 11 15 18 28 29 34 40 45 57 59 64 70 75 77 79 81 85 87 93 96 97 107 108 110 111 114 119 124 128 130 132 146 149 154 **P**6 **S** Duke LifePoint Healthcare, Brentwood, TN
Primary Contact: David Ziolkowski, Chief Executive Officer
CFO: Jessi Ayers, Chief Financial Officer
CIO: Rhonda M. Elliott, Director Information Technology and Meaningful Use
CHR: Mary Barksdale, Director Human Resources
CNO: Lynn Peoples, Interim Chief Nursing Officer
Web address: www.personhospital.com
**Control**: Partnership, Investor–owned (for–profit) **Service**: General medical and surgical

**Staffed Beds: 77 Admissions: 1191 Census: 60 Outpatient Visits: 35893 Births: 0 Total Expense ($000): 33951 Payroll Expense ($000): 9070**

**RUTHERFORDTON—Rutherford County**

✠ **RUTHERFORD REGIONAL HEALTH SYSTEM (340013)**, 288 South Ridgecrest Avenue, Zip 28139–2838; tel. 828/286–5000, (Nonreporting) **A**1 2 10 **F**3 13 15 18 20 28 29 30 31 34 35 40 45 48 49 50 57 59 64 70 75 76 77 78 79 81 85 86 87 89 93 97 98 100 101 102 104 107 108 110 111 114 115 118 119 130 131 132 135 146 147 149 **S** Duke LifePoint Healthcare, Brentwood, TN
Primary Contact: Rebecca Segal, Chief Executive Officer
COO: John Domansky, Vice President Operations
CFO: Jeff Rush, Chief Financial Officer
CIO: Tommy Finley, Chief Information Officer
CHR: Robin B Callas, Vice President Human Resources
Web address: www.rutherfordhosp.org
**Control**: Partnership, Investor–owned (for–profit) **Service**: General medical and surgical

**Staffed Beds: 112 Admissions: 3307 Census: 40 Outpatient Visits: 69627 Births: 97 Total Expense ($000): 75167 Payroll Expense ($000): 29151 Personnel: 432**

**RUTHERFORD REGIONAL MEDICAL CENTER** See Rutherford Regional Health System

## SALISBURY—Rowan County

☒ **NOVANT HEALTH ROWAN MEDICAL CENTER (340015)**, 612 Mocksville Avenue, Zip 28144–2799; tel. 704/210–5000, (Nonreporting) **A**1 2 5 10 19 **S** Novant Health, Winston Salem, NC
Primary Contact: Dari Caldwell, R.N., Ph.D., FACHE, President and Chief Operating Officer
CFO: Fred M Hargett, Executive Vice President and Chief Financial Officer
CMO: Thomas Zweng, Executive Vice President and Chief Medical Officer
CIO: David B Garrett, Senior Vice President and Chief Information Officer
CNO: Cora Greene, Senior Director, Chief Nursing Officer
Web address: www.https://www.novanthealth.org/rowan-medical-center.aspx
**Control:** Other not-for-profit (including NFP Corporation) **Service:** General medical and surgical

**Staffed Beds: 149**

**ROWAN REGIONAL MEDICAL CENTER** See Novant Health Rowan Medical Center

**VETERANS AFFAIRS MEDICAL CENTER** See W. G. (Bill) Heffner Veterans Affairs Medical Center

☒ **W. G. (BILL) HEFFNER VETERANS AFFAIRS MEDICAL CENTER**, 1601 Brenner Avenue, Zip 28144–2559; tel. 704/638–9000, (Nonreporting) **A**1 3 5 **S** Department of Veterans Affairs, Washington, DC
Primary Contact: Joseph Vaughn, Director
CFO: Steve Patil, Chief Financial Officer
CIO: Deborah Gunn, Chief Information Officer
CHR: Sandra Fischer, Director Human Resources
Web address: www.salisbury.va.gov
**Control:** Veterans Affairs, Government, federal **Service:** Psychiatric

**Staffed Beds: 171**

## SANFORD—Lee County

**AMI CENTRAL CAROLINA HOSPITAL** See Central Carolina Hospital

☒ **CENTRAL CAROLINA HOSPITAL (340020)**, 1135 Carthage Street, Zip 27330–4162; tel. 919/774–2100, (Nonreporting) **A**1 10 **S** Duke LifePoint Healthcare, Brentwood, TN
Primary Contact: Spencer Thomas, Chief Executive Officer
CFO: Jared M. Stimpson, Chief Financial Officer
CIO: Jimmy Whitaker, Director Information Systems
CHR: Deanna Lamb, Director Human Resources
Web address: www.centralcarolinahosp.com
**Control:** Corporation, Investor–owned (for–profit) **Service:** General medical and surgical

**Staffed Beds: 137**

## SHELBY—Cleveland County

☒ **ATRIUM HEALTH CLEVELAND (340021)**, 201 East Grover Street, Zip 28150–3917; tel. 980/487–3000, (Includes ATRIUM HEALTH KINGS MOUNTAIN, Mailing address: 706 West King Street, Kings Mountain, North Carolina, Zip 28086–2708; tel. 980/487–5000; Brian Gwyn, West Market President- Atrium Health), (Nonreporting) **A**1 2 10 19 **F**3 4 8 13 15 18 20 28 29 30 31 32 34 35 39 40 43 44 45 47 48 49 50 53 55 56 57 59 64 65 70 71 74 75 76 77 78 79 80 81 82 85 86 87 89 93 98 100 107 108 110 111 115 118 119 120 121 123 126 129 130 131 132 135 145 146 147 148 149 154 156 **S** Atrium Health, Charlotte, NC
Primary Contact: Brian Gwyn, West Market President- Atrium Health
COO: Brian Gwyn, West Market President- Atrium Health
CFO: Christine M Martin, Vice President and Chief Financial Officer
CMO: Charles M Tomlinson, M.D., Chief Medical Officer
CHR: Debra Kale, Vice President Human Resources
CNO: Veronica Poole-Adams, R.N., Vice President, Chief Operating Officer and Chief Nursing Executive
Web address: www.clevelandregional.org
**Control:** Hospital district or authority, Government, Nonfederal **Service:** General medical and surgical

**Staffed Beds: 230 Admissions: 11646 Census: 136 Outpatient Visits: 262245 Births: 1421 Total Expense ($000): 245249 Payroll Expense ($000): 83897 Personnel: 1454**

**CAROLINAS HEALTHCARE SYSTEM CLEVELAND** See Atrium Health Cleveland

## SILER CITY—Chatham County

☒ **CHATHAM HOSPITAL (341311)**, 475 Progress Boulevard, Zip 27344–6787, Mailing Address: P.O. Box 649, Zip 27344–0649; tel. 919/799–4000, (Nonreporting) **A**1 10 18 **F**3 15 18 26 28 29 30 34 35 39 40 45 46 57 59 68 70 75 77 79 81 85 92 93 107 110 111 114 119 130 133 135 154 156 **S** UNC Health Care, Chapel Hill, NC
Primary Contact: Jeffery C. Strickler, R.N., President and Chief Executive Officer
CFO: Jeff LeGay, Chief Financial Officer
CMO: Andrew Hannapel, Chief Medical Officer
CIO: Deborah Taylor, Chief Information Officer
CHR: Jodie Sartor Solow, Director of Human Resources
CNO: Tammy Needham, Chief Nursing Officer
Web address: www.chathamhospital.org
**Control:** Other not-for-profit (including NFP Corporation) **Service:** General medical and surgical

**Staffed Beds: 25 Admissions: 884 Census: 12 Outpatient Visits: 38151 Births: 0 Total Expense ($000): 36333 Payroll Expense ($000): 11226 Personnel: 199**

## SMITHFIELD—Johnston County

☒ **JOHNSTON HEALTH (340090)**, 509 North Bright Leaf Blvd, Zip 27577–4407, Mailing Address: P.O. Box 1376, Zip 27577–1376; tel. 919/934–8171, (Nonreporting) **A**1 2 10 **F**3 11 13 15 17 18 20 22 26 28 29 30 31 32 34 35 38 40 45 49 50 53 57 59 61 62 63 64 66 68 70 73 74 75 76 79 81 82 85 86 87 89 92 93 98 100 107 108 110 111 114 115 119 120 121 126 130 132 144 146 147 148 149 154 156 **S** UNC Health Care, Chapel Hill, NC
Primary Contact: Tom Williams, Chief Executive Officer
COO: Ruth Marler, Chief Nursing Officer and Chief Operating Officer
CFO: Edward A Klein, Chief Financial Officer
CMO: Rodney McCaskill, M.D., Interim Chief Medical Officer
CIO: Teresa Chappell, Chief Information Officer
CHR: Timothy A Hays, Vice President Human Resources
CNO: Ruth Marler, Chief Nursing Officer and Chief Operating Officer
Web address: www.johnstonhealth.org
**Control:** Hospital district or authority, Government, Nonfederal **Service:** General medical and surgical

**Staffed Beds: 153 Admissions: 10801 Census: 112 Outpatient Visits: 168357 Births: 1507 Total Expense ($000): 224541 Payroll Expense ($000): 89526 Personnel: 1489**

**JOHNSTON UNC HEALTH CARE** See Johnston Health

## SOUTHPORT—Brunswick County

★ **J. ARTHUR DOSHER MEMORIAL HOSPITAL (341327)**, 924 North Howe Street, Zip 28461–3099; tel. 910/457–3800, (Nonreporting) **A**10 18 **F**3 11 12 15 28 30 34 35 40 45 47 50 54 57 59 64 68 75 77 79 81 91 93 97 107 110 111 114 115 118 119 127 129 130 131 132 133 144 146 148 149 154 156 **P**6
Primary Contact: Brad L. Hilaman, M.D., JD, Chief Executive Officer
COO: Carol Northup, R.N., Chief Nursing Officer and Chief Operating Officer
CFO: Daniel J. Porter, Senior Vice President and Chief Financial Officer
CMO: Brad L Hilaman, M.D., JD, Chief Medical Officer
CIO: Susan Shomaker, Director Information Management Systems
CHR: Deanna Parker, Director Human Resources
CNO: Carol Northup, R.N., Chief Nursing Officer and Chief Operating Officer
Web address: www.dosher.org
**Control:** Hospital district or authority, Government, Nonfederal **Service:** General medical and surgical

**Staffed Beds: 12 Admissions: 794 Census: 6 Outpatient Visits: 73110 Births: 0 Total Expense ($000): 42597 Payroll Expense ($000): 16744 Personnel: 247**

## SPARTA—Alleghany County

**ALLEGHANY CNTY MEM HOSPITAL** See Alleghany Memorial Hospital

☒ **ALLEGHANY MEMORIAL HOSPITAL (341320)**, 233 Doctors Street, Zip 28675–9247; tel. 336/372–5511, (Nonreporting) **A**1 10 18
Primary Contact: Craig James, President
CFO: Brett Liverman, Chief Financial Officer
CMO: Joe Arocha, Chief of Staff
CIO: Darlene Keith, Chief Information Systems
CHR: Courtney Bennett, Human Resource Manager
CNO: Wendy Orton, Chief Nursing Officer
Web address: www.amhsparta.org
**Control:** Other not-for-profit (including NFP Corporation) **Service:** General medical and surgical

**Staffed Beds: 25**

## SPRUCE PINE—Mitchell County

☒ **BLUE RIDGE REGIONAL HOSPITAL (341329)**, 125 Hospital Drive, Zip 28777–3035; tel. 828/765–4201, (Includes BLUE RIDGE MEDICAL CENTER - YANCEY CAMPUS, Mailing address: 800 Medical Campus Drive, Burnsville, North Carolina, Zip 28714–9010; tel. 828/682–0200), (Nonreporting) **A**1 3 10 18 **S** HCA Healthcare, Nashville, TN
Primary Contact: Tonia Hale, R.N., Chief Executive Officer and Chief Nursing Officer
CFO: Clint Stewart, Chief Financial Officer
CMO: Jennifer Larson, M.D., Chief of Staff
CIO: Pam Blevins, R.N., Director, Clinical Informatics
CNO: Tonia Hale, R.N., Chief Executive Officer and Chief Nursing Officer
Web address: www.spchospital.org
**Control:** Other not-for-profit (including NFP Corporation) **Service:** General medical and surgical

**Staffed Beds: 46**

**SPRUCE PINE COMMUNITY HOSPITAL** See Blue Ridge Regional Hospital

**NC**

*Many Facility Codes have changed. Please refer to the AHA Guide Code Chart.* © 2021 AHA Guide

## STATESVILLE—Iredell County

⊞ **DAVIS REGIONAL MEDICAL CENTER (340144)**, 218 Old Mocksville Road, Zip 28625–1930, Mailing Address: P.O. Box 1823, Zip 28687–1823; tel. 704/873–0281, (Nonreporting) **A**1 10 19 **S** Community Health Systems, Inc., Franklin, TN
Primary Contact: Josh Snow, Chief Executive Officer
CFO: Hugh Tobin, Chief Financial Officer
CMO: Christopher Lariscy, M.D., Chief of Staff
CIO: Janie Stikeleather, Director Marketing and Community Relations
CNO: Janice S Martin, R.N., Chief Nursing Officer
Web address: www.davisregional.com
**Control**: Corporation, Investor–owned (for–profit) **Service**: General medical and surgical

**Staffed Beds**: 130

**DAVIS REGIONAL MEDICAL CTR** See Davis Regional Medical Center

⊞ **IREDELL HEALTH SYSTEM (340039)**, 557 Brookdale Drive, Zip 28677–4107, Mailing Address: P.O. Box 1828, Zip 28687–1828; tel. 704/873–5661, (Total facility includes 48 beds in nursing home–type unit) (Nonreporting) **A**1 2 10 **F**3 8 11 13 15 17 18 20 22 28 29 30 31 32 34 35 40 41 44 45 47 49 50 56 57 58 59 60 62 64 68 70 74 75 76 77 78 79 81 82 85 86 87 89 91 93 97 107 108 110 111 114 115 116 117 118 119 120 121 123 126 127 128 129 130 132 135 146 147 148 156 **P**6
Primary Contact: John Green, President and Chief Executive Officer
COO: John Green, Chief Operating Officer
CFO: Skip Smith, Vice President Finance
CMO: Brent Warren, President Medical Staff
CIO: Kyle Smith, Director Information Systems
CHR: Cindy Smale, Director, Human Resources
CNO: Becky Quate, Vice President Nursing and Patient Care Services
Web address: www.iredellhealth.org
**Control**: Other not–for–profit (including NFP Corporation) **Service**: General medical and surgical

**Staffed Beds**: 199 **Admissions**: 7583 **Census**: 126 **Outpatient Visits**: 114559 **Births**: 445 **Total Expense ($000)**: 178777 **Payroll Expense ($000)**: 83139 **Personnel**: 1364

**IREDELL MEMORIAL HOSPITAL** See Iredell Health System

## SYLVA—Jackson County

⊞ **HARRIS REGIONAL HOSPITAL (340016)**, 68 Hospital Road, Zip 28779–2722; tel. 828/586–7000, (Nonreporting) **A**1 10 **S** Duke LifePoint Healthcare, Brentwood, TN
Primary Contact: Steve Heatherly, Chief Executive Officer
CHR: Janet Millsaps, Chief Human Resources Officer
Web address: www.westcare.org
**Control**: Other not–for–profit (including NFP Corporation) **Service**: General medical and surgical

**Staffed Beds**: 86

**MEDWEST - HARRIS** See Harris Regional Hospital

## TARBORO—Edgecombe County

**HERITAGE HOSPITAL** See Vidant Edgecombe Hospital

⊞ **VIDANT EDGECOMBE HOSPITAL (340107)**, 111 Hospital Drive, Zip 27886–2011; tel. 252/641–7700, (Nonreporting) **A**1 2 3 10 **F**3 11 13 15 28 29 30 31 34 35 40 45 50 57 59 60 64 70 73 75 76 78 79 81 82 83 84 85 87 92 93 107 110 111 119 127 130 131 132 145 146 149 154 **S** Vidant Health, Greenville, NC
Primary Contact: Patrick Heins, President
CFO: Charles Alford, Vice President Financial Services
CMO: Barry Bunn, M.D., Chief of Staff
CHR: David Prafka, Ed.D., Director of Human Resources
Web address: www.https://www.vidanthealth.com/edgecombe/default.aspx
**Control**: Other not–for–profit (including NFP Corporation) **Service**: General medical and surgical

**Staffed Beds**: 58 **Admissions**: 3352 **Census**: 39 **Outpatient Visits**: 78803 **Births**: 401 **Total Expense ($000)**: 81443 **Payroll Expense ($000)**: 27832 **Personnel**: 426

## THOMASVILLE—Davidson County

⊞ **NOVANT HEALTH THOMASVILLE MEDICAL CENTER (340085)**, 207 Old Lexington Road, Zip 27360–3428, Mailing Address: P.O. Box 789, Zip 27361–0789; tel. 336/472–2000, (Nonreporting) **A**1 3 10 **S** Novant Health, Winston Salem, NC
Primary Contact: Jon D. Applebaum, President and Chief Operating Officer
CFO: Fred M Hargett, Executive Vice President and Chief Financial Officer
CMO: Thomas Zweng, Executive Vice President and Chief Medical Officer
CIO: David B Garrett, Senior Vice President and Chief Information Officer
CNO: Nancy Pearson, MSN, R.N., Director, Nursing
Web address: www.thomasvillemedicalcenter.org
**Control**: Other not–for–profit (including NFP Corporation) **Service**: General medical and surgical

**Staffed Beds**: 87

**THOMASVILLE MEDICAL CENTER** See Novant Health Thomasville Medical Center

## TROY—Montgomery County

**FIRSTHEALTH MONTGOMERY HOSP** See Firsthealth Montgomery Memorial Hospital

⊞ **FIRSTHEALTH MONTGOMERY MEMORIAL HOSPITAL (341303)**, 520 Allen Street, Zip 27371–2802; tel. 910/571–5000, (Nonreporting) **A**1 10 18 **S** FirstHealth of the Carolinas, Pinehurst, NC
Primary Contact: Rebecca W. Carter, MSN, R.N., FACHE, President
CFO: Bryan Hawkins, Controller
CIO: David B Dillehunt, Chief Information Officer
CHR: Tina H Thompson, Coordinator Human Resources
CNO: Pam Gaddy, Director, Patient Care Services and Chief Nursing Officer
Web address: www.firsthealth.org
**Control**: Other not–for–profit (including NFP Corporation) **Service**: General medical and surgical

**Staffed Beds**: 5

## VALDESE—Burke County

**VALDESE GENERAL HOSPITAL** See Carolinas Healthcare System - Blue Ridge - Valdese Campus

## WADESBORO—Anson County

⊞ **ATRIUM HEALTH ANSON (340084)**, 2301 US Highway 74 W, Zip 28170–7554, Mailing Address: 2301 U.S Highway 74 West, Zip 28170; tel. 704/994–4500, (Nonreporting) **A**1 10 **F**15 18 29 34 35 40 57 59 64 71 75 77 81 86 87 93 97 100 107 110 114 119 129 130 131 132 135 143 146 154 **S** Atrium Health, Charlotte, NC
Primary Contact: Dave Anderson, FACHE, Vice President and Administrator
CFO: Jeff Griffin, Assistant Vice President Finance
CMO: Edward Blasko, Chief of Staff
CIO: Lisa Sykes, IS/Communications Director
CHR: Rhonda McFarland, Director Human Resources
CNO: Denise White, MSN, Chief Nurse Executive
Web address: www.carolinashealthcare.org/anson
**Control**: Hospital district or authority, Government, Nonfederal **Service**: General medical and surgical

**Staffed Beds**: 15 **Admissions**: 419 **Census**: 3 **Outpatient Visits**: 35417 **Births**: 0 **Total Expense ($000)**: 18276 **Payroll Expense ($000)**: 7372 **Personnel**: 122

**CAROLINAS HEALTHCARE SYSTEM ANSON** See Atrium Health Anson

## WASHINGTON—Beaufort County

**BEAUFORT COUNTY MEDICAL CENTER** See Vidant Beaufort Hospital

⊞ **VIDANT BEAUFORT HOSPITAL (340186)**, 628 East 12th Street, Zip 27889–3409; tel. 252/975–4100, (Nonreporting) **A**1 3 10 **S** Vidant Health, Greenville, NC
Primary Contact: Debra T. Hernandez, R.N., FACHE, President
CFO: Lucinda Crawford, Vice President of Patient Care Services
CMO: James Egbert, Chief of Staff
CHR: Jenny Brown, Director of Human Resources
CNO: Lou Montana-Rhodes, Vice President of Patient Care Services
Web address: www.vidanthealth.com
**Control**: Hospital district or authority, Government, Nonfederal **Service**: General medical and surgical

**Staffed Beds**: 84

## WHITEVILLE—Columbus County

⇑ **COLUMBUS COUNTY HOSPITAL** See Columbus Regional Healthcare System

★ ⇑ **COLUMBUS REGIONAL HEALTHCARE SYSTEM (340068)**, 500 Jefferson Street, Zip 28472–3634; tel. 910/642–8011, (Nonreporting) **A**10 19 21 **S** Atrium Health, Charlotte, NC
Primary Contact: John E. Young, Interim Chief Executive Officer
CFO: Carl Biber, Chief Financial Officer
CMO: Samuel N Wheatley, Chief Medical Officer
CIO: Lisa Ward, Director Information Systems
CHR: Andrea West, MS, Vice President of Human Resources
CNO: Terri Veneziano, Interim Chief Nursing Officer
Web address: www.crhealthcare.org/
**Control**: Hospital district or authority, Government, Nonfederal **Service**: General medical and surgical

**Staffed Beds**: 85

---

**NC**

## WILLIAMSTON—Martin County

✠ **MARTIN GENERAL HOSPITAL (340133)**, 310 South McCaskey Road, Zip 27892–2150, Mailing Address: P.O. Box 1128, Zip 27892–1128; tel. 252/809–6300, (Nonreporting) **A**1 10 **S** Quorum Health, Brentwood, TN
Primary Contact: John Jacobson, Interim Chief Executive Officer
CFO: John Jacobson, Chief Financial Officer
CIO: Blaine Chappel, Director Information Technology
CHR: Rebecca Edwards, Director Human Resources
CNO: Hayley Taffer, Chief Nursing Officer
Web address: www.martingeneral.com
**Control:** Corporation, Investor–owned (for–profit) **Service:** General medical and surgical

**Staffed Beds:** 49

## WILMINGTON—New Hanover County

**CAPE FEAR MEMORIAL HOSPITAL** See Cape Fear Hospital

**LIFE CENTER** See Wilmington Treatment Center

★ △ ⇑ **NEW HANOVER REGIONAL MEDICAL CENTER (340141)**, 2131 South 17th Street, Zip 28401–7483, Mailing Address: P.O. Box 9000, Zip 28402–9000; tel. 910/343–7000, (Includes CAPE FEAR HOSPITAL, Mailing address: 5301 Wrightsville Avenue, Wilmington, North Carolina, Zip 28403–6599; tel. 910/452–8100), (Nonreporting) **A**2 3 5 7 10 21 **F**3 7 8 11 12 13 15 17 18 20 22 24 26 28 29 30 31 34 35 36 37 39 40 42 43 44 45 46 47 48 49 50 53 54 56 57 58 59 60 61 64 65 66 68 70 72 73 74 75 76 77 78 79 80 81 82 84 85 86 87 88 89 90 92 93 94 96 97 98 100 101 102 107 108 110 111 114 115 117 118 119 121 123 126 130 131 132 135 144 146 147 148 149 154 155 **S** New Hanover Regional Medical Center, Wilmington, NC
Primary Contact: Andre Boyd Sr, Executive Vice President, Hospital Division
CFO: Edwin J Ollie, Executive Vice President and Chief Financial Officer
CMO: Sam Spicer, M.D., Vice President Medical Affairs
CIO: Avery Cloud, Vice President and Chief Information Officer
CHR: Keith A Strawn, Vice President Human Resources
CNO: Mary Ellen Bonczek, R.N., Chief Nursing Executive
Web address: www.nhrmc.org
**Control:** County, Government, Nonfederal **Service:** General medical and surgical

**Staffed Beds:** 720 **Admissions:** 37708 **Census:** 597 **Outpatient Visits:** 459087 **Births:** 4122 **Total Expense ($000):** 1069292 **Payroll Expense ($000):** 380005 **Personnel:** 5714

**WILMINGTON TREATMENT CENTER (340168)**, 2520 Troy Drive, Zip 28401–7643; tel. 910/762–2727, (Nonreporting) **A**10 **S** CRC Health Group, Inc., Cupertino, CA
Primary Contact: Robert Pitts, Executive Director
COO: Paige Bottom, Director Operations
CFO: Virginia Powell, Director Finance
CMO: Patrick Martin, M.D., Medical Director
Web address: www.wilmtreatment.com
**Control:** Corporation, Investor–owned (for–profit) **Service:** Alcoholism and other chemical dependency

**Staffed Beds:** 44

## WILSON—Wilson County

**WILMED NURSING CARE CENTER** See Wilmed Nursing Care Center

✠ **WILSON MEDICAL CENTER (340126)**, 1705 Tarboro Street, SW, Zip 27893–3428; tel. 252/399–8040, (Nonreporting) **A**1 2 10 19 **S** Duke LifePoint Healthcare, Brentwood, TN
Primary Contact: Mark C. Holyoak, FACHE, Chief Executive Officer
CMO: Rick Guarino, M.D., Vice President Medical Affairs
CIO: Brian Dietrick, Director Information Systems
CHR: Denise O'Hara, Vice President Human Resources
Web address: www.wilmed.org
**Control:** Other not–for–profit (including NFP Corporation) **Service:** General medical and surgical

**Staffed Beds:** 244

**WILSON MEMORIAL CENTER** See Wilson Medical Center

## WINDSOR—Bertie County

**BERTIE MEMORIAL HOSPITAL** See Vidant Bertie Hospital

✠ **VIDANT BERTIE HOSPITAL (341304)**, 1403 South King Street, Zip 27983–9666, Mailing Address: P.O. Box 40, Zip 27983–0040; tel. 252/794–6600, (Nonreporting) **A**1 10 18 **F**3 15 29 30 34 35 40 45 46 47 48 49 57 59 64 77 79 81 82 93 94 97 107 110 114 119 127 132 135 146 148 154 156 **S** Vidant Health, Greenville, NC
Primary Contact: Brian Harvill, President
CMO: William Ballance, Chief of Medical Staff
CIO: Brian White, Director Strategic Planning
CHR: Nicole Spell, Director Human Resources
Web address: www.vidanthealth.com
**Control:** Other not–for–profit (including NFP Corporation) **Service:** General medical and surgical

**Staffed Beds:** 6 **Admissions:** 397 **Census:** 4 **Outpatient Visits:** 24288 **Births:** 0 **Total Expense ($000):** 18212 **Payroll Expense ($000):** 7763 **Personnel:** 102

## WINSTON SALEM—Forsyth County

**BRENNER CHILDREN'S HOSPITAL & HEALTH SERVICES** See Wake Forest Baptist Medical Center, Winston-Salem

## WINSTON—SALEM—Forsyth County

**FORSYTH MEDICAL CENTER** See Novant Health Forsyth Medical Center

**MEDICAL PARK HOSPITAL** See Novant Health Medical Park Hospital

**NORTH CAROLINA BAPTIST HOSPITAL** See Wake Forest Baptist Medical Center

✠ **NOVANT HEALTH FORSYTH MEDICAL CENTER (340014)**, 3333 Silas Creek Parkway, Zip 27103–3090; tel. 336/718–5000, (Includes KERNERSVILLE MEDICAL CENTER, Mailing address: 2911750 Kernersville Medical Parkway, Kernersville, North Carolina, Zip 27284–2932, 1750 Kernersville Medical Parkway, Zip 27284–2932, tel. 336/564–4000; Chad Setliff, President and Chief Operating Officer; NOVANT HEALTH CLEMMONS MEDICAL CENTER, Mailing address: 6915 Village Medical Circle, Clemmons, North Carolina, Zip 27012–8002; tel. 336/893–1000; Chad Setliff, President and Chief Operating Officer), (Nonreporting) **A**1 2 3 5 10 **S** Novant Health, Winston Salem, NC
Primary Contact: Chad Setliff, President and Chief Operating Officer
CFO: Fred M Hargett, Executive Vice President and Chief Financial Officer
CMO: Thomas Zweng, Executive Vice President and Chief Medical Officer
CIO: David B Garrett, Senior Vice President and Chief Information Officer
CNO: Loraine Frank-Lightfoot, Vice President and Market Chief Nursing Officer
Web address: www.https://www.novanthealth.org
**Control:** Other not–for–profit (including NFP Corporation) **Service:** General medical and surgical

**Staffed Beds:** 740

✠ **NOVANT HEALTH MEDICAL PARK HOSPITAL (340148)**, 1950 South Hawthorne Road, Zip 27103–3993; tel. 336/718–0600, (Nonreporting) **A**1 10 **S** Novant Health, Winston Salem, NC
Primary Contact: Kirsten Royster, President and Chief Operating Officer
CFO: Fred M Hargett, Executive Vice President and Chief Financial Officer
CMO: Thomas Zweng, Executive Vice President and Chief Medical Officer
CIO: David B Garrett, Senior Vice President and Chief Information Officer
CNO: Carol A Smith, R.N., Director Operations and Nursing
Web address: www.novanthealth.org
**Control:** Other not–for–profit (including NFP Corporation) **Service:** General medical and surgical

**Staffed Beds:** 21

☐ **OLD VINEYARD BEHAVIORAL HEALTH SERVICES (344007)**, 3637 Old Vineyard Road, Zip 27104–4842; tel. 336/794–3550, (Nonreporting) **A**1 10 **S** Universal Health Services, Inc., King of Prussia, PA
Primary Contact: Kevin Patton, Chief Executive Officer
CFO: Ernest C Priddy IIIChief Financial Officer
CMO: Raj Thotakura, M.D., Medical Director
CHR: Jackie Pennino, Director Human Resources
CNO: Susan Evans, Chief Nursing Officer
Web address: www.oldvineyardbhs.com
**Control:** Corporation, Investor–owned (for–profit) **Service:** Psychiatric

**Staffed Beds:** 148

**OLD VINEYARD YOUTH SERVICES** See Old Vineyard Behavioral Health Services

✠ △ **WAKE FOREST BAPTIST MEDICAL CENTER (340047)**, Medical Center Boulevard, Zip 27157–0001; tel. 336/716–2011, (Includes BRENNER CHILDREN'S HOSPITAL & HEALTH SERVICES, Mailing address: Medical Center Boulevard, Winston Salem, North Carolina, Zip 27157, One Medical Center Boulevard, Zip 27157, tel. 336/716–2255), (Nonreporting) **A**1 2 3 5 7 8 10 **F**3 5 6 7 9 11 12 15 16 17 18 19 20 21 22 23 24 25 26 27 28 29 30 31 32 34 35 36 37 38 40 41 43 44 45 46 47 48 49 50 52 53 54 55 56 57 58 59 60 61 62 64 65 66 68 70 72 73 74 75 77 78 79 81 82 84 85 86 87 88 89 90 91 92 93 96 97 98 99 100 101 102 103 104 107 108 110 111 113 114 115 116 117 118 119 120 121 123 124 126 127 129 130 131 132 134 135 136 137 138 141 142 143 145 146 147 148 149 150 153 154 155 156 157 **S** Wake Forest Baptist Health, Winston-Salem, NC
Primary Contact: Cathleen Wheatley, R.N., President and System Chief Nurse Executive and Senior Vice President of Clinical Operations
CMO: Russell M Howerton, M.D., Chief Medical Officer
CHR: Cheryl Locke, Vice President and Chief Human Resource Officer
Web address: www.wakehealth.edu
**Control:** Other not–for–profit (including NFP Corporation) **Service:** General medical and surgical

**Staffed Beds:** 800 **Admissions:** 39125 **Census:** 664 **Outpatient Visits:** 925593 **Births:** 30 **Total Expense ($000):** 1761494 **Payroll Expense ($000):** 557328 **Personnel:** 9341

**NC**

*Many Facility Codes have changed. Please refer to the AHA Guide Code Chart.*

© 2021 AHA Guide

# NORTH DAKOTA

## ASHLEY—Mcintosh County

★ **ASHLEY MEDICAL CENTER (351322)**, 612 North Center Avenue,
Zip 58413–7013, Mailing Address: P.O. Box 450, Zip 58413–0450;
tel. 701/288–3433, (Nonreporting) **A**10 18
Primary Contact: Eric Heupel, Interim Chief Executive Officer
CMO: Udom Tinsa, M.D., Medical Director
Web address: www.amctoday.org
**Control:** Other not-for-profit (including NFP Corporation) **Service:** General
medical and surgical

**Staffed Beds:** 60

## BELCOURT—Rolette County

☐ **INDIAN HEALTH SERVICE - QUENTIN N. BURDICK MEMORIAL HEALTH CARE
FACILITY (350063)**, 1300 Hospital Loop, Zip 58316, Mailing Address: P.O. Box
160, Zip 58316–0160; tel. 701/477–6111, (Nonreporting) **A**1 10 **S** U. S. Indian
Health Service, Rockville, MD
Primary Contact: Shelly Harris, Chief Executive Officer
CFO: Deland Davis, Chief Financial Officer
CMO: Paula Bercier, M.D., Chief Medical Officer
CIO: Chance Wilkie, Information Technology Specialist
CHR: Donna Belgarde, Human Resources Specialist
CNO: Lynelle Hunt, Director of Nursing
Web address: www.ihs.gov
**Control:** PHS, Indian Service, Government, federal **Service:** General medical and
surgical

**Staffed Beds:** 29

**PUBLIC HEALTH SERVICE INDIAN HOSPITAL - QUENTIN N. BURDICK
MEMORIAL HEALTH FACILITY** See Indian Health Service - Quentin N. Burdick
Memorial Health Care Facility

## BISMARCK—Burleigh County

✠ **CHI ST. ALEXIUS HEALTH (350002)**, 900 East Broadway, Zip 58501–4586,
Mailing Address: P.O. Box 5510, Zip 58506–5510; tel. 701/530–7000, (Total
facility includes 19 beds in nursing home–type unit) (Nonreporting) **A**1 2 3 5 10 **F**3
5 8 9 11 12 13 15 17 18 19 20 21 22 23 24 25 26 28 29 30 31 32 34 35 38
40 43 45 46 49 53 54 56 57 58 59 60 64 68 70 72 73 74 75 76 77 78 79 81
82 84 85 87 88 89 92 93 94 96 97 98 99 100 101 102 103 104 105 107 110
111 114 115 118 119 126 128 129 130 131 132 135 144 146 147 148 149
150 152 154 **P**8 **S** CommonSpirit Health, Chicago, IL
Primary Contact: Kurt Schley, Chief Executive Officer
CFO: Susan Sisk, Chief Financial Officer
CMO: Shiraz Hyder, M.D., Director Medical Affairs
CIO: Todd Bortke, Director Information Systems
CHR: Tom Gregg, Vice President Human Resources
CNO: Rosanne Schmidt, R.N., Chief Nursing Officer
Web address: www.st.alexius.org
**Control:** Church operated, Nongovernment, not-for-profit **Service:** General
medical and surgical

**Staffed Beds:** 237 **Admissions:** 8733 **Census:** 122 **Outpatient
Visits:** 141546 **Births:** 1069 **Total Expense ($000):** 307481 **Payroll
Expense ($000):** 136010 **Personnel:** 1356

**SANFORD BISMARCK** See Sanford Medical Center Bismarck

✠ **SANFORD MEDICAL CENTER BISMARCK (350015)**, 300 North Seventh
Street, Zip 58501–4439, Mailing Address: P.O. Box 5525, Zip 58506–5525;
tel. 701/323–6000, (Nonreporting) **A**1 2 3 5 10 19 **F**3 8 9 11 12 13 15 17 18
20 22 24 26 28 29 30 31 32 33 34 35 36 37 38 40 43 44 45 49 51 53 54 55
56 57 58 59 60 61 62 63 64 65 66 68 69 70 71 72 73 74 75 76 77 78 79 81
82 84 85 86 87 88 89 92 93 96 97 98 100 101 102 104 107 108 110 111
115 118 119 126 129 130 131 132 134 135 138 141 142 146 147 148 149
150 154 156 157 **P**6 **S** Sanford Health, Sioux Falls, SD
Primary Contact: Michael LeBeau, President
CFO: Kirk Cristy, Vice President Finance
CMO: Chris Meeker, M.D., Chief Medical Officer
CHR: Leah Kelsch, Executive Director
CNO: Patrick Schultz, Vice President Nursing
Web address: www.bismarck.sanfordhealth.org/
**Control:** Other not-for-profit (including NFP Corporation) **Service:** General
medical and surgical

**Staffed Beds:** 227 **Admissions:** 13555 **Census:** 164 **Outpatient
Visits:** 203383 **Births:** 1419 **Total Expense ($000):** 563038 **Payroll
Expense ($000):** 257883 **Personnel:** 2689

**ST. ALEXIUS MEDICAL CENTER** See Chi St. Alexius Health

## BOTTINEAU—Bottineau County

**ST ANDREW'S MEDICAL CENTER** See St. Andrew'S Health Center

**ST. ANDREW'S HEALTH CENTER (351307)**, 316 Ohmer Street,
Zip 58318–1045; tel. 701/228–9300, (Nonreporting) **A**10 18 **S** Sisters of Mary of
the Presentation Health System, Fargo, ND
Primary Contact: Alfred Sams, President and Chief Executive Officer
CFO: Sean Rinkenberger, Chief Financial Officer
CMO: Jessica Skjolden, M.D., Chief of Staff
CHR: Brenda Arneson, Administrative Assistant
CNO: Karla Spence, Director of Nursing
Web address: www.standrewshealth.com
**Control:** Church operated, Nongovernment, not-for-profit **Service:** General
medical and surgical

**Staffed Beds:** 25

## BOWMAN—Bowman County

**SOUTHWEST HEALTHCARE SERVICES (351313)**, 802 2nd Street
Northwest, Zip 58623–4483, Mailing Address: P O Drawer 'C', Zip 58623;
tel. 701/523–5265, (Nonreporting) **A**10 18
Primary Contact: Jerry Wiesner, Administrator and Chief Executive Officer
Web address: www.swhealthcare.net
**Control:** Other not-for-profit (including NFP Corporation) **Service:** General
medical and surgical

**Staffed Beds:** 55

**ST LUKE'S TRI-STATE HOSPITAL** See Southwest Healthcare Services

## CANDO—Towner County

★ **TOWNER COUNTY MEDICAL CENTER (351331)**, State Highway 281 North,
Zip 58324, Mailing Address: P.O. Box 688, Zip 58324–0688; tel. 701/968–4411,
(Nonreporting) **A**10 18
Primary Contact: Ben Bucher, Chief Executive Officer
CFO: Tammy Larson, Chief Financial Officer
CMO: Russ Petty, M.D., Chief of Staff
CIO: David Fite, Director Information Technology
CHR: Pat Klingenberg, Director Human Resources
Web address: www.tcmedcenter.org
**Control:** Other not-for-profit (including NFP Corporation) **Service:** General
medical and surgical

**Staffed Beds:** 55

**TOWNER COUNTY MEMORIAL HOSP** See Towner County Medical Center

---

## CARRINGTON—Foster County

**CHI CARRINGTON HEALTH** See Chi St Alexius Health Carrington Medical Center

★ **CHI ST ALEXIUS HEALTH CARRINGTON MEDICAL CENTER (351318)**, 800 North Fourth Street, Zip 58421–1217, Mailing Address: P.O. Box 461, Zip 58421–0461; tel. 701/652–3141, (Nonreporting) **A**10 18 **F**3 7 11 15 28 34 40 45 46 64 75 81 87 104 107 108 110 114 119 127 132 133 143 146 154 **S** CommonSpirit Health, Chicago, IL
Primary Contact: Mariann Doeling, R.N., President
COO: Brenda Rask, Vice President Operations
CFO: Kurt Sargent, CPA, Vice President, Operational Finance
CIO: Keith Stauffer, Regional Chief Information Officer
CHR: Carol Risovi, Human Resources
CNO: Jodi Lynn Hovdenes, R.N., Vice President Patient Care
Web address: www.carringtonhealthcenter.org
**Control:** Other not–for–profit (including NFP Corporation) **Service:** General medical and surgical

**Staffed Beds:** 25 **Admissions:** 292 **Census:** 3 **Outpatient Visits:** 18620 **Births:** 0 **Total Expense ($000):** 11132 **Payroll Expense ($000):** 2889 **Personnel:** 45

## CAVALIER—Pembina County

★ **PEMBINA COUNTY MEMORIAL HOSPITAL AND WEDGEWOOD MANOR (351319)**, 301 Mountain Street East, Zip 58220–4015, Mailing Address: P.O. Box 380, Zip 58220–0380; tel. 701/265–8461, (Nonreporting) **A**10 18
Primary Contact: Lisa LeTexier, Chief Executive Officer
CFO: Katie Werner, Chief Financial Officer
CMO: K S Sumra, M.D., Chief of Staff
CIO: Robert Heidt, Director Information Systems
CHR: Chelsey Terault, Manager Human Resources
CNO: ArvaDell Sharp, Director of Nursing
Web address: www.cavalierhospital.com
**Control:** Other not–for–profit (including NFP Corporation) **Service:** General medical and surgical

**Staffed Beds:** 70

## COOPERSTOWN—Griggs County

**COOPERSTOWN MEDICAL CENTER (351306)**, 1200 Roberts Avenue NorthEast, Zip 58425–7101; tel. 701/797–2221, (Nonreporting) **A**10 18
Primary Contact: Nikki Johnson, Administrator and Chief Executive Officer
CMO: Jeffrey Peterson, M.D., Medical Director
CHR: Pamela VenHuizen, Chief Human Resources Officer
Web address: www.coopermc.com
**Control:** Other not–for–profit (including NFP Corporation) **Service:** General medical and surgical

**Staffed Beds:** 62

**GRIGGS CNTY HOSPITAL & NRSG HM** See Cooperstown Medical Center

## CROSBY—Divide County

**ST. LUKE'S HOSPITAL** See St. Luke's Medical Center

★ **ST. LUKE'S MEDICAL CENTER (351325)**, 702 First Street Southwest, Zip 58730–3329, Mailing Address: P.O. Box 10, Zip 58730–0010; tel. 701/965–6384, (Total facility includes 27 beds in nursing home–type unit) (Nonreporting) **A**5 10 18 **F**29 30 32 34 40 43 45 50 59 64 69 77 81 82 83 84 86 87 92 93 94 96 97 119 127 128 130 132 133 148 149 150 154
Primary Contact: Jody Nelson, Chief Executive Officer
Web address: www.dcstlukes.org/
**Control:** Other not–for–profit (including NFP Corporation) **Service:** General medical and surgical

**Staffed Beds:** 43 **Admissions:** 142 **Census:** 36 **Outpatient Visits:** 887 **Births:** 0 **Personnel:** 111

## DEVILS LAKE—Ramsey County

**CHI MERCY HOSPITAL** See Chi St. Alexius Health Devils Lake Hospital

✠ **CHI ST. ALEXIUS HEALTH DEVILS LAKE HOSPITAL (351333)**, 1031 Seventh Street NE, Zip 58301–2798; tel. 701/662–2131, (Nonreporting) **A**1 10 18 **F**3 11 13 28 29 34 40 45 50 54 57 64 75 76 77 81 85 87 93 97 107 108 111 115 119 131 132 133 148 149 150 **S** CommonSpirit Health, Chicago, IL
Primary Contact: Andrew Lankowicz, FACHE, President
CFO: Kurt Sargent, CPA, Vice President Operational Finance
CMO: Richard Johnson, M.D., Chief of Medical Staff
CHR: Bonnie Mattern, Director Human Resources
CNO: Aaron Johnson, Vice President Patient Care Services and Chief Nursing Officer
Web address: www.mercyhospitaldl.com
**Control:** Church operated, Nongovernment, not–for–profit **Service:** General medical and surgical

**Staffed Beds:** 25 **Admissions:** 827 **Census:** 9 **Outpatient Visits:** 20793 **Births:** 300 **Total Expense ($000):** 18585 **Payroll Expense ($000):** 6366 **Personnel:** 124

## DICKINSON—Stark County

✠ **CHI ST. ALEXIUS HEALTH - DICKINSON MEDICAL CENTER (351336)**, 2500 Fairway Street, Zip 58601–4399; tel. 701/456–4000, (Nonreporting) **A**1 10 18 **S** CommonSpirit Health, Chicago, IL
Primary Contact: DeeAnna Opstedahl, R.N., Interim President
CFO: Stephanie Franken, Vice President Operational Finance
CHR: Denise Lutz, Chief Human Resources Officer
CNO: DeeAnna Opstedahl, R.N., Vice President Patient Care Services
Web address: www.stjoeshospital.org
**Control:** Church operated, Nongovernment, not–for–profit **Service:** General medical and surgical

**Staffed Beds:** 25

**ST. JOSEPH'S HOSPITAL AND HEALTH CENTER** See Chi St. Alexius Health - Dickinson Medical Center

## ELGIN—Grant County

**JACOBSON MEMORIAL HOSPITAL CARE CENTER (351314)**, 601 East Street North, Zip 58533–7105, Mailing Address: P.O. Box 367, Zip 58533–0367; tel. 701/584–2792, (Nonreporting) **A**10 18
Primary Contact: Theo Stoller, Chief Executive Officer
CFO: Scott Ostenson, Chief Financial Officer
CMO: Deepak Goyal, M.D., Chief of Staff
CHR: Rynae Golke, Director Human Resources
CNO: Connie Gustafson, Director of Nursing
Web address: www.jacobsonhospital.org
**Control:** Other not–for–profit (including NFP Corporation) **Service:** General medical and surgical

**Staffed Beds:** 30

## FARGO—Cass County

△ **COBALT REHABILITATION HOSPITAL**, 4671 38th Avenue South, Zip 58104; tel. 701/404–5100, (Nonreporting) **A**7
Primary Contact: Karissa Olson, Chief Executive Officer
Web address: www.curahealth.com/inpatient-rehabilitation-facilities/cobalt-rehabilitation-fargo/
**Control:** Corporation, Investor–owned (for–profit) **Service:** Rehabilitation

**Staffed Beds:** 42

**ESSENTIA HEALTH** See Essentia Health Fargo

✠ **ESSENTIA HEALTH FARGO (350070)**, 3000 32nd Avenue South, Zip 58103–6132; tel. 701/364–8000, (Nonreporting) **A**1 2 3 5 10 **F**3 9 11 12 13 15 17 18 19 20 22 24 26 28 29 30 31 32 33 34 35 38 40 41 43 44 45 46 47 48 49 50 51 55 56 57 58 59 60 61 64 65 70 72 74 75 76 77 78 79 81 82 83 84 85 86 87 89 91 92 93 97 107 108 109 110 111 112 113 114 115 116 117 118 119 120 121 122 123 124 126 129 130 131 132 135 144 145 146 147 148 154 156 157 **P**6 **S** Essentia Health, Duluth, MN
Primary Contact: Al Hurley, West Region Chief Operating Officer
COO: Al Hurley, West Region Chief Operating Officer
CFO: Dennis Fuhrman, Vice President Finance
CMO: Michael Briggs, M.D., Chief Medical Officer
CIO: Ken Gilles, Chief Information Officer
CHR: Keith Wahlund, Vice President Human Resources
Web address: www.essentiahealth.com
**Control:** Other not–for–profit (including NFP Corporation) **Service:** General medical and surgical

**Staffed Beds:** 137 **Admissions:** 8532 **Census:** 90 **Outpatient Visits:** 125756 **Births:** 1296 **Total Expense ($000):** 378468 **Payroll Expense ($000):** 172766 **Personnel:** 1583

*Many Facility Codes have changed. Please refer to the AHA Guide Code Chart.* © 2021 AHA Guide

**FARGO NURSING HOME** See Rosewood on Broadway

**⊞ FARGO VETERANS AFFAIRS HEALTH CARE SYSTEM**, 2101 Elm Street North, Zip 58102; tel. 701/232–3241, (Nonreporting) **A**1 3 5 **S** Department of Veterans Affairs, Washington, DC
Primary Contact: Breton Weintraub, Director
COO: Dale DeKrey, MS, Associate Director Operations and Resources
CFO: Roger Sayler, Finance Officer
CMO: J Brian Hancock, M.D., Chief of Staff
CIO: Raymond Nelson, Acting Chief Information Resource Management
CHR: Jason Wells, Chief Human Resources Management Service
CNO: Julie Bruhn, R.N., MS, Associate Director Patient Care and Nurse Executive
Web address: www.fargo.va.gov/
**Control**: Veterans Affairs, Government, federal **Service**: General medical and surgical

**Staffed Beds:** 72

**KINDRED HOSPITAL FARGO** See Vibra Hospital of Fargo

**MERITCARE MEDICAL CENTER** See Sanford Medical Center Fargo

**MERITCARE SOUTH UNIVERSITY** See Sanford South University

**PRAIRIE AT ST JOHN'S** See Prairie St. John's

**☐ PRAIRIE ST. JOHN'S (354004)**, 510 4th Street South, Zip 58103–1914; tel. 701/476–7200, (Nonreporting) **A**1 3 10 **S** Universal Health Services, Inc., King of Prussia, PA
Primary Contact: Jeff Herman, Chief Executive Officer
COO: Jennifer Faul, Chief Operating Officer
CFO: Tom Eide, Chief Financial Officer
CMO: Eduardo Meza, M.D., Medical Director
CHR: Michelle A Parkinson, Director Human Resources
CNO: Jacki Toppen, Director of Nursing
Web address: www.prairie-stjohns.com
**Control**: Partnership, Investor–owned (for–profit) **Service**: Psychiatric

**Staffed Beds:** 94

**⊞ △ SANFORD MEDICAL CENTER FARGO (350011)**, 801 Broadway North, Zip 58122–3641; tel. 701/234–2000, (Includes SANFORD SOUTH UNIVERSITY, Mailing address: 1720 South University Drive, Fargo, North Dakota, Zip 58103–4994; tel. 701/234–2000; Nate White, Executive Vice President), (Nonreporting) **A**1 2 3 5 7 10 19 **F**3 7 8 9 11 12 13 15 17 18 19 20 21 22 23 24 25 26 27 28 29 30 31 32 33 34 35 36 37 38 39 40 43 44 45 46 48 49 50 51 52 53 54 55 56 57 58 59 60 61 62 63 64 65 66 67 68 70 71 72 74 75 76 78 79 81 82 83 84 85 86 87 88 89 90 91 92 93 94 96 97 98 99 100 101 102 103 104 105 107 108 110 111 112 114 115 116 117 118 119 120 121 123 124 126 129 130 131 132 135 138 141 142 143 144 145 146 147 148 149 150 153 154 155 156 157 **P**6 8 **S** Sanford Health, Sioux Falls, SD
Primary Contact: Bryan Nermoe, President
CFO: Tiffany Lawrence, Vice President of Finance
CMO: Douglas Griffin, M.D., Vice President Medical Officer
CIO: Arlyn Broekhuis, Chief Information Officer
CNO: Roberta Jo Young, Vice President Nursing
Web address: www.sanfordhealth.org
**Control**: Other not–for–profit (including NFP Corporation) **Service**: General medical and surgical

**Staffed Beds:** 546 **Admissions:** 27720 **Census:** 382 **Outpatient Visits:** 356826 **Births:** 2871 **Total Expense ($000):** 1293833 **Payroll Expense ($000):** 542673 **Personnel:** 5413

**VETERANS AFFAIRS HEALTH CARE SYSTEM** See Fargo Veterans Affairs Health Care System

**⊞ VIBRA HOSPITAL OF FARGO (352004)**, 1720 University Drive South, Zip 58103–4940; tel. 701/241–9099, (Nonreporting) **A**1 10 **S** Vibra Healthcare, Mechanicsburg, PA
Primary Contact: Custer Huseby, Chief Executive Officer
Web address: www.vhfargo.com
**Control**: Corporation, Investor–owned (for–profit) **Service**: Acute long–term care hospital

**Staffed Beds:** 31

### FORT YATES—Sioux County

**☐ STANDING ROCK SERVICE UNIT, FORT YATES HOSPITAL, INDIAN HEALTH SERVICE, DHHS (350064)**, 10 North River Road, Zip 58538, Mailing Address: P.O. Box 'J', Zip 58538; tel. 701/854–3831, (Nonreporting) **A**1 10 **S** U. S. Indian Health Service, Rockville, MD
Primary Contact: Jana Gipp, Chief Executive Officer
CFO: Byron Wilcox, Chief Financial Management Officer
CMO: Sara Jumping Eagle, Clinical Director
CNO: Joelle Keepseagle, Director of Nursing
Web address: www.ihs.gov
**Control**: PHS, Indian Service, Government, federal **Service**: General medical and surgical

**Staffed Beds:** 14

**U. S. PUBLIC HEALTH SERVICE INDIAN HOSPITAL** See Standing Rock Service Unit, Fort Yates Hospital, Indian Health Service, Dhhs

### GARRISON—Mclean County

**CHI ST. ALEXIUS HEALTH GARRISON** See Chi St. Alexius Health-Garrison Memorial Hospital

**★ CHI ST. ALEXIUS HEALTH-GARRISON MEMORIAL HOSPITAL (351303)**, 407 Third Avenue SE, Zip 58540–7235; tel. 701/463–2275, (Nonreporting) **A**10 18 **S** CommonSpirit Health, Chicago, IL
Primary Contact: Tod Graeber, Administrator
CMO: Vern Harchenko, M.D., Chief of Staff
CNO: Beth Hetletved, Director of Nurses
Web address: www.garrisonmh.com
**Control**: Other not–for–profit (including NFP Corporation) **Service**: General medical and surgical

**Staffed Beds:** 50

### GRAFTON—Walsh County

**UNITY HOSPITAL** See Unity Medical Center

**★ UNITY MEDICAL CENTER (351320)**, 164 West 13th Street, Zip 58237–1896; tel. 701/352–1620, (Nonreporting) **A**10 18
Primary Contact: Alan O'Neil, Chief Executive Officer
CFO: Rachel Ray, Chief Financial Officer
Web address: www.unitymedcenter.com
**Control**: Other not–for–profit (including NFP Corporation) **Service**: General medical and surgical

**Staffed Beds:** 14

### GRAND FORKS—Grand Forks County

**⊞ △ ALTRU HEALTH SYSTEM (350019)**, 1200 South Columbia Road, Zip 58201–4036, Mailing Address: P.O. Box 6002, Zip 58206–6002; tel. 701/780–5000, (Includes ALTRU HOSPITAL, Mailing address: 1200 South Columbia Road, Grand Forks, North Dakota, Zip 58201, PO Box 6002, Zip 58206–6002, tel. 701/780–5000; Steven Weiser, M.D., President; ALTRU REHABILITATION CENTER, Mailing address: 1300 South Columbia Road, Grand Forks, North Dakota, Zip 58201; tel. 701/780–2311; Steven Weiser, M.D., President), (Nonreporting) **A**1 2 3 5 7 10 20 **F**3 4 7 9 11 12 13 14 15 17 18 20 22 24 26 28 29 30 31 32 33 34 35 36 37 38 40 43 44 45 46 48 49 50 52 55 56 57 58 59 60 61 62 63 64 65 68 70 71 72 73 74 75 76 77 78 79 81 82 83 84 85 86 87 89 90 91 92 93 94 96 97 98 99 100 101 102 103 104 107 108 110 111 114 115 116 117 119 120 121 123 124 126 129 130 131 132 135 144 146 147 148 149 151 153 154 155 156 157 **P**6
Primary Contact: David R. Molmen, Interim Chief Executive Officer
CFO: Craig Faerber, Interim Chief Financial Officer
CIO: Mark Waind, Chief Information Officer
CHR: Kellee J. Fisk, Chief People and Strategy Officer
CNO: Margaret M Reed, R.N., Chief Nursing Officer
Web address: www.altru.org
**Control**: Other not–for–profit (including NFP Corporation) **Service**: General medical and surgical

**Staffed Beds:** 299 **Admissions:** 10613 **Census:** 150 **Outpatient Visits:** 952028 **Births:** 1586 **Total Expense ($000):** 626771 **Payroll Expense ($000):** 298418 **Personnel:** 2150

**ALTRU REHAB CENTER** See Altru Rehabilitation Center

---

**Hospital, Medicare Provider Number, Address, Telephone, Approval, Facility, and Physician Codes, Health Care System**

★ American Hospital Association (AHA) membership
☐ The Joint Commission accreditation
○ Healthcare Facilities Accreditation Program
◇ DNV Healthcare Inc. accreditation
⇧ Center for Improvement in Healthcare Quality Accreditation
△ Commission on Accreditation of Rehabilitation Facilities (CARF) accreditation

**RED RIVER BEHAVIORAL HEALTH SYSTEM (354005)**, 1451 44th Avenue South Unit A, Zip 58201–3434; tel. 701/772–2500, (Nonreporting) **A**10
Primary Contact: Jacqueline Hanson, Chief Executive Officer
CFO: Michelle Currie, Chief Financial Officer
CHR: Amanda Altendorf, Chief Human Resources and Quality Management
Web address: www.redriverbhs.com
**Control:** Corporation, Investor–owned (for–profit) **Service:** Psychiatric

**Staffed Beds:** 70

**RICHARD P. STADTER PSYCHIATRIC CENTER** See Red River Behavioral Health System

**UNITED HEALTH SERVICES** See Altru Health System

**UNITED HOSPITAL** See Altru Hospital

**HARVEY—Wells County**

★ **ST. ALOISIUS MEDICAL CENTER (351327)**, 325 East Brewster Street, Zip 58341–1653; tel. 701/324–4651, (Total facility includes 85 beds in nursing home–type unit) (Nonreporting) **A**10 18 **F**15 28 30 40 45 53 56 57 59 77 81 93 107 110 114 125 128 130 131 132 133 146 147 156 **S** Sisters of Mary of the Presentation Health System, Fargo, ND
Primary Contact: Mike Zwicker, Chief Executive Officer
CFO: Sandra Teubner, Chief Financial Officer
Web address: www.staloisius.com
**Control:** Church operated, Nongovernment, not–for–profit **Service:** General medical and surgical

**Staffed Beds:** 110 **Admissions:** 406 **Census:** 77 **Outpatient Visits:** 9934 **Births:** 0 **Total Expense ($000):** 17297 **Payroll Expense ($000):** 8431 **Personnel:** 211

**HAZEN—Mercer County**

★ **SAKAKAWEA MEDICAL CENTER (351310)**, 510 Eighth Avenue NE, Zip 58545–4637; tel. 701/748–2225, (Nonreporting) **A**10 18
Primary Contact: Darrold Bertsch, Chief Executive Officer
CFO: Renae Snyder, Chief Financial Officer
CHR: Laurie Miller, Administrative Assistant
CNO: Marcie Schulz, Director Patient Care
Web address: www.smcnd.org
**Control:** Other not–for–profit (including NFP Corporation) **Service:** General medical and surgical

**Staffed Beds:** 18

**HETTINGER—Adams County**

**WEST RIVER REGIONAL MEDICAL CENTER (351330)**, 1000 Highway 12, Zip 58639–7530; tel. 701/567–4561, (Nonreporting) **A**3 5 10 18
Primary Contact: Matthew Shahan, Chief Executive Officer
CFO: Nathan Stadheim, Chief Financial Officer
CMO: Jennifer Shefield, M.D., Chief of Staff
CIO: Julia Gochenour, Manager Information Systems
CHR: Tera Fried, Manager Human Resources
CNO: Barbara Stadheim, Chief Nursing Officer
Web address: www.wrhs.com
**Control:** Other not–for–profit (including NFP Corporation) **Service:** General medical and surgical

**Staffed Beds:** 25

**HILLSBORO—Traill County**

**HILLSBORO MEDICAL CENTER** See Sanford Hillsboro Medical Center

**HILLSBORO NURSING HOME** See Hillsboro Community Nursing Home

★ **SANFORD HILLSBORO MEDICAL CENTER (351329)**, 12 Third Street SE, Zip 58045–4840, Mailing Address: P.O. Box 609, Zip 58045–0609; tel. 701/636–3200, (Total facility includes 30 beds in nursing home–type unit) (Nonreporting) **A**10 18 **F**7 10 11 34 35 40 64 65 68 75 81 93 97 103 125 128 143 146 148 154 156 158 **P**6 **S** Sanford Health, Sioux Falls, SD
Primary Contact: Jac McTaggart, Chief Executive Officer
CFO: Scott Awalt, Chief Financial Officer
CMO: Charles J Breen, M.D., Medical Director
CHR: Jenny Jacobson, Manager Human Resources
Web address: www.https://www.sanfordhealth.org/locations/sanford-hillsboro-medical-center
**Control:** Other not–for–profit (including NFP Corporation) **Service:** General medical and surgical

**Staffed Beds:** 46 **Admissions:** 170 **Census:** 36 **Outpatient Visits:** 14879 **Births:** 0 **Total Expense ($000):** 13459 **Payroll Expense ($000):** 5792 **Personnel:** 87

**JAMESTOWN—Stutsman County**

**JAMESTOWN HOSPITAL** See Jamestown Regional Medical Center

✠ **JAMESTOWN REGIONAL MEDICAL CENTER (351335)**, 2422 20th Street SW, Zip 58401–6201; tel. 701/252–1050, (Nonreporting) **A**1 10 18 **F**3 11 13 15 28 29 30 31 34 35 40 43 45 50 53 57 59 62 63 64 68 70 75 76 77 78 79 81 82 84 85 86 87 93 107 108 110 111 115 118 119 130 131 132 133 135 146 148 149 156
Primary Contact: Michael Delfs, President and Chief Executive Officer
COO: Ricki Ramlo, Chief Operating Officer and Human Resources
CFO: Brandon Vaughan, Chief Financial Officer and Vice President Finance
CMO: Derek Brickner, President Medical Staff
CIO: Jeff Gunkel, Chief Information Officer
CHR: Ricki Ramlo, Chief Operating Officer and Human Resources
CNO: Trisha Jungels, R.N., Chief Nursing Officer and Vice President Clinical Services
Web address: www.jamestownhospital.com
**Control:** Other not–for–profit (including NFP Corporation) **Service:** General medical and surgical

**Staffed Beds:** 25 **Admissions:** 961 **Census:** 8 **Outpatient Visits:** 35552 **Births:** 357 **Total Expense ($000):** 51685 **Payroll Expense ($000):** 21027 **Personnel:** 279

☐ **NORTH DAKOTA STATE HOSPITAL (354003)**, 2605 Circle Drive SE, Zip 58401–6905; tel. 701/253–3964, (Nonreporting) **A**1 3 5 10
Primary Contact: Rosalie Etherington, Superintendent and Chief Executive Officer
COO: Ken Schulz, Chief Operating Officer
CMO: Eduardo Yabut, M.D., Medical Director
CIO: Amy Shape, Information Technology
CNO: Leah Schulz, Director of Nursing
Web address: www.nd.gov/
**Control:** State, Government, Nonfederal **Service:** Psychiatric

**Staffed Beds:** 100

**KENMARE—Ward County**

**KENMARE COMMUNITY HOSPITAL (351305)**, 317 First Avenue NW, Zip 58746–7104, Mailing Address: P.O. Box 697, Zip 58746–0697; tel. 701/385–4296, (Nonreporting) **A**10 18
Primary Contact: Danielle Alsadon, Clinic/Hospital Manager
COO: Bev Heninger, Director of Nursing
CFO: Dennis Empey, Chief Financial Officer
CMO: Buki Oni, M.D., Chief Medical Officer
CIO: David Wanner, Director Information Technology
CHR: Ranae Ehlke, Administrative Secretary and Coordinator Risk Management and Human Resources
CNO: Bev Heninger, Director of Nursing
Web address: www.kenmarend.net/hospital.htm
**Control:** Corporation, Investor–owned (for–profit) **Service:** General medical and surgical

**Staffed Beds:** 25

**LANGDON—Cavalier County**

**CAVALIER COUNTY MEMORIAL HOSPITAL** See Cavalier County Memorial Hospital and Clinics

★ **CAVALIER COUNTY MEMORIAL HOSPITAL AND CLINICS (351323)**, 909 Second Street, Zip 58249–2407; tel. 701/256–6100, (Nonreporting) **A**10 18
Primary Contact: Jeff Stanley, Chief Executive Officer
COO: Darla Roder, Chief Operating Officer
CFO: Richard Fromme, Chief Financial Officer
CMO: Lynne Didrikson, M.D., Chief Medical Officer
CHR: Linda Benoit, Human Resource Officer
CNO: Jamie Nienhuis, Chief Nursing Officer
Web address: www.cavaliercountyhospital.com
**Control:** Other not–for–profit (including NFP Corporation) **Service:** General medical and surgical

**Staffed Beds:** 20

**LINTON—Emmons County**

★ **LINTON HOSPITAL (351328)**, 518 North Broadway, Zip 58552–7308, Mailing Address: P.O. Box 850, Zip 58552–0850; tel. 701/254–4511, (Nonreporting) **A**10 18
Primary Contact: Robert O. Black, Chief Executive Officer
CMO: John Knecht, Chief Medical Staff
CHR: Sue Meidinger, Manager Business Office
Web address: www.lintonhospital.com
**Control:** Other not–for–profit (including NFP Corporation) **Service:** General medical and surgical

**Staffed Beds:** 14

*Many Facility Codes have changed. Please refer to the AHA Guide Code Chart.*

© 2021 AHA Guide

## LISBON—Ransom County

★ **CHI LISBON HEALTH (351311)**, 905 Main Street, Zip 58054–4334, Mailing Address: P.O. Box 353, Zip 58054–0353; tel. 701/683–6400, (Nonreporting) **A**10 18 **S** CommonSpirit Health, Chicago, IL
Primary Contact: Keith E. Heuser, Administrator
COO: Sheri Heinisch, Compliance Officer
CFO: Amber Stowman, Controller
CHR: Janet Froemke, Human Resources Officer
Web address: www.lisbonhospital.com
**Control**: Church operated, Nongovernment, not–for–profit **Service**: General medical and surgical

| Staffed Beds: 25 |
| --- |

**LISBON AREA HEALTH SERVICES** See Chi Lisbon Health

## MANDAN—Morton County

**KINDRED HOSPITAL-CENTRAL DAKOTAS** See Vibra Hospital of Central Dakotas

⊞ **VIBRA HOSPITAL OF CENTRAL DAKOTAS (352005)**, 1000 18th Street NW, Zip 58554–1612; tel. 701/667–2000, (Nonreporting) **A**1 10 **S** Vibra Healthcare, Mechanicsburg, PA
Primary Contact: Glynda Troyo-Sauviac, Chief Executive Officer
Web address: www.vhcentraldakotas.com
**Control**: Corporation, Investor–owned (for–profit) **Service**: Acute long–term care hospital

| Staffed Beds: 41 |
| --- |

## MAYVILLE—Traill County

★ **SANFORD MAYVILLE MEDICAL CENTER (351309)**, 42 Sixth Avenue SE, Zip 58257–1598; tel. 701/786–3800, (Nonreporting) **A**10 18 **F**5 7 40 43 45 65 77 81 93 97 107 119 128 129 130 133 156 **P**6 **S** Sanford Health, Sioux Falls, SD
Primary Contact: Jac McTaggart, Chief Executive Officer
CFO: Shauna Slabik, Chief Financial Officer
CMO: Jane Ostlig, Chief Medical Officer
Web address: www.unionhospital.com
**Control**: Other not–for–profit (including NFP Corporation) **Service**: General medical and surgical

| Staffed Beds: 10 Admissions: 272 Census: 4 Outpatient Visits: 18340 Births: 0 Total Expense ($000): 9555 Payroll Expense ($000): 4860 Personnel: 61 |
| --- |

**SANFORD MEDICAL CENTER MAYVILLE** See Sanford Mayville Medical Center

## MCVILLE—Nelson County

**COMM HOSP IN NELSON CNTY** See Nelson County Health System

**NELSON COUNTY HEALTH SYSTEM (351308)**, 200 Main Street, Zip 58254, Mailing Address: P.O. Box 367, Zip 58254–0367; tel. 701/322–4328, (Nonreporting) **A**10 18
Primary Contact: Steve Forde, Chief Executive Officer
CMO: Erling Martinson, M.D., Medical Director
Web address: www.nelsoncountyhealthsystem.org
**Control**: Other not–for–profit (including NFP Corporation) **Service**: General medical and surgical

| Staffed Beds: 58 |
| --- |

## MINOT—Ward County

⊞ △ **TRINITY HEALTH (350006)**, One Burdick Expressway West, Zip 58701–4406, Mailing Address: P.O. Box 5020, Zip 58702–5020; tel. 701/857–5766, (Includes TRINITY HOSPITAL-ST. JOSEPH'S, Mailing address: 407 3rd Street SE, Minot, North Dakota, Zip 58702–5001; tel. 701/857–2000) (Total facility includes 215 beds in nursing home–type unit) **A**1 2 3 5 7 10 **F**3 4 5 7 8 11 13 15 18 20 22 24 28 29 30 31 34 35 38 39 40 43 45 46 50 54 55 56 57 59 60 62 63 64 65 68 70 72 73 74 75 76 77 78 79 81 82 84 85 86 87 89 90 92 93 94 97 98 99 100 101 103 104 105 107 108 110 111 113 114 115 116 117 118 119 120 121 124 126 127 128 129 130 131 132 133 143 144 146 147 148 149 151 152 154 155 156 **P**6
Primary Contact: John M. Kutch, President and Chief Executive Officer
CFO: Dennis Empey, Chief Financial Officer
CIO: David Wanner, Chief Information Officer
CHR: Paul Simonson, Vice President
Web address: www.trinityhealth.org
**Control**: Other not–for–profit (including NFP Corporation) **Service**: General medical and surgical

| Staffed Beds: 580 Admissions: 8757 Census: 300 Outpatient Visits: 565897 Births: 1480 Total Expense ($000): 463169 Payroll Expense ($000): 224670 Personnel: 2553 |
| --- |

**UNIMED MEDICAL CENTER** See Trinity Hospital-St. Joseph's

## NORTHWOOD—Grand Forks County

★ **NORTHWOOD DEACONESS HEALTH CENTER (351312)**, 4 North Park Street, Zip 58267–4102, Mailing Address: P.O. Box 190, Zip 58267–0190; tel. 701/587–6060, (Nonreporting) **A**10 18 **S** Sanford Health, Sioux Falls, SD
Primary Contact: Pete Antonson, Chief Executive Officer
CMO: Jon Berg, M.D., Chief of Staff
CIO: Chad Peterson, Chief Information Officer
Web address: www.ndhc.net
**Control**: Church operated, Nongovernment, not–for–profit **Service**: General medical and surgical

| Staffed Beds: 57 |
| --- |

**SANFORD NORTHWOOD DEACONESS HEALTH CENTER** See Northwood Deaconess Health Center

## OAKES—Dickey County

⊞ **CHI OAKES HOSPITAL (351315)**, 1200 North Seventh Street, Zip 58474–2502; tel. 701/742–3291, (Nonreporting) **A**1 10 18 **S** CommonSpirit Health, Chicago, IL
Primary Contact: Becki Thompson, President
CFO: Bethany Smith, Director of Finance
CMO: Katie O'Brien-Paradis, M.D., Chief Medical Officer
CHR: Julie Entzminger, Manager Human Resources
CNO: Kimberly A. Ketterling, R.N., Vice President Patient Care Services
Web address: www.oakeshospital.com
**Control**: Other not–for–profit (including NFP Corporation) **Service**: General medical and surgical

| Staffed Beds: 20 |
| --- |

**OAKES COMMUNITY HOSPITAL** See Chi Oakes Hospital

## PARK RIVER—Walsh County

★ **FIRST CARE HEALTH CENTER (351326)**, 115 Vivian Street, Zip 58270–4540, Mailing Address: PO Box I, Zip 58270–0708; tel. 701/284–7500, (Nonreporting) **A**10 18
Primary Contact: Marcus Lewis, Chief Executive Officer
CFO: Layne Ensrude, Chief Financial Officer
CMO: Joel Johnson, M.D., Chief Medical Staff
CNO: Lori Seim, R.N., Director Nursing Services
Web address: www.firstcarehc.com
**Control**: Other not–for–profit (including NFP Corporation) **Service**: General medical and surgical

| Staffed Beds: 14 |
| --- |

**ST ANSGAR'S HEALTH CENTER** See First Care Health Center

## ROLLA—Rolette County

**PRESENTATION MED CENTER** See Presentation Medical Center

★ **PRESENTATION MEDICAL CENTER (351316)**, 213 Second Avenue NE, Zip 58367–7153, Mailing Address: P.O. Box 759, Zip 58367–0759; tel. 701/477–3161, (Nonreporting) **A**10 18 **S** Sisters of Mary of the Presentation Health System, Fargo, ND
Primary Contact: Chris Albertson, Chief Executive Officer and President
CFO: Paula Wilkie, Chief Financial Officer
CMO: Roy Cordy, M.D., President Medical Staff
CHR: Chris Albertson, Director Human Resources
Web address: www.pmc-rolla.com
**Control**: Church operated, Nongovernment, not–for–profit **Service**: General medical and surgical

| Staffed Beds: 25 |
| --- |

## RUGBY—Pierce County

★ **HEART OF AMERICA MEDICAL CENTER (351332)**, 800 Main Avenue South, Zip 58368–2198; tel. 701/776–5261, (Nonreporting) **A**10 18
Primary Contact: Erik Christenson, Chief Executive Officer
CFO: Melissa Shepard, Chief Financial Officer
CIO: Jeremy Schonebery, Director Information Technology
Web address: www.hamc.com
**Control**: Other not–for–profit (including NFP Corporation) **Service**: General medical and surgical

| Staffed Beds: 85 |
| --- |

**HEART OF AMERICAN MEDICAL CNTR** See Heart of America Medical Center

---

**Hospital, Medicare Provider Number, Address, Telephone, Approval, Facility, and Physician Codes, Health Care System**

★ American Hospital Association (AHA) membership
□ The Joint Commission accreditation
○ Healthcare Facilities Accreditation Program
◇ DNV Healthcare Inc. accreditation
⇑ Center for Improvement in Healthcare Quality Accreditation
△ Commission on Accreditation of Rehabilitation Facilities (CARF) accreditation

## STANLEY—Mountrail County

★ **MOUNTRAIL COUNTY MEDICAL CENTER (351301)**, 615 6th Street SE, Zip 58784–4444, Mailing Address: P.O. Box 399, Zip 58784–0399; tel. 701/628–2424, (Nonreporting) **A**10 18
Primary Contact: Ben Bucher, Interim Chief Executive Officer
CFO: Susan Weston, CPA, Chief Financial Officer
CMO: Marla Longmuir, M.D., Chief Medical Officer
CIO: Kathy Janssen, Director Medical Records
CHR: Alisha McMahon, Director Human Resources
CNO: Belinda Moen, R.N., MSN, Interim Director of Nursing
Web address: www.stanleyhealth.org
**Control:** Other not–for–profit (including NFP Corporation) **Service:** General medical and surgical

**Staffed Beds:** 11

**STANLEY COMMUNITY HOSPITAL** See Mountrail County Medical Center

## TIOGA—Williams County

**TIOGA COMMUNITY HOSPITAL** See Tioga Medical Center

★ **TIOGA MEDICAL CENTER (351300)**, 810 North Welo Street, Zip 58852–7157, Mailing Address: P.O. Box 159, Zip 58852–0159; tel. 701/664–3305, (Nonreporting) **A**5 10 18
Primary Contact: Randall K. Pederson, Chief Executive Officer
CMO: Swami P Gade, M.D., Medical Director
CHR: Mary Ann Holm, Office Clerk
Web address: www.tiogahealth.org
**Control:** Other not–for–profit (including NFP Corporation) **Service:** General medical and surgical

**Staffed Beds:** 55

## TURTLE LAKE—McLean County

★ **CHI ST. ALEXIUS HEALTH-TURTLE LAKE HOSPITAL (351304)**, 220 Fifth Avenue, Zip 58575–4005, Mailing Address: P.O. Box 280, Zip 58575–0280; tel. 701/448–2331, (Nonreporting) **A**10 18 **S** CommonSpirit Health, Chicago, IL
Primary Contact: Tod Graeber, Administrator
CFO: Tom Spain, Director Operations Finance
CNO: Jessie Martin, R.N., Chief Nursing Executive
Web address: www.wrtc.com/cullum/hospital
**Control:** Church operated, Nongovernment, not–for–profit **Service:** General medical and surgical

**Staffed Beds:** 25

**COMMUNITY MEMORIAL HOSPITAL** See Chi St. Alexius Health-Turtle Lake Hospital

## VALLEY CITY—Barnes County

★ **CHI MERCY HEALTH (351324)**, 570 Chautauqua Boulevard, Zip 58072–3199; tel. 701/845–6400, (Nonreporting) **A**10 18 **S** CommonSpirit Health, Chicago, IL
Primary Contact: Keith E. Heuser, President
CFO: Bethany Smith, Vice President Finance
CHR: Nicole Nestler, Division Director Human Resources
Web address: www.mercyhospitalvalleycity.org
**Control:** Church operated, Nongovernment, not–for–profit **Service:** General medical and surgical

**Staffed Beds:** 19

**MERCY HOSPITAL** See Chi Mercy Health

## WATFORD CITY—Mckenzie County

★ **MCKENZIE COUNTY HEALTHCARE SYSTEM (351302)**, 516 North Main Street, Zip 58854–7310; tel. 701/842–3000, (Total facility includes 47 beds in nursing home–type unit) (Nonreporting) **A**10 18 **F**3 11 15 28 29 32 34 40 43 45 56 57 59 64 65 67 68 75 79 81 84 86 87 93 94 97 107 110 111 115 119 127 128 133 144 154 156
Primary Contact: Daniel R. Kelly, Chief Executive Officer
COO: Michael Curtis, Chief Administrative Officer
CFO: Kenneth Cox, Interim Chief Financial Officer
CMO: Gary Ramage, M.D., Chief Medical Officer
CIO: Karn Pederson, Manager Health Information Management
CHR: Amy Gonzales, Director of Human Resources
CNO: Cheryl Faulkner, Director of Nursing
Web address: www.mckenziehealth.com
**Control:** Other not–for–profit (including NFP Corporation) **Service:** General medical and surgical

**Staffed Beds:** 80 **Admissions:** 742 **Census:** 38 **Outpatient Visits:** 19420 **Births:** 0 **Total Expense ($000):** 29255 **Payroll Expense ($000):** 9516 **Personnel:** 90

**MCKENZIE COUNTY MEM HOSPITAL** See Mckenzie County Healthcare System

## WILLISTON—Williams County

✉ **CHI ST. ALEXIUS HEALTH - WILLISTON MEDICAL CENTER (351334)**, 1301 15th Avenue West, Zip 58801–3896; tel. 701/774–7400, (Nonreporting) **A**1 3 10 18 **S** CommonSpirit Health, Chicago, IL
Primary Contact: Dan Bjerknes, President
CMO: Brett Vibeto, M.D., Chief of Staff
CIO: Jeff Rust, Information Technology Systems Site Manager
CHR: Dan Bjerknes, Director Human Resources
CNO: Lori Hahn, Vice President Nursing Services
Web address: www.mercy-williston.org
**Control:** Church operated, Nongovernment, not–for–profit **Service:** General medical and surgical

**Staffed Beds:** 25

**MERCY MEDICAL CENTER** See Chi St. Alexius Health - Williston Medical Center

## WISHEK—Mcintosh County

★ **SOUTH CENTRAL HEALTH (351321)**, 1007 Fourth Avenue South, Zip 58495–7527, Mailing Address: P.O. Box 647, Zip 58495–0647; tel. 701/452–2326, (Nonreporting) **A**10 18 **F**3 7 11 15 17 28 29 32 34 35 36 40 44 45 50 53 56 57 59 64 65 68 75 81 82 83 87 91 92 93 97 107 114 127 128 130 131 133 143 146 147 148 149 156
Primary Contact: Beverly Vilhauer, Chief Executive Officer
CFO: Megan Rath, Chief Financial Officer
CMO: Joseph Thirumalareddy, M.D., Chief of Staff
CIO: Kari Buchholz, Director Health Information Management
CHR: Shar Bauer, Executive Secretary
Web address: www.https://schealthnd.com
**Control:** Other not–for–profit (including NFP Corporation) **Service:** General medical and surgical

**Staffed Beds:** 19 **Admissions:** 187 **Census:** 2 **Outpatient Visits:** 8380 **Births:** 0 **Total Expense ($000):** 7917 **Payroll Expense ($000):** 3620 **Personnel:** 73

**WISHEK COMMUNITY HOSPITAL AND CLINICS** See South Central Health

*Many Facility Codes have changed. Please refer to the AHA Guide Code Chart.*

© 2021 AHA Guide

# OHIO

## AKRON—Summit County

✠ △ **AKRON CHILDREN'S HOSPITAL (363303)**, One Perkins Square, Zip 44308–1063; tel. 330/543–1000, (Nonreporting) **A**1 2 3 5 7 10 **F**3 7 11 13 16 18 19 20 21 22 23 25 26 27 29 30 31 32 33 34 35 36 37 38 39 40 41 43 44 48 50 54 55 58 59 60 61 62 63 64 65 66 68 72 73 74 75 76 77 78 79 81 82 84 85 86 87 88 89 91 92 93 94 96 97 98 99 100 101 102 104 105 106 107 108 111 112 114 115 116 117 118 119 120 126 129 130 131 132 134 135 136 141 143 144 146 148 149 153 154 155 156 **P**6
Primary Contact: Grace Wakulchik, R.N., MSN, President and Chief Executive Officer
COO: Lisa Aurilio, R.N., MSN, Chief Operating Officer
CFO: Michael Trainer, Chief Financial Officer
CMO: Robert McGregor, M.D., Chief Medical Officer
CIO: Harun Rashid, Vice President and Chief Information Officer
CHR: Bernett Williams, Interim Chief Human Resource Officer
CNO: Christine Young, MSN, R.N., Vice President of Patient Services and Chief Nursing Officer
Web address: www.akronchildrens.org
**Control:** Other not-for-profit (including NFP Corporation) **Service:** Children's general medical and surgical

**Staffed Beds:** 462 **Admissions:** 9543 **Census:** 223 **Outpatient Visits:** 1229524 **Births:** 0 **Total Expense ($000):** 904968 **Payroll Expense ($000):** 456787 **Personnel:** 5663

**AKRON CITY HOSPITAL** See Summa Akron City Hospital

**AKRON GENERAL MEDICAL CENTER** See Cleveland Clinic Akron General

**CHILDREN'S HOSP MEDICAL CENTER** See Akron Children's Hospital

✠ **CLEVELAND CLINIC AKRON GENERAL (360027)**, 1 Akron General Avenue, Zip 44307–2433; tel. 330/344–6000, (Nonreporting) **A**1 2 3 5 8 10 **F**3 5 8 11 12 13 15 17 18 20 22 24 26 28 29 30 31 34 35 36 37 38 40 42 43 44 45 46 47 48 49 50 51 52 53 54 58 59 60 61 62 63 64 65 66 68 70 71 72 74 75 76 77 78 79 81 82 84 85 87 93 94 96 97 98 100 101 102 103 104 105 107 108 110 111 112 114 115 117 118 119 120 121 123 124 126 129 130 131 132 135 138 144 146 147 148 149 152 153 154 155 156 **S** Cleveland Clinic Health System, Cleveland, OH
Primary Contact: Brian J. Harte, M.D., President
CFO: Dave Frigo,  Vice President Financial Planning and Treasury
CMO: David Peter, M.D., Senior Vice President Medical Affairs and Chief Medical Director
CIO: David Fiser, Vice President and Chief Information Officer
CHR: Don Corpora, Executive Vice President and Chief Human Resources Officer
CNO: Cherie M Guster, R.N., MSN, Senior Vice President and Chief Nursing Officer
Web address: www.akrongeneral.org
**Control:** Other not-for-profit (including NFP Corporation) **Service:** General medical and surgical

**Staffed Beds:** 482 **Admissions:** 24620 **Census:** 317 **Outpatient Visits:** 553279 **Births:** 2254 **Total Expense ($000):** 582562 **Payroll Expense ($000):** 243225 **Personnel:** 4246

**SAINT THOMAS HOSPITAL** See Summa Saint Thomas Hospital

✠ **SELECT SPECIALTY HOSPITAL-AKRON (362027)**, 200 East Market Street, Zip 44308–2015; tel. 330/761–7500, (Nonreporting) **A**1 10 **S** Select Medical Corporation, Mechanicsburg, PA
Primary Contact: Dawne Wheeler, Chief Executive Officer
Web address: www.selectspecialtyhospitals.com/company/locations/akron.aspx
**Control:** Corporation, Investor-owned (for-profit) **Service:** Acute long-term care hospital

**Staffed Beds:** 60

**SUMMA AKRON CITY HOSPITAL** See Summa Health System, Akron

**SUMMA AKRON CITY HOSPITAL** See Summa Health System

✠ **SUMMA HEALTH SYSTEM (360020)**, 525 East Market Street, Zip 44304–1619; tel. 330/375–3000, (Includes SUMMA AKRON CITY HOSPITAL, Mailing address: 525 East Market Street, Akron, Ohio, Zip 44309–2090, P O Box 2090, Zip 44309–2090, tel. 330/375–3000; David Custodio, M.D., President Summa Akron City and St. Thomas Campuses; SUMMA HEALTH SYSTEM BARBERTON HOSPITAL, Mailing address: 155 Fifth Street NE, Barberton, Ohio, Zip 44203–3332; tel. 330/615–3000; Michael Hughes, M.D., President, Summa Barberton Campus; SUMMA SAINT THOMAS HOSPITAL, Mailing address: 444 North Main Street, Akron, Ohio, Zip 44310; tel. 330/375–3000; David Custodio, M.D., President Summa Akron City and St. Thomas Campuses), (Nonreporting) **A**1 2 3 5 8 10 19 **F**3 4 5 8 11 12 13 15 17 18 20 22 24 26 28 29 30 31 34 35 36 37 38 39 40 42 43 44 45 46 47 48 49 51 53 54 56 57 58 59 61 64 65 66 70 71 74 75 76 77 78 79 80 81 82 83 84 85 86 87 90 92 93 97 98 100 101 102 103 104 105 107 108 110 111 114 115 116 117 119 120 121 123 124 126 129 130 131 132 133 135 144 146 147 148 149 152 153 154 156 157 **P**6 8 **S** Summa Health, Akron, OH
Primary Contact: David Custodio, M.D., President Summa Akron City and St. Thomas Campuses
CIO: Tanya Authur, Chief Information Officer
CHR: Kyle Klawitter, Vice President Human Resources
Web address: www.summahealth.org
**Control:** Other not-for-profit (including NFP Corporation) **Service:** General medical and surgical

**Staffed Beds:** 721 **Admissions:** 34560 **Census:** 416 **Outpatient Visits:** 473071 **Births:** 4502 **Total Expense ($000):** 870326 **Payroll Expense ($000):** 252030 **Personnel:** 6720

✠ △ **SUMMA REHAB HOSPITAL (363035)**, 29 North Adams Street, Zip 44304–1641; tel. 330/572–7300, (Nonreporting) **A**1 7 10 **S** Summa Health, Akron, OH
Primary Contact: Michelle Dudek, President and Chief Executive Officer
Web address: www.summarehabhospital.com/
**Control:** Corporation, Investor-owned (for-profit) **Service:** Rehabilitation

**Staffed Beds:** 60

**SUMMA SAINT THOMAS HOSPITAL** See Summa Health System, Akron

## ALLIANCE—Stark County

○ **ALLIANCE COMMUNITY HOSPITAL (360131)**, 200 East State Street, Zip 44601–4936; tel. 330/596–6000, (Total facility includes 78 beds in nursing home-type unit) (Nonreporting) **A**2 5 10 11 **F**3 11 15 28 29 30 34 35 36 37 40 44 45 50 51 56 57 59 60 63 64 68 69 70 71 74 75 77 79 81 82 84 85 86 87 93 96 98 103 107 108 110 111 114 115 118 119 128 130 131 132 135 143 144 146 147 148 154 156 157 **P**7 8 **S** Aultman Health Foundation, Canton, OH
Primary Contact: Ryan Jones, Chief Executive Officer
COO: Dale W. Wells, Chief Financial and Operating Officer
CFO: Dale W. Wells, Chief Financial and Operating Officer
CMO: Ashraf Ahmed, M.D., Senior Vice President Physician and Hospital Services
CIO: David W Shroades, Vice President Technology Services
CHR: Nicole L Russ, Director Colleague Relations
CNO: Amy Antonacci, MSN, R.N., Vice President Nursing Services
Web address: www.achosp.org
**Control:** Other not-for-profit (including NFP Corporation) **Service:** General medical and surgical

**Staffed Beds:** 202 **Admissions:** 2711 **Census:** 94 **Outpatient Visits:** 184745 **Births:** 0 **Total Expense ($000):** 89538 **Payroll Expense ($000):** 36637 **Personnel:** 871

## AMHERST—Lorain County

□ **SPECIALTY HOSPITAL OF LORAIN (362025)**, 254 Cleveland Avenue, Zip 44001–1620; tel. 440/988–6260, (Nonreporting) **A**1 10
Primary Contact: Rajive Khanna, Chief Executive Officer
COO: Susan Adams, Chief Nursing Officer and Chief Operating Officer
CNO: Susan Adams, Chief Nursing Officer and Chief Operating Officer
**Control:** Other not-for-profit (including NFP Corporation) **Service:** Acute long-term care hospital

**Staffed Beds:** 30

---

**Hospital, Medicare Provider Number, Address, Telephone, Approval, Facility, and Physician Codes, Health Care System**

★ American Hospital Association (AHA) membership
□ The Joint Commission accreditation
○ Healthcare Facilities Accreditation Program
◇ DNV Healthcare Inc. accreditation
⇑ Center for Improvement in Healthcare Quality Accreditation
△ Commission on Accreditation of Rehabilitation Facilities (CARF) accreditation

**OH**

## ARCHBOLD—Fulton County

**ARCHBOLD HOSPITAL** See Community Hospitals and Wellness Centers, Bryan

## ASHLAND—Ashland County

☒ **UH SAMARITAN MEDICAL CENTER (360002)**, 1025 Center Street, Zip 44805–4011; tel. 419/289–0491, (Nonreporting) **A**1 10 **F**3 11 13 15 18 28 29 30 31 34 35 40 45 50 51 57 59 60 62 64 68 70 75 76 77 78 79 81 82 84 85 86 87 93 96 102 107 111 114 115 116 117 118 119 129 130 131 132 135 144 146 147 148 149 154 **S** University Hospitals, Cleveland, OH
Primary Contact: Todd Harford, President
CFO: Mary Griest, Vice President Finance and Chief Financial Officer
CMO: Philip Myers, M.D., Vice President Medical Affairs
CIO: Kathleen Metcalf, Chief Information Officer
CHR: Alyce Legg, Vice President Human Resources
CNO: Karin Schwan, Chief Nursing Officer, Vice President Patient Care Services
Web address: www.samaritanhospital.org
**Control:** Other not–for–profit (including NFP Corporation) **Service:** General medical and surgical

**Staffed Beds:** 39 **Admissions:** 2585 **Census:** 22 **Outpatient Visits:** 136276 **Births:** 254 **Total Expense ($000):** 70750 **Payroll Expense ($000):** 22337 **Personnel:** 399

**UNIVERSITY HOSPITALS SAMARITAN MEDICAL CENTER** See UH Samaritan Medical Center

## ASHTABULA—Ashtabula County

☒ **ASHTABULA COUNTY MEDICAL CENTER (360125)**, 2420 Lake Avenue, Zip 44004–4954; tel. 440/997–2262, (Total facility includes 16 beds in nursing home–type unit) (Nonreporting) **A**1 5 10 20 **F**3 4 5 11 13 15 18 20 28 29 30 31 34 35 38 40 45 46 47 50 51 53 57 59 60 62 64 65 68 70 74 75 76 77 78 79 80 81 82 83 85 87 89 91 92 93 94 97 98 100 101 102 103 104 107 108 109 110 111 112 113 114 115 116 118 119 128 130 131 132 135 146 147 148 149 152 153 154 156 157
Primary Contact: Michael J. Habowski, President and Chief Executive Officer
COO: Lewis Hutchison, Vice President Operations and Quality
CFO: Donald L Kepner, Chief Financial Officer
CMO: Jude Cauwenberg, M.D., Chief of Staff
CIO: Jared Swiger, Director Information Systems
CHR: Jonathan Forbes, Director Human Resources
CNO: Ken Frame, Chief Nursing Officer
Web address: www.acmchealth.org
**Control:** Other not–for–profit (including NFP Corporation) **Service:** General medical and surgical

**Staffed Beds:** 154 **Admissions:** 5757 **Census:** 64 **Outpatient Visits:** 263779 **Births:** 312 **Total Expense ($000):** 145206 **Payroll Expense ($000):** 65534

## ATHENS—Athens County

☐ **APPALACHIAN BEHAVIORAL HEALTHCARE (364015)**, 100 Hospital Drive, Zip 45701–2301; tel. 740/594–5000, (Nonreporting) **A**1 3 5 10 **S** Ohio Department of Mental Health, Columbus, OH
Primary Contact: Jane E. Krason, R.N., Chief Executive Officer
COO: Kelly Sole, Chief Operating Officer
CMO: Todd Jamrose IChief Clinical Officer
CHR: Donovan Workman, Director Human Capital Management
CNO: Karen Durniat-Sushrstedt, Nurse Executive
Web address: www.mh.state.oh.us
**Control:** State, Government, Nonfederal **Service:** Psychiatric

**Staffed Beds:** 224

**APPALACHIAN PSYCHIATRIC HLTH** See Appalachian Behavioral Healthcare

☒ **O'BLENESS MEMORIAL HOSPITAL (360014)**, 55 Hospital Drive, Zip 45701–2302; tel. 740/593–5551, (Nonreporting) **A**1 2 3 5 10 12 13 **F**3 13 15 18 28 29 30 31 34 35 36 40 41 44 45 50 51 53 57 59 64 68 70 71 74 75 76 77 78 79 81 82 85 87 93 107 108 110 111 114 115 118 119 120 121 129 130 135 141 146 154 **S** OhioHealth, Columbus, OH
Primary Contact: Mark R. Seckinger, President
CFO: Robert Melaragno, Vice President Finance
CIO: Kristine Barr, Vice President Communication Services
CHR: Sandie Leasure, Senior Vice President Human Resources
CNO: Sandy Wood, MSN, R.N., Vice President Patient Services and Chief Nursing Officer
Web address: www.obleness.org
**Control:** Other not–for–profit (including NFP Corporation) **Service:** General medical and surgical

**Staffed Beds:** 69 **Admissions:** 2098 **Census:** 12 **Outpatient Visits:** 125279 **Births:** 652 **Total Expense ($000):** 95648 **Payroll Expense ($000):** 28216 **Personnel:** 500

## AVON—Lorain County

☒ **CLEVELAND CLINIC AVON HOSPITAL (360364)**, 33300 Cleveland Clinic Boulevard, Zip 44011; tel. 440/695–5000, (Nonreporting) **A**1 2 3 10 **F**3 15 18 20 29 30 34 35 36 40 45 49 50 51 64 68 70 74 75 77 78 79 80 81 82 85 87 92 100 107 108 110 111 114 115 119 130 131 146 147 148 149 154 155 156 **P**6 **S** Cleveland Clinic Health System, Cleveland, OH
Primary Contact: Rebecca Starck, M.D., President
COO: John Mills, Chief Operating Officer
CFO: Lori Koenig, Assistant Finance Director
CMO: Michael Taylor, M.D., Chief Medical Officer
CNO: Mary R Sauer, R.N., Chief Nursing Officer
Web address: www.my.clevelandclinic.org
**Control:** Other not–for–profit (including NFP Corporation) **Service:** General medical and surgical

**Staffed Beds:** 126 **Admissions:** 7016 **Census:** 66 **Outpatient Visits:** 101648 **Births:** 0 **Total Expense ($000):** 120397 **Payroll Expense ($000):** 43279 **Personnel:** 586

☒ **CLEVELAND CLINIC REHABILITATION HOSPITAL (363038)**, 33355 Health Campus Boulevard, Zip 44011; tel. 440/937–9099, (Includes CLEVELAND CLINIC REHABILITATION HOSPITAL, Mailing address: 3025 Science Park Drive, Beachwood, Ohio, Zip 44122; tel. 216/455–6400; R David Richer, Chief Executive Officer), (Nonreporting) **A**1 3 10 **F**3 34 60 68 69 75 90 91 92 94 96 119 130 132 135 143 148 149 157 **S** Select Medical Corporation, Mechanicsburg, PA
Primary Contact: Sam Bayoumy, Chief Executive Officer
Web address: www.my.clevelandclinic.org
**Control:** Partnership, Investor–owned (for–profit) **Service:** Rehabilitation

**Staffed Beds:** 180 **Admissions:** 3306 **Census:** 125 **Outpatient Visits:** 0 **Births:** 0

☐ **UH AVON REHABILITATION HOSPITAL (363039)**, 37900 Chester Road, Zip 44011–1044; tel. 440/695–7100, (Nonreporting) **A**1 10 **S** Kindred Healthcare, Louisville, KY
Primary Contact: Andrew Goldfrach, Chief Executive Officer
CFO: Jason DiGuilio, Controller
CHR: Abby Hoag, Director, Human Resources
CNO: Katie Kasper, Chief Clinical Officer
Web address: www.uhhospitals.org/uh-avon-rehabilitation-hospital
**Control:** Corporation, Investor–owned (for–profit) **Service:** Rehabilitation

**Staffed Beds:** 50

**UNIVERSITY HOSPITALS AVON REHABILITATION HOSPITALS** See UH Avon Rehabilitation Hospital

## BARBERTON—Summit County

**SUMMA BARBERTON CITIZENS HOSPITAL** See Summa Health System Barberton Hospital

## BARNESVILLE—Belmont County

**BARNESVILLE HOSPITAL** See Wvu Medicine - Barnesville Hospital

☒ **WVU MEDICINE - BARNESVILLE HOSPITAL (361321)**, 639 West Main Street, Zip 43713–1039, Mailing Address: P.O. Box 309, Zip 43713–0309; tel. 740/425–3941, (Nonreporting) **A**1 10 18 **S** West Virginia University Health System, Morgantown, WV
Primary Contact: David D. Phillips, Chief Executive Officer and Administrator
CFO: Willie Cooper-Lohr, Chief Financial Officer
CMO: David J Hilliard, D.O., Chief of Staff
CHR: Beth K. Brill, Senior Director Human Resources
CNO: Cynthia Touvelle, R.N., Senior Director Care Management and Chief Nursing Officer
Web address: www.barnesvillehospital.com
**Control:** Other not–for–profit (including NFP Corporation) **Service:** General medical and surgical

**Staffed Beds:** 25

## BATAVIA—Clermont County

☐ **MERCY HEALTH - CLERMONT HOSPITAL (360236)**, 3000 Hospital Drive, Zip 45103–1921; tel. 513/732–8200, (Nonreporting) **A**1 2 10 **F**3 8 11 15 18 19 28 29 30 31 34 35 37 38 40 42 44 45 46 47 48 49 50 51 54 56 57 59 60 61 64 66 68 70 75 77 79 80 81 84 85 86 87 92 93 94 95 98 100 101 102 103 104 105 107 110 111 115 118 119 126 130 131 132 134 146 148 149 152 153 154 **S** Mercy Health, Cincinnati, OH
Primary Contact: Shane Knisley, President
CFO: Philip Wheeler, Director Finance
CMO: Parma Hariharan, M.D., Chief of Staff
CHR: Angie Ferrell, Director Human Resources
Web address: www.https://www.mercy.com
**Control:** Church operated, Nongovernment, not–for–profit **Service:** General medical and surgical

**Staffed Beds:** 178 **Admissions:** 7508 **Census:** 84 **Outpatient Visits:** 129991

**MERCY HOSPITAL CLERMONT** See Mercy Health - Clermont Hospital

*Many Facility Codes have changed. Please refer to the AHA Guide Code Chart.* © 2021 AHA Guide

## BEACHWOOD—Cuyahoga County

⇧ **LAKE HEALTH BEACHWOOD MEDICAL CENTER (360367)**, 25501 Chagrin Boulevard, Zip 44122–5603; tel. 216/545–4800, (Nonreporting) **A**21
Primary Contact: Christopher Truax, FACHE, Chief Administrative Officer
Web address: www.beachwoodmedical.org
**Control**: Corporation, Investor–owned (for–profit) **Service**: General medical and surgical

**Staffed Beds**: 24

⊞ **UH AHUJA MEDICAL CENTER (360359)**, 3999 Richmond Road, Zip 44122–6046; tel. 216/593–5500, (Nonreporting) **A**1 3 10 **F**3 5 9 14 15 17 18 19 20 22 24 26 28 29 30 31 34 35 36 37 40 41 42 45 46 47 48 49 50 51 56 57 58 59 60 61 63 64 65 68 70 74 75 77 78 79 80 81 82 84 85 87 91 92 93 97 100 102 107 108 109 110 111 115 119 126 130 131 132 144 145 146 148 149 152 154 156 **S** University Hospitals, Cleveland, OH
Primary Contact: Alan Papa, President
Web address: www.https://www.uhhospitals.org
**Control**: Other not–for–profit (including NFP Corporation) **Service**: General medical and surgical

**Staffed Beds**: 144 **Admissions**: 9061 **Census**: 92 **Outpatient Visits**: 172972 **Births**: 0 **Total Expense ($000)**: 195457 **Payroll Expense ($000)**: 56715 **Personnel**: 976

☐ **UH REHABILITATION HOSPITAL (363036)**, 23333 Harvard Road, Zip 44122–6232; tel. 216/593–2200, (Nonreporting) **A**1 3 **S** Kindred Healthcare, Louisville, KY
Primary Contact: Mirza Baig, M.D., Medical Director
Web address: www.uhhospitals.org
**Control**: Corporation, Investor–owned (for–profit) **Service**: Rehabilitation

**Staffed Beds**: 50

**UNIVERSITY HOSPITALS AHUJA MEDICAL CENTER** See UH Ahuja Medical Center

## BEAVERCREEK—Greene County

★ ○ **SOIN MEDICAL CENTER (360360)**, 3535 Pentagon Boulevard, Zip 45431–1705; tel. 937/702–4000, (Nonreporting) **A**2 3 10 11 **F**3 11 13 15 18 20 22 26 29 30 31 34 35 36 40 43 45 56 70 73 74 75 76 77 78 79 81 82 85 87 93 97 102 107 108 109 110 111 115 116 117 118 119 120 121 126 130 131 132 135 146 147 149 154 157 **S** Kettering Health Network, Dayton, OH
Primary Contact: Rick A. Dodds, President
COO: Ron D Connovich, Chief Financial Officer and Chief Operating Officer
CFO: Ron D Connovich, Chief Financial Officer and Chief Operating Officer
CMO: Michael Caccamo, M.D., Chief Medical Officer
CIO: Andy Lehman, Vice President Information Systems
CNO: Belinda Mallett, R.N., MS, Vice President, Patient Care and Clinical Services
Web address: www.khnetwork.org/soin
**Control**: Church operated, Nongovernment, not–for–profit **Service**: General medical and surgical

**Staffed Beds**: 133 **Admissions**: 8135 **Census**: 80 **Outpatient Visits**: 116411 **Births**: 786 **Total Expense ($000)**: 226541 **Payroll Expense ($000)**: 84178 **Personnel**: 1042

## BELLEFONTAINE—Logan County

★ ⇧ **MARY RUTAN HOSPITAL (360197)**, 205 Palmer Avenue, Zip 43311–2281; tel. 937/592–4015, (Nonreporting) **A**3 5 10 20 21 **F**3 11 12 13 14 15 18 20 28 29 30 31 32 34 50 51 54 57 59 64 68 70 75 76 77 79 81 82 85 86 87 89 97 107 108 110 111 115 118 119 129 130 131 132 133 135 144 146 147 149 154 156
Primary Contact: Mandy C. Goble, President and Chief Executive Officer
COO: Chad A. Ross, Chief Operating Officer
CFO: Steven Brown, Vice President Fiscal Affairs
CMO: Grant Varian, M.D., Medical Director
CIO: Robert Reynolds, Director Information Systems
CHR: Vickie L Crumley, Chief Human Resources Officer
CNO: Wendy Rodenberger, Chief Nursing Officer and Vice President, Patient Services
Web address: www.maryrutan.org
**Control**: Other not–for–profit (including NFP Corporation) **Service**: General medical and surgical

**Staffed Beds**: 46 **Admissions**: 1400 **Census**: 11 **Outpatient Visits**: 126991 **Births**: 341 **Total Expense ($000)**: 102702 **Payroll Expense ($000)**: 52116 **Personnel**: 642

## BELLEVUE—Sandusky County

⊞ **BELLEVUE HOSPITAL (360107)**, 1400 West Main Street, Zip 44811–9088, Mailing Address: P.O. Box 8004, Zip 44811–8004; tel. 419/483–4040, (Nonreporting) **A**1 3 5 10 **F**3 13 15 28 29 30 31 34 35 40 41 44 45 46 50 53 56 57 59 61 68 70 74 75 76 77 79 81 82 85 87 89 91 93 107 110 111 115 118 119 127 129 130 131 132 133 135 143 144 146 147 148 149 154 156 **P**8
Primary Contact: Timothy Buit, President and Chief Executive Officer
CMO: Corey Fazio, M.D., Chief Medical Officer
CIO: Kim Stults, Director, Information Systems
CHR: Lisa M. Sartain, Vice President, Human Resources
CNO: Sara Brokaw, Vice President Patient Care Services
Web address: www.bellevuehospital.com
**Control**: Other not–for–profit (including NFP Corporation) **Service**: General medical and surgical

**Staffed Beds**: 50 **Admissions**: 1459 **Census**: 12 **Outpatient Visits**: 84758 **Births**: 371 **Total Expense ($000)**: 53565 **Payroll Expense ($000)**: 18703 **Personnel**: 342

## BLUFFTON—Allen County

**BLANCHARD VALLEY REG HLTH CTR** See Bluffton Hospital

★ **BLUFFTON HOSPITAL (361322)**, 139 Garau Street, Zip 45817–1027; tel. 419/358–9010, (Nonreporting) **A**10 18 **F**3 8 11 13 15 18 29 30 35 40 45 59 63 64 68 70 75 76 77 79 81 82 84 85 87 89 91 93 107 110 114 119 126 127 146 147 154 **P**5 6 **S** Blanchard Valley Health System, Findlay, OH
Primary Contact: Christine Keller, Chief Administrative Officer
CFO: David Cytlak, Vice President Finance
CMO: William H Kose, M.D., Vice President Quality and Medical Affairs
CIO: David Cytlak, Vice President Finance
CHR: Ryan Fisher, Director Human Resources
CNO: Barbara J. Pasztor, R.N., Vice President Nursing and Patient Care Services
Web address: www.bvhealthsystem.org/
**Control**: Other not–for–profit (including NFP Corporation) **Service**: General medical and surgical

**Staffed Beds**: 25 **Admissions**: 290 **Census**: 2 **Outpatient Visits**: 26191 **Births**: 174 **Total Expense ($000)**: 16482 **Payroll Expense ($000)**: 7944 **Personnel**: 117

## BOARDMAN—Mahoning County

**MAHONING VALLEY HOSPITAL** See Vibra Hospital of Mahoning Valley

☐ **MERCY HEALTH - ST. ELIZABETH BOARDMAN HOSPITAL (360276)**, 8401 Market Street, Zip 44512–6777; tel. 330/729–2929, (Nonreporting) **A**1 3 5 10 13 **S** Mercy Health, Cincinnati, OH
Primary Contact: Eugenia Aubel, President, St. Elizabeth Boardman Hospital
CFO: Anthony J. Seminaro, Chief Financial Youngstown
CMO: Heath Dorion, Physician Administrator
CIO: Maureen Kordupel, Director Information Technology Relationship Manager
CNO: Stacie Call, Chief Nursing Officer
Web address: www.https://www.mercy.com/youngstown
**Control**: Church operated, Nongovernment, not–for–profit **Service**: General medical and surgical

**Staffed Beds**: 217

★ **SELECT SPECIALTY HOSPITAL - BOARDMAN (360363)**, 8401 Market Street, 7 South, Zip 44512–6725; tel. 330/729–1750, (Nonreporting) **S** Select Medical Corporation, Mechanicsburg, PA
Primary Contact: Jodi Costello, Chief Executive Officer
Web address: www.selectspecialtyhospitals.com/
**Control**: Corporation, Investor–owned (for–profit) **Service**: Acute long–term care hospital

**Staffed Beds**: 24

**SELECT SPECIALTY HOSPITAL - YOUNGSTOWN** See Select Specialty Hospital - Boardman

**ST. ELIZABETH BOARDMAN HEALTH CENTER** See Mercy Health - St. Elizabeth Boardman Hospital

---

**Hospital, Medicare Provider Number, Address, Telephone, Approval, Facility, and Physician Codes, Health Care System**

★ American Hospital Association (AHA) membership ○ Healthcare Facilities Accreditation Program ⇧ Center for Improvement in Healthcare Quality Accreditation
☐ The Joint Commission accreditation ◇ DNV Healthcare Inc. accreditation △ Commission on Accreditation of Rehabilitation Facilities (CARF) accreditation

---

**OH**

⊞ **VIBRA HOSPITAL OF MAHONING VALLEY (362023)**, 8049 South Avenue, Zip 44512–6154; tel. 330/726–5000, (Includes VIBRA HOSPITAL OF MAHONING VALLEY-TRUMBULL CAMPUS, Mailing address: 1350 E Market Street, 9th Floor, Warren, Ohio, Zip 44483–6608; tel. 330/675–5555; Nathan Mast, Chief Executive Officer), (Nonreporting) **A**1 10 **S** Vibra Healthcare, Mechanicsburg, PA
Primary Contact: Nathan Mast, Chief Executive Officer
CMO: Lawrence Goldstein, M.D., Chief Medical Officer
Web address: www.vhmvalley.com
**Control**: Corporation, Investor–owned (for–profit) **Service**: Acute long–term care hospital

| Staffed Beds: 42 |
| --- |

### BOWLING GREEN—Wood County

⊞ **WOOD COUNTY HOSPITAL (360029)**, 950 West Wooster Street, Zip 43402–2603; tel. 419/354–8900, (Nonreporting) **A**1 5 10 **F**3 11 12 13 15 17 28 29 30 31 32 33 34 35 36 40 44 45 50 54 56 57 59 64 65 68 69 70 74 75 76 77 78 79 81 82 85 87 89 93 107 108 110 111 114 115 118 119 120 121 123 124 126 129 130 131 132 135 144 146 147 148 149 154 156 **P**6 8
Primary Contact: Stanley R. Korducki, President
CFO: Karol Bortel, Vice President Financial Services
CMO: Shawn Stansbery, M.D., Chief of Staff
CIO: Joanne White, Chief Information Officer
CHR: Michael Ford, Vice President Patient Services
CNO: Sandra Beidelschies, MSN, R.N., Vice President Patient Services
Web address: www.woodcountyhospital.org
**Control**: Other not–for–profit (including NFP Corporation) **Service**: General medical and surgical

| Staffed Beds: 108 Admissions: 2609 Census: 21 Outpatient Visits: 99338 Births: 335 Total Expense ($000): 94231 Payroll Expense ($000): 34183 Personnel: 655 |
| --- |

### BRYAN—Williams County

**BRYAN COMMUNITY HOSPITAL** See Bryan Hospital

**COMM HOSPS OF WILLIAMS CNTY** See Community Hospitals and Wellness Centers

☐ **COMMUNITY HOSPITALS AND WELLNESS CENTERS (360121)**, 433 West High Street, Zip 43506–1679; tel. 419/636–1131, (Includes ARCHBOLD HOSPITAL, Mailing address: 121 Westfield Drive, Archbold, Ohio, Zip 43502; tel. 419/445–4415; BRYAN HOSPITAL, Mailing address: 433 West High Street, Bryan, Ohio, Zip 43506; tel. 419/636–1131; MONTPELIER HOSPITAL, Mailing address: 909 East Snyder Avenue, Montpelier, Ohio, Zip 43543; tel. 419/485–3154), (Nonreporting) **A**1 2 5 10
Primary Contact: Chad Tinkel, President and Chief Executive Officer
CFO: Leroy P Feather, Vice President Finance
CIO: Greg Slattery, Vice President Information
CHR: Mary Ann Potts, Director Personnel
Web address: www.chwchospital.com
**Control**: Other not–for–profit (including NFP Corporation) **Service**: General medical and surgical

| Staffed Beds: 113 |
| --- |

### BUCYRUS—Crawford County

⇑ **BUCYRUS COMMUNITY HOSPITAL** See Bucyrus Hospital

★ ⇑ **BUCYRUS HOSPITAL (361316)**, 629 North Sandusky Avenue, Zip 44820–1821; tel. 419/562–4677, (Nonreporting) **A**10 18 21 **S** Avita Health System, Galion, OH
Primary Contact: Jerome Morasko, Chief Executive Officer
CMO: Amanda Kovolyan, M.D., Chief Medical Officer
CIO: Alex Reed, Chief Information Officer
CHR: Traci Oswald, Vice President Human Resources
Web address: www.bchonline.org
**Control**: Other not–for–profit (including NFP Corporation) **Service**: General medical and surgical

| Staffed Beds: 25 |
| --- |

### CADIZ—Harrison County

☐ **HARRISON COMMUNITY HOSPITAL (361311)**, 951 East Market Street, Zip 43907–9799; tel. 740/942–4631, (Nonreporting) **A**1 10 18
Primary Contact: John DeBlasis, Vice President
CFO: Donald Huelskamp, Interim Chief Financial Officer
CMO: Anandhi Murthy, Chief Medical Officer
CIO: Will Combs, Director Information Technology
CHR: Peter Giordano, Senior Director Human Resources
CNO: Janis Olinski, R.N., Vice President Clinical Services
Web address: www.harrisoncommunity.com
**Control**: Other not–for–profit (including NFP Corporation) **Service**: General medical and surgical

| Staffed Beds: 25 |
| --- |

### CAMBRIDGE—Guernsey County

**GUERNSEY MEMORIAL HOSPITAL** See Southeastern Ohio Regional Medical Center

⊞ **SOUTHEASTERN OHIO REGIONAL MEDICAL CENTER (360203)**, 1341 North Clark Street, Zip 43725–9614, Mailing Address: P.O. Box 610, Zip 43725–0610; tel. 740/439–8000, (Nonreporting) **A**1 2 3 10 20 **F**11 13 15 28 29 30 31 32 34 35 40 43 44 45 48 49 50 51 57 59 60 62 64 68 70 75 76 77 78 79 81 83 84 85 86 87 91 93 96 107 108 110 111 114 115 118 119 120 121 123 130 131 132 135 146 147 148 149 156
Primary Contact: Wendy C. Elliott, President and Chief Executive Officer
CFO: Timothy R. Evancho, Chief Financial Officer
CMO: E Edwin Conaway, M.D., Vice President Medical Affairs and Chief Medical Officer
CHR: Steven Michael Brooks, Vice President Human Resources
CNO: Gina F. Woods, Chief Nursing Officer
Web address: www.seormc.org
**Control**: Other not–for–profit (including NFP Corporation) **Service**: General medical and surgical

| Staffed Beds: 94 Admissions: 3064 Census: 28 |
| --- |

### CANAL WINCHESTER—Fairfield County

☐ **DILEY RIDGE MEDICAL CENTER (360358)**, 7911 Diley Road, Zip 43110–9653; tel. 614/838–7911, (Nonreporting) **A**1 10 **F**3 4 15 29 35 40 50 54 64 68 85 87 107 110 111 114 119 130 147 **P**1
Primary Contact: Jodi Wilson, President and Chief Operating Officer
COO: Jodi Wilson, President and Chief Operating Officer
Web address: www.dileyridgemedicalcenter.com
**Control**: Other not–for–profit (including NFP Corporation) **Service**: General medical and surgical

| Staffed Beds: 10 Admissions: 247 Census: 2 Outpatient Visits: 47549 Births: 0 Total Expense ($000): 14272 Payroll Expense ($000): 5818 Personnel: 92 |
| --- |

### CANTON—Stark County

**ACUTE CARE SPECIALTY HOSPITAL OF AULTMAN** See Aultman Specialty Hospital

**ALUTMAN HOSPITAL PEDIATRIC SERVICES** See Aultman Hospital Pediatric Services

⊞ △ **AULTMAN HOSPITAL (360084)**, 2600 Sixth Street SW, Zip 44710–1702; tel. 330/452–9911, (Includes AULTMAN HOSPITAL PEDIATRIC SERVICES, Mailing address: 2600 Sixth Street, SW, Canton, Ohio, Zip 44710–1702; tel. 330/363–5455) (Total facility includes 60 beds in nursing home–type unit) **A**1 2 3 5 7 8 10 13 19 **F**3 7 8 11 12 13 15 17 18 20 22 24 26 28 29 30 31 34 35 39 40 42 43 44 45 48 49 50 51 53 54 55 56 57 58 59 60 61 62 63 64 68 70 71 72 74 75 76 77 78 79 81 82 83 84 85 86 87 89 90 93 96 97 102 104 105 107 108 109 110 111 114 115 116 117 118 119 120 121 123 126 127 128 129 130 131 132 133 134 135 144 145 146 147 148 149 150 154 155 156 157 **P**6 7 **S** Aultman Health Foundation, Canton, OH
Primary Contact: Tony Snyder, Chief Executive Officer
CFO: Mark Wright, Vice President
CMO: Allison Oprandi, M.D., Chief Medical Officer
CIO: Liz Getz, Chief Information Officer
CHR: Sue Olivera, Vice President
CNO: Nicole Kolacz, Chief Nursing Officer
Web address: www.aultman.com
**Control**: Other not–for–profit (including NFP Corporation) **Service**: General medical and surgical

| Staffed Beds: 532 Admissions: 26981 Census: 317 Outpatient Visits: 452876 Births: 2995 Total Expense ($000): 435838 Payroll Expense ($000): 173853 Personnel: 5784 |
| --- |

*Many Facility Codes have changed. Please refer to the AHA Guide Code Chart.*

**AULTMAN SPECIALTY HOSPITAL (362032)**, 2600 Sixth Street, SW, Zip 44710–1702; tel. 330/363–4000, (Nonreporting) **A**1 10 **S** Aultman Health Foundation, Canton, OH
Primary Contact: Ryan Kuharich, Chief Executive Officer
CFO: Mark Wright, Chief Financial Officer
CMO: George Kefalas, Chief Medical Officer
Web address: www.aultman.org
**Control**: Other not–for–profit (including NFP Corporation) **Service**: Acute long–term care hospital

**Staffed Beds:** 16

**COLUMBIA MERCY MEDICAL CENTER** See Mercy Medical Center

**MERCY MEDICAL CENTER (360070)**, 1320 Mercy Drive NW, Zip 44708–2641; tel. 330/489–1000, (Nonreporting) **A**1 2 3 5 10 19 **F**3 12 13 15 17 18 20 22 24 26 28 29 30 31 34 35 39 40 43 44 46 48 49 50 51 53 54 57 58 59 60 61 62 63 64 66 68 70 72 74 75 76 77 78 79 80 81 82 84 85 86 87 89 90 91 92 93 96 97 100 102 107 108 110 111 114 115 116 117 118 119 120 121 123 124 126 129 130 131 132 135 144 146 147 148 149 150 156 **P**6 7 **S** Sisters of Charity Health System, Cleveland, OH
Primary Contact: Thomas J. Strauss, Interim President and Chief Executive Officer
CFO: David K Stewart, Senior Vice President and Chief Financial Officer
CMO: David Gormsen, D.O., Senior Vice President and Chief Medical Officer
CIO: Robin Stursa, Vice President, Chief Information Officer
CHR: Patti Bresnahan, Director Human Resources
CNO: Barbara Yingling, R.N., Senior Vice President Patient Care Services and Chief Nursing Officer
Web address: www.cantonmercy.org
**Control**: Other not–for–profit (including NFP Corporation) **Service**: General medical and surgical

**Staffed Beds:** 338 **Admissions:** 15880 **Census:** 198 **Outpatient Visits:** 726298 **Births:** 1281 **Total Expense ($000):** 551948 **Payroll Expense ($000):** 149717 **Personnel:** 2237

**SELECT SPECIALTY HOSPITAL** See Select Specialty Hospital-Canton

**SELECT SPECIALTY HOSPITAL-CANTON (362016)**, 1320 Mercy Drive NW, 6th Floor, Zip 44708–2614; tel. 330/489–8189, (Nonreporting) **A**1 10 **S** Select Medical Corporation, Mechanicsburg, PA
Primary Contact: Sherri Becker, Chief Executive Officer
Web address: www.selectspecialtyhospitals.com/company/locations/canton.aspx
**Control**: Corporation, Investor–owned (for–profit) **Service**: Acute long–term care hospital

**Staffed Beds:** 30

**CHARDON—Geauga County**

**HEATHERHILL CARE COMMUNITIES (362014)**, 12340 Bass Lake Road, Zip 44024–8327; tel. 440/285–4040, (Nonreporting)
Primary Contact: Jim Homa, Chief Executive Officer
COO: Lisa Deering, Administrator
CFO: Valerie Love, Manager Business Office
CMO: Beejadi Makunda, M.D., Chief Medical Officer
CHR: Pam McCall, Director Human Resources
CNO: Alice Harvey, Director of Nursing
Web address: www.heatherhill.com
**Control**: Other not–for–profit (including NFP Corporation) **Service**: Acute long–term care hospital

**Staffed Beds:** 214

**UH GEAUGA MEDICAL CENTER (360192)**, 13207 Ravenna Road, Zip 44024–7032; tel. 440/269–6000, (Nonreporting) **A**1 2 3 10 **F**3 11 12 13 15 18 20 22 26 28 29 30 31 32 34 35 36 38 39 40 41 42 43 44 50 51 54 56 57 58 59 60 62 63 64 65 68 70 74 75 76 77 78 79 81 82 84 85 86 87 91 92 93 96 98 100 101 102 103 107 108 109 110 111 114 115 116 117 118 119 120 121 123 124 129 130 131 132 134 135 143 144 145 146 147 148 149 154 **S** University Hospitals, Cleveland, OH
Primary Contact: Donald DeCarlo, M.D., President
CFO: Paul Amantea, Director Finance
CMO: David Kosnosky, M.D., Chief Medical Officer
CIO: Lou Ciraldo, Information Services Representative
CHR: Danialle Lynce, Manager Human Resources
CNO: Peggy A Kuhar, R.N., MSN, Chief Nursing Officer
Web address: www.uhhospitals.org
**Control**: Other not–for–profit (including NFP Corporation) **Service**: General medical and surgical

**Staffed Beds:** 143 **Admissions:** 8283 **Census:** 85 **Outpatient Visits:** 170341 **Births:** 1016 **Total Expense ($000):** 172171 **Payroll Expense ($000):** 47460 **Personnel:** 826

**UNIVERSITY HOSPITALS EXTENDED CARE CAMPUS** See Heatherhill Care Communities

**UNIVERSITY HOSPITALS GEAUGA MEDICAL CENTER** See UH Geauga Medical Center

**CHILLICOTHE—Ross County**

**ADENA HEALTH SYSTEM** See Adena Medical Center

**ADENA MEDICAL CENTER (360159)**, 272 Hospital Road, Zip 45601–9031; tel. 740/779–7500, (Nonreporting) **A**1 2 3 5 10 19 **F**3 5 8 13 15 18 20 22 24 26 28 29 30 31 32 34 35 37 38 40 41 45 46 47 48 49 51 54 57 59 62 63 64 66 70 71 73 74 75 76 77 78 79 81 82 83 84 85 86 87 89 91 93 96 97 98 100 101 102 104 107 108 110 111 114 115 117 118 119 120 121 123 126 127 129 130 131 132 135 144 146 147 148 149 154 156 **S** Adena Health System, Chillicothe, OH
Primary Contact: Jeff Graham, President and Chief Executive Officer
COO: Eric Cecava, Chief Operating Officer
CMO: John Fortney, Senior System Medical Advisor
CIO: Linn Weimer, Chief Information Officer
CHR: Jay D. Justice, Chief Human Resource Officer
Web address: www.adena.org
**Control**: Other not–for–profit (including NFP Corporation) **Service**: General medical and surgical

**Staffed Beds:** 226 **Admissions:** 10962 **Census:** 111 **Outpatient Visits:** 708601 **Births:** 1285 **Total Expense ($000):** 374839 **Payroll Expense ($000):** 138581 **Personnel:** 2552

**CHILLICOTHE VETERANS AFFAIRS MEDICAL CENTER**, 17273 State Route 104, Zip 45601–9718; tel. 740/773–1141, (Nonreporting) **A**1 3 5 **F**3 4 5 7 12 18 29 30 33 34 35 36 38 39 44 45 46 47 48 50 53 54 56 57 58 59 62 63 64 65 68 71 74 75 77 79 82 84 86 87 90 92 93 94 96 97 98 100 101 102 103 104 105 106 107 108 111 115 119 127 128 129 130 132 135 143 144 146 147 148 149 150 152 153 154 156 157 **S** Department of Veterans Affairs, Washington, DC
Primary Contact: Kathy Berger, R.N., Medical Center Director
CFO: Rick Deckard, Chief Fiscal Service
CMO: Deborah Meesig, M.D., Chief of Staff
CIO: William Gawler, Chief Information Officer
CHR: Angela Young, Human Resources Officer
Web address: www.chillicothe.va.gov/
**Control**: Veterans Affairs, Government, federal **Service**: General medical and surgical

**Staffed Beds:** 295 **Admissions:** 2928 **Census:** 247 **Outpatient Visits:** 323416 **Births:** 0 **Total Expense ($000):** 257660 **Payroll Expense ($000):** 116553 **Personnel:** 1534

**VETERANS AFFAIRS MEDICAL CENTER** See Chillicothe Veterans Affairs Medical Center

---

OH

## CINCINNATI—Hamilton County

☒ **BETHESDA NORTH HOSPITAL (360179)**, 10500 Montgomery Road, Zip 45242–4402; tel. 513/865–1111, (Includes BETHESDA BUTLER HOSPITAL, Mailing address: 3125 Hamilton Mason Road, Hamilton, Ohio, Zip 45011–5307; tel. 513/894–8888; Chuck Brown, Administrator), (Nonreporting) **A**1 3 5 10 **F**3 5 8 9 11 12 13 15 17 18 20 22 24 26 28 29 30 31 34 35 36 37 38 39 40 41 42 43 44 45 46 47 48 49 50 53 54 55 56 57 58 59 61 63 64 65 66 68 70 71 73 74 75 76 77 78 79 81 82 83 84 85 86 87 91 92 93 94 96 97 100 101 102 104 107 108 109 110 111 114 115 116 117 118 119 120 121 123 124 126 129 130 131 132 134 135 141 143 144 145 146 147 148 149 153 154 156 **P**6 8
Primary Contact: Mark C. Clement, President
COO: Jenny Oliphant, Executive Vice President and Chief Operating Officer
CFO: Michael Crofton, Senior Vice President and Chief Financial Officer
CMO: Georges Feghali, M.D., Senior Vice President Quality and Chief Medical Officer
CIO: Rick Moore, Chief Information Officer
CHR: Walter L McLarty, Chief Human Resources Officer
CNO: Mary Irvin, R.N., MSN, Senior Vice President and Chief Nursing Officer
Web address: www.trihealth.com
**Control:** Other not–for–profit (including NFP Corporation) **Service:** General medical and surgical

**Staffed Beds:** 384 **Admissions:** 23698 **Census:** 274 **Outpatient Visits:** 362646 **Births:** 3802 **Total Expense ($000):** 554396 **Payroll Expense ($000):** 176721 **Personnel:** 3195

**CHILDREN'S HOSP MEDICAL CENTER** See Cincinnati Children's Hospital Medical Center

☐ △ **CHRIST HOSPITAL (360163)**, 2139 Auburn Avenue, Zip 45219–2906; tel. 513/585–2000, (Nonreporting) **A**1 2 3 5 7 10 **F**3 6 8 9 12 13 15 17 18 20 22 24 26 28 29 30 31 34 35 36 37 38 39 40 42 44 45 46 47 48 49 50 51 53 54 55 56 57 58 59 60 64 65 66 68 70 73 74 75 76 77 78 79 80 81 82 83 84 85 86 87 90 92 93 94 96 97 98 100 103 107 108 109 110 111 114 115 116 117 118 119 120 121 123 124 126 129 130 131 132 135 138 141 144 145 146 147 148 149 154 156 **P**6
Primary Contact: Arturo Polizzi, President and Chief Executive Officer
COO: Deborah Marie Hayes, R.N., MS, MSN, Chief Operating Officer
CMO: Bernard B Gawne, M.D., Vice President and Chief Medical Officer
CIO: Alex Vaillancourt, Chief Information Officer
CHR: Rick Tolson, Chief Administrative Officer and Chief Human Resources Officer
Web address: www.thechristhospital.com
**Control:** Other not–for–profit (including NFP Corporation) **Service:** General medical and surgical

**Staffed Beds:** 592 **Admissions:** 23548 **Census:** 304 **Outpatient Visits:** 657541 **Births:** 3477 **Total Expense ($000):** 759824 **Payroll Expense ($000):** 264284 **Personnel:** 4036

☒ △ **CINCINNATI CHILDREN'S HOSPITAL MEDICAL CENTER (363300)**, 3333 Burnet Avenue MLC 8006, Zip 45229–3039, Mailing Address: 3333 Burnet Avenue, Zip 45229–3039; tel. 513/636–4200, (Includes CHILDREN'S HOSPITAL, Mailing address: 3300 Elland Avenue, Cincinnati, Ohio, Zip 45229–2804; tel. 513/894–8888), (Nonreporting) **A**1 2 3 5 7 8 10 **F**3 7 9 11 12 17 18 19 20 21 22 23 24 25 26 27 28 29 30 31 32 34 35 36 37 38 39 40 41 42 43 44 45 46 47 48 49 50 51 54 55 57 58 59 60 61 62 63 64 65 66 68 72 74 75 76 77 78 79 81 82 84 85 86 87 88 89 90 91 92 93 94 95 96 97 98 99 100 101 102 104 105 106 107 108 111 112 113 115 117 118 119 120 122 126 129 130 131 132 134 135 136 137 138 139 140 141 142 144 146 148 149 150 154 155 157 **P**8
Primary Contact: Michael Fisher, President and Chief Executive Officer
CIO: Marianne Speight, Vice President Information System and Chief Information Officer
CHR: Nerissa E. Morris, Senior Vice President and Chief Human Resource Officer
CNO: Barbara F. Tofani, R.N., MSN, Senior Vice President and Chief Nursing Officer
Web address: www.cincinnatichildrens.org
**Control:** Other not–for–profit (including NFP Corporation) **Service:** Children's general medical and surgical

**Staffed Beds:** 654 **Admissions:** 19803 **Census:** 462 **Outpatient Visits:** 1259706 **Births:** 39 **Total Expense ($000):** 2386357 **Payroll Expense ($000):** 1160601 **Personnel:** 13669

☒ **CINCINNATI VETERANS AFFAIRS MEDICAL CENTER**, 3200 Vine Street, Zip 45220–2288; tel. 513/475–6300, (Nonreporting) **A**1 2 3 5 **S** Department of Veterans Affairs, Washington, DC
Primary Contact: Jane Johnson, Interim Medical Director and Chief Nursing Officer
COO: David Ninneman, Associate Director
CFO: Sandra Selvidge, Chief Fiscal Service
CIO: Vique Caro, Chief Information Officer
CHR: Sandra Stenger, Acting Chief Human Resources
CNO: Jane Johnson, Chief Nursing Officer
Web address: www.cincinnati.va.gov/
**Control:** Veterans Affairs, Government, federal **Service:** General medical and surgical

**Staffed Beds:** 268

☐ **DANIEL DRAKE CENTER FOR POST ACUTE CARE (362004)**, 151 West Galbraith Road, Zip 45216–1015; tel. 513/418–2500, (Nonreporting) **A**1 3 5 10 **S** UC Health, Cincinnati, OH
Primary Contact: Lafe Bauer, Vice President, Post Acute Care Services and Chief Administrative Officer
CFO: Duane Pifko, Interim Director Financial Services
Web address: www.uchealth.com/danieldrakecenter/
**Control:** Other not–for–profit (including NFP Corporation) **Service:** Acute long–term care hospital

**Staffed Beds:** 202

**DRAKE CENTER** See Daniel Drake Center for Post Acute Care

☒ **ENCOMPASS HEALTH REHABILITATION HOSPITAL AT CINCINNATI (363034)**, 151 West Galbraith Road, Zip 45216–1015; tel. 513/418–5600, (Includes HEALTHSOUTH REHABILITATION HOSPITAL OF CINCINNATI AT NORWOOD, Mailing address: 4953 Section Avenue, Cincinnati, Ohio, Zip 45212–2120; tel. 513/712–9200; Ryan Smokovitz, Chief Executive Officer), (Nonreporting) **A**1 3 10 **F**29 34 35 56 57 74 90 91 130 148 **S** Encompass Health Corporation, Birmingham, AL
Primary Contact: Ryan Smokovitz, Chief Executive Officer
CFO: Scott Corder, Controller
CMO: Mark Goddard, M.D., Medical Director
CHR: Jason Sparks, Director, Human Resources
CNO: Kathy McNally, Chief Nursing Officer
Web address: www.healthsouthatdrake.com
**Control:** Corporation, Investor–owned (for–profit) **Service:** Rehabilitation

**Staffed Beds:** 100 **Admissions:** 1711 **Census:** 66 **Outpatient Visits:** 0 **Births:** 0 **Total Expense ($000):** 26224 **Payroll Expense ($000):** 13566 **Personnel:** 177

**EVENDALE MEDICAL CENTER** See Trihealth Evendale Hospital

☒ **GOOD SAMARITAN HOSPITAL (360134)**, 375 Dixmyth Avenue, Zip 45220–2489; tel. 513/862–1400, (Nonreporting) **A**1 2 3 5 8 10 **F**3 5 6 8 9 11 12 13 15 18 20 22 24 26 28 29 30 31 34 35 36 37 38 39 40 41 42 44 45 46 47 48 49 50 53 54 55 56 57 58 59 61 63 64 65 66 68 70 71 72 74 75 76 77 78 79 81 82 83 84 85 86 87 91 92 93 94 96 97 98 100 101 102 103 104 105 107 108 109 110 111 114 115 116 117 118 119 120 121 123 124 126 129 130 131 132 134 135 141 143 144 145 146 147 148 149 152 153 154 156 **P**6 8 **S** CommonSpirit Health, Chicago, IL
Primary Contact: Jamie Easterling, Executive Director, Operations
COO: Gerald P Oliphant, Executive Vice President and Chief Operating Officer
CFO: Michael Crofton, Chief Financial Officer
CMO: Georges Feghali, M.D., Senior Vice President Quality and Chief Medical Officer
CIO: Rick Moore, Chief Information Officer
CHR: Walter L McLarty, Chief Human Resources Officer
Web address: www.trihealth.com
**Control:** Church operated, Nongovernment, not–for–profit **Service:** General medical and surgical

**Staffed Beds:** 355 **Admissions:** 21680 **Census:** 282 **Outpatient Visits:** 325342 **Births:** 5344 **Total Expense ($000):** 540108 **Payroll Expense ($000):** 179408 **Personnel:** 2740

**HEALTHSOUTH REHABILITATION HOSPITAL AT DRAKE** See Encompass Health Rehabilitation Hospital at Cincinnati

**HEALTHSOUTH REHABILITATION HOSPITAL OF CINCINNATI AT NORWOOD** See Healthsouth Rehabilitation Hospital of Cincinnati at Norwood

☐ **MERCY HEALTH - ANDERSON HOSPITAL (360001)**, 7500 State Road, Zip 45255–2492; tel. 513/624–4500, (Nonreporting) **A**1 2 3 10 **S** Mercy Health, Cincinnati, OH
Primary Contact: Ken James, President and Chief Executive Officer of East Market
COO: Robert Maloney JrChief Operating Officer
CFO: Patrick A Kowalski, Chief Financial Officer
CMO: Dan Roth, M.D., Vice President Medical Affairs
CIO: Matt Eversole, Regional Vice President Information Services
CHR: Angie Ferrell, Director Human Resources
Web address: www.e-mercy.com
**Control:** Church operated, Nongovernment, not–for–profit **Service:** General medical and surgical

**Staffed Beds:** 281

*Many Facility Codes have changed. Please refer to the AHA Guide Code Chart.*   © 2021 AHA Guide

☐ **MERCY HEALTH - WEST HOSPITAL (360234)**, 3300 Mercy Health Boulevard, Zip 45211–1103; tel. 513/215–5000, (Nonreporting) **A**1 2 3 10 **S** Mercy Health, Cincinnati, OH
Primary Contact: Michael Kramer, Chief Executive Officer
COO: Jason Asic, Chief Operating Officer
CFO: Kyle Klein, Assistant Chief Financial Officer
CMO: Creighton Wright, M.D., Vice President Medical Administration
CHR: Bridget Mentzel, Director Human Resources
Web address: www.e-mercy.com/west-hospital
**Control**: Church operated, Nongovernment, not–for–profit **Service**: General medical and surgical

**Staffed Beds: 250**

**MERCY HOSPITAL ANDERSON** See Mercy Health - Anderson Hospital

**PAULINE WARFIELD LEWIS CENTER** See Summit Behavioral Healthcare

**REGENCY HOSPITAL OF CINCINNATI** See Select Specialty Hospital - Cincinnati North

★ **SELECT SPECIALTY HOSPITAL - CINCINNATI NORTH (362034)**, 10500 Montgomery Road, Zip 45242–4402; tel. 513/865–5300, (Nonreporting) **A**10 **S** Select Medical Corporation, Mechanicsburg, PA
Primary Contact: David D. Muggli, FACHE, Interim Chief Executive Officer
CMO: Sunil Dama, M.D., Medical Director
CHR: Elizabeth M Wilson, Coordinator Human Resources
Web address: www.cincinnatinorth.selectspecialtyhospitals.com/
**Control**: Corporation, Investor–owned (for–profit) **Service**: Acute long–term care hospital

**Staffed Beds: 41**

⊞ **SELECT SPECIALTY HOSPITAL-CINCINNATI (362019)**, 375 Dixmyth Avenue, 15th Floor, Zip 45220–2475; tel. 513/862–4444, (Nonreporting) **A**1 10 **S** Select Medical Corporation, Mechanicsburg, PA
Primary Contact: David D. Muggli, FACHE, Chief Executive Officer
CMO: Brian Boster, M.D., Medical Director
CNO: Bobbi Schmidt, Chief Nursing Officer
Web address: www.selectspecialtyhospitals.com/company/locations/cincinnati.aspx
**Control**: Corporation, Investor–owned (for–profit) **Service**: Acute long–term care hospital

**Staffed Beds: 30**

☐ **SHRINERS HOSPITALS FOR CHILDREN - CINCINNATI (363308)**, 3229 Burnet Avenue, Zip 45229–3095; tel. 513/872–6000, (Nonreporting) **A**1 3 5 10 **S** Shriners Hospitals for Children, Tampa, FL
Primary Contact: Mark D. Shugarman, Administrator
CFO: Susan Harris, Director Fiscal Services
CMO: Petra Warner, Chief of Staff
CIO: David Brian, Chief Information Officer
CHR: Gretchen Long, Manager Human Resources
Web address: www.shrinershospitalsforchildren.org/Hospitals/Locations/Cincinnati.aspx
**Control**: Other not–for–profit (including NFP Corporation) **Service**: Children's other specialty

**Staffed Beds: 30**

**SHRINERS HOSPITALS FOR CHILDREN-CINCINNATI BURNS HOSPITAL** See Shriners Hospitals for Children - Cincinnati

⊞ **SUMMIT BEHAVIORAL HEALTHCARE (364035)**, 1101 Summit Road, Zip 45237–2652; tel. 513/948–3600, (Nonreporting) **A**1 3 5 10 **S** Ohio Department of Mental Health, Columbus, OH
Primary Contact: Elizabeth Banks, Chief Executive Officer
COO: Steven Burns, Director Fiscal Services
CFO: Steven Burns, Director Fiscal Services
CMO: Patrick McCullough, M.D., Chief Medical Services
CIO: Eric Bradley, Director Computer Information Services
CHR: Bobbie Carrelli, Director Human Resources
CNO: Kathy A. Smith, MSN, R.N., Nurse Executive
Web address: www.mh.state.oh.us/
**Control**: State, Government, Nonfederal **Service**: Psychiatric

**Staffed Beds: 291**

**THE JEWISH HOSPITAL** See The Jewish Hospital - Mercy Health

☐ **THE JEWISH HOSPITAL - MERCY HEALTH (360016)**, 4777 East Galbraith Road, Zip 45236–2725; tel. 513/686–3000, (Nonreporting) **A**1 2 3 5 10 **S** Mercy Health, Cincinnati, OH
Primary Contact: Patricia Davis-Hagens, R.N., Central Market Leader and President
COO: Jack Hill, Chief Operating Officer and Administrator
Web address: www.jewishhospitalcincinnati.com/
**Control**: Other not–for–profit (including NFP Corporation) **Service**: General medical and surgical

**Staffed Beds: 209**

☐ **TRIHEALTH EVENDALE HOSPITAL (360362)**, 3155 Glendale Milford Road, Zip 45241–3134; tel. 513/454–2222, (Nonreporting) **A**1 2 10 **F**3 8 29 30 34 35 44 46 50 57 59 64 68 70 75 79 81 82 85 86 87 107 111 115 119 130 131 143 146 149 154 156 **P**6 8
Primary Contact: Kelvin Hanger, Chief Executive Officer
CFO: Michael Crofton, Chief Financial Officer
Web address: www.evendalemedical.com
**Control**: Other not–for–profit (including NFP Corporation) **Service**: Surgical

**Staffed Beds: 19 Admissions: 651 Census: 2 Outpatient Visits:** 37919 **Births:** 0 **Total Expense ($000):** 57073 **Payroll Expense ($000):** 15480 **Personnel:** 227

⊞ **TRIHEALTH REHABILITATION HOSPITAL (363041)**, 2155 Dana Avenue, Zip 45207; tel. 513/601–0600, (Nonreporting) **A**1 10 **F**74 79 90 **S** Select Medical Corporation, Mechanicsburg, PA
Primary Contact: Daphne Glenn, Chief Executive Officer
Web address: www.trihealthrehab.com
**Control**: Corporation, Investor–owned (for–profit) **Service**: Rehabilitation

**Staffed Beds: 60 Admissions: 1203 Census: 42 Outpatient Visits:** 0 **Births:** 0

**UNIVERSITY HOSPITAL** See University of Cincinnati Medical Center

☐ **UNIVERSITY OF CINCINNATI MEDICAL CENTER (360003)**, 234 Goodman Street, Zip 45219–2316; tel. 513/584–1000, (Nonreporting) **A**1 2 3 5 8 10 **F**3 7 9 11 12 13 15 16 17 18 20 22 24 26 29 30 31 34 35 37 38 39 40 41 43 44 45 46 47 48 49 50 51 54 55 56 57 58 59 60 61 63 64 66 68 70 71 72 74 75 76 77 78 79 80 81 82 84 85 86 87 91 92 97 98 100 101 102 103 104 107 108 110 111 112 114 115 116 117 118 119 120 121 122 123 124 126 129 130 131 132 134 135 136 137 138 139 141 142 143 145 146 147 148 149 150 154 155 156 157 **P**6 **S** UC Health, Cincinnati, OH
Primary Contact: Ann Smith, Senior Vice President, Inpatient Services and Interim Chief Administrative Officer
CFO: Matthew Nealon, Vice President, Chief Financial Officer
CMO: Bill Hurford, Chief Medical Officer
CIO: Jay Brown, Vice President and Chief Information Officer
CHR: Clarence Pauley, Senior Vice President and Chief Human Resources Officer
CNO: Beverly A Bokovitz, R.N., Chief Nursing Officer
Web address: www.uchealth.com/university-of-cincinnati-medical-center/
**Control**: Other not–for–profit (including NFP Corporation) **Service**: General medical and surgical

**Staffed Beds: 577 Admissions: 25868 Census: 456 Outpatient Visits:** 788539 **Births:** 2220 **Total Expense ($000):** 967484 **Payroll Expense ($000):** 299293 **Personnel:** 4579

**VETERANS AFFAIRS MEDICAL CENTER** See Cincinnati Veterans Affairs Medical Center

**CIRCLEVILLE—Pickaway County**

**BERGER HEALTH SYSTEM** See Ohiohealth Berger Hospital

⊞ **OHIOHEALTH BERGER HOSPITAL (360170)**, 600 North Pickaway Street, Zip 43113–1447; tel. 740/474–2126, (Data for 91 days) (Nonreporting) **A**1 2 3 5 10 **F**3 13 15 17 18 20 24 28 29 30 31 34 35 40 45 46 50 53 54 59 63 64 70 76 77 78 79 81 85 87 92 93 96 107 108 110 111 115 119 124 129 130 131 132 135 146 148 157 **S** OhioHealth, Columbus, OH
Primary Contact: Tim A. Colburn, President and Chief Executive Officer
CFO: Richard Filler, Chief Financial Officer
CMO: Jill Barno, M.D., Chief Medical Officer
CIO: Andy Chileski, Chief Information Officer and Vice President Facilities
CHR: Diane Guglielmi, Vice President, Human Resources
CNO: Kristin Day Gardner, Chief Nursing Officer
Web address: www.bergerhealth.com
**Control**: Church operated, Nongovernment, not–for–profit **Service**: General medical and surgical

**Staffed Beds: 56 Admissions: 332 Census: 11 Outpatient Visits:** 20287 **Births:** 66 **Total Expense ($000):** 17518 **Payroll Expense ($000):** 6012

**OH**

## CLEVELAND—Cuyahoga County

**BABIES AND CHILDREN'S HOSPITAL** See Rainbow Babies and Children's Hospital

☒ **CLEVELAND CLINIC (360180)**, 9500 Euclid Avenue, Zip 44195–5108; tel. 216/444–2200, (Includes CLEVELAND CLINIC CHILDREN'S HOSPITAL, Mailing address: 9500 Euclid Avenue, Cleveland, Ohio, Zip 44103; tel. 800/223–2273), (Nonreporting) **A1** 2 3 5 8 10 **F3** 6 7 8 9 12 13 14 15 17 18 19 20 21 22 23 24 25 26 27 28 29 30 31 32 33 34 35 36 37 38 39 40 42 44 45 46 47 48 49 50 51 52 53 54 55 56 57 58 59 60 61 62 63 64 65 66 68 70 71 72 74 75 76 77 78 79 80 81 82 84 85 86 87 88 89 91 92 93 94 95 96 97 100 101 104 107 108 109 110 111 112 113 114 115 116 117 118 119 120 121 123 124 126 129 130 131 132 134 135 136 137 138 139 140 141 142 143 144 145 146 147 148 149 150 156 **P6 S** Cleveland Clinic Health System, Cleveland, OH
Primary Contact: Tomislav Mihaljevic, M.D., President and Chief Executive Officer
CFO: Steven Glass, Chief Financial Officer
CMO: Joseph Hahn, M.D., Chief of Staff
CIO: Edward Marx, Chief Information Officer
CNO: Katherine Hancock, R.N., Executive Chief Nursing Officer
Web address: www.clevelandclinic.org
**Control:** Other not–for–profit (including NFP Corporation) **Service:** General medical and surgical

**Staffed Beds:** 1294 **Admissions:** 53558 **Census:** 1030 **Outpatient Visits:** 8091607 **Births:** 133 **Total Expense ($000):** 6160617 **Payroll Expense ($000):** 3010630 **Personnel:** 30614

**CLEVELAND CLINIC CHILD HOSPITA** See Cleveland Clinic Children's Hospital for Rehabilitation

☒ △ **CLEVELAND CLINIC CHILDREN'S HOSPITAL FOR REHABILITATION (363304)**, 2801 Martin Luther King Jr Drive, Zip 44104–3865; tel. 216/448–6400, (Nonreporting) **A1** 3 7 10 **F**28 29 30 32 34 35 36 44 50 60 68 74 75 79 80 82 84 90 91 93 94 96 100 130 131 132 143 146 148 149 154 **P6 S** Cleveland Clinic Health System, Cleveland, OH
Primary Contact: Michelle Marks, D.O., Medical Director
COO: Alec G Kulik, Administrator
CFO: Debra Nyikes, Director Finance and Chief Financial Officer
CMO: Roberta Bauer, M.D., Acting Chair Medical Staff
CIO: C Martin Harris, M.D., Chief Information Officer
CHR: Jan Hlahol, Manager Human Resources
Web address: www.my.clevelandclinic.org/childrens-hospital/default.aspx
**Control:** Other not–for–profit (including NFP Corporation) **Service:** Children's rehabilitation

**Staffed Beds:** 25 **Admissions:** 207 **Census:** 14 **Outpatient Visits:** 46604 **Births:** 0 **Total Expense ($000):** 50598 **Payroll Expense ($000):** 29598 **Personnel:** 423

☒ **CLEVELAND CLINIC FAIRVIEW HOSPITAL (360077)**, 18101 Lorain Avenue, Zip 44111–5656; tel. 216/476–7000, (Nonreporting) **A1** 2 3 5 10 **F3** 8 11 12 13 15 17 18 20 22 24 26 28 29 30 31 32 34 35 36 40 41 43 45 46 47 49 50 51 53 55 57 58 59 60 64 65 66 68 70 71 72 73 74 75 76 77 78 79 80 81 82 84 85 86 87 89 92 93 97 98 99 100 107 108 110 111 114 115 116 117 118 119 120 121 123 124 126 130 131 132 135 143 146 147 148 149 150 154 155 156 **P6 S** Cleveland Clinic Health System, Cleveland, OH
Primary Contact: Neil Smith, D.O., President
COO: John C Mills, Senior Vice President Operations
CFO: Ankit Chhabra, Director Finance
CIO: C Martin Harris, M.D., Chief Information Officer
CHR: Ann Beatty, Director Human Resources
Web address: www.fairviewhospital.org
**Control:** Other not–for–profit (including NFP Corporation) **Service:** General medical and surgical

**Staffed Beds:** 460 **Admissions:** 27519 **Census:** 296 **Outpatient Visits:** 232372 **Births:** 5422 **Total Expense ($000):** 412217 **Payroll Expense ($000):** 157735 **Personnel:** 2285

**CLEVELAND CLINIC FOUNDATION** See Cleveland Clinic

**FAIRVIEW HOSPITAL** See Cleveland Clinic Fairview Hospital

☐ **GRACE HOSPITAL (362015)**, 2307 West 14th Street, Zip 44113–3698; tel. 216/687–1500, (Nonreporting) **A1** 10
Primary Contact: Rajive Khanna, Chief Executive Officer
COO: Rajive Khanna, Chief Executive Officer
CFO: Michelle Hennis, Administrative Director Financial Services
CMO: John Nickels, M.D., President Medical Staff
Web address: www.gracehospital.org
**Control:** Other not–for–profit (including NFP Corporation) **Service:** Acute long–term care hospital

**Staffed Beds:** 87

**HANNA HOUSE** See Hanna House Skilled Nursing Facility

☒ **HILLCREST HOSPITAL (360230)**, 6780 Mayfield Road, Zip 44124–2203; tel. 440/312–4500, (Nonreporting) **A1** 2 3 5 7 8 **F3** 8 12 13 15 17 18 20 22 24 26 28 29 30 31 34 35 36 37 38 40 41 43 46 49 50 51 53 54 55 56 57 59 60 62 63 64 65 68 70 72 74 75 76 77 78 79 81 82 84 85 86 89 93 97 99 100 107 108 110 111 114 115 116 117 118 119 120 121 126 129 130 131 132 135 143 145 146 147 148 149 154 155 156 **P6 S** Cleveland Clinic Health System, Cleveland, OH
Primary Contact: Richard Parker, M.D., President, Hillcrest Hospital
Web address: www.hillcresthospital.org
**Control:** Other not–for–profit (including NFP Corporation) **Service:** General medical and surgical

**Staffed Beds:** 440 **Admissions:** 26116 **Census:** 327 **Outpatient Visits:** 214388 **Births:** 4408 **Total Expense ($000):** 426863 **Payroll Expense ($000):** 148856 **Personnel:** 2164

**KINDRED HOSPITAL CLEVELAND-GATEWAY** See Select Specialty Hospital - Cleveland Gateway

**KINDRED HOSPITAL OF CLEVELAND** See Select Specialty Hospital - Cleveland Fairhill

☒ △ **LOUIS STOKES CLEVELAND VETERANS AFFAIRS MEDICAL CENTER**, 10701 East Boulevard, Zip 44106–1702; tel. 216/791–3800, (Total facility includes 123 beds in nursing home–type unit) (Nonreporting) **A1** 2 3 5 7 8 **F3** 4 5 6 8 9 12 14 15 17 18 20 22 24 26 28 29 30 31 33 35 36 38 39 40 44 45 46 47 48 49 50 54 56 57 58 59 60 61 62 63 64 65 67 70 74 75 77 78 79 80 81 82 83 84 85 86 87 90 91 92 94 95 96 97 98 100 101 102 103 104 105 106 107 108 110 111 115 116 117 118 119 120 121 123 124 126 127 128 129 130 131 132 135 136 138 139 140 141 143 146 147 148 149 152 153 154 156 157 158 **S** Department of Veterans Affairs, Washington, DC
Primary Contact: Jill Dietrich, JD, FACHE, Executive Director
COO: Andrew Pacyna, Deputy Director
CFO: Michael Pappas, Chief Fiscal Service Officer
CMO: Murray Altose, M.D., Chief of Staff
CIO: Steve Gaj, Facility Chief Information Officer
CHR: Charles Franks, Chief Human Resources
CNO: Innette Mary Sarduy, M.P.H., R.N., Associate Director Patient Care Services and Nurse Executive
Web address: www.cleveland.va.gov/
**Control:** Veterans Affairs, Government, federal **Service:** General medical and surgical

**Staffed Beds:** 578 **Admissions:** 8430 **Census:** 474 **Outpatient Visits:** 1571804 **Births:** 0 **Personnel:** 5981

☒ **LUTHERAN HOSPITAL (360087)**, 1730 West 25th Street, Zip 44113–3170; tel. 216/696–4300, (Nonreporting) **A1** 3 10 **F3** 4 5 12 15 29 30 34 35 37 40 45 50 56 57 58 59 60 64 65 68 70 74 75 77 79 81 82 85 86 87 93 94 98 100 102 103 104 107 108 110 111 114 115 119 126 130 131 132 135 143 146 148 149 152 153 154 156 **P6 S** Cleveland Clinic Health System, Cleveland, OH
Primary Contact: Donald A. Malone Jr, M.D., President
COO: Matthew Mattner, Chief Operating Officer
CFO: Don Urbancsik, Director Finance
CMO: Ronald Golovan, M.D., Vice President Medical Operations
CIO: C Martin Harris, M.D., Chief Information Officer
CHR: Judith Santora, Chief Human Resource Officer
CNO: Janet Schuster, Chief Nursing Officer
Web address: www.lutheranhospital.org
**Control:** Other not–for–profit (including NFP Corporation) **Service:** General medical and surgical

**Staffed Beds:** 194 **Admissions:** 7171 **Census:** 89 **Outpatient Visits:** 77060 **Births:** 0 **Total Expense ($000):** 113623 **Payroll Expense ($000):** 45602 **Personnel:** 652

**LUTHERAN MEDICAL CENTER** See Lutheran Hospital

**MACDONALD HOSPITAL FOR WOMEN** See University Macdonald Women's Hospital

**MERIDIA HILLCREST HOSPITAL** See Hillcrest Hospital

**METROHEALTH CTR FOR NRSG CARE** See Metrohealth Center for Skilled Nursing Care

**OH**

⊠ △ **METROHEALTH MEDICAL CENTER (360059)**, 2500 MetroHealth Drive, Zip 44109–1998; tel. 216/778–7800, (Total facility includes 137 beds in nursing home–type unit) (Nonreporting) **A**1 2 3 5 7 8 10 **F**3 5 6 7 8 9 11 12 13 15 16 17 18 19 20 22 24 26 27 28 29 30 31 32 34 35 36 38 39 40 42 43 44 45 46 47 48 49 50 51 52 53 54 55 56 57 58 59 60 61 63 64 65 66 68 70 71 72 74 75 76 77 78 79 80 81 82 83 84 85 86 87 88 89 90 91 92 93 94 95 96 97 98 100 101 102 104 105 107 108 110 111 114 115 116 117 118 119 120 121 123 124 126 128 129 130 131 132 134 135 143 144 146 147 148 149 150 153 154 155 156 157 **P**1
Primary Contact: Akram Boutros, M.D., FACHE, President and Chief Executive Officer
COO: Daniel Lewis, Executive Vice President and Chief Operating Officer
CFO: Craig Richmond, Senior Vice President and Chief Financial Officer
CMO: Alfred Connors, M.D., Executive Vice President and Chief Quality Officer and Interim Chief Medical Officer
CHR: Debbie Warman, Vice President Human Resources
CNO: Melissa Kline, Chief Nursing Officer
Web address: www.metrohealth.org
**Control**: County, Government, Nonfederal **Service**: General medical and surgical

**Staffed Beds:** 760 **Admissions:** 23317 **Census:** 465 **Outpatient Visits:** 1444050 **Births:** 2495 **Total Expense ($000):** 1228463 **Payroll Expense ($000):** 645905 **Personnel:** 6888

☐ **RAINBOW BABIES AND CHILDREN'S HOSPITAL (363302)**, 2101 Adelbert Road, Zip 44106–2624; tel. 216/844–3911, (Nonreporting) **A**1 10 **S** University Hospitals, Cleveland, OH
Primary Contact: Patricia DePompei, President
**Control**: Other not–for–profit (including NFP Corporation) **Service**: Children's general medical and surgical

**Staffed Beds:** 190

**SELECT SPECIALTY HOSPITAL - CLEVELAND FAIRHILL** See Select Specialty Hospital - Cleveland Gateway, Cleveland

⊠ **SELECT SPECIALTY HOSPITAL - CLEVELAND GATEWAY (362026)**, 2351 East 22nd Street, 7th Floor, Zip 44115–3111; tel. 216/363–2671, (Includes SELECT SPECIALTY HOSPITAL - CLEVELAND FAIRHILL, Mailing address: 11900 Fairhill Road, Cleveland, Ohio, Zip 44120–1062; tel. 216/983–8030; Julie Idoine-Fries, Chief Executive Officer), (Nonreporting) **A**1 3 10 **S** Select Medical Corporation, Mechanicsburg, PA
Primary Contact: Julie Idoine-Fries, Chief Executive Officer
Web address: www.selectspecialtyhospitals.com/
**Control**: Corporation, Investor–owned (for–profit) **Service**: Acute long–term care hospital

**Staffed Beds:** 143

**ST. VINCENT CHARITY HOSPITAL** See St. Vincent Charity Medical Center

☐ **ST. VINCENT CHARITY MEDICAL CENTER (360037)**, 2351 East 22nd Street, Zip 44115–3111; tel. 216/861–6200, (Nonreporting) **A**1 3 5 10 **S** Sisters of Charity Health System, Cleveland, OH
Primary Contact: Janice G. Murphy, President and Chief Executive Office
COO: Shannan Ritchie, Chief Operating Officer
CFO: John Rusnaczyk, Senior Vice President and Chief Financial Officer
CMO: Joseph A. Sopko, M.D., Chief Medical Officer
CIO: Robin Stursa, Chief Information Officer
CHR: Ted Monczewski, Vice President Human Resources
CNO: Barbara Moran, R.N., Chief Nursing Officer
Web address: www.stvincentcharity.com/
**Control**: Other not–for–profit (including NFP Corporation) **Service**: General medical and surgical

**Staffed Beds:** 208

**THE METROHEALTH SYSTEM** See Metrohealth Medical Center

⊠ **UH CLEVELAND MEDICAL CENTER (360137)**, 11100 Euclid Avenue, Zip 44106–1716; tel. 216/844–1000, (Includes HANNA HOUSE SKILLED NURSING FACILITY, Mailing address: 11100 Euclid Avenue, Cleveland, Ohio, Zip 44106; tel. 216/983–8030; UNIVERSITY MACDONALD WOMEN'S HOSPITAL, Mailing address: 2101 Adelbert Road, Cleveland, Ohio, Zip 44106–2624; tel. 216/844–3911; Patricia DePompei, President) (Total facility includes 19 beds in nursing home–type unit) **A**1 2 3 5 8 10 **F**3 5 6 8 9 11 12 13 14 15 17 18 19 20 21 22 23 24 25 26 27 28 29 30 31 32 34 35 36 37 38 39 40 41 42 43 44 45 46 47 48 49 50 51 52 53 54 55 56 57 58 59 60 61 62 63 64 65 69 70 71 72 73 74 75 76 77 78 79 80 81 82 84 85 86 87 88 91 92 93 94 96 97 98 99 100 101 102 104 105 107 108 109 110 111 112 113 114 115 116 117 118 119 120 121 122 123 124 126 128 129 130 131 132 134 135 136 137 138 139 140 141 142 144 145 146 147 148 149 150 152 153 154 156 157 **P**6 7 **S** University Hospitals, Cleveland, OH
Primary Contact: Daniel I. Simon, M.D., President
COO: Ron Dziedzicki, R.N., Chief Operating Officer
CFO: Sonia Salvino, Vice President Finance
CIO: Sue Schade, Interim Chief Information Officer
CHR: Julie Chester, Vice President Human Resources
CNO: Jean Blake, Chief Nursing Officer
Web address: www.UHhospitals.org
**Control**: Other not–for–profit (including NFP Corporation) **Service**: General medical and surgical

**Staffed Beds:** 916 **Admissions:** 39963 **Census:** 674 **Outpatient Visits:** 939378 **Births:** 4203 **Total Expense ($000):** 1711907 **Payroll Expense ($000):** 512925 **Personnel:** 8980

⊠ **UH REGIONAL HOSPITALS (360075)**, 27100 Chardon Road, Zip 44143–1116; tel. 440/585–6500, (Includes UNIVERSITY HOSPITALS BEDFORD MEDICAL CENTER, Mailing address: 44 Blaine Avenue, Cleveland, Ohio, Zip 44146–2709; tel. 440/735–3900; UNIVERSITY HOSPITALS RICHMOND MEDICAL CENTER, Mailing address: 27100 Chardon Road, Cleveland, Ohio, Zip 44143–1116; tel. 440/585–6500), (Nonreporting) **A**1 3 5 10 12 13 **F**8 14 15 18 20 26 29 30 34 35 39 40 50 56 57 59 60 61 64 65 66 68 70 74 75 77 78 79 81 82 84 85 86 87 91 92 93 96 97 100 107 108 109 110 111 114 115 116 117 118 119 130 131 132 133 135 143 146 147 148 149 154 **S** University Hospitals, Cleveland, OH
Primary Contact: Roberta Rowell, President
CFO: Scott Platz, Director Finance
CMO: Rosemary Leeming, M.D., Chief Medical Officer
CHR: Stephanie W Neonakis, Manager Human Resources
CNO: Michelle Giltner, Interim Chief Nursing Officer
Web address: www.uhhospitals.org
**Control**: Other not–for–profit (including NFP Corporation) **Service**: General medical and surgical

**Staffed Beds:** 101 **Admissions:** 4011 **Census:** 42 **Outpatient Visits:** 126896 **Births:** 0 **Total Expense ($000):** 117600 **Payroll Expense ($000):** 44406 **Personnel:** 736

**UNIVERSITY HOSPITAL RICHMOND** See University Hospitals Richmond Medical Center

**UNIVERSITY HOSPITALS BEDFORD** See University Hospitals Bedford Medical Center

**UNIVERSITY HOSPITALS CLEVELAND MEDICAL CENTER** See UH Cleveland Medical Center

**VETERANS AFFAIRS MEDICAL CENTER** See Louis Stokes Cleveland Veterans Affairs Medical Center

## COLDWATER—Mercer County

**MERCER COUNTY JOINT TOWNSHIP COMMUNITY HOSPITAL** See Mercer Health

⊠ **MERCER HEALTH (360058)**, 800 West Main Street, Zip 45828–1698; tel. 419/678–2341, (Nonreporting) **A**1 10 **F**3 7 11 12 13 15 18 28 29 30 31 32 34 35 40 44 45 47 50 51 54 57 59 61 62 64 65 70 75 76 77 78 79 81 82 85 87 92 93 94 95 97 107 108 110 111 114 118 119 130 131 132 133 134 135 143 144 145 146 147 148 149 150 156 **P**3
Primary Contact: Lisa R. Klenke, R.N., Chief Executive Officer
CFO: Jon Dingledine, Chief Financial Officer and Chief Operating Officer
CMO: John Terpstra, M.D., Chief Medical Officer
CIO: DeWayne Marsee, Director Information Systems
CHR: Jon Dingledine, Chief Financial Officer and Chief Operating Officer
CNO: Cindy Liette, Vice President Patient Care Services
Web address: www.mercer-health.com
**Control**: Hospital district or authority, Government, Nonfederal **Service**: General medical and surgical

**Staffed Beds:** 60 **Admissions:** 2310 **Census:** 16 **Outpatient Visits:** 11545 **Births:** 358 **Total Expense ($000):** 63499 **Payroll Expense ($000):** 19746 **Personnel:** 368

**OH**

## COLUMBUS—Franklin County

**CHILDREN'S HOSPITAL** See Nationwide Children's Hospital

**DOCTORS HOSPITAL** See Ohiohealth Doctors Hospital

**GRANT MEDICAL CENTER** See Ohiohealth Grant Medical Center

☒ **JAMES CANCER HOSPITAL AND SOLOVE RESEARCH INSTITUTE (360242)**, 460 West Tenth Avenue, Zip 43210–1240; tel. 614/293–3300, (Nonreporting) **A**1 2 3 5 10 **F**3 15 29 30 31 32 34 35 36 37 38 39 44 46 47 48 49 50 52 54 55 57 58 59 61 64 65 66 68 70 71 74 75 77 78 79 80 81 82 84 85 86 87 93 97 100 107 108 110 111 112 114 115 116 117 118 119 120 121 123 124 126 130 132 134 135 136 141 143 145 146 147 148 149 154 157 **P**6 **S** Ohio State University Health System, Columbus, OH
Primary Contact: William Farrar, M.D., Interim Chief Executive Officer
CFO: Bell Julian, Associate Executive Director and Chief Financial Officer
CIO: Michael Townsend, Chief Information Officer
CHR: Jill Hannah, Director Human Resources
CNO: Kris M Kipp, Executive Director, Patient Services and Chief Nursing Officer
Web address: www.https://cancer.osu.edu/
**Control:** State, Government, Nonfederal **Service:** Cancer

**Staffed Beds:** 344 **Admissions:** 15151 **Census:** 290 **Outpatient Visits:** 413002 **Births:** 0 **Total Expense ($000):** 1161151 **Payroll Expense ($000):** 276216 **Personnel:** 4784

**MOUNT CARMEL** See Mount Carmel West

**MOUNT CARMEL MEDICAL CENTER** See Mount Carmel West Hospital

☒ **MOUNT CARMEL WEST (360035)**, 793 West State Street, Zip 43222–1551; tel. 614/234–5000, (Includes MOUNT CARMEL EAST HOSPITAL, Mailing address: 6001 East Broad Street, Columbus, Ohio, Zip 43213; tel. 614/234–6000; Michael Wilkins, President; MOUNT CARMEL WEST HOSPITAL, Mailing address: 793 West State Street, Columbus, Ohio, Zip 43222; tel. 614/234–5000), (Nonreporting) **A**1 2 3 5 10 **F**3 11 12 13 15 17 18 20 22 24 26 28 29 30 31 34 35 37 40 42 43 44 45 46 47 48 49 50 51 54 55 57 58 59 61 63 64 65 66 68 70 72 74 75 76 77 78 79 81 82 83 84 85 86 87 97 107 108 109 110 111 114 115 116 117 118 119 120 121 123 126 130 131 132 141 146 147 148 149 154 **P**1 **S** Trinity Health, Livonia, MI
Primary Contact: Sean McKibben, President and Chief Operating Officer
COO: Mary R Trimmer, Interim Chief Operating Officer
Web address: www.mountcarmelhealth.com
**Control:** Church operated, Nongovernment, not–for–profit **Service:** General medical and surgical

**Staffed Beds:** 488 **Admissions:** 32361 **Census:** 399 **Outpatient Visits:** 333850 **Births:** 3046 **Total Expense ($000):** 768794 **Payroll Expense ($000):** 254819 **Personnel:** 2968

☒ △ **NATIONWIDE CHILDREN'S HOSPITAL (363305)**, 700 Children's Drive, Zip 43205–2664; tel. 614/722–2000, (Nonreporting) **A**1 2 3 5 7 8 10 18 **F**3 5 7 8 12 16 17 18 19 20 21 22 23 24 25 26 27 28 29 30 31 32 34 35 36 38 39 40 41 42 43 44 45 47 48 50 51 52 53 54 55 57 58 59 60 61 62 63 64 65 66 68 71 72 73 74 75 77 78 79 81 82 83 84 85 86 87 88 89 90 92 96 97 98 99 100 101 102 104 105 107 108 111 112 114 115 116 117 118 119 126 127 129 130 131 132 133 134 135 136 137 138 139 140 141 143 144 145 146 148 149 150 153 154 155 156 157 158 **P**6 8
Primary Contact: Tim Robinson, Chief Executive Officer
COO: Rick Miller, President and Chief Operating Officer
CMO: Richard Brilli, M.D., Chief Medical Officer
CIO: Denise Zabawski, Vice President Information Services and Chief Information Officer
Web address: www.nationwidechildrens.org
**Control:** Other not–for–profit (including NFP Corporation) **Service:** Children's general medical and surgical

**Staffed Beds:** 673 **Admissions:** 18718 **Census:** 455 **Outpatient Visits:** 1617311 **Births:** 0 **Total Expense ($000):** 1355996 **Payroll Expense ($000):** 629947 **Personnel:** 10402

**OHIO HOSPITAL FOR CHILD AND ADOLESCENT PSYCHIATRY** See Ohio Hospital for Psychiatry

☐ **OHIO HOSPITAL FOR PSYCHIATRY (364041)**, 880 Greenlawn Avenue, Zip 43223–2616; tel. 614/449–9664, (Nonreporting) **A**1 10 **F**64 98 103 130 153 **S** Acadia Healthcare Company, Inc., Franklin, TN
Primary Contact: Angel Piper, Chief Executive Officer
COO: Shannon Robbins, Chief Operating Officer
CFO: Steve Snyder, Chief Financial Officer
CMO: Richard Nockowitz, M.D., Medical Director
CNO: Jayne Zink, Director of Nursing
Web address: www.ohiohospitalforpsychiatry.com/
**Control:** Corporation, Investor–owned (for–profit) **Service:** Psychiatric

**Staffed Beds:** 130 **Admissions:** 3517 **Census:** 69 **Outpatient Visits:** 5182 **Births:** 0 **Total Expense ($000):** 16822 **Payroll Expense ($000):** 9052 **Personnel:** 227

**OHIO STATE UNIVERSITY MEDICAL CENTER** See Ohio State University Wexner Medical Center

☒ △ **OHIO STATE UNIVERSITY WEXNER MEDICAL CENTER (360085)**, 410 West 10th Avenue, Zip 43210–1240; tel. 614/293–8000, (Includes OHIO STATE UNIVERSITY HOSPITALS EAST, Mailing address: 1492 East Broad Street, Columbus, Ohio, Zip 43205–1546; tel. 614/257–3000), (Nonreporting) **A**1 3 5 7 8 10 **F**3 4 5 6 8 9 11 12 13 15 16 17 18 20 22 24 26 28 29 30 31 33 34 35 36 37 38 39 40 42 43 44 45 46 47 48 49 50 51 52 53 54 55 56 57 58 59 60 61 64 65 66 68 70 72 73 74 75 76 77 78 79 80 81 82 84 85 86 87 90 91 92 93 95 96 97 98 99 100 101 102 103 104 105 107 108 110 111 112 113 114 115 118 119 126 129 130 131 132 134 135 137 138 139 140 141 142 143 145 146 147 148 149 152 153 154 156 157 **P**6 **S** Ohio State University Health System, Columbus, OH
Primary Contact: David P. McQuaid, FACHE, Chief Operating Officer
COO: David P. McQuaid, FACHE, Chief Operating Officer
CFO: Mark Larmore, Chief Financial Officer
CMO: Andrew Thomas, M.D., Chief Medical Officer
CIO: Phyllis Teater, Chief Information Officer
CHR: Kim Shumate, Human Resources Officer
CNO: Cheryl L Hoying, Ph.D., R.N., FACHE, Chief Nurse Executive and Patient Services Officer
Web address: www.medicalcenter.osu.edu
**Control:** State, Government, Nonfederal **Service:** General medical and surgical

**Staffed Beds:** 1124 **Admissions:** 49383 **Census:** 876 **Outpatient Visits:** 1502174 **Births:** 5246 **Total Expense ($000):** 1751852 **Payroll Expense ($000):** 527937 **Personnel:** 11841

☒ **OHIOHEALTH DOCTORS HOSPITAL (360152)**, 5100 West Broad Street, Zip 43228–1607; tel. 614/544–1000, (Nonreporting) **A**1 2 3 5 10 12 13 **F**3 13 15 17 18 20 22 26 27 28 29 30 31 34 35 36 40 45 46 47 48 49 50 58 59 64 65 66 68 70 72 73 74 75 76 77 78 79 81 82 84 85 87 90 92 93 97 100 107 109 110 111 114 115 116 117 119 120 121 123 126 130 131 135 145 146 147 148 154 **S** OhioHealth, Columbus, OH
Primary Contact: Michael L. Reichfield, President
CMO: Dean Colwell, D.O., Vice President Medical Affairs
CIO: Michael Krouse, Chief Information Officer
CHR: David Sullivan, Director Human Resources
Web address: www.ohiohealth.com
**Control:** Church operated, Nongovernment, not–for–profit **Service:** General medical and surgical

**Staffed Beds:** 206 **Admissions:** 8388 **Census:** 95 **Outpatient Visits:** 136404 **Births:** 1009 **Total Expense ($000):** 227933 **Payroll Expense ($000):** 100697 **Personnel:** 1198

☒ **OHIOHEALTH GRANT MEDICAL CENTER (360017)**, 111 South Grant Avenue, Zip 43215–1898; tel. 614/566–9000, (Nonreporting) **A**1 2 3 5 8 10 **F**3 7 8 9 11 13 15 17 18 20 22 24 26 28 29 30 31 34 35 36 37 40 41 42 43 45 46 47 48 49 50 53 54 56 57 58 59 60 61 64 66 67 68 70 72 74 75 76 78 79 81 82 84 85 86 87 97 100 107 108 109 110 111 114 115 116 117 118 119 120 121 123 124 126 130 131 132 135 146 147 148 149 150 154 155 156 157 **S** OhioHealth, Columbus, OH
Primary Contact: Michael Lawson, President and Chief Operating Officer
COO: Kevin Lutz, DPM, Chief Operating Officer, Grant
CFO: Heather Brandon, Vice President of Finance, Grant
CMO: Michael Ezzie, Director of Medical Education and Interim Vice President of Medical Affairs
CIO: Michael Krouse, Chief Information Officer
CHR: Qiana Williams, Director, Human Resource Business Partner, Grant
CNO: Sharon Neenan, Interim Chief Nursing Officer, Grant
Web address: www.ohiohealth.com
**Control:** Church operated, Nongovernment, not–for–profit **Service:** General medical and surgical

**Staffed Beds:** 471 **Admissions:** 18565 **Census:** 274 **Outpatient Visits:** 124680 **Births:** 2161 **Total Expense ($000):** 593502 **Payroll Expense ($000):** 233587 **Personnel:** 2526

☒ △ **OHIOHEALTH REHABILITATION HOSPITAL (363037)**, 1087 Dennison Avenue, 4th Floor, Zip 43201–3201; tel. 614/484–9600, (Nonreporting) **A**1 7 10 **F**3 29 30 34 35 50 57 90 95 96 130 132 135 146 148 149 **S** Select Medical Corporation, Mechanicsburg, PA
Primary Contact: Eric Yap, Chief Executive Officer
CFO: Ted Bolcavage, Vice President Division Controller, Inpatient
CMO: Lisa Lombard, Chief Medical Officer
CHR: Josette Alexander, Director, Human Resources
CNO: Graydon Todd Auckerman, Chief Nursing Officer
Web address: www.ohiohealth-rehab.com
**Control:** Partnership, Investor–owned (for–profit) **Service:** Rehabilitation

**Staffed Beds:** 74 **Admissions:** 1587 **Census:** 60 **Outpatient Visits:** 0 **Births:** 0 **Personnel:** 204

*Many Facility Codes have changed. Please refer to the AHA Guide Code Chart.*
© 2021 AHA Guide

**OHIOHEALTH RIVERSIDE METHODIST HOSPITAL (360006)**, 3535 Olentangy River Road, Zip 43214–3998; tel. 614/566–5000, (Nonreporting) **A**1 2 3 5 8 10 **S** OhioHealth, Columbus, OH
Primary Contact: Brian Jepson, President
CFO: Peter Bury, Vice President Finance
CMO: Thomas Harmon, M.D., Vice President Medical Affairs
CIO: Michael Krouse, Chief Information Officer
CHR: Shereen Solaiman, Vice President Human Resources
CNO: Lisa Gossett, MSN, R.N., Chief Nursing Officer
Web address: www.ohiohealth.com
**Control:** Church operated, Nongovernment, not–for–profit **Service:** General medical and surgical

| Staffed Beds: 754 |
|---|

**OSU JAMES CANCER HOSPITAL** See James Cancer Hospital and Solove Research Institute

**PARK MEDICAL CENTER** See Ohio State University Hospitals East

**REGENCY HOSPITAL OF COLUMBUS (362037)**, 1430 South High Street, Zip 43207–1045; tel. 614/456–0300, (Includes SELECT SPECIALTY HOSPITAL - COLUMBUS EAST, Mailing address: 1492 East Broad Street, 6th Floor, Columbus, Ohio, Zip 43205–1546; tel. 614/685–1703; Nabarun Kundu, Chief Executive Officer), (Nonreporting) **A**1 10 **S** Select Medical Corporation, Mechanicsburg, PA
Primary Contact: Kindra Marks, Chief Executive Officer
Web address: www.regencyhospital.com/
**Control:** Corporation, Investor–owned (for–profit) **Service:** Acute long–term care hospital

| Staffed Beds: 66 |
|---|

**RIVERSIDE METHODIST HOSPITAL** See Ohiohealth Riverside Methodist Hospital

**SELECT SPECIALTY HOSPITAL-COLUMBUS (362022)**, 1087 Dennison Avenue, Zip 43201–3201; tel. 614/458–9000, (Nonreporting) **A**1 10 **S** Select Medical Corporation, Mechanicsburg, PA
Primary Contact: Lisa J. Pettrey, MSN, R.N., Chief Executive Officer
CMO: Victoria Ruff, M.D., Medical Director
CHR: Charles Pankowski, Manager Human Resources
Web address: www.selectspecialtyhospitals.com/company/locations/columbus.aspx
**Control:** Corporation, Investor–owned (for–profit) **Service:** Acute long–term care hospital

| Staffed Beds: 162 |
|---|

**SEQUEL POMEGRANATE HEALTH SYSTEMS (364045)**, 765 Pierce Drive, Zip 43223, Mailing Address: 975 Pierce Avenue, Zip 43227; tel. 614/223–1650, (Nonreporting) **A**1 10
Primary Contact: Angela Nickell, Executive Director
Web address: www.pomegranatehealthsystems.com
**Control:** Other not–for–profit (including NFP Corporation) **Service:** Psychiatric

| Staffed Beds: 90 |
|---|

**SUN BEHAVIORAL COLUMBUS (364058)**, 900 Dublin Granville Road, Zip 43229–2452; tel. 614/706–2786, (Nonreporting) **A**1 10
Primary Contact: Lance Folske, Chief Executive Officer
Web address: www.https://www.suncolumbus.com
**Control:** Corporation, Investor–owned (for–profit) **Service:** Psychiatric

| Staffed Beds: 72 |
|---|

**TWIN VALLEY BEHAVIORAL HEALTHCARE (364007)**, 2200 West Broad Street, Zip 43223–1297; tel. 614/752–0333, (Nonreporting) **A**1 3 10 **S** Ohio Department of Mental Health, Columbus, OH
Primary Contact: Veronica Lofton, Acting Chief Executive Officer
COO: David Blahnik, Chief Operating Officer
CFO: Tracy Gladen, Chief Financial Officer
CMO: R Alan Freeland, M.D., Chief Clinical Officer
CIO: Missy McGarvey, Chief Information Officer
CHR: Marcia McKeen, Director Human Resources
CNO: Michael Breakwell, R.N., Nurse Executive
Web address: www.mh.state.oh.us/ibhs/bhos/tvbh.html
**Control:** State, Government, Nonfederal **Service:** Psychiatric

| Staffed Beds: 178 |
|---|

**TWIN VALLEY PSYCHIATRIC SYSTEM** See Twin Valley Behavioral Healthcare

## CONCORD TOWNSHIP—Lake County

**LAKE HEALTH (360098)**, 7590 Auburn Road, Zip 44077–9176; tel. 440/953–9600, (Includes TRIPOINT MEDICAL CENTER, Mailing address: 7590 Auburn Road, Concord Township, Ohio, Zip 44077; tel. 614/685–1703; Cynthia Moore-Hardy, FACHE, President and Chief Executive Officer), (Nonreporting) **A**1 10 **F**3 5 11 12 13 15 18 20 22 24 26 28 29 30 32 33 34 35 36 40 42 44 45 50 51 53 54 56 57 58 59 60 62 63 64 65 68 70 75 76 77 79 81 82 84 85 86 87 90 93 97 98 103 107 108 110 111 112 113 114 115 116 117 119 120 121 122 123 124 126 129 130 131 132 133 135 143 144 146 147 148 154 156 **P**1
Primary Contact: Cynthia Moore-Hardy, FACHE, President and Chief Executive Officer
CFO: Robert B Tracz, CPA, Senior Vice President and Chief Financial Officer
CMO: John Baniewicz, M.D., Chief Medical Officer
CIO: Gerald Peters, Vice President Information Technologies and Chief Information Officer
CHR: Craig J Ghidotti, Vice President Human Resources
Web address: www.lakehealth.org
**Control:** Other not–for–profit (including NFP Corporation) **Service:** General medical and surgical

| Staffed Beds: 352 Admissions: 15365 Census: 170 Outpatient Visits: 396293 Births: 1621 Total Expense ($000): 374224 Payroll Expense ($000): 131508 Personnel: 3038 |
|---|

**LAKE HOSPITAL SYSTEM, INC** See Lake Health

## CONNEAUT—Ashtabula County

**UH CONNEAUT MEDICAL CENTER (361308)**, 158 West Main Road, Zip 44030–2039; tel. 440/593–1131, (Nonreporting) **A**1 10 18 **F**3 11 15 18 28 29 31 34 35 37 40 45 56 57 59 64 68 70 75 77 78 79 81 82 85 86 87 93 107 110 111 115 119 130 132 133 135 143 144 146 147 148 149 154 156 **S** University Hospitals, Cleveland, OH
Primary Contact: M Steven. Jones, President
COO: Jason Glowczewski, Chief Operating Officer
CFO: Lara Eggleston, Finance Manager
CMO: Abirammy Sundaramoorthy, M.D., Chief Medical Officer
CIO: Kirsten Hale, Coordinator Health Information Services
CHR: Danialle Lynce, Business Partner Human Resources
CNO: Ashley Fertig, Chief Nursing Officer
Web address: www.uhhospitals.org
**Control:** Other not–for–profit (including NFP Corporation) **Service:** General medical and surgical

| Staffed Beds: 25 Admissions: 592 Census: 5 Outpatient Visits: 28360 Births: 0 Total Expense ($000): 25952 Payroll Expense ($000): 9047 Personnel: 150 |
|---|

**UNIVERSITY HOSPITALS CONNEAUT MEDICAL CENTER** See UH Conneaut Medical Center

## COPLEY—Summit County

**EDWIN SHAW HOSPITAL** See Edwin Shaw Rehab

★ **EDWIN SHAW REHAB (360241)**, 4389 Medina Road, Zip 44321–1388; tel. 234/815–5100, (Nonreporting) **A**5 10 **S** Cleveland Clinic Health System, Cleveland, OH
Primary Contact: Geoffrey Hall, Chief Executive Officer
CFO: Dave Frigo, Chief Financial Officer
CMO: Anthony Hayek, D.O., Medical Director
CHR: Heather Saus, Human Resource Generalist
Web address: www.edwinshaw.com
**Control:** County, Government, Nonfederal **Service:** Rehabilitation

| Staffed Beds: 35 |
|---|

## COSHOCTON—Coshocton County

**COSHOCTON COUNTY MEMORIAL HOSPITAL** See Coshocton Regional Medical Center

---

| Hospital, Medicare Provider Number, Address, Telephone, Approval, Facility, and Physician Codes, Health Care System |
|---|

★ American Hospital Association (AHA) membership    ○ Healthcare Facilities Accreditation Program    ⇑ Center for Improvement in Healthcare Quality Accreditation
□ The Joint Commission accreditation    ◇ DNV Healthcare Inc. accreditation    △ Commission on Accreditation of Rehabilitation Facilities (CARF) accreditation

**OH**

☐ **COSHOCTON REGIONAL MEDICAL CENTER (360109)**, 1460 Orange Street, Zip 43812–2229, Mailing Address: P.O. Box 1330, Zip 43812–6330; tel. 740/622–6411, (Nonreporting) **A**1 10 20 **F**3 15 20 26 28 29 30 31 34 35 40 47 57 59 64 70 77 79 81 82 85 92 93 97 107 108 111 114 115 117 119 132 144 147 149 154 **S** Prime Healthcare, Ontario, CA
Primary Contact: Stephanie Conn, Administrator and Chief Nursing Officer
CFO: Dennis Lockard, FACHE, Chief Financial Officer
CMO: Gary J. Carver, M.D., Chief Medical Officer
CIO: Seth Peterson, Director Information Services
CHR: Rick Davis, Chief Operating Officer and Support Services
Web address: www.https://www.coshoctonhospital.org
**Control:** Other not–for–profit (including NFP Corporation) **Service:** General medical and surgical

**Staffed Beds:** 44 **Admissions:** 1827 **Census:** 17 **Outpatient Visits:** 74538 **Births:** 0 **Total Expense ($000):** 39913 **Payroll Expense ($000):** 15052 **Personnel:** 354

### CUYAHOGA FALLS—Summit County

**SUMMA WESTERN RESERVE HOSPITAL** See Western Reserve Hospital

○ **WESTERN RESERVE HOSPITAL (360150)**, 1900 23rd Street, Zip 44223–1499; tel. 330/971–7000, (Nonreporting) **A**3 5 10 11 **F**3 12 26 29 30 31 33 34 35 36 38 40 44 45 47 49 50 51 54 57 58 59 60 64 65 66 68 70 74 75 77 78 79 81 82 84 85 86 87 92 93 94 96 97 107 108 111 114 115 119 129 130 132 135 144 146 148 **P**6 8
Primary Contact: Robert Kent, D.O., President and Chief Executive Officer
CFO: Jill Hiner, Vice President and Chief Financial Officer
CMO: Charles Feunning, M.D., Chief Medical Officer
CIO: Pamela Banchy, Chief Information Officer
CHR: Heather Milicevic, Director Human Resources
CNO: Carrie Gallo, Chief Nursing Officer
Web address: www.westernreservehospital.org
**Control:** Partnership, Investor–owned (for–profit) **Service:** General medical and surgical

**Staffed Beds:** 83 **Admissions:** 3164 **Census:** 32 **Outpatient Visits:** 129322 **Births:** 0 **Total Expense ($000):** 126075 **Payroll Expense ($000):** 41988 **Personnel:** 721

### DAYTON—Montgomery County

☐ **ACCESS HOSPITAL DAYTON (364050)**, 2611 Wayne Avenue, Zip 45420–1833; tel. 937/256–7801, (Nonreporting) **A**1 10
Primary Contact: Lauren Biles, Administrator
Web address: www.accesshospital.com/
**Control:** Corporation, Investor–owned (for–profit) **Service:** Psychiatric

**Staffed Beds:** 28

**CHILDREN'S MEDICAL CENTER** See Dayton Children's Hospital

☐ **DAYTON CHILDREN'S HOSPITAL (363306)**, One Children's Plaza, Zip 45404–1815; tel. 937/641–3000, (Nonreporting) **A**1 2 3 5 10 **F**3 7 8 11 19 21 29 30 31 32 34 35 38 39 40 41 42 43 44 45 50 54 55 57 58 59 60 61 62 63 64 65 66 68 72 74 75 77 78 79 81 82 84 85 86 87 88 89 93 97 98 99 100 101 102 104 107 111 115 119 129 130 131 132 134 135 144 146 148 149 154 156 **P**6
Primary Contact: Deborah A. Feldman, President and Chief Executive Officer
COO: Matthew P Graybill, Vice President, Human Resources and Chief Administrative Officer
CFO: Chris Bergman, Chief Financial Officer
CMO: Adam Mezoff, M.D., Vice President and Chief Medical Officer
CIO: Beth Fredette, Chief Information Officer
Web address: www.childrensdayton.org
**Control:** Other not–for–profit (including NFP Corporation) **Service:** Children's general medical and surgical

**Staffed Beds:** 170 **Admissions:** 5148 **Census:** 75 **Outpatient Visits:** 445570 **Births:** 0 **Total Expense ($000):** 448499 **Personnel:** 3068

⊞ △ **DAYTON VETERANS AFFAIRS MEDICAL CENTER**, 4100 West Third Street, Zip 45428–9000; tel. 937/268–6511, (Nonreporting) **A**1 3 5 7 8 **S** Department of Veterans Affairs, Washington, DC
Primary Contact: Mark Murdock, FACHE, Medical Center Director
CFO: Shannon Rappach, Chief Fiscal Services
CMO: James Hardy, D.O., Chief of Staff
CIO: Susan Sherer, Chief Information Resource Management
CHR: Rolanda Watkins, Chief Human Resources Management Service
CNO: Penelope Franklin Gorsuch, Associate Director Patient Care Services
Web address: www.dayton.va.gov/
**Control:** Veterans Affairs, Government, federal **Service:** General medical and surgical

**Staffed Beds:** 486

**GRANDVIEW HOSPITAL AND MEDICAL CENTER** See Grandview Medical Center

★ ○ **GRANDVIEW MEDICAL CENTER (360133)**, 405 West Grand Avenue, Zip 45405–4796; tel. 937/723–3200, (Includes SOUTHVIEW MEDICAL CENTER, Mailing address: 1997 Miamisburg-Centerville Road, Dayton, Ohio, Zip 45459–3800; tel. 937/439–6000; Richard Manchur, President), (Nonreporting) **A**2 3 5 10 11 12 13 19 **F**3 11 12 13 15 18 20 22 24 26 28 29 30 31 34 35 36 38 40 42 43 44 45 47 48 49 50 51 53 54 56 57 58 59 60 61 64 65 66 68 70 73 74 75 76 77 78 79 81 82 85 86 87 93 96 97 98 100 101 102 104 106 107 108 110 111 114 115 117 118 119 120 121 123 124 129 130 131 132 135 141 144 145 146 147 148 149 157 **P**6 **S** Kettering Health Network, Dayton, OH
Primary Contact: Rebecca Lewis, President
CFO: Luis Chanaga, Chief Financial Officer
CMO: Paul Martin, Chief Medical Officer
CIO: Andy Lehman, Senior Vice President Technology and Analytics
CHR: Keith Jenkins, Director, Human Resources
CNO: Ronda Brandstater, Vice President Patient Care
Web address: www.ketteringhealth.org/grandview/
**Control:** Church operated, Nongovernment, not–for–profit **Service:** General medical and surgical

**Staffed Beds:** 301 **Admissions:** 14478 **Census:** 171 **Outpatient Visits:** 476339 **Births:** 2054 **Total Expense ($000):** 586580 **Payroll Expense ($000):** 148131 **Personnel:** 1908

☐ **HAVEN BEHAVIORAL SENIOR CARE OF DAYTON (364048)**, One Elizabeth Place, 4th Floor Southwest Tower, Zip 45417–3445; tel. 937/234–0100, (Nonreporting) **A**1 10 **S** Haven Behavioral Healthcare, Nashville, TN
Primary Contact: Keith Kuhn, Chief Executive Officer
CMO: Amita Patel, M.D., Medical Director
CNO: Cheryl Meyer, MSN, Director of Nursing
Web address: www.havenbehavioraldayton.com/
**Control:** Corporation, Investor–owned (for–profit) **Service:** Psychiatric

**Staffed Beds:** 32

⊞ **HEALTHSOUTH REHABILITATION HOSPITAL OF DAYTON (363033)**, One Elizabeth Place, Zip 45417–3445; tel. 937/424–8200, (Nonreporting) **A**1 10 **F**29 57 59 90 148 **P**5 **S** Encompass Health Corporation, Birmingham, AL
Primary Contact: Lynne Blinco, Chief Executive Officer
Web address: www.reliantdayton.com
**Control:** Corporation, Investor–owned (for–profit) **Service:** Rehabilitation

**Staffed Beds:** 50 **Admissions:** 818 **Census:** 26 **Outpatient Visits:** 0 **Births:** 0 **Total Expense ($000):** 11299 **Payroll Expense ($000):** 6155 **Personnel:** 109

**HEALTHSOUTH REHABILITATION HOSPITAL OF DAYTON** See Healthsouth Rehabilitation Hospital of Dayton

**KETTERING YOUTH SERVICES** See Kettering Behavioral Medical Center

⊞ **KINDRED HOSPITAL-DAYTON (362033)**, 707 South Edwin C Moses Boulevard, Zip 45417–3462; tel. 937/222–5963, (Nonreporting) **A**1 10 **S** Kindred Healthcare, Louisville, KY
Primary Contact: Phillip Underwood, Chief Executive Officer
CMO: Felipe Rubio, M.D., Medical Director
Web address: www.khdayton.com
**Control:** Corporation, Investor–owned (for–profit) **Service:** Acute long–term care hospital

**Staffed Beds:** 67

⊞ △ **MIAMI VALLEY HOSPITAL (360051)**, One Wyoming Street, Zip 45409–2793; tel. 937/208–8000, (Includes MIAMI VALLEY HOSPITAL SOUTH, Mailing address: 2400 Miami Valley Drive, Centerville, Ohio, Zip 45459–4774; tel. 937/438–2400), (Nonreporting) **A**1 2 3 5 7 10 19 **F**3 5 7 8 11 12 13 15 16 17 18 20 22 24 26 28 29 30 31 32 34 35 37 40 41 42 43 44 45 46 47 48 49 50 53 54 55 56 57 58 59 60 61 63 64 68 70 71 72 73 74 75 76 77 78 79 80 81 82 84 85 86 87 90 91 92 93 95 96 98 100 101 102 103 104 107 108 110 111 114 115 116 117 118 119 120 121 123 124 126 129 130 131 132 134 135 141 146 147 148 149 153 154 155 156 **P**6 **S** Premier Health, Dayton, OH
Primary Contact: Michael J. Maiberger, President
COO: Mikki Clancy, Chief Operating Officer
CFO: Thomas M Duncan, Executive Vice President and Chief Financial Officer
CMO: Marc Belcastro, D.O., Chief Medical Officer
CIO: Gary Ginter, System Vice President and Chief Information Officer
Web address: www.miamivalleyhospital.org
**Control:** Other not–for–profit (including NFP Corporation) **Service:** General medical and surgical

**Staffed Beds:** 754 **Admissions:** 41967 **Census:** 574 **Outpatient Visits:** 794241 **Births:** 4870 **Total Expense ($000):** 1141689 **Payroll Expense ($000):** 453924 **Personnel:** 7043

**VETERANS AFFAIRS MEDICAL CENTER** See Dayton Veterans Affairs Medical Center

*Many Facility Codes have changed. Please refer to the AHA Guide Code Chart.*
© 2021 AHA Guide

## DEFIANCE—Defiance County

**DEFIANCE REGIONAL MEDICAL CENTER** See Promedica Defiance Regional Hospital

☐ **MERCY HOSPITAL OF DEFIANCE (360270)**, 1404 East Second Street, Zip 43512–2440; tel. 419/782–8444, (Nonreporting) **A**1 10 **S** Mercy Health, Cincinnati, OH
Primary Contact: B Lynn. Detterman, President and Chief Executive Officer
COO: Kerry Knuth, Chief Operating Officer
CFO: James Puffenberger, Vice President and Chief Financial Officer
CMO: Jeffrey Pruitt, M.D., Chief of Staff
CHR: Susan Pscodna, Director Human Resources
CNO: Sonya Selhorst, R.N., Administrator and Chief Nursing Officer
Web address: www.ehealthconnection.com/regions/toledo/
**Control**: Partnership, Investor–owned (for–profit) **Service**: General medical and surgical

**Staffed Beds:** 23

☒ **PROMEDICA DEFIANCE REGIONAL HOSPITAL (361328)**, 1200 Ralston Avenue, Zip 43512–1396; tel. 419/783–6955, (Nonreporting) **A**1 5 10 18 **F**3 11 13 15 18 20 28 31 32 34 40 43 55 57 59 64 66 68 70 75 76 77 78 79 81 82 85 86 87 93 98 100 101 102 104 105 107 108 110 111 114 118 119 129 130 132 135 144 146 147 148 153 156 157 **P**6 **S** ProMedica Health System, Toledo, OH
Primary Contact: Doug Bush, President
CFO: Ken Swint, Director Finance
CMO: Stanislaw Dajczak, M.D., Chief of Staff
CIO: Patricia Swint, Director Information Management Systems
CHR: Carrie Miller, Director Human Resources
Web address: www.promedica.org
**Control**: Other not–for–profit (including NFP Corporation) **Service**: General medical and surgical

**Staffed Beds:** 35 **Admissions:** 1712 **Census:** 15 **Outpatient Visits:** 91106 **Births:** 378 **Total Expense ($000):** 59201 **Payroll Expense ($000):** 16001 **Personnel:** 256

## DELAWARE—Delaware County

**GRADY MEMORIAL HOSPITAL** See Ohiohealth Grady Memorial Hospital

☒ **OHIOHEALTH GRADY MEMORIAL HOSPITAL (360210)**, 561 West Central Avenue, Zip 43015–1410; tel. 740/615–1000, (Nonreporting) **A**1 2 10 **F**3 13 15 18 20 28 29 30 31 34 35 40 42 45 49 50 54 55 57 59 64 70 74 76 78 79 81 82 84 85 86 87 96 97 102 107 108 109 110 111 114 118 119 124 126 131 132 135 141 146 147 148 149 154 **S** OhioHealth, Columbus, OH
Primary Contact: Steve Bunyard, President
COO: Anna Hensley, Chief Operating Officer
CFO: David Hensel, Director Financial Operations
CMO: Barbara Evert, M.D., Vice President Medical Affairs
CIO: Michael Krouse, Chief Information Officer Information Services
CHR: Victoria L. Matlack, Director and Human Resources Business Partner
CNO: Elizabeth Anne Biegler, R.N., Chief Nursing Officer
Web address: www.ohiohealth.com
**Control**: Church operated, Nongovernment, not–for–profit **Service**: General medical and surgical

**Staffed Beds:** 61 **Admissions:** 1876 **Census:** 15 **Outpatient Visits:** 69099 **Births:** 307 **Total Expense ($000):** 91492 **Payroll Expense ($000):** 34170 **Personnel:** 386

## DENNISON—Tuscarawas County

☒ **TRINITY HOSPITAL TWIN CITY (361302)**, 819 North First Street, Zip 44621–1098; tel. 740/922–2800, (Nonreporting) **A**1 10 18 **F**11 15 18 28 29 30 34 35 40 45 50 57 59 64 70 75 77 81 85 86 87 91 93 97 107 114 119 127 128 129 130 132 133 146 147 148 **P**6 **S** CommonSpirit Health, Chicago, IL
Primary Contact: Teresa Gagliardi, R.N., Vice President of Hospital Operations and Site Administrator
CMO: Tim McKnight, M.D., Chief of Staff
CHR: Bianca Love, Assistant Administrator Human Resources
CNO: Teresa Gagliardi, R.N., Chief Nursing Officer
Web address: www.trinitytwincity.org
**Control**: Church operated, Nongovernment, not–for–profit **Service**: General medical and surgical

**Staffed Beds:** 12 **Admissions:** 135 **Census:** 1 **Outpatient Visits:** 42838 **Births:** 0 **Total Expense ($000):** 22510 **Payroll Expense ($000):** 9723 **Personnel:** 202

**TWIN CITY HOSPITAL** See Trinity Hospital Twin City

## DOVER—Tuscarawas County

★ △ ⇑ **CLEVELAND CLINIC UNION HOSPITAL (360010)**, 659 Boulevard, Zip 44622–2077; tel. 330/343–3311, (Nonreporting) **A**5 7 10 19 21 **F**3 8 11 13 15 18 28 29 34 35 36 40 48 50 51 53 54 57 59 62 64 65 70 74 75 76 77 78 79 81 82 85 90 93 100 102 104 105 107 108 110 111 115 119 124 129 130 131 132 135 144 146 148 149 153 154 156 157 **P**6 **S** Cleveland Clinic Health System, Cleveland, OH
Primary Contact: Bruce James, President and Chief Executive Officer
CFO: Eugene A Thorn IIIVice President Finance and Chief Financial Officer
CMO: Todd Meyerhoefer, M.D., Vice President Medical Affairs
CIO: David Baumgardner, Director Information Management
CHR: Darwin K Smith, Vice President Human Resources
CNO: Diana Boyd, Vice President Nursing
Web address: www.unionhospital.org
**Control**: Other not–for–profit (including NFP Corporation) **Service**: General medical and surgical

**Staffed Beds:** 136 **Admissions:** 4022 **Census:** 43 **Outpatient Visits:** 262992 **Births:** 544 **Total Expense ($000):** 137224 **Payroll Expense ($000):** 78039 **Personnel:** 969

⇑ **UNION HOSPITAL** See Cleveland Clinic Union Hospital

## DUBLIN—Franklin County

☐ **COLUMBUS DUBLIN SPRINGS (364049)**, 7625 Hospital Drive, Zip 43016–9649; tel. 614/717–1800, (Includes COLUMBUS SPRINGS EAST HOSPITAL, Mailing address: 2085 Citygate Drive, Columbus, Ohio, Zip 43219–3656; tel. 614/412–1772; Garry W Hoyes, Chief Executive Officer), (Nonreporting) **A**1 3 10 **S** Springstone, Louisville, KY
Primary Contact: Garry W. Hoyes, Chief Executive Officer
COO: Merissa McKinstry, Chief Operating Officer
CFO: Alexis Barbour, Director Finance
CMO: Mark Blair, M.D., Medical Director
CHR: Tam Wisler, Director Human Resources
Web address: www.dublinsprings.com
**Control**: Corporation, Investor–owned (for–profit) **Service**: Psychiatric

**Staffed Beds:** 144

**DUBLIN METHODIST HOSPITAL** See Ohiohealth Dublin Methodist Hospital

**DUBLIN SPRINGS** See Columbus Dublin Springs

☒ **OHIOHEALTH DUBLIN METHODIST HOSPITAL (360348)**, 7500 Hospital Drive, Zip 43016–8518; tel. 614/544–8000, (Nonreporting) **A**1 2 3 5 10 **F**3 13 15 18 20 28 29 30 34 40 45 50 57 59 60 64 68 70 76 79 81 84 85 87 97 100 102 107 108 109 110 111 113 114 115 118 119 120 126 130 132 135 141 146 147 148 149 154 **S** OhioHealth, Columbus, OH
Primary Contact: Steve Bunyard, President
COO: Anna Hensley, Chief Operating Officer
CFO: Keely Pummel, Director, Financial Operations
CMO: Barbara Evert, M.D., Vice President Medical Affairs
CIO: Michael Krouse, Senior Vice President Chief Information Officer
CHR: Victoria L. Matlack, Director and Human Resources Business Partner
CNO: Elizabeth Anne Biegler, R.N., Chief Nursing Officer
Web address: www.ohiohealth.com
**Control**: Church operated, Nongovernment, not–for–profit **Service**: General medical and surgical

**Staffed Beds:** 120 **Admissions:** 6471 **Census:** 47 **Outpatient Visits:** 72769 **Births:** 2539 **Total Expense ($000):** 169116 **Payroll Expense ($000):** 59302

## EAST LIVERPOOL—Columbiana County

☐ **EAST LIVERPOOL CITY HOSPITAL (360096)**, 425 West Fifth Street, Zip 43920–2498; tel. 330/385–7200, (Nonreporting) **A**1 3 5 10 **S** Prime Healthcare, Ontario, CA
Primary Contact: Keith Richardson, President and Chief Executive Officer
CFO: Kyle Johnson, Vice President Finance
CMO: Steve LaTulippe, President Medical Staff
CIO: Frank Mader, Director Information Services
CHR: Teri Pasco, Director Human Resources
CNO: Stacie Call, R.N., Vice President Patient Care and Chief Nursing Officer
Web address: www.elch.org
**Control**: Other not–for–profit (including NFP Corporation) **Service**: General medical and surgical

**Staffed Beds:** 120

**OH**

### ELYRIA—Lorain County

⊠ **UH ELYRIA MEDICAL CENTER (360145)**, 630 East River Street,
Zip 44035–5902; tel. 440/329–7500, (Nonreporting) **A**1 2 5 10 **F**3 11 12 13 15
17 18 20 22 24 26 28 29 30 31 32 34 36 37 40 42 43 44 45 49 50 53 54 57
59 60 64 68 70 73 74 75 76 77 78 79 81 82 85 86 87 89 91 92 93 94 98 100
107 108 110 111 114 115 116 117 118 119 126 129 130 131 132 133 135
146 147 148 149 154 **S** University Hospitals, Cleveland, OH
Primary Contact: Kristi M. Sink, President
CFO: David A Cook, Vice President and Chief Financial Officer
CHR: Daniel Miller, Vice President Human Resources
CNO: Sandra Jean Kantelas, Chief Nursing Officer
Web address: www.uhhospitals.org/elyria
**Control**: Other not–for–profit (including NFP Corporation) **Service**: General
medical and surgical

> **Staffed Beds: 202 Admissions: 9459 Census: 101 Outpatient**
> **Visits: 234866 Births: 653 Total Expense ($000): 203631 Payroll Expense**
> **($000): 66395 Personnel: 1162**

**UNIVERSITY HOSPITALS ELYRIA MEDICAL CENTER** See UH Elyria Medical
Center

### EUCLID—Cuyahoga County

⊠ **EUCLID HOSPITAL (360082)**, 18901 Lake Shore Boulevard, Zip 44119–1090;
tel. 216/531–9000, (Total facility includes 40 beds in nursing home–type unit)
(Nonreporting) **A**1 3 10 **F**3 8 15 18 28 29 30 34 35 40 45 56 57 59 60 64 70
74 75 77 79 81 82 85 87 91 93 94 96 98 100 102 103 107 108 111 114
118 119 128 130 131 135 146 148 154 155 156 **P**6 **S** Cleveland Clinic Health
System, Cleveland, OH
Primary Contact: Teresa Dews, M.D., President
COO: Rich Lea, Vice President Operations
CFO: Don Urbancsik, Director Finance
CMO: John Bertsch, M.D., Chief of Staff
CNO: Dawn A Bailey, R.N., Vice President Nursing and Chief Nursing Officer
Web address: www.euclidhospital.org
**Control**: Other not–for–profit (including NFP Corporation) **Service**: General
medical and surgical

> **Staffed Beds: 166 Admissions: 7072 Census: 99 Outpatient Visits: 69639**
> **Births: 0 Total Expense ($000): 110897 Payroll Expense ($000): 46787**
> **Personnel: 656**

**MERIDIA EUCLID HOSPITAL** See Euclid Hospital

### FAIRFIELD—Butler County

☐ △ **MERCY HEALTH - FAIRFIELD HOSPITAL (360056)**, 3000 Mack Road,
Zip 45014–5335; tel. 513/870–7000, (Nonreporting) **A**1 2 7 10 **F**3 8 11 12 13
15 17 18 20 22 24 35 37 40 43 45 46 47 48 49 50 51 54
57 59 60 64 68 70 73 74 76 77 78 79 81 82 84 85 86 87 90 93 96 100 107
108 110 111 114 115 118 119 126 129 130 131 135 146 147 148 149 154
156 **S** Mercy Health, Cincinnati, OH
Primary Contact: Justin Krueger, FACHE, President
CFO: Liz Mohr, Assistant Chief Financial Officer
CMO: John Kennedy, M.D., Vice President of Medical Affairs
CIO: Rebecca S Sykes, Chief Information Officer
CNO: Ramona Cheek, MS, R.N., Chief Nursing Officer
Web address: www.https://www.mercy.com
**Control**: Church operated, Nongovernment, not–for–profit **Service**: General
medical and surgical

> **Staffed Beds: 145 Admissions: 12651 Census: 144 Outpatient**
> **Visits: 174700 Births: 1490 Total Expense ($000): 241710 Payroll**
> **Expense ($000): 71817 Personnel: 1039**

**MERCY HOSPITAL FAIRFIELD** See Mercy Health - Fairfield Hospital

### FINDLAY—Hancock County

**BLANCHARD VALLEY HEALTH SYSTEM** See Blanchard Valley Hospital

⊠ **BLANCHARD VALLEY HOSPITAL (360095)**, 1900 South Main Street,
Zip 45840–1214; tel. 419/423–4500, (Includes BLANCHARD VALLEY
HOSPITAL, Mailing address: 1900 South Main Street, Findlay, Ohio, Zip 45840;
tel. 419/423–4500), (Nonreporting) **A**1 2 5 10 19 **F**3 11 13 15 17 18 20 22 24
26 28 29 30 31 34 35 40 41 43 44 45 48 49 50 54 55 57 58 59 60 64 65 68
70 73 74 76 77 78 79 81 82 84 85 87 91 93 96 98 100 102 107 108 110 111
114 115 117 118 119 120 121 129 130 131 132 135 146 147 148
149 154 **P**5 6 **S** Blanchard Valley Health System, Findlay, OH
Primary Contact: Scott C. Malaney, FACHE, President and Chief Executive Officer
CFO: David Cytlak, Chief Financial Officer
CMO: Michael Denike, D.O., Vice President, Medical Affairs
CIO: David Cytlak, Chief Financial Officer
CHR: Ryan Fisher, Director of Human Resources
CNO: Barbara J. Pasztor, R.N., Vice President Patient Care Services and Chief
Nursing Officer
Web address: www.bvhealthsystem.org
**Control**: Other not–for–profit (including NFP Corporation) **Service**: General
medical and surgical

> **Staffed Beds: 159 Admissions: 7798 Census: 75 Outpatient**
> **Visits: 151950 Births: 1199 Total Expense ($000): 225150 Payroll**
> **Expense ($000): 90643 Personnel: 1310**

**BLANCHARD VALLEY REG HLTH CTR** See Blanchard Valley Hospital

### FOSTORIA—Hancock County

**FOSTORIA COMMUNITY HOSPITAL** See Promedica Fostoria Community Hospital

⊠ **PROMEDICA FOSTORIA COMMUNITY HOSPITAL (361318)**, 501 Van Buren
Street, Zip 44830–1534, Mailing Address: P.O. Box 907, Zip 44830–0907;
tel. 419/435–7734, (Nonreporting) **A**1 10 18 **F**3 11 15 28 29 30 31 34 35 40
45 46 57 59 60 64 70 75 78 79 81 82 85 87 89 93 96 104 107 108 110 111
115 119 128 129 130 131 132 133 135 146 147 148 149 156 157 **P**6 **S**
ProMedica Health System, Toledo, OH
Primary Contact: Pamela M. Jensen, FACHE, President
COO: Tom Borer, Vice President Operations
CFO: Ken Swint, Vice President Finance and Chief Financial Officer
CMO: Terrence Fondessy, M.D., Vice President Medical Affairs
CIO: Rose Ann Laureto, Chief Information Officer
Web address: www.promedica.org
**Control**: Other not–for–profit (including NFP Corporation) **Service**: General
medical and surgical

> **Staffed Beds: 25 Admissions: 469 Census: 3 Outpatient Visits: 66432**
> **Births: 0 Total Expense ($000): 34073 Payroll Expense ($000): 8839**
> **Personnel: 152**

### FREMONT—Sandusky County

**MEMORIAL HOSPITAL** See Promedica Memorial Hospital

⊠ **PROMEDICA MEMORIAL HOSPITAL (360156)**, 715 South Taft Avenue,
Zip 43420–3237; tel. 419/332–7321, (Nonreporting) **A**1 3 5 10 **F**3 11 13 15 18
19 28 29 30 31 34 35 38 40 44 45 46 47 48 51 53 56 57 59 64 65 70 74 75
76 77 78 79 80 81 82 84 85 87 89 93 96 97 107 108 110 111 114 115 119
123 124 129 130 131 132 135 141 142 146 147 148 149 156 157 **P**1 6 **S**
ProMedica Health System, Toledo, OH
Primary Contact: Pamela M. Jensen, FACHE, President, Regional Acute Care
COO: Corey Leber, R.N., Associate Vice President Operations
CFO: Ken Swint, Adminstrative Director Finance
CMO: John J. Hiestand, M.D., Vice President Medical Affairs
CHR: Warrenette Parthemore, Director Human Resources
CNO: Jodi Rucker, MSN, R.N., Vice President Patient Care Services and Chief
Nursing Officer
Web address: www.https://www.promedica.org
**Control**: Other not–for–profit (including NFP Corporation) **Service**: General
medical and surgical

> **Staffed Beds: 76 Admissions: 1167 Census: 9 Outpatient Visits: 62271**
> **Births: 179 Total Expense ($000): 63671 Payroll Expense ($000): 16253**
> **Personnel: 288**

### GAHANNA—Franklin County

☐ **THE WOODS AT PARKSIDE (360247)**, 349 Olde Ridenour Road,
Zip 43230–2528; tel. 614/471–2552, (Nonreporting) **A**1 10
Primary Contact: Chauncey Wallace, Director of Hospital Operations
Web address: www.thewoodsatparkside.com
**Control**: Partnership, Investor–owned (for–profit) **Service**: Alcoholism and other
chemical dependency

> **Staffed Beds: 50**

## GALION—Crawford County

⇑ **GALION COMMUNITY HOSPITAL** See Galion Hospital

★ ⇑ **GALION HOSPITAL (361325)**, 269 Portland Way South, Zip 44833–2399; tel. 419/468–4841, (Nonreporting) **A**10 18 21 **S** Avita Health System, Galion, OH
Primary Contact: Jerome Morasko, President and Chief Executive Officer
CFO: D. Eric Draime, Vice President and Chief Financial Officer
CIO: Alex Reed, Chief Information Officer
CHR: Traci L Oswald, Vice President of Human Resources
CNO: Kathy Durflinger, Vice President and Chief Nursing Officer
Web address: www.avitahs.org
**Control:** Other not-for-profit (including NFP Corporation) **Service:** General medical and surgical

**Staffed Beds:** 35

## GALLIPOLIS—Gallia County

⊠ △ **HOLZER MEDICAL CENTER (360054)**, 100 Jackson Pike, Zip 45631–1563; tel. 740/446–5000, (Nonreporting) **A**1 2 3 5 7 10 19 **F**3 12 13 15 18 20 22 26 28 29 30 31 33 34 35 37 40 42 45 49 55 57 59 60 62 63 64 70 74 76 77 78 79 81 82 85 87 89 90 93 96 97 98 103 107 108 110 111 114 115 118 119 120 121 123 126 129 130 131 132 144 146 149 **S** Holzer Health System, Jackson, OH
Primary Contact: Michael R. Canady, M.D., Interim Chief Executive Officer
CFO: Kenneth G Payne, Chief Financial Officer
CMO: John Viall, M.D., Vice President Medical Affairs
CIO: John Allen, Chief Information Officer
CHR: Lisa B Halley, Vice President Human Resources
Web address: www.holzer.org
**Control:** Other not-for-profit (including NFP Corporation) **Service:** General medical and surgical

**Staffed Beds:** 195 **Admissions:** 4663 **Census:** 62 **Births:** 580 **Total Expense ($000):** 167606 **Payroll Expense ($000):** 52788 **Personnel:** 597

## GARFIELD HEIGHTS—Cuyahoga County

⊠ **MARYMOUNT HOSPITAL (360143)**, 12300 McCracken Road, Zip 44125–2975; tel. 216/581–0500, (Nonreporting) **A**1 2 3 10 **F**3 7 8 10 11 15 18 28 29 30 31 34 35 38 40 44 50 51 53 54 56 57 59 60 62 63 64 65 68 70 74 75 77 78 79 81 82 84 85 86 87 92 93 96 97 98 100 102 103 104 107 108 110 111 114 115 118 119 125 130 131 132 143 144 146 147 148 149 153 154 155 157 158 **P**6 **S** Cleveland Clinic Health System, Cleveland, OH
Primary Contact: Daniel Napierkowski, M.D., President
COO: Mark Nussbaum, Vice President Operations
CFO: Mike Stilgenbauer, Director Finance
CMO: Douglas Kohler, M.D., Vice President Medical Operations
CIO: Ralph A Cagna, Director Information Technology Operations, Cleveland Clinic Health System South Market
CHR: Judith Santora, Human Resources Business Partner
CNO: Barbara Zinner, Chief Nursing Officer
Web address: www.marymount.org
**Control:** Other not-for-profit (including NFP Corporation) **Service:** General medical and surgical

**Staffed Beds:** 269 **Admissions:** 9405 **Census:** 126 **Outpatient Visits:** 75835 **Births:** 0 **Total Expense ($000):** 160939 **Payroll Expense ($000):** 58274 **Personnel:** 829

## GENEVA—Ashtabula County

⊠ **UH GENEVA MEDICAL CENTER (361307)**, 870 West Main Street, Zip 44041–1295; tel. 440/466–1141, (Nonreporting) **A**1 3.10 18 **F**3 5 7 11 15 18 29 31 34 35 40 46 51 56 57 59 60 64 68 70 75 77 78 79 81 82 85 86 87 91 93 107 110 111 115 116 119 129 130 132 133 135 143 146 147 148 149 154 **S** University Hospitals, Cleveland, OH
Primary Contact: M Steven. Jones, President
COO: Jason Glowczewski, Chief Operating Officer
CFO: Lara Eggleston, Finance Manager
CMO: Amitabh Goel, M.D., Chief Medical Officer
CIO: Kirsten Hale, Coordinator Health Information Systems and Coding
CHR: Danialle Lynce, Business Partner Human Resources
CNO: Ashley Fertig, Chief Nursing Officer
Web address: www.uhhs.com
**Control:** Other not-for-profit (including NFP Corporation) **Service:** General medical and surgical

**Staffed Beds:** 25 **Admissions:** 1390 **Census:** 15 **Outpatient Visits:** 52496 **Births:** 0 **Total Expense ($000):** 41495 **Payroll Expense ($000):** 13590 **Personnel:** 240

**UNIVERSITY HOSPITALS GENEVA MEDICAL CENTER** See UH Geneva Medical Center

## GEORGETOWN—Brown County

**GEORGETOWN BEHAVIORAL HOSPITAL**, 425 Home Street, Zip 45121–1407; tel. 937/483–4933, (Nonreporting) **S** Oglethorpe Recovery and Behavioral Hospitals, Tampa, FL
Primary Contact: Arthur Douglas. Owens, Administrator
Web address: www.https://www.gbhoh.com
**Control:** Corporation, Investor–owned (for–profit) **Service:** Psychiatric

**Staffed Beds:** 46

## GREEN SPRINGS—Sandusky County

**EDEN SPRINGS HEALTH CARE CENTER (362007)**, 401 North Broadway, Zip 44836–9653; tel. 419/639–2626, (Nonreporting) **A**10
Primary Contact: Deanna Turner, Executive Director
CFO: Douglas Morris, Chief Financial Officer
CMO: John Yuhas, D.O., Medical Director
CHR: Joan E Schmidt, Director Human Resources
**Control:** Church operated, Nongovernment, not–for–profit **Service:** Acute long–term care hospital

**Staffed Beds:** 186

**ELMWOOD HEALTHCARE CENTER AT THE SPRINGS** See Eden Springs Health Care Center

## GREENFIELD—Highland County

☐ △ **ADENA GREENFIELD MEDICAL CENTER (361304)**, 550 Mirabeau Street, Zip 45123–1617; tel. 937/981–9400, (Nonreporting) **A**1 7 10 18 **F**3 15 18 29 30 34 35 40 41 45 50 54 57 59 68 74 75 77 79 81 82 90 93 107 110 111 114 119 130 131 132 133 135 146 147 148 154 **S** Adena Health System, Chillicothe, OH
Primary Contact: Josh McCoy, Administrator
CFO: Ralph W Sorrell Sr Chief Financial Officer
CIO: Marcus Bost, Director Information Services and Chief Information Officer
CHR: Brandt Lippert, Vice President Human Resources
Web address: www.adena.org
**Control:** Other not-for-profit (including NFP Corporation) **Service:** General medical and surgical

**Staffed Beds:** 25 **Admissions:** 359 **Census:** 9 **Outpatient Visits:** 42585 **Births:** 0 **Total Expense ($000):** 17705 **Payroll Expense ($000):** 7127 **Personnel:** 123

**GREENFIELD AREA MEDICAL CENTER** See Adena Greenfield Medical Center

## GREENVILLE—Darke County

★ ○ **WAYNE HEALTHCARE (360044)**, 835 Sweitzer Street, Zip 45331–1077; tel. 937/548–1141, (Nonreporting) **A**2 3 10 11 **F**3 8 11 13 15 28 29 30 31 34 35 39 40 41 45 57 59 64 65 70 75 76 77 78 79 81 82 84 85 86 87 89 93 98 103 107 108 110 111 114 117 118 119 124 126 129 130 131 132 135 141 146 147 148 149 154 156
Primary Contact: Wayne G. Deschambeau, President and Chief Executive Officer
COO: Kimberlee Freeman, Vice President of Patient Care Services/Chief Nursing Officer
CFO: Jennifer Williams, Vice President of Finance/Chief Financial Officer
CMO: Safet Hatic, M.D., President Medical Staff
CIO: Shelton Monger, Director Information Technology
CHR: Peggy Schwartz, Vice President Human Resources
CNO: Kimberlee Freeman, Vice President Patient Care Services and Chief Nursing Officer
Web address: www.waynehealthcare.org
**Control:** Other not-for-profit (including NFP Corporation) **Service:** General medical and surgical

**Staffed Beds:** 53 **Admissions:** 1836 **Census:** 20 **Outpatient Visits:** 74784 **Births:** 303 **Total Expense ($000):** 62866 **Payroll Expense ($000):** 19738 **Personnel:** 376

**WAYNE HOSPITAL** See Wayne Healthcare

## HAMILTON—Butler County

**BUTLER COUNTY MEDICAL CENTER** See Bethesda Butler Hospital

---

**Hospital, Medicare Provider Number, Address, Telephone, Approval, Facility, and Physician Codes, Health Care System**

★ American Hospital Association (AHA) membership
☐ The Joint Commission accreditation
○ Healthcare Facilities Accreditation Program
◇ DNV Healthcare Inc. accreditation
⇑ Center for Improvement in Healthcare Quality Accreditation
△ Commission on Accreditation of Rehabilitation Facilities (CARF) accreditation

**OH**

★ ○ **FORT HAMILTON HOSPITAL (360132)**, 630 Eaton Avenue, Zip 45013–2770; tel. 513/867–2000, (Nonreporting) **A**2 10 11 **F**3 11 13 15 18 20 22 26 28 29 30 31 34 35 36 38 40 43 45 46 47 48 49 50 53 54 55 56 57 59 60 64 68 69 70 73 74 75 76 78 79 81 82 84 85 86 87 90 92 93 94 96 97 98 102 107 108 109 110 111 112 113 115 116 117 118 119 120 121 124 126 129 130 131 132 146 147 148 154 156 **P**6 **S** Kettering Health Network, Dayton, OH
Primary Contact: Michael Mewhirter, President
CFO: William Villegas, Vice President Finance
CMO: Marcus Romanello, Chief Medical Officer
CIO: Andy Lehman, Senior Vice President Technology and Analytics
CHR: Joseph Geigle, Director Human Resources
CNO: Carol Applegeet, MSN, R.N., Vice President and Chief Nursing Officer
Web address: www.khnetwork.org/forthamilton
**Control**: Church operated, Nongovernment, not–for–profit **Service**: General medical and surgical

**Staffed Beds: 200 Admissions: 6816 Census: 79 Outpatient Visits: 111081 Births: 598 Total Expense ($000): 175973 Payroll Expense ($000): 74291 Personnel: 927**

**FORT HAMILTON-HUGHES MEM HOSP** See Fort Hamilton Hospital

### HICKSVILLE—Defiance County

☐ **COMMUNITY MEMORIAL HOSPITAL (361301)**, 208 North Columbus Street, Zip 43526–1299; tel. 419/542–6692, (Nonreporting) **A**1 10 18
Primary Contact: Michelle Waggoner, Chief Executive Officer
CFO: Steve Caryer, Chief Financial Officer
CNO: Betty Clevinger, Chief Nursing Officer
Web address: www.cmhosp.com
**Control**: Hospital district or authority, Government, Nonfederal **Service**: General medical and surgical

**Staffed Beds: 25**

### HIGHLAND HILLS—Cuyahoga County

☐ **HIGHLAND SPRINGS HOSPITAL (364053)**, 4199 Mill Pond Drive, Zip 44122–5731; tel. 602/314–7800, (Nonreporting) **A**1 **S** Springstone, Louisville, KY
Primary Contact: Matthew Winchester, Chief Executive Officer
Web address: www.https://www.highlandspringshealth.com
**Control**: Corporation, Investor–owned (for–profit) **Service**: Psychiatric

**Staffed Beds: 72**

### HILLSBORO—Highland County

**HIGHLAND DISTRICT HOSP** See Highland District Hospital

⊞ **HIGHLAND DISTRICT HOSPITAL (361332)**, 1275 North High Street, Zip 45133–8273; tel. 937/393–6100, (Nonreporting) **A**1 10 18 **F**3 11 13 15 29 30 31 34 35 40 44 45 47 49 50 57 59 62 64 74 76 77 78 79 81 82 85 86 87 92 93 94 96 98 103 107 108 110 111 115 118 119 127 130 131 132 133 135 146 148 149 156
Primary Contact: Randal P. Lennartz, CPA, President and Chief Executive Officer
COO: Timothy Parry, R.N., Chief Operating Officer
CMO: Ron Zile, M.D., Chief of Staff
CIO: Tim Bogard, Manager Information Technology
CHR: Melanie Wymer, Director Human Resources
CNO: Pam Barnett, R.N., Director of Nursing
Web address: www.hdh.org
**Control**: Hospital district or authority, Government, Nonfederal **Service**: General medical and surgical

**Staffed Beds: 35 Admissions: 1392 Census: 15 Outpatient Visits: 82863 Births: 217 Total Expense ($000): 50923 Payroll Expense ($000): 17906 Personnel: 311**

### JACKSON—Jackson County

⊠ **HOLZER MEDICAL CENTER - JACKSON (361320)**, 500 Burlington Road, Zip 45640–9360; tel. 740/288–4625, (Nonreporting) **A**1 10 18 **F**18 29 30 40 64 68 75 77 79 82 85 87 97 107 108 114 118 119 130 131 133 146 148 149 154 **S** Holzer Health System, Jackson, OH
Primary Contact: Michael R. Canady, M.D., Chief Executive Officer
CFO: Kevin Yeager, Vice President Fiscal Services
CMO: Nimal Dutla, M.D., Chief Medical Staff
CHR: Sandy Carlisle, Manager Human Resources
Web address: www.holzer.org
**Control**: Other not–for–profit (including NFP Corporation) **Service**: General medical and surgical

**Staffed Beds: 24 Admissions: 513 Census: 4 Outpatient Visits: 47229 Total Expense ($000): 17985 Payroll Expense ($000): 7290 Personnel: 176**

### KENTON—Hardin County

**HARDIN MEMORIAL HOSPITAL** See Ohiohealth Hardin Memorial Hospital

⊞ **OHIOHEALTH HARDIN MEMORIAL HOSPITAL (361315)**, 921 East Franklin Street, Zip 43326–2099; tel. 419/673–0761, (Nonreporting) **A**1 10 18 **F**11 15 29 30 34 40 45 50 57 59 61 68 75 77 78 79 81 86 87 93 97 102 107 108 110 111 114 115 116 119 129 130 131 132 133 135 144 146 147 154 156 **S** OhioHealth, Columbus, OH
Primary Contact: Ron Snyder, Chief Operating Officer
Web address: www.hardinmemorial.org
**Control**: Other not–for–profit (including NFP Corporation) **Service**: General medical and surgical

**Staffed Beds: 25 Admissions: 420 Census: 4 Total Expense ($000): 24869 Payroll Expense ($000): 10502 Personnel: 169**

### KETTERING—Montgomery County

**CHARLES F KETTERING MEM CENTER** See Kettering Medical Center

★ ○ △ **KETTERING MEDICAL CENTER (360079)**, 3535 Southern Boulevard, Zip 45429–1221; tel. 937/298–4331, (Nonreporting) **A**2 3 5 7 8 10 11 19 **F**3 8 11 13 17 18 20 22 24 26 28 29 30 31 34 35 36 37 38 39 40 42 43 44 45 46 47 48 49 50 51 52 53 54 55 56 57 58 59 60 61 62 64 65 66 68 70 71 72 74 75 76 77 78 79 81 82 84 85 86 87 90 91 92 93 96 97 102 107 108 110 111 114 115 116 117 118 119 120 123 124 126 129 130 131 132 135 141 145 146 147 149 154 157 **S** Kettering Health Network, Dayton, OH
Primary Contact: Terry M. Burns, President
CFO: Steven Chavez, Vice President Finance and Operations
CMO: Robert T. Smith, M.D., Chief Medical Officer
CIO: Andy Lehman, Senior Vice President Technology and Analytics
CHR: Derek Morgan, Vice President Human Resources
CNO: Brenda Kuhn, Ph.D., R.N., FACHE, Chief Nursing Officer
Web address: www.ketteringhealth.org/kettering
**Control**: Church operated, Nongovernment, not–for–profit **Service**: General medical and surgical

**Staffed Beds: 426 Admissions: 23146 Census: 294 Outpatient Visits: 320495 Births: 2685 Total Expense ($000): 827048 Payroll Expense ($000): 309231 Personnel: 2909**

### LANCASTER—Fairfield County

☐ **FAIRFIELD MEDICAL CENTER (360072)**, 401 North Ewing Street, Zip 43130–3371; tel. 740/687–8000, (Nonreporting) **A**1 2 3 5 10 13 **F**3 8 11 12 13 15 18 20 22 24 26 28 29 30 31 34 35 36 37 38 40 42 44 45 46 47 48 49 50 53 54 57 58 59 64 70 71 74 75 76 77 78 79 81 82 83 84 85 87 89 92 93 96 97 98 100 102 104 107 108 110 111 115 118 119 120 121 123 124 126 129 130 131 132 135 141 142 144 145 146 147 148 149 154 156
Primary Contact: John R. Janoso, Chief Executive Officer
CFO: Sky Gettys, Chief Financial Officer
CMO: Renee Wagner, M.D., Chief Medical Officer
CIO: Martha Buckley, Chief Medical Informatics Officer
CHR: Debra L Palmer, MS, R.N., Chief Human Resources Officer and Corporate Compliance Officer
CNO: Helen Harding, Chief Nursing Officer
Web address: www.fmchealth.org
**Control**: Other not–for–profit (including NFP Corporation) **Service**: General medical and surgical

**Staffed Beds: 222 Admissions: 10078 Census: 114 Outpatient Visits: 290087 Births: 875 Total Expense ($000): 263593 Payroll Expense ($000): 96639 Personnel: 1888**

**LANCASTER-FAIRFIELD COMM HOSP** See Fairfield Medical Center

*Many Facility Codes have changed. Please refer to the AHA Guide Code Chart.* © 2021 AHA Guide

## LIMA—Allen County

☐ **INSTITUTE FOR ORTHOPAEDIC SURGERY (360263)**, 801 Medical Drive, Suite B, Zip 45804–4030; tel. 419/224–7586, (Nonreporting) **A**1 10 **S** Mercy Health, Cincinnati, OH
Primary Contact: Mark McDonald, M.D., President and Chief Executive Officer
CMO: Mark McDonald, M.D., President and Chief Executive Officer
CHR: Pat Farmer, Coordinator Human Resources and Safety Officer
Web address: www.ioshospital.com
**Control**: Partnership, Investor–owned (for–profit) **Service**: Orthopedic

**Staffed Beds**: 3

✖ **KINDRED HOSPITAL LIMA (362020)**, 730 West Market Street, 6th Floor, Zip 45801–4602; tel. 419/224–1888, (Nonreporting) **A**1 10 **S** Kindred Healthcare, Louisville, KY
Primary Contact: Susan Krinke, Chief Executive Officer
Web address: www.khlima.com
**Control**: Corporation, Investor–owned (for–profit) **Service**: Acute long–term care hospital

**Staffed Beds**: 26

✖ △ **LIMA MEMORIAL HEALTH SYSTEM (360009)**, 1001 Bellefontaine Avenue, Zip 45804–2899; tel. 419/228–3335, (Nonreporting) **A**1 2 7 10 **F**3 11 13 15 17 18 20 22 24 26 28 29 30 31 34 35 36 40 41 43 45 46 47 48 49 50 54 57 59 60 62 63 64 68 70 73 74 75 76 77 78 79 81 84 85 86 87 89 90 93 96 107 108 110 111 114 115 116 119 121 126 129 130 131 132 135 146 147 148 149 154 156 **P**8
Primary Contact: Michael D. Swick, President and Chief Executive Officer
COO: Robert E. Armstrong, Senior Vice President and Chief Operating Officer
CFO: John T. Fischbach, Vice President of Finance, Chief Financial Officer
CIO: Mathew P. Gaug, Executive Director of Information Technology
CHR: Denise G Kiraly, Director, Human Resources and Organization Development
CNO: Ann-Marie J Pohl, Vice President and Chief Nursing Officer
Web address: www.limamemorial.org
**Control**: Other not–for–profit (including NFP Corporation) **Service**: General medical and surgical

**Staffed Beds**: 159 **Admissions**: 6117 **Census**: 67 **Outpatient Visits**: 203134 **Births**: 529 **Total Expense ($000)**: 173165 **Payroll Expense ($000)**: 64559 **Personnel**: 1176

**LIMA MEMORIAL HOSPITAL** See Lima Memorial Health System

☐ △ **MERCY HEALTH - ST. RITA'S MEDICAL CENTER (360066)**, 730 West Market Street, Zip 45801–4602; tel. 419/227–3361, (Nonreporting) **A**1 2 3 5 7 10 **S** Mercy Health, Cincinnati, OH
Primary Contact: Dale Gisi, President
COO: Ronda Lehman, PharmD, Chief Operating Officer, SRPS
CFO: Tim Rieger, Chief Financial Officer
CMO: Kevin Casey, M.D., Chief Clinical Officer
CHR: Will Cason, Vice President Human Resources
CNO: Jodi Pahl, Chief Nurse Executive
Web address: www.stritas.org
**Control**: Church operated, Nongovernment, not–for–profit **Service**: General medical and surgical

**Staffed Beds**: 271

**ST. RITA'S MEDICAL CENTER** See Mercy Health - St. Rita's Medical Center

**TRIUMPH HOSPITAL LIMA** See Kindred Hospital Lima

## LODI—Medina County

✖ **CLEVELAND CLINIC AKRON GENERAL LODI HOSPITAL (361303)**, 225 Elyria Street, Zip 44254–1096; tel. 330/948–1222, (Nonreporting) **A**1 10 18 **F**3 15 18 28 29 30 34 35 40 45 57 59 64 65 75 81 90 93 96 97 107 111 114 119 128 129 130 133 135 146 147 154 **P**6 **S** Cleveland Clinic Health System, Cleveland, OH
Primary Contact: Dana Kocsis, Vice President, Nursing and Operations
COO: Dana Kocsis, Vice President Nursing and Operations
CFO: Dave Frigo, Director Finance and Controller
CMO: David Peter, M.D., Senior Vice President Medical Affairs and Chief Medical Officer
CIO: Robb Baldauf, Coordinator Information Systems
CHR: Lynn Moraca, Director Human Resources
CNO: Dana Kocsis, Vice President, Nursing and Operations
Web address: www.lodihospital.org
**Control**: Other not–for–profit (including NFP Corporation) **Service**: General medical and surgical

**Staffed Beds**: 20 **Admissions**: 224 **Census**: 6 **Outpatient Visits**: 24725 **Births**: 0 **Total Expense ($000)**: 15707 **Payroll Expense ($000)**: 7616 **Personnel**: 97

**LODI COMMUNITY HOSPITAL** See Cleveland Clinic Akron General Lodi Hospital

## LOGAN—Hocking County

✖ **HOCKING VALLEY COMMUNITY HOSPITAL (361330)**, 601 State Route 664 North, Zip 43138–8541, Mailing Address: P.O. Box 966, Zip 43138–0966; tel. 740/380–8000, (Nonreporting) **A**1 10 18 **F**3 8 11 15 28 29 30 31 34 40 56 57 59 64 70 75 77 79 81 82 85 86 87 93 98 103 107 111 114 118 119 127 129 130 133 135 144 146 147 148 152 154 156
Primary Contact: Stacey Gabriel, R.N., President and Chief Executive Officer
CFO: Julie E Grow, Chief Financial Officer
CMO: Duane Mast, M.D., Medical Director
CIO: John Burgess, Director Information Services
CHR: Robert F Schmidt, Director Human Resources
CNO: Janelle Hicks, R.N., Vice President Patient Services
Web address: www.hvch.org
**Control**: County, Government, Nonfederal **Service**: General medical and surgical

**Staffed Beds**: 35 **Admissions**: 852 **Census**: 17 **Outpatient Visits**: 231388 **Births**: 0 **Total Expense ($000)**: 41500 **Payroll Expense ($000)**: 12792 **Personnel**: 259

## LONDON—Madison County

**MADISON COUNTY HOSPITAL** See Madison Health

✖ **MADISON HEALTH (360189)**, 210 North Main Street, Zip 43140–1115; tel. 740/845–7000, (Nonreporting) **A**1 10 **F**3 11 13 15 18 29 30 31 34 35 40 45 50 53 57 59 64 68 70 75 76 77 78 79 81 85 89 93 97 107 108 110 111 114 118 119 129 130 131 132 135 146 **P**6
Primary Contact: Dana E. Engle, Chief Executive Officer
CFO: Michael Browning, Chief Financial Officer
CMO: Bernard Oppong, D.O., Chief of Staff
CIO: Dennis Vogt, Director Information Technology
CHR: Becky Rozell, Vice President, Human Resources
CNO: Jennifer Piccione, Chief Nursing and Clinical Services Officer
Web address: www.madison-health.com
**Control**: Other not–for–profit (including NFP Corporation) **Service**: General medical and surgical

**Staffed Beds**: 53 **Admissions**: 1272 **Census**: 10 **Outpatient Visits**: 57226 **Births**: 232 **Total Expense ($000)**: 44141 **Payroll Expense ($000)**: 16643 **Personnel**: 375

## LORAIN—Lorain County

☐ **CLEARVISTA HEALTH AND WELLNESS (364052)**, 3364 Kolbe Road, Zip 44053–1628; tel. 440/960–7960, (Nonreporting) **A**1
Primary Contact: Cecile M. Mahr, Chief Executive Officer
Web address: www.clearvistahealth.com
**Control**: Corporation, Investor–owned (for–profit) **Service**: Psychiatric

**Staffed Beds**: 30

**COMMUNITY HEALTH PARTNERS REGIONAL MEDICAL CENTER** See Mercy Regional Medical Center

☐ △ **MERCY REGIONAL MEDICAL CENTER (360172)**, 3700 Kolbe Road, Zip 44053–1697; tel. 440/960–4000, (Nonreporting) **A**1 2 7 10 **S** Mercy Health, Cincinnati, OH
Primary Contact: Edwin M. Oley, President and Chief Executive Officer
CMO: Sam El-Dalati, M.D., Chief Medical Officer
CHR: JC Fischer, Director Human Resources
CNO: Catherine Walsh, Interim Nursing Executive
Web address: www.community-health-partners.com
**Control**: Church operated, Nongovernment, not–for–profit **Service**: General medical and surgical

**Staffed Beds:** 259

---

### MANSFIELD—Richland County

**MANSFIELD GENERAL HOSPITAL** See Mansfield Hospital

**MEDCENTRAL - MANSFIELD HOSPITAL** See Ohiohealth Medcentral Mansfield Hospital

☒ **OHIOHEALTH MEDCENTRAL MANSFIELD HOSPITAL (360118)**, 335 Glessner Avenue, Zip 44903–2265; tel. 419/526–8000, (Includes MANSFIELD HOSPITAL, Mailing address: 335 Glessner Avenue, Mansfield, Ohio, Zip 44903–2265; tel. 419/526–8000), (Nonreporting) **A**1 2 3 5 10 **F**3 8 11 13 15 17 18 20 22 24 26 28 29 30 31 34 40 42 43 45 46 47 48 50 51 53 54 57 58 59 61 62 63 64 65 67 68 70 74 75 76 77 78 79 80 81 84 85 86 89 90 91 92 93 96 97 98 99 100 101 102 104 107 108 110 111 115 116 117 119 120 121 126 129 130 131 132 135 146 147 148 149 153 154 156 **S** OhioHealth, Columbus, OH
Primary Contact: Vinson Yates, President
CFO: Joseph Lyren, Chief Financial Officer
CMO: Terry Weston, M.D., Vice President Physician Services
CIO: Cindy Sheets, Vice President Information Systems and Chief Information Officer
CHR: Beth Hildreth, Vice President Human Resources
CNO: Pam Crawford, R.N., Ph.D., Vice President of Nursing and Chief Nursing Officer
Web address: www.medcentral.org
**Control**: Church operated, Nongovernment, not–for–profit **Service**: General medical and surgical

**Staffed Beds:** 249 **Admissions:** 10818 **Census:** 144 **Outpatient Visits:** 305813 **Births:** 881 **Total Expense ($000):** 266033 **Payroll Expense ($000):** 101999 **Personnel:** 1531

---

### MARIETTA—Washington County

★ ○ **MARIETTA MEMORIAL HOSPITAL (360147)**, 401 Matthew Street, Zip 45750–1699; tel. 740/374–1400, (Nonreporting) **A**2 3 5 10 11 19 **S** Memorial Health System, Marietta, OH
Primary Contact: J Scott. Cantley, President and Chief Executive Officer
CFO: Eric L Young, Vice President Finance and Chief Financial Officer
CMO: Matthew Macatol, M.D., President Medical Staff
CHR: Dee Ann Gehlauf, Senior Vice President Business and Organization Development
Web address: www.mhsystem.org
**Control**: Other not–for–profit (including NFP Corporation) **Service**: General medical and surgical

**Staffed Beds:** 218

★ ○ △ **SELBY GENERAL HOSPITAL (361319)**, 1106 Colegate Drive, Zip 45750–1323; tel. 740/568–2000, (Nonreporting) **A**7 10 11 18 **F**11 29 34 40 42 59 69 79 81 87 90 107 116 117 119 133 147 148 **S** Memorial Health System, Marietta, OH
Primary Contact: Paige Leann. Smith, President
CFO: Eric L Young, Chief Financial Officer
CMO: David Spears, D.O., Chief of Staff
CHR: Tricia A Engfehr, Chief Human Resources
CNO: Misti Spencer, Director Inpatient Services
Web address: www.selbygeneral.org
**Control**: Other not–for–profit (including NFP Corporation) **Service**: General medical and surgical

**Staffed Beds:** 35 **Admissions:** 1139 **Census:** 15 **Outpatient Visits:** 22091 **Births:** 0 **Total Expense ($000):** 41478 **Payroll Expense ($000):** 11162

---

### MARION—Marion County

**MARION GENERAL HOSPITAL** See Ohiohealth Marion General Hospital

---

☒ **OHIOHEALTH MARION GENERAL HOSPITAL (360011)**, 1000 McKinley Park Drive, Zip 43302–6397; tel. 740/383–8400, (Nonreporting) **A**1 2 10 19 **F**3 8 13 15 18 20 22 26 28 29 30 31 35 40 53 54 57 59 60 63 64 68 70 72 74 75 76 77 78 79 81 82 84 87 89 93 94 98 104 105 107 111 114 116 119 126 129 130 132 135 146 147 148 149 153 154 **S** OhioHealth, Columbus, OH
Primary Contact: Curtis Gingrich, M.D., Chief Operating Officer
CIO: Chris King, Director Information Services
CHR: Gianna Ferrarotti, Director Human Resources North Region
Web address: www.ohiohealth.com/mariongeneral
**Control**: Church operated, Nongovernment, not–for–profit **Service**: General medical and surgical

**Staffed Beds:** 229 **Admissions:** 7157 **Census:** 82 **Outpatient Visits:** 290583 **Births:** 873 **Total Expense ($000):** 204945 **Payroll Expense ($000):** 77895 **Personnel:** 1083

---

### MARYSVILLE—Union County

★ **MEMORIAL HEALTH (360092)**, 500 London Avenue, Zip 43040–1594; tel. 937/644–6115, (Nonreporting) **A**10 **F**3 8 11 13 15 18 20 28 29 30 31 32 34 35 38 40 45 48 49 50 51 53 54 56 57 59 60 62 64 69 74 75 76 77 78 79 80 81 82 85 86 87 91 92 93 96 100 107 108 110 111 114 115 116 118 119 120 124 129 130 131 132 135 144 145 146 148 149 150 152 156 **P**6
Primary Contact: Olas A. Hubbs III, FACHE, President and Chief Executive Officer
COO: Laurie A Whittington, Chief Operating Officer
CFO: Jeffrey Ehlers, Chief Financial Officer
CMO: Matthew Hazelbaker, M.D., President Medical Staff
CIO: Carl Zani, Chief Technology Director
CHR: Larry C Schleeter, Chief Human Resources Officer
CNO: Robin Slattman, Chief Nursing Officer
Web address: www.memorialhosp.org
**Control**: County, Government, Nonfederal **Service**: General medical and surgical

**Staffed Beds:** 74 **Admissions:** 2083 **Census:** 16 **Outpatient Visits:** 138101 **Births:** 593 **Total Expense ($000):** 127181 **Payroll Expense ($000):** 42960 **Personnel:** 628

**MEMORIAL HOSPITAL OF UNION COUNTY** See Memorial Health

---

### MASON—Warren County

☐ **LINDNER CENTER OF HOPE (364044)**, 4075 Old Western Row Road, Zip 45040–3104; tel. 513/536–0311, (Nonreporting) **A**1 2 3 10
Primary Contact: Paul Keck, M.D., President and Chief Executive Officer
COO: Brian Owens, Chief Operating Officer
CFO: David McAdams, Chief Financial Officer
CIO: Cliff McClintick, Chief Information Officer
CHR: Debbie A Strawser, Director Human Resources
Web address: www.lindnercenterofhope.org
**Control**: Other not–for–profit (including NFP Corporation) **Service**: Psychiatric

**Staffed Beds:** 48

**THE LINDNER CENTER OF HOPE** See Lindner Center of Hope

---

### MASSILLON—Stark County

☐ **HEARTLAND BEHAVIORAL HEALTHCARE (364031)**, 3000 Erie Stree South, Zip 44646–7993, Mailing Address: 3000 Erie Street South, Zip 44646–7976; tel. 330/833–3135, (Nonreporting) **A**1 3 5 10 **S** Ohio Department of Mental Health, Columbus, OH
Primary Contact: Jeffrey Sims, Chief Executive Officer
CFO: Patricia Eddleman, Fiscal Officer
CMO: Steven Thomson, M.D., Medical Director
CIO: Robert Hobart, Director Management Information Systems
CHR: Jerald Wilhite, Administrator Human Resources
Web address: www.mh.state.oh.us/ibhs/bhos/hoh.html
**Control**: State, Government, Nonfederal **Service**: Psychiatric

**Staffed Beds:** 152

**MASSILLON PSYCHIATRIC CENTER** See Heartland Behavioral Healthcare

---

### MAUMEE—Lucas County

☐ **ARROWHEAD BEHAVIORAL HEALTH HOSPITAL (364036)**, 1725 Timber Line Road, Zip 43537–4015; tel. 419/891–9333, (Nonreporting) **A**1 10 **S** Universal Health Services, Inc., King of Prussia, PA
Primary Contact: Theresa Contreras, Chief Executive Officer
CFO: Allison Duncan, Chief Financial Officer
CMO: Kenneth Adler, M.D., Medical Director
CIO: Peggy Montgomery, Director Medical Records
CHR: Dawn Bosworth, Director Human Resources
CNO: Anita Zych, Director of Nursing
Web address: www.arrowheadbehavioral.com
**Control**: Corporation, Investor–owned (for–profit) **Service**: Psychiatric

**Staffed Beds:** 48

**CHARTER HOSPITAL OF TOLEDO** See Arrowhead Behavioral Health Hospital

⇑ **PROMEDICA ST. LUKE'S HOSPITAL** See St. Luke's Hospital

⇑ **ST. LUKE'S HOSPITAL (360090)**, 5901 Monclova Road, Zip 43537–1899; tel. 419/893–5911, (Nonreporting) **A**3 5 10 21
Primary Contact: Jennifer Montgomery, President and Chief Executive Officer
CMO: Stephen Bazeley, M.D., Vice President Medical Affairs
CIO: Patricia Swint, Director Information Technology
CHR: Connie Sessler, Director Human Resources
CNO: Jill A. Trosin, R.N., MSN, Vice President Patient Care Services, Chief Nursing Officer
Web address: www.stlukeshospital.com
**Control:** Other not–for–profit (including NFP Corporation) **Service:** General medical and surgical

| Staffed Beds: 170 |
| --- |

### MEDINA—Medina County

⊠ **CLEVELAND CLINIC, MEDINA HOSPITAL (360091)**, 1000 East Washington Street, Zip 44256–2170; tel. 330/725–1000, (Nonreporting) **A**1 2 3 5 10 **F**3 7 8 15 18 20 28 29 30 31 34 35 40 47 49 50 51 57 59 60 64 70 74 75 77 78 79 81 82 85 86 93 96 107 111 115 117 119 129 130 131 132 133 135 146 148 154 **P**6 **S** Cleveland Clinic Health System, Cleveland, OH
Primary Contact: Richard K. Shewbridge, President
COO: Vicky Snyder, Chief Operating Officer
CFO: Becky Molnar, Director of Finance
CMO: Matthew Vrobel, Vice President, Medical Operations
CIO: Frank Longley, Business Partner Information Technology
CHR: Tracie Curtis, Business Partner Human Resources
CNO: Julie Fetto, R.N., Chief Nursing Officer
Web address: www.medinahospital.org
**Control:** Other not–for–profit (including NFP Corporation) **Service:** General medical and surgical

| Staffed Beds: 148 Admissions: 6451 Census: 69 Outpatient Visits: 78253 Births: 0 Total Expense ($000): 118539 Payroll Expense ($000): 43340 Personnel: 663 |
| --- |

**MEDINA HOSPITAL** See Cleveland Clinic, Medina Hospital

### MIAMISBURG—Montgomery County

**KETTERING MEDICAL CENTER-SYCAMORE** See Sycamore Medical Center

**LIFECARE HOSPITAL OF DAYTON** See Pam Specialty Hospital of Dayton

⊠ **PAM SPECIALTY HOSPITAL OF DAYTON (362028)**, 4000 Miamisburg-Centerville Road, Zip 45342–7615; tel. 937/384–8300, (Data for 92 days) (Nonreporting) **A**1 10 **F**1 12 29 120 148 154 **S** Post Acute Medical, LLC, Enola, PA
Primary Contact: Karla Cody, Chief Executive Officer
CMO: Richard Gregg, M.D., Medical Director
Web address: www.https://postacutemedical.com
**Control:** Corporation, Investor–owned (for–profit) **Service:** Acute long–term care hospital

| Staffed Beds: 44 Admissions: 98 Census: 32 Outpatient Visits: 0 Births: 0 Total Expense ($000): 4172 Payroll Expense ($000): 1724 Personnel: 130 |
| --- |

★ ◯ **SYCAMORE MEDICAL CENTER (360239)**, 4000 Miamisburg-Centerville Road, Zip 45342–7615; tel. 937/866–0551, (Includes KETTERING BEHAVIORAL MEDICAL CENTER, Mailing address: 5350 Lamme Road, Dayton, Ohio, Zip 45439; tel. 937/534–4600; Jason Brown, Director), (Nonreporting) **A**10 11 **F**3 8 12 15 19 20 34 35 38 40 41 42 45 49 53 54 56 60 64 68 70 74 75 78 79 81 82 84 85 86 87 91 92 93 96 97 98 100 101 102 103 104 105 107 108 110 111 114 115 119 125 129 130 131 132 143 146 147 148 149 153 154 156 157 **S** Kettering Health Network, Dayton, OH
Primary Contact: Walter Sackett, President
CMO: Robert T. Smith, M.D., Chief Medical Officer
CIO: Andy Lehman, Senior Vice President Technology and Analytics
CHR: Derek Morgan, Vice President Human Resources
Web address: www.khnetwork.org/sycamore
**Control:** Church operated, Nongovernment, not–for–profit **Service:** General medical and surgical

| Staffed Beds: 168 Admissions: 8890 Census: 91 Outpatient Visits: 147358 Births: 0 Total Expense ($000): 194059 Payroll Expense ($000): 69573 Personnel: 830 |
| --- |

### MIDDLE POINT—Van Wert County

☐ **RIDGEVIEW BEHAVIORAL HOSPITAL (364047)**, 17872 Lincoln Highway, Zip 45863–9700; tel. 419/968–2950, (Nonreporting) **A**1 10 **S** Oglethorpe Recovery and Behavioral Hospitals, Tampa, FL
Primary Contact: Pat Tracy, Administrator
Web address: www.ridgeviewhospital.net/
**Control:** Corporation, Investor–owned (for–profit) **Service:** Psychiatric

| Staffed Beds: 40 |
| --- |

### MIDDLEBURG HEIGHTS—Cuyahoga County

**SOUTHWEST COMM HLTH SYSTEM** See Southwest General Health Center

☐ **SOUTHWEST GENERAL HEALTH CENTER (360155)**, 18697 Bagley Road, Zip 44130–3497; tel. 440/816–8000, (Nonreporting) **A**1 2 3 5 10
Primary Contact: William A. Young Jr, President and Chief Executive Officer
COO: Bradley W. Rauh, Vice President, Chief Operating Officer
CFO: Mary Ann Freas, Senior Vice President and Chief Financial Officer
CMO: Marilyn McNamara, M.D., Chief Medical Officer
CIO: Alec Williams, Chief Information Officer
CHR: Dee Weber, Vice President Human Resources
CNO: Martha F. Bauschka, R.N., Vice President and Chief Nursing Officer
Web address: www.swgeneral.com
**Control:** Other not–for–profit (including NFP Corporation) **Service:** General medical and surgical

| Staffed Beds: 252 |
| --- |

### MIDDLETOWN—Warren County

⊠ △ **ATRIUM MEDICAL CENTER (360076)**, One Medical Center Drive, Zip 45005–1066; tel. 513/424–2111, (Nonreporting) **A**1 2 3 7 10 **F**3 8 11 13 15 17 18 20 22 24 26 28 29 30 31 32 34 35 36 38 39 40 41 43 44 45 46 48 49 50 54 55 56 57 58 59 61 63 64 65 66 68 70 71 73 74 75 76 77 78 79 80 81 82 84 85 86 87 90 91 92 93 96 98 100 101 102 103 107 108 110 111 114 115 118 119 126 130 131 132 134 135 141 146 147 148 149 154 156 157 **P**6 **S** Premier Health, Dayton, OH
Primary Contact: Michael Uhl, President
CMO: Matthew Reeves, D.O., EsqChief Medical Officer
CHR: Ted Ripperger, Administrative Director Human Resources
CNO: Marquita Turner, Chief Operating Officer and Chief Nursing Officer
Web address: www.PremierHealth.com
**Control:** Other not–for–profit (including NFP Corporation) **Service:** General medical and surgical

| Staffed Beds: 129 Admissions: 8920 Census: 105 Outpatient Visits: 216396 Births: 914 Total Expense ($000): 204751 Payroll Expense ($000): 77261 Personnel: 1301 |
| --- |

**MIDDLETOWN REGIONAL HOSPITAL** See Atrium Medical Center

### MILLERSBURG—Holmes County

**POMERENE HOSPITAL (360148)**, 981 Wooster Road, Zip 44654–1094; tel. 330/674–1015, (Nonreporting) **A**10 22 **F**3 11 13 15 18 28 29 30 34 35 40 50 53 55 57 59 70 75 76 77 79 81 85 86 87 89 93 107 108 110 115 119 127 130 131 132 135 143 144 146 147 149
Primary Contact: Jason Justus, Chief Executive Officer
CFO: Tia A Cernava, Chief Financial Officer
CMO: Yasser Omran, M.D., President Medical Staff
CIO: Brent Edington, Director Information Services
CHR: Kim Croft, R.N., Executive Director Human Resources
CNO: Fran Lauriha, Chief Nursing Officer
Web address: www.pomerenehospital.org
**Control:** Other not–for–profit (including NFP Corporation) **Service:** General medical and surgical

| Staffed Beds: 41 Admissions: 1510 Census: 13 Outpatient Visits: 40423 Births: 515 Total Expense ($000): 29180 Payroll Expense ($000): 11377 Personnel: 260 |
| --- |

**POMERENE MEMORIAL HOSPITAL** See Pomerene Hospital

---

**Hospital, Medicare Provider Number, Address, Telephone, Approval, Facility, and Physician Codes, Health Care System**

★ American Hospital Association (AHA) membership
☐ The Joint Commission accreditation
◯ Healthcare Facilities Accreditation Program
◇ DNV Healthcare Inc. accreditation
⇑ Center for Improvement in Healthcare Quality Accreditation
△ Commission on Accreditation of Rehabilitation Facilities (CARF) accreditation

**OH**

## MONTPELIER—Williams County

**COMMUNITY HOSPITALS AND WELLNESS CENTERS** See Community Hospitals and Wellness Centers-Montpelier

**COMMUNITY HOSPITALS AND WELLNESS CENTERS-MONTPELIER (361327)**, 909 East Snyder Avenue, Zip 43543–1251; tel. 419/636–1131, (Nonreporting) **A**10 18
Primary Contact: Chad Tinkel, President and Chief Executive Officer
Web address: www.https://www.chwchospital.com
**Control**: Corporation, Investor–owned (for–profit) **Service**: General medical and surgical

**Staffed Beds:** 35

**MONTPELIER HOSPITAL** See Community Hospitals and Wellness Centers, Bryan

**WILLIAMS COUNTY GEN HOSPITAL** See Montpelier Hospital

## MOUNT GILEAD—Morrow County

✉ **MORROW COUNTY HOSPITAL (361313)**, 651 West Marion Road, Zip 43338–1027; tel. 419/946–5015, (Nonreporting) **A**1 10 18 **S** OhioHealth, Columbus, OH
Primary Contact: Chad J. Miller, President and Chief Executive Officer
CFO: Joe Schueler, Chief Financial Officer
Web address: www.morrowcountyhospital.com
**Control**: County, Government, Nonfederal **Service**: General medical and surgical

**Staffed Beds:** 22

## MOUNT VERNON—Knox County

✉ **KNOX COMMUNITY HOSPITAL (360040)**, 1330 Coshocton Road, Zip 43050–1495; tel. 740/393–9000, (Nonreporting) **A**1 2 10 20 **F**3 5 11 12 13 15 18 20 22 26 28 29 31 34 35 36 40 41 44 45 46 48 49 50 53 57 59 62 64 68 69 70 74 75 76 77 78 79 81 82 83 84 85 86 87 93 94 96 97 104 107 108 110 111 112 113 114 115 118 119 120 121 123 129 130 131 132 144 146 147 149 150 154 156 157 **P**6 **S** QHR Health, Brentwood, TN
Primary Contact: Bruce D. White, Chief Executive Officer
COO: Bruce M Behner, Chief Operating Officer
CFO: Michael Ambrosiani, Chief Financial Officer
CMO: Jeffrey Northup, D.O., Chief Medical Officer
CIO: Kwi Holland, Vice President Information Services
CHR: Lisa Bragg, Vice President Human Resources
CNO: James Middleton, MSN, R.N., Chief Nursing Officer
Web address: www.kch.org
**Control**: Other not–for–profit (including NFP Corporation) **Service**: General medical and surgical

**Staffed Beds:** 71 **Admissions:** 3123 **Census:** 30 **Outpatient Visits:** 149482 **Births:** 407 **Total Expense ($000):** 174653 **Payroll Expense ($000):** 82126 **Personnel:** 1100

## NAPOLEON—Henry County

★ ⚕ **HENRY COUNTY HOSPITAL (361309)**, 1600 East Riverview Avenue, Zip 43545–9399; tel. 419/592–4015, (Nonreporting) **A**5 10 18 21 **F**3 5 11 13 15 28 29 30 31 34 35 36 40 45 50 53 57 59 64 65 68 70 75 76 77 78 79 81 82 85 86 87 93 100 101 104 107 108 110 114 119 130 132 133 135 146 148 149 156
Primary Contact: Kristi Barnd, Interim Chief Executive Officer
COO: Kristi Barnd, Chief Operating Officer
CFO: Diane Walther, Controller
CIO: William Grimm, Chief Information Officer
CHR: Jennifer A Fisher, Manager Human Resources
CNO: Patricia Frank, Chief Nursing Officer
Web address: www.henrycountyhospital.org
**Control**: Other not–for–profit (including NFP Corporation) **Service**: General medical and surgical

**Staffed Beds:** 25 **Admissions:** 698 **Census:** 7 **Outpatient Visits:** 60556 **Births:** 199 **Total Expense ($000):** 32808 **Payroll Expense ($000):** 13094 **Personnel:** 221

## NEW ALBANY—Franklin County

✉ **MOUNT CARMEL NEW ALBANY SURGICAL HOSPITAL (360266)**, 7333 Smith's Mill Road, Zip 43054–9291; tel. 614/775–6600, (Nonreporting) **A**1 3 5 10 **F**3 29 34 35 37 44 57 58 59 64 65 68 74 75 79 81 85 86 87 107 111 114 119 141 146 **P**1 **S** Trinity Health, Livonia, MI
Primary Contact: Diane Doucette, R.N., President
Web address: www.mountcarmelhealth.com
**Control**: Church operated, Nongovernment, not–for–profit **Service**: Surgical

**Staffed Beds:** 60 **Admissions:** 3679 **Census:** 16 **Outpatient Visits:** 15831 **Births:** 0 **Total Expense ($000):** 82273 **Payroll Expense ($000):** 15698 **Personnel:** 247

**NEW ALBANY SURGICAL HOSPITAL** See Mount Carmel New Albany Surgical Hospital

## NEWARK—Licking County

☐ ⚕ **LICKING MEMORIAL HOSPITAL (360218)**, 1320 West Main Street, Zip 43055–3699; tel. 740/348–4000, (Nonreporting) **A**1 2 10 21 **F**3 4 5 13 15 18 20 22 28 29 30 31 32 34 35 40 41 45 46 48 49 50 53 57 59 62 64 65 68 70 71 72 74 75 76 77 78 79 81 82 85 86 89 90 92 93 97 98 100 101 102 104 107 108 110 111 114 115 116 117 118 119 129 130 131 132 135 144 146 147 148 152 154 156 **P**6
Primary Contact: Robert A. Montagnese, President and Chief Executive Officer
CFO: Cindy Webster, Vice President Financial Services
CMO: Craig Cairns, M.D., Vice President Medical Affairs
CIO: Sallie Arnett, Vice President Information Systems
CHR: Anne Peterson, Vice President Human Resources and Support Services
Web address: www.lmhealth.org
**Control**: Other not–for–profit (including NFP Corporation) **Service**: General medical and surgical

**Staffed Beds:** 227 **Admissions:** 7831 **Census:** 76 **Outpatient Visits:** 312777 **Births:** 988 **Total Expense ($000):** 202946 **Payroll Expense ($000):** 83627 **Personnel:** 1530

✉ **SELECT SPECIALTY HOSPITAL OF SOUTHEAST OHIO (362031)**, 2000 Tamarack Road, Zip 43055; tel. 740/588–7888, (Nonreporting) **A**1 10 **S** Select Medical Corporation, Mechanicsburg, PA
Primary Contact: Linda Supplee, Chief Executive Officer
CMO: Armand Bermudez, M.D., Medical Director
CHR: Jacqueline Nezbeth, Human Resources Officer
CNO: Taryn Vierling, Chief Nursing Officer
Web address: www.selectspecialtyhospitals.com/company/locations/zanesville.aspx
**Control**: Corporation, Investor–owned (for–profit) **Service**: Acute long–term care hospital

**Staffed Beds:** 35

**SELECT SPECIALTY HOSPITAL-ZANESVILLE** See Select Specialty Hospital of Southeast Ohio

## NORTHFIELD—Summit County

☐ **NORTHCOAST BEHAVIORAL HEALTHCARE (364011)**, 1756 Sagamore Road, Zip 44067–1086; tel. 330/467–7131, (Nonreporting) **A**1 5 10 **S** Ohio Department of Mental Health, Columbus, OH
Primary Contact: Douglas W. Kern, Chief Executive Officer
CIO: Karl Donenwirth, Vice President Information Services
Web address: www.mha.ohio.gov
**Control**: State, Government, Nonfederal **Service**: Psychiatric

**Staffed Beds:** 258

**NORTHCOAST BEHAVIORAL HEALTHCARE SYSTEM** See Northcoast Behavioral Healthcare

## NORWALK—Huron County

★ ○ **FISHER-TITUS MEDICAL CENTER (360065)**, 272 Benedict Avenue, Zip 44857–2374; tel. 419/668–8101, (Total facility includes 69 beds in nursing home–type unit) (Nonreporting) **A**2 3 5 10 11 19 **F**3 10 11 13 15 18 20 22 26 28 29 31 32 34 35 36 38 40 43 44 45 48 49 50 51 55 56 57 59 61 62 64 65 68 70 74 75 76 77 78 79 81 82 84 85 86 87 92 93 94 96 107 108 110 111 115 118 119 126 128 129 130 131 132 135 143 146 147 148 149 154 156 **P**6
Primary Contact: Brent Burkey, M.D., President and Chief Executive Officer
COO: Matthew Mattner, Chief Operations Officer
CFO: Scott Endsley, Chief Financial Officer
CMO: Gary L Moorman, D.O., Chief Medical Officer
CIO: Linda Stevenson, Chief Information Officer
CHR: Miriam Batke, Interim Chief Human Resource Officer
CNO: Katie Chieda, Chief Nursing Officer
Web address: www.fisher-titus.org
**Control**: Other not–for–profit (including NFP Corporation) **Service**: General medical and surgical

**Staffed Beds:** 147 **Admissions:** 3839 **Census:** 91 **Outpatient Visits:** 179986 **Births:** 444 **Total Expense ($000):** 121418 **Payroll Expense ($000):** 49659 **Personnel:** 972

## OBERLIN—Lorain County

**ALLEN COMMUNITY HOSPITAL** See Mercy Allen Hospital

*Many Facility Codes have changed. Please refer to the AHA Guide Code Chart.* © 2021 AHA Guide

☐ **MERCY ALLEN HOSPITAL (361306)**, 200 West Lorain Street, Zip 44074–1077; tel. 440/775–1211, (Nonreporting) **A**1 10 18 **S** Mercy Health, Cincinnati, OH
Primary Contact: Ed Ruth, President
COO: Ken Hale, Executive Director of Operations
CFO: Cynthia Dennison, Chief Financial Officer
CMO: Rafik Massouh, M.D., Chief of Staff
CHR: Kathy Dolbin, Director of Human Resources
CNO: Cheryl Rieves, Chief Nurse Executive Lorain Region
Web address: www.mercyonline.org/mercy_allen_hospital.aspx
**Control**: Other not–for–profit (including NFP Corporation) **Service**: General medical and surgical

| Staffed Beds: 25 |
|---|

### ONTARIO—Richland County

★ ⇑ **AVITA ONTARIO HOSPITAL (360365)**, 715 Richland Mall, Zip 44906–3802; tel. 567/307–7666, (Nonreporting) **A**10 21 **S** Avita Health System, Galion, OH
Primary Contact: Jerome Morasko, President and Chief Executive Officer
CFO: D. Eric Draime, Vice President and Chief Financial Officer
CIO: Alex Reed, Chief Information Officer
CHR: Traci L Oswald, Vice President, Chief Human Resources
CNO: Kathy Durflinger, Vice President and Chief Nursing Officer
Web address: www.avitahealth.org
**Control**: Other not–for–profit (including NFP Corporation) **Service**: General medical and surgical

| Staffed Beds: 26 |
|---|

### OREGON—Lucas County

**BAY PARK COMMUNITY HOSPITAL** See Promedica Bay Park Hospital

☐ △ **MERCY HEALTH - ST. CHARLES HOSPITAL (360081)**, 2600 Navarre Avenue, Zip 43616–3297; tel. 419/696–7200, (Nonreporting) **A**1 2 3 5 7 10 **S** Mercy Health, Cincinnati, OH
Primary Contact: Craig Albers, President and Chief Operating Officer
COO: Craig Albers, President and Chief Operating Officer
CFO: Mark Thompson, Market Chief Financial Officer Northern Region and Chief Financial Officer
CMO: Riaz Chaudhry, M.D., Chief Medical Officer
CIO: Rebecca S Sykes, Senior Vice President Resource Management, Chief Information Officer
Web address: www.mercyweb.org
**Control**: Church operated, Nongovernment, not–for–profit **Service**: General medical and surgical

| Staffed Beds: 279 |
|---|

**MERCY ST. CHARLES HOSPITAL** See Mercy Health - St. Charles Hospital

⊞ **PROMEDICA BAY PARK HOSPITAL (360259)**, 2801 Bay Park Drive, Zip 43616–4920; tel. 419/690–7900, (Nonreporting) **A**1 10 **F**3 11 13 15 18 28 29 30 31 34 35 40 45 49 50 54 57 59 64 68 70 74 75 76 77 78 79 81 82 85 86 92 93 97 107 108 110 111 114 118 119 124 126 129 130 131 132 134 135 143 146 147 148 149 154 156 **P**6 **S** ProMedica Health System, Toledo, OH
Primary Contact: Neeraj Kanwal, M.D., Interim President, Metro Region
COO: Darrell Wachowiak, Associate Vice President Operations
CFO: Scott Fought, Vice President Finance
CMO: David Lindstrom, M.D., Vice President Medical Affairs
CIO: Rose Ann Laureto, Corporate Vice President Information Resources
CHR: Kara Zimmerly, Manager Human Resources
Web address: www.promedica.org
**Control**: Other not–for–profit (including NFP Corporation) **Service**: General medical and surgical

| Staffed Beds: 44 Admissions: 3416 Census: 32 Outpatient Visits: 105897 Births: 550 Total Expense ($000): 79248 Payroll Expense ($000): 22259 Personnel: 396 |
|---|

### ORRVILLE—Wayne County

⊞ **AULTMAN ORRVILLE HOSPITAL (361323)**, 832 South Main Street, Zip 44667–2208; tel. 330/682–3010, (Nonreporting) **A**1 10 18 **F**3 8 9 11 12 13 14 15 28 29 30 34 35 40 45 49 50 51 53 55 57 59 68 71 75 76 77 79 81 82 85 86 87 93 107 108 110 111 112 114 115 118 119 126 127 129 130 131 132 133 135 143 146 147 152 154 156 **P**8 **S** Aultman Health Foundation, Canton, OH
Primary Contact: Jennifer Kessel, Chief Executive Officer
CFO: Adam Luntz, Chief Financial Officer
CIO: Vince Logozzo, Director Information Technology
CNO: Angela McGee, Vice President Nursing Services
Web address: www.aultmanorrville.org
**Control**: Other not–for–profit (including NFP Corporation) **Service**: General medical and surgical

| Staffed Beds: 25 Admissions: 1096 Census: 8 Outpatient Visits: 39377 Births: 489 Total Expense ($000): 29699 Payroll Expense ($000): 12149 Personnel: 215 |
|---|

**DUNLAP COMMUNITY HOSPITAL** See Aultman Orrville Hospital

### OXFORD—Butler County

**MCCULLOUGH-HYDE MEMORIAL HOSPITAL** See Mccullough-Hyde Memorial Hospital/Trihealth

★ ○ **MCCULLOUGH-HYDE MEMORIAL HOSPITAL/TRIHEALTH (360046)**, 110 North Poplar Street, Zip 45056–1292; tel. 513/523–2111, (Nonreporting) **A**2 10 11 **F**3 11 13 15 18 28 29 30 31 34 35 36 40 45 47 50 54 57 59 64 68 69 70 75 76 77 78 79 81 82 84 85 86 87 93 102 107 108 110 111 114 119 129 130 131 132 144 146 147 149 154 156 **P**6 8
Primary Contact: Brett Kirkpatrick, Executive Director
CFO: John R Clements, Chief Financial Officer
CMO: Amy Spivey, Chief Medical Officer
CHR: Sharon Hancock, Chief Human Resources Officer
CNO: Pamela Collins, Vice President Chief Patient Services Officer
Web address: www.mhmh.org
**Control**: Other not–for–profit (including NFP Corporation) **Service**: General medical and surgical

| Staffed Beds: 48 Admissions: 2091 Census: 17 Outpatient Visits: 58134 Births: 408 Total Expense ($000): 51911 Payroll Expense ($000): 18997 Personnel: 316 |
|---|

### PARMA—Cuyahoga County

**PARMA COMMUNITY GENERAL HOSPITAL** See University Hospitals Parma Medical Center

⊞ △ **UNIVERSITY HOSPITALS PARMA MEDICAL CENTER (360041)**, 7007 Powers Boulevard, Zip 44129–5495; tel. 440/743–3000, (Nonreporting) **A**1 2 3 7 10 13 **F**3 11 12 15 17 18 20 22 24 26 28 29 30 31 34 35 36 40 43 44 45 48 49 50 51 53 54 56 57 58 59 60 62 64 65 68 69 70 71 74 75 77 78 79 81 82 84 85 86 87 90 92 93 94 96 97 98 100 101 103 107 108 111 114 115 116 117 119 120 121 129 130 131 132 135 143 145 146 147 148 149 154 **S** University Hospitals, Cleveland, OH
Primary Contact: Brian Monter, MSN, R.N., President
CMO: Christopher Loyke, Chief Medical Officer
CHR: Daniel Miller, Human Resources Business Partner
Web address: www.uhhospitals.org/parma
**Control**: Other not–for–profit (including NFP Corporation) **Service**: General medical and surgical

| Staffed Beds: 261 Admissions: 9123 Census: 111 Outpatient Visits: 191775 Births: 176 Total Expense ($000): 190562 Payroll Expense ($000): 60396 Personnel: 1006 |
|---|

### PAULDING—Paulding County

⊞ **PAULDING COUNTY HOSPITAL (361300)**, 1035 West Wayne Street, Zip 45879–1544; tel. 419/399–4080, (Nonreporting) **A**1 10 18
Primary Contact: Ronald Goedde, Chief Executive Officer
CFO: Rob Goshia, Chief Financial Officer
CMO: Wendell J Spangler, M.D., Chief of Staff
CIO: Dan Kaufman, Director Information Services
CHR: Melanie Rittenour, Director Human Resources
Web address: www.pauldingcountyhospital.com
**Control**: County, Government, Nonfederal **Service**: General medical and surgical

| Staffed Beds: 25 |
|---|

**OH**

### PORT CLINTON—Ottawa County

**H. B. MAGRUDER MEMORIAL HOSPITAL** See Magruder Memorial Hospital

✉ **MAGRUDER MEMORIAL HOSPITAL (361314)**, 615 Fulton Street, Zip 43452–2001; tel. 419/734–3131, (Nonreporting) **A**1 5 10 18 **F**3 11 15 18 28 29 31 34 35 40 44 45 46 48 50 53 57 59 64 65 68 70 75 77 78 79 81 82 85 86 87 89 93 107 108 110 115 118 119 129 130 131 132 133 135 144 146 147 148 149 156 **P**6 8
Primary Contact: J Todd. Almendinger, President and Chief Executive Officer
COO: Nick Marsico, Vice President and Chief Operating Officer
CFO: Julie Georgoff, Vice President of Finance and Chief Financial Officer
CHR: Jason Kraus, Director Human Resources
CNO: Kimberly D Schreiner, MSN, R.N., Vice President of Nursing & Chief Nursing Officer
Web address: www.magruderhospital.com
**Control:** Other not–for–profit (including NFP Corporation) **Service:** General medical and surgical

**Staffed Beds:** 25 **Admissions:** 393 **Census:** 3 **Outpatient Visits:** 125081 **Births:** 0 **Total Expense ($000):** 55001 **Payroll Expense ($000):** 25732 **Personnel:** 370

### PORTSMOUTH—Scioto County

**KINGS DAUGHTERS MEDICAL CENTER OHIO** See King's Daughters Medical Center Ohio

☐ **KING'S DAUGHTERS MEDICAL CENTER OHIO (360361)**, 2001 Scioto Trail, Zip 45662–2845; tel. 740/991–4000, (Nonreporting) **A**1 10
Primary Contact: Kim Grooms, Administrator
Web address: www.kdmcohio.com/
**Control:** Other not–for–profit (including NFP Corporation) **Service:** General medical and surgical

**Staffed Beds:** 10

✉ △ **SOUTHERN OHIO MEDICAL CENTER (360008)**, 1805 27th Street, Zip 45662–2640, Mailing Address: 1805 27th Street, Waller Building Suite B01, Zip 45662–2640; tel. 740/356–5000, (Nonreporting) **A**1 2 3 5 7 10 **F**3 11 13 15 17 18 20 22 24 26 28 29 30 31 34 35 37 38 40 41 44 45 46 47 48 49 50 53 54 57 59 62 63 64 65 70 74 75 76 77 78 79 81 82 83 84 85 86 87 90 92 97 100 104 107 108 109 110 111 114 115 116 117 118 119 120 121 122 123 124 129 130 131 132 135 145 146 147 149 152 154 156 157 **P**3
Primary Contact: Randal M. Arnett, President and Chief Executive Officer
CFO: Dean Wray, Vice President Finance
CMO: Kendall Stewart, M.D., Chief Medical Officer
CIO: Brent Richard, Administrative Director Information Systems
CHR: Vicki Noel, Vice President Human Resources
CNO: Claudia L Burchett, R.N., Vice President of Patient Services
Web address: www.somc.org
**Control:** Other not–for–profit (including NFP Corporation) **Service:** General medical and surgical

**Staffed Beds:** 248 **Admissions:** 12375 **Census:** 151 **Outpatient Visits:** 451502 **Births:** 1078 **Total Expense ($000):** 340150 **Payroll Expense ($000):** 128997 **Personnel:** 2581

**U S HLTH CORP OF SOUTHERN OHIO** See Southern Ohio Medical Center

### PROCTORVILLE—Lawrence County

☐ **THREE GABLES SURGERY CENTER (360261)**, 5897 County Road 107, Zip 45669–8852, Mailing Address: P.O. Box 490, Zip 45669–0490; tel. 740/886–9911, (Nonreporting) **A**1 10
Primary Contact: Tony Aluise, Chief Executive Officer
Web address: www.threegablessurgery.com
**Control:** Partnership, Investor–owned (for–profit) **Service:** Surgical

**Staffed Beds:** 8

### RAVENNA—Portage County

✉ **UH PORTAGE MEDICAL CENTER (360078)**, 6847 North Chestnut Street, Zip 44266–3929, Mailing Address: P.O. Box 1204, Zip 44266–1204; tel. 330/297–0811, (Nonreporting) **A**1 2 3 5 10 **F**3 11 13 15 18 20 22 26 28 29 30 31 34 35 36 40 42 43 44 45 46 47 48 49 50 51 54 56 57 58 59 60 64 65 68 70 74 75 76 77 78 79 81 82 84 85 87 89 92 93 100 107 108 109 110 111 115 117 119 129 130 131 132 135 143 144 145 146 147 148 149 154 156 **S** University Hospitals, Cleveland, OH
Primary Contact: William Benoit, President
CFO: Jen Hahn, Finance Manager
CMO: Benjamin Prestegaard, Chief Medical Officer
CIO: Rhonda Smith, Applications Support Manager
CHR: Neil Everett, Vice President Human Resources
Web address: www.uhportage.org
**Control:** Other not–for–profit (including NFP Corporation) **Service:** General medical and surgical

**Staffed Beds:** 130 **Admissions:** 7167 **Census:** 75 **Outpatient Visits:** 234866 **Births:** 640 **Total Expense ($000):** 132691 **Payroll Expense ($000):** 46306 **Personnel:** 865

**UH ROBINSON MEDICAL CENTER** See UH Portage Medical Center

### ROCK CREEK—Ashtabula County

**GLENBEIGH HEALTH SOURCES** See Glenbeigh Hospital and Outpatient Centers

**GLENBEIGH HOSPITAL AND OUTPATIENT CENTERS (360245)**, 2863 Route 45, Zip 44084, Mailing Address: P.O. Box 298, Zip 44084–0298; tel. 440/563–3400, (Nonreporting) **A**10 **F**4 5 29 30 34 36 53 54 57 75 86 87 100 130 132 135 149 152
Primary Contact: Patricia Weston-Hall, Chief Executive Officer
CFO: Phil Pawlowski, Chief Financial Officer
CIO: Linda Advey, Manager Information Systems
CHR: Shirley Deary, Director Human Resources
Web address: www.glenbeigh.com
**Control:** Other not–for–profit (including NFP Corporation) **Service:** Alcoholism and other chemical dependency

**Staffed Beds:** 114 **Admissions:** 3309 **Census:** 121 **Outpatient Visits:** 69412 **Births:** 0 **Total Expense ($000):** 23223 **Payroll Expense ($000):** 11362 **Personnel:** 266

### SAINT MARYS—Auglaize County

⇑ **JOINT TOWNSHIP DISTRICT MEMORIAL HOSPITAL (360032)**, 200 St Clair Street, Zip 45885–2400; tel. 419/394–3335, (Nonreporting) **A**10 21
Primary Contact: Kevin W. Harlan, President
CFO: Jeffrey W Vossler, Chief Financial Officer
CIO: Joshua Miller, Director Information Systems
CHR: Art Swain, Vice President Support Services
CNO: Debra McKee, R.N., Chief Clinical Officer and Chief Nursing Officer
Web address: www.grandlakehealth.org
**Control:** Other not–for–profit (including NFP Corporation) **Service:** General medical and surgical

**Staffed Beds:** 60

### SALEM—Columbiana County

**SALEM COMMUNITY HOSPITAL** See Salem Regional Medical Center

✉ **SALEM REGIONAL MEDICAL CENTER (360185)**, 1995 East State Street, Zip 44460–2423; tel. 330/332–1551, (Nonreporting) **A**1 3 5 10
Primary Contact: Anita Hackstedde, M.D., President and Chief Executive Officer
COO: Keith Meredith, Chief Operating Officer
CFO: Mike Giangardella, Vice President Finance and Administration
CMO: Anita Hackstedde, M.D., Vice President Medical Affairs
CIO: Mark L'Italien, Director Information Services
CHR: Barb Hirst, R.N., Vice President Human Resources and Chief Nursing Officer
CNO: Barb Hirst, R.N., Vice President Human Resources and Chief Nursing Officer
Web address: www.salemregional.com
**Control:** Other not–for–profit (including NFP Corporation) **Service:** General medical and surgical

**Staffed Beds:** 116

### SANDUSKY—Erie County

**FIRELANDS COMMUNITY HOSPITAL** See Firelands Regional Medical Center - Main Campus

*Many Facility Codes have changed. Please refer to the AHA Guide Code Chart.*

○ **FIRELANDS REGIONAL HEALTH SYSTEM (360025)**, 1111 Hayes Avenue, Zip 44870–3323; tel. 419/557–7400, (Includes FIRELANDS REGIONAL MEDICAL CENTER - MAIN CAMPUS, Mailing address: 1111 Hayes Avenue, Sandusky, Ohio, Zip 44870; tel. 419/557–7400; FIRELANDS REGIONAL MEDICAL CENTER SOUTH CAMPUS, Mailing address: 1912 Hayes Avenue, Sandusky, Ohio, Zip 44870–4736; tel. 419/557–7000), (Nonreporting) **A**2 3 5 10 11 19
Primary Contact: Daniel J. Moncher, Interim President and Chief Executive Officer
CFO: Daniel J Moncher, Vice President and Chief Financial Officer
CMO: Brenda Violette, M.D., Director Medical Staff
CIO: Robert Ayres, Director Information Systems
CHR: James Sennish, Vice President Human Resources
Web address: www.firelands.com
**Control**: Other not–for–profit (including NFP Corporation) **Service**: General medical and surgical

**Staffed Beds**: 239

**FIRELANDS REGIONAL MEDICAL CTR** See Firelands Regional Health System

**PROVIDENCE HOSPITAL** See Firelands Regional Medical Center South Campus

## SEAMAN—Adams County

**ADAMS COUNTY HOSPITAL** See Adams County Regional Medical Center

☐ **ADAMS COUNTY REGIONAL MEDICAL CENTER (361326)**, 230 Medical Center Drive, Zip 45679–8002; tel. 937/386–3400, (Nonreporting) **A**1 10 18
Primary Contact: Alan Bird, Chief Executive Officer
CFO: Pete Dagenbach, Chief Financial Officer
CHR: Heather Hoop, Human Resources Generalist
CNO: Sharon Ashley, MSN, Chief Nursing Officer
Web address: www.acrmc.com
**Control**: County, Government, Nonfederal **Service**: General medical and surgical

**Staffed Beds**: 25

## SHELBY—Richland County

**MEDCENTRAL - SHELBY HOSPITAL** See Ohiohealth Medcentral Shelby Hospital

★ **OHIOHEALTH MEDCENTRAL SHELBY HOSPITAL (361324)**, 199 West Main Street, Zip 44875–1490; tel. 419/342–5015, (Nonreporting) **A**10 18 **F**3 8 11 13 18 28 29 30 31 35 40 45 50 59 63 65 68 75 76 77 78 79 81 85 89 93 97 107 108 110 115 119 128 130 133 135 146 154 156 **S** OhioHealth, Columbus, OH
Primary Contact: Vinson Yates, President
CNO: Trish DelGreco, Director of Nursing
Web address: www.medcentral.org/body.cfm?id=153
**Control**: Church operated, Nongovernment, not–for–profit **Service**: General medical and surgical

**Staffed Beds**: 25 **Admissions**: 1034 **Census**: 16 **Outpatient Visits**: 40514 **Births**: 147 **Total Expense ($000)**: 29880 **Payroll Expense ($000)**: 9530

## SIDNEY—Shelby County

★ ○ **WILSON MEMORIAL HOSPITAL (360013)**, 915 West Michigan Street, Zip 45365–2491; tel. 937/498–2311, (Nonreporting) **A**10 11 **F**3 11 12 13 15 18 20 22 28 29 30 34 40 45 49 51 56 57 59 62 63 64 68 70 75 76 77 79 81 82 84 85 86 87 89 93 97 107 108 111 115 118 119 129 130 131 132 135 146 147 156 157 **P**6
Primary Contact: Mark Klosterman, FACHE, President and Chief Executive Officer
COO: Craig Lannoye, Vice President Operations
CFO: Julie Covault, Vice President Finance
CMO: Robert J McDevitt, M.D., Chief of Staff
CIO: Larry Meyers, Chief Information Officer
CHR: John Eve, Vice President Human Resources and Education
CNO: Linda Maurer, Vice President Patient Care Services
Web address: www.https://www.wilsonhealth.org
**Control**: Other not–for–profit (including NFP Corporation) **Service**: General medical and surgical

**Staffed Beds**: 71 **Admissions**: 2077 **Census**: 16 **Outpatient Visits**: 208033 **Births**: 705 **Total Expense ($000)**: 78106 **Payroll Expense ($000)**: 30075 **Personnel**: 527

## SPRINGFIELD—Clark County

☐ **MENTAL HEALTH SERVICES FOR CLARK AND MADISON COUNTIES (364040)**, 474 North Yellow Springs Street, Zip 45504–2463; tel. 937/399–9500, (Nonreporting) **A**1
Primary Contact: Curt Gillespie, Chief Executive Officer
Web address: www.mhscc.org
**Control**: County, Government, Nonfederal **Service**: Psychiatric

**Staffed Beds**: 16

**OHIO VALLEY MEDICAL CENTER** See Ohio Valley Surgical Hospital

☐ **OHIO VALLEY SURGICAL HOSPITAL (360355)**, 100 West Main Street, Zip 45502–1312; tel. 937/521–3900, (Nonreporting) **A**1 10
Primary Contact: Steve Eisentrager, President
CFO: Amanda martin, Manager Human Resources
CMO: Thales Pavlatos, Medical Director
CIO: Jonathan Bisdorf, Director Information Technology
CNO: Beth Lizza, Chief Nursing Officer
Web address: www.ovsurgical.com/
**Control**: Partnership, Investor–owned (for–profit) **Service**: Surgical

**Staffed Beds**: 24

☐ **SPRINGFIELD REGIONAL MEDICAL CENTER (360086)**, 100 Medical Center Drive, Zip 45504–2687; tel. 937/523–1000, (Nonreporting) **A**1 2 3 10 **S** Mercy Health, Cincinnati, OH
Primary Contact: Adam Groshans, President
CFO: William J. Kusnierz, Vice President and Chief Financial Officer
CNO: Elaine Storrs, Chief Nursing Officer
Web address: www.community-mercy.org
**Control**: Church operated, Nongovernment, not–for–profit **Service**: General medical and surgical

**Staffed Beds**: 259

**SPRINGFIELD REGIONAL MEDICAL CENTER - HIGH STREET CAMPUS** See Springfield Regional Medical Center

## STEUBENVILLE—Jefferson County

★ **ACUITY SPECIALTY HOSPITALS OHIO VALLEY (362035)**, 380 Summit Avenue, 3rd Floor, Zip 43952–2667; tel. 740/283–7600, (Includes ACUITY SPECIALTY HOSPITALS OHIO VALLEY AT BELMONT, Mailing address: 4697 Harrison Street, Bellaire, Ohio, Zip 43906–1338; tel. 740/671–2086; Dusty A. Bowers, Chief Executive Officer) **F**1 3 29 34 57 85 91 148 **S** AcuityHealthcare, LP, Charlotte, NC
Primary Contact: Dusty A. Bowers, Chief Executive Officer
Web address: www.acuityhealthcare.net
**Control**: Partnership, Investor–owned (for–profit) **Service**: Acute long–term care hospital

**Staffed Beds**: 52 **Admissions**: 532 **Census**: 41 **Outpatient Visits**: 0 **Births**: 0 **Total Expense ($000)**: 23472 **Payroll Expense ($000)**: 10524 **Personnel**: 165

**LIFE LINE HOSPITAL (362039)**, 200 School Street, Zip 43953–9610; tel. 740/346–2600, (Nonreporting) **A**10
Primary Contact: Patricia Cross, Chief Executive Officer
Web address: www.llhospital.com
**Control**: Partnership, Investor–owned (for–profit) **Service**: Acute long–term care hospital

**Staffed Beds**: 30

**OHIO VALLEY HOSPITAL** See Trinity Medical Center East

**ST JOHN MEDICAL CENTER** See Trinity Medical Center West

---

**Hospital, Medicare Provider Number, Address, Telephone, Approval, Facility, and Physician Codes, Health Care System**

★ American Hospital Association (AHA) membership    ○ Healthcare Facilities Accreditation Program    ⇑ Center for Improvement in Healthcare Quality Accreditation
☐ The Joint Commission accreditation    ◇ DNV Healthcare Inc. accreditation    △ Commission on Accreditation of Rehabilitation Facilities (CARF) accreditation

**OH**

✠ **TRINITY HEALTH SYSTEM (360211)**, 380 Summit Avenue, Zip 43952–2699; tel. 740/283–7000, (Includes TRINITY MEDICAL CENTER EAST, Mailing address: 380 Summit Avenue, Steubenville, Ohio, Zip 43952–2699; tel. 740/283–7000; TRINITY MEDICAL CENTER WEST, Mailing address: 4000 Johnson Road, Steubenville, Ohio, Zip 43952–2393; tel. 740/264–8000), (Nonreporting) **A**1 2 3 5 10 **F**3 4 5 12 13 15 17 18 20 22 24 26 28 29 30 31 32 33 34 35 38 40 44 45 46 47 48 49 51 54 56 57 59 62 64 65 69 70 71 74 75 76 77 78 79 81 82 85 86 87 89 90 91 92 93 94 96 97 98 100 101 102 104 105 106 107 108 110 111 115 117 118 119 120 121 123 124 126 128 129 130 131 132 135 144 146 147 148 149 152 153 156 **S** CommonSpirit Health, Chicago, IL
Primary Contact: Matthew Grimshaw, Market Chief Executive Officer
COO: JoAnn M Mulrooney, R.N., Chief Operating Officer
CFO: Dave Werkin, Vice President Finance and Chief Financial Officer
CMO: Gray Goncz, Vice President of Medical Affairs
CIO: Tom Kiger, Director Information Systems
CHR: Lewis C Musso, Vice President Human Resources
Web address: www.trinityhealth.com
**Control**: Other not–for–profit (including NFP Corporation) **Service**: General medical and surgical

**Staffed Beds: 277 Admissions: 8452 Census: 122 Outpatient Visits: 275702 Births: 502 Total Expense ($000): 226821 Payroll Expense ($000): 91925 Personnel: 1579**

**TRINITY MEDICAL CENTER** See Trinity Health System

### SYLVANIA—Lucas County

**FLOWER HOSPITAL** See Promedica Flower Hospital

✠ **REGENCY HOSPITAL OF TOLEDO (362036)**, 5220 Alexis Road, Zip 43560–2504; tel. 419/318–5700, (Nonreporting) **A**1 5 10 **S** Select Medical Corporation, Mechanicsburg, PA
Primary Contact: Gary Zaciewski, Chief Executive Officer
Web address: www.regencyhospital.com
**Control**: Corporation, Investor–owned (for–profit) **Service**: Acute long–term care hospital

**Staffed Beds: 45**

### TIFFIN—Seneca County

**MERCY HOSPITAL OF TIFFIN** See Mercy Tiffin Hospital

☐ **MERCY TIFFIN HOSPITAL (360089)**, 45 St Lawrence Drive, Zip 44883–8310; tel. 419/455–7000, (Nonreporting) **A**1 2 5 10 **S** Mercy Health, Cincinnati, OH
Primary Contact: B Lynn. Detterman, President and Chief Executive Officer
CMO: Steven Bruhl, Chief Medical Officer
CHR: Diana Olson, Director Human Resources
CNO: Anne Zimmerman, Senior Director Patient Care Services and Chief Nursing Officer
Web address: www.mercyweb.org
**Control**: Church operated, Nongovernment, not–for–profit **Service**: General medical and surgical

**Staffed Beds: 45**

☐ **SOJOURN AT SENECA SENIOR BEHAVIORAL HEALTH (364055)**, 50 St Lawrence Drive, Zip 44883–8310; tel. 567/207–2230, (Nonreporting) **A**1
Primary Contact: Kelly Tripp, Executive Director
CNO: Patricia Huber, Chief Nursing Officer
Web address: www.voaseniorliving.org
**Control**: Other not–for–profit (including NFP Corporation) **Service**: Psychiatric

**Staffed Beds: 24**

### TOLEDO—Lucas County

**ADVANCED SPECIALTY HOSPITAL** See Advanced Specialty Hospital of Toledo

☐ **ADVANCED SPECIALTY HOSPITAL OF TOLEDO (362038)**, 1015 Garden Lake Parkway, Zip 43614–2779; tel. 419/381–0037, (Nonreporting) **A**1 3 10
Primary Contact: Troy Holmes, Interim Chief Executive Officer and Chief Financial Officer
CFO: Troy Holmes, Chief Financial Officer
CMO: B Sarroui, M.D., Chief of Staff
CHR: Lauren Avigdor, Director Human Resources
CNO: Bridgett Mitchell, Chief Clinical Officer
Web address: www.advancedspecialtyhospitals.com
**Control**: Corporation, Investor–owned (for–profit) **Service**: Acute long–term care hospital

**Staffed Beds: 25**

**MEDICAL UNIVERSITY OF OHIO** See The University of Toledo Medical Center

☐ **MERCY ST. ANNE HOSPITAL (360262)**, 3404 West Sylvania Avenue, Zip 43623–4467; tel. 419/407–2663, (Nonreporting) **A**1 2 3 5 10 **S** Mercy Health, Cincinnati, OH
Primary Contact: Bradley J. Bertke, President and Chief Operating Officer
CFO: Michael Whipple, Chief Financial Officer
CMO: Herbert Stockard, M.D., Chief Medical Officer
CIO: Rebecca S Sykes, Chief Information Officer
CNO: Barb Dianda-Martin, Chief Nursing Officer
Web address: www.mercyweb.org
**Control**: Church operated, Nongovernment, not–for–profit **Service**: General medical and surgical

**Staffed Beds: 96**

☐ **MERCY ST. VINCENT MEDICAL CENTER (360112)**, 2213 Cherry Street, Zip 43608–2691; tel. 419/251–3232, (Includes MERCY CHILDREN'S HOSPITAL, Mailing address: 2213 Cherry Street, Toledo, Ohio, Zip 43608–2691; tel. 419/251–8000), (Nonreporting) **A**1 2 3 5 10 13 **S** Mercy Health, Cincinnati, OH
Primary Contact: Jeffrey Dempsey, President
CMO: Thomas Welch, M.D., Chief Medical Officer
CHR: Gary George, Senior Vice President Human Resources
CNO: Barbara Martin, Chief Nursing Officer
Web address: www.mercyweb.org
**Control**: Church operated, Nongovernment, not–for–profit **Service**: General medical and surgical

**Staffed Beds: 350**

☐ **NORTHWEST OHIO PSYCHIATRIC HOSPITAL (364014)**, 930 Detroit Avenue, Zip 43614–2701; tel. 419/381–1881, (Nonreporting) **A**1 3 10 **F**29 30 50 53 75 87 98 101 102 106 130 146 149 154 **S** Ohio Department of Mental Health, Columbus, OH
Primary Contact: Brett M. Johnson, Chief Executive Officer
COO: Kyle Hurst, Chief Operations Officer
CIO: Michael Carter, Administrator Information Technology
CHR: Ursula Barrera-Richards, Human Resource Director
CNO: Deb Duris, Director of Nursing
Web address: www.mh.state.oh.us/
**Control**: State, Government, Nonfederal **Service**: Psychiatric

**Staffed Beds: 112 Admissions: 600 Census: 106 Outpatient Visits: 0 Births: 0 Total Expense ($000): 27642 Payroll Expense ($000): 17471 Personnel: 202**

✠ **PROMEDICA TOLEDO HOSPITAL (360068)**, 2142 North Cove Boulevard, Zip 43606–3896; tel. 419/291–4000, (Includes PROMEDICA FLOWER HOSPITAL, Mailing address: 5200 Harroun Road, Sylvania, Ohio, Zip 43560–2196; tel. 419/824–1444; Neeraj Kanwal, M.D., Interim President, Metro Region; PROMEDICA RUSSELL J. EBEID CHILDREN'S HOSPITAL, Mailing address: 2142 North Cove Boulevard, Toledo, Ohio, Zip 43606; tel. 419/291–4000; Dawn M. Buskey, President, Regional Acute Care; PROMEDICA WILDWOOD ORTHOPAEDIC AND SPINE HOSPITAL, Mailing address: 2901 North Reynolds Road, Toledo, Ohio, Zip 43615; tel. 419/578–7700; Dawn M. Buskey, President), (Nonreporting) **A**1 2 3 5 10 **F**3 7 8 11 12 13 15 17 18 20 22 24 26 29 30 31 32 34 35 36 38 39 40 41 43 45 46 47 48 49 50 51 53 54 55 57 58 59 60 64 65 67 68 70 72 74 75 76 77 78 79 81 82 84 85 86 87 88 89 90 91 92 93 94 96 97 98 99 100 101 102 103 104 105 107 108 109 110 111 113 114 115 116 117 118 119 120 121 123 124 126 129 130 131 132 134 135 143 144 146 147 148 149 150 153 154 155 157 **P**6 **S** ProMedica Health System, Toledo, OH
Primary Contact: Dawn M. Buskey, President
COO: Gary Akenberger, Chief Operating Officer
CFO: Steven Cavanaugh, Chief Financial Officer
CMO: Neeraj Kanwal, M.D., Vice President, Medical Affairs
CIO: Murry Mercier, Chief Information Officer
CHR: Les Thompson, Chief Human Resources Officer
CNO: Deana Sievert, MSN, R.N., Chief Nursing Officer
Web address: www.promedica.org
**Control**: Other not–for–profit (including NFP Corporation) **Service**: General medical and surgical

**Staffed Beds: 815 Admissions: 42958 Census: 593 Outpatient Visits: 787748 Births: 4515 Total Expense ($000): 977925 Payroll Expense ($000): 293613 Personnel: 5186**

**PROMEDICA TOLEDO HOSPITAL** See Promedica Toledo Hospital

☐ **REHABILITATION HOSPITAL OF NORTHWEST OHIO (363040)**, 1455 West Medical Loop, Zip 43614; tel. 419/214–6600, (Nonreporting) **A**1 3 10 **S** Ernest Health, Inc., Albuquerque, NM
Primary Contact: Scott Williams, Chief Executive Officer
**Control**: Corporation, Investor–owned (for–profit) **Service**: Rehabilitation

**Staffed Beds: 40**

**ST. ANNE MERCY HOSPITAL** See Mercy St. Anne Hospital

**ST. VINCENT MERCY MEDICAL CENTER** See Mercy St. Vincent Medical Center

*Many Facility Codes have changed. Please refer to the AHA Guide Code Chart.* © 2021 AHA Guide

**THE UNIVERSITY OF TOLEDO MEDICAL CENTER (360048)**, 3000 Arlington Avenue, Zip 43614–2595; tel. 419/383–4000, (Nonreporting) **A**1 2 3 5 8 10 **F**3 4 5 8 11 12 15 17 18 20 22 24 26 28 29 30 31 32 34 35 36 37 38 39 40 43 44 45 46 47 48 49 50 51 52 53 54 55 56 57 58 59 60 61 64 65 67 68 70 74 75 77 78 79 81 82 85 86 87 91 92 93 94 96 97 98 99 100 101 102 103 104 105 107 108 110 111 114 115 116 117 118 119 120 121 123 124 126 130 131 132 134 135 138 145 146 147 148 149 152 153 156
Primary Contact: Daniel Barbee, Chief Executive Officer
CMO: Michael Ellis, M.D., Chief Medical Officer
CIO: William McCreary, Vice President and Chief Information Officer
CHR: Wendy Davis, Associate Vice President and Chief Human Resource Officer
CNO: Moneca Smith, Chief Nursing Officer
Web address: www.utoledo.edu
**Control:** State, Government, Nonfederal **Service:** General medical and surgical

| |
|---|
| **Staffed Beds:** 246 **Admissions:** 11626 **Census:** 159 **Outpatient Visits:** 367314 **Births:** 2 **Total Expense ($000):** 304256 **Payroll Expense ($000):** 114492 **Personnel:** 1713 |

**TOLEDO CHILDREN'S HOSPITAL** See Promedica Russell J. Ebeid Children's Hospital

### TROY—Miami County

○ **KETTERING HEALTH NETWORK TROY HOSPITAL (360368)**, 600 W Main Street, Zip 45373–3384; tel. 937/980–7000, (Data for 200 days) (Nonreporting) **A**11 **F**18 29 30 40 50 56 64 70 74 78 79 81 82 85 87 97 100 107 108 111 114 115 118 119 120 121 124 126 130 143 146 148 154 **S** Kettering Health Network, Dayton, OH
Primary Contact: Eric E. Lunde, President
Web address: www.https://ketteringhealth.org/troy
**Control:** Church operated, Nongovernment, not–for–profit **Service:** General medical and surgical

| |
|---|
| **Staffed Beds:** 28 **Admissions:** 595 **Census:** 9 **Outpatient Visits:** 15773 **Births:** 0 **Total Expense ($000):** 25135 **Payroll Expense ($000):** 10471 **Personnel:** 197 |

△ **UPPER VALLEY MEDICAL CENTER (360174)**, 3130 North County Road 25A, Zip 45373–1309; tel. 937/440–4000, (Nonreporting) **A**1 2 5 7 10 **F**3 8 11 13 15 18 20 22 26 28 29 30 31 32 34 35 36 37 38 40 41 44 45 46 48 49 50 54 55 56 57 58 59 60 61 63 68 70 71 73 74 75 76 78 79 80 81 85 86 87 90 91 92 93 96 97 98 100 101 102 103 104 107 108 110 111 114 118 119 129 130 131 132 134 135 141 145 147 148 149 154 156 **P**6 **S** Premier Health, Dayton, OH
Primary Contact: Thomas Parker, President
CFO: Tim Snider, Senior Vice President for Finance
CMO: Jennifer Hauler, D.O., Chief Medical Officer
CIO: James Kaiser, Site Director Information Technology
CHR: Kathy Boerger, Director Human Resources
CNO: Terry Fry, R.N., Chief Nursing Officer
Web address: www.uvmc.com
**Control:** Other not–for–profit (including NFP Corporation) **Service:** General medical and surgical

| |
|---|
| **Staffed Beds:** 85 **Admissions:** 6406 **Census:** 66 **Outpatient Visits:** 253125 **Births:** 583 **Total Expense ($000):** 153402 **Payroll Expense ($000):** 66622 **Personnel:** 913 |

### UPPER SANDUSKY—Wyandot County

★ **WYANDOT MEMORIAL HOSPITAL (361329)**, 885 North Sandusky Avenue, Zip 43351–1098; tel. 419/294–4991, (Nonreporting) **A**10 18 **F**3 11 15 17 18 28 29 30 31 34 35 40 45 46 50 53 57 59 64 65 71 74 75 77 78 79 81 82 85 86 87 89 92 93 97 107 108 110 111 115 116 117 118 119 124 126 127 129 130 131 132 133 135 144 146 147 148 149
Primary Contact: Ty Shaull, President and Chief Executive Officer
CFO: Alan H Yeates, Vice President Fiscal Services
CHR: Vickie Underwood, Director Human Resources
CNO: Marty Gray, R.N., Director of Nursing
Web address: www.wyandotmemorial.org
**Control:** Hospital district or authority, Government, Nonfederal **Service:** General medical and surgical

| |
|---|
| **Staffed Beds:** 25 **Admissions:** 609 **Census:** 7 **Outpatient Visits:** 69340 **Births:** 37 **Total Expense ($000):** 47881 **Payroll Expense ($000):** 18349 **Personnel:** 258 |

### URBANA—Champaign County

**MERCY MEMORIAL HOSPITAL (361312)**, 904 Scioto Street, Zip 43078–2200; tel. 937/653–5231, (Nonreporting) **A**10 18 **S** Mercy Health, Cincinnati, OH
Primary Contact: Matthew T. Caldwell, President and Chief Executive Officer
Web address: www.health-partners.org
**Control:** Church operated, Nongovernment, not–for–profit **Service:** General medical and surgical

| |
|---|
| **Staffed Beds:** 25 |

### VAN WERT—Van Wert County

**VAN WERT COUNTY HOSPITAL (360071)**, 1250 South Washington Street, Zip 45891–2599; tel. 419/238–2390, (Nonreporting) **A**1 5 10 **F**3 8 13 15 18 28 29 32 34 35 36 40 44 48 50 53 54 57 59 62 64 65 68 70 75 76 77 79 81 82 85 87 89 93 94 97 107 108 110 113 119 129 130 131 135 146 147 148 154 157
Primary Contact: James W. Pope, FACHE, President and Chief Executive Officer
CFO: Karen Shadowens, CPA, Chief Financial Officer
CMO: Thomas Conte, M.D., President, Medical Staff
CIO: Brett Taylor, Director Hospital Information Systems
CNO: Elizabeth Neuschwanger, Chief Nursing Officer
Web address: www.vanwerthealth.org
**Control:** Other not–for–profit (including NFP Corporation) **Service:** General medical and surgical

| |
|---|
| **Staffed Beds:** 27 **Admissions:** 898 **Census:** 8 **Outpatient Visits:** 66449 **Births:** 156 **Total Expense ($000):** 64353 **Payroll Expense ($000):** 24218 **Personnel:** 343 |

### WARREN—Trumbull County

**FORUM HEALTH TRUMBULL MEMORIAL HOSPITAL** See Trumbull Memorial Hospital

**FORUM HILLSIDE REHABILITATION HOSPITAL** See Hillside Rehabilitation Hospital

△ **HILLSIDE REHABILITATION HOSPITAL (363026)**, 8747 Squires Lane NE, Zip 44484–1649; tel. 330/841–3700, (Nonreporting) **A**1 5 7 10 **S** Steward Health Care System, LLC, Dallas, TX
Primary Contact: Steven Ryland, Interim Chief Executive Officer
CMO: Joseph Cerimele, D.O., Medical Director
CIO: Barry Fitts, Chief Information Officer
CHR: Jody Roman, Chief Human Resource Officer
CNO: Susan Joy, Chief Nursing Officer
Web address: www.https://valleycareofohio.steward.org
**Control:** Corporation, Investor–owned (for–profit) **Service:** Rehabilitation

| |
|---|
| **Staffed Beds:** 65 |

☐ **MERCY HEALTH - ST. JOSEPH WARREN HOSPITAL (360161)**, 667 Eastland Avenue SE, Zip 44484–4531, Mailing Address: 627 Eastland Avenue, Zip 44484–4531; tel. 330/841–4000, (Nonreporting) **A**1 2 3 5 10 13 **S** Mercy Health, Cincinnati, OH
Primary Contact: Kathy Cook, FACHE, MSN, President
COO: Donald E. Koenig Jr., Chief Operating Officer
CMO: Nicholas Kreatsoulas, Vice President Medical Affairs
Web address: www.hmpartners.org
**Control:** Church operated, Nongovernment, not–for–profit **Service:** General medical and surgical

| |
|---|
| **Staffed Beds:** 136 |

**ST. JOSEPH HEALTH CENTER** See Mercy Health - St. Joseph Warren Hospital

☐ **TRUMBULL MEMORIAL HOSPITAL (360055)**, 1350 East Market Street, Zip 44483–6628; tel. 330/841–9011, (Nonreporting) **A**1 2 3 5 10 **S** Steward Health Care System, LLC, Dallas, TX
Primary Contact: Krista McFadden, President
CMO: Thomas L James, M.D., Chief Medical Officer
CIO: Barry Fitts, Chief Information Officer
CHR: Robert Sincich, Vice President Human Resources
CNO: Melissa Bennett, Chief Nursing Officer
Web address: www.https://trumbullmemorial.org/?_ga=2.209137234.1564767671.1497292183-315051339.1497292183
**Control:** Corporation, Investor–owned (for–profit) **Service:** General medical and surgical

| |
|---|
| **Staffed Beds:** 292 |

---

**Hospital, Medicare Provider Number, Address, Telephone, Approval, Facility, and Physician Codes, Health Care System**

★ American Hospital Association (AHA) membership
☐ The Joint Commission accreditation
○ Healthcare Facilities Accreditation Program
◇ DNV Healthcare Inc. accreditation
⇑ Center for Improvement in Healthcare Quality Accreditation
△ Commission on Accreditation of Rehabilitation Facilities (CARF) accreditation

**OH**

## WARRENSVILLE HEIGHTS—Cuyahoga County

**MERIDIA SOUTH POINTE HOSPITAL** See South Pointe Hospital

**REGENCY HOSPITAL CLEVELAND EAST**(Includes REGENCY HOSPITAL OF CLEVELAND - WEST, Mailing address: 6990 Engle Road, Middleburg Heights, Ohio, Zip 44130–3420; tel. 440/202–4200; Timothy Rolsen, Chief Executive Officer) **A**1 10
Web address: www.regencyhospital.com/

**REGENCY HOSPITAL CLEVELAND EAST (362029)**, 4200 Interchange Corporate Center Road, Zip 44128–5631; tel. 216/910–3800, (Includes REGENCY HOSPITAL OF CLEVELAND - WEST, Mailing address: 6990 Engle Road, Middleburg Heights, Ohio, Zip 44130–3420; tel. 440/202–4200; Timothy Rolsen, Chief Executive Officer), (Nonreporting) **A**1 10 **S** Select Medical Corporation, Mechanicsburg, PA
Primary Contact: Lisa Deering, Chief Executive Officer
Web address: www.regencyhospital.com/
**Control**: Corporation, Investor–owned (for–profit) **Service**: Acute long–term care hospital

**Staffed Beds**: 87

**SOUTH POINTE HOSPITAL (360144)**, 20000 Harvard Road, Zip 44122–6805; tel. 216/491–6000, (Nonreporting) **A**1 2 3 5 10 13 **F**3 15 18 26 28 29 30 31 34 35 36 38 39 40 44 50 51 55 56 57 58 59 60 61 64 65 66 68 70 74 75 77 78 79 81 82 84 85 86 87 93 97 100 102 107 108 110 111 114 117 119 130 132 143 144 146 148 154 156 **P**6 **S** Cleveland Clinic Health System, Cleveland, OH
Primary Contact: Margaret McKenzie, M.D., President
COO: Andrea Jacobs, Chief Operating Officer
CFO: Lindsay Bird, Director Finance
CMO: Arun Gupta, M.D., Vice President Medical Affairs
CIO: Ralph A Cagna, Director Information Technology
CHR: Doris A. Zajec, Director Human Resources
Web address: www.southpointehospital.org
**Control**: Other not–for–profit (including NFP Corporation) **Service**: General medical and surgical

**Staffed Beds**: 163 **Admissions**: 7468 **Census**: 96 **Outpatient Visits**: 86302 **Births**: 0 **Total Expense ($000)**: 134937 **Payroll Expense ($000)**: 52889 **Personnel**: 722

## WASHINGTON COURT HOUSE—Fayette County

**FAYETTE COUNTY MEMORIAL HOSPITAL (361331)**, 1430 Columbus Avenue, Zip 43160–1791; tel. 740/335–1210, (Nonreporting) **A**1 10 18 **F**3 7 8 11 15 18 29 34 35 40 41 44 45 51 57 59 64 68 70 75 77 78 79 81 82 85 86 87 89 91 92 93 97 100 108 110 114 119 127 128 130 131 132 133 135 144 146 147 148 149 154 156 **P**5
Primary Contact: D Michael. Diener, Chief Executive Officer
CFO: Trent Lemle, Chief Financial Officer
CNO: Tammie Wilson, R.N., MSN, Chief Nursing Officer
Web address: www.fcmh.org
**Control**: County, Government, Nonfederal **Service**: General medical and surgical

**Staffed Beds**: 25 **Admissions**: 558 **Census**: 4 **Outpatient Visits**: 175415 **Births**: 0 **Total Expense ($000)**: 49095 **Payroll Expense ($000)**: 21896 **Personnel**: 371

## WAUSEON—Fulton County

**FULTON COUNTY HEALTH CENTER (361333)**, 725 South Shoop Avenue, Zip 43567–1701; tel. 419/335–2015, (Total facility includes 71 beds in nursing home–type unit) (Nonreporting) **A**1 2 3 5 10 18 **F**3 8 11 12 13 15 18 26 28 29 31 34 40 53 57 59 67 69 70 75 76 77 78 79 81 87 89 93 98 101 102 103 104 105 107 108 111 115 118 119 128 129 130 131 132 135 146 148 149 153 156
Primary Contact: Patricia Finn, Chief Executive Officer
COO: Kristine Snyder, Chief Operating Officer
CFO: Jenee Seibert, Chief Finance Officer
CIO: Larry Hefflinger, Chief Information Officer
CHR: Rachel Geckle, Chief Human Resource Officer
CNO: Tiffany Siegel, Chief Nursing Officer
Web address: www.fultoncountyhealthcenter.org
**Control**: Other not–for–profit (including NFP Corporation) **Service**: General medical and surgical

**Staffed Beds**: 106 **Admissions**: 1178 **Census**: 75 **Outpatient Visits**: 154550 **Births**: 208 **Total Expense ($000)**: 66280 **Payroll Expense ($000)**: 23778 **Personnel**: 655

## WAVERLY—Pike County

☐ **ADENA PIKE MEDICAL CENTER (361334)**, 100 Dawn Lane, Zip 45690–9138; tel. 740/947–2186, (Nonreporting) **A**1 10 18 **F**3 11 18 29 30 34 35 40 43 45 50 56 57 59 62 63 64 65 79 81 82 85 86 91 93 96 104 105 107 111 114 115 130 131 133 135 146 148 149 154 156 **S** Adena Health System, Chillicothe, OH
Primary Contact: David M. Zanni, Administrator
COO: Eric Cecava, Chief Operating Officer
CFO: Lisa Carlson, Chief Financial Officer
CMO: John Fortney, Chief Medical Officer
CIO: Tom Bialorucki, Chief Information Officer
CHR: Jay D. Justice, Chief Human Resources Officer
Web address: www.adena.org
**Control**: Other not–for–profit (including NFP Corporation) **Service**: General medical and surgical

**Staffed Beds**: 25 **Admissions**: 545 **Census**: 9 **Outpatient Visits**: 36067 **Births**: 0 **Total Expense ($000)**: 19714 **Payroll Expense ($000)**: 7346 **Personnel**: 124

**PIKE COMMUNITY HOSPITAL** See Adena Pike Medical Center

## WEST CHESTER—Butler County

☐ **BECKETT SPRINGS (364051)**, 8614 Shepherd Farm Drive, Zip 45069; tel. 513/942–9500, (Nonreporting) **A**1 10 **F**4 5 98 105 152 153 **S** Springstone, Louisville, KY
Primary Contact: Neicole Knott, Chief Executive Officer
Web address: www.springstone.com/hospitals.stmhl
**Control**: Corporation, Investor–owned (for–profit) **Service**: Psychiatric

**Staffed Beds**: 96 **Admissions**: 2809 **Census**: 85 **Outpatient Visits**: 27727 **Births**: 0 **Total Expense ($000)**: 23915 **Payroll Expense ($000)**: 13908 **Personnel**: 249

**UNIVERSITY POINTE SURGICAL HOSPITAL** See West Chester Hospital Surgical Center

☐ **WEST CHESTER HOSPITAL (360354)**, 7700 University Drive, Zip 45069–2505; tel. 513/298–3000, (Includes WEST CHESTER HOSPITAL SURGICAL CENTER, Mailing address: 7750 University Court, West Chester, Ohio, Zip 45069; tel. 513/475–8300; Tom G Daskalakis, Chief Administrative Officer), (Nonreporting) **A**1 3 5 10 **F**3 9 12 13 15 18 20 22 26 29 30 31 34 35 37 38 40 41 43 44 45 46 47 48 49 50 51 54 57 58 59 60 61 63 64 70 73 74 75 76 77 78 79 80 81 82 84 85 86 87 91 92 100 107 108 110 111 114 115 116 117 119 120 126 129 130 131 132 134 135 141 145 146 147 148 149 150 154 155 156 157 **P**6 **S** UC Health, Cincinnati, OH
Primary Contact: Tom G. Daskalakis, Chief Administrative Officer
CIO: Jay Brown, Senior Vice President, Chief Information Officer
CHR: Jack Talbot, Director, Human Resources
CNO: Kathie Hays, MSN, R.N., Chief Nursing Officer
Web address: www.uchealth.com/westchesterhospital
**Control**: Other not–for–profit (including NFP Corporation) **Service**: General medical and surgical

**Staffed Beds**: 174 **Admissions**: 9242 **Census**: 97 **Outpatient Visits**: 252627 **Births**: 945 **Total Expense ($000)**: 255688 **Payroll Expense ($000)**: 71387 **Personnel**: 1145

## WESTERVILLE—Delaware County

△ **MOUNT CARMEL REHABILITATION HOSPITAL (363042)**, 597 Executive Campus Drive, Zip 43082–8870; tel. 614/392–3400, (Nonreporting) **A**1 7 **S** Encompass Health Corporation, Birmingham, AL
Primary Contact: Angela Bridges, R.N., Chief Executive Officer
CFO: Ibrahima Loume, Controller
CMO: Sarah Grove, M.D., Medical Director
CHR: Merri Foltz, Director of Human Resources
CNO: Jan Bricker, R.N., Chief Nursing Officer
Web address: www.encompasshealth.com
**Control**: Corporation, Investor–owned (for–profit) **Service**: Rehabilitation

**Staffed Beds**: 60

*Many Facility Codes have changed. Please refer to the AHA Guide Code Chart.*   © 2021 AHA Guide

## WESTERVILLE—Franklin County

☒ **MOUNT CARMEL ST. ANN'S (360012)**, 500 South Cleveland Avenue, Zip 43081–8998; tel. 614/898–4000, (Nonreporting) **A**1 2 3 5 10 **F**3 11 13 15 17 18 20 21 22 24 26 28 29 30 31 34 35 37 40 42 44 45 47 48 49 50 51 54 55 57 58 59 61 63 64 65 66 68 70 74 75 76 77 78 79 81 82 83 84 85 86 87 97 100 107 108 109 110 111 114 115 116 118 119 120 121 123 124 126 130 131 132 141 146 147 148 154 **P**1 **S** Trinity Health, Livonia, MI
Primary Contact: Kim Unhee, President
Web address: www.mountcarmelhealth.com
**Control**: Church operated, Nongovernment, not–for–profit **Service**: General medical and surgical

**Staffed Beds:** 281 **Admissions:** 17667 **Census:** 190 **Outpatient Visits:** 162337 **Births:** 3835 **Total Expense ($000):** 346567 **Payroll Expense ($000):** 110796 **Personnel:** 1607

**ST ANN'S HOSPITAL** See Mount Carmel St. Ann's

## WESTLAKE—Cuyahoga County

**ST. JOHN MEDICAL CENTER** See UH St. John Medical Center

☒ **UH ST. JOHN MEDICAL CENTER (360123)**, 29000 Center Ridge Road, Zip 44145–5293; tel. 440/835–8000, (Nonreporting) **A**1 2 3 5 10 13 **F**3 11 13 15 17 18 19 20 22 24 26 28 29 30 31 34 35 36 39 40 41 43 44 45 46 47 49 50 51 54 55 56 57 58 59 60 63 64 65 67 68 69 70 71 74 75 76 78 79 81 82 83 84 85 86 87 89 92 93 100 102 107 108 110 111 114 115 119 126 130 131 132 135 143 146 147 148 149 154 **S** University Hospitals, Cleveland, OH
Primary Contact: Robert G. David, President
CFO: Allen R Tracy, Senior Vice President and Chief Financial Officer
CMO: Michael Dobrovich, M.D., Chief Medical Officer
CIO: James H Carroll, Chief Information Officer
CHR: Gary Lazroff, Vice President Human Resources
Web address: www.https://www.uhhospitals.org
**Control**: Other not–for–profit (including NFP Corporation) **Service**: General medical and surgical

**Staffed Beds:** 179 **Admissions:** 8427 **Census:** 77 **Outpatient Visits:** 191775 **Births:** 779 **Total Expense ($000):** 166791 **Payroll Expense ($000):** 53105 **Personnel:** 882

## WILLARD—Huron County

☐ **MERCY HEALTH - WILLARD HOSPITAL (361310)**, 1100 Neal Zick Road, Zip 44890–9287; tel. 419/964–5000, (Nonreporting) **A**1 5 10 18 **S** Mercy Health, Cincinnati, OH
Primary Contact: B Lynn. Detterman, President and Chief Executive Officer
CMO: Christopher Bohach, DPM, Chief of Staff
CHR: Diana Olson, Chief Human Resources Officer
Web address: www.mercyweb.org
**Control**: Church operated, Nongovernment, not–for–profit **Service**: General medical and surgical

**Staffed Beds:** 20

**MERCY WILLARD HOSPITAL** See Mercy Health - Willard Hospital

## WILLOUGHBY—Lake County

**LAURELWOOD HOSPITAL** See Windsor-Laurelwood Center for Behavioral Medicine

☐ **WINDSOR-LAURELWOOD CENTER FOR BEHAVIORAL MEDICINE (364029)**, 35900 Euclid Avenue, Zip 44094–4648; tel. 440/953–3000, (Nonreporting) **A**1 10 **S** Universal Health Services, Inc., King of Prussia, PA
Primary Contact: Shelley Zimmerman, Chief Executive Officer
CFO: Leanne Smith, Chief Financial Officer
CMO: James Psarras, M.D., Chief Medical Officer
CHR: Pam Connell, Manager Human Resources
CNO: Erika Quintana, Chief Nursing Officer
Web address: www.windsorlaurelwood.com
**Control**: Individual, Investor–owned (for–profit) **Service**: Psychiatric

**Staffed Beds:** 159

## WILMINGTON—Clinton County

**CLINTON MEMORIAL HOSPITAL** See Cmh Regional Health System

☒ **CMH REGIONAL HEALTH SYSTEM (360175)**, 610 West Main Street, Zip 45177–2125; tel. 937/382–6611, (Nonreporting) **A**1 2 5 10 **S** LifePoint Health, Brentwood, TN
Primary Contact: Lance Beus, Chief Executive Officer
CFO: Bradley Boggus, Chief Financial Officer
CIO: Ray Doherty, Director Information Technology
CHR: Jan Blair, Director Human Resources
CNO: Sheila Martin, Chief Nursing Officer
Web address: www.cmhregional.com
**Control**: Corporation, Investor–owned (for–profit) **Service**: General medical and surgical

**Staffed Beds:** 119

## WOOSTER—Wayne County

⇑ **WOOSTER COMMUNITY HOSPITAL (360036)**, 1761 Beall Avenue, Zip 44691–2342; tel. 330/263–8100, (Nonreporting) **A**2 10 19 21
Primary Contact: William E. Sheron, Chief Executive Officer
Web address: www.woosterhospital.org
**Control**: City, Government, Nonfederal **Service**: General medical and surgical

**Staffed Beds:** 152

## WRIGHT—PATTERSON AFB—Greene County

**USAF MED CTR WRIGHT-PATTERSON** See Wright Patterson Medical Center

☒ **WRIGHT PATTERSON MEDICAL CENTER**, 4881 Sugar Maple Drive, Zip 45433–5529; tel. 937/257–0837, (Nonreporting) **A**1 2 3 5 **S** Department of the Air Force, Washington, DC
Primary Contact: Colonel Freddie Jenkins, Administrator
COO: ColonelBrent J Erickson, Administrator
CFO: MajorKelly Lesnick, Resource Manager Flight Commander
CMO: Gregory Sweitzer, Chief Medical Officer
CIO: John Beighle, Flight Chief Medical Information Systems
CHR: Hubert Chatman, Chief Civilian Personnel
CNO: ColonelDaniel Gerke, Chief Nursing Officer
Web address: www.wpafb.af.mil/units/wpmc/
**Service**: General medical and surgical

**Staffed Beds:** 62

## XENIA—Greene County

★ ◯ **GREENE MEMORIAL HOSPITAL (360026)**, 1141 North Monroe Drive, Zip 45385–1600; tel. 937/352–2000, (Nonreporting) **A**2 5 10 11 **F**3 11 15 18 28 29 30 34 35 36 40 43 54 56 64 70 74 75 77 78 79 81 85 87 93 96 102 107 108 110 111 115 118 119 127 129 130 132 135 146 148 149 154 157 **P**6 **S** Kettering Health Network, Dayton, OH
Primary Contact: Rick A. Dodds, President
CFO: Ron D Connovich, Chief Financial Officer
CMO: Michael Caccamo, M.D., Chief Medical Officer
CIO: Andy Lehman, Senior Vice President Technology & Analytics
CHR: Jeff Jones, Director Human Resources
CNO: Brenda Kuhn, Ph.D., R.N., FACHE, Chief Nursing Officer
Web address: www.ketteringhealth.org/greene
**Control**: Church operated, Nongovernment, not–for–profit **Service**: General medical and surgical

**Staffed Beds:** 49 **Admissions:** 2198 **Census:** 23 **Outpatient Visits:** 106843 **Births:** 0 **Total Expense ($000):** 133522 **Payroll Expense ($000):** 68900 **Personnel:** 255

## YOUNGSTOWN—Trumbull County

☐ **BELMONT PINES HOSPITAL (364038)**, 615 Churchill-Hubbard Road, Zip 44505–1379; tel. 330/759–2700, (Nonreporting) **A**1 10 **S** Universal Health Services, Inc., King of Prussia, PA
Primary Contact: Lisa Cocca, Chief Executive Officer
CFO: Sylvia Kuppler, Chief Financial Officer
CMO: Phillip G Maiden, M.D., Medical Director
CHR: Deidre L Watson, Director Human Resources
CNO: Tammy Shells, Chief Nursing Officer
Web address: www.belmontpines.com
**Control**: Corporation, Investor–owned (for–profit) **Service**: Psychiatric

**Staffed Beds:** 96

**BHC BELMONT PINES HOSPITAL** See Belmont Pines Hospital

---

**Hospital, Medicare Provider Number, Address, Telephone, Approval, Facility, and Physician Codes, Health Care System**

★ American Hospital Association (AHA) membership
☐ The Joint Commission accreditation
◯ Healthcare Facilities Accreditation Program
◇ DNV Healthcare Inc. accreditation
⇑ Center for Improvement in Healthcare Quality Accreditation
△ Commission on Accreditation of Rehabilitation Facilities (CARF) accreditation

**OH**

## YOUNGSTOWN—Mahoning County

☐ △ **MERCY HEALTH - ST. ELIZABETH YOUNGSTOWN HOSPITAL (360064)**, 1044 Belmont Avenue, Zip 44504–1096, Mailing Address: P.O. Box 1790, Zip 44501–1790; tel. 330/746–7211, (Nonreporting) **A**1 2 3 5 7 10 19 **S** Mercy Health, Cincinnati, OH
Primary Contact: Donald E. Kline, President and Chief Executive Officer
COO: Donald E. Koenig JrExecutive Vice President and Regional Chief Operating Officer, President, St. Elizabeth Youngstown Hospital
CFO: Anthony J. Seminaro, Chief Financial Officer
CIO: Maureen Kordupel, Director Relationship Manager
CNO: Lori DeNiro, Regional Chief Nursing Officer
Web address: www.mercy.com
**Control**: Church operated, Nongovernment, not–for–profit **Service**: General medical and surgical

**Staffed Beds**: 396

✉ **SELECT SPECIALTY HOSPITAL-YOUNGSTOWN (362024)**, 1044 Belmont Avenue, Zip 44504–1006; tel. 330/480–2349, (Includes SELECT SPECIALTY HOSPITAL-YOUNGSTOWN, BOARDMAN CAMPUS, Mailing address: 667 Eastland Avenue SE, Warren, Ohio, Zip 44484–4503; tel. 330/729–1700), (Nonreporting) **A**1 10 **S** Select Medical Corporation, Mechanicsburg, PA
Primary Contact: Jodi Costello, Chief Executive Officer
Web address: www.selectspecialtyhospitals.com/company/locations/youngstown.aspx
**Control**: Corporation, Investor–owned (for–profit) **Service**: Acute long–term care hospital

**Staffed Beds**: 56

**SELECT SPECIALTY HOSPITAL-YOUNGSTOWN-BOARDMAN** See Select Specialty Hospital-Youngstown

**ST. ELIZABETH HEALTH CENTER** See Mercy Health - St. Elizabeth Youngstown Hospital

☐ **SURGICAL HOSPITAL AT SOUTHWOODS (360352)**, 7630 Southern Boulevard, Zip 44512–5633; tel. 330/729–8000, (Nonreporting) **A**1 3 10
Primary Contact: Ed Muransky, Owner
Web address: www.surgeryatsouthwoods.com/
**Control**: Individual, Investor–owned (for–profit) **Service**: Surgical

**Staffed Beds**: 12

## ZANESVILLE—Muskingum County

★ ○ **GENESIS HEALTHCARE SYSTEM (360039)**, 2951 Maple Avenue, Zip 43701–1406; tel. 740/454–5000, (Includes BETHESDA HOSPITAL, Mailing address: 2951 Maple Avenue, Zanesville, Ohio, Zip 43701–1465; tel. 614/454–4000; GENESIS BEHAVIORAL HEALTH, Mailing address: 2951 Maple Avenue, Zanesville, Ohio, Zip 43701–1406; tel. 740/454–4000; Matthew J Perry, President and Chief Executive Officer; GOOD SAMARITAN MEDICAL AND REHABILITATION CENTER, Mailing address: 800 Forest Avenue, Zanesville, Ohio, Zip 43701–2881; tel. 614/454–5000), (Nonreporting) **A**2 3 10 11 **F**3 5 8 9 11 13 15 17 18 20 22 24 26 28 29 30 31 32 34 35 40 42 43 44 45 46 47 48 50 51 54 57 58 59 60 63 64 65 68 70 73 74 75 76 77 78 79 81 82 84 85 86 87 89 91 92 93 94 96 98 99 100 101 102 104 105 106 107 108 109 110 111 114 115 116 117 118 119 120 121 123 124 126 129 130 131 132 135 144 146 147 148 151 154 156 157 **P**6 **S** Franciscan Sisters of Christian Charity Sponsored Ministries, Inc., Manitowoc, WI
Primary Contact: Matthew J. Perry, President and Chief Executive Officer
COO: Richard S Helsper, Chief Operating Officer
CFO: Paul Masterson, Chief Financial Officer
CMO: Dan Scheerer, M.D., Chief Medical Officer
CIO: Edmund J Romito, Chief Information Officer
CHR: Dianna LeVeck, Chief Human Resources Officer
CNO: Abby Nguyen, R.N., Chief Nursing Officer
Web address: www.genesishcs.org
**Control**: Other not–for–profit (including NFP Corporation) **Service**: General medical and surgical

**Staffed Beds**: 321 **Admissions**: 13628 **Census**: 160 **Outpatient Visits**: 467618 **Births**: 1456 **Total Expense ($000)**: 406876 **Payroll Expense ($000)**: 137768 **Personnel**: 3298

*Many Facility Codes have changed. Please refer to the AHA Guide Code Chart.*

**OK**

# OKLAHOMA

## ADA—Pontotoc County

**CHICKASAW NATION HEALTH SYSTEM** See Chickasaw Nation Medical Center

☒ **CHICKASAW NATION MEDICAL CENTER (370180)**, 1921 Stonecipher Boulevard, Zip 74820–3439; tel. 580/436–3980, (Nonreporting) **A**1 3 5 10 13 **F**3 5 7 8 13 15 18 29 30 34 35 38 39 40 41 43 45 50 53 54 57 58 59 60 64 65 68 69 70 71 75 76 79 81 82 85 86 87 89 91 93 97 100 101 102 104 107 110 111 115 117 119 127 130 133 135 143 144 146 147 148 149 154 156 157 158
Primary Contact: Charles Grim, D.D.S., Secretary of Health
CFO: Marty Wafford, Under Secretary of Support and Programs
CMO: Richard McClain, M.D., Chief Medical Officer
CIO: Desiree Traylor, Chief Information Officer
CHR: Jalinda Kelley, Secretary of Interior Services
CNO: Jerod Waters, Chief Nursing Officer
Web address: www.chickasaw.net
**Control:** PHS, Indian Service, Government, federal **Service:** General medical and surgical

**Staffed Beds:** 72 **Admissions:** 2751 **Census:** 24 **Outpatient Visits:** 742848 **Births:** 922 **Total Expense ($000):** 260763 **Payroll Expense ($000):** 107482 **Personnel:** 1650

☒ **MERCY HOSPITAL ADA (370020)**, 430 North Monte Vista, Zip 74820–4610; tel. 580/332–2323, (Nonreporting) **A**1 2 10 **F**3 7 11 13 15 18 29 30 31 35 40 43 44 45 50 59 64 68 69 70 72 75 76 77 78 79 81 85 86 87 89 90 93 98 100 107 108 110 111 114 116 117 119 120 121 124 129 130 131 132 143 146 147 148 149 154 156 **S** Mercy, Chesterfield, MO
Primary Contact: Terence Farrell, President
CFO: Mary Garber, Vice President Finance
CMO: Imtiaz Ahmed, Chief of Staff
CHR: Katrina Godfrey, Director Human Resources
CNO: Cynthia Standlee, R.N., Chief Nursing Officer
Web address: www.https://www.mercy.net/practice/mercy-hospital-ada/
**Control:** Church operated, Nongovernment, not–for–profit **Service:** General medical and surgical

**Staffed Beds:** 156 **Admissions:** 3351 **Census:** 40 **Outpatient Visits:** 126664 **Births:** 433 **Total Expense ($000):** 92625 **Payroll Expense ($000):** 41094 **Personnel:** 469

☐ **ROLLING HILLS HOSPITAL (374016)**, 1000 Rolling Hills Lane, Zip 74820–9415; tel. 580/436–3600, (Nonreporting) **A**1 3 10 **F**34 35 38 98 100 101 103 106 130 135 154 **S** Acadia Healthcare Company, Inc., Franklin, TN
Primary Contact: Dennis Gober, Interim Chief Executive Officer
CMO: Robert Morton, M.D., Medical Director
CIO: Sherry Barnes, Director Health Information and Quality Management
CHR: Timothy Blackwell, Manager Human Resources
Web address: www.rollinghillshospital.com
**Control:** Corporation, Investor–owned (for–profit) **Service:** Psychiatric

**Staffed Beds:** 108 **Admissions:** 961 **Census:** 77 **Outpatient Visits:** 0 **Births:** 0 **Total Expense ($000):** 15775 **Payroll Expense ($000):** 7905 **Personnel:** 168

**VALLEY VIEW REGIONAL HOSPITAL** See Mercy Hospital Ada

## ALTUS—Jackson County

☒ **JACKSON COUNTY MEMORIAL HOSPITAL (370022)**, 1200 East Pecan Street, Zip 73521–6192, Mailing Address: P.O. Box 8190, Zip 73522–8190; tel. 580/379–5000, (Nonreporting) **A**1 3 10 **F**3 10 11 13 15 29 30 34 35 40 43 45 49 56 57 59 62 63 64 65 70 75 76 77 79 81 85 86 87 93 100 101 104 107 110 111 114 115 119 127 129 130 131 132 133 135 146 147 148 149 **P**6
Primary Contact: Steve L. Hartgraves, President and Chief Executive Officer
COO: Casey D. Miranda, Executive Vice President and Chief Operating Officer
CFO: Jennifer Combs, Chief Financial Officer
CMO: Julia Rivera, M.D., Chief of Staff
CIO: Mark Driscoll, Chief Information Officer
CHR: Richard Pope, Vice President Human Resources
CNO: Shelley Simmons, Chief Nursing Officer
Web address: www.jcmh.com
**Control:** Hospital district or authority, Government, Nonfederal **Service:** General medical and surgical

**Staffed Beds:** 49 **Admissions:** 2476 **Census:** 24 **Outpatient Visits:** 162007 **Births:** 310 **Total Expense ($000):** 75742 **Payroll Expense ($000):** 39613 **Personnel:** 677

## ALVA—Woods County

⇑ **SHARE MEDICAL CENTER (371341)**, 800 Share Drive, Zip 73717–3618, Mailing Address: P.O. Box 727, Zip 73717–0727; tel. 580/327–2800, (Nonreporting) **A**10 18 20 21 **F**3 15 29 40 43 45 59 64 65 68 69 77 81 93 96 97 107 110 114 127 128 129 130 133 144 149
Primary Contact: Kandice K. Allen, R.N., Chief Executive Officer
CMO: Elizabeth Kinzic, M.D., Chief of Staff
CIO: Alan Vaughan, Director Information Technology
CHR: Mary Herold, Director Human Resources
CNO: Regina Wilson, R.N., Director of Nursing
Web address: www.smcok.com
**Control:** Hospital district or authority, Government, Nonfederal **Service:** General medical and surgical

**Staffed Beds:** 21 **Admissions:** 299 **Census:** 5 **Outpatient Visits:** 16770 **Births:** 0 **Total Expense ($000):** 10948 **Payroll Expense ($000):** 4862 **Personnel:** 91

## ANADARKO—Caddo County

**ANADARKO MUNICIPAL HOSPITAL** See Physicians' Hospital in Anadarko

**PHYSICIANS' HOSPITAL IN ANADARKO (371314)**, 1002 Central Boulevard East, Zip 73005–4496; tel. 405/247–2551, (Nonreporting) **A**10 18 **S** First Physicians Capital Group, Inc., Oklahoma City, OK
Primary Contact: Travis A. Villani, FACHE, Chief Executive Officer and Administrator
Web address: www.anadarkohospital.com
**Control:** Partnership, Investor–owned (for–profit) **Service:** General medical and surgical

**Staffed Beds:** 25

## ANTLERS—Pushmataha County

**PUSHMATAHA HOSPITAL (370083)**, 510 East Main Street, Zip 74523–3262, Mailing Address: P.O. Box 518, Zip 74523–0518; tel. 580/298–3341, (Nonreporting) **A**10
Primary Contact: Nick Rowland, Chief Executive Officer
COO: Nick Rowland, Chief Operating Officer
CFO: Rory Ward, Chief Financial Officer
CMO: G Wayne Flatt, D.O., Chief Medical Director
CHR: Paula Schalski, Director Human Resources
CNO: Marla Barnes, Director of Nursing
Web address: www.pushhospital.com
**Control:** State, Government, Nonfederal **Service:** General medical and surgical

**Staffed Beds:** 23

**PUSHMATAHA HOSPITAL & HOME HEALTH** See Pushmataha Hospital

---

**Hospital, Medicare Provider Number, Address, Telephone, Approval, Facility, and Physician Codes, Health Care System**

★ American Hospital Association (AHA) membership
☐ The Joint Commission accreditation
○ Healthcare Facilities Accreditation Program
○ DNV Healthcare Inc. accreditation
⇑ Center for Improvement in Healthcare Quality Accreditation
△ Commission on Accreditation of Rehabilitation Facilities (CARF) accreditation

**OK**

## ARDMORE—Carter County

✠ **MERCY HOSPITAL ARDMORE (370047)**, 1011 14th Avenue NW,
Zip 73401–1828; tel. 580/223–5400, (Nonreporting) **A**1 10 **F**3 13 15 18 20 22
28 29 30 31 34 35 40 43 45 47 48 50 57 59 62 64 67 68 70 74 75 76 77 78
79 81 82 84 85 87 89 90 93 98 103 107 108 110 111 114 115 117 119 120
121 123 126 129 130 146 148 149 156 **S** Mercy, Chesterfield, MO
Primary Contact: Daryle Voss, FACHE, President and Chief Executive Officer
CMO: Pam Kimbrough, M.D., Vice President Medical Affairs
CHR: Melinda Sharum, Director Human Resources
CNO: Debra Pender, MS, R.N., Vice President Nursing
Web address: www.mercyok.net
**Control**: Church operated, Nongovernment, not–for–profit **Service**: General
medical and surgical

> **Staffed Beds**: 190 **Admissions**: 6225 **Census**: 75 **Outpatient
> Visits**: 207016 **Births**: 789 **Total Expense ($000)**: 143153 **Payroll Expense
> ($000)**: 54474 **Personnel**: 726

**MERCY MEMORIAL HEALTH CENTER** See Mercy Hospital Ardmore

## ATOKA—Atoka County

★ **ATOKA COUNTY MEDICAL CENTER (371300)**, 1590 West Liberty
Road, Zip 74525–1621, Mailing Address: PO Box 1107, Zip 74525–1621;
tel. 580/364–8205, (Nonreporting) **A**10 18 **F**3 29 34 40 45 46 53 56 57 59 64
77 81 91 93 107 119 128 133 146 154
Primary Contact: John Rains, Chief Executive Officer
CMO: Ted Rowland, Chief of Medical Staff
CHR: Courtney Jackson, Coordinator Human Resources
CNO: Sally Finch, Chief Nursing Officer
Web address: www.atokamedicalcenter.org
**Control**: Hospital district or authority, Government, Nonfederal **Service**: General
medical and surgical

> **Staffed Beds**: 25 **Admissions**: 603 **Census**: 10 **Outpatient Visits**: 7555
> **Births**: 0 **Total Expense ($000)**: 9086 **Payroll Expense ($000)**: 3981
> **Personnel**: 112

**ATOKA MEMORIAL HOSPITAL** See Atoka County Medical Center

## BARTLESVILLE—Washington County

★ ⇑ **ASCENSION ST. JOHN JANE PHILLIPS (370018)**, 3500 East Frank Phillips
Boulevard, Zip 74006–2411; tel. 918/333–7200, (Nonreporting) **A**5 10 21 **F**8
11 13 15 17 18 20 22 24 28 29 30 31 34 35 40 46 49 50 51 53 57 58 59 60
61 64 68 74 75 76 77 78 79 81 82 84 85 86 87 90 92 93 96 98 102 105 107
111 114 115 116 117 118 119 121 123 127 129 130 131 135 143 145 146
147 148 154 156 **P**4 **S** Ascension Healthcare, Saint Louis, MO
Primary Contact: Mike Moore, President and Chief Operating Officer
CFO: James Brasel, Chief Financial Officer
CMO: Paul McQuillen, M.D., Chief Medical Officer
CNO: Angie Bidleman, Chief Nursing Officer
Web address: www.jpmc.org
**Control**: Church operated, Nongovernment, not–for–profit **Service**: General
medical and surgical

> **Staffed Beds**: 106 **Admissions**: 4068 **Census**: 45 **Outpatient Visits**: 95000
> **Births**: 482 **Total Expense ($000)**: 102549 **Payroll Expense ($000)**: 31387
> **Personnel**: 505

⇑ **JANE PHILLIPS MEDICAL CENTER** See Ascension St. John Jane Phillips

## BEAVER—Beaver County

**BEAVER COUNTY MEMORIAL HOSPITAL (371322)**, 212 East Eighth Street,
Zip 73932, Mailing Address: P.O. Box 640, Zip 73932–0640; tel. 580/625–4551,
(Nonreporting) **A**10 18 **F**40 57 64 107 133 154
Primary Contact: Alissa Schlessman, Administrator
CFO: Cody Gregory, Comptroller
CMO: Gary Mathews, M.D., Medical Doctor
CHR: Karla Leisher, Business Office Manager
CNO: Lyn Sizelove, Director of Nursing
Web address: www.beavercountyhospitalauthority.com
**Control**: Hospital district or authority, Government, Nonfederal **Service**: General
medical and surgical

> **Staffed Beds**: 12 **Admissions**: 116 **Census**: 2 **Outpatient Visits**: 4627
> **Births**: 0 **Total Expense ($000)**: 5457 **Payroll Expense ($000)**: 2255

## BETHANY—Oklahoma County

**CHILDREN'S CENTER** See The Children's Center Rehabilitation Hospital

△ **THE CHILDREN'S CENTER REHABILITATION HOSPITAL (373302)**, 6800 NW
39th Expressway, Zip 73008–2513; tel. 405/789–6711, (Nonreporting) **A**3 5 7
10 **F**1 3 29 30 34 35 39 53 58 59 68 74 75 79 84 87 90 91 93 96 107 130
132 146 148 149 **P**6
Primary Contact: Nico Gomez, Chief Executive Officer
Web address: www.tccokc.org
**Control**: Other not–for–profit (including NFP Corporation) **Service**: Children's
general and surgical

> **Staffed Beds**: 160 **Admissions**: 184 **Census**: 110 **Outpatient Visits**: 19000
> **Births**: 0 **Total Expense ($000)**: 50219 **Payroll Expense ($000)**: 30199

## BLACKWELL—Kay County

⇑ **ALLIANCEHEALTH BLACKWELL** See Blackwell Regional Hospital

★ ⇑ **BLACKWELL REGIONAL HOSPITAL (370030)**, 710 South 13th Street,
Zip 74631–3700; tel. 580/363–2311, (Nonreporting) **A**10 21 **F**3 15 29 34 40 43
65 67 68 87 89 93 107 110 119 130 146 149 154
Primary Contact: Steven Taylor, Regional Chief Executive Officer
CFO: Courtney Kozikuski, Chief Financial Officer
CMO: Jeffery Shuart, M.D., Chief of Staff
CHR: Deb Ellis, Director Human Resource
Web address: www.blackwellregional.org
**Control**: Hospital district or authority, Government, Nonfederal **Service**: General
medical and surgical

> **Staffed Beds**: 28 **Admissions**: 383 **Census**: 3 **Outpatient Visits**: 20081
> **Births**: 0 **Total Expense ($000)**: 9625 **Payroll Expense ($000)**: 3470
> **Personnel**: 47

## BOISE CITY—Cimarron County

**CIMARRON MEMORIAL HOSPITAL (371307)**, 100 South Ellis
Street, Zip 73933, Mailing Address: P.O. Box 1059, Zip 73933–1059;
tel. 580/544–2501, (Nonreporting) **A**10 18
Primary Contact: Tim Beard, Chief Executive Officer
CFO: Jamie Jacoby, Chief Financial Officer
CIO: Tim Beard, Director, Information Technology
CNO: Barbara Carter, Chief Nursing Officer
Web address: www.cimarronmemorialhospital.org
**Control**: County, Government, Nonfederal **Service**: General medical and surgical

> **Staffed Beds**: 15

## BRISTOW—Creek County

**BRISTOW MEDICAL CENTER (370041)**, 700 West 7th Avenue, Suite 6,
Zip 74010–2302; tel. 918/367–2215, (Nonreporting) **A**10
Primary Contact: Jan Winter-Clark, Chief Executive Officer
CFO: Robin Van Vickle, Chief Financial Officer
Web address: www.bristowmedcenter.com
**Control**: Corporation, Investor–owned (for–profit) **Service**: General medical and
surgical

> **Staffed Beds**: 30

**BRISTOW MEMORIAL HOSPITAL** See Bristow Medical Center

## BROKEN ARROW—Tulsa County

**JOHN REHABILITATION HOSPITAL** See St. John Rehabilitation Hospital

✠ **ST. JOHN BROKEN ARROW (370235)**, 1000 West Boise Circle,
Zip 74012–4900; tel. 918/994–8100, (Nonreporting) **A**1 10 **F**3 11 14 15 18
29 30 34 35 37 40 43 45 50 57 59 64 65 68 74 79 81 84 85 87 94 107 108
110 111 114 115 119 130 132 135 143 146 **S** Ascension Healthcare, Saint
Louis, MO
Primary Contact: David L. Phillips, Chief Operating Officer
CFO: Katie Caughman, Chief Financial Officer
CMO: Jason Lepak, M.D., Medical Director
CNO: Dwan Borens, Chief Nursing Officer
Web address: www.stjohnbrokenarrow.com
**Control**: Church operated, Nongovernment, not–for–profit **Service**: General
medical and surgical

> **Staffed Beds**: 44 **Admissions**: 2027 **Census**: 13 **Outpatient Visits**: 72805
> **Births**: 0 **Total Expense ($000)**: 56490 **Payroll Expense ($000)**: 12875
> **Personnel**: 251

*Many Facility Codes have changed. Please refer to the AHA Guide Code Chart.*   © 2021 AHA Guide

⊠ **ST. JOHN REHABILITATION HOSPITAL (373034)**, 1200 West Albany Drive, Zip 74012–8146; tel. 918/744–2338, (Nonreporting) **A1 F3** 29 68 74 79 86 90 91 95 96 132 146 148 **S** Encompass Health Corporation, Birmingham, AL
Primary Contact: David Nicholas, Chief Executive Officer
Web address: www.stjohnrehab.com
**Control**: Corporation, Investor–owned (for–profit) **Service**: Rehabilitation

**Staffed Beds**: 40 **Admissions**: 1251 **Census**: 39 **Outpatient Visits**: 0 **Births**: 0

### BUFFALO—Harper County

★ **HARPER COUNTY COMMUNITY HOSPITAL (371324)**, Highway 64 North, Zip 73834, Mailing Address: P.O. Box 60, Zip 73834–0060; tel. 580/735–2555, (Nonreporting) **A**10 18 **F**7 40 69 93 107 114 119 133
Primary Contact: Kevin O'Brien, Chief Executive Officer
COO: Pam Dodd, Chief Operating Officer
CFO: Lisa Oakley, Chief Financial Officer
CNO: Melissa Madrid, R.N., Chief Nursing Officer
Web address: www.hcchospital.com/
**Control**: County, Government, Nonfederal **Service**: General medical and surgical

**Staffed Beds**: 12 **Admissions**: 177 **Census**: 1 **Outpatient Visits**: 8414 **Births**: 0 **Total Expense ($000)**: 4221 **Payroll Expense ($000)**: 2443 **Personnel**: 37

### CARNEGIE—Caddo County

**CARNEGIE TRI-COUNTY MUNICIPAL HOSPITAL (371334)**, 102 North Broadway, Zip 73015, Mailing Address: P.O. Box 97, Zip 73015–0097; tel. 580/654–1050, (Nonreporting) **A**10 18 **F**29 40 41 56 68 75 84 91 93 97 104 107 119 128 130 133 149 154 **S** First Physicians Capital Group, Inc., Oklahoma City, OK
Primary Contact: Thomas Henton, Chief Executive Officer
Web address: www.carnegiehospital.org/
**Control**: Other not–for–profit (including NFP Corporation) **Service**: General medical and surgical

**Staffed Beds**: 17 **Admissions**: 373 **Census**: 12 **Outpatient Visits**: 5407 **Births**: 0 **Total Expense ($000)**: 14108 **Payroll Expense ($000)**: 6337 **Personnel**: 89

### CHEYENNE—Roger Mills County

★ **ROGER MILLS MEMORIAL HOSPITAL (371303)**, 501 South L.L. Males, Zip 73628, Mailing Address: P.O. Box 219, Zip 73628; tel. 580/497–3336, (Nonreporting) **A**10 18 **F**3 7 34 40 57 59 64 65 93 107 115 119 127 133 135 **P**6
Primary Contact: Cynthia Duncan, Chief Executive Officer
Web address: www.rmmhonline.com
**Control**: Hospital district or authority, Government, Nonfederal **Service**: General medical and surgical

**Staffed Beds**: 15 **Admissions**: 106 **Census**: 2 **Outpatient Visits**: 5833 **Births**: 0 **Total Expense ($000)**: 6443 **Payroll Expense ($000)**: 3340 **Personnel**: 43

### CHICKASHA—Grady County

★ **GRADY MEMORIAL HOSPITAL (370054)**, 2220 West Iowa Avenue, Zip 73018–2738; tel. 405/224–2300, (Nonreporting) **A**10 **F**3 8 11 15 17 29 30 34 35 40 43 45 50 51 54 57 59 65 66 70 76 79 81 82 85 87 89 91 93 107 110 111 114 115 119 127 130 131 132 133 144 146 147 148 149 155 **P**6
Primary Contact: Warren K. Spellman, Chief Executive Officer
CFO: Jackie McAdoo, Chief Financial Officer
CMO: Mitch Coppedge, M.D., Chief Medical Officer
CIO: Mike Townsend, Interim Director Health Information Systems
CHR: Rebel Rutledge, Director Human Resources
CNO: Cathy Groseclose, Vice President Patient Care Services
Web address: www.gradymem.org
**Control**: Hospital district or authority, Government, Nonfederal **Service**: General medical and surgical

**Staffed Beds**: 48 **Admissions**: 929 **Census**: 9 **Outpatient Visits**: 67784 **Births**: 2 **Total Expense ($000)**: 45022 **Payroll Expense ($000)**: 21147 **Personnel**: 289

### CLAREMORE—Rogers County

☐ **CLAREMORE INDIAN HOSPITAL (370173)**, 101 South Moore Avenue, Zip 74017–5091; tel. 918/342–6200, (Nonreporting) **A1** 10 **S** U. S. Indian Health Service, Rockville, MD
Primary Contact: George Valliere, Chief Executive Officer
CFO: LaLana Spears, Supervisor Accounting
CMO: Gary Lang, M.D., Clinical Director
CIO: David Ponder, Information Technology Officer
CHR: Quinn Proctor, Director Human Resources
CNO: Alonna Adair-Triplett, Chief Nurse Executive
Web address: www.ihs.gov
**Control**: PHS, Indian Service, Government, federal **Service**: General medical and surgical

**Staffed Beds**: 44

⇑ **CLAREMORE REGIONAL HOSPITAL** See Hillcrest Hospital Claremore

★ ⇑ **HILLCREST HOSPITAL CLAREMORE (370039)**, 1202 North Muskogee Place, Zip 74017–3036; tel. 918/341–2556, (Nonreporting) **A**10 21 **F**3 8 11 13 15 18 20 22 26 28 29 30 34 35 37 40 45 49 51 59 64 70 74 76 77 79 81 82 85 86 87 89 93 107 108 110 111 119 129 130 131 133 135 145 146 147 148 156 **S** Ardent Health Services, Nashville, TN
Primary Contact: David Chaussard, Chief Executive Officer
CIO: Celeste Rodden, Chief Information Officer
CHR: Pat Goad, Director Human Resources
CNO: Randy Walker, Chief Nursing Officer
Web address: www.hillcrestclaremore.com
**Control**: Corporation, Investor–owned (for–profit) **Service**: General medical and surgical

**Staffed Beds**: 49 **Admissions**: 2696 **Census**: 25 **Outpatient Visits**: 42761 **Births**: 626 **Total Expense ($000)**: 48510 **Payroll Expense ($000)**: 17064 **Personnel**: 296

**PHS COMP INDIAN HLTH FACILITY** See Claremore Indian Hospital

### CLEVELAND—Pawnee County

**CLEVELAND AREA HOSPITAL (371320)**, 1401 West Pawnee Street, Zip 74020–3019; tel. 918/358–2501, (Nonreporting) **A**10 18 **F**11 15 29 32 34 35 40 41 43 57 59 64 65 75 77 87 90 91 93 96 97 107 110 111 115 119 127 128 130 133 135 147 148 154 156 **P**6
Primary Contact: Edred Benton, Chief Executive Officer and Chief Operating Officer
COO: Edred Benton, Chief Executive Officer and Chief Operating Officer
CMO: Jason Sims, M.D., Chief Medical Officer
CHR: Sherry Brown, Director Human Resources
Web address: www.clevelandareahospital.com
**Control**: Hospital district or authority, Government, Nonfederal **Service**: General medical and surgical

**Staffed Beds**: 14 **Admissions**: 201 **Census**: 8 **Outpatient Visits**: 25187 **Births**: 0 **Total Expense ($000)**: 15974 **Payroll Expense ($000)**: 10441 **Personnel**: 182

### CLINTON—Custer County

⊠ **ALLIANCEHEALTH CLINTON (370029)**, 100 North 30th Street, Zip 73601–3117; tel. 580/323–2363, (Nonreporting) **A1** 10 20 **S** Community Health Systems, Inc., Franklin, TN
Primary Contact: Landon E. Hise, Chief Executive Officer
CFO: Jay Johnson, Chief Financial Officer
CHR: Julie Graumann, Director
CNO: Kimberly Todd, Chief Nursing Officer
Web address: www.alliancehealthclinton.com
**Control**: Partnership, Investor–owned (for–profit) **Service**: General medical and surgical

**Staffed Beds**: 49

**CLINTON REGIONAL HOSPITAL** See Alliancehealth Clinton

---

**Hospital, Medicare Provider Number, Address, Telephone, Approval, Facility, and Physician Codes, Health Care System**

★ American Hospital Association (AHA) membership
☐ The Joint Commission accreditation
○ Healthcare Facilities Accreditation Program
◇ DNV Healthcare Inc. accreditation
⇑ Center for Improvement in Healthcare Quality Accreditation
△ Commission on Accreditation of Rehabilitation Facilities (CARF) accreditation

**OK**

### COALGATE—Coal County

★ **COAL COUNTY GENERAL HOSPITAL (371319)**, 6 North Covington Street, Zip 74538–2002, Mailing Address: P.O. Box 326, Zip 74538–0326; tel. 580/927–2327, (Nonreporting) **A**10 18 **F**29 30 38 40 41 56 62 63 64 68 75 77 89 97 100 104 105 107 114 115 119 127 128 130 133 135 148 152 154 **P**5
Primary Contact: Trent Bourland, Chief Executive Officer
CFO: Diane Downard, Chief Financial Officer
CMO: R.J Helton, D.O., Chief of Staff
CIO: Matt Balliett, Chief Information Officer
CHR: Cyndie Martin, Director
CNO: Farra Ybarra, R.N., Chief Nursing Officer
Web address: www.hillcrest.com
**Control:** Hospital district or authority, Government, Nonfederal **Service:** General medical and surgical

**Staffed Beds:** 20 **Admissions:** 423 **Census:** 4 **Outpatient Visits:** 6349 **Births:** 0

**HURLEY HEALTH CENTER** See Coal County General Hospital

### CORDELL—Washita County

★ ⇑ **CORDELL MEMORIAL HOSPITAL (371325)**, 1220 North Glenn English Street, Zip 73632–2010; tel. 580/832–3339, (Nonreporting) **A**10 18 21 **F**7 29 40 57 59 107 115 127 133 154
Primary Contact: Kenny Downs, Chief Executive Officer
CFO: Sue Kelley, Chief Financial Officer
Web address: www.cordellmemorialhospital.com
**Control:** Hospital district or authority, Government, Nonfederal **Service:** General medical and surgical

**Staffed Beds:** 14 **Admissions:** 161 **Census:** 1 **Outpatient Visits:** 4912 **Births:** 0 **Total Expense ($000):** 6049 **Payroll Expense ($000):** 2893 **Personnel:** 57

### CUSHING—Payne County

**CUSHING REGIONAL HOSPITAL** See Hillcrest Hospital Cushing

★ **HILLCREST HOSPITAL CUSHING (370099)**, 1027 East Cherry Street, Zip 74023–4101; tel. 918/225–2915, (Nonreporting) **A**10 **F**11 15 18 29 34 35 39 40 43 44 45 46 50 51 56 57 59 64 68 71 75 77 79 81 86 87 93 94 97 107 110 111 114 115 119 129 130 131 143 146 148 **S** Ardent Health Services, Nashville, TN
Primary Contact: David Long, Interim Chief Executive Officer
CFO: Joseph Mendoza, Chief Financial Officer
CHR: Bethany Leininger, Manager Human Resource
CNO: Tina Petersen, Chief Nursing Officer
Web address: www.hillcrestcushing.com/
**Control:** Corporation, Investor–owned (for–profit) **Service:** General medical and surgical

**Staffed Beds:** 54 **Admissions:** 881 **Census:** 7 **Outpatient Visits:** 24743 **Births:** 0 **Total Expense ($000):** 18044 **Payroll Expense ($000):** 6026 **Personnel:** 104

### DRUMRIGHT—Creek County

**DRUMRIGHT REGIONAL HOSPITAL (371331)**, 610 West Bypass, Zip 74030–5957; tel. 918/382–2300, (Data for 158 days) (Nonreporting) **A**10 18 **F**3 29 40 43 45 65 68 77 79 81 85 91 93 97 107 114 127 128 130 133 154 **S** Rural Community Hospitals of America, Kansas City, MO
Primary Contact: Rebecca Benham, Interim Chief Executive Officer
CFO: Mark Conrath, Chief Financial Officer
Web address: www.drumrighthospital.com/
**Control:** Corporation, Investor–owned (for–profit) **Service:** General medical and surgical

**Staffed Beds:** 15 **Admissions:** 179 **Census:** 10 **Outpatient Visits:** 1496 **Births:** 0 **Personnel:** 57

### DUNCAN—Stephens County

⊞ **DUNCAN REGIONAL HOSPITAL (370023)**, 1407 North Whisenant Drive, Zip 73533–1650, Mailing Address: P.O. Box 2000, Zip 73534–2000; tel. 580/252–5300, (Nonreporting) **A**1 5 10 20 **S** DRH Health, Duncan, OK
Primary Contact: Jay R. Johnson, FACHE, President and Chief Executive Officer
COO: Roger Neal, Chief Operating Officer
CFO: Douglas R. Volinski, Vice President and Chief Financial Officer
CMO: Krystal Vonfeldt, M.D., Chief of Staff
CHR: Michelle Bivans, Director Human Resources
CNO: Kristen Webb, Chief Nursing Officer
Web address: www.duncanregional.com
**Control:** Other not–for–profit (including NFP Corporation) **Service:** General medical and surgical

**Staffed Beds:** 117

### DURANT—Bryan County

⊞ **ALLIANCEHEALTH DURANT (370014)**, 1800 University Boulevard, Zip 74701–3006, Mailing Address: P.O. Box 1207, Zip 74702–1207; tel. 580/924–3080, (Nonreporting) **A**1 3 5 10 13 19 **F**3 8 11 12 13 15 17 18 20 22 28 29 30 34 35 39 40 43 45 50 51 56 57 59 70 74 75 76 77 79 80 81 82 85 86 89 97 102 107 110 111 114 115 119 126 130 131 135 145 146 147 148 154 **P**8 **S** Community Health Systems, Inc., Franklin, TN
Primary Contact: Kevin Samrow, Chief Executive Officer
CFO: Cindy Rios, Chief Financial Officer
CMO: Kevin Gordon, M.D., Chief of Staff
CIO: Katy Stinson, Director Information Services
Web address: www.alliancehealthdurant.com/
**Control:** Corporation, Investor–owned (for–profit) **Service:** General medical and surgical

**Staffed Beds:** 140 **Admissions:** 5822 **Census:** 50 **Outpatient Visits:** 54054 **Births:** 912

**MEDICAL CENTER OF SOUTHEASTERN OKLAHOMA** See Alliancehealth Durant

### EDMOND—Oklahoma County

**EDMOND MEDICAL CENTER** See Ou Medical Center Edmond

**FOUNDATION BARIATRIC HOSPITAL OF OKLAHOMA** See Summit Medical Center

⊞ **INTEGRIS HEALTH EDMOND (370236)**, 4801 Integris Parkway, Zip 73034–8864; tel. 405/657–3000, (Nonreporting) **A**1 3 5 10 **F**3 8 11 13 15 18 20 22 29 30 34 35 40 43 45 46 47 49 53 54 57 59 60 64 68 70 73 74 76 77 78 79 81 82 85 87 93 97 100 102 107 108 110 111 114 115 118 119 130 131 132 135 146 147 148 149 154 155 **P**6 7 **S** INTEGRIS Health, Oklahoma City, OK
Primary Contact: Jonathan Rule, Chief Hospital Executive
CNO: Angela K Kamermayer, MS, Chief Nursing Officer
Web address: www.integrisok.com/edmond
**Control:** Other not–for–profit (including NFP Corporation) **Service:** General medical and surgical

**Staffed Beds:** 40 **Admissions:** 2792 **Census:** 25 **Outpatient Visits:** 54847 **Births:** 782 **Total Expense ($000):** 65740 **Payroll Expense ($000):** 18492 **Personnel:** 292

**OU MEDICAL CENTER EDMOND** See Ou Medical Center, Oklahoma City

★ **SUMMIT MEDICAL CENTER (370225)**, 1800 S Renaissance Boulevard, Zip 73013–3023; tel. 405/359–2400, (Nonreporting) **A**5 10 **F**3 12 29 40 41 45 54 64 70 75 79 81 82 85 107 111 119 129 131 148 149 156
Primary Contact: Curtis Summers, Chief Executive Officer
Web address: www.summitmedcenter.com/
**Control:** Partnership, Investor–owned (for–profit) **Service:** General medical and surgical

**Staffed Beds:** 9 **Admissions:** 649 **Census:** 4 **Outpatient Visits:** 19928 **Births:** 0 **Total Expense ($000):** 40908 **Payroll Expense ($000):** 10707 **Personnel:** 185

### ELK CITY—Beckham County

**COMMUNITY HOSPITAL** See Great Plains Regional Medical Center

⊞ **GREAT PLAINS REGIONAL MEDICAL CENTER (370019)**, 1801 West Third Street, Zip 73644–5145, Mailing Address: P.O. Box 2339, Zip 73648–2339; tel. 580/225–2511, (Nonreporting) **A**1 5 10 20 **F**3 11 12 13 15 18 28 29 30 31 34 35 40 43 50 56 57 59 62 64 68 70 74 75 76 77 78 79 81 82 85 87 89 90 91 93 96 98 100 101 103 107 108 110 111 115 118 119 120 121 123 127 129 130 131 132 133 146 147 148 149 156
Primary Contact: Corey Lively, Chief Executive Officer
COO: Jon Gill, Chief Operating Officer
CFO: Monica Scott, Chief Financial Officer
CMO: Craig Phelps, M.D., Chief of Staff
CIO: Terry Price, Director Information Technology
CHR: Misty Carter, Chief Human Resource Officer and Ancillary Services
CNO: Gayle Ann Sturgis, Chief Nursing Officer, Risk Management
Web address: www.gprmc-ok.com
**Control:** Other not–for–profit (including NFP Corporation) **Service:** General medical and surgical

**Staffed Beds:** 60 **Admissions:** 1811 **Census:** 24 **Outpatient Visits:** 57326 **Births:** 319 **Total Expense ($000):** 50912 **Payroll Expense ($000):** 18008 **Personnel:** 373

## ENID—Garfield County

**INTEGRIS BASS BEHAVIORAL HEALTH SYSTEM** See Integris Bass Meadowlake

☒ **INTEGRIS BASS BAPTIST HEALTH CENTER (370016)**, 600 South Monroe Street, Zip 73701–7211, Mailing Address: P.O. Box 3168, Zip 73702–3168; tel. 580/233–2300, (Includes INTEGRIS BASS MEADOWLAKE, Mailing address: 2216 South Van Buren Street, Enid, Oklahoma, Zip 73703–8299; tel. 580/234–2220), (Nonreporting) **A**1 10 **F**3 11 13 15 17 18 20 22 28 30 31 35 40 43 45 49 51 56 57 59 62 64 65 70 74 75 76 78 79 81 85 89 97 98 99 107 108 109 110 111 114 115 118 119 120 121 126 127 129 130 131 132 146 147 148 149 154 **P**6 7 **S** INTEGRIS Health, Oklahoma City, OK
Primary Contact: Finny Mathew, President
CFO: Stacie Mason, Vice President, Regional Chief Financial Officer
CMO: Michael Jackson, M.D., Assistant Chief Medical Officer
CNO: Kenna Wilson, Vice President, Chief Nursing Officer
Web address: www.integris-health.com
**Control**: Other not–for–profit (including NFP Corporation) **Service**: General medical and surgical

**Staffed Beds:** 132 **Admissions:** 3344 **Census:** 61 **Outpatient Visits:** 63991
**Births:** 888 **Total Expense ($000):** 97763 **Payroll Expense ($000):** 29491
**Personnel:** 437

**INTEGRIS BASS BAPTIST HOSPITAL** See Integris Bass Baptist Health Center

**ST MARY'S MERCY HOSPITAL** See St. Mary's Regional Medical Center

☐ △ **ST. MARY'S REGIONAL MEDICAL CENTER (370026)**, 305 South Fifth Street, Zip 73701–5899, Mailing Address: P.O. Box 232, Zip 73702–0232; tel. 580/233–6100, (Nonreporting) **A**1 7 10 **F**3 11 13 15 18 20 22 28 29 30 31 34 35 39 40 43 45 51 56 57 59 60 64 68 70 73 74 75 76 78 79 80 81 82 85 86 87 89 90 92 93 96 98 100 101 107 108 110 111 114 115 118 119 126 129 130 131 132 135 146 147 149 **S** Universal Health Services, Inc., King of Prussia, PA
Primary Contact: Krista Roberts, Chief Executive Officer
COO: Anthony Rodebush, Chief Operating Officer
CFO: David Jamin, Chief Financial Officer
CMO: Michael Pontious, M.D., Chief of Staff
CIO: Tracy Andersen, Chief Information Officer
CHR: David Camp, Director Human Resources
CNO: Douglas W Coffey, R.N., MSN, Chief Nursing Officer
Web address: www.stmarysregional.com
**Control**: Corporation, Investor–owned (for–profit) **Service**: General medical and surgical

**Staffed Beds:** 124 **Admissions:** 5147 **Census:** 62 **Outpatient Visits:** 88596
**Births:** 273 **Total Expense ($000):** 86624 **Payroll Expense ($000):** 34112
**Personnel:** 468

## FAIRFAX—Osage County

**FAIRFAX COMMUNITY HOSPITAL (371318)**, 40 Hospital Road, Zip 74637–5084; tel. 918/642–3291, (Nonreporting) **A**10 18 **S** Rural Community Hospitals of America, Kansas City, MO
Primary Contact: Hunter Thoms, Chief Executive Officer
COO: Linda Thompson, Chief Operating Officer
CMO: Arman Janloo, M.D., Chief Medical Staff
CIO: Lisa Drymon, Manager
CHR: Sharon Binkley, Director Human Resources
**Control**: Corporation, Investor–owned (for–profit) **Service**: General medical and surgical

**Staffed Beds:** 15

**FAIRFAX MEMORIAL HOSPITAL** See Fairfax Community Hospital

## FAIRVIEW—Major County

**FAIRVIEW HOSPITAL** See Fairview Regional Medical Center

**FAIRVIEW REGIONAL MEDICAL CENTER (371329)**, 523 East State Road, Zip 73737–1453, Mailing Address: P.O. Box 548, Zip 73737–0548; tel. 580/227–3721, (Nonreporting) **A**10 18 **F**3 28 34 35 38 40 43 45 57 59 64 65 68 69 75 77 81 84 85 91 93 100 107 114 127 128 130 131 132 133 135 146 148 149 154 156 **P**5
Primary Contact: Roger Knak, Administrator and Chief Executive Officer
CMO: John Stephen Price, M.D., Chief of Staff
CIO: Bob Maynard, Chief Information Officer
CHR: Elisabeth Hughes, Director Human Resources and Community Relations
CNO: Tamara Eitzen, Chief Nursing Officer
Web address: www.fairviewregionalmedicalcenter.com
**Control**: Hospital district or authority, Government, Nonfederal **Service**: General medical and surgical

**Staffed Beds:** 25 **Admissions:** 146 **Census:** 2 **Outpatient Visits:** 9780
**Births:** 0 **Total Expense ($000):** 6385 **Payroll Expense ($000):** 3460
**Personnel:** 73

## FORT SUPPLY—Woodward County

**NORTHWEST CENTER FOR BEHAVIORAL HEALTH (374001)**, 193461 East County Road, #304, Zip 73841, Mailing Address: 1222 10th Street, Suite 211, Woodward, Zip 73801–3156; tel. 580/766–2311, (Nonreporting) **A**3 10 **F**98 104 130 132 135 149 154 **S** Oklahoma Department of Mental Health and Substance Abuse Services, Oklahoma City, OK
Primary Contact: Cathy Billings, Interim Executive Director
Web address: www.ncbhok.org/
**Control**: State, Government, Nonfederal **Service**: Psychiatric

**Staffed Beds:** 24 **Admissions:** 586 **Census:** 18 **Outpatient Visits:** 49427
**Births:** 0 **Total Expense ($000):** 13010 **Payroll Expense ($000):** 6647
**Personnel:** 185

**WESTERN STATE PSYCHIATRIC CTR** See Northwest Center for Behavioral Health

## GROVE—Delaware County

**INTEGRIS GROVE HOSPITAL** See Integris Grove Hospital

☒ **INTEGRIS GROVE HOSPITAL (370113)**, 1001 East 18th Street, Zip 74344–2907; tel. 918/786–2243, (Nonreporting) **A**1 10 20 **F**3 7 11 13 15 18 20 22 29 30 31 34 35 40 43 45 51 54 57 59 62 64 70 76 77 78 79 81 85 91 93 107 108 109 110 111 115 119 129 146 147 148 154 **P**6 7 **S** INTEGRIS Health, Oklahoma City, OK
Primary Contact: Jonas Rabel, President
CFO: Stacie Mason, Vice President and Chief Financial Officer
CMO: Kyle Schauf, M.D., President Medical Staff
CNO: Brandi Stewart, R.N., Vice President and Chief Nursing Officer
Web address: www.integris-health.com
**Control**: Other not–for–profit (including NFP Corporation) **Service**: General medical and surgical

**Staffed Beds:** 58 **Admissions:** 1764 **Census:** 16 **Outpatient Visits:** 37478
**Births:** 315 **Total Expense ($000):** 46968 **Payroll Expense ($000):** 13074
**Personnel:** 203

## GUTHRIE—Logan County

**LOGAN MEDICAL CENTER** See Mercy Hospital Logan County

★ **MERCY HOSPITAL LOGAN COUNTY (371317)**, 200 South Academy Road, Zip 73044–8727, Mailing Address: P.O. Box 1017, Zip 73044–1017; tel. 405/282–6700, (Nonreporting) **A**10 18 **F**3 15 29 30 34 35 40 44 50 57 59 68 75 77 87 93 107 110 111 114 119 127 129 130 131 133 144 146 148 149 **S** Mercy, Chesterfield, MO
Primary Contact: Bobby Stitt, R.N., Administrator
CMO: Jignesh Veragiwala, Chief of Staff
CHR: Mary Jo Messelt, Senior Human Resources Manager
Web address: www.mercy.net
**Control**: Church operated, Nongovernment, not–for–profit **Service**: General medical and surgical

**Staffed Beds:** 25 **Admissions:** 406 **Census:** 6 **Outpatient Visits:** 84105
**Births:** 0 **Total Expense ($000):** 17465 **Payroll Expense ($000):** 10663
**Personnel:** 121

## GUYMON—Texas County

⇑ **MEMORIAL HOSPITAL** See Memorial Hospital of Texas County

---

**Hospital, Medicare Provider Number, Address, Telephone, Approval, Facility, and Physician Codes, Health Care System**

★ American Hospital Association (AHA) membership
☐ The Joint Commission accreditation
○ Healthcare Facilities Accreditation Program
◇ DNV Healthcare Inc. accreditation
⇑ Center for Improvement in Healthcare Quality Accreditation
△ Commission on Accreditation of Rehabilitation Facilities (CARF) accreditation

**OK**

⇑ **MEMORIAL HOSPITAL OF TEXAS COUNTY (371340)**, 520 Medical Drive,
Zip 73942–4438; tel. 580/338–6515, (Nonreporting) **A**10 18 21
Primary Contact: Pamela McFarland, Interim Chief Executive Officer
CFO: Michele Reust, Controller
CIO: Sheldon Spence, Director of Revenue Cycle, IT
CHR: Sarah Wagner, Human Resources Officer
CNO: Dondie Rodgers, Interim Chief Nursing Officer
Web address: www.mhtcguymon.org
**Control**: County, Government, Nonfederal **Service**: General medical and surgical

**Staffed Beds:** 14

### HEALDTON—Carter County

**HEALDTON MERCY HOSPITAL** See Mercy Hospital Healdton

★ **MERCY HOSPITAL HEALDTON (371310)**, 3462 Hospital Road,
Zip 73438–6124, Mailing Address: P.O. Box 928, Zip 73438–0928;
tel. 580/229–0701, (Nonreporting) **A**10 18 **F**3 29 35 40 43 44 64 68 107 114
127 133 146 149 154 157 **S** Mercy, Chesterfield, MO
Primary Contact: Nichole Barrett, R.N., Interim Administrator
CMO: Mark Newey, D.O., Chief of Staff
CHR: Melinda Sharum, Director Human Resources
Web address: www.mercyok.com
**Control**: Church operated, Nongovernment, not–for–profit **Service**: General medical and surgical

**Staffed Beds:** 22 **Admissions:** 173 **Census:** 6 **Outpatient Visits:** 11365
**Births:** 0 **Total Expense ($000):** 6187 **Payroll Expense ($000):** 3467
**Personnel:** 52

### HENRYETTA—Okmulgee County

**HENRYETTA MEDICAL CENTER** See Hillcrest Hospital Henryetta

★ **HILLCREST HOSPITAL HENRYETTA (370183)**, 2401 West Main Street,
Zip 74437–3893, Mailing Address: P.O. Box 1269, Zip 74437–1269;
tel. 918/650–1100, (Nonreporting) **A**10 **F**3 15 18 29 35 40 45 54 56 64 75 79
81 87 91 93 107 108 110 111 114 119 127 129 130 131 133 143 148 152
154 **S** Ardent Health Services, Nashville, TN
Primary Contact: Dee Renshaw, Chief Executive Officer
CFO: Joseph Mendoza, Chief Financial Officer
CHR: Sheree Snyder, Manager Human Resources
CNO: April Secor, R.N., Chief Nursing Officer
Web address: www.hillcresthenryetta.com/
**Control**: Corporation, Investor–owned (for–profit) **Service**: General medical and surgical

**Staffed Beds:** 39 **Admissions:** 719 **Census:** 11 **Outpatient Visits:** 53672
**Births:** 0 **Total Expense ($000):** 17337 **Payroll Expense ($000):** 7346
**Personnel:** 101

### HOBART—Kiowa County

★ **ELKVIEW GENERAL HOSPITAL (370153)**, 429 West Elm Street,
Zip 73651–1615; tel. 580/726–1900, (Nonreporting) **A**10 20 **F**3 15 29 34 40 57
59 79 81 85 89 93 107 108 110 111 115 119 129 133 146 148 154 **P**6
Primary Contact: Lisa Hart, Chief Executive Officer
CMO: Ross Riddle, D.O., Medical Director
CIO: Dennis Tarver, Director Information Technology
CHR: Sharon Moad, Human Resources Director Health Information Management
CNO: Debbie Norman, MSN, R.N., Chief Nursing Officer
Web address: www.elkviewhospital.com
**Control**: Hospital district or authority, Government, Nonfederal **Service**: General medical and surgical

**Staffed Beds:** 25 **Admissions:** 666 **Census:** 6 **Outpatient Visits:** 20483
**Births:** 1 **Total Expense ($000):** 11841 **Payroll Expense ($000):** 5568
**Personnel:** 120

### HOLDENVILLE—Hughes County

★ **HOLDENVILLE GENERAL HOSPITAL (371321)**, 100 McDougal Drive,
Zip 74848–2822; tel. 405/379–4200, (Nonreporting) **A**10 18 **F**3 11 29 30 34 40
57 59 64 65 79 81 97 107 111 115 119 127 128 133 146
Primary Contact: Stephen C. Stewart, Chief Executive Officer
CFO: Drew Johnson, Chief Financial Officer
CMO: Tom Osborn, D.O., Chief Medical Staff
CIO: Mike Combs, Manager Information Technology
CHR: Heather Heard, Director Human Resources
CNO: Jackie Smith, R.N., Chief Nursing Officer
Web address: www.holdenvillehospital.com/
**Control**: City, Government, Nonfederal **Service**: General medical and surgical

**Staffed Beds:** 25 **Admissions:** 406 **Census:** 6 **Outpatient Visits:** 34789
**Births:** 0 **Total Expense ($000):** 11089 **Payroll Expense ($000):** 5311
**Personnel:** 121

### HOLLIS—Harmon County

**HARMON MEMORIAL HOSPITAL (371338)**, 400 East Chestnut Street,
Zip 73550–2030, Mailing Address: P.O. Box 791, Zip 73550–0791;
tel. 580/688–3363, (Nonreporting) **A**10 18 **F**40 68 75 85 93 107 128 133 149
154
Primary Contact: Dena Daniel, Chief Administrative Officer
CFO: Willie Mae Copeland, Chief Financial Officer
CMO: Akram Abraham, M.D., Chief of Staff
CHR: Abbey Welch, Director Human Resources
Web address: www.harmonmemorial.com/
**Control**: Hospital district or authority, Government, Nonfederal **Service**: General medical and surgical

**Staffed Beds:** 14 **Admissions:** 401 **Census:** 5 **Outpatient Visits:** 4239
**Births:** 0 **Total Expense ($000):** 5669 **Payroll Expense ($000):** 2349
**Personnel:** 57

### HUGO—Choctaw County

**CHOCTAW MEMORIAL HOSPITAL (370100)**, 1405 East Kirk Street,
Zip 74743–3603; tel. 580/317–9500, (Nonreporting) **A**10
Primary Contact: Nick Rowland, Interim Chief Executive Officer
CIO: Andy Richmond, Director Information Technology
CHR: Darlene Galyon, Director Human Resources
Web address: www.choctawmemorial.com
**Control**: Hospital district or authority, Government, Nonfederal **Service**: General medical and surgical

**Staffed Beds:** 32

### IDABEL—Mccurtain County

⇑ **MCCURTAIN MEMORIAL HOSPITAL (371342)**, 1301 Lincoln Road,
Zip 74745–7341; tel. 580/286–7623, (Nonreporting) **A**10 18 20 21 **F**3 11 13 14
15 18 28 29 30 34 35 40 41 45 46 47 48 49 50 53 54 59 63 64 66 68 75 76
77 81 85 87 89 91 93 102 107 110 111 114 115 119 124 127 133 144 145
146 147 148 154
Primary Contact: Brad S. Morse, FACHE, Interim Chief Executive Officer
CFO: Ray B Whitmore, Chief Financial Officer
CMO: Michael C West, M.D., Chief of Staff
CIO: Dana A Stowell, Chief Information Officer
CNO: Pamela Johnson, R.N., Chief Nursing Officer
Web address: www.mmhok.com
**Control**: Other not–for–profit (including NFP Corporation) **Service**: General medical and surgical

**Staffed Beds:** 25 **Admissions:** 997 **Census:** 11 **Outpatient Visits:** 30000
**Births:** 200 **Total Expense ($000):** 14134 **Payroll Expense ($000):** 6725
**Personnel:** 151

### KINGFISHER—Kingfisher County

**KINGFISHER REGIONAL HOSPITAL** See Mercy Hospital Kingfisher

⊞ **MERCY HOSPITAL KINGFISHER (371313)**, 1000 Hospital Cirle,
Zip 73750–5002, Mailing Address: P.O. Box 59, Zip 73750–0059;
tel. 405/375–3141, (Nonreporting) **A**1 10 18 **F**3 11 15 29 30 34 35 40 41 43
45 50 59 64 68 75 77 79 81 82 85 87 89 93 107 110 111 115 119 129 133
146 148 149 154 157 **S** Mercy, Chesterfield, MO
Primary Contact: Brian Denton, Administrator
CMO: Brett Krablin, M.D., Chief of Staff
CIO: Chad Kliewer, Information Technology Specialist
CHR: Carolyn Bjerke, Director Human Resources
CNO: Hannah Powell, Chief Nursing Officer
Web address: www.https://www.mercy.net/practice/mercy-hospital-kingfisher/
**Control**: Church operated, Nongovernment, not–for–profit **Service**: General medical and surgical

**Staffed Beds:** 25 **Admissions:** 332 **Census:** 5 **Outpatient Visits:** 19187
**Births:** 0 **Total Expense ($000):** 12209 **Payroll Expense ($000):** 6467
**Personnel:** 71

*Many Facility Codes have changed. Please refer to the AHA Guide Code Chart.*   © 2021 AHA Guide

OK

## LAWTON—Comanche County

**COLUMBIA SOUTHWESTERN MED CTR** See Southwestern Medical Center

☒ △ **COMANCHE COUNTY MEMORIAL HOSPITAL (370056)**, 3401 West Gore Boulevard, Zip 73505–6332, Mailing Address: P.O. Box 129, Zip 73502–0129; tel. 580/355–8620, (Total facility includes 146 beds in nursing home–type unit) (Nonreporting) **A**1 3 5 7 10 13 **F**3 6 7 8 11 12 13 15 17 18 20 22 24 26 28 29 30 31 32 34 35 40 43 45 46 47 48 49 50 51 54 56 57 59 62 63 64 65 66 68 70 72 74 75 76 77 78 79 80 81 82 84 85 86 89 90 91 92 93 96 97 98 103 104 107 108 110 111 114 115 116 117 118 119 120 121 127 129 130 131 132 134 135 143 146 147 148 156
Primary Contact: Brent Smith, Chief Executive Officer
CFO: George Kruger, CPA, Chief Financial Officer
CMO: Scott Michener, M.D., Chief Medical Officer
CIO: James Wellman, Senior Director Information Services
CHR: Donna Wade, Senior Director Human Resources
CNO: Chris Ward, Chief Nursing Officer
Web address: www.ccmhonline.com
**Control:** Hospital district or authority, Government, Nonfederal **Service:** General medical and surgical

**Staffed Beds:** 352 **Admissions:** 10982 **Census:** 270 **Outpatient Visits:** 184855 **Births:** 1292 **Total Expense ($000):** 264159 **Payroll Expense ($000):** 110463 **Personnel:** 1473

**JIM TALIAFERRO COMMUNITY MENTAL HEALTH (374008)**, 602 SW 38th Street, Zip 73505; tel. 580/248–5780, (Nonreporting) **A**3 10
Primary Contact: Debbie Moran, Executive Director
Web address: www.odmhsas.org
**Control:** State, Government, Nonfederal **Service:** Psychiatric

**Staffed Beds:** 22

☐ **LAWTON INDIAN HOSPITAL (370170)**, 1515 Lawrie Tatum Road, Zip 73507–3099; tel. 580/353–0350, (Nonreporting) **A**1 5 10 **S** U. S. Indian Health Service, Rockville, MD
Primary Contact: Lenora Littledeer, R.N., Chief Executive Officer and Chief Nursing Officer
COO: John Bear, Hospital Administrator Officer and Supervisor Human Resources
CFO: Sarabeth Sahmaunt, Supervisory Accountant
CMO: Richard Chadek, M.D., Clinical Director
CIO: William R Harris, Chief Information Officer
CHR: John Bear, Hospital Administrator Officer and Supervisor Human Resources
CNO: Lenora Littledeer, R.N., Chief Executive Officer and Chief Nursing Officer
Web address: www.ihs.gov
**Control:** PHS, Indian Service, Government, federal **Service:** General medical and surgical

**Staffed Beds:** 26

**PHS INDIAN HOSPITAL** See Lawton Indian Hospital

☒ ○ △ **SOUTHWESTERN MEDICAL CENTER (370097)**, 5602 SW Lee Boulevard, Zip 73505–9635; tel. 580/531–4700, (Nonreporting) **A**1 5 7 10 11 19 **F**3 8 13 29 30 34 38 40 41 45 47 49 50 51 57 59 60 64 65 67 68 70 74 76 77 79 81 85 87 89 90 91 92 93 98 99 100 101 102 104 106 107 108 111 114 118 119 129 130 131 133 135 146 147 148 **P**6 **S** LifePoint Health, Brentwood, TN
Primary Contact: Elizabeth Jones, Chief Executive Officer
CFO: Wayne Colson, Chief Financial Officer
CMO: Aryan Kadivar, M.D., Chief Medical Officer
CIO: Kent Lewis, Director Information Services
CHR: Danny Hale, Director Human Resources
CNO: Jayne Thomas, Chief Nursing Officer
Web address: www.swmconline.com
**Control:** Corporation, Investor–owned (for–profit) **Service:** General medical and surgical

**Staffed Beds:** 178 **Admissions:** 4948 **Census:** 80 **Outpatient Visits:** 61299 **Births:** 669 **Total Expense ($000):** 88617 **Payroll Expense ($000):** 40252 **Personnel:** 496

## LINDSAY—Garvin County

**LINDSAY MUNICIPAL HOSPITAL (370214)**, Highway 19 West, Zip 73052, Mailing Address: P.O. Box 888, Zip 73052–0888; tel. 405/756–1404, (Nonreporting) **A**10
Primary Contact: Jeff Walraven, Chief Executive Officer
**Control:** City, Government, Nonfederal **Service:** General medical and surgical

**Staffed Beds:** 26

## MADILL—Marshall County

☒ **ALLIANCEHEALTH MADILL (371326)**, 901 South Fifth Avenue, Zip 73446–3640, Mailing Address: P.O. Box 827, Zip 73446–0827; tel. 580/795–3384, (Nonreporting) **A**1 10 18 **F**29 35 40 43 45 75 81 93 107 114 119 127 133 146 157 **S** Community Health Systems, Inc., Franklin, TN
Primary Contact: Kevin Samrow, Chief Executive Officer
CFO: Thomas Briggs, Chief Financial Officer
CMO: Heidi Haislip, M.D., Chief of Staff
CHR: D.J. Shawn, Director Human Resources
CNO: Carol Wright, Chief Nursing Officer
Web address: www.myalliancehealth.com
**Control:** Corporation, Investor–owned (for–profit) **Service:** General medical and surgical

**Staffed Beds:** 23 **Admissions:** 129 **Census:** 1 **Outpatient Visits:** 43154 **Births:** 0 **Total Expense ($000):** 14671 **Payroll Expense ($000):** 6781

**MARSHALL COUNTY MEDICAL CENTER** See Alliancehealth Madill

## MANGUM—Greer County

**MANGUM CITY HOSPITAL** See Mangum Regional Medical Center

**MANGUM REGIONAL MEDICAL CENTER (371330)**, One Wickersham Drive, Zip 73554–9116, Mailing Address: P.O. Box 280, Zip 73554–0280; tel. 580/782–3353, (Nonreporting) **A**10 18 **F**3 29 40 91 93 97 101 104 107 114 119 127 133 148 153 154
Primary Contact: Nicholas (Ty) Weston, Interim Chief Executive Officer
COO: Danny Avery, Chief Financial Officer and Chief Operating Officer
CIO: Gregg Burnam, Chief Information Officer and Manager Business Office
Web address: www.https://mangumregional.net
**Control:** City, Government, Nonfederal **Service:** General medical and surgical

**Staffed Beds:** 18 **Admissions:** 379 **Census:** 2 **Outpatient Visits:** 7983 **Births:** 0 **Total Expense ($000):** 15403 **Payroll Expense ($000):** 4294 **Personnel:** 70

## MARIETTA—Love County

**LOVE COUNTY HEALTH CENTER** See Mercy Health Love County

★ **MERCY HEALTH LOVE COUNTY (371306)**, 300 Wanda Street, Zip 73448–1200; tel. 580/276–3347, (Nonreporting) **A**10 18 **F**2 3 7 11 29 34 40 43 44 50 57 59 77 87 91 107 114 119 127 133 135 146 148 149 **S** Mercy, Chesterfield, MO
Primary Contact: Richard Barker, Administrator and Chief Executive Officer
CIO: Connie Graham, Public Information Officer
Web address: www.mercyhealthlovecounty.com
**Control:** Church operated, Nongovernment, not–for–profit **Service:** General medical and surgical

**Staffed Beds:** 25 **Admissions:** 301 **Census:** 9 **Outpatient Visits:** 26336 **Births:** 0 **Total Expense ($000):** 16260 **Payroll Expense ($000):** 9386 **Personnel:** 127

## MCALESTER—Pittsburg County

**CARL ALBERT COMMUNITY MENTAL HEALTH CENTER (374006)**, 1101 East Monroe Avenue, Zip 74501–4826; tel. 918/426–7800, (Nonreporting) **A**3 10
Primary Contact: Debbie Moran, Executive Director
CFO: Konnie Taylor, Chief Financial Officer
CMO: William Mings, M.D., Medical Director
CHR: Judy Allen, Human Resource Specialist
Web address: www.odmhsas.org
**Control:** State, Government, Nonfederal **Service:** Psychiatric

**Staffed Beds:** 15

---

OK

★ ⇑ **MCALESTER REGIONAL HEALTH CENTER (370034)**, One East Clark Bass Boulevard, Zip 74501–4267, Mailing Address: 3473 E Hereford LN, Zip 74501; tel. 918/426–1800, (Total facility includes 60 beds in nursing home–type unit) (Nonreporting) **A**3 5 10 13 21 **F**3 8 10 11 13 15 18 20 22 26 29 30 34 35 40 43 45 49 50 51 53 54 56 57 59 61 62 63 64 66 68 69 70 75 76 77 79 81 82 85 86 87 90 91 92 93 98 101 102 103 104 107 108 109 110 111 114 115 116 117 118 119 125 129 130 131 132 135 144 146 147 148 154 158 **P**6
Primary Contact: David N. Keith, FACHE, President and Chief Executive Officer
CFO: Darryl Linnington, Chief Financial Officer
CIO: Jason Bray, Chief Information Officer
CHR: Scott Lowe, Director Human Resource
CNO: Kimberly Dawn Stout, Chief Nursing Officer and Chief Operating Officer
Web address: www.mrhcok.com
**Control**: City, Government, Nonfederal **Service**: General medical and surgical

**Staffed Beds:** 209 **Admissions:** 4519 **Census:** 94 **Outpatient Visits:** 79973 **Births:** 543 **Total Expense ($000):** 96483 **Payroll Expense ($000):** 41117 **Personnel:** 647

### MIAMI—Ottawa County

**INTEGRIS BAPTIST REGIONAL HEALTH CENTER** See Integris Miami Hospital

⊠ **INTEGRIS MIAMI HOSPITAL (370004)**, 200 Second Avenue SW, Zip 74354–6830; tel. 918/542–6611, (Nonreporting) **A**1 10 20 **F**3 7 11 13 15 18 26 28 29 30 34 35 40 43 44 45 53 57 59 62 63 70 75 76 77 79 81 85 89 93 107 108 109 110 111 115 119 120 121 123 131 132 135 144 146 147 148 154 **P**6 7 **S** INTEGRIS Health, Oklahoma City, OK
Primary Contact: Jonas Rabel, President
CFO: Valerie Reeves, Chief Financial Officer
CMO: Elaine Mader, M.D., Chief of Staff
CHR: Jamil Haynes, Regional Director Human Resources
CNO: Lisa Halstead, Chief Nursing Officer
Web address: www.integrisok.com/miami-hospital
**Control**: Other not–for–profit (including NFP Corporation) **Service**: General medical and surgical

**Staffed Beds:** 39 **Admissions:** 1955 **Census:** 20 **Outpatient Visits:** 47111 **Births:** 299 **Total Expense ($000):** 46941 **Payroll Expense ($000):** 15890 **Personnel:** 234

★ **WILLOW CREST HOSPITAL (374017)**, 130 'A' Street SW, Zip 74354–6800; tel. 918/542–1836, (Nonreporting) **A**10
Primary Contact: Shari Murphree, Chief Executive Officer
COO: Steven Goodman, Chief Operating Officer
CFO: Cindy Bell, Director Finance
CMO: Mark Elkington, M.D., Chief Medical Officer
CIO: Steven Goodman, Chief Operating Officer
CHR: Kathy Henderson, Director Human Resources
CNO: Kassi Davis, Director Patient Care Services
Web address: www.willowcresthospital.com
**Control**: Corporation, Investor–owned (for–profit) **Service**: Children's hospital psychiatric

**Staffed Beds:** 76

### MIDWEST CITY—Oklahoma County

⊠ **ALLIANCEHEALTH MIDWEST (370094)**, 2825 Parklawn Drive, Zip 73110–4258; tel. 405/610–4411, (Nonreporting) **A**1 3 5 10 **S** Community Health Systems, Inc., Franklin, TN
Primary Contact: Clay Franklin, Chief Executive Officer
COO: Lisa Ellis, Chief Operating Officer
CFO: Cynthia Gray, Interim Chief Financial Officer
CMO: Rockey Talley, M.D., Chief Medical Officer
CHR: Dana Leach, Director Human Resources
CNO: Jaconna Joni"" Tiller, Chief Nursing Officer
Web address: www.myalliancehealth.com
**Control**: Corporation, Investor–owned (for–profit) **Service**: General medical and surgical

**Staffed Beds:** 255

☐ **INSPIRE SPECIALTY HOSPITAL (372012)**, 8210 National Avenue, Zip 73110–8518; tel. 405/739–0800, (Nonreporting) **A**1 10 **S** Concord Healthcare Group, Lakewood, NJ
Primary Contact: Bobby Snyder, Chief Executive Officer
CFO: Veronica Scott, Business Office Manager
CHR: Anna Emamghoraishi, Human Resources
CNO: Jason Farris, Chief Nursing Officer
Web address: www.inspirehospital.com
**Control**: Corporation, Investor–owned (for–profit) **Service**: Acute long–term care hospital

**Staffed Beds:** 31

**MIDWEST CITY SPECIALTY HOSPITAL** See Inspire Specialty Hospital

**MIDWEST REGIONAL MEDICAL CENTER** See Alliancehealth Midwest

### MOORE—Cleveland County

**MOORE MEDICAL CENTER** See Norman Regional Moore

**NORMAN REGIONAL MOORE** See Norman Regional Health System, Norman

### MUSKOGEE—Muskogee County

**CORNERSTONE HOSPITAL OF OKLAHOMA-MUSKOGEE (372022)**, 351 South 40th Street, Zip 74401–4916; tel. 918/682–6161, (Includes CORNERSTONE HOSPITAL OF OKLAHOMA-BROKEN ARROW, Mailing address: 1000 West Boise Circle, Third Floor, Broken Arrow, Oklahoma, Zip 74012–4900, 1000 West Boise Circle, Zip 74012–4900, tel. 918/994–8300; Craig Koele, Chief Executive Officer), (Nonreporting) **A**10 22 **S** Cornerstone Healthcare Group, Dallas, TX
Primary Contact: Craig Koele, Chief Executive Officer
CMO: Jeremiah Rutherford, Chief Medical Officer
Web address: www.chghospitals.com/muskogee/
**Control**: Corporation, Investor–owned (for–profit) **Service**: Acute long–term care hospital

**Staffed Beds:** 41

**EASTAR HEALTH SYSTEM** See Saint Francis Hospital Muskogee

**EASTAR HEALTH SYSTEM, EAST CAMPUS** See Saint Francis Hospital Muskogee, Muskogee

**JACK C. MONTGOMERY VETERAN AFFAIRS MEDICAL CENTER** See Jack C. Montgomery Veterans Affairs Medical Center

⊠ △ **JACK C. MONTGOMERY VETERANS AFFAIRS MEDICAL CENTER**, 1011 Honor Heights Drive, Zip 74401–1318; tel. 918/577–3000, (Nonreporting) **A**1 3 5 7 **S** Department of Veterans Affairs, Washington, DC
Primary Contact: Mark E. Morgan, Medical Center Director
CFO: Dwight Beal, Chief Fiscal Services
CMO: Thomas D Schneider, D.O., Chief of Staff
Web address: www.muskogee.va.gov
**Control**: Veterans Affairs, Government, federal **Service**: General medical and surgical

**Staffed Beds:** 89

**MUSKOGEE COMMUNITY HOSPITAL** See Eastar Health System, East Campus

⊠ **SAINT FRANCIS HOSPITAL MUSKOGEE (370025)**, 300 Rockefeller Drive, Zip 74401–5081; tel. 918/682–5501, (Includes EASTAR HEALTH SYSTEM, EAST CAMPUS, Mailing address: 2900 North Main Street, Muskogee, Oklahoma, Zip 74401–4078; tel. 918/687–7777), (Nonreporting) **A**1 3 10 19 **F**3 8 11 13 15 18 20 22 28 29 30 31 35 37 40 43 45 53 54 56 57 60 64 68 70 74 75 76 78 79 81 82 85 86 87 89 90 92 96 98 100 102 103 107 108 110 111 114 115 119 120 121 123 124 126 129 130 131 141 143 146 147 148 **P**6 **S** Saint Francis Health System, Tulsa, OK
Primary Contact: Michele A. Keeling, Vice President and Administrator
COO: Tony Capuano, Chief Operating Officer
CFO: Scott Bailey, Chief Financial Officer
CMO: Jay Gregory, M.D., Chief Medical Officer
CIO: James Tolbert, Director Information Systems
CHR: Bill Peterson, Director Human Resources
Web address: www.https://www.saintfrancis.com/muskogee/Pages/default.aspx
**Control**: Church operated, Nongovernment, not–for–profit **Service**: General medical and surgical

**Staffed Beds:** 185 **Admissions:** 8536 **Census:** 124 **Outpatient Visits:** 78414 **Births:** 590 **Total Expense ($000):** 127960 **Payroll Expense ($000):** 49435 **Personnel:** 707

**SOLARA HOSPITAL OF MUSKOGEE** See Cornerstone Hospital of Oklahoma-Muskogee

## NORMAN—Cleveland County

**GRIFFIN MEM HOSP** See Griffin Memorial Hospital

☐ **GRIFFIN MEMORIAL HOSPITAL (374000)**, 900 East Main Street,
Zip 73071–5305, Mailing Address: P.O. Box 151, Zip 73070–0151;
tel. 405/573–6600, (Nonreporting) **A**1 3 5 10 **F**29 58 75 87 98 100 102
103 130 132 135 143 149 154 **S** Oklahoma Department of Mental Health and
Substance Abuse Services, Oklahoma City, OK
Primary Contact: Henry Hartsell, Ph.D., Executive Director
CFO: Cheryl Cupps, Director Finance
CMO: Clayton Morris, Medical Director
CNO: Mike Abla, Director of Nursing
Web address: www.odmhsas.org
**Control**: State, Government, Nonfederal **Service**: Psychiatric

**Staffed Beds**: 120 **Admissions**: 1391 **Census**: 116 **Outpatient Visits**: 2013
**Births**: 0 **Total Expense ($000)**: 24314 **Payroll Expense ($000)**: 11371
**Personnel**: 311

**J D MCCARTHY CTR FOR CHILDREN** See J. D. Mccarty Center for Children
With Developmental Disabilities

**J. D. MCCARTY CENTER FOR CHILDREN WITH DEVELOPMENTAL
DISABILITIES (373300)**, 2002 East Robinson, Zip 73071–7420;
tel. 405/307–2800, (Nonreporting) **A**10 **F**3 29 35 64 65 75 77 87 90 91 93 119
130 134 135 146
Primary Contact: Vicki Kuerstersteffen, Director and Chief Executive Officer
CFO: Erik Paulson, Director of Finance
CMO: Thomas Thurston, M.D., Medical Director
CIO: Jeffery Setzer, Administrator Information Systems
CHR: Tina Martinez, Director Human Resources
Web address: www.jdmc.org
**Control**: State, Government, Nonfederal **Service**: Children's rehabilitation

**Staffed Beds**: 36 **Admissions**: 133 **Census**: 30 **Outpatient Visits**: 9746
**Births**: 0 **Total Expense ($000)**: 23541 **Payroll Expense ($000)**: 10219
**Personnel**: 229

⊞ **NORMAN REGIONAL HEALTH SYSTEM (370008)**, 901 North Porter
Avenue, Zip 73071–6404, Mailing Address: P.O. Box 1308, Zip 73070–1308;
tel. 405/515–1000, (Includes NORMAN REGIONAL HOSPITAL, Mailing address:
901 North Porter Street, Norman, Oklahoma, Zip 73071–6482, P O Box 1308,
Zip 73070–1308, tel. 405/307–1000; Richie Splitt, FACHE, President and Chief
Executive Office; NORMAN REGIONAL MOORE, Mailing address: 700 South
Telephone Road, Moore, Oklahoma, Zip 73160; tel. 405/793–9355; Richie Splitt,
FACHE, President and Chief Executive Officer), (Nonreporting) **A**1 3 5 10 13 **F**3 7
11 12 13 15 17 18 20 22 24 28 29 30 31 32 34 35 36 37 39 40 43 44 45 47
48 49 50 53 54 55 56 57 58 59 63 64 65 69 70 72 74 75 76 77 78 79 80 81
82 83 84 85 86 87 89 90 93 94 96 97 98 100 101 102 103 104 107 110 111
114 115 117 118 119 120 123 126 127 129 130 131 132 135 143 145 146
147 148 154 156 157 **P**5 8
Primary Contact: Richie Splitt, FACHE, President and Chief Executive Officer
COO: John Manfredo, Chief Operating Officer
CFO: Ken Hopkins, Vice President Finance and Chief Financial Officer
CMO: Aaron Boyd, M.D., Chief Medical Officer
CIO: Danny Kelley, Administrative Director, Health Information Technology
CHR: Jim Beyer, Administrative Director Human Resources
CNO: Brittini McGill, MSN, R.N., Chief Nursing Officer
Web address: www.normanregional.com
**Control**: Hospital district or authority, Government, Nonfederal **Service**: General
medical and surgical

**Staffed Beds**: 387 **Admissions**: 17473 **Census**: 206 **Outpatient
Visits**: 380780 **Births**: 2408 **Total Expense ($000)**: 437870 **Payroll
Expense ($000)**: 202972 **Personnel**: 3350

## NOWATA—Nowata County

★ **JANE PHILLIPS NOWATA HEALTH CENTER (371305)**, 237 South Locust
Street, Zip 74048–3660; tel. 918/273–3102, (Nonreporting) **A**10 18 **F**3 29 30
34 35 40 50 57 64 68 107 114 119 128 133 146 154 **S** Ascension Healthcare,
Saint Louis, MO
Primary Contact: Jason McCauley, Administrator
CMO: David Caughell, M.D., Chief of Staff
Web address: www.jpmc.org
**Control**: Church operated, Nongovernment, not–for–profit **Service**: General
medical and surgical

**Staffed Beds**: 15 **Admissions**: 173 **Census**: 5 **Outpatient Visits**: 4792
**Births**: 0 **Total Expense ($000)**: 5255 **Payroll Expense ($000)**: 2377
**Personnel**: 29

## OKEENE—Blaine County

★ **OKEENE MUNICIPAL HOSPITAL (371327)**, 207 East 'F' Street,
Zip 73763–9441, Mailing Address: P.O. Box 489, Zip 73763–0489;
tel. 580/822–4417, (Nonreporting) **A**10 18 **F**3 29 34 40 45 59 64 65 68 77 81
85 93 97 107 119 130 133 135 148 149 154 **P**6
Primary Contact: Shelly Dunham, Chief Executive Officer
COO: Tammi Jantzen, Chief Operating Officer
CFO: Sandra Lamle, Chief Financial Officer
CMO: George S. Stenger, D.O., Chief of Staff
CHR: Barbara Creps, Director Human Resources and Accounting
CNO: Tamara Fischer, Chief Nursing Officer
Web address: www.okeenehospital.com
**Control**: Hospital district or authority, Government, Nonfederal **Service**: General
medical and surgical

**Staffed Beds**: 17 **Admissions**: 163 **Census**: 4 **Outpatient Visits**: 22855
**Births**: 0 **Total Expense ($000)**: 6845 **Payroll Expense ($000)**: 3166
**Personnel**: 49

## OKEMAH—Okfuskee County

★ ⚕ **CREEK NATION COMMUNITY HOSPITAL (371333)**, 1800 East Coplin
Street, Zip 74859–4642; tel. 918/623–1424, (Nonreporting) **A**10 18 21 **F**3 7 29
35 40 45 64 65 81 107 115 119 133
Primary Contact: Phillip Barnoski, Administrator
COO: Rhonda Beaver, Chief Operating Officer
CFO: Tyler McIntosh, Chief Financial Officer
CMO: Lawrence Vark, M.D., Chief Medical Officer
CIO: Robert Coffee, Chief Information Officer
CHR: Russell B Torbett, Director Human Resources
CNO: Annette James, R.N., MSN, Chief Nursing Officer
Web address: www.creekhealth.org
**Control**: Other not–for–profit (including NFP Corporation) **Service**: General
medical and surgical

**Staffed Beds**: 25 **Admissions**: 300 **Census**: 2 **Outpatient Visits**: 23558
**Births**: 0 **Total Expense ($000)**: 13959 **Payroll Expense ($000)**: 5046
**Personnel**: 126

## OKLAHOMA CITY—Oklahoma County

**ALLIANCEHEALTH DEACONESS** See Integris Deaconess

**AMG MERCY** See OKC-AMG Specialty Hospital

**BONE AND JOINT HOSPITAL** See Ssm Health Bone and Joint Hospital at St.
Anthony

☐ **CEDAR RIDGE HOSPITAL (374023)**, 6501 NE 50th Street, Zip 73141–9118;
tel. 405/605–6111, (Includes BETHANY BEHAVIORAL HEALTH, Mailing address:
7600 NW 23rd Street, Bethany, Oklahoma, Zip 73008–4944; tel. 405/792–5360;
Heather Joseph, Chief Executive Officer), (Nonreporting) **A**1 10 **F**98 99 103 105
106 130 149 153 154 **P**5 6 **S** Universal Health Services, Inc., King of Prussia, PA
Primary Contact: Heather Joseph, Chief Executive Officer
Web address: www.cedarridgebhs.com
**Control**: Corporation, Investor–owned (for–profit) **Service**: Psychiatric

**Staffed Beds**: 172 **Admissions**: 4312 **Census**: 118 **Outpatient Visits**: 2622
**Births**: 0 **Total Expense ($000)**: 23231 **Payroll Expense ($000)**: 12667
**Personnel**: 255

**CHILDREN'S HOSPITAL OF OKLAHOMA** See Ou Medical Center, Oklahoma City

---

## OKLAHOMA CITY—Cleveland County

⇑ **COMMUNITY HOSPITAL (370203)**, 3100 SW 89th Street, Zip 73159–7900, Mailing Address: 3125 SW 89th Street, Zip 73159–7900; tel. 405/602–8100, (Nonreporting) **A**10 21
Primary Contact: Debbie Kearns, Chief Executive Officer
Web address: www.communityhospitalokc.com
**Control**: Corporation, Investor–owned (for–profit) **Service**: Surgical

**Staffed Beds**: 45

## OKLAHOMA CITY—Oklahoma County

**CURAHEALTH HOSPITAL OKLAHOMA CITY (372004)**, 1407 North Robinson Avenue, Zip 73103–4823; tel. 405/232–8000, (Includes CURAHEALTH OKLAHOMA, Mailing address: 2129 SW 59th Street, Oklahoma City, Oklahoma, Zip 73119; tel. 405/713–5955; Brenda Hood, Chief Executive Officer), (Nonreporting) **A**10 **S** Curahealth Hospitals, Garland, TX
Primary Contact: Brenda Hood, Chief Executive Officer
Web address: www.curahealth.com
**Control**: Corporation, Investor–owned (for–profit) **Service**: Acute long–term care hospital

**Staffed Beds**: 93

**CURAHEALTH OKLAHOMA** See Curahealth Hospital Oklahoma City

**EVERETT TOWER** See Ou Medical Center, Oklahoma City

**INTEGRIS BAPTIST MEDICAL CENTER** See Integris Baptist Medical Center

⊠ △ **INTEGRIS BAPTIST MEDICAL CENTER (370028)**, 3300 NW Expressway, Zip 73112–4418; tel. 405/949–3011, (Includes INTEGRIS MENTAL HEALTH SYSTEM–SPENCER, Mailing address: 2601 North Spencer Road, Spencer, Oklahoma, Zip 73084–3699, P O Box 11137, Oklahoma City, Zip 73136–0137, tel. 405/717–9800), (Nonreporting) **A**1 2 3 5 7 10 **F**3 8 11 12 13 15 16 17 18 19 20 22 24 26 28 29 30 31 34 35 39 40 43 44 45 46 47 49 50 51 54 55 57 58 59 60 62 63 64 68 70 71 72 74 75 76 77 78 79 80 81 82 84 85 86 87 88 89 90 92 93 96 97 98 99 100 101 102 104 105 106 107 108 109 110 111 114 115 116 118 119 120 121 123 124 126 129 130 131 132 135 137 138 139 140 141 142 146 147 148 149 153 154 156 157 **P**6 7 **S** INTEGRIS Health, Oklahoma City, OK
Primary Contact: Rex Van Meter, Chief Hospital Executive
COO: Rex Van Meter, Chief Hospital Executive
CFO: Cheryl Perry, Chief Financial Officer
CIO: Mark Pasquale, Chief Information Officer
CHR: Jason L Eliot, Vice President Human Resources
CNO: Lewis L. Perkins, R.N., MSN, JrChief Nursing Officer
Web address: www.integrisok.com
**Control**: Other not–for–profit (including NFP Corporation) **Service**: General medical and surgical

**Staffed Beds**: 955 **Admissions**: 28545 **Census**: 515 **Outpatient Visits**: 310327 **Births**: 3060 **Total Expense ($000)**: 893988 **Payroll Expense ($000)**: 256094 **Personnel**: 3117

⇑ **INTEGRIS COMMUNITY HOSPITAL AT COUNCIL CROSSING**, 9417 North Council Road, Zip 73134–2521; tel. 405/500–3280, (Nonreporting) **A**21 **F**3 29 40 41 107 114 115 119 130 154 **S** Emerus, The Woodlands, TX
Primary Contact: Shannon Crinole, Chief Executive Officer
Web address: www.https://www.integriscommunityhospital.com/locations/council-crossing/
**Control**: Partnership, Investor–owned (for–profit) **Service**: General medical and surgical

**Staffed Beds**: 64 **Admissions**: 413 **Census**: 2 **Outpatient Visits**: 31732 **Births**: 0 **Total Expense ($000)**: 28504 **Payroll Expense ($000)**: 7306 **Personnel**: 170

★ △ **INTEGRIS DEACONESS (370032)**, 5501 North Portland Avenue, Zip 73112–2099; tel. 405/604–6000, (Nonreporting) **A**3 5 7 10 **S** INTEGRIS Health, Oklahoma City, OK
Primary Contact: Rex Van Meter, President
COO: Brett Kirkham, Chief Operating Officer
CIO: Don Bandy, Director Information Technology
CHR: Ellen Gifford, Director Human Resources
CNO: Jayne Thomas, Chief Nursing Officer
Web address: www.https://integrisok.com/locations/hospital/integris-deaconess
**Control**: Other not–for–profit (including NFP Corporation) **Service**: General medical and surgical

**Staffed Beds**: 141

⊠ **INTEGRIS SOUTHWEST MEDICAL CENTER (370106)**, 4401 South Western, Zip 73109–3413; tel. 405/636–7000, (Nonreporting) **A**1 2 3 5 10 13 **F**3 11 13 15 18 20 22 24 26 28 29 30 31 34 35 40 43 44 45 47 49 50 51 53 57 58 59 60 64 68 70 71 74 75 76 77 78 79 80 81 82 85 86 87 90 91 92 93 95 96 97 100 102 107 108 110 111 114 115 118 119 120 121 123 124 126 129 130 131 132 135 146 147 148 149 154 156 157 **P**6 7 **S** INTEGRIS Health, Oklahoma City, OK
Primary Contact: John Adams, Chief Hospital Executive
CFO: Dan Davis, Managing Director and Chief Financial Officer
CMO: Philip Mosca, M.D., President, Medical Staff
CIO: Mark Pasquale, Chief Information Officer
CHR: Lynn Ketch, Regional Director Integris Southwest Medical Center
CNO: Marva Harrison, R.N., Vice President and Chief Nursing Officer
Web address: www.integrisok.com
**Control**: Other not–for–profit (including NFP Corporation) **Service**: General medical and surgical

**Staffed Beds**: 273 **Admissions**: 11831 **Census**: 184 **Outpatient Visits**: 168399 **Births**: 1134 **Total Expense ($000)**: 249288 **Payroll Expense ($000)**: 76350 **Personnel**: 1278

**INTEGRIS SOUTHWEST MEDICAL CENTER** See Integris Southwest Medical Center

**KINDRED HOSPITAL-OKLAHOMA CITY SOUTH** See Curahealth Oklahoma

⊠ **LAKESIDE WOMEN'S HOSPITAL (370199)**, 11200 North Portland Avenue, Zip 73120–5045; tel. 405/936–1500, (Nonreporting) **A**1 10 **F**3 13 15 29 30 35 36 40 45 59 64 73 76 81 85 87 110 119 126 130 132 147 **P**6 **S** INTEGRIS Health, Oklahoma City, OK
Primary Contact: Kelley Brewer, R.N., MSN, President
CFO: Darla McCallister, Chief Financial Officer
CMO: Margaret Hall, M.D., Chief Medical Officer
Web address: www.lakeside-wh.net
**Control**: Corporation, Investor–owned (for–profit) **Service**: Obstetrics and gynecology

**Staffed Beds**: 23 **Admissions**: 1429 **Census**: 9 **Outpatient Visits**: 21367 **Births**: 1342 **Total Expense ($000)**: 23241 **Payroll Expense ($000)**: 8989 **Personnel**: 115

⇑ **MCBRIDE CLINIC ORTHOPEDIC HOSPITAL** See Mcbride Orthopedic Hospital

⇑ **MCBRIDE ORTHOPEDIC HOSPITAL (370222)**, 9600 Broadway Extension, Zip 73114–7408; tel. 405/486–2100, (Nonreporting) **A**3 5 10 21 **F**3 29 34 40 64 68 77 79 81 82 85 86 87 93 97 107 111 114 119 126 130 131 146 149
Primary Contact: Mark Galliart, Chief Executive Officer
CFO: Greg Gisler, Chief Financial Officer
CNO: Krista Reyna, Chief Nursing Officer
Web address: www.mcboh.com
**Control**: Corporation, Investor–owned (for–profit) **Service**: Orthopedic

**Staffed Beds**: 60 **Admissions**: 3512 **Census**: 24 **Outpatient Visits**: 164213 **Births**: 0 **Total Expense ($000)**: 154717 **Payroll Expense ($000)**: 59541 **Personnel**: 772

**MERCY HEALTH CENTER** See Mercy Hospital Oklahoma City

⊠ **MERCY HOSPITAL OKLAHOMA CITY (370013)**, 4300 West Memorial Road, Zip 73120–8362; tel. 405/755–1515, (Nonreporting) **A**1 2 3 10 **F**3 8 11 12 13 15 28 29 30 31 32 34 35 40 42 43 44 45 46 47 48 49 50 53 55 57 58 59 60 61 62 63 64 65 68 69 70 72 74 75 76 77 78 79 81 82 83 84 85 86 87 89 91 92 93 94 96 100 101 107 108 110 111 114 115 117 118 119 120 121 124 126 129 130 131 132 134 135 143 146 147 148 149 154 156 **S** Mercy, Chesterfield, MO
Primary Contact: Jim Gebhart Jr, FACHE, President
COO: Aaron Steffens, Chief Operating Officer
CFO: Jon Vitiello, Senior Vice President, Finance Operations and Analytics
CIO: Ellen Stephens, Vice President Information Services
CHR: Becky J Payton, Vice President Human Resources
Web address: www.mercyok.net
**Control**: Church operated, Nongovernment, not–for–profit **Service**: General medical and surgical

**Staffed Beds**: 349 **Admissions**: 16588 **Census**: 221 **Outpatient Visits**: 550304 **Births**: 3852 **Total Expense ($000)**: 483460 **Payroll Expense ($000)**: 156515 **Personnel**: 2104

☐ △ **MERCY REHABILITATION HOSPITAL OKLAHOMA CITY (373033)**, 5401 West Memorial Rd, Zip 73142–2026; tel. 405/384–5211, (Nonreporting) **A**1 7 10
Primary Contact: Thomas Elliott, President
Web address: www.https://www.mercy.net/practice/mercy-rehabilitation-hospital-oklahoma-city/
**Control**: Partnership, Investor–owned (for–profit) **Service**: Rehabilitation

**Staffed Beds**: 50

**OK**

⇑ **NORTHWEST SURGICAL HOSPITAL (370192)**, 9204 North May Avenue, Zip 73120–4419; tel. 405/848–1918, (Nonreporting) **A**3 5 10 21
Primary Contact: Debbie Kearns, Chief Executive Officer
CFO: Cindy Thompson, Chief Financial Officer
CMO: Jimmy Conway, M.D., President Medical Staff
Web address: www.nwsurgicalokc.com/
**Control:** Corporation, Investor–owned (for–profit) **Service:** Orthopedic

**Staffed Beds:** 9

☐ **OAKWOOD SPRINGS (374025)**, 13101 Memorial Springs Court, Zip 73114–2226; tel. 405/438–3000, (Nonreporting) **A**1 10 **F**4 5 29 34 38 53 68 98 100 101 102 104 105 132 135 143 144 148 149 152 153 **P**6 **S** Springstone, Louisville, KY
Primary Contact: Casey McMahan, Chief Executive Officer
Web address: www.oakwoodsprings.com/
**Control:** Corporation, Investor–owned (for–profit) **Service:** Psychiatric

**Staffed Beds:** 72 **Admissions:** 2068 **Census:** 48 **Outpatient Visits:** 10005
**Births:** 0 **Total Expense ($000):** 15322 **Payroll Expense ($000):** 8793

**OKC–AMG SPECIALTY HOSPITAL (372005)**, 4300 West Memorial Road, 2nd Floor, Zip 73120–8304; tel. 405/936–5822, (Nonreporting) **A**22 **S** AMG Integrated Healthcare Management, Lafayette, LA
Primary Contact: Erick Heflin, R.N., Chief Executive Officer
Web address: www.https://amgmercy.com/
**Control:** Corporation, Investor–owned (for–profit) **Service:** Acute long–term care hospital

**Staffed Beds:** 30

☐ **OKLAHOMA CENTER FOR ORTHOPEDIC AND MULTI-SPECIALTY SURGERY (370212)**, 8100 South Walker, Suite C, Zip 73139–9402, Mailing Address: P.O. Box 890609, Zip 73189–0609; tel. 405/602–6500, (Nonreporting) **A**1 10 **F**3 12 29 34 35 37 39 40 45 47 48 54 57 59 64 74 79 81 82 85 86 93 94 107 111 126 131 148 149 **S** United Surgical Partners International, Addison, TX
Primary Contact: Daniel J. Coats, Chief Executive Officer
COO: Jeff Bibb, Chief Operating Officer
CFO: Amy Taylor, Chief Financial Officer
CHR: Emily Phipps, Director Human Resources
CNO: Jolena Wyer, R.N., Chief Nursing Officer
Web address: www.ocomhospital.com
**Control:** Partnership, Investor–owned (for–profit) **Service:** Orthopedic

**Staffed Beds:** 9 **Admissions:** 761 **Census:** 4 **Outpatient Visits:** 32442
**Births:** 0 **Total Expense ($000):** 43879 **Payroll Expense ($000):** 11929
**Personnel:** 182

⊠ △ **OKLAHOMA CITY VETERANS AFFAIRS MEDICAL CENTER**, 921 NE 13th Street, Zip 73104–5028; tel. 405/456–1000, (Nonreporting) **A**1 3 5 7 8 **S** Department of Veterans Affairs, Washington, DC
Primary Contact: Kristopher Wade. Vlosich, Director
CFO: Michele Pipgrass, Chief Fiscal Service
CIO: David Buckley, Acting Chief Information Management Services
CHR: Kyle Inhofe, Chief Human Resources Officer
Web address: www.oklahoma.va.gov
**Control:** Veterans Affairs, Government, federal **Service:** General medical and surgical

**Staffed Beds:** 192

**OKLAHOMA CTR FOR ORTHOPAEDIC** See Oklahoma Center for Orthopedic and Multi-Specialty Surgery

**OKLAHOMA HEART HOSPITAL (370215)**, 4050 West Memorial Road, Zip 73120–8382; tel. 405/608–3200, (Nonreporting) **A**3 10 **F**17 18 20 22 24 26 28 29 30 34 35 40 50 59 64 68 75 81 82 85 86 87 100 102 107 108 111 114 115 117 118 119 126 127 129 130 135 146 154 **P**6
Primary Contact: John Harvey, M.D., Chief Executive Officer
COO: Peggy Tipton, Chief Operating Officer and Chief Nursing Officer
CFO: Carol Walker, Chief Financial Officer
CMO: John Harvey, M.D., Chief Executive Officer
CIO: Michelle Mullins, Chief Information Officer
CHR: Katherine Wynn, Director Human Resource
Web address: www.okheart.com
**Control:** Corporation, Investor–owned (for–profit) **Service:** Heart

**Staffed Beds:** 98 **Admissions:** 6674 **Census:** 80 **Outpatient Visits:** 293575
**Births:** 0 **Total Expense ($000):** 235954 **Payroll Expense ($000):** 97895
**Personnel:** 2174

⇑ **OKLAHOMA HEART HOSPITAL SOUTH CAMPUS (370234)**, 5200 East I-240 Service Road, Zip 73135; tel. 405/628–6000, (Nonreporting) **A**10 21 **F**17 18 20 22 24 26 28 29 30 34 35 40 50 59 64 68 75 81 82 85 86 87 100 107 111 115 117 118 119 126 129 130 135 146 154 **P**6
Primary Contact: John Harvey, M.D., Chief Executive Officer
Web address: www.okheart.com
**Control:** Corporation, Investor–owned (for–profit) **Service:** Heart

**Staffed Beds:** 44 **Admissions:** 3933 **Census:** 39 **Outpatient Visits:** 89583
**Births:** 0 **Total Expense ($000):** 142211 **Payroll Expense ($000):** 52729
**Personnel:** 847

**OKLAHOMA SPINE HOSPITAL (370206)**, 14101 Parkway Commons Drive, Zip 73134–6012; tel. 405/749–2700, (Nonreporting) **A**10
Primary Contact: Kevin Blaylock, Chief Executive Officer
Web address: www.oklahomaspine.com
**Control:** Corporation, Investor–owned (for–profit) **Service:** Surgical

**Staffed Beds:** 12

**ONECORE HEALTH (370220)**, 1044 SW 44th Street, Suite 350, Zip 73109–3609; tel. 405/631–3085, (Nonreporting) **A**10
Primary Contact: Mike Kimzey, Chief Executive Officer
CMO: Joel L Frazier, M.D., Medical Director
CNO: Teresa Carter, Vice President Patient Care Services
Web address: www.onecorehealth.com
**Control:** Corporation, Investor–owned (for–profit) **Service:** Orthopedic

**Staffed Beds:** 8

**ORTHOPEDIC HOSPITAL** See Onecore Health

**OU MED CTR** See Ou Medical Center

⊠ **OU MEDICAL CENTER (370093)**, 1200 Everett Drive, Zip 73104–5047, Mailing Address: P.O. Box 26307, Zip 73126–0307; tel. 405/271–3636, (Includes CHILDREN'S HOSPITAL OF OKLAHOMA, Mailing address: 940 NE 13th Street, Oklahoma City, Oklahoma, Zip 73104, P O Box 26307, Zip 73126, tel. 405/271–6165; EVERETT TOWER, Mailing address: 1200 Everett Drive, Oklahoma City, Oklahoma, Zip 73104; tel. 405/271–4700; OU MEDICAL CENTER EDMOND, Mailing address: 1 South Bryant Avenue, Edmond, Oklahoma, Zip 73034–6309; tel. 405/341–6100; PRESBYTERIAN TOWER, Mailing address: 700 NE 13th Street, Oklahoma City, Oklahoma, Zip 73104–5070; tel. 405/271–5100), (Nonreporting) **A**1 2 3 5 8 10 **F**3 5 6 8 11 12 13 15 17 18 19 20 21 22 23 24 25 26 27 28 29 30 31 32 34 35 36 37 38 39 40 41 43 44 45 46 47 48 49 50 51 52 54 55 56 57 58 59 60 61 63 64 65 66 68 70 71 72 74 75 76 77 78 79 80 81 82 83 84 85 86 87 88 89 91 92 93 94 96 97 98 99 100 101 102 103 107 108 110 111 114 115 116 117 118 119 120 121 122 123 124 126 129 130 131 132 134 135 136 138 139 141 142 145 146 147 148 149 150 153 154
Primary Contact: Kristina Wallace, R.N., Chief Executive Officer
CFO: Mike Reese, Chief Financial Officer
CMO: Curt Steinhart, M.D., Chief Medical Officer
CIO: Larry Forsyth, Director Information Services
CHR: Jed M Liuzza, Chief Human Resources Officer
Web address: www.oumedicine.com/oumedicalcenter
**Control:** Other not–for–profit (including NFP Corporation) **Service:** General medical and surgical

**Staffed Beds:** 748 **Admissions:** 34790 **Census:** 581 **Outpatient Visits:** 279427 **Births:** 3727 **Total Expense ($000):** 1203122 **Payroll Expense ($000):** 284393 **Personnel:** 4338

**OKLAHOMA CITY—Cleveland County**

⇑ **PHYSICIANS HOSPITAL** See Community Hospital

**OKLAHOMA CITY—Oklahoma County**

**PINNACLE REHABILITATION HOSP** See Valir Rehabilitation Hospital

**PRESBYTERIAN HOSPITAL** See Presbyterian Tower

**PRESBYTERIAN TOWER** See Ou Medical Center, Oklahoma City

---

**Hospital, Medicare Provider Number, Address, Telephone, Approval, Facility, and Physician Codes, Health Care System**

★ American Hospital Association (AHA) membership ☐ The Joint Commission accreditation
○ Healthcare Facilities Accreditation Program ◇ DNV Healthcare Inc. accreditation
⇑ Center for Improvement in Healthcare Quality Accreditation △ Commission on Accreditation of Rehabilitation Facilities (CARF) accreditation

**OK**

⊞ **SELECT SPECIALTY HOSPITAL-OKLAHOMA CITY (372009)**, 3524 NW 56th Street, Zip 73112–4518; tel. 405/606–6700, (Nonreporting) **A**1 10 **F**1 3 12 29 74 75 79 87 107 119 130 148 **S** Select Medical Corporation, Mechanicsburg, PA
Primary Contact: Kelly Duke, Chief Executive Officer
CNO: LieutenantAutumn Pulis, Chief Nursing Officer
Web address: www.https://oklahomacity.selectspecialtyhospitals.com/
**Control**: Corporation, Investor–owned (for–profit) **Service**: Acute long–term care hospital

**Staffed Beds**: 72 **Admissions**: 864 **Census**: 64 **Outpatient Visits**: 0
**Births**: 0 **Total Expense ($000)**: 36523 **Payroll Expense ($000)**: 15892
**Personnel**: 220

⊞ **SSM HEALTH ST. ANTHONY HOSPITAL - OKLAHOMA CITY (370037)**, 1000 North Lee Street, Zip 73102–1080, Mailing Address: P.O. Box 205, Zip 73101–0205; tel. 405/272–7000, (Includes SSM HEALTH BONE AND JOINT HOSPITAL AT ST. ANTHONY, Mailing address: 1111 North Dewey Avenue, Oklahoma City, Oklahoma, Zip 73103–2609; tel. 405/272–9671; Tammy Powell, FACHE, M.P.H., President; SSM HEALTH ST. ANTHONY SOUTH, Mailing address: 2129 SW 59th Street, Oklahoma City, Oklahoma, Zip 73119–7001; tel. 405/713–5700), (Nonreporting) **A**1 2 3 5 10 12 13 **F**3 4 5 7 8 11 12 13 15 17 18 20 22 24 26 28 29 30 31 34 35 36 37 38 40 42 43 45 46 47 48 49 50 54 56 57 58 59 64 67 70 71 72 74 76 77 78 79 81 82 84 85 86 87 89 90 91 92 93 96 97 98 99 100 101 102 103 104 105 106 107 108 110 111 114 115 117 118 119 120 121 123 124 126 127 129 130 131 132 144 146 147 148 149 152 153 154 **P**4 **S** SSM Health, Saint Louis, MO
Primary Contact: Tammy Powell, FACHE, M.P.H., President
COO: Marti Jourden, FACHE, Chief Quality Officer
CFO: Shasta Manuel, Executive Director Finance
CMO: Kersey Winfree, M.D., Chief Medical Officer
CIO: Kevin Olson, Director Information Systems
CHR: Cynthia Brundise, Vice President Human Resources
Web address: www.saintsok.com
**Control**: Church operated, Nongovernment, not–for–profit **Service**: General medical and surgical

**Staffed Beds**: 615 **Admissions**: 22935 **Census**: 437 **Outpatient Visits**: 357872 **Births**: 1142 **Total Expense ($000)**: 538351 **Payroll Expense ($000)**: 158699 **Personnel**: 2554

**ST. ANTHONY HOSPITAL** See Ssm Health St. Anthony Hospital - Oklahoma City

**ST. ANTHONY SOUTH** See Ssm Health St. Anthony South

**SURGICAL HOSPITAL OF OKLAHOMA (370201)**, 100 SE 59th Street, Zip 73129–3616; tel. 405/634–9300, (Nonreporting) **A**3 10 22
Primary Contact: Phil Ross, Chief Executive Officer
CNO: Cindy Ridge Braly, MAAL, R.N., Chief Nursing Officer
Web address: www.sh-ok.com
**Control**: Partnership, Investor–owned (for–profit) **Service**: Other specialty treatment

**Staffed Beds**: 12

**UNIVERSITY EVERETT TOWER** See Everett Tower

⊞ **VALIR REHABILITATION HOSPITAL (373025)**, 700 NW Seventh Street, Zip 73102–1212; tel. 405/236–3131, (Nonreporting) **A**1 10
Primary Contact: Andy Marlette, Interim Chief Executive Officer
COO: Ginger Castleberry, Corporate Risk Manager, Quality and Patient Safety
CFO: Scott Brown, Chief Financial Officer
CMO: Tonya Washburn, M.D., Medical Director
CIO: Mark Dickey, Director Business Development
CHR: Bill Turner, Vice President Human Resources
Web address: www.valir.com
**Control**: Corporation, Investor–owned (for–profit) **Service**: Rehabilitation

**Staffed Beds**: 49

**VETERANS AFFAIRS MEDICAL CENTER** See Oklahoma City Veterans Affairs Medical Center

---

**OKMULGEE—Okmulgee County**

**MUSCOGEE CREEK NATION MEDICAL CENTER (370057)**, 1401 Morris Drive, Zip 74447–6429, Mailing Address: P.O. Box 1038, Zip 74447–1038; tel. 918/756–4233, (Nonreporting) **A**10 **F**11 29 40 43 45 56 57 59 81 82 87 93 98 103 107 108 111 115 119 133 146
Primary Contact: Tim Hicks, Administrator
CFO: John W Crawford, Chief Financial Officer
CMO: Michael Sandlin, M.D., Chief of Staff
CHR: Stacey R. Burton, Director Human Resources
Web address: www.creekhealth.org/medical-center/
**Control**: Other not–for–profit (including NFP Corporation) **Service**: General medical and surgical

**Staffed Beds**: 45 **Admissions**: 954 **Census**: 16 **Outpatient Visits**: 27069
**Births**: 0 **Total Expense ($000)**: 20079 **Payroll Expense ($000)**: 7525
**Personnel**: 155

**MUSCOGEE CREEK NATION PHYSICAL REHABILITATION CENTER (372023)**, 1401 Morris Drive, Zip 74447–6429, Mailing Address: P.O. Box 1038, Zip 74447–1938; tel. 918/756–4233, (Nonreporting) **F**1 28 29 64 74 77 93
Primary Contact: Tim Hicks, Administrator
**Control**: Other not–for–profit (including NFP Corporation) **Service**: Acute long–term care hospital

**Staffed Beds**: 4 **Admissions**: 33 **Census**: 3 **Outpatient Visits**: 8028
**Births**: 0 **Total Expense ($000)**: 3453 **Payroll Expense ($000)**: 1676
**Personnel**: 34

**OKMULGEE MEMORIAL HOSPITAL** See Muscogee Creek Nation Medical Center

**OWASSO—Tulsa County**

★ ⇑ **BAILEY MEDICAL CENTER (370228)**, 10502 North 110th East Avenue, Zip 74055–6655; tel. 918/376–8000, (Nonreporting) **A**10 21 **F**3 12 13 15 18 29 34 40 45 51 57 64 70 75 76 77 79 81 82 85 91 93 107 108 110 111 115 119 129 132 146 147 149 **S** Ardent Health Services, Nashville, TN
Primary Contact: Keith Mason, Chief Executive Officer
CFO: Carol Barlow, Chief Financial Officer
CHR: Tandy Groves, Director Human Resources
CNO: Ruby Triplett, Chief Nursing Officer
Web address: www.baileymedicalcenter.com
**Control**: Corporation, Investor–owned (for–profit) **Service**: General medical and surgical

**Staffed Beds**: 37 **Admissions**: 1584 **Census**: 9 **Outpatient Visits**: 41018
**Births**: 320 **Total Expense ($000)**: 40428 **Payroll Expense ($000)**: 14389
**Personnel**: 215

⊞ **ST. JOHN OWASSO (370227)**, 12451 East 100th Street North, Zip 74055–4600; tel. 918/274–5000, (Nonreporting) **A**1 10 **F**3 11 13 15 18 29 30 34 35 40 43 45 57 59 64 68 76 79 81 85 87 93 107 108 110 111 114 115 119 130 131 132 146 147 149 156 **S** Ascension Healthcare, Saint Louis, MO
Primary Contact: David L. Phillips, President and Chief Operating Officer
CFO: Katie Caughman, Chief Financial Officer
CMO: Tim Hepner, M.D., Chief Medical Officer
CIO: Mike Reeves, Chief Information Officer
CNO: Dan Hall, R.N., Chief Operating Officer
Web address: www.stjohnowasso.com
**Control**: Church operated, Nongovernment, not–for–profit **Service**: General medical and surgical

**Staffed Beds**: 36 **Admissions**: 1408 **Census**: 11 **Outpatient Visits**: 63750
**Births**: 497 **Total Expense ($000)**: 28669 **Payroll Expense ($000)**: 9948
**Personnel**: 156

**PAWHUSKA—Osage County**

★ **PAWHUSKA HOSPITAL (371309)**, 1101 East 15th Street, Zip 74056–1920; tel. 918/287–3232, (Nonreporting) **A**10 18
Primary Contact: Jason McBride, Chief Executive Officer
CMO: Mike Priest, M.D., Chief of Staff
Web address: www.https://pawhuskahospital.com/
**Control**: City, Government, Nonfederal **Service**: General medical and surgical

**Staffed Beds**: 15

## PERRY—Noble County

⇑ **PERRY MEMORIAL HOSPITAL** See Stillwater Medical Perry

★ ⇑ **STILLWATER MEDICAL PERRY (370139)**, 501 North 14th Street,
Zip 73077–5099; tel. 580/336–3541, (Nonreporting) **A**10 20 21 **F**3 11 15 28 29
34 40 59 62 81 93 107 114 133 146 148 154
Primary Contact: Steven Taylor, Regional Chief Executive Officer
CFO: Courtney Kozikuski, Chief Financial Officer
CMO: Michael Hartwig, M.D., EsqChief of Staff
CIO: Jeff Ware, Information Technology Support Technician
CHR: Deb Ellis, Director Human Resources
CNO: Brenda Quiring, R.N., Director of Nursing
Web address: www.https://www.stillwater-medical.org/locations/stillwater-medical-perry
**Control**: Hospital district or authority, Government, Nonfederal **Service**: General
medical and surgical

**Staffed Beds**: 23 **Admissions**: 373 **Census**: 4 **Outpatient Visits**: 12560
**Births**: 0 **Total Expense ($000)**: 7249 **Payroll Expense ($000)**: 3115
**Personnel**: 66

## PONCA CITY—Kay County

⊠ **ALLIANCEHEALTH PONCA CITY (370006)**, 1900 North 14th Street,
Zip 74601–2099; tel. 580/765–3321, (Nonreporting) **A**1 10 19 **F**3 13 15 18 28
29 30 34 40 43 45 46 50 51 53 55 57 59 64 65 68 70 75 76 77 79 81 82 85
89 90 93 107 108 110 111 115 119 127 130 131 132 133 145 146 147 148
149 154 156 **P**6 **S** Community Health Systems, Inc., Franklin, TN
Primary Contact: Christopher Mendoza, Chief Executive Officer
CFO: Sheryl Schmidtberger, Chief Financial Officer
CIO: William Gazaway, Information Technology Security Officer
CHR: Calvin Hodges, Director Human Resources
CNO: Jeanne Stara, R.N., MSN, Chief Nursing Officer
Web address: www.AllianceHealthPoncaCity.com/
**Control**: Corporation, Investor–owned (for–profit) **Service**: General medical and
surgical

**Staffed Beds**: 74 **Admissions**: 2357 **Census**: 22 **Outpatient Visits**: 63173
**Births**: 460 **Total Expense ($000)**: 59329 **Payroll Expense ($000)**: 24050
**Personnel**: 356

**PONCA CITY MEDICAL CENTER** See Alliancehealth Ponca City

## POTEAU—Le Flore County

⇑ **EASTERN OKLAHOMA MEDICAL CENTER (371337)**, 105 Wall Street,
Zip 74953–4433, Mailing Address: P.O. Box 1148, Zip 74953–1148;
tel. 918/647–8161, (Nonreporting) **A**10 18 21 **F**3 15 29 30 34 35 40 45 50 57
59 64 68 76 81 85 87 93 97 98 100 103 107 108 110 111 115 119 127 129
130 132 133 144 146 148 154 **P**6
Primary Contact: Bob Carter, Interim Chief Executive Officer
CFO: Shaun Keef, Chief Financial Officer
CMO: Dennis Carter, M.D., Chief of Staff
CIO: Michael C Huggins, Administrator Network System
Web address: www.eomchospital.com
**Control**: County, Government, Nonfederal **Service**: General medical and surgical

**Staffed Beds**: 25 **Admissions**: 481 **Census**: 4 **Outpatient Visits**: 64074
**Births**: 161 **Total Expense ($000)**: 23832 **Payroll Expense ($000)**: 11617
**Personnel**: 174

## PRAGUE—Lincoln County

**PRAGUE COMMUNITY HOSPITAL (371301)**, 1322 Klabzuba Avenue,
Zip 74864–9005, Mailing Address: P.O. Box S, Zip 74864–1090;
tel. 405/567–4922, (Nonreporting) **A**10 18 **F**3 29 40 43 64 82 83 93 97 107
114 127 128 133 148 154 **P**6 **S** Rural Community Hospitals of America, Kansas
City, MO
Primary Contact: Jamal Bandeh, Interim Chief Executive Officer
CFO: Doug Erickson, Chief Financial Officer
CMO: Darryl Jackson, D.O., Chief of Staff
CIO: Rhonda Whitnum, Director Health Improvement Management
CHR: Angie Brezny, Director Human Resources
Web address: www.praguehospital.com
**Control**: Other not–for–profit (including NFP Corporation) **Service**: General
medical and surgical

**Staffed Beds**: 25 **Admissions**: 76 **Census**: 5 **Outpatient Visits**: 9691
**Births**: 0 **Personnel**: 67

**PRAGUE MUNICIPAL HOSPITAL** See Prague Community Hospital

## PRYOR—Mayes County

⇑ **ALLIANCEHEALTH PRYOR** See Hillcrest Hospital Pryor

★ ⇑ **HILLCREST HOSPITAL PRYOR (370015)**, 111 North Bailey Street,
Zip 74361–4201; tel. 918/825–1600, (Nonreporting) **A**10 **F**3 11 15 18 26 29
30 34 35 45 50 57 59 64 65 79 81 93 107 108 110 111 114 119 127 147 **S**
Ardent Health Services, Nashville, TN
Primary Contact: Douglas K. Weaver, FACHE, Chief Executive Officer
CMO: Jason Joice, M.D., Chief Medical Staff
CHR: Pamela A Guthrie, Chief Human Resources Officer
CNO: Mary Ozment, Chief Nursing Officer
Web address: www.hillcrestpryor.com/
**Control**: Corporation, Investor–owned (for–profit) **Service**: General medical and
surgical

**Staffed Beds**: 22 **Admissions**: 764 **Census**: 5 **Outpatient Visits**: 75784
**Births**: 0 **Total Expense ($000)**: 25910 **Payroll Expense ($000)**: 10844
**Personnel**: 160

## PURCELL—McClain County

**PURCELL MUNICIPAL HOSPITAL (370158)**, 1500 North Green Avenue,
Zip 73080–1699, Mailing Address: P.O. Box 511, Zip 73080–0511;
tel. 405/527–6524, (Nonreporting) **A**10 **F**3 11 18 29 30 35 40 45 48 59 64 65
75 79 81 82 86 87 89 107 119 133 135 144 154
Primary Contact: Kem Scully, Chief Executive Officer and Chief Nursing Officer
CFO: Mary Morris, Chief Financial Officer
CMO: David Bryan Dye, M.D., Chief Medical Officer
CIO: Jennifer Coates, Coordinator Information Technology
CHR: Tara Selfridge, Manager Human Resources
CNO: Kem Scully, Chief Executive Officer and Chief Nursing Officer
Web address: www.purcellhospital.com
**Control**: City, Government, Nonfederal **Service**: General medical and surgical

**Staffed Beds**: 28 **Admissions**: 526 **Census**: 5 **Outpatient Visits**: 45132
**Births**: 0 **Total Expense ($000)**: 13609 **Payroll Expense ($000)**: 4739
**Personnel**: 97

## SALLISAW—Sequoyah County

**NORTHEASTERN HEALTH SYSTEM SEQUOYAH (370112)**, 213 East Redwood
Street, Zip 74955–2811, Mailing Address: P.O. Box 505, Zip 74955–0505;
tel. 918/774–1100, (Nonreporting) **A**10 **F**3 15 18 29 30 34 40 43 50 59 62 63
64 68 81 83 84 85 93 97 102 107 109 110 111 115 119 127 129 133 146
154 157
Primary Contact: Stephanie Six, Chief Executive Officer
CMO: Jennifer Scoufos, M.D., Chief of Staff
CIO: Gary McClanahan, Chief Information Officer
CHR: Shayna Brooke Roberts, Director Human Resources
CNO: Ozalina Martinez, R.N., Director of Nursing
Web address: www.pmtc.ok.gov/sequoyah-memorial-hospital-sallisaw-ok
**Control**: City–county, Government, Nonfederal **Service**: General medical and
surgical

**Staffed Beds**: 26 **Admissions**: 533 **Census**: 7 **Outpatient Visits**: 97227
**Births**: 0 **Total Expense ($000)**: 11218 **Payroll Expense ($000)**: 4674
**Personnel**: 161

**SEQUOYAH MEMORIAL HOSPITAL** See Northeastern Health System Sequoyah

## SAPULPA—Creek County

**BARTLETT MEM MEDICAL CENTER** See St. John Sapulpa

★ **ST. JOHN SAPULPA (371312)**, 1004 East Bryan Avenue, Zip 74066–4513,
Mailing Address: P.O. Box 1368, Zip 74067–1368; tel. 918/224–4280,
(Nonreporting) **A**10 18 **F**3 8 11 14 29 30 34 35 40 45 57 59 64 68 79 81 85 86
87 107 111 119 130 132 133 135 143 149 154 **S** Ascension Healthcare, Saint
Louis, MO
Primary Contact: Michael Christian, Chief Operating Officer
COO: Michael Christian, Chief Operating Officer
CFO: John W Crawford, Chief Financial Officer
CMO: Jason Lepak, M.D., Medical Director
CNO: Kelly Johnson, R.N., Chief Nursing Officer
Web address: www.stjohnhealthsystem.com/sapulpa
**Control**: Church operated, Nongovernment, not–for–profit **Service**: General
medical and surgical

**Staffed Beds**: 25 **Admissions**: 586 **Census**: 15 **Outpatient Visits**: 39882
**Births**: 0 **Total Expense ($000)**: 20394 **Payroll Expense ($000)**: 7197
**Personnel**: 113

---

**Hospital, Medicare Provider Number, Address, Telephone, Approval, Facility, and Physician Codes, Health Care System**

★ American Hospital Association (AHA) membership
☐ The Joint Commission accreditation
○ Healthcare Facilities Accreditation Program
◇ DNV Healthcare Inc. accreditation
⇑ Center for Improvement in Healthcare Quality Accreditation
△ Commission on Accreditation of Rehabilitation Facilities (CARF) accreditation

**OK**

### SEILING—Dewey County

⋔ **SEILING MUNICIPAL HOSPITAL** See Seiling Regional Medical Center

⋔ **SEILING REGIONAL MEDICAL CENTER (371332)**, Highway 60 NE, Zip 73663, Mailing Address: P.O. Box 720, Zip 73663–0720; tel. 580/922–7361, (Nonreporting) **A**10 18 21
Primary Contact: Miranda Walz-Allen, Chief Executive Officer
COO: Rachel Farrow, Chief Operations Officer
CFO: Nancy Freed, Chief Financial Officer
CMO: Kenneth Duffy, M.D., Medical Director
CHR: Sandy Landreth, Director Human Resources
Web address: www.seilingmunicipalhospital.org/
**Control**: City, Government, Nonfederal **Service**: General medical and surgical

| **Staffed Beds**: 18 |
|---|

### SEMINOLE—Seminole County

⊠ **ALLIANCEHEALTH SEMINOLE (370229)**, 2401 Wrangler Boulevard, Zip 74868–1917; tel. 405/303–4000, (Nonreporting) **A**1 10 **S** Community Health Systems, Inc., Franklin, TN
Primary Contact: Damon Brown, Interim Chief Executive Officer
CMO: Nikki Chawla, M.D., Medical Director
CHR: Lori Friend, Human Resources Director
CNO: Barbara Lewis, Chief Nursing Officer
Web address: www.alliancehealthseminole.com/
**Control**: Partnership, Investor–owned (for–profit) **Service**: General medical and surgical

| **Staffed Beds**: 32 |
|---|

**SEMINOLE MEDICAL CENTER** See Alliancehealth Seminole

### SHATTUCK—Ellis County

**NEWMAN MEMORIAL HOSPITAL (371336)**, 905 South Main Street, Zip 73858–9205; tel. 580/938–2551, (Nonreporting) **A**10 18 **F**3 8 11 15 18 19 29 32 34 35 40 41 43 45 57 64 65 69 75 77 81 85 89 93 97 107 110 111 115 119 128 129 130 133 147 149 156
Primary Contact: Ed Majors, Chief Executive Officer
CFO: Kellcie Skinner, Controller
CMO: Danna Stuart, M.D., Chief Medical Officer
CIO: Robert Neal, Manager Information Technology Services
Web address: www.newmanmemorialhospital.org
**Control**: City, Government, Nonfederal **Service**: General medical and surgical

| **Staffed Beds**: 25 **Admissions**: 183 **Census**: 1 **Outpatient Visits**: 9201 **Births**: 1 **Total Expense ($000)**: 7692 **Payroll Expense ($000)**: 2295 **Personnel**: 51 |
|---|

### SHAWNEE—Pottawatomie County

**CORNERSTONE HOSPITAL OF OKLAHOMA-SHAWNEE (372019)**, 1900 Gordon Cooper Drive, 2nd Floor, Zip 74801–8603, Mailing Address: P.O. Box 1245, Zip 74802–1245; tel. 405/395–5800, (Nonreporting) **A**10 22 **S** Cornerstone Healthcare Group, Dallas, TX
Primary Contact: Kristopher Karns, Chief Executive Officer
CMO: Rakesh Shrivastava, M.D., Chief Medical Officer
Web address: www.chghospitals.com/shawnee/
**Control**: Corporation, Investor–owned (for–profit) **Service**: Acute long–term care hospital

| **Staffed Beds**: 34 |
|---|

**SOLARA HOSPITAL OF SHAWNEE** See Cornerstone Hospital of Oklahoma-Shawnee

⊠ **SSM HEALTH ST. ANTHONY HOSPITAL - SHAWNEE (370149)**, 1102 West MacArthur Street, Zip 74804–1744; tel. 405/273–2270, (Nonreporting) **A**1 10 19 **F**3 11 13 15 18 20 22 29 30 31 34 35 40 43 45 50 57 59 60 64 65 68 69 70 75 76 77 78 79 81 82 84 87 94 107 110 111 114 115 116 117 119 120 121 123 129 130 131 132 135 146 147 148 **P**6 **S** SSM Health, Saint Louis, MO
Primary Contact: Angela Mohr, R.N., MS, President
CFO: Jennifer Pierce, Administrative Director of Finance
CMO: Gaynell Anderson, M.D., Medical Director
CHR: Michael Spears, Human Resource Leader
Web address: www.stanthonyshawnee.com
**Control**: Other not–for–profit (including NFP Corporation) **Service**: General medical and surgical

| **Staffed Beds**: 70 **Admissions**: 3887 **Census**: 31 **Outpatient Visits**: 130049 **Births**: 856 **Total Expense ($000)**: 87659 **Payroll Expense ($000)**: 26891 **Personnel**: 413 |
|---|

**ST. ANTHONY SHAWNEE HOSPITAL** See Ssm Health St. Anthony Hospital - Shawnee

### SPENCER—Oklahoma County

**INTEGRIS MENTAL HEALTH SYSTEM-SPENCER** See Integris Baptist Medical Center, Oklahoma City

**WILLOW VIEW MENTAL HLTH SYSTEM** See Integris Mental Health System-Spencer

### STIGLER-Haskell County

**HASKELL COUNTY COMMUNITY HOSPITAL (371335)**, 401 Northwest 'H' Street, Zip 74462–1625; tel. 918/967–4682, (Nonreporting) **A**10 18 **S** Rural Community Hospitals of America, Kansas City, MO
Primary Contact: Andrea Randall, Chief Executive Officer
CMO: Stephen Woodson, D.O., Chief of Staff
CIO: Steve Hurst, Information Technology Specialist
Web address: www.haskellhospital.com
**Control**: Corporation, Investor–owned (for–profit) **Service**: General medical and surgical

| **Staffed Beds**: 20 |
|---|

**HASKELL COUNTY HEALTHCARE SYSTEM** See Haskell County Community Hospital

### STILLWATER—Payne County

★ ⋔ **STILLWATER MEDICAL CENTER (370049)**, 1323 West Sixth Avenue, Zip 74074–4399, Mailing Address: P.O. Box 2408, Zip 74076–2408; tel. 405/372–1480, (Nonreporting) **A**2 10 21 **F**3 11 13 15 18 20 22 28 29 30 31 34 35 40 43 44 45 47 49 50 51 53 54 55 57 59 62 63 64 65 66 68 70 75 76 77 78 79 81 82 85 86 87 89 90 93 94 97 107 108 110 111 115 117 118 119 120 121 124 126 127 129 130 131 132 135 144 145 146 147 148 149 154 156 **P**6 7
Primary Contact: Denise Webber, President and Chief Executive Officer
CFO: Alan Lovelace, Vice President and Chief Financial Officer
CMO: Steve Cummings, M.D., Chief of Medical Staff
CIO: Chris Roark, Chief Information Officer
CHR: Keith Hufnagel, Director Human Resources
CNO: Elizabeth Michael, R.N., MS, Vice President Patient Care Services and Chief Nursing Officer
Web address: www.stillwater-medical.org
**Control**: Hospital district or authority, Government, Nonfederal **Service**: General medical and surgical

| **Staffed Beds**: 100 **Admissions**: 4096 **Census**: 43 **Outpatient Visits**: 149171 **Births**: 829 **Total Expense ($000)**: 223218 **Payroll Expense ($000)**: 98966 **Personnel**: 1409 |
|---|

### STILWELL—Adair County

**MEMORIAL HOSPITAL OF STILWELL (370178)**, 1401 West Locust, Zip 74960–3275, Mailing Address: P.O. Box 272, Zip 74960–0272; tel. 918/696–3101, (Nonreporting) **A**10
Primary Contact: Alan L. Adams, Administrator
Web address: www.stilwellmemorialhospital.com
**Control**: Corporation, Investor–owned (for–profit) **Service**: General medical and surgical

| **Staffed Beds**: 34 |
|---|

**STILWELL MEMORIAL HOSPITAL** See Memorial Hospital of Stilwell

### SULPHUR—Murray County

★ **ARBUCKLE MEMORIAL HOSPITAL (371328)**, 2011 West Broadway Street, Zip 73086–4221, Mailing Address: P.O. Box 1109, Zip 73086–8109; tel. 580/622–2161, (Nonreporting) **A**10 18 **F**3 11 29 32 40 45 56 57 81 87 93 107 119 127 128 133 135 148 **S** Preferred Management Corporation, Shawnee, OK
Primary Contact: Jeremy A. Jones, Chief Executive Officer
CFO: Denise Welch, Chief Financial Officer
CMO: Ryan Oden, D.O., Chief of Staff
CIO: Tiffany Sands, Manager Health Information
CHR: Sallie Tomlinson, Manager Human Resources
CNO: Sarah Freehill, Chief Nursing Officer
Web address: www.arbucklehospital.com/
**Control**: County, Government, Nonfederal **Service**: General medical and surgical

| **Staffed Beds**: 15 **Admissions**: 809 **Census**: 17 **Outpatient Visits**: 32189 **Births**: 0 **Total Expense ($000)**: 16838 **Payroll Expense ($000)**: 9624 **Personnel**: 148 |
|---|

*Many Facility Codes have changed. Please refer to the AHA Guide Code Chart.* © 2021 AHA Guide

OK

## TAHLEQUAH—Cherokee County

★ ⇑ **CHEROKEE NATION W.W. HASTINGS INDIAN HOSPITAL (370171)**, 100 South Bliss Avenue, Zip 74464–2512; tel. 918/458–3100, (Nonreporting) **A**3 10 21
Primary Contact: Brian Hail, Deputy Executive Director of External Operations
COO: Mitchell Thornbrugh, Administrative Officer
CMO: Douglas Nolan, M.D., Medical Director
CIO: Mitchell Thornbrugh, Acting Chief Information Officer
CNO: Valerie J Rogers, Director of Nursing
Web address: www.cherokee.org
**Control:** Public Health Service other than 47, Government, federal **Service:** General medical and surgical

**Staffed Beds:** 58

★ **NORTHEASTERN HEALTH SYSTEM (370089)**, 1400 East Downing Street, Zip 74464–3324, Mailing Address: P.O. Box 1008, Zip 74465–1008; tel. 918/456–0641, (Nonreporting) **A**3 5 10 13 20 **F**3 7 11 13 15 17 18 20 22 24 26 28 29 30 40 43 45 47 48 49 51 64 70 75 76 77 80 81 85 87 89 90 92 93 96 97 98 103 107 108 110 111 115 117 118 119 120 121 123 124 127 130 135 144 146 147 148 **P**4 7
Primary Contact: James T. Berry, FACHE, Executive Vice President and Administrator
COO: Mark McCroskey, Vice President Operations
CFO: Julie Ward, Vice President Finance
CIO: Julie Ward, Vice President Finance
CHR: Phyllis Smith, Vice President Human Resources
CNO: Donna Dallis, R.N., Vice President Patient Care
Web address: www.nhs-ok.org/
**Control:** City, Government, Nonfederal **Service:** General medical and surgical

**Staffed Beds:** 90 **Admissions:** 4301 **Census:** 50 **Outpatient Visits:** 178370 **Births:** 290 **Total Expense ($000):** 111130 **Payroll Expense ($000):** 39206 **Personnel:** 877

**TAHLEQUAH CITY HOSPITAL** See Northeastern Health System

⇑ **WILLIAM W. HASTINGS INDIAN HOSPITAL** See Cherokee Nation W.W. Hastings Indian Hospital

## TALIHINA—Latimer County

⊞ **CHOCTAW NATION HEALTH CARE CENTER (370172)**, One Choctaw Way, Zip 74571–2022; tel. 918/567–7000, (Nonreporting) **A**1 3 10 13 20 **F**3 5 7 12 13 15 18 29 34 35 38 39 40 43 45 50 53 54 56 57 58 59 64 65 68 71 74 75 76 79 81 87 89 92 93 97 100 101 104 107 110 111 114 115 119 127 129 130 135 141 142 143 144 147 148 149 154 156 157
Primary Contact: Todd Hallmark, Chief Executive Officer
COO: Todd Hallmark, Chief Operating Officer
CMO: Jason Hill, M.D., Chief Medical Officer
CIO: Dwane Sorrells, Chief Information Officer
CHR: Jami Beckwith, Director Human Resources
CNO: Lisa Isaac, Chief Nursing Officer
Web address: www.cnhsa.com
**Control:** PHS, Indian Service, Government, federal **Service:** General medical and surgical

**Staffed Beds:** 46 **Admissions:** 1203 **Census:** 11 **Outpatient Visits:** 292858 **Births:** 482 **Total Expense ($000):** 240159 **Payroll Expense ($000):** 98699 **Personnel:** 2014

**CHOCTAW NATION INDIAN HOSPITAL** See Choctaw Nation Health Care Center

## TISHOMINGO—Johnston County

**JOHNSTON MEMORIAL HOSPITAL** See Mercy Hospital Tishomingo

★ **MERCY HOSPITAL TISHOMINGO (371304)**, 1000 South Byrd Street, Zip 73460–3299; tel. 580/371–2327, (Nonreporting) **A**10 18 **F**3 29 34 40 43 44 50 59 64 68 75 84 107 114 119 133 143 146 148 149 154 **S** Mercy, Chesterfield, MO
Primary Contact: Lori McMillin, Administrator
CFO: Lisa Dowling, Manager Finance
CHR: Arlita Hummelke, Manager Human Resources
Web address: www.mercy.net/
**Control:** Church operated, Nongovernment, not–for–profit **Service:** General medical and surgical

**Staffed Beds:** 12 **Admissions:** 219 **Census:** 5 **Outpatient Visits:** 5479 **Births:** 0 **Total Expense ($000):** 7427 **Payroll Expense ($000):** 4319 **Personnel:** 33

## TULSA—Tulsa County

△ **BROOKHAVEN HOSPITAL (374012)**, 201 South Garnett Road, Zip 74128–1805; tel. 918/438–4257, (Nonreporting) **A**7 10 **F**4 5 29 30 54 64 74 75 77 98 101 102 104 106 130 132 154 **P**5
Primary Contact: Thomas W. Brown, Chief Executive Officer
CFO: Kenneth Pierce, Chief Financial Officer
CMO: Mark Gage, D.O., Medical Director
CHR: Heather Dudley, Director Administrative Services
CNO: Debbie Jones, Director of Nursing
Web address: www.brookhavenhospital.com
**Control:** Corporation, Investor–owned (for–profit) **Service:** Psychiatric

**Staffed Beds:** 64 **Admissions:** 684 **Census:** 48 **Outpatient Visits:** 991 **Births:** 0 **Total Expense ($000):** 18130 **Payroll Expense ($000):** 8011 **Personnel:** 183

**CANCER TREATMENT CENTER** See Southwestern Regional Medical Center

⇑ **HILLCREST HEALTHCARE SYSTEM** See Hillcrest Medical Center

★ ⇑ **HILLCREST HOSPITAL - SOUTH (370202)**, 8801 South 101st East Avenue, Zip 74133–5716; tel. 918/294–4000, (Nonreporting) **A**3 10 21 **F**3 13 15 18 20 22 24 26 28 29 34 35 40 43 45 46 47 48 49 51 57 70 73 74 76 79 81 82 85 86 87 91 93 107 108 110 111 115 119 126 129 130 146 147 148 **S** Ardent Health Services, Nashville, TN
Primary Contact: Bennett Geister, Chief Executive Officer
COO: Matthew Morgan, Associate Administrator
CFO: James Washecka, Chief Financial Officer
CMO: David L. Pohl, M.D., Chief of Staff
CIO: David Graser, Vice President and Chief Information Officer
CHR: Rachel Steward, Director Human Resources
CNO: Dava Baldridge, R.N., Chief Nursing Officer
Web address: www.southcresthospital.com
**Control:** Corporation, Investor–owned (for–profit) **Service:** General medical and surgical

**Staffed Beds:** 168 **Admissions:** 10306 **Census:** 125 **Outpatient Visits:** 102437 **Births:** 1397 **Total Expense ($000):** 158959 **Payroll Expense ($000):** 52229 **Personnel:** 806

★ ⇑ **HILLCREST MEDICAL CENTER (370001)**, 1120 South Utica Avenue, Zip 74104–4090; tel. 918/579–1000, (Nonreporting) **A**3 5 10 19 21 **F**1 3 4 10 11 13 15 16 17 18 20 22 24 26 28 29 30 31 34 35 37 39 40 43 45 46 49 50 51 53 58 59 60 64 67 68 70 72 73 74 75 76 77 78 79 80 81 83 84 85 86 87 88 89 90 93 98 100 107 108 110 111 114 115 116 117 118 119 120 121 123 124 126 128 129 130 131 135 145 146 147 148 154 156 **P**6 **S** Ardent Health Services, Nashville, TN
Primary Contact: Xavier Villarreal, FACHE, Chief Executive Officer
COO: Farron Sneed, Chief Operating Officer
CFO: Joseph Mendoza, Chief Financial Officer
CIO: Richard Gomez, Assistant Vice President Information Technology Division
CHR: Donald Morris, Vice President Human Resources
CNO: Jodi Simmons, Chief Nursing Officer
Web address: www.hillcrestmedicalcenter.com
**Control:** Corporation, Investor–owned (for–profit) **Service:** General medical and surgical

**Staffed Beds:** 510 **Admissions:** 22731 **Census:** 360 **Outpatient Visits:** 119313 **Births:** 2613 **Total Expense ($000):** 454409 **Payroll Expense ($000):** 135519 **Personnel:** 2137

**KINDRED HOSPITAL TULSA** See Post Acute Medical Specialty Hospital of Tulsa

⊞ **LAUREATE PSYCHIATRIC CLINIC AND HOSPITAL (374020)**, 6655 South Yale Avenue, Zip 74136–3329; tel. 918/481–4000, (Nonreporting) **A**1 3 5 10 **F**4 5 98 99 100 101 102 103 104 105 106 146 151 152 153 **P**6 **S** Saint Francis Health System, Tulsa, OK
Primary Contact: Brandon Keppner, Administrator
CFO: Eric Schick, Senior Vice President, Chief Administrative Officer and Chief Financial Officer
CMO: Mark I Frost, M.D., Senior Vice President Medical Affairs
Web address: www.laureate.com
**Control:** Other not–for–profit (including NFP Corporation) **Service:** Psychiatric

**Staffed Beds:** 106 **Admissions:** 3607 **Census:** 80 **Outpatient Visits:** 11428 **Births:** 0 **Total Expense ($000):** 37455 **Payroll Expense ($000):** 21455 **Personnel:** 347

---

**Hospital, Medicare Provider Number, Address, Telephone, Approval, Facility, and Physician Codes, Health Care System**

★ American Hospital Association (AHA) membership
□ The Joint Commission accreditation
○ Healthcare Facilities Accreditation Program
◇ DNV Healthcare Inc. accreditation
⇑ Center for Improvement in Healthcare Quality Accreditation
△ Commission on Accreditation of Rehabilitation Facilities (CARF) accreditation

OK

○ **OKLAHOMA STATE UNIVERSITY MEDICAL CENTER (370078)**, 744 West Ninth Street, Zip 74127–9020; tel. 918/599–1000, (Nonreporting) **A**3 5 8 10 11 12 13 19 **S** Saint Francis Health System, Tulsa, OK
Primary Contact: Lynn A. Sund, Interim Administrator
COO: Jeff Stroup, Chief Operating Officer
CFO: Sara Bradley, Chief Financial Officer
CMO: Damon Baker, D.O., Chief Medical Officer
CIO: Heidi Holmes, Chief Information Officer
CNO: Joy Upshaw, Chief Nursing Officer
Web address: www.osumc.net
**Control**: City, Government, Nonfederal **Service**: General medical and surgical

**Staffed Beds**: 191

○ **OKLAHOMA SURGICAL HOSPITAL (370210)**, 2408 East 81st Street, Suite 300, Zip 74137–4215; tel. 918/477–5000, (Nonreporting) **A**3 5 10 11 **F**3 12 18 20 22 24 26 29 30 34 37 40 44 45 46 49 50 51 58 64 65 68 70 74 75 79 81 82 85 86 87 93 107 108 111 115 118 119 120 121 123 124 126 129 130 131 148 149 **P**2
Primary Contact: Rick Ferguson, Chief Executive Officer
CFO: Dub Cleland, Chief Financial Officer
Web address: www.oklahomasurgicalhospital.com
**Control**: Partnership, Investor–owned (for–profit) **Service**: Surgical

**Staffed Beds**: 55 **Admissions**: 3892 **Census**: 23 **Outpatient Visits**: 30469
**Births**: 0 **Total Expense ($000)**: 115909 **Payroll Expense ($000)**: 26415
**Personnel**: 480

**ORTHOPEDIC SURGICAL HOSPITAL** See Oklahoma Surgical Hospital

☒ **PAM REHABILITATION HOSPITAL OF TULSA (373035)**, 10020 East 91st Street, Zip 74133; tel. 918/893–2400, (Nonreporting) **A**1 10 **S** Post Acute Medical, LLC, Enola, PA
Primary Contact: Thomas Biby, Chief Executive Officer
Web address: www.warmsprings.org/our-facilities/outpatient-rehabilitation
**Control**: Corporation, Investor–owned (for–profit) **Service**: Rehabilitation

**Staffed Beds**: 41

**PARKSIDE HOSPITAL** See Parkside Psychiatric Hospital and Clinic

**PARKSIDE PSYCHIATRIC HOSPITAL AND CLINIC (374021)**, 1619 East 13th Street, Zip 74120–5407; tel. 918/582–2131, (Nonreporting) **A**10 **F**3 4 5 29 34 35 38 40 41 44 50 56 57 59 64 87 98 99 100 101 102 103 104 106 130 132 143 146 149 151 153 154
Primary Contact: Debra Moore-Jones, Chief Executive Officer
CFO: Saunya Moore, Chief Financial Officer
CMO: Marvin Jin, M.D., Medical Director
CIO: Joe Vitali, Director Information Technology
CHR: David Patterson, Director Human Resources
Web address: www.parksideinc.org
**Control**: Other not–for–profit (including NFP Corporation) **Service**: Psychiatric

**Staffed Beds**: 71 **Admissions**: 2311 **Census**: 62 **Outpatient Visits**: 10335
**Births**: 0 **Total Expense ($000)**: 14985 **Payroll Expense ($000)**: 10028
**Personnel**: 176

☒ **POST ACUTE MEDICAL SPECIALTY HOSPITAL OF TULSA (372018)**, 3219 South 79th East Avenue, Zip 74145–1343; tel. 918/663–8183, (Nonreporting) **A**1 10 **S** Post Acute Medical, LLC, Enola, PA
Primary Contact: Anthony Young, Chief Executive Officer
Web address: www.postacutetulsa.com
**Control**: Corporation, Investor–owned (for–profit) **Service**: Acute long–term care hospital

**Staffed Beds**: 60

**SAINT FRANCIS HEALTH SYSTEM** See Saint Francis Hospital

**SAINT FRANCIS HEART HOSPITAL** See Saint Francis Hospital, Tulsa

**SAINT FRANCIS HOSPITAL** See Saint Francis Hospital South

☒ **SAINT FRANCIS HOSPITAL (370091)**, 6161 South Yale Avenue, Zip 74136–1902; tel. 918/494–2200, (Includes CHILDREN'S HOSPITAL AT SAINT FRANCIS, Mailing address: 6161 South Yale Avenue, Tulsa, Oklahoma, Zip 74136–1902; tel. 918/502–6714; Shannon M. Filosa, Executive Director Women's and Children; SAINT FRANCIS HEART HOSPITAL, Mailing address: 6151 South Yale Avenue, Tulsa, Oklahoma, Zip 74136–1902; tel. 918/494–1817; Douglas Williams, Vice President, Saint Francis Heart Hospital), (Nonreporting) **A**1 2 3 5 10 **F**3 7 8 11 12 13 15 17 18 19 20 21 22 23 24 25 26 27 28 29 30 31 32 35 37 39 40 41 43 44 45 46 47 48 49 50 51 54 55 56 57 58 59 60 61 64 66 68 70 72 73 74 75 76 77 78 79 80 81 82 83 84 85 86 87 88 89 90 92 93 100 102 107 108 110 111 114 115 116 117 118 119 120 121 123 124 126 129 130 131 132 135 136 138 141 146 147 148 154 **P**6 **S** Saint Francis Health System, Tulsa, OK
Primary Contact: Douglas Williams, Senior Vice President, Administrator
COO: Barry L Steichen, Executive Vice President and Chief Operating Officer, Saint Francis Health System
CFO: Eric Schick, Senior Vice President and Chief Financial Officer, Saint Francis Health System
CMO: Mark I Frost, M.D., Senior Vice President Medical Affairs, Saint Francis Health System
CIO: Meridith Coburn, Vice President Information Services
Web address: www.saintfrancis.com
**Control**: Other not–for–profit (including NFP Corporation) **Service**: General medical and surgical

**Staffed Beds**: 880 **Admissions**: 49070 **Census**: 675 **Outpatient Visits**: 475283 **Births**: 4110 **Total Expense ($000)**: 930838 **Payroll Expense ($000)**: 357280 **Personnel**: 4987

☒ **SAINT FRANCIS HOSPITAL SOUTH (370218)**, 10501 East 91st Street, Zip 74133–5790; tel. 918/307–6010, (Nonreporting) **A**1 10 **F**11 13 15 18 20 22 26 29 30 34 35 37 39 40 42 44 48 49 50 51 57 58 60 61 64 68 70 72 75 76 79 80 81 82 85 87 107 108 110 111 114 115 118 119 130 146 148 154 **P**6 **S** Saint Francis Health System, Tulsa, OK
Primary Contact: Todd Schuster, Vice President and Administrator
COO: Barry L Steichen, Executive Vice President and Chief Operating Officer
CFO: Eric Schick, Chief Financial Officer
CMO: Mark I Frost, M.D., Senior Vice President Medical Affairs
CIO: Meridith Coburn, Vice President, Information Systems
Web address: www.saintfrancis.com/south/
**Control**: Other not–for–profit (including NFP Corporation) **Service**: General medical and surgical

**Staffed Beds**: 102 **Admissions**: 5830 **Census**: 56 **Outpatient Visits**: 98397
**Births**: 793 **Total Expense ($000)**: 86694 **Payroll Expense ($000)**: 35346
**Personnel**: 411

**SELECT SPECIALTY HOSPITAL-MIDTOWN** See Select Specialty Hospital-Tulsa Midtown

☒ **SELECT SPECIALTY HOSPITAL-TULSA MIDTOWN (372007)**, 1125 South Trenton Avenue, 3rd Floor, Zip 74120–5418; tel. 918/579–7300, (Nonreporting) **A**1 10 **F**1 3 29 75 85 87 130 148 **S** Select Medical Corporation, Mechanicsburg, PA
Primary Contact: Charles D. Nasem, FACHE, Chief Executive Officer
CMO: E Joe Schelbar, M.D., Medical Director
CNO: Connie Ryan, Chief Nursing Officer
Web address: www.tulsa.selectspecialtyhospitals.com/
**Control**: Corporation, Investor–owned (for–profit) **Service**: Acute long–term care hospital

**Staffed Beds**: 52 **Admissions**: 360 **Census**: 26 **Outpatient Visits**: 0
**Births**: 0 **Total Expense ($000)**: 15086 **Payroll Expense ($000)**: 6883
**Personnel**: 91

⇑ **SOUTHCREST HOSPITAL** See Hillcrest Hospital - South

☐ **SOUTHWESTERN REGIONAL MEDICAL CENTER (370190)**, 10109 East 79th Street, Zip 74133–4564; tel. 918/286–5000, (Nonreporting) **A**1 2 3 10 13 **S** Cancer Treatment Centers of America, Schaumburg, IL
Primary Contact: Jay Foley, President and Chief Executive Officer
CFO: David Hedges, Chief Financial Officer
CMO: Daniel Nader, D.O., Chief of Staff
CIO: Craig Olson, Director Information Technology
CHR: Ryan Crawford, Director Talent
CNO: Denise Geuder, Vice President Patient Care Service and Chief Nursing Officer
Web address: www.cancercenter.com
**Control**: Corporation, Investor–owned (for–profit) **Service**: General medical and surgical

**Staffed Beds**: 40

*Many Facility Codes have changed. Please refer to the AHA Guide Code Chart.*   © 2021 AHA Guide

⊞ **ST. JOHN MEDICAL CENTER (370114)**, 1923 South Utica Avenue, Zip 74104–6502; tel. 918/744–2345, (Nonreporting) **A**1 2 3 5 10 19 **F**3 8 9 11 12 13 14 15 17 18 19 20 22 24 26 28 29 30 31 34 35 37 38 39 40 43 45 46 47 48 49 50 51 53 54 56 57 58 59 60 61 63 64 65 66 68 70 72 73 74 75 76 77 78 79 80 81 82 83 84 85 86 87 88 89 90 92 93 94 96 97 100 104 107 108 110 111 114 115 116 117 118 119 120 121 123 124 126 129 130 131 132 135 138 141 143 145 146 147 148 149 154 156 **P**1 5 **S** Ascension Healthcare, Saint Louis, MO
Primary Contact: Jeffrey D. Nowlin, President and Chief Operating Officer
COO: Jeffrey D. Nowlin, President and Chief Operating Officer
CFO: Wayne Walthall, Vice President and Chief Financial Officer
CMO: William Allred, M.D., Vice President Medical Affairs
CIO: Mike Reeves, Vice President
CHR: John Page Bachman, Corporate Vice President
CNO: Pamela Kiser, R.N., MS, Chief Nursing Executive and Vice President of Nursing
Web address: www.sjmc.org
**Control**: Church operated, Nongovernment, not–for–profit **Service**: General medical and surgical

**Staffed Beds: 523 Admissions: 28152 Census: 408 Outpatient Visits: 239222 Births: 2312 Total Expense ($000): 519965 Payroll Expense ($000): 156923 Personnel: 2291**

**THE CHILDREN'S HOSPITAL AT SAINT FRANCIS** See Children's Hospital at Saint Francis

☐ **TULSA CENTER FOR BEHAVIORAL HEALTH (374026)**, 2323 South Harvard Ave, Zip 74114–3301; tel. 918/293–2140, (Nonreporting) **A**1 3
Primary Contact: Lea Price, Administrator
Web address: www.https://www.ok.gov/odmhsas/
**Control**: State, Government, Nonfederal **Service**: Psychiatric

**Staffed Beds: 56**

**TULSA REGIONAL MEDICAL CENTER** See Oklahoma State University Medical Center

⊞ **TULSA SPINE AND SPECIALTY HOSPITAL (370216)**, 6901 South Olympia Avenue, Zip 74132–1843; tel. 918/388–5701, (Nonreporting) **A**1 3 10 **F**3 29 40 45 68 74 78 79 81 82 85 87 107 111 116 117 126 129 **S** Ardent Health Services, Nashville, TN
Primary Contact: Trent Gastineau, Chief Executive Officer
CMO: David Fell, M.D., Chief Medical Officer
Web address: www.tulsaspinehospital.com
**Control**: Partnership, Investor–owned (for–profit) **Service**: Surgical

**Staffed Beds: 38 Admissions: 993 Census: 8 Outpatient Visits: 19169 Births: 0 Total Expense ($000): 50181 Payroll Expense ($000): 12835**

**TULSA SPINE HOSPITAL** See Tulsa Spine and Specialty Hospital

### VINITA—Craig County

⇧ **CRAIG GENERAL HOSPITAL** See Saint Francis Hospital Vinita

**EASTERN STATE HOSPITAL** See Oklahoma Forensic Center

**OKLAHOMA FORENSIC CENTER**, 24800 South 4420 Road, Zip 74301–5544, Mailing Address: P.O. Box 69, Zip 74301–0069; tel. 918/256–7841, (Nonreporting) **A**3 **F**39 98 100 106 130 154 **S** Oklahoma Department of Mental Health and Substance Abuse Services, Oklahoma City, OK
Primary Contact: Kevan Finley, Chief Executive Officer
CFO: Miriam Harris, Director Finance
CMO: Satwant Tandon, M.D., Director of Clinical Services
CIO: Kevin Marble, Director Information Technology
CHR: Julie Jacobs, Director Human Resources
CNO: Glenda Satterwhite, Director of Nursing
Web address: www.odmhsas.org
**Control**: State, Government, Nonfederal **Service**: Psychiatric

**Staffed Beds: 200 Admissions: 309 Census: 191 Outpatient Visits: 0 Births: 0 Personnel: 240**

★ ⇧ **SAINT FRANCIS HOSPITAL VINITA (370237)**, 735 North Foreman Street, Zip 74301–1418; tel. 918/256–7551, (Nonreporting) **A**10 20 21 **F**3 11 15 18 29 30 34 35 36 40 45 50 53 57 59 68 74 75 77 79 80 82 86 87 93 94 98 100 102 103 104 107 108 111 114 115 119 127 129 130 133 143 146 147 148 154 **P**6 **S** Saint Francis Health System, Tulsa, OK
Primary Contact: Todd Schuster, Administrator
CMO: Ed Allensworth, M.D., Medical Director
CHR: Darlene R Nolte, Chief Human Resource Officer
CNO: Ann Carr, R.N., Chief Nursing Officer
Web address: www.https://www.saintfrancis.com/vinita/Pages/default.aspx
**Control**: Other not–for–profit (including NFP Corporation) **Service**: General medical and surgical

**Staffed Beds: 70 Admissions: 1117 Census: 19 Outpatient Visits: 31222 Births: 0 Total Expense ($000): 15747 Payroll Expense ($000): 7505 Personnel: 110**

### WAGONER—Wagoner County

**COLUMBIA WAGONER HOSPITAL** See Wagoner Community Hospital

**WAGONER COMMUNITY HOSPITAL (370166)**, 1200 West Cherokee Street, Zip 74467–4624, Mailing Address: P.O. Box 407, Zip 74477–0407; tel. 918/485–5514, (Nonreporting) **A**10 **F**3 11 15 18 28 29 34 39 40 41 45 50 51 56 57 59 64 65 70 74 75 79 81 82 85 87 93 98 100 102 107 108 110 111 115 118 119 129 130 131 132 135 146 147 148 149 154 156 157
Primary Contact: Jimmy Leopard, FACHE, Chief Executive Officer
COO: Louise Dodson, R.N., Chief Operating Officer and Chief Nursing Officer
CFO: Rebecca Sharp, Chief Financial Officer
CMO: Casey Hanna, M.D., Chief of Staff
CIO: Jim Riley, Director Information Technology
CHR: Barnetta Pofahl, Director Human Resources
CNO: Louise Dodson, R.N., Chief Nursing Officer
Web address: www.wagonerhospital.com
**Control**: Hospital district or authority, Government, Nonfederal **Service**: General medical and surgical

**Staffed Beds: 100 Admissions: 2599 Census: 37 Outpatient Visits: 34219 Births: 0 Total Expense ($000): 21976 Payroll Expense ($000): 9369 Personnel: 188**

### WATONGA—Blaine County

★ **MERCY HOSPITAL WATONGA (371302)**, 500 North Clarence Nash Boulevard, Zip 73772–2845, Mailing Address: P.O. Box 370, Zip 73772–0370; tel. 580/623–7211, (Nonreporting) **A**10 18 **F**3 11 29 30 34 40 43 50 57 59 64 68 75 85 87 93 107 114 119 128 130 132 133 135 149 154 **S** Mercy, Chesterfield, MO
Primary Contact: Bobby Stitt, R.N., Administrator
CHR: Mary Jo Messelt, Manager Human Resources
Web address: www.mercy.net/watongaok/practice/mercy-hospital-watonga
**Control**: Church operated, Nongovernment, not–for–profit **Service**: General medical and surgical

**Staffed Beds: 25 Admissions: 133 Census: 2 Outpatient Visits: 9450 Births: 0 Total Expense ($000): 6669 Payroll Expense ($000): 3746 Personnel: 56**

**WATONGA MUNICIPAL HOSPITAL** See Mercy Hospital Watonga

### WAURIKA—Jefferson County

★ **JEFFERSON COUNTY HOSPITAL (371311)**, Highway 70 and 81, Zip 73573–3075, Mailing Address: P.O. Box 90, Zip 73573–0090; tel. 580/228–2344, (Nonreporting) **A**10 18 **F**40 57 59 64 66 68 87 93 107 127 128 130 148 149 154 **S** DRH Health, Duncan, OK
Primary Contact: Richard Gillespie, President
CFO: Richard Tallon, Chief Financial Officer
CMO: Rob Linzman, D.O., Chief of Staff
CIO: Nikki McGahey, Information Officer
Web address: www.jeffersoncountyhospital.net
**Control**: Other not–for–profit (including NFP Corporation) **Service**: General medical and surgical

**Staffed Beds: 8 Admissions: 28 Census: 1 Outpatient Visits: 4356 Births: 0**

---

**Hospital, Medicare Provider Number, Address, Telephone, Approval, Facility, and Physician Codes, Health Care System**

★ American Hospital Association (AHA) membership
☐ The Joint Commission accreditation
○ Healthcare Facilities Accreditation Program
◇ DNV Healthcare Inc. accreditation
⇧ Center for Improvement in Healthcare Quality Accreditation
△ Commission on Accreditation of Rehabilitation Facilities (CARF) accreditation

**OK**

### WEATHERFORD—Custer County

**SOUTHWESTERN MEMORIAL HOSPITAL** See Weatherford Regional Hospital

★ **WEATHERFORD REGIONAL HOSPITAL (371323)**, 3701 East Main Street,
Zip 73096–3309; tel. 580/772–5551, (Nonreporting) **A**10 18 **F**3 11 13 15 29 31
34 40 43 45 59 64 68 75 76 77 79 81 86 87 93 97 107 108 110 111 115 119
129 130 133 135 144 146 147 148 149 **S** SSM Health, Saint Louis, MO
Primary Contact: Debbie Howe, Chief Executive Officer
CFO: Stephanie Helton, Chief Financial Officer
CMO: Jonathan Ray Long, M.D., Chief of Staff
CIO: Amy Outhier, Director Health Information Management
CHR: Tawnya Paden, Director Human Resources
CNO: Delvin Mast, R.N., Director of Nursing
Web address: www.weatherfordhospital.com
**Control:** Hospital district or authority, Government, Nonfederal **Service:** General
medical and surgical

**Staffed Beds:** 22 **Admissions:** 510 **Census:** 4 **Outpatient Visits:** 43672
**Births:** 148 **Total Expense ($000):** 17839 **Payroll Expense ($000):** 6399
**Personnel:** 128

### WOODWARD—Woodward County

⊞ **ALLIANCEHEALTH WOODWARD (370002)**, 900 17th Street, Zip 73801–2448;
tel. 580/256–5511, (Nonreporting) **A**1 10 20 **S** Community Health Systems, Inc.,
Franklin, TN
Primary Contact: Landon E. Hise, Interim Chief Executive Officer
CFO: Tom Earley, Chief Financial Officer
CIO: Larry Churchill, Director Information Services
CHR: Melinda Brock, Director Human Resources
CNO: Kimberly N Arnold, R.N., Chief Nursing Officer and Interim Chief Quality
Officer
Web address: www.woodwardhospital.com
**Control:** Corporation, Investor–owned (for–profit) **Service:** General medical and
surgical

**Staffed Beds:** 40

**WOODWARD REGIONAL HOSPITAL** See Alliancehealth Woodward

### YUKON—Canadian County

⊞ **INTEGRIS CANADIAN VALLEY HOSPITAL (370211)**, 1201 Health Center
Parkway, Zip 73099–6381; tel. 405/717–6800, (Nonreporting) **A**1 3 10 **F**3 11 13
15 18 29 30 39 40 43 44 45 46 49 52 60 64 68 70 76 77 79 81 85 87 93 96
107 108 110 111 115 118 119 130 135 146 147 156 **P**6 7 **S** INTEGRIS Health,
Oklahoma City, OK
Primary Contact: Teresa Gray, President
COO: Cindy White, CPA, Vice President of Operations
CFO: Errol Mitchell, Chief Financial Officer
CHR: Lynn Ketch, Human Resources Recruiter Generalist
Web address: www.integris-health.com
**Control:** Other not–for–profit (including NFP Corporation) **Service:** General
medical and surgical

**Staffed Beds:** 75 **Admissions:** 3526 **Census:** 34 **Outpatient Visits:** 64852
**Births:** 907 **Total Expense ($000):** 64956 **Payroll Expense ($000):** 19306
**Personnel:** 302

**INTEGRIS CANADIAN VALLEY REGIONAL HOSPITAL** See Integris Canadian
Valley Hospital

*Many Facility Codes have changed. Please refer to the AHA Guide Code Chart.*

# OREGON

## ALBANY—Linn County

⇑ **ALBANY GENERAL HOSPITAL** See Samaritan Albany General Hospital

★ ⇑ **SAMARITAN ALBANY GENERAL HOSPITAL (380022)**, 1046 Sixth Avenue, SW, Zip 97321–1999; tel. 541/812–4000, (Nonreporting) **A**3 10 21 **F**3 5 11 13 15 18 28 29 30 31 34 35 36 37 40 43 45 47 49 53 54 57 59 61 63 64 67 68 70 73 74 75 76 77 78 79 81 84 85 86 87 89 92 93 97 104 107 108 110 111 114 116 117 119 129 130 131 132 135 144 146 147 148 149 150 154 156 **P**6 **S** Samaritan Health Services, Corvallis, OR
Primary Contact: Dan Keteri, R.N., Chief Executive Officer
CFO: Daniel B Smith, Vice President Finance
Web address: www.samhealth.org
**Control:** Other not–for–profit (including NFP Corporation) **Service:** General medical and surgical

> **Staffed Beds:** 70 **Admissions:** 2723 **Census:** 23 **Outpatient Visits:** 314562 **Births:** 502 **Total Expense ($000):** 205805 **Payroll Expense ($000):** 83425 **Personnel:** 889

## ASHLAND—Jackson County

★ ⇑ **ASANTE ASHLAND COMMUNITY HOSPITAL (380005)**, 280 Maple Street, Zip 97520–1593; tel. 541/201–4000, (Nonreporting) **A**10 21 **F**3 13 15 29 30 34 35 36 40 45 46 48 50 57 59 64 65 70 75 76 79 81 85 87 93 107 110 114 119 130 131 132 143 145 146 147 148 **S** Asante Health System, Medford, OR
Primary Contact: Sheila Clough, Chief Executive Officer
CFO: Patrick Hocking, Chief Financial Officer
CMO: Bill Steinsick, M.D., Chief Medical Staff
CIO: Mark Hetz, Chief Information Officer
CHR: Gregg Edwards, Vice President Human Resources
CNO: Susan Montgomery, Chief Nursing Officer
Web address: www.ashlandhospital.org
**Control:** Other not–for–profit (including NFP Corporation) **Service:** General medical and surgical

> **Staffed Beds:** 38 **Admissions:** 1163 **Census:** 11 **Outpatient Visits:** 39305 **Births:** 227 **Total Expense ($000):** 57162 **Payroll Expense ($000):** 20233 **Personnel:** 227

⇑ **ASHLAND COMMUNITY HOSPITAL** See Asante Ashland Community Hospital

## ASTORIA—Clatsop County

★ ○ **COLUMBIA MEMORIAL HOSPITAL (381320)**, 2111 Exchange Street, Zip 97103–3329; tel. 503/325–4321, (Nonreporting) **A**3 5 10 11 18 **F**3 11 13 15 18 26 28 29 30 31 32 34 35 36 40 41 43 44 45 50 51 57 58 59 63 64 65 68 70 75 76 77 78 79 81 85 86 87 89 91 93 97 107 108 110 111 114 115 116 117 119 127 130 131 132 133 134 135 143 144 146 147 148 149 154 **P**5 8
Primary Contact: Erik Thorsen, President and Chief Executive Officer
COO: Nicole Williams, Chief Operating Officer
CFO: Stephanie D Brenden, Vice President Finance
CMO: Bruce Bobek, President Professional Staff
CIO: Galina Gandy, Vice President Information Technology
CHR: Lucy G Dupree, Director Human Resources
CNO: Trece Gurrad, Vice President Patient Care Services
Web address: www.columbiamemorial.org
**Control:** Other not–for–profit (including NFP Corporation) **Service:** General medical and surgical

> **Staffed Beds:** 25 **Admissions:** 1754 **Census:** 14 **Outpatient Visits:** 247583 **Births:** 308 **Total Expense ($000):** 127351 **Payroll Expense ($000):** 47992 **Personnel:** 739

## BAKER CITY—Baker County

⊞ **SAINT ALPHONSUS MEDICAL CENTER - BAKER CITY (381315)**, 3325 Pocahontas Road, Zip 97814–1464; tel. 541/523–6461, (Nonreporting) **A**1 10 18 **F**3 11 13 15 29 30 31 34 35 40 43 44 45 50 57 59 64 68 70 76 77 78 79 81 83 85 87 97 107 110 111 115 119 127 128 129 131 133 143 146 147 148 154 **P**6 **S** Trinity Health, Livonia, MI
Primary Contact: Priscilla Lynn, President and Chief Executive Officer
CFO: Robert D Wehling, Interim Chief Financial Officer
CHR: Jerry Nickell, Vice President Human Resource and Mission
Web address: www.https://www.saintalphonsus.org/bakercity
**Control:** Other not–for–profit (including NFP Corporation) **Service:** General medical and surgical

> **Staffed Beds:** 25 **Admissions:** 760 **Census:** 7 **Outpatient Visits:** 40279 **Births:** 117 **Total Expense ($000):** 36278 **Payroll Expense ($000):** 14654 **Personnel:** 192

**ST. ELIZABETH HEALTH SERVICES** See Saint Alphonsus Medical Center - Baker City

## BANDON—Coos County

**SOUTHERN COOS GENERAL HOSPITAL** See Southern Coos Hospital and Health Center

★ **SOUTHERN COOS HOSPITAL AND HEALTH CENTER (381304)**, 900 11th Street SE, Zip 97411–9114; tel. 541/347–2426, (Nonreporting) **A**10 18 **F**3 11 15 29 34 35 40 45 50 57 59 64 65 75 81 82 85 87 97 107 110 111 115 119 130 132 133 135 146 148 149 154 156 **P**6
Primary Contact: Eugene Suksi, Chief Executive Officer
CFO: Alan Dow, Chief Financial Officer
CMO: Megan Holland, Chief Medical Officer and Family Practitioner
CIO: Mandy Calvert, Director Information Systems
CHR: Kalen M Mills, Director Human Resources
CNO: Rachel Beissel, Chief Nursing Officer
Web address: www.southerncoos.org
**Control:** Hospital district or authority, Government, Nonfederal **Service:** General medical and surgical

> **Staffed Beds:** 19 **Admissions:** 374 **Census:** 5 **Outpatient Visits:** 58808 **Births:** 0 **Total Expense ($000):** 21853 **Payroll Expense ($000):** 9379 **Personnel:** 139

## BEND—Deschutes County

⊞ **ST. CHARLES BEND (380047)**, 2500 NE Neff Road, Zip 97701–6015; tel. 541/382–4321, (Nonreporting) **A**1 2 3 5 10 19 **F**3 8 11 12 13 15 18 19 20 21 22 24 26 28 29 30 31 34 35 36 37 38 40 43 44 45 46 47 49 50 51 53 54 57 58 59 60 62 63 64 65 67 68 70 72 74 75 76 77 78 79 81 82 84 85 86 87 89 90 91 92 93 97 98 100 101 102 104 107 108 111 114 115 119 120 121 123 124 126 129 130 132 135 144 146 147 148 149 154 156 **P**6 **S** St. Charles Health System, Inc., Bend, OR
Primary Contact: Aaron Adams, President
CFO: Jennifer Welander, CPA, Senior Vice President Finance and Chief Financial Officer
CMO: Jeffrey Absalon, M.D., Chief Physician Officer
CIO: Jerimiah Brickhouse, Chief Information Officer
CHR: Rebecca Berry, Vice President Human Resources
Web address: www.stcharleshealthcare.org
**Control:** Other not–for–profit (including NFP Corporation) **Service:** General medical and surgical

> **Staffed Beds:** 305 **Admissions:** 16903 **Census:** 184 **Outpatient Visits:** 171418 **Births:** 1955 **Total Expense ($000):** 466669 **Payroll Expense ($000):** 183064 **Personnel:** 3023

**ST. CHARLES HEALTH SYSTEM-BEND** See St. Charles Bend

---

**Hospital, Medicare Provider Number, Address, Telephone, Approval, Facility, and Physician Codes, Health Care System**

★ American Hospital Association (AHA) membership    ○ Healthcare Facilities Accreditation Program    ⇑ Center for Improvement in Healthcare Quality Accreditation
□ The Joint Commission accreditation    ◇ DNV Healthcare Inc. accreditation    △ Commission on Accreditation of Rehabilitation Facilities (CARF) accreditation

OR

## BURNS—Harney County

**HARNEY COUNTY HOSPITAL** See Harney District Hospital

★ **HARNEY DISTRICT HOSPITAL (381307)**, 557 West Washington Street, Zip 97720–1497; tel. 541/573–7281, (Nonreporting) **A**10 18 **F**3 7 12 13 15 29 31 34 35 40 43 45 50 53 57 59 64 65 70 75 76 78 81 82 85 93 97 107 111 114 119 127 131 132 133 146 149 156
Primary Contact: Dan Grigg, Chief Executive Officer
CFO: Catherine White, Chief Financial Officer
CMO: Sarah Laiosa, M.D., Chief Medical Staff
CIO: Tanya Strong, Manager Information Technology
CHR: Sammie Masterson, Director Human Resources
CNO: Deana Altman, Interim Chief Nursing Officer
Web address: www.harneydh.com
**Control:** Hospital district or authority, Government, Nonfederal **Service:** General medical and surgical

**Staffed Beds:** 21 **Admissions:** 325 **Census:** 3 **Outpatient Visits:** 36414 **Births:** 65 **Total Expense ($000):** 26929 **Payroll Expense ($000):** 12378 **Personnel:** 182

## CLACKAMAS—Clackamas County

**KAISER PERMANENTE SUNNYSIDE MEDICAL CENTER** See Kaiser Sunnyside Medical Center

✠ **KAISER SUNNYSIDE MEDICAL CENTER (380091)**, 10180 SE Sunnyside Road, Zip 97015–8970; tel. 503/652–2880, (Nonreporting) **A**1 2 3 5 10 **F**3 11 12 13 15 17 18 20 22 24 26 29 30 31 34 35 40 45 46 47 49 51 60 61 64 65 68 70 72 74 75 76 77 78 79 81 85 86 87 93 94 97 102 107 108 110 111 114 115 118 119 130 135 141 146 147 148 154 **P**6 **S** Kaiser Foundation Hospitals, Oakland, CA
Primary Contact: James L. Robinson III, PsyD, Hospital Adminstrator
CFO: Justin N. Evander, Chief Financial Officer
CMO: Richard Hunt, M.D., Chief Operating Officer
CIO: Mark A Burmester, Vice President Strategy and Communications
CHR: Rich Smith, Vice President Human Resources
CNO: Lauren M Bridge, R.N., Chief Nursing Officer
Web address: www.kaiserpermanente.org
**Control:** Other not–for–profit (including NFP Corporation) **Service:** General medical and surgical

**Staffed Beds:** 301 **Admissions:** 20513 **Census:** 197 **Outpatient Visits:** 71573 **Births:** 2333 **Total Expense ($000):** 418633 **Payroll Expense ($000):** 178089 **Personnel:** 2251

## COOS BAY—Coos County

✠ **BAY AREA HOSPITAL (380090)**, 1775 Thompson Road, Zip 97420–2198; tel. 541/269–8111, (Nonreporting) **A**1 2 3 10 **F**3 11 12 13 15 18 20 22 26 28 29 31 34 35 40 43 45 46 48 50 51 57 59 62 68 70 73 74 75 76 77 78 79 81 84 85 89 91 92 93 98 100 101 102 107 108 110 111 115 118 119 120 121 123 126 129 130 132 135 146 147 148 149 156 157
Primary Contact: Brian Moore, President and Chief Executive Officer
COO: Ben Pfau, Chief Facility and Information Officer
CFO: Sam Patterson, Chief Financial Officer
CMO: Michael van Duren, M.D., Chief Medical Officer
CIO: Bob Adams, Director Information Services
CHR: Suzie Q McDaniel, Chief Human Resource Officer
Web address: www.bayareahospital.org
**Control:** Hospital district or authority, Government, Nonfederal **Service:** General medical and surgical

**Staffed Beds:** 134 **Admissions:** 5654 **Census:** 64 **Outpatient Visits:** 98007 **Births:** 632 **Total Expense ($000):** 180935 **Payroll Expense ($000):** 75233 **Personnel:** 889

## COQUILLE—Coos County

★ **COQUILLE VALLEY HOSPITAL (381312)**, 940 East Fifth Street, Zip 97423–1699; tel. 541/396–3101, (Nonreporting) **A**10 18 **F**3 11 15 29 30 34 40 43 56 57 68 77 79 81 82 107 108 111 114 119 133 135 146 148 **P**6
Primary Contact: Jeff Lang, Chief Executive Officer
CFO: Robert E Fisher, Chief Financial Officer
CMO: James Sinnott, M.D., Chief Medical Staff
CIO: Curt Carpenter, Manager Information Technology
CHR: Monte Johnston, Manager Human Resources
Web address: www.cvhospital.org
**Control:** Hospital district or authority, Government, Nonfederal **Service:** General medical and surgical

**Staffed Beds:** 17 **Admissions:** 596 **Census:** 8 **Outpatient Visits:** 31109 **Births:** 0 **Total Expense ($000):** 30632 **Payroll Expense ($000):** 14468 **Personnel:** 156

## CORVALLIS—Benton County

⇑ **GOOD SAMARITAN HOSP CORVALLIS** See Good Samaritan Regional Medical Center

★ ⇑ **GOOD SAMARITAN REGIONAL MEDICAL CENTER (380014)**, 3600 NW Samaritan Drive, Zip 97330–3737, Mailing Address: P.O. Box 1068, Zip 97339–1068; tel. 541/768–5111, (Nonreporting) **A**2 3 5 10 12 13 19 21 **F**3 11 12 13 15 17 18 20 22 24 26 28 29 30 31 34 35 36 37 40 43 53 54 56 57 58 59 61 64 68 70 71 73 74 76 77 78 79 81 82 85 86 87 89 92 93 97 98 100 101 102 104 107 108 110 111 114 115 116 117 118 119 120 121 123 124 126 130 131 132 135 144 146 147 148 149 154 156 **S** Samaritan Health Services, Corvallis, OR
Primary Contact: Becky A. Pape, R.N., Chief Executive Officer
CFO: Daniel B Smith, Vice President Finance
CIO: Bob Power, Vice President Information Services
CHR: Doug Boysen, Chief Legal Counsel and Vice President Human Resources
CNO: William Howden, Vice President Nursing
Web address: www.samhealth.org
**Control:** Other not–for–profit (including NFP Corporation) **Service:** General medical and surgical

**Staffed Beds:** 185 **Admissions:** 8199 **Census:** 109 **Outpatient Visits:** 415651 **Births:** 973 **Total Expense ($000):** 456763 **Payroll Expense ($000):** 179283 **Personnel:** 1757

## COTTAGE GROVE—Lane County

**COTTAGE GROVE COMMUNITY HOSPITAL** See Peacehealth Cottage Grove Community Medical Center

★ **PEACEHEALTH COTTAGE GROVE COMMUNITY MEDICAL CENTER (381301)**, 1515 Village Drive, Zip 97424–9700; tel. 541/942–0511, (Nonreporting) **A**10 18 **F**3 11 15 29 30 34 35 40 59 64 65 93 97 100 107 110 111 115 119 127 130 132 133 146 148 149 154 **S** PeaceHealth, Vancouver, WA
Primary Contact: Tim Herrmann, R.N., Administrator
Web address: www.peacehealth.org
**Control:** Church operated, Nongovernment, not–for–profit **Service:** General medical and surgical

**Staffed Beds:** 14 **Admissions:** 264 **Census:** 2 **Outpatient Visits:** 39740 **Births:** 0 **Total Expense ($000):** 18530 **Payroll Expense ($000):** 6962 **Personnel:** 83

## DALLAS—Polk County

**SALEM HEALTH WEST VALLEY (381308)**, 525 SE Washington Street, Zip 97338–2834, Mailing Address: P.O. Box 378, Zip 97338–0378; tel. 503/623–8301, (Nonreporting) **A**10 18 **F**3 15 35 40 50 59 64 75 79 81 85 93 97 107 108 110 111 114 119 131 132 133 143 146 148 **P**6 **S** Salem Health, Salem, OR
Primary Contact: Brandon Schmidgall, Chief Executive Officer
CFO: James Parr, Chief Financial Officer
CMO: Ralph Yates, D.O., Chief Medical Officer
CNO: Sarah Horn, Chief Nursing Officer
Web address: www.salemhealth.org/wvh/
**Control:** Other not–for–profit (including NFP Corporation) **Service:** General medical and surgical

**Staffed Beds:** 6 **Admissions:** 172 **Census:** 1 **Outpatient Visits:** 73155 **Births:** 0 **Total Expense ($000):** 28933 **Payroll Expense ($000):** 13208 **Personnel:** 128

**WEST VALLEY HOSPITAL** See Salem Health West Valley

## ENTERPRISE—Wallowa County

★ ⇑ **WALLOWA MEMORIAL HOSPITAL (381306)**, 601 Medical Parkway, Zip 97828–5124; tel. 541/426–3111, (Nonreporting) **A**3 5 10 18 21 **F**3 7 10 11 13 15 29 30 31 34 35 40 43 45 46 56 57 59 64 68 75 76 77 78 79 81 82 85 87 93 97 102 107 110 115 119 127 128 131 132 133 134 135 143 145 148 149
Primary Contact: Larry Davy, Chief Executive Officer
CFO: Daniel Jessup, Chief Financial Officer
CMO: Keith DeYoung, M.D., Chief Medical Staff
CIO: John Straughan, Director Information Technology
CHR: Linda Childers, Director Human Resources
CNO: Jenni Word, R.N., Chief Nursing Officer
Web address: www.wchcd.org
**Control:** Hospital district or authority, Government, Nonfederal **Service:** General medical and surgical

**Staffed Beds:** 25 **Admissions:** 604 **Census:** 7 **Outpatient Visits:** 35741 **Births:** 50 **Total Expense ($000):** 24052 **Payroll Expense ($000):** 10732 **Personnel:** 134

*Many Facility Codes have changed. Please refer to the AHA Guide Code Chart.* © 2021 AHA Guide

**OR**

## EUGENE—Lane County

★ △ ⇑ **PEACEHEALTH SACRED HEART MEDICAL CENTER UNIVERSITY DISTRICT (380033)**, 1255 Hilyard Street, Zip 97401–3700, Mailing Address: P.O. Box 10905, Zip 97440–2905; tel. 541/686–7300, (Nonreporting) **A**7 10 21 **F**3 29 30 31 38 40 43 56 62 63 68 84 90 93 98 102 105 107 115 130 146 148 153 154 **S** PeaceHealth, Vancouver, WA
Primary Contact: Mary Anne McMurren, R.N., Chief Administrative Officer
CFO: Wendy Apland, Interim Chief Financial Officer
CMO: Bill Moshofsky, M.D., Chief of Staff
CIO: Donn McMillan, Chief Information Officer
CHR: Craig Mills, Vice President Human Resources
Web address: www.peacehealth.org
**Control**: Church operated, Nongovernment, not–for–profit **Service**: General medical and surgical

| | |
|---|---|
| **Staffed Beds**: 93 **Admissions**: 2849 **Census**: 60 **Outpatient Visits**: 77516 **Births**: 0 **Total Expense ($000)**: 101322 **Payroll Expense ($000)**: 49573 **Personnel**: 555 | |

⇑ **PEACEHEALTH SACRED HEART MEDICAL CENTER, UNIVERSITY DISTRICT** See Peacehealth Sacred Heart Medical Center University District

**VALLEY WEST HEALTH CENTER** See Valley West Health Care Center

## FLORENCE—Lane County

⇑ **PEACE HARBOR HOSPITAL** See Peacehealth Peace Harbor Medical Center

★ ⇑ **PEACEHEALTH PEACE HARBOR MEDICAL CENTER (381316)**, 400 Ninth Street, Zip 97439–7398; tel. 541/997–8412, (Nonreporting) **A**10 18 21 **F**3 8 13 15 18 28 29 30 34 38 40 43 45 50 57 59 62 63 68 70 75 76 79 81 82 84 93 97 100 104 107 110 111 115 118 119 130 133 135 147 148 149 154 156 **S** PeaceHealth, Vancouver, WA
Primary Contact: Jason F. Hawkins, Chief Administrative Officer
CMO: Ron Shearer, M.D., Regional Medical Director
CIO: Ginni Boughal, Director Health Information and Information Technology
CHR: Don Bourland, Vice President Human Resources
Web address: www.peacehealth.org
**Control**: Church operated, Nongovernment, not–for–profit **Service**: General medical and surgical

| | |
|---|---|
| **Staffed Beds**: 21 **Admissions**: 892 **Census**: 7 **Outpatient Visits**: 68197 **Births**: 0 **Total Expense ($000)**: 54521 **Payroll Expense ($000)**: 23753 **Personnel**: 357 | |

## FOREST GROVE—Washington County

**FOREST GROVE COMM HOSPITAL** See Tuality Forest Grove Hospital

**TUALITY FOREST GROVE HOSPITAL** See Tuality Healthcare, Hillsboro

## GOLD BEACH—Curry County

★ ⇑ **CURRY GENERAL HOSPITAL (381322)**, 94220 Fourth Street, Zip 97444–7756; tel. 541/247–3000, (Nonreporting) **A**10 18 21 **F**3 11 15 18 28 29 34 40 43 50 51 54 59 64 75 79 81 82 85 87 90 97 107 110 111 114 119 127 128 130 133 135 144 148 149
Primary Contact: Virginia Razo, Chief Executive Officer
CFO: Carl Gerlach, Chief Financial Officer
CMO: Reginald Williams, M.D., Medical Staff President
CIO: Kristina Martin, Chief Information Officer
Web address: www.curryhealthnetwork.com
**Control**: Hospital district or authority, Government, Nonfederal **Service**: General medical and surgical

| | |
|---|---|
| **Staffed Beds**: 18 **Admissions**: 523 **Census**: 5 **Outpatient Visits**: 111040 **Births**: 0 **Total Expense ($000)**: 46987 **Payroll Expense ($000)**: 23222 **Personnel**: 287 | |

## GRANTS PASS—Josephine County

★ ⇑ **ASANTE THREE RIVERS MEDICAL CENTER (380002)**, 500 SW Ramsey Avenue, Zip 97527–5554; tel. 541/472–7000, (Nonreporting) **A**3 5 10 21 **F**3 11 13 15 28 29 30 31 34 35 36 40 43 45 46 48 49 50 53 54 57 59 64 65 70 75 76 78 79 81 85 87 93 94 107 108 110 111 114 115 118 119 120 129 130 132 143 144 145 146 147 148 154 **S** Asante Health System, Medford, OR
Primary Contact: Win Howard, Chief Executive Officer
COO: David Kinyon, Vice President of Operations and Outpatient Services
CFO: Patrick Hocking, Chief Financial Officer
CMO: Eric Loeliger, Vice President of Medical Affairs
CIO: Mark Hetz, Chief Information Officer
CHR: Gregg Edwards, Chief People Officer
Web address: www.asante.org/trmc/
**Control**: Other not–for–profit (including NFP Corporation) **Service**: General medical and surgical

| | |
|---|---|
| **Staffed Beds**: 122 **Admissions**: 6928 **Census**: 72 **Outpatient Visits**: 309195 **Births**: 738 **Total Expense ($000)**: 181047 **Payroll Expense ($000)**: 68503 **Personnel**: 920 | |

⇑ **THREE RIVERS MEDICAL CENTER** See Asante Three Rivers Medical Center

## GRESHAM—Multnomah County

⊞ **LEGACY MOUNT HOOD MEDICAL CENTER (380025)**, 24800 SE Stark, Zip 97030–3378; tel. 503/667–1122, (Nonreporting) **A**1 2 10 **F**3 11 13 15 18 20 26 28 29 30 31 32 34 35 38 40 44 45 46 48 49 50 51 57 59 60 64 68 70 74 75 76 77 78 79 81 85 86 87 93 100 101 102 107 108 110 111 114 115 118 119 120 121 123 126 129 130 132 146 147 148 149 156 **P**6 **S** Legacy Health, Portland, OR
Primary Contact: Tanya Shanks-Connors, R.N., MSN, Interim President
COO: Michael Newcomb, D.O., Senior Vice President and Chief Operating Officer
CFO: Linda Hoff, Senior Vice President and Chief Financial Officer
CMO: Lewis Low, M.D., Chief Medical Officer
CIO: John Jay Kenagy, Ph.D., Senior Vice President and Chief Information Officer
CHR: Sonja Steves, Senior Vice President Human Resources
CNO: Marcia Soderling, R.N., Hospital Nurse Executive
Web address: www.legacyhealth.org
**Control**: Other not–for–profit (including NFP Corporation) **Service**: General medical and surgical

| | |
|---|---|
| **Staffed Beds**: 98 **Admissions**: 6065 **Census**: 62 **Outpatient Visits**: 166382 **Births**: 935 **Total Expense ($000)**: 151125 **Payroll Expense ($000)**: 59962 **Personnel**: 603 | |

**MOUNT HOOD MEDICAL CENTER** See Legacy Mount Hood Medical Center

## HEPPNER—Morrow County

**PIONEER MEMORIAL HOSPITAL (381310)**, 564 East Pioneer Drive, Zip 97836–7318, Mailing Address: P.O. Box 9, Zip 97836–0009; tel. 541/676–9133, (Nonreporting) **A**10 18 **F**3 7 34 35 40 43 45 50 57 59 62 63 64 66 68 75 81 97 107 119 127 130 133 135 146 147 148 154 **P**6
Primary Contact: Robert Houser, FACHE, Chief Executive Officer
CFO: Nicole Mahoney, Chief Financial Officer
CIO: Shawn Cutsforth, Information Systems Officer
CHR: Patti Allstott, Administrative Coordinator Human Resources and Grant Writer
Web address: www.morrowcountyhealthdistrict.org
**Control**: Hospital district or authority, Government, Nonfederal **Service**: General medical and surgical

| | |
|---|---|
| **Staffed Beds**: 11 **Admissions**: 90 **Census**: 6 **Outpatient Visits**: 6639 **Births**: 0 **Total Expense ($000)**: 13543 **Payroll Expense ($000)**: 7265 **Personnel**: 114 | |

---

## HERMISTON—Umatilla County

★ ⇑ **GOOD SHEPHERD HEALTH CARE SYSTEM (381325)**, 610 NW 11th Street, Zip 97838–6601; tel. 541/667–3400, (Nonreporting) **A**10 18 21 **F**3 11 13 15 28 29 30 31 33 34 35 36 40 43 45 46 50 53 54 57 59 62 63 64 65 68 70 75 76 79 81 85 86 87 97 107 108 110 111 115 119 126 127 132 133 135 143 144 146 147 148 149 154 156
Primary Contact: Dennis E. Burke, President and Chief Executive Officer
COO: Jim Schlenker, Chief Operating Officer
CFO: Jan D Peter, Vice President Fiscal Services and Chief Financial Officer
CMO: Jeremy Anderson, M.D., Medical Staff President
CIO: Rob Rizk, Director Information Technology
CHR: Kelly B. Sanders, Vice President Human Resources
CNO: Theresa Brock, Vice President Nursing
Web address: www.gshealth.org
**Control:** Other not–for–profit (including NFP Corporation) **Service:** General medical and surgical

**Staffed Beds:** 25 **Admissions:** 1561 **Census:** 13 **Outpatient Visits:** 74398 **Births:** 387 **Total Expense ($000):** 92088 **Payroll Expense ($000):** 37092 **Personnel:** 650

⇑ **GOOD SHEPHERD HEALTHCARE SYSTEM** See Good Shepherd Health Care System

## HILLSBORO—Washington County

**KAISER FOUNDATION HOSPITAL WESTSIDE MEDICAL CENTER** See Kaiser Westside Medical Center

⊠ **KAISER WESTSIDE MEDICAL CENTER (380103)**, 2875 NE Stucki Avenue, Zip 97124–5806; tel. 971/310–1000, (Nonreporting) **A**1 10 **F**3 13 15 29 30 31 34 35 40 45 46 47 49 51 59 60 61 64 65 68 70 74 75 76 77 79 81 85 86 87 93 94 96 97 102 107 108 110 111 114 115 118 119 126 130 135 141 146 147 148 149 154 **P**6 **S** Kaiser Foundation Hospitals, Oakland, CA
Primary Contact: James L. Robinson III, PsyD, Hospital Administrator
COO: Brantley Dettmer, Chief Operating Officer
CMO: Carol Unitan, M.D., Chief Medical Officer
CIO: Charles Stearns, Area Information Officer
CHR: Rich Smith, Vice President Human Resources
CNO: Janet Lee Reeder, MSN, R.N., Chief Nurse Executive
Web address: www.kp.org
**Control:** Other not–for–profit (including NFP Corporation) **Service:** General medical and surgical

**Staffed Beds:** 122 **Admissions:** 8975 **Census:** 70 **Outpatient Visits:** 48984 **Births:** 1562 **Total Expense ($000):** 176923 **Payroll Expense ($000):** 73735 **Personnel:** 877

⊠ **TUALITY HEALTHCARE (380021)**, 335 SE Eighth Avenue, Zip 97123–4246; tel. 503/681–1111, (Includes TUALITY COMMUNITY HOSPITAL, Mailing address: 335 SE Eighth Avenue, Hillsboro, Oregon, Zip 97123, P O Box 309, Zip 97123, tel. 503/681–1111; Manuel S Berman, FACHE, President and Chief Executive Officer; TUALITY FOREST GROVE HOSPITAL, Mailing address: 1809 Maple Street, Forest Grove, Oregon, Zip 97116–1995; tel. 503/357–2173; Manuel S Berman, FACHE, President and Chief Executive Officer), (Nonreporting) **A**1 3 5 10 **F**3 11 13 15 18 20 22 24 26 28 29 30 31 32 34 35 40 44 45 47 49 50 53 54 56 57 59 62 64 68 70 71 74 75 76 77 78 79 80 81 82 85 86 87 92 93 97 98 100 103 104 107 108 110 111 114 115 118 119 126 129 130 131 132 135 143 144 145 146 147 148 **P**1 6
Primary Contact: Lori James-Nielsen, President
COO: Steven P Krautscheid, Ancillary Services Administrator
CFO: Tim Fleischmann, Chief Financial Officer
CMO: Joe Hardman, M.D., Chief Medical Officer
CHR: Cheryl Gebhart, Chief Human Resources Officer
Web address: www.tuality.org
**Control:** Other not–for–profit (including NFP Corporation) **Service:** General medical and surgical

**Staffed Beds:** 122 **Admissions:** 4519 **Census:** 46 **Outpatient Visits:** 224628 **Births:** 564 **Total Expense ($000):** 210642 **Payroll Expense ($000):** 87497 **Personnel:** 1073

## HOOD RIVER—Hood River County

**HOOD RIVER MEMORIAL HOSPITAL** See Providence Hood River Memorial Hospital

⊠ **PROVIDENCE HOOD RIVER MEMORIAL HOSPITAL (381318)**, 810 12th Street, Zip 97031–1587, Mailing Address: P.O. Box 149, Zip 97031–0055; tel. 541/386–3911, (Nonreporting) **A**1 3 10 18 **F**3 5 9 10 11 12 13 15 18 28 29 30 31 34 35 36 40 43 45 47 48 53 54 56 57 59 60 64 65 68 70 75 76 77 78 79 81 82 84 85 86 89 90 92 97 100 101 102 104 107 108 110 111 114 118 119 125 130 131 132 133 134 135 143 146 147 148 149 154 156 **P**6 **S** Providence St. Joseph Health, Renton, WA
Primary Contact: Jeanette Vieira, Chief Executive
CHR: Jami McCaslin, Director Human Resources
Web address: www.providence.org/hoodriver
**Control:** Church operated, Nongovernment, not–for–profit **Service:** General medical and surgical

**Staffed Beds:** 25 **Admissions:** 1459 **Census:** 11 **Outpatient Visits:** 178967 **Births:** 401 **Total Expense ($000):** 99912 **Payroll Expense ($000):** 33906 **Personnel:** 422

## JOHN DAY—Grant County

**BLUE MOUNTAIN HOSPITAL** See Blue Mountain Hospital District

★ **BLUE MOUNTAIN HOSPITAL DISTRICT (381305)**, 170 Ford Road, Zip 97845–2009; tel. 541/575–1311, (Total facility includes 40 beds in nursing home–type unit) (Nonreporting) **A**3 5 10 18 **F**7 8 11 13 15 29 30 34 35 36 40 41 43 45 50 57 59 62 63 64 65 67 68 70 75 76 77 81 82 85 86 87 93 97 107 110 111 114 119 127 130 132 133 134 135 143 145 146 148 149 156 158 **S** HealthTech Management Services, Brentwood, TN
Primary Contact: Derek Daly, Chief Executive Officer
CMO: Keith Thomas, M.D., Chief of Staff
CIO: Sean Tsao, Director Information Technology
CHR: Verlene Davis, Director Human Resources
CNO: Les McLeod, Director of Nursing Services
Web address: www.bluemountainhospital.org
**Control:** Hospital district or authority, Government, Nonfederal **Service:** General medical and surgical

**Staffed Beds:** 56 **Admissions:** 380 **Census:** 24 **Outpatient Visits:** 30466 **Births:** 44 **Total Expense ($000):** 26203 **Payroll Expense ($000):** 15456 **Personnel:** 248

## KLAMATH FALLS—Klamath County

⇑ **MERLE WEST MEDICAL CENTER** See Sky Lakes Medical Center

★ ⇑ **SKY LAKES MEDICAL CENTER (380050)**, 2865 Daggett Avenue, Zip 97601–1106; tel. 541/882–6311, (Nonreporting) **A**3 5 10 21 **F**3 8 11 13 15 18 20 22 29 31 34 35 37 40 43 44 45 46 47 48 50 51 53 54 56 57 59 61 62 64 68 70 71 75 76 77 78 79 81 84 85 86 87 92 93 94 96 97 100 102 107 108 110 111 114 115 116 117 118 119 120 121 123 130 131 132 134 135 141 142 143 144 145 146 147 148 149 156 157 **P**6
Primary Contact: Paul R. Stewart, President and Chief Executive Officer
CFO: Richard Rico, Vice President and Chief Financial Officer
CMO: Grant Niskanen, M.D., Vice President Medical Affairs
CHR: Don York, Vice President and Chief Human Resource Officer
CNO: Annette E. Cole, R.N., MSN, Vice President and Chief Nursing Officer
Web address: www.skylakes.org
**Control:** Other not–for–profit (including NFP Corporation) **Service:** General medical and surgical

**Staffed Beds:** 105 **Admissions:** 6827 **Census:** 47 **Outpatient Visits:** 271969 **Births:** 801 **Total Expense ($000):** 257337 **Payroll Expense ($000):** 100201 **Personnel:** 1262

## LA GRANDE—Union County

⊠ **GRANDE RONDE HOSPITAL (381321)**, 900 Sunset Drive, Zip 97850–1387, Mailing Address: P.O. Box 3290, Zip 97850–7290; tel. 541/963–8421, (Nonreporting) **A**1 10 18 **F**3 11 13 15 17 18 26 29 30 31 34 35 37 39 40 43 44 45 50 54 59 62 63 64 66 70 74 75 76 78 79 81 82 84 85 86 87 89 91 92 93 96 97 107 108 110 111 115 118 119 127 128 129 130 131 132 133 144 146 147 148 149 154
Primary Contact: Jeremy P. Davis, President and Chief Executive Officer
CFO: Robert Seymour, Chief Financial Officer/Senior Director Finance
CMO: Stacy Whitaker, M.D., Medical Staff President
CIO: Parhez Sattar, Senior Director Information Technology
CHR: Steve Lyon, Senior Director Human Resources
CNO: Laurie Marcum, MSN, R.N., Executive Director Patient Care Services
Web address: www.grh.org
**Control:** Other not–for–profit (including NFP Corporation) **Service:** General medical and surgical

**Staffed Beds:** 25 **Admissions:** 1604 **Census:** 11 **Outpatient Visits:** 197741 **Births:** 232 **Total Expense ($000):** 106836 **Payroll Expense ($000):** 56413 **Personnel:** 696

*Many Facility Codes have changed. Please refer to the AHA Guide Code Chart.*        © 2021 AHA Guide

OR

**OR**

## LAKEVIEW—Lake County

★ **LAKE DISTRICT HOSPITAL (381309)**, 700 South 'J' Street, Zip 97630–1679; tel. 541/947–2114, (Nonreporting) **A**5 10 18 **F**3 13 15 29 30 31 32 34 35 37 38 40 45 46 57 59 62 63 64 68 75 76 77 78 79 81 82 84 85 87 90 93 97 100 107 111 115 119 127 129 130 132 133 134 135 146 148 149 153 **P**6
Primary Contact: Charles B. Tveit, Chief Executive Officer
CFO: Cheryl J Cornwell, Chief Financial Officer
CMO: Stephen Hussey, M.D., Chief of Staff
CIO: Steven Vance, Information Technology Director
CHR: Lesley Hanson, Director Human Resources
CNO: Teresa Squires, R.N., Chief Nursing Officer
Web address: www.lakehealthdistrict.org
**Control**: Hospital district or authority, Government, Nonfederal **Service**: General medical and surgical

**Staffed Beds**: 24 **Admissions**: 390 **Census**: 3 **Outpatient Visits**: 59537
**Births**: 67 **Total Expense ($000)**: 33905 **Payroll Expense ($000)**: 15000
**Personnel**: 251

## LEBANON—Linn County

⇑ **LEBANON COMMUNITY HOSPITAL** See Samaritan Lebanon Community Hospital

★ ⇑ **SAMARITAN LEBANON COMMUNITY HOSPITAL (381323)**, 525 North Santiam Highway, Zip 97355–4363, Mailing Address: P.O. Box 739, Zip 97355–0739; tel. 541/258–2101, (Nonreporting) **A**3 10 18 21 **F**3 10 11 13 15 28 29 30 31 34 35 40 43 44 45 46 47 53 59 64 68 70 75 76 78 79 81 85 86 87 89 92 93 97 107 108 110 111 114 116 117 118 119 125 127 130 131 132 135 144 146 147 148 149 156 **P**6 **S** Samaritan Health Services, Corvallis, OR
Primary Contact: Marty Cahill, Chief Executive Officer
CFO: Daniel B Smith, Vice President Finance
CMO: Alan Blake, M.D., President Medical Staff
CIO: Robert Power, Vice President Information Services
CHR: Connie Erwin, Manager
CNO: Wendie Wunderwald, R.N., Vice President Patient Care Services
Web address: www.samhealth.org
**Control**: Other not–for–profit (including NFP Corporation) **Service**: General medical and surgical

**Staffed Beds**: 25 **Admissions**: 1554 **Census**: 15 **Outpatient Visits**: 250141
**Births**: 264 **Total Expense ($000)**: 130820 **Payroll Expense ($000)**: 54545
**Personnel**: 646

## LINCOLN CITY—Lincoln County

⇑ **NORTH LINCOLN HOSPITAL** See Samaritan North Lincoln Hospital

★ ⇑ **SAMARITAN NORTH LINCOLN HOSPITAL (381302)**, 3043 NE 28th Street, Zip 97367–4518, Mailing Address: P.O. Box 767, Zip 97367–0767; tel. 541/994–3661, (Nonreporting) **A**3 5 10 18 21 **F**3 8 11 13 15 26 29 30 31 34 35 40 43 44 45 51 57 58 59 64 65 68 70 75 76 77 78 79 81 85 87 93 97 104 107 110 111 115 116 117 118 119 127 130 132 133 135 144 146 147 148 149 156 **P**6 **S** Samaritan Health Services, Corvallis, OR
Primary Contact: Lesley Ogden, M.D., Chief Executive Officer
CFO: Kathryn Doksum, Director Finance
CMO: Raj Baman, D.O., President Medical Staff
CHR: Gina Tapp, Director Human Resources
CNO: Virginia Riffle, Vice President Patient Care Services
Web address: www.samhealth.org
**Control**: Other not–for–profit (including NFP Corporation) **Service**: General medical and surgical

**Staffed Beds**: 25 **Admissions**: 893 **Census**: 11 **Outpatient Visits**: 105886
**Births**: 112 **Total Expense ($000)**: 66698 **Payroll Expense ($000)**: 29579
**Personnel**: 290

## MADRAS—Jefferson County

**MOUNTAIN VIEW HOSPITAL DISTRICT** See St. Charles Madras

★ **ST. CHARLES MADRAS (381324)**, 470 NE 'A' Street, Zip 97741–1844; tel. 541/475–3882, (Nonreporting) **A**10 18 **F**3 13 15 29 34 35 40 43 45 57 59 62 63 64 70 75 76 77 81 82 83 84 85 86 87 89 90 93 97 107 110 115 119 130 132 133 135 146 147 156 **P**6 **S** St. Charles Health System, Inc., Bend, OR
Primary Contact: David Golda, Vice President Hospital and Administrator
Web address: www.stcharleshealthcare.org/Our-Locations/Madras
**Control**: Other not–for–profit (including NFP Corporation) **Service**: General medical and surgical

**Staffed Beds**: 25 **Admissions**: 704 **Census**: 10 **Outpatient Visits**: 26731
**Births**: 166 **Total Expense ($000)**: 31142 **Payroll Expense ($000)**: 14681
**Personnel**: 168

## MCMINNVILLE—Yamhill County

⊞ **WILLAMETTE VALLEY MEDICAL CENTER (380071)**, 2700 SE Stratus Avenue, Zip 97128–6255; tel. 503/472–6131, (Nonreporting) **A**1 2 10 **F**3 11 12 13 15 18 20 24 26 27 28 29 30 31 34 35 40 41 43 45 46 48 50 51 56 57 58 59 60 64 65 70 74 75 76 78 79 80 81 82 84 85 86 87 91 92 93 98 103 107 108 110 111 114 115 118 119 120 123 124 130 131 132 135 146 147 148 154 156 **S** LifePoint Health, Brentwood, TN
Primary Contact: Lorinda Bergen, Chief Executive Officer
CFO: Meredith Nelson, Chief Financial Officer
CMO: Jeanne Savage, M.D., Chief Medical Officer
CIO: Diane Farrow, Manager Information Technology and Systems
CHR: Lisa Clark, Director Human Resources
CNO: Connie Pullen, R.N., Chief Nursing Officer
Web address: www.willamettevalleymedical.com/
**Control**: Corporation, Investor–owned (for–profit) **Service**: General medical and surgical

**Staffed Beds**: 60 **Admissions**: 3337 **Census**: 36 **Outpatient Visits**: 116784
**Births**: 423 **Total Expense ($000)**: 90562 **Payroll Expense ($000)**: 33722
**Personnel**: 465

**WILLIAMETTE VALLEY MEDICAL CTR** See Willamette Valley Medical Center

## MEDFORD—Jackson County

★ ⇑ **ASANTE ROGUE REGIONAL MEDICAL CENTER (380018)**, 2825 East Barnett Road, Zip 97504–8332; tel. 541/789–7000, (Nonreporting) **A**2 3 5 10 19 21 **F**3 11 12 13 15 17 18 20 22 24 26 28 29 30 31 32 34 35 36 37 40 43 45 46 48 49 50 57 58 59 60 63 64 65 70 72 74 75 76 78 79 81 85 86 87 89 90 93 94 96 97 98 100 101 102 107 108 110 111 112 115 119 120 121 122 126 129 130 132 143 145 146 147 148 154 **S** Asante Health System, Medford, OR
Primary Contact: Mick Zdeblick, Chief Executive Officer
COO: Kristi Blackhurst, Interim Vice President Operations
CFO: Patrick Hocking, Chief Financial Officer
CMO: Jamie Grebosky, M.D., Vice President of Medical Affairs
CIO: Mark Hetz, Chief Information Officer
CHR: Gregg Edwards, Chief People Officer
Web address: www.asante.org
**Control**: Other not–for–profit (including NFP Corporation) **Service**: General medical and surgical

**Staffed Beds**: 343 **Admissions**: 15867 **Census**: 246 **Outpatient Visits**: 515346 **Births**: 1540 **Total Expense ($000)**: 561808 **Payroll Expense ($000)**: 176831 **Personnel**: 2332

**PROVIDENCE HOSP & MEDICAL CTR** See Providence Medford Medical Center

---

OR

⊞ **PROVIDENCE MEDFORD MEDICAL CENTER (380075)**, 1111 Crater Lake Avenue, Zip 97504–6241; tel. 541/732–5000, (Nonreporting) **A**1 2 10 19 **F**3 11 13 15 18 19 20 21 22 28 29 30 31 32 34 35 40 43 45 49 50 55 56 57 59 61 64 68 70 74 75 76 77 78 79 81 82 84 85 86 87 90 91 92 93 96 97 102 107 110 114 115 118 119 120 121 123 124 126 129 130 131 132 146 147 148 **P**6 **S** Providence St. Joseph Health, Renton, WA
Primary Contact: Tom Lorish, M.D., Interim Chief Executive
COO: Chris Pizzi, Chief Operating Officer and Chief Financial Officer
CFO: Chris Pizzi, Chief Operating Officer and Chief Financial Officer
CHR: Julie Levison, Director Human Resources
CNO: Sherri Steele, Chief Nursing Officer
Web address: www.providence.org
**Control**: Church operated, Nongovernment, not–for–profit **Service**: General medical and surgical

**Staffed Beds**: 138 **Admissions**: 6080 **Census**: 78 **Outpatient Visits**: 362171 **Births**: 506 **Total Expense ($000)**: 228179 **Payroll Expense ($000)**: 73499 **Personnel**: 987

⇑ **ROGUE VALLEY MEDICAL CENTER** See Asante Rogue Regional Medical Center

**MILWAUKIE—Clackamas County**

⊞ **PROVIDENCE MILWAUKIE HOSPITAL (380082)**, 10150 SE 32nd Avenue, Zip 97222–6516; tel. 503/513–8300, (Nonreporting) **A**1 3 5 10 **F**3 15 18 29 30 34 35 36 40 44 45 46 50 53 54 56 57 59 63 64 68 70 71 74 75 77 79 81 82 84 85 87 91 92 93 97 98 100 102 103 104 107 108 110 111 114 115 119 129 130 131 132 133 135 146 147 148 154 **P**6 **S** Providence St. Joseph Health, Renton, WA
Primary Contact: Sherri Kulink, Chief Executive Officer
COO: Sherri Paris, Chief Operating Officer
CFO: Sheila Waldron, Finance Manager
CHR: Julie Smith, Senior Human Resources Strategic Partner
CNO: Lisa Halvorsen, Chief Nurse Executive
Web address: www.providence.org
**Control**: Church operated, Nongovernment, not–for–profit **Service**: General medical and surgical

**Staffed Beds**: 60 **Admissions**: 2812 **Census**: 43 **Outpatient Visits**: 273856 **Births**: 0 **Total Expense ($000)**: 124632 **Payroll Expense ($000)**: 41702 **Personnel**: 487

**NEWBERG—Yamhill County**

**PROVIDENCE NEWBERG HOSPITAL** See Providence Newberg Medical Center

⊞ **PROVIDENCE NEWBERG MEDICAL CENTER (380037)**, 1001 Providence Drive, Zip 97132–7485; tel. 503/537–1555, (Nonreporting) **A**1 10 **F**3 11 13 15 18 20 29 30 34 35 40 45 46 47 49 50 51 57 59 60 64 68 70 74 75 76 77 79 81 84 85 87 92 93 100 107 108 110 111 114 118 119 129 130 132 135 146 147 148 149 **P**6 **S** Providence St. Joseph Health, Renton, WA
Primary Contact: Lorinda Van Zanten, MSN, Chief Executive
CFO: Jack R Sumner, Assistant Administrator Finance
CMO: George Weghorst, M.D., Chief Medical Officer
CIO: Laureen O'Brien, Chief Information Officer
CHR: Cheryl Gebhart, Director Human Resources Providence Health Plan and Providence Medical Group
Web address: www.phsor.org
**Control**: Church operated, Nongovernment, not–for–profit **Service**: General medical and surgical

**Staffed Beds**: 40 **Admissions**: 2380 **Census**: 22 **Outpatient Visits**: 262296 **Births**: 467 **Total Expense ($000)**: 112238 **Payroll Expense ($000)**: 33018 **Personnel**: 390

**NEWPORT—Lincoln County**

⇑ **SAMARITAN PACIFIC COMM HOSPITA** See Samaritan Pacific Communities Hospital

★ ⇑ **SAMARITAN PACIFIC COMMUNITIES HOSPITAL (381314)**, 930 SW Abbey Street, Zip 97365–4820, Mailing Address: P.O. Box 945, Zip 97365–0072; tel. 541/265–2244, (Nonreporting) **A**10 18 21 **F**3 8 11 13 15 26 28 29 30 31 34 35 40 43 44 45 47 53 54 59 64 65 68 70 75 76 77 78 79 81 82 85 86 87 92 93 97 107 108 110 111 114 119 127 129 130 132 133 135 144 146 147 148 149 156 **P**6 **S** Samaritan Health Services, Corvallis, OR
Primary Contact: Lesley Ogden, M.D., Chief Executive Officer
CFO: Daniel B Smith, Chief Financial Officer
CIO: Robert Power, Chief Information Officer
CHR: Gina Tapp, Director Human Resources
CNO: Lorie Williams, R.N., Vice President Nursing
Web address: www.samhealth.org
**Control**: Other not–for–profit (including NFP Corporation) **Service**: General medical and surgical

**Staffed Beds**: 25 **Admissions**: 1327 **Census**: 12 **Outpatient Visits**: 167820 **Births**: 201 **Total Expense ($000)**: 105640 **Payroll Expense ($000)**: 41181 **Personnel**: 392

**ONTARIO—Malheur County**

**HOLY ROSARY MEDICAL CENTER** See Saint Alphonsus Medical Center - Ontario

⊞ **SAINT ALPHONSUS MEDICAL CENTER - ONTARIO (380052)**, 351 SW Ninth Street, Zip 97914–2693; tel. 541/881–7000, (Nonreporting) **A**1 3 5 10 20 **F**3 11 13 15 28 29 30 31 34 35 39 40 43 44 45 46 50 54 56 57 59 63 64 65 68 70 75 76 77 78 79 81 83 85 87 93 97 107 108 110 111 114 118 119 127 129 130 131 132 135 144 146 147 148 149 154 **S** Trinity Health, Livonia, MI
Primary Contact: Kenneth Hart, President
CFO: Lannie Checketts, Chief Financial Officer
CMO: Paul Gering, M.D., Vice President Medical Affairs
CHR: Stefanie Thiel, Senior Human Resources Business Partner
Web address: www.saintalphonsus.org/ontario
**Control**: Other not–for–profit (including NFP Corporation) **Service**: General medical and surgical

**Staffed Beds**: 35 **Admissions**: 2022 **Census**: 14 **Outpatient Visits**: 70103 **Births**: 429 **Total Expense ($000)**: 76980 **Payroll Expense ($000)**: 24477 **Personnel**: 371

**OREGON CITY—Clackamas County**

**PROVIDENCE WILLAMETTE FALLS HOSPITAL** See Providence Willamette Falls Medical Center

⊞ **PROVIDENCE WILLAMETTE FALLS MEDICAL CENTER (380038)**, 1500 Division Street, Zip 97045–1597; tel. 503/656–1631, (Nonreporting) **A**1 10 **F**13 15 29 30 34 35 36 40 44 45 46 50 53 54 57 59 63 64 68 70 74 75 76 77 78 79 81 82 84 85 87 91 92 93 97 98 100 107 108 111 114 119 130 131 132 133 135 146 147 **P**6 **S** Providence St. Joseph Health, Renton, WA
Primary Contact: Russ Reinhard, Chief Executive
COO: Patricia A Markesino, FACHE, Chief Nurse Executive and Chief Operating Officer
CFO: Elizabeth Sublette, Director Finance
CMO: James Watkins, M.D., President Medical Staff
CHR: Joann M Pfister, Director Human Resources
CNO: Jessica Bailey-Oetker, Director Quality and Medical Staff
Web address: www.providence.org/pwfmc
**Control**: Church operated, Nongovernment, not–for–profit **Service**: General medical and surgical

**Staffed Beds**: 111 **Admissions**: 4188 **Census**: 45 **Outpatient Visits**: 191388 **Births**: 809 **Total Expense ($000)**: 136458 **Payroll Expense ($000)**: 46496 **Personnel**: 515

**PENDLETON—Umatilla County**

⊞ **CHI ST. ANTHONY HOSPITAL (381319)**, 2801 St Anthony Way, Zip 97801–3800; tel. 541/276–5121, (Nonreporting) **A**1 10 18 **F**3 11 13 15 18 29 30 31 35 37 40 43 45 50 53 54 57 59 64 65 68 70 75 76 77 78 79 81 85 86 87 91 93 97 107 108 110 111 114 118 119 127 129 130 131 132 133 134 135 146 147 148 149 156 157 **P**6 **S** CommonSpirit Health, Chicago, IL
Primary Contact: Harold S. Geller, Chief Executive Officer
CFO: Scott Attridge, Chief Financial Officer
CMO: John McBee, Chief of Staff
CHR: Janeen K. Reding, Ed.D., Market Vice President of Human Resources
CNO: Joyce Bailey, Vice President Patient Care
Web address: www.sahpendleton.org
**Control**: Church operated, Nongovernment, not–for–profit **Service**: General medical and surgical

**Staffed Beds**: 25 **Admissions**: 1231 **Census**: 11 **Outpatient Visits**: 87299 **Births**: 305 **Total Expense ($000)**: 72610 **Payroll Expense ($000)**: 27101 **Personnel**: 305

**ST. ANTHONY HOSPITAL** See Chi St. Anthony Hospital

*Many Facility Codes have changed. Please refer to the AHA Guide Code Chart.* © 2021 AHA Guide

**OR**

## PORTLAND—Multnomah County

✠ **ADVENTIST HEALTH PORTLAND (380060)**, 10123 SE Market Street, Zip 97216–2599; tel. 503/257–2500, (Nonreporting) **A**1 2 3 5 10 **F**3 9 11 13 15 17 18 20 22 24 26 28 29 30 31 34 35 36 37 40 44 45 46 49 53 54 57 58 59 64 68 70 71 74 75 76 77 78 79 81 82 84 85 86 93 97 100 102 104 105 107 108 110 111 114 115 117 118 119 120 121 123 126 129 130 131 132 135 143 144 146 147 148 149 153 154 157 **P**6 **S** Adventist Health, Roseville, CA
Primary Contact: Joyce Newmyer, President
CFO: V Mark Perry, Chief Financial Officer
CMO: Wesley E Rippey, M.D., Chief Medical Officer
CHR: Shane Voshell, Director Human Resources
CNO: Ellen Tryon, R.N., Chief Nursing Officer
Web address: www.adventisthealthnw.com
**Control:** Church operated, Nongovernment, not–for–profit **Service:** General medical and surgical

**Staffed Beds:** 170 **Admissions:** 9279 **Census:** 87 **Outpatient Visits:** 511641 **Births:** 728 **Total Expense ($000):** 336345 **Payroll Expense ($000):** 124862 **Personnel:** 1829

**ADVENTIST MEDICAL CENTER-PORTLAND** See Adventist Health Portland

## PORTLAND—Washington County

☐ **CEDAR HILLS HOSPITAL (384012)**, 10300 SW Eastridge Street, Zip 97225–5004; tel. 503/944–5000, (Nonreporting) **A**1 10 **S** Universal Health Services, Inc., King of Prussia, PA
Primary Contact: Elizabeth Hutter, Chief Executive Officer
Web address: www.cedarhillshospital.com
**Control:** Corporation, Investor–owned (for–profit) **Service:** Psychiatric

**Staffed Beds:** 78

## PORTLAND—Multnomah County

**GOOD SAMARITAN HOSPITAL AND MEDICAL CENTER** See Legacy Good Samaritan Medical Center, Portland

**LEGACY EMANUEL CHILDREN'S HOSPITAL** See Randall Children's Hospital

**LEGACY EMANUEL HOSPITAL AND HEALTH CENTER** See Legacy Emanuel Medical Center

✠ **LEGACY EMANUEL MEDICAL CENTER (380007)**, 2801 North Gantenbein Avenue, Zip 97227–1674; tel. 503/413–2200, (Includes RANDALL CHILDREN'S HOSPITAL, Mailing address: 2801 North Gantenbein Avenue, Portland, Oregon, Zip 97227–1623; tel. 503/413–2200), (Nonreporting) **A**1 2 3 5 8 10 **F**3 7 11 13 15 16 17 18 19 20 21 22 24 25 26 27 28 29 30 31 34 35 37 38 39 40 41 43 44 45 46 47 48 49 50 51 54 55 56 57 59 60 61 64 65 66 68 72 74 75 76 77 78 79 80 81 83 84 85 86 87 88 89 91 93 97 98 99 100 101 102 103 107 108 110 111 114 115 118 119 126 127 130 131 132 135 144 146 147 148 149 154 **P**6 **S** Legacy Health, Portland, OR
Primary Contact: Trent Green, President
CHR: Sonja Steves, Senior Vice President Human Resources and Marketing
Web address: www.legacyhealth.org
**Control:** Other not–for–profit (including NFP Corporation) **Service:** General medical and surgical

**Staffed Beds:** 536 **Admissions:** 19972 **Census:** 369 **Outpatient Visits:** 431500 **Births:** 1742 **Total Expense ($000):** 968527 **Payroll Expense ($000):** 482136 **Personnel:** 3393

**LEGACY GOOD SAMARITAN HOSPITAL AND MEDICAL CENTER** See Legacy Good Samaritan Medical Center

✠ △ **LEGACY GOOD SAMARITAN MEDICAL CENTER (380017)**, 1015 NW 22nd Avenue, Zip 97210–3099; tel. 503/413–7711, (Includes GOOD SAMARITAN HOSPITAL AND MEDICAL CENTER, Mailing address: 1015 NW 22nd Avenue, Portland, Oregon, Zip 97210; tel. 503/229–7711; REHABILITATION INSTITUTE OF OREGON, Mailing address: 2010 NW Kearney Street, Portland, Oregon, Zip 97209; tel. 503/226–3774), (Nonreporting) **A**1 2 3 5 7 10 **F**3 8 11 12 15 18 20 22 26 28 29 30 31 34 35 38 40 44 45 46 47 48 49 50 51 55 56 57 58 59 60 61 64 65 68 70 74 75 76 77 78 79 80 81 82 83 84 85 86 87 90 91 93 94 95 96 97 107 108 110 111 114 115 116 117 118 119 120 121 123 124 126 129 130 132 135 138 142 143 144 145 146 147 148 149 154 **P**6 **S** Legacy Health, Portland, OR
Primary Contact: Jonathan Avery, President
CIO: C Matthew Calais, Senior Vice President and Chief Information Officer
CHR: Sonja Steves, Vice President Marketing
CNO: Cindy Evans, R.N., MS, Chief Nursing Officer
Web address: www.legacyhealth.org
**Control:** Other not–for–profit (including NFP Corporation) **Service:** General medical and surgical

**Staffed Beds:** 218 **Admissions:** 9521 **Census:** 135 **Outpatient Visits:** 208304 **Births:** 966 **Total Expense ($000):** 331164 **Payroll Expense ($000):** 128167 **Personnel:** 1294

★ ⇑ **OHSU HOSPITAL (380009)**, 3181 SW Sam Jackson Park Road, Zip 97239–3098; tel. 503/494–8311, (Includes DOERNBECHER CHILDREN'S HOSPITAL, Mailing address: 700 SW Campus Drive, Portland, Oregon, Zip 97239; tel. 503/494–8811; Timothy Goldfarb, Interim Chief Executive Officer), (Nonreporting) **A**2 3 5 8 10 21 **F**3 6 8 9 12 13 15 17 18 19 20 21 22 23 24 25 26 27 28 29 30 31 32 33 34 35 36 37 38 39 40 41 43 44 45 46 47 48 49 50 51 52 53 54 55 56 57 58 59 60 61 64 66 67 68 70 71 72 74 75 76 77 78 79 81 82 84 85 86 87 88 89 90 91 92 93 95 96 97 100 101 104 107 108 109 110 111 112 114 115 116 117 118 119 120 121 123 124 126 127 129 130 131 132 134 135 136 137 138 139 141 142 144 145 146 147 148 149 153 154 156
Primary Contact: John G. Hunter, M.D., FACS, Executive Vice President and Chief Executive Officer
COO: Joe Ness, Chief Operating Officer
CFO: Diana Gernhart, Senior Vice President and Hospital Chief Financial Officer
CMO: Michael Bonazzola, M.D., Interim Chief Medical Officer
CIO: Bridget Barnes, Vice President and Chief Information Officer
CHR: Dan Forbes, Vice President Human Resources
CNO: Dana Bjarnason, Ph.D., R.N., Vice President and Chief Nursing Officer
Web address: www.ohsu.edu
**Control:** Hospital district or authority, Government, Nonfederal **Service:** General medical and surgical

**Staffed Beds:** 562 **Admissions:** 29174 **Census:** 476 **Outpatient Visits:** 1058407 **Births:** 2245 **Total Expense ($000):** 1802917 **Payroll Expense ($000):** 661892 **Personnel:** 7962

⇑ **OREGON HLTH SCIENCES UNIV HOSP** See Ohsu Hospital

**PROVIDENCE HEALTH SYSTEM** See Providence Portland Medical Center

## PORTLAND—Washington County

**PROVIDENCE PORTLAND MED CTR** See Providence St. Vincent Medical Center

## PORTLAND—Multnomah County

✠ **PROVIDENCE PORTLAND MEDICAL CENTER (380061)**, 4805 NE Glisan Street, Zip 97213–2933; tel. 503/215–5526, (Nonreporting) **A**1 2 3 5 10 **F**3 5 13 15 18 20 22 24 26 29 30 31 34 35 36 37 38 40 44 45 46 49 50 51 54 55 56 57 58 59 60 61 64 66 68 70 72 74 75 76 77 78 79 81 82 84 85 86 87 90 92 93 98 100 101 102 104 105 106 107 108 109 110 111 114 116 117 118 119 121 123 124 126 129 130 131 132 133 135 136 145 146 147 148 153 154 156 **P**6 **S** Providence St. Joseph Health, Renton, WA
Primary Contact: Krista Farnham, Chief Executive
COO: Kendall Sawa, R.N., Chief Operating Officer
CFO: Eric Olson, Chief Financial Officer
CMO: Robert Wells, M.D., Chief Medical Officer
CIO: Mark Premo, Senior Director HC Intelligence
CHR: Jeannie Mikulic, Director Human Resources
Web address: www.providence.org
**Control:** Church operated, Nongovernment, not–for–profit **Service:** General medical and surgical

**Staffed Beds:** 407 **Admissions:** 19432 **Census:** 316 **Outpatient Visits:** 1387979 **Births:** 2644 **Total Expense ($000):** 878634 **Payroll Expense ($000):** 259880 **Personnel:** 3004

**Hospital, Medicare Provider Number, Address, Telephone, Approval, Facility, and Physician Codes, Health Care System**

★ American Hospital Association (AHA) membership
☐ The Joint Commission accreditation
○ Healthcare Facilities Accreditation Program
◇ DNV Healthcare Inc. accreditation
⇑ Center for Improvement in Healthcare Quality Accreditation
△ Commission on Accreditation of Rehabilitation Facilities (CARF) accreditation

**OR**

## PORTLAND—Washington County

☒ **PROVIDENCE ST. VINCENT MEDICAL CENTER (380004)**, 9205 SW Barnes Road, Zip 97225–6661; tel. 503/216–1234, (Includes CHILDREN AT PROVIDENCE ST. VINCENT, Mailing address: 9205 SW Barnes Road, Portland, Oregon, Zip 97225–6603; tel. 503/216–4400), (Nonreporting) **A**1 2 3 5 10 **F**3 5 13 15 17 18 20 22 24 26 28 29 30 31 34 35 36 37 38 40 41 44 45 46 47 48 49 50 53 54 56 57 58 59 60 61 64 65 70 72 74 75 76 77 78 79 81 82 84 85 86 87 88 89 91 92 93 97 98 100 102 104 105 106 107 108 109 110 111 112 114 115 116 117 118 119 120 121 123 126 129 130 131 132 135 146 147 148 149 153 156 **P**6 **S** Providence St. Joseph Health, Renton, WA
Primary Contact: Janice Burger, Chief Executive
COO: Nancy Roberts, Chief Operating Officer
CFO: Scott Pfister, Director Finance
Web address: www.providence.org/portland/hospitals
**Control**: Church operated, Nongovernment, not–for–profit **Service**: General medical and surgical

**Staffed Beds:** 528 **Admissions:** 24793 **Census:** 341 **Outpatient Visits:** 974047 **Births:** 3475 **Total Expense ($000):** 895239 **Payroll Expense ($000):** 266214 **Personnel:** 3096

## PORTLAND—Multnomah County

**REHABILITATION INSTITUTE OF OREGON** See Legacy Good Samaritan Medical Center, Portland

**SHRINERS HOSPITALS FOR CHILDREN, PORTLAND** See Shriners Hospitals for Children-Portland

☐ **SHRINERS HOSPITALS FOR CHILDREN-PORTLAND (383300)**, 3101 SW Sam Jackson Park Road, Zip 97239–3009; tel. 503/241–5090, (Nonreporting) **A**1 3 5 10 **F**3 29 34 35 37 50 58 64 68 75 77 79 81 85 86 87 91 93 94 130 131 132 134 146 148 149 154 **P**6 **S** Shriners Hospitals for Children, Tampa, FL
Primary Contact: Dereesa Reid, Administrator
CFO: Mark Knudsen, Director Fiscal Services
CMO: Michael Aiona, M.D., Chief of Staff
CIO: Carl Montante, Director Information Systems and Information Technology
CHR: Rhonda Smith, Director Human Resources
CNO: Suzanne Diers, R.N., Director Patient Care Services
Web address: www.shrinershospitalsforchildren.org/portland
**Control**: Other not–for–profit (including NFP Corporation) **Service**: Children's general medical and surgical

**Staffed Beds:** 12 **Admissions:** 348 **Census:** 5 **Outpatient Visits:** 16455 **Births:** 0 **Total Expense ($000):** 44397 **Payroll Expense ($000):** 24440 **Personnel:** 255

**VA PORTLAMD HEALTHCARE SYSTEM** See VA Portland Healthcare System

☒ **VA PORTLAND HEALTHCARE SYSTEM**, 3710 SW U S Veterans Hospital Road, Zip 97239–2964, Mailing Address: 3710 SW US Veterans Hospital Road, Zip 97207–1034; tel. 503/220–8262, (Nonreporting) **A**1 2 3 5 8 **S** Department of Veterans Affairs, Washington, DC
Primary Contact: Michael W. Fisher, Director
CFO: Josh Wiseman, Chief Financial Officer
CMO: Sahana Misra, Acting Chief of Staff
CHR: Karla Azcuy, Acting Chief Human Resources Officer
CNO: Kathleen Chapman EsqDeputy Director, Patient Care Services
Web address: www.portland.va.gov/
**Control**: Veterans Affairs, Government, federal **Service**: General medical and surgical

**Staffed Beds:** 176

☒ **VIBRA SPECIALTY HOSPITAL OF PORTLAND (382004)**, 10300 NE Hancock Street, Zip 97220–3831; tel. 503/257–5500, (Nonreporting) **A**1 10 **S** Vibra Healthcare, Mechanicsburg, PA
Primary Contact: Victor Jackson, Chief Executive Officer
CFO: Stephanie Lawrence, Chief Financial Officer
CMO: Cynthia Wallace, M.D., Medical Director
CIO: Marie Roof, Executive Vice President Information Systems
CHR: Kellie Bernert-Yap, Director Human Resources
CNO: Susan E Brooker, R.N., Chief Clinical Officer
Web address: www.vshportland.com
**Control**: Corporation, Investor–owned (for–profit) **Service**: Acute long–term care hospital

**Staffed Beds:** 68

## PRINEVILLE—Crook County

**PIONEER MEMORIAL HOSPITAL** See St. Charles Prineville

★ **ST. CHARLES PRINEVILLE (381313)**, 384 SE Combs Flat Road, Zip 97754–1206; tel. 541/447–6254, (Nonreporting) **A**10 18 **F**3 11 15 29 30 34 35 40 43 45 50 57 59 64 65 74 75 77 79 80 81 82 84 85 86 87 93 97 107 110 115 119 127 130 132 133 135 **P**6 **S** St. Charles Health System, Inc., Bend, OR
Primary Contact: Todd Shields, Vice President and Administrator
CFO: Karen Shepard, Senior Vice President and Chief Financial Officer
CMO: Michel Boileau, M.D., Chief Clinical Officer
CHR: Rebecca Berry, Senior Director Human Resources
Web address: www.stcharleshealthcare.org
**Control**: Other not–for–profit (including NFP Corporation) **Service**: General medical and surgical

**Staffed Beds:** 16 **Admissions:** 583 **Census:** 8 **Outpatient Visits:** 45423 **Births:** 0 **Total Expense ($000):** 31295 **Payroll Expense ($000):** 14343 **Personnel:** 205

## REDMOND—Deschutes County

**ST. CHARLES MEDICAL CENTER - REDMOND** See St. Charles Redmond

☒ **ST. CHARLES REDMOND (380040)**, 1253 NW Canal Boulevard, Zip 97756–1395; tel. 541/548–8131, (Nonreporting) **A**1 10 20 **F**3 11 15 18 20 22 24 26 28 29 30 31 32 34 35 37 38 40 44 45 46 47 48 49 50 51 53 57 59 64 65 68 70 75 77 78 79 81 82 84 85 87 97 107 111 115 119 126 129 130 132 135 146 149 154 156 **P**6 **S** St. Charles Health System, Inc., Bend, OR
Primary Contact: Aaron Adams, President
CFO: Jennifer Welander, CPA, Senior Vice President Finance and Chief Financial Officer
CMO: Jeffrey Absalon, M.D., Chief Physician Officer
CIO: Jerimiah Brickhouse, Chief Information Officer
CHR: Rebecca Berry, Vice President Human Resources
Web address: www.stcharleshealthcare.org
**Control**: Other not–for–profit (including NFP Corporation) **Service**: General medical and surgical

**Staffed Beds:** 36 **Admissions:** 2421 **Census:** 23 **Outpatient Visits:** 57988 **Births:** 228 **Total Expense ($000):** 72803 **Payroll Expense ($000):** 34780 **Personnel:** 468

## REEDSPORT—Douglas County

★ **LOWER UMPQUA HOSPITAL DISTRICT (381311)**, 600 Ranch Road, Zip 97467–1795; tel. 541/271–2171, (Nonreporting) **A**5 10 18 **F**3 7 11 15 29 34 35 40 43 45 46 50 57 59 64 65 70 75 77 79 81 82 85 87 93 97 104 107 108 115 119 127 130 131 132 133 135 143 148 153 154 **P**6
Primary Contact: Ryan Fowler, Chief Administrative Officer
CMO: Ronald Vail, M.D., Chief of Staff
CIO: Timothy Picou, Manager Information Technology
Web address: www.lowerumpquahospital.com
**Control**: Hospital district or authority, Government, Nonfederal **Service**: General medical and surgical

**Staffed Beds:** 20 **Admissions:** 465 **Census:** 5 **Outpatient Visits:** 20605 **Births:** 0 **Total Expense ($000):** 29596 **Payroll Expense ($000):** 12298 **Personnel:** 173

## ROSEBURG—Douglas County

☒ **MERCY MEDICAL CENTER (380027)**, 2700 Stewart Parkway, Zip 97471–1281; tel. 541/673–0611, (Nonreporting) **A**1 3 10 **F**3 8 11 13 15 17 18 19 20 22 24 26 28 29 30 31 35 37 40 43 45 47 50 51 56 57 59 60 62 63 70 73 76 81 84 85 87 89 93 102 107 108 110 111 115 118 119 126 129 130 146 148 149 154 **P**3 4 5 **S** CommonSpirit Health, Chicago, IL
Primary Contact: Kelly C. Morgan, President and Chief Executive Officer
COO: Debbie Boswell, Chief Operating Officer and Chief Nursing Officer
CFO: Grant L Glines, Vice President Operation Finance
CMO: Jason Gray, M.D., Chief Medical Officer
CIO: Kathleen Nickel, Director Communications
CHR: Debora Lightcap, Director Human Resources
CNO: Debbie Boswell, Chief Operating Officer and Chief Nursing Officer
Web address: www.mercyrose.org
**Control**: Church operated, Nongovernment, not–for–profit **Service**: General medical and surgical

**Staffed Beds:** 140 **Admissions:** 6490 **Census:** 72 **Outpatient Visits:** 427006 **Births:** 880 **Total Expense ($000):** 194639 **Payroll Expense ($000):** 68532 **Personnel:** 795

**VA ROSEBURG HLTH CARE SYSTEM** See Veterans Affairs Roseburg Healthcare System

*Many Facility Codes have changed. Please refer to the AHA Guide Code Chart.*

© 2021 AHA Guide

⊞ **VETERANS AFFAIRS ROSEBURG HEALTHCARE SYSTEM**, 913 NW Garden
Valley Boulevard, Zip 97471–6513; tel. 541/440–1000, (Nonreporting) **A**1 3 **S**
Department of Veterans Affairs, Washington, DC
Primary Contact: Douglas V. Paxton, Director
CHR: Larry Mentzer, Chief Human Resources Officer
CNO: Tracy Weistreich, Ph.D., R.N., Associate Director Patient Care Services/
Nurse Executive
Web address: www.roseburg.va.gov/
**Control:** Veterans Affairs, Government, federal **Service:** General medical and
surgical

Staffed Beds: 88

**SALEM—Marion County**

☐ **OREGON STATE HOSPITAL (384008)**, 2600 Center Street NE,
Zip 97301–2682; tel. 503/945–2870, (Nonreporting) **A**1 3 5 10 **F**3 30 39 50 53
56 57 59 65 69 75 77 91 98 100 101 103 106 107 130 132 135 146 148 149
154 156 157
Primary Contact: Dolly Matteucci, Superintendent
Web address: www.oregon.gov/OHA/amh/osh/
**Control:** State, Government, Nonfederal **Service:** Psychiatric

Staffed Beds: 680 Admissions: 1086 Census: 607 Outpatient Visits: 0
Births: 0

**REGIONAL REHABILITATION CENTER** See Salem Health Rehabilitation Center

⊞ **SALEM HOSPITAL (380051)**, 890 Oak Street SE, Zip 97301–3959, Mailing
Address: P.O. Box 14001, Zip 97309–5014; tel. 503/561–5200, (Includes
PSYCHIATRIC MEDICINE CENTER, Mailing address: 1127 Oak Street SE, Salem,
Oregon, Zip 97301, P O Box 14001, Zip 97309–5014, tel. 503/561–5761;
SALEM HEALTH REHABILITATION CENTER, Mailing address: 755 Mission
St SE, Salem, Oregon, Zip 97301, P O Box 14001, Zip 97309–5014,
tel. 503/561–5986), (Nonreporting) **A**1 2 10 **F**3 11 12 13 15 17 18 20 22 24 26
28 29 30 31 34 35 36 37 38 40 43 44 45 46 47 48 49 50 53 54 55 56 57 58
59 64 67 68 70 72 74 75 76 77 78 79 81 82 84 85 86 87 90 91 92 93 94 96
97 98 100 102 106 107 108 109 110 111 114 115 116 117 118 119 120 121
122 123 124 126 129 130 131 132 135 144 145 146 147 148 149 154 156
**P**6 **S** Salem Health, Salem, OR
Primary Contact: Cheryl R. Nester Wolfe, R.N., President and Chief Executive
Officer
COO: Bahaa Wanly, Interim Chief Operating Officer
CFO: James Parr, Chief Financial Officer
CMO: Ralph Yates, D.O., Chief Medical Officer
CIO: Leah Mitchell, R.N., Interim Chief Information Officer
CNO: Sarah Horn, Chief Nursing Officer
Web address: www.salemhealth.org
**Control:** Other not–for–profit (including NFP Corporation) **Service:** General
medical and surgical

Staffed Beds: 475 Admissions: 27225 Census: 340 Outpatient
Visits: 452805 Births: 3432 Total Expense ($000): 770619 Payroll
Expense ($000): 352212 Personnel: 3815

**SEASIDE—Clatsop County**

⊞ **PROVIDENCE SEASIDE HOSPITAL (381303)**, 725 South Wahanna Road,
Zip 97138–7735; tel. 503/717–7000, (Nonreporting) **A**1 3 10 18 **F**3 12 13 15
18 29 30 31 32 34 35 40 45 46 56 57 59 61 64 65 66 70 75 76 78 79 81 82
83 84 85 86 87 91 92 93 97 107 108 110 111 114 119 127 130 132 133 135
143 146 147 148 149 154 **P**6 **S** Providence St. Joseph Health, Renton, WA
Primary Contact: Don Lemmon, Chief Executive Officer
COO: Janiece Zauner, Chief Operating Officer
CFO: Pamela Cooper, Director Finance
CMO: Julie Paquette, M.D., Chief Medical Officer
CHR: John Anglim, Human Resources Client Manager
CNO: Janiece Zauner, Chief Nursing Officer
Web address: www.providence.org
**Control:** Church operated, Nongovernment, not–for–profit **Service:** General
medical and surgical

Staffed Beds: 25 Admissions: 847 Census: 10 Outpatient Visits: 151276
Births: 91 Total Expense ($000): 74364 Payroll Expense ($000): 31575
Personnel: 372

**SEASIDE GENERAL HOSPITAL** See Providence Seaside Hospital

**SILVERTON—Marion County**

⊞ **LEGACY SILVERTON MEDICAL CENTER (380029)**, 139 Breyonna
Way, Zip 97381, Mailing Address: 342 Fairview Street, Zip 97381–1993;
tel. 503/873–1500, (Nonreporting) **A**1 10 **F**3 11 13 15 28 29 30 34 35 40 43
45 47 50 54 59 64 65 68 70 75 76 77 79 81 85 86 87 93 96 107 108 110
111 114 115 119 124 127 130 131 132 135 143 144 146 147 148 149 154
**P**6 **S** Legacy Health, Portland, OR
Primary Contact: Sarah Brewer, President
COO: Karen Brady, R.N., MSN, Vice President, Chief Nursing Officer
CFO: Daniel Jessup, Chief Financial Officer
CMO: Joseph Huang, M.D., Chief Medical and Quality Officer
CIO: Karen Brady, R.N., MSN, Vice President, Chief Nursing Officer
CHR: Natalie Britton, Manager Employee Relations
CNO: Karen Brady, R.N., MSN, Vice President, Chief Nursing Officer
Web address: www.legacyhealth.org/locations/hospitals/legacy-silverton-medical-
center.aspx
**Control:** Other not–for–profit (including NFP Corporation) **Service:** General
medical and surgical

Staffed Beds: 47 Admissions: 3127 Census: 21 Outpatient Visits: 266851
Births: 1214 Total Expense ($000): 159904 Payroll Expense
($000): 50620 Personnel: 511

**SILVERTON HOSPITAL** See Legacy Silverton Medical Center

**SPRINGFIELD—Lane County**

**MCKENZIE-WILLAMETTE HOSPITAL** See Mckenzie-Willamette Medical Center

☐ **MCKENZIE-WILLAMETTE MEDICAL CENTER (380020)**, 1460 'G' Street,
Zip 97477–4197; tel. 541/726–4400, (Nonreporting) **A**1 10 **F**3 11 13 18 20 22
24 26 28 29 34 35 39 40 41 43 45 46 47 49 50 57 59 70 73 76 79 81 82 85
87 89 107 108 111 115 118 119 126 130 132 146 147 148 154 **P**6 **S** Quorum
Health, Brentwood, TN
Primary Contact: David Elgarico, Chief Executive Officer
CFO: Rosanne Devault, Chief Financial Officer
CIO: David Blomquist, Director Information Technology
CHR: Megan A O'Leary, Vice President Human Resources and Rehabilitation
Services
Web address: www.mckweb.com
**Control:** Corporation, Investor–owned (for–profit) **Service:** General medical and
surgical

Staffed Beds: 112 Admissions: 8644 Census: 77 Outpatient Visits: 92777
Total Expense ($000): 211956 Payroll Expense ($000): 76677
Personnel: 888

★ ⇧ **PEACEHEALTH SACRED HEART MEDICAL CENTER AT RIVERBEND
(380102)**, 3333 Riverbend Drive, Zip 97477–8800; tel. 541/222–7300,
(Nonreporting) **A**10 21 **F**3 11 12 13 19 20 21 22 24 26 28 29 30 34 37 38 40
43 45 46 47 48 49 51 53 57 58 59 60 68 70 72 74 75 76 77 78 79 81 84 85
89 107 108 111 112 114 115 118 119 124 126 129 130 132 135 145 146
147 148 149 154 **S** PeaceHealth, Vancouver, WA
Primary Contact: Mary E. Kingston, FACHE, R.N., Chief Executive
COO: Shannon Surber, Chief Operating Officer
CHR: Marie F Stehmer, Senior Director of Human Resources
CNO: Heather Wall, Chief Nursing Officer
Web address: www.peacehealth.org
**Control:** Church operated, Nongovernment, not–for–profit **Service:** General
medical and surgical

Staffed Beds: 379 Admissions: 26443 Census: 332 Outpatient
Visits: 164775 Births: 2587 Total Expense ($000): 660048 Payroll
Expense ($000): 237649 Personnel: 2569

⇧ **SACRED HEART MEDICAL CENTER AT RIVERBEND** See Peacehealth Sacred
Heart Medical Center at Riverbend

**OR**

## STAYTON—Marion County

✠ **SANTIAM HOSPITAL (380056)**, 1401 North 10th Avenue, Zip 97383–1399; tel. 503/769–2175, (Nonreporting) **A**1 10 **F**1 3 4 7 11 13 15 16 17 29 30 40 41 43 50 65 67 70 72 73 76 79 80 81 85 87 88 89 90 98 107 111 115 119 128 130 133 135 143 154
Primary Contact: Terry L. Fletchall, President and Chief Executive Officer
COO: Maggie Hudson, Chief Financial and Operations Officer
CFO: Rachael Seeder, Controller
CMO: Scott Hadden, M.D., Medical Staff President
CIO: Trace Jacobs, Director Information Technology
CNO: Sherri Steele, Chief Nursing Officer
Web address: www.santiamhospital.org
**Control:** Other not–for–profit (including NFP Corporation) **Service:** General medical and surgical

**Staffed Beds:** 40 **Admissions:** 948 **Census:** 9 **Outpatient Visits:** 46683 **Births:** 135 **Total Expense ($000):** 57347 **Payroll Expense ($000):** 29071 **Personnel:** 378

**SANTIAM MEMORIAL HOSPITAL** See Santiam Hospital

## THE DALLES—Wasco County

✠ △ **MID-COLUMBIA MEDICAL CENTER (380001)**, 1700 East 19th Street, Zip 97058–3317; tel. 541/296–1111, (Nonreporting) **A**1 2 7 10 **F**3 11 13 15 18 28 29 30 31 32 34 35 36 40 43 45 46 50 53 54 57 59 62 64 65 66 68 70 75 76 77 78 79 81 82 85 87 89 90 91 92 93 96 97 100 101 104 107 108 110 111 114 118 119 120 121 123 126 127 129 130 131 132 133 134 135 146 147 148 149 154 156 157 **P**6
Primary Contact: Dennis M. Knox, Chief Executive Officer
COO: Larry Kahl, Chief Operating Officer
CFO: Edwin J Bode, Chief Financial Officer
CMO: Judy Richardson, M.D., President Medical Staff
CIO: Erick Larson, Vice President and Chief Information Officer
CHR: Christine Espy, Division Director
CNO: Felicia M Adams, MS, Chief Nursing Officer
Web address: www.mcmc.net
**Control:** Other not–for–profit (including NFP Corporation) **Service:** General medical and surgical

**Staffed Beds:** 46 **Admissions:** 1942 **Census:** 17 **Outpatient Visits:** 104396 **Births:** 242 **Total Expense ($000):** 104766 **Payroll Expense ($000):** 47538 **Personnel:** 937

## TILLAMOOK—Tillamook County

✠ **ADVENTIST HEALTHTILLAMOOK (381317)**, 1000 Third Street, Zip 97141–3430; tel. 503/842–4444, (Nonreporting) **A**1 10 18 **F**2 3 7 13 15 17 18 29 30 31 33 34 35 37 40 43 45 50 59 64 65 68 75 76 77 78 79 81 82 85 87 93 94 97 102 107 108 110 111 115 119 127 129 130 131 132 133 134 135 144 146 147 148 149 154 156 **P**6 **S** Adventist Health, Roseville, CA
Primary Contact: Kathy Saxon, R.N., Interim President
CFO: Walt Larson, Vice President Finance
CMO: Mark Bowman, M.D., President Medical Staff
CNO: Kathy Saxon, R.N., Vice President Patient Care Services
Web address: www.https://www.adventisthealth.org/tillamook/
**Control:** Church operated, Nongovernment, not–for–profit **Service:** General medical and surgical

**Staffed Beds:** 25 **Admissions:** 1366 **Census:** 12 **Outpatient Visits:** 195954 **Births:** 177 **Total Expense ($000):** 91499 **Payroll Expense ($000):** 32509 **Personnel:** 356

**TILLAMOOK REGIONAL MEDICAL CENTER** See Adventist Healthtillamook

## TUALATIN—Clackamas County

**LEGACY MERIDIAN PARK HOSPITAL** See Legacy Meridian Park Medical Center

✠ **LEGACY MERIDIAN PARK MEDICAL CENTER (380089)**, 19300 SW 65th Avenue, Zip 97062–9741; tel. 503/692–1212, (Nonreporting) **A**1 2 10 **F**3 13 15 18 20 22 28 29 30 31 32 34 35 38 40 44 45 46 49 50 51 56 57 59 60 64 68 70 74 75 76 77 78 79 80 81 85 86 87 91 93 97 107 108 110 111 114 115 116 117 118 119 120 121 126 129 130 132 145 146 147 148 149 154 **P**6 **S** Legacy Health, Portland, OR
Primary Contact: Melinda Stibal, R.N., MSN, Interim President
COO: Michael Newcomb, D.O., Senior Vice President and Chief Operating Officer
CMO: Lewis Low, M.D., Senior Vice President and Chief Medical Officer
CIO: John Jay Kenagy, Ph.D., Senior Vice President and Chief Information Officer
CHR: Sonja Steves, Vice President Human Resources and Marketing
Web address: www.legacyhealth.org
**Control:** Other not–for–profit (including NFP Corporation) **Service:** General medical and surgical

**Staffed Beds:** 149 **Admissions:** 8776 **Census:** 87 **Outpatient Visits:** 272764 **Births:** 953 **Total Expense ($000):** 217142 **Payroll Expense ($000):** 82120 **Personnel:** 827

## WHITE CITY—Jackson County

**VETERANS AFFAIRS DOMICILIARY** See Southern Oregon-White City Veterans Affairs Rehabilitation Center and Clinics

*Many Facility Codes have changed. Please refer to the AHA Guide Code Chart.* © 2021 AHA Guide

PA

# PENNSYLVANIA

## ABINGTON—Montgomery County

**ABINGTON JEFFERSON HEALTH (390231)**, 1200 Old York Road,
Zip 19001–3720; tel. 215/481–2000, (Nonreporting) **A**1 2 3 5 10 13 **F**3 6 8 9
11 12 13 15 17 18 20 22 24 26 28 29 30 31 32 34 35 36 37 38 39 40 43 44
45 46 47 48 49 50 52 53 54 55 56 57 58 59 61 62 63 64 65 66 68 70 72 73
74 75 76 77 78 79 80 81 82 84 85 86 87 89 90 91 93 96 97 98 100 101 102
103 104 107 108 110 111 114 115 118 119 120 121 123 124 126 129 130
131 132 135 144 145 146 147 148 149 150 154 156 **P**1 **S** Jefferson Health,
Philadelphia, PA
Primary Contact: Alison Ferren, Interim President and Chief Operating Officer
COO: Alison Ferren, Interim President and Chief Operating Officer
CFO: Michael Walsh, Senior Vice President Finance and Chief Financial Officer
CMO: Gerard M. Cleary, M.D., Senior Vice President, Chief of Staff and Chief
Medical Officer
CHR: Meghan Patton, Vice President Human Resources
CNO: Annmarie Chavarria, Senior Vce President Patient Care Services, Chief
Nursing Officer
Web address: www.abingtonhealth.org
**Control:** Other not–for–profit (including NFP Corporation) **Service:** General
medical and surgical

**Staffed Beds:** 623 **Admissions:** 30593 **Census:** 384 **Outpatient
Visits:** 578664 **Births:** 4379 **Total Expense ($000):** 858888 **Payroll
Expense ($000):** 400194 **Personnel:** 4802

**ABINGTON MEMORIAL HOSPITAL** See Abington Jefferson Health

## ALLENTOWN—Lehigh County

**ALLENTOWN HOSP-LEHIGH CTR** See Lehigh Valley Hospital

**ALLENTOWN OSTEOPATHIC MED CTR** See St Luke's Hospital - Allentown
Campus

△ **GOOD SHEPHERD REHABILITATION HOSPITAL (393035)**, 850 South 5th
Street, Zip 18103–3308; tel. 610/776–3299, (Nonreporting) **A**1 3 5 7 10 **F**28 29
30 32 34 35 36 53 54 56 57 58 59 64 65 66 68 74 75 82 86 87 90 91 92 93
94 95 96 100 107 119 130 131 132 146 147 148 154 157 **S** Good Shepherd
Rehabilitation Network, Allentown, PA
Primary Contact: Gary R. Schmidt, Interim President and Chief Executive Officer
CFO: Ronald J. Petula, Chief Financial Officer
Web address: www.goodshepherdrehab.org
**Control:** Other not–for–profit (including NFP Corporation) **Service:** Rehabilitation

**Staffed Beds:** 106 **Admissions:** 1234 **Census:** 72 **Outpatient
Visits:** 254134 **Births:** 0 **Total Expense ($000):** 90515 **Payroll Expense
($000):** 37256 **Personnel:** 944

**GOOD SHEPHERD REHABILITATION HOSPITAL-ALLENTOWN** See Good
Shepherd Rehabilitation Hospital

**LEHIGH VALLEY HEALTH NETWORK AT COORDINATED HEALTH (390321)**,
1503 North Cedar Crest Boulevard, Zip 18104–2302; tel. 610/861–8080,
(Nonreporting) **A**1 5 10
Primary Contact: Amy Nyberg, President
Web address: www.coordinatedhealth.com
**Control:** Other not–for–profit (including NFP Corporation) **Service:** Surgical

**Staffed Beds:** 20

**LEHIGH VALLEY HEALTH NETWORK PEDIATRICS** See Lehigh Valley Health
Network Pediatrics

**LEHIGH VALLEY HOSPITAL (390133)**, 1200 South Cedar Crest Boulevard,
Zip 18103–6248, Mailing Address: P.O. Box 689, Zip 18105–1556;
tel. 610/402–8000, (Includes LEHIGH VALLEY HEALTH NETWORK PEDIATRICS,
Mailing address: 1200 South Cedar Crest Boulevard, Allentown, Pennsylvania,
Zip 18103–6202, P.O. Box 689, Zip 18105, tel. 484/862–3131; LEHIGH VALLEY
HOSPITAL-MUHLENBERG, Mailing address: 2545 Schoenersville Road, Bethlehem,
Pennsylvania, Zip 18017–7300; tel. 484/884–2200; Brian A. Nester, D.O.,
President and Chief Executive Officer), (Nonreporting) **A**1 2 3 5 8 10 13 19 **F**3 6
7 8 9 12 13 15 16 17 18 20 22 24 26 28 29 30 31 32 33 34 35 36 37 38 39
40 41 42 43 44 45 46 47 48 49 50 51 53 54 55 56 57 58 59 60 61 62 63 64
65 66 68 70 71 72 74 76 77 78 79 80 81 82 84 85 86 87 88 89 90 92 93 96
97 98 99 100 101 102 104 105 106 107 108 110 111 114 115 116 117 118
119 120 121 123 124 126 128 129 130 131 132 134 135 138 141 142 143
144 145 146 147 148 149 154 155 157 **P**1 5 6 **S** Lehigh Valley Health Network,
Allentown, PA
Primary Contact: Brian A. Nester, D.O., President and Chief Executive Officer
COO: Terry Ann Capuano, R.N., MSN, FACHE, Executive Vice President and Chief
Operating Officer
CFO: Edward O'Dea, Executive Vice President and Chief Financial Officer
CMO: Thomas V. Whalen, M.D., Chief Medical Officer
CIO: Michael N. Minear, Senior Vice President and Chief Information Officer
CNO: Marie Kim Jordan, R.N., Senior Vice President and Chief Nursing Officer
Web address: www.lvhn.org
**Control:** Other not–for–profit (including NFP Corporation) **Service:** General
medical and surgical

**Staffed Beds:** 1044 **Admissions:** 57596 **Census:** 845 **Outpatient
Visits:** 805755 **Births:** 4690 **Total Expense ($000):** 1975457 **Payroll
Expense ($000):** 576433 **Personnel:** 9185

**SACRED HEART HOSPITAL** See St. Luke's Sacred Heart Campus

**ST LUKE'S HOSPITAL - ALLENTOWN CAMPUS** See St. Luke's University
Hospital - Bethlehem Campus, Bethlehem

△ **ST. LUKE'S SACRED HEART CAMPUS (390197)**, 421 West Chew Street,
Zip 18102–3490; tel. 610/776–4500, (Total facility includes 22 beds in nursing
home–type unit) (Nonreporting) **A**1 3 5 7 10 **F**3 11 12 15 18 29 30 31 34 35 38
40 44 45 49 50 54 56 57 59 64 70 74 75 78 79 81 85 86 87 92 93 97 98 100
101 102 103 107 108 110 111 114 115 117 118 119 128 130 132 134 135
146 147 149 154 **S** St. Luke's University Health Network, Bethlehem, PA
Primary Contact: Frank Ford, President
CMO: Farrokh Sadr, M.D., Chief Medical Officer
CIO: Tracy Burkhart, Vice President Information Services
CHR: Joseph Mikitka, Vice President Human Resources
Web address: www.shh.org
**Control:** Other not–for–profit (including NFP Corporation) **Service:** General
medical and surgical

**Staffed Beds:** 197 **Admissions:** 3947 **Census:** 103 **Outpatient
Visits:** 78696 **Births:** 0 **Total Expense ($000):** 74149 **Payroll Expense
($000):** 36397 **Personnel:** 530

## ALTOONA—Blair County

**ALTOONA REGIONAL HEALTH SYSTEM** See UPMC Altoona

**ENCOMPASS HEALTH REHABILITATION HOSPITAL OF ALTOONA (393040)**,
2005 Valley View Boulevard, Zip 16602–4598; tel. 814/944–3535, (Nonreporting)
**A**1 10 **S** Encompass Health Corporation, Birmingham, AL
Primary Contact: Scott Filler, Chief Executive Officer
CFO: George Berger, Controller
CMO: Rakesh Patel, D.O., Medical Director
CIO: Kathleen Edwards, Manager Information Systems Operation
CHR: Christine Filer, Director Human Resources
CNO: Mary Gen Boyles, Chief Nursing Officer
Web address: www.healthsouthaltoona.com
**Control:** Corporation, Investor–owned (for–profit) **Service:** Rehabilitation

**Staffed Beds:** 80

**HEALTHSOUTH REHABILITATION HOSPITAL OF ALTOONA** See Encompass
Health Rehabilitation Hospital of Altoona

---

**Hospital, Medicare Provider Number, Address, Telephone, Approval, Facility, and Physician Codes, Health Care System**

★ American Hospital Association (AHA) membership
□ The Joint Commission accreditation
○ Healthcare Facilities Accreditation Program
◇ DNV Healthcare Inc. accreditation
⇑ Center for Improvement in Healthcare Quality Accreditation
△ Commission on Accreditation of Rehabilitation Facilities (CARF) accreditation

---

**PA**

✠ **JAMES E. VAN ZANDT VETERANS AFFAIRS MEDICAL CENTER**, 2907 Pleasant Valley Boulevard, Zip 16602–4305; tel. 877/626–2500, (Nonreporting) **A**1 **S** Department of Veterans Affairs, Washington, DC
Primary Contact: Sigrid Andrew, Director
CFO: Carl Parrish, Chief Fiscal Service
CIO: Michael Hynoski, Chief Information Resource Management
CHR: Gina Dunio, Chief Human Resources
Web address: www.altoona.va.gov/
**Control:** Veterans Affairs, Government, federal **Service:** General medical and surgical

| Staffed Beds: 68 |
| --- |

✠ **UPMC ALTOONA (390073)**, 620 Howard Avenue, Zip 16601–4804; tel. 814/889–2011, (Nonreporting) **A**1 2 3 5 10 12 13 **F**3 8 11 12 13 15 17 18 20 22 24 26 28 29 30 31 34 35 37 38 39 40 43 44 45 47 48 49 50 51 56 57 59 60 61 64 65 66 68 70 73 74 75 76 77 78 79 81 83 84 85 86 87 89 97 98 100 101 102 103 107 108 110 111 114 115 117 118 119 120 121 123 126 129 130 131 132 135 146 147 148 149 154 155 156 **P**6 **S** UPMC, Pittsburgh, PA
Primary Contact: Jan E. Fisher, President
COO: Ron McConnell, Chief Operating Officer
CFO: Monica Klatt, Chief Financial Officer
CMO: Linnane Batzel, M.D., Senior Vice President Quality and Medical Affairs and Chief Medical Officer
CIO: Dale Fuller, Vice President and Chief Information Officer
CHR: Michelle A Speck, Vice President Human Resources
CNO: Chris Rickens, R.N., MS, Senior Vice President and Chief Nursing Officer
Web address: www.altoonaregional.org
**Control:** Other not–for–profit (including NFP Corporation) **Service:** General medical and surgical

| Staffed Beds: 346 Admissions: 18805 Census: 243 Outpatient Visits: 341872 Births: 1251 Total Expense ($000): 475245 Payroll Expense ($000): 142416 Personnel: 1897 |
| --- |

### AMBLER—Montgomery County

☐ **HORSHAM CLINIC (394034)**, 722 East Butler Pike, Zip 19002–2310; tel. 215/643–7800, (Nonreporting) **A**1 3 5 10 **S** Universal Health Services, Inc., King of Prussia, PA
Primary Contact: Phyllis Weisfield, Chief Executive Officer and Managing Director
CFO: Jeffrey Beiler, Chief Operating Officer
CMO: James B Congdon, M.D., Medical Director
CIO: Suzanne Scholz, Director Medical Records
CHR: Kathleen Nichelson, Director Human Resources
CNO: Calvin Litka, R.N., Director of Nursing
Web address: www.horshamclinic.com
**Control:** Individual, Investor–owned (for–profit) **Service:** Psychiatric

| Staffed Beds: 206 |
| --- |

### BEAVER—Beaver County

**CURAHEALTH HERITAGE VALLEY (392043)**, 1000 Dutch Ridge Road, Zip 15009–9727; tel. 724/773–8480, (Nonreporting) **A**10 **S** Curahealth Hospitals, Garland, TX
Primary Contact: Carol Falo, R.N., Chief Executive Officer
CFO: Chad Deardorff, Chief Financial Officer
CMO: Jeffrey Erukhimou, M.D., Medical Director
CNO: Geri Reichenbach, Nurse Executive
Web address: www.curahealth.com
**Control:** Corporation, Investor–owned (for–profit) **Service:** Acute long–term care hospital

| Staffed Beds: 35 |
| --- |

**HERITAGE VALLEY BEAVER** See Heritage Valley Health System

☐ **HERITAGE VALLEY HEALTH SYSTEM (390036)**, 1000 Dutch Ridge Road, Zip 15009–9727; tel. 724/728–7000, (Nonreporting) **A**1 3 5 10 13 **S** Heritage Valley Health System, Beaver, PA
Primary Contact: Norman F. Mitry, President and Chief Executive Officer
COO: John Luellen, M.D., Chief Operating Officer
CFO: Robert Rosenberger, Chief Financial Officer
CMO: Michael Cratty, M.D., Chief Medical Officer
CIO: David Carleton, Chief Information Officer
CHR: Bruce Edwards, Vice President Human Resources
CNO: Linda Homyk, Chief Nursing Officer
Web address: www.heritagevalley.org
**Control:** Other not–for–profit (including NFP Corporation) **Service:** General medical and surgical

| Staffed Beds: 271 |
| --- |

**KINDRED HOSPITAL-HERITAGE VALLEY** See Curahealth Heritage Valley

### BENSALEM—Bucks County

**LIVENGRIN FOUNDATION**, 4833 Hulmeville Road, Zip 19020–3099; tel. 215/638–5200, (Nonreporting)
Primary Contact: Richard M. Pine, President and Chief Executive Officer
CFO: James D Flis, Chief Financial Officer
CMO: William J Lorman, Ph.D., Clinical Director
CIO: William Miller, Coordinator Management Information Systems
Web address: www.livengrin.org
**Control:** Other not–for–profit (including NFP Corporation) **Service:** Alcoholism and other chemical dependency

| Staffed Beds: 76 |
| --- |

☐ **ROTHMAN SPECIALTY HOSPITAL (390322)**, 3300 Tillman Drive, Zip 19020–2071; tel. 215/244–7400, (Nonreporting) **A**1 3 10
Primary Contact: Kelly Doyle, Chief Executive Officer
Web address: www.rothmanspecialtyhospital.com/
**Control:** Partnership, Investor–owned (for–profit) **Service:** Orthopedic

| Staffed Beds: 24 |
| --- |

### BERWICK—Columbia County

✠ **BERWICK HOSPITAL CENTER (390072)**, 701 East 16th Street, Zip 18603–2397; tel. 570/759–5000, (Nonreporting) **A**1 10 **S** Community Health Systems, Inc., Franklin, TN
Primary Contact: Thomas Neal, Chief Executive Officer
CFO: Whitney Holloway, Chief Financial Officer
CMO: John A. Guerriero, D.O., IIIChief of Staff
CIO: Kerry Yeager, Director Information Technology
CHR: Gail Kauffman, Director Human Resources
CNO: Maribeth Angeli, Chief Nursing Officer
Web address: www.commonwealthhealth.net
**Control:** Corporation, Investor–owned (for–profit) **Service:** General medical and surgical

| Staffed Beds: 101 |
| --- |

### BETHLEHEM—Northampton County

☐ **COORDINATED HEALTH-BETHLEHEM (390314)**, 2310 Highland Avenue, Zip 18020–8920, Mailing Address: 2300 Highland Avenue, Zip 18020; tel. 610/861–8080, (Nonreporting) **A**1 3 10
Primary Contact: Amy Nyberg, President and Chief Operating Officer
Web address: www.coordinatedhealth.com
**Control:** Partnership, Investor–owned (for–profit) **Service:** General medical and surgical

| Staffed Beds: 20 |
| --- |

### BETHLEHEM—Lehigh County

☐ △ **GOOD SHEPHERD SPECIALTY HOSPITAL (392033)**, 2545 Schoenersville Road, 4th Floor, Zip 18017–7300; tel. 484/884–5051, (Nonreporting) **A**1 7 10 **F**1 3 29 30 36 77 85 87 91 95 130 148 **S** Good Shepherd Rehabilitation Network, Allentown, PA
Primary Contact: Jessica Florkowski, Administrator
CFO: Ronald J. Petula, Chief Financial Officer
CIO: Michael Cirba, Chief Information Officer
CHR: Kristen Melan, Director Human Resources Administration
CNO: Samuel Miranda JrChief Nursing Officer
Web address: www.goodshepherdrehab.org
**Control:** Other not–for–profit (including NFP Corporation) **Service:** Acute long–term care hospital

| Staffed Beds: 32 Admissions: 349 Census: 28 Outpatient Visits: 0 Births: 0 Total Expense ($000): 12661 Payroll Expense ($000): 6143 Personnel: 119 |
| --- |

**MUHLENBERG HOSPITAL CENTER** See Lehigh Valley Hospital-Muhlenberg

**ST. LUKE'S HOSPITAL - BETHLEHEM CAMPUS** See St. Luke's University Hospital - Bethlehem Campus

*Many Facility Codes have changed. Please refer to the AHA Guide Code Chart.*   © 2021 AHA Guide

☐ △ **ST. LUKE'S UNIVERSITY HOSPITAL - BETHLEHEM CAMPUS (390049)**, 801 Ostrum Street, Zip 18015–1065; tel. 484/526–4000, (Includes ST LUKE'S HOSPITAL - ALLENTOWN CAMPUS, Mailing address: 1736 Hamilton Street, Allentown, Pennsylvania, Zip 18104–5656; tel. 610/628–8300; William Moyer, President), (Nonreporting) **A**1 2 3 5 7 8 10 12 13 **F**3 9 11 12 13 15 17 18 19 20 22 24 26 27 28 29 30 31 32 34 35 36 37 38 39 40 43 44 45 46 47 48 49 50 51 52 53 54 55 56 57 58 59 60 61 63 64 65 68 70 71 72 73 74 75 76 77 78 79 81 82 84 85 86 87 89 90 92 93 96 97 100 101 102 104 105 107 108 109 110 111 115 117 118 119 120 121 123 124 126 129 130 131 132 134 135 144 145 146 147 148 149 153 154 **S** St. Luke's University Health Network, Bethlehem, PA
Primary Contact: Carol Kuplen, R.N., MSN, President
CFO: Tom Lichtenwalner, Vice President Finance
CMO: Jeffrey Jahre, M.D., Vice President Medical and Academic Affairs
CIO: Chad Brisendine, Chief Information Officer
CHR: Robert Zimmel, Senior Vice President Human Resources
Web address: www.slhn-lehighvalley.org
**Control**: Other not–for–profit (including NFP Corporation) **Service**: General medical and surgical

| | |
|---|---|
| **Staffed Beds:** 550 **Admissions:** 29742 **Census:** 389 **Outpatient Visits:** 676776 **Births:** 4291 **Total Expense ($000):** 682791 **Payroll Expense ($000):** 296172 **Personnel:** 5640 | |

### BLOOMSBURG—Columbia County

**BLOOMSBURG HOSPITAL** See Geisinger-Bloomsburg Hospital

★ **GEISINGER-BLOOMSBURG HOSPITAL (390003)**, 549 Fair Street, Zip 17815–1419; tel. 570/387–2100, (Nonreporting) **A**3 10 **F**3 8 11 12 13 15 26 27 28 29 30 32 34 35 36 38 40 41 44 45 46 50 51 53 55 56 57 59 62 63 65 68 70 74 75 76 81 85 86 87 91 92 93 97 98 100 101 102 103 104 107 108 110 111 115 119 130 131 132 135 144 145 146 147 148 149 150 153 154 156 **P**1 5 8 **S** Geisinger, Danville, PA
Primary Contact: Lissa Bryan-Smith, Chief Administrative Officer
COO: Joseph M DeVito, Vice President Finance and Chief Operating Officer
CFO: Joseph M DeVito, Vice President Finance and Chief Operating Officer
CMO: James Joseph, M.D., President Medical Staff
CIO: Thomas Wray, Director Information
Web address: www.bloomhealth.net
**Control**: Other not–for–profit (including NFP Corporation) **Service**: General medical and surgical

| | |
|---|---|
| **Staffed Beds:** 76 **Admissions:** 2156 **Census:** 24 **Outpatient Visits:** 72919 **Births:** 472 **Total Expense ($000):** 50046 **Payroll Expense ($000):** 18011 **Personnel:** 349 | |

### BRADFORD—Mckean County

**BRADFORD HOSPITAL** See Bradford Regional Medical Center

### BRISTOL—Bucks County

☐ **LOWER BUCKS HOSPITAL (390070)**, 501 Bath Road, Zip 19007–3190; tel. 215/785–9200, (Nonreporting) **A**1 3 5 10 13 **F**3 11 15 17 18 20 22 28 29 30 34 35 40 45 46 50 51 56 57 59 60 64 68 70 74 75 77 79 81 83 92 93 98 102 103 107 109 110 111 112 114 115 119 130 146 148 149 154 **S** Prime Healthcare, Ontario, CA
Primary Contact: Michael J. Motte, Chief Executive Officer
CMO: Sanjay Bhatia, Chief Medical Officer
CIO: Steve Kane, Director Information Technology
CNO: Pat Bain, Chief Nursing Officer
Web address: www.lowerbuckshosp.com
**Control**: Individual, Investor–owned (for–profit) **Service**: General medical and surgical

| | |
|---|---|
| **Staffed Beds:** 100 **Admissions:** 4251 **Census:** 58 **Outpatient Visits:** 19668 **Births:** 0 **Total Expense ($000):** 71400 **Payroll Expense ($000):** 29094 | |

**TEMPLE LOWER BUCKS HOSPITAL** See Lower Bucks Hospital

### BROOKVILLE—Jefferson County

**BROOKVILLE HOSPITAL** See Penn Highlands Brookville

**PENN HIGHLANDS BROOKVILLE (391312)**, 100 Hospital Road, Zip 15825–1367; tel. 814/849–2312, (Nonreporting) **A**3 10 18
Primary Contact: Julianne Peer, President
CFO: Jessica Park, Director Accounting
CMO: Timothy Pendleton, M.D., President Medical Staff
CIO: Thomas Johnson, Director Information Systems
CHR: Rebecca Edwards, Chief Human Resources Officer
CNO: Debra A. Thomas, Vice President of Patient Care Services and Chief Nursing Officer
Web address: www.phhealthcare.org/
**Control**: Other not–for–profit (including NFP Corporation) **Service**: General medical and surgical

| | |
|---|---|
| **Staffed Beds:** 35 | |

### BRYN MAWR—Montgomery County

⊞ **BRYN MAWR HOSPITAL (390139)**, 130 South Bryn Mawr Avenue, Zip 19010–3160; tel. 484/337–3000, (Nonreporting) **A**1 2 3 5 10 13 **F**3 11 12 13 15 17 18 20 22 26 28 29 30 31 34 35 36 37 38 39 40 41 44 45 49 50 54 55 56 57 58 59 62 63 64 65 66 70 72 74 75 76 78 79 80 81 82 84 85 86 87 89 93 96 97 98 100 102 104 105 107 108 110 111 114 115 118 119 124 126 129 130 131 134 135 141 145 146 147 148 149 153 154 156 **S** Main Line Health, Ontario, CA
Primary Contact: Andrea F. Gilbert, FACHE, President
CFO: Michael J Buongiorno, Executive Vice President Finance and Chief Financial Officer
CMO: Andrew J Norton, M.D., Chief Medical Officer
CIO: Kay Carr, Chief Information Officer
CHR: Terry Dougherty, Director Human Resources
CNO: Barbara A Wadsworth, MSN, R.N., FACHE, Chief Nursing Officer
Web address: www.brynmawrhospital.org
**Control**: Other not–for–profit (including NFP Corporation) **Service**: General medical and surgical

| | |
|---|---|
| **Staffed Beds:** 253 **Admissions:** 14680 **Census:** 151 **Outpatient Visits:** 222018 **Births:** 1423 **Total Expense ($000):** 336045 **Payroll Expense ($000):** 102741 **Personnel:** 1422 | |

### BUTLER—Butler County

★ **BUTLER HEALTH SYSTEM (390168)**, 1 Hospital Way, Zip 16001–4697; tel. 724/283–6666, (Nonreporting) **A**10
Primary Contact: Ken DeFurio, President and Chief Executive Officer
COO: Jason R. Sciarro, Chief Operating Officer
CFO: Eric Huss, Chief Financial Officer
CMO: David Rottinghaus, M.D., Director
CIO: Roger Lutz, Chief Information Officer
CHR: Thomas A Genevro, Vice President Human Resources
CNO: Karen A Allen, R.N., Chief Nursing Officer
Web address: www.butlerhealthsystem.org
**Control**: Other not–for–profit (including NFP Corporation) **Service**: General medical and surgical

| | |
|---|---|
| **Staffed Beds:** 288 | |

**BUTLER MEMORIAL HOSPITAL** See Butler Health System

### CAMP HILL—Cumberland County

⊞ **GEISINGER HOLY SPIRIT (390004)**, 503 North 21st Street, Zip 17011–2204; tel. 717/763–2100, (Nonreporting) **A**1 3 5 10 **F**3 8 13 14 15 17 18 20 21 22 24 26 28 29 30 31 34 35 38 40 43 44 45 46 47 48 49 50 54 57 59 64 65 70 72 74 75 76 77 78 79 81 82 84 85 86 87 89 93 98 100 101 102 104 105 107 108 110 111 114 115 118 119 120 121 123 124 126 129 130 132 134 135 143 146 147 148 149 153 154 156 **P**1 5 8 **S** Geisinger, Danville, PA
Primary Contact: Kyle C. Snyder, Chief Administrative Officer
CNO: Lisa F Torchia, MSN, R.N., Vice President and Chief Nursing Officer
Web address: www.hsh.org
**Control**: Other not–for–profit (including NFP Corporation) **Service**: General medical and surgical

| | |
|---|---|
| **Staffed Beds:** 311 **Admissions:** 10750 **Census:** 149 **Outpatient Visits:** 237074 **Births:** 1135 **Total Expense ($000):** 304700 **Payroll Expense ($000):** 103459 **Personnel:** 1939 | |

**HOLY SPIRIT - A GEISINGER AFFILIATE** See Geisinger Holy Spirit

---

**Hospital, Medicare Provider Number, Address, Telephone, Approval, Facility, and Physician Codes, Health Care System**

★ American Hospital Association (AHA) membership
☐ The Joint Commission accreditation
○ Healthcare Facilities Accreditation Program
◇ DNV Healthcare Inc. accreditation
⇑ Center for Improvement in Healthcare Quality Accreditation
△ Commission on Accreditation of Rehabilitation Facilities (CARF) accreditation

⊠ **SELECT SPECIALTY HOSPITAL-CAMP HILL (392039)**, 503 North 21st Street, 5th Floor, Zip 17011–2204; tel. 717/972–4575, (Includes SELECT SPECIALTY HOSPITAL-HARRISBURG, Mailing address: 111 South Front Street, Alex Grass Building, 5th Floor, Harrisburg, Pennsylvania, Zip 17101; tel. 717/724–6610; John E Simodejka, Marketing Chief Executive Officer; SELECT SPECIALTY HOSPITAL-YORK, Mailing address: 1001 South George Street, York, Pennsylvania, Zip 17403–3676; tel. 717/851–2661; Marcia Medlin, Chief Executive Officer), (Nonreporting) **A**1 10 **S** Select Medical Corporation, Mechanicsburg, PA
Primary Contact: John E. Simodejka, Chief Executive Officer
Web address: www.camphill.selectspecialtyhospitals.com/
**Control**: Corporation, Investor–owned (for–profit) **Service**: Acute long–term care hospital

**Staffed Beds:** 92

**SELECT SPECIALTY HOSPITAL-CENTRAL PENNSYLVANIA** See Select Specialty Hospital-Camp Hill

**STATE CORRECTIONAL INSTITUTION AT CAMP HILL**, 2500 Lisburn Road, Zip 17011–8005, Mailing Address: P.O. Box 200, Zip 17001–0200; tel. 717/737–4531, (Nonreporting)
Primary Contact: Beth Herb, Administrator
Web address: www.cor.state.pa.us/
**Control**: State, Government, Nonfederal **Service**: Hospital unit of an institution (prison hospital, college infirmary, etc.)

**Staffed Beds:** 34

### CANONSBURG—Washington County

**CANONSBURG GENERAL HOSPITAL** See Canonsburg Hospital

⊠ **CANONSBURG HOSPITAL (390160)**, 100 Medical Boulevard, Zip 15317–9762; tel. 724/745–6100, (Nonreporting) **A**1 10 **F**3 7 11 15 18 28 29 30 34 35 40 44 45 46 47 49 50 54 57 59 64 70 74 75 77 79 81 84 85 86 87 90 92 93 96 102 107 108 110 111 114 115 118 119 129 130 131 132 135 141 143 146 148 149 154 **S** Allegheny Health Network, Pittsburgh, PA
Primary Contact: Chong Park, M.D., President
COO: Kelly Kassab, Chief Operating Officer
CMO: Thomas B Corkery, D.O., Chief Medical Officer
CIO: David Vincent, Director Information Systems
CHR: Martha L Clister, Director Human Resources
Web address: www.wpahs.org
**Control**: Other not–for–profit (including NFP Corporation) **Service**: General medical and surgical

**Staffed Beds:** 42 **Admissions:** 1604 **Census:** 21 **Outpatient Visits:** 70045 **Births:** 0 **Total Expense ($000):** 49973 **Payroll Expense ($000):** 19238 **Personnel:** 318

### CARLISLE—Cumberland County

⊠ **UPMC CARLISLE (390058)**, 361 Alexander Spring Road, Zip 17015–6940; tel. 717/249–1212, (Nonreporting) **A**1 3 10 **F**3 8 11 13 14 15 18 20 29 30 31 34 35 38 40 44 45 46 48 49 50 51 54 55 57 59 60 64 65 68 70 74 75 76 77 78 79 81 85 87 90 96 107 108 109 110 111 114 115 116 117 118 119 120 121 123 126 129 130 132 141 144 146 147 148 149 154 **S** UPMC, Pittsburgh, PA
Primary Contact: Lou Baverso, President
CFO: Alison Bernhardt, Chief Financial Officer
CMO: Ivan' Sola', President Medical Staff
CHR: Sylvia Rockwood, Director Human Resources
Web address: www.https://www.pinnaclehealth.org/carlisle/
**Control**: Other not–for–profit (including NFP Corporation) **Service**: General medical and surgical

**Staffed Beds:** 153 **Admissions:** 4602 **Census:** 73 **Outpatient Visits:** 127304 **Births:** 407 **Total Expense ($000):** 115482 **Payroll Expense ($000):** 30624 **Personnel:** 564

**UPMC PINNACLE CARLISLE** See UPMC Carlisle

### CENTRE HALL—Centre County

⊠ **MEADOWS PSYCHIATRIC CENTER (394040)**, 132 The Meadows Drive, Zip 16828–9231; tel. 814/364–2161, (Nonreporting) **A**1 10 **F**29 40 59 98 99 100 103 130 135 **S** Universal Health Services, Inc., King of Prussia, PA
Primary Contact: David Grabowski, Chief Executive Officer
CFO: David Witt, Chief Financial Officer
CMO: Craig Richman, M.D., Medical Director
CHR: Mary Jane Schreffler, Director Human Resources
CNO: Dana Thies, Director of Nursing
Web address: www.themeadows.net
**Control**: Corporation, Investor–owned (for–profit) **Service**: Psychiatric

**Staffed Beds:** 119 **Admissions:** 2683 **Census:** 102 **Outpatient Visits:** 151 **Births:** 0 **Personnel:** 200

### CHAMBERSBURG—Franklin County

**CHAMBERSBURG HOSPITAL** See Wellspan Chambersburg Hospital

⊠ **WELLSPAN CHAMBERSBURG HOSPITAL (390151)**, 112 North Seventh Street, Zip 17201–1720; tel. 717/267–3000, (Nonreporting) **A**1 2 3 5 10 19 **F**3 13 15 17 18 20 22 26 28 29 30 40 44 45 49 50 58 68 70 72 75 76 77 81 85 86 87 90 98 100 102 104 107 108 110 111 114 115 119 126 129 130 146 148 149 154 **P**8 **S** WellSpan Health, York, PA
Primary Contact: Patrick W. O'Donnell, President and Chief Executive Officer
COO: John P. Massimilla, FACHE, Vice President and Chief Operating Officer
CFO: Kimberly Rzomp, Vice President and Chief Financial Officer
CMO: Thomas Anderson, M.D., Vice President Medical Affairs
CIO: Michele Zeigler, Vice President and Chief Information Officer
CHR: Harry Dieuveuil, Vice President Human Resources
CNO: Elyse Fisler, Chief Nursing Officer
Web address: www.summithealth.org
**Control**: Other not–for–profit (including NFP Corporation) **Service**: General medical and surgical

**Staffed Beds:** 285 **Admissions:** 11400 **Census:** 131 **Outpatient Visits:** 428028 **Births:** 1319 **Total Expense ($000):** 298397 **Payroll Expense ($000):** 126785 **Personnel:** 1713

### CLARION—Clarion County

⊠ ○ **CLARION HOSPITAL (390093)**, One Hospital Drive, Zip 16214–8501; tel. 814/226–9500, (Nonreporting) **A**1 3 5 10 11 12 13
Primary Contact: Steven T. Davis, Chief Executive Officer
CFO: Will Grant, Interim Chief Financial Officer
CMO: Anie Perard, M.D., President, Medical Staff
CIO: James Confer, Manager Information Systems
CHR: Brooke N. Divins, Director Human Resources
CNO: Leslie Walters, MSN, Chief Nursing Officer
Web address: www.clarionhospital.org
**Control**: Other not–for–profit (including NFP Corporation) **Service**: General medical and surgical

**Staffed Beds:** 66

☐ **CLARION PSYCHIATRIC CENTER (394043)**, 2 Hospital Drive, Zip 16214–8502; tel. 814/226–9545, (Nonreporting) **A**1 10 **F**98 99 105 **S** Universal Health Services, Inc., King of Prussia, PA
Primary Contact: Wendy Shapiro, Chief Executive Officer
CFO: Shelly Rhoades, Chief Financial Officer
CMO: Jeffrey Moll, M.D., Medical Director
CHR: Dianne C Bilunka, Director Human Resources
CNO: Rhonda Massa, Director of Nursing
Web address: www.clarioncenter.com
**Control**: Corporation, Investor–owned (for–profit) **Service**: Psychiatric

**Staffed Beds:** 96 **Admissions:** 2677 **Census:** 86 **Outpatient Visits:** 0 **Births:** 0

### CLARKS SUMMIT—Lackawanna County

**CLARKS SUMMIT STATE HOSPITAL (394012)**, 1451 Hillside Drive, Zip 18411–9504; tel. 570/586–2011, (Nonreporting) **A**10
Primary Contact: Monica Bradbury, Chief Executive Officer
COO: Gordon Weber, Chief Operating Officer
CMO: David Waibel, M.D., Medical Director
CHR: William Abda, Chief Human Resources Officer
Web address: www.dpw.state.pa.us/
**Control**: State, Government, Nonfederal **Service**: Psychiatric

**Staffed Beds:** 210

### CLEARFIELD—Clearfield County

**CLEARFIELD HOSPITAL** See Penn Highlands Clearfield

**PENN HIGHLANDS CLEARFIELD (390052)**, 809 Turnpike Avenue, Zip 16830–1232, Mailing Address: P.O. Box 992, Zip 16830–0992; tel. 814/765–5341, (Nonreporting) **A**3 10 **F**3 8 11 14 15 18 28 29 30 32 34 40 45 50 57 59 68 75 77 79 81 82 84 85 86 87 93 97 98 103 104 107 108 110 111 115 119 130 131 132 133 146 148
Primary Contact: Rhonda Halstead, President
CFO: William Cain, Controller
CMO: Kevin L Tyler, M.D., President Medical Staff
CNO: Kathy Bedger, Chief Nursing Officer
Web address: www.phhealthcare.org
**Control**: Other not–for–profit (including NFP Corporation) **Service**: General medical and surgical

**Staffed Beds:** 43 **Admissions:** 1448 **Census:** 19 **Outpatient Visits:** 107578 **Births:** 0 **Total Expense ($000):** 44203 **Payroll Expense ($000):** 15104

**COAL TOWNSHIP—Northumberland County**

**GEISINGER SHAMOKIN AREA COMMUNITY HOSPITAL** See Geisinger-Shamokin Area Community Hospital

**COALDALE—Schuylkill County**

☐ **ST. LUKE'S HOSPITAL - MINERS CAMPUS (390183)**, 360 West Ruddle Street, Zip 18218–1027; tel. 570/645–2131, (Total facility includes 48 beds in nursing home–type unit) (Nonreporting) **A**1 3 10 **F**3 15 18 28 29 31 34 35 38 40 43 44 45 50 51 53 54 56 57 58 59 60 63 64 65 70 74 75 77 78 79 81 82 85 86 93 102 107 108 110 111 115 118 119 127 128 129 130 131 132 143 144 145 146 148 149 154 156 **S** St. Luke's University Health Network, Bethlehem, PA
Primary Contact: Wendy Lazo, President
COO: Joel Fagerstrom, Executive Vice President and Chief Operating Officer
CFO: Michele Levitz, Director Finance
CIO: Chad Brisendine, Vice President and Chief Information Officer
CHR: Susan Van Why, Director Human Resources
CNO: Kimberly Sargent, Vice President Patient Services
Web address: www.slhn.org
**Control**: Other not–for–profit (including NFP Corporation) **Service**: General medical and surgical

**Staffed Beds**: 97 **Admissions**: 2790 **Census**: 69 **Outpatient Visits**: 129115
**Births**: 0 **Total Expense ($000)**: 68188 **Payroll Expense ($000)**: 31219
**Personnel**: 362

**ST. LUKE'S MINERS MEMORIAL HOSPITAL** See St. Luke's Hospital - Miners Campus

**COATESVILLE—Chester County**

**BRANDYWINE HOSP & TRAUMA CNTR** See Brandywine Hospital

⊞ **BRANDYWINE HOSPITAL (390076)**, 201 Reeceville Road, Zip 19320–1536; tel. 610/383–8000, (Nonreporting) **A**1 3 10 **S** Tower Health, West Reading, PA
Primary Contact: Vik Acharya, M.P.H., Chief Executive Officer
COO: Jill Tillman, Assistant Chief Executive Officer
CFO: Mark Reyngoudt, Chief Financial Officer
Web address: www.https://brandywine.towerhealth.org/
**Control**: Other not–for–profit (including NFP Corporation) **Service**: General medical and surgical

**Staffed Beds**: 169

⊞ **COATESVILLE VETERANS AFFAIRS MEDICAL CENTER**, 1400 Black Horse Hill Road, Zip 19320–2040; tel. 610/384–7711, (Nonreporting) **A**1 3 5 **S** Department of Veterans Affairs, Washington, DC
Primary Contact: Carla Sivek, Director
CFO: Tony Wolfgang, Chief Financial Officer
CMO: Sheila Chellappa, M.D., Chief of Staff
CIO: Ryan McGettigan, Chief Information Officer
CHR: Andrew Sutton, Chief Human Resources Officer
CNO: Nancy A Schmid, R.N., MS, Associate Director Patient Care Services
Web address: www.coatesville.va.gov/
**Control**: Veterans Affairs, Government, federal **Service**: Alcoholism and other chemical dependency

**Staffed Beds**: 118

**VETERANS AFFAIRS MEDICAL CENTER** See Coatesville Veterans Affairs Medical Center

**CONNELLSVILLE—Fayette County**

**HIGHLANDS HOSPITAL (390184)**, 401 East Murphy Avenue, Zip 15425–2700; tel. 724/628–1500, (Nonreporting) **A**10
Primary Contact: John S. Andursky, President and Chief Executive Officer
CMO: Paul Means, M.D., President Medical Staff
CHR: Mary June Krosoff, Chief Human Resources Officer
CNO: Vicki Rough, Chief Nursing Officer
Web address: www.highlandshospital.org
**Control**: Other not–for–profit (including NFP Corporation) **Service**: General medical and surgical

**Staffed Beds**: 64

**HIGHLANDS HOSPITAL & HLTH CTR** See Highlands Hospital

**CORRY—Erie County**

**CORRY MEMORIAL HOSPITAL** See Lecom Corry Memorial Hospital

**LECOM CORRY MEMORIAL HOSPITAL (391308)**, 965 Shamrock Lane, Zip 16407; tel. 814/664–4641, (Nonreporting) **A**10 18
Primary Contact: Barbara Nichols, R.N., President and Chief Executive Officer
CFO: Michael Heller, Chief Financial Officer
CMO: Paul McGeehan, M.D., Chief Medical Staff
CHR: Brenda Cooper, Director Quality and Human Resources
CNO: Patty White, R.N., Director Patient Care Services
Web address: www.corryhospital.com
**Control**: Other not–for–profit (including NFP Corporation) **Service**: General medical and surgical

**Staffed Beds**: 25

**COUDERSPORT—Potter County**

**COLE MEMORIAL** See UPMC Cole

⊞ **UPMC COLE (391313)**, 1001 East Second Street, Zip 16915–8161; tel. 814/274–9300, (Total facility includes 44 beds in nursing home–type unit) (Nonreporting) **A**1 10 18 **F**3 13 15 18 28 29 31 39 40 50 70 76 77 78 79 81 82 84 85 87 93 97 107 108 110 111 115 119 121 127 128 129 131 133 146 147 148 154 156 **P**6
Primary Contact: Janie Marie. Hilfiger, President
CFO: Ronald Rapp, Vice President Finance
CMO: Brenda Wahlers, M.D., Chief of Staff
CHR: James Evens, Executive Director, Human Resources and General Services
CNO: Emily Ann Bunnell, Chief Nurse Executive, Senior Director of Acute Care
Web address: www.colememorial.org/
**Control**: Other not–for–profit (including NFP Corporation) **Service**: General medical and surgical

**Staffed Beds**: 69 **Admissions**: 1668 **Census**: 55 **Outpatient Visits**: 250363
**Births**: 183 **Total Expense ($000)**: 91707 **Payroll Expense ($000)**: 32475
**Personnel**: 786

**CRANBERRY—Butler County**

**ST FRANCIS HOSPITAL CRANBERRY** See UPMC Passavant Cranberry

**UPMC PASSAVANT CRANBERRY** See UPMC Passavant, Pittsburgh

**DANVILLE—Montour County**

**DANVILLE STATE HOSPITAL (394004)**, 200 State Hospital Drive, Zip 17821–9198; tel. 570/271–4500, (Nonreporting) **A**3 10 **F**65 75 77 98 106 130 135 154 156 157
Primary Contact: Theresa Long, Chief Executive Officer
COO: Thomas J Burk, Chief Operating Officer
CFO: Patricia Riegert, Director Fiscal Services
CMO: Vikrant Mittal, M.D., Chief Medical Officer
CHR: Thomas J Burk, Chief Operating Officer
CNO: Brenda Lahout, Chief Nurse Executive
Web address: www.dpw.state.pa.us/foradults/statehospitals/danvillestatehospital/index.htm
**Control**: State, Government, Nonfederal **Service**: Psychiatric

**Staffed Beds**: 161 **Admissions**: 65 **Census**: 158 **Outpatient Visits**: 0
**Births**: 0 **Total Expense ($000)**: 35713 **Personnel**: 354

⊞ **GEISINGER ENCOMPASS HEALTH REHABILITATION HOSPITAL (393047)**, 64 Rehab Lane, Zip 17821–8498; tel. 570/271–6733, (Nonreporting) **A**1 3 10 **S** Encompass Health Corporation, Birmingham, AL
Primary Contact: Lorie Dillon, Chief Executive Officer
CMO: Greg Burke, M.D., Medical Director
CHR: Christian Shirley, Director Human Resources
Web address: www.geisingerhealthsouth.com
**Control**: Corporation, Investor–owned (for–profit) **Service**: Rehabilitation

**Staffed Beds**: 42

**GEISINGER HEALTHSOUTH REHABILITATION HOSPITAL** See Geisinger Encompass Health Rehabilitation Hospital

---

**Hospital, Medicare Provider Number, Address, Telephone, Approval, Facility, and Physician Codes, Health Care System**

★ American Hospital Association (AHA) membership
☐ The Joint Commission accreditation
○ Healthcare Facilities Accreditation Program
◇ DNV Healthcare Inc. accreditation
⇑ Center for Improvement in Healthcare Quality Accreditation
△ Commission on Accreditation of Rehabilitation Facilities (CARF) accreditation

PA

✠ **GEISINGER MEDICAL CENTER (390006)**, 100 North Academy Avenue, Zip 17822–2201; tel. 570/271–6211, (Includes GEISINGER-SHAMOKIN AREA COMMUNITY HOSPITAL, Mailing address: 4200 Hospital Road, Coal Township, Pennsylvania, Zip 17866–9697; tel. 570/644–4200), (Nonreporting) **A**1 2 3 5 8 10 13 19 **F**3 4 7 8 9 11 12 13 14 15 17 18 19 20 21 22 23 24 25 26 27 28 29 30 31 32 34 35 36 37 39 40 41 43 44 45 46 47 48 49 50 51 52 53 54 55 56 57 58 59 60 61 62 63 64 65 66 67 68 69 70 71 72 73 74 75 76 77 78 79 80 81 82 83 84 85 86 87 88 89 91 92 93 94 96 97 98 99 100 101 102 104 107 108 110 111 114 115 117 118 119 120 121 123 124 126 129 130 131 132 134 135 136 138 139 141 145 146 147 148 149 150 153 154 155 156 **P**1 5 8 **S** Geisinger, Danville, PA
Primary Contact: Thomas P. Sokola, Chief Administrative Officer
CFO: Kevin F Brennan, CPA, Executive Vice President and Chief Financial Officer
CIO: Frank Richards, Chief Information Officer
CHR: Amy Brayford, Chief Human Resources Officer
CNO: Susan M Robel, R.N., Executive Vice President and Chief Nursing Officer
Web address: www.geisinger.org
**Control**: Other not–for–profit (including NFP Corporation) **Service**: General medical and surgical

| | |
|---|---|
| **Staffed Beds:** 527 **Admissions:** 27777 **Census:** 394 **Outpatient Visits:** 1148340 **Births:** 2000 **Total Expense ($000):** 1173124 **Payroll Expense ($000):** 346403 **Personnel:** 7274 | |

**SELECT SPECIALTY HOSP-DANVILLE** See Select Specialty Hospital-Danville

✠ **SELECT SPECIALTY HOSPITAL-DANVILLE (392047)**, 100 North Academy Avenue, 3rd Floor, Zip 17822–3050; tel. 570/214–9653, (Nonreporting) **A**1 10 **S** Select Medical Corporation, Mechanicsburg, PA
Primary Contact: Brian Mann, Chief Executive Officer
Web address: www.https://danville.selectspecialtyhospitals.com
**Control**: Corporation, Investor–owned (for–profit) **Service**: Acute long–term care hospital

| | |
|---|---|
| **Staffed Beds:** 30 | |

### DARBY—Delaware County

**FITZGERALD MERCY HOSPITAL** See Mercy Fitzgerald Hospital

✠ **MERCY CATHOLIC MEDICAL CENTER - MERCY FITZGERALD CAMPUS (390156)**, 1500 Lansdowne Avenue, Zip 19023–1200; tel. 610/237–4000, (Includes MERCY FITZGERALD HOSPITAL, Mailing address: 1500 South Lansdowne Avenue, Darby, Pennsylvania, Zip 19023; tel. 610/237–4000), (Nonreporting) **A**1 2 3 5 10 **F**3 4 11 12 15 18 20 22 24 26 28 29 30 31 34 35 38 39 40 45 46 49 50 51 54 57 59 61 64 66 70 74 75 77 78 79 81 82 85 86 87 90 91 92 93 97 98 100 101 102 107 108 110 111 114 115 118 119 120 121 123 124 130 131 132 135 145 146 147 148 149 150 154 **S** Trinity Health, Livonia, MI
Primary Contact: Christopher Cullom, President
COO: Ruth Thomas, Chief Operating Officer
CFO: Don Snenk, Chief Financial Officer
CMO: Jeff Komins, M.D., Chief Medical Officer
CIO: Jeff Byda, Vice President Information Technology
Web address: www.mercyhealth.org
**Control**: Other not–for–profit (including NFP Corporation) **Service**: General medical and surgical

| | |
|---|---|
| **Staffed Beds:** 340 **Admissions:** 14845 **Census:** 204 **Outpatient Visits:** 385643 **Births:** 0 **Total Expense ($000):** 334946 **Payroll Expense ($000):** 122885 **Personnel:** 1469 | |

**MERCY FITZGERALD HOSPITAL** See Mercy Catholic Medical Center - Mercy Fitzgerald Campus

### DOWNINGTOWN—Chester County

★ **ST. JOHN VIANNEY HOSPITAL**, 151 Woodbine Road, Zip 19335–3057; tel. 610/269–2600, (Nonreporting)
Primary Contact: David Shellenberger, President
CMO: James MacFadyen, M.D., Medical Director
CHR: Linda Rava EsqDirector Human Resources
CNO: Diana Karanja, R.N., Director of Nursing
Web address: www.sjvcenter.org
**Control**: Church operated, Nongovernment, not–for–profit **Service**: Psychiatric

| | |
|---|---|
| **Staffed Beds:** 47 | |

**VILLA ST JOHN VIANNEY HOSPITAL** See St. John Vianney Hospital

### DOYLESTOWN—Bucks County

**DEL VLY MENTAL HLTH FOUNDATION** See Foundations Behavioral Health

✠ △ **DOYLESTOWN HOSPITAL (390203)**, 595 West State Street, Zip 18901–2597; tel. 215/345–2200, (Nonreporting) **A**1 2 3 5 7 10 **F**3 8 13 15 17 18 20 22 24 28 29 30 31 32 34 35 40 45 46 49 50 51 54 55 57 58 59 62 63 64 70 73 74 75 76 77 78 79 81 85 86 87 89 92 93 94 96 107 108 110 111 114 115 118 119 124 126 129 130 131 132 134 146 147 149 154
Primary Contact: James L. Brexler, President and Chief Executive Officer
COO: Eleanor Wilson, R.N., MSN, Vice President and Chief Operating Officer
CFO: Daniel Upton, Vice President and Chief Financial Officer
CMO: Scott S Levy, M.D., Vice President and Chief Medical Officer
CIO: Richard Lang, Ed.D., Vice President and Chief Information Officer
CHR: Barbara Hebel, Vice President Human Resources
CNO: Patricia A Stover, Administrator Nursing
Web address: www.doylestownhealth.org
**Control**: Other not–for–profit (including NFP Corporation) **Service**: General medical and surgical

| | |
|---|---|
| **Staffed Beds:** 189 **Admissions:** 12230 **Census:** 130 **Outpatient Visits:** 262957 **Births:** 1196 **Total Expense ($000):** 263606 **Payroll Expense ($000):** 113508 **Personnel:** 2107 | |

☐ **FOUNDATIONS BEHAVIORAL HEALTH (394038)**, 833 East Butler Avenue, Zip 18901–2280; tel. 215/345–0444, (Nonreporting) **A**1 10 **S** Universal Health Services, Inc., King of Prussia, PA
Primary Contact: Gina Fusco, M.D., Chief Executive Officer
Web address: www.fbh.com
**Control**: Other not–for–profit (including NFP Corporation) **Service**: Children's hospital psychiatric

| | |
|---|---|
| **Staffed Beds:** 58 | |

### DREXEL HILL—Delaware County

☐ **DELAWARE COUNTY MEMORIAL HOSPITAL (390081)**, 501 North Lansdowne Avenue, Zip 19026–1114; tel. 610/284–8100, (Nonreporting) **A**1 2 3 5 10 **S** Prospect Medical Holdings, Los Angeles, CA
Primary Contact: Patrick Kerrwood, President
CFO: Richard I Bennett, Senior Vice President and Chief Financial Officer
CMO: Seth Malin, M.D., President Medical and Dental Staff
CIO: Robert E Wilson, Vice President and Chief Information Officer
Web address: www.crozer.org
**Control**: Other not–for–profit (including NFP Corporation) **Service**: General medical and surgical

| | |
|---|---|
| **Staffed Beds:** 168 | |

### DUBOIS—Clearfield County

⇑ **DUBOIS REGIONAL MEDICAL CENTER** See Penn Highlands Dubois

⇑ **PENN HIGHLANDS DUBOIS (390086)**, 100 Hospital Avenue, Zip 15801–1440, Mailing Address: P.O. Box 447, Zip 15801–0447; tel. 814/371–2200, (Nonreporting) **A**3 10 13 19 21
Primary Contact: John Sutika, President
CFO: Brian S Kline, Vice President and Chief Financial Officer
CMO: Gary Dugan, M.D., Vice President Medical Affairs
CHR: Jake Maijala, Chief Human Resource Officer
Web address: www.drmc.org
**Control**: Other not–for–profit (including NFP Corporation) **Service**: General medical and surgical

| | |
|---|---|
| **Staffed Beds:** 219 | |

### EAGLEVILLE—Montgomery County

★ **EAGLEVILLE HOSPITAL (390278)**, 100 Eagleville Road, Zip 19403–1829, Mailing Address: P.O. Box 45, Zip 19408–0045; tel. 610/539–6000, (Nonreporting) **A**5 10
Primary Contact: Eugene J. Ott Jr, Chief Executive Officer
CFO: Alfred P Salvitti, Chief Financial Officer
CMO: Robert Wilson, D.O., Director Medical Services
CIO: Richard R Mitchell, Director Information Technology
CHR: Zoe Yousaitis, Director Human Resources
Web address: www.eaglevillehospital.org
**Control**: Other not–for–profit (including NFP Corporation) **Service**: Alcoholism and other chemical dependency

| | |
|---|---|
| **Staffed Beds:** 83 | |

*Many Facility Codes have changed. Please refer to the AHA Guide Code Chart.*

PA

## EAST NORRITON—Montgomery County

☐ **EINSTEIN MEDICAL CENTER MONTGOMERY (390329)**, 559 West Germantown Pike, Zip 19403–4250; tel. 484/622–1000, (Nonreporting) **A**1 2 3 10 **F**3 8 11 12 13 15 18 20 22 24 26 29 30 31 34 35 40 45 46 49 55 57 59 62 63 64 68 70 72 74 75 76 78 79 80 81 82 84 85 87 92 100 107 108 110 111 115 117 119 120 121 123 126 129 130 131 132 135 146 147 149 **S** Einstein Healthcare Network, Philadelphia, PA
Primary Contact: Beth Duffy, Chief Operating Officer
COO: Beth Duffy, Chief Operating Officer
CFO: Gerard Blaney, Vice President, Finance
CMO: Angela Nicholas, Vice President, Medical Affairs
CIO: Mary Carroll Ford, Chief Information Officer
CHR: Kenneth Levitan, Chief Administrative Officer
CNO: AnnMarie Papa, R.N., Vice President and Chief Nursing Officer
**Control:** Other not–for–profit (including NFP Corporation) **Service:** General medical and surgical

**Staffed Beds: 171 Admissions: 10686 Census: 129 Outpatient Visits: 206110 Births: 2085 Total Expense ($000): 238019 Payroll Expense ($000): 85032 Personnel: 1443**

**MERCY SUBURBAN HOSPITAL** See Suburban Community Hospital

☐ **SUBURBAN COMMUNITY HOSPITAL (390116)**, 2701 Dekalb Pike, Zip 19401–1820; tel. 610/278–2000, (Nonreporting) **A**1 3 5 10 12 13 **S** Prime Healthcare, Ontario, CA
Primary Contact: Matt Shelak, Chief Executive Officer
COO: Joseph Schofield, Chief Operating Officer
CFO: Joseph Marino, Chief Financial Officer
CMO: Andrea D Pedano, D.O., Chief Medical Officer
CIO: Jason Wayne, Network Administrator
CHR: Gretchen Pendleton, Director Human Resources
CNO: Mary Ellen Rauner, R.N., Chief Nursing Officer
Web address: www.suburbanhosp.org
**Control:** Corporation, Investor–owned (for–profit) **Service:** General medical and surgical

**Staffed Beds: 126**

## EAST STROUDSBURG—Monroe County

☒ **LEHIGH VALLEY HOSPITAL - POCONO (390201)**, 206 East Brown Street, Zip 18301–3006; tel. 570/421–4000, (Nonreporting) **A**1 2 10 **S** Lehigh Valley Health Network, Allentown, PA
Primary Contact: Elizabeth Wise, President and Chief Executive Officer
CMO: William K. Cors, M.D., Senior Medical Director
CIO: Ferd Feola, Chief Information Officer
CHR: Lynn Lansdowne, Vice President Labor Relations and Human Resources
Web address: www.pmchealthsystem.org
**Control:** Other not–for–profit (including NFP Corporation) **Service:** General medical and surgical

**Staffed Beds: 239**

**POCONO MEDICAL CENTER** See Lehigh Valley Hospital - Pocono

## EASTON—Northampton County

☐ **ST. LUKE'S EASTON CAMPUS (390162)**, 250 South 21st Street, Zip 18042–3892; tel. 610/250–4000, (Nonreporting) **A**1 3 5 10 **S** St. Luke's University Health Network, Bethlehem, PA
Primary Contact: Linda J. Grass, President
COO: Ronald Ziobro, Chief Operating Officer
CFO: Arthur Comito, Chief Financial Officer
CMO: Roman Tuma, Chief Medical Officer
CIO: Don Lutz, Director Information Technology
CHR: Tanya Segal, Director
CNO: Karen Vadyak, Chief Nursing Officer
Web address: www.https://www.easton-hospital.org/
**Control:** Other not–for–profit (including NFP Corporation) **Service:** General medical and surgical

**Staffed Beds: 196**

☐ **ST. LUKE'S HOSPITAL - ANDERSON CAMPUS (390326)**, 1872 Riverside Circle, Zip 18045–5669; tel. 484/503–3000, (Nonreporting) **A**1 3 10 **F**3 8 11 15 18 20 22 24 26 28 29 30 31 34 35 38 40 44 45 46 49 50 51 53 54 55 57 59 60 63 64 68 70 71 74 75 77 78 79 81 82 84 85 86 87 92 93 96 100 102 107 108 110 111 115 118 119 121 123 124 126 130 132 144 145 146 147 148 149 154 **S** St. Luke's University Health Network, Bethlehem, PA
Primary Contact: Edward Nawrocki, President
CMO: Justin P Psaila, M.D., Vice President Medical Affairs
CNO: Darla Frack, MSN, Vice President, Patient Services
Web address: www.mystlukesonline.org
**Control:** Other not–for–profit (including NFP Corporation) **Service:** General medical and surgical

**Staffed Beds: 108 Admissions: 7789 Census: 75 Outpatient Visits: 218493 Births: 0 Total Expense ($000): 178928 Payroll Expense ($000): 62159 Personnel: 691**

## ELKINS PARK—Montgomery County

**MOSS REHAB, EINSTEIN AT ELKINS PARK** See Einstein Medical Center Elkins Park

## EPHRATA—Lancaster County

⇑ **EPHRATA COMMUNITY HOSPITAL** See Wellspan Ephrata Community Hospital

★ ⇑ **WELLSPAN EPHRATA COMMUNITY HOSPITAL (390225)**, 169 Martin Avenue, Zip 17522–1724, Mailing Address: P.O. Box 1002, Zip 17522–1002; tel. 717/733–0311, (Nonreporting) **A**2 10 21 **F**3 7 13 15 18 20 22 26 28 29 30 31 34 40 44 45 46 49 50 51 54 57 59 60 64 70 72 75 76 77 78 79 80 81 82 85 86 87 89 90 93 98 100 107 108 110 111 114 115 116 117 118 119 120 121 123 126 129 130 131 132 146 147 148 149 154 156 **P**6 8 **S** WellSpan Health, York, PA
Primary Contact: , MSN
CFO: David Kreider, Controller
CMO: Mark Jacobson, D.O., Vice President Medical Affairs
CIO: Leon John Jabour, Regional Chief Information Officer
CHR: Jana Salaki, Regional Director Human Resources
CNO: Tina Citro, R.N., Chief Nursing Officer, Vice President, Patient Services
Web address: www.wellspan.org
**Control:** Other not–for–profit (including NFP Corporation) **Service:** General medical and surgical

**Staffed Beds: 141 Admissions: 7469 Census: 77 Outpatient Visits: 302700 Births: 863 Total Expense ($000): 214290 Payroll Expense ($000): 57255 Personnel: 906**

## ERIE—Erie County

☒ **ENCOMPASS HEALTH REHABILITATION HOSPITAL OF ERIE (393046)**, 143 East Second Street, Zip 16507–1501; tel. 814/878–1200, (Nonreporting) **A**1 10 **S** Encompass Health Corporation, Birmingham, AL
Primary Contact: Janet Hein, Chief Executive Officer
CFO: Lori Gibbens, Controller
CMO: Douglas Grisier, D.O., Medical Director
CIO: Sharon Zielinski, Manager Health Information
CHR: William Robinson, Director Human Resources
Web address: www.healthsoutherie.com
**Control:** Corporation, Investor–owned (for–profit) **Service:** Rehabilitation

**Staffed Beds: 100**

☒ **ERIE VETERANS AFFAIRS MEDICAL CENTER**, 135 East 38th Street, Zip 16504–1559; tel. 814/860–2576, (Nonreporting) **A**1 **S** Department of Veterans Affairs, Washington, DC
Primary Contact: John Gennaro, FACHE, Director
CFO: Joann Pritchard, Chief Financial Officer
CMO: Anthony Behm, D.O., Chief of Staff
CIO: Jonathan Seale, Chief Information Officer
CHR: Lynn Nies, Human Resources Officer
CNO: Dorene M. Sommers, Associate Director Patient Care Services
Web address: www.erie.va.gov/
**Control:** Veterans Affairs, Government, federal **Service:** General medical and surgical

**Staffed Beds: 52**

**HAMOT MEDICAL CENTER** See UPMC Hamot

**HEALTHSOUTH REHABILITATION HOSPITAL OF ERIE** See Encompass Health Rehabilitation Hospital of Erie

---

**Hospital, Medicare Provider Number, Address, Telephone, Approval, Facility, and Physician Codes, Health Care System**

★ American Hospital Association (AHA) membership
☐ The Joint Commission accreditation
○ Healthcare Facilities Accreditation Program
◇ DNV Healthcare Inc. accreditation
⇑ Center for Improvement in Healthcare Quality Accreditation
△ Commission on Accreditation of Rehabilitation Facilities (CARF) accreditation

○ **LECOM HEALTH MILLCREEK COMMUNITY HOSPITAL (390198)**, 5515 Peach Street, Zip 16509–2695; tel. 814/864–4031, (Nonreporting) **A**3 5 10 11 12 13
Primary Contact: Mary L. Eckert, President and Chief Executive Officer
CFO: Richard P Olinger, Chief Financial Officer
CMO: James Y Lin, D.O., Chief of Staff
CIO: Cheryl Girardier, Director Information Technology
CHR: Polly Momeyer, Manager Human Resources
CNO: Katie Agresti, R.N., Director Patient Care Services
Web address: www.millcreekcommunityhospital.com
**Control:** Other not–for–profit (including NFP Corporation) **Service:** General medical and surgical

| Staffed Beds: 168 |
| --- |

**MILLCREEK COMMUNITY HOSPITAL** See Lecom Health Millcreek Community Hospital

**SAINT VINCENT HEALTH CENTER** See Saint Vincent Hospital

☒ **SAINT VINCENT HOSPITAL (390009)**, 232 West 25th Street, Zip 16544–0002; tel. 814/452–5000, (Nonreporting) **A**1 3 5 10 12 13 19 **F**3 7 8 11 12 13 15 17 18 20 22 24 26 28 29 30 31 34 35 37 39 40 44 45 46 47 48 49 50 54 56 57 58 59 60 61 64 65 70 71 72 74 75 76 77 78 79 80 81 84 85 86 87 89 90 92 96 98 100 101 102 103 107 108 110 111 115 118 119 121 123 124 126 130 132 135 141 146 147 148 149 154 **S** Allegheny Health Network, Pittsburgh, PA
Primary Contact: Christopher Clark, D.O., President and Chief Executive Officer
COO: Jason Roeback, Chief Operating Officer
CFO: Randolph Levis, Chief Financial Officer
CIO: Richard B Ong, Chief Information Officer
CHR: Johnie M Atkinson, Chief Human Resources Officer
Web address: www.svhs.org
**Control:** Other not–for–profit (including NFP Corporation) **Service:** General medical and surgical

| Staffed Beds: 280 Admissions: 13401 Census: 176 Outpatient Visits: 170855 Births: 1066 Total Expense ($000): 294747 Payroll Expense ($000): 90751 Personnel: 1802 |
| --- |

**SELECT SPECIALTY HOSPITAL** See Select Specialty Hospital-Erie

☒ **SELECT SPECIALTY HOSPITAL-ERIE (392037)**, 252 West 11th Street, Zip 16501–1702; tel. 814/874–5300, (Nonreporting) **A**1 10 **S** Select Medical Corporation, Mechanicsburg, PA
Primary Contact: Michael A. Post, Chief Executive Officer
CNO: Keith Christiansen, Chief Nursing Officer
Web address: www.erie.selectspecialtyhospitals.com/
**Control:** Corporation, Investor–owned (for–profit) **Service:** Acute long–term care hospital

| Staffed Beds: 50 |
| --- |

**TWINBROOK NURSING & CONV HOME** See Twinbrook Medical Center

☒ **UPMC HAMOT (390063)**, 201 State Street, Zip 16550–0002; tel. 814/877–6000, (Nonreporting) **A**1 2 3 5 10 19 **F**3 5 9 12 13 15 17 18 20 22 24 26 28 29 30 31 34 35 36 37 38 39 40 43 44 45 46 47 48 49 50 51 54 56 57 58 59 60 61 64 65 66 68 70 72 74 75 76 77 78 79 80 81 82 84 85 86 87 89 91 92 93 96 97 100 101 102 104 106 107 108 109 110 111 114 115 118 119 124 126 129 130 131 132 134 135 138 141 147 148 149 150 154 **P**6 **S** UPMC, Pittsburgh, PA
Primary Contact: David Gibbons, President
CFO: Bradley Dinger, Chief Financial Officer
CMO: Richard Long, M.D., Chief Medical Officer
CIO: Lisa D McChesney, R.N., Senior Director Information Systems
CNO: James E Donnelly, Chief Nursing Officer and Vice President Patient Care Services
Web address: www.upmc.com/locations/hospitals/hamot
**Control:** Other not–for–profit (including NFP Corporation) **Service:** General medical and surgical

| Staffed Beds: 345 Admissions: 20443 Census: 263 Outpatient Visits: 225760 Births: 2168 Total Expense ($000): 421768 Payroll Expense ($000): 108995 Personnel: 2028 |
| --- |

**VETERANS AFFAIRS MEDICAL CENTER** See Erie Veterans Affairs Medical Center

**EVERETT—Bedford County**

**MEM HOSPITAL OF BEDFORD COUNTY** See UPMC Bedford

☒ **UPMC BEDFORD (390117)**, 10455 Lincoln Highway, Zip 15537–7046; tel. 814/623–6161, (Nonreporting) **A**1 10 20 **F**3 8 11 15 18 28 29 30 31 34 35 36 38 40 45 50 51 56 57 59 61 64 65 68 70 74 75 77 78 79 81 85 86 87 89 102 107 108 110 111 114 119 129 130 131 132 135 146 147 148 149 154 156 **P**6 **S** UPMC, Pittsburgh, PA
Primary Contact: Jan E. Fisher, President
CFO: Monica Klatt, Chief Financial Officer
CIO: Mark Wiley, Manager Information Systems Development
CHR: Michelle A Speck, Vice President Human Resources
CNO: Paula Thomas, Vice President Patient Services
Web address: www.upmcbedfordmemorial.com
**Control:** Other not–for–profit (including NFP Corporation) **Service:** General medical and surgical

| Staffed Beds: 24 Admissions: 1201 Census: 11 Outpatient Visits: 108816 Births: 0 Total Expense ($000): 59288 Payroll Expense ($000): 13375 Personnel: 223 |
| --- |

**FARRELL—Mercer County**

**SHENANGO VALLEY CAMPUS** See UPMC Horizon, Farrell

**SHENANGO VALLEY MEDICAL CENTER** See Shenango Valley Campus

**UMPC HORIZON** See UPMC Horizon

☒ **UPMC HORIZON (390178)**, 2200 Memorial Drive, Zip 16121–1357; tel. 724/588–2100, (Includes GREENVILLE CAMPUS, Mailing address: 110 North Main Street, Greenville, Pennsylvania, Zip 16125–1795; tel. 724/588–2100; SHENANGO VALLEY CAMPUS, Mailing address: 2200 Memorial Drive, Farrell, Pennsylvania, Zip 16121–1398; tel. 724/981–3500), (Nonreporting) **A**1 3 5 10 13 **F**3 11 12 13 15 18 26 28 29 30 31 32 34 35 40 43 44 45 46 49 50 51 54 57 59 64 65 68 73 74 75 76 77 78 79 81 82 85 86 87 92 93 100 107 110 111 114 115 118 119 120 129 130 131 132 133 135 146 147 148 149 154 156 157 **S** UPMC, Pittsburgh, PA
Primary Contact: Robert Charles. Jackson Jr, President
CFO: Brian Fritz, Chief Financial Officer
CMO: Samuel Daisley, D.O., Vice President Medical Affairs
CHR: Connie Mayle, Vice President Administrative Services
Web address: www.upmc.com
**Control:** Other not–for–profit (including NFP Corporation) **Service:** General medical and surgical

| Staffed Beds: 66 Admissions: 4061 Census: 39 Outpatient Visits: 210035 Births: 853 Total Expense ($000): 136601 Payroll Expense ($000): 34840 Personnel: 553 |
| --- |

**FORT WASHINGTON—Montgomery County**

☐ **BROOKE GLEN BEHAVIORAL HOSPITAL (394049)**, 7170 Lafayette Avenue, Zip 19034–2301; tel. 215/641–5300, (Nonreporting) **A**1 10 **S** Universal Health Services, Inc., King of Prussia, PA
Primary Contact: Neil Callahan, Chief Executive Officer
COO: William R Mason, Chief Operating Officer
CFO: Robert Zagerman, Chief Financial Officer
CMO: Chand Nair, M.D., Medical Director
CHR: Dawn Kownacki, Director Human Resources
Web address: www.brookeglenhospital.com
**Control:** Corporation, Investor–owned (for–profit) **Service:** Psychiatric

| Staffed Beds: 146 |
| --- |

**NORTHWESTERN INSTITUTE** See Brooke Glen Behavioral Hospital

**GETTYSBURG—Adams County**

★ ⇑ **WELLSPAN GETTYSBURG HOSPITAL (390065)**, 147 Gettys Street, Zip 17325–2534; tel. 717/334–2121, (Nonreporting) **A**2 3 10 21 **F**3 8 11 13 15 18 20 22 26 28 29 30 31 34 35 40 45 46 50 51 54 56 59 64 68 70 74 75 76 77 78 79 81 82 84 85 87 91 92 93 94 96 102 107 108 110 111 115 119 120 121 123 124 129 130 131 132 134 135 146 147 148 149 154 157 **S** WellSpan Health, York, PA
Primary Contact: Jane E. Hyde, President
COO: Joseph H Edgar, Senior Vice President Operations
CMO: Charles Marley, D.O., Vice President Medical Affairs
CIO: Robin Kimple, Director Information Services
CHR: Kim Brister, Director Human Resources
Web address: www.wellspan.org
**Control:** Other not–for–profit (including NFP Corporation) **Service:** General medical and surgical

| Staffed Beds: 76 Admissions: 5062 Census: 45 Outpatient Visits: 247161 Births: 461 Total Expense ($000): 190172 Payroll Expense ($000): 45200 Personnel: 716 |
| --- |

⇑ **WELLSPANGETTYSBURG HOSPITAL** See Wellspan Gettysburg Hospital

*Many Facility Codes have changed. Please refer to the AHA Guide Code Chart.* © 2021 AHA Guide

**GREENSBURG—Westmoreland County**

☐ **EXCELA HEALTH WESTMORELAND HOSPITAL (390145)**, 532 West Pittsburgh Street, Zip 15601–2282; tel. 724/832–4000, (Nonreporting) **A**1 3 5 10 **S** Excela Health, Greensburg, PA
Primary Contact: John Sphon, Chief Executive Officer
COO: Jeffrey Tiesi, Executive Vice President and Chief Operating Officer
CFO: Jeffrey T Curry, Executive Vice President and Chief Financial Officer
CMO: Jerome Granato, M.D., Senior Vice President and Chief Medical Officer
CIO: David Gawaluck, Vice President and Chief Information Officer
CHR: John Caverno, Chief Human Resources Officer
CNO: Helen K Burns, Ph.D., R.N., Senior Vice President and Chief Nursing Officer
Web address: www.excelahealth.org
**Control**: Other not–for–profit (including NFP Corporation) **Service**: General medical and surgical

| Staffed Beds: 270 |
|---|

**EXCELA WESTMORELAND REGIONAL HOSPITAL** See Excela Health Westmoreland Hospital

**GREENVILLE—Mercer County**

**GREENVILLE REGIONAL HOSPITAL** See Greenville Campus

**GROVE CITY—Mercer County**

★ **AHN GROVE CITY (390266)**, 631 North Broad Street Extension, Zip 16127–4603; tel. 724/450–7000, (Nonreporting) **A**10 **F**3 15 20 26 28 29 31 34 35 40 45 46 51 57 59 64 68 70 75 78 79 81 82 85 87 91 92 93 107 108 110 111 115 117 119 129 130 132 146 148 149 **S** Allegheny Health Network, Pittsburgh, PA
Primary Contact: Allan Klapper, M.D., Chief Executive Officer
COO: Jason Roeback, Chief Operating Officer
CFO: Richard W Fries, Vice President Finance
CMO: Daniel Ferguson, Chief of Staff
CIO: Philip Swartwood, Director Information Systems
CHR: David Poland, Interim Chief Human Resource Officer
CNO: Anthony Bono JrChief Nursing Officer
Web address: www.gcmcpa.org
**Control**: Other not–for–profit (including NFP Corporation) **Service**: General medical and surgical

| Staffed Beds: 35 Admissions: 1200 Census: 11 Outpatient Visits: 98567 Births: 0 Total Expense ($000): 43131 Payroll Expense ($000): 15910 Personnel: 314 |
|---|

**UNITED COMMUNITY HOSPITAL** See Ahn Grove City

**HANOVER—York County**

⊞ **UPMC HANOVER (390233)**, 300 Highland Avenue, Zip 17331–2297; tel. 717/316–3711, (Nonreporting) **A**1 10 **F**3 11 13 15 18 20 22 26 28 29 30 31 34 35 40 44 45 47 49 50 51 53 54 57 59 64 65 71 75 76 79 81 84 85 86 87 89 93 94 96 107 108 110 111 115 118 119 126 129 130 132 135 143 146 147 148 149 154 **P**1 6 **S** UPMC, Pittsburgh, PA
Primary Contact: Michael W. Gaskins, President
COO: Michael A. Hockenberry, Senior Vice President and Chief Operating Officer
CFO: Donna L. Muller, Vice President Finance, Southern Region
CMO: Michael H Ader, M.D., Vice President Medical Affairs
CIO: William C. Tandy, Chief Information Officer
CHR: Christine Miller, General Counsel and Vice President Human Resources
CNO: M Patricia Saunders, R.N., MS, Vice President Nursing
Web address: www.hanoverhospital.org
**Control**: Other not–for–profit (including NFP Corporation) **Service**: General medical and surgical

| Staffed Beds: 93 Admissions: 5386 Census: 88 Outpatient Visits: 208757 Births: 309 Total Expense ($000): 168934 Payroll Expense ($000): 59377 Personnel: 884 |
|---|

**UPMC PINNACLE HANOVER** See UPMC Hanover

**HARRISBURG—Dauphin County**

**COMMUNITY HOSPITAL** See Pinnaclehealth at Community General Osteopathic Hospital

**HARRISBURG HOSPITAL** See Pinnaclehealth at Harrisburg Hospital

⊞ **HELEN M. SIMPSON REHABILITATION HOSPITAL (393056)**, 4300 Londonderry Road, Zip 17109–5317; tel. 717/920–4300, (Nonreporting) **A**1 10 13 **F**28 29 74 77 86 90 91 96 130 132 135 148 149 156 **S** Select Medical Corporation, Mechanicsburg, PA
Primary Contact: Mark Freeburn, Chief Executive Officer
Web address: www.simpson-rehab.com/
**Control**: Partnership, Investor–owned (for–profit) **Service**: Rehabilitation

| Staffed Beds: 50 Admissions: 1217 Census: 39 Outpatient Visits: 0 Births: 0 Personnel: 111 |
|---|

**PENNSYLVANIA PSYCHIATRIC HOSPITAL** See Pennsylvania Psychiatric Institute

⊞ **PENNSYLVANIA PSYCHIATRIC INSTITUTE (394051)**, 2501 North Third Street, Zip 17110–1904; tel. 717/782–6420, (Nonreporting) **A**1 3 5 10
Primary Contact: Kimberly Feeman, Interim Chief Executive Officer
CFO: Robert Fotter, Chief Financial Officer
CMO: Elisabeth J. Kunkel, M.D., Professor, Pennsylvania State College of Medicine
CHR: Wanda Geesey, Director Human Resources
CNO: Teresa Terry-Williams, R.N., Chief Nursing Officer
Web address: www.ppimhs.org/
**Control**: Other not–for–profit (including NFP Corporation) **Service**: Psychiatric

| Staffed Beds: 72 |
|---|

**PINNACLEHEALTH AT COMMUNITY GENERAL OSTEOPATHIC HOSPITAL** See UPMC Pinnacle Harrisburg, Harrisburg

**SELECT SPECIALTY HOSPITAL-HARRISBURG** See Select Specialty Hospital-Camp Hill, Camp Hill

⊞ **UPMC PINNACLE HARRISBURG (390067)**, 111 South Front Street, Zip 17101–2010, Mailing Address: P.O. Box 8700, Zip 17105–8700; tel. 717/231–8900, (Includes PINNACLEHEALTH AT COMMUNITY GENERAL OSTEOPATHIC HOSPITAL, Mailing address: 4300 Londonderry Road, Harrisburg, Pennsylvania, Zip 17109–5397, P O Box 3000, Zip 17105–3000, tel. 717/652–3000; PINNACLEHEALTH AT HARRISBURG HOSPITAL, Mailing address: 111 South Front Street, Harrisburg, Pennsylvania, Zip 17101–2099; tel. 717/782–3131; PINNACLEHEALTH WEST SHORE HOSPITAL, Mailing address: 1995 Technology Parkway, Mechanicsburg, Pennsylvania, Zip 17050–8522; tel. 717/791–2600; Lou Baverso, President), (Nonreporting) **A**1 2 3 5 10 12 19 **F**3 7 8 11 12 13 14 15 17 18 19 20 22 24 26 27 28 29 30 31 32 34 35 36 37 38 40 44 45 46 47 48 49 50 51 52 54 55 56 57 58 59 60 61 64 65 66 68 70 72 74 75 76 77 78 79 81 84 85 86 87 89 93 97 100 107 108 109 110 111 114 115 116 117 118 119 120 121 123 124 126 129 130 131 132 134 138 141 142 143 144 145 146 147 148 149 150 154 156 157 **P**1 6 **S** UPMC, Pittsburgh, PA
Primary Contact: Philip Guarneschelli, President and Chief Executive Officer
COO: Mark Sevco, Chief Operating Officer
CFO: Alison Bernhardt, Chief Financial Officer
CMO: Nirmal Joshi, M.D., Senior Vice President Medical Affairs and Chief Medical Officer
CHR: Ann H Gormley, Senior Vice President Human Resources
CNO: Susan Comp, Senior Vice President and Chief Nursing Officer
Web address: www.pinnaclehealth.org
**Control**: Other not–for–profit (including NFP Corporation) **Service**: General medical and surgical

| Staffed Beds: 665 Admissions: 35285 Census: 432 Outpatient Visits: 875561 Births: 3716 Total Expense ($000): 985287 Payroll Expense ($000): 338357 Personnel: 4465 |
|---|

**UPMC PINNACLE HARRISBURG CAMPUS** See UPMC Pinnacle Harrisburg

---

**Hospital, Medicare Provider Number, Address, Telephone, Approval, Facility, and Physician Codes, Health Care System**

★ American Hospital Association (AHA) membership  ○ Healthcare Facilities Accreditation Program  ⇑ Center for Improvement in Healthcare Quality Accreditation
☐ The Joint Commission accreditation  ◇ DNV Healthcare Inc. accreditation  △ Commission on Accreditation of Rehabilitation Facilities (CARF) accreditation

**PA**

## HASTINGS—Cambria County

☒ **CONEMAUGH MINERS MEDICAL CENTER (390130)**, 290 Haida Avenue, Zip 16646–5610, Mailing Address: P.O. Box 689, Zip 16646–0689; tel. 814/247–3100, (Nonreporting) **A**1 10 20 **F**3 15 18 29 30 35 36 40 45 48 50 56 59 64 75 81 86 92 93 96 97 102 107 108 110 119 129 133 148 **S** Duke LifePoint Healthcare, Brentwood, TN
Primary Contact: Timothy Harclerode, Chief Executive Officer
COO: Debbie Spells-Wilson, R.N., Chief Operating Officer and Chief Nursing Officer
CFO: Linda Fanale, Chief Financial Officer
CMO: Susan Williams, M.D., Chief Medical Officer
CIO: Joe Dado, Chief Information Officer
CNO: Debbie Spells-Wilson, R.N., Chief Operating Officer and Chief Nursing Officer
Web address: www.conemaugh.org
**Control**: Corporation, Investor–owned (for–profit) **Service**: General medical and surgical

**Staffed Beds**: 25 **Admissions**: 485 **Census**: 5 **Outpatient Visits**: 36939 **Births**: 0 **Total Expense ($000)**: 16701 **Payroll Expense ($000)**: 5357 **Personnel**: 102

**MINERS MEDICAL CENTER** See Conemaugh Miners Medical Center

## HAZLETON—Luzerne County

★ ○ **LEHIGH VALLEY HOSPITAL - HAZLETON (390185)**, 700 East Broad Street, Zip 18201–6897; tel. 570/501–4000, (Nonreporting) **A**10 11 **F**3 7 8 9 11 12 13 15 18 28 29 30 31 32 33 34 35 40 41 43 44 50 53 55 57 59 60 62 64 68 69 70 75 76 77 78 79 81 82 85 86 87 89 90 93 107 108 110 111 114 118 119 129 131 132 135 143 144 146 147 148 154 155 157 **P**5 6 8 **S** Lehigh Valley Health Network, Allentown, PA
Primary Contact: John R. Fletcher, President
CFO: William Bauer, Vice President Finance and Chief Financial Officer
CMO: Anthony Valente, M.D., Vice President Medical Affairs
CIO: Carl Shoener, Chief Information Officer
CHR: Lynn Lansdowne, Vice President Labor Relations and Human Resources
Web address: www.lvhn.org/hazleton/
**Control**: Other not–for–profit (including NFP Corporation) **Service**: General medical and surgical

**Staffed Beds**: 120 **Admissions**: 6006 **Census**: 68 **Outpatient Visits**: 136813 **Births**: 745 **Total Expense ($000)**: 116622 **Payroll Expense ($000)**: 36691 **Personnel**: 582

**LEIGH VALLEY HOSPITAL - HAZLETON** See Lehigh Valley Hospital - Hazleton

## HERSHEY—Dauphin County

**MILTON S HERSHEY MEDICAL CTR** See Penn State Milton S. Hershey Medical Center

☒ **PENN STATE MILTON S. HERSHEY MEDICAL CENTER (390256)**, 500 University Drive, Zip 17033–2360, Mailing Address: P.O. Box 850, Zip 17033–0850; tel. 717/531–8521, (Includes PENN STATE CHILDREN'S HOSPITAL, Mailing address: 600 University Drive, Hershey, Pennsylvania, Zip 17033–2360; tel. 717/531–8521; Stephen M. Massini, Chief Executive Officer, Penn State Health), (Nonreporting) **A**1 2 3 5 8 10 19 **F**3 5 6 7 8 9 11 12 13 14 15 17 18 19 20 21 22 23 24 25 26 27 28 29 30 31 32 34 35 36 37 38 40 41 43 44 45 46 47 48 49 50 51 52 53 54 55 56 57 58 59 60 61 64 65 66 67 68 70 71 72 73 74 75 76 77 78 79 80 81 82 84 85 86 87 88 89 91 92 93 96 97 98 100 101 102 104 105 107 108 110 111 114 115 116 117 118 119 120 121 123 124 126 129 130 131 132 134 135 136 137 138 139 141 142 143 144 145 146 147 148 149 150 153 154 155 156 157 **P**6 **S** Penn State Hershey Health System, Hershey, PA
Primary Contact: Deborah Berini, President
CMO: Thomas Tracy JrChief Medical Officer
CHR: Jane Mannon, Vice President Human Resources
CNO: Judy N. Himes, MSN, R.N., Chief Nursing Officer
Web address: www.pennstatehershey.org/
**Control**: Other not–for–profit (including NFP Corporation) **Service**: General medical and surgical

**Staffed Beds**: 531 **Admissions**: 27207 **Census**: 453 **Outpatient Visits**: 1092367 **Births**: 2004 **Total Expense ($000)**: 1543293 **Payroll Expense ($000)**: 448761 **Personnel**: 10732

## HONESDALE—Wayne County

**WAYNE COUNTY MEMORIAL HOSPITAL** See Wayne Memorial Hospital

★ **WAYNE MEMORIAL HOSPITAL (390125)**, 601 Park Street, Zip 18431–1498; tel. 570/253–8100, (Nonreporting) **A**10 20
Primary Contact: David L. Hoff, Chief Executive Officer
COO: John Conte, Director Facility Services and Real Estate
CFO: Michael J Clifford, Director Finance
CMO: William Dewar, M.D., Chief of Staff
CIO: Tom Hoffman, Manager Information Systems
CHR: Elizabeth McDonald, Director Human Resources
CNO: Jim Pettinato, Director Patient Care Services
Web address: www.wmh.org
**Control**: Other not–for–profit (including NFP Corporation) **Service**: General medical and surgical

**Staffed Beds**: 87

## HUMMELSTOWN—Dauphin County

**PENN STATE HERSEY REHAB** See Penn State Hershey Rehabilitation Hospital

☒ △ **PENN STATE HERSHEY REHABILITATION HOSPITAL (393053)**, 1135 Old West Chocolate Avenue, Zip 17036; tel. 717/832–2600, (Total facility includes 22 beds in nursing home–type unit) (Nonreporting) **A**1 3 5 7 10 **F**3 29 60 90 93 96 128 130 132 148 149 **S** Select Medical Corporation, Mechanicsburg, PA
Primary Contact: Michelle Von Arx, Chief Executive Officer
CMO: Brenda Mallory, M.D., Medical Director
Web address: www.psh-rehab.com
**Control**: Corporation, Investor–owned (for–profit) **Service**: Rehabilitation

**Staffed Beds**: 98 **Admissions**: 1850 **Census**: 70 **Outpatient Visits**: 0 **Births**: 0 **Personnel**: 196

## HUNTINGDON—Huntingdon County

**J. C. BLAIR MEMORIAL HOSPITAL** See Penn Highlands Huntingdon

☒ **PENN HIGHLANDS HUNTINGDON (390056)**, 1225 Warm Springs Avenue, Zip 16652–2398; tel. 814/643–2290, (Nonreporting) **A**1 10 20 **F**3 11 13 15 18 20 22 26 28 29 34 35 40 45 50 53 55 56 59 64 70 75 77 79 81 84 85 86 87 89 93 96 98 100 103 107 108 110 111 115 118 119 129 130 132 133 135 144 146 148 154 156
Primary Contact: Joseph Myers, President and Chief Executive Officer
COO: Adam Dimm, Chief Executive Officer
CMO: James Hayden, M.D., Chief Medical Officer
CIO: Armen Arakelian, Chief Information Officer
CHR: Susan Hess, Director Human Resources
CNO: Joye Gingrich, Director Patient Care Services and Chief Nursing Officer
Web address: www.jcblair.org
**Control**: Other not–for–profit (including NFP Corporation) **Service**: General medical and surgical

**Staffed Beds**: 59 **Admissions**: 2210 **Census**: 28 **Outpatient Visits**: 116976 **Births**: 89 **Total Expense ($000)**: 51558 **Payroll Expense ($000)**: 21710 **Personnel**: 333

## INDIANA—Indiana County

**INDIANA HOSPITAL** See Indiana Regional Medical Center

★ **INDIANA REGIONAL MEDICAL CENTER (390173)**, 835 Hospital Road, Zip 15701–3629, Mailing Address: P.O. Box 788, Zip 15701–0788; tel. 724/357–7000, (Nonreporting) **A**10 20 22 **F**3 11 15 18 20 22 28 29 31 34 35 40 44 45 46 47 49 53 56 57 59 64 65 70 71 74 75 76 77 78 79 81 82 83 84 85 90 91 96 98 102 103 107 108 111 114 115 118 119 120 121 123 124 126 129 130 132 144 145 146 147 148 149 154 156 157
Primary Contact: Stephen A. Wolfe, President and Chief Executive Officer
COO: Dominic Paccapaniccia, Chief Operating Officer
CFO: Robert Gongaware, Chief Financial Officer
CMO: Bruce A. Bush, M.D., Interim Chief Medical Officer
CIO: Mark Volovic, Chief Information Officer
CHR: James W. Kinneer, Chief Human Resource Officer
CNO: Wendy Haislip, Chief Nursing Officer
Web address: www.indianarmc.org
**Control**: Other not–for–profit (including NFP Corporation) **Service**: General medical and surgical

**Staffed Beds**: 166 **Admissions**: 6147 **Census**: 70 **Outpatient Visits**: 250924 **Births**: 509 **Total Expense ($000)**: 168556 **Payroll Expense ($000)**: 71285 **Personnel**: 910

*Many Facility Codes have changed. Please refer to the AHA Guide Code Chart.* © 2021 AHA Guide

**JEFFERSON HILLS—Allegheny County**

**AHN/JEFFERSON HOSPITAL** See Jefferson Hospital

☒ **JEFFERSON HOSPITAL (390265)**, 565 Coal Valley Road, Zip 15025–3703,
Mailing Address: Box 18119, Pittsburgh, Zip 15236–0119; tel. 412/469–5000,
(Nonreporting) **A**1 2 3 10 **F**3 11 12 13 15 17 18 20 22 24 26 28 29 30 31 34
35 36 40 44 45 46 47 48 49 50 54 57 59 60 64 70 73 74 75 76 77 78 79 80
81 82 84 85 86 87 90 92 93 96 98 100 102 104 107 108 110 111 114 115
117 118 119 120 121 123 124 126 129 130 131 132 135 141 146 147 148
149 153 154 **S** Allegheny Health Network, Pittsburgh, PA
Primary Contact: Chong Park, M.D., President
COO: Kelly Kassab, Chief Operating Officer
CMO: Richard F Collins, M.D., Executive Vice President and Chief Medical Officer
CIO: James Witenske, Chief Information Officer
CNO: Kimberley Finnerty, MSN, R.N., Chief Nursing Officer
Web address: www.jeffersonregional.com
**Control:** Other not–for–profit (including NFP Corporation) **Service:** General
medical and surgical

Staffed Beds: 303 Admissions: 13276 Census: 165 Outpatient
Visits: 278497 Births: 1310 Total Expense ($000): 245646 Payroll
Expense ($000): 83330 Personnel: 1433

**JERSEY SHORE—Lycoming County**

☒ **GEISINGER JERSEY SHORE HOSPITAL (391300)**, 1020 Thompson Street,
Zip 17740–1794; tel. 570/398–0100, (Nonreporting) **A**1 10 18 **F**3 7 12 15 18
28 29 34 35 40 45 50 54 57 59 65 68 75 79 81 85 93 97 107 108 110 111
115 119 129 130 132 133 135 144 147 154 155 156 **P**1 5 8 **S** Geisinger,
Danville, PA
Primary Contact: Tammy Anderer, Acting President
CFO: Mark Rice, CPA, Chief Financial Officer
CMO: Stephen Goykovich, D.O., Chief Medical Officer
CIO: Christine Haas, Chief Information Officer
CHR: Joan Rounsley, Director Human Resources
CNO: Paulette Nish, Chief Nursing Officer
Web address: www.jsh.org
**Control:** Other not–for–profit (including NFP Corporation) **Service:** General
medical and surgical

Staffed Beds: 25 Admissions: 597 Census: 4 Outpatient Visits: 64497
Births: 0 Total Expense ($000): 26790 Payroll Expense ($000): 11489
Personnel: 220

**JERSEY SHORE HOSPITAL** See Geisinger Jersey Shore Hospital

**JOHNSTOWN—Cambria County**

☒ **CONEMAUGH MEMORIAL MEDICAL CENTER (390110)**, 1086 Franklin Street,
Zip 15905–4398; tel. 814/534–9000, (Includes MEMORIAL MEDICAL CENTER
- LEE CAMPUS, Mailing address: 320 Main Street, Johnstown, Pennsylvania,
Zip 15901–1601; tel. 814/533–0123), (Nonreporting) **A**1 3 5 10 13 **F**3 5 7 8
12 13 14 15 17 18 20 22 24 26 28 29 30 31 32 34 35 36 37 40 43 44 45 46
49 50 53 54 55 56 57 58 59 60 61 64 65 70 72 74 75 76 77 78 79 81 82 83
84 85 86 87 89 90 92 93 96 97 98 99 100 101 102 103 104 107 108 109
110 111 114 115 116 117 118 119 120 121 123 126 128 129 130 131 132
134 144 145 146 147 148 149 150 154 155 156 **S** Duke LifePoint Healthcare,
Brentwood, TN
Primary Contact: William E. Caldwell Jr, FACHE, Chief Executive Officer
CMO: Susan Williams, M.D., Chief Medical Officer
CIO: Joe Dado, Chief Information Officer
CNO: Claudia Rager, R.N., Vice President Patient Care Services
Web address: www.conemaugh.org
**Control:** Corporation, Investor–owned (for–profit) **Service:** General medical and
surgical

Staffed Beds: 509 Admissions: 18291 Census: 256 Outpatient
Visits: 470684 Births: 1769 Total Expense ($000): 340413 Payroll
Expense ($000): 129123 Personnel: 2346

**MEM MED CTR LEE CAMPUS** See Memorial Medical Center - Lee Campus

**MEMORIAL MEDICAL CENTER** See Conemaugh Memorial Medical Center

**MEMORIAL MEDICAL CENTER - LEE CAMPUS** See Conemaugh Memorial
Medical Center, Johnstown

☒ **SELECT SPECIALTY HOSPITAL-JOHNSTOWN (392031)**, 320 Main Street,
3rd Floor, Zip 15901–1601; tel. 814/534–7300, (Nonreporting) **A**1 10 **S** Select
Medical Corporation, Mechanicsburg, PA
Primary Contact: Kelly Blake, Chief Executive Officer
CMO: Gary Davidson, M.D., Medical Director
Web address: www.selectspecialtyhospitals.com/company/locations/johnstown.
aspx
**Control:** Corporation, Investor–owned (for–profit) **Service:** Acute long–term care
hospital

Staffed Beds: 39

**KANE—Mckean County**

**KANE COMMUNITY HOSPITAL** See UPMC Kane

★ **UPMC KANE (390104)**, 4372 Route 6, Zip 16735–3060; tel. 814/837–8585,
(Nonreporting) **A**10 20 **F**3 11 15 17 18 28 29 30 34 35 40 45 46 50 53 57 59
64 65 70 75 77 79 81 82 85 89 107 108 110 111 115 117 118 128 130 131
132 133 135 146 147 149 156 **P**4 **S** UPMC, Pittsburgh, PA
Primary Contact: Mark Papalia, President
CFO: Bradley Dinger, Chief Financial Officer
CMO: Linda Rettger, M.D., President Medical Staff
CIO: Deano Cherry, Chief Information Officer
CHR: Marsha Keller, Director Human Resources
CNO: Pam Bray, Director of Nursing and Director Inpatient Services
Web address: www.kanehosp.com
**Control:** Other not–for–profit (including NFP Corporation) **Service:** General
medical and surgical

Staffed Beds: 31 Admissions: 334 Census: 3 Outpatient Visits: 70245
Births: 0 Total Expense ($000): 21139 Payroll Expense ($000): 9459
Personnel: 133

**KINGSTON—Luzerne County**

☒ **FIRST HOSPITAL WYOMING VALLEY (394039)**, 562 Wyoming Avenue,
Zip 18704–3721; tel. 570/552–3900, (Nonreporting) **A**1 10 **F**98 99 130 **S**
Community Health Systems, Inc., Franklin, TN
Primary Contact: Christine Mathews, Interim President and Chief Executive Officer,
Chief Nursing Officer
CMO: David Liskov, M.D., Medical Director
CNO: Christine Mathews, Chief Nursing Officer
Web address: www.commonwealthhealth.net/locations/first-hospital
**Control:** Corporation, Investor–owned (for–profit) **Service:** Psychiatric

Staffed Beds: 149 Admissions: 3368 Census: 99 Outpatient Visits: 0
Births: 0

**KITTANNING—Armstrong County**

⇑ **ACMH** See ACMH Hospital

⇑ **ACMH HOSPITAL (390163)**, One Nolte Drive, Zip 16201–7111;
tel. 724/543–8500, (Total facility includes 17 beds in nursing home–type unit)
(Nonreporting) **A**2 10 19 21 **F**3 4 11 13 15 17 18 20 22 26 28 29 30 34 35 40
45 47 49 59 70 74 75 76 77 78 79 81 82 85 90 93 98 100 102 107 108 110
111 112 114 119 120 126 127 128 129 130 131 132 135 136 141 142 146
148 149 151 154 156
Primary Contact: John I. Lewis, President and Chief Executive Officer
COO: Nichole Geraci, Chief Operating Officer
CFO: Patrick Burns, Vice President Finance
CMO: Harold Altman, M.D., Chief Medical Officer
CIO: Dianne Emminger, Vice President Information Services
CHR: Anne Remaley, Vice President Human Resources
Web address: www.acmh.org
**Control:** Other not–for–profit (including NFP Corporation) **Service:** General
medical and surgical

Staffed Beds: 164 Admissions: 4304 Census: 54 Outpatient
Visits: 260135 Births: 392 Total Expense ($000): 99500 Payroll Expense
($000): 43640 Personnel: 820

---

**PA**

## LANCASTER—Lancaster County

**LANCASTER GENERAL HOSPITAL** See Penn Medicine Lancaster General Hospital

☐ **LANCASTER REHABILITATION HOSPITAL (393054)**, 675 Good Drive, Zip 17601–2426; tel. 717/406–3000, (Nonreporting) **A**1 10
Primary Contact: Amy Teal, Chief Executive Officer
CFO: David Stark, Chief Financial Officer
CHR: Lisa Andrews, Director Human Resources
Web address: www.lancastergeneral.org
**Control**: Corporation, Investor–owned (for–profit) **Service**: Rehabilitation

**Staffed Beds**: 10

☒ **PENN MEDICINE LANCASTER GENERAL HOSPITAL (390100)**, 555 North Duke Street, Zip 17602–2250; tel. 717/544–5511, (Nonreporting) **A**1 2 3 5 10 **F**3 11 12 13 14 15 17 18 20 22 24 26 28 29 30 31 32 33 34 35 36 38 39 40 43 44 45 46 47 48 49 50 51 54 55 56 57 58 59 60 61 64 65 66 68 70 72 73 74 75 76 77 78 79 80 81 82 84 85 86 87 89 91 92 93 94 95 96 97 100 101 102 107 108 110 114 115 118 119 120 121 123 124 126 129 130 132 134 135 141 142 145 146 147 148 149 150 154 156 157 **P**6 **S** University of Pennsylvania Health System, Philadelphia, PA
Primary Contact: Jan L. Bergen, President and Chief Executive Officer
COO: Steven G Littleson, FACHE, Chief Operating and Integration Officer
CFO: Joseph Byorick, Senior Vice President and Chief Financial Officer
CMO: Lee M Duke, M.D., IISenior Vice President and Chief Physician Executive
CIO: Gary Davidson, Senior Vice President and Chief Information Officer
CHR: Regina Mingle, Senior Vice President and Chief Leadership Officer
CNO: Lanyce Roldan, Chief Nursing Officer
Web address: www.lancastergeneralhealth.org
**Control**: Other not–for–profit (including NFP Corporation) **Service**: General medical and surgical

**Staffed Beds**: 603 **Admissions**: 32283 **Census**: 414 **Outpatient Visits**: 1688959 **Births**: 4145 **Total Expense ($000)**: 1001522 **Payroll Expense ($000)**: 383060 **Personnel**: 5558

## LANGHORNE—Bucks County

**BARIX CLINICS OF PENNSYLVANIA (390302)**, 280 Middletown Boulevard, Zip 19047–1816; tel. 267/572–3100, (Nonreporting) **A**10
Primary Contact: Tony Adams, President
Web address: www.barixclinics.com
**Control**: Partnership, Investor–owned (for–profit) **Service**: Surgical

**Staffed Beds**: 40

**BUCK COUNTY CAMPUS** See Bucks County Campus

**BUCKS COUNTY CAMPUS** See Jefferson Health Northeast, Philadelphia

**MARY REHABILITATION HOSPITAL** See St. Mary Rehabilitation Hospital

**SAINT MARY HOSPITAL** See St. Mary Medical Center

☒ **ST. MARY MEDICAL CENTER (390258)**, 1201 Langhorne-Newtown Road, Zip 19047–1201; tel. 215/710–2000, (Nonreporting) **A**1 2 3 5 10 19 **S** Trinity Health, Livonia, MI
Primary Contact: Lawrence Brilliant, M.D., Vice President and Chief Medical Officer
COO: Jeffrey N Yarmel, Chief Operating Officer
CFO: Daniel Confalone, Chief Financial Officer and Vice President Finance
CMO: Lawrence Brilliant, M.D., Vice President and Chief Medical Officer
CIO: Bonnie J. Buehler, Chief Information Officer
CNO: Sharon Brown, Vice President Patient Care and Chief Nursing Officer
Web address: www.stmaryhealthcare.org
**Control**: Church operated, Nongovernment, not–for–profit **Service**: General medical and surgical

**Staffed Beds**: 353

☐ △ **ST. MARY REHABILITATION HOSPITAL (393055)**, 1201 Langhorne Newtown Road, Zip 19047–1201, Mailing Address: 1208 Langhorne Newtown Road, Zip 19047–1234; tel. 267/560–1111, (Nonreporting) **A**1 7 10
Primary Contact: Lisa Haney, Chief Executive Officer
Web address: www.stmaryhealthcare.org
**Control**: Church operated, Nongovernment, not–for–profit **Service**: Rehabilitation

**Staffed Beds**: 50

## LANSDALE—Montgomery County

**ABINGTON HEALTH LANSDALE HOSPITAL** See Abington-Lansdale Hospital Jefferson Health

☒ **ABINGTON-LANSDALE HOSPITAL JEFFERSON HEALTH (390012)**, 100 Medical Campus Drive, Zip 19446–1200; tel. 215/368–2100, (Nonreporting) **A**1 3 10 **F**2 3 11 15 18 28 29 32 34 35 36 37 40 44 45 49 50 53 56 57 59 63 64 65 66 68 70 74 75 77 79 81 82 84 85 86 87 93 96 97 107 108 110 111 114 115 119 129 130 131 132 135 146 147 148 149 150 154 156 **S** Jefferson Health, Philadelphia, PA
Primary Contact: Alison Ferren, President
CFO: Michael Walsh, Senior Vice President Finance and Chief Financial Officer
CMO: Michel Taupin, M.D., Chief Medical Officer
CHR: Meghan Patton, Vice President Human Resources
CNO: Kelly Cummings, Chief Nursing Officer
Web address: www.abingtonhealth.org/find-a-location/abington-lansdale-hospital/#.V5dyWVL9yk4
**Control**: Other not–for–profit (including NFP Corporation) **Service**: General medical and surgical

**Staffed Beds**: 127 **Admissions**: 6012 **Census**: 57 **Outpatient Visits**: 78846 **Births**: 0 **Total Expense ($000)**: 88105 **Payroll Expense ($000)**: 33238 **Personnel**: 351

## LATROBE—Westmoreland County

☐ **EXCELA LATROBE AREA HOSPITAL (390219)**, One Mellon Way, Zip 15650–1096; tel. 724/537–1000, (Nonreporting) **A**1 2 3 5 10 13 **S** Excela Health, Greensburg, PA
Primary Contact: John Sphon, Chief Executive Officer
COO: Jeffrey Tiesi, Executive Vice President and Chief Operating Officer
CMO: Carol J. Fox, M.D., Senior Vice President and Chief Medical Officer
CIO: David Gawaluck, Vice President and Chief Information Officer
CHR: Laurie English, Senior Vice President and Chief Human Resource Officer
CNO: Helen K Burns, Ph.D., R.N., Senior Vice President and Chief Nursing Officer
Web address: www.excelahealth.org
**Control**: Other not–for–profit (including NFP Corporation) **Service**: General medical and surgical

**Staffed Beds**: 114

**LATROBE AREA HOSPITAL** See Excela Latrobe Area Hospital

☒ **SELECT SPECIALTY HOSPITAL-LAUREL HIGHLANDS (392036)**, One Mellon Way, 3rd Floor, Zip 15650–1197; tel. 724/539–3870, (Nonreporting) **A**1 10 **S** Select Medical Corporation, Mechanicsburg, PA
Primary Contact: Stacy Carson, Chief Executive Officer
Web address: www.laurelhighlands.selectspecialtyhospitals.com/
**Control**: Corporation, Investor–owned (for–profit) **Service**: Acute long–term care hospital

**Staffed Beds**: 40

## LEBANON—Lebanon County

☒ **LEBANON VETERANS AFFAIRS MEDICAL CENTER**, 1700 South Lincoln Avenue, Zip 17042–7529; tel. 717/272–6621, (Nonreporting) **A**1 3 5 **S** Department of Veterans Affairs, Washington, DC
Primary Contact: Margaret G. Wilson, R.N., MSN, Acting Director
CFO: Geoffrey Smith, Chief Financial Officer
CMO: Kanan Chatterjee, M.D., Chief of Staff
CIO: Andru Ditzler, Chief Information Officer
CHR: Cindy Shiner, Manager Human Resources
Web address: www.lebanon.va.gov
**Control**: Veterans Affairs, Government, federal **Service**: General medical and surgical

**Staffed Beds**: 213

**THE GOOD SAMARITAN HOSPITAL** See Wellspan Good Samaritan Hospital

**VETERANS AFFAIRS MEDICAL CENTER** See Lebanon Veterans Affairs Medical Center

*Many Facility Codes have changed. Please refer to the AHA Guide Code Chart.* © 2021 AHA Guide

**PA**

✠ **WELLSPAN GOOD SAMARITAN HOSPITAL (390066)**, 252 South 4th Street, Fourth and Walnut Streets, Zip 17042–1281, Mailing Address: P.O. Box 1281, Zip 17042–1281; tel. 717/270–7500, (Nonreporting) **A**1 3 10 13 **F**3 8 11 13 14 15 17 18 20 22 24 26 28 29 30 31 34 35 40 45 49 50 55 57 58 59 64 68 70 74 75 76 77 78 79 80 81 82 85 87 90 91 92 93 96 107 110 111 114 115 118 119 120 121 124 126 129 130 132 135 146 148 149 156 **P**8 **S** WellSpan Health, York, PA
Primary Contact: Thomas R. Harlow, FACHE, President
COO: Kimberly Feeman, Senior Vice President and Chief Operating Officer
CMO: Robert D Shaver, M.D., Vice President Medical Affairs
CIO: Leon John Jabour, Regional Chief Information Officer
CHR: Denise M Garman, Director Human Resources
CNO: Jacquelyn M Gould, MS, R.N., Vice President Patient Care Services and Chief Nursing Officer
Web address: www.gshleb.org
**Control**: Other not–for–profit (including NFP Corporation) **Service**: General medical and surgical

**Staffed Beds:** 159 **Admissions:** 7187 **Census:** 89 **Outpatient Visits:** 294263 **Births:** 720 **Total Expense ($000):** 224516 **Payroll Expense ($000):** 59240 **Personnel:** 907

### LEHIGHTON—Carbon County

**ST. LUKE'S - GNADEN HUETTEN CAMPUS** See St. Luke's - Lehighton Campus

☐ △ **ST. LUKE'S - LEHIGHTON CAMPUS (390194)**, 211 North 12th Street, Zip 18235–1138; tel. 610/377–1300, (Includes ST. LUKE'S - PALMERTON CAMPUS, Mailing address: 135 Lafayette Avenue, Palmerton, Pennsylvania, Zip 18071–1596; tel. 610/826–3141; John L Nespoli, President) (Total facility includes 91 beds in nursing home–type unit) **A**1 7 10 **F**2 3 11 15 18 28 29 30 34 35 38 40 46 49 50 54 56 57 59 60 64 68 70 74 75 79 81 85 87 90 93 98 100 102 103 104 105 107 108 110 111 114 119 128 130 132 146 148 149 153 154 **S** St. Luke's University Health Network, Bethlehem, PA
Primary Contact: John L. Nespoli, President
CFO: Andrea Andrae, Chief Financial Officer
CMO: Patrick Hanley, D.O., Interim Vice President Medical Affairs
CIO: Steve Kinkaid, Director Information Systems
Web address: www.blmtn.org
**Control**: Other not–for–profit (including NFP Corporation) **Service**: General medical and surgical

**Staffed Beds:** 242 **Admissions:** 2563 **Census:** 106 **Outpatient Visits:** 67115 **Births:** 0 **Total Expense ($000):** 71436 **Payroll Expense ($000):** 33616 **Personnel:** 403

### LEWISBURG—Union County

**EVANGELICAL COMMUNITY HOSPITAL (390013)**, One Hospital Drive, Zip 17837–9350; tel. 570/522–2000, (Nonreporting) **A**2 10 19 **F**3 7 8 12 13 15 18 20 22 28 29 30 31 34 35 40 43 45 49 50 51 54 57 59 63 64 65 68 71 74 75 76 77 78 79 80 81 82 84 85 86 87 90 91 92 93 96 97 107 108 110 111 114 115 116 117 118 119 129 130 131 132 135 144 146 147 148 156 157 **P**7
Primary Contact: Kendra A. Aucker, President and Chief Executive Officer
COO: Kendra A. Aucker, Vice President Operations
CFO: Jim Stopper, CPA, Chief Financial Officer
CIO: Dale Moyer, Vice President Information Systems
CHR: Angela Hummel, Vice President Human Resources
CNO: Tamara F. Persing MHA, BSNChief Nursing Officer
Web address: www.evanhospital.com
**Control**: Other not–for–profit (including NFP Corporation) **Service**: General medical and surgical

**Staffed Beds:** 132 **Admissions:** 5739 **Census:** 49 **Outpatient Visits:** 244034 **Births:** 782 **Total Expense ($000):** 172628 **Payroll Expense ($000):** 70497 **Personnel:** 1426

**U S PENITENTIARY HOSPITAL** See U.S. Penitentiary Infirmary

**U. S. PENITENTIARY INFIRMARY**, Route 7, Zip 17837–9303; tel. 570/523–1251, (Nonreporting)
Primary Contact: Steve Brown, Health Services Director
**Control**: Department of Justice, Government, federal **Service**: Hospital unit of an institution (prison hospital, college infirmary, etc.)

**Staffed Beds:** 17

### LEWISTOWN—Mifflin County

✠ **GEISINGER-LEWISTOWN HOSPITAL (390048)**, 400 Highland Avenue, Zip 17044–1198; tel. 717/248–5411, (Nonreporting) **A**1 2 3 10 **F**3 11 13 15 17 18 28 29 30 31 34 35 40 41 45 48 49 50 51 57 59 64 70 71 74 75 76 78 79 81 82 84 85 86 87 98 100 101 102 103 107 108 110 111 114 115 116 117 118 119 120 121 123 124 129 130 131 132 135 146 147 148 149 154 156 157 **P**1 5 8 **S** Geisinger, Danville, PA
Primary Contact: Kirk E. Thomas, Chief Administrative Officer
COO: Aaron Hartsock, Director of Operations
CFO: Kristy Hine, Associate Vice President Finance
CMO: Michael T Hegstrom, M.D., Chief Medical Officer
CIO: Ronald M Cowan, Vice President Information Systems
CNO: Stacey M. Osborne, Chief Nursing Officer
Web address: www.geisinger.org
**Control**: Other not–for–profit (including NFP Corporation) **Service**: General medical and surgical

**Staffed Beds:** 123 **Admissions:** 4261 **Census:** 45 **Outpatient Visits:** 192784 **Births:** 549 **Total Expense ($000):** 116094 **Payroll Expense ($000):** 40474 **Personnel:** 927

**LEWISTOWN HOSPITAL** See Geisinger-Lewistown Hospital

### LITITZ—Lancaster County

✠ **UPMC LITITZ (390068)**, 1500 Highlands Drive, Zip 17543–7694; tel. 717/625–5000, (Nonreporting) **A**1 3 5 10 13 **F**3 13 15 18 20 22 28 29 30 31 34 35 37 40 44 45 46 48 49 50 51 57 59 60 64 65 68 70 72 74 75 76 77 78 79 81 82 85 87 89 93 107 108 110 111 114 115 119 126 129 130 135 146 147 148 149 154 **S** UPMC, Pittsburgh, PA
Primary Contact: Brooks M. Turkel, President
CIO: David Fisher, Director Information Systems
Web address: www.heartoflancaster.com
**Control**: Other not–for–profit (including NFP Corporation) **Service**: General medical and surgical

**Staffed Beds:** 90 **Admissions:** 2844 **Census:** 40 **Outpatient Visits:** 74324 **Births:** 975 **Total Expense ($000):** 101211 **Payroll Expense ($000):** 27361 **Personnel:** 567

**UPMC PINNACLE LITITZ** See UPMC Lititz

### LOCK HAVEN—Clinton County

**LOCK HAVEN HOSPITAL** See UPMC Lock Haven

✠ **UPMC LOCK HAVEN (390071)**, 24 Cree Drive, Zip 17745–2699; tel. 570/893–5000, (Total facility includes 90 beds in nursing home–type unit) (Nonreporting) **A**1 10 **F**3 6 11 15 29 30 34 35 40 45 46 50 54 56 57 59 62 67 68 77 79 81 82 86 87 90 93 96 97 107 108 110 111 114 118 119 128 130 131 132 146 150 154 157 **S** UPMC, Pittsburgh, PA
Primary Contact: Ronald J. Reynolds, President
CFO: Jennifer Lesher, Chief Financial Officer
CMO: Rajesh Patel, M.D., Chief of Staff
CIO: Judy Chapman, Interim Director Information Systems
CHR: Courtney Kunes, Director Human Resources
Web address: www.lockhavenhospital.com
**Control**: Other not–for–profit (including NFP Corporation) **Service**: General medical and surgical

**Staffed Beds:** 105 **Admissions:** 1104 **Census:** 86 **Outpatient Visits:** 29826 **Births:** 0 **Total Expense ($000):** 32314 **Payroll Expense ($000):** 11823 **Personnel:** 186

**PA**

---

**Hospital, Medicare Provider Number, Address, Telephone, Approval, Facility, and Physician Codes, Health Care System**

★ American Hospital Association (AHA) membership   ○ Healthcare Facilities Accreditation Program   ⇑ Center for Improvement in Healthcare Quality Accreditation
☐ The Joint Commission accreditation   ◇ DNV Healthcare Inc. accreditation   △ Commission on Accreditation of Rehabilitation Facilities (CARF) accreditation

## MALVERN—Chester County

☒ △ **BRYN MAWR REHABILITATION HOSPITAL (393025)**, 414 Paoli Pike, Zip 19355–3300, Mailing Address: P.O. Box 3007, Zip 19355–0707; tel. 484/596–5400, (Nonreporting) **A**1 3 7 10 **F**3 11 28 29 30 34 35 36 64 65 71 75 82 86 87 90 91 93 95 96 119 130 131 132 134 143 146 157 **P**5 **S** Main Line Health, Pittsburgh, PA
Primary Contact: Donna Phillips, President
CFO: Dave Schmotzer, Chief Financial Officer
CMO: John Kraus, M.D., Chief Medical Officer
CIO: Kay Carr, Chief Information Officer
Web address: www.brynmawrrehab.org
**Control:** Other not–for–profit (including NFP Corporation) **Service:** Rehabilitation

**Staffed Beds:** 148 **Admissions:** 1860 **Census:** 84 **Outpatient Visits:** 79587 **Births:** 0 **Total Expense ($000):** 72395 **Payroll Expense ($000):** 36574 **Personnel:** 533

**DEVEREUX CHILDREN'S BEHAVIORAL HEALTH CENTER**, 655 Sugartown Road, Zip 19355–3303, Mailing Address: 655 Sugartown Rd, Zip 19355–3303; tel. 800/345–1292, (Nonreporting) **S** Devereux, Villanova, PA
Primary Contact: Patricia Hillis-Clark, Executive Director
CFO: Tim Evans, Assistant Financial Director
CMO: Jacquelyn Zavodnick, M.D., Medical Director
CIO: MaryLou Hettinger, Director Quality Management
CHR: Sean Maher, Director Human Resources
CNO: Deanna Reiss, Hospital Director of Nursing
Web address: www.devereux.org
**Control:** Other not–for–profit (including NFP Corporation) **Service:** Children's hospital psychiatric

**Staffed Beds:** 49

**DEVEREUX MAPLETON PSYCH INST** See Devereux Children's Behavioral Health Center

**MALVERN INSTITUTE**, 940 King Road, Zip 19355–3166; tel. 610/647–0330, (Nonreporting)
Primary Contact: Geoff Botak, Chief Executive Officer
CFO: Janet Corley, Accountant
Web address: www.malverninstitute.com
**Control:** Corporation, Investor–owned (for–profit) **Service:** Alcoholism and other chemical dependency

**Staffed Beds:** 40

## MC CONNELLSBURG—Fulton County

★ **FULTON COUNTY MEDICAL CENTER (391303)**, 214 Peach Orchard Road, Zip 17233–8559, Mailing Address: McConnellsburg, tel. 717/485–3155, (Total facility includes 67 beds in nursing home–type unit) (Nonreporting) **A**10 18 **F**3 11 15 18 28 29 30 34 35 39 40 45 46 50 53 57 59 62 64 70 75 77 78 79 81 87 91 93 97 107 108 110 111 115 118 119 127 128 129 130 132 133 135 144 146 147 148 149 154 156
Primary Contact: Michael D. Makosky, Chief Executive Officer
COO: Kim Slee, Chief Operating Officer
CFO: Deborah A Shughart, Chief Financial Officer
CMO: Sharon E Martin, M.D., Ph.D., President Medical Staff
CIO: Armen Arakelian, Chief Information Officer
CHR: Cheryl Rose, Human Resources Director
Web address: www.fcmcpa.org
**Control:** Other not–for–profit (including NFP Corporation) **Service:** General medical and surgical

**Staffed Beds:** 88 **Admissions:** 622 **Census:** 72 **Outpatient Visits:** 77263 **Births:** 0 **Total Expense ($000):** 52106 **Payroll Expense ($000):** 24011 **Personnel:** 372

## MCKEES ROCKS—Allegheny County

☒ **HERITAGE VALLEY KENNEDY (390157)**, 25 Heckel Road, Zip 15136–1694; tel. 412/777–6161, (Nonreporting) **A**1 10 **S** Heritage Valley Health System, Beaver, PA
Primary Contact: Michael S. Miller, President and Chief Executive Officer
CFO: Jack Nelson, Vice President Finance and Chief Financial Officer
CHR: Erin J Frohnhofer, Vice President Human Resources
CNO: Paulette Bingham, Director Nursing Services
Web address: www.ohiovalleyhospital.org
**Control:** Other not–for–profit (including NFP Corporation) **Service:** General medical and surgical

**Staffed Beds:** 124

**OHIO VALLEY HOSPITAL** See Heritage Valley Kennedy

## MCKEESPORT—Allegheny County

**MCKEESPORT HOSPITAL** See UPMC Mckeesport

☒ **SELECT SPECIALTY HOSPITAL-MCKEESPORT (392045)**, 1500 Fifth Avenue, 6th Floor, Zip 15132–2422; tel. 412/664–2900, (Nonreporting) **A**1 10 **S** Select Medical Corporation, Mechanicsburg, PA
Primary Contact: Laurie Kozorosky, Chief Executive Officer
Web address: www.mckeesport.selectspecialtyhospitals.com/
**Control:** Corporation, Investor–owned (for–profit) **Service:** Acute long–term care hospital

**Staffed Beds:** 30

☒ **UPMC MCKEESPORT (390002)**, 1500 Fifth Avenue, Zip 15132–2422; tel. 412/664–2000, (Total facility includes 18 beds in nursing home–type unit) (Nonreporting) **A**1 3 5 10 13 **F**3 4 18 20 22 28 29 30 31 34 35 40 45 49 50 54 56 57 59 60 62 64 65 68 70 74 75 77 78 79 81 82 84 85 86 87 90 96 98 100 101 102 103 107 108 111 114 115 119 120 121 123 128 130 132 135 143 146 148 154 156 157 **S** UPMC, Pittsburgh, PA
Primary Contact: Mark O'Hern, President
COO: Amy Bush, Vice President Operations
CFO: Laurene Timmons, Chief Financial Officer
CMO: R Curtis Waligura, D.O., Vice President Medical Affairs, Chief Medical Officer
CIO: Terri Keeling, Vice President Information Systems
CHR: Kelli Reale, Vice President Human Resources
CNO: Leeanna McKibben, R.N., MSN, Vice President Patient Services and Chief Nursing Officer
Web address: www.mckeesport.upmc.com
**Control:** Other not–for–profit (including NFP Corporation) **Service:** General medical and surgical

**Staffed Beds:** 184 **Admissions:** 7419 **Census:** 131 **Outpatient Visits:** 116117 **Births:** 0 **Total Expense ($000):** 146362 **Payroll Expense ($000):** 44578 **Personnel:** 748

## MEADOWBROOK—Montgomery County

⇑ **HOLY REDEEMER HOSPITAL (390097)**, 1648 Huntingdon Pike, Zip 19046–8001; tel. 215/947–3000, (Nonreporting) **A**2 3 5 10 21
Primary Contact: Michael B. Laign, President and Chief Executive Officer
CFO: Russell R Wagner, Executive Vice President and Chief Financial Officer
CMO: Henry D. Unger, M.D., Senior Vice President and Chief Medical Officer
CIO: Donald F. Friel, Executive Vice President
CHR: Joseph J Cassidy, Vice President
CNO: Anne Catino, MS, R.N., Vice President and Chief Nursing Officer
Web address: www.holyredeemer.com
**Control:** Other not–for–profit (including NFP Corporation) **Service:** General medical and surgical

**Staffed Beds:** 263

⇑ **HOLY REDEEMER HOSPITAL AND MEDICAL CENTER** See Holy Redeemer Hospital

## MEADVILLE—Crawford County

★ ⇑ **MEADVILLE MEDICAL CENTER (390113)**, 751 Liberty Street, Zip 16335–2559; tel. 814/333–5000, (Nonreporting) **A**2 3 10 12 13 21 **S** Meadville Medical Center, Meadville, PA
Primary Contact: Philip E. Pandolph, FACHE, Chief Executive Officer
CFO: Renato Suntay, Chief Financial Officer
CMO: Denise Johnson, M.D., Medical Director
CHR: Greg Maras, Vice President Human Resources
CNO: MaryAnn Hewston, R.N., Chief Nurse Executive
Web address: www.mmchs.org
**Control:** Other not–for–profit (including NFP Corporation) **Service:** General medical and surgical

**Staffed Beds:** 234

## MECHANICSBURG—Cumberland County

☒ **ENCOMPASS HEALTH REHABILITATION HOSPITAL OF MECHANICSBURG (393031)**, 175 Lancaster Boulevard, Zip 17055–3562; tel. 717/691–3700, (Nonreporting) **A**1 10 **S** Encompass Health Corporation, Birmingham, AL
Primary Contact: Josette M. Myers, Chief Executive Officer
CMO: Michael Lupinacci, M.D., Medical Director
CHR: David Staskin, Director Human Resources
Web address: www.healthsouthpa.com
**Control:** Corporation, Investor–owned (for–profit) **Service:** Rehabilitation

**Staffed Beds:** 75

**HEALTHSOUTH REHABILITATION HOSPITAL OF MECHANICSBURG** See Encompass Health Rehabilitation Hospital of Mechanicsburg

*Many Facility Codes have changed. Please refer to the AHA Guide Code Chart.*
© 2021 AHA Guide

PA

## MEDIA—Delaware County

✠ **RIDDLE HOSPITAL (390222)**, 1068 West Baltimore Pike, Zip 19063–5177; tel. 484/227–9400, (Total facility includes 23 beds in nursing home–type unit) (Nonreporting) **A**1 2 3 10 **F**3 7 11 13 15 18 20 22 26 28 29 30 31 34 35 36 37 38 40 41 44 45 49 50 51 53 54 55 56 57 58 59 63 64 65 70 72 74 75 76 78 79 80 81 82 84 85 86 87 93 96 97 100 102 107 108 110 111 114 115 119 120 124 126 128 129 130 131 132 135 141 143 145 146 147 148 149 154 156 157 **S** Main Line Health, Birmingham, AL
Primary Contact: Shelly Buck, President
CFO: Ed McKillip, Vice President Finance
CMO: David Thomas, President Medical Staff
CHR: Mary Louise Ciciretti, Director Human Resources
Web address: www.riddlehospital.org
**Control**: Other not–for–profit (including NFP Corporation) **Service**: General medical and surgical

**Staffed Beds**: 227 **Admissions**: 10884 **Census**: 122 **Outpatient Visits**: 163460 **Births**: 956 **Total Expense ($000)**: 198258 **Payroll Expense ($000)**: 69405 **Personnel**: 884

**RIDDLE MEMORIAL HOSPITAL** See Riddle Hospital

## MEYERSDALE—Somerset County

✠ **CONEMAUGH MEYERSDALE MEDICAL CENTER (391302)**, 200 Hospital Drive, Zip 15552–1249; tel. 814/634–5911, (Nonreporting) **A**1 10 18 **F**29 34 40 45 50 59 64 75 81 107 111 114 119 127 130 132 133 146 148 154 **S** Duke LifePoint Healthcare, Brentwood, TN
Primary Contact: Heather Smith, Chief Executive Officer
CMO: Dwayne Platt, M.D., Chief Medical Officer
CNO: Pam Swansboro, R.N., Chief Nursing Officer
Web address: www.conemaugh.org
**Control**: Corporation, Investor–owned (for–profit) **Service**: General medical and surgical

**Staffed Beds**: 20 **Admissions**: 265 **Census**: 4 **Outpatient Visits**: 48084 **Births**: 0 **Total Expense ($000)**: 14585 **Payroll Expense ($000)**: 4941 **Personnel**: 102

**MEYERSDALE MEDICAL CENTER** See Conemaugh Meyersdale Medical Center

## MONONGAHELA—Washington County

✠ **MONONGAHELA VALLEY HOSPITAL (390147)**, 1163 Country Club Road, Zip 15063–1095; tel. 724/258–1000, (Nonreporting) **A**1 2 10 **F**3 8 9 11 12 15 17 18 20 22 28 29 30 31 32 34 35 40 45 48 51 54 55 56 57 59 61 64 68 70 74 75 77 78 79 80 81 82 85 86 87 89 90 92 93 96 98 100 101 102 103 107 108 110 111 114 115 118 119 120 121 123 124 129 130 131 132 134 135 146 147 148 149 154 156 **P**8
Primary Contact: Louis J. Panza Jr, President and Chief Executive Officer
COO: Patrick J Alberts, Senior Vice President and Chief Operating Officer
CFO: Daniel F Simmons, Senior Vice President and Treasurer
CMO: L. Douglas Pepper, M.D., President, Medical Staff
CIO: Matt Rashilla, Chief Information and Application Officer
CHR: Christopher Kovski, Senior Vice President Human Resources
Web address: www.monvalleyhospital.com
**Control**: Other not–for–profit (including NFP Corporation) **Service**: General medical and surgical

**Staffed Beds**: 200 **Admissions**: 5991 **Census**: 91 **Outpatient Visits**: 284089 **Births**: 0 **Total Expense ($000)**: 130476 **Payroll Expense ($000)**: 56190 **Personnel**: 953

## MONROEVILLE—Allegheny County

✠ **FORBES HOSPITAL (390267)**, 2570 Haymaker Road, Zip 15146–3513; tel. 412/858–2000, (Nonreporting) **A**1 2 3 5 10 **F**3 8 11 13 15 17 18 20 22 24 26 28 29 30 31 34 35 36 40 44 49 50 54 55 57 58 59 64 65 69 70 73 74 75 76 77 78 79 80 81 82 84 85 86 87 90 92 96 98 100 102 107 108 110 111 115 117 118 119 120 121 123 124 126 130 132 135 141 145 146 147 148 149 154 155 **P**6 **S** Allegheny Health Network, Pittsburgh, PA
Primary Contact: Mark Rubino, M.D., President
COO: Krista A. Bragg, MSN, Chief Operating Officer
CFO: Tom Hipkiss, Vice President Finance
CMO: Mark Rubino, M.D., Chief Medical Officer
CIO: Sharon Lewis, Director Information Systems
CHR: Georgia Redding, Director Human Resources
Web address: www.ahn.org
**Control**: Other not–for–profit (including NFP Corporation) **Service**: General medical and surgical

**Staffed Beds**: 315 **Admissions**: 13405 **Census**: 199 **Outpatient Visits**: 157045 **Births**: 1338 **Total Expense ($000)**: 258434 **Payroll Expense ($000)**: 87164 **Personnel**: 1386

**FORBES REGIONAL HOSPITAL** See Forbes Hospital

✠ **UPMC EAST (390328)**, 2775 Mosside Boulevard, Zip 15146–2760; tel. 412/357–3000, (Nonreporting) **A**1 2 3 10 **F**3 18 20 22 29 30 34 35 40 45 47 49 50 57 59 62 65 68 70 74 75 77 78 79 81 82 84 85 87 90 96 100 107 108 111 115 119 120 121 123 130 132 135 146 148 154 156 157 **S** UPMC, Pittsburgh, PA
Primary Contact: Mark O'Hern, President
CFO: Laurene Timmons, Chief Financial Officer
CNO: Tamra Minton, R.N., MSN, Vice President Patient Care Services and Chief Nursing Officer
Web address: www.upmc.com/locations/hospitals/east/Pages/default.aspx
**Control**: Other not–for–profit (including NFP Corporation) **Service**: General medical and surgical

**Staffed Beds**: 155 **Admissions**: 8453 **Census**: 120 **Outpatient Visits**: 85504 **Births**: 0 **Total Expense ($000)**: 157701 **Payroll Expense ($000)**: 42405 **Personnel**: 711

## MONTROSE—Susquehanna County

★ **ENDLESS MOUNTAIN HEALTH SYSTEMS (391306)**, 100 Hospital Drive, Zip 18801–6402; tel. 570/278–3801, (Nonreporting) **A**10 18
Primary Contact: Loren Stone, Chief Executive Officer
CIO: Gary Passmore, Chief Information Officer
CHR: Paula Anderson, Administrative Director Human Resources
Web address: www.endlesscare.org
**Control**: Other not–for–profit (including NFP Corporation) **Service**: General medical and surgical

**Staffed Beds**: 25

**MONTROSE GENERAL HOSPITAL** See Endless Mountain Health Systems

## MOUNT GRETNA—Lebanon County

**PHILHAVEN** See Wellspan Philhaven

✠ **WELLSPAN PHILHAVEN (394020)**, 283 South Butler Road, Zip 17064–6085, Mailing Address: P.O. Box 550, Zip 17064–0550; tel. 717/273–8871, (Nonreporting) **A**1 10 **F**30 98 99 100 101 102 103 104 105 106 130 153 **P**6 **S** WellSpan Health, York, PA
Primary Contact: Philip D. Hess, President
COO: Philip D. Hess, President
CFO: Matt Rogers, Chief Financial Officer
CMO: Francis D Sparrow, M.D., Medical Director
CIO: Lori Nolt, Director Information Technology
CHR: Denis Orthaus, Director Human Resources
CNO: Heidi McMullan, R.N., Chief Nursing Officer
Web address: www.philhaven.org
**Control**: Other not–for–profit (including NFP Corporation) **Service**: Psychiatric

**Staffed Beds**: 118 **Admissions**: 1954 **Census**: 97 **Outpatient Visits**: 0 **Births**: 0 **Total Expense ($000)**: 88904 **Payroll Expense ($000)**: 41889 **Personnel**: 775

---

Hospital, Medicare Provider Number, Address, Telephone, Approval, Facility, and Physician Codes, Health Care System

★ American Hospital Association (AHA) membership    ○ Healthcare Facilities Accreditation Program    ⇑ Center for Improvement in Healthcare Quality Accreditation
□ The Joint Commission accreditation    ◇ DNV Healthcare Inc. accreditation    △ Commission on Accreditation of Rehabilitation Facilities (CARF) accreditation

## MOUNT PLEASANT—Westmoreland County

☐ **EXCELA FRICK HOSPITAL (390217)**, 508 South Church Street,
Zip 15666–1790; tel. 724/547–1500, (Nonreporting) **A**1 10 **S** Excela Health,
Greensburg, PA
Primary Contact: John Sphon, Chief Executive Officer
COO: Jeffrey Tiesi, Executive Vice President and Chief Operating Officer
CFO: Jeffrey T Curry, Executive Vice President and Chief Financial Officer
CMO: Jerome Granato, M.D., Senior Vice President and Chief Medical Officer
CIO: David Gawaluck, Vice President and Chief Information Officer
CHR: John Caverno, Chief Human Resources Officer
CNO: Helen K Burns, Ph.D., R.N., Senior Vice President and Chief Nursing Officer
Web address: www.excelahealth.org/PatientsandVisitors/HospitalsFacilities/
Hospitals/Frick.aspx
**Control:** Other not–for–profit (including NFP Corporation) **Service:** General
medical and surgical

| Staffed Beds: 33 |
|---|

**FRICK HOSPITAL** See Excela Frick Hospital

## MUNCY—Lycoming County

**MUNCY VALLEY HOSPITAL** See UPMC Muncy

☒ **UPMC MUNCY (391301)**, 215 East Water Street, Zip 17756–8700;
tel. 570/546–8282, (Total facility includes 125 beds in nursing home–type unit)
(Nonreporting) **A**1 3 10 18 **F**6 11 15 29 30 34 35 40 44 45 46 50 56 57 59 62
67 68 77 81 86 87 90 93 96 97 107 108 110 111 114 118 119 128 130 131
132 133 146 154 157 **S** UPMC, Pittsburgh, PA
Primary Contact: Ronald J. Reynolds, President
CFO: Eric Pohjala, Executive Vice President and Chief Financial Officer
CIO: Timothy E Schoener, Chief Information Officer
CHR: Dawn Wright, Vice President Human Resources
CNO: C Cynthia Whipple, Director of Nursing
Web address: www.susquehannahealth.org
**Control:** Other not–for–profit (including NFP Corporation) **Service:** General
medical and surgical

| Staffed Beds: 158 Admissions: 863 Census: 136 Outpatient Visits: 48042 |
|---|
| Births: 0 Total Expense ($000): 50091 Payroll Expense ($000): 16896 |
| Personnel: 269 |

## NATRONA HEIGHTS—Allegheny County

**ALLE KISKI MEDICAL CENTER** See Select Specialty Hospital - Alle Kiski

☒ **ALLEGHENY VALLEY HOSPITAL (390032)**, 1301 Carlisle Street,
Zip 15065–1152; tel. 724/224–5100, (Nonreporting) **A**1 2 3 10 **F**3 11 15 17
18 24 28 29 30 31 34 35 39 40 44 45 47 49 50 56 57 58 59 64 65 70 72 74
75 77 78 79 80 81 84 85 86 87 90 92 93 96 98 100 102 103 107 108 110
111 115 118 119 120 121 124 126 129 130 132 135 146 149 154 **P**6 **S**
Allegheny Health Network, Pittsburgh, PA
Primary Contact: Vicenta Gaspar-Yoo, M.D., President and Chief Executive Officer
COO: Krista A. Bragg, MSN, Chief Operating Officer
CFO: James A Kanuch, Vice President Finance
CMO: Suzanne M. Labriola, D.O., Chief Medical Officer
CIO: Linda Fergus, Manager Information Technology
CHR: Cindy Moser, Director Human Resources
Web address: www.wpahs.org
**Control:** Other not–for–profit (including NFP Corporation) **Service:** General
medical and surgical

| Staffed Beds: 83 Admissions: 4456 Census: 60 Outpatient Visits: 169790 |
|---|
| Births: 0 Total Expense ($000): 102237 Payroll Expense ($000): 43219 |
| Personnel: 767 |

**ALLE-KISKI MEDICAL CENTER** See Allegheny Valley Hospital

## NEW CASTLE—Lawrence County

☒ **UPMC JAMESON (390016)**, 1211 Wilmington Avenue, Zip 16105–2516;
tel. 724/658–9001, (Nonreporting) **A**1 3 10 19 **F**3 12 15 18 20 22 28 29 30 32
34 35 40 43 45 46 49 50 57 59 61 64 65 68 70 74 75 77 78 79 81 82 85 86
87 90 92 93 96 100 105 107 108 110 111 114 115 118 119 126 130 135
146 147 148 149 154 156 157 **S** UPMC, Pittsburgh, PA
Primary Contact: Robert Charles. Jackson Jr, President
COO: Albert Boland, Vice President Operations
CFO: Brian Fritz, Chief Financial Officer
CMO: Elizabeth Piccione, M.D., Chief Medical Officer
CIO: Charles M. Rudek, Chief Information Officer
CHR: Eric D. McIntosh, Vice President Human Resources
CNO: Marianna Stoneburner, R.N., Chief Nursing Officer
Web address: www.upmcjameson.com
**Control:** Other not–for–profit (including NFP Corporation) **Service:** General
medical and surgical

| Staffed Beds: 90 Admissions: 5083 Census: 69 Outpatient Visits: 139657 |
|---|
| Births: 0 Total Expense ($000): 105191 Payroll Expense ($000): 36490 |
| Personnel: 722 |

**UPMC JAMESON HOSPITAL** See UPMC Jameson

## NORRISTOWN—Montgomery County

☐ **MONTGOMERY COUNTY EMERGENCY SERVICE (394033)**, 50 Beech Drive,
Zip 19403–5421; tel. 610/279–6100, (Nonreporting) **A**1 10
Primary Contact: William Myers, Chief Executive Officer
CFO: Wendy Wait, Chief Financial Officer
CMO: Marina Cooney, Medical Director
CHR: Byanka Meacham, Director Human Resources
CNO: Naomi Finkel, Nurse Executive
Web address: www.mces.org
**Control:** County, Government, Nonfederal **Service:** Psychiatric

| Staffed Beds: 81 |
|---|

☐ **NORRISTOWN STATE HOSPITAL (394001)**, 1001 Sterigere Street,
Zip 19401–5300; tel. 610/270–1000, (Nonreporting) **A**10
Primary Contact: Edna I. McCutcheon, Chief Executive Officer
COO: Gary Raisner, Chief Operating Officer
CMO: Mia Marcovici, M.D., Chief Medical Officer
CHR: Richard Szczurowski, Director Human Resources
CNO: Taryn Mason-Jones, Chief Nurse Executive
**Control:** State, Government, Nonfederal **Service:** Psychiatric

| Staffed Beds: 259 |
|---|

**VALLEY FORGE MED CNTR & HOSP** See Valley Forge Medical Center and
Hospital

☐ **VALLEY FORGE MEDICAL CENTER AND HOSPITAL (390272)**, 1033 West
Germantown Pike, Zip 19403–3905; tel. 610/539–8500, (Nonreporting) **A**1 10
Primary Contact: Gregg Y. Slocum, Chief Executive Officer
CMO: Robert E Colcher, M.D., Medical Director
CHR: Frederick D Jackes, Assistant Administrator and Director Human Resources
Web address: www.vfmc.net
**Control:** Corporation, Investor–owned (for–profit) **Service:** Alcoholism and other
chemical dependency

| Staffed Beds: 50 |
|---|

## OAKDALE—Allegheny County

**CURAHEALTH PITTSBURGH (392028)**, 7777 Steubenville Pike,
Zip 15071–3409; tel. 412/494–5500, (Nonreporting) **A**10 **S** Curahealth Hospitals,
Garland, TX
Primary Contact: Carol Falo, R.N., Chief Executive Officer
CFO: Kevin Varley, Chief Financial Officer
CMO: Ravi Alagar, M.D., Medical Director
Web address: www.curahealth.com
**Control:** Corporation, Investor–owned (for–profit) **Service:** Acute long–term care
hospital

| Staffed Beds: 31 |
|---|

**KINDRED HOSPITAL-PITTSBURGH** See Curahealth Pittsburgh

**PA**

**OREFIELD—Lehigh County**

**KIDSPEACE CHILDREN'S HOSPITAL (394047)**, 5300 Kids Peace Drive, Zip 18069–2044; tel. 610/799–7900, (Nonreporting) **A**3 10
Primary Contact: William R. Isemann, President and Chief Executive Officer
CFO: Michael Callan, Executive Vice President and Chief Financial Officer
CMO: Matthew Koval, M.D., Vice President Medical Affairs
CIO: Joan Lesko, Director Technical Support and Services
CHR: Sheila Rulli, Director Human Resources
CNO: Tamara Wasilick, Director Operations
Web address: www.kidspeace.org
**Control**: Other not–for–profit (including NFP Corporation) **Service**: Children's hospital psychiatric

| Staffed Beds: 120 |
| --- |

**NATIONAL HOSPITAL FOR KIDS** See Kidspeace Children's Hospital

**PALMERTON—Carbon County**

**BLUE MOUNTAIN HOSPITAL PALMERTON CAMPUS** See St. Luke's - Palmerton Campus

**PAOLI—Chester County**

☒ **PAOLI HOSPITAL (390153)**, 255 West Lancaster Avenue, Zip 19301–1763; tel. 484/565–1000, (Nonreporting) **A**1 3 10 **F**3 11 13 15 18 20 22 24 26 28 29 30 31 32 34 35 36 38 39 40 41 43 44 45 49 50 54 55 56 57 59 63 64 65 68 70 72 74 75 76 78 79 80 81 82 84 85 86 87 93 96 100 102 107 108 110 111 114 115 118 119 120 121 124 126 129 130 131 132 134 135 141 145 146 147 148 149 150 154 156 157 **S** Main Line Health, Garland, TX
Primary Contact: James Paradis, President
CFO: John Doyle, Vice President Finance
CMO: Andrew J Norton, M.D., Chief Medical Officer
CIO: Kay Carr, Senior Vice President and Chief Information Officer
CHR: Deborah Fedora, Director Human Resources
Web address: www.mainlinehealth.org
**Control**: Other not–for–profit (including NFP Corporation) **Service**: General medical and surgical

| Staffed Beds: 231 Admissions: 14237 Census: 140 Outpatient Visits: 260997 Births: 1987 Total Expense ($000): 295065 Payroll Expense ($000): 88176 Personnel: 1147 |
| --- |

**PAOLI MEMORIAL HOSPITAL** See Paoli Hospital

**PHILADELPHIA—Philadelphia County**

**ALBERT EINSTEIN MEDICAL CENTER** See Einstein Medical Center Philadelphia

**AMERICAN ONCOLOGIC HOSPITAL** See Fox Chase Cancer Center-American Oncologic Hospital

☐ **BELMONT BEHAVIORAL HOSPITAL (394023)**, 4200 Monument Road, Zip 19131–1625; tel. 215/877–2000, (Nonreporting) **A**1 3 5 10 **F**29 98 99 101 103 104 105 130 153 154 **S** Acadia Healthcare Company, Inc., Franklin, TN
Primary Contact: Laura Longstreet, Chief Executive Officer
CFO: Guy Romaniello, Director Fiscal Services
CMO: Richard Jaffe, M.D., Medical Director
CHR: Jenna Pacini, Human Resources Specialist
CNO: Nona Fain, Ph.D., R.N., Director of Nursing
Web address: www.einstein.edu/locations/belmont-behavioral-health/
**Control**: Individual, Investor–owned (for–profit) **Service**: Psychiatric

| Staffed Beds: 180 Admissions: 3703 Census: 164 Outpatient Visits: 58718 Births: 0 Total Expense ($000): 52782 Payroll Expense ($000): 31936 Personnel: 413 |
| --- |

**BELMONT CENTER FOR COMPREHENSIVE TREATMENT** See Belmont Behavioral Hospital

☐ **CANCER TREATMENT CENTERS OF AMERICA-EASTERN REGIONAL MEDICAL CENTER (390312)**, 1331 East Wyoming Avenue, Zip 19124–3808; tel. 215/537–7400, (Nonreporting) **A**1 2 3 5 10 **S** Cancer Treatment Centers of America, Schaumburg, IL
Primary Contact: Maria Scenna, Chief Executive Officer
COO: Jeffrey Ryan, Chief Operating Officer
CFO: Jeffrey Ryan, Senior Vice President, Finance and Business Development
CMO: Steven B. Standiford, M.D., Chief of Staff
CIO: Kristin Darby, Chief Information Officer
CHR: Ronald Gilg, Assistant Vice President Talent
CNO: Joanne McGovern, MSN, R.N., Chief Nursing Officer
Web address: www.cancercenter.com
**Control**: Corporation, Investor–owned (for–profit) **Service**: Cancer

| Staffed Beds: 56 |
| --- |

**CHARTER FAIRMOUNT BEHAVIORAL** See Fairmount Behavioral Health System

**CHESTNUT HILL HEALTH SYSTEM** See Chestnut Hill Hospital

☒ **CHESTNUT HILL HOSPITAL (390026)**, 8835 Germantown Avenue, Zip 19118–2718; tel. 215/248–8200, (Nonreporting) **A**1 3 5 10 **S** Tower Health, West Reading, PA
Primary Contact: John D. Cacciamani, M.D., Chief Executive Officer
CFO: Marc Costner, Chief Financial Officer
CMO: John Scanlon, DPM, Chief Medical Officer
CHR: Marilyn DiCicco, Director Human Resources
CNO: Teresa M Kelly, MSN, R.N., Chief Nursing Officer
Web address: www.chhealthsystem.com
**Control**: Other not–for–profit (including NFP Corporation) **Service**: General medical and surgical

| Staffed Beds: 212 |
| --- |

**CHILDREN'S HOSPITAL OF PHILADE** See Children's Hospital of Philadelphia

☐ **CHILDREN'S HOSPITAL OF PHILADELPHIA (393303)**, 3401 Civic Center Boulevard, Zip 19104–4319; tel. 215/590–1000, (Nonreporting) **A**1 3 5 8 10 **F**3 5 8 11 12 13 17 18 19 20 21 22 23 24 25 26 27 28 29 30 31 32 33 34 35 36 37 38 39 40 41 43 44 45 46 48 49 50 53 54 55 57 58 59 60 61 62 64 65 66 68 71 72 74 75 76 77 78 79 81 82 83 84 85 86 87 88 89 90 91 92 93 95 96 97 99 100 101 102 104 107 111 112 113 114 115 116 117 118 119 126 129 130 131 132 134 135 136 137 138 139 140 141 142 143 144 146 148 149 150 151 152 153 154 156 157 **P**6
Primary Contact: Madeline Bell, President and Chief Executive Officer
COO: Douglas G Hock, Executive Vice President and Chief Operating Officer
CFO: Thomas Todorow, Chief Financial Officer and Executive Vice President
CMO: Jan Boswinkel, M.D., Vice President Medical Operations and Chief Safety Officer
CHR: Robert Croner, Senior Vice President and Chief Human Resources Officer
CNO: Paula M Agosto, R.N., MSN, Senior Vice President and Chief Nursing Officer
Web address: www.chop.edu
**Control**: Other not–for–profit (including NFP Corporation) **Service**: Children's general medical and surgical

| Staffed Beds: 564 Admissions: 29091 Census: 473 Outpatient Visits: 1421406 Births: 446 Total Expense ($000): 2373723 Payroll Expense ($000): 1065873 Personnel: 12930 |
| --- |

**EASTERN REGIONAL MEDICAL CENTER** See Cancer Treatment Centers of America-Eastern Regional Medical Center

☐ △ **EINSTEIN MEDICAL CENTER PHILADELPHIA (390142)**, 5501 Old York Road, Zip 19141–3098; tel. 215/456–7890, (Includes EINSTEIN MEDICAL CENTER ELKINS PARK, Mailing address: 60 Township Line Road, Elkins Park, Pennsylvania, Zip 19027–2220; tel. 215/663–6000; Barry R Freedman, President and Chief Executive Officer) (Total facility includes 44 beds in nursing home–type unit) **A**1 2 3 5 7 8 10 **F**3 8 11 12 13 15 17 18 20 22 24 26 28 29 30 31 32 34 35 36 37 38 39 40 43 44 45 46 47 48 49 54 55 56 57 58 59 61 64 65 66 68 70 72 73 74 75 76 77 78 79 80 81 82 84 85 86 87 90 91 92 93 94 95 97 98 100 101 102 103 104 106 107 108 110 111 114 115 119 120 121 123 124 126 128 129 130 131 132 138 139 142 143 145 146 147 148 149 150 154 156 157 158 **S** Einstein Healthcare Network, Philadelphia, PA
Primary Contact: Dixie James, President and Chief Operating Officer
COO: Ruth Lefton, Chief Operating Officer
CFO: Gerard Blaney, Vice President Finance and Interim Chief Financial Officer
CMO: Steven Sivak, M.D., Chief Medical Officer, Einstein Physicians Philadelphia
CIO: Brenda West, Vice President, Information Services and Interim Chief Information Officer
CHR: Lynne R Kornblatt, Chief Human Resources Officer
CNO: Jill Stunkard, R.N., MSN, Associate Chief Nurse Executive and Interim Chief Nursing Officer
Web address: www.einstein.edu
**Control**: Other not–for–profit (including NFP Corporation) **Service**: General medical and surgical

**Staffed Beds**: 504 **Admissions**: 27570 **Census**: 480 **Outpatient Visits**: 579113 **Births**: 2844 **Total Expense ($000)**: 823030 **Payroll Expense ($000)**: 380028 **Personnel**: 4898

**EPISCOPAL HOSPITAL** See Temple University Hospital - Episcopal Division

☐ **FAIRMOUNT BEHAVIORAL HEALTH SYSTEM (394027)**, 561 Fairthorne Avenue, Zip 19128–2499; tel. 215/487–4000, (Nonreporting) **A**1 10 **S** Universal Health Services, Inc., King of Prussia, PA
Primary Contact: Mark L. Howard, Chief Executive Officer
CFO: Anthony Tortella, Chief Financial Officer
CMO: Silvia Gratz, D.O., Chief Medical Officer
CIO: Anthony Tortella, Chief Financial Officer
CHR: Brendan Aurand, Director, Human Resources
CNO: Wanda Nolasco, Chief Nursing Officer
Web address: www.fairmountbhs.com
**Control**: Corporation, Investor–owned (for–profit) **Service**: Psychiatric

**Staffed Beds**: 235

☒ **FOX CHASE CANCER CENTER-AMERICAN ONCOLOGIC HOSPITAL (390196)**, 333 Cottman Avenue, Zip 19111–2434; tel. 215/728–6900, (Nonreporting) **A**1 2 3 5 10 **F**11 15 29 30 31 34 35 36 45 46 47 49 50 55 57 58 59 60 63 64 68 70 71 75 77 78 79 81 82 84 85 86 87 93 100 104 107 108 109 110 111 114 115 116 117 118 119 120 121 123 124 126 130 132 135 136 145 146 147 148 149 157 **P**6 **S** Temple University Health System, Philadelphia, PA
Primary Contact: Richard Fisher, M.D., President and Chief Executive Officer
COO: Judith Lynn Bachman, Chief Operating Officer
CFO: Anthony J Diasio, Chief Financial Officer
CMO: James Helstrom, Chief Medical Officer
CIO: Michael Sweeney, Chief Information Officer
CNO: Anne Jadwin, R.N., MSN, Chief Nursing Officer
Web address: www.fccc.org
**Control**: Other not–for–profit (including NFP Corporation) **Service**: Cancer

**Staffed Beds**: 72 **Admissions**: 3814 **Census**: 59 **Outpatient Visits**: 120087 **Births**: 0 **Total Expense ($000)**: 385945 **Payroll Expense ($000)**: 97715 **Personnel**: 1575

**FRIENDS BEHAVIORAL HEALTH SYSTEM** See Friends Hospital

☐ **FRIENDS HOSPITAL (394008)**, 4641 Roosevelt Boulevard, Zip 19124–2343; tel. 215/831–4600, (Nonreporting) **A**1 3 5 10 **S** Universal Health Services, Inc., King of Prussia, PA
Primary Contact: Elizabeth Conlin, PsyD, Chief Executive Officer
COO: Diane Carugati, Chief Operating Officer
CFO: Michael Terwilliger, Chief Financial Officer
CMO: Marc Rothman, M.D., Medical Director
CIO: John Healy, Manager Information Technology
CHR: Paul Cavanaugh, Director Human Resources
Web address: www.friendshospital.com
**Control**: Corporation, Investor–owned (for–profit) **Service**: Psychiatric

**Staffed Beds**: 192

☒ **GOOD SHEPHERD PENN PARTNERS SPECIALTY HOSPITAL AT RITTENHOUSE (392050)**, 1800 Lombard Street, Zip 19146–1414; tel. 877/969–7342, (Nonreporting) **A**1 10 **F**1 3 28 29 30 34 35 44 50 56 57 58 59 60 64 68 74 75 77 79 82 84 85 86 87 90 91 93 94 95 96 100 130 131 132 143 146 148 149 154
Primary Contact: Laura Porter, Executive Director
CFO: Ronald J. Petula, Vice President Finance
CMO: Michael Grippi, M.D., Chief Medical Officer
CHR: Mark Sneff, Vice President Human Resources
CNO: Jean Romano, Chief Nursing Officer
Web address: www.phillyrehab.com
**Control**: Other not–for–profit (including NFP Corporation) **Service**: Acute long–term care hospital

**Staffed Beds**: 38 **Admissions**: 250 **Census**: 26 **Outpatient Visits**: 238659 **Births**: 0 **Total Expense ($000)**: 57015 **Payroll Expense ($000)**: 27562 **Personnel**: 407

☐ **HAVEN BEHAVIORAL HOSPITAL OF PHILADELPHIA (394053)**, 3300 Henry Avenue, Four Falls Building, Suite 100, Zip 19129–1141; tel. 215/475–3400, (Nonreporting) **A**1 3 5 10 **S** Haven Behavioral Healthcare, Nashville, TN
Primary Contact: Robert Scheffler, Chief Executive Officer
Web address: www.https://philadelphia.havenbehavioral.com
**Control**: Corporation, Investor–owned (for–profit) **Service**: Psychiatric

**Staffed Beds**: 36

**HOSPITAL OF THE UNIV OF PENN** See Hospital of The University of Pennsylvania

☒ **HOSPITAL OF THE UNIVERSITY OF PENNSYLVANIA (390111)**, 3400 Spruce Street, Zip 19104–4206; tel. 215/662–4000, (Includes SCHEIE EYE INSTITUTE OF THE HOSPITAL OF THE UNIVERSITY OF PENNSYLVANIA, Mailing address: 3400 Civic Center Blvd FL 3, West Pavilion, 3rd Floor, Philadelphia, Pennsylvania, Zip 19104–5127; tel. 215/662–8100; Sheara Hollin, Chief Operating Officer), (Nonreporting) **A**1 2 5 8 10 **F**3 6 **F**3 8 9 11 12 13 15 17 18 20 22 24 26 29 30 31 34 35 36 38 39 40 44 45 46 47 48 49 50 52 54 55 56 57 58 59 60 61 62 64 65 66 68 69 70 72 73 74 75 76 77 78 79 80 81 82 84 85 86 87 90 91 92 93 94 95 96 97 100 102 104 107 108 110 111 113 115 116 117 118 119 120 121 122 123 124 126 129 130 131 132 135 136 137 138 139 140 141 142 145 146 147 148 149 150 154 155 156 **P**6 **S** University of Pennsylvania Health System, Philadelphia, PA
Primary Contact: Regina Cunningham, Ph.D., R.N., Chief Executive Officer
CFO: Joseph M Huber, Chief Financial Officer
CMO: Patrick J Brennan, M.D., Senior Vice President and Chief Medical Officer
CIO: Michael Restuccia, Chief Information Officer
CHR: Denise J. Mariotti, Chief Human Resource Officer
Web address: www.pennmedicine.org
**Control**: Other not–for–profit (including NFP Corporation) **Service**: General medical and surgical

**Staffed Beds**: 807 **Admissions**: 34895 **Census**: 718 **Outpatient Visits**: 1998941 **Births**: 4184 **Total Expense ($000)**: 3021861 **Payroll Expense ($000)**: 1145469 **Personnel**: 15042

☒ **JEFFERSON HEALTH NORTHEAST (390115)**, 10800 Knights Road, Zip 19114–4200; tel. 215/612–4000, (Includes BUCKS COUNTY CAMPUS, Mailing address: 380 North Oxford Valley Road, Langhorne, Pennsylvania, Zip 19047–8399; tel. 215/949–5000; FRANKFORD CAMPUS, Mailing address: Frankford Avenue and Wakeling Street, Philadelphia, Pennsylvania, Zip 19124; tel. 215/831–2000), (Nonreporting) **A**1 2 3 5 10 **F**3 11 12 15 17 18 20 22 24 26 28 29 30 31 34 35 39 40 43 44 45 46 49 50 53 54 57 58 59 61 64 65 66 68 70 74 75 77 79 80 81 82 84 85 86 87 92 93 94 96 100 107 108 110 111 114 115 117 118 119 120 121 123 124 126 129 130 131 132 135 144 145 146 147 148 149 154 **P**8 **S** Jefferson Health, Philadelphia, PA
Primary Contact: Richard Galup, President
COO: Sandra Gomberg, Chief Operating Officer
CFO: William Degnan, Vice President Finance
CMO: Stanton Segal, M.D., Chief Medical Officer
CHR: Dorinda Carolina, Chief Human Resources Officer
CNO: Michelle E Conley, R.N., Chief Nursing Officer
Web address: www.ariahealth.org
**Control**: Other not–for–profit (including NFP Corporation) **Service**: General medical and surgical

**Staffed Beds**: 450 **Admissions**: 24263 **Census**: 307 **Outpatient Visits**: 224236 **Births**: 0 **Total Expense ($000)**: 479790 **Payroll Expense ($000)**: 200981 **Personnel**: 3249

**JEFFERSON HEALTH NORTHEST** See Jefferson Health Northeast

**JEFFERSON METHODIST HOSPITAL** See Thomas Jefferson University Hospitals, Philadelphia

*Many Facility Codes have changed. Please refer to the AHA Guide Code Chart.*
© 2021 AHA Guide

PA

☐ **KENSINGTON HOSPITAL (390025)**, 136 West Diamond Street,
Zip 19122–1721; tel. 215/426–8100, (Nonreporting) **A**1 10
Primary Contact: Kathleen Lalli, Chief Executive Officer
CFO: Kenneth Biddle, Controller
CMO: Luis F Vera, M.D., Medical Director
CHR: Maria Dimichele, Administrative Assistant
CNO: Aleyamma John, R.N., Director of Nursing
**Control**: State, Government, Nonfederal **Service**: General medical and surgical

**Staffed Beds**: 33

⊞ **KINDRED HOSPITAL-PHILADELPHIA (392027)**, 6129 Palmetto Street,
Zip 19111–5729; tel. 215/722–8555, (Includes KINDRED HOSPITAL
PHILADELPHIA - HAVERTOWN, Mailing address: 2000 Old West Chester Pike,
Havertown, Pennsylvania, Zip 19083–2712; tel. 610/536–2100; Margaret M
Murphy, Chief Executive Officer), (Nonreporting) **A**1 10 **F**1 3 29 30 35 50 60 65
70 74 75 77 85 86 90 96 107 130 148 149 **S** Kindred Healthcare, Louisville, KY
Primary Contact: Michele S. Basile, Chief Executive Officer
CFO: Kathy Andrews, Chief Financial Officer
CNO: Erin McCullough, Chief Clinical Officer
Web address: www.kindredphila.com/
**Control**: Corporation, Investor–owned (for–profit) **Service**: Acute long–term care hospital

**Staffed Beds**: 82 **Admissions**: 784 **Census**: 57 **Outpatient Visits**: 0
**Births**: 0 **Total Expense ($000)**: 39493 **Payroll Expense ($000)**: 18128
**Personnel**: 213

⊞ △ **MAGEE REHABILITATION HOSPITAL (393038)**, 1513 Race Street,
Zip 19102–1177; tel. 215/587–3000, (Nonreporting) **A**1 3 5 7 10
Primary Contact: Richard Webster, R.N., President and Chief Executive Officer,
Thomas Jefferson University Hospital
CFO: Stephen DeStefano, Chief Financial Officer
CMO: Guy Fried, M.D., Chief Medical Officer
CIO: Shawna White, Chief Information Officer
CHR: Cindy Tobin-Payne, Director
Web address: www.mageerehab.org
**Control**: Other not–for–profit (including NFP Corporation) **Service**: Rehabilitation

**Staffed Beds**: 96

**METHODIST HOSPITAL** See Jefferson Methodist Hospital

⊞ △ **NAZARETH HOSPITAL (390204)**, 2601 Holme Avenue, Zip 19152–2096;
tel. 215/335–6000, (Nonreporting) **A**1 3 5 7 10 **S** Trinity Health, Livonia, MI
Primary Contact: Michael Magro, D.O., President
CFO: David Wajda, Chief Financial Officer
CMO: Edward O'Dell, D.O., Chief Medical Officer
CIO: Bonnie J. Buehler, Chief Information Technology
CHR: Kathleen M. Pries, Director Human Resources
CNO: Linda Kauffman, R.N., Chief Nursing Officer
Web address: www.nazarethhospital.org
**Control**: Other not–for–profit (including NFP Corporation) **Service**: General medical and surgical

**Staffed Beds**: 162

**NORTH PHILADELPHIA HEALTH SYST** See Girard Medical Center

**NORTH PHILADELPHIA HEALTH SYST** See North Philadelphia Health System

**NORTH PHILADELPHIA HEALTH SYSTEM (390132)**, 801 West Girard Ave,
Zip 19122–4212, Mailing Address: 801 West Girard Avenue, Zip 19122–4212;
tel. 215/787–9000, (Includes GIRARD MEDICAL CENTER, Mailing address:
Girard Avenue at Eighth Street, Philadelphia, Pennsylvania, Zip 19122;
tel. 215/787–2000; Gerri H. Walker, President and Chief Executive Officer),
(Nonreporting) **A**10
Primary Contact: Gerri H. Walker, President and Chief Executive Officer
CFO: Ronald Kaplan, Chief Financial Officer
CIO: Tony Iero, Director Management Information Systems
CHR: James Gloner, Senior Vice President
Web address: www.nphs.com
**Control**: Other not–for–profit (including NFP Corporation) **Service**: General medical and surgical

**Staffed Beds**: 175

⊞ **PENN PRESBYTERIAN MEDICAL CENTER (390223)**, 51 North 39th Street,
Zip 19104–2699; tel. 215/662–8000, (Total facility includes 25 beds in nursing
home–type unit) (Nonreporting) **A**1 2 3 5 10 **F**3 4 5 7 8 9 11 12 15 17 18 20
22 24 26 29 30 31 32 34 35 36 37 38 39 40 43 44 45 46 49 50 51 52 54 56
57 58 59 60 61 62 63 64 65 66 68 70 74 77 78 79 81 82 84 85 86 87 92 94
96 97 98 100 101 104 107 108 110 111 115 118 119 120 121 126 128 130
131 132 134 135 141 142 146 147 148 149 150 154 155 **P**6 **S** University of
Pennsylvania Health System, Philadelphia, PA
Primary Contact: Michele M. Volpe, Chief Executive Officer
COO: Robert J Russell, Associate Executive Director Operations
CFO: Anthony Zumpano, Chief Financial Officer
CMO: Kevin Fosnocht, M.D., Chief Medical Officer and Associate Executive Director
CIO: Theresa Hiltunen, Entity Information Officer
CHR: Margorie Michele, Chief Human Resources Officer
CNO: James R Ballinghoff, MSN, R.N., Chief Nursing Officer and Associate Executive Director
Web address: www.pennmedicine.org/pmc/
**Control**: Other not–for–profit (including NFP Corporation) **Service**: General medical and surgical

**Staffed Beds**: 375 **Admissions**: 18375 **Census**: 306 **Outpatient Visits**: 325168 **Births**: 0 **Total Expense ($000)**: 738838 **Payroll Expense ($000)**: 259154 **Personnel**: 2760

⊞ △ **PENNSYLVANIA HOSPITAL (390226)**, 800 Spruce Street,
Zip 19107–6192; tel. 215/829–3000, (Nonreporting) **A**1 2 3 5 7 10 13 **F**3 8 12
13 15 17 18 20 22 24 26 28 29 30 31 34 35 36 37 38 39 40 44 45 46 49 50
51 52 54 55 56 57 58 59 60 61 62 63 64 65 68 70 72 74 75 76 77 78 79 80
81 82 84 85 86 87 92 96 97 98 100 101 102 103 104 107 108 110 111 114
115 116 117 118 119 120 121 123 124 126 129 130 131 132 135 136 141
142 145 146 147 148 149 150 154 156 **P**6 **S** University of Pennsylvania Health
System, Philadelphia, PA
Primary Contact: Theresa M. Larivee, Chief Executive Officer
CFO: Frank Anastasi, Chief Financial Officer
CMO: Daniel Feinberg, M.D., Chief Medical Officer
CIO: Kwon Lee, Chief Information Officer
CNO: Joanne Ruggiero, Interim Chief Nursing Officer
Web address: www.pahosp.com
**Control**: Other not–for–profit (including NFP Corporation) **Service**: General medical and surgical

**Staffed Beds**: 440 **Admissions**: 17957 **Census**: 257 **Outpatient Visits**: 387979 **Births**: 5131 **Total Expense ($000)**: 652361 **Payroll Expense ($000)**: 222742 **Personnel**: 2536

⊞ △ **PHILADELPHIA VETERANS AFFAIRS MEDICAL CENTER**, 3900 Woodland
Avenue, Zip 19104–4594; tel. 215/823–5800, (Nonreporting) **A**1 3 5 7 **S**
Department of Veterans Affairs, Washington, DC
Primary Contact: Admiral Karen Ann. Flaherty-Oxler, MSN, R.N., Director
CMO: Dave Oslin, M.D., Chief of Staff
CIO: Adrienne Ficchi, Vice President Information Management
CHR: Gerald Morelli, Director Human Resources
Web address: www.philadelphia.va.gov/
**Control**: Veterans Affairs, Government, federal **Service**: General medical and surgical

**Staffed Beds**: 317

**PHILADEPHIA VETERANS AFFAIRS MEDICAL CENTER** See Philadelphia
Veterans Affairs Medical Center

**PRESBYTERIAN MEDICAL CENTER OF THE UNIVERSITY OF PENNSYLVANIA
HEALTH SYSTEM** See Penn Presbyterian Medical Center

☐ **ROXBOROUGH MEMORIAL HOSPITAL (390304)**, 5800 Ridge Avenue,
Zip 19128–1737; tel. 215/483–9900, (Nonreporting) **A**1 3 5 10 **S** Prime
Healthcare, Ontario, CA
Primary Contact: Matt Shelak, Chief Executive Officer
CFO: Thomas Reinboth, Chief Financial Officer
CHR: Michael Henrici, Associate Administrator
Web address: www.roxboroughmemorial.com
**Control**: Corporation, Investor–owned (for–profit) **Service**: General medical and surgical

**Staffed Beds**: 131

**SCHEIE INSTITUTE OF THE HOSPITAL OF THE UNIVERSITY OF
PENNSYLVANIA** See Scheie Eye Institute of The Hospital of The University of
Pennsylvania

**PA**

---

**PA**

⊞ **SHRINERS HOSPITALS FOR CHILDREN-PHILADELPHIA (393309)**, 3551 North Broad Street, Zip 19140–4160; tel. 215/430–4000, (Nonreporting) **A**1 3 5 10 **S** Shriners Hospitals for Children, Tampa, FL
Primary Contact: Ed Myers, Administrator
CFO: Mario Salvati, Director Fiscal Services
CMO: Scott Kozin, M.D., Chief of Staff
CHR: Megan Hauser, Director Human Resources
CNO: Krista Miller, R.N., Chief Nursing Officer
Web address: www.shrinershospitalsforchildren.org/Hospitals/Locations/Philadelphia.aspx
**Control**: Other not–for–profit (including NFP Corporation) **Service**: Children's orthopedic

**Staffed Beds**: 39

**SHRINERS HOSPS FOR CHILD** See Shriners Hospitals for Children-Philadelphia

⊞ **ST. CHRISTOPHER'S HOSPITAL FOR CHILDREN (393307)**, 3601 A Street, Zip 19134–1043, Mailing Address: 160 E. Erie Avenue, Zip 19134–1011; tel. 215/427–5000, (Nonreporting) **A**1 3 5 10 **S** Tower Health, West Reading, PA
Primary Contact: Donald Mueller, Chief Executive Officer
COO: Thomas Runkle, MS, Ph.D., Chief Operating Officer
CMO: Mary Moran, M.D., Pediatrician in Chief
CIO: Robert Taylor, Director Information Services
CHR: Kellie T. Pearson, Chief Human Resource Officer
CNO: Joanna Horst, MSN, R.N., Chief Nursing Officer
Web address: www.stchristophershospital.com
**Control**: Other not–for–profit (including NFP Corporation) **Service**: Children's general medical and surgical

**Staffed Beds**: 121

⊞ **TEMPLE UNIVERSITY HOSPITAL (390027)**, 3401 North Broad Street, Zip 19140–5103; tel. 215/707–2000, (Includes TEMPLE UNIVERSITY HOSPITAL - EPISCOPAL DIVISION, Mailing address: 100 East Lehigh Avenue, Philadelphia, Pennsylvania, Zip 19125–1098; tel. 215/427–7000; Kathleen Barron, Executive Director), (Nonreporting) **A**1 2 3 5 8 10 **F**3 6 8 12 13 15 16 17 18 20 22 24 26 28 29 30 31 34 35 36 37 38 40 43 44 45 46 47 48 49 50 53 54 55 56 57 58 59 60 61 64 68 70 72 73 74 75 76 77 79 81 82 83 84 85 86 87 92 93 94 96 97 98 100 101 102 107 108 109 110 111 112 114 115 118 119 120 121 124 126 129 130 131 132 135 136 137 138 139 140 141 142 145 146 147 148 149 154 156 157 **S** Temple University Health System, Philadelphia, PA
Primary Contact: Michael A. Young, FACHE, President and Chief Executive Officer
CFO: Gerald P Oetzel, Chief Financial Officer
CMO: Herbert Cushing, M.D., Chief Medical Officer
CIO: David Kamowski, Vice President and Chief Information Officer
CHR: John Lasky JrVice President, Chief Human Resources Officer
CNO: Elizabeth J Craig, MSN, Chief Nursing Officer and Vice President Patient Services
Web address: www.tuh.templehealth.org/content/default.htm
**Control**: Other not–for–profit (including NFP Corporation) **Service**: General medical and surgical

**Staffed Beds**: 732 **Admissions**: 35462 **Census**: 562 **Outpatient Visits**: 330597 **Births**: 2331 **Total Expense ($000)**: 1232091 **Payroll Expense ($000)**: 400646 **Personnel**: 4757

⊞ **TEMPLE UNIVERSITY HOSPITAL - JEANES CAMPUS (390080)**, 7600 Central Avenue, Zip 19111–2499; tel. 215/728–2000, (Nonreporting) **A**1 3 5 10 **F**3 11 12 15 17 18 20 22 24 26 28 29 30 31 34 35 40 44 45 49 50 51 56 57 59 60 61 62 65 68 70 74 75 77 78 79 81 82 84 85 86 87 91 92 93 96 107 108 110 111 115 118 119 130 132 135 146 148 149 154 **S** Temple University Health System, Philadelphia, PA
Primary Contact: Marc P. Hurowitz, D.O., Chief Executive Officer
COO: Judith Lynn Bachman, Chief Operating Officer
CFO: Ray Lefton, Chief Financial Officer
CMO: Rebecca Armbruster, M.D., Chief Medical Officer
CIO: Michael Sweeney, Chief Informatics Officer
CHR: Beverly Sherbondy, Assistant Vice President, Human Resources
CNO: Denise Anne Lavery Frasca, MSN, R.N., Vice President Patient Care Services and Chief Nursing Officer
Web address: www.jeanes.com
**Control**: Other not–for–profit (including NFP Corporation) **Service**: General medical and surgical

**Staffed Beds**: 146 **Admissions**: 6889 **Census**: 84 **Outpatient Visits**: 109606 **Births**: 0 **Total Expense ($000)**: 157702 **Payroll Expense ($000)**: 64914 **Personnel**: 951

**TEMPLE UNIVERSITYHOSPITAL - JEANES CAMPUS** See Temple University Hospital - Jeanes Campus

⊞ △ **THOMAS JEFFERSON UNIVERSITY HOSPITALS (390174)**, 111 South 11th Street, Zip 19107–5084; tel. 215/955–6000, (Includes JEFFERSON METHODIST HOSPITAL, Mailing address: 2301 South Broad Street, Philadelphia, Pennsylvania, Zip 19148; tel. 215/952–9000; Stephen K Klasko, M.D., President), (Nonreporting) **A**1 2 3 5 7 8 10 **F**1 3 4 5 6 7 8 9 11 12 13 14 15 16 17 18 20 22 24 26 28 29 30 31 34 35 36 37 38 39 40 43 44 45 48 49 50 51 52 53 54 55 56 57 58 59 60 61 64 65 66 67 68 69 70 71 72 74 75 76 77 78 79 80 81 82 84 85 86 87 89 90 92 93 94 96 97 98 100 101 103 104 107 108 110 111 114 115 116 117 118 119 120 121 123 124 126 128 129 130 131 132 134 135 136 137 138 139 141 142 144 145 146 147 148 149 150 153 154 155 156 **P**2 6 8 **S** Jefferson Health, Philadelphia, PA
Primary Contact: Richard Webster, R.N., President
CFO: Neil Lubarsky, Senior Vice President, Finance and Chief Financial Officer
CMO: Edmund A. Pribitkin, M.D., Chief Medical Officer
CIO: Nassar Nizami, Chief Information Officer
CHR: Jeffrey Stevens, Executive Vice President and Chief Human Resource Officer
CNO: Mary Ann McGinley, Ph.D., Senior Vice President, Patient Services and Chief Nursing Officer
Web address: www.jefferson.edu
**Control**: Other not–for–profit (including NFP Corporation) **Service**: General medical and surgical

**Staffed Beds**: 883 **Admissions**: 39122 **Census**: 622 **Outpatient Visits**: 408759 **Births**: 1979 **Total Expense ($000)**: 1821315 **Payroll Expense ($000)**: 510245 **Personnel**: 6793

**VENCOR HOSPITAL-PHILADELPHIA** See Kindred Hospital-Philadelphia

### PHOENIXVILLE—Chester County

⊞ △ **PHOENIXVILLE HOSPITAL (390127)**, 140 Nutt Road, Zip 19460–3900, Mailing Address: P.O. Box 3001, Zip 19460–0916; tel. 610/983–1000, (Nonreporting) **A**1 2 3 7 10 **F**3 8 13 15 18 20 22 24 26 28 29 31 32 34 35 36 38 39 40 45 46 49 50 51 55 56 57 59 61 64 68 69 70 72 74 75 76 77 78 79 80 81 82 85 86 87 91 92 93 96 102 107 108 110 111 114 115 117 118 119 126 130 132 134 135 146 147 154 156 **S** Tower Health, West Reading, PA
Primary Contact: Stephen M. Tullman, President and Chief Executive Officer
CFO: Edward Chabalowski, Chief Financial Officer
CMO: David Stepansky, M.D., Chief Medical Officer
CIO: Terry Murphy, Director Information Services
CHR: Denise Chiolo, Chief Human Resources Officer
CNO: Sarah Strzelecki, Ed.D., R.N., Chief Nursing Officer
Web address: www.https://phoenixville.towerhealth.org
**Control**: Other not–for–profit (including NFP Corporation) **Service**: General medical and surgical

**Staffed Beds**: 137 **Admissions**: 6238 **Census**: 75 **Outpatient Visits**: 84894 **Births**: 724 **Total Expense ($000)**: 174945 **Payroll Expense ($000)**: 51617 **Personnel**: 809

### PITTSBURGH—Allegheny County

⊞ **ALLEGHENY GENERAL HOSPITAL (390050)**, 320 East North Avenue, Zip 15212–4756; tel. 412/359–3131, (Nonreporting) **A**1 2 3 5 8 10 12 **F**3 6 11 12 15 17 18 20 22 24 26 28 29 30 31 34 35 36 37 39 40 43 44 45 46 47 48 49 50 53 54 57 58 59 64 65 66 70 74 75 77 78 79 80 81 82 84 85 86 87 89 92 93 96 100 102 104 105 107 108 110 111 114 115 117 118 119 121 123 124 126 130 131 132 135 137 138 139 141 146 147 148 149 153 154 155 **S** Allegheny Health Network, Pittsburgh, PA
Primary Contact: David S. Parda, M.D., President
COO: Duke Rupert, Chief Operating Officer
CFO: Richard W Fries, Vice President Finance
CMO: Tony Farah, M.D., President Medical Staff
CIO: John Foley, Chief Information Officer
Web address: www.wpahs.org/locations/allegheny-general-hospital
**Control**: Other not–for–profit (including NFP Corporation) **Service**: General medical and surgical

**Staffed Beds**: 401 **Admissions**: 23597 **Census**: 356 **Outpatient Visits**: 330077 **Births**: 0 **Total Expense ($000)**: 813844 **Payroll Expense ($000)**: 224614 **Personnel**: 3493

**ALLEGHENY UNIVERSITY HOSPITALS** See Allegheny General Hospital

**CHILDREN INST OF PITTSBURGH** See The Children's Institute of Pittsburgh

**CHILDREN'S HOSPITAL OF PITTSBURGH OF UPMC** See UPMC Children's Hospital of Pittsburgh

**ENCOMPASS HEALTH HARMARVILLE REHABILITATION HOSPITAL** See Encompass Health Rehabilitation Hospital of Hamarville

*Many Facility Codes have changed. Please refer to the AHA Guide Code Chart.*
© 2021 AHA Guide

⊞ **ENCOMPASS HEALTH REHABILITATION HOSPITAL OF HAMARVILLE (393027)**, 320 Guys Run Road, Zip 15238–0460, Mailing Address: P.O. Box 11460, Zip 15238–0460; tel. 412/828–1300, (Nonreporting) **A**1 10 **F**28 29 34 56 64 75 77 79 82 86 87 90 91 93 94 96 130 131 132 146 148 149 154 156 157 **S** Encompass Health Corporation, Birmingham, AL
Primary Contact: Michelle P. Cunningham, Chief Executive Officer
CFO: Daniel A Vrana, Controller
CMO: James Kreshon, M.D., Medical Director
CHR: Kathy Grills, Director Human Resources
CNO: Eileen Skalski, Chief Nursing Officer
Web address: www.healthsouthharmarville.com
**Control**: Corporation, Investor–owned (for–profit) **Service**: Rehabilitation

Staffed Beds: 50 Admissions: 1129 Census: 48 Outpatient Visits: 7029
Births: 0 Total Expense ($000): 17001 Payroll Expense ($000): 11213
Personnel: 178

**EYE AND EAR HOSPITAL OF PITTSBURGH** See UPMC Presbyterian, Pittsburgh

⊞ **LIFECARE BEHAVIORAL HEALTH HOSPITAL (394054)**, 225 Penn Avenue, Zip 15221–2148; tel. 469/247–2000, (Includes LIFECARE HOSPITALS OF PITTSBURGH - SUBURBAN, Mailing address: 100 South Jackson Avenue, Pittsburgh, Pennsylvania, Zip 15202–3428, 100 South Jackson Avenue, 4th Floor, Zip 15202–3428, tel. 412/734–7600; Trisha Niemuth, Market Chief Executive Officer), (Nonreporting) **A**1 10 **F**3 29 98 100 101 103 **S** LifeCare Management Services, Plano, TX
Primary Contact: Steven Jarrell, Chief Executive Officer
CFO: Asia Holyfield, Manager Business Office
CMO: Steven Sotos, M.D., President Medical Staff
CIO: Mike Wattenbarger, Chief Information Officer
CHR: Robin F. Arslanpay, Director Human Resources
CNO: Paula Pawloski, Chief Nursing Officer
Web address: www.lifecare-hospitals.com
**Control**: Corporation, Investor–owned (for–profit) **Service**: Psychiatric

Staffed Beds: 49 Admissions: 425 Census: 7 Outpatient Visits: 0 Births: 0
Personnel: 73

**LIFECARE HOSPITALS OF PITTSBURGH** See Lifecare Behavioral Health Hospital

**LIFECARE HOSPITALS OF PITTSBURGH - SUBURBAN CAMPUS** See Lifecare Hospitals of Pittsburgh - Suburban

**MAGEE-WOMENS HOSPITAL OF UPMC** See UPMC Magee-Womens Hospital

**MERCY HOSPITAL OF PITTSBURGH** See UPMC Mercy

**MONTEFIORE HOSPITAL** See UPMC Montefiore

⊞ **SELECT SPECIALTY HOSPITAL-PITTSBURGH/UPMC (392044)**, 200 Lothrop Street, E824, Zip 15213–2536; tel. 412/586–9800, (Includes SELECT SPECIALTY HOSPITAL - ALLE KISKI, Mailing address: 1301 Carlisle Street, Natrona Heights, Pennsylvania, Zip 15065–1152; tel. 724/226–7312), (Nonreporting) **A**1 10 **S** Select Medical Corporation, Mechanicsburg, PA
Primary Contact: Darrell Jones, Interim Chief Executive Officer
CMO: Michael Donahue, M.D., Medical Director
CHR: Prudence Sloan, Coordinator Human Resources
CNO: Eli Babich, Chief Nursing Officer
Web address: www.pittsburghupmc.selectspecialtyhospitals.com/
**Control**: Corporation, Investor–owned (for–profit) **Service**: Acute long–term care hospital

Staffed Beds: 32

**SELECT SPECIALTY HOSPITAL-UPMC** See Select Specialty Hospital-Pittsburgh/UPMC

**SHADYSIDE HOSPITAL** See UPMC Shadyside

☐ **SOUTHWOOD PSYCHIATRIC HOSPITAL**, 2575 Boyce Plaza Road, Zip 15241–3925; tel. 412/257–2290, (Nonreporting) **A**1 **S** Acadia Healthcare Company, Inc., Franklin, TN
Primary Contact: Stephen J. Quigley, Chief Executive Officer
CFO: Frank Urban, Chief Financial Officer
CMO: Allan W Clark, M.D., Medical Director
CHR: Erin J Frohnhofer, Director Human Resources
Web address: www.southwoodhospital.com
**Control**: Corporation, Investor–owned (for–profit) **Service**: Children's hospital psychiatric

Staffed Beds: 156

⊞ **ST. CLAIR HOSPITAL (390228)**, 1000 Bower Hill Road, Zip 15243–1873; tel. 412/942–4000, (Nonreporting) **A**1 2 3 10 **F**3 8 13 15 17 18 20 22 24 26 28 29 30 31 34 35 40 45 46 47 48 49 51 53 54 57 59 60 64 67 70 73 74 75 76 77 78 79 81 84 85 86 87 89 92 93 96 97 98 100 102 105 107 108 110 111 114 115 117 119 120 121 126 129 130 131 132 134 135 142 143 144 145 146 147 148 149 153 156 **P**6
Primary Contact: James M. Collins, President and Chief Executive Officer
COO: Michael J Flanagan, Senior Vice President and Chief Operating Officer
CFO: Richard C Chesnos, Senior Vice President Finance and Chief Financial Officer
CMO: John Sullivan, M.D., Chief Medical Officer
CIO: Richard Schaeffer, Vice President Information Systems and Chief Information Officer
CHR: Andrea Kalina, Vice President External Affairs and Chief Human Resources Officer
CNO: Joan Massella, Administrative Vice President and Chief Nursing Officer
Web address: www.stclair.org
**Control**: Other not–for–profit (including NFP Corporation) **Service**: General medical and surgical

Staffed Beds: 302 Admissions: 15386 Census: 174 Outpatient
Visits: 312257 Births: 1445 Total Expense ($000): 275305 Payroll
Expense ($000): 105886 Personnel: 1727

**ST. CLAIR MEMORIAL HOSPITAL** See St. Clair Hospital

★ **THE CHILDREN'S HOME OF PITTSBURGH (393304)**, 5324 Penn Avenue, Zip 15224–1733; tel. 412/441–4884, (Nonreporting) **A**10
Primary Contact: Pamela R. Keen, Chief Executive Officer
COO: Kimberly Reblock, M.D., Chief Operating Officer
CFO: Kimberly A Phillips, Chief Financial Officer
CMO: Frederick C Sherman, M.D., Chief Medical Officer
Web address: www.childrenshomepgh.org
**Control**: Other not–for–profit (including NFP Corporation) **Service**: Children's general medical and surgical

Staffed Beds: 30

**THE CHILDREN'S INSTITUTE OF PITTSBURGH (393308)**, 1405 Shady Avenue, Zip 15217–1350; tel. 412/420–2400, (Nonreporting) **A**10
Primary Contact: Wendy Ann. Pardee, President and Chief Executive Officer
COO: Stacey Vaccaro, Chief Operating Officer
CFO: John Jubas, Vice President Finance
CMO: Matthew Masiello, M.D., Chief Medical Officer
CIO: Sharon Dorogy, Chief Information Officer
CHR: Linda M Allen, Vice President Human Resources
Web address: www.amazingkids.org
**Control**: Other not–for–profit (including NFP Corporation) **Service**: Children's rehabilitation

Staffed Beds: 62

**UNIV MEDICAL CENTER-PASSAVANT** See UPMC Passavant

⊞ **UPMC CHILDREN'S HOSPITAL OF PITTSBURGH (393302)**, One Children's Hospital Drive, Zip 15224–1334; tel. 412/692–5325, (Nonreporting) **A**1 3 5 10 **F**3 8 12 17 18 19 20 21 22 23 24 25 26 27 28 29 30 31 32 34 35 36 38 39 40 41 43 45 46 48 49 50 53 54 55 57 58 59 60 61 64 65 66 68 71 72 74 75 77 78 79 81 82 84 86 87 88 89 90 91 92 93 94 97 100 107 108 109 111 112 114 115 116 117 118 119 120 121 123 124 126 127 129 130 131 132 134 135 136 137 138 139 140 141 142 143 144 146 148 150 154 **S** UPMC, Pittsburgh, PA
Primary Contact: Mark Sevco, President
CFO: Mario Wilfong, Chief Financial Officer
CMO: Brian Martin, Vice President Medical Affairs
CIO: Srinivasan Suresh, M.D., Chief Medical Information Officer
CHR: Rhonda Larimore, Vice President, Human Resources
CNO: Diane Hupp, R.N., Vice President Support Services and Patient Care Services
Web address: www.chp.edu
**Control**: Other not–for–profit (including NFP Corporation) **Service**: Children's general medical and surgical

Staffed Beds: 303 Admissions: 12986 Census: 229 Outpatient
Visits: 353559 Births: 1 Total Expense ($000): 731951 Payroll Expense
($000): 176888 Personnel: 2739

**PA**

---

Hospital, Medicare Provider Number, Address, Telephone, Approval, Facility, and Physician Codes, Health Care System

★ American Hospital Association (AHA) membership    ◯ Healthcare Facilities Accreditation Program    ⇧ Center for Improvement in Healthcare Quality Accreditation
☐ The Joint Commission accreditation    ◇ DNV Healthcare Inc. accreditation    △ Commission on Accreditation of Rehabilitation Facilities (CARF) accreditation

**UPMC MAGEE-WOMENS HOSPITAL (390114)**, 300 Halket Street, Zip 15213–3108; tel. 412/641–1000, (Total facility includes 20 beds in nursing home–type unit) (Nonreporting) **A**1 2 3 5 10 **F**3 8 11 12 13 15 18 29 30 31 34 35 36 40 44 45 46 52 54 55 56 57 58 59 64 65 66 68 70 72 74 75 76 77 78 79 80 81 82 84 85 86 87 90 91 97 100 107 108 110 111 115 117 119 120 121 123 124 126 128 130 132 134 135 146 147 148 149 150 154 **S** UPMC, Pittsburgh, PA
Primary Contact: Richard Beigi, M.D., President
COO: Lou Baverso, Vice President Operations
CFO: Jared Weiner, Chief Financial Officer
CMO: Dennis English, M.D., Vice President Medical Affairs
CHR: Rhonda Larimore, Vice President Human Resources
CNO: Maribeth McLaughlin, R.N., Vice President Patient Care Services
Web address: www.magee.edu
**Control:** Other not–for–profit (including NFP Corporation) **Service:** Obstetrics and gynecology

**Staffed Beds:** 321 **Admissions:** 18488 **Census:** 232 **Outpatient Visits:** 599105 **Births:** 8701 **Total Expense ($000):** 973926 **Payroll Expense ($000):** 146943 **Personnel:** 2381

**UPMC MERCY (390028)**, 1400 Locust Street, Zip 15219–5166; tel. 412/232–8111, (Nonreporting) **A**1 3 5 10 13 **F**3 4 16 18 20 22 24 26 28 29 30 31 34 35 36 39 40 43 44 45 46 47 48 49 50 51 54 56 57 58 59 60 61 64 65 66 68 70 74 75 77 78 79 81 82 84 85 86 87 90 91 92 93 94 95 96 97 100 101 102 107 108 111 114 115 116 118 119 126 129 130 131 132 135 141 142 146 148 154 156 157 **S** UPMC, Pittsburgh, PA
Primary Contact: Michael A. Grace, President
COO: Julie Hecker, Vice President, Operations
CFO: Jared Weiner, Chief Financial Officer
CIO: Kevin Conway, Chief Information Officer
CHR: Tracey Stange-Kolo, Vice President, Human Resources
CNO: Leeanna McKibben, R.N., MSN, Vice President Patient Services and Chief Nursing Officer
Web address: www.upmc.com/HospitalsFacilities/HFHome/Hospitals/Mercy/
**Control:** Other not–for–profit (including NFP Corporation) **Service:** General medical and surgical

**Staffed Beds:** 383 **Admissions:** 17036 **Census:** 302 **Outpatient Visits:** 168240 **Births:** 729 **Total Expense ($000):** 405599 **Payroll Expense ($000):** 126011 **Personnel:** 2276

**UPMC MONTEFIORE** See UPMC Presbyterian, Pittsburgh

**UPMC PASSAVANT (390107)**, 9100 Babcock Boulevard, Zip 15237–5815; tel. 412/748–6700, (Includes UPMC PASSAVANT CRANBERRY, Mailing address: One St Francis Way, Cranberry, Pennsylvania, Zip 16066; tel. 724/772–5300; Teresa G Petrick, President), (Nonreporting) **A**1 2 3 5 10 **F**3 8 9 11 15 17 18 20 22 24 26 28 29 30 31 34 35 40 44 45 46 47 48 49 51 54 56 57 58 59 60 61 63 64 65 68 70 74 75 77 78 79 81 82 84 85 86 87 90 96 97 100 107 108 111 114 115 117 118 119 120 121 123 126 129 130 131 132 135 143 146 147 148 154 156 157 **S** UPMC, Pittsburgh, PA
Primary Contact: Susan E. Hoolahan, R.N., MSN, President
CFO: Brian Fritz, Chief Financial Officer
CMO: James W Boyle, M.D., Chief Medical Officer
CNO: Susan E Hoolahan, R.N., MSN, Vice President Patient Care Services and Chief Nursing Officer
Web address: www.https://www.upmc.com/locations/hospitals/passavant
**Control:** Other not–for–profit (including NFP Corporation) **Service:** General medical and surgical

**Staffed Beds:** 306 **Admissions:** 15542 **Census:** 216 **Outpatient Visits:** 293081 **Births:** 0 **Total Expense ($000):** 376061 **Payroll Expense ($000):** 98313 **Personnel:** 1786

**UPMC PRESBYTERIAN (390164)**, 200 Lothrop Street, Zip 15213–2536; tel. 412/647–2345, (Includes EYE AND EAR HOSPITAL OF PITTSBURGH, Mailing address: 200 Lothrop Street, Pittsburgh, Pennsylvania, Zip 15213–2592; tel. 412/647–2345; UPMC MONTEFIORE, Mailing address: 3459 Fifth Avenue, Pittsburgh, Pennsylvania, Zip 15213; tel. 412/647–2345; John Innocenti Sr, President; UPMC PRESBYTERIAN HOSPITAL, Mailing address: 200 Lothrop Street, Pittsburgh, Pennsylvania, Zip 15213; tel. 412/647–2345; UPMC SHADYSIDE, Mailing address: 5230 Centre Avenue, Pittsburgh, Pennsylvania, Zip 15232–1381; tel. 412/623–2121; Timothy Kagle, Vice President, Operations; WESTERN PSYCHIATRIC INSTITUTE AND CLINIC, Mailing address: 3811 O'Hara Street, Pittsburgh, Pennsylvania, Zip 15213–2593; tel. 412/624–2100; Deborah Brodine, President), (Nonreporting) **A**1 2 3 5 8 10 **F**3 5 6 7 8 9 11 12 14 17 18 20 22 24 26 28 29 30 31 34 35 36 37 38 39 40 43 44 45 46 47 48 49 50 51 54 55 56 57 58 59 60 61 63 64 65 66 68 70 71 74 75 77 78 79 81 82 84 85 86 87 90 91 92 93 94 95 96 97 98 99 100 101 102 103 104 105 106 107 108 111 113 114 115 116 117 118 119 120 121 123 124 126 129 130 131 132 135 136 137 138 139 140 141 142 145 146 148 149 153 154 155 156 157 158 **S** UPMC, Pittsburgh, PA
Primary Contact: John Innocenti Sr, President
CFO: Jared Weiner, Chief Financial Officer
CMO: Margaret Reidy, M.D., Vice President Medical Affairs
CHR: Kathryn Devine, Vice President Human Resources
Web address: www.https://www.upmc.com/locations/hospitals/presbyterian/
**Control:** Other not–for–profit (including NFP Corporation) **Service:** General medical and surgical

**Staffed Beds:** 1409 **Admissions:** 55976 **Census:** 1132 **Outpatient Visits:** 1042376 **Births:** 0 **Total Expense ($000):** 2210108 **Payroll Expense ($000):** 538216 **Personnel:** 13088

**UPMC PRESBYTERIAN SHADYSIDE** See UPMC Presbyterian

**UPMC ST. MARGARET (390102)**, 815 Freeport Road, Zip 15215–3301; tel. 412/784–4000, (Nonreporting) **A**1 3 5 10 13 **F**3 6 7 8 9 11 15 18 20 29 30 31 34 35 40 44 45 49 51 54 56 57 58 59 60 61 63 64 65 68 70 74 75 77 78 79 81 82 84 85 86 87 90 96 97 100 104 107 108 111 114 115 119 120 121 123 126 129 130 131 132 134 135 143 146 147 148 154 156 157 **S** UPMC, Pittsburgh, PA
Primary Contact: David J. Patton, President
COO: Merle Taylor, Vice President Operations
CFO: Brian Fritz, Chief Financial Officer
CMO: John Lagnese, M.D., Vice President Medical Affairs
CIO: Charles M. Rudek, Chief Information Officer
CHR: Tracey Stange-Kolo, Vice President Human Resources
CNO: Mary C Barkhymer, R.N., MSN, Vice President Patient Care Services and Chief Nursing Officer
Web address: www.upmc.com/locations/hospitals/st-margaret/Pages/default.aspx
**Control:** Other not–for–profit (including NFP Corporation) **Service:** General medical and surgical

**Staffed Beds:** 175 **Admissions:** 10217 **Census:** 134 **Outpatient Visits:** 156862 **Births:** 0 **Total Expense ($000):** 236542 **Payroll Expense ($000):** 65552 **Personnel:** 1342

**UPMC-PRESBYTERIAN HOSPITAL** See UPMC Presbyterian Hospital

**UPMC-ST MARGARET** See UPMC St. Margaret

**VETERANS ADM MEDICAL CENTER** See Veterans Affairs Medical Center

**VETERANS AFF MEDICAL CENTER** See Veterans Affairs Medical Center

△ **VETERANS AFFAIRS PITTSBURGH HEALTHCARE SYSTEM**, University Drive C, Zip 15240; tel. 866/482–7488, (Includes VETERANS AFFAIRS MEDICAL CENTER, Mailing address: 7180 Highland Drive, Pittsburgh, Pennsylvania, Zip 15206–1297; tel. 412/365–4900; VETERANS AFFAIRS MEDICAL CENTER, Mailing address: University Drive 'C', Pittsburgh, Pennsylvania, Zip 15240–1001; tel. 412/688–6000), (Nonreporting) **A**1 3 5 7 8 **S** Department of Veterans Affairs, Washington, DC
Primary Contact: Donald E. Koenig, Director
CMO: Ali Sonel, M.D., Chief of Staff
CIO: John Kovac, Facility Chief Information Officer
CHR: Amber Mesoras, Chief Human Resources Officer
CNO: Ira Richmond, Associate Director Patient Care Services
Web address: www.pittsburgh.va.gov/
**Control:** Veterans Affairs, Government, federal **Service:** Psychiatric

**Staffed Beds:** 549

⊞ **WEST PENN HOSPITAL (390090)**, 4800 Friendship Avenue, Zip 15224–1722; tel. 412/578–5000, (Nonreporting) **A**1 2 3 5 8 10 **F**3 11 12 13 15 16 17 18 20 22 24 26 29 30 31 34 35 36 37 40 44 45 46 47 48 49 50 51 54 55 57 58 59 64 66 70 72 73 74 75 76 77 78 79 80 81 82 84 85 86 87 90 96 102 107 108 110 111 115 118 119 120 121 123 124 126 129 130 132 135 136 141 142 145 146 147 148 149 154 **S** Allegheny Health Network, Pittsburgh, PA
Primary Contact: Ronald J. Andro, R.N., MS, President and Chief Executive Officer
CFO: James A Kanuch, Vice President Finance
CMO: I William Goldfarb, Chief Medical Officer
CIO: Jacqueline Dailey, Chief Information Officer
CHR: Sally Carozza, Director Human Resources
CNO: Paula A Lacher, MSN, R.N., Chief Nursing Officer
Web address: www.wpahs.org
**Control**: Other not–for–profit (including NFP Corporation) **Service**: General medical and surgical

**Staffed Beds**: 270 **Admissions**: 13620 **Census**: 213 **Outpatient Visits**: 164871 **Births**: 4420 **Total Expense ($000)**: 486321 **Payroll Expense ($000)**: 113385 **Personnel**: 1879

**WESTERN PENNSYLVANIA HOSPITAL** See West Penn Hospital

**WESTERN PSYCHIATRIC INSTITUTE AND CLINIC** See UPMC Presbyterian, Pittsburgh

## PLEASANT GAP—Centre County

⊞ **ENCOMPASS HEALTH NITTANY VALLEY REHABILITATION HOSPITAL (393039)**, 550 West College Avenue, Zip 16823–7401; tel. 814/359–3421, (Nonreporting) **A**1 10 **S** Encompass Health Corporation, Birmingham, AL
Primary Contact: Amy Lynn. Adams, Chief Executive Officer
CFO: Alan M Phillips, Controller
CMO: Richard Allatt, M.D., Medical Director
CHR: Michelle Katz, Director Human Resources
CNO: Penny Frownfelter, Chief Nursing Officer
Web address: www.nittanyvalleyrehab.com
**Control**: Corporation, Investor–owned (for–profit) **Service**: Rehabilitation

**Staffed Beds**: 73

**HEALTHSOUTH NITTANY VALLEY REHABILITATION HOSPITAL** See Encompass Health Nittany Valley Rehabilitation Hospital

## POTTSTOWN—Montgomery County

⊞ **POTTSTOWN HOSPITAL (390123)**, 1600 East High Street, Zip 19464–5093; tel. 610/327–7000, (Nonreporting) **A**1 3 10 **S** Tower Health, West Reading, PA
Primary Contact: Richard Newell, Chief Executive Officer
COO: Bryce Sillyman, Chief Operating Officer
CFO: Debbie Konarski, Chief Financial Officer
CMO: Richard McLaughlin, M.D., Chief Medical Officer
CIO: Chad Paine, Director Client Services
CHR: Kimberly Schneider, Director Human Resources
CNO: Ann Blankenhorn, Chief Nursing Officer
Web address: www.https://pottstown.towerhealth.org/
**Control**: Other not–for–profit (including NFP Corporation) **Service**: General medical and surgical

**Staffed Beds**: 232

**POTTSTOWN MEMORIAL MEDICAL CENTER** See Pottstown Hospital

## POTTSVILLE—Schuylkill County

⊞ △ **LEHIGH VALLEY HOSPITAL - SCHUYLKILL (390030)**, 420 South Jackson Street, Zip 17901–3625; tel. 570/621–5000, (Includes LEHIGH VALLEY HOSPITAL - SCHUYLKILL EAST NORWEGIAN STREET, Mailing address: 700 East Norwegian Street, Pottsville, Pennsylvania, Zip 17901–2710; tel. 570/621–4000; William Reppy, President), (Nonreporting) **A**1 7 10 19 **F**3 11 13 15 28 29 30 31 34 35 40 45 46 49 56 57 59 62 64 70 74 75 76 77 78 79 81 82 84 85 86 89 90 92 93 96 97 98 99 100 101 102 103 107 108 110 111 115 117 118 119 124 126 130 132 135 146 147 148 149 154 156 **S** Lehigh Valley Health Network, Allentown, PA
Primary Contact: William Reppy, President
CFO: Diane Boris, Chief Financial Officer
CIO: Tina Zanis, Director Information Systems
CHR: Lynn Lansdowne, Vice President Labor Relations and Human Resources
CNO: Darnell F Furer, MS, R.N., Vice President Patient Care Services and Chief Nursing Officer
Web address: www.schuylkillhealth.com
**Control**: Other not–for–profit (including NFP Corporation) **Service**: General medical and surgical

**Staffed Beds**: 186 **Admissions**: 7614 **Census**: 127 **Outpatient Visits**: 179222 **Births**: 593 **Total Expense ($000)**: 138133 **Payroll Expense ($000)**: 57456 **Personnel**: 837

**LEHIGH VALLEY HOSPITAL - SCHUYLKILL SOUTH JACKSON STREET** See Lehigh Valley Hospital - Schuylkill

**SCHUYLKILL MEDICAL CENTER - EAST NORWEGIAN STREET** See Lehigh Valley Hospital - Schuylkill East Norwegian Street

## PUNXSUTAWNEY—Jefferson County

**PUNXSUTAWNEY AREA HOSPITAL (390199)**, 81 Hillcrest Drive, Zip 15767–2616; tel. 814/938–1800, (Nonreporting) **A**10 20
Primary Contact: Daniel D. Blough Jr, Chief Executive Officer
CFO: Jack Sisk, Chief Financial Officer
CMO: Dajani Zuhd, M.D., President Medical Staff
CIO: Chuck States, Director Information Systems
CHR: Barbara Kostok, Manager Human Resources
CNO: Paula Spack, R.N., MSN, Vice President Nursing
Web address: www.pah.org
**Control**: Other not–for–profit (including NFP Corporation) **Service**: General medical and surgical

**Staffed Beds**: 49

## QUAKERTOWN—Bucks County

☐ **ST. LUKE'S HOSPITAL - QUAKERTOWN CAMPUS (390035)**, 1021 Park Avenue, Zip 18951–1573; tel. 215/538–4500, (Nonreporting) **A**1 2 3 10 **F**3 11 15 18 28 29 30 31 34 35 38 40 43 44 45 49 50 51 54 56 57 59 60 63 64 65 70 71 74 75 77 78 79 81 82 85 86 87 92 93 98 100 102 107 108 109 110 111 115 118 119 129 130 131 132 135 144 146 148 149 154 **S** St. Luke's University Health Network, Bethlehem, PA
Primary Contact: Dennis Pfleiger, President
CFO: Theresa Corrado, Director Finance
CMO: Thomas Filipowicz, M.D., Medical Director
CIO: Chad Brisendine, Chief Information Officer
CHR: Shelley Maley, Director Human Resources
Web address: www.https://www.slhn.org/quakertown
**Control**: Other not–for–profit (including NFP Corporation) **Service**: General medical and surgical

**Staffed Beds**: 62 **Admissions**: 3530 **Census**: 43 **Outpatient Visits**: 94958 **Births**: 0 **Total Expense ($000)**: 71990 **Payroll Expense ($000)**: 30527 **Personnel**: 336

**ST. LUKE'S QUAKERTOWN HOSPITAL** See St. Luke's Hospital - Quakertown Campus

**PA**

Hospital, Medicare Provider Number, Address, Telephone, Approval, Facility, and Physician Codes, Health Care System

★ American Hospital Association (AHA) membership
☐ The Joint Commission accreditation
○ Healthcare Facilities Accreditation Program
◇ DNV Healthcare Inc. accreditation
⇑ Center for Improvement in Healthcare Quality Accreditation
△ Commission on Accreditation of Rehabilitation Facilities (CARF) accreditation

© 2021 AHA Guide          *Many Facility Codes have changed. Please refer to the AHA Guide Code Chart.*          Hospitals **A605**

## READING—Berks County

⊞ **ENCOMPASS HEALTH READING REHABILITATION HOSPITAL (393026)**, 1623 Morgantown Road, Zip 19607–9455; tel. 610/796–6000, (Nonreporting) **A**1 10 19 **S** Encompass Health Corporation, Birmingham, AL
Primary Contact: Shelby Olind, Chief Executive Officer
CFO: Jason Pulaski, Controller
CMO: Suzanne Adam, D.O., Medical Director
CHR: Kelly Kozik, Director Human Resources
Web address: www.https://www.encompasshealth.com/readingrehab
**Control**: Corporation, Investor–owned (for–profit) **Service**: Rehabilitation

**Staffed Beds:** 60

**HAVEN BEHAVIORAL HEALTH OF EASTERN PENNSYLVANIA** See Haven Behavioral Hospital of Eastern Pennsylvania

☐ **HAVEN BEHAVIORAL HOSPITAL OF EASTERN PENNSYLVANIA (394052)**, 145 North 6th Street, 3rd Floor, Zip 19601–3096; tel. 610/406–4340, (Nonreporting) **A**1 10 **S** Haven Behavioral Healthcare, Nashville, TN
Primary Contact: Robert Scheffler, Chief Executive Officer
CMO: Mark Putnam, M.D., Medical Director
CHR: Kathy Copenhaver, Director Human Resources
Web address: www.https://havenbehavioral.com/
**Control**: Corporation, Investor–owned (for–profit) **Service**: Psychiatric

**Staffed Beds:** 48

**HEALTHSOUTH READING REHABILITATION HOSPITAL** See Encompass Health Reading Rehabilitation Hospital

⊞ **PENN STATE HEALTH ST. JOSEPH (390096)**, 2500 Bernville Road, Zip 19605–9453, Mailing Address: P.O. Box 316, Zip 19603–0316; tel. 610/378–2000, (Includes PENN STATE HEALTH ST. JOSEPH - DOWNTOWN CAMPUS, Mailing address: 145 North Sixth Street, Reading, Pennsylvania, Zip 19601, P O Box 316, Zip 19603–0316, tel. 610/378–2000; Joseph Frank, Interim President), (Nonreporting) **A**1 2 5 10 13 19 **F**3 12 13 15 18 20 22 24 26 28 29 30 31 32 34 35 39 40 44 45 46 49 50 51 53 54 57 58 59 64 66 68 70 71 72 74 75 76 77 78 79 81 82 84 85 87 89 93 97 107 108 110 111 113 114 115 116 117 118 119 120 121 126 130 131 132 135 144 146 147 148 149 156 157 **P**1 6 **S** Penn State Hershey Health System, Hershey, PA
Primary Contact: Joseph Frank, Interim President
CFO: Courtney Coffman, Vice President, Finance and Chief Financial Officer
CMO: Jeffrey Held, M.D., Vice President, Medical Affairs
CIO: Amanda Klopp, Director, Innovation and Clinical Integration
CHR: Scott Mengle, Vice President Human Resources
CNO: Sharon Strohecker, R.N., MSN, Vice President Clinical Operations and Chief Nursing Officer
Web address: www.thefutureofhealthcare.org
**Control**: Other not–for–profit (including NFP Corporation) **Service**: General medical and surgical

**Staffed Beds:** 180 **Admissions:** 7724 **Census:** 94 **Outpatient Visits:** 242079 **Births:** 575 **Total Expense ($000):** 223362 **Payroll Expense ($000):** 74686 **Personnel:** 1550

**ST. JOSEPH MEDICAL CENTER-DOWNTOWN READING** See Penn State Health St. Joseph - Downtown Campus

**ST. JOSEPH REGIONAL HEALTH NETWORK** See Penn State Health St. Joseph

## RENOVO—Clinton County

**BUCKTAIL MEDICAL CENTER (391304)**, 1001 Pine Street, Zip 17764–1620; tel. 570/923–1000, (Nonreporting) **A**10 18
Primary Contact: Timothy Reeves, Administrator
CFO: Wendy Janerella, Controller
CMO: Alvin Berlot, M.D., Medical Director
Web address: www.bucktailmed.org
**Control**: Other not–for–profit (including NFP Corporation) **Service**: General medical and surgical

**Staffed Beds:** 64

## RIDLEY PARK—Delaware County

**TAYLOR HOSPITAL** See Crozer-Chester Medical Center, Upland

## ROARING SPRING—Blair County

⊞ **CONEMAUGH NASON MEDICAL CENTER (390062)**, 105 Nason Drive, Zip 16673–1202; tel. 814/224–2141, (Nonreporting) **A**1 10 **F**3 11 15 17 18 20 22 29 30 34 35 39 40 45 46 50 57 59 64 65 70 74 75 76 77 79 81 85 87 91 107 108 110 111 114 119 124 127 130 141 146 147 148 149 154 **S** LifePoint Health, Brentwood, TN
Primary Contact: Timothy Harclerode, Chief Executive Officer
CFO: Kimberly Semelsberger, CPA, Chief Financial Officer
CHR: Lorie Smith, Director Human Resources
Web address: www.nasonhospital.com
**Control**: Corporation, Investor–owned (for–profit) **Service**: General medical and surgical

**Staffed Beds:** 45 **Admissions:** 1758 **Census:** 12 **Outpatient Visits:** 70196 **Births:** 262 **Total Expense ($000):** 37282 **Payroll Expense ($000):** 13310 **Personnel:** 245

**NASON HOSPITAL** See Conemaugh Nason Medical Center

## ROYERSFORD—Montgomery County

⇧ **PHYSICIANS CARE SURGICAL HOSPITAL (390324)**, 454 Enterprise Drive, Zip 19468–1200; tel. 610/495–3330, (Nonreporting) **A**10 21
Primary Contact: Christopher Doyle, Chief Executive Officer
Web address: www.phycarehospital.com
**Control**: Partnership, Investor–owned (for–profit) **Service**: Surgical

**Staffed Beds:** 12

## SAINT MARYS—Elk County

**ELK REGIONAL HEALTH CENTER** See Penn Highlands Elk

★ **PENN HIGHLANDS ELK (391315)**, 763 Johnsonburg Road, Zip 15857–3498; tel. 814/788–8000, (Nonreporting) **A**3 10 18
Primary Contact: Bradley Chapman, President
CFO: Laurie MacDonald, Vice President Finance
CMO: David Johe, M.D., President Medical Staff
CIO: Mary Ann Schwabenbauer, Director Information Technology
CHR: Seanna D'Amore, Director Human Resources
Web address: www.phhealthcare.org
**Control**: Other not–for–profit (including NFP Corporation) **Service**: General medical and surgical

**Staffed Beds:** 173

## SAYRE—Bradford County

⊞ **GUTHRIE ROBERT PACKER HOSPITAL (390079)**, 1 Guthrie Square, Zip 18840–1698; tel. 570/888–6666, (Nonreporting) **A**1 2 3 5 10 13 19 **F**3 11 12 13 15 18 20 22 24 26 28 29 30 31 34 37 38 40 41 43 44 45 46 47 48 49 50 57 58 59 61 64 70 73 74 75 76 78 79 81 82 84 85 86 87 89 91 92 93 96 98 100 102 105 107 108 110 111 114 115 116 117 118 119 120 121 123 126 129 130 132 141 142 145 146 148 149 150 154 **S** Guthrie Clinic, Sayre, PA
Primary Contact: Joseph T. Sawyer Jr, President and Chief Operating Officer
CFO: Scott Silvestri, Chief Financial Officer, Hospital Financial Operations
CMO: Brian Fillipo, M.D., Chief Medical Officer
CIO: Burt Robles, Vice President Information Services
CHR: Frank Pinkosky, Senior Vice President
CNO: Catherine Mohr, R.N., MSN, Chief Nursing Officer
Web address: www.https://www.guthrie.org/location/robert-packer-hospital
**Control**: Other not–for–profit (including NFP Corporation) **Service**: General medical and surgical

**Staffed Beds:** 267 **Admissions:** 14792 **Census:** 175 **Outpatient Visits:** 154937 **Births:** 739 **Total Expense ($000):** 338656 **Payroll Expense ($000):** 85218 **Personnel:** 1401

**ROBERT PACKER HOSPITAL** See Guthrie Robert Packer Hospital

## SCRANTON—Lackawanna County

☐ **ALLIED SERVICES REHABILITATION HOSPITAL (393030)**, 475 Morgan Highway, Zip 18508–2605, Mailing Address: P.O. Box 1103, Zip 18501–1103; tel. 570/348–1300, (Nonreporting) **A**1 10
Primary Contact: William P. Conaboy, Chief Executive Officer
CFO: Michael Avvisato, Senior Vice President and Chief Financial Officer
CMO: Gregory Basting, M.D., Vice President Medical Affairs
CIO: John Regula, Chief Information Officer
CHR: Judy P Oprisko, Vice President
CNO: Jeana Sluck, R.N., Executive Director Nursing Clinical Inpatient Departments
Web address: www.allied-services.org
**Control**: Other not–for–profit (including NFP Corporation) **Service**: Rehabilitation

**Staffed Beds:** 117

**PA**

**ALLIED SERVS INST REHAB HOSP** See Allied Services Rehabilitation Hospital

**COMMUNITY MEDICAL CENTER HEALTHCARE SYSTEM** See Geisinger-Community Medical Center

✠ **GEISINGER-COMMUNITY MEDICAL CENTER (390001)**, 1800 Mulberry Street, Zip 18510–2369; tel. 570/703–8000, (Nonreporting) **A**1 2 3 5 10 19 **F**3 11 12 15 18 20 22 24 26 28 29 30 31 34 35 37 39 40 43 44 45 46 47 49 53 54 56 58 59 61 64 65 68 70 74 75 77 78 79 80 81 82 84 85 86 87 89 91 92 93 94 97 98 100 102 107 108 110 111 114 115 117 118 119 126 129 130 131 132 135 145 146 147 148 149 154 156 **P**1 5 8 **S** Geisinger, Danville, PA
Primary Contact: Ronald R. Beer, FACHE, Chief Administrative Officer
CMO: Anthony Aquilina, D.O., Chief Medical Officer
CHR: Lois Wolfe, Director Human Resources
Web address: www.geisinger.org/for-patients/locations-directions/gcmc/
**Control:** Other not-for-profit (including NFP Corporation) **Service:** General medical and surgical

> **Staffed Beds: 213 Admissions: 12446 Census: 156 Outpatient Visits: 262951 Births: 0 Total Expense ($000): 316877 Payroll Expense ($000): 103345 Personnel: 1570**

**MERCY HOSPITAL OF SCRANTON** See Regional Hospital of Scranton

✠ **MOSES TAYLOR HOSPITAL (390119)**, 700 Quincy Avenue, Zip 18510–1724; tel. 570/770–5000, (Nonreporting) **A**1 3 5 10 19 **F**3 7 13 15 18 29 30 31 34 40 44 45 49 50 51 54 56 57 59 60 61 64 65 66 68 70 72 74 75 76 77 78 79 81 85 86 87 92 93 98 103 107 108 110 111 114 115 116 117 119 124 129 130 132 135 146 147 154 **S** Community Health Systems, Inc., Franklin, TN
Primary Contact: Michael L. Brown, President and Chief Executive Officer
CFO: Thomas Bisignani, Chief Financial Officer
CMO: Mary Sewatsky, M.D., Chief Medical Officer
CHR: Elizabeth Leo, Chief Human Resources Officer
CNO: Patricia Seliga, R.N., Chief Nursing Officer
Web address: www.https://www.commonwealthhealth.net/
**Control:** Corporation, Investor-owned (for-profit) **Service:** General medical and surgical

> **Staffed Beds: 213 Admissions: 7357 Census: 96 Outpatient Visits: 162264 Births: 2153 Total Expense ($000): 150568 Payroll Expense ($000): 44674 Personnel: 785**

✠ **REGIONAL HOSPITAL OF SCRANTON (390237)**, 746 Jefferson Avenue, Zip 18510–1624; tel. 570/348–7100, (Nonreporting) **A**1 2 3 5 10 19 **F**7 8 11 12 15 17 18 20 22 24 26 28 29 31 34 35 39 40 44 45 46 47 48 49 50 51 53 54 57 58 59 60 61 64 65 66 68 70 74 75 77 78 79 81 82 85 86 87 91 92 93 97 100 107 108 109 110 111 112 113 114 115 116 117 118 119 120 121 122 123 124 126 130 132 143 144 145 146 147 148 149 157 **S** Community Health Systems, Inc., Franklin, TN
Primary Contact: Michael L. Brown, Chief Executive Officer
CFO: Stephen Franko, Vice President Finance and Chief Financial Officer
CMO: Anthony Yanni, M.D., Vice President Medical Affairs
CIO: Jorge Coronel, Chief Information Officer
Web address: www.regionalhospitalofscranton.net
**Control:** Corporation, Investor-owned (for-profit) **Service:** General medical and surgical

> **Staffed Beds: 186 Admissions: 7778 Census: 100 Outpatient Visits: 77457 Births: 0 Total Expense ($000): 170552 Payroll Expense ($000): 50842 Personnel: 756**

**SELLERSVILLE—Bucks County**

✠ **GRAND VIEW HEALTH (390057)**, 700 Lawn Avenue, Zip 18960–1548, Mailing Address: P.O. Box 902, Zip 18960–0902; tel. 215/453–4000, (Nonreporting) **A**1 2 3 10 **F**3 7 11 12 13 15 18 20 22 28 29 31 34 35 37 40 45 46 50 54 56 57 59 62 63 64 65 68 70 72 74 75 76 77 78 79 81 84 85 86 87 89 90 93 96 97 107 108 110 111 114 115 116 117 118 119 120 121 123 126 130 131 132 135 143 146 149 156 157 **P**6
Primary Contact: Jean M. Keeler, President and Chief Executive Officer
COO: J Mark Horne, Senior Vice President, Ambulatory Services and Chief Operating Officer
CFO: Michael Keen, Senior Vice President and Chief Financial Officer
CMO: Jane Ferry, M.D., Vice President Medical Affairs
CIO: Jane Doll Loveless, Vice President, Chief Information Officer
CNO: Kathleen Burkey, R.N., MSN, Vice President, Patient Care Service and Chief Nursing Officer
Web address: www.gvh.org
**Control:** Other not-for-profit (including NFP Corporation) **Service:** General medical and surgical

> **Staffed Beds: 176 Admissions: 7862 Census: 88 Outpatient Visits: 329464 Births: 1132 Total Expense ($000): 207503 Payroll Expense ($000): 108944 Personnel: 1082**

**GRAND VIEW HOSPITAL** See Grand View Health

**SENECA—Venango County**

✠ **UPMC NORTHWEST (390091)**, 100 Fairfield Drive, Zip 16346–2130; tel. 814/676–7600, (Total facility includes 16 beds in nursing home–type unit) (Nonreporting) **A**1 3 10 19 **F**3 11 12 13 15 18 20 26 28 29 31 34 35 40 41 44 45 46 47 50 51 57 59 60 63 64 65 68 70 71 74 75 76 77 78 79 81 82 83 84 85 86 87 90 91 93 94 96 98 100 101 102 103 107 108 110 111 114 115 119 121 123 128 130 132 135 141 142 146 147 148 154 155 156 157 **S** UPMC, Pittsburgh, PA
Primary Contact: Brian Durniok, President
COO: Brian Durniok, Vice President Operations
CFO: Bradley Dinger, Chief Financial Officer
CMO: David McCandless, Vice President Medical Affairs
CHR: Brian Durniok, President
Web address: www.upmc.com/locations/hospitals/northwest/Pages/default.aspx
**Control:** Other not-for-profit (including NFP Corporation) **Service:** General medical and surgical

> **Staffed Beds: 128 Admissions: 5946 Census: 92 Outpatient Visits: 143164 Births: 613 Total Expense ($000): 114971 Payroll Expense ($000): 30126 Personnel: 623**

**UPMC NORTHWEST MEDICAL CENTER** See UPMC Northwest

**SEWICKLEY—Allegheny County**

✠ **ENCOMPASS HEALTH REHABILITATION HOSPITAL OF SEWICKLEY (393045)**, 303 Camp Meeting Road, Zip 15143–8322; tel. 412/741–9500, (Nonreporting) **A**1 10 **F**29 34 56 57 59 60 62 64 65 74 75 87 90 91 92 93 95 96 100 132 146 148 154 **S** Encompass Health Corporation, Birmingham, AL
Primary Contact: Leah Laffey, R.N., Chief Executive Officer
CFO: Daniel A Vrana, Area Controller
CMO: Shelana Gibbs-McElvy, M.D., Medical Director
CIO: Jamie Smith, Supervisor Health Information Management Systems
CHR: Melissa Coleman, Director Human Resources
CNO: Christie Ryan, Chief Nursing Officer
Web address: www.healthsouthsewickley.com
**Control:** Corporation, Investor-owned (for-profit) **Service:** Rehabilitation

> **Staffed Beds: 55 Admissions: 1164 Census: 43 Outpatient Visits: 4010 Births: 0 Total Expense ($000): 17838 Payroll Expense ($000): 8550 Personnel: 161**

**HEALTHSOUTH REHABILITATION HOSPITAL OF SEWICKLEY** See Encompass Health Rehabilitation Hospital of Sewickley

**SEWICKLEY VALLEY HOSPITAL** See Sewickley Valley Hospital, (A Division of Valley Medical Facilities)

**PA**

---

☐ **SEWICKLEY VALLEY HOSPITAL, (A DIVISION OF VALLEY MEDICAL FACILITIES) (390037)**, 720 Blackburn Road, Zip 15143–1459; tel. 412/741–6600, (Nonreporting) **A**1 3 10 **S** Heritage Valley Health System, Beaver, PA
Primary Contact: Norman F. Mitry, President and Chief Executive Officer
COO: John Luellen, M.D., Chief Operating Officer
CFO: Robert Rosenberger, Chief Financial Officer
CMO: Michael Cratty, M.D., Chief Medical Officer
CIO: David Carleton, Chief Information Officer
CHR: Bruce Edwards, Vice President Human Resources
CNO: Linda Homyk, Chief Nursing Officer
Web address: www.heritagevalley.org
**Control:** Other not–for–profit (including NFP Corporation) **Service:** General medical and surgical

**Staffed Beds:** 179

### SHARON—Mercer County

**SHARON REGIONAL HEALTH SYSTEM** See Sharon Regional Medical Center

☐ **SHARON REGIONAL MEDICAL CENTER (390211)**, 740 East State Street, Zip 16146–3395; tel. 724/983–3911, (Nonreporting) **A**1 3 10 **S** Steward Health Care System, LLC, Dallas, TX
Primary Contact: Robert Rogalski, President
Web address: www.https://www.sharonregionalmedical.org
**Control:** Corporation, Investor–owned (for–profit) **Service:** General medical and surgical

**Staffed Beds:** 218

### SHICKSHINNY—Luzerne County

**CLEAR BROOK LODGE** See Huntington Creek Recovery Center

**HUNTINGTON CREEK RECOVERY CENTER**, 890 Bethel Road, Zip 18655; tel. 570/864–3116, (Nonreporting)
Primary Contact: Kelly McKenna, Chief Executive Officer
Web address: www.clearbrookinc.com
**Control:** Other not–for–profit (including NFP Corporation) **Service:** Alcoholism and other chemical dependency

**Staffed Beds:** 65

### SHIPPENSBURG—Franklin County

☐ **ROXBURY TREATMENT CENTER (394050)**, 601 Roxbury Road, Zip 17257–9302; tel. 800/648–4673, (Nonreporting) **A**1 10 **S** Universal Health Services, Inc., King of Prussia, PA
Primary Contact: Shauna Mogerman, Chief Executive Officer
Web address: www.roxburyhospital.com
**Control:** Corporation, Investor–owned (for–profit) **Service:** Psychiatric

**Staffed Beds:** 94

### SOMERSET—Somerset County

⊞ **UPMC SOMERSET (390039)**, 225 South Center Avenue, Zip 15501–2088; tel. 814/443–5000, (Nonreporting) **A**1 10 20 **F**3 8 11 15 17 18 20 22 26 28 29 30 31 32 34 35 39 40 45 49 50 53 57 59 62 63 64 65 68 75 77 79 80 81 82 84 85 86 87 89 97 98 100 102 103 107 108 110 111 115 119 129 130 131 132 133 135 146 149 154 156 **S** UPMC, Pittsburgh, PA
Primary Contact: Andrew G. Rush, President
CFO: Monica Klatt, Chief Financial Officer
CIO: Dale Fuller, Vice President, Chief Information Officer
CHR: Tracey Stange-Kolo, Vice President Human Resources
CNO: Kristine Keefer Wolff, Vice President and Chief Nursing Officer
Web address: www.somersethospital.com
**Control:** Other not–for–profit (including NFP Corporation) **Service:** General medical and surgical

**Staffed Beds:** 98 **Admissions:** 2527 **Census:** 33 **Outpatient Visits:** 129828 **Births:** 0 **Total Expense ($000):** 65683 **Payroll Expense ($000):** 25748 **Personnel:** 581

**UPMC SOMERSET HOSPITAL** See UPMC Somerset

### SPRINGFIELD—Delaware County

**METRO HOSP-SPRINGFIELD DIV** See Springfield Hospital

**SPRINGFIELD HOSPITAL** See Crozer-Chester Medical Center, Upland

### STATE COLLEGE—Centre County

**MOUNT NITTANY HEALTH** See Mount Nittany Medical Center

⊞ **MOUNT NITTANY MEDICAL CENTER (390268)**, 1800 East Park Avenue, Zip 16803–6797; tel. 814/231–7000, (Nonreporting) **A**1 2 3 5 10 20 **F**3 7 8 13 15 17 20 22 26 28 29 30 31 35 40 46 49 51 57 59 64 68 70 73 74 75 76 77 78 79 80 81 82 84 85 87 89 93 98 100 101 102 107 108 111 114 115 118 119 121 126 129 130 132 135 143 146 148 149 154
Primary Contact: Kathleen Rhine, President and Chief Executive Officer
CFO: Bryan Roach, Executive Vice President and Chief Financial Officer
CMO: Nirmal Joshi, M.D., System Chief Medical Officer
CIO: Michael Martz, Senior Vice President and Chief Information Officer
CNO: Tiffany Cabibbo, Executive Vice President and Chief Nursing Officer
Web address: www.mountnittany.org
**Control:** Other not–for–profit (including NFP Corporation) **Service:** General medical and surgical

**Staffed Beds:** 260 **Admissions:** 13082 **Census:** 131 **Outpatient Visits:** 312422 **Births:** 1283 **Total Expense ($000):** 416311 **Payroll Expense ($000):** 186276 **Personnel:** 1653

### STROUDSBURG—Monroe County

☐ **ST. LUKE'S MONROE (390330)**, 100 St. Lukes Lane, Zip 18360–6217, Mailing Address: 100 St. Luke's Lane, Zip 18360; tel. 484/526–2116, (Nonreporting) **A**1 10 **F**3 7 12 15 18 20 22 26 29 30 31 34 35 38 40 44 45 46 47 49 50 51 54 56 57 59 60 63 64 70 74 75 77 78 79 81 85 86 87 93 100 102 107 108 109 110 111 115 118 119 120 121 123 129 130 132 144 145 146 147 149 154 155
Primary Contact: Donald Seiple, President
Web address: www.slhn.org/Choose/choose-monroe
**Control:** Other not–for–profit (including NFP Corporation) **Service:** General medical and surgical

**Staffed Beds:** 90 **Admissions:** 6712 **Census:** 69 **Outpatient Visits:** 127668 **Births:** 0 **Total Expense ($000):** 128389 **Payroll Expense ($000):** 44548 **Personnel:** 538

**ST.LUKE'S MONROE** See St. Luke's Monroe

### SUSQUEHANNA—Susquehanna County

**BARNES-KASSON COUNTY HOSPITAL (391309)**, 2872 Turnpike Street, Zip 18847–2771; tel. 570/853–3135, (Nonreporting) **A**10 18
Primary Contact: Sara F. Adornato, Executive Director
CFO: Kelli R Kane, Director of Finance
CMO: Pravinchandra Patel, M.D., Chief Medical Officer
CIO: Eric Detwiler, Director Information Technology
Web address: www.barnes-kasson.org
**Control:** Other not–for–profit (including NFP Corporation) **Service:** General medical and surgical

**Staffed Beds:** 83

### TITUSVILLE—Crawford County

★ **TITUSVILLE AREA HOSPITAL (391314)**, 406 West Oak Street, Zip 16354–1404; tel. 814/827–1851, (Nonreporting) **A**10 18 **S** Meadville Medical Center, Meadville, PA
Primary Contact: Lee M. Clinton, FACHE, President and Chief Executive Officer
CFO: Jill Neely, Chief Financial Officer
CMO: William Sonnenberg, M.D., President Medical Staff
CIO: Karen Humes, Chief Information Officer
CHR: Jeffrey Saintz, Vice President Human Resources
CNO: Brenda Burnett, R.N., Vice President Patient Care Services and Chief Nursing Officer
Web address: www.titusvillehospital.org
**Control:** Other not–for–profit (including NFP Corporation) **Service:** General medical and surgical

**Staffed Beds:** 25

### TORRANCE—Westmoreland County

**TORRANCE STATE HOSPITAL (394026)**, Torrance Road, Zip 15779–0111, Mailing Address: P.O. Box 111, Zip 15779–0111; tel. 724/459–8000, (Nonreporting) **A**10 **F**39 53 65 75 77 97 98 100 101 130 135 143 146 147 148 154
Primary Contact: Stacey Keilman, Chief Executive Officer
COO: R Brad Snyder, Chief Operating Officer
CFO: Michael Yahner, Chief Financial Officer
CMO: Herbert G Chissell, M.D., Chief Medical Officer
Web address: www.dpw.state.pa.us
**Control:** State, Government, Nonfederal **Service:** Psychiatric

**Staffed Beds:** 357 **Admissions:** 348 **Census:** 303 **Outpatient Visits:** 0 **Births:** 0 **Total Expense ($000):** 87993 **Payroll Expense ($000):** 41307 **Personnel:** 690

*Many Facility Codes have changed. Please refer to the AHA Guide Code Chart.*

© 2021 AHA Guide

## TOWANDA—Bradford County

★ **GUTHRIE TOWANDA MEMORIAL HOSPITAL (390236)**, 91 Hospital Drive, Zip 18848–9702; tel. 570/265–2191, (Total facility includes 160 beds in nursing home–type unit) (Nonreporting) **A**10 **F**3 7 10 11 28 29 34 35 36 40 50 57 59 64 75 77 79 81 82 85 87 93 107 108 111 115 119 128 129 130 133 135 143 146 154 157 **S** Guthrie Clinic, Sayre, PA
Primary Contact: Felissa Koernig, President and Chief Operating Officer
CIO: Karen Brown, Manager Information Technology
CHR: Linda Berry, Vice President Human Resources
CNO: Lynn Dibble, Vice President Patient Care Services
Web address: www.https://www.guthrie.org/location/guthrie-towanda-memorial-hospital
**Control**: Other not–for–profit (including NFP Corporation) **Service**: General medical and surgical

**Staffed Beds**: 195 **Admissions**: 1311 **Census**: 137 **Outpatient Visits**: 69439 **Births**: 0 **Total Expense ($000)**: 36639 **Payroll Expense ($000)**: 12385 **Personnel**: 279

**MEMORIAL HOSPITAL** See Guthrie Towanda Memorial Hospital

## TRANSFER—Mercer County

**EDGEWOOD SURGICAL HOSPITAL (390307)**, 239 Edgewood Drive Extension, Zip 16154–1817; tel. 724/646–0400, (Nonreporting) **A**10
Primary Contact: Tom Roskos, Chief Executive Officer
Web address: www.edgewoodsurgical.com
**Control**: Corporation, Investor–owned (for–profit) **Service**: Surgical

**Staffed Beds**: 10

## TROY—Bradford County

★ ○ **GUTHRIE TROY COMMUNITY HOSPITAL (391305)**, 275 Guthrie Drive, Zip 16947; tel. 570/297–2121, (Nonreporting) **A**10 11 18 **F**3 11 15 28 29 30 40 43 45 50 59 68 75 81 82 85 87 92 93 107 110 111 119 129 130 133 135 146 148 149 157 **S** Guthrie Clinic, Sayre, PA
Primary Contact: Lori Barnett, R.N., MSN, President and Chief Operating Officer
CFO: Bernie Smith, Chief Financial Officer
CMO: Vance A Good, M.D., Chief Medical Staff
CIO: Dale Swingle, Vice President Information Services
CHR: Frank Pinkosky, Executive Vice President
Web address: www.guthrie.org
**Control**: Other not–for–profit (including NFP Corporation) **Service**: General medical and surgical

**Staffed Beds**: 25 **Admissions**: 686 **Census**: 7 **Outpatient Visits**: 8123 **Births**: 0 **Total Expense ($000)**: 15343 **Payroll Expense ($000)**: 6494 **Personnel**: 134

**TROY COMMUNITY HOSPITAL** See Guthrie Troy Community Hospital

## TUNKHANNOCK—Wyoming County

**MERCY TYLER HOSPITAL** See Tyler Memorial Hospital

⊞ **TYLER MEMORIAL HOSPITAL (390192)**, 5950 State Route 6, Zip 18657–7905; tel. 570/836–2161, (Nonreporting) **A**1 10 **S** Community Health Systems, Inc., Franklin, TN
Primary Contact: Ann Marie. Stevens, R.N., Chief Executive Officer
CMO: Terrance Chilson, Chief of Staff
CNO: Judith Ragukas, Interim Chief Nursing Officer
Web address: www.tylermemorialhospital.net
**Control**: Corporation, Investor–owned (for–profit) **Service**: General medical and surgical

**Staffed Beds**: 44

## TYRONE—Blair County

**TYRONE HOSPITAL (391307)**, 187 Hospital Drive, Zip 16686–1808; tel. 814/684–1255, (Nonreporting) **A**10 18
Primary Contact: Joseph J. Peluso, Chief Executive Officer
CMO: Kelly Biggs, M.D., Chief Medical Officer
CHR: Rosemary Jorden Best, Director Human Resources
CNO: Sharon Fisher, R.N., Chief Nursing Officer
Web address: www.tyronehospital.org
**Control**: Other not–for–profit (including NFP Corporation) **Service**: General medical and surgical

**Staffed Beds**: 25

## UNIONTOWN—Fayette County

⊞ **UNIONTOWN HOSPITAL (390041)**, 500 West Berkeley Street, Zip 15401–5596; tel. 724/430–5000, (Nonreporting) **A**1 10
Primary Contact: Steven P. Handy, CPA, Chief Executive Officer
CHR: James Proud, Vice President Human Resources and Marketing
CNO: Betty Ann Rock, Vice President Nursing and Chief Nursing Officer
Web address: www.uniontownhospital.com
**Control**: Other not–for–profit (including NFP Corporation) **Service**: General medical and surgical

**Staffed Beds**: 142

## UPLAND—Delaware County

☐ **CROZER-CHESTER MEDICAL CENTER (390180)**, One Medical Center Boulevard, Zip 19013–3995; tel. 610/447–2000, (Includes SPRINGFIELD HOSPITAL, Mailing address: 190 West Sproul Road, Springfield, Pennsylvania, Zip 19064–2097; tel. 610/328–8700; TAYLOR HOSPITAL, Mailing address: 175 East Chester Pike, Ridley Park, Pennsylvania, Zip 19078–2212; tel. 610/595–6000), (Nonreporting) **A**1 2 3 5 10 12 13 **S** Prospect Medical Holdings, Los Angeles, CA
Primary Contact: Michael Curran, President
CMO: Sat Arora, M.D., President Medical and Dental Staff
CIO: Robert E Wilson, Vice President and Chief Information Officer
Web address: www.crozer.org
**Control**: Other not–for–profit (including NFP Corporation) **Service**: General medical and surgical

**Staffed Beds**: 384

## WARREN—Warren County

**WARREN GENERAL HOSPITAL (390146)**, Two Crescent Park West, Zip 16365–0068, Mailing Address: P.O. Box 68, Zip 16365–0068; tel. 814/723–4973, (Nonreporting) **A**10 **F**3 4 11 13 15 18 26 27 28 29 31 34 35 40 44 45 47 48 50 51 57 59 62 64 68 70 75 76 77 78 79 81 85 87 89 90 92 93 97 98 99 100 101 102 103 107 108 109 110 111 114 115 116 117 118 119 120 121 123 130 133 145 146 148 149 157
Primary Contact: Richard Allen, Chief Executive Officer
COO: Randy California, Chief Operating Officer
CFO: Julie Jacobs, Chief Financial Officer
CMO: John Maljovec, M.D., Medical Director
CIO: Helen Rosequist, Manager Information Systems
CHR: Matthew Franklin, Director Human Resources
CNO: Joe Akif, Chief Clinical Officer and Chief Nursing Officer
Web address: www.wgh.org
**Control**: Other not–for–profit (including NFP Corporation) **Service**: General medical and surgical

**Staffed Beds**: 87 **Admissions**: 2645 **Census**: 29 **Outpatient Visits**: 164677 **Births**: 266 **Total Expense ($000)**: 74595 **Payroll Expense ($000)**: 32119 **Personnel**: 397

**WARREN STATE HOSPITAL (394016)**, 33 Main Drive, Zip 16365–5001; tel. 814/723–5500, (Nonreporting) **A**10 **F**29 39 50 75 77 82 98 100 128 130 132 135 146 149 **P**6
Primary Contact: Charlotte M. Uber, Chief Executive Officer
COO: Ronnie Cropper, Chief Operating Officer
CFO: Terry Crambes, Manager Finance
CMO: Andrea J. Richard, M.D., Chief Medical Officer
CIO: Karen Byler, Information Technology Generalist
CNO: Sara Flasher, Chief Nurse Executive
Web address: www.https://www.dhs.pa.gov/Services/Assistance/Pages/Warren-State-Hospital.aspx
**Control**: State, Government, Nonfederal **Service**: Psychiatric

**Staffed Beds**: 152 **Admissions**: 91 **Census**: 142 **Outpatient Visits**: 0 **Births**: 0 **Total Expense ($000)**: 48701 **Payroll Expense ($000)**: 20865 **Personnel**: 363

## WASHINGTON—Washington County

☐ **ADVANCED SURGICAL HOSPITAL (390323)**, 100 Trich Drive Suite 1, Zip 15301–5990; tel. 724/884–0710, (Nonreporting) **A**1 10
Primary Contact: Anne S. Hast, R.N., Chief Executive Officer
CFO: Diane Hritz, Chief Financial Officer
CNO: Anne S Hast, R.N., Director of Nursing
Web address: www.ashospital.net
**Control**: Partnership, Investor–owned (for–profit) **Service**: Orthopedic

**Staffed Beds**: 14

---

**Hospital, Medicare Provider Number, Address, Telephone, Approval, Facility, and Physician Codes, Health Care System**

★ American Hospital Association (AHA) membership
☐ The Joint Commission accreditation
○ Healthcare Facilities Accreditation Program
◇ DNV Healthcare Inc. accreditation
⇑ Center for Improvement in Healthcare Quality Accreditation
△ Commission on Accreditation of Rehabilitation Facilities (CARF) accreditation

**PA**

☒ **WASHINGTON HOSPITAL (390042)**, 155 Wilson Avenue, Zip 15301–3398; tel. 724/225–7000, (Nonreporting) **A**1 3 5 10 13 **F**5 11 12 13 15 18 20 22 24 26 28 29 30 31 32 34 35 36 38 39 40 44 45 46 49 50 53 54 56 57 59 60 64 65 74 75 77 78 79 81 82 84 85 86 87 91 92 93 94 96 97 100 101 102 103 107 108 110 111 114 115 118 119 126 127 130 131 132 134 135 146 147 148 154 156 **S** Washington Health System, Washington, PA
Primary Contact: Brook Ward, President and Chief Executive Officer
CFO: Alisa Rucker, Vice President Finance and Chief Financial Officer
CIO: Rodney Louk, Vice President Information Systems
CHR: Barbara A McCullough, Vice President Human Resources
CNO: Karen A Bray, R.N., MSN, Vice President Patient Care Services
Web address: www.washingtonhospital.org
**Control**: Other not–for–profit (including NFP Corporation) **Service**: General medical and surgical

**Staffed Beds**: 181 **Admissions**: 9643 **Census**: 116 **Outpatient Visits**: 732772 **Births**: 817 **Total Expense ($000)**: 235785 **Payroll Expense ($000)**: 101737 **Personnel**: 1606

### WAYNESBORO—Franklin County

**WAYNESBORO HOSPITAL** See Wellspan Waynesboro Hospital

☒ **WELLSPAN WAYNESBORO HOSPITAL (390138)**, 501 East Main Street, Zip 17268–2394; tel. 717/765–4000, (Nonreporting) **A**1 10 **F**3 11 13 15 29 30 34 40 44 45 49 50 54 56 57 59 61 64 65 68 74 75 76 77 79 81 85 86 87 93 94 100 107 108 110 111 115 118 119 130 131 132 133 135 146 147 148 149 150 154 157 **P**8 **S** WellSpan Health, York, PA
Primary Contact: Melissa Dubrow, Vice President and Chief Operating Officer
COO: Melissa Dubrow, Vice President and Chief Operating Officer
CFO: Kimberly Rzomp, Vice President Finance
CMO: Thomas Anderson, M.D., Vice President Medical Affairs
CIO: Michele Zeigler, Vice President Information Services
CHR: Jennifer Knight, Manager Human Resources
CNO: Elyse Fisler, Chief Nursing Officer
Web address: www.https://www.wellspan.org/offices-locations/wellspan-waynesboro-hospital/
**Control**: Other not–for–profit (including NFP Corporation) **Service**: General medical and surgical

**Staffed Beds**: 57 **Admissions**: 2308 **Census**: 19 **Outpatient Visits**: 95970 **Births**: 407 **Total Expense ($000)**: 66243 **Payroll Expense ($000)**: 29257 **Personnel**: 433

### WAYNESBURG—Greene County

**SOUTHWEST REGIONAL MEDICAL CENTER** See Washington Health System Greene

★ **WASHINGTON HEALTH SYSTEM GREENE (390150)**, 350 Bonar Avenue, Zip 15370–1608; tel. 724/627–3101, (Nonreporting) **A**3 5 10 **F**3 11 15 29 30 34 35 40 44 57 59 64 87 107 108 110 111 114 119 130 133 135 146 **S** Washington Health System, Washington, PA
Primary Contact: Terry Wiltrout, President
COO: Janel Mudry, Chief Operating Officer
CMO: Jamie Boris, M.D., President Medical Staff
CIO: Leslie Hayhurst, Director Information Systems
CHR: Patricia Marshall, Assistant Administrator Human Resources
Web address: www.southwestregionalmedical.com/
**Control**: Other not–for–profit (including NFP Corporation) **Service**: General medical and surgical

**Staffed Beds**: 23 **Admissions**: 789 **Census**: 8 **Outpatient Visits**: 50001 **Births**: 0 **Total Expense ($000)**: 18363 **Payroll Expense ($000)**: 8861 **Personnel**: 140

### WELLSBORO—Tioga County

**UPMC SUSQUEHANNA SOLDIERS + SAILORS** See UPMC Wellsboro

☒ **UPMC WELLSBORO (391316)**, 32 Central Avenue, Zip 16901–1899; tel. 570/723–7764, (Nonreporting) **A**1 10 18 **F**3 10 11 13 15 28 29 30 31 32 34 35 40 44 45 46 54 56 57 59 62 63 67 68 75 76 77 78 79 81 84 86 87 90 93 96 97 107 108 110 111 115 118 119 120 128 129 130 131 132 146 147 150 154 157 **P**6 **S** UPMC, Pittsburgh, PA
Primary Contact: Janie Marie. Hilfiger, Chief Administrative Officer
CFO: Eric Pohjala, Chief Financial Officer
CMO: Walter Laibinis, M.D., Chief Medical Officer
CIO: Timothy E Schoener, Senior Vice President and Chief Information Officer
CHR: Dawn Wright, Vice President Human Resources
CNO: Matt Romania, Director of Nursing
Web address: www.susquehannahealth.org
**Control**: Other not–for–profit (including NFP Corporation) **Service**: General medical and surgical

**Staffed Beds**: 20 **Admissions**: 1563 **Census**: 15 **Outpatient Visits**: 89728 **Births**: 169 **Total Expense ($000)**: 64740 **Payroll Expense ($000)**: 22043 **Personnel**: 564

### WERNERSVILLE—Berks County

**WERNERSVILLE STATE HOSPITAL (394014)**, 160 Main Street, Zip 19565–9490; tel. 610/678–3411, (Nonreporting) **A**10
Primary Contact: Shirley Sowizral, Chief Executive Officer
COO: Cheryl Benson, Chief Operating Officer
CMO: Dale K Adair, M.D., Chief Medical Officer
CIO: William Edwards, Information Technology Generalist
CHR: Melvin McMinn, Director Human Resources
Web address: www.dhs.pa.gov/citizens/statehospitals/wernersvillestatehospital/
**Control**: State, Government, Nonfederal **Service**: Psychiatric

**Staffed Beds**: 266

### WEST CHESTER—Chester County

☒ **CHESTER COUNTY HOSPITAL (390179)**, 701 East Marshall Street, Zip 19380–4412; tel. 610/431–5000, (Nonreporting) **A**1 2 3 5 10 **F**3 11 13 15 18 20 22 24 26 28 29 30 31 34 35 36 39 40 44 45 46 49 50 51 54 55 56 57 58 59 60 62 64 65 66 68 70 72 74 75 76 77 78 79 81 84 85 86 87 89 92 93 96 107 108 110 111 114 115 116 117 118 119 120 121 126 130 131 132 135 141 142 146 147 148 149 154 156 **S** University of Pennsylvania Health System, Philadelphia, PA
Primary Contact: Michael J. Duncan, President and Chief Executive Officer
COO: Michael Barber, Chief Operating Officer
CFO: Kenneth E Flickinger, Chief Financial Officer
CMO: Richard D Donze, D.O., Senior Vice President Medical Affairs
CIO: Karen Pinsky, M.D., Chief Medical Information Officer
CHR: Jacqueline Felicetti, Chief Human Resource Officer
CNO: Angela R. Coladonato, R.N., MSN, Chief Nursing Officer
Web address: www.chestercountyhospital.org
**Control**: Other not–for–profit (including NFP Corporation) **Service**: General medical and surgical

**Staffed Beds**: 224 **Admissions**: 14749 **Census**: 157 **Outpatient Visits**: 268895 **Births**: 2874 **Total Expense ($000)**: 346612 **Payroll Expense ($000)**: 127827 **Personnel**: 1891

**CHESTER COUNTY HOSPITAL** See Chester County Hospital

### WEST GROVE—Chester County

☒ **JENNERSVILLE HOSPITAL (390220)**, 1015 West Baltimore Pike, Zip 19390–9459; tel. 610/869–1000, (Nonreporting) **A**1 10 **F**3 18 34 40 45 49 50 51 57 59 65 70 74 75 79 81 85 87 92 93 107 108 110 111 115 119 129 130 146 149 154 **S** Tower Health, West Reading, PA
Primary Contact: Claire Bradley. Mooney, R.N., President and Chief Executive Officer
CFO: Tracey Claxton, Chief Financial Officer
CMO: Tracy Carmellini, M.D., Chief of Staff
CHR: Debra Basquill, Director Human Resources
CNO: Claire Bradley Mooney, R.N., Vice President and Chief Nursing Officer
Web address: www.jennersville.com
**Control**: Other not–for–profit (including NFP Corporation) **Service**: General medical and surgical

**Staffed Beds**: 63 **Admissions**: 2288 **Census**: 19 **Outpatient Visits**: 31472 **Births**: 0 **Total Expense ($000)**: 49379 **Payroll Expense ($000)**: 16788 **Personnel**: 276

**JENNERSVILLE REGIONAL HOSPITAL** See Jennersville Hospital

### WEST READING—Berks County

**READING HEALTH** See Reading Hospital

☒ **READING HOSPITAL (390044)**, Sixth Avenue and Spruce Street, Zip 19611–1428, Mailing Address: P.O. Box 16052, Zip 19612–6052; tel. 610/988–8000, (Nonreporting) **A**1 2 3 5 8 10 13 **S** Tower Health, West Reading, PA
Primary Contact: William Jennings, President and Chief Executive Officer
COO: Dawn Anuszkiewicz, Chief Operating Officer
CFO: Richard W Jones, Chief Financial Officer
CMO: Ron Nutting, M.D., Chief Medical Officer
CIO: Jayashree Raman, Vice President and Chief Information Officer
CNO: Rosemary Wurster, M.P.H., R.N., Chief Nursing Officer
Web address: www.readinghospital.org
**Control**: Other not–for–profit (including NFP Corporation) **Service**: General medical and surgical

**Staffed Beds**: 732

*Many Facility Codes have changed. Please refer to the AHA Guide Code Chart.* © 2021 AHA Guide

**PA**

## WILKES BARRE—Luzerne County

✠ **GEISINGER WYOMING VALLEY MEDICAL CENTER (390270)**, 1000 East Mountain Boulevard, Zip 18711–0027; tel. 570/808–7300, (Nonreporting) **A**1 2 3 5 10 13 19 **F**3 6 9 11 12 13 15 17 18 19 20 22 24 26 28 29 30 31 32 34 35 37 39 40 43 44 45 46 47 48 49 52 53 54 56 57 58 59 61 64 65 68 70 71 72 74 75 76 77 78 79 80 81 82 84 85 86 87 89 90 91 92 93 94 96 97 100 107 108 110 111 114 115 116 117 118 119 120 121 123 124 126 129 130 131 132 135 144 145 146 147 148 149 154 156 **P**1 5 8 **S** Geisinger, Danville, PA
Primary Contact: Ronald R. Beer, FACHE, Chief Administrative Officer
CFO: Thomas A Bielecki, Chief Financial Officer
CMO: Steven Pierdon, M.D., Executive Vice President and Chief Medical Officer
CIO: Frank Richards, Chief Information Officer
CHR: Margaret Heffers, Assistant Vice President Human Resources
Web address: www.geisinger.org
**Control**: Other not–for–profit (including NFP Corporation) **Service**: General medical and surgical

**Staffed Beds: 277 Admissions: 18932 Census: 212 Outpatient Visits: 863001 Births: 1816 Total Expense ($000): 520360 Payroll Expense ($000): 142006 Personnel: 2753**

★ **PAM SPECIALTY HOSPITAL OF WILKES-BARRE (392025)**, 575 North River Street, 7th Floor, Zip 18702–2634; tel. 570/208–3310, (Nonreporting) **A**10 **S** Post Acute Medical, LLC, Enola, PA
Primary Contact: David Long, Chief Executive Officer
Web address: www.warmsprings.org/our-facilities/hospitals/post-acute-medical-specialty-hospital-wilkes-barre/
**Control**: Corporation, Investor–owned (for–profit) **Service**: Acute long–term care hospital

**Staffed Beds: 36**

**PENN STATE GEISINGER WYOMING** See Geisinger Wyoming Valley Medical Center

## WILKES-BARRE—Luzerne County

☐ **JOHN HEINZ INSTITUTE OF REHABILITATION MEDICINE (393036)**, 150 Mundy Street, Zip 18702–6830; tel. 570/826–3800, (Nonreporting) **A**1 10
Primary Contact: Karen Kearney, Vice President Inpatient Rehabilitation Services
CFO: Mike Avvisato, Vice President and Chief Financial Officer
CMO: Gregory Basting, M.D., Vice President Medical Affairs
CIO: John Regula, Chief Information Officer
CNO: Maria Berlyn, Assistant Vice President Nursing Services
Web address: www.allied-services.org
**Control**: Other not–for–profit (including NFP Corporation) **Service**: Rehabilitation

**Staffed Beds: 71**

**VETERANS AFFAIRS MEDICAL CENTER** See Wilkes-Barre Veterans Affairs Medical Center

✠ △ **WILKES-BARRE GENERAL HOSPITAL (390137)**, 575 North River Street, Zip 18764–0001; tel. 570/829–8111, (Includes WILKES-BARRE GENERAL HOSPITAL, Mailing address: 575 North River Street, Wilkes-Barre, Pennsylvania, Zip 18764; tel. 570/829–8111), (Nonreporting) **A**1 2 3 5 7 10 19 **F**3 8 12 13 15 17 18 20 22 24 26 28 29 30 31 34 37 40 43 44 45 46 47 48 49 50 51 54 56 57 59 61 64 66 70 73 74 75 76 79 81 82 83 84 85 86 87 89 90 92 93 96 107 108 110 111 112 114 115 116 117 118 119 120 121 123 124 126 129 130 132 145 146 147 149 154 **S** Community Health Systems, Inc., Franklin, TN
Primary Contact: Cornelio R. Catena, President and Chief Executive Officer
COO: Robert Stiekes, Chief Operating Officer
CFO: Roy Boyd, Chief Financial Officer
CIO: Denis Tucker, Chief Information Officer
CHR: James Carmody, Vice President Human Resources
CNO: Robert P Hoffman, R.N., Chief Nursing Officer
Web address: www.wvhc.org
**Control**: Corporation, Investor–owned (for–profit) **Service**: General medical and surgical

**Staffed Beds: 374 Admissions: 11134 Census: 155 Outpatient Visits: 401972 Births: 772 Total Expense ($000): 307472 Payroll Expense ($000): 78299 Personnel: 1306**

✠ **WILKES-BARRE VETERANS AFFAIRS MEDICAL CENTER**, 1111 East End Boulevard, Zip 18711–0030; tel. 570/824–3521, (Nonreporting) **A**1 2 3 5 **S** Department of Veterans Affairs, Washington, DC
Primary Contact: Russell E. Lloyd, Director
COO: Joesph P. Sharon, Associate Director
CFO: Donald E Foote, Fiscal Officer
CMO: Mirza Z Ali, M.D., Chief of Staff
CIO: David Longmore, Chief Information Officer
CHR: Dawn P DeMorrow, Chief Human Resources Service
Web address: www.va.gov/vamcwb
**Control**: Veterans Affairs, Government, federal **Service**: General medical and surgical

**Staffed Beds: 146**

**WYOMING VALLEY HEALTH CARE SYSTEM** See Wilkes-Barre General Hospital

## WILLIAMSPORT—Lycoming County

**UPMC SUSQUEHANNA DIVINE PROVIDENCE** See UPMC Susquehanna Divine Providence Campus

**UPMC SUSQUEHANNA WILLIAMSPORT REGIONAL MEDICAL CENTER** See UPMC Williamsport

✠ **UPMC WILLIAMSPORT (390045)**, 700 High Street, Zip 17701–3100; tel. 570/321–1000, (Includes UPMC SUSQUEHANNA DIVINE PROVIDENCE CAMPUS, Mailing address: 1100 Grampian Boulevard, Williamsport, Pennsylvania, Zip 17701–1995; tel. 570/326–8000; Robert E. Kane, President), (Nonreporting) **A**1 2 3 5 10 13 19 **F**3 4 5 7 11 13 15 17 18 20 22 24 26 28 29 30 31 32 34 35 38 40 44 45 46 47 48 49 50 54 55 56 57 59 60 61 62 63 64 65 66 68 70 74 75 76 77 78 79 81 82 84 85 86 87 89 90 91 92 93 96 97 98 99 100 103 104 107 108 110 111 114 115 117 118 119 120 121 123 124 125 126 129 130 131 132 134 135 138 139 143 146 147 148 150 151 152 154 156 157 158 **S** UPMC, Pittsburgh, PA
Primary Contact: Donald R. Owrey, President
COO: Jan E Fisher, Executive Vice President, Chief Operating Officer and Chief Administrative Officer
CFO: Eric Pohjala, Executive Vice President and Chief Financial Officer
CIO: Timothy E Schoener, Vice President and Chief Information Officer
CHR: Donald Wilver JrVice President Human Resources
CNO: Lori A Beucler, MSN, RN, BS-NE, FACHE, R.N., Vice President and Chief Nursing Officer
Web address: www.susquehannahealth.org
**Control**: Other not–for–profit (including NFP Corporation) **Service**: General medical and surgical

**Staffed Beds: 250 Admissions: 11691 Census: 157 Outpatient Visits: 363390 Births: 1153 Total Expense ($000): 394650 Payroll Expense ($000): 128219 Personnel: 1449**

## WINDBER—Somerset County

★ **CHAN SOON-SHIONG MEDICAL CENTER (390112)**, 600 Somerset Avenue, Zip 15963–1331; tel. 814/467–3000, (Nonreporting) **A**10 **F**3 11 12 15 18 20 22 28 29 30 34 35 36 40 45 48 53 55 56 57 58 59 62 63 70 75 79 81 83 84 85 93 107 108 110 111 114 118 119 129 130 131 132 135 145 146 147
Primary Contact: Thomas M. Kurtz, President and Chief Executive Officer
CFO: Richard Sukenik, CPA, Vice President Finance and Chief Financial Officer
CIO: Renee Adams, Director Information Technology
CHR: Jamie Brock, Vice President Human Resources
CNO: Michelle Hamula, Director of Nursing and Quality
Web address: www.windbercare.org
**Control**: Other not–for–profit (including NFP Corporation) **Service**: General medical and surgical

**Staffed Beds: 54 Admissions: 1088 Census: 7 Outpatient Visits: 98848 Births: 0 Total Expense ($000): 45263 Payroll Expense ($000): 20320 Personnel: 349**

**WINDBER MEDICAL CENTER** See Chan Soon-Shiong Medical Center

## WYNNEWOOD—Montgomery County

**LANKENAU HOSPITAL** See Lankenau Medical Center

---

**Hospital, Medicare Provider Number, Address, Telephone, Approval, Facility, and Physician Codes, Health Care System**

★ American Hospital Association (AHA) membership
☐ The Joint Commission accreditation
○ Healthcare Facilities Accreditation Program
◇ DNV Healthcare Inc. accreditation
⇑ Center for Improvement in Healthcare Quality Accreditation
△ Commission on Accreditation of Rehabilitation Facilities (CARF) accreditation

☒ **LANKENAU MEDICAL CENTER (390195)**, 100 East Lancaster Avenue, Zip 19096–3411; tel. 484/476–2000, (Nonreporting) **A**1 2 3 5 8 10 12 13 **F**3 11 13 15 17 18 20 22 24 26 28 29 30 31 32 34 35 36 37 38 39 40 41 43 44 45 46 47 48 49 50 54 55 56 57 58 59 63 64 65 66 70 72 73 74 75 76 78 79 80 81 82 84 85 86 87 93 96 97 100 102 107 108 110 111 114 115 118 119 120 121 124 126 129 130 131 132 135 138 141 146 148 149 154 156 157 **S** Main Line Health, Pittsburgh, PA
Primary Contact: Phillip D. Robinson, President
COO: John Schwarz, Vice President Administration
CFO: Michael J Buongiorno, Vice President Finance
CMO: Robert Benz, M.D., Chief Medical Officer
CIO: Kay Carr, Chief Information Officer
CHR: Paul Yakulis, MS, R.N., Senior Vice President Human Resources
Web address: www.https://www.mainlinehealth.org/
**Control**: Other not–for–profit (including NFP Corporation) **Service**: General medical and surgical

Staffed Beds: 370 Admissions: 19153 Census: 234 Outpatient Visits: 311630 Births: 2982 Total Expense ($000): 534791 Payroll Expense ($000): 148031 Personnel: 2323

### WYOMISSING—Berks County

**READING HEALTH REHABILITATION HOSPITAL** See Reading Hospital Rehabilitation at Wyomissing

☐ △ **READING HOSPITAL REHABILITATION AT WYOMISSING**, 2802 Papermill Road, Zip 19610–1065; tel. 484/628–2388, (Nonreporting) **A**1 7
Primary Contact: Clinton Matthews, President and Chief Executive Officer
Web address: www.https://www.readinghealth.org/locations/locations-module/reading-health-rehabilitation-hospital-2802-papermill-road-wyomissing-pa-19610-889615952/
**Control**: Other not–for–profit (including NFP Corporation) **Service**: Rehabilitation

Staffed Beds: 112

☒ **SURGICAL INSTITUTE OF READING (390316)**, 2752 Century Boulevard, Zip 19610–3345; tel. 610/378–8800, (Nonreporting) **A**1 10
Primary Contact: James Bennett, Chief Executive Officer
CFO: Cheryl Peterson, Business Office Manager
CHR: Megan Schaffer, Administrative Assistant
Web address: www.sireading.com
**Control**: Partnership, Investor–owned (for–profit) **Service**: Surgical

Staffed Beds: 15

### YORK—York County

☒ **ENCOMPASS HEALTH REHABILITATION HOSPITAL OF YORK (393037)**, 1850 Normandie Drive, Zip 17408–1534; tel. 717/767–6941, (Nonreporting) **A**1 10 **S** Encompass Health Corporation, Birmingham, AL
Primary Contact: Michelle Fitzgerald, R.N., Chief Executive Officer
CFO: Joyce Henry, Controller
CMO: Bruce Sicilia, M.D., Medical Director
CIO: Laura Emig, Director Marketing Operations
CHR: Bradley Teahl, Director Human Resources
CNO: Julie Scott, Chief Nursing Officer
Web address: www.https://encompasshealth.com/yorkrehab
**Control**: Corporation, Investor–owned (for–profit) **Service**: Rehabilitation

Staffed Beds: 90

**HEALTHSOUTH REHABILITATION HOSPITAL OF YORK** See Encompass Health Rehabilitation Hospital of York

☒ **OSS HEALTH (390325)**, 1861 Powder Mill Road, Zip 17402–4723; tel. 717/718–2000, (Nonreporting) **A**1 10
Primary Contact: Michael Enriquez, Chief Executive Officer
COO: Cynthia Page, FACHE, Chief Operating Officer
CFO: Dale Bushey, Chief Financial Officer
CMO: Todd A. Curran, M.D., President Medical Staff
CIO: Tricia Wolf, Director Information Technology
CHR: Maureen M Putnam, Director Human Resources
CNO: Debra Garton, R.N., Chief Nursing Officer
Web address: www.osshealth.com
**Control**: Partnership, Investor–owned (for–profit) **Service**: Orthopedic

Staffed Beds: 30

**OSS ORTHOPAEDIC SPECIALTY HOSPITAL** See Oss Health

**SELECT SPECIALTY HOSP - YORK** See Select Specialty Hospital-York

**SELECT SPECIALTY HOSPITAL-YORK** See Select Specialty Hospital-Camp Hill, Camp Hill

★ ○ **UPMC MEMORIAL (390101)**, 1701 Innovation Drive, Zip 17408–8815, Mailing Address: P.O. Box 15118, Zip 17405–7118; tel. 717/843–8623, (Nonreporting) **A**3 10 11 13 **F**3 13 15 18 20 22 26 29 30 31 34 35 37 40 44 45 46 47 48 49 50 51 52 54 55 56 57 58 59 60 61 62 64 65 66 68 70 74 75 76 77 78 79 81 85 87 92 93 97 107 108 109 110 111 114 115 116 117 118 119 126 129 130 132 135 146 147 154 156 **P**1 6 **S** UPMC, Pittsburgh, PA
Primary Contact: Michael W. Gaskins, President
CFO: Donna L. Muller, Vice President Finance, Southern Region
CIO: James Mahoney, Chief Information Officer
CHR: Corey Hudak, Director Human Resources
CNO: Susan Gordon, R.N., Chief Nursing Officer
Web address: www.mhyork.org
**Control**: Other not–for–profit (including NFP Corporation) **Service**: General medical and surgical

Staffed Beds: 100 Admissions: 3802 Census: 57 Outpatient Visits: 128823 Births: 424 Total Expense ($000): 93147 Payroll Expense ($000): 32212 Personnel: 563

**UPMC PMEMORIAL** See UPMC Memorial

△ ⇑ **WELLSPAN SURGERY AND REHABILLITATION HOSPITAL (390327)**, 55 Monument Road, Zip 17403–5023; tel. 717/812–6100, (Nonreporting) **A**3 7 10 21 **F**29 30 68 74 77 79 81 82 84 85 87 90 93 94 100 107 112 114 119 130 132 146 148 149 154 **S** WellSpan Health, York, PA
Primary Contact: Victoria Diamond, R.N., MS, President
Web address: www.wellspan.org
**Control**: Other not–for–profit (including NFP Corporation) **Service**: Rehabilitation

Staffed Beds: 72 Admissions: 1720 Census: 45 Outpatient Visits: 2889 Births: 0 Total Expense ($000): 80327 Payroll Expense ($000): 20040

☒ △ **WELLSPAN YORK HOSPITAL (390046)**, 1001 South George Street, Zip 17403–3645; tel. 717/851–2345, (Nonreporting) **A**1 2 3 5 7 8 10 12 13 **F**3 11 12 13 14 15 17 18 20 22 24 26 28 29 30 31 34 35 39 40 43 44 45 46 47 48 49 50 54 55 56 57 58 59 60 61 64 65 66 68 70 72 74 75 76 77 78 79 81 82 84 85 86 87 89 91 92 93 96 97 98 100 101 102 103 107 108 110 111 114 115 117 118 119 120 121 123 124 126 129 130 131 132 135 141 146 147 148 149 154 **S** WellSpan Health, York, PA
Primary Contact: Victoria Diamond, R.N., MS, President
COO: Raymond Rosen, FACHE, Vice President Operations
CFO: Michael F O'Connor, Senior Vice President Finance
CMO: Peter M Hartmann, M.D., Vice President Medical Affairs
CIO: R Hal Baker, M.D., Vice President and Chief Information Officer
CHR: Robert J Batory, Vice President Human Resources
CNO: Astrid Davis, R.N., Chief Nursing Officer
Web address: www.wellspan.org
**Control**: Other not–for–profit (including NFP Corporation) **Service**: General medical and surgical

Staffed Beds: 573 Admissions: 29629 Census: 470 Outpatient Visits: 760000 Births: 3070 Total Expense ($000): 1015696 Payroll Expense ($000): 265419 Personnel: 4015

**YORK HOSPITAL** See Wellspan York Hospital

*Many Facility Codes have changed. Please refer to the AHA Guide Code Chart.*

# RHODE ISLAND

## CRANSTON—Providence County

☐ **ELEANOR SLATER HOSPITAL (412001)**, 111 Howard Avenue,
Zip 02920–0269, Mailing Address: P.O. Box 8269, Zip 02920–0269;
tel. 401/462–3085, (Nonreporting) **A**1 3 10
Primary Contact: Jennifer White, Interim Chief Executive Officer
CMO: Charlene Tate, M.D., Chief Medical Staff and Clinical Services
Web address: www.https://bhddh.ri.gov/esh/
**Control**: State, Government, Nonfederal **Service**: Acute long–term care hospital

**Staffed Beds: 284**

## EAST PROVIDENCE—Providence County

☐ **EMMA PENDLETON BRADLEY HOSPITAL (414003)**, 1011 Veterans Memorial
Parkway, Zip 02915–5099; tel. 401/432–1000, (Nonreporting) **A**1 3 5 10 **F**5
29 30 35 55 75 98 99 101 104 105 106 130 132 153 154 **P**7 **S** Lifespan
Corporation, Providence, RI
Primary Contact: Daniel J. Wall, President and Chief Executive Officer
CFO: Mamie Wakefield, Vice President Finance and Chief Financial Officer
CMO: Henry T Sachs, M.D., IIIMedical Director
CIO: Carole Cotter, Senior Vice President and Chief Information Officer
CHR: Rob Duval, Chief Human Resources Officer
CNO: Vareen O'Keefe Domaleski, MS, R.N., Vice Patient Care Services and Chief
Nursing Officer
Web address: www.lifespan.org
**Control**: Other not–for–profit (including NFP Corporation) **Service**: Children's
hospital psychiatric

**Staffed Beds: 70 Admissions: 1068 Census: 67 Outpatient Visits: 3670
Births: 0 Total Expense ($000): 80200 Payroll Expense ($000): 47540
Personnel: 644**

## NEWPORT—Newport County

☐ △ **NEWPORT HOSPITAL (410006)**, 11 Friendship Street, Zip 02840–2299;
tel. 401/846–6400, (Nonreporting) **A**1 2 3 5 7 10 **F**3 8 9 13 15 18 20 28 29 30
31 34 35 37 40 45 50 51 53 54 56 57 59 60 64 65 68 70 74 75 76 77 78 79
81 82 85 86 87 90 91 92 93 94 96 97 98 100 102 104 105 107 108 111 114
118 119 129 130 131 132 135 146 147 148 154 156 157 **P**3 5 6 7 **S** Lifespan
Corporation, Providence, RI
Primary Contact: Crista F. Durand, President
CFO: Frank J Byrne, Vice President Finance
CMO: Jeffrey Gaines, M.D., Vice President and Chief Medical Officer
CHR: Barbara J. Arcangeli, Vice President Human Resources
CNO: Orla Brandos, Vice President of Patient Care Services and Chief Nursing Officer
Web address: www.newporthospital.org
**Control**: Other not–for–profit (including NFP Corporation) **Service**: General
medical and surgical

**Staffed Beds: 104 Admissions: 5147 Census: 65 Outpatient Visits: 89721
Births: 451 Total Expense ($000): 117104 Payroll Expense ($000): 53076
Personnel: 678**

## NORTH PROVIDENCE—Providence County

**ST JOSEPH HOSP OF RHODE ISLAND** See St. Joseph Health Services of Rhode Island

☐ △ **ST. JOSEPH HEALTH SERVICES OF RHODE ISLAND (410005)**, 200 High
Service Avenue, Zip 02904–5199; tel. 401/456–3000, (Includes OUR LADY OF
FATIMA HOSPITAL, Mailing address: 200 High Service Avenue, North Providence,
Rhode Island, Zip 2904; tel. 401/456–3000; Thomas Hughes, President; ST.
JOSEPH HOSPITAL FOR SPECIALTY CARE, Mailing address: 21 Peace Street,
Providence, Rhode Island, Zip 2907; tel. 401/456–3000), (Nonreporting) **A**1 7 10
**S** Prospect Medical Holdings, Los Angeles, CA
Primary Contact: John J. Holiver, Chief Executive Officer
CFO: Michael E Conklin JrChief Financial Officer
CIO: Susan Cerrone Abely, Chief Information Officer
CHR: Darlene Souza, Vice President
CNO: Patricia A Nadle, R.N., Chief Nursing Officer
Web address: www.saintjosephri.com
**Control**: Other not–for–profit (including NFP Corporation) **Service**: General
medical and surgical

**Staffed Beds: 125**

## NORTH SMITHFIELD—Providence County

**LANDMARK MEDICAL CENTER-FOGARTY UNIT** See Landmark Medical Center,
Woonsocket

☐ **REHABILITATION HOSPITAL OF RHODE ISLAND (413025)**, 116 Eddie Dowling
Highway, Zip 02896–7327; tel. 401/766–0800, (Nonreporting) **A**1 10 **S** Prime
Healthcare, Ontario, CA
Primary Contact: Michael Souza, Chief Executive Officer
COO: Demetra Ouellette, Chief Operating Officer
CFO: Thomas Klessens, Chief Financial Officer
CMO: Khin Yin, Medical Director
CIO: Vincent Larosa, Director of Information Technology Services
CHR: Gail Gosselin, Director Human Resources
CNO: Kathy Keeling, Director of Nursing
Web address: www.rhri.net
**Control**: Other not–for–profit (including NFP Corporation) **Service**: Rehabilitation

**Staffed Beds: 70**

## PROVIDENCE—Providence County

⊞ **BUTLER HOSPITAL (414000)**, 345 Blackstone Boulevard, Zip 02906–4829;
tel. 401/455–6200, (Nonreporting) **A**1 3 5 10 **S** Care New England Health
System, Providence, RI
Primary Contact: Mary Marran, MS, President and Chief Operating Officer
CFO: Bonnie Baker, Vice President Finance and Chief Financial Officer
CMO: James Sullivan, M.D., Chief Medical Officer
CIO: Summa Gaddam, Chief Information Officer
CHR: Timothy Bigelow, Director Human Resources
CNO: Mary Leveillee, Senior Vice President Patient Care Services and Chief
Nursing Officer
Web address: www.butler.org
**Control**: Other not–for–profit (including NFP Corporation) **Service**: Psychiatric

**Staffed Beds: 143**

☐ **MIRIAM HOSPITAL (410012)**, 164 Summit Avenue, Zip 02906–2853;
tel. 401/793–2500, (Nonreporting) **A**1 2 3 5 8 10 **F**3 8 9 12 15 18 20 22 26 28
29 30 31 34 35 37 39 40 44 45 46 49 50 51 54 55 56 57 58 59 60 61 64 65
67 68 70 74 75 77 78 79 81 82 84 85 87 91 92 93 97 100 107 108 110 111
114 115 118 119 126 130 132 135 146 147 148 149 156 157 **P**3 5 6 7 **S**
Lifespan Corporation, Providence, RI
Primary Contact: Arthur J. Sampson, FACHE, President
COO: Maria Ducharme, R.N., Senior Vice President Patient Care Services and Chief
Nursing Officer
CFO: Mamie Wakefield, Chief Financial Officer
CMO: G. Dean Roye, M.D., Senior Vice President of Medical Affairs and Chief
Medical Officer
CIO: Carole Cotter, Vice President and Chief Information Officer
CHR: Nancy McMahon, Vice President Human Resources
Web address: www.lifespan.org
**Control**: Other not–for–profit (including NFP Corporation) **Service**: General
medical and surgical

**Staffed Beds: 247 Admissions: 19583 Census: 204 Outpatient
Visits: 239224 Births: 0 Total Expense ($000): 501331 Payroll Expense
($000): 211095 Personnel: 2677**

⊞ **PROVIDENCE VETERANS AFFAIRS MEDICAL CENTER**, 830 Chalkstone
Avenue, Zip 02908–4799; tel. 401/273–7100, (Nonreporting) **A**1 2 3 5 **S**
Department of Veterans Affairs, Washington, DC
Primary Contact: Lawrence B. Connell, Director
COO: Erin Clare Sears, Associate Director of Operations
CMO: Satish C Sharma, M.D., Chief of Staff
Web address: www.providence.va.gov/
**Control**: Veterans Affairs, Government, federal **Service**: General medical and
surgical

**Staffed Beds: 73**

---

**Hospital, Medicare Provider Number, Address, Telephone, Approval, Facility, and Physician Codes, Health Care System**

★ American Hospital Association (AHA) membership  ○ Healthcare Facilities Accreditation Program  ⇑ Center for Improvement in Healthcare Quality Accreditation
☐ The Joint Commission accreditation  ◇ DNV Healthcare Inc. accreditation  △ Commission on Accreditation of Rehabilitation Facilities (CARF) accreditation

**RI**

☐ **RHODE ISLAND HOSPITAL (410007)**, 593 Eddy Street, Zip 02903–4900; tel. 401/444–4000, (Includes HASBRO CHILDREN'S HOSPITAL, Mailing address: 593 Eddy Street, Providence, Rhode Island, Zip 02903–4923; tel. 401/444–4000), (Nonreporting) **A**1 2 3 5 8 10 **F**3 6 7 8 11 15 16 17 18 19 20 21 22 23 24 26 29 30 31 32 34 35 38 39 40 41 43 44 45 46 47 48 49 50 51 53 54 55 56 57 58 59 60 61 64 65 67 68 70 74 75 77 78 79 81 82 84 85 86 87 88 89 90 91 92 93 94 96 97 98 99 100 101 102 103 104 105 107 108 110 111 114 115 116 117 118 119 120 121 122 123 124 126 129 130 131 132 133 134 135 138 145 146 147 148 149 156 157 **P**3 5 6 7 **S** Lifespan Corporation, Providence, RI
Primary Contact: Margaret M. Van Bree, Dr.PH, President
COO: Fredrick Macri, Executive Vice President
CFO: Mamie Wakefield, Senior Vice President and Chief Financial Officer
CMO: John B Murphy, M.D., Vice President Medical Affairs and Chief Medical Officer
CIO: Carole Cotter, Senior Vice President and Chief Information Officer
CHR: Louis J Sperling, Vice President Human Resources
Web address: www.rhodeislandhospital.org/
**Control**: Other not-for-profit (including NFP Corporation) **Service**: General medical and surgical

**Staffed Beds**: 682 **Admissions**: 36896 **Census**: 575 **Outpatient Visits**: 507437 **Births**: 0 **Total Expense ($000)**: 1477373 **Payroll Expense ($000)**: 597390 **Personnel**: 6460

☐ **ROGER WILLIAMS MEDICAL CENTER (410004)**, 825 Chalkstone Avenue, Zip 02908–4735; tel. 401/456–2000, (Nonreporting) **A**1 2 3 5 10 **S** Prospect Medical Holdings, Los Angeles, CA
Primary Contact: Jeffrey H. Liebman, Chief Executive Officer
CFO: Addy Kane, Chief Financial Officer
CMO: Elaine Jones, M.D., President Medical Staff
CIO: Susan Cerrone Abely, Vice President and Chief Information Officer
Web address: www.rwmc.org/
**Control**: Other not-for-profit (including NFP Corporation) **Service**: General medical and surgical

**Staffed Beds**: 86

**ROGER WILLIAMS MEDICAL CNTR** See Roger Williams Medical Center

**ST. JOSEPH HOSPITAL FOR SPECIALTY CARE** See St. Joseph Health Services of Rhode Island, North Providence

**VETERANS AFFAIRS MEDICAL CENTER** See Providence Veterans Affairs Medical Center

☒ **WOMEN & INFANTS HOSPITAL OF RHODE ISLAND (410010)**, 101 Dudley Street, Zip 02905–2499; tel. 401/274–1100, (Nonreporting) **A**1 2 3 5 8 10 **S** Care New England Health System, Providence, RI
Primary Contact: Shannon Sullivan, President and Chief Operating Officer
CFO: Robert W Pacheco, Vice President Finance
CMO: Raymond Powrie, M.D., Senior Vice President Quality and Clinical Effectiveness
CHR: Paul F Heffernan, Vice President Human Resources
Web address: www.womenandinfants.org
**Control**: Other not-for-profit (including NFP Corporation) **Service**: Obstetrics and gynecology

**Staffed Beds**: 247

**WAKEFIELD—Washington County**

☐ **SOUTH COUNTY HOSPITAL (410008)**, 100 Kenyon Avenue, Zip 02879–4299; tel. 401/782–8000, (Nonreporting) **A**1 2 10 **F**3 11 13 15 18 20 26 28 29 30 31 34 35 36 37 39 40 44 45 46 47 49 50 51 53 54 56 57 59 60 61 64 65 68 70 74 76 77 78 79 81 85 86 87 89 107 108 110 111 114 119 126 129 130 131 135 141 145 146 149 154 156 157
Primary Contact: Aaron Robinson, President and Chief Executive Officer
CFO: Thomas Breen, Vice President and Chief Financial Officer
CMO: John Russell Corcoran, Vice President Medical Affairs
CIO: Gary Croteau, Assistant Vice President and Chief Information Officer
CHR: Maggie Thomas, Vice President Human Resources and Practice Management
Web address: www.https://www.southcountyhealth.org/
**Control**: Other not-for-profit (including NFP Corporation) **Service**: General medical and surgical

**Staffed Beds**: 91 **Admissions**: 5567 **Census**: 56 **Outpatient Visits**: 233247 **Births**: 683 **Total Expense ($000)**: 188007 **Payroll Expense ($000)**: 83704 **Personnel**: 1028

**WARWICK—Kent County**

☒ △ **KENT COUNTY MEMORIAL HOSPITAL (410009)**, 455 Tollgate Road, Zip 02886–2770; tel. 401/737–7000, (Nonreporting) **A**1 2 3 5 7 10 13 **F**3 4 8 11 12 13 15 18 20 22 26 29 30 31 34 35 36 40 44 45 46 47 48 49 50 51 55 56 57 58 59 60 61 63 64 65 68 70 74 75 76 77 78 79 80 81 82 84 85 86 87 90 93 94 96 97 98 100 102 107 108 110 111 114 115 116 117 118 119 126 129 130 131 132 143 146 147 148 149 151 154 156 **S** Care New England Health System, Providence, RI
Primary Contact: Robert Haffey, R.N., President and Chief Operating Officer
CFO: James M. Burke, Vice President Finance, Chief Nursing Executive Medical Surgical Hospitals
CMO: Paari Gopalakrishnan, M.D., Chief Medical Officer
CIO: Sumalatha Gaddam, Senior Vice President and Chief Information Officer
CHR: Marilyn J Walsh, Vice President Human Resources
CNO: Rebecca Burke, R.N., MS, Senior Vice President and Chief Nursing Officer
Web address: www.kentri.org
**Control**: Other not-for-profit (including NFP Corporation) **Service**: General medical and surgical

**Staffed Beds**: 306 **Admissions**: 12918 **Census**: 152 **Outpatient Visits**: 344038 **Births**: 696 **Total Expense ($000)**: 365868 **Payroll Expense ($000)**: 117847 **Personnel**: 2122

**WESTERLY—Washington County**

☒ **WESTERLY HOSPITAL (410013)**, 25 Wells Street, Zip 02891–2934; tel. 401/596–6000, (Nonreporting) **A**1 10 **F**3 11 15 18 20 26 31 34 35 40 44 49 51 57 59 64 68 70 75 78 79 81 85 86 87 93 94 98 101 103 107 108 110 111 115 118 119 130 132 135 146 149 **S** Yale New Haven Health, New Haven, CT
Primary Contact: Patrick Green, FACHE, President and Chief Executive Officer
CFO: Seth Van Essendelft, Vice President and Chief Financial Officer
CMO: Oliver Mayorga, M.D., Chief Medical Officer
CIO: Kimberly Kalajainen, Vice President, Operations and Information Technology, Chief Information Officer
CHR: Donna Epps, Vice President, Chief Human Resource Officer
Web address: www.westerlyhospital.org
**Control**: Other not-for-profit (including NFP Corporation) **Service**: General medical and surgical

**Staffed Beds**: 93 **Admissions**: 2730 **Census**: 32 **Outpatient Visits**: 105815 **Births**: 0 **Total Expense ($000)**: 73094 **Payroll Expense ($000)**: 30879 **Personnel**: 425

**WOONSOCKET—Providence County**

☐ **LANDMARK MEDICAL CENTER (410011)**, 115 Cass Avenue, Zip 02895–4731; tel. 401/769–4100, (Includes LANDMARK MEDICAL CENTER-FOGARTY UNIT, Mailing address: 116 Eddie Dowling Highway, North Smithfield, Rhode Island, Zip 02896–7327; tel. 401/766–0800; LANDMARK MEDICAL CENTER-WOONSOCKET UNIT, Mailing address: 115 Cass Avenue, Woonsocket, Rhode Island, Zip 2895; tel. 401/769–4100), (Nonreporting) **A**1 10 **S** Prime Healthcare, Ontario, CA
Primary Contact: Michael Souza, Chief Executive Officer
CFO: Thomas Klessens, Chief Financial Officer
CMO: Glenn Fort, Chief Medical Officer
CIO: Vincent Larosa, Director of Information Systems
CHR: Gail Gosselin, Director Human Resources
Web address: www.landmarkmedcenter.com
**Control**: Other not-for-profit (including NFP Corporation) **Service**: General medical and surgical

**Staffed Beds**: 140

*Many Facility Codes have changed. Please refer to the AHA Guide Code Chart.*

RI

# SOUTH CAROLINA

## ABBEVILLE—Abbeville County

★ ⇧ **ABBEVILLE AREA MEDICAL CENTER (421301)**, 420 Thomson Circle, Zip 29620–5656, Mailing Address: P.O. Box 887, Zip 29620–0887; tel. 864/366–5011, (Nonreporting) **A**10 18 21 **S** QHR Health, Brentwood, TN
Primary Contact: Cindy Buck, Interim Chief Executive Officer
CFO: Timothy Wren, Chief Financial Officer
CMO: Christopher Ceraldi, M.D., Chief of Staff
CIO: Tim Stewart, Chief Information Officer
CHR: Alice Rigney, Chief Human Resources Officer
CNO: Ernest Shock, Chief Nursing Officer
Web address: www.abbevilleareamc.com
**Control**: County, Government, Nonfederal **Service**: General medical and surgical

Staffed Beds: 25

⇧ **ABBEVILLE COUNTY MEM HOSPITAL** See Abbeville Area Medical Center

## AIKEN—Aiken County

**AIKEN REGIONAL MEDICAL CENTER** See Aiken Regional Medical Centers

☐ **AIKEN REGIONAL MEDICAL CENTERS (420082)**, 302 University Parkway, Zip 29801–6302; tel. 803/641–5000, (Includes AURORA PAVILION, Mailing address: 655 Medical Park Drive, Aiken, South Carolina, Zip 29801; tel. 803/641–5900), (Nonreporting) **A**1 3 5 10 **F**3 4 11 15 18 20 22 24 29 30 31 34 35 40 44 46 49 56 57 58 59 64 70 73 74 76 77 78 79 80 81 85 86 87 89 90 94 98 99 100 101 102 103 104 107 108 110 111 114 115 119 121 123 126 129 130 131 132 135 146 147 148 149 **P**5 **S** Universal Health Services, Inc., King of Prussia, PA
Primary Contact: James F. O'Loughlin, Chief Executive Officer
COO: Matt Merrifield, Chief Operating Officer
Web address: www.aikenregional.com
**Control**: Corporation, Investor–owned (for–profit) **Service**: General medical and surgical

Staffed Beds: 299 Admissions: 12366 Census: 155 Outpatient Visits: 128077 Births: 1068 Total Expense ($000): 175980 Payroll Expense ($000): 61934 Personnel: 738

## ANDERSON—Anderson County

★ ⇧ **ANMED HEALTH MEDICAL CENTER (420027)**, 800 North Fant Street, Zip 29621–5793; tel. 864/512–1000, (Includes ANMED HEALTH WOMEN'S and CHILDREN'S HOSPITAL, Mailing address: 2000 East Greenville Street, Anderson, South Carolina, Zip 29621; tel. 864/512–1000; William T Manson III, FACHE, Chief Executive Officer), (Nonreporting) **A**2 3 5 10 21 **F**3 4 8 11 12 13 15 17 18 20 22 24 26 28 29 30 31 34 35 37 39 40 43 45 46 47 48 49 50 51 53 54 56 57 58 59 60 62 64 65 68 70 71 73 74 75 76 77 78 79 80 81 84 85 86 87 89 90 91 97 98 100 101 102 103 104 107 108 110 111 112 114 115 117 118 119 120 121 123 126 127 129 130 131 132 146 147 148 149 156 **S** AnMed Health, Anderson, SC
Primary Contact: William A. Kenley, Chief Executive Officer
COO: Tina M. Jury, R.N., Chief Hospital Operations
CFO: Christine Pearson, Chief Financial Officer
CMO: Thomas Kayrouz, M.D., Chief Medical Officer
CIO: Marty Stewart, Chief Information Officer
CNO: Shaunda Trotter, R.N., Chief Nursing Officer
Web address: www.anmedhealth.org
**Control**: Other not–for–profit (including NFP Corporation) **Service**: General medical and surgical

Staffed Beds: 358 Admissions: 23226 Census: 251 Outpatient Visits: 726509 Births: 1548 Total Expense ($000): 523508 Payroll Expense ($000): 228797 Personnel: 3401

⇧ **ANMED HEALTH MEDICAL CENTER** See Anmed Health Medical Center

**ANMED HEALTH REHAB HOSP** See Anmed Health Rehabilitation Hospital

⊞ **ANMED HEALTH REHABILITATION HOSPITAL (423029)**, 1 Spring Back Way, Zip 29621–2676; tel. 864/716–2600, (Nonreporting) **A**1 10 **S** Encompass Health Corporation, Birmingham, AL
Primary Contact: Denise R. Murray, Chief Executive Officer
CFO: Julie Harris, Controller
CMO: William Vogentiz, M.D., Medical Director
CHR: Morgan Clements, Director of Human Resources
CNO: Kelly Davis, Chief Nursing Officer
Web address: www.anmedrehab.com
**Control**: Corporation, Investor–owned (for–profit) **Service**: Rehabilitation

Staffed Beds: 60

☐ **PATRICK B. HARRIS PSYCHIATRIC HOSPITAL (424011)**, 130 Highway 252, Zip 29621–5054; tel. 864/231–2600, (Nonreporting) **A**1 3 5 10
Primary Contact: Allen McEniry, Executive Director
Web address: www.patrickbharris.com/
**Control**: State, Government, Nonfederal **Service**: Psychiatric

Staffed Beds: 131

## BEAUFORT—Beaufort County

⊞ **BEAUFORT MEMORIAL HOSPITAL (420067)**, 955 Ribaut Road, Zip 29902–5441; tel. 843/522–5200, (Nonreporting) **A**1 2 10 **F**3 11 12 13 15 18 20 22 28 29 30 31 32 34 35 40 45 46 49 50 51 53 54 57 59 60 64 65 69 70 71 73 74 75 76 77 78 79 81 85 86 87 89 90 91 93 94 96 97 98 100 101 102 103 104 107 108 110 111 114 115 118 119 120 121 126 127 130 132 134 145 146 147 148 149 154 Primary Contact: Edmond Russell, Baxley III, President and Chief Executive Officer
CFO: Ken Miller, Chief Financial Officer
CMO: Kurt Gambla, D.O., Chief Medical Officer
CIO: Edward Ricks, Vice President and Chief Information Officer
CHR: Doug Douglas, Interim Vice President Human Resources
CNO: Karen Manuel Carroll, R.N., Vice President Patient Care Services
Web address: www.bmhsc.org
**Control**: County, Government, Nonfederal **Service**: General medical and surgical

Staffed Beds: 203 Admissions: 8592 Census: 106 Outpatient Visits: 186305 Births: 903

**NAVAL HOSPITAL** See Naval Hospital Beaufort

⊞ **NAVAL HOSPITAL BEAUFORT**, 1 Pinckney Boulevard, Zip 29902–6122; tel. 843/228–5301, (Nonreporting) **A**1 5 **S** Bureau of Medicine and Surgery, Department of the Navy, Falls Church, VA
Primary Contact: Lieutenant Commander Willie Brown, Director Administration
Web address: www.med.navy.mil/sites/nhbeaufort/Pages/Welcome_Page.aspx
**Service**: General medical and surgical

Staffed Beds: 20

## CAMDEN—Kershaw County

**KERSHAW COUNTY MEDICAL CENTER** See Kershawhealth

⊞ **KERSHAWHEALTH (420048)**, 1315 Roberts Street, Zip 29020–3737, Mailing Address: P.O. Box 7003, Zip 29021–7003; tel. 803/432–4311, (Nonreporting) **A**1 10 **F**3 11 13 15 18 20 24 28 29 30 31 32 34 35 40 44 45 49 50 51 54 57 59 61 62 63 64 66 68 70 75 76 77 78 79 81 85 86 87 89 90 94 97 98 103 107 108 110 111 114 115 118 119 127 129 130 132 144 146 147 148 154 **S** LifePoint Health, Brentwood, TN
Primary Contact: Susan C. Shugart, Chief Executive Officer
COO: Susan R Burroughs, FACHE, Chief Operating Officer
CFO: Mike Bunch, Executive Vice President, Chief Operating Officer and Chief Financial Officer
CMO: Tallulah Holmstrom, M.D., Chief Medical Officer
CIO: Diane Arrants, Chief Information Officer
CHR: Angela F Nettles, Vice President, Human Resources and Support Services
Web address: www.kershawhealth.org
**Control**: Corporation, Investor–owned (for–profit) **Service**: General medical and surgical

Staffed Beds: 76 Admissions: 3924 Census: 49 Outpatient Visits: 134162 Births: 274 Total Expense ($000): 99654 Payroll Expense ($000): 38671 Personnel: 651

---

**Hospital, Medicare Provider Number, Address, Telephone, Approval, Facility, and Physician Codes, Health Care System**

★ American Hospital Association (AHA) membership
☐ The Joint Commission accreditation
○ Healthcare Facilities Accreditation Program
◇ DNV Healthcare Inc. accreditation
⇧ Center for Improvement in Healthcare Quality Accreditation
△ Commission on Accreditation of Rehabilitation Facilities (CARF) accreditation

## CHARLESTON—Charleston County

☒ **BON SECOURS ST. FRANCIS HOSPITAL (420065)**, 2095 Henry Tecklenburg Drive, Zip 29414–5733; tel. 843/402–1000, (Nonreporting) **A**1 10 **F**3 7 12 13 14 15 28 29 30 31 34 35 40 45 48 49 50 51 56 57 59 64 68 70 73 74 75 76 77 78 79 80 81 82 84 85 86 87 93 94 100 102 107 108 110 111 114 115 117 118 119 120 121 123 124 129 130 131 132 145 146 147 148 149 **S** Roper St. Francis Healthcare, Charleston, SC
Primary Contact: Gretchen Morin, Chief Administrative Officer
CFO: Bret Johnson, Chief Financial Officer
CMO: Steven D Shapiro, M.D., Chief Medical Officer
CIO: Michael Taylor, Chief Information Officer
CNO: Pennie Peralta, R.N., VP, Nursing & Chief Nursing Officer
Web address: www.rsfh.com/
**Control:** Other not–for–profit (including NFP Corporation) **Service:** General medical and surgical

**Staffed Beds:** 157 **Admissions:** 9414 **Census:** 95 **Outpatient Visits:** 162045 **Births:** 2450 **Total Expense ($000):** 200613 **Payroll Expense ($000):** 56940 **Personnel:** 995

**BON SECOURS ST. FRANCIS XAVIER HOSPITAL** See Bon Secours St. Francis Hospital

**CHARTER CHARLESTON BEHAV HLTH** See Palmetto Lowcountry Behavioral Health

**COLUMBIA TRIDENT MEDICAL CTR** See Trident Medical Center

☒ **ENCOMPASS HEALTH REHABILITATION HOSPITAL OF CHARLESTON (423027)**, 9181 Medcom Street, Zip 29406–9168; tel. 843/820–7777, (Nonreporting) **A**1 10 **F**90 94 96 **S** Encompass Health Corporation, Birmingham, AL
Primary Contact: Michele M. Skripps, R.N., Chief Executive Officer
CFO: Beckye Lariviere, Controller
CMO: William Livesay, D.O., JrMedical Director
CHR: Traxler Littlejohn, Human Resources Director
CNO: Patricia Simon, Chief Nursing Officer
Web address: www.healthsouthcharleston.com
**Control:** Corporation, Investor–owned (for–profit) **Service:** Rehabilitation

**Staffed Beds:** 49 **Admissions:** 856 **Census:** 30 **Outpatient Visits:** 0 **Births:** 0 **Personnel:** 97

**HEALTHSOUTH REHABILITATION HOSPITAL OF CHARLESTON** See Encompass Health Rehabilitation Hospital of Charleston

**MUSC CHILDREN'S HOSPITAL** See Children's Hospital of South Carolina at Musc

☒ **MUSC HEALTH OF MEDICAL UNIVERSITY OF SOUTH CAROLINA (420004)**, 169 Ashley Avenue, Zip 29425–8905; tel. 843/792–2300, (Includes CHILDREN'S HOSPITAL OF SOUTH CAROLINA AT MUSC, Mailing address: 171 Ashley Avenue, Charleston, South Carolina, Zip 29425–8908; tel. 843/792–1414; Patrick J Cawley, Chief Executive Officer, MUSC Health and Vice President for Health Affairs, University), (Nonreporting) **A**1 2 3 5 8 10 **F**3 4 5 6 7 8 9 11 12 13 14 15 16 17 18 19 20 21 22 24 25 26 27 28 29 30 31 32 34 35 36 37 38 39 40 41 43 44 45 46 47 48 49 50 51 52 53 54 55 56 57 58 59 60 61 64 65 66 67 68 70 71 72 73 74 75 76 77 78 79 80 81 82 84 85 86 87 88 89 91 92 93 94 97 98 99 100 101 102 103 104 105 107 108 110 111 114 115 116 117 118 119 120 121 123 124 126 129 130 131 132 134 135 136 137 138 139 140 141 142 144 145 146 147 148 149 150 151 152 153 154 155 156 **S** MUSC Health, Charleston, SC
Primary Contact: Patrick J. Cawley, Chief Executive Officer, MUSC Health and Vice President for Health Affairs, University
CFO: Lisa Goodlett, Administrator Finance and Support Services
CMO: Daniel Handel, M.D., Chief Medical Officer
CIO: Mark W McMath, Chief Information Officer
CHR: Darrick Paul, Chief People Officer
Web address: www.muschealth.com
**Control:** Hospital district or authority, Government, Nonfederal **Service:** General medical and surgical

**Staffed Beds:** 779 **Admissions:** 37439 **Census:** 714 **Outpatient Visits:** 1100415 **Births:** 2864 **Total Expense ($000):** 1586188 **Payroll Expense ($000):** 527401 **Personnel:** 7035

**MUSC MEDICAL CENTER OF MEDICAL UNIVERSITY OF SOUTH CAROLINA** See Musc Health of Medical University of South Carolina

☐ **PALMETTO LOWCOUNTRY BEHAVIORAL HEALTH (424006)**, 2777 Speissegger Drive, Zip 29405–8229; tel. 843/747–5830, (Nonreporting) **A**1 10 **F**4 5 98 99 102 103 104 105 152 153 **S** Universal Health Services, Inc., King of Prussia, PA
Primary Contact: Timothy Miller, Interim Chief Executive Officer
CFO: Stan Markowski, Chief Financial Officer
CMO: Steven Lopez, M.D., Chief Medical Officer
CHR: Sheila Simpson, Vice President Human Resources
CNO: Jo Good, Director of Nursing
Web address: www.palmettobehavioralhealth.com
**Control:** Corporation, Investor–owned (for–profit) **Service:** Psychiatric

**Staffed Beds:** 100 **Admissions:** 3141 **Census:** 67 **Outpatient Visits:** 4779 **Births:** 0 **Personnel:** 172

☒ **RALPH H. JOHNSON VETERANS AFFAIRS MEDICAL CENTER**, 109 Bee Street, Zip 29401–5799; tel. 843/577–5011, (Nonreporting) **A**1 2 3 5 8 **S** Department of Veterans Affairs, Washington, DC
Primary Contact: Scott R. Isaacks, FACHE, Director and Chief Executive Officer
CFO: Cassandra Helfer, Chief Financial Officer
CMO: Florence N. Hutchison, M.D., Chief of Staff
CIO: LaBon Hardy, Chief Information Officer
CHR: Renae A. Jacobson, Human Resources Officer
CNO: Garett E. Schreier, R.N., Associate Director, Nursing and Patient Care Services
Web address: www.charleston.va.gov/
**Control:** Veterans Affairs, Government, federal **Service:** General medical and surgical

**Staffed Beds:** 98

☒ △ **ROPER HOSPITAL (420087)**, 316 Calhoun Street, Zip 29401–1125; tel. 843/724–2000, (Nonreporting) **A**1 2 3 5 7 10 **F**3 7 8 9 14 15 17 18 20 22 24 26 28 29 30 31 34 35 37 40 42 45 49 50 51 53 54 55 56 57 58 59 60 61 62 63 64 65 67 68 70 74 75 77 78 79 80 81 82 84 85 86 87 90 92 93 94 95 96 102 107 108 110 111 115 118 119 120 121 123 126 129 130 131 132 135 136 143 146 147 148 149 **S** Roper St. Francis Healthcare, Charleston, SC
Primary Contact: Matthew Desmond, Chief Administrative Officer
CFO: Bret Johnson, Chief Financial Officer
CMO: Steven D Shapiro, M.D., Vice President Medical Affairs
CIO: Melinda H. Cardell, Interim Vice President and Chief Information Officer
CHR: Melanie Stith, Vice President Human Resources
Web address: www.rsfh.com/
**Control:** Other not–for–profit (including NFP Corporation) **Service:** General medical and surgical

**Staffed Beds:** 290 **Admissions:** 11973 **Census:** 181 **Outpatient Visits:** 179368 **Births:** 0 **Total Expense ($000):** 350565 **Payroll Expense ($000):** 109274 **Personnel:** 1862

**ROPER ST. FRANCIS** See Roper Hospital

☒ **TRIDENT MEDICAL CENTER (420079)**, 9330 Medical Plaza Drive, Zip 29406–9195; tel. 843/797–7000, (Includes MONCKS CORNER MEDICAL CENTER, Mailing address: 401 North Live Oak Drive, Highway 17A, Moncks Corner, South Carolina, Zip 29461–5603; tel. 843/761–8721; SUMMERVILLE MEDICAL CENTER, Mailing address: 295 Midland Parkway, Summerville, South Carolina, Zip 29485–8104; tel. 843/832–5000; Jeff Taylor, Chief Executive Officer), (Nonreporting) **A**1 3 5 10 **F**3 5 8 12 13 15 16 18 20 22 24 26 28 29 30 31 34 35 37 40 41 42 43 45 46 47 48 49 50 54 55 56 57 59 60 61 64 70 72 73 74 75 76 77 78 79 80 81 84 85 86 87 89 90 93 94 98 100 102 107 108 110 111 114 115 116 117 118 121 123 126 130 131 132 135 145 146 147 148 152 **S** HCA Healthcare, Nashville, TN
Primary Contact: Todd Gallati, FACHE, President and Chief Executive Officer
COO: Scott Weiskittel, Chief Operating Officer
CFO: Andy Miller, Chief Financial Officer
CMO: Lee Biggs, M.D., Chief Medical Officer
CHR: Vickie Cummings, Vice President of Human Resources
CNO: Mary Kaye Halterman, R.N., Chief Nursing Officer
Web address: www.tridenthealthsystem.com
**Control:** Corporation, Investor–owned (for–profit) **Service:** General medical and surgical

**Staffed Beds:** 451 **Admissions:** 26374 **Census:** 337

**VETERANS AFFAIRS MED CENTER** See Ralph H. Johnson Veterans Affairs Medical Center

SC

## CHERAW—Chesterfield County

⇑ **CHESTERFIELD GENERAL HOSPITAL** See Mcleod Health Cheraw

⇑ **MCLEOD HEALTH CHERAW (420107)**, 711 Chesterfield Highway,
Zip 29520–7002; tel. 843/537–7881, (Nonreporting) **A**3 10 21 **F**1 3 15 18 28
29 30 34 35 40 45 56 57 59 70 79 80 81 85 86 87 89 107 108 111 114 118
119 128 130 132 133 135 **P**3 **S** McLeod Health, Florence, SC
Primary Contact: Virginia Hardee, Interim Administrator
CFO: Louis Anderson, Chief Financial Officer
CMO: David Bersinger, M.D., Chief of Staff
CIO: Jim Spencer, Director Information System
Web address: www.chesterfieldgeneral.com
**Control:** Other not–for–profit (including NFP Corporation) **Service:** General
medical and surgical

**Staffed Beds:** 32 **Admissions:** 1856 **Census:** 27 **Outpatient Visits:** 35519
**Births:** 12 **Total Expense ($000):** 40525 **Payroll Expense ($000):** 16330
**Personnel:** 235

## CHESTER—Chester County

**CHESTER REGIONAL MEDICAL CENTER** See Musc Health Chester Medical Center

⊠ **MUSC HEALTH CHESTER MEDICAL CENTER (420019)**, 1 Medical Park Drive,
Zip 29706–9769; tel. 803/581–3151, (Nonreporting) **A**1 10 **F**15 18 28 29 34 35
40 45 50 56 57 59 70 75 77 79 81 85 86 87 89 90 94 107 108 110 111 119
128 130 131 132 135 149 154 157 **S** MUSC Health, Charleston, SC
Primary Contact: J. Scott Broome, Chief Executive Officer
CFO: Tracey Claxton, Chief Financial Officer
CMO: Terry Dodge, M.D., Chief of Staff
CIO: Shaw Laird, Chief Information Officer
CHR: Karen Chapman, Director Human Resources
CNO: Betty Griffin, Interim Chief Nursing Officer
Web address: www.muschealth.org/locations/chester-medical-center
**Control:** Hospital district or authority, Government, Nonfederal **Service:** General
medical and surgical

**Staffed Beds:** 12 **Admissions:** 879 **Census:** 9 **Outpatient Visits:** 48453
**Births:** 0 **Personnel:** 146

## CLINTON—Laurens County

**BAILEY MEMORIAL HOSPITAL** See Ghs - Laurens County Memorial Hospital

**LAURENS COUNTY HOSPITAL** See Prisma Health Laurens County Hospital

☐ **PRISMA HEALTH LAURENS COUNTY HOSPITAL (420038)**, 22725 Highway
76 East, Zip 29325–5527, Mailing Address: P O Drawer 976, Zip 29325–0976;
tel. 864/833–9100, (Includes GHS - LAURENS COUNTY MEMORIAL HOSPITAL,
Mailing address: 22725 Highway 76 E, PO Box 976, Clinton, South Carolina,
Zip 29325–7527, PO Box 976, Zip 29325–0976, tel. 803/833–9100; Justin
Benfield, Southern Region Chief Operating Officer), (Nonreporting) **A**1 5 10 20
**F**3 13 15 18 28 29 30 40 45 46 59 70 76 79 80 81 87 94 97 107 110 111
114 115 119 127 128 129 130 132 146 147 **S** Prisma Health - Midlands,
Columbia, SC
Primary Contact: Justin Benfield, Southern Region Chief Operating Officer
CFO: Michael Norrick, Director of Campus Operations
CMO: Vincent Green, Medical Director
CIO: Kathleen Anderson, Director, Acute Clinical Systems
CHR: Cathy M Rogers, Manager Human Resources
CNO: Kay Swisher, Chief Nursing Officer
Web address: www.ghs.org/laurens
**Control:** Other not–for–profit (including NFP Corporation) **Service:** General
medical and surgical

**Staffed Beds:** 57 **Admissions:** 2010 **Census:** 23 **Outpatient Visits:** 131085
**Births:** 306 **Total Expense ($000):** 61611 **Payroll Expense ($000):** 18291
**Personnel:** 301

## COLUMBIA—Richland County

★ **CONTINUECARE HOSPITAL AT PALMETTO HEALTH BAPTIST (422006)**,
Taylor at Marion Street, Zip 29220, Mailing Address: PO BOX 11069,
Zip 29211–1069; tel. 803/296–3757, (Nonreporting) **A**10 22 **S** Community
Hospital Corporation, Plano, TX
Primary Contact: Wayne B. Boutwell, Chief Executive Officer
Web address: www.continuecare.org/palmetto//
**Control:** Other not–for–profit (including NFP Corporation) **Service:** Acute long–
term care hospital

**Staffed Beds:** 35

**DORN VETERANS HOSPITAL** See Wm. Jennings Bryan Dorn Veterans Affairs
Medical Center

**EARLE E. MORRIS ALCOHOL AND DRUG TREATMENT CENTER** See Morris
Village Alcohol and Drug Addiction Treatment Center

⊞ **ENCOMPASS HEALTH REHABILITATION HOSPITAL OF COLUMBIA (423025)**,
2935 Colonial Drive, Zip 29203–6811; tel. 803/254–7777, (Nonreporting) **A**1 10
**F**29 50 53 60 64 77 90 91 92 93 94 95 96 97 119 149 156 157 **S** Encompass
Health Corporation, Birmingham, AL
Primary Contact: Chris Daughtry, Chief Executive Officer
CFO: Jessica Burriss, Chief Financial Officer
CMO: Devin Troyer, M.D., Medical Director
CHR: Luanne Burton, Director Human Resources
CNO: April Brooks, Chief Nursing Officer
Web address: www.healthsouthcolumbia.com
**Control:** Corporation, Investor–owned (for–profit) **Service:** Rehabilitation

**Staffed Beds:** 96 **Admissions:** 2053 **Census:** 71 **Outpatient Visits:** 0
**Births:** 0 **Total Expense ($000):** 20919 **Payroll Expense ($000):** 12263
**Personnel:** 221

☐ **G. WERBER BRYAN PSYCHIATRIC HOSPITAL (424005)**, 220 Faison Drive,
Zip 29203–3210; tel. 803/935–7140, (Nonreporting) **A**1 3 10 **F**4 30 50 74 75
97 98 99 101 103 130 132 135 146
Primary Contact: Stuart Shields, Director
COO: Jaclyn Upfield, Chief Operating Officer
CIO: Sam Livingston, Information Resource Consultant
CHR: Kim Church, Manager Human Resources
Web address: www.scdmh.org
**Control:** State, Government, Nonfederal **Service:** Psychiatric

**Staffed Beds:** 240 **Admissions:** 591 **Census:** 193 **Outpatient Visits:** 0
**Births:** 0 **Personnel:** 565

**HEALTHSOUTH REHABILITATION HOSPITAL OF COLUMBIA** See Encompass
Health Rehabilitation Hospital of Columbia

**INTERMEDICAL HOSPITAL OF SOUTH CAROLINA** See Continuecare Hospital at
Palmetto Health Baptist

**MORRIS VILLAGE ALCOHOL AND DRUG ADDICTION TREATMENT CENTER**,
610 Faison Drive, Zip 29203–3218; tel. 803/935–7100, (Nonreporting) **A**3 **F**4 29
39 53 61 67 74 75 87 98 130 132 146
Primary Contact: George McConnell, Director
Web address: www.state.sc.us/dmh/morrisvillage/home.html
**Control:** State, Government, Nonfederal **Service:** Alcoholism and other chemical
dependency

**Staffed Beds:** 103 **Admissions:** 1398 **Census:** 98 **Outpatient Visits:** 0
**Births:** 0 **Personnel:** 180

## COLUMBIA—Lexington County

**PALMETTO HEALTH BAPTIST PARKRIDGE** See Prisma Health Baptist Parkridge
Hospital

## COLUMBIA—Richland County

**PALMETTO HEALTH CHILDREN'S HOSPITAL** See Prisma Health Children's
Hospital

**PALMETTO HEALTH RICHLAND** See Prisma Health Richland Hospital

**PRISMA HEALTH BAPTIST** See Prisma Health Baptist Hospital

**SC**

---

**Hospital, Medicare Provider Number, Address, Telephone, Approval, Facility, and Physician Codes, Health Care System**

★ American Hospital Association (AHA) membership
☐ The Joint Commission accreditation
○ Healthcare Facilities Accreditation Program
◇ DNV Healthcare Inc. accreditation
⇑ Center for Improvement in Healthcare Quality Accreditation
△ Commission on Accreditation of Rehabilitation Facilities (CARF) accreditation

☐ **PRISMA HEALTH BAPTIST HOSPITAL (420086)**, Taylor at Marion Street, Zip 29220–0001; tel. 803/296–5010, (Nonreporting) **A**1 2 3 5 10 **F**3 4 5 11 12 13 15 18 20 29 30 31 34 35 38 40 45 46 47 48 49 57 59 61 62 63 64 65 66 70 72 73 74 75 76 77 78 79 80 81 84 85 86 87 90 98 99 100 101 102 103 104 105 107 108 110 111 114 115 117 118 119 126 130 132 146 147 153 154 156 **S** Prisma Health - Midlands, Columbia, SC
Primary Contact: Michael N. Bundy, Chief Operating Officer
COO: James M Bridges, Executive Vice President and Chief Operating Officer
CFO: Paul K Duane, Chief Financial Officer and Office of Health Reform
CMO: Mark J Mayson, M.D., Medical Director
CIO: Michelle Edwards, Executive Vice President Information Technology
CHR: Trip Gregory, Senior Vice President Human Resources
Web address: www.palmettohealth.org
**Control:** Other not–for–profit (including NFP Corporation) **Service:** General medical and surgical

**Staffed Beds:** 344 **Admissions:** 20574 **Census:** 225 **Outpatient Visits:** 187880 **Births:** 3030 **Total Expense ($000):** 339388 **Payroll Expense ($000):** 104082 **Personnel:** 2148

### COLUMBIA—Lexington County

☐ **PRISMA HEALTH BAPTIST PARKRIDGE HOSPITAL (420106)**, 400 Palmetto Health Parkway, Zip 29212–1760, Mailing Address: P.O. Box 2266, Zip 29202–2266; tel. 803/907–7000, (Nonreporting) **A**1 3 10 **F**1 3 8 11 13 15 29 30 34 35 40 45 46 50 57 59 64 70 75 76 77 79 81 85 86 87 90 107 110 111 115 119 128 130 132 146 147 154 **S** Prisma Health - Midlands, Columbia, SC
Primary Contact: Michael N. Bundy, Chief Operating Officer
COO: Emilie Keene, FACHE, Interim Chief Operating Officer
Web address: www.palmettohealth.org
**Control:** Other not–for–profit (including NFP Corporation) **Service:** General medical and surgical

**Staffed Beds:** 76 **Admissions:** 4561 **Census:** 55 **Outpatient Visits:** 187880 **Births:** 786 **Total Expense ($000):** 128286 **Payroll Expense ($000):** 35199 **Personnel:** 830

### COLUMBIA—Richland County

☐ **PRISMA HEALTH RICHLAND HOSPITAL (420018)**, Five Richland Medical Park Drive, Zip 29203–6897; tel. 803/434–7000, (Includes PRISMA HEALTH CHILDREN'S HOSPITAL, Mailing address: Five Richland Medical Park Dr, Columbia, South Carolina, Zip 29203–6863; tel. 803/434–6882), (Nonreporting) **A**1 2 3 5 8 10 19 **F**3 4 7 11 13 15 16 17 18 19 20 22 24 26 28 29 30 31 32 34 35 38 39 40 41 43 45 46 47 48 49 50 53 54 56 57 58 59 61 64 65 66 70 72 73 74 75 76 77 78 79 81 84 85 86 87 88 89 90 92 93 94 97 98 99 100 101 102 103 104 105 107 110 111 114 115 119 124 126 129 130 131 132 146 147 148 153 154 156 **S** Prisma Health - Midlands, Columbia, SC
Primary Contact: Robert Cofield, Dr.PH, Chief Executive Officer
CFO: Paul K Duane, Chief Financial Officer and Office of Health Reform
CMO: Eric Brown, M.D., Physician Executive
CNO: Carole A Siegfried, MSN, R.N., Campus Nurse Executive
Web address: www.palmettohealth.org
**Control:** Other not–for–profit (including NFP Corporation) **Service:** General medical and surgical

**Staffed Beds:** 699 **Admissions:** 32339 **Census:** 587 **Outpatient Visits:** 467983 **Births:** 2601 **Total Expense ($000):** 856041 **Payroll Expense ($000):** 287040 **Personnel:** 4818

☒ **PROVIDENCE HOSPITAL (420026)**, 2435 Forest Drive, Zip 29204–2098; tel. 803/865–4500, (Includes PROVIDENCE HOSPITAL NORTHEAST, Mailing address: 120 Gateway Corporate Boulevard, Columbia, South Carolina, Zip 29203–9611; tel. 803/865–4500; Ryan Hall, Vice President), (Nonreporting) **A**1 10 19 **F**3 11 15 17 18 20 22 24 26 28 29 30 34 35 38 40 42 44 45 49 50 53 54 57 58 59 60 63 64 70 74 75 77 79 81 84 85 86 87 90 93 94 100 107 108 110 111 115 119 129 130 132 135 141 146 148 **S** LifePoint Health, Brentwood, TN
Primary Contact: Terry Gunn, FACHE, Chief Executive Officer
COO: W. Carl Martin, Chief Operating Officer
CFO: Pamela Gallagher, Chief Financial Officer
CMO: Wayne Sribnick, M.D., Senior Vice President and Chief Medical Officer
CIO: Lib Cumbee, Director Information Systems
CHR: Justin A Lofurno, Director Human Resources
Web address: www.sistersofcharityhealth.org/health-care/providence-hospitals/
**Control:** Corporation, Investor–owned (for–profit) **Service:** General medical and surgical

**Staffed Beds:** 216 **Admissions:** 9673 **Census:** 112 **Outpatient Visits:** 127945 **Births:** 0 **Total Expense ($000):** 189710 **Payroll Expense ($000):** 56784 **Personnel:** 756

**PROVIDENCE HOSPITAL NORTHEAST** See Providence Hospital, Columbia

**SISTERS OF CHARITY PROVIDENCE HOSPITALS** See Providence Hospital

**SOUTH CAROLINA DEPARTMENT OF CORRECTIONS HOSPITAL**, 4344 Broad River Road, Zip 29210–4098; tel. 803/896–8567, (Nonreporting) **A**3
Primary Contact: John Solomon, M.D., Director
Web address: www.doc.sc.gov/
**Control:** State, Government, Nonfederal **Service:** Hospital unit of an institution (prison hospital, college infirmary, etc.)

**Staffed Beds:** 70

**WILLIAM S. HALL PSYCHIATRIC INSTITUTE (424003)**, 1800 Colonial Drive, Zip 29203–6827; tel. 803/898–1693, (Nonreporting) **A**3
Primary Contact: Mary Jane Hicks, Hospital Director
COO: Doug Glover, Controller
CFO: Doug Glover, Controller
CMO: Phyllis Bryant-Mobley, M.D., Director Medical Services
CIO: Mesa Foard, Director Information technology
CHR: Kim Church, Manager Human Resources
Web address: www.scdmh.org
**Control:** State, Government, Nonfederal **Service:** Psychiatric

**Staffed Beds:** 37

☒ △ **WM. JENNINGS BRYAN DORN VETERANS AFFAIRS MEDICAL CENTER**, 6439 Garners Ferry Road, Zip 29209–1639; tel. 803/776–4000, (Nonreporting) **A**1 2 3 5 7 **S** Department of Veterans Affairs, Washington, DC
Primary Contact: David Omura, MS, Director
CMO: Bernard L. DeKoning, M.D., Chief of Staff
CIO: Steve Chalphant, Director Information Management Service Line
CHR: Phyllis Jones, Chief Human Resources
CNO: Ruth W. Mustard, R.N., MSN, Associate Director Nursing and Patient Services
Web address: www.columbiasc.va.gov/
**Control:** Veterans Affairs, Government, federal **Service:** General medical and surgical

**Staffed Beds:** 216

### CONWAY—Horry County

⇑ **CONWAY HOSPITAL** See Conway Medical Center

★ ⇑ **CONWAY MEDICAL CENTER (420049)**, 300 Singleton Ridge Road, Zip 29526–9142, Mailing Address: P.O. Box 829, Zip 29528–0829; tel. 843/347–7111, (Nonreporting) **A**3 10 21
Primary Contact: Bret A. Barr, President and Chief Executive Officer
CMO: Paul McKinley Richardson Jr Chief Medical Officer
CIO: David Crutchfield, Vice President, Information Services & Chief Information Officer
CHR: Matthew J. Securro, Vice President, Human Resources
CNO: Tony L. Minshew, Vice President, Patient Care Services
Web address: www.conwaymedicalcenter.com
**Control:** Other not–for–profit (including NFP Corporation) **Service:** General medical and surgical

**Staffed Beds:** 266

☐ **LIGHTHOUSE BEHAVIORAL HEALTH HOSPITAL (424002)**, 152 Waccamaw Medical Park Drive, Zip 29526–8901; tel. 843/347–8871, (Nonreporting) **A**1 3 10 **F**4 98 99 101 102 103 130 **S** Universal Health Services, Inc., King of Prussia, PA
Primary Contact: Thomas L. Ryba, Chief Executive Officer
CFO: Gabrielle Gale, Chief Financial Officer
CMO: Adedapo Oduwole, M.D., Medical Director
CIO: Gabrielle Gale, Chief Financial Officer
CHR: Lois Woodall, Director Human Resources
Web address: www.lighthousecarecenterofconway.com/
**Control:** Corporation, Investor–owned (for–profit) **Service:** Psychiatric

**Staffed Beds:** 105 **Admissions:** 3577 **Census:** 83 **Outpatient Visits:** 0 **Births:** 0 **Personnel:** 173

**LIGHTHOUSE CARE CENTER OF CONWAY** See Lighthouse Behavioral Health Hospital

### DARLINGTON—Darlington County

⇑ **MCLEOD HEALTH DARLINGTON (420057)**, 701 Cashua Ferry Road, Zip 29532–8488, Mailing Address: P.O. Box 1859, Zip 29540; tel. 843/395–1100, (Nonreporting) **A**10 21 **F**3 4 15 34 35 38 56 57 59 64 77 85 90 97 98 100 101 103 104 107 110 119 127 128 130 133 135 147 148 **P**3 **S** McLeod Health, Florence, SC
Primary Contact: Virginia Hardee, Administrator
Web address: www.mcleodhealth.org
**Control:** Other not–for–profit (including NFP Corporation) **Service:** General medical and surgical

**Staffed Beds:** 40 **Admissions:** 1182 **Census:** 40 **Outpatient Visits:** 5543 **Births:** 0 **Total Expense ($000):** 18669 **Payroll Expense ($000):** 8417 **Personnel:** 115

⇑ **MCLEOD MEDICAL CENTER DARLINGTON** See Mcleod Health Darlington

*Many Facility Codes have changed. Please refer to the AHA Guide Code Chart.*

## DILLON—Dillon County

⇧ **MCLEOD HEALTH DILLON (420005)**, 301 East Jackson Street, Zip 29536–2509, Mailing Address: P.O. Box 1327, Zip 29536–1327; tel. 843/774–4111, (Nonreporting) **A**10 21 **F**3 11 13 15 28 29 30 34 35 40 50 57 59 64 70 75 76 79 81 85 87 89 90 94 107 111 114 119 130 132 133 134 135 146 147 148 149 **P**3 **S** McLeod Health, Florence, SC
Primary Contact: Joan Ervin, Administrator
CFO: Samuel Fulton Ervin IIISenior Vice President and Chief Financial Officer
CMO: Walter B Blum, M.D., Chief of Staff
CIO: Jenean Blackmon, Assistant Vice President and Chief Information Officer
CHR: Cynthia Causey, Associate Administrator Human and Mission Services
Web address: www.mcleodhealth.org
**Control**: Other not–for–profit (including NFP Corporation) **Service**: General medical and surgical

**Staffed Beds: 34 Admissions: 2199 Census: 21 Outpatient Visits: 87919 Births: 292 Total Expense ($000): 40060 Payroll Expense ($000): 17545 Personnel: 278**

⇧ **MCLEOD MEDICAL CENTER DILLON** See Mcleod Health Dillon

## EASLEY—Pickens County

**BAPTIST EASLEY HOSPITAL** See Prisma Health Baptist Easley Hospital

☐ **PRISMA HEALTH BAPTIST EASLEY HOSPITAL (420015)**, 200 Fleetwood Drive, Zip 29640–2022, Mailing Address: P.O. Box 2129, Zip 29641–2129; tel. 864/442–7200, (Nonreporting) **A**1 5 10 **F**3 11 13 15 18 28 29 30 34 35 40 56 57 59 64 70 74 75 76 79 81 85 87 89 107 108 111 114 115 119 129 130 132 146 147
Primary Contact: Todd Walker, President
CFO: Kathleen Stapleton, Chief Financial Officer
CIO: Cynthia Ellenburg, Director Health Information Services
CHR: Richard B Posey, Director Human Resources
CNO: Mary Ann Hunter, Director Nursing Services
Web address: www.https://www.ghs.org/locations/baptist-easley-medical-campus/
**Control**: Other not–for–profit (including NFP Corporation) **Service**: General medical and surgical

**Staffed Beds: 73 Admissions: 2836 Census: 33 Outpatient Visits: 123250 Births: 386**

## EDGEFIELD—Edgefield County

**EDGEFIELD COUNTY HEALTHCARE (421304)**, 300 Ridge Medical Plaza, Zip 29824–4525, Mailing Address: PO Box 590, Zip 29824–4525; tel. 803/637–3174, (Nonreporting) **A**10 18 **F**3 15 18 28 29 34 35 40 45 59 65 68 77 79 81 94 107 119 127 128 130 133 146 154
Primary Contact: Carlos Milanes, Chief Executive Officer
CFO: Lori Jacobs, Chief Financial Officer
CMO: Tami Massey, M.D., Chief of Medical Staff
CIO: Juli Corley, Chief Information Officer
CHR: Theresa Stover, Chief Human Resource Officer
CNO: Cheryl Faust, Chief Nursing Officer
Web address: www.myech.org
**Control**: County, Government, Nonfederal **Service**: General medical and surgical

**Staffed Beds: 25 Admissions: 218 Census: 7 Outpatient Visits: 13515 Births: 0 Personnel: 145**

**EDGEFIELD COUNTY HOSPITAL** See Edgefield County Healthcare

## FAIRFAX—Allendale County

★ **ALLENDALE COUNTY HOSPITAL (421300)**, 1787 Allendale Fairfax Highway, Zip 29827–9133, Mailing Address: P.O. Box 218, Zip 29827–0218; tel. 803/632–3311, (Nonreporting) **A**10 18
Primary Contact: Lari Gooding, Chief Executive Officer
CFO: Teresa Hicks, Chief Financial Officer
CIO: Tammy Smith, Director
CHR: Tammy Smith, Director
CNO: Becky Rowell, R.N., Director
Web address: www.achospital.org
**Control**: County, Government, Nonfederal **Service**: General medical and surgical

**Staffed Beds: 69**

## FLORENCE—Florence County

**CAROLINAS HOSPITAL SYSTEM** See Musc Health Florence Medical Center

⊞ **ENCOMPASS HEALTH REHABILITATION HOSPITAL OF FLORENCE (423026)**, 900 East Cheves Street, Zip 29506–2704; tel. 843/679–9000, (Nonreporting) **A**1 10 **F**9 28 29 34 35 56 57 59 75 77 82 86 87 90 91 92 93 94 95 96 148 149 **S** Encompass Health Corporation, Birmingham, AL
Primary Contact: Brian Nunn, R.N., Chief Executive Officer
CFO: Robert Wheeler, Controller
CMO: Adora Matthews, M.D., Medical Director
CHR: Susan Trantham, Director Human Resources
Web address: www.healthsouthflorence.com
**Control**: Corporation, Investor–owned (for–profit) **Service**: Rehabilitation

**Staffed Beds: 88 Admissions: 1198 Census: 45 Outpatient Visits: 0 Births: 0 Personnel: 171**

**HEALTHSOUTH REHABILITATION HOSPITAL OF FLORENCE** See Encompass Health Rehabilitation Hospital of Florence

⇧ **MCLEOD HEALTH** See Mcleod Regional Medical Center

★ ⇧ **MCLEOD REGIONAL MEDICAL CENTER (420051)**, 555 East Cheves Street, Zip 29506–2617, Mailing Address: P.O. Box 100551, Zip 29502–0551; tel. 843/777–2000, (Nonreporting) **A**2 3 5 10 21 **F**3 7 8 11 13 15 17 18 19 20 22 24 26 28 29 30 31 32 34 35 39 40 43 44 45 46 47 48 49 50 51 53 54 56 57 58 59 60 61 62 63 64 65 66 70 71 72 73 74 75 76 77 78 79 80 81 84 85 86 87 88 89 90 92 94 96 97 100 102 107 108 110 111 115 117 118 119 120 121 123 124 126 129 130 131 132 135 143 145 146 147 148 149 150 155 156 **P**3 **S** McLeod Health, Florence, SC
Primary Contact: Robert L. Colones, President and Chief Executive Officer
COO: Ron Boring, Senior Vice President and Chief Operating Officer
CFO: Samuel Fulton Ervin IIIChief Financial Officer
CMO: Alva W Whitehead, M.D., Vice President Medical Services
CIO: Jenean Blackmon, Associate Vice President and Chief Information Officer
CHR: Jeannette Glenn, Vice President Human Resources, Education and Training
Web address: www.mcleodhealth.org
**Control**: Other not–for–profit (including NFP Corporation) **Service**: General medical and surgical

**Staffed Beds: 464 Admissions: 27982 Census: 305 Outpatient Visits: 212026 Births: 2118 Total Expense ($000): 674241 Payroll Expense ($000): 229160 Personnel: 3389**

⊞ △ **MUSC HEALTH FLORENCE MEDICAL CENTER (420091)**, 805 Pamplico Highway, Zip 29505–6050, Mailing Address: P.O. Box 100550, Zip 29502–0550; tel. 843/674–5000, (Nonreporting) **A**1 5 7 10 **F**3 4 11 13 15 17 18 20 22 24 26 28 29 31 34 35 40 43 45 46 47 49 53 56 57 59 64 70 72 74 75 76 77 78 79 81 82 87 89 90 94 107 108 110 111 115 119 120 121 128 129 130 132 135 146 147 149 157 **S** MUSC Health, Charleston, SC
Primary Contact: Vance V. Reynolds, FACHE, CPA, Chief Executive Officer
COO: Kyle Baxter, Chief Operating Officer
CFO: Loren Rials, Chief Financial Officer
CIO: Lynn Northcutt, Chief Information Officer
CHR: Kay Douglas, Human Resources Director
CNO: Costa Cockfield, Chief Nursing Officer
Web address: www.carolinashospital.com
**Control**: Hospital district or authority, Government, Nonfederal **Service**: General medical and surgical

**Staffed Beds: 384 Admissions: 12754 Census: 233 Outpatient Visits: 117330 Births: 828 Personnel: 841**

**REGENCY HOSPITAL** See Regency Hospital of Florence

⊞ **REGENCY HOSPITAL OF FLORENCE (422007)**, 121 East Cedar Street, 4th Floor, Zip 29506–2576; tel. 843/661–3471, (Nonreporting) **A**1 10 **F**1 3 29 34 35 57 58 77 80 85 90 100 130 148 **S** Select Medical Corporation, Mechanicsburg, PA
Primary Contact: Amy Metz, Chief Executive Officer
CMO: Stephen Dersch, M.D., President Medical Staff
CHR: Tina Stokes, Manager Human Resources
Web address: www.regencyhospital.com
**Control**: Corporation, Investor–owned (for–profit) **Service**: Acute long–term care hospital

**Staffed Beds: 40 Admissions: 498 Census: 38 Outpatient Visits: 0 Births: 0 Personnel: 143**

**SC**

---

**Hospital, Medicare Provider Number, Address, Telephone, Approval, Facility, and Physician Codes, Health Care System**

★ American Hospital Association (AHA) membership
☐ The Joint Commission accreditation
○ Healthcare Facilities Accreditation Program
◇ DNV Healthcare Inc. accreditation
⇧ Center for Improvement in Healthcare Quality Accreditation
△ Commission on Accreditation of Rehabilitation Facilities (CARF) accreditation

## FORT JACKSON—Richland County

★ **MONCRIEF ARMY COMMUNITY HOSPITAL**, 4500 Stuart Street, Zip 29207–5700; tel. 803/751–2160, (Nonreporting) **A**5 **S** Department of the Army, Office of the Surgeon General, Falls Church, VA
Primary Contact: Colonel Traci Crawford, R.N., Commander
Web address: www.moncrief.amedd.army.mil
**Service:** General medical and surgical

| Staffed Beds: 60 |
|---|

## GAFFNEY—Cherokee County

★ ⇑ **CHEROKEE MEDICAL CENTER (420043)**, 1530 North Limestone Street, Zip 29340–4738; tel. 864/487–4271, (Nonreporting) **A**10 21 **F**3 11 15 18 29 34 35 40 45 46 57 59 64 70 75 79 81 85 86 87 107 108 110 111 115 119 128 129 130 131 132 146 148 149 154 **S** Spartanburg Regional Healthcare System, Spartanburg, SC
Primary Contact: Cody Butts, President
CFO: Christine Poplawski, Chief Financial Officer
CMO: Frank Phillips, M.D., Chief of Staff
CIO: John Odonell, Director Information Systems
CHR: Angie Benfield, Director Human Resources
CNO: Mychelle Ross, R.N., Chief Nursing Officer
Web address: www.maryblackgaffney.com/mary-black-gaffney/home.aspx
**Control:** Hospital district or authority, Government, Nonfederal **Service:** General medical and surgical

| Staffed Beds: 44 Admissions: 2088 Census: 19 Outpatient Visits: 45985 Births: 0 Personnel: 197 |
|---|

⇑ **MARY BLACK HEALTH SYSTEM - GAFFNEY** See Cherokee Medical Center

## GEORGETOWN—Georgetown County

**GEORGETOWN MEMORIAL HOSPITAL** See Tidelands Georgetown Memorial Hospital

⊠ **TIDELANDS GEORGETOWN MEMORIAL HOSPITAL (420020)**, 606 Black River Road, Zip 29440–3368, Mailing Address: Drawer 421718, Zip 29442–4203; tel. 843/527–7000, (Nonreporting) **A**1 3 5 10 19 **F**3 8 11 12 13 15 17 18 20 22 26 28 29 30 31 32 34 35 39 40 45 46 49 50 51 53 56 57 59 60 61 64 65 68 70 73 74 75 76 77 78 79 80 81 82 85 86 87 89 90 93 94 97 100 102 107 108 110 111 115 118 119 130 131 132 135 146 147 148 **S** Tidelands Health, Georgetown, SC
Primary Contact: Bruce P. Bailey, Chief Executive Officer
COO: Gayle L Resetar, Vice President and Chief Operating Officer
CFO: Elizabeth S. Ward, Chief Financial Officer
CHR: James F Harper, Senior Vice President and Chief Human Resources Officer
Web address: www.tidelandshealth.org
**Control:** Other not–for–profit (including NFP Corporation) **Service:** General medical and surgical

| Staffed Beds: 136 Admissions: 3926 Census: 45 Outpatient Visits: 203785 Births: 229 Total Expense ($000): 150147 Payroll Expense ($000): 57253 Personnel: 887 |
|---|

## GREENVILLE—Greenville County

**BON SECOURS ST. FRANCIS EASTSIDE** See St. Francis Eastside

☐ △ **BON SECOURS ST. FRANCIS HEALTH SYSTEM (420023)**, One St Francis Drive, Zip 29601–3207; tel. 864/255–1000, (Includes ST. FRANCIS EASTSIDE, Mailing address: 125 Commonwealth Drive, Greenville, South Carolina, Zip 29615–4812; tel. 864/675–4000), (Nonreporting) **A**1 2 7 10 **F**1 3 8 17 18 20 22 24 26 28 29 30 31 34 35 36 39 40 44 45 46 47 48 49 50 51 53 54 57 58 59 60 61 62 63 64 66 68 69 70 71 74 75 77 78 79 80 81 82 83 84 85 86 87 90 94 96 97 107 108 111 114 115 118 119 124 126 128 129 130 132 135 136 141 146 147 **S** Bon Secours Mercy Health, Marriottsville, MD
Primary Contact: Matthew T. Caldwell, President
CFO: Ronnie Hyatt, Senior Vice President Finance and Chief Financial Officer
CIO: Rita Hooker, Administrative Director Information Services
CHR: Fernando Fleites, Senior Vice President Human Resources
CNO: Teri Ficicchy, R.N., MSN, Chief Nursing Officer
Web address: www.stfrancishealth.org
**Control:** Other not–for–profit (including NFP Corporation) **Service:** General medical and surgical

| Staffed Beds: 352 Admissions: 19345 Census: 249 Outpatient Visits: 203070 Births: 2022 Total Expense ($000): 408073 Payroll Expense ($000): 124709 |
|---|

**CHILDREN'S HOSPITAL** See Ghs Children's Hospital

**GHS GREENVILLE MEMORIAL HOSPITAL** See Prisma Health Greenville Memorial Hospital

**PATEWOOD HOSPITAL** See Prisma Health Patewood Hospital

☐ △ **PRISMA HEALTH GREENVILLE MEMORIAL HOSPITAL (420078)**, 701 Grove Road, Zip 29605–4295; tel. 864/455–7000, (Includes GHS CHILDREN'S HOSPITAL, Mailing address: 701 Grove Road, Greenville, South Carolina, Zip 29605–5611; tel. 864/455–7000; MARSHALL I. PICKENS HOSPITAL, Mailing address: 701 Grove Road, Greenville, South Carolina, Zip 29605–5601; tel. 864/455–8988; ROGER C. PEACE REHABILITATION HOSPITAL, Mailing address: 701 Grove Road, Greenville, South Carolina, Zip 29605–4295; tel. 864/455–7000), (Nonreporting) **A**1 2 3 5 7 8 10 **F**3 4 11 13 15 17 18 19 20 22 24 26 27 28 29 30 31 32 34 35 36 38 39 40 41 43 44 45 46 47 48 49 50 51 52 53 54 56 57 58 59 61 64 65 66 68 70 72 73 74 75 76 77 78 79 80 81 82 83 84 85 86 87 88 89 90 92 93 94 96 97 98 99 100 101 102 103 104 105 106 107 108 110 111 114 115 116 117 118 119 120 121 123 124 126 129 130 132 134 136 141 142 145 146 147 148 153 154 156 **S** Prisma Health - Midlands, Columbia, SC
Primary Contact: James Agnew, Chief Executive Officer
COO: Greg Rusnak, Executive Vice President and Chief Operating Officer
CFO: Terri T. Newsom, Vice President of Finance and Chief Financial Officer
CMO: Angelo Sinopoli, M.D., Vice President Clinical Integration and Chief Medical Officer
CIO: Rich Rogers, Vice President Information Services
CHR: Doug Dorman, Vice President Human Resources
CNO: Michelle T Smith, R.N., MSN, FACHE, Vice President Nursing Chief Nursing Officer Chief Experience Officer
Web address: www.ghs.org
**Control:** Other not–for–profit (including NFP Corporation) **Service:** General medical and surgical

| Staffed Beds: 811 Admissions: 35531 Census: 598 Outpatient Visits: 805170 Births: 3906 Total Expense ($000): 1068549 Payroll Expense ($000): 288400 Personnel: 4191 |
|---|

☐ **PRISMA HEALTH PATEWOOD HOSPITAL (420102)**, 175 Patewood Drive, Zip 29615–3570; tel. 864/797–1000, (Nonreporting) **A**1 5 10 **F**3 11 13 29 30 37 45 50 64 74 76 77 79 80 81 85 86 130 146 147 **S** Prisma Health - Midlands, Columbia, SC
Primary Contact: Tim Brookshire, Chief Operating Officer
Web address: www.ghs.org/patewood
**Control:** Other not–for–profit (including NFP Corporation) **Service:** Surgical

| Staffed Beds: 72 Admissions: 4027 Census: 20 Outpatient Visits: 124887 Births: 2075 Personnel: 285 |
|---|

⊠ **REGENCY HOSPITAL OF GREENVILLE (422009)**, One St Francis Drive, 4th Floor, Zip 29601–3955; tel. 864/255–1438, (Nonreporting) **A**1 10 **F**1 3 29 75 77 85 **S** Select Medical Corporation, Mechanicsburg, PA
Primary Contact: Tammy Ratliff, Chief Executive Officer
Web address: www.regencyhospital.com
**Control:** Corporation, Investor–owned (for–profit) **Service:** Acute long–term care hospital

| Staffed Beds: 32 Admissions: 327 Census: 24 Outpatient Visits: 0 Births: 0 Total Expense ($000): 13361 Payroll Expense ($000): 7158 Personnel: 97 |
|---|

☐ **SHRINERS HOSPITALS FOR CHILDREN-GREENVILLE (423300)**, 950 West Faris Road, Zip 29605–4277; tel. 864/271–3444, (Nonreporting) **A**1 3 10 **F**1 29 59 64 68 75 77 79 81 85 87 89 90 93 94 128 130 131 146 148 154 **P**6 **S** Shriners Hospitals for Children, Tampa, FL
Primary Contact: William Munley, Administrator
CFO: John Conti, Director Finance
CMO: J. Michael Wattenbarger, M.D., Chief of Staff
CHR: Willis E Tisdale, Director Human Resources
CNO: Allison Leigh Windas, Director of Patient Care Services-Nurse Executive
Web address: www.greenvilleshrinershospital.org
**Control:** Other not–for–profit (including NFP Corporation) **Service:** Children's orthopedic

| Staffed Beds: 15 Admissions: 261 Census: 3 Outpatient Visits: 21314 Births: 0 Total Expense ($000): 28574 Payroll Expense ($000): 15066 Personnel: 178 |
|---|

**SHRINERS HOSPS FOR CRPLD CHILD** See Shriners Hospitals for Children-Greenville

**ST FRANCIS HEALTH SYSTEM** See Bon Secours St. Francis Health System

*Many Facility Codes have changed. Please refer to the AHA Guide Code Chart.*

© 2021 AHA Guide

## GREENWOOD—Greenwood County

☐ **GREENWOOD REGIONAL REHABILITATION HOSPITAL (423030)**, 1530 Parkway, Zip 29646–4027; tel. 864/330–1800, (Nonreporting) **A**1 10 **S** Ernest Health, Inc., Albuquerque, NM
Primary Contact: Kristin Manske, Chief Executive Officer
CFO: Charity Martin, Controller and Regional Business Officer Manager
CMO: Cam Monda, D.O., Medical Director
CHR: Michelle Watkins, Human Resources Manager
CNO: Jessica Lawson, Director of Nursing
Web address: www.grrh.ernesthealth.com
**Control:** Corporation, Investor–owned (for–profit) **Service:** Rehabilitation

| Staffed Beds: 54 |
|---|

⇑ **SELF MEMORIAL HOSPITAL** See Self Regional Healthcare

★ ⇑ **SELF REGIONAL HEALTHCARE (420071)**, 1325 Spring Street, Zip 29646–3860; tel. 864/725–4111, (Nonreporting) **A**2 3 5 10 21 **F**1 3 8 11 13 15 17 18 19 20 22 24 26 28 29 30 31 32 34 35 39 40 43 44 45 46 48 49 50 51 53 55 57 58 59 60 61 62 64 68 70 71 72 73 74 75 76 77 78 79 80 81 82 85 86 87 89 90 91 94 96 97 98 102 103 107 108 110 111 114 115 117 119 120 121 123 124 127 128 129 130 131 132 134 135 144 146 147 148 149 156
Primary Contact: James A. Pfeiffer, FACHE, President and Chief Executive Officer
CFO: Timothy Evans, Vice President and Chief Financial Officer
CMO: Matthew Logan, M.D., Vice President Medical Affairs and Chief Medical Officer
CIO: Andy Hartung, Assistant Vice President of Information Systems and Chief Information Officer
CHR: Michael Dixon, Vice President of Human Resources
CNO: Linda Russell, Vice President and Chief Nursing Officer
Web address: www.selfregional.org
**Control:** State, Government, Nonfederal **Service:** General medical and surgical

| Staffed Beds: 322 Admissions: 12141 Census: 154 Outpatient Visits: 263978 Births: 1381 Total Expense ($000): 334825 Payroll Expense ($000): 115284 Personnel: 2333 |
|---|

## GREER—Greenville County

☐ **CAROLINA CENTER FOR BEHAVIORAL HEALTH (424010)**, 2700 East Phillips Road, Zip 29650–4816; tel. 864/235–2335, (Nonreporting) **A**1 3 10 **S** Universal Health Services, Inc., King of Prussia, PA
Primary Contact: Jerry Chapman, Chief Executive Officer
CFO: James P Boynton Jr Chief Financial Officer
CMO: Gergana Dimitrova, M.D., Medical Director
CHR: Ginny Savage, Director of Human Resources
CNO: Jennifer Daigle, R.N., Director of Nursing and Utilization Review
Web address: www.thecarolinacenter.com
**Control:** Corporation, Investor–owned (for–profit) **Service:** Psychiatric

| Staffed Beds: 130 |
|---|

**CHARTER GREENVILLE HLTH SYST** See Carolina Center for Behavioral Health

**GREER MEMORIAL HOSPITAL** See Prisma Health Greer Memorial Hospital

## GREER—Spartanburg County

★ ⇑ **PELHAM MEDICAL CENTER (420103)**, 250 Westmoreland Road, Zip 29651–9013; tel. 864/530–6000, (Nonreporting) **A**10 21 **F**3 11 15 18 20 26 29 30 34 35 37 40 45 49 50 54 57 59 64 68 70 74 75 77 79 81 82 84 85 86 87 90 94 107 108 110 111 114 115 118 119 130 146 148 149 154 **S** Spartanburg Regional Healthcare System, Spartanburg, SC
Primary Contact: Anthony Kouskolekas, FACHE, President
CNO: Connie Spykerman, Chief Nursing Officer
Web address: www.pelhammedicalcenter.com
**Control:** Hospital district or authority, Government, Nonfederal **Service:** General medical and surgical

| Staffed Beds: 48 Admissions: 2601 Census: 34 Outpatient Visits: 56867 Births: 0 Total Expense ($000): 82543 Payroll Expense ($000): 24145 Personnel: 693 |
|---|

## GREER—Greenville County

☐ **PRISMA HEALTH GREER MEMORIAL HOSPITAL (420033)**, 830 South Buncombe Road, Zip 29650–2400; tel. 864/797–8000, (Nonreporting) **A**1 3 5 10 **F**1 3 11 13 15 18 28 29 30 34 35 40 44 45 49 50 51 57 59 64 65 68 70 76 77 79 80 81 85 87 89 94 107 110 111 114 115 119 126 128 129 130 146 147 148 **S** Prisma Health - Midlands, Columbia, SC
Primary Contact: John F. Mansure, FACHE, President
Web address: www.ghs.org
**Control:** Other not–for–profit (including NFP Corporation) **Service:** General medical and surgical

| Staffed Beds: 70 Admissions: 3071 Census: 29 Outpatient Visits: 95308 Births: 792 Total Expense ($000): 82713 Payroll Expense ($000): 25756 Personnel: 390 |
|---|

## GREER—Spartanburg County

⇑ **VILLAGE HOSPITAL** See Pelham Medical Center

## HARDEEVILLE—Jasper County

⊠ **COASTAL CAROLINA HOSPITAL (420101)**, 1000 Medical Center Drive, Zip 29927–3446; tel. 843/784–8000, (Nonreporting) **A**1 10 **S** TENET Healthcare Corporation, Dallas, TX
Primary Contact: Joel Taylor, Chief Executive Officer
COO: Christopher Borgstrom, Associate Administrator
CFO: Ronald J. Groteluschen, Chief Financial Officer
CIO: Cheryl Grant, Director Information Systems
CHR: Darlene E. Nester, Market Chief Human Resources Officer
CNO: Christina Brzezinski, Chief Nursing Officer
Web address: www.coastalhospital.com
**Control:** Corporation, Investor–owned (for–profit) **Service:** General medical and surgical

| Staffed Beds: 35 |
|---|

**COASTAL CAROLINA MEDICAL CTR** See Coastal Carolina Hospital

## HARTSVILLE—Darlington County

**BYERLY HOSPITAL** See Carolina Pines Regional Medical Center

⊠ ○ **CAROLINA PINES REGIONAL MEDICAL CENTER (420010)**, 1304 West Bobo Newsom Highway, Zip 29550–4710; tel. 843/339–2100, (Nonreporting) **A**1 10 11 19 **S** LifePoint Health, Brentwood, TN
Primary Contact: William Little, Chief Executive Officer
COO: Susan C Shugart, Chief Operating Officer
CFO: Rodney VanDonkelaar, Chief Financial Officer
CMO: Tallulah Holmstrom, M.D., Chief Medical Officer
CIO: Denise Barefoot, Director of Information Technology
CHR: Charlotte Adams, Director of Human Resources
CNO: Christy Moody, R.N., Chief Nursing Officer
Web address: www.cprmc.com
**Control:** Corporation, Investor–owned (for–profit) **Service:** General medical and surgical

| Staffed Beds: 105 |
|---|

## HILTON HEAD ISLAND—Beaufort County

⊠ **HILTON HEAD HOSPITAL (420080)**, 25 Hospital Center Boulevard, Zip 29926–2738; tel. 843/681–6122, (Nonreporting) **A**1 10 20 **S** TENET Healthcare Corporation, Dallas, TX
Primary Contact: Jeremy L. Clark, Market Chief Executive Officer
CMO: Glenn Neil Love, M.D., Medical Director
CIO: Stephen Brendler, Director Information Systems
CHR: Darlene E. Nester, Chief Human Resources Officer
Web address: www.hiltonheadregional.com
**Control:** Partnership, Investor–owned (for–profit) **Service:** General medical and surgical

| Staffed Beds: 93 |
|---|

**HILTON HEAD REGIONAL MED CTR** See Hilton Head Hospital

## KINGSTREE—Williamsburg County

**CAROLINAS HOSP SYST-KINGSTREE** See Williamsburg Regional Hospital

✉ **WILLIAMSBURG REGIONAL HOSPITAL (421303)**, 500 Nelson Boulevard, Zip 29556-4027; tel. 843/355-8888, (Nonreporting) **A**1 10 18
Primary Contact: Allen Abernethy, Interim Chief Executive Officer
COO: Dan Harrington, Chief Operating Officer and Director Human Resources
CMO: Troy B Gamble, M.D., JrChief Medical Staff
CIO: David Slenszak, Director, Information Services
CHR: Dan Harrington, Chief Operating Officer and Director Human Resources
CNO: Kelly Lawson, Chief Nursing Officer
Web address: www.https://wmbgrh.org/
**Control:** Other not-for-profit (including NFP Corporation) **Service:** General medical and surgical

**Staffed Beds:** 25

### LAKE CITY—Florence County

**CAROLINAS HOSP SYST-LAKE CITY** See Lake City Community Hospital

★ **LAKE CITY COMMUNITY HOSPITAL (420066)**, 258 N Ron McNair Boulevard, Zip 29560-2462, Mailing Address: P.O. Box 1479, Zip 29560-1479; tel. 843/374-2036, (Nonreporting) **A**10
Primary Contact: Michael Faucett, Chief Operating Officer
COO: Michael Faucett, Chief Operating Officer
CMO: Stephen Askins, M.D., Chief of Staff
CIO: David Moon JrDirector Information Systems
CHR: Anne Poston, Director of Human Resources/Compliance
CNO: Renate Browder, R.N., Director of Nursing
Web address: www.lcchospital.org
**Control:** Hospital district or authority, Government, Nonfederal **Service:** General medical and surgical

**Staffed Beds:** 26

### LANCASTER—Lancaster County

✉ **MUSC HEALTH LANCASTER MEDICAL CENTER (420036)**, 800 West Meeting Street, Zip 29720-2298; tel. 803/286-1214, (Nonreporting) **A**1 5 10 **F**1 3 11 13 15 17 18 20 28 29 30 34 35 40 45 47 48 49 54 57 59 60 64 70 73 74 75 76 77 78 79 80 81 82 85 87 89 90 93 94 98 102 103 107 108 110 111 114 115 118 119 128 129 130 131 132 135 146 147 148 149 157 **S** MUSC Health, Charleston, SC
Primary Contact: J. Scott Broome, Chief Executive Officer
COO: Richard Warrin, Chief Operating Officer
CFO: Holt Smith, Chief Financial Officer
CMO: Douglas Tiedt, M.D., Chief of Staff
CIO: Chrys Steele, Director Information Systems
CHR: Karen Chapman, Human Resources Director
CNO: Karen Martin, Chief Nursing Officer
Web address: www.springsmemorial.com
**Control:** Hospital district or authority, Government, Nonfederal **Service:** General medical and surgical

**Staffed Beds:** 111 **Admissions:** 5363 **Census:** 82 **Outpatient Visits:** 64112 **Births:** 478 **Total Expense ($000):** 99824 **Payroll Expense ($000):** 32592 **Personnel:** 619

☐ **REBOUND BEHAVIORAL HEALTH (424014)**, 134 East Rebound Road, Zip 29720-7712; tel. 855/999-9501, (Nonreporting) **A**1 10 **S** Acadia Healthcare Company, Inc., Franklin, TN
Primary Contact: Cameron Bolish, Chief Executive Officer
Web address: www.reboundbehavioralhealth.com
**Control:** Corporation, Investor-owned (for-profit) **Service:** Psychiatric

**Staffed Beds:** 42

**SPRINGS MEMORIAL HOSPITAL** See Musc Health Lancaster Medical Center

### LORIS—Horry County

⇑ **MCLEOD HEALTH LORIS (420105)**, 3655 Mitchell Street, Zip 29569-2827; tel. 843/716-7000, (Includes MCLEOD SEACOAST, Mailing address: 4000 Highway 9 East, Little River, South Carolina, Zip 29566-7833; tel. 843/390-8100; Monica Vehige, Administrator), (Nonreporting) **A**10 21 **F**1 3 11 13 15 18 20 29 30 32 34 35 40 44 50 53 57 59 63 64 70 74 75 76 77 79 80 81 85 86 87 90 94 96 102 107 108 110 111 115 118 119 128 130 131 132 134 135 143 146 148 149 **P**3 **S** McLeod Health, Florence, SC
Primary Contact: Scott Montgomery, Administrator
CMO: John Charles, M.D., Chief Medical Officer
CNO: Amanda Mills, Chief Nursing Officer
Web address: www.mcleodhealth.org
**Control:** Other not-for-profit (including NFP Corporation) **Service:** General medical and surgical

**Staffed Beds:** 132 **Admissions:** 7569 **Census:** 61 **Outpatient Visits:** 97705 **Births:** 423 **Total Expense ($000):** 145754 **Payroll Expense ($000):** 52838 **Personnel:** 323

⇑ **MCLEOD LORIS HEALTH** See Mcleod Health Loris

### MANNING—Clarendon County

⇑ **CLARENDON HEALTH SYSTEM** See Mcleod Health Clarendon

⇑ **MCLEOD HEALTH CLARENDON (420109)**, 10 Hospital Street, Zip 29102-3153, Mailing Address: P.O. Box 550, Zip 29102-0550; tel. 803/433-3000, (Nonreporting) **A**3 10 21 **F**1 3 13 15 28 29 34 35 40 45 53 59 62 64 70 75 76 79 80 81 85 87 90 94 97 107 108 111 119 127 128 130 133 135 146 149 **P**3 **S** McLeod Health, Florence, SC
Primary Contact: Rachel Gainey, Administrator
COO: Paul Schumacher, Chief Operating Officer
CMO: Catherine Rabon, M.D., Chief Medical Officer
CIO: Pat Kolb, Manager Information Technology
CHR: Gail A Richbourg, Director Human Resources
CNO: Natalie Davis, R.N., Interim Chief Nursing Officer
Web address: www.clarendonhealth.com
**Control:** Other not-for-profit (including NFP Corporation) **Service:** General medical and surgical

**Staffed Beds:** 36 **Admissions:** 2236 **Census:** 20 **Outpatient Visits:** 17908 **Births:** 332 **Total Expense ($000):** 44509 **Payroll Expense ($000):** 22147 **Personnel:** 372

### MONCKS CORNER—Berkeley County

**BERKELEY REGIONAL MEDICAL CENTER** See Moncks Corner Medical Center

### MOUNT PLEASANT—Charleston County

✉ **EAST COOPER MEDICAL CENTER (420089)**, 2000 Hospital Drive, Zip 29464-3764; tel. 843/881-0100, (Nonreporting) **A**1 3 5 10 **F**1 3 12 13 15 18 20 29 31 34 35 37 40 43 45 46 49 50 51 57 59 60 64 68 70 73 74 75 76 77 78 79 80 81 82 84 85 86 90 92 93 94 100 107 108 110 111 114 115 119 126 128 129 130 131 132 146 147 148 **S** TENET Healthcare Corporation, Dallas, TX
Primary Contact: Patrick Downes, Chief Executive Officer
COO: Ramona Pickens, Chief Operating Officer
CFO: Patrick C Bolander, Chief Financial Officer
CMO: Kevin Keenan, M.D., Physician Advisor
CIO: Michael Foster, Director Information Systems
CHR: Tracy Hunter, Chief Human Resources Officer
CNO: Patrick Beaver, MSN, R.N., Chief Nursing Officer
Web address: www.eastcoopermedctr.com
**Control:** Corporation, Investor-owned (for-profit) **Service:** General medical and surgical

**Staffed Beds:** 140 **Admissions:** 5081 **Census:** 42 **Outpatient Visits:** 53816 **Births:** 1442 **Total Expense ($000):** 125788 **Payroll Expense ($000):** 34456 **Personnel:** 494

**EAST COOPER REGIONAL MEDICAL CENTER** See East Cooper Medical Center

**MOUNT PLEASANT HOSPITAL** See Roper St. Francis Mount Pleasant Hospital

✉ **ROPER ST. FRANCIS MOUNT PLEASANT HOSPITAL (420104)**, 3500 Highway 17 North, Zip 29466-9123, Mailing Address: 3500 North Highway 17, Zip 29466-9123; tel. 843/606-7000, (Nonreporting) **A**1 10 **F**3 7 13 15 28 29 30 34 40 45 46 54 59 67 68 70 75 76 79 81 84 85 86 87 89 94 102 107 108 110 111 115 118 119 129 143 146 147 148 149 156 **S** Roper St. Francis Healthcare, Charleston, SC
Primary Contact: Tavia Buck, Chief Administrative Officer
CFO: Bret Johnson, Chief Financial Officer
CMO: Steven D Shapiro, M.D., Chief Medical Officer
CIO: Melinda H. Cardell, Interim Chief Information Officer
CHR: Melanie Stith, Vice President Human Resources
Web address: www.rsfh.com/mount-pleasant-hospital
**Control:** Other not-for-profit (including NFP Corporation) **Service:** General medical and surgical

**Staffed Beds:** 73 **Admissions:** 2734 **Census:** 22 **Outpatient Visits:** 50814 **Births:** 518 **Total Expense ($000):** 82233 **Payroll Expense ($000):** 20037 **Personnel:** 359

### MT. PLEASANT—Mt. Pleasant County

✉ **VIBRA HOSPITAL OF CHARLESTON (422005)**, 1200 Hospital Drive, Zip 29464; tel. 843/375-4000, (Nonreporting) **A**1 10 **S** Vibra Healthcare, Mechanicsburg, PA
Primary Contact: Donald Becker, Chief Executive Officer
CFO: Julia Smith, Chief Financial Officer
CMO: Athena Beldecos, M.D., Medical Director
CHR: Julia Taylor, Area Director Human Resources
Web address: www.vhcharleston.com
**Control:** Corporation, Investor-owned (for-profit) **Service:** Acute long-term care hospital

**Staffed Beds:** 59

**VIBRA HOSPITAL OF CHARLESTON-TCU** See Vibra Hospital of Charleston

*Many Facility Codes have changed. Please refer to the AHA Guide Code Chart.*

## MULLINS—Marion County

**CAROLINAS HOSPITAL SYSTEM MARION** See Musc Health Marion Medical Center

✠ **MUSC HEALTH MARION MEDICAL CENTER (420055)**, 2829 East Highway 76, Zip 29574–6035, Mailing Address: P O Drawer 1150, Marion, Zip 29571–1150; tel. 843/431–2000, (Total facility includes 92 beds in nursing home–type unit) (Nonreporting) **A**1 10 **F**3 15 18 28 29 34 35 40 45 46 53 57 59 67 70 75 77 79 81 82 87 89 94 107 108 110 111 115 119 128 130 131 133 135 146 149 157 **S** MUSC Health, Charleston, SC
Primary Contact: Vance V. Reynolds, FACHE, CPA, Chief Executive Officer
CFO: Loren Rials, Chief Financial Officer
CMO: Robert DeGrood, M.D., Chief Medical Staff
CIO: Charlie Grantham, Manager Information Systems
CHR: Christi Meggs, Director
CNO: Linda Parnell, Chief Nursing Officer
Web address: www.https://muschealth.org/locations/marion-medical-center
**Control**: Hospital district or authority, Government, Nonfederal **Service**: General medical and surgical

**Staffed Beds**: 138 **Admissions**: 1916 **Census**: 107 **Outpatient Visits**: 43046 **Births**: 0

## MURRELLS INLET—Georgetown County

✠ **TIDELANDS WACCAMAW COMMUNITY HOSPITAL (420098)**, 4070 Highway 17 Bypass, Zip 29576–5033, Mailing Address: P O Drawer 3350, Zip 29576–2673; tel. 843/652–1000, (Nonreporting) **A**1 10 **F**3 11 13 15 17 18 28 29 30 31 32 35 37 39 40 45 50 51 56 60 61 64 65 68 70 73 74 75 76 77 78 79 80 81 82 85 86 87 89 90 93 94 97 102 107 108 110 111 114 115 118 119 130 131 146 147 148 **S** Tidelands Health, Georgetown, SC
Primary Contact: Bruce P. Bailey, Chief Executive Officer
CFO: Elizabeth S. Ward, Chief Financial Officer
Web address: www.tidelandswaccamawcommunity.org
**Control**: Other not–for–profit (including NFP Corporation) **Service**: General medical and surgical

**Staffed Beds**: 126 **Admissions**: 7022 **Census**: 67 **Outpatient Visits**: 125543 **Births**: 569 **Total Expense ($000)**: 154420 **Payroll Expense ($000)**: 31969 **Personnel**: 570

**WACCAMAW COMMUNITY HOSPITAL** See Tidelands Waccamaw Community Hospital

## MYRTLE BEACH—Horry County

✠ **GRAND STRAND MEDICAL CENTER (420085)**, 809 82nd Parkway, Zip 29572–4607; tel. 843/692–1000, (Nonreporting) **A**1 3 5 10 19 **F**1 3 11 13 15 17 18 20 22 24 26 28 29 30 31 34 35 37 38 39 40 41 42 43 45 47 49 50 54 57 58 59 60 64 70 73 74 75 76 77 78 79 80 81 84 85 86 87 88 89 90 94 96 98 101 102 105 107 108 109 110 111 114 115 118 119 120 121 123 124 126 128 130 132 135 146 147 149 153 154 157 **S** HCA Healthcare, Nashville, TN
Primary Contact: Mark E. Sims, Chief Executive Officer
CFO: Turner Wortham, Chief Financial Officer
Web address: www.grandstrandmed.com
**Control**: Corporation, Investor–owned (for–profit) **Service**: General medical and surgical

**Staffed Beds**: 371 **Admissions**: 24950 **Census**: 335 **Outpatient Visits**: 197106 **Births**: 893 **Personnel**: 1393

**GRAND STRAND REGIONAL MEDICAL CENTER** See Grand Strand Medical Center

## NEWBERRY—Newberry County

✠ **NEWBERRY COUNTY MEMORIAL HOSPITAL (420053)**, 2669 Kinard Street, Zip 29108–2911, Mailing Address: P.O. Box 497, Zip 29108–0497; tel. 803/276–7570, (Nonreporting) **A**1 10 20 **F**1 3 7 11 13 15 17 28 29 30 31 32 34 35 37 40 45 47 53 56 57 59 64 68 70 75 76 77 78 79 81 82 85 86 87 89 90 94 107 108 109 110 111 115 119 128 130 133 135 143 146 147 148 149 **P**6 **S** QHR Health, Brentwood, TN
Primary Contact: Bruce A. Baldwin, Chief Executive Officer
CFO: Mike Reynolds, Chief Financial Officer
CMO: Mark Davis, M.D., Chief of Staff
CIO: David Wolff, Director Information Technology
CHR: Dyan Bowman, Director Human Resources
Web address: www.newberryhospital.org
**Control**: County, Government, Nonfederal **Service**: General medical and surgical

**Staffed Beds**: 54 **Admissions**: 1931 **Census**: 18 **Outpatient Visits**: 44476 **Births**: 246 **Total Expense ($000)**: 50844 **Payroll Expense ($000)**: 18943 **Personnel**: 348

## ORANGEBURG—Orangeburg County

✠ **REGIONAL MEDICAL CENTER (420068)**, 3000 St Matthews Road, Zip 29118–1442; tel. 803/395–2200, (Nonreporting) **A**1 10
Primary Contact: Charles E. Williams, President and Chief Executive Officer
COO: Nicole Smith Hendricks, Chief Operating Officer
CIO: Michelle E. Edwards, Chief Information Officer
CHR: Sonya L. Medley, Director of Human Resources
CNO: Dana L Dalton, Vice President and Chief Nursing Officer
Web address: www.trmhealth.org
**Control**: County, Government, Nonfederal **Service**: General medical and surgical

**Staffed Beds**: 283

**REGIONAL MEDICAL CENTER OF ORANGEBURG AND CALHOUN COUNTIES** See Regional Medical Center

**WILLIAM J. MCCORD ADOLESCENT AND TREATMENT CENTER** See William J. Mccord Adolescent Treatment Facility

☐ **WILLIAM J. MCCORD ADOLESCENT TREATMENT FACILITY (424013)**, 910 Cook Road, Zip 29118–2124, Mailing Address: P.O. Box 1166, Zip 29116–1166; tel. 803/534–2328, (Nonreporting) **A**1 10 **F**4 29 34 38 57 61 98 99 130 132 134 135 151
Primary Contact: Michael Dennis, Director
CFO: Laura Murdaugh, Finance Director
CMO: Dorothy Kendall, Medical Director
CNO: Linda Mitchum, Director of Nursing
Web address: www.tccada.com
**Control**: Other not–for–profit (including NFP Corporation) **Service**: Children's hospital psychiatric

**Staffed Beds**: 15 **Admissions**: 89 **Census**: 8 **Outpatient Visits**: 0 **Births**: 0 **Personnel**: 33

## PICKENS—Pickens County

★ ⇑ **ANMED HEALTH CANNON (420011)**, 123 W G Acker Drive, Zip 29671–2739, Mailing Address: P.O. Box 188, Zip 29671–0188; tel. 864/878–4791, (Nonreporting) **A**10 21 **S** AnMed Health, Anderson, SC
Primary Contact: Brandon Clary, President and Chief Executive Officer
CFO: Will Grant, Chief Financial Officer
CMO: Daniel J Dahlhausen, M.D., President of Medical Staff/Chief Medical Officer
CIO: Robert Furr, Director Information Services
CHR: Lisa G Bryant, Director Human Resources
CNO: Donna K Anderson, R.N., Chief Nursing Officer
Web address: www.cannonhospital.org
**Control**: Other not–for–profit (including NFP Corporation) **Service**: General medical and surgical

**Staffed Beds**: 24

⇑ **CANNON MEMORIAL HOSPITAL** See Anmed Health Cannon

## ROCK HILL—York County

✠ **ENCOMPASS HEALTH REHABILITATION HOSPITAL OF ROCK HILL (423028)**, 1795 Dr. Frank Gaston Boulevard, Zip 29732–1190; tel. 803/326–3500, (Nonreporting) **A**1 10 **F**29 90 95 96 148 149 **S** Encompass Health Corporation, Birmingham, AL
Primary Contact: Deanna Martin, Chief Executive Officer
Web address: www.healthsouthrockhill.com
**Control**: Corporation, Investor–owned (for–profit) **Service**: Rehabilitation

**Staffed Beds**: 50 **Admissions**: 1424 **Census**: 43 **Outpatient Visits**: 0 **Births**: 0 **Personnel**: 149

**HEALTHSOUTH REHABILITATION HOSPITAL OF ROCK HILL** See Encompass Health Rehabilitation Hospital of Rock Hill

**PIEDMONT HEALTHCARE SYSTEM** See Piedmont Medical Center

⊠ **PIEDMONT MEDICAL CENTER (420002)**, 222 Herlong Avenue, Zip 29732; tel. 803/329–1234, (Nonreporting) **A**1 2 10 **F**1 3 7 11 12 13 15 17 18 20 22 24 26 28 29 30 31 34 35 40 43 45 49 50 57 59 60 64 67 70 72 73 74 75 76 77 78 79 81 82 85 86 89 90 91 93 98 100 102 103 107 108 110 111 114 115 118 119 126 128 130 132 135 146 147 148 **S** TENET Healthcare Corporation, Dallas, TX
Primary Contact: Mark Nosacka, Chief Executive Officer
COO: Ramona Pickens, Chief Operating Officer
CFO: Stephen Gilmore, Chief Financial Officer
CIO: Joel Dean, Director Information Services
CHR: Elizabeth Elich, Chief Human Resources Officer
CNO: Elaine Hastings, MSN, R.N., Chief Nursing Officer
Web address: www.piedmontmedicalcenter.com
**Control**: Corporation, Investor–owned (for–profit) **Service**: General medical and surgical

**Staffed Beds:** 279 **Admissions:** 15915 **Census:** 212 **Outpatient Visits:** 139684 **Births:** 1587 **Total Expense ($000):** 258793 **Payroll Expense ($000):** 86930 **Personnel:** 1747

### SENECA—Oconee County

**OCONEE MEMORIAL HOSPITAL** See Prisma Health Oconee Memorial Hospital

☐ **PRISMA HEALTH OCONEE MEMORIAL HOSPITAL (420009)**, 298 Memorial Drive, Zip 29672–9499; tel. 864/882–3351, (Nonreporting) **A**1 3 5 10 20 **F**1 3 7 11 13 15 17 18 20 28 29 30 31 34 35 39 40 51 54 56 57 59 63 64 65 67 70 75 76 77 78 79 80 81 82 84 85 86 87 89 90 94 97 107 108 111 114 115 119 128 130 132 143 146 149 **S** Prisma Health - Midlands, Columbia, SC
Primary Contact: Hunter Kome, Campus President
CMO: Conrad K Shuler, M.D., Chief Medical Officer
CIO: Jay Hansen, Director Information Services
CNO: Patricia Smith, Chief Nursing Officer
Web address: www.oconeemed.org
**Control**: Other not–for–profit (including NFP Corporation) **Service**: General medical and surgical

**Staffed Beds:** 136 **Admissions:** 5244 **Census:** 57 **Outpatient Visits:** 129501 **Births:** 481 **Total Expense ($000):** 116306 **Payroll Expense ($000):** 39434 **Personnel:** 646

### SIMPSONVILLE—Greenville County

**HILLCREST HOSPITAL** See Prisma Health Hillcrest Hospital

☐ **PRISMA HEALTH HILLCREST HOSPITAL (420037)**, 729 SE Main Street, Zip 29681–3280; tel. 864/454–6100, (Nonreporting) **A**1 5 10 **F**1 3 11 12 15 18 29 34 35 40 44 45 50 57 59 64 68 70 79 80 81 85 86 90 107 108 110 111 114 115 119 128 129 130 132 146 **S** Prisma Health - Midlands, Columbia, SC
Primary Contact: Scott R. Jones, FACHE, Chief Operating Officer
Web address: www.ghs.org
**Control**: Other not–for–profit (including NFP Corporation) **Service**: General medical and surgical

**Staffed Beds:** 43 **Admissions:** 1865 **Census:** 15 **Outpatient Visits:** 81509 **Births:** 0 **Personnel:** 259

### SPARTANBURG—Spartanburg County

**MARY BLACK HEALTH SYSTEM-SPARTANBURG** See Spartanburg Medical Center - Mary Black

★ **SPARTANBURG HOSPITAL FOR RESTORATIVE CARE (422004)**, 389 Serpentine Drive, Zip 29303–3026; tel. 864/560–3280, (Total facility includes 25 beds in nursing home–type unit) (Nonreporting) **A**10 **F**1 3 29 30 31 35 70 75 77 79 82 85 87 90 119 128 130 148 149 **S** Spartanburg Regional Healthcare System, Spartanburg, SC
Primary Contact: Jill Jolley Greene, MSN, R.N., President
Web address: www.https://www.spartanburgregional.com/locations/spartanburg-hospital-for-restorative-care/restorative-care-medical-staff
**Control**: Hospital district or authority, Government, Nonfederal **Service**: Acute long–term care hospital

**Staffed Beds:** 116 **Admissions:** 686 **Census:** 40 **Outpatient Visits:** 0 **Births:** 0 **Total Expense ($000):** 23956 **Payroll Expense ($000):** 11864 **Personnel:** 185

⚕ **SPARTANBURG MEDICAL CENTER** See Spartanburg Medical Center - Church Street Campus

★ ⚕ **SPARTANBURG MEDICAL CENTER - CHURCH STREET CAMPUS (420007)**, 101 East Wood Street, Zip 29303–3040; tel. 864/560–6000, (Nonreporting) **A**2 3 10 21 **F**1 3 7 11 12 13 15 17 18 20 22 24 26 28 29 30 31 34 35 36 37 38 39 40 43 44 45 46 47 48 49 50 53 54 56 57 58 59 60 61 62 63 64 65 66 68 70 71 72 73 74 75 76 77 78 79 81 82 83 84 85 86 87 88 89 90 94 97 98 99 100 101 102 103 104 107 108 110 111 114 115 117 118 119 120 123 124 126 128 129 130 131 132 143 144 145 146 147 148 149 154 **S** Spartanburg Regional Healthcare System, Spartanburg, SC
Primary Contact: J Philip. Feisal, President and Chief Executive Officer
COO: Mark Aycock, Chief Operating Officer
CFO: Kenneth Meinke, Senior Vice President Administrative Services, Finance and Chief Financial Officer
CMO: Charles Morrow, M.D., Chief Medical Officer
CIO: Harold Moore, Chief Information Technology Officer
CHR: Kathy Sinclair, Vice President Human Resources
CNO: Susan Duggar, MSN, Vice President Nursing
Web address: www.spartanburgregional.com
**Control**: Hospital district or authority, Government, Nonfederal **Service**: General medical and surgical

**Staffed Beds:** 531 **Admissions:** 26558 **Census:** 427 **Outpatient Visits:** 441539 **Births:** 2786 **Total Expense ($000):** 851824 **Payroll Expense ($000):** 274417 **Personnel:** 4164

★ △ **SPARTANBURG MEDICAL CENTER - MARY BLACK (420083)**, 1700 Skylyn Drive, Zip 29307–1061, Mailing Address: P.O. Box 3217, Zip 29304–3217; tel. 864/573–3000, (Nonreporting) **A**5 7 10 **F**1 3 11 13 15 18 20 29 30 31 34 35 40 45 47 49 50 51 56 57 59 60 64 68 70 73 74 75 76 77 78 79 80 81 85 87 89 90 93 94 96 98 100 101 102 103 107 108 110 111 114 115 119 126 128 129 130 132 145 146 147 148 149 154 **S** Spartanburg Regional Healthcare System, Spartanburg, SC
Primary Contact: Parkes Coggins, Vice President Hospital Integration
CFO: Brett English, Chief Financial Officer
CMO: Howard Bean, M.D., Chief Medical Officer
CIO: John O'Donnell, Director of Information Technology Services
CHR: Lee Ann Roque, Director of Human Resources
CNO: Chanda Flynn, R.N., MSN, Chief Nursing Officer
Web address: www.maryblackhealthsystem.com
**Control**: Hospital district or authority, Government, Nonfederal **Service**: General medical and surgical

**Staffed Beds:** 160 **Admissions:** 5234 **Census:** 66 **Outpatient Visits:** 70466 **Births:** 1013 **Personnel:** 697

### SUMMERVILLE—Dorchester County

**GUMMERVILLE MEDICAL CENTER** See Summerville Medical Center

### SUMMERVILLE—Berkeley County

⊠ **ROPER ST. FRANCIS HOSPITAL-BERKELEY (420110)**, 100 Callen Boulevard, Zip 29486–2807; tel. 854/529–3100, (Data for 89 days) (Nonreporting) **A**1 **F**1 3 7 13 15 29 30 35 40 45 51 64 68 70 76 79 81 84 94 102 107 108 110 111 115 118 119 126 128 146 148 149 154 **S** Roper St. Francis Healthcare, Charleston, SC
Primary Contact: Patrick Bosse, Chief Administrative Officer
Web address: www.https://www.rsfh.com/berkeley-hospital/
**Control**: Other not–for–profit (including NFP Corporation) **Service**: General medical and surgical

**Staffed Beds:** 50 **Admissions:** 638 **Census:** 20 **Outpatient Visits:** 11674 **Births:** 134 **Personnel:** 329

### SUMTER—Sumter County

**PALMETTO HEALTH TUOMEY** See Prisma Health Tuomey Hospital

☐ **PRISMA HEALTH TUOMEY HOSPITAL (420070)**, 129 North Washington Street, Zip 29150–4983; tel. 803/774–9000, (Nonreporting) **A**1 3 10 19 **F**1 3 11 13 15 18 20 28 29 30 31 34 35 40 47 48 49 50 51 54 56 59 62 63 64 68 70 71 73 75 76 77 78 79 80 81 84 85 86 87 89 90 94 102 107 108 110 111 114 119 120 121 126 128 129 130 131 132 135 146 147 148 154 **S** Prisma Health - Midlands, Columbia, SC
Primary Contact: Michelle Logan-Owens, Ph.D., R.N., Chief Operating Officer
CFO: Mark Lovell, Vice President and Chief Financial Officer
CMO: Gene Dickerson, M.D., Vice President Medical Affairs
CIO: Cheryl Martin, Chief Information Officer
CHR: Letitia Pringle-Miller, Administrative Director
CNO: Terrie Carlton, R.N., Vice President & Chief Nursing Officer
Web address: www.tuomey.com
**Control**: Other not–for–profit (including NFP Corporation) **Service**: General medical and surgical

**Staffed Beds:** 230 **Admissions:** 9075 **Census:** 131 **Outpatient Visits:** 149250 **Births:** 1275 **Total Expense ($000):** 178522 **Payroll Expense ($000):** 69277 **Personnel:** 1368

*Many Facility Codes have changed. Please refer to the AHA Guide Code Chart.* © 2021 AHA Guide

**TRAVELERS REST—Greenville County**

**NORTH GREENVILLE HOSPITAL** See Prisma Health North Greenville

☐ △ **PRISMA HEALTH NORTH GREENVILLE (422008)**, 807 North Main Street, Zip 29690–1551; tel. 864/455–9206, (Nonreporting) **A**1 5 7 10 **F**1 3 15 29 30 34 35 40 44 50 75 79 80 85 86 87 107 110 111 114 119 128 130 146 148 **S** Prisma Health - Midlands, Columbia, SC
Primary Contact: Adrienne Talbert, Interim Administrator
CMO: Amy Treece, M.D., Medical Director
CHR: Carol Bish, Human Resources Coordinator
CNO: Marian Lorraine McVey, Chief Nursing Officer
Web address: www.ghs.org
**Control**: Other not–for–profit (including NFP Corporation) **Service**: Acute long–term care hospital

**Staffed Beds:** 28 **Admissions:** 228 **Census:** 20 **Outpatient Visits:** 28126 **Total Expense ($000):** 30323 **Payroll Expense ($000):** 9117 **Personnel:** 146

**SPRINGBROOK AUTISM BEHAVIORAL HEALTH SYSTEM** See Springbrook Behavioral Health

☐ **SPRINGBROOK BEHAVIORAL HEALTH (424007)**, One Havenwood Lane, Zip 29690–9447, Mailing Address: P.O. Box 1005, Zip 29690–1005; tel. 864/834–8013, (Nonreporting) **A**1 10 **F**1 4 98 99 103 128
Primary Contact: Mike Rowley, Chief Executive Officer
COO: Mary Ann Bennett, Chief Operating Officer and Chief Nursing Officer
CFO: Bart Bennett, Chief Financial Officer
CMO: Mathew Fisher, M.D., Medical Director
CIO: Bart Bennett, Chief Information Technology Officer
CHR: Robin B Callas, Human Resource Director
CNO: Mary Ann Bennett, Director of Nursing
Web address: www.springbrookbehavioral.com
**Control**: Corporation, Investor–owned (for–profit) **Service**: Psychiatric

**Staffed Beds:** 62 **Admissions:** 950 **Census:** 27 **Outpatient Visits:** 0 **Births:** 0 **Personnel:** 149

**UNION—Union County**

★ ⇑ **UNION MEDICAL CENTER (420108)**, 322 West South Street, Zip 29379–2857, Mailing Address: P.O. Box 789, Zip 29379–0789; tel. 864/301–2000, (Nonreporting) **A**10 21 **F**1 3 11 29 30 34 35 40 57 59 64 75 107 111 115 119 127 128 130 146 149 154 **S** Spartanburg Regional Healthcare System, Spartanburg, SC
Primary Contact: Paul R. Newhouse, President
CFO: Cindy L. Gault, Chief Financial Officer
CHR: Angie Benfield, Human Resources Generalist
CNO: Beth Lawson, Chief Nursing Officer
Web address: www.https://www.spartanburgregional.com/locations/union-medical-center/
**Control**: Hospital district or authority, Government, Nonfederal **Service**: General medical and surgical

**Staffed Beds:** 50 **Admissions:** 385 **Census:** 5 **Outpatient Visits:** 7925 **Total Expense ($000):** 26531 **Payroll Expense ($000):** 11652 **Personnel:** 177

⇑ **WALLACE THOMSON HOSPITAL** See Union Medical Center

**VARNVILLE—Hampton County**

**HAMPTON GENERAL HOSPITAL** See Hampton Regional Medical Center

★ **HAMPTON REGIONAL MEDICAL CENTER (420072)**, 503 West Carolina Avenue, Zip 29944–4735, Mailing Address: P.O. Box 338, Zip 29944–0338; tel. 803/943–2771, (Nonreporting) **A**10 20 **F**1 15 17 18 24 28 29 31 34 40 57 59 65 67 70 75 78 79 81 90 93 94 102 107 108 110 111 115 119 127 128 133 146
Primary Contact: Dave H. Hamill, President and Chief Executive Officer
Web address: www.hamptonregional.com
**Control**: Other not–for–profit (including NFP Corporation) **Service**: General medical and surgical

**Staffed Beds:** 32 **Admissions:** 696 **Census:** 6 **Outpatient Visits:** 12939 **Births:** 0 **Total Expense ($000):** 22524 **Payroll Expense ($000):** 10424

**WALTERBORO—Colleton County**

⊞ **COLLETON MEDICAL CENTER (420030)**, 501 Robertson Boulevard, Zip 29488–5714; tel. 843/782–2000, (Nonreporting) **A**1 3 10 20 **S** HCA Healthcare, Nashville, TN
Primary Contact: Jimmy O. Hiott III, Chief Executive Officer
CFO: Cassie Ball, Chief Financial Officer
CMO: Mark Greenslit, M.D., Chief Medical Staff
CIO: Phil Gansz, Director Information Technology
CHR: Robert Valenca, Director, Human Resources
Web address: www.colletonmedical.com
**Control**: Corporation, Investor–owned (for–profit) **Service**: General medical and surgical

**Staffed Beds:** 135

**COLUMBIA COLLETON MEDICAL CTR** See Colleton Medical Center

**WEST COLUMBIA—Lexington County**

★ ⇑ **LEXINGTON MEDICAL CENTER (420073)**, 2720 Sunset Boulevard, Zip 29169–4810; tel. 803/791–2000, (Nonreporting) **A**2 5 10 21 **F**1 3 8 11 12 13 15 18 20 22 24 26 28 29 30 31 32 34 35 38 39 40 43 44 45 46 48 49 50 51 53 54 57 58 59 60 61 64 68 70 72 73 74 75 76 77 78 79 80 81 82 84 85 86 87 90 92 93 94 96 107 108 110 111 114 115 117 118 119 120 121 123 124 126 127 128 129 130 131 132 135 141 142 144 145 146 147 148 **P**6
Primary Contact: Tod Augsburger, FACHE, President and Chief Executive Officer
CFO: Melinda Kruzner, Chief Financial Officer
CMO: Brent Powers, M.D., Vice President/Chief Medical Officer
CIO: Kathleen R Herald, Vice President and Chief Information Officer
CHR: Brian Smith, Vice President Human Resources
CNO: Melissa Taylor, R.N., MSN, Chief Nursing Officer
Web address: www.lexmed.com
**Control**: Hospital district or authority, Government, Nonfederal **Service**: General medical and surgical

**Staffed Beds:** 505 **Admissions:** 30333 **Census:** 341 **Outpatient Visits:** 189453 **Births:** 3425 **Total Expense ($000):** 720501 **Payroll Expense ($000):** 256079 **Personnel:** 3820

☐ **THREE RIVERS BEHAVIORAL HEALTH (424008)**, 2900 Sunset Boulevard, Zip 29169–3422; tel. 803/796–9911, (Nonreporting) **A**1 10 **S** Universal Health Services, Inc., King of Prussia, PA
Primary Contact: Shannon Marcus, Chief Executive Officer
CFO: Christopher Jensen, Chief Financial Officer
CMO: Christina Lynn, M.D., Medical Director
CHR: Nita Sundberg, Director Human Resources
CNO: Lilly Wing, Chief Nursing Officer
Web address: www.threeriversbehavioral.org
**Control**: Corporation, Investor–owned (for–profit) **Service**: Psychiatric

**Staffed Beds:** 122

**THREE RIVERS CENTER FOR HEALTH** See Three Rivers Behavioral Health

SC

---

**Hospital, Medicare Provider Number, Address, Telephone, Approval, Facility, and Physician Codes, Health Care System**

★ American Hospital Association (AHA) membership
☐ The Joint Commission accreditation
○ Healthcare Facilities Accreditation Program
◇ DNV Healthcare Inc. accreditation
⇑ Center for Improvement in Healthcare Quality Accreditation
△ Commission on Accreditation of Rehabilitation Facilities (CARF) accreditation

# SOUTH DAKOTA

**SD**

## ABERDEEN—Brown County

**AVERA ST. LUKE'S** See Avera St. Luke's Hospital

☒ **AVERA ST. LUKE'S HOSPITAL (430014)**, 305 South State Street, Zip 57401–4527; tel. 605/622–5000, (Nonreporting) **A**1 2 5 10 19 **S** Avera Health, Sioux Falls, SD
Primary Contact: Todd Forkel, President and Chief Executive Officer
CFO: Geoff Durst, Vice President Finance
CMO: Shahid Chaudhary, M.D., Chief Medical Officer
CIO: Julie Kusler, Manager Information Services
CHR: Tracy L Olson, Human Resource Officer
CNO: Jan Patterson, Chief Nursing Officer
Web address: www.avera.org/st-lukes-hospital/
**Control:** Church operated, Nongovernment, not–for–profit **Service:** General medical and surgical

**Staffed Beds:** 212

**DAKOTA PLAINS SURGICAL CENTER (430092)**, 701 8th Avenue NW, Suite C, Zip 57401–1865; tel. 605/225–3300, (Nonreporting)
Primary Contact: Charles Livingston, Administrator
**Control:** Corporation, Investor–owned (for–profit) **Service:** Surgical

**Staffed Beds:** 15

★ **SANFORD ABERDEEN MEDICAL CENTER (430097)**, 2905 3rd Avenue SE, Zip 57401–5420; tel. 605/626–4200, (Nonreporting) **A**10 **F**3 13 15 18 20 22 26 28 29 31 32 34 35 40 43 45 46 50 56 57 59 61 64 65 70 75 76 77 78 79 81 85 89 90 93 94 97 107 110 111 115 119 130 131 132 144 146 147 148 156 **P**6 **S** Sanford Health, Sioux Falls, SD
Primary Contact: Ashley M. Erickson, Chief Executive Officer
CFO: Jeffrey Poppen, Chief Financial Officer
CMO: Samuel Nyamu, M.D., Chief Medical Officer
CHR: Katie Palmer, Manager Human Resources
CNO: Kila Legrand, Chief Nursing Officer
Web address: www.sanfordaberdeen.org/
**Control:** Other not–for–profit (including NFP Corporation) **Service:** General medical and surgical

**Staffed Beds:** 54 **Admissions:** 1618 **Census:** 9 **Outpatient Visits:** 80230
**Births:** 305 **Total Expense ($000):** 69763 **Payroll Expense ($000):** 31402
**Personnel:** 384

**SANFORD MEDICAL CENTER ABERDEEN** See Sanford Aberdeen Medical Center

## ARMOUR—Douglas County

**DOUGLAS COUNTY MEMORIAL HOSPITAL (431305)**, 708 Eighth Street, Zip 57313–2102; tel. 605/724–2159, (Nonreporting) **A**10 18 **F**3 8 10 28 31 34 40 41 43 46 53 57 59 62 64 65 78 81 91 100 102 107 114 119 127 133 154 **P**6
Primary Contact: Heath Brouwer, Administrator
CFO: Dorothy Spease, Manager Business Office
Web address: www.dcmhsd.org
**Control:** Other not–for–profit (including NFP Corporation) **Service:** General medical and surgical

**Staffed Beds:** 11 **Admissions:** 135 **Census:** 2 **Outpatient Visits:** 9129
**Births:** 0 **Total Expense ($000):** 9961 **Payroll Expense ($000):** 4523
**Personnel:** 81

## BOWDLE—Edmunds County

★ **BOWDLE HOSPITAL (431318)**, 8001 West Fifth Street, Zip 57428, Mailing Address: P.O. Box 556, Zip 57428–0556; tel. 605/285–6146, (Nonreporting) **A**10 18
Primary Contact: Sandy Schlechter, Chief Executive Officer
CFO: Brooke Heilman, Chief Financial Officer
CMO: John Ottenbacher, Chief of Staff
CNO: Bobbi Noess, Director of Nursing
Web address: www.bowdlehc.com
**Control:** City, Government, Nonfederal **Service:** General medical and surgical

**Staffed Beds:** 50

## BRITTON—Marshall County

★ **MARSHALL COUNTY HEALTHCARE CENTER AVERA (431312)**, 413 Ninth Street, Zip 57430–2274; tel. 605/448–2253, (Nonreporting) **A**10 18 **S** Avera Health, Sioux Falls, SD
Primary Contact: Nick Fosness, Chief Executive Officer
Web address: www.avera.org
**Control:** Other not–for–profit (including NFP Corporation) **Service:** General medical and surgical

**Staffed Beds:** 18

**MARSHALL COUNTY MEM HOSPITAL** See Marshall County Healthcare Center Avera

## BROOKINGS—Brookings County

★ **BROOKINGS HEALTH SYSTEM (430008)**, 300 22nd Avenue, Zip 57006–2496; tel. 605/696–9000, (Total facility includes 79 beds in nursing home–type unit) (Nonreporting) **A**10 20 **F**3 7 8 11 13 28 29 30 31 32 34 37 40 41 45 51 53 57 59 62 63 64 65 70 74 75 76 77 79 81 82 85 86 87 89 92 93 102 107 108 111 114 118 119 125 126 127 128 129 130 133 135 146 147 148 149 154
Primary Contact: Jason R. Merkley, Chief Executive Officer
CFO: Steve Lindemann, Chief Financial Officer
CMO: Shelby Eischens, Chief Medical Officer
CHR: September Bessler, Director, Human Resources
CNO: Tammy Hillestad, Chief Nursing Officer
Web address: www.brookingshealth.org
**Control:** City, Government, Nonfederal **Service:** General medical and surgical

**Staffed Beds:** 128 **Admissions:** 1300 **Census:** 87 **Outpatient Visits:** 72833
**Births:** 339 **Total Expense ($000):** 73458 **Payroll Expense ($000):** 31472

**BROOKINGS HOSPITAL** See Brookings Health System

## BURKE—Gregory County

★ **COMMUNITY MEMORIAL HOSPITAL (431309)**, 809 Jackson Street, Zip 57523–2065, Mailing Address: P.O. Box 319, Zip 57523–0319; tel. 605/775–2621, (Nonreporting) **A**10 18 **S** Sanford Health, Sioux Falls, SD
Primary Contact: Mistie Sachtjen, Chief Executive Officer
CMO: Megan Smith, M.D., Chief Medical Staff
CHR: Tami Lyon, Director Human Resources
Web address: www.sanfordhealth.org
**Control:** Other not–for–profit (including NFP Corporation) **Service:** General medical and surgical

**Staffed Beds:** 16

## CANTON—Lincoln County

★ **SANFORD CANTON-INWOOD MEDICAL CENTER (431333)**, 440 North Hiawatha Drive, Zip 57013–5800; tel. 605/764–1400, (Nonreporting) **A**10 18 **F**7 10 28 29 31 34 35 40 43 45 56 57 59 61 64 65 81 86 89 93 94 97 128 130 133 135 148 149 154 156 **P**6 **S** Sanford Health, Sioux Falls, SD
Primary Contact: Scott C. Larson, Chief Executive Officer
CFO: Paul Gerhart, Chief Financial Officer
Web address: www.sanfordcantoninwood.org
**Control:** Other not–for–profit (including NFP Corporation) **Service:** General medical and surgical

**Staffed Beds:** 27 **Admissions:** 210 **Census:** 4 **Outpatient Visits:** 19785
**Births:** 0 **Total Expense ($000):** 10769 **Payroll Expense ($000):** 5164
**Personnel:** 78

**SANFORD HOSPITAL CANTON-INWOOD** See Sanford Canton-Inwood Medical Center

*Many Facility Codes have changed. Please refer to the AHA Guide Code Chart.*   © 2021 AHA Guide

## CHAMBERLAIN—Brule County

★ **SANFORD CHAMBERLAIN MEDICAL CENTER (431329)**, 300 South Byron Boulevard, Zip 57325–9741; tel. 605/234–5511, (Total facility includes 44 beds in nursing home–type unit) (Nonreporting) **A**10 18 **F**3 13 15 18 19 28 29 31 34 35 40 43 45 50 57 59 64 65 68 75 77 78 81 85 86 87 89 93 100 101 102 104 107 110 115 119 130 131 132 133 148 149 154 156 157 **P**6 **S** Sanford Health, Sioux Falls, SD
Primary Contact: Erica Peterson, Chief Executive Officer
COO: Paul Miller, Director of Operations
CFO: Erica Peterson, Chief Executive Officer and Chief Financial Officer
CMO: Lacey Olson, M.D., Chief Medical Staff
CHR: Dorothy Hieb, Director Human Resources
CNO: Sarah Talbott, Chief Nursing Officer
Web address: www.sanfordchamberlain.org
**Control**: Other not–for–profit (including NFP Corporation) **Service**: General medical and surgical

**Staffed Beds:** 68 **Admissions:** 498 **Census:** 48 **Outpatient Visits:** 26743
**Births:** 52 **Total Expense ($000):** 21541 **Payroll Expense ($000):** 10255
**Personnel:** 184

**SANFORD MEDICAL CENTER CHAMBERLAIN** See Sanford Chamberlain Medical Center

## CLEAR LAKE—Deuel County

★ **SANFORD CLEAR LAKE MEDICAL CENTER (431307)**, 701 Third Avenue South, Zip 57226–2016; tel. 605/874–2141, (Nonreporting) **A**10 18 **F**28 29 34 35 40 43 53 56 57 59 64 65 77 81 85 89 90 93 94 96 97 107 114 119 127 128 133 144 154 156 **P**6 **S** Sanford Health, Sioux Falls, SD
Primary Contact: Lori Sisk, R.N., Chief Executive Officer
CFO: Allison Nelson, Chief Financial Officer
CMO: Terrance Smith, M.D., Chairman Medical Staff
CNO: Stephanie Dobbs, Chief Nursing Officer
Web address: www.sanforddeuelcounty.org
**Control**: Other not–for–profit (including NFP Corporation) **Service**: General medical and surgical

**Staffed Beds:** 15 **Admissions:** 145 **Census:** 3 **Outpatient Visits:** 8839
**Births:** 0 **Total Expense ($000):** 6391 **Payroll Expense ($000):** 3220
**Personnel:** 48

**SANFORD DEUEL COUNTY MEDICAL CENTER** See Sanford Clear Lake Medical Center

## CUSTER—Custer County

**CUSTER REGIONAL HOSPITAL** See Monument Health Custer Hospital

★ **MONUMENT HEALTH CUSTER HOSPITAL (431323)**, 1039 Montgomery Street, Zip 57730–1397; tel. 605/673–2229, (Total facility includes 60 beds in nursing home–type unit) (Nonreporting) **A**10 18 **F**3 10 12 15 29 40 59 64 65 67 68 75 77 87 89 90 93 97 102 107 108 110 114 119 127 128 132 133 149 154 156 **S** Monument Health, Rapid City, SD
Primary Contact: Mark C. Schmidt, President
Web address: www.regionalhealth.com
**Control**: Other not–for–profit (including NFP Corporation) **Service**: General medical and surgical

**Staffed Beds:** 87 **Admissions:** 385 **Census:** 56 **Outpatient Visits:** 2783
**Births:** 0 **Total Expense ($000):** 23939 **Payroll Expense ($000):** 10583
**Personnel:** 158

## DAKOTA DUNES—Union County

☐ **DUNES SURGICAL HOSPITAL (430089)**, 600 North Sioux Point Road, Zip 57049–5000; tel. 605/232–3332, (Nonreporting) **A**1 10
Primary Contact: Greg Miner, Administrator
Web address: www.dunessurgicalhospital.com
**Control**: Corporation, Investor–owned (for–profit) **Service**: Surgical

**Staffed Beds:** 40

**SIOUXLAND SURGERY CENTER** See Dunes Surgical Hospital

## DE SMET—Kingsbury County

★ **AVERA DE SMET MEMORIAL HOSPITAL (431332)**, 306 Prairie Avenue SW, Zip 57231–2285, Mailing Address: P.O. Box 160, Zip 57231–0160; tel. 605/854–6100, (Nonreporting) **A**10 18 **F**3 15 28 34 35 40 59 68 93 107 133 154 **P**6 **S** Avera Health, Sioux Falls, SD
Primary Contact: Stephanie Reasy, Administrator and Chief Executive Officer
Web address: www.avera.org
**Control**: Other not–for–profit (including NFP Corporation) **Service**: General medical and surgical

**Staffed Beds:** 6 **Admissions:** 55 **Census:** 1 **Outpatient Visits:** 9993
**Births:** 0 **Total Expense ($000):** 4989 **Payroll Expense ($000):** 1901
**Personnel:** 29

**DE SMET MEMORIAL HOSPITAL** See Avera De Smet Memorial Hospital

## DEADWOOD—Lawrence County

**LEAD-DEADWOOD REGIONAL HOSPITAL** See Monument Health Lead-Deadwood Hospital

★ **MONUMENT HEALTH LEAD-DEADWOOD HOSPITAL (431320)**, 61 Charles Street, Zip 57732–1303; tel. 605/717–6000, (Nonreporting) **A**10 18 **F**3 7 15 28 29 30 34 40 43 45 59 64 68 69 70 71 75 77 81 87 93 94 97 107 110 115 119 132 133 148 154 **P**6 **S** Monument Health, Rapid City, SD
Primary Contact: Mark C. Schmidt, President
CMO: Elizabeth Sayler, M.D., Chief of Staff
CHR: Kathryn L Shockey, Director Human Resources
Web address: www.regionalhealth.com
**Control**: State, Government, Nonfederal **Service**: General medical and surgical

**Staffed Beds:** 8 **Admissions:** 292 **Census:** 8 **Outpatient Visits:** 2528
**Births:** 0 **Total Expense ($000):** 13432 **Payroll Expense ($000):** 7239
**Personnel:** 109

## DELL RAPIDS—Minnehaha County

**AVERA DELLS AREA HEALTH CENTER** See Avera Dells Area Hospital

★ **AVERA DELLS AREA HOSPITAL (431331)**, 909 North Iowa Avenue, Zip 57022–1231; tel. 605/428–5431, (Nonreporting) **A**10 18 **F**3 15 28 34 35 40 41 45 53 57 59 64 65 75 81 86 92 93 94 97 107 110 128 129 132 133 134 144 148 154 **P**6 **S** Avera Health, Sioux Falls, SD
Primary Contact: Scott James. Hargens, Administrator and Chief Executive Officer
CFO: Kory Holt, Division Controller Network Operations
CMO: Valerie Larson, M.D., Chief Medical Officer
CIO: Val Witham, Director of Health Information
CHR: Nikki Tiff, Regional Manager Human Resources
CNO: Karla Carstensen, Director Patient Care
Web address: www.https://www.avera.org/locations/profile/avera-dells-area-hospital/
**Control**: Other not–for–profit (including NFP Corporation) **Service**: General medical and surgical

**Staffed Beds:** 23 **Admissions:** 154 **Census:** 2 **Outpatient Visits:** 17053
**Births:** 0 **Total Expense ($000):** 5627 **Payroll Expense ($000):** 2580
**Personnel:** 51

## EAGLE BUTTE—Dewey County

☐ **U. S. PUBLIC HEALTH SERVICE INDIAN HOSPITAL (430083)**, 317 Main Street, Zip 57625–1012, Mailing Address: P.O. Box 1012, Zip 57625–1012; tel. 605/964–7724, (Nonreporting) **A**1 10 **S** U. S. Indian Health Service, Rockville, MD
Primary Contact: Charles Fisher, Chief Executive Officer
CFO: Lisa Deal, Budget Analyst
Web address: www.ihs.gov
**Control**: PHS, Indian Service, Government, federal **Service**: General medical and surgical

**Staffed Beds:** 8

**SD**

---

**Hospital, Medicare Provider Number, Address, Telephone, Approval, Facility, and Physician Codes, Health Care System**

★ American Hospital Association (AHA) membership
☐ The Joint Commission accreditation
○ Healthcare Facilities Accreditation Program
◇ DNV Healthcare Inc. accreditation
⇑ Center for Improvement in Healthcare Quality Accreditation
△ Commission on Accreditation of Rehabilitation Facilities (CARF) accreditation

## EUREKA—Mcpherson County

★ **EUREKA COMMUNITY HEALTH SERVICES AVERA (431308)**, 410 Ninth Street, Zip 57437–2182, Mailing Address: P.O. Box 517, Zip 57437–0517; tel. 605/284–2661, (Nonreporting) **A**10 18 **F**3 10 28 34 35 40 41 45 59 65 81 93 107 127 133 154 156 **P**4 5 **S** Avera Health, Sioux Falls, SD
Primary Contact: Carmen Weber, Administrator
CFO: Joyce Schwingler, Chief Financial Officer
Web address: www.avera.org
**Control:** Other not–for–profit (including NFP Corporation) **Service:** General medical and surgical

| | |
|---|---|
| **Staffed Beds:** 4 **Admissions:** 98 **Census:** 1 **Outpatient Visits:** 6304 **Births:** 0 **Total Expense ($000):** 3677 **Payroll Expense ($000):** 1485 **Personnel:** 35 | |

**EUREKA COMMUNITY HOSPITAL** See Eureka Community Health Services Avera

## FAULKTON—Faulk County

**FAULK COUNTY MEMORIAL HOSPITAL** See Faulkton Area Medical Center

**FAULKTON AREA MEDICAL CENTER (431301)**, 1300 Oak Street, Zip 57438–2149, Mailing Address: P.O. Box 100, Zip 57438–0100; tel. 605/598–6262, (Nonreporting) **A**10 18 **F**3 17 28 29 31 40 45 59 64 77 78 82 93 97 107 115 127 128 133
Primary Contact: Dirkland T. Smith, Chief Executive Officer
COO: Jay A Jahnig, Chief Executive Officer
CFO: Susan Miller, Financial Administrator
CMO: K A Bartholomew, M.D., Medical Director
CIO: Cheryl Bue, Health Information Transcriptionist
CHR: Blythe Smith, Administrative Assistant
CNO: Shannon Stuwe, Director of Nursing
Web address: www.faulktonmedical.org
**Control:** Other not–for–profit (including NFP Corporation) **Service:** General medical and surgical

| | |
|---|---|
| **Staffed Beds:** 12 **Admissions:** 247 **Census:** 3 **Outpatient Visits:** 9191 **Births:** 0 **Total Expense ($000):** 10697 **Payroll Expense ($000):** 4679 **Personnel:** 76 | |

## FLANDREAU—Moody County

★ **AVERA FLANDREAU HOSPITAL (431310)**, 214 North Prairie Street, Zip 57028–1243; tel. 605/997–2433, (Nonreporting) **A**10 18 **F**3 28 34 35 40 41 45 57 59 64 65 75 81 86 92 93 97 107 127 128 129 133 134 144 146 148 154 **P**6 **S** Avera Health, Sioux Falls, SD
Primary Contact: Scott James. Hargens, Administrator and Chief Executive Officer
CFO: Kory Holt, Assistant Vice President for Financial Integration
CIO: Val Witham, Director Health Information
CHR: Nikki Tiff, Human Resources Analyst
CNO: Heather Hubbell, Director of Patient Care
Web address: www.avera.org/flandreau-medical/
**Control:** Other not–for–profit (including NFP Corporation) **Service:** General medical and surgical

| | |
|---|---|
| **Staffed Beds:** 18 **Admissions:** 139 **Census:** 1 **Outpatient Visits:** 16641 **Births:** 0 **Total Expense ($000):** 6013 **Payroll Expense ($000):** 2434 **Personnel:** 47 | |

**AVERA FLANDREAU MEDICAL CENTER** See Avera Flandreau Hospital

## FORT MEADE—Meade County

✠ **VETERANS AFFAIRS BLACK HILLS HEALTH CARE SYSTEM**, 113 Comanche Road, Zip 57741–1099; tel. 605/347–2511, (Includes VETERANS AFFAIRS MEDICAL CENTER HOT SPRINGS CAMPUS, Mailing address: 500 North Fifth Street, Hot Springs, South Dakota, Zip 57747; tel. 605/745–2052), (Nonreporting) **A**1 5 **S** Department of Veterans Affairs, Washington, DC
Primary Contact: Sandra Horsman, Director
CFO: Joseph Ferris, Chief Financial Officer
CHR: Denis Sullivan, Chief Human Resources Management
Web address: www.blackhills.va.gov/
**Control:** Veterans Affairs, Government, federal **Service:** General medical and surgical

| | |
|---|---|
| **Staffed Beds:** 247 | |

## FREEMAN—Hutchinson County

**FREEMAN COMMUNITY HOSPITAL** See Freeman Regional Health Services

★ **FREEMAN REGIONAL HEALTH SERVICES (431313)**, 510 East Eighth Street, Zip 57029–2086, Mailing Address: P.O. Box 370, Zip 57029–0370; tel. 605/925–4000, (Total facility includes 56 beds in nursing home–type unit) (Nonreporting) **A**10 18 **F**2 3 6 11 15 28 30 34 35 40 43 45 49 54 56 57 59 64 65 68 69 75 77 79 81 82 86 89 90 93 97 107 115 119 125 127 128 130 132 133 146 154 158 **P**6
Primary Contact: Nicholas R. Brandner, Chief Executive Officer
CFO: Mark Miller, Chief Financial Officer
Web address: www.freemanregional.com
**Control:** Other not–for–profit (including NFP Corporation) **Service:** General medical and surgical

| | |
|---|---|
| **Staffed Beds:** 74 **Admissions:** 199 **Census:** 44 **Outpatient Visits:** 1172 **Births:** 0 **Total Expense ($000):** 11476 **Payroll Expense ($000):** 5227 **Personnel:** 81 | |

## GETTYSBURG—Potter County

★ **AVERA GETTYSBURG HOSPITAL (431302)**, 606 East Garfield Avenue, Zip 57442–1398; tel. 605/765–2488, (Total facility includes 53 beds in nursing home–type unit) (Nonreporting) **A**10 18 **F**3 6 11 29 30 31 34 40 43 44 50 59 62 63 64 65 67 68 81 83 85 86 87 89 90 97 107 119 125 128 130 133 135 148 149 154 **P**6 **S** Avera Health, Sioux Falls, SD
Primary Contact: Kristi Livermont, Administrator
Web address: www.avera.org/st-marys-pierre/gettysburg-hospital/
**Control:** Church operated, Nongovernment, not–for–profit **Service:** General medical and surgical

| | |
|---|---|
| **Staffed Beds:** 59 **Admissions:** 189 **Census:** 46 **Outpatient Visits:** 5221 **Births:** 0 **Total Expense ($000):** 7517 **Payroll Expense ($000):** 3468 **Personnel:** 60 | |

**GETTYSBURG MEMORIAL HOSPITAL** See Avera Gettysburg Hospital

## GREGORY—Gregory County

**AVERA GREGORY HEALTHCARE CENTER** See Avera Gregory Hospital

★ **AVERA GREGORY HOSPITAL (431338)**, 400 Park Avenue, Zip 57533–1302, Mailing Address: P.O. Box 408, Zip 57533–0408; tel. 605/835–8394, (Nonreporting) **A**10 18 **S** Avera Health, Sioux Falls, SD
Primary Contact: Anthony Timanus, Chief Executive Officer
CFO: Trish Keiser, Comptroller
CMO: Rich Kafka, M.D., Chief Medical Officer
CIO: Justin Keegan, Director Support Services
CHR: Carol Postulka, Administrative Coordinator
Web address: www.gregoryhealthcare.org
**Control:** Church operated, Nongovernment, not–for–profit **Service:** General medical and surgical

| | |
|---|---|
| **Staffed Beds:** 65 | |

## HOT SPRINGS—Fall River County

★ **FALL RIVER HOSPITAL (431322)**, 1201 Highway 71 South, Zip 57747–8800; tel. 605/745–3159, (Total facility includes 59 beds in nursing home–type unit) (Nonreporting) **A**10 18 **F**3 28 29 34 40 45 48 56 57 59 64 65 68 74 77 81 89 93 104 107 119 127 128 129 130 131 132 133 146 148 154
Primary Contact: Tricia Uhlir, Chief Executive Officer
CFO: Jesse Naze, Chief Financial Officer
CMO: Rodney Larson, M.D., Medical Director
CIO: Dustin Kleinsasser, Information Technology and BioMed
CHR: Cindy Trent, Manager Personnel
Web address: www.frhssd.org
**Control:** Other not–for–profit (including NFP Corporation) **Service:** General medical and surgical

| | |
|---|---|
| **Staffed Beds:** 84 **Admissions:** 346 **Census:** 54 **Outpatient Visits:** 20422 **Births:** 0 **Total Expense ($000):** 22104 **Payroll Expense ($000):** 10158 | |

**SOUTHERN HILLS GEN HOSPITAL** See Fall River Hospital

**VETERANS AFFAIRS MEDICAL CENTER** See Veterans Affairs Medical Center Hot Springs Campus

**VETERANS AFFAIRS MEDICAL CENTER HOT SPRINGS CAMPUS** See Veterans Affairs Black Hills Health Care System, Fort Meade

*Many Facility Codes have changed. Please refer to the AHA Guide Code Chart.*

© 2021 AHA Guide

**SD**

## HURON—Beadle County

★ **HURON REGIONAL MEDICAL CENTER (431335)**, 172 Fourth Street SE, Zip 57350–2590; tel. 605/353–6200, (Nonreporting) **A**10 18 **S** QHR Health, Brentwood, TN
Primary Contact: Erick J. Larson, President and Chief Executive Officer
CFO: Marcia Zwanziger, Vice President Finance
CMO: Bill Miner, M.D., Chief of Staff
CHR: Rhonda Hanson, Director Human Resources
CNO: Gail Robeson, Vice President Patient Services
Web address: www.huronregional.org
**Control:** Other not–for–profit (including NFP Corporation) **Service:** General medical and surgical

**Staffed Beds:** 30

## MADISON—Lake County

**MADISON COMMUNITY HOSPITAL D/B/A MADISON REGIONAL HEALTH SYSTEM** See Madison Regional Health System

★ **MADISON REGIONAL HEALTH SYSTEM (431300)**, 323 SW 10th Street, Zip 57042–3200; tel. 605/256–6551, (Nonreporting) **A**10 18 **F**7 13 15 28 31 34 35 40 41 43 50 57 59 62 64 65 70 75 76 77 81 82 85 87 89 93 97 107 110 111 114 119 129 132 133 135 143 144 146 148 156 **P**6
Primary Contact: Tamara Miller, FACHE, Chief Executive Officer and Administrator
CFO: Teresa Mallett, Chief Financial Officer
CNO: Charlotte Charles, Director Acute Patient Services
Web address: www.madisonregionalhealth.org
**Control:** Other not–for–profit (including NFP Corporation) **Service:** General medical and surgical

**Staffed Beds:** 22 **Admissions:** 605 **Census:** 10 **Outpatient Visits:** 27618 **Births:** 57 **Total Expense ($000):** 27953 **Payroll Expense ($000):** 13185 **Personnel:** 236

## MARTIN—Bennett County

**BENNETT CNTY HEALTHCARE CENTER** See Bennett County Hospital and Nursing Home

★ **BENNETT COUNTY HOSPITAL AND NURSING HOME (431314)**, 102 Major Allen Street, Zip 57551–6005, Mailing Address: P.O. Box 70, Zip 57551–0070; tel. 605/685–6622, (Nonreporting) **A**10 18
Primary Contact: Andrew Riggin, Chief Executive Officer
CFO: Jean Kirk, Chief Financial Officer
CMO: Peter Knowles-Smith, M.D., Medical Director
CIO: Jean Kirk, Chief Financial Officer
CHR: T J Porter, Director Human Resources
Web address: www.bennettcountyhospital.com/
**Control:** Other not–for–profit (including NFP Corporation) **Service:** General medical and surgical

**Staffed Beds:** 62

## MILBANK—Grant County

**AVERA MILBANK AREA HOSPITAL** See Milbank Area Hospital Avera

★ **MILBANK AREA HOSPITAL AVERA (431326)**, 301 Flynn Drive, Zip 57252–1508; tel. 605/432–4538, (Nonreporting) **A**10 18 **S** Avera Health, Sioux Falls, SD
Primary Contact: Natalie Gauer, Administrator
CMO: Kevin Bjordahl, M.D., Chief Medical Officer
CHR: Mona Schafer, Regional Manager Human Resources
Web address: www.averamilbank.org
**Control:** Other not–for–profit (including NFP Corporation) **Service:** General medical and surgical

**Staffed Beds:** 25

## MILLER—Hand County

★ **AVERA HAND COUNTY MEMORIAL HOSPITAL (431337)**, 300 West Fifth Street, Zip 57362–1238; tel. 605/853–2421, (Nonreporting) **A**10 18 **S** Avera Health, Sioux Falls, SD
Primary Contact: Bryan Breitling, Administrator
CFO: Debbie Pullman, Director Finance
CMO: John Hopkins, M.D., Chief of Staff
CIO: Janice Purrington, Coordinator Medical Records
CNO: Sarah DeHaai, R.N., Director of Nursing
Web address: www.avera.org
**Control:** Other not–for–profit (including NFP Corporation) **Service:** General medical and surgical

**Staffed Beds:** 9

**AVERA HAND COUNTY MEMORIAL HOSPITAL & CLINIC** See Avera Hand County Memorial Hospital

## MITCHELL—Davison County

**AVERA QUEEN OF PEACE** See Avera Queen of Peace Hospital

⊞ **AVERA QUEEN OF PEACE HOSPITAL (430013)**, 525 North Foster, Zip 57301–2999; tel. 605/995–2000, (Total facility includes 109 beds in nursing home–type unit) (Nonreporting) **A**1 2 10 **F**3 10 13 15 28 29 30 31 34 40 43 45 48 50 51 53 54 57 59 64 69 70 71 75 76 77 78 79 81 82 83 84 85 86 89 93 94 96 104 107 108 110 111 114 117 118 119 121 123 127 128 129 130 131 132 133 135 146 147 148 154 155 156 **P**6 **S** Avera Health, Sioux Falls, SD
Primary Contact: Douglas R. Ekeren, FACHE, Interim Regional President and Chief Executive Officer
CFO: Will Flett, Vice President Finance and Chief Financial Officer
CMO: David Balt, D.O., Chief Medical Officer
CIO: Jim Hanson, Director Information Systems
CHR: Rita Lemon, Director Human Resources
CNO: Rochelle Reider, Vice President Patient Care
Web address: www.averaqueenofpeace.org
**Control:** Church operated, Nongovernment, not–for–profit **Service:** General medical and surgical

**Staffed Beds:** 159 **Admissions:** 1999 **Census:** 97 **Outpatient Visits:** 113125 **Births:** 472 **Total Expense ($000):** 104499 **Payroll Expense ($000):** 45668 **Personnel:** 490

## MOBRIDGE—Walworth County

★ **MOBRIDGE REGIONAL HOSPITAL (431325)**, 1401 Tenth Avenue West, Zip 57601–1106, Mailing Address: P.O. Box 580, Zip 57601–0580; tel. 605/845–3692, (Nonreporting) **A**10 18 **F**3 7 10 11 13 15 28 29 32 34 35 40 43 45 50 56 57 59 62 64 65 66 70 76 77 78 81 82 83 84 85 89 93 97 101 102 107 110 114 119 125 127 128 129 130 131 132 133 147 148 154 156 **P**6
Primary Contact: John J. Ayoub, FACHE, Chief Executive Officer
COO: Beth Jensen, Director Clinic Operations
CFO: Renae Tisdall, Chief Financial Officer
CMO: Travis Henderson, M.D., Chief of Staff
CIO: Josiah Barton, Director Information Technology
CHR: Keri Wientjes, Director Human Resources
CNO: Kristi Voller, Director of Nursing
Web address: www.mobridgehospital.org
**Control:** Other not–for–profit (including NFP Corporation) **Service:** General medical and surgical

**Staffed Beds:** 25 **Admissions:** 546 **Census:** 6 **Outpatient Visits:** 57187 **Births:** 67 **Total Expense ($000):** 21847 **Payroll Expense ($000):** 10657 **Personnel:** 171

**SD**

## PARKSTON—Hutchinson County

★ **AVERA ST. BENEDICT HEALTH CENTER (431330)**, 401 West Glynn Drive, Zip 57366–9605; tel. 605/928–3311, (Total facility includes 74 beds in nursing home–type unit) (Nonreporting) **A**10 18 **F**2 3 8 10 13 15 28 29 30 31 32 34 35 38 40 45 53 56 57 59 62 64 65 69 71 75 76 81 82 83 85 86 87 89 107 110 111 115 116 119 127 128 129 130 131 132 133 135 146 147 148 154 156 **P**6 **S** Avera Health, Sioux Falls, SD
Primary Contact: Rita Blasius, President and Chief Executive Officer
CFO: Rita Blasius, Assistant Administrator and Chief Financial Officer
CMO: Antoinette VanderPol, Chief of Staff
CIO: Adam Popp, Director Information Systems
CHR: Phyllis Ehler, Director Human Resources
CNO: Denise Muntefering, Vice President Patient Care Services
Web address: www.averastbenedict.org
**Control:** Church operated, Nongovernment, not–for–profit **Service:** General medical and surgical

**Staffed Beds:** 99 **Admissions:** 602 **Census:** 55 **Outpatient Visits:** 19440 **Births:** 57 **Total Expense ($000):** 22131 **Payroll Expense ($000):** 10947 **Personnel:** 176

**AVERA ST. BENEDICT HOSPITAL** See Avera St. Benedict Health Center

## PHILIP—Haakon County

**HANS P. PETERSON MEMORIAL HOSPITAL** See Philip Health Services

★ **PHILIP HEALTH SERVICES (431319)**, 503 West Pine Street, Zip 57567–3300, Mailing Address: P.O. Box 790, Zip 57567–0790; tel. 605/859–2511, (Total facility includes 30 beds in nursing home–type unit) (Nonreporting) **A**10 18 **F**10 40 43 57 59 62 67 85 90 93 107 114 127 128 130 131 133 147 148 149 150 **P**6 **S** Monument Health, Rapid City, SD
Primary Contact: Jeremy Schultes, Administrator and Chief Executive Officer
Web address: www.philiphealthservices.com/
**Control:** Other not–for–profit (including NFP Corporation) **Service:** General medical and surgical

**Staffed Beds:** 48 **Admissions:** 181 **Census:** 29 **Outpatient Visits:** 14947 **Births:** 0 **Total Expense ($000):** 12756 **Payroll Expense ($000):** 6945 **Personnel:** 106

## PIERRE—Hughes County

⊞ **AVERA ST. MARY'S HOSPITAL (430015)**, 801 East Sioux Avenue, Zip 57501–3323; tel. 605/224–3100, (Nonreporting) **A**1 2 3 10 20 **S** Avera Health, Sioux Falls, SD
Primary Contact: Mikel Holland, M.D., President and Chief Medical Officer
CFO: Tom Wagner, Interim Vice President Finance
CMO: Denise Hanisch, M.D., Chief of Staff
CIO: Jamie Raske, Information Technology Lead
CHR: Paul Marso, Vice President Human Resources
Web address: www.avera.org/st-marys-pierre/
**Control:** Church operated, Nongovernment, not–for–profit **Service:** General medical and surgical

**Staffed Beds:** 110

**ST. MARY'S HEALTHCARE CENTER** See Avera St. Mary's Hospital

## PINE RIDGE—Shannon County

**U. S. PUBLIC HEALTH SERVICE INDIAN HOSPITAL (430081)**, East Highway 18, Zip 57770, Mailing Address: P.O. Box 1201, Zip 57770–1201; tel. 605/867–5131, (Nonreporting) **A**10 **S** U. S. Indian Health Service, Rockville, MD
Primary Contact: Travis Scott, Service Unit Director
CFO: Sophia Conny, Deputy Administrative Officer
CMO: Jan Colton, M.D., Acting Clinical Director
CHR: Annabelle Blackbear, Human Resources Specialist
Web address: www.ihs.gov
**Control:** PHS, Indian Service, Government, federal **Service:** General medical and surgical

**Staffed Beds:** 45

## PLATTE—Charles Mix County

**PLATTE HEALTH CENTER** See Platte Health Center Avera

★ **PLATTE HEALTH CENTER AVERA (431306)**, 601 East Seventh, Zip 57369–2123, Mailing Address: P.O. Box 200, Zip 57369–0200; tel. 605/337–3364, (Nonreporting) **A**10 18 **S** Avera Health, Sioux Falls, SD
Primary Contact: Mark Burket, Chief Executive Officer
CFO: Jerry Hoffman, Chief Financial Officer
Web address: www.phcavera.org
**Control:** Other not–for–profit (including NFP Corporation) **Service:** General medical and surgical

**Staffed Beds:** 59

## RAPID CITY—Pennington County

**BLACK HILLS SURGERY HOSPITAL** See Black Hills Surgical Hospital

**BLACK HILLS SURGICAL HOSPITAL (430091)**, 216 Anamaria Drive, Zip 57701–7366, Mailing Address: 1868 Lombardy Drive, Zip 57703–4130; tel. 605/721–4900, (Nonreporting) **A**10 22
Primary Contact: Jack Kaup, Chief Executive Officer
COO: Greg Loos, Chief Operating Officer
Web address: www.bhsc.com
**Control:** Partnership, Investor–owned (for–profit) **Service:** Surgical

**Staffed Beds:** 26

**INDIAN HEALTH SERV HOSP** See Indian Health Service Hospital

**INDIAN HEALTH SERVICE HOSPITAL (430082)**, 3200 Canyon Lake Drive, Zip 57702–8197; tel. 605/355–2280, (Nonreporting) **A**10 **S** U. S. Indian Health Service, Rockville, MD
Primary Contact: Kevin J. Stiffarm, Chief Executive Officer
Web address: www.ihs.gov
**Control:** PHS, Indian Service, Government, federal **Service:** General medical and surgical

**Staffed Beds:** 9

⊞ **MONUMENT HEALTH RAPID CITY HOSPITAL (430077)**, 353 Fairmont Boulevard, Zip 57701–7393, Mailing Address: P.O. Box 6000, Zip 57709–6000; tel. 605/755–1000, (Nonreporting) **A**1 3 5 10 **F**3 12 13 15 17 18 20 22 24 26 28 29 30 31 34 40 43 45 46 48 49 51 56 58 59 60 61 64 70 72 74 76 77 78 79 81 82 84 85 87 89 90 92 93 97 98 99 102 104 107 108 111 115 118 119 120 121 124 126 129 130 131 144 146 148 149 154 **P**8 **S** Monument Health, Rapid City, SD
Primary Contact: John Pierce, Acting President
CFO: Mark Thompson, Vice President Financial Services
CMO: David Houser, M.D., Vice President Medical Affairs
CIO: Richard Latuchie, Vice President Business Development
CHR: Maureen Henson, Vice President Human Resources
Web address: www.regionalhealth.com
**Control:** Other not–for–profit (including NFP Corporation) **Service:** General medical and surgical

**Staffed Beds:** 375 **Admissions:** 18755 **Census:** 243 **Outpatient Visits:** 524939 **Births:** 2026 **Total Expense ($000):** 530391 **Payroll Expense ($000):** 215121 **Personnel:** 2950

**RAPID CITY REGIONAL HOSPITAL** See Monument Health Rapid City Hospital

**SAME DAY SURGERY CENTER (430093)**, 651 Cathedral Drive, Zip 57701–7368; tel. 605/755–9900, (Nonreporting) **A**10
Primary Contact: Doris Fritts, R.N., Executive Director
Web address: www.samedaysurgerycenter.org
**Control:** Corporation, Investor–owned (for–profit) **Service:** Surgical

**Staffed Beds:** 8

## REDFIELD—Spink County

**COMMUNITY MEMORIAL HOSPITAL (431316)**, 110 West Tenth Avenue, Zip 57469–1520, Mailing Address: P.O. Box 420, Zip 57469–0420; tel. 605/472–1110, (Nonreporting) **A**10 18 **F**3 7 11 28 34 40 53 56 57 59 62 64 65 67 68 75 77 86 87 91 93 97 107 115 127 129 133 135 144 146 148 149 150
Primary Contact: Tom Snyder, Interim Chief Executive Officer
CFO: William Boyer, Chief Financial Officer
CHR: Rhonda Stroh, Chief Human Resources Officer
CNO: Julene J Cass, R.N., Director of Nursing
Web address: www.redfieldcmh.org/
**Control:** City, Government, Nonfederal **Service:** General medical and surgical

**Staffed Beds:** 25 **Admissions:** 350 **Census:** 4 **Outpatient Visits:** 17158 **Births:** 0 **Total Expense ($000):** 11272 **Payroll Expense ($000):** 5898

**SD**

## ROSEBUD—Todd County

☐ **U. S. PUBLIC HEALTH SERVICE INDIAN HOSPITAL (430084)**, Highway 18, Soldier Creek Road, Zip 57570; tel. 605/747–2231, (Nonreporting) **A**1 10 **S** U. S. Indian Health Service, Rockville, MD
Primary Contact: Kathey Wilson, Acting Chief Executive Officer
COO: Romeo Vivit, Chief Surgeon
CMO: Valerie Parker, M.D., Clinical Director
CHR: Michelle Zephier, Human Resource Specialist
Web address: www.ihs.gov
**Control**: PHS, Indian Service, Government, federal **Service**: General medical and surgical

**Staffed Beds**: 35

## SCOTLAND—Bon Homme County

**LANDMANN-JUNGMAN MEMORIAL HOSPITAL** See Landmann-Jungman Memorial Hospital Avera

★ **LANDMANN-JUNGMAN MEMORIAL HOSPITAL AVERA (431317)**, 600 Billars Street, Zip 57059–2026; tel. 605/583–2226, (Nonreporting) **A**10 18 **F**3 28 29 34 35 38 40 41 43 53 55 56 57 58 59 64 65 67 68 71 84 89 93 97 107 114 125 128 131 132 133 134 135 147 148 149 150 154 **S** Avera Health, Sioux Falls, SD
Primary Contact: Melissa Gale, Chief Executive Officer
CFO: Darcy Permann, Manager Business Office
Web address: www.ljmh.org
**Control**: Other not–for–profit (including NFP Corporation) **Service**: General medical and surgical

**Staffed Beds**: 10 **Admissions**: 87 **Census**: 1 **Outpatient Visits**: 17057 **Births**: 0

## SIOUX FALLS—Lincoln County

☐ **AVERA HEART HOSPITAL OF SOUTH DAKOTA (430095)**, 4500 West 69th Street, Zip 57108–8148; tel. 605/977–7000, (Nonreporting) **A**1 5 10 **S** Avera Health, Sioux Falls, SD
Primary Contact: Michael Gibbs, President
CFO: Jean White, Vice President Finance
Web address: www.avera.org/heart-hospital
**Control**: Church operated, Nongovernment, not–for–profit **Service**: General medical and surgical

**Staffed Beds**: 53

## SIOUX FALLS—Minnehaha County

⊠ △ **AVERA MCKENNAN HOSPITAL AND UNIVERSITY HEALTH CENTER (430016)**, 1325 South Cliff Avenue, Zip 57105–1007, Mailing Address: P.O. Box 5045, Zip 57117–5045; tel. 605/322–8000, (Includes AVERA BEHAVIORAL HEALTH CENTER, Mailing address: 440 West 69th Street, Sioux Falls, South Dakota, Zip 57108; tel. 605/322–4065; Steve Lindquist, Assistant Vice President, Behavioral Health; AVERA CHILDREN'S HOSPITAL, Mailing address: 1325 South Cliff Avenue, Sioux Falls, South Dakota, Zip 57105–1016, PO Box 5045, Zip 57117–5045, tel. 605/322–5437) (Total facility includes 114 beds in nursing home–type unit) **A**1 2 3 5 7 10 **F**3 5 7 8 11 12 13 15 18 19 20 21 22 23 24 28 29 31 32 34 35 36 38 39 40 41 42 43 44 45 46 47 48 49 50 53 54 55 56 57 58 59 60 61 64 65 66 68 70 71 72 74 75 76 77 78 79 81 82 83 84 85 86 87 88 89 90 91 92 93 94 96 97 98 99 100 101 102 103 104 105 107 108 109 110 111 112 114 115 116 117 118 119 120 121 123 124 126 127 128 129 130 131 132 134 135 136 138 139 141 142 143 144 145 146 147 148 149 152 153 154 155 156 157 **P**6 **S** Avera Health, Sioux Falls, SD
Primary Contact: David Flicek, President and Chief Executive Officer
COO: Judy Blauwet, M.P.H., R.N., Senior Vice President Operations and Chief Nursing Officer
CFO: Julie Norton, Vice President, Operational Finance
CMO: Michael Elliott, M.D., Chief Medical Officer and Senior Vice President of Medical Affairs
CIO: Kristin Gross, Director Information Technology Center
CHR: Lynne D Hagen, SHRM-CP, Human Resources Officer
CNO: Judy Blauwet, M.P.H., R.N., Senior Vice President of Hospital Operations and Chief Nursing Officer
Web address: www.averamckennan.org
**Control**: Church operated, Nongovernment, not–for–profit **Service**: General medical and surgical

**Staffed Beds**: 500 **Admissions**: 23651 **Census**: 349 **Outpatient Visits**: 344425 **Births**: 2151 **Total Expense ($000)**: 1058370 **Payroll Expense ($000)**: 429252 **Personnel**: 5780

**CHILDRENS CARE HOSPITAL AND SCHOOL** See Lifescape

## SIOUX FALLS—Lincoln County

**ENCOMPASS HEALTH REHABILITATION HOSPITAL OF SIOUX FALLS**, 4700 W 69th Street, Zip 57108–8757; tel. 605/305–5600, (Nonreporting) **S** Encompass Health Corporation, Birmingham, AL
Primary Contact: Michael N. O'Keefe, Chief Executive Officer
Web address: www.encompasshealth.com/siouxfallsrehab
**Service**: Rehabilitation

**Staffed Beds**: 40

**HEART HOSPITAL OF SOUTH DAKOTA** See Avera Heart Hospital of South Dakota

## SIOUX FALLS—Minnehaha County

**LIFESCAPE (433300)**, 2501 West 26th Street, Zip 57105–2498; tel. 605/444–9500, (Nonreporting) **A**10
Primary Contact: Steve Watkins, Chief Executive Officer
CFO: Stephan A. Wilson, Chief Financial Officer
CMO: Christiane Maroun, M.D., Chief of Staff
CHR: Tiffany Reilly, Director Human Resources
Web address: www.cchs.org
**Control**: Other not–for–profit (including NFP Corporation) **Service**: Children's rehabilitation

**Staffed Beds**: 114

**MCKENNAN HOSPITAL** See Avera Mckennan Hospital and University Health Center

**ROYAL C. JOHNSON VETERANS MEMORIAL MEDICAL CENTER** See Sioux Falls Veterans Affairs Health Care System

**SANFORD USD MED CTR** See Sanford USD Medical Center

⊠ △ **SANFORD USD MEDICAL CENTER (430027)**, 1305 West 18th Street, Zip 57105–0496, Mailing Address: P.O. Box 5039, Zip 57117–5039; tel. 605/333–1000, (Includes SANFORD CHILDREN'S HOSPITAL, Mailing address: 1600 West 22nd Street, Sioux Falls, South Dakota, Zip 57105, PO Box 5039, Zip 57117–5039, tel. 605/333–1000), (Nonreporting) **A**1 2 3 5 7 8 10 **F**3 7 8 9 11 12 13 14 15 17 18 19 20 21 22 23 24 25 26 27 28 29 30 31 32 34 35 36 37 38 40 43 44 45 46 47 48 49 50 51 52 53 54 55 56 57 58 59 60 61 62 63 64 65 66 67 68 69 70 71 72 73 74 75 76 77 78 79 80 81 82 83 84 85 86 87 88 89 90 91 92 93 94 96 97 99 100 101 102 103 104 105 106 107 108 110 111 114 115 116 117 118 119 120 121 123 124 125 126 129 130 131 132 134 135 138 141 142 143 144 146 147 148 149 150 153 154 155 156 157 **P**6 8 **S** Sanford Health, Sioux Falls, SD
Primary Contact: Paul A. Hanson, FACHE, President
COO: Brad J. Schipper, Chief Operating Officer
CFO: Merrilee Schultz, Chief Finance
CIO: Arlyn Broekhuis, Vice President and Chief Information Officer
CHR: Evan Burkett, Chief Human Resource Officer
Web address: www.sanfordhealth.org
**Control**: Other not–for–profit (including NFP Corporation) **Service**: General medical and surgical

**Staffed Beds**: 500 **Admissions**: 26698 **Census**: 327 **Outpatient Visits**: 536720 **Births**: 3125 **Total Expense ($000)**: 984254 **Payroll Expense ($000)**: 418101 **Personnel**: 5452

⊠ **SELECT SPECIALTY HOSPITAL-SIOUX FALLS (432002)**, 1305 West 18th Street, Zip 57105–0401; tel. 605/312–9500, (Nonreporting) **A**1 10 **S** Select Medical Corporation, Mechanicsburg, PA
Primary Contact: Carol Ulmer, Chief Executive Officer
CNO: Alison Anderson, Chief Nursing Officer
Web address: www.selectspecialtyhospitals.com/company/locations/siouxfalls.aspx
**Control**: Corporation, Investor–owned (for–profit) **Service**: Acute long–term care hospital

**Staffed Beds**: 24

◯ **SIOUX FALLS SPECIALTY HOSPITAL (430090)**, 910 East 20th Street, Zip 57105–1012; tel. 605/334–6730, (Nonreporting) **A**10 11
Primary Contact: R Blake. Curd, M.D., Chief Executive Officer
CFO: Kyle Goldammer, Chief Financial Officer
Web address: www.sfsurgical.com
**Control**: Partnership, Investor–owned (for–profit) **Service**: Surgical

**Staffed Beds**: 35

**SIOUX FALLS SURGICAL CENTER** See Sioux Falls Specialty Hospital

**SD**

⊠ **SIOUX FALLS VETERANS AFFAIRS HEALTH CARE SYSTEM**, 2501 West 22nd Street, Zip 57105–1305, Mailing Address: P.O. Box 5046, Zip 57117–5046; tel. 605/336–3230, (Nonreporting) **A**1 3 5 **S** Department of Veterans Affairs, Washington, DC
Primary Contact: Lisa J. Simoneau, FACHE, Director
COO: Sara Ackert, Associate Director
CFO: Daniel Hubbard, Chief Financial Officer
CMO: John M Wempe, M.D., Chief of Staff
CIO: Eric Heiser, Chief Information Resource Management
CHR: Betsy Geiver, Chief Human Resources Officer
CNO: Barbara Teal, R.N., Associate Director Patient Care Services and Nurse Executive
Web address: www.siouxfalls.va.gov
**Control**: Veterans Affairs, Government, federal **Service**: General medical and surgical

| **Staffed Beds**: 92 |
| --- |

### SISSETON—Roberts County

★ **COTEAU DES PRAIRIES HOSPITAL (431339)**, 205 Orchard Drive, Zip 57262–2398; tel. 605/698–7647, (Nonreporting) **A**10 18 **S** Sanford Health, Sioux Falls, SD
Primary Contact: Craig A. Kantos, Chief Executive Officer
CFO: Larry Moen, Chief Financial Officer
CMO: David Staub, M.D., Chief of Staff
CIO: Cheryl Kaufman, Information Technology Technician
CHR: Leslie Hendrickson, Director Human Resources
CNO: Brenda Bostrom, Director of Nursing
Web address: www.cdphospital.com
**Control**: Other not–for–profit (including NFP Corporation) **Service**: General medical and surgical

| **Staffed Beds**: 25 |
| --- |

**COTEAU DES PRAIRIES HOSPITAL** See Coteau Des Prairies Hospital

### SPEARFISH—Lawrence County

★ **MONUMENT HEALTH SPEARFISH HOSPITAL (430048)**, 1440 North Main Street, Zip 57783–1504; tel. 605/644–4000, (Includes SPEARFISH REGIONAL SURGERY CENTER, Mailing address: 1316 N 10th St, Spearfish, South Dakota, Zip 57783–1530, 1316 North 10th Street, Zip 57783–1530, tel. 605/642–3113), (Nonreporting) **A**10 20 **F**3 12 13 15 18 28 29 34 40 56 57 59 64 68 70 75 76 79 81 82 85 89 93 97 107 108 110 111 115 119 127 129 131 132 144 147 148 154 156 **P**6 **S** Monument Health, Rapid City, SD
Primary Contact: Thomas Worsley, Chief Executive Officer
CFO: Marcia Olson, Director Finance and Controller
CMO: Christopher Gasbarre, D.O., Community Medical Director
CIO: Richard Latuchie, Chief Information Officer
CHR: Patsy Aiken, Coordinator Human Resource
CNO: Suzanne Campbell, R.N., Director Patient Services
Web address: www.regionalhealth.com/Our-Locations/Regional-Hospitals/Spearfish-Regional-Hospital.aspx
**Control**: Other not–for–profit (including NFP Corporation) **Service**: General medical and surgical

| **Staffed Beds**: 35 **Admissions**: 1558 **Census**: 9 **Outpatient Visits**: 202894 **Births**: 440 **Total Expense ($000)**: 87332 **Payroll Expense ($000)**: 40897 **Personnel**: 454 |
| --- |

**SPEARFISH REGIONAL HOSPITAL** See Monument Health Spearfish Hospital

**SPEARFISH SURGERY CENTER** See Spearfish Regional Surgery Center

### STURGIS—Meade County

★ **MONUMENT HEALTH STURGIS HOSPITAL (431321)**, 2140 Junction Avenue, Zip 57785–2452; tel. 605/720–2400, (Total facility includes 84 beds in nursing home–type unit) (Nonreporting) **A**10 18 **F**11 15 28 29 40 43 70 75 77 81 82 93 97 107 111 115 119 128 130 133 144 148 149 156 **S** Monument Health, Rapid City, SD
Primary Contact: Mark Schulte, FACHE, President
CFO: Jodie Mitchell, Facility Financial Director
CMO: Constance Stock, M.D., Chief Medical Officer
CHR: Ginger Chord, Coordinator Human Resources
CNO: Rikki Plaggemeyer, Director Acute Care Nursing
Web address: www.https://directory.monument.health/facility/sd/sturgis/2140-junction-avenue-6671505
**Control**: Other not–for–profit (including NFP Corporation) **Service**: General medical and surgical

| **Staffed Beds**: 109 **Admissions**: 709 **Census**: 81 **Births**: 0 **Total Expense ($000)**: 26450 **Payroll Expense ($000)**: 11702 **Personnel**: 190 |
| --- |

**STURGIS REGIONAL HOSPITAL** See Monument Health Sturgis Hospital

### TYNDALL—Bon Homme County

**ST. MICHAEL'S HOSPITAL** See St. Michael's Hospital Avera

★ **ST. MICHAEL'S HOSPITAL AVERA (431327)**, 410 West 16th Avenue, Zip 57066–2318; tel. 605/589–2100, (Nonreporting) **A**10 18 **S** Avera Health, Sioux Falls, SD
Primary Contact: Carol Deurmier, Chief Executive Officer
CFO: Lisa Ronke, Director Finance
CMO: Melvin Wallinga, M.D., Medical Director
Web address: www.stmichaels-bhfp.org
**Control**: Church operated, Nongovernment, not–for–profit **Service**: General medical and surgical

| **Staffed Beds**: 25 |
| --- |

### VERMILLION—Clay County

★ **SANFORD VERMILLION MEDICAL CENTER (431336)**, 20 South Plum Street, Zip 57069–3346; tel. 605/677–3500, (Total facility includes 66 beds in nursing home–type unit) (Nonreporting) **A**10 18 **F**10 13 15 28 29 31 32 34 35 40 43 45 56 59 61 64 65 67 75 76 77 81 85 86 93 94 96 97 99 100 101 103 104 107 110 111 114 119 130 131 133 135 144 148 149 154 156 **P**6 **S** Sanford Health, Sioux Falls, SD
Primary Contact: Timothy J. Tracy, Senior Director
CFO: Valerie Osterberg, Chief Financial Officer
CMO: Roy Mortinsen, M.D., Chief of Staff
CIO: Mary C Merrigan, Manager Public Relations
CHR: Cindy Benzel, Manager Human Resources
CNO: Jeff Berens, MS, Chief Nursing Officer
Web address: www.sanfordvermillion.org
**Control**: Other not–for–profit (including NFP Corporation) **Service**: General medical and surgical

| **Staffed Beds**: 120 **Admissions**: 530 **Census**: 69 **Outpatient Visits**: 39330 **Births**: 100 **Total Expense ($000)**: 24131 **Payroll Expense ($000)**: 11453 **Personnel**: 200 |
| --- |

**SIOUX VALLEY VERMILLION MED** See Sanford Vermillion Medical Center

### VIBORG—Turner County

★ **PIONEER MEMORIAL HOSPITAL AND HEALTH SERVICES (431328)**, 315 North Washington Street, Zip 57070–2002, Mailing Address: P.O. Box 368, Zip 57070–0368; tel. 605/326–5161, (Total facility includes 52 beds in nursing home–type unit) (Nonreporting) **A**10 18 **F**6 10 15 28 30 34 40 43 45 53 56 57 59 63 65 69 75 79 81 87 97 107 111 119 125 127 128 130 132 133 154 156 158 **P**6 **S** Sanford Health, Sioux Falls, SD
Primary Contact: Thomas V. Richter, Chief Executive Officer
CFO: Anne Christiansen, Chief Financial Officer
CMO: Syed Shah, M.D., Chief of Staff
Web address: www.pioneermemorial.org
**Control**: Other not–for–profit (including NFP Corporation) **Service**: General medical and surgical

| **Staffed Beds**: 64 **Admissions**: 112 **Census**: 40 **Outpatient Visits**: 19301 **Births**: 0 **Total Expense ($000)**: 10771 **Payroll Expense ($000)**: 6179 **Personnel**: 136 |
| --- |

### WAGNER—Charles Mix County

★ **WAGNER COMMUNITY MEMORIAL HOSPITAL AVERA (431315)**, 513 Third Street SW, Zip 57380–9675, Mailing Address: P.O. Box 280, Zip 57380–0280; tel. 605/384–3611, (Nonreporting) **A**10 18 **F**3 11 28 31 34 40 43 45 57 59 64 67 70 77 81 93 97 107 114 119 128 130 133 148 154 **S** Avera Health, Sioux Falls, SD
Primary Contact: Bryan Slaba, Chief Executive Officer
CFO: Lisa Weisser, Supervisor Finance
CHR: Marcia Podzimek, Chief Human Resources Officer
Web address: www.avera.org/wagnerhospital
**Control**: Other not–for–profit (including NFP Corporation) **Service**: General medical and surgical

| **Staffed Beds**: 20 **Admissions**: 132 **Census**: 1 **Outpatient Visits**: 15216 **Births**: 0 **Total Expense ($000)**: 9540 **Payroll Expense ($000)**: 5086 **Personnel**: 70 |
| --- |

**SD**

*Many Facility Codes have changed. Please refer to the AHA Guide Code Chart.* © 2021 AHA Guide

## WATERTOWN—Codington County

★ **PRAIRIE LAKES HEALTHCARE SYSTEM (430005)**, 401 9th Avenue NW, Zip 57201–1548, Mailing Address: P.O. Box 1210, Zip 57201–6210; tel. 605/882–7000, (Nonreporting) **A**10 20 **F**3 8 12 13 18 20 22 28 29 30 31 34 35 38 40 43 47 50 57 58 59 60 62 63 64 75 76 77 78 79 80 81 82 83 84 85 87 89 93 107 111 114 115 118 119 120 121 123 130 132 133 146 148 154
Primary Contact: K. C. DeBoer, President and Chief Executive Officer
COO: Traci Rabine, Vice President Clinic Operations
CFO: Adam Popp, Chief Financial Officer
CMO: Leighton Singh, M.D., Chief of Staff
CIO: Grant Tillett, Chief Information Officer
CHR: Nathan Lake, Vice President Human Resources
CNO: Shelly Turbak, R.N., Chief Nursing Officer
Web address: www.prairielakes.com
**Control:** Other not–for–profit (including NFP Corporation) **Service:** General medical and surgical

**Staffed Beds:** 79 **Admissions:** 2720 **Census:** 22 **Outpatient Visits:** 98123 **Births:** 595 **Total Expense ($000):** 96690 **Payroll Expense ($000):** 43879 **Personnel:** 435

**PRAIRIE LAKES HOSP & CARE CTR** See Prairie Lakes Healthcare System

## WEBSTER—Day County

**SANFORD MEDICAL CENTER WEBSTER** See Sanford Webster Medical Center

★ **SANFORD WEBSTER MEDICAL CENTER (431311)**, 1401 West 1st Street, Zip 57274–1054, Mailing Address: P.O. Box 489, Zip 57274–0489; tel. 605/345–3336, (Nonreporting) **A**10 18 **F**28 29 31 32 34 35 40 43 53 56 57 59 61 64 65 67 75 81 85 89 90 93 94 97 107 110 115 119 127 128 130 132 133 144 146 **P**6 **S** Sanford Health, Sioux Falls, SD
Primary Contact: Isaac Gerdes, Chief Executive Officer
CFO: Sheryl L Pappas, Chief Financial Officer
Web address: www.sanfordhealth.org
**Control:** Other not–for–profit (including NFP Corporation) **Service:** General medical and surgical

**Staffed Beds:** 20 **Admissions:** 209 **Census:** 2 **Outpatient Visits:** 15017 **Births:** 0 **Total Expense ($000):** 8094 **Payroll Expense ($000):** 3918 **Personnel:** 61

## WESSINGTON SPRINGS—Jerauld County

★ **AVERA WESKOTA MEMORIAL HOSPITAL (431324)**, 604 First Street NE, Zip 57382–2166; tel. 605/539–1201, (Nonreporting) **A**10 18 **F**3 15 28 34 35 40 53 57 59 64 75 77 85 93 107 114 119 128 130 131 133 **P**5 **S** Avera Health, Sioux Falls, SD
Primary Contact: Stephanie Reasy, Administrator and Chief Executive Officer
CFO: Linda Jager, Director Finance
CMO: Thomas Dean, M.D., Chief of Staff
CNO: JoAnn Hettinger, R.N., Director of Patient Care Services
Web address: www.averaweskota.org
**Control:** Other not–for–profit (including NFP Corporation) **Service:** General medical and surgical

**Staffed Beds:** 23 **Admissions:** 88 **Census:** 2 **Outpatient Visits:** 4387 **Births:** 0 **Total Expense ($000):** 3968 **Payroll Expense ($000):** 1608 **Personnel:** 21

**AVERA WESKOTA MEMORIAL MEDICAL CENTER** See Avera Weskota Memorial Hospital

## WINNER—Tripp County

**BAPTIST HOSPITAL** See Winner Regional Healthcare Center

★ **WINNER REGIONAL HEALTHCARE CENTER (431334)**, 745 East Eighth Street, Zip 57580–2631; tel. 605/842–7100, (Nonreporting) **A**10 18 **S** Sanford Health, Sioux Falls, SD
Primary Contact: Kevin Coffey, Chief Executive Officer
COO: Debra K. Davis, Director of Operations
CFO: Earl Pierce, Chief Financial Officer
CMO: Tony L. Berg, M.D., Chief of Staff
CIO: Gary Burrus, Director Information Technology
CHR: Susan Hughes, Interim Director Human Resources
CNO: Julie Hennebold, R.N., Interim Chief Nursing Officer
Web address: www.winnerregional.org
**Control:** Other not–for–profit (including NFP Corporation) **Service:** General medical and surgical

**Staffed Beds:** 104

## YANKTON—Yankton County

**AVERA SACRED HEART** See Avera Sacred Heart Hospital

⊞ **AVERA SACRED HEART HOSPITAL (430012)**, 501 Summit Avenue, Zip 57078–3855; tel. 605/668–8000, (Total facility includes 187 beds in nursing home–type unit) (Nonreporting) **A**1 2 3 5 10 **F**2 3 6 8 10 13 15 18 20 28 29 30 31 34 35 39 40 43 45 46 47 48 53 57 59 60 63 64 70 71 73 75 76 77 78 79 81 82 84 85 86 87 89 91 93 96 97 100 104 107 108 110 111 114 115 118 119 120 121 125 128 129 130 131 132 133 146 147 148 154 156 **P**6 **S** Avera Health, Sioux Falls, SD
Primary Contact: Douglas R. Ekeren, FACHE, Regional President and Chief Executive Officer, Administration
CFO: Jamie Schaefer, Vice President Finance
CIO: Kathy Quinlivan, Director Management Information Systems
CHR: Jane E. Miller, Human Resources Officer
CNO: Lindsay Flannery, R.N., Vice President Patient Care Services
Web address: www.averasacredheart.com
**Control:** Church operated, Nongovernment, not–for–profit **Service:** General medical and surgical

**Staffed Beds:** 286 **Admissions:** 3460 **Census:** 204 **Outpatient Visits:** 85912 **Births:** 541 **Total Expense ($000):** 112311 **Payroll Expense ($000):** 43889 **Personnel:** 630

**LEWIS AND CLARK SPECIALTY HOSPITAL (430096)**, 2601 Fox Run Parkway, Zip 57078–5341; tel. 605/665–5100, (Nonreporting) **A**10
Primary Contact: Douglas Doorn, Chief Executive Officer
CFO: Terry Steichen, Business Officer
CHR: Elizabeth Steichen, Human Resources
Web address: www.lewisandclarkspecialty.com
**Control:** Corporation, Investor–owned (for–profit) **Service:** Surgical

**Staffed Beds:** 6

**SD**

---

# TENNESSEE

## ASHLAND CITY—Cheatham County

☒ **TRISTAR ASHLAND CITY MEDICAL CENTER (441311)**, 313 North Main Street, Zip 37015–1347; tel. 615/792–3030, (Nonreporting) **A**1 10 18 **S** HCA Healthcare, Nashville, TN
Primary Contact: Darrell White, R.N., Administrator and Chief Nursing Officer
CFO: Joe Bowman, Chief Financial Officer
CMO: Divya Shroff, Chief Medical Officer
CIO: David Archer, Director Information Systems
CNO: Darrell White, R.N., Administrator and Chief Nursing Officer
Web address: www.tristarashlandcity.com/
**Control**: Corporation, Investor–owned (for–profit) **Service**: General medical and surgical

| **Staffed Beds:** 12 |
| --- |

**TRISTAR CENTENNIAL MEDICAL CENTER AT ASHLAND CITY** See Tristar Ashland City Medical Center

## ATHENS—Mcminn County

**ATHENS REGIONAL MEDICAL CENTER** See Starr Regional Medical Center

☒ **STARR REGIONAL MEDICAL CENTER (440068)**, 1114 West Madison Avenue, Zip 37303–4150, Mailing Address: P.O. Box 250, Zip 37371–0250; tel. 423/745–1411, (Nonreporting) **A**1 3 10 **S** LifePoint Health, Brentwood, TN
Primary Contact: John R. McLain, Chief Executive Officer
COO: Michael Herr, Chief Operating Officer
CFO: David Alley, Chief Financial Officer
Web address: www.starrregional.com
**Control**: Corporation, Investor–owned (for–profit) **Service**: General medical and surgical

| **Staffed Beds:** 63 |
| --- |

## BARTLETT—Shelby County

☒ **SAINT FRANCIS HOSPITAL-BARTLETT (440228)**, 2986 Kate Bond Road, Zip 38133–4003; tel. 901/820–7000, (Nonreporting) **A**1 10 **F**3 11 13 15 18 20 22 29 30 31 34 35 38 40 45 46 49 50 54 57 59 64 70 72 74 75 76 77 78 79 81 85 86 87 93 102 107 108 110 111 115 118 119 126 130 131 132 146 147 148 149 **P**5 **S** TENET Healthcare Corporation, Dallas, TX
Primary Contact: Christopher Locke, Chief Executive Officer
COO: Gwen Bonner, Chief Operating Officer
CFO: Tina Kovacs, Chief Financial Officer
CMO: David Schwartz, M.D., Chief Medical Officer
CIO: Mark Lawrence, Director Information Systems
CHR: Adrienne Huntley, Chief Human Resources Officer
Web address: www.saintfrancisbartlett.com
**Control**: Corporation, Investor–owned (for–profit) **Service**: General medical and surgical

| **Staffed Beds:** 156 **Admissions:** 8515 **Census:** 100 **Outpatient Visits:** 71376 **Births:** 406 **Total Expense ($000):** 116606 **Payroll Expense ($000):** 36924 **Personnel:** 545 |
| --- |

## BOLIVAR—Hardeman County

☒ **BOLIVAR GENERAL HOSPITAL (441320)**, 650 Nuckolls Road, Zip 38008–1532, Mailing Address: PO Box 509, Zip 38008–0509; tel. 731/658–3100, (Nonreporting) **A**1 10 18 **F**3 15 29 30 35 40 44 57 59 64 75 87 93 107 119 130 132 133 146 149 **S** West Tennessee Healthcare, Jackson, TN
Primary Contact: Ruby Kirby, Chief Executive Officer
CFO: Dana Lawrence, Controller
CMO: Felix Nnaji, Chief Medical Staff
Web address: www.wth.net
**Control**: Hospital district or authority, Government, Nonfederal **Service**: General medical and surgical

| **Staffed Beds:** 12 **Admissions:** 169 **Census:** 1 **Outpatient Visits:** 15734 **Births:** 1 **Total Expense ($000):** 7060 **Payroll Expense ($000):** 3027 **Personnel:** 53 |
| --- |

**BOLIVAR MEDICAL CENTER** See Bolivar General Hospital

☐ **WESTERN MENTAL HEALTH INSTITUTE (444008)**, 11100 Old Highway 64, West, Zip 38008–1554; tel. 731/228–2000, (Nonreporting) **A**1 10
Primary Contact: Roger Pursley, Chief Executive Officer
CFO: Richard Taylor, Chief Financial Officer
CMO: Doug King, M.D., Director Clinical Services
CIO: Earl Bates, Director Information Technology
CHR: Barry Young, Director Human Resources
**Control**: State, Government, Nonfederal **Service**: Psychiatric

| **Staffed Beds:** 150 |
| --- |

## BRISTOL—Sullivan County

☒ **BRISTOL REGIONAL MEDICAL CENTER (440012)**, 1 Medical Park Boulevard, Zip 37620–7430; tel. 423/844–1121, (Nonreporting) **A**1 3 5 10 19 **F**1 3 4 8 11 13 15 17 18 20 22 24 28 29 30 31 34 35 37 38 39 40 43 44 45 46 47 48 49 51 54 56 57 58 59 60 61 62 64 67 70 72 73 74 75 76 77 78 79 80 81 82 84 85 86 87 88 89 90 91 92 93 94 96 97 98 100 102 107 108 109 110 111 114 115 116 117 118 119 120 121 123 124 126 129 130 131 132 135 144 145 146 147 148 149 154 157 **P**6 8 **S** Ballad Health, Johnson City, TN
Primary Contact: Chad Couch, M.D., Interim Chief Executive Officer
COO: Christopher Brian Hobson, Chief Operating Officer
CFO: Bob Bender, Vice-President Hospital Finance and Operations, Northeast Market
CMO: Chad Couch, M.D., Chief Medical Officer, Northeast Market
CIO: Pam Austin, Senior Vice-President, Chief Information Officer
CHR: Deborah L Dover, Senior Vice-President of Human Resources
CNO: Bobbie Murphy, R.N., Chief Nursing Officer
Web address: www.balladhealth.org
**Control**: Other not–for–profit (including NFP Corporation) **Service**: General medical and surgical

| **Staffed Beds:** 296 **Admissions:** 17117 **Census:** 202 **Outpatient Visits:** 316892 **Births:** 1066 **Total Expense ($000):** 224331 **Payroll Expense ($000):** 78469 **Personnel:** 1343 |
| --- |

☒ **SELECT SPECIALTY HOSPITAL-TRI CITIES (442016)**, One Medical Park Boulevard, 5th Floor, Zip 37620–8964; tel. 423/844–5900, (Nonreporting) **A**1 10 **S** Select Medical Corporation, Mechanicsburg, PA
Primary Contact: Jeffrey Radford, Chief Executive Officer
CMO: John Byers, M.D., Medical Director
CHR: William G Ison, Human Resources Manager
CNO: Valerie Anderson, Chief Nursing Officer
Web address: www.tricities.selectspecialtyhospitals.com/
**Control**: Corporation, Investor–owned (for–profit) **Service**: Acute long–term care hospital

| **Staffed Beds:** 33 |
| --- |

**SELECT SPECIALTY HOSPITAL-TRICITIES** See Select Specialty Hospital-Tri Cities

**WELLMONT BRISTOL REGIONAL MEDICAL CENTER** See Bristol Regional Medical Center

## CAMDEN—Benton County

☒ **CAMDEN GENERAL HOSPITAL (441316)**, 175 Hospital Drive, Zip 38320–1617; tel. 731/593–6300, (Nonreporting) **A**1 10 18 **F**3 15 29 30 35 40 44 57 59 64 75 79 81 85 87 93 107 111 119 130 132 133 146 149 **S** West Tennessee Healthcare, Jackson, TN
Primary Contact: Scott Barber, Administrator
CFO: Terry Swindell, Chief Financial Officer
CMO: Jon R. Winter, D.O., Chief of Staff
CIO: Jeff Frieling, Vice President Information Systems
CHR: Barry Phillips, Executive Director Human Resources
Web address: www.wth.net
**Control**: Hospital district or authority, Government, Nonfederal **Service**: General medical and surgical

| **Staffed Beds:** 8 **Admissions:** 283 **Census:** 4 **Outpatient Visits:** 11527 **Births:** 0 **Total Expense ($000):** 8180 **Payroll Expense ($000):** 3413 **Personnel:** 63 |
| --- |

**VALLEY REGIONAL HOSPITAL** See Camden General Hospital

TN

## CARTHAGE—Smith County

☒ **RIVERVIEW REGIONAL MEDICAL CENTER (441307)**, 158 Hospital Drive, Zip 37030–1096; tel. 615/735–1560, (Nonreporting) **A**1 10 18 **S** LifePoint Health, Brentwood, TN
Primary Contact: Michael Herman, Chief Executive Officer
CHR: Gina Anderson, Human Resources Officer
CNO: Patricia Anderson, Chief Nursing Officer
Web address: www.myriverviewmedical.com/
**Control**: Corporation, Investor–owned (for–profit) **Service**: General medical and surgical

**Staffed Beds:** 35

**RIVERVIEW REGIONAL MEDICAL CENTER NORTH** See Riverview Regional Medical Center

## CENTERVILLE—Hickman County

**HICKMAN COMMUNITY HOSPITAL** See Saint Thomas Hickman Hospital

☒ **SAINT THOMAS HICKMAN HOSPITAL (441300)**, 135 East Swan Street, Zip 37033–1417; tel. 931/729–4271, (Nonreporting) **A**1 10 18 **S** Ascension Healthcare, Saint Louis, MO
Primary Contact: Kevin Campbell, Chief Executive Officer
COO: Robin Crowell, Chief Nursing Officer and Chief Operating Officer
CMO: Zachary Hutchens, M.D., Chief Medical Officer
CHR: Patty Matney, Human Resources Consultant
CNO: Robin Crowell, Chief Nursing Officer and Chief Operating Officer
Web address: www.sths.com/hickman
**Control**: Other not–for–profit (including NFP Corporation) **Service**: General medical and surgical

**Staffed Beds:** 25

## CHATTANOOGA—Hamilton County

☒ **CHI MEMORIAL (440091)**, 2525 De Sales Avenue, Zip 37404–1161; tel. 423/495–2525, (Includes MEMORIAL HOSPITAL HIXSON, Mailing address: 2051 Hamill Road, Hixson, Tennessee, Zip 37343–4026; tel. 423/495–7100; Janelle Reilly, Chief Executive Officer), (Nonreporting) **A**1 2 3 5 10 **F**3 7 8 11 12 15 17 18 20 22 24 26 28 29 30 31 34 35 36 37 40 44 45 46 47 48 49 50 53 54 55 56 57 58 59 60 64 67 70 71 74 75 77 78 79 81 82 85 86 87 93 107 108 109 110 111 114 115 116 117 118 119 120 121 124 126 129 130 132 135 143 145 146 147 148 149 150 154 156 **P**3 6 7 8 **S** CommonSpirit Health, Chicago, IL
Primary Contact: Janelle Reilly, Chief Executive Officer
COO: Anthony Houston, FACHE, Chief Operating Officer
CFO: Michael Sutton, Chief Financial Officer
CHR: Brad W Pope, Vice President Human Resources
CNO: Rhonda Hatfield, Chief Nursing Officer and Vice President of Clinical Operations
Web address: www.memorial.org
**Control**: Church operated, Nongovernment, not–for–profit **Service**: General medical and surgical

**Staffed Beds:** 423 **Admissions:** 22385 **Census:** 308 **Outpatient Visits:** 374570 **Births:** 0 **Total Expense ($000):** 520632 **Payroll Expense ($000):** 156681 **Personnel:** 2682

**COLUMBIA PARKRIDGE MEDICAL CTR** See Parkridge Medical Center

☒ **ENCOMPASS HEALTH REHABILITATION HOSPITAL OF CHATTANOOGA (443032)**, 2412 McCallie Avenue, Zip 37404–3398; tel. 423/698–0221, (Nonreporting) **A**1 10 **F**3 28 29 90 91 95 96 132 135 148 149 154 **S** Encompass Health Corporation, Birmingham, AL
Primary Contact: Scott Rowe, Chief Executive Officer
COO: Scott Rowe, Chief Executive Officer
CFO: Karen Klassen, Controller
CMO: Amjad Munir, M.D., Medical Director
CIO: Denise Smith, Director Health Information
CHR: Rebekah McNair, Director Human Resources
CNO: Cinthia Campbell, Chief Nursing Officer
Web address: www.healthsouthchattanooga.com
**Control**: Corporation, Investor–owned (for–profit) **Service**: Rehabilitation

**Staffed Beds:** 50 **Admissions:** 1247 **Census:** 42 **Outpatient Visits:** 0 **Total Expense ($000):** 16532 **Payroll Expense ($000):** 8483 **Personnel:** 143

☐ **ERLANGER BEHAVIORAL HOSPITAL (444026)**, 804 North Holtzclaw Avenue, Zip 37404–1235; tel. 423/834–7176, (Nonreporting) **A**1
Primary Contact: Tyler Davis, Chief Executive Officer and Chief Nursing Officer
Web address: www.https://www.erlangerbh.com/
**Control**: Corporation, Investor–owned (for–profit) **Service**: Psychiatric

**Staffed Beds:** 88

⇑ **ERLANGER HEALTH SYSTEM** See Erlanger Medical Center

★ ⇑ **ERLANGER MEDICAL CENTER (440104)**, 975 East Third Street, Zip 37403–2147; tel. 423/778–7000, (Includes ERLANGER EAST HOSPITAL, Mailing address: 1755 Gunbarrel Road, Chattanooga, Tennessee, Zip 37421; tel. 423/778–8700; ERLANGER NORTH HOSPITAL, Mailing address: 632 Morrison Springs Road, Chattanooga, Tennessee, Zip 37415; tel. 615/778–3300; T. C. THOMPSON CHILDREN'S HOSPITAL, Mailing address: 910 Blackford Street, Chattanooga, Tennessee, Zip 37403; tel. 615/778–6011; WILLIE D. MILLER EYE CENTER, Mailing address: 975 East Third Street, Chattanooga, Tennessee, Zip 37403; tel. 615/778–6011), (Nonreporting) **A**2 5 8 10 21 **F**3 8 9 11 12 13 14 15 17 18 19 20 21 22 23 24 25 26 27 28 29 30 31 32 34 35 37 38 39 40 41 42 43 44 45 46 47 48 49 50 51 52 53 54 55 56 57 58 59 60 61 62 64 65 66 68 70 71 72 73 74 75 76 77 78 79 80 81 82 83 84 85 86 87 88 89 92 93 96 97 100 101 102 107 108 109 110 111 112 114 115 116 117 118 119 120 121 123 124 126 127 129 130 131 132 133 134 135 136 138 141 142 144 145 146 147 148 149 150 154 155 156 157 **P**6 **S** Erlanger Health System, Chattanooga, TN
Primary Contact: William L. Jackson Jr, M.D., President and Chief Executive Officer
CFO: J. Britton Tabor, Executive Vice President, Chief Financial Officer
CMO: William L. Jackson, M.D., JrExecutive Vice President, Chief Medical Officer
CIO: David Peterson, Senior Vice President, Chief Technology Officer
CHR: Floyd Chasse, Vice President Human Resources
Web address: www.erlanger.org
**Control**: Hospital district or authority, Government, Nonfederal **Service**: General medical and surgical

**Staffed Beds:** 690 **Admissions:** 40554 **Census:** 546 **Outpatient Visits:** 919076 **Births:** 5500 **Total Expense ($000):** 1006528 **Payroll Expense ($000):** 430010 **Personnel:** 5852

**ERLANGER WOMEN'S EAST HOSPITAL** See Erlanger East Hospital

**HEALTHSOUTH CHATTANOOGA REHABILITATION HOSPITAL** See Encompass Health Rehabilitation Hospital of Chattanooga

☒ **KINDRED HOSPITAL-CHATTANOOGA (442007)**, 709 Walnut Street, Zip 37402–1916; tel. 423/266–7721, (Nonreporting) **A**1 10 **S** Kindred Healthcare, Louisville, KY
Primary Contact: Andrea White, Chief Executive Officer
COO: Rick Rheinheimer, Chief Clinical Officer
CFO: Julia Smith, Chief Financial Officer
CMO: Randy Heisser, M.D., Medical Director
CHR: Kellie McCampbell, Coordinator Human Resources
CNO: Gigi Johnson, Chief Nursing Officer
Web address: www.kindredchattanooga.com/
**Control**: Corporation, Investor–owned (for–profit) **Service**: Acute long–term care hospital

**Staffed Beds:** 39

**MEMORIAL HEALTH CARE SYSTEM** See Chi Memorial

☐ **MOCCASIN BEND MENTAL HEALTH INSTITUTE (444002)**, 100 Moccasin Bend Road, Zip 37405–4415; tel. 423/265–2271, (Nonreporting) **A**1 10 **F**34 57 59 65 75 77 86 98 101 102 130 135
Primary Contact: Mary C. Young, Chief Executive Officer
CFO: Sylvia Harris, Fiscal Director
CMO: Terry R Holmes, M.D., Clinical Director
CIO: Mickey Williams, Manager Information Technology
CHR: Cynthia Honeycutt, Director Human Resources
CNO: Charlynne Parson, Nurse Executive
Web address: www.state.tn.us/mental/mhs/mbhmhi/moc.htm
**Control**: State, Government, Nonfederal **Service**: Psychiatric

**Staffed Beds:** 165 **Admissions:** 2606 **Census:** 123 **Outpatient Visits:** 0 **Births:** 0 **Total Expense ($000):** 39532 **Payroll Expense ($000):** 20354 **Personnel:** 461

**TN**

**TN**

✠ **PARKRIDGE MEDICAL CENTER (440156)**, 2333 McCallie Avenue, Zip 37404–3258; tel. 423/698–6061, (Includes EAST RIDGE HOSPITAL, Mailing address: 941 Spring Creek Road, East Ridge, Tennessee, Zip 37412, P O Box 91229, Zip 37412–6229, tel. 423/855–3500; Jarrett B. Millsaps Jr, FACHE, Chief Executive Officer; PARKRIDGE EAST HOSPITAL, Mailing address: 941 Spring Creek Road, Chattanooga, Tennessee, Zip 37412–3909; tel. 423/894–7870; Jarrett B. Millsaps Jr, FACHE, Chief Executive Officer; PARKRIDGE VALLEY CHILD AND ADOLESCENT CAMPUS, Mailing address: 2200 Morris Hill Road, Chattanooga, Tennessee, Zip 37421; tel. 423/894–4220; Melissa Arkin, Chief Executive Officer; PARKRIDGE WEST HOSPITAL, Mailing address: 1000 Highway 28, Jasper, Tennessee, Zip 37347–3638; tel. 423/837–9500; Shirley K Scarlatti, Associate Chief Nursing Officer), (Nonreporting) **A**1 2 3 5 10 **S** HCA Healthcare, Nashville, TN
Primary Contact: Thomas H. Ozburn, Chief Executive Officer
CMO: Timothy M. Grant, M.D., Chief Medical Officer
CIO: David Cornelius, Director Information Systems
CHR: Carole Hoffman, Vice President
CNO: Jerri C Underwood, R.N., Chief Nursing Officer
Web address: www.parkridgemedicalcenter.com
**Control**: Corporation, Investor–owned (for–profit) **Service**: General medical and surgical

| Staffed Beds: 645 |
|---|

**PARKRIDGE VALLEY HOSPTIAL** See Parkridge Valley Child and Adolescent Campus

✠ △ **SISKIN HOSPITAL FOR PHYSICAL REHABILITATION (443025)**, One Siskin Plaza, Zip 37403–1306; tel. 423/634–1200, (Nonreporting) **A**1 7 10
Primary Contact: Matt Gibson, Chief Executive Officer
CFO: Carol Arnhart, Vice President Finance and Chief Financial Officer
CMO: David N Bowers, M.D., Medical Director
CIO: Shane Pilcher, Administrative Director Information Systems
CHR: Kristi Delaney, Director, Human Resources
CNO: Tracy Collings Reed, Vice President Patient Care Services, Chief Nursing Officer
Web address: www.siskinrehab.com
**Control**: Other not–for–profit (including NFP Corporation) **Service**: Rehabilitation

| Staffed Beds: 195 |
|---|

**T. C. THOMPSON CHILDREN'S HOSPITAL** See Erlanger Medical Center, Chattanooga

**VENCOR HOSPITAL-CHATTANOOGA** See Kindred Hospital-Chattanooga

### CLARKSVILLE—Montgomery County

**BEHAVIORAL HEALTHCARE CENTER AT CLARKSVILLE** See Unity Psychiatric Care-Clarksville

**GATEWAY MEDICAL CENTER** See Tennova Healthcare-Clarksville

✠ **TENNOVA HEALTHCARE-CLARKSVILLE (440035)**, 651 Dunlop Lane, Zip 37040–5015, Mailing Address: P.O. Box 31629, Zip 37040–0028; tel. 931/502–1000, (Nonreporting) **A**1 10 19 **F**3 12 13 15 18 20 22 26 28 29 30 34 39 40 41 42 49 60 63 70 72 75 76 77 78 79 81 82 85 90 93 107 108 110 111 115 116 119 126 127 130 146 147 148 154 156 **S** Community Health Systems, Inc., Franklin, TN
Primary Contact: Alex Villa, Chief Executive Officer
CFO: George Sprinkel, Chief Financial Officer
CMO: Thomas L Ely, D.O., Chief Medical Officer
CIO: Scott Greene, Chief Information Officer
CHR: Liza Edmunds, Director Human Resources
CNO: Faye Perry, Chief Nursing Officer
Web address: www.tennova.com/
**Control**: Partnership, Investor–owned (for–profit) **Service**: General medical and surgical

| Staffed Beds: 172 Admissions: 10900 Census: 115 Outpatient Visits: 140754 Births: 2090 Total Expense ($000): 151335 Payroll Expense ($000): 54908 Personnel: 1067 |
|---|

**UNITY PSYCHIATRIC CARE-CLARKSVILLE (444019)**, 930 Professional Park Drive, Zip 37040–5136; tel. 931/538–6420, (Nonreporting) **A**10 **S** Tennessee Health Management, Parsons, TN
Primary Contact: Jennifer Robinson, Administrator
CMO: Michael McGhee, M.D., Medical Director
CNO: Chrissy Myers, R.N., Director of Nursing
Web address: www.unitypsych.com
**Control**: Partnership, Investor–owned (for–profit) **Service**: Psychiatric

| Staffed Beds: 26 |
|---|

### CLEVELAND—Bradley County

**CLEVELAND COMMUNITY HOSPITAL** See Skyridge Medical Center - Westside Campus

**SKYRIDGE MEDICAL CENTER** See Tennova Healthcare - Cleveland

✠ **TENNOVA HEALTHCARE - CLEVELAND (440185)**, 2305 Chambliss Avenue NW, Zip 37311–3847, Mailing Address: P.O. Box 3060, Zip 37320–3060; tel. 423/559–6000, (Includes SKYRIDGE MEDICAL CENTER - WESTSIDE CAMPUS, Mailing address: 2800 Westside Drive NW, Cleveland, Tennessee, Zip 37312–3599; tel. 423/339–4100; R Coleman Foss, Chief Executive Officer), (Nonreporting) **A**1 3 10 **F**3 5 13 15 18 20 22 28 29 30 31 34 35 39 40 41 44 45 46 49 50 51 57 59 60 68 70 73 74 75 76 77 78 79 81 82 85 87 89 93 98 100 101 102 104 107 108 110 111 114 115 119 126 129 135 136 141 146 148 149 153 154 **S** Community Health Systems, Inc., Franklin, TN
Primary Contact: J. T. Barnhart, Chief Executive Officer
CFO: H. Wes Griffith, Chief Financial Officer
CMO: William F Johnson, Chief Medical Officer
CHR: Kristine Godfrey, Director Human Resources
Web address: www.skyridgemedicalcenter.net
**Control**: Corporation, Investor–owned (for–profit) **Service**: General medical and surgical

| Staffed Beds: 183 Admissions: 9140 Census: 108 Outpatient Visits: 97590 Births: 949 Total Expense ($000): 129318 Payroll Expense ($000): 48252 Personnel: 903 |
|---|

### COLLIERVILLE—Shelby County

★ **BAPTIST MEMORIAL HOSPITAL-COLLIERVILLE (440217)**, 1500 West Poplar Avenue, Zip 38017–0601; tel. 901/861–9400, (Nonreporting) **A**5 10 **F**3 7 8 11 12 15 18 29 30 34 35 36 38 40 41 45 46 47 48 49 50 53 57 58 59 60 61 64 65 68 70 74 75 77 79 81 84 85 87 91 92 93 96 107 108 109 110 111 114 115 119 120 129 130 132 135 146 147 148 149 154 **S** Baptist Memorial Health Care Corporation, Memphis, TN
Primary Contact: Lindsay Stencel, Chief Administrative Officer
CFO: Terri Seago, Chief Financial Officer
CIO: Doug Reiselt, Vice President and Chief Information Officer
CHR: Brenda Johnson, Director Human Resources
CNO: Denise Ferguson, Chief Nursing Officer
Web address: www.baptistonline.org/collierville/
**Control**: Other not–for–profit (including NFP Corporation) **Service**: General medical and surgical

| Staffed Beds: 51 Admissions: 3426 Census: 28 Outpatient Visits: 39510 Births: 0 Total Expense ($000): 55472 Payroll Expense ($000): 18587 Personnel: 264 |
|---|

### COLUMBIA—Maury County

**BEHAVIORAL HEALTHCARE CENTER AT COLUMBIA** See Unity Psychiatric Care-Columbia

✠ **MAURY REGIONAL HOSPITAL (440073)**, 1224 Trotwood Avenue, Zip 38401–4802; tel. 931/381–1111, (Nonreporting) **A**1 2 10 19 **F**3 7 8 11 12 13 15 18 20 22 26 28 29 30 31 34 35 37 38 40 41 44 45 46 47 48 49 50 51 53 54 55 57 58 59 60 62 64 68 70 71 73 74 75 76 77 78 79 80 81 82 84 85 86 87 89 91 92 93 96 102 107 108 110 111 114 115 116 117 118 119 120 121 123 124 126 129 130 131 132 135 146 147 149 154 **S** Maury Regional Health System, Columbia, TN
Primary Contact: H. Alan. Watson, FACHE, Chief Executive Officer
COO: Kenneth Boyd, Chief Operating Officer
CFO: Nick Swift, Chief Financial Officer
CMO: Martin Chaney, M.D., Chief Medical Officer
CIO: Jim Parcel, Director Information Technology
CHR: Kaye Brewer, Chief Human Resources Officer
CNO: Deborah Lumpkins, MSN, Chief Nursing Officer
Web address: www.mauryregional.com
**Control**: County, Government, Nonfederal **Service**: General medical and surgical

| Staffed Beds: 208 Admissions: 12573 Census: 139 Outpatient Visits: 156014 Births: 1425 Total Expense ($000): 325869 Payroll Expense ($000): 117535 Personnel: 2283 |
|---|

★ **PINEWOOD SPRINGS**, 1001 North James M Campbell Boulevard, Zip 38401; tel. 931/777–6000, (Nonreporting) **S** HCA Healthcare, Nashville, TN
Primary Contact: Troy Chisolm, Chief Executive Officer
Web address: www.pinewoodsprings.com/
**Control**: Corporation, Investor–owned (for–profit) **Service**: Psychiatric

| Staffed Beds: 60 |
|---|

*Many Facility Codes have changed. Please refer to the AHA Guide Code Chart.* © 2021 AHA Guide

**UNITY PSYCHIATRIC CARE-COLUMBIA (444021)**, 1400 Rosewood Drive, Zip 38401–4878; tel. 931/388–6573, (Nonreporting) **A**10 **S** Tennessee Health Management, Parsons, TN
Primary Contact: Paula Chennault, Administrator
CMO: Rodney Poling, M.D., Medical Director
CHR: Pam Brown, Human Resources Manager
CNO: Sheila Ridner, R.N., Director of Nursing
Web address: www.unitypsych.com
**Control**: Partnership, Investor–owned (for–profit) **Service**: Psychiatric

| Staffed Beds: 16 |
|---|

## COOKEVILLE—Putnam County

**COOKEVILLE GENERAL HOSPITAL** See Cookeville Regional Medical Center

✠ **COOKEVILLE REGIONAL MEDICAL CENTER (440059)**, 1 Medical Center Boulevard, Zip 38501–4294; tel. 931/783–2000, (Nonreporting) **A**1 2 10 19
Primary Contact: Paul Korth, Chief Executive Officer
COO: Scott Williams, Chief Operating Officer
CFO: Paul Korth, Chief Financial Officer
CMO: Jeffrey J Gleason, M.D., Chief Medical Officer
CIO: Les Bernstein, Chief Information Officer
CHR: Angela Lewis, Senior Vice President Administration
CNO: Linda Crawford, R.N., MSN, Chief Nursing Officer
Web address: www.crmchealth.org
**Control**: City, Government, Nonfederal **Service**: General medical and surgical

| Staffed Beds: 243 |
|---|

## COVINGTON—Tipton County

✠ **BAPTIST MEMORIAL HOSPITAL-TIPTON (440131)**, 1995 Highway 51 South, Zip 38019–3635; tel. 901/476–2621, (Nonreporting) **A**1 2 10 **F**3 11 15 29 30 31 34 35 40 45 55 57 58 59 65 70 74 75 76 78 79 81 85 87 89 93 100 107 108 110 111 114 115 119 120 121 130 146 148 154 **S** Baptist Memorial Health Care Corporation, Memphis, TN
Primary Contact: Parker Harris, Chief Executive Officer and Administrator
CFO: Monique Hart, Chief Financial Officer
CMO: Kenneth Afenya, M.D., Chief of Staff
CHR: Myra Cousar, Director Human Resources
Web address: www.baptistonline.org/tipton/
**Control**: Other not–for–profit (including NFP Corporation) **Service**: General medical and surgical

| Staffed Beds: 50 **Admissions**: 1160 **Census**: 7 **Outpatient Visits**: 64672 **Births**: 340 **Total Expense ($000)**: 117310 **Payroll Expense ($000)**: 17238 **Personnel**: 219 |
|---|

## CROSSVILLE—Cumberland County

☐ **CUMBERLAND MEDICAL CENTER (440009)**, 421 South Main Street, Zip 38555–5031; tel. 931/484–9511, (Nonreporting) **A**1 2 10 20 **F**3 11 13 15 18 20 22 28 29 30 31 34 35 40 44 45 47 48 51 53 57 58 59 61 64 68 70 74 75 76 77 78 79 81 82 85 86 87 93 94 102 107 108 110 111 114 115 119 120 121 129 130 132 135 146 147 148 154 156 **P**6 **S** Covenant Health, Knoxville, TN
Primary Contact: David V. Bunch, President and Chief Administrative Officer
CFO: April VonAchen, Chief Financial Officer and Vice President Financial Services
CIO: Joe Lowe, Director Management Information Systems
CHR: Charles Sexton, Manager Human Resources
CNO: Rebecca Foster, MSN, R.N., Chief Nursing Officer
Web address: www.cmchealthcare.org
**Control**: Other not–for–profit (including NFP Corporation) **Service**: General medical and surgical

| Staffed Beds: 85 **Admissions**: 5445 **Census**: 55 **Outpatient Visits**: 90344 **Births**: 644 **Total Expense ($000)**: 83104 **Payroll Expense ($000)**: 29563 **Personnel**: 597 |
|---|

## DAYTON—Rhea County

**RHEA COUNTY MEDICAL CENTER** See Rhea Medical Center

✠ **RHEA MEDICAL CENTER (441310)**, 9400 Rhea County Highway, Zip 37321–7922; tel. 423/775–1121, (Nonreporting) **A**1 10 18 **S** QHR Health, Brentwood, TN
Primary Contact: David Bixler, Chief Executive Officer
CFO: Harv Sanders, Chief Financial Officer
CMO: Benjamin Kellogg, M.D., Chief of Staff
CNO: Samantha Bryant, Chief Nursing Officer
Web address: www.rheamedical.org
**Control**: County, Government, Nonfederal **Service**: General medical and surgical

| Staffed Beds: 25 |
|---|

## DICKSON—Dickson County

**HORIZON MEDICAL CENTER** See Tristar Horizon Medical Center

✠ **TRISTAR HORIZON MEDICAL CENTER (440046)**, 111 Highway 70 East, Zip 37055–2080; tel. 615/446–0446, (Nonreporting) **A**1 2 10 **S** HCA Healthcare, Nashville, TN
Primary Contact: Jason E. Boyd, Chief Executive Officer
CFO: Clarence Gray, Chief Financial Officer
CIO: Rick Stoker, Director Management Information Systems
CHR: Sheila Kight, Director Human Resources
CNO: Gina Bullington, Chief Nursing Officer
Web address: www.horizonmedicalcenter.com
**Control**: Corporation, Investor–owned (for–profit) **Service**: General medical and surgical

| Staffed Beds: 157 |
|---|

## DYERSBURG—Dyer County

**TENNOVA HEALTHCARE DYERSBURG REGIONAL MEDICAL CENTER** See West Tennessee Healthcare Dyersburg Hospital

✠ **WEST TENNESSEE HEALTHCARE DYERSBURG HOSPITAL (440072)**, 400 East Tickle Street, Zip 38024–3120; tel. 731/285–2410, (Nonreporting) **A**1 10 20 **F**3 8 11 13 15 18 20 22 26 28 29 30 34 35 39 40 44 45 46 47 48 49 50 51 57 59 60 70 76 79 81 82 85 87 92 93 97 107 108 110 111 115 119 120 121 124 127 129 130 145 146 147 149 157 **S** West Tennessee Healthcare, Jackson, TN
Primary Contact: Scott Barber, Interim Chief Executive Officer
CFO: Meredith Malone, Chief Financial Officer
CMO: Darren Johnson, M.D., Chief of Staff
CIO: Russ Shephard, Senior Systems Analyst
CHR: Beverly Ray, Director Human Resources
CNO: Jan Leann Zimmer, R.N., MSN, R.N., MS, Chief Nursing Officer
Web address: www.wth.org/locations/west-tennessee-healthcare-dyersburg-hospital
**Control**: Hospital district or authority, Government, Nonfederal **Service**: General medical and surgical

| Staffed Beds: 115 **Admissions**: 4414 **Census**: 46 **Outpatient Visits**: 58577 **Births**: 466 **Total Expense ($000)**: 63979 **Payroll Expense ($000)**: 21675 **Personnel**: 341 |
|---|

## EAST RIDGE—Hamilton County

**COLUMBIA EAST RIDGE HOSPITAL** See East Ridge Hospital

**EAST RIDGE HOSPITAL** See Parkridge Medical Center, Chattanooga

## ELIZABETHTON—Carter County

**COLUMBIA SYCAMORE SHOALS HOSP** See Sycamore Shoals Hospital

☐ **SYCAMORE SHOALS HOSPITAL (440018)**, 1501 West Elk Avenue, Zip 37643–2874; tel. 423/542–1300, (Nonreporting) **A**1 10 **F**3 11 15 18 29 30 34 35 40 41 44 45 48 50 53 54 56 57 59 62 63 64 68 70 75 77 79 81 84 85 87 93 97 98 103 107 110 111 115 118 119 130 144 146 147 148 154 **S** Ballad Health, Johnson City, TN
Primary Contact: Dwayne Taylor, Chief Executive Officer
COO: Melanie Stanton, R.N., Chief Nursing Officer
CFO: Chase Wilson, Chief Financial Officer
CMO: Morris H Seligman, M.D., Chief Medical Officer and Chief Medical Information Officer
CIO: Paul Merrywell, Chief Information Officer
CHR: Sharon Sheppard, Manager Human Resources
Web address: www.msha.com
**Control**: Other not–for–profit (including NFP Corporation) **Service**: General medical and surgical

| Staffed Beds: 74 **Admissions**: 3701 **Census**: 45 **Outpatient Visits**: 65256 **Births**: 0 **Total Expense ($000)**: 43803 **Payroll Expense ($000)**: 17850 **Personnel**: 1144 |
|---|

| Hospital, Medicare Provider Number, Address, Telephone, Approval, Facility, and Physician Codes, Health Care System |
|---|
| ★ American Hospital Association (AHA) membership ☐ The Joint Commission accreditation ○ Healthcare Facilities Accreditation Program ◇ DNV Healthcare Inc. accreditation ⇑ Center for Improvement in Healthcare Quality Accreditation △ Commission on Accreditation of Rehabilitation Facilities (CARF) accreditation |

**TN**

## ERIN—Houston County

✠ **HOUSTON COUNTY COMMUNITY HOSPITAL (441322)**, 5001 East Main Street, Zip 37061–4115, Mailing Address: P.O. Box 489, Zip 37061–0489; tel. 931/289–4211, (Nonreporting) **A**1 10 18
Primary Contact: Doug Martin, Chief Executive Officer
CFO: Alisha Harvey, Director of Finance
CMO: Michael Carter, M.D., Chief Medical Officer
CIO: Richard Christy, Information Technology Manager
CHR: Leslie Booth, Human Resources Director
CNO: Doug Martin, Chief Nursing Officer
Web address: www.hhc.org/
**Control**: County, Government, Nonfederal **Service**: General medical and surgical

**Staffed Beds**: 25

**PATIENTS' CHOICE MEDICAL CENTER OF ERIN** See Houston County Community Hospital

## ERWIN—Unicoi County

✠ **UNICOI COUNTY MEMORIAL HOSPITAL (440001)**, 2030 Temple Hill Road, Zip 37650, Mailing Address: P.O. Box 802, Zip 37650–0802; tel. 423/743–3141, (Total facility includes 46 beds in nursing home–type unit) (Nonreporting) **A**1 10 **F**15 29 30 34 35 40 50 64 67 68 75 77 85 93 107 110 111 115 119 130 131 146 154 **S** Ballad Health, Johnson City, TN
Primary Contact: Eric Carroll, Chief Executive Officer
CFO: Toni Buchanan, Chief Financial Officer
CMO: Jose Picaza, M.D., Chief of Staff
CIO: Maggie Tipton, Chief Information Officer
CHR: Susan Broyles, Director Human Resources and Safety
CNO: Melanie Stanton, R.N., Chief Nursing Officer
Web address: www.msha.com
**Control**: Other not–for–profit (including NFP Corporation) **Service**: General medical and surgical

**Staffed Beds**: 50 **Admissions**: 535 **Census**: 26 **Outpatient Visits**: 33439 **Births**: 0 **Total Expense ($000)**: 11835 **Payroll Expense ($000)**: 4766 **Personnel**: 225

## FAYETTEVILLE—Lincoln County

☐ **LINCOLN COUNTY HEALTH SYSTEM (440102)**, 106 Medical Center Boulevard, Zip 37334–2684, Mailing Address: PO Box 637, Zip 37334–2684; tel. 931/438–1100, (Nonreporting) **A**1 10
Primary Contact: Darrell Blaylock, Chief Executive Officer
CFO: Robert M Lonis, CPA, Chief Financial Officer
CIO: John Kenneth Lavender, Chief Information Officer
CHR: Wendy Nogler, Director Human Resources
CNO: Vicky Groce, Chief Nursing Officer
Web address: www.lchealthsystem.com
**Control**: County, Government, Nonfederal **Service**: General medical and surgical

**Staffed Beds**: 313

**LINCOLN COUNTY HEALTH SYSTEMS** See Lincoln County Health System

## FRANKLIN—Williamson County

✠ **ENCOMPASS HEALTH REHABILITATION HOSPITAL OF FRANKLIN (443035)**, 1000 Physicians Way, Zip 37067–1471; tel. 615/721–4000, (Nonreporting) **A**1 10 **S** Encompass Health Corporation, Birmingham, AL
Primary Contact: Scott J. Peterson, Chief Executive Officer
CFO: Patricia Huffman, Controller
CMO: Scott Craig, M.D., Medical Director
CHR: Dawn McMaster, Human Resources Director
CNO: Valerie Shoulders, R.N., Chief Nursing Officer
Web address: www.https://encompasshealth.com/franklinrehab
**Control**: Corporation, Investor–owned (for–profit) **Service**: Rehabilitation

**Staffed Beds**: 40

**HEALTHSOUTH REHABILITATION HOSPITAL OF FRANKLIN** See Encompass Health Rehabilitation Hospital of Franklin

☐ **ROLLING HILLS HOSPITAL (444007)**, 2014 Quail Hollow Circle, Zip 37067–5967; tel. 615/628–5700, (Nonreporting) **A**1 10 **S** Universal Health Services, Inc., King of Prussia, PA
Primary Contact: James Miller, Chief Executive Officer
COO: Laurel Roberts, R.N., MSN, Chief Operating Officer
CFO: Ray Brocato, Chief Financial Officer
CMO: James Hart, M.D., Medical Director
CHR: Lisa Hodge, Director, Human Resources
CNO: Hilary Gipson, Director of Nursing
Web address: www.RollingHillsHospital.org/
**Control**: Corporation, Investor–owned (for–profit) **Service**: Psychiatric

**Staffed Beds**: 130

☐ **WILLIAMSON MEDICAL CENTER (440029)**, 4321 Carothers Parkway, Zip 37067–8542; tel. 615/435–5000, (Nonreporting) **A**1 2 3 5 10 **F**3 7 8 11 12 13 15 18 19 20 21 24 25 28 29 30 31 34 35 37 40 41 50 51 54 56 57 59 60 64 65 68 70 72 74 75 76 77 78 79 81 82 84 85 86 87 89 97 107 126 129 130 131 132 135 136 140 141 142 143 144 146 147 148 149 155 156 **P**6
Primary Contact: Donald Webb, Chief Executive Officer
COO: Julie Miller, Chief Operating Officer
CMO: Starling C Evins, M.D., Chief of Staff
CIO: Steve Dycus, Director Marketing and Public Relations
CHR: Phyllis Molyneux, Associate Administrator Human Resources and Education
Web address: www.williamsonmedicalcenter.org
**Control**: County, Government, Nonfederal **Service**: General medical and surgical

**Staffed Beds**: 185 **Admissions**: 9915 **Census**: 94 **Outpatient Visits**: 148975 **Births**: 1666

## GALLATIN—Sumner County

**SUMNER MEMORIAL HOSPITAL** See Sumner Regional Medical Center

✠ **SUMNER REGIONAL MEDICAL CENTER (440003)**, 555 Hartsville Pike, Zip 37066–2400, Mailing Address: P.O. Box 1558, Zip 37066–1558; tel. 615/452–4210, (Nonreporting) **A**1 2 3 10 **S** LifePoint Health, Brentwood, TN
Primary Contact: Susan M. Peach, R.N., Chief Executive Officer
CMO: Geoffrey Lifferth, M.D., Chief Medical Officer
CIO: Vickie Carter, Information Systems Director
CNO: Anne Melton, Chief Nursing Officer
Web address: www.mysumnermedical.com
**Control**: Corporation, Investor–owned (for–profit) **Service**: General medical and surgical

**Staffed Beds**: 110

## GERMANTOWN—Shelby County

☐ △ **BAPTIST MEMORIAL REHABILITATION HOSPITAL (443034)**, 1240 South Germantown Road, Zip 38138–2226; tel. 901/275–3300, (Nonreporting) **A**1 7 10 **S** Baptist Memorial Health Care Corporation, Memphis, TN
Primary Contact: Christopher L. Bariola, Chief Executive Officer
CFO: Carlos Mendoza, Controller
CHR: Stacie Schroeppel, Director of Human Resources
CNO: Donna Hale, Director of Nursing
Web address: www.baptistrehab.com
**Control**: Partnership, Investor–owned (for–profit) **Service**: Rehabilitation

**Staffed Beds**: 49

**METHODIST HLTHCARE-GERMANTOWN** See Methodist Le Bonheur Germantown Hospital

**METHODIST LE BONHEUR GERMANTOWN HOSPITAL** See Methodist Healthcare Memphis Hospitals, Memphis

## GREENEVILLE—Greene County

✠ **GREENEVILLE COMMUNITY HOSPITAL WEST (440050)**, 401 Takoma Avenue, Zip 37743–4647; tel. 423/639–3151, (Includes GREENEVILLE COMMUNITY HOSPITAL EAST, Mailing address: 1420 Tusculum Boulevard, Greeneville, Tennessee, Zip 37745–5825; tel. 423/787–5000; Tammy Albright, Chief Executive Officer), (Nonreporting) **A**1 10 **F**3 6 11 12 13 15 18 29 30 32 34 35 40 44 45 46 49 50 54 56 57 59 64 65 68 74 75 77 81 85 87 97 98 100 102 103 104 107 108 110 111 115 119 129 130 131 132 135 144 146 147 149 154 156 **S** Ballad Health, Johnson City, TN
Primary Contact: Tammy Albright, Chief Executive Officer
COO: Chris Miller, Chief Operating Officer
CFO: Lindsay Haun, Chief Financial Officer
CMO: Daniel Lewis, Chief Medical Officer
CHR: Jack Lister, Director Human Resources
CNO: Robin Roberts, R.N., Chief Nursing Officer
Web address: www.balladhealth.org
**Control**: Other not–for–profit (including NFP Corporation) **Service**: Psychiatric

**Staffed Beds**: 15 **Admissions**: 1325 **Census**: 15 **Outpatient Visits**: 222901 **Births**: 309 **Total Expense ($000)**: 52941 **Payroll Expense ($000)**: 24335 **Personnel**: 466

**LAUGHLIN MEMORIAL HOSPITAL** See Greeneville Community Hospital East

**TAKOMA REGIONAL HOSPITAL** See Greeneville Community Hospital West

## HARRIMAN—Roane County

**HARRIMAN CITY HOSPITAL** See Roane Medical Center

*Many Facility Codes have changed. Please refer to the AHA Guide Code Chart.*

☐ **ROANE MEDICAL CENTER (440031)**, 8045 Roane Medical Center Dr, Zip 37748–8333; tel. 865/316–1000, (Nonreporting) **A**1 3 10 **F**3 11 15 18 20 28 29 30 34 35 40 44 45 50 57 58 59 61 64 68 69 70 75 78 79 81 82 85 86 87 93 94 102 107 108 110 111 115 118 119 129 130 132 143 146 148 154 156 **S** Covenant Health, Knoxville, TN
Primary Contact: Jason B. Pilant, President and Chief Administrative Officer
CFO: Julie Utterback, Chief Financial Officer
CMO: Mark Browne, M.D., Chief Medical Officer
CIO: Mike Ward, Senior Vice President Chief Information Officer
CHR: Randall Carr, Director Human Resources
CNO: Carolyn Shipley, R.N., Chief Nursing Officer
Web address: www.roanemedical.com
**Control**: Other not–for–profit (including NFP Corporation) **Service**: General medical and surgical

| Staffed Beds: 52 | Admissions: 2679 | Census: 26 | Outpatient Visits: 60760 |
| Births: 0 | Total Expense ($000): 35413 | Payroll Expense ($000): 13441 |
| Personnel: 234 |

### HARTSVILLE—Trousdale County

**HARTSVILLE MEDICAL CENTER** See Trousdale Medical Center

⊞ **TROUSDALE MEDICAL CENTER (441301)**, 500 Church Street, Zip 37074–1744; tel. 615/374–2221, (Nonreporting) **A**1 10 18 **S** LifePoint Health, Brentwood, TN
Primary Contact: Michael Herman, Chief Executive Officer
COO: William D Mize, Chief Operating Officer
CFO: David Wilhoite, CPA, Senior Vice President Finance and Chief Financial Officer
CIO: David Young, Senior Vice President Planning and Technology
CHR: Amy Overstreet, Director Human Resources
CNO: Jennifer Holder, Chief Nursing Officer
Web address: www.mytrousdalemedical.com
**Control**: Corporation, Investor–owned (for–profit) **Service**: General medical and surgical

| Staffed Beds: 25 |

### HENDERSONVILLE—Sumner County

**HENDERSONVILLE MEDICAL CENTER** See Tristar Hendersonville Medical Center

⊞ **TRISTAR HENDERSONVILLE MEDICAL CENTER (440194)**, 355 New Shackle Island Road, Zip 37075–2479; tel. 615/338–1000, (Nonreporting) **A**1 3 10 **S** HCA Healthcare, Nashville, TN
Primary Contact: Regina Bartlett, Chief Executive Officer
CFO: Stephen Bearden, Chief Financial Officer
CMO: Tamie Babb, Chief Medical Officer
CIO: Hal Schultheis, Director Information Systems
CHR: Amy L Hobdy, Vice President of Human Resources
CNO: Lisa Hochstetler, R.N., Chief Nursing Officer
Web address: www.hendersonvillemedicalcenter.com
**Control**: Corporation, Investor–owned (for–profit) **Service**: General medical and surgical

| Staffed Beds: 159 |

### HERMITAGE—Davidson County

**SUMMIT MEDICAL CENTER** See Tristar Summit Medical Center

⊞ **TRISTAR SUMMIT MEDICAL CENTER (440150)**, 5655 Frist Boulevard, Zip 37076–2053; tel. 615/316–3000, (Nonreporting) **A**1 2 10 **S** HCA Healthcare, Nashville, TN
Primary Contact: Brian Marger, Chief Executive Officer
CFO: Bryan Shephard, Chief Financial Officer
CMO: Kevin M. Hamilton, M.D., Chief Medical Officer
CIO: Joel Bain, Director Information Services
CHR: Emily Dye, Vice President Human Resources
CNO: Mary Ann Angle, R.N., FACHE, Chief Nursing Officer
Web address: www.summitmedctr.com
**Control**: Corporation, Investor–owned (for–profit) **Service**: General medical and surgical

| Staffed Beds: 218 |

### HIXSON—Hamilton County

**MEMORIAL NORTH PARK HOSPITAL** See Memorial Hospital Hixson

### HUNTINGDON—Carroll County

⊞ **BAPTIST MEMORIAL HOSPITAL-CARROLL COUNTY (440016)**, 631 R.B. Wilson Drive, Zip 38344–1727; tel. 731/986–4461, (Nonreporting) **A**1 10 **F**3 11 15 18 28 29 30 34 35 38 40 44 50 56 57 59 61 64 65 66 70 75 77 79 81 85 86 87 91 93 97 98 101 102 103 107 108 110 111 115 118 119 130 132 133 134 135 145 146 148 149 154 156 **S** Baptist Memorial Health Care Corporation, Memphis, TN
Primary Contact: Susan M. Breeden, Administrator and Chief Executive Officer
CFO: Sharron Holland, Chief Financial Officer
CHR: Kim King, Director Human Resources and Public Relations
CNO: Kimberly Sanders, Chief Nursing Officer
Web address: www.baptistonline.org/huntingdon/
**Control**: Other not–for–profit (including NFP Corporation) **Service**: General medical and surgical

| Staffed Beds: 35 | Admissions: 1040 | Census: 14 | Outpatient Visits: 26265 |
| Births: 1 | Total Expense ($000): 22002 | Payroll Expense ($000): 9301 |
| Personnel: 168 |

**BAPTIST MEMORIAL HOSPITAL-HUNTINGDON** See Baptist Memorial Hospital-Carroll County

### JACKSON—Madison County

⊞ **JACKSON-MADISON COUNTY GENERAL HOSPITAL (440002)**, 620 Skyline Drive, Zip 38301–3923; tel. 731/541–5000, (Includes WEST TENNESSEE HEALTHCARE NORTH HOSPITAL, Mailing address: 367 Hospital Boulevard, Jackson, Tennessee, Zip 38305–2080; tel. 731/661–2000; Kevin Rinks, Chief Executive Officer), (Nonreporting) **A**1 2 3 5 10 19 **F**3 7 8 11 13 15 17 18 20 22 24 26 28 29 30 31 34 35 37 39 40 42 44 45 46 47 48 49 51 53 55 56 57 58 59 60 63 64 65 68 70 72 74 75 76 77 78 79 80 81 82 84 85 86 87 89 92 93 94 96 97 107 108 109 110 111 114 115 116 117 118 119 120 121 124 126 129 130 131 132 135 145 146 147 148 149 156 **S** West Tennessee Healthcare, Jackson, TN
Primary Contact: Deann Thelen, Vice President and Administrator
CFO: Jeff Blankenship, CPA, Vice President and Chief Financial Officer
CMO: David Roberts, M.D., Chief Medical Officer
CIO: Jeff Frieling, Vice President and Chief Information Officer
CHR: Wendie Carlson, Chief Human Resources Officer
CNO: Tina Prescott, Vice President, Hospital Services
Web address: www.wth.org
**Control**: Hospital district or authority, Government, Nonfederal **Service**: General medical and surgical

| Staffed Beds: 632 | Admissions: 31445 | Census: 433 | Outpatient Visits: 199493 | Births: 3200 | Total Expense ($000): 684410 | Payroll Expense ($000): 248108 | Personnel: 4272 |

**OAK HILLS BEHAVIORAL CENTER** See Perimeter Behavioral Hospital of Jackson

**PATHWAYS** See Pathways of Tennessee

★ **PATHWAYS OF TENNESSEE (444010)**, 238 Summar Drive, Zip 38301–3906; tel. 731/541–8200, (Nonreporting) **A**10 **F**4 5 29 35 38 44 57 59 98 99 100 101 102 103 104 132 134 135 149 150 153 154 157 **S** West Tennessee Healthcare, Jackson, TN
Primary Contact: Pam Henson, Executive Director
CFO: Jeff Blankenship, CPA, Chief Financial Officer
CMO: Kevin Turner, M.D., Medical Director
CIO: Jeff Frieling, Chief Information Officer
CHR: Wendy Carlson, Director Human Resources
CNO: Angela Hensley, Director of Nursing
Web address: www.wth.net/pathways
**Control**: Hospital district or authority, Government, Nonfederal **Service**: Psychiatric

| Staffed Beds: 25 | Admissions: 1072 | Census: 12 | Outpatient Visits: 97989 |
| Births: 0 | Total Expense ($000): 19898 | Payroll Expense ($000): 10352 |
| Personnel: 208 |

☐ **PERIMETER BEHAVIORAL HOSPITAL OF JACKSON (444023)**, 49 Old Hickory Boulevard, Zip 38305–4551; tel. 731/668–7073, (Nonreporting) **A**1
Web address: www.https://www.perimeterhealthcare.com/facilities/perimeter-behavioral-hospital-of-jackson/
**Control**: Corporation, Investor–owned (for–profit) **Service**: Psychiatric

| Staffed Beds: 45 |

**TENNOVA HEALTHCARE REGIONAL HOSPITAL OF JACKSON** See West Tennessee Healthcare North Hospital

**TN**

✠ **WEST TENNESSEE HEALTHCARE REHABILITATION HOSPITAL JACKSON (443036)**, 616 West Forest Avenue, Zip 38301–3902; tel. 731/574–3000, (Nonreporting) **A**1 10 **S** Encompass Health Corporation, Birmingham, AL
Primary Contact: Julie Taylor, Chief Executive Officer
Web address: www.https://encompasshealth.com/locations/jacksonrehab/
**Control:** Corporation, Investor–owned (for–profit) **Service:** Rehabilitation

**Staffed Beds:** 48

### JAMESTOWN—Fentress County

**JAMESTOWN REGIONAL MEDICAL CENTER (440083)**, 436 Central Ave W, Zip 38556–3031, Mailing Address: P.O. Box 1500, Zip 38556–1500; tel. 931/879–8171, (Nonreporting) **A**10 20
Primary Contact: Michael D. Alexander, MS, Chief Executive Officer
CMO: Mark Hendrixson, M.D., Chief Medical Officer
CIO: Rick Smith, Director Information Systems
CHR: Shelia Russell, Director Human Resources
Web address: www.https://jrmcnd.com
**Control:** Corporation, Investor–owned (for–profit) **Service:** General medical and surgical

**Staffed Beds:** 85

**TENNOVA HEALTHCARE-JAMESTOWN** See Jamestown Regional Medical Center

### JASPER—Marion County

**GRANDVIEW MEDICAL CENTER** See Parkridge West Hospital

### JEFFERSON CITY—Jefferson County

✠ **TENNOVA HEALTHCARE-JEFFERSON MEMORIAL HOSPITAL (440056)**, 110 Hospital Drive, Zip 37760–5281; tel. 865/471–2500, (Nonreporting) **A**1 10 **F**3 15 29 30 34 35 40 45 49 50 57 59 68 70 75 77 79 81 87 93 108 110 111 115 119 129 130 133 135 141 146 154 157 **S** Community Health Systems, Inc., Franklin, TN
Primary Contact: Colin McRae, Chief Executive Officer
CFO: Roseann M Devault, Chief Financial Officer
CMO: Richard Carter, M.D., Chief of Staff
Web address: www.tennova.com/
**Control:** Corporation, Investor–owned (for–profit) **Service:** General medical and surgical

**Staffed Beds:** 58 **Admissions:** 2432 **Census:** 26 **Outpatient Visits:** 61893 **Births:** 0 **Total Expense ($000):** 43158 **Payroll Expense ($000):** 15228 **Personnel:** 284

**TENNOVA-JEFFERSON MEMORIAL HOSPITAL** See Tennova Healthcare-Jefferson Memorial Hospital

### JELLICO—Campbell County

★ **JELLICO COMMUNITY HOSPITAL (440180)**, 188 Hospital Lane, Zip 37762–4400; tel. 423/784–7252, (Nonreporting) **A**10 22 **S** Community Hospital Corporation, Plano, TX
Primary Contact: Gene Miller, Interim Chief Executive Officer
COO: Pamela Hodge, R.N., Chief Nursing Officer and Coordinator Performance Improvement
CFO: Evelyn Ghulum, Chief Financial Officer
CMO: Gregory Wilkens, M.D., Chief of Staff
CIO: Derek Brown, Chief Information Officer
CHR: Vince Vannett, Director Human Resources
Web address: www.jellicomc.com/
**Control:** Other not–for–profit (including NFP Corporation) **Service:** General medical and surgical

**Staffed Beds:** 47

### JOHNSON CITY—Washington County

✠ **FRANKLIN WOODS COMMUNITY HOSPITAL (440184)**, 300 MedTech Parkway, Zip 37604–2277; tel. 423/302–1000, (Total facility includes 34 beds in nursing home–type unit) (Nonreporting) **A**1 10 **F**3 11 13 29 30 34 35 36 38 40 44 45 50 51 56 57 63 65 68 70 74 75 76 77 81 85 87 100 107 108 111 114 115 118 119 126 128 130 146 147 148 149 154 157 **S** Ballad Health, Johnson City, TN
Primary Contact: Melanie Steagall. Stanton, Chief Executive Officer
CFO: Andrew R. Wampler, Chief Financial Officer
CHR: Brooke Graham, Human Resources Manager
CNO: Rhonda Mann, Chief Nursing Officer
Web address: www.msha.com
**Control:** Other not–for–profit (including NFP Corporation) **Service:** General medical and surgical

**Staffed Beds:** 102 **Admissions:** 5470 **Census:** 63 **Outpatient Visits:** 50837 **Births:** 1231 **Total Expense ($000):** 68064 **Payroll Expense ($000):** 21556 **Personnel:** 945

**JAMES H & CECILE C QUILLEN** See Quillen Rehabilitation Hospital

**JOHNSON CITY MED CENTER** See Johnson City Medical Center

✠ **JOHNSON CITY MEDICAL CENTER (440063)**, 400 North State of Franklin Road, Zip 37604–6094; tel. 423/431–6111, (Includes NISWONGER CHILDREN'S HOSPITAL, Mailing address: 400 North State of Franklin Road, Johnson City, Tennessee, Zip 37604–6035; tel. 423/431–6111; Lisa Carter, Chief Executive Officer; WOODRIDGE HOSPITAL, Mailing address: 403 State of Franklin Road, Johnson City, Tennessee, Zip 37604–6034; tel. 423/431–7111; Patricia Baise, R.N., FACHE, Chief Executive Officer), (Nonreporting) **A**1 3 5 8 10 19 **F**3 4 5 7 11 12 13 15 17 18 19 20 21 22 24 26 28 29 30 31 32 34 35 38 39 40 41 43 44 45 46 47 48 49 50 51 52 53 54 55 56 57 58 59 60 61 62 63 64 68 70 72 74 75 76 77 78 79 81 82 84 85 86 87 88 89 91 93 97 98 99 100 101 102 103 104 107 108 110 111 114 115 117 118 119 120 121 123 124 129 130 131 132 134 135 143 146 147 148 153 154 **S** Ballad Health, Johnson City, TN
Primary Contact: Stan Hickson, FACHE, Chief Executive Officer
COO: Kenny Shafer, Chief Operating Officer
CFO: Richard Boone, Chief Financial Officer
CMO: Clay Runnels, Vice President Chief Medical Officer Washington County
CHR: Barry Tourigny, Human Resources Director
CNO: Dru Malcolm, Vice President and Chief Nursing Officer
Web address: www.msha.com
**Control:** Other not–for–profit (including NFP Corporation) **Service:** General medical and surgical

**Staffed Beds:** 585 **Admissions:** 27927 **Census:** 392 **Outpatient Visits:** 268372 **Births:** 1263 **Total Expense ($000):** 388888 **Payroll Expense ($000):** 124593 **Personnel:** 2161

**NORTH SIDE HOSPITAL** See Franklin Woods Community Hospital

✠ **QUILLEN REHABILITATION HOSPITAL (443033)**, 2511 Wesley Street, Zip 37601–1723; tel. 423/952–1700, (Nonreporting) **A**1 10 **F**29 75 90 132 148 149 **S** Encompass Health Corporation, Birmingham, AL
Primary Contact: Brian Luff, Chief Executive Officer
CFO: Debbie Wyse, Controller
CHR: Penny Lawson, Human Resource Director
CNO: Lynn Langan, Chief Nursing Officer
Web address: www.quillenrehabilitationhospital.com/
**Control:** Corporation, Investor–owned (for–profit) **Service:** Rehabilitation

**Staffed Beds:** 31 **Admissions:** 666 **Census:** 26 **Outpatient Visits:** 0 **Births:** 0 **Total Expense ($000):** 10712 **Payroll Expense ($000):** 5554 **Personnel:** 95

### KINGSPORT-Sullivan County

☐ **CREEKSIDE BEHAVIORAL HEALTH (444027)**, 1025 Executive Park Boulevard, Zip 37660–4620; tel. 423/830–8110, (Nonreporting) **A**1
Primary Contact: Ric McAllister, Chief Executive Officer
Web address: www.creeksidebh.com
**Control:** Corporation, Investor–owned (for–profit) **Service:** Psychiatric

**Staffed Beds:** 72

✠ **ENCOMPASS HEALTH REHABILITATION HOSPITAL OF KINGSPORT (443027)**, 113 Cassel Drive, Zip 37660–3775; tel. 423/246–7240, (Nonreporting) **A**1 10 **S** Encompass Health Corporation, Birmingham, AL
Primary Contact: Troy Clark, Chief Executive Officer
CFO: Natalie Tilson, Controller
CMO: James P Little, M.D., Medical Director
CIO: Natalie Tilson, Controller
CHR: Joyce Jones, Director Human Resources
CNO: Debra Smith, Chief Nursing Officer
Web address: www.healthsouthkingsport.com
**Control:** Corporation, Investor–owned (for–profit) **Service:** Rehabilitation

**Staffed Beds:** 50

**HEALTHSOUTH REHABILITATION HOSPITAL** See Encompass Health
Rehabilitation Hospital of Kingsport

✠ **HOLSTON VALLEY MEDICAL CENTER (440017)**, 130 West Ravine
Street, Zip 37660–3837, Mailing Address: P.O. Box 238, Zip 37662–0238;
tel. 423/224–4000, (Nonreporting) **A**1 3 5 10 13 19 **F**3 13 15 18 20 22 24 26
28 29 30 31 34 35 37 40 41 43 45 46 47 49 50 51 55 56 57 58 59 65 68 75
77 78 79 81 97 107 108 109 110 111 116 117 119 129 130 131 132 135
146 147 149 154 156 157 **S** Ballad Health, Johnson City, TN
Primary Contact: Lindy P. White, Vice President and Chief Executive Officer
COO: Dale Clark, Chief Operating Officer
CFO: Dale Poe, Vice President Finance and Operations
CMO: Daniel Carlson, M.D., Chief Medical Officer
CHR: Hamlin J Wilson, Senior Vice President Human Resources
CNO: Kathy Campbell, Interim Chief Nursing Officer
Web address: www.wellmont.org
**Control**: Other not–for–profit (including NFP Corporation) **Service**: General
medical and surgical

**Staffed Beds:** 336 **Admissions:** 18916 **Census:** 217 **Outpatient
Visits:** 391293 **Births:** 758 **Total Expense ($000):** 336158 **Payroll Expense
($000):** 96114 **Personnel:** 1854

☐ **INDIAN PATH COMMUNITY HOSPITAL (440176)**, 2000 Brookside Drive,
Zip 37660–4627; tel. 423/857–7000, (Nonreporting) **A**1 5 10 **F**3 8 11 13 15 18
29 30 31 34 35 40 45 46 47 49 50 51 54 55 57 59 60 64 65 68 70 74 75 77
78 79 81 84 85 86 87 93 97 107 108 110 111 114 116 117 118 119 123 129
130 132 135 146 147 149 154 156 157 **S** Ballad Health, Johnson City, TN
Primary Contact: Lindy P. White, Vice President, Chief Executive Officer of
Kingsport Market Operations
COO: Dale M. Clark, Chief Operating Officer
CFO: Andrew R. Wampler, Vice President, Operational Excellence
CMO: Herbert D. Ladley, M.D., Chief Medical Officer
CIO: Randy F. Hart, Manager, Information Technology Regional Operations
CHR: Rowena L. Lyons, Human Resource Manager
CNO: Stephanie L. Rhoton, Director, Patient Care Services
Web address: www.balladhealth.org
**Control**: Other not–for–profit (including NFP Corporation) **Service**: General
medical and surgical

**Staffed Beds:** 117 **Admissions:** 4241 **Census:** 47 **Outpatient
Visits:** 130427 **Births:** 809 **Total Expense ($000):** 100937 **Payroll Expense
($000):** 27678 **Personnel:** 2201

**INDIAN PATH MEDICAL CENTER** See Indian Path Community Hospital

**WELLMONT HOLSTON VALLEY MEDICAL CENTER** See Holston Valley Medical
Center

## KNOXVILLE—Knox County

☐ **EAST TENNESSEE CHILDREN'S HOSPITAL (443303)**, 2018 Clinch Avenue,
Zip 37916–2393, Mailing Address: P.O. Box 15010, Zip 37901–5010;
tel. 865/541–8000, (Nonreporting) **A**1 3 5 10
Primary Contact: Matthew Schaefer, President and Chief Executive Officer
COO: Steven Godbold, Vice President Operations and Chief Operating Officer
CFO: Caryn Hawthorne, Vice President Finance and Chief Finance Officer
CMO: Joe Childs, M.D., Vice President Medical Services
CIO: John Hanks, Director Information Systems
CHR: Sue Wilburn, Vice President Human Resources and Organizational
Development
CNO: Hella Ewing, Vice President Patient Care Services and Chief Nursing Officer
Web address: www.etch.com
**Control**: Other not–for–profit (including NFP Corporation) **Service**: Children's
general medical and surgical

**Staffed Beds:** 152

**FORT SANDERS REG MEDICAL CNTR** See Fort Sanders Regional Medical Center

☐ △ **FORT SANDERS REGIONAL MEDICAL CENTER (440125)**, 1901 West
Clinch Avenue, Zip 37916–2307; tel. 865/541–1111, (Total facility includes 24
beds in nursing home–type unit) (Nonreporting) **A**1 2 7 10 19 **F**3 11 12 13 15 17
18 20 22 24 26 28 29 30 31 34 35 39 40 44 45 46 47 49 50 51 54 55 57 58
59 60 61 64 68 70 74 75 76 78 79 80 81 82 84 85 86 87 90 91 92 93 94 96
100 101 102 107 108 110 111 114 115 116 117 118 119 120 121 123 124
126 128 129 130 132 135 143 146 147 148 149 154 156 157 **S** Covenant
Health, Knoxville, TN
Primary Contact: Keith Altshuler, President and Chief Administrative Officer
CNO: Lynda Watts, Vice President, Chief Nursing Officer
Web address: www.covenanthealth.com
**Control**: Other not–for–profit (including NFP Corporation) **Service**: General
medical and surgical

**Staffed Beds:** 389 **Admissions:** 19401 **Census:** 279 **Outpatient
Visits:** 231760 **Births:** 3147 **Total Expense ($000):** 305390 **Payroll
Expense ($000):** 101968 **Personnel:** 1596

**PARKWEST MED CTR** See Parkwest Medical Center

✠ **PARKWEST MEDICAL CENTER (440173)**, 9352 Park West Boulevard,
Zip 37923–4325, Mailing Address: P.O. Box 22993, Zip 37933–0993;
tel. 865/373–1000, (Includes PENINSULA HOSPITAL, Mailing address: 2347
Jones Bend Road, Louisville, Tennessee, Zip 37777–5213, P O Box 2000,
Zip 37777–2000, tel. 865/970–9800; Elizabeth P Clary, Vice President Behavioral
Health), (Nonreporting) **A**1 2 10 **F**3 11 12 13 15 17 18 20 22 24 26 28 29 30 31
34 35 37 38 39 40 44 45 46 48 49 50 51 57 58 59 60 61 64 68 70 74 75
76 77 78 79 80 81 82 84 85 86 87 92 93 94 96 98 99 100 101 102 103 104
107 108 110 111 115 116 117 118 119 120 121 123 126 129 130 132 135
143 146 148 153 154 156 **S** Covenant Health, Knoxville, TN
Primary Contact: Neil Heatherly, Chief Executive Officer
COO: Jason Draper, Vice President and Chief Support Officer
CFO: Scott Hamilton, Vice President and Chief Financial Officer
CHR: Stephen Wilder, Director Human Resources
CNO: Lynn Cagle, Chief Nursing Officer
Web address: www.treatedwell.com/
**Control**: Other not–for–profit (including NFP Corporation) **Service**: General
medical and surgical

**Staffed Beds:** 417 **Admissions:** 24036 **Census:** 309 **Outpatient
Visits:** 278363 **Births:** 1853 **Total Expense ($000):** 343889 **Payroll
Expense ($000):** 112394 **Personnel:** 1887

**TURKEY CREEK MEDICAL CENTER** See Tennova Turkey Creek Medical Center

**UNIV OF TN MEM HOSPITAL** See University of Tennessee Medical Center

✠ **UNIVERSITY OF TENNESSEE MEDICAL CENTER (440015)**, 1924 Alcoa Highway,
Zip 37920–6900; tel. 865/305–9000, (Nonreporting) **A**1 2 3 5 8 10 19 **F**3 6 8 9 11
12 13 15 17 18 20 22 24 26 28 29 30 31 34 35 36 37 39 40 41 43 44 45 46 47
48 49 50 51 52 53 54 55 56 57 58 59 60 61 64 65 70 71 72 74 75 76 77 78 79
81 82 84 85 86 87 88 91 92 93 94 96 97 100 102 105 107 108 109 110 111
114 115 116 117 118 119 120 121 123 124 126 129 130 131 132 135 138 141
142 144 145 146 147 148 149 150 153 154 155 156 **P**5 6
Primary Contact: Joseph Landsman, President and Chief Executive Officer
COO: David Hall, Senior Vice President and Chief Operating Officer
CFO: Thomas Fisher, Senior Vice President and Chief Financial Officer
CMO: Jerry Epps, M.D., Senior Vice President and Chief Medical Officer
CIO: Michael Saad, Vice President and Chief Information Officer
CHR: Julie Simpson, Vice President Human Resources
CNO: Janell Cecil, R.N., MSN, Senior Vice President and Chief Nursing Officer
Web address: www.utmedicalcenter.org
**Control**: Other not–for–profit (including NFP Corporation) **Service**: General
medical and surgical

**Staffed Beds:** 685 **Admissions:** 32731 **Census:** 476 **Outpatient
Visits:** 339618 **Births:** 4710 **Total Expense ($000):** 980284 **Payroll
Expense ($000):** 346628 **Personnel:** 4711

## LA FOLLETTE—Campbell County

**LAFOLLETTE MEDICAL CENTER** See Tennova Healthcare-Lafollette Medical
Center

**TN**

⊠ **TENNOVA HEALTHCARE-LAFOLLETTE MEDICAL CENTER (440033)**, 923 East Central Avenue, Zip 37766–2768, Mailing Address: P.O. Box 1301, Zip 37766–1301; tel. 423/907–1200, (Nonreporting) **A**1 10 20 **F**1 3 11 15 18 29 30 34 35 40 41 45 47 48 50 51 56 64 68 70 71 78 79 81 85 97 98 100 103 107 110 111 119 120 121 123 127 129 131 146 148 154 **P**5 **S** Community Health Systems, Inc., Franklin, TN
Primary Contact: Mark Cain, Chief Executive Officer
COO: Sara Heatherly-Lloyd, Chief Operating Officer
CFO: Michael Cherry, Chief Financial Officer
CMO: George O'Neal Vinsant, M.D., Chief Medical Officer
CIO: Dillon Ward, Management Information Systems Specialist
CHR: Bess Stout, Director Human Resources
CNO: Kathy R Myers, MS, R.N., Chief Nursing Officer
Web address: www.tennova.com
**Control:** Corporation, Investor–owned (for–profit) **Service:** General medical and surgical

**Staffed Beds:** 164 **Admissions:** 1982 **Census:** 41 **Outpatient Visits:** 57346 **Births:** 0 **Total Expense ($000):** 40870 **Payroll Expense ($000):** 16127

### LAFAYETTE—Macon County

★ ⇧ **MACON COMMUNITY HOSPITAL (441305)**, 204 Medical Drive, Zip 37083–1799, Mailing Address: P.O. Box 378, Zip 37083–0378; tel. 615/666–2147, (Nonreporting) **A**10 18 21 **S** QHR Health, Brentwood, TN
Primary Contact: Thomas J. Kidd, CPA, Chief Executive Officer
CFO: Scott A. Tongate, Chief Financial Officer
Web address: www.mcgh.net
**Control:** Other not–for–profit (including NFP Corporation) **Service:** General medical and surgical

**Staffed Beds:** 25

⇧ **MACON COUNTY GENERAL HOSPITAL** See Macon Community Hospital

### LAWRENCEBURG—Lawrence County

**CROCKETT HOSPITAL** See Southern Tennessee Regional Health System-Lawrenceburg

⊠ **SOUTHERN TENNESSEE REGIONAL HEALTH SYSTEM-LAWRENCEBURG (440175)**, 1607 South Locust Avenue, Zip 38464–4011, Mailing Address: P.O. Box 847, Zip 38464–0847; tel. 931/762–6571, (Nonreporting) **A**1 10 **F**3 15 18 28 29 30 34 35 39 40 41 46 50 57 59 64 68 70 74 75 76 77 79 81 82 87 89 90 93 107 108 110 111 114 115 119 124 129 130 131 133 147 148 154 **S** LifePoint Health, Brentwood, TN
Primary Contact: Adam Martin, Chief Executive Officer
CFO: Kristie Taylor, Chief Financial Officer
CIO: Jason Weaver, Director Information Systems
CHR: Robert Augustin, Director Human Resources
CNO: Carrie Rogers, Chief Nursing Officer
Web address: www.crocketthospital.com
**Control:** Corporation, Investor–owned (for–profit) **Service:** General medical and surgical

**Staffed Beds:** 80 **Admissions:** 1892 **Census:** 19 **Outpatient Visits:** 43636 **Births:** 391 **Total Expense ($000):** 32277 **Payroll Expense ($000):** 12034 **Personnel:** 238

### LEBANON—Wilson County

**TENNOVA HEALTHCARE-LEBANON** See Vanderbilt Wilson County Hospital

**TENNOVA HEALTHCARE-LEBANON MCFARLAND CAMPUS** See Vanderbilt Wilson County Hospital-Mcfarland Hospital

⊠ **VANDERBILT WILSON COUNTY HOSPITAL (440193)**, 1411 Baddour Parkway, Zip 37087–2513; tel. 615/444–8262, (Includes VANDERBILT WILSON COUNTY HOSPITAL-MCFARLAND HOSPITAL, Mailing address: 500 Park Avenue, Lebanon, Tennessee, Zip 37087–3720; tel. 615/449–0500), (Nonreporting) **A**1 10 **F**3 8 12 13 15 18 20 28 29 30 34 35 37 40 45 54 57 59 60 64 68 70 74 76 77 78 79 81 82 84 85 90 93 96 97 98 107 108 110 111 115 118 119 126 129 130 131 132 135 141 146 148 149 154 **S** Vanderbilt Health, Nashville, TN
Primary Contact: Jay Hinesley, FACHE, Chief Executive Officer
CMO: Andrew Jordan, M.D., Chief of Staff
CIO: Adrian Fung, Director Information Systems
Web address: www.universitymedicalcenter.com
**Control:** Other not–for–profit (including NFP Corporation) **Service:** General medical and surgical

**Staffed Beds:** 137 **Admissions:** 4622 **Census:** 59 **Outpatient Visits:** 60819 **Births:** 441 **Total Expense ($000):** 78409 **Payroll Expense ($000):** 29800 **Personnel:** 590

### LENOIR CITY—Loudon County

☐ **FORT LOUDOUN MEDICAL CENTER (440110)**, 550 Fort Loudoun Medical Center Drive, Zip 37772–5673; tel. 865/271–6000, (Nonreporting) **A**1 10 **F**3 11 15 28 29 30 34 35 39 40 44 45 50 57 58 59 61 64 68 70 75 78 79 81 82 85 86 87 93 94 102 107 108 110 111 115 118 119 130 132 135 146 148 154 156 **S** Covenant Health, Knoxville, TN
Primary Contact: Jeffrey Feike, President and Chief Administrative Officer
CNO: Teresa Fisher, R.N., Chief Nursing Officer
Web address: www.covenanthealth.com
**Control:** Other not–for–profit (including NFP Corporation) **Service:** General medical and surgical

**Staffed Beds:** 30 **Admissions:** 2207 **Census:** 24 **Outpatient Visits:** 67498 **Births:** 0 **Total Expense ($000):** 32108 **Payroll Expense ($000):** 13421 **Personnel:** 222

**FORT SANDERS LOUDON MED CENTER** See Fort Loudoun Medical Center

### LEWISBURG—Marshall County

**LEWISBURG COMMUNITY HOSPITAL** See Marshall Medical Center

⊠ **MARSHALL MEDICAL CENTER (441309)**, 1080 North Ellington Parkway, Zip 37091–2227, Mailing Address: P.O. Box 1609, Zip 37091–1609; tel. 931/359–6241, (Nonreporting) **A**1 10 18 **F**3 11 15 29 30 34 40 45 50 56 57 59 68 75 77 81 85 86 92 93 102 104 107 108 110 111 114 119 129 131 132 133 135 146 149 **S** Maury Regional Health System, Columbia, TN
Primary Contact: Phyllis Brown, Chief Executive Officer
CFO: Kyle Jones, Chief Financial Officer
CMO: Tim Nash, M.D., Chief of Staff, Board Vice Chairman
CHR: Jeff M Pierce, Chief Human Resource Officer
CNO: Karen Martin, R.N., MSN, Chief Nursing Officer
Web address: www.mauryregional.com
**Control:** County, Government, Nonfederal **Service:** General medical and surgical

**Staffed Beds:** 12 **Admissions:** 139 **Census:** 1 **Outpatient Visits:** 28245 **Births:** 0 **Total Expense ($000):** 14861 **Payroll Expense ($000):** 7223 **Personnel:** 164

### LEXINGTON—Henderson County

☐ **HENDERSON COUNTY COMMUNITY HOSPITAL (440008)**, 200 West Church Street, Zip 38351–2038; tel. 731/968–3646, (Nonreporting) **A**1 10
Primary Contact: Pamela W. Roberts, Chief Executive Officer
CFO: John Bostwick, Interim Chief Financial Officer
CHR: Linda Durham, Director Human Resources
CNO: Charlene Morgan, Chief Nursing Officer
Web address: www.hendersoncchospital.com
**Control:** Corporation, Investor–owned (for–profit) **Service:** General medical and surgical

**Staffed Beds:** 45

**METHODIST HEALTHCARE-LEXINGTON** See Henderson County Community Hospital

### LINDEN—Perry County

**BAPTIST PERRY COMMUNITY HOSP** See Perry Community Hospital

**PERRY COMMUNITY HOSPITAL (440040)**, 2718 Squirrel Hollow Drive, Zip 37096–3526; tel. 931/589–2121, (Nonreporting) **A**10
Primary Contact: John B. Avery III, Administrator
Web address: www.3riverscommunityhealth.com/
**Control:** Other not–for–profit (including NFP Corporation) **Service:** General medical and surgical

**Staffed Beds:** 53

### LIVINGSTON—Overton County

**COLUMBIA LIVINGSTON REG HOSP** See Livingston Regional Hospital

⊠ **LIVINGSTON REGIONAL HOSPITAL (440187)**, 315 Oak Street, Zip 38570–1728, Mailing Address: P.O. Box 550, Zip 38570–0550; tel. 931/823–5611, (Nonreporting) **A**1 10 **S** LifePoint Health, Brentwood, TN
Primary Contact: Timothy W. McGill, Chief Executive Officer
CMO: Christopher Nahm, M.D., Chief Medical Officer
CIO: Mark Hambridge, Director Information Systems
CNO: Penny V Kirby, MSN, Chief Nursing Officer
Web address: www.MyLivingstonHospital.com
**Control:** Corporation, Investor–owned (for–profit) **Service:** General medical and surgical

**Staffed Beds:** 82

*Many Facility Codes have changed. Please refer to the AHA Guide Code Chart.*
© 2021 AHA Guide

TN

## MADISON—Davidson County

**SKYLINE MADISON CAMPUS** See Tristar Skyline Madison Campus

## MANCHESTER—Coffee County

**UNITED REGIONAL MEDICAL CENTER** See Unity Medical Center

**UNITY MEDICAL CENTER (440007)**, 1001 McArthur Drive, Zip 37355–2455, Mailing Address: P.O. Box 1079, Zip 37349–1079; tel. 931/728–3586, (Nonreporting) **A**10
Primary Contact: Martha McCormick, Chief Executive Officer
CFO: Pam Jernigan, Chief Financial Officer
CMO: James Van Winkle, M.D., Chief of Staff
CIO: Matt Burks, Director Information Technology
CHR: Sherry Holt, Director Human Resources
CNO: Stephanie Byars, Chief Nursing Officer
Web address: www.unitymedicalmanchester.com
**Control**: Corporation, Investor–owned (for–profit) **Service**: General medical and surgical

**Staffed Beds:** 36

## MARTIN—Weakley County

**BEHAVIORAL HEALTHCARE CENTER AT MARTIN** See Unity Psychiatric Care-Martin

**SPIRE CANE CREEK REHABILITATION HOSPITAL** See West Tennessee Rehabilitation Hospital Cane Creek

**TENNOVA HEALTHCARE VOLUNTEER COMMUNITY HOSPITAL** See West Tennessee Healthcare Volunteer Hospital

**UNITY PSYCHIATRIC CARE-MARTIN (444005)**, 458 Hannings Lane, Zip 38237–3308; tel. 731/588–2830, (Nonreporting) **A**10 **S** Tennessee Health Management, Parsons, TN
Primary Contact: Carrie Brawley, Administrator
Web address: www.unitypsych.com
**Control**: Partnership, Investor–owned (for–profit) **Service**: Psychiatric

**Staffed Beds:** 16

⊞ **WEST TENNESSEE HEALTHCARE VOLUNTEER HOSPITAL (440061)**, 161 Mount Pelia Road, Zip 38237–3811; tel. 731/587–4261, (Nonreporting) **A**1 10 **F**3 11 13 15 18 28 29 34 35 40 45 50 53 57 59 60 68 70 76 79 81 85 89 91 93 108 110 111 115 119 127 129 133 135 **S** West Tennessee Healthcare, Jackson, TN
Primary Contact: Donna Barfield, Interim Chief Executive Officer
CFO: Jason Draper, Chief Financial Officer
CMO: Elizabeth Lund, M.D., Chief of Staff
CHR: Tammie Bell, Director Human Resources
CNO: Donna Barfield, Chief Nursing Officer
Web address: www.wth.org/locations/west-tennessee-healthcare-volunteer-hospital
**Control**: Hospital district or authority, Government, Nonfederal **Service**: General medical and surgical

**Staffed Beds:** 38 **Admissions:** 1259 **Census:** 11 **Outpatient Visits:** 33960 **Births:** 344 **Total Expense ($000):** 28358 **Payroll Expense ($000):** 11734 **Personnel:** 194

⊞ **WEST TENNESSEE REHABILITATION HOSPITAL CANE CREEK (443030)**, 180 Mount Pelia Road, Zip 38237–3812; tel. 731/587–4231, (Nonreporting) **A**1 10 **S** Encompass Health Corporation, Birmingham, AL
Primary Contact: Rick Johnson, Chief Executive Officer
CFO: Bethany Smith, Controller
CMO: Belinda Merritt, M.D., Medical Director
CIO: Jan Trowhill, Director Health Information Management Systems
CHR: Sharon Shihady, Director Human Resources
CNO: Lindsey Rotger, Chief Nursing Officer
Web address: www.healthsouthcanecreek.com
**Control**: Corporation, Investor–owned (for–profit) **Service**: Rehabilitation

**Staffed Beds:** 40

## MARYVILLE—Blount County

⊞ **BLOUNT MEMORIAL HOSPITAL (440011)**, 907 East Lamar Alexander Parkway, Zip 37804–5016; tel. 865/983–7211, (Total facility includes 76 beds in nursing home–type unit) (Nonreporting) **A**1 2 10 19 **F**3 4 10 11 12 13 15 17 18 20 22 26 28 29 30 31 35 38 40 45 46 48 49 53 54 56 57 59 62 63 64 67 70 74 75 76 77 78 79 80 81 82 84 85 86 87 90 93 96 97 98 100 101 102 103 104 105 107 108 110 111 115 116 119 120 121 123 125 126 128 129 130 131 132 135 144 146 147 148 153 154 156
Primary Contact: Don Heinemann, Administrator and Chief Executive Officer
CFO: Jonathan Smith, Assistant Administrator and Chief Financial Officer
CMO: G Harold Naramore, M.D., Chief Medical Officer and in house Legal Counsel
CIO: Clay Puckett, Assistant Administrator and Chief Information Officer
CHR: Chris Wilkes, MS, Executive Director, Human Resources
CNO: Sonya Newman, R.N., Chief Nursing Officer
Web address: www.blountmemorial.org
**Control**: County, Government, Nonfederal **Service**: General medical and surgical

**Staffed Beds:** 275 **Admissions:** 13055 **Census:** 207 **Outpatient Visits:** 373278 **Births:** 725 **Total Expense ($000):** 307377 **Payroll Expense ($000):** 151426 **Personnel:** 2185

## MC MINNVILLE—Warren County

**RIVER PARK HOSPITAL** See Saint Thomas River Park Hospital

⊞ **SAINT THOMAS RIVER PARK HOSPITAL (440151)**, 1559 Sparta Street, Zip 37110–1316; tel. 931/815–4000, (Nonreporting) **A**1 10 **S** Ascension Healthcare, Saint Louis, MO
Primary Contact: Dale Humphrey, Chief Executive Officer
CFO: Christina Patterson, Chief Financial Officer
CMO: Randal D Rampp, M.D., Chief Medical Officer
CIO: Jeff Johnson, Director Information Systems
CHR: Deeann Johnson, Director Human Resources
Web address: www.riverparkhospital.com
**Control**: Church operated, Nongovernment, not–for–profit **Service**: General medical and surgical

**Staffed Beds:** 85

## MEMPHIS—Shelby County

⊞ **BAPTIST MEMORIAL HOSPITAL - MEMPHIS (440048)**, 6019 Walnut Grove Road, Zip 38120–2173; tel. 901/226–5000, (Nonreporting) **A**1 2 8 10 **F**3 6 8 12 17 18 20 22 26 27 28 29 30 31 34 35 36 40 41 45 46 47 48 49 50 53 54 56 57 58 59 60 63 64 65 68 70 74 75 77 78 79 80 81 82 84 85 86 87 91 92 93 102 107 108 109 111 112 114 115 116 118 119 120 121 122 123 124 126 130 132 135 136 137 143 146 148 154 157 **S** Baptist Memorial Health Care Corporation, Memphis, TN
Primary Contact: Brad H. Parsons, FACHE, Chief Executive Officer
CFO: Cyndi Pittman, Chief Financial Officer
CMO: Christian C Patrick, M.D., Chief Medical Officer
CIO: Doug Reiselt, Vice President and Chief Information Officer
CHR: Jerry Barbaree, Director Human Resources
CNO: Dana Dye, R.N., Vice President
Web address: www.baptistonline.org/memphis/
**Control**: Other not–for–profit (including NFP Corporation) **Service**: General medical and surgical

**Staffed Beds:** 584 **Admissions:** 28152 **Census:** 482 **Outpatient Visits:** 136811 **Births:** 0 **Total Expense ($000):** 521840 **Payroll Expense ($000):** 167787 **Personnel:** 2756

**BAPTIST MEMORIAL HOSPITAL EAST** See Baptist Memorial Hospital - Memphis

---

TN

★ **BAPTIST MEMORIAL HOSPITAL FOR WOMEN (440222)**, 6225 Humphreys Boulevard, Zip 38120–2373; tel. 901/227–9000, (Nonreporting) **A**3 10 **F**3 7 12 13 15 19 29 30 32 34 35 38 41 45 46 47 48 49 54 55 56 57 58 59 64 65 68 70 71 72 73 74 75 76 77 78 79 81 82 85 86 87 88 89 107 108 109 110 111 114 115 119 124 126 130 132 135 146 147 148 154 **S** Baptist Memorial Health Care Corporation, Memphis, TN
Primary Contact: Kevin R. Hammeran, Chief Executive Officer and Administrator
CFO: Margaret Williams, Chief Financial Officer
CMO: Judi Carney, M.D., President Medical Staff
CIO: Melissa Nelson, Assistant Administrator
CHR: Karen Ingram, Director Human Resources
CNO: Carol Thetford, Chief Nursing Officer
Web address: www.baptistonline.org/womens/
**Control:** Other not–for–profit (including NFP Corporation) **Service:** Obstetrics and gynecology

**Staffed Beds:** 140 **Admissions:** 7016 **Census:** 47 **Outpatient Visits:** 71094 **Births:** 5785 **Total Expense ($000):** 108820 **Payroll Expense ($000):** 47613 **Personnel:** 619

⊞ **BAPTIST MEMORIAL RESTORATIVE CARE HOSPITAL (442010)**, 6019 Walnut Grove Road, Zip 38120–2113; tel. 901/226–4200, (Nonreporting) **A**1 10 **F**1 3 29 68 75 77 130 148 **P**3 **S** Baptist Memorial Health Care Corporation, Memphis, TN
Primary Contact: William Fox, Chief Executive Officer
Web address: www.baptistonline.org/restorative-care/
**Control:** Other not–for–profit (including NFP Corporation) **Service:** Acute long–term care hospital

**Staffed Beds:** 30 **Admissions:** 206 **Census:** 19 **Outpatient Visits:** 0 **Births:** 0 **Total Expense ($000):** 11948 **Payroll Expense ($000):** 4528 **Personnel:** 65

**CHARTER LAKESIDE HLTH SYSTEM** See Lakeside Behavioral Health System

□ **CRESTWYN BEHAVIORAL HEALTH (444025)**, 9485 Crestwyn Hills Cove, Zip 38125–8515; tel. 901/248–1500, (Nonreporting) **A**1 3 10 **F**5 98 102 103 104 105 152 153 154 **S** Acadia Healthcare Company, Inc., Franklin, TN
Primary Contact: Debby Willis, Chief Executive Officer
Web address: www.crestwynbh.com
**Control:** Corporation, Investor–owned (for–profit) **Service:** Psychiatric

**Staffed Beds:** 80 **Admissions:** 290 **Census:** 8 **Outpatient Visits:** 0 **Births:** 0

**DELTA MEDICAL CENTER** See Delta Specialty Hospital

□ **DELTA SPECIALTY HOSPITAL (440159)**, 3000 Getwell Road, Zip 38118–2299; tel. 901/369–8100, (Nonreporting) **A**1 10 **S** Acadia Healthcare Company, Inc., Franklin, TN
Primary Contact: Andre Cromwell, Chief Executive Officer
CFO: Mike Reynolds, Chief Financial Officer
CMO: David Richardson, M.D., Chief of Staff
CIO: Patrick Duffee, Director Medical Information Systems
CHR: Karyn Erickson, Director Human Resources
CNO: Donna Lanier, R.N., Chief Nursing Officer
Web address: www.deltaspecialtyhospital.com
**Control:** Corporation, Investor–owned (for–profit) **Service:** General medical and surgical

**Staffed Beds:** 167

⊞ **ENCOMPASS HEALTH REHABILITATION HOSPITAL OF MEMPHIS (443029)**, 1282 Union Avenue, Zip 38104–3414; tel. 901/722–2000, (Nonreporting) **A**1 3 10 **S** Encompass Health Corporation, Birmingham, AL
Primary Contact: Toni Wackerfuss, Chief Executive Officer
CFO: Eric Gray, Chief Financial Officer
CMO: Jonathan D Ellen, M.D., Medical Director
CHR: Sandra Milburn, Director Human Resources
CNO: Jennifer Ferrell, Chief Nursing Officer
Web address: www.healthsouthmemphis.com
**Control:** Partnership, Investor–owned (for–profit) **Service:** Rehabilitation

**Staffed Beds:** 72

⊞ **ENCOMPASS HEALTH REHABILITATION HOSPITAL OF NORTH MEMPHIS (443031)**, 4100 Austin Peay Highway, Zip 38128–2502; tel. 901/213–5400, (Nonreporting) **A**1 10 **S** Encompass Health Corporation, Birmingham, AL
Primary Contact: Adam Yoe, Chief Executive Officer
CFO: Thaddeus Williams, Controller
CMO: Donald Sullivan, M.D., Medical Director
CHR: Adrienne Huntley, Director Human Resources
CNO: Charlotte Boyce, Chief Nursing Officer
Web address: www.healthsouthnorthmemphis.com
**Control:** Corporation, Investor–owned (for–profit) **Service:** Rehabilitation

**Staffed Beds:** 50

**ENCOMPASS HEALTH REHABILITATION HOSPITAL OF NORTH MEMPHIS-NORTH** See Encompass Health Rehabilitation Hospital of North Memphis

**HEALTHSOUTH REHABILITATION HOSPITAL OF MEMPHIS** See Encompass Health Rehabilitation Hospital of Memphis

□ **LAKESIDE BEHAVIORAL HEALTH SYSTEM (444004)**, 2911 Brunswick Road, Zip 38133–4199; tel. 901/377–4700, (Nonreporting) **A**1 3 5 10 **S** Universal Health Services, Inc., King of Prussia, PA
Primary Contact: Joy Golden, Chief Executive Officer
CFO: Thomas Joyner, Chief Financial Officer
CMO: C Hal Brunt, M.D., Medical Director
CIO: Jacob Arnett, Chief Information Technology Officer
CHR: Terri Starling, Director of Human Resources
CNO: Robert Edwards, Chief Nursing Officer
Web address: www.lakesidebhs.com
**Control:** Corporation, Investor–owned (for–profit) **Service:** Psychiatric

**Staffed Beds:** 345

**LE BONHEUR CHILDREN'S HOSPITAL** See Methodist Healthcare Memphis Hospitals, Memphis

**LE BONHEUR CHILDREN'S MEDICAL CENTER** See Le Bonheur Children's Hospital

□ **MEMPHIS MENTAL HEALTH INSTITUTE (444001)**, 951 Court Ave, Zip 38103–2813, Mailing Address: P.O. Box 63656, Zip 38163–3656; tel. 901/577–1800, (Nonreporting) **A**1 3 5 10
Primary Contact: Josh Carter, Chief Executive Officer
CFO: Donny Hornsby, Director Fiscal Services
CHR: Claudette Seymour, Director Personnel
Web address: www.tn.gov/mental/mhs/mhs2.html
**Control:** State, Government, Nonfederal **Service:** Psychiatric

**Staffed Beds:** 55

⊞ △ **MEMPHIS VETERANS AFFAIRS MEDICAL CENTER**, 1030 Jefferson Avenue, Zip 38104–2193; tel. 901/523–8990, (Nonreporting) **A**1 3 5 7 **S** Department of Veterans Affairs, Washington, DC
Primary Contact: David K. Dunning, Medical Center Director and Chief Executive Officer
CFO: Kristi Depperman, Chief Financial Officer
CMO: Christopher Marino, M.D., Chief of Staff
CIO: Robert Page IIIChief Information and Technology Officer
CHR: Natalie Brown, Chief Human Resources Management Services
CNO: Karen Gillette, Associate Director Patient Care Services
Web address: www.memphis.va.gov/
**Control:** Veterans Affairs, Government, federal **Service:** General medical and surgical

**Staffed Beds:** 251

**METH HEALTHCARE - SOUTH HOSP** See Methodist Healthcare-South Hospital

★ ⇑ **METHODIST HEALTHCARE MEMPHIS HOSPITALS (440049)**, 1265 Union Avenue, Zip 38104–3415; tel. 901/516–7000, (Includes LE BONHEUR CHILDREN'S HOSPITAL, Mailing address: 848 Adams Avenue, Memphis, Tennessee, Zip 38103; tel. 901/287–5437; Michael Wiggins, President; METHODIST HEALTHCARE-NORTH HOSPITAL, Mailing address: 3960 New Covington Pike, Memphis, Tennessee, Zip 38128; tel. 901/516–5200; Florence Jones, President; METHODIST HEALTHCARE-SOUTH HOSPITAL, Mailing address: 1300 Wesley Drive, Memphis, Tennessee, Zip 38116; tel. 901/516–3700; Jessie Lee Tucker III, Ph.D., Chief Executive Officer; METHODIST LE BONHEUR GERMANTOWN HOSPITAL, Mailing address: 7691 Poplar Avenue, Germantown, Tennessee, Zip 38138; tel. 901/516–6000; Rebecca Cullison, President), (Nonreporting) **A**2 3 5 8 10 21 **F**3 7 8 9 11 12 13 15 17 18 19 20 21 22 23 24 25 26 27 28 29 30 31 32 34 35 37 38 39 40 41 43 44 45 46 47 48 49 50 54 55 56 57 58 59 60 61 64 65 68 70 71 72 73 74 75 76 78 79 80 81 82 84 85 86 87 88 89 91 92 93 94 96 97 98 100 101 102 103 104 107 108 110 111 112 113 114 115 116 117 118 119 120 121 123 126 129 130 131 132 134 135 136 137 138 139 141 142 143 144 146 147 148 149 150 154 156 **P**5 6 8 **S** Methodist Le Bonheur Healthcare, Memphis, TN
Primary Contact: Michael Ugwueke Sr, President and Chief Executive Officer
CFO: Chris McLean, Chief Administrative Officer
CHR: Carol Ross-Spang, Chief Human Resources Officer
CNO: Nikki S Polis, Ph.D., Chief Nurse Executive
Web address: www.methodisthealth.org
**Control:** Other not–for–profit (including NFP Corporation) **Service:** General medical and surgical

**Staffed Beds:** 1362 **Admissions:** 63558 **Census:** 1004 **Outpatient Visits:** 1122680 **Births:** 4754 **Total Expense ($000):** 1541494 **Payroll Expense ($000):** 524983 **Personnel:** 7550

**METHODIST NORTH-J HARRIS HSP** See Methodist Healthcare-North Hospital

*Many Facility Codes have changed. Please refer to the AHA Guide Code Chart.* © 2021 AHA Guide

**TN**

⇑ **METHODIST UNIVERSITY HOSPITAL** See Methodist Healthcare Memphis Hospitals

**REGIONAL MEDICAL CENTER AT MEMPHIS** See Regional One Health

⊞ △ **REGIONAL ONE HEALTH (440152)**, 877 Jefferson Avenue, Zip 38103–2897; tel. 901/545–7100, (Total facility includes 14 beds in nursing home–type unit) (Nonreporting) **A**1 3 5 7 10 **F**1 3 8 11 13 15 16 18 20 22 29 30 35 40 43 44 45 46 48 49 50 54 57 58 59 61 64 68 70 72 74 75 76 77 79 80 81 82 85 86 87 90 92 93 96 97 100 107 108 110 111 115 119 128 130 131 132 141 146 147 148 149 150 154
Primary Contact: Reginald W. Coopwood, M.D., President and Chief Executive Officer
COO: Rob Sumter, Executive Vice President and Chief Operating Officer
CFO: Rick Wagers, Senior Executive Vice President and Chief Financial Officer
CMO: Martin Croce, M.D., Senior Vice President and Chief Medical Officer
CIO: Rob Sumter, Executive Vice President and Chief Operation Officer
CHR: Sarah Colley, Senior Vice President Human Resources
CNO: Pam Castleman, MSN, Chief Nursing Officer
Web address: www.regionalonehealth.org
**Control:** Other not–for–profit (including NFP Corporation) **Service:** General medical and surgical

**Staffed Beds:** 382 **Admissions:** 11861 **Census:** 275 **Outpatient Visits:** 244457 **Births:** 3009 **Total Expense ($000):** 512898 **Payroll Expense ($000):** 173360 **Personnel:** 3222

**REGIONAL ONE HEALTH EXTENDED CARE HOSPITAL (442017)**, 890 Madison Avenue, Turner Tower, Zip 38103–3409; tel. 901/515–3000, (Nonreporting) **A**10
Primary Contact: Mark Kelly, Administrator
CNO: Paula Harrell, Chief Nursing Officer
Web address: www.regionalonehealth.org/extended-care-hospital/
**Control:** Other not–for–profit (including NFP Corporation) **Service:** Acute long–term care hospital

**Staffed Beds:** 21

⊞ △ **SAINT FRANCIS HOSPITAL (440183)**, 5959 Park Avenue, Zip 38119–5198; tel. 901/765–1000, (Nonreporting) **A**1 3 5 7 10 **S** TENET Healthcare Corporation, Dallas, TX
Primary Contact: Sally A. Hurt-Deitch, FACHE, R.N., MSN, Chief Executive Officer
COO: Manoucheka Thermitus, Chief Operating Officer
CFO: Tina Kovacs, Chief Financial Officer
CMO: David Schwartz, M.D., Chief Medical Officer
CIO: Keith Scarbrough, Director, Information Systems
CHR: Marty Keith, Chief Human Resources Officer
CNO: Jennifer Chiusano, R.N., Chief Nursing Officer
Web address: www.saintfrancishosp.com
**Control:** Corporation, Investor–owned (for–profit) **Service:** General medical and surgical

**Staffed Beds:** 415

⊞ **SELECT SPECIALTY HOSPITAL-MEMPHIS (442014)**, 5959 Park Avenue, 12th Floor, Zip 38119–5200; tel. 901/765–1245, (Nonreporting) **A**1 10 **S** Select Medical Corporation, Mechanicsburg, PA
Primary Contact: Marcia Taylor, Chief Executive Officer
Web address: www.selectspecialtyhospitals.com/company/locations/memphis.aspx
**Control:** Corporation, Investor–owned (for–profit) **Service:** Acute long–term care hospital

**Staffed Beds:** 39

**ST FRANCIS HOSPITAL** See Saint Francis Hospital

⊞ **ST. JUDE CHILDREN'S RESEARCH HOSPITAL (443302)**, 262 Danny Thomas Place, Zip 38105–3678; tel. 901/595–3300, (Nonreporting) **A**1 3 5 10
Primary Contact: James R. Downing, M.D., Chief Executive Officer
COO: Mary Anna Quinn, Executive Vice President, Chief Administrative Officer
CFO: Abed Abdo, Chief Financial Officer
CMO: Ellis Neufeld, M.D., Chief Medical Officer
CIO: Darrin Keith Perry, Chief Information Officer and Senior Vice President
CHR: Dana Bottenfield, Vice President Human Resources
Web address: www.stjude.org
**Control:** Other not–for–profit (including NFP Corporation) **Service:** Children's other specialty

**Staffed Beds:** 68

**UNITY PSYCH CARE-MEMPHIS (444024)**, 1505 North Second Street, Zip 38107–1003; tel. 901/791–0600, (Nonreporting)
Primary Contact: Robert Edwards, Administrator
Web address: www.https://www.unitypsych.com/memphis
**Control:** Corporation, Investor–owned (for–profit) **Service:** Psychiatric

**Staffed Beds:** 16

**VETERANS AFFAIRS MEDICAL CENTER** See Memphis Veterans Affairs Medical Center

### MILAN—Gibson County

**CITY OF MILAN HOSPITAL** See Milan General Hospital

⊞ **MILAN GENERAL HOSPITAL (440060)**, 4039 Highland Street, Zip 38358–3483; tel. 731/686–1591, (Nonreporting) **A**1 10 **F**3 15 29 30 35 40 44 45 57 59 64 68 70 81 87 107 110 114 119 130 132 133 135 146 149 **S** West Tennessee Healthcare, Jackson, TN
Primary Contact: Sherry Scruggs, Administrator
CMO: Joe Appleton, M.D., Chief of Surgery
CNO: Carolyn Drake, Director of Nursing
Web address: www.wth.org
**Control:** Hospital district or authority, Government, Nonfederal **Service:** General medical and surgical

**Staffed Beds:** 28 **Admissions:** 499 **Census:** 5 **Outpatient Visits:** 14351 **Births:** 1 **Total Expense ($000):** 10651 **Payroll Expense ($000):** 4172 **Personnel:** 71

### MORRISTOWN—Hamblen County

☐ **MORRISTOWN-HAMBLEN HEALTHCARE SYSTEM (440030)**, 908 West Fourth North Street, Zip 37814–3894, Mailing Address: P.O. Box 1178, Zip 37816–1178; tel. 423/492–9000, (Nonreporting) **A**1 2 3 5 10 **F**3 11 13 15 18 20 22 26 28 29 30 31 34 35 39 40 41 44 45 46 47 49 50 51 56 57 58 59 60 61 64 68 74 75 76 78 79 80 81 82 85 86 87 93 94 96 98 101 102 103 107 108 110 111 114 115 117 118 119 120 121 123 129 130 131 132 135 146 147 148 154 156 **S** Covenant Health, Knoxville, TN
Primary Contact: Gordon Lintz, President and Chief Administrative Officer
CFO: Amy Herndon, Chief Finance Officer
CIO: Mike Ward, Chief Information Officer
CNO: Wilma Hart-Flynn, Ph.D., R.N., Chief Nursing Officer
Web address: www.morristownhamblen.com
**Control:** Other not–for–profit (including NFP Corporation) **Service:** General medical and surgical

**Staffed Beds:** 115 **Admissions:** 7255 **Census:** 85 **Outpatient Visits:** 119345 **Births:** 837 **Total Expense ($000):** 90861 **Payroll Expense ($000):** 34209 **Personnel:** 604

**MORRISTOWN-HAMBLEN HOSPITAL** See Morristown-Hamblen Healthcare System

### MOUNTAIN CITY—Johnson County

**JOHNSON COUNTY COMMUNITY HOSPITAL (441304)**, 1901 South Shady Street, Zip 37683–2271; tel. 423/727–1100, (Nonreporting) **A**5 10 18 **F**3 15 18 28 30 34 35 40 44 50 56 57 62 64 68 87 93 97 107 108 110 111 114 119 127 154 **S** Ballad Health, Johnson City, TN
Primary Contact: Chastity Trivette, Chief Executive Officer
CNO: Helen Pardue, Interim Chief Nursing Officer
Web address: www.msha.com
**Control:** Other not–for–profit (including NFP Corporation) **Service:** General medical and surgical

**Staffed Beds:** 2 **Admissions:** 29 **Census:** 1 **Outpatient Visits:** 39729 **Births:** 0 **Total Expense ($000):** 8807 **Payroll Expense ($000):** 4082 **Personnel:** 163

**JOHNSON COUNTY HEALTH CENTER** See Johnson County Community Hospital

**TN**

---

**Hospital, Medicare Provider Number, Address, Telephone, Approval, Facility, and Physician Codes, Health Care System**

★ American Hospital Association (AHA) membership
☐ The Joint Commission accreditation
○ Healthcare Facilities Accreditation Program
◇ DNV Healthcare Inc. accreditation
⇑ Center for Improvement in Healthcare Quality Accreditation
△ Commission on Accreditation of Rehabilitation Facilities (CARF) accreditation

## MOUNTAIN HOME—Washington County

⊠ **JAMES H. QUILLEN VETERANS AFFAIRS MEDICAL CENTER**, Corner of Lamont & Veterans Way, Zip 37684, Mailing Address: P.O. Box 4000, Zip 37684–4000; tel. 423/926–1171, (Nonreporting) **A**1 3 5 **S** Department of Veterans Affairs, Washington, DC
Primary Contact: Dean B. Borsos, Medical Center Director
CFO: Sandra Nash, Chief Fiscal Service
CMO: David Hecht, M.D., Chief of Staff
CIO: Karen Perry, Chief Information Resource Management Services
CHR: John Henderson, Chief Human Resources Management
CNO: Linda M McConnell, R.N., MSN, FACHE, Associate Medical Center Director Patient Care Services
Web address: www.mountainhome.va.gov/
**Control**: Veterans Affairs, Government, federal **Service**: General medical and surgical

| Staffed Beds: 98 |
|---|

**VETERANS AFFAIRS MEDICAL CTR** See James H. Quillen Veterans Affairs Medical Center

## MURFREESBORO—Rutherford County

**ALVIN C. YORK CAMPUS** See Tennessee Valley Healthcare System, Nashville

**ALVIN C. YORK VETERANS AFFAIRS MEDICAL CENTER** See Alvin C. York Campus

**MIDDLE TENNESSEE MEDICAL CENTER** See Saint Thomas Rutherford Hospital

⊠ **SAINT THOMAS RUTHERFORD HOSPITAL (440053)**, 1700 Medical Center Parkway, Zip 37129–2245; tel. 615/396–4100, (Nonreporting) **A**1 2 3 5 10 **S** Ascension Healthcare, Saint Louis, MO
Primary Contact: Gordon B. Ferguson, President and Chief Executive Officer
COO: Thomas Roddy, Chief Operating Officer
CFO: Bailey Pratt, Chief Financial Officer
CMO: Richard Rogers, M.D., Chief Medical Officer
CHR: Carol Bragdon, Director Human Resources
Web address: www.mtmc.org
**Control**: Church operated, Nongovernment, not–for–profit **Service**: General medical and surgical

| Staffed Beds: 286 |
|---|

☐ **TRUSTPOINT HOSPITAL (440231)**, 1009 North Thompson Lane, Zip 37129–4351; tel. 615/867–1111, (Nonreporting) **A**1 10 **F**3 29 34 59 64 75 77 90 98 99 100 101 103 104 130 132 135 148 149 150 153 154 **S** Acadia Healthcare Company, Inc., Franklin, TN
Primary Contact: Beth Goodner, Chief Executive Officer
Web address: www.trustpointhospital.com
**Control**: Corporation, Investor–owned (for–profit) **Service**: General medical and surgical

| Staffed Beds: 155 Admissions: 4082 Census: 110 Outpatient Visits: 16069 Births: 0 Total Expense ($000): 39648 Payroll Expense ($000): 20920 Personnel: 359 |
|---|

## NASHVILLE—Davidson County

**BAPTIST HOSPITAL** See Saint Thomas Midtown Hospital

**CENTER FOR SPINAL SURGERY** See Saint Thomas Hospital for Spinal Surgery

☐ **CURAHEALTH NASHVILLE (442006)**, 1412 County Hospital Road, Zip 37218–3007; tel. 615/687–2600, (Nonreporting) **A**1 10 **F**1 3 29 75 130 148 **S** Curahealth Hospitals, Garland, TX
Primary Contact: Matt Pearson, Chief Executive Officer
CFO: Philip L Jones, Chief Financial Officer
CMO: Clyde Heflin, M.D., Chief Medical Officer
Web address: www.curahealth.com
**Control**: Corporation, Investor–owned (for–profit) **Service**: Acute long–term care hospital

| Staffed Beds: 60 Admissions: 104 Census: 9 Outpatient Visits: 0 Births: 0 Total Expense ($000): 5017 Payroll Expense ($000): 2244 Personnel: 34 |
|---|

**KINDRED HOSPITAL–NASHVILLE** See Curahealth Nashville

**METRO NASHVILLE GEN HOSPITAL** See Nashville General Hospital

☐ **MIDDLE TENNESSEE MENTAL HEALTH INSTITUTE (444014)**, 221 Stewarts Ferry Pike, Zip 37214–3325; tel. 615/902–7535, (Nonreporting) **A**1 3 5 10 **F**3 29 30 75 98 101 103 130
Primary Contact: Rob Cotterman, Chief Executive Officer
CFO: Mark Stanley, Director Fiscal Services
CMO: Mohammad S Jahan, M.D., Clinical Director
CHR: Margie Dunn, Director Human Resources
Web address: www.tn.gov/mental/mhs/mhs2.html
**Control**: State, Government, Nonfederal **Service**: Psychiatric

| Staffed Beds: 207 Admissions: 3298 Census: 161 Outpatient Visits: 0 Births: 0 Total Expense ($000): 50906 Payroll Expense ($000): 28721 Personnel: 533 |
|---|

**MONROE CARELL JR. CHILDREN'S HOSPITAL AT VANDERBILT** See Vanderbilt University Medical Center, Nashville

☐ **NASHVILLE GENERAL HOSPITAL (440111)**, 1818 Albion Street, Zip 37208–2918; tel. 615/341–4000, (Nonreporting) **A**1 2 3 5 10
Primary Contact: Joseph Webb, Chief Executive Officer
CMO: Deann Bullock, M.D., Chief Medical Officer
CIO: Chris Whorley, Chief Information Officer
CHR: Diana Wohlfardt, Director Human Resources
CNO: Leonora Collins, Chief Nursing Officer
Web address: www.nashvillegeneral.org/
**Control**: City–county, Government, Nonfederal **Service**: General medical and surgical

| Staffed Beds: 116 |
|---|

**PSYCHIATRIC HOSPITAL AT VANDERBILT** See Vanderbilt Psychiatric Hospital

**SAINT THOMAS HOSPITAL** See Saint Thomas West Hospital

⊠ **SAINT THOMAS HOSPITAL FOR SPINAL SURGERY (440218)**, 2011 Murphy Avenue, Suite 400, Zip 37203–2065; tel. 615/341–7500, (Nonreporting) **A**1 10 **S** Ascension Healthcare, Saint Louis, MO
Primary Contact: Kathy Watson, R.N., Administrator and Chief Nursing Officer
CFO: Angie Crow, Director Finance
CMO: Carl Hampf, M.D., Chief Medical Officer
Web address: www.hospitalforspinalsurgery.com
**Control**: Partnership, Investor–owned (for–profit) **Service**: General medical and surgical

| Staffed Beds: 23 |
|---|

⊠ **SAINT THOMAS WEST HOSPITAL (440082)**, 4220 Harding Road, Zip 37205–2095, Mailing Address: P.O. Box 380, Zip 37202–0380; tel. 615/222–2111, (Includes SAINT THOMAS MIDTOWN HOSPITAL, Mailing address: 2000 Church Street, Nashville, Tennessee, Zip 37236–0002; tel. 615/284–5555; Fahad Tahir, Chief Executive Officer), (Nonreporting) **A**1 2 3 5 10 **S** Ascension Healthcare, Saint Louis, MO
Primary Contact: Fahad Tahir, Chief Executive Officer
COO: Harrison Kiser, Chief Operating Officer
CFO: Pamela Hess, Chief Financial Officer
CMO: Dale Batchelor, M.D., Chief Medical Officer
CHR: Bud Wood, Chief Human Resources Officer
CNO: Sam Straton, Chief Nursing Officer
Web address: www.stthomas.org
**Control**: Church operated, Nongovernment, not–for–profit **Service**: General medical and surgical

| Staffed Beds: 395 |
|---|

⊠ **SELECT SPECIALTY HOSPITAL–NASHVILLE (442011)**, 2000 Hayes Street, Zip 37203–2318; tel. 615/284–4599, (Nonreporting) **A**1 10 **S** Select Medical Corporation, Mechanicsburg, PA
Primary Contact: Jennifer Causey, Chief Executive Officer
CNO: Karen Cagle, Chief Nursing Officer
Web address: www.selectspecialtyhospitals.com/company/locations/nashville.aspx
**Control**: Corporation, Investor–owned (for–profit) **Service**: Acute long–term care hospital

| Staffed Beds: 70 |
|---|

**SKYLINE MEDICAL CENTER** See Tristar Skyline Medical Center

**SOUTHERN HILLS MEDICAL CENTER** See Tristar Southern Hills Medical Center

**TN**

*Many Facility Codes have changed. Please refer to the AHA Guide Code Chart.*   © 2021 AHA Guide

✠ **TENNESSEE VALLEY HEALTHCARE SYSTEM**, 1310 24th Avenue South, Zip 37212–2637; tel. 615/327–4751, (Includes ALVIN C. YORK CAMPUS, Mailing address: 3400 Lebanon Pike, Murfreesboro, Tennessee, Zip 37129–1236; tel. 615/867–6000; NASHVILLE CAMPUS, Mailing address: 1310 24th Avenue South, Nashville, Tennessee, Zip 37212–2637; tel. 615/327–4751), (Nonreporting) **A**1 3 5 **S** Department of Veterans Affairs, Washington, DC
Primary Contact: Jennifer Vedral-Baron, Health System Director
COO: Suzanne L. Jene, Chief Operating Officer
CFO: Lynn Menthcoast, Chief Fiscal Service
CMO: Roger Jones, M.D., Interim Chief of Staff
CIO: Paul Mardy, Chief Information Technology Officer
CHR: Shirley F Pettite, Chief Human Resources Officer
CNO: Janice M Cobb, R.N., Chief Nursing Officer
Web address: www.tennesseevalley.va.gov
**Control**: Veterans Affairs, Government, federal **Service**: General medical and surgical

**Staffed Beds:** 437

✠ **TRISTAR CENTENNIAL MEDICAL CENTER (440161)**, 2300 Patterson Street, Zip 37203–1528; tel. 615/342–1000, (Includes TRISTAR CENTENNIAL WOMEN'S & CHILDREN'S, Mailing address: 2221 Murphy Avenue, Nashville, Tennessee, Zip 37203; tel. 615/342–1000), (Nonreporting) **A**1 2 3 5 10 **S** HCA Healthcare, Nashville, TN
Primary Contact: Scott A. Cihak, President and Chief Executive Officer
COO: Justin Coury, Chief Operating Officer
CFO: Tom Jackson, Chief Financial Officer
CHR: Jennifer Burden, Human Resources Director
Web address: www.tristarcentennial.com
**Control**: Corporation, Investor–owned (for–profit) **Service**: General medical and surgical

**Staffed Beds:** 733

**TRISTAR CENTENNIAL MEDICAL CENTER** See Tristar Centennial Medical Center

✠ △ **TRISTAR SKYLINE MEDICAL CENTER (440006)**, 3441 Dickerson Pike, Zip 37207–2539; tel. 615/769–2000, (Includes TRISTAR SKYLINE MADISON CAMPUS, Mailing address: 500 Hospital Drive, Madison, Tennessee, Zip 37115–5032; tel. 615/769–5000; Dustin Greene, Chief Executive Officer), (Nonreporting) **A**1 2 7 10 **S** HCA Healthcare, Nashville, TN
Primary Contact: Dustin Greene, Chief Executive Officer
COO: Nick Howald, Chief Operating Officer
CFO: Michael Morrison, Chief Financial Officer
CMO: Christopher Conley, M.D., President of the Medical Staff
CIO: Troy Sypien, Director Information Technology and Systems
CHR: Robert A Hooper, Director Human Resources
CNO: Christine Staigl, Chief Nursing Officer
Web address: www.tristarskyline.com
**Control**: Corporation, Investor–owned (for–profit) **Service**: General medical and surgical

**Staffed Beds:** 407

✠ **TRISTAR SOUTHERN HILLS MEDICAL CENTER (440197)**, 391 Wallace Road, Zip 37211–4859, Mailing Address: 3441 Dickerson Pike, Zip 37207; tel. 615/781–4000, (Nonreporting) **A**1 2 10 **S** HCA Healthcare, Nashville, TN
Primary Contact: Joanna J. Conley, FACHE, Chief Executive Officer
COO: Joe White, Chief Operating Officer
CFO: John Porada, Chief Financial Officer
CMO: Eric Schuck, M.D., Chief Medical Officer
CIO: Ronnie Gannon, Director Information Services
CHR: Gary Briggs, Vice President Human Resources
Web address: www.tristarsouthernhills.com
**Control**: Corporation, Investor–owned (for–profit) **Service**: General medical and surgical

**Staffed Beds:** 126

**VANDERBILT HOSPITAL AND CLINICS** See Vanderbilt University Medical Center

**VANDERBILT PSYCHIATRIC HOSPITAL** See Vanderbilt University Medical Center, Nashville

✠ **VANDERBILT STALLWORTH REHABILITATION HOSPITAL (443028)**, 2201 Childrens Way, Zip 37212–3165; tel. 615/320–7600, (Nonreporting) **A**1 3 5 10 **F**29 68 75 77 90 96 143 148 149 **S** Encompass Health Corporation, Birmingham, AL
Primary Contact: Jeffrey Palmucci, Chief Executive Officer
CFO: Christine Campbell, Controller
CMO: Jeffery Johns, M.D., Medical Director
CHR: Ruth Beasley, Director Human Resources
CNO: Karen Lasher, Chief Nursing Officer
Web address: www.vanderbiltstallworthrehab.com
**Control**: Partnership, Investor–owned (for–profit) **Service**: Rehabilitation

**Staffed Beds:** 80 **Admissions:** 1328 **Census:** 51 **Outpatient Visits:** 0 **Births:** 0 **Total Expense ($000):** 23554 **Payroll Expense ($000):** 11002 **Personnel:** 224

✠ **VANDERBILT UNIVERSITY MEDICAL CENTER (440039)**, 1211 Medical Center Drive, Zip 37232–2102; tel. 615/322–5000, (Includes MONROE CARELL JR. CHILDREN'S HOSPITAL AT VANDERBILT, Mailing address: 2200 Children's Way, Nashville, Tennessee, Zip 37232; tel. 615/936–1000; Meg Rush, M.D., Interim President; VANDERBILT PSYCHIATRIC HOSPITAL, Mailing address: 1601 23rd Avenue South, Nashville, Tennessee, Zip 37212–3198; tel. 615/320–7770), (Nonreporting) **A**1 2 3 5 8 10 **F**3 4 5 6 7 8 9 11 12 13 15 16 17 18 19 20 21 22 23 24 25 26 27 28 29 30 31 32 34 35 36 37 38 39 40 41 43 44 45 46 47 48 49 50 51 52 53 54 55 56 57 59 60 61 62 63 64 65 66 68 70 71 72 74 75 76 77 78 79 80 81 82 83 84 85 86 87 88 89 90 91 92 93 94 96 97 98 99 100 101 102 103 104 105 107 108 109 110 111 114 115 116 117 118 119 120 121 123 124 126 129 130 131 132 134 135 136 137 138 139 140 141 142 144 146 147 148 149 150 151 152 153 154 156 157 158 **P**1 2 6 **S** Vanderbilt Health, Nashville, TN
Primary Contact: Jeffrey R. Balsar, President and Chief Executive Officer Vanderbilt Medical Center and Dean, Vanderbilt University Scho
CFO: Cecelia B Moore, CPA, Associate Vice Chancellor Finance
CMO: Paul Sternberg, M.D., Professor and Chairman
CIO: William Stead, Associate Vice Chancellor Health Affairs, Director Informatics Center and Chief Strategy and Information Officer
CHR: Traci Nordberg, Chief Human Resources Officer
CNO: Pam Jones, MSN, R.N., Associate Hospital Director and Chief Nursing Officer
Web address: www.mc.vanderbilt.edu
**Control**: Other not–for–profit (including NFP Corporation) **Service**: General medical and surgical

**Staffed Beds:** 1058 **Admissions:** 60854 **Census:** 946 **Outpatient Visits:** 2796696 **Births:** 4389 **Total Expense ($000):** 3463884 **Payroll Expense ($000):** 1248176 **Personnel:** 22037

**VETERANS ADM MEDICAL CENTER** See Nashville Campus

**VETERANS AFFAIRS TENNESSEE VALLEY HEALTHCARE SYSTEM** See Tennessee Valley Healthcare System

### NEWPORT—Cocke County

**NEWPORT MEDICAL CENTER** See Tennova Newport Medical Center

✠ **TENNOVA NEWPORT MEDICAL CENTER (440153)**, 435 Second Street, Zip 37821–3799; tel. 423/625–2200, (Nonreporting) **A**1 10 **S** Community Health Systems, Inc., Franklin, TN
Primary Contact: Matthew Littlejohn, Chief Executive Officer
CFO: Jon Richards, Chief Financial Officer
CMO: Larry Mathers, M.D., Chief of Staff
Web address: www.tennova.com
**Control**: Corporation, Investor–owned (for–profit) **Service**: General medical and surgical

**Staffed Beds:** 47

---

**Hospital, Medicare Provider Number, Address, Telephone, Approval, Facility, and Physician Codes, Health Care System**

★ American Hospital Association (AHA) membership
□ The Joint Commission accreditation
○ Healthcare Facilities Accreditation Program
◇ DNV Healthcare Inc. accreditation
î Center for Improvement in Healthcare Quality Accreditation
△ Commission on Accreditation of Rehabilitation Facilities (CARF) accreditation

**TN**

## OAK RIDGE—Anderson County

☐ **METHODIST MEDICAL CENTER OF OAK RIDGE (440034)**, 990 Oak Ridge Turnpike, Zip 37830–6976, Mailing Address: P.O. Box 2529, Zip 37831–2529; tel. 865/835–1000, (Nonreporting) **A**1 2 3 5 10 **F**3 11 13 15 17 18 20 22 24 26 28 29 30 31 34 35 37 39 40 44 45 46 49 50 51 54 57 58 59 60 61 64 68 70 74 75 76 78 79 80 81 82 84 85 86 87 92 93 94 96 102 107 108 110 111 114 115 118 119 120 121 123 126 129 130 132 135 143 146 148 154 156 **S** Covenant Health, Knoxville, TN
Primary Contact: Jeremy Biggs, President and Chief Administrative Officer
COO: Connie Martin, Vice President and Chief Support Officer
CFO: Rick Carringer, Vice President and Chief Financial Officer
CMO: Mark Browne, M.D., Covenant Health, Senior Vice President and Chief Medical Officer
CIO: Mike Ward, Covenant Health, Senior Vice President and Chief Information Officer
CHR: Rick Akens, Director Human Resources and Labor Relations
CNO: Mike P. Cavacos, MSN, Chief Nursing Officer
Web address: www.mmcoakridge.com
**Control:** Other not–for–profit (including NFP Corporation) **Service:** General medical and surgical

**Staffed Beds:** 210 **Admissions:** 10415 **Census:** 126 **Outpatient Visits:** 161903 **Births:** 457 **Total Expense ($000):** 158992 **Payroll Expense ($000):** 57465 **Personnel:** 835

**RIDGEVIEW PSYCHIATRIC HOSPITAL AND CENTER (444003)**, 240 West Tyrone Road, Zip 37830–6571; tel. 865/482–1076, (Nonreporting) **A**10
Primary Contact: Brian Buuck, Chief Executive Officer
CFO: Mary Claire Duff, CPA, Chief Financial Officer
CMO: Renu Bhateja, M.D., President Medical Staff
CHR: Julie M Wright, Director Human Resources
Web address: www.ridgeviewresources.com
**Control:** Other not–for–profit (including NFP Corporation) **Service:** Psychiatric

**Staffed Beds:** 20

## ONEIDA—Scott County

⚕ **BIG SOUTH FORK MEDICAL CENTER (440235)**, 18797 Alberta Street, Zip 37841–2127; tel. 423/286–5500, (Nonreporting) **A**10 21
Primary Contact: Hal W. Leftwich, FACHE, Chief Executive Officer
Web address: www.bsfmedical.com
**Control:** Other not–for–profit (including NFP Corporation) **Service:** General medical and surgical

**Staffed Beds:** 25

## PARIS—Henry County

☒ **HENRY COUNTY MEDICAL CENTER (440132)**, 301 Tyson Avenue, Zip 38242–4544, Mailing Address: P.O. Box 1030, Zip 38242–1030; tel. 731/642–1220, (Total facility includes 116 beds in nursing home–type unit) (Nonreporting) **A**1 10 **F**3 7 11 13 15 18 20 28 29 30 32 34 35 37 40 44 50 51 53 56 57 59 62 63 64 65 67 68 70 71 76 77 79 81 85 86 87 89 93 98 100 102 103 107 108 110 111 114 115 118 119 126 127 128 129 130 131 132 133 135 143 146 147 148 154 156 **P**6
Primary Contact: Lisa Casteel, Chief Executive Officer
CIO: Pam Ridley, Director Information Systems
CHR: Edwin L Ledden, Assistant Administrator and Director Human Resources
CNO: Cynthia Whitaker, Chief Nursing Officer
Web address: www.hcmc-tn.org
**Control:** Hospital district or authority, Government, Nonfederal **Service:** General medical and surgical

**Staffed Beds:** 202 **Admissions:** 4159 **Census:** 133 **Outpatient Visits:** 161166 **Births:** 550 **Total Expense ($000):** 95754 **Payroll Expense ($000):** 45724 **Personnel:** 659

## PIKEVILLE—Bledsoe County

⚕ **BLEDSOE COMMUNITY MEDICAL CTR** See Erlanger Bledsoe Hospital

⚕ **ERLANGER BLEDSOE HOSPITAL (441306)**, 71 Wheeler Avenue, Zip 37367, Mailing Address: P.O. Box 699, Zip 37367–0699; tel. 423/447–2112, (Nonreporting) **A**10 18 21 **F**3 11 18 29 30 34 35 38 40 42 44 50 54 56 57 58 59 61 63 64 65 66 68 74 75 77 79 82 84 86 87 102 107 108 114 119 127 130 132 133 135 146 147 148 154 156 157 **P**6 **S** Erlanger Health System, Chattanooga, TN
Primary Contact: Stephanie Boynton, Administrator
CMO: Arturo L Quito, M.D., Chief of Staff
CIO: Debbie Rains, Coordinator Health Information Management
CHR: Patsy Brown, Site Coordinator Human Resources
Web address: www.erlanger.org
**Control:** Hospital district or authority, Government, Nonfederal **Service:** General medical and surgical

**Staffed Beds:** 25 **Admissions:** 254 **Census:** 6 **Outpatient Visits:** 29235 **Births:** 0 **Total Expense ($000):** 13772 **Payroll Expense ($000):** 6335 **Personnel:** 90

## POWELL—Knox County

**NORTH KNOXVILLE MEDICAL CENTER** See Tennova North Knoxville Medical Center

☒ **SELECT SPECIALTY HOSPITAL–NORTH KNOXVILLE (442015)**, 7557B Dannaher Drive, Suite 145, Zip 37849–3568; tel. 865/512–2450, (Includes SELECT SPECIALTY HOSPITAL–KNOXVILLE, Mailing address: 1901 Clinch Avenue, 4th Floor North, Knoxville, Tennessee, Zip 37916–2307; tel. 865/541–2615; Andrew Howard, Chief Executive Officer), (Nonreporting) **A**1 10 **S** Select Medical Corporation, Mechanicsburg, PA
Primary Contact: Steve Plumlee, Chief Executive Officer
CFO: David Elledge, Controller
CMO: Jeff Summers, M.D., Medical Director
CIO: Steve Plumlee, Chief Executive Officer
CHR: Mallory Wilson, Administrative Assistant and Human Resources Coordinator
CNO: Nancy Johnson, Chief Nursing Officer
Web address: www.northknoxville.selectspecialtyhospitals.com/
**Control:** Corporation, Investor–owned (for–profit) **Service:** Acute long–term care hospital

**Staffed Beds:** 33

☒ **TENNOVA NORTH KNOXVILLE MEDICAL CENTER (440120)**, 7565 Dannaher Way, Zip 37849–4029; tel. 865/859–8000, (Includes TENNOVA TURKEY CREEK MEDICAL CENTER, Mailing address: 10820 Parkside Drive, Knoxville, Tennessee, Zip 37934–1956; tel. 865/218–7092; Ben Youree, Chief Executive Officer), (Nonreporting) **A**1 2 10 **S** Community Health Systems, Inc., Franklin, TN
Primary Contact: Clyde Wood, Chief Executive Officer
Web address: www.https://www.tennovanorthknoxville.com/
**Control:** Corporation, Investor–owned (for–profit) **Service:** General medical and surgical

**Staffed Beds:** 220

## PULASKI—Giles County

☒ **SOUTHERN TENNESSEE REGIONAL HEALTH SYSTEM–PULASKI (440020)**, 1265 East College Street, Zip 38478–4541; tel. 931/363–7531, (Nonreporting) **A**1 10 **F**3 13 15 28 29 30 34 39 40 41 44 45 50 51 56 57 59 65 68 70 74 75 76 77 79 81 82 83 84 85 87 89 91 93 98 103 107 111 114 119 129 133 146 147 148 154 **S** LifePoint Health, Brentwood, TN
Primary Contact: James H. Edmondson, Chief Executive Officer
CFO: Donald Gavin, Chief Financial Officer
CMO: J Michael Windland, M.D., Chief of Staff
CIO: Mitzi Foster, Director Information Services
CHR: Jane Petty, Director Human Resources
CNO: Sherry Sands, R.N., Chief Nursing Officer
Web address: www.southerntnpulaski.com/
**Control:** Corporation, Investor–owned (for–profit) **Service:** General medical and surgical

**Staffed Beds:** 38 **Admissions:** 1826 **Census:** 22 **Outpatient Visits:** 35996 **Births:** 149 **Total Expense ($000):** 32312 **Payroll Expense ($000):** 11942 **Personnel:** 238

**SOUTHERN TENNESSESS REGIONAL HEALTH SYSTEM–PULASKI** See Southern Tennessee Regional Health System–Pulaski

## ROCKY TOP—Anderson County

☐ **BEHAVIORAL HEALTH OF ROCKY TOP (444028)**, 210 Industrial Park Lane, Zip 37769–2301; tel. 865/630–9200, (Nonreporting) **A**1
Primary Contact: Bobby Brown, Chief Executive Officer
Web address: www.https://www.behavioralhealthofrockytop.com/
**Control:** Corporation, Investor–owned (for–profit) **Service:** Psychiatric

**Staffed Beds:** 18

## ROGERSVILLE—Hawkins County

☒ **HAWKINS COUNTY MEMORIAL HOSPITAL (440032)**, 851 Locust Street, Zip 37857–2407, Mailing Address: P.O. Box 130, Zip 37857–0130; tel. 423/921–7000, (Nonreporting) **A**1 5 10 **F**3 15 29 30 34 40 45 50 57 59 64 70 75 80 81 82 85 87 93 107 108 114 119 129 130 133 135 146 154 **S** Ballad Health, Johnson City, TN
Primary Contact: Regina Day, Chief Executive Officer
CFO: Dale Poe, Vice President and Chief Financial Officer
CHR: Robin Poteete, Manager Human Resources
Web address: www.wellmont.org
**Control:** Other not–for–profit (including NFP Corporation) **Service:** General medical and surgical

**Staffed Beds:** 16 **Admissions:** 818 **Census:** 8 **Outpatient Visits:** 43440 **Births:** 0 **Total Expense ($000):** 18106 **Payroll Expense ($000):** 6267 **Personnel:** 130

**WELLMONT HAWKINS COUNTY MEMORIAL HOSPITAL** See Hawkins County Memorial Hospital

*Many Facility Codes have changed. Please refer to the AHA Guide Code Chart.*
© 2021 AHA Guide

TN

## SAVANNAH—Hardin County

⇧ **HARDIN COUNTY GENERAL HOSPITAL** See Hardin Medical Center

★ ⇧ **HARDIN MEDICAL CENTER (440109)**, 935 Wayne Road, Zip 38372–1904;
tel. 731/926–8000, (Total facility includes 73 beds in nursing home–type unit)
(Nonreporting) **A**10 21 **F**2 3 7 11 13 15 18 19 28 29 31 34 40 45 57 59 62 65
68 69 75 76 77 78 79 80 81 89 93 107 110 111 115 119 124 128 129 130
133 144 148 **P**6
Primary Contact: Nicholas P. Lewis, Chief Executive Officer
CFO: Leigh Ann Hughes, Chief Financial Officer
CMO: Gilbert M. Thayer, M.D., Chief Medical Staff
CIO: Jacob Bomar, Director Information Technology
CNO: Jesse Wint, Director of Nursing
Web address: www.hardinmedicalcenter.org
**Control:** County, Government, Nonfederal **Service:** General medical and surgical

**Staffed Beds:** 122 **Admissions:** 1471 **Census:** 73 **Outpatient Visits:** 64714
**Births:** 289 **Total Expense ($000):** 39520 **Payroll Expense ($000):** 17027
**Personnel:** 392

## SEVIERVILLE—Sevier County

**FORT SANDERS-SEVIER MEDICAL CENTER** See Leconte Medical Center

☐ **LECONTE MEDICAL CENTER (440081)**, 742 Middle Creek Road,
Zip 37862–5019, Mailing Address: P.O. Box 8005, Zip 37864–8005;
tel. 865/446–7000, (Total facility includes 51 beds in nursing home–type unit)
(Nonreporting) **A**1 5 10 **F**3 11 13 15 18 20 28 29 30 31 34 35 39 40 44 45
46 50 51 53 57 58 59 61 64 67 68 70 74 75 76 77 78 79 80 81 82 85 86
87 93 94 96 102 107 108 110 111 114 115 116 117 118 119 120 121 123
128 130 131 132 133 135 143 146 147 148 149 154 156 **S** Covenant Health,
Knoxville, TN
Primary Contact: Gaye Jolly, FACHE, President and Chief Administrative Officer
COO: Michael Hatmaker, Vice President Support Services and Admin Nursing Home
CFO: Jacqueline Hounshell, Chief Financial Officer
CMO: William Clifford Cole, M.D., Chief of Staff
CHR: Tami McClain, Human Resources Operations Specialist
Web address: www.lecontemedicalcenter.com
**Control:** Other not–for–profit (including NFP Corporation) **Service:** General
medical and surgical

**Staffed Beds:** 128 **Admissions:** 4799 **Census:** 74 **Outpatient
Visits:** 138129 **Births:** 1088 **Total Expense ($000):** 99736 **Payroll Expense
($000):** 30295 **Personnel:** 469

## SEWANEE—Franklin County

**EMERALD-HODGSON HOSPITAL** See Southern Tennessee Regional Health
System-Sewanee

**SOUTHERN TENNESSEE REGIONAL HEALTH SYSTEM-SEWANEE** See
Southern Tennessee Regional Health System-Winchester, Winchester

## SHELBYVILLE—Bedford County

**HERITAGE MEDICAL CENTER** See Tennova Healthcare-Shelbyville

⊞ **TENNOVA HEALTHCARE-SHELBYVILLE (440137)**, 2835 Highway 231 North,
Zip 37160–7327; tel. 931/685–5433, (Nonreporting) **A**1 10 **S** Community Health
Systems, Inc., Franklin, TN
Primary Contact: Bill Rich, Chief Executive Officer
CFO: Tammy Cobb, Chief Financial Officer
CIO: Jonathon Willis, Director Information Services
CHR: Charisse Parker, Director Human Resources
CNO: Vickie Vaughn, Chief Nursing Officer
Web address: www.Tennova.com
**Control:** County, Government, Nonfederal **Service:** General medical and surgical

**Staffed Beds:** 49

## SMITHVILLE—Dekalb County

**DEKALB COMMUNITY HOSPITAL** See Saint Thomas Dekalb Hospital

⊞ **SAINT THOMAS DEKALB HOSPITAL (440148)**, 520 West Main Street,
Zip 37166–1138, Mailing Address: P.O. Box 640, Zip 37166–0640;
tel. 615/215–5000, (Nonreporting) **A**1 10 **S** Ascension Healthcare, Saint
Louis, MO
Primary Contact: Bradley Mullinax, Chief Administrative Officer
CFO: Alan Sharp, Chief Financial Officer
CMO: Kimberly Collins, M.D., Chief of Staff
CNO: Emily Elrod, R.N., Chief Nursing Officer
Web address: www.dekalbcommunityhospital.com
**Control:** Church operated, Nongovernment, not-for-profit **Service:** General
medical and surgical

**Staffed Beds:** 56

## SMYRNA—Rutherford County

**STONECREST MEDICAL CENTER** See Tristar Stonecrest Medical Center

⊞ **TRISTAR STONECREST MEDICAL CENTER (440227)**, 200 StoneCrest
Boulevard, Zip 37167–6810; tel. 615/768–2000, (Nonreporting) **A**1 2 10 **S** HCA
Healthcare, Nashville, TN
Primary Contact: Louis Caputo, Chief Executive Officer
COO: Joe Gleason, Chief Operating Officer
CFO: Joseph E Bowman, Chief Financial Officer
CMO: William Mayfield, M.D., Chief of Staff
CHR: Cynthia Adams, Vice President Human Resources
CNO: Amy Cason, MSN, Chief Nursing Officer
Web address: www.stonecrestmedical.com
**Control:** Corporation, Investor–owned (for–profit) **Service:** General medical and
surgical

**Staffed Beds:** 119

## SNEEDVILLE—Hancock County

★ **HANCOCK COUNTY HOSPITAL (441313)**, 1519 Main Street, Zip 37869–3657;
tel. 423/733–5000, (Nonreporting) **A**10 18 **F**3 29 30 34 40 50 57 59 85 87 107
108 119 127 133 135 154 **S** Ballad Health, Johnson City, TN
Primary Contact: Rebecca Beck, President
COO: Eric Deaton, Executive Vice President, Chief Operating Officer and Corporate
Operating
CFO: Regina Day, Director of Finance
CIO: Martha O'Regan Chill, Interim Chief Information Officer
CHR: Denise Adams, Human Resources Generalist
CNO: Phyllis Dossett, Director of Clinical Services
Web address: www.wellmont.org/Hospitals/Hancock-County-Hospital.aspx
**Control:** Other not–for–profit (including NFP Corporation) **Service:** General
medical and surgical

**Staffed Beds:** 10 **Admissions:** 218 **Census:** 2 **Outpatient Visits:** 21268
**Births:** 0 **Total Expense ($000):** 6856 **Payroll Expense ($000):** 2467
**Personnel:** 43

**WELLMONT HANCOCK COUNTY HOSPITAL** See Hancock County Hospital

## SPARTA—White County

**HIGHLANDS MEDICAL CENTER** See Saint Thomas Highlands Hospital

⊞ **SAINT THOMAS HIGHLANDS HOSPITAL (440192)**, 401 Sewell Road,
Zip 38583–1299; tel. 931/738–9211, (Nonreporting) **A**1 10 **S** Ascension
Healthcare, Saint Louis, MO
Primary Contact: Richard Tumlin, Chief Administrative Officer
CFO: Rodney VanDonkelaar, Chief Financial Officer
CMO: Robert Knowles, M.D., Chief of Staff
CIO: Glenn Wade, Director Information Systems
CHR: Kent Frisbee, Director Human Resources
CNO: Gearline Copeland, R.N., Chief Nursing Officer
Web address: www.whitecountyhospital.com
**Control:** Church operated, Nongovernment, not-for-profit **Service:** General
medical and surgical

**Staffed Beds:** 60

## SPRINGFIELD—Robertson County

**NORTH CREST MEDICAL CENTER** See Northcrest Medical Center

---

**Hospital, Medicare Provider Number, Address, Telephone, Approval, Facility, and Physician Codes, Health Care System**

★ American Hospital Association (AHA) membership
☐ The Joint Commission accreditation
○ Healthcare Facilities Accreditation Program
◇ DNV Healthcare Inc. accreditation
⇧ Center for Improvement in Healthcare Quality Accreditation
△ Commission on Accreditation of Rehabilitation Facilities (CARF) accreditation

TN

✠ **NORTHCREST MEDICAL CENTER (440065)**, 100 North Crest Drive, Zip 37172–3961; tel. 615/384–2411, (Nonreporting) **A**1 3 10 **F**3 13 18 20 22 28 29 30 34 40 46 57 59 63 64 68 70 75 76 78 79 81 84 85 87 89 107 111 115 116 117 119 128 129 130 131 133 135 146 147 148 149 154 156
Primary Contact: Randy Davis, Chief Executive Officer
CFO: Kim Pridgen, Chief Financial Officer
CHR: Kimberly Walker, Director of Human Resources
CNO: Angie Beard, R.N., Chief Nursing Officer
Web address: www.northcrest.com
**Control:** Other not–for–profit (including NFP Corporation) **Service:** General medical and surgical

**Staffed Beds:** 72 **Admissions:** 3023 **Census:** 30 **Outpatient Visits:** 76055

### SWEETWATER—Monroe County

✠ **SWEETWATER HOSPITAL (440084)**, 304 Wright Street, Zip 37874–2823; tel. 865/213–8200, (Nonreporting) **A**1 10
Primary Contact: Scott Bowman, Administrator
CFO: Debbie Thompson, Chief Financial Officer
CMO: David Norris, Chief Medical Staff
CIO: Tony Sharp, Supervisor Information System
CHR: Lucretia Allen, Director Human Resources
CNO: Andrea Henry, Director of Nursing
Web address: www.sweetwaterhospital.org
**Control:** Other not–for–profit (including NFP Corporation) **Service:** General medical and surgical

**Staffed Beds:** 59

### TAZEWELL—Claiborne County

**CLAIBORNE COUNTY HOSPITAL** See Claiborne Medical Center

☐ **CLAIBORNE MEDICAL CENTER (440057)**, 1850 Old Knoxville Road, Zip 37879–3625; tel. 423/626–4211, (Total facility includes 72 beds in nursing home–type unit) (Nonreporting) **A**1 10 **F**7 11 15 18 28 29 34 35 39 40 44 45 50 56 57 58 59 64 67 68 70 75 81 85 86 87 93 94 101 102 107 108 115 119 128 130 131 132 135 143 146 148 154 **S** Covenant Health, Knoxville, TN
Primary Contact: Patricia P. Ketterman, R.N., President and Chief Administrative Officer
CFO: Tracee McFarland, Chief Financial Officer
CHR: Susan Stone, Director Human Resources
Web address: www.claibornehospital.org
**Control:** Other not–for–profit (including NFP Corporation) **Service:** General medical and surgical

**Staffed Beds:** 105 **Admissions:** 1333 **Census:** 92 **Outpatient Visits:** 36572
**Births:** 0 **Total Expense ($000):** 29874 **Payroll Expense ($000):** 14395
**Personnel:** 258

### TULLAHOMA—Coffee County

**HARTON REGIONAL MEDICAL CENTER** See Tennova Healthcare-Harton

✠ **TENNOVA HEALTHCARE-HARTON (440144)**, 1801 North Jackson Street, Zip 37388–8259; tel. 931/393–3000, (Nonreporting) **A**1 10 **S** Community Health Systems, Inc., Franklin, TN
Primary Contact: Richard Ellis, Chief Executive Officer
CFO: Shaun Adams, Chief Financial Officer
CMO: John D Crabtree, M.D., Chief of Staff
CIO: Donald Cooper, Director Information Systems
CHR: Lenore Blackwell, Director Human Resources
Web address: www.hartonmedicalcenter.com
**Control:** Corporation, Investor–owned (for–profit) **Service:** General medical and surgical

**Staffed Beds:** 135

### UNION CITY—Obion County

✠ **BAPTIST MEMORIAL HOSPITAL-UNION CITY (440130)**, 1201 Bishop Street, Zip 38261–5403, Mailing Address: P.O. Box 310, Zip 38281–0310; tel. 731/885–2410, (Nonreporting) **A**1 2 10 **F**11 13 15 18 20 26 28 29 30 34 35 40 45 48 50 51 53 57 59 63 64 70 75 76 78 79 81 82 84 85 86 87 89 91 93 107 108 109 110 111 115 118 119 121 124 130 132 135 146 156 **S** Baptist Memorial Health Care Corporation, Memphis, TN
Primary Contact: Barry Bondurant, Administrator and Chief Executive Officer
CFO: Mike Perryman, Chief Financial Officer
CMO: Kofi Nuako, M.D., President Medical Staff
CIO: David Mercer, Coordinator Information Systems
CHR: Nicky Thomas, Director Human Resources
CNO: Lori Brown, Chief Nursing Officer
Web address: www.baptistonline.org/union-city/
**Control:** Other not–for–profit (including NFP Corporation) **Service:** General medical and surgical

**Staffed Beds:** 63 **Admissions:** 2659 **Census:** 22 **Outpatient Visits:** 47432
**Births:** 345 **Total Expense ($000):** 43803 **Payroll Expense ($000):** 15009
**Personnel:** 258

### WAVERLY—Humphreys County

**BAPTIST THREE RIVERS HOSPITAL** See Three Rivers Hospital

**THREE RIVERS HOSPITAL (441303)**, 451 Highway 13 South, Zip 37185–2109, Mailing Address: P.O. Box 437, Zip 37185–0437; tel. 931/296–4203, (Nonreporting) **A**10 18
Primary Contact: David A. Shannon, President and Chief Executive Officer
CFO: Sandra Patrick, Chief Financial Officer
CMO: George Mathai, M.D., Chief of Staff
CIO: Joe Hildreth, Director Information Technology
CHR: Linda Rawlings, Director Human Resources and Personnel
CNO: Freda Russell, R.N., Chief Executive Officer and Chief Nursing Officer
Web address: www.threerivershealth.org
**Control:** Other not–for–profit (including NFP Corporation) **Service:** General medical and surgical

**Staffed Beds:** 25

### WAYNESBORO—Wayne County

**WAYNE COUNTY GENERAL HOSPITAL** See Wayne Medical Center

✠ **WAYNE MEDICAL CENTER (440010)**, 103 J V Mangubat Drive, Zip 38485–2440, Mailing Address: P.O. Box 580, Zip 38485–0580; tel. 931/722–5411, (Nonreporting) **A**1 10 20 **F**3 7 15 29 34 35 40 41 45 57 59 68 75 77 81 82 85 86 93 102 107 110 111 114 119 129 130 133 135 149 **S** Maury Regional Health System, Columbia, TN
Primary Contact: Tyler Taylor, Chief Executive Officer
CMO: Harish Veeramachaneni, M.D., Chief of Staff
CHR: Jeff M Pierce, Manager Human Resources
Web address: www.mauryregional.com
**Control:** County, Government, Nonfederal **Service:** General medical and surgical

**Staffed Beds:** 25 **Admissions:** 319 **Census:** 3 **Outpatient Visits:** 22798
**Births:** 0 **Total Expense ($000):** 13022 **Payroll Expense ($000):** 6385
**Personnel:** 167

### WINCHESTER—Franklin County

**SOUTHERN TENNESSEE MEDICAL CENTER** See Southern Tennessee Regional Health System-Winchester

✠ **SOUTHERN TENNESSEE REGIONAL HEALTH SYSTEM-WINCHESTER (440058)**, 185 Hospital Road, Zip 37398–2404; tel. 931/967–8200, (Includes SOUTHERN TENNESSEE REGIONAL HEALTH SYSTEM-SEWANEE, Mailing address: 1260 University Avenue, Sewanee, Tennessee, Zip 37375–2303; tel. 931/598–5691; William R Spray, Interim Chief Executive Officer), (Nonreporting) **A**1 10 **S** LifePoint Health, Brentwood, TN
Primary Contact: William R. Spray, Chief Executive Officer
COO: Clifford Wilson, Chief Operating Officer
CFO: Steve Moore, Chief Financial Officer
CIO: James Payne, Director Information Systems
CHR: Linda Tipps, Director Human Resources
CNO: Jean Ann McMurrey, R.N., MSN, Chief Nursing Officer
Web address: www.southerntennessee.com
**Control:** Corporation, Investor–owned (for–profit) **Service:** General medical and surgical

**Staffed Beds:** 190

### WOODBURY—Cannon County

✠ **SAINT THOMAS STONES RIVER HOSPITAL (440200)**, 324 Doolittle Road, Zip 37190–1139; tel. 615/563–4001, (Nonreporting) **A**1 10 **S** Ascension Healthcare, Saint Louis, MO
Primary Contact: Robert Peglow, Interim Chief Administrative Officer
CFO: Alan Sharp, Chief Financial Officer
CMO: James Spurlock, D.O., Chief of Staff
CNO: Emily Elrod, R.N., Director of Nursing
Web address: www.stonesriverhospital.com
**Control:** Church operated, Nongovernment, not–for–profit **Service:** General medical and surgical

**Staffed Beds:** 60

**STONES RIVER HOSPITAL** See Saint Thomas Stones River Hospital

**TN**

# TEXAS

## ABILENE—Taylor County

✠ **ABILENE REGIONAL MEDICAL CENTER (450558)**, 6250 US Highway 83/84, Zip 79606–5299; tel. 325/428–1000, (Nonreporting) **A**1 3 10 **F**8 11 13 15 17 18 20 22 24 26 28 29 30 31 34 35 40 41 43 45 46 49 50 53 56 57 59 64 68 70 72 75 76 77 78 79 81 85 86 87 89 91 93 107 108 110 111 114 115 118 119 126 128 130 132 135 146 147 148 149 154 **S** Community Health Systems, Inc., Franklin, TN
Primary Contact: Michael D. Murphy, FACHE, Chief Executive Officer
COO: Matthew Conrad, Chief Operating Officer
CFO: Matt Butler, Chief Financial Officer
CMO: Eric Schackmuth, M.D., EsqChief of Staff
CIO: Dennis Newquist, Director Information Systems
CHR: Ethan Shepherd, Director Human Resources
CNO: Katherine Mary Degenstein-Gartman, MSN, R.N., Chief Nursing Officer
Web address: www.abileneregional.com
**Control**: Partnership, Investor–owned (for–profit) **Service**: General medical and surgical

**Staffed Beds**: 205 **Admissions**: 5865 **Census**: 64 **Outpatient Visits**: 71036 **Births**: 883 **Total Expense ($000)**: 97598 **Payroll Expense ($000)**: 33831 **Personnel**: 631

**CONTINUE CARE HOSPITAL AT HENDRICK MEDICAL CENTER** See Continuecare Hospital at Hendrick Medical Center

★ **CONTINUECARE HOSPITAL AT HENDRICK MEDICAL CENTER (452029)**, 1900 Pine Street, Zip 79601–2432; tel. 325/670–6251, (Nonreporting) **A**10 **F**1 3 29 34 35 68 85 87 149 **S** Community Hospital Corporation, Plano, TX
Primary Contact: Holly Powell, Interim Chief Executive Officer
CFO: Lisa Young, CPA, Chief Financial Officer
CHR: Trisha Kane, Director Human Resources
CNO: Sherry Hendricksen, R.N., MSN, Chief Nursing Officer
Web address: www.continuecare.org/hendrick/
**Control**: Other not–for–profit (including NFP Corporation) **Service**: Acute long–term care hospital

**Staffed Beds**: 23 **Admissions**: 223 **Census**: 14 **Outpatient Visits**: 0 **Births**: 0 **Total Expense ($000)**: 7765 **Payroll Expense ($000)**: 3567 **Personnel**: 42

✠ **ENCOMPASS HEALTH REHABILITATION HOSPITAL OF ABILENE (673039)**, 6401 Directors Parkway, Zip 79606–5869; tel. 325/691–1600, (Nonreporting) **A**1 10 **F**3 29 57 59 74 75 77 90 96 130 143 148 149 **S** Encompass Health Corporation, Birmingham, AL
Primary Contact: Joe Roberson, Chief Executive Officer
Web address: www.reliantabilene.com
**Control**: Corporation, Investor–owned (for–profit) **Service**: Rehabilitation

**Staffed Beds**: 60 **Admissions**: 1185 **Census**: 43 **Outpatient Visits**: 0 **Births**: 0 **Total Expense ($000)**: 17860 **Payroll Expense ($000)**: 9714 **Personnel**: 154

**HEALTHSOUTH REHABILITATION HOSPITAL - ABILENE** See Encompass Health Rehabilitation Hospital of Abilene

✠ **HENDRICK HEALTH SYSTEM (450229)**, 1900 Pine Street, Zip 79601–2432; tel. 325/670–2000, (Total facility includes 20 beds in nursing home–type unit) (Nonreporting) **A**1 10 **F**3 11 12 13 14 15 17 18 20 22 24 26 28 29 30 31 34 35 39 40 42 43 44 45 46 48 49 50 51 53 54 55 56 57 58 59 60 61 62 64 68 70 72 74 75 76 77 78 79 80 81 82 84 85 86 87 88 90 91 92 93 96 97 102 107 108 110 111 114 115 118 119 120 121 123 124 126 128 129 130 131 132 143 146 147 148 149 154 **P**6 8
Primary Contact: Brad D. Holland, President and Chief Executive Officer
CFO: Jeremy Tyler Walker, Vice President and Chief Financial Officer
CIO: Duane Donaway, Director Information Technology
CHR: Susan Wade, Vice President
CNO: Susie Cassle, R.N., MSN, Vice President Nursing Services
Web address: www.ehendrick.org
**Control**: Church operated, Nongovernment, not–for–profit **Service**: General medical and surgical

**Staffed Beds**: 407 **Admissions**: 17514 **Census**: 260 **Outpatient Visits**: 349086 **Births**: 1836 **Total Expense ($000)**: 408622 **Payroll Expense ($000)**: 148733 **Personnel**: 3050

**HENDRICK MEDICAL CENTER** See Hendrick Health System

**HUMANA HOSPITAL-ABILENE** See Abilene Regional Medical Center

✠ **OCEANS BEHAVIORAL HOSPITAL ABILENE (454122)**, 4225 Woods Place, Zip 79602–7991; tel. 325/691–0030, (Nonreporting) **A**1 10 **F**29 34 35 98 99 100 101 103 104 130 132 149 153 154 **P**6 **S** Oceans Healthcare, Plano, TX
Primary Contact: Stacy Sanford, Chief Executive Officer
Web address: www.oceansabilene.com
**Control**: Corporation, Investor–owned (for–profit) **Service**: Psychiatric

**Staffed Beds**: 90 **Admissions**: 2155 **Census**: 64 **Outpatient Visits**: 27525 **Births**: 0 **Total Expense ($000)**: 15484 **Payroll Expense ($000)**: 8175 **Personnel**: 292

## ADDISON—Dallas County

⇧ **METHODIST HOSPITAL FOR SURGERY (670073)**, 17101 North Dallas Parkway, Zip 75001–7103; tel. 469/248–3900, (Nonreporting) **A**10 21 **F**3 29 37 40 64 68 70 75 81 85 93 107 111 114 119 129 146 148 149
Primary Contact: John Friesen, President and Chief Operating Officer
CFO: Kelly Hayes, Chief Financial Officer
CMO: Robert Fischer, M.D., Medical Director
CHR: Erik Leopard, Manager Human Resource
CNO: Patti Griffith, R.N., MS, Chief Nursing Officer
Web address: www.methodisthospitalforsurgery.com/
**Control**: Partnership, Investor–owned (for–profit) **Service**: Surgical

**Staffed Beds**: 32 **Admissions**: 2461 **Census**: 18 **Outpatient Visits**: 33567 **Births**: 0 **Total Expense ($000)**: 141073 **Payroll Expense ($000)**: 18075 **Personnel**: 223

## ALICE—Jim Wells County

✠ **CHRISTUS SPOHN HOSPITAL ALICE (450828)**, 2500 East Main Street, Zip 78332–4169; tel. 361/661–8000, (Nonreporting) **A**1 10 20 **F**3 13 18 20 22 24 28 29 40 43 70 76 77 78 81 93 107 111 115 127 146 **P**8 **S** CHRISTUS Health, Irving, TX
Primary Contact: Richard Morin, R.N., Interim Chief Executive Officer
CFO: Michael Guajardo, Director Finance
CMO: Jerry Liles, D.O., Chief Medical Officer
CHR: Mindy Soliz, Director Human Resources
CNO: Margot Rios, R.N., Chief Nursing Officer
Web address: www.https://www.christushealth.org/spohn/alice
**Control**: Church operated, Nongovernment, not–for–profit **Service**: General medical and surgical

**Staffed Beds**: 54 **Admissions**: 2273 **Census**: 22 **Outpatient Visits**: 64362 **Births**: 57 **Total Expense ($000)**: 43004 **Payroll Expense ($000)**: 13567 **Personnel**: 177

**CHRISTUS SPOHN HOSPITAL ALICE** See Christus Spohn Hospital Alice

## ALLEN—Collin County

✠ **PAM REHABILITATION HOSPITAL OF ALLEN (673025)**, 1001 Raintree Circle, Zip 75013–4912; tel. 972/908–2015, (Nonreporting) **A**1 10 **F**3 29 34 35 40 56 59 60 64 68 70 75 81 85 93 94 96 100 130 132 146 148 149 **S** Post Acute Medical, LLC, Enola, PA
Primary Contact: Jennifer Beuerlein, Chief Executive Officer
Web address: www.warmsprings.org
**Control**: Partnership, Investor–owned (for–profit) **Service**: Rehabilitation

**Staffed Beds**: 40 **Admissions**: 1092 **Census**: 33 **Outpatient Visits**: 3596 **Births**: 0 **Total Expense ($000)**: 16399 **Payroll Expense ($000)**: 8080 **Personnel**: 134

**POST ACUTE REHABILITATION HOSPITAL OF ALLEN** See Pam Rehabilitation Hospital of Allen

**PRESBYTERIAN HOSPITAL OF ALLEN** See Texas Health Presbyterian Hospital Allen

**TX**

---

**Hospital, Medicare Provider Number, Address, Telephone, Approval, Facility, and Physician Codes, Health Care System**

★ American Hospital Association (AHA) membership
□ The Joint Commission accreditation
○ Healthcare Facilities Accreditation Program
◇ DNV Healthcare Inc. accreditation
⇧ Center for Improvement in Healthcare Quality Accreditation
△ Commission on Accreditation of Rehabilitation Facilities (CARF) accreditation

✉ **TEXAS HEALTH PRESBYTERIAN HOSPITAL ALLEN (450840)**, 1105 Central Expressway North, Suite 140, Zip 75013–6103; tel. 972/747–1000, (Nonreporting) **A**1 10 **F**3 13 15 18 20 22 28 29 30 34 35 38 40 44 45 47 49 51 55 57 59 64 65 70 72 73 74 75 76 78 79 81 84 85 89 90 91 93 102 107 108 110 111 115 118 119 126 130 132 135 146 147 148 149 154 **P**6 **S** Texas Health Resources, Arlington, TX
Primary Contact: Jared Shelton, President
COO: Crispin P Hocate, Professional and Support Services Officer
CFO: Lisa Gildon, Group Financial Officer
CMO: Bob Schwab, M.D., Chief Medical Officer
CHR: Sharon Chisholm, Entity Human Resource Officer
Web address: www.texashealth.org
**Control**: Other not-for-profit (including NFP Corporation) **Service**: General medical and surgical

**Staffed Beds**: 52 **Admissions**: 2626 **Census**: 22 **Outpatient Visits**: 43266 **Births**: 210 **Total Expense ($000)**: 84734 **Payroll Expense ($000)**: 30102 **Personnel**: 341

### ALPINE—Brewster County

☐ **BIG BEND REGIONAL MEDICAL CENTER (451378)**, 2600 North State Highway 118, Zip 79830–2002; tel. 432/837–3447, (Nonreporting) **A**1 3 10 18 **F**3 11 13 29 34 40 43 45 50 56 57 59 64 65 68 70 75 76 77 79 81 84 93 97 107 111 115 119 127 131 132 133 135 146 147 148 149 **S** Quorum Health, Brentwood, TN
Primary Contact: Rick Flores, Interim Chief Executive Officer
CNO: Keith Ellison, Chief Nursing Officer
Web address: www.bigbendhealthcare.com
**Control**: Corporation, Investor-owned (for-profit) **Service**: General medical and surgical

**Staffed Beds**: 25 **Admissions**: 602 **Census**: 5 **Outpatient Visits**: 16888 **Births**: 161 **Total Expense ($000)**: 21585 **Payroll Expense ($000)**: 8417 **Personnel**: 142

**BREWSTER MEMORIAL HOSPITAL** See Big Bend Regional Medical Center

### ALVIN—Brazoria County

**ALVIN DIAGNOSTIC AND URGENT CARE CENTER** See Hca Houston Healthcare Clear Lake, League City

**ALVIN MEDICAL CENTER** See Alvin Diagnostic and Urgent Care Center

### AMARILLO—Potter County

✉ **AMARILLO VETERANS AFFAIRS HEALTH CARE SYSTEM**, 6010 West Amarillo Boulevard, Zip 79106–1992; tel. 806/355–9703, (Nonreporting) **A**1 2 3 5 **S** Department of Veterans Affairs, Washington, DC
Primary Contact: Zachary Sage, Interim Director
CHR: Ken Creamer, Chief Human Resource
Web address: www.amarillo.va.gov/
**Control**: Veterans Affairs, Government, federal **Service**: General medical and surgical

**Staffed Beds**: 55

⇑ **BAPTIST ST. ANTHONY HEALTH SYSTEM** See Bsa Hospital, LLC

★ ⇑ **BSA HOSPITAL, LLC (450231)**, 1600 Wallace Boulevard, Zip 79106–1799; tel. 806/212–2000, (Nonreporting) **A**2 3 5 10 21 **F**3 7 8 11 12 13 15 17 18 20 22 24 26 28 29 30 31 34 35 40 43 45 46 48 49 51 53 54 56 57 58 59 64 70 71 72 74 75 76 77 78 79 81 82 84 86 87 88 89 90 91 92 93 96 107 108 109 110 111 114 115 116 117 118 119 120 121 123 124 126 129 130 143 145 146 147 148 **S** Ardent Health Services, Nashville, TN
Primary Contact: Bob Williams, President and Chief Executive Officer
COO: Michael Cruz, Senior Vice President Operations
CFO: Lorenzo Olivarez, Senior Vice President and Chief Financial Officer
CMO: Mike Lamanteer, M.D., Senior Vice President Medical Affairs
CIO: Lewis Brown, Director Information Technology
CHR: Mona Tucker, Vice President Human Resources
CNO: Belinda D Gibson, R.N., Senior Vice President Patient Services
Web address: www.bsahs.org
**Control**: Corporation, Investor-owned (for-profit) **Service**: General medical and surgical

**Staffed Beds**: 355 **Admissions**: 21436 **Census**: 244 **Outpatient Visits**: 142764 **Births**: 1839 **Total Expense ($000)**: 350512 **Payroll Expense ($000)**: 135470 **Personnel**: 2063

**BSA-PANHANDLE SURGICAL HOSP** See Physicians Surgical Hospital - Panhandle Campus

**KINDRED HOSPITAL-AMARILLO** See Vibra Hospital of Amarillo

**KINDRED REHABILITATION HOSPITAL AMARILLO** See Vibra Rehabilitation Hospital of Amarillo

☐ **NORTHWEST TEXAS HEALTHCARE SYSTEM (450209)**, 1501 South Coulter Avenue, Zip 79106–1770, Mailing Address: P.O. Box 1110, Zip 79105–1110; tel. 806/354–1000, (Includes NORTHWEST CHILDREN'S HOSPITAL, Mailing address: 1501 South Coulter Street, Amarillo, Texas, Zip 79106–1770; tel. 806/354–1000; NORTHWEST PAVILION, Mailing address: 7201 Evans, Amarillo, Texas, Zip 79106, P O Box 1110, Zip 79105–1110, tel. 806/354–1000; Ryan Chandler, Chief Executive Officer; NORTHWEST TEXAS SURGERY CENTER, Mailing address: 3501 South Soncy Road Suite 118, Amarillo, Texas, Zip 79119–6405; tel. 806/359–7999; Ryan Chandler, Chief Executive Officer), (Nonreporting) **A**1 3 5 10 19 **F**3 4 5 8 11 12 13 15 17 18 20 22 24 26 28 29 30 31 32 35 37 38 39 40 42 43 44 45 46 49 50 54 56 57 59 60 61 64 65 66 68 70 72 74 75 76 77 78 79 81 82 84 85 86 87 88 89 90 92 93 94 96 97 98 99 100 101 102 103 104 105 107 108 110 111 115 118 119 126 129 130 132 135 144 146 147 148 152 153 154 **S** Universal Health Services, Inc., King of Prussia, PA
Primary Contact: Ryan Chandler, Chief Executive Officer
COO: John McDonald, Chief Operating Officer
CFO: Divya Matai, Chief Financial Officer
CMO: Brian Weis, M.D., Chief Medical Officer
CIO: Bach Nguyen, Director Information Systems
CHR: Samuel Lynn, Director Human Resources
Web address: www.nwtexashealthcare.com
**Control**: Corporation, Investor-owned (for-profit) **Service**: General medical and surgical

**Staffed Beds**: 431 **Admissions**: 18914 **Census**: 248 **Outpatient Visits**: 228624 **Births**: 2348 **Total Expense ($000)**: 284940 **Payroll Expense ($000)**: 100452 **Personnel**: 1789

**NORTHWEST TEXAS HOSPITAL** See Northwest Texas Healthcare System

★ ⇑ **PHYSICIANS SURGICAL HOSPITAL - QUAIL CREEK (450875)**, 6819 Plum Creek, Zip 79124–1602; tel. 806/354–6100, (Includes PHYSICIANS SURGICAL HOSPITAL - PANHANDLE CAMPUS, Mailing address: 7100 West 9th Avenue, Amarillo, Texas, Zip 79106–1704; tel. 806/212–0247; Todd Greene, Chief Executive Officer), (Nonreporting) **A**10 21 **F**3 29 30 40 64 68 79 81 82 93 130 131 154 **S** Ardent Health Services, Nashville, TN
Primary Contact: Todd Greene, Chief Executive Officer
CFO: Austin Jones, CPA, Chief Financial Officer
CMO: Robert Crabtree, M.D., Chief of Staff and Medical Director
CNO: Debbie Inman, Chief Nursing Officer
Web address: www.physurg.com
**Control**: Partnership, Investor-owned (for-profit) **Service**: Surgical

**Staffed Beds**: 40 **Admissions**: 2161 **Census**: 11 **Outpatient Visits**: 7454 **Births**: 0 **Total Expense ($000)**: 51537 **Payroll Expense ($000)**: 12937 **Personnel**: 201

**THE CHILDREN'S HOSPITAL** See Northwest Children's Hospital

**VETERANS AFFAIRS MED CENTER** See Amarillo Veterans Affairs Health Care System

✉ **VIBRA HOSPITAL OF AMARILLO (452060)**, 7501 Wallace Boulevard, Zip 79124–2150; tel. 806/467–7000, (Nonreporting) **A**1 10 **F**1 3 29 45 46 56 59 60 61 70 74 75 77 79 82 84 85 86 87 91 96 107 114 130 148 154 **S** Vibra Healthcare, Mechanicsburg, PA
Primary Contact: Eric Mueller, Chief Executive Officer and Market Chief Executive Officer
CFO: Carlene Wright, Chief Financial Officer
CMO: Pablo Rodrigues, M.D., Medical Director
CNO: Melany McCarty, R.N., Chief Clinical Officer
Web address: www.vhamarillo.com
**Control**: Corporation, Investor-owned (for-profit) **Service**: Acute long-term care hospital

**Staffed Beds**: 37 **Admissions**: 586 **Census**: 36 **Outpatient Visits**: 0 **Births**: 0 **Total Expense ($000)**: 15374 **Payroll Expense ($000)**: 7820 **Personnel**: 128

✉ △ **VIBRA REHABILITATION HOSPITAL OF AMARILLO (453096)**, 7200 West 9th Avenue, Zip 79106–1703; tel. 806/468–2900, (Nonreporting) **A**1 7 10 **F**3 28 29 34 56 57 75 77 79 82 87 90 91 96 130 132 143 148 154 **P**4 **S** Vibra Healthcare, Mechanicsburg, PA
Primary Contact: Tammie Tabor, Chief Executive Officer
Web address: www.vrhamarillo.com
**Control**: Corporation, Investor-owned (for-profit) **Service**: Rehabilitation

**Staffed Beds**: 44 **Admissions**: 633 **Census**: 20 **Outpatient Visits**: 0 **Births**: 0 **Total Expense ($000)**: 10470 **Payroll Expense ($000)**: 4730 **Personnel**: 127

**TX**

*Many Facility Codes have changed. Please refer to the AHA Guide Code Chart.* © 2021 AHA Guide

## ANAHUAC—Chambers County

★ **BAYSIDE COMMUNITY HOSPITAL (451320)**, 200 Hospital Drive, Zip 77514, Mailing Address: P.O. Box 398, Zip 77514–0398; tel. 409/267–3143, (Nonreporting) **A**10 18 **F**11 29 34 35 40 41 45 50 53 54 56 57 59 64 81 86 107 119 130 133
Primary Contact: Jay Hodges, Interim Chief Executive Officer
CFO: Peggy Hamilton, Chief Financial Officer
CMO: Anthony Capili, M.D., Chief of Staff
CNO: Christi Morris, Director of Nursing
Web address: www.chambershealth.org/html/bayside_hospital.html
**Control:** Hospital district or authority, Government, Nonfederal **Service:** General medical and surgical

**Staffed Beds:** 10 **Admissions:** 98 **Census:** 1 **Outpatient Visits:** 15320
**Births:** 0 **Total Expense ($000):** 27279 **Payroll Expense ($000):** 6376
**Personnel:** 104

**CHAMBERS COUNTY PUBLIC HOSPITAL DISTRICT NO. 1** See Bayside Community Hospital

## ANDREWS—Andrews County

⇑ **PERMIAN GENERAL HOSPITAL** See Permian Regional Medical Center

★ ⇑ **PERMIAN REGIONAL MEDICAL CENTER (450144)**, 720 Hospital Drive, Zip 79714–3617, Mailing Address: P.O. Box 2108, Zip 79714–2108; tel. 432/523–2200, (Nonreporting) **A**3 10 20 21 **F**3 11 13 15 29 34 35 36 38 40 43 44 50 53 56 57 59 62 63 64 65 68 70 75 76 77 81 82 84 85 86 87 93 97 107 108 110 111 115 119 127 129 130 131 132 133 135 145 146 148 **P**6
Primary Contact: Donny Booth, Chief Executive Officer
CFO: Sandra Cox, Controller
CIO: Dan Smart, Chief Information Management Officer
CHR: Pam McCormick, Director Human Resources
Web address: www.permianregional.com
**Control:** Hospital district or authority, Government, Nonfederal **Service:** General medical and surgical

**Staffed Beds:** 34 **Admissions:** 1159 **Census:** 5 **Outpatient Visits:** 59736
**Births:** 333 **Total Expense ($000):** 54568 **Payroll Expense ($000):** 22518
**Personnel:** 210

## ANGLETON—Brazoria County

**ANGLETON DANBURY MEDICAL CENTER** See Angleton Danbury Campus

## ANSON—Jones County

**ANSON GENERAL HOSPITAL (450078)**, 101 Avenue 'J', Zip 79501–2198; tel. 325/823–3231, (Nonreporting) **A**10 **F**11 29 40 75 77 81 93 107 127 133 **P**8
Primary Contact: Nathan Staggs, Chief Executive Officer
CIO: Lynna B Cox, Director Health Information Services
**Control:** Hospital district or authority, Government, Nonfederal **Service:** General medical and surgical

**Staffed Beds:** 13 **Admissions:** 305 **Census:** 5 **Outpatient Visits:** 6909
**Births:** 0 **Total Expense ($000):** 6047 **Payroll Expense ($000):** 3529
**Personnel:** 66

## ARLINGTON—Tarrant County

**ARLINGTON MEMORIAL HOSPITAL** See Texas Health Arlington Memorial Hospital

☐ **BAYLOR ORTHOPEDIC AND SPINE HOSPITAL AT ARLINGTON (670067)**, 707 Highlander Boulevard, Zip 76015–4319; tel. 817/583–7100, (Nonreporting) **A**1 3 10 **F**3 29 37 40 79 81 82 97 107 111 119 126
Primary Contact: Allan Beck, Chief Executive Officer
Web address: www.baylorarlington.com/
**Control:** Partnership, Investor–owned (for–profit) **Service:** Orthopedic

**Staffed Beds:** 20 **Admissions:** 1678 **Census:** 10 **Outpatient Visits:** 12122
**Births:** 0 **Total Expense ($000):** 65485 **Payroll Expense ($000):** 13528
**Personnel:** 154

**BHC MILLWOOD HOSPITAL** See Millwood Hospital

⊠ **ENCOMPASS HEALTH REHABILITATION HOSPITAL OF ARLINGTON (453040)**, 3200 Matlock Road, Zip 76015–2911; tel. 817/468–4000, (Nonreporting) **A**1 10 **F**3 29 74 75 77 79 90 91 95 96 130 148 154 **S** Encompass Health Corporation, Birmingham, AL
Primary Contact: Tyrrell Taplin, Chief Executive Officer
CFO: Kathy Dickerson, Chief Financial Officer
CMO: Todd Daniels, M.D., Medical Director
CHR: Nancy Rosiles, Director Human Resources
Web address: www.healthsoutharlington.com
**Control:** Corporation, Investor–owned (for–profit) **Service:** Rehabilitation

**Staffed Beds:** 85 **Admissions:** 1798 **Census:** 57 **Outpatient Visits:** 0
**Births:** 0 **Total Expense ($000):** 28321 **Payroll Expense ($000):** 12895
**Personnel:** 160

**HEALTHSOUTH REHABILITATION HOSPITAL OF ARLINGTON** See Encompass Health Rehabilitation Hospital of Arlington

**KINDRED HOSPITAL** See Kindred Hospital Tarrant County-Arlington

⊠ **KINDRED HOSPITAL TARRANT COUNTY-ARLINGTON (452028)**, 1000 North Cooper Street, Zip 76011–5540; tel. 817/548–3400, (Includes KINDRED HOSPITAL TARRANT COUNTY-FORT WORTH SOUTHWEST, Mailing address: 7800 Oakmont Boulevard, Fort Worth, Texas, Zip 76132–4299; tel. 817/346–0400; Susan Schaetti, Chief Executive Officer), (Nonreporting) **A**1 10 **F**1 3 29 30 40 45 49 56 57 64 70 77 80 82 93 105 130 148 **S** Kindred Healthcare, Louisville, KY
Primary Contact: Christina Richard, Chief Executive Officer
CFO: Jennifer Penland, Controller
CMO: Bernard A McGowen, M.D., Medical Director
Web address: www.kindredhospitalarl.com/
**Control:** Corporation, Investor–owned (for–profit) **Service:** Acute long–term care hospital

**Staffed Beds:** 147 **Admissions:** 1049 **Census:** 80 **Outpatient Visits:** 6491
**Births:** 0 **Total Expense ($000):** 39241 **Payroll Expense ($000):** 20011
**Personnel:** 330

**MEDICAL CENTER ARLINGTON** See Medical City Arlington

⊠ **MEDICAL CITY ARLINGTON (450675)**, 3301 Matlock Road, Zip 76015–2908; tel. 817/465–3241, (Nonreporting) **A**1 2 3 10 **F**3 11 12 13 17 18 20 22 24 26 28 29 31 34 35 39 40 41 42 43 45 47 49 50 57 59 64 70 72 74 75 76 78 79 81 84 85 86 87 90 93 96 107 108 111 114 115 118 119 126 130 131 132 135 146 147 148 149 154 **S** HCA Healthcare, Nashville, TN
Primary Contact: Keith Zimmerman, Chief Executive Officer
COO: Ben Coogan, Chief Operating Officer
CFO: Jeff Ardemagni, Chief Financial Officer
CMO: Eric Benink, M.D., Chief Medical Officer
CIO: Craig Santangelo, Director Information Services
CNO: Cathy McLaughlin, R.N., MSN, Chief Nursing Officer
Web address: www.medicalcenterarlington.com
**Control:** Partnership, Investor–owned (for–profit) **Service:** General medical and surgical

**Staffed Beds:** 351 **Admissions:** 19954 **Census:** 267 **Outpatient Visits:** 147614 **Births:** 4381 **Total Expense ($000):** 288140 **Payroll Expense ($000):** 105913 **Personnel:** 1457

☐ **MILLWOOD HOSPITAL (454012)**, 1011 North Cooper Street, Zip 76011–5517; tel. 817/261–3121, (Nonreporting) **A**1 10 **F**4 5 29 30 35 75 87 98 99 100 101 102 103 104 105 130 132 143 148 152 153 154 **S** Universal Health Services, Inc., King of Prussia, PA
Primary Contact: Brian Gill, Chief Executive Officer
CFO: Jeff Epperson, Chief Financial Officer
CMO: Robert Bennett, M.D., Medical Director
CIO: Morgan Wilson, Director Health Information Management
CHR: Yolanda Ross, Director Human Resources
CNO: Stacy Jacobs, Chief Nursing Officer
Web address: www.millwoodhospital.com
**Control:** Partnership, Investor–owned (for–profit) **Service:** Psychiatric

**Staffed Beds:** 134 **Admissions:** 4461 **Census:** 109 **Outpatient Visits:** 28389 **Births:** 0 **Total Expense ($000):** 32405 **Payroll Expense ($000):** 15494 **Personnel:** 263

☐ **PERIMETER BEHAVIORAL HOSPITAL OF ARLINGTON (454148)**, 7000 US Highway 287 South, Zip 76001; tel. 817/662–6342, (Nonreporting) **A**1 **S** Perimeter Healthcare, Alpharetta, GA
Primary Contact: Keith Morehouse, Chief Executive Officer
Web address: www.https://www.perimeterhealthcare.com/facilities/perimeter-behavioral-hospital-of-arlington/
**Control:** Corporation, Investor–owned (for–profit) **Service:** Psychiatric

**Staffed Beds:** 116

---

**Hospital, Medicare Provider Number, Address, Telephone, Approval, Facility, and Physician Codes, Health Care System**

★ American Hospital Association (AHA) membership
☐ The Joint Commission accreditation
○ Healthcare Facilities Accreditation Program
◇ DNV Healthcare Inc. accreditation
⇑ Center for Improvement in Healthcare Quality Accreditation
△ Commission on Accreditation of Rehabilitation Facilities (CARF) accreditation

**TX**

✠ **TEXAS HEALTH ARLINGTON MEMORIAL HOSPITAL (450064)**, 800 West Randol Mill Road, Zip 76012–2503; tel. 817/548–6100, (Nonreporting) **A**1 2 10 **F**3 5 11 13 15 18 28 29 30 31 34 35 37 40 43 45 46 47 48 49 51 53 54 57 59 60 64 65 66 68 70 72 74 75 76 77 78 79 80 81 85 86 87 93 98 100 101 102 103 104 105 107 108 110 111 114 115 118 119 120 123 124 126 130 131 132 135 145 146 147 148 149 152 153 156 **P**6 **S** Texas Health Resources, Arlington, TX
Primary Contact: Blake Kretz, FACHE, President
CMO: Robert N Cluck, M.D., Vice President and Medical Director
CHR: Yvonne Kyler, Director Human Resources
Web address: www.arlingtonmemorial.org
**Control:** Other not-for-profit (including NFP Corporation) **Service:** General medical and surgical

**Staffed Beds:** 234 **Admissions:** 11926 **Census:** 157 **Outpatient Visits:** 111935 **Births:** 1417 **Total Expense ($000):** 270187 **Payroll Expense ($000):** 106442 **Personnel:** 1415

☐ **TEXAS HEALTH HEART & VASCULAR HOSPITAL ARLINGTON (670071)**, 811 Wright Street, Zip 76012–4708; tel. 817/960–3500, (Nonreporting) **A**1 10 **F**3 17 18 20 22 24 26 29 30 58 64 65 68 81 85 130
Primary Contact: Sherri Leigh. Emerson, Chief Executive Officer
COO: Sherri Leigh Emerson, Chief Operating Officer
CFO: Kay Mason, Chief Financial Officer
CMO: Baron L Hamman, M.D., Chief Medical Officer
CHR: Yvonne Kyler, Director Human Resources
Web address: www.texashealthheartandvascular.org/
**Control:** Partnership, Investor-owned (for-profit) **Service:** Heart

**Staffed Beds:** 26 **Admissions:** 932 **Census:** 12 **Outpatient Visits:** 2804 **Births:** 0 **Total Expense ($000):** 48624 **Payroll Expense ($000):** 12402 **Personnel:** 160

☐ △ **TEXAS REHABILITATION HOSPITAL OF ARLINGTON (673060)**, 900 W Arbrook Blvd, Zip 76015; tel. 682/304–6000, (Nonreporting) **A**1 7 **F**3 28 29 34 35 90 95 96 130 132 135 148 149 156
Primary Contact: Teresa Huffman, Chief Executive Officer
CFO: Debbie Horn, Controller
CMO: Camelia Mitchell, M.D., Medical Director
CHR: Stanley Coleman, Director Human Resources
Web address: www.texasrehabarlington.com
**Control:** Partnership, Investor-owned (for-profit) **Service:** Rehabilitation

**Staffed Beds:** 40 **Admissions:** 975 **Census:** 32 **Outpatient Visits:** 0 **Births:** 0 **Total Expense ($000):** 14630 **Payroll Expense ($000):** 7530 **Personnel:** 141

**TX**

✠ **USMD HOSPITAL AT ARLINGTON (450872)**, 801 West Interstate 20, Zip 76017–5851; tel. 817/472–3400, (Nonreporting) **A**1 10 **F**3 12 29 34 35 36 39 40 45 46 49 50 51 57 59 64 70 74 75 78 79 81 82 85 86 87 107 108 111 114 115 119 126 132 **S** USMD Health System, Irving, TX
Primary Contact: Marcia Crim, R.N., MSN, Chief Executive Officer
CFO: Tonya Smith, Chief Financial Officer
CMO: M. Patrick Collini, M.D., President Medical Staff
CIO: Bob Rick, Vice President Information Technology
CHR: Bernardo Valle, Vice President Human Resources
CNO: Marcia Crim, R.N., MSN, Chief Nursing Officer and Chief Executive Officer
Web address: www.usmdarlington.com
**Control:** Partnership, Investor-owned (for-profit) **Service:** General medical and surgical

**Staffed Beds:** 34 **Admissions:** 1009 **Census:** 9 **Outpatient Visits:** 19244 **Births:** 0 **Total Expense ($000):** 65349 **Payroll Expense ($000):** 15613 **Personnel:** 306

### ASPERMONT—Stonewall County

**STONEWALL MEMORIAL HOSPITAL (451318)**, 821 North Broadway, Zip 79502–2029, Mailing Address: P.O. Box 'C', Zip 79502–0902; tel. 940/989–3551, (Nonreporting) **A**10 18 **F**3 29 34 35 40 41 56 57 59 64 93 97 103 107 114 119 127 133 148 **P**5
Primary Contact: Billie Carter, Chief Executive Officer
CMO: Frederic K Passmann, M.D., Chief of Staff
CNO: Jan Harris, R.N., Director of Nursing
Web address: www.smhdhealth.org/
**Control:** Hospital district or authority, Government, Nonfederal **Service:** General medical and surgical

**Staffed Beds:** 20 **Admissions:** 101 **Census:** 2 **Outpatient Visits:** 4440 **Births:** 0 **Total Expense ($000):** 10382 **Payroll Expense ($000):** 5064 **Personnel:** 54

### ATHENS—Henderson County

**EAST TEXAS MEDICAL CENTER ATHENS** See UT Health Athens

✠ **UT HEALTH ATHENS (450389)**, 2000 South Palestine Street, Zip 75751–5610; tel. 903/676–1000, (Nonreporting) **A**1 10 **F**3 11 13 15 18 29 34 40 42 43 45 49 50 57 68 70 74 75 76 78 79 81 82 85 89 107 108 110 111 114 115 118 119 130 132 145 146 148 156 **S** Ardent Health Services, Nashville, TN
Primary Contact: Scott Campbell, Chief Executive Officer
CFO: David A Travis, Chief Financial Officer
CHR: Jennifer Rummel, Director Human Resources
CNO: Kevin M Jablonski, Chief Nursing Officer
Web address: www.https://uthealthathens.com/
**Control:** Corporation, Investor-owned (for-profit) **Service:** General medical and surgical

**Staffed Beds:** 90 **Admissions:** 5282 **Census:** 48 **Outpatient Visits:** 66172 **Births:** 765 **Total Expense ($000):** 78667 **Payroll Expense ($000):** 29369 **Personnel:** 439

### ATLANTA—Cass County

**CHRISTUS ST. MICHAEL'S HEALTH SYSTEM** See Christus St. Michael Hospital-Atlanta

### AUBREY—Denton County

⇑ **BAYLOR SCOTT & WHITE EMERGENCY HOSPITAL—AUBREY** See Baylor Scott & White Emergency Hospitals—Aubrey

⇑ **BAYLOR SCOTT & WHITE EMERGENCY HOSPITALS—AUBREY (670062)**, 26791 Highway 380, Zip 76227; tel. 972/347–2525, (Includes BAYLOR EMERGENCY MEDICAL CENTER MURPHY, Mailing address: 511 FM 544, Suite 100, Plano, Texas, Zip 75094; tel. 214/294–6150; Vic Schmerbeck, Chief Executive Officer; BAYLOR EMERGENCY MEDICAL CENTERS - COLLEYVILLE, Mailing address: 5500 Colleyville Boulevard, Colleyville, Texas, Zip 76034–5835; tel. 214/294–6350; Vic Schmerbeck, Chief Executive Officer; BAYLOR EMERGENCY MEDICAL CENTERS - KELLER, Mailing address: 620 S Main Street, Suite 100, Keller, Texas, Zip 76248–4960; tel. 214/294–6100; Vic Schmerbeck, Chief Executive Officer), (Nonreporting) **A**10 21 **F**3 29 40 75 87 107 119 149 **S** Emerus, The Woodlands, TX
Primary Contact: Vic Schmerbeck, Chief Executive Officer
CMO: Amynah Kara, M.D., Chief Medical Officer
CIO: Trang Dawson, Chief Information Officer
CHR: Larry Guillory, Chief Human Resources Officer
Web address: www.bemcataubrey.com
**Control:** Corporation, Investor-owned (for-profit) **Service:** General medical and surgical

**Staffed Beds:** 40 **Admissions:** 674 **Census:** 4 **Outpatient Visits:** 42573 **Births:** 1 **Total Expense ($000):** 37685 **Payroll Expense ($000):** 10465 **Personnel:** 113

### AUSTIN—Travis County

☐ **ARISE AUSTIN MEDICAL CENTER (450871)**, 3003 Bee Caves Road, Zip 78746–5542; tel. 512/314–3800, (Nonreporting) **A**1 10 **F**3 29 40 64 68 70 75 79 81 82 85 107 111 114 119 126 149
Primary Contact: Tammy Smittle, R.N., Chief Executive Officer
CFO: Lawrence Oldham, Chief Financial Officer
CMO: Robert Wills, M.D., Chief Medical Officer
CHR: Marilyn Jennings, Director Human Resources
Web address: www.austinsurgicalhospital.com
**Control:** Corporation, Investor-owned (for-profit) **Service:** General medical and surgical

**Staffed Beds:** 19 **Admissions:** 451 **Census:** 2 **Outpatient Visits:** 3942 **Births:** 0 **Total Expense ($000):** 29534 **Payroll Expense ($000):** 5639 **Personnel:** 87

✠ **ASCENSION SETON MEDICAL CENTER AUSTIN (450056)**, 1201 West 38th Street, Zip 78705–1006; tel. 512/324–1000, (Nonreporting) **A**1 2 3 5 10 **F**3 11 12 13 15 17 18 20 22 24 26 28 29 30 31 34 35 40 43 44 45 46 49 50 51 57 58 59 60 61 64 68 70 72 74 75 76 77 78 79 80 81 82 84 85 86 87 93 107 108 110 111 114 115 118 119 120 131 132 135 145 146 147 148 149 154 **S** Ascension Healthcare, Saint Louis, MO
Primary Contact: Christann Vasquez, Regional Hospital President
COO: Tad Hatton, Vice President Chief Operating Officer
CFO: Robert Scott Herndon, Vice President Chief Financial Officer
CMO: David W Martin, M.D., Vice President Chief Medical Officer
CIO: Michael H. Minks, Chief Information Officer VI
CHR: Joe Canales, Vice President Human Resources
CNO: Elizabeth Steger, FACHE, R.N., Chief Nursing Officer
Web address: www.seton.net/locations/smc/
**Control:** Church operated, Nongovernment, not-for-profit **Service:** General medical and surgical

**Staffed Beds:** 382 **Admissions:** 18410 **Census:** 259 **Outpatient Visits:** 94716 **Births:** 5157 **Total Expense ($000):** 440145 **Payroll Expense ($000):** 107967 **Personnel:** 2031

*Many Facility Codes have changed. Please refer to the AHA Guide Code Chart.* © 2021 AHA Guide

✠ **ASCENSION SETON NORTHWEST (450867)**, 11113 Research Boulevard, Zip 78759–5236; tel. 512/324–6000, (Nonreporting) **A**1 2 3 5 10 **F**3 11 13 29 30 34 35 37 40 41 45 47 49 51 57 59 70 72 75 76 79 80 81 85 87 107 108 111 114 115 119 126 130 132 146 147 154 **S** Ascension Healthcare, Saint Louis, MO
Primary Contact: Katherine Henderson, Regional Hospital President
COO: Tony DeDominico, Chief Operating Officer
CFO: Scott Herndon, FACHE, Chief Financial Officer, Texas Market
CMO: Jason Martin, M.D., Medical Director
CIO: Michael H. Minks, Chief Information Officer
CHR: Joe Canales, Vice President, Ascension and Human Resources Officer, Texas Market
CNO: Yvonne VanDyke, R.N., MSN, Chief Nursing Officer, Texas Market
Web address: www.seton.net
**Control**: Church operated, Nongovernment, not–for–profit **Service**: General medical and surgical

**Staffed Beds**: 117 **Admissions**: 4984 **Census**: 44 **Outpatient Visits**: 50062
**Births**: 1406 **Total Expense ($000)**: 86044 **Payroll Expense ($000)**: 24274
**Personnel**: 431

✠ **ASCENSION SETON SHOAL CREEK (454029)**, 3501 Mills Avenue, Zip 78731–6391; tel. 512/324–2000, (Nonreporting) **A**1 3 5 10 **F**4 29 30 68 98 100 101 105 130 132 135 153 154 **S** Ascension Healthcare, Saint Louis, MO
Primary Contact: Christann Vasquez, Regional Hospital President
COO: William Henricks, Ph.D., Vice President and Chief Operating Officer
CFO: Robert Scott Herndon, Chief Financial Officer
CMO: Amy E. Walton, M.D., Chief Medical Officer
CIO: Michael H. Minks, Chief Information Officer
CHR: Joe Canales, Director Human Resources
Web address: www.seton.net
**Control**: Church operated, Nongovernment, not–for–profit **Service**: Psychiatric

**Staffed Beds**: 70 **Admissions**: 2177 **Census**: 38 **Outpatient Visits**: 20916
**Births**: 0 **Total Expense ($000)**: 21579 **Payroll Expense ($000)**: 9507
**Personnel**: 171

✠ **ASCENSION SETON SOUTHWEST (450865)**, 7900 F M 1826, Building 1, Zip 78737–1407; tel. 512/324–9000, (Nonreporting) **A**1 10 **F**3 11 28 29 30 40 41 45 50 57 64 68 79 81 85 87 107 111 119 126 130 131 135 146 **S** Ascension Healthcare, Saint Louis, MO
Primary Contact: Katherine Henderson, Regional Hospital President
Web address: www.seton.net
**Control**: Church operated, Nongovernment, not–for–profit **Service**: General medical and surgical

**Staffed Beds**: 11 **Admissions**: 234 **Census**: 2 **Outpatient Visits**: 25818
**Births**: 0 **Total Expense ($000)**: 24210 **Payroll Expense ($000)**: 6297
**Personnel**: 102

☐ **AUSTIN LAKES HOSPITAL (454069)**, 1025 East 32nd Street, Zip 78705–2714; tel. 512/544–5253, (Nonreporting) **A**1 10 **F**98 103 104 105 130 153 **S** Universal Health Services, Inc., King of Prussia, PA
Primary Contact: Robert J. Lerma, MS, Chief Executive Officer
CFO: Greg Wysocki, Chief Financial Officer
CMO: Shiva Lam, M.D., Executive Medical Director
CHR: Dan Smith, Director Human Resources
CNO: Barbara Powers, R.N., Chief Nursing Officer
Web address: www.austinlakeshospital.com
**Control**: Corporation, Investor–owned (for–profit) **Service**: Psychiatric

**Staffed Beds**: 58 **Admissions**: 2692 **Census**: 49 **Outpatient Visits**: 6940
**Births**: 0 **Total Expense ($000)**: 13546 **Payroll Expense ($000)**: 7407
**Personnel**: 128

☐ **AUSTIN OAKS HOSPITAL (454121)**, 1407 West Stassney Lane, Zip 78745–2947; tel. 512/440–4800, (Nonreporting) **A**1 10 **F**5 29 30 38 64 98 99 100 101 103 104 105 130 147 153 154 **S** Universal Health Services, Inc., King of Prussia, PA
Primary Contact: Steve Kelly, Chief Executive Officer
COO: Meg Haden, Chief Operating Officer
CFO: Margo Wilhelm, Chief Financial Officer
Web address: www.austinoakshospital.com
**Control**: Partnership, Investor–owned (for–profit) **Service**: Psychiatric

**Staffed Beds**: 80 **Admissions**: 2754 **Census**: 52 **Outpatient Visits**: 6576
**Births**: 0 **Total Expense ($000)**: 13520 **Payroll Expense ($000)**: 7378
**Personnel**: 159

☐ **AUSTIN STATE HOSPITAL (454084)**, 4110 Guadalupe Street, Zip 78751–4296; tel. 512/452–0381, (Nonreporting) **A**1 3 5 10 **F**29 30 39 50 56 59 65 68 75 86 98 99 101 103 106 130 132 143 146 149 154 157 **P**1 **S** Texas Department of State Health Services, Austin, TX
Primary Contact: Stacey Thompson, Superintendent
CMO: Ross Taylor, M.D., Clinical Director
CIO: Cindy Reed, Director Community Relations
Web address: www.dshs.state.tx.us/mhhospitals/austinsh/default.shtm
**Control**: State, Government, Nonfederal **Service**: Psychiatric

**Staffed Beds**: 263 **Admissions**: 850 **Census**: 243 **Outpatient Visits**: 0
**Births**: 0 **Total Expense ($000)**: 67773 **Payroll Expense ($000)**: 54588
**Personnel**: 929

**AUSTIN SURGICAL HOSPITAL** See Arise Austin Medical Center

☐ **BAYLOR SCOTT & WHITE MEDICAL CENTER - AUSTIN**, 5251 West US Highway 290, Zip 78735; tel. 512/654–2100, (Nonreporting) **S** Baylor Scott & White Health, Dallas, TX
Primary Contact: Jay Fox, Chief Executive Officer
Web address: www.https://www.bswhealth.com/locations/austin-medical-center/pages/default.aspx
**Control**: Other not–for–profit (including NFP Corporation) **Service**: General medical and surgical

**Staffed Beds**: 25

☐ **CENTRAL TEXAS REHABILITATION HOSPITAL (673027)**, 700 West 45th Street, Zip 78751–2800; tel. 512/407–2111, (Nonreporting) **A**1 3 5 10 **F**3 29 60 68 90 91 94 95 96 100 132 148 157
Primary Contact: John Wood, Chief Executive Officer
CFO: Lisa Donnely, Controller II
CMO: Christopher Garrison, M.D., Medical Director
CHR: Trena Robinson, Director, Human Resources
CNO: Lauren Brandt, Chief Clinical Officer
Web address: www.khrehabcentraltexas.com/
**Control**: Corporation, Investor–owned (for–profit) **Service**: Rehabilitation

**Staffed Beds**: 50 **Admissions**: 824 **Census**: 31 **Outpatient Visits**: 0
**Births**: 0 **Total Expense ($000)**: 8674 **Payroll Expense ($000)**: 6591
**Personnel**: 98

**CHILDREN'S HOSPITAL OF AUSTIN** See Dell Children's Medical Center of Central Texas

**COLUMBIA ST DAVID'S HOSPITAL** See St. David's Medical Center

**CORNERSTONE HOSPITAL OF AUSTIN** See Cornerstone Specialty Hospitals Austin

**CORNERSTONE HOSPITAL OF CENTRAL TEXAS** See Cross Creek Hospital

☐ **CORNERSTONE SPECIALTY HOSPITALS AUSTIN (452034)**, 4207 Burnet Road, Zip 78756–3396; tel. 512/706–1900, (Includes CORNERSTONE HOSPITAL OF AUSTIN, Mailing address: 1005 East 32nd Street, Austin, Texas, Zip 78705; tel. 512/867–5822; Edward J Sherwood, M.D., Chief Executive Officer; CORNERSTONE HOSPITAL OF ROUND ROCK, Mailing address: 4681 College Park Drive, Round Rock, Texas, Zip 78665; tel. 512/533–2525; Edward L Dyer, Chief Executive Officer), (Nonreporting) **A**10 22 **F**1 3 29 30 45 64 70 75 77 87 107 148 **S** Cornerstone Healthcare Group, Dallas, TX
Primary Contact: Curt L. Roberts, Market Chief Executive Officer
CMO: David F. Pohl, M.D., Chief of Staff
Web address: www.chghospitals.com/austin/
**Control**: Corporation, Investor–owned (for–profit) **Service**: Acute long–term care hospital

**Staffed Beds**: 86 **Admissions**: 640 **Census**: 50 **Outpatient Visits**: 1582
**Births**: 0 **Total Expense ($000)**: 26378 **Payroll Expense ($000)**: 12529
**Personnel**: 180

☐ **CROSS CREEK HOSPITAL (454133)**, 8402 Cross Park Drive, Zip 78754; tel. 512/215–3900, (Nonreporting) **A**1 **F**4 98 99 103 105 153 154 **P**5 **S** Acadia Healthcare Company, Inc., Franklin, TN
Primary Contact: Kay McKennery, Chief Executive Officer
Web address: www.cornerstonehealthcaregroup.com
**Control**: Corporation, Investor–owned (for–profit) **Service**: Psychiatric

**Staffed Beds**: 90 **Admissions**: 2889 **Census**: 59 **Outpatient Visits**: 795
**Births**: 0 **Total Expense ($000)**: 14264 **Payroll Expense ($000)**: 7132
**Personnel**: 138

**TX**

---

**Hospital, Medicare Provider Number, Address, Telephone, Approval, Facility, and Physician Codes, Health Care System**

★ American Hospital Association (AHA) membership
☐ The Joint Commission accreditation
○ Healthcare Facilities Accreditation Program
◇ DNV Healthcare Inc. accreditation
⇑ Center for Improvement in Healthcare Quality Accreditation
△ Commission on Accreditation of Rehabilitation Facilities (CARF) accreditation

✠ **DELL CHILDREN'S MEDICAL CENTER OF CENTRAL TEXAS (453310)**, 4900 Mueller Boulevard, Zip 78723–3079; tel. 512/324–0000, (Nonreporting) **A**1 2 3 5 10 **F**3 11 17 18 19 20 21 22 23 24 25 26 27 29 30 31 32 34 35 39 40 41 43 44 46 49 50 53 54 55 57 58 59 60 61 64 65 66 68 71 72 74 75 77 78 79 81 82 84 85 86 87 88 89 90 92 93 96 98 99 100 101 102 104 107 108 111 112 113 114 115 118 119 129 130 131 132 133 135 143 146 148 149 150 153 154 156 **S** Ascension Healthcare, Saint Louis, MO
Primary Contact: Debra M. Brown, Vice President Patient Care and Chief Operating Officer
CNO: Elizabeth E. Fredeboelling, Chief Nursing Officer
Web address: www.dellchildrens.net
**Control**: Church operated, Nongovernment, not–for–profit **Service**: Children's general medical and surgical

**Staffed Beds:** 240 **Admissions:** 8419 **Census:** 125 **Outpatient Visits:** 125584 **Births:** 3 **Total Expense ($000):** 490826 **Payroll Expense ($000):** 150430 **Personnel:** 2449

✠ **DELL SETON MEDICAL CENTER AT THE UNIVERSITY OF TEXAS (450124)**, 1500 Red River Street, Zip 78701; tel. 512/324–7000, (Nonreporting) **A**1 2 3 5 **S** Ascension Healthcare, Saint Louis, MO
Primary Contact: Christann Vasquez, Regional Hospital President
CFO: Scott Herndon, FACHE, Chief Financial Officer, Ministry Market Texas
CMO: Tom Caven, M.D., Vice President, Medical Director
CIO: Michael H. Minks, Chief Information Officer VI
CHR: Joe Canales, Vice President Human Resources, Ministry Market Texas
Web address: www.seton.net/locations/dell-seton/
**Control**: Church operated, Nongovernment, not–for–profit **Service**: General medical and surgical

**Staffed Beds:** 211

✠ **ENCOMPASS HEALTH REHABILITATION HOSPITAL OF AUSTIN (673054)**, 330 West Ben White Boulevard, Zip 78704; tel. 512/730–4800, (Nonreporting) **A**1 10 **F**3 29 90 91 **S** Encompass Health Corporation, Birmingham, AL
Primary Contact: Lauren Suarez, Chief Executive Officer
CFO: Pamela McLaughlin, Chief Financial Officer
CMO: Johnny Shane Ross, Executive Medical Director
Web address: www.healthsouthaustin.com
**Control**: Corporation, Investor–owned (for–profit) **Service**: Rehabilitation

**Staffed Beds:** 60 **Admissions:** 1097 **Census:** 37 **Outpatient Visits:** 0 **Births:** 0 **Total Expense ($000):** 20876 **Payroll Expense ($000):** 8874 **Personnel:** 154

**HEALTHSOUTH REHABILITATION HOSPITAL OF AUSTIN** See Encompass Health Rehabilitation Hospital of Austin

**NORTH AUSTIN MEDICAL CENTER** See St. David's North Austin Medical Center

☐ **NORTHWEST HILLS SURGICAL HOSPITAL (450808)**, 6818 Austin Center Boulevard, Suite 100, Zip 78731–3199; tel. 512/346–1994, (Nonreporting) **A**1 5 10 **F**3 18 40 45 64 74 75 79 81 157 **P**2
Primary Contact: Cullen Scott, Chief Executive Officer
CFO: Jenny Salome, Chief Financial Officer and Assistant Administrator
Web address: www.northwesthillssurgical.com
**Control**: Partnership, Investor–owned (for–profit) **Service**: General medical and surgical

**Staffed Beds:** 8 **Admissions:** 505 **Census:** 2 **Outpatient Visits:** 5303 **Births:** 0 **Total Expense ($000):** 29708 **Payroll Expense ($000):** 6875 **Personnel:** 113

**SETON MEDICAL CENTER AUSTIN** See Ascension Seton Medical Center Austin

**SETON NORTHWEST HOSPITAL** See Ascension Seton Northwest

**SETON SHOAL CREEK HOSPITAL** See Ascension Seton Shoal Creek

**SETON SOUTHWEST HEALTHCARE CENTER** See Ascension Seton Southwest

**ST DAVID'S PAVILION** See Austin Lakes Hospital

**ST DAVID'S REHAB HOSPITAL** See St. David's Rehabilitation Center

✠ **ST. DAVID'S MEDICAL CENTER (450431)**, 919 East 32nd Street, Zip 78705–2709, Mailing Address: P.O. Box 4039, Zip 78765–4039; tel. 512/476–7111, (Includes HEART HOSPITAL OF AUSTIN, Mailing address: 3801 North Lamar Boulevard, Austin, Texas, Zip 78756–4080; tel. 512/407–7000; David Laird, Chief Executive Officer; ST. DAVID'S GEORGETOWN HOSPITAL, Mailing address: 2000 Scenic Drive, Georgetown, Texas, Zip 78626–7726; tel. 512/943–3000; Hugh Brown, Chief Executive Officer; ST. DAVID'S REHABILITATION CENTER, Mailing address: 1005 East 32nd Street, Austin, Texas, Zip 78705–2713, P O Box 4270, Zip 78765–4270, tel. 512/544–5100; Diane Owens, Assistant Administrator), (Nonreporting) **A**1 2 3 5 10 **F**3 8 11 12 13 15 17 18 20 22 24 26 28 29 30 31 34 35 36 37 39 40 43 45 46 47 48 49 53 57 58 59 60 61 64 70 72 73 74 75 76 77 78 79 81 82 84 85 86 87 90 93 95 96 107 108 110 111 114 115 116 119 126 129 130 131 132 135 144 146 147 148 149 154 155 **P**3 6 **S** HCA Healthcare, Nashville, TN
Primary Contact: Todd E. Steward, FACHE, Chief Executive Officer
COO: Esther Chung, Chief Operating Officer
CFO: Daniel Huffine, Chief Financial Officer
CMO: John Marietta, M.D., Chief Medical Officer
CIO: Richard Lear, Director Information Systems
CHR: Julie Hajek, Director Human Resources
Web address: www.stdavids.com
**Control**: Other not–for–profit (including NFP Corporation) **Service**: General medical and surgical

**Staffed Beds:** 607 **Admissions:** 28342 **Census:** 406 **Outpatient Visits:** 186810 **Births:** 4551 **Total Expense ($000):** 567014 **Payroll Expense ($000):** 177778 **Personnel:** 2362

✠ **ST. DAVID'S NORTH AUSTIN MEDICAL CENTER (450809)**, 12221 North MoPac Expressway, Zip 78758–2496; tel. 512/901–1000, (Nonreporting) **A**1 2 3 10 **F**3 8 12 13 15 18 20 22 24 28 29 30 31 34 35 37 40 41 42 43 45 46 47 49 52 53 54 55 57 58 59 60 64 70 72 73 74 75 76 77 78 79 81 84 85 86 87 88 89 90 91 92 93 96 107 108 110 111 114 115 118 119 124 126 129 130 138 146 147 148 149 154 157 **P**3 6 **S** HCA Healthcare, Nashville, TN
Primary Contact: Thomas W. Jackson, Chief Executive Officer
COO: Becky Barnes, Chief Operating Officer
CFO: Natalie Pack, Chief Financial Officer
CMO: Ryan Charbeneau, M.D., Chief Medical Officer
CIO: Marshall Pearson, Director Management Information Systems
CHR: Laura Light, Director Human Resources
Web address: www.northaustin.com
**Control**: Other not–for–profit (including NFP Corporation) **Service**: General medical and surgical

**Staffed Beds:** 398 **Admissions:** 23238 **Census:** 308 **Outpatient Visits:** 169986 **Births:** 7554 **Total Expense ($000):** 350890 **Payroll Expense ($000):** 123363 **Personnel:** 1717

**ST. DAVID'S SOUTH AUSTIN HOSPITAL** See St. David's South Austin Medical Center

✠ **ST. DAVID'S SOUTH AUSTIN MEDICAL CENTER (450713)**, 901 West Ben White Boulevard, Zip 78704–6903; tel. 512/447–2211, (Nonreporting) **A**1 2 3 5 10 **F**3 11 12 18 20 22 24 26 28 29 30 31 34 35 37 40 41 42 43 45 46 49 54 56 58 59 64 70 73 74 75 76 77 78 79 80 81 82 84 85 87 93 107 108 110 111 115 119 126 129 130 136 145 146 147 148 154 **P**3 6 **S** HCA Healthcare, Nashville, TN
Primary Contact: Todd E. Steward, FACHE, Chief Executive Officer
COO: Kyle Landry, Chief Operating Officer
CFO: Wesley D Fountain, Chief Financial Officer
CMO: DeVry Anderson, Chief Medical Officer
CIO: Richard Lear, Director Information Systems
CHR: Lisa Talbot, Director Human Resources
CNO: Sally A Gillam, R.N., Chief Nursing Officer
Web address: www.southaustinmc.com
**Control**: Other not–for–profit (including NFP Corporation) **Service**: General medical and surgical

**Staffed Beds:** 325 **Admissions:** 20617 **Census:** 284 **Outpatient Visits:** 154407 **Births:** 2584 **Total Expense ($000):** 319788 **Payroll Expense ($000):** 107985 **Personnel:** 1470

**SURGICAL HOSPITAL OF AUSTIN** See Northwest Hills Surgical Hospital

**TEXAS NEURO REHAB CENTER** See Texas Neurorehab Center

*Many Facility Codes have changed. Please refer to the AHA Guide Code Chart.*
© 2021 AHA Guide

★ **TEXAS NEUROREHAB CENTER (452038)**, 1106 West Dittmar Road, Building 9, Zip 78745–6328, Mailing Address: P.O. Box 150459, Zip 78715–0459; tel. 512/444–4835, (Nonreporting) **A**10 **F**1 3 29 30 54 74 75 77 79 93 108 130 148 154 **P**5 **S** Universal Health Services, Inc., King of Prussia, PA
Primary Contact: Edgar E. Prettyman, PsyD, Chief Executive Officer
COO: Janet Bitner, Chief Operating Officer
CFO: Omar Correa, Chief Financial Officer
CMO: James Boysen, M.D., Executive Medical Director
CHR: Colleen Lewis, Director Human Resources
Web address: www.texasneurorehab.com
**Control:** Partnership, Investor–owned (for–profit) **Service:** Acute long–term care hospital

**Staffed Beds:** 47 **Admissions:** 549 **Census:** 38 **Outpatient Visits:** 8033
**Births:** 0 **Total Expense ($000):** 19339 **Payroll Expense ($000):** 11628
**Personnel:** 285

☐ **TEXAS STAR RECOVERY (454111)**, 1106 West Dittmar Road, Zip 78745–6328; tel. 512/462–6729, (Nonreporting) **A**1 10
Primary Contact: Edgar E. Prettyman, PsyD, Chief Executive Officer
Web address: www.texasstarrecovery.com
**Control:** Partnership, Investor–owned (for–profit) **Service:** Psychiatric

**Staffed Beds:** 28

⇑ **THE HOSPITAL AT WESTLAKE MEDICAL CENTER (670006)**, 5656 Bee Caves Road, Suite M302, Zip 78746–5280; tel. 512/327–0000, (Nonreporting) **A**10 21 **F**3 29 39 40 45 47 53 59 64 70 75 77 79 81 82 85 107 108 111 114 119 130 131 148 149
Primary Contact: Tammy Smittle, R.N., Chief Executive Officer
CFO: Devon Culbert, Controller
CMO: Tom Burns, M.D., Chief of Staff
CHR: Kellie Bryson, Director Human Resources
Web address: www.westlakemedical.com
**Control:** Partnership, Investor–owned (for–profit) **Service:** General medical and surgical

**Staffed Beds:** 23 **Admissions:** 800 **Census:** 5 **Outpatient Visits:** 10647
**Births:** 0 **Total Expense ($000):** 43466 **Payroll Expense ($000):** 10068
**Personnel:** 201

## AZLE—Tarrant County

**HARRIS METHODIST NORTHWEST** See Texas Health Harris Methodist Hospital Azle

✠ **TEXAS HEALTH HARRIS METHODIST HOSPITAL AZLE (450419)**, 108 Denver Trail, Zip 76020–3614; tel. 817/444–8600, (Nonreporting) **A**1 10 **F**3 11 15 18 29 30 34 35 40 43 45 57 59 64 70 75 77 79 81 85 93 107 110 114 119 130 135 146 148 149 150 154 156 **P**6 **S** Texas Health Resources, Arlington, TX
Primary Contact: Tonya Sosebee, MSN, R.N., Chief Operating and Nursing Officer
COO: Tonya Sosebee, MSN, R.N., Chief Operating and Nursing Officer
CFO: Brian Blessing, Chief Financial Officer
CMO: Judy Laviolette, M.D., Chief Medical Officer
CIO: Patricia Johnston, Vice President Information Services
CHR: Lance Waring, Director Human Resources
CNO: Tonya Sosebee, MSN, R.N., Chief Operating and Nursing Officer
Web address: www.texashealth.org/Azle
**Control:** Other not–for–profit (including NFP Corporation) **Service:** General medical and surgical

**Staffed Beds:** 31 **Admissions:** 1540 **Census:** 12 **Outpatient Visits:** 31132
**Births:** 0 **Total Expense ($000):** 33844 **Payroll Expense ($000):** 14895
**Personnel:** 189

## BALLINGER—Runnels County

★ **BALLINGER MEMORIAL HOSPITAL (451310)**, 608 Avenue 'B', Zip 76821–2499, Mailing Address: P.O. Box 617, Zip 76821–0617; tel. 325/365–2531, (Nonreporting) **A**10 18 **F**3 7 11 29 34 40 43 53 64 65 68 77 93 107 114 127 130 133 135 154 156
Primary Contact: Rhett D. Fricke, Chief Executive Officer
CFO: Josilyn Peterson, Chief Financial Officer
CHR: Roselyn Hudgens, Director Human Resources
Web address: www.ballingerhospital.org
**Control:** Hospital district or authority, Government, Nonfederal **Service:** General medical and surgical

**Staffed Beds:** 16 **Admissions:** 192 **Census:** 4 **Outpatient Visits:** 28506
**Births:** 0 **Total Expense ($000):** 13676 **Payroll Expense ($000):** 5233
**Personnel:** 120

## BASTROP—Bastrop County

★ **ASCENSION SETON BASTROP (670143)**, 630 TX-71 West, Zip 78602–4234; tel. 737/881–7400, (Nonreporting) **S** Ascension Healthcare, Saint Louis, MO
Primary Contact: Andy Davis, Chief Executive Officer
COO: Robbie G. Rabe, Chief Operatiang Officer
Web address: www.https://healthcare.ascension.org/Locations/Texas/TXAUS/Bastrop-Ascension-Seton-Bastrop
**Control:** Church operated, Nongovernment, not–for–profit **Service:** General medical and surgical

**Staffed Beds:** 7

## BAY CITY—Matagorda County

**MATAGORDA COUNTY HOSPITAL DISTRICT** See Matagorda Regional Medical Center

✠ **MATAGORDA REGIONAL MEDICAL CENTER (450465)**, 104 7th Street, Zip 77414–4853; tel. 979/245–6383, (Nonreporting) **A**1 10 20 **F**3 11 12 13 15 18 20 22 28 29 30 34 38 39 40 43 45 46 47 50 51 53 56 57 59 64 65 66 68 70 75 76 77 79 81 82 85 86 89 93 98 103 107 108 110 111 114 119 130 132 135 144 146 147 148 154 156 **S** QHR Health, Brentwood, TN
Primary Contact: James Warren. Robicheaux, FACHE, Chief Executive Officer
CFO: Bryan Prochnow, Chief Financial Officer
CIO: Beverly Trombatore, R.N., Director Managed Information Systems
CHR: Cindy Krebs, District Director Human Resources
CNO: Mike Lee, R.N., Chief Nursing Officer
Web address: www.matagordaregional.org
**Control:** Hospital district or authority, Government, Nonfederal **Service:** General medical and surgical

**Staffed Beds:** 58 **Admissions:** 2136 **Census:** 26 **Outpatient Visits:** 62284
**Births:** 466 **Total Expense ($000):** 64038 **Payroll Expense ($000):** 23265
**Personnel:** 317

## BAYTOWN—Harris County

⇑ **ALTUS BAYTOWN HOSPITAL (670109)**, 1626 West Baker Road, Zip 77521–2271; tel. 281/837–7600, (Nonreporting) **A**21 **F**3 12 29 40 42 44 45 49 77 79 81 82 85 87 107 108 111 114 116 117 119 124 130 149
Primary Contact: Sourabh Sanduja, Administrator
Web address: www.altusbaytownhospital.org
**Control:** Partnership, Investor–owned (for–profit) **Service:** Surgical

**Staffed Beds:** 10 **Admissions:** 534 **Census:** 2 **Outpatient Visits:** 4812
**Births:** 0 **Total Expense ($000):** 24849 **Payroll Expense ($000):** 7181
**Personnel:** 84

★ ⇑ **HOUSTON METHODIST BAYTOWN HOSPITAL (450424)**, 4401 Garth Road, Zip 77521–2122; tel. 281/420–8600, (Nonreporting) **A**2 3 10 21 **F**3 4 8 11 12 13 15 18 20 22 24 26 28 29 30 31 34 35 38 40 41 44 45 49 50 51 53 55 56 57 59 60 61 63 64 65 68 70 73 74 75 76 77 78 79 81 82 84 85 86 87 91 93 94 96 102 107 110 111 115 117 118 119 120 121 123 126 129 130 131 132 145 146 147 148 149 154 156 **P**5 6 **S** Houston Methodist, Houston, TX
Primary Contact: David P. Bernard, FACHE, Chief Executive Officer
CFO: Jonathan Sturgis, Chief Financial Officer
CMO: Klaus Thaler, FACS, M.D., Chief Medical Officer
CHR: Courtney Lewis, Director Human Resources
CNO: Rebecca Chalupa, MSN, R.N., Chief Nursing Officer
Web address: www.houstonmethodist.org
**Control:** Other not–for–profit (including NFP Corporation) **Service:** General medical and surgical

**Staffed Beds:** 224 **Admissions:** 14515 **Census:** 185 **Outpatient Visits:** 181295 **Births:** 1782 **Total Expense ($000):** 280504 **Payroll Expense ($000):** 111089 **Personnel:** 1646

⇑ **HOUSTON METHODIST SAN JACINTO HOSPITAL** See Houston Methodist Baytown Hospital

**TX**

## BEAUMONT—Jefferson County

★ **BAPTIST HOSPITALS OF SOUTHEAST TEXAS (450346)**, 3080 College Street, Zip 77701–4689, Mailing Address: P.O. Box 1591, Zip 77704–1591; tel. 409/212–5000, (Includes BAPTIST HOSPITALS OF SOUTHEAST TEXAS FANNIN BEHAVIORAL HEALTH CENTER, Mailing address: 3250 Fannin Street, Beaumont, Texas, Zip 77701; tel. 409/212–7000; David N Parmer, FACHE, Chief Executive Officer), (Nonreporting) **A**2 10 19 22 **F**3 11 12 13 15 17 18 20 22 24 26 28 29 30 31 34 35 40 41 43 44 45 46 48 49 50 51 54 57 59 60 61 64 70 72 73 76 78 79 81 85 88 89 90 93 98 99 100 103 104 105 107 108 110 111 114 115 116 117 118 119 120 121 123 129 130 146 148 153 154 **S** Community Hospital Corporation, Plano, TX
Primary Contact: David N. Parmer, FACHE, Chief Executive Officer
COO: Patrick Shannon, Chief Operating Officer
CFO: Gary Troutman, CPA, Chief Financial Officer
CMO: Shariq Ahmad, M.D., Chief of Staff
CIO: William Toon, Chief Information Officer
CHR: Hannah Schiesler, Interim Assistant Director Human Resources
CNO: Karen Garcia, MSN, R.N., Chief Nursing Officer
Web address: www.bhset.net
**Control:** Other not–for–profit (including NFP Corporation) **Service:** General medical and surgical

**Staffed Beds: 307 Admissions: 15146 Census: 192 Outpatient Visits: 172552 Births: 1312 Total Expense ($000): 265213 Payroll Expense ($000): 93515 Personnel: 1497**

**BEAUMONT MEDICAL & SURG HOSP** See Baptist Hospitals of Southeast Texas

☐ **CHRISTUS DUBUIS HOSPITAL OF BEAUMONT (452042)**, 2830 Calder Avenue, 4th Floor, Zip 77702–1809; tel. 409/899–7680, (Includes CHRISTUS DUBUIS HOSPITAL OF PORT ARTHUR, Mailing address: 3600 Gates Boulevard, 3rd Floor West, Port Arthur, Texas, Zip 77642–3858; tel. 409/989–5300; Tuan Le, Chief Executive Officer), (Nonreporting) **A**1 10 **F**1 3 18 29 31 148 154 **S** LHC Group, Lafayette, LA
Primary Contact: Jason Baker, Administrator
Web address: www.christusdubuis.org/BeaumontandPortArthurSystem-CHRISTUSDubuisHospitalofBeaumont
**Control:** Corporation, Investor–owned (for–profit) **Service:** Acute long–term care hospital

**Staffed Beds: 33 Admissions: 356 Census: 25 Outpatient Visits: 0 Births: 0 Total Expense ($000): 11444 Payroll Expense ($000): 5231 Personnel: 69**

**CHRISTUS ORTHOPEDIC SPECIALTY CENTER - ST. ELIZABETH** See Christus Southeast Texas Orthopedic Specialty Center

**CHRISTUS SOUTHEAST TEXAS HOSPITAL** See Christus Southeast Texas Hospital - St. Elizabeth

⊞ **CHRISTUS SOUTHEAST TEXAS HOSPITAL - ST. ELIZABETH (450034)**, 2830 Calder Avenue, Zip 77702–1809, Mailing Address: P.O. Box 5405, Zip 77726–5405; tel. 409/892–7171, (Nonreporting) **A**1 3 10 19 **F**3 11 12 13 15 17 18 20 22 24 26 28 29 30 31 34 35 36 38 40 42 43 44 45 46 49 50 51 54 57 59 60 63 64 70 72 74 75 76 77 78 79 81 82 84 85 86 87 89 93 94 107 108 110 111 114 118 119 126 130 131 132 144 146 147 148 149 156 **P**8 **S** CHRISTUS Health, Irving, TX
Primary Contact: Paul Trevino, President and Chief Executive Officer
CFO: Shawn Adams, Chief Financial Officer
CMO: Rick Tyler, M.D., Vice President Medical Affairs
CIO: Robert Jacobs, Regional Director Information Management
CHR: Charles Foster, Regional Director Human Resources
Web address: www.christushospital.org
**Control:** Church operated, Nongovernment, not–for–profit **Service:** General medical and surgical

**Staffed Beds: 367 Admissions: 16203 Census: 181 Outpatient Visits: 394897 Births: 2106 Total Expense ($000): 340792 Payroll Expense ($000): 102970 Personnel: 1843**

**CHRISTUS SOUTHEAST TEXAS ORTHOPEDIC SPECIALTY CENTER (670007)**, 3650 Laurel Street, Zip 77707–2216; tel. 409/838–0346, (Nonreporting) **A**10
Primary Contact: William Klamfoth, Administrator
Web address: www.orthodoc.aaos.org/bbji/
**Control:** Partnership, Investor–owned (for–profit) **Service:** General medical and surgical

**Staffed Beds: 6**

**DUBUIS HOSPITAL OF BEAUMONT** See Christus Dubuis Hospital of Beaumont

**HEALTHSOUTH REHABILITATION HOSPITAL OF BEAUMONT** See Pam Rehabilitation Hospital of Beaumont

☐ **KATE DISHMAN REHABILITATION HOSPITAL (673030)**, 2830 Calder Street, 6th Floor, Zip 77702–1809; tel. 409/899–8380, (Nonreporting) **A**1 **F**29 86 87 90 96 97 100 **S** CHRISTUS Health, Irving, TX
Primary Contact: David Pipkins, Chief Executive Officer
Web address: www.christushospital.org
**Control:** Partnership, Investor–owned (for–profit) **Service:** Rehabilitation

**Staffed Beds: 27 Admissions: 405 Census: 15 Outpatient Visits: 0 Births: 0 Total Expense ($000): 6645 Payroll Expense ($000): 3691 Personnel: 66**

**MEDICAL CENTER OF SOUTHEAST TEXAS**, 6025 Metropolitan Drive, Zip 77706–2407; tel. 409/617–7700, (Nonreporting) **S** Steward Health Care System, LLC, Dallas, TX
Primary Contact: Becky Ames, Chief Executive Officer
Web address: www.medicalcentersetexas.com/
**Control:** Other not–for–profit (including NFP Corporation) **Service:** Surgical

**Staffed Beds: 17**

**MEMORIAL HERMANN BAPTIST FANNIN BEHAVIORAL HEALTH CENTER** See Baptist Hospitals of Southeast Texas Fannin Behavioral Health Center

**MID-JEFFERSON EXTENDED CARE HOSPITAL OF BEAUMONT (452083)**, 860 South 8th Street, Zip 77701–4626; tel. 409/363–5800, (Includes MID-JEFFERSON EXTENDED CARE HOSPITAL, Mailing address: 2600 Highway 365, Nederland, Texas, Zip 77627–6237; tel. 409/726–8700; Mark J. Rice, Chief Executive Officer) **F**1 3 4 16 17 29 30 34 35 40 70 72 73 74 75 76 77 79 80 85 88 90 98 128 130 148
Primary Contact: Mark J. Rice, Chief Executive Officer
Web address: www.midjeffextendedcare.com
**Control:** Corporation, Investor–owned (for–profit) **Service:** Acute long–term care hospital

**Staffed Beds: 78 Admissions: 715 Census: 40 Outpatient Visits: 0 Births: 0 Total Expense ($000): 15156 Payroll Expense ($000): 8288 Personnel: 176**

⊞ **PAM REHABILITATION HOSPITAL OF BEAUMONT (453048)**, 3340 Plaza 10 Boulevard, Zip 77707–2551; tel. 409/835–0835, (Nonreporting) **A**1 10 **F**3 29 34 35 57 74 75 90 93 96 148 **S** Post Acute Medical, LLC, Enola, PA
Primary Contact: Todd Lorenz, Administrator
CHR: Joanna Donica, Director Human Resource
CNO: Barbara Morris, R.N., Chief Nursing Officer
Web address: www.postacutemedical.com/our-facilities/outpatient-rehabilitation/rehabilitation-hospital-beaumont/
**Control:** Partnership, Investor–owned (for–profit) **Service:** Rehabilitation

**Staffed Beds: 61 Admissions: 729 Census: 22 Outpatient Visits: 4365 Births: 0 Total Expense ($000): 11539 Payroll Expense ($000): 5598 Personnel: 122**

**VICTORY MEDICAL CENTER BEAUMONT** See Medical Center of Southeast Texas

## BEDFORD—Tarrant County

⊞ **ENCOMPASS HEALTH REHABILITATION HOSPITAL OF THE MID-CITIES (673044)**, 2304 State Highway 121, Zip 76021–5985; tel. 817/684–2000, (Nonreporting) **A**1 10 **F**3 29 90 96 148 **S** Encompass Health Corporation, Birmingham, AL
Primary Contact: Robert M. Smart, Chief Executive Officer
CFO: Mary Mwaniki, Chief Financial Officer
CMO: Toni Willis, M.D., Medical Director
CHR: Christie Moore, Director Human Resources
Web address: www.relianthcp.com
**Control:** Partnership, Investor–owned (for–profit) **Service:** Rehabilitation

**Staffed Beds: 60 Admissions: 1358 Census: 46 Outpatient Visits: 0 Births: 0 Total Expense ($000): 23989 Payroll Expense ($000): 10570 Personnel: 172**

**HARRIS METHODIST-HEB** See Texas Health Harris Methodist Hospital Hurst-Euless-Bedford

**HEALTHSOUTH REHABILITATION HOSPITAL - MID-CITIES** See Encompass Health Rehabilitation Hospital of The Mid-Cities

*Many Facility Codes have changed. Please refer to the AHA Guide Code Chart.*

© 2021 AHA Guide

✠ **TEXAS HEALTH HARRIS METHODIST HOSPITAL HURST-EULESS-BEDFORD (450639)**, 1600 Hospital Parkway, Zip 76022–6913; tel. 817/685–4000, (Includes TEXAS HEALTH SPRINGWOOD BEHAVIORAL HEALTH HOSPITAL, Mailing address: 1608 Hospital Parkway, Bedford, Texas, Zip 76022; tel. 817/355–7700; Jay Frayser, MSN, R.N., Administrator), (Nonreporting) **A**1 10 **F**3 4 5 11 13 18 20 22 24 26 28 29 30 31 34 35 40 43 45 46 47 48 49 50 53 57 59 60 64 70 72 74 75 76 78 79 80 81 82 84 85 86 87 93 98 99 100 101 102 104 105 106 107 108 111 114 119 126 130 131 132 134 135 146 147 148 149 151 152 153 154 **S** Texas Health Resources, Arlington, TX
Primary Contact: Fraser Hay, President
COO: Alice Landers, Administrative Director Operations
CFO: Jaime James, Entity Finance Officer
CMO: Susann Land, M.D., Chief Medical Officer
CHR: Lee Mulvey, Human Resource Officer
CNO: Ray Kelly, R.N., MSN, Vice President Chief Nursing Officer
Web address: www.texashealth.org
**Control:** Other not-for-profit (including NFP Corporation) **Service:** General medical and surgical

**Staffed Beds:** 285 **Admissions:** 13408 **Census:** 145 **Outpatient Visits:** 85818 **Births:** 2301 **Total Expense ($000):** 238766 **Payroll Expense ($000):** 94590 **Personnel:** 1136

**TEXAS HEALTH SPRINGWOOD** See Texas Health Springwood Behavioral Health Hospital

## BEEVILLE—Bee County

**CHRISTUS SPOHN HOSPITAL** See Christus Spohn Hospital Beeville

✠ **CHRISTUS SPOHN HOSPITAL BEEVILLE (450082)**, 1500 East Houston Street, Zip 78102–5312; tel. 361/354–2000, (Nonreporting) **A**1 10 20 **F**3 11 13 29 30 32 34 35 40 43 45 50 53 57 59 63 64 68 70 75 76 79 81 85 87 93 97 107 108 111 114 115 119 127 130 146 147 148 154 **P**8 **S** CHRISTUS Health, Irving, TX
Primary Contact: Genifer Rucker, President
Web address: www.christusspohn.org
**Control:** Church operated, Nongovernment, not-for-profit **Service:** General medical and surgical

**Staffed Beds:** 49 **Admissions:** 1859 **Census:** 15 **Outpatient Visits:** 46967 **Births:** 186 **Total Expense ($000):** 29730 **Payroll Expense ($000):** 10417 **Personnel:** 159

## BELLAIRE—Harris County

⇧ **FIRST STREET HOSPITAL** See First Surgical Hospital

⇧ **FIRST SURGICAL HOSPITAL (670029)**, 4801 Bissonnet Street, Zip 77401–4028; tel. 713/275–1111, (Data for 92 days) (Nonreporting) **A**10 21 **F**8 12 29 37 40 45 48 77 78 79 81 85 107 149
Primary Contact: Tricia D. Lynch, Chief Nursing Officer
Web address: www.firststreethospital.com
**Control:** Corporation, Investor-owned (for-profit) **Service:** Surgical

**Staffed Beds:** 19 **Admissions:** 269 **Census:** 1 **Outpatient Visits:** 1143 **Births:** 0 **Total Expense ($000):** 6096 **Payroll Expense ($000):** 1604 **Personnel:** 102

**MEMORIAL HERMANN HOUSTON ORTHOPEDIC AND SPINE HOSPITAL** See Memorial Hermann Orthopedic and Spine Hospital

## BELLVILLE—Austin County

✠ **BELLVILLE MEDICAL CENTER (450253)**, 44 North Cummings Street, Zip 77418–1347, Mailing Address: P.O. Box 977, Zip 77418–0977; tel. 979/413–7400, (Nonreporting) **A**1 10 **F**3 11 15 29 34 35 40 43 45 50 53 57 59 64 65 68 75 77 81 87 91 93 97 107 110 111 114 119 133 146 154 157
Primary Contact: Daniel J. Bonk, Chief Executive Officer
CMO: Christophe Gay, M.D., Chief of Staff
CHR: Jacqueline McEuen, Coordinator Human Resources
Web address: www.https://www.bellvillemc.org/home/
**Control:** Other not-for-profit (including NFP Corporation) **Service:** General medical and surgical

**Staffed Beds:** 10 **Admissions:** 113 **Census:** 2 **Outpatient Visits:** 22175 **Births:** 0 **Total Expense ($000):** 11878 **Payroll Expense ($000):** 3902 **Personnel:** 49

**CHI ST. JOSEPH HEALTH BELLVILLE HOSPITAL** See Bellville Medical Center

## BELTON—Bell County

**CEDAR CREST HOSPITAL** See Cedar Crest Hospital and Residential Treatment Center

☐ **CEDAR CREST HOSPITAL AND RESIDENTIAL TREATMENT CENTER (454114)**, 3500 I-35 South, Zip 76513; tel. 254/939–2100, (Nonreporting) **A**1 10 **F**4 29 34 35 59 68 86 87 98 99 100 101 103 104 105 106 130 143 152 153 **P**4
Primary Contact: Caanan Blakemore, Chief Executive Officer
CFO: Melissa West, Chief Financial Officer
CMO: Alejandro Munoz, M.D., Chief Medical Officer
CIO: Cesar Osario, Specialist Information Technology
CHR: Allison Liston, Director, Human Resources
CNO: Caanan Blakemore, Chief Executive Officer
Web address: www.cedarcresthospital.com
**Control:** Corporation, Investor-owned (for-profit) **Service:** Psychiatric

**Staffed Beds:** 68 **Admissions:** 2470 **Census:** 44 **Outpatient Visits:** 2487 **Births:** 0 **Total Expense ($000):** 10064 **Payroll Expense ($000):** 5449 **Personnel:** 174

## BIG LAKE—Reagan County

★ **REAGAN MEMORIAL HOSPITAL (451301)**, 1300 North Main, Zip 76932–3938; tel. 325/884–2561, (Nonreporting) **A**10 18 **F**3 40 43 53 57 89 93 107 114 115 128 130 133 143 154 156 157 **P**5
Primary Contact: Jonathon Voelkel, Chief Executive Officer
CMO: Joseph Sudolcan, M.D., Medical Director
Web address: www.reaganhealth.com/getpage.php?name=index
**Control:** Hospital district or authority, Government, Nonfederal **Service:** General medical and surgical

**Staffed Beds:** 7 **Admissions:** 13 **Census:** 1 **Outpatient Visits:** 9347 **Births:** 0 **Total Expense ($000):** 15731 **Payroll Expense ($000):** 6235 **Personnel:** 40

## BIG SPRING—Howard County

☐ **BIG SPRING STATE HOSPITAL (454000)**, 1901 North Highway 87, Zip 79720–0283; tel. 432/267–8216, (Nonreporting) **A**1 3 5 10 **F**30 39 50 56 59 61 74 75 77 86 87 97 98 101 103 130 135 146 154 158 **P**6 **S** Texas Department of State Health Services, Austin, TX
Primary Contact: Traci Phillips, Superintendent
CFO: Adrienne Bides, Assistant Chief Financial Officer and Budget Analyst
CMO: Guido Spangher, M.D., Clinical Director
CIO: Elizabeth Correa, Director Information Management
CNO: Stormy Ward, Chief Nurse Executive
Web address: www.dshs.state.tx.us/mhhospitals/BigSpringSH/default.shtm
**Control:** State, Government, Nonfederal **Service:** Psychiatric

**Staffed Beds:** 144 **Admissions:** 166 **Census:** 159 **Outpatient Visits:** 0 **Births:** 0 **Total Expense ($000):** 40587 **Payroll Expense ($000):** 22504 **Personnel:** 462

✠ **SCENIC MOUNTAIN MEDICAL CENTER (450653)**, 1601 West 11th Place, Zip 79720–4198; tel. 432/263–1211, (Nonreporting) **A**1 10 20 **S** Steward Health Care System, LLC, Dallas, TX
Primary Contact: Stacey L. Brown, President
CFO: Rodger W Bowen, M.P.H., Chief Financial Officer
CMO: Keith Ledford, M.D., Chief of Staff
CIO: Gene Mills, Director Information Technology
CHR: Deborah Elder, Director Human Resources
CNO: Judy Roever, MSN, R.N., Chief Nursing Officer
Web address: www.smmccares.com
**Control:** Corporation, Investor-owned (for-profit) **Service:** General medical and surgical

**Staffed Beds:** 82

**WEST TEXAS VA HEALTH CARE SYSTEM** See West Texas Veterans Affairs Health Care System

**TX**

---

**Hospital, Medicare Provider Number, Address, Telephone, Approval, Facility, and Physician Codes, Health Care System**

★ American Hospital Association (AHA) membership
☐ The Joint Commission accreditation
○ Healthcare Facilities Accreditation Program
◇ DNV Healthcare Inc. accreditation
⇧ Center for Improvement in Healthcare Quality Accreditation
△ Commission on Accreditation of Rehabilitation Facilities (CARF) accreditation

★ **WEST TEXAS VETERANS AFFAIRS HEALTH CARE SYSTEM**, 300 Veterans
Boulevard, Zip 79720–5500, Mailing Address: Big Springs, tel. 432/263–7361,
(Nonreporting) **A**3 5 **S** Department of Veterans Affairs, Washington, DC
Primary Contact: Kalautie JangDhari, Director
CFO: Ray Olivas, Chief Fiscal Service
CMO: Martin Schnier, D.O., Chief of Staff
CIO: Mike McKinley, Information Security Officer
CHR: Anna Osborne, Chief Human Resources Management Service
Web address: www.bigspring.va.gov/about/
**Control**: Veterans Affairs, Government, federal **Service**: General medical and
surgical

> **Staffed Beds:** 149

### BONHAM—Fannin County

**RED RIVER REGIONAL HOSPITAL** See Tmc Bonham Hospital

**SAM RAYBURN MEMORIAL VETERANS CENTER** See Veterans Affairs North
Texas Health Care System, Dallas

**TMC BONHAM HOSPITAL (451370)**, 504 Lipscomb Street, Zip 75418–4028;
tel. 903/583–8585, (Nonreporting) **A**10 18 **F**3 11 15 29 30 34 35 40 43 46 50
57 59 64 65 75 81 87 93 107 108 110 111 118 119 130 133 135 148 154
Primary Contact: Michael Daines. Hall, Interim Chief Executive Officer
CMO: Michael Brown, D.O., Chief of Staff
CIO: Jack Farguson, Director Information Technology
CHR: Brenda Bagley, Director Human Resources
CNO: William Kiefer, Chief Nursing Officer
Web address: www.https://tmcbonham.com/
**Control**: Hospital district or authority, Government, Nonfederal **Service**: General
medical and surgical

> **Staffed Beds:** 19 **Admissions:** 601 **Census:** 12 **Outpatient Visits:** 19984
> **Births:** 0 **Total Expense ($000):** 19124 **Payroll Expense ($000):** 9040
> **Personnel:** 124

### BORGER—Hutchinson County

**BOLDEN PLAINS COMM HOSPITAL** See Golden Plains Community Hospital

**GOLDEN PLAINS COMMUNITY HOSPITAL (451369)**, 100 Medical Drive,
Zip 79007–7579; tel. 806/467–5700, (Nonreporting) **A**10 18 **F**11 13 15 29 30
34 35 40 43 45 50 54 56 57 59 62 64 65 66 68 70 75 76 77 79 81 85 86 87
89 93 107 108 110 115 119 127 130 131 132 133 143 146 147 148 153 154
156 **P**6
Primary Contact: Don Bates, Chief Executive Officer
COO: Melody Lynn Henderson, Ph.D., R.N., Chief Operating Officer and Chief
Nursing Officer
CFO: Dina Hermes, Chief Financial Officer
CMO: Tanay M. Patel, M.D., Chief of Staff
CHR: Jennifer Harvey, Director Human Resources
Web address: www.goldenplains.org
**Control**: Corporation, Investor–owned (for–profit) **Service**: General medical and
surgical

> **Staffed Beds:** 17 **Admissions:** 631 **Census:** 5 **Outpatient Visits:** 38805
> **Births:** 257 **Total Expense ($000):** 28195 **Payroll Expense ($000):** 7630
> **Personnel:** 159

### BRADY—Mcculloch County

**HEART OF TEXAS MEMORIAL HOSPITAL (451348)**, 2008 Nine Road,
Zip 76825–7210, Mailing Address: P.O. Box 1150, Zip 76825–1150;
tel. 325/597–2901, (Nonreporting) **A**10 18 **F**15 28 40 43 45 64 81 93 107 111
114 119 127 133 152 154 156 157 **P**4
Primary Contact: Tim Jones, Chief Executive Officer
CFO: Brad Burnett, Chief Financial Officer
CMO: Pete Castro, D.O., Chief of Staff
Web address: www.bradyhospital.com/
**Control**: Other not–for–profit (including NFP Corporation) **Service**: General
medical and surgical

> **Staffed Beds:** 25 **Admissions:** 225 **Census:** 3 **Outpatient Visits:** 16092
> **Births:** 0 **Total Expense ($000):** 15288 **Payroll Expense ($000):** 4183
> **Personnel:** 97

### BRECKENRIDGE—Stephens County

★ **STEPHENS MEMORIAL HOSPITAL (450498)**, 200 South Geneva Street,
Zip 76424–4799; tel. 254/559–2242, (Nonreporting) **A**10 20 **F**3 8 11 15 28 30
34 35 40 43 45 50 53 54 56 57 59 63 64 68 69 81 85 87 89 93 97 107 114
127 130 133 144 146
Primary Contact: Doug Smith, Interim Chief Executive Officer and Chief Financial
Officer
CFO: Doug Smith, Chief Financial Officer
CMO: Cynthia Perry, M.D., Chief of Staff
CIO: Bobby Thompson, Director Information Technology
CHR: Michelle Funderburg, Director Human Resources
CNO: Alicia Whitt, R.N., Chief Nursing Officer
Web address: www.smhtx.com
**Control**: Hospital district or authority, Government, Nonfederal **Service**: General
medical and surgical

> **Staffed Beds:** 14 **Admissions:** 203 **Census:** 2 **Outpatient Visits:** 14500
> **Births:** 0 **Total Expense ($000):** 13098 **Payroll Expense ($000):** 5947
> **Personnel:** 124

### BRENHAM—Washington County

⊞ **BAYLOR SCOTT & WHITE MEDICAL CENTER - BRENHAM (450187)**, 700
Medical Parkway, Zip 77833–5498; tel. 979/337–5000, (Nonreporting) **A**1 10
**F**3 13 18 28 29 30 40 45 50 51 54 56 68 70 76 79 81 82 85 87 89 93 102
107 114 115 119 130 132 146 149 154 157 **S** Baylor Scott & White Health,
Dallas, TX
Primary Contact: Jason Jennings, FACHE, President
CFO: Jane Wellmann, Chief Financial Officer
CMO: Michael Schlabach, M.D., Chief Medical Officer
CIO: Sharon Schwartz, Director Medical Records
CHR: Virginia Counts, Manager Human Resources
Web address: www.swbrenham.org
**Control**: Other not–for–profit (including NFP Corporation) **Service**: General
medical and surgical

> **Staffed Beds:** 44 **Admissions:** 1361 **Census:** 12 **Outpatient Visits:** 47485
> **Births:** 253 **Total Expense ($000):** 37705 **Payroll Expense ($000):** 13476
> **Personnel:** 165

**BAYLOR SCOTT & WHITEMEDICAL CENTER - BRENHAM** See Baylor Scott &
White Medical Center - Brenham

### BROWNFIELD—Terry County

★ **BROWNFIELD REGIONAL MEDICAL CENTER (450399)**, 705 East Felt Street,
Zip 79316–3439; tel. 806/637–3551, (Nonreporting) **A**10 20 **F**3 7 13 28 29 30
34 40 43 45 50 53 57 59 62 64 65 68 75 76 80 81 85 86 87 93 97 102 107
111 114 119 127 129 130 135 148 149 154 **P**4
Primary Contact: Jerry Jasper, Chief Executive Officer
CFO: Grady Paul Gafford, Chief Financial Officer
CIO: Edgar Rivera, Chief Information Officer
CHR: Kelly Barnett, Human Resource Officer
CNO: Chris Beard, Chief Nursing Officer
Web address: www.brownfield-rmc.org
**Control**: Hospital district or authority, Government, Nonfederal **Service**: General
medical and surgical

> **Staffed Beds:** 26 **Admissions:** 499 **Census:** 4 **Outpatient Visits:** 38386
> **Births:** 51 **Total Expense ($000):** 16408 **Payroll Expense ($000):** 7413
> **Personnel:** 152

### BROWNSVILLE—Cameron County

**BROWNSVILLE MEDICAL CENTER** See Valley Baptist Medical Center-Brownsville

**COLUMBIA VALLEY REG MED CTR** See Valley Regional Medical Center

**SOLARA HOSPITAL HARLINGEN-BROWNSVILLE CAMPUS** See Solara Hospital
- Brownsville Campus

**TX**

☐ **SOUTH TEXAS REHABILITATION HOSPITAL (453092)**, 425 East Alton Gloor Boulevard, Zip 78526–3361; tel. 956/554–6000, (Nonreporting) **A**1 10 **F**3 28 29 34 35 59 64 75 77 86 87 90 93 94 96 130 132 148 149 **S** Ernest Health, Inc., Albuquerque, NM
Primary Contact: Leo Garza, Chief Executive Officer
CFO: Ernest Nash, Chief Financial Officer
CMO: Christopher Wilson, M.D., Inpatient Medical Director
CIO: Deborah Alcocer, Chief Information Officer
CHR: Tony Rodriguez, Director Human Resources
CNO: Aaron Cepeda, Director Nursing Operations
Web address: www.strh.ernesthealth.com
**Control:** Partnership, Investor–owned (for–profit) **Service:** Rehabilitation

> **Staffed Beds:** 40 **Admissions:** 765 **Census:** 30 **Outpatient Visits:** 7910
> **Total Expense ($000):** 15463 **Payroll Expense ($000):** 6679
> **Personnel:** 128

✠ **VALLEY BAPTIST MEDICAL CENTER-BROWNSVILLE (450028)**, 1040 West Jefferson Street, Zip 78520–6338, Mailing Address: P.O. Box 3590, Zip 78523–3590; tel. 956/698–5400, (Nonreporting) **A**1 5 10 **F**3 11 12 13 15 18 20 22 24 26 29 30 34 35 37 40 42 43 44 45 49 50 51 54 56 57 59 60 63 64 65 68 70 72 74 75 76 77 79 81 82 84 85 86 87 89 93 101 102 103 104 107 108 110 111 114 115 118 119 126 129 130 132 146 147 148 149 153 154 157 **S** TENET Healthcare Corporation, Dallas, TX
Primary Contact: Leslie Bingham, Senior Vice President and Chief Executive Officer
COO: Marisa Aguilar, Chief Operating Officer
CFO: Edwin Cordero, Chief Financial Officer
CMO: Jose L Ayala, M.D., Chief Medical Officer
CNO: Marisa Aguilar, Interim Chief Nursing Officer
Web address: www.https://www.valleybaptist.net/location/detail/vbmc-brownsville
**Control:** Corporation, Investor–owned (for–profit) **Service:** General medical and surgical

> **Staffed Beds:** 225 **Admissions:** 10773 **Census:** 125 **Outpatient Visits:** 83158 **Births:** 1926 **Total Expense ($000):** 137095 **Payroll Expense ($000):** 54216 **Personnel:** 695

✠ **VALLEY REGIONAL MEDICAL CENTER (450662)**, 100A Alton Gloor Boulevard, Zip 78526–3354; tel. 956/350–7101, (Nonreporting) **A**1 3 10 **F**3 11 13 15 18 20 22 24 26 29 30 31 32 34 35 40 43 44 45 47 49 50 53 57 59 60 61 64 65 68 70 72 73 74 75 76 77 78 79 81 82 84 85 86 87 89 93 107 108 110 111 114 115 118 119 124 126 130 132 135 146 147 148 149 156 **P**7 **S** HCA Healthcare, Nashville, TN
Primary Contact: Art Garza, FACHE, Chief Executive Officer
COO: Steven C Hoelscher, Chief Operating Officer
CFO: Marcia Patterson, Chief Financial Officer
CIO: Carlos Leal, Director Information Technology
CHR: Vicky Kahl, Director Human Resources
Web address: www.valleyregionalmedicalcenter.com
**Control:** Partnership, Investor–owned (for–profit) **Service:** General medical and surgical

> **Staffed Beds:** 214 **Admissions:** 8670 **Census:** 101 **Outpatient Visits:** 76467 **Births:** 2160 **Total Expense ($000):** 124108 **Payroll Expense ($000):** 53678 **Personnel:** 674

**BROWNWOOD—Brown County**

✠ **BROWNWOOD REGIONAL MEDICAL CENTER (450587)**, 1501 Burnet Road, Zip 76801–8520, Mailing Address: P.O. Box 760, Zip 76804–0760; tel. 325/646–8541, (Nonreporting) **A**1 10 20 **F**3 11 13 15 18 20 22 28 29 30 31 34 35 39 40 43 45 50 51 54 57 59 64 68 70 74 75 76 77 78 79 81 85 86 87 93 97 107 108 110 111 115 119 120 121 123 127 129 130 135 146 147 148 **P**3 8 **S** Community Health Systems, Inc., Franklin, TN
Primary Contact: Jace Jones, Interim Chief Executive Officer
CFO: Joseph Wooldridge, Chief Financial Officer
CMO: Sammy Horton, Chief of Staff
CIO: Jay Smith, Director Information Systems
CHR: Mikeana Bailey, Director Human Resources
CNO: Alicia R. Kayga, R.N., Chief Nursing Officer
Web address: www.brmc-cares.com
**Control:** Partnership, Investor–owned (for–profit) **Service:** General medical and surgical

> **Staffed Beds:** 148 **Admissions:** 2777 **Census:** 28 **Outpatient Visits:** 80189 **Births:** 573 **Total Expense ($000):** 65959 **Payroll Expense ($000):** 21113 **Personnel:** 466

**COLUMBIA BROWNWOOD MED CTR** See Brownwood Regional Medical Center

**BRYAN—Brazos County**

**CAPROCK HOSPITAL**, 3134 Briarcrest Drive, Zip 77802–3014; tel. 979/314–2323, (Nonreporting) **F**3 40 41 42 82 107 114 115 **P**4
Primary Contact: Braden Anderson, Chief Executive Officer
**Control:** Partnership, Investor–owned (for–profit) **Service:** General medical and surgical

> **Staffed Beds:** 10 **Admissions:** 27 **Census:** 1 **Outpatient Visits:** 5686 **Births:** 0 **Total Expense ($000):** 10447 **Payroll Expense ($000):** 2728 **Personnel:** 55

✠ **CHI ST. JOSEPH HEALTH REHABILITATION HOSPITAL, AN AFFILIATE OF ENCOMPASS HEALTH (673065)**, 1600 Joseph Drive, Suite 2000, Zip 77802–1502; tel. 979/213–4300, (Nonreporting) **A**1 **S** Encompass Health Corporation, Birmingham, AL
Primary Contact: Amy Gray, Chief Executive Officer
CFO: Kris Smith, Controller
Web address: www.encompasshealth.com/locations/stjrehab
**Control:** Corporation, Investor–owned (for–profit) **Service:** Rehabilitation

> **Staffed Beds:** 49

✠ **CHI ST. JOSEPH REGIONAL HEALTH CENTER (450011)**, 2801 Franciscan Drive, Zip 77802–2599; tel. 979/776–3777, (Nonreporting) **A**1 2 3 5 10 **F**3 7 11 12 13 15 17 18 20 22 24 28 29 30 31 32 34 35 37 40 42 43 44 45 46 48 49 50 53 54 57 59 64 65 67 68 70 72 74 75 76 77 78 79 80 81 82 84 85 86 87 89 93 96 107 110 111 114 118 119 121 123 124 126 127 129 130 131 132 135 143 144 146 148 **P**4 **S** CommonSpirit Health, Chicago, IL
Primary Contact: Theron Park, Chief Executive Officer
CFO: Lisa McNair, CPA, Senior Vice President and Chief Financial Officer
CMO: Kia Parsi, M.D., Chief Medical Officer
CIO: John Phillips, Vice President Information Services
CHR: Michael G Costa, Vice President Human Resources
Web address: www.st-joseph.org
**Control:** Church operated, Nongovernment, not–for–profit **Service:** General medical and surgical

> **Staffed Beds:** 222 **Admissions:** 13670 **Census:** 150 **Outpatient Visits:** 312138 **Births:** 2082 **Total Expense ($000):** 267987 **Payroll Expense ($000):** 93734 **Personnel:** 1445

**PHYSICIANS CENTRE** See The Physicians Centre Hospital

**ST. JOSEPH REGIONAL HEALTH CENTER** See Chi St. Joseph Regional Health Center

☐ **THE PHYSICIANS CENTRE HOSPITAL (450834)**, 3131 University Drive East, Zip 77802–3473; tel. 979/731–3100, (Nonreporting) **A**1 3 10 **F**3 12 15 29 40 44 45 51 64 74 75 77 79 81 82 85 87 107 111 114 119 126 130 131 135 149 157
Primary Contact: Kori Rich, Chief Executive Officer
CFO: Paul Tannos, Chief Financial Officer
CMO: Barry Solcher, M.D., Chief of Staff
CIO: Shawn Clark, Director Information Systems
CHR: LeeAnn Ford, Director Human Resources and Imaging
CNO: Robert Raymond Lemay, R.N., Chief Nursing Officer
Web address: www.thephysicianscentre.com
**Control:** Corporation, Investor–owned (for–profit) **Service:** Surgical

> **Staffed Beds:** 16 **Admissions:** 314 **Census:** 2 **Outpatient Visits:** 10654 **Births:** 0 **Total Expense ($000):** 16847 **Payroll Expense ($000):** 4655 **Personnel:** 94

**BUDA—Hays County**

☐ **BAYLOR SCOTT & WHITE MEDICAL CENTER - BUDA**, 5330 Overpass Drive, Zip 78610–2300; tel. 737/999–6200, (Nonreporting) **A**1 **S** Baylor Scott & White Health, Dallas, TX
Primary Contact: Jay Fox, President
Web address: www.https://www.bswhealth.com/locations/buda/Pages/default.aspx
**Control:** Other not–for–profit (including NFP Corporation) **Service:** General medical and surgical

> **Staffed Beds:** 15

**BURLESON—Tarrant County**

⇑ **BAYLOR EMERGENCY MEDICAL CENTERS - BURLESON** See Baylor Scott & White Emergency Hospital—Burleson

---

**Hospital, Medicare Provider Number, Address, Telephone, Approval, Facility, and Physician Codes, Health Care System**

★ American Hospital Association (AHA) membership    ◇ Healthcare Facilities Accreditation Program    ⇑ Center for Improvement in Healthcare Quality Accreditation
☐ The Joint Commission accreditation    ◇ DNV Healthcare Inc. accreditation    △ Commission on Accreditation of Rehabilitation Facilities (CARF) accreditation

⇑ **BAYLOR SCOTT & WHITE EMERGENCY HOSPITAL—BURLESON (670107)**, 12500 South Freeway Suite 100, Zip 76028-7128; tel. 214/294-6250, (Includes BAYLOR EMERGENCY MEDICAL CENTERS - MANSFIELD, Mailing address: 1776 US 287, Suite 100, Mansfield, Texas, Zip 76063; tel. 214/294-6300; Vic Schmerbeck, Chief Executive Officer), (Nonreporting) **A**10 21 **F3** 40 107 119 149 **S** Emerus, The Woodlands, TX
Primary Contact: Vic Schmerbeck, Chief Executive Officer
Web address: www.bayloremc.com/burleson
**Control**: Corporation, Investor-owned (for-profit) **Service**: General medical and surgical

**Staffed Beds:** 24 **Admissions:** 539 **Census:** 3 **Outpatient Visits:** 32745 **Births:** 0 **Total Expense ($000):** 25254 **Payroll Expense ($000):** 6800 **Personnel:** 82

**HUGULEY MEMORIAL MEDICAL CENTER** See Texas Health Huguley Hospital Fort Worth South

⊞ **TEXAS HEALTH HUGULEY HOSPITAL FORT WORTH SOUTH (450677)**, 11801 South Freeway, Zip 76028-7021, Mailing Address: P.O. Box 6337, Fort Worth, Zip 76115-0337; tel. 817/293-9110, (Nonreporting) **A**1 10 **F3** 5 11 13 15 17 18 20 22 24 26 28 29 30 31 32 34 35 37 38 40 41 43 45 46 48 49 50 51 53 54 56 57 59 60 64 65 68 70 71 73 74 75 76 77 78 79 80 81 84 85 86 87 91 93 98 100 101 102 104 105 107 108 110 111 114 115 118 119 126 130 131 132 135 146 147 148 152 153 154 156 **P6 S** AdventHealth, Altamonte Springs, FL
Primary Contact: Penny Johnson, Chief Executive Officer
CFO: Jesse Sutton, Senior Vice President and Chief Financial Officer
CMO: Edward Laue, M.D., Chief Medical Officer
CIO: John Delano, Chief Information Officer, Southwest Region
CHR: Amber Owen, Regional Vice President, Human Resources
CNO: Tammy Ellis, FACHE, R.N., Vice President Patient Services
Web address: www.TexasHealthHuguley.org
**Control**: Church operated, Nongovernment, not-for-profit **Service**: General medical and surgical

**Staffed Beds:** 193 **Admissions:** 10889 **Census:** 127 **Outpatient Visits:** 134170 **Births:** 1255 **Total Expense ($000):** 190515 **Payroll Expense ($000):** 73979 **Personnel:** 1143

**BURNET—Burnet County**

⊞ **ASCENSION SETON HIGHLAND LAKES (451365)**, 3201 South Water Street, Zip 78611-4510, Mailing Address: P.O. Box 1219, Zip 78611-7219; tel. 512/715-3000, (Nonreporting) **A**1 3 5 10 18 **F**1 3 11 15 28 29 30 34 35 40 43 45 46 50 51 57 59 64 67 68 71 74 79 81 85 87 89 92 93 97 107 108 109 110 111 115 118 119 126 127 130 132 133 146 148 154 **S** Ascension Healthcare, Saint Louis, MO
Primary Contact: Scott O. Fuller, President and Chief Executive Officer
COO: Karen Christine Litterer, R.N., MSN, Administrator and Chief Operating Officer
CFO: Douglas D Waite, Senior Vice President and Chief Financial Officer
Web address: www.seton.net
**Control**: Church operated, Nongovernment, not-for-profit **Service**: General medical and surgical

**Staffed Beds:** 19 **Admissions:** 618 **Census:** 7 **Outpatient Visits:** 96697 **Births:** 0 **Total Expense ($000):** 43336 **Payroll Expense ($000):** 12602 **Personnel:** 247

**SETON HIGHLAND LAKES** See Ascension Seton Highland Lakes

**CALDWELL—Burleson County**

**BURLESON ST. JOSEPH HEALTH CENTER** See Chi St. Joseph Health Burleson Hospital

⊞ **CHI ST. JOSEPH HEALTH BURLESON HOSPITAL (451305)**, 1101 Woodson Drive, Zip 77836-1052, Mailing Address: P.O. Box 360, Zip 77836-0360; tel. 979/567-3245, (Nonreporting) **A**1 10 18 **F3** 7 11 28 29 30 34 35 40 43 57 59 64 93 119 130 133 135 143 **S** CommonSpirit Health, Chicago, IL
Primary Contact: Theron Park, Chief Executive Officer
CFO: Daniel Goggin, Senior Vice President and Chief Financial Officer
CMO: Kristel Leubner, D.O., Chief of Staff
CHR: Jackie Stradtman, Director Human Resources
CNO: Heather Page, MSN, Director of Nursing
Web address: www.chistjoseph.org/
**Control**: Church operated, Nongovernment, not-for-profit **Service**: General medical and surgical

**Staffed Beds:** 12 **Admissions:** 189 **Census:** 5 **Outpatient Visits:** 8175 **Births:** 0 **Total Expense ($000):** 10229 **Payroll Expense ($000):** 3942 **Personnel:** 58

**CAMERON—Milam County**

**CAMERON HOSPITAL (670094)**, 806 North Crockett Avenue, Zip 76520-2553; tel. 254/605-1300, (Nonreporting)
Primary Contact: Troy Zinn, Chief Executive Officer
Web address: www.lrhealthcare.com/cameronhospital
**Control**: Corporation, Investor-owned (for-profit) **Service**: General medical and surgical

**Staffed Beds:** 6

**LITTLE RIVER CAMERON HOSPITAL** See Cameron Hospital

**CANADIAN—Hemphill County**

**HEMPHILL COUNTY HOSPITAL (450578)**, 1020 South Fourth Street, Zip 79014-3315; tel. 806/323-6422, (Total facility includes 45 beds in nursing home-type unit) (Nonreporting) **A**10 20 **F2** 3 7 10 29 35 40 45 56 57 59 62 63 64 68 69 87 89 93 97 102 104 107 108 119 127 128 129 130 133 146 147 148
Primary Contact: Christy Francis, Chief Executive Officer
CFO: Bob Ericson, Chief Financial Officer
CMO: G. Anthony Cook, M.D., Medical Director
CIO: Brian Goza, Chief Information Officer
CHR: David G Troublefield, Director, Human Resources
CNO: Debra Sappenfield, R.N., Chief Nursing Officer
Web address: www.hchdst.org
**Control**: Hospital district or authority, Government, Nonfederal **Service**: General medical and surgical

**Staffed Beds:** 64 **Admissions:** 277 **Census:** 36 **Outpatient Visits:** 18155 **Births:** 0 **Total Expense ($000):** 13369 **Payroll Expense ($000):** 5828 **Personnel:** 102

**CARRIZO SPRINGS—Dimmit County**

**DIMMIT COUNTY MEMORIAL HOSPITAL** See Dimmit Regional Hospital

★ **DIMMIT REGIONAL HOSPITAL (451390)**, 704 Hospital Drive, Zip 78834-3836, Mailing Address: P.O. Box 1016, Zip 78834-7016; tel. 830/876-2424, (Nonreporting) **A**10 18 **F**11 13 15 40 43 57 64 70 76 81 89 93 107 115 119 133 154
Primary Contact: John A. Graves, Chief Executive Officer
CFO: Alma Melendez, Controller
Web address: www.dimmitregionalhospital.com/
**Control**: Other not-for-profit (including NFP Corporation) **Service**: General medical and surgical

**Staffed Beds:** 35 **Admissions:** 503 **Census:** 6 **Outpatient Visits:** 21281 **Births:** 157 **Total Expense ($000):** 18610 **Payroll Expense ($000):** 7461 **Personnel:** 147

**CARROLLTON—Denton County**

**BAYLOR SCOTT & WHITE MEDICAL CENTER - CARROLLTON** See Carrollton Regional Medical Center

**TX**

✠ **CARROLLTON REGIONAL MEDICAL CENTER (450730)**, 4343 North Josey Lane, Zip 75010–4691; tel. 972/394–1010, (Nonreporting) **A**1 10 **F**3 11 14 15 18 20 22 29 30 31 34 35 40 41 45 46 47 48 49 50 51 54 56 57 59 60 64 66 68 70 74 75 78 79 80 81 84 85 93 107 108 109 110 111 112 113 114 115 116 117 118 119 126 129 130 132 134 146 148 154
Primary Contact: William Leyhe, Chief Executive Officer
CFO: James McNatt, Chief Financial Officer
CMO: Matthew Smith, M.D., Vice President Medical Affairs and Chief Medical Officer
CIO: Paul Ratcliff, Director Information Services
CHR: Erica Calime, Director Human Resources
CNO: Barbara Vaughn, R.N., Chief Nursing Officer
Web address: www.https://www.crmc.health/
**Control**: Other not–for–profit (including NFP Corporation) **Service**: General medical and surgical

**Staffed Beds**: 89 **Admissions**: 4095 **Census**: 49 **Outpatient Visits**: 51440 **Births**: 0 **Total Expense ($000)**: 102604 **Payroll Expense ($000)**: 35593 **Personnel**: 359

☐ **CARROLLTON SPRINGS (454119)**, 2225 Parker Road, Zip 75010–4711; tel. 972/242–4114, (Nonreporting) **A**1 10 **F**4 98 102 103 104 105 151 152 153 154 **S** Springstone, Louisville, KY
Primary Contact: Samantha Castle, Chief Executive Officer
Web address: www.carrolltonsprings.com
**Control**: Corporation, Investor–owned (for–profit) **Service**: Psychiatric

**Staffed Beds**: 78 **Admissions**: 2393 **Census**: 61 **Outpatient Visits**: 36288 **Births**: 0 **Total Expense ($000)**: 21073 **Payroll Expense ($000)**: 13473 **Personnel**: 192

**LEGENT ORTHOPEDIC HOSPITAL CARROLLTON (670265)**, 1401 East Trinity Mills Road, Zip 75006; tel. 972/810–0700, (Data for 134 days) (Nonreporting) **A**10 **F**3 29 40 50 68 75 79 81 85 87 107 119 130
Primary Contact: Brittani James, R.N., Vice President Operations
Web address: www.https://www.psnaffiliates.com/
**Control**: Corporation, Investor–owned (for–profit) **Service**: Surgical

**Staffed Beds**: 18 **Admissions**: 377 **Census**: 3 **Outpatient Visits**: 2451 **Births**: 0 **Total Expense ($000)**: 20069 **Payroll Expense ($000)**: 4941 **Personnel**: 73

**SAGECREST HOSPITAL** See Legent Orthopedic Hospital Carrollton

✠ **SELECT SPECIALTY HOSPITAL-DALLAS (452022)**, 2329 West Parker Road, Zip 75010–4713; tel. 469/892–1400, (Nonreporting) **A**1 10 **F**1 3 29 56 74 75 77 85 91 107 114 119 130 135 148 **S** Select Medical Corporation, Mechanicsburg, PA
Primary Contact: John O'Hearn, Chief Executive Officer
Web address: www.firsttexashospital.com/
**Control**: Corporation, Investor–owned (for–profit) **Service**: Acute long–term care hospital

**Staffed Beds**: 60 **Admissions**: 314 **Census**: 24 **Outpatient Visits**: 0 **Births**: 0 **Total Expense ($000)**: 19272 **Payroll Expense ($000)**: 7468 **Personnel**: 97

**SELECT SPECIALTY HOSPITAL-NORTH DALLAS** See Select Specialty Hospital-Dallas

**CARTHAGE—Panola County**

**EAST TEXAS MEDICAL CENTER CARTHAGE** See UT Health Carthage

✠ **UT HEALTH CARTHAGE (450210)**, 409 Cottage Road, Zip 75633–1466; tel. 903/693–3841, (Nonreporting) **A**1 10 20 **F**3 8 11 15 28 29 30 34 35 40 43 45 50 57 59 64 65 75 81 85 107 108 110 111 115 119 127 129 145 146 149 150 155 157 **P**6 **S** Ardent Health Services, Nashville, TN
Primary Contact: Mark Leitner, Chief Executive Officer
CMO: Salah Almohammed, Chief of Staff
CIO: Renee Lawhorn, Director Medical Records
CHR: Amber Cox, Director Human Resources
CNO: Judy Peterson, R.N., Chief Nursing Officer
Web address: www.https://uthealthcarthage.com/
**Control**: Corporation, Investor–owned (for–profit) **Service**: General medical and surgical

**Staffed Beds**: 23 **Admissions**: 626 **Census**: 5 **Outpatient Visits**: 67343 **Births**: 0 **Total Expense ($000)**: 19726 **Payroll Expense ($000)**: 6985 **Personnel**: 135

**CEDAR PARK—Williamson County**

**BAYLOR SCOTT & WHITE EMERGENCY HOSPITAL- CEDAR PARK** See Baylor Scott & White Emergency Medical Center- Cedar Park

**BAYLOR SCOTT & WHITE EMERGENCY MEDICAL CENTER- CEDAR PARK (670087)**, 900 East Whitestone Boulevard, Zip 78613–9093; tel. 512/684–4911, (Data for 181 days) (Nonreporting) **A**10 **F**3 40 107 119 149 **P**5
Primary Contact: Vic Schmerbeck, Chief Executive Officer
Web address: www.sweh.org
**Control**: Corporation, Investor–owned (for–profit) **Service**: General medical and surgical

**Staffed Beds**: 8 **Admissions**: 3 **Census**: 1 **Outpatient Visits**: 3326 **Births**: 0 **Total Expense ($000)**: 3127 **Payroll Expense ($000)**: 981 **Personnel**: 34

✠ **CEDAR PARK REGIONAL MEDICAL CENTER (670043)**, 1401 Medical Parkway, Zip 78613–7763; tel. 512/528–7000, (Nonreporting) **A**1 5 10 **F**3 12 13 15 18 20 22 28 29 31 34 35 37 39 40 42 43 45 46 47 49 50 54 57 59 64 70 73 74 75 76 77 78 79 81 82 85 87 89 93 107 108 110 111 114 115 116 118 119 126 129 130 132 135 146 147 148 154 **S** Community Health Systems, Inc., Franklin, TN
Primary Contact: Carl (Bo) Beaudry, Chief Executive Officer
CFO: Erich Wallschlaeger, Chief Financial Officer
CIO: Brad Hoar, Director Information and Technology
CHR: Jeffery Ward, Director Human Resources
CNO: Krista Baty, R.N., Chief Nursing Officer
Web address: www.cedarparkregional.com
**Control**: Corporation, Investor–owned (for–profit) **Service**: General medical and surgical

**Staffed Beds**: 108 **Admissions**: 5165 **Census**: 51 **Outpatient Visits**: 62723 **Births**: 916 **Total Expense ($000)**: 102294 **Payroll Expense ($000)**: 35740 **Personnel**: 627

**CHILDRESS—Childress County**

**CHILDRESS GENERAL HOSPITAL** See Childress Regional Medical Center

★ **CHILDRESS REGIONAL MEDICAL CENTER (450369)**, 901 Highway 83 North, Zip 79201–5800, Mailing Address: P.O. Box 1030, Zip 79201–1030; tel. 940/937–6371, (Nonreporting) **A**10 20 **F**3 7 8 13 15 29 31 32 34 35 40 43 45 50 56 57 59 60 61 62 63 64 65 66 68 75 77 78 79 81 84 91 92 93 107 108 111 114 119 126 127 129 130 133 154 157
Primary Contact: Kevin Latimer, Chief Executive Officer
COO: Holly Holcomb, R.N., Chief Operating Officer
CFO: Emilee Stratton, Chief Financial Officer
CMO: Dustin Pratt, M.D., Chief of Staff
CIO: Holly Holcomb, R.N., Chie Operating Officer
CHR: Gayle Cannon, Director Human Resources
CNO: Sulynn Mester, R.N., Chief Nursing Officer
Web address: www.childresshospital.com
**Control**: Hospital district or authority, Government, Nonfederal **Service**: General medical and surgical

**Staffed Beds**: 35 **Admissions**: 727 **Census**: 9 **Outpatient Visits**: 214235 **Births**: 164 **Total Expense ($000)**: 30152 **Payroll Expense ($000)**: 15611 **Personnel**: 234

**CLEBURNE—Johnson County**

✠ **TEXAS HEALTH HARRIS METHODIST HOSPITAL CLEBURNE (450148)**, 201 Walls Drive, Zip 76033–4007; tel. 817/641–2551, (Nonreporting) **A**1 10 **F**3 11 13 15 18 29 30 34 35 40 43 47 48 59 64 65 66 68 70 75 76 77 79 81 85 87 93 107 108 110 111 114 119 124 126 132 135 146 147 148 149 154 **P**6 **S** Texas Health Resources, Arlington, TX
Primary Contact: Ajith Pai, PharmD, FACHE, President
CFO: Shelly Miland, Group Finance Officer
CMO: Judy Laviolette, M.D., Chief Medical Officer
CIO: Brenda Taylor, Director Information Systems
CHR: Marsha Adams, Interim Director Human Resources
CNO: Vicki Brockman, R.N., Chief Nursing Officer
Web address: www.texashealth.org
**Control**: Other not–for–profit (including NFP Corporation) **Service**: General medical and surgical

**Staffed Beds**: 92 **Admissions**: 2967 **Census**: 26 **Outpatient Visits**: 43946 **Births**: 481 **Total Expense ($000)**: 68424 **Payroll Expense ($000)**: 26053 **Personnel**: 325

**WALLS REGIONAL HOSPITAL** See Texas Health Harris Methodist Hospital Cleburne

**TX**

**Hospital, Medicare Provider Number, Address, Telephone, Approval, Facility, and Physician Codes, Health Care System**

★ American Hospital Association (AHA) membership
☐ The Joint Commission accreditation
○ Healthcare Facilities Accreditation Program
◇ DNV Healthcare Inc. accreditation
⇑ Center for Improvement in Healthcare Quality Accreditation
△ Commission on Accreditation of Rehabilitation Facilities (CARF) accreditation

© 2021 AHA Guide *Many Facility Codes have changed. Please refer to the AHA Guide Code Chart.* Hospitals **A663**

## CLEVELAND—Liberty County

☐ **CLEVELAND EMERGENCY HOSPITAL (670115)**, 1017 South Travis Avenue, Zip 77327–5152; tel. 281/592–5400, (Includes TEXAS EMERGENCY HOSPITAL, Mailing address: 300 East Crockett Street, Cleveland, Texas, Zip 77327–4029; tel. 281/592–5410; David Way, Chief Executive Officer), (Nonreporting) **A**1 10 **F**3 18 20 22 29 40 42 45 46 47 48 49 57 79 81 82 87 107 108 109 111 114 115 119 127
Primary Contact: Don Vickers, Chief Executive Officer
**Control**: Partnership, Investor–owned (for–profit) **Service**: General medical and surgical

**Staffed Beds**: 16 **Admissions**: 363 **Census**: 3 **Outpatient Visits**: 18795 **Births**: 0 **Total Expense ($000)**: 42914 **Payroll Expense ($000)**: 15898 **Personnel**: 253

## CLIFTON—Bosque County

★ ⬆ **GOODALL-WITCHER HOSPITAL (451385)**, 101 Posey Avenue, Zip 76634–1289, Mailing Address: P.O. Box 549, Zip 76634–0549; tel. 254/675–8322, (Nonreporting) **A**10 18 21 **F**3 11 13 15 28 29 30 34 35 36 40 43 45 50 53 57 59 62 64 65 68 76 77 81 93 107 108 114 119 127 129 130 133 146 147 148 **P**4 5 6
Primary Contact: Adam Willmann, President and Chief Executive Officer
CFO: Jerry Pickett, Chief Financial Officer
CMO: Kevin Blanton, D.O., Chief of Staff
CHR: Jennie Oldham, Director Human Resources
CNO: Donna Nichols, R.N., Chief Nursing Officer
Web address: www.gwhf.org
**Control**: Hospital district or authority, Government, Nonfederal **Service**: General medical and surgical

**Staffed Beds**: 25 **Admissions**: 621 **Census**: 11 **Outpatient Visits**: 53174 **Births**: 60 **Total Expense ($000)**: 22101 **Payroll Expense ($000)**: 9666 **Personnel**: 187

⬆ **GOODALL-WITCHER HOSPITAL AUTHORITY** See Goodall-Witcher Hospital

## COLEMAN—Coleman County

**COLEMAN COUNTY COMMUNITY HOSP** See Coleman County Medical Center

**COLEMAN COUNTY MEDICAL CENTER (451347)**, 310 South Pecos Street, Zip 76834–4159; tel. 325/625–2135, (Nonreporting) **A**10 18 **F**3 11 13 28 29 32 34 40 43 44 45 50 56 57 59 64 65 68 81 84 86 87 93 97 107 114 119 127 130 132 133 147 148 149 150 154 **S** Preferred Management Corporation, Shawnee, OK
Primary Contact: Clay Vogel, Administrator and Chief Executive Officer
CMO: Paul Reynolds, M.D., Medical Director
CIO: Harvey Ramirez, Chief Information Officer
CHR: Sue Titsworth, Director Human Resources
CNO: Melissa Ereman, R.N., Chief Nursing Officer
Web address: www.colemantexas.org/hospital.html
**Control**: Corporation, Investor–owned (for–profit) **Service**: General medical and surgical

**Staffed Beds**: 25 **Admissions**: 613 **Census**: 8 **Outpatient Visits**: 23575 **Births**: 24 **Total Expense ($000)**: 11392 **Payroll Expense ($000)**: 5201 **Personnel**: 112

## COLLEGE STATION—Brazos County

⊞ **BAYLOR SCOTT & WHITE HOSPITAL MEDICAL CENTER - COLLEGE STATION (670088)**, 700 Scott & White Drive, Zip 77845; tel. 979/207–0100, (Nonreporting) **A**1 5 10 **F**3 10 12 13 14 15 18 20 22 24 26 28 29 30 31 34 35 40 43 45 46 47 48 49 50 51 56 57 59 61 63 64 65 67 68 70 72 73 74 75 76 77 78 79 81 82 83 84 85 87 89 93 94 97 101 102 104 107 108 110 111 114 115 118 119 120 121 122 123 124 125 126 127 129 130 131 135 145 146 147 148 156 157 158 **S** Baylor Scott & White Health, Dallas, TX
Primary Contact: Jason Jennings, FACHE, President
Web address: www.sw.org/location/college-station-hospital
**Control**: Other not–for–profit (including NFP Corporation) **Service**: General medical and surgical

**Staffed Beds**: 119 **Admissions**: 7346 **Census**: 70 **Outpatient Visits**: 429595 **Births**: 1534 **Total Expense ($000)**: 182788 **Payroll Expense ($000)**: 48800 **Personnel**: 917

⊞ **CHI ST. JOSEPH COLLEGE STATION HOSPITAL (450299)**, 1604 Rock Prairie Road, Zip 77845–8345; tel. 979/764–5100, (Data for 304 days) (Nonreporting) **A**1 5 10 **F**3 11 12 15 18 20 22 24 26 28 29 30 34 40 43 45 46 57 74 79 80 81 85 87 93 107 110 111 114 119 124 126 129 130 146 148 157 **P**7 **S** CommonSpirit Health, Chicago, IL
Primary Contact: Theron Park, Chief Executive Officer
COO: Vicky Cha Bridier, Chief Operating Officer
CFO: Kenneth Pannell, Chief Financial Officer
CIO: Daphane Hartman, Director Information Systems
CHR: Sharon Bond, Director Human Resources
CNO: Sherri Welch, R.N., Chief Nursing Officer
Web address: www.csmedcenter.com
**Control**: Corporation, Investor–owned (for–profit) **Service**: General medical and surgical

**Staffed Beds**: 144 **Admissions**: 2835 **Census**: 35 **Outpatient Visits**: 38020 **Births**: 0 **Total Expense ($000)**: 63447 **Payroll Expense ($000)**: 21176 **Personnel**: 291

**COLLEGE STATION MEDICAL CENTER** See Chi St. Joseph College Station Hospital

☐ **ROCK PRAIRIE BEHAVIORAL HEALTH (454125)**, 3550 Normand Drive, Zip 77845–6399; tel. 979/703–8848, (Nonreporting) **A**1 10 **F**5 29 34 35 38 40 56 57 98 99 101 102 103 105 130 135 149 152 153 **S** Strategic Behavioral Health, LLC, Memphis, TN
Primary Contact: Jennifer Kelly, Chief Executive Officer
CMO: Jason Boley, M.D., Medical Director
CHR: MaxAnne Jones, Director Human Resources
Web address: www.rockprairiebh.com/
**Control**: Partnership, Investor–owned (for–profit) **Service**: Psychiatric

**Staffed Beds**: 72 **Admissions**: 1910 **Census**: 37 **Outpatient Visits**: 2486 **Births**: 0 **Total Expense ($000)**: 12249 **Payroll Expense ($000)**: 7210 **Personnel**: 126

## COLORADO CITY—Mitchell County

★ **MITCHELL COUNTY HOSPITAL (451342)**, 997 West Interstate 20, Zip 79512–2685; tel. 325/728–3431, (Nonreporting) **A**10 18 **F**3 7 11 28 29 34 35 40 43 45 50 53 57 59 64 65 68 71 81 86 87 93 107 108 109 114 119 127 133 135 146 **P**6
Primary Contact: Robbie Dewberry, Chief Executive Officer
CFO: Joe Wright, Chief Financial Officer
CMO: Dee A Roach, M.D., Chief of Staff
CHR: Deana Overton, Director Human Resources
CNO: Donna Goebel, M.D., Chief Nursing Officer
Web address: www.mitchellcountyhospital.com
**Control**: Hospital district or authority, Government, Nonfederal **Service**: General medical and surgical

**Staffed Beds**: 17 **Admissions**: 458 **Census**: 7 **Outpatient Visits**: 14867 **Births**: 0 **Total Expense ($000)**: 19440 **Payroll Expense ($000)**: 9093 **Personnel**: 215

## COLUMBUS—Colorado County

**COLUMBUS COMMUNITY HOSPITAL (450370)**, 110 Shult Drive, Zip 78934–3010; tel. 979/732–2371, (Nonreporting) **A**5 10 20 **F**11 13 15 29 35 40 43 57 68 76 79 81 107 110 111 114 119 127 130 133 135 149 154 156
Primary Contact: James Vanek, Chief Executive Officer
CFO: Regina Wicke, Chief Financial Officer
CMO: Robert Katz, M.D., Chief of Staff
CIO: Ashley Mathis, Privacy Officer
CHR: Janie Hammonds, Human Resources Officer
CNO: Jeno Hargrove, R.N., Director of Nursing
Web address: www.columbusch.com
**Control**: Other not–for–profit (including NFP Corporation) **Service**: General medical and surgical

**Staffed Beds**: 40 **Admissions**: 846 **Census**: 8 **Outpatient Visits**: 90771 **Births**: 329 **Total Expense ($000)**: 29338 **Payroll Expense ($000)**: 9254 **Personnel**: 173

## COMANCHE—Comanche County

**COMANCHE COMMUNITY HOSPITAL** See Comanche County Medical Center

**TX**

★ **COMANCHE COUNTY MEDICAL CENTER (451382)**, 10201 Highway 16; Zip 76442–4462; tel. 254/879–4900, (Nonreporting) **A**10 18 **F**3 11 15 28 29 30 34 35 40 43 45 50 53 57 59 64 65 75 77 79 81 85 86 87 93 97 107 108 110 111 115 119 127 129 130 131 133 145 146 147 148 156
Primary Contact: Larry Troxell, Chief Executive Officer
CMO: Guyle Donham, M.D., Chief of Staff
CIO: Ismelda Garza, Director Information Systems
CHR: Karen DeLavan, Interim Director Human Resources
CNO: Colleen Jedlicka, R.N., JD, Chief Nursing Officer
Web address: www.comanchecmc.org
**Control**: Other not–for–profit (including NFP Corporation) **Service**: General medical and surgical

**Staffed Beds**: 23 **Admissions**: 759 **Census**: 9 **Outpatient Visits**: 31714 **Births**: 0 **Total Expense ($000)**: 28211 **Payroll Expense ($000)**: 10198 **Personnel**: 223

### CONROE—Montgomery County

**ASPIRE BEHAVIORAL HEALTH OF CONROE** See Aspire Hospital

⊞ **ASPIRE HOSPITAL (670093)**, 2006 South Loop 336 West, Suite 500, Zip 77304–3315; tel. 936/647–3500, (Nonreporting) **A**1 10 **F**3 34 57 59 78 93 98 100 101 103 104 105 107 108 111 112 113 114 115 118 119 120 121 123 124 129 130 131 148 153
Primary Contact: Kostas Gotsoulias, Interim Chief Executive Officer
CFO: Bob Gray, Chief Financial Officer
CIO: John Heemann, Vice President and Chief Information Officer
CHR: Angela Walker, Manager Human Resources
Web address: www.aspirehospital.com
**Control**: Partnership, Investor–owned (for–profit) **Service**: Psychiatric

**Staffed Beds**: 30 **Admissions**: 818 **Census**: 17 **Outpatient Visits**: 35981 **Births**: 0 **Total Expense ($000)**: 12577 **Payroll Expense ($000)**: 5134 **Personnel**: 105

**CHG CORNERSTONE HOSPITAL CONROE (452107)**, 1500 Grand Lake Drive, Zip 77304–2891; tel. 936/523–1800, (Nonreporting) **A**10 22 **F**1 3 29 40 70 75 77 79 85 86 87 91 119 130 148 153 **P**5 **S** Cornerstone Healthcare Group, Dallas, TX
Primary Contact: Suzanne Kretschmer, Chief Executive Officer
Web address: www.chghospitals.com/conroe/
**Control**: Partnership, Investor–owned (for–profit) **Service**: Acute long–term care hospital

**Staffed Beds**: 41 **Admissions**: 402 **Census**: 26 **Outpatient Visits**: 0 **Births**: 0 **Total Expense ($000)**: 14095 **Payroll Expense ($000)**: 5988 **Personnel**: 80

**CONROE REGIONAL MEDICAL CENTER** See Hca Houston Healthcare Conroe

⊞ **ENCOMPASS HEALTH REHABILITATION HOSPITAL THE WOODLANDS (453059)**, 18550 'IH' 45 South, Zip 77384; tel. 281/364–2000, (Nonreporting) **A**1 10 **F**3 28 29 34 35 44 57 59 65 68 74 75 77 78 79 82 86 87 90 91 95 96 130 132 148 149 **S** Encompass Health Corporation, Birmingham, AL
Primary Contact: Jennifer Brewer, Chief Executive Officer
CMO: Ben Agana, M.D., Medical Director
CHR: Valerie Wells, Manager Human Resources
Web address: www.healthsouththewoodlands.com
**Control**: Corporation, Investor–owned (for–profit) **Service**: Rehabilitation

**Staffed Beds**: 84 **Admissions**: 724 **Census**: 23 **Outpatient Visits**: 0 **Births**: 0 **Total Expense ($000)**: 14157 **Payroll Expense ($000)**: 6463 **Personnel**: 115

⊞ **HCA HOUSTON HEALTHCARE CONROE (450222)**, 504 Medical Boulevard, Zip 77304, Mailing Address: P.O. Box 1538, Zip 77305–1538; tel. 936/539–1111, (Nonreporting) **A**1 3 10 **F**3 11 12 13 17 18 20 22 24 26 28 29 31 33 34 40 43 45 46 47 48 49 51 53 54 56 57 59 60 64 67 68 70 72 74 75 76 77 78 79 81 82 85 89 90 91 93 107 108 111 112 114 115 116 117 118 119 121 123 126 129 130 131 132 135 142 144 146 147 148 154 156 157 **S** HCA Healthcare, Nashville, TN
Primary Contact: Matt Davis, FACHE, Chief Executive Officer
CFO: Thomas A Holt, Chief Financial Officer
CMO: Mujtaba Ali-Khan, D.O., Chief Medical Officer
CIO: Jeremy Fuller, Director Information Systems
CHR: Diana Howell, Director Human Resources
Web address: www.conroeregional.com/
**Control**: Partnership, Investor–owned (for–profit) **Service**: General medical and surgical

**Staffed Beds**: 310 **Admissions**: 16165 **Census**: 202 **Outpatient Visits**: 114682 **Births**: 1406 **Total Expense ($000)**: 215458 **Payroll Expense ($000)**: 77015 **Personnel**: 1104

**HEALTHSOUTH REHABILITATION HOSPITAL THE WOODLANDS** See Encompass Health Rehabilitation Hospital The Woodlands

**SOLARA HOSPITAL CONROE** See Chg Cornerstone Hospital Conroe

☐ **WOODLAND SPRINGS HOSPITAL (454144)**, 15680 Old Conroe Road, Zip 77384; tel. 936/270–7520, (Nonreporting) **A**1 **F**87 98 99 103 105 153 **S** Springstone, Louisville, KY
Primary Contact: Dustin Davis, Chief Executive Officer
Web address: www.https://www.woodlandspringshealth.com/
**Control**: State, Government, Nonfederal **Service**: Psychiatric

**Staffed Beds**: 96 **Admissions**: 2129 **Census**: 55 **Outpatient Visits**: 8510 **Births**: 0 **Total Expense ($000)**: 16135 **Payroll Expense ($000)**: 9035 **Personnel**: 131

### CORPUS CHRISTI—Nueces County

**ADA WILSON HOSP OF PHYS MED** See ADA Wilson Children's Center for Rehabilitation

**CHRISTUS SPOHN HOSP SHORELINE** See Christus Spohn Hospital Corpus Christi Shoreline

**CHRISTUS SPOHN HOSPITAL CORPUS CHRISTI** See Christus Spohn Hospital Corpus Christi Memorial

⊞ **CHRISTUS SPOHN HOSPITAL CORPUS CHRISTI MEMORIAL (450046)**, 2606 Hospital Boulevard, Zip 78405–1804, Mailing Address: P.O. Box 5280, Zip 78405; tel. 361/902–4000, (Includes CHRISTUS SPOHN HOSPITAL CORPUS CHRISTI SHORELINE, Mailing address: 600 Elizabeth Street, Corpus Christi, Texas, Zip 78404–2235; tel. 361/881–3000; Brian Connor, FACHE, President; CHRISTUS SPOHN HOSPITAL CORPUS CHRISTUS SOUTH, Mailing address: 5950 Saratoga, Corpus Christi, Texas, Zip 78414–4100; tel. 361/985–5000) (Total facility includes 10 beds in nursing home–type unit) **A**1 2 3 5 8 10 **F**3 11 13 17 18 20 22 24 26 28 29 30 31 34 35 37 38 39 40 43 45 46 47 48 49 50 51 53 54 56 57 59 60 64 65 66 68 70 71 72 74 75 76 77 78 79 81 84 85 87 90 91 92 93 94 96 98 101 102 103 107 108 111 114 115 118 119 120 121 123 124 126 127 128 130 131 141 142 144 145 146 147 148 154 156 **S** CHRISTUS Health, Irving, TX
Primary Contact: Osbert Blow, M.D., Ph.D., FACS, President and Chief Medical Officer
CFO: Brower Pam, Chief Financial Officer
CMO: Charles T. Volk, M.D., Regional Chief Medical Officer
CHR: Mary LaFrancois, Vice President Human Resources
CNO: Jennifer Gentry, R.N., Chief Nursing Officer
Web address: www.christusspohn.org
**Control**: Church operated, Nongovernment, not–for–profit **Service**: General medical and surgical

**Staffed Beds**: 488 **Admissions**: 27031 **Census**: 402 **Outpatient Visits**: 291284 **Births**: 2474 **Total Expense ($000)**: 594568 **Payroll Expense ($000)**: 161959 **Personnel**: 2434

**COLUMBIA DOCTORS REG MED CTR** See Corpus Christi Medical Center

**TX**

**Hospital, Medicare Provider Number, Address, Telephone, Approval, Facility, and Physician Codes, Health Care System**

★ American Hospital Association (AHA) membership  ○ Healthcare Facilities Accreditation Program  î Center for Improvement in Healthcare Quality Accreditation
☐ The Joint Commission accreditation  ◇ DNV Healthcare Inc. accreditation  △ Commission on Accreditation of Rehabilitation Facilities (CARF) accreditation

© 2021 AHA Guide  *Many Facility Codes have changed. Please refer to the AHA Guide Code Chart.*  Hospitals **A665**

⊞ **CORPUS CHRISTI MEDICAL CENTER (450788)**, 3315 South Alameda Street, Zip 78411–1883, Mailing Address: P.O. Box 8991, Zip 78468–8991; tel. 361/761–1400, (Includes CORPUS CHRISTI MEDICAL CENTER - BAYVIEW BEHAVIORAL HOSPITAL, Mailing address: 6629 Wooldridge Road, Corpus Christi, Texas, Zip 78414; tel. 361/986–9444; CORPUS CHRISTI MEDICAL CENTER - THE HEART HOSPITAL, Mailing address: 7002 Williams Drive, Corpus Christi, Texas, Zip 78412–4911; tel. 361/761–1000; Eric Evans, Chief Executive Officer; CORPUS CHRISTI MEDICAL CENTER BAY AREA, Mailing address: 7101 South Padre Island Drive, Corpus Christi, Texas, Zip 78412–4999; tel. 361/985–1200; Eric Evans, Chief Executive Officer), (Nonreporting) **A**1 3 5 10 13 **F**3 4 5 11 12 13 15 17 18 20 22 24 26 28 29 31 34 35 37 38 40 42 44 47 49 50 53 57 58 59 64 67 68 70 72 73 74 75 76 77 78 79 81 82 85 86 87 90 93 97 98 99 103 104 105 107 108 110 111 114 115 118 119 120 121 123 124 126 130 131 132 146 147 148 149 150 153 156 157 **P**3 8 **S** HCA Healthcare, Nashville, TN
Primary Contact: Eric Evans, Chief Executive Officer
CFO: Chris Nicosia, Chief Financial Officer
CHR: Michael Conwill, Director Human Resources
CNO: Kathleen A Rubano, MSN, R.N., Chief Nursing Officer
Web address: www.ccmedicalcenter.com
**Control**: Partnership, Investor–owned (for–profit) **Service**: General medical and surgical

**Staffed Beds**: 426 **Admissions**: 23337 **Census**: 310 **Outpatient Visits**: 141507 **Births**: 4033 **Total Expense ($000)**: 343789 **Payroll Expense ($000)**: 103463 **Personnel**: 1432

**CORPUS CHRUSTI MEDICAL CENTER** See Corpus Christi Medical Center Bay Area

⊞ △ **DRISCOLL CHILDREN'S HOSPITAL (453301)**, 3533 South Alameda Street, Zip 78411–1785, Mailing Address: P.O. Box 6530, Zip 78466–6530; tel. 361/694–5000, (Nonreporting) **A**1 3 5 7 10 **F**3 7 11 12 18 21 23 25 27 29 30 31 32 34 35 38 39 40 41 43 49 50 54 55 57 58 59 60 61 64 65 68 72 74 75 77 78 79 81 82 85 86 87 88 89 92 93 97 104 107 108 111 115 118 119 130 131 132 134 138 143 144 146 148 149 150 153 155 156
Primary Contact: Eric Hamon, Interim President and Chief Executive Officer
COO: Donna Quinn, Vice President Operations
CFO: Eric Hamon, Executive Vice President and Chief Financial Officer
CIO: Miguel Perez, III, Chief Information Officer
CHR: Bill Larsen, Vice President Human Resources
CNO: Julie A. Pina, Assistant Vice President Patient Care Services and Chief Nursing Officer
Web address: www.driscollchildrens.org
**Control**: Other not–for–profit (including NFP Corporation) **Service**: Children's general medical and surgical

**Staffed Beds**: 162 **Admissions**: 3776 **Census**: 76 **Outpatient Visits**: 186743 **Births**: 0 **Total Expense ($000)**: 311211 **Payroll Expense ($000)**: 114243 **Personnel**: 2047

**DRISCOLL FDN CHILDREN'S HOSP** See Driscoll Children's Hospital

**PADRE BEHAVIORAL HOSPITAL** See Corpus Christi Medical Center - Bayview Behavioral Hospital

⊞ **PAM REHABILITATION HOSPITAL OF CORPUS CHRISTI (673067)**, 345 South Water Street, Zip 78401–2819; tel. 361/500–0600, (Nonreporting) **A**1 **S** Post Acute Medical, LLC, Enola, PA
Primary Contact: Hector Bernal, Chief Executive Officer
Web address: www.postacutemedical.com
**Service**: Rehabilitation

**Staffed Beds**: 40

**POST ACUTE MEDICAL SPECIALTY HOSPITAL OF CORPUS CHRISTI** See Post Acute Medical Specialty Hospital of Corpus Christi - North

⊞ **POST ACUTE MEDICAL SPECIALTY HOSPITAL OF CORPUS CHRISTI - NORTH (452086)**, 600 Elizabeth Street, 3rd Floor, Zip 78404–2235; tel. 361/881–3223, (Includes PAM SPECIALTY HOSPITAL OF CORPUS CHRISTI BAYFRONT, Mailing address: 345 South Water Street, Corpus Christi, Texas, Zip 78401–2819; tel. 361/500–0600; Hector Bernal, Chief Executive Officer), (Nonreporting) **A**1 10 **F**1 3 29 75 85 87 91 148 **S** Post Acute Medical, LLC, Enola, PA
Primary Contact: Hector Bernal, Chief Executive Officer
Web address: www.postacutemedical.com/our-facilities/hospitals/post-acute-medical-specialty-hospital-corpus-christi/
**Control**: Corporation, Investor–owned (for–profit) **Service**: Acute long–term care hospital

**Staffed Beds**: 41 **Admissions**: 519 **Census**: 35 **Outpatient Visits**: 0 **Births**: 0 **Total Expense ($000)**: 16733 **Payroll Expense ($000)**: 6741 **Personnel**: 103

☐ **SOUTH TEXAS SURGICAL HOSPITAL (670061)**, 6130 Parkway Drive, Zip 78414–2455; tel. 361/993–2000, (Nonreporting) **A**1 3 10 **F**3 12 29 40 45 54 64 68 75 79 81 82 85 107 119 126 130 149 **S** National Surgical Healthcare, Chicago, IL
Primary Contact: David G. Covert, Chief Executive Officer
CFO: Julie Wittwer, Chief Financial Officer
CMO: Michael Mintz, M.D., Chief Medical Officer
CHR: Lory Beth Smith, Manager Human Resource
CNO: Jan O'Donnell, Chief Nursing Officer
Web address: www.southtexassurgicalhospital.com
**Control**: Partnership, Investor–owned (for–profit) **Service**: Surgical

**Staffed Beds**: 20 **Admissions**: 968 **Census**: 6 **Outpatient Visits**: 17144 **Births**: 0 **Total Expense ($000)**: 41897 **Payroll Expense ($000)**: 10353 **Personnel**: 172

## CORSICANA—Navarro County

**COLUMBIA NAVARRO REGIONAL HOSP** See Navarro Regional Hospital

⊞ **NAVARRO REGIONAL HOSPITAL (450447)**, 3201 West State Highway 22, Zip 75110–2469; tel. 903/654–6800, (Nonreporting) **A**1 10 19 **F**3 11 13 15 18 20 28 29 30 34 35 39 40 43 46 47 49 50 51 54 57 60 64 68 70 75 76 79 81 82 85 89 93 107 108 111 114 115 119 127 132 135 146 149 154 **S** Community Health Systems, Inc., Franklin, TN
Primary Contact: Curt M. Junkins, Chief Executive Officer
CFO: Shea C. Brock, Chief Financial Officer
CIO: Bryan Chilton, Director Information Systems
CHR: Melodee Pugh, Director Human Resources
CNO: Dona E Townsend, Chief Nursing Officer
Web address: www.navarrohospital.com
**Control**: Partnership, Investor–owned (for–profit) **Service**: General medical and surgical

**Staffed Beds**: 49 **Admissions**: 2306 **Census**: 19 **Outpatient Visits**: 65919 **Births**: 543 **Total Expense ($000)**: 47268 **Payroll Expense ($000)**: 15519 **Personnel**: 273

## CRANE—Crane County

★ **CRANE MEMORIAL HOSPITAL (451353)**, 1310 South Alford Street, Zip 79731–3899; tel. 432/558–3555, (Nonreporting) **A**10 18 **F**3 29 32 34 40 57 59 64 65 68 75 81 86 97 107 114 119 127 133 145 147 148 **P**2 6
Primary Contact: Dianne Yeager, Chief Executive Officer
CFO: Daniel Ibarra, Chief Financial Officer
CMO: Sixta Gumato, M.D., Chief Medical Officer
CHR: Becky Esparza, Human Resources
CNO: Pat Touchstone, Chief Nursing Officer
Web address: www.cranememorial.org
**Control**: Hospital district or authority, Government, Nonfederal **Service**: General medical and surgical

**Staffed Beds**: 10 **Admissions**: 89 **Census**: 2 **Outpatient Visits**: 11667 **Births**: 0 **Total Expense ($000)**: 8260 **Payroll Expense ($000)**: 3508 **Personnel**: 57

## CROCKETT—Houston County

○ **CROCKETT MEDICAL CENTER (451393)**, 1100 East Loop 304, Zip 75835–1810; tel. 936/546–3891, (Nonreporting) **A**11 18
Primary Contact: Tommy Johnson, Chief Executive Officer
Web address: www.crockettmedicalcenter.com
**Control**: Corporation, Investor–owned (for–profit) **Service**: General medical and surgical

**Staffed Beds**: 25

## CROSBYTON—Crosby County

**CROSBYTON CLINIC HOSPITAL (451345)**, 710 West Main Street, Zip 79322–2143; tel. 806/675–2382, (Nonreporting) **A**10 18 **F**7 40 57 59 68 93 119 127 133 **P**6
Primary Contact: Debra Miller, Administrator
CFO: Cherie Parkhill, Chief Financial Officer
CMO: Steve B Alley, M.D., Chief of Staff
CHR: Janie Cantu, Director Human Resources
CNO: Freda Bartlett, Director of Nursing
Web address: www.crosbytonclinichospital.com
**Control**: Other not–for–profit (including NFP Corporation) **Service**: General medical and surgical

**Staffed Beds**: 2 **Admissions**: 49 **Census**: 1 **Outpatient Visits**: 13276 **Births**: 0 **Total Expense ($000)**: 5462 **Payroll Expense ($000)**: 2410 **Personnel**: 55

## CUERO—Dewitt County

**CUERO COMMUNITY HOSPITAL** See Cuero Regional Hospital

**TX**

*Many Facility Codes have changed. Please refer to the AHA Guide Code Chart.*
© 2021 AHA Guide

★ **CUERO REGIONAL HOSPITAL (450597)**, 2550 North Esplanade Street, Zip 77954–4716; tel. 361/275–6191, (Nonreporting) **A**3 10 **F**3 7 11 13 15 29 34 40 43 45 53 57 59 62 64 68 70 75 76 77 79 81 85 86 93 107 108 110 111 115 118 119 127 129 130 131 154 **P**6
Primary Contact: Lynn Falcone, Chief Executive Officer
CFO: Greg Pritchett, Chief Financial Officer
CMO: Michael McLeod, M.D., Chief Medical Officer
CIO: Arthur Mueller, Director Management Information Systems
CHR: Wanda S Kolodziejcyk, Director Human Resources
CNO: Judith Krupala, R.N., Chief Nursing Officer
Web address: www.cuerohospital.org
**Control:** Hospital district or authority, Government, Nonfederal **Service:** General medical and surgical

**Staffed Beds:** 24 **Admissions:** 914 **Census:** 8 **Outpatient Visits:** 121918
**Births:** 135 **Total Expense ($000):** 39937 **Payroll Expense ($000):** 15984
**Personnel:** 300

### CYPRESS—Harris County

See Lone Star Behavioral Health

☐ **LONE STAR BEHAVIORAL HEALTH (454118)**, 16303 Grant Road, Zip 77429–1253; tel. 281/516–6200, (Nonreporting) **A**1 10 **F**98 105 149 153
Primary Contact: Nathan Daniel. Ingram, Chief Executive Officer and Owner
Web address: www.lonestarbehavioralhealth.com
**Control:** Corporation, Investor–owned (for–profit) **Service:** Psychiatric

**Staffed Beds:** 24 **Admissions:** 394 **Census:** 11 **Outpatient Visits:** 33812
**Births:** 0 **Total Expense ($000):** 5969 **Payroll Expense ($000):** 3665
**Personnel:** 78

**MEMORIAL HERMAN HOSPITAL CYPRESS** See Memorial Herman Cypress

**NORTH CYPRESS MEDICAL CENTER** See Hca Houston Healthcare North Cypress

### DALHART—Hartley County

★ **COON MEMORIAL HOSPITAL (451331)**, 1411 Denver Avenue, Zip 79022–4809, Mailing Address: P.O. Box 2014, Zip 79022–6014; tel. 806/244–4571, (Nonreporting) **A**10 18 **F**3 7 10 11 13 30 34 35 40 43 45 50 53 57 59 62 63 64 65 68 69 71 76 77 79 81 82 83 85 87 93 97 103 107 114 119 125 127 131 133 143 144 146 148 **P**5
Primary Contact: Loree Tamayo, Chief Executive Officer
CFO: Donny Pettit, Chief Financial Officer
CMO: Randy Herring, M.D., Chief of Staff
CIO: Anthony Lovato, Director Information Technology
CHR: Dee Dawn McCormick, Director Personnel and Human Resources
Web address: www.dhchd.org/
**Control:** Hospital district or authority, Government, Nonfederal **Service:** General medical and surgical

**Staffed Beds:** 21 **Admissions:** 439 **Census:** 5 **Outpatient Visits:** 145719
**Births:** 131 **Total Expense ($000):** 31936 **Payroll Expense ($000):** 10104
**Personnel:** 192

**COON MEMORIAL HOSPITAL AND HOME** See Coon Memorial Hospital

### DALLAS—Dallas County

**BAYLOR INSTITUTE FOR REHABILITATION** See Baylor Scott & White Institute for Rehabilitation - Dallas

**BAYLOR JACK AND JANE HAMILTON HEART AND VASCULAR HOSPITAL** See Baylor Scott & White Heart & Vascular Hospital-Dallas

**BAYLOR MEDICAL CENTER AT UPTOWN** See Baylor Scott & White Medical Center-Uptown

⊞ **BAYLOR SCOTT & WHITE HEART & VASCULAR HOSPITAL-DALLAS (450851)**, 621 North Hall Street, Suite 150, Zip 75226–1339; tel. 214/820–0600, (Nonreporting) **A**1 5 10 **F**3 11 17 18 20 22 24 26 28 29 30 34 35 44 50 57 58 59 60 63 64 65 68 75 77 81 85 86 87 93 96 100 107 111 115 119 130 132 135 146 149 154 156
Primary Contact: Nancy Vish, Ph.D., FACHE, R.N., President
CFO: Julius Wicke IllVice President Finance and Hospital Financial Officer
CMO: Kevin Wheelan, M.D., Medical Director
CHR: Kim Krause, Director Human Resources
Web address: www.baylorhearthospital.com
**Control:** Partnership, Investor–owned (for–profit) **Service:** General medical and surgical

**Staffed Beds:** 53 **Admissions:** 2620 **Census:** 24 **Outpatient Visits:** 42373
**Births:** 0 **Total Expense ($000):** 150874 **Payroll Expense ($000):** 39094
**Personnel:** 433

⊞ **BAYLOR SCOTT & WHITE INSTITUTE FOR REHABILITATION - DALLAS (453036)**, 909 North Washington Avenue, Zip 75246–1520; tel. 214/820–9300, (Nonreporting) **A**1 3 10 **F**3 28 29 30 34 35 38 44 58 59 60 62 64 65 68 74 75 77 78 79 85 86 87 90 91 92 93 94 95 96 100 130 131 132 135 143 148 149 154 156
Primary Contact: David Smith, Chief Executive Officer
CMO: Amy Wilson, M.D., Medical Director
CHR: Karen Hill, Director Human Resources
CNO: Beth Hudson, Chief Nursing Officer
Web address: www.baylorhealth.com/PhysiciansLocations/BIR/Pages/Default.aspx
**Control:** Partnership, Investor–owned (for–profit) **Service:** Rehabilitation

**Staffed Beds:** 89 **Admissions:** 1459 **Census:** 76 **Outpatient Visits:** 12031
**Births:** 0 **Total Expense ($000):** 74903 **Payroll Expense ($000):** 47962
**Personnel:** 368

**BAYLOR SCOTT & WHITE MEDICAL CENTER - WHITE ROCK** See City Hospital at White Rock

⊞ **BAYLOR SCOTT & WHITE MEDICAL CENTER-UPTOWN (450422)**, 2727 East Lemmon Avenue, Zip 75204–2895; tel. 214/443–3000, (Nonreporting) **A**1 3 5 10 **F**29 34 40 79 81 85 107 111 114 126 130 **P**2 **S** United Surgical Partners International, Addison, TX
Primary Contact: Nick Taylor, Chief Executive Officer
CFO: Colene Fielding, Manager Business Office
CMO: Mark Armstrong, M.D., Medical Director
CIO: Javier Vela, Director Information Technology
CHR: Emalie Sanchez, Director Human Resources
CNO: Verette Neeb, R.N., MSN, Chief Nursing Officer
Web address: www.bmcuptown.com
**Control:** Partnership, Investor–owned (for–profit) **Service:** Surgical

**Staffed Beds:** 24 **Admissions:** 1087 **Census:** 6 **Outpatient Visits:** 10857
**Births:** 0 **Total Expense ($000):** 58666 **Payroll Expense ($000):** 14179
**Personnel:** 241

TX

---

**Hospital, Medicare Provider Number, Address, Telephone, Approval, Facility, and Physician Codes, Health Care System**

★ American Hospital Association (AHA) membership
☐ The Joint Commission accreditation
○ Healthcare Facilities Accreditation Program
◇ DNV Healthcare Inc. accreditation
⇑ Center for Improvement in Healthcare Quality Accreditation
△ Commission on Accreditation of Rehabilitation Facilities (CARF) accreditation

⊞ **BAYLOR UNIVERSITY MEDICAL CENTER (450021)**, 3500 Gaston Avenue, Zip 75246–2088; tel. 214/820–0111, (Includes A. WEBB ROBERTS HOSPITAL, Mailing address: 3500 Gaston Avenue, Dallas, Texas, Zip 75246–2017; tel. 361/500–0600; ERIK AND MARGARET JONSSON HOSPITAL, Mailing address: 3500 Gaston Avenue, Dallas, Texas, Zip 75246–2017; tel. 361/500–0600; GEORGE W. TRUETT MEMORIAL HOSPITAL, Mailing address: 3500 Gaston Avenue, Dallas, Texas, Zip 75246; tel. 361/500–0600; KARL AND ESTHER HOBLITZELLE MEMORIAL HOSPITAL, Mailing address: 3500 Gaston Avenue, Dallas, Texas, Zip 75246; tel. 361/500–0600), (Nonreporting) **A**1 2 3 5 8 10 **F**3 6 8 11 12 13 14 15 17 18 19 20 21 23 24 26 29 30 31 34 35 36 37 38 39 40 41 42 43 44 45 46 47 48 49 50 51 52 53 54 55 56 57 58 59 60 61 63 64 65 66 68 70 71 72 74 75 76 77 78 79 80 81 82 84 85 86 87 100 101 102 107 108 110 111 112 114 115 116 117 119 120 121 122 123 124 126 129 130 131 132 135 136 137 138 139 140 141 142 143 144 145 146 147 148 149 150 154 156 157 **S** Baylor Scott & White Health, Dallas, TX
Primary Contact: Steven R. Newton, FACHE, President
COO: Kyle Armstrong, Chief Operating Officer
CFO: Jay Whitfield, Chief Financial Officer
CMO: Brad Lembcke, M.D., Vice President Medical Staff Affairs
CHR: Julie Strittmatter, Director Human Resources
Web address: www.baylorhealth.com/PhysiciansLocations/Dallas/Pages/Default.aspx
**Control**: Other not-for-profit (including NFP Corporation) **Service**: General medical and surgical

**Staffed Beds**: 857 **Admissions**: 37738 **Census**: 625 **Outpatient Visits**: 220172 **Births**: 3936 **Total Expense ($000)**: 1027992 **Payroll Expense ($000)**: 310323 **Personnel**: 3822

**CHARLTON METHODIST HOSPITAL** See Methodist Charlton Medical Center

**CHILDREN'S HEALTH SYSTEM OF TEXAS** See Children's Medical Center Dallas

⊞ **CHILDREN'S MEDICAL CENTER DALLAS (453302)**, 1935 Medical District Drive, Zip 75235–7701; tel. 214/456–7000, (Nonreporting) **A**1 3 5 8 10 **F**3 5 7 8 11 12 17 18 19 20 21 22 23 24 25 26 27 28 29 30 31 32 34 35 36 38 39 40 41 43 44 45 46 48 49 51 54 55 57 58 59 60 61 62 64 65 66 68 72 74 75 77 78 79 81 82 84 85 86 87 88 89 91 92 93 94 96 97 98 99 100 101 102 104 105 107 108 111 115 116 117 118 119 126 127 129 130 131 132 134 136 137 138 139 141 142 143 145 146 148 152 153 154 155 **S** Children's Health, Dallas, TX
Primary Contact: David T. Berry, President
CFO: Richard P. Goode, Executive Vice President and Chief Financial Officer
CMO: W. Robert Morrow, M.D., Executive Vice President and Chief Medical Officer
CIO: Pamela Arora, Senior Vice President Information Systems
CHR: Kim Besse, Executive Vice President and Chief Human Resource Officer
CNO: Mary Stowe, Senior Vice President and Chief Nursing Officer
Web address: www.childrens.com
**Control**: Other not-for-profit (including NFP Corporation) **Service**: Children's general medical and surgical

**Staffed Beds**: 386 **Admissions**: 11976 **Census**: 250 **Outpatient Visits**: 540468 **Births**: 0 **Total Expense ($000)**: 1129714 **Payroll Expense ($000)**: 320488 **Personnel**: 4237

⊞ **CITY HOSPITAL AT WHITE ROCK (450678)**, 9440 Poppy Drive, Zip 75218–3694; tel. 214/324–6100, (Nonreporting) **A**1 10 **F**3 11 12 13 15 17 18 20 22 24 26 28 29 30 31 34 35 37 40 42 45 47 49 50 51 53 56 57 59 64 70 72 74 75 76 77 78 79 81 85 93 107 108 110 111 114 115 119 120 124 126 129 130 132 135 146 147 148
Primary Contact: Chad W. Wable, Chief Executive Officer
CFO: Drew Shea, Chief Financial Officer
CMO: William Jones, M.D., IIChief Medical Officer
CHR: David Olmstead, Director, Human Resources
CNO: Cheryl Nail, R.N., Chief Nursing Officer
Web address: www.https://cityhospital.co/
**Control**: Partnership, Investor-owned (for-profit) **Service**: General medical and surgical

**Staffed Beds**: 151 **Admissions**: 6723 **Census**: 67 **Outpatient Visits**: 59919 **Births**: 1169 **Total Expense ($000)**: 108742 **Payroll Expense ($000)**: 33717 **Personnel**: 559

**DALLAS COUNTY HOSPITAL DIST** See Parkland Health & Hospital System

☐ **DALLAS MEDICAL CENTER (450379)**, Seven Medical Parkway, Zip 75234–7823, Mailing Address: P.O. Box 819094, Zip 75381–9094; tel. 972/247–1000, (Nonreporting) **A**1 10 **F**3 12 15 18 20 22 26 29 34 40 43 44 45 46 49 50 51 56 57 59 64 68 70 74 75 77 78 79 81 82 84 85 86 93 97 107 108 111 114 116 119 130 131 141 142 146 147 148 149 **P**6 **S** Prime Healthcare, Ontario, CA
Primary Contact: Ruben Garza, Chief Executive Officer
CFO: Jade E. Andrews, Chief Financial Officer
CHR: Sheila K Richards, Human Resources Director
Web address: www.dallasmedcenter.com
**Control**: Corporation, Investor-owned (for-profit) **Service**: General medical and surgical

**Staffed Beds**: 71 **Admissions**: 2408 **Census**: 25 **Outpatient Visits**: 28597 **Births**: 0 **Total Expense ($000)**: 65384 **Payroll Expense ($000)**: 21903 **Personnel**: 462

⊞ **ENCOMPASS HEALTH REHABILITATION HOSPITAL OF DALLAS (673043)**, 7930 Northaven Road, Zip 75230–3331; tel. 214/706–8200, (Nonreporting) **A**1 10 **F**3 29 90 96 130 148 149 **S** Encompass Health Corporation, Birmingham, AL
Primary Contact: Daniel MacNicol, Chief Executive Officer
CFO: Elizabeth Robertson, Area Controller
CMO: Anna Freed-Sigurdsson, M.D., Medical Director
CHR: Lindsay Battles, Director Human Resources
CNO: Elysia Clay, Chief Nursing Officer
Web address: www.healthsouthdallas.com
**Control**: Corporation, Investor-owned (for-profit) **Service**: Rehabilitation

**Staffed Beds**: 40 **Admissions**: 843 **Census**: 36 **Outpatient Visits**: 0 **Births**: 0 **Total Expense ($000)**: 21959 **Payroll Expense ($000)**: 9093 **Personnel**: 132

⊞ **FIRST BAPTIST MEDICAL CENTER**, 8111 Meadow Road, Zip 75231; tel. 469/329–3700, (Nonreporting) **A**1 **F**3 12 29 37 40 45 49 64 70 79 81 82 85 86 87 107 114 119 130 149
Primary Contact: Harold V. Gaskill III, M.D., Chief Executive Officer
Web address: www.fbmcdallas.com
**Control**: Corporation, Investor-owned (for-profit) **Service**: Surgical

**Staffed Beds**: 18 **Admissions**: 656 **Census**: 3 **Outpatient Visits**: 1626 **Births**: 0 **Total Expense ($000)**: 29271 **Payroll Expense ($000)**: 8556 **Personnel**: 105

**GREEN OAKS HOSPITAL** See Medical City Green Oaks Hospital

**HEALTHSOUTH REHABILITATION HOSPITAL - DALLAS** See Encompass Health Rehabilitation Hospital of Dallas

⊞ **KINDRED HOSPITAL DALLAS CENTRAL (452108)**, 8050 Meadow Road, Zip 75231–3406; tel. 469/232–6500, (Nonreporting) **A**1 10 **F**1 3 29 75 77 85 87 96 107 114 148 **P**8 **S** Kindred Healthcare, Louisville, KY
Primary Contact: Kyron J. Kooken, MS, Chief Executive Officer
CFO: Robin Fry, CPA, Market Controller
CNO: Traci Brewer, R.N., Chief Clinical Officer
Web address: www.khdallascentral.com/
**Control**: Partnership, Investor-owned (for-profit) **Service**: Acute long-term care hospital

**Staffed Beds**: 60 **Admissions**: 538 **Census**: 42 **Outpatient Visits**: 0 **Births**: 0 **Total Expense ($000)**: 25947 **Payroll Expense ($000)**: 9864 **Personnel**: 159

☐ **KPC PROMISE HOSPITAL OF DALLAS (452067)**, 7955 Harry Hines Boulevard, Zip 75235–3305; tel. 214/637–0000, (Nonreporting) **A**1 10 **S** KPC Healthcare, Inc., Santa Ana, CA
Primary Contact: Kiley P. Cedotal, FACHE, Chief Executive Officer
CFO: Diana B Smith, Chief Financial Officer
CMO: Gary E. Goff, M.D., Medical Director
CHR: Ginger Davenport, Director Human Resources
Web address: www.dallas.kpcph.com/
**Control**: Corporation, Investor-owned (for-profit) **Service**: Acute long-term care hospital

**Staffed Beds**: 66

*Many Facility Codes have changed. Please refer to the AHA Guide Code Chart.*
© 2021 AHA Guide

✠ **LIFECARE HOSPITALS OF DALLAS (452044)**, 1950 Record Crossing Road, Zip 75235–6223; tel. 214/640–9600, (Includes LIFECARE HOSPITALS OF NORTH TEXAS-FORT WORTH, Mailing address: 6201 Overton Ridge Boulevard, Fort Worth, Texas, Zip 76132–3613; tel. 817/370–6078; LIFECARE HOSPITALS OF NORTH TEXAS-PLANO, Mailing address: 6800 Preston Road, Plano, Texas, Zip 75024–2505; tel. 214/473–8822; Kathleen Wallace, R.N., MSN, Administrator and Chief Executive Officer), (Nonreporting) **A**1 10 **S** LifeCare Management Services, Plano, TX
Primary Contact: Joy Patel, Chief Executive Officer
CFO: Amie Gratch, Director Financial Services
CMO: Jonathan Weissler, M.D., Chief Medical Officer
CHR: Linzie Riley, Interim Human Resource Manager
CNO: Kathy Mason, R.N., MSN, Chief Nursing Officer
Web address: www.lifecare-hospitals.com/hospital/dallas
**Control**: Partnership, Investor–owned (for–profit) **Service**: Acute long–term care hospital

**Staffed Beds:** 113

**LIFECARE HOSPITALS OF NORTH TEXAS** See Lifecare Hospitals of Dallas

✠ **MEDICAL CITY DALLAS (450647)**, 7777 Forest Lane, Zip 75230–2598; tel. 972/566–7000, (Includes MEDICAL CITY CHILDREN'S HOSPITAL, Mailing address: 7777 Forest Lane, Dallas, Texas, Zip 75230–2505; tel. 972/566–7000; Jessica O'Neal, Chief Executive Officer; MEDICAL CITY HEART HOSPITAL, Mailing address: 11970 North Central Expressway, Dallas, Texas, Zip 75243–3768; tel. 972/940–8000, Josh Kempf, Chief Operating Officer; MEDICAL CITY SPINE HOSPITAL, Mailing address: 11970 North Central Expressway, Dallas, Texas, Zip 75243–3768; tel. 972/940–8000), (Nonreporting) **A**1 2 3 5 10 **F**3 8 11 12 13 17 18 19 20 21 22 23 24 25 28 29 31 35 37 40 41 42 43 44 45 46 47 48 49 50 51 55 56 57 58 59 60 64 65 68 70 72 73 74 75 76 77 78 79 81 82 84 85 86 87 88 89 90 91 93 96 107 108 111 114 115 116 117 118 119 124 126 130 132 135 136 137 138 141 142 143 146 147 148 149 157 **S** HCA Healthcare, Nashville, TN
Primary Contact: Chris Mowan, Chief Executive Officer
CFO: Mark Atchley, Vice President and Chief Financial Officer
CMO: Kenneth Rothfield, M.D., Chief Medical Officer
CIO: Troy Sypien, Director Information Technology and Systems
CHR: Jenifer K Tertel, Director Human Resources
CNO: Joyce Soule, R.N., MSN, Chief Nursing Officer
Web address: www.medicalcityhospital.com
**Control**: Corporation, Investor–owned (for–profit) **Service**: General medical and surgical

**Staffed Beds:** 876 **Admissions:** 32251 **Census:** 535 **Outpatient Visits:** 208642 **Births:** 4173 **Total Expense ($000):** 629962 **Payroll Expense ($000):** 225695 **Personnel:** 2733

**MEDICAL CITY DALLAS HOSPITAL** See Medical City Dallas

✠ **MEDICAL CITY GREEN OAKS HOSPITAL (454094)**, 7808 Clodus Fields Drive, Zip 75251–2206; tel. 972/991–9504, (Nonreporting) **A**1 5 10 **F**4 5 29 30 50 68 87 98 99 101 102 103 104 105 130 132 135 149 151 152 153 154 **P**7 **S** HCA Healthcare, Nashville, TN
Primary Contact: Thomas M. Collins, President, Chairman and Chief Executive Officer
COO: Pam Whitley, R.N., Chief Operating Officer and Chief Nursing Officer
CMO: Joel Holiner, M.D., Executive Medical Director
CIO: Richard Fontenault, Director Information Systems
CHR: Kevin Adkins, Director Human Resources
CNO: Pam Whitley, R.N., Chief Nursing Officer and Chief Operating Officer
Web address: www.https://medicalcitygreenoaks.com/
**Control**: Corporation, Investor–owned (for–profit) **Service**: Psychiatric

**Staffed Beds:** 124 **Admissions:** 5818 **Census:** 115 **Outpatient Visits:** 20133 **Births:** 0 **Total Expense ($000):** 39589 **Payroll Expense ($000):** 18327 **Personnel:** 275

✠ **METHODIST CHARLTON MEDICAL CENTER (450723)**, 3500 West Wheatland Road, Zip 75237–3460, Mailing Address: P.O. Box 225357, Zip 75222–5357; tel. 214/947–7777, (Nonreporting) **A**1 2 3 10 **F**3 11 13 15 18 20 22 24 28 29 30 31 34 35 40 43 45 46 47 49 50 53 58 59 60 64 66 68 70 74 76 78 79 81 82 84 85 86 87 97 107 108 110 111 114 115 118 119 126 130 131 132 146 148 156 **P**5 6 **S** Methodist Health System, Dallas, TX
Primary Contact: Fran Laukaitis, FACHE, R.N., President
COO: Pamela Stoyanoff, President and Chief Operating Officer
CFO: Michael J Schaefer, Executive Vice President and Chief Financial Officer
CIO: Pamela McNutt, Vice President Information Systems
CHR: Merridth Simpson, Director Human Resources
CNO: Teresa Kay Land, R.N., Chief Nursing Officer, Vice President Nursing
Web address: www.methodisthealthsystem.org/charlton
**Control**: Other not–for–profit (including NFP Corporation) **Service**: General medical and surgical

**Staffed Beds:** 273 **Admissions:** 14305 **Census:** 204 **Outpatient Visits:** 151378 **Births:** 1610 **Total Expense ($000):** 251584 **Payroll Expense ($000):** 119621 **Personnel:** 1558

✠ **METHODIST DALLAS MEDICAL CENTER (450051)**, 1441 North Beckley Avenue, Zip 75203–1201, Mailing Address: P.O. Box 655999, Zip 75265–5999; tel. 214/947–8181, (Nonreporting) **A**1 2 5 10 **F**3 11 12 13 15 18 20 22 24 26 28 29 30 31 34 35 37 40 43 45 46 47 48 49 50 53 54 58 59 60 64 66 68 70 72 74 76 78 79 81 82 84 85 87 92 93 97 107 108 110 111 114 115 118 119 126 130 132 138 139 142 146 148 149 150 156 **P**5 6 **S** Methodist Health System, Dallas, TX
Primary Contact: John E. Phillips, FACHE, President
COO: Pamela Stoyanoff, Executive Vice President and Chief Operating Officer
CFO: Randy Walker, Vice President
CMO: Leslie Cler, M.D., Chief Medical Officer
CIO: Pamela McNutt, Senior Vice President and Chief Information Officer
CHR: Jackie Middleton, Vice President Human Resources
Web address: www.methodisthealthsystem.org/Dallas
**Control**: Other not–for–profit (including NFP Corporation) **Service**: General medical and surgical

**Staffed Beds:** 387 **Admissions:** 15168 **Census:** 245 **Outpatient Visits:** 173184 **Births:** 2170 **Total Expense ($000):** 456518 **Payroll Expense ($000):** 171490 **Personnel:** 2155

**METHODIST MEDICAL CENTER** See Methodist Dallas Medical Center

☐ △ **METHODIST REHABILITATION HOSPITAL (673031)**, 3020 West Wheatland Road, Zip 75237–3537; tel. 972/708–8600, (Nonreporting) **A**1 7 10 **F**29 30 90 91 93 95 96 111 119
Primary Contact: Shari Moore, Chief Executive Officer
CFO: Darline Kennemer, Controller
Web address: www.methodist-rehab.com
**Control**: Partnership, Investor–owned (for–profit) **Service**: Rehabilitation

**Staffed Beds:** 50 **Admissions:** 1199 **Census:** 39 **Outpatient Visits:** 11697 **Births:** 0 **Total Expense ($000):** 18290 **Payroll Expense ($000):** 9808 **Personnel:** 178

☐ **NORTH CENTRAL SURGICAL CENTER (670049)**, 9301 North Central Expressway, Suite 100, Zip 75231–0802; tel. 214/265–2810, (Nonreporting) **A**1 3 10 **F**3 8 29 40 45 68 79 81 82 85 93 96 107 111 115 119 146
Primary Contact: Thanh Tran, FACHE, Chief Executive Officer
COO: Ben Magestro, Chief Operating Officer
CFO: Mike Quaglieri, Chief Financial Officer
CMO: Stuart Simon, M.D., Medical Director
CNO: Katherine Martinez, Chief Nursing Officer
Web address: www.northcentralsurgical.com
**Control**: Partnership, Investor–owned (for–profit) **Service**: Surgical

**Staffed Beds:** 23 **Admissions:** 1654 **Census:** 9 **Outpatient Visits:** 19748 **Births:** 0 **Total Expense ($000):** 76729 **Payroll Expense ($000):** 18258 **Personnel:** 236

**TX**

⊞ **OUR CHILDREN'S HOUSE (453308)**, 1340 Empire Central Drive, Zip 75247–4022; tel. 214/867–6700, (Nonreporting) **A**1 3 5 10 **F**3 29 30 35 89 129 130 132 146 154 **S** Children's Health, Dallas, TX
Primary Contact: David T. Berry, President, System Clinical Operations
CMO: Andrew Gelfand, M.D., Medical Director
CNO: Kelli Terpstra, R.N., Senior Director
Web address: www.https://www.childrens.com/och
**Control**: Other not–for–profit (including NFP Corporation) **Service**: Children's general medical and surgical

| | |
|---|---|
| **Staffed Beds**: 39 **Admissions**: 403 **Census**: 24 **Outpatient Visits**: 20721 **Births**: 0 **Total Expense ($000)**: 34341 **Payroll Expense ($000)**: 13012 **Personnel**: 221 | |

**OUR CHILDREN'S HOUSE AT BAYLOR** See Our Children's House

⊞ **PARKLAND HEALTH & HOSPITAL SYSTEM (450015)**, 2370 Victory Avenue, Zip 75219, Mailing Address: 5200 Harry Hines Boulevard, Zip 75235–7708; tel. 214/590–8000, (Nonreporting) **A**1 2 3 5 8 10 **F**3 8 9 11 13 15 16 18 20 22 26 28 29 30 31 34 36 37 38 39 40 43 45 46 47 48 49 50 51 54 55 56 57 58 59 60 61 64 65 66 68 70 72 74 75 76 77 78 79 81 82 83 84 87 90 93 94 96 97 98 100 101 102 107 108 110 111 113 114 115 118 119 126 129 130 132 135 138 141 144 145 146 147 148 149 154 156 157 **P**1
Primary Contact: Fred Cerise, M.D., Chief Executive Officer
COO: David S Lopez, FACHE, Executive Vice President and Chief Operating Officer
CFO: Richard Humphrey, Executive Vice President and Chief Financial Officer
CIO: Joseph Longo, Chief Information Officer
CHR: Corey D. Jackson, Executive Vice President and Chief Talent Officer
Web address: www.parklandhospital.com
**Control**: Hospital district or authority, Government, Nonfederal **Service**: General medical and surgical

| | |
|---|---|
| **Staffed Beds**: 853 **Admissions**: 38147 **Census**: 636 **Outpatient Visits**: 1356718 **Births**: 12642 **Total Expense ($000)**: 1889067 **Payroll Expense ($000)**: 847956 **Personnel**: 12248 | |

**PINE CREEK MEDICAL CENTER (450894)**, 9032 Harry Hines Boulevard, Zip 75235–1720; tel. 214/231–2273, (Nonreporting) **A**10
Primary Contact: Daniel L. Gideon, FACHE, Chief Executive Officer
CFO: Michael Conroy, Chief Financial Officer
CIO: Kevin Carney, Senior Information Systems Analyst
Web address: www.pinecreekmedicalcenter.com
**Control**: Partnership, Investor–owned (for–profit) **Service**: Surgical

| | |
|---|---|
| **Staffed Beds**: 15 | |

**PRESBYTERIAN HOSPITAL DALLAS** See Texas Health Presbyterian Hospital Dallas

**PROMISE HOSPITAL OF DALLAS** See Kpc Promise Hospital of Dallas

**SELECT SPECIAL HOSPITAL - DALLAS DOWNTOWN** See Select Specialty Hospital - Dallas Downtown

★ **SELECT SPECIALTY HOSPITAL - DALLAS DOWNTOWN (452119)**, 3500 Gaston Avenue, Floors 3&4 Jonsson, Zip 75246–2017; tel. 469/801–4500, (Nonreporting) **F**1 3 29 74 77 85 86 87 91 96 148 **S** Select Medical Corporation, Mechanicsburg, PA
Primary Contact: Michael McAlister, Chief Executive Officer
Web address: www.dallasdowntown.selectspecialtyhospitals.com/
**Control**: Corporation, Investor–owned (for–profit) **Service**: Acute long–term care hospital

| | |
|---|---|
| **Staffed Beds**: 26 **Admissions**: 295 **Census**: 23 **Outpatient Visits**: 0 **Births**: 0 **Total Expense ($000)**: 16433 **Payroll Expense ($000)**: 6678 **Personnel**: 85 | |

⊞ △ **TEXAS HEALTH PRESBYTERIAN HOSPITAL DALLAS (450462)**, 8200 Walnut Hill Lane, Zip 75231–4426; tel. 214/345–6789, (Nonreporting) **A**1 2 3 5 7 10 **F**3 5 11 12 13 15 17 18 20 22 24 29 30 31 34 35 37 38 39 40 43 44 45 46 47 49 50 51 53 54 55 56 57 58 59 60 61 64 65 66 68 69 70 71 72 73 74 75 76 77 78 79 81 84 85 86 87 90 91 92 93 94 95 96 97 98 100 101 102 104 105 106 107 108 110 111 112 114 115 118 119 126 132 135 141 143 146 148 149 151 152 153 157 **P**6 **S** Texas Health Resources, Arlington, TX
Primary Contact: James Parobek, President
CFO: Brian Craft, Group Finance Officer
CMO: Aurora Estevez, M.D., Chief Medical Officer
CIO: Tammy Phillips, Director, Information Systems
CHR: Stacy Miller, Entity Human Resources Officer
Web address: www.texashealth.org
**Control**: Other not–for–profit (including NFP Corporation) **Service**: General medical and surgical

| | |
|---|---|
| **Staffed Beds**: 632 **Admissions**: 26495 **Census**: 372 **Outpatient Visits**: 138184 **Births**: 4976 **Total Expense ($000)**: 613561 **Payroll Expense ($000)**: 214700 **Personnel**: 2267 | |

**TEXAS HOSPITAL FOR ADVANCED MEDICINE** See Dallas Medical Center

**TEXAS INSTITUTE FOR SURGERY AT PRESBYTERIAN HOSPITAL OF DALLAS** See Texas Institute for Surgery at Texas Health Presbyterian Dallas

**TEXAS INSTITUTE FOR SURGERY AT TEXAS HEALTH PRESBYTERIAN DALLAS (450889)**, 7115 Greenville Avenue, Suite 100, Zip 75231–5100; tel. 214/647–5300, (Nonreporting) **A**10 22 **F**40 51 64 79 81 82 107 114 115 119
Primary Contact: John S. Croley, Chief Executive Officer and Chief Financial Officer
CFO: John S. Croley, Chief Executive Officer and Chief Financial Officer
CMO: Presley Mock, M.D., Chief of Staff
CHR: Jennifer C. Levy, Director Human Resources
CNO: Tammy Jarvis, Vice President Clinical Services and Chief Nursing Officer
Web address: www.texasinstituteforsurgery.com
**Control**: Partnership, Investor–owned (for–profit) **Service**: General medical and surgical

| | |
|---|---|
| **Staffed Beds**: 9 **Admissions**: 624 **Census**: 4 **Outpatient Visits**: 9829 **Births**: 0 **Total Expense ($000)**: 55215 **Payroll Expense ($000)**: 14219 **Personnel**: 170 | |

⊞ **TEXAS SCOTTISH RITE HOSPITAL FOR CHILDREN (453314)**, 2222 Welborn Street, Zip 75219–3924; tel. 214/559–5000, (Nonreporting) **A**1 3 5 10 **F**3 9 11 29 34 35 39 50 53 54 57 58 64 68 74 75 77 79 81 82 85 86 87 89 92 93 94 107 111 115 119 130 131 132 146 157
Primary Contact: Robert L. Walker, FACHE, President and Chief Executive Officer
CFO: William R Huston, Senior Vice President and Chief Financial Officer
CMO: Daniel J Sucato, M.D., MS, Chief of Staff
CIO: Les Clonch, Chief Information Officer
CHR: Connie Wright, Vice President Human Resources
CNO: Debbie A Sayles, R.N., Vice President and Chief Nursing Officer
Web address: www.tsrhc.org
**Control**: Other not–for–profit (including NFP Corporation) **Service**: Children's orthopedic

| | |
|---|---|
| **Staffed Beds**: 52 **Admissions**: 607 **Census**: 11 **Outpatient Visits**: 61779 **Births**: 0 **Total Expense ($000)**: 232268 **Payroll Expense ($000)**: 99648 **Personnel**: 710 | |

**TRIUMPH HOSPITAL DALLAS** See Kindred Hospital Dallas Central

**TX**

⊞ △ **UNIVERSITY OF TEXAS SOUTHWESTERN MEDICAL CENTER (450044)**, 5323 Harry Hines Boulevard, Zip 75390–9265; tel. 214/648–3111, (Includes UNIVERSITY OF TEXAS SOUTHWESTERN MEDICAL CENTER - ZALE LIPSHY, Mailing address: 5151 Harry Hines Boulevard, Dallas, Texas, Zip 75390–9265; tel. 214/645–8300; Daniel Podolsky, M.D., President; WILLIAM P. CLEMENTS, JR. UNIVERSITY HOSPITAL, Mailing address: 6201 Harry Hines Boulevard, Dallas, Texas, Zip 75235–5202; tel. 214/633–5555; Daniel Podolsky, M.D., President), (Nonreporting) **A**1 2 3 5 7 8 10 19 **F**3 5 6 8 9 11 12 13 14 15 17 18 19 20 21 22 23 24 25 26 27 28 29 30 31 32 34 35 36 37 38 39 40 41 44 45 46 47 48 49 50 52 53 54 55 56 57 58 59 60 61 62 63 64 65 68 70 71 72 74 75 76 77 78 79 80 81 82 83 84 85 86 87 90 91 92 93 94 95 96 97 98 99 100 101 102 103 104 107 108 109 110 111 113 114 115 116 117 118 119 120 121 123 124 126 127 129 130 131 132 134 135 136 137 138 139 140 141 142 143 145 146 147 148 149 150 151 152 153 154 156 **P**4 6
Primary Contact: John Warner, M.D., Chief Executive Officer
COO: Becky McCulley, Chief Operations Officer
CMO: John Warner, M.D., Chief Executive Officer, Interim Chief Medical Officer
CIO: Marc E. Milstein, Vice President Information Resources
CHR: Ivan Thompson, Vice President, Chief Human Resource Officer
CNO: Susan Hernandez, R.N., Chief Nurse Executive
Web address: www.utsouthwestern.edu
**Control**: State, Government, Nonfederal **Service**: General medical and surgical

**Staffed Beds: 608 Admissions: 27910 Census: 483 Outpatient Visits: 579841 Births: 1996 Total Expense ($000): 1443879 Payroll Expense ($000): 542002 Personnel: 6292**

⊞ △ **VETERANS AFFAIRS NORTH TEXAS HEALTH CARE SYSTEM**, 4500 South Lancaster Road, Zip 75216–7167; tel. 214/742–8387, (Includes SAM RAYBURN MEMORIAL VETERANS CENTER, Mailing address: 1201 East Ninth Street, Bonham, Texas, Zip 75418–4091; tel. 903/583–2111; Angela Nix, Administrator), (Nonreporting) **A**1 2 3 5 7 **S** Department of Veterans Affairs, Washington, DC
Primary Contact: Stephen R. Holt, M.D., Director
CFO: Alton McKinley, Chief Financial Officer
CIO: Lucy Rogers, Chief Information Resource Management Systems
Web address: www.northtexas.va.gov/
**Control**: Veterans Affairs, Government, federal **Service**: General medical and surgical

**Staffed Beds: 853**

**ZALE LIPSHY UNIV HOSPITAL** See University of Texas Southwestern Medical Center - Zale Lipshy

⊞ **WISE HEALTH SYSTEM (450271)**, 609 Medical Center Drive, Zip 76234–3836; tel. 940/627–5921, (Includes WISE HEALTH SYSTEM, WEST CAMPUS DECATUR, Mailing address: 2000 South Fm 51, Decatur, Texas, Zip 76234–3702; tel. 940/627–5921; Jason Wren, Chief Executive Officer), (Nonreporting) **A**1 2 10 **F**3 11 12 13 15 17 18 20 22 24 26 28 29 30 31 32 34 38 40 43 45 47 49 51 53 54 56 57 59 60 64 70 74 75 76 77 78 79 81 82 85 87 89 90 93 96 97 98 103 104 107 108 110 111 114 115 117 118 119 121 124 126 129 130 131 132 135 144 147 148 149 154 156
Primary Contact: Jason Wren, President and Chief Executive Officer
COO: Leon Fuqua, Chief Operating Officer
CFO: Todd Scroggins, Chief Financial Officer
CMO: Jon W. Walker, M.D., Chief Medical Officer
CIO: Joe Arispe, Director Information Systems
CHR: Mike McQuiston, Administrative Director Human Resources
CNO: Lee Ann Jennings, R.N., Vice President, Nursing Services
Web address: www.wiseregional.com
**Control**: Hospital district or authority, Government, Nonfederal **Service**: General medical and surgical

**Staffed Beds: 133 Admissions: 5398 Census: 75 Outpatient Visits: 610020 Births: 568 Total Expense ($000): 351458 Payroll Expense ($000): 96599 Personnel: 1444**

**WISE REGIONAL HEALTH SYSTEM** See Wise Health System

**VAL VERDE MEMORIAL HOSPITAL** See Val Verde Regional Medical Center

★ **VAL VERDE REGIONAL MEDICAL CENTER (450154)**, 801 Bedell Avenue, Zip 78840–4112, Mailing Address: 801 North Bedell Avenue, Zip 78840–4112; tel. 830/775–8566, (Nonreporting) **A**10 20 22 **F**3 7 11 13 15 18 20 28 29 30 34 35 40 43 46 48 54 56 57 59 63 64 73 75 76 77 79 81 82 84 85 87 89 93 96 101 104 107 108 110 111 114 119 127 129 130 131 132 133 146 147 149 153 154 155 156
Primary Contact: Linda Walker, Chief Executive Officer
CFO: Eddie Read, Interim Chief Financial Officer
CMO: Mohamed Shafiu, M.D., Chief of Staff
CIO: Val King, Chief Information Officer
CNO: Kathy Fletcher, R.N., MSN, Interim Chief Nursing Officer
Web address: www.vvrmc.org
**Control**: Hospital district or authority, Government, Nonfederal **Service**: General medical and surgical

**Staffed Beds: 80 Admissions: 2495 Census: 22 Outpatient Visits: 72308 Births: 746 Total Expense ($000): 71349 Payroll Expense ($000): 27802 Personnel: 517**

**TEXOMA HEALTHCARE SYSTEM** See Texoma Medical Center

□ **TEXOMA MEDICAL CENTER (450324)**, 5016 South US Highway 75, Zip 75020–4584, Mailing Address: P.O. Box 890, Zip 75021–0890; tel. 903/416–4000, (Includes TMC BEHAVIORAL HEALTH CENTER, Mailing address: 2601 North Cornerstone Drive, Sherman, Texas, Zip 75092–2551; tel. 903/416–3000; Ryan Tatu, Chief Executive Officer), (Nonreporting) **A**1 3 5 10 13 **F**3 11 12 13 15 17 18 20 22 24 28 29 30 31 34 35 40 42 43 45 46 47 48 49 50 53 54 57 59 62 64 70 72 74 75 77 78 79 80 81 82 85 86 87 89 90 91 93 96 98 99 100 101 102 103 104 107 108 110 111 115 118 119 126 129 130 132 144 145 146 147 148 149 150 153 156 **S** Universal Health Services, Inc., King of Prussia, PA
Primary Contact: Ronald T. Seal, Chief Executive Officer
CFO: Gerard Hebert, Chief Financial Officer
CMO: Robert Sanders, M.D., Chief Medical Officer
CIO: Lisa Engle, Director Information Technology
CHR: Bill Heinzmann, Director Human Resources
CNO: Andrea Brenn, R.N., Chief Nursing Officer
Web address: www.texomamedicalcenter.net
**Control**: Corporation, Investor–owned (for–profit) **Service**: General medical and surgical

**Staffed Beds: 414 Admissions: 21674 Census: 293 Outpatient Visits: 145119 Births: 1225 Total Expense ($000): 291203 Payroll Expense ($000): 120284 Personnel: 2033**

⊞ **BAYLOR SCOTT & WHITE THE HEART HOSPITAL DENTON (450893)**, 2801 South Mayhill Road, Zip 76208–5910, Mailing Address: 2891 South Mayhill Road, Zip 76208; tel. 469/814–3278, (Nonreporting) **A**1 10 **F**3 17 18 20 22 24 26 28 29 30 34 35 40 53 54 57 60 64 68 70 74 75 77 81 82 84 85 87 90 107 111 115 119 126 129 130 132 135 146 148 149 154 157
Primary Contact: Mark Valentine, President
COO: Brad D. McCall, Vice President Operations
CFO: Bryan Nichols, Chief Financial Officer
CMO: Trent Pettijohn, M.D., EsqChief Medical Officer
CHR: Anna Gemeny, Regional Director Human Resources
CNO: Susan K. Moats, R.N., Chief Nursing Officer
Web address: www.https://denton.thehearthospitalbaylor.com
**Control**: Partnership, Investor–owned (for–profit) **Service**: Heart

**Staffed Beds: 22 Admissions: 677 Census: 8 Outpatient Visits: 6936 Births: 0 Total Expense ($000): 44804 Payroll Expense ($000): 12903 Personnel: 132**

**BAYLOR SCOTT & WHITE THE HEART HOSPITAL—DENTON** See Baylor Scott & White The Heart Hospital Denton

**DENTON COMMUNITY HOSPITAL** See Texas Health Presbyterian Hospital Denton

**DENTON REGIONAL MEDICAL CENTER** See Medical City Denton

**HORIZON MEDICAL CENTER** See Horizon Medical Center, LLC

**TX**

☐ **HORIZON MEDICAL CENTER, LLC (452111)**, 2813 South Mayhill Road, Zip 76208–5910; tel. 940/565–8580, (Nonreporting) **A**1 **F**1 3 8 29 64 75 81 129 148 **P**3
Primary Contact: Decha Brooks, Chief Operations Officer
CNO: Tonia Torregrossa, Chief Nursing Officer
Web address: www.https://www.horizonmedcenter.com/
**Control**: Partnership, Investor–owned (for–profit) **Service**: Acute long–term care hospital

> **Staffed Beds**: 22 **Admissions**: 148 **Census**: 11 **Outpatient Visits**: 1385 **Births**: 0 **Total Expense ($000)**: 10545 **Payroll Expense ($000)**: 2424 **Personnel**: 65

⊞ **MAYHILL HOSPITAL (670010)**, 2809 South Mayhill Road, Zip 76208–5910; tel. 940/239–3000, (Nonreporting) **A**1 10 **F**4 5 29 40 44 56 57 59 64 86 87 98 100 101 102 103 104 105 106 130 132 135 151 152 153 154 157 **S** Universal Health Services, Inc., King of Prussia, PA
Primary Contact: Loren Fouch, Chief Executive Officer
CFO: Emmy Adams, Chief Financial Officer
CMO: Asad Islam, M.D., Chief Medical Officer
CIO: Kyle Murphy, Director Information Technology
CHR: Patricia Gloria-Barraza, Coordinator Human Resources
Web address: www.mayhillhospital.com
**Control**: Partnership, Investor–owned (for–profit) **Service**: Psychiatric

> **Staffed Beds**: 59 **Admissions**: 2045 **Census**: 49 **Outpatient Visits**: 3287 **Births**: 0 **Total Expense ($000)**: 12567 **Payroll Expense ($000)**: 6493 **Personnel**: 136

⊞ **MEDICAL CITY DENTON (450634)**, 3535 South 1-35 East, Zip 76210; tel. 940/384–3535, (Nonreporting) **A**1 3 10 **F**3 15 18 20 22 24 26 28 29 30 34 35 40 43 45 46 47 49 50 57 64 70 74 75 77 79 80 81 82 84 85 86 87 93 107 108 110 111 114 115 118 119 126 130 132 144 146 148 149 154 **S** HCA Healthcare, Nashville, TN
Primary Contact: Steven Edgar, FACHE, President and Chief Executive Officer
COO: John Walker, Chief Operating Officer
CFO: Todd Gibson, Chief Financial Officer
CMO: Howard Shaw, M.D., Chief Medical Officer
CHR: Stacey Bravo, Vice President Human Resources
CNO: Brandy H Farrer, R.N., Chief Nursing Officer
Web address: www.dentonregional.com
**Control**: Partnership, Investor–owned (for–profit) **Service**: General medical and surgical

> **Staffed Beds**: 185 **Admissions**: 9852 **Census**: 129 **Outpatient Visits**: 81225 **Births**: 0 **Total Expense ($000)**: 160586 **Payroll Expense ($000)**: 56455 **Personnel**: 823

⊞ **SELECT REHABILITATION HOSPITAL OF DENTON (673036)**, 2620 Scripture Street, Zip 76201–4315; tel. 940/297–6500, (Nonreporting) **A**1 10 **F**3 29 64 68 74 75 77 79 86 87 90 93 96 132 135 148 149 **S** Select Medical Corporation, Mechanicsburg, PA
Primary Contact: Michelle Powell, Chief Executive Officer
CFO: Doug Selsor, Director Finance
CHR: Patsy Martin, Manager Human Resources
CNO: Lee Ann Elliott, R.N., Director of Nursing
Web address: www.selectrehab-denton.com/
**Control**: Partnership, Investor–owned (for–profit) **Service**: Rehabilitation

> **Staffed Beds**: 44 **Admissions**: 735 **Census**: 26 **Outpatient Visits**: 12148 **Births**: 0 **Total Expense ($000)**: 15070 **Payroll Expense ($000)**: 8073 **Personnel**: 100

⊞ **TEXAS HEALTH PRESBYTERIAN HOSPITAL DENTON (450743)**, 3000 North I-35, Zip 76201–5119; tel. 940/898–7000, (Nonreporting) **A**1 10 **F**3 12 13 15 18 20 22 24 26 28 29 30 31 34 35 39 40 45 46 47 48 49 57 59 65 66 68 70 72 74 75 76 78 79 81 83 84 85 86 87 93 107 108 110 111 115 118 119 126 130 132 135 146 147 148 149 156 **P**6 **S** Texas Health Resources, Arlington, TX
Primary Contact: Jeff Reecer, FACHE, Chief Executive Officer
CFO: David B Meltzer, Chief Financial Officer
CMO: Timothy Harris, M.D., Chief Quality Officer
CIO: Melissa Smart, Communication ad Public Relations Specialist
CHR: Kathy Hardcastle, Director Human Resources
CNO: Deborah Bostic, R.N., Chief Nursing Officer
Web address: www.dentonhospital.com
**Control**: Other not–for–profit (including NFP Corporation) **Service**: General medical and surgical

> **Staffed Beds**: 236 **Admissions**: 10892 **Census**: 123 **Outpatient Visits**: 75130 **Births**: 2209 **Total Expense ($000)**: 201334 **Payroll Expense ($000)**: 75342 **Personnel**: 924

**UNIV BEHAVIORAL HEALTH CENTER** See University Behavioral Health of Denton

⊞ **UNIVERSITY BEHAVIORAL HEALTH OF DENTON (454104)**, 2026 West University Drive, Zip 76201–0644; tel. 940/320–8100, (Nonreporting) **A**1 10 **F**4 5 59 68 75 98 99 100 101 102 103 104 105 106 132 134 135 144 151 152 153 154 **S** Universal Health Services, Inc., King of Prussia, PA
Primary Contact: Ronald Rains, Chief Executive Officer
CFO: Ed Sopiarz, Chief Financial Officer
CMO: Atique Khan, M.D., Medical Director
CIO: Marsh Smith, Manager Health Information
CHR: Dorie Atherton, Manager Human Resources
CNO: Vicki Stoker, Chief Nursing Officer
Web address: www.ubhdenton.com
**Control**: Partnership, Investor–owned (for–profit) **Service**: Psychiatric

> **Staffed Beds**: 104 **Admissions**: 2936 **Census**: 72 **Outpatient Visits**: 7541 **Births**: 0 **Total Expense ($000)**: 24434 **Payroll Expense ($000)**: 10093 **Personnel**: 168

## DENVER CITY—Yoakum County

★ **YOAKUM COUNTY HOSPITAL (451308)**, 412 Mustang Avenue, Zip 79323–2762, Mailing Address: P.O. Box 1130, Zip 79323–1130; tel. 806/592–2121, (Nonreporting) **A**10 18 **F**3 11 13 28 34 35 40 41 43 50 53 57 59 60 62 64 76 81 87 89 93 107 114 119 127 129 133 149
Primary Contact: Newman Wheeler, Chief Executive Officer
CFO: Suann Parrish, Chief Financial Officer
CMO: Dan Khan, M.D., Chief Medical Officer
CIO: Todd Carrillo, Chief Information Officer
CHR: Teresa Howard, Manager Human Resources
Web address: www.ych.us
**Control**: County, Government, Nonfederal **Service**: General medical and surgical

> **Staffed Beds**: 22 **Admissions**: 457 **Census**: 4 **Outpatient Visits**: 55687 **Births**: 258 **Total Expense ($000)**: 26997 **Payroll Expense ($000)**: 9314 **Personnel**: 179

## DESOTO—Dallas County

**CEDARS HOSPITAL** See Hickory Trail Hospital

☐ **DALLAS BEHAVIORAL HEALTHCARE HOSPITAL (454126)**, 800 Kirnwood Drive, Zip 75115–2000; tel. 855/982–0897, (Nonreporting) **A**1 **F**4 5 56 87 98 99 100 101 103 104 105 130 151 152 153 154 **S** Signature Healthcare Services, Corona, CA
Primary Contact: Terrance O'Reilly, Chief Executive Officer
CMO: Rahim Haqqani, M.D., Medical Director
CHR: Henry In, Director Human Resources
CNO: Susie Edler, R.N., Chief Nursing Officer
Web address: www.dallasbehavioral.com
**Control**: Individual, Investor–owned (for–profit) **Service**: Psychiatric

> **Staffed Beds**: 116 **Admissions**: 3912 **Census**: 75 **Outpatient Visits**: 7554 **Births**: 0 **Total Expense ($000)**: 24912 **Payroll Expense ($000)**: 13187 **Personnel**: 259

☐ **HICKORY TRAIL HOSPITAL (454065)**, 2000 Old Hickory Trail, Zip 75115–2242; tel. 972/298–7323, (Nonreporting) **A**1 10 **F**4 5 29 38 98 99 100 101 103 105 130 152 153 154 **S** Universal Health Services, Inc., King of Prussia, PA
Primary Contact: Daniel Martinez-Torres, Chief Executive Officer
CFO: Terri Logsdon, Chief Financial Officer
CMO: Manoochehr Khatami, M.D., Medical Director
CHR: Sarah Warren, Coordinator Human Resources
Web address: www.hickorytrail.com
**Control**: Corporation, Investor–owned (for–profit) **Service**: Psychiatric

> **Staffed Beds**: 86 **Admissions**: 3004 **Census**: 65 **Outpatient Visits**: 9892 **Births**: 0 **Total Expense ($000)**: 18606 **Payroll Expense ($000)**: 9942 **Personnel**: 153

**TX**

⊞ **VIBRA SPECIALTY HOSPITAL AT DESOTO (452097)**, 2700 Walker
Way, Zip 75115–2088; tel. 972/298–1100, (Includes VIBRA HOSPITAL OF
RICHARDSON, Mailing address: 401 West Campbell Road, Richardson, Texas,
Zip 75080–3416; tel. 210/941–4886; Tracy Penny, Interim Chief Executive
Officer), (Nonreporting) **A**1 10 **F**1 3 29 70 74 75 77 82 85 91 107 114 130 135
148 154 **S** Vibra Healthcare, Mechanicsburg, PA
Primary Contact: Tracy Penny, Interim Chief Executive Officer
CFO: Donald Trimble, CPA, Chief Financial Officer
CMO: Ed Dominguez, President Medical Staff
CHR: Tim Lozier, Director Human Resources
CNO: Mae C Weathersby, R.N., Chief Clinical Officer
Web address: www.vshdesoto.com
**Control**: Corporation, Investor–owned (for–profit) **Service**: Acute long–term care
hospital

| | |
|---|---|
| **Staffed Beds:** 60 **Admissions:** 673 **Census:** 42 **Outpatient Visits:** 0 | |
| **Births:** 0 **Total Expense ($000):** 23106 **Payroll Expense ($000):** 11129 | |
| **Personnel:** 178 | |

**VIBRA SPECIALTY HOSPITAL OF DALLAS** See Vibra Specialty Hospital at
Desoto

**DIMMITT—Castro County**

★ **PLAINS MEMORIAL HOSPITAL (451350)**, 310 West Halsell Street,
Zip 79027–1846, Mailing Address: P.O. Box 278, Zip 79027–0278;
tel. 806/647–2191, (Nonreporting) **A**10 18 **F**3 7 32 34 35 40 43 53 57 59 64
65 69 75 77 85 86 87 93 97 107 114 115 119 127 130 133 135 149 156
Primary Contact: Linda Rasor, R.N., Chief Executive Officer
CFO: Terri Martinez, Chief Financial Officer
CMO: Gary R Hardee, M.D., Medical Director
CIO: Terry Young, Chief Information Officer
CHR: Debbie Underwood, Manager Human Resources
CNO: Renee Castillo, Chief Nursing Officer
Web address: www.plainsmemorial.com
**Control**: Hospital district or authority, Government, Nonfederal **Service**: General
medical and surgical

| | |
|---|---|
| **Staffed Beds:** 17 **Admissions:** 136 **Census:** 4 **Outpatient Visits:** 20694 | |
| **Births:** 0 **Total Expense ($000):** 13293 **Payroll Expense ($000):** 5781 | |
| **Personnel:** 104 | |

**DUMAS—Moore County**

**MEMORIAL HOSPITAL** See Moore County Hospital District

☐ **MOORE COUNTY HOSPITAL DISTRICT (451386)**, 224 East Second Street,
Zip 79029–3808; tel. 806/935–7171, (Nonreporting) **A**1 10 18 **F**3 7 11 13 15
28 34 35 40 43 46 50 51 57 59 62 63 70 75 76 79 81 85 86 89 91 93 107
110 111 115 119 127 130 131 132 133 135 146 147 148 154
Primary Contact: Jeff Turner, FACHE, Chief Executive Officer
COO: Ashleigh Wiswell, Chief Operations Officer
CFO: John E. Bailey, Chief Financial Officer
CHR: Kathie Fuston, Director Human Resources
CNO: Ronda Crow, Chief Nursing Officer
Web address: www.mchd.net
**Control**: Hospital district or authority, Government, Nonfederal **Service**: General
medical and surgical

| | |
|---|---|
| **Staffed Beds:** 25 **Admissions:** 1285 **Census:** 10 **Outpatient Visits:** 25448 | |
| **Births:** 353 **Total Expense ($000):** 41965 **Payroll Expense ($000):** 20315 | |
| **Personnel:** 336 | |

**EAGLE LAKE—Colorado County**

**RICE DISTRICT COMMUNITY HOSP** See Rice Medical Center

**RICE MEDICAL CENTER (451312)**, 600 South Austin Road, Zip 77434–3298,
Mailing Address: P.O. Box 277, Zip 77434–0277; tel. 979/234–5571,
(Nonreporting) **A**10 18 **F**3 11 15 29 34 35 40 43 56 59 64 65 75 77 79 80 81
85 101 104 107 114 119 127 133 153 154 156 **P**6
Primary Contact: James D. Janek, Chief Executive Officer
CMO: Russell Thomas, M.D., Chief of Staff
CHR: Velma Loya, Administrative Human Resource Coordinator
CNO: Susan Hernandez, R.N., Chief Nursing Officer
Web address: www.ricemedicalcenter.net/
**Control**: Corporation, Investor–owned (for–profit) **Service**: General medical and
surgical

| | |
|---|---|
| **Staffed Beds:** 12 **Admissions:** 132 **Census:** 2 **Outpatient Visits:** 25094 | |
| **Births:** 0 **Total Expense ($000):** 13885 **Payroll Expense ($000):** 3582 | |
| **Personnel:** 90 | |

**EAGLE PASS—Maverick County**

**FORT DUNCAN MEDICAL CENTER** See Fort Duncan Regional Medical Center

☐ **FORT DUNCAN REGIONAL MEDICAL CENTER (450092)**, 3333 North Foster
Maldonado Boulevard, Zip 78852–5893; tel. 830/773–5321, (Nonreporting) **A**1
10 20 **F**3 11 13 15 18 20 22 29 40 43 45 57 60 65 68 70 75 76 77 79 81 85
87 89 90 91 93 107 108 110 111 114 115 119 129 130 146 147 148 149 **S**
Universal Health Services, Inc., King of Prussia, PA
Primary Contact: Eladio Montalvo, Chief Executive Officer
COO: Alan Gonzalez, Chief Operating Officer
CFO: Joel Morales, Chief Financial Officer
CMO: Ruben de los Santos, M.D., Chief Medical Officer
CIO: Jose Elias, Director Information Technology
CHR: Daisy Rodriquez, Director Human Resources
CNO: Scott Lethi, R.N., FACHE, Chief Nursing Officer
Web address: www.fortduncanmedicalcenter.com
**Control**: Partnership, Investor–owned (for–profit) **Service**: General medical and
surgical

| | |
|---|---|
| **Staffed Beds:** 101 **Admissions:** 4410 **Census:** 48 **Outpatient Visits:** 53687 | |
| **Births:** 1049 **Total Expense ($000):** 53719 **Payroll Expense ($000):** 22080 | |
| **Personnel:** 337 | |

**EASTLAND—Eastland County**

**EASTLAND MEMORIAL HOSPITAL (450411)**, 304 South Daugherty
Street, Zip 76448–2609, Mailing Address: P.O. Box 897, Zip 76448–0897;
tel. 254/629–2601, (Nonreporting) **A**10 20 **F**7 11 12 15 28 29 30 34 35 40 43
45 50 53 57 59 60 64 68 77 81 85 86 87 89 93 107 110 114 130 131 133
146 148
Primary Contact: Ted Matthews, Chief Executive Officer
CFO: Jamie Hayden, Chief Financial Officer
CHR: Leisha Hodges, Human Resources Officer
Web address: www.eastlandmemorial.com
**Control**: Hospital district or authority, Government, Nonfederal **Service**: General
medical and surgical

| | |
|---|---|
| **Staffed Beds:** 36 **Admissions:** 562 **Census:** 9 **Outpatient Visits:** 42899 | |
| **Births:** 0 **Total Expense ($000):** 16431 **Payroll Expense ($000):** 7007 | |
| **Personnel:** 146 | |

**EDEN—Concho County**

**CONCHO COUNTY HOSPITAL (451325)**, 614 Eaker Street, Zip 76837–0359,
Mailing Address: P.O. Box 987, Zip 76837–0987; tel. 325/869–5911,
(Nonreporting) **A**10 18 **F**3 34 40 43 50 53 59 77 87 107 115 129 133 146
Primary Contact: Brian Lady, Administrator and Chief Executive Officer
CFO: Melanie Lozano, Chief Financial Officer
CNO: Toby Lehn, Director of Nurses
Web address: www.conchocountyhospital.com/
**Control**: Hospital district or authority, Government, Nonfederal **Service**: General
medical and surgical

| | |
|---|---|
| **Staffed Beds:** 16 **Admissions:** 74 **Census:** 1 **Outpatient Visits:** 3621 | |
| **Births:** 0 **Total Expense ($000):** 7740 **Payroll Expense ($000):** 2651 | |
| **Personnel:** 46 | |

**EDINBURG—Hidalgo County**

⊞ **CORNERSTONE REGIONAL HOSPITAL (450825)**, 2302 Cornerstone
Boulevard, Zip 78539–8471; tel. 956/618–4444, (Nonreporting) **A**1 10 **F**3 8
29 34 35 37 39 40 45 46 47 51 57 59 68 74 79 81 82 85 119 126 145 **S**
Universal Health Services, Inc., King of Prussia, PA
Primary Contact: Andrew Wilson, Chief Executive Officer
CFO: Janie Alvarez, Accounting Director
CMO: Omar Gomez, M.D., Chief of Staff
CHR: Erika Betancourt, Coordinator Human Resources
CNO: Roxanne Reyes, Director of Nursing
Web address: www.cornerstoneregional.com
**Control**: Partnership, Investor–owned (for–profit) **Service**: General medical and
surgical

| | |
|---|---|
| **Staffed Beds:** 14 **Admissions:** 429 **Census:** 2 **Outpatient Visits:** 2845 | |
| **Births:** 0 **Total Expense ($000):** 15235 **Payroll Expense ($000):** 4262 | |
| **Personnel:** 79 | |

**TX**

□ △ **DOCTOR'S HOSPITAL AT RENAISSANCE (450869)**, 5501 South McColl Road, Zip 78539–9152; tel. 956/362–7360, (Nonreporting) **A**1 2 3 5 7 8 10 **F**1 3 4 5 8 9 12 13 15 16 17 18 19 20 21 22 23 24 25 26 27 28 29 30 31 34 35 38 39 40 41 43 45 46 47 48 49 50 51 53 54 55 56 57 58 59 60 63 64 65 66 68 70 71 72 73 74 75 76 77 78 79 80 81 82 83 84 85 86 87 88 89 90 91 92 93 95 96 97 98 99 100 101 102 103 104 107 108 109 110 111 112 113 114 115 116 117 118 119 120 121 123 124 126 127 130 131 132 135 138 139 144 145 146 147 148 149 154 155 156 157 **P**1 3 6
Primary Contact: Manish Singh, M.D., Chief Executive Officer
COO: Marissa Castaneda, Chief Operating Officer and Director Marketing
Web address: www.dhr-rgv.com
**Control**: Partnership, Investor–owned (for–profit) **Service**: General medical and surgical

> **Staffed Beds:** 519 **Admissions:** 31411 **Census:** 421 **Outpatient Visits:** 461443 **Births:** 8635 **Total Expense ($000):** 614920 **Payroll Expense ($000):** 226545 **Personnel:** 5064

**EDINBURG REGIONAL HOSPITAL** See Edinburg Regional Medical Center

□ **SOUTH TEXAS HEALTH SYSTEM (450119)**, 1400 West Trenton Road, Zip 78539–9105, Mailing Address: 1102 West Trenton Road, Zip 78539–9105; tel. 956/388–6000, (Includes EDINBURG CHILDREN'S HOSPITAL, Mailing address: 1400 West Trenton Road, Edinburg, Texas, Zip 78539; tel. 956/388–8000; EDINBURG REGIONAL MEDICAL CENTER, Mailing address: 1102 West Trenton Road, Edinburg, Texas, Zip 78539–6199; tel. 956/388–6000; Lance Ames, Interim Chief Executive Officer; MCALLEN HEART HOSPITAL, Mailing address: 1900 South D Street, McAllen, Texas, Zip 78503; tel. 956/994–2000; Dan Caldwell, Chief Executive Officer; MCALLEN MEDICAL CENTER, Mailing address: 301 West Expressway 83, McAllen, Texas, Zip 78503–3045; tel. 956/632–4000; Todd Mann, Chief Executive Officer; SOUTH TEXAS BEHAVIORAL HEALTH CENTER, Mailing address: 2101 West Trenton Road, Edinburg, Texas, Zip 78539; tel. 956/388–1300; Joe Rodriguez, Chief Executive Officer), (Nonreporting) **A**1 3 10 19 **F**3 4 5 11 12 13 15 17 18 19 20 22 24 26 29 31 34 35 38 40 41 42 43 45 46 47 48 49 50 56 57 58 59 64 68 70 72 74 75 76 77 78 79 81 85 86 87 88 89 90 93 96 97 98 99 100 101 102 103 104 105 107 108 110 111 114 115 119 126 130 132 135 146 148 149 150 153 154 **P**7 **S** Universal Health Services, Inc., King of Prussia, PA
Primary Contact: Lance Ames, Chief Executive Officer
CFO: Carlos Guajardo, Chief Financial Officer
CMO: Yuri Bermudez, M.D., Chief of Staff
CIO: Rosie L Mendiola-Balderas, Director Information Systems
CHR: Patricia Mcclelland, Director Human Resources
CNO: Candida Constantine-Castillo, MSN, R.N., Chief Nursing Officer
Web address: www.https://www.edinburgregional.com/
**Control**: Partnership, Investor–owned (for–profit) **Service**: General medical and surgical

> **Staffed Beds:** 820 **Admissions:** 30531 **Census:** 406 **Outpatient Visits:** 245098 **Births:** 1470 **Total Expense ($000):** 403681 **Payroll Expense ($000):** 145005 **Personnel:** 2641

**JACKSON COUNTY HOSPITAL** See Jackson County Hospital District

★ **JACKSON COUNTY HOSPITAL DISTRICT (451363)**, 1013 South Wells Street, Zip 77957–4098; tel. 361/782–7800, (Nonreporting) **A**10 18 **F**3 7 15 29 34 35 40 43 44 45 50 53 57 59 62 64 65 68 75 81 87 97 102 107 110 114 119 127 130 133 143 146 156 157 **P**8
Primary Contact: Bill Jones, Chief Executive Officer
CFO: Lance Smiga, Chief Financial Officer
CMO: Francisco Ortiz, M.D., Chief of Staff
CIO: Jeff Prukop, Director Professional Services
CHR: Donna Coleman, Coordinator Human Resources
CNO: Tammy Zajicek, Director of Nursing
Web address: www.jchd.org
**Control**: Hospital district or authority, Government, Nonfederal **Service**: General medical and surgical

> **Staffed Beds:** 17 **Admissions:** 256 **Census:** 4 **Outpatient Visits:** 20260 **Births:** 0 **Total Expense ($000):** 19576 **Payroll Expense ($000):** 8076 **Personnel:** 124

★ **EL CAMPO MEMORIAL HOSPITAL (450694)**, 303 Sandy Corner Road, Zip 77437–9535; tel. 979/543–6251, (Nonreporting) **A**10 20 **F**3 11 15 18 20 28 29 30 32 34 35 40 45 54 57 59 60 64 65 66 68 70 77 79 81 85 86 91 92 93 97 107 108 110 111 112 114 119 127 129 130 133 135 147 148 154 **P**6
Primary Contact: Nathan Tudor, Chief Executive Officer
CFO: David Mak, Chief Financial Officer
CMO: Thai Huynh, M.D., Chief of Medical Staff
CIO: Bill Eller, Director Information Technology
CHR: Ginger Andreas, Coordinator Personnel and Credentialing
CNO: Desiree Cernoch, Director of Nurses
Web address: www.ecmh.org
**Control**: Other not–for–profit (including NFP Corporation) **Service**: General medical and surgical

> **Staffed Beds:** 30 **Admissions:** 783 **Census:** 9 **Outpatient Visits:** 100397 **Births:** 0 **Total Expense ($000):** 31203 **Payroll Expense ($000):** 14398 **Personnel:** 306

**MEMORIAL HOSPITAL-EL CAMPO** See El Campo Memorial Hospital

**CHILDREN'S HOSPITAL AT PROVIDENCE** See Providence Children's Hospital

**COBALT REHABILITATION HOSPITAL EL PASO**, 1600 East Cliff Drive, Zip 79902–5130; tel. 915/975–8630, (Nonreporting) **S** Curahealth Hospitals, Garland, TX
Primary Contact: Jack Boggess, Chief Executive Officer
Web address: www.cobaltrehab.com/el-paso-tx/
**Control**: Corporation, Investor–owned (for–profit) **Service**: Rehabilitation

> **Staffed Beds:** 42

**COLUMBIA MEDICAL CENTER-EAST** See Del Sol Medical Center

**DEL SOL REHABILITATION HOSP** See Las Palmas Rehabilitation Hospital

□ **EL PASO BEHAVIORAL HEALTH SYSTEM (454109)**, 1900 Denver Avenue, Zip 79902–3008; tel. 915/544–4000, (Nonreporting) **A**1 10 **F**4 5 56 57 75 86 87 98 99 101 102 103 104 105 130 135 149 150 152 153 154 **P**5 **S** Universal Health Services, Inc., King of Prussia, PA
Primary Contact: Phuong Cardoza, Chief Executive Officer
CFO: Phillip Sosa, Chief Financial Officer
CMO: Arthur L. Ramirez, M.D., Medical Director
CIO: Victor Torres, Information Technology Specialist Administrator
CHR: Brenda Holguin, Manager Human Resources
CNO: Susan Brown, Chief Nursing Officer
Web address: www.ubhelpaso.com
**Control**: Corporation, Investor–owned (for–profit) **Service**: Psychiatric

> **Staffed Beds:** 166 **Admissions:** 6142 **Census:** 136 **Outpatient Visits:** 30621 **Births:** 0 **Total Expense ($000):** 45596 **Payroll Expense ($000):** 17039 **Personnel:** 306

□ **EL PASO CHILDREN'S HOSPITAL (453313)**, 4845 Alameda Avenue, Zip 79905–2705; tel. 915/242–8614, (Nonreporting) **A**1 3 5 10 **F**3 19 27 29 30 31 34 35 38 39 40 41 44 45 48 49 50 57 58 59 61 64 68 72 73 74 75 78 79 81 82 85 86 87 88 89 93 96 108 111 119 130 132 146 148 149 150 156 **P**6
Primary Contact: Cindy Stout, R.N., Chief Executive Officer
COO: Ellen Pitcher, Chief Nursing Officer and Chief Operating Officer
CFO: Andrew Rybolt, Chief Financial Officer
CMO: Bradley Fuhrman, M.D., Physician in Chief
CIO: Janina Prada, Director Information Technology
CHR: Marina Estrada, Director Human Resources
CNO: Ellen Pitcher, Chief Nursing Officer and Chief Operating Officer
Web address: www.elpasochildrens.org
**Control**: Other not–for–profit (including NFP Corporation) **Service**: Children's general medical and surgical

> **Staffed Beds:** 122 **Admissions:** 4035 **Census:** 62 **Outpatient Visits:** 70437 **Births:** 0 **Total Expense ($000):** 105897 **Payroll Expense ($000):** 34102 **Personnel:** 569

**TX**

**EL PASO LTAC HOSPITAL (670127)**, 1221 North Cotton Street, 3rd Floor, Zip 79902–3015; tel. 915/546–5822, (Nonreporting) **A**10 22 **F**1 3 29 30 34 57 60 75 77 82 84 85 86 87 100 119 130 148
Primary Contact: Skylier Blake, R.N., Chief Executive Officer
CFO: Eddie Martinez, Chief Financial Officer
Web address: www.https://el-paso-ltac-hospital.business.site/
**Control**: Partnership, Investor–owned (for–profit) **Service**: Acute long–term care hospital

**Staffed Beds**: 33 **Admissions**: 245 **Census**: 11 **Outpatient Visits**: 0 **Births**: 0 **Total Expense ($000)**: 5481 **Payroll Expense ($000)**: 2626 **Personnel**: 46

**EL PASO PSYCHIATRIC CENTER (454100)**, 4615 Alameda Avenue, Zip 79905–2702; tel. 915/532–2202, (Nonreporting) **A**1 3 5 10 **F**29 98 99 103 130 135 **P**6 **S** Texas Department of State Health Services, Austin, TX
Primary Contact: Zulema Carrillo, Superintendent
CFO: David Osterhout, Assistant Superintendent and Chief Financial Officer
CNO: Raul D. Luna, Chief Nurse Executive
Web address: www.dshs.state.tx.us/mhhospitals/ElPasoPC/default.shtm
**Control**: State, Government, Nonfederal **Service**: Psychiatric

**Staffed Beds**: 74 **Admissions**: 847 **Census**: 64 **Outpatient Visits**: 0 **Births**: 0 **Total Expense ($000)**: 16675 **Payroll Expense ($000)**: 13904 **Personnel**: 218

**FOUNDATION SURGICAL HOSPITAL OF EL PASO** See Legent Hospital of El Paso

**△ HIGHLANDS REHABILITATION HOSPITAL (453086)**, 1395 George Dieter Drive, Zip 79936–7410; tel. 915/298–7222, (Nonreporting) **A**1 7 10 **F**3 29 30 34 57 59 64 74 75 79 86 87 90 93 96 100 130 132 143 148 149 **S** Vibra Healthcare, Mechanicsburg, PA
Primary Contact: Steven Alwine, Chief Executive Officer
CHR: Janet Straughan, Manager Human Resources
CNO: Oscar Mendizabal, Chief Nursing Officer
Web address: www.vrhhighlands.com/
**Control**: Partnership, Investor–owned (for–profit) **Service**: Rehabilitation

**Staffed Beds**: 41 **Admissions**: 666 **Census**: 24 **Outpatient Visits**: 5720 **Births**: 0 **Total Expense ($000)**: 14049 **Payroll Expense ($000)**: 7702 **Personnel**: 131

**KINDRED HOSPITAL EL PASO (452079)**, 1740 Curie Drive, Zip 79902–2901; tel. 915/351–9044, (Nonreporting) **A**1 10 **F**1 3 29 45 46 70 75 148 149 **S** Kindred Healthcare, Louisville, KY
Primary Contact: America Jones, R.N., Chief Executive Officer
CFO: Melissa Campa, Controller
CMO: Edward Juarez, M.D., Chief Medical Officer
CHR: Laura Anchondo, Administrator Human Resources
Web address: www.khelpaso.com
**Control**: Corporation, Investor–owned (for–profit) **Service**: Acute long–term care hospital

**Staffed Beds**: 52 **Admissions**: 544 **Census**: 39 **Outpatient Visits**: 48 **Births**: 0 **Total Expense ($000)**: 17128 **Payroll Expense ($000)**: 8171 **Personnel**: 114

**LAS PALMAS DEL SOL HEALTHCARE** See Las Palmas Medical Center

**LAS PALMAS MEDICAL CENTER (450107)**, 1801 North Oregon Street, Zip 79902–3591; tel. 915/521–1200, (Includes DEL SOL MEDICAL CENTER, Mailing address: 10301 West Gateway Boulevard, El Paso, Texas, Zip 79925–7798; tel. 915/595–9000; David Shimp, Chief Executive Officer; LAS PALMAS REHABILITATION HOSPITAL, Mailing address: 300 Waymore Drive, El Paso, Texas, Zip 79902–1628; tel. 915/577–2600; Don Karl, Interim Chief Executive Officer), (Nonreporting) **A**1 2 3 5 10 **F**3 8 9 11 12 13 15 17 18 19 20 22 24 26 28 29 30 31 34 35 37 38 39 40 41 42 43 45 46 47 48 49 50 51 54 56 57 58 59 60 63 64 68 70 72 73 74 75 76 77 78 79 81 82 83 84 85 86 87 88 89 90 91 92 93 96 102 107 108 110 111 112 114 115 119 120 121 122 124 126 127 129 130 132 134 135 138 143 144 145 146 147 148 149 154 157 **P**3 6 **S** HCA Healthcare, Nashville, TN
Primary Contact: Don Karl, Interim Chief Executive Officer
COO: Don Karl, Chief Operating Officer
CMO: Oscar Vega, M.D., Chief Medical Officer
CNO: Jerry Gonzalez, Interim Chief Nursing Officer
Web address: www.laspalmashealth.com
**Control**: Partnership, Investor–owned (for–profit) **Service**: General medical and surgical

**Staffed Beds**: 576 **Admissions**: 26879 **Census**: 362 **Outpatient Visits**: 191124 **Births**: 5068 **Total Expense ($000)**: 366127 **Payroll Expense ($000)**: 141513 **Personnel**: 2050

**LEGENT HOSPITAL OF EL PASO (450877)**, 1416 George Dieter Drive, Zip 79936–7601; tel. 915/598–4240, (Nonreporting) **A**3 10 11 **F**3 29 40 45 49 79 81 82 85 86 107 111 114 119 126 148
Primary Contact: Jim Wilcox, Chief Executive Officer
COO: Sheila Floyd Adams, MSN, R.N., Chief Operating Officer and Chief Nursing Officer
CIO: Louie Aguilera, Director Information Technology
CHR: Grace Beltran, Director Human Resources
CNO: Sheila Floyd Adams, MSN, R.N., Chief Operating Officer and Chief Nursing Officer
Web address: www.psnaffiliates.com/legent-hospital-of-el-paso
**Control**: Partnership, Investor–owned (for–profit) **Service**: Surgical

**Staffed Beds**: 20 **Admissions**: 483 **Census**: 3 **Outpatient Visits**: 7088 **Births**: 0 **Total Expense ($000)**: 38656 **Payroll Expense ($000)**: 6958 **Personnel**: 137

**MESA HILLS SPECIALTY HOSPITAL** See Premier Specialty Hospital of El Paso

**PREMIER SPECIALTY HOSPITAL OF EL PASO (452035)**, 2311 North Oregon Street, 5th Floor, Zip 79902–3216; tel. 915/545–1823, (Nonreporting) **A**1 10 **F**1 3 8 29 64 75 81 148 **S** Concord Healthcare Group, Lakewood, NJ
Primary Contact: Jose Huerta, Chief Executive Officer
COO: Elena Pino, Chief Operating Officer and Chief Nursing Officer
CFO: Priscilla Carter, Chief Financial Officer
Web address: www.specialtyhospitalmesahills.com/
**Control**: Corporation, Investor–owned (for–profit) **Service**: Acute long–term care hospital

**Staffed Beds**: 32 **Admissions**: 171 **Census**: 11 **Outpatient Visits**: 1131 **Births**: 0 **Total Expense ($000)**: 12364 **Payroll Expense ($000)**: 3803 **Personnel**: 41

**PROVIDENCE MEMORIAL HOSPITAL** See The Hospitals of Providence Memorial Campus

**R E THOMASON GENERAL HOSPITAL** See University Medical Center of El Paso

**RIO BRAVO BEHAVIORAL HEALTH** See Rio Vista Behavioral Health

**RIO VISTA BEHAVIORAL HEALTH (454146)**, 1390 Northwestern Drive, Zip 79912–8003; tel. 915/209–4513, (Nonreporting) **A**1 **F**98 103 105 152 153 154 **S** Acadia Healthcare Company, Inc., Franklin, TN
Primary Contact: Diana Schultz, Chief Executive Officer
Web address: www.https://www.riovistabehavioral.com/
**Control**: Corporation, Investor–owned (for–profit) **Service**: Psychiatric

**Staffed Beds**: 80 **Admissions**: 806 **Census**: 20 **Outpatient Visits**: 1202 **Births**: 0 **Total Expense ($000)**: 8302 **Payroll Expense ($000)**: 3760 **Personnel**: 79

**SIERRA MEDICAL CENTER** See The Hospitals of Providence Sierra Campus

TX

---

**Hospital, Medicare Provider Number, Address, Telephone, Approval, Facility, and Physician Codes, Health Care System**

★ American Hospital Association (AHA) membership   ○ Healthcare Facilities Accreditation Program   ⇑ Center for Improvement in Healthcare Quality Accreditation
□ The Joint Commission accreditation   ◇ DNV Healthcare Inc. accreditation   △ Commission on Accreditation of Rehabilitation Facilities (CARF) accreditation

✠ **THE HOSPITALS OF PROVIDENCE EAST CAMPUS (670047)**, 3280 Joe Battle Boulevard, Zip 79938–2622; tel. 915/832–2000, (Nonreporting) **A**1 10 **F**3 13 15 18 20 22 26 29 30 31 34 35 39 40 41 42 43 45 49 50 51 57 58 59 60 64 70 72 73 74 75 76 77 78 79 81 84 85 86 87 93 107 108 110 111 114 115 119 126 130 134 146 147 148 149 154 156 **S** TENET Healthcare Corporation, Dallas, TX
Primary Contact: Monica Vargas-Mahar, FACHE, Chief Executive Officer
COO: Brandon May, Chief Operating Officer
Web address: www.sphn.com
**Control:** Individual, Investor–owned (for–profit) **Service:** General medical and surgical

**Staffed Beds:** 182 **Admissions:** 13711 **Census:** 167 **Outpatient Visits:** 108825 **Births:** 2344 **Total Expense ($000):** 204706 **Payroll Expense ($000):** 63229 **Personnel:** 859

✠ **THE HOSPITALS OF PROVIDENCE MEMORIAL CAMPUS (450002)**, 2001 North Oregon Street, Zip 79902–3368; tel. 915/577–6625, (Includes PROVIDENCE CHILDREN'S HOSPITAL, Mailing address: 2001 North Oregon Street, El Paso, Texas, Zip 79902–3320; tel. 915/577–7746; Nicholas R Tejeda, FACHE, Market Chief Executive Officer), (Nonreporting) **A**1 2 3 10 **F**3 8 11 12 13 14 15 17 18 19 20 21 22 23 26 30 31 32 34 35 37 40 41 42 43 45 46 48 49 50 54 55 56 57 58 59 60 64 65 70 71 72 74 75 76 77 78 79 81 84 85 86 88 89 93 97 98 100 101 102 103 105 107 110 111 115 119 126 130 132 133 134 141 143 145 146 147 148 149 150 154 157 **S** TENET Healthcare Corporation, Dallas, TX
Primary Contact: Nicholas R. Tejeda, FACHE, Market Chief Executive Officer
COO: Roddex Barlow, Chief Operating Officer
CFO: Charles Handley, Chief Financial Officer
CIO: Vince Randazzo, Texas Regional Director Information Systems, Tenet Account
CHR: Stephanie S. Talley, Market Chief Human Resource Officer
CNO: Mark Phillips, Chief Nursing Officer
Web address: www.thehospitalsofprovidence.com
**Control:** Partnership, Investor–owned (for–profit) **Service:** General medical and surgical

**Staffed Beds:** 332 **Admissions:** 15553 **Census:** 182 **Outpatient Visits:** 121347 **Births:** 2978 **Total Expense ($000):** 258402 **Payroll Expense ($000):** 81960 **Personnel:** 1220

✠ △ **THE HOSPITALS OF PROVIDENCE SIERRA CAMPUS (450668)**, 1625 Medical Center Drive, Zip 79902–5005; tel. 915/747–4000, (Nonreporting) **A**1 5 7 10 **F**11 15 17 18 20 22 24 26 28 29 34 40 43 46 47 49 50 54 57 59 60 61 64 70 74 77 78 79 81 85 90 92 93 96 107 108 109 110 111 114 115 119 126 130 132 146 148 149 154 157 **S** TENET Healthcare Corporation, Dallas, TX
Primary Contact: Rob J. Anderson, Chief Executive Officer
COO: Sereka Barlow, Chief Operating Officer
CFO: Charles Handley, Chief Financial Officer
CIO: Charlie Ortega, Administrative Director Information Systems
CHR: Stephanie S. Talley, Chief Human Resource Officer
CNO: Carlos Castillo, R.N., Chief Nursing Officer
Web address: www.thehospitalsofprovidence.com
**Control:** Partnership, Investor–owned (for–profit) **Service:** General medical and surgical

**Staffed Beds:** 180 **Admissions:** 8041 **Census:** 118 **Outpatient Visits:** 72150 **Births:** 0 **Total Expense ($000):** 184306 **Payroll Expense ($000):** 49212 **Personnel:** 642

✠ **THE HOSPITALS OF PROVIDENCE TRANSMOUNTAIN CAMPUS (670120)**, 2000 Transmountain Road, Zip 79911; tel. 915/877–8300, (Nonreporting) **A**1 3 10 **F**3 11 13 18 20 22 26 29 30 34 35 40 41 43 44 45 46 48 49 50 51 57 59 60 64 68 70 73 74 75 76 77 78 79 81 85 93 107 108 111 115 118 119 126 130 146 148 149 154 **S** TENET Healthcare Corporation, Dallas, TX
Primary Contact: Tasha Hopper, Chief Executive Officer
COO: David Byrd, Chief Operating Officer
CFO: David Byrd, Chief Financial Officer
CMO: Gustavo Martell, M.D., Chief Medical Officer
CIO: Vince Randazzo, Interim Chief Information Officer
CHR: Stephanie S. Talley, Chief Human Resource Officer
CNO: Linda B. Lawson, Chief Nursing Officer
Web address: www.https://www.thehospitalsofprovidence.com/our-locations/transmountain
**Control:** Corporation, Investor–owned (for–profit) **Service:** General medical and surgical

**Staffed Beds:** 106 **Admissions:** 5985 **Census:** 64 **Outpatient Visits:** 43391 **Births:** 495 **Total Expense ($000):** 99730 **Payroll Expense ($000):** 32765 **Personnel:** 385

**THE HOSPITALS OF SIERRA PROVIDENCE EAST CAMPUS** See The Hospitals of Providence East Campus

**TRIUMPH HOSPITAL EL PASO** See Kindred Hospital El Paso

**UNIVERSITY BEHAVIORAL HEALTH OF EL PASO** See El Paso Behavioral Health System

✠ **UNIVERSITY MEDICAL CENTER OF EL PASO (450024)**, 4815 Alameda Avenue, Zip 79905–2794; tel. 915/544–1200, (Nonreporting) **A**1 2 3 5 10 **F**3 8 11 13 15 17 18 20 22 24 26 28 29 30 31 34 35 37 40 43 45 46 47 48 49 50 51 53 54 57 59 60 61 64 65 68 70 74 75 76 77 78 79 80 81 82 85 86 87 91 92 93 94 96 97 100 102 107 108 110 111 112 113 114 115 118 119 126 127 130 131 134 143 144 145 146 147 148 149 150 157
Primary Contact: Jacob Cintron, FACHE, President and Chief Executive Officer
COO: Maria Zampini, Chief Operating Officer
CFO: Michael Nunez, Chief Financial Officer
CMO: Joel Hendryx, M.D., Chief Medical Officer
CIO: Janina Prada, Director Information Services
CHR: Janice M Harris, Director Human Resources
CNO: Amyra Daher, MSN, R.N., Chief Nursing Officer
Web address: www.thomasoncares.org
**Control:** Hospital district or authority, Government, Nonfederal **Service:** General medical and surgical

**Staffed Beds:** 290 **Admissions:** 15912 **Census:** 214 **Outpatient Visits:** 937427 **Births:** 2684 **Total Expense ($000):** 530428 **Payroll Expense ($000):** 177406 **Personnel:** 3005

**VIBRA HIGHLANDS REHABILITATION HOSPITAL OF EL PASO** See Highlands Rehabilitation Hospital

✠ **WILLIAM BEAUMONT ARMY MEDICAL CENTER**, 5005 North Piedras Street, Zip 79920–5001; tel. 915/742–2121, (Nonreporting) **A**1 2 3 5 **S** Department of the Army, Office of the Surgeon General, Falls Church, VA
Primary Contact: Colonel Erik G. Rude, Commander
CIO: MajorRion Koon, Chief Information Management Division
Web address: www.https://www.wbamc.amedd.army.mil/NewPersonnel/CDR.aspx
**Service:** General medical and surgical

**Staffed Beds:** 209

**ELDORADO—Schleicher County**

★ **SCHLEICHER COUNTY MEDICAL CENTER (451304)**, 102 North US Highway 277, Zip 76936–4010; tel. 325/853–2507, (Nonreporting) **A**10 18 **F**29 34 40 43 57 59 64 65 68 87 93 97 107 127 133 154 **S** Preferred Management Corporation, Shawnee, OK
Primary Contact: Paul Burke, Administrator
CFO: Larry Stephens, Chief Financial Officer
CMO: Gordy Day, M.D., Medical Director
CHR: Beverly Minor, Chief Human Resources
Web address: www.scmc.us
**Control:** Corporation, Investor–owned (for–profit) **Service:** General medical and surgical

**Staffed Beds:** 14 **Admissions:** 54 **Census:** 1 **Outpatient Visits:** 7622 **Births:** 0 **Total Expense ($000):** 5514 **Payroll Expense ($000):** 2666 **Personnel:** 53

**SCHLEICHER COUNTY MEDICAL CNTR** See Schleicher County Medical Center

**ELECTRA—Wichita County**

★ **ELECTRA MEMORIAL HOSPITAL (451343)**, 1207 South Bailey Street, Zip 76360–3221, Mailing Address: P.O. Box 1112, Zip 76360–1112; tel. 940/495–3981, (Nonreporting) **A**10 18 **F**3 7 11 28 29 32 34 35 40 43 53 57 59 62 64 65 66 75 77 86 93 97 107 114 119 127 129 130 131 133 148
Primary Contact: Rebecca J. McCain, Chief Executive Officer
CFO: Ginnie Holmes, Chief Financial Officer
CIO: Brandon Huffstutler, Chief Information Officer
CNO: Kim Gilbert, R.N., Chief Nursing Officer
Web address: www.electrahospital.com
**Control:** Hospital district or authority, Government, Nonfederal **Service:** General medical and surgical

**Staffed Beds:** 19 **Admissions:** 346 **Census:** 6 **Outpatient Visits:** 34235 **Births:** 0 **Total Expense ($000):** 20209 **Payroll Expense ($000):** 10055 **Personnel:** 103

*Many Facility Codes have changed. Please refer to the AHA Guide Code Chart.*   © 2021 AHA Guide

TX

## ENNIS—Ellis County

**ENNIS REGIONAL MEDICAL CENTER (450833)**, 2201 West Lampasas Street, Zip 75119–5644; tel. 972/875–0900, (Nonreporting) **A**1 10 **F**3 11 15 18 29 30 34 35 40 43 45 50 51 57 59 64 65 70 75 77 79 81 82 85 91 93 107 108 110 111 115 119 146 147 149 157 **S** LifePoint Health, Brentwood, TN
Primary Contact: Robert Rupp, Chief Executive Officer
CFO: Jack Wilcox, Chief Financial Officer
CMO: John M. Sullivan, M.D., Chief of Staff
CHR: Selena Cryer, Director Human Resources
CNO: Edwina A Miner, R.N., Chief Nursing Officer
Web address: www.ennisregional.com
**Control:** Partnership, Investor–owned (for–profit) **Service:** General medical and surgical

**Staffed Beds:** 58 **Admissions:** 619 **Census:** 5 **Outpatient Visits:** 29328 **Births:** 0 **Total Expense ($000):** 22000 **Payroll Expense ($000):** 7963 **Personnel:** 138

## FAIRFIELD—Freestone County

**FREESTON MEDICAL CENTER** See Freestone Medical Center

★ **FREESTONE MEDICAL CENTER (450658)**, 125 Newman Street, Zip 75840–1499; tel. 903/389–2121, (Nonreporting) **A**10 22 **F**3 11 15 28 29 34 35 40 43 45 57 59 64 65 75 81 97 107 108 110 115 119 127 128 **P**6 **S** Community Hospital Corporation, Plano, TX
Primary Contact: John M. Yeary, FACHE, Chief Executive Officer
CFO: David A Travis, Chief Financial Officer
CMO: Darryl White, M.D., Chief of Staff
CHR: Jennifer Rummel, Director Human Resources
CNO: Tonya Basque, Chief Nursing Officer
Web address: www.freestonemc.com/
**Control:** Hospital district or authority, Government, Nonfederal **Service:** General medical and surgical

**Staffed Beds:** 28 **Admissions:** 316 **Census:** 2 **Outpatient Visits:** 29222 **Births:** 0 **Total Expense ($000):** 13106 **Payroll Expense ($000):** 6000 **Personnel:** 118

## FLORESVILLE—Wilson County

**CONNALLY MEDICAL CENTER** See Connally Memorial Medical Center

**CONNALLY MEMORIAL MEDICAL CENTER (450108)**, 499 10th Street, Zip 78114–3175; tel. 830/393–1300, (Nonreporting) **A**10 **F**3 15 18 29 34 35 40 43 45 47 49 54 57 59 62 64 65 75 81 97 107 108 110 111 114 119 130 132 133 144 146 148 154 156 **P**6
Primary Contact: Bob Gillespie, Chief Executive Officer
COO: Bob Gillespie, Chief Operating Officer
CFO: Curtis Rojas, Interim Chief Financial Officer
CMO: Wade Krause, M.D., Chief Medical Officer
CHR: Loretta Y Morgan, Director Human Resources
CNO: Sue Tackitt, Chief Nursing Officer
Web address: www.connallymmc.org
**Control:** Hospital district or authority, Government, Nonfederal **Service:** General medical and surgical

**Staffed Beds:** 26 **Admissions:** 817 **Census:** 8 **Outpatient Visits:** 144793 **Births:** 3 **Total Expense ($000):** 37097 **Payroll Expense ($000):** 16386 **Personnel:** 278

## FLOWER MOUND—Denton County

**CONTINUUM REHABILITATION HOSPITAL OF NORTH TEXAS** See Icare Rehabilitation Hospital

**ICARE REHABILITATION HOSPITAL (673064)**, 3100 Peters Colony Road, Zip 75022–2949; tel. 214/513–0310, (Nonreporting) **A**10
Primary Contact: Gina Tomaseski, Chief Executive Officer
Web address: www.https://www.icarerehabilitation.com/
**Control:** Corporation, Investor–owned (for–profit) **Service:** Rehabilitation

**Staffed Beds:** 41

☐ **TEXAS HEALTH PRESBYTERIAN HOSPITAL FLOWER MOUND (670068)**, 4400 Long Prairie Road, Zip 75028–1892; tel. 469/322–7000, (Nonreporting) **A**1 10 **F**3 12 13 15 18 20 29 30 31 34 40 45 49 51 54 57 59 64 70 73 74 75 76 77 78 79 81 82 85 87 93 107 108 110 111 114 115 119 126 130 132 146 147 149 157
Primary Contact: Spencer Turner, FACHE, President
COO: Shelley R Tobey, R.N., MS, Chief Operating Officer and Chief Nursing Officer
CFO: Tom Howard, Chief Financial Officer
CHR: Nicole Schweigert, Director Human Resources
CNO: Shelley R Tobey, R.N., MS, Chief Operating Officer and Chief Nursing Officer
Web address: www.texashealthflowermound.com/
**Control:** Partnership, Investor–owned (for–profit) **Service:** General medical and surgical

**Staffed Beds:** 99 **Admissions:** 5932 **Census:** 57 **Outpatient Visits:** 39017 **Births:** 1914 **Total Expense ($000):** 132805 **Payroll Expense ($000):** 47609 **Personnel:** 619

## FORT HOOD—Coryell County

**CARL R. DARNALL ARMY MEDICAL CENTER**, 36065 Santa Fe Avenue, Zip 76544–5060; tel. 254/288–8000, (Nonreporting) **A**1 3 5 **S** Department of the Army, Office of the Surgeon General, Falls Church, VA
Primary Contact: Colonel Richard Malish, M.D., Commander
CHR: Charles Burton, Chief Human Resources
Web address: www.https://www.crdamc.amedd.army.mil/Default.aspx
**Service:** General medical and surgical

**Staffed Beds:** 109

**DARNALL ARMY COMM HOSPITAL** See Carl R. Darnall Army Medical Center

## FORT SAM HOUSTON—Bexar County

**BROOKE ARMY MEDICAL CENTER**, 3551 Roger Brooke Drive, Zip 78234–4501; tel. 210/916–4141, (Nonreporting) **A**1 2 3 5 **S** Department of the Army, Office of the Surgeon General, Falls Church, VA
Primary Contact: Brigadier General Jeffrey Johnson, Commander
CMO: ColonelJoseph P Chozinski, M.D., Deputy Commander Clinical Services
CHR: Rose Juarez, Chief Civilian Personnel Branch
CNO: ColonelSheri Howell, Deputy Commander Nursing
Web address: www.https://www.bamc.health.mil/
**Service:** General medical and surgical

**Staffed Beds:** 483

**SAN ANTONIO MILITARY MEDICAL CENTER** See Brooke Army Medical Center

## FORT STOCKTON—Pecos County

★ **PECOS COUNTY MEMORIAL HOSPITAL (451389)**, 387 West I H–10, Zip 79735–8912, Mailing Address: P.O. Box 1648, Zip 79735–1648; tel. 432/336–2004, (Nonreporting) **A**3 10 18 **F**3 11 13 28 29 30 34 35 40 43 45 46 50 53 57 59 62 63 64 65 75 76 81 93 107 111 119 127 130 133 144 146 148 **P**6
Primary Contact: Betsy Briscoe, Chief Executive Officer
COO: Margaret Davis, Chief Operating Officer
CFO: Sharon Hunt, Interim Chief Financial Officer
CMO: Subodh Mallik, M.D., Chief of Staff
CHR: Malissa Trevino, Director Human Resources
CNO: Gina Kalka, R.N., Chief Nursing Officer
Web address: www.pcmhfs.com
**Control:** County, Government, Nonfederal **Service:** General medical and surgical

**Staffed Beds:** 25 **Admissions:** 450 **Census:** 4 **Outpatient Visits:** 57673 **Births:** 144 **Total Expense ($000):** 29249 **Payroll Expense ($000):** 13082 **Personnel:** 254

## FORT WORTH—Tarrant County

**BAYLOR ALL SAINTS MEDICAL CENTER AT FORT WORTH** See Baylor Scott & White All Saints Medical Center - Fort Worth

**BAYLOR INSTITUTE FOR REHABILITATION AT FORT WORTH** See Baylor Scott & White Institute for Rehabilitation-Fort Worth

---

Hospital, Medicare Provider Number, Address, Telephone, Approval, Facility, and Physician Codes, Health Care System

★ American Hospital Association (AHA) membership
☐ The Joint Commission accreditation
◯ Healthcare Facilities Accreditation Program
◇ DNV Healthcare Inc. accreditation
⇑ Center for Improvement in Healthcare Quality Accreditation
△ Commission on Accreditation of Rehabilitation Facilities (CARF) accreditation

⊞ **BAYLOR SCOTT & WHITE ALL SAINTS MEDICAL CENTER - FORT WORTH (450137)**, 1400 Eighth Avenue, Zip 76104–4192; tel. 817/926–2544, (Nonreporting) **A**1 2 5 10 **F**3 11 13 17 18 24 26 28 29 30 31 34 35 38 40 43 45 46 47 49 55 59 64 70 72 73 74 75 76 77 78 79 80 81 84 86 87 96 97 100 102 107 108 111 114 115 119 124 126 130 131 132 138 139 142 146 147 148 149 154 **S** Baylor Scott & White Health, Dallas, TX
Primary Contact: Michael Sanborn, FACHE, MS, President
COO: Janice L Walker, R.N., Senior Executive Vice President and System Chief Nursing Officer
CFO: Lucy Catala, Vice President Finance
CMO: Dahlia Hassani, Vice President of Medical Affairs
CIO: Sandy Vaughn, Director Information Services
CHR: Tracy Stanford, Director Human Resources
Web address: www.baylorhealth.com/PhysiciansLocations/AllSaints/Pages/Default.aspx
**Control:** Other not-for-profit (including NFP Corporation) **Service:** General medical and surgical

**Staffed Beds: 377 Admissions: 18486 Census: 250 Outpatient Visits: 69088 Births: 5689 Total Expense ($000): 371040 Payroll Expense ($000): 125362 Personnel: 1416**

⊞ **BAYLOR SCOTT & WHITE INSTITUTE FOR REHABILITATION-FORT WORTH (673035)**, 6601 Harris Parkway, Zip 76132–6108; tel. 817/433–9600, (Nonreporting) **A**1 10 **F**3 28 29 30 64 75 90 93 130 131 135 149 154 **S** Select Medical Corporation, Mechanicsburg, PA
Primary Contact: Ryan Seymour, Chief Executive Officer
CMO: Asher Light, M.D., Medical Director
CHR: Nissi Dalton, Manager Human Resources
CNO: Catherine Ewing, M.D., Chief Nursing Officer
Web address: www.baylorhealth.com/PhysiciansLocations/BIR/Pages/Default.aspx
**Control:** Partnership, Investor–owned (for–profit) **Service:** Rehabilitation

**Staffed Beds: 42 Admissions: 593 Census: 20 Outpatient Visits: 6467 Births: 0 Total Expense ($000): 14955 Payroll Expense ($000): 7334 Personnel: 107**

☐ **BAYLOR SCOTT & WHITE SURGICAL HOSPITAL FORT WORTH (450880)**, 1800 Park Place Avenue, Zip 76110–1302; tel. 682/703–5600, (Nonreporting) **A**1 3 10 **F**3 8 12 29 40 51 64 70 79 81 82 85 87 107 111 115 119 126 131
Primary Contact: Paul Debona, Chief Executive Officer
CFO: Jane Mathis, Chief Financial Officer
CMO: Bruce Bollinger, M.D., Medical Director
CNO: Stacie Merrill, Chief Nursing Officer
Web address: www.mcsh-hospital.com
**Control:** Partnership, Investor–owned (for–profit) **Service:** General medical and surgical

**Staffed Beds: 30 Admissions: 1780 Census: 10 Outpatient Visits: 11326 Births: 0 Total Expense ($000): 93572 Payroll Expense ($000): 19048 Personnel: 210**

⊞ **COOK CHILDREN'S MEDICAL CENTER (453300)**, 801 Seventh Avenue, Zip 76104–2796; tel. 682/885–4000, (Nonreporting) **A**1 3 5 10 **F**3 7 8 17 19 21 23 25 27 29 30 31 32 34 35 37 38 39 40 41 43 44 45 46 47 48 49 50 54 55 57 58 59 60 61 62 64 65 68 72 74 75 77 78 79 80 81 82 84 85 86 87 88 89 90 91 92 93 94 95 97 98 99 100 101 102 104 105 107 108 111 112 113 114 115 118 119 126 129 130 131 132 136 138 143 144 146 148 149 150 154 155
Primary Contact: Rick W. Merrill, System President and Chief Executive Officer
CFO: Stephen Kimmel, Chief Financial Officer
CMO: James C Cunningham, M.D., Chief Medical Officer
CIO: Theresa Meadows, Chief Information Officer
CNO: Teresa J Clark, R.N., MS, Chief Nursing Officer
Web address: www.cookchildrens.org
**Control:** Other not-for-profit (including NFP Corporation) **Service:** Children's general medical and surgical

**Staffed Beds: 391 Admissions: 12997 Census: 236 Outpatient Visits: 318752 Births: 0 Total Expense ($000): 919333 Payroll Expense ($000): 284217 Personnel: 4522**

**COOK-FORT WORTH CHILD MED CTR** See Cook Children's Medical Center

⊞ **ENCOMPASS HEALTH REHABILITATION HOSPITAL OF CITY VIEW (453042)**, 6701 Oakmont Boulevard, Zip 76132–2957; tel. 817/370–4700, (Nonreporting) **A**1 10 **F**3 29 75 77 90 91 94 95 96 130 148 154 **S** Encompass Health Corporation, Birmingham, AL
Primary Contact: Janell Briscoe, Chief Executive Officer
Web address: www.healthsouthcityview.com
**Control:** Corporation, Investor–owned (for–profit) **Service:** Rehabilitation

**Staffed Beds: 62 Admissions: 1392 Census: 49 Outpatient Visits: 0 Births: 0 Total Expense ($000): 21434 Payroll Expense ($000): 11188 Personnel: 195**

**FOREST PARK MEDICAL CENTER** See Texas Health Hospital Clearfork

**HARRIS CONTINUED CARE HOSPITAL** See Texas Health Specialty Hospital

**HARRIS METHODIST FORT WORTH** See Texas Health Harris Methodist Hospital Fort Worth

**HARRIS METHODIST SOUTHWEST** See Texas Health Harris Methodist Hospital Southwest Fort Worth

**HEALTHSOUTH CITY VIEW REHABILITATION HOSPITAL** See Encompass Health Rehabilitation Hospital of City View

**JOHN PETER SMITH HOSPITAL** See Jps Health Network, Fort Worth

⊞ **JPS HEALTH NETWORK (450039)**, 1500 South Main Street, Zip 76104–4917; tel. 817/921–3431, (Includes JOHN PETER SMITH HOSPITAL, Mailing address: 1500 South Main Street, Fort Worth, Texas, Zip 76104; tel. 817/921–3431; TRINITY SPRINGS PAVILION, Mailing address: 1500 South Main Street, Fort Worth, Texas, Zip 76104–4917; tel. 817/927–3636; Lily Wong, Director Psychiatry), (Nonreporting) **A**1 2 3 5 8 10 **F**3 8 11 13 18 20 22 24 26 28 29 30 31 32 34 35 36 39 40 43 44 45 46 47 49 50 54 56 57 58 59 60 61 64 65 66 68 70 71 72 74 75 76 77 78 79 80 81 82 84 85 86 87 91 92 93 97 98 100 101 102 104 105 107 108 110 111 114 115 118 119 121 123 124 126 130 131 132 135 141 143 144 146 147 148 153 154 156 **P**6
Primary Contact: Robert Earley, President and Chief Executive Officer
CFO: Alan Townsend, Interim Chief Financial Officer
CIO: Melinda Custin, Chief Information Officer
CHR: Nikki Sumpter, Senior Vice President Human Resources
CNO: Wanda V. Peebles, Chief Nursing Officer
Web address: www.jpshealthnet.org
**Control:** Hospital district or authority, Government, Nonfederal **Service:** General medical and surgical

**Staffed Beds: 540 Admissions: 32703 Census: 501 Outpatient Visits: 1098198 Births: 3925 Total Expense ($000): 1003040 Payroll Expense ($000): 406800 Personnel: 6035**

**KINDRED HOSP-FORT WORTH SW** See Kindred Hospital Tarrant County-Fort Worth Southwest

**LIFECARE HOSP OF FORT WORTH** See Lifecare Hospitals of North Texas-Fort Worth

**MEDICAL CENTER ALLIANCE** See Medical City Alliance

**MEDICAL CENTRE SURGICAL HOSP** See Baylor Scott & White Surgical Hospital Fort Worth

⊞ **MEDICAL CITY ALLIANCE (670103)**, 3101 North Tarrant Parkway, Zip 76177; tel. 817/639–1000, (Nonreporting) **A**1 **F**3 11 12 13 15 18 20 22 24 26 29 30 34 35 40 42 45 46 47 48 49 50 54 56 57 59 64 70 72 74 75 76 77 79 81 82 85 86 87 92 107 108 110 111 114 115 119 126 130 132 135 145 146 147 148 149 154 156 **S** HCA Healthcare, Nashville, TN
Primary Contact: Glenn Wallace, Chief Executive Officer
Web address: www.baylorhealth.com/PhysiciansLocations/BIR/Pages/Default.aspx
**Control:** Corporation, Investor–owned (for–profit) **Service:** General medical and surgical

**Staffed Beds: 75 Admissions: 4711 Census: 43 Outpatient Visits: 58266 Births: 805 Total Expense ($000): 87580 Payroll Expense ($000): 29791 Personnel: 404**

⊞ **MEDICAL CITY FORT WORTH (450672)**, 900 Eighth Avenue, Zip 76104–3902; tel. 817/336–2100, (Nonreporting) **A**1 2 3 5 10 **F**3 12 17 18 20 22 24 26 28 29 30 31 37 40 42 45 46 47 48 49 56 58 64 67 70 74 77 78 79 81 85 87 90 91 93 107 108 111 114 115 119 126 130 138 139 145 146 148 **S** HCA Healthcare, Nashville, TN
Primary Contact: Jyric Sims, FACHE, Chief Executive Officer
COO: JW Newman, Chief Operating Officer
CFO: Andrew Lane, Chief Financial Officer
CMO: Terry Loftus, M.D., Chief Medical Officer
CIO: Kelley Fredrickson, Director Information Services
CHR: Cyndi Roberts, Director Human Resources
CNO: Damita Williams, Ed.D., R.N., MSN, Chief Nursing Officer
Web address: www.medicalcityfortworth.com/about/
**Control:** Partnership, Investor–owned (for–profit) **Service:** General medical and surgical

**Staffed Beds: 218 Admissions: 11286 Census: 172 Outpatient Visits: 52815 Births: 0 Total Expense ($000): 287526 Payroll Expense ($000): 88622 Personnel: 1043**

*Many Facility Codes have changed. Please refer to the AHA Guide Code Chart.* © 2021 AHA Guide

**TX**

☐ **MESA SPRINGS (454124)**, 5560 Mesa Springs Drive, Zip 76123; tel. 817/292–4600, (Nonreporting) **A**1 10 **F**5 29 54 98 101 104 105 135 153 **S** Springstone, Louisville, KY
Primary Contact: Barbara Schmidt, Chief Executive Officer
CFO: Kent Ashley, Chief Financial Officer
CMO: Stewart Keller, M.D., Medical Director
CHR: Jill Housand, Director Human Resources
CNO: Ana Ramirez, Director of Nursing
Web address: www.springstone.com/hospitals.stmhl
**Control**: Corporation, Investor–owned (for–profit) **Service**: Psychiatric

**Staffed Beds**: 72 **Admissions**: 3059 **Census**: 60 **Outpatient Visits**: 30402
**Births**: 0 **Total Expense ($000)**: 22070 **Payroll Expense ($000)**: 13805
**Personnel**: 234

**OCEANS BEHAVIORAL HOSPITAL FORT WORTH** See Wellbridge Healthcare of Fort Worth

**PARKWAY SURGICAL & CARDIOVASCULAR HOSPITAL** See Wise Health Surgical Hospital at Parkway

**PLAZA MEDICAL CENTER OF FORT WORTH** See Medical City Fort Worth

**TARRANT COUNTY HOSP DISTRICT** See Jps Health Network

☒ **TEXAS HEALTH HARRIS METHODIST HOSPITAL ALLIANCE (670085)**, 10864 Texas Health Trail, Zip 76244–4897; tel. 682/212–2000, (Nonreporting) **A**1 10 **F**3 11 12 13 15 18 20 22 24 26 28 29 30 34 35 40 45 48 49 50 57 59 64 70 72 74 75 76 77 79 80 81 82 84 85 86 93 107 108 110 111 113 114 115 118 119 126 130 131 132 135 146 147 148 149 **P**6 **S** Texas Health Resources, Arlington, TX
Primary Contact: Clint Abernathy, President
Web address: www.https://www.texashealth.org/alliance/Pages/default.aspx
**Control**: Other not–for–profit (including NFP Corporation) **Service**: General medical and surgical

**Staffed Beds**: 101 **Admissions**: 6614 **Census**: 61 **Outpatient Visits**: 42850
**Births**: 2028 **Total Expense ($000)**: 105609 **Payroll Expense ($000)**: 42675 **Personnel**: 506

☒ **TEXAS HEALTH HARRIS METHODIST HOSPITAL FORT WORTH (450135)**, 1301 Pennsylvania Avenue, Zip 76104–2122; tel. 817/250–2000, (Nonreporting) **A**1 2 3 5 10 **F**3 11 13 15 17 18 20 22 24 26 28 29 30 31 34 35 36 40 42 43 45 46 47 48 49 53 54 56 58 59 60 61 64 65 66 67 68 70 71 72 73 74 75 76 77 78 79 81 83 84 85 86 87 91 92 93 94 96 100 107 108 110 111 112 113 114 115 116 117 118 119 120 126 130 131 132 135 138 145 146 147 148 149 150 154 156 **P**6 **S** Texas Health Resources, Arlington, TX
Primary Contact: Joseph DeLeon, President
CFO: Shelly Miland, Group Financial Officer
CMO: Joseph Prosser, M.D., Chief Medical Officer
CHR: Ginger Morrow, Entity Human Resources Officer
CNO: Elaine Nelson, R.N., MSN, Chief Nursing Officer
Web address: www.texashealth.org
**Control**: Other not–for–profit (including NFP Corporation) **Service**: General medical and surgical

**Staffed Beds**: 647 **Admissions**: 35919 **Census**: 530 **Outpatient Visits**: 215096 **Births**: 3037 **Total Expense ($000)**: 786679 **Payroll Expense ($000)**: 288092 **Personnel**: 3900

☒ **TEXAS HEALTH HARRIS METHODIST HOSPITAL SOUTHWEST FORT WORTH (450779)**, 6100 Harris Parkway, Zip 76132–4199; tel. 817/433–5000, (Includes TEXAS HEALTH HOSPITAL CLEARFORK, Mailing address: 5400 Clearfork Main Street, Fort Worth, Texas, Zip 76109–3553; tel. 682/703–5000; Rebecca Tucker, President), (Nonreporting) **A**1 2 10 **F**3 8 11 13 15 18 20 28 29 34 35 36 37 40 45 46 47 48 49 50 53 57 59 60 64 68 70 72 75 76 77 78 79 80 81 84 85 86 87 93 102 107 110 111 114 115 119 126 130 131 146 147 148 149 **S** Texas Health Resources, Arlington, TX
Primary Contact: Rebecca Tucker, President
CFO: Charlotte Ward, Entity Financial Officer
CMO: Mark Montgomery, M.D., Chief Medical Officer
CHR: Leanna W Nalley, Director Human Resources
CNO: Mary Robinson, Chief Nursing Officer and Vice President Patient Care Services
Web address: www.texashealth.org
**Control**: Other not–for–profit (including NFP Corporation) **Service**: General medical and surgical

**Staffed Beds**: 231 **Admissions**: 13881 **Census**: 131 **Outpatient Visits**: 104459 **Births**: 3086 **Total Expense ($000)**: 289823 **Payroll Expense ($000)**: 90364 **Personnel**: 1097

☒ **TEXAS HEALTH SPECIALTY HOSPITAL (452018)**, 1301 Pennsylvania Avenue, 4th Floor, Zip 76104–2190; tel. 817/250–5500, (Nonreporting) **A**1 10 **F**1 3 87 130 148 149 **P**6 **S** Texas Health Resources, Arlington, TX
Primary Contact: Barclay E. Berdan, FACHE, Chief Executive Officer
CFO: Shelly Miland, Chief Financial Officer
CMO: Michael Thornsberry, M.D., Chief Medical Officer
CNO: Pamela Duffey, DNP, RN, NEA-BC, MSN, R.N., Chief Nursing Officer
Web address: www.https://www.texashealth.org/texas-health-specialty-hospital/
**Control**: Other not–for–profit (including NFP Corporation) **Service**: Acute long–term care hospital

**Staffed Beds**: 10 **Admissions**: 107 **Census**: 8 **Outpatient Visits**: 0 **Births**: 0
**Total Expense ($000)**: 7861 **Payroll Expense ($000)**: 3233 **Personnel**: 33

☐ △ **TEXAS REHABILITATION HOSPITAL OF FORT WORTH (673048)**, 425 Alabama Avenue, Zip 76104–1022; tel. 817/820–3400, (Nonreporting) **A**1 7 10 **F**3 29 34 57 68 74 79 90 91 96 130 132 148 156
Primary Contact: Jake Daggett, Chief Executive Officer
Web address: www.texasrehabhospital.com/
**Control**: Corporation, Investor–owned (for–profit) **Service**: Rehabilitation

**Staffed Beds**: 66 **Admissions**: 1569 **Census**: 50 **Outpatient Visits**: 0
**Births**: 0 **Total Expense ($000)**: 18793 **Payroll Expense ($000)**: 10947
**Personnel**: 167

**TEXAS REHABILITATION OF FORT WORTH** See Texas Rehabilitation Hospital of Fort Worth

**TRINITY SPRINGS PAVILION-EAST** See Trinity Springs Pavilion

☐ **WELLBRIDGE HEALTHCARE OF FORT WORTH (454128)**, 6200 Overton Ridge Boulevard, Zip 76132–3614; tel. 817/361–1991, (Nonreporting) **A**1 **F**56 98 101 103 130 153 154
Primary Contact: Soni Helmicki, Chief Executive Officer
Web address: www.oceanshealthcare.com
**Control**: Corporation, Investor–owned (for–profit) **Service**: Psychiatric

**Staffed Beds**: 48 **Admissions**: 913 **Census**: 29 **Outpatient Visits**: 1286
**Births**: 0 **Total Expense ($000)**: 8862 **Payroll Expense ($000)**: 4297
**Personnel**: 86

☐ **WISE HEALTH SURGICAL HOSPITAL AT PARKWAY (670116)**, 3200 North Tarrant Parkway, Zip 76177–8611; tel. 817/502–7300, (Includes WISE HEALTH SURGICAL HOSPITAL AT ARGYLE, Mailing address: 7218 Crawford Road, Argyle, Texas, Zip 76226; tel. 940/293–2885; Jason Wren, President and Chief Executive Officer), (Nonreporting) **A**1 **F**18 20 22 24 26 29 40 68 81 82 107 119 130 149 154
Primary Contact: Dustin Lee. Davis, Administrator
Web address: www.wiseregional.com
**Control**: Hospital district or authority, Government, Nonfederal **Service**: Surgical

**Staffed Beds**: 36 **Admissions**: 509 **Census**: 4 **Outpatient Visits**: 10458
**Births**: 0 **Total Expense ($000)**: 100692 **Payroll Expense ($000)**: 15652
**Personnel**: 250

**FREDERICKSBURG—Gillespie County**

☒ **HILL COUNTRY MEMORIAL HOSPITAL (450604)**, 1020 South State Highway 16, Zip 78624–4471; Mailing Address: P.O. Box 835, Zip 78624–0835; tel. 830/997–4353, (Nonreporting) **A**1 10 **F**3 11 13 15 18 20 28 29 30 31 32 34 35 37 40 43 45 49 50 51 53 57 59 62 63 64 68 70 74 75 76 77 78 79 81 82 84 85 86 87 93 96 97 107 108 110 111 114 115 119 124 126 129 130 131 132 135 144 146 148 149 **P**6 8
Primary Contact: Jayne E. Pope, R.N., FACHE, Chief Executive Officer
COO: Mike Reno, Chief Operating Officer
CFO: Mark Jones, Chief Financial Officer
CMO: James R Partin, M.D., Chief Medical Director
CIO: John Mason, Chief Information Officer
CHR: Alysha Metzger, Director Human Resources
CNO: Maureen Polivka, Chief Nursing Officer
Web address: www.hillcountrymemorial.org
**Control**: Other not–for–profit (including NFP Corporation) **Service**: General medical and surgical

**Staffed Beds**: 57 **Admissions**: 2448 **Census**: 19 **Outpatient Visits**: 96315
**Births**: 437 **Total Expense ($000)**: 78773 **Payroll Expense ($000)**: 26031
**Personnel**: 418

**FRIONA—Parmer County**

**PARMER COUNTY COMMUNITY HOSPITAL** See Parmer Medical Center

**TX**

---

**Hospital, Medicare Provider Number, Address, Telephone, Approval, Facility, and Physician Codes, Health Care System**

★ American Hospital Association (AHA) membership  ○ Healthcare Facilities Accreditation Program  ⇑ Center for Improvement in Healthcare Quality Accreditation
☐ The Joint Commission accreditation  ◇ DNV Healthcare Inc. accreditation  △ Commission on Accreditation of Rehabilitation Facilities (CARF) accreditation

★ **PARMER MEDICAL CENTER (451300)**, 1307 Cleveland Street, Zip 79035–1121; tel. 806/250–2754, (Nonreporting) **A**10 18 **F**11 30 34 35 40 57 59 64 75 77 89 93 107 119 127 130 133 148 **S** Preferred Management Corporation, Shawnee, OK
Primary Contact: Gayla Quillin, Administrator
Web address: www.parmermedicalcenter.com
**Control**: Other not–for–profit (including NFP Corporation) **Service**: General medical and surgical

| Staffed Beds: 15 Admissions: 92 Census: 3 Outpatient Visits: 18319 Births: 0 Total Expense ($000): 10685 Payroll Expense ($000): 4709 Personnel: 94 |
| --- |

### FRISCO—Collin County

**BAYLOR INSTITUTE FOR REHABILITATION AT FRISCO** See Baylor Scott & White Institute for Rehabilitation-Frisco

**BAYLOR MEDICAL CENTER AT FRISCO** See Baylor Scott & White Medical Center—Frisco

⊠ **BAYLOR SCOTT & WHITE INSTITUTE FOR REHABILITATION-FRISCO (673046)**, 2990 Legacy Drive, Zip 75034–6066; tel. 469/888–5100, (Nonreporting) **A**1 10 **F**3 29 30 34 35 36 64 75 90 91 92 93 96 130 132 148 149 **S** Select Medical Corporation, Mechanicsburg, PA
Primary Contact: Ryan Seymour, Chief Executive Officer
Web address: www.baylorhealth.com/bir
**Control**: Partnership, Investor–owned (for–profit) **Service**: Rehabilitation

| Staffed Beds: 44 Admissions: 793 Census: 30 Outpatient Visits: 18793 Births: 0 Total Expense ($000): 22284 Payroll Expense ($000): 11693 Personnel: 216 |
| --- |

⊠ **BAYLOR SCOTT & WHITE MEDICAL CENTER - CENTENNIAL (450885)**, 12505 Lebanon Road, Zip 75035–8298; tel. 972/963–3333, (Nonreporting) **A**1 10 **F**3 13 15 17 18 20 22 26 29 30 34 35 40 41 43 45 46 47 48 49 50 51 57 59 64 65 70 72 74 75 76 77 78 79 81 82 85 89 93 107 110 111 114 115 119 126 130 132 146 154 **S** Baylor Scott & White Health, Dallas, TX
Primary Contact: Ryan Gebhart, President
CFO: Blaise Bondi, Chief Financial Officer
CIO: Dianne Yarborough, Director of Information Technology
CHR: Stephanie S. Talley, Director Human Resources
CNO: Calee Travis, R.N., Chief Nursing Officer
Web address: www.https://www.bswhealth.com/
**Control**: Other not–for–profit (including NFP Corporation) **Service**: General medical and surgical

| Staffed Beds: 106 Admissions: 3986 Census: 45 Outpatient Visits: 40931 Births: 1289 Total Expense ($000): 103726 Payroll Expense ($000): 33185 Personnel: 321 |
| --- |

☐ **BAYLOR SCOTT & WHITE MEDICAL CENTER—FRISCO (450853)**, 5601 Warren Parkway, Zip 75034–4069; tel. 214/407–5000, (Nonreporting) **A**1 3 5 10 **F**3 13 29 34 40 45 51 54 57 64 68 72 75 76 79 81 85 86 87 107 111 115 119 126 129 130 131 144 **S** United Surgical Partners International, Addison, TX
Primary Contact: Trevor Castaneda, Chief Executive Officer
COO: Kevin Coats, Chief Operating Officer and Chief Financial Officer
CFO: Kevin Coats, Chief Financial Officer
CMO: Jimmy Laferney, M.D., Vice President Medical Staff Affairs
CIO: Rick Barry, Director Information Systems
CHR: Margaret Garcia, Manager Human Resources
CNO: Randi Elliott, MSN, Chief Nursing Officer
Web address: www.bmcf.com
**Control**: Partnership, Investor–owned (for–profit) **Service**: Surgical

| Staffed Beds: 68 Admissions: 4040 Census: 31 Outpatient Visits: 28662 Births: 2294 Total Expense ($000): 132985 Payroll Expense ($000): 47573 Personnel: 541 |
| --- |

**CENTENNIAL MEDICAL CENTER** See Baylor Scott & White Medical Center - Centennial

☐ **HAVEN BEHAVIORAL HOSPITAL OF FRISCO (454134)**, 5680 Frisco Square Boulevard, Suite 3000, Zip 75034–3300; tel. 469/353–2219, (Nonreporting) **A**1
Primary Contact: Angie Crawford, Chief Executive Officer
Web address: www.frisco.havenbehavioral.com/
**Control**: Corporation, Investor–owned (for–profit) **Service**: Psychiatric

| Staffed Beds: 36 |
| --- |

**MEDICAL CENTER FRISCO** See Medical City Frisco

★ **TEXAS HEALTH FRISCO**, 12400 Dallas Parkway, Zip 75033–4224; tel. 469/495–2000, (Nonreporting) **S** Texas Health Resources, Arlington, TX
Primary Contact: Brett D. Lee, President
Web address: www.https://www.texashealth.org/locations/texas-health-frisco
**Control**: Other not–for–profit (including NFP Corporation) **Service**: General medical and surgical

| Staffed Beds: 63 |
| --- |

### GAINESVILLE—Cooke County

**GAINESVILLE MEMORIAL HOSPITAL** See North Texas Medical Center

**NORTH TEXAS MEDICAL CENTER (450090)**, 1900 Hospital Boulevard, Zip 76240–2002; tel. 940/665–1751, (Data for 212 days) (Nonreporting) **A**10 20 22 **F**3 11 13 15 28 29 30 34 35 40 43 45 50 59 62 64 65 66 68 70 75 76 77 79 81 82 85 86 87 93 107 108 110 111 115 119 127 129 130 132 133 135 146 147 149 154 156
Primary Contact: Thomas Sledge, Chief Executive Officer
CFO: Melissa Walker, CPA, Chief Financial Officer
CHR: Teresa Westover, Director Human Resources
CNO: Becky Small, Chief Nursing Officer
Web address: www.ntmconline.net
**Control**: Other not–for–profit (including NFP Corporation) **Service**: General medical and surgical

| Staffed Beds: 48 Admissions: 791 Census: 16 Outpatient Visits: 32054 Births: 60 Total Expense ($000): 21778 Payroll Expense ($000): 8916 Personnel: 204 |
| --- |

### GALVESTON—Galveston County

☐ **SHRINERS HOSPITALS FOR CHILDREN-GALVESTON (453311)**, 815 Market Street, Zip 77550–2725; tel. 409/770–6600, (Nonreporting) **A**1 3 5 10 **F**3 11 16 29 34 35 50 64 68 75 77 81 82 85 86 93 94 100 119 130 132 146 148 154 **S** Shriners Hospitals for Children, Tampa, FL
Primary Contact: Mary Jaco, Administrator
CFO: Michael B Schimming, Director Financial Services
CMO: Steven Wolf, D.O., Chief of Staff
CIO: Michael Lyons, Regional Director Information Services
CHR: Robert A Magee, Director Human Resources
CNO: Jeannie Keith, R.N., Nurse Executive
Web address: www.shrinershospitalsforchildren.org/Hospitals/Locations/Galveston.aspx
**Control**: Other not–for–profit (including NFP Corporation) **Service**: Children's other specialty

| Staffed Beds: 15 Admissions: 132 Census: 8 Outpatient Visits: 7212 Births: 0 Total Expense ($000): 38813 Payroll Expense ($000): 16589 Personnel: 244 |
| --- |

**SHRINERS HOSPITALS FOR CHILDREN-GALVESTON BURNS HOSPITAL** See Shriners Hospitals for Children-Galveston

⊠ **UNIVERSITY OF TEXAS MEDICAL BRANCH (450018)**, 301 University Boulevard, Zip 77555–0128; tel. 409/772–1011, (Includes ANGLETON DANBURY CAMPUS, Mailing address: 132 East Hospital Drive, Angleton, Texas, Zip 77515–4112; tel. 979/849–7721; Elizabeth Meagan Reimschissel, Administrator and Associate Chief Nursing Officer), (Nonreporting) **A**1 2 3 5 10 **F**3 11 12 13 15 16 17 18 19 20 22 24 26 28 29 30 31 34 35 36 38 39 40 41 43 44 45 46 49 50 51 52 53 54 55 56 57 58 59 60 61 63 64 65 68 70 71 72 73 74 75 76 77 78 79 81 82 84 85 86 87 88 89 92 93 96 97 100 101 104 107 108 110 111 112 114 115 116 117 118 119 120 121 123 124 126 129 130 131 132 134 135 137 138 139 141 142 144 145 146 147 148 149 150 156 **S** University of Texas System, Austin, TX
Primary Contact: Timothy J. Harlin, M.D., Chief Executive Officer and Executive Vice President
COO: Deborah A McGrew, Vice President and Chief Operating Officer
CFO: Cheryl A Sadro, Executive Vice President Chief Business and Finance Officer
CIO: Todd Leach, Vice President and Chief Information Officer
CHR: Ronald McKinley, Ph.D., Vice President Human Resources and Employee Services
CNO: Merry Philip, M.D., Chief Nursing Officer
Web address: www.utmb.edu
**Control**: State, Government, Nonfederal **Service**: General medical and surgical

| Staffed Beds: 541 Admissions: 33454 Census: 418 Outpatient Visits: 1252618 Births: 6516 Total Expense ($000): 1094217 Payroll Expense ($000): 352653 Personnel: 5015 |
| --- |

**UNIVERSITY OF TEXAS MEDICAL BRANCH HOSPITALS** See University of Texas Medical Branch

*Many Facility Codes have changed. Please refer to the AHA Guide Code Chart.* © 2021 AHA Guide

**GARLAND—Dallas County**

☐ **GARLAND BEHAVIORAL HOSPITAL (454138)**, 2300 Marie Curie Boulevard, 5th Floor, Zip 75402; tel. 972/487–5309, (Nonreporting) **A**1 **F**98 101 103 104 105 153 **S** Universal Health Services, Inc., King of Prussia, PA
Primary Contact: Kimberly Lynn. Bunnell, Chief Executive Officer
CFO: Scott Cook, Chief Financial Officer
Web address: www.garlandbehavioralhospital.com/
**Control**: Corporation, Investor–owned (for–profit) **Service**: Psychiatric

Staffed Beds: 72 Admissions: 2162 Census: 57 Outpatient Visits: 2185
Births: 0 Total Expense ($000): 15756 Payroll Expense ($000): 7522
Personnel: 118

☐ **PERIMETER BEHAVIORAL HOSPITAL OF DALLAS (454149)**, 2696 West Walnut Street, Zip 75042–6441; tel. 972/370–5517, (Nonreporting) **A**1 **S** Perimeter Healthcare, Alpharetta, GA
Primary Contact: Phillip Wilcoxon, Chief Executive Officer
Web address: www.https://www.perimeterhealthcare.com/facilities/perimeter-behavioral-hospital-of-dallas/
**Control**: Corporation, Investor–owned (for–profit) **Service**: Psychiatric

Staffed Beds: 100

**GATESVILLE—Coryell County**

☐ **CORYELL HEALTH (451379)**, 1507 West Main Street, Zip 76528–1098; tel. 254/865–8251, (Nonreporting) **A**1 10 18 **F**3 7 10 11 12 15 18 20 28 34 35 40 43 45 50 57 58 59 60 62 64 65 70 74 79 81 82 84 86 87 93 97 102 104 107 108 110 111 115 116 117 119 125 127 129 130 131 133 146 148 154 **P**6
Primary Contact: David Byrom, Chief Executive Officer
COO: David Byrom, Chief Executive Officer
CFO: Carol Jones, Controller and Manager Business Office
CMO: Diedra Wuenschel, D.O., President Medical Staff
CIO: Mike Huckabee, Network Administrator
CHR: Paula Smithhart, Director Human Resources
CNO: Jeanne Griffith, Chief Nursing Officer
Web address: www.cmhos.org
**Control**: Hospital district or authority, Government, Nonfederal **Service**: General medical and surgical

Staffed Beds: 25 Admissions: 762 Census: 7 Outpatient Visits: 80145
Births: 0 Total Expense ($000): 60210 Payroll Expense ($000): 18151
Personnel: 527

**CORYELL MEMORIAL HOSPITAL** See Coryell Health

**GEORGETOWN—Williamson County**

☐ **GEORGETOWN BEHAVIORAL HEALTH INSTITUTE (454129)**, 3101 South Austin Avenue, Zip 78626–7541; tel. 512/819–1100, (Nonreporting) **A**1 **F**4 5 98 99 100 102 104 105 130 132 135 151 152 153 154 **S** Signature Healthcare Services, Corona, CA
Primary Contact: Monica Ochoa, Chief Executive Officer
COO: Ellen Payne, Chief Operating Officer
CFO: Shelli Surcouf, Chief Financial Officer
CHR: Kristi Hynes, Director Human Resources
CNO: Nini Perry, Chief Nursing Officer
Web address: www.georgetownbehavioral.com
**Control**: Corporation, Investor–owned (for–profit) **Service**: Psychiatric

Staffed Beds: 118 Admissions: 3415 Census: 61 Outpatient Visits: 4686
Births: 0 Total Expense ($000): 19729 Payroll Expense ($000): 8749
Personnel: 165

**GEORGETOWN HEALTHCARE SYSTEM** See St. David's Georgetown Hospital

⌧ **ROCK SPRINGS (454127)**, 700 Southeast Inner Loop, Zip 78626; tel. 512/819–9400, (Nonreporting) **A**1 **F**4 5 54 98 100 104 105 152 153 154 **S** Springstone, Louisville, KY
Primary Contact: Mark Puckett, Chief Executive Officer
COO: Erin Basalay, PsyD, Director Clinical Services
CFO: Amy Jordan, Chief Financial Officer
CHR: Sharon McMurray, Director, Human Resources
CNO: Jennifer Cooley, Director of Nursing
Web address: www.rockspringshealth.com/
**Control**: Corporation, Investor–owned (for–profit) **Service**: Psychiatric

Staffed Beds: 72 Admissions: 2248 Census: 54 Outpatient Visits: 11710
Births: 0 Total Expense ($000): 17508 Payroll Expense ($000): 9800
Personnel: 184

**ROCK SPRINGS, LLC** See Rock Springs

**GLEN ROSE—Somervell County**

☐ **GLEN ROSE MEDICAL CENTER (450451)**, 1021 Holden Street, Zip 76043–4937, Mailing Address: P.O. Box 2099, Zip 76043–2099; tel. 254/897–2215, (Nonreporting) **A**1 10 **F**2 3 15 29 34 40 43 45 48 51 53 54 56 57 59 65 68 81 90 93 97 98 100 103 104 107 110 114 119 141 143 146 148 153
Primary Contact: Ray Reynolds, Chief Executive Officer
CFO: Michael Honea, Chief Financial Officer
CHR: Ladonna Green, Director Human Resources
CNO: Laura Hodnett, Interim Chief Nursing Officer
Web address: www.glenrosemedicalcenter.com
**Control**: Hospital district or authority, Government, Nonfederal **Service**: General medical and surgical

Staffed Beds: 10 Admissions: 261 Census: 2 Outpatient Visits: 41540
Births: 0 Total Expense ($000): 34038 Payroll Expense ($000): 6910
Personnel: 172

**HARRIS METHODIST-GLEN ROSE** See Glen Rose Medical Center

**GONZALES—Gonzales County**

★ **GONZALES HEALTHCARE SYSTEMS (450235)**, 1110 Sarah Dewitt Drive, Zip 78629–3311, Mailing Address: P.O. Box 587, Zip 78629–0587; tel. 830/672–7581, (Nonreporting) **A**10 20 **F**3 8 11 13 15 34 40 53 57 59 62 65 76 77 79 81 85 87 93 107 108 110 111 114 115 119 127 130 **S** QHR Health, Brentwood, TN
Primary Contact: Patty Stewart, Chief Executive Officer
CFO: Patty Stewart, Chief Financial Officer
CMO: Commie Hisey, D.O., Chief of Staff
CHR: Joni Leland, Director Human Resources
CNO: Lori Parker, Chief Nursing Officer
Web address: www.gonzaleshealthcare.com
**Control**: Hospital district or authority, Government, Nonfederal **Service**: General medical and surgical

Staffed Beds: 33 Admissions: 749 Census: 6 Outpatient Visits: 30161
Births: 145 Total Expense ($000): 50877 Payroll Expense ($000): 11155
Personnel: 262

**MEMORIAL HOSPITAL** See Gonzales Healthcare Systems

**GRAHAM—Young County**

**GRAHAM GENERAL HOSPITAL** See Graham Regional Medical Center

**GRAHAM REGIONAL MEDICAL CENTER (450085)**, 1301 Montgomery Road, Zip 76450–4240, Mailing Address: P.O. Box 1390, Zip 76450–1390; tel. 940/549–3400, (Nonreporting) **A**10 20 **F**3 7 11 15 28 29 40 43 45 50 53 57 59 62 63 75 77 79 81 85 89 93 104 107 111 115 119 127 130 133 135
Primary Contact: Shane Kernell, Chief Executive Officer
CIO: Jeff Clark, Director Information Systems
Web address: www.grahamrmc.com
**Control**: Hospital district or authority, Government, Nonfederal **Service**: General medical and surgical

Staffed Beds: 17 Admissions: 612 Census: 6 Outpatient Visits: 34380
Births: 0 Total Expense ($000): 20990 Payroll Expense ($000): 7838
Personnel: 168

TX

## GRANBURY—Hood County

**HOOD GENERAL HOSPITAL** See Lake Granbury Medical Center

✠ **LAKE GRANBURY MEDICAL CENTER (450596)**, 1310 Paluxy Road,
Zip 76048–5655; tel. 817/573–2273, (Nonreporting) **A**1 10 **F**3 8 11 12 13 15
18 20 22 26 28 29 30 34 37 40 43 45 49 53 57 59 64 68 70 74 75 76 77 79
81 82 85 86 93 107 108 110 111 114 118 119 126 129 146 147 149 154
157 **S** Community Health Systems, Inc., Franklin, TN
Primary Contact: David Orcutt, Chief Executive Officer
CFO: Noe Gutierrez, Chief Financial Officer
CIO: Kevin Myers, Director Information Systems
CHR: Brooke Montoya, Director Human Resources
CNO: Abigail Kendall, Chief Nursing Officer
Web address: www.lakegranburymedicalcenter.com
**Control:** Corporation, Investor–owned (for–profit) **Service:** General medical and
surgical

**Staffed Beds:** 73 **Admissions:** 3551 **Census:** 37 **Outpatient Visits:** 82381
**Births:** 539 **Total Expense ($000):** 75453 **Payroll Expense ($000):** 26775
**Personnel:** 353

## GRAND PRAIRIE—Tarrant County

**BAYLOR SCOTT & WHITE EMERGENCY HOSPIOTAL - GRAND PRAIRIE** See
Baylor Scott & White Emergency Hospital - Grand Prairie

**BAYLOR SCOTT & WHITE EMERGENCY HOSPITAL - GRAND PRAIRIE**, 3095
Kingswood Boulevard, Zip 75052–4512; tel. 972/854–0009, (Nonreporting) **S**
Emerus, The Woodlands, TX
Primary Contact: Vic Schmerbeck, Chief Executive Officer
Web address: www.https://www.bsweh.org/locations/grand-prairie/?utm_
source=google&utm_medium=organic&utm_campaign=gmb
**Control:** Corporation, Investor–owned (for–profit) **Service:** General medical and surgical

**Staffed Beds:** 24

## GRAND PRAIRIE—Dallas County

**TEXAS GENERAL HOSPITAL (670083)**, 2709 Hospital Boulevard,
Zip 75051–1017; tel. 469/557–9430, (Nonreporting) **A**10
Primary Contact: Suleman Hashmi, President and Chief Executive Officer
Web address: www.texasgeneralhospital.com
**Control:** Partnership, Investor–owned (for–profit) **Service:** General medical and
surgical

**Staffed Beds:** 41

## GRAPEVINE—Tarrant County

**BAYLOR REGIONAL MEDICAL CENTER AT GRAPEVINE** See Baylor Scott &
White Medical Center - Grapevine

✠ **BAYLOR SCOTT & WHITE MEDICAL CENTER - GRAPEVINE (450563)**, 1650
West College Street, Zip 76051–3565; tel. 817/481–1588, (Nonreporting) **A**1 2 3
5 10 **F**3 8 12 13 15 18 20 22 24 26 28 29 30 31 34 35 40 43 45 46 47 48 49
56 57 59 64 65 70 72 74 75 76 77 78 79 80 81 82 84 86 87 90 107 108 110
111 115 119 126 130 131 132 145 146 147 148 149 **S** Baylor Scott & White
Health, Dallas, TX
Primary Contact: Christopher York, FACHE, President
CFO: Terri Foster, Hospital Finance Officer
CMO: Ron Jensen, D.O., Chief Medical Officer and Vice President
CIO: Sandy Vaughn, Director Information Systems
CHR: Donna Stark, Director Human Resources
Web address: www.https://www.baylorhealth.com/PhysiciansLocations/Grapevine/
Pages/Default.aspx
**Control:** Other not–for–profit (including NFP Corporation) **Service:** General
medical and surgical

**Staffed Beds:** 270 **Admissions:** 12638 **Census:** 159 **Outpatient
Visits:** 61786 **Births:** 2210 **Total Expense ($000):** 212026 **Payroll Expense
($000):** 74499 **Personnel:** 825

## GREENVILLE—Hunt County

✠ **GLEN OAKS HOSPITAL (454050)**, 301 Division Street, Zip 75401–4101;
tel. 903/454–6000, (Nonreporting) **A**1 10 **F**4 5 29 34 35 75 86 87 98 100 101
102 104 105 132 152 153 **S** Universal Health Services, Inc., King of Prussia, PA
Primary Contact: Brittney Nolan, Chief Executive Officer
Web address: www.glenoakshospital.com
**Control:** Corporation, Investor–owned (for–profit) **Service:** Psychiatric

**Staffed Beds:** 54 **Admissions:** 1931 **Census:** 39 **Outpatient Visits:** 2113
**Births:** 0 **Total Expense ($000):** 11706 **Payroll Expense ($000):** 6029
**Personnel:** 105

**HUNT MEMORIAL HOSPITAL DISTRICT** See Hunt Regional Medical Center

☐ **HUNT REGIONAL MEDICAL CENTER (450352)**, 4215 Joe Ramsey Boulevard
East, Zip 75401–7899, Mailing Address: P.O. Box 1059, Zip 75403–1059;
tel. 903/408–5000, (Nonreporting) **A**1 10 **F**3 11 12 13 15 28 29 30 34 37 40
42 43 44 45 46 49 50 53 56 57 59 62 64 65 68 70 71 72 73 74 75 76 77 78
79 81 82 84 85 86 87 90 91 92 93 94 96 98 102 103 104 107 108 110 111
114 115 118 119 120 121 123 129 132 135 141 143 144 146 147 148
149 154 156 157 **S** Hunt Regional Healthcare, Greenville, TX
Primary Contact: Richard Carter, District Chief Executive Officer
CFO: Lee Boles, Assistant Administrator and Chief Financial Officer
CMO: James H Sandin, M.D., Assistant Administrator Medical Affairs
CIO: Richard Montanye, Director Information Systems
CNO: Deborah Clack, Chief Nursing Officer
Web address: www.huntregional.org
**Control:** Hospital district or authority, Government, Nonfederal **Service:** General
medical and surgical

**Staffed Beds:** 167 **Admissions:** 7122 **Census:** 88 **Outpatient
Visits:** 139512 **Births:** 1385 **Total Expense ($000):** 164021 **Payroll
Expense ($000):** 71663 **Personnel:** 1081

## GROESBECK—Limestone County

**LIMESTONE MEDICAL CENTER (451303)**, 701 McClintic Drive,
Zip 76642–2128; tel. 254/729–3281, (Nonreporting) **A**10 18 **F**3 7 11 28 29 32
34 35 40 41 43 45 57 64 65 77 84 85 90 93 96 97 104 107 111 115
119 127 129 130 133 135 146 148 153
Primary Contact: Larry Price, Chief Executive Officer
CFO: Michael F. Williams, Chief Financial Officer
CMO: Jeffrey Rettig, D.O., Chief of Staff
CIO: Byong Lee, Chief Information Officer
CHR: Jean Koester, Manager Human Resources
CNO: Jean Wragge, Chief Nursing Officer
Web address: www.lmchospital.com
**Control:** Hospital district or authority, Government, Nonfederal **Service:** General
medical and surgical

**Staffed Beds:** 20 **Admissions:** 157 **Census:** 5 **Outpatient Visits:** 13343
**Births:** 0 **Total Expense ($000):** 21780 **Payroll Expense ($000):** 11692
**Personnel:** 232

**SOUTH LIMESTONE HOSPITAL** See Limestone Medical Center

## HALLETTSVILLE—Lavaca County

**LAVACA MEDICAL CENTER (451376)**, 1400 North Texana Street,
Zip 77964–2099; tel. 361/798–3671, (Nonreporting) **A**10 18 **F**3 11 15 18 28 29
34 40 41 43 45 47 53 56 57 59 64 65 68 75 77 81 85 86 87 93 107 108 110
111 114 118 119 127 133 135 146 148 149 154
Primary Contact: Stephen Bowen, Administrator
**Control:** Hospital district or authority, Government, Nonfederal **Service:** General
medical and surgical

**Staffed Beds:** 25 **Admissions:** 415 **Census:** 5 **Outpatient Visits:** 41294
**Births:** 0 **Total Expense ($000):** 19814 **Payroll Expense ($000):** 6853
**Personnel:** 146

## HAMILTON—Hamilton County

★ ⇑ **HAMILTON GENERAL HOSPITAL (451392)**, 400 North Brown Street,
Zip 76531–1518; tel. 254/386–1600, (Nonreporting) **A**10 18 20 21 **F**3 5 7 11
15 28 29 34 35 40 43 44 45 50 53 57 59 64 65 68 75 79 81 82 85 86 87 93
97 100 104 107 108 110 111 115 119 127 129 130 131 132 133 148 149
153 154 156 157
Primary Contact: Grady A. Hooper, Chief Executive Officer
CMO: James R Lee, M.D., Chief of Staff
CIO: Chad Reinert, Chief Information Officer
CHR: Keela Payne, Director Human Resources
CNO: Debra Martin, Chief Nursing Officer
Web address: www.hamiltonhospital.org
**Control:** Hospital district or authority, Government, Nonfederal **Service:** General
medical and surgical

**Staffed Beds:** 25 **Admissions:** 569 **Census:** 5 **Outpatient Visits:** 81234
**Births:** 0 **Total Expense ($000):** 31745 **Payroll Expense ($000):** 14013
**Personnel:** 351

*Many Facility Codes have changed. Please refer to the AHA Guide Code Chart.* © 2021 AHA Guide

## HARKER HEIGHTS—Bell County

☒ **SETON MEDICAL CENTER HARKER HEIGHTS (670080)**, 850 West Central Texas Expressway, Zip 76548–1890; tel. 254/690–0900, (Nonreporting) **A**1 10 **F**3 13 15 18 20 22 26 28 29 30 34 35 40 43 45 49 50 51 57 59 60 66 70 74 75 76 79 81 91 93 107 108 110 111 115 119 129 146 147 148 154 **S** Ardent Health Services, Nashville, TN
Primary Contact: Patrick Swindle, Chief Executive Officer
CFO: John K Sharp, Chief Financial Officer
CNO: Pamela Craig, R.N., Chief Nursing Officer
Web address: www.setonharkerheights.net
**Control**: Partnership, Investor–owned (for–profit) **Service**: General medical and surgical

**Staffed Beds:** 83 **Admissions:** 5167 **Census:** 31 **Outpatient Visits:** 87597 **Births:** 874 **Total Expense ($000):** 85734 **Payroll Expense ($000):** 26631 **Personnel:** 538

## HARLINGEN—Cameron County

☐ **HARLINGEN MEDICAL CENTER (450855)**, 5501 South Expressway 77, Zip 78550–3213; tel. 956/365–1000, (Nonreporting) **A**1 3 5 10 **S** Prime Healthcare, Ontario, CA
Primary Contact: Matt Wolthoff, Chief Executive Officer
CFO: Michael Bergstrom, Chief Financial Officer
CMO: Elizabeth Juarez, M.D., Chief Medical Officer
CHR: Emmett Craig, Director Human Resources
CNO: Deborah Meeks, Chief Nursing Officer
Web address: www.harlingenmedicalcenter.com
**Control**: Partnership, Investor–owned (for–profit) **Service**: General medical and surgical

**Staffed Beds:** 88

☐ **RIO GRANDE STATE CENTER/SOUTH TEXAS HEALTH CARE SYSTEM (454088)**, 1401 South Rangerville Road, Zip 78552–7638; tel. 956/364–8000, (Includes RIO GRANDE STATE CENTER, Mailing address: 1401 South Rangerville Road, Harlingen, Texas, Zip 78552–7638; tel. 956/364–8000; SOUTH TEXAS HEALTH CARE SYSTEM, Mailing address: 1401 Rangerville Road, Harlingen, Texas, Zip 78552–7609; tel. 956/364–8000), (Nonreporting) **A**1 3 5 10 **F**3 30 53 57 65 66 68 75 87 97 98 101 107 119 130 132 135 143 146 147 154 156 **S** Texas Department of State Health Services, Austin, TX
Primary Contact: Sonia Hernandez-Keeble, Superintendent
CFO: Tom Garza, Director Fiscal and Support
CMO: David Moron, M.D., Clinical Director
CIO: Blas Ortiz JrAssistant Superintendent and Public Information Officer
CHR: Irma Garcia, Job Coordinator
CNO: Maia Baker, MSN, Chief Nurse Executive
Web address: www.dshs.state.tx.us/mhhospitals/RioGrandeSC/default.shtm
**Control**: State, Government, Nonfederal **Service**: Psychiatric

**Staffed Beds:** 55 **Admissions:** 775 **Census:** 51 **Outpatient Visits:** 0 **Births:** 0 **Total Expense ($000):** 16776 **Payroll Expense ($000):** 13660 **Personnel:** 232

☐ **SOLARA HOSPITAL HARLINGEN (452101)**, 508 Victoria Lane, Zip 78550–3225; tel. 956/425–9600, (Includes SOLARA HOSPITAL - BROWNSVILLE CAMPUS, Mailing address: 333 Lorenaly Drive, Brownsville, Texas, Zip 78526–4333; tel. 956/546–0808; Cynthia Issacs, Chief Executive Officer), (Nonreporting) **A**1 10 22 **F**1 3 29 35 40 57 70 85 86 91 130 148 **S** Cornerstone Healthcare Group, Dallas, TX
Primary Contact: Alberto Sanchez, Chief Executive Officer
CFO: Kurt Schultz, Chief Financial Officer
CHR: Dan Perkins, Vice President of Human Resources
CNO: Nesa Caldwell, Chief Nursing Officer
Web address: www.chghospitals.com/harlingen/
**Control**: Partnership, Investor–owned (for–profit) **Service**: Acute long–term care hospital

**Staffed Beds:** 70 **Admissions:** 791 **Census:** 58 **Outpatient Visits:** 0 **Births:** 0 **Total Expense ($000):** 22967 **Payroll Expense ($000):** 11179 **Personnel:** 173

**SOUTH TEXAS HOSPITAL** See South Texas Health Care System

**VALLEY BAPTIST HEALTH SYSTEM** See Valley Baptist Medical Center-Harlingen

☒ △ **VALLEY BAPTIST MEDICAL CENTER-HARLINGEN (450033)**, 2101 Pease Street, Zip 78550–8307, Mailing Address: P O Drawer 2588, Zip 78551–2588; tel. 956/389–1100, (Nonreporting) **A**1 3 5 7 10 **F**3 11 12 13 14 15 17 18 20 22 24 26 28 29 30 31 34 35 39 40 41 42 43 44 45 46 47 48 49 50 53 54 56 57 58 59 60 63 64 65 68 70 72 73 74 75 76 77 78 79 80 81 82 84 85 86 87 88 89 90 92 93 94 98 100 101 102 103 104 105 107 108 110 111 112 114 115 119 126 129 130 132 144 146 147 148 153 156 157 **S** TENET Healthcare Corporation, Dallas, TX
Primary Contact: Manuel Vela, President and Chief Executive Officer
CFO: Marco Rodriguez, Chief Financial Officer
CNO: Stephen Hill, Vice President and Chief Nursing Officer
Web address: www.valleybaptist.net/harlingen/index.htm
**Control**: Corporation, Investor–owned (for–profit) **Service**: General medical and surgical

**Staffed Beds:** 432 **Admissions:** 18792 **Census:** 244 **Outpatient Visits:** 136785 **Births:** 1731 **Total Expense ($000):** 275525 **Payroll Expense ($000):** 96303 **Personnel:** 932

## HASKELL—Haskell County

**HASKELL MEMORIAL HOSPITAL (451341)**, 1 North Avenue 'N', Zip 79521–5499, Mailing Address: P.O. Box 1117, Zip 79521–1117; tel. 940/864–2621, (Nonreporting) **A**10 18 **F**11 28 29 34 35 40 53 54 57 59 64 68 75 77 86 87 93 97 107 119 130 131 133 146
Primary Contact: Christopher Strickland, Chief Executive Officer
CHR: Emily Moore, Director Human Resources and Information Technology
CNO: Teri Turner, Chief Nursing Officer
Web address: www.haskellmemorialhospital.com/
**Control**: Hospital district or authority, Government, Nonfederal **Service**: General medical and surgical

**Staffed Beds:** 15 **Admissions:** 197 **Census:** 2 **Outpatient Visits:** 24847 **Births:** 0 **Total Expense ($000):** 8255 **Payroll Expense ($000):** 3520 **Personnel:** 80

## HEMPHILL—Sabine County

**SABINE COUNTY HOSPITAL (451361)**, 2301 Worth Street, Zip 75948–7216, Mailing Address: P.O. Box 750, Zip 75948–0750; tel. 409/787–3300, (Nonreporting) **A**10 18 **F**3 29 40 43 93 97 107 114 119 127 133 154 **S** Preferred Management Corporation, Shawnee, OK
Primary Contact: Jerry Howell, Administrator
COO: Mike Easley, Vice President and Chief Operating Officer
CFO: Larry Stephens, Chief Financial Officer
CMO: Vera Luther, M.D., Chief of Staff
CIO: Margaret Moore, Director Business Office
CHR: Laura Simpson, Director Human Resources
CNO: Margie Watson MSN, RN-BChief Nursing Officer
Web address: www.sabinecountyhospital.com/
**Control**: Corporation, Investor–owned (for–profit) **Service**: General medical and surgical

**Staffed Beds:** 25 **Admissions:** 199 **Census:** 3 **Outpatient Visits:** 18167 **Births:** 0 **Total Expense ($000):** 9405 **Payroll Expense ($000):** 4318 **Personnel:** 85

## HENDERSON—Rusk County

**EAST TEXAS MEDICAL CENTER HENDERSON** See UT Health Henderson

☒ **UT HEALTH HENDERSON (450475)**, 300 Wilson Street, Zip 75652–5956; tel. 903/657–7541, (Nonreporting) **A**1 10 **F**3 8 11 13 15 18 28 29 30 34 35 37 40 43 45 50 57 59 64 65 75 76 79 81 87 107 108 110 111 115 119 127 129 135 145 146 147 148 149 152 156 **P**6 **S** Ardent Health Services, Nashville, TN
Primary Contact: Mark Leitner, FACHE, Administrator
CFO: Wesley Knight, Chief Financial Officer
CHR: William Henry, Director Human Resources
CNO: Donna K Stanley, R.N., Chief Nursing Officer
Web address: www.https://uthealthhenderson.com/
**Control**: Corporation, Investor–owned (for–profit) **Service**: General medical and surgical

**Staffed Beds:** 41 **Admissions:** 1220 **Census:** 10 **Outpatient Visits:** 55549 **Births:** 213 **Total Expense ($000):** 29593 **Payroll Expense ($000):** 9088 **Personnel:** 156

**TX**

## HENRIETTA—Clay County

**CLAY COUNTY MEMORIAL HOSPITAL (451362)**, 310 West South Street, Zip 76365–3346; tel. 940/538–5621, (Nonreporting) **A**10 18 **F**7 8 11 28 34 35 40 50 53 57 62 68 80 81 90 93 107 111 119 130 132 133 144 146 148 **P**5
Primary Contact: Jeff Huskey, Chief Executive Officer and Administrator
CFO: Debra Haehn, Chief Financial Officer
CMO: Lexi Mitchell Sanchez, D.O., Chief of Staff
CHR: Linda Burleson, Administrative Secretary
CNO: Kelley McMillion, Chief Nursing Officer
Web address: www.ccmhospital.com
**Control:** County, Government, Nonfederal **Service:** General medical and surgical

**Staffed Beds:** 25 **Admissions:** 140 **Census:** 2 **Outpatient Visits:** 8264
**Births:** 0 **Total Expense ($000):** 8126 **Payroll Expense ($000):** 3536
**Personnel:** 83

## HEREFORD—Deaf Smith County

**DEAF SMITH GENERAL HOSPITAL** See Hereford Regional Medical Center

**HEREFORD REGIONAL MEDICAL CENTER (450155)**, 540 West 15th Street, Zip 79045–2820; tel. 806/364–2141, (Nonreporting) **A**10 **F**3 7 11 13 15 29 35 40 43 50 57 59 65 70 76 77 81 85 93 107 111 114 119 127 130 132 133 147 **P**6
Primary Contact: Jeff Barnhart, FACHE, Chief Executive Officer
CFO: Sharon Hunt, Chief Financial Officer
CIO: Laura Garza, Manager Information Technology
CHR: Patsy Smith, Director Human Resources
CNO: Candice Smith, MSN, Chief Nursing Officer
Web address: www.dschd.org/
**Control:** Hospital district or authority, Government, Nonfederal **Service:** General medical and surgical

**Staffed Beds:** 42 **Admissions:** 589 **Census:** 5 **Outpatient Visits:** 62933
**Births:** 279 **Total Expense ($000):** 25358 **Payroll Expense ($000):** 8891
**Personnel:** 171

## HILLSBORO—Hill County

✠ **HILL REGIONAL HOSPITAL (451395)**, 101 Circle Drive, Zip 76645–2670; tel. 254/580–8500, (Nonreporting) **A**1 10 18 20 **F**3 13 15 29 34 35 40 43 45 50 57 59 64 65 68 75 76 78 79 81 86 87 93 107 114 118 119 146 147 149 154 156 **S** Community Health Systems, Inc., Franklin, TN
Primary Contact: Michael J. Ellis, FACHE, Chief Executive Officer
CFO: Judy Culp, Chief Financial Officer
CHR: Becky Hale, Director Human Resources
Web address: www.https://www.hillregionalhospital.com/
**Control:** Corporation, Investor–owned (for–profit) **Service:** General medical and surgical

**Staffed Beds:** 25 **Admissions:** 838 **Census:** 6 **Outpatient Visits:** 20234
**Births:** 179 **Total Expense ($000):** 32080 **Payroll Expense ($000):** 7525
**Personnel:** 125

## HONDO—Medina County

**MEDINA COMMUNITY HOSPITAL** See Medina Regional Hospital

**MEDINA REGIONAL HOSPITAL (451330)**, 3100 Avenue E, Zip 78861–3599; tel. 830/426–7700, (Nonreporting) **A**10 18 **F**3 11 13 15 28 29 34 35 40 43 45 50 57 59 64 65 66 68 75 76 77 81 82 84 85 93 107 110 111 114 115 119 127 130 132 133 134 135 146 147 148 154 156 **P**4
Primary Contact: Janice Simons, FACHE, Chief Executive Officer
CFO: Kevin Frosch, Chief Financial Officer
CMO: Matthew Windrow, M.D., Chief of Staff
CIO: Ken Gallegos, Director Support Services and Information Technology
CHR: Sharon Garcia, Human Resources Representative
CNO: Billie Bell, Chief Nursing Officer
Web address: www.medinahospital.net
**Control:** Hospital district or authority, Government, Nonfederal **Service:** General medical and surgical

**Staffed Beds:** 25 **Admissions:** 670 **Census:** 7 **Outpatient Visits:** 57768
**Births:** 150 **Total Expense ($000):** 28786 **Payroll Expense ($000):** 11632
**Personnel:** 245

## HOUSTON—Harris County

☐ **AD HOSPITAL EAST (670102)**, 12950 East Freeway, Zip 77015–5710; tel. 713/330–3887, (Includes RIVER OAKS HOSPITALS & CLINICS, Mailing address: 4200 Twelve Oaks Drive, Houston, Texas, Zip 77027–6812; tel. 713/980–7900; Robert A Turner, Chief Executive Officer), (Nonreporting) **A**1
Primary Contact: Robert A. Turner, Chief Executive Officer
**Control:** Other not–for–profit (including NFP Corporation) **Service:** General medical and surgical

**Staffed Beds:** 25

☐ **ADVANCED DIAGNOSTICS HOSPITAL (670203)**, 12950 East Freeway, Zip 77015–5710; tel. 713/330–3887, (Nonreporting) **A**1 **F**3 12 15 29 35 40 44 45 54 64 68 75 79 81 82 85 87 92 107 110 111 115 119 131 148 149 156
Primary Contact: Steve Winnett, Chief Executive Officer
CFO: Carol Files, Chief Financial Officer
CMO: Ian Reynolds, Chief Medical Officer
CIO: Yobi Kasper, Chief Information Officer
CHR: Gabby Myers, Human Resources Director
CNO: David Gonzalez, Chief Clinical Officer
**Control:** Individual, Investor–owned (for–profit) **Service:** General medical and surgical

**Staffed Beds:** 16 **Admissions:** 687 **Census:** 3 **Outpatient Visits:** 20531
**Births:** 0 **Total Expense ($000):** 25820 **Payroll Expense ($000):** 9278
**Personnel:** 241

**ALTUS HOUSTON HOSPITAL**, 6011 West Sam Houston Parkway South, Zip 77072–1646; tel. 713/773–0556, (Nonreporting)
Primary Contact: Kris Jenkins, Administrator
Web address: www.https://altushospital.org
**Control:** Partnership, Investor–owned (for–profit) **Service:** General medical and surgical

**Staffed Beds:** 10

**BAYLOR COLLEGE OF MEDICINE MEDICAL CENTER** See Baylor St. Luke's Medical Center Mcnair Campus

★ ⇧ **BAYLOR ST. LUKE'S MEDICAL CENTER (450193)**, 6720 Bertner Avenue, Zip 77030–2697, Mailing Address: P.O. Box 20269, Zip 77225–0269; tel. 832/355–1000, (Nonreporting) **A**2 3 5 8 10 21 **F**3 8 11 12 14 15 17 18 20 22 24 26 28 29 30 31 34 35 36 37 39 40 42 45 46 47 48 49 50 51 52 54 55 56 57 58 59 60 61 63 64 65 66 68 70 74 75 77 78 79 81 82 84 85 86 87 90 91 92 93 100 107 108 109 110 111 112 113 114 115 116 117 118 119 120 121 122 123 124 126 129 130 131 132 137 138 139 140 141 146 148 149 154 156 **S** CommonSpirit Health, Chicago, IL
Primary Contact: Elizabeth Youngblood, President and Chief Executive Officer
CMO: John Byrne, M.D., Vice President and Chief Medical Officer
CIO: James Albin, Chief Information Officer
CHR: Susan Bailey-Newell, Vice President Human Resources
CNO: Loretta Lee, Acting Chief Nursing Officer
Web address: www.stlukestexas.com
**Control:** Church operated, Nongovernment, not–for–profit **Service:** General medical and surgical

**Staffed Beds:** 634 **Admissions:** 23480 **Census:** 419 **Outpatient Visits:** 155740 **Births:** 0 **Total Expense ($000):** 956403 **Payroll Expense ($000):** 316936 **Personnel:** 3554

★ **BAYLOR ST. LUKE'S MEDICAL CENTER MCNAIR CAMPUS**, One Baylor Plaza, BCM 100, Zip 77030–3411; tel. 713/798–4951, (Nonreporting) **A**3 **S** CommonSpirit Health, Chicago, IL
Primary Contact: Elizabeth Youngblood, President and Chief Executive Officer
Web address: www.bcm.edu
**Control:** Other not–for–profit (including NFP Corporation) **Service:** General medical and surgical

**Staffed Beds:** 256

☐ **BEHAVIORAL HOSPITAL OF BELLAIRE (454107)**, 5314 Dashwood Drive, Zip 77081–4603; tel. 713/600–9500, (Nonreporting) **A**1 10 **F**4 5 29 98 99 100 101 103 105 130 152 153 154 **S** Universal Health Services, Inc., King of Prussia, PA
Primary Contact: Eric Amoh, Chief Executive Officer
CFO: Autumn Crouse, Chief Financial Officer
Web address: www.bhbhospital.com
**Control:** Corporation, Investor–owned (for–profit) **Service:** Psychiatric

**Staffed Beds:** 122 **Admissions:** 3850 **Census:** 93 **Outpatient Visits:** 5810
**Births:** 0 **Total Expense ($000):** 20782 **Payroll Expense ($000):** 11327
**Personnel:** 197

**BEN TAUB GENERAL HOSPITAL** See Ben Taub Hospital

**TX**

*Many Facility Codes have changed. Please refer to the AHA Guide Code Chart.*

★ ⇑ **CHI ST. LUKE'S HOSPITAL - THE VINTAGE HOSPITAL (670075)**, 20171 Chasewood Park Drive, Zip 77070–1437; tel. 832/534–5000, (Nonreporting) **A**10 21 **F**3 13 15 18 20 22 24 26 29 30 34 35 40 44 45 46 49 50 57 59 60 64 68 70 72 74 75 76 77 79 81 85 87 107 108 110 111 114 115 118 119 130 146 147 149 **S** CommonSpirit Health, Chicago, IL
Primary Contact: Mario J. Garner, Ed.D., FACHE, Chief Executive Officer
Web address: www.https://www.chistlukeshealth.org/locations/vintage-hospital
**Control**: Church operated, Nongovernment, not-for-profit **Service**: General medical and surgical

| | |
|---|---|
| **Staffed Beds**: 78 **Admissions**: 4070 **Census**: 45 **Outpatient Visits**: 28022 **Births**: 742 **Total Expense ($000)**: 75675 **Payroll Expense ($000)**: 29046 **Personnel**: 389 | |

⇑ **CHRISTUS ST JOSEPH HOSPITAL** See St. Joseph Medical Center

**COBALT REHABILITATION HOUSTON HEIGHTS**, 1917 Ashland Street, 4th Floor, Zip 77008–3907; tel. 713/814–9114, (Nonreporting) **A**22 **S** Curahealth Hospitals, Garland, TX
Primary Contact: Jeff Crawford, Chief Executive Officer
Web address: www.curahealth.com/locations/rehabilitation-houston-heights/
**Control**: Corporation, Investor–owned (for–profit) **Service**: Rehabilitation

| | |
|---|---|
| **Staffed Beds**: 35 | |

**COLUMBIA TEXAS ORTHOPEDIC HOSP** See Texas Orthopedic Hospital

**CORNERSTONE HOSPITAL OF SOUTH HOUSTON** See Cornerstone Hospital-Medical Center of Houston

**CORNERSTONE HOSPITAL-MEDICAL CENTER OF HOUSTON (452055)**, 2001 Hermann Drive, Zip 77004; tel. 832/649–6200, (Nonreporting) **A**10 **F**1 3 29 70 85 86 87 91 119 130 148 149 **S** Cornerstone Healthcare Group, Dallas, TX
Primary Contact: Guido J. Cubellis, Chief Executive Officer
Web address: www.chghospitals.com
**Control**: Corporation, Investor–owned (for–profit) **Service**: Acute long–term care hospital

| | |
|---|---|
| **Staffed Beds**: 35 **Admissions**: 368 **Census**: 29 **Outpatient Visits**: 0 **Births**: 0 **Total Expense ($000)**: 17446 **Payroll Expense ($000)**: 7856 **Personnel**: 96 | |

☐ **CYPRESS CREEK HOSPITAL (454108)**, 17750 Cali Drive, Zip 77090–2700; tel. 281/586–7600, (Nonreporting) **A**1 10 **F**4 5 29 64 75 87 98 100 102 104 105 130 132 153 154 **S** Universal Health Services, Inc., King of Prussia, PA
Primary Contact: Rae Oliver, Chief Executive Officer
CFO: Stephen Copeland, Chief Financial Officer
CMO: Marshall Lucas, M.D., Medical Director
CIO: James Harmon, Information Technology
CHR: Brenda Dominguez, Director Human Resources
CNO: Michael Smith, Director of Nursing
Web address: www.cypresscreekhospital.com
**Control**: Corporation, Investor–owned (for–profit) **Service**: Psychiatric

| | |
|---|---|
| **Staffed Beds**: 128 **Admissions**: 4247 **Census**: 102 **Outpatient Visits**: 8571 **Births**: 0 **Total Expense ($000)**: 27232 **Payroll Expense ($000)**: 13074 **Personnel**: 229 | |

**CYPRESS FAIRBANKS MEDICAL CENTER** See Hca Houston Healthcare Cypress Fairbanks

⊞ **ENCOMPASS HEALTH REHABILITATION HOSPITAL OF CYPRESS (673050)**, 13031 Wortham Center Drive, Zip 77065–5662; tel. 832/280–2500, (Nonreporting) **A**1 10 **F**3 29 34 57 59 62 75 77 82 86 87 90 91 95 96 130 132 148 149 156 **S** Encompass Health Corporation, Birmingham, AL
Primary Contact: Sheila A. Bollier, Chief Executive Officer
CFO: Melissa Haddox, Controller
CMO: Ignazio LaChina, M.D., Medical Director
CNO: Roshonda Henry, Chief Nursing Officer
Web address: www.healthsouthcypress.com
**Control**: Corporation, Investor–owned (for–profit) **Service**: Rehabilitation

| | |
|---|---|
| **Staffed Beds**: 60 **Admissions**: 1336 **Census**: 48 **Outpatient Visits**: 0 **Births**: 0 **Total Expense ($000)**: 20350 **Payroll Expense ($000)**: 10718 **Personnel**: 192 | |

⊞ **ENCOMPASS HEALTH REHABILITATION HOSPITAL THE VINTAGE (673052)**, 20180 Chasewood Park Drive, Zip 77070–1436; tel. 281/205–5100, (Nonreporting) **A**1 10 **F**3 28 29 65 90 91 96 130 132 148 149 154 **S** Encompass Health Corporation, Birmingham, AL
Primary Contact: Krista Uselman, Chief Executive Officer
CNO: Stanley F Kiebzak, R.N., Chief Nursing Officer
Web address: www.reliantnwhouston.com
**Control**: Corporation, Investor–owned (for–profit) **Service**: Rehabilitation

| | |
|---|---|
| **Staffed Beds**: 60 **Admissions**: 1277 **Census**: 41 **Outpatient Visits**: 3770 **Births**: 0 **Total Expense ($000)**: 21649 **Payroll Expense ($000)**: 10309 **Personnel**: 147 | |

**FOREST SPRINGS HOSPITAL** See Intracare North Hospital

⇑ **HARRIS COUNTY HOSPITAL DISTRICT** See Harris Health System

⇑ **HARRIS HEALTH SYSTEM (450289)**, 2525 Holly Hall Street, Zip 77054–4108, Mailing Address: P.O. Box 66769, Zip 77266–6769; tel. 713/566–6403, (Includes BEN TAUB HOSPITAL, Mailing address: 1504 Taub Loop, Houston, Texas, Zip 77030; tel. 713/873–2000; Esmaeil Porsa, M.D., Chief Executive Officer; LYNDON B JOHNSON GENERAL HOSPITAL, Mailing address: 5656 Kelley, Houston, Texas, Zip 77026; tel. 713/566–5000; Colonel Patricia Darnauer, Administrator; QUENTIN MEASE HOSPITAL, Mailing address: 3601 North MacGregor, Houston, Texas, Zip 77004; tel. 713/873–3700; Jeffrey Webster, Administrator) (Total facility includes 22 beds in nursing home–type unit) **A**2 3 5 10 21 **F**1 3 4 5 7 8 13 15 16 17 18 20 22 24 26 29 30 31 32 34 35 39 40 41 43 45 46 49 50 51 54 55 56 57 58 59 60 61 64 65 67 68 70 71 72 73 74 75 76 77 78 79 80 81 82 84 87 88 89 90 91 92 93 94 97 98 100 101 102 104 107 110 111 112 114 115 118 119 120 121 124 128 129 130 132 134 135 143 144 146 147 148 149 150 153 154 156
Primary Contact: Esmaeil Porsa, M.D., President and Chief Executive Officer
CFO: Michael Norby, Chief Financial Officer
CMO: Fred Sutton, M.D., Chief Medical Officer
CIO: Tim Tindle, Chief Information Officer
CHR: Diane Poirot, Vice President Human Resources
CNO: Toni Cotton, R.N., Chief Nursing Officer
Web address: www.https://www.harrishealth.org
**Control**: Hospital district or authority, Government, Nonfederal **Service**: General medical and surgical

| | |
|---|---|
| **Staffed Beds**: 711 **Admissions**: 29477 **Census**: 475 **Outpatient Visits**: 1764025 **Births**: 5407 **Total Expense ($000)**: 1441259 **Payroll Expense ($000)**: 556334 **Personnel**: 8115 | |

⊞ **HCA HOUSTON HEALTHCARE MEDICAL CENTER (450659)**, 1313 Hermann Drive, Zip 77004–7092; tel. 713/527–5000, (Nonreporting) **A**1 5 10 **F**3 12 15 17 18 20 22 24 26 29 30 37 40 49 50 58 70 74 75 79 81 85 86 92 100 101 102 104 105 106 107 108 110 111 114 115 118 119 120 121 123 129 130 146 148 153 **S** HCA Healthcare, Nashville, TN
Primary Contact: Peyton Elliott, Chief Executive Officer
COO: Mary Jo Goodman, Chief Operating Officer
CIO: Terry Janis, Assistant Vice President
CHR: Melanie R Webb, Vice President Human Resources
Web address: www.https://hcahoustonhealthcare.com/locations/medical-center/
**Control**: Corporation, Investor–owned (for–profit) **Service**: General medical and surgical

| | |
|---|---|
| **Staffed Beds**: 147 **Admissions**: 3724 **Census**: 56 **Outpatient Visits**: 25252 **Births**: 0 **Total Expense ($000)**: 87263 **Payroll Expense ($000)**: 34425 **Personnel**: 420 | |

⊞ **HCA HOUSTON HEALTHCARE NORTHWEST (450638)**, 710 Cypress Creek Parkway, Zip 77090–3402; tel. 281/440–1000, (Nonreporting) **A**1 3 5 10 **F**3 11 12 13 18 20 22 24 26 28 29 30 31 34 35 40 43 45 46 47 48 49 50 57 59 64 65 70 72 74 75 76 77 78 79 81 82 84 85 86 87 90 92 102 107 108 111 115 119 126 129 130 132 135 144 145 146 147 148 149 **S** HCA Healthcare, Nashville, TN
Primary Contact: Scott Davis, Chief Executive Officer
COO: Michael Adkins, Chief Operating Officer
CFO: Cameron Pophan, Chief Financial Officer
CIO: Ed Roberson, Director Information Systems
CHR: Melanie R Webb, Vice President Human Resources
CNO: Cindy Henning, R.N., Chief Nursing Officer
Web address: www.hnmc.com
**Control**: Partnership, Investor–owned (for–profit) **Service**: General medical and surgical

| | |
|---|---|
| **Staffed Beds**: 254 **Admissions**: 14782 **Census**: 184 **Outpatient Visits**: 107785 **Births**: 3225 **Total Expense ($000)**: 246568 **Payroll Expense ($000)**: 94505 **Personnel**: 1209 | |

**TX**

**Hospital, Medicare Provider Number, Address, Telephone, Approval, Facility, and Physician Codes, Health Care System**

★ American Hospital Association (AHA) membership
☐ The Joint Commission accreditation
○ Healthcare Facilities Accreditation Program
◇ DNV Healthcare Inc. accreditation
⇑ Center for Improvement in Healthcare Quality Accreditation
△ Commission on Accreditation of Rehabilitation Facilities (CARF) accreditation

© 2021 AHA Guide     *Many Facility Codes have changed. Please refer to the AHA Guide Code Chart.*     Hospitals **A685**

⊞ **HCA HOUSTON HEALTHCARE WEST (450644)**, 12141 Richmond Avenue, Zip 77082–2499; tel. 281/558–3444, (Nonreporting) **A**1 3 10 **F**3 11 12 13 15 18 20 22 24 26 29 31 39 40 45 46 47 48 49 50 51 56 57 59 60 64 70 73 74 75 76 77 78 79 80 81 82 85 90 93 96 98 102 103 107 110 111 115 116 117 118 119 121 124 126 129 130 132 145 146 147 148 149 **S** HCA Healthcare, Nashville, TN
Primary Contact: Megan Marietta, Chief Executive Officer
COO: Philip Morris, Chief Operating Officer
CFO: Stanley K Nord, Chief Financial Officer
CMO: Magdy Rizk, M.D., Chief of Staff
CIO: Sergio Almeida, Director Information Systems
CHR: Carol Melville, Director Human Resources
Web address: www.https://hcahoustonhealthcare.com/locations/west/
**Control**: Partnership, Investor–owned (for–profit) **Service**: General medical and surgical

**Staffed Beds**: 264 **Admissions**: 13210 **Census**: 179 **Outpatient Visits**: 110568 **Births**: 2508 **Total Expense ($000)**: 209734 **Payroll Expense ($000)**: 80225 **Personnel**: 860

⇑ **HEALTHBRIDGE CHILDREN'S HOSPITAL OF HOUSTON** See Nexus Children's Hospital Houston

**HEALTHSOUTH REHABILITATION HOSPITAL OF CYPRESS** See Encompass Health Rehabilitation Hospital of Cypress

**HEALTHSOUTH REHABILITATION HOSPITAL THE VINTAGE** See Encompass Health Rehabilitation Hospital The Vintage

☐ **HOUSTON BEHAVIORAL HEALTHCARE HOSPITAL (454135)**, 2801 Gessner Road, Zip 77080–2503; tel. 832/834–7710, (Nonreporting) **A**1 **S** Signature Healthcare Services, Corona, CA
Primary Contact: Roy Hollis, Chief Executive Officer
Web address: www.houstonbehavioralhealth.com/
**Control**: Individual, Investor–owned (for–profit) **Service**: Psychiatric

**Staffed Beds**: 25

★ △ ⇑ **HOUSTON METHODIST HOSPITAL (450358)**, 6565 Fannin Street, D200, Zip 77030–2707; tel. 713/790–3311, (Total facility includes 18 beds in nursing home–type unit) (Nonreporting) **A**2 3 5 7 8 10 21 **F**3 5 6 8 9 11 12 13 14 15 17 18 20 22 24 26 29 30 31 34 35 36 37 38 39 40 41 42 44 45 47 48 49 50 51 53 54 55 56 57 58 59 60 61 62 63 64 65 66 68 70 73 74 75 76 77 78 79 80 81 82 84 85 86 87 90 91 92 93 95 96 97 98 100 101 102 103 104 105 107 108 110 111 112 114 115 117 118 119 120 121 123 124 126 128 129 130 131 132 135 136 138 139 140 141 142 145 146 147 148 149 150 153 154 156 **P**5 6 **S** Houston Methodist, Houston, TX
Primary Contact: Roberta Schwartz, Ph.D., Executive Vice President
CMO: Robert Phillips, M.D., Ph.D., FACC, Executive Vice President and Chief Medical Officer
CIO: Robert K Eardley, Senior Vice President and Chief Information Officer
CNO: Katherine Walsh, MS, R.N., Dr.PH, Vice President and Chief Nursing Officer
Web address: www.methodisthealth.com
**Control**: Other not–for–profit (including NFP Corporation) **Service**: General medical and surgical

**Staffed Beds**: 954 **Admissions**: 41976 **Census**: 780 **Outpatient Visits**: 464879 **Births**: 1247 **Total Expense ($000)**: 1985730 **Payroll Expense ($000)**: 548637 **Personnel**: 11191

★ ⇑ **HOUSTON METHODIST WEST HOSPITAL (670077)**, 18500 Katy Freeway, Zip 77094–1110; tel. 832/522–1000, (Nonreporting) **A**2 10 21 **F**3 11 12 13 15 18 20 22 24 26 28 29 30 31 34 35 36 39 40 42 44 45 49 50 51 53 54 57 59 60 61 63 64 68 70 72 74 75 76 77 78 79 81 82 84 85 86 87 93 107 108 109 110 111 114 115 116 117 118 119 120 121 123 124 126 130 131 132 135 146 147 148 149 156 **P**6 **S** Houston Methodist, Houston, TX
Primary Contact: Wayne M. Voss, Chief Executive Officer
CNO: Victoria Brownewell, Chief Nursing Officer
Web address: www.methodisthealth.com
**Control**: Other not–for–profit (including NFP Corporation) **Service**: General medical and surgical

**Staffed Beds**: 216 **Admissions**: 12717 **Census**: 129 **Outpatient Visits**: 186946 **Births**: 2417 **Total Expense ($000)**: 312310 **Payroll Expense ($000)**: 109167 **Personnel**: 1534

★ ⇑ **HOUSTON METHODIST WILLOWBROOK HOSPITAL (450844)**, 18220 State Highway 249, Zip 77070–4347; tel. 281/477–1000, (Nonreporting) **A**3 10 21 **F**3 8 11 12 13 15 17 18 20 22 24 26 28 29 30 31 34 35 36 37 40 42 44 45 49 50 53 54 57 59 64 65 70 72 73 74 75 76 77 78 79 81 85 86 87 93 97 100 102 107 108 110 111 112 115 119 120 121 123 126 129 130 131 132 135 146 147 149 156 **P**6 **S** Houston Methodist, Houston, TX
Primary Contact: Keith Barber, CPA, Chief Executive Officer
CHR: Elizabeth Acevedo, Director Human Resources
CNO: Nancy C Keenan, R.N., Senior Vice President and Chief Nursing Officer
Web address: www.houstonmethodist.org/locations/willowbrook/
**Control**: Other not–for–profit (including NFP Corporation) **Service**: General medical and surgical

**Staffed Beds**: 312 **Admissions**: 20712 **Census**: 238 **Outpatient Visits**: 272093 **Births**: 4053 **Total Expense ($000)**: 410812 **Payroll Expense ($000)**: 148436 **Personnel**: 1923

**HOUSTON NORTHWEST MEDICAL CENTER** See Hca Houston Healthcare Northwest

☐ **INTRACARE NORTH HOSPITAL (454083)**, 1120 Cypress Station Drive, Zip 77090–3031; tel. 281/893–7200, (Nonreporting) **A**1 10 **F**98 99 100 101 103 104 105 153
Primary Contact: Terry Scovill, Chief Executive Officer
CFO: Fred Chan, Chief Financial Officer
CMO: Javier Ruiz, M.D., Medical Director
Web address: www.intracare.org
**Control**: Other not–for–profit (including NFP Corporation) **Service**: Psychiatric

**Staffed Beds**: 90 **Admissions**: 2283 **Census**: 54 **Outpatient Visits**: 27145 **Births**: 0 **Total Expense ($000)**: 17120 **Payroll Expense ($000)**: 8330 **Personnel**: 175

**JEFFERSON DAVIS HOSPITAL** See Lyndon B Johnson General Hospital

⊞ **KINDRED HOSPITAL HOUSTON MEDICAL CENTER (452023)**, 6441 Main Street, Zip 77030–1596; tel. 713/790–0500, (Nonreporting) **A**1 3 5 10 **F**1 3 29 30 70 75 77 85 107 130 148 **S** Kindred Healthcare, Louisville, KY
Primary Contact: Robert Stein, Chief Executive Officer
CFO: Sara Langlitz, Controller
Web address: www.khhouston.com/
**Control**: Corporation, Investor–owned (for–profit) **Service**: Acute long–term care hospital

**Staffed Beds**: 105 **Admissions**: 656 **Census**: 67 **Outpatient Visits**: 0 **Births**: 0 **Total Expense ($000)**: 40562 **Payroll Expense ($000)**: 18877 **Personnel**: 273

**KINDRED HOSPITAL–HOUSTON** See Kindred Hospital Houston Medical Center

⊞ **KINDRED HOSPITAL–HOUSTON NORTHWEST (452039)**, 11297 Fallbrook Drive, Zip 77065–4292; tel. 281/897–8114, (Nonreporting) **A**1 10 **F**1 3 29 49 57 64 70 77 85 87 107 114 130 148 **S** Kindred Healthcare, Louisville, KY
Primary Contact: Tracy Kohler, Chief Executive Officer
Web address: www.khhoustonnw.com/
**Control**: Corporation, Investor–owned (for–profit) **Service**: Acute long–term care hospital

**Staffed Beds**: 84 **Admissions**: 499 **Census**: 45 **Outpatient Visits**: 481 **Births**: 0 **Total Expense ($000)**: 26284 **Payroll Expense ($000)**: 10915 **Personnel**: 180

**LYNDON B JOHNSON GENERAL HOSPITAL** See Harris Health System, Houston

**MEM HERMANN CHILDREN'S HOSP** See Children's Memorial Hermann Hospital

*Many Facility Codes have changed. Please refer to the AHA Guide Code Chart.*

TX

✠ △ **MEMORIAL HERMANN - TEXAS MEDICAL CENTER (450068)**, 6411 Fannin Street, Zip 77030–1501; tel. 713/704–4000, (Includes CHILDREN'S MEMORIAL HERMANN HOSPITAL, Mailing address: 6411 Fannin, Houston, Texas, Zip 77030; tel. 713/704–5437; MEMORIAL HERMAN CYPRESS, Mailing address: 27700 NW Freeway, Suite 380, Cypress, Texas, Zip 77433; tel. 832/658–3102; Jerry Ashworth, Senior Vice President and Chief Executive Officer; MEMORIAL HERMANN ORTHOPEDIC AND SPINE HOSPITAL, Mailing address: 5410 West Loop South, Bellaire, Texas, Zip 77401–2103; tel. 713/314–4500; Gregory Haralson, FACHE, Senior Vice President and Chief Executive Officer) (Total facility includes 8 beds in nursing home–type unit) **A**1 2 3 5 7 8 10 **F**3 7 8 11 12 13 15 16 17 18 19 20 21 22 23 24 25 26 27 28 29 30 31 32 34 35 36 37 39 40 41 43 44 45 46 47 48 49 50 53 54 55 56 57 58 59 60 61 63 64 65 68 70 71 72 74 76 77 78 80 81 82 83 84 85 86 87 88 89 90 92 93 97 102 107 108 109 110 111 113 114 115 116 117 118 119 120 121 123 124 126 128 129 130 131 132 135 136 137 138 139 140 141 142 144 146 147 148 149 150 154 155 **P**5 6 **S** Memorial Hermann Health System, Houston, TX
Primary Contact: Gregory Haralson, FACHE, Senior Vice President and Chief Executive Officer
CFO: William Pack, Chief Financial Officer
CMO: Jeffrey Katz, M.D., Chief Medical Officer
CIO: David Bradshaw, Chief Information Officer
CHR: Vivian Kardow, Chief Human Resources Officer
Web address: www.mhhs.org
**Control**: Other not–for–profit (including NFP Corporation) **Service**: General medical and surgical

**Staffed Beds:** 1068 **Admissions:** 42024 **Census:** 724 **Outpatient Visits:** 283423 **Births:** 5930 **Total Expense ($000):** 1626114 **Payroll Expense ($000):** 478472 **Personnel:** 5439

**MEMORIAL HERMANN - THE INSTITUTE FOR REHABILITATION AND RESEARCH** See Tirr Memorial Hermann

✠ △ **MEMORIAL HERMANN GREATER HEIGHTS HOSPITAL (450184)**, 1635 North Loop West, Zip 77008–1532; tel. 713/867–3380, (Includes MEMORIAL HERMANN PEARLAND MEDICAL CENTER, Mailing address: 16100 South Freeway, Pearland, Texas, Zip 77584–1895; tel. 713/413–5000; Colonel Noel J. Cardenas, FACHE, Senior Vice President and Chief Executive Officer; MEMORIAL HERMANN SOUTHEAST HOSPITAL, Mailing address: 11800 Astoria Boulevard, Houston, Texas, Zip 77089–6041; tel. 281/929–6100; Colonel Noel J. Cardenas, FACHE, Senior Vice President and Chief Executive Officer; MEMORIAL HERMANN SOUTHWEST HOSPITAL, Mailing address: 7600 Beechnut, Houston, Texas, Zip 77074–1850; tel. 713/456–5000; Malisha Patel, Senior Vice President and Chief Executive Officer; MEMORIAL HERMANN THE WOODLANDS HOSPITAL, Mailing address: 9250 Pinecroft Drive, The Woodlands, Texas, Zip 77380–3225; tel. 281/364–2300; Justin Kendrick, Senior Vice President and Chief Executive Officer), (Nonreporting) **A**1 2 3 5 7 10 **F**3 8 11 12 13 15 17 18 20 22 24 26 28 29 30 31 34 35 36 37 40 41 42 43 44 45 46 47 48 49 50 51 54 55 56 57 58 59 60 62 64 65 70 72 73 74 75 76 77 78 79 80 81 82 84 85 86 87 90 91 92 93 94 96 97 100 101 102 107 108 109 110 111 112 113 114 115 116 117 119 120 121 123 124 126 129 130 131 132 135 143 144 146 147 148 149 154 **P**5 6 **S** Memorial Hermann Health System, Houston, TX
Primary Contact: Paul O'Sullivan, FACHE, Chief Executive Officer
COO: Wesley Tidwell, Chief Operating Officer
CFO: James R Shallock, Chief Financial Officer
CMO: Maurice Leibman, M.D., Chief Medical Officer
CIO: David Bradshaw, Chief Information Officer
CNO: Ann Szapor, Vice President and Chief Nursing Officer
Web address: www.memorialhermann.org
**Control**: Other not–for–profit (including NFP Corporation) **Service**: General medical and surgical

**Staffed Beds:** 1521 **Admissions:** 72424 **Census:** 936 **Outpatient Visits:** 657764 **Births:** 9276 **Total Expense ($000):** 1443351 **Payroll Expense ($000):** 490920 **Personnel:** 5499

**MEMORIAL HERMANN HOSPITAL** See Memorial Hermann - Texas Medical Center

**MEMORIAL HERMANN MEMORIAL CITY HOSPITAL** See Memorial Hermann Memorial City Medical Center

✠ **MEMORIAL HERMANN MEMORIAL CITY MEDICAL CENTER (450610)**, 1760 Barker Cypress Rd, Zip 77084, Mailing Address: 921 Gessner Road, Zip 77024–2501; tel. 713/242–3000, (Nonreporting) **A**1 2 3 5 10 **F**3 12 13 15 18 20 22 24 26 28 29 30 31 34 35 37 40 41 43 45 46 47 49 50 51 56 57 59 60 65 70 72 74 75 76 77 78 79 80 81 82 84 85 86 87 89 107 108 110 111 114 115 117 118 119 120 121 123 124 126 129 130 131 132 135 146 147 148 149 156 **P**5 6 **S** Memorial Hermann Health System, Houston, TX
Primary Contact: Paul O'Sullivan, FACHE, Chief Executive Officer
COO: Allen Tseng, Chief Operations Officer
CFO: Lisa Kendler, Chief Financial Officer
CMO: Harold Gottlieb, M.D., Chief Medical Officer
CIO: David Bradshaw, Chief Information, Planning and Marketing Officer
CHR: Suzanne S Meier, System Director, Compensation and Human Resources Technology
CNO: Dan Kelly, R.N., Chief Nursing Officer
Web address: www.memorialhermann.org
**Control**: Other not–for–profit (including NFP Corporation) **Service**: General medical and surgical

**Staffed Beds:** 421 **Admissions:** 21178 **Census:** 241 **Outpatient Visits:** 188375 **Births:** 3240 **Total Expense ($000):** 492915 **Payroll Expense ($000):** 129801 **Personnel:** 1559

**MEMORIAL HERMANN NORTHWEST HOSPITAL** See Memorial Hermann Greater Heights Hospital

**MEMORIAL HERMANN SOUTHEAST** See Memorial Hermann Southeast Hospital

**MEMORIAL HERMANN SOUTHEAST HOSPITAL** See Memorial Hermann Greater Heights Hospital, Houston

**MEMORIAL HERMANN SOUTHWEST HOSPITAL** See Memorial Hermann Greater Heights Hospital, Houston

**MEMORIAL HOSPITAL SOUTHWEST** See Memorial Hermann Southwest Hospital

☐ **MENNINGER CLINIC**, 12301 Main Street, Zip 77035–6207; tel. 713/275–5000, (Nonreporting) **A**1 3 5 **F**30 35 74 98 101 104 106 130 132 154
Primary Contact: Armando Colombo, Chief Executive Officer
CFO: Anthony Gaglio, CPA, Senior Vice President and Chief Financial Officer
CIO: M. Justin Coffey, Vice President and Chief Information Officer, Medical Director Center for Brain Stimulation
CHR: Andrea Preisinger, Director Human Resources
Web address: www.menningerclinic.com
**Control**: Other not–for–profit (including NFP Corporation) **Service**: Psychiatric

**Staffed Beds:** 102 **Admissions:** 682 **Census:** 60 **Outpatient Visits:** 11996 **Births:** 0 **Total Expense ($000):** 59443 **Payroll Expense ($000):** 25448 **Personnel:** 471

⇧ **METHODIST WEST HOUSTON HOSPITAL** See Houston Methodist West Hospital

⇧ **METHODIST WILLOWBROOK HOSPITAL** See Houston Methodist Willowbrook Hospital

✠ △ **MICHAEL E. DEBAKEY VETERANS AFFAIRS MEDICAL CENTER**, 2002 Holcombe Boulevard, Zip 77030–4298; tel. 713/791–1414, (Nonreporting) **A**1 3 5 7 **S** Department of Veterans Affairs, Washington, DC
Primary Contact: Francisco Vazquez, Director
CFO: Alisa Cooper, Manager Financial Resources
CMO: Jagadeesh S Kalavar, M.D., Chief of Staff
CIO: Kevin Lenamond, Information Management Service Line Executive
CHR: Mark Muhammad, Manager Human Resources
CNO: Kelly Ann Irving MSN, RN-BAssociate Director for Patient Care Services
Web address: www.houston.va.gov
**Control**: Veterans Affairs, Government, federal **Service**: General medical and surgical

**Staffed Beds:** 479

**NEW HORIZON HOSPITAL**, 17506 Red Oak Drive, Zip 77090–1248; tel. 281/937–1530, (Nonreporting)
Primary Contact: Debbie Cormier, Chief Executive Officer
Web address: www.newhorizonhospital.com
**Control**: Partnership, Investor–owned (for–profit) **Service**: Psychiatric

**Staffed Beds:** 24

**TX**

---

**Hospital, Medicare Provider Number, Address, Telephone, Approval, Facility, and Physician Codes, Health Care System**

★ American Hospital Association (AHA) membership
☐ The Joint Commission accreditation
○ Healthcare Facilities Accreditation Program
◇ DNV Healthcare Inc. accreditation
⇧ Center for Improvement in Healthcare Quality Accreditation
△ Commission on Accreditation of Rehabilitation Facilities (CARF) accreditation

⇑ **NEXUS CHILDREN'S HOSPITAL HOUSTON (453309)**, 2929 Woodland Park Drive, Zip 77082–2687; tel. 281/293–7774, (Nonreporting) **A**3 5 10 21 **F**3 29 74 75 79 85 87 89 91 93 100 130 146 148 **S** Nexus Health Systems, Houston, TX
Primary Contact: Mary Harbeson, R.N., Chief Executive Officer
CMO: Robert Yetman, M.D., Medical Director
CHR: Guy Murdock, Vice President Human Resources
Web address: www.https://www.nexuscontinuum.com/services/childrens-hospital/
**Control:** Partnership, Investor–owned (for–profit) **Service:** Children's general medical and surgical

**Staffed Beds:** 40 **Admissions:** 137 **Census:** 24 **Outpatient Visits:** 276 **Births:** 0 **Total Expense ($000):** 14290 **Payroll Expense ($000):** 5989 **Personnel:** 105

**PARK PLAZA HOSPITAL** See Hca Houston Healthcare Medical Center

⊠ **PLAZA SPECIALTY HOSPITAL (452046)**, 1300 Binz Street, Zip 77004–7016; tel. 713/285–1000, (Nonreporting) **A**1 10 **F**1 3 70 85 87 **S** HCA Healthcare, Nashville, TN
Primary Contact: Peyton Elliott, Chief Executive Officer
CFO: Charles Handley, Chief Financial Officer
CMO: Wasae S Tabibi, M.D., President Medical Staff
CIO: Michael Turner, Chief Information Officer
Web address: www.plazaspecialtyhospital.com
**Control:** Corporation, Investor–owned (for–profit) **Service:** Acute long–term care hospital

**Staffed Beds:** 46 **Admissions:** 253 **Census:** 20 **Outpatient Visits:** 0 **Births:** 0 **Total Expense ($000):** 16168 **Payroll Expense ($000):** 6556 **Personnel:** 76

☐ **SACRED OAK MEDICAL CENTER (454142)**, 11500 Space Center Boulevard, Zip 77059–3603; tel. 281/241–6460, (Nonreporting) **A**1 10 **F**5 98 104 105 152 153
Primary Contact: Raquel Diati, Chief Executive Officer
Web address: www.sacredoakmedical.com/
**Control:** Partnership, Investor–owned (for–profit) **Service:** Psychiatric

**Staffed Beds:** 20 **Admissions:** 936 **Census:** 16 **Outpatient Visits:** 1123 **Births:** 0 **Total Expense ($000):** 12168 **Payroll Expense ($000):** 5511 **Personnel:** 86

☐ **SHRINERS HOSPITALS FOR CHILDREN-HOUSTON (453312)**, 6977 Main Street, Zip 77030–3701; tel. 713/797–1616, (Nonreporting) **A**1 3 5 10 **F**3 29 30 35 50 59 64 68 74 75 77 79 81 86 87 89 93 94 96 130 131 132 134 143 146 148 154 **P**6 **S** Shriners Hospitals for Children, Tampa, FL
Primary Contact: Cathy Moniaci, Administrator
COO: Cathy Moniaci, Administrator
CFO: Michael B Schimming, Director Fiscal Services
CMO: Douglas A Barnes, M.D., Chief of Staff
CHR: Robert A Magee, Director Human Resources
CNO: Jeannie Keith, R.N., Nurse Executive
Web address: www.shrinershospitalsforchildren.org/Locations/houston
**Control:** Other not–for–profit (including NFP Corporation) **Service:** Children's orthopedic

**Staffed Beds:** 40 **Admissions:** 445 **Census:** 10 **Outpatient Visits:** 8478 **Births:** 0 **Total Expense ($000):** 30462 **Payroll Expense ($000):** 16420 **Personnel:** 171

**SHRINERS HOSPS FOR CRPLD CHILD** See Shriners Hospitals for Children-Houston

**SPECIALTY HOSPITAL OF HOUSTON** See Cornerstone Hospital of Houston - Bellaire

⇑ **ST. JOSEPH MEDICAL CENTER (450035)**, 1401 St Joseph Parkway, Zip 77002–8301; tel. 713/757–1000, (Nonreporting) **A**3 5 10 21 **F**3 11 12 13 15 18 20 22 24 26 29 30 34 35 40 43 45 49 50 51 53 55 57 59 60 64 68 70 72 74 75 76 77 78 79 81 82 84 85 86 87 90 93 98 101 102 107 108 110 111 114 115 116 117 118 119 121 123 124 126 130 131 132 135 143 146 147 148 149 156 **P**8 **S** Steward Health Care System, LLC, Dallas, TX
Primary Contact: Kimberly S. Bassett, R.N., President
COO: Laura Fortin, R.N., Chief Operating Officer
CFO: Mark Hartman, Interim Chief Financial Officer
CIO: Robin Brown, Chief Information Officer and Compliance Officer
CHR: Kris Clatanoff, Director Human Resources
Web address: www.sjmctx.com
**Control:** Partnership, Investor–owned (for–profit) **Service:** General medical and surgical

**Staffed Beds:** 463 **Admissions:** 13862 **Census:** 176 **Outpatient Visits:** 107235 **Births:** 4135 **Total Expense ($000):** 257212 **Payroll Expense ($000):** 89809 **Personnel:** 1244

⇑ **ST. LUKE'S HOSPITAL - THE VINTAGE HOSPITAL** See Chi St. Luke's Hospital - The Vintage Hospital

⇑ **ST. LUKE'S MEDICAL CENTER** See Baylor St. Luke's Medical Center

☐ **SUN BEHAVIORAL HOUSTON (454139)**, 7601 Fannin Street, Zip 77054–1905; tel. 713/796–2273, (Nonreporting) **A**1 3 **F**98 99 100 101 102 103 104 105 106 153
Primary Contact: Brennan Francois, Chief Executive Officer
CMO: Vernon Walling, M.D., Chief Medical Officer
Web address: www.sunhouston.com
**Control:** Corporation, Investor–owned (for–profit) **Service:** Psychiatric

**Staffed Beds:** 148 **Admissions:** 4288 **Census:** 96 **Outpatient Visits:** 6429 **Births:** 0 **Total Expense ($000):** 23615 **Payroll Expense ($000):** 13293 **Personnel:** 204

☐ △ **TEXAS CHILDREN'S HOSPITAL (453304)**, 6621 Fannin Street, Zip 77030–2399, Mailing Address: Box 300630, Zip 77230–0630; tel. 832/824–1000, (Includes TEXAS CHILDREN'S HOSPITAL THE WOODLANDS, Mailing address: 17600 Interstate 45 South, The Woodlands, Texas, Zip 77384–5148; tel. 936/267–5000; Michelle Riley-Brown, President; TEXAS CHILDREN'S HOSPITAL WEST CAMPUS, Mailing address: 18200 Katy Freeway, Houston, Texas, Zip 77094–1285; tel. 832/227–1000; Michelle Riley-Brown, President), (Nonreporting) **A**1 3 5 7 8 10 **F**3 7 11 12 13 17 19 20 21 22 23 24 25 26 27 29 30 31 32 34 35 38 39 40 41 42 43 46 48 49 50 51 52 54 55 57 58 59 60 61 64 65 66 68 71 72 73 74 75 76 77 78 79 80 81 82 84 85 86 87 88 89 90 92 93 94 95 96 97 100 101 102 104 107 108 111 112 113 114 115 116 117 118 119 124 126 129 130 131 132 134 136 137 138 139 140 143 146 147 148 149 150 154 155
Primary Contact: Mark A. Wallace, FACHE, President and Chief Executive Officer
CMO: Jim Versalovic, M.D., Ph.D., Interim Physican-in-Chief
CIO: Myra Davis, Senior Vice President and Chief Information Officer
CHR: Linda W Aldred, Senior Vice President
Web address: www.texaschildrens.org
**Control:** Other not–for–profit (including NFP Corporation) **Service:** Children's general medical and surgical

**Staffed Beds:** 813 **Admissions:** 31015 **Census:** 615 **Outpatient Visits:** 1678478 **Births:** 6706 **Total Expense ($000):** 2409081 **Payroll Expense ($000):** 901215 **Personnel:** 9971

⊠ **TEXAS ORTHOPEDIC HOSPITAL (450804)**, 7401 South Main Street, Zip 77030–4509; tel. 713/799–8600, (Nonreporting) **A**1 3 5 10 **F**3 29 30 40 59 64 68 70 79 81 82 85 86 87 93 94 97 107 111 119 146 149 **S** HCA Healthcare, Nashville, TN
Primary Contact: Eric Becker, Chief Executive Officer
CFO: Blair Callaway, Chief Financial Officer
CMO: Gregory Stocks, M.D., Chief of Staff
CNO: Troy Sarver, R.N., Chief Nursing Officer
Web address: www.texasorthopedic.com
**Control:** Partnership, Investor–owned (for–profit) **Service:** Orthopedic

**Staffed Beds:** 49 **Admissions:** 3919 **Census:** 20 **Outpatient Visits:** 43091 **Births:** 0 **Total Expense ($000):** 101591 **Payroll Expense ($000):** 27224 **Personnel:** 339

**TEXAS WEST OAKS HOSPITAL** See West Oaks Hospital

⇑ **THE METHODIST HOSPITAL** See Houston Methodist Hospital

**THE WOMAN'S HOSPITAL OF TEXAS** See Woman's Hospital of Texas

⊠ **TIRR MEMORIAL HERMANN (453025)**, 1333 Moursund Street, Zip 77030–3405; tel. 713/799–5000, (Nonreporting) **A**1 3 5 10 **F**3 11 29 30 34 35 44 50 54 58 59 60 64 68 74 75 77 79 82 86 87 90 91 92 93 95 96 97 100 104 107 114 119 129 130 131 132 146 148 149 157 **P**5 6 **S** Memorial Hermann Health System, Houston, TX
Primary Contact: Rhonda Abbott, Interim Chief Executive Officer
CFO: Wayne Gordon, Chief Financial Officer
CMO: Gerard E Francisco, M.D., Chief Medical Officer
CIO: Gina Tripp, Director Information Systems
CHR: Vivian Kardow, Chief Human Resources Officer
Web address: www.memorialhermann.org/locations/tirr.html
**Control:** Other not–for–profit (including NFP Corporation) **Service:** Rehabilitation

**Staffed Beds:** 134 **Admissions:** 1593 **Census:** 103 **Outpatient Visits:** 34552 **Births:** 0 **Total Expense ($000):** 130574 **Payroll Expense ($000):** 63001 **Personnel:** 821

**TOPS SURGICAL SPECIALTY HOSP** See Tops Surgical Specialty Hospital

**TX**

*Many Facility Codes have changed. Please refer to the AHA Guide Code Chart.*

© 2021 AHA Guide

□ **TOPS SURGICAL SPECIALTY HOSPITAL (450774)**, 17080 Red Oak Drive, Zip 77090–2602; tel. 281/539–2900, (Nonreporting) **A**1 10 **F**3 15 29 40 45 47 64 78 79 81 82 85 86 87 107 110 114 119 148 **P**2 **S** United Surgical Partners International, Addison, TX
Primary Contact: Samuel H. Rossmann, Chief Executive Officer
CFO: Daniel Smith, Chief Financial Officer
CMO: Thomas Barton, M.D., Medical Director
CIO: Maud Jones, Manager Medical Records
CHR: Ashley Monzingo, Human Resources, Accounts Payable and Payroll
CNO: Andrea Wappelhorst, Chief Nursing Officer
Web address: www.tops-hospital.com
**Control:** Partnership, Investor–owned (for–profit) **Service:** Surgical

**Staffed Beds:** 15 **Admissions:** 673 **Census:** 4 **Outpatient Visits:** 46360
**Births:** 0 **Total Expense ($000):** 34432 **Payroll Expense ($000):** 9902
**Personnel:** 142

**UNITED MEMORIAL MEDICAL CARE** See United Memorial Medical Center

**UNITED MEMORIAL MEDICAL CENTER (450803)**, 510 West Tidwell Road, Zip 77091–4399; tel. 281/618–8500, (Includes UNITED MEMORIAL MEDICAL CENTER - NORTH HOUSTON, Mailing address: 17400 Red Oak Drive, Houston, Texas, Zip 77090–1246; tel. 936/267–5000; Farida Moeen, M.D., Chief Executive Officer), (Nonreporting) **A**10 22 **F**40 43 50 64 70 75 79 81 92 107 114 119 130
Primary Contact: Farida Moeen, M.D., Chief Executive Officer
COO: Farida Moeen, M.D., Chief Executive Officer
CFO: Theresa Eatherly, Chief Financial Officer
CMO: Cesar Ortega, M.D., Chief of Staff
CIO: Dell Davis, Director Information Systems
CHR: Carolyn Washington, Director of Human Resources
Web address: www.ummc.care/
**Control:** Partnership, Investor–owned (for–profit) **Service:** General medical and surgical

**Staffed Beds:** 42 **Admissions:** 7087 **Census:** 21 **Outpatient Visits:** 17106
**Births:** 0

**UNIVERSITY OF TEXAS HARRIS COUNTY PSYCHIATRIC CENTER** See Uthealth Harris County Psychiatric Center

**UNIVERSITY OF TEXAS M. D. ANDERSON CANCER CENTER** See University of Texas M.D. Anderson Cancer Center

✠ **UNIVERSITY OF TEXAS M.D. ANDERSON CANCER CENTER (450076)**, 1515 Holcombe Boulevard, Unit 1491, Zip 77030–4000; tel. 713/792–2121, (Nonreporting) **A**1 2 3 5 8 10 **F**3 11 14 15 18 20 22 26 29 30 31 32 34 35 36 37 38 39 40 41 44 45 46 47 48 49 50 54 55 56 57 58 59 64 68 70 71 74 75 77 78 79 80 81 82 83 84 85 86 87 88 89 90 92 93 96 97 100 101 102 104 107 108 110 111 112 114 115 116 117 118 119 120 121 122 123 124 126 129 130 132 134 135 136 141 142 145 146 147 148 149 150 157 **P**6 **S** University of Texas System, Austin, TX
Primary Contact: Peter Pisters, M.D., President
COO: Stephen Hahn, Deputy to the President and Chief Operating Officer
CFO: Weldon Gage, Chief Financial Officer
CIO: Chris Belmont, Chief Information Officer and Vice President
CHR: Shibu Varghese, Vice President Human Resources
CNO: Barbara L. Summers, Ph.D., R.N., Vice President Nursing Practice and Chief Nursing Officer
Web address: www.mdanderson.org
**Control:** State, Government, Nonfederal **Service:** Cancer

**Staffed Beds:** 670 **Admissions:** 30339 **Census:** 598 **Outpatient Visits:** 1559050 **Births:** 0 **Total Expense ($000):** 5063250 **Payroll Expense ($000):** 2082895 **Personnel:** 21247

✠ **UTHEALTH HARRIS COUNTY PSYCHIATRIC CENTER (454076)**, 2800 South MacGregor Way, Zip 77021–1000; tel. 713/741–7870, (Nonreporting) **A**1 3 5 10 **F**29 30 34 35 57 58 68 75 86 87 98 99 100 101 103 104 130 146 **P**6 **S** University of Texas System, Austin, TX
Primary Contact: Jair C. Soares, M.D., Executive Director
COO: Stephen Glazier, Chief Operating Officer
CFO: Lois K. Pierson, Chief Financial Officer
CMO: R Andrew Harper, M.D., Medical Director
CNO: Margaret Pung, R.N., Chief Nursing Officer
Web address: www.https://hcpc.uth.edu/
**Control:** State, Government, Nonfederal **Service:** Psychiatric

**Staffed Beds:** 217 **Admissions:** 8358 **Census:** 192 **Outpatient Visits:** 509 **Births:** 0 **Total Expense ($000):** 54716 **Payroll Expense ($000):** 36495 **Personnel:** 483

**VENCOR HOSP-HOUSTON NORTHWEST** See Kindred Hospital-Houston Northwest

**VETERANS AFFAIRS MED CENTER** See Michael E. Debakey Veterans Affairs Medical Center

**VICTORY SURGICAL HOSPITAL EAST HOUSTON** See Advanced Diagnostics Hospital

**WEST HOUSTON MEDICAL CENTER** See Hca Houston Healthcare West

**WEST OAKS AT CYPRESS CREEK** See Cypress Creek Hospital

□ **WEST OAKS HOSPITAL (454026)**, 6500 Hornwood Drive, Zip 77074–5095; tel. 713/995–0909, (Nonreporting) **A**1 5 10 **F**5 29 54 56 64 68 98 99 101 104 105 132 152 153 **S** Universal Health Services, Inc., King of Prussia, PA
Primary Contact: Mandy Westerman, Chief Executive Officer
CFO: Rob Tyler, Chief Financial Officer
CMO: Vernon Walling, M.D., Executive Medical Director
CIO: James Harmon, Network Administrator
CHR: Janice Webster, Director Human Resources
CNO: Israel Ahaine, Chief Nursing Officer
Web address: www.westoakshospital.com
**Control:** Corporation, Investor–owned (for–profit) **Service:** Psychiatric

**Staffed Beds:** 160 **Admissions:** 6402 **Census:** 144 **Outpatient Visits:** 14270 **Births:** 0 **Total Expense ($000):** 29847 **Payroll Expense ($000):** 18504 **Personnel:** 303

**WESTSIDE SURGICAL HOSPITAL**, 4200 Twelve Oaks Drive, Zip 77027; tel. 713/621–5010, (Nonreporting)
Primary Contact: Chad Baldwin, Interim Chief Executive Officer
CNO: Jimmy Wells, Chief Nursing and Administrative Officer
Web address: www.westsidesurgical.net
**Control:** Partnership, Investor–owned (for–profit) **Service:** Surgical

**Staffed Beds:** 12

✠ **WOMAN'S HOSPITAL OF TEXAS (450674)**, 7600 Fannin Street, Zip 77054–1906; tel. 713/790–1234, (Nonreporting) **A**1 3 5 10 **F**3 7 8 13 15 19 29 30 34 35 40 41 45 46 50 53 54 55 58 64 65 68 70 71 72 73 75 76 77 78 81 85 86 87 88 89 90 93 100 107 108 110 111 114 119 126 130 132 146 147 155 156 **S** HCA Healthcare, Nashville, TN
Primary Contact: Elizbeth Ortega, Chief Executive Officer
CFO: Scott Bentley, Chief Financial Officer
CMO: Eberhard Lotze, M.D., Chief Medical Officer
CIO: Emily Le, Director Information Technology and Services
CHR: Arnita Crawford, Director Human Resources
CNO: Holley Tyler, R.N., Chief Nursing Officer
Web address: www.womanshospital.com
**Control:** Partnership, Investor–owned (for–profit) **Service:** Obstetrics and gynecology

**Staffed Beds:** 367 **Admissions:** 16331 **Census:** 257 **Outpatient Visits:** 56190 **Births:** 11076 **Total Expense ($000):** 218078 **Payroll Expense ($000):** 96180 **Personnel:** 1147

**HUMBLE—Harris County**

✠ **ENCOMPASS HEALTH REHABILITATION HOSPITAL OF HUMBLE (453029)**, 19002 McKay Drive, Zip 77338–5701; tel. 281/446–6148, (Nonreporting) **A**1 10 **F**29 56 75 77 78 79 82 86 87 90 91 92 95 96 130 132 143 148 149 **P**5 **S** Encompass Health Corporation, Birmingham, AL
Primary Contact: Angela L. Simmons, Chief Executive Officer
CFO: Sheila Shepard, Controller
CMO: Emile Mathurin, M.D., JrMedical Director
CHR: Christy Dixon, Chief Human Resources Officer
CNO: Christie Griffin-Jones, R.N., Chief Nursing Officer
Web address: www.healthsouthhumble.com
**Control:** Corporation, Investor–owned (for–profit) **Service:** Rehabilitation

**Staffed Beds:** 60 **Admissions:** 1189 **Census:** 42 **Outpatient Visits:** 0 **Births:** 0 **Total Expense ($000):** 15952 **Payroll Expense ($000):** 10703 **Personnel:** 168

**HEALTHSOUTH REHABILITATION HOSPITAL OF HUMBLE, LLC** See Encompass Health Rehabilitation Hospital of Humble

**ICON HOSPITAL** See Se Texas Er & Hospital

**TX**

✠ **MEMORIAL HERMANN NORTHEAST (450684)**, 18951 North Memorial Drive, Zip 77338–4297; tel. 281/540–7700, (Nonreporting) **A**1 2 3 5 10 **F**3 11 13 15 18 20 22 24 26 29 30 31 34 35 40 42 44 45 46 49 53 54 57 59 64 65 68 70 72 73 74 75 76 77 78 79 80 81 84 85 87 91 93 100 107 108 109 111 114 115 119 120 121 126 129 130 131 132 135 146 147 148 154 157 **S** Memorial Hermann Health System, Houston, TX
Primary Contact: Justin Kendrick, Senior Vice President and Chief Executive Officer
CFO: Rebecca Tucker, Chief Financial Officer
CMO: Susan Curling, M.D., Chief Medical Officer
CHR: Monica Baisden, Director Human Resources
CNO: Linda Stephens, R.N., Chief Nursing Officer
Web address: www.memorialhermann.org/locations/northeast/
**Control:** Other not–for–profit (including NFP Corporation) **Service:** General medical and surgical

**Staffed Beds: 242 Admissions: 12507 Census: 146 Outpatient Visits: 142661 Total Expense ($000): 249149 Payroll Expense ($000): 85543 Personnel: 1020**

**NORTHEAST MEDICAL CENTER HOSP** See Memorial Hermann Northeast

✠ **PAM REHABILITATION HOSPITAL OF HUMBLE (673061)**, 18839 McKay Drive, Zip 77338–5721; tel. 281/446–3655, (Data for 153 days) (Nonreporting) **A**1 **F**3 29 90 91 93 96 130 148 **S** Post Acute Medical, LLC, Enola, PA
Primary Contact: Mikael Simpson, Chief Executive Officer
Web address: www.https://postacutemedical.com/facilities/find-facility/rehabilitation-hospitals/PAM-Rehabilitation-Hospital-of-Humble
**Control:** Partnership, Investor–owned (for–profit) **Service:** Rehabilitation

**Staffed Beds: 46 Admissions: 841 Census: 71 Outpatient Visits: 3922 Births: 0 Total Expense ($000): 15896 Payroll Expense ($000): 7452 Personnel: 136**

**SE TEXAS ER & HOSPITAL (452112)**, 19211 McKay Boulevard, Zip 77338–5502; tel. 281/883–5500, (Data for 245 days) (Nonreporting) **A**10 22 **F**1 3 40 107 114
Primary Contact: Michelle Heinrich, Ph.D., MS, R.N., Chief Executive Officer and Chief Nursing Officer
Web address: www.https://setexaser.com/
**Control:** Partnership, Investor–owned (for–profit) **Service:** Acute long–term care hospital

**Staffed Beds: 9 Admissions: 60 Census: 1 Outpatient Visits: 1594 Births: 0 Total Expense ($000): 2475 Payroll Expense ($000): 1335 Personnel: 43**

### HUNTSVILLE—Walker County

□ **HUNTSVILLE MEMORIAL HOSPITAL (450347)**, 110 Memorial Hospital Drive, Zip 77340–4940, Mailing Address: P.O. Box 4001, Zip 77342–4001; tel. 936/291–3411, (Nonreporting) **A**1 10 **F**3 11 12 13 15 18 20 22 26 28 29 32 34 35 40 43 45 46 47 49 50 57 59 60 65 66 67 70 75 76 77 79 81 84 85 86 87 89 90 92 93 96 97 102 107 108 110 111 114 115 119 126 127 130 131 132 135 146 147 148 149 150 154 **P**3
Primary Contact: Steven L. Smith, Chief Executive Officer
CFO: John Moore, Interim Chief Financial Officer
CHR: Brenda Ray, Director Human Resources
CNO: Sheila Ard, Chief Nursing Officer
Web address: www.huntsvillememorial.com
**Control:** Other not–for–profit (including NFP Corporation) **Service:** General medical and surgical

**Staffed Beds: 98 Admissions: 4467 Census: 57 Outpatient Visits: 106632 Births: 332 Total Expense ($000): 81549 Payroll Expense ($000): 32274 Personnel: 492**

### HURST—Tarrant County

**SAINT CAMILLUS MEDICAL CENTER (670121)**, 1612 Hurst Town Center Drive, Zip 76054–6236; tel. 817/519–3700, (Nonreporting) **A**22 **F**3 12 29 40 45 64 74 75 79 81 82 85 87 107 135 149
Primary Contact: Corazon Ramirez, M.D., Chief Executive Officer
COO: Karen Sperduti, Chief Operating Officer
Web address: www.https://saintcamillusmedicalcenter.com/
**Control:** Corporation, Investor–owned (for–profit) **Service:** Surgical

**Staffed Beds: 5 Admissions: 152 Census: 1 Outpatient Visits: 1309 Births: 0 Total Expense ($000): 25146 Payroll Expense ($000): 3949 Personnel: 45**

### IRAAN—Pecos County

★ **IRAAN GENERAL HOSPITAL (451307)**, 600 349 North, Zip 79744, Mailing Address: P.O. Box 665, Zip 79744–0665; tel. 432/639–2871, (Nonreporting) **A**10 18 **F**28 40 43 56 57 59 64 65 75 82 86 93 107 119 127 130 131 133 154
Primary Contact: Keith L. Butler, Chief Executive Officer
CFO: Tami Burks, Chief Fiscal Services
CMO: Robert W Garcia, M.D., Chief Medical Officer
CHR: Cathy Tucker, Director Human Resources
Web address: www.igh-hospital.com
**Control:** Hospital district or authority, Government, Nonfederal **Service:** General medical and surgical

**Staffed Beds: 14 Admissions: 34 Census: 1 Outpatient Visits: 9077 Births: 0 Total Expense ($000): 8116 Payroll Expense ($000): 3918 Personnel: 76**

**PECOS COUNTY GENERAL HOSPITAL** See Iraan General Hospital

### IRVING—Dallas County

**BAYLOR MEDICAL CENTER AT IRVING** See Baylor Scott & White Medical Center-Irving

✠ **BAYLOR SCOTT & WHITE MEDICAL CENTER-IRVING (450079)**, 1901 North MacArthur Boulevard, Zip 75061–2220; tel. 972/579–8100, (Nonreporting) **A**1 2 3 5 10 **F**3 8 11 13 15 17 18 20 22 24 26 28 29 30 31 34 35 40 45 46 47 49 54 55 57 58 59 64 65 66 70 73 74 75 76 77 78 79 80 81 82 84 85 86 87 90 93 94 100 107 108 110 111 114 115 116 117 118 119 120 121 122 126 129 130 141 143 146 147 148 149 150 156 **S** Baylor Scott & White Health, Dallas, TX
Primary Contact: Cindy K. Schamp, FACHE, President
CFO: Steve Roussel, Vice President Finance
CMO: Jeffrey Embrey, M.D., Chief Medical Officer
CIO: Tim Huffman, Western Region Director, Information Systems Business Relationships
CHR: Vonetta Fuller-Williams, Director Human Resources Strategic and Business Services
Web address: www.bswhealth.com
**Control:** Other not–for–profit (including NFP Corporation) **Service:** General medical and surgical

**Staffed Beds: 233 Admissions: 10117 Census: 127 Outpatient Visits: 95336 Births: 1433 Total Expense ($000): 222913 Payroll Expense ($000): 69990 Personnel: 791**

□ **BAYLOR SURGICAL HOSPITAL AT LAS COLINAS (450874)**, 400 West Lyndon B Johnson Freeway, Zip 75063–3718; tel. 972/868–4000, (Nonreporting) **A**1 10 **F**3 29 30 40 51 79 81 107 111 119 126 130 **S** United Surgical Partners International, Addison, TX
Primary Contact: Deonna Unell, Chief Executive Officer
CFO: Gabrielle Holland, Chief Financial Officer
CMO: Scott McGraw, M.D., Medical Director
Web address: www.baylorhealth.com/About/Community/Assessments/West/ICSH/Pages/Default.aspx
**Control:** Partnership, Investor–owned (for–profit) **Service:** General medical and surgical

**Staffed Beds: 12 Admissions: 799 Census: 4 Outpatient Visits: 7593 Births: 0 Total Expense ($000): 48638 Payroll Expense ($000): 11076 Personnel: 169**

**IRVING COPPELL SURGICAL HOSPITAL** See Baylor Surgical Hospital at Las Colinas

**LAS COLINAS MEDICAL CENTER** See Medical City Las Colinas

✠ **MEDICAL CITY LAS COLINAS (450822)**, 6800 North MacArthur Boulevard, Zip 75039–2422; tel. 972/969–2000, (Nonreporting) **A**1 10 **F**3 8 12 13 15 18 20 22 24 29 30 34 35 37 40 45 46 47 48 49 50 57 59 60 63 64 68 70 72 74 75 76 77 78 79 80 81 87 93 100 102 107 108 110 111 114 118 119 126 130 147 148 149 **S** HCA Healthcare, Nashville, TN
Primary Contact: Daniela Decell, Chief Executive Officer
COO: Chip Zahn, Chief Operating Officer
CFO: Nick Galt, Chief Financial Officer
CMO: Miguel Benet, M.D., Chief Medical Officer
Web address: www.lascolinasmedical.com
**Control:** Corporation, Investor–owned (for–profit) **Service:** General medical and surgical

**Staffed Beds: 72 Admissions: 5759 Census: 53 Outpatient Visits: 60087 Births: 2205 Total Expense ($000): 87345 Payroll Expense ($000): 30204 Personnel: 368**

*Many Facility Codes have changed. Please refer to the AHA Guide Code Chart.*

TX

## JACKSBORO—Jack County

**FAITH COMMUNITY HOSPITAL (450241)**, 215 Chisholm Trail,
Zip 76458–1111; tel. 940/567–6633, (Nonreporting) **A**10 20 **F**7 11 13 15 28 34
35 40 43 45 57 59 65 66 68 75 76 77 81 93 97 107 110 114 119 127 130
133 135 148 149 156 **P**6
Primary Contact: Frank Beaman, Chief Executive Officer
COO: Kim Lee, Chief Operating Officer
CFO: Bonnie Blevins, R.N., Chief Financial Officer
CMO: Robert Cooper, M.D., Chief Medical Officer
CIO: Troy McKenzie, Chief information Officer
CHR: Deborah White, Human Resource Coordinator
CNO: Joy Henry, R.N., Chief of Nursing
Web address: www.fchtexas.com
**Control**: Hospital district or authority, Government, Nonfederal **Service**: General
medical and surgical

**Staffed Beds: 17 Admissions: 348 Census: 3 Outpatient Visits: 57384
Births: 63 Total Expense ($000): 25303 Payroll Expense ($000): 8306
Personnel: 151**

**JACK COUNTY HOSPITAL** See Faith Community Hospital

## JACKSONVILLE—Cherokee County

✠ **CHRISTUS MOTHER FRANCES HOSPITAL - JACKSONVILLE (451319)**, 2026
South Jackson, Zip 75766–5822; tel. 903/541–4500, (Nonreporting) **A**1 10 18
**F**3 15 18 29 30 32 34 35 40 43 45 50 53 56 57 59 64 65 68 79 81 82 85
89 93 97 107 108 110 111 114 119 129 130 133 145 147 148 **P**5 6 7 8 **S**
CHRISTUS Health, Irving, TX
Primary Contact: Barry D. Lofquist, Chief Executive Officer
CFO: Elizabeth Pulliam, Chief Financial Officer
CMO: Peter Sirianni, M.D., President Medical Staff
CNO: Jamie Maddox, Chief Nursing Officer
Web address: www.tmfhs.org/jacksonville
**Control**: Other not–for–profit (including NFP Corporation) **Service**: General
medical and surgical

**Staffed Beds: 23 Admissions: 803 Census: 11 Outpatient Visits: 64507
Births: 0 Total Expense ($000): 39755 Payroll Expense ($000): 11079
Personnel: 220**

**EAST TEXAS MEDICAL CENTER JACKSONVILLE** See UT Health Jacksonville

**MOTHER FRANCES HOSPITAL - JACKSONVILLE** See Christus Mother Frances
Hospital - Jacksonville

✠ **UT HEALTH JACKSONVILLE (450194)**, 501 South Ragsdale Street,
Zip 75766–2413; tel. 903/541–5000, (Nonreporting) **A**1 3 10 20 **F**3 8 11 13 15
18 26 29 34 35 39 40 43 45 50 57 59 64 65 70 75 76 79 81 82 85 97 107
108 110 111 115 119 127 129 145 146 147 148 155 156 **P**6 **S** Ardent Health
Services, Nashville, TN
Primary Contact: DeLeigh Haley, Chief Executive Officer
CMO: Todd Parrish, M.D., Chief of Staff
CHR: Elysia Epperson, Director Human Resources
CNO: Jana Bateman, R.N., Chief Nursing Officer
Web address: www.https://uthealthjacksonville.com/
**Control**: Corporation, Investor–owned (for–profit) **Service**: General medical and
surgical

**Staffed Beds: 38 Admissions: 1264 Census: 11 Outpatient Visits: 100962
Births: 280 Total Expense ($000): 33617 Payroll Expense ($000): 10926
Personnel: 154**

## JASPER—Jasper County

✠ **CHRISTUS SOUTHEAST TEXAS JASPER MEMORIAL (450573)**, 1275 Marvin
Hancock Drive, Zip 75951–4995; tel. 409/384–5461, (Nonreporting) **A**1 10 **F**3
11 13 15 29 30 34 40 43 50 51 57 59 64 70 76 77 79 81 82 107 110 111
114 119 127 130 135 146 149 **P**8 **S** CHRISTUS Health, Irving, TX
Primary Contact: Wayne Moore, Interim Administrator
COO: Mark Durand, Assistant Administrator Operations
CFO: Nikki Martin, Chief Financial Officer
CIO: Robert Jacobs, Regional Information Management Executive
CHR: Kay Powell, Director Human Resources
Web address: www.christusjasper.org
**Control**: Church operated, Nongovernment, not–for–profit **Service**: General
medical and surgical

**Staffed Beds: 38 Admissions: 704 Census: 6 Outpatient Visits: 67945
Births: 115 Total Expense ($000): 25666 Payroll Expense ($000): 8670
Personnel: 128**

**CHRISTUS SOUTHEAST TEXAS JASPER MEMORIALA** See Christus Southeast
Texas Jasper Memorial

## JOURDANTON—Atascosa County

✠ **METHODIST HOSPITAL SOUTH (450165)**, 1905 Highway 97 East,
Zip 78026–1504; tel. 830/769–3515, (Nonreporting) **A**1 10 20 **F**3 13 15 18
29 30 34 35 39 40 45 49 57 59 63 64 68 70 74 75 76 77 79 81 85 93 107
108 110 111 115 119 129 130 132 146 147 152 154 **P**7 **S** HCA Healthcare,
Nashville, TN
Primary Contact: Gregory A. Seiler, Chief Executive Officer
COO: Pamela Guillory, Chief Operating Officer and Chief Nursing Officer
CFO: Joe Vazquez, Chief Financial Officer
CIO: Rita S Castillo, R.N., Vice President, Quality, Risk and Safety
CNO: Pamela Guillory, Chief Operating Officer and Chief Nursing Officer
Web address: www.https://sahealth.com/locations/methodisthospitalsouth/
**Control**: Partnership, Investor–owned (for–profit) **Service**: General medical and
surgical

**Staffed Beds: 42 Admissions: 1663 Census: 13 Outpatient Visits: 43524
Births: 230 Total Expense ($000): 36874 Payroll Expense ($000): 11750
Personnel: 157**

**SOUTH TEXAS REGIONAL MEDICAL CENTER** See Methodist Hospital South

## JUNCTION—Kimble County

**KIMBLE HOSPITAL (451306)**, 349 Reid Road, Zip 76849–3049;
tel. 325/446–3321, (Nonreporting) **A**10 18 **F**3 29 34 40 43 45 57 59 64 65 68
93 97 107 119 127 133 146 148 154 **S** Preferred Management Corporation,
Shawnee, OK
Primary Contact: Duke Young, Chief Executive Officer
COO: Teena Hagood, Chief Nursing Officer
CFO: Larry Stephens, Chief Financial Officer
CMO: Ben Udall, M.D., Chief of Staff
CIO: Anna Henry, Chief Information Officer
CHR: Hope Lamb, Manager Human Resources
Web address: www.kimblehospital.org/
**Control**: Corporation, Investor–owned (for–profit) **Service**: General medical and
surgical

**Staffed Beds: 15 Admissions: 125 Census: 2 Outpatient Visits: 13555
Births: 0 Total Expense ($000): 7645 Payroll Expense ($000): 3290
Personnel: 74**

## KATY—Harris County

☐ **ENCOMPASS HEALTH REHABILITATION HOSPITAL OF KATY**, 23331 Grand
Reserve Drive, Zip 77494; tel. 281/505–3500, (Nonreporting) **A**1 **S** Encompass
Health Corporation, Birmingham, AL
Primary Contact: Nicholas Hardin, FACHE, Chief Executive Officer
Web address: www.https://www.encompasshealth.com/katyrehab
**Control**: Corporation, Investor–owned (for–profit) **Service**: Rehabilitation

**Staffed Beds: 40**

★ ⇧ **HOUSTON METHODIST CONTINUING CARE HOSPITAL (452118)**, 701 Fry Road, Zip 77450–2255; tel. 281/599–5700, (Nonreporting) **A**10 21 **F**1 75 82 84 86 87 130 132 149 150 **S** Houston Methodist, Houston, TX
Primary Contact: Gary L. Kempf, R.N., Administrator
CFO: Nancy Brock, Chief Financial Officer
CHR: James A Fitch, Director Human Resources
Web address: www.houstonmethodist.org/katy-st-catherine-hospital
**Control**: Other not–for–profit (including NFP Corporation) **Service**: Acute long–term care hospital

**Staffed Beds: 58 Admissions: 488 Census: 43 Outpatient Visits: 0 Births: 0 Total Expense ($000): 39645 Payroll Expense ($000): 16907 Personnel: 244**

⇧ **HOUSTON METHODIST ST. CATHERINE HOSPITAL** See Houston Methodist Continuing Care Hospital

**KATY MEDICAL CENTER** See Memorial Hermann Katy Hospital

**KATY REHABILITATION HOSPITAL** See Memorial Hermann Rehabilitation Hospital - Katy

⊞ **MEMORIAL HERMANN KATY HOSPITAL (450847)**, 23900 Katy Freeway, Zip 77494–1323; tel. 281/644–7000, (Nonreporting) **A**1 2 3 5 10 **F**3 11 13 15 18 20 22 26 29 30 34 35 37 39 40 41 42 43 45 46 49 50 51 54 57 59 61 64 65 68 70 72 73 74 75 76 77 78 79 80 81 85 87 89 93 102 107 108 110 111 114 119 126 130 131 132 144 145 146 147 149 154 **P**5 6 **S** Memorial Hermann Health System, Houston, TX
Primary Contact: Jerry Ashworth, Senior Vice President and Chief Executive Officer
CFO: Linda Kulhanek, Chief Financial Officer
Web address: www.memorialhermann.org/locations/katy/
**Control**: Other not–for–profit (including NFP Corporation) **Service**: General medical and surgical

**Staffed Beds: 199 Admissions: 11629 Census: 116 Outpatient Visits: 123585 Births: 2107 Total Expense ($000): 223320 Payroll Expense ($000): 79006 Personnel: 890**

**MEMORIAL HERMANN REHABILITATION HOSPITAL - KATY** See Oceans Behavioral Hospital Katy

⊞ △ **MEMORIAL HERMANN REHABILITATION HOSPITAL - KATY (673038)**, 21720 Kingsland Boulevard, 2nd Floor, Zip 77450–2550; tel. 800/447–3422, (Nonreporting) **A**1 2 7 10 **F**3 29 30 64 74 75 77 79 90 92 93 96 100 107 111 114 119 129 130 131 146 148 149 **S** Memorial Hermann Health System, Houston, TX
Primary Contact: Rhonda Abbott, Interim Chief Executive Officer
COO: Mary Ann Euliarte, R.N., Chief Operating Officer
CFO: Wayne Gordon, Chief Financial Officer
CMO: Shalin Patel, M.D., Chief Medical Officer
CHR: Joyce Williams, Consultant Human Resources and Organizational Development
CNO: Mary Ann Euliarte, R.N., Chief Nursing Officer
Web address: www.memorialhermann.org/locations/katy-rehab/
**Control**: Partnership, Investor–owned (for–profit) **Service**: Rehabilitation

**Staffed Beds: 35 Admissions: 781 Census: 28 Outpatient Visits: 14599 Births: 0 Total Expense ($000): 24573 Payroll Expense ($000): 11239 Personnel: 116**

☐ **OCEANS BEHAVIORAL HOSPITAL KATY (454136)**, 455 Park Grove Lane, Zip 77450–1572; tel. 281/492–8888, (Nonreporting) **A**1 **F**29 34 35 64 98 100 101 103 104 149 153 154 **S** Oceans Healthcare, Plano, TX
Primary Contact: Stuart Archer, Chief Executive Officer
Web address: www.memorialhermann.org/locations/katy-rehab/
**Control**: Corporation, Investor–owned (for–profit) **Service**: Psychiatric

**Staffed Beds: 48 Admissions: 1030 Census: 36 Outpatient Visits: 15038 Births: 0 Total Expense ($000): 11266 Payroll Expense ($000): 5117 Personnel: 158**

**PRESBYTERIAN HOSP OF KAUFMAN** See Texas Health Presbyterian Hospital Kaufman

⊞ **TEXAS HEALTH PRESBYTERIAN HOSPITAL KAUFMAN (450292)**, 850 Ed Hall Drive, Zip 75142–1861, Mailing Address: P.O. Box 1108, Zip 75142–5401; tel. 972/932–7200, (Nonreporting) **A**1 10 **F**3 11 15 29 30 34 35 40 45 53 57 59 64 65 70 75 79 81 82 85 86 87 93 102 107 108 110 111 112 114 115 118 119 130 132 146 149 **P**6 **S** Texas Health Resources, Arlington, TX
Primary Contact: Mark Sij, D.O., Chief Executive Officer
CMO: Benjamin Bradshaw, M.D., President Medical Staff
CHR: Mark J Rainey, Director Human Resources
CNO: Denise Claussen, R.N., MSN, Chief Nursing Officer
Web address: www.texashealth.org/Kaufman
**Control**: Other not–for–profit (including NFP Corporation) **Service**: General medical and surgical

**Staffed Beds: 47 Admissions: 1086 Census: 7 Outpatient Visits: 32623 Births: 0 Total Expense ($000): 32971 Payroll Expense ($000): 13073 Personnel: 156**

★ **OTTO KAISER MEMORIAL HOSPITAL (451364)**, 3349 South Highway 181, Zip 78119–5247; tel. 830/583–3401, (Nonreporting) **A**10 18 **F**3 11 15 29 30 34 40 43 45 46 53 57 59 62 64 68 77 81 93 107 111 115 119 132 133 135 148 154 **P**8
Primary Contact: David Lee, Chief Executive Officer
CIO: Joseph Wiatrek, Director Information Technology
CHR: Christina Benavides, Director Employee Services
CNO: Vincent Sowell, Chief Nursing Officer
Web address: www.okmh.org/
**Control**: Hospital district or authority, Government, Nonfederal **Service**: General medical and surgical

**Staffed Beds: 25 Admissions: 238 Census: 4 Outpatient Visits: 22823 Births: 0 Total Expense ($000): 23882 Payroll Expense ($000): 9434 Personnel: 154**

**MEMORIAL HOSPITAL** See Winkler County Memorial Hospital

**WINKLER COUNTY MEMORIAL HOSPITAL (451314)**, 821 Jeffee Drive, Zip 79745–4696, Mailing Address: P.O. Box H, Zip 79745–6008; tel. 432/586–5864, (Nonreporting) **A**10 18 **F**3 32 34 36 40 57 59 64 65 69 93 107 119 127 133
Primary Contact: Lorenzo Serrano, Chief Executive Officer
CFO: Wannah Hartley, Controller
CMO: K Pham, M.D., Chief of Staff
CIO: Keith Palmer, Assistant Administrator
**Control**: County, Government, Nonfederal **Service**: General medical and surgical

**Staffed Beds: 19 Admissions: 139 Census: 1 Outpatient Visits: 8276 Births: 0 Total Expense ($000): 9064 Payroll Expense ($000): 4083 Personnel: 77**

**KERRVILLE DIVISION** See South Texas Veterans Health Care System, San Antonio

☐ **KERRVILLE STATE HOSPITAL (454014)**, 721 Thompson Drive, Zip 78028–5154; tel. 830/896–2211, (Nonreporting) **A**1 10 **F**11 30 34 39 44 50 56 65 68 75 86 87 97 98 101 103 130 132 135 146 149 157 **S** Texas Department of State Health Services, Austin, TX
Primary Contact: Leigh Ann Fitzpatrick, Superintendent
CFO: Laurie Harris, Chief Accountant
CMO: Matthew Faubion, M.D., Clinical Director
CNO: Amanda McDonald, MSN, Chief Nurse Executive
Web address: www.dshs.state.tx.us/mhhospitals/KerrvilleSH/default.shtm
**Control**: State, Government, Nonfederal **Service**: Psychiatric

**Staffed Beds: 218 Admissions: 89 Census: 215 Outpatient Visits: 0 Births: 0 Total Expense ($000): 35032 Payroll Expense ($000): 23921 Personnel: 551**

TX

✠ **PETERSON HEALTH (450007)**, 551 Hill Country Drive, Zip 78028–6085; tel. 830/896–4200, (Nonreporting) **A**1 10 **F**3 8 11 13 15 18 20 22 28 29 30 31 34 35 39 40 44 45 47 49 51 54 57 59 62 63 64 65 68 70 74 75 76 77 78 79 81 82 85 86 87 90 93 96 97 107 108 109 110 111 114 115 118 119 126 130 131 132 135 145 146 147 148 149 154 156 157 **P**8
Primary Contact: Cory Edmondson, President and Chief Executive Officer
CFO: Lisa Medovich, Chief Financial Officer
CMO: Al Roschmann, M.D., Chief of Staff
CIO: Brian Robicheaux, Chief Information Officer
CHR: Buddy Volpe, Director Human Resources
CNO: Kaeli Dressler, R.N., MSN, Chief Nursing Officer
Web address: www.petersonhealth.com
**Control:** Other not–for–profit (including NFP Corporation) **Service:** General medical and surgical

> **Staffed Beds: 124 Admissions: 4712 Census: 48 Outpatient Visits:** 147181 **Births:** 434 **Total Expense ($000):** 143656 **Payroll Expense ($000):** 57049 **Personnel:** 967

**PETERSON REGIONAL MEDICAL CENTER** See Peterson Health

**VETERANS AFFAIRS MED CENTER** See Kerrville Division

### KILLEEN—Bell County

✠ **ADVENTHEALTH CENTRAL TEXAS (450152)**, 2201 South Clear Creek Road, Zip 76549–4110; tel. 254/526–7523, (Includes METROPLEX BEHAVIORAL HEALTH CENTER, Mailing address: 2201 South Clear Creek Road, Killeen, Texas, Zip 76549–4110; tel. 254/628–1000; Kevin A. Roberts, FACHE, President and Chief Executive Officer), (Nonreporting) **A**1 3 10 **F**3 8 11 12 13 15 18 20 22 26 28 29 30 34 35 39 40 43 45 46 48 49 54 57 59 62 65 68 70 71 74 75 76 77 78 79 81 82 83 85 86 87 89 91 93 98 100 101 102 104 107 108 110 111 114 115 118 119 129 130 131 132 135 146 147 148 154 156 **S** AdventHealth, Altamonte Springs, FL
Primary Contact: Kevin A. Roberts, FACHE, President and Chief Executive Officer
CMO: Frederick Barnett, M.D., Chief of Staff
CHR: Brenda Coley, Executive Director
CNO: Tammy Rodriguez, Vice President Patient Care Services
Web address: www.mplex.org
**Control:** Church operated, Nongovernment, not–for–profit **Service:** General medical and surgical

> **Staffed Beds: 177 Admissions: 6742 Census: 73 Outpatient Visits:** 100563 **Births:** 1220 **Total Expense ($000):** 117819 **Payroll Expense ($000):** 47858 **Personnel:** 809

**METROPLEX ADVENTIST HOSPITAL** See Adventhealth Central Texas

### KINGSVILLE—Kleberg County

**CHRISTUS SPOHN HOSP KLEBERG** See Christus Spohn Hospital Kleberg

✠ **CHRISTUS SPOHN HOSPITAL KLEBERG (450163)**, 1311 General Cavazos Boulevard, Zip 78363–7130; tel. 361/595–1661, (Nonreporting) **A**1 10 20 **F**3 11 13 15 28 29 30 34 35 40 43 53 54 57 59 64 65 70 75 76 77 79 81 85 86 87 89 93 102 107 108 110 111 115 119 130 146 **P**8 **S** CHRISTUS Health, Irving, TX
Primary Contact: Richard Morin, R.N., Interim Chief Executive Officer
COO: David LeMonte, Vice President and Chief Operating Officer
CFO: Jessica Pena, Manager Finance
CHR: Mindy Soliz, Director Human Resource Strategy
CNO: LieutenantLaci Lasater, R.N., Chief Nursing Officer
Web address: www.christusspohn.org
**Control:** Church operated, Nongovernment, not–for–profit **Service:** General medical and surgical

> **Staffed Beds: 50 Admissions: 2663 Census: 30 Outpatient Visits:** 58548 **Births:** 309 **Total Expense ($000):** 36981 **Payroll Expense ($000):** 13782 **Personnel:** 189

### KINGWOOD—Montgomery County

✠ **HCA HOUSTON HEALTHCARE KINGWOOD (450775)**, 22999 U S Highway 59 North, Zip 77339; tel. 281/348–8000, (Includes HCA HOUSTON HEALTHCARE NORTH CYPRESS, Mailing address: 21214 Northwest Freeway, Cypress, Texas, Zip 77429–3373; tel. 832/912–3500; Jim Brown, Chief Executive Officer), (Nonreporting) **A**1 3 10 **F**3 12 13 18 19 20 22 24 26 28 29 34 35 40 41 42 46 47 48 49 57 59 70 72 74 76 77 79 81 85 87 89 90 91 92 96 107 108 111 114 115 118 119 126 130 132 146 148 149 154 **S** HCA Healthcare, Nashville, TN
Primary Contact: John Corbeil, Chief Executive Officer
CFO: Daniel E Davis, Chief Financial Officer
CMO: Eugene Ogrod, M.D., Chief Medical Officer
Web address: www.kingwoodmedical.com
**Control:** Corporation, Investor–owned (for–profit) **Service:** General medical and surgical

> **Staffed Beds: 563 Admissions: 31699 Census: 411 Outpatient Visits:** 254798 **Births:** 2605 **Total Expense ($000):** 535521 **Payroll Expense ($000):** 177971 **Personnel:** 2527

### KINGWOOD—Harris County

**KINGWOOD EMERGENCY HOSPITAL**, 23330 US 59 North, Zip 77339–3043; tel. 832/777–6165, (Nonreporting) **F**3 34 40 57 64 75 87 107 115 154
Primary Contact: Jeremy M. Brynes, Chief Executive Officer
**Control:** Partnership, Investor–owned (for–profit) **Service:** General medical and surgical

> **Staffed Beds: 3 Admissions: 158 Census: 1 Outpatient Visits:** 5607 **Births:** 0 **Total Expense ($000):** 9100 **Payroll Expense ($000):** 2264 **Personnel:** 30

**KINGWOOD HEALTH CENTER** See Kingwood Pines Hospital

### KINGWOOD—Montgomery County

**KINGWOOD MEDICAL CENTER** See Hca Houston Healthcare Kingwood

### KINGWOOD—Harris County

☐ **KINGWOOD PINES HOSPITAL (454103)**, 2001 Ladbrook Drive, Zip 77339–3004; tel. 281/404–1001, (Nonreporting) **A**1 10 **F**4 5 75 86 87 98 99 101 102 103 104 105 130 149 153 **S** Universal Health Services, Inc., King of Prussia, PA
Primary Contact: Kristin Harris, Chief Executive Officer
COO: Beryl Shorter, Chief Operating Officer, Director Performance Improvement
CFO: Sharon Corum, Chief Financial Officer
CMO: Bharath Raj, M.D., Medical Director
CHR: Robert Fontenot, Director Human Resources
CNO: Barbara Vasquez, Chief Nursing Officer
Web address: www.kingwoodpines.com
**Control:** Corporation, Investor–owned (for–profit) **Service:** Psychiatric

> **Staffed Beds: 52 Admissions: 3340 Census: 80 Outpatient Visits:** 2928 **Births:** 0 **Total Expense ($000):** 22966 **Payroll Expense ($000):** 11772 **Personnel:** 184

### KINGWOOD—Montgomery County

**KINGWOOD SPECIALTY HOSPITAL** See Memorial Hermann Surgical Hospital Kingwood

☐ **MEMORIAL HERMANN SURGICAL HOSPITAL KINGWOOD (670005)**, 300 Kingwood Medical Drive, Zip 77339–6400; tel. 281/312–4000, (Nonreporting) **A**1 10 **F**3 29 34 45 51 79 81 82 85 111 119 126 131 149 **P**2
Primary Contact: Teal A. Holden, Chief Executive Officer
CFO: Jay Michael Gomez, Chief Financial Officer
CNO: Shawna Fugler, R.N., Chief Nursing Officer
Web address: www.memorialhermannkingwood.com
**Control:** Partnership, Investor–owned (for–profit) **Service:** Surgical

> **Staffed Beds: 10 Admissions: 335 Census: 2 Outpatient Visits:** 9461 **Births:** 0 **Total Expense ($000):** 25817 **Payroll Expense ($000):** 5776 **Personnel:** 86

**TX**

---

## KNOX CITY—Knox County

⇧ **KNOX COUNTY HOSPITAL (451394)**, 701 South Fifth Street, Zip 79529–2107, Mailing Address: P.O. Box 608, Zip 79529–0608; tel. 940/657–3535, (Nonreporting) **A**10 18 20 21 **F**7 11 28 33 34 35 40 43 57 59 62 127 130 133 149 **P**6
Primary Contact: Stephen A. Kuehler, Administrator
CFO: Dan Offutt, Manager Finance
CMO: Ezekiel Duke, M.D., Chief of Staff
CNO: Sheila Kuehler, R.N., Director of Nursing
Web address: www.knoxcountyhospital-texas.com
**Control:** Hospital district or authority, Government, Nonfederal **Service:** General medical and surgical

**Staffed Beds:** 14 **Admissions:** 92 **Census:** 1 **Outpatient Visits:** 32250 **Births:** 0 **Total Expense ($000):** 27266 **Payroll Expense ($000):** 6031 **Personnel:** 87

## KYLE—Hays County

✠ **ASCENSION SETON HAYS (670056)**, 6001 Kyle Parkway, Zip 78640–6112; tel. 512/504–5000, (Nonreporting) **A**1 3 5 10 **F**3 11 12 13 15 17 18 20 22 24 28 29 30 34 35 40 41 43 45 46 47 48 49 50 53 54 56 57 59 62 63 64 68 70 72 74 76 78 79 81 82 84 85 87 93 100 107 108 110 111 115 119 126 129 130 131 132 135 143 144 145 146 148 154 156 **S** Ascension Healthcare, Saint Louis, MO
Primary Contact: Katherine Henderson, Regional Hospital President
COO: Neal Kelley, Vice President and Chief Operating Officer
CNO: Nikki Rivers, R.N., Regional Chief Nursing Officer, South Market
Web address: www.seton.net/locations/seton_medical_center_hays/
**Control:** Church operated, Nongovernment, not–for–profit **Service:** General medical and surgical

**Staffed Beds:** 150 **Admissions:** 7798 **Census:** 92 **Outpatient Visits:** 74300 **Births:** 1084 **Total Expense ($000):** 148458 **Payroll Expense ($000):** 42157 **Personnel:** 849

**SETON MEDICAL CENTER HAYS** See Ascension Seton Hays

✠ **WARM SPRINGS REHABILITATION HOSPITAL OF KYLE (673057)**, 5980 Kyle Parkway, Zip 78640–2400; tel. 512/262–0821, (Nonreporting) **A**1 **F**3 29 74 75 79 90 93 95 96 130 131 132 148 154 **S** Post Acute Medical, LLC, Enola, PA
Primary Contact: Duke Saldivar, FACHE, Chief Executive Officer
Web address: www.warmsprings.org/our-facilities/outpatient-rehabilitation/warm-springs-rehabilitation-center-kyle/
**Control:** Corporation, Investor–owned (for–profit) **Service:** Rehabilitation

**Staffed Beds:** 40 **Admissions:** 1036 **Census:** 33 **Outpatient Visits:** 7088 **Births:** 0 **Total Expense ($000):** 16280 **Payroll Expense ($000):** 7746 **Personnel:** 150

## LA GRANGE—Fayette County

**FAYETTE MEMORIAL HOSPITAL** See St. Mark'S Medical Center

★ **ST. MARK'S MEDICAL CENTER (670004)**, One St Mark's Place, Zip 78945; tel. 979/242–2200, (Nonreporting) **A**5 10 **F**3 11 15 28 29 34 40 45 50 57 59 64 74 75 77 79 81 85 93 107 108 110 111 114 119 130 132 133 145 147 **P**6 **S** Community Hospital Corporation, Plano, TX
Primary Contact: Barry Harding, Interim Chief Executive Officer
COO: Carol Drozd, Chief Operating Officer
CFO: Barbara Brooks, Interim Chief Financial Officer
CMO: Russell Juno, M.D., Chief of Staff
CHR: Tammy Oehlke, Director Human Resources
Web address: www.smmctx.org
**Control:** Other not–for–profit (including NFP Corporation) **Service:** General medical and surgical

**Staffed Beds:** 38 **Admissions:** 1056 **Census:** 10 **Outpatient Visits:** 37657 **Births:** 0 **Total Expense ($000):** 28052 **Payroll Expense ($000):** 10468 **Personnel:** 145

## LAKE JACKSON—Brazoria County

**BRAZOSPORT REGIONAL HEALTH SYSTEM** See Chi St. Luke's Health Brazosport

## CHI ST. LUKE'S HEALTH BRAZOSPORT (450072), 100 Medical Drive,

✠ **CHI ST. LUKE'S HEALTH BRAZOSPORT (450072)**, 100 Medical Drive, Zip 77566–5674; tel. 979/297–4411, (Nonreporting) **A**1 10 **F**3 11 13 15 18 20 22 28 29 30 31 34 37 40 41 43 45 47 48 49 51 54 59 60 62 64 65 70 74 75 76 78 79 81 82 85 86 87 90 91 93 94 107 108 110 111 114 115 117 118 119 120 121 123 129 130 131 132 146 147 148 149 154 **P**8 **S** CommonSpirit Health, Chicago, IL
Primary Contact: Al Guevara Jr, FACHE, President
CFO: Chuck Jeffress, Vice President Fiscal Services
CMO: Michael Gilliand, M.D., Chief of Staff
CIO: Todd Edwards, Director Information Management Systems
CHR: Christopher Calia, Vice President Human Resources
CNO: Shannon Haltom, Vice President, Patient Care Services
Web address: www.chistlukesbrazosport.org
**Control:** Church operated, Nongovernment, not–for–profit **Service:** General medical and surgical

**Staffed Beds:** 103 **Admissions:** 3600 **Census:** 38 **Outpatient Visits:** 120086 **Births:** 390 **Total Expense ($000):** 72973 **Payroll Expense ($000):** 29500 **Personnel:** 551

## LAKEWAY—Travis County

✠ △ **BAYLOR SCOTT & WHITE INSTITUTE FOR REHABILITATION - LAKEWAY (673058)**, 2000 Medical Drive, Zip 78734–4200; tel. 512/263–4500, (Nonreporting) **A**1 7 **F**3 29 30 60 68 90 91 96 119 132 148 154 **S** Select Medical Corporation, Mechanicsburg, PA
Primary Contact: Deborah Hopps, R.N., FACHE, Chief Executive Officer
CMO: Maria Elena Arizmendez, M.D., Medical Director
CHR: Debbie Belcher, Director Human Resources
CNO: Ramon Austria, R.N., Chief Nursing Officer
Web address: www.vrhlaketravis.com
**Control:** Partnership, Investor–owned (for–profit) **Service:** Rehabilitation

**Staffed Beds:** 36 **Admissions:** 468 **Census:** 15 **Outpatient Visits:** 0 **Births:** 0 **Total Expense ($000):** 13331 **Payroll Expense ($000):** 5501 **Personnel:** 85

**LAKEWAY REGIONAL MEDICAL CENTER** See Baylor Scott & White Medical Center - Lakeway

**VIBRA REHABILITATION HOSPITAL LAKE TRAVIS** See Baylor Scott & White Institute for Rehabilitation - Lakeway

## LAMESA—Dawson County

**MEDICAL ARTS HOSPITAL (450489)**, 2200 North Bryan Avenue, Zip 79331–2451; tel. 806/872–2183, (Nonreporting) **A**10 20
Primary Contact: Letha Stokes, Chief Executive Officer
COO: Jo Beth Smith, Chief Operating Officer
CMO: Michael Sprys, D.O., Chief of Staff
CHR: Traci Brown, Director Human Resources
CNO: Diane Sherrill, R.N., Director of Nursing
Web address: www.medicalartshospital.org
**Control:** Hospital district or authority, Government, Nonfederal **Service:** General medical and surgical

**Staffed Beds:** 22

## LAMPASAS—Lampasas County

✠ **ADVENTHEALTH ROLLINS BROOK (451323)**, 608 North Key Avenue, Zip 76550–1106, Mailing Address: P.O. Box 589, Zip 76550–0032; tel. 512/556–3682, (Nonreporting) **A**1 10 18 **F**3 8 15 29 35 40 43 45 46 61 81 85 87 93 97 107 110 111 114 119 130 131 133 146 **P**4 8 **S** AdventHealth, Altamonte Springs, FL
Primary Contact: Ashley Underwood, Administrator
CFO: Robert Brock, Chief Financial Officer and Vice President
CMO: Don Daniels, M.D., Chief Medical Officer
CIO: Carl Elkins, Director Information Technology
CHR: Brenda Coley, Executive Director
Web address: www.mplex.org
**Control:** Church operated, Nongovernment, not–for–profit **Service:** General medical and surgical

**Staffed Beds:** 35 **Admissions:** 481 **Census:** 9 **Outpatient Visits:** 13404 **Births:** 0 **Total Expense ($000):** 16292 **Payroll Expense ($000):** 4889 **Personnel:** 40

**ROLLINS BROOK COMMUNITY HOSPITAL** See Adventhealth Rollins Brook

**TX**

*Many Facility Codes have changed. Please refer to the AHA Guide Code Chart.* © 2021 AHA Guide

**LANCASTER—Dallas County**

⇑ **CRESCENT MEDICAL CENTER LANCASTER (670090)**, 2600 West Pleasant Run Road, Zip 75146–1114; tel. 972/230–8888, (Nonreporting) **A**10 21 **F**3 29 30 34 40 51 57 59 60 64 68 70 77 79 81 82 85 107 108 111 114 119 129 130 143 148
Primary Contact: Raji Kumar, Chief Executive Officer
CFO: Becky Speight, Chief Financial Officer and Administrator
Web address: www.cmcl.us/
**Control**: Partnership, Investor–owned (for–profit) **Service**: General medical and surgical

**Staffed Beds**: 35 **Admissions**: 1063 **Census**: 9 **Outpatient Visits**: 26388 **Births**: 0 **Total Expense ($000)**: 43690 **Payroll Expense ($000)**: 13192 **Personnel**: 237

**LAREDO—Webb County**

**COLUMBIA DOCTORS HOSPITAL** See Doctors Hospital of Laredo

☐ **DOCTORS HOSPITAL OF LAREDO (450643)**, 10700 McPherson Road, Zip 78045–6268; tel. 956/523–2000, (Nonreporting) **A**1 2 10 **F**3 11 12 13 15 18 20 22 24 26 28 29 31 32 34 35 37 39 40 42 43 45 48 49 50 54 57 59 60 63 64 70 71 72 74 75 76 77 78 79 81 85 87 89 90 91 107 108 111 115 118 119 121 126 129 130 131 132 146 147 148 154 156 **P**5 7 **S** Universal Health Services, Inc., King of Prussia, PA
Primary Contact: Emma Krabill, Chief Executive Officer
COO: Raymond Ramos, FACHE, Chief Operating Officer
CFO: Faraz Khan, Chief Financial Officer
CMO: Santiago Gutierrez, M.D., Chief Medical Officer
CIO: Maribel Mata, Director Information Services
CHR: Roseann Figueroa, Director Human Resources
CNO: Daman Mott, MSN, Chief Nursing Officer
Web address: www.doctorshospitallaredo.com
**Control**: Partnership, Investor–owned (for–profit) **Service**: General medical and surgical

**Staffed Beds**: 183 **Admissions**: 7169 **Census**: 97 **Outpatient Visits**: 130422 **Births**: 1861 **Total Expense ($000)**: 127528 **Payroll Expense ($000)**: 49678 **Personnel**: 767

**LAREDO HEALTH CENTER** See Laredo Medical Center

✠ **LAREDO MEDICAL CENTER (450029)**, 1700 East Saunders Avenue, Zip 78041–5474, Mailing Address: P.O. Box 2068, Zip 78044–2068; tel. 956/796–5000, (Total facility includes 18 beds in nursing home–type unit) (Nonreporting) **A**1 2 3 10 19 **F**3 8 11 12 13 15 18 20 22 24 26 28 29 30 31 34 35 40 43 45 46 49 50 51 53 54 57 59 60 64 65 68 70 72 74 75 76 77 78 79 81 85 86 87 89 91 92 93 107 108 110 111 114 119 120 121 123 126 128 132 135 144 146 147 148 149 **S** Community Health Systems, Inc., Franklin, TN
Primary Contact: Enrique Gallegos, Chief Executive Officer
CIO: Joe Rivera, Chief Information Technology Officer
Web address: www.laredomedical.com
**Control**: Corporation, Investor–owned (for–profit) **Service**: General medical and surgical

**Staffed Beds**: 326 **Admissions**: 13608 **Census**: 210 **Outpatient Visits**: 139346 **Births**: 3238 **Total Expense ($000)**: 187083 **Payroll Expense ($000)**: 65071 **Personnel**: 1036

☐ **LAREDO REHABILITATION HOSPITAL (673059)**, 2005a East Bustamante Street, Zip 78041; tel. 956/764–8555, (Nonreporting) **A**1 **F**3 29 75 90 91 96 **S** Ernest Health, Inc., Albuquerque, NM
Primary Contact: Hanna Huang, Administrator and Chief Operating Officer
Web address: www.lrh.ernesthealth.com
**Control**: Corporation, Investor–owned (for–profit) **Service**: Rehabilitation

**Staffed Beds**: 20 **Admissions**: 453 **Census**: 18 **Outpatient Visits**: 0 **Births**: 0 **Total Expense ($000)**: 6786 **Payroll Expense ($000)**: 3616 **Personnel**: 55

☐ **LAREDO SPECIALTY HOSPITAL (452096)**, 2005 Bustamente Street, Zip 78041–5470; tel. 956/753–5353, (Nonreporting) **A**1 10 **F**1 3 29 75 85 91 96 130 **S** Ernest Health, Inc., Albuquerque, NM
Primary Contact: Hanna Huang, Administrator and Chief Operating Officer
CFO: Robert Voss, Chief Financial Officer
CMO: Marisa Guerrero, Director Human Resources
Web address: www.lsh.ernesthealth.com
**Control**: Partnership, Investor–owned (for–profit) **Service**: Acute long–term care hospital

**Staffed Beds**: 40 **Admissions**: 407 **Census**: 26 **Outpatient Visits**: 0 **Births**: 0 **Total Expense ($000)**: 14835 **Payroll Expense ($000)**: 5364 **Personnel**: 108

**LEAGUE CITY—Harris County**

**CLEAR LAKE REGIONAL MEDICAL CENTER** See Hca Houston Healthcare Clear Lake

**LEAGUE CITY—Galveston County**

**DEVEREUX HOSPITAL** See Devereux Texas Treatment Network

☐ **DEVEREUX TEXAS TREATMENT NETWORK (454085)**, 1150 Devereux Drive, Zip 77573–2043; tel. 281/335–1000, (Nonreporting) **A**1 3 10 **F**4 29 32 35 38 53 59 75 86 87 98 101 106 130 132 134 **S** Devereux, Villanova, PA
Primary Contact: Pamela E. Helm, Executive Director
Web address: www.devereux.org
**Control**: Other not–for–profit (including NFP Corporation) **Service**: Children's hospital psychiatric

**Staffed Beds**: 31 **Admissions**: 33 **Census**: 34 **Outpatient Visits**: 0 **Births**: 0 **Total Expense ($000)**: 6841 **Payroll Expense ($000)**: 2457 **Personnel**: 55

**LEAGUE CITY—Harris County**

⊞ **HCA HOUSTON HEALTHCARE CLEAR LAKE (450617)**, 620 Power St., Zip 77598–4220, Mailing Address: 500 West Medical Center Boulevard, Webster, Zip 77598–4220; tel. 281/332–2511, (Includes ALVIN DIAGNOSTIC and URGENT CARE CENTER, Mailing address: 301 Medic Lane, Alvin, Texas, Zip 77511–5597; tel. 281/331–6141; MAINLAND MEDICAL CENTER, Mailing address: 6801 'E' 'F' Lowry Expressway, Texas City, Texas, Zip 77591; tel. 409/938–5000; Tripp Montalbo, Chief Executive Officer), (Nonreporting) **A**1 2 3 5 10 **F**3 11 12 13 17 18 19 20 22 24 26 28 29 31 34 35 40 41 42 43 44 45 46 47 49 50 51 56 57 59 60 64 70 72 74 75 76 78 79 81 85 86 87 88 89 90 91 93 94 96 107 108 110 111 114 115 119 124 126 129 130 132 135 146 147 148 149 **S** HCA Healthcare, Nashville, TN
Primary Contact: Todd Caliva, FACHE, Chief Executive Officer
CFO: Jeff Sliwinski, Chief Financial Officer
CMO: Richard Marietta, M.D., Medical Director
CIO: Ley Samson, Director Management Information Systems
CHR: Brad Horst, Director Human Resources
Web address: www.clearlakermc.com
**Control**: Partnership, Investor–owned (for–profit) **Service**: General medical and surgical

**Staffed Beds**: 591 **Admissions**: 31318 **Census**: 454 **Outpatient Visits**: 175891 **Births**: 3211 **Total Expense ($000)**: 416963 **Payroll Expense ($000)**: 188038 **Personnel**: 2022

**LEVELLAND—Hockley County**

★ **COVENANT HOSPITAL-LEVELLAND (450755)**, 1900 College Avenue, Zip 79336–6508; tel. 806/894–4963, (Nonreporting) **A**10 **F**7 11 13 15 29 30 34 40 43 45 57 59 64 65 68 75 76 77 81 85 87 93 97 107 110 115 119 127 133 149 **P**3 **S** Providence St. Joseph Health, Renton, WA
Primary Contact: Bruce White, Administrator
CMO: Harry Weaver, M.D., Chief of Staff
CIO: Kevin Elmore, Chief Information Officer
CHR: Tammy Franklin, Manager Personnel and Marketing
CNO: Connie Thomman, Director of Nursing
Web address: www.https://www.covenanthealth.org/contact-us/locations/covenant-health-levelland2/
**Control**: Church operated, Nongovernment, not–for–profit **Service**: General medical and surgical

**Staffed Beds**: 26 **Admissions**: 729 **Census**: 6 **Outpatient Visits**: 35848 **Births**: 217 **Total Expense ($000)**: 20703 **Payroll Expense ($000)**: 10168 **Personnel**: 189

**METHODIST HOSPITAL-LEVELLAND** See Covenant Hospital-Levelland

**TX**

**Hospital, Medicare Provider Number, Address, Telephone, Approval, Facility, and Physician Codes, Health Care System**

★ American Hospital Association (AHA) membership
☐ The Joint Commission accreditation
○ Healthcare Facilities Accreditation Program
◇ DNV Healthcare Inc. accreditation
⇑ Center for Improvement in Healthcare Quality Accreditation
△ Commission on Accreditation of Rehabilitation Facilities (CARF) accreditation

© 2021 AHA Guide    *Many Facility Codes have changed. Please refer to the AHA Guide Code Chart.*    Hospitals **A695**

## LEWISVILLE—Denton County

**MEDICAL CENTER OF LEWISVILLE** See Medical City Lewisville

☒ **MEDICAL CITY LEWISVILLE (450669)**, 500 West Main, Zip 75057–3699; tel. 972/420–1000, (Nonreporting) **A**1 10 **F**3 12 13 18 20 22 24 26 28 29 30 34 35 37 40 41 42 43 45 46 47 49 50 56 57 59 60 63 65 68 70 72 74 75 76 77 78 79 81 82 84 87 89 90 91 92 93 96 97 107 108 110 111 114 119 126 129 130 132 135 146 147 148 149 154 **S** HCA Healthcare, Nashville, TN
Primary Contact: LaSharndra Barbarin, Chief Executive Officer
CFO: Lisa Brodbeck, Chief Financial Officer
CIO: Shirley Archambeault, Chief Information Officer
CHR: Dara Biegert, Vice President Human Resources
CNO: Lynn O'Neill, R.N., Chief Nursing Officer
Web address: www.lewisvillemedical.com
**Control**: Corporation, Investor–owned (for–profit) **Service**: General medical and surgical

**Staffed Beds**: 156 **Admissions**: 7217 **Census**: 90 **Outpatient Visits**: 87357 **Births**: 1285 **Total Expense ($000)**: 144950 **Payroll Expense ($000)**: 55208 **Personnel**: 678

## LIBERTY—Liberty County

**LIBERTY DAYTON REGIONAL MEDICAL CENTER (451375)**, 1353 North Travis, Zip 77575–3549; tel. 936/336–7316, (Nonreporting) **A**10 18 **F**3 29 40 45 59 64 89 107 115 119 127 128 130 133
Primary Contact: Ray Mason, Chief Executive Officer
CFO: Hal Mayo, Chief Financial Officer
CMO: Don Callens, M.D., Chief Medical Officer
CNO: Cindy Griffin, Chief Nursing Officer
Web address: www.libertydaytonrmc.com
**Control**: Hospital district or authority, Government, Nonfederal **Service**: General medical and surgical

**Staffed Beds**: 15 **Admissions**: 91 **Census**: 1 **Outpatient Visits**: 21746 **Births**: 0 **Total Expense ($000)**: 6842 **Payroll Expense ($000)**: 4690 **Personnel**: 104

**LIBERTY-DAYTON REGIONAL MEDICAL CENTER** See Liberty Dayton Regional Medical Center

## LITTLEFIELD—Lamb County

**LAMB HEALTHCARE CENTER (450698)**, 1500 South Sunset, Zip 79339–4899; tel. 806/385–6411, (Nonreporting) **A**10 20 **F**3 35 40 43 50 57 59 64 66 75 76 81 86 87 107 114 119 127 132 133 134 146 147 149 156
Primary Contact: Cindy Klein, Chief Executive Officer
CMO: Isabel Molina, M.D., Chief Medical Officer
CHR: Joan Williams, Administrative Assistant/Human Resources
CNO: Stacie Styron, Chief Nursing Officer
Web address: www.littlefieldtexas.net/index.php/our-community/lamb-healthcare-center
**Control**: County, Government, Nonfederal **Service**: General medical and surgical

**Staffed Beds**: 41 **Admissions**: 285 **Census**: 3 **Outpatient Visits**: 27875 **Births**: 74 **Total Expense ($000)**: 13068 **Payroll Expense ($000)**: 4078 **Personnel**: 116

## LIVE OAK—Bexar County

**VILLAGE OAKS MEDICAL CENTER** See Northeast Methodist Hospital

## LIVINGSTON—Polk County

☒ **CHI ST. LUKE'S HEALTH MEMORIAL LIVINGSTON (450395)**, 1717 Highway 59 Loop North, Zip 77351–5710, Mailing Address: P.O. Box 1257, Zip 77351–0022; tel. 936/329–8700, (Nonreporting) **A**1 10 **F**3 11 13 15 29 34 35 40 42 43 45 46 50 57 59 64 68 70 74 75 76 79 81 85 87 89 107 108 110 111 114 119 129 130 132 146 149 156 **S** CommonSpirit Health, Chicago, IL
Primary Contact: Kristi Froese, R.N., Vice President Clinical Operations
CFO: Duane Miller, Chief Financial Officer
CMO: Verner Nellsch, M.D., Chief of Staff
CIO: Kathy DeFiguieredo, Director, Information Technology
CHR: Heather Jordan, Director Human Resources
CNO: Kristi Froese, R.N., Chief Nursing Officer
Web address: www.https://www.chistlukeshealthmemorial.org/centers/livingston
**Control**: Other not–for–profit (including NFP Corporation) **Service**: General medical and surgical

**Staffed Beds**: 66 **Admissions**: 1936 **Census**: 17 **Outpatient Visits**: 49655 **Births**: 391 **Total Expense ($000)**: 41499 **Payroll Expense ($000)**: 14680 **Personnel**: 221

**MEMORIAL MEDICAL CENTER - LIVINGSTON** See Chi St. Luke's Health Memorial Livingston

## LLANO—Llano County

★ **BAYLOR SCOTT & WHITE MEDICAL CENTER - LLANO (450219)**, 200 West Ollie Street, Zip 78643–2628; tel. 325/247–5040, (Nonreporting) **A**10 20 **F**3 7 29 40 85 107 115 127 129 130 149 154 **S** Baylor Scott & White Health, Dallas, TX
Primary Contact: Timothy A. Ols, FACHE, Chief Executive Officer
COO: Royce Bramer Owens, Chief Operating Officer
CFO: Jennie Campbell, Chief Financial Officer
CMO: Paul Cook, M.D., Chief Medical Officer
CIO: Rodney Lott, Director Management Information Systems and Facility Operations
CHR: Jane Frasure, Human Resources
CNO: Betsy B Patterson, R.N., FACHE, Chief Nursing Officer
Web address: www.bwshealth.com
**Control**: Other not–for–profit (including NFP Corporation) **Service**: General medical and surgical

**Staffed Beds**: 10 **Admissions**: 181 **Census**: 1 **Outpatient Visits**: 5836 **Births**: 0 **Total Expense ($000)**: 27309 **Payroll Expense ($000)**: 12956 **Personnel**: 132

**SCOTT & WHITE HOSPITAL - LLANO** See Baylor Scott & White Medical Center - Llano

## LOCKNEY—Floyd County

**LOCKNEY GENERAL HOSPITAL** See W. J. Mangold Memorial Hospital

★ **W. J. MANGOLD MEMORIAL HOSPITAL (451337)**, 320 North Main Street, Zip 79241–0037, Mailing Address: Box 37, Zip 79241–0037; tel. 806/652–3373, (Nonreporting) **A**10 18 **F**3 35 40 43 45 53 57 59 62 64 65 81 85 93 97 107 111 119 127 130 133 148 157 **P**4
Primary Contact: Vincent DiFranco, Chief Executive Officer
CFO: Alyssa McCarter, Chief Financial Officer
CMO: Kevin T Stennett, M.D., Chief of Staff
CIO: David Green, Manager Information Technology
CNO: Billie Hendrix, R.N., Director of Nursing
Web address: www.mangoldmemorial.org
**Control**: Hospital district or authority, Government, Nonfederal **Service**: General medical and surgical

**Staffed Beds**: 25 **Admissions**: 266 **Census**: 3 **Outpatient Visits**: 21828 **Births**: 0 **Total Expense ($000)**: 11307 **Payroll Expense ($000)**: 4674 **Personnel**: 115

## LONGVIEW—Gregg County

**AUDUBON BEHAVIORAL HOSPITAL LONGVIEW** See Oceans Behavioral Hospital Longview

**BEHAVIORAL HOSPITAL OF LONGVIEW** See Magnolia Behavioral Hospital of East Texas

**COLUMBIA LONGVIEW REG MED CTR** See Longview Regional Medical Center

**EVEREST REHABILITATION HOSPITAL LONGVIEW**, 701 East Loop 281, Zip 75605–5006; tel. 430/240–4600, (Nonreporting) **A**22 **S** Everest Rehabilitation Hospitals, LLC, Dallas, TX
Primary Contact: Jay Lindsey, Chief Executive Officer
Web address: www.everestrehab.com
**Control**: Corporation, Investor–owned (for–profit) **Service**: Rehabilitation

**Staffed Beds**: 36

**GOOD SHEPHERD MEDICAL CENTER** See Christus Good Shepherd Medical Center

**LONGVIEW REGIONAL MEDICAL CENTER (450702)**, 2901 North Fourth Street, Zip 75605–5191, Mailing Address: P.O. Box 14000, Zip 75607–4000; tel. 903/758–1818, (Nonreporting) **A**1 3 10 **F**3 8 11 13 15 18 20 22 24 26 28 29 30 31 34 35 37 39 40 43 45 46 47 49 50 57 59 61 64 65 70 72 74 75 76 77 78 79 81 85 86 87 89 91 93 107 108 110 111 114 115 118 119 120 126 130 146 148 **P**8 **S** Community Health Systems, Inc., Franklin, TN
Primary Contact: Douglas R. Luckett, Interim Chief Executive Officer
COO: Roy Finch, Chief Operating Officer
CFO: Todd Johnson, Chief Financial Officer
CMO: Kenneth McClure, M.D., Chief of Staff
CIO: Keith Jarvis, Director Information Systems
CHR: Terry Hardan, Director Human Resources
CNO: Stephanie Foster, MSN, R.N., Chief Nursing Officer
Web address: www.longviewregional.com
**Control:** Partnership, Investor–owned (for–profit) **Service:** General medical and surgical

**Staffed Beds: 168 Admissions: 11078 Census: 135 Outpatient Visits: 112668 Births: 2011 Total Expense ($000): 191209 Payroll Expense ($000): 59508 Personnel: 893**

**MAGNOLIA BEHAVIORAL HOSPITAL OF EAST TEXAS (454143)**, 22 Bermuda Lane, Zip 75605–2902; tel. 903/291–3456, (Nonreporting)
Primary Contact: Allison Debruycker, Administrator
Web address: www.magnoliabehavioralhospital.com/
**Control:** Corporation, Investor–owned (for–profit) **Service:** Psychiatric

**Staffed Beds: 20**

**OCEANS BEHAVIORAL HOSPITAL LONGVIEW (454117)**, 615 Clinic Drive, Zip 75605–5172; tel. 903/212–3105, (Nonreporting) **A**1 10 **F**29 64 98 100 101 103 104 130 132 149 153 154 **S** Oceans Healthcare, Plano, TX
Primary Contact: Lauren Weber, Administrator
Web address: www.oceanslongview.com/
**Control:** Corporation, Investor–owned (for–profit) **Service:** Psychiatric

**Staffed Beds: 24 Admissions: 584 Census: 22 Outpatient Visits: 25292 Births: 0 Total Expense ($000): 5886 Payroll Expense ($000): 2948 Personnel: 113**

**SELECT SPECIALTY HOSPITAL-LONGVIEW (452087)**, 700 East Marshall Avenue, 1st Floor, Zip 75601–5580; tel. 903/315–1100, (Nonreporting) **A**1 10 **F**1 3 28 29 75 77 85 91 92 130 148 **S** Select Medical Corporation, Mechanicsburg, PA
Primary Contact: Andrew Meade, Chief Executive Officer
Web address: www.longview.selectspecialtyhospitals.com/
**Control:** Corporation, Investor–owned (for–profit) **Service:** Acute long–term care hospital

**Staffed Beds: 32 Admissions: 304 Census: 21 Outpatient Visits: 0 Births: 0 Total Expense ($000): 12105 Payroll Expense ($000): 5531 Personnel: 75**

## LUBBOCK—Lubbock County

**COVENANT CHILDREN'S HOSPITAL (453306)**, 4015 22nd Place, Zip 79410; tel. 806/725–1011, (Nonreporting) **A**1 3 5 10 **F**3 4 19 21 23 25 27 30 31 32 40 41 43 50 59 70 72 73 76 78 81 88 89 98 102 104 154 **P**8 **S** Providence St. Joseph Health, Renton, WA
Primary Contact: Amy Thompson, M.D., Chief Executive Officer
COO: Clay Thomas, Chief Operating Officer
CMO: Craig Rhyne, M.D., FACS, Chief Medical Officer
CIO: Jim Reid, Vice President and Chief Information Officer
CHR: Chris Shaver, Vice President Human Resources
Web address: www.covenanthealth.org/About-Us/Facilities/Childrens-Hospital.aspx
**Control:** Other not–for–profit (including NFP Corporation) **Service:** Children's general medical and surgical

**Staffed Beds: 204 Admissions: 5440 Census: 76 Outpatient Visits: 119326 Births: 4136 Total Expense ($000): 198315 Payroll Expense ($000): 56467 Personnel: 793**

**COVENANT MEDICAL CENTER (450040)**, 3615 19th Street, Zip 79410–1203, Mailing Address: P.O. Box 1201, Zip 79408–1201; tel. 806/725–0000, (Includes COVENANT MEDICAL CENTER-LAKESIDE, Mailing address: 4000 24th Street, Lubbock, Texas, Zip 79410–1894; tel. 806/725–0000), (Nonreporting) **A**1 3 5 10 **F**7 8 12 15 17 18 19 20 22 23 26 27 28 30 34 35 37 39 40 42 43 46 47 48 49 50 51 53 54 55 57 58 59 60 61 63 64 65 68 70 71 74 75 77 78 79 80 81 82 83 84 85 86 87 91 92 93 94 107 108 109 111 114 115 116 117 119 120 121 123 129 130 131 132 135 143 144 146 147 148 **P**6 8 **S** Providence St. Joseph Health, Renton, WA
Primary Contact: Walt Cathey, Chief Executive Officer
CFO: John A Grigson, Vice President and Chief Financial Officer
CMO: Craig Rhyne, M.D., FACS, Chief Medical Officer
CIO: Troy Pratt, Information Technology Site Director
CHR: Chris Shaver, Vice President Human Resources
CNO: Karen Baggerly, Chief Nursing Officer and Vice President
Web address: www.covenanthealth.org
**Control:** Other not–for–profit (including NFP Corporation) **Service:** General medical and surgical

**Staffed Beds: 380 Admissions: 17641 Census: 263 Outpatient Visits: 283421 Births: 0 Total Expense ($000): 397302 Payroll Expense ($000): 136512 Personnel: 2449**

★ **COVENANT SPECIALTY HOSPITAL (452102)**, 3815 20th Street, Zip 79410–1235; tel. 806/725–9200, (Nonreporting) **A**10 **F**1 3 29 30 31 60 63 68 75 77 78 79 87 119 130 143 148 **P**8 **S** Providence St. Joseph Health, Renton, WA
Primary Contact: Ely Perea, Director and Chief Executive Officer
CFO: John Carigson, Chief Financial Officer
CMO: Naidu Chekuru, M.D., Chief Medical Officer
CHR: Chris Shaver, Vice President Human Resources
Web address: www.covenanthealth.org/view/Facilities/Specialty_Hospital
**Control:** Partnership, Investor–owned (for–profit) **Service:** Acute long–term care hospital

**Staffed Beds: 56 Admissions: 391 Census: 28 Outpatient Visits: 0 Births: 0 Total Expense ($000): 18645 Payroll Expense ($000): 7777 Personnel: 109**

**GRACE MEDICAL CENTER (450162)**, 2412 50th Street, Zip 79412–2494; tel. 806/788–4100, (Nonreporting) **A**1 5 10 **F**3 8 11 12 15 29 34 35 37 40 45 47 49 50 51 54 55 59 64 65 70 75 79 81 82 85 87 107 108 110 111 114 115 118 119 130 135 146 149 157 **S** Providence St. Joseph Health, Renton, WA
Primary Contact: Vanessa Reasoner, Chief Executive Officer
CMO: Howard Beck, M.D., Chief of Staff
CIO: Jason Derouen, Director Management Information Systems
CHR: Sally Charles, Coordinator Human Resources
Web address: www.gracehealthsystem.com
**Control:** Other not–for–profit (including NFP Corporation) **Service:** General medical and surgical

**Staffed Beds: 43 Admissions: 738 Census: 5 Outpatient Visits: 100512 Births: 0 Total Expense ($000): 55415 Payroll Expense ($000): 11616 Personnel: 261**

**HIGHLAND COMMUNITY HOSPITAL** See Grace Medical Center

⇑ **LUBBOCK GEN HOSPITAL** See University Medical Center

**LUBBOCK HEART & SURGICAL HOSPITAL (450876)**, 4810 North Loop 289, Zip 79416–3025; tel. 806/687–7777, (Nonreporting) **A**5 10 **F**3 17 18 20 22 24 26 28 29 34 37 40 45 57 59 75 77 79 81 82 85 107 108 115 119 130 131 148 149
Primary Contact: Maridel Acosta-Cruz, Chief Executive Officer
Web address: www.https://lubbockheart.com/
**Control:** Partnership, Investor–owned (for–profit) **Service:** Heart

**Staffed Beds: 73 Admissions: 2569 Census: 22 Outpatient Visits: 37252 Births: 0 Total Expense ($000): 84426 Payroll Expense ($000): 23628 Personnel: 407**

**LUBBOCK HEART HOSPITAL** See Lubbock Heart & Surgical Hospital

**METHODIST CHILDREN'S HOSPITAL** See Covenant Children's Hospital

**METHODIST HOSPITAL** See Covenant Medical Center

---

**Hospital, Medicare Provider Number, Address, Telephone, Approval, Facility, and Physician Codes, Health Care System**

★ American Hospital Association (AHA) membership
□ The Joint Commission accreditation
○ Healthcare Facilities Accreditation Program
◇ DNV Healthcare Inc. accreditation
⇑ Center for Improvement in Healthcare Quality Accreditation
△ Commission on Accreditation of Rehabilitation Facilities (CARF) accreditation

☐ **SOUTH PLAINS REHABILITATION HOSPITAL (673070)**, 5406 Colgate Street, Zip 79416; tel. 806/507–3500, (Data for 214 days) (Nonreporting) **A**1 **F**3 29 56 60 74 75 77 79 82 87 90 96 100 130 132 148 149 154 157 **S** Encompass Health Corporation, Birmingham, AL
Primary Contact: Christopher Wortham, Chief Executive Officer
Web address: www.https://www.encompasshealth.com/locations/southplainsrehab
**Control**: Partnership, Investor–owned (for–profit) **Service**: Rehabilitation

> **Staffed Beds:** 40 **Admissions:** 596 **Census:** 35 **Outpatient Visits:** 0
> **Births:** 0 **Total Expense ($000):** 9681 **Payroll Expense ($000):** 5147
> **Personnel:** 145

**ST MARY OF THE PLAINS HOSPITAL** See Covenant Medical Center-Lakeside

☐ **SUNRISE CANYON HOSPITAL (454093)**, 1950 Aspen Ave, Zip 79404–1211, Mailing Address: P.O. Box 2828, Zip 79408–2828; tel. 806/740–1420, (Nonreporting) **A**1 10 **F**35 38 98 101 130 135 154
Primary Contact: Leonard Valderaz, Administrator
CFO: Jerome Flores, Chief Financial Officer
CMO: Dana Butler, M.D., Medical Director
CIO: Wendy Potitadkul, Chief Information Officer
CHR: Barbara McCann, Director Human Resources
Web address: www.starcarelubbock.org
**Control**: Other not–for–profit (including NFP Corporation) **Service**: Psychiatric

> **Staffed Beds:** 30 **Admissions:** 802 **Census:** 25 **Outpatient Visits:** 0
> **Births:** 0 **Total Expense ($000):** 7857 **Payroll Expense ($000):** 2836
> **Personnel:** 61

**TRUSTPOINT HOSPITAL** See Trustpoint Rehabilitation Hospital of Lubbock

☐ **TRUSTPOINT REHABILITATION HOSPITAL OF LUBBOCK (673063)**, 4302A Princeton Street, Zip 79415–1304; tel. 806/749–2222, (Nonreporting) **A**1 5 10 **F**3 29 34 35 56 57 74 75 77 79 85 86 87 90 91 96 130 132 **S** Ernest Health, Inc., Albuquerque, NM
Primary Contact: Craig Bragg, Chief Executive Officer
CFO: Crystal Roach, Chief Financial Officer
CNO: John Parsons, R.N., Chief Nursing Officer
Web address: www.trustpointhospital.com/
**Control**: Partnership, Investor–owned (for–profit) **Service**: Rehabilitation

> **Staffed Beds:** 72 **Admissions:** 1404 **Census:** 64 **Outpatient Visits:** 3438
> **Births:** 0 **Total Expense ($000):** 26028 **Payroll Expense ($000):** 12353
> **Personnel:** 238

⇑ **UNIVERSITY MEDICAL CENTER (450686)**, 602 Indiana Avenue, Zip 79415–3364, Mailing Address: P.O. Box 5980, Zip 79408–5980; tel. 806/775–8200, (Nonreporting) **A**2 3 5 8 10 21 **F**3 7 9 11 12 13 15 16 17 18 19 20 22 24 26 28 29 30 31 34 35 38 40 41 43 45 46 47 48 49 50 54 55 57 58 59 62 64 65 66 67 68 70 72 74 75 76 77 78 79 81 83 84 85 86 87 88 89 93 96 97 107 108 110 111 114 115 116 117 118 119 120 121 122 123 124 126 130 131 132 135 136 141 142 143 144 146 147 148 149 150
Primary Contact: Mark Funderburk, President and Chief Executive Officer
CFO: Jeff Dane, Executive Vice President and Chief Financial Officer
CMO: Michael Ragain, M.D., Chief Medical Officer and Senior Vice President
CIO: Bill Eubanks, Senior Vice President and Chief Information Officer
CHR: Adrienne Cozart, Senior Vice President Human Resources
CNO: Timothy W. Howell, R.N., Senior Vice President and Chief Nursing Officer
Web address: www.umchealthsystem.com
**Control**: Hospital district or authority, Government, Nonfederal **Service**: General medical and surgical

> **Staffed Beds:** 476 **Admissions:** 32844 **Census:** 395 **Outpatient Visits:** 211839 **Births:** 3043 **Total Expense ($000):** 615316 **Payroll Expense ($000):** 238404 **Personnel:** 3564

**LUFKIN—Angelina County**

⊞ **CHI ST. LUKE'S HEALTH MEMORIAL LUFKIN (450211)**, 1201 West Frank Avenue, Zip 75904–3357, Mailing Address: P.O. Box 1447, Zip 75902–1447; tel. 936/634–8111, (Nonreporting) **A**1 10 19 **F**3 11 12 13 14 15 17 18 20 21 22 23 24 26 28 29 30 31 34 35 37 38 40 42 43 44 45 46 47 48 49 50 51 56 57 59 60 61 64 68 70 71 74 75 76 77 78 79 81 82 83 84 85 86 87 90 91 92 93 97 100 101 102 107 108 110 111 112 114 115 116 117 119 121 126 129 130 132 135 143 144 146 147 148 149 156 **S** CommonSpirit Health, Chicago, IL
Primary Contact: Monte J. Bostwick, Market Chief Executive Officer
CFO: Kristi Gay, Chief Financial Officer
CHR: Tanya Tyler, Vice President Human Resources
Web address: www.memorialhealth.us/centers/lufkin
**Control**: Other not–for–profit (including NFP Corporation) **Service**: General medical and surgical

> **Staffed Beds:** 194 **Admissions:** 6640 **Census:** 87 **Outpatient Visits:** 89757
> **Births:** 324 **Total Expense ($000):** 166048 **Payroll Expense ($000):** 47453
> **Personnel:** 723

**CHI ST. LUKE'S HEALTH-MEMORIAL LUFKIN** See Pam Specialty Hospital of Lufkin

**COLUMBIA WOODLAND HEIGHTS CTR** See Woodland Heights Medical Center

**MEMORIAL MEDICAL CENTER - LUFKIN** See Chi St. Luke's Health Memorial Lufkin

**OCEANS BEHAVIORAL HOSPITAL** See Oceans Behavioral Hospital Lufkin

☐ **OCEANS BEHAVIORAL HOSPITAL LUFKIN (454123)**, 302 Gobblers Knob Road, Zip 75904–5419; tel. 936/632–2276, (Nonreporting) **A**1 10 **F**29 35 64 98 100 101 103 104 130 153 154 **S** Oceans Healthcare, Plano, TX
Primary Contact: Laci Laird, Chief Executive Officer
Web address: www.oceanslufkin.com/
**Control**: Corporation, Investor–owned (for–profit) **Service**: Psychiatric

> **Staffed Beds:** 24 **Admissions:** 535 **Census:** 19 **Outpatient Visits:** 17971
> **Births:** 0 **Total Expense ($000):** 5515 **Payroll Expense ($000):** 2640
> **Personnel:** 103

★ **PAM SPECIALTY HOSPITAL OF LUFKIN (452031)**, 1201 West Frank Avenue, D5, Zip 75904–3357, Mailing Address: P.O. Box 1447, Zip 75902–1447; tel. 936/639–7530, (Nonreporting) **A**10 **F**1 3 29 31 50 61 68 74 75 86 149 **S** Post Acute Medical, LLC, Enola, PA
CMO: David Todd, M.D., President Medical Staff
Web address: www.postacutemedical.com/facilities/find-facility/specialty-hospitals/PAM-Specialty-Hospital-Lufkin
**Control**: Other not–for–profit (including NFP Corporation) **Service**: Acute long–term care hospital

> **Staffed Beds:** 26 **Admissions:** 364 **Census:** 20 **Outpatient Visits:** 0
> **Births:** 0 **Total Expense ($000):** 11270 **Payroll Expense ($000):** 4064
> **Personnel:** 50

⊞ **WOODLAND HEIGHTS MEDICAL CENTER (450484)**, 505 South John Redditt Drive, Zip 75904–3157, Mailing Address: P.O. Box 150610, Zip 75904; tel. 936/634–8311, (Nonreporting) **A**1 10 19 **F**8 11 12 13 15 18 20 22 24 26 28 29 30 34 35 40 41 46 49 50 51 53 57 59 64 68 70 72 74 75 76 77 78 79 81 82 85 86 87 93 102 107 108 111 114 115 118 119 126 129 130 131 146 147 148 156 **S** Community Health Systems, Inc., Franklin, TN
Primary Contact: Andrew Emery, Chief Executive Officer
COO: Conner Hickey, Chief Operating Officer
CFO: William Whiddon, Chief Financial Officer
CMO: Imran Nazeer, M.D., Chief of Staff
CIO: Kalvin Buckley, Director Information Systems
CHR: Emilie Hobbs, Director Human Resources
Web address: www.woodlandheights.net
**Control**: Partnership, Investor–owned (for–profit) **Service**: General medical and surgical

> **Staffed Beds:** 124 **Admissions:** 5905 **Census:** 65 **Outpatient Visits:** 55297
> **Births:** 1095 **Total Expense ($000):** 82030 **Payroll Expense ($000):** 30173
> **Personnel:** 493

**TX**

*Many Facility Codes have changed. Please refer to the AHA Guide Code Chart.*  © 2021 AHA Guide

## LULING—Caldwell County

✠ **ASCENSION SETON EDGAR B. DAVIS HOSPITAL (451371)**, 130 Hays Street, Zip 78648–3207; tel. 830/875–7000, (Nonreporting) **A**1 10 18 **F**3 11 15 29 30 31 35 40 45 46 50 56 57 59 64 65 66 67 68 71 81 85 97 104 107 110 111 115 119 127 128 130 133 135 146 150 **S** Ascension Healthcare, Saint Louis, MO
Primary Contact: Scott O. Fuller, President and Chief Executive Officer
CMO: Arjun Mohandas, M.D., Chief of Staff
CIO: Michael H. Minks, Chief Information Officer
CHR: Joe Canales, Director Human Resources
Web address: www.seton.net/locations/edgar_davis/
**Control**: Church operated, Nongovernment, not–for–profit **Service**: General medical and surgical

**Staffed Beds:** 25 **Admissions:** 553 **Census:** 7 **Outpatient Visits:** 67806 **Births:** 0 **Total Expense ($000):** 25858 **Payroll Expense ($000):** 8955 **Personnel:** 191

✠ **PAM SPECIALTY HOSPITAL OF LULING (452062)**, 200 Memorial Drive, Zip 78648–3213; tel. 830/875–8400, (Nonreporting) **A**1 10 **F**1 3 29 53 64 93 96 130 133 148 **S** Post Acute Medical, LLC, Enola, PA
Primary Contact: Jana Kuykendall, Chief Executive Officer
Web address: www.warmsprings.org
**Control**: Partnership, Investor–owned (for–profit) **Service**: Acute long–term care hospital

**Staffed Beds:** 34 **Admissions:** 614 **Census:** 29 **Outpatient Visits:** 15281 **Births:** 0 **Total Expense ($000):** 16223 **Payroll Expense ($000):** 7545 **Personnel:** 143

**POST ACUTE/WARM SPRINGS SPECIALTY HOSPITAL OF LULING** See Pam Specialty Hospital of Luling

**SETON EDGAR B. DAVIS HOSPITAL** See Ascension Seton Edgar B. Davis Hospital

## MADISONVILLE—Madison County

✠ **CHI ST. JOSEPH HEALTH MADISON HOSPITAL (451316)**, 100 West Cross Street, Zip 77864–2432, Mailing Address: Box 698, Zip 77864–0698; tel. 936/348–2631, (Nonreporting) **A**1 10 18 **F**3 7 11 15 30 34 40 43 50 56 57 59 64 68 75 77 93 102 107 110 119 130 133 146 148 **S** CommonSpirit Health, Chicago, IL
Primary Contact: Theron Park, Chief Executive Officer
CMO: Grover Hubley, M.D., President Medical Staff
CIO: Maurita Turner, Team Leader Health Information Systems Services
CNO: Roxanne Hass, Director of Nursing
Web address: www.st-joseph.org
**Control**: Church operated, Nongovernment, not–for–profit **Service**: General medical and surgical

**Staffed Beds:** 25 **Admissions:** 232 **Census:** 9 **Outpatient Visits:** 12487 **Births:** 0 **Total Expense ($000):** 11293 **Payroll Expense ($000):** 4617 **Personnel:** 66

**MADISON ST. JOSEPH HEALTH CENTER** See Chi St. Joseph Health Madison Hospital

## MANSFIELD—Tarrant County

✠ **KINDRED HOSPITAL-MANSFIELD (452019)**, 1802 Highway 157 North, Zip 76063–3923; tel. 817/473–6101, (Nonreporting) **A**1 10 **F**1 3 29 30 45 46 64 70 75 82 85 107 130 132 148 **S** Kindred Healthcare, Louisville, KY
Primary Contact: Tyler Cummings, Administrator and Chief Executive Officer
CFO: Judy Baker, Chief Financial Officer
Web address: www.kindredmansfield.com
**Control**: Corporation, Investor–owned (for–profit) **Service**: Acute long–term care hospital

**Staffed Beds:** 55 **Admissions:** 433 **Census:** 26 **Outpatient Visits:** 163 **Births:** 0 **Total Expense ($000):** 13045 **Payroll Expense ($000):** 6560 **Personnel:** 92

✠ **METHODIST MANSFIELD MEDICAL CENTER (670023)**, 2700 East Broad Street, Zip 76063–5899; tel. 682/622–2000, (Nonreporting) **A**1 10 **F**3 11 13 15 18 20 22 24 29 30 31 34 35 37 40 43 45 46 48 49 50 58 59 60 64 68 70 72 74 76 78 79 81 82 85 87 93 97 107 108 110 111 115 118 119 126 130 132 146 148 156 **P**5 6 **S** Methodist Health System, Dallas, TX
Primary Contact: Juan Fresquez, President
CFO: Jary Ganske, Chief Financial Officer
CIO: Pamela McNutt, Senior Vice President and Chief Information Officer
CNO: Nora Frasier, R.N., FACHE, Chief Nursing Officer
Web address: www.methodisthealthsystem.org/mansfield
**Control**: Other not–for–profit (including NFP Corporation) **Service**: General medical and surgical

**Staffed Beds:** 254 **Admissions:** 12061 **Census:** 164 **Outpatient Visits:** 92850 **Births:** 2165 **Total Expense ($000):** 213030 **Payroll Expense ($000):** 92514 **Personnel:** 1085

**TRUSTED MEDICAL CENTERS-MANSFIELD**, 1710 North Highway 287 Frontage Road, Zip 76063; tel. 817/225–4809, (Data for 211 days) (Nonreporting) **F**3 34 40 64 70 75 87 89 102 107 111 114 148 149
Primary Contact: Lori Guerrero, Chief Executive Officer
CNO: Paula Sims, Chief Nursing Officer
Web address: www.themansfieldhospital.com
**Control**: Corporation, Investor–owned (for–profit) **Service**: General medical and surgical

**Staffed Beds:** 10 **Admissions:** 21 **Census:** 1 **Outpatient Visits:** 1542 **Births:** 0 **Total Expense ($000):** 3472 **Payroll Expense ($000):** 1887 **Personnel:** 23

**VENCOR HOSPITAL-MANSFIELD** See Kindred Hospital-Mansfield

## MARBLE FALLS—Burnet County

✠ **BAYLOR SCOTT & WHITE MEDICAL CENTER - MARBLE FALLS (670108)**, 800 West Highway 71, Zip 78654; tel. 830/201–8000, (Nonreporting) **A**1 **F**3 11 13 15 18 20 26 29 31 34 35 40 45 59 64 65 68 70 75 76 77 79 81 85 87 93 107 111 115 116 119 130 131 132 144 146 149 154 **S** Baylor Scott & White Health, Dallas, TX
Primary Contact: Timothy A. Ols, FACHE, President
Web address: www.sw.org/location/marble-falls-hospital
**Control**: Other not–for–profit (including NFP Corporation) **Service**: General medical and surgical

**Staffed Beds:** 46 **Admissions:** 2584 **Census:** 21 **Outpatient Visits:** 120042 **Births:** 363 **Total Expense ($000):** 81409 **Payroll Expense ($000):** 22275 **Personnel:** 325

**SCOTT & WHITE HOSPITAL - MARBLE FALLS** See Baylor Scott & White Medical Center - Marble Falls

## MARLIN—Falls County

**FALLS COMM HOSP & CLINIC** See Falls Community Hospital and Clinic

**FALLS COMMUNITY HOSPITAL AND CLINIC (450348)**, 322 Coleman Street, Zip 76661–2358, Mailing Address: P.O. Box 60, Zip 76661–0060; tel. 254/803–3561, (Nonreporting) **A**10 20 **F**3 11 18 32 33 34 35 36 40 53 56 57 59 64 65 66 68 75 82 87 91 93 97 100 102 104 107 114 119 127 129 131 135 146 147 148
Primary Contact: Jessica Ford, Interim Chief Executive Officer
COO: Becca Brewer, Chief Operations Officer
CMO: James Scott Crockett, M.D., Chief of Staff
CIO: Chris Smith, Chief Information Officer
CHR: Peggy Polster, Manager Personnel and Administrative Assistant
CNO: Tasha Burnett, Director of Nursing
Web address: www.fallshospital.com
**Control**: Other not–for–profit (including NFP Corporation) **Service**: General medical and surgical

**Staffed Beds:** 32 **Admissions:** 138 **Census:** 1 **Outpatient Visits:** 40009 **Births:** 0 **Total Expense ($000):** 12144 **Payroll Expense ($000):** 5068 **Personnel:** 142

---

**TX**

## MARSHALL—Harrison County

⊞ △ **CHRISTUS GOOD SHEPHERD MEDICAL CENTER-MARSHALL (450032)**, 811 South Washington Avenue, Zip 75670–5336, Mailing Address: P.O. Box 1599, Zip 75671–1599; tel. 903/927–6000, (Includes CHRISTUS GOOD SHEPHERD MEDICAL CENTER, Mailing address: 700 East Marshall Avenue, Longview, Texas, Zip 75601–5580; tel. 903/315–1800; Todd Hancock, President and Chief Executive Officer) (Data for 273 days)**A**1 3 7 10 **F**3 8 11 12 13 15 18 20 22 24 26 28 29 30 31 34 35 38 40 42 43 44 45 46 47 48 49 50 51 53 56 57 59 60 61 64 65 68 70 71 72 73 74 75 76 77 78 79 80 81 82 84 85 86 87 89 90 97 102 104 107 110 111 114 115 117 119 129 130 131 132 135 143 145 146 147 148 149 150 154 156 **P**8 **S** CHRISTUS Health, Irving, TX
Primary Contact: Todd Hancock, President and Chief Executive Officer
COO: Keith Creel, Vice President Operations
CFO: Michael Cheek, Chief Financial Officer
CMO: Larry Verfurth, D.O., Executive Vice President and Chief Medical Officer
CIO: Walter Grimes, Director Information Technology
CNO: Keith Kirbow, R.N., Vice President and Chief Nursing Officer
Web address: www.https://www.christushealth.org/good-shepherd/marshall
**Control:** Church operated, Nongovernment, not–for–profit **Service:** General medical and surgical

**Staffed Beds: 368 Admissions: 13640 Census: 200 Outpatient Visits: 207426 Births: 1211 Total Expense ($000): 287721 Payroll Expense ($000): 97880 Personnel: 1962**

**GOOD SHEPHERD MEDICAL CENTER-MARSHALL** See Christus Good Shepherd Medical Center-Marshall

## MCALLEN—Hidalgo County

**COLUMBIA RIO GRANDE REG HOSP** See Rio Grande Regional Hospital

⊞ **RIO GRANDE REGIONAL HOSPITAL (450711)**, 101 East Ridge Road, Zip 78503–1299; tel. 956/632–6000, (Nonreporting) **A**1 10 19 **F**3 8 11 12 13 15 18 19 20 21 22 23 25 26 27 29 30 31 34 35 39 40 41 42 43 45 46 49 50 54 56 57 59 60 64 65 66 68 70 72 73 74 75 76 77 78 79 81 82 85 87 88 89 93 107 108 110 111 114 118 119 126 130 132 146 147 148 149 154 156 157 **S** HCA Healthcare, Nashville, TN
Primary Contact: Cristina Rivera, Chief Executive Officer
CFO: William Saller, Chief Financial Officer
CHR: Marjorie Whittemore, Director Human Resources
Web address: www.riohealth.com
**Control:** Partnership, Investor–owned (for–profit) **Service:** General medical and surgical

**Staffed Beds: 304 Admissions: 15283 Census: 182 Outpatient Visits: 129115 Births: 2059 Total Expense ($000): 168219 Payroll Expense ($000): 68750 Personnel: 768**

**SOLARA HOSPITAL MCALLEN (452095)**, 301 West Expressway 83, 8th Floor, Zip 78503–3045; tel. 956/632–4880, (Nonreporting) **A**10 22 **F**1 3 29 30 56 70 75 77 85 86 87 91 130 148 **S** Cornerstone Healthcare Group, Dallas, TX
Primary Contact: David Tupper, Chief Executive Officer
Web address: www.chghospitals.com/mcallen/
**Control:** Corporation, Investor–owned (for–profit) **Service:** Acute long–term care hospital

**Staffed Beds: 78 Admissions: 653 Census: 50 Outpatient Visits: 0 Births: 0 Total Expense ($000): 19599 Payroll Expense ($000): 9910 Personnel: 143**

## MCCAMEY—Upton County

★ **MCCAMEY COUNTY HOSPITAL DISTRICT (451309)**, 2500 Highway 305 South, Zip 79752, Mailing Address: P.O. Box 1200, Zip 79752–1200; tel. 432/652–8626, (Total facility includes 30 beds in nursing home–type unit) (Nonreporting) **A**10 18 **F**3 40 53 59 64 65 66 93 127 128 133
Primary Contact: Jaime Ramirez, Chief Executive Officer
CFO: Jason J Menefee, Chief Financial Officer
CMO: John Bruce Addison, D.O., Chief Medical Officer
CIO: Larry Rollins, Supervisor Information Technology
CHR: Ashley Johnson, Director Human Resource
CNO: Erin Mann, R.N., Chief Nursing Officer
Web address: www.mccameyhospitaldistrict.org
**Control:** Hospital district or authority, Government, Nonfederal **Service:** General medical and surgical

**Staffed Beds: 41 Admissions: 70 Census: 29 Outpatient Visits: 9430 Births: 0 Total Expense ($000): 14439 Payroll Expense ($000): 4776 Personnel: 71**

**MCCAMEY HOSPITAL** See Mccamey County Hospital District

## MCKINNEY—Collin County

**BAYLOR MEDICAL CENTER AT MCKINNEY** See Baylor Scott & White Medical Center at - Mckinney

⊞ **BAYLOR SCOTT & WHITE MEDICAL CENTER AT - MCKINNEY (670082)**, 5252 West University Drive, Zip 75071–7822; tel. 469/764–1000, (Nonreporting) **A**1 2 10 **F**3 13 15 18 20 22 26 29 30 31 34 35 40 43 45 46 47 49 50 51 57 59 60 70 72 73 74 75 76 77 78 79 81 84 85 87 107 110 111 114 115 116 119 126 130 131 132 146 147 148 **S** Baylor Scott & White Health, Dallas, TX
Primary Contact: Erin Blair, Interim Chief Executive Officer
COO: Melissa Winter, R.N., MSN, Chief Operating Officer and Chief Nursing Officer
CFO: Steve Roussel, Chief Financial Officer
CMO: Jeff Kerr, M.D., Chief Medical Officer
CNO: Melissa Winter, R.N., MSN, Chief Operating Officer and Chief Nursing Officer
Web address: www.baylorhealth.com/PhysiciansLocations/McKinney/Pages/Default.aspx
**Control:** Other not–for–profit (including NFP Corporation) **Service:** General medical and surgical

**Staffed Beds: 143 Admissions: 8621 Census: 91 Outpatient Visits: 62177 Births: 2026 Total Expense ($000): 166771 Payroll Expense ($000): 56846 Personnel: 624**

**MEDICAL CENTER MCKINNEY** See Medical City Mckinney

⊞ **MEDICAL CITY MCKINNEY (450403)**, 4500 Medical Center Drive, Zip 75069–1650; tel. 972/547–8000, (Includes WYSONG CAMPUS, Mailing address: 130 South Central Expressway, McKinney, Texas, Zip 75070; tel. 972/548–5300), (Nonreporting) **A**1 10 **F**3 4 11 13 18 20 22 24 26 28 29 30 34 37 40 42 43 45 49 50 56 57 59 60 64 68 70 72 74 75 76 77 78 79 81 82 85 87 90 91 92 93 94 96 97 98 102 103 107 108 109 111 114 115 119 126 130 131 132 146 147 148 149 **S** HCA Healthcare, Nashville, TN
Primary Contact: Ernest C. Lynch III, FACHE, President and Chief Executive Officer
COO: Andrew Zenger, Chief Operating Officer
CFO: Anthony Villigran, Chief Financial Officer
CMO: Jaya Kumar, M.D., Chief Medical Officer
CIO: Kevin Fletcher, Director Information Systems
CHR: Alayne Sewick, Vice President Human Resources
CNO: Cassidi Roberts, Chief Nursing Officer
Web address: www.medicalcenterofmckinney.com
**Control:** Partnership, Investor–owned (for–profit) **Service:** General medical and surgical

**Staffed Beds: 222 Admissions: 13060 Census: 176 Outpatient Visits: 90421 Births: 1778 Total Expense ($000): 166416 Payroll Expense ($000): 71102 Personnel: 840**

☐ **METHODIST MCKINNEY HOSPITAL (670069)**, 8000 West Eldorado Parkway, Zip 75070–5940; tel. 972/569–2700, (Nonreporting) **A**1 10 **F**3 8 29 34 37 40 45 64 75 79 81 82 85 93 107 111 119 126 130 131
Primary Contact: Joseph Minissale, President
CFO: Mike Conroy, Chief Financial Officer
CIO: Sharon Stark, R.N., Manager Clinical Information Systems
CHR: Diana Hume, Manager Human Resources
CNO: Staci Jones, R.N., Chief Nursing Officer
Web address: www.methodistmckinneyhospital.com
**Control:** Partnership, Investor–owned (for–profit) **Service:** Surgical

**Staffed Beds: 23 Admissions: 1243 Census: 7 Outpatient Visits: 47129 Births: 0 Total Expense ($000): 58715 Payroll Expense ($000): 11576 Personnel: 209**

**WESTPARK SURGERY CENTER** See Wysong Campus

## MESQUITE—Dallas County

☐ **DALLAS REGIONAL MEDICAL CENTER (450688)**, 1011 North Galloway Avenue, Zip 75149–2433; tel. 214/320–7000, (Nonreporting) **A**1 10 **F**3 12 13 15 18 20 22 24 26 29 30 34 35 37 39 40 41 43 45 46 49 50 56 57 59 65 67 70 74 75 76 78 79 81 85 86 87 102 105 107 108 110 111 115 118 119 126 129 130 134 135 146 147 148 149 154 157 **S** Prime Healthcare, Ontario, CA
Primary Contact: Glenda Matchett, Chief Executive Officer
CMO: Srinivas Gunukula, M.D., Chief of Staff
Web address: www.dallasregionalmedicalcenter.com
**Control:** Individual, Investor–owned (for–profit) **Service:** General medical and surgical

**Staffed Beds: 127 Admissions: 6919 Census: 74 Outpatient Visits: 47509 Births: 993 Total Expense ($000): 87825 Payroll Expense ($000): 35160 Personnel: 492**

**MESQUITE REHABILITATION HOSPITAL** See Mesquite Rehabilitation Institute

☐ **MESQUITE REHABILITATION INSTITUTE (673045)**, 1023 North Belt Line Road, Zip 75149–1788; tel. 972/216–2400, (Nonreporting) **A**1 10 **F**3 28 29 34 90 93 96 130 132 148 149 **S** Ernest Health, Inc., Albuquerque, NM
Primary Contact: Michael Ridgeway, Chief Executive Officer
Web address: www.mesquiterehab.ernesthealth.com/
**Control:** Corporation, Investor–owned (for–profit) **Service:** Rehabilitation

**Staffed Beds:** 30 **Admissions:** 616 **Census:** 24 **Outpatient Visits:** 4388
**Births:** 0 **Total Expense ($000):** 8706 **Payroll Expense ($000):** 5409
**Personnel:** 74

☐ **MESQUITE SPECIALTY HOSPITAL (452100)**, 1024 North Galloway Avenue, Zip 75149–2434; tel. 972/216–2300, (Nonreporting) **A**1 10 **F**1 3 29 75 148 149 154 **S** Ernest Health, Inc., Albuquerque, NM
Primary Contact: Michael Ridgeway, Chief Executive Officer
Web address: www.msh.ernesthealth.com
**Control:** Partnership, Investor–owned (for–profit) **Service:** Acute long–term care hospital

**Staffed Beds:** 40 **Admissions:** 284 **Census:** 19 **Outpatient Visits:** 0
**Births:** 0 **Total Expense ($000):** 10491 **Payroll Expense ($000):** 4983
**Personnel:** 91

### MEXIA—Limestone County

**HARRIS METHODIST-MEXIA** See Parkview Regional Hospital

⊞ **PARKVIEW REGIONAL HOSPITAL (450400)**, 600 South Bonham, Zip 76667–3603; tel. 254/562–5332, (Nonreporting) **A**1 10 **F**3 11 15 29 30 34 35 40 43 45 51 53 56 57 59 64 65 70 75 77 78 79 81 85 86 87 90 93 97 98 103 107 108 110 111 114 119 127 130 132 133 146 **S** LifePoint Health, Brentwood, TN
Primary Contact: Robert Rupp, Chief Executive Officer
COO: R. Austin Wratchford, Chief Operating Officer
CFO: Jack Wilcox, Chief Financial Officer
CNO: Edwina J Henry, Assistant Chief Nursing Officer
Web address: www.parkviewregional.com
**Control:** Partnership, Investor–owned (for–profit) **Service:** General medical and surgical

**Staffed Beds:** 58 **Admissions:** 641 **Census:** 6 **Outpatient Visits:** 23356
**Births:** 0 **Total Expense ($000):** 22321 **Payroll Expense ($000):** 6901
**Personnel:** 149

### MIDLAND—Midland County

**BEHAVIORAL HEALTH CENTER OF THE PERMIAN BASIN** See Oceans Behavioral Health Center Permian Basin

⊞ **ENCOMPASS HEALTH REHABILITATION HOSPITAL MIDLAND ODESSA (453057)**, 1800 Heritage Boulevard, Zip 79707–9750; tel. 432/520–1600, (Nonreporting) **A**1 10 **F**3 29 57 59 65 75 77 82 90 91 96 130 143 148 154 **S** Encompass Health Corporation, Birmingham, AL
Primary Contact: Jason Dan. Hudson, R.N., Chief Executive Officer
CFO: Vivian Irwin, Chief Financial Officer and Controller
CMO: Mark A Fredrickson, M.D., Medical Director
CHR: Tina Parker, Director Human Resources
Web address: www.healthsouthmidland.com
**Control:** Corporation, Investor–owned (for–profit) **Service:** Rehabilitation

**Staffed Beds:** 80 **Admissions:** 1681 **Census:** 61 **Outpatient Visits:** 0
**Births:** 0 **Total Expense ($000):** 29985 **Payroll Expense ($000):** 14818
**Personnel:** 190

**HEALTHSOUTH REHABILITATION HOSPITAL MIDLAND-ODESSA** See Encompass Health Rehabilitation Hospital Midland Odessa

⇧ **MEMORIAL HOSPITAL & MED CENTER** See Midland Memorial Hospital

**MIDLAND MEM HOSP WEST CAMPUS** See Midland Memorial Hospital

★ ⇧ **MIDLAND MEMORIAL HOSPITAL (450133)**, 400 Rosalind Redfern Grover Parkway, Zip 79701–6499; tel. 432/221–1111, (Includes MIDLAND MEMORIAL HOSPITAL, Mailing address: 400 Rosalind Redfern Grover Pkwy, Midland, Texas, Zip 79701–5846; tel. 432/221–1111), (Nonreporting) **A**3 5 10 21 **F**3 8 11 12 13 15 17 18 20 22 24 26 28 29 30 32 34 35 37 40 43 45 49 50 53 56 57 59 61 64 68 70 73 74 75 76 77 78 79 80 81 82 84 86 87 88 89 93 97 107 108 110 111 114 115 116 117 118 119 124 126 129 130 131 132 135 145 146 147 148 154 156 157 **P**8
Primary Contact: Russell Meyers, FACHE, President and Chief Executive Officer
CFO: Stephen Bowerman, Senior Vice President, Chief Financial Officer
CMO: Lawrence Wilson, M.D., Vice President, Chief Medical Officer
CIO: Taylor Weems, Vice President, Chief Information Officer
CHR: Roberta SoloRio, Vice President, Chief Human Resource Officer
Web address: www.https://www.midlandhealth.org/
**Control:** Hospital district or authority, Government, Nonfederal **Service:** General medical and surgical

**Staffed Beds:** 244 **Admissions:** 10777 **Census:** 132 **Outpatient Visits:** 165391 **Births:** 2612 **Total Expense ($000):** 280586 **Payroll Expense ($000):** 108865 **Personnel:** 1753

☐ **OCEANS BEHAVIORAL HEALTH CENTER PERMIAN BASIN (454110)**, 3300 South FM 1788, Zip 79706–2601; tel. 432/561–5915, (Nonreporting) **A**1 3 10 **F**29 34 35 64 68 98 99 100 101 103 104 130 132 153 154 **P**6 **S** Oceans Healthcare, Plano, TX
Primary Contact: Emileh Flitton, Administrator
Web address: www.oceanspermianbasin.com/
**Control:** Corporation, Investor–owned (for–profit) **Service:** Psychiatric

**Staffed Beds:** 62 **Admissions:** 1725 **Census:** 45 **Outpatient Visits:** 15379
**Births:** 0 **Total Expense ($000):** 11286 **Payroll Expense ($000):** 6550
**Personnel:** 221

### MINERAL WELLS—Palo Pinto County

⊞ **PALO PINTO GENERAL HOSPITAL (450565)**, 400 SW 25th Avenue, Zip 76067–8246; tel. 940/325–7891, (Nonreporting) **A**1 10 **F**11 13 15 18 28 29 34 35 40 43 45 46 51 53 54 57 59 64 65 66 68 69 70 71 74 75 76 77 78 79 81 82 86 87 91 93 107 108 110 111 114 119 127 129 130 131 133 135 146 147 148 154
Primary Contact: Ross Korkmas, Chief Executive Officer
COO: Shane Coleman, Chief Operating Officer
CFO: Daniel Smith, Chief Financial Officer
CMO: George Thomas, M.D., Chief of Staff
CHR: Mary B Braddock, Director Human Resources
CNO: James Fesser, Chief Nursing Officer
Web address: www.ppgh.com
**Control:** Hospital district or authority, Government, Nonfederal **Service:** General medical and surgical

**Staffed Beds:** 54 **Admissions:** 1607 **Census:** 16 **Outpatient Visits:** 84454
**Births:** 278 **Total Expense ($000):** 42261 **Payroll Expense ($000):** 19494
**Personnel:** 366

### MISSION—Hidalgo County

**MISSION HOSPITAL** See Mission Regional Medical Center

☐ △ **MISSION REGIONAL MEDICAL CENTER (450176)**, 900 South Bryan Road, Zip 78572–6613; tel. 956/323–9103, (Nonreporting) **A**1 7 10 **F**3 11 12 13 15 18 20 22 29 34 35 40 43 45 46 49 50 51 57 59 60 64 65 66 68 70 72 74 75 76 77 79 81 85 87 89 90 93 96 107 108 110 111 115 118 119 130 132 146 147 148 149 154 **P**8 **S** Prime Healthcare, Ontario, CA
Primary Contact: Kane A. Dawson, Chief Executive Officer
CFO: Lester Surrock, Chief Financial Officer
CMO: Humberto F. Nunez, M.D., Chief Medical Officer
CNO: Kennetha Foster, Chief Nursing Officer
Web address: www.missionrmc.org
**Control:** Other not–for–profit (including NFP Corporation) **Service:** General medical and surgical

**Staffed Beds:** 228 **Admissions:** 8924 **Census:** 109 **Outpatient Visits:** 79679 **Births:** 1735 **Total Expense ($000):** 104900 **Payroll Expense ($000):** 45177 **Personnel:** 796

**TX**

---

**Hospital, Medicare Provider Number, Address, Telephone, Approval, Facility, and Physician Codes, Health Care System**

★ American Hospital Association (AHA) membership
☐ The Joint Commission accreditation
○ Healthcare Facilities Accreditation Program
◇ DNV Healthcare Inc. accreditation
⇧ Center for Improvement in Healthcare Quality Accreditation
△ Commission on Accreditation of Rehabilitation Facilities (CARF) accreditation

## MONAHANS—Ward County

★ **WARD MEMORIAL HOSPITAL (451373)**, 406 South Gary Street, Zip 79756–4798, Mailing Address: P.O. Box 40, Zip 79756–0040; tel. 432/943–2511, (Nonreporting) **A**10 18 **F**3 40 43 45 64 65 66 81 82 89 93 107 114 119 127 131 133 148 **P**6
Primary Contact: Leticia Rodriguez, Chief Executive Officer
CFO: Alison Cooper, Chief Financial Officer
CMO: Htin Thaung, M.D., Chief Medical Officer
CIO: David Hargrave, Chief Information Officer
CHR: Corina Subia, Director Human Resources
CNO: Jason Harbin, Director of Nursing
Web address: www.wardmemorial.com
**Control:** County, Government, Nonfederal **Service:** General medical and surgical

**Staffed Beds: 25 Admissions: 372 Census: 4 Outpatient Visits: 46111 Births: 0 Total Expense ($000): 17005 Payroll Expense ($000): 7684 Personnel: 103**

## MORTON—Cochran County

**COCHRAN MEMORIAL HOSPITAL (451366)**, 201 East Grant Street, Zip 79346–3444; tel. 806/266–5565, (Nonreporting) **A**10 18 **F**7 34 40 57 59 65 127 149 **P**6
Primary Contact: Larry Turney, Administrator
CFO: Maggie Ramon, Chief Financial Officer
CIO: David Turney, Chief Information Officer
CHR: Amanda Turney, Director Human Resources
CNO: Rosemary Franco, Chief Nursing Officer
**Control:** Hospital district or authority, Government, Nonfederal **Service:** General medical and surgical

**Staffed Beds: 13 Admissions: 6 Census: 1 Outpatient Visits: 5334 Births: 0 Total Expense ($000): 4242 Payroll Expense ($000): 2243 Personnel: 47**

## MOUNT PLEASANT—Titus County

⊞ **TITUS REGIONAL MEDICAL CENTER (450080)**, 2001 North Jefferson Avenue, Zip 75455–2398; tel. 903/577–6000, (Nonreporting) **A**1 10 **F**3 7 11 12 13 15 18 20 22 24 28 29 30 34 35 39 40 43 45 47 50 51 53 54 56 57 58 59 64 68 70 73 74 75 76 77 78 79 81 82 85 87 89 90 93 97 98 103 107 108 110 111 114 115 117 118 119 121 123 126 127 129 130 131 132 135 147 148 149 154 156
Primary Contact: Terry Scoggin, Chief Executive Officer
CFO: Terry Scoggin, Chief Financial Officer
CMO: Chris Burling, M.D., Chief of Staff
CIO: Kevin Harris, Director Information Systems
CHR: Tony Piazza, Director Human Resources
CNO: Carol Slider, Chief Nursing Officer
Web address: www.titusregional.com
**Control:** Hospital district or authority, Government, Nonfederal **Service:** General medical and surgical

**Staffed Beds: 73 Admissions: 4346 Census: 45 Outpatient Visits: 180228 Births: 826 Total Expense ($000): 98023 Payroll Expense ($000): 34390 Personnel: 612**

**TITUS REGIONAL MEDICAL CTR** See Titus Regional Medical Center

## MUENSTER—Cooke County

**MUENSTER HOSPITAL DISTRICT** See Muenster Memorial Hospital

**MUENSTER MEMORIAL HOSPITAL (451335)**, 605 North Maple Street, Zip 76252–2424, Mailing Address: P.O. Box 370, Zip 76252–0370; tel. 940/759–2271, (Nonreporting) **A**10 18 **F**11 35 40 43 45 53 57 59 64 65 75 77 81 93 107 114 119 127 130 133 146 **P**8
Primary Contact: Brian Roland, Chief Executive Officer
CFO: Julie Williams, Chief Financial Officer
CNO: Tiffany Lutkenhaus, Chief Nursing Officer
Web address: www.muensterhospital.com
**Control:** Hospital district or authority, Government, Nonfederal **Service:** General medical and surgical

**Staffed Beds: 18 Admissions: 104 Census: 9 Outpatient Visits: 4492 Births: 0 Total Expense ($000): 13483 Payroll Expense ($000): 5728 Personnel: 85**

## MULESHOE—Bailey County

**MULESHOE AREA MEDICAL CENTER (451372)**, 708 South First Street, Zip 79347–3627; tel. 806/272–4524, (Nonreporting) **A**10 18 **F**29 34 40 57 59 64 93 97 107 119 127 133 135 154 **S** Preferred Management Corporation, Shawnee, OK
Primary Contact: Dennis Fleenor, R.N., Administrator
CMO: Bruce Purdy, M.D., Chief of Staff
CHR: Suzanne Nichols, Director Human Resources
Web address: www.mahdtx.org
**Control:** Corporation, Investor–owned (for–profit) **Service:** General medical and surgical

**Staffed Beds: 25 Admissions: 228 Census: 4 Outpatient Visits: 18454 Births: 0 Total Expense ($000): 8725 Payroll Expense ($000): 3685 Personnel: 89**

## NACOGDOCHES—Nacogdoches County

**AMI NACOGDOCHES MEDICAL CENTER** See Nacogdoches Medical Center

**MEMORIAL HOSPITAL** See Nacogdoches Memorial Hospital

⊠ **NACOGDOCHES MEDICAL CENTER (450656)**, 4920 NE Stallings Drive, Zip 75965–1200; tel. 936/569–9481, (Nonreporting) **A**1 10 19 **F**3 13 15 17 18 20 22 24 26 29 30 31 34 35 40 42 43 45 46 49 50 54 56 57 59 64 65 68 70 72 74 75 76 77 78 79 81 82 84 85 86 87 89 93 96 97 100 102 107 108 110 111 114 115 118 119 120 121 122 123 126 129 130 131 132 135 141 146 147 154 **S** TENET Healthcare Corporation, Dallas, TX
Primary Contact: Jeff Patterson, Chief Executive Officer
CFO: Randy Slack, Chief Financial Officer
CMO: Charles Thompson, M.D., Chief Medical Officer
CIO: Teresa Simon, Director Information Systems
CHR: Teresa Farrell, Chief Human Resources Officer
CNO: Patti Bennett, Chief Nursing Officer
Web address: www.nacmedicalcenter.com
**Control:** Partnership, Investor–owned (for–profit) **Service:** General medical and surgical

**Staffed Beds: 117 Admissions: 5084 Census: 49 Outpatient Visits: 72650 Births: 743 Total Expense ($000): 87154 Payroll Expense ($000): 26296 Personnel: 398**

⊠ **NACOGDOCHES MEMORIAL HOSPITAL (450508)**, 1204 North Mound Street, Zip 75961–4061; tel. 936/564–4611, (Nonreporting) **A**1 10 19 **F**3 7 11 13 15 18 20 22 26 28 29 30 31 34 38 40 43 45 50 57 59 64 65 66 70 72 73 74 75 76 77 78 79 80 81 82 85 87 90 93 96 97 107 108 110 111 114 115 119 127 130 135 143 146 147 148 149 155 **P**6
Primary Contact: Gary L. Stokes, Interim Chief Executive Officer
CFO: Jane Ann Bridges, Chief Financial Officer
CNO: Beth Knight, Chief Nursing Officer
Web address: www.nacmem.org
**Control:** Hospital district or authority, Government, Nonfederal **Service:** General medical and surgical

**Staffed Beds: 130 Admissions: 3682 Census: 50 Outpatient Visits: 94843 Births: 507 Total Expense ($000): 98385 Payroll Expense ($000): 30072 Personnel: 607**

## NASSAU BAY—Harris County

★ ⇑ **HOUSTON METHODIST CLEAR LAKE HOSPITAL (450709)**, 18300 St John Drive, Zip 77058–6302; tel. 281/333–5503, (Nonreporting) **A**5 10 21 **F**3 8 11 12 13 15 18 20 22 24 26 28 29 30 31 34 35 39 40 41 44 45 48 49 50 51 53 54 57 59 60 63 64 65 68 70 72 73 74 75 76 77 78 79 81 82 84 85 86 87 93 94 96 102 107 108 110 111 115 118 119 120 121 123 126 130 131 132 135 146 147 148 149 150 154 **P**5 6 **S** Houston Methodist, Houston, TX
Primary Contact: Dan Newman, Chief Executive Officer
CFO: David A Witt, Vice President Finances
CHR: Becky A Merritt, Director Human Resources
Web address: www.houstonmethodist.org/st-john-clear-lake
**Control:** Other not–for–profit (including NFP Corporation) **Service:** General medical and surgical

**Staffed Beds: 138 Admissions: 6912 Census: 81 Outpatient Visits: 163439 Births: 678 Total Expense ($000): 171919 Payroll Expense ($000): 65550 Personnel: 847**

⇑ **HOUSTON METHODIST ST. JOHN HOSPITAL** See Houston Methodist Clear Lake Hospital

*Many Facility Codes have changed. Please refer to the AHA Guide Code Chart.*

© 2021 AHA Guide

## NAVASOTA—Grimes County

☒ **CHI ST. JOSEPH HEALTH GRIMES HOSPITAL (451322)**, 210 South Judson Street, Zip 77868–3704; tel. 936/825–6585, (Nonreporting) **A**1 10 18 **F**3 28 29 34 40 43 56 57 59 75 77 93 104 107 111 119 130 132 133 135 146 **S** CommonSpirit Health, Chicago, IL
Primary Contact: Theron Park, Chief Executive Officer
CFO: Daniel Goggin, Senior Vice President and Chief Financial Officer
CMO: Luke P Scamardo, M.D., llChief of Staff
CIO: Mike Russo, Vice President Information Systems
CHR: Kristina Lee, Director Human Resources
CNO: Cesar Lopez, R.N., Director of Nurses
Web address: www.st-joseph.org
**Control**: Church operated, Nongovernment, not–for–profit **Service**: General medical and surgical

**Staffed Beds**: 18 **Admissions**: 159 **Census**: 6 **Outpatient Visits**: 11299
**Births**: 0 **Total Expense ($000)**: 10570 **Payroll Expense ($000)**: 4427
**Personnel**: 66

**GRIMES ST. JOSEPH HEALTH CENTER** See Chi St. Joseph Health Grimes Hospital

## NEDERLAND—Jefferson County

**PROMISE SPECIALTY HOSPITAL OF SOUTHEAST TEXAS** See Mid-Jefferson Extended Care Hospital

## NEW BRAUNFELS—Comal County

**CHRISTUS SANTA ROSA HOSPITAL - NEW BRAUNFELS** See Christus Santa Rosa Hospital - New Braunfels

☐ **NEW BRAUNFELS REGIONAL REHABILITATION HOSPITAL (673049)**, 2041 Sundance Parkway, Zip 78130–2779; tel. 830/625–6700, (Nonreporting) **A**1 10 **F**3 29 34 57 64 90 93 96 130 132 148 **S** Ernest Health, Inc., Albuquerque, NM
Primary Contact: Nicholas Nilest, Chief Executive Officer
CFO: Sue Thomsen, Chief Financial Officer
CMO: Maria R Lomba, Medical Director
CHR: Cheryl Smith, Manager Human Resources
CNO: Peggy Schmits, Director, Nursing Operations
Web address: www.nbrrh.ernesthealth.com
**Control**: Corporation, Investor–owned (for–profit) **Service**: Rehabilitation

**Staffed Beds**: 40 **Admissions**: 861 **Census**: 32 **Outpatient Visits**: 8062
**Births**: 0 **Total Expense ($000)**: 12182 **Payroll Expense ($000)**: 6992
**Personnel**: 150

☒ **PAM SPECIALTY HOSPITAL OF NEW BRAUNFELS (452106)**, 1445 Hanz Drive, Zip 78130–2567; tel. 830/627–7600, (Nonreporting) **A**1 10 **F**1 3 29 30 34 85 130 148 **S** Post Acute Medical, LLC, Enola, PA
Primary Contact: Angela Jaco, Chief Executive Officer
Web address: www.warmsprings.org/locations/hos/h1/
**Control**: Partnership, Investor–owned (for–profit) **Service**: Acute long–term care hospital

**Staffed Beds**: 40 **Admissions**: 652 **Census**: 27 **Outpatient Visits**: 0
**Births**: 0 **Total Expense ($000)**: 13740 **Payroll Expense ($000)**: 5443
**Personnel**: 70

**POST ACUTE/WARM SPRINGS SPECIALTY HOSPITAL OF NEW BRAUNFELS** See Pam Specialty Hospital of New Braunfels

☒ **RESOLUTE HEALTH (670098)**, 555 Creekside Crossing, Zip 78130–2594; tel. 830/500–6000, (Nonreporting) **A**1 10 **F**3 13 15 18 20 22 29 30 34 35 40 45 48 49 50 53 60 64 65 70 72 74 75 76 77 79 81 85 87 107 108 111 114 115 119 126 130 146 147 149 150 156 **S** TENET Healthcare Corporation, Dallas, TX
Primary Contact: Mark L. Bernard, Chief Executive Officer
Web address: www.resolutehealth.com
**Control**: Corporation, Investor–owned (for–profit) **Service**: General medical and surgical

**Staffed Beds**: 70 **Admissions**: 5048 **Census**: 50 **Outpatient Visits**: 41710
**Births**: 818 **Total Expense ($000)**: 87411 **Payroll Expense ($000)**: 30766
**Personnel**: 492

## NOCONA—Montague County

**NOCONA GENERAL HOSPITAL (450641)**, 100 Park Road, Zip 76255–3616; tel. 940/825–3235, (Nonreporting) **A**10 **F**3 7 28 29 30 34 35 40 43 45 50 53 57 59 62 64 68 75 81 82 86 87 93 107 108 115 119 127 130 133 146 148 **P**5
Primary Contact: Lance Meekins, Chief Executive Officer
CFO: Lance Meekins, Chief Executive Officer
CMO: Chance Dingler, M.D., Chief Medical Officer
CHR: Paula Monkres, Administrative Assistant and Director Human Resources
Web address: www.noconageneral.com/
**Control**: Hospital district or authority, Government, Nonfederal **Service**: General medical and surgical

**Staffed Beds**: 18 **Admissions**: 363 **Census**: 5 **Outpatient Visits**: 5264
**Births**: 1 **Total Expense ($000)**: 9517 **Payroll Expense ($000)**: 4569
**Personnel**: 125

## NORTH RICHLAND HILLS—Tarrant County

☒ **MEDICAL CITY NORTH HILLS (450087)**, 4401 Booth Calloway Road, Zip 76180–7399; tel. 817/255–1000, (Nonreporting) **A**1 3 10 **F**3 12 15 17 18 20 22 24 26 28 29 31 34 35 37 39 40 41 43 45 49 50 56 57 64 67 70 74 75 77 78 79 81 85 86 87 93 98 103 107 108 110 111 115 118 119 126 130 132 135 146 148 149 **S** HCA Healthcare, Nashville, TN
Primary Contact: Mark S. Deno, Chief Executive Officer
COO: Nancy L Hill, R.N., MSN, Chief Operating Officer
CFO: Nick Galt, Chief Financial Officer
CMO: John McDonald, M.D., Chief Medical Officer
CIO: Jason Sims, Facility Information Security Officer
CHR: Cynthia Dang, Vice President Human Resources
CNO: John Marker, MSN, R.N., Chief Nursing Officer
Web address: www.northhillshospital.com
**Control**: Partnership, Investor–owned (for–profit) **Service**: General medical and surgical

**Staffed Beds**: 138 **Admissions**: 6920 **Census**: 92 **Outpatient Visits**: 77219
**Births**: 0 **Total Expense ($000)**: 120660 **Payroll Expense ($000)**: 41686
**Personnel**: 553

**NORTH HILLS HOSPITAL** See Medical City North Hills

## ODESSA—Ector County

**BASIN HEALTHCARE CENTER** See Odessa Regional Medical Center South Campus

★ **CONTINUECARE HOSPITAL AT MEDICAL CENTER (ODESSA) (452121)**, 500 West Fourth Street, 4th Floor, Zip 79761–5001; tel. 432/640–4380, (Nonreporting) **A**10 22 **F**1 3 29 34 35 79 85 87 **S** Community Hospital Corporation, Plano, TX
Primary Contact: Laci Harris, Chief Executive Officer
CNO: Ade Adelekan, Chief Nursing Officer
Web address: www.continuecare.org/odessa//
**Control**: Other not–for–profit (including NFP Corporation) **Service**: Acute long–term care hospital

**Staffed Beds**: 25 **Admissions**: 233 **Census**: 18 **Outpatient Visits**: 0
**Births**: 0 **Total Expense ($000)**: 9657 **Payroll Expense ($000)**: 4334
**Personnel**: 39

☒ **MEDICAL CENTER HEALTH SYSTEM (450132)**, 500 West Fourth Street, Zip 79761–5059, Mailing Address: P O Drawer 7239, Zip 79760–7239; tel. 432/640–4000, (Nonreporting) **A**1 3 5 10 **F**3 11 12 13 15 17 18 20 22 24 26 28 29 30 31 34 35 40 42 43 45 46 47 48 49 50 53 54 57 59 64 65 66 68 70 71 72 74 75 76 77 78 79 81 85 87 89 90 93 107 111 114 115 116 117 118 119 126 131 132 135 144 146 147 148 155 157 **P**1 6 7
Primary Contact: Russell Tippin, Chief Executive Officer
COO: Tony Ruiz, Senior Vice President, Chief Operating Officer
CMO: Sari A. Nabulshi, M.D., Chief Medical Officer
CIO: Gary Barnes, Senior Vice President, Chief Information Officer
CHR: Robbi Banks, Vice President, Human Resources
CNO: Chad Dunavan, R.N., Vice President, Chief Nursing Officer
Web address: www.mchodessa.com
**Control**: Hospital district or authority, Government, Nonfederal **Service**: General medical and surgical

**Staffed Beds**: 368 **Admissions**: 14102 **Census**: 198 **Outpatient Visits**: 350088 **Births**: 2083 **Total Expense ($000)**: 325306 **Payroll Expense ($000)**: 114042 **Personnel**: 1784

**MEDICAL CENTER HOSPITAL** See Medical Center Health System

---

**Hospital, Medicare Provider Number, Address, Telephone, Approval, Facility, and Physician Codes, Health Care System**

★ American Hospital Association (AHA) membership
☐ The Joint Commission accreditation
○ Healthcare Facilities Accreditation Program
◇ DNV Healthcare Inc. accreditation
⇧ Center for Improvement in Healthcare Quality Accreditation
△ Commission on Accreditation of Rehabilitation Facilities (CARF) accreditation

**TX**

⇑ **ODESSA REGIONAL HOSPITAL** See Odessa Regional Medical Center

⇑ **ODESSA REGIONAL MEDICAL CENTER (450661)**, 520 East Sixth Street, Zip 79761–4565, Mailing Address: P.O. Box 4859, Zip 79760–4859; tel. 432/582–8000, (Nonreporting) **A**3 5 10 21 **F**3 12 13 15 17 18 20 22 23 24 25 29 34 35 40 43 46 49 50 51 52 55 57 59 60 64 66 72 74 75 76 79 81 82 85 86 87 89 90 91 107 108 111 115 119 124 130 132 146 147 148 154 **S** Steward Health Care System, LLC, Dallas, TX
Primary Contact: Stacey L. Brown, Chief Executive Officer
CIO: Jimmy Diaz, Director Information Technology
CHR: Jill Sparkman, Director Human Resources
CNO: Levi Ross Stone, R.N., Chief Nursing Officer and Chief Operating Officer
Web address: www.https://www.odessaregionalmedicalcenter.org/
**Control:** Partnership, Investor–owned (for–profit) **Service:** General medical and surgical

**Staffed Beds:** 213 **Admissions:** 6284 **Census:** 81 **Outpatient Visits:** 50630 **Births:** 2407 **Total Expense ($000):** 135040 **Payroll Expense ($000):** 37486 **Personnel:** 559

**ODESSA REGIONAL MEDICAL CENTER SOUTH CAMPUS (670066)**, 900 East 4th Street, Zip 79761–5255; tel. 432/362–9900, (Nonreporting) **A**10
Primary Contact: Stacey L. Brown, Chief Executive Officer
CMO: Richard Bartlett, M.D., Chief Medical Officer
Web address: www.bhcodessa.com/
**Control:** Partnership, Investor–owned (for–profit) **Service:** General medical and surgical

**Staffed Beds:** 14

### OLNEY—Young County

★ **HAMILTON HOSPITAL (451354)**, 901 West Hamilton Street, Zip 76374–1725, Mailing Address: P.O. Box 158, Zip 76374–0158; tel. 940/564–5521, (Nonreporting) **A**10 18 **F**7 11 13 28 29 30 34 40 43 53 57 76 77 81 86 89 93 98 107 114 127 129 130 133 146 148
Primary Contact: Michael H. Huff, Chief Executive Officer
CFO: Coy Noles, Chief Financial Officer Consultant
CMO: Mark L Mankins, M.D., Chief of Staff
CIO: Rick Oliver, Information Technology
CHR: Amy Moore, Human Resources
CNO: Samantha Isbell, R.N., Chief Nursing Officer
Web address: www.olneyhamiltonhospital.com
**Control:** Hospital district or authority, Government, Nonfederal **Service:** General medical and surgical

**Staffed Beds:** 25 **Admissions:** 282 **Census:** 8 **Outpatient Visits:** 19455 **Births:** 39 **Total Expense ($000):** 15849 **Payroll Expense ($000):** 5900 **Personnel:** 131

### PALACIOS—Matagorda County

★ **PALACIOS COMMUNITY MEDICAL CENTER (451332)**, 311 Green Street, Zip 77465–3213; tel. 361/972–2511, (Nonreporting) **A**10 18 **F**3 29 32 34 40 41 50 57 59 64 65 87 91 93 96 97 107 119 128 133 146 148 **P**6
Primary Contact: Nathan Tudor, Chief Executive Officer
COO: Lisa Henderson, Chief Operating Officer
CFO: Claude Manning, Chief Financial Officer
CIO: Angela Yeager, Director Information Technology
CHR: Lisa Henderson, Chief Operations Officer
CNO: Susan Easter, Chief Nursing Officer
Web address: www.palacioshospital.net/
**Control:** Other not–for–profit (including NFP Corporation) **Service:** General medical and surgical

**Staffed Beds:** 17 **Admissions:** 71 **Census:** 2 **Outpatient Visits:** 5149 **Births:** 0 **Total Expense ($000):** 4330 **Payroll Expense ($000):** 1907 **Personnel:** 43

**WAGNER GENERAL HOSPITAL** See Palacios Community Medical Center

### PALESTINE—Anderson County

⊞ **PALESTINE REGIONAL MEDICAL CENTER-EAST (450747)**, 2900 South Loop 256, Zip 75801–6958; tel. 903/731–1000, (Includes PALESTINE REGIONAL MEDICAL CENTER, Mailing address: 2900 S Loop 256, Palestine, Texas, Zip 75801–6958; tel. 903/731–1000; Roy Finch, Chief Executive Officer), (Nonreporting) **A**1 5 10 **F**3 7 13 15 18 20 26 28 29 31 34 40 43 44 47 48 49 50 51 56 57 59 60 62 63 70 76 79 81 82 85 86 87 89 90 93 96 97 98 100 107 108 110 111 114 118 119 129 130 131 146 147 148 154 **P**6 **S** LifePoint Health, Brentwood, TN
Primary Contact: Roy Finch, Chief Executive Officer
CFO: Celena Brim, Chief Financial Officer
CIO: Rebecca Chou, Director Information Systems
CHR: Rhonda Beard, Director Human Resources
Web address: www.palestineregional.com
**Control:** Partnership, Investor–owned (for–profit) **Service:** General medical and surgical

**Staffed Beds:** 120 **Admissions:** 3231 **Census:** 48 **Outpatient Visits:** 57045 **Births:** 552 **Total Expense ($000):** 66956 **Payroll Expense ($000):** 33978 **Personnel:** 488

**PALESTINE REGIONAL REHABILITATION CENTER** See Palestine Regional Medical Center

**TRINITY VALLEY MEDICAL CENTER** See Palestine Regional Medical Center-East

### PAMPA—Gray County

**COLUMBIA MEDICAL CENTER** See Pampa Regional Medical Center

☐ **PAMPA REGIONAL MEDICAL CENTER (450099)**, One Medical Plaza, Zip 79065; tel. 806/665–3721, (Nonreporting) **A**1 10 20 **F**3 11 13 15 18 20 22 29 34 35 40 41 45 46 50 51 55 56 57 64 66 70 76 77 79 81 85 87 91 92 93 96 97 98 101 102 103 104 107 110 111 115 119 129 130 132 133 134 135 143 144 146 147 148 149 153 154 **S** Prime Healthcare, Ontario, CA
Primary Contact: Edwin Leon, Chief Executive Officer
CFO: Ronald Collins, Chief Financial Officer
CMO: James Hall, M.D., Chief Medical Officer
CIO: Joy Patton, Director Information Technology
CHR: Debbie Dixon, Director Human Resources
CNO: Twilla Thomas, Chief Nursing Officer
Web address: www.prmctx.com
**Control:** Other not–for–profit (including NFP Corporation) **Service:** General medical and surgical

**Staffed Beds:** 91 **Admissions:** 1618 **Census:** 14 **Outpatient Visits:** 22396 **Births:** 163 **Total Expense ($000):** 37184 **Payroll Expense ($000):** 11026 **Personnel:** 194

### PARIS—Lamar County

**CHRISTUS ST JOSEPH HOSP NORTH** See Paris Regional Medical Center

⊞ **PARIS REGIONAL MEDICAL CENTER (450196)**, 865 Deshong Drive, Zip 75460–9313, Mailing Address: P.O. Box 9070, Zip 75461–9070; tel. 903/785–4521, (Includes PARIS REGIONAL MEDICAL CENTER, Mailing address: 865 Deshong Drive, Paris, Texas, Zip 75462–2097; tel. 903/785–4521), (Nonreporting) **A**1 10 **F**3 8 11 13 15 17 18 20 22 24 26 28 29 30 31 34 35 36 39 40 43 44 45 49 50 51 55 57 59 60 64 65 66 68 70 74 75 76 77 78 79 81 82 85 86 87 89 90 91 93 97 102 107 108 110 111 115 118 119 126 127 129 130 132 135 145 146 147 148 149 **P**5 **S** LifePoint Health, Brentwood, TN
Primary Contact: Steve Hyde, Chief Executive Officer
COO: Scott B. Avery, Chief Operating Officer
CFO: Donald E McDaniel IIIChief Financial Officer
CMO: Richard Bercher, M.D., Chief Medical Officer
CHR: Cheryl Perry, Executive Director Human Resources
CNO: Debra Taylor, Chief Nursing Officer
Web address: www.https://parisregionalmedical.com/
**Control:** Partnership, Investor–owned (for–profit) **Service:** General medical and surgical

**Staffed Beds:** 171 **Admissions:** 7547 **Census:** 80 **Outpatient Visits:** 77802 **Births:** 825 **Total Expense ($000):** 119480 **Payroll Expense ($000):** 40788 **Personnel:** 687

### PASADENA—Harris County

**BAYSHORE MEDICAL CENTER** See Hca Houston Healthcare Southeast

**TX**

★ ⇑ **CHI ST. LUKE'S HEALTH - PATIENTS MEDICAL CENTER (670031)**, 4600 East Sam Houston Parkway South, Zip 77505–3948; tel. 713/948–7000, (Nonreporting) **A**10 21 **F**12 15 17 18 20 22 24 26 28 29 30 34 35 40 42 45 46 51 54 64 70 74 77 79 81 82 86 87 91 93 94 107 111 114 115 116 117 119 129 130 145 146 147 148 154 157 **S** CommonSpirit Health, Chicago, IL
Primary Contact: Steven Foster, Chief Executive Officer
Web address: www.stlukestexas.com
**Control**: Partnership, Investor–owned (for–profit) **Service**: General medical and surgical

| | | |
|---|---|---|
| **Staffed Beds:** 61 **Admissions:** 3740 **Census:** 51 **Outpatient Visits:** 38962 **Births:** 1 **Total Expense ($000):** 77857 **Payroll Expense ($000):** 30672 **Personnel:** 487 | | |

⊞ **HCA HOUSTON HEALTHCARE SOUTHEAST (450097)**, 4000 Spencer Highway, Zip 77504–1202; tel. 713/359–2000, (Nonreporting) **A**1 10 **F**3 8 11 12 13 15 17 18 20 22 24 26 28 32 34 35 40 42 43 45 46 49 50 51 54 56 57 59 60 64 67 70 72 74 75 76 77 78 79 81 82 84 85 90 93 96 100 102 107 108 110 111 114 115 118 119 121 123 124 126 129 130 131 132 146 147 154 **S** HCA Healthcare, Nashville, TN
Primary Contact: Jeanna Bamburg, FACHE, Chief Executive Officer
CFO: John Armour, Chief Financial Officer
CIO: Clifford Ferguson, Director Information Technology and Systems
Web address: www.bayshoremedical.com
**Control**: Partnership, Investor–owned (for–profit) **Service**: General medical and surgical

| | | |
|---|---|---|
| **Staffed Beds:** 269 **Admissions:** 13721 **Census:** 197 **Outpatient Visits:** 139110 **Births:** 2441 **Total Expense ($000):** 234400 **Payroll Expense ($000):** 84181 **Personnel:** 1071 | | |

☐ **OCEANS BEHAVIORAL HOSPITAL OF PASADENA (454147)**, 4001 Preston Drive, Zip 77505–2069; tel. 832/619–8836, (Nonreporting) **A**1 **S** Oceans Healthcare, Plano, TX
Primary Contact: Shamieka Thomas, Administrator
Web address: www.https://oceanshealthcare.com/pasadena
**Control**: Corporation, Investor–owned (for–profit) **Service**: Psychiatric

| | | |
|---|---|---|
| **Staffed Beds:** 22 | | |

⇑ **ST. LUKE'S PATIENTS MEDICAL CENTER** See Chi St. Luke's Health - Patients Medical Center

○ **SURGERY SPECIALTY HOSPITALS OF AMERICA (450831)**, 4301B Vista Road, Zip 77504; tel. 713/378–3000, (Nonreporting) **A**10 11 **F**3 12 29 40 45 60 68 70 75 77 79 81 82 85 107 111 119 131 132
Primary Contact: Eric Chan, M.D., Chief Executive Officer
COO: Hemant Khemka, Chief Operating Officer
CFO: Hemant Khemka, Chief Financial Officer
CMO: Xiao H. Li, M.D., Chief of Staff
CIO: Ringo Cheng, Director Information Technology
Web address: www.surgeryspecialty.com/
**Control**: Partnership, Investor–owned (for–profit) **Service**: General medical and surgical

| | | |
|---|---|---|
| **Staffed Beds:** 37 **Admissions:** 183 **Census:** 1 **Outpatient Visits:** 2246 **Births:** 0 **Total Expense ($000):** 7337 **Payroll Expense ($000):** 4019 **Personnel:** 95 | | |

**VISTA MEDICAL CENTER HOSPITAL** See Surgery Specialty Hospitals of America

### PEARLAND—Brazoria County

⊞ **ENCOMPASS HEALTH REHABILITATION HOSPITAL OF PEARLAND (673066)**, 2121 Business Center Drive, Zip 77584–2153; tel. 346/907–3000, (Nonreporting) **A**1 10 **F**3 29 90 96 130 132 **P**5 **S** Encompass Health Corporation, Birmingham, AL
Primary Contact: Michael Cabiro, Chief Executive Officer
Web address: www.https://www.encompasshealth.com/locations/pearlandrehab
**Control**: Corporation, Investor–owned (for–profit) **Service**: Rehabilitation

| | | |
|---|---|---|
| **Staffed Beds:** 40 **Admissions:** 1107 **Census:** 38 **Outpatient Visits:** 0 **Births:** 0 **Total Expense ($000):** 16886 **Payroll Expense ($000):** 9998 **Personnel:** 118 | | |

⊞ **HCA HOUSTON HEALTHCARE PEARLAND (670106)**, 11100 Shadow Creek Parkway, Zip 77584–7285; tel. 713/770–7000, (Nonreporting) **A**1 **F**3 18 20 22 26 29 31 34 35 37 40 41 45 49 50 51 57 59 68 74 75 77 78 79 81 82 85 86 87 107 108 110 111 114 119 126 130 143 146 148 **S** HCA Healthcare, Nashville, TN
Primary Contact: David S. Wagner, Chief Executive Officer
Web address: www.pearlandmc.com
**Control**: Partnership, Investor–owned (for–profit) **Service**: General medical and surgical

| | | |
|---|---|---|
| **Staffed Beds:** 53 **Admissions:** 3349 **Census:** 37 **Outpatient Visits:** 32474 **Births:** 0 **Total Expense ($000):** 51345 **Payroll Expense ($000):** 18878 **Personnel:** 225 | | |

**PEARLAND MEDICAL CENTER** See Hca Houston Healthcare Pearland

### PEARSALL—Frio County

**FRIO HOSPITAL** See Frio Regional Hospital

★ **FRIO REGIONAL HOSPITAL (451391)**, 200 South I H 35, Zip 78061–3998; tel. 830/334–3617, (Nonreporting) **A**10 18 **F**3 13 15 29 34 35 40 43 45 57 59 62 64 68 76 77 81 87 96 107 110 115 119 130 133 146 148 **P**6
Primary Contact: John R. Hughson, Chief Executive Officer
CMO: Oscar Garza, M.D., Chief Medical Staff
CIO: Jacob Flores, Chief Information Officer
CHR: Nancy Ortiz, Director Human Resource and Marketing
CNO: Louisa Martinez, Director of Nursing
Web address: www.frioregionalhospital.com
**Control**: Other not–for–profit (including NFP Corporation) **Service**: General medical and surgical

| | | |
|---|---|---|
| **Staffed Beds:** 22 **Admissions:** 303 **Census:** 5 **Outpatient Visits:** 21185 **Births:** 99 **Total Expense ($000):** 18202 **Payroll Expense ($000):** 7364 **Personnel:** 117 | | |

### PECOS—Reeves County

**REEVES COUNTY HOSPITAL** See Reeves County Hospital District

**REEVES COUNTY HOSPITAL DISTRICT (451377)**, 2323 Texas Street, Zip 79772–7338; tel. 432/447–3551, (Nonreporting) **A**10 18 **F**3 11 13 15 35 40 43 57 60 64 68 70 76 81 87 89 93 107 110 114 119 127 130 131 133 146 147 148
Primary Contact: Brenda McKinney, Chief Executive Officer
COO: Yvette Riker, Chief Operating Officer
CFO: Bomi Bharucha, Chief Financial Officer
CMO: Deitrick Gorman, M.D., Chief of Staff
CHR: Nadine Smith, Director Human Resources
CNO: Faye Lease, Chief Nursing Officer
Web address: www.reevescountyhospital.com
**Control**: Hospital district or authority, Government, Nonfederal **Service**: General medical and surgical

| | | |
|---|---|---|
| **Staffed Beds:** 25 **Admissions:** 804 **Census:** 8 **Outpatient Visits:** 79704 **Births:** 172 **Total Expense ($000):** 33555 **Payroll Expense ($000):** 16976 **Personnel:** 239 | | |

### PERRYTON—Ochiltree County

★ **OCHILTREE GENERAL HOSPITAL (451359)**, 3101 Garrett Drive, Zip 79070–5323; tel. 806/435–3606, (Nonreporting) **A**10 18 **F**10 11 13 15 30 35 40 43 57 59 62 63 64 65 69 76 81 85 89 93 104 107 108 114 119 127 130 133 143 146 147 **P**1
Primary Contact: Leroy Schaffner, Interim Chief Executive Officer
CFO: Debbie Blodgett, Director Fiscal Services
CMO: Rex Mann, M.D., Chief Medical Officer
CIO: Dyan Harrison, Manager Health Information
CHR: Debbie Beck, Manager Human Resource and Payroll
Web address: www.ochiltreehospital.com
**Control**: Hospital district or authority, Government, Nonfederal **Service**: General medical and surgical

| | | |
|---|---|---|
| **Staffed Beds:** 25 **Admissions:** 424 **Census:** 6 **Outpatient Visits:** 46248 **Births:** 139 **Total Expense ($000):** 20066 **Payroll Expense ($000):** 8844 **Personnel:** 158 | | |

**TX**

---

**Hospital, Medicare Provider Number, Address, Telephone, Approval, Facility, and Physician Codes, Health Care System**

★ American Hospital Association (AHA) membership ○ Healthcare Facilities Accreditation Program ⇑ Center for Improvement in Healthcare Quality Accreditation
☐ The Joint Commission accreditation ◇ DNV Healthcare Inc. accreditation △ Commission on Accreditation of Rehabilitation Facilities (CARF) accreditation

## PFLUGERVILLE—Travis County

☐ **BAYLOR SCOTT & WHITE MEDICAL CENTER - PFLUGERVILLE (670128)**, 2600 East Pflugerville Parkway, Zip 78660–5998; tel. 512/654–6100, (Data for 211 days) (Nonreporting) **A**1 **F**3 15 18 29 34 35 40 45 50 54 57 59 64 68 74 75 77 79 81 84 85 87 102 107 108 110 111 119 130 131 148 149 154 **S** Baylor Scott & White Health, Dallas, TX
Primary Contact: Jay Fox, Chief Executive Officer
Web address: www.https://www.bswhealth.com/locations/pflugerville-mc
**Control:** Other not-for-profit (including NFP Corporation) **Service:** General medical and surgical

**Staffed Beds:** 12 **Admissions:** 248 **Census:** 3 **Outpatient Visits:** 8468
**Births:** 0 **Total Expense ($000):** 16044 **Payroll Expense ($000):** 5903
**Personnel:** 83

## PITTSBURG—Camp County

**EAST TEXAS MEDICAL CENTER PITTSBURG** See UT Health Pittsburg

★ **UT HEALTH PITTSBURG (451367)**, 2701 Highway 271 North, Zip 75686–1032; tel. 903/946–5000, (Nonreporting) **A**3 10 18 **F**3 11 12 28 29 34 35 40 43 45 50 57 59 64 65 75 77 79 81 82 84 85 87 92 93 97 107 108 111 115 119 127 129 130 133 **S** Ardent Health Services, Nashville, TN
Primary Contact: Casey Mayben, Interim Chief Executive Officer
CFO: Janet Andersen, Chief Financial Officer
CMO: W R Christensen, M.D., Chief of Staff
CIO: Paula Anthony, Vice President Information Services
CHR: Kathy Shelton, Director Human Resources
CNO: Casey Mayben, Chief Nursing Officer
Web address: www.https://uthealthpittsburg.com/
**Control:** Partnership, Investor-owned (for-profit) **Service:** General medical and surgical

**Staffed Beds:** 25 **Admissions:** 789 **Census:** 9 **Outpatient Visits:** 81422
**Births:** 0 **Total Expense ($000):** 29349 **Payroll Expense ($000):** 10310
**Personnel:** 171

## PLAINVIEW—Hale County

**ALLEGIANCE BEHAVIORAL HEALTH CENTER OF PLAINVIEW (454101)**, 2601 Dimmit Road, Suite 400, Zip 79072–1833; tel. 806/296–9191, (Nonreporting) **A**10 **F**29 35 56 64 98 101 103 104 **S** Allegiance Health Management, Shreveport, LA
Primary Contact: William E. Ernst, Chief Executive Officer
COO: Don Cameron, Chief Operating Officer
CMO: Victor A Gutierrez, M.D., Medical Director
CIO: Joe Monsour, Chief Information Officer
CHR: Danny J. Wagner, Chief Human Resource Officer
Web address: www.ahmgt.com
**Control:** Corporation, Investor-owned (for-profit) **Service:** Psychiatric

**Staffed Beds:** 20 **Admissions:** 291 **Census:** 12 **Outpatient Visits:** 30195
**Births:** 0 **Total Expense ($000):** 5421 **Payroll Expense ($000):** 2206
**Personnel:** 40

⊠ **COVENANT HOSPITAL PLAINVIEW (450539)**, 2601 Dimmit Road, Zip 79072–1833; tel. 806/296–5531, (Nonreporting) **A**1 10 20 **F**3 11 13 15 18 29 30 32 34 35 38 40 41 43 44 45 46 48 50 51 54 56 57 59 61 64 65 68 70 75 76 77 79 80 81 85 86 87 97 107 108 110 111 114 119 127 129 130 131 132 135 146 147 148 149 156 **S** Providence St. Joseph Health, Renton, WA
Primary Contact: Alan N. King, FACHE, Chief Executive Officer
COO: Mike McNutt, Assistant Administrator
CFO: Cassie Mogg, Chief Financial Officer
CMO: Sergio Lara, M.D., Chief Medical Officer
CNO: Leslie Hackett, Chief Nursing Officer
Web address: www.covenantplainview.org
**Control:** Other not-for-profit (including NFP Corporation) **Service:** General medical and surgical

**Staffed Beds:** 68 **Admissions:** 1591 **Census:** 13 **Outpatient Visits:** 82289
**Births:** 389 **Total Expense ($000):** 39067 **Payroll Expense ($000):** 13942
**Personnel:** 219

**METHODIST HOSPITAL PLAINVIEW** See Covenant Hospital Plainview

## PLANO—Denton County

See Accel Rehabilitation Hospital of Plano

☐ **ACCEL REHABILITATION HOSPITAL OF PLANO (673055)**, 2301 Marsh Lane, #200, Zip 75093–8497; tel. 972/899–5510, (Nonreporting) **A**1 **F**3 29 90 96 130 132
Primary Contact: Rick Tichenor, Chief Executive Officer
Web address: www.accelrehab.com
**Control:** Partnership, Investor-owned (for-profit) **Service:** Rehabilitation

**Staffed Beds:** 30 **Admissions:** 506 **Census:** 17 **Outpatient Visits:** 920
**Births:** 0 **Total Expense ($000):** 8598 **Payroll Expense ($000):** 3050
**Personnel:** 63

## PLANO—Collin County

**BAYLOR REGIONAL MEDICAL CENTER AT PLANO** See Baylor Scott & White Medical Center - Plano

⊠ **BAYLOR SCOTT & WHITE MEDICAL CENTER - PLANO (450890)**, 4700 Alliance Boulevard, Zip 75093–5323; tel. 469/814–2000, (Nonreporting) **A**1 2 3 5 10 **F**3 12 15 29 30 31 34 35 40 45 46 47 48 49 51 54 55 57 58 59 60 64 70 75 77 78 79 80 81 87 107 108 110 111 114 115 118 119 126 130 131 132 133 135 145 146 147 148 149 154 **S** Baylor Scott & White Health, Dallas, TX
Primary Contact: Jerri Garison, R.N., President
COO: Joseph C. Brown, Vice President Operations
CFO: Deanne Kindred, Vice President Finance
CMO: John Marcucci, M.D., Vice President Medical Affairs
CHR: Kriss Gamez, Director Human Resources
Web address: www.baylorhealth.com/PhysiciansLocations/Plano/Pages/Default.aspx
**Control:** Other not-for-profit (including NFP Corporation) **Service:** General medical and surgical

**Staffed Beds:** 124 **Admissions:** 6656 **Census:** 83 **Outpatient Visits:** 66087
**Births:** 0 **Total Expense ($000):** 180632 **Payroll Expense ($000):** 56834
**Personnel:** 607

⊠ **BAYLOR SCOTT & WHITE THE HEART HOSPITAL PLANO (670025)**, 1100 Allied Drive, Zip 75093–5348; tel. 469/814–3278, (Nonreporting) **A**1 2 3 5 10 **F**3 17 18 20 22 24 26 28 29 30 34 35 38 40 46 49 53 54 57 58 59 60 64 68 74 75 77 81 82 84 85 86 87 90 107 108 111 112 115 119 126 130 132 135 146 148 149 154 157
Primary Contact: Mark Valentine, President
COO: Brad D. McCall, Vice President Operations
CFO: Bryan Nichols, Chief Financial Officer
CMO: Trent Pettijohn, M.D., EsqChief Medical Officer
CHR: Anna Gemeny, Regional Director Human Resources
CNO: Susan K. Moats, R.N., Vice President Patient Care Services and Chief Nursing Officer
Web address: www.https://www.thehearthospitalbaylor.com
**Control:** Partnership, Investor-owned (for-profit) **Service:** Heart

**Staffed Beds:** 114 **Admissions:** 5524 **Census:** 88 **Outpatient Visits:** 34022
**Births:** 0 **Total Expense ($000):** 256438 **Payroll Expense ($000):** 73232
**Personnel:** 819

☐ **CHILDREN'S MEDICAL CENTER PLANO (453316)**, 7601 Preston Road, Zip 75024–3214; tel. 469/303–7000, (Nonreporting) **A**1 3 5 **F**3 19 21 23 29 30 31 34 39 40 41 43 54 59 64 68 74 75 77 78 79 81 82 85 86 87 88 89 93 97 98 99 104 105 107 108 111 114 115 118 119 126 129 130 131 146 148 153 154 156 **S** Children's Health, Dallas, TX
Primary Contact: Jeremiah Radandt, President
CIO: Pamela Arora, Senior Vice President and Chief Information Officer
CHR: Kim Besse, Executive Vice President and Chief Human Resource Officer
CNO: Mary Stowe, Senior Vice President and Chief Nursing Officer
Web address: www.https://www.childrens.com/location-landing/locations-and-directions/childrens-health-plano
**Control:** Other not-for-profit (including NFP Corporation) **Service:** Children's general medical and surgical

**Staffed Beds:** 72 **Admissions:** 2675 **Census:** 26 **Outpatient Visits:** 143096
**Births:** 0 **Total Expense ($000):** 180525 **Payroll Expense ($000):** 52578
**Personnel:** 812

*Many Facility Codes have changed. Please refer to the AHA Guide Code Chart.*  © 2021 AHA Guide

**ENCOMPASS HEALTH REHABILITATION HOSPITAL OF PLANO (453047)**, 2800 West 15th Street, Zip 75075–7526; tel. 972/612–9000, (Nonreporting) **A**1 10 **F**34 57 59 90 93 95 96 130 132 148 **S** Encompass Health Corporation, Birmingham, AL
Primary Contact: Brandon Tudor, Chief Executive Officer
CFO: Catrina Madkins, Controller and Chief Financial Officer
CMO: Omar Colon, M.D., Medical Director
Web address: www.healthsouthplano.com
**Control**: Corporation, Investor–owned (for–profit) **Service**: Rehabilitation

**Staffed Beds: 83 Admissions: 1627 Census: 53 Outpatient Visits: 0 Births: 0 Total Expense ($000): 22027 Payroll Expense ($000): 12078 Personnel: 207**

**HEALTHSOUTH PLANO REHABILITATION HOSPITAL** See Encompass Health Rehabilitation Hospital of Plano

⇑ **LEGENT HOSPITAL FOR SPECIAL SURGERY**, 4100 Mapleshade Lane, Zip 75093–0012; tel. 972/265–1050, (Nonreporting) **A**21
Primary Contact: Ethel Johnson, Chief Nursing Officer
Web address: www.https://www.legenthealth.com/
**Control**: Corporation, Investor–owned (for–profit) **Service**: Surgical

**Staffed Beds: 8**

**LIFECARE HOSPITALS OF PLANO** See Lifecare Hospitals of North Texas-Plano

**MEDICAL CENTER OF PLANO** See Medical City Plano

**MEDICAL CITY PLANO (450651)**, 3901 West 15th Street, Zip 75075–7738; tel. 972/596–6800, (Includes MEDICAL CITY FRISCO, Mailing address: 5500 Frisco Square Boulevard, Frisco, Texas, Zip 75034–3305; tel. 214/618–0500; Patrick Rohan, Chief Executive Officer), (Nonreporting) **A**1 2 3 10 **F**3 12 13 15 18 19 20 22 24 26 28 29 30 31 34 35 40 41 43 45 46 47 48 49 51 55 57 58 59 60 64 70 72 73 74 75 76 78 79 81 82 84 85 86 87 90 93 107 108 110 111 112 114 115 117 118 119 124 126 130 132 135 145 146 147 148 157 **S** HCA Healthcare, Nashville, TN
Primary Contact: Carlton Ulmer, Chief Executive Officer
COO: Cameron Howard, Chief Operating Officer
CFO: Brad Stein, Chief Financial Officer
CMO: Ann Arnold, M.D., Medical Director
CIO: Michael Gfeller, Director Information Systems
CHR: Shanna Warren, Director Human Resources
CNO: Damita Williams, Ed.D., R.N., MSN, Chief Nursing Officer
Web address: www.medicalcenterplano.com
**Control**: Partnership, Investor–owned (for–profit) **Service**: General medical and surgical

**Staffed Beds: 611 Admissions: 26298 Census: 387 Outpatient Visits: 170435 Births: 3522 Total Expense ($000): 492887 Payroll Expense ($000): 164470 Personnel: 2899**

**OCEANS BEHAVIORAL HOSPITAL PLANO** See Wellbridge Healthcare Greater Dallas

**PRESBYTERIAN HOSPITAL OF PLANO** See Texas Health Presbyterian Hospital Plano

**PRESBYTERIAN PLANO CENTER FOR DIAGNOSTIC & SURGERY** See Texas Health Center for Diagnostic & Surgery

⇑ **STAR MEDICAL CENTER** See Legent Hospital for Special Surgery

**TEXAS HEALTH CENTER FOR DIAGNOSTIC & SURGERY (450891)**, 6020 West Parker Road, Suite 100, Zip 75093–8171; tel. 972/403–2700, (Nonreporting) **A**1 3 10 **F**3 29 40 45 51 54 64 79 81 82 85 87 107 111 115 119 126 129 149
Primary Contact: Larry Robertson, President
CFO: Douglas Browning, Chief Financial Officer
CHR: Cookie Tedder, Human Resources Manager
CNO: Ellen Baldwin, R.N., Chief Nursing Officer
Web address: www.thcds.com
**Control**: Partnership, Investor–owned (for–profit) **Service**: General medical and surgical

**Staffed Beds: 18 Admissions: 714 Census: 3 Outpatient Visits: 15796 Births: 0 Total Expense ($000): 61332 Payroll Expense ($000): 14918 Personnel: 169**

**TEXAS HEALTH PRESBYTERIAN HOSPITAL PLANO (450771)**, 6200 West Parker Road, Zip 75093–8185; tel. 972/981–8000, (Nonreporting) **A**1 2 3 10 **F**3 12 13 15 18 20 22 24 26 28 29 30 31 32 34 35 36 38 40 42 43 44 45 46 49 50 52 53 54 55 57 58 59 60 64 65 68 70 72 74 75 76 77 78 79 81 84 85 86 87 89 93 98 104 105 107 108 110 111 114 115 118 119 126 130 131 132 134 135 141 145 146 147 148 149 150 153 157 **P**6 **S** Texas Health Resources, Arlington, TX
Primary Contact: Joshua Floren, President
CFO: Lisa Gildon, Vice President and Chief Financial Officer
CMO: Gwen Webster, M.D., President Medical Staff
CIO: Susan Anderson, Director Information Systems
CHR: Kelly K Martin, Human Resource Officer
Web address: www.texashealth.org
**Control**: Other not–for–profit (including NFP Corporation) **Service**: General medical and surgical

**Staffed Beds: 309 Admissions: 19444 Census: 244 Outpatient Visits: 102079 Births: 4132 Total Expense ($000): 373197 Payroll Expense ($000): 127780 Personnel: 1548**

**THE HEART HOSPITAL BAYLOR PLANO** See Baylor Scott & White The Heart Hospital Plano

**WELLBRIDGE HEALTHCARE GREATER DALLAS (454130)**, 4301 Mapleshade Lane, Zip 75093–0010; tel. 972/596–5445, (Nonreporting) **A**1
Primary Contact: John Sannuto, Chief Executive Officer
Web address: www.wellbridgedallas.com/
**Control**: Corporation, Investor–owned (for–profit) **Service**: Psychiatric

**Staffed Beds: 48**

## PORT ARTHUR—Jefferson County

**CHRISTUS DUBUIS HOSPITAL OF PORT ARTHUR** See Christus Dubuis Hospital of Port Arthur

⇑ **THE MEDICAL CENTER OF SOUTHEAST TEXAS (450518)**, 2555 Jimmy Johnson Boulevard, Zip 77640–2007; tel. 409/724–7389, (Nonreporting) **A**10 21 **F**3 8 11 12 13 15 17 18 20 22 24 26 28 29 30 34 35 40 43 44 45 47 49 50 56 57 59 64 70 72 74 76 77 78 79 81 82 85 86 87 89 90 91 92 93 94 98 101 102 103 104 105 107 108 110 111 114 115 119 121 129 130 132 135 146 147 148 153 154 **S** Steward Health Care System, LLC, Dallas, TX
Primary Contact: Phillip Craig. Desmond, Chief Executive Officer
COO: Chris McMahon, Chief Operating Officer
CFO: Jason R. Miller, Chief Financial Officer
CMO: Ryan McHugh, M.D., Chief of Staff
CIO: Bryan Hebert, Director Information Systems
CHR: Carol Hebert, Director Human Resources
CNO: Debbie Vaughn, Chief Nursing Officer
Web address: www.https://www.medicalcentersetexas.org/
**Control**: Partnership, Investor–owned (for–profit) **Service**: General medical and surgical

**Staffed Beds: 136 Admissions: 7490 Census: 93 Outpatient Visits: 83605 Births: 1034 Total Expense ($000): 151735 Payroll Expense ($000): 47634 Personnel: 753**

## PORT LAVACA—Calhoun County

★ **MEMORIAL MEDICAL CENTER (451356)**, 815 North Virginia Street, Zip 77979–3025, Mailing Address: P.O. Box 25, Zip 77979–0025; tel. 361/552–6713, (Nonreporting) **A**10 18 **F**3 11 13 15 18 28 29 30 34 35 40 43 44 45 46 50 57 59 64 65 68 70 75 76 77 79 81 82 84 85 86 87 93 97 107 108 111 115 118 119 127 129 130 131 132 133 135 146 147 148 153 154 **P**6
Primary Contact: Jason Anglin, Chief Executive Officer
COO: Roshanda Gray, Assistant Administrator
CFO: Diane C. Moore, Chief Financial Officer
CMO: Jeannine Griffin, M.D., Chief of Staff
CIO: Adam Besio, Chief Information Officer
CNO: Erin R Clevenger, Chief Nursing Officer and Director of Quality
Web address: www.mmcportlavaca.com
**Control**: County, Government, Nonfederal **Service**: General medical and surgical

**Staffed Beds: 25 Admissions: 1079 Census: 12 Outpatient Visits: 65431 Births: 111 Total Expense ($000): 30866 Payroll Expense ($000): 11478 Personnel: 222**

TX

## QUANAH—Hardeman County

**HARDEMAN COUNTY MEMORIAL HOSPITAL (451352)**, 402 Mercer Street, Zip 79252-4026, Mailing Address: P.O. Box 90, Zip 79252-0090; tel. 940/663-2795, (Nonreporting) **A**10 18 **F**28 29 34 40 43 50 56 57 59 64 75 93 94 100 101 104 107 127 130 133 148 149 153 **P**5
Primary Contact: Dennis Thomas, Chief Executive Officer
CFO: Tracy Betts, Chief Financial Officer
CMO: Kevin Lane, D.O., Chief of Staff
Web address: www.hcmhosp.net/
**Control:** Hospital district or authority, Government, Nonfederal **Service:** General medical and surgical

**Staffed Beds:** 18 **Admissions:** 217 **Census:** 4 **Outpatient Visits:** 17774 **Births:** 0 **Total Expense ($000):** 8495 **Payroll Expense ($000):** 3893 **Personnel:** 79

**HARDEMAN MEMORIAL HOSPITAL** See Hardeman County Memorial Hospital

## QUITMAN—Wood County

**EAST TEXAS MEDICAL CENTER-QUITMAN** See UT Health Quitman

★ **UT HEALTH QUITMAN (451380)**, 117 Winnsboro Street, Zip 75783-2144, Mailing Address: P.O. Box 1000, Zip 75783-1000; tel. 903/763-6300, (Nonreporting) **A**3 10 18 **F**3 11 28 29 30 34 35 40 43 45 50 57 59 64 65 77 79 81 82 84 85 87 107 108 111 115 119 127 129 130 133 144 148 149 **S** Ardent Health Services, Nashville, TN
Primary Contact: Robert Terry, Interim Chief Executive Officer
CFO: Janet Andersen, Chief Financial Officer
CHR: William Henry, Director Human Resources
CNO: Allicia Settles, Chief Nursing Officer
Web address: www.https://uthealthquitman.com/
**Control:** Partnership, Investor-owned (for-profit) **Service:** General medical and surgical

**Staffed Beds:** 25 **Admissions:** 995 **Census:** 11 **Outpatient Visits:** 73624 **Births:** 0 **Total Expense ($000):** 24853 **Payroll Expense ($000):** 9395 **Personnel:** 191

## RANKIN—Upton County

★ **RANKIN COUNTY HOSPITAL DISTRICT (451329)**, 1105 Elizabeth Street, Zip 79778, Mailing Address: P.O. Box 327, Zip 79778-0327; tel. 432/693-2443, (Nonreporting) **A**10 18 **F**3 7 34 35 40 50 53 54 55 56 57 59 64 65 66 68 75 86 87 93 97 102 107 119 130 131 133 135 147 148 156 **P**6
Primary Contact: Jim Horton, Chief Executive Officer
CFO: Tami Burks, Comptroller
CMO: Thomas J Curvin, M.D., Chief of Staff
Web address: www.rankincountyhospital.com/
**Control:** Hospital district or authority, Government, Nonfederal **Service:** General medical and surgical

**Staffed Beds:** 14 **Admissions:** 52 **Census:** 1 **Outpatient Visits:** 9546 **Births:** 0 **Total Expense ($000):** 13048 **Payroll Expense ($000):** 6142 **Personnel:** 80

**RANKIN HOSPITAL DISTRICT** See Rankin County Hospital District

## REFUGIO—Refugio County

**REFUGIO COUNTY MEMORIAL HOSPITAL (451317)**, 107 Swift Street, Zip 78377-2425; tel. 361/526-2321, (Nonreporting) **A**10 18 **F**3 7 29 40 43 57 61 64 75 81 86 87 93 97 107 119 127 133 155 **P**6
Primary Contact: Horace Whitt, Chief Executive Officer and Chief Operating Officer
Web address: www.refugiohospital.com/
**Control:** Hospital district or authority, Government, Nonfederal **Service:** General medical and surgical

**Staffed Beds:** 20 **Admissions:** 56 **Census:** 1 **Outpatient Visits:** 20509 **Births:** 0 **Total Expense ($000):** 13351 **Payroll Expense ($000):** 5513 **Personnel:** 113

## RICHARDSON—Collin County

⇑ **EMINENT MEDICAL CENTER**, 1351 West President George Bush Hwy, Zip 75080; tel. 469/910-8800, (Nonreporting) **A**21 **F**3 29 37 40 75 77 79 81 85 86 87 119 126 149 **P**2
Primary Contact: Rhonda Lopp, Chief Executive Officer
CNO: Erin Baker, Chief Nursing Officer
Web address: www.eminentmedicalcenter.com
**Control:** Partnership, Investor-owned (for-profit) **Service:** Surgical

**Staffed Beds:** 5 **Admissions:** 182 **Census:** 1 **Outpatient Visits:** 2674 **Births:** 0 **Total Expense ($000):** 22309 **Payroll Expense ($000):** 3213 **Personnel:** 50

⊠ **ENCOMPASS HEALTH REHABILITATION HOSPITAL OF RICHARDSON (673029)**, 3351 Waterview Parkway, Zip 75080-1449; tel. 972/398-5700, (Nonreporting) **A**1 10 **F**3 29 30 90 96 132 148 149 156 **S** Encompass Health Corporation, Birmingham, AL
Primary Contact: LaDessa Forrest, Administrator
CMO: Richard Jones, M.D., Medical Director
CNO: Pam Smith, Chief Nursing Officer
Web address: www.relianthcp.com
**Control:** Corporation, Investor-owned (for-profit) **Service:** Rehabilitation

**Staffed Beds:** 50 **Admissions:** 1372 **Census:** 46 **Outpatient Visits:** 0 **Births:** 0 **Total Expense ($000):** 18374 **Payroll Expense ($000):** 10852 **Personnel:** 140

**HEALTHSOUTH REHABILITATION HOSPITAL NORTH TEXAS** See Encompass Health Rehabilitation Hospital of Richardson

⊠ **METHODIST RICHARDSON MEDICAL CENTER (450537)**, 2831 East President George Bush Highway, Zip 75082-3561; tel. 469/204-1000, (Nonreporting) **A**1 2 3 10 **F**3 5 11 13 15 18 20 22 24 29 30 31 34 35 38 40 45 46 49 54 55 56 57 59 64 65 68 70 72 74 75 76 77 78 79 81 82 85 86 87 93 97 98 100 101 102 103 104 105 107 108 109 110 111 112 115 116 117 119 120 121 123 124 126 129 130 131 132 135 146 147 148 153 156 **P**5 6 **S** Methodist Health System, Dallas, TX
Primary Contact: E. Kenneth. Hutchenrider Jr, FACHE, President
COO: Robert Simpson, Vice President Operations
CFO: Ed Abbott, Vice President Finance
CMO: Mark Smith, M.D., Chief Medical Officer
CIO: Pamela McNutt, Senior Vice President and Chief Information Officer
CHR: Chris Loyd, Director Human Resources
CNO: Irene T Strejc, M.P.H., R.N., Vice President, Nursing
Web address: www.methodisthealthsystem.org/richardson
**Control:** Other not-for-profit (including NFP Corporation) **Service:** General medical and surgical

**Staffed Beds:** 259 **Admissions:** 12891 **Census:** 190 **Outpatient Visits:** 106130 **Births:** 1796 **Total Expense ($000):** 263872 **Payroll Expense ($000):** 106011 **Personnel:** 1137

**RICHARDSON REGIONAL MEDICAL CENTER** See Methodist Richardson Medical Center

## RICHMOND—Fort Bend County

**OAKBEND MEDICAL CENTER** See Oakbend Medical Center

☐ **OAKBEND MEDICAL CENTER (450330)**, 1705 Jackson Street, Zip 77469-3289; tel. 281/341-3000, (Includes HOSPITAL FOR SURGICAL EXCELLENCE, Mailing address: 1211 Highway 6, Suite 70, Sugar Land, Texas, Zip 77478-4940; tel. 281/238-3900; Joe Freudenberger, Chief Executive Officer; OAKBEND MEDICAL CENTER WILLIAMS WAY CAMPUS, Mailing address: 22003 Southwest Freeway, Richmond, Texas, Zip 77469-7003; tel. 281/341-2000; Joe Freudenberger, Chief Executive Officer) (Total facility includes 36 beds in nursing home-type unit) **A**1 10 **F**3 8 13 15 18 20 22 24 26 28 29 30 34 35 40 42 43 45 46 48 49 50 51 53 56 57 59 70 72 74 75 76 77 78 79 81 85 87 93 97 98 103 107 108 110 111 114 115 119 128 129 130 131 146 147 148 154 **P**6
Primary Contact: Joe Freudenberger, Chief Executive Officer
CFO: Rodney Lenfant, Chief Financial Officer
CMO: Douglas Thibodeaux, M.D., Chief Medical Officer
CIO: Tim McCarty, Chief Information Officer
CHR: Eileen Gamboa, Vice President Human Resources, HCA Houston Healthcare Southeast
Web address: www.oakbendmedcenter.org
**Control:** Hospital district or authority, Government, Nonfederal **Service:** General medical and surgical

**Staffed Beds:** 237 **Admissions:** 5441 **Census:** 78 **Outpatient Visits:** 91134 **Births:** 1118 **Total Expense ($000):** 162972 **Payroll Expense ($000):** 54632 **Personnel:** 838

☐ **WESTPARK SPRINGS (454131)**, 6902 South Peek Road, Zip 77407; tel. 832/532-8107, (Nonreporting) **A**1 **F**4 5 54 64 68 75 86 87 98 99 101 104 105 106 130 151 152 153 154 **S** Springstone, Louisville, KY
Primary Contact: Dustin Davis, Market Chief Executive Officer
Web address: www.westparksprings.com/why-westpark-springs/
**Control:** Corporation, Investor-owned (for-profit) **Service:** Psychiatric

**Staffed Beds:** 72 **Admissions:** 2478 **Census:** 51 **Outpatient Visits:** 12180 **Births:** 0 **Total Expense ($000):** 15896 **Payroll Expense ($000):** 9050 **Personnel:** 130

**TX**

*Many Facility Codes have changed. Please refer to the AHA Guide Code Chart.* © 2021 AHA Guide

## RIO GRANDE CITY—Starr County

★ **STARR COUNTY MEMORIAL HOSPITAL (450654)**, 128 N FM 3167, Zip 78582–6211, Mailing Address: P.O. Box 78, Zip 78582–0078; tel. 956/487–5561, (Nonreporting) **A**10 20 **F**7 11 13 15 29 34 35 39 40 43 45 46 50 57 59 64 65 66 68 75 76 81 89 97 107 110 111 115 119 127 130 135 145 146 148 154 **P**5
Primary Contact: Thalia H. Munoz, R.N., MS, Chief Executive Officer
CFO: Rafael Olivares, Controller
CHR: Amaro Salinas, Assistant Administrator and Human Resource Officer
CNO: Mario Segura, Director of Nursing
Web address: www.starrcountyhospital.com
**Control:** Hospital district or authority, Government, Nonfederal **Service:** General medical and surgical

| | |
|---|---|
| Staffed Beds: 47 Admissions: 878 Census: 8 Outpatient Visits: 41227 Births: 145 Total Expense ($000): 36631 Payroll Expense ($000): 14249 Personnel: 274 | |

## ROCKWALL—Rockwall County

**BAYLOR SCOTT & WHITE EMERGENCY HOSPITAL - ROCKWALL (670097)**, 1975 Alpha Drive Suite 100, Zip 75087–4951; tel. 214/294–6200, (Nonreporting) **A**10 **S** Emerus, The Woodlands, TX
Primary Contact: Vic Schmerbeck, Chief Executive Officer
Web address: www.bayloremc.com/rockwall
**Control:** Partnership, Investor–owned (for–profit) **Service:** General medical and surgical

| | |
|---|---|
| Staffed Beds: 8 | |

**BAYLOR SCOTT & WHITE EMERGENCY HOSPITAL—ROCKWALL** See Baylor Scott & White Emergency Hospital - Rockwall

**PRESBYTERIAN HOSPITAL OF ROCKWALL** See Texas Health Presbyterian Hospital of Rockwall

⊞ **TEXAS HEALTH PRESBYTERIAN HOSPITAL OF ROCKWALL (670044)**, 3150 Horizon Road, Zip 75032–7805; tel. 469/698–1000, (Nonreporting) **A**1 3 10 **F**3 11 12 13 15 29 30 34 35 40 42 45 46 47 49 50 51 54 68 70 75 76 77 79 81 82 84 85 87 107 108 110 111 115 119 126 130 131 146 147
Primary Contact: Cynthia K. Perrin, President and Chief Executive Officer
COO: Jason Linscott, CPA, Chief Operating Officer and Chief Financial Officer
CFO: Jason Linscott, CPA, Chief Financial Officer
CMO: Gary Bonacquisti, M.D., Chief Medical Officer
CHR: Candy Marie Stewart, Vice President People and Culture, Chief Human Resouces Officer
CNO: Tami Hawkins, R.N., MSN, Vice President Patient Care and Chief Nursing Officer
Web address: www.phrtexas.com
**Control:** Corporation, Investor–owned (for–profit) **Service:** General medical and surgical

| | |
|---|---|
| Staffed Beds: 61 Admissions: 3448 Census: 28 Outpatient Visits: 61329 Births: 727 Total Expense ($000): 113199 Payroll Expense ($000): 37986 Personnel: 487 | |

## ROTAN—Fisher County

**FISHER COUNTY HOSPITAL DISTRICT (451313)**, 774 State Highway 70 North, Zip 79546–6918, Mailing Address: P O Drawer 'F', Zip 79546–4019; tel. 325/735–2256, (Nonreporting) **A**10 18 **F**7 28 32 34 35 40 43 50 53 56 57 59 64 66 75 93 97 107 119 127 133 155 **P**6
Primary Contact: Leanne Martinez, Chief Executive Officer and Administrator
CFO: Debbie Hull, Chief Financial Officer
CMO: Joseph Lampley, D.O., Chief of Staff
CHR: Teresa Terry, Director Human Resource, Payroll
CNO: D'Linda Benham, Director of Nursing
Web address: www.fishercountyhospital.com
**Control:** Hospital district or authority, Government, Nonfederal **Service:** General medical and surgical

| | |
|---|---|
| Staffed Beds: 14 Admissions: 100 Census: 2 Outpatient Visits: 15736 Births: 0 Total Expense ($000): 8694 Payroll Expense ($000): 4167 Personnel: 75 | |

## ROUND ROCK—Williamson County

⊞ **ASCENSION SETON WILLIAMSON (670041)**, 201 Seton Parkway, Zip 78665–8000; tel. 512/324–4000, (Nonreporting) **A**1 2 3 5 10 **F**3 11 12 13 18 20 22 24 26 28 29 30 35 37 40 43 44 45 46 47 48 49 64 68 70 72 74 76 77 79 81 85 87 92 100 107 108 111 114 115 118 119 120 126 130 131 132 146 147 148 154 **S** Ascension Healthcare, Saint Louis, MO
Primary Contact: Katherine Henderson, Regional Hospital President
CFO: Douglas D Waite, Senior Vice President and Chief Financial Officer
CMO: Hugh V Gilmore, M.D., Vice President Medical Affairs
CHR: Thomas Wilken, Vice President Human Resources
Web address: www.seton.net/williamson
**Control:** Church operated, Nongovernment, not–for–profit **Service:** General medical and surgical

| | |
|---|---|
| Staffed Beds: 140 Admissions: 7192 Census: 93 Outpatient Visits: 48672 Births: 277 Total Expense ($000): 152247 Payroll Expense ($000): 40173 Personnel: 734 | |

⊞ **BAYLOR SCOTT & WHITE MEDICAL CENTER - ROUND ROCK (670034)**, 300 University Boulevard, Zip 78665–1032; tel. 512/509–0100, (Includes BAYLOR SCOTT & WHITE MEDICAL CENTER - LAKEWAY, Mailing address: 100 Medical Parkway, Lakeway, Texas, Zip 78738–5621; tel. 512/571–5000; Philippe Bochaton, President), (Nonreporting) **A**1 2 3 10 **F**3 11 13 15 18 20 22 24 28 29 30 34 36 40 42 45 46 47 49 50 51 54 56 58 60 62 63 65 68 72 74 75 76 78 79 81 82 84 85 87 89 91 92 93 97 100 107 108 110 111 114 115 116 117 119 126 129 130 132 133 135 143 146 147 148 149 154 156 **S** Baylor Scott & White Health, Dallas, TX
Primary Contact: John M. Lambert, President
COO: Joseph C. Brown, Vice President Operations
CFO: Jason Cole, Regional Chief Financial Officer
CMO: Rob Watson, M.D., Chief Medical Officer
CIO: Matthew Chambers, Chief Information Officer
CHR: Mark A. Sherry, Regional Director Human Resource Strategic Services, Austin/Round Rock Region
CNO: Leslie Gembol, MSN, R.N., Chief Nursing Officer
Web address: www.sw.org
**Control:** Other not–for–profit (including NFP Corporation) **Service:** General medical and surgical

| | |
|---|---|
| Staffed Beds: 173 Admissions: 10191 Census: 102 Outpatient Visits: 664105 Births: 883 Total Expense ($000): 321180 Payroll Expense ($000): 84886 Personnel: 1411 | |

⊞ **ENCOMPASS HEALTH REHABILITATION HOSPITAL OF ROUND ROCK (673032)**, 1400 Hesters Crossing Road, Zip 78681–8025; tel. 512/244–4400, (Nonreporting) **A**1 10 **F**3 29 90 95 96 130 132 148 149 **S** Encompass Health Corporation, Birmingham, AL
Primary Contact: David Jones, Chief Executive Officer
CFO: Joe Griffin, Controller
CHR: Amelia Leudecke, Director Human Resources
CNO: Randi Cruz, Chief Nursing Officer
Web address: www.https://www.encompasshealth.com/roundrockrehab
**Control:** Corporation, Investor–owned (for–profit) **Service:** Rehabilitation

| | |
|---|---|
| Staffed Beds: 75 Admissions: 1438 Census: 48 Outpatient Visits: 0 Births: 0 Total Expense ($000): 24693 Payroll Expense ($000): 11114 Personnel: 161 | |

**HEALTHSOUTH REHABILITATION HOSPITAL ROUND ROCK** See Encompass Health Rehabilitation Hospital of Round Rock

⊞ **PAM REHABILITATION HOSPITAL OF ROUND ROCK (673069)**, 351 Seton Parkway, Zip 78665–8001; tel. 737/708–9800, (Nonreporting) **A**1 **S** Post Acute Medical, LLC, Enola, PA
Primary Contact: Troy Lee, Chief Executive Officer
Web address: www.postacutemedical.com
**Service:** Rehabilitation

| | |
|---|---|
| Staffed Beds: 40 | |

**ROUND ROCK MEDICAL CENTER** See St. David's Round Rock Medical Center

**SCOTT & WHITE HOSPITAL AT ROUND ROCK** See Baylor Scott & White Medical Center - Round Rock

**SETON MEDICAL CENTER WILLIAMSON** See Ascension Seton Williamson

**TX**

---

✠ **ST. DAVID'S ROUND ROCK MEDICAL CENTER (450718)**, 2400 Round Rock Avenue, Zip 78681–4097; tel. 512/341-1000, (Nonreporting) **A**1 2 10 **F**3 12 13 15 18 20 22 24 26 28 29 30 31 34 35 37 40 42 43 45 49 54 59 64 67 69 70 72 74 75 76 77 78 79 81 84 85 87 93 102 107 108 110 111 115 116 117 119 124 126 129 130 132 135 146 147 148 149 152 154 157 **P**6 **S** HCA Healthcare, Nashville, TN
Primary Contact: Jeremy Barclay, Chief Executive Officer
COO: Katie Lattanzi, Chief Operating Officer
CFO: Cindy Sexton, Chief Financial Officer
CHR: Amy Noak, Director Human Resources
Web address: www.stdavids.com
**Control:** Other not–for–profit (including NFP Corporation) **Service:** General medical and surgical

**Staffed Beds:** 169 **Admissions:** 10612 **Census:** 129 **Outpatient Visits:** 80249 **Births:** 1571 **Total Expense ($000):** 177605 **Payroll Expense ($000):** 60371 **Personnel:** 805

### ROWLETT—Rockwall County

✠ **BAYLOR SCOTT & WHITE MEDICAL CENTER - LAKE POINTE (450742)**, 6800 Scenic Drive, Zip 75088–4552, Mailing Address: P.O. Box 1550, Zip 75030–1550; tel. 972/412–2273, (Nonreporting) **A**1 10 **F**3 13 15 18 20 22 26 28 29 30 34 35 40 42 43 45 46 49 50 59 64 68 70 72 73 74 75 76 77 79 81 82 85 86 87 93 97 100 107 108 110 111 114 115 119 126 129 146 147 148 149 156 **S** Baylor Scott & White Health, Dallas, TX
Primary Contact: Donas Cole, FACHE, President
COO: Benson Chacko, Vice President, Operations
Web address: www.https://www.bswhealth.com/locations/lake-pointe/
**Control:** Other not–for–profit (including NFP Corporation) **Service:** General medical and surgical

**Staffed Beds:** 176 **Admissions:** 7010 **Census:** 77 **Outpatient Visits:** 93337 **Births:** 1610 **Total Expense ($000):** 165502 **Payroll Expense ($000):** 52378 **Personnel:** 577

**LAKE POINTE MEDICAL CENTER** See Baylor Scott & White Medical Center - Lake Pointe

### RUSK—Cherokee County

☐ **RUSK STATE HOSPITAL (454009)**, 805 North Dickinson, Zip 75785–2333, Mailing Address: P.O. Box 318, Zip 75785–0318; tel. 903/683–3421, (Nonreporting) **A**1 3 5 10 **F**3 29 30 39 44 77 86 87 91 98 100 103 106 130 135 146 148 149 **P**6 **S** Texas Department of State Health Services, Austin, TX
Primary Contact: Brenda Slaton, Superintendent
COO: Lynda Roberson, Senior Program Director
CFO: Rhonda Transier, Financial Officer
CMO: Joe Bates, M.D., Clinical Director
CHR: Kendra Brown, Job Requisition Coordinator
Web address: www.dshs.state.tx.us/mhhospitals/RuskSH/default.shtm
**Control:** State, Government, Nonfederal **Service:** Psychiatric

**Staffed Beds:** 277 **Admissions:** 984 **Census:** 276 **Outpatient Visits:** 0 **Births:** 0 **Total Expense ($000):** 60439 **Payroll Expense ($000):** 47436 **Personnel:** 869

### SAN ANGELO—Tom Green County

**COLUMBIA MEDICAL CENTER** See San Angelo Community Medical Center

**CONCHO VALLEY REGIONAL HOSP** See Shannon Medical Center- St. John's Campus

☐ **RIVER CREST HOSPITAL (454064)**, 1636 Hunters Glen Road, Zip 76901–5016; tel. 325/949–5722, (Nonreporting) **A**1 3 10 **F**4 5 29 64 87 98 99 100 101 102 103 104 105 130 132 151 152 153 **S** Universal Health Services, Inc., King of Prussia, PA
Primary Contact: Angela Harris, Chief Executive Officer
CMO: Raymond Mays, M.D., Medical Director
CHR: Lydia Cardenas, Director Human Resources
CNO: Debra Millsap, Director of Nursing
Web address: www.rivercresthospital.com
**Control:** Corporation, Investor–owned (for–profit) **Service:** Psychiatric

**Staffed Beds:** 80 **Admissions:** 2751 **Census:** 48 **Outpatient Visits:** 3551 **Births:** 0 **Total Expense ($000):** 14027 **Payroll Expense ($000):** 7017 **Personnel:** 142

✠ ○ **SAN ANGELO COMMUNITY MEDICAL CENTER (450340)**, 3501 Knickerbocker Road, Zip 76904–7698; tel. 325/949–9511, (Nonreporting) **A**1 10 11 **F**3 8 11 12 13 15 18 20 22 24 26 28 29 30 34 35 37 40 43 45 49 51 53 54 57 59 60 63 64 68 70 72 74 75 76 77 78 79 81 85 89 93 107 108 110 111 115 118 119 126 129 130 131 135 144 145 146 147 148 **P**8 **S** Community Health Systems, Inc., Franklin, TN
Primary Contact: Rodney Schumacher, Interim Chief Executive Officer
CFO: Steven Ewing, Chief Financial Officer
CHR: Lisa Bibb, Director Human Resources
Web address: www.sacmc.com
**Control:** Partnership, Investor–owned (for–profit) **Service:** General medical and surgical

**Staffed Beds:** 131 **Admissions:** 3743 **Census:** 41 **Outpatient Visits:** 77330 **Births:** 668 **Total Expense ($000):** 90016 **Payroll Expense ($000):** 27859 **Personnel:** 519

★ **SHANNON MEDICAL CENTER (450571)**, 120 East Harris Street, Zip 76903–5976, Mailing Address: P.O. Box 1879, Zip 76902–1879; tel. 325/653–6741, (Includes SHANNON MEDICAL CENTER- ST. JOHN'S CAMPUS, Mailing address: 2018 Pulliam Street, San Angelo, Texas, Zip 76905–5197; tel. 325/659–7100; Bryan Horner, President and Chief Executive Officer) (Total facility includes 21 beds in nursing home–type unit) **A**3 5 10 22 **F**3 8 11 12 13 15 18 20 22 24 26 28 29 30 31 32 34 35 37 38 40 43 44 45 47 48 49 50 51 53 54 56 57 58 59 60 61 62 64 68 70 71 72 73 74 75 76 77 78 79 80 81 82 84 85 86 87 89 90 92 93 94 96 98 100 101 102 107 108 110 111 114 115 117 119 126 128 130 132 145 146 147 148 149 155 **P**6
Primary Contact: Shane Plymell, Chief Executive Officer
COO: Pamela Bradshaw, R.N., Vice President, Chief Operating Officer and Chief Nursing Officer
CFO: Staci Wetz, Chief Financial Officer
CMO: Irvin Zeitler, D.O., Vice President Medical Affairs
CIO: Tom Perkins, Chief Information Officer
CHR: Teresa Morgan, Assistant Vice President Human Resources
CNO: Pamela Bradshaw, R.N., Vice President, Chief Operating Officer and Chief Nursing Officer
Web address: www.shannonhealth.com
**Control:** Other not–for–profit (including NFP Corporation) **Service:** General medical and surgical

**Staffed Beds:** 320 **Admissions:** 14621 **Census:** 206 **Outpatient Visits:** 128239 **Births:** 1325 **Total Expense ($000):** 312059 **Payroll Expense ($000):** 103293 **Personnel:** 1760

### SAN ANTONIO—Bexar County

**AUDIE L MURPHY MEM HOSPITAL** See San Antonio Division

⇧ **BAPTIST EMERGENCY HOSPITAL (670078)**, 16088 San Pedro, Zip 78232–2249; tel. 210/402–4092, (Includes BAPTIST EMERGENCY HOSPITAL - HAUSMAN, Mailing address: 8230 North 1604 West, San Antonio, Texas, Zip 78249; tel. 210/572–8885; Shannon Crinion, Chief Executive Officer; BAPTIST EMERGENCY HOSPITAL - OVERLOOK, Mailing address: 25615 US Highway 281 North, San Antonio, Texas, Zip 78258–7135; tel. 210/572–2911; Shannon Crinion, Chief Executive Officer; BAPTIST EMERGENCY HOSPITAL - SCHERTZ, Mailing address: 16977 Interstate 35 North, Schertz, Texas, Zip 78154–1466; tel. 210/572–8400; Sandra Diaz, Administrator; BAPTIST EMERGENCY HOSPITAL - WESTOVER HILLS, Mailing address: 10811 Town Center Drive, San Antonio, Texas, Zip 78251–4585; tel. 210/572–0911; Shannon Crinion, Chief Executive Officer), (Nonreporting) **A**10 21 **F**1 3 29 40 42 67 102 107 114 149 **P**5 **S** Emerus, The Woodlands, TX
Primary Contact: Shannon Crinion, Chief Executive Officer
CNO: David Mitchell, Vice President Nursing
Web address: www.baptistemergencyhospital.com
**Control:** Corporation, Investor–owned (for–profit) **Service:** General medical and surgical

**Staffed Beds:** 33 **Admissions:** 1494 **Census:** 9 **Outpatient Visits:** 109203 **Births:** 0 **Total Expense ($000):** 65423 **Payroll Expense ($000):** 18392 **Personnel:** 322

⇧ **BAPTIST EMERGENCY HOSPITAL - THOUSAND OAKS** See Baptist Emergency Hospital

**BAPTIST HEALTH SYSTEM** See Baptist Medical Center

*Many Facility Codes have changed. Please refer to the AHA Guide Code Chart.* © 2021 AHA Guide

⊞ △ **BAPTIST MEDICAL CENTER (450058)**, 111 Dallas Street, Zip 78205–1230; tel. 210/297–7000, (Includes MISSION TRAIL BAPTIST HOSPITAL, Mailing address: 3333 Research Plaza, San Antonio, Texas, Zip 78235–5154; tel. 210/297–3000; Gina Temple, Chief Executive Officer; NORTH CENTRAL BAPTIST HOSPITAL, Mailing address: 520 Madison Oak Drive, San Antonio, Texas, Zip 78258–3912; tel. 210/297–4000; NORTHEAST BAPTIST HOSPITAL, Mailing address: 8811 Village Drive, San Antonio, Texas, Zip 78217–5440; tel. 210/297–2000; J Phillip Young, FACHE, Chief Executive Officer; ST. LUKE'S BAPTIST HOSPITAL, Mailing address: 7930 Floyd Curl Drive, San Antonio, Texas, Zip 78229–0100; tel. 210/297–5000; Philip Koovakada, Chief Executive Officer), (Nonreporting) **A**1 2 3 5 7 10 **F**3 11 12 13 14 15 17 18 19 20 22 24 26 28 29 30 31 35 37 38 40 41 43 44 45 46 47 50 54 55 56 57 59 60 64 65 68 70 72 73 74 75 76 77 78 79 80 81 82 85 86 87 88 89 90 91 92 93 95 96 98 101 102 103 107 108 111 114 115 116 117 119 124 126 129 130 132 135 145 146 147 148 149 **P**8 **S** TENET Healthcare Corporation, Dallas, TX
Primary Contact: Jorge Trevino, Chief Executive Officer
COO: Sandy Ethridge, Interim Chief Operating Officer
CIO: Gary Davis, Vice President Information Systems
Web address: www.baptisthealthsystem.com
**Control**: Partnership, Investor–owned (for-profit) **Service**: General medical and surgical

**Staffed Beds:** 1570 **Admissions:** 61235 **Census:** 771 **Outpatient Visits:** 463865 **Births:** 10376 **Total Expense ($000):** 955543 **Payroll Expense ($000):** 324169 **Personnel:** 5532

**BEXAR COUNTY HOSPITAL DISTRICT** See University Health System

**BRADY-GREEN COMM HEALTH CENTER** See University Health Center - Downtown

⊞ **CHILDREN'S HOSPITAL OF SAN ANTONIO (453315)**, 333 North Santa Rosa Street, Zip 78207; tel. 210/704–2011, (Nonreporting) **A**1 3 5 10 **F**3 8 11 13 19 21 23 25 27 28 29 30 31 32 34 37 39 40 41 42 43 45 46 48 49 54 55 58 59 60 64 65 68 70 71 72 74 75 76 77 78 79 81 82 83 84 85 86 87 88 89 93 97 107 108 111 114 115 117 118 119 126 130 131 132 144 146 147 148 156 157 **S** CHRISTUS Health, Irving, TX
Primary Contact: Cris Daskevich, Chief Executive Officer
Web address: www.chofsa.org/
**Control**: Church operated, Nongovernment, not-for-profit **Service**: General medical and surgical

**Staffed Beds:** 220 **Admissions:** 5657 **Census:** 104 **Outpatient Visits:** 188046 **Births:** 968 **Total Expense ($000):** 267932 **Payroll Expense ($000):** 79030 **Personnel:** 1259

**CHILDREN'S HOSPITAL OF SANTA ROSA** See Children's Hospital of San Antonio

**CHRISTUS SANTA ROSA HEALTH CARE** See Christus Santa Rosa Health System

⊞ **CHRISTUS SANTA ROSA HEALTH SYSTEM (450237)**, 333 North Santa Rosa Street, Zip 78207-3108, Mailing Address: 100 NE Loop 410 Suite 800, Zip 78216–4749; tel. 210/704–2000, (Includes CHRISTUS SANTA ROSA HOSPITAL - ALAMO HEIGHTS, Mailing address: 403 Treeline Park Building, San Antonio, Texas, Zip 78209–2042; tel. 210/294–8000; Lanell Scott, Chief Executive Officer; CHRISTUS SANTA ROSA HOSPITAL - NEW BRAUNFELS, Mailing address: 600 North Union Avenue, New Braunfels, Texas, Zip 78130–4191; tel. 830/606–9111; Jim D Wesson, President and Administrator; CHRISTUS SANTA ROSA-MEDICAL CENTER, Mailing address: 2827 Babcock Road, San Antonio, Texas, Zip 78229–4813; tel. 210/705–6300; Ian Thompson Jr, M.D., President), (Nonreporting) **A**1 3 5 10 **F**3 12 13 15 18 19 20 21 22 23 24 25 26 27 28 29 30 31 32 34 35 37 39 40 41 42 43 45 46 48 49 54 56 57 58 59 60 62 63 64 65 68 70 71 72 74 75 76 77 78 79 81 82 83 84 85 86 87 88 89 92 93 95 97 107 108 110 111 112 113 114 115 116 117 118 119 124 126 130 131 132 134 138 141 144 146 147 149 154 **S** CHRISTUS Health, Irving, TX
Primary Contact: Dean Alexander, President and Chief Executive Officer
CFO: Linda Kirks, Vice President and Chief Financial Officer
CMO: Kenneth Davis, M.D., Chief Medical Officer
CHR: Crystal H Kohanke, Group Vice President, Human Resources
CNO: Patty Toney, R.N., MSN, Chief Nurse Executive
Web address: www.christussantarosa.org
**Control**: Church operated, Nongovernment, not-for-profit **Service**: General medical and surgical

**Staffed Beds:** 397 **Admissions:** 20971 **Census:** 259 **Outpatient Visits:** 387095 **Births:** 1976 **Total Expense ($000):** 395100 **Payroll Expense ($000):** 120375 **Personnel:** 1700

**CHRISTUS SANTA ROSA REHABILITATION HOSPITAL** See Christus Santa Rosa-Medical Center

☐ **CLARITY CHILD GUIDANCE CENTER**, 8535 Tom Slick, Zip 78229–3363; tel. 210/616–0300, (Nonreporting) **A**1 3 5 **F**29 34 50 98 99 101 102 104 105 146 154
Primary Contact: Jessica Knudsen, Chief Executive Officer
CFO: Michael Bernick, Executive Vice President and Chief Financial Officer
CMO: Soad Michelson, M.D., Senior Medical Director
CHR: Gina Massey, Vice President Human Resources
CNO: Carol Carver, MSN, R.N., Vice President Patient Services
Web address: www.claritycgc.org
**Control**: Other not–for–profit (including NFP Corporation) **Service**: Children's hospital psychiatric

**Staffed Beds:** 66 **Admissions:** 3353 **Census:** 65 **Outpatient Visits:** 21560 **Births:** 0 **Total Expense ($000):** 26819 **Payroll Expense ($000):** 14240 **Personnel:** 260

⊞ **ENCOMPASS HEALTH REHABILITATION HOSPITAL OF SAN ANTONIO (453031)**, 9119 Cinnamon Hill, Zip 78240–5401; tel. 210/691–0737, (Nonreporting) **A**1 10 **F**29 90 91 96 130 132 148 **S** Encompass Health Corporation, Birmingham, AL
Primary Contact: Andrew Meade, Chief Executive Officer
CFO: Larry Floyd Spriggs, CPA, Controller
CMO: Chaula Rana, M.D., Medical Director
CHR: Vanessa Tejada, Director Human Resources
CNO: Matthew D'Ambrosio, MSN, R.N., Chief Nursing Officer
Web address: www.hsriosa.com
**Control**: Corporation, Investor–owned (for-profit) **Service**: Rehabilitation

**Staffed Beds:** 96 **Admissions:** 1109 **Census:** 36 **Outpatient Visits:** 0 **Births:** 0 **Total Expense ($000):** 18836 **Payroll Expense ($000):** 9447 **Personnel:** 151

**ENCOMPASS HEALTH REHABILITATION HOSPITAL OF SAN ANTONIO (RIOSA)** See Encompass Health Rehabilitation Hospital of San Antonio

⇑ **FOUNDATION BARIATRIC HOSPITAL OF SAN ANTONIO** See Foundation Surgical Hospital of San Antonio

⇑ **FOUNDATION SURGICAL HOSPITAL OF SAN ANTONIO (670054)**, 9522 Huebner Road, Zip 78240–1548; tel. 210/478–5400, (Nonreporting) **A**3 5 10 21 **F**3 12 29 37 40 79 81 107 114 149 **P**2
Primary Contact: Blake W. Hubbard, FACHE, Chief Executive Officer
CNO: Beckie Leonard, R.N., Chief Nursing Officer
Web address: www.https://www.fshsanantonio.com/
**Control**: Corporation, Investor–owned (for-profit) **Service**: Surgical

**Staffed Beds:** 20 **Admissions:** 1258 **Census:** 7 **Outpatient Visits:** 3816 **Births:** 0 **Total Expense ($000):** 33517 **Payroll Expense ($000):** 7183 **Personnel:** 129

**GLOBALREHAB HOSPITAL - SAN ANTONIO** See Methodist Hospital Stone Oak Rehabilitation Center

⊞ **KINDRED HOSPITAL SAN ANTONIO CENTRAL (452073)**, 111 Dallas Street, 4th Floor, Zip 78205–1201; tel. 210/297–7185, (Nonreporting) **A**1 10 **F**1 29 75 77 87 91 130 148 157 **S** Kindred Healthcare, Louisville, KY
Primary Contact: Kyle E. Sinclair, Chief Executive Officer
Web address: www.kindredsanantoniocentral.com/
**Control**: Corporation, Investor–owned (for-profit) **Service**: Acute long–term care hospital

**Staffed Beds:** 44 **Admissions:** 413 **Census:** 27 **Outpatient Visits:** 0 **Births:** 0 **Total Expense ($000):** 16620 **Payroll Expense ($000):** 7050 **Personnel:** 87

⊞ **KINDRED HOSPITAL-SAN ANTONIO (452016)**, 3636 Medical Drive, Zip 78229–2183; tel. 210/616–0616, (Nonreporting) **A**1 10 **F**1 3 29 30 70 75 77 85 87 91 107 130 148 157 **S** Kindred Healthcare, Louisville, KY
Primary Contact: Abiola Anyebe, Interim Chief Executive Officer
CFO: Erin Russell, Controller
CMO: Charles Duncan, M.D., Medical Director
CHR: Stanley Richardson, Coordinator Human Resources and Payroll Benefits
Web address: www.khsanantonio.com/
**Control**: Corporation, Investor–owned (for-profit) **Service**: Acute long–term care hospital

**Staffed Beds:** 59 **Admissions:** 341 **Census:** 23 **Outpatient Visits:** 0 **Births:** 0 **Total Expense ($000):** 15831 **Payroll Expense ($000):** 6540 **Personnel:** 92

**LAUREL RIDGE HOSPITAL** See Laurel Ridge Treatment Center

**TX**

⊞ **LAUREL RIDGE TREATMENT CENTER (454060)**, 17720 Corporate Woods Drive, Zip 78259–3500; tel. 210/491–9400, (Nonreporting) **A**1 3 5 10 **F**4 5 29 35 38 75 87 98 99 100 101 102 103 105 106 130 132 135 151 152 153 **S** Universal Health Services, Inc., King of Prussia, PA
Primary Contact: Jacob Cuellar, M.D., Chief Executive Officer
CFO: Linda Maenius, Chief Financial Officer
CMO: Benigno J Fernandez, M.D., Executive Medical Director
CHR: Brenda Frederick, Director Human Resources
CNO: Kathy Rosetta, Chief Nursing Officer
Web address: www.laurelridgetc.com
**Control:** Partnership, Investor–owned (for–profit) **Service:** Psychiatric

Staffed Beds: 208 Admissions: 7816 Census: 183 **Outpatient Visits:** 25151 **Births:** 0 Total Expense ($000): 55990 **Payroll Expense** ($000): 23871 **Personnel:** 350

**LEGENT ORTHOPEDIC & SPINE HOSPITAL** See Legent Orthopedic + Spine Hospital

☐ **LEGENT ORTHOPEDIC + SPINE HOSPITAL (670112)**, 5330 North Loop 1604 West, Zip 78249; tel. 210/877–8000, (Nonreporting) **A**1 10 **F**3 14 29 40 64 68 74 79 80 81 85 107 141
Primary Contact: Dan Plummer, Senior Vice President, Operations
CNO: Lisa Kuopus, Chief Nursing Officer
Web address: www.https://www.legenthealth.com/
**Control:** Partnership, Investor–owned (for–profit) **Service:** Surgical

Staffed Beds: 25 Admissions: 1416 Census: 6 **Outpatient Visits:** 3165 **Births:** 0 Total Expense ($000): 37174 **Payroll Expense ($000):** 7206 **Personnel:** 137

**LIFECARE HOSPITALS OF SAN ANTONIO** See Pam Specialty Hospital of San Antonio Center

**MEDICAL CENTER HOSPITAL** See University Hospital

**METHODIST AMBULATORY SURGERY HOSPITAL** See Methodist Ambulatory Surgery Hospital - Northwest

⊞ **METHODIST AMBULATORY SURGERY HOSPITAL - NORTHWEST (450780)**, 9150 Huebner Road, Suite 100, Zip 78240–1545; tel. 210/575–5000, (Nonreporting) **A**1 3 10 **F**3 29 40 50 65 68 79 81 85 87 107 114 **S** HCA Healthcare, Nashville, TN
Primary Contact: Scott Rausch, Chief Executive Officer
COO: Megan Cool, Chief Operating Officer
CFO: Tim Carr, Chief Financial Officer
CHR: Barry Burns, Vice President
CNO: Cathy Bump, R.N., Chief Nursing Officer
Web address: www.sahealth.com
**Control:** Partnership, Investor–owned (for–profit) **Service:** Surgical

Staffed Beds: 21 Admissions: 429 Census: 3 **Outpatient Visits:** 6238 **Births:** 0 Total Expense ($000): 23110 **Payroll Expense ($000):** 6777 **Personnel:** 97

⊞ **METHODIST HOSPITAL (450388)**, 7700 Floyd Curl Drive, Zip 78229–3993; tel. 210/575–4000, (Includes METHODIST CHILDREN'S HOSPITAL, Mailing address: 7700 Floyd Curl Drive, San Antonio, Texas, Zip 78229–3383; tel. 210/575–7000; Robert Lenza, Chief Executive Officer; METHODIST SPECIALTY AND TRANSPLANT HOSPITAL, Mailing address: 8026 Floyd Curl Drive, San Antonio, Texas, Zip 78229–3915; tel. 210/575–8090; Jeffrey Wilson, Chief Executive Officer; METHODIST TEXSAN HOSPITAL, Mailing address: 6700 IH-10 West, San Antonio, Texas, Zip 78201; tel. 210/736–6700; Scott Rausch, Chief Executive Officer; METROPOLITAN METHODIST HOSPITAL, Mailing address: 1310 McCullough Avenue, San Antonio, Texas, Zip 78212–2617; tel. 210/757–2909; Gregory A Seiler, Chief Executive Officer; NORTHEAST METHODIST HOSPITAL, Mailing address: 12412 Judson Road, Live Oak, Texas, Zip 78233–3255; tel. 210/757–5000; Michael D Beaver, Chief Executive Officer), (Nonreporting) **A**1 2 3 5 10 **F**3 5 8 11 12 13 15 17 18 19 20 21 22 23 24 25 26 27 28 29 30 31 34 35 38 40 41 42 43 44 45 46 47 48 49 51 53 54 56 57 58 59 60 64 65 68 70 72 74 75 76 77 78 79 80 81 82 84 85 86 87 88 89 90 93 95 96 98 100 101 102 103 104 105 107 108 111 112 114 115 118 119 120 121 124 126 127 129 130 132 135 136 137 138 139 142 143 144 145 146 147 148 152 153 154 156 **S** HCA Healthcare, Nashville, TN
Primary Contact: Daniel Miller, FACHE, Chief Executive Officer
CFO: Nancy Meadows, Chief Financial Officer
CMO: Russell Woodward, M.D., Chief Medical Officer
CIO: Eddie Cuellar, Vice President Information Systems
CHR: Nancy Edgar, Vice President Human Resources
CNO: Lori Townsend, Chief Nursing Officer
Web address: www.sahealth.com
**Control:** Partnership, Investor–owned (for–profit) **Service:** General medical and surgical

Staffed Beds: 1667 Admissions: 87824 Census: 1254 **Outpatient Visits:** 496461 **Births:** 8925 Total Expense ($000): 1439487 **Payroll Expense ($000):** 505160 **Personnel:** 6582

☐ **METHODIST HOSPITAL STONE OAK REHABILITATION CENTER**, 19126 Stonehue Road, Zip 78258–3490; tel. 210/482–3400, (Nonreporting) **A**1 10 **F**3 29 30 34 35 75 90 91 96 130 148 149 156
Primary Contact: John Deleon, Chief Executive Officer
Web address: www.sanantonio-rehab.com/
**Control:** Partnership, Investor–owned (for–profit) **Service:** Rehabilitation

Staffed Beds: 42 Admissions: 660 Census: 22 **Outpatient Visits:** 0 **Births:** 0 Total Expense ($000): 13825 **Payroll Expense ($000):** 7186 **Personnel:** 140

⊞ **METHODIST STONE OAK HOSPITAL (670055)**, 1139 E Sonterra Boulevard, Zip 78258–4347, Mailing Address: 1139 East Sonterra Boulevard, Zip 78258–4347; tel. 210/638–2100, (Nonreporting) **A**1 3 5 10 **F**3 13 15 18 20 22 24 28 29 30 31 34 35 38 40 41 44 45 46 47 49 52 56 57 59 60 65 68 70 72 74 75 76 77 78 79 80 81 82 85 87 90 102 107 108 114 119 126 130 145 146 147 148 149 154 **P**7 **S** HCA Healthcare, Nashville, TN
Primary Contact: Marc Strode, Chief Executive Officer
CFO: Gabriel Marrufo, Chief Financial Officer
CMO: Peter DeYoung, M.D., Chief Medical Officer
CNO: Ann M Winn, M.D., R.N., FACHE, Chief Nursing Officer
Web address: www.sahealth.com/locations/methodist-stone-oak-hospital/
**Control:** Partnership, Investor–owned (for–profit) **Service:** General medical and surgical

Staffed Beds: 242 Admissions: 14137 Census: 186 **Outpatient Visits:** 51785 **Births:** 2072 Total Expense ($000): 202241 **Payroll Expense ($000):** 66270 **Personnel:** 997

**METHODIST WOMEN'S & CHILD HOSP** See Methodist Children's Hospital

**METROPOLITAN HOSPITAL** See Metropolitan Methodist Hospital

⊞ **PAM SPECIALTY HOSPITAL OF SAN ANTONIO CENTER (452059)**, 8902 Floyd Curl Drive, Zip 78240–1681; tel. 210/690–7000, (Data for 92 days) (Nonreporting) **A**1 10 **F**1 3 29 45 60 70 77 85 86 87 107 114 130 148 **S** Post Acute Medical, LLC, Enola, PA
Primary Contact: Armando Morales, Chief Executive Officer
CMO: Randall C Bell, M.D., Medical Director
Web address: www.lifecare-hospitals.com
**Control:** Corporation, Investor–owned (for–profit) **Service:** Acute long–term care hospital

Staffed Beds: 62 Admissions: 127 Census: 35 **Outpatient Visits:** 0 **Births:** 0 Total Expense ($000): 6017 **Payroll Expense ($000):** 2476 **Personnel:** 189

**POST ACUTE/WARM SPRINGS REHABILITATION HOSPITAL OF SAN ANTONIO** See Warm Springs Rehabilitation Hospital of San Antonio

⊞ **POST ACUTE/WARM SPRINGS SPECIALTY HOSPITAL OF SAN ANTONIO (452090)**, 5418 N Loop 1604 W, Zip 78247; tel. 210/921–3550, (Nonreporting) **A**1 10 **F**1 3 29 30 74 75 77 82 85 86 87 148 154 **S** Post Acute Medical, LLC, Enola, PA
Primary Contact: Kristen Lowe, Chief Executive Officer
CNO: Carrie Nims, Director of Nursing
Web address: www.postacutemedical.com
**Control:** Partnership, Investor–owned (for–profit) **Service:** Acute long–term care hospital

**Staffed Beds:** 26 **Admissions:** 345 **Census:** 24 **Outpatient Visits:** 0 **Births:** 0 **Total Expense ($000):** 15412 **Payroll Expense ($000):** 6184 **Personnel:** 94

☐ **SAN ANTONIO BEHAVIORAL HEALTHCARE HOSPITAL (454132)**, 8550 Huebner Road, Zip 78240–1803; tel. 210/541–5300, (Nonreporting) **A**1 **F**5 87 98 99 100 101 103 104 105 132 152 153 154 **S** Signature Healthcare Services, Corona, CA
Primary Contact: Aleen Davis. Arabit, Chief Executive Officer
CFO: Sam Silberman, Chief Financial Officer
CMO: Joseph Hernandez, M.D., Medical Director
CNO: Shawn Larabie, Chief Nursing Officer
Web address: www.sanantoniobehavioral.com
**Control:** Individual, Investor–owned (for–profit) **Service:** Psychiatric

**Staffed Beds:** 198 **Admissions:** 6755 **Census:** 121 **Outpatient Visits:** 8088 **Births:** 0 **Total Expense ($000):** 25720 **Payroll Expense ($000):** 14586 **Personnel:** 333

**SAN ANTONIO COMMUNITY HOSPITAL** See Methodist Specialty and Transplant Hospital

☐ **SAN ANTONIO STATE HOSPITAL (454011)**, 6711 South New Braunfels, Suite 100, Zip 78223–3006; tel. 210/531–7711, (Nonreporting) **A**1 3 5 10 **F**30 39 53 56 57 59 68 75 77 86 87 91 98 99 100 101 103 130 132 135 146 **P**1 **S** Texas Department of State Health Services, Austin, TX
Primary Contact: Robert C. Arizpe, Superintendent
CFO: Janie Rabago, Chief Accountant
CMO: Terresa Stallworth, M.D., Clinical Director
CIO: Chris Stanush, Director Information Management
CHR: Renee Bourland, Human Resources Specialist
CNO: Maria DC Ostrander, R.N., MSN, Chief Nurse Executive
Web address: www.dshs.state.tx.us/mhhospitals/SanAntonioSH/default.shtm
**Control:** State, Government, Nonfederal **Service:** Psychiatric

**Staffed Beds:** 264 **Admissions:** 602 **Census:** 235 **Outpatient Visits:** 0 **Births:** 0 **Total Expense ($000):** 65310 **Payroll Expense ($000):** 36610 **Personnel:** 798

**SELECT SPECIALTY HOSPITAL-SAN ANTONIO** See Kindred Hospital San Antonio Central

☐ **SOUTH TEXAS SPINE AND SURGICAL HOSPITAL (450856)**, 18600 Hardy Oak Boulevard, Zip 78258–4206; tel. 210/507–4090, (Nonreporting) **A**1 3 5 10 **F**3 29 40 41 75 77 79 81 82 85 86 87 126 **S** National Surgical Healthcare, Chicago, IL
Primary Contact: Angie Kauffman, Chief Executive Officer
CFO: Sylvia Garcia, Chief Accounting Officer
CHR: Sally Hall, Manager Human Resources
CNO: Jennifer West, R.N., Chief Nursing Officer
Web address: www.southtexassurgical.com
**Control:** Partnership, Investor–owned (for–profit) **Service:** Orthopedic

**Staffed Beds:** 30 **Admissions:** 1634 **Census:** 9 **Outpatient Visits:** 2129 **Births:** 0 **Total Expense ($000):** 45018 **Payroll Expense ($000):** 9020 **Personnel:** 145

⊞ △ **SOUTH TEXAS VETERANS HEALTH CARE SYSTEM**, 7400 Merton Minter Boulevard, Zip 78229–4404; tel. 210/617–5300, (Includes KERRVILLE DIVISION, Mailing address: 3600 Memorial Boulevard, Kerrville, Texas, Zip 78028; tel. 210/896–2020; SAN ANTONIO DIVISION, Mailing address: 7400 Merton Minter Boulevard, San Antonio, Texas, Zip 78284–5799; tel. 210/617–5300), (Nonreporting) **A**1 2 3 5 7 8 **S** Department of Veterans Affairs, Washington, DC
Primary Contact: Christopher R. Sandles, FACHE, Medical Center Director
COO: Joe Perez, Associate Director
CFO: Eloisa Salazar, Chief Financial Officer
CMO: Julianne Flynn, M.D., Chief of Staff
CIO: Simon Willett, Director Administrative Operations
CHR: Jeffrey Young, Chief Human Resource Officer
CNO: Sharon Millican, Associate Director, Patient Care Services
Web address: www.southtexas.va.gov/
**Control:** Veterans Affairs, Government, federal **Service:** General medical and surgical

**Staffed Beds:** 268

**SOUTHEAST BAPTIST HOSPITAL** See Mission Trail Baptist Hospital

⇑ **SOUTHWEST GENERAL HOSPITAL (450697)**, 7400 Barlite Boulevard, Zip 78224–1399; tel. 210/921–2000, (Nonreporting) **A**3 10 21 **F**3 12 13 18 20 22 24 26 29 30 35 37 40 43 44 45 46 49 50 51 56 57 59 60 64 65 70 71 72 74 75 76 77 79 80 81 85 87 90 96 98 100 102 103 104 107 108 111 114 115 119 130 132 135 146 147 148 149 153 **P**6 **S** Steward Health Care System, LLC, Dallas, TX
Primary Contact: Jonathan Turton, FACHE, President
COO: Sarah Humme, MSN, R.N., Chief Operating Officer
CFO: Colin B. Brooks, Chief Financial Officer
CIO: Debbie Mora, Director
CHR: Christina Rivera, Director Human Resources
CNO: Sarah Humme, MSN, R.N., Chief Nursing Officer
Web address: www.https://www.southwestgeneralhospital.org/
**Control:** Corporation, Investor–owned (for–profit) **Service:** General medical and surgical

**Staffed Beds:** 253 **Admissions:** 8637 **Census:** 113 **Outpatient Visits:** 48959 **Births:** 1162 **Total Expense ($000):** 115988 **Payroll Expense ($000):** 38376 **Personnel:** 660

**SOUTHWEST MENTAL HEALTH CENTER** See Clarity Child Guidance Center

**SOUTHWEST TEXAS METHODIST HOSP** See Methodist Hospital

**SPINE HOSP OF SOUTH TEXAS** See South Texas Spine and Surgical Hospital

**ST LUKE'S LUTHERAN HOSPITAL** See St. Luke's Baptist Hospital

**ST. LUKE'S BAPTIST HOSPITAL** See Baptist Medical Center, San Antonio

☐ **TEXAS CENTER FOR INFECTIOUS DISEASE (670125)**, 2303 SE Military Drive, Zip 78223–3597; tel. 210/534–8857, (Nonreporting) **A**1 3 5 10 **F**3 29 30 50 53 58 59 61 65 68 75 80 86 87 130 132 135 143 146 149 **S** Texas Department of State Health Services, Austin, TX
Primary Contact: James N. Elkins, FACHE, Director
CFO: Glenda Armstrong-Huff, Assistant Superintendent
CMO: David Griffith, M.D., Medical Director
CIO: Andre Avant, Facility Automation Manager
CHR: Gerald Shackelford, Staff Support Specialist
CNO: Rebecca Sanchez, R.N., M.P.H., Director of Nursing
Web address: www.dshs.state.tx.us/tcid/default.shtm
**Control:** State, Government, Nonfederal **Service:** Tuberculosis and other respiratory diseases

**Staffed Beds:** 50 **Admissions:** 89 **Census:** 34 **Outpatient Visits:** 108 **Births:** 0 **Total Expense ($000):** 14127 **Payroll Expense ($000):** 6460 **Personnel:** 167

**TEXSAN HEART HOSPITAL** See Methodist Texsan Hospital

**TX CTR FOR INFECTIOUS DESEASE** See Texas Center for Infectious Disease

**TX**

---

**Hospital, Medicare Provider Number, Address, Telephone, Approval, Facility, and Physician Codes, Health Care System**

★ American Hospital Association (AHA) membership
☐ The Joint Commission accreditation
○ Healthcare Facilities Accreditation Program
◇ DNV Healthcare Inc. accreditation
⇑ Center for Improvement in Healthcare Quality Accreditation
△ Commission on Accreditation of Rehabilitation Facilities (CARF) accreditation

⊞ **UNIVERSITY HEALTH SYSTEM (450213)**, 4502 Medical Drive, Zip 78229–4493; tel. 210/358–2000, (Includes UNIVERSITY HEALTH CENTER - DOWNTOWN, Mailing address: 4502 Medical Drive, San Antonio, Texas, Zip 78229–4493; tel. 210/358–3400; UNIVERSITY HOSPITAL, Mailing address: 4502 Medical Drive, San Antonio, Texas, Zip 78229–4493; tel. 210/358–4000; Michael Roussos, Administrator), (Nonreporting) **A**1 2 3 5 8 10 19 **F**3 4 11 12 13 14 15 16 17 18 19 20 21 22 23 24 25 26 27 28 29 30 31 32 34 35 36 38 40 41 43 44 45 46 47 48 49 50 51 54 55 56 57 58 59 60 61 64 65 66 68 70 72 73 74 75 76 77 78 79 81 82 84 85 86 87 88 89 90 92 93 95 98 100 101 102 107 110 111 115 118 119 126 129 130 132 138 139 140 141 142 144 145 146 147 148 149 154 **P**6
Primary Contact: George B. Hernandez Jr, President and Chief Executive Officer
COO: Christann Vasquez, Executive Vice President and Chief Operating Officer
CFO: Peggy Deming, Executive Vice President and Chief Financial Officer
CMO: Bryan Alsip, M.D., Executive Vice President, Chief Medical Officer
CIO: Bill Phillips, Vice President Information Services
CHR: Theresa Scepanski, Vice President People and Organizational Development
CNO: Tommye Austin, Ph.D., R.N., MSN, Chief Nursing Executive
Web address: www.universityhealthsystem.com
**Control:** Hospital district or authority, Government, Nonfederal **Service:** General medical and surgical

**Staffed Beds:** 681 **Admissions:** 31372 **Census:** 528 **Outpatient Visits:** 1906793 **Births:** 3213 **Total Expense ($000):** 1377981 **Payroll Expense ($000):** 504405 **Personnel:** 8007

**VENCOR HOSPITAL-SAN ANTONIO** See Kindred Hospital-San Antonio

⊞ **WARM SPRINGS REHABILITATION HOSPITAL OF SAN ANTONIO (453035)**, 5101 Medical Drive, Zip 78229–4801; tel. 210/616–0100, (Includes WARM SPRINGS REHABILITATION HOSPITAL OF THOUSAND OAKS, Mailing address: 14747 Jones Maltsberger Road, San Antonio, Texas, Zip 78247–3713; tel. 210/581–5300; Kyle Sinclair, Chief Executive Officer; WARM SPRINGS REHABILITATION HOSPITAL OF WESTOVER HILLS, Mailing address: 10323 State Highway 151, San Antonio, Texas, Zip 78251–4557; tel. 210/581–5306; Brian Lidiak, Chief Executive Officer), (Nonreporting) **A**1 3 5 10 **F**3 11 29 30 34 57 64 68 74 75 79 82 90 93 94 95 96 100 130 132 146 148 154 **S** Post Acute Medical, LLC, Enola, PA
Primary Contact: Peter Drew, Chief Executive Officer
CIO: Rick Marek, Vice President Medical Information Systems
Web address: www.postacutemedical.com/our-facilities/hospitals/warm-springs-rehabilitation-hospital-san-antonio/
**Control:** Partnership, Investor–owned (for–profit) **Service:** Rehabilitation

**Staffed Beds:** 139 **Admissions:** 3168 **Census:** 104 **Outpatient Visits:** 30475 **Births:** 0 **Total Expense ($000):** 54128 **Payroll Expense ($000):** 26897 **Personnel:** 519

**WARM SPRINGS SPECIALTY HOSPITAL OF SAN ANTONIO** See Post Acute/ Warm Springs Specialty Hospital of San Antonio

### SAN AUGUSTINE—San Augustine County

★ **CHI ST. LUKE'S HEALTH MEMORIAL SAN AUGUSTINE (451360)**, 511 East Hospital Street, Zip 75972–2121, Mailing Address: P.O. Box 658, Zip 75972–0658; tel. 936/275–3446, (Nonreporting) **A**10 18 **F**29 30 35 40 57 59 64 102 107 119 132 133 149 **S** CommonSpirit Health, Chicago, IL
Primary Contact: Darlene Williams, R.N., Administrator
CFO: Kristi Gay, Chief Financial Officer
Web address: www.memorialhealth.org
**Control:** Other not–for–profit (including NFP Corporation) **Service:** General medical and surgical

**Staffed Beds:** 9 **Admissions:** 231 **Census:** 2 **Outpatient Visits:** 9757 **Births:** 0 **Total Expense ($000):** 7259 **Payroll Expense ($000):** 2735 **Personnel:** 40

**MEMORIAL MEDICAL CENTER - SAN AUGUSTINE** See Chi St. Luke's Health Memorial San Augustine

### SAN MARCOS—Hays County

**CENTRAL TEXAS MEDICAL CENTER** See Christus Santa Rosa Hospital - San Marcos

⊞ **CHRISTUS SANTA ROSA HOSPITAL - SAN MARCOS (450272)**, 1301 Wonder World Drive, Zip 78666–7544; tel. 512/353–8979, (Nonreporting) **A**1 10 **F**3 11 13 15 18 20 29 30 32 34 35 39 40 43 44 45 49 50 51 56 57 59 60 62 63 64 65 66 68 70 72 75 76 77 79 80 81 82 85 86 87 92 93 94 98 107 108 109 110 111 114 116 117 118 119 126 129 130 131 132 146 147 148 152 157 **P**6 8 **S** CHRISTUS Health, Irving, TX
Primary Contact: Thomas McKinney, Chief Executive Officer
CFO: Stephanie Nelson, CPA, Vice President and Chief Financial Officer
CMO: Lee Johannsen, M.D., Vice President and Chief Medical Officer
CHR: Debbie D. Cox, Administrative Director Human Resources
CNO: Catherine Amitrano, MSN, R.N., Vice President and Chief Nursing Officer
Web address: www.https://www.christushealth.org/santa-rosa/san-marcos
**Control:** Church operated, Nongovernment, not–for–profit **Service:** General medical and surgical

**Staffed Beds:** 111 **Admissions:** 3564 **Census:** 31 **Outpatient Visits:** 79587 **Births:** 679 **Total Expense ($000):** 92382 **Payroll Expense ($000):** 31663 **Personnel:** 474

**OCEANS BEHAVIORAL HOSPITAL SAN MARCOS** See Wellbridge Heatlhcare of San Marcos

☐ **WELLBRIDGE HEATLHCARE OF SAN MARCOS (454137)**, 1106 North Interstate 35, Zip 78666–7030; tel. 512/353–0194, (Nonreporting) **A**1 **F**29 98 100 101 103 130 132 135 149 153 154
Primary Contact: Wiley B. Barner, Chief Executive Officer
Web address: www.oceanssanmarcos.com
**Control:** Partnership, Investor–owned (for–profit) **Service:** Psychiatric

**Staffed Beds:** 24 **Admissions:** 522 **Census:** 16 **Outpatient Visits:** 368 **Births:** 0 **Total Expense ($000):** 4786 **Payroll Expense ($000):** 2187 **Personnel:** 50

### SEGUIN—Guadalupe County

⊞ **GUADALUPE REGIONAL MEDICAL CENTER (450104)**, 1215 East Court Street, Zip 78155–5189; tel. 830/379–2411, (Nonreporting) **A**1 10 **F**3 5 11 13 15 18 20 22 24 28 29 30 31 34 35 38 39 40 43 45 46 49 50 51 53 57 58 59 60 63 66 68 70 73 74 75 76 77 78 79 81 82 84 85 90 93 96 104 107 108 110 111 112 114 115 118 119 126 129 132 135 143 146 148 149 150 154 156 **P**8
Primary Contact: Robert Gerard. Haynes, FACHE, Chief Executive Officer
COO: Sheri Williams, Chief Operating Officer
CFO: Penny Wallace, Chief Financial Officer
CMO: Robert Ryan, M.D., Chief Medical Officer
CIO: Steve Ratliff, Director Information Technology
CHR: Fay Bennett, Vice President Employee Services
CNO: Daphne Blake, R.N., MSN, Chief Nursing Officer
Web address: www.grmedcenter.com
**Control:** City–county, Government, Nonfederal **Service:** General medical and surgical

**Staffed Beds:** 99 **Admissions:** 3621 **Census:** 37 **Outpatient Visits:** 137462 **Births:** 781 **Total Expense ($000):** 103513 **Payroll Expense ($000):** 38262 **Personnel:** 721

**GUADALUPE VALLEY HOSPITAL** See Guadalupe Regional Medical Center

### SEMINOLE—Gaines County

★ **MEMORIAL HOSPITAL (451358)**, 209 NW Eighth Street, Zip 79360–3447; tel. 432/758–5811, (Total facility includes 58 beds in nursing home–type unit) (Nonreporting) **A**10 18 **F**3 10 11 13 28 29 30 32 34 35 40 43 45 53 56 57 59 62 63 64 65 75 76 81 87 93 97 102 107 111 114 119 127 130 131 132 133 143 146 147 148
Primary Contact: Larry Gray, Chief Executive Officer
COO: Heath Mitchell, Chief Operating Officer
CFO: Traci Anderson, Chief Financial Officer
CMO: Michael Watson, M.D., Chief of Staff
Web address: www.seminolehospitaldistrict.com
**Control:** Hospital district or authority, Government, Nonfederal **Service:** General medical and surgical

**Staffed Beds:** 83 **Admissions:** 900 **Census:** 44 **Outpatient Visits:** 48675 **Births:** 621 **Total Expense ($000):** 47427 **Payroll Expense ($000):** 11909 **Personnel:** 226

**TX**

*Many Facility Codes have changed. Please refer to the AHA Guide Code Chart.*

## SEYMOUR—Baylor County

**SEYMOUR HOSPITAL (450586)**, 200 Stadium Drive, Zip 76380–2344; tel. 940/889–5572, (Nonreporting) **A**10 20 **F**3 7 8 11 13 14 28 29 34 36 40 43 45 50 53 56 57 59 62 64 65 66 68 70 75 76 81 85 86 87 89 93 94 100 102 103 104 107 119 127 130 133 135 146 147 148 154 **P**1
Primary Contact: Leslie Hardin, Chief Executive Officer and Chief Financial Officer
CFO: Leslie Hardin, Chief Executive Officer and Chief Financial Officer
CMO: Kory Lann Martin, M.D., Chief of Staff
CHR: Linda Moore, Manager Human Resources
CNO: Julie Smajstrla, Director Nursing
Web address: www.seymourhospital.com/
**Control:** Hospital district or authority, Government, Nonfederal **Service:** General medical and surgical

**Staffed Beds:** 40 **Admissions:** 395 **Census:** 5 **Outpatient Visits:** 39893 **Births:** 34 **Total Expense ($000):** 27157 **Payroll Expense ($000):** 5740 **Personnel:** 132

**SEYMOUR HOSPITAL AUTHORITY** See Seymour Hospital

## SHAMROCK—Wheeler County

★ **SHAMROCK GENERAL HOSPITAL (451340)**, 1000 South Main Street, Zip 79079–2896, Mailing Address: P O Box 511, Zip 79079–0511; tel. 806/256–2114, (Nonreporting) **A**10 18 **F**7 11 29 32 34 35 40 43 63 65 68 93 107 119 127 130 133 **P**4 6
Primary Contact: Wiley M. Fires, Administrator
CFO: Wiley M Fires, Administrator
CHR: Cecille Williams, Assistant Administrator
CNO: Jeanne Crossland, Director of Nursing
**Control:** Hospital district or authority, Government, Nonfederal **Service:** General medical and surgical

**Staffed Beds:** 13 **Admissions:** 106 **Census:** 2 **Outpatient Visits:** 10103 **Births:** 0 **Total Expense ($000):** 7065 **Payroll Expense ($000):** 3681 **Personnel:** 74

## SHENANDOAH—Montgomery County

**BEACON SPECIALTY HOSPITAL** See Nexus Specialty Hospital

⊞ **ENCOMPASS HEALTH REHABILITATION HOSPITAL VISION PARK (673034)**, 117 Vision Park Boulevard, Zip 77384–3001; tel. 936/444–1700, (Nonreporting) **A**1 10 **F**3 28 29 34 35 44 57 59 65 68 71 74 75 77 78 79 82 86 87 90 91 95 96 130 132 148 149 **S** Encompass Health Corporation, Birmingham, AL
Primary Contact: Jennifer Brewer, Chief Executive Officer
CFO: Terri Weiss, Chief Financial Officer
Web address: www.healthsouthvisionpark.com/
**Control:** Corporation, Investor–owned (for–profit) **Service:** Rehabilitation

**Staffed Beds:** 60 **Admissions:** 1495 **Census:** 47 **Outpatient Visits:** 0 **Births:** 0 **Total Expense ($000):** 20911 **Payroll Expense ($000):** 10900 **Personnel:** 166

**HEALTHSOUTH REHABILITATION HOSPITAL VISION PARK** See Encompass Health Rehabilitation Hospital Vision Park

**NEXUS SPECIALTY HOSPITAL**, 123 Vision Park Boulevard, Zip 77384–3001; tel. 281/364–0317, (Nonreporting) **F**1 3 70 74 75 77 82 84 85 91 92 93 100 101 107 119 130 132 135 148 **S** Nexus Health Systems, Houston, TX
Primary Contact: Eric Cantrell, Chief Executive Officer
CFO: David Strickler, Chief Financial Officer
CMO: Ather Siddiqi, M.D., Medical Director
CIO: Noe Salinas, Vice President Information Technology
CHR: Kevin McAndrews, Vice President Human Resources
CNO: Rhena Anderson, Chief Nursing Officer
Web address: www.nexusspecialty.com/
**Control:** Partnership, Investor–owned (for–profit) **Service:** Acute long–term care hospital

**Staffed Beds:** 76 **Admissions:** 484 **Census:** 36 **Outpatient Visits:** 276 **Births:** 0 **Total Expense ($000):** 23247 **Payroll Expense ($000):** 9134 **Personnel:** 162

## SHERMAN—Grayson County

⇑ **BAYLOR SCOTT & WHITE SURGICAL HOSPITAL AT SHERMAN** See Baylor Scott & White Surgical Hospital-Sherman

⇑ **BAYLOR SCOTT & WHITE SURGICAL HOSPITAL-SHERMAN (670076)**, 3601 North Calais Street, Zip 75090–1785; tel. 903/870–0999, (Nonreporting) **A**10 21 **F**3 29 37 40 45 47 77 81 85 107 111 119 126 131 145 **S** Baylor Scott & White Health, Dallas, TX
Primary Contact: Marc Devorsetz, Chief Executive Officer
CMO: Curtis Holbrook, M.D., Chief Medical Officer
CIO: Grant Hulsey, Director Information Technology
CHR: Terrie Langford, Director Human Resources
CNO: Teresa Dutton, R.N., Chief Nursing Officer
Web address: www.heritageparksurgicalhospital.com
**Control:** Partnership, Investor–owned (for–profit) **Service:** General medical and surgical

**Staffed Beds:** 12 **Admissions:** 593 **Census:** 4 **Outpatient Visits:** 25322 **Births:** 0 **Total Expense ($000):** 41028 **Payroll Expense ($000):** 11757 **Personnel:** 189

☐ **CARRUS REHABILITATION HOSPITAL (673041)**, 1810 West US Highway 82, Suite 100, Zip 75092–7069; tel. 903/870–2600, (Nonreporting) **A**1 10 **F**3 29 40 41 44 65 74 75 77 79 85 86 87 90 91 96 130 **S** Carrus Hospitals, Sherman, TX
Primary Contact: Brad Sidlo, Chief Executive Officer
CFO: Michael Exline, Chief Financial Officer
CMO: Jose Matus, M.D., Director Medical
CIO: Gary Glenn, Director Information Technology
CHR: Charlene Shupert, Director Staff Services
CNO: Marie Johnson, Chief Nursing Officer
Web address: www.carrushospital.com
**Control:** Corporation, Investor–owned (for–profit) **Service:** Rehabilitation

**Staffed Beds:** 24 **Admissions:** 704 **Census:** 22 **Outpatient Visits:** 0 **Births:** 0 **Total Expense ($000):** 10830 **Payroll Expense ($000):** 4441 **Personnel:** 102

☐ **CARRUS SPECIALTY HOSPITAL (452041)**, 1810 West US Highway 82, Zip 75092–7069; tel. 903/870–2600, (Nonreporting) **A**1 10 **F**1 3 29 40 41 44 56 65 74 75 77 78 79 82 83 85 86 87 91 107 114 119 129 130 148 **S** Carrus Hospitals, Sherman, TX
Primary Contact: Brad Sidlo, Chief Executive Officer
CFO: Michael Exline, Chief Financial Officer
CMO: Nathan Watson, M.D., JrChief of Staff
CIO: Gary Glenn, Director Information Technology
CHR: Charlene Shupert, Director Staff Services
CNO: Marie Johnson, Chief Nursing Officer
Web address: www.carrushospital.com
**Control:** Corporation, Investor–owned (for–profit) **Service:** Acute long–term care hospital

**Staffed Beds:** 33 **Admissions:** 470 **Census:** 26 **Outpatient Visits:** 1853 **Births:** 0 **Total Expense ($000):** 14723 **Payroll Expense ($000):** 6577 **Personnel:** 135

**TEXAS HEALTH PRESBYTERIAN HOSPITAL-WNJ** See Wilson N. Jones Regional Medical Center

**TEXOMA MEDICAL CENTER RESTORATIVE CARE HOSPITAL** See Carrus Specialty Hospital

**TX**

☐ **WILSON N. JONES REGIONAL MEDICAL CENTER (450469)**, 500 North Highland Avenue, Zip 75092–7354; tel. 903/870–4611, (Nonreporting) **A**1 10 **F**3 12 13 15 18 20 22 24 28 29 30 34 35 40 41 43 45 47 49 53 56 57 58 59 64 70 74 75 76 77 79 81 83 84 85 87 91 92 93 96 98 103 107 108 110 111 119 129 130 132 135 146 147 148 149 154 156 157 **S** Alecto Healthcare, Irvine, CA
Primary Contact: Cory Countryman, Chief Executive Officer
CFO: Andrea Lane, Chief Financial Officer
CMO: Michael Benson, M.D., President Medical Staff
CIO: Prabhu Bollu, Director Information Technology
CHR: Bill Barrett, Manager Human Resources
CNO: Mandy Dick EsqChief Nursing Officer
Web address: www.wnj.org
**Control**: Corporation, Investor–owned (for–profit) **Service**: General medical and surgical

**Staffed Beds**: 109 **Admissions**: 5267 **Census**: 66 **Outpatient Visits**: 38643 **Births**: 387 **Total Expense ($000)**: 78768 **Payroll Expense ($000)**: 29676 **Personnel**: 524

### SMITHVILLE—Bastrop County

✉ **ASCENSION SETON SMITHVILLE (450143)**, 1201 Hill Road, Zip 78957; tel. 512/237–3214, (Nonreporting) **A**1 10 **F**3 11 15 29 30 35 40 45 46 47 50 53 57 77 79 81 82 85 87 92 93 97 107 110 111 114 119 127 130 143 146 147 148 149 **S** Ascension Healthcare, Saint Louis, MO
Primary Contact: Andy Davis, Chief Executive Officer
COO: Robbie G. Rabe, Chief Operating Officer
CFO: Melissa Nordyke, Chief Financial Officer
CHR: Sara Rodriguez, Human Resources
CNO: Christine Laflamme, R.N., MSN, Chief Nursing Officer
Web address: www.https://healthcare.ascension.org/Locations/Texas/TXAUS/Smithville-Ascension-Seton-Smithville
**Control**: Church operated, Nongovernment, not–for–profit **Service**: General medical and surgical

**Staffed Beds**: 5 **Admissions**: 185 **Census**: 2 **Outpatient Visits**: 27983 **Births**: 0 **Total Expense ($000)**: 14593 **Payroll Expense ($000)**: 5055 **Personnel**: 96

**SETON SMITHVILLE REGIONAL HOSPITAL** See Ascension Seton Smithville

### SNYDER—Scurry County

**COGDELL MEMORIAL HOSPITAL (451384)**, 1700 Cogdell Boulevard, Zip 79549–6198; tel. 325/573–6374, (Nonreporting) **A**10 18 **F**3 8 11 12 13 15 18 19 29 30 34 35 40 43 45 46 47 48 49 50 53 56 57 59 62 63 64 65 66 68 75 76 77 79 81 83 84 85 86 87 91 92 93 97 107 110 111 115 119 127 130 131 132 133 145 146 147 148 149 154 156 157
Primary Contact: Ella Raye. Helms, Chief Executive Officer
CFO: John Everett, Chief Financial Officer
CMO: Robert Rakov, M.D., Chief Medical Officer
CHR: Linda Warren, Director Human Resources
Web address: www.cogdellhospital.com
**Control**: Hospital district or authority, Government, Nonfederal **Service**: General medical and surgical

**Staffed Beds**: 25 **Admissions**: 744 **Census**: 8 **Outpatient Visits**: 92800 **Births**: 157 **Total Expense ($000)**: 40310 **Payroll Expense ($000)**: 17674 **Personnel**: 292

**D. M. COGDELL MEMORIAL HOSPITAL** See Cogdell Memorial Hospital

### SONORA—Sutton County

★ **LILLIAN M. HUDSPETH MEMORIAL HOSPITAL (451324)**, 308 Hudspeth Avenue, Zip 76950–8003, Mailing Address: P.O. Box 455, Zip 76950–0455; tel. 325/387–2521, (Nonreporting) **A**10 18 **F**3 7 15 26 28 29 30 34 35 40 41 43 50 53 57 59 63 64 65 66 68 75 79 86 87 90 93 96 97 107 110 111 115 119 127 128 131 133 135 154
Primary Contact: Lance W. Keilers, Interim Chief Executive Officer
COO: Joe Marshall, Chief Operating Officer
CFO: Michelle Schaefer, Chief Financial Officer
CNO: Lara Ellen Teague, R.N., Chief Nursing Officer
Web address: www.sonora-hospital.org
**Control**: Hospital district or authority, Government, Nonfederal **Service**: General medical and surgical

**Staffed Beds**: 12 **Admissions**: 127 **Census**: 2 **Outpatient Visits**: 9981 **Births**: 0 **Total Expense ($000)**: 9746 **Payroll Expense ($000)**: 4336 **Personnel**: 79

### SOUTHLAKE—Tarrant County

**FOREST PARK MEDICAL CENTER-SOUTHLAKE** See Methodist Southlake Hospital

**HARRIS METHODIST SOUTHLAKE CENTER FOR DIAGNOSTICS AND SURGERY** See Texas Health Harris Methodist Hospital Southlake

☐ **METHODIST SOUTHLAKE HOSPITAL**, 421 East State Highway 114, Zip 76092; tel. 817/865–4400, (Nonreporting) **A**1 **F**3 12 29 40 45 49 50 51 68 70 75 79 81 82 85 107 111 115 119 124 126 130 135 149 **S** Methodist Health System, Dallas, TX
Primary Contact: John McGreevy, FACHE, President
Web address: www.https://methodistsouthlake.com/
**Control**: Partnership, Investor–owned (for–profit) **Service**: General medical and surgical

**Staffed Beds**: 12 **Admissions**: 404 **Census**: 2 **Outpatient Visits**: 4297 **Births**: 0 **Total Expense ($000)**: 44909 **Payroll Expense ($000)**: 11013 **Personnel**: 146

☐ **TEXAS HEALTH HARRIS METHODIST HOSPITAL SOUTHLAKE (450888)**, 1545 East Southlake Boulevard, Zip 76092–6422; tel. 817/748–8700, (Nonreporting) **A**1 10 **F**3 29 30 40 64 74 75 79 81 85 107 111 115 119 130 **P**2
Primary Contact: Traci Bernard, R.N., President, Chief Executive Officer and Chief Operating Officer
CFO: Mitchell Mulvehill, Group Financial Officer
CMO: David Taunton, M.D., Chief of Staff
CHR: Tasha Sledge, Director Human Resources
CNO: Debra Ennis, Vice President and Chief Nursing Officer
Web address: www.texashealthsouthlake.com
**Control**: Corporation, Investor–owned (for–profit) **Service**: Surgical

**Staffed Beds**: 23 **Admissions**: 986 **Census**: 4 **Outpatient Visits**: 15554 **Births**: 0 **Total Expense ($000)**: 61688 **Payroll Expense ($000)**: 11612 **Personnel**: 145

### SPEARMAN—Hansford County

★ ⌂ **HANSFORD HOSPITAL (451344)**, 707 South Roland Street, Zip 79081–3441; tel. 806/659–2535, (Nonreporting) **A**10 18 21 **F**3 7 11 32 34 35 40 43 56 57 59 62 63 64 65 68 69 77 78 93 107 114 127 130 133 148 158 **P**6
Primary Contact: Jonathan D. Bailey, Chief Executive Officer and Administrator
CFO: Scott Beedy, Chief Financial Officer
CMO: Mark Garnett, M.D., Chief of Staff
CHR: Jackie Nelson, Director Human Resources
Web address: www.hchd.net
**Control**: Hospital district or authority, Government, Nonfederal **Service**: General medical and surgical

**Staffed Beds**: 14 **Admissions**: 143 **Census**: 3 **Outpatient Visits**: 22615 **Births**: 0 **Total Expense ($000)**: 12826 **Payroll Expense ($000)**: 5189 **Personnel**: 105

### STAFFORD—Fort Bend County

**ATRIUM MEDICAL CENTER (452114)**, 11929 West Airport Boulevard, Zip 77477–2451; tel. 281/207–8200, (Nonreporting) **A**10 22 **F**3 18 28 29 56 59 60 64 65 68 74 77 82 83 85 91 107 114 119 130 148
Primary Contact: Ahmad Zaid, Chief Executive Officer
COO: Rachid Al Rayes, Chief Operating Officer
CFO: Gloria Carrion, Chief Financial Offricer
CMO: Shatish Patel, M.D., Chief Medical Officer
CNO: Vivian Bradly, Chief Nursing Officer
Web address: www.atriummedicalcenter.com
**Control**: Partnership, Investor–owned (for–profit) **Service**: Acute long–term care hospital

**Staffed Beds**: 68 **Admissions**: 239 **Census**: 16 **Outpatient Visits**: 11 **Births**: 0 **Total Expense ($000)**: 12788 **Payroll Expense ($000)**: 3397 **Personnel**: 97

**TX**

*Many Facility Codes have changed. Please refer to the AHA Guide Code Chart.*
© 2021 AHA Guide

## STANTON—Martin County

**MARTIN COUNTY HOSPITAL DISTRICT (451333)**, 600 Interstate 20E, Zip 79782, Mailing Address: P.O. Box 640, Zip 79782–0640; tel. 432/607–3200, (Nonreporting) **A**10 18 **F**3 7 29 34 35 39 40 45 53 57 59 62 63 64 65 75 77 81 82 87 93 107 112 114 119 127 133 154 157 **P**6
Primary Contact: Nancy Cooke, Chief Executive Officer
CFO: Michele Cathey, Interim Chief Financial officer
CIO: Freddy Oliveras, Chief Information Officer
CHR: Paula Dority, Director Human Resources
CNO: Brandi Avila, Chief Nursing Officer
Web address: www.martincountyhospital.org/
**Control:** Hospital district or authority, Government, Nonfederal **Service:** General medical and surgical

**Staffed Beds:** 18 **Admissions:** 120 **Census:** 4 **Outpatient Visits:** 7319
**Births:** 0 **Total Expense ($000):** 27544 **Payroll Expense ($000):** 11878
**Personnel:** 171

## STEPHENVILLE—Erath County

**HARRIS METHODIST-ERATH COUNTY** See Texas Health Harris Methodist Hospital Stephenville

☒ **TEXAS HEALTH HARRIS METHODIST HOSPITAL STEPHENVILLE (450351)**, 411 North Belknap Street, Zip 76401–3415; tel. 254/965–1500, (Nonreporting) **A**1 10 20 **F**3 11 15 28 29 30 34 35 39 40 41 43 50 57 59 63 64 65 68 70 75 77 79 81 85 86 87 89 107 110 111 114 117 119 130 146 148 149 154 156 **P**6 **S** Texas Health Resources, Arlington, TX
Primary Contact: Christopher Leu, President
CMO: Marilyn Brister, M.D., Chief of Staff
CHR: Kimberly Leondar, Director Human Resources
CNO: Cynthia L McCarthy, Chief Nursing Officer
Web address: www.texashealth.org/landing.cfm?id=108
**Control:** Other not–for–profit (including NFP Corporation) **Service:** General medical and surgical

**Staffed Beds:** 41 **Admissions:** 1333 **Census:** 9 **Outpatient Visits:** 28422
**Births:** 194 **Total Expense ($000):** 43847 **Payroll Expense ($000):** 15836
**Personnel:** 184

## SUGAR LAND—Fort Bend County

**EMERUS HOSPITAL - SUGAR LAND** See Memorial Hermann First Colony Hospital

☒ **ENCOMPASS HEALTH REHABILITATION HOSPITAL OF SUGAR LAND (673042)**, 1325 Highway 6, Zip 77478–4906; tel. 281/276–7574, (Nonreporting) **A**1 10 **F**3 29 30 34 75 87 90 91 95 96 130 132 146 148 149 154 **S** Encompass Health Corporation, Birmingham, AL
Primary Contact: Bindu Varghese, R.N., Chief Executive Officer
CFO: Carol Neilson, CPA, Controller
CNO: Steve Midgett, R.N., Chief Nursing Officer
Web address: www.healthsouthsugarland.com
**Control:** Corporation, Investor–owned (for–profit) **Service:** Rehabilitation

**Staffed Beds:** 50 **Admissions:** 1374 **Census:** 45 **Outpatient Visits:** 0
**Births:** 0 **Total Expense ($000):** 20918 **Payroll Expense ($000):** 10779
**Personnel:** 188

**HEALTHSOUTH SUGAR LAND REHABILITATION HOSPITAL** See Encompass Health Rehabilitation Hospital of Sugar Land

★ ⇑ **HOUSTON METHODIST SUGAR LAND HOSPITAL (450820)**, 16655 SW Freeway, Zip 77479–2329; tel. 281/274–7000, (Nonreporting) **A**2 3 10 21 **F**3 12 13 15 18 20 22 24 26 28 29 30 31 32 33 34 35 36 37 38 40 41 42 44 45 48 49 50 51 53 55 57 59 60 61 63 64 65 68 70 73 74 75 76 77 78 79 80 81 82 84 85 86 87 91 92 93 94 96 100 102 107 108 110 111 114 115 116 117 118 119 120 121 123 124 126 130 131 132 135 145 146 147 148 149 150 154 156 **P**5 6 **S** Houston Methodist, Houston, TX
Primary Contact: Christopher Siebenaler, Regional Senior Vice President and Chief Executive Officer
CMO: Jeffrey Jackson, M.D., Medical Director
CHR: Luis Mario Garcia JrDirector Human Resources
Web address: www.methodisthealth.com
**Control:** Other not–for–profit (including NFP Corporation) **Service:** General medical and surgical

**Staffed Beds:** 318 **Admissions:** 17799 **Census:** 225 **Outpatient Visits:** 280795 **Births:** 2457 **Total Expense ($000):** 455196 **Payroll Expense ($000):** 155340 **Personnel:** 2533

☒ **KINDRED HOSPITAL SUGAR LAND (452080)**, 1550 First Colony Boulevard, Zip 77479–4000; tel. 281/275–6000, (Nonreporting) **A**1 10 **F**1 3 29 30 64 75 77 82 84 87 107 130 146 148 149 154 **S** Kindred Healthcare, Louisville, KY
Primary Contact: John D. Cross, Chief Executive Officer
CFO: Sara Rodriguez, Chief Financial Officer
CMO: Subodh Bhuchar, M.D., Chief of Staff
CIO: Feisal Ndomea, Director Case Management
CHR: Lupe Delgado, Coordinator Human Resources
CNO: Hala Alameddine, Chief Nursing Executive
Web address: www.kindred.com
**Control:** Corporation, Investor–owned (for–profit) **Service:** Acute long–term care hospital

**Staffed Beds:** 105 **Admissions:** 842 **Census:** 61 **Outpatient Visits:** 420
**Births:** 0 **Total Expense ($000):** 41171 **Payroll Expense ($000):** 13795
**Personnel:** 215

**MEM HERMANN FORT BEND HOSP** See Memorial Hermann Sugar Land Hospital

**MEMORIAL HERMANN FIRST COLONY HOSPITAL (670058)**, 16000 Southwest Freeway, Suite 100, Zip 77479–2674; tel. 281/277–0911, (Data for 243 days) (Nonreporting) **A**3 10 **F**3 40 75 107 114 119 149 **P**5 **S** Emerus, The Woodlands, TX
Primary Contact: Brenda Villafranco, Administrator
Web address: www.emerus.com
**Control:** Corporation, Investor–owned (for–profit) **Service:** General medical and surgical

**Staffed Beds:** 15 **Admissions:** 129 **Census:** 2 **Outpatient Visits:** 7868
**Births:** 0 **Total Expense ($000):** 7595 **Payroll Expense ($000):** 2656
**Personnel:** 29

☒ **MEMORIAL HERMANN SUGAR LAND HOSPITAL (450848)**, 17500 West Grand Parkway South, Zip 77479–2562; tel. 281/725–5000, (Nonreporting) **A**1 3 5 10 **F**3 4 8 11 12 13 15 18 20 22 26 29 30 34 35 37 40 41 43 44 45 46 47 48 49 50 51 55 56 57 58 59 64 68 70 72 74 75 76 77 78 79 80 81 82 85 86 87 89 91 107 108 109 110 111 112 114 119 126 129 130 146 147 148 154 **S** Memorial Hermann Health System, Houston, TX
Primary Contact: Malisha Patel, Senior Vice President and Chief Executive Officer
CFO: Lisa Kendler, Chief Financial Officer
CMO: William Riley, M.D., JrChief of Staff
CHR: Robert Blake, Chief Human Resources Officer Southwest Market
Web address: www.memorialhermann.org
**Control:** Other not–for–profit (including NFP Corporation) **Service:** General medical and surgical

**Staffed Beds:** 149 **Admissions:** 8734 **Census:** 80 **Outpatient Visits:** 111726 **Births:** 1896 **Total Expense ($000):** 177357 **Payroll Expense ($000):** 59279 **Personnel:** 703

⇑ **METHODIST SUGAR LAND HOSPITAL** See Houston Methodist Sugar Land Hospital

**MICHAEL'S ELITE HOSPITAL** See St. Michael's Elite Hospital

**ST LUKE'S SUGAR LAND HOSPITAL** See St. Luke's Sugar Land Hospital

☒ **ST. LUKE'S SUGAR LAND HOSPITAL (670053)**, 1317 Lake Pointe Parkway, Zip 77478–3997; tel. 281/637–7000, (Nonreporting) **A**1 10 **F**3 13 15 18 20 22 26 29 30 35 37 39 40 41 44 45 46 49 57 60 64 68 70 72 74 75 76 79 81 82 85 107 108 110 111 115 119 126 130 146 147 148 **P**5 **S** CommonSpirit Health, Chicago, IL
Primary Contact: Steven Foster, President and Interim Chief Executive Officer
CFO: Bill Beauchamp, Chief Financial Officer
CNO: Wes Garrison
Web address: www.https://www.chistlukeshealth.org/locations/sugar-land-hospital?utm_source=localListing&utm_medium=organic&utm_campaign=website-link
**Control:** Church operated, Nongovernment, not–for–profit **Service:** General medical and surgical

**Staffed Beds:** 96 **Admissions:** 4379 **Census:** 52 **Outpatient Visits:** 22114
**Births:** 1046 **Total Expense ($000):** 74595 **Payroll Expense ($000):** 29931
**Personnel:** 335

TX

---

**Hospital, Medicare Provider Number, Address, Telephone, Approval, Facility, and Physician Codes, Health Care System**

★ American Hospital Association (AHA) membership  ○ Healthcare Facilities Accreditation Program  ⇑ Center for Improvement in Healthcare Quality Accreditation
☐ The Joint Commission accreditation  ◇ DNV Healthcare Inc. accreditation  △ Commission on Accreditation of Rehabilitation Facilities (CARF) accreditation

**ST. MICHAEL'S ELITE HOSPITAL**, 16000 Southwest Freeway, Zip 77479–2673; tel. 281/980–4357, (Nonreporting)
Primary Contact: Don Vickers, Chief Executive Officer
Web address: www.https://23hrer.com
**Control**: Partnership, Investor–owned (for–profit) **Service**: Other specialty treatment

| Staffed Beds: 7 |
|---|

**TRIUMPH HOSPITAL SOUTHWEST** See Kindred Hospital Sugar Land

### SULPHUR SPRINGS—Hopkins County

✠ **CHRISTUS MOTHER FRANCES HOSPITAL - SULPHUR SPRINGS (450236)**, 115 Airport Road, Zip 75482–2105; tel. 903/885–7671, (Nonreporting) **A**1 10 **F**1 3 11 13 15 28 29 30 34 35 40 43 45 47 49 51 53 57 59 64 66 70 72 76 79 80 81 82 85 93 96 97 107 108 110 111 115 119 129 130 131 146 147 148 **S** CHRISTUS Health, Irving, TX
Primary Contact: Paul Harvey, President and Chief Executive Officer
COO: Donna Geiken Wallace, Chief Operating Officer and Chief Financial Officer
CFO: Donna Geiken Wallace, Chief Operating Officer and Chief Financial Officer
CMO: Chris Gallagher, M.D., Chief Medical Officer
CHR: Donna Rudzik, Director Human Resources
Web address: www.tmfhc.org/maps-and-locations/locations-profile/?id=72&searchid=8bcb329f-a152-e611-b37f-2c768a4e1b84&sort=11&page=1&pageSize=10
**Control**: Other not–for–profit (including NFP Corporation) **Service**: General medical and surgical

| Staffed Beds: 62 Admissions: 3106 Census: 33 Outpatient Visits: 120570 Births: 553 Total Expense ($000): 74093 Payroll Expense ($000): 19873 Personnel: 387 |
|---|

**HOPKINS COUNTY MEMORIAL HOSPITAL** See Christus Mother Frances Hospital - Sulphur Springs

### SUNNYVALE—Dallas County

✠ **BAYLOR SCOTT & WHITE MEDICAL CENTER - SUNNYVALE (670060)**, 231 South Collins Road, Zip 75182–4624; tel. 972/892–3000, (Nonreporting) **A**1 10 **F**15 18 20 22 26 28 29 40 64 70 77 79 80 81 82 85 93 107 108 110 111 115 119 130 **S** United Surgical Partners International, Addison, TX
Primary Contact: Jon Duckert, FACHE, Chief Executive Officer
COO: Josiah De La Garza, Chief Operating Officer
CMO: William G. Jones, M.D., Chief Medical Officer
CNO: Deborah A Moeller, R.N., MS, Interim Chief Nursing Officer
Web address: www.BaylorScottandWhite.com/Sunnyvale
**Control**: Partnership, Investor–owned (for–profit) **Service**: General medical and surgical

| Staffed Beds: 70 Admissions: 4470 Census: 52 Outpatient Visits: 46622 Births: 0 Total Expense ($000): 89802 Payroll Expense ($000): 29625 Personnel: 344 |
|---|

**TEXAS REGIONAL MEDICAL CENTER AT SUNNYVALE** See Baylor Scott & White Medical Center - Sunnyvale

### SWEENY—Brazoria County

★ **SWEENY COMMUNITY HOSPITAL (451311)**, 305 North McKinney Street, Zip 77480–2895; tel. 979/548–1500, (Nonreporting) **A**10 18 **F**7 10 11 15 29 34 35 40 43 53 56 57 59 64 65 69 70 75 81 85 93 104 107 110 114 119 127 132 133 143 148 149 153 156
Primary Contact: Kelly Park, R.N., Interim Chief Executive Officer
CFO: Hong Wade, Chief Financial Officer
CMO: Fabio Aglieco, D.O., Chief of Staff
CIO: Stuart Butler, Director Information Technology
CHR: Dana Quintanilla, Director Human Resources
CNO: Kelly Park, R.N., Chief Nursing Officer
Web address: www.sweenyhospital.org
**Control**: Hospital district or authority, Government, Nonfederal **Service**: General medical and surgical

| Staffed Beds: 14 Admissions: 258 Census: 3 Outpatient Visits: 29761 Births: 2 Total Expense ($000): 49266 Payroll Expense ($000): 9342 Personnel: 173 |
|---|

### SWEETWATER—Nolan County

★ ⇑ **ROLLING PLAINS MEMORIAL HOSPITAL (450055)**, 200 East Arizona Street, Zip 79556–7199, Mailing Address: P.O. Box 690, Zip 79556–0690; tel. 325/235–1701, (Nonreporting) **A**3 10 20 21 **F**3 11 13 15 28 29 34 40 43 45 53 57 59 62 70 76 77 79 81 85 93 107 108 114 119 127 130 133 135 146 148 156
Primary Contact: Doug Dippel, R.N., MSN, Chief Executive Officer
COO: Rhonda Guelker, Senior Director Finance
CFO: Rhonda Guelker, Senior Director Finance
CIO: Rhonda Guelker, Senior Director Finance
CHR: Ame Monroe, Director Human Resources
CNO: Maxine Montano, R.N., Chief Nursing Officer
Web address: www.rpmh.net
**Control**: Hospital district or authority, Government, Nonfederal **Service**: General medical and surgical

| Staffed Beds: 57 Admissions: 991 Census: 11 Outpatient Visits: 68488 Births: 233 Total Expense ($000): 38695 Payroll Expense ($000): 17578 Personnel: 296 |
|---|

### TAHOKA—Lynn County

★ **LYNN COUNTY HOSPITAL DISTRICT (451351)**, 2600 Lockwood, Zip 79373–4118; tel. 806/998–4533, (Nonreporting) **A**10 18 **F**3 7 10 28 29 30 32 34 35 40 43 44 53 54 56 57 59 64 65 66 75 84 86 87 93 97 107 119 133 135 147 148 149 154 **P**5
Primary Contact: Melanie Richburg, Chief Executive Officer
CFO: Steve Brock, Chief Financial Officer
CMO: Donald Freitag, M.D., Chief Medical Officer
CIO: Jim Brown, Director Information Technology
CHR: Jill Stone, Manager Human Resources
CNO: Angie Jalomo, Chief Nursing Officer
Web address: www.lchdhealthcare.org
**Control**: Hospital district or authority, Government, Nonfederal **Service**: General medical and surgical

| Staffed Beds: 24 Admissions: 85 Census: 6 Outpatient Visits: 10802 Births: 0 Total Expense ($000): 13045 Payroll Expense ($000): 6615 Personnel: 137 |
|---|

### TAYLOR—Williamson County

✠ **BAYLOR SCOTT & WHITE MEDICAL CENTER - TAYLOR (451374)**, 305 Mallard Lane, Zip 76574–1208; tel. 512/352–7611, (Nonreporting) **A**1 10 18 **F**3 18 29 34 35 40 45 50 56 59 63 64 65 68 75 77 79 81 82 84 85 87 91 92 93 97 107 108 114 119 129 130 132 133 135 143 146 147 148 **S** Baylor Scott & White Health, Dallas, TX
Primary Contact: Jay Fox, Chief Executive Officer
Web address: www.https://www.bswhealth.com/locations/taylor/pages/default.aspx?utm_source=BSWHealth.com-Taylor&utm_medium=offline&utm_campaign=BSWHealth.com&utm_term=BSWHealth.com-Taylor&utm_content=redirect
**Control**: Other not–for–profit (including NFP Corporation) **Service**: General medical and surgical

| Staffed Beds: 25 Admissions: 376 Census: 7 Outpatient Visits: 58471 Births: 0 Total Expense ($000): 22656 Payroll Expense ($000): 10388 Personnel: 116 |
|---|

**SCOTT & WHITE HOSPITAL - TAYLOR** See Baylor Scott & White Medical Center - Taylor

### TEMPLE—Bell County

★ **BAYLOR SCOTT & WHITE CONTINUING CARE HOSPITAL-TEMPLE (452105)**, 546 North Kegley Road, Zip 76502–4069; tel. 254/215–0900, (Total facility includes 23 beds in nursing home–type unit) (Nonreporting) **A**10 **F**1 3 29 30 60 107 119 128 148 **S** Baylor Scott & White Health, Dallas, TX
Primary Contact: Michael Davis, Administrator
CMO: David P Ciceri, M.D., Chief Medical Officer
CNO: Robert Pisicotta, Chief Nursing Officer
Web address: www.sw.org/location/temple-cch
**Control**: Other not–for–profit (including NFP Corporation) **Service**: Acute long–term care hospital

| Staffed Beds: 48 Admissions: 458 Census: 40 Outpatient Visits: 187 Births: 0 Total Expense ($000): 20304 Payroll Expense ($000): 9350 Personnel: 102 |
|---|

*Many Facility Codes have changed. Please refer to the AHA Guide Code Chart.*  © 2021 AHA Guide

⊞ **BAYLOR SCOTT & WHITE MEDICAL CENTER - TEMPLE (450054)**, 2401 South 31st Street, Zip 76508–0002; tel. 254/724–2111, (Includes MCLANE CHILDREN'S HOSPITAL SCOTT & WHITE, Mailing address: 1901 SW H K Dodgen Loop, Temple, Texas, Zip 76502–1896; tel. 254/771–8600; Shahin Motakef, FACHE, Chief Executive Officer; MCLANE CHILDREN'S HOSPITAL SCOTT & WHITE, Mailing address: 2401 South 31st Street, Temple, Texas, Zip 76508–0001; tel. 877/724–5437; Shahin Motakef, FACHE, President), (Nonreporting) **A**1 2 3 5 8 10 **F**3 5 7 8 9 11 12 13 14 15 17 18 19 20 22 23 24 25 26 27 28 29 30 31 32 34 35 36 37 38 39 40 41 43 45 46 47 48 49 50 51 52 54 55 56 57 58 59 60 61 63 64 65 66 67 68 70 71 72 73 74 75 76 77 78 79 81 82 83 84 85 86 87 88 89 91 92 93 96 97 98 100 104 107 108 109 110 111 112 113 114 115 116 117 118 119 120 121 123 124 126 127 129 130 131 132 134 135 136 137 138 141 142 143 144 146 147 148 149 150 153 154 156 157 **S** Baylor Scott & White Health, Dallas, TX
Primary Contact: Shahin Motakef, FACHE, President
CFO: Alita Prosser, Chief Financial Officer
CMO: Stephen Sibbitt, M.D., Chief Medical Officer
CIO: Matthew Chambers, Chief Information Officer
CHR: Pat Balz, Vice President Operations Human Resources
CNO: Gerald W Bryant, R.N., Chief Nursing Officer
Web address: www.https://www.bswhealth.com/locations/temple/Pages/default.aspx
**Control**: Other not–for–profit (including NFP Corporation) **Service**: General medical and surgical

| | |
|---|---|
| **Staffed Beds**: 644 **Admissions**: 35621 **Census**: 469 **Outpatient Visits**: 1880078 **Births**: 2509 **Total Expense ($000)**: 984221 **Payroll Expense ($000)**: 292450 **Personnel**: 5404 | |

**BAYLOR SCOTT AND WHITE CONTINUING CARE HOSPITAL** See Baylor Scott & White Continuing Care Hospital-Temple

**CENTRAL TEXAS VETERANS AFFAIRS HEALTH CARE SYSTEM, OLIN E. TEAGUE VETERANS CENTER** See Central Texas Veterans Affairs Health Care System, Olin E. Teague Veterans Medical Center

**CENTRAL TEXAS VETERANS AFFAIRS HEALTH CARE SYSTEM, OLIN E. TEAGUE VETERANS MEDICAL CENTER** See Central Texas Veterans Health Care System, Temple

⊞ △ **CENTRAL TEXAS VETERANS HEALTH CARE SYSTEM**, 1901 Veterans Memorial Drive, Zip 76504–7493; tel. 254/778–4811, (Includes CENTRAL TEXAS VETERANS AFFAIRS HEALTH CARE SYSTEM, OLIN E. TEAGUE VETERANS MEDICAL CENTER, Mailing address: 1901 Veterans Memorial Drive, Temple, Texas, Zip 76504; tel. 254/778–4811; Colonel Michael L Kiefer, FACHE, Director; CENTRAL TEXAS VETERANS HEALTH CARE SYSTEM, DORIS MILLER VETERANS MEDICAL CENTER, Mailing address: 4800 Memorial Drive, Waco, Texas, Zip 76711–1397; tel. 254/752–6581; Colonel Michael L Kiefer, FACHE, Director), (Nonreporting) **A**1 3 5 7 8 **S** Department of Veterans Affairs, Washington, DC
Primary Contact: Colonel Michael L. Kiefer, FACHE, Director
CFO: Rosey Anzures, Acting Chief Financial Officer
CMO: Olawale Fashina, M.D., Chief of Staff
CIO: Victor Vitolas, Acting Chief Information Technology Services
CHR: Mary P. Doerfler, Chief Human Resources Officer
Web address: www.centraltexas.va.gov/
**Control**: Veterans Affairs, Government, federal **Service**: General medical and surgical

| | |
|---|---|
| **Staffed Beds**: 1532 | |

**CENTRAL TEXAS VETERANS HEALTHCARE SYSTEM** See Central Texas Veterans Health Care System

**CHILDREN'S HOSPITAL AT SCOTT & WHITE** See Mclane Children's Hospital Scott & White

**EVEREST REHABILITATION HOSPITAL TEMPLE**, 23621 SE H.K. Dodgen Loop, Zip 76504–0555, (Nonreporting) **A**22 **S** Everest Rehabilitation Hospitals, LLC, Dallas, TX
Primary Contact: Michael Hutka, Chief Executive Officer
**Control**: Corporation, Investor–owned (for–profit) **Service**: Rehabilitation

| | |
|---|---|
| **Staffed Beds**: 36 | |

**KING'S DAUGHTERS HOSPITAL** See Mclane Children's Hospital Scott & White

**MCLANE CHILDREN'S HOSPITAL SCOTT & WHITE** See Baylor Scott & White Medical Center - Temple, Temple

**SCOTT & WHITE MEDICAL CENTER - TEMPLE** See Baylor Scott & White Medical Center - Temple

**TERRELL—Kaufman County**

**COLONIAL HOSPITAL** See Terrell Community Hospital, Colonial Campus

☐ **TERRELL STATE HOSPITAL (454006)**, 1200 East Brin Street, Zip 75160–2938, Mailing Address: P.O. Box 70, Zip 75160–9000; tel. 972/524–6452, (Nonreporting) **A**1 3 5 10 **F**30 34 39 57 68 75 86 87 98 99 100 101 103 130 132 135 146 **P**6 **S** Texas Department of State Health Services, Austin, TX
Primary Contact: Dorothy Floyd, Ph.D., Superintendent
CFO: David R. Teel, Financial Officer
CMO: Mark Messer, D.O., Clinical Director
CIO: Sims Anderson, Manager Facility Automation
CNO: Kathryn Griffin, Chief Nurse Executive
Web address: www.dshs.state.tx.us/mhhospitals/terrellsh
**Control**: State, Government, Nonfederal **Service**: Psychiatric

| | |
|---|---|
| **Staffed Beds**: 288 **Admissions**: 1359 **Census**: 270 **Outpatient Visits**: 0 **Births**: 0 **Total Expense ($000)**: 60912 **Payroll Expense ($000)**: 50698 **Personnel**: 859 | |

**TEXARKANA—Bowie County**

**CHRISTUS ST MICHAEL HLTH SYST** See Christus St. Michael Health System

**CHRISTUS ST MICHAEL REHAB HOSP** See Christus St. Michael Rehabilitation Hospital

⊞ **CHRISTUS ST. MICHAEL HEALTH SYSTEM (450801)**, 2600 St Michael Drive, Zip 75503–5220; tel. 903/614–1000, (Includes CHRISTUS ST. MICHAEL HOSPITAL-ATLANTA, Mailing address: 1007 South William Street, Atlanta, Texas, Zip 75551–3245; tel. 903/799–3000; William Micah Johnson, Administrator and Chief Nursing Officer), (Nonreporting) **A**1 10 19 **F**3 11 13 15 17 18 20 22 24 26 28 29 30 31 34 35 37 40 41 43 45 48 49 51 53 55 56 57 59 60 64 65 68 70 71 72 73 74 75 76 77 78 79 80 81 82 84 85 86 87 89 92 93 102 107 108 109 110 111 114 115 118 119 120 121 122 123 124 126 129 130 131 132 135 143 146 147 148 149 154 156 **P**8 **S** CHRISTUS Health, Irving, TX
Primary Contact: Jason Rounds, FACHE, President
COO: Jennifer Wright, Vice President Operations
CFO: Glen Boles, Vice President and Chief Financial Officer
CMO: Mike Finley, M.D., Chief Medical Officer
CIO: Stephen DeLoach, Regional Information Management Executive
CHR: Wendy Chandler, Vice President Human Resources
CNO: Louise Thornell, Ph.D., R.N., Chief Nursing Officer
Web address: www.christusstmichael.org
**Control**: Church operated, Nongovernment, not–for–profit **Service**: General medical and surgical

| | |
|---|---|
| **Staffed Beds**: 354 **Admissions**: 14147 **Census**: 164 **Outpatient Visits**: 297827 **Births**: 1623 **Total Expense ($000)**: 289435 **Payroll Expense ($000)**: 86672 **Personnel**: 1314 | |

⊞ △ **CHRISTUS ST. MICHAEL REHABILITATION HOSPITAL (453065)**, 2400 St Michael Drive, Zip 75503–2374; tel. 903/614–4000, (Nonreporting) **A**1 7 10 **F**11 18 28 29 30 34 35 57 59 65 68 75 77 79 82 87 90 93 96 132 135 143 148 149 154 **P**8 **S** CHRISTUS Health, Irving, TX
Primary Contact: Patrick Flannery, Administrator
CFO: Glen Boles, Vice President and Chief Financial Officer
CMO: Richard Sharp, M.D., Medical Director
CIO: Alana Higgins, Regional Information Management Executive
CHR: Jennifer Wright, Vice President Human Resources
CNO: Stacey Breedlove, Chief Nursing Officer
Web address: www.christusstmichael.org/rehab
**Control**: Church operated, Nongovernment, not–for–profit **Service**: Rehabilitation

| | |
|---|---|
| **Staffed Beds**: 50 **Admissions**: 909 **Census**: 28 **Outpatient Visits**: 48605 **Births**: 0 **Total Expense ($000)**: 22952 **Payroll Expense ($000)**: 10873 **Personnel**: 152 | |

**TX**

---

**Hospital, Medicare Provider Number, Address, Telephone, Approval, Facility, and Physician Codes, Health Care System**

★ American Hospital Association (AHA) membership  ○ Healthcare Facilities Accreditation Program  ⇑ Center for Improvement in Healthcare Quality Accreditation
☐ The Joint Commission accreditation  ◇ DNV Healthcare Inc. accreditation  △ Commission on Accreditation of Rehabilitation Facilities (CARF) accreditation

© 2021 AHA Guide          *Many Facility Codes have changed. Please refer to the AHA Guide Code Chart.*          Hospitals **A719**

⊠ **ENCOMPASS HEALTH REHABILITATION HOSPITAL OF TEXARKANA (453053)**, 515 West 12th Street, Zip 75501–4416; tel. 903/735–5000, (Nonreporting) **A**1 10 **F**3 28 29 64 74 77 79 90 91 93 96 130 131 132 143 148 154 **P**5 **S** Encompass Health Corporation, Birmingham, AL
Primary Contact: Harlo McCall, Chief Executive Officer
CFO: Phylis Buck, Controller
CMO: Mark A Wren, M.D., Medical Director
CHR: Ann R Clapp, Director Human Resources
CNO: Lorri Oglesby, Chief Nursing Officer
Web address: www.healthsouthtexarkana.com
**Control:** Corporation, Investor–owned (for–profit) **Service:** Rehabilitation

**Staffed Beds:** 60 **Admissions:** 1233 **Census:** 44 **Outpatient Visits:** 7241 **Births:** 0 **Total Expense ($000):** 18555 **Payroll Expense ($000):** 10469 **Personnel:** 146

**HEALTHSOUTH REHABILITATION HOSPITAL OF TEXARKANA** See Encompass Health Rehabilitation Hospital of Texarkana

**POST ACUTE MEDICAL SPECIALTY HOSPITAL OF TEXARKANA** See Post Acute Medical Specialty Hospital of Texarkana - North

⊠ **POST ACUTE MEDICAL SPECIALTY HOSPITAL OF TEXARKANA - NORTH (452061)**, 2400 St Michael Drive, 2nd Floor, Zip 75503–2372; tel. 903/614–7600, (Nonreporting) **A**1 10 **F**1 3 29 60 68 85 148 154 **S** Post Acute Medical, LLC, Enola, PA
Primary Contact: Greg Lessard, Chief Executive Officer
Web address: www.postacutemedical.com
**Control:** Corporation, Investor–owned (for–profit) **Service:** Acute long–term care hospital

**Staffed Beds:** 30 **Admissions:** 350 **Census:** 21 **Outpatient Visits:** 0 **Births:** 0 **Total Expense ($000):** 11029 **Payroll Expense ($000):** 4362 **Personnel:** 77

☐ **WADLEY REGIONAL MEDICAL CENTER (450200)**, 1000 Pine Street, Zip 75501–5170; tel. 903/798–8000, (Nonreporting) **A**1 3 10 19 **F**3 11 13 15 18 20 22 28 29 30 31 34 35 40 43 45 49 50 56 57 59 60 64 65 70 71 72 74 75 76 77 78 79 81 85 86 87 89 93 98 103 107 108 110 111 114 115 119 126 130 146 147 148 149 154 **S** Steward Health Care System, LLC, Dallas, TX
Primary Contact: Thomas D. Gilbert, FACHE, Chief Executive Officer
CFO: Bonny Sorensen, Chief Financial Officer
CIO: Matt Kesterson, Director Information Services
CHR: Debby Butler, Director Human Resources
CNO: Shelly Strayhorn, R.N., Chief Nursing Officer
Web address: www.wadleyhealth.com
**Control:** Corporation, Investor–owned (for–profit) **Service:** General medical and surgical

**Staffed Beds:** 178 **Admissions:** 6160 **Census:** 76 **Outpatient Visits:** 79308 **Births:** 835 **Total Expense ($000):** 96853 **Payroll Expense ($000):** 36464 **Personnel:** 659

### TEXAS CITY—Galveston County

**COLUMBIA MAINLAND MEDICAL CTR** See Mainland Medical Center

### THE COLONY—Denton County

**THE COLONY ER HOSPITAL**, 4780 State Highway 121, Zip 75056–2913; tel. 214/469–1119, (Nonreporting) **A**22
Primary Contact: Russell Kaiser, Interim Chief Executive Officer and Chief Nursing Officer
Web address: www.https://thecolonyer.com/
**Control:** Individual, Investor–owned (for–profit) **Service:** General medical and surgical

**Staffed Beds:** 13

### THE WOODLANDS—Montgomery County

⊠ **CHI ST. LUKE'S HEALTH-LAKESIDE HOSPITAL (670059)**, 17400 St. Luke's Way, Zip 77384–8036; tel. 936/266–9000, (Nonreporting) **A**1 10 **F**3 18 20 22 26 29 30 34 35 40 50 57 59 64 68 75 79 81 87 94 107 111 115 119 130 131 135 157 **P**5 **S** CommonSpirit Health, Chicago, IL
Primary Contact: James Parisi, Chief Executive Officer
CHR: Debra Roberts, Director of Human Resources
CNO: Diane Freeman, R.N., Assistant Vice President and Chief Nursing Officer
Web address: www.stlukeslakeside.com/
**Control:** Corporation, Investor–owned (for–profit) **Service:** Surgical

**Staffed Beds:** 30 **Admissions:** 791 **Census:** 4 **Outpatient Visits:** 14201 **Births:** 0 **Total Expense ($000):** 37414 **Payroll Expense ($000):** 7612 **Personnel:** 106

⊠ **CHI ST. LUKE'S HEALTH-THE WOODLANDS HOSPITAL (450862)**, 17200 St. Luke's Way, Zip 77384–8007; tel. 936/266–2000, (Nonreporting) **A**1 5 10 **F**3 11 12 13 15 18 20 22 24 26 28 29 30 34 35 38 40 41 42 45 49 50 57 58 59 64 68 70 72 74 75 76 78 79 81 82 85 86 87 89 90 93 107 108 109 110 111 114 118 119 124 126 129 130 131 135 145 146 147 148 **P**5 **S** CommonSpirit Health, Chicago, IL
Primary Contact: James Parisi, Chief Executive Officer
CMO: Charles Sims, M.D., Chief of Staff
Web address: www.stlukeswoodlands.com
**Control:** Church operated, Nongovernment, not–for–profit **Service:** General medical and surgical

**Staffed Beds:** 204 **Admissions:** 11416 **Census:** 147 **Outpatient Visits:** 90121 **Births:** 1728 **Total Expense ($000):** 219816 **Payroll Expense ($000):** 73408 **Personnel:** 981

★ ⇑ **HOUSTON METHODIST THE WOODLANDS HOSPITAL (670122)**, 17201 Interstate 45 South, Zip 77385; tel. 713/790–3333, (Nonreporting) **A**3 10 21 **F**3 11 12 13 15 18 20 22 24 26 28 29 30 31 34 35 36 37 40 41 42 44 45 46 47 48 49 50 51 53 57 59 64 65 68 70 72 74 75 76 77 78 79 80 81 84 85 86 87 93 95 96 97 102 107 108 110 111 115 117 118 119 120 121 123 124 126 130 131 132 135 146 147 149 154 **P**5 6 **S** Houston Methodist, Houston, TX
Primary Contact: Debra F. Sukin, Ph.D., Regional Senior Vice President and Chief Executive Officer
CNO: Kerrie Guerrero, R.N., MSN, Vice President and Chief Nursing Officer
Web address: www.houstonmethodist.org/locations/the-woodlands/
**Control:** Other not–for–profit (including NFP Corporation) **Service:** General medical and surgical

**Staffed Beds:** 187 **Admissions:** 10919 **Census:** 114 **Outpatient Visits:** 146835 **Births:** 1651 **Total Expense ($000):** 266154 **Payroll Expense ($000):** 84872 **Personnel:** 1244

**MEMORIAL HERMANN THE WOODLANDS HOSPITAL** See Memorial Hermann Greater Heights Hospital, Houston

**MEMORIAL HOSPITAL** See Memorial Hermann The Woodlands Hospital

⇑ **NEXUS SPECIALTY HOSPITAL THE WOODLANDS (452057)**, 9182 Six Pines Drive, Zip 77380–3670; tel. 281/364–0317, (Nonreporting) **A**10 21
Primary Contact: Eric Cantrell, Chief Executive Officer
CFO: David Strickler, Chief Financial Officer
CMO: Ather Siddiqi, M.D., Medical Director
CIO: Noe Salinas, Vice President Information Technology
CHR: Kevin McAndrews, Vice President, Human Resources
CNO: Rhena Anderson, Chief Nursing Officer
Web address: www.nexusspecialty.com
**Control:** Partnership, Investor–owned (for–profit) **Service:** Acute long–term care hospital

**Staffed Beds:** 21

**ST. LUKE'S LAKESIDE HOSPITAL** See Chi St. Luke's Health-Lakeside Hospital

**ST. LUKE'S THE WOODLANDS HOSPITAL** See Chi St. Luke's Health-The Woodlands Hospital

*Many Facility Codes have changed. Please refer to the AHA Guide Code Chart.*
© 2021 AHA Guide

★ **WOODLANDS SPECIALTY HOSPITAL**, 9182 Six Pines Drive, Zip 77380–3670, Mailing Address: 25540 I-45 North, Suite 100, Spring, Zip 77380–3670; tel. 281/602–8160, (Nonreporting) **A**22 **F3** 18 20 22 24 26 29 40 45 46 47 48 49 79 80 81 107 108 109 111 115 118 119 120 149 156 **P4** 5 8
Primary Contact: Jody Randall, MSN, R.N., Chief Executive Officer/Chief Nursing Officer
CFO: Virginia de Bond, Chief Financial Officer
Web address: www.woodlandsspecialtyhospital.com/
**Control:** Individual, Investor–owned (for–profit) **Service:** General medical and surgical

**Staffed Beds:** 8 **Admissions:** 78 **Census:** 1 **Outpatient Visits:** 3042 **Births:** 0 **Total Expense ($000):** 14323 **Payroll Expense ($000):** 7789 **Personnel:** 179

**WOODLANS SPECIALTY HOSPITAL** See Woodlands Specialty Hospital

## THROCKMORTON—Throckmorton County

**THROCKMORTON COUNTY MEMORIAL HOSPITAL (451339)**, 802 North Minter Avenue, Zip 76483–5357, Mailing Address: P.O. Box 729, Zip 76483–0729; tel. 940/849–2151, (Nonreporting) **A**10 18 **F**1 4 7 34 40 41 43 44 50 59 61 64 65 67 68 79 87 97 102 127 128 130 133 148 **P**6
Primary Contact: Kirby Gober, Chief Executive Officer
CMO: Craig Beasley, M.D., Chief Medical Officer
CHR: Karla Benson, Executive Assistant
CNO: Kinsi Voss, R.N., Chief Nursing Officer
Web address: www.throckmortonhospital.com
**Control:** County, Government, Nonfederal **Service:** General medical and surgical

**Staffed Beds:** 14 **Admissions:** 78 **Census:** 2 **Outpatient Visits:** 14971 **Births:** 0 **Total Expense ($000):** 4502 **Payroll Expense ($000):** 1894 **Personnel:** 54

## TOMBALL—Harris County

✉ **HCA HOUSTON HEALTHCARE TOMBALL (450670)**, 605 Holderrieth Street, Zip 77375–6445; tel. 281/401–7500, (Includes HCA HOUSTON HEALTHCARE CYPRESS FAIRBANKS, Mailing address: 10655 Steepletop Drive, Houston, Texas, Zip 77065–4297; tel. 281/890–4285; Robert Marmerstein, Chief Executive Officer), (Nonreporting) **A**1 10 **F**3 8 12 13 15 18 20 22 24 26 28 29 30 31 34 35 40 42 43 44 45 46 47 48 49 50 51 53 54 57 59 64 65 70 72 74 75 76 77 78 79 80 81 82 85 86 87 90 91 93 94 96 98 103 107 108 110 111 114 115 119 120 121 124 126 129 130 131 132 144 145 146 147 148 149 154 **S** HCA Healthcare, Nashville, TN
Primary Contact: Robert Marmerstein, Chief Executive Officer
COO: Saumya Sutaria, M.D., Chief Operating Officer
CFO: Richard Ervin, Chief Financial Officer
CMO: Ian Glass, M.D., Chief Medical Officer
CIO: Marisa Smith, Director
CHR: Vanessa Hunt, Director Human Resources
Web address: www.tomballregionalmedicalcenter.com
**Control:** Corporation, Investor–owned (for–profit) **Service:** General medical and surgical

**Staffed Beds:** 261 **Admissions:** 10958 **Census:** 155 **Outpatient Visits:** 112104 **Births:** 1395 **Total Expense ($000):** 307473 **Payroll Expense ($000):** 86747 **Personnel:** 798

**TOMBALL REGIONAL MEDICAL CENTER** See Hca Houston Healthcare Tomball

## TROPHY CLUB—Denton County

**BAYLOR MEDICAL CENTER AT TROPHY CLUB** See Baylor Scott & White Medical Center - Trophy Club

☐ **BAYLOR SCOTT & WHITE MEDICAL CENTER - TROPHY CLUB (450883)**, 2850 East State Highway 114, Zip 76262–5302; tel. 817/837–4600, (Nonreporting) **A**1 10 **F**3 29 40 70 75 79 81 85 87 107 108 111 114 118 121 123 141
Primary Contact: Melanie Chick, Chief Executive Officer
CFO: Jonathan Saunders, Chief Financial Officer
CMO: Mike Stanton, D.O., Medical Director
CIO: Scot Bradford, Chief Information Officer
CHR: Donna Irvin, Director Human Resources
CNO: Tina Huddleston, R.N., Chief Nursing Officer
Web address: www.baylortrophyclub.com
**Control:** Partnership, Investor–owned (for–profit) **Service:** General medical and surgical

**Staffed Beds:** 22 **Admissions:** 1225 **Census:** 6 **Outpatient Visits:** 7567 **Births:** 0 **Total Expense ($000):** 54703 **Payroll Expense ($000):** 12384 **Personnel:** 173

## TULIA—Swisher County

★ **SWISHER MEMORIAL HEALTHCARE SYSTEM (451349)**, 539 Southeast Second, Zip 79088–2400, Mailing Address: P.O. Box 808, Zip 79088–0808; tel. 806/995–3581, (Nonreporting) **A**3 10 18 **F**3 7 10 11 29 33 34 35 36 40 43 50 53 57 59 64 65 68 75 77 93 104 107 114 127 130 132 133 **P**4
Primary Contact: Luke Brewer, Acting Chief Executive Officer
CFO: Connie Wilhelm, Chief Financial Officer
CIO: Brad Roberts, Network Administrator
Web address: www.swisherhospital.com
**Control:** Other not–for–profit (including NFP Corporation) **Service:** General medical and surgical

**Staffed Beds:** 20 **Admissions:** 158 **Census:** 4 **Outpatient Visits:** 22824 **Births:** 0 **Total Expense ($000):** 11381 **Payroll Expense ($000):** 4286 **Personnel:** 78

**SWISHER MEMORIAL HOSPITAL DISTRICT** See Swisher Memorial Healthcare System

## TYLER—Smith County

**BAYLOR SCOTT & WHITE TEXAS SPINE & JOINT HOSPITAL** See Baylor Scott & White Texas Spine & Joint Hospital-Tyler

✉ **BAYLOR SCOTT & WHITE TEXAS SPINE & JOINT HOSPITAL-TYLER (450864)**, 1814 Roseland Boulevard, Suite 100, Zip 75701–4262; tel. 903/525–3300, (Nonreporting) **A**1 10 **F**8 29 39 40 53 77 79 81 82 107 111 114 119 129 131 144
Primary Contact: Tony Wahl, Chief Executive Officer
CFO: Greg Cummings, Chief Financial Officer
CMO: Kim Foreman, M.D., Chief of Staff
CNO: Aaron Fleet, R.N., Chief Nursing Officer
Web address: www.tsjh.org
**Control:** Partnership, Investor–owned (for–profit) **Service:** Orthopedic

**Staffed Beds:** 20 **Admissions:** 2264 **Census:** 14 **Outpatient Visits:** 47419 **Births:** 0 **Total Expense ($000):** 94166 **Payroll Expense ($000):** 22752 **Personnel:** 473

✉ **CHRISTUS MOTHER FRANCES HOSPITAL - TYLER (450102)**, 800 East Dawson Street, Zip 75701–2036; tel. 903/593–8441, (Includes LOUIS & PEACHES OWEN HEART HOSPITAL, Mailing address: 703 South Fleishel Avenue, Tyler, Texas, Zip 75701–2015; tel. 903/606–3000; John McGreevy, FACHE, Chief Executive Officer), (Nonreporting) **A**1 2 3 10 **F**3 8 11 12 13 15 17 18 20 22 24 26 28 29 30 31 34 37 40 42 43 45 46 47 48 49 50 51 53 54 55 57 58 59 60 64 68 70 71 72 73 74 75 76 78 79 80 81 82 84 85 86 87 89 93 97 107 108 109 110 111 113 114 115 119 126 127 129 130 131 132 144 145 146 147 148 156 157 **P**5 6 7 8 **S** CHRISTUS Health, Irving, TX
Primary Contact: Jason J. Proctor, Chief Executive Officer
COO: Jason J Proctor, Chief Operating Officer
CFO: Joyce Hester, CPA, Senior Vice President and Chief Financial Officer
CMO: Fadi Nasrallah, M.D., Vice President Medical Affairs
CIO: Jeff Pearson, Vice President and Chief Information Officer
CHR: Thomas Wilken, Senior Vice President and Chief Human Resources Officer
Web address: www.tmfhc.org
**Control:** Other not–for–profit (including NFP Corporation) **Service:** General medical and surgical

**Staffed Beds:** 463 **Admissions:** 25549 **Census:** 308 **Outpatient Visits:** 543408 **Births:** 2990 **Total Expense ($000):** 629602 **Payroll Expense ($000):** 232798 **Personnel:** 4261

**CHRISTUS TRINITY MOTHER FRANCES REHABILITATION HOSPITAL** See Christus Trinity Mother Frances Rehabilitation Hospital, A Partner of Encompass Health

✉ **CHRISTUS TRINITY MOTHER FRANCES REHABILITATION HOSPITAL, A PARTNER OF ENCOMPASS HEALTH (453056)**, 3131 Troup Highway, Zip 75701–8352; tel. 903/510–7000, (Nonreporting) **A**1 10 **F**3 9 12 28 29 56 60 74 75 77 79 82 87 90 91 95 96 130 132 143 148 149 154 156 157 **S** Encompass Health Corporation, Birmingham, AL
Primary Contact: Sharla Anderson, Chief Executive Officer
CFO: Michael G Treadway, Controller
CMO: Bradley Merritt, M.D., Medical Director
Web address: www.tmfrehabhospital.com
**Control:** Partnership, Investor–owned (for–profit) **Service:** Rehabilitation

**Staffed Beds:** 94 **Admissions:** 2112 **Census:** 69 **Outpatient Visits:** 78 **Births:** 0 **Total Expense ($000):** 26331 **Payroll Expense ($000):** 12680 **Personnel:** 226

TX

| Hospital, Medicare Provider Number, Address, Telephone, Approval, Facility, and Physician Codes, Health Care System |
| --- |

★ American Hospital Association (AHA) membership  ○ Healthcare Facilities Accreditation Program  ⇑ Center for Improvement in Healthcare Quality Accreditation
☐ The Joint Commission accreditation  ◇ DNV Healthcare Inc. accreditation  △ Commission on Accreditation of Rehabilitation Facilities (CARF) accreditation

**EAST TEXAS MEDICAL CENTER BEHAVIORAL HEALTH CENTER** See UT Health Behavioral Health Center

**EAST TEXAS MEDICAL CENTER SPECIALTY HOSPITAL** See UT Health Specialty Hospital

**EAST TEXAS MEDICAL CENTER TYLER** See UT Health Tyler

**MOTHER FRANCES HOSPITAL - TYLER** See Christus Mother Frances Hospital - Tyler

**TYLER CONTINUECARE HOSPITAL** See Tyler Continuecare Hospital

★ **TYLER CONTINUECARE HOSPITAL (452091)**, 800 East Dawson, 4th Floor, Zip 75701–2036; tel. 903/531–4080, (Nonreporting) **A**10 22 **F**1 3 29 34 57 59 85 86 130 148 **P**4 **S** Community Hospital Corporation, Plano, TX
Primary Contact: Stephanie Hyde, R.N., MSN, Chief Executive Officer
Web address: www.continuecare.org
**Control:** Other not-for-profit (including NFP Corporation) **Service:** Acute long–term care hospital

**Staffed Beds:** 51 **Admissions:** 522 **Census:** 36 **Outpatient Visits:** 0
**Births:** 0 **Total Expense ($000):** 20745 **Payroll Expense ($000):** 7649
**Personnel:** 98

**UNIVERSITY OF TEXAS HEALTH NORTHEAST** See UT Health North Campus Tyler

⊞ **UT HEALTH EAST TEXAS REHABILITATION HOSPITAL (453072)**, 701 Olympic Plaza Circle, Zip 75701–1950, Mailing Address: P.O. Box 7530, Zip 75711–7530; tel. 903/596–3000, (Nonreporting) **A**1 2 10 **F**3 28 29 30 34 53 57 75 86 90 91 93 96 130 131 132 148 149 **S** Ardent Health Services, Nashville, TN
Primary Contact: Laurie Lehnhof-Watts, Administrator and Chief Nursing Officer
CFO: James Blanton, Chief Financial Officer
CMO: Perry Wallach, M.D., Chief Medical Officer
CIO: Paul Campbell, Director Technology Support and Operations
CHR: Wes Griffin, Division Human Resources Manager
CNO: Laurie Lehnhof-Watts, Administrator and Chief Nursing Officer
Web address: www.https://uthealthrehab.com/
**Control:** Corporation, Investor–owned (for–profit) **Service:** Rehabilitation

**Staffed Beds:** 36 **Admissions:** 911 **Census:** 34 **Outpatient Visits:** 72895
**Births:** 0 **Total Expense ($000):** 25277 **Payroll Expense ($000):** 13712
**Personnel:** 235

⊞ **UT HEALTH NORTH CAMPUS TYLER (450690)**, 11937 Highway 271, Zip 75708–3154; tel. 903/877–7777, (Nonreporting) **A**1 2 8 10 **F**3 11 15 18 20 22 26 28 29 30 31 32 34 35 39 40 43 45 46 47 49 50 53 54 55 56 57 58 59 64 65 68 71 75 77 78 79 84 85 86 87 93 97 98 100 101 102 103 104 105 107 108 110 111 114 115 116 117 118 119 120 121 123 129 130 132 135 143 146 147 148 153 156 **S** University of Texas System, Austin, TX
Primary Contact: Cody Boyd, Chief Executive Officer
COO: Joe Woelkers, Executive Vice President and Chief Staff
CFO: Juie Krc, Chief Financial Officer
CMO: Steven Cox, M.D., Chief Medical Officer
CIO: Vernon Moore, Senior Vice President Chief Business and Finance
CHR: Jesse Gomez, Vice President Human Resources
CNO: Don Hunt, M.D., Vice President Patient Centered Care and Chief Nursing Officer
Web address: www.https://uthealthnorth.com/
**Control:** State, Government, Nonfederal **Service:** General medical and surgical

**Staffed Beds:** 114 **Admissions:** 875 **Census:** 16 **Outpatient Visits:** 284731
**Births:** 0 **Total Expense ($000):** 202069 **Payroll Expense ($000):** 64598
**Personnel:** 1183

**UT HEALTH REHABILITATION HOSPITAL** See UT Health East Texas Rehabilitation Hospital

⊞ **UT HEALTH SPECIALTY HOSPITAL (452051)**, 1000 South Beckham, 5th Floor, Zip 75701–1908, Mailing Address: P.O. Box 7018, Zip 75711–7018; tel. 903/596–3600, (Nonreporting) **A**1 10 **F**1 3 29 30 75 84 130 148 149 **S** Ardent Health Services, Nashville, TN
Primary Contact: Jimmy Clark, Administrator
CFO: James Blanton, Chief Financial Officer
CMO: J David Johnson, M.D., Chief of Staff
CIO: Paula Anthony, Vice President Information Services
CHR: David L Langston, Corporate Vice President Human Resources
CNO: Laurie Lehnhof-Watts, Administrator and Chief Nursing Officer
Web address: www.https://uthealthtylerhospital.com/
**Control:** Corporation, Investor–owned (for–profit) **Service:** Acute long–term care hospital

**Staffed Beds:** 30 **Admissions:** 326 **Census:** 25 **Outpatient Visits:** 0
**Births:** 0 **Total Expense ($000):** 11058 **Payroll Expense ($000):** 4843
**Personnel:** 69

⊞ **UT HEALTH TYLER (450083)**, 1000 South Beckham Street, Zip 75701–1908, Mailing Address: Box 6400, Zip 75711–6400; tel. 903/597–0351, (Includes UT HEALTH BEHAVIORAL HEALTH CENTER, Mailing address: 4101 University Boulevard, Tyler, Texas, Zip 75701–6600; tel. 903/566–8668; Marcey Davis, Chief Executive Officer), (Nonreporting) **A**1 2 3 5 10 **F**3 5 8 11 12 13 15 17 18 20 22 24 26 28 29 30 31 34 35 37 38 40 42 43 44 45 46 47 48 49 51 56 58 59 60 61 64 65 68 70 71 73 74 75 76 78 79 80 81 82 84 85 86 87 89 93 98 99 100 101 102 104 107 110 111 115 117 118 119 126 129 130 132 141 145 146 147 148 149 150 152 153 156 **S** Ardent Health Services, Nashville, TN
Primary Contact: Vicki R. Briggs, Chief Executive Officer
CFO: Byron Hale, Chief Financial Officer
CMO: John Andrews, M.D., Chief of Staff
CIO: Paula Anthony, Vice President Information Services
CHR: Mike Gray, Corporate Vice President Human Resources
CNO: Mariarose Kulma, R.N., Vice President Patient Services
Web address: www.https://uthealthtylerhospital.com/
**Control:** Individual, Investor–owned (for–profit) **Service:** General medical and surgical

**Staffed Beds:** 399 **Admissions:** 22657 **Census:** 317 **Outpatient Visits:** 163393 **Births:** 810 **Total Expense ($000):** 379087 **Payroll Expense ($000):** 125635 **Personnel:** 2239

### UVALDE—Uvalde County

**UVALDE COUNTY HOSPITAL AUTHORITY** See Uvalde Memorial Hospital

⊞ **UVALDE MEMORIAL HOSPITAL (451387)**, 1025 Garner Field Road, Zip 78801–4809; tel. 830/278–6251, (Nonreporting) **A**1 10 18 **F**3 11 13 15 18 29 30 34 39 40 43 45 50 57 59 63 64 70 76 79 81 84 85 86 87 88 89 93 104 107 108 110 111 115 118 119 127 130 132 133 146 147 148 149 **P**3
Primary Contact: Thomas Nordwick, FACHE, Chief Executive Officer
CFO: Valerie Lopez, CPA, Chief Financial Officer
CMO: Jared Reading, M.D., Chief of Staff
CIO: Blake Eaker, Interim Director Information Services
CHR: Charla Garcia, Human Resource Officer
CNO: Adam Apolinar, Chief Nursing Officer
Web address: www.umhtx.org
**Control:** Hospital district or authority, Government, Nonfederal **Service:** General medical and surgical

**Staffed Beds:** 25 **Admissions:** 1154 **Census:** 12 **Outpatient Visits:** 168965
**Births:** 428 **Total Expense ($000):** 57842 **Payroll Expense ($000):** 25572
**Personnel:** 436

### VAN HORN—Culberson County

**CULBERSON HOSPITAL (451338)**, Eisenhower-Farm Market Road 2185, Zip 79855, Mailing Address: P.O. Box 609, Zip 79855–0609; tel. 432/283–2760, (Nonreporting) **A**10 18 **F**3 7 29 34 40 43 50 57 59 64 65 68 93 97 107 114 119 127 133 154 **S** Preferred Management Corporation, Shawnee, OK
Primary Contact: Rick Gray, Chief Executive Officer
CMO: John Garner, D.O., Medical Director
Web address: www.culbersonhospital.org
**Control:** Corporation, Investor–owned (for–profit) **Service:** General medical and surgical

**Staffed Beds:** 14 **Admissions:** 165 **Census:** 3 **Outpatient Visits:** 9497
**Births:** 0 **Total Expense ($000):** 7422 **Payroll Expense ($000):** 3405
**Personnel:** 67

**CULBERSON HOSPITAL DISTRICT** See Culberson Hospital

**TX**

## VERNON—Wilbarger County

**NORTH TEXAS STATE HOSPITAL**, 4730 College Drive, Zip 76384–4009, Mailing Address: P.O. Box 2231, Zip 76385–2231; tel. 940/552–9901, (Nonreporting) **F**30 39 50 56 57 68 75 87 96 97 98 99 100 101 103 130 132 135 143 146 149 154 **P**6 **S** Texas Department of State Health Services, Austin, TX
Primary Contact: James E. Smith, Superintendent
CFO: Robin Moreno, Financial Officer
CIO: Chad Hughes, Information Officer
Web address: www.online.dshs.state.tx.us/northtexassh/default.htm
**Control:** State, Government, Nonfederal **Service:** Psychiatric

**Staffed Beds:** 562 **Admissions:** 1696 **Census:** 529 **Outpatient Visits:** 0 **Births:** 0 **Total Expense ($000):** 89355 **Payroll Expense ($000):** 73822 **Personnel:** 1990

**VERNON STATE HOSPITAL** See North Texas State Hospital

★ **WILBARGER GENERAL HOSPITAL (450584)**, 920 Hillcrest Drive, Zip 76384–3196; tel. 940/552–9351, (Nonreporting) **A**10 20 **F**3 6 11 15 28 29 35 40 43 45 55 57 60 62 63 75 77 81 85 86 87 93 107 108 110 111 115 119 124 130 132 133 146 148 153 155 **S** QHR Health, Brentwood, TN
Primary Contact: Tom Siemers, Chief Executive Officer
CFO: Chris Dover, CPA, Chief Financial Officer
CMO: Travis Lehman, M.D., Medical Director
CHR: Alisha Nix, Director Human Resources
CNO: Tonya Price, Chief Nursing Officer
Web address: www.wghospital.com
**Control:** Hospital district or authority, Government, Nonfederal **Service:** General medical and surgical

**Staffed Beds:** 27 **Admissions:** 747 **Census:** 8 **Outpatient Visits:** 19564 **Births:** 2 **Total Expense ($000):** 21876 **Payroll Expense ($000):** 9615 **Personnel:** 225

## VICTORIA—Victoria County

★ ⇑ **CITIZENS MEDICAL CENTER (450023)**, 2701 Hospital Drive, Zip 77901–5749; tel. 361/573–9181, (Total facility includes 20 beds in nursing home–type unit) (Nonreporting) **A**2 10 19 21 **F**3 11 12 13 15 18 20 22 24 28 29 30 31 34 35 40 41 43 45 46 49 50 51 53 54 56 57 59 62 64 65 70 72 74 75 76 78 79 81 82 85 86 87 89 93 97 107 108 109 110 111 113 114 115 116 117 118 119 120 121 123 126 128 129 130 131 132 135 146 147 148 149 154
Primary Contact: Michael R. Olson, Chief Executive Officer
CFO: Carolyn Zafereo, Chief Accounting Officer
CMO: Daniel Cano, M.D., Chief Medical Officer
CIO: Russell Witte, Director Information Technology
CHR: Kathleen C Mosmeyer, Director Human Resources
Web address: www.citizensmedicalcenter.org
**Control:** County, Government, Nonfederal **Service:** General medical and surgical

**Staffed Beds:** 265 **Admissions:** 6872 **Census:** 94 **Outpatient Visits:** 120948 **Births:** 810 **Total Expense ($000):** 154276 **Payroll Expense ($000):** 65804 **Personnel:** 1044

⊞ **DETAR HEALTHCARE SYSTEM (450147)**, 506 San Antonio Street, Zip 77901–6060, Mailing Address: P.O. Box 2089, Zip 77902–2089; tel. 361/575–7441, (Includes DETAR HOSPITAL NORTH, Mailing address: 101 Medical Drive, Victoria, Texas, Zip 77904–3198; tel. 361/573–6100; Bernard Leger, Chief Executive Officer), (Nonreporting) **A**1 3 10 **F**3 12 13 15 18 20 22 24 26 28 29 30 31 34 39 40 41 43 45 47 49 50 51 53 56 64 70 72 74 75 76 77 78 79 81 82 85 86 87 89 90 93 107 108 110 111 114 118 119 126 130 132 146 147 148 149 156 **P**5 **S** Community Health Systems, Inc., Franklin, TN
Primary Contact: Bernard Leger, Chief Executive Officer
COO: George N Parsley, Chief Operating Officer
CFO: Donald E Hagan, Chief Financial Officer
CMO: Conde Nevin Anderson, M.D., Chief of Staff
CIO: Kim Tompkins, Director Information Services
CHR: Dwight Linton, Director Human Resources
CNO: Sammie Drehr, Chief Nursing Officer
Web address: www.detar.com
**Control:** Corporation, Investor–owned (for–profit) **Service:** General medical and surgical

**Staffed Beds:** 235 **Admissions:** 8317 **Census:** 100 **Outpatient Visits:** 112926 **Births:** 1249 **Total Expense ($000):** 156421 **Payroll Expense ($000):** 53405 **Personnel:** 1011

**DETAR HOSPITAL NAVARRO** See Detar Healthcare System

⊞ **PAM REHABILITATION HOSPITAL OF VICTORIA (673056)**, 101 James Coleman Drive, Zip 77904–3147; tel. 361/220–7900, (Nonreporting) **A**1 **S** Post Acute Medical, LLC, Enola, PA
Primary Contact: Tommy Beyer, Director of Operations
Web address: www.warmsprings.org/our-facilities/outpatient-rehabilitation/warm-springs-rehabilitation-center-victoria/
**Control:** Partnership, Investor–owned (for–profit) **Service:** Rehabilitation

**Staffed Beds:** 26

⊞ **PAM SPECIALTY HOSPITAL OF VICTORIA NORTH (452094)**, 102 Medical Drive, Zip 77904–3101; tel. 361/576–6200, (Includes PAM SPECIALTY HOSPITAL OF VICTORIA SOUTHEAST, Mailing address: 2701 Hospital Drive, 6th Floor, Victoria, Texas, Zip 77901–5748; tel. 361/237–1957; Christina Adrean, Chief Executive Officer), (Nonreporting) **A**1 10 **F**1 3 29 64 75 77 85 93 94 157 **S** Post Acute Medical, LLC, Enola, PA
Primary Contact: Christina Adrean, Chief Executive Officer
CMO: Adam Burick, M.D., Chief Medical Officer
Web address: www.warmsprings.org
**Control:** Partnership, Investor–owned (for–profit) **Service:** Acute long–term care hospital

**Staffed Beds:** 26 **Admissions:** 448 **Census:** 27 **Outpatient Visits:** 10380 **Births:** 0 **Total Expense ($000):** 15405 **Payroll Expense ($000):** 5636 **Personnel:** 123

⊞ **PAM SPECIALTY HOSPITAL OF VICTORIA SOUTH (452056)**, 506 East San Antonio Street, 3rd Floor, Zip 77901–6060; tel. 361/575–1445, (Nonreporting) **A**1 10 **F**1 3 29 82 85 86 87 97 130 148 **S** Post Acute Medical, LLC, Enola, PA
Primary Contact: Christina Adrean, Chief Executive Officer
CMO: Adam Burick, M.D., Chief Medical Officer
Web address: www.warmsprings.org/our-facilities/hospitals/post-acute-medical-specialty-hospital-victoria/
**Control:** Partnership, Investor–owned (for–profit) **Service:** Acute long–term care hospital

**Staffed Beds:** 23 **Admissions:** 325 **Census:** 22 **Outpatient Visits:** 0 **Births:** 0 **Total Expense ($000):** 10853 **Payroll Expense ($000):** 4894 **Personnel:** 73

**POST ACUTE MEDICAL SPECIALTY HOSPITAL OF VICTORIA** See Pam Specialty Hospital of Victoria South

**POST ACUTE/WARM SPRINGS SPECIALTY HOSPITAL OF VICTORIA** See Pam Specialty Hospital of Victoria North

**REGIONAL MEDICAL CENTER** See Detar Hospital North

## WACO—McLennan County

⊞ **ASCENSION PROVIDENCE (450042)**, 6901 Medical Parkway, Zip 76712–7998, Mailing Address: P.O. Box 2589, Zip 76702–2589; tel. 254/751–4000, (Includes DEPAUL CENTER, Mailing address: 301 Londonderry Drive, Waco, Texas, Zip 76712; tel. 254/776–5970; Vicky Campbell, Vice President Mental Health and Support Services), (Nonreporting) **A**1 2 3 10 **S** Ascension Healthcare, Saint Louis, MO
Primary Contact: Philip A. Patterson, President
CFO: Karen K. Richardson, Senior Vice President and Chief Financial Officer
CMO: Brian Becker, Vice President Medical Affairs and Chief Medical Officer
CIO: Jay Scherler, Vice President Finance and Chief Information Officer
CNO: Cyndy Dunlap, R.N., FACHE, Chief Nursing Officer
Web address: www.providence.net
**Control:** Church operated, Nongovernment, not–for–profit **Service:** General medical and surgical

**Staffed Beds:** 284

---

**Hospital, Medicare Provider Number, Address, Telephone, Approval, Facility, and Physician Codes, Health Care System**

★ American Hospital Association (AHA) membership
☐ The Joint Commission accreditation
◯ Healthcare Facilities Accreditation Program
◇ DNV Healthcare Inc. accreditation
⇑ Center for Improvement in Healthcare Quality Accreditation
△ Commission on Accreditation of Rehabilitation Facilities (CARF) accreditation

## WACO—Mclennan County

**BAYLOR SCOTT & WHITE HILLCREST MEDICAL CENTER** See Baylor Scott & White Medical Center - Hillcrest

☒ △ **BAYLOR SCOTT & WHITE MEDICAL CENTER - HILLCREST (450101)**, 100 Hillcrest Medical Boulevard, Zip 76712–8897; tel. 254/202–2000, (Nonreporting) **A**1 2 3 7 10 19 **F**3 8 11 13 15 18 20 22 24 26 28 29 30 31 34 40 43 45 46 49 50 54 55 56 57 59 60 63 64 68 70 72 74 75 76 77 78 79 81 82 83 84 85 87 89 90 93 96 97 107 108 110 111 115 118 119 120 121 123 126 129 130 131 132 135 145 146 148 149 154 **S** Baylor Scott & White Health, Dallas, TX
Primary Contact: Rebecca Kay. Hardie, Interim President
COO: David Blackwell, Vice President Operations
CFO: Richard Perkins, Chief Financial Officer
CMO: J. E. Morrison, M.D., M.P.H., Chief Medical Officer
CNO: Rebecca Kay Hardie, Chief Nursing Officer
Web address: www.sw.org/hillcrest-medical-center
**Control:** Other not-for-profit (including NFP Corporation) **Service:** General medical and surgical

**Staffed Beds:** 226 **Admissions:** 14108 **Census:** 165 **Outpatient Visits:** 189360 **Births:** 2825 **Total Expense ($000):** 287923 **Payroll Expense ($000):** 82225 **Personnel:** 1182

## WACO—McLennan County

**CENTRAL TEXAS VETERANS HEALTH CARE SYSTEM, DORIS MILLER VETERANS MEDICAL CENTER** See Central Texas Veterans Health Care System, Temple

**PROVIDENCE HEALTHCARE NETWORK** See Ascension Providence

**WACO VETERANS AFFAIRS HOSPITAL** See Central Texas Veterans Health Care System, Doris Miller Veterans Medical Center

## WAXAHACHIE—Ellis County

☒ **BAYLOR SCOTT & WHITE MEDICAL CENTER-WAXAHACHIE (450372)**, 2400 North I-35E, Zip 75165; tel. 469/843–4000, (Nonreporting) **A**1 2 3 10 **F**3 8 11 12 13 15 18 28 29 30 31 34 35 37 39 40 43 44 45 47 48 49 50 51 56 57 58 59 60 61 64 68 70 74 75 76 77 78 79 80 81 84 85 96 100 102 107 108 109 110 111 114 115 116 117 118 119 120 121 123 126 129 130 131 132 135 145 146 147 148 149 154 156 **S** Baylor Scott & White Health, Dallas, TX
Primary Contact: Will Turner, President
COO: Cindy Murray, R.N., Chief Nursing Officer and Chief Operating Officer
CFO: Cheryl McMullan, Chief Financial Officer
CMO: Thomas Glenn Ledbetter, M.D., Chief Medical Officer
CNO: Cindy Murray, R.N., Chief Nursing Officer and Chief Operating Officer
Web address: www.baylorhealth.com/PhysiciansLocations/Waxahachie/Pages/Default.aspx
**Control:** Other not-for-profit (including NFP Corporation) **Service:** General medical and surgical

**Staffed Beds:** 129 **Admissions:** 7356 **Census:** 72 **Outpatient Visits:** 98971 **Births:** 1056 **Total Expense ($000):** 168944 **Payroll Expense ($000):** 52625 **Personnel:** 639

**BAYLOR SCOTT & WHITE MEDICAL CENTER—WAXAHACHIE** See Baylor Scott & White Medical Center-Waxahachie

## WEATHERFORD—Parker County

☐ **CLEARSKY REHABILITATION HOSPITAL OF WEATHERFORD (673062)**, 703 Eureka Street, Zip 76086–6547; tel. 682/803–0100, (Nonreporting) **A**1
Primary Contact: Brian Abraham, Chief Executive Officer
Web address: www.https://www.clearskyhealth.com/Weatherford/
**Control:** Corporation, Investor-owned (for-profit) **Service:** Rehabilitation

**Staffed Beds:** 26

☒ **MEDICAL CITY WEATHERFORD (450203)**, 713 East Anderson Street, Zip 76086–5705; tel. 682/582–1000, (Nonreporting) **A**1 3 5 10 **F**3 13 15 17 18 20 22 28 29 40 43 45 46 47 48 49 59 60 64 68 70 74 75 76 79 81 82 85 93 94 107 110 111 119 130 146 148 154 **P**6 **S** HCA Healthcare, Nashville, TN
Primary Contact: Sean Kamber, Chief Executive Officer
CMO: Sanjeeb Shrestha, M.D., Chief Medical Staff
CIO: Brett Cates, Director Information Services
CNO: Donna Boone, MS, R.N., Chief Nursing Officer
Web address: www.weatherfordregional.com
**Control:** Corporation, Investor-owned (for-profit) **Service:** General medical and surgical

**Staffed Beds:** 82 **Admissions:** 6122 **Census:** 49 **Outpatient Visits:** 36880 **Births:** 844 **Total Expense ($000):** 96444 **Payroll Expense ($000):** 27524 **Personnel:** 421

**WEATHERFORD REGIONAL MEDICAL CENTER** See Medical City Weatherford

**WEATHERFORD REHABILITATION HOSPITAL** See Clearsky Rehabilitation Hospital of Weatherford

## WEBSTER—Harris County

**CORNERSTONE HOSPITAL OF HOUSTON AT CLEARLAKE (452032)**, 709 Medical Center Boulevard, Zip 77598; tel. 281/332–3322, (Includes CORNERSTONE HOSPITAL OF HOUSTON - BELLAIRE, Mailing address: 5314 Dashwood, Houston, Texas, Zip 77081–4603; tel. 713/295–5300; Austin B. Cleveland, Chief Executive Officer), (Nonreporting) **A**10 22 **F**1 3 29 30 50 74 75 77 82 85 86 87 107 130 148 **S** Cornerstone Healthcare Group, Dallas, TX
Primary Contact: Amy Stasney, R.N., Chief Executive Officer
COO: Brenda Lucero, Chief Clinical Officer
CFO: A Shane Wells, Chief Financial Officer
CMO: Mark Barlow, M.D., Chief Medical Officer and President Medical Staff
CIO: Jerald Harris, Chief Information Officer
CHR: Yolanda Jacobs, Coordinator Human Resources
Web address: www.cornerstonehealthcaregroup.com
**Control:** Partnership, Investor–owned (for–profit) **Service:** Acute long–term care hospital

**Staffed Beds:** 148 **Admissions:** 915 **Census:** 61 **Outpatient Visits:** 1666 **Births:** 0 **Total Expense ($000):** 32199 **Payroll Expense ($000):** 14557 **Personnel:** 200

⇑ **HOUSTON PHYSICIANS HOSPITAL (670008)**, 333 North Texas Avenue, Suite 1000, Zip 77598–4966; tel. 281/557–5620, (Nonreporting) **A**10 21 **F**3 29 37 40 51 64 74 79 81 82 85 86 91 93 107 111 114 141 149
Primary Contact: Heather Womack, Chief Executive Officer
Web address: www.houstonphysicianshospital.com
**Control:** Corporation, Investor–owned (for–profit) **Service:** Surgical

**Staffed Beds:** 21 **Admissions:** 27065 **Census:** 5 **Outpatient Visits:** 87960 **Births:** 0 **Total Expense ($000):** 57422 **Payroll Expense ($000):** 19169 **Personnel:** 260

☒ **KINDRED HOSPITAL CLEAR LAKE (452075)**, 350 Blossom Street, Zip 77598; tel. 281/316–7800, (Nonreporting) **A**1 **F**1 3 29 30 45 57 60 64 75 77 84 85 91 95 96 107 130 148 **S** Kindred Healthcare, Louisville, KY
Primary Contact: Angel Gradney, Chief Executive Officer
Web address: www.khclearlake.com
**Control:** Corporation, Investor–owned (for–profit) **Service:** Acute long–term care hospital

**Staffed Beds:** 110 **Admissions:** 770 **Census:** 54 **Outpatient Visits:** 3168 **Births:** 0 **Total Expense ($000):** 40643 **Payroll Expense ($000):** 13019 **Personnel:** 261

☒ **PAM REHABILITATION HOSPITAL OF CLEAR LAKE (453052)**, 110 East Medical Center Boulevard, Zip 77598–4301; tel. 832/224–9500, (Includes PAM REHABILITATION HOSPITAL OF CLEAR LAKE - NORTH, Mailing address: 655 East Medical Center Boulevard, Webster, Texas, Zip 77598–4328; tel. 281/286–1500; Elena Pugh, Chief Executive Officer), (Nonreporting) **A**1 **F**3 29 64 67 77 90 93 96 130 148 154 **S** Post Acute Medical, LLC, Enola, PA
Primary Contact: Claudia Hauser, Chief Executive Officer
Web address: www.https://postacutemedical.com
**Control:** Partnership, Investor–owned (for–profit) **Service:** Rehabilitation

**Staffed Beds:** 90 **Admissions:** 1960 **Census:** 66 **Outpatient Visits:** 5739 **Births:** 0 **Total Expense ($000):** 34818 **Payroll Expense ($000):** 16472 **Personnel:** 101

**PAM REHABILITATION HOSPITAL OF CLEAR LAKE** See Pam Rehabilitation Hospital of Clear Lake - North

⇑ **SURGICAL ARTS CENTER** See Houston Physicians Hospital

**TRIUMPH HOSPITAL CLEAR LAKE** See Kindred Hospital Clear Lake

## WELLINGTON—Collingsworth County

**COLLINGSWORTH GENERAL HOSPITAL (451355)**, 1013 15th Street, Zip 79095–3703, Mailing Address: P.O. Box 1112, Zip 79095–1112; tel. 806/447–2521, (Nonreporting) **A**10 18 **F**3 29 40 57 59 64 65 68 93 97 107 114 127 130 133 154 **S** Preferred Management Corporation, Shawnee, OK
Primary Contact: Candy Powell, Administrator
CFO: Larry Stephens, Chief Financial Officer
CMO: Wesley Nickens, M.D., Chief of Staff
CIO: Thomas T. Ng, Chief Information Officer
CHR: April Wright, Human Resources Officer
CNO: Vikki Barton, R.N., Chief Nursing Officer
Web address: www.collingsworthgeneral.net
**Control:** Corporation, Investor–owned (for–profit) **Service:** General medical and surgical

**Staffed Beds:** 13 **Admissions:** 152 **Census:** 2 **Outpatient Visits:** 9559 **Births:** 0 **Total Expense ($000):** 7209 **Payroll Expense ($000):** 3031 **Personnel:** 65

**TX**

*Many Facility Codes have changed. Please refer to the AHA Guide Code Chart.*

© 2021 AHA Guide

## WESLACO—Hidalgo County

☐ **KNAPP MEDICAL CENTER (450128)**, 1401 East Eighth Street, Zip 78596–6640, Mailing Address: P.O. Box 1110, Zip 78599–1110; tel. 956/968–8567, (Nonreporting) **A**1 3 5 10 **F**3 8 11 13 15 22 26 29 30 31 34 35 39 40 43 44 46 49 50 51 56 57 59 60 64 70 73 74 75 76 77 78 79 81 82 84 85 86 87 89 93 107 108 110 111 114 115 119 130 131 132 134 135 146 147 148 149 154 156 **P**8 **S** Prime Healthcare, Ontario, CA
Primary Contact: Rene Lopez, Chief Executive Officer
CFO: Dinah L. Gonzalez, Chief Financial Officer
CIO: Teri Garza, Director Health Information Services
CHR: Emmett Craig, Chief Human Resources Officer
CNO: Anna Hinojosa, MSN, R.N., Interim Chief Nursing Officer
Web address: www.knappmed.org
**Control:** Other not–for–profit (including NFP Corporation) **Service:** General medical and surgical

**Staffed Beds:** 186 **Admissions:** 8482 **Census:** 78 **Outpatient Visits:** 65832 **Births:** 1394 **Total Expense ($000):** 101857 **Payroll Expense ($000):** 39665 **Personnel:** 591

☐ **WESLACO REGIONAL REHABILITATION HOSPITAL (453091)**, 906 South James Street, Zip 78596–9840; tel. 956/969–2222, (Nonreporting) **A**1 10 **F**3 29 34 35 68 82 86 87 90 96 130 132 148 149 154
Primary Contact: Corina Humphreys, Chief Executive Officer
CFO: Ernest Nash, Chief Financial Officer
CMO: Daisy Arce, President Medical Staff
CHR: Debbie Pemelton, Director Human Resources
CNO: Rita Mata-Guerrero, Director of Nursing
Web address: www.wrrh.ernesthealth.com
**Control:** Corporation, Investor–owned (for–profit) **Service:** Rehabilitation

**Staffed Beds:** 32 **Admissions:** 585 **Census:** 22 **Outpatient Visits:** 340 **Births:** 0 **Total Expense ($000):** 8996 **Payroll Expense ($000):** 4998 **Personnel:** 83

**WESLACO REHABILITATION HOSPITAL** See Weslaco Regional Rehabilitation Hospital

## WHEELER—Wheeler County

**PARKVIEW HOSPITAL (451334)**, 901 Sweetwater Street, Zip 79096–2421, Mailing Address: P.O. Box 1030, Zip 79096–1030; tel. 806/826–5581, (Nonreporting) **A**10 18 **F**3 7 10 40 43 59 62 64 65 68 91 93 107 114 127 128 130 133 148
Primary Contact: Monica Kidd, R.N., MSN, Administrator
CFO: Jace Henderson, Chief Financial Officer
CMO: John P. Lavelle, M.D., Chief Medical Officer
CNO: Melisa Scales, Director of Nursing
Web address: www.parkviewhosp.org
**Control:** Hospital district or authority, Government, Nonfederal **Service:** General medical and surgical

**Staffed Beds:** 16 **Admissions:** 91 **Census:** 2 **Outpatient Visits:** 3819 **Births:** 0 **Total Expense ($000):** 8873 **Payroll Expense ($000):** 4337 **Personnel:** 75

## WICHITA FALLS—Wichita County

**BETHANIA REGIONAL HEALTH CNTR** See United Regional Health Care System-Eleventh Street Campus

⊠ **ENCOMPASS HEALTH REHABILITATION HOSPITAL OF WICHITA FALLS (453054)**, 3901 Armory Road, Zip 76302–2204; tel. 940/720–5700, (Nonreporting) **A**1 10 **F**3 28 29 68 74 75 77 79 86 87 90 91 94 95 96 130 132 **S** Encompass Health Corporation, Birmingham, AL
Primary Contact: Boyd Davis III, Chief Executive Officer
CMO: Virgil Frardo, M.D., Medical Director
CIO: Mary Walker, Manager Information Technology
CHR: Kathleen Pirtle, Director Human Resources
CNO: Jody S Gregory, R.N., Chief Nursing Officer
Web address: www.healthsouthwichitafalls.com
**Control:** Partnership, Investor–owned (for–profit) **Service:** Rehabilitation

**Staffed Beds:** 63 **Admissions:** 1671 **Census:** 55 **Outpatient Visits:** 0 **Births:** 0 **Total Expense ($000):** 18052 **Payroll Expense ($000):** 11119 **Personnel:** 176

**HEALTHSOUTH REHABILITATION HOSPITAL-WICHITA FALLS** See Encompass Health Rehabilitation Hospital of Wichita Falls

**KELL WEST REGIONAL HOSPITAL (450827)**, 5420 Kell West Boulevard, Zip 76310–1610; tel. 940/692–5888, (Nonreporting) **A**10 22 **F**3 37 39 40 51 59 65 74 75 78 79 81 85 97 107 108 114 119 126 129 130 135 149 154
Primary Contact: Jerry Myers, M.D., Chief Executive Officer and Medical Director
CFO: Fran Lindemann, Director Finance
Web address: www.kellwest.com
**Control:** Partnership, Investor–owned (for–profit) **Service:** General medical and surgical

**Staffed Beds:** 25 **Admissions:** 1209 **Census:** 10 **Outpatient Visits:** 24151 **Births:** 0 **Total Expense ($000):** 33149 **Payroll Expense ($000):** 10455 **Personnel:** 256

☐ **KPC PROMISE HOSPITAL OF WICHITA FALLS (452068)**, 1103 Grace Street, Zip 76301–4414; tel. 940/720–6633, (Nonreporting) **A**1 10 **S** KPC Healthcare, Inc., Santa Ana, CA
Primary Contact: Rachel Bailey, Chief Executive Officer
CFO: Debbie Herder, Controller
CMO: Robert McBroom, M.D., Medical Director
CIO: Gail McIlroy, Director Medical Records
CNO: Deanna Dowling, R.N., Chief Nursing Officer
Web address: www.wichitafalls.kpcph.com/
**Control:** Corporation, Investor–owned (for–profit) **Service:** Acute long–term care hospital

**Staffed Beds:** 31

☐ **NORTH TEXAS STATE HOSPITAL, WICHITA FALLS CAMPUS (454008)**, 6515 Lake Road, Zip 76308–5419, Mailing Address: Box 300, Zip 76307–0300; tel. 940/692–1220, (Nonreporting) **A**1 10
Primary Contact: James E. Smith, Superintendent
CFO: Robin Moreno, Chief Financial Officer
CMO: Eulon Ross Taylor, Clinical Director
CIO: Chad Hughes, Chief Information Officer
Web address: www.online.dshs.state.tx.us/northtexassh/default.htm
**Control:** State, Government, Nonfederal **Service:** Psychiatric

**Staffed Beds:** 640

**PROMISE HOSPITAL OF WICHITA FALLS** See Kpc Promise Hospital of Wichita Falls

**RED RIVER HOSPITAL** See Red River Hospital, LLC

☐ **RED RIVER HOSPITAL, LLC (454018)**, 1505 Eighth Street, Zip 76301–3106; tel. 940/322–3171, (Nonreporting) **A**1 10 **F**4 5 29 38 50 86 87 98 99 100 101 102 103 104 105 130 135 143 152 153 157 **P**5 **S** Acadia Healthcare Company, Inc., Franklin, TN
Primary Contact: Jon Lasell, Chief Executive Officer
CFO: Bruce Porter, Chief Financial Officer
CMO: Harvey C Martin, M.D., Medical Director
CIO: Fay Helton, Director Medical Records
CHR: Kimberley Pellegrin, Director, Human Resources
CNO: Glenda Lawrence, R.N., Chief Nursing Officer
Web address: www.redriverhospital.com
**Control:** Corporation, Investor–owned (for–profit) **Service:** Psychiatric

**Staffed Beds:** 96 **Admissions:** 2314 **Census:** 69 **Outpatient Visits:** 4601 **Births:** 0 **Total Expense ($000):** 13867 **Payroll Expense ($000):** 7693 **Personnel:** 236

⊠ **UNITED REGIONAL HEALTH CARE SYSTEM (450010)**, 1600 11th Street, Zip 76301–4300; tel. 940/764–7000, (Includes UNITED REGIONAL HEALTH CARE SYSTEM-ELEVENTH STREET CAMPUS, Mailing address: 1600 11th Street, Wichita Falls, Texas, Zip 76301–9988; tel. 940/764–7000), (Nonreporting) **A**1 10 20 **F**3 11 12 13 15 17 18 20 21 22 24 26 28 29 30 31 32 34 35 37 39 40 43 44 45 46 47 48 49 50 51 53 57 59 60 61 64 65 68 70 74 75 76 77 78 79 80 81 82 84 85 86 87 89 92 93 102 107 110 111 114 115 116 117 118 119 126 130 131 132 134 146 147 148 149 **P**3
Primary Contact: Phyllis A. Cowling, CPA, President and Chief Executive Officer
COO: Nancy Townley, R.N., Senior Vice President Operations
CFO: Robert M Pert, Vice President Finance and Chief Financial Officer
CIO: Stephanie McDonell, Vice President and Chief Information Officer
CHR: Kristi Faulkner, Vice President Organizational Growth
CNO: Jane Ritter, R.N., Vice President, Patient Care and Clinical Services
Web address: www.unitedregional.org
**Control:** Other not–for–profit (including NFP Corporation) **Service:** General medical and surgical

**Staffed Beds:** 278 **Admissions:** 15988 **Census:** 173 **Outpatient Visits:** 132792 **Births:** 2006 **Total Expense ($000):** 336027 **Payroll Expense ($000):** 133004 **Personnel:** 1905

**WICHITA FALLS STATE HOSPITAL** See North Texas State Hospital, Wichita Falls Campus

---

**Hospital, Medicare Provider Number, Address, Telephone, Approval, Facility, and Physician Codes, Health Care System**

★ American Hospital Association (AHA) membership
☐ The Joint Commission accreditation
○ Healthcare Facilities Accreditation Program
◇ DNV Healthcare Inc. accreditation
⇑ Center for Improvement in Healthcare Quality Accreditation
△ Commission on Accreditation of Rehabilitation Facilities (CARF) accreditation

## WINNIE—Chambers County

**RICELAND MEDICAL CENTER (451328)**, 538 Broadway, Zip 77665–7600; tel. 409/296–6000, (Nonreporting) **A**10 18 **F**3 8 15 29 34 40 54 57 59 65 81 93 105 107 110 111 114 119 127 133 146
Primary Contact: Steve Deatrick, Administrator
CFO: Julie Harris, Chief Financial Officer
CMO: Leonidas Andres, M.D., Chief of Staff
CHR: Anha Simon, Director Human Resources
Web address: www.energis.in/index.html
**Control:** Partnership, Investor–owned (for–profit) **Service:** General medical and surgical

**Staffed Beds:** 25 **Admissions:** 276 **Census:** 3 **Outpatient Visits:** 75812 **Births:** 0 **Total Expense ($000):** 31131 **Payroll Expense ($000):** 11330 **Personnel:** 251

**WINNIE COMMUNITY HOSPITAL** See Riceland Medical Center

## WINNSBORO—Wood County

✉ **CHRISTUS MOTHER FRANCES HOSPITAL - WINNSBORO (451381)**, 719 West Coke Road, Zip 75494–3011; tel. 903/342–5227, (Nonreporting) **A**1 10 18 **F**3 11 29 30 35 40 43 56 57 64 81 82 85 87 89 114 119 127 128 129 130 132 133 146 148 156 **P**5 6 7 8 **S** CHRISTUS Health, Irving, TX
Primary Contact: Paul Harvey, Chief Executive Officer
CFO: Glenn Peltier, Chief Financial Officer
CNO: Kevin Jablonski, Chief Nursing Officer
Web address: www.tmfhs.org
**Control:** Other not–for–profit (including NFP Corporation) **Service:** General medical and surgical

**Staffed Beds:** 23 **Admissions:** 417 **Census:** 6 **Outpatient Visits:** 23608 **Births:** 0 **Total Expense ($000):** 17690 **Payroll Expense ($000):** 5432 **Personnel:** 135

**MOTHER FRANCES HOSPITAL - WINNSBORO** See Christus Mother Frances Hospital - Winnsboro

## WINTERS—Runnels County

★ **NORTH RUNNELS HOSPITAL (451315)**, 7821 State Highway 153, Zip 79567–7345, Mailing Address: P.O. Box 185, Zip 79567–0185; tel. 325/754–1317, (Nonreporting) **A**10 18 **F**7 11 40 57 59 62 65 66 68 93 97 107 119 127 133
Primary Contact: Joe Wright, Chief Executive Officer
CMO: Mark McKinnon, M.D., Chief of Staff
CNO: Bobbie Collom, Nursing Director
**Control:** Hospital district or authority, Government, Nonfederal **Service:** General medical and surgical

**Staffed Beds:** 15 **Admissions:** 99 **Census:** 1 **Outpatient Visits:** 5873 **Births:** 0 **Total Expense ($000):** 18893 **Payroll Expense ($000):** 3991 **Personnel:** 57

## WOODVILLE—Tyler County

**TYLER COUNTY HOSPITAL (450460)**, 1100 West Bluff Street, Zip 75979–4799, Mailing Address: P.O. Box 549, Zip 75979–0549; tel. 409/283–8141, (Nonreporting) **A**10 20 **F**3 11 30 35 40 43 57 59 64 75 107 114 119 127 146
Primary Contact: Sondra Dianne. Wilson, R.N., MSN, Chief Executive Officer
CFO: Scott Elton McCluskey, Chief Financial Officer
CMO: Paula Lajean Denson, M.D., President
CIO: Rachel Joy Haygood, Director Information Technology
CHR: Kenneth Lynn Jobe, Director Human Resources
Web address: www.tchospital.us
**Control:** County, Government, Nonfederal **Service:** General medical and surgical

**Staffed Beds:** 25 **Admissions:** 305 **Census:** 2 **Outpatient Visits:** 25745 **Births:** 0 **Total Expense ($000):** 11310 **Payroll Expense ($000):** 4330 **Personnel:** 121

## YOAKUM—Lavaca County

★ **YOAKUM COMMUNITY HOSPITAL (451346)**, 1200 Carl Ramert Drive, Zip 77995–4868; tel. 361/293–2321, (Nonreporting) **A**10 18 **F**3 11 15 29 34 35 40 43 56 57 59 64 70 79 81 85 86 93 104 107 108 111 114 119 129 132 133 134 146 148 153 **S** Community Hospital Corporation, Plano, TX
Primary Contact: Karen Barber, R.N., Chief Executive Officer
CFO: Robert Foret, Chief Financial Officer
CMO: Timothy Wagner, M.D., Chief Medical Staff
CIO: Barbara Vasek, Director Information Technology
CHR: Karen Roznovsky, Director Human Resources
CNO: Jennifer Franklin, R.N., Chief Clinical Officer
Web address: www.yoakumhospital.org
**Control:** Other not–for–profit (including NFP Corporation) **Service:** General medical and surgical

**Staffed Beds:** 23 **Admissions:** 551 **Census:** 6 **Outpatient Visits:** 20791 **Births:** 0 **Total Expense ($000):** 18060 **Payroll Expense ($000):** 7678 **Personnel:** 123

**TX**

*Many Facility Codes have changed. Please refer to the AHA Guide Code Chart.*

# UTAH

## AMERICAN FORK—Utah County

⊞ **AMERICAN FORK HOSPITAL (460023)**, 170 North 1100 East, Zip 84003–2096; tel. 801/855–3300, (Nonreporting) **A**1 10 **F**3 9 11 13 15 29 30 31 34 35 38 40 43 44 45 50 53 54 57 60 68 70 72 75 76 77 78 79 81 82 84 85 86 87 92 93 100 102 104 107 108 110 111 115 118 119 120 121 123 124 129 130 131 132 135 141 144 145 146 147 148 149 154 **S** Intermountain Healthcare, Inc., Salt Lake City, UT
Primary Contact: Jason Wilson, Administrator and Chief Executive Officer
CFO: Craig Carrier, Chief Financial Officer
CMO: Scott Van Wagoner, M.D., Chief Medical Officer
CIO: Mary Gathers, Manager Information Systems
CHR: Scott Walker, Chief Human Resource Officer
CNO: Terri Lynn Hunter, R.N., Nurse Administrator
Web address: www.intermountainhealthcare.org
**Control:** Other not–for–profit (including NFP Corporation) **Service:** General medical and surgical

**Staffed Beds:** 78 **Admissions:** 5880 **Census:** 41 **Outpatient Visits:** 60351 **Births:** 2880 **Total Expense ($000):** 130387 **Payroll Expense ($000):** 39141 **Personnel:** 641

## BEAVER—Beaver County

**BEAVER VALLEY HOSPITAL (461335)**, 1109 North 100 West, Zip 84713, Mailing Address: P.O. Box 1670, Zip 84713–1670; tel. 435/438–7100, (Total facility includes 17 beds in nursing home–type unit) (Nonreporting) **A**10 18 **F**13 34 40 41 43 44 45 50 56 57 59 62 63 64 68 75 76 77 79 81 84 87 89 90 91 101 102 104 107 111 119 128 130 133 146 147 148 149 150 154
Primary Contact: Scott Langford, Administrator
Web address: www.bvhospital.com/
**Control:** City–county, Government, Nonfederal **Service:** General medical and surgical

**Staffed Beds:** 27 **Admissions:** 221 **Census:** 17

## BLANDING—San Juan County

★ **BLUE MOUNTAIN HOSPITAL (461310)**, 802 South 200 West, Suite A, Zip 84511–3910; tel. 435/678–3993, (Nonreporting) **A**10 18
Primary Contact: Jeremy Lyman, Chief Executive Officer
CFO: Jimmy Johnson, Chief Financial Officer
CMO: Mahana Fisher, M.D., Medical Director
CIO: Anthony Torres, Manager Information Technology
CHR: Gail M. Northern, Director Human Resources
CNO: Derrill Kent Turek, R.N., Chief Nursing Officer
Web address: www.bmhutah.org/
**Control:** Other not–for–profit (including NFP Corporation) **Service:** General medical and surgical

**Staffed Beds:** 11

## BOUNTIFUL—Davis County

⊞ **LAKEVIEW HOSPITAL (460042)**, 630 East Medical Drive, Zip 84010–4908; tel. 801/299–2200, (Nonreporting) **A**1 10 **F**3 8 11 13 15 18 20 22 26 28 29 30 34 37 38 40 43 44 45 49 50 51 53 56 57 59 60 64 65 67 68 70 72 74 75 76 77 79 81 82 85 86 87 93 96 97 98 100 101 102 107 108 110 111 114 115 118 119 129 130 132 135 146 147 148 **S** HCA Healthcare, Nashville, TN
Primary Contact: Troy Wood, Chief Executive Officer
CFO: Wayne Dalton, Chief Financial Officer
CMO: Michael Hess, M.D., Chief Medical Officer
CIO: Mark Ellis, Director Information Technology
CHR: Julie Isom, Director Human Resources
CNO: Marilyn Mariani, R.N., Chief Nursing Officer
Web address: www.lakeviewhospital.com
**Control:** Corporation, Investor–owned (for–profit) **Service:** General medical and surgical

**Staffed Beds:** 119 **Admissions:** 3839 **Census:** 39

## SOUTH DAVIS COMMUNITY HOSPITAL (462003)

**SOUTH DAVIS COMMUNITY HOSPITAL (462003)**, 401 South 400 East, Zip 84010–4933; tel. 801/295–2361, (Nonreporting) **A**3 10
Primary Contact: David Bland, Chief Executive Officer
CMO: Scott Southworth, M.D., Medical Director
CHR: Jamey Sulser, Director Human Resources
Web address: www.sdch.com
**Control:** Other not–for–profit (including NFP Corporation) **Service:** Acute long–term care hospital

**Staffed Beds:** 176

## BRIGHAM CITY—Box Elder County

⊞ **BRIGHAM CITY COMMUNITY HOSPITAL (460017)**, 950 South Medical Drive, Zip 84302–4724; tel. 435/734–9471, (Nonreporting) **A**1 10 **S** HCA Healthcare, Nashville, TN
Primary Contact: Richard Spuhler, Chief Executive Officer
CMO: Derrick Walker, M.D., Chief Medical Officer
CIO: Steve Reichard, Manager Information Systems
CHR: Tracie Greene, Director Human Resources
CNO: Jerry Bushman, Chief Nursing Officer
Web address: www.brighamcityhospital.com
**Control:** Corporation, Investor–owned (for–profit) **Service:** General medical and surgical

**Staffed Beds:** 40

**COLUMBIA BRIGHAM CITY HOSP** See Brigham City Community Hospital

## CEDAR CITY—Iron County

⊞ **CEDAR CITY HOSPITAL (460007)**, 1303 North Main Street, Zip 84721–9746; tel. 435/868–5000, (Nonreporting) **A**1 10 20 **F**3 11 13 15 18 28 29 31 34 35 38 40 43 45 46 50 53 57 60 64 70 74 75 76 77 78 79 81 85 86 87 93 100 102 107 108 110 111 115 118 119 120 121 123 124 130 131 132 135 141 146 147 148 149 154 156 157 **S** Intermountain Healthcare, Inc., Salt Lake City, UT
Primary Contact: Eric Packer, Chief Executive Officer
CFO: Craig Corry, Chief Financial Officer
CMO: Gerald Rowland, M.D., Chief Medical Officer
CIO: Becki Bronson, Chief Information Officer
CHR: Amy Martin, Chief Human Resource Officer
CNO: Cyndi Wallace, R.N., MSN, Chief Nursing Officer
Web address: www.https://intermountainhealthcare.org/locations/cedar-city-hospital/
**Control:** Other not–for–profit (including NFP Corporation) **Service:** General medical and surgical

**Staffed Beds:** 48 **Admissions:** 2229 **Census:** 13 **Outpatient Visits:** 41446 **Births:** 799 **Total Expense ($000):** 81262 **Payroll Expense ($000):** 22353 **Personnel:** 384

**VALLEY VIEW MEDICAL CENTER** See Cedar City Hospital

## DELTA—Millard County

★ **DELTA COMMUNITY MEDICAL CENTER (461300)**, 126 South White Sage Avenue, Zip 84624–8937; tel. 435/864–5591, (Nonreporting) **A**10 18 **F**3 13 15 29 34 35 38 40 43 44 45 50 64 68 75 76 77 81 85 87 100 102 107 110 111 114 119 133 146 147 148 149 154 157 **S** Intermountain Healthcare, Inc., Salt Lake City, UT
Primary Contact: Kurt Forsyth, Administrator
CFO: Vince Donohue, Chief Financial Officer
CHR: Mathias Moyano, Chief Human Resource Officer
CNO: Ches Jacobson, Chief Nursing Officer
Web address: www.https://intermountainhealthcare.org/locations/delta-community-hospital/
**Control:** Other not–for–profit (including NFP Corporation) **Service:** General medical and surgical

**Staffed Beds:** 18 **Admissions:** 210 **Census:** 2 **Outpatient Visits:** 4813 **Births:** 80 **Total Expense ($000):** 10320 **Payroll Expense ($000):** 4085 **Personnel:** 48

---

**Hospital, Medicare Provider Number, Address, Telephone, Approval, Facility, and Physician Codes, Health Care System**

★ American Hospital Association (AHA) membership
☐ The Joint Commission accreditation
○ Healthcare Facilities Accreditation Program
◇ DNV Healthcare Inc. accreditation
⇧ Center for Improvement in Healthcare Quality Accreditation
△ Commission on Accreditation of Rehabilitation Facilities (CARF) accreditation

UT

## DRAPER—Salt Lake County

✠ **LONE PEAK HOSPITAL (460060)**, 1925 South State Street, Zip 84020;
tel. 801/545–8000, (Nonreporting) **A**1 10 **S** HCA Healthcare, Nashville, TN
Primary Contact: Brian Lines, Chief Executive Officer
Web address: www.lonepeakhospital.com
**Control:** Corporation, Investor–owned (for–profit) **Service:** General medical and
surgical

**Staffed Beds:** 32

## FILLMORE—Millard County

★ **FILLMORE COMMUNITY HOSPITAL (461301)**, 674 South Highway 99,
Zip 84631–5013; tel. 435/743–5591, (Nonreporting) **A**10 18 **F**3 15 29 34 35
38 40 44 50 68 75 76 77 81 85 86 87 97 100 102 107 110 111 114 119
130 132 133 146 147 148 149 154 **S** Intermountain Healthcare, Inc., Salt Lake
City, UT
Primary Contact: Kurt Forsyth, Administrator
CFO: Vince Donohue, Chief Financial Officer
CHR: Mathias Moyano, Chief Human Resource Officer
CNO: Andrea Wardle, Chief Nursing Officer
Web address: www.ihc.com
**Control:** Other not–for–profit (including NFP Corporation) **Service:** General
medical and surgical

**Staffed Beds:** 7 **Admissions:** 177 **Census:** 10 **Outpatient Visits:** 2978
**Births:** 37 **Total Expense ($000):** 9918 **Payroll Expense ($000):** 3844
**Personnel:** 50

**FILLMORE COMMUNITY MEDICAL CENTER** See Fillmore Community Hospital

## GUNNISON—Sanpete County

★ **GUNNISON VALLEY HOSPITAL (461306)**, 64 East 100 North, Zip 84634,
Mailing Address: P.O. Box 759, Zip 84634–0759; tel. 435/528–7246,
(Nonreporting) **A**10 18
Primary Contact: Mark F. Dalley, Administrator
CFO: Brian Murray, Chief Financial Officer
CIO: Mike Ryan, Director of Information Services
CNO: Brenda Bartholomew, Chief Nursing Officer
Web address: www.gvhospital.org
**Control:** County, Government, Nonfederal **Service:** General medical and surgical

**Staffed Beds:** 119

## HEBER CITY—Wasatch County

★ **HEBER VALLEY HOSPITAL (461307)**, 1485 South Highway 40,
Zip 84032–3522; tel. 435/654–2500, (Nonreporting) **A**10 18 **F**3 13 15 29 34 35
38 40 43 44 50 51 53 57 59 60 64 68 75 76 77 79 81 85 86 87 93 102 107
110 111 115 119 128 129 130 131 133 135 141 144 146 148 149 154 156 **S**
Intermountain Healthcare, Inc., Salt Lake City, UT
Primary Contact: Si William. Hutt, Administrator
CFO: Jennilyn Ferry, Chief Financial Officer
CMO: Stanton B McDonald, M.D., Medical Director
CIO: Dennis De Melo, Chief Information Officer
CHR: Bruce Dent, Human Resources Director
CNO: Jill Teuscher, Chief Nursing Officer
Web address: www.https://intermountainhealthcare.org/locations/heber-valley-
hospital/
**Control:** Other not–for–profit (including NFP Corporation) **Service:** General
medical and surgical

**Staffed Beds:** 19 **Admissions:** 726 **Census:** 5 **Outpatient Visits:** 12535
**Births:** 186 **Total Expense ($000):** 35651 **Payroll Expense ($000):** 12252
**Personnel:** 141

**HEBER VALLEY MEDICAL CENTER** See Heber Valley Hospital

## KANAB—Kane County

**KANE COUNTY HOSPITAL (461309)**, 355 North Main Street, Zip 84741–3260;
tel. 435/644–5811, (Nonreporting) **A**10 18
Primary Contact: Sherrie Pandya, Administrator
CFO: Stephen Howells, Chief Financial Officer
CMO: Darin Ott, D.O., Chief of Staff
CHR: Laurali Noteman, Director Human Resources
Web address: www.kanecountyhospital.net
**Control:** Hospital district or authority, Government, Nonfederal **Service:** General
medical and surgical

**Staffed Beds:** 25

## LAYTON—Davis County

⇑ **DAVIS HOSPITAL & MEDICAL CNTR** See Davis Hospital and Medical Center

★ ⇑ **DAVIS HOSPITAL AND MEDICAL CENTER (460041)**, 1600 West Antelope
Drive, Zip 84041–1142; tel. 801/807–1000, (Nonreporting) **A**3 10 21 **S** Steward
Health Care System, LLC, Dallas, TX
Primary Contact: Michael Jensen, Chief Executive Officer
COO: Jared Spackman, Chief Operating Officer
CFO: Jared Spackman, Chief Financial Officer
CMO: Les Greenwood, M.D., President, Medical Staff
CIO: Shane Williams, Director Information Systems
CHR: Tara Figgins, Director Human Resources
CNO: Chris Johnson, Chief Nursing Officer
Web address: www.davishospital.com
**Control:** Partnership, Investor–owned (for–profit) **Service:** General medical and
surgical

**Staffed Beds:** 221

✠ **LAYTON HOSPITAL (460061)**, 201 West Layton Parkway, Zip 84041–3692;
tel. 801/543–6000, (Nonreporting) **A**1 **F**3 11 13 29 31 35 38 40 49 50 60 68
70 73 75 76 77 79 81 85 86 87 93 100 102 107 108 111 115 118 119 130
131 132 141 144 146 147 148 149 154 **S** Intermountain Healthcare, Inc., Salt
Lake City, UT
Primary Contact: Judy Williamson, R.N., Administrator
CFO: Trever Porter, Chief Financial Officer
CMO: Glen Morrell, M.D., Chief Medical Officer
CHR: Jennifer L. Jensen, Chief Human Resource Officer
CNO: Tiffany Bears, Chief Nursing Officer
Web address: www.https://intermountainhealthcare.org/locations/layton-hospital/
medical-services/
**Control:** Other not–for–profit (including NFP Corporation) **Service:** General
medical and surgical

**Staffed Beds:** 33 **Admissions:** 1839 **Census:** 13 **Outpatient Visits:** 98997
**Births:** 622 **Total Expense ($000):** 77112 **Payroll Expense ($000):** 21860
**Personnel:** 334

## LOGAN—Cache County

✠ **LOGAN REGIONAL HOSPITAL (460015)**, 1400 North 500 East,
Zip 84341–2455; tel. 435/716–1000, (Total facility includes 11 beds in nursing
home–type unit) (Nonreporting) **A**1 10 **F**3 9 13 15 18 20 22 28 29 31 34 35 38
39 40 43 44 45 49 50 56 57 59 60 64 68 70 73 75 76 77 78 79 81 85 86 87
92 93 98 100 102 107 108 110 111 115 116 117 118 119 121 123 124
126 128 129 130 131 132 141 146 147 148 149 154 156 157 **S** Intermountain
Healthcare, Inc., Salt Lake City, UT
Primary Contact: Brandon McBride, Administrator
COO: Brandon McBride, Operations Officer
CFO: Justin Wiser, Chief Financial Officer
CMO: Todd A Brown, M.D., Medical Director
CIO: Dave Felts, Chief Information Systems
CHR: Jolene Clonts, Director Human Resources
CNO: Neil C Perkes, Operations Officer
Web address: www.loganregionalhospital.org
**Control:** Other not–for–profit (including NFP Corporation) **Service:** General
medical and surgical

**Staffed Beds:** 133 **Admissions:** 6296 **Census:** 51 **Outpatient Visits:** 50295
**Births:** 2152 **Total Expense ($000):** 185784 **Payroll Expense
($000):** 50960 **Personnel:** 886

## MIDVALE—Salt Lake County

☐ **HIGHLAND RIDGE HOSPITAL (464015)**, 7309 South 180 West,
Zip 84047–3769; tel. 801/569–2153, (Nonreporting) **A**1 **S** Acadia Healthcare
Company, Inc., Franklin, TN
Primary Contact: Jim Hess, Chief Executive Officer
COO: Robert Beatty, Chief Operating Officer
CFO: Sheri Sorenson, Manager Business Office
CHR: Carol Cunningham, Administrative Assistant
Web address: www.highlandridgehospital.com
**Control:** Corporation, Investor–owned (for–profit) **Service:** Psychiatric

**Staffed Beds:** 83

*Many Facility Codes have changed. Please refer to the AHA Guide Code Chart.*

UT

## MILFORD—Beaver County

★ **MILFORD VALLEY MEMORIAL HOSPITAL (461305)**, 850 North Main Street, Zip 84751–0640, Mailing Address: P.O. Box 640, Zip 84751–0640; tel. 435/387–2411, (Nonreporting) **A**10 18
Primary Contact: Scott Langford, Administrator
COO: Michelle Barton, Chief Operating Officer
CFO: Tyler Moss, Chief Financial Officer
CNO: Amy Contreras EsqChief Nursing Officer
Web address: www.milfordmemorialhospital.org
**Control**: Hospital district or authority, Government, Nonfederal **Service**: General medical and surgical

**Staffed Beds**: 25

## MOAB—Grand County

**ALLEN MEMORIAL HOSPITAL** See Moab Regional Hospital

★ **MOAB REGIONAL HOSPITAL (461302)**, 450 West Williams Way, Zip 84532–2065, Mailing Address: P.O. Box 998, Zip 84532–0998; tel. 435/719–3500, (Nonreporting) **A**10 18 **F**3 5 8 15 29 31 34 35 40 43 45 46 63 64 65 75 76 78 79 81 82 84 97 100 101 102 104 107 110 111 114 115 119 130 131 133 148 153 154 156 **P**6
Primary Contact: Jennifer Sadoff, Chief Executive Officer
COO: Vicki Gigliotti, Chief Clinical Officer
CFO: Craig M Daniels, Chief Financial Officer
CMO: Dylan Cole, Chief Medical Officer
CIO: Mike Foster, Manager Information Systems
CHR: Katherine Sullivan, Director, Human Resources
Web address: www.mrhmoab.org
**Control**: Other not–for–profit (including NFP Corporation) **Service**: General medical and surgical

**Staffed Beds**: 17 **Admissions**: 302 **Census**: 2 **Outpatient Visits**: 18442 **Births**: 67 **Total Expense ($000)**: 29245 **Payroll Expense ($000)**: 14889 **Personnel**: 216

## MONTICELLO—San Juan County

★ **SAN JUAN HEALTH SERVICE DISTRICT (461308)**, 380 West 100 North, Zip 84535, Mailing Address: P.O. Box 308, Zip 84535–0308; tel. 435/587–2116, (Nonreporting) **A**10 18 **F**3 12 13 15 29 32 34 35 38 40 41 44 45 47 50 56 57 59 64 65 66 68 76 79 80 81 82 87 97 107 110 111 114 119 127 128 131 133 145 148 154 **P**6
Primary Contact: Clayton Holt, Chief Executive Officer
CFO: Lyman Duncan, Chief Financial Officer
CMO: Kelly Jeppesen, Chief Medical Officer
CIO: Julie Bingham, IT Supervisor
CHR: Deana Dalton, Human Resources
CNO: Laurie Schafer, Chief Nursing Officer
Web address: www.sanjuanhealthservices.org/
**Control**: Hospital district or authority, Government, Nonfederal **Service**: General medical and surgical

**Staffed Beds**: 25 **Admissions**: 276 **Census**: 2 **Outpatient Visits**: 2088 **Births**: 57 **Total Expense ($000)**: 17344 **Payroll Expense ($000)**: 7326 **Personnel**: 100

**SAN JUAN HEALTH SERVICES DISTRICT** See San Juan Health Service District

## MOUNT PLEASANT—Sanpete County

★ **SANPETE VALLEY HOSPITAL (461303)**, 1100 South Medical Drive, Zip 84647–2222; tel. 435/462–2441, (Nonreporting) **A**10 18 **F**3 13 15 29 34 35 38 40 43 44 50 57 59 68 75 76 77 79 81 82 84 85 86 87 97 100 102 107 110 111 115 119 129 130 131 132 133 135 147 148 149 154 156 157 **S** Intermountain Healthcare, Inc., Salt Lake City, UT
Primary Contact: Aaron C. Wood, Chief Executive Officer and Administrator
COO: Kristina Skinner, Director Quality
CFO: Vince Donohue, Chief Financial Officer
CMO: Robert Armstrong, M.D., Chief Medical Officer
CIO: Michael Ence, Computer Specialist
CHR: Katey Nelson, Chief Human Resource Officer
CNO: Ryan Robison, Chief Nursing Officer
Web address: www.intermountainhealthcare.com
**Control**: Other not–for–profit (including NFP Corporation) **Service**: General medical and surgical

**Staffed Beds**: 13 **Admissions**: 439 **Census**: 4 **Outpatient Visits**: 9779 **Births**: 120 **Total Expense ($000)**: 21268 **Payroll Expense ($000)**: 7304 **Personnel**: 96

## MURRAY—Salt Lake County

**COTTONWOOD HOSPITAL MED CNTR** See Intermountain Medical Center

☐ △ **INTERMOUNTAIN MEDICAL CENTER (460010)**, 5121 South Cottonwood Street, Zip 84107–5701; tel. 801/507–7000, (Nonreporting) **A**1 2 3 5 7 10 **F**3 8 11 13 15 17 18 20 22 24 26 28 29 30 31 34 35 37 38 39 40 43 44 45 46 47 48 49 50 51 52 53 54 55 56 57 58 59 60 61 63 64 66 68 70 71 72 74 75 76 77 78 79 80 81 82 84 85 86 87 90 91 92 93 94 96 97 100 102 107 108 109 110 111 115 116 117 118 119 120 121 123 124 126 129 130 131 132 135 137 138 139 141 142 146 147 148 149 150 154 155 156 157 **S** Intermountain Healthcare, Inc., Salt Lake City, UT
Primary Contact: Blair M. Kent, Administrator
COO: Kelly L Duffin, Operations Officer
CFO: Royce Stephens, Director Finance
CMO: Mark Ott, M.D., Regional Chief Medical Director
CIO: Heather Romualdo, Chief Information Officer
CHR: Cammie Cable, Chief Human Resource Officer
CNO: Suzanne P. Anderson, Nurse Administrator
Web address: www.https://intermountainhealthcare.org/locations/intermountain-medical-center/
**Control**: Other not–for–profit (including NFP Corporation) **Service**: General medical and surgical

**Staffed Beds**: 502 **Admissions**: 27003 **Census**: 336 **Outpatient Visits**: 218802 **Births**: 4301 **Total Expense ($000)**: 945973 **Payroll Expense ($000)**: 271550 **Personnel**: 3989

**THE ORTHOPEDIC SPECIALTY HOSP** See The Orthopedic Specialty Hospital

⊞ **THE ORTHOPEDIC SPECIALTY HOSPITAL (460049)**, 5848 South 300 East, Zip 84107–6121; tel. 801/314–4100, (Nonreporting) **A**1 10 **F**3 9 29 34 35 44 50 53 57 58 59 64 68 75 77 79 81 85 86 87 92 93 94 107 111 115 119 130 131 132 141 146 149 154 **S** Intermountain Healthcare, Inc., Salt Lake City, UT
Primary Contact: Adam Chandio, Administrator
CFO: Dan Brady, Chief Financial Officer
CMO: Bill Gowski, M.D., Chief Medical Officer
CIO: David Baird, Chief Information Officer
CHR: Shawn Elizabeth Bonifay, Chief Human Resource Officer
CNO: Lisa Bagley, Chief Nursing Officer
Web address: www.intermountainhealthcare.org
**Control**: Other not–for–profit (including NFP Corporation) **Service**: Orthopedic

**Staffed Beds**: 40 **Admissions**: 1673 **Census**: 7 **Outpatient Visits**: 48624 **Births**: 0 **Total Expense ($000)**: 71677 **Payroll Expense ($000)**: 20839 **Personnel**: 335

## NEPHI—Juab County

★ **CENTRAL VALLEY MEDICAL CENTER (461304)**, 48 West 1500 North, Zip 84648–8900; tel. 435/623–3000, (Nonreporting) **A**10 18 **F**3 8 13 15 29 34 35 36 37 40 43 45 50 57 59 62 63 64 65 68 75 76 77 79 81 82 85 86 87 89 93 94 97 101 102 104 107 110 114 119 126 129 130 131 133 146 147 148 154 156 **S** Rural Health Group, Nephi, UT
Primary Contact: Mark R. Stoddard, Chief Executive Officer
COO: Randy Cuff, Chief Operating Officer
CFO: Brent Davis, Chief Financial Officer
CMO: Mark Oveson, M.D., Chief Medical Staff
CIO: Ken Richens, Chief Information Officer
CHR: Brian Allsop, Director Human Resources
CNO: Randy Allinson, R.N., Chief Nursing Officer
Web address: www.cvmed.net
**Control**: Other not–for–profit (including NFP Corporation) **Service**: General medical and surgical

**Staffed Beds**: 25 **Admissions**: 825 **Census**: 9 **Outpatient Visits**: 32589 **Births**: 144 **Total Expense ($000)**: 41480 **Payroll Expense ($000)**: 12898

## NORTH LOGAN—Cache County

⊞ **CACHE VALLEY HOSPITAL (460054)**, 2380 North 400 East, Zip 84341–6000; tel. 435/713–9700, (Nonreporting) **A**1 5 10 **S** HCA Healthcare, Nashville, TN
Primary Contact: Daren Wells, Chief Executive Officer
CFO: David S Geary, Chief Financial Officer
CMO: Jess Jewett, Chief Medical Officer
Web address: www.cachevalleyhospital.com/
**Control**: Corporation, Investor–owned (for–profit) **Service**: General medical and surgical

**Staffed Beds**: 28

**CACHE VALLEY SPECIALTY HOSPITAL** See Cache Valley Hospital

---

## OGDEN—Weber County

**COLUMBIA OGDEN REG MED CTR** See Ogden Regional Medical Center

✠ **MCKAY-DEE HOSPITAL (460004)**, 4401 Harrison Boulevard, Zip 84403–3195; tel. 801/387–2800, (Nonreporting) **A**1 3 5 10 **F**3 8 9 11 12 13 15 17 18 20 22 24 26 28 29 30 31 34 35 36 38 39 40 43 44 45 48 49 50 51 53 54 55 57 59 60 64 68 70 72 74 75 76 77 78 79 80 81 82 84 85 86 87 89 90 91 92 93 94 96 97 98 99 100 102 104 105 107 108 110 111 115 116 117 118 119 120 121 123 124 126 129 130 131 132 134 135 141 146 147 148 149 154 156 157 **S** Intermountain Healthcare, Inc., Salt Lake City, UT
Primary Contact: Michael A. Clark, Administrator
COO: Michael A Clark, Chief Operating Officer
CFO: Trever Porter, Chief Financial Officer
CMO: Masood Safaee Semiromi, M.D., Chief Medical Officer
CIO: Mary Gathers, Director Information Systems
CHR: Christopher Saling, Chief Human Resource Officer
CNO: Donna Lynn Chapman, R.N., Chief Nursing Officer
Web address: www.mckay-dee.org
**Control:** Other not–for–profit (including NFP Corporation) **Service:** General medical and surgical

**Staffed Beds:** 299 **Admissions:** 18585 **Census:** 187 **Births:** 3362
**Total Expense ($000):** 488790 **Payroll Expense ($000):** 131506
**Personnel:** 2195

**MCKAY-DEE HOSPITAL CENTER** See Mckay-Dee Hospital

✠ **OGDEN REGIONAL MEDICAL CENTER (460005)**, 5475 South 500 East, Zip 84405–6905; tel. 801/479–2111, (Nonreporting) **A**1 2 10 13 **S** HCA Healthcare, Nashville, TN
Primary Contact: Mark B. Adams, Chief Executive Officer
COO: Brian Lines, Chief Operating Officer
CFO: Judd Taylor, Chief Financial Officer
CMO: Jeffrey Abel, M.D., Chief Medical Officer
CIO: Eric Peterson, Director
CHR: Chris Bissenden, Director Human Resources
CNO: Elizabeth B. Later, R.N., Chief Nursing Officer
Web address: www.ogdenregional.com
**Control:** Corporation, Investor–owned (for–profit) **Service:** General medical and surgical

**Staffed Beds:** 232

## OREM—Utah County

✠ **OREM COMMUNITY HOSPITAL (460043)**, 331 North 400 West, Zip 84057–1999; tel. 801/224–4080, (Nonreporting) **A**1 10 **F**3 13 15 29 34 35 38 40 44 50 59 64 68 75 76 77 81 85 86 87 93 100 102 107 110 111 115 119 130 132 141 146 147 149 154 **S** Intermountain Healthcare, Inc., Salt Lake City, UT
Primary Contact: Lenny Lyons, Administrator
CFO: Craig Carrier, Chief Financial Officer
CMO: Tracy Hill, M.D., Chief Medical Officer
CIO: Diane Rindlisbacher, Manager Information Systems
CHR: Jeremy H Rogers, Chief Human Resource Officer
CNO: Amber Iverson, Chief Nursing Officer
Web address: www.intermountainhealthcare.org
**Control:** Other not–for–profit (including NFP Corporation) **Service:** General medical and surgical

**Staffed Beds:** 23 **Admissions:** 856 **Census:** 4 **Outpatient Visits:** 20408
**Births:** 845 **Total Expense ($000):** 29037 **Payroll Expense ($000):** 10254
**Personnel:** 157

☐ **PROVO CANYON BEHAVIORAL HOSPITAL (464014)**, 1350 East 750 North, Zip 84097–4345; tel. 801/852–2273, (Nonreporting) **A**1 10 **S** Universal Health Services, Inc., King of Prussia, PA
Primary Contact: Jeremy Cottle, Ph.D., Chief Executive Officer
CFO: Emmy Adams, Chief Financial Officer
CHR: Diann Decker, Chief Human Resource Officer
Web address: www.pcbh.com
**Control:** Corporation, Investor–owned (for–profit) **Service:** Psychiatric

**Staffed Beds:** 80

✠ **TIMPANOGOS REGIONAL HOSPITAL (460052)**, 750 West 800 North, Zip 84057–3660; tel. 801/714–6000, (Nonreporting) **A**1 5 10 **F**3 11 12 13 15 17 18 19 20 22 24 26 28 29 30 31 34 35 39 40 41 45 46 47 48 49 50 68 70 72 73 74 76 78 79 81 82 85 88 89 93 97 107 108 109 110 111 115 116 117 119 120 121 123 126 130 131 135 146 147 149 154 156 **S** HCA Healthcare, Nashville, TN
Primary Contact: Kimball S. Anderson, FACHE, Chief Executive Officer
COO: Ryan LeMasters, Chief Operating Officer
CFO: Jody S Dial, Chief Financial Officer
CMO: Randle L Likes, M.D., Chief Medical Officer
CIO: Richard Neilson, Director of Information Services
CHR: Tim Black, Director Human Resources
CNO: Sandy Ewell, Chief Nursing Officer
Web address: www.timpanogosregionalhospital.com
**Control:** Corporation, Investor–owned (for–profit) **Service:** General medical and surgical

**Staffed Beds:** 106 **Admissions:** 5489 **Census:** 52

## PANGUITCH—Garfield County

★ **GARFIELD MEMORIAL HOSPITAL (461333)**, 200 North 400 East, Zip 84759, Mailing Address: P.O. Box 389, Zip 84759–0389; tel. 435/676–8811, (Nonreporting) **A**10 18 **F**15 29 34 38 40 44 45 50 57 59 65 66 68 71 75 76 77 85 86 87 97 100 102 107 110 115 119 127 128 130 132 133 149 154 156 **S** Intermountain Healthcare, Inc., Salt Lake City, UT
Primary Contact: Alberto Vasquez, Administrator
CFO: Craig Corry, Chief Financial Officer
CMO: Mitchell Miller, M.D., Chief Medical Officer
CHR: Carla Ramsay, Chief Human Resource Officer
CNO: DeAnn Brown, Chief Nursing Officer
Web address: www.ihc.com/hospitals/garfield
**Control:** County, Government, Nonfederal **Service:** General medical and surgical

**Staffed Beds:** 15 **Admissions:** 284 **Census:** 4 **Outpatient Visits:** 11924
**Births:** 35 **Total Expense ($000):** 12028 **Payroll Expense ($000):** 6504
**Personnel:** 94

**GARFIELD MEMORIAL HOSPITAL AND CLINICS** See Garfield Memorial Hospital

## PARK CITY—Summit County

✠ **PARK CITY HOSPITAL (460057)**, 900 Round Valley Drive, Zip 84060–7552; tel. 435/658–7000, (Nonreporting) **A**1 10 **F**3 13 15 18 29 34 35 36 38 40 43 44 45 46 48 50 53 57 59 64 68 70 75 76 77 79 81 85 86 87 92 93 97 100 102 107 108 110 111 115 118 119 129 130 131 132 135 141 146 147 148 149 154 156 157 **S** Intermountain Healthcare, Inc., Salt Lake City, UT
Primary Contact: Lori Weston, Administrator
CFO: Jennilyn Ferry, Chief Financial Officer
CMO: Wing Province, M.D., Chief Medical Officer
CHR: Celene Roberts, Chief Human Resource Officer
CNO: Dan Davis, MSN, R.N., Nurse Administrator
Web address: www.intermountainhealthcare.org
**Control:** Other not–for–profit (including NFP Corporation) **Service:** General medical and surgical

**Staffed Beds:** 37 **Admissions:** 2040 **Census:** 10 **Outpatient Visits:** 20740
**Births:** 319 **Total Expense ($000):** 89713 **Payroll Expense ($000):** 24962
**Personnel:** 373

**PARK CITY MEDICAL CENTER** See Park City Hospital

## PAYSON—Utah County

✠ **MOUNTAIN VIEW HOSPITAL (460013)**, 1000 East 100 North, Zip 84651–1600; tel. 801/465–7000, (Nonreporting) **A**1 10 **S** HCA Healthcare, Nashville, TN
Primary Contact: Kevin Johnson, Chief Executive Officer
COO: Ric Johnson, Associate Administrator
CFO: Steven R Schramm, Chief Financial Officer
CMO: Jeffrey Wallentine, Chief of Staff
CIO: Cindy Mecham, Health Information Director
CHR: Wally Trotter, Director Human Resources
CNO: Katie King, R.N., Chief Nursing Officer
Web address: www.mvhpayson.com
**Control:** Corporation, Investor–owned (for–profit) **Service:** General medical and surgical

**Staffed Beds:** 124

UT

## PRICE—Carbon County

✦ **CASTLEVIEW HOSPITAL (460011)**, 300 North Hospital Drive, Zip 84501–4200; tel. 435/637–4800, (Nonreporting) **A**1 10 20 **F**3 8 11 12 13 15 18 29 31 34 39 40 41 45 50 51 54 56 57 59 64 65 68 70 75 76 77 78 79 81 82 84 86 87 89 92 93 97 107 108 110 111 115 119 127 130 131 144 146 147 148 149 154 156 157 **S** LifePoint Health, Brentwood, TN
Primary Contact: Greg Cook, Chief Executive Officer
CMO: Glen T. Etzel, M.D., Chief of Staff
CIO: Fiore Wilson, Director Information Systems
CHR: Misty Birch, Director Human Resources
CNO: Grant Barraclough, R.N., Chief Nursing Officer
Web address: www.castleviewhospital.net
**Control**: Corporation, Investor–owned (for–profit) **Service**: General medical and surgical

**Staffed Beds:** 49 **Admissions:** 1721 **Census:** 13

## PROVO—Utah County

☐ **UTAH STATE HOSPITAL (464001)**, 1300 East Center Street, Zip 84606–3554, Mailing Address: P.O. Box 270, Zip 84603–0270; tel. 801/344–4400, (Nonreporting) **A**1 3 10 **F**30 34 56 59 75 77 86 87 91 98 99 100 101 103 106 130 135 143 146 149 150 157
Primary Contact: Dallas Earnshaw, Superintendent
COO: Dallas Earnshaw, Superintendent
CFO: Robert Burton, Manager Finance
CMO: Madhu Gundlapalli, M.D., Clinical Director
CIO: Jill Hill, Director Information Technology
CHR: Devin Patrick, Manager Human Resources
CNO: Chris Metcalf, Director of Nursing
Web address: www.ush.utah.gov
**Control**: State, Government, Nonfederal **Service**: Psychiatric

**Staffed Beds:** 348 **Admissions:** 292 **Census:** 319 **Outpatient Visits:** 0
**Births:** 0 **Total Expense ($000):** 71618 **Payroll Expense ($000):** 36362

✦ △ **UTAH VALLEY HOSPITAL (460001)**, 1034 North 500 West, Zip 84604–3337; tel. 801/357–7850, (Nonreporting) **A**1 2 3 5 7 10 **F**3 9 12 15 17 18 20 22 24 26 28 29 30 31 32 34 35 37 38 39 40 43 44 45 46 47 48 49 50 51 53 54 55 56 57 58 59 60 63 64 68 70 72 74 75 76 77 78 79 81 82 84 85 86 87 88 89 90 91 92 93 94 98 100 102 107 108 110 111 115 116 117 118 119 120 121 123 124 126 129 130 131 132 141 144 145 146 147 148 149 154 156 157 **S** Intermountain Healthcare, Inc., Salt Lake City, UT
Primary Contact: Kyle A. Hansen, Chief Executive Officer
CFO: Nathan Empey, Chief Finanial Officer
CMO: Tracy Hill, M.D., Chief Medical Officer
CIO: Mary Gathers, Director Information Systems
CHR: Brady Anderson, Chief Human Resource Officer
CNO: Maria Black, Chief Nursing Officer
Web address: www.https://intermountainhealthcare.org/locations/utah-valley-hospital/
**Control**: Other not–for–profit (including NFP Corporation) **Service**: General medical and surgical

**Staffed Beds:** 385 **Admissions:** 20390 **Census:** 232 **Outpatient Visits:** 193256 **Births:** 4147 **Total Expense ($000):** 568748 **Payroll Expense ($000):** 159649 **Personnel:** 2654

**UTAH VALLEY REGIONAL MEDICAL CENTER** See Utah Valley Hospital

☐ **UTAH VALLEY SPECIALTY HOSPITAL (462005)**, 306 River Bend Lane, Zip 84604–5625; tel. 801/226–8880, (Nonreporting) **A**1 10 **S** Ernest Health, Inc., Albuquerque, NM
Primary Contact: Brynn Beck, Chief Executive Officer
Web address: www.uvsh.ernesthealth.com
**Control**: Corporation, Investor–owned (for–profit) **Service**: Acute long–term care hospital

**Staffed Beds:** 40

## RICHFIELD—Sevier County

✦ **SEVIER VALLEY HOSPITAL (460026)**, 1000 North Main Street, Zip 84701–1857; tel. 435/893–4100, (Nonreporting) **A**1 10 20 **F**3 15 29 31 34 35 38 40 44 45 50 59 64 68 75 76 77 78 79 81 85 86 87 100 102 107 108 110 111 115 118 119 129 130 132 141 146 147 148 149 154 **S** Intermountain Healthcare, Inc., Salt Lake City, UT
Primary Contact: Brent Schmidt, Administrator
CFO: Bert Zimmerli, Executive Vice President and Chief Financial Officer
CMO: Justin Abbott, M.D., Medical Director
CHR: Katey Nelson, Director Human Resources
CNO: Cami Blackham, R.N., Nurse Administrator
Web address: www.sevierhospital.org
**Control**: Other not–for–profit (including NFP Corporation) **Service**: General medical and surgical

**Staffed Beds:** 29 **Admissions:** 852 **Census:** 6 **Outpatient Visits:** 13184
**Births:** 224 **Total Expense ($000):** 43395 **Payroll Expense ($000):** 10741
**Personnel:** 167

**SEVIER VALLEY MEDICAL CENTER** See Sevier Valley Hospital

## RIVERTON—Salt Lake County

✦ **RIVERTON HOSPITAL (460058)**, 3741 West 12600 South, Zip 84065–7215; tel. 801/285–4000, (Nonreporting) **A**1 3 10 **F**3 9 13 15 29 31 34 35 38 39 40 41 44 45 49 50 54 56 57 59 64 68 70 73 75 76 77 78 79 81 85 86 87 89 93 100 102 107 108 110 111 115 118 119 120 121 123 124 129 130 131 132 141 144 146 147 148 149 154 156 **S** Intermountain Healthcare, Inc., Salt Lake City, UT
Primary Contact: Todd Neubert, Chief Executive Officer
CFO: Andrew Ozmun, Chief Financial Officer
CMO: Dean Mayer, M.D., Chief Medical Officer
CIO: Susan Hanks, Chief Information Officer
CHR: Kimberly Dansie, Chief Human Resource Officer
CNO: Brian Pendleton, Chief Nursing Officer
Web address: www.intermountainhealthcare.org/
**Control**: Other not–for–profit (including NFP Corporation) **Service**: General medical and surgical

**Staffed Beds:** 88 **Admissions:** 5759 **Census:** 36 **Outpatient Visits:** 59063
**Births:** 2340 **Total Expense ($000):** 137830 **Payroll Expense ($000):** 37231 **Personnel:** 588

## ROOSEVELT—Duchesne County

**DUCHESNE COUNTY HOSPITAL** See Uintah Basin Medical Center

★ **UINTAH BASIN MEDICAL CENTER (460019)**, 250 West 300 North, 75-2, Zip 84066–2336; tel. 435/722–6163, (Total facility includes 75 beds in nursing home–type unit) (Nonreporting) **A**10 20 **F**6 7 11 13 15 17 35 40 45 50 52 53 54 57 59 60 62 63 70 73 76 77 79 81 82 84 85 87 89 93 107 108 110 111 115 119 127 128 129 130 131 132 135 146 147 148 154 155 156 **P**3
Primary Contact: James I. Marshall, President and Chief Executive Officer
CFO: Brent Hales, Chief Financial Officer
CMO: Gary B White, M.D., Chief Medical Staff
CHR: Randall Bennett, Assistant Administrator
Web address: www.ubmc.org
**Control**: Other not–for–profit (including NFP Corporation) **Service**: General medical and surgical

**Staffed Beds:** 124 **Admissions:** 1670 **Census:** 60 **Outpatient Visits:** 70899
**Births:** 577 **Total Expense ($000):** 63027 **Payroll Expense ($000):** 26412
**Personnel:** 695

**UT**

---

**Hospital, Medicare Provider Number, Address, Telephone, Approval, Facility, and Physician Codes, Health Care System**

★ American Hospital Association (AHA) membership  ○ Healthcare Facilities Accreditation Program  ⇑ Center for Improvement in Healthcare Quality Accreditation
☐ The Joint Commission accreditation  ◇ DNV Healthcare Inc. accreditation  △ Commission on Accreditation of Rehabilitation Facilities (CARF) accreditation

## SAINT GEORGE—Washington County

**DIXIE MEDICAL CENTER** See Dixie Regional Medical Center

☒ △ **DIXIE REGIONAL MEDICAL CENTER (460021)**, 1380 East Medical Center Drive, Zip 84790–2123; tel. 435/251–1000, (Includes DIXIE REGIONAL MEDICAL CENTER, Mailing address: 544 South 400 East, St George, Utah, Zip 84770; tel. 940/764–7000), (Nonreporting) **A**1 7 10 **F**3 9 11 12 13 15 17 18 20 22 24 26 28 29 30 31 34 35 37 38 39 40 43 44 46 49 50 51 52 53 54 55 56 57 58 59 60 64 68 70 71 72 74 75 76 77 78 79 80 81 82 84 85 86 87 89 90 91 92 93 94 96 97 98 100 102 104 107 108 110 111 112 114 115 116 117 118 119 120 121 123 124 126 129 130 131 132 141 144 146 147 148 149 154 155 156 **S** Intermountain Healthcare, Inc., Salt Lake City, UT
Primary Contact: Mitchell Cloward, Administrator
CFO: Don Cannon, Chief Financial Officer
CMO: Patrick Carroll, M.D., Chief Medical Officer
CIO: Kenley Brinkerhoff, Chief Information Officer
CHR: Colette Eppley, Chief Human Resource Officer
CNO: Natalie Ashby, Chief Nursing Officer
Web address: www.intermountainhealthcare.org
**Control:** Other not–for–profit (including NFP Corporation) **Service:** General medical and surgical

**Staffed Beds:** 284 **Admissions:** 18189 **Census:** 182 **Outpatient Visits:** 222057 **Births:** 2424 **Total Expense ($000):** 568339 **Payroll Expense ($000):** 140172 **Personnel:** 2376

## SALT LAKE CITY—Salt Lake County

**COLUMBIA ST MARK'S HOSPITAL** See St. Mark'S Hospital

⇑ **HOLY CROSS HOSPITAL** See Salt Lake Regional Medical Center

**KPC PROMISE HOSPITAL OF SALT LAKE (462004)**, 8 Avenue, C Street, Zip 84143; tel. 801/408–7110, (Nonreporting) **A**10 **S** KPC Healthcare, Inc., Santa Ana, CA
Primary Contact: Wayne Kinsey, Chief Executive Officer
CMO: Geoff Harding, Chief Clinical Officer
Web address: www.saltlake.kpcph.com/
**Control:** Corporation, Investor–owned (for–profit) **Service:** Acute long–term care hospital

**Staffed Beds:** 41

☒ **LDS HOSPITAL (460006)**, Eighth Avenue and 'C' Street, Zip 84143–0001; tel. 801/408–1100, (Nonreporting) **A**1 3 5 10 **F**3 4 9 11 12 15 29 31 34 35 38 40 44 45 46 47 48 49 50 51 55 56 57 58 59 60 64 68 70 73 74 75 76 77 78 79 81 82 84 85 86 87 92 93 96 98 100 102 104 107 108 110 111 115 118 119 120 121 123 124 126 129 130 131 132 135 136 141 146 147 148 149 154 157 **S** Intermountain Healthcare, Inc., Salt Lake City, UT
Primary Contact: Shawn Morrow, Chief Executive Officer
CFO: Dan Brady, Chief Financial Officer
CMO: Kerry Fisher, M.D., Medical Director
CIO: David Baird, Chief Information Officer
CHR: Andy Lawson, Chief Human Resource Officer
CNO: Hallie Rector, Chief Nursing Officer
Web address: www.https://intermountainhealthcare.org/locations/lds-hospital/
**Control:** Other not–for–profit (including NFP Corporation) **Service:** General medical and surgical

**Staffed Beds:** 256 **Admissions:** 10764 **Census:** 115 **Outpatient Visits:** 54331 **Births:** 2003 **Total Expense ($000):** 265520 **Payroll Expense ($000):** 72276 **Personnel:** 1194

☒ **MARIAN CENTER (464012)**, 451 East Bishop Federal Lane, Zip 84115–2357; tel. 801/487–7557, (Nonreporting) **A**1 10 **F**29 34 98 100 101 103 130
Primary Contact: Lee Kilpack, Chief Executive Officer
Web address: www.stjosephvilla.com
**Control:** Corporation, Investor–owned (for–profit) **Service:** Psychiatric

**Staffed Beds:** 14 **Admissions:** 255 **Census:** 9 **Outpatient Visits:** 0 **Births:** 0 **Total Expense ($000):** 2504 **Payroll Expense ($000):** 1470 **Personnel:** 27

☐ △ **PRIMARY CHILDREN'S HOSPITAL (463301)**, 100 North Mario Capecchi Drive, Zip 84113–1100; tel. 801/662–1000, (Nonreporting) **A**1 3 5 7 10 **F**3 8 11 17 19 21 23 25 27 28 29 30 31 32 34 35 36 37 38 39 40 41 43 44 45 47 48 50 51 53 54 57 58 59 60 64 65 66 68 71 72 74 75 77 78 79 80 81 82 84 85 86 87 88 89 92 93 96 98 99 100 101 102 104 105 106 107 108 111 115 118 119 129 130 132 134 135 136 137 138 139 141 146 148 149 153 154 156 157 **S** Intermountain Healthcare, Inc., Salt Lake City, UT
Primary Contact: Katy Welkie MBA, R.N., Chief Executive Officer
CFO: Sidney P. Norton, Chief Financial Officer
CMO: Angelo Giardino, M.D., Chief Medical Officer
CIO: Joe Hales, Chief Information Officer
CHR: Ben Buckworth, Human Resources Administrative Director
CNO: Angie Scartezina, Chief Nursing Officer
Web address: www.intermountainhealthcare.org
**Control:** Other not–for–profit (including NFP Corporation) **Service:** Children's general medical and surgical

**Staffed Beds:** 292 **Admissions:** 13080 **Census:** 209 **Outpatient Visits:** 76163 **Births:** 0 **Total Expense ($000):** 609872 **Payroll Expense ($000):** 190975 **Personnel:** 2914

**PRIMARY CHILDREN'S MEDICAL CENTER** See Primary Children's Hospital

**PROMISE HOSPITAL OF SALT LAKE** See Kpc Promise Hospital of Salt Lake

☐ **SALT LAKE BEHAVIORAL HEALTH (464013)**, 3802 South 700 East, Zip 84106–1182; tel. 801/264–6000, (Nonreporting) **A**1 10 **F**4 5 29 38 75 98 104 130 135 **S** Universal Health Services, Inc., King of Prussia, PA
Primary Contact: Kreg Gillman, Chief Executive Officer
CFO: Daren Woolstenhulme, Chief Financial Officer
CMO: Monica Polk, M.D., Chief Medical Officer
CHR: Robyn Holsten, Human Resources Director
CNO: Suzanne Nelson, R.N., Director of Nursing
Web address: www.saltlakebehavioralhealth.com
**Control:** Corporation, Investor–owned (for–profit) **Service:** Psychiatric

**Staffed Beds:** 118 **Admissions:** 2468 **Census:** 66 **Outpatient Visits:** 6043 **Births:** 0 **Total Expense ($000):** 26795 **Payroll Expense ($000):** 10776 **Personnel:** 199

★ ⇑ **SALT LAKE REGIONAL MEDICAL CENTER (460003)**, 1050 East South Temple, Zip 84102–1507; tel. 801/350–4111, (Nonreporting) **A**3 5 10 21 **S** Steward Health Care System, LLC, Dallas, TX
Primary Contact: Dale Johns, FACHE, Chief Executive Officer
CFO: Brian Ebright, Chief Financial Officer
CMO: Blake Johnson, M.D., Chief of Staff
CIO: Mark Runyan, Director Information Services
CHR: Carolyn Livingston, Director Human Resources
CNO: Terron Arbon, R.N., Chief Nursing Officer
Web address: www.saltlakeregional.com
**Control:** Corporation, Investor–owned (for–profit) **Service:** General medical and surgical

**Staffed Beds:** 132

**SHRINERS HOSPITALS FOR CHILDREN-INTERMOUNTAIN** See Shriners Hospitals for Children-Salt Lake City

☐ **SHRINERS HOSPITALS FOR CHILDREN-SALT LAKE CITY (463302)**, 1275 East Fairfax Road, Zip 84103–4399; tel. 801/536–3500, (Nonreporting) **A**1 3 5 10 **F**29 35 37 50 57 64 68 74 75 77 79 81 82 85 87 89 93 94 119 127 130 131 132 143 146 154 **S** Shriners Hospitals for Children, Tampa, FL
Primary Contact: Kevin Martin, M.P.H., R.N., FACHE, Administrator
CFO: Heath Braby, Director Fiscal Services
CMO: Kristen Carroll, M.D., Chief of Staff
CIO: Mike Allen, Director Information Technology
CHR: Kris Goldman, Director Human Resources
CNO: Gail McGuill, R.N., MSN, Chief Nursing Officer and Administrative Director of Patient Care Services
Web address: www.shrinershospitalsforchildren.org/Hospitals/Locations/SaltLakeCity.aspx
**Control:** Other not–for–profit (including NFP Corporation) **Service:** Children's orthopedic

**Staffed Beds:** 12 **Admissions:** 196 **Census:** 3 **Outpatient Visits:** 11849 **Births:** 0 **Total Expense ($000):** 26439 **Payroll Expense ($000):** 13661

**UT**

*Many Facility Codes have changed. Please refer to the AHA Guide Code Chart.*   © 2021 AHA Guide

☒ **ST. MARK'S HOSPITAL (460047)**, 1200 East 3900 South, Zip 84124–1390; tel. 801/268–7111, (Nonreporting) **A**1 2 3 5 10 **S** HCA Healthcare, Nashville, TN
Primary Contact: Mark Robinson, FACHE, Chief Executive Officer
CFO: Bryan McKinley, Chief Financial Officer
CMO: J Eric Vanderhooft, M.D., President Medical Staff
CIO: Jesse Trujillo, Chief Information Officer
CHR: Robyn Opheikens, Assistant Administrator Human Resources
Web address: www.stmarkshospital.com
**Control**: Corporation, Investor–owned (for–profit) **Service**: General medical and surgical

**Staffed Beds**: 298

★ △ ⇑ **UNIVERSITY OF UTAH HEALTH (460009)**, 50 North Medical Drive, Zip 84132–0002; tel. 801/581–2121, (Includes UNIVERSITY OF UTAH NEUROPSYCHIATRIC INSTITUTE, Mailing address: 501 South Chipeta Way, Salt Lake City, Utah, Zip 84108–1222; tel. 801/583–2500; Ross Van Vranken, Executive Director), (Nonreporting) **A**2 3 5 7 8 10 21 **F**3 5 6 7 8 9 11 12 13 15 16 17 18 20 22 24 26 28 29 30 31 34 35 36 37 38 39 40 42 43 44 45 46 47 48 49 50 51 52 53 54 55 56 57 58 59 60 61 62 64 65 68 70 71 72 73 74 75 76 77 78 79 80 81 82 83 84 85 86 87 90 91 92 93 94 95 96 97 98 100 101 102 103 107 108 109 110 111 112 113 114 115 117 118 119 120 121 123 124 126 129 130 131 132 134 135 136 137 138 139 140 141 142 143 144 145 146 147 148 149 150 152 154 155 156 157 **P**1
Primary Contact: Gordon Crabtree, Interim Chief Executive Officer
COO: Dan Lundergan, Chief Operating Officer
CFO: Gordon Crabtree, Chief Financial Officer
CMO: Thomas Miller, M.D., Medical Director
CIO: James Turnbull, Chief Information Officer
CHR: Dale A Spartz, Chief Human Resources Officer
CNO: Margaret Pearce, R.N., Ph.D., Chief Nursing Officer
Web address: www.uuhsc.utah.edu
**Control**: State, Government, Nonfederal **Service**: General medical and surgical

**Staffed Beds**: 613 **Admissions**: 29074 **Census**: 460 **Outpatient Visits**: 2469237 **Births**: 4417 **Total Expense ($000)**: 1779148 **Payroll Expense ($000)**: 624847 **Personnel**: 11503

⇑ **UNIVERSITY OF UTAH HEALTH CARE - HOSPITAL AND CLINICS** See University of Utah Health

**UTAH NEUROPSYCHIATRIC INST** See University of Utah Neuropsychiatric Institute

**VETERANS AFFAIRS MED CENTER** See Veterans Affairs Salt Lake City Health Care System

☒ △ **VETERANS AFFAIRS SALT LAKE CITY HEALTH CARE SYSTEM**, 500 Foothill Drive, Zip 84148–0002; tel. 801/582–1565, (Nonreporting) **A**1 3 5 7 **F**3 4 5 8 12 18 20 22 24 26 28 29 30 31 33 34 35 36 38 39 40 44 45 46 47 48 49 50 53 54 55 56 57 58 59 60 61 62 63 64 65 70 71 74 75 77 78 79 81 82 83 84 85 86 87 90 92 93 94 96 97 98 100 101 102 104 105 106 107 108 109 111 114 115 116 117 118 119 126 127 129 130 132 133 135 143 144 146 147 148 149 151 152 153 154 156 158 **S** Department of Veterans Affairs, Washington, DC
Primary Contact: Shella D. Stovall, R.N., Interim Director
CFO: Val Martin, Director Financial Management Services Center
CMO: Ronald J Gebhart, M.D., Chief of Staff
CIO: Lisa Leonelis, Chief Information Officer
CHR: Lisa Porter, Director Human Resources, Leadership and Education
Web address: www.saltlakecity.va.gov/
**Control**: Veterans Affairs, Government, federal **Service**: General medical and surgical

**Staffed Beds**: 123 **Admissions**: 5503 **Census**: 85 **Births**: 0

SANDY—Salt Lake County

☒ **ALTA VIEW HOSPITAL (460044)**, 9660 South 1300 East, Zip 84094–3793; tel. 801/501–2600, (Nonreporting) **A**1 10 **F**3 9 11 12 13 15 29 31 34 35 38 40 43 44 45 49 50 54 57 59 60 64 68 70 75 76 77 79 81 85 86 87 92 93 102 107 108 110 111 115 118 119 129 130 131 132 141 144 146 147 149 154 **S** Intermountain Healthcare, Inc., Salt Lake City, UT
Primary Contact: Scott Roberson, Administrator
CFO: Andrew Ozmun, Chief Financial Officer
CMO: Laurie Niederee, M.D., Chief Medical Officer
CHR: Marissa Johnson, Chief Human Resource Officer
CNO: David Hurst, Chief Nursing Officer
Web address: www.intermountainhealthcare.org
**Control**: Other not–for–profit (including NFP Corporation) **Service**: General medical and surgical

**Staffed Beds**: 59 **Admissions**: 2873 **Census**: 18 **Outpatient Visits**: 48482 **Births**: 1026 **Total Expense ($000)**: 109823 **Payroll Expense ($000)**: 28629 **Personnel**: 459

☒ **ENCOMPASS HEALTH REHABILITATION HOSPITAL OF UTAH (463025)**, 8074 South 1300 East, Zip 84094–0743; tel. 801/561–3400, (Nonreporting) **A**1 10 **F**29 30 90 91 100 107 130 148 154 **S** Encompass Health Corporation, Birmingham, AL
Primary Contact: Charles Smith, Chief Executive Officer
CMO: Joseph VickRoy, M.D., Medical Director
CHR: Troy Jensen, Director Human Resources
Web address: www.https://www.encompasshealth.com/utahrehab
**Control**: Corporation, Investor–owned (for–profit) **Service**: Rehabilitation

**Staffed Beds**: 45 **Admissions**: 808 **Census**: 31 **Outpatient Visits**: 0 **Births**: 0 **Total Expense ($000)**: 13048 **Payroll Expense ($000)**: 7905

**HEALTHSOUTH REHABILITATION HOSPITAL OF UTAH** See Encompass Health Rehabilitation Hospital of Utah

SOUTH OGDEN—Weber County

☐ **NORTHERN UTAH REHABILITATION HOSPITAL (463027)**, 5825 Harrison Boulevard, Zip 84403–4316; tel. 801/475–5254, (Nonreporting) **A**1 **S** Ernest Health, Inc., Albuquerque, NM
Primary Contact: Scot Stevens, Chief Executive Officer
COO: Reuben Jessop, Chief Operating Officer
CFO: Daniel J Foster, Chief Financial Officer
CNO: Terina Chapman, Director of Nursing
Web address: www.ernesthealth.com/gallery-item/northern-utah-rehabilitation-hospital/
**Control**: Other not–for–profit (including NFP Corporation) **Service**: Rehabilitation

**Staffed Beds**: 20

TOOELE—Tooele County

☐ **MOUNTAIN WEST MEDICAL CENTER (460014)**, 2055 North Main Street, Zip 84074–9819; tel. 435/843–3600, (Nonreporting) **A**1 10 **F**3 7 11 13 15 29 30 34 37 40 43 45 47 50 51 64 68 70 74 75 76 77 79 81 85 87 89 93 97 102 107 110 111 114 115 119 126 130 144 146 148 149 154 156 **S** Quorum Health, Brentwood, TN
Primary Contact: Philip Eaton, Chief Executive Officer
CMO: James Antinori, M.D., Chief of Staff
CIO: Marc Taylor, IS Director
CHR: Matthew Flygare, Director Human Resources
CNO: Yvonne Nielson, Chief Nursing Officer, Director Quality Management and Regulatory Compliance
Web address: www.mountainwestmc.com
**Control**: Corporation, Investor–owned (for–profit) **Service**: General medical and surgical

**Staffed Beds**: 44 **Admissions**: 1700 **Census**: 10 **Births**: 464 **Total Expense ($000)**: 37550 **Payroll Expense ($000)**: 15664

**TOOELE VALLEY REG MED CTR** See Mountain West Medical Center

**UT**

---

## TREMONTON—Box Elder County

★ **BEAR RIVER VALLEY HOSPITAL (460039)**, 905 North 1000 West,
Zip 84337–2497; tel. 435/207–4500, (Nonreporting) **A**10 **F**3 13 15 29 34 35 38
40 44 45 50 68 75 76 77 79 81 82 85 87 93 100 102 107 108 110 111 115
118 119 129 130 131 132 141 146 149 154 **S** Intermountain Healthcare, Inc.,
Salt Lake City, UT
Primary Contact: Brandon Vonk, Administrator
CFO: Justin Wiser, Chief Financial Officer
CMO: Brett Nance, M.D., Chief Medical Officer
CHR: Joy Sadler, Director Human Resources
CNO: James Montgomery, Chief Nursing Officer
Web address: www.https://intermountainhealthcare.org/locations/bear-river-valley-
hospital/
**Control**: Other not–for–profit (including NFP Corporation) **Service**: General
medical and surgical

**Staffed Beds:** 16 **Admissions:** 442 **Census:** 2 **Outpatient Visits:** 13847
**Births:** 128 **Total Expense ($000):** 26861 **Payroll Expense ($000):** 9740
**Personnel:** 124

## VERNAL—Uintah County

✉ **ASHLEY REGIONAL MEDICAL CENTER (460030)**, 150 West 100 North,
Zip 84078–2036; tel. 435/789–3342, (Nonreporting) **A**1 10 20 **S** LifePoint
Health, Brentwood, TN
Primary Contact: Wes Taylor, Chief Executive Officer
CFO: Chad Labrum, Chief Financial Officer
CMO: Dennis Lewis, M.D., Chief of Staff
CIO: Cameron Winn, Director Information Services
CHR: Deena Mansfield, Director Human Resources
CNO: Greg Gardiner, Chief Clinical Officer
Web address: www.ashleyregional.com
**Control**: Corporation, Investor–owned (for–profit) **Service**: General medical and
surgical

**Staffed Beds:** 39

**ASHLEY VALLEY MEDICAL CENTER** See Ashley Regional Medical Center

## WEST JORDAN—Salt Lake County

⇑ **JORDAN VALLEY MED CENTER** See Jordan Valley Medical Center

★ ⇑ **JORDAN VALLEY MEDICAL CENTER (460051)**, 3580 West 9000 South,
Zip 84088–8812; tel. 801/561–8888, (Includes MOUNTAIN POINT MEDICAL
CENTER, Mailing address: 3000 North Triumph Boulevard, Lehii, Utah, Zip 84043,
Lehi, tel. 385/345–3000), (Nonreporting) **A**5 10 21 **S** Steward Health Care
System, LLC, Dallas, TX
Primary Contact: Jon Butterfield, Administrator and Chief Executive Officer
CFO: Kurt Shipley, Chief Financial Officer
CMO: B Dee Allred, M.D., President Medical Staff
Web address: www.jordanvalleymc.com
**Control**: Partnership, Investor–owned (for–profit) **Service**: General medical and
surgical

**Staffed Beds:** 183

## WEST VALLEY CITY—Salt Lake County

★ **JORDAN VALLEY MEDICAL CENTER WEST VALLEY CAMPUS**, 3460 South
Pioneer Parkway, Zip 84120–2049; tel. 801/561–8888, (Nonreporting) **S** Steward
Health Care System, LLC, Dallas, TX
Primary Contact: Nathanael Budge, Administrator
CFO: Steven Payne, Chief Financial Officer
CMO: Justin Parkinson, M.D., President Medical Staff
CIO: Mark Runyan, Director Information Systems
CHR: Rob Burnett, Director Human Resources
Web address: www.https://www.jordanwestvalley.org
**Control**: Corporation, Investor–owned (for–profit) **Service**: General medical and
surgical

**Staffed Beds:** 101

**PIONEER VALLEY HOSPITAL** See Jordan Valley Medical Center West Valley
Campus

**UT**

*Many Facility Codes have changed. Please refer to the AHA Guide Code Chart.* © 2021 AHA Guide

# VERMONT

## BENNINGTON—Bennington County

⊠ **SOUTHWESTERN VERMONT MEDICAL CENTER (470012)**, 100 Hospital Drive, Zip 05201–5004; tel. 802/442–6361, (Nonreporting) **A**1 2 5 10
Primary Contact: Thomas A. Dee, President and Chief Executive Officer
CFO: Stephen D Majetich, CPA, Chief Financial Officer
CMO: Trey Dobson, M.D., Chief Medical Officer
CIO: Richard Ogilvie, Chief Information Officer
CHR: Rudolph D Weaver, Vice President Human Resources
CNO: Pamela Duchene, R.N., Vice President Patient Care Services and Chief Nursing Officer
Web address: www.svhealthcare.org
**Control**: Other not–for–profit (including NFP Corporation) **Service**: General medical and surgical

| | |
|---|---|
| **Staffed Beds**: 77 | |

## BERLIN—Washington County

**CENTRAL VERMONT MEDICAL CENTER** See The University of Vermont Health Network Central Vermont Medical Center

⊠ **THE UNIVERSITY OF VERMONT HEALTH NETWORK CENTRAL VERMONT MEDICAL CENTER (470001)**, 130 Fisher Road, Zip 05602–9516, Mailing Address: P.O. Box 547, Barre, Zip 05641–0547; tel. 802/371–4100, (Total facility includes 153 beds in nursing home–type unit) (Nonreporting) **A**1 3 5 10 **F**3 5 11 13 15 18 28 29 30 31 34 35 36 40 44 45 48 49 50 51 53 54 59 63 64 65 68 70 74 75 76 77 78 79 81 82 84 85 86 87 92 93 94 96 97 98 99 100 102 103 104 107 108 110 111 114 118 119 120 121 123 128 130 131 132 135 141 143 144 146 147 148 149
Primary Contact: Anna T. Noonan, President and Chief Operating Officer
CFO: Stephen F. Kenney, Chief Financial Officer
CMO: Philip Brown, D.O., Vice President Medical Affairs
CHR: Robert Patterson, Vice President Human Resources and Rehabilitation Services
CNO: Matthew Choate, Chief Nursing Officer
Web address: www.cvmc.org/
**Control**: Other not–for–profit (including NFP Corporation) **Service**: General medical and surgical

| | |
|---|---|
| **Staffed Beds**: 245 **Admissions**: 4236 **Census**: 183 **Outpatient Visits**: 434835 **Births**: 256 **Total Expense ($000)**: 187449 **Payroll Expense ($000)**: 79207 **Personnel**: 1310 | |

☐ **VERMONT PSYCHIATRIC CARE HOSPITAL (474004)**, 350 Fisher Road, Zip 5602; tel. 802/828–3300, (Nonreporting) **A**1 10 **F**75 92 98 102 130 135 143 146 149 154
Primary Contact: Sarah Squirrell, Commissioner of Vermont Department of Mental Health
Web address: www.mentalhealth.vermont.gov/Vermont-psychiatric-care-hospital
**Control**: State, Government, Nonfederal **Service**: Psychiatric

| | |
|---|---|
| **Staffed Beds**: 25 **Admissions**: 90 **Census**: 23 **Outpatient Visits**: 0 **Births**: 0 **Total Expense ($000)**: 22716 **Payroll Expense ($000)**: 10144 **Personnel**: 188 | |

## BRATTLEBORO—Windham County

★ **BRATTLEBORO MEMORIAL HOSPITAL (470011)**, 17 Belmont Avenue, Zip 05301–3498; tel. 802/257–0341, (Nonreporting) **A**5 10 **F**3 11 13 15 18 28 29 30 31 34 35 37 40 45 49 50 51 53 55 59 61 64 68 70 74 75 76 78 79 81 85 87 93 97 107 108 110 111 115 118 119 131 132 135 146 147 148 149 154 156 **P**6
Primary Contact: Steven R. Gordon, President and Chief Executive Officer
CFO: Andre Bissonnette, Chief Financial Officer
CMO: Kathleen McGraw, M.D., Chief Medical Officer
CIO: Jonathan Farina, Chief Information Officer
CHR: William Norwood, Vice President, Human Resources
CNO: Mary Urquhart, R.N., Vice President Patient Care
Web address: www.bmhvt.org
**Control**: Other not–for–profit (including NFP Corporation) **Service**: General medical and surgical

| | |
|---|---|
| **Staffed Beds**: 42 **Admissions**: 1780 **Census**: 15 **Outpatient Visits**: 159200 **Births**: 316 **Total Expense ($000)**: 87095 **Payroll Expense ($000)**: 37858 **Personnel**: 514 | |

⊠ **BRATTLEBORO RETREAT (474001)**, Anna Marsh Lane, Zip 5301, Mailing Address: P.O. Box 803, Zip 05302–0803; tel. 802/257–7785, (Nonreporting) **A**1 5 10 **F**5 29 34 35 44 50 68 75 82 87 98 99 100 101 102 103 104 105 106 135 149 152 153 154
Primary Contact: Louis Josephson, Ph.D., President and Chief Executive Officer
COO: Gerri Cote, Chief Operating Officer
CFO: Steven Monette, Chief Financial Officer
CMO: Frederick Engstrom, M.D., Chief Medical Officer
CHR: Jeffrey T. Corrigan, Vice President Human Resources
CNO: Linda J. Nagy, MSN, R.N., Chief Nursing Officer
Web address: www.brattlebororetreat.org
**Control**: Other not–for–profit (including NFP Corporation) **Service**: Psychiatric

| | |
|---|---|
| **Staffed Beds**: 119 **Admissions**: 3700 **Census**: 99 **Outpatient Visits**: 27670 **Births**: 0 **Total Expense ($000)**: 78833 **Payroll Expense ($000)**: 50265 **Personnel**: 538 | |

## BURLINGTON—Chittenden County

**THE UNIVERSITY OF VERMONT HEALTH NETWORK UNIVERSITY OF VERMONT MEDICAL CENTER** See University of Vermont Medical Center

⊠ **UNIVERSITY OF VERMONT MEDICAL CENTER (470003)**, 111 Colchester Avenue, Zip 05401–1473; tel. 802/847–0000, (Includes FANNY ALLEN CAMPUS, Mailing address: 101 College Parkway, Colchester, Vermont, Zip 05446–3035; tel. 802/655–1234; MEDICAL CENTER HOSPITAL CAMPUS, Mailing address: 111 Colchester Avenue, Burlington, Vermont, Zip 5401; tel. 802/847–2345; VERMONT CHILDREN'S HOSPITAL, Mailing address: 111 Colchester Avenue, Burlington, Vermont, Zip 05401–1473; tel. 802/847–0000), (Nonreporting) **A**1 2 3 5 8 10 **F**3 4 5 6 7 9 11 12 13 15 17 18 19 20 21 22 23 24 25 26 28 29 30 31 32 34 35 36 37 39 40 43 44 45 46 47 48 49 50 51 52 54 55 56 57 58 59 60 61 63 64 65 66 68 70 72 73 74 75 76 77 78 79 81 82 84 85 86 87 88 89 90 91 92 93 94 96 97 98 99 100 101 102 103 104 105 107 108 110 111 114 115 116 117 118 119 120 121 123 124 126 129 130 131 132 135 136 138 141 142 143 144 145 146 147 148 151 152 153 154 155 **P**6
Primary Contact: Stephen Leffler, M.D., President and Chief Operating Officer
CFO: Todd Keating, Chief Financial Officer
CMO: Isabelle Desjardins, M.D., Chief Medical Officer
CHR: Jerald Novak, Chief People Officer
CNO: Margaret Gagne, R.N., MS, Interim Chief Nursing Officer
Web address: www.uvmhealth.org/medcenter/Pages/default.aspx
**Control**: Other not–for–profit (including NFP Corporation) **Service**: General medical and surgical

| | |
|---|---|
| **Staffed Beds**: 499 **Admissions**: 21084 **Census**: 352 **Outpatient Visits**: 1138161 **Births**: 2291 **Total Expense ($000)**: 1394632 **Payroll Expense ($000)**: 637495 **Personnel**: 7584 | |

VT

**Hospital, Medicare Provider Number, Address, Telephone, Approval, Facility, and Physician Codes, Health Care System**

★ American Hospital Association (AHA) membership
☐ The Joint Commission accreditation
○ Healthcare Facilities Accreditation Program
◇ DNV Healthcare Inc. accreditation
⇑ Center for Improvement in Healthcare Quality Accreditation
△ Commission on Accreditation of Rehabilitation Facilities (CARF) accreditation

© 2021 AHA Guide     *Many Facility Codes have changed. Please refer to the AHA Guide Code Chart.*     Hospitals **A735**

## COLCHESTER—Chittenden County

**FANNY ALLEN CAMPUS** See University of Vermont Medical Center, Burlington

**FANNY ALLEN CAMPUS**
Primary Contact: , R.N., MS

## MIDDLEBURY—Addison County

**PORTER HOSPITAL** See Porter Medical Center

★ **PORTER MEDICAL CENTER (471307)**, 115 Porter Drive, Zip 05753–8423; tel. 802/388–4701, (Nonreporting) **A**10 18 **F**3 8 11 13 15 18 28 29 30 34 35 40 45 50 59 64 68 75 76 79 81 83 84 85 87 97 107 108 110 111 115 119 132 133 135 144 146 147 148 149 154 156 157
Primary Contact: Seleem Choudhury, R.N., MSN, President and Chief Operating Officer
CFO: Steve Ciampa, Vice President Finance
CMO: Fred Kniffin, M.D., Chief Medical Officer
CIO: Rebecca Woods, Chief Information Officer
CHR: David Fuller, Vice President of Human Resources
CNO: Lorraina Smith-Zuba, R.N., MSN, Chief Nursing Officer
Web address: www.portermedical.org
**Control:** Other not–for–profit (including NFP Corporation) **Service:** General medical and surgical

**Staffed Beds:** 25 **Admissions:** 1575 **Census:** 14 **Births:** 336 **Total Expense ($000):** 86649 **Payroll Expense ($000):** 42711 **Personnel:** 495

## MORRISVILLE—Lamoille County

★ **COPLEY HOSPITAL (471305)**, 528 Washington Highway, Zip 05661–8973; tel. 802/888–8888, (Nonreporting) **A**10 18
Primary Contact: Joseph L. Woodin, Chief Executive Officer
COO: Vera A. Jones, Chief Operating Officer
CFO: Debbie Dorain, Chief Financial Officer
CMO: Joel Silverstein, M.D., Chief Medical Officer
CIO: Randy Chesley, Director Information Technology
CHR: Amy Fitzgerald, Human Resources Manager
CNO: Lori Profota, Chief Nursing Officer
Web address: www.copleyvt.org
**Control:** Other not–for–profit (including NFP Corporation) **Service:** General medical and surgical

**Staffed Beds:** 25

## NEWPORT—Orleans County

★ ⇑ **NORTH COUNTRY HOSPITAL AND HEALTH CENTER (471304)**, 189 Prouty Drive, Zip 05855–9326; tel. 802/334–7331, (Nonreporting) **A**10 18 21 **F**11 13 15 28 29 30 34 35 40 43 45 50 53 70 74 75 76 77 79 81 82 84 85 89 91 93 107 108 110 111 114 118 119 127 129 130 131 133 135 146 148 149
Primary Contact: Brian Nall, Chief Executive Officer
COO: Thomas Frank, Chief Operating Officer
CHR: William Perket, Vice President Human Resources
CNO: Avril Cochran, R.N., Vice President Patient Care Services
Web address: www.nchsi.org
**Control:** Other not–for–profit (including NFP Corporation) **Service:** General medical and surgical

**Staffed Beds:** 25 **Admissions:** 1386 **Census:** 16 **Outpatient Visits:** 72850 **Births:** 214 **Total Expense ($000):** 86375 **Payroll Expense ($000):** 40391 **Personnel:** 457

## RANDOLPH—Orange County

★ **GIFFORD MEDICAL CENTER (471301)**, 44 South Main Street, Zip 05060–1381, Mailing Address: P.O. Box 2000, Zip 05060–2000; tel. 802/728–7000, (Nonreporting) **A**5 10 18
Primary Contact: Dan Bennett, President and Chief Executive Officer
CMO: Joshua Plavin, M.D., Medical Director Medicine Division
CIO: Sean Patrick, Director Information Systems
CHR: Janice Davis, Interim Director Human Resources
CNO: Linda Minsinger, Vice President Hospital Division
Web address: www.giffordmed.org
**Control:** Other not–for–profit (including NFP Corporation) **Service:** General medical and surgical

**Staffed Beds:** 52

**GIFFORD MEMORIAL HOSPITAL** See Gifford Medical Center

## RUTLAND—Rutland County

⊞ **RUTLAND REGIONAL MEDICAL CENTER (470005)**, 160 Allen Street, Zip 05701–4595; tel. 802/775–7111, (Nonreporting) **A**1 2 10 **F**3 5 13 15 18 28 29 31 34 37 40 44 45 50 55 57 59 64 65 70 74 76 78 79 81 82 83 84 85 87 92 93 98 100 101 102 104 107 108 109 110 111 115 117 118 119 120 121 123 124 129 130 133 135 146 147 148 149 154 156 157
Primary Contact: Claudio D. Fort, President and Chief Executive Officer
CFO: Judi Kennedy Fox, Chief Financial Officer
CMO: Baxter C Holland, M.D., Chief Medical Officer
CNO: Carol Egan, R.N., MSN, Chief Nursing Officer
Web address: www.rrmc.org
**Control:** Other not–for–profit (including NFP Corporation) **Service:** General medical and surgical

**Staffed Beds:** 120 **Admissions:** 6272 **Census:** 83 **Outpatient Visits:** 244443 **Births:** 352 **Total Expense ($000):** 274017 **Payroll Expense ($000):** 135829 **Personnel:** 1411

## SAINT ALBANS—Franklin County

⊞ **NORTHWESTERN MEDICAL CENTER (470024)**, 133 Fairfield Street, Zip 05478–1726; tel. 802/524–5911, (Nonreporting) **A**1 2 10 20 **F**5 11 15 28 29 30 32 34 35 36 40 45 46 48 50 53 54 55 57 58 59 60 61 64 65 68 70 74 75 77 79 81 82 84 86 87 93 96 97 102 107 109 110 111 115 119 131 132 133 135 143 144 146 147 148 149 154 156 157 **P**6 **S** QHR Health, Brentwood, TN
Primary Contact: Gerald J. Barbini, Interim Chief Executive Officer
COO: Jane Catton, R.N., Chief Operating Officer and Chief Nursing Officer
CFO: Christopher Hickey, Chief Financial Officer
CMO: Lowery Sullivan, M.D., Chief Medical Officer
CIO: Joel Benware, Vice President Information Technology and Compliance
CHR: Thomas C Conley, Vice President, Human Resources and Organizational Development
CNO: Jane Catton, R.N., Chief Operating Officer and Chief Nursing Officer
Web address: www.northwesternmedicalcenter.org
**Control:** Other not–for–profit (including NFP Corporation) **Service:** General medical and surgical

**Staffed Beds:** 47 **Admissions:** 2348 **Census:** 21 **Births:** 343 **Total Expense ($000):** 119729 **Payroll Expense ($000):** 56737

## SAINT JOHNSBURY—Caledonia County

★ **NORTHEASTERN VERMONT REGIONAL HOSPITAL (471303)**, 1315 Hospital Drive, Zip 05819–9210, Mailing Address: PO Box 905, Zip 05819–0905; tel. 802/748–8141, (Nonreporting) **A**5 10 18
Primary Contact: Shawn Tester, Chief Executive Officer
CFO: Robert Hersey, Chief Financial Officer
CMO: Michael Rousse, M.D., Chief Medical Officer
CIO: Shawn Burroughs, Director of Information Services
CHR: Elizabeth Gwatkin, Vice President Human Resources
Web address: www.nvrh.org
**Control:** Other not–for–profit (including NFP Corporation) **Service:** General medical and surgical

**Staffed Beds:** 25

## SPRINGFIELD—Windsor County

★ **SPRINGFIELD HOSPITAL (471306)**, 25 Ridgewood Road, Zip 05156–3050, Mailing Address: 25 Ridgewood Rd, Zip 05156–3050; tel. 802/885–2151, (Nonreporting) **A**5 10 18
Primary Contact: Joshua Dufresne, Chief of Practice Operations
CFO: Scott Whittemore, Chief Financial Officer and Chief of Ancillary Services
CMO: Richard Marasa, M.D., President Medical Staff
CIO: Kyle Peoples, Director Technology Management Services
CHR: Janet Lyle, Chief Human Resources and Allied Health Services
CNO: Janet Sherer, Chief of Patient Care Services
Web address: www.springfieldmed.org
**Control:** Other not–for–profit (including NFP Corporation) **Service:** General medical and surgical

**Staffed Beds:** 35

VT

## TOWNSHEND—Windham County

★ **GRACE COTTAGE HOSPITAL (471300)**, 185 Grafton Road, Zip 05353–0216,
Mailing Address: P.O. Box 216, Zip 05353–0216; tel. 802/365–7357,
(Nonreporting) **A**5 10 18 **F**3 29 30 34 35 40 50 57 59 64 65 66 68 77 85 93 96
97 104 107 115 119 127 130 132 133 135 146 147 149
Primary Contact: Douglas F. DiVello, FACHE, M.P.H., President and Chief Executive
Officer
CFO: Stephen A Brown, Chief Financial Officer
CMO: George Terwilliger, Chief Medical Officer
CIO: Christopher Paul Boucher, Director of Information Services
CHR: Jennifer Newman, Director of Human Resources
CNO: Lisa J. Eaton, R.N., Chief Nursing Officer
Web address: www.gracecottage.org
**Control:** Other not–for–profit (including NFP Corporation) **Service:** General
medical and surgical

**Staffed Beds:** 19 **Admissions:** 335 **Census:** 11 **Outpatient Visits:** 19255
**Births:** 0 **Total Expense ($000):** 20743 **Payroll Expense ($000):** 12050
**Personnel:** 157

## WHITE RIVER JUNCTION—Windsor County

**VETERANS AFFAIRS MEDICAL CENTER** See White River Junction Veterans
Affairs Medical Center

⊞ **WHITE RIVER JUNCTION VETERANS AFFAIRS MEDICAL CENTER**, 215 North
Main Street, Zip 05009–0001; tel. 802/295–9363, (Nonreporting) **A**1 3 5 8 **S**
Department of Veterans Affairs, Washington, DC
Primary Contact: Brett Rusch, M.D., Acting Director
CFO: Joan Wilmot, Chief Finance Officer
CMO: M. Ganga Hematillake, M.D., Chief of Staff
CIO: Matthew Rafus, Chief Information Officer
CHR: Barbara Nadeau, Chief Human Resources Management Service
Web address: www.whiteriver.va.gov/
**Control:** Veterans Affairs, Government, federal **Service:** General medical and
surgical

**Staffed Beds:** 74

## WINDSOR—Windsor County

**MT ASCUTNEY HOSP AND HLTH CTR** See Mt. Ascutney Hospital and Health
Center

★ △ **MT. ASCUTNEY HOSPITAL AND HEALTH CENTER (471302)**, 289 County
Road, Zip 05089–9000; tel. 802/674–6711, (Nonreporting) **A**5 7 10 18 **F**3 8 11
15 28 29 30 31 32 34 40 44 45 49 50 54 56 57 59 63 65 68 70 75 77 78
81 82 84 87 90 91 92 93 94 95 96 97 104 107 110 114 119 129 130 132
133 135 146 148 154 156 157 **P**6
Primary Contact: Joseph L. Perras, M.D., President and Chief Executive Officer
COO: Paul Calandrella, Chief Operating Officer
CFO: David Sanville, Chief Financial Officer
CMO: Joseph L. Perras, M.D., Chief Medical Officer
CHR: Jean Martaniuk, Director Human Resources
CNO: Amy Visser-Lynch, Chief Nursing Officer
Web address: www.mtascutneyhospital.org
**Control:** Other not–for–profit (including NFP Corporation) **Service:** General
medical and surgical

**Staffed Beds:** 35 **Admissions:** 1057 **Census:** 28 **Outpatient Visits:** 47771
**Births:** 0 **Total Expense ($000):** 54567 **Payroll Expense ($000):** 26789
**Personnel:** 367

VT

---

**Hospital, Medicare Provider Number, Address, Telephone, Approval, Facility, and Physician Codes, Health Care System**

★ American Hospital Association (AHA) membership    ○ Healthcare Facilities Accreditation Program    ⇑ Center for Improvement in Healthcare Quality Accreditation
□ The Joint Commission accreditation    ◇ DNV Healthcare Inc. accreditation    △ Commission on Accreditation of Rehabilitation Facilities (CARF) accreditation

# VIRGINIA

## ABINGDON—Washington County

✠ **JOHNSTON MEMORIAL HOSPITAL (490053)**, 16000 Johnston Memorial Drive, Zip 24211–7659; tel. 276/258–1000, (Nonreporting) **A**1 2 3 5 10 13 **F**3 8 11 13 15 18 20 22 24 26 28 29 30 31 34 35 36 39 40 44 45 46 47 48 49 51 54 55 57 58 59 60 62 63 64 68 70 74 75 76 77 78 79 81 82 84 85 87 92 93 97 100 107 110 111 114 115 118 119 120 121 122 123 124 129 130 132 135 136 141 144 145 146 147 148 149 154 156 157 **S** Ballad Health, Johnson City, TN
Primary Contact: John Jeter, Chief Executive Officer
COO: Bryan Mullins, Chief Operating Officer
CMO: Brian Condit, M.D., Chief Medical Officer
CIO: Jackson Dale, Director Management Information Services
CHR: Jackie G Phipps, Director Human Resources
CNO: Linda Shepherd, R.N., Chief Nursing Officer
Web address: www.jmh.org
**Control:** Other not–for–profit (including NFP Corporation) **Service:** General medical and surgical

**Staffed Beds:** 116 **Admissions:** 7157 **Census:** 74 **Outpatient Visits:** 223654 **Births:** 581 **Total Expense ($000):** 144339 **Payroll Expense ($000):** 48213 **Personnel:** 651

## ALDIE—Loudoun County

✠ **ENCOMPASS HEALTH REHABILITATION HOSPITAL OF NORTHERN VIRGINIA (493033)**, 24430 Millstream Drive, Zip 20105–3098; tel. 703/957–2000, (Nonreporting) **A**1 10 **F**29 90 **P**5 **S** Encompass Health Corporation, Birmingham, AL
Primary Contact: Alfred Santos, Chief Executive Officer
Web address: www.healthsouthnorthernvirginia.com
**Control:** Corporation, Investor–owned (for–profit) **Service:** Rehabilitation

**Staffed Beds:** 60 **Admissions:** 1732 **Census:** 54 **Outpatient Visits:** 0 **Births:** 0 **Total Expense ($000):** 23330 **Payroll Expense ($000):** 13146 **Personnel:** 197

**HEALTHSOUTH REHABILITATION HOSPITAL OF NORTHERN VIRGINIA** See Encompass Health Rehabilitation Hospital of Northern Virginia

## ALEXANDRIA—Alexandria City County

**ALEXANDRIA HOSPITAL** See Inova Alexandria Hospital

✠ **INOVA ALEXANDRIA HOSPITAL (490040)**, 4320 Seminary Road, Zip 22304–1535; tel. 703/504–3167, (Nonreporting) **A**1 2 5 10 **F**3 11 13 14 15 18 20 22 26 28 29 30 31 34 35 38 39 40 41 42 44 45 46 47 48 49 50 51 54 55 56 57 58 59 60 61 63 64 65 68 70 72 74 75 76 77 78 79 81 82 84 85 86 87 91 92 93 100 101 102 107 110 111 114 115 118 119 120 121 123 124 126 129 130 131 132 135 145 146 147 148 149 154 156 157 **P**6 **S** Inova Health System, Falls Church, VA
Primary Contact: Rina Bansal, M.D., President
CFO: Todd Lockcuff, Chief Financial Officer
CMO: William L Jackson, Chief Medical Officer
CHR: Hugo Aguas, Vice President Human Resources
Web address: www.inova.org
**Control:** Other not–for–profit (including NFP Corporation) **Service:** General medical and surgical

**Staffed Beds:** 302 **Admissions:** 15001 **Census:** 174 **Outpatient Visits:** 184850 **Births:** 3211 **Total Expense ($000):** 1646975 **Payroll Expense ($000):** 524164 **Personnel:** 1438

## ALEXANDRIA—Fairfax County

✠ **INOVA MOUNT VERNON HOSPITAL (490122)**, 2501 Parker's Lane, Zip 22306–3209; tel. 703/664–7000, (Nonreporting) **A**1 2 3 5 10 **F**3 11 14 15 18 28 29 30 31 34 35 38 40 42 44 45 48 49 50 51 54 55 57 58 59 60 61 63 64 65 68 70 74 75 77 78 79 81 84 85 86 87 90 91 92 93 94 95 96 98 100 101 102 104 105 107 108 110 111 115 118 119 130 131 132 135 145 146 147 148 149 154 156 157 **P**6 **S** Inova Health System, Falls Church, VA
Primary Contact: Joseph Pina, M.D., Chief Executive Officer
CFO: Tammy Razmic, Associate Administrator Finance and Chief Financial Officer
CHR: Bev Sugar, Associate Administrator and Director Human Resources
Web address: www.inova.org
**Control:** Other not–for–profit (including NFP Corporation) **Service:** General medical and surgical

**Staffed Beds:** 237 **Admissions:** 8466 **Census:** 141 **Outpatient Visits:** 107238 **Births:** 0 **Total Expense ($000):** 214745 **Payroll Expense ($000):** 79773 **Personnel:** 1063

**MOUNT VERNON HOSPITAL** See Inova Mount Vernon Hospital

## ARLINGTON—Arlington County

**CAPITAL HOSPICE (490129)**, 4715 15th Street North, Zip 22205–2640; tel. 703/538–2065, (Nonreporting) **A**3 10
Primary Contact: Malene S. Davis, R.N., President and Chief Executive Officer
CFO: David Schwind, Chief Financial Officer
CIO: Diane Rigsby, Chief Information Officer
Web address: www.capitalhospice.org
**Control:** Other not–for–profit (including NFP Corporation) **Service:** Other specialty treatment

**Staffed Beds:** 15

**HOSPICE OF NORTHERN VIRGINIA** See Capital Hospice

✠ △ **VIRGINIA HOSPITAL CENTER (490050)**, 1701 North George Mason Drive, Zip 22205–3698; tel. 703/558–5000, (Nonreporting) **A**1 2 3 5 7 10 **F**3 4 5 8 11 12 13 15 17 18 20 22 24 26 28 29 30 31 34 35 37 38 40 45 46 47 48 49 50 51 53 54 56 57 58 59 60 61 64 65 66 68 70 72 73 74 75 76 77 78 79 81 82 83 84 85 86 87 89 90 91 92 93 94 95 96 97 98 100 102 103 104 105 107 108 110 111 114 115 116 117 118 119 120 121 123 124 126 129 130 132 135 144 145 146 147 148 149 152 153 154 156 157 **P**6
Primary Contact: James B. Cole, President and Chief Executive Officer
CFO: John Zabrowski, Senior Vice President and Chief Financial Officer
CMO: Jeffrey P. DiLisi, M.D., Senior Vice President, Chief Medical Officer
CIO: Michael Mistretta, Vice President and Chief Information Officer
CHR: Michael Malone, Vice President and Chief Human Resources Officer
CNO: Melody Dickerson, R.N., MSN, Senior Vice President, Chief Nursing Officer
Web address: www.virginiahospitalcenter.com
**Control:** Other not–for–profit (including NFP Corporation) **Service:** General medical and surgical

**Staffed Beds:** 365 **Admissions:** 23238 **Census:** 290 **Outpatient Visits:** 396685 **Births:** 4504 **Total Expense ($000):** 533914 **Payroll Expense ($000):** 238333 **Personnel:** 2737

**VIRGINIA HOSPITAL CENTER - ARLINGTON** See Virginia Hospital Center

## BEDFORD—Bedford City County

**BEDFORD MEMORIAL HOSPITAL** See Centra Bedford Memorial Hospital

☒ **CENTRA BEDFORD MEMORIAL HOSPITAL (490088)**, 1613 Oakwood Street, Zip 24523–1213; tel. 540/586–2441, (Total facility includes 111 beds in nursing home–type unit) (Nonreporting) **A**1 5 10 **F**2 3 11 15 28 29 30 34 35 40 46 53 57 59 63 67 70 81 84 85 86 87 97 107 110 115 119 128 130 143 146 148 **S** Centra Health, Inc., Lynchburg, VA
Primary Contact: Patti Jurkus, Vice President and Chief Executive Officer
CFO: Donald E Lorton, Executive Vice President
CMO: E Allen Joslyn, M.D., Chief Medical Officer
Web address: www.bmhva.com
**Control**: Other not–for–profit (including NFP Corporation) **Service**: General medical and surgical

**Staffed Beds:** 145 **Admissions:** 2265 **Census:** 111 **Outpatient Visits:** 51146 **Births:** 0 **Total Expense ($000):** 43431 **Payroll Expense ($000):** 18319 **Personnel:** 306

## BIG STONE GAP—Wise County

☒ **LONESOME PINE HOSPITAL (490114)**, 1990 Holton Avenue East, Zip 24219–3350; tel. 276/523–3111, (Nonreporting) **A**1 3 5 10 13 **F**3 11 15 29 30 31 34 40 45 50 57 59 63 70 76 77 78 79 81 82 85 87 93 107 108 110 111 114 118 119 120 121 129 130 135 146 148 **S** Ballad Health, Johnson City, TN
Primary Contact: Mark T. Leonard, Interim Chief Executive Officer
CFO: Regina Day, Executive Vice President of Finance
CMO: Michael Ketcham, President, Medical Staff
CHR: Bobby Collins, Director Human Resources
Web address: www.wellmont.org
**Control**: Other not–for–profit (including NFP Corporation) **Service**: General medical and surgical

**Staffed Beds:** 16 **Admissions:** 2811 **Census:** 29 **Outpatient Visits:** 113565 **Births:** 217 **Total Expense ($000):** 60951 **Payroll Expense ($000):** 12146 **Personnel:** 184

**WELLMONT LONESOME PINE HOSPITAL** See Lonesome Pine Hospital

## BLACKSBURG—Montgomery County

☒ **LEWISGALE HOSPITAL MONTGOMERY (490110)**, 3700 South Main Street, Zip 24060–7081, Mailing Address: P.O. Box 90004, Zip 24062–9004; tel. 540/951–1111, (Nonreporting) **A**1 3 5 10 12 13 **S** HCA Healthcare, Nashville, TN
Primary Contact: Alan J. Fabian, Chief Executive Officer
CFO: Timothy W Haasken, Chief Financial Officer
CIO: Diron Lane, Director Information Systems
CNO: Ellen Y Linkenhoker, Chief Nursing Officer
Web address: www.lewisgale.com
**Control**: Corporation, Investor–owned (for–profit) **Service**: General medical and surgical

**Staffed Beds:** 146

**MONTGOMERY REGIONAL HOSPITAL** See Lewisgale Hospital Montgomery

## BOONES MILL—Salem City County

**COLUMBIA LEWIS-GALE MED CTR** See Lewis-Gale Medical Center

☒ **LEWIS-GALE MEDICAL CENTER (490048)**, 8633 Grassy Hill Rd, Zip 24065, Mailing Address: 1900 Electric Road, Salem, Zip 24153–7494; tel. 540/776–4000, (Includes LEWIS-GALE PAVILION, Mailing address: 1902 Braeburn Drive, Salem, Virginia, Zip 24153–7391; tel. 703/772–2800), (Nonreporting) **A**1 2 3 5 10 **S** HCA Healthcare, Nashville, TN
Primary Contact: Lance Jones, Chief Executive Officer
COO: Michael Abbott, Chief Operating Officer
CFO: Angela D Reynolds, Chief Financial Officer
CMO: Joseph Nelson, M.D., President Medical Staff
CIO: Beth Cole, Director Information Services
CHR: Dale Beaudoin, Vice President Human Resources
Web address: www.lewis-gale.com
**Control**: Corporation, Investor–owned (for–profit) **Service**: General medical and surgical

**Staffed Beds:** 506

## BRISTOL—Bristol City County

☒ **REHABILITATION HOSPITAL OF BRISTOL (493034)**, 103 North Street, Zip 24201–3201; tel. 276/642–7900, (Nonreporting) **A**1 10 **S** Encompass Health Corporation, Birmingham, AL
Primary Contact: Troy Clark, Chief Executive Officer
Web address: www.rehabilitationhospitalsvvirginia.com
**Control**: Corporation, Investor–owned (for–profit) **Service**: Rehabilitation

**Staffed Beds:** 25

**REHABILITATION HOSPITAL OF SOUTHWEST VIRGINIA** See Rehabilitation Hospital of Bristol

## BURKEVILLE—Nottoway County

☐ **PIEDMONT GERIATRIC HOSPITAL (490134)**, 5001 East Patrick Henry Hwy, Zip 23922–3460, Mailing Address: P.O. Box 427, Zip 23922–0427; tel. 434/767–4401, (Nonreporting) **A**1 **S** Virginia Department of Mental Health, Richmond, VA
Primary Contact: Emma L. Lowry, M.D., Acting Facility Director, Chief Executive Officer
COO: Jarvis T. Griffin, Assistant Director Administration and Chief Operating Officer
CFO: Cynthia Arthur, Fiscal Director
CMO: Ramesh Chaudry, M.D., Medical Director
CHR: Michelle Wingo, Director Human Resources
CNO: Regina E. Johnson, Chief Nurse Executive
Web address: www.pgh.dmhmrsas.virginia.gov
**Control**: State, Government, Nonfederal **Service**: Other specialty treatment

**Staffed Beds:** 135

## CATAWBA—Roanoke County

☐ **CATAWBA HOSPITAL (490135)**, 5525 Catawba Hospital Drive, Zip 24070–2115, Mailing Address: P.O. Box 200, Zip 24070–0200; tel. 540/375–4200, (Nonreporting) **A**1 3 5 10 **F**29 30 35 39 44 50 68 75 77 98 103 130 143 146 149 **P**6 **S** Virginia Department of Mental Health, Richmond, VA
Primary Contact: Walton F. Mitchell III, Director
COO: Charles Law, Ph.D., Chief Operating Officer
CFO: Cecil Hardin, CPA, Chief Financial Officer
CMO: Yad Jabbarpour, M.D., Chief of Staff
CIO: Charles Law, Ph.D., Chief Operating Officer
CHR: Patricia Ebbett, Chief Human Resources Officer
CNO: Vicky Fisher, Ph.D., R.N., Chief Nurse Executive
Web address: www.catawba.dbhds.virginia.gov
**Control**: State, Government, Nonfederal **Service**: Psychiatric

**Staffed Beds:** 110 **Admissions:** 620 **Census:** 102 **Outpatient Visits:** 0 **Births:** 0 **Total Expense ($000):** 26192 **Payroll Expense ($000):** 13691 **Personnel:** 263

## CHARLOTTESVILLE—Charlottesville City County

⇑ **MARTHA JEFFERSON HOSPITAL** See Sentara Martha Jefferson Hospital

★ ⇑ **SENTARA MARTHA JEFFERSON HOSPITAL (490077)**, 500 Martha Jefferson Drive, Zip 22911–4668; tel. 434/654–7000, (Nonreporting) **A**2 10 21 **F**3 8 11 12 13 15 18 20 22 26 28 29 30 31 34 35 36 40 41 42 44 45 46 47 48 49 50 53 54 55 56 57 58 59 64 65 68 70 74 75 76 77 78 79 81 82 84 85 86 87 92 93 94 97 107 108 110 111 114 115 116 117 118 119 120 121 123 124 129 130 131 132 134 135 141 145 146 147 148 149 154 156 **P**8 **S** Sentara Healthcare, Norfolk, VA
Primary Contact: Jonathan S. Davis, FACHE, President
COO: Amy Black, R.N., MSN, Chief Operating Officer
CFO: Stewart R Nelson, Vice President and Chief Financial Officer
CMO: F Michael Ashby, M.D., Vice President and Medical Director
CIO: Marijo Lecker, Vice President
CHR: Debbie Desmond, Director Human Resources
Web address: www.marthajefferson.org
**Control**: Other not–for–profit (including NFP Corporation) **Service**: General medical and surgical

**Staffed Beds:** 144 **Admissions:** 9685 **Census:** 96 **Outpatient Visits:** 619677 **Births:** 1372 **Total Expense ($000):** 255320 **Payroll Expense ($000):** 86060 **Personnel:** 1536

## CHARLOTTESVILLE—Albemarle County

**TRANSITIONAL CARE HOSPITAL** See UVA Transitional Care Hospital

**VA**

---

**Hospital, Medicare Provider Number, Address, Telephone, Approval, Facility, and Physician Codes, Health Care System**

★ American Hospital Association (AHA) membership
☐ The Joint Commission accreditation
○ Healthcare Facilities Accreditation Program
◇ DNV Healthcare Inc. accreditation
⇑ Center for Improvement in Healthcare Quality Accreditation
△ Commission on Accreditation of Rehabilitation Facilities (CARF) accreditation

## CHARLOTTESVILLE—Charlottesville City County

**UNIVERSITY OF VIRGINIA HOSPS** See University of Virginia Medical Center

⊞ **UNIVERSITY OF VIRGINIA MEDICAL CENTER (490009)**, 1215 Lee Street, Zip 22908–0001, Mailing Address: P.O. Box 800809, Zip 22908–0809; tel. 434/924–0211, (Includes UNIVERSITY OF VIRGINIA CHILDREN'S HOSPITAL, Mailing address: 1215 Lee Street, Charlottesville, Virginia, Zip 22908, PO Box 800566, Zip 22908, tel. 434/243–5500), (Nonreporting) **A**1 2 3 5 8 10 **F**3 5 7 8 9 11 12 13 15 16 17 18 19 20 21 22 23 24 25 26 27 28 29 30 31 32 34 35 36 37 38 39 40 41 43 44 45 46 47 48 49 50 51 52 54 55 56 57 58 59 60 61 62 63 64 65 66 68 70 71 72 73 74 75 76 77 78 79 80 81 82 83 84 85 86 87 88 89 90 91 92 93 94 97 98 100 101 102 103 104 107 108 110 111 112 114 115 116 117 118 119 120 121 123 124 126 129 130 131 132 134 135 136 137 138 139 140 141 142 143 145 146 147 148 149 153 154 155 156 **P**3 **S** UVA Health System, Charlottesville, VA
Primary Contact: Craig Kent, Interim Chief Executive Officer
COO: William T. Fulkerson, Chief Operating Officer
CFO: Nick Mendyka, Chief Financial Officer
CMO: Chris A. Ghaemmaghami, M.D., Chief Medical Officer
CIO: Richard Skinner, Chief Information Technology Officer
CHR: John Boswell, Chief Human Resources Officer
CNO: Mary E. Dixon, MSN, R.N., Interim Chief Nursing Officer
Web address: www.healthsystem.virginia.edu
**Control:** State, Government, Nonfederal **Service:** General medical and surgical

**Staffed Beds:** 612 **Admissions:** 28838 **Census:** 496 **Outpatient Visits:** 2003694 **Births:** 1929 **Total Expense ($000):** 1650528 **Payroll Expense ($000):** 577644 **Personnel:** 8208

## CHARLOTTESVILLE—Albemarle County

⊞ **UVA ENCOMPASS HEALTH REHABILITATION HOSPITAL (493029)**, 515 Ray C Hunt Drive, Zip 22903–2981; tel. 434/244–2000, (Nonreporting) **A**1 3 5 10 **F**3 28 29 34 35 57 59 74 75 77 90 91 132 148 149 154 **P**5 **S** Encompass Health Corporation, Birmingham, AL
Primary Contact: Louis Collier, Chief Executive Officer
CFO: Dianna Gomez, Controller
CMO: Alan Alfano, M.D., Medical Director
CIO: Michael Vanhoy, Director of Quality
CHR: Tonya Loving, Director of Human Resources
CNO: Sherry Herring, Chief Nursing Officer
Web address: www.uvahealthsouth.com
**Control:** Corporation, Investor–owned (for–profit) **Service:** Rehabilitation

**Staffed Beds:** 50 **Admissions:** 1277 **Census:** 43 **Outpatient Visits:** 17328 **Births:** 0 **Total Expense ($000):** 20614 **Payroll Expense ($000):** 11842 **Personnel:** 173

⊞ **UVA TRANSITIONAL CARE HOSPITAL (492011)**, 2965 Ivy Rd (250 West), Zip 22903–9330; tel. 434/924–8245, (Nonreporting) **A**1 10 **F**1 3 29 30 60 77 85 94 130 146 148 149 **P**3 **S** UVA Health System, Charlottesville, VA
Primary Contact: Tracy Turman, Administrator
Web address: www.uvahealth.com/services/transitional-care-hospital
**Control:** State, Government, Nonfederal **Service:** Acute long–term care hospital

**Staffed Beds:** 30 **Admissions:** 315 **Census:** 25 **Outpatient Visits:** 0 **Births:** 0 **Total Expense ($000):** 18597 **Payroll Expense ($000):** 6643 **Personnel:** 111

**UVA-HEALTHSOUTH REHABILITATION HOSPITAL** See UVA Encompass Health Rehabilitation Hospital

## CHESAPEAKE—Chesapeake City County

**CHESAPEAKE REGIONAL HEALTHCARE** See Chesapeake Regional Medical Center

★ ○ **CHESAPEAKE REGIONAL MEDICAL CENTER (490120)**, 736 Battlefield Boulevard North, Zip 23320–4941, Mailing Address: P.O. Box 2028, Zip 23327–2028; tel. 757/312–8121, (Nonreporting) **A**2 3 10 11
Primary Contact: Reese Jackson, President and Chief Executive Officer
COO: Amber Egyud, R.N., Chief Nursing Officer and Chief Operating Officer
CFO: Stephen C McDonnell, Chief Financial Officer
CMO: Raymond McCue, M.D., Vice President, Medical Affairs and Chief Medical Officer
CIO: Maurice Bastarache, Chief Information Officer
CHR: Deborah L Rosenburg, Vice President Human Resources
CNO: Amber Egyud, R.N., Chief Nursing Officer and Chief Operating Officer
Web address: www.chesapeakeregional.com
**Control:** Hospital district or authority, Government, Nonfederal **Service:** General medical and surgical

**Staffed Beds:** 310

## CHRISTIANSBURG—Montgomery County

⊞ **CARILION NEW RIVER VALLEY MEDICAL CENTER (490042)**, 2900 Lamb Circle, Zip 24073–6344, Mailing Address: P.O. Box 5, Radford, Zip 24143–0005; tel. 540/731–2000, (Includes CARILION CLINIC SAINT ALBANS HOSPITAL, Mailing Address: 2900 Lamb Circle, Christiansburg, Virginia, Zip 24073–6344; tel. 540/731–2000), (Nonreporting) **A**1 3 5 10 19 **F**3 5 8 12 13 15 18 20 22 24 26 28 29 30 31 34 35 36 40 43 45 47 48 49 50 51 53 57 59 60 62 63 64 65 68 70 74 75 76 77 79 81 82 84 85 86 87 89 91 92 93 96 98 99 102 103 104 105 107 108 110 111 114 115 118 119 126 129 130 131 135 146 147 148 149 154 156 **P**6 **S** Carilion Clinic, Roanoke, VA
Primary Contact: William Flattery, Vice President and Administrator Western Division
CFO: Rob Vaughan, Chief Financial Officer
CMO: Dennis Means, M.D., Vice President Medical Affairs
CIO: Daniel Borchi, Chief Information Officer
CHR: Patti Jurkus, Director Human Resources
Web address: www.carilionclinic.org/Carilion/cnrv
**Control:** Other not–for–profit (including NFP Corporation) **Service:** General medical and surgical

**Staffed Beds:** 95 **Admissions:** 8491 **Census:** 94 **Outpatient Visits:** 107748 **Births:** 949 **Total Expense ($000):** 192771 **Payroll Expense ($000):** 67664 **Personnel:** 1012

**CARILION RADFORD COMM HOSP** See Carilion New River Valley Medical Center

**CARILION SAINT ALBANS HOSPITAL** See Carilion Clinic Saint Albans Hospital

## CLINTWOOD—Dickenson County

☐ **DICKENSON COMMUNITY HOSPITAL (491303)**, 312 Hospital Drive, Zip 24228, Mailing Address: P.O. Box 1440, Zip 24228–1440; tel. 276/926–0300, (Nonreporting) **A**1 10 18 **F**3 29 40 44 64 77 93 97 98 103 104 107 119 130 148 153 154 156 **S** Ballad Health, Johnson City, TN
Primary Contact: Mark T. Leonard, Chief Executive Officer
CFO: Kevin Morrison, Chief Financial Officer
CMO: Erin Mullins, D.O., Chief Medical Staff
CHR: Valeri J Colyer, Director Human Resources
CNO: Terri Roop, Director Patient Care Services
Web address: www.msha.com/dch
**Control:** Other not–for–profit (including NFP Corporation) **Service:** General medical and surgical

**Staffed Beds:** 11 **Admissions:** 260 **Census:** 7 **Outpatient Visits:** 26032 **Births:** 0 **Total Expense ($000):** 8929 **Payroll Expense ($000):** 3498 **Personnel:** 139

## CULPEPER—Culpeper County

⊞ **NOVANT HEALTH UVA HEALTH SYSTEM CULPEPER MEDICAL CENTER (490019)**, 501 Sunset Lane, Zip 22701–3917, Mailing Address: P.O. Box 592, Zip 22701–0500; tel. 540/829–4100, (Nonreporting) **A**1 3 5 10 **S** Novant Health, Winston Salem, NC
Primary Contact: Jeff Hetmanski, President and Chief Operating Officer
CFO: David J Plaviak, Interim Chief Financial Officer
CMO: Morton Chiles, M.D., Chief Medical Officer
CIO: Steven Speelman, Director Information Systems
CHR: Susan Edwards, Vice President Human Resources
Web address: www.culpeperhealth.org
**Control:** Other not–for–profit (including NFP Corporation) **Service:** General medical and surgical

**Staffed Beds:** 68

**UVA CULPEPER HOSPITAL** See Novant Health UVA Health System Culpeper Medical Center

*Many Facility Codes have changed. Please refer to the AHA Guide Code Chart.*

VA

## DANVILLE—Danville City County

**DANVILLE REGIONAL MEDICAL CENTER** See Sovah Health-Danville

☐ **SOUTHERN VIRGINIA MENTAL HEALTH INSTITUTE (494017)**, 382 Taylor Drive, Zip 24541–4023; tel. 434/799–6220, (Nonreporting) **A**1 10 **S** Virginia Department of Mental Health, Richmond, VA
Primary Contact: William Cook, Director
CFO: Wayne Peters, Administrator
CMO: Pravin Patel, M.D., Acting President and Chief Executive Officer
CIO: Larry Hays, Director Information Technology
CHR: Stephanie Haywood, Director Human Resources
CNO: Kathy M Dodd, Director of Nursing
Web address: www.svmhi.dbhds.virginia.gov
**Control**: State, Government, Nonfederal **Service**: Psychiatric

**Staffed Beds:** 72

☒ **SOVAH HEALTH-DANVILLE (490075)**, 142 South Main Street, Zip 24541–2922; tel. 434/799–2100, (Nonreporting) **A**1 2 3 5 10 13 **S** LifePoint Health, Brentwood, TN
Primary Contact: Alan Larson, Chief Executive Officer
CFO: Mark T Anderson, Chief Financial Officer
CMO: James F Starling, M.D., Chief Medical Officer
CIO: David Cartwright, Director Management Information Systems
CNO: Aundrea Mills, R.N., Chief Nursing Officer
Web address: www.danvilleregional.com/
**Control**: Other not-for-profit (including NFP Corporation) **Service**: General medical and surgical

**Staffed Beds:** 250

## DULLES—Loudoun County

☒ **STONESPRINGS HOSPITAL CENTER (490145)**, 24440 Stone Spring Boulevard, Zip 20166–2247; tel. 571/349–4000, (Nonreporting) **A**1 10 **S** HCA Healthcare, Nashville, TN
Primary Contact: Matt Mathias, Chief Executive Officer
COO: Benjamin Brown, Chief Operating Officer
CFO: Candi Christopher, CPA, Chief Financial Officer
CMO: Walter R Zolkiwsky, M.D., Chief Medical Officer
CHR: Tiffani Smith, Chief Human Resources Officer
CNO: Michelle L. Epps, MSN, R.N., Chief Nursing Officer
Web address: www.stonespringshospital.com
**Control**: Corporation, Investor–owned (for–profit) **Service**: General medical and surgical

**Staffed Beds:** 124

## EMPORIA—Emporia City County

**GREENSVILLE MEMORIAL HOSPITAL** See Southern Virginia Regional Medical Center

☒ **SOUTHERN VIRGINIA REGIONAL MEDICAL CENTER (490097)**, 727 North Main Street, Zip 23847–1274; tel. 434/348–4400, (Nonreporting) **A**1 10 **S** Bon Secours Mercy Health, Marriottsville, MD
Primary Contact: Wilson A. Thomas, Chief Executive Officer
CFO: Jim Porter, Chief Financial Officer
CMO: Fitzgerald Marcelin, M.D., Chief of Staff
CIO: Larry Gold, Vice President, Information Services
CHR: Becky Parrish, Director Human Resources
Web address: www.svrmc.com
**Control**: Corporation, Investor–owned (for–profit) **Service**: General medical and surgical

**Staffed Beds:** 80

## FAIRFAX—Fairfax County

**FAIR OAKS HOSPITAL** See Inova Fair Oaks Hospital

☒ **INOVA FAIR OAKS HOSPITAL (490101)**, 3600 Joseph Siewick Drive, Zip 22033–1798; tel. 703/391–3600, (Nonreporting) **A**1 2 3 5 10 **F**3 11 12 13 14 15 18 28 29 30 31 34 35 37 38 39 40 41 44 45 47 48 49 50 51 54 55 57 58 59 60 61 64 65 68 70 72 74 75 76 77 78 79 80 81 82 84 85 86 87 89 91 92 93 100 101 102 107 108 110 111 114 115 118 119 120 121 123 124 126 129 130 131 132 135 145 146 147 148 149 154 156 157 **P**6 **S** Inova Health System, Falls Church, VA
Primary Contact: Donald Brideau, M.D., Chief Executive Officer
CFO: Jerry Seager, Assistant Vice President and Chief Financial Officer
CMO: G Michael Lynch, M.D., Chief Medical Officer
CIO: Marshall Ruffin, Chief Information Officer
CHR: Jeanne Robinson, Director Human Resources
Web address: www.inova.org
**Control**: Other not-for-profit (including NFP Corporation) **Service**: General medical and surgical

**Staffed Beds:** 201 **Admissions:** 11356 **Census:** 111 **Outpatient Visits:** 94130 **Births:** 3100 **Total Expense ($000):** 268652 **Payroll Expense ($000):** 81808 **Personnel:** 1119

## FALLS CHURCH—Fairfax County

☒ **DOMINION HOSPITAL (494023)**, 2960 Sleepy Hollow Road, Zip 22044–2030; tel. 703/536–2000, (Nonreporting) **A**1 3 10 **S** HCA Healthcare, Nashville, TN
Primary Contact: Lee Higginbotham, Chief Executive Officer
CFO: Edward R Stojakovich, Chief Financial Officer
CMO: Gary Litovitz, M.D., Medical Director
CIO: Leslie Gilliam, Director Health Information Management
CHR: Lesley Channell, Vice President Human Resources
Web address: www.dominionhospital.com
**Control**: Corporation, Investor–owned (for–profit) **Service**: Psychiatric

**Staffed Beds:** 116

**FAIRFAX HOSPITAL** See Inova Fairfax Hospital

**HCA DOMINION HOSPITAL** See Dominion Hospital

☒ **INOVA FAIRFAX HOSPITAL (490063)**, 3300 Gallows Road, Zip 22042–3300; tel. 703/776–4001, (Includes INOVA FAIRFAX HOSPITAL FOR CHILDREN, Mailing address: 3300 Gallows Road, Falls Church, Virginia, Zip 22042–3307; tel. 703/776–4002), (Nonreporting) **A**1 2 3 5 8 10 **F**3 4 5 8 9 11 13 14 15 17 18 19 20 21 22 23 24 25 26 27 28 29 30 31 32 34 35 36 37 38 39 40 41 42 43 44 45 46 47 48 49 50 51 53 54 55 56 57 58 59 60 61 63 64 65 68 70 72 74 75 76 77 78 79 80 81 82 83 84 85 86 87 88 89 90 91 92 93 98 100 101 102 104 105 107 108 109 110 111 114 115 118 119 120 121 123 124 126 129 130 131 132 135 137 138 140 141 142 145 146 147 148 149 152 154 156 157 **P**6 **S** Inova Health System, Falls Church, VA
Primary Contact: Susan T. Carroll, FACHE, Acting President
CFO: Ronald Ewald, Chief Financial Officer
CMO: Joseph Hallal, M.D., Chief Medical Officer
CIO: Geoffrey Brown, Vice President Information Systems
CHR: Ken Hull, Director Human Resources
Web address: www.inova.org
**Control**: Other not-for-profit (including NFP Corporation) **Service**: General medical and surgical

**Staffed Beds:** 1056 **Admissions:** 52191 **Census:** 747 **Outpatient Visits:** 455401 **Births:** 10364 **Total Expense ($000):** 334923 **Payroll Expense ($000):** 115100 **Personnel:** 8263

☐ **NORTHERN VIRGINIA MENTAL HEALTH INSTITUTE (494010)**, 3302 Gallows Road, Zip 22042–3398; tel. 703/207–7100, (Nonreporting) **A**1 3 5 10 **S** Virginia Department of Mental Health, Richmond, VA
Primary Contact: Tammy Peacock, Ph.D., Facility Director
CFO: John Poffenbarger, Director Fiscal Services
CMO: R Maximilien del Rio, M.D., Medical Director
CHR: Cynthia Lott, Director Human Resources
Web address: www.nvmhi.dbhds.virginia.gov
**Control**: State, Government, Nonfederal **Service**: Psychiatric

**Staffed Beds:** 134

VA

**VA**

---

### FARMVILLE—Prince Edward County

✠ **CENTRA SOUTHSIDE COMMUNITY HOSPITAL (490090)**, 800 Oak Street, Zip 23901–1199; tel. 434/392–8811, (Nonreporting) **A**1 5 10 20 **F**3 11 13 15 18 20 22 26 28 29 30 31 34 35 40 44 45 49 50 57 59 62 63 64 70 74 75 76 77 78 79 81 82 84 85 86 87 89 107 108 110 111 115 118 119 129 130 132 133 146 147 148 154 **S** Centra Health, Inc., Lynchburg, VA
Primary Contact: Thomas Angelo, Chief Executive Officer
Web address: www.sch.centrahealth.com/
**Control:** Other not–for–profit (including NFP Corporation) **Service:** General medical and surgical

**Staffed Beds: 86 Admissions:** 4141 **Census:** 39 **Outpatient Visits:** 87254 **Births:** 299 **Total Expense ($000):** 80890 **Payroll Expense ($000):** 27399 **Personnel:** 417

**SOUTHSIDE COMMUNITY HOSPITAL** See Centra Southside Community Hospital

---

### FISHERSVILLE—Augusta County

✠ ⋔ **AUGUSTA HEALTH (490018)**, 78 Medical Center Drive, Zip 22939–2332, Mailing Address: P.O. Box 1000, Zip 22939–1000; tel. 540/932–4000, (Nonreporting) **A**1 2 3 5 10 21 **F**3 5 7 11 13 15 18 20 22 26 28 29 30 31 32 34 35 38 40 41 44 45 46 48 50 51 53 54 55 57 58 59 62 63 64 65 66 68 70 74 75 76 77 78 79 81 82 83 84 85 86 87 89 90 92 93 96 97 98 100 101 102 103 104 107 108 110 111 113 114 115 118 119 120 121 123 124 126 128 129 130 131 132 143 144 146 148 149 153 154 156 157 **P**8
Primary Contact: Mary N. Mannix, FACHE, President and Chief Executive Officer
CMO: Richard Embrey, M.D., Chief Medical Officer
CIO: Michael Canfield, Chief Information Officer
CHR: Sue Krzastek, Vice President Human Resources
Web address: www.augustahealth.com
**Control:** Other not–for–profit (including NFP Corporation) **Service:** General medical and surgical

**Staffed Beds:** 209 **Admissions:** 11472 **Census:** 127 **Outpatient Visits:** 904362 **Births:** 1021 **Total Expense ($000):** 360018 **Payroll Expense ($000):** 155361 **Personnel:** 2074

⋔ **AUGUSTA MEDICAL CENTER** See Augusta Health

---

### FORT BELVOIR—Fairfax County

**DEWITT ARMY COMMUNITY HOSPITAL** See Fort Belvoir Community Hospital

✠ **FORT BELVOIR COMMUNITY HOSPITAL**, 9300 Dewitt Loop, Zip 22060–5285; tel. 571/231–3224, (Nonreporting) **A**1 3 5 **S** Department of the Army, Office of the Surgeon General, Falls Church, VA
Primary Contact: Colonel Jason S. Wieman, Director
CMO: Lieutenant Colonel Mark D Harris, Deputy Commander Clinical Services
CIO: Terrance Branch, Chief Information Management
Web address: www.fbch.capmed.mil/SitePages/Home.aspx
**Service:** General medical and surgical

**Staffed Beds:** 46

---

### FRANKLIN—Franklin City County

✠ **SOUTHAMPTON MEMORIAL HOSPITAL (490092)**, 100 Fairview Drive, Zip 23851–1238, Mailing Address: P.O. Box 817, Zip 23851–0817; tel. 757/569–6100, (Nonreporting) **A**1 10 20 **S** Bon Secours Mercy Health, Marriottsville, MD
Primary Contact: Kimberly W. Marks, Chief Executive Officer
CFO: Steve Ramey, Chief Financial Officer
CMO: Donald Bowling, M.D., Chief Medical Staff
CIO: Kristie Howell, System Information Technology Director
CHR: Loretha Ricks, Human Resources Supervisor
CNO: Laurie Ross, Chief Nursing Officer
Web address: www.smhfranklin.com
**Control:** Corporation, Investor–owned (for–profit) **Service:** General medical and surgical

**Staffed Beds:** 72

---

### FREDERICKSBURG—Fredericksburg City County

✠ **ENCOMPASS HEALTH REHABILITATION HOSPITAL OF FREDERICKSBURG (493032)**, 300 Park Hill Drive, Zip 22401–3387; tel. 540/368–7300, (Nonreporting) **A**1 10 **S** Encompass Health Corporation, Birmingham, AL
Primary Contact: David Cashwell, Chief Executive Officer
Web address: www.fredericksburgrehabhospital.com
**Control:** Corporation, Investor–owned (for–profit) **Service:** Rehabilitation

**Staffed Beds:** 40

**HEALTHSOUTH REHABILITATION HOSPITAL OF FREDERICKSBURG** See Encompass Health Rehabilitation Hospital of Fredericksburg

✠ **MARY WASHINGTON HOSPITAL (490022)**, 1001 Sam Perry Boulevard, Zip 22401–3354; tel. 540/741–1100, (Includes SNOWDEN AT FREDERICKSBURG, Mailing address: 1200 Sam Perry Boulevard, Fredericksburg, Virginia, Zip 22401–4456; tel. 540/741–3900; Charles Scercy, Corporate Director), (Nonreporting) **A**1 2 3 5 10 **F**3 5 13 18 22 24 26 28 29 30 31 34 35 36 40 42 43 44 45 46 47 48 49 50 54 55 57 58 59 62 64 70 72 74 75 76 77 78 79 81 83 84 85 86 87 89 92 93 96 98 99 100 101 102 104 105 107 108 111 114 115 118 119 120 121 124 126 129 130 131 132 135 146 147 148 152 153 154 **P**5 8 **S** Mary Washington Healthcare, Fredericksburg, VA
Primary Contact: Michael P. McDermott, M.D., President and Chief Executive Officer
COO: Thomas Gettinger, Executive Vice President and Chief Operating Officer
CFO: Sean Barden, Executive Vice President and Chief Financial Officer
CMO: Rebecca Bigoney, Executive Vice President and Chief Medical Officer
CIO: Justin K. Box, Senior Vice President & Chief Information Officer
CHR: Kathryn S Wall, Executive Vice President, Human Resources and Organizational Development
CNO: Eileen L Dohmann, R.N., Senior Vice President and Chief Nursing Officer
Web address: www.marywashingtonhealthcare.com
**Control:** Other not–for–profit (including NFP Corporation) **Service:** General medical and surgical

**Staffed Beds:** 451 **Admissions:** 25010 **Census:** 304 **Outpatient Visits:** 354159 **Births:** 2297 **Total Expense ($000):** 469945 **Payroll Expense ($000):** 129281 **Personnel:** 1967

---

### FREDERICKSBURG—Spotsylvania County

✠ **SPOTSYLVANIA REGIONAL MEDICAL CENTER (490141)**, 4600 Spotsylvania Parkway, Zip 22408–7762; tel. 540/498–4000, (Nonreporting) **A**1 5 10 **S** HCA Healthcare, Nashville, TN
Primary Contact: David McKnight, CPA, Chief Executive Officer
COO: Roberta Tinch, Chief Operations Officer
Web address: www.spotsrmc.com
**Control:** Corporation, Investor–owned (for–profit) **Service:** General medical and surgical

**Staffed Beds:** 137

---

### FRONT ROYAL—Warren County

✠ **VALLEY HEALTH - WARREN MEMORIAL HOSPITAL (490033)**, 1000 North Shenandoah Avenue, Zip 22630–3598; tel. 540/636–0300, (Total facility includes 120 beds in nursing home–type unit) (Nonreporting) **A**1 3 5 10 **F**3 11 13 15 18 20 22 28 29 30 34 35 36 40 50 53 54 56 57 59 64 65 67 70 75 77 79 81 82 85 86 87 93 96 107 108 111 114 118 119 128 130 132 135 144 146 147 148 154 156 **S** Valley Health System, Winchester, VA
Primary Contact: Floyd Heater, President
CFO: Phillip Graybeal, CPA, Chief Financial Officer
CMO: Robert Meltvedt, M.D., JrVice President Medical Affairs
CNO: Terri Mayes, Vice President and Chief Nursing Officer
Web address: www.valleyhealthlink.com/WMH
**Control:** Other not–for–profit (including NFP Corporation) **Service:** General medical and surgical

**Staffed Beds:** 180 **Admissions:** 2257 **Census:** 132 **Outpatient Visits:** 74098 **Births:** 0 **Total Expense ($000):** 74276 **Payroll Expense ($000):** 24200 **Personnel:** 435

**WARREN MEMORIAL HOSPITAL** See Valley Health - Warren Memorial Hospital

---

*Many Facility Codes have changed. Please refer to the AHA Guide Code Chart.*

## GALAX—Galax City County

⊠ **TWIN COUNTY REGIONAL HEALTHCARE (490115)**, 200 Hospital Drive, Zip 24333–2227; tel. 276/236–8181, (Nonreporting) **A**1 5 10 20 **F**3 13 14 15 28 29 30 32 34 35 38 40 45 50 51 57 64 65 68 70 75 76 77 79 81 82 85 87 89 93 98 100 101 102 104 107 108 110 111 116 117 119 129 132 144 146 147 **S** Duke LifePoint Healthcare, Brentwood, TN
Primary Contact: Dale Alward, Chief Executive Officer
CFO: Marita Caldwell, Chief Financial Officer
CHR: Kristal Herrington, Senior Director, Human Resources
CNO: Agnes A Smith, MSN, R.N., Chief Nursing Officer
Web address: www.tcrh.org
**Control**: Partnership, Investor–owned (for–profit) **Service**: General medical and surgical

**Staffed Beds:** 66 **Admissions:** 3182 **Census:** 29 **Outpatient Visits:** 55447 **Births:** 240 **Total Expense ($000):** 44019 **Payroll Expense ($000):** 18053 **Personnel:** 394

**TWIN COUNTY REGIONAL HOSPITAL** See Twin County Regional Healthcare

## GLOUCESTER—Gloucester County

⇧ **RIVERSIDE MIDDLE PENINSULA HSP** See Riverside Walter Reed Hospital

⇧ **RIVERSIDE WALTER REED HOSPITAL (490130)**, 7519 Hospital Drive, Zip 23061–4178, Mailing Address: P.O. Box 1130, Zip 23061–1130; tel. 804/693–8800, (Nonreporting) **A**2 10 21 **F**3 15 28 29 34 35 40 44 45 50 51 57 59 60 64 70 71 75 77 78 79 81 85 86 87 92 93 96 107 108 110 111 114 115 116 118 119 120 121 123 130 132 146 147 148 149 **P**6 **S** Riverside Health System, Newport News, VA
Primary Contact: Esther Muscari. Desimini, Interim Administrator
CHR: Tabetha Holt, Director of Human Resources
Web address: www.riversideonline.com
**Control**: Other not–for–profit (including NFP Corporation) **Service**: General medical and surgical

**Staffed Beds:** 27 **Admissions:** 2710 **Census:** 27 **Outpatient Visits:** 95351 **Births:** 0 **Total Expense ($000):** 60986 **Payroll Expense ($000):** 21711 **Personnel:** 317

## GRUNDY—Buchanan County

⊠ **BUCHANAN GENERAL HOSPITAL (490127)**, 1535 Slate Creek Road, Zip 24614–6974; tel. 276/935–1000, (Nonreporting) **A**1 10 20 **F**3 15 18 28 29 30 34 35 40 41 45 57 59 62 64 70 81 85 87 89 93 107 108 110 115 119 129 130 132 135 146 148
Primary Contact: Robert D. Ruchti, Chief Executive Officer
COO: Scott M Pittman, Chief Operating Officer
CFO: Kim Boyd, Chief Financial Officer
CIO: Rita Ramey, Director Information Systems
CHR: Wanda B. Stiltner, Director Human Resources
CNO: Patty Dorton, Director of Nursing
Web address: www.bgh.org
**Control**: Other not–for–profit (including NFP Corporation) **Service**: General medical and surgical

**Staffed Beds:** 49 **Admissions:** 1067 **Census:** 14 **Outpatient Visits:** 41957 **Births:** 0 **Total Expense ($000):** 23391 **Payroll Expense ($000):** 8818 **Personnel:** 205

## HAMPTON—Hampton City County

⊠ **HAMPTON VETERANS AFFAIRS MEDICAL CENTER**, 100 Emancipation Drive, Zip 23667–0001; tel. 757/722–9961, (Nonreporting) **A**1 3 5 **S** Department of Veterans Affairs, Washington, DC
Primary Contact: Taquisa Simmons, Interim Director
COO: Lorraine B Price, Associate Director
CFO: Terry Grew, Chief Business Office
CMO: Val Gibberman, M.D., Acting Chief of Staff
CIO: Cary Parks, Chief Information Resource Management
Web address: www.hampton.va.gov/
**Control**: Veterans Affairs, Government, federal **Service**: General medical and surgical

**Staffed Beds:** 451

**PENINSULA BEHAVIORAL CENTER** See Riverside Behavioral Health Center

★ ⇧ **SENTARA CAREPLEX HOSPITAL (490093)**, 3000 Coliseum Drive, Zip 23666–5963; tel. 757/736–1000, (Nonreporting) **A**2 3 5 10 21 **F**3 8 11 12 13 15 18 20 22 26 28 29 30 31 33 34 35 36 37 38 39 40 41 42 44 45 46 47 48 49 50 51 54 56 57 58 59 60 61 63 64 68 70 71 74 75 76 77 78 79 80 81 82 84 85 86 87 91 92 93 96 100 107 110 111 113 117 118 119 120 126 129 130 131 132 134 135 141 146 147 148 149 150 154 156 **S** Sentara Healthcare, Norfolk, VA
Primary Contact: Kirkpatrick Conley, President
COO: Rita A. Bunch, M.P.H., FACHE, Vice President of Operations
CFO: Cheryl Larner, Chief Financial Officer
CMO: Arthur Greene, M.D., Vice President Medical Affairs
CIO: Thomas Ewing, Director Information Technology
CHR: David Kidd, Manager Human Resources
Web address: www.sentara.com
**Control**: Other not–for–profit (including NFP Corporation) **Service**: General medical and surgical

**Staffed Beds:** 169 **Admissions:** 8902 **Census:** 107 **Outpatient Visits:** 426894 **Births:** 472 **Total Expense ($000):** 226562 **Payroll Expense ($000):** 86706 **Personnel:** 1355

⇧ **SENTARA HAMPTON GEN HOSPITAL** See Sentara Careplex Hospital

**U S AIR FORCE REGIONAL HOSP** See U.S. Air Force Hospital

⊠ **U. S. AIR FORCE HOSPITAL**, 77 Nealy Avenue, Zip 23665–2040; tel. 757/764–6969, (Nonreporting) **A**1 3 **S** Department of the Air Force, Washington, DC
Primary Contact: Colonel Susan Pietrykowski, Commander
COO: ColonelMichael Dietz, Administrator
CFO: MajorSteven Dadd, Flight Commander Resource Management
CMO: ColonelPaul Gourley, M.D., Chief Hospital Services
CIO: MajorMerlinda Vergonio, Chief Information Management and Technology
CHR: MajorSteven Dadd, Flight Commander Resource Management
CNO: ColonelMarlene Kerchenski, Chief Nurse
Web address: www.jble.af.mil
**Service**: General medical and surgical

**Staffed Beds:** 60

**VETERANS AFFAIRS MEDICAL CENTER** See Hampton Veterans Affairs Medical Center

## HARRISONBURG—Harrisonburg City County

⇧ **ROCKINGHAM MEMORIAL HOSPITAL** See Sentara Rmh Medical Center

★ ⇧ **SENTARA RMH MEDICAL CENTER (490004)**, 2010 Health Campus Drive, Zip 22801–3293; tel. 540/689–1000, (Nonreporting) **A**2 5 10 21 **F**3 5 11 12 13 15 17 18 20 22 24 26 28 29 30 31 32 34 35 36 40 41 44 45 46 47 48 49 50 53 54 55 56 57 58 59 60 61 64 65 68 70 71 73 74 75 76 77 78 79 81 82 84 85 86 87 89 91 92 93 97 98 100 102 104 105 107 108 110 111 114 115 116 117 118 119 120 121 129 130 131 132 135 141 145 146 147 148 149 152 153 154 156 **P**6 7 8 **S** Sentara Healthcare, Norfolk, VA
Primary Contact: Douglas J. Moyer, President
COO: Richard L Haushalter, Senior Vice President Operations and Chief Operating Officer
CFO: Stewart R Nelson, Vice President and Chief Financial Officer
CMO: Susan McDonald, Vice President, Medical Affairs
CNO: Donna S Hahn, R.N., Vice President Acute Care and Chief Nurse Executive
Web address: www.rmhonline.com
**Control**: Other not–for–profit (including NFP Corporation) **Service**: General medical and surgical

**Staffed Beds:** 244 **Admissions:** 13240 **Census:** 139 **Outpatient Visits:** 715244 **Births:** 1829 **Total Expense ($000):** 357409 **Payroll Expense ($000):** 120583 **Personnel:** 2205

**VA**

---

**Hospital, Medicare Provider Number, Address, Telephone, Approval, Facility, and Physician Codes, Health Care System**

★ American Hospital Association (AHA) membership   ○ Healthcare Facilities Accreditation Program   ⇧ Center for Improvement in Healthcare Quality Accreditation
☐ The Joint Commission accreditation   ◇ DNV Healthcare Inc. accreditation   △ Commission on Accreditation of Rehabilitation Facilities (CARF) accreditation

## HAYMARKET—Prince William County

**NOVANT HEALTH HAYMARKET MEDICAL CENTER** See Novant Health UVA Health System Haymarket Medical Center

☒ **NOVANT HEALTH UVA HEALTH SYSTEM HAYMARKET MEDICAL CENTER (490144)**, 15225 Heathcote Boulevard, Zip 20155–4023, Mailing Address: 14535 John Marshall Hwy, Gainesville, Zip 20155–4023; tel. 571/284–1000, (Nonreporting) **A**1 2 10 **S** Novant Health, Winston Salem, NC
Primary Contact: Stephen Smith, President and Chief Operating Officer
CFO: Charles Coder, Vice President
CMO: Doug Wall, M.D., Vice President of Medical Affairs
CIO: David B Garrett, Senior Vice President and Chief Information Officer
CHR: Tracy Bowers, Vice President Human Resources and Administrative Services
CNO: Maggie C Conklin, M.P.H., Interim Chief Nursing Officer
Web address: www.novanthealth.org
**Control:** Other not–for–profit (including NFP Corporation) **Service:** General medical and surgical

**Staffed Beds:** 18

## HOPEWELL—Hopewell City County

**COLUMBIA JOHN RANDOLPH MED CTR** See John Randolph Medical Center

☒ **JOHN RANDOLPH MEDICAL CENTER (490020)**, 411 West Randolph Road, Zip 23860–2938; tel. 804/541–1600, (Nonreporting) **A**1 2 5 10 **S** HCA Healthcare, Nashville, TN
Primary Contact: Joseph Mazzo, Chief Executive Officer
CFO: Jennifer Honaker, Chief Financial Officer
CHR: MaDena DuChemin, Assistant Administrator Human Resources
Web address: www.johnrandolphmed.com
**Control:** Corporation, Investor–owned (for–profit) **Service:** General medical and surgical

**Staffed Beds:** 147

## HOT SPRINGS—Bath County

☒ **BATH COMMUNITY HOSPITAL (491300)**, 106 Park Drive, Zip 24445–2921, Mailing Address: P.O. Box Z, Zip 24445–0750; tel. 540/839–7000, (Nonreporting) **A**1 10 18
Primary Contact: Kathy Landreth, Chief Executive Officer
COO: Mitzi Grey, Chief Operating Officer
CMO: James Redington, M.D., Chief of Staff
CIO: Tracy Bartley, Manager Information Technology
CHR: Patricia Foutz, Director Human Resources
CNO: Kyna Moore, R.N., Director of Nursing
Web address: www.https://bathhospital.org
**Control:** Other not–for–profit (including NFP Corporation) **Service:** General medical and surgical

**Staffed Beds:** 25

**BATH COUNTY COMMUNITY HOSPITAL** See Bath Community Hospital

## KILMARNOCK—Lancaster County

☐ **RAPPAHANNOCK GENERAL HOSPITAL (491308)**, 101 Harris Drive, Zip 22482–3880, Mailing Address: P.O. Box 1449, Zip 22482–1449; tel. 804/435–8000, (Nonreporting) **A**1 10 18 **S** Bon Secours Mercy Health, Marriottsville, MD
Primary Contact: Chris Accashian, Chief Executive Officer
Web address: www.https://bonsecours.com/richmond/find-a-facility/rappahannock-general-hospital
**Control:** Other not–for–profit (including NFP Corporation) **Service:** General medical and surgical

**Staffed Beds:** 35

## LEBANON—Russell County

**RUSSELL CNTY MEDICAL CENTER** See Russell County Medical Center

☐ **RUSSELL COUNTY MEDICAL CENTER (490002)**, 58 Carroll Street, Zip 24266, Mailing Address: P.O. Box 3600, Zip 24266–0200; tel. 276/883–8000, (Nonreporting) **A**1 5 10 **F**3 11 15 28 29 30 31 34 35 40 44 45 54 56 57 59 63 64 65 68 70 75 77 78 79 81 85 93 97 98 100 101 102 104 107 108 110 111 114 118 119 127 129 130 133 135 146 147 148 154 **S** Ballad Health, Johnson City, TN
Primary Contact: Stephen K. Givens, Assistant Vice President and Administrator
CMO: Brian Condit, M.D., Vice President Chief Medical Officer, Virginia Operations Medical Staff Services
CHR: Beth Hill, Director Human Resources
Web address: www.mountainstateshealth.com/rcmc
**Control:** Other not–for–profit (including NFP Corporation) **Service:** General medical and surgical

**Staffed Beds:** 78 **Admissions:** 1712 **Census:** 21 **Outpatient Visits:** 30977 **Births:** 0 **Total Expense ($000):** 26000 **Payroll Expense ($000):** 8089 **Personnel:** 467

## LEESBURG—Loudoun County

☒ **INOVA LOUDOUN HOSPITAL (490043)**, 44045 Riverside Parkway, Zip 20176–5101, Mailing Address: P.O. Box 6000, Zip 20177–0600; tel. 703/858–6000, (Total facility includes 100 beds in nursing home–type unit) (Nonreporting) **A**1 2 5 10 **F**3 5 11 13 14 15 18 20 22 26 28 29 30 31 34 35 37 38 39 40 41 42 43 44 45 48 49 50 54 55 56 57 58 59 60 61 63 64 65 66 67 68 70 71 72 74 75 76 77 78 79 80 81 82 84 85 86 87 89 91 92 93 94 96 98 100 101 102 103 104 105 107 108 110 111 114 115 118 119 120 121 123 126 128 130 131 132 135 145 146 147 148 149 154 156 157 **P**6 **S** Inova Health System, Falls Church, VA
Primary Contact: Deborah Addo, Chief Executive Officer
CFO: William Bane, Chief Financial Officer
CMO: Christopher Chiantella, M.D., Chief Medical Officer
CHR: Sarah Pavik, Director Human Resources and Guest Services
CNO: Elizabeth Dugan, Ph.D., R.N., MSN, Chief Nursing Officer
Web address: www.inova.org
**Control:** Other not–for–profit (including NFP Corporation) **Service:** General medical and surgical

**Staffed Beds:** 288 **Admissions:** 14011 **Census:** 237 **Outpatient Visits:** 157142 **Births:** 2381 **Total Expense ($000):** 325061 **Payroll Expense ($000):** 107416 **Personnel:** 1487

**LOUDOUN HOSPITAL CENTER** See Inova Loudoun Hospital

## LEXINGTON—Lexington City County

☒ **CARILION STONEWALL JACKSON HOSPITAL (491304)**, 1 Health Circle, Zip 24450–2492; tel. 540/458–3300, (Nonreporting) **A**1 3 10 18 **F**3 8 11 15 18 28 29 34 35 40 45 50 53 56 57 59 65 68 70 75 77 79 81 85 87 91 93 97 107 108 110 111 115 119 127 129 130 131 132 133 135 146 148 149 **P**6 **S** Carilion Clinic, Roanoke, VA
Primary Contact: Greg T. Madsen, Chief Executive Officer
CMO: Lyle McClung, M.D., Chief of Staff
Web address: www.carilionclinic.org
**Control:** Other not–for–profit (including NFP Corporation) **Service:** General medical and surgical

**Staffed Beds:** 14 **Admissions:** 1191 **Census:** 12 **Outpatient Visits:** 32563 **Births:** 3 **Total Expense ($000):** 37459 **Payroll Expense ($000):** 13898 **Personnel:** 211

**STONEWALL JACKSON HOSPITAL** See Carilion Stonewall Jackson Hospital

**VA**

## LOW MOOR—Alleghany County

**ALLEGHANY REGIONAL HOSPITAL** See Lewisgale Hospital Alleghany

☒ **LEWISGALE HOSPITAL ALLEGHANY (490126)**, One ARH Lane, Zip 24457, Mailing Address: P.O. Box 7, Zip 24457–0007; tel. 540/862–6011, (Nonreporting) **A**1 5 10 20 **S** HCA Healthcare, Nashville, TN
Primary Contact: William Windham, Chief Executive Officer
CMO: Michele Ballou, M.D., Chief Medical Staff
CIO: Jeffrey Steelman, Director Information Systems
CHR: Bernard M Campbell, Administrator Human Resources
CNO: Robin Broughman, R.N., Ph.D., Chief Nursing Officer
Web address: www.alleghanyregional.com
**Control**: Corporation, Investor–owned (for–profit) **Service**: General medical and surgical

| Staffed Beds: 205 |

## LURAY—Page County

**PAGE MEMORIAL HOSPITAL** See Valley Health - Page Memorial Hospital

☒ **VALLEY HEALTH - PAGE MEMORIAL HOSPITAL (491307)**, 200 Memorial Drive, Zip 22835–1005; tel. 540/743–4561, (Nonreporting) **A**1 10 18 **F**3 7 8 11 15 28 29 30 34 35 40 53 56 57 59 60 64 66 68 69 74 75 77 79 81 85 93 107 108 110 111 114 119 127 129 130 133 135 143 146 148 154 155 156 **P**2 **S** Valley Health System, Winchester, VA
Primary Contact: N. Travis. Clark, President
CFO: Phillip Graybeal, CPA, Chief Financial Officer
Web address: www.valleyhealthlink.com/page
**Control**: Other not–for–profit (including NFP Corporation) **Service**: General medical and surgical

| Staffed Beds: 25 Admissions: 469 Census: 9 Outpatient Visits: 85587 Births: 0 Total Expense ($000): 34758 Payroll Expense ($000): 15109 Personnel: 183 |

## LYNCHBURG—Lynchburg City County

**CENTER FOR RESTORATIVE CARE AND REHABILITATION** See Centra Specialty Hospital

**CENTRA HEALTH** See Centra Lynchburg General Hospital

☒ **CENTRA LYNCHBURG GENERAL HOSPITAL (490021)**, 1901 Tate Springs Road, Zip 24501–1109; tel. 434/200–4700, (Includes CENTRA VIRGINIA BAPTIST HOSPITAL, Mailing address: 3300 Rivermont Avenue, Lynchburg, Virginia, Zip 24503–2053; tel. 434/200–4000; LYNCHBURG GENERAL HOSPITAL, Mailing address: 1901 Tate Springs Road, Lynchburg, Virginia, Zip 24501–1167; tel. 434/200–3000) (Total facility includes 413 beds in nursing home–type unit) **A**1 2 3 5 10 **F**2 3 4 5 7 10 11 12 13 15 17 18 19 20 22 24 26 28 29 30 31 34 35 37 38 40 42 43 44 45 46 47 48 49 50 53 54 55 56 57 59 60 61 62 63 64 67 68 70 71 72 73 74 75 76 77 78 79 80 81 82 84 85 86 87 89 90 91 92 93 94 96 97 98 99 100 101 102 103 104 105 106 107 108 109 110 111 114 115 119 120 121 123 124 125 126 127 128 129 130 131 132 133 135 143 144 146 147 148 149 152 155 156 **P**7 **S** Centra Health, Inc., Lynchburg, VA
Primary Contact: Michael Elliott, Acting Chief Executive Officer
CFO: Lewis C Addison, Senior Vice President and Chief Financial Officer
CMO: Chalmers Nunn, M.D., Chief Medical Officer and Senior Vice President
CIO: Ben Clark, Vice President and Chief Information Officer
CHR: Jan Walker, Director Human Resources
Web address: www.centrahealth.com
**Control**: Other not–for–profit (including NFP Corporation) **Service**: General medical and surgical

| Staffed Beds: 1037 Admissions: 32252 Census: 759 Outpatient Visits: 201613 Births: 2670 Total Expense ($000): 849744 Payroll Expense ($000): 303363 Personnel: 5849 |

**CENTRA SPECIALTY HOSPITAL (492010)**, 3300 Rivermont Avenue, Zip 24503–2030; tel. 434/200–1799, (Nonreporting) **A**10
Primary Contact: Kay Bowling, Chief Executive Officer
**Control**: Partnership, Investor–owned (for–profit) **Service**: Acute long–term care hospital

| Staffed Beds: 26 |

## LYNCHBURG—Lynchburg (City) County

**VIRGINIA BAPTIST HOSPITAL** See Centra Virginia Baptist Hospital

## MADISON HEIGHTS—Amherst County

**CENTRAL VIRGINIA TRAINING CENTER (490108)**, 210 East Colony Road, Zip 24572–2005, Mailing Address: P.O. Box 1098, Lynchburg, Zip 24505–1098; tel. 434/947–6326, (Nonreporting) **S** Virginia Department of Mental Health, Richmond, VA
Primary Contact: David Cole, Assistant Director of Administration, Chief Financial Officer, Department of Behavioral Health and D
CFO: Charles Felmlee, Assistant Director Fiscal Services
CMO: Balraj Bawa, M.D., Assistant Director Medical Services
CHR: Burchkhard Blob, Manager Human Resources
Web address: www.cvtc.dmhmrsas.virginia.gov/
**Control**: State, Government, Nonfederal **Service**: Intellectual disabilities

| Staffed Beds: 1112 |

## MANASSAS—Manassas City County

**NOVANT HEALTH PRINCE WILLIAM MEDICAL CENTER** See Novant Health UVA Health System Prince William Medical Center

☒ **NOVANT HEALTH UVA HEALTH SYSTEM PRINCE WILLIAM MEDICAL CENTER (490045)**, 8700 Sudley Road, Zip 20110–4418, Mailing Address: P.O. Box 2610, Zip 20108–0867; tel. 703/369–8000, (Nonreporting) **A**1 2 3 5 10 **S** Novant Health, Winston Salem, NC
Primary Contact: Stephen Smith, President and Chief Operating Officer
CFO: Charles Coder, Vice President
CMO: Doug Wall, M.D., Vice President Medical Affairs
CIO: David B Garrett, Senior Vice President and Chief Information Officer
CHR: Tracy Bowers, Vice President Human Resources and Administrative Services
CNO: Maggie C Conklin, M.P.H., Interim Chief Nurse Officer
Web address: www.pwhs.org
**Control**: Other not–for–profit (including NFP Corporation) **Service**: General medical and surgical

| Staffed Beds: 87 |

## MARION—Smyth County

☐ **SMYTH COUNTY COMMUNITY HOSPITAL (490038)**, 245 Medical Park Drive, Zip 24354, Mailing Address: P.O. Box 880, Zip 24354–0880; tel. 276/378–1000, (Total facility includes 109 beds in nursing home–type unit) **A**1 5 10 **F**3 11 15 18 28 29 30 31 34 35 40 45 50 51 54 57 59 62 64 67 68 70 75 77 78 79 81 85 87 90 93 97 107 110 111 115 118 119 127 128 129 131 132 133 135 144 146 147 148 149 **S** Ballad Health, Johnson City, TN
Primary Contact: James E. Tyler, Chief Executive Officer
CHR: Sue Henderson, Human Resource Manager
CNO: Ethan Collins, R.N., Chief Nursing Officer
Web address: www.msha.com/scch
**Control**: Other not–for–profit (including NFP Corporation) **Service**: General medical and surgical

| Staffed Beds: 153 Admissions: 1400 Census: 105 Outpatient Visits: 60677 Births: 0 Total Expense ($000): 38178 Payroll Expense ($000): 11833 Personnel: 774 |

**SOUTHWESTERN STATE HOSPITAL** See Southwestern Virginia Mental Health Institute

☐ **SOUTHWESTERN VIRGINIA MENTAL HEALTH INSTITUTE (494029)**, 340 Bagley Circle, Zip 24354–3390; tel. 276/783–1200, (Nonreporting) **A**1 10 **S** Virginia Department of Mental Health, Richmond, VA
Primary Contact: Cynthia McClaskey, Ph.D., Director
CIO: Kim Ratliff, Director Health Information Management
Web address: www.swvmhi.dmhmrsas.virginia.gov/
**Control**: State, Government, Nonfederal **Service**: Psychiatric

| Staffed Beds: 166 |

**VA**

## MARTINSVILLE—Martinsville City County

**MEMORIAL HOSPITAL** See Sovah Health-Martinsville

★ **SOVAH HEALTH-MARTINSVILLE (490079)**, 320 Hospital Drive,
Zip 24112–1981, Mailing Address: P.O. Box 4788, Zip 24115–4788;
tel. 276/666–7200, (Nonreporting) **A**5 19 **S** LifePoint Health, Brentwood, TN
Primary Contact: Alan Larson, Market President
CFO: Brandy Hanners, Chief Financial Officer
CIO: Jeff Butker, Chief Information Officer
CHR: Sherry Schofield, Director Human Resources
CNO: Michael Pittman, Chief Nursing Officer
Web address: www.martinsvillehospital.com
**Control:** Corporation, Investor–owned (for–profit) **Service:** General medical and surgical

**Staffed Beds:** 150

## MECHANICSVILLE—Hanover County

☐ **BON SECOURS MEMORIAL REGIONAL MEDICAL CENTER (490069)**, 8260
Atlee Road, Zip 23116–1844; tel. 804/764–6000, (Nonreporting) **A**1 2 3 5 10 **S**
Bon Secours Mercy Health, Marriottsville, MD
Primary Contact: Leigh Sewell, Chief Executive Officer
COO: Gary A. Welch, Assistant to the Chief Executive Officer and Administrative Director Support Systems
CFO: Stephan F Quiriconi, Vice President Finance
CMO: Sunil K. Sinha, M.D., FACHE, Chief Medical Officer
CIO: Gwen Harding, Site Manager Information Systems
CHR: Rebecca Kamguia, Administrative Director Human Resources
CNO: Jill M Kennedy, R.N., Vice President, Ambulatory Patient Care Services
Web address: www.bonsecours.com
**Control:** Church operated, Nongovernment, not–for–profit **Service:** General medical and surgical

**Staffed Beds:** 225

**MEMORIAL REGIONAL MEDICAL CENTER** See Bon Secours Memorial Regional Medical Center

☐ **SHELTERING ARMS REHABILITATION HOSPITAL (493025)**, 8254 Atlee Road,
Zip 23116–1844; tel. 804/764–1000, (Nonreporting) **A**1 3 10 **F**3 28 29 30 34
35 50 53 54 57 58 59 64 74 75 77 79 82 86 87 90 91 92 93 94 95 96 104
130 131 132 146 147 148
Primary Contact: Mary A. Zweifel, MS, President and Chief Executive Officer
COO: Amy J Showalter, R.N., Chief Operating Officer
CFO: James Litsinger, CPA, Vice President and Chief Financial Officer
CMO: Hillary Hawkins, M.D., Medical Director
CIO: Chris Sorenson, Chief Information Officer
CHR: Amanda Worley, Chief Human Resources Officer
CNO: Sandra Eyler, MS, Chief Nursing Officer
Web address: www.shelteringarms.com
**Control:** Other not–for–profit (including NFP Corporation) **Service:** Rehabilitation

**Staffed Beds:** 40 **Admissions:** 840 **Census:** 38 **Outpatient Visits:** 96517
**Births:** 0

## MIDLOTHIAN—Chesterfield County

☐ **BON SECOURS ST. FRANCIS MEDICAL CENTER (490136)**, 13710 St Francis
Boulevard, Zip 23114–3267; tel. 804/594–7300, (Nonreporting) **A**1 2 3 5 10 **F**3
8 11 13 15 17 18 20 22 26 28 29 30 31 34 35 40 42 45 46 47 48 49 50 54
55 57 59 60 61 64 65 68 70 71 72 74 75 76 77 78 79 81 84 85 86 87 93 96
107 108 109 110 111 115 118 119 120 121 123 126 130 131 132 135 146
147 148 149 154 **S** Bon Secours Mercy Health, Marriottsville, MD
Primary Contact: Chris Accashian, Chief Executive Officer
CFO: Stephan F Quiriconi, Vice President, Finance
CMO: Michael Menen, M.D., Chief Medical Officer
CIO: Terri Spence, Vice President and Regional Chief Information Officer
CNO: Barbara L. Gesme, MSN, Vice President Patient Care Services & Chief Nurse Executive
Web address: www.bonsecours.com/sfmc/default.asp
**Control:** Other not–for–profit (including NFP Corporation) **Service:** General medical and surgical

**Staffed Beds:** 130 **Admissions:** 9972 **Census:** 102 **Outpatient
Visits:** 45588 **Births:** 2260 **Total Expense ($000):** 222949 **Payroll Expense
($000):** 58400

☐ **SHELTERING ARMS HOSPITAL SOUTH (493030)**, 13700 St. Francis
Boulevard, Suite 400, Zip 23114–3222; tel. 804/764–1000, (Nonreporting) **A**1 5
10 **F**3 29 30 34 35 50 54 56 57 58 59 64 74 75 77 79 82 84 86 87 90 91 92
93 94 95 96 100 104 130 131 132 146 148 **P**6
Primary Contact: Mary A. Zweifel, MS, President and Chief Executive Officer
COO: Amy J Showalter, R.N., Chief Operating Officer
CFO: James Litsinger, CPA, Chief Operating Officer
CMO: Timothy Silver, M.D., Medical Director, SAH-S
CIO: Chris Sorenson, Chief Health Information Officer
CHR: Ellen B Vance, Chief Human Resources Officer
CNO: Sandra Eyler, MS, Chief Nursing Officer
Web address: www.shelteringarms.com
**Control:** Other not–for–profit (including NFP Corporation) **Service:** Rehabilitation

**Staffed Beds:** 28 **Admissions:** 599 **Census:** 24 **Outpatient Visits:** 7730
**Births:** 0

**ST FRANCIS MEDICAL CENTER** See Bon Secours St. Francis Medical Center

## NEW KENT—New Kent County

**CUMBERLAND HOSPITAL** See Cumberland Hospital for Children and Adolescents

☐ **CUMBERLAND HOSPITAL FOR CHILDREN AND ADOLESCENTS (493300)**,
9407 Cumberland Road, Zip 23124–2029; tel. 804/966–2242, (Nonreporting) **A**1
10 **S** Universal Health Services, Inc., King of Prussia, PA
Primary Contact: Patrice Gay. Brooks, Chief Executive Officer
CFO: Joanne Rial, Chief Financial Officer
CMO: Daniel N Davidow, M.D., Medical Director
CIO: Leslie Bowery, Director of Standards and Compliance
CHR: Kim Ivey, Director of Human Resources
CNO: Paula Roberts, Chief Nursing Officer
Web address: www.cumberlandhospital.com
**Control:** Corporation, Investor–owned (for–profit) **Service:** Children's rehabilitation

**Staffed Beds:** 118

## NEWPORT NEWS—Newport News City County

☐ **BON SECOURS MARY IMMACULATE HOSPITAL (490041)**, 2 Bernardine Drive,
Zip 23602–4499; tel. 757/886–6000, (Nonreporting) **A**1 10 **S** Bon Secours
Mercy Health, Marriottsville, MD
Primary Contact: Darlene Stephenson, Chief Executive Officer
COO: Darlene Stephenson, Vice President Operations
CIO: Terri Spence, Vice President Information Services
CHR: Vickie Witcher Humphries, Vice President Human Resources
Web address: www.bonsecourshamptonroads.com
**Control:** Other not–for–profit (including NFP Corporation) **Service:** General medical and surgical

**Staffed Beds:** 238

⊠ ⇑ **COASTAL VIRGINIA REHABILITATION (493027)**, 245 Chesapeake Avenue,
Zip 23607–6038; tel. 757/928–8000, (Nonreporting) **A**1 10 21 **S** Select Medical
Corporation, Mechanicsburg, PA
Primary Contact: Daniel Ballin, Administrator
COO: William B Downey, President and Chief Executive Officer
CFO: Bill Austin, Senior Vice President of Finance
CMO: C Renee Moss, M.D., Chief Medical Officer
CIO: Dennis Loftis, Senior Vice President of Information Systems
CHR: Rob Cuthrell, Director of Human Resources
CNO: Debbie Outlaw, R.N., Director Patient Care Services
Web address: www.riversideonline.com/rri/index.cfm
**Control:** Other not–for–profit (including NFP Corporation) **Service:** Rehabilitation

**Staffed Beds:** 35

⇑ **HAMPTON ROADS SPECIALTY HOSPITAL** See Select Specialty Hospital
Hampton Roads

**KEYSTONE NEWPORT NEWS** See Newport News Behavioral Health Center

**MARY IMMACULATE HOSPITAL** See Bon Secours Mary Immaculate Hospital

**NEWPORT NEWS BEHAVIORAL HEALTH CENTER**, 17579 Warwick Boulevard, Zip 23603–1343; tel. 757/888–0400, (Nonreporting)
Primary Contact: Larry Kirkland, Chief Executive Officer
CFO: Holly Hernandez, Chief Financial Officer
CMO: Avtar Dhillon, M.D., Medical Director
CIO: Terry Rethamel, Director of Support Services
CHR: Kristine Pierce, Director Human Resources
CNO: Karen Bruce, Director of Nursing
Web address: www.newportnewsbhc.com/
**Control**: Corporation, Investor–owned (for–profit) **Service**: Psychiatric

**Staffed Beds**: 132

⇑ **RIVERSIDE REGIONAL MED CTR** See Riverside Regional Medical Center

⇑ **RIVERSIDE REGIONAL MEDICAL CENTER (490052)**, 500 J Clyde Morris Boulevard, Zip 23601–1929; tel. 757/594–2000, (Includes RIVERSIDE BEHAVIORAL HEALTH CENTER, Mailing address: 2244 Executive Drive, Hampton, Virginia, Zip 23666–2430; tel. 757/827–1001; Debra Campbell, R.N., Administrator), (Nonreporting) **A**2 3 5 10 21 **F**3 4 8 13 15 18 20 22 24 26 28 30 31 36 38 40 43 44 45 49 50 51 54 56 58 60 64 70 72 74 75 76 77 78 79 81 82 84 85 86 87 91 93 94 96 98 99 100 102 103 107 108 110 111 114 115 116 117 118 119 120 121 123 124 126 129 130 131 132 141 143 146 148 149 154 **S** Riverside Health System, Newport News, VA
Primary Contact: Michael J. Doucette, Senior Vice President and Administrator
COO: William B Downey, Chief Operating Officer
CFO: Wade Broughman, Executive Vice President and Chief Financial Officer
CMO: Barry L Gross, M.D., Executive Vice President and Chief Medical Officer
CIO: Dennis Loftis, Senior Vice President and Chief Information Officer
CHR: Sally Hartman, Senior Vice President
CNO: Candice R. Carroll, Nurse Executive
Web address: www.https://www.riversideonline.com/rrmc/index.cfm
**Control**: Other not–for–profit (including NFP Corporation) **Service**: General medical and surgical

**Staffed Beds**: 307 **Admissions**: 19184 **Census**: 264 **Outpatient Visits**: 148321 **Births**: 2527 **Total Expense ($000)**: 564407 **Payroll Expense ($000)**: 150630 **Personnel**: 2397

⇑ **RIVERSIDE REHABILITATION INSTITUTE** See Coastal Virginia Rehabilitation

★ ⇑ **SELECT SPECIALTY HOSPITAL HAMPTON ROADS (492008)**, 245 Chesapeake Avenue, Zip 23607–6038; tel. 757/534–5000, (Nonreporting) **A**10 21 **F**3 90 **S** Select Medical Corporation, Mechanicsburg, PA
Primary Contact: Phillip L. Wright, FACHE, Chief Executive Officer
Web address: www.hamptonroadsspecialtyhospital.com
**Control**: Corporation, Investor–owned (for–profit) **Service**: Rehabilitation

**Staffed Beds**: 50 **Admissions**: 901 **Census**: 32 **Outpatient Visits**: 0 **Births**: 0 **Personnel**: 136

## NORFOLK—Norfolk City County

**BON SECOUR-DEPAUL MEDICAL CTR** See Bon Secours-Depaul Medical Center

☐ **BON SECOURS-DEPAUL MEDICAL CENTER (490011)**, 150 Kingsley Lane, Zip 23505–4650; tel. 757/889–5000, (Nonreporting) **A**1 2 3 5 10 **S** Bon Secours Mercy Health, Marriottsville, MD
Primary Contact: Paul Gaden, Chief Executive Officer
CFO: Charmaine Rochester, Vice President Finance
CIO: Lynne Zultanky, Director Corporate Communications and Media Relations
CHR: Vickie Witcher Humphries, Vice President Human Resources
CNO: Michael J. Bratton, R.N., Market Chief Nursing and Quality Officer
Web address: www.bonsecourshamptonroads.com
**Control**: Other not–for–profit (including NFP Corporation) **Service**: General medical and surgical

**Staffed Beds**: 204

⇑ **CHILDREN'S HOSPITAL OF THE KING'S DAUGHTERS (493301)**, 601 Children's Lane, Zip 23507–1910; tel. 757/668–7000, (Nonreporting) **A**3 5 10 21 **F**3 7 8 9 12 16 17 19 21 23 25 27 29 30 31 32 34 35 39 40 41 43 44 45 48 49 50 55 57 58 59 60 61 64 65 66 68 72 73 74 75 77 78 79 80 81 82 84 85 86 87 88 89 90 91 92 93 97 99 100 102 107 108 111 115 118 119 129 130 131 132 134 138 144 145 146 148 149 153 154 156 **P**8
Primary Contact: James D. Dahling, President and Chief Executive Officer
COO: John P Harding, Chief Operating Officer
CFO: Dennis Ryan, Senior Vice President and Chief Financial Officer
CMO: Chris Foley, Chief of Medicine
CIO: Deborah Barnes, Vice President and Chief Information Officer
CHR: Paul J Morlock, FACHE, Vice President Human Resources and Occupational Health
CNO: Karen Mitchell, Vice President Patient Care Services
Web address: www.chkd.org
**Control**: Other not–for–profit (including NFP Corporation) **Service**: Children's general medical and surgical

**Staffed Beds**: 185 **Admissions**: 5639 **Census**: 131 **Outpatient Visits**: 341681 **Births**: 0 **Total Expense ($000)**: 392597 **Payroll Expense ($000)**: 160876 **Personnel**: 2530

**HOSPITAL FOR EXTENDED RECOVERY (492007)**, 600 Gresham Drive, Suite 700, Zip 23507–1904; tel. 757/388–1700, (Nonreporting) **A**10
Primary Contact: Aimee Vergara, Chief Executive Officer
**Control**: Other not–for–profit (including NFP Corporation) **Service**: Acute long–term care hospital

**Staffed Beds**: 25

☐ **KEMPSVILLE CENTER FOR BEHAVIORAL HEALTH**, 860 Kempsville Road, Zip 23502–3980; tel. 757/461–4565, (Nonreporting) **A**1
Primary Contact: Jaime Fernandez, Chief Executive Officer
**Control**: Corporation, Investor–owned (for–profit) **Service**: Psychiatric

**Staffed Beds**: 77

**LAKE TAYLOR HOSPITAL** See Lake Taylor Transitional Care Hospital

**LAKE TAYLOR TRANSITIONAL CARE HOSPITAL (492001)**, 1309 Kempsville Road, Zip 23502–2286; tel. 757/461–5001, (Nonreporting) **A**3 5 10
Primary Contact: Thomas J. Orsini, President and Chief Executive Officer
CFO: Robert W Fogg, Director Finance
CMO: Kevin Murray, M.D., Director Medical Services
CIO: Mark Davis, Director Information Systems
CHR: LeeAnn Lowman, Director Human Resources
Web address: www.laketaylor.org
**Control**: Hospital district or authority, Government, Nonfederal **Service**: Acute long–term care hospital

**Staffed Beds**: 284

★ ⇑ **SENTARA LEIGH HOSPITAL (490046)**, 830 Kempsville Road, Zip 23502–3920; tel. 757/261–6000, (Nonreporting) **A**2 3 5 10 21 **F**3 8 9 13 15 18 20 22 26 28 29 30 31 34 35 36 37 38 39 40 41 44 45 46 47 48 49 50 53 56 57 58 59 60 61 63 64 65 68 70 71 74 75 76 77 78 79 80 81 82 84 85 86 87 91 92 93 94 96 97 100 102 107 108 110 111 114 126 130 131 132 135 141 146 147 148 149 154 156 **P**6 **S** Sentara Healthcare, Norfolk, VA
Primary Contact: Joanne Inman, President
COO: Howard P. Kern, President and Chief Operating Officer
CFO: Robert Broermann, Senior Vice President and Chief Financial Officer
CMO: Terry Gilliland, M.D., Chief Medical Officer
CIO: Bert Reese, Chief Information Officer
CHR: Michael V Taylor, Senior Vice President Human Resources
CNO: Genemarie McGee, R.N., MS, Chief Nursing Officer
Web address: www.sentara.com
**Control**: Other not–for–profit (including NFP Corporation) **Service**: General medical and surgical

**Staffed Beds**: 247 **Admissions**: 18225 **Census**: 206 **Outpatient Visits**: 513068 **Births**: 2243 **Total Expense ($000)**: 326197 **Payroll Expense ($000)**: 122682 **Personnel**: 1866

⇑ **SENTARA NORFOLK GEN HOSP** See Sentara Norfolk General Hospital

**VA**

---

★ ⚕ **SENTARA NORFOLK GENERAL HOSPITAL (490007)**, 600 Gresham Drive, Zip 23507–1904; tel. 757/388–3000, (Nonreporting) **A**2 3 5 8 10 21 **F**3 12 13 15 16 17 18 20 22 24 26 28 29 30 31 34 35 36 37 38 39 40 41 43 44 45 46 47 49 50 51 52 53 54 55 56 57 58 59 60 61 63 64 65 66 68 70 71 72 74 75 76 77 78 79 80 81 82 84 85 86 87 90 91 92 93 94 96 97 98 100 102 103 107 108 110 111 112 114 115 116 117 118 119 120 121 123 124 126 129 130 131 132 135 136 137 138 141 142 145 146 147 148 149 150 154 155 156 **P**6 **S** Sentara Healthcare, Norfolk, VA
Primary Contact: Jessica Melton, Interim President
CFO: Robert Broermann, Senior Vice President and Chief Financial Officer
CIO: Bert Reese, Chief Information Officer
Web address: www.sentara.com
**Control:** Other not–for–profit (including NFP Corporation) **Service:** General medical and surgical

> **Staffed Beds:** 500 **Admissions:** 26213 **Census:** 434 **Outpatient Visits:** 1232562 **Births:** 3217 **Total Expense ($000):** 965657 **Payroll Expense ($000):** 280732 **Personnel:** 4020

**TIDEWATER PSYCH INST-NORFOLK** See Kempsville Center for Behavioral Health

---

### NORTON—Norton City County

**BON SECOURS ST MARY'S HOSPITAL** See Mountain View Regional Medical Center

★ **MOUNTAIN VIEW REGIONAL MEDICAL CENTER (490027)**, 310 Third Street NE, Zip 24273–1137; tel. 276/679–9100, (Total facility includes 44 beds in nursing home–type unit) (Nonreporting) **F**3 11 15 28 29 40 45 50 59 70 75 77 81 85 87 93 107 108 110 111 115 119 128 130 135 **S** Ballad Health, Johnson City, TN
Primary Contact: Mark T. Leonard, Interim Chief Executive Officer
CFO: Regina Day, Executive Director Finance
CMO: Michael Ketcham, Chief Medical Officer
CHR: Bobby Collins, Director Human Resources
Web address: www.wellmont.org
**Control:** Other not–for–profit (including NFP Corporation) **Service:** General medical and surgical

> **Staffed Beds:** 70 **Admissions:** 937 **Census:** 37 **Outpatient Visits:** 38392 **Births:** 0 **Total Expense ($000):** 20248 **Payroll Expense ($000):** 5522 **Personnel:** 120

☐ **NORTON COMMUNITY HOSPITAL (490001)**, 100 15th Street NW, Zip 24273–1616; tel. 276/679–9600, (Nonreporting) **A**1 3 5 10 13 **F**3 11 13 15 18 28 29 30 31 32 34 35 40 45 46 51 53 55 56 57 59 62 64 65 66 68 70 75 76 77 78 79 81 87 90 93 107 108 110 111 115 116 117 118 119 129 130 131 133 135 146 147 148 154 **S** Ballad Health, Johnson City, TN
Primary Contact: Mark T. Leonard, Chief Executive Officer
CFO: Stephen Sawyer, Chief Financial Officer
CMO: Allen Mullens, M.D., Chief Medical Staff
CIO: Judy Lawson, Director Information Services
CHR: Valeri J Colyer, Director Human Resources
Web address: www.msha.com/nch
**Control:** Other not–for–profit (including NFP Corporation) **Service:** General medical and surgical

> **Staffed Beds:** 66 **Admissions:** 2648 **Census:** 29 **Outpatient Visits:** 76230 **Births:** 199 **Total Expense ($000):** 55207 **Payroll Expense ($000):** 18613 **Personnel:** 969

---

### ONANCOCK—Accomack County

★ ⚕ **RIVERSIDE SHORE MEMORIAL HOSPITAL (490037)**, 20480 Market Street, Zip 23417–4309, Mailing Address: P.O. Box 430, Zip 23417; tel. 757/302–2100, (Nonreporting) **A**2 3 10 20 21 **S** Riverside Health System, Newport News, VA
Primary Contact: John Peterman, Vice President and Administrator
CFO: W William Austin JrSenior Vice President Finance
CMO: David Jones, Service Chief
CHR: Nicole Miller, Director Human Resources
Web address: www.riversideonline.com
**Control:** Other not–for–profit (including NFP Corporation) **Service:** General medical and surgical

> **Staffed Beds:** 24

⚕ **SHORE MEMORIAL HOSPITAL** See Riverside Shore Memorial Hospital

---

### PEARISBURG—Giles County

⊞ **CARILION GILES COMMUNITY HOSPITAL (491302)**, 159 Hartley Way, Zip 24134–2471; tel. 540/921–6000, (Nonreporting) **A**1 5 10 18 **F**3 11 15 18 28 29 30 34 35 36 40 45 50 53 54 57 59 64 65 68 70 75 77 79 81 85 86 87 91 93 96 107 108 110 111 119 127 130 133 135 146 147 148 149 154 156 **P**6 **S** Carilion Clinic, Roanoke, VA
Primary Contact: William Flattery, Vice President and Administrator Western Division
CMO: John Tamminen, M.D., President Medical Staff
CHR: Carrie Boggess, Human Resource Generalist
CNO: Veronica Stump, Director of Nursing
Web address: www.https://www.carilionclinic.org
**Control:** Other not–for–profit (including NFP Corporation) **Service:** General medical and surgical

> **Staffed Beds:** 12 **Admissions:** 958 **Census:** 12 **Outpatient Visits:** 26683 **Births:** 2 **Total Expense ($000):** 32055 **Payroll Expense ($000):** 11949 **Personnel:** 183

**CARILION GILES MEMORIAL HOSPITAL** See Carilion Giles Community Hospital

---

### PETERSBURG—Petersburg City County

☐ **CENTRAL STATE HOSPITAL**, 26317 West Washington Street, Zip 23803–2727, Mailing Address: P.O. Box 4030, Zip 23803–0030; tel. 804/524–7000, (Nonreporting) **A**1 3 **F**29 30 35 38 75 77 87 98 100 101 102 106 130 132 143 146 149 157 **S** Virginia Department of Mental Health, Richmond, VA
Primary Contact: Brandi Justice, Interim Director
COO: Ann Bailey, Assistant Director Administration
CFO: Robert Kaufman, Director Financial Services
CMO: Ronald O Forbes, M.D., Medical Director
CIO: Jonathan Baber, Director Information Technology
CHR: Tracy Salisbury, Regional Manager Human Resources
CNO: Eva Parham, R.N., Chief Nurse Executive
Web address: www.csh.dbhds.virginia.gov
**Control:** State, Government, Nonfederal **Service:** Psychiatric

> **Staffed Beds:** 277 **Admissions:** 1204 **Census:** 240 **Outpatient Visits:** 0 **Births:** 0 **Total Expense ($000):** 69597 **Payroll Expense ($000):** 38637 **Personnel:** 874

⊞ **ENCOMPASS HEALTH REHABILITATION HOSPITAL OF PETERSBURG (493031)**, 95 Medical Park Boulevard, Zip 23805–9233; tel. 804/504–8100, (Nonreporting) **A**1 10 **S** Encompass Health Corporation, Birmingham, AL
Primary Contact: Dale Poe, Chief Executive Officer
Web address: www.https://www.encompasshealth.com
**Control:** Corporation, Investor–owned (for–profit) **Service:** Rehabilitation

> **Staffed Beds:** 53

**HCA POPLAR SPRINGS HOSPITAL** See Poplar Springs Hospital

**HEALTHSOUTH REHABILITATION HOSPITAL OF PETERSBURG** See Encompass Health Rehabilitation Hospital of Petersburg

☐ **HIRAM W. DAVIS MEDICAL CENTER (490104)**, 26317 West Washington Street, Zip 23803–2727, Mailing Address: P.O. Box 4030, Zip 23803–0030; tel. 804/524–7420, (Nonreporting) **A**1 10 **S** Virginia Department of Mental Health, Richmond, VA
Primary Contact: Nichelle Williams, Director
CFO: Robert Kaufman, Fiscal Officer
CHR: Tracy Salisbury, Director Human Resources
**Control:** State, Government, Nonfederal **Service:** Other specialty treatment

> **Staffed Beds:** 10

⊞ **POPLAR SPRINGS HOSPITAL (494022)**, 350 Poplar Drive, Zip 23805–9367; tel. 804/733–6874, (Nonreporting) **A**1 10 **S** Universal Health Services, Inc., King of Prussia, PA
Primary Contact: Nelson Smith, Chief Executive Officer
COO: Rachel Beal, Chief Operating Officer
CFO: Michael Felice, Chief Financial Officer
CMO: Thresa Simon, M.D., Medical Director
CHR: Morris Mitchell, Director Human Resources
Web address: www.poplarsprings.com
**Control:** Corporation, Investor–owned (for–profit) **Service:** Psychiatric

> **Staffed Beds:** 180

**VA**

*Many Facility Codes have changed. Please refer to the AHA Guide Code Chart.*   © 2021 AHA Guide

⊠ **SOUTHSIDE REGIONAL MEDICAL CENTER (490067)**, 200 Medical Park Boulevard, Zip 23805–9274; tel. 804/765–5000, (Nonreporting) **A**1 2 3 5 10 **S** Bon Secours Mercy Health, Marriottsville, MD
Primary Contact: Trent Nobles, Chief Executive Officer
COO: Jerad Hanlon, Chief Operating Officer
CMO: Boyd Wickizer, M.D., JrChief Medical Officer
CIO: Eric Synnestvedt, Director Information Technology
CHR: Irene Buskey, Director Human Resources
CNO: Beverly Bzdek Smith, Chief Nursing Officer
Web address: www.srmconline.com
**Control**: Church operated, Nongovernment, not–for–profit **Service**: General medical and surgical

| Staffed Beds: 294 |
|---|

### PORTSMOUTH—Portsmouth City County

☐ **BON SECOURS MARYVIEW MEDICAL CENTER (490017)**, 3636 High Street, Zip 23707–3270; tel. 757/398–2200, (Nonreporting) **A**1 2 3 5 10 **S** Bon Secours Mercy Health, Marriottsville, MD
Primary Contact: Paul Gaden, Chief Executive Officer
CFO: Ernest C Padden, Chief Financial Officer
CMO: Warren Austin, M.D., Vice President Medical Affairs
CIO: Terri Spence, Chief Information Officer
CHR: Vickie Witcher Humphries, Director Human Resources
CNO: Leana Fox, Interim Chief Nurse Executive
Web address: www.bonsecourshamptonroads.com
**Control**: Other not–for–profit (including NFP Corporation) **Service**: General medical and surgical

| Staffed Beds: 466 |
|---|

**MARYVIEW MEDICAL CENTER** See Bon Secours Maryview Medical Center

**NAVAL HOSPITAL** See Naval Medical Center

⊠ **NAVAL MEDICAL CENTER**, 620 John Paul Jones Circle, Zip 23708–2197; tel. 757/953–1980, (Nonreporting) **A**1 2 3 5 **S** Bureau of Medicine and Surgery, Department of the Navy, Falls Church, VA
Primary Contact: Captain Lisa Mulligan, Commanding Officer
CMO: CaptainCynthia J Gantt, Chief of Staff
CIO: Lieutenant ColonelKaren Albany, Chief Information Officer
Web address: www.https://www.med.navy.mil/sites/nmcp/SitePages/home.aspx
**Service**: General medical and surgical

| Staffed Beds: 274 |
|---|

### PULASKI—Pulaski County

**LEWISGALE HOSPITAL AT PULASKI** See Lewisgale Hospital Pulaski

⊠ **LEWISGALE HOSPITAL PULASKI (490116)**, 2400 Lee Highway, Zip 24301–2326, Mailing Address: P.O. Box 759, Zip 24301–0759; tel. 540/994–8100, (Nonreporting) **A**1 2 5 10 **S** HCA Healthcare, Nashville, TN
Primary Contact: Sean Pressman, Chief Executive Officer
CFO: Jeff Kurcab, Chief Financial Officer
CMO: Karanita Ojomo, M.D., Chief of Staff
CIO: Diron Lane, Director Information Systems
CHR: Jana Beckner, Director Human Resources
Web address: www.lewisgale.com/
**Control**: Corporation, Investor–owned (for–profit) **Service**: General medical and surgical

| Staffed Beds: 147 |
|---|

### RESTON—Fairfax County

⊠ **RESTON HOSPITAL CENTER (490107)**, 1850 Town Center Parkway, Zip 20190–3219; tel. 703/689–9000, (Nonreporting) **A**1 2 10 **S** HCA Healthcare, Nashville, TN
Primary Contact: John A. Deardorff, President and Chief Executive, Northern Virginia Market
COO: Jane Raymond, Vice President and Chief Operating Officer
CFO: Edward R Stojakovich, Chief Financial Officer
CMO: Walter R Zolkiwsky, M.D., Chief Medical Officer
CIO: Paresh Shah, Director Information Systems
CHR: Lesley Channell, Vice President Human Resources
CNO: Cynthia Glover, R.N., Vice President and Chief Nursing Officer
Web address: www.restonhospital.com
**Control**: Corporation, Investor–owned (for–profit) **Service**: General medical and surgical

| Staffed Beds: 247 |
|---|

**RESTON HOSPITAL CTR** See Reston Hospital Center

### RICHLANDS—Tazewell County

⊠ **CLINCH VALLEY MEDICAL CENTER (490060)**, 6801 Governor G C Peery Highway, Zip 24641–2194; tel. 276/596–6000, (Total facility includes 24 beds in nursing home–type unit) (Nonreporting) **A**1 5 10 **F**3 12 13 14 15 17 18 20 22 28 29 30 31 34 35 39 40 41 45 46 50 55 56 57 59 64 70 75 76 77 78 79 81 85 86 87 89 93 94 97 107 108 110 111 114 115 118 119 120 121 128 129 130 132 134 135 143 144 146 147 148 149 150 154 **S** LifePoint Health, Brentwood, TN
Primary Contact: Peter Mulkey, Chief Executive Officer
CFO: Jason Schmiedt, Chief Financial Officer
CMO: George Farrell, M.D., Chief Medical Officer
CIO: Chris Perkins, Director Information Services
CHR: John Knowles, Director Human Resources
Web address: www.clinchvalleymedicalcenter.com
**Control**: Corporation, Investor–owned (for–profit) **Service**: General medical and surgical

| Staffed Beds: 95 Admissions: 3146 Census: 38 Outpatient Visits: 102685 Births: 265 Personnel: 463 |
|---|

**COLUMBIA CLINCH VALLEY MED CTR** See Clinch Valley Medical Center

### RICHMOND—Henrico County

☐ **BON SECOURS ST. MARY'S HOSPITAL (490059)**, 5801 Bremo Road, Zip 23226–1907; tel. 804/285–2011, (Includes BON SECOURS ST. MARY'S CHILDREN'S SERVICES, Mailing address: 5801 Bremo Road, Richmond, Virginia, Zip 23226–1907; tel. 804/285–2011), (Nonreporting) **A**1 2 3 5 10 **S** Bon Secours Mercy Health, Marriottsville, MD
Primary Contact: Francine Barr, R.N., MS, Chief Executive Officer
COO: Francine Barr, R.N., MS, Vice President and Chief Operating Officer
CFO: Stephan F Quiriconi, Chief Financial Officer
CMO: Khiet Trinh, M.D., Chief Medical Officer
CIO: Terri Spence, Chief Information Officer
CHR: Kishah White, Director Human Resources
CNO: Jody A. Bishop, Chief Nursing Officer
Web address: www.bonsecours.com
**Control**: Church operated, Nongovernment, not–for–profit **Service**: General medical and surgical

| Staffed Beds: 391 |
|---|

### RICHMOND—Richmond City County

☐ **BON SECOURS-RICHMOND COMMUNITY HOSPITAL (490094)**, 1500 North 28th Street, Zip 23223–5396, Mailing Address: P.O. Box 27184, Zip 23261–7184; tel. 804/225–1700, (Nonreporting) **A**1 10 **S** Bon Secours Mercy Health, Marriottsville, MD
Primary Contact: Leigh Sewell, Chief Executive Officer
CIO: Jeff Burke, Chief Information Officer
CHR: Shelia White, Director Human Resources
Web address: www.bonsecours.com
**Control**: Church operated, Nongovernment, not–for–profit **Service**: General medical and surgical

| Staffed Beds: 85 |
|---|

**CHILDREN'S HOSPITAL OF RICHMOND** See Children's Hospital of Richmond at Vcu-Brook Road Campus

**VA**

---

**Hospital, Medicare Provider Number, Address, Telephone, Approval, Facility, and Physician Codes, Health Care System**

★ American Hospital Association (AHA) membership
☐ The Joint Commission accreditation
○ Healthcare Facilities Accreditation Program
◇ DNV Healthcare Inc. accreditation
⇑ Center for Improvement in Healthcare Quality Accreditation
△ Commission on Accreditation of Rehabilitation Facilities (CARF) accreditation

★ **CHILDREN'S HOSPITAL OF RICHMOND AT VCU-BROOK ROAD CAMPUS (493302)**, 2924 Brook Road, Zip 23220–1298; tel. 804/321–7474, (Nonreporting) **A**3 5 10 **S** VCU Health System, Richmond, VA
Primary Contact: Elias Neujahr, Chief Executive Officer
CFO: James A Deyarmin, Controller
CMO: Eugene A Monasterio, M.D., Medical Director
CIO: Tim Gibbs, Director of Information Technology, Information Security Officer
CNO: Sharon Darby, R.N., FACHE, Vice President, Clinical Operations
Web address: www.chrichmond.org
**Control:** Other not–for–profit (including NFP Corporation) **Service:** Children's rehabilitation

Staffed Beds: 36

⊞ **CHIPPENHAM HOSPITAL (490112)**, 7101 Jahnke Road, Zip 23225–4044; tel. 804/483–0000, (Includes CHIPPENHAM MEDICAL CENTER, Mailing address: 7101 Jahnke Road, Richmond, Virginia, Zip 23225; tel. 804/320–3911; JOHNSTON-WILLIS HOSPITAL, Mailing address: 1401 Johnston-Willis Drive, Richmond, Virginia, Zip 23235; tel. 804/330–2000; Zachary McCluskey, Chief Executive Officer), (Nonreporting) **A**1 3 5 10 **F**3 4 5 8 9 13 15 17 18 19 20 22 24 26 28 29 30 31 32 34 35 37 38 40 41 42 43 44 45 46 47 48 49 50 51 55 56 58 59 60 61 63 64 68 70 72 73 74 75 76 77 78 79 80 81 82 84 85 86 87 88 89 90 92 93 94 96 98 99 100 101 102 103 104 105 107 108 109 110 111 112 114 115 116 117 118 119 120 121 123 124 126 129 130 132 134 135 145 146 147 148 149 150 151 152 153 154 156 157 **S** HCA Healthcare, Nashville, TN
Primary Contact: William Lunn, M.D., Chief Executive Officer
CFO: Lynn Strader, Chief Financial Officer
CMO: Georgean DeBlois, M.D., Chairman Medical Staff
CIO: Tracy Hechler, Healthcare Director Information Services
CHR: Kris Lukish, Human Resources Officer
Web address: www.cjwmedical.com
**Control:** Individual, Investor–owned (for–profit) **Service:** General medical and surgical

Staffed Beds: 702 Admissions: 37921 Census: 547 Outpatient Visits: 308421 Births: 2815 Total Expense ($000): 553033 Payroll Expense ($000): 190798

**CJW MEDICAL CENTER** See Chippenham Hospital

### RICHMOND—Henrico County

⊞ **ENCOMPASS HEALTH REHABILITATION HOSPITAL OF RICHMOND (493028)**, 5700 Fitzhugh Avenue, Zip 23226–1800; tel. 804/288–5700, (Nonreporting) **A**1 10 **S** Encompass Health Corporation, Birmingham, AL
Primary Contact: Vivian White, Chief Executive Officer
CMO: Roger Giordano, M.D., Medical Director
CIO: Faye Encke, Director Information Management
CHR: Tonya Ferguson, Director Human Resources
CNO: Michelle Anthony, Chief Nursing Officer
Web address: www.https://www.encompasshealth.com
**Control:** Corporation, Investor–owned (for–profit) **Service:** Rehabilitation

Staffed Beds: 28

**ENCOMPASS HEALTH REHABILITATION HOSPITAL OF VIRGINIA** See Encompass Health Rehabilitation Hospital of Richmond

### RICHMOND—Richmond City County

**HCA CHIPPENHAM MEDICAL CENTER** See Chippenham Medical Center

### RICHMOND—Chesterfield County

**HCA JOHNSTON-WILLIS HOSPITAL** See Johnston-Willis Hospital

### RICHMOND—Henrico County

**HEALTHSOUTH MEDICAL CENTER** See Henrico Doctors' Hospital - Parham

**HENRICO DOCTOR'S HOSPITAL** See Henrico Doctors' Hospital - Forest

⊞ **HENRICO DOCTORS' HOSPITAL (490118)**, 1602 Skipwith Road, Zip 23229–5205; tel. 804/289–4500, (Includes HENRICO DOCTORS' HOSPITAL - FOREST, Mailing address: 1602 Skipwith Road, Richmond, Virginia, Zip 23229–5298; tel. 804/289–4500; HENRICO DOCTORS' HOSPITAL - PARHAM, Mailing address: 7700 East Parham Road, Richmond, Virginia, Zip 23294–4301; tel. 804/747–5600; Chase Christianson, Chief Executive Officer; HENRICO DOCTORS' HOSPITAL - RETREAT CAMPUS, Mailing address: 2621 Grove Avenue, Richmond, Virginia, Zip 23220–4308; tel. 804/254–5100; Elizabeth Matish, Chief Executive Officer), (Nonreporting) **A**1 2 10 **S** HCA Healthcare, Nashville, TN
Primary Contact: Ryan Jensen, Chief Executive Officer
COO: Zachary Reed, Chief Operating Officer
CFO: Christopher Denton, Chief Financial Officer
CIO: Daniel Patton, Director Information Systems
CHR: Steven Burgess, Administrator Human Resources
Web address: www.henricodoctorshospital.com
**Control:** Corporation, Investor–owned (for–profit) **Service:** General medical and surgical

Staffed Beds: 767

### RICHMOND—Richmond City County

⊞ △ **HUNTER HOLMES MCGUIRE VETERANS AFFAIRS MEDICAL CENTER-RICHMOND**, 1201 Broad Rock Boulevard, Zip 23249–0002; tel. 804/675–5000, (Nonreporting) **A**1 3 5 7 8 **S** Department of Veterans Affairs, Washington, DC
Primary Contact: J. Ronald. Johnson, Director
COO: Alan Lombardo, Associate Director
CFO: Tanza Westry, Chief Financial Officer
CMO: Julie Beales, M.D., Chief of Staff
CIO: David Dahlstrand, Chief, OI&T
CHR: Adriana H Hamilton, Chief Human Resources Officer
CNO: Marjorie Lyne, Associate Director for Patient Care Services
Web address: www.richmond.va.gov/
**Control:** Veterans Affairs, Government, federal **Service:** General medical and surgical

Staffed Beds: 381

**HUNTER HOLMES MCGUIRE VETERANS AFFAIRS MEDICAL CENTER-RICHMOND, VA** See Hunter Holmes Mcguire Veterans Affairs Medical Center-Richmond

### RICHMOND—Chesterfield County

**JOHNSTON-WILLIS HOSPITAL** See Chippenham Hospital, Richmond

### RICHMOND—Henrico County

**KINDRED HOSPITAL RICHMOND** See Vibra Hospital of Richmond

### RICHMOND—Richmond City County

**RETREAT DOCTORS' HOSPITAL** See Henrico Doctors' Hospital - Retreat Campus

**RICHMOND COMMUNITY HOSPITAL** See Bon Secours-Richmond Community Hospital

### RICHMOND—Henrico County

**ST MARY'S HOSPITAL** See Bon Secours St. Mary's Hospital

### RICHMOND—Richmond City County

**VCU HEALTH SYSTEM** See Vcu Medical Center

**VCU HEALTH SYSTEM CHILDREN'S MEDICAL CENTER** See Children's Hospital of Richmond at Vcu

⊞ **VCU MEDICAL CENTER (490032)**, 1250 East Marshall Street,
Zip 23298–5051, Mailing Address: P.O. Box 980510, Zip 23298–0510;
tel. 804/828–9000, (Includes CHILDREN'S HOSPITAL OF RICHMOND AT VCU,
Mailing address: 1000 East Broad Street, Richmond, Virginia, Zip 23219–1918,
PO Box 980646, Zip 23298–0646, tel. 804/828–2467; Elias Neujahr, Chief
Executive Officer), (Nonreporting) **A**1 3 5 8 10 **F**2 3 5 6 8 9 10 11 12 13 15 16 17
18 19 20 21 22 23 24 25 26 27 28 29 30 31 32 34 35 36 37 38 39 40 41 43
44 45 46 47 48 49 50 51 52 54 55 56 57 58 59 60 61 62 64 65 66 68 70
72 73 74 75 76 78 79 80 81 82 83 84 85 86 87 88 89 90 91 92 93 95 96
97 98 99 100 101 102 103 104 107 108 109 110 111 114 115 116 117 118
119 120 121 123 124 126 129 130 131 132 134 135 136 137 138 139 141
142 143 145 146 147 148 149 150 153 154 156 **P**6 **S** VCU Health System,
Richmond, VA
Primary Contact: Ron Clark, M.D., Interim Chief Executive Officer
COO: Paul J Wesolowski, Chief Operating Officer
CFO: Melinda Hancock, Chief Financial Officer
CMO: Ron Clark, M.D., Vice President Clinical Activities and Chief Medical Officer
CIO: Susan Steagall, Vice President Information Services
CHR: Maria Curran, Vice President Human Resources
CNO: Deb Zimmermann, R.N., Chief Nursing Officer and Vice President Patient
Care Services
Web address: www.vcuhealth.org
**Control**: Hospital district or authority, Government, Nonfederal **Service**: General
medical and surgical

**Staffed Beds: 812 Admissions: 36465 Census: 663 Outpatient
Visits: 954042 Births: 2633 Total Expense ($000): 1638648 Payroll
Expense ($000): 542567 Personnel: 8879**

### RICHMOND—Henrico County

⊞ **VIBRA HOSPITAL OF RICHMOND (492009)**, 2220 Edward Holland Drive,
Zip 23230–2519; tel. 804/678–7000, (Nonreporting) **A**1 3 10 **S** Vibra Healthcare,
Mechanicsburg, PA
Primary Contact: Linda Tiemens, Chief Executive Officer
CMO: Gerard Weeden, Chief Medical Officer
CHR: Jonnitra Peeples, Chief Human Resource Officer
CNO: Crystal Richardson, Chief Nursing Officer
Web address: www.vhrichmond.com
**Control**: Corporation, Investor–owned (for–profit) **Service**: Acute long–term care
hospital

**Staffed Beds: 60**

### ROANOKE—Roanoke City County

**CARILION MEDICAL CENTER** See Carilion Roanoke Memorial Hospital

**CARILION ROANOKE COMM HOSP** See Carilion Roanoke Community Hospital

⊞ **CARILION ROANOKE MEMORIAL HOSPITAL (490024)**, 1906 Belleview Avenue
Southeast, Zip 24014–1838, Mailing Address: P.O. Box 13367, Zip 24033–3367;
tel. 540/981–7000, (Includes CARILION CLINIC CHILDREN'S HOSPITAL, Mailing
address: 1906 Belleview Avenue, SE, Roanoke, Virginia, Zip 24014–1838;
tel. 540/981–7000; CARILION ROANOKE COMMUNITY HOSPITAL, Mailing address:
101 Elm Avenue SE, Roanoke, Virginia, Zip 24013–2230, P O Box 12946,
Zip 24029–2946, tel. 540/985–8000; ROANOKE MEMORIAL REHABILITATION
CENTER, Mailing address: South Jefferson and McClanahan Streets, Roanoke,
Virginia, Zip 24014, P O Box 13367, Zip 24033, tel. 703/342–4541),
(Nonreporting) **A**1 2 3 5 8 10 13 **F**3 4 5 7 8 9 11 12 18 19 20 22 24
26 28 29 30 31 32 33 34 35 36 37 38 39 40 41 43 44 45 46 47 48 49 50 51
52 53 54 55 56 57 58 59 60 61 62 63 64 65 66 70 71 72 73 74 75 76 77
78 79 81 82 83 84 85 86 87 88 89 90 91 92 93 95 96 97 98 99 100 101 102
103 104 106 107 108 110 111 113 114 115 116 117 118 119 120 121 123
124 126 129 130 131 132 134 135 143 144 146 147 148 149 150 151 154
155 156 157 **P**6 **S** Carilion Clinic, Roanoke, VA
Primary Contact: Steven C. Arner, President
COO: Steven C. Arner, President
CFO: Donald B Halliwill, Executive Vice President and Chief Financial Officer
CHR: Heather S Shepardson, Vice President Human Resources
Web address: www.carilionclinic.org
**Control**: Other not–for–profit (including NFP Corporation) **Service**: General
medical and surgical

**Staffed Beds: 641 Admissions: 37258 Census: 543 Outpatient
Visits: 276689 Births: 3143 Total Expense ($000): 1297088 Payroll
Expense ($000): 567287 Personnel: 6708**

### ROCKY MOUNT—Franklin County

⊞ **CARILION FRANKLIN MEMORIAL HOSPITAL (490089)**, 180 Floyd Avenue,
Zip 24151–1389; tel. 540/483–5277, (Nonreporting) **A**1 3 10 **F**3 11 15 18 28
29 30 34 35 40 45 50 53 57 59 62 63 65 68 70 75 81 82 84 85 93 96 107
110 111 115 119 130 132 146 148 149 154 **P**6 **S** Carilion Clinic, Roanoke, VA
Primary Contact: Carl T. Cline, Vice President, Carilion Clinic and Hospital
Administrator
COO: Steven C. Arner, Executive Vice President of Administration
CFO: Donald B Halliwill, Chief Financial Officer
CMO: Patrice M. Weiss, Executive Vice President, Administration
CIO: Robert Keith Perry, Senior Vice President, Chief Information Officer
CHR: Paul C. Hudgins, Senior Vice President
Web address: www.carilionclinic.org/CFMH
**Control**: Other not–for–profit (including NFP Corporation) **Service**: General
medical and surgical

**Staffed Beds: 17 Admissions: 1328 Census: 14 Outpatient Visits: 44870
Births: 2 Total Expense ($000): 43152 Payroll Expense ($000): 16768
Personnel: 279**

**FRANKLIN MEMORIAL HOSPITAL** See Carilion Franklin Memorial Hospital

### SALEM—Roanoke County

**LEWIS-GALE PSYCHIATRIC CENTER** See Lewis-Gale Pavilion

### SALEM—Salem City County

⊞ **SALEM VETERANS AFFAIRS MEDICAL CENTER**, 1970 Roanoke Boulevard,
Zip 24153–6478; tel. 540/982–2463, (Total facility includes 50 beds in nursing
home–type unit) (Nonreporting) **A**1 3 5 8 **F**3 4 5 11 18 20 22 24 26 29 30 31 35
36 38 39 40 44 45 46 53 55 56 57 58 59 60 61 63 64 67 70 74 75 77 78 79
80 81 82 83 84 85 86 87 90 92 93 94 96 97 98 100 101 102 104 107 108
111 114 115 116 117 118 119 128 129 130 132 135 146 147 148 149 154
156 157 158 **S** Department of Veterans Affairs, Washington, DC
Primary Contact: Rebecca J. Stackhouse, Medical Center Director
CFO: Codie Walker, Chief Financial Officer
CMO: Anne Hutchins, M.D., Chief of Staff
CIO: Sharon Collins, Chief Information Officer
CHR: Brian Zeman, Chief Human Resources
CNO: Teresa England, R.N., Ph.D., Nurse Executive
Web address: www.salem.va.gov
**Control**: Veterans Affairs, Government, federal **Service**: General medical and
surgical

**Staffed Beds: 191 Admissions: 3556 Census: 66 Outpatient
Visits: 465528 Births: 0 Total Expense ($000): 398239 Payroll Expense
($000): 156086 Personnel: 1904**

**VETERANS AFFAIRS MEDICAL CENTER** See Salem Veterans Affairs Medical
Center

### SOUTH BOSTON—Halifax County

⇑ **HALIFAX REGIONAL HEALTH SYSTEM** See Sentara Halifax Regional Hospital

★ ⇑ **SENTARA HALIFAX REGIONAL HOSPITAL (490013)**, 2204 Wilborn Avenue,
Zip 24592–1638; tel. 434/517–3100, (Total facility includes 384 beds in nursing
home–type unit) (Nonreporting) **A**5 10 21 **F**3 5 11 13 14 15 18 20 22 28 29 30
31 34 35 38 39 40 45 46 47 48 56 57 59 61 62 63 64 65 68 70 74 75 76 77
78 79 81 84 85 87 91 92 93 96 97 104 105 107 108 110 111 114 115 118
119 128 129 130 131 132 135 141 145 146 147 148 149 152 153 154 **P**4 7
**S** Sentara Healthcare, Norfolk, VA
Primary Contact: Jason A. Studley, FACHE, President
CFO: Stewart R Nelson, Vice President and Chief Financial Officer
CMO: Said Iskandar, M.D., Chief Medical Officer
CIO: William Zirkle, Manager Information Systems
CHR: Catherine Howard, Director Human Resources
CNO: Patricia F Thomas, Chief Nursing Officer
Web address: www.hrhs.org
**Control**: Other not–for–profit (including NFP Corporation) **Service**: General
medical and surgical

**Staffed Beds: 441 Admissions: 4054 Census: 367 Outpatient
Visits: 116569 Births: 366 Total Expense ($000): 122222 Payroll Expense
($000): 46028 Personnel: 853**

**VA**

---

**Hospital, Medicare Provider Number, Address, Telephone, Approval, Facility, and Physician Codes, Health Care System**

★ American Hospital Association (AHA) membership ○ Healthcare Facilities Accreditation Program ⇑ Center for Improvement in Healthcare Quality Accreditation
□ The Joint Commission accreditation ◇ DNV Healthcare Inc. accreditation △ Commission on Accreditation of Rehabilitation Facilities (CARF) accreditation

## SOUTH HILL—Mecklenburg County

**VCU COMMUNITY MEMORIAL HOSPITAL** See Vcu Health Community Memorial Hospital

☒ **VCU HEALTH COMMUNITY MEMORIAL HOSPITAL (490098)**, 125 Buena Vista Circle, Zip 23970–1431, Mailing Address: P.O. Box 90, Zip 23970–0090; tel. 434/447–3151, (Total facility includes 136 beds in nursing home–type unit) (Nonreporting) **A**1 2 10 20 **F**3 11 12 13 15 18 28 29 30 31 34 35 39 40 45 46 49 50 53 54 56 59 62 63 64 65 70 74 75 76 77 78 79 81 82 84 85 86 87 93 96 97 107 108 110 111 115 118 119 121 123 128 130 131 132 133 135 143 146 147 148 154 **S** VCU Health System, Richmond, VA
Primary Contact: W Scott. Burnette, Chief Executive Officer
CFO: Kenneth Libby, Vice President Finance
CMO: Manhal Saleeby, M.D., Chief of Staff
CIO: Brian Rock, Director of Information Systems
CHR: Maria Stephens, Director Human Resources, Education and Occupational Health and Wellness
CNO: Ursula N Butts, FACHE, Vice President of Patient Care Services
Web address: www.cmh-sh.org
**Control:** Other not–for–profit (including NFP Corporation) **Service:** General medical and surgical

> **Staffed Beds:** 210 **Admissions:** 3888 **Census:** 138 **Outpatient Visits:** 166662 **Births:** 174 **Total Expense ($000):** 118090 **Payroll Expense ($000):** 57155 **Personnel:** 733

## STAFFORD—Stafford County

☒ **STAFFORD HOSPITAL (490140)**, 101 Hospital Center Boulevard, Zip 22554–6200; tel. 540/741–9000, (Nonreporting) **A**1 5 10 **F**3 13 15 18 20 22 26 29 30 31 34 35 36 39 40 44 45 46 47 48 49 50 54 57 58 59 64 70 73 74 75 76 77 78 79 81 84 85 86 87 92 93 96 102 107 108 110 111 115 118 119 120 121 129 130 131 132 135 146 147 148 149 **P**5 8 **S** Mary Washington Healthcare, Fredericksburg, VA
Primary Contact: Michael P. McDermott, M.D., President and Chief Executive Officer
COO: Thomas Gettinger, Executive Vice President and Chief Operating Officer
CFO: Sean Barden, Executive Vice President and Chief Financial Officer
CMO: Rebecca Bigoney, Executive Vice President and Chief Medical Officer
CIO: Justin K. Box, Senior Vice President and Chief Information Officer
CHR: Kathryn S Wall, Executive Vice President Human Resources and Organizational Development
CNO: Eileen L Dohmann, R.N., Senior Vice President and Chief Nursing Officer
Web address: www.mwhc.com
**Control:** Other not–for–profit (including NFP Corporation) **Service:** General medical and surgical

> **Staffed Beds:** 82 **Admissions:** 4924 **Census:** 46 **Outpatient Visits:** 70199 **Births:** 1239 **Total Expense ($000):** 101106 **Payroll Expense ($000):** 29200 **Personnel:** 425

**STAFFORD HOSPITAL CENTER** See Stafford Hospital

## STAUNTON—Staunton City County

**COMMONWEALTH CENTER FOR CHILDREN AND ADOLESCENTS**, 1355 Richmond Road, Zip 24401–9146, Mailing Address: Box 4000, Zip 24402–4000; tel. 540/332–2100, (Nonreporting) **A**3 5 **S** Virginia Department of Mental Health, Richmond, VA
Primary Contact: Jaime Bamford, M.D., Director
Web address: www.ccca.dbhds.virginia.gov
**Control:** State, Government, Nonfederal **Service:** Children's hospital psychiatric

> **Staffed Beds:** 60

**DE JARNETTE CENTER** See Commonwealth Center for Children and Adolescents

☐ **WESTERN STATE HOSPITAL (494021)**, 103 Valley Center Drive, Zip 24401–9146, Mailing Address: P.O. Box 2500, Zip 24402–2500; tel. 540/332–8000, (Nonreporting) **A**1 3 5 10 **F**3 29 30 34 39 44 50 53 59 65 68 75 77 86 87 97 98 100 101 130 132 135 146 149 154 **S** Virginia Department of Mental Health, Richmond, VA
Primary Contact: Mary Clare. Smith, Director
CFO: Jon Chapman, Fiscal Officer
CMO: Jonathan Anderson, Medical Director
CIO: Sharon Johnson, Director Health Information Management
CHR: Kimberly Harman, Regional Manager Human Resources
CNO: Diane Pavalonis, Chief Nurse Executive
Web address: www.dbhds.virginia.gov
**Control:** State, Government, Nonfederal **Service:** Psychiatric

> **Staffed Beds:** 246 **Admissions:** 1214 **Census:** 234 **Outpatient Visits:** 188 **Births:** 0 **Total Expense ($000):** 66359 **Payroll Expense ($000):** 34852 **Personnel:** 669

## SUFFOLK—Suffolk City County

⇑ **LOUISE OBICI MEMORIAL HOSPITAL** See Sentara Obici Hospital

★ ⇑ **SENTARA OBICI HOSPITAL (490044)**, 2800 Godwin Boulevard, Zip 23434–8038; tel. 757/934–4000, (Nonreporting) **A**2 3 5 10 21 **F**3 8 11 13 15 18 20 22 26 28 29 30 31 33 34 35 36 37 38 39 40 41 42 44 45 46 47 48 49 50 51 54 56 57 58 59 60 61 63 64 65 68 70 74 75 76 77 78 79 81 82 84 85 86 87 91 92 93 94 96 97 98 100 102 107 108 110 111 114 115 118 119 120 121 123 124 126 129 130 131 132 135 141 142 145 146 147 148 149 154 **P**6 **S** Sentara Healthcare, Norfolk, VA
Primary Contact: Coleen F. Santa Ana, President
CFO: Mike Mounie, Director Finance
CMO: Steve Julian, M.D., Vice President Medical Affairs
CIO: Alice Oxton, Director Information Technology
CHR: Deborah Ferguson, Human Resources Consultant
Web address: www.sentara.com
**Control:** Other not–for–profit (including NFP Corporation) **Service:** General medical and surgical

> **Staffed Beds:** 175 **Admissions:** 11456 **Census:** 131 **Outpatient Visits:** 395144 **Births:** 1365 **Total Expense ($000):** 219451 **Payroll Expense ($000):** 87295 **Personnel:** 1262

## TAPPAHANNOCK—Essex County

⇑ **RIVERSIDE TAPPAHANNOCK HOSPITAL (490084)**, 618 Hospital Road, Zip 22560–5000; tel. 804/443–3311, (Nonreporting) **A**10 20 21 **S** Riverside Health System, Newport News, VA
Primary Contact: Elizabeth J. Martin, Hospital President
CFO: Jeri Sibley, Director Revenue Cycle
CMO: Richard Dunn, M.D., Chief Medical Officer
CHR: Lindsey Custer, Director Human Resources
CNO: Judith Matthews, Nurse Executive
Web address: www.https://www.riversideonline.com
**Control:** Other not–for–profit (including NFP Corporation) **Service:** General medical and surgical

> **Staffed Beds:** 18

## TAZEWELL—Tazewell County

☒ **CARILION TAZEWELL COMMUNITY HOSPITAL (490117)**, 388 Ben Bolt Avenue, Zip 24651–9700; tel. 276/988–8700, (Nonreporting) **A**1 5 10 **F**3 11 15 29 30 34 40 44 50 57 59 62 64 65 68 75 77 85 87 91 93 107 111 114 119 133 135 146 149 **P**6 **S** Carilion Clinic, Roanoke, VA
Primary Contact: Alicia Bales, Senior Director, Chief Executive Officer and Chief Nursing Officer
CMO: Michael Rorrer, M.D., Chief of Medical Staff
CHR: Carrie Boggess, Human Resources Generalist
CNO: Alicia Bales, Senior Director, Chief Executive Officer and Chief Nursing Officer
Web address: www.carilionclinic.org
**Control:** Other not–for–profit (including NFP Corporation) **Service:** General medical and surgical

> **Staffed Beds:** 5 **Admissions:** 560 **Census:** 6 **Outpatient Visits:** 15196 **Births:** 0 **Total Expense ($000):** 16763 **Payroll Expense ($000):** 6003 **Personnel:** 122

**TAZEWELL COMMUNITY HOSPITAL** See Carilion Tazewell Community Hospital

**VA**

*Many Facility Codes have changed. Please refer to the AHA Guide Code Chart.* © 2021 AHA Guide

## VIRGINIA BEACH—Virginia Beach City County

⇑ **SENTARA BAYSIDE HOSPITAL** See Sentara Princess Anne Hospital

★ ⇑ **SENTARA PRINCESS ANNE HOSPITAL (490119)**, 2025 Glenn Mitchell Drive, Zip 23456–0178; tel. 757/507–1000, (Nonreporting) **A**2 3 5 10 21 **F**3 8 11 13 15 18 20 22 26 28 29 30 31 34 35 36 37 38 39 40 41 44 45 46 47 48 49 50 53 55 56 57 58 59 60 61 63 64 65 68 70 71 74 75 76 77 78 79 81 82 84 85 86 87 91 92 93 94 96 97 100 102 107 108 110 111 114 115 118 119 126 129 130 131 132 135 141 146 147 148 149 154 **S** Sentara Healthcare, Norfolk, VA
Primary Contact: Paul Gaden, Chief Executive Officer
COO: Howard P. Kern, Chief Operating Officer
CFO: Robert Broermann, Senior Vice President and Chief Financial Officer
CMO: Terry Gilliland, M.D., Senior Vice President and Chief Medical Officer
CIO: Bert Reese, Chief Information Officer
CHR: Michael V Taylor, Vice President Human Resources
CNO: Grace Myers, MSN, Vice President, Nurse Executive
Web address: www.sentara.com
**Control**: Other not–for–profit (including NFP Corporation) **Service**: General medical and surgical

**Staffed Beds: 153 Admissions:** 12474 **Census:** 149 **Outpatient Visits:** 401913 **Births:** 2105 **Total Expense ($000):** 267264 **Payroll Expense ($000):** 80837 **Personnel:** 1439

★ ⇑ **SENTARA VIRGINIA BEACH GENERAL HOSPITAL (490057)**, 1060 First Colonial Road, Zip 23454–3002; tel. 757/395–8000, (Nonreporting) **A**2 3 5 10 21 **F**3 4 5 11 15 17 18 20 22 24 26 28 29 30 31 33 34 35 36 37 38 39 40 41 42 43 44 45 46 47 48 49 50 51 53 54 55 56 57 58 59 60 61 62 63 64 65 68 70 71 74 75 77 78 79 80 81 82 84 85 86 87 90 91 92 93 94 96 97 98 100 102 104 105 107 108 110 111 114 115 118 119 120 121 123 126 129 130 131 132 135 141 142 145 146 147 148 149 152 153 154 155 156 **P**6 **S** Sentara Healthcare, Norfolk, VA
Primary Contact: Elwood Bernard. Boone III, FACHE, President
CFO: Marley Nacey, Director Finance
CHR: Michelle Meekins, Manager Human Resources
CNO: Peggy Braun, R.N., Vice President Patient Care Services and Chief Nurse Executive
Web address: www.sentara.com
**Control**: Other not–for–profit (including NFP Corporation) **Service**: General medical and surgical

**Staffed Beds: 204 Admissions:** 14653 **Census:** 204 **Outpatient Visits:** 448534 **Births:** 0 **Total Expense ($000):** 285306 **Payroll Expense ($000):** 116702 **Personnel:** 1733

⇑ **VIRGINIA BEACH GEN HOSPITAL** See Sentara Virginia Beach General Hospital

☐ **VIRGINIA BEACH PSYCHIATRIC CENTER (494025)**, 1100 First Colonial Road, Zip 23454–2403; tel. 757/496–6000, (Nonreporting) **A**1 10 **S** Universal Health Services, Inc., King of Prussia, PA
Primary Contact: Kurt Hooks, Chief Executive Officer
Web address: www.vbpcweb.com
**Control**: Corporation, Investor–owned (for–profit) **Service**: Psychiatric

**Staffed Beds: 100**

## WARRENTON—Fauquier County

⊞ **FAUQUIER HOSPITAL (490023)**, 500 Hospital Drive, Zip 20186–3099; tel. 540/316–5000, (Nonreporting) **A**1 2 10 **S** LifePoint Health, Brentwood, TN
Primary Contact: Chad Melton, Chief Executive Officer
CFO: Lionel J Phillips, Vice President Financial Services
CIO: Donna Staton, Chief Information Officer
CHR: Katy Reeves, Vice President Human Resources
CNO: Linda Sharkey, R.N., MSN, Vice President Patient Care Services and Chief Nurse Executive
Web address: www.fauquierhealth.org/
**Control**: Other not–for–profit (including NFP Corporation) **Service**: General medical and surgical

**Staffed Beds: 86**

## WILLIAMSBURG—James City County

☐ **EASTERN STATE HOSPITAL (490109)**, 4601 Ironbound Road, Zip 23188–2652; tel. 757/253–5161, (Nonreporting) **A**1 5 10 **S** Virginia Department of Mental Health, Richmond, VA
Primary Contact: Donna Moore, PsyD, Director
CFO: E Clifford Love, Director Fiscal Services
CMO: Guillermo Schrader, M.D., Acting Medical Director
CIO: Barbara Lambert, Director Healthcare Compliance
CHR: Edie Rogan, Manager Human Resources
Web address: www.esh.dmhmrsas.virginia.gov/
**Control**: State, Government, Nonfederal **Service**: Psychiatric

**Staffed Beds: 300**

⇑ **RIVERSIDE DOCTORS' HOSPITAL** See Riverside Doctors' Hospital Williamsburg

⇑ **RIVERSIDE DOCTORS' HOSPITAL WILLIAMSBURG (490143)**, 1500 Commonwealth Avenue, Zip 23185–5229; tel. 757/585–2200, (Nonreporting) **A**10 21 **S** Riverside Health System, Newport News, VA
Primary Contact: Steve C. McCary, Administrator
CNO: Arlene Messina, R.N., MSN, Director of Nursing
Web address: www.riversideonline.com/rdhw
**Control**: Other not–for–profit (including NFP Corporation) **Service**: General medical and surgical

**Staffed Beds: 14**

## WILLIAMSBURG—York County

⇑ **SENTARA WILLIAMSBURG COMM HOSP** See Sentara Williamsburg Regional Medical Center

★ ⇑ **SENTARA WILLIAMSBURG REGIONAL MEDICAL CENTER (490066)**, 100 Sentara Circle, Zip 23188–5713; tel. 757/984–6000, (Nonreporting) **A**2 10 21 **F**3 8 11 13 15 18 20 22 28 29 30 31 34 35 36 37 38 39 40 44 45 46 47 49 50 51 54 55 56 57 58 59 60 63 64 65 68 70 74 75 76 77 78 79 81 84 85 86 87 89 90 91 92 93 96 97 100 107 108 110 111 114 115 118 119 124 129 130 131 132 135 141 142 146 147 148 149 154 156 **P**6 **S** Sentara Healthcare, Norfolk, VA
Primary Contact: David J. Masterson, President
CFO: Andreas Roehrle, Director Finance
CMO: Joe Robbins, M.D., Vice President Medical Affairs
CIO: Mike Freeman, Director Information Technology
CHR: Lois B Demerich, Director Human Resources
CNO: Donna Wilmoth, Vice President Patient Care Services and Chief Nursing Officer
Web address: www.sentara.com
**Control**: Other not–for–profit (including NFP Corporation) **Service**: General medical and surgical

**Staffed Beds: 145 Admissions:** 7550 **Census:** 84 **Outpatient Visits:** 308577 **Births:** 869 **Total Expense ($000):** 176646 **Payroll Expense ($000):** 64754 **Personnel:** 932

☐ **THE PAVILION AT WILLIAMSBURG PLACE (494032)**, 5483 Mooretown Road, Zip 23188–2108; tel. 757/565–0106, (Nonreporting) **A**1 10
Primary Contact: Michael A. Post, Chief Executive Officer
CMO: Avtar Dhillon, M.D., Medical Director
CNO: Nicole K. Beer, Chief Nursing Officer
Web address: www.pavilionwp.com
**Control**: Corporation, Investor–owned (for–profit) **Service**: Psychiatric

**Staffed Beds: 66**

**VA**

---

| | Hospital, Medicare Provider Number, Address, Telephone, Approval, Facility, and Physician Codes, Health Care System | |
|---|---|---|
| ★ American Hospital Association (AHA) membership | ○ Healthcare Facilities Accreditation Program | ⇑ Center for Improvement in Healthcare Quality Accreditation |
| ☐ The Joint Commission accreditation | ◇ DNV Healthcare Inc. accreditation | △ Commission on Accreditation of Rehabilitation Facilities (CARF) accreditation |

## WINCHESTER—Winchester City County

✠ **VALLEY HEALTH - WINCHESTER MEDICAL CENTER (490005)**, 1840 Amherst Street, Zip 22601-2808, Mailing Address: P.O. Box 3340, Zip 22604-2540; tel. 540/536-8000, (Nonreporting) **A**1 2 3 5 10 20 **F**3 5 8 11 12 13 15 17 18 20 22 24 26 28 29 30 31 32 34 35 36 38 39 40 41 43 44 45 46 47 49 50 51 54 55 56 57 58 59 61 62 64 65 66 68 70 71 72 74 75 76 77 78 79 80 81 82 84 85 86 87 89 90 91 92 93 97 98 100 101 102 103 104 107 108 110 111 114 115 116 117 118 119 120 121 123 124 126 129 130 131 132 135 136 146 147 148 149 153 154 155 156 **P**6 **S** Valley Health System, Winchester, VA
Primary Contact: Grady W. Philips III, President
CFO: Robert Amos, Vice President and Chief Financial Officer
CMO: Nicolas Restrepo, M.D., Vice President Medical Affairs
CHR: Elizabeth Savage, Senior Vice President and Chief Human Resource Officer and Vice President Community Health and Wellness
CNO: Anne Whiteside, Vice President Nursing
Web address: www.valleyhealthlink.com/WMC
**Control**: Other not-for-profit (including NFP Corporation) **Service**: General medical and surgical

**Staffed Beds:** 541 **Admissions:** 23191 **Census:** 344 **Outpatient Visits:** 368151 **Births:** 2219 **Total Expense ($000):** 622556 **Payroll Expense ($000):** 181342 **Personnel:** 2393

**WINCHESTER MEDICAL CENTER** See Valley Health - Winchester Medical Center

## WOODBRIDGE—Prince William County

★ ⓕ **SENTARA NORTHERN VIRGINIA MEDICAL CENTER (490113)**, 2300 Opitz Boulevard, Zip 22191-3399; tel. 703/523-1000, (Nonreporting) **A**2 10 21 **F**3 8 11 12 13 15 18 20 22 26 28 29 30 31 34 35 36 38 40 41 42 43 44 45 48 49 50 53 54 55 56 57 58 59 60 61 62 63 64 65 66 68 70 71 72 74 75 76 77 78 79 81 82 84 85 86 87 91 92 93 94 96 97 102 107 108 110 111 114 115 118 119 121 126 130 131 132 135 141 143 145 146 147 148 149 154 156 **P**6 **S** Sentara Healthcare, Norfolk, VA
Primary Contact: Katherine Johnson, Ph.D., President
CMO: David M Schwartz, D.O., Vice President, Medical Affairs
CIO: Thomas Ewing, Director Information Technology
CHR: Brett Willsie, Vice President Human Resources
CNO: Valerie E Keane, FACHE, Chief Nursing Executive
Web address: www.sentara.com/northernvirginia
**Control**: Other not-for-profit (including NFP Corporation) **Service**: General medical and surgical

**Staffed Beds:** 183 **Admissions:** 10267 **Census:** 115 **Outpatient Visits:** 335327 **Births:** 1390 **Total Expense ($000):** 239085 **Payroll Expense ($000):** 87540 **Personnel:** 998

ⓕ **SENTARA POTOMAC HOSPITAL** See Sentara Northern Virginia Medical Center

## WOODSTOCK—Shenandoah County

✠ **VALLEY HEALTH - SHENANDOAH MEMORIAL HOSPITAL (491305)**, 759 South Main Street, Zip 22664-1127; tel. 540/459-1100, (Nonreporting) **A**1 10 18 **F**3 11 15 18 28 29 30 35 40 45 50 53 57 59 64 65 68 69 70 75 77 79 81 82 87 92 93 97 104 107 108 110 111 114 118 119 127 129 130 132 133 135 146 147 148 153 154 155 156 **P**6 **S** Valley Health System, Winchester, VA
Primary Contact: N. Travis. Clark, President
CFO: Phillip Graybeal, CPA, Vice President, Finance
CMO: Greg Byrd, Vice President Medical Affairs
CIO: James Burton, Vice President and Chief Information Officer, Valley Health
CHR: Abbey Rembold, Manager, Human Resource Business Partnerships
CNO: April McClain, Director, Acute Care
Web address: www.valleyhealthlink.com/shenandoah
**Control**: Other not-for-profit (including NFP Corporation) **Service**: General medical and surgical

**Staffed Beds:** 25 **Admissions:** 1365 **Census:** 17 **Outpatient Visits:** 142580 **Births:** 0 **Total Expense ($000):** 62187 **Payroll Expense ($000):** 25917 **Personnel:** 321

**VALLEY HEALTH SHENANDOAH MEMORIAL HOSPITAL** See Valley Health - Shenandoah Memorial Hospital

## WYTHEVILLE—Wythe County

✠ **WYTHE COUNTY COMMUNITY HOSPITAL (490111)**, 600 West Ridge Road, Zip 24382-1099; tel. 276/228-0200, (Nonreporting) **A**1 5 10 20 **F**3 12 13 15 18 26 27 28 29 34 35 37 40 50 51 57 59 65 68 70 75 76 77 79 81 82 86 87 91 92 93 97 107 110 111 114 119 128 129 130 131 132 133 135 144 146 147 148 154 156 **S** LifePoint Health, Brentwood, TN
Primary Contact: Joseph Wilkins, Chief Executive Officer
COO: Adam Martin, Chief Operating Officer
CFO: John D White, Chief Financial Officer
CMO: George Farrell, M.D., Chief of Staff
CIO: Andrea Harless, Director Information Services
CHR: Kristie E Walker, M.P.H., Director of Human Resources
CNO: Theresa Dix, R.N., Chief Nursing Officer
Web address: www.wcchcares.com
**Control**: Corporation, Investor-owned (for-profit) **Service**: General medical and surgical

**Staffed Beds:** 70 **Admissions:** 2350 **Census:** 20 **Outpatient Visits:** 58228 **Births:** 342 **Total Expense ($000):** 51859 **Payroll Expense ($000):** 15468 **Personnel:** 238

*Many Facility Codes have changed. Please refer to the AHA Guide Code Chart.*
© 2021 AHA Guide

# WASHINGTON

## ABERDEEN—Grays Harbor County

⇧ **GRAYS HARBOR COMMUNITY HOSPITAL (500031)**, 915 Anderson Drive,
Zip 98520–1006; tel. 360/532–8330, (Nonreporting) **A**10 20 21
Primary Contact: Tom Jensen, Chief Executive Officer
CMO: Anne Marie Wong, M.D., Chief Medical Officer
CIO: Brad Wallace, Director Information Services
CHR: Julie Feller, Executive Director Human Resources
CNO: Melanie Brandt EsqChief Nursing Officer
Web address: www.ghcares.org
**Control**: Other not–for–profit (including NFP Corporation) **Service**: General
medical and surgical

| Staffed Beds: 105 |
| --- |

⇧ **SUMMIT PACIFIC MEDICAL CENTER** See Grays Harbor Community Hospital

## ANACORTES—Skagit County

⇧ **ISLAND HEALTH NORTHWEST** See Island Hospital

★ ⇧ **ISLAND HOSPITAL (500007)**, 1211 24th Street, Zip 98221–2562;
tel. 360/299–1300, (Nonreporting) **A**5 10 21 **F**3 8 11 13 15 28 29 30 31 34 35
40 43 45 50 53 57 59 64 70 75 76 77 78 79 81 82 84 85 86 89 93 96 97 99
100 101 104 107 108 110 111 114 115 119 127 129 130 131 132 134 135
144 146 147 148 149 154 156 157
Primary Contact: Charles Hall, Chief Executive Officer
CFO: Elise Cutter, Chief Financial Officer
CIO: Tom Bluhm, Director Information Systems
CNO: Lois Pate, R.N., Chief Nursing Officer
Web address: www.islandhospital.org
**Control**: Hospital district or authority, Government, Nonfederal **Service**: General
medical and surgical

| Staffed Beds: 43 Admissions: 2471 Census: 19 Outpatient Visits: 117272 |
| --- |
| Births: 424 Total Expense ($000): 99480 Payroll Expense ($000): 41891 |
| Personnel: 589 |

## ARLINGTON—Snohomish County

⇧ **CASCADE VALLEY HOSPITAL (500060)**, 330 South Stillaguamish Avenue,
Zip 98223–1642; tel. 360/435–2133, (Nonreporting) **A**10 21 **S** Skagit Regional
Health, Mount Vernon, WA
Primary Contact: Brian K. Ivie, President and Chief Executive Officer
COO: Danny Vera, PharmD, Regional Vice President and Chief Operating Officer
CFO: Paul Ishizuka, Regional Vice President and Chief Financial Officer
CMO: James Fletcher, M.D., Medical Staff President
CIO: Lisa Buller, Regional Vice President and Chief Information Officer
CHR: Deborah Martin, Regional Vice President Human Resources
CNO: Michelle Sand, R.N., MSN, Vice President and Chief Nursing Officer
Web address: www.cascadevalley.org
**Control**: Hospital district or authority, Government, Nonfederal **Service**: General
medical and surgical

| Staffed Beds: 48 |
| --- |

⇧ **CASCADE VALLEY HOSPITAL AND CLINICS** See Cascade Valley Hospital

## AUBURN—King County

☐ **MULTICARE AUBURN MEDICAL CENTER (500015)**, 202 North Division, Plaza
One, Zip 98001–4908; tel. 253/833–7711, (Nonreporting) **A**1 3 10 **F**3 13 18 20
22 28 29 30 34 35 40 43 45 49 50 51 56 57 64 65 68 70 73 74 75 76 77 79
81 84 85 87 93 96 98 102 103 107 108 111 114 115 119 126 129 130 132
135 146 147 148 149 **S** MultiCare Health System, Tacoma, WA
Primary Contact: Mark T. Smith, JD, CPA, President and Chief Operating Officer
CMO: Chad Krilich, M.D., Chief Med Officer-AMC/CMC
CHR: Kevin B Dull, Senior Vice President Human Potential
CNO: Roseanna Bell, Chief Nurse Executive
Web address: www.https://www.multicare.org/auburn-medical-center/
**Control**: Other not–for–profit (including NFP Corporation) **Service**: General
medical and surgical

| Staffed Beds: 153 Admissions: 7121 Census: 120 Outpatient |
| --- |
| Visits: 77092 Births: 1108 Total Expense ($000): 184098 Payroll Expense |
| ($000): 84725 Personnel: 831 |

**MULTICARE AUBURN MEDICAL CENTER** See Multicare Auburn Medical Center

## BELLEVUE—King County

**OVERLAKE HOSPITAL MEDICAL CENTER** See Overlake Medical Center

⊞ **OVERLAKE MEDICAL CENTER (500051)**, 1035 116th Avenue NE,
Zip 98004–4604; tel. 425/688–5000, (Nonreporting) **A**1 3 10 **F**3 8 12 13 15
17 18 20 22 24 26 28 29 30 31 34 35 36 37 38 40 41 43 45 46 47 48 49 54
55 56 58 59 60 61 64 65 68 70 72 73 74 75 76 77 78 79 81 82 84 85 86 87
92 93 97 98 100 101 102 103 104 105 107 108 110 111 114 115 118 119
120 121 123 124 126 130 131 132 135 146 147 148 149 153 154 156 **P**6
Primary Contact: J. Michael. Marsh, President and Chief Executive Officer
COO: Thomas DeBord, Chief Operating Officer
CFO: Andrew Tokar, Chief Financial Officer
CMO: David Knoepfler, M.D., Chief Medical Officer
CHR: Lisa M Brock, Chief Human Resource Officer
Web address: www.overlakehospital.org
**Control**: Other not–for–profit (including NFP Corporation) **Service**: General
medical and surgical

| Staffed Beds: 291 Admissions: 17165 Census: 182 Outpatient |
| --- |
| Visits: 236547 Births: 3651 Total Expense ($000): 558603 Payroll |
| Expense ($000): 247016 Personnel: 2134 |

## BELLINGHAM—Whatcom County

⇧ **PEACEHEALTH ST. JOSEPH HOSPITAL** See Peacehealth St. Joseph Medical
Center

★ ⇧ **PEACEHEALTH ST. JOSEPH MEDICAL CENTER (500030)**, 2901 Squalicum
Parkway, Zip 98225–1851; tel. 360/734–5400, (Nonreporting) **A**2 5 10 20 21
**F**11 13 18 20 22 24 26 28 29 30 31 34 35 36 39 40 43 45 47 48 49 50 51
57 58 59 63 64 68 70 73 75 76 77 80 81 83 85 87 89 90 93 96 98 100 102
107 108 111 115 119 120 121 123 124 126 130 132 146 148 149 154 **S**
PeaceHealth, Vancouver, WA
Primary Contact: Charles Prosper, Chief Executive NW
COO: Stephen R Omta, Chief Operating Officer
CMO: Chris Sprowl, M.D., Vice President
CIO: Kelly Lundy, Chief Information Officer
CHR: Cindy C Klein, Vice President Human Resources
Web address: www.peacehealth.org
**Control**: Church operated, Nongovernment, not–for–profit **Service**: General
medical and surgical

| Staffed Beds: 255 Admissions: 15031 Census: 187 Outpatient |
| --- |
| Visits: 164655 Births: 1906 Total Expense ($000): 435509 Payroll |
| Expense ($000): 156416 Personnel: 1691 |

**WA**

---

**Hospital, Medicare Provider Number, Address, Telephone, Approval, Facility, and Physician Codes, Health Care System**

★ American Hospital Association (AHA) membership
☐ The Joint Commission accreditation
○ Healthcare Facilities Accreditation Program
◇ DNV Healthcare Inc. accreditation
⇧ Center for Improvement in Healthcare Quality Accreditation
△ Commission on Accreditation of Rehabilitation Facilities (CARF) accreditation

## BREMERTON—Kitsap County

**HARRISON MEDICAL CENTER** See St. Michael Medical Center

**NAVAL HOSPITAL** See Naval Hospital Bremerton

☒ **NAVAL HOSPITAL BREMERTON**, One Boone Road, Zip 98312–1898; tel. 360/475–4000, (Nonreporting) **A**1 3 5 **F**3 5 8 12 13 15 18 29 30 32 33 34 35 38 39 45 50 53 54 57 59 64 65 67 74 75 76 77 79 81 82 85 86 87 92 93 97 98 99 100 101 104 107 108 111 114 115 119 130 131 132 134 135 144 146 147 149 151 153 154 156 157 **S** Bureau of Medicine and Surgery, Department of the Navy, Falls Church, VA
Primary Contact: Captain Shannon J. Johnson, Commanding Officer
CFO: Judith Hogan, Comptroller and Director Resources and Logistics
CIO: Patrick Flaherty, Director Management Information
Web address: www.https://www.med.navy.mil/sites/nhbrem/Pages/Default.aspx
**Control**: Department of Defense, Government, federal **Service**: General medical and surgical

**Staffed Beds**: 23 **Admissions**: 823 **Census**: 5 **Outpatient Visits**: 254922 **Births**: 516

☒ **ST. MICHAEL MEDICAL CENTER (500039)**, 2520 Cherry Avenue, Zip 98310–4229; tel. 360/744–3911, (Nonreporting) **A**1 2 3 10 19 **F**3 11 12 13 15 18 20 22 24 26 28 29 30 31 34 35 38 40 43 44 45 46 49 50 54 57 59 60 64 70 73 74 75 76 77 78 79 80 81 82 84 85 86 87 93 94 96 107 108 110 111 114 115 117 118 119 120 121 124 126 129 130 132 135 144 146 147 148 149 154 **S** CommonSpirit Health, Chicago, IL
Primary Contact: David W. Schultz, FACHE, President, Peninsula Region
COO: Matthew Wheelus, Vice President, Chief Operating Officer
CFO: Mike Fitzgerald, Chief Financial Officer
CMO: David Weiss, M.D., Vice President, Medical Operations, Peninsula Region
CIO: Rand Strobel, Regional Chief Information Officer, Information Technology Services
CHR: Vickie Lackman, Human Resource Director, Peninsula Region
CNO: Jeanell Rasmussen, R.N., Vice President Patient Care Services and Chief Nursing Officer
Web address: www.chifranciscan.org/harrison
**Control**: Church operated, Nongovernment, not–for–profit **Service**: General medical and surgical

**Staffed Beds**: 232 **Admissions**: 13385 **Census**: 169 **Outpatient Visits**: 402271 **Births**: 1972 **Total Expense ($000)**: 466493 **Payroll Expense ($000)**: 135720 **Personnel**: 1963

## BREWSTER—Okanogan County

**OKANOGAN DOUGLAS DISTRICT HOSPITAL** See Three Rivers Hospital

★ **THREE RIVERS HOSPITAL (501324)**, 507 Hospital Way, Zip 98812–0577, Mailing Address: P.O. Box 577, Zip 98812–0577; tel. 509/689–2517, (Nonreporting) **A**10 18
Primary Contact: Scott Graham, Chief Executive Officer
CFO: Jennifer Munson, Chief Financial Officer
CMO: Gordon Tagge, M.D., President Medical Staff
CIO: Edgar Alejandro Arellano, Chief Information Technologist
CHR: Anita Fisk, Director Human Resources
CNO: Gretchen Aguilar, Director Patient Care and Chief Nursing Officer
Web address: www.threerivershospital.net
**Control**: Hospital district or authority, Government, Nonfederal **Service**: General medical and surgical

**Staffed Beds**: 20

## BURIEN—King County

**HIGHLINE MEDICAL CENTER** See St. Anne Hospital

☒ **ST. ANNE HOSPITAL (500011)**, 16251 Sylvester Road SW, Zip 98166–3052; tel. 206/244–9970, (Nonreporting) **A**1 2 10 **F**3 11 13 15 18 28 29 30 31 34 35 38 40 43 44 45 49 50 51 57 59 60 64 70 72 74 75 76 77 78 79 80 81 85 86 87 92 93 102 107 108 110 111 114 115 117 118 119 126 129 130 131 132 135 146 147 148 149 **S** CommonSpirit Health, Chicago, IL
Primary Contact: Russell Woolley, Chief Operating Officer
COO: Russell Woolley, Chief Operating Officer
CMO: Dennis De Leon, M.D., Associate Chief Medical Officer and Vice President Medical Affairs
CHR: Sharon Royne, Senior Vice President: Human Resources
CNO: Kim Baisch, R.N., Associate Vice President Patient Care Services
Web address: www.https://www.chifranciscan.org/highline-medical-center.html
**Control**: Church operated, Nongovernment, not–for–profit **Service**: General medical and surgical

**Staffed Beds**: 115 **Admissions**: 5899 **Census**: 77 **Outpatient Visits**: 118803 **Births**: 845 **Total Expense ($000)**: 197192 **Payroll Expense ($000)**: 61104 **Personnel**: 824

## CENTRALIA—Lewis County

☒ **PROVIDENCE CENTRALIA HOSPITAL (500019)**, 914 S Scheuber RD, Zip 98531–9027, Mailing Address: 914 South Scheuber Road, Zip 98531–9027; tel. 360/736–2803, (Nonreporting) **A**1 3 10 20 **F**3 8 11 13 15 29 30 31 34 35 40 43 50 51 57 58 59 64 68 70 75 76 77 78 79 80 81 82 84 85 86 87 93 107 108 110 111 114 115 116 117 118 119 120 121 123 124 130 132 146 148 149 150 154 **S** Providence St. Joseph Health, Renton, WA
Primary Contact: Darin Goss, FACHE, Site Administrator
CFO: Denise Marroni, Chief Financial Officer
CMO: Kevin Caserta, M.D., Chief Medical Officer
CIO: Kerry Miles, Site Director
CHR: Dana Vandewege, Director Human Resources
CNO: Michelle James, Regional Chief Nursing Officer
Web address: www.providence.org
**Control**: Church operated, Nongovernment, not–for–profit **Service**: General medical and surgical

**Staffed Beds**: 91 **Admissions**: 4381 **Census**: 55 **Outpatient Visits**: 314606 **Births**: 642 **Total Expense ($000)**: 621974 **Payroll Expense ($000)**: 552162 **Personnel**: 661

**PROVIDENCE HOSPITAL** See Providence Centralia Hospital

## CHELAN—Chelan County

**LAKE CHELAN COMMUNITY HOSPITAL** See Lake Chelan Community Hospital and Clinics

★ **LAKE CHELAN COMMUNITY HOSPITAL AND CLINICS (501334)**, 503 East Highland Avenue, Zip 98816–8631, Mailing Address: P.O. Box 908, Zip 98816–0908; tel. 509/682–3300, (Nonreporting) **A**3 10 18
Primary Contact: George A. Rohrich, FACHE, Chief Executive Officer
COO: Brad Hankins, Chief Operating Quality Officer
CFO: Mike Ellis, Chief Financial Officer
CMO: Ty Witt, M.D., Chief Medical Officer
CIO: Ross Hurd, Chief Information Officer
CHR: DeLynn K Barnett, Director Human Resources
Web address: www.lakechelancommunityhospital.com
**Control**: Hospital district or authority, Government, Nonfederal **Service**: General medical and surgical

**Staffed Beds**: 25

## CHEWELAH—Stevens County

☒ **PROVIDENCE ST. JOSEPH'S HOSPITAL (501309)**, 500 East Webster Street, Zip 99109–9523; tel. 509/935–8211, (Nonreporting) **A**1 10 18 **S** Providence St. Joseph Health, Renton, WA
Primary Contact: Ronald G. Rehn, Chief Executive Officer
CFO: Helen Andrus, Chief Financial Officer
CMO: Jeff Collins, Chief Medical Officer
CNO: Deborah Watson, R.N., Chief Nursing Officer
Web address: www.washington.providence.org/hospitals/st-josephs-hospital/
**Control**: Church operated, Nongovernment, not–for–profit **Service**: General medical and surgical

**Staffed Beds**: 55

**ST. JOSEPH'S HOSPITAL** See Providence St. Joseph's Hospital

## CLARKSTON—Asotin County

★ ⋔ **TRI-STATE MEMORIAL HOSPITAL (501332)**, 1221 Highland Avenue, Zip 99403–2829, Mailing Address: P.O. Box 189, Zip 99403–0189; tel. 509/758–5511, (Nonreporting) **A**10 18 21
Primary Contact: Donald Wee, Chief Executive Officer
CFO: Alex Town, Vice President Finance
CMO: Don Greggain, M.D., Physician Network Director
CIO: Joleen Carper, Vice President Quality and Risk
CHR: Regana Davis, Vice President Human Resources
CNO: Rhonda Mason, Vice President of Patient Care Services
Web address: www.tsmh.org
**Control**: Other not–for–profit (including NFP Corporation) **Service**: General medical and surgical

**Staffed Beds**: 25

## COLFAX—Whitman County

**WHITMAN HOSPITAL** See Whitman Hospital and Medical Center

★ **WHITMAN HOSPITAL AND MEDICAL CENTER (501327)**, 1200 West Fairview Street, Zip 99111–9579; tel. 509/397–3435, (Nonreporting) **A**10 18 **F**3 13 15 29 34 35 36 40 43 45 50 53 56 64 68 75 76 79 81 82 84 85 87 93 97 107 110 111 119 130 131 133 154 156 **P**6 **S** Providence St. Joseph Health, Renton, WA
Primary Contact: Hank Hanigan, FACHE, Chief Executive Officer
CFO: Hank Hanigan, FACHE, Interim Chief Financial Officer
CMO: Bryan N Johnson, M.D., Chief Medical Officer
CHR: Michelle Ellis, Director Human Resources
CNO: Pam Akin, R.N., MSN, Chief Nursing Officer
Web address: www.whitmanhospital.org
**Control:** Hospital district or authority, Government, Nonfederal **Service:** General medical and surgical

**Staffed Beds:** 21 **Admissions:** 746 **Census:** 4 **Outpatient Visits:** 36179 **Births:** 35 **Total Expense ($000):** 34092 **Payroll Expense ($000):** 13761 **Personnel:** 223

## COLVILLE—Stevens County

**MOUNT CARMEL HOSPITAL** See Providence Mount Carmel Hospital

▣ **PROVIDENCE MOUNT CARMEL HOSPITAL (501326)**, 982 East Columbia Avenue, Zip 99114–3352; tel. 509/685–5100, (Nonreporting) **A**1 3 10 18 **S** Providence St. Joseph Health, Renton, WA
Primary Contact: Ronald G. Rehn, Chief Executive Officer
CFO: Helen Andrus, Chief Financial Officer
CNO: Deborah Watson, R.N., Chief Nursing Officer
Web address: www.mtcarmelhospital.org
**Control:** Church operated, Nongovernment, not–for–profit **Service:** General medical and surgical

**Staffed Beds:** 25

## COUPEVILLE—Island County

**WHIDBEY GENERAL HOSPITAL** See Whidbeyhealth

★ **WHIDBEYHEALTH (501339)**, 101 North Main Street, Zip 98239–3413; tel. 360/678–5151, (Nonreporting) **A**2 10 18 **F**3 7 8 11 12 13 15 20 28 29 30 31 34 35 36 38 40 43 44 45 46 47 49 50 54 59 62 63 64 65 70 75 76 77 78 79 81 83 84 86 87 93 97 102 107 108 109 110 111 112 119 127 128 129 130 133 135 143 144 146 147 148 154 156
Primary Contact: Ron Telles, Interim Chief Executive Officer
CFO: Ron Telles, Chief Financial Officer
CMO: Gabe Barrio, M.D., Chief of Staff
CNO: Linda Stephens Gipson, MSN, Ph.D., Chief Nursing Officer
Web address: www.https//whidbeyhealth.org/
**Control:** Hospital district or authority, Government, Nonfederal **Service:** General medical and surgical

**Staffed Beds:** 25 **Admissions:** 1364 **Census:** 12 **Outpatient Visits:** 192464 **Births:** 224 **Total Expense ($000):** 117418 **Payroll Expense ($000):** 53079

## COVINGTON—King County

☐ **MULTICARE COVINGTON MEDICAL CENTER (500154)**, 17700 SE 272nd Street, Zip 98042–4951; tel. 253/372–6500, (Nonreporting) **A**1 **S** MultiCare Health System, Tacoma, WA
Primary Contact: Mark T. Smith, JD, CPA, President and Chief Operating Officer
**Control:** Corporation, Investor–owned (for–profit) **Service:** General medical and surgical

**Staffed Beds:** 58

## DAVENPORT—Lincoln County

**LINCOLN CNTY HOSP DISTRICT 3** See Lincoln Hospital

★ **LINCOLN HOSPITAL (501305)**, 10 Nicholls Street, Zip 99122–9729; tel. 509/725–7101, (Nonreporting) **A**10 18
Primary Contact: Tyson Lacy, Chief Executive Officer and Superintendent
CFO: Tim O'Connell, Chief Financial Officer
CMO: Fred Reed, M.D., Chief of Staff
CIO: Elliott Donson, Chief Information Specialist
CHR: Becky Bailey, Director Human Resources
CNO: Jennifer Larmer, R.N., Chief Clinical Officer
Web address: www.lincolnhospital.org
**Control:** Hospital district or authority, Government, Nonfederal **Service:** General medical and surgical

**Staffed Beds:** 50

## DAYTON—Columbia County

★ **COLUMBIA COUNTY HEALTH SYSTEM (501302)**, 1012 South Third Street, Zip 99328–1696; tel. 509/382–2531, (Nonreporting) **A**10 18
Primary Contact: Shane McGuire, Chief Executive Officer
CHR: Steven J Stahl, Director Human Resources
CNO: Stephanie Carpenter, Director of Nursing Services
Web address: www.cchd-wa.org
**Control:** County, Government, Nonfederal **Service:** General medical and surgical

**Staffed Beds:** 44

**DAYTON GENERAL HOSPITAL** See Columbia County Health System

## EDMONDS—Snohomish County

⇧ **STEVENS HEALTHCARE** See Swedish/Edmonds

★ ⇧ **SWEDISH/EDMONDS (500026)**, 21601 76th Avenue West, Zip 98026–7506; tel. 425/640–4000, (Nonreporting) **A**2 3 10 21 **F**2 3 11 13 15 18 20 22 26 28 29 30 31 34 35 38 40 41 43 45 49 56 59 61 64 65 68 70 73 74 75 76 77 78 79 81 82 84 85 87 91 92 93 96 98 100 101 102 104 107 108 111 114 115 116 119 124 126 129 130 131 132 135 141 146 147 148 149 154 **S** Swedish Health Services, Seattle, WA
Primary Contact: David R. West, Vice President, Operations
CMO: Sandeep Sachdeva, M.D., Vice President Medical Affairs
CNO: Jean Doerge, R.N., MSN, Nurse Executive
Web address: www.swedish.org
**Control:** Other not–for–profit (including NFP Corporation) **Service:** General medical and surgical

**Staffed Beds:** 185 **Admissions:** 9879 **Census:** 133 **Outpatient Visits:** 135019 **Births:** 1336 **Total Expense ($000):** 278725 **Payroll Expense ($000):** 97608 **Personnel:** 801

## ELLENSBURG—Kittitas County

**KITTITAS VALLEY COMMUNITY HOSPITAL** See Kittitas Valley Healthcare

★ **KITTITAS VALLEY HEALTHCARE (501333)**, 603 South Chestnut Street, Zip 98926–3875; tel. 509/962–7302, (Nonreporting) **A**3 10 18 **F**3 13 15 29 30 34 35 37 40 41 43 44 45 46 50 56 57 59 62 63 64 65 68 70 73 75 76 77 79 81 84 85 87 89 93 96 102 107 110 111 115 119 127 130 131 132 133 144 146 147 148 149 154 156
Primary Contact: Julie Petersen, CPA, Chief Executive Officer
CFO: Libby Allgood, Chief Financial Officer
CMO: Don Solberg, M.D., Chief Medical Officer
CIO: Jack Schwartz, Director Information Technology
CHR: Carrie Youngblood, Director of Human Resources
CNO: Vicky Machorro, R.N., Chief Nursing Officer
Web address: www.kvhealthcare.org
**Control:** Hospital district or authority, Government, Nonfederal **Service:** General medical and surgical

**Staffed Beds:** 25 **Admissions:** 941 **Census:** 8 **Outpatient Visits:** 65526 **Births:** 309 **Total Expense ($000):** 80626 **Payroll Expense ($000):** 41754 **Personnel:** 528

## ELMA—Grays Harbor County

**MARK REED HEALTH CARE DISTRICT** See Summit Pacific Medical Center

**SUMMIT PACIFIC MEDICAL CENTER (501304)**, 600 East Main Street, Zip 98541–9560; tel. 360/346–2222, (Nonreporting) **A**3 10 18
Primary Contact: Josh Martin, Chief Executive Officer
COO: Josh Martin, Chief Operating Officer
CFO: James Hansen, Chief Financial Officer
CMO: William Hurley, M.D., Chief Medical Officer
CIO: Jeff Painter, Manager Information Technology
CHR: Mindy Portchy, Manager Human Resources
Web address: www.markreed.org
**Control:** Corporation, Investor–owned (for–profit) **Service:** General medical and surgical

**Staffed Beds:** 6

**WA**

---

## ENUMCLAW—King County

**ENUMCLAW REGIONAL HOSPITAL** See St. Elizabeth Hospital

★ **ST. ELIZABETH HOSPITAL (501335)**, 1455 Battersby Avenue, Zip 98022–3634, Mailing Address: P.O. Box 218, Zip 98022–0218; tel. 360/802–8800, (Nonreporting) **A**10 18 **F**3 13 15 18 29 30 35 38 40 44 45 50 59 64 70 74 75 76 79 81 85 87 93 107 108 110 111 114 115 119 130 132 133 135 146 147 149 154 **S** CommonSpirit Health, Chicago, IL
Primary Contact: Tim O'Haver, Market President
COO: Joseph Wilczek, Chief Executive Officer
CFO: Philip Hjembo, Chief Financial Officer
CHR: Jerilyn Ray, Manager Human Resources
Web address: www.fhshealth.org
**Control:** Church operated, Nongovernment, not–for–profit **Service:** General medical and surgical

**Staffed Beds:** 25 **Admissions:** 1506 **Census:** 14 **Outpatient Visits:** 35108 **Births:** 357 **Total Expense ($000):** 51499 **Payroll Expense ($000):** 17705 **Personnel:** 283

## EPHRATA—Grant County

★ **COLUMBIA BASIN HOSPITAL (501317)**, 200 Nat Washington Way, Zip 98823–1982; tel. 509/754–4631, (Total facility includes 12 beds in nursing home–type unit) (Nonreporting) **A**10 18 **F**3 10 11 15 29 30 32 34 35 40 50 56 59 65 75 77 84 91 93 97 107 108 111 114 119 127 128 130 132 133 146
Primary Contact: Rosalinda Kibby, Superintendent and Administrator
CFO: Rhonda Handley, Chief Financial Officer
CMO: Lowell C Allred, M.D., Chief of Staff
CHR: Suzanne Little, Human Resources Specialist
Web address: www.columbiabasinhospital.org
**Control:** Hospital district or authority, Government, Nonfederal **Service:** General medical and surgical

**Staffed Beds:** 69 **Admissions:** 270 **Census:** 25 **Outpatient Visits:** 17525 **Births:** 0 **Total Expense ($000):** 20345 **Payroll Expense ($000):** 8523 **Personnel:** 124

## EVERETT—Snohomish County

**PROVIDENCE EVERETT MEDICAL CTR** See Providence Regional Medical Center Everett

**PROVIDENCE GENERAL MEDICAL CTR** See Providence Everett Medical Center - Colby Campus

**PROVIDENCE GENERAL MEDICAL CTR** See Providence Everett Medical Center - Pacific Campus

⊞ △ **PROVIDENCE REGIONAL MEDICAL CENTER EVERETT (500014)**, 1321 Colby Avenue, Zip 98201–1665, Mailing Address: P.O. Box 1147, Zip 98206–1147; tel. 425/261–2000, (Includes PROVIDENCE EVERETT MEDICAL CENTER - COLBY CAMPUS, Mailing address: 1321 Colby Avenue, Everett, Washington, Zip 98206, P O Box 1147, Zip 98206, tel. 425/261–2000; PROVIDENCE EVERETT MEDICAL CENTER - PACIFIC CAMPUS, Mailing address: Pacific and Nassau Streets, Everett, Washington, Zip 98201, P O Box 1067, Zip 98206–1067, tel. 206/258–7123), (Nonreporting) **A**1 2 3 5 7 10 **F**3 4 5 11 12 13 15 18 20 22 24 26 28 29 30 31 32 34 35 36 37 38 40 43 44 45 46 47 48 49 50 54 55 56 57 58 59 61 64 68 70 72 73 74 75 76 77 78 79 80 81 84 85 86 87 89 90 93 94 96 100 101 107 108 109 110 111 114 115 116 117 118 119 120 121 123 124 126 129 130 132 135 146 147 148 149 150 154 157 **P**6 **S** Providence St. Joseph Health, Renton, WA
Primary Contact: Kim Williams, R.N., MS, Chief Executive Officer
CFO: Sheri Feeney, Chief Financial Officer
CMO: Frank Andersen, Interim Chief Medical Officer
CIO: Matt Wonser, Director, Information Services
CHR: Lori A Vocca, Vice President Human Resources
CNO: Barbara M Hyland-Hill, R.N., Chief Nursing Officer
Web address: www.providence.org
**Control:** Church operated, Nongovernment, not–for–profit **Service:** General medical and surgical

**Staffed Beds:** 571 **Admissions:** 29446 **Census:** 430 **Outpatient Visits:** 492902 **Births:** 4531

## FEDERAL WAY—King County

**ST FRANCIS COMM HOSPITAL** See St. Francis Hospital

⊞ **ST. FRANCIS HOSPITAL (500141)**, 34515 Ninth Avenue South, Zip 98003–6799; tel. 253/944–8100, (Nonreporting) **A**1 3 5 10 **F**3 8 11 12 13 15 18 20 22 26 28 29 30 31 34 35 38 40 43 44 45 49 50 51 57 59 60 64 70 72 74 75 76 77 78 79 80 81 85 86 87 92 93 107 108 110 111 114 115 117 118 119 126 129 130 131 132 135 146 147 149 154 **S** CommonSpirit Health, Chicago, IL
Primary Contact: Dino Johnson, R.N., Chief Operating Officer
COO: Dino Johnson, R.N., Chief Operating Officer
CFO: Mike Fitzgerald, Chief Financial Officer
CMO: Dennis deLeon, M.D., Chief Medical Officer, King Region
CIO: Rand Strobel, Regional Chief Information Officer
CHR: Les Soltis, Director - Human Resources
Web address: www.fhshealth.org
**Control:** Church operated, Nongovernment, not–for–profit **Service:** General medical and surgical

**Staffed Beds:** 124 **Admissions:** 7805 **Census:** 89 **Outpatient Visits:** 172882 **Births:** 1288 **Total Expense ($000):** 220440 **Payroll Expense ($000):** 71755 **Personnel:** 1014

## FORKS—Clallam County

⇑ **FORKS COMMUNITY HOSPITAL (501325)**, 530 Bogachiel Way, Zip 98331–9120; tel. 360/374–6271, (Nonreporting) **A**10 18 21
Primary Contact: Heidi Anderson, Chief Executive Officer
CFO: Joe Bradick, Chief Financial Officer
CIO: Andrea Perkins-Peppers, Chief Information Officer
CHR: Cindy Paget, Chief Human Resources Officer
CNO: Laura Kripinski, Chief Nursing Officer
Web address: www.forkshospital.org
**Control:** Hospital district or authority, Government, Nonfederal **Service:** General medical and surgical

**Staffed Beds:** 45

## FRIDAY HARBOR—San Juan County

★ ⇑ **PEACEHEALTH PEACE ISLAND MEDICAL CENTER (501340)**, 1117 Spring Street, Zip 98250–9782; tel. 360/378–2141, (Nonreporting) **A**5 10 18 21 **F**29 30 31 34 40 45 59 64 65 68 75 78 79 81 97 100 102 104 107 115 119 130 132 135 146 149 154 **S** PeaceHealth, Vancouver, WA
Primary Contact: Jack Estrada, Chief Administrative Officer
CFO: Carolyn Foster, Chief Financial Officer
CMO: Michael Sullivan, M.D., Medical Director Emergency Services
CHR: Lorraine Allison, Human Resource Partner
CNO: Sheryl Murphy, Chief Nursing Officer and Director of Clinical Services
Web address: www.peacehealth.org
**Control:** Church operated, Nongovernment, not–for–profit **Service:** General medical and surgical

**Staffed Beds:** 10 **Admissions:** 82 **Census:** 1 **Outpatient Visits:** 18912 **Births:** 0 **Total Expense ($000):** 17010 **Payroll Expense ($000):** 6704 **Personnel:** 67

## GIG HARBOR—Pierce County

⊞ **ST. ANTHONY HOSPITAL (500151)**, 11567 Canterwood Boulevard NW, Zip 98332–5812; tel. 253/530–2000, (Nonreporting) **A**1 3 10 **F**3 11 15 18 20 29 30 31 34 38 40 44 45 49 50 51 59 60 64 70 74 75 77 78 79 81 85 86 87 92 93 107 108 110 111 114 115 118 119 126 129 130 131 132 135 146 147 154 **S** CommonSpirit Health, Chicago, IL
Primary Contact: David W. Schultz, FACHE, President, Peninsula Region
Web address: www.chifranciscan.org/
**Control:** Church operated, Nongovernment, not–for–profit **Service:** General medical and surgical

**Staffed Beds:** 112 **Admissions:** 5254 **Census:** 69 **Outpatient Visits:** 82381 **Births:** 0 **Total Expense ($000):** 148744 **Payroll Expense ($000):** 45153 **Personnel:** 646

*Many Facility Codes have changed. Please refer to the AHA Guide Code Chart.*

## GOLDENDALE—Klickitat County

**KLICKITAT VALLEY HEALTH (501316)**, 310 South Roosevelt Avenue, Zip 98620–9201; tel. 509/773–4022, (Nonreporting) **A**10 18
Primary Contact: Leslie Hiebert, Chief Executive Officer
CFO: Jamie Eldred, Controller
CMO: Rod Krehbiel, M.D., Chief of Staff
CIO: Jonathan Hatfield, Supervisor Information Technology
CHR: Herbert Hill, Director Human Resources
CNO: Gwen Cox, Director Nursing Services
Web address: www.kvhealth.net
**Control**: Hospital district or authority, Government, Nonfederal **Service**: General medical and surgical

**Staffed Beds: 17**

**KLICKITAT VALLEY HEALTH SERVS** See Klickitat Valley Health

## GRAND COULEE—Grant County

**COULEE COMMUNITY HOSPITAL** See Coulee Medical Center

★ **COULEE MEDICAL CENTER (501308)**, 411 Fortuyn Road, Zip 99133–8718; tel. 509/633–1753, (Nonreporting) **A**10 18 **F**8 15 29 32 40 41 43 45 47 48 50 56 57 59 64 65 75 76 79 81 82 83 84 85 86 87 93 97 107 110 114 119 127 128 130 133 144 147 148 149 154 156
Primary Contact: Ramona Hicks, Chief Executive Officer
CFO: Paul Babcock, Chief Financial Officer
CMO: Andrew Castrodale, M.D., Chief Medical Officer
CHR: Heather McCleary, Director Human Resources
Web address: www.cmccares.org
**Control**: Hospital district or authority, Government, Nonfederal **Service**: General medical and surgical

**Staffed Beds: 25 Admissions: 429 Census: 17 Outpatient Visits: 25376 Births: 60 Total Expense ($000): 38495 Payroll Expense ($000): 15469 Personnel: 210**

## ILWACO—Pacific County

★ **OCEAN BEACH HOSPITAL (501314)**, 174 First Avenue North, Zip 98624–9137, Mailing Address: P.O. Box H, Zip 98624–0258; tel. 360/642–3181, (Nonreporting) **A**10 18 **F**3 11 15 18 28 29 30 34 35 40 43 45 56 57 59 68 75 77 78 79 81 85 86 87 93 97 102 107 108 111 115 119 127 128 130 132 133 135 149 154 156 **P**6
Primary Contact: Larry Cohen, Chief Executive Officer
CFO: Kathy Hubbard, Controller
CMO: Patty Malone, M.D., Chief Medical Officer
CIO: Julie P Oakes, R.N., Manager Risk and Quality
CHR: Beth Whitton, Director Human Resources
CNO: Linda Kaino, Chief Nursing Officer
Web address: www.oceanbeachhospital.com
**Control**: Hospital district or authority, Government, Nonfederal **Service**: General medical and surgical

**Staffed Beds: 25 Admissions: 399 Census: 5 Outpatient Visits: 38938 Births: 0 Total Expense ($000): 27758 Payroll Expense ($000): 12150 Personnel: 141**

## ISSAQUAH—King County

★ ⇑ **SWEDISH/ISSAQUAH (500152)**, 751 NE Blakely Drive, Zip 98029–6201; tel. 425/313–4000, (Nonreporting) **A**3 10 21 **F**3 12 13 15 18 20 22 29 30 31 34 35 37 38 40 41 45 48 49 50 56 57 58 59 61 64 65 68 70 73 74 75 76 77 78 79 81 82 85 86 87 89 92 93 96 97 102 107 108 110 111 114 115 126 129 130 131 132 134 135 141 143 146 147 148 149 154 **S** Swedish Health Services, Seattle, WA
Primary Contact: R. Guy Hudson, Chief Executive Officer
COO: Jeffery Robert, Chief Operating Officer
Web address: www.swedish.org/issaquah
**Control**: Other not–for–profit (including NFP Corporation) **Service**: General medical and surgical

**Staffed Beds: 153 Admissions: 6607 Census: 58 Outpatient Visits: 129917 Births: 1593 Total Expense ($000): 231709 Payroll Expense ($000): 63239 Personnel: 503**

## KENNEWICK—Benton County

**KENNEWICK GENERAL HOSPITAL** See Trios Health

✚ **TRIOS HEALTH (500053)**, 900 South Auburn Street, Zip 99336–5621, Mailing Address: P.O. Box 6128, Zip 99336–0128; tel. 509/586–6111, (Nonreporting) **A**1 2 3 5 10 13 **F**3 11 13 15 18 22 28 29 31 34 35 40 43 45 49 50 56 57 59 64 65 70 73 75 76 77 78 81 82 84 85 87 89 97 107 108 110 111 115 118 119 126 129 130 132 144 146 147 148 156 157 **S** LifePoint Health, Brentwood, TN
Primary Contact: John H. Solheim, Chief Executive Officer
CFO: Jason Hotchkiss, CPA, Chief Financial Officer
CIO: Michael Cloutier, Director Information Services
CHR: Russ Keefer, Chief Human Resources Officer
Web address: www.trioshealth.org
**Control**: Corporation, Investor–owned (for–profit) **Service**: General medical and surgical

**Staffed Beds: 109 Admissions: 5496 Census: 53 Outpatient Visits: 67539 Births: 1397 Total Expense ($000): 168600 Payroll Expense ($000): 70382 Personnel: 904**

## KIRKLAND—King County

**EVERGREEN HOSPITAL MEDICAL CENTER** See Evergreenhealth

✚ **EVERGREENHEALTH (500124)**, 12040 NE 128th Street, Zip 98034–3013; tel. 425/899–1000, (Nonreporting) **A**1 **F**3 8 12 13 15 18 20 22 28 29 30 34 35 37 38 40 42 43 44 45 46 49 50 51 54 55 56 57 58 59 61 62 63 64 65 68 70 71 72 73 74 75 76 78 79 80 81 82 84 85 86 87 89 90 91 92 93 94 95 96 97 100 104 107 108 110 111 114 115 118 119 120 121 123 124 126 129 130 131 132 134 135 142 146 147 148 149 154 156 **P**4 6
Primary Contact: Jeffrey Tomlin, M.D., Chief Executive Officer
COO: Christopher Bredeson, Chief Operating Officer
CFO: Tina Mycroft, Senior Vice President, Chief Financial Officer
CIO: Tom Martin, Senior Vice President, Strategy and Information Technology Officer
CHR: Bob Sampson, Senior Vice President, Human Resources
CNO: Mary Shepler, R.N., Seniro Vice President, Chief Nursing Officer
Web address: www.evergreenhealth.com
**Control**: Hospital district or authority, Government, Nonfederal **Service**: General medical and surgical

**Staffed Beds: 318 Admissions: 15200 Census: 169 Outpatient Visits: 1229575 Births: 4673 Total Expense ($000): 739267 Payroll Expense ($000): 396534 Personnel: 3737**

✚ **FAIRFAX BEHAVIORAL HEALTH (504002)**, 10200 NE 132nd Street, Zip 98034–2899; tel. 425/821–2000, (Includes FAIRFAX BEHAVIORAL HEALTH EVERETT, Mailing address: 916 Pacific Avenue, Everett, Washington, Zip 98201–4147; tel. 425/821–2000), (Nonreporting) **A**1 10 **F**29 50 64 87 97 98 99 100 101 103 105 130 153 **P**6 **S** Universal Health Services, Inc., King of Prussia, PA
Primary Contact: Ron Escarda, Interim Chief Executive Officer
COO: Todd Thama, Chief Operating Officer
CFO: Pam Rhoads, Chief Financial Officer
CMO: Samir Aziz, M.D., Medical Director
CHR: Anne Schreiber, Manager Human Resources
Web address: www.fairfaxhospital.com
**Control**: Corporation, Investor–owned (for–profit) **Service**: Psychiatric

**Staffed Beds: 221 Admissions: 5245 Census: 190 Outpatient Visits: 5869 Births: 0 Total Expense ($000): 74814 Payroll Expense ($000): 30468 Personnel: 435**

**FAIRFAX HOSPITAL** See Fairfax Behavioral Health

**WA**

---

**Hospital, Medicare Provider Number, Address, Telephone, Approval, Facility, and Physician Codes, Health Care System**

★ American Hospital Association (AHA) membership    ○ Healthcare Facilities Accreditation Program    ⇑ Center for Improvement in Healthcare Quality Accreditation
□ The Joint Commission accreditation    ◇ DNV Healthcare Inc. accreditation    △ Commission on Accreditation of Rehabilitation Facilities (CARF) accreditation

## LAKEWOOD—Pierce County

**ST CLARE HOSPITAL** See St. Clare Hospital

⊠ **ST. CLARE HOSPITAL (500021)**, 11315 Bridgeport Way SW, Zip 98499–3004; tel. 253/985–1711, (Nonreporting) **A**1 3 10 **F**3 8 18 29 30 31 34 35 38 40 44 45 49 50 51 57 59 60 64 70 74 75 77 78 79 80 81 82 85 86 87 92 93 107 108 111 114 118 119 126 129 130 131 132 135 146 149 154 **S** CommonSpirit Health, Chicago, IL
Primary Contact: Tim O'Haver, President
CFO: Mike Fitzgerald, Chief Financial Officer
CIO: Bruce Elkington, Regional Chief Information Officer
CHR: David C. Lawson, Senior Vice President Human Resources
Web address: www.fhshealth.org
**Control:** Church operated, Nongovernment, not–for–profit **Service:** General medical and surgical

**Staffed Beds:** 104 **Admissions:** 5319 **Census:** 87 **Outpatient Visits:** 96206
**Births:** 0 **Total Expense ($000):** 149536 **Payroll Expense ($000):** 49626
**Personnel:** 680

## LEAVENWORTH—Chelan County

**CASCADE GENERAL HOSPITAL** See Cascade Medical Center

★ **CASCADE MEDICAL CENTER (501313)**, 817 Commercial Street, Zip 98826–1316; tel. 509/548–5815, (Nonreporting) **A**5 10 18 **F**3 7 15 34 40 41 45 50 59 64 65 68 77 87 93 94 97 104 107 110 114 127 130 131 132 133 148 **P**6
Primary Contact: Diane Blake, Chief Executive Officer
COO: Pat Songer, Chief Operations Officer
CFO: Jim Hopkins, Chief Financial Officer
CMO: Jerome Jerome, M.D., Clinic Medical Director
CIO: Charles Amstutz, Director of Information Technology
CHR: Reyne Boik, Director Human Resources
CNO: Shawn Ottley, R.N., Chief Clinical Officer
Web address: www.cascademedical.org
**Control:** Hospital district or authority, Government, Nonfederal **Service:** General medical and surgical

**Staffed Beds:** 9 **Admissions:** 141 **Census:** 4 **Outpatient Visits:** 39023
**Births:** 0 **Total Expense ($000):** 20168 **Payroll Expense ($000):** 10596
**Personnel:** 165

## LONGVIEW—Cowlitz County

★ ⇑ **PEACEHEALTH ST. JOHN MEDICAL CENTER (500041)**, 1615 Delaware Street, Zip 98632–2367, Mailing Address: P.O. Box 3002, Zip 98632–0302; tel. 360/414–2000, (Nonreporting) **A**2 10 21 **F**11 15 18 20 29 30 31 34 40 43 68 70 75 76 78 79 81 82 98 107 111 119 129 130 146 147 148 **S** PeaceHealth, Vancouver, WA
Primary Contact: Cherelle Montanye-Ireland, Chief Administrative Officer
CFO: Ronald K Benfield, Chief Financial Officer
CMO: Sheila Lynam, M.D., Chief Medical Officer
CHR: Kelley Frengle, Director, Human Resources
Web address: www.peacehealth.org
**Control:** Church operated, Nongovernment, not–for–profit **Service:** General medical and surgical

**Staffed Beds:** 180 **Admissions:** 7722 **Census:** 84 **Outpatient Visits:** 158405 **Births:** 783 **Total Expense ($000):** 204421 **Payroll Expense ($000):** 80495 **Personnel:** 1048

⇑ **ST. JOHN MEDICAL CENTER** See Peacehealth St. John Medical Center

## MARYSVILLE—Snohomish County

☐ **SMOKEY POINT BEHAVIORAL HOSPITAL (504012)**, 3955 156th Street Northeast, Zip 98271; tel. 844/202–5555, (Nonreporting) **A**1 10
Primary Contact: Christopher D. Burke, Ph.D., Chief Executive Officer
Web address: www.smokeypointbehavioralhospital.com
**Control:** Other not–for–profit (including NFP Corporation) **Service:** Psychiatric

**Staffed Beds:** 115

## MEDICAL LAKE—Spokane County

☐ **EASTERN STATE HOSPITAL (504004)**, Maple Street, Zip 99022–0045, Mailing Address: P.O. Box 800, Zip 99022–0800; tel. 509/565–4705, (Nonreporting) **A**1 3 10 **F**29 30 39 59 65 68 75 77 86 98 100 101 103 130 132 135 143 146 149
Primary Contact: Mark Kettner, Chief Executive Officer
COO: Ronda Kenney, Chief Operating Officer
CMO: Kamal Floura, M.D., Medical Director
CNO: Chet Roshetko, Chief Nursing Officer
Web address: www.dshs.wa.gov/bha/division-state-hospitals/eastern-state-hospital-overview
**Control:** State, Government, Nonfederal **Service:** Psychiatric

**Staffed Beds:** 342 **Admissions:** 444 **Census:** 256 **Outpatient Visits:** 0
**Births:** 0 **Total Expense ($000):** 96222 **Payroll Expense ($000):** 57767
**Personnel:** 697

## MONROE—Snohomish County

★ ⇑ **EVERGREENHEALTH MONROE (500084)**, 14701 179th SE, Zip 98272–1108, Mailing Address: P.O. Box 646, Zip 98272–0646; tel. 360/794–7497, (Nonreporting) **A**10 21 **F**3 4 5 11 15 29 30 31 34 35 40 43 45 50 68 70 75 77 78 79 81 82 85 87 91 93 107 110 111 114 115 118 119 130 131 132 146 148 149 151 152 154
Primary Contact: Lisa LaPlante, Chief Administrative Officer
CFO: Scott Olander, Chief Financial Officer
CMO: Jack Handley, M.D., Chief Medical Officer
CIO: John Gepford, Director Information Systems
CHR: Kathryn Rothberg, Director Human Resources
CNO: Brenda West, R.N., MSN, Chief Nursing Officer
Web address: www.evergreenhealthmonroe.com
**Control:** Hospital district or authority, Government, Nonfederal **Service:** General medical and surgical

**Staffed Beds:** 67 **Admissions:** 910 **Census:** 9 **Outpatient Visits:** 97000
**Births:** 0 **Total Expense ($000):** 53824 **Payroll Expense ($000):** 24387
**Personnel:** 228

⇑ **VALLEY GENERAL HOSPITAL** See Evergreenhealth Monroe

## MORTON—Lewis County

★ **ARBOR HEALTH, MORTON HOSPITAL (501319)**, 521 Adams Avenue, Zip 98356–9323, Mailing Address: P.O. Box 1138, Zip 98356–0019; tel. 360/496–5112, (Nonreporting) **A**10 18 **F**29 34 40 45 50 64 68 81 93 97 107 110 111 114 119 127 129 130 133 135 147 148 154 **P**6
Primary Contact: Leianne Everett, Chief Executive Officer
CFO: Geoff Hamilton, Interim Chief Financial Officer
CIO: Randy Nielsen, Director Information Technology
CHR: Shannon Kelly, Director Human Resources
CNO: Heidi Anderson, Chief Nursing Officer
Web address: www.https://www.myarborhealth.org/
**Control:** Hospital district or authority, Government, Nonfederal **Service:** General medical and surgical

**Staffed Beds:** 24 **Admissions:** 194 **Census:** 4 **Outpatient Visits:** 29933
**Births:** 0 **Total Expense ($000):** 28930 **Payroll Expense ($000):** 14807
**Personnel:** 183

**MORTON GENERAL HOSPITAL** See Arbor Health, Morton Hospital

## MOSES LAKE—Grant County

★ ⇑ **SAMARITAN HEALTHCARE (500033)**, 801 East Wheeler Road, Zip 98837–1899; tel. 509/765–5606, (Nonreporting) **A**10 20 21
Primary Contact: Theresa Sullivan, Chief Executive Officer
COO: Kris Neff, Chief Operating Officer
CFO: Alex Town, Chief Financial Officer
CMO: Andrea Carter, M.D., Chief Medical Officer
CNO: Becky DeMers, R.N., Chief Nursing Officer
Web address: www.samaritanhealthcare.com
**Control:** Hospital district or authority, Government, Nonfederal **Service:** General medical and surgical

**Staffed Beds:** 50

⇑ **SAMARITAN HOSPITAL** See Samaritan Healthcare

**WA**

*Many Facility Codes have changed. Please refer to the AHA Guide Code Chart.* © 2021 AHA Guide

## MOUNT VERNON—Skagit County

⇑ **SKAGIT REGIONAL HEALTH** See Skagit Valley Hospital

★ ⇑ **SKAGIT VALLEY HOSPITAL (500003)**, 300 Hospital Parkway, Zip 98273,
Mailing Address: P.O. Box 1376, Zip 98273–1376; tel. 360/424–4111,
(Nonreporting) **A**2 3 5 10 13 19 21 **S** Skagit Regional Health, Mount Vernon, WA
Primary Contact: Brian K. Ivie, President and Chief Executive Officer
COO: Jim Geist, Executive Vice President and Chief Operating Officer
CFO: Paul Ishizuka, Chief Financial Officer
CMO: Jeffrey S. Gibbs, M.D., Regional Vice President Medical Affairs
CIO: John Dwight, Regional Vice President and Chief Information Officer
CHR: Deborah Martin, Regional Vice President Human Resources
CNO: Roxanne Olason, R.N., FACHE, Vice President and Chief Nursing Officer
Web address: www.skagitregionalhealth.org
**Control**: Hospital district or authority, Government, Nonfederal **Service**: General
medical and surgical

**Staffed Beds: 173**

## NEWPORT—Pend Oreille County

**NEWPORT COMMUNITY HOSPITAL** See Newport Hospital and Health Services

**NEWPORT HOSPITAL AND HEALTH SERVICES (501310)**, 714 West Pine
Street, Zip 99156–9046; tel. 509/447–2441, (Nonreporting) **A**10 18
Primary Contact: Thomas W. Wilbur, Chief Executive Officer and Superintendent
COO: Lynn Peterson, R.N., Director Nursing Services
CMO: Jeremy Lewis, D.O., Chief of Medical Staff
CIO: Walter Price, Director Information Technology
CHR: Joseph Clouse, Chief Administrative Officer
Web address: www.newporthospitalandhealth.org
**Control**: Hospital district or authority, Government, Nonfederal **Service**: General
medical and surgical

**Staffed Beds: 74**

## OAK HARBOR—Island County

**NAVAL HOSPITAL** See Naval Hospital Oak Harbor

⊠ **NAVAL HOSPITAL OAK HARBOR**, 3475 North Saratoga Street,
Zip 98278–8800; tel. 360/257–9500, (Nonreporting) **A**1 **S** Bureau of Medicine
and Surgery, Department of the Navy, Falls Church, VA
Primary Contact: Commander Frederick Joseph. McDonald, Commanding Officer
COO: LieutenantMichael Bowers, Interim Director for Administration
CFO: LieutenantMatthew Martin, Director Resource Management
CMO: Lieutenant CommanderCatherine Borja, M.D., Chairman Executive
Committee Medical Staff
CIO: Gregory Carruth, Head Information Management
CHR: LieutenantMichael Bowers, Head Human Resources
CNO: CaptainKaren Pruett-Baer, Senior Nurse Executive
Web address: www.med.navy.mil/sites/nhoh/Pages/default.aspx
**Service**: General medical and surgical

**Staffed Beds: 29**

## ODESSA—Lincoln County

★ **ODESSA MEMORIAL HEALTHCARE CENTER (501307)**, 502 East Amende
Drive, Zip 99159–7003, Mailing Address: P.O. Box 368, Zip 99159–0368;
tel. 509/982–2611, (Nonreporting) **A**10 18
Primary Contact: Emmett Schuster, Interim Chief Executive Officer
CFO: Annette Edwards, Chief Financial Officer
CMO: Linda J Powel, M.D., Medical Director
CHR: Jodi J Bailey, Human Resources Director
CNO: Megan Shepard, Director Clinical Services
Web address: www.omhc.org
**Control**: Hospital district or authority, Government, Nonfederal **Service**: General
medical and surgical

**Staffed Beds: 13**

**ODESSA MEMORIAL HOSPITAL** See Odessa Memorial Healthcare Center

## OLYMPIA—Thurston County

⊠ **CAPITAL MEDICAL CENTER (500139)**, 3900 Capital Mall Drive SW,
Zip 98502–5026; tel. 360/754–5858, (Nonreporting) **A**1 10 **S** LifePoint Health,
Brentwood, TN
Primary Contact: Mark S. Turner, Chief Executive Officer
COO: D Christopher Sloan, Chief Operating Officer
CFO: Brian Anderson, Chief Financial Officer
CMO: Rojesh Sharangpani, M.D., Chief of Staff
CIO: Renee Crotty, Coordinator Marketing and Public Relations
CHR: Dana Vandewege, Director Human Resources
Web address: www.capitalmedical.com
**Control**: Partnership, Investor–owned (for–profit) **Service**: General medical and
surgical

**Staffed Beds: 52**

**COLUMBIA CAPITAL MEDICAL CTR** See Capital Medical Center

⊠ **PROVIDENCE ST. PETER HOSPITAL (500024)**, 413 Lilly Road NE,
Zip 98506–5166; tel. 360/491–9480, (Nonreporting) **A**1 3 5 10 **F**3 5 8 11 13 15
18 20 22 24 26 28 29 30 31 34 35 38 40 43 44 46 49 51 53 56 57 58 59 64
68 70 73 74 75 76 77 78 79 80 81 82 84 85 86 87 89 90 91 92 93 95 96 98
99 100 101 102 104 107 108 111 114 115 118 119 126 129 130 132 135
145 146 148 149 150 152 154 **S** Providence St. Joseph Health, Renton, WA
Primary Contact: Darin Goss, FACHE, Chief Executive Officer
CFO: Denise Marroni, Chief Financial Officer
CMO: Kevin Caserta, M.D., Chief Medical Officer
CIO: Kerry Miles, Chief Information Officer
CHR: Susan Meenk, Vice President Human Resources
CNO: Michelle James, Chief Nursing Officer
Web address: www.providence.org/swsa/facilities/st_peter_hospital
**Control**: Church operated, Nongovernment, not–for–profit **Service**: General
medical and surgical

**Staffed Beds: 349 Admissions: 19567 Census: 29 Outpatient
Visits: 420185 Births: 2197 Total Expense ($000): 389453 Payroll
Expense ($000): 193177 Personnel: 2292**

**ST PETER HOSPITAL** See Providence St. Peter Hospital

## OMAK—Okanogan County

**MID-VALLEY HOSPITAL (501328)**, 810 Jasmine, Zip 98841–9578, Mailing
Address: P.O. Box 793, Zip 98841–0793; tel. 509/826–1760, (Nonreporting) **A**5
10 18 **F**3 8 13 15 18 19 26 27 29 34 35 38 40 43 45 48 50 54 56 57 59 61
64 65 68 75 76 77 79 81 85 87 93 97 102 105 107 108 110 111 115 119
127 130 131 133 147 148 149 152 154 156 **P**6
Primary Contact: Alan Fisher, Chief Executive Officer
CFO: Scott Attridge, Chief Financial Officer
CMO: Jennifer Thill, Chief of Staff
CIO: Ethan Harris, Manager Information Systems
CHR: Randy Coffell, Manager Human Resources
CNO: Rebecca Christoph, Director Nursing and Patient Care Services
Web address: www.mvhealth.org
**Control**: Hospital district or authority, Government, Nonfederal **Service**: General
medical and surgical

**Staffed Beds: 25 Admissions: 638 Census: 3 Outpatient Visits: 55173
Births: 232**

## OTHELLO—Adams County

★ **OTHELLO COMMUNITY HOSPITAL (501318)**, 315 North 14th Avenue,
Zip 99344–1297; tel. 509/488–2636, (Nonreporting) **A**10 18
Primary Contact: Connie Agenbroad, Chief Executive Officer
CFO: Mark Bunch, Director Finance
CHR: Mindy Gonzales, Chief Human Resources Officer
CNO: Tina Bernsen, Chief Nursing Officer
Web address: www.othellocommunityhospital.org
**Control**: Hospital district or authority, Government, Nonfederal **Service**: General
medical and surgical

**Staffed Beds: 25**

**WA**

## PASCO—Franklin County

✠ △ **LOURDES MEDICAL CENTER (501337)**, 520 North Fourth Avenue, Zip 99301–5257; tel. 509/547–7704, (Nonreporting) **A**1 3 7 10 18 **S** LifePoint Health, Brentwood, TN
Primary Contact: John Serle, FACHE, President and Chief Executive Officer
CFO: Frank Becker, Chief Financial Officer
CMO: Venkataraman Sambasivan, M.D., Chief Medical Officer
CIO: Deb Carpenter, Director Information Technology
CHR: Barbara Blood, Executive Director Human Resources
CNO: Denise Clapp, Chief Nursing Officer
Web address: www.lourdeshealth.net
**Control**: Corporation, Investor–owned (for–profit) **Service**: General medical and surgical

**Staffed Beds**: 53

**OUR LADY OF LOURDES HEALTH CTR** See Lourdes Medical Center

## POMEROY—Garfield County

**GARFIELD COUNTY HOSP DISTRICT** See Garfield County Public Hospital District

★ **GARFIELD COUNTY PUBLIC HOSPITAL DISTRICT (501301)**, 66 North 6th Street, Zip 99347–9705; tel. 509/843–1591, (Nonreporting) **A**10 18
Primary Contact: Jayd Keener, Co-Chief Executive Officer
CFO: Julie Leonard, Chief Financial Officer
CMO: Glenn Jefferson, Chief Medical Officer
CHR: Alicia Scharnhorst, Human Resources and Administrative Assistant
CNO: Barbara DeHerrera, Chief Nursing Officer
Web address: www.pomeroymd.com
**Control**: Hospital district or authority, Government, Nonfederal **Service**: General medical and surgical

**Staffed Beds**: 45

## PORT ANGELES—Clallam County

★ ⇑ **OLYMPIC MEDICAL CENTER (500072)**, 939 Caroline Street, Zip 98362–3997; tel. 360/417–7000, (Nonreporting) **A**2 3 10 21 **F**3 13 15 18 28 29 30 31 34 40 43 44 45 54 57 58 62 64 70 74 75 76 77 78 79 81 82 85 87 91 93 97 107 108 110 111 114 115 117 119 120 121 123 127 129 131 132 144 146 147 148 156
Primary Contact: Darryl Wolfe, Chief Executive Officer
COO: Darryl Wolfe, Chief Operating Officer
CFO: Lorraine Cannon, Chief Financial Officer
CMO: R. Scott Kennedy, M.D., Chief Medical Officer and Safety Officer
CHR: Jennifer Burkhardt, Chief Human Resources Officer
CNO: Ralph Parker, Chief Nursing Officer
Web address: www.olympicmedical.org
**Control**: Hospital district or authority, Government, Nonfederal **Service**: General medical and surgical

**Staffed Beds**: 67 **Admissions**: 4342 **Census**: 38 **Outpatient Visits**: 501049 **Births**: 445 **Total Expense ($000)**: 211428 **Payroll Expense ($000)**: 100088 **Personnel**: 1285

⇑ **OLYMPIC MEMORIAL HOSPITAL** See Olympic Medical Center

## PORT TOWNSEND—Jefferson County

⇑ **JEFFERSON GENERAL HOSPITAL** See Jefferson Healthcare

★ ⇑ **JEFFERSON HEALTHCARE (501323)**, 834 Sheridan Street, Zip 98368–2443; tel. 360/385–2200, (Nonreporting) **A**2 10 18 21
Primary Contact: Mike Glenn, Chief Executive Officer
COO: Paula Dowdle, Chief Operating Officer
CFO: Hilary Whittington, Chief Financial Officer
CMO: Joe Mattern, M.D., Chief Medical Officer
CHR: Heather Bailey, Chief Human Resources Officer
CNO: Tina Toner, Chief Nursing Officer
Web address: www.jeffersonhealthcare.org
**Control**: Hospital district or authority, Government, Nonfederal **Service**: General medical and surgical

**Staffed Beds**: 25

## PROSSER—Benton County

**PMH MEDICAL CENTER** See Prosser Memorial Health

★ **PROSSER MEMORIAL HEALTH (501312)**, 723 Memorial Street, Zip 99350–1524; tel. 509/786–2222, (Nonreporting) **A**3 10 18 **F**3 7 11 12 13 15 29 30 34 35 37 40 43 44 50 54 57 59 65 68 75 76 77 79 81 82 85 87 89 91 93 97 107 108 109 110 111 114 115 119 127 128 130 131 132 133 135 143 146 147 148 149 154 **P**8
Primary Contact: Craig J. Marks, FACHE, Chief Executive Officer
CFO: Tim Cooper, Chief Financial Officer
CIO: Jim Zoesch, Information Technology Director
CNO: Marla Davis, Interim Chief Nursing Officer
Web address: www.pmhmedicalcenter.com/
**Control**: Hospital district or authority, Government, Nonfederal **Service**: General medical and surgical

**Staffed Beds**: 25 **Admissions**: 992 **Census**: 12 **Outpatient Visits**: 92127 **Births**: 439 **Total Expense ($000)**: 58587 **Payroll Expense ($000)**: 27476 **Personnel**: 312

## PULLMAN—Whitman County

⇑ **PULLMAN MEMORIAL HOSPITAL** See Pullman Regional Hospital

⇑ **PULLMAN REGIONAL HOSPITAL (501331)**, 835 SE Bishop Boulevard, Zip 99163–5512; tel. 509/332–2541, (Nonreporting) **A**10 18 21
Primary Contact: Scott K. Adams, FACHE, Chief Executive Officer
CFO: Steven Febus, Chief Financial Officer
CMO: Gerald L Early, M.D., Chief Medical Officer
CHR: Bernadette Berney, Director Human Resources
Web address: www.pullmanhospital.org
**Control**: Hospital district or authority, Government, Nonfederal **Service**: General medical and surgical

**Staffed Beds**: 25

## PUYALLUP—Pierce County

☐ △ **MULTICARE GOOD SAMARITAN HOSPITAL (500079)**, 401 15th Avenue SE, Zip 98372–3770, Mailing Address: P.O. Box 1247, Zip 98371–0192; tel. 253/697–4000, (Nonreporting) **A**1 3 5 7 10 **F**3 11 13 17 18 20 22 24 28 29 30 31 34 35 38 40 41 42 43 45 47 48 50 51 55 56 57 58 59 61 64 65 66 68 70 71 73 74 76 77 78 79 80 81 82 83 84 85 87 89 90 91 93 96 97 102 106 107 108 111 114 115 116 117 118 119 126 129 130 132 146 147 148 149 154 **S** MultiCare Health System, Tacoma, WA
Primary Contact: James Beatty, President and Chief Operating Officer
CMO: Walter Fink, Chief Medical Officer
CHR: Kevin B Dull, Senior Vice President Human Potential
CNO: Lucy Norris, Administrator Interim Chief Nursing Officer
Web address: www.multicare.org/good-samaritan-hospital/
**Control**: Other not–for–profit (including NFP Corporation) **Service**: General medical and surgical

**Staffed Beds**: 350 **Admissions**: 19842 **Census**: 281 **Outpatient Visits**: 160839 **Births**: 2227 **Total Expense ($000)**: 490754 **Payroll Expense ($000)**: 230926 **Personnel**: 2023

**MULTICARE GOOD SAMARITAN HOSPITAL** See Multicare Good Samaritan Hospital

## QUINCY—Grant County

**QUINCY VALLEY HOSPITAL** See Quincy Valley Medical Center

**QUINCY VALLEY MEDICAL CENTER (501320)**, 908 10th Avenue SW, Zip 98848–1376; tel. 509/787–3531, (Nonreporting) **A**10 18
Primary Contact: Glenda Bishop, Interim Chief Executive Officer
CFO: Dean Taplett, Controller
CMO: Mark Vance, M.D., Chief Medical Officer
CIO: Ruth Vance, Director Information Systems
CHR: Alene Walker, Director Human Resources
Web address: www.quincyhospital.org
**Control**: County, Government, Nonfederal **Service**: General medical and surgical

**Staffed Beds**: 25

## RENTON—King County

✠ **UW MEDICINE/VALLEY MEDICAL CENTER (500088)**, 400 South 43rd Street, Zip 98055–5714, Mailing Address: P.O. Box 50010, Zip 98058–5010; tel. 425/228–3450, (Nonreporting) **A**1 2 3 5 10 **F**3 8 11 12 13 15 18 19 20 22 26 28 29 30 31 32 34 35 36 37 38 40 43 44 45 48 49 50 51 53 54 55 56 57 58 59 60 63 64 65 66 68 70 72 74 75 76 77 78 79 81 82 83 84 85 86 87 89 91 92 93 94 96 97 100 101 102 104 107 110 111 114 115 118 119 120 121 123 124 126 129 130 131 132 135 144 146 147 148 149 153 156 **P**6 **S** UW Medicine, Seattle, WA
Primary Contact: Richard D. Roodman, Chief Executive Officer
CFO: Larry Smith, Senior Vice President and Chief Financial Officer
CMO: Kathryn Beattie, M.D., Senior Vice President and Chief Medical Officer
CHR: Barbara Mitchell, Senior Vice President Marketing and Human Resources
CNO: Scott Alleman, Senior Vice President Patient Care Services and Chief Nursing Officer
Web address: www.valleymed.org
**Control**: Hospital district or authority, Government, Nonfederal **Service**: General medical and surgical

**Staffed Beds:** 311 **Admissions:** 18271 **Census:** 208 **Outpatient Visits:** 764294 **Births:** 3180 **Total Expense ($000):** 702359 **Payroll Expense ($000):** 347820 **Personnel:** 3353

**VALLEY MEDICAL CENTER** See UW Medicine/Valley Medical Center

## REPUBLIC—Ferry County

★ **FERRY COUNTY MEMORIAL HOSPITAL (501322)**, 36 Klondike Road, Zip 99166–9701; tel. 509/775–3333, (Nonreporting) **A**10 18
Primary Contact: Aaron Edwards, Chief Executive Officer
CFO: Kelly Leslie, Chief Financial Officer
CMO: Farhad H Alrashedy, M.D., Chief Medical Officer
CIO: James Davidson, Director of Information Services
CHR: Michelle Loftis, Human Resources Officer
CNO: Thomas Durham, Chief Nursing Officer
Web address: www.fcphd.org
**Control**: Hospital district or authority, Government, Nonfederal **Service**: General medical and surgical

**Staffed Beds:** 25

## RICHLAND—Benton County

**CARONDELET BEHAVIORAL HLTH CTR** See Lourdes Counseling Center

**KADLEC MEDICAL CENTER** See Kadlec Regional Medical Center

✠ △ **KADLEC REGIONAL MEDICAL CENTER (500058)**, 888 Swift Boulevard, Zip 99352–3514; tel. 509/946–4611, (Nonreporting) **A**1 2 3 5 7 10 **S** Providence St. Joseph Health, Renton, WA
Primary Contact: Reza Kaleel, Chief Executive
COO: Kirk Harper, R.N., Chief Operating Officer/Chief Nursing Officer
CFO: Spencer Harris, Chief Financial Officer
CMO: Kevin Pieper, Chief Medical Officer
CHR: Angela N Mager, Director, Human Resources
CNO: Kirk Harper, R.N., Chief Operating Officer and Chief Nursing Officer
Web address: www.https://www.kadlec.org
**Control**: Other not–for–profit (including NFP Corporation) **Service**: General medical and surgical

**Staffed Beds:** 260

★ **LOURDES COUNSELING CENTER (504008)**, 1175 Carondelet Drive, Zip 99354–3300; tel. 509/943–9104, (Nonreporting) **A**10 **S** LifePoint Health, Brentwood, TN
Primary Contact: Robert Monical, Chief Executive Officer
CFO: Frank Becker, Chief Financial Officer
CIO: Jared Fleming, Director, Information Services
CHR: Barbara Blood, Director Human Resources
CNO: Denise Clapp, Chief Nursing Officer
Web address: www.lourdeshealth.net
**Control**: Corporation, Investor–owned (for–profit) **Service**: Psychiatric

**Staffed Beds:** 20

## RITZVILLE—Adams County

★ **EAST ADAMS RURAL HEALTHCARE (501311)**, 903 South Adams Street, Zip 99169–2298; tel. 509/659–1200, (Nonreporting) **A**10 18
Primary Contact: Corey J. Fedie, Chief Executive Officer
COO: Dina McBride, Chief Operating Officer and Director Human Resources
CFO: Gary Bostrom, Chief Executive Officer and Chief Financial Officer
CMO: Charles Sackmann, M.D., Chief of Staff
CIO: Kellie Ottmar, Manager Information Services
CHR: Dina McBride, Chief Operating Officer and Director Human Resources
CNO: Brenda Herr, Chief Nursing Officer
Web address: www.earh.com
**Control**: Hospital district or authority, Government, Nonfederal **Service**: General medical and surgical

**Staffed Beds:** 20

**EAST ADAMS RURAL HOSPITAL** See East Adams Rural Healthcare

## SEATTLE—King County

**BALLARD COMMUNITY HOSPITAL** See Swedish Medical Center-Ballard

⇑ **CHILDREN'S HOSPITAL AND REGIONAL MEDICAL CENTER** See Seattle Children's Hospital

⇑ **GROUP HEALTH COOPERATIVE CENTRAL HOSPITAL** See Kaiser Permanente Capitol Hill Campus

**HARBORVIEW MEDICAL CENTER** See UW Medicine/Harborview Medical Center

⇑ **KAISER PERMANENTE CAPITOL HILL CAMPUS (500052)**, 201 16th Avenue East, Zip 98112–5226; tel. 206/326–3000, (Nonreporting) **A**10 21
Primary Contact: Carol M. Taylor, R.N., Regional Director Clinical Operations
Web address: www.https://www.ghc.org/html/public/locations/capitol-hill
**Control**: Corporation, Investor–owned (for–profit) **Service**: General medical and surgical

**Staffed Beds:** 306

✠ **KINDRED HOSPITAL SEATTLE-FIRST HILL (502002)**, 1334 Terry Avenue, Zip 98101–2747; tel. 206/682–2661, (Nonreporting) **A**1 10 **S** Kindred Healthcare, Louisville, KY
Primary Contact: Minta Albietz, Resource Chief Executive Officer
Web address: www.khseattlefirsthill.com
**Control**: Corporation, Investor–owned (for–profit) **Service**: Acute long–term care hospital

**Staffed Beds:** 10

☐ **NAVOS (504009)**, 2600 SW Holden Street, Zip 98126–3505; tel. 206/933–7299, (Nonreporting) **A**1 10
Primary Contact: Tim Holmes, President, Behavioral Health
COO: Cassie Undlin, Chief Operating Officer
CIO: Mary Sellers, Chief Information Officer
CHR: Karen White, Interim Vice President of Human Resources
CNO: Terry McInerney, Director of Nursing, Inpatient
Web address: www.navos.org
**Control**: Other not–for–profit (including NFP Corporation) **Service**: Psychiatric

**Staffed Beds:** 40

**NAVOS INPATIENT SERVICES** See Navos

**NORTHWEST HOSPITAL & MEDICAL CENTER** See UW Medicine/Northwest Hospital & Medical Center

△ **SCHICK SHADEL HOSPITAL**, 12101 Ambaum Boulevard SW, Zip 98146–2651, Mailing Address: P.O. Box 48149, Zip 98148–0149; tel. 206/244–8100, (Nonreporting) **A**7
Primary Contact: Philip Herink, Administrator
CFO: Troy Cherry, Chief Financial Officer
CMO: Kayyan Danbdala, M.D., Medical Director
CIO: Peter Vermulen, Director Information Technology
CHR: Elaine Oksendahl, Director Human Resources and Risk Management
Web address: www.schickshadel.com
**Control**: Corporation, Investor–owned (for–profit) **Service**: Alcoholism and other chemical dependency

**Staffed Beds:** 55

**WA**

---

**Hospital, Medicare Provider Number, Address, Telephone, Approval, Facility, and Physician Codes, Health Care System**

★ American Hospital Association (AHA) membership
☐ The Joint Commission accreditation
○ Healthcare Facilities Accreditation Program
◇ DNV Healthcare Inc. accreditation
⇑ Center for Improvement in Healthcare Quality Accreditation
△ Commission on Accreditation of Rehabilitation Facilities (CARF) accreditation

⊞ **SEATTLE CANCER CARE ALLIANCE (500138)**, 825 Eastlake Avenue East, Zip 98109–4405, Mailing Address: P.O. Box 19023, Zip 98109–1023; tel. 206/288–1400, (Nonreporting) **A**1 3 10 **F**3 14 15 29 30 31 34 35 36 38 39 44 45 50 52 55 57 58 59 64 65 68 71 75 77 78 80 81 82 84 85 86 87 93 100 104 107 108 110 111 115 117 118 119 120 121 123 130 132 135 136 143 146 147 148 149 154 **P**1
Primary Contact: Aaron Crane, Executive Vice President
CFO: Jonathan Tingstad, Vice President and Chief Financial Officer
CMO: Marc Stewart, M.D., Vice President and Medical Director
CIO: David Ackerson, Chief Information Officer
CHR: Han Nachtrieb, Vice President Human Resources
Web address: www.seattlecca.org
**Control:** Other not–for–profit (including NFP Corporation) **Service:** Cancer

**Staffed Beds:** 20 **Admissions:** 564 **Census:** 18 **Outpatient Visits:** 88296 **Births:** 0 **Total Expense ($000):** 684666 **Payroll Expense ($000):** 127817 **Personnel:** 1406

△ ⇑ **SEATTLE CHILDREN'S HOSPITAL (503300)**, 4800 Sand Point Way NE, Zip 98105–3901, Mailing Address: P.O. Box 5371, Zip 98145–5005; tel. 206/987–2000, (Nonreporting) **A**2 3 5 7 10 21
Primary Contact: Jeff Sperring, M.D., Chief Executive Officer
COO: Cindy Gazecki, Senior Vice President, Hospital Operations
CFO: Suzanne Beitel, Senior Vice President and Chief Financial Officer
CMO: Ruth A. McDonald, M.D., Chief Medical Officer
CIO: Zafar Chaudry, M.D., Senior Vice President and Chief Information Officer
CHR: Steven Hurwitz, Senior Vice President Shared Services
CNO: Susan Heath, R.N., Senior Vice President and Chief Nursing Officer
Web address: www.seattlechildrens.org
**Control:** Other not–for–profit (including NFP Corporation) **Service:** Children's general medical and surgical

**Staffed Beds:** 316

⇑ **SWEDISH HEALTH SERVICES** See Swedish Medical Center-First Hill

⇑ **SWEDISH MED CTR PROVIDENCE CMP** See Swedish Medical Center-Cherry Hill Campus

★ △ ⇑ **SWEDISH MEDICAL CENTER-CHERRY HILL CAMPUS (500025)**, 500 17th Avenue, Zip 98122–5711; tel. 206/320–2000, (Nonreporting) **A**3 5 7 10 21 **F**3 8 11 17 18 20 21 22 23 24 26 27 28 29 30 31 34 35 37 38 40 45 46 53 57 58 59 61 64 65 68 74 75 77 78 79 80 81 82 83 84 85 87 90 91 92 93 97 100 101 102 107 108 109 111 114 124 126 129 130 131 132 135 141 143 146 148 149 154 **S** Swedish Health Services, Seattle, WA
Primary Contact: David R. West, Chief Operating Officer
COO: David R. West, Chief Operating Officer
CFO: Jeffrey Veilleux, Senior Vice President and Chief Financial Officer
CIO: Janice Newell, Chief Information Officer
Web address: www.swedish.org
**Control:** Other not–for–profit (including NFP Corporation) **Service:** General medical and surgical

**Staffed Beds:** 208 **Admissions:** 9520 **Census:** 159 **Outpatient Visits:** 155842 **Births:** 0 **Total Expense ($000):** 489202 **Payroll Expense ($000):** 135347 **Personnel:** 1066

★ ⇑ **SWEDISH MEDICAL CENTER-FIRST HILL (500027)**, 747 Broadway, Zip 98122–4307; tel. 206/386–6000, (Includes SWEDISH MEDICAL CENTER-BALLARD, Mailing address: 5300 Tallman Avenue NW, Seattle, Washington, Zip 98107–3932; tel. 206/782–2700; Jennifer Graves, R.N., MS, Chief Executive), (Nonreporting) **A**2 3 5 10 21 **F**3 4 5 7 8 11 12 13 15 18 19 20 21 22 23 25 26 29 30 31 32 34 35 36 37 38 39 40 41 42 45 46 47 48 49 52 54 55 56 57 58 59 60 61 64 65 66 68 70 71 72 74 75 76 77 78 79 80 81 82 83 84 85 86 87 88 89 91 92 93 96 97 98 100 101 102 104 107 108 109 110 111 114 115 116 117 118 119 120 121 123 126 127 130 131 132 134 135 136 138 139 141 142 144 146 147 148 149 154 156 **S** Swedish Health Services, Seattle, WA
Primary Contact: Elizabeth Wako, Chief Operating Officer
COO: Kevin Brooks, Chief Operating Officer
CFO: Jeffrey Veilleux, Executive Vice President and Chief Financial Officer
CIO: Janice Newell, Chief Information Officer
Web address: www.swedish.org
**Control:** Other not–for–profit (including NFP Corporation) **Service:** General medical and surgical

**Staffed Beds:** 689 **Admissions:** 34286 **Census:** 464 **Outpatient Visits:** 540551 **Births:** 8245 **Total Expense ($000):** 1415787 **Payroll Expense ($000):** 416379 **Personnel:** 3012

⊞ △ **UNIVERSITY OF WASHINGTON MEDICAL CENTER (500008)**, 1959 NE Pacific Street, Zip 98195–6151; tel. 206/598–3300, (Nonreporting) **A**1 2 3 5 7 8 10 **F**3 9 11 12 13 15 17 18 20 22 24 26 28 29 30 31 32 34 35 36 40 44 45 46 47 48 49 50 52 54 55 56 57 58 59 60 61 64 65 68 70 72 74 75 76 77 78 79 81 82 84 85 86 87 90 91 92 93 94 95 96 97 98 100 101 102 104 105 107 108 110 111 114 115 116 117 118 119 120 121 123 124 126 130 131 132 135 136 137 138 139 140 141 142 144 145 146 147 148 149 154 156 **S** UW Medicine, Seattle, WA
Primary Contact: Cynthia Hecker, R.N., Executive Director
COO: Geoff Austin, Chief Operating Officer
CFO: Jacque Cabe, Chief Financial Officer
CMO: Tom Staiger, Medical Director
CIO: Joy Grosser, Chief Information Officer
CHR: Jennifer J Petritz, Director Human Resources
CNO: Cindy Sayre, Ph.D., R.N., Chief Nursing Officer
Web address: www.uwmedicine.org/uw-medical-center
**Control:** State, Government, Nonfederal **Service:** General medical and surgical

**Staffed Beds:** 476 **Admissions:** 18948 **Census:** 380 **Outpatient Visits:** 364006 **Births:** 1338 **Total Expense ($000):** 1364512 **Payroll Expense ($000):** 404831 **Personnel:** 4815

⊞ △ **UW MEDICINE/HARBORVIEW MEDICAL CENTER (500064)**, 325 Ninth Avenue, Zip 98104–2499, Mailing Address: P.O. Box 359717, Zip 98195–9717; tel. 206/744–3000, (Nonreporting) **A**1 3 5 7 8 10 **F**3 5 6 16 17 20 22 26 29 30 31 32 33 34 35 36 37 38 40 43 44 45 46 47 48 49 50 56 58 59 60 61 64 65 66 68 70 74 75 77 78 79 80 81 82 84 85 86 87 90 91 92 93 94 96 97 98 100 101 102 104 107 108 111 114 115 118 119 124 129 130 131 132 135 146 147 148 149 150 154 156 **P**6 **S** UW Medicine, Seattle, WA
Primary Contact: Paul Hayes, R.N., Executive Director
CFO: Kera Dennis, Assistant Administrator, Finance
CMO: J. Richard Goss, M.D., Medical Director
CIO: Joy Grosser, Chief Information Officer
CHR: Nicki McCraw, Assistant Vice President Human Resources
CNO: Jerome Dayao, Chief Nursing Officer
Web address: www.uwmedicine.org/Patient-Care/Locations/HMC/Pages/default.aspx
**Control:** County, Government, Nonfederal **Service:** General medical and surgical

**Staffed Beds:** 413 **Admissions:** 16073 **Census:** 405 **Outpatient Visits:** 313951 **Total Expense ($000):** 1050508 **Payroll Expense ($000):** 390088 **Personnel:** 4604

⊞ **UW MEDICINE/NORTHWEST HOSPITAL & MEDICAL CENTER (500001)**, 1550 North 115th Street, Zip 98133–8401; tel. 206/364–0500, (Nonreporting) **A**1 2 3 5 10 **F**3 9 13 15 18 20 22 24 26 28 29 30 31 34 35 40 41 43 44 45 46 47 49 51 53 54 56 57 58 59 61 64 68 70 73 74 75 76 77 78 79 81 84 85 86 87 92 93 96 97 98 100 102 103 104 105 107 108 110 111 114 115 119 126 130 131 132 146 148 155 **P**6 **S** UW Medicine, Seattle, WA
Primary Contact: Cynthia Hecker, R.N., Executive Director
CFO: Ketty Hsieh, Senior Director Finance
CMO: Greg Schroedl, M.D., Vice President, Medical and Chief Medical Officer
CIO: Eric Neil, Interim Chief Information Officer
CHR: Linda Olmstead, Director, Human Resources
CNO: Susan Manfredi, R.N., Vice President and Chief Nursing Officer
Web address: www.uwmedicine.org/Patient-Care/Locations/nwh/Pages/default.aspx
**Control:** Other not–for–profit (including NFP Corporation) **Service:** General medical and surgical

**Staffed Beds:** 203 **Admissions:** 9767 **Census:** 142 **Outpatient Visits:** 216116 **Births:** 1049 **Total Expense ($000):** 397932 **Payroll Expense ($000):** 169014 **Personnel:** 1914

⊞ △ **VETERANS AFFAIRS PUGET SOUND HEALTH CARE SYSTEM**, 1660 South Columbian Way, Zip 98108–1597; tel. 206/762–1010, (Includes VETERANS AFFAIRS PUGET SOUND HEALTH CARE SYSTEM-AMERICAN LAKE DIVISION, Mailing address: 9600 Veterans Drive, Tacoma, Washington, Zip 98493–0003; tel. 253/582–8440), (Nonreporting) **A**1 2 3 5 7 8 **S** Department of Veterans Affairs, Washington, DC
Primary Contact: Michael C. Tadych, FACHE, Director
CFO: Kenneth J Hudson, Chief Financial Officer
CMO: Gordon Starkebaum, M.D., Chief of Staff
CIO: Glenn Zwinger, Manager Information Systems Services
Web address: www.pugetsound.va.gov/
**Control:** Veterans Affairs, Government, federal **Service:** General medical and surgical

**Staffed Beds:** 416

**VIRGINIA MASON HOSPITAL** See Virginia Mason Medical Center

**WA**

*Many Facility Codes have changed. Please refer to the AHA Guide Code Chart.*     © 2021 AHA Guide

✠ **VIRGINIA MASON MEDICAL CENTER (500005)**, 1100 Ninth Avenue, Zip 98101–2756, Mailing Address: P.O. Box 900, Zip 98111–0900; tel. 206/223–6600, (Total facility includes 35 beds in nursing home–type unit) (Nonreporting) **A**1 2 3 5 10 **F**2 3 8 11 12 15 17 18 20 22 24 26 28 29 30 31 34 36 40 44 45 46 47 48 49 50 51 54 55 56 57 58 59 60 61 62 63 64 65 68 70 74 75 77 78 79 80 81 82 83 84 85 86 87 91 92 93 94 96 97 98 100 101 102 104 107 108 110 111 114 115 117 118 119 120 121 123 126 128 129 130 131 132 135 138 141 142 144 145 146 148 154 156 157 **S** Virginia Mason Health System, Seattle, WA
Primary Contact: Suzanne Anderson, President
CFO: Craig Goodrich, Chief Financial Officer
CMO: Michael Glenn, M.D., Chief Medical Officer
CIO: Bill Poppy, Chief Information Officer
CHR: Kathy J. Shingleton, Ed.D., Vice President, Human Resources
CNO: Charleen Tachibana, R.N., Senior Vice President and Chief Nursing Officer
Web address: www.VirginiaMason.org
**Control**: Other not–for–profit (including NFP Corporation) **Service**: General medical and surgical

**Staffed Beds:** 255 **Admissions:** 12284 **Census:** 210 **Outpatient Visits:** 1011596 **Births:** 0 **Total Expense ($000):** 1165450 **Payroll Expense ($000):** 562986 **Personnel:** 4919

### SEDRO–WOOLLEY—Skagit County

★ ⇑ **PEACEHEALTH UNITED GENERAL MEDICAL CENTER (501329)**, 2000 Hospital Drive, Zip 98284–4327; tel. 360/856–6021, (Nonreporting) **A**2 10 18 21 **F**3 11 15 29 30 31 34 35 40 43 45 50 57 59 64 68 70 75 77 78 79 81 85 92 93 107 108 110 115 118 119 120 121 123 129 130 132 133 143 146 148 149 **S** PeaceHealth, Vancouver, WA
Primary Contact: Christopher Johnston, Chief Administrative Officer
CFO: Carolyn Haupt, Chief Financial Officer
CHR: Tracie Skrinde, Senior Human Resources Partner
Web address: www.peacehealth.org/united-general
**Control**: Church operated, Nongovernment, not–for–profit **Service**: General medical and surgical

**Staffed Beds:** 25 **Admissions:** 535 **Census:** 4 **Outpatient Visits:** 42938 **Births:** 0 **Total Expense ($000):** 46150 **Payroll Expense ($000):** 16966 **Personnel:** 221

⇑ **PEACEHEALTH UNITED MEDICAL CENTER** See Peacehealth United General Medical Center

### SHELTON—Mason County

⇑ **MASON GENERAL HOSPITAL** See Mason General Hospital and Family of Clinics

★ ⇑ **MASON GENERAL HOSPITAL AND FAMILY OF CLINICS (501336)**, 901 Mountain View Drive, Zip 98584–4401, Mailing Address: P.O. Box 1668, Zip 98584–5001; tel. 360/426–1611, (Nonreporting) **A**5 10 18 21 **F**3 11 13 15 29 30 34 35 40 43 45 50 55 57 59 68 70 75 76 79 81 83 85 93 94 97 104 107 110 111 115 119 127 130 132 146 147 148 149 154 156 157
Primary Contact: Eric Moll, Chief Executive Officer
COO: Mark Batty, Chief Operating Officer
CFO: Rick Smith, Chief Financial Officer
CMO: Dean Gushee, M.D., Medical Director
CIO: Tom Hornburg, Director Information Systems
CNO: Melissa D Strong, Chief Nursing Officer
Web address: www.masongeneral.com
**Control**: Hospital district or authority, Government, Nonfederal **Service**: General medical and surgical

**Staffed Beds:** 25 **Admissions:** 1448 **Census:** 12 **Outpatient Visits:** 193840 **Births:** 302 **Total Expense ($000):** 105643 **Payroll Expense ($000):** 50759 **Personnel:** 593

### SNOQUALMIE—King County

**SNOQUALMIE VALLEY HOSPITAL** See Snoqualmie Valley Hospital District

**SNOQUALMIE VALLEY HOSPITAL DISTRICT (501338)**, 9801 Frontier Avenue SE, Zip 98065–9577; tel. 425/831–2300, (Nonreporting) **A**10 18
Primary Contact: Kimberly Witkop, M.D., Interim Chief Executive Officer
CMO: Kimberly Witkop, M.D., Chief Medical Officer
Web address: www.snoqualmiehospital.org/
**Control**: Hospital district or authority, Government, Nonfederal **Service**: General medical and surgical

**Staffed Beds:** 18

### SOUTH BEND—Pacific County

**WILLAPA HARBOR HOSPITAL (501303)**, 800 Alder Street, Zip 98586–4900, Mailing Address: P.O. Box 438, Zip 98586–0438; tel. 360/875–5526, (Nonreporting) **A**10 18 **F**3 11 15 28 29 34 35 40 41 43 45 47 48 50 54 56 59 68 77 81 87 97 102 107 114 115 119 127 148 149 154 156 157
Primary Contact: Matthew Kempton, Chief Executive Officer
CFO: Terry Stone, Chief Financial Officer and Chief Information Officer
CIO: Terry Stone, Chief Financial Officer and Chief Information Officer
CHR: Krisy L Funkhouser, Manager Human Resources
Web address: www.willapaharborhospital.com
**Control**: Hospital district or authority, Government, Nonfederal **Service**: General medical and surgical

**Staffed Beds:** 10 **Admissions:** 216 **Census:** 2 **Outpatient Visits:** 18000 **Births:** 0 **Total Expense ($000):** 21391 **Payroll Expense ($000):** 11345 **Personnel:** 116

### SPOKANE—Spokane County

**HOLY FAMILY HOSPITAL** See Providence Holy Family Hospital

☐ **INLAND NORTHWEST BEHAVIORAL HEALTH (504014)**, 104 West 5th Avenue, Zip 99204–4820; tel. 509/992–1888, (Nonreporting) **A**1
Primary Contact: Dorothy Sawyer, Chief Executive Officer
Web address: www.https://inlandnorthwestbh.com/
**Control**: Corporation, Investor–owned (for–profit) **Service**: Psychiatric

**Staffed Beds:** 100

✠ **MANN-GRANDSTAFF VETERANS AFFAIRS MEDICAL CENTER**, 4815 North Assembly Street, Zip 99205–6197; tel. 509/434–7000, (Nonreporting) **A**1 3 5 **S** Department of Veterans Affairs, Washington, DC
Primary Contact: Robert Fischer, M.D., Medical Center Director
COO: Perry Klein, Chief Engineering
CFO: Michael Stuhlmiller, Chief Financial Officer
CIO: Rob Fortenberry, Chief Information Officer
CHR: Jacqueline Ross, Chief Human Resources Officer
CNO: Nancy Benton, Assistant Director Patient Care Services
Web address: www.spokane.va.gov/
**Control**: Veterans Affairs, Government, federal **Service**: General medical and surgical

**Staffed Beds:** 68

☐ **MULTICARE DEACONESS HOSPITAL (500044)**, 800 West Fifth Avenue, Zip 99204–2803, Mailing Address: P.O. Box 248, Zip 99210–0248; tel. 509/458–5800, (Nonreporting) **A**1 3 5 10 **F**3 12 13 15 17 18 20 22 24 26 28 29 30 31 35 40 42 43 45 46 47 48 49 50 51 53 60 64 65 68 70 72 73 74 76 77 78 79 81 82 85 86 87 91 92 94 100 102 107 108 109 110 111 114 115 119 124 126 129 130 131 132 146 147 148 149 **P**6 **S** MultiCare Health System, Tacoma, WA
Primary Contact: Gregory George. Repetti III, FACHE, President
CFO: Rodney Higgins, Chief Financial Officer
CMO: David Chen, M.D., Chief Medical Officer
CIO: Richard DeRoche, Manager Information Technology
CHR: Melinda Moore, Director Human Resources
CNO: Jennifer Petrik, Interim Chief Nursing Officer
Web address: www.https://www.multicare.org/deaconess-hospital/
**Control**: Other not–for–profit (including NFP Corporation) **Service**: General medical and surgical

**Staffed Beds:** 352 **Admissions:** 10111 **Census:** 140 **Outpatient Visits:** 119251 **Births:** 1384 **Total Expense ($000):** 366701 **Payroll Expense ($000):** 111408 **Personnel:** 1393

**MULTICARE DEACONESS HOSPITAL** See Multicare Deaconess Hospital

**WA**

✠ **PROVIDENCE HOLY FAMILY HOSPITAL (500077)**, 5633 North Lidgerwood Street, Zip 99208–1224; tel. 509/482–0111, (Nonreporting) **A**1 3 5 10 **F**3 8 11 12 13 15 18 29 30 31 34 35 37 38 39 40 41 43 45 46 47 48 49 50 53 56 57 58 59 60 61 64 68 70 73 74 75 76 77 78 79 80 81 82 84 85 86 87 92 100 107 108 126 129 130 131 132 143 145 146 147 148 149 154 156 **S** Providence St. Joseph Health, Renton, WA
Primary Contact: Peggy M. Currie, R.N., Chief Operating Officer
COO: Cathy J Simchuk, Chief Operating Officer
CFO: Shelby Stokoe, Chief Financial Officer
CMO: Dean Martz, Chief Medical Officer
CIO: Mark Vogelsang, Director Information Services
CHR: Mark Smith, Director Human Resources
CNO: Sharon Hershman, R.N., Chief Nursing Officer
Web address: www.providence.org
**Control:** Church operated, Nongovernment, not–for–profit **Service:** General medical and surgical

**Staffed Beds:** 191 **Admissions:** 7752 **Census:** 97 **Outpatient Visits:** 199155 **Births:** 1231 **Total Expense ($000):** 210285 **Payroll Expense ($000):** 61388 **Personnel:** 783

**PROVIDENCE SACRED HEART MEDICAL CENTER** See Providence Sacred Heart Medical Center & Children's Hospital

✠ **PROVIDENCE SACRED HEART MEDICAL CENTER & CHILDREN'S HOSPITAL (500054)**, 101 West Eighth Avenue, Zip 99204–2364, Mailing Address: P.O. Box 2555, Zip 99220–2555; tel. 509/474–3131, (Includes SACRED HEART CHILDREN'S HOSPITAL, Mailing address: 101 West Eight Avenue, Spokane, Washington, Zip 99204–2307, PO Box 2555, Zip 99220–2555, tel. 509/474–4841; Keith Georgeson, M.D., Chief Executive), (Nonreporting) **A**1 2 3 5 10 **F**8 13 17 18 19 20 21 22 23 24 25 26 27 29 30 31 35 36 37 40 41 43 45 46 47 48 49 56 58 60 70 72 73 74 75 76 78 79 80 81 82 83 84 85 86 87 88 89 92 98 100 101 102 104 107 108 109 111 114 115 118 119 120 121 123 124 126 130 131 132 136 137 138 142 145 146 147 148 149 150 154 156 **P**6 **S** Providence St. Joseph Health, Renton, WA
Primary Contact: Peggy M. Currie, R.N., Chief Operating Officer
CFO: Shelby Stokoe, Senior Director Finance
CMO: Dean Martz, Chief Medical Officer
CHR: Mark Smith, Director Human Resources
CNO: Susan Stacey, Chief Nursing Officer
Web address: www.shmc.org
**Control:** Church operated, Nongovernment, not–for–profit **Service:** General medical and surgical

**Staffed Beds:** 656 **Admissions:** 29259 **Census:** 460 **Outpatient Visits:** 690222 **Births:** 3203 **Total Expense ($000):** 694697 **Payroll Expense ($000):** 314425 **Personnel:** 3369

**SACRED HEART CHILDEN'S HOSPITAL** See Sacred Heart Children's Hospital

☐ **SHRINERS HOSPITALS FOR CHILDREN-SPOKANE (503302)**, 911 West Fifth Avenue, Zip 99204–2901, Mailing Address: P.O. Box 2472, Zip 99210–2472; tel. 509/455–7844, (Nonreporting) **A**1 3 5 10 **S** Shriners Hospitals for Children, Tampa, FL
Primary Contact: Peter G. Brewer, Administrator
CFO: Monica Hickman, Director Fiscal Services
CMO: Glen Baird, M.D., Chief of Staff
CIO: Mike Allen, Director Information Services
CHR: Karen Mattern, Director of Human Resources
CNO: Lynda Vilanova, Director Patient Care Services
Web address: www.shrinershospitalsforchildren.org/Hospitals/Locations/Spokane.aspx
**Control:** Other not–for–profit (including NFP Corporation) **Service:** Children's orthopedic

**Staffed Beds:** 30

**SHRINERS HOSPS FOR CRPLD CHILD** See Shriners Hospitals for Children-Spokane

**SPOKANE VETERANS AFFAIRS MEDICAL CENTER** See Mann-Grandstaff Veterans Affairs Medical Center

**ST LUKES REHAB INSTITUTE** See St. Luke's Rehabilitation Institute

✠ △ **ST. LUKE'S REHABILITATION INSTITUTE (503025)**, 711 South Cowley Street, Zip 99202–1388; tel. 509/473–6000, (Nonreporting) **A**1 7 10 **F**28 29 30 34 35 36 38 43 50 53 57 58 64 68 74 75 77 79 86 87 90 91 92 93 95 96 130 131 132 135 146 148 149 154 156 157 **P**6 **S** Providence St. Joseph Health, Renton, WA
Primary Contact: Nancy Webster, Administrator and Chief Operating Officer
CFO: Helen Andrus, Chief Financial Officer
CMO: Gregory Carter, M.D., Chief Medical Officer
CIO: Fred Galusha, Chief Information Officer
CHR: Staci Franz, Director Human Resources
CNO: Kimberly J Ward, Chief Nurse Officer
Web address: www.st-lukes.org
**Control:** Other not–for–profit (including NFP Corporation) **Service:** Rehabilitation

**Staffed Beds:** 72 **Admissions:** 1471 **Census:** 54 **Outpatient Visits:** 107285 **Births:** 0 **Total Expense ($000):** 54250 **Payroll Expense ($000):** 33654 **Personnel:** 589

**SPOKANE VALLEY—Spokane County**

✠ **MULTICARE VALLEY HOSPITAL (500119)**, 12606 East Mission Avenue, Zip 99216–1090; tel. 509/924–6650, (Nonreporting) **A**1 3 10 **F**3 13 20 29 30 40 45 46 49 50 60 68 70 74 76 79 81 85 87 107 108 111 114 115 118 119 131 146 **S** MultiCare Health System, Tacoma, WA
Primary Contact: Gregory George. Repetti III, FACHE, Chief Executive Officer
COO: David Martin, Assistant Administrator
CFO: Justin Voelker, Chief Financial Officer
CMO: David Chen, M.D., Chief Medical Officer
CIO: Brain Jones, Director of Information Technology
CHR: Jamie Caine, Director of Human Resources
CNO: Shannon S Holland, R.N., MSN, Chief Nursing Officer
Web address: www.valleyhospital.org
**Control:** Other not–for–profit (including NFP Corporation) **Service:** General medical and surgical

**Staffed Beds:** 123 **Admissions:** 5152 **Census:** 53 **Outpatient Visits:** 57897 **Births:** 604 **Total Expense ($000):** 129017 **Payroll Expense ($000):** 55199 **Personnel:** 605

**MULTICARE VALLEY HOSPITAL** See Multicare Valley Hospital

**SUNNYSIDE—Yakima County**

★ **ASTRIA SUNNYSIDE HOSPITAL (501330)**, 1016 Tacoma Avenue, Zip 98944–2263, Mailing Address: P.O. Box 719, Zip 98944–0719; tel. 509/837–1500, (Nonreporting) **A**3 10 18 **S** Astria Health, Sunnyside, WA
Primary Contact: Brian P. Gibbons Jr, Chief Executive Officer
CFO: Cary Rowan, Chief Financial Officer
CIO: John Andersen, Manager Information Systems
CHR: Elaina Wagner, Director Human Resources
CNO: Mary Beth Tubbs, Chief Nursing Officer
Web address: www.astria.health/
**Control:** Other not–for–profit (including NFP Corporation) **Service:** General medical and surgical

**Staffed Beds:** 25

**SUNNYSIDE COMMUNITY HOSPITAL AND CLINICS** See Astria Sunnyside Hospital

**TACOMA—Pierce County**

**ALLENMORE HOSPITAL** See Multicare Tacoma General Hospital, Tacoma

☐ **CHI FRANCISCAN REHABILITATION (503026)**, 815 S Vassault Street, Zip 98465–2008; tel. 253/444–3320, (Nonreporting) **A**1
Primary Contact: Gregory Jackson, Chief Executive Officer
Web address: www.https://www.chifranciscan.org/rehabilitation-hospital.html
**Control:** Corporation, Investor–owned (for–profit) **Service:** Rehabilitation

**Staffed Beds:** 60

**HUMANA HOSPITAL-TACOMA** See Allenmore Hospital

**WA**

*Many Facility Codes have changed. Please refer to the AHA Guide Code Chart.*

⊞ **MADIGAN ARMY MEDICAL CENTER**, 9040 Jackson Avenue, Zip 98431–1100; tel. 253/968–1110, (Nonreporting) **A**1 2 3 5 **F**3 4 5 7 8 9 11 12 13 14 15 18 19 20 22 29 30 31 32 33 34 35 36 37 38 39 40 41 43 44 45 46 47 48 49 50 51 52 53 54 55 56 57 58 59 60 61 64 65 68 70 72 74 75 76 77 78 79 80 81 82 83 84 85 86 87 88 89 91 92 93 94 96 97 98 100 101 102 104 107 110 111 114 115 116 117 118 119 120 121 122 123 124 125 131 132 134 135 136 144 145 146 147 148 149 152 153 154 156 157 **S** Department of the Army, Office of the Surgeon General, Falls Church, VA
Primary Contact: Colonel Christopher Warner, Commander
CFO: Lieutenant ColonelNolan Brandt, Chief Finance Officer
CMO: ColonelGeorge Leonard, M.D., Chief Medical Officer
CIO: ColonelJames A Morrison, Chief Information Officer
CHR: Anthony Munoz, Chief, Civilian Human Resources Branch
CNO: ColonelLouis Stout, Chief Nursing Officer and Deputy Commander Health Readiness
Web address: www.mamc.health.mil/
**Control**: Department of Defense, Government, federal **Service**: General medical and surgical

**Staffed Beds**: 203 **Admissions**: 12143 **Census**: 108 **Outpatient Visits**: 925339 **Births**: 1796 **Total Expense ($000)**: 623560 **Payroll Expense ($000)**: 265661 **Personnel**: 5397

**MADIGAN HEALTHCARE SYSTEM** See Madigan Army Medical Center

**MARY BRIDGE CHILDREN'S HOSPITAL AND HEALTH CENTER** See Multicare Mary Bridge Children's Hospital and Health Center

☐ **MULTICARE MARY BRIDGE CHILDREN'S HOSPITAL AND HEALTH CENTER (503301)**, 317 Martin Luther King Jr Way, Zip 98405–4234, Mailing Address: P.O. Box 5299, Zip 98415–0299; tel. 253/403–1400, (Nonreporting) **A**1 3 5 10 **F**3 8 19 21 23 25 27 29 30 31 32 34 35 38 39 40 41 43 45 46 48 49 53 54 55 57 58 59 60 61 62 64 65 66 68 71 74 75 78 79 81 82 84 85 86 87 88 89 91 92 93 94 96 97 100 104 107 108 111 114 115 116 117 119 120 121 123 124 126 129 130 131 132 143 144 146 148 149 150 153 154 156 158 **S** MultiCare Health System, Tacoma, WA
Primary Contact: Jeffrey S. Poltawsky, President and Market Leader
COO: Jennifer Hamilton, COO - Mary Bridge
CMO: Iain Asplin, Chief Medical Officer
CHR: Kevin B Dull, Senior Vice President Human Potential
CNO: Diana Brovold, Chief Nurse Executive
Web address: www.multicare.org/marybridge
**Control**: Other not–for–profit (including NFP Corporation) **Service**: Children's general medical and surgical

**Staffed Beds**: 75 **Admissions**: 4316 **Census**: 43 **Outpatient Visits**: 154606 **Births**: 0 **Total Expense ($000)**: 283227 **Payroll Expense ($000)**: 125295 **Personnel**: 886

⊞ **MULTICARE TACOMA GENERAL HOSPITAL (500129)**, 315 Martin Luther King Jr Way, Zip 98405–4234, Mailing Address: P.O. Box 5299, Zip 98415–0299; tel. 253/403–1000, (Includes ALLENMORE HOSPITAL, Mailing address: 1901 South Union Avenue, Tacoma, Washington, Zip 98405, P O Box 11414, Zip 98411–0414, tel. 253/459–6633; Laureen Driscoll, President), (Nonreporting) **A**1 2 3 5 10 **F**3 8 12 13 15 17 18 20 22 24 26 28 29 30 31 34 35 36 40 43 45 46 47 48 49 50 51 53 54 55 57 58 59 64 70 72 73 74 75 76 78 79 80 81 82 84 85 87 98 99 100 102 107 108 109 111 114 115 116 117 119 120 121 123 124 126 129 130 131 132 135 146 147 148 149 154 157 **S** MultiCare Health System, Tacoma, WA
Primary Contact: Laureen Driscoll, President
COO: Julia Truman, Chief Operating Officer
CHR: Kevin B Dull, Senior Vice President Human Potential
CNO: Anita Wolfe, Chief Nurse Executive
Web address: www.multicare.org
**Control**: Other not–for–profit (including NFP Corporation) **Service**: General medical and surgical

**Staffed Beds**: 458 **Admissions**: 22266 **Census**: 320 **Outpatient Visits**: 222561 **Births**: 2921 **Total Expense ($000)**: 804711 **Payroll Expense ($000)**: 392493 **Personnel**: 2403

**ST JOSEPH HOSP & HLTH CARE CTR** See St. Joseph Medical Center

⊞ **ST. JOSEPH MEDICAL CENTER (500108)**, 1717 South 'J' Street, Zip 98405–3004, Mailing Address: P.O. Box 2197, Zip 98401–2197; tel. 253/426–4101, (Nonreporting) **A**1 2 3 5 10 **F**3 11 12 13 18 20 22 24 26 28 29 30 31 34 35 38 40 43 44 45 46 47 48 49 50 51 55 57 58 59 60 63 64 65 70 72 73 74 75 76 77 78 79 80 81 82 84 85 86 87 92 93 98 102 107 108 111 114 115 118 119 124 126 130 131 132 135 136 145 146 148 149 154 **S** CommonSpirit Health, Chicago, IL
Primary Contact: Tim O'Haver, President
CFO: Mike Fitzgerald, Chief Financial Officer
CMO: Michael Anderson, M.D., Chief Medical Officer
CIO: Shawn Shuffield, Interim Chief Information Officer
CNO: Ruth Flint, Chief Nursing Officer
Web address: www.chifranciscan.org
**Control**: Church operated, Nongovernment, not–for–profit **Service**: General medical and surgical

**Staffed Beds**: 366 **Admissions**: 20309 **Census**: 293 **Outpatient Visits**: 205959 **Births**: 4361 **Total Expense ($000)**: 645128 **Payroll Expense ($000)**: 204010 **Personnel**: 3140

**TACOMA GENERAL HOSPITAL** See Multicare Tacoma General Hospital

**VETERANS AFFAIRS MED CENTER** See Veterans Affairs Puget Sound Health Care System-American Lake Division

**VETERANS AFFAIRS PUGET SOUND HEALTH CARE SYSTEM-AMERICAN LAKE DIVISION** See Veterans Affairs Puget Sound Health Care System, Seattle

☐ **WELLFOUND BEHAVIORAL HEALTH HOSPITAL (504016)**, 3402 South 19th Street, Zip 98405–2487; tel. 253/301–5400, (Nonreporting) **A**1
Primary Contact: Matt Crockett, Chief Executive Officer
Web address: www.https://www.wellfound.org/
**Control**: Corporation, Investor–owned (for–profit) **Service**: Psychiatric

**Staffed Beds**: 120

**WESTERN STATE HOSPITAL (504003)**, 9601 Steilacom Boulevard SW, Zip 98498–7213; tel. 253/582–8900, (Nonreporting) **F**29 30 34 35 38 39 44 50 56 57 58 59 65 68 75 77 84 86 87 96 98 100 101 103 130 132 135 143 146 147 148 149 150 154 156 157 **P**6
Primary Contact: David Holt, Chief Executive Officer
CFO: Sue Breen, Chief Financial Officer
CMO: James A Polo, M.D., Chief Medical Officer
CHR: Lori Manning, Administrator Human Resources
CNO: Rae Simpson, R.N., Chief Nursing Officer
Web address: www.dshs.wa.gov/bhsia/division-state-hospitals/western-state-hospital
**Control**: State, Government, Nonfederal **Service**: Psychiatric

**Staffed Beds**: 857 **Admissions**: 1029 **Census**: 780 **Outpatient Visits**: 0 **Births**: 0 **Total Expense ($000)**: 232205 **Payroll Expense ($000)**: 137411 **Personnel**: 2888

**TONASKET—Okanogan County**

★ **NORTH VALLEY HOSPITAL (501321)**, 203 South Western Avenue, Zip 98855–8803; tel. 509/486–2151, (Total facility includes 42 beds in nursing home–type unit) (Nonreporting) **A**10 18 **F**13 15 29 40 43 45 50 59 64 68 75 76 77 85 86 93 107 110 114 119 128 130 132 133 148
Primary Contact: Scott Graham, Chief Executive Officer
COO: John McReynolds, Chief Operating Officer
CMO: Paul Lacey, M.D., Chief Medical Staff
CIO: Kelly Cariker, Chief Information Officer
CHR: Jan Gonzales, Director Human Resources
Web address: www.nvhospital.org
**Control**: Hospital district or authority, Government, Nonfederal **Service**: General medical and surgical

**Staffed Beds**: 67 **Admissions**: 217 **Census**: 46 **Outpatient Visits**: 11969 **Births**: 45 **Total Expense ($000)**: 23275 **Payroll Expense ($000)**: 10652 **Personnel**: 135

**WA**

**Hospital, Medicare Provider Number, Address, Telephone, Approval, Facility, and Physician Codes, Health Care System**

★ American Hospital Association (AHA) membership ☐ The Joint Commission accreditation ○ Healthcare Facilities Accreditation Program ◇ DNV Healthcare Inc. accreditation ⇑ Center for Improvement in Healthcare Quality Accreditation △ Commission on Accreditation of Rehabilitation Facilities (CARF) accreditation

© 2021 AHA Guide *Many Facility Codes have changed. Please refer to the AHA Guide Code Chart.* Hospitals **A767**

## TOPPENISH—Yakima County

✠ **ASTRIA TOPPENISH HOSPITAL (500037)**, 502 West Fourth Avenue,
Zip 98948–1616, Mailing Address: P.O. Box 672, Zip 98948–0672;
tel. 509/865–3105, (Nonreporting) **A**1 3 10 **S** Astria Health, Sunnyside, WA
Primary Contact: Michael J. Arno, President
CHR: Rosa Solorzano, Interim Director Human Resources
Web address: www.astria.health/
**Control:** Corporation, Investor–owned (for–profit) **Service:** General medical and surgical

| Staffed Beds: 48 |
| --- |

**TOPPENISH COMMUNITY HOSPITAL** See Astria Toppenish Hospital

## TUKWILA—King County

☐ **CASCADE BEHAVIORAL HOSPITAL (504011)**, 12844 Military Road South,
Zip 98168–3045; tel. 206/244–0180, (Nonreporting) **A**1 10 **S** Acadia Healthcare
Company, Inc., Franklin, TN
Primary Contact: Christopher West, Chief Executive Officer
CFO: Gregg Terreson, Chief Financial Officer
CHR: Sherry Cochran, Manager Human Resources
Web address: www.cascadebh.com
**Control:** Corporation, Investor–owned (for–profit) **Service:** Psychiatric

| Staffed Beds: 63 |
| --- |

**RIVERTON HOSPITAL** See Cascade Behavioral Hospital

## VANCOUVER—Clark County

**LEGACY SALMON CREEK HOSPITAL** See Legacy Salmon Creek Medical Center

✠ **LEGACY SALMON CREEK MEDICAL CENTER (500150)**, 2211 NE 139th
Street, Zip 98686–2742; tel. 360/487–1000, (Nonreporting) **A**1 2 5 10 **F**3 11 13
15 18 20 26 28 29 30 31 32 34 35 37 38 39 40 41 44 45 46 47 49 50 51 55
57 59 60 65 68 70 72 74 75 76 77 78 79 81 82 84 85 87 93 94 96 97 107
108 110 111 114 115 116 117 118 119 120 121 126 130 132 146 147 148
149 150 **P**6 **S** Legacy Health, Portland, OR
Primary Contact: Jon Hersen, President
COO: Michael Newcomb, D.O., Senior Vice President and Chief Operating Officer
CMO: Lewis Low, M.D., Senior Vice President and Chief Medical Officer
CHR: Sonja Steves, Senior Vice President Human Resources
Web address: www.legacyhealth.org
**Control:** Other not–for–profit (including NFP Corporation) **Service:** General
medical and surgical

| Staffed Beds: 208 Admissions: 15285 Census: 158 Outpatient |
| --- |
| Visits: 399680 Births: 3517 Total Expense ($000): 342978 Payroll |
| Expense ($000): 176914 Personnel: 1790 |

★ △ ⇑ **PEACEHEALTH SOUTHWEST MEDICAL CENTER (500050)**, 400
NE Mother Joseph Place, Zip 98664–3200, Mailing Address: P.O. Box 1600,
Zip 98668–1600; tel. 360/256–2000, (Includes VANCOUVER MEMORIAL
CAMPUS, Mailing address: 3400 Main Street, Vancouver, Washington, Zip 98663;
tel. 360/514–2000; Sean Gregory, Chief Executive, Columbia Network),
(Nonreporting) **A**2 3 5 7 10 21 **F**3 11 12 13 15 17 18 20 22 24 26 28 29 30
31 34 35 40 42 43 44 45 46 49 50 51 54 57 58 59 60 61 62 63 64 65 68 70
72 73 74 75 76 77 78 79 81 82 84 85 86 87 88 89 90 92 93 96 97 98 100
101 102 103 104 105 107 108 109 110 111 114 115 116 117 119 120 121
122 124 126 129 130 131 132 135 144 145 146 147 148 153 154 156 **S**
PeaceHealth, Vancouver, WA
Primary Contact: Sean Gregory, Chief Executive
COO: Gary Foster, R.N., Chief Operating Officer
CFO: Ronald K Benfield, Chief Financial Officer
CMO: Lawrence Neville, Chief Medical Officer
CIO: Donn McMillan, Senior Director, IST Client Liaison
CHR: Kelley Frengle, Senior Director, Human Resources
CNO: Helen Vos, R.N., Interim Chief Nursing Officer
Web address: www.peacehealth.org
**Control:** Church operated, Nongovernment, not–for–profit **Service:** General
medical and surgical

| Staffed Beds: 436 Admissions: 19955 Census: 246 Outpatient |
| --- |
| Visits: 218504 Births: 1925 Total Expense ($000): 541748 Payroll |
| Expense ($000): 197650 Personnel: 2401 |

☐ **RAINIER SPRINGS HOSPITAL (504013)**, 2805 Northeast 129th Street,
Zip 98686–3324; tel. 360/356–1890, (Nonreporting) **A**1 **S** Springstone,
Louisville, KY
Primary Contact: Jeff Serrano, Chief Executive Officer
Web address: www.https://www.rainiersprings.com
**Control:** Corporation, Investor–owned (for–profit) **Service:** Psychiatric

| Staffed Beds: 72 |
| --- |

⇑ **SOUTHWEST WASHINGTON MEDICAL CENTER** See Peacehealth Southwest
Medical Center

**VANCOUVER MEMORIAL HOSPITAL** See Vancouver Memorial Campus

## WALLA WALLA—Walla Walla County

✠ △ **PROVIDENCE ST. MARY MEDICAL CENTER (500002)**, 401 W Poplar
Street, Zip 99362–2846, Mailing Address: P.O. Box 1477, Zip 99362–0312;
tel. 509/897–3320, (Nonreporting) **A**1 2 7 10 19 **F**3 13 15 18 20 22 28 29 30
31 34 35 40 43 45 46 49 51 58 59 60 62 64 69 74 75 77 78 79 81 84 85
92 93 96 97 100 107 108 110 111 114 115 119 120 121 123 124 129 130
131 132 135 144 146 147 148 149 154 156 **S** Providence St. Joseph Health,
Renton, WA
Primary Contact: Susan Blackburn, Chief Administrative Officer
COO: Susan Blackburn, Chief Operating Officer
CMO: Tim Davidson, Chief Executive Physician Services
CIO: Martin Manny, Director, I.S.
CNO: Yvonne M Strader, Chief Nursing Officer
Web address: www.washington.providence.org/hospitals/st-mary/
**Control:** Church operated, Nongovernment, not–for–profit **Service:** General
medical and surgical

| Staffed Beds: 92 Admissions: 5632 Census: 58 Outpatient Visits: 203772 |
| --- |
| Births: 682 Total Expense ($000): 135650 Payroll Expense ($000): 65513 |
| Personnel: 1138 |

**ST. MARY MEDICAL CENTER** See Providence St. Mary Medical Center

**STATE PENITENTIARY HOSPITAL**, 1313 North 13th Street, Zip 99362–8817;
tel. 509/525–3610, (Nonreporting)
Primary Contact: Donald Holbrook, Chief Executive Officer
**Control:** State, Government, Nonfederal **Service:** Hospital unit of an institution
(prison hospital, college infirmary, etc.)

| Staffed Beds: 36 |
| --- |

## WENATCHEE—Chelan County

⇑ **CENTRAL WASHINGTON HOSPITAL** See Confluence Health/Central Washington
Hospital

★ ⇑ **CONFLUENCE HEALTH/CENTRAL WASHINGTON HOSPITAL (500016)**,
1201 South Miller Street, Zip 98801–3201, Mailing Address: P.O. Box 1887,
Zip 98807–1887; tel. 509/662–1511, (Nonreporting) **A**2 3 10 21 **F**3 12 13 17
18 20 22 24 26 28 29 30 31 34 35 40 43 45 46 47 49 50 53 62 63 64 68 69
70 73 74 75 76 78 79 81 82 84 85 86 89 91 93 94 95 100 102 107 108 111
114 115 119 126 129 130 146 147 148 149 154 156
Primary Contact: Peter Rutherford, M.D., Chief Executive Officer
COO: Vikki Noyes, Executive Vice President and Chief Operating Officer
CFO: John Doyle, Chief Financial Officer
CMO: Stuart Freed, M.D., Chief Medical Officer
CIO: Robert Pageler, Chief Information Officer
CHR: Jim Wood, Chief Administrative Officer
CNO: Tracey A Kasnic, Senior Vice President Inpatient and Chief Nursing Officer
Web address: www.cwhs.com
**Control:** Other not–for–profit (including NFP Corporation) **Service:** General
medical and surgical

| Staffed Beds: 176 Admissions: 11279 Census: 124 Outpatient |
| --- |
| Visits: 286180 Births: 1349 Total Expense ($000): 427711 Payroll |
| Expense ($000): 115675 Personnel: 1554 |

△ **CONFLUENCE HEALTH/WENATCHEE VALLEY HOSPITAL (500148)**, 820
North Chelan Avenue, Zip 98801–2028; tel. 509/663–8711, (Nonreporting) **A**2 3
7 10
Primary Contact: Peter Rutherford, M.D., Chief Executive Officer
COO: Kevin Gilbert, R.N., Vice President
CFO: John Doyle, Chief Financial Officer
CMO: Stuart Freed, M.D., Medical Director
CIO: Robert Pageler, Chief Information Officer
CHR: Jim Wood, Chief Human Resources Officer
CNO: Tracey A Kasnic, Chief Nursing Officer
Web address: www.confluencehealth.org
**Control:** Partnership, Investor–owned (for–profit) **Service:** General medical and
surgical

| Staffed Beds: 198 |
| --- |

**WENATCHEE VALLEY HOSPITAL** See Confluence Health/Wenatchee Valley
Hospital

**WA**

*Many Facility Codes have changed. Please refer to the AHA Guide Code Chart.*
© 2021 AHA Guide

## WHITE SALMON—Klickitat County

**SKYLINE HOSPITAL (501315)**, 211 Skyline Drive, Zip 98672–1918, Mailing Address: P.O. Box 99, Zip 98672–0099; tel. 509/493–1101, (Nonreporting) **A**10 18
Primary Contact: Robert P. Kimmes, Chief Executive Officer
CFO: Brenda Schneider, Chief Financial Officer
CMO: Christopher Samuels, Chief of Staff
CIO: Steve Opbroek, Manager Information Technology
CHR: Jessie Ramos, Manager Human Resources
CNO: Stefanie Boen, Chief Nursing Officer
Web address: www.skylinehospital.org
**Control:** Hospital district or authority, Government, Nonfederal **Service:** General medical and surgical

**Staffed Beds:** 16

## YAKIMA—Yakima County

✠ **VIRGINIA MASON MEMORIAL (500036)**, 2811 Tieton Drive, Zip 98902–3761; tel. 509/575–8000, (Nonreporting) **A**1 2 3 5 10 **F**3 8 9 11 13 15 17 18 20 22 26 28 29 30 31 32 34 35 36 40 41 43 44 45 46 47 48 49 50 51 54 55 57 58 59 62 63 64 68 70 72 73 74 75 76 77 78 79 81 82 84 85 86 87 89 91 92 93 96 97 98 100 102 103 104 107 108 110 111 114 115 116 117 118 119 120 121 123 124 126 129 130 131 132 135 146 147 148 149 154 156 **P**6 **S** Virginia Mason Health System, Seattle, WA
Primary Contact: Carole Peet, R.N., MSN, Chief Executive Officer
COO: Diane Patterson, Senior Vice President, Chief Operating Officer and Chief Nursing Officer
CFO: Tim Reed, Vice President and Chief Financial Officer
CMO: Marty Brueggemann, Chief Medical Officer
CIO: Jeff Yamada, Vice President
CHR: Jolene R. Seda, Vice President Chief Experience Officer
CNO: Diane Patterson, Senior Vice President, Chief Operating Officer and Chief Nursing Officer
Web address: www.yakimamemorial.org
**Control:** Other not–for–profit (including NFP Corporation) **Service:** General medical and surgical

**Staffed Beds:** 226 **Admissions:** 11832 **Census:** 134 **Outpatient Visits:** 417682 **Births:** 2385 **Total Expense ($000):** 499176 **Payroll Expense ($000):** 204987 **Personnel:** 2575

**YAKIMA VALLEY MEMORIAL HOSPITAL** See Virginia Mason Memorial

**WA**

# WEST VIRGINIA

## BECKLEY—Raleigh County

⇑ **BECKLEY APPALACHIAN REGIONAL HOSPITAL** See Beckley Arh Hospital

○ ⇑ **BECKLEY ARH HOSPITAL (510062)**, 306 Stanaford Road, Zip 25801–3142; tel. 304/255–3000, (Nonreporting) **A**10 11 21 **F**3 6 11 15 17 18 20 22 24 26 28 29 30 31 34 35 40 43 44 45 46 47 48 49 50 51 54 56 57 59 60 61 62 64 65 70 74 75 77 78 79 81 82 84 85 86 87 89 90 92 93 97 98 99 100 101 102 103 107 108 109 110 111 114 115 116 118 119 129 130 132 146 148 154 155 156 **S** Appalachian Regional Healthcare, Inc., Lexington, KY
Primary Contact: Rocco K. Massey, Community Chief Executive Officer
CMO: Ahmad Khiami, Chief of Staff
CHR: Sue Thomas, Manager Human Resources
CNO: Angela Rivera, Chief Nursing Officer
Web address: www.arh.org
**Control**: Other not–for–profit (including NFP Corporation) **Service**: General medical and surgical

**Staffed Beds:** 167 **Admissions:** 5924 **Census:** 101 **Outpatient Visits:** 77769 **Births:** 0 **Personnel:** 506

✠ **BECKLEY VETERANS AFFAIRS MEDICAL CENTER**, 200 Veterans Avenue, Zip 25801–6499; tel. 304/255–2121, (Nonreporting) **A**1 3 5 **S** Department of Veterans Affairs, Washington, DC
Primary Contact: Stacy J. Vasquez, Director
CFO: Terry Massey, Chief Fiscal Services
CMO: John David Berryman, M.D., Chief of Staff
CIO: Sherry Gregg, Chief Information Technology Officer
CNO: Debra Lynn Legg, Associate Director Patient Care Services and Nurse Executive
Web address: www.beckley.va.gov/
**Control**: Veterans Affairs, Government, federal **Service**: General medical and surgical

**Staffed Beds:** 173

✠ **RALEIGH GENERAL HOSPITAL (510070)**, 1710 Harper Road, Zip 25801–3397; tel. 304/256–4100, (Nonreporting) **A**1 3 5 10 19 **F**3 13 15 17 18 20 22 29 30 31 34 35 40 43 45 49 50 57 59 60 64 70 74 75 76 78 79 81 85 87 89 107 108 110 111 114 115 116 117 119 120 126 130 132 146 147 148 149 156 **S** LifePoint Health, Brentwood, TN
Primary Contact: Matthew S. Roberts, Chief Executive Officer
CFO: Randy Harrison, Chief Financial Officer
CMO: Syed Siddiqi, M.D., President Medical Staff
CIO: Kevin Sexton, Director Information Systems
CHR: Chris T Beebe, Director Human Resources
CNO: Alene Lewis, R.N., Chief Nursing Officer
Web address: www.raleighgeneral.com
**Control**: Corporation, Investor–owned (for–profit) **Service**: General medical and surgical

**Staffed Beds:** 229 **Admissions:** 11586 **Census:** 145 **Outpatient Visits:** 106605 **Births:** 890 **Total Expense ($000):** 159802 **Payroll Expense ($000):** 47666 **Personnel:** 833

**VETERANS AFFAIRS MEDICAL CENTER** See Beckley Veterans Affairs Medical Center

## BERKELEY SPRINGS—Morgan County

✠ **VALLEY HEALTH - WAR MEMORIAL HOSPITAL (511309)**, One Healthy Way, Zip 25411–7463; tel. 304/258–1234, (Total facility includes 16 beds in nursing home–type unit) (Nonreporting) **A**1 10 18 **F**3 11 15 18 28 29 30 34 35 40 45 50 53 54 57 59 64 65 75 77 79 81 85 86 87 93 97 107 110 114 119 129 130 132 133 135 147 155 156 **P**6 **S** Valley Health System, Winchester, VA
Primary Contact: Thomas S. Kluge, President
CFO: Kathryn Morales, Director of Finance
CMO: Gerald Bechamps, M.D., Vice President Medical Affairs
CHR: Abbey Rembold, Human Resources Senior Generalist
CNO: Heather Sigel, Director of Clinical Services
Web address: www.valleyhealthlink.com/war
**Control**: Other not–for–profit (including NFP Corporation) **Service**: General medical and surgical

**Staffed Beds:** 41 **Admissions:** 537 **Census:** 25 **Outpatient Visits:** 44270 **Births:** 0 **Total Expense ($000):** 25263 **Payroll Expense ($000):** 9637 **Personnel:** 141

**WAR MEMORIAL HOSPITAL** See Valley Health - War Memorial Hospital

## BRIDGEPORT—Harrison County

✠ **UNITED HOSPITAL CENTER (510006)**, 327 Medical Park Drive, Zip 26330–9006; tel. 681/342–1000, (Nonreporting) **A**1 2 3 5 10 12 13 **F**3 11 13 15 17 18 20 22 26 28 29 30 31 32 34 35 40 44 45 46 47 48 49 50 51 54 55 57 58 59 60 62 63 64 68 70 74 75 76 77 78 79 81 82 84 85 86 87 89 92 93 96 97 98 100 101 107 108 110 111 114 115 117 119 120 121 126 128 129 130 131 132 135 145 146 147 148 149 **P**1 6 **S** West Virginia University Health System, Morgantown, WV
Primary Contact: Michael C. Tillman, President and Chief Executive Officer
COO: John Fernandez, Chief Operating Officer
CFO: Jim Rutkowski, Chief Financial Officer
CMO: Eric Radcliffe, M.D., Medical Director
CIO: Brian Cottrill, Chief Information Officer
CHR: Timothy M Allen, Vice President Human Resources
CNO: Stephanie Smart, Chief Nursing Officer
Web address: www.thenewuhc.com
**Control**: Other not–for–profit (including NFP Corporation) **Service**: General medical and surgical

**Staffed Beds:** 264 **Admissions:** 13782 **Census:** 184 **Outpatient Visits:** 561036 **Births:** 1019 **Total Expense ($000):** 375448 **Payroll Expense ($000):** 136715 **Personnel:** 2323

**WVU MEDICINE UNITED HOSPITAL CENTER** See United Hospital Center

## BUCKEYE—Pocahontas County

★ **POCAHONTAS MEMORIAL HOSPITAL (511314)**, 150 Duncan Road, Zip 24924; tel. 304/799–7400, (Nonreporting) **A**10 18 **F**3 7 11 29 30 34 35 40 43 50 56 57 59 64 65 68 75 77 86 89 90 93 97 107 119 127 128 130 132 133 135 149 156
Primary Contact: Mary Beth. Barr, R.N., Chief Executive Officer
COO: Terry Wagner, R.N., Chief Operating Officer
CFO: Jon Boyette, Chief Financial Officer
CMO: Jeffrey Pilney, Chief Medical Officer
CIO: Samuel Walker, Director of IT
CHR: Katie Brown, Coordinator Human Resources
CNO: Kyna Moore, R.N., Chief Nursing Officer
Web address: www.pmhwv.org/
**Control**: County, Government, Nonfederal **Service**: General medical and surgical

**Staffed Beds:** 24 **Admissions:** 262 **Census:** 4 **Outpatient Visits:** 24390 **Births:** 0 **Total Expense ($000):** 16087 **Payroll Expense ($000):** 8036 **Personnel:** 139

**WV**

*Many Facility Codes have changed. Please refer to the AHA Guide Code Chart.* © 2021 AHA Guide

## BUCKHANNON—Upshur County

**ST JOSEPH'S HOSPITAL** See St. Joseph's Hospital of Buckhannon

⊞ **ST. JOSEPH'S HOSPITAL OF BUCKHANNON (511321)**, 1 Amalia Drive, Zip 26201–2276; tel. 304/473–2000, (Total facility includes 26 beds in nursing home–type unit) (Nonreporting) **A**1 10 18 **F**3 11 13 15 18 28 29 30 31 34 35 40 43 44 45 50 57 59 64 65 70 75 76 81 83 84 85 87 89 107 110 115 119 128 129 130 132 133 135 144 146 147 154 156 **P**6 **S** West Virginia University Health System, Morgantown, WV
Primary Contact: Skip Gjolberg, FACHE, Administrator
CFO: Russell J. Plywaczynski, CPA, Director of Finance
CMO: Bartley Brown, D.O., Chief of Staff
CIO: Brian Williams, Web Services and Information Technology Manager
CHR: Anissa J Hite Davis, Vice President Human Resources
CNO: Annamarie Chidester, R.N., Vice President, Patient Care Services
Web address: www.stj.net
**Control**: Other not–for–profit (including NFP Corporation) **Service**: General medical and surgical

**Staffed Beds:** 51 **Admissions:** 947 **Census:** 29 **Outpatient Visits:** 83321
**Births:** 319 **Total Expense ($000):** 60503 **Payroll Expense ($000):** 22012
**Personnel:** 403

## CHARLESTON—Kanawha County

**CAMC MEMORIAL HOSPITAL** See Charleston Area Medical Center, Charleston

**CAMC WOMEN AND CHILDREN'S HOSPITAL** See Charleston Area Medical Center, Charleston

★ △ ⇑ **CHARLESTON AREA MEDICAL CENTER (510022)**, 501 Morris Street, Zip 25301–1300, Mailing Address: P.O. Box 1547, Zip 25326–1547; tel. 304/388–5432, (Includes CAMC MEMORIAL HOSPITAL, Mailing address: PO Box 2069, Charleston, West Virginia, Zip 25327, 3200 MacCorkle Avenue SE, Zip 25304, tel. 304/388–5973; Jeffrey L. Oskin, Vice President and Administrator; CAMC TEAYS VALLEY HOSPITAL, Mailing address: 1400 Hospital Drive, Hurricane, West Virginia, Zip 25526–9202; tel. 304/757–1700; Randall H Hodges, FACHE, Vice President and Administrator; CAMC WOMEN AND CHILDREN'S HOSPITAL, Mailing address: 800 Pennsylvania Avenue, Charleston, West Virginia, Zip 25302, P O Box 6669, Zip 25362, tel. 304/388–5432; Andrew Weber, Vice President and Administrator; GENERAL HOSPITAL, Mailing address: 501 Morris Street, Charleston, West Virginia, Zip 25301, Box 1393, Zip 25325, tel. 304/388–5432; Michael D Williams, Vice President and Administrator), (Nonreporting) **A**2 3 5 7 8 10 21 **F**3 7 8 11 12 13 15 17 18 19 20 22 24 26 28 29 30 31 32 34 35 38 39 40 41 43 44 45 46 47 48 49 50 51 52 54 55 56 57 59 60 61 64 65 68 70 72 74 75 76 77 78 79 81 82 84 85 86 87 88 89 90 91 92 93 94 95 96 97 98 100 101 102 104 107 108 110 111 114 115 116 117 118 119 120 121 123 124 126 129 130 131 132 134 135 138 143 144 145 146 147 148 149 150 154 156 157
Primary Contact: David L. Ramsey, President and Chief Executive Officer
COO: Glenn Crotty, M.D., JrExecutive Vice President and Chief Operating Officer
CFO: Larry C Hudson, Executive Vice President and Chief Financial Officer
CMO: T Pinckney McIlwain, M.D., Vice President and Chief Medical Officer
CIO: Eileen Clark, Vice President Information Services
CHR: Kristi Snyder, Vice President Human Resources
CNO: Ronald E Moore, R.N., MSN, Vice President Professional Practice and Chief Nursing Officer
Web address: www.camc.org
**Control**: Other not–for–profit (including NFP Corporation) **Service**: General medical and surgical

**Staffed Beds:** 846 **Admissions:** 37199 **Census:** 576 **Outpatient Visits:** 780168 **Births:** 2817 **Total Expense ($000):** 1189520 **Payroll Expense ($000):** 470315 **Personnel:** 6924

**CHARLESTON GENERAL HOSPITAL** See General Hospital

☐ **CHARLESTON SURGICAL HOSPITAL (510091)**, 1306 Kanawha Boulevard East, Zip 25301–3001, Mailing Address: P.O. Box 2271, Zip 25328–2271; tel. 304/343–4371, (Nonreporting) **A**1 10
Primary Contact: Christina Arvon, Administrator and Chief Executive Officer
CMO: James W Candill, M.D., President Medical Staff
Web address: www.eyeandearclinicwv.org
**Control**: Corporation, Investor–owned (for–profit) **Service**: General medical and surgical

**Staffed Beds:** 6

**EYE AND EAR CLINIC OF CHARLESTON** See Charleston Surgical Hospital

**GENERAL HOSPITAL** See Charleston Area Medical Center, Charleston

⊞ **HIGHLAND HOSPITAL (514001)**, 300 56th Street SE, Zip 25304–2361, Mailing Address: P.O. Box 4107, Zip 25364–4107; tel. 304/926–1600, (Nonreporting) **A**1 10 **F**3 34 35 38 98 99 101 106 130 132 135
Primary Contact: Cynthia A. Persily, Ph.D., R.N., Chief Executive Officer
COO: Rick Rucker, Chief Operating Officer
CFO: Chris K. Miller, Chief Financial Officer
CMO: Kiran S. Devaraj, Chief Medical Officer and Chief Clinical Officer
CIO: Damon Carradine, Director Information Technology
CNO: Leigh Dalton, Director of Nursing and Patient Care Services
Web address: www.highlandhosp.com
**Control**: Individual, Investor–owned (for–profit) **Service**: Psychiatric

**Staffed Beds:** 115 **Admissions:** 1972 **Census:** 79 **Outpatient Visits:** 0
**Births:** 0 **Total Expense ($000):** 26173 **Payroll Expense ($000):** 11060
**Personnel:** 243

**MEMORIAL DIVISION** See Camc Memorial Hospital

⊞ **SAINT FRANCIS HOSPITAL (510031)**, 333 Laidley Street, Zip 25301–1628, Mailing Address: P.O. Box 471, Zip 25322–0471; tel. 304/347–6500, (Total facility includes 25 beds in nursing home–type unit) (Nonreporting) **A**1 10 **F**3 4 11 15 18 20 22 29 30 33 34 35 45 46 47 48 49 51 57 58 59 64 75 77 81 82 97 100 107 108 110 111 115 118 119 128 130 144 146 147 148 **S** Thomas Health System, Inc., South Charleston, WV
Primary Contact: Daniel Lauffer, FACHE, President and Chief Executive Officer
COO: Brian Ulery, Senior Vice President and Chief Operating Officer
CFO: Renee Cross, Senior Vice President and Chief Financial Officer
CMO: Matthew Upton, Chief Medical Officer and Chief Medical Information Officer
CIO: Jeremy Taylor, Director Information Services
CHR: Patrick Rawlings, Chief Human Resource Officer
CNO: Rebecca Brannon, R.N., Senior Vice President and Chief Nursing Officer
Web address: www.stfrancishospital.com
**Control**: Other not–for–profit (including NFP Corporation) **Service**: General medical and surgical

**Staffed Beds:** 65 **Admissions:** 912 **Census:** 37 **Outpatient Visits:** 65409
**Births:** 0 **Total Expense ($000):** 61789 **Payroll Expense ($000):** 19403
**Personnel:** 360

⊞ **SELECT SPECIALTY HOSPITAL-CHARLESTON (512002)**, 333 Laidley Street, 3rd Floor East, Zip 25301–1614; tel. 304/720–7234, (Nonreporting) **A**1 10 **F**1 29 74 75 85 130 148 149 **S** Select Medical Corporation, Mechanicsburg, PA
Primary Contact: Frank Weber, Chief Executive Officer
CHR: Sabrina White, Coordinator Human Resources
Web address: www.selectspecialtyhospitals.com/company/locations/charleston.aspx
**Control**: Corporation, Investor–owned (for–profit) **Service**: Acute long–term care hospital

**Staffed Beds:** 32 **Admissions:** 356 **Census:** 27 **Outpatient Visits:** 0
**Births:** 0 **Total Expense ($000):** 17291 **Payroll Expense ($000):** 7194
**Personnel:** 77

**ST FRANCIS HOSPITAL** See Saint Francis Hospital

**WOMEN AND CHILDREN'S HOSP** See Camc Women and Children's Hospital

## CLARKSBURG—Harrison County

⊞ **HIGHLAND-CLARKSBURG HOSPITAL (514011)**, 3 Hospital Plaza, Zip 26301–9316; tel. 304/969–3100, (Nonreporting) **A**1 3 10 **F**29 38 98 99 103 149 154 **P**6
Primary Contact: Vickie Jones, Interim Chief Executive Officer
CFO: Shelly Giaguinto, Chief Financial Officer
CMO: Christi Cooper-Lehki, Chief Clinical Officer
CIO: Kimberly Samuelson, Director of Information Management
CHR: Robert L Boyles, Director of Human Resources
CNO: Melissa Hitt, Director of Nursing
Web address: www.highlandhosp.com
**Control**: Other not–for–profit (including NFP Corporation) **Service**: Psychiatric

**Staffed Beds:** 115 **Admissions:** 620 **Census:** 75 **Outpatient Visits:** 0
**Births:** 0 **Total Expense ($000):** 23022 **Payroll Expense ($000):** 12991
**Personnel:** 283

**LOUIS A JOHNSON VETERANS CNTR** See Louis A. Johnson Veterans Affairs Medical Center

**WV**

---

**Hospital, Medicare Provider Number, Address, Telephone, Approval, Facility, and Physician Codes, Health Care System**

★ American Hospital Association (AHA) membership
☐ The Joint Commission accreditation
○ Healthcare Facilities Accreditation Program
◇ DNV Healthcare Inc. accreditation
⇑ Center for Improvement in Healthcare Quality Accreditation
△ Commission on Accreditation of Rehabilitation Facilities (CARF) accreditation

✠ **LOUIS A. JOHNSON VETERANS AFFAIRS MEDICAL CENTER**, 1 Medical
Center Drive, Zip 26301–4199; tel. 304/623–3461, (Nonreporting) **A**1 3 5 **S**
Department of Veterans Affairs, Washington, DC
Primary Contact: Glenn R. Snider, M.D., Interim Director
CMO: Glenn R Snider, M.D., Chief of Staff
CIO: Michael Matthey, Facility Chief Information Officer
CHR: Ian Jacobs, Chief, Human Resource Management Service
Web address: www.clarksburg.va.gov
**Control:** Veterans Affairs, Government, federal **Service:** General medical and
surgical

| Staffed Beds: 71 |
|---|

### ELKINS—Randolph County

✠ **DAVIS MEDICAL CENTER (510030)**, Gorman Avenue and Reed
Street, Zip 26241, Mailing Address: P.O. Box 1484, Zip 26241–1484;
tel. 304/636–3300, (Nonreporting) **A**1 2 10 20 **F**11 13 15 28 29 30 31 32 34
35 40 49 50 51 54 56 57 59 64 68 69 70 71 75 76 78 79 81 82 84 85 86 87
92 94 97 98 103 107 108 109 110 111 115 116 117 118 119 121 123 129
130 132 135 146 147 148 154 **P**3 8 **S** Davis Health System, Elkins, WV
Primary Contact: Vance Jackson, FACHE, Chief Executive Officer
COO: Carl W Nichols IIISenior Vice President, Chief Operating Officer
CFO: Melanie Dempsey, Vice President and Chief Financial Officer
CMO: Catherine Chua, M.D., Chief Medical Officer
CIO: Steve Crowl, Director of Information Services
CHR: Jon Steen, Director Human Resources
CNO: Kathy Sturm, R.N., Vice President, Chief Nursing Officer
Web address: www.davishealthsystem.com
**Control:** Other not–for–profit (including NFP Corporation) **Service:** General
medical and surgical

| Staffed Beds: 80 Admissions: 2684 Census: 29 Outpatient Visits: 111921 |
|---|
| Births: 270 Total Expense ($000): 103391 Payroll Expense ($000): 45161 |
| Personnel: 708 |

**DAVIS MEMORIAL HOSPITAL** See Davis Medical Center

### GASSAWAY—Braxton County

★ **BRAXTON COUNTY MEMORIAL HOSPITAL (511308)**, 100 Hoylman DR,
Zip 26624–9318, Mailing Address: 100 Hoylman Drive, Zip 26624–9318;
tel. 304/364–5156, (Nonreporting) **A**10 18 **F**3 8 11 15 29 30 32 34 35 40 43
45 57 59 62 64 75 81 97 107 108 114 119 127 130 133 146 147 149 154
156 **P**6
Primary Contact: Karen L. Bowling, MSN, R.N., Interim Chief Executive Officer
CFO: Kimber Knight, Chief Financial Officer
CMO: Russell L Stewart, D.O., Medical Director
CNO: Julia Rose, R.N., Director of Nursing
Web address: www.braxtonmemorial.org
**Control:** Other not–for–profit (including NFP Corporation) **Service:** General
medical and surgical

| Staffed Beds: 25 Admissions: 320 Census: 3 Outpatient Visits: 108519 |
|---|
| Births: 0 Total Expense ($000): 18449 Payroll Expense ($000): 7506 |
| Personnel: 144 |

### GLEN DALE—Marshall County

✠ **REYNOLDS MEMORIAL HOSPITAL (510013)**, 800 Wheeling Avenue,
Zip 26038–1697; tel. 304/845–3211, (Nonreporting) **A**1 10 **S** West Virginia
University Health System, Morgantown, WV
Primary Contact: David F. Hess, M.D., Chief Executive Officer
COO: Kevin Britt, Chief Operating Officer
CFO: William Robert Hunt, Chief Financial Officer
CMO: David F. Hess, M.D., President Medical Staff
CIO: Warren Kelley, Chief Information Officer
CHR: R. Craig Madden, Director Employee Relations
CNO: Carol R Miller, R.N., Chief Nursing Officer
Web address: www.reynoldsmemorial.com
**Control:** Other not–for–profit (including NFP Corporation) **Service:** General
medical and surgical

| Staffed Beds: 50 |
|---|

### GRAFTON—Taylor County

**GRAFTON CITY HOSPITAL (511307)**, 1 Hospital Plaza, Zip 26354–1283;
tel. 304/265–0400, (Nonreporting) **A**10 18
Primary Contact: George C. Boyles, Interim President and Chief Administrative
Officer
CFO: Kevin M. Gessler, Interim Chief Financial Officer
CMO: David B Bender, M.D., Chief Medical Staff
CIO: Jim Harris, Director Information Technology
CHR: Missey Kimbrew, Director Human Resources
CNO: Violet Shaw, R.N., Director of Nursing
Web address: www.graftonhospital.com
**Control:** City, Government, Nonfederal **Service:** General medical and surgical

| Staffed Beds: 101 |
|---|

### GRANTSVILLE—Calhoun County

**CALHOUN GENERAL HOSPITAL** See Minnie Hamilton Healthcare Center

★ **MINNIE HAMILTON HEALTHCARE CENTER (511303)**, 186 Hospital Drive,
Zip 26147–7100; tel. 304/354–9244, (Nonreporting) **A**10 18
Primary Contact: Steve Whited, Chief Executive Officer
CMO: Suresh Balasubramony, M.D., Chief Medical Officer
CIO: Brent Barr, Chief Information Officer
CHR: Sheila Gherke, Director Human Resources
CNO: Kim Houchin, Chief Nursing Officer
Web address: www.mhhcc.com
**Control:** Other not–for–profit (including NFP Corporation) **Service:** General
medical and surgical

| Staffed Beds: 42 |
|---|

### HINTON—Summers County

⇑ **SUMMERS COUNTY APPALACHIAN REGIONAL HOSPITAL** See Summers
County Arh Hospital

⇑ **SUMMERS COUNTY ARH HOSPITAL (511310)**, 115 Summers Hospital
Road, Zip 25951–5172, Mailing Address: P.O. Box 940, Zip 25951–0940;
tel. 304/466–1000, (Nonreporting) **A**10 18 21 **F**11 15 29 30 32 34 35 40 43
44 50 54 57 59 62 64 65 71 77 81 82 85 86 87 93 97 107 110 114 119
127 130 133 146 147 148 154 155 **S** Appalachian Regional Healthcare, Inc.,
Lexington, KY
Primary Contact: Wesley Dangerfield, Community Chief Executive Officer
CMO: Waheed Khan, M.D., President Medical Staff
CIO: Brent Styer, Chief Information Officer
CHR: Beth Elswick, Administrative Assistant
CNO: Sharon Milburn, Chief Nursing Officer
Web address: www.arh.org
**Control:** Other not–for–profit (including NFP Corporation) **Service:** General
medical and surgical

| Staffed Beds: 25 Admissions: 251 Census: 6 Outpatient Visits: 29343 |
|---|
| Births: 0 |

### HUNTINGTON—Cabell County

✠ **CABELL HUNTINGTON HOSPITAL (510055)**, 1340 Hal Greer Boulevard,
Zip 25701–0195; tel. 304/526–2000, (Includes HOOPS FAMILY CHILDREN'S
HOSPITAL, Mailing address: 1340 Hal Greer Boulevard, Huntington, West Virginia,
Zip 25701–3800; tel. 304/526–2000), (Nonreporting) **A**1 2 3 5 8 10 **F**2 3 5 8
9 11 12 13 15 16 18 20 22 26 28 29 30 31 34 35 37 38 40 41 43 44 45 46
47 48 49 50 51 52 54 55 56 57 58 59 61 62 64 65 70 72 73 74 75 76 77 78
79 81 82 83 84 85 86 87 88 89 91 92 93 94 96 97 104 107 108 110 111
114 115 116 117 118 119 120 121 123 124 126 129 130 131 132 134 135
144 145 146 147 148 149 150 154 156 157 **P**6 **S** Mountain Health Network,
Huntington, WV
Primary Contact: Kevin N. Fowler, President and Chief Executive Officer
CFO: David M Ward, Chief Financial Officer and Chief Acquisition Officer
CMO: Hoyt J Burdick, M.D., Vice President Medical Affairs
CIO: Dennis Lee, Vice President and Chief Information Officer
CHR: Barry Tourigny, Vice President Human Resources and Organizational
Development
CNO: Joy S Pelfrey, R.N., MSN, Vice President and Chief Nursing Officer
Web address: www.cabellhuntington.org
**Control:** Other not–for–profit (including NFP Corporation) **Service:** General
medical and surgical

| Staffed Beds: 319 Admissions: 15645 Census: 246 Outpatient |
|---|
| Visits: 677430 Births: 2636 Total Expense ($000): 643357 Payroll |
| Expense ($000): 182577 Personnel: 2695 |

**COLUMBIA RIVER PARK HOSPITAL** See River Park Hospital

**WV**

*Many Facility Codes have changed. Please refer to the AHA Guide Code Chart.*

☐ **CORNERSTONE HOSPITAL OF HUNTINGTON (512003)**, 2900 First Avenue, Two East, Zip 25702–1241; tel. 304/399–2600, (Nonreporting) **A**1 10 **F**1 29 148 **S** Cornerstone Healthcare Group, Dallas, TX
Primary Contact: Cynthia Isaacs, Chief Executive Officer
CFO: Carla Jeffs, Chief Financial Officer
CMO: William Beam, M.D., Chief of Staff
Web address: www.chghospitals.com
**Control:** Corporation, Investor–owned (for–profit) **Service:** Acute long–term care hospital

**Staffed Beds:** 28 **Admissions:** 384 **Census:** 27 **Outpatient Visits:** 0
**Births:** 0 **Total Expense ($000):** 11694 **Payroll Expense ($000):** 5251
**Personnel:** 74

⊞ **ENCOMPASS HEALTH REHABILITATION HOSPITAL OF HUNTINGTON (513028)**, 6900 West Country Club Drive, Zip 25705–2000; tel. 304/733–1060, (Nonreporting) **A**1 10 **F**29 34 90 96 148 149 **S** Encompass Health Corporation, Birmingham, AL
Primary Contact: Michael E. Zuliani, Chief Executive Officer
CHR: Helen Arigan, Director Human Resources
CNO: Lisa Caldwell, Chief Nursing Officer
Web address: www.https://www.encompasshealth.com/huntingtonrehab
**Control:** Corporation, Investor–owned (for–profit) **Service:** Rehabilitation

**Staffed Beds:** 60 **Admissions:** 1600 **Census:** 55 **Outpatient Visits:** 0
**Births:** 0 **Total Expense ($000):** 18008 **Payroll Expense ($000):** 9991
**Personnel:** 183

**HEALTHSOUTH HUNTINGTON REHABILITATION HOSPITAL** See Encompass Health Rehabilitation Hospital of Huntington

### HUNTINGTON—Wayne County

⊞ **HUNTINGTON VETERANS AFFAIRS MEDICAL CENTER**, 1540 Spring Valley Drive, Zip 25704–9300; tel. 304/429–6741, (Nonreporting) **A**1 3 5 **S** Department of Veterans Affairs, Washington, DC
Primary Contact: Brian Nimmo, Director
CIO: Gary Henderson, Chief Information Resources Management Services
Web address: www.huntington.va.gov/
**Control:** Veterans Affairs, Government, federal **Service:** General medical and surgical

**Staffed Beds:** 80

### HUNTINGTON—Cabell County

**MILDRED MITCHELL BATEMAN HOSP** See Mildred Mitchell-Bateman Hospital

☐ **MILDRED MITCHELL-BATEMAN HOSPITAL (514009)**, 1530 Norway Avenue, Zip 25705–1358, Mailing Address: P.O. Box 448, Zip 25709–0448; tel. 304/525–7801, (Nonreporting) **A**1 3 5 10 **F**3 4 11 30 68 86 87 97 98 103 130 132 135 143 146 148 149 150 154
Primary Contact: Craig A. Richards, Chief Executive Officer
CFO: Lucille Gedies, Chief Financial Officer
CMO: Shahid Masood, M.D., Clinical Director
CIO: Elias Majdalani, Director Management Information Systems
CHR: Kieth Anne Worden, Director Human Resources
CNO: Patricia Hamilton, R.N., Director of Nursing
Web address: www.batemanhospital.org
**Control:** State, Government, Nonfederal **Service:** Psychiatric

**Staffed Beds:** 110 **Admissions:** 529 **Census:** 98 **Outpatient Visits:** 0
**Births:** 0 **Total Expense ($000):** 42875 **Payroll Expense ($000):** 14484
**Personnel:** 300

☐ **RIVER PARK HOSPITAL (514008)**, 1230 Sixth Avenue, Zip 25701–2312, Mailing Address: P.O. Box 1875, Zip 25719–1875; tel. 304/526–9111, (Nonreporting) **A**1 3 5 10 **S** Universal Health Services, Inc., King of Prussia, PA
Primary Contact: Terry A. Stephens, Chief Executive Officer
CFO: Steve Kuhn, Chief Financial Officer
CMO: Mark A. Hughes, M.D., Medical Director
CIO: James Martin, Chief Information Officer
CHR: Mary Stratton, Director Human Resources
CNO: Michelle Gilliland, Director of Nursing
Web address: www.riverparkhospital.net
**Control:** Corporation, Investor–owned (for–profit) **Service:** Psychiatric

**Staffed Beds:** 175

**ST MARY'S HOSPITAL** See St. Mary's Medical Center

⊞ **ST. MARY'S MEDICAL CENTER (510007)**, 2900 First Avenue, Zip 25702–1272; tel. 304/526–1234, (Total facility includes 19 beds in nursing home–type unit) (Nonreporting) **A**1 2 3 5 10 **F**3 11 12 13 15 17 18 20 22 24 26 28 29 30 31 32 34 35 36 39 40 42 43 44 45 46 47 48 49 50 53 54 55 56 57 58 59 60 61 62 64 65 66 67 68 70 74 76 77 78 79 81 82 84 85 87 90 93 98 100 102 103 105 107 108 110 111 114 115 118 119 120 121 123 124 126 128 129 130 132 135 144 146 147 154 156 157 **P**4 **S** Mountain Health Network, Huntington, WV
Primary Contact: Todd Campbell, Chief Executive Officer
CFO: Angela Swearingen, Vice President Finance
CMO: Ernest Lee Taylor, M.D., Vice President Medical Affairs
CIO: David Wendell, Manager, Information Systems
CHR: Susan Beth Robinson, Vice President Human Resources
CNO: Elizabeth Bosley, R.N., FACHE, Vice President Patient Services and Chief Nursing Officer
Web address: www.st-marys.org
**Control:** Other not–for–profit (including NFP Corporation) **Service:** General medical and surgical

**Staffed Beds:** 393 **Admissions:** 16564 **Census:** 272 **Outpatient Visits:** 256406 **Births:** 364 **Total Expense ($000):** 417529 **Payroll Expense ($000):** 146341 **Personnel:** 2821

### HUNTINGTON—Wayne County

**VETERANS AFFAIRS MEDICAL CENTER** See Huntington Veterans Affairs Medical Center

### HURRICANE—Putnam County

**TEAYS VALLEY HOSPITAL** See Camc Teays Valley Hospital

### KEYSER—Mineral County

⊞ **POTOMAC VALLEY HOSPITAL (511315)**, 100 Pin Oak Lane, Zip 26726–5908; tel. 304/597–3500, (Nonreporting) **A**1 10 18 **F**3 15 18 28 29 34 35 40 44 45 50 54 57 59 63 64 65 66 68 70 71 74 75 77 79 81 82 85 86 87 92 93 97 107 108 110 111 114 119 127 130 131 132 133 135 143 146 148 149 154 156 **S** West Virginia University Health System, Morgantown, WV
Primary Contact: Mark G. Boucot, FACHE, President and Chief Executive Officer
CFO: Marian Cardwell, Chief Financial Officer
CMO: Charles Bess, M.D., Medical Director
CIO: Micah Reel, Director of Bio-Med
CHR: Dianne Smith, Director Personnel and Human Resources
CNO: Mary Ann Billings, Director of Nursing
Web address: www.potomacvalleyhospital.com
**Control:** Other not–for–profit (including NFP Corporation) **Service:** General medical and surgical

**Staffed Beds:** 25 **Admissions:** 1738 **Census:** 13 **Outpatient Visits:** 35905
**Births:** 0 **Total Expense ($000):** 32223 **Payroll Expense ($000):** 13968
**Personnel:** 234

### KINGWOOD—Preston County

★ **PRESTON MEMORIAL HOSPITAL (511312)**, 150 Memorial Drive, Zip 26537–1495; tel. 304/329–1400, (Nonreporting) **A**10 18 **F**3 12 15 18 28 29 30 34 35 40 43 45 47 48 50 53 55 57 59 64 65 68 70 74 75 77 79 81 92 93 97 107 108 110 111 114 119 129 132 133 135 144 146 147 148 154 **P**6 **S** Mon Health System, Morgantown, WV
Primary Contact: Melissa Lockwood, Chief Executive Officer
CFO: Kevin M. Gessler, Chief Financial Officer
CIO: Beth Horne, System Administrator Information Technology
CHR: Michele Batiste, Director Human Resources
Web address: www.prestonmemorial.org
**Control:** Other not–for–profit (including NFP Corporation) **Service:** General medical and surgical

**Staffed Beds:** 25 **Admissions:** 688 **Census:** 9 **Outpatient Visits:** 78136
**Births:** 1 **Total Expense ($000):** 43944 **Payroll Expense ($000):** 19829
**Personnel:** 344

**WV**

---

**Hospital, Medicare Provider Number, Address, Telephone, Approval, Facility, and Physician Codes, Health Care System**

★ American Hospital Association (AHA) membership    ○ Healthcare Facilities Accreditation Program    ⇑ Center for Improvement in Healthcare Quality Accreditation
☐ The Joint Commission accreditation    ◇ DNV Healthcare Inc. accreditation    △ Commission on Accreditation of Rehabilitation Facilities (CARF) accreditation

## LOGAN—Logan County

**LOGAN GENERAL HOSPITAL** See Logan Regional Medical Center

☒ **LOGAN REGIONAL MEDICAL CENTER (510048)**, 20 Hospital Drive, Zip 25601–3452; tel. 304/831–1101, (Nonreporting) **A**1 10 20 **S** LifePoint Health, Brentwood, TN
Primary Contact: Simon Ratliff, Interim Chief Executive Officer
COO: Simon Ratliff, Chief Operating Officer
CFO: Tim Matney, Chief Financial Officer
CMO: Kathy Harvey, D.O., Chief Medical Officer
CIO: Barry Hensley, Director Information Systems
CHR: Jessica Martin, Director Human Resources
CNO: Karen Barnes, Interim Chief Nursing Officer
Web address: www.loganregionalmedicalcenter.com
**Control**: Corporation, Investor–owned (for–profit) **Service**: General medical and surgical

**Staffed Beds:** 129

## MADISON—Boone County

☒ **BOONE MEMORIAL HOSPITAL (511313)**, 701 Madison Avenue, Zip 25130–1699; tel. 304/369–1230, (Nonreporting) **A**1 10 18 **F**3 5 11 15 18 28 29 30 34 35 40 45 47 48 50 53 57 59 65 75 81 87 93 97 100 104 107 108 110 111 114 118 119 127 129 130 131 133 135 144 146 154 156 **P**6
Primary Contact: Virgil Underwood, Chief Executive Officer
CFO: Randy Foxx, Chief Financial Officer
CMO: Ziad Chanaa, M.D., Chief of Staff
CIO: Susan Shreve, Executive Director Information Technology
CHR: Sheliah Cook, Director Human Resources
CNO: Teresa Meade, R.N., Chief Nursing Officer
Web address: www.bmh.org
**Control**: Other not–for–profit (including NFP Corporation) **Service**: General medical and surgical

**Staffed Beds:** 25 **Admissions:** 1673 **Census:** 15 **Outpatient Visits:** 81006 **Births:** 0 **Total Expense ($000):** 46047 **Payroll Expense ($000):** 19338 **Personnel:** 307

## MARTINSBURG—Berkeley County

☒ **BERKELEY MEDICAL CENTER (510008)**, 2500 Hospital Drive, Zip 25401–3402; tel. 304/264–1000, (Nonreporting) **A**1 2 3 5 10 **F**3 8 11 12 15 17 18 20 22 28 29 30 31 34 35 38 40 43 44 45 47 49 51 53 54 56 57 59 62 64 70 72 74 75 76 77 78 79 81 82 84 85 86 87 92 93 98 102 103 104 105 107 108 110 111 114 115 118 119 124 126 129 130 131 132 135 143 145 146 147 148 154 157 **P**6 8 **S** West Virginia University Health System, Morgantown, WV
Primary Contact: Anthony Zelenka, President and Chief Operating Officer
CFO: Anna Buchanan, Vice President Finance and Chief Financial Officer
CIO: Mark Combs, Interim Director System Information Technology
CHR: Justin Ruble, Director, Human Resources
CNO: Donna Clews, Ph.D., R.N., Vice President Patient Care Services
Web address: www.cityhospital.org
**Control**: Other not–for–profit (including NFP Corporation) **Service**: General medical and surgical

**Staffed Beds:** 195 **Admissions:** 8710 **Census:** 108 **Outpatient Visits:** 293034 **Births:** 1047 **Total Expense ($000):** 232794 **Payroll Expense ($000):** 69393 **Personnel:** 1509

**CITY HOSPITAL** See Berkeley Medical Center

☒ **MARTINSBURG VETERANS AFFAIRS MEDICAL CENTER**, 510 Butler Avenue, Zip 25405–9990; tel. 304/263–0811, (Nonreporting) **A**1 3 5 **S** Department of Veterans Affairs, Washington, DC
Primary Contact: Kenneth W. Allensworth, Interim Medical Center Director
CMO: Jonathan Fierer, M.D., Chief of Staff
CIO: Mary Ann Creel, Chief Information Resource Management
CHR: Brenda Byrd-Pelaez, Chief Human Resources Management Office
CNO: Susan George, R.N., M.P.H., Associate Director Patient Care Services
Web address: www.martinsburg.va.gov/
**Control**: Veterans Affairs, Government, federal **Service**: General medical and surgical

**Staffed Beds:** 487

**VETERANS AFFAIRS MEDICAL CENTER** See Martinsburg Veterans Affairs Medical Center

## MONTGOMERY—Fayette County

☒ **MONTGOMERY GENERAL HOSPITAL (511318)**, 401 Sixth Avenue, Zip 25136–2116, Mailing Address: P.O. Box 270, Zip 25136–0270; tel. 304/442–5151, (Total facility includes 44 beds in nursing home–type unit) (Nonreporting) **A**1 10 18 **F**3 11 15 29 30 34 35 40 45 49 50 53 57 59 64 67 68 77 81 87 93 96 97 107 110 111 114 119 128 129 130 131 133 135 146 147 149
Primary Contact: Vickie Lynn. Gay, Chief Executive Officer
CFO: Sherri Murray, Chief Financial Officer
CMO: Traci Acklin, M.D., Chief of Staff
CIO: Denzil Blevins, Director Information Systems
CHR: Kelly D Frye, Director Human Resources
Web address: www.mghwv.com
**Control**: Other not–for–profit (including NFP Corporation) **Service**: General medical and surgical

**Staffed Beds:** 69 **Admissions:** 485 **Census:** 42 **Outpatient Visits:** 53184 **Births:** 0 **Total Expense ($000):** 23105 **Payroll Expense ($000):** 10923 **Personnel:** 210

## MORGANTOWN—Monongalia County

**CHESTNUT RIDGE HOSPITAL** See West Virginia University Hospitals, Morgantown

☒ **ENCOMPASS HEALTH REHABILITATION HOSPITAL OF MORGANTOWN (513030)**, 1160 Van Voorhis Road, Zip 26505–3437; tel. 304/598–1100, (Nonreporting) **A**1 5 10 **S** Encompass Health Corporation, Birmingham, AL
Primary Contact: Tracy Vinciguerra, Chief Executive Officer
CFO: Jason Gizzi, Controller
CMO: Govind Patel, M.D., Medical Director
CIO: Robin Wherry, Risk Manager and Director Quality Assurance and Health Information Management
CHR: Shannon Hyde, Director Human Resources
CNO: Stacy Jones, Chief Nursing Officer
Web address: www.healthsouthmountainview.com
**Control**: Corporation, Investor–owned (for–profit) **Service**: Rehabilitation

**Staffed Beds:** 96

**HEALTHSOUTH MOUNTAINVIEW REGIONAL REHABILITATION HOSPITAL** See Encompass Health Rehabilitation Hospital of Morgantown

☒ **MON HEALTH MEDICAL CENTER (510024)**, 1200 J D Anderson Drive, Zip 26505–3486; tel. 304/598–1200, (Nonreporting) **A**1 2 3 10 19 **F**3 13 15 17 18 20 22 24 26 28 29 30 31 32 34 35 40 43 45 46 49 50 51 54 55 57 59 60 64 65 68 70 74 75 76 77 78 79 81 82 84 85 86 87 89 97 100 104 107 108 110 111 114 115 116 118 119 120 121 123 126 127 129 130 132 135 145 146 147 148 149 154 156 **P**6 **S** Mon Health System, Morgantown, WV
Primary Contact: David Goldberg, President and Chief Executive Officer
CMO: Matthew P Darmelio, Chief of Staff
CIO: Steve Carter, Chief Information Officer
CHR: Melissa Shreves Shahnam, Director Human Resources
Web address: www.mongeneral.com
**Control**: Other not–for–profit (including NFP Corporation) **Service**: General medical and surgical

**Staffed Beds:** 185 **Admissions:** 7412 **Census:** 83 **Outpatient Visits:** 421799 **Births:** 1100 **Total Expense ($000):** 269975 **Payroll Expense ($000):** 98262 **Personnel:** 1648

**MONONGALIA GENERAL HOSPITAL** See Mon Health Medical Center

**WV**

*Many Facility Codes have changed. Please refer to the AHA Guide Code Chart.*

⊞ **WEST VIRGINIA UNIVERSITY HOSPITALS (510001)**, 1 Medical Center Drive, Zip 26506–4749; tel. 304/598–4000, (Includes CHESTNUT RIDGE HOSPITAL, Mailing address: 930 Chestnut Ridge Road, Morgantown, West Virginia, Zip 26505–2854; tel. 304/293–4000; WEST VIRGINIA UNIVERSITY CHILDREN'S HOSPITAL, Mailing address: 1 Medical Center Drive, Morgantown, West Virginia, Zip 26506–1200; tel. 800/982–6277), (Nonreporting) **A**1 2 3 5 8 10 19 **F**3 4 5 7 8 9 11 12 13 15 17 18 19 20 21 22 23 24 25 26 27 28 29 30 31 32 33 34 35 36 37 38 39 40 41 43 44 45 46 47 48 49 50 51 52 53 54 55 56 57 58 59 60 61 62 63 64 65 68 70 71 72 74 75 76 77 78 79 80 81 82 83 84 85 86 87 88 89 91 92 93 97 98 99 100 101 102 103 104 105 106 107 108 109 110 111 114 115 116 117 118 119 120 121 123 124 126 127 129 130 131 132 133 135 136 137 138 141 143 144 145 146 147 148 149 152 153 154 155 156 157 **S** West Virginia University Health System, Morgantown, WV
Primary Contact: Albert L. Wright Jr, President and Chief Executive Officer
COO: Ron Pellegrino, Chief Operating Officer
CFO: Melissa McCoy, Vice President and Chief Financial Officer
CMO: Judie Charlton, M.D., Chief Medical Officer
CIO: James Venturella, Vice President Information Technology
CHR: Leeann Cerimele, Vice President Human Resources
CNO: Douglas W Mitchell, Vice President and Chief Nursing Officer
Web address: www.health.wvu.edu
**Control:** Other not–for–profit (including NFP Corporation) **Service:** General medical and surgical

**Staffed Beds:** 657 **Admissions:** 33439 **Census:** 579 **Outpatient Visits:** 914239 **Births:** 1731 **Total Expense ($000):** 1309325 **Payroll Expense ($000):** 358970 **Personnel:** 6367

### NEW MARTINSVILLE—Wetzel County

⊞ **WETZEL COUNTY HOSPITAL (510072)**, 3 East Benjamin Drive, Zip 26155–2758; tel. 304/455–8000, (Nonreporting) **A**1 10 20 **F**8 15 18 28 29 30 34 35 40 43 45 50 57 59 68 70 75 77 78 79 81 82 90 93 107 110 111 115 119 127 130 133 146 148 154 156 157 **P**5 **S** West Virginia University Health System, Morgantown, WV
Primary Contact: David F. Hess, M.D., Chief Executive Officer
CFO: Edwin Szewczyk, Chief Financial Officer
CMO: Donald A. Blum, M.D., Chief of Staff
CIO: Amy Frazier, Supervisor Management Information Systems
CHR: Sarah Boley, Director Human Resources
Web address: www.wetzelcountyhospital.com
**Control:** City–county, Government, Nonfederal **Service:** General medical and surgical

**Staffed Beds:** 58 **Admissions:** 483 **Census:** 7 **Outpatient Visits:** 85740 **Births:** 0 **Total Expense ($000):** 20190 **Payroll Expense ($000):** 8530 **Personnel:** 195

### OAK HILL—Fayette County

⊞ **PLATEAU MEDICAL CENTER (511317)**, 430 Main Street, Zip 25901–3455; tel. 304/469–8600, (Nonreporting) **A**1 3 10 18 **F**3 11 15 18 29 34 40 45 46 50 53 57 68 70 75 76 77 79 81 87 93 104 107 108 110 111 115 119 126 129 133 146 **S** Community Health Systems, Inc., Franklin, TN
Primary Contact: Christopher L. Howe, R.N., Chief Executive Officer
CFO: Heather Hylton, Chief Financial Officer
CMO: Jacob McNeel, D.O., Chief of Staff
CIO: Nick Stover, Director Information Systems
CHR: Tammie Chinn, Director Marketing and Public Relations
CNO: Randell Thompson, Chief Nursing Officer
Web address: www.plateaumedicalcenter.com
**Control:** Corporation, Investor–owned (for–profit) **Service:** General medical and surgical

**Staffed Beds:** 25 **Admissions:** 866 **Census:** 7 **Outpatient Visits:** 38856 **Births:** 0 **Total Expense ($000):** 24481 **Payroll Expense ($000):** 9999 **Personnel:** 204

**PLATEAU MEDICAL CENTER INC** See Plateau Medical Center

### PARKERSBURG—Wood County

⊞ **CAMDEN CLARK MEDICAL CENTER (510058)**, 800 Garfield Avenue, Zip 26101–5378, Mailing Address: P.O. Box 718, Zip 26102–0718; tel. 304/424–2111, (Nonreporting) **A**1 2 3 5 10 19 **F**3 7 8 11 12 13 15 17 18 20 22 24 28 29 30 31 34 35 40 43 45 48 49 50 53 54 57 58 59 60 64 65 66 67 68 70 74 75 76 77 78 79 80 81 82 84 85 86 87 89 92 97 98 100 107 108 110 111 115 117 119 120 121 123 124 129 130 131 132 135 144 146 147 154 156 157 **P**6 8 **S** West Virginia University Health System, Morgantown, WV
Primary Contact: Steve Altmiller, President and Chief Executive Officer
CFO: Carolyn Allen, Vice President and Chief Financial Officer
CMO: David Gnegy, M.D., Vice President of Medical Affairs
CIO: Josh Woods, Director Information Systems
CHR: Tom Heller, Vice President Operations and Human Resources
CNO: Christine S. Daniels, R.N., Chief Nursing Officer
Web address: www.camdenclark.org
**Control:** Other not–for–profit (including NFP Corporation) **Service:** General medical and surgical

**Staffed Beds:** 284 **Admissions:** 17619 **Census:** 185 **Outpatient Visits:** 93048 **Births:** 1209 **Total Expense ($000):** 226139 **Payroll Expense ($000):** 76607 **Personnel:** 2226

**CAMDEN-CLARK MEMORIAL HOSPITAL** See Camden Clark Medical Center

⊞ **ENCOMPASS HEALTH REHABILITATION HOSPITAL OF PARKERSBURG (513027)**, 3 Western Hills Drive, Zip 26105–8122; tel. 304/420–1300, (Nonreporting) **A**1 10 **F**29 90 96 130 148 149 **S** Encompass Health Corporation, Birmingham, AL
Primary Contact: Alvin R. Lawson, JD, Chief Executive Officer
CFO: Jessica Gum, Controller
CMO: Kalapala Rao, M.D., Medical Director
CHR: Olivia Morrison, Human Resource Manager
**Control:** Corporation, Investor–owned (for–profit) **Service:** Rehabilitation

**Staffed Beds:** 40 **Admissions:** 1122 **Census:** 36 **Outpatient Visits:** 0 **Births:** 0 **Total Expense ($000):** 14368 **Payroll Expense ($000):** 7049 **Personnel:** 129

**HEALTHSOUTH WESTERN HILLS REGIONAL REHABILITATION HOSPITAL** See Encompass Health Rehabilitation Hospital of Parkersburg

### PETERSBURG—Grant County

★ **GRANT MEMORIAL HOSPITAL (511316)**, 117 Hospital Drive, Zip 26847–9566, Mailing Address: P.O. Box 1019, Zip 26847–1019; tel. 304/257–1026, (Total facility includes 20 beds in nursing home–type unit) (Nonreporting) **A**10 18 **F**3 11 13 15 28 29 34 35 40 45 50 57 59 64 65 67 70 75 76 77 79 81 87 93 107 108 110 111 114 118 119 128 130 131 132 133 135 146 147 149 156 157
Primary Contact: Robert W. Milvet Jr, Chief Executive Officer
CFO: David Applewood, Chief Financial Officer
CMO: Caroline Armstrong, D.O., M.D., Chief of Staff
CIO: Derek Nesselrodt, Director Information Systems
CHR: Ronnie Arbaugh, Director Human Resources
CNO: Kelley M. Scott, Interim Chief Nursing Officer
Web address: www.grantmemorial.com
**Control:** County, Government, Nonfederal **Service:** General medical and surgical

**Staffed Beds:** 45 **Admissions:** 1343 **Census:** 25 **Outpatient Visits:** 45775 **Births:** 285 **Total Expense ($000):** 38438 **Payroll Expense ($000):** 14368 **Personnel:** 314

### PHILIPPI—Barbour County

★ **BROADDUS HOSPITAL (511300)**, 1 Healthcare Drive, Zip 26416–9405, Mailing Address: P.O. Box 930, Zip 26416–0930; tel. 304/457–1760, (Total facility includes 60 beds in nursing home–type unit) (Nonreporting) **A**10 18 **F**3 15 29 30 34 35 40 57 59 64 75 85 87 107 110 115 119 128 130 132 133 135 143 146 148 **S** Davis Health System, Elkins, WV
Primary Contact: Dana L. Gould, Chief Executive Officer
CHR: Penny D. Brown, Human Resource Representative
CNO: Lesa Corley, Director of Nursing
Web address: www.davishealthsystem.org/
**Control:** Other not–for–profit (including NFP Corporation) **Service:** General medical and surgical

**Staffed Beds:** 72 **Admissions:** 222 **Census:** 57 **Outpatient Visits:** 22936 **Births:** 0 **Total Expense ($000):** 18371 **Payroll Expense ($000):** 7850 **Personnel:** 158

---

**Hospital, Medicare Provider Number, Address, Telephone, Approval, Facility, and Physician Codes, Health Care System**

★ American Hospital Association (AHA) membership    ○ Healthcare Facilities Accreditation Program    ⇑ Center for Improvement in Healthcare Quality Accreditation
□ The Joint Commission accreditation    ◇ DNV Healthcare Inc. accreditation    △ Commission on Accreditation of Rehabilitation Facilities (CARF) accreditation

## POINT PLEASANT—Mason County

☒ **PLEASANT VALLEY HOSPITAL (510012)**, 2520 Valley Drive, Zip 25550–2031; tel. 304/675–4340, (Total facility includes 100 beds in nursing home–type unit) (Nonreporting) **A**1 10 **F**3 11 13 15 17 18 24 26 28 29 30 31 34 35 40 43 45 46 47 48 50 53 56 57 59 64 65 70 74 75 76 77 78 79 81 85 86 87 89 93 107 108 110 111 114 115 118 119 128 129 130 131 132 133 135 143 144 146 147 148 156 **P**6 **S** Mountain Health Network, Huntington, WV
Primary Contact: Glen A. Washington, Chief Executive Officer
COO: William A Barker JrVice President Administration
CFO: Richard Hogan, Chief Financial Officer
CMO: Agnes Enrico-Simon, M.D., President Medical Staff
CIO: Paula Brooker, Director Information Services
CNO: Amber Findley, Senior Director Nursing Services and NRC Administrator
Web address: www.pvalley.org
**Control**: Other not–for–profit (including NFP Corporation) **Service**: General medical and surgical

**Staffed Beds:** 149 **Admissions:** 1688 **Census:** 114 **Outpatient Visits:** 113619 **Births:** 96 **Total Expense ($000):** 64326 **Payroll Expense ($000):** 20724 **Personnel:** 478

## PRINCETON—Mercer County

☒ **ENCOMPASS HEALTH REHABILITATION HOSPITAL OF PRINCETON (513026)**, 120 Twelfth Street, Zip 24740–2352; tel. 304/487–8000, (Nonreporting) **A**1 10 **S** Encompass Health Corporation, Birmingham, AL
Primary Contact: Robert Williams, Chief Executive Officer
CFO: Amy Flowers, Controller
CMO: Robert Walker, M.D., Medical Director
CIO: Brian Bales, Director Plant Operations
CHR: Jan Thibodeau, Director Human Resources
CNO: Lisa Lester, Chief Nursing Officer
Web address: www.healthsouthsouthernhills.com
**Control**: Corporation, Investor–owned (for–profit) **Service**: Rehabilitation

**Staffed Beds:** 45

**HEALTHSOUTH SOUTHERN HILLS REHABILITATION HOSPITAL** See Encompass Health Rehabilitation Hospital of Princeton

☒ ⋔ **PRINCETON COMMUNITY HOSPITAL (510046)**, 122 12th Street, Zip 24740–2352, Mailing Address: P.O. Box 1369, Zip 24740–1369; tel. 304/487–7000, (Nonreporting) **A**1 2 10 19 21 **F**3 11 12 13 15 17 29 30 31 32 34 35 39 40 44 45 46 48 49 50 51 53 57 59 64 65 70 74 75 76 77 78 79 81 85 86 87 89 93 98 100 101 102 103 104 107 108 110 111 114 115 118 119 127 129 130 131 132 135 141 142 144 146 147 149 153 **P**1
Primary Contact: Jeffrey Lilley, CPA, Chief Executive Officer
CFO: Frank J Sinicrope JrVice President Financial Services
CMO: Wesley Asbury, M.D., President Medical Staff
CIO: Stephen A Curry, Director Information Services
CHR: Heather Poff, Director Human Resources
CNO: Rose Morgan, MS, R.N., Vice President Patient Care Services
Web address: www.pchonline.org
**Control**: City, Government, Nonfederal **Service**: General medical and surgical

**Staffed Beds:** 164 **Admissions:** 8173 **Census:** 114 **Outpatient Visits:** 303023 **Births:** 525 **Total Expense ($000):** 148574 **Payroll Expense ($000):** 55092 **Personnel:** 1079

## RANSON—Jefferson County

☒ **JEFFERSON MEDICAL CENTER (511319)**, 300 South Preston Street, Zip 25438–1631; tel. 304/728–1600, (Nonreporting) **A**1 3 5 10 18 **F**3 13 30 35 38 40 43 45 64 70 76 79 81 82 86 87 93 97 107 119 130 131 133 146 147 154 157 **P**6 8 **S** West Virginia University Health System, Morgantown, WV
Primary Contact: Anthony Zelenka, President and Chief Executive Officer
CFO: Anna Buchanan, Vice President Finance and Chief Financial Officer
CMO: David A. Baltierra, M.D., President Medical Staff
CIO: Mark Combs, Chief Information Security Officer
CHR: Justin Ruble, Director Human Resources
CNO: Linda Blanc, R.N., Administrative Director of Nursing
Web address: www.wvuniversityhealthcare.com/locations/Jefferson-Medical-Center.aspx
**Control**: Other not–for–profit (including NFP Corporation) **Service**: General medical and surgical

**Staffed Beds:** 25 **Admissions:** 1393 **Census:** 11 **Outpatient Visits:** 71055 **Births:** 225 **Total Expense ($000):** 50786 **Payroll Expense ($000):** 16618 **Personnel:** 293

**JEFFERSON MEMORIAL HOSPITAL** See Jefferson Medical Center

## RIPLEY—Jackson County

☒ **JACKSON GENERAL HOSPITAL (511320)**, 122 Pinnell Street, Zip 25271–9101, Mailing Address: P.O. Box 720, Zip 25271–0720; tel. 304/372–2731, (Nonreporting) **A**10 18
Primary Contact: Stephanie McCoy, President and Chief Executive Officer
CFO: Angela Frame, Chief Financial Officer
CMO: James G Gaal, M.D., Chief of Medical Staff
CIO: John Manley, Director Information Systems
CHR: Jeffrey Tabor, Director Human Resources
Web address: www.jacksongeneral.com
**Control**: Other not–for–profit (including NFP Corporation) **Service**: General medical and surgical

**Staffed Beds:** 25

## ROMNEY—Hampshire County

**HAMPSHIRE MEMORIAL HOSPITAL** See Valley Health - Hampshire Memorial Hospital

☒ **VALLEY HEALTH - HAMPSHIRE MEMORIAL HOSPITAL (511311)**, 363 Sunrise Boulevard, Zip 26757–4607; tel. 304/822–4561, (Total facility includes 30 beds in nursing home–type unit) (Nonreporting) **A**1 10 18 **F**3 15 18 29 30 40 45 50 54 59 64 65 71 77 79 81 85 86 93 97 107 110 114 119 127 128 129 130 133 148 154 155 156 157 **P**6 **S** Valley Health System, Winchester, VA
Primary Contact: Thomas S. Kluge, President
CFO: Kathryn Morales, Director of Finance
CMO: Gerald Bechamps, M.D., Vice President Medical Affairs
CHR: Abbey Rembold, Human Resources Senior Generalist
CNO: Mary Sas, Vice President
Web address: www.valleyhealthlink.com/hampshire
**Control**: Other not–for–profit (including NFP Corporation) **Service**: General medical and surgical

**Staffed Beds:** 44 **Admissions:** 754 **Census:** 37 **Outpatient Visits:** 52268 **Births:** 0 **Total Expense ($000):** 27243 **Payroll Expense ($000):** 10147 **Personnel:** 156

## RONCEVERTE—Greenbrier County

★ ○ **GREENBRIER VALLEY MEDICAL CENTER (510002)**, 202 Maplewood Avenue, Zip 24970–1334, Mailing Address: P.O. Box 497, Zip 24970–0497; tel. 304/647–4411, (Nonreporting) **A**3 5 10 11 12 13 **S** Community Health Systems, Inc., Franklin, TN
Primary Contact: Jim Hobson, Chief Executive Officer
CFO: Paige Adkins, Chief Financial Officer
CMO: John Johnson, M.D., Chief of Staff
CIO: Matt Turley, Interim Director Information Systems
CHR: Melissa Wickline, Director Marketing
CNO: Charlene Warren, R.N., Chief Nursing Officer
Web address: www.gvmc.com
**Control**: Corporation, Investor–owned (for–profit) **Service**: General medical and surgical

**Staffed Beds:** 113

**HUMANA HOSP-GREENBRIER VALLEY** See Greenbrier Valley Medical Center

## SISTERSVILLE—Tyler County

★ **SISTERSVILLE GENERAL HOSPITAL (511304)**, 314 South Wells Street, Zip 26175–1098; tel. 304/652–2611, (Nonreporting) **A**10 18
Primary Contact: Brandon Chadock, Interim Chief Executive Officer
COO: Brandon Chadock, Director of Operations
CMO: Amanda Nichols, M.D., Chief of Staff
CIO: Casey Tuttle, Director Information Technology
CNO: Stephen Todd Strickler, Director of Nursing
Web address: www.sistersvillehospital.com
**Control**: City, Government, Nonfederal **Service**: General medical and surgical

**Staffed Beds:** 12

## SOUTH CHARLESTON—Kanawha County

☒ **THOMAS MEMORIAL HOSPITAL (510029)**, 4605 MacCorkle Avenue SW, Zip 25309–1398; tel. 304/766–3600, (Nonreporting) **A**1 5 10 **F**3 5 11 13 15 17 18 19 20 22 26 28 29 30 31 32 34 35 40 43 45 49 57 59 64 70 72 76 78 79 81 85 86 89 92 93 97 98 100 102 103 105 107 108 110 111 114 115 118 119 120 121 123 126 129 130 146 147 153 **S** Thomas Health System, Inc., South Charleston, WV
Primary Contact: Daniel Lauffer, FACHE, President and Chief Executive Officer
COO: Brian Ulery, Chief Operating Officer
CFO: Timothy Skeldon, Chief Financial Officer
CMO: Matthew Upton, Chief Medical Information Officer
CHR: Patrick Rawlings, Human Resources Director
CNO: Rebecca Brannon, R.N., Chief Nursing Officer
Web address: www.thomashealth.org
**Control**: Other not–for–profit (including NFP Corporation) **Service**: General medical and surgical

**Staffed Beds**: 214 **Admissions**: 6764 **Census**: 89 **Outpatient Visits**: 168657 **Births**: 753 **Total Expense ($000)**: 177668 **Payroll Expense ($000)**: 62928 **Personnel**: 1549

## SPENCER—Roane County

☒ **ROANE GENERAL HOSPITAL (511306)**, 200 Hospital Drive, Zip 25276–1050; tel. 304/927–4444, (Total facility includes 35 beds in nursing home–type unit) (Nonreporting) **A**1 10 18 **F**1 3 11 15 18 28 29 34 35 40 43 45 53 57 59 64 65 67 68 81 82 85 89 90 93 97 107 108 110 114 119 127 128 130 132 133 135 148 156 **P**6
Primary Contact: Douglas E. Bentz, Chief Executive Officer
CFO: Kyle A. Pierson, Chief Financial Officer
CMO: Hong-Kin Ng, M.D., Chief Medical Officer
CIO: Tony Keaton, Director Information Systems
CHR: Jeffery B Hunt, Vice President, Business Development and Support Services
CNO: Julie R. Carr, Chief Nursing Officer
Web address: www.roanegeneralhospital.com
**Control**: Other not–for–profit (including NFP Corporation) **Service**: General medical and surgical

**Staffed Beds**: 60 **Admissions**: 188 **Census**: 36 **Outpatient Visits**: 43912 **Births**: 0 **Total Expense ($000)**: 38865 **Payroll Expense ($000)**: 17505 **Personnel**: 283

## SUMMERSVILLE—Nicholas County

**SUMMERSVILLE MEMORIAL HOSPITAL** See Summersville Regional Medical Center

★ **SUMMERSVILLE REGIONAL MEDICAL CENTER (511322)**, 400 Fairview Heights Road, Zip 26651–9308; tel. 304/872–2891, (Total facility includes 52 beds in nursing home–type unit) (Nonreporting) **A**10 18 20 **F**3 15 28 29 34 35 40 43 45 57 59 64 65 68 70 75 77 81 85 97 107 108 110 111 115 119 127 128 130 133 135 154
Primary Contact: Karen L. Bowling, MSN, R.N., Interim Chief Executive Officer
CFO: Brian Kelbaugh, Chief Financial Officer
CMO: Bandy Mullins, M.D., Chief of Staff
CIO: Mike Ellison, Information Systems Lead
CHR: David M Henderson, Director Human Resources
CNO: Jennifer McCue, Director Patient Care
Web address: www.https://www.summersvilleregional.org/
**Control**: Other not–for–profit (including NFP Corporation) **Service**: General medical and surgical

**Staffed Beds**: 77 **Admissions**: 1454 **Census**: 68 **Outpatient Visits**: 114719 **Births**: 0 **Total Expense ($000)**: 43084 **Payroll Expense ($000)**: 23134 **Personnel**: 387

## WEBSTER SPRINGS—Webster County

★ **WEBSTER COUNTY MEMORIAL HOSPITAL (511301)**, 324 Miller Mountain Drive, Zip 26288–1087, Mailing Address: P.O. Box 312, Zip 26288–0312; tel. 304/847–5682, (Nonreporting) **A**10 18 **S** Davis Health System, Elkins, WV
Primary Contact: Jim Parker, FACHE, Chief Executive Officer
CFO: Kenneth Chad Wright, Chief Financial Officer
CIO: Jeannie Fisher, Coordinator Information Technology
CHR: Michelle Holcomb, Human Resources
Web address: www.wcmhw.org
**Control**: Other not–for–profit (including NFP Corporation) **Service**: General medical and surgical

**Staffed Beds**: 15

## WEIRTON—Brooke County

☒ **WEIRTON MEDICAL CENTER (510023)**, 601 Colliers Way, Zip 26062–5091; tel. 304/797–6000, (Total facility includes 33 beds in nursing home–type unit) (Nonreporting) **A**1 10 **F**3 9 11 13 15 17 18 20 22 28 29 30 32 35 37 40 41 43 45 46 47 48 49 50 51 54 56 57 59 60 61 62 64 68 70 74 75 76 77 78 79 81 82 85 86 87 89 90 92 93 96 97 100 102 107 108 110 111 114 115 116 118 119 124 126 128 129 130 131 132 135 143 145 146 147 148 149 154 **P**6
Primary Contact: John C. Frankovitch, President and Chief Executive Officer
COO: David S Artman, Chief Operating Officer
CFO: Eugene Trout, Chief Financial Officer
CMO: Atul Shetty, Chief of Staff
CIO: Cristen Nopwaskey, Chief Information Officer
CHR: Gabe D'Ortenzio, Director of Human Resources
CNO: Denise P Westwood, Chief Nursing Officer
Web address: www.weirtonmedical.com
**Control**: Other not–for–profit (including NFP Corporation) **Service**: General medical and surgical

**Staffed Beds**: 167 **Admissions**: 6593 **Census**: 89 **Outpatient Visits**: 508912 **Births**: 456 **Total Expense ($000)**: 196096 **Payroll Expense ($000)**: 87175 **Personnel**: 1201

## WELCH—Mcdowell County

**WELCH COMMUNITY HOSPITAL (510086)**, 454 McDowell Street, Zip 24801–2097; tel. 304/436–8461, (Total facility includes 59 beds in nursing home–type unit) (Nonreporting) **A**10 20 **F**3 15 29 35 40 45 50 57 59 64 65 66 67 68 70 75 81 86 87 89 97 107 110 114 119 127 130 135 146 147 148 156
Primary Contact: Mark Simpson, Chief Executive Officer
COO: Heather Smith, Chief Operating Officer
CFO: Johnny Brant, Chief Financial Officer
CMO: Chandra Sharma, M.D., Chief of Staff
CHR: Diana Blankenship, Director Human Resources
**Control**: State, Government, Nonfederal **Service**: General medical and surgical

**Staffed Beds**: 108 **Admissions**: 593 **Census**: 35 **Outpatient Visits**: 28431 **Births**: 0 **Total Expense ($000)**: 28978 **Payroll Expense ($000)**: 7225 **Personnel**: 224

**WELCH EMERGENCY HOSPITAL** See Welch Community Hospital

## WESTON—Lewis County

**SHARPE HOSPITAL** See William R. Sharpe, Jr. Hospital

☒ **STONEWALL JACKSON MEMORIAL HOSPITAL (510038)**, 230 Hospital Plaza, Zip 26452–8558; tel. 304/269–8000, (Nonreporting) **A**1 10 **F**3 11 13 15 28 29 30 31 35 40 43 45 48 50 56 57 59 62 64 68 70 75 76 78 79 81 85 86 87 93 94 97 107 108 111 114 118 119 129 130 131 132 135 145 146 147 148 157 **P**6 **S** Mon Health System, Morgantown, WV
Primary Contact: Avah Stalnaker, Chief Executive Officer
CFO: Daris Rosencrance, Chief Financial Officer
CMO: Doyle R. Sickles, M.D., Chief of Medical Staff
CIO: Kay Butcher, Director Health Information Management
CHR: Rhonda K. Mitchell, Director Human Resources
CNO: Carole Norton, Chief Nursing Officer
Web address: www.stonewallhospital.com
**Control**: Other not–for–profit (including NFP Corporation) **Service**: General medical and surgical

**Staffed Beds**: 70 **Admissions**: 1572 **Census**: 15 **Outpatient Visits**: 79759 **Births**: 154 **Total Expense ($000)**: 49281 **Payroll Expense ($000)**: 23009 **Personnel**: 393

☐ **WILLIAM R. SHARPE, JR. HOSPITAL (514012)**, 936 Sharpe Hospital Road, Zip 26452–8550; tel. 304/269–1210, (Nonreporting) **A**1 3 5 **F**3 11 30 50 53 56 68 75 86 87 98 100 101 103 130 132 143 146 157
Primary Contact: Parker Haddix, Chief Executive Officer
COO: Terry L. Small, Assistant Chief Executive Officer
CFO: Robert J. Kimble, Chief Financial Officer
CIO: Pam Lewis, Chief Compliance Officer
CNO: Cheryl France, M.D., Chief Medical Officer
Web address: www.wvdhhr.org/sharpe
**Control**: State, Government, Nonfederal **Service**: Psychiatric

**Staffed Beds**: 200 **Admissions**: 150 **Census**: 117 **Outpatient Visits**: 0 **Births**: 0 **Total Expense ($000)**: 58739 **Payroll Expense ($000)**: 13165 **Personnel**: 575

**WV**

---

**Hospital, Medicare Provider Number, Address, Telephone, Approval, Facility, and Physician Codes, Health Care System**

★ American Hospital Association (AHA) membership
☐ The Joint Commission accreditation
○ Healthcare Facilities Accreditation Program
◇ DNV Healthcare Inc. accreditation
⇑ Center for Improvement in Healthcare Quality Accreditation
△ Commission on Accreditation of Rehabilitation Facilities (CARF) accreditation

**WHEELING—Ohio County**

★ **PETERSON HEALTHCARE AND REHABILITATION HOSPITAL (513025)**, 20
Homestead Avenue, Zip 26003–6638; tel. 304/234–0500, (Nonreporting) **A**10
Primary Contact: Diane Miller, Administrator
CFO: Tammy Bortz, Director of Finance
CMO: William Mercer, M.D., Director
CIO: Hope Miller, Director of Medical Records
CHR: Spencer McIlvain, Director of Human Resources
CNO: Charlene Jones, Chief Nursing Officer
Web address: www.https://guardianeldercare.com/locations/peterson/
**Control**: Corporation, Investor–owned (for–profit) **Service**: Rehabilitation

**Staffed Beds:** 172

**PETERSON REHABILITATION HOSPITAL** See Peterson Healthcare and
Rehabilitation Hospital

✠ **WHEELING HOSPITAL (510050)**, 1 Medical Park, Zip 26003–6379;
tel. 304/243–3000, (Nonreporting) **A**1 2 3 5 10 **F**3 8 9 11 12 13 15 17 18 20
22 24 26 28 29 30 31 32 34 35 36 40 43 44 45 46 47 48 49 50 51 53 55 56
57 58 59 60 61 62 64 65 66 68 70 72 73 74 75 76 77 78 79 80 81 82 84 85
86 87 89 91 92 93 96 97 100 107 108 110 111 114 115 116 117 118 119
120 121 123 126 129 130 131 132 135 136 143 144 146 147 148 149 150
154 156 **S** West Virginia University Health System, Morgantown, WV
Primary Contact: Douglass Harrison, Chief Executive Officer
CFO: James B. Murdy, Chief Financial Officer
CMO: Angelo Georges, M.D., President Medical and Dental Staff
CIO: David Rapp, Chief Information Officer
CHR: Kareen Simon, Vice President of Operations
CNO: Kathy Stahl, Chief Nursing Officer
Web address: www.wheelinghospital.org
**Control**: Other not–for–profit (including NFP Corporation) **Service**: General
medical and surgical

**Staffed Beds:** 223 **Admissions:** 11196 **Census:** 138 **Outpatient
Visits:** 716989 **Births:** 1239 **Total Expense ($000):** 401387 **Payroll
Expense ($000):** 168641 **Personnel:** 2737

WV

*Many Facility Codes have changed. Please refer to the AHA Guide Code Chart.*

# WISCONSIN

## ALTOONA—Eau Claire County

**OAKLEAF SURGICAL CENTER** See Oakleaf Surgical Hospital

☐ **OAKLEAF SURGICAL HOSPITAL (520196)**, 1000 OakLeaf Way,
Zip 54701–3016; tel. 715/831–8130, (Nonreporting) **A**1 10 **F**3 37 45 47 48 51
64 68 75 79 80 81 82 85 107 111 114 119 126 130 149 **S** National Surgical
Healthcare, Chicago, IL
Primary Contact: Anne Hargrave-Thomas, Chief Executive Officer
COO: Erma Radke, Director of Operations
CFO: Denise Freid-Scheppke, Chief Accounting Officer
CHR: Nikki Yankton, Director Human Resources
CNO: Jacquelyn Maki, Chief Nursing Officer
Web address: www.oakleafmedical.com
**Control**: Corporation, Investor–owned (for–profit) **Service**: General medical and
surgical

> **Staffed Beds:** 13 **Admissions:** 408 **Census:** 2 **Outpatient Visits:** 11397
> **Births:** 0 **Total Expense ($000):** 53113 **Payroll Expense ($000):** 15135
> **Personnel:** 220

## AMERY—Polk County

☒ **AMERY HOSPITAL AND CLINIC (521308)**, 265 Griffin Street East,
Zip 54001–1439; tel. 715/268–8000, (Nonreporting) **A**1 3 5 10 18 **F**3 6 11 13
15 18 28 29 30 32 34 35 36 38 40 44 45 53 54 56 57 59 64 65 75 76 77
78 79 80 81 82 85 86 87 89 93 96 97 98 99 100 103 104 107 108 110 111
115 119 129 130 131 132 133 144 146 148 149 154 156 **S** HealthPartners,
Bloomington, MN
Primary Contact: Debra Rudquist, FACHE, President and Chief Executive Officer
CMO: James Quenan, M.D., Chief Medical Officer
CIO: Patrice P Wolff, Director Management Information Systems
CHR: Joanne Jackson, Administrator Human Resources, Community Relations and
Quality Improvement
Web address: www.amerymedicalcenter.org
**Control**: Other not–for–profit (including NFP Corporation) **Service**: General
medical and surgical

> **Staffed Beds:** 17 **Admissions:** 1215 **Census:** 14 **Outpatient Visits:** 113870
> **Births:** 93 **Total Expense ($000):** 59232 **Payroll Expense ($000):** 34673
> **Personnel:** 309

**AMERY REGIONAL MEDICAL CENTER** See Amery Hospital and Clinic

## ANTIGO—Langlade County

☒ **ASPIRUS LANGLADE HOSPITAL (521350)**, 112 East Fifth Avenue,
Zip 54409–2796; tel. 715/623–2331, (Nonreporting) **A**1 3 5 10 18 **F**3 11 13 15
28 29 30 31 34 35 40 43 50 53 56 57 59 64 65 66 68 69 70 75 76 77 78 79
81 82 84 85 86 87 89 92 93 96 97 107 108 110 111 115 118 119 121 127
129 130 132 133 135 143 144 146 148 154 156 **S** Aspirus, Inc., Wausau, WI
Primary Contact: Andrew J. Barth, Executive Director
CFO: Pat Tincher, Director Finance
CHR: Janelle K. Markgraf, SHRM-SCP, SPHR, Director Human Resources and Off
Campus Services
CNO: Sherry Bunten, Director Patient Care Services
Web address: www.aspirus.org
**Control**: Church operated, Nongovernment, not–for–profit **Service**: General
medical and surgical

> **Staffed Beds:** 24 **Admissions:** 1238 **Census:** 11 **Outpatient Visits:** 110754
> **Births:** 261 **Total Expense ($000):** 93621 **Payroll Expense ($000):** 35761
> **Personnel:** 372

**LANGLADE HOSPITAL** See Aspirus Langlade Hospital

## APPLETON—Outagamie County

**APPLETON MEDICAL CENTER** See Thedacare Regional Medical Center-Appleton

☒ △ **ASCENSION NORTHEAST WISCONSIN ST. ELIZABETH HOSPITAL
(520009)**, 1506 South Oneida Street, Zip 54915–1305; tel. 920/738–2000,
(Nonreporting) **A**1 2 3 5 7 10 **F**3 4 5 9 13 15 17 18 20 22 24 26 28 29 30 31
34 35 40 43 45 46 47 48 49 50 53 54 56 58 60 64 68 70 72 74 75 76 78 79
80 81 84 85 86 87 89 92 93 98 99 100 101 102 103 104 105 107 108 110
111 115 116 118 119 120 121 123 124 126 129 130 131 135 144 146 147
148 149 154 157 **S** Ascension Healthcare, Saint Louis, MO
Primary Contact: Monica Hilt, President and Regional Vice President
CFO: Jeff Badger, Chief Financial Officer
CMO: Lawrence Donatelle, M.D., Vice President Medical Affairs
CIO: Will Weider, Chief Information Officer
CHR: Vince Gallucci, Senior Vice President Human Resources
Web address: www.https://healthcare.ascension.org
**Control**: Church operated, Nongovernment, not–for–profit **Service**: General
medical and surgical

> **Staffed Beds:** 190 **Admissions:** 7968 **Census:** 95 **Outpatient
> Visits:** 257030 **Births:** 1146 **Total Expense ($000):** 196107 **Payroll
> Expense ($000):** 54218 **Personnel:** 843

**ASCENSION ST. ELIZABETH HOSPITAL** See Ascension Northeast Wisconsin St.
Elizabeth Hospital

☐ **THEDACARE REGIONAL MEDICAL CENTER-APPLETON (520160)**, 1818
North Meade Street, Zip 54911–3496; tel. 920/731–4101, (Nonreporting) **A**1 2 3
5 10 **F**3 4 9 13 15 17 18 24 28 29 30 31 34 35 40 41 47 48 49 51 54 57 59
64 70 74 75 76 78 79 80 81 82 84 85 86 88 89 92 96 101 107 108 110 111
112 115 117 118 119 120 121 123 124 126 129 130 132 145 146 148 149
154 **S** ThedaCare, Inc., Appleton, WI
Primary Contact: Thomas J. Arquilla, Chief Strategy Officer
CFO: Tim Olson, Senior Vice President Finance
CMO: Gregory L Long, M.D., Chief Medical Officer
CIO: Keith Livingston, Senior Vice President and Chief Information Officer
Web address: www.thedacare.org
**Control**: Other not–for–profit (including NFP Corporation) **Service**: General
medical and surgical

> **Staffed Beds:** 147 **Admissions:** 8754 **Census:** 87 **Outpatient
> Visits:** 195201 **Births:** 1024 **Total Expense ($000):** 236937 **Payroll
> Expense ($000):** 72849 **Personnel:** 1083

## ASHLAND—Ashland County

**MEMORIAL MEDICAL CENTER - ASHLAND** See Memorial Medical Center of
Ashland

☒ **MEMORIAL MEDICAL CENTER OF ASHLAND (521359)**, 1615 Maple Lane,
Zip 54806–3689; tel. 715/685–5500, (Nonreporting) **A**1 2 5 10 18 **F**3 5 13 15
28 30 31 34 37 40 43 45 46 48 49 57 59 65 68 75 76 78 79 80 81 85 86 87
89 90 93 94 96 98 99 100 101 102 103 104 107 108 110 111 114 115 118
119 120 121 123 126 129 130 132 135 144 146 148 149 152 153 158
Primary Contact: Jason T. Douglas, Chief Executive Officer
COO: Karen Hansen, Vice President and Chief Operating Officer
CFO: Kent Dumonseau, Vice President Finance and Information Services
CIO: Todd Reynolds, Chief Information Officer
CHR: Diane Lulich, Director Human Resources
CNO: Kathryn Tuttle, R.N., Director of Nursing
Web address: www.ashlandmmc.com
**Control**: Other not–for–profit (including NFP Corporation) **Service**: General
medical and surgical

> **Staffed Beds:** 35 **Admissions:** 2156 **Census:** 19 **Outpatient Visits:** 16122
> **Births:** 203 **Total Expense ($000):** 88604 **Payroll Expense ($000):** 33975
> **Personnel:** 499

WI

---

## BALDWIN—St. Croix County

**BALDWIN AREA MEDICAL CENTER** See Western Wisconsin Health

★ **WESTERN WISCONSIN HEALTH (521347)**, 1100 Bergslien Street, Zip 54002–2600; tel. 715/684–3311, (Nonreporting) **A**10 18 **F**3 6 8 11 13 15 28 29 32 34 35 36 38 40 41 43 50 53 55 56 57 59 64 65 68 75 76 77 78 79 80 81 83 85 86 87 89 90 93 94 96 97 99 100 101 102 103 104 107 111 114 115 116 117 118 119 126 127 130 131 132 133 135 143 146 147 148 154 156 157
Primary Contact: Alison Page, Chief Executive Officer
CIO: Kendra Shaw, Chief Information Officer
CHR: Chris Riba, Director Human Resources
Web address: www.https://www.wwhealth.org
**Control:** Other not–for–profit (including NFP Corporation) **Service:** General medical and surgical

**Staffed Beds:** 15 **Admissions:** 503 **Census:** 4 **Outpatient Visits:** 64301 **Births:** 217 **Total Expense ($000):** 43980 **Payroll Expense ($000):** 20353 **Personnel:** 265

## BARABOO—Sauk County

✠ **SSM HEALTH ST. CLARE HOSPITAL-BARABOO (520057)**, 707 14th Street, Zip 53913–1597; tel. 608/356–1400, (Nonreporting) **A**1 3 5 10 **F**11 13 15 28 29 34 36 40 56 64 69 70 75 76 77 78 80 81 82 86 89 93 107 108 116 118 119 130 131 144 154 **P**2 **S** SSM Health, Saint Louis, MO
Primary Contact: Laura Walczak, President
CFO: Troy Walker, Director Finance
CMO: Maureen Murphy, M.D., Director of Medical Affairs
CIO: Heather Stephens, Director of Information Health Technology
CHR: Jason Stelzer, Director Human Resources
CNO: Ginger Selle, Vice President Patient Care Services
Web address: www.stclare.com
**Control:** Church operated, Nongovernment, not–for–profit **Service:** General medical and surgical

**Staffed Beds:** 54 **Admissions:** 1949 **Census:** 17 **Outpatient Visits:** 101459 **Births:** 194 **Total Expense ($000):** 53242 **Payroll Expense ($000):** 20660 **Personnel:** 275

**ST. CLARE HOSPITAL** See Ssm Health St. Clare Hospital-Baraboo

## BARRON—Barron County

**LUTHER MIDELFORT NORTHLAND** See Mayo Clinic Health System - Northland in Barron

☐ **MAYO CLINIC HEALTH SYSTEM - NORTHLAND IN BARRON (521315)**, 1222 East Woodland Avenue, Zip 54812–1798; tel. 715/537–3186, (Nonreporting) **A**1 10 18 **F**3 13 15 18 28 29 30 31 32 34 35 38 40 43 44 45 53 54 55 56 57 59 64 65 74 76 77 78 79 80 81 82 85 86 87 89 90 93 96 97 100 104 107 110 111 115 129 130 131 132 133 144 145 146 147 148 149 154 156 **P**2 **S** Mayo Clinic, Rochester, MN
Primary Contact: Richard Helmers, M.D., Regional Vice President
COO: Karolyn Bartlett, Assistant Administrator
CFO: Paul Bammel, Vice President
CMO: Richard Nagler, M.D., Chief of Staff
CIO: Todd Muden, Section Head Information Management
CHR: Blythe Rinaldi, Vice President
CNO: Patricia Keller, MSN, R.N., Nurse Administrator
Web address: www.luthermidelfortnorthland.org
**Control:** Other not–for–profit (including NFP Corporation) **Service:** General medical and surgical

**Staffed Beds:** 23 **Admissions:** 1071 **Census:** 13 **Outpatient Visits:** 67423 **Births:** 106 **Total Expense ($000):** 66176 **Payroll Expense ($000):** 25523 **Personnel:** 287

## BEAVER DAM—Dodge County

✠ **MARSHFIELD MEDICAL CENTER - BEAVER DAM (520076)**, 707 South University Avenue, Zip 53916–3089; tel. 920/887–7181, (Total facility includes 115 beds in nursing home–type unit) (Nonreporting) **A**1 10 19 **F**3 5 6 8 10 11 13 15 17 28 29 30 31 33 34 36 37 40 41 43 44 45 47 53 56 57 59 62 63 64 65 69 70 74 75 76 77 78 79 80 81 82 85 86 87 89 93 96 97 107 110 111 114 115 116 118 119 126 128 129 130 131 132 135 143 144 146 147 148 149 150 154 156 157 158 **S** Marshfield Clinic Health System, Marshfield, WI
Primary Contact: Angelia Foster, Chief Administrative Officer
CMO: Jason Smith, Chief Medical Officer
CHR: Melanie Bruins, Chief Talent Officer
CNO: Carolyn Catton, Interim Chief Patient Care Officer
Web address: www.bdch.com
**Control:** Other not–for–profit (including NFP Corporation) **Service:** General medical and surgical

**Staffed Beds:** 163 **Admissions:** 1824 **Census:** 108 **Outpatient Visits:** 89165 **Births:** 272 **Total Expense ($000):** 93333 **Payroll Expense ($000):** 33521 **Personnel:** 531

## BELOIT—Rock County

☐ **BELOIT HEALTH SYSTEM (520100)**, 1969 West Hart Road, Zip 53511–2299; tel. 608/364–5011, (Nonreporting) **A**1 3 10 **F**5 6 9 10 11 12 13 15 17 20 22 24 28 29 34 36 40 43 51 53 54 56 60 62 63 75 76 77 78 80 81 82 86 87 89 93 99 100 101 102 103 104 108 111 116 118 119 130 131 144 147 154 **P**2
Primary Contact: Timothy M. McKevett, President and Chief Executive Officer
CFO: William E Groeper, Vice President Finance
CMO: Kenneth Klein, M.D., Vice President Medical Affairs
CHR: Thomas J McCawley, Vice President
CNO: Doris Mulder, Vice President Nursing
Web address: www.beloithealthsystem.org
**Control:** Other not–for–profit (including NFP Corporation) **Service:** General medical and surgical

**Staffed Beds:** 97 **Admissions:** 4221 **Census:** 44 **Outpatient Visits:** 347326 **Births:** 402 **Total Expense ($000):** 231996 **Payroll Expense ($000):** 101738 **Personnel:** 1317

**BELOIT MEMORIAL HOSPITAL** See Beloit Health System

## BERLIN—Green Lake County

☐ **THEDACARE MEDICAL CENTER-BERLIN (521355)**, 225 Memorial Drive, Zip 54923–1295; tel. 920/361–1313, (Nonreporting) **A**1 10 18 **F**11 13 15 17 24 28 29 34 40 43 51 53 56 70 75 76 78 80 81 82 86 87 88 89 90 93 107 108 111 116 118 119 130 131 144 147 **P**2 **S** ThedaCare, Inc., Appleton, WI
Primary Contact: Tammy Bending, Vice President, Critical Access Hospital
CFO: Thomas P Krystowiak, Chief Financial Officer
Web address: www.chnwi.org
**Control:** Other not–for–profit (including NFP Corporation) **Service:** General medical and surgical

**Staffed Beds:** 25 **Admissions:** 1065 **Census:** 10 **Outpatient Visits:** 62942 **Births:** 85 **Total Expense ($000):** 38421 **Payroll Expense ($000):** 15702 **Personnel:** 251

**THEDACARE REGIONAL MEDICAL CENTER-BERLIN** See Thedacare Medical Center-Berlin

## BLACK RIVER FALLS—Jackson County

☐ **BLACK RIVER MEMORIAL HOSPITAL (521333)**, 711 West Adams Street, Zip 54615–9113; tel. 715/284–5361, (Nonreporting) **A**1 5 10 18 **F**3 8 11 13 29 30 34 35 40 41 53 56 57 59 62 63 65 69 75 76 77 79 81 84 85 86 89 93 107 111 114 115 116 118 119 129 130 131 132 133 135 144 146 148 149 152 156
Primary Contact: Mary Beth White-Jacobs, FACHE, R.N., Chief Executive Officer
COO: Holly Winn, FACHE, Chief Operating Officer
CFO: Robert Daley, CPA, Chief Financial Officer
CMO: Esteban Miller, Chief Medical Officer
CIO: Robert Daley, CPA, Vice President Fiscal and Information Technology Services
CNO: Melissa Bergerson, R.N., Chief Nursing Officer
Web address: www.brmh.net
**Control:** Other not–for–profit (including NFP Corporation) **Service:** General medical and surgical

**Staffed Beds:** 25 **Admissions:** 847 **Census:** 8 **Outpatient Visits:** 11811 **Births:** 155 **Total Expense ($000):** 61283 **Payroll Expense ($000):** 25358 **Personnel:** 311

**WI**

*Many Facility Codes have changed. Please refer to the AHA Guide Code Chart.*

## BLOOMER—Chippewa County

**LUTHER MIDELFORT CHIPPEWA VALLEY** See Mayo Clinic Health System - Chippewa Valley in Bloomer

☐ **MAYO CLINIC HEALTH SYSTEM - CHIPPEWA VALLEY IN BLOOMER (521314)**, 1501 Thompson Street, Zip 54724–1299; tel. 715/568–2000, (Nonreporting) **A**1 10 18 **F**3 15 18 28 29 30 32 34 35 38 40 43 44 45 53 54 56 57 59 64 65 77 78 79 80 81 84 85 86 87 89 90 93 96 97 104 107 110 115 129 130 132 133 144 145 146 147 148 149 154 156 **S** Mayo Clinic, Rochester, MN
Primary Contact: Richard Helmers, M.D., Regional Vice President
Web address: www.bloomermedicalcenter.org
**Control:** Other not–for–profit (including NFP Corporation) **Service:** General medical and surgical

**Staffed Beds: 18 Admissions:** 425 **Census:** 15 **Outpatient Visits:** 43168
**Births:** 0 **Total Expense ($000):** 36239 **Payroll Expense ($000):** 15737
**Personnel:** 190

## BOSCOBEL—Grant County

**GUNDERSEN BOSCOBEL AREA HEALTH CARE AND CLINICS** See Gundersen Boscobel Area Hospital and Clinics

★ **GUNDERSEN BOSCOBEL AREA HOSPITAL AND CLINICS (521344)**, 205 Parker Street, Zip 53805–1698; tel. 608/375–4112, (Nonreporting) **A**10 18 **F**11 15 28 29 34 36 38 40 43 53 54 56 63 64 75 77 78 81 82 86 93 99 100 101 102 104 107 108 111 118 119 125 130 144 154
Primary Contact: David Hartberg, Chief Executive Officer
CFO: Melissa Uselman, Chief Financial Officer
CMO: Marilu Bintz, M.D., Chief of Staff
CIO: Tonia Midtlien, Information Systems Support Specialist
CHR: Jennifer Dax, Director Human Resources
CNO: Theresa Lynn Braudt, Chief Nursing Officer
Web address: www.gundersenhealth.org/boscobel
**Control:** Other not–for–profit (including NFP Corporation) **Service:** General medical and surgical

**Staffed Beds: 8 Admissions:** 172 **Census:** 2 **Outpatient Visits:** 34208
**Births:** 0 **Total Expense ($000):** 18813 **Payroll Expense ($000):** 6585
**Personnel:** 124

## BROOKFIELD—Waukesha County

★ **ASCENSION SOUTHEAST WISCONSIN HOSPITAL - ELMBROOK CAMPUS (520170)**, 19333 West North Avenue, Zip 53045–4198; tel. 262/785–2000, (Nonreporting) **A**5 **F**3 11 12 13 15 17 18 20 22 24 26 28 29 30 31 34 35 36 40 43 44 45 46 47 48 49 50 51 54 56 59 64 65 68 70 74 76 77 78 79 80 81 82 84 85 86 87 90 92 93 100 107 108 109 110 111 112 114 115 116 117 118 119 120 121 122 123 124 126 130 131 132 135 143 144 145 146 148 149 154 156 157 **P**2 **S** Ascension Healthcare, Saint Louis, MO
Primary Contact: Timothy Richman, President and Chief Executive Officer
CFO: Michael Petitt, Director of Finance
CMO: Rita Hanson, M.D., Vice President Medical Affairs
CIO: Andrew Donovan, Director Information Technology
CHR: Christopher Morris, Director Human Resources
Web address: www.https://www.mywheaton.org
**Control:** Church operated, Nongovernment, not–for–profit **Service:** General medical and surgical

**Staffed Beds: 60 Admissions:** 4202 **Census:** 49 **Outpatient Visits:** 151744
**Births:** 429 **Total Expense ($000):** 148343 **Payroll Expense ($000):** 41401
**Personnel:** 567

**WHEATON FRANCISCAN - ELMBROOK MEMORIAL CAMPUS** See Ascension Southeast Wisconsin Hospital - Elmbrook Campus

## BROWN DEER—Milwaukee County

**CHARTER NORTHBROOKE BEHAVIORAL HEALTH SYSTEM OF MILWAUKEE/ BROWN DEER** See Rogers Memorial Hospital-Brown Deer

## BURLINGTON—Racine County

⊞ **AURORA MEDICAL CENTER BURLINGTON (520059)**, 252 McHenry Street, Zip 53105–1828; tel. 262/767–6000, (Nonreporting) **A**1 2 10 **F**3 8 11 15 17 18 20 26 28 29 30 34 35 36 40 43 44 46 49 50 51 53 57 59 60 68 70 74 75 79 80 81 82 85 86 87 89 93 94 96 100 107 108 109 110 111 115 116 118 119 130 131 132 134 135 146 148 149 150 **P**2 **S** Advocate Aurora Health, Downers Grove, IL
Primary Contact: Bob Miller, President
CFO: Stuart Arnett, Vice President Finance and Chief Financial Officer
CIO: Jean Chase, Regional Manager Information Services
CHR: Gene Krauklis, Regional Vice President Human Resources
Web address: www.aurorahealthcare.org
**Control:** Other not–for–profit (including NFP Corporation) **Service:** General medical and surgical

**Staffed Beds: 38 Admissions:** 2083 **Census:** 21 **Outpatient Visits:** 100561
**Births:** 0 **Total Expense ($000):** 78587 **Payroll Expense ($000):** 26053
**Personnel:** 532

**AURORA MEMORIAL HOSPITAL OF BURLINGTON** See Aurora Medical Center Burlington

## CHILTON—Calumet County

⊞ **ASCENSION CALUMET HOSPITAL (521317)**, 614 Memorial Drive, Zip 53014–1597; tel. 920/849–2386, (Nonreporting) **A**1 10 18 **F**3 5 7 15 18 28 29 30 31 34 35 40 43 45 50 53 56 58 64 68 74 75 78 79 80 81 82 85 86 87 93 97 107 108 110 111 115 116 118 119 129 130 131 133 144 146 148 149 154 **S** Ascension Healthcare, Saint Louis, MO
Primary Contact: Jenny Derks, Chief Administrative Officer
CFO: Jeff Badger, Chief Financial Officer
CMO: Mark W Kehrberg, M.D., Chief Medical Officer
CIO: Will Weider, Chief Information Officer
CHR: Beth O'laire, Manager Human Resources
Web address: www.affinityhealth.org
**Control:** Church operated, Nongovernment, not–for–profit **Service:** General medical and surgical

**Staffed Beds: 25 Admissions:** 278 **Census:** 3 **Outpatient Visits:** 63066
**Births:** 0 **Total Expense ($000):** 27036 **Payroll Expense ($000):** 6725
**Personnel:** 109

**CALUMET MEDICAL CENTER** See Ascension Calumet Hospital

## CHIPPEWA FALLS—Chippewa County

⊞ **HSHS ST. JOSEPH'S HOSPITAL (520017)**, 2661 County Highway I, Zip 54729–5407; tel. 715/723–1811, (Nonreporting) **A**1 3 10 **F**3 4 5 11 13 15 17 28 29 30 34 38 40 41 43 53 54 56 59 62 63 64 69 70 75 76 79 80 81 82 84 85 86 87 88 89 100 101 102 107 110 115 119 129 130 132 145 146 147 148 149 **S** HSHS Hospital Sisters Health System, Springfield, IL
Primary Contact: John Wagner, President and Chief Executive Officer
CFO: David Nelson, FACHE, Divisional Chief Financial Officer
CIO: Kevin Groskreutz, Division Chief Information Officer, Ancillary Systems
CHR: Rick Tolson, Divisional Chief People Officer
CNO: Stella Clark, MSN, R.N., Chief Nursing Officer
Web address: www.stjoeschipfalls.com
**Control:** Church operated, Nongovernment, not–for–profit **Service:** General medical and surgical

**Staffed Beds: 124 Admissions:** 2872 **Census:** 38 **Outpatient Visits:** 44185
**Births:** 0 **Total Expense ($000):** 64645 **Payroll Expense:** 24068 **Personnel:** 280

**ST. JOSEPH'S HOSPITAL** See Hshs St. Joseph's Hospital

## COLUMBUS—Columbia County

**PRAIRIE RIDGE HEALTH** See Prairie Ridge Health, Inc.

WI

✠ **PRAIRIE RIDGE HEALTH, INC. (521338)**, 1515 Park Avenue, Zip 53925–2402; tel. 920/623–2200, (Nonreporting) **A**1 10 18 **F**3 8 13 15 16 17 18 28 29 34 35 40 45 47 50 51 54 56 57 59 64 70 75 76 77 78 79 80 81 85 86 88 93 97 115 118 119 130 131 132 133 135 144 146 147 149 156
Primary Contact: John D. Russell, President and Chief Executive Officer
CFO: Melissa Mangan, Vice President of Finance and Chief Financial Officer
CMO: Matthew Niesen, M.D., Chief of the Medical Staff
CIO: Melissa Mangan, Vice President of Finance and Chief Financial Officer
CHR: Ann Roundy, Vice President of Employee and Support Services
CNO: Jamie Hendrix, Vice President Patient Care Services
Web address: www.prairieridge.health
**Control:** Other not–for–profit (including NFP Corporation) **Service:** General medical and surgical

**Staffed Beds: 25 Admissions: 851 Census: 7 Outpatient Visits:** 59552 **Births: 84 Total Expense ($000):** 44772 **Payroll Expense ($000):** 18898 **Personnel:** 214

### CUBA CITY—Grant County

**CUBA CITY MEDICAL CENTER** See Southwest Health Center Nursing Home

**SOUTHWEST HEALTH CENTER NURSING HOME** See Southwest Health, Platteville

### CUDAHY—Milwaukee County

**AURORA ST. LUKE'S SOUTH SHORE** See Aurora St. Luke's Medical Center, Milwaukee

**ST LUKE'S SOUTH SHORE** See Aurora St. Luke's South Shore

### CUMBERLAND—Barron County

☐ **CUMBERLAND HEALTHCARE (521353)**, 1110 Seventh Avenue, Zip 54829–9138; tel. 715/822–2741, (Nonreporting) **A**1 10 18 **F**3 11 13 15 28 29 30 34 40 43 44 45 46 50 53 55 56 57 59 64 65 75 76 77 78 81 82 86 87 89 92 93 96 97 99 100 103 104 107 114 127 129 130 131 132 133 135 144 146 148 154 156
Primary Contact: Michael Gutsch, Chief Executive Officer and Administrator
COO: Bob Lindberg, Chief Operating Officer
CFO: Angela Martens, Chief Financial Officer
CMO: Tom Lingen, M.D., Chief of Staff
CIO: Jason Morse, Director Information Technology
CHR: Hilary Butzler, Director Human Resources
Web address: www.cumberlandhealthcare.com
**Control:** Other not–for–profit (including NFP Corporation) **Service:** General medical and surgical

**Staffed Beds: 7 Admissions: 414 Census: 6 Outpatient Visits:** 12267 **Births: 27 Total Expense ($000):** 24471 **Payroll Expense ($000):** 11078 **Personnel:** 170

**CUMBERLAND MEMORIAL HOSPITAL** See Cumberland Healthcare

### DARLINGTON—Lafayette County

★ **MEMORIAL HOSPITAL OF LAFAYETTE COUNTY (521312)**, 800 Clay Street, Zip 53530–1228, Mailing Address: P.O. Box 70, Zip 53530–0070; tel. 608/776–4466, (Nonreporting) **A**10 18 **F**1 3 11 15 18 26 28 29 32 35 40 45 46 47 48 54 56 57 64 68 74 75 79 80 81 82 86 89 90 93 102 107 110 111 114 116 117 119 130 131 133 144 156 **S** UnityPoint Health, West Des Moines, IA
Primary Contact: Kathleen Kuepers, Chief Executive Officer
CFO: Marie Wamsley, Chief Financial Officer
Web address: www.memorialhospitaloflafayettecounty.org
**Control:** County, Government, Nonfederal **Service:** General medical and surgical

**Staffed Beds: 25 Admissions: 282 Census: 3 Outpatient Visits:** 24401 **Births: 0 Total Expense ($000):** 21079 **Payroll Expense ($000):** 7225 **Personnel:** 125

### DODGEVILLE—Iowa County

✠ **UPLAND HILLS HEALTH (521352)**, 800 Compassion Way, Zip 53533–1956, Mailing Address: P.O. Box 800, Zip 53533–0800; tel. 608/930–8000, (Total facility includes 44 beds in nursing home–type unit) (Nonreporting) **A**1 3 5 10 18 **F**3 8 11 13 15 17 28 29 34 36 40 41 43 44 45 50 53 54 56 57 59 62 63 64 67 68 70 75 76 77 78 79 80 81 82 83 84 85 86 87 88 89 90 93 96 97 107 110 111 114 115 119 127 128 129 130 131 132 133 144 146 147 148 149 156 157
Primary Contact: Lisa W. Schnedler, FACHE, President and Chief Executive Officer
CFO: Karl Pustina, Vice President Finance
CIO: Karen Thuli, Information Systems Coordinator
CHR: Troy Marx, Human Resources Director
CNO: Lynn Hebgen, MSN, R.N., Vice President of Nursing
Web address: www.uplandhillshealth.org
**Control:** Other not–for–profit (including NFP Corporation) **Service:** General medical and surgical

**Staffed Beds: 69 Admissions: 954 Census: 46 Outpatient Visits:** 56392 **Births: 230 Total Expense ($000):** 53682 **Payroll Expense ($000):** 25005 **Personnel:** 328

**UPLAND HILLS HEALTH, INC** See Upland Hills Health

### DURAND—Pepin County

**ADVENTHEALTH CHIPPEWA** See Adventhealth Durand

★ **ADVENTHEALTH DURAND (521307)**, 1220 Third Avenue West, Zip 54736–1600, Mailing Address: P.O. Box 224, Zip 54736–0224; tel. 715/672–4211, (Nonreporting) **A**10 18 **F**3 15 18 19 28 29 30 34 35 40 44 56 57 59 65 68 75 79 81 86 87 97 107 109 110 114 117 129 130 132 152 156 **S** AdventHealth, Altamonte Springs, FL
Primary Contact: Douglas R. Peterson, President and Chief Executive Officer
Web address: www.chippewavalleyhospital.com/
**Control:** Church operated, Nongovernment, not–profit **Service:** General medical and surgical

**Staffed Beds: 25 Admissions: 185 Census: 3 Outpatient Visits:** 25757 **Births: 0 Total Expense ($000):** 14072 **Payroll Expense ($000):** 5073 **Personnel:** 73

### EAGLE RIVER—Vilas County

★ **ASCENSION EAGLE RIVER HOSPITAL (521300)**, 201 Hospital Road, Zip 54521–8835; tel. 715/479–7411, (Nonreporting) **A**10 18 **F**3 11 15 28 29 30 34 35 40 45 64 75 79 81 82 85 86 87 89 93 107 110 111 115 119 130 133 146 149 154 **S** Ascension Healthcare, Saint Louis, MO
Primary Contact: Laurie Oungst, Chief Administrative Officer
COO: Laurie Oungst, Vice President, Operations
CFO: Jamon Lamers, Chief Financial Officer
CMO: Roderick Brodhead, Chief Medical Officer
CIO: Howard Dobizl, Director Information Technology Services
CHR: Michelle Cornelius, Director Human Resources for Northern Region
CNO: Jacqualyn Monge, Director of Nursing
Web address: www.ministryhealth.org
**Control:** Church operated, Nongovernment, not–profit **Service:** General medical and surgical

**Staffed Beds: 14 Admissions: 376 Census: 4 Outpatient Visits:** 22752 **Births: 0 Total Expense ($000):** 13962 **Payroll Expense ($000):** 4161 **Personnel:** 52

**MINISTRY EAGLE RIVER MEMORIAL HOSPITAL** See Ascension Eagle River Hospital

**WI**

## EAU CLAIRE—Eau Claire County

☒ △ **HSHS SACRED HEART HOSPITAL (520013)**, 900 West Clairemont Avenue, Zip 54701–6122; tel. 715/717–4121, (Nonreporting) **A**1 2 3 5 7 10 **F**3 6 11 12 13 15 17 18 20 22 24 28 29 30 31 34 35 38 40 41 43 47 48 49 51 53 54 56 57 59 60 64 69 70 72 74 75 76 78 79 80 81 82 83 84 85 86 87 88 89 90 92 93 96 98 99 100 101 102 103 107 108 110 111 112 115 116 117 118 119 120 121 123 124 126 129 130 132 141 144 145 146 147 149 154 **S** HSHS Hospital Sisters Health System, Springfield, IL
Primary Contact: Sandy Anderson, Interim President
CFO: David Nelson, FACHE, Chief Financial Officer
CMO: Humayun Khan, M.D., Chief Medical Officer
CIO: Kevin Groskreutz, Chief Information Officer
CHR: Craig Brenholt, Division Director People Services
CNO: Amy L. Dwyer, R.N., MSN, Chief Nursing Officer
Web address: www.sacredhearteauclaire.org
**Control**: Church operated, Nongovernment, not–for–profit **Service**: General medical and surgical

**Staffed Beds:** 205 **Admissions:** 7311 **Census:** 96 **Outpatient Visits:** 70155 **Births:** 552 **Total Expense ($000):** 195376 **Payroll Expense ($000):** 55353 **Personnel:** 862

**LUTHER HOSPITAL** See Mayo Clinic Health System in Eau Claire

☒ **MARSHFIELD MEDICAL CENTER - EAU CLAIRE HOSPITAL**, 2310 Craig Road, Zip 54701–6128; tel. 715/858–8100, (Nonreporting) **A**1 5 **F**3 6 8 11 12 13 15 17 18 19 20 22 24 26 28 29 30 31 32 34 40 41 43 44 56 57 59 64 70 74 75 76 77 78 79 80 81 82 85 86 87 91 93 96 97 107 108 110 111 114 115 116 118 119 120 121 123 126 129 130 131 135 144 146 147 148 154 **S** Marshfield Clinic Health System, Marshfield, WI
Primary Contact: Bill Priest, Chief Administrative Officer
Web address: www.https://www.marshfieldclinic.org
**Control**: Other not–for–profit (including NFP Corporation) **Service**: General medical and surgical

**Staffed Beds:** 44 **Admissions:** 2833 **Census:** 28 **Outpatient Visits:** 181354 **Births:** 552 **Total Expense ($000):** 219345 **Payroll Expense ($000):** 75834 **Personnel:** 794

☐ **MAYO CLINIC HEALTH SYSTEM IN EAU CLAIRE (520070)**, 1221 Whipple Street, Zip 54703–5270, Mailing Address: P.O. Box 4105, Zip 54702; tel. 715/838–3311, (Nonreporting) **A**1 2 3 5 10 19 **F**3 4 5 6 12 13 15 17 18 20 22 24 26 28 29 30 31 32 34 35 37 38 40 43 44 45 46 48 49 53 55 56 57 58 59 60 61 64 65 70 72 74 76 77 78 79 80 81 82 84 85 86 87 89 90 92 93 94 96 97 98 99 100 101 102 103 104 105 107 108 110 111 115 116 117 118 119 120 121 124 126 129 130 131 132 134 144 145 146 147 148 149 154 156 157 **S** Mayo Clinic, Rochester, MN
Primary Contact: Richard Helmers, M.D., Regional Vice President
COO: John M Dickey, Chief Administrative Officer
CFO: Denise Mattison, Director Finance and Accounting Services
CMO: Robert C Peck, M.D., Chief Medical Officer
CHR: Kenneth Lee, Division Chair, Human Resource Advisory
CNO: Pamela K. White, R.N., MSN, Chief Nursing Officer
Web address: www.mhs.mayo.edu
**Control**: Other not–for–profit (including NFP Corporation) **Service**: General medical and surgical

**Staffed Beds:** 201 **Admissions:** 11104 **Census:** 131 **Outpatient Visits:** 417270 **Births:** 984 **Total Expense ($000):** 581383 **Payroll Expense ($000):** 273719 **Personnel:** 2768

**SACRED HEART HOSPITAL** See Hshs Sacred Heart Hospital

## EDGERTON—Rock County

☒ **EDGERTON HOSPITAL AND HEALTH SERVICES (521319)**, 11101 North Sherman Road, Zip 53534–9002; tel. 608/884–3441, (Nonreporting) **A**1 10 18 **F**3 11 15 18 28 34 40 43 59 64 75 77 81 86 90 93 97 107 108 109 111 119 129 130 133 144 146 148 **P**2
Primary Contact: Jim Schultz, Chief Executive Officer
CFO: Charles Roader, Vice President Finance
CMO: Brian Stubitsch, M.D., Chief Medical Officer
CIO: JT Johrendt, Information Technology Network Specialist
CHR: Mark Kindschi, Director Human Resources
CNO: Sue Alwin-Popp, Chief Clinical Officer
Web address: www.edgertonhospital.com
**Control**: Other not–for–profit (including NFP Corporation) **Service**: General medical and surgical

**Staffed Beds:** 18 **Admissions:** 337 **Census:** 7 **Outpatient Visits:** 21990 **Births:** 0 **Total Expense ($000):** 21011 **Payroll Expense ($000):** 9819 **Personnel:** 137

**MEMORIAL COMMUNITY HOSPITAL** See Edgerton Hospital and Health Services

## ELK MOUND—Dunn County

**VERNON MEMORIAL HEALTHCARE (521348)**, E8270 660th Ave, Zip 54739–4401, Mailing Address: 507 South Main Street, Viroqua, Zip 54665–2096; tel. 608/637–2101, (Nonreporting) **A**10 18 **F**5 13 15 28 29 34 36 40 43 56 62 63 64 75 76 77 80 81 82 86 87 89 93 99 100 103 104 107 119 130 131 144
Primary Contact: Kyle Bakkum, Chief Executive Officer and Administrator
COO: Kristy Wiltrout, R.N., Chief Operating Officer
CFO: Mary Koenig, Chief Financial Officer
CIO: Scott Adkins, Manager Information Technology
CHR: Kay Starr, Manager Human Resources
Web address: www.vmh.org
**Control**: Other not–for–profit (including NFP Corporation) **Service**: General medical and surgical

**Staffed Beds:** 25 **Admissions:** 1460 **Census:** 10 **Outpatient Visits:** 140818 **Births:** 158 **Total Expense ($000):** 73151 **Payroll Expense ($000):** 32244 **Personnel:** 374

**VERNON MEMORIAL HOSPITAL** See Vernon Memorial Healthcare

## ELKHORN—Walworth County

☒ △ **AURORA LAKELAND MEDICAL CENTER (520102)**, W3985 County Road NN, Zip 53121–4389; tel. 262/741–2000, (Nonreporting) **A**1 2 3 7 10 **F**3 11 13 17 18 29 30 34 35 36 40 43 44 50 51 57 59 60 68 70 74 75 76 79 80 81 82 84 85 86 89 90 93 94 96 100 107 108 111 115 118 119 127 129 130 131 132 135 146 148 149 150 **P**2 **S** Advocate Aurora Health, Downers Grove, IL
Primary Contact: Bob Miller, President
CFO: Stuart Arnett, Regional Vice President Finance
CMO: Greg Gerber, M.D., Chief Medical Officer
CIO: Jean Chase, Regional Manager Information Services
CHR: Gene Krauklis, Regional Vice President Human Resources
Web address: www.aurorahealthcare.org
**Control**: Other not–for–profit (including NFP Corporation) **Service**: General medical and surgical

**Staffed Beds:** 64 **Admissions:** 2668 **Census:** 25 **Outpatient Visits:** 71202 **Births:** 678 **Total Expense ($000):** 55280 **Payroll Expense ($000):** 20852 **Personnel:** 433

**LAKELAND MEDICAL CENTER** See Aurora Lakeland Medical Center

## FOND DU LAC—Fond Du Lac County

**AGNESIAN HEALTHCARE** See St. Agnes Hospital

**FOND DU LAC CNTY MENTAL HLTH** See Fond Du Lac County Mental Health Center

**WI**

**FOND DU LAC COUNTY MENTAL HEALTH CENTER (524025)**, 459 East First Street, Zip 54935–4599; tel. 920/929–3502, (Nonreporting) **A**10 **F**4 38 98 99 102 103 130 152
Primary Contact: J.R. Musunuru, M.D., Executive Director
Web address: www.fdlco.wi.gov
**Control:** County, Government, Nonfederal **Service:** Psychiatric

> **Staffed Beds:** 25 **Admissions:** 837 **Census:** 12 **Outpatient Visits:** 1209
> **Births:** 0 **Total Expense ($000):** 3418 **Payroll Expense ($000):** 2473
> **Personnel:** 50

☒ △ **ST. AGNES HOSPITAL (520088)**, 430 East Division Street, Zip 54935–4560, Mailing Address: P.O. Box 385, Zip 54936–0385; tel. 920/929–2300, (Nonreporting) **A**1 2 7 10 20 **F**2 3 5 6 8 11 13 15 18 20 22 24 26 28 29 30 31 33 34 35 36 38 40 43 44 45 46 47 48 49 50 51 53 54 55 56 57 59 60 62 63 64 66 68 69 74 75 76 77 78 79 80 81 82 84 85 86 87 90 92 93 96 97 98 99 100 101 102 103 104 105 107 108 109 110 111 115 118 119 120 121 123 124 126 129 130 131 132 134 135 143 144 146 147 148 149 150 152 153 154 156 **P**2 **S** SSM Health, Saint Louis, MO
Primary Contact: Katherine Vergos, FACHE, President
CFO: Bonnie Schmitz, Vice President and Chief Financial Officer
CMO: Derek Colmenares, M.D., Chief Medical Officer
CIO: Nancy Birschbach, Vice President and Chief Information Officer
CHR: Sue Edminster, Vice President Human Resources
CNO: Tami Schattschneider, Chief Nursing Officer
Web address: www.agnesian.com
**Control:** Church operated, Nongovernment, not–for–profit **Service:** General medical and surgical

> **Staffed Beds:** 146 **Admissions:** 6591 **Census:** 71 **Outpatient Visits:** 306516 **Births:** 751 **Total Expense ($000):** 252495 **Payroll Expense ($000):** 110242 **Personnel:** 1348

### FORT ATKINSON—Jefferson County

☒ **FORT HEALTHCARE (520071)**, 611 Sherman Avenue East, Zip 53538–1998; tel. 920/568–5000, (Nonreporting) **A**1 10 **F**3 11 12 13 15 28 29 34 40 47 48 50 53 55 56 57 59 68 75 76 77 79 80 81 85 86 87 89 90 93 94 96 107 108 110 111 114 118 119 130 132 135 144 146 147 149 150 **P**2
Primary Contact: Michael S. Wallace, President and Chief Executive Officer
CFO: James J Nelson, Senior Vice President Finance and Strategic Planning
CMO: William Cannon, M.D., Medical Director
CIO: Jennifer Winter, Chief Medical Information Officer
CHR: Nancy Alstad, Director Human Resources
CNO: Marie Wiesmann, Vice President of Nursing and Chief Nursing Officer
Web address: www.forthealthcare.com
**Control:** Other not–for–profit (including NFP Corporation) **Service:** General medical and surgical

> **Staffed Beds:** 49 **Admissions:** 1613 **Census:** 13 **Outpatient Visits:** 271396 **Births:** 352 **Total Expense ($000):** 119280 **Payroll Expense ($000):** 39904 **Personnel:** 651

**FORT HEALTHCARE** See Fort Healthcare

### FRANKLIN—Milwaukee County

★ **ASCENSION SOUTHEAST WISCONSIN HOSPITAL - FRANKLIN CAMPUS (520204)**, 10101 South 27th Street, Zip 53132–7209; tel. 414/325–4700, (Nonreporting) **F**3 15 17 18 20 22 26 29 30 34 40 43 45 47 49 50 57 64 68 70 74 77 79 80 81 82 84 85 86 87 91 92 93 96 107 108 110 111 115 119 126 130 131 135 145 146 147 148 149 156 **S** Ascension Healthcare, Saint Louis, MO
Primary Contact: Seth R. Teigen, President
CFO: Aaron Bridgeland, Director Finance
CMO: Michelle Graham, M.D., Vice President Medical Affairs
CIO: Gregory Smith, Senior Vice President and Chief Information Officer
CNO: Sheila Gansemer, R.N., Vice President Patient Care Services and Chief Nursing Officer
Web address: www.mywheaton.org/
**Control:** Church operated, Nongovernment, not–for–profit **Service:** General medical and surgical

> **Staffed Beds:** 46 **Admissions:** 2920 **Census:** 34 **Outpatient Visits:** 90383 **Births:** 0 **Total Expense ($000):** 76110 **Payroll Expense ($000):** 23605 **Personnel:** 322

☒ **MIDWEST ORTHOPEDIC SPECIALTY HOSPITAL (520205)**, 10101 South 27th Street, 2nd Floor, Zip 53132–7209; tel. 414/817–5800, (Nonreporting) **A**1 3 5 10 **F**3 29 30 34 50 57 68 79 80 81 82 85 86 91 92 94 96 130 131 149 **P**2 **S** Ascension Healthcare, Saint Louis, MO
Primary Contact: Bernie Sherry, Ministry Market Executive for Ascension Wisconsin
CFO: Aaron Bridgeland, Director Finance
CMO: Daniel Guehlstorf, M.D., Chief of Staff
CIO: Gregory Smith, Senior Vice President and Chief Information Officer
Web address: www.mymosh.com/
**Control:** Partnership, Investor–owned (for–profit) **Service:** General medical and surgical

> **Staffed Beds:** 16 **Admissions:** 1484 **Census:** 8 **Outpatient Visits:** 6039
> **Births:** 0 **Total Expense ($000):** 40572 **Payroll Expense ($000):** 7490
> **Personnel:** 116

**WHEATON FRANCISCAN HEALTHCARE - FRANKLIN** See Ascension Southeast Wisconsin Hospital - Franklin Campus

### FRIENDSHIP—Adams County

★ **GUNDERSEN MOUNDVIEW HOSPITAL & CLINICS (521309)**, 402 West Lake Street, Zip 53934–9699, Mailing Address: P.O. Box 40, Zip 53934–0040; tel. 608/339–3331, (Nonreporting) **A**10 18 **F**6 11 15 28 29 34 36 40 53 56 64 77 81 82 86 87 93 107 108 111 119 130 131 154 **P**2
Primary Contact: Francisco Perez-Guerra, Chief Executive Officer
Web address: www.moundview.org
**Control:** Other not–for–profit (including NFP Corporation) **Service:** General medical and surgical

> **Staffed Beds:** 25 **Admissions:** 158 **Census:** 2 **Outpatient Visits:** 39594
> **Births:** 0 **Total Expense ($000):** 16804 **Payroll Expense ($000):** 7085
> **Personnel:** 128

**GUNDERSEN MOUNDVIEW MEMORIAL HOSPITAL & CLINICS** See Gundersen Moundview Hospital & Clinics

### GLENDALE—Milwaukee County

**ORTHOPAEDIC HOSPITAL OF WISCONSIN (520194)**, 475 West River Woods Parkway, Zip 53212–1081; tel. 414/961–6800, (Nonreporting) **A**10 **F**3 29 34 38 53 64 79 80 81 82 86 93 94 96 107 111 114 119 130 131
Primary Contact: Brian J. Cramer, Chief Executive Officer
CFO: Tom Swiderski, Chief Financial Officer
CMO: Rory Wright, M.D., President Medical Staff
CIO: Todd Heikkinen, Manager Sports Medicine and Rehabilitation Services
CNO: Nanette Johnson, Chief Nursing Officer
Web address: www.ohow.org
**Control:** Partnership, Investor–owned (for–profit) **Service:** Orthopedic

> **Staffed Beds:** 30 **Admissions:** 1588 **Census:** 9 **Outpatient Visits:** 42672
> **Births:** 0 **Total Expense ($000):** 46468 **Payroll Expense ($000):** 15641
> **Personnel:** 237

**ORTHOPAEDIC HOSPITAL OF WISCONSIN - GLENDALE** See Orthopaedic Hospital of Wisconsin

### GRAFTON—Ozaukee County

☒ **AURORA MEDICAL CENTER GRAFTON (520207)**, 975 Port Washington Road, Zip 53024–9201; tel. 262/329–1000, (Nonreporting) **A**1 2 3 5 10 **F**3 8 12 13 15 17 18 20 22 24 26 28 29 30 31 34 35 36 37 40 41 43 44 45 46 47 48 49 50 51 53 54 59 60 64 65 68 70 72 74 75 76 79 80 81 82 85 86 87 89 92 93 94 107 108 110 111 114 115 116 117 118 119 121 124 126 130 131 135 146 147 148 149 154 **P**2 **S** Advocate Aurora Health, Downers Grove, IL
Primary Contact: David Graebner, President
CMO: Doug McManus, Chief Medical Officer
Web address: www.aurorahealthcare.org
**Control:** Other not–for–profit (including NFP Corporation) **Service:** General medical and surgical

> **Staffed Beds:** 132 **Admissions:** 7267 **Census:** 79 **Outpatient Visits:** 150612 **Births:** 1160 **Total Expense ($000):** 207625 **Payroll Expense ($000):** 63195 **Personnel:** 1299

### GRANTSBURG—Burnett County

**BURNETT GENERAL HOSPITAL** See Burnett Medical Center

*Many Facility Codes have changed. Please refer to the AHA Guide Code Chart.*

© 2021 AHA Guide

**WI**

★ **BURNETT MEDICAL CENTER (521331)**, 257 West St George Avenue, Zip 54840–7827; tel. 715/463–5353, (Total facility includes 50 beds in nursing home–type unit) (Nonreporting) **A**10 18 **F**2 3 15 28 29 34 35 40 43 44 50 56 57 59 64 75 77 78 80 81 86 87 89 90 93 97 107 110 115 127 128 130 131 132 133 135 144 146 149 152 156 157 **P**2
Primary Contact: Gordon Lewis, Chief Executive Officer
CFO: Gordy Forbort, Interim Chief Financial Officer
CMO: Hans Rechsteiner, M.D., Chief of Staff
CIO: Andy Douglas, Manager Information Technology
CHR: Sandy Hinrichs, Director Human Resources
Web address: www.burnettmedicalcenter.com
**Control**: Other not-for-profit (including NFP Corporation) **Service**: General medical and surgical

**Staffed Beds**: 67 **Admissions**: 209 **Census**: 3 **Outpatient Visits**: 29909
**Births**: 0 **Total Expense ($000)**: 16048 **Payroll Expense ($000)**: 7934
**Personnel**: 133

### GREEN BAY—Brown County

★ ⇑ **AURORA BAYCARE MEDICAL CENTER (520193)**, 2845 Greenbrier Road, Zip 54311–6519, Mailing Address: P.O. Box 8900, Zip 54308–8900; tel. 920/288–8000, (Nonreporting) **A**2 3 10 19 21 **F**3 12 13 15 17 18 20 22 24 26 28 29 30 31 32 33 34 35 36 37 40 43 44 45 46 47 48 49 50 53 54 57 58 59 64 65 68 70 72 74 75 76 78 79 80 81 82 84 85 86 87 89 90 91 92 93 94 97 107 108 109 110 111 114 115 116 117 118 119 123 124 126 129 130 131 132 134 135 144 146 147 148 149 154 156 157 **S** Advocate Aurora Health, Downers Grove, IL
Primary Contact: Daniel T. Meyer, President
COO: Daniel T Meyer, President
CFO: Gwen Christensen, Vice President, Finance
CMO: Brian Johnson, M.D., Chief Medical Officer
CIO: Chuck Geurts, Manager Information Technology Client Services
CHR: Elizabeth A Kirby, Senior Director Human Resources
CNO: Heather Schroeder, R.N., Vice President Nursing
Web address: www.aurorabaycare.com
**Control**: Partnership, Investor-owned (for-profit) **Service**: General medical and surgical

**Staffed Beds**: 167 **Admissions**: 9971 **Census**: 117 **Outpatient Visits**: 425221 **Births**: 1732 **Total Expense ($000)**: 392923 **Payroll Expense ($000)**: 125894 **Personnel**: 1864

★ ⇑ **BELLIN HOSPITAL (520049)**, 744 South Webster Avenue, Zip 54301–3581, Mailing Address: P.O. Box 23400, Zip 54305–3400; tel. 920/433–3500, (Nonreporting) **A**2 10 21 **F**3 12 13 15 17 18 20 22 24 28 29 30 31 32 34 35 36 37 40 41 43 45 46 47 48 49 51 53 54 59 62 64 71 74 75 76 77 78 79 80 81 82 83 84 85 86 87 89 90 91 92 96 97 107 108 110 111 115 116 117 118 119 123 124 126 127 129 131 132 144 145 146 148 149 154 156 **P**2
Primary Contact: Chris Woleske, President and Chief Executive Officer
CFO: Jim Dietsche, Chief Financial Officer
CMO: Cynthia Lasecki, M.D., Chief Medical Officer
CIO: John Rocheleau, Vice President Business Support and Information Technology
CHR: Troy L Koebke, Director Human Resources Management
CNO: Laura Hieb, R.N., Chief Nursing Officer
Web address: www.bellin.org
**Control**: Other not-for-profit (including NFP Corporation) **Service**: General medical and surgical

**Staffed Beds**: 167 **Admissions**: 8227 **Census**: 84 **Outpatient Visits**: 1249880 **Births**: 1396 **Total Expense ($000)**: 512463 **Payroll Expense ($000)**: 276276 **Personnel**: 3130

⇑ **BELLIN MEMORIAL HOSPITAL** See Bellin Hospital

⇑ **BELLIN PSYCHIATRIC CENTER (524038)**, 301 East St Joseph Street, Zip 54301, Mailing Address: P.O. Box 23725, Zip 54305–3725; tel. 920/433–3630, (Nonreporting) **A**3 5 10 21 **F**4 5 6 29 34 36 38 53 54 56 64 75 86 87 98 99 100 101 102 103 104 130 154
Primary Contact: Sharla Baenen, MSN, R.N., President Mental Well Being, Vice President Emergency Medicine, Hospitalists & Medical Subspecialist
CFO: Kevin McGurk, Controller
CIO: Troy Schiesl, Director Information Services
CHR: Troy L Koebke, Director Human Resources
CNO: Crystal Malakar, Team Leader Inpatient Nursing
Web address: www.bellin.org
**Control**: Other not-for-profit (including NFP Corporation) **Service**: Psychiatric

**Staffed Beds**: 53 **Admissions**: 1662 **Census**: 21 **Outpatient Visits**: 78819
**Births**: 0 **Total Expense ($000)**: 24878 **Payroll Expense ($000)**: 16702
**Personnel**: 173

**BROWN COUNTY COMMUNITY TREATMENT CENTER (524014)**, 3150 Gershwin Drive, Zip 54311–5899; tel. 920/391–4700, (Nonreporting) **A**3 10 **F**98 102 130
Primary Contact: Roberta Morschauser, Administrator
CFO: Margaret Hoff, Account Manager
CMO: Yogesh Pareek, M.D., Clinical Director
CIO: Dawn LaPlant, Manager Health Information Management
CHR: Brent R Miller, Manager Human Resources
Web address: www.co.brown.wi.us/
**Control**: County, Government, Nonfederal **Service**: Psychiatric

**Staffed Beds**: 16 **Admissions**: 682 **Census**: 12 **Outpatient Visits**: 0
**Births**: 0 **Total Expense ($000)**: 3482 **Payroll Expense ($000)**: 2613
**Personnel**: 52

**BROWN COUNTY HUMAN SERVICES MENTAL HEALTH CENTER** See Brown County Community Treatment Center

✉ **HSHS ST. MARY'S HOSPITAL MEDICAL CENTER (520097)**, 1726 Shawano Avenue, Zip 54303–3282; tel. 920/498–4200, (Nonreporting) **A**1 2 10 **F**3 13 15 17 18 20 22 26 28 29 30 31 34 35 40 43 44 45 46 47 48 49 50 51 53 55 57 59 64 65 70 74 75 76 77 78 79 80 82 84 85 86 87 92 94 96 102 107 108 110 111 115 116 117 118 119 131 132 143 145 146 147 148 149 150 154 **P**2 **S** HSHS Hospital Sisters Health System, Springfield, IL
Primary Contact: Brian Charlier, President and Chief Executive Officer
COO: Lawrence J Connors, Chief Operating Officer
CFO: Greg Simia, Chief Financial Officer
CMO: Ken Johnson, Chief Physician Executive
CIO: Shane Miller, Chief Information Officer
CHR: Christine Jensema, Chief People Officer
CNO: Paula Hafeman, Chief Nursing Officer
Web address: www.stmgb.org
**Control**: Church operated, Nongovernment, not-for-profit **Service**: General medical and surgical

**Staffed Beds**: 83 **Admissions**: 3495 **Census**: 34 **Outpatient Visits**: 99876
**Births**: 344 **Total Expense ($000)**: 129421 **Payroll Expense ($000)**: 34641
**Personnel**: 416

✉ **HSHS ST. VINCENT HOSPITAL (520075)**, 835 South Van Buren Street, Zip 54301–3526, Mailing Address: P.O. Box 13508, Zip 54307–3508; tel. 920/433–0111, (Nonreporting) **A**1 2 10 **F**3 5 9 11 12 13 15 17 18 19 20 22 24 26 29 30 31 32 34 35 36 40 43 44 45 49 50 51 56 57 58 59 60 62 64 65 70 72 74 75 76 77 78 79 80 81 83 84 85 86 87 88 89 90 91 92 94 96 107 108 110 111 114 115 116 117 118 119 120 121 123 124 126 129 130 132 135 143 144 146 147 148 149 150 151 152 154 **P**2 **S** HSHS Hospital Sisters Health System, Springfield, IL
Primary Contact: Brian Charlier, President and Chief Executive Officer
CFO: Greg Simia, Chief Financial Officer
CMO: Ken Johnson, Chief Physician Executive
CIO: Shane Miller, Chief Information Officer
CHR: Christine Jensema, Chief Human Resources Officer
CNO: Kenneth E Nelson, R.N., IIIChief Nursing Officer
Web address: www.stvincenthospital.org
**Control**: Church operated, Nongovernment, not-for-profit **Service**: General medical and surgical

**Staffed Beds**: 255 **Admissions**: 10461 **Census**: 134 **Outpatient Visits**: 173719 **Births**: 1096 **Total Expense ($000)**: 327163 **Payroll Expense ($000)**: 94293 **Personnel**: 1619

**ST. MARY'S HOSPITAL MEDICAL CENTER** See Hshs St. Mary's Hospital Medical Center

**ST. VINCENT HOSPITAL** See Hshs St. Vincent Hospital

☐ **WILLOW CREEK BEHAVIORAL HEALTH (524041)**, 1351 Ontario Road, Zip 54311–8302; tel. 920/328–1220, (Nonreporting) **A**1 10 **F**98 99 103 104 154 **S** Strategic Behavioral Health, LLC, Memphis, TN
Primary Contact: Teena Ahuja, Interim Chief Executive Officer and Regional Vice President of Operations
Web address: www.willowcreekbh.com
**Control**: Corporation, Investor-owned (for-profit) **Service**: Psychiatric

**Staffed Beds**: 72 **Admissions**: 2209 **Census**: 42 **Outpatient Visits**: 0
**Births**: 0 **Total Expense ($000)**: 14978 **Payroll Expense ($000)**: 8542
**Personnel**: 147

**WI**

## HARTFORD—Washington County

✠ **AURORA MEDICAL CENTER IN WASHINGTON COUNTY (520038)**, 1032 East Sumner Street, Zip 53027–1698; tel. 262/673–2300, (Nonreporting) **A**1 2 10 **F**3 8 11 15 28 29 30 34 35 36 40 41 43 44 45 46 47 48 49 50 53 54 56 57 59 60 64 65 68 75 77 79 80 81 82 84 85 86 87 89 90 91 92 93 94 95 96 107 111 112 113 114 118 119 129 130 132 135 146 148 149 150 157 **P**2 **S** Advocate Aurora Health, Downers Grove, IL
Primary Contact: Jessica Bauer, President
CIO: John Sipek, Supervisor Client Services
CNO: Terry Kabitzke-Groth, R.N., Chief Nursing Officer
Web address: www.aurorahealthcare.org
**Control:** Other not–for–profit (including NFP Corporation) **Service:** General medical and surgical

| | |
|---|---|
| **Staffed Beds:** 35 **Admissions:** 1495 **Census:** 14 **Outpatient Visits:** 87881 **Births:** 0 **Total Expense ($000):** 51321 **Payroll Expense ($000):** 19750 **Personnel:** 355 | |

**AURORA MEDICAL CENTER OF WASHINGTON COUNTY** See Aurora Medical Center in Washington County

## HAYWARD—Sawyer County

**HAYWARD AREA MEMORIAL HOSPITAL AND NURSING HOME** See Hayward Area Memorial Hospital and Water's Edge

★ **HAYWARD AREA MEMORIAL HOSPITAL AND WATER'S EDGE (521336)**, 11040 North State Road 77, Zip 54843–6391; tel. 715/934–4321, (Total facility includes 70 beds in nursing home–type unit) (Nonreporting) **A**10 18 **F**10 11 13 15 29 34 40 43 51 53 64 75 76 78 80 81 82 86 93 107 111 119 125 128 130 147 154 **P**2
Primary Contact: Luke Beirl, PharmD, Chief Executive Officer
COO: Brad Zeller, Vice President Operations
CFO: Kent Dumonseau, Vice President Finance and Information Services
CHR: Rose Gates, Director Human Resources
Web address: www.https://haywardmemorialhospital.com
**Control:** Other not–for–profit (including NFP Corporation) **Service:** General medical and surgical

| | |
|---|---|
| **Staffed Beds:** 75 **Admissions:** 867 **Census:** 76 **Outpatient Visits:** 14143 **Births:** 125 **Total Expense ($000):** 42942 **Payroll Expense ($000):** 18413 **Personnel:** 234 | |

## HILLSBORO—Vernon County

★ **GUNDERSEN ST. JOSEPH'S HOSPITAL AND CLINICS (521304)**, 400 Water Avenue, Zip 54634–9054, Mailing Address: P.O. Box 527, Zip 54634–0527; tel. 608/489–8000, (Nonreporting) **A**10 18 **F**15 28 29 34 36 38 40 43 53 56 64 69 75 77 80 81 82 86 87 89 90 93 99 100 101 103 104 107 108 130 131 144 147 **P**2
Primary Contact: Robin Nelson, Interim Chief Executive Officer
CFO: Robin Nelson, Chief Financial Officer
CMO: William Cooke, M.D., Chief of Staff
CIO: Danial Phetteplace, Director Information Technology
CHR: Kristie McCoic, Clinic Operations Officer and Director Human Resources
Web address: www.gundersenhealth.org/st-josephs
**Control:** Other not–for–profit (including NFP Corporation) **Service:** General medical and surgical

| | |
|---|---|
| **Staffed Beds:** 13 **Admissions:** 291 **Census:** 3 **Outpatient Visits:** 37234 **Births:** 0 **Total Expense ($000):** 20788 **Payroll Expense ($000):** 8666 **Personnel:** 151 | |

**ST. JOSEPH'S HEALTH SERVICES-GUNDERSEN LUTHERAN** See Gundersen St. Joseph's Hospital and Clinics

## HUDSON—St. Croix County

☐ **HUDSON HOSPITAL AND CLINIC (521335)**, 405 Stageline Road, Zip 54016–7848; tel. 715/531–6000, (Nonreporting) **A**1 3 10 18 **F**5 13 15 28 29 34 38 40 43 53 55 56 64 75 76 78 80 81 86 87 89 93 107 111 119 130 **P**2 **S** HealthPartners, Bloomington, MN
Primary Contact: Thomas Borowski, FACHE, President
CFO: Douglas E Johnson, Vice President, Chief Financial Officer
CMO: Levon O'hAodha, Chief of Staff
CHR: Kristen Novak, Director, Human Resources
CNO: Kristy Yaeger, Vice President, Patient Care Services and Chief Nursing Officer
Web address: www.hudsonhospital.org
**Control:** Other not–for–profit (including NFP Corporation) **Service:** General medical and surgical

| | |
|---|---|
| **Staffed Beds:** 24 **Admissions:** 1435 **Census:** 10 **Outpatient Visits:** 49090 **Births:** 510 **Total Expense ($000):** 56644 **Payroll Expense ($000):** 20655 **Personnel:** 220 | |

**HUDSON HOSPITAL AND CLINICS** See Hudson Hospital and Clinic

## JANESVILLE—Rock County

✠ **MERCY HOSPITAL AND TRAUMA CENTER** See Mercyhealth Hospital and Trauma Center - Janesville

✠ **MERCYHEALTH HOSPITAL AND TRAUMA CENTER - JANESVILLE (520066)**, 1000 Mineral Point Avenue, Zip 53548–2982, Mailing Address: P.O. Box 5003, Zip 53547–5003; tel. 608/756–6000, (Nonreporting) **A**1 2 3 5 10 **S** Mercy Health System, Janesville, WI
Primary Contact: Javon R. Bea, President and Chief Executive Officer
CFO: John Cook, Vice President and Chief Financial Officer
CMO: Mark L. Goelzer, M.D., Director Medical Affairs
CHR: Kathy Harris, Vice President
CNO: Debra Potempa, Vice President
Web address: www.mercyhealthsystem.org
**Control:** Other not–for–profit (including NFP Corporation) **Service:** General medical and surgical

| | |
|---|---|
| **Staffed Beds:** 135 | |

✠ **SSM HEALTH ST. MARY'S HOSPITAL JANESVILLE (520208)**, 3400 East Racine Street, Zip 53546–2344, Mailing Address: 3400 East Racine Steeet, Zip 53546–2344; tel. 608/373–8000, (Nonreporting) **A**1 10 **F**13 28 29 34 38 40 43 64 70 75 76 80 81 86 87 89 90 107 108 111 119 130 154 **P**2 **S** SSM Health, Saint Louis, MO
Primary Contact: Benjamin Layman, President
Web address: www.stmarysjanesville.com
**Control:** Church operated, Nongovernment, not–for–profit **Service:** General medical and surgical

| | |
|---|---|
| **Staffed Beds:** 50 **Admissions:** 2703 **Census:** 24 **Outpatient Visits:** 81220 **Births:** 458 **Total Expense ($000):** 63162 **Payroll Expense ($000):** 19961 **Personnel:** 293 | |

**ST. MARY'S JANESVILLE HOSPITAL** See Ssm Health St. Mary's Hospital Janesville

## KENOSHA—Kenosha County

**AURORA MEDICAL CENTER** See Aurora Medical Center Kenosha

✠ **AURORA MEDICAL CENTER KENOSHA (520189)**, 10400 75th Street, Zip 53142–7884; tel. 262/948–5600, (Nonreporting) **A**1 2 3 5 10 **F**3 8 11 13 15 17 18 19 20 22 26 28 29 30 31 34 35 36 40 43 44 45 46 47 48 49 50 51 54 57 59 60 64 68 70 72 74 75 76 79 80 81 82 84 85 86 87 89 93 94 96 100 107 108 110 111 114 115 116 117 118 119 120 121 123 126 129 130 131 132 135 146 147 148 149 150 154 **S** Advocate Aurora Health, Downers Grove, IL
Primary Contact: Lisa Just, President
COO: Linda A. Gump, Chief Clinical Services Officer
CFO: Laurie B. Yake, Vice President Finance
CMO: James Santarelli, M.D., President Medical Staff
CIO: Debora R. Chapdelaine, Manager Information Technology
CHR: Kellie Nelson, Director Human Resources
CNO: Donna F. Jamieson, Ph.D., R.N., Chief Nursing Officer
Web address: www.aurorahealthcare.org
**Control:** Other not–for–profit (including NFP Corporation) **Service:** General medical and surgical

| | |
|---|---|
| **Staffed Beds:** 83 **Admissions:** 5717 **Census:** 56 **Outpatient Visits:** 210704 **Births:** 909 **Total Expense ($000):** 160497 **Payroll Expense ($000):** 51293 **Personnel:** 1324 | |

☐ **FROEDTERT SOUTH - KENOSHA MEDICAL CENTER (520021)**, 6308 Eighth Avenue, Zip 53143–5082; tel. 262/656–2011, (Includes FROEDTERT SOUTH - ST. CATHERINE'S MEDICAL CENTER, Mailing address: 9555 76th Street, Pleasant Prairie, Wisconsin, Zip 53158–1984, 6308 Eighth Avenue, Kenosha, Zip 53143–5082, tel. 262/577–8000; Richard O Schmidt Jr, President and Chief Executive Officer), (Nonreporting) **A**1 2 10
Primary Contact: Richard O. Schmidt Jr, President and Chief Executive Officer
CFO: Thomas J. Kelley, Executive Vice President and Chief Financial Officer
Web address: www.froedtertsouth.com
**Control:** Other not–for–profit (including NFP Corporation) **Service:** General medical and surgical

| | |
|---|---|
| **Staffed Beds:** 232 | |

**UNITED HOSPITAL SYSTEM-KENOSHA CAMPUS** See Froedtert South - Kenosha Medical Center

## LA CROSSE—La Crosse County

**FRANCISCAN SKEMP HEALTHCARE-LA CROSSE CAMPUS** See Mayo Clinic Health System - Franciscan Healthcare in La Crosse

**GUNDERSEN HEALTH SYSTEM** See Gundersen Lutheran Medical Center

✠ △ **GUNDERSEN LUTHERAN MEDICAL CENTER (520087)**, 1900 South Avenue, Zip 54601–5467; tel. 608/782–7300, (Nonreporting) **A**1 2 3 5 7 8 10 **F**3 4 5 6 9 12 13 15 18 19 20 22 24 26 28 29 30 31 32 33 34 35 36 38 40 43 44 45 46 47 48 49 50 51 52 54 55 56 57 59 60 61 63 64 65 68 71 72 74 75 76 77 78 79 80 81 82 84 85 86 87 88 89 90 91 92 93 94 96 97 98 99 100 101 102 103 104 105 107 109 110 111 113 115 116 117 118 119 120 121 123 124 126 129 130 131 132 134 135 143 144 145 146 147 148 149 150 152 153 154 156 **P**2
Primary Contact: Scott W. Rathgaber, M.D., Chief Executive Officer
COO: Kathy Klock, R.N., Senior Vice President Clinical Operations and Human Resources
CFO: Dara Bartels, Chief Financial Officer
CMO: Greg Thompson, Chief Medical Officer
CIO: Deb Rislow, Chief Information Officer
CHR: Kathy Klock, R.N., Senior Vice President Clinical Operations and Human Resources
Web address: www.gundluth.org
**Control**: Other not–for–profit (including NFP Corporation) **Service**: General medical and surgical

**Staffed Beds**: 293 **Admissions**: 13132 **Census**: 188 **Outpatient Visits**: 663272 **Births**: 1667 **Total Expense ($000)**: 981570 **Payroll Expense ($000)**: 419490 **Personnel**: 2945

✠ **MAYO CLINIC HEALTH SYSTEM - FRANCISCAN HEALTHCARE IN LA CROSSE (520004)**, 700 West Avenue South, Zip 54601–4783; tel. 608/785–0940, (Nonreporting) **A**1 2 3 5 10 19 **F**3 6 8 11 13 15 18 19 20 22 26 28 29 30 31 34 35 36 40 41 43 44 45 46 48 49 51 54 56 57 58 59 60 64 65 66 68 69 70 74 75 76 77 78 79 80 81 82 84 85 87 89 90 97 102 107 108 110 111 115 116 117 118 119 120 121 123 126 129 130 135 144 145 146 148 149 154 156 157 **S** Mayo Clinic, Rochester, MN
Primary Contact: Paul S. Mueller, Regional Vice President
COO: Michael A Morrey, Executive Vice President
CFO: Tom Tiggelaar, Vice President Finance
CMO: David Rushlow, Vice President Medical Affairs
CIO: Neal Sanger, Vice President Information Services
Web address: www.franciscanskemp.org
**Control**: Other not–for–profit (including NFP Corporation) **Service**: General medical and surgical

**Staffed Beds**: 100 **Admissions**: 4480 **Census**: 50 **Outpatient Visits**: 334718 **Births**: 673 **Total Expense ($000)**: 354578 **Payroll Expense ($000)**: 169443 **Personnel**: 2106

## LADYSMITH—Rusk County

★ **MARSHFIELD MEDICAL CENTER - LADYSMITH (521328)**, 900 College Avenue West, Zip 54848–2116; tel. 715/532–5561, (Nonreporting) **A**10 18 **F**3 11 15 28 29 30 34 35 40 43 44 45 50 53 57 59 81 85 86 87 89 93 107 110 111 115 116 117 118 119 127 132 133 144 146 148 154 **S** Marshfield Clinic Health System, Marshfield, WI
Primary Contact: Jeff Euclide, R.N., Chief Administrative Officer
CFO: David Kuehn, Chief Financial Officer
CMO: Ganesh Pawar, M.D., Chief of Staff
CHR: Rita Telitz, Chief Administrative Officer
Web address: www.ruskhospital.org
**Control**: Other not–for–profit (including NFP Corporation) **Service**: General medical and surgical

**Staffed Beds**: 25 **Admissions**: 347 **Census**: 3 **Outpatient Visits**: 53981 **Births**: 0 **Total Expense ($000)**: 32186 **Payroll Expense ($000)**: 12028 **Personnel**: 110

**RUSK COUNTY MEMORIAL HOSPITAL** See Marshfield Medical Center - Ladysmith

## LAKE GENEVA—Walworth County

**MERCY WALWORTH HOSPITAL AND MEDICAL CENTER** See Mercyhealth Hospital and Medical Center - Walworth

**MERCYHEALTH HOSPITAL AND MEDICAL CENTER - WALWORTH (521357)**, N2950 State Road 67, Zip 53147–2655; tel. 262/245–0535, (Nonreporting) **A**10 18 **F**9 11 13 15 17 29 38 40 64 70 75 76 77 78 80 81 82 87 89 93 100 101 103 104 107 108 111 118 119 130 131 144 147 154 **S** Mercy Health System, Janesville, WI
Primary Contact: Javon R. Bea, President and Chief Executive Officer
COO: Jennifer Hallatt, Vice President
CNO: Caryn Lynn Oleston, FACHE, MSN, R.N., Chief Nursing Officer
Web address: www.mercyhealthsystem.org
**Control**: Other not–for–profit (including NFP Corporation) **Service**: General medical and surgical

**Staffed Beds**: 17 **Admissions**: 1387 **Census**: 10 **Outpatient Visits**: 166070 **Births**: 178 **Total Expense ($000)**: 83165 **Payroll Expense ($000)**: 19627 **Personnel**: 362

## LANCASTER—Grant County

✠ **GRANT REGIONAL HEALTH CENTER (521322)**, 507 South Monroe Street, Zip 53813–2054; tel. 608/723–2143, (Nonreporting) **A**1 5 10 18 **F**3 8 11 13 15 28 29 34 35 36 40 43 45 52 53 54 55 56 57 59 64 65 66 68 69 75 76 77 79 80 81 82 85 86 87 89 90 93 97 107 110 111 115 119 127 130 131 132 133 135 144 146 148 149 154 157 **S** HealthTech Management Services, Brentwood, TN
Primary Contact: David Smith, President and Chief Executive Officer
CFO: Dawn Bandy, Chief Financial Officer
CMO: Jessica Varnam, Chief of Staff
CIO: Ken Kaiser, Coordinator Information Systems
CHR: Stacy L Martin, Director Human Resources
CNO: Jennifer Rutkowski, R.N., MSN, Vice President Professional Services
Web address: www.grantregional.com
**Control**: Other not–for–profit (including NFP Corporation) **Service**: General medical and surgical

**Staffed Beds**: 7 **Admissions**: 593 **Census**: 6 **Outpatient Visits**: 40876 **Births**: 155 **Total Expense ($000)**: 33109 **Payroll Expense ($000)**: 14739 **Personnel**: 184

**LANCASTER MEMORIAL HOSPITAL** See Grant Regional Health Center

## MADISON—Dane County

☐ **MENDOTA MENTAL HEALTH INSTITUTE (524008)**, 301 Troy Drive, Zip 53704–1599; tel. 608/301–1000, (Nonreporting) **A**1 3 5 10 **F**6 29 34 38 56 75 82 86 87 98 100 101 103 104 130 154 **P**2
Primary Contact: Greg Van Rybroek, Chief Executive Officer
CFO: Stacie Schiereck, Director Management Services
CMO: Molli Martha Rolli, M.D., Medical Director
CNO: Jane Walters, Director of Nursing
Web address: www.dhfs.state.wi.us
**Control**: State, Government, Nonfederal **Service**: Psychiatric

**Staffed Beds**: 293 **Admissions**: 541 **Census**: 284 **Outpatient Visits**: 0 **Births**: 0 **Total Expense ($000)**: 92846 **Payroll Expense ($000)**: 50814 **Personnel**: 791

**MERITER UNITYPOINT HEALTH** See Unitypoint Health Meriter

✠ **SELECT SPECIALTY HOSPITAL-MADISON (522008)**, 801 Braxton Place, Zip 53715–1415; tel. 608/260–2700, (Nonreporting) **A**1 10 **F**1 29 34 75 82 86 107 119 130 154 **S** Select Medical Corporation, Mechanicsburg, PA
Primary Contact: Catherine Heimbecher, Chief Executive Officer
CHR: Mallary Stramowski, Chief Human Resources Officer
CNO: Dana McKinney, Chief Nursing Officer
Web address: www.madison.selectspecialtyhospitals.com
**Control**: Corporation, Investor–owned (for–profit) **Service**: Acute long–term care hospital

**Staffed Beds**: 58 **Admissions**: 440 **Census**: 38 **Outpatient Visits**: 0 **Births**: 0 **Total Expense ($000)**: 27070 **Payroll Expense ($000)**: 10513 **Personnel**: 146

WI

**Hospital, Medicare Provider Number, Address, Telephone, Approval, Facility, and Physician Codes, Health Care System**

★ American Hospital Association (AHA) membership
☐ The Joint Commission accreditation
○ Healthcare Facilities Accreditation Program
◇ DNV Healthcare Inc. accreditation
⇑ Center for Improvement in Healthcare Quality Accreditation
△ Commission on Accreditation of Rehabilitation Facilities (CARF) accreditation

✠ **SSM HEALTH ST. MARY'S HOSPITAL (520083)**, 700 South Park Street, Zip 53715–1830; tel. 608/251–6100, (Nonreporting) **A**1 3 5 10 **F**2 9 11 13 15 17 20 22 24 28 29 34 40 43 53 56 64 70 72 76 77 78 80 81 82 86 89 90 98 100 101 102 103 107 108 118 119 130 141 154 **P**2 **S** SSM Health, Saint Louis, MO
Primary Contact: Jon Rozenfeld, President
CFO: Steve Caldwell, Vice President Finance and Chief Financial Officer
CHR: Linda Taplin Statz, System Director, Employee Experience
CNO: Ginger Malone MSN, RN-BChief Nursing Officer
Web address: www.stmarysmadison.com
**Control:** Church operated, Nongovernment, not–for–profit **Service:** General medical and surgical

**Staffed Beds:** 362 **Admissions:** 18329 **Census:** 248 **Outpatient Visits:** 99430 **Births:** 2115 **Total Expense ($000):** 394929 **Payroll Expense ($000):** 133112 **Personnel:** 1824

**ST. MARY'S HOSPITAL** See Ssm Health St. Mary's Hospital

✠ **UNITYPOINT HEALTH MERITER (520089)**, 202 South Park Street, Zip 53715–1507; tel. 608/417–6000, (Nonreporting) **A**1 3 5 10 **F**3 4 5 9 11 12 13 15 17 18 20 22 26 28 29 30 31 32 34 35 36 37 40 41 43 45 46 48 49 50 53 56 57 58 59 64 65 66 68 70 71 72 74 75 76 78 79 80 81 84 85 86 87 90 92 93 96 97 98 99 100 101 102 103 104 107 108 110 111 115 118 119 126 130 132 135 145 146 147 148 149 154 156 **S** UnityPoint Health, West Des Moines, IA
Primary Contact: Sue Erickson, President and Chief Executive Officer
CFO: Beth Erdman, Chief Financial Officer
CMO: Geoff Priest, M.D., Chief Medical Officer
CIO: Denise Gomez, Assistant Vice President Information Systems
CHR: James Arnett, Vice President Human Resources
CNO: Pat Grunwald, MSN, Chief Nursing Officer
Web address: www.meriter.com
**Control:** Other not–for–profit (including NFP Corporation) **Service:** General medical and surgical

**Staffed Beds:** 214 **Admissions:** 16149 **Census:** 200 **Outpatient Visits:** 328296 **Births:** 4813 **Total Expense ($000):** 443499 **Payroll Expense ($000):** 186490 **Personnel:** 2195

✠ **UNIVERSITY HOSPITAL (520098)**, 600 Highland Avenue, Zip 53792–0002; tel. 608/263–6400, (Includes AMERICAN FAMILY CHILDREN'S HOSPITAL, Mailing address: 1675 Highland Avenue, Madison, Wisconsin, Zip 53705; tel. 608/890–5437; Jeffrey S Poltawsky, Senior Vice President), (Nonreporting) **A**1 2 3 5 8 10 **F**3 5 8 9 12 15 16 17 18 19 20 21 22 23 24 25 26 27 28 29 30 31 32 34 35 36 37 40 41 43 45 46 47 48 49 50 51 53 54 56 57 58 59 60 61 62 64 65 68 70 72 74 77 78 79 80 81 82 83 84 85 86 87 88 89 92 93 94 96 97 98 100 102 103 107 108 110 111 112 114 115 116 117 118 119 120 121 123 124 126 129 130 131 132 134 135 136 137 138 139 140 141 142 145 146 147 148 149 150 154 157 **P**2 **S** UW Health System, Madison, WI
Primary Contact: Alan Kaplan, M.D., Chief Executive Officer
COO: Ron Sliwinski, Chief of Hospital Division
CFO: Robert Flannery, Chief Financial Officer
CMO: Peter Newcomer, M.D., Chief Medical Officer
CIO: Jocelyn DeWitt, Ph.D., Vice President and Chief Information Officer
Web address: www.uwhealth.org
**Control:** Other not–for–profit (including NFP Corporation) **Service:** General medical and surgical

**Staffed Beds:** 624 **Admissions:** 33537 **Census:** 477 **Outpatient Visits:** 1066401 **Births:** 3 **Total Expense ($000):** 1888147 **Payroll Expense ($000):** 595449 **Personnel:** 9227

**UNIVERSITY OF WISCONSIN HOSPITALS AND CLINICS AUTHORITY** See University Hospital

☐ **UW HEALTH REHABILITATION HOSPITAL (523028)**, 5115 North Biltmore Lane, Zip 53718–2161; tel. 608/592–8100, (Nonreporting) **A**1 10 **F**29 34 75 86 90 **P**2 **S** UW Health System, Madison, WI
Primary Contact: Mary Kay Diderrich, R.N., Chief Executive Officer
CFO: Karen Bindl, CPA, Controller
Web address: www.uwhealth.org
**Control:** Partnership, Investor–owned (for–profit) **Service:** Rehabilitation

**Staffed Beds:** 43 **Admissions:** 1112 **Census:** 37 **Outpatient Visits:** 0 **Births:** 0 **Total Expense ($000):** 19866 **Payroll Expense ($000):** 8918 **Personnel:** 114

✠ **WILLIAM S. MIDDLETON MEMORIAL VETERANS HOSPITAL**, 2500 Overlook Terrace, Zip 53705–2286; tel. 608/256–1901, (Nonreporting) **A**1 3 5 **S** Department of Veterans Affairs, Washington, DC
Primary Contact: John J. Rohrer, Director
CFO: Evarista Mikell, Assistant Finance Officer
CMO: Alan J Bridges, M.D., Chief of Staff
CIO: Randall Margenau, Chief Information Officer
CHR: Stuart Souders, Chief, Human Resources
CNO: Rebecca Kordahl, R.N., Associate Director, Patient Care Services
Web address: www.madison.va.gov
**Control:** Veterans Affairs, Government, federal **Service:** General medical and surgical

**Staffed Beds:** 87

**WM S MIDDLETON MEM VET HOSP** See William S. Middleton Memorial Veterans Hospital

## MANITOWOC—Manitowoc County

✠ **HOLY FAMILY MEMORIAL (520107)**, 2300 Western Avenue, Zip 54220–3712, Mailing Address: P.O. Box 1450, Zip 54221–1450; tel. 920/320–2011, (Nonreporting) **A**1 3 5 **F**3 5 11 13 15 18 20 22 28 29 30 31 32 33 34 35 36 40 43 45 46 47 48 49 50 51 53 54 56 57 58 59 62 63 64 65 70 75 76 77 78 79 80 81 82 85 86 89 91 92 93 96 97 104 107 108 109 110 111 114 115 118 119 120 121 122 123 130 132 135 143 148 149 157 **S** Franciscan Sisters of Christian Charity Sponsored Ministries, Inc., Manitowoc, WI
Primary Contact: Brett William. Norell, Interim Chief Executive Officer
COO: Jane Curran-Meuli, Chief Operating Officer
CFO: Patricia Huettl, Vice President Finance and Chief Financial Officer
CMO: Steve Driggers, M.D., Chief Medical Officer
CIO: Theron Pappas, Director Management Information Systems
CHR: Laura M Fielding, Administrative Director Organizational Development
CNO: Bonny Range, MSN, Chief Nursing Officer
Web address: www.hfmhealth.org
**Control:** Church operated, Nongovernment, not–for–profit **Service:** General medical and surgical

**Staffed Beds:** 67 **Admissions:** 2562 **Census:** 24 **Outpatient Visits:** 227250 **Births:** 127 **Total Expense ($000):** 111811 **Payroll Expense ($000):** 55595 **Personnel:** 696

**HOLY FAMILY MEMORIAL MEDICAL CENTER** See Holy Family Memorial

## MARINETTE—Marinette County

✠ **AURORA MEDICAL CENTER - BAY AREA (520113)**, 3003 University Drive, Zip 54143–4110; tel. 715/735–4200, (Nonreporting) **A**1 2 10 20 **F**3 7 11 13 15 17 28 29 30 31 34 40 43 44 45 50 51 54 57 59 70 74 75 76 77 78 79 80 81 82 85 86 87 89 93 96 107 108 109 110 111 114 115 119 120 121 123 124 130 131 135 143 146 147 148 154 **P**2 **S** Advocate Aurora Health, Downers Grove, IL
Primary Contact: Edward A. Harding, FACHE, President
CFO: Daniel Cook, Director of Finance
CMO: Syed Ali, M.D., Chief Medical Officer
CNO: Nicole Swanson, Vice President of Nursing
Web address: www.bamc.org
**Control:** Other not–for–profit (including NFP Corporation) **Service:** General medical and surgical

**Staffed Beds:** 59 **Admissions:** 2902 **Census:** 26 **Outpatient Visits:** 374372 **Births:** 185 **Total Expense ($000):** 113740 **Payroll Expense ($000):** 40289 **Personnel:** 472

**BAY AREA MEDICAL CENTER** See Aurora Medical Center - Bay Area

**WI**

## MARSHFIELD—Wood County

☒ △ **MARSHFIELD MEDICAL CENTER (520037)**, 611 St Joseph Avenue, Zip 54449–1898; tel. 715/387-1713, (Includes MARSHFIELD CHILDEN'S HOSPITAL, Mailing address: 611 Saint Joseph Avenue, Marshfield, Wisconsin, Zip 54449–1832; tel. 715/387-1713), (Nonreporting) **A**1 2 3 5 7 10 20 **F**3 4 6 8 9 11 12 13 15 16 17 18 20 22 24 26 28 29 30 31 32 34 35 36 37 40 41 43 44 45 46 47 48 49 50 51 53 55 56 57 59 66 68 69 70 71 72 74 75 76 77 78 79 80 81 82 83 84 85 86 87 88 89 90 92 93 94 96 97 98 100 101 107 108 110 111 114 116 117 118 119 120 121 122 123 124 126 129 130 131 132 135 136 144 145 146 147 148 149 150 152 153 154 156 **P**2 **S** Marshfield Clinic Health System, Marshfield, WI
Primary Contact: Pat Board, Chief Administrative Officer
CFO: William J Hinner, Vice President Financial Analysis and Planning Ministry Health Care
CMO: Peter Stamas, M.D., Vice President Medical Affairs
CIO: Will Weider, Chief Information Officer
CHR: Cheryl F Zima, Vice President Human Resources Ministry Health Care
CNO: Robin Kretschman, MSN, R.N., Vice President Patient Care Services
Web address: www.stjosephs-marshfield.org
**Control**: Other not–for–profit (including NFP Corporation) **Service**: General medical and surgical

**Staffed Beds:** 200 **Admissions:** 12935 **Census:** 186 **Outpatient Visits:** 434660 **Births:** 969 **Total Expense ($000):** 694325 **Payroll Expense ($000):** 257066 **Personnel:** 3052

**MINISTRY SAINT JOSEPH'S HOSPITAL** See Marshfield Medical Center

**NORWOOD HEALTH CENTER (524019)**, 1600 North Chestnut Avenue, Zip 54449–1499; tel. 715/384–2188, (Total facility includes 28 beds in nursing home–type unit) (Nonreporting) **A**10 **F**3 4 30 69 75 98 99 100 101 102 103 104 105 128 130 143 146 148 154 **P**2
Primary Contact: Jordan Bruce, Administrator
CFO: Jo Timmerman, Manager Accounting
CHR: Larry Shear, Administrative Assistant
Web address: www.co.wood.wi.us/norwood/index.htm
**Control**: County, Government, Nonfederal **Service**: Psychiatric

**Staffed Beds:** 44 **Admissions:** 444 **Census:** 32 **Outpatient Visits:** 0 **Births:** 0 **Total Expense ($000):** 4813 **Payroll Expense ($000):** 2265 **Personnel:** 38

**SAINT JOSEPH'S CHILDEN'S HOSPITAL** See Marshfield Childen's Hospital

## MAUSTON—Juneau County

**HESS MEMORIAL HOSPITAL** See Mile Bluff Medical Center

☐ **MILE BLUFF MEDICAL CENTER (520109)**, 1050 Division Street, Zip 53948–1997; tel. 608/847–6161, (Total facility includes 72 beds in nursing home–type unit) (Nonreporting) **A**1 5 10 20 **F**10 11 13 15 28 29 34 36 40 43 54 56 60 64 69 75 76 77 78 80 81 82 86 87 89 93 107 108 111 118 119 125 128 130 131 144 **P**2
Primary Contact: James M. O'Keefe, President and Chief Executive Officer
CFO: Francis James Fish, Vice President and Chief Financial Officer
CMO: Tim Bjelland EsqPhysician
CHR: Sue Wafle, Director, Human Resources
CNO: Jean Surguy, Vice President, Chief Nursing Officer
Web address: www.milebluff.com
**Control**: Other not–for–profit (including NFP Corporation) **Service**: General medical and surgical

**Staffed Beds:** 79 **Admissions:** 1053 **Census:** 110 **Outpatient Visits:** 172080 **Births:** 135 **Total Expense ($000):** 84052 **Payroll Expense ($000):** 44632 **Personnel:** 505

## MEDFORD—Taylor County

**ASPIRUS MEDFORD HOSPITAL** See Aspirus Medford Hospital & Clinics, Inc.

☒ **ASPIRUS MEDFORD HOSPITAL & CLINICS, INC. (521324)**, 135 South Gibson Street, Zip 54451; tel. 715/748–8100, (Total facility includes 109 beds in nursing home–type unit) (Nonreporting) **A**1 3 5 10 18 **F**3 8 10 11 13 15 28 29 31 34 35 36 40 41 43 45 50 53 55 56 57 58 59 60 64 68 71 75 76 77 78 81 82 85 86 87 89 90 93 97 107 110 111 115 116 117 118 119 125 127 128 129 130 131 132 133 135 144 146 147 148 149 154 156 **P**2 **S** Aspirus, Inc., Wausau, WI
Primary Contact: Dale Hustedt, President
CFO: Greg Shaw, Vice President, Finance
CMO: Clint Semrau, President Medical Staff
CIO: Todd Richardson, Chief Information Officer
CHR: Julie Zeps, Vice President Human Resources
CNO: Barb Lato, Chief Nursing Officer
Web address: www.aspirus.org
**Control**: Other not–for–profit (including NFP Corporation) **Service**: General medical and surgical

**Staffed Beds:** 124 **Admissions:** 847 **Census:** 58 **Outpatient Visits:** 86413 **Births:** 202 **Total Expense ($000):** 68309 **Payroll Expense ($000):** 27875 **Personnel:** 454

## MENOMONEE FALLS—Waukesha County

☒ △ **FROEDTERT MENOMONEE FALLS HOSPITAL (520103)**, W180 N8085 Town Hall Road, Zip 53051–3518, Mailing Address: P.O. Box 408, Zip 53052–0408; tel. 262/251–1000, (Nonreporting) **A**1 2 3 5 7 10 **F**3 4 5 8 9 11 13 15 17 20 22 24 26 28 29 30 31 34 35 37 38 40 43 44 45 46 47 49 50 51 54 56 57 58 59 60 62 64 65 66 68 70 72 74 75 76 77 78 79 80 81 82 84 85 86 87 89 90 93 97 98 100 101 102 103 104 105 107 108 110 111 114 115 116 117 118 119 120 121 123 126 129 130 131 132 135 145 146 147 148 149 150 153 156 **S** Froedtert Health, Milwaukee, WI
Primary Contact: Teresa M. Lux, President and Chief Operating Officer
COO: Allen Ericson, Chief Operating Officer, Community Hospital Division and President, St. Joseph's Hospital
CFO: Scott Hawig, Senior Vice President of Finance, Chief Financial Officer and Treasurer
CMO: David Goldberg, M.D., Vice President Medical Affairs and Chief Medical Officer
CHR: Keith Allen, Senior Vice President and Chief Human Resources Officer
Web address: www.https://www.froedtert.com
**Control**: Other not–for–profit (including NFP Corporation) **Service**: General medical and surgical

**Staffed Beds:** 202 **Admissions:** 9907 **Census:** 105 **Outpatient Visits:** 116674 **Births:** 750 **Total Expense ($000):** 298093 **Payroll Expense ($000):** 94206 **Personnel:** 1236

## MENOMONIE—Dunn County

**MAYO CLINIC HEALTH SYSTEM - RED CEDAR** See Mayo Clinic Health System - Red Cedar in Menomonie

☐ **MAYO CLINIC HEALTH SYSTEM - RED CEDAR IN MENOMONIE (521340)**, 2321 Stout Road, Zip 54751–2397; tel. 715/235–5531, (Nonreporting) **A**1 3 5 10 18 **F**3 13 15 17 18 28 29 30 31 32 34 35 38 40 43 44 45 53 54 55 56 57 59 64 65 70 74 76 77 78 79 80 81 82 85 86 87 89 90 93 94 96 97 99 100 101 102 103 104 107 108 110 111 115 119 129 130 131 132 133 144 145 146 147 148 149 154 156 **P**2 **S** Mayo Clinic, Rochester, MN
Primary Contact: Richard Helmers, M.D., Regional Vice President
CFO: Jeanie Lubinsky, Chief Financial Officer
CMO: Mark Deyo Svendsen, M.D., Medical Director
CIO: Frank Wrogg, Director Information Technology
CHR: Leann Wurtzel, Director Human Resources
Web address: www.rcmc-mhs.org
**Control**: Other not–for–profit (including NFP Corporation) **Service**: General medical and surgical

**Staffed Beds:** 19 **Admissions:** 1009 **Census:** 12 **Outpatient Visits:** 107274 **Births:** 239 **Total Expense ($000):** 90343 **Payroll Expense ($000):** 37724 **Personnel:** 398

WI

---

**Hospital, Medicare Provider Number, Address, Telephone, Approval, Facility, and Physician Codes, Health Care System**

★ American Hospital Association (AHA) membership
☐ The Joint Commission accreditation
○ Healthcare Facilities Accreditation Program
◇ DNV Healthcare Inc. accreditation
⇑ Center for Improvement in Healthcare Quality Accreditation
△ Commission on Accreditation of Rehabilitation Facilities (CARF) accreditation

### MEQUON—Ozaukee County

✠ **ASCENSION COLUMBIA ST. MARY'S HOSPITAL OZAUKEE (520027)**, 13111 North Port Washington Road, Zip 53097–2416; tel. 262/243–7300, (Nonreporting) **A**1 2 10 **F**3 4 5 9 13 15 17 18 20 22 24 26 28 29 30 31 34 35 36 38 40 43 44 46 48 49 50 51 53 54 56 57 58 59 64 66 68 70 74 76 77 78 79 80 81 84 85 86 89 91 93 94 96 97 98 100 102 103 105 107 108 110 111 114 116 118 119 120 121 123 126 130 132 135 144 145 146 147 148 149 153 156 **P**2 **S** Ascension Healthcare, Saint Louis, MO
Primary Contact: Kelly Elkins, President and Chief Executive Officer
CFO: Rhonda Anderson, Executive Vice President Finance and Chief Financial Officer
CMO: David Shapiro, M.D., Vice President Medical Affairs and Chief Medical Officer
CIO: Mary Paul, Chief Information Officer
CHR: Cheryl Hill, Vice President Human Resources
Web address: www.columbia-stmarys.org
**Control:** Church operated, Nongovernment, not–for–profit **Service:** General medical and surgical

**Staffed Beds:** 124 **Admissions:** 4673 **Census:** 57 **Outpatient Visits:** 254767 **Births:** 450 **Total Expense ($000):** 117344 **Payroll Expense ($000):** 34965 **Personnel:** 688

**COLUMBIA ST. MARY'S HOSPITAL OZAUKEE** See Ascension Columbia St. Mary's Hospital Ozaukee

### MERRILL—Lincoln County

✠ **ASCENSION GOOD SAMARITAN HOSPITAL (521339)**, 601 South Center Avenue, Zip 54452–3404; tel. 715/536–5511, (Nonreporting) **A**1 10 18 **F**3 11 15 28 29 30 31 34 35 40 43 45 50 57 64 65 75 80 81 82 86 87 89 93 97 107 108 110 111 115 119 130 133 144 146 147 149 154 **P**2 **S** Ascension Healthcare, Saint Louis, MO
Primary Contact: Jeremy Normington-Slay, FACHE, Chief Executive Officer
CFO: David Jirovec, Director Finance
CHR: Nancy Kwiesielewicz, Human Resources Manager
CNO: Kristine McGarigle, R.N., Vice President Patient Care
Web address: www.ministryhealth.org
**Control:** Church operated, Nongovernment, not–for–profit **Service:** General medical and surgical

**Staffed Beds:** 3 **Admissions:** 375 **Census:** 3 **Outpatient Visits:** 18562 **Births:** 0 **Total Expense ($000):** 17795 **Payroll Expense ($000):** 4458 **Personnel:** 57

**MINISTRY GOOD SAMARITAN HEALTH CENTER** See Ascension Good Samaritan Hospital

### MILWAUKEE—Milwaukee County

✠ △ **ASCENSION COLUMBIA ST. MARY'S HOSPITAL MILWAUKEE (520051)**, 2301 North Lake Drive, Zip 53211–4508; tel. 414/291–1000, (Includes COLUMBIA ST. MARY'S COLUMBIA HOSPITAL, Mailing address: 2025 East Newport Avenue, Milwaukee, Wisconsin, Zip 53211–2990; tel. 414/961–3300; COLUMBIA ST. MARY'S MILWAUKEE HOSPITAL, Mailing address: 2323 North Lake Drive, Milwaukee, Wisconsin, Zip 53211–9682, P O Box 503, Zip 53201–0503, tel. 414/291–1000), (Nonreporting) **A**1 2 3 5 7 10 19 **S** Ascension Healthcare, Saint Louis, MO
Primary Contact: Travis Andersen, Chief Executive Officer
CFO: Rhonda Anderson, Executive Vice President Finance and Chief Financial Officer
CMO: David Shapiro, M.D., Vice President Medical Affairs and Chief Medical Officer
CIO: Mary Paul, Chief Information Officer
CHR: Cheryl Hill, Vice President Human Resources
Web address: www.columbia-stmarys.org
**Control:** Church operated, Nongovernment, not–for–profit **Service:** General medical and surgical

**Staffed Beds:** 277

✠ **ASCENSION COLUMBIA ST. MARY'S MILWAUKEE HOSPITAL (523025)**, 2323 North Lake Drive, Zip 53211–4508, Mailing Address: 2301 North Lake Drive, Zip 53211–4508; tel. 414/585–1000, (Nonreporting) **A**1 10 **F**9 29 30 34 56 64 77 86 90 93 100 102 103 130 131 132 **P**2 **S** Ascension Healthcare, Saint Louis, MO
Primary Contact: Kelly Elkins, President and Chief Executive Officer
CFO: Rhonda Anderson, Executive Vice President Finance and Chief Financial Officer
CMO: David Shapiro, M.D., Vice President Medical Affairs and Chief Medical Officer
CIO: Mary Paul, Vice President and Chief Information Officer
CHR: Cheryl Hill, Vice President Human Resources
Web address: www.columbia-stmarys.org/SHRI
**Control:** Church operated, Nongovernment, not–for–profit **Service:** Rehabilitation

**Staffed Beds:** 15 **Admissions:** 137 **Census:** 7 **Outpatient Visits:** 14566 **Births:** 0 **Total Expense ($000):** 10975 **Payroll Expense ($000):** 4722 **Personnel:** 58

✠ **ASCENSION SOUTHEAST WISCONSIN HOSPITAL - ST. FRANCIS CAMPUS (520078)**, 3237 South 16th Street, Zip 53215; tel. 414/647–5000, (Nonreporting) **A**1 2 10 **F**3 4 5 11 13 15 17 18 20 22 24 26 28 29 30 31 34 38 40 43 44 45 46 47 49 50 54 56 64 65 66 68 70 74 76 77 78 79 80 81 82 84 85 86 87 92 93 98 100 101 102 103 104 105 107 108 110 111 114 115 118 119 120 121 122 129 130 133 145 146 147 148 149 152 157 **P**2 **S** Ascension Healthcare, Saint Louis, MO
Primary Contact: Seth R. Teigen, President
CFO: Aaron Bridgeland, Director Finance
CMO: Michelle Graham, M.D., Vice President Medical Affairs
CIO: Gregory Smith, Senior Vice President and Chief Information Officer
Web address: www.mywheaton.org/stfrancis
**Control:** Church operated, Nongovernment, not–for–profit **Service:** General medical and surgical

**Staffed Beds:** 120 **Admissions:** 5411 **Census:** 72 **Outpatient Visits:** 148793 **Births:** 484 **Total Expense ($000):** 158509 **Payroll Expense ($000):** 45444 **Personnel:** 618

✠ **ASCENSION SOUTHEAST WISCONSIN HOSPITAL - ST. JOSEPH'S CAMPUS (520136)**, 5000 West Chambers Street, Zip 53210–1650; tel. 414/447–2000, (Nonreporting) **A**1 3 5 10 **F**3 4 5 11 15 17 18 20 22 28 29 30 31 34 35 40 43 44 45 46 49 50 53 54 56 57 59 64 65 68 70 72 74 76 77 78 79 80 81 82 83 84 85 86 87 89 91 92 93 96 97 100 104 107 108 110 111 114 117 118 119 130 131 132 135 144 145 146 147 148 149 150 154 156 **S** Ascension Healthcare, Saint Louis, MO
Primary Contact: Kevin Kluesner, Chief Administrative Officer
CFO: Michael Petitt, Director of Finance
CMO: Rita Hanson, M.D., Vice President Medical Affairs
CIO: Andrew Donovan, Regional Director Information Services
CHR: Christopher Morris, Senior Director, Human Resources
Web address: www.mywheaton.org/stjoseph
**Control:** Church operated, Nongovernment, not–for–profit **Service:** General medical and surgical

**Staffed Beds:** 170 **Admissions:** 5708 **Census:** 79 **Outpatient Visits:** 175952 **Births:** 1867 **Total Expense ($000):** 154328 **Payroll Expense ($000):** 49701 **Personnel:** 625

★ △ **AURORA SINAI MEDICAL CENTER (520064)**, 945 North 12th Street, Zip 53233–1337, Mailing Address: P.O. Box 342, Zip 53201–0342; tel. 414/219–2000, (Nonreporting) **A**2 3 5 7 8 **F**3 6 11 12 13 15 18 29 30 31 32 34 35 36 37 38 40 43 44 45 46 49 50 51 54 56 57 59 60 65 68 72 74 75 76 77 78 79 80 81 84 85 86 87 89 91 92 93 94 96 102 107 108 110 111 114 115 119 120 121 123 126 129 130 131 132 135 146 147 148 149 150 154 **P**2 **S** Advocate Aurora Health, Downers Grove, IL
Primary Contact: Carrie Killoran, President
CHR: Heidi Grow, Director Human Resources
CNO: Ania Horner, R.N., MSN, Vice President and Chief Nurse Executive
Web address: www.aurorahealthcare.org
**Control:** Other not–for–profit (including NFP Corporation) **Service:** General medical and surgical

**Staffed Beds:** 202 **Admissions:** 6085 **Census:** 100 **Outpatient Visits:** 233477 **Births:** 2364 **Total Expense ($000):** 201743 **Payroll Expense ($000):** 73507 **Personnel:** 1837

✠ △ **AURORA ST. LUKE'S MEDICAL CENTER (520138)**, 2900 West Oklahoma Avenue, Zip 53215–4330, Mailing Address: P.O. Box 2901, Zip 53201–2901; tel. 414/649–6000, (Includes AURORA ST. LUKE'S SOUTH SHORE, Mailing address: 5900 South Lake Drive, Cudahy, Wisconsin, Zip 53110–8903; tel. 414/769–9000), (Nonreporting) **A**1 2 3 5 7 8 10 19 **F**1 3 4 5 11 12 15 17 18 20 22 24 26 28 29 30 31 34 35 36 37 38 40 41 43 44 45 46 47 48 49 50 51 54 56 57 58 59 60 64 65 66 68 70 74 75 78 79 80 81 82 84 85 86 87 89 90 91 92 93 94 95 96 98 100 103 104 105 107 108 109 110 111 115 116 117 118 119 120 121 123 124 126 129 130 132 135 136 137 138 139 140 142 145 146 148 149 153 154 **S** Advocate Aurora Health, Downers Grove, IL
Primary Contact: Marie Golanowski, R.N., MS, President
CFO: Nan Nelson, Senior Vice President Finance
CMO: Jeffrey A. Smith, Senior Vice President and Chief Medical Officer
CIO: Philip Loftus, Ph.D., Vice President and Chief Information Officer
CHR: Thomas C Ter Horst, Vice President Human Resources
CNO: Faye Zwieg, R.N., Vice President and Chief Nursing Officer
Web address: www.aurorahealthcare.org
**Control:** Other not–for–profit (including NFP Corporation) **Service:** General medical and surgical

**Staffed Beds:** 711 **Admissions:** 30154 **Census:** 533 **Outpatient Visits:** 618774 **Births:** 0 **Total Expense ($000):** 1236346 **Payroll Expense ($000):** 354033 **Personnel:** 6909

*Many Facility Codes have changed. Please refer to the AHA Guide Code Chart.*

© 2021 AHA Guide

**WI**

✠ **CHILDREN'S HOSPITAL OF WISCONSIN (523300)**, 9000 West Wisconsin Avenue, Zip 53226–4810, Mailing Address: P.O. Box 1997, Zip 53201–1997; tel. 414/266–2000, (Nonreporting) **A**1 3 5 10 **F**12 20 22 24 28 29 34 36 38 40 43 51 54 60 61 64 72 75 77 78 81 82 86 87 88 89 93 99 100 102 104 107 108 111 116 118 119 130 131 136 137 138 140 141 **P**2 **S** Children's Hospital and Health System, Milwaukee, WI
Primary Contact: Peggy N. Troy, President and Chief Executive Officer
CFO: Marc Cadieux, Corporate Vice President and Chief Financial Officer
CMO: Michael Gutzeit, M.D., Chief Medical Officer
CIO: Michael B Nauman, Chief Information Officer
CHR: Thomas Shanahan, Vice President, Human Resources
CNO: Nancy K Korom, Chief Nursing Officer and Vice President
Web address: www.chw.org
**Control**: Other not–for–profit (including NFP Corporation) **Service**: Children's general medical and surgical

**Staffed Beds:** 185 **Admissions:** 9467 **Census:** 185 **Outpatient Visits:** 429709 **Births:** 0 **Total Expense ($000):** 637618 **Payroll Expense ($000):** 195360 **Personnel:** 2688

✠ △ **CLEMENT J. ZABLOCKI VETERANS AFFAIRS MEDICAL CENTER**, 5000 West National Avenue, Zip 53295–0001; tel. 414/384–2000, (Nonreporting) **A**1 2 3 5 7 **S** Department of Veterans Affairs, Washington, DC
Primary Contact: Daniel Zomchek, Ph.D., Chief Executive Officer and Medical Center Director
COO: James McClain, Deputy Director
CFO: John Lasota, Assistant Finance Officer
CMO: Michael Erdmann, M.D., Chief of Staff
CIO: Bryan Vail, Chief Information Officer
CHR: Kay Schwieger, Chief Human Resources Officer
CNO: Mary E. Brunn, R.N., Acting Associate Director Nursing
Web address: www.milwaukee.va.gov/
**Control**: Veterans Affairs, Government, federal **Service**: General medical and surgical

**Staffed Beds:** 637

**COLUMBIA ST MARY'S-COLUMBIA** See Columbia St. Mary's Columbia Hospital

**COLUMBIA ST MARY'S-MILWAUKEE** See Columbia St. Mary's Milwaukee Hospital

**COLUMBIA ST. MARY'S HOSPITAL MILWAUKEE** See Ascension Columbia St. Mary's Hospital Milwaukee

**COLUMBIA ST. MARY'S MILWAUKEE HOSPITAL** See Ascension Columbia St. Mary's Milwaukee Hospital

**FROEDTERT & THE MEDICAL COLLEGE OF WISCONSIN FROEDTERT HOSPITAL** See Froedtert and The Medical College of Wisconsin Froedtert Hospital

✠ △ **FROEDTERT AND THE MEDICAL COLLEGE OF WISCONSIN FROEDTERT HOSPITAL (520177)**, 9200 West Wisconsin Avenue, Zip 53226–3596, Mailing Address: P.O. Box 26099, Zip 53226–0099; tel. 414/805–3000, (Nonreporting) **A**1 2 3 5 7 8 10 19 **F**3 4 6 8 9 12 13 15 17 18 20 22 24 26 28 29 30 31 34 35 37 38 40 43 44 45 46 47 48 49 50 51 52 54 55 56 57 58 59 60 61 64 65 66 68 70 72 74 75 76 77 78 79 80 81 82 84 85 86 87 89 90 91 92 93 94 95 96 97 98 100 107 108 110 111 112 113 114 115 116 117 118 119 120 121 123 124 126 129 130 131 132 135 136 137 138 139 140 141 142 143 145 146 147 148 149 150 154 **S** Froedtert Health, Milwaukee, WI
Primary Contact: Catherine Buck, MSN, R.N., President
CFO: Scott Hawig, Senior Vice President Finance, Chief Financial Officer and Treasurer
CMO: Lee Biblo, M.D., Chief Medical Officer
CHR: Keith Allen, Senior Vice President and Chief Human Resources Officer
CNO: Kathleen Bechtel, MSN, R.N., Vice President Patient Care Services and Chief Nursing Officer
Web address: www.froedtert.com
**Control**: Other not–for–profit (including NFP Corporation) **Service**: General medical and surgical

**Staffed Beds:** 607 **Admissions:** 31126 **Census:** 508 **Outpatient Visits:** 873918 **Births:** 3103 **Total Expense ($000):** 1651772 **Payroll Expense ($000):** 415261 **Personnel:** 6377

★ **MILWAUKEE COUNTY BEHAVIORAL HEALTH DIVISION (524001)**, 9455 Watertown Plank Road, Zip 53226–3559; tel. 414/257–6995, (Nonreporting) **A**3 5 10 **F**35 50 98 99 100 101 102 104 106 134 146 149 153
Primary Contact: Michael Lappen, Chief Executive Officer
COO: Jennifer Bergersen, Interim Chief Operating Officer
CFO: Randy Oleszak, Director Fiscal Services
CMO: John Schneider, M.D., Medical Director
CIO: Chris Lindberg, Chief Information Officer
CHR: Ara Garcia, Manager Human Resources
CNO: Nancy Ann Marigomen, R.N., Director of Nursing
Web address: www.milwaukeecounty.org
**Control**: County, Government, Nonfederal **Service**: Psychiatric

**Staffed Beds:** 54 **Admissions:** 1353 **Census:** 49 **Outpatient Visits:** 7764 **Births:** 0 **Total Expense ($000):** 210061 **Payroll Expense ($000):** 35714 **Personnel:** 494

**MILWAUKEE MENTAL HLTH DIVISION** See Milwaukee County Behavioral Health Division

✠ **SELECT SPECIALTY HOSPITAL-MILWAUKEE (522006)**, 8901 West Lincoln Avenue, 2nd Floor, Zip 53227–2409, Mailing Address: West Allis, tel. 414/328–7700, (Nonreporting) **A**1 10 **F**1 29 60 78 100 130 **S** Select Medical Corporation, Mechanicsburg, PA
Primary Contact: Dennis Mattes, Chief Executive Officer
CMO: Matt Mathai, M.D., Medical Director
CHR: Chris Froh, Senior Coordinator Human Resources
CNO: Jane Cerra, Market Nurse Executive and Chief Nursing Officer
Web address: www.selectspecialtyhospitals.com/company/locations/milwaukee.aspx
**Control**: Corporation, Investor–owned (for–profit) **Service**: Acute long–term care hospital

**Staffed Beds:** 63 **Admissions:** 516 **Census:** 45 **Outpatient Visits:** 0 **Births:** 0 **Total Expense:** 29862 **Payroll Expense:** 10467 **Personnel:** 147

**SELECT SPECIALTY HOSPITAL-MILWAUKEE ST. LUKES** See Select Specialty Hospital-Milwaukee

**SINAI SAMARITAN MEDICAL CENTER** See Aurora Sinai Medical Center

**ST LUKE'S MEDICAL CENTER** See Aurora St. Luke's Medical Center

**VETERANS AFFAIRS MED CENTER** See Clement J. Zablocki Veterans Affairs Medical Center

**WHEATON FRANCISCAN HEALTHCARE - ST. FRANCIS** See Ascension Southeast Wisconsin Hospital - St. Francis Campus

**WHEATON FRANCISCAN HEALTHCARE - ST. JOSEPH'S** See Ascension Southeast Wisconsin Hospital - St. Joseph's Campus

**MINOCQUA—Oneida County**

**MARSHFIELD MEDICAL CENTER - MINOCQUA (520212)**, 9576 State Highway 70, Zip 54548; tel. 715/358–1710, (Nonreporting) **S** Marshfield Clinic Health System, Marshfield, WI
Primary Contact: David R. Olejniczak, Chief Administrative Officer
Web address: www.marshfieldclinic.org
**Control**: Other not–for–profit (including NFP Corporation) **Service**: General medical and surgical

**Staffed Beds:** 19

WI

## MONROE—Green County

✠ **MONROE CLINIC (520028)**, 515 22nd Avenue, Zip 53566–1598;
tel. 608/324–2000, (Nonreporting) **A**1 3 5 10 13 **F**6 9 13 15 17 28 29 34 38 40
43 55 56 62 63 70 75 76 77 80 81 82 86 89 90 93 99 100 101 102 103 104
107 108 111 119 130 131 144 147 154 **P**2 **S** SSM Health, Saint Louis, MO
Primary Contact: Michael B. Sanders, President
CMO: Darren Pipp, M.D., Chief Medical Officer
CHR: Jane Monahan, Vice President Ministry, Spiritual Care and Human Resources
Web address: www.monroeclinic.org
**Control:** Other not–for–profit (including NFP Corporation) **Service:** General
medical and surgical

**Staffed Beds:** 58 **Admissions:** 2553 **Census:** 23 **Outpatient Visits:** 272527
**Births:** 436 **Total Expense ($000):** 174214 **Payroll Expense ($000):** 90039
**Personnel:** 1019

**MONROE CLINIC HOSPITAL** See Monroe Clinic

## NEENAH—Winnebago County

**CHILDREN'S HOSP OF WI-FOX VLY** See Children's Hospital of Wisconsin-Fox
Valley

☐ **CHILDREN'S HOSPITAL OF WISCONSIN-FOX VALLEY (523302)**, 130 Second
Street, Zip 54956–2883; tel. 920/969–7900, (Nonreporting) **A**1 10 **F**34 64 72
75 86 89 93 130 154 **S** Children's Hospital and Health System, Milwaukee, WI
Primary Contact: Peggy N. Troy, President and Chief Executive Officer
COO: Debra Franckowiak, Executive Director
CFO: Marc Cadieux, Corporate Vice President and Chief Financial Officer
CMO: Paul Myers, M.D., Neonatologist and Chief Medical Officer
CIO: Michael B Nauman, Chief Information Officer and Corporate Vice President
CHR: Thomas Shanahan, Vice President, Human Resources
CNO: Nancy K Korom, Chief Nursing Officer and Vice President
Web address: www.chw.org
**Control:** Other not–for–profit (including NFP Corporation) **Service:** Children's
general medical and surgical

**Staffed Beds:** 16 **Admissions:** 519 **Census:** 15 **Outpatient Visits:** 15774
**Births:** 0 **Total Expense ($000):** 31447 **Payroll Expense ($000):** 13399
**Personnel:** 150

**THEDA CLARK MEDICAL CENTER** See Thedacare Regional Medical Center-
Neenah

☐ **THEDACARE REGIONAL MEDICAL CENTER-NEENAH (520045)**, 130 Second
Street, Zip 54956–2883, Mailing Address: P.O. Box 2021, Zip 54957–2021;
tel. 920/729–3100, (Nonreporting) **A**1 10 **F**4 5 9 12 13 15 17 28 29 34 40 43
51 64 70 75 76 78 80 81 82 86 88 90 98 101 107 108 111 118 119 130 **P**2
**S** ThedaCare, Inc., Appleton, WI
Primary Contact: Mark Thompson, System Chief Financial Officer
CFO: Tim Olson, Senior Vice President Finance
CMO: Gregory L Long, M.D., Chief Medical Officer
CIO: Keith Livingston, Senior Vice President and Chief Information Officer
Web address: www.thedacare.org
**Control:** Other not–for–profit (including NFP Corporation) **Service:** General
medical and surgical

**Staffed Beds:** 164 **Admissions:** 8602 **Census:** 108 **Outpatient
Visits:** 120954 **Births:** 1493 **Total Expense ($000):** 184431 **Payroll
Expense ($000):** 66462 **Personnel:** 888

## NEILLSVILLE—Clark County

★ **MARSHFIELD MEDICAL CENTER - NEILSVILLE (521323)**, 216 Sunset Place,
Zip 54456–1799; tel. 715/743–3101, (Total facility includes 13 beds in nursing
home–type unit) (Nonreporting) **A**10 18 **F**3 10 11 15 28 29 30 34 40 41 43 45
56 64 75 77 79 80 81 82 85 86 89 93 97 107 111 114 119 127 130 131 133
135 144 146 147 148 154 **P**2 **S** Marshfield Clinic Health System, Marshfield, WI
Primary Contact: Ryan T. Neville, FACHE, President and Chief Executive Officer
CMO: Timothy Meyer, M.D., Chief of Staff
CIO: Derrick Longdo, Director Information Systems
CHR: Tamie Zarak, Director Human Resources
Web address: www.memorialmedcenter.org
**Control:** Other not–for–profit (including NFP Corporation) **Service:** General
medical and surgical

**Staffed Beds:** 16 **Admissions:** 330 **Census:** 13 **Outpatient Visits:** 20960
**Births:** 0 **Total Expense ($000):** 27382 **Payroll Expense ($000):** 11362
**Personnel:** 161

**MEMORIAL MEDICAL CENTER - NEILLSVILLE** See Marshfield Medical Center -
Neillsville

## NEW LONDON—Outagamie County

**NEW LONDON FAMILY MEDICAL CENTER** See Thedacare Medical Center-New
London

☐ **THEDACARE MEDICAL CENTER-NEW LONDON (521326)**, 1405 Mill
Street, Zip 54961–0307, Mailing Address: P.O. Box 307, Zip 54961–0307;
tel. 920/531–2000, (Nonreporting) **A**1 10 18 **F**7 11 13 15 28 29 34 40 43
56 64 75 76 80 81 82 86 87 89 90 93 107 108 111 119 131 141 **P**2 **S**
ThedaCare, Inc., Appleton, WI
Primary Contact: William Schmidt, President and Chief Executive Officer
CFO: Betty Gehring, Finance Director, Operations
CMO: Paul Hoell, M.D., President Medical Staff
CNO: Peggy School, Director of Nursing
Web address: www.thedacare.org
**Control:** Other not–for–profit (including NFP Corporation) **Service:** General
medical and surgical

**Staffed Beds:** 25 **Admissions:** 829 **Census:** 9 **Outpatient Visits:** 42782
**Births:** 69 **Total Expense ($000):** 25511 **Payroll Expense ($000):** 10532
**Personnel:** 139

## NEW RICHMOND—St. Croix County

**WESTFIELDS HOSPITAL** See Westfields Hospital and Clinic

✠ **WESTFIELDS HOSPITAL AND CLINIC (521345)**, 535 Hospital Road,
Zip 54017–1449; tel. 715/243–2600, (Nonreporting) **A**1 3 10 18 **F**1 3 13 15
18 28 29 30 31 32 34 35 37 38 40 43 44 45 47 50 56 57 59 64 65 68 70
75 76 77 78 80 81 82 86 87 89 90 93 94 97 104 105 107 110 111 115 119
129 130 131 132 133 144 145 146 148 149 152 153 154 156 157 **P**2 **S**
HealthPartners, Bloomington, MN
Primary Contact: Steven Massey, President and Chief Executive Officer
CFO: Jason J. Luhrs, Vice President Fiscal Services
CMO: David O DeGear, M.D., Vice President Medical Affairs
CIO: Patrice P Wolff, Director Information Services
CHR: Chad P Engstrom, Director Human Resources
Web address: www.westfieldshospital.com
**Control:** Other not–for–profit (including NFP Corporation) **Service:** General
medical and surgical

**Staffed Beds:** 25 **Admissions:** 912 **Census:** 6 **Outpatient Visits:** 105599
**Births:** 129 **Total Expense ($000):** 64498 **Payroll Expense ($000):** 21472
**Personnel:** 300

## OCONOMOWOC—Waukesha County

**MEMORIAL HOSPITAL** See Oconomowoc Memorial Hospital

✠ **OCONOMOWOC MEMORIAL HOSPITAL (520062)**, 791 Summit Avenue,
Zip 53066–3896; tel. 262/569–9400, (Nonreporting) **A**1 2 10 **F**3 11 12 13 15
18 20 22 26 28 29 30 31 32 34 37 40 43 44 45 46 47 48 49 50 56 57 59 64
65 68 74 75 76 78 79 81 83 84 85 87 89 93 97 100 101 102 107 108 109
110 111 112 114 115 117 118 120 121 126 130 133 135 146 147 148 149
153 154 156 157 **P**2 **S** ProHealth Care, Inc., Waukesha, WI
Primary Contact: Susan A. Edwards, President and Chief Executive Officer
COO: Mary Jo O'Malley, R.N., MS, Vice President Diagnostics and Support Services
CMO: Brian Lipman, M.D., Medical Director and Medical Staff Services
CIO: Christine Bessler, Vice President Information Services
CHR: Edward Malindzak, Chief Human Resources Officer
CNO: Catherine Rapp, R.N., MS, Vice President Nursing
Web address: www.prohealthcare.org/locations/locations-v2-detail/?id=1123
**Control:** Other not–for–profit (including NFP Corporation) **Service:** General
medical and surgical

**Staffed Beds:** 58 **Admissions:** 2941 **Census:** 25 **Outpatient Visits:** 75911
**Births:** 279 **Total Expense ($000):** 98438 **Payroll Expense ($000):** 25838
**Personnel:** 288

**ROGERS MEMORIAL HOSPITAL** See Rogers Memorial Hospital, Inc.

**WI**

*Many Facility Codes have changed. Please refer to the AHA Guide Code Chart.*    © 2021 AHA Guide

⊠ **ROGERS MEMORIAL HOSPITAL, INC. (524018)**, 34700 Valley Road, Zip 53066–4599; tel. 262/646–4411, (Includes ROGERS MEMORIAL HOSPITAL-BROWN DEER, Mailing address: 4600 West Schroeder Drive, Brown Deer, Wisconsin, Zip 53223; tel. 414/865–2500; Jim Kubicek, Vice President, Operations; ROGERS MEMORIAL HOSPITAL-WEST ALLIS, Mailing address: 11101 West Lincoln Avenue, West Allis, Wisconsin, Zip 53227; tel. 414/327–3000; T Orvin Fillman, Dr.PH, Vice President, Operations), (Nonreporting) **A**1 3 5 10 **F**4 5 29 34 38 53 54 75 86 87 98 99 100 101 102 103 104 130 154 **P**2
Primary Contact: Paul A. Mueller, Chief Executive Officer, Hospital Division
CFO: Gerald A Noll, Chief Financial Officer
CMO: Peter M Lake, M.D., Chief Medical Officer
CIO: Wayne Mattson, Management Information Systems Specialist
CHR: Renee A. Patterson, Vice President Employment and Training Services
CNO: Teresa L Schultz, R.N., Vice President of Patient Care
Web address: www.rogershospital.org
**Control:** Other not–for–profit (including NFP Corporation) **Service:** Psychiatric

| | |
|---|---|
| Staffed Beds: 200 **Admissions:** 9514 **Census:** 169 **Outpatient Visits:** 77277 **Births:** 0 **Total Expense:** 154464 **Payroll Expense:** 81686 **Personnel:** 1104 | |

## OCONTO—Oconto County

⇑ **BELLIN HEALTH OCONTO HOSPITAL (521356)**, 820 Arbutus Avenue, Zip 54153–2004, Mailing Address: P.O. Box 357, Zip 54153–0357; tel. 920/835–1100, (Nonreporting) **A**10 18 21 **F**15 29 40 43 51 62 64 78 80 81 82 90 99 100 101 107 111 119 130 144 154
Primary Contact: Julie Bieber, Vice President
CHR: Troy L Koebke, Human Resource Director
Web address: www.bellin.org/facilities_amenities/oconto_hospital_medical_center/
**Control:** Other not–for–profit (including NFP Corporation) **Service:** General medical and surgical

| | |
|---|---|
| Staffed Beds: 10 **Admissions:** 145 **Census:** 2 **Outpatient Visits:** 19009 **Births:** 0 **Total Expense ($000):** 57880 **Payroll Expense ($000):** 22450 **Personnel:** 269 | |

⇑ **OCONTO HOSPITAL & MEDICAL CENTER** See Bellin Health Oconto Hospital

## OCONTO FALLS—Oconto County

**COMMUNITY MEMORIAL HOSPITAL** See Hshs St. Clare Memorial Hospital

★ **HSHS ST. CLARE MEMORIAL HOSPITAL (521310)**, 855 South Main Street, Zip 54154–1296; tel. 920/846–3444, (Nonreporting) **A**10 18 **F**3 11 15 28 29 30 34 35 40 43 44 50 56 57 59 64 65 75 77 79 80 81 85 86 87 89 90 94 96 107 108 110 111 114 119 127 129 130 132 133 144 146 148 154 **S** HSHS Hospital Sisters Health System, Springfield, IL
Primary Contact: Christopher Brabant, President and Chief Executive Officer
CFO: Greg Simia, Chief Financial Officer
CMO: Richard Cooley, M.D., Chief Physician Executive
CIO: Shane Miller, Chief Information Officer
CHR: Christine Jensema, Chief Human Resources Officer
CNO: Paula Hafeman, Chief Nursing Officer
Web address: www.stclaremorial.org
**Control:** Church operated, Nongovernment, not–for–profit **Service:** General medical and surgical

| | |
|---|---|
| Staffed Beds: 20 **Admissions:** 291 **Census:** 2 **Outpatient Visits:** 17475 **Births:** 0 **Total Expense ($000):** 29441 **Payroll Expense ($000):** 8241 **Personnel:** 121 | |

## OSCEOLA—Polk County

**LADD MEMORIAL HOSPITAL** See Osceola Medical Center

★ **OSCEOLA MEDICAL CENTER (521318)**, 2600 65th Avenue, Zip 54020–4370, Mailing Address: P.O. Box 218, Zip 54020–0218; tel. 715/294–2111, (Nonreporting) **A**10 18 **F**3 8 11 13 15 28 29 31 32 34 35 40 43 45 50 53 56 57 59 65 66 70 75 76 77 78 81 85 86 87 93 96 97 107 110 111 115 119 129 132 133 135 144 146 148 149 150 154 **P**2
Primary Contact: Jeffrey K. Meyer, Interim Chief Executive Officer
CMO: Rene Milner, Chief Medical Officer
CIO: Shawn Kammerud, Manager Information Services
CHR: Margie Evenson, Manager Human Resources
Web address: www.osceolamedicalcenter.com
**Control:** Other not–for–profit (including NFP Corporation) **Service:** General medical and surgical

| | |
|---|---|
| Staffed Beds: 18 **Admissions:** 478 **Census:** 4 **Outpatient Visits:** 18825 **Births:** 101 **Total Expense ($000):** 37591 **Payroll Expense ($000):** 12959 **Personnel:** 222 | |

## OSHKOSH—Winnebago County

★ △ **ASCENSION NORTHEAST WISCONSIN MERCY HOSPITAL (520048)**, 500 South Oakwood Road, Zip 54904–7944; tel. 920/223–2000, (Nonreporting) **A**2 7 10 **F**3 4 5 9 13 15 17 18 20 22 26 28 29 30 31 34 35 40 43 45 46 47 48 49 50 53 56 58 60 64 68 70 74 75 76 78 79 80 81 82 84 85 86 87 90 92 93 96 98 100 101 102 103 104 107 108 110 111 114 115 116 118 119 120 121 123 124 126 129 130 131 135 144 146 147 148 149 154 157 **P**2 **S** Ascension Healthcare, Saint Louis, MO
Primary Contact: Denise Parrish, Interim Chief Administrative Officer
CFO: Jeff Badger, Chief Financial Officer
CMO: Mark W Kehrberg, M.D., Senior Vice President and Chief Medical Officer
CIO: Will Weider, Chief Information Officer
CHR: Vince Gallucci, Senior Vice President Human Resources
Web address: www.affinityhealth.org
**Control:** Church operated, Nongovernment, not–for–profit **Service:** General medical and surgical

| | |
|---|---|
| Staffed Beds: 132 **Admissions:** 3570 **Census:** 38 **Outpatient Visits:** 128084 **Births:** 411 **Total Expense ($000):** 84968 **Payroll Expense ($000):** 24339 **Personnel:** 381 | |

**ASCENSION NORTHEAST WISCONSON MERCY HOSPITAL** See Ascension Northeast Wisconsin Mercy Hospital

★ ○ ⇑ **AURORA MEDICAL CENTER OF OSHKOSH (520198)**, 855 North Westhaven Drive, Zip 54904–7668; tel. 920/456–6000, (Nonreporting) **A**2 10 11 21 **F**3 8 11 12 13 15 17 18 20 22 26 28 29 30 34 36 37 40 43 47 49 53 54 56 60 64 68 70 71 72 74 75 76 78 79 80 81 82 85 86 87 89 92 93 94 107 109 110 111 113 114 115 117 118 119 120 121 122 123 129 130 131 135 145 146 147 148 149 150 154 **S** Advocate Aurora Health, Downers Grove, IL
Primary Contact: John B. Newman, M.D., President
CFO: Brian McGinnis, Director Finance
CMO: John B. Newman, M.D., Chief Medical Officer
CIO: Philip Loftus, Ph.D., Vice President and Chief Information Officer
CHR: Russ Haase, Director Human Resources
CNO: Mary Beth Kingston, Ph.D., R.N., MSN, Executive Vice President and Chief Nursing Officer
Web address: www.aurorahealthcare.com
**Control:** Other not–for–profit (including NFP Corporation) **Service:** General medical and surgical

| | |
|---|---|
| Staffed Beds: 72 **Admissions:** 3922 **Census:** 36 **Outpatient Visits:** 164468 **Births:** 717 **Total Expense ($000):** 138830 **Payroll Expense ($000):** 40230 **Personnel:** 1207 | |

## OSSEO—Trempealeau County

**LUTHER MIDELFORT OAKRIDGE** See Mayo Clinic Health System - Oakridge in Osseo

☐ **MAYO CLINIC HEALTH SYSTEM - OAKRIDGE IN OSSEO (521302)**, 13025 Eighth Street, Zip 54758–7634, Mailing Address: P.O. Box 70, Zip 54758–0070; tel. 715/597–3121, (Nonreporting) **A**1 10 18 **F**3 15 18 28 29 30 32 34 35 38 40 43 44 45 53 54 56 57 59 64 65 77 79 80 85 86 87 90 93 96 97 107 110 115 129 130 132 133 144 146 148 149 154 156 **P**2 **S** Mayo Clinic, Rochester, MN
Primary Contact: Richard Helmers, M.D., Regional Vice President
Web address: www.mayoclinichealthsystem.org/locations/osseo
**Control:** Other not–for–profit (including NFP Corporation) **Service:** General medical and surgical

| | |
|---|---|
| Staffed Beds: 14 **Admissions:** 415 **Census:** 11 **Outpatient Visits:** 27533 **Births:** 0 **Total Expense ($000):** 24750 **Payroll Expense ($000):** 11126 **Personnel:** 151 | |

**WI**

| | |
|---|---|
| **Hospital, Medicare Provider Number, Address, Telephone, Approval, Facility, and Physician Codes, Health Care System** | |
| ★ American Hospital Association (AHA) membership | ○ Healthcare Facilities Accreditation Program | ⇑ Center for Improvement in Healthcare Quality Accreditation |
| ☐ The Joint Commission accreditation | ◇ DNV Healthcare Inc. accreditation | △ Commission on Accreditation of Rehabilitation Facilities (CARF) accreditation |

## PARK FALLS—Price County

★ **FLAMBEAU HOSPITAL (521325)**, 98 Sherry Avenue, Zip 54552–1467, Mailing Address: P.O. Box 310, Zip 54552–0310; tel. 715/762–2484, (Nonreporting) **A**10 18 **F**11 15 28 29 34 40 43 53 56 62 63 64 69 75 77 80 81 82 86 87 89 90 93 107 108 119 130 131 144 154 **P**2 **S** Marshfield Clinic Health System, Marshfield, WI
Primary Contact: James R. Braun, Chief Administrative Officer and Chief Financial Officer
CMO: Yusuf Kasirye, M.D., Chief of Staff
CHR: Elizabeth Harrop, Director, Human Resources
CNO: Elizabeth Schreiber, R.N., Director Patient Care Services
Web address: www.flambeauhospital.org
**Control:** Other not–for–profit (including NFP Corporation) **Service:** General medical and surgical

**Staffed Beds:** 25 **Admissions:** 455 **Census:** 5 **Outpatient Visits:** 26455 **Births:** 0 **Total Expense ($000):** 24225 **Payroll Expense ($000):** 9333 **Personnel:** 172

**FLAMBEAU MEDICAL CENTER** See Flambeau Hospital

## PLATTEVILLE—Grant County

✠ **SOUTHWEST HEALTH (521354)**, 1400 Eastside Road, Zip 53818–9800; tel. 608/348–2331, (Includes SOUTHWEST HEALTH CENTER NURSING HOME, Mailing address: 808 South Washington Street, Cuba City, Wisconsin, Zip 53807; tel. 608/744–2161) (Total facility includes 78 beds in nursing home–type unit) **A**1 10 18 **F**2 3 6 7 13 15 28 29 34 35 36 40 43 45 46 47 48 49 50 56 57 59 64 65 75 76 77 79 80 81 82 83 84 85 86 87 93 94 96 97 98 100 101 102 103 104 107 110 111 112 115 119 127 128 129 130 131 132 133 135 143 144 146 147 148 149 153 156
Primary Contact: Dan D. Rohrbach, President
CFO: Matthew Streeter, Chief Financial Officer
CMO: Andrew Klann, D.O., Chief of Staff
CIO: Todd Lull, Director Information Technology
CHR: Holly Beehn, Director Human Resources
CNO: Suzi Okey, Director of Nursing
Web address: www.southwesthealth.org
**Control:** Other not–for–profit (including NFP Corporation) **Service:** General medical and surgical

**Staffed Beds:** 113 **Admissions:** 967 **Census:** 84 **Outpatient Visits:** 80770 **Births:** 147 **Total Expense ($000):** 60266 **Payroll Expense ($000):** 29381 **Personnel:** 526

**SOUTHWEST HEALTH CENTER** See Southwest Health

## PLEASANT PRAIRIE—Kenosha County

**UNITED HOSPITAL SYSTEM, ST. CATHERINE'S MEDICAL CENTER CAMPUS** See Froedtert South - St. Catherine's Medical Center

## PORTAGE—Columbia County

☐ **DIVINE SAVIOR HEALTHCARE (520041)**, 2817 New Pinery Road, Zip 53901–9240, Mailing Address: P.O. Box 387, Zip 53901–0387; tel. 608/742–4131, (Total facility includes 123 beds in nursing home–type unit) (Nonreporting) **A**1 10 **F**7 11 12 13 15 28 34 36 40 43 54 55 60 62 64 69 70 75 76 77 78 80 81 82 86 87 90 93 107 108 111 118 119 128 130 131 144 147 154 **P**2
Primary Contact: Michael Decker, President and Chief Executive Officer
CFO: Marlin Pete Nelson, Vice President Fiscal Services
CMO: Elizabeth Strabel, M.D., Chief Medical Staff
CHR: Carol J Bank, Vice President Human Resources
Web address: www.dshealthcare.com
**Control:** Church operated, Nongovernment, not–for–profit **Service:** General medical and surgical

**Staffed Beds:** 132 **Admissions:** 2035 **Census:** 114 **Outpatient Visits:** 172548 **Births:** 208 **Total Expense ($000):** 83362 **Payroll Expense ($000):** 44599 **Personnel:** 635

**DIVINE SAVIOR HOSPITAL** See Divine Savior Healthcare

## PRAIRIE DU CHIEN—Crawford County

★ **CROSSING RIVERS HEALTH MEDICAL CENTER (521330)**, 37868 US Highway 18, Zip 53821–8416; tel. 608/357–2000, (Nonreporting) **A**10 18 **F**11 13 15 28 29 31 34 35 36 40 41 43 50 53 56 57 59 63 64 65 68 75 76 77 79 81 82 83 84 86 87 93 97 107 110 111 115 117 119 126 129 130 131 132 133 135 144 146 147 148 154 **P**2
Primary Contact: William P. Sexton, Chief Executive Officer
CFO: Dave Breitbach, Chief Financial Officer
CMO: Steven Bush, Chief Medical Officer
CIO: John Daane, Information Systems Officer
CHR: Samantha Donahue, Director Human Resources
Web address: www.crossingrivers.org
**Control:** Other not–for–profit (including NFP Corporation) **Service:** General medical and surgical

**Staffed Beds:** 25 **Admissions:** 784 **Census:** 8 **Outpatient Visits:** 9888 **Births:** 143 **Total Expense ($000):** 51808 **Payroll Expense ($000):** 20172 **Personnel:** 296

**PRAIRIE DU CHIEN MEMORIAL HOSPITAL** See Crossing Rivers Health Medical Center

## PRAIRIE DU SAC—Sauk County

○ **SAUK PRAIRIE HEALTHCARE (520095)**, 260 26th Street, Zip 53578–1599; tel. 608/643–3311, (Nonreporting) **A**3 5 10 11 **F**3 8 11 13 15 28 29 32 34 35 36 38 40 41 43 45 48 53 54 55 56 57 59 65 69 75 76 77 79 80 81 82 85 86 89 90 93 97 102 107 108 110 111 115 118 119 127 129 130 131 132 133 135 144 146 147 149 156 **P**2
Primary Contact: Shawn Lerch, Chief Executive Officer
CFO: James Dregney, Vice President Finance and Operations, Chief Financial Officer
CMO: Todd Schad, M.D., Medical Director
CIO: Richard C Bonjour, Chief Information Officer
CHR: Robbi E Bos, Vice President Human Resources
CNO: Lisa Pickarts, Vice President Patient Services
Web address: www.saukprairiehealthcare.org/
**Control:** Other not–for–profit (including NFP Corporation) **Service:** General medical and surgical

**Staffed Beds:** 36 **Admissions:** 1988 **Census:** 11 **Outpatient Visits:** 135330 **Births:** 354 **Total Expense ($000):** 92752 **Payroll Expense ($000):** 43893 **Personnel:** 508

**SAUK PRAIRIE MEMORIAL HOSPITAL & CLINICS** See Sauk Prairie Healthcare

## RACINE—Racine County

✠ △ **ASCENSION ALL SAINTS (520096)**, 3801 Spring Street, Zip 53405–1690; tel. 262/687–4011, (Nonreporting) **A**1 2 5 7 10 19 **F**3 4 5 6 13 15 17 18 20 22 24 26 28 29 30 31 34 38 40 43 44 45 46 47 48 49 50 51 53 56 57 58 59 64 65 66 70 72 74 76 77 78 79 80 81 82 84 85 86 87 89 90 91 92 93 94 96 97 98 99 100 101 102 103 104 105 107 108 110 111 114 115 117 118 119 120 121 123 124 126 129 130 131 132 134 135 143 146 147 148 149 150 152 153 157 **P**2 **S** Ascension Healthcare, Saint Louis, MO
Primary Contact: Kristin McManmon, President
CFO: Jeanne Gramza, Director Finance
CMO: Jerry Hardacre, M.D., Chief of Staff
CIO: Joanne Bisterfeldt, Chief Information Officer
CHR: Mary Jo Wodicka, Vice President Human Resources
Web address: www.allsaintshealth.com
**Control:** Church operated, Nongovernment, not–for–profit **Service:** General medical and surgical

**Staffed Beds:** 278 **Admissions:** 11954 **Census:** 159 **Outpatient Visits:** 547311 **Births:** 1507 **Total Expense ($000):** 319634 **Payroll Expense ($000):** 93598 **Personnel:** 1666

**WHEATON FRANCISCAN HEALTHCARE - ALL SAINTS** See Ascension All Saints

**WI**

## REEDSBURG—Sauk County

✠ **REEDSBURG AREA MEDICAL CENTER (521351)**, 2000 North Dewey Street, Zip 53959–1097; tel. 608/524–6487, (Nonreporting) **A**1 5 10 18 **F**3 8 11 13 15 17 28 29 30 31 32 34 35 40 41 43 45 48 49 50 51 53 54 57 59 64 65 66 70 75 76 77 78 79 80 81 82 85 86 87 88 89 93 96 97 107 110 111 114 127 129 130 131 132 133 135 144 146 147 148 154 156 **P**2
Primary Contact: Robert Van Meeteren, President and Chief Executive Officer
COO: Dale Turner, Chief Operating Officer
CFO: Barry Borchert, Vice President Finance
Web address: www.ramchealth.com
**Control**: Other not–for–profit (including NFP Corporation) **Service**: General medical and surgical

**Staffed Beds**: 25 **Admissions**: 899 **Census**: 6 **Outpatient Visits**: 114942
**Births**: 209 **Total Expense ($000)**: 76111 **Payroll Expense ($000)**: 33542
**Personnel**: 542

**REEDSBURG MEMORIAL HOSPITAL** See Reedsburg Area Medical Center

## RHINELANDER—Oneida County

**ASCENSION SAINT MARY'S HOSPITALS** See Ascension St. Mary's Hospital

✠ **ASCENSION ST. MARY'S HOSPITAL (520019)**, 2251 North Shore Drive, Zip 54501–6710; tel. 715/361–2000, (Includes ST. MARY'S HOSPITAL, Mailing address: 1044 Kabel Avenue, Rhinelander, Wisconsin, Zip 54501; tel. 715/369–6600), (Nonreporting) **A**1 3 5 10 20 **F**3 4 5 13 15 28 29 30 31 34 35 40 45 54 59 64 74 75 76 78 79 80 81 82 84 85 86 87 89 93 97 98 99 100 102 103 104 107 108 110 111 115 116 119 120 121 123 126 127 130 131 132 135 144 146 148 149 154 156 **S** Ascension Healthcare, Saint Louis, MO
Primary Contact: Laurie Oungst, Chief Administrative Officer
CFO: Jamon Lamers, Director Finance
CMO: Mark Banas, M.D., Chief Medical Officer
CIO: Howard Dobizl, Director Information Services for the Northern Region
CHR: Michelle Cornelius, Director Human Resources for the Northern Region
CNO: Christine Krebs, Director or Nursing
Web address: www.ministryhealth.org
**Control**: Church operated, Nongovernment, not–for–profit **Service**: General medical and surgical

**Staffed Beds**: 64 **Admissions**: 2574 **Census**: 28 **Outpatient Visits**: 119719
**Births**: 269 **Total Expense ($000)**: 82385 **Payroll Expense ($000)**: 20873
**Personnel**: 340

## RICE LAKE—Barron County

**LAKEVIEW MEDICAL CENTER** See Marshfield Medical Center - Rice Lake

✠ **MARSHFIELD MEDICAL CENTER - RICE LAKE (520011)**, 1700 West Stout Street, Zip 54868–5000; tel. 715/234–1515, (Nonreporting) **A**1 10 20 **F**3 7 8 11 13 15 18 26 28 29 31 32 34 35 40 43 45 51 53 56 57 59 60 62 63 64 65 70 75 76 77 78 79 80 81 84 85 86 89 93 97 107 110 111 115 119 124 129 130 132 135 146 147 156 **P**2 **S** Marshfield Clinic Health System, Marshfield, WI
Primary Contact: Bradley D. Groseth, Chief Administrative Officer
COO: Cindy Arts-Strenke, R.N., Chief Operating Officer and Chief Nursing Officer
CFO: Jacqueline Klein, Chief Financial Officer
CMO: John L. Olson, M.D., Medical Director
CIO: Brad Gerrits, Director Information Systems
CHR: Kathy Mitchell, Director Human Resources
Web address: www.lakeviewmedical.com
**Control**: Other not–for–profit (including NFP Corporation) **Service**: General medical and surgical

**Staffed Beds**: 40 **Admissions**: 2042 **Census**: 17 **Outpatient Visits**: 157388
**Births**: 443 **Total Expense ($000)**: 133053 **Payroll Expense ($000)**: 49204
**Personnel**: 526

## RICHLAND CENTER—Richland County

✠ **RICHLAND HOSPITAL (521341)**, 333 East Second Street, Zip 53581–1914; tel. 608/647–6321, (Nonreporting) **A**1 5 10 18 **F**3 12 13 15 28 31 34 35 37 40 43 49 50 56 57 59 64 65 70 75 76 78 79 80 81 85 86 89 92 93 97 107 110 112 115 119 127 129 130 131 132 133 135 143 146 148 149 154 **P**2
Primary Contact: Bruce E. Roesler, FACHE, Chief Executive Officer
CFO: Karen Traynor, Chief Financial Officer
CMO: David May, Chief of Staff
CIO: Jerry Cooper, Manager Data Processing
CHR: Rhonda Sutton, Director Human Resources
CNO: Cindy Hanold, Chief Nursing Officer
Web address: www.richlandhospital.com
**Control**: Other not–for–profit (including NFP Corporation) **Service**: General medical and surgical

**Staffed Beds**: 25 **Admissions**: 968 **Census**: 9 **Outpatient Visits**: 37412
**Births**: 130 **Total Expense ($000)**: 39368 **Payroll Expense ($000)**: 18048
**Personnel**: 252

## RIPON—Fond Du Lac County

✠ **RIPON MEDICAL CENTER (521321)**, 845 Parkside Street, Zip 54971–8505, Mailing Address: P.O. Box 390, Zip 54971–0390; tel. 920/748–3101, (Nonreporting) **A**1 5 10 18 **F**11 15 17 28 29 34 40 43 51 53 69 70 75 77 80 81 82 86 87 88 89 93 107 108 111 118 119 130 131 144 147 **P**2 **S** SSM Health, Saint Louis, MO
Primary Contact: DeAnn Thurmer, President and Chief Nursing Officer
CFO: Bonnie Schmitz, Chief Financial Officer
CMO: Derek Colmenares, M.D., Chief Medical Officer
CIO: Nancy Birschbach, Vice President and Chief Information Officer
CHR: Sue Edminster, Vice President Human Resources
CNO: DeAnn Thurmer, President and Chief Nursing Officer
Web address: www.agnesian.com
**Control**: Church operated, Nongovernment, not–for–profit **Service**: General medical and surgical

**Staffed Beds**: 16 **Admissions**: 486 **Census**: 5 **Outpatient Visits**: 30157
**Births**: 0 **Total Expense ($000)**: 27606 **Payroll Expense ($000)**: 12279
**Personnel**: 107

**RIPON MEMORIAL HOSPITAL** See Ripon Medical Center

## RIVER FALLS—St. Croix County

✠ **RIVER FALLS AREA HOSPITAL (521349)**, 1629 East Division Street, Zip 54022–1571; tel. 715/425–6155, (Nonreporting) **A**1 2 10 18 **F**11 13 15 28 29 34 40 43 51 53 64 75 76 78 80 81 82 86 87 89 90 93 107 111 119 130 131 147 154 **P**2 **S** Allina Health, Minneapolis, MN
Primary Contact: Helen J. Strike, R.N., President
COO: William Frommelt, Director Operations and Finance
CFO: William Frommelt, Director Operations and Finance
CHR: Kristen Novak, Manager Human Resources
Web address: www.allina.com
**Control**: Other not–for–profit (including NFP Corporation) **Service**: General medical and surgical

**Staffed Beds**: 18 **Admissions**: 775 **Census**: 5 **Outpatient Visits**: 18605
**Births**: 87 **Total Expense ($000)**: 37993 **Payroll Expense ($000)**: 14856
**Personnel**: 137

## SHAWANO—Shawano County

**SHAWANO MEDICAL CENTER** See Thedacare Medical Center-Shawano

☐ **THEDACARE MEDICAL CENTER-SHAWANO (521346)**, 100 County Road B, Zip 54166–2127; tel. 715/526–2111, (Nonreporting) **A**1 5 10 18 **F**11 13 15 28 29 34 40 53 64 75 76 77 78 80 81 82 86 87 89 90 102 107 108 111 118 119 130 131 154 **P**2 **S** ThedaCare, Inc., Appleton, WI
Primary Contact: William Schmidt, Chief Executive Officer
CFO: Kerry Lee Blanke, Chief Financial Officer
CMO: Mindy Frimodig, D.O., President Medical Staff ThedaCare Physicians Shawano
CIO: Jennifer Quinn, Quality and Safety Coordinator
CNO: Patricia A Angelucci, MS, R.N., Director Patient Care Services
Web address: www.shawanomed.org
**Control**: Other not–for–profit (including NFP Corporation) **Service**: General medical and surgical

**Staffed Beds**: 22 **Admissions**: 1527 **Census**: 12 **Outpatient Visits**: 81056
**Births**: 243 **Total Expense ($000)**: 39073 **Payroll Expense ($000)**: 18293
**Personnel**: 218

**WI**

## SHEBOYGAN—Sheboygan County

✠ **AURORA SHEBOYGAN MEMORIAL MEDICAL CENTER (520035)**, 2629 North Seventh Street, Zip 53083–4998; tel. 920/451–5000, (Nonreporting) **A**1 2 10 19 **F**3 4 5 13 17 18 20 22 26 28 29 30 31 32 34 35 36 40 41 43 44 45 49 50 53 56 57 58 59 60 64 65 68 70 72 74 75 76 78 79 80 81 82 84 85 86 87 89 92 93 94 98 99 100 102 103 104 105 107 108 111 112 114 115 117 118 119 120 121 123 126 129 130 131 132 135 143 146 147 148 149 150 152 153 154 **P**2 **S** Advocate Aurora Health, Downers Grove, IL
Primary Contact: David Graebner, President
CFO: Pamela Ott, Vice President Finance
CMO: Andrea Gavin, M.D., Chief Medical officer
CIO: Steve Serketich, Manager Information Services
CHR: Stacie A Schneider, Director Human Resources
CNO: Lori Knitt, Chief Nursing Officer
Web address: www.aurorahealthcare.org
**Control:** Other not–for–profit (including NFP Corporation) **Service:** General medical and surgical

**Staffed Beds:** 127 **Admissions:** 5149 **Census:** 47 **Outpatient Visits:** 101191 **Births:** 896 **Total Expense ($000):** 132886 **Payroll Expense ($000):** 41821 **Personnel:** 772

✠ **HSHS ST. NICHOLAS HOSPITAL (520044)**, 3100 Superior Avenue, Zip 53081–1948; tel. 920/459–8300, (Nonreporting) **A**1 2 10 **F**3 8 11 13 15 17 18 20 22 28 29 30 31 34 35 36 38 40 43 44 45 47 50 53 54 57 59 60 62 63 64 65 70 71 74 75 76 77 79 80 81 84 85 86 87 89 90 93 107 108 110 111 114 115 116 117 118 119 120 126 129 130 132 146 148 149 154 **P**2 **S** HSHS Hospital Sisters Health System, Springfield, IL
Primary Contact: Justin Selle, Chief Executive Officer
CFO: Greg Simia, Chief Financial Officer
CMO: Richard Cooley, M.D., Chief Physician Executive
CIO: Shane Miller, Chief Information Officer
CHR: Christine Jensema, Chief People Officer
CNO: Mary Martin, MSN, R.N., Chief Nursing Officer
Web address: www.stnicholashospital.org
**Control:** Church operated, Nongovernment, not–for–profit **Service:** General medical and surgical

**Staffed Beds:** 46 **Admissions:** 1956 **Census:** 18 **Outpatient Visits:** 83451 **Births:** 254 **Total Expense ($000):** 84805 **Payroll Expense ($000):** 22763 **Personnel:** 276

**SHEBOYGAN MEMORIAL MEDICAL CTR** See Aurora Sheboygan Memorial Medical Center

**ST. NICHOLAS HOSPITAL** See Hshs St. Nicholas Hospital

## SHELL LAKE—Washburn County

☐ **INDIANHEAD MEDICAL CENTER (521342)**, 113 Fourth Avenue, Zip 54871–4457, Mailing Address: P.O. Box 300, Zip 54871–0300; tel. 715/468–7833, (Nonreporting) **A**1 10 18 **F**15 28 34 40 43 56 62 64 80 81 86 89 93 107 119 130 144
Primary Contact: Shannon Jack, Administrator
CFO: Michael Elliott, Controller
CMO: Allan Haesemeyer, M.D., Chief of Staff
CHR: Gwen Nielsen, Manager Human Resources
Web address: www.indianheadmedicalcenter.com
**Control:** Corporation, Investor–owned (for–profit) **Service:** General medical and surgical

**Staffed Beds:** 16 **Admissions:** 247 **Census:** 3 **Outpatient Visits:** 19177 **Births:** 0 **Total Expense ($000):** 8999 **Payroll Expense ($000):** 3566 **Personnel:** 85

## SPARTA—Monroe County

**FRANCISCAN SKEMP HEALTHCARE-SPARTA CAMPUS** See Mayo Clinic Health System - Franciscan Healthcare in Sparta

★ **MAYO CLINIC HEALTH SYSTEM - FRANCISCAN HEALTHCARE IN SPARTA (521305)**, 310 West Main Street, Zip 54656–2171; tel. 608/269–2132, (Nonreporting) **A**10 18 **F**3 6 8 11 15 28 29 30 34 35 40 41 43 45 54 56 57 59 64 65 66 68 77 79 82 84 85 93 97 102 107 110 115 119 127 130 133 146 148 149 154 156 **P**2 **S** Mayo Clinic, Rochester, MN
Primary Contact: Paul S. Mueller, Regional Vice President
COO: Michael A Morrey, Regional Chair-Admin SWWI
CFO: Julie S Hansen, Chief Financial Officer
CMO: Tracy Warsing, M.D., Site Leader Chief of Staff
CHR: Cathryn H. Fraser, Chief Human Resources Officer
CNO: Jason J Fratzke, Chief Nursing Officer
Web address: www.mayoclinichealthsystem.org
**Control:** Other not–for–profit (including NFP Corporation) **Service:** General medical and surgical

**Staffed Beds:** 15 **Admissions:** 333 **Census:** 9 **Outpatient Visits:** 48729 **Births:** 0 **Total Expense ($000):** 33225 **Payroll Expense ($000):** 14823 **Personnel:** 151

## SPOONER—Washburn County

★ **SPOONER HEALTH (521332)**, 1280 Chandler Drive, Zip 54801–1299; tel. 715/635–2111, (Nonreporting) **A**10 18 **F**3 11 15 29 30 31 34 35 40 43 45 50 56 57 59 62 64 65 68 75 78 79 80 81 82 85 86 87 89 90 93 103 107 111 119 129 130 132 133 135 146 148 **S** HealthTech Management Services, Brentwood, TN
Primary Contact: Michael Schafer, Chief Executive Officer and Administrator
CFO: Rebecca Busch, Chief Financial Officer
CMO: Mark Van Etten, M.D., Chief of Staff
CHR: Cindy Rouzer, Director Human Resources
CNO: Clint Miller, Chief Nursing Officer
Web address: www.spoonerhealth.com
**Control:** Other not–for–profit (including NFP Corporation) **Service:** General medical and surgical

**Staffed Beds:** 20 **Admissions:** 419 **Census:** 6 **Outpatient Visits:** 28882 **Births:** 0 **Total Expense ($000):** 25745 **Payroll Expense ($000):** 8228 **Personnel:** 113

**SPOONER HEALTH SYSTEM** See Spooner Health

## ST CROIX FALLS—Polk County

**ST CROIX VALLEY MEM HOSPITAL** See St. Croix Regional Medical Center

★ **ST. CROIX REGIONAL MEDICAL CENTER (521337)**, 235 State Street, Zip 54024–4117; tel. 715/483–3261, (Nonreporting) **A**10 18 **F**6 9 11 13 15 28 29 34 36 40 43 51 55 56 64 70 75 76 77 78 81 82 86 87 93 99 100 101 104 107 108 111 116 118 119 130 131 144 147 **P**2
Primary Contact: David Dobosenski, Chief Executive Officer
CFO: Sally Bajak, Chief Financial Officer
CMO: Jeffrey Hall, DPM, Chief Medical Officer
CIO: Brent McCurdy, Director Management Information
CHR: Betsy Nordby, Director of Human Resources
CNO: Laura J. Jensen, Vice President Patient Care Services
Web address: www.scrmc.org
**Control:** Other not–for–profit (including NFP Corporation) **Service:** General medical and surgical

**Staffed Beds:** 25 **Admissions:** 1548 **Census:** 12 **Outpatient Visits:** 198467 **Births:** 246 **Total Expense ($000):** 100508 **Payroll Expense ($000):** 44652 **Personnel:** 474

## STANLEY—Chippewa County

★ **ASCENSION OUR LADY OF VICTORY HOSPITAL (521311)**, 1120 Pine Street, Zip 54768–1297; tel. 715/644–5571, (Nonreporting) **A**10 18 **F**3 15 28 29 30 34 35 40 43 45 50 59 64 65 75 80 81 85 86 87 89 93 96 97 107 110 114 127 130 131 133 144 146 147 148 149 154 **P**2 **S** Ascension Healthcare, Saint Louis, MO
Primary Contact: Jeremy Normington-Slay, FACHE, President
CFO: Terri Lewandowski, Director Financial Services
Web address: www.ministryhealth.org
**Control:** Church operated, Nongovernment, not–for–profit **Service:** General medical and surgical

**Staffed Beds:** 2 **Admissions:** 207 **Census:** 3 **Outpatient Visits:** 40085 **Births:** 0 **Total Expense ($000):** 12980 **Payroll Expense ($000):** 4075 **Personnel:** 57

**MINISTRY OUR LADY OF VICTORY HOSPITAL** See Ascension Our Lady of Victory Hospital

## STEVENS POINT—Portage County

✠ **ASCENSION ST. MICHAEL'S HOSPITAL (520002)**, 900 Illinois Avenue, Zip 54481–3196; tel. 715/346–5000, (Nonreporting) **A**1 3 5 10 19 **F**3 5 13 15 17 18 29 30 31 34 40 43 44 45 48 50 51 56 57 59 64 65 68 70 72 74 76 77 78 79 80 81 84 85 86 87 89 90 93 97 98 99 100 101 102 103 104 106 107 108 111 114 115 116 117 118 119 123 124 126 130 131 132 135 144 146 147 148 149 150 154 **P**2 **S** Ascension Healthcare, Saint Louis, MO
Primary Contact: Teresa Theiler, Chief Administrative Officer
CFO: William J Hinner, Vice President Financial Analysis and Planning
CIO: Will Weider, Chief Information Officer
CHR: Celia Shaunessy, Vice President Human Resources
CNO: Tom Veeser, Chief Nursing Officer
Web address: www.ministryhealth.org/SMH/home.nws
**Control:** Church operated, Nongovernment, not–for–profit **Service:** General medical and surgical

**Staffed Beds:** 27 **Admissions:** 3601 **Census:** 31 **Outpatient Visits:** 430937 **Births:** 404 **Total Expense ($000):** 111835 **Payroll Expense ($000):** 25289 **Personnel:** 411

**MINISTRY SAINT MICHAEL'S HOSPITAL** See Ascension St. Michael's Hospital

**WI**

*Many Facility Codes have changed. Please refer to the AHA Guide Code Chart.* © 2021 AHA Guide

## STOUGHTON—Dane County

☐ **STOUGHTON HOSPITAL ASSOCIATION (521343)**, 900 Ridge Street,
Zip 53589–1864; tel. 608/873–6611, (Nonreporting) **A**1 5 10 18 **F**3 4 6 15 28
29 34 35 36 40 43 50 53 54 56 57 59 62 64 65 68 70 75 77 79 80 81 86 87
89 90 93 98 100 103 107 110 115 129 130 131 132 133 144 146 147 148
**P**2
Primary Contact: Daniel DeGroot, President and Chief Executive Officer
CFO: Michelle Abey, Chief Financial Officer
CHR: Christopher Schmitz, Associate Vice President, Director Human Resources
CNO: Teresa Lindfors, Vice President Growth and Development
Web address: www.stoughtonhospital.com
**Control**: Other not–for–profit (including NFP Corporation) **Service**: General
medical and surgical

**Staffed Beds:** 32 **Admissions:** 854 **Census:** 14 **Outpatient Visits:** 61758
**Births:** 0 **Total Expense ($000):** 43638 **Payroll Expense ($000):** 19207
**Personnel:** 249

## STURGEON BAY—Door County

★ **DOOR COUNTY MEDICAL CENTER (521358)**, 323 South 18th Avenue,
Zip 54235–1495; tel. 920/743–5566, (Total facility includes 30 beds in nursing
home–type unit) (Nonreporting) **A**10 18 **F**3 6 8 11 13 15 17 28 29 30 34
35 36 40 43 44 45 47 50 56 57 59 61 64 65 66 70 75 76 77 79 80 81 82 84
85 86 87 89 90 93 97 107 108 111 118 119 126 127 128 129 130 132 133
135 144 145 146 147 148 149 156 **P**2
Primary Contact: Brian Stephens, President and Chief Executive Officer
CFO: Andrew LaLuzerne, Chief Financial Officer
CMO: James Heise, Chief Medical Officer
CIO: Mary Lopas, Chief Information Officer
CHR: Kelli Bowling, Chief Culture Officer
CNO: Christa Krause, Chief Nursing Officer
Web address: www.dcmedical.org
**Control**: Church operated, Nongovernment, not–for–profit **Service**: General
medical and surgical

**Staffed Beds:** 55 **Admissions:** 1310 **Census:** 37 **Outpatient Visits:** 145630
**Births:** 132 **Total Expense ($000):** 84495 **Payroll Expense ($000):** 41517
**Personnel:** 507

**MINISTRY DOOR COUNTY MEDICAL CENTER** See Door County Medical Center

## SUMMIT—Waukesha County

☒ ○ **AURORA MEDICAL CENTER SUMMIT (520206)**, 36500 Aurora Drive,
Zip 53066–4899; tel. 262/434–1000, (Nonreporting) **A**1 2 3 10 11 **F**3 8 11 12
13 15 17 18 20 22 26 28 29 31 32 34 35 36 40 41 43 44 45 47 48 49 50 53
54 57 58 59 60 64 68 70 72 74 75 76 79 80 81 82 85 86 87 89 90 93 94 96
102 107 108 110 111 114 115 116 117 118 119 120 121 123 126 129 130
131 132 134 135 146 147 148 149 150 154 157 **P**2 **S** Advocate Aurora Health,
Downers Grove, IL
Primary Contact: Jessica Bauer, President
Web address: www.aurorahealthcare.org
**Control**: Other not–for–profit (including NFP Corporation) **Service**: General
medical and surgical

**Staffed Beds:** 91 **Admissions:** 4524 **Census:** 48 **Outpatient Visits:** 111674
**Births:** 440 **Total Expense ($000):** 122462 **Payroll Expense ($000):** 40178
**Personnel:** 1050

## SUPERIOR—Douglas County

☒ **ESSENTIA HEALTH ST. MARY'S HOSPITAL OF SUPERIOR (521329)**, 3500
Tower Avenue, Zip 54880–5395; tel. 715/817–7000, (Nonreporting) **A**1 10 18
**F**11 15 28 29 34 40 56 75 77 78 80 81 82 86 87 90 93 99 104 107 119 130
**P**2 **S** Essentia Health, Duluth, MN
Primary Contact: Kim Renee. Pearson, Administrator
CFO: Scott Nigon, Finance Senior Manager
CNO: Kim Renee Pearson, Nursing Director
Web address: www.essentiahealth.org/
EssentiaHealthStMarysHospitalofSuperiorFoundation/overview.aspx
**Control**: Other not–for–profit (including NFP Corporation) **Service**: General
medical and surgical

**Staffed Beds:** 25 **Admissions:** 651 **Census:** 8 **Outpatient Visits:** 55671
**Births:** 0 **Total Expense ($000):** 57605 **Payroll Expense ($000):** 29974
**Personnel:** 327

**ST. MARY'S HOSPITAL OF SUPERIOR** See Essentia Health St. Mary's Hospital of
Superior

## TOMAH—Monroe County

☒ **TOMAH HEALTH (521320)**, 321 Butts Avenue, Zip 54660–1412;
tel. 608/372–2181, (Nonreporting) **A**1 10 18 **F**12 13 28 34 40 43 54 63 64
76 77 80 81 82 86 87 89 90 93 107 108 111 119 130 144 154 **S** HealthTech
Management Services, Brentwood, TN
Primary Contact: Philip J. Stuart, Administrator and Chief Executive Officer
CFO: Joseph Zeps, Vice President Finance
CIO: LaVonne Smith, Director Health Information Technology
CHR: Brenda Reinert, Director Human Resources
CNO: Tracy Myhre, R.N., MSN, Chief Nursing Officer
Web address: www.tomahhospital.org
**Control**: Other not–for–profit (including NFP Corporation) **Service**: General
medical and surgical

**Staffed Beds:** 25 **Admissions:** 897 **Census:** 8 **Outpatient Visits:** 42586
**Births:** 254 **Total Expense ($000):** 55149 **Payroll Expense ($000):** 23384
**Personnel:** 313

**TOMAH MEMORIAL HOSPITAL** See Tomah Health

**TOMAH VETERANS AFFAIRS MEDICAL CENTER** See VA Medical Center

☒ **VA MEDICAL CENTER**, 500 East Veterans Street, Zip 54660–3105;
tel. 608/372–3971, (Nonreporting) **A**1 3 5 **S** Department of Veterans Affairs,
Washington, DC
Primary Contact: Victoria Brahm, R.N., MSN, Medical Center Director
CFO: Jane Mashak-Ekern, Fiscal Officer
CMO: David Houlihan, M.D., Chief of Staff
CIO: Edward Hensel, Chief Information Officer
CHR: David Dechant, Chief Human Resources Officer
Web address: www.tomah.va.gov
**Control**: Veterans Affairs, Government, federal **Service**: General medical and surgical

**Staffed Beds:** 71

## TOMAHAWK—Lincoln County

★ **ASCENSION SACRED HEART HOSPITAL (521313)**, 401 West Mohawk Drive,
Zip 54487–2274; tel. 715/453–7700, (Nonreporting) **A**10 18 **F**3 5 15 28 29 30
34 40 45 57 59 64 75 80 81 85 86 87 89 93 97 107 115 119 130 131 133
146 148 149 154 **S** Ascension Healthcare, Saint Louis, MO
Primary Contact: Laurie Oungst, Chief Administrative Officer
CFO: Jamon Lamers, Director Finance
CMO: Russ Sudbury, M.D., President Medical Staff
CIO: Howard Dobizl, Director Information Technology Services
CHR: Michelle Cornelius, Director Human Resources
CNO: Christine Krebs, Director of Nursing
Web address: www.ministryhealth.org
**Control**: Church operated, Nongovernment, not–for–profit **Service**: General
medical and surgical

**Staffed Beds:** 8 **Admissions:** 234 **Census:** 2 **Outpatient Visits:** 24742
**Births:** 0 **Total Expense ($000):** 11351 **Payroll Expense ($000):** 3401
**Personnel:** 45

**MINISTRY SACRED HEART HOSPITAL** See Ascension Sacred Heart Hospital

## TWO RIVERS—Manitowoc County

☒ ⇑ **AURORA MEDICAL CENTER - MANITOWOC COUNTY (520034)**, 5000
Memorial Drive, Zip 54241–3900; tel. 920/794–5000, (Nonreporting) **A**1 2 10 21
**F**3 8 11 13 28 29 30 33 34 35 36 40 41 43 46 48 49 56 57 58 59 64 65 75
76 78 79 80 81 82 86 87 89 91 93 94 96 97 107 108 109 110 111 112 115
117 119 120 121 123 124 129 130 131 132 135 146 147 148 149 150 154
156 **S** Advocate Aurora Health, Downers Grove, IL
Primary Contact: Cathie A. Kocourek, President
CFO: Joyce Nwatuobi, Vice President Finance
CMO: Scott Voskuil, M.D., Chief Medical Officer
CIO: Bobbie Byrne, M.D., Chief Information Officer
CHR: Elizabeth A Kirby, Senior Director Human Resources
Web address: www.aurorahealthcare.org
**Control**: Other not–for–profit (including NFP Corporation) **Service**: General
medical and surgical

**Staffed Beds:** 62 **Admissions:** 2080 **Census:** 15 **Outpatient Visits:** 92199
**Births:** 398 **Total Expense ($000):** 61390 **Payroll Expense ($000):** 18756
**Personnel:** 362

⇑ **TWO RIVERS COMMUNITY HOSPITAL** See Aurora Medical Center - Manitowoc
County

**WI**

## WATERFORD—Racine County

☐ **LAKEVIEW SPECIALTY HOSPITAL AND REHAB (522005)**, 1701 Sharp Road, Zip 53185–5214; tel. 262/534–7297, (Nonreporting) **A**1 10 **F**1 29 34 38 53 60 64 75 86 87 90 93 130
**Primary Contact:** Andy Olivares, Chief Executive Officer
**Web address:** www.lakeviewsystem.com
**Control:** Corporation, Investor–owned (for–profit) **Service:** Acute long–term care hospital

**Staffed Beds:** 39 **Admissions:** 266 **Census:** 31 **Outpatient Visits:** 3835
**Births:** 0 **Total Expense ($000):** 17565 **Payroll Expense ($000):** 7850
**Personnel:** 143

**LAKEVIEW SPECIALTY HOSPITAL AND REHABILITATION CENTER** See Lakeview Specialty Hospital and Rehab

## WATERTOWN—Dodge County

**WATERTOWN MEMORIAL HOSPITAL** See Watertown Regional Medical Center

☒ **WATERTOWN REGIONAL MEDICAL CENTER (520116)**, 125 Hospital Drive, Zip 53098–3303; tel. 920/261–4210, (Nonreporting) **A**1 10 **F**10 11 13 15 20 22 28 29 34 36 40 53 54 56 64 69 75 76 77 80 81 82 86 87 89 90 93 98 103 104 107 108 111 118 119 125 130 131 144 147 154 **P**2 **S** LifePoint Health, Brentwood, TN
**Primary Contact:** Richard Keddington, Chief Executive Officer
**COO:** John P Kosanovich, President
**CFO:** John Graf, Senior Vice President
**CIO:** Jennifer Laughlin, Chief Information Officer
**CHR:** Duane Floyd, Vice President Human Resources and Professional Services
**Web address:** www.watertownregional.com/Main/Home.aspx
**Control:** Corporation, Investor–owned (for–profit) **Service:** General medical and surgical

**Staffed Beds:** 64 **Admissions:** 2315 **Census:** 24 **Outpatient Visits:** 79401
**Births:** 187 **Total Expense ($000):** 95130 **Payroll Expense ($000):** 41770
**Personnel:** 462

## WAUKESHA—Waukesha County

☐ **REHABILITATION HOSPITAL OF WISCONSIN (523027)**, 1625 Coldwater Creek Drive, Zip 53188–8028; tel. 262/521–8800, (Nonreporting) **A**1 10 **F**28 29 34 64 75 86 90 93 100 130 **S** Kindred Healthcare, Louisville, KY
**Primary Contact:** Brad Anderson, Chief Executive Officer
**CFO:** Kim Stoltz, Controller
**CMO:** Tim McAvoy, M.D., Medical Director
**CHR:** Katelyn Gonyo, Director of Human Resources
**CNO:** Vanessa Plante, Chief Clinical Officer
**Web address:** www.rehabhospitalwi.com
**Control:** Partnership, Investor–owned (for–profit) **Service:** Rehabilitation

**Staffed Beds:** 40 **Admissions:** 927 **Census:** 32 **Outpatient Visits:** 6789
**Births:** 0 **Total Expense ($000):** 15100 **Payroll Expense ($000):** 8239
**Personnel:** 126

**WAUKESHA COUNTY MENTAL HEALTH CENTER (524026)**, 1501 Airport Road, Zip 53188; tel. 262/548–7950, (Nonreporting) **A**10 **F**4 29 50 87 98 103 130 **P**2
**Primary Contact:** Jeff Lewis, Administrator
**CFO:** Randy R Setzer, Financial Services Manager
**Web address:** www.waukeshacounty.gov/
**Control:** County, Government, Nonfederal **Service:** Psychiatric

**Staffed Beds:** 28 **Admissions:** 478 **Census:** 19 **Outpatient Visits:** 0
**Births:** 0 **Total Expense ($000):** 8015 **Payroll Expense ($000):** 4251
**Personnel:** 63

☒ **WAUKESHA MEMORIAL HOSPITAL (520008)**, 725 American Avenue, Zip 53188–5099; tel. 262/928–1000, (Nonreporting) **A**1 2 3 5 10 **F**3 4 5 11 12 13 18 20 22 24 26 28 29 30 31 32 33 34 37 40 41 43 44 45 46 47 48 49 50 56 57 58 59 64 65 66 68 72 74 75 76 78 79 80 81 82 83 84 85 87 89 93 97 98 100 101 102 104 105 107 108 109 110 111 112 114 115 116 117 118 119 120 121 126 129 130 132 133 135 146 147 148 149 151 152 153 154 156 157 **P**2 **S** ProHealth Care, Inc., Waukesha, WI
**Primary Contact:** Susan A. Edwards, President and Chief Executive Officer
**CMO:** James D Gardner, M.D., Vice President and Chief Medical Officer
**CIO:** Rodney Dykehouse, Senior Vice President Information Services
**CHR:** Nadine T Guirl, Senior Vice President Human Resources
**Web address:** www.prohealthcare.org/locations/locations-v2-detail/?id=1119
**Control:** Other not–for–profit (including NFP Corporation) **Service:** General medical and surgical

**Staffed Beds:** 262 **Admissions:** 7446 **Census:** 138 **Outpatient Visits:** 360674 **Births:** 1642 **Total Expense ($000):** 449409 **Payroll Expense ($000):** 122367 **Personnel:** 1740

## WAUPACA—Waupaca County

**RIVERSIDE MEDICAL CENTER** See Thedacare Medical Center-Waupaca

☐ **THEDACARE MEDICAL CENTER-WAUPACA (521334)**, 800 Riverside Drive, Zip 54981–1999; tel. 715/258–1000, (Nonreporting) **A**1 5 10 18 **F**11 13 17 28 29 34 40 64 70 75 76 78 80 81 82 86 87 88 89 90 107 111 119 130 144 147 **P**2 **S** ThedaCare, Inc., Appleton, WI
**Primary Contact:** David Corso, Vice President Critical Access Hospitals
**CFO:** Kerry Lee Blanke, Director Financial Services
**CMO:** James Williams, M.D., Chief of Staff
**CHR:** Kevin Gossens, Director Human Resources
**Web address:** www.riversidemedical.org
**Control:** Other not–for–profit (including NFP Corporation) **Service:** General medical and surgical

**Staffed Beds:** 25 **Admissions:** 1010 **Census:** 8 **Outpatient Visits:** 71086
**Births:** 128 **Total Expense ($000):** 31765 **Payroll Expense ($000):** 13417
**Personnel:** 177

## WAUPUN—Dodge County

☒ **WAUPUN MEMORIAL HOSPITAL (521327)**, 620 West Brown Street, Zip 53963–1799; tel. 920/324–5581, (Nonreporting) **A**1 10 18 **F**3 11 13 15 18 28 29 30 31 34 35 40 43 44 45 50 51 57 59 60 66 68 69 70 75 76 77 79 81 82 85 86 87 93 96 97 107 108 109 111 114 118 119 124 130 131 132 133 134 135 143 144 146 147 148 149 150 156 **S** SSM Health, Saint Louis, MO
**Primary Contact:** DeAnn Thurmer, President and Chief Nursing Officer
**CFO:** Bonnie Schmitz, Chief Financial Officer
**CMO:** Derek Colmenares, M.D., Chief Medical Officer
**CIO:** Nancy Birschbach, Vice President and Chief Information Officer
**CHR:** Sue Edminster, Vice President Human Resources
**CNO:** DeAnn Thurmer, President and Chief Nursing Officer
**Web address:** www.agnesian.com
**Control:** Church operated, Nongovernment, not–for–profit **Service:** General medical and surgical

**Staffed Beds:** 25 **Admissions:** 1011 **Census:** 8 **Outpatient Visits:** 68372
**Births:** 158 **Total Expense ($000):** 37820 **Payroll Expense ($000):** 16812
**Personnel:** 169

## WAUSAU—Marathon County

**ASPIRUS WAUSAU HOSPITAL** See Aspirus Wausau Hospital, Inc.

☒ △ **ASPIRUS WAUSAU HOSPITAL, INC. (520030)**, 333 Pine Ridge Boulevard, Zip 54401–4187; tel. 715/847–2121, (Nonreporting) **A**1 2 3 5 7 10 **F**3 5 6 7 8 11 12 13 15 16 17 18 20 22 24 26 28 29 30 31 34 35 36 37 40 43 44 45 46 47 49 50 51 54 55 56 57 58 59 60 64 65 68 69 70 71 72 74 75 76 78 79 80 81 82 83 84 85 86 87 88 89 90 92 93 96 97 100 102 103 107 108 110 111 114 115 116 117 118 119 120 121 123 124 126 129 130 132 134 135 144 145 146 147 148 154 156 **S** Aspirus, Inc., Wausau, WI
**Primary Contact:** Darrell Lentz, President
**CFO:** Sidney C Sczygelski, Senior Vice President Finance and Chief Financial Officer
**CMO:** Ryan Andrews, M.D., Chief Medical Officer
**CNO:** Jeannine Nosko, Vice President Patient Care
**Web address:** www.aspirus.org
**Control:** Other not–for–profit (including NFP Corporation) **Service:** General medical and surgical

**Staffed Beds:** 307 **Admissions:** 14714 **Census:** 173 **Outpatient Visits:** 137200 **Births:** 1467 **Total Expense ($000):** 472420 **Payroll Expense ($000):** 154817 **Personnel:** 2406

☒ **NORTH CENTRAL HEALTH CARE (524017)**, 1100 Lake View Drive, Zip 54403–6785; tel. 715/848–4600, (Total facility includes 172 beds in nursing home–type unit) (Nonreporting) **A**1 3 5 10 **F**4 5 29 38 75 80 87 98 99 102 103 104 128 130 154
**Primary Contact:** Michael Loy, FACHE, Chief Executive Officer
**COO:** Jarret Nickel, Operations Executive
**CFO:** Brenda Glodowski, Chief Financial Officer
**CMO:** Robert Gouthro, M.D., Chief Medical Officer
**CIO:** Thomas Boutain, Information Services Executive
**Web address:** www.norcen.org
**Control:** County, Government, Nonfederal **Service:** Psychiatric

**Staffed Beds:** 188 **Admissions:** 1030 **Census:** 193 **Outpatient Visits:** 173150 **Births:** 0 **Total Expense ($000):** 54554 **Payroll Expense ($000):** 20031 **Personnel:** 512

**NORTH CENTRAL HEALTH CARE FACILITIES** See North Central Health Care

*Many Facility Codes have changed. Please refer to the AHA Guide Code Chart.*

**WI**

## WAUWATOSA—Milwaukee County

⊠ **AURORA PSYCHIATRIC HOSPITAL (524000)**, 1220 Dewey Avenue,
Zip 53213–2598; tel. 414/454–6600, (Nonreporting) **A**1 3 5 10 **F**4 5 11 29 30
32 34 35 36 38 44 50 54 59 64 68 75 86 87 98 99 100 101 103 104 105
106 130 132 134 135 149 152 153 158 **S** Advocate Aurora Health, Downers
Grove, IL
Primary Contact: Peter Carlson, President, Behavioral Health Services
CFO: Susan Dwyer, Vice President Finance
CMO: Anthony Meyer, M.D., Medical Director
CIO: Philip Loftus, Ph.D., Vice President and Chief Information Officer
CHR: Pamela Gamb, Manager Human Resources
CNO: Jamie Lewiston, R.N., MSN, Chief Nursing Officer
Web address: www.aurorahealthcare.org
**Control**: Other not–for–profit (including NFP Corporation) **Service**: Psychiatric

| | |
|---|---|
| **Staffed Beds:** 91 **Admissions:** 5942 **Census:** 71 **Outpatient Visits:** 75617 **Births:** 0 **Total Expense ($000):** 41718 **Payroll Expense ($000):** 21950 **Personnel:** 472 | |

**MILWAUKEE PSYCHIATRIC HOSPITAL** See Aurora Psychiatric Hospital

## WEST ALLIS—Milwaukee County

⊠ **AURORA WEST ALLIS MEDICAL CENTER (520139)**, 8901 West Lincoln
Avenue, Zip 53227–2409, Mailing Address: P.O. Box 27901, Zip 53227–0901;
tel. 414/328–6000, (Nonreporting) **A**1 2 3 10 **F**3 11 12 13 15 28 29 30 31 32
34 35 36 37 38 40 43 44 45 46 49 50 52 54 55 56 57 59 64 65 68 70 72 74
75 76 78 79 80 81 82 84 85 86 87 89 91 93 94 95 96 97 107 108 110 111
114 115 116 117 118 119 120 121 123 126 130 132 134 135 146 147 148
149 150 154 **S** Advocate Aurora Health, Downers Grove, IL
Primary Contact: Holly Schmidtke, R.N., Interim President
COO: Gerard Colman, Chief Operating Officer
CFO: Chris Hemmer, Director Finance
CMO: Andrew McDonagh, M.D., Chief Medical Officer
CIO: Philip Loftus, Ph.D., Chief Information Officer
CHR: Shannon Christenson, Director Human Resources
CNO: Kathy Becker, Ph.D., R.N., Vice President and Chief Nursing Officer
Web address: www.aurorahealthcare.org
**Control**: Other not–for–profit (including NFP Corporation) **Service**: General
medical and surgical

| | |
|---|---|
| **Staffed Beds:** 219 **Admissions:** 9945 **Census:** 110 **Outpatient Visits:** 163984 **Births:** 3526 **Total Expense ($000):** 212622 **Payroll Expense ($000):** 74478 **Personnel:** 2186 | |

**CHARTER BEHAVIORAL HEALTH SYSTEM OF MILWAUKEE/WEST ALLIS** See
Rogers Memorial Hospital-West Allis

**WEST ALLIS MEMORIAL HOSPITAL** See Aurora West Allis Medical Center

## WEST BEND—Washington County

⊠ **FROEDTERT WEST BEND HOSPITAL (520063)**, 3200 Pleasant Valley Road,
Zip 53095–9274; tel. 262/836–5533, (Nonreporting) **A**1 2 3 5 10 **F**3 9 13 15 17
26 28 29 30 31 34 35 38 40 43 44 45 46 47 50 51 54 56 57 58 59 60 61 64
65 66 68 70 72 74 75 76 77 78 79 80 81 82 84 85 86 87 89 90 101 107 108
110 111 114 115 116 117 118 119 120 121 123 126 129 130 132 135 145
146 147 148 149 150 154 156 **S** Froedtert Health, Milwaukee, WI
Primary Contact: Allen Ericson, President
COO: Teresa M Lux, President and Chief Operating Officer
CFO: Scott Hawig, Senior Vice President of Finance, Chief Financial Officer and
Treasurer
CMO: Patrick Gardner, M.D., Associate Vice President, Medical Affairs, St. Joseph's
Hospital
CIO: Kathryn McClellan, Senior Vice President and Chief Information Officer
CHR: Eric Humphrey, Senior Vice President, Chief Human Resources Officer
CNO: Shelly Waala, Vice President Patient Care Services and Chief Nursing Officer
Web address: www.froedtert.com
**Control**: Other not–for–profit (including NFP Corporation) **Service**: General
medical and surgical

| | |
|---|---|
| **Staffed Beds:** 70 **Admissions:** 4100 **Census:** 40 **Outpatient Visits:** 91228 **Births:** 661 **Total Expense ($000):** 144685 **Payroll Expense ($000):** 40652 **Personnel:** 531 | |

**ST. JOSEPH'S HOSPITAL** See Froedtert West Bend Hospital

## WESTON—Marathon County

⊠ **MARSHFIELD MEDICAL CENTER - WESTON (520202)**, 3400 Ministry
Parkway, Zip 54476–5220; tel. 715/393–3000, (Nonreporting) **A**1 10 **F**3 11 13
17 18 20 22 24 26 29 30 31 34 35 40 43 44 45 46 47 48 49 50 51 57 59 64
65 68 70 74 76 78 79 80 81 82 84 85 86 87 89 97 126 130 132 135 144 146
147 148 149 150 154 **S** Marshfield Clinic Health System, Marshfield, WI
Primary Contact: Jeremy Normington-Slay, FACHE, President, North Central Region
CFO: Charlotte Esselman, Director Finance
CIO: Tammy Hawkey, Manager Information Technology Client Services
CHR: Nancy Kwiesielewicz, Human Resources Manager
CNO: Sally E. Zillman, Interim Vice President, Patient Care Services
Web address: www.ministryhealth.org
**Control**: Church operated, Nongovernment, not–for–profit **Service**: General
medical and surgical

| | |
|---|---|
| **Staffed Beds:** 49 **Admissions:** 4680 **Census:** 47 **Outpatient Visits:** 24529 **Births:** 447 **Total Expense ($000):** 124924 **Payroll Expense ($000):** 25161 **Personnel:** 339 | |

**MINISTRY GOOD SAMARITAN HEALTH CENTER** See Marshfield Medical Center
- Weston

## WHITEHALL—Trempealeau County

★ **GUNDERSEN TRI-COUNTY HOSPITAL AND CLINICS (521316)**, 18601 Lincoln
Street, Zip 54773–8605; tel. 715/538–4361, (Total facility includes 35 beds in
nursing home–type unit) (Nonreporting) **A**10 18 **F**6 7 10 11 15 28 34 40 43 53
54 56 64 75 78 81 82 86 87 93 99 100 103 104 107 108 128 130 144 154
**P**2
Primary Contact: Joni Olson, Chief Executive Officer
CFO: Roxane K Schliech, Chief Financial Officer
CMO: Kim B Breidenbach, Medical Director
CIO: John Waldera, Director Information Technology
CHR: Jill Wesener Dieck, Human Resources Operations Manager
CNO: Kelsey N Underwood, Director of Nursing
Web address: www.gundersenhealth.org/tri-county
**Control**: Other not–for–profit (including NFP Corporation) **Service**: General
medical and surgical

| | |
|---|---|
| **Staffed Beds:** 50 **Admissions:** 373 **Census:** 39 **Outpatient Visits:** 32605 **Births:** 0 **Total Expense ($000):** 18875 **Payroll Expense ($000):** 8347 **Personnel:** 158 | |

**TRI-COUNTY MEMORIAL HOSPITAL** See Gundersen Tri-County Hospital and
Clinics

## WILD ROSE—Waushara County

**THEDA CARE MEDICAL CENTER - WILD ROSE (521303)**, 601 Grove
Avenue, Zip 54984–6903, Mailing Address: P.O. Box 243, Zip 54984–0243;
tel. 920/622–3257, (Nonreporting) **A**10 18 **F**11 15 28 29 34 40 43 56 64 75 77
80 81 86 87 89 90 93 99 100 101 102 103 104 107 111 119 131 144 147 **S**
ThedaCare, Inc., Appleton, WI
Primary Contact: Tammy Bending, Vice President
CFO: Joanne Horvath, Vice President Finance
CMO: Chandler Caves, M.D., Chief Medical Officer
CIO: James Albin, Chief Information Officer
CHR: Maggie A. Lund, Chief Human Resources Officer
CNO: Jacqueline Kay Anhalt, Chief Nursing Officer
Web address: www.https://www.thedacare.org
**Control**: Other not–for–profit (including NFP Corporation) **Service**: General
medical and surgical

| | |
|---|---|
| **Staffed Beds:** 25 **Admissions:** 213 **Census:** 5 **Outpatient Visits:** 17338 **Births:** 0 **Total Expense ($000):** 8299 **Payroll Expense ($000):** 5677 **Personnel:** 68 | |

**WILD ROSE COMMUNITY MEMORIAL HOSPITAL** See Theda Care Medical
Center - Wild Rose

**WI**

---

| Hospital, Medicare Provider Number, Address, Telephone, Approval, Facility, and Physician Codes, Health Care System |
|---|

★ American Hospital Association (AHA) membership ○ Healthcare Facilities Accreditation Program ⇑ Center for Improvement in Healthcare Quality Accreditation
□ The Joint Commission accreditation ◇ DNV Healthcare Inc. accreditation △ Commission on Accreditation of Rehabilitation Facilities (CARF) accreditation

## WINNEBAGO—Winnebago County

☐ **WINNEBAGO MENTAL HEALTH INSTITUTE (524002)**, 1300 South Drive,
Zip 54985, Mailing Address: Box 9, Zip 54985–0009; tel. 920/235–4910,
(Nonreporting) **A**1 3 5 10 **F**3 4 29 30 34 57 59 75 82 86 87 98 99 103 130 132
135 146 149
Primary Contact: Byran Bartow, Director
COO: Chris Craggs, Deputy Director
CFO: Lisa Spanbauer, Financial Program Supervisor
CMO: Randy Kerswill, M.D., Medical Director
CIO: Terrance J. Sweet, Director Information Technology
CHR: Mary Howard, Director Human Resources
CNO: Lori Monroe, Director of Nursing
Web address: www.dhfs.state.wi.us/mh_winnebago
**Control:** State, Government, Nonfederal **Service:** Psychiatric

**Staffed Beds:** 188 **Admissions:** 3392 **Census:** 175 **Outpatient Visits:** 0
**Births:** 0 **Total Expense ($000):** 80744 **Payroll Expense ($000):** 37647
**Personnel:** 586

## WISCONSIN RAPIDS—Wood County

☒ **ASPIRUS RIVERVIEW HOSPITAL AND CLINICS, INC. (520033)**, 410 Dewey
Street, Zip 54494–4715, Mailing Address: P.O. Box 8080, Zip 54495–8080;
tel. 715/423–6060, (Nonreporting) **A**1 10 **F**3 4 13 15 17 28 30 31 32 34 35 40
43 45 50 56 57 59 64 65 68 69 70 74 75 76 77 78 79 80 81 84 85 86 88 89
90 93 97 98 107 108 110 111 115 117 118 119 120 121 124 127 129 130
131 132 135 143 146 148 154 156 157 **S** Aspirus, Inc., Wausau, WI
Primary Contact: Todd Burch, Chief Executive Officer
CFO: Nancy Roth-Mallek, Vice President of Finance
CMO: Thomas Voelker, M.D., Chief Medical Officer
CIO: Marjorie Tell, Vice President Information Technology
CHR: Jessica Fox, Director of Human Resources
CNO: Peggy Ose, FACHE, MSN, R.N., Chief Nursing Officer
Web address: www.aspirus.org
**Control:** Other not-for-profit (including NFP Corporation) **Service:** General
medical and surgical

**Staffed Beds:** 91 **Admissions:** 3009 **Census:** 26 **Outpatient Visits:** 49965
**Births:** 473 **Total Expense ($000):** 123383 **Payroll Expense ($000):** 46756
**Personnel:** 506

**RIVERVIEW HOSPITAL ASSOCIATION** See Aspirus Riverview Hospital and
Clinics, Inc.

## WOODRUFF—Oneida County

☒ **HOWARD YOUNG MEDICAL CENTER (520091)**, 240 Maple Street,
Zip 54568–9190, Mailing Address: P.O. Box 470, Zip 54568–0470;
tel. 715/356–8000, (Nonreporting) **A**1 10 20 **F**3 11 13 15 28 29 30 34 35 40
43 45 51 59 64 75 76 79 80 81 82 84 85 86 87 88 89 93 95 96 97 107 110
111 115 119 126 129 130 135 146 148 149 154 **S** Ascension Healthcare, Saint
Louis, MO
Primary Contact: Laurie Oungst, Chief Administrative Officer
CFO: Jamon Lamers, Director Finance
CMO: John Crump, M.D., Medical Staff President
CIO: Howard Dobizl, Director Information Technology Services
CHR: Michelle Cornelius, Director Human Resources
CNO: Jacqualyn Monge, Director of Nursing
Web address: www.ministryhealth.org
**Control:** Church operated, Nongovernment, not-for-profit **Service:** General
medical and surgical

**Staffed Beds:** 50 **Admissions:** 2335 **Census:** 22 **Outpatient Visits:** 37675
**Births:** 241 **Total Expense ($000):** 46317 **Payroll Expense ($000):** 14908
**Personnel:** 223

**WI**

# WYOMING

## AFTON—Lincoln County

★ **STAR VALLEY HEALTH (531313)**, 901 Adams Street, Zip 83110–9621, Mailing Address: P.O. Box 579, Zip 83110–0579; tel. 307/885–5800, (Total facility includes 24 beds in nursing home–type unit) (Nonreporting) **A**5 10 18 **F**3 7 11 12 13 15 28 29 31 34 35 36 40 41 43 45 46 47 48 49 50 51 56 57 59 64 65 70 75 76 77 78 79 81 82 84 85 87 92 93 97 107 108 109 110 111 112 115 119 128 129 130 131 132 133 141 144 145 146 148 149 152 154 156 157 **P**6
Primary Contact: Bren Lowe, Chief Executive Officer
COO: Mike Hunsaker, Chief Operating Officer
CFO: Chad Turner, Chief Financial Officer
CMO: Donald Kirk, M.D., Chief of Staff
CIO: Amy R Johnson, R.N., Quality Improvement Safety Officer
CHR: Trevor Merritt, Director Human Resources
CNO: Derek Greenwald, Chief Nursing Officer
Web address: www.https://starvalleyhealth.org/
**Control**: Hospital district or authority, Government, Nonfederal **Service**: General medical and surgical

| | |
|---|---|
| **Staffed Beds:** 46 **Admissions:** 800 **Census:** 27 **Outpatient Visits:** 40209 **Births:** 100 **Total Expense ($000):** 52616 **Payroll Expense ($000):** 24834 **Personnel:** 362 | |

**STAR VALLEY MEDICAL CENTER** See Star Valley Health

## BASIN—Big Horn County

★ **SOUTH BIG HORN COUNTY HOSPITAL (531301)**, 388 South U S Highway 20, Zip 82410–8902; tel. 307/568–3311, (Nonreporting) **A**10 18
Primary Contact: Tadd S. Greenfield, Chief Executive Officer
Web address: www.midwayclinic.com
**Control**: Hospital district or authority, Government, Nonfederal **Service**: General medical and surgical

| | |
|---|---|
| **Staffed Beds:** 47 | |

## BUFFALO—Johnson County

**JOHNSON COUNTY HEALTCARE CTR** See Johnson County Healthcare Center

★ **JOHNSON COUNTY HEALTHCARE CENTER (531308)**, 497 West Lott Street, Zip 82834–1691; tel. 307/684–5521, (Total facility includes 44 beds in nursing home–type unit) (Nonreporting) **A**10 18 **F**3 11 13 15 28 31 34 40 45 53 57 59 62 63 67 70 76 78 79 81 89 93 97 107 119 130 131 132 133 146
Primary Contact: Sean McCallister, Chief Executive Officer
CMO: Blaine Ruby, M.D., Chief of Staff
CIO: Laurie Hansen, Director of Administration
CHR: Karen Ferguson, Director Human Resources
CNO: Mary Whaley, Director of Acute Care
Web address: www.jchealthcare.com
**Control**: Hospital district or authority, Government, Nonfederal **Service**: General medical and surgical

| | |
|---|---|
| **Staffed Beds:** 59 **Admissions:** 379 **Census:** 47 **Outpatient Visits:** 17344 **Births:** 41 **Total Expense ($000):** 22776 **Payroll Expense ($000):** 11775 | |

## CASPER—Natrona County

**CRESTVIEW HOSPITAL** See Wyoming Behavioral Institute

☐ **ELKHORN VALLEY REHABILITATION HOSPITAL (533027)**, 5715 East 2nd Street, Zip 82609–4322; tel. 307/265–0005, (Nonreporting) **A**1 10 **F**29 34 35 50 75 77 82 86 87 91 93 96 132 143 148 149 154 **S** Ernest Health, Inc., Albuquerque, NM
Primary Contact: Connie Longwell, Chief Executive Officer
Web address: www.evrh.ernesthealth.com/
**Control**: Corporation, Investor–owned (for–profit) **Service**: Rehabilitation

| | |
|---|---|
| **Staffed Beds:** 41 **Admissions:** 685 **Census:** 29 **Outpatient Visits:** 3827 **Births:** 0 | |

☐ ⇑ **SUMMIT MEDICAL CENTER (530034)**, 6350 East 2nd Street, Zip 82609–4264; tel. 307/232–6600, (Nonreporting) **A**1 21 **F**3 15 29 39 45 46 47 49 79 81 82 107 110 111 114 119 120 124
Primary Contact: Raymond Vucetic, Chief Executive Officer
COO: Mindi L. Pile, Chief Operations Officer
CFO: Calvin Carey, Chief Financial Officer
CMO: Joseph Vigneri, M.D., Chief Medical Officer
CNO: Vanessa Sorensen, Chief Nursing Officer
Web address: www.summitmedicalcasper.com/
**Control**: Partnership, Investor–owned (for–profit) **Service**: General medical and surgical

| | |
|---|---|
| **Staffed Beds:** 16 **Admissions:** 351 **Census:** 2 **Outpatient Visits:** 6662 **Births:** 0 **Total Expense ($000):** 13060 **Payroll Expense ($000):** 4399 **Personnel:** 64 | |

⇑ **SUMMITT MEDICAL CENTER** See Summit Medical Center

☐ **WYOMING BEHAVIORAL INSTITUTE (534004)**, 2521 East 15th Street, Zip 82609–4126; tel. 307/237–7444, (Nonreporting) **A**1 10 **F**98 102 106 146 154 **S** Universal Health Services, Inc., King of Prussia, PA
Primary Contact: Mike Phillips, Chief Executive Officer
CFO: Carmel Bickford, Chief Financial Officer
CMO: Steven Brown, M.D., Medical Director
CHR: Jon Barra, Director Human Resources
Web address: www.wbihelp.com
**Control**: State, Government, Nonfederal **Service**: Psychiatric

| | |
|---|---|
| **Staffed Beds:** 114 **Admissions:** 2357 **Census:** 99 **Births:** 0 **Total Expense ($000):** 22730 **Payroll Expense ($000):** 11968 | |

⊞ **WYOMING MEDICAL CENTER (530012)**, 1233 East Second Street, Zip 82601–2988; tel. 307/577–7201, (Nonreporting) **A**1 3 5 10 20 **F**3 7 11 12 13 18 20 22 24 28 29 30 31 34 35 36 40 41 43 45 46 48 49 50 51 53 57 59 60 61 68 70 74 75 76 77 79 81 82 85 86 87 89 97 102 107 108 115 118 119 120 121 123 124 126 129 130 132 135 144 146 147 148 **P**6
Primary Contact: Michele Chulick, President and Chief Executive Officer
CFO: Jeanne Ehlebracht, Senior Vice President and Chief Financial Officer
CMO: Carol M. Solie, M.D., Vice President, Quality and Medical Safety
CIO: Rob Pettigrew, Director Information Technology
CNO: Connie Coleman, R.N., Chief Nursing Officer
Web address: www.https://wyomingmedicalcenter.org/
**Control**: Other not–for–profit (including NFP Corporation) **Service**: General medical and surgical

| | |
|---|---|
| **Staffed Beds:** 249 **Admissions:** 9119 **Census:** 99 **Outpatient Visits:** 90169 **Births:** 981 **Total Expense ($000):** 252726 **Payroll Expense ($000):** 92127 **Personnel:** 1143 | |

## CHEYENNE—Laramie County

⊞ △ **CHEYENNE REGIONAL MEDICAL CENTER (530014)**, 214 East 23rd Street, Zip 82001–3790; tel. 307/634–2273, (Nonreporting) **A**1 3 5 7 10 20 **F**3 5 8 12 13 15 18 20 22 24 26 28 29 30 31 32 34 35 37 38 40 43 44 45 46 47 48 49 50 51 55 56 57 59 60 61 62 63 64 65 68 70 73 74 76 77 78 79 81 82 83 84 85 86 87 89 90 91 92 93 96 97 98 100 101 102 104 107 108 111 115 116 117 118 119 120 121 122 123 124 126 130 131 135 143 146 147 148 149 153 154 157 **P**6
Primary Contact: Timothy Thornell, FACHE, President and Chief Executive Officer
COO: Robin Roling, FACHE, MS, R.N., Chief Operating Officer
CFO: Neil W Bertrand, Interim Chief Financial Officer
CMO: Jeffrey Chapman, M.D., Chief Medical Officer
CNO: Tracy Garcia, MS, Chief Nursing Officer
Web address: www.cheyenneregional.org/
**Control**: County, Government, Nonfederal **Service**: General medical and surgical

| | |
|---|---|
| **Staffed Beds:** 222 **Admissions:** 9807 **Census:** 121 **Outpatient Visits:** 188922 **Births:** 1191 **Total Expense ($000):** 303308 **Payroll Expense ($000):** 121883 **Personnel:** 1553 | |

✠ **CHEYENNE VETERANS AFFAIRS MEDICAL CENTER**, 2360 East Pershing Boulevard, Zip 82001–5392; tel. 307/778–7550, (Total facility includes 10 beds in nursing home–type unit) (Nonreporting) **A**1 3 **F**3 4 5 30 31 33 35 36 39 40 44 45 54 56 61 62 63 64 67 68 70 71 74 75 77 78 79 81 82 83 84 85 91 93 94 97 100 102 104 106 107 111 114 115 119 120 127 129 130 132 135 143 146 147 148 149 153 154 157 **S** Department of Veterans Affairs, Washington, DC
Primary Contact: Paul L. Roberts, Director
CFO: Melvin Cranford, Chief Fiscal Services
CMO: Roger Johnson, M.D., Chief of Staff
CIO: Liz McCulloch, Chief Information Resource Management Systems
CHR: Ron Lester, Chief Human Resources
Web address: www.cheyenne.va.gov/
**Control**: Veterans Affairs, Government, federal **Service**: General medical and surgical

**Staffed Beds**: 32 **Admissions**: 1406 **Census**: 53 **Outpatient Visits**: 4752

**UNITED MEDICAL CENTER** See Cheyenne Regional Medical Center

**VETERANS AFFAIRS MEDICAL CENTER** See Cheyenne Veterans Affairs Medical Center

### CODY—Park County

★ **WEST PARK HOSPITAL (531312)**, 707 Sheridan Avenue, Zip 82414–3409; tel. 307/527–7501, (Total facility includes 87 beds in nursing home–type unit) (Nonreporting) **A**10 18 **F**3 4 5 7 13 15 28 29 30 31 34 35 37 38 40 41 43 45 46 50 54 55 56 57 59 63 64 65 68 70 74 75 76 77 78 79 81 84 85 86 87 93 97 101 102 104 107 108 110 111 114 115 119 126 127 128 130 131 132 133 146 147 148 149 154 156 **S** QHR Health, Brentwood, TN
Primary Contact: Douglas A. McMillan, Administrator and Chief Executive Officer
CFO: Patrick G McConnell, Chief Financial Officer
CMO: Gary Hart, M.D., Chief Medical Officer
CHR: Dick Smith, Director Human Resources
Web address: www.westparkhospital.org
**Control**: Hospital district or authority, Government, Nonfederal **Service**: General medical and surgical

**Staffed Beds**: 112 **Admissions**: 1410 **Census**: 86 **Outpatient Visits**: 92958 **Births**: 197 **Total Expense ($000)**: 99015 **Payroll Expense ($000)**: 40231 **Personnel**: 501

### DOUGLAS—Converse County

**CONVERSE COUNTY MEM HOSPITAL** See Memorial Hospital of Converse County

★ **MEMORIAL HOSPITAL OF CONVERSE COUNTY (531302)**, 111 South Fifth Street, Zip 82633–2434, Mailing Address: P.O. Box 1450, Zip 82633–1450; tel. 307/358–2122, (Nonreporting) **A**10 18 **F**3 7 8 11 13 15 28 29 30 32 34 35 38 40 43 45 46 50 57 59 64 65 69 70 74 75 76 79 81 82 85 86 87 89 94 97 107 109 110 111 115 116 117 118 119 126 127 128 129 130 131 133 135 143 144 146 147 148 149 150 154 156
Primary Contact: Matt Dammeyer, Ph.D., Chief Executive Officer
COO: Karl Edward Hertz, Assistant Administrator
CFO: Curtis R. Dugger, Chief Financial Officer
CMO: James Morgan, M.D., Chief Medical Officer
CIO: Dave Patterson, Chief Information Officer
CHR: Linda York, Director Human Resource
CNO: Cristy Dicklich-Cobb, Chief Nursing Officer
Web address: www.conversehospital.com
**Control**: County, Government, Nonfederal **Service**: General medical and surgical

**Staffed Beds**: 25 **Admissions**: 951 **Census**: 8

### EVANSTON—Uinta County

✠ **EVANSTON REGIONAL HOSPITAL (530032)**, 190 Arrowhead Drive, Zip 82930–9266; tel. 307/789–3636, (Nonreporting) **A**1 10 20 **F**3 11 13 15 29 34 35 40 43 45 48 60 64 65 70 74 75 76 77 79 81 82 85 86 87 89 93 97 107 108 111 115 119 126 127 128 129 131 133 146 147 148 149 **P**6 **S** Quorum Health, Brentwood, TN
Primary Contact: Cheri Willard, MSN, R.N., Interim Chief Executive Officer
CHR: Joshua Jones, Director Human Resources
CNO: Cheri Willard, MSN, R.N., Chief Nursing Officer
Web address: www.evanstonregionalhospital.com
**Control**: Corporation, Investor–owned (for–profit) **Service**: General medical and surgical

**Staffed Beds**: 42 **Admissions**: 695 **Census**: 4 **Outpatient Visits**: 32270 **Births**: 144 **Total Expense ($000)**: 31384 **Payroll Expense ($000)**: 14237 **Personnel**: 184

**IHC EVANSTON REGIONAL HOSPITAL** See Evanston Regional Hospital

**WYOMING STATE HOSPITAL (534001)**, 830 Highway 150 South, Zip 82931–5341, Mailing Address: P.O. Box 177, Zip 82931–0177; tel. 307/789–3464, (Nonreporting) **A**10 **F**29 30 50 75 77 98 100 102 103 130

Primary Contact: Bill Rein, Administrator
CFO: Paul Mullenax, Business Manager
CIO: Steve Baldwin, Manager Information Technology
Web address: www.health.wyo.gov/statehospital/index.html
**Control**: State, Government, Nonfederal **Service**: Psychiatric

**Staffed Beds**: 104 **Admissions**: 189 **Census**: 76 **Births**: 0 **Total Expense ($000)**: 26503 **Payroll Expense ($000)**: 16856

### GILLETTE—Campbell County

★ ⇑ **CAMPBELL COUNTY HEALTH (530002)**, 501 South Burma Avenue, Zip 82716–3426, Mailing Address: P.O. Box 3011, Zip 82717–3011; tel. 307/682–8811, (Total facility includes 160 beds in nursing home–type unit) (Nonreporting) **A**10 20 21 **F**3 5 7 8 11 13 15 18 20 22 26 28 29 30 31 34 35 38 40 41 43 45 46 47 48 49 50 54 56 59 60 62 63 64 65 70 73 76 77 78 79 81 84 85 91 92 93 94 96 97 98 99 100 101 102 104 107 108 109 110 111 115 116 117 118 119 120 121 123 129 130 131 132 134 135 144 146 147 148 152 153 154 157
Primary Contact: Colleen Heeter, R.N., Chief Executive Officer
CFO: Dalton Huber, Chief Financial Officer
CIO: Chris Harrison, Manager Information Systems
CHR: John A Fitch, Vice President Human Resources
CNO: Deb L Tonn, Vice President Patient Care
Web address: www.ccmh.net
**Control**: Hospital district or authority, Government, Nonfederal **Service**: General medical and surgical

**Staffed Beds**: 215 **Admissions**: 2497 **Census**: 167 **Outpatient Visits**: 171420 **Births**: 648 **Total Expense ($000)**: 192344 **Payroll Expense ($000)**: 86337

⇑ **CAMPBELL COUNTY MEMORIAL HOSPITAL** See Campbell County Health

### JACKSON—Teton County

⇑ **ST JOHN'S HOSP & LIVING CTR** See St. John's Health

★ ⇑ **ST. JOHN'S HEALTH (530015)**, 625 East Broadway Street, Zip 83001–8642, Mailing Address: P.O. Box 428, Zip 83001–0428; tel. 307/733–3636, (Total facility includes 60 beds in nursing home–type unit) (Nonreporting) **A**10 20 21 **F**3 10 11 13 15 18 19 26 28 29 30 31 32 34 35 36 37 38 39 40 43 44 45 46 47 48 49 50 51 53 54 56 57 59 62 63 65 66 68 70 74 75 76 77 78 79 81 82 84 85 86 87 93 94 97 99 100 101 104 107 108 110 111 114 115 119 120 126 127 128 129 130 131 132 133 135 143 144 145 146 147 148 149 150 153 154 156 157
Primary Contact: Paul Beaupre', M.D., Chief Executive Officer
CFO: John Kren, Chief Financial Officer
CIO: Lance Spranger, Chief Information Officer
CHR: Thomas Kinney, Chief Human Resource Officer
CNO: Marsha Sensat, Chief Nursing Officer
Web address: www.tetonhospital.org
**Control**: Hospital district or authority, Government, Nonfederal **Service**: General medical and surgical

**Staffed Beds**: 105 **Admissions**: 2380 **Census**: 60 **Outpatient Visits**: 86746 **Births**: 382 **Total Expense ($000)**: 127329 **Payroll Expense ($000)**: 53596 **Personnel**: 812

### KEMMERER—Lincoln County

★ **SOUTH LINCOLN MEDICAL CENTER (531315)**, 711 Onyx Street, Zip 83101–3214; tel. 307/877–4401, (Nonreporting) **A**10 18
Primary Contact: Karl Sundberg, Chief Executive Officer
CFO: Curtis Nielson, Chief Financial Officer
CMO: G Christopher Krell, M.D., Chief of Staff
CNO: Kathi Parks, Director of Nursing
Web address: www.southlincolnmedical.com
**Control**: Hospital district or authority, Government, Nonfederal **Service**: General medical and surgical

**Staffed Beds**: 38

### LANDER—Fremont County

**SAGEWEST HEALTHCARE-LANDER** See Sagewest Health Care at Lander

*Many Facility Codes have changed. Please refer to the AHA Guide Code Chart.*
© 2021 AHA Guide

## LARAMIE—Albany County

⊠ **IVINSON MEMORIAL HOSPITAL (530025)**, 255 North 30th Street, Zip 82072–5140; tel. 307/742–2141, (Nonreporting) **A**1 3 10 20
Primary Contact: Doug Faus, FACHE, Chief Executive Officer
COO: Holly Zajic, Chief Operating Officer
CFO: James G Bands IVChief Financial Officer
CMO: John Ullrich, M.D., Chief of Staff
CIO: Brandon Lewis, Director of Information Technology
CHR: Kayla Parry, Manager Human Resources
CNO: Nicole Roonery, Chief Nursing Officer
Web address: www.ivinsonhospital.org
**Control**: Hospital district or authority, Government, Nonfederal **Service**: General medical and surgical

| Staffed Beds: 99 |
| --- |

## LOVELL—Big Horn County

**NORTH BIG HORN HOSPITAL** See North Big Horn Hospital District

★ **NORTH BIG HORN HOSPITAL DISTRICT (531309)**, 1115 Lane 12, Zip 82431–9537; tel. 307/548–5200, (Total facility includes 72 beds in nursing home–type unit) (Nonreporting) **A**10 18 **F**1 7 10 15 18 29 30 31 32 34 35 38 40 45 50 57 59 62 63 65 68 71 75 77 78 79 81 85 87 90 93 97 107 108 110 114 119 127 128 129 130 131 132 133 135 146 148 154 155 156
Primary Contact: Rick Schroeder, Chief Executive Officer
CFO: Lori Smith, Chief Financial Officer
CMO: Richard Jay, D.O., Chief of Staff
CIO: Lisa Strom, Director Information Systems
CHR: Barbara Shumway, Director Human Resources
Web address: www.nbhh.com
**Control**: Hospital district or authority, Government, Nonfederal **Service**: General medical and surgical

| Staffed Beds: 81 Admissions: 361 Census: 73 Births: 0 |
| --- |

## LUSK—Niobrara County

★ **NIOBRARA COMMUNITY HOSPITAL (531314)**, 921 Ballencee Avenue, Zip 82225, Mailing Address: P.O. Box 780, Zip 82225–0780; tel. 307/334–4000, (Nonreporting) **A**10 18
Primary Contact: Nick Doucette, Chief Executive Officer
Web address: www.niobrarahospital.com
**Control**: Hospital district or authority, Government, Nonfederal **Service**: General medical and surgical

| Staffed Beds: 24 |
| --- |

**NIOBRARA COUNTY HOSPITAL DIST** See Niobrara Community Hospital

## NEWCASTLE—Weston County

★ **WESTON COUNTY HEALTH SERVICES (531303)**, 1124 Washington Boulevard, Zip 82701–2972; tel. 307/746–4491, (Total facility includes 58 beds in nursing home–type unit) (Nonreporting) **A**10 18 **F**3 28 29 35 40 41 43 50 57 59 62 64 77 93 107 114 119 129 130 135 148 **S** Monument Health, Rapid City, SD
Primary Contact: Maureen K. Cadwell, Chief Executive Officer
CFO: Lynn Moller, Chief Financial Officer
CMO: Chuck Franklin, M.D., Chief Medical Staff
CIO: Terri Frye, Information Technology Officer
CHR: Julie A Sindlinger, Director of Human Resources
Web address: www.wchs-wy.org
**Control**: Hospital district or authority, Government, Nonfederal **Service**: General medical and surgical

| Staffed Beds: 70 Admissions: 259 Census: 61 Outpatient Visits: 26281 Births: 0 Total Expense ($000): 20155 Payroll Expense ($000): 8765 Personnel: 159 |
| --- |

**WESTON COUNTY MEM HOSPITAL** See Weston County Health Services

## POWELL—Park County

**POWELL HOSPITAL** See Powell Valley Healthcare

★ **POWELL VALLEY HEALTHCARE (531310)**, 777 Avenue 'H', Zip 82435–2296; tel. 307/754–2267, (Total facility includes 100 beds in nursing home–type unit) (Nonreporting) **A**10 18 **F**7 10 11 13 14 15 18 28 29 34 35 40 45 56 57 59 65 67 70 75 76 79 81 82 85 87 97 107 110 111 115 128 130 131 133 135 144 146 147 149 156
Primary Contact: Terry Odom, Chief Executive Officer
CFO: Mike Long, Chief Financial Officer
CMO: Valerie Lengfelder, M.D., Chief of Staff
CIO: Joshua Baxter, Director, Information Systems
CHR: Cassie Tinsley, Director, Human Resources
CNO: Arleen Campeau, R.N., Vice President of Patient Care Services, Chief Nursing Officer
Web address: www.pvhc.org
**Control**: Hospital district or authority, Government, Nonfederal **Service**: General medical and surgical

| Staffed Beds: 125 Admissions: 445 Census: 87 Outpatient Visits: 28067 Births: 127 Total Expense ($000): 45992 Payroll Expense ($000): 22568 |
| --- |

## RAWLINS—Carbon County

★ **MEMORIAL HOSPITAL OF CARBON COUNTY (531316)**, 2221 West Elm Street, Zip 82301–5108, Mailing Address: P.O. Box 460, Zip 82301–0460; tel. 307/324–2221, (Nonreporting) **A**10 18 **F**3 7 11 13 15 28 29 34 35 37 40 43 45 56 57 59 64 65 70 76 79 81 82 85 93 97 107 111 115 119 126 133 135 146 147 148 154 156 **S** QHR Health, Brentwood, TN
Primary Contact: Kenneth Harman, Chief Executive Officer
CFO: David Pike, Interim Chief Financial Officer
CMO: David Cesko, M.D., Chief of Staff
CIO: Toby Schaef, Director Information Technology
Web address: www.imhcc.com
**Control**: County, Government, Nonfederal **Service**: General medical and surgical

| Staffed Beds: 25 Admissions: 629 Census: 5 Outpatient Visits: 35076 Births: 85 Total Expense ($000): 14756 Payroll Expense ($000): 11339 |
| --- |

## RIVERTON—Fremont County

**RIVERTON MEMORIAL HOSPITAL** See Sagewest Health Care

⊠ **SAGEWEST HEALTH CARE (530008)**, 2100 West Sunset Drive, Zip 82501–2274; tel. 307/856–4161, (Includes SAGEWEST HEALTH CARE AT LANDER, Mailing address: 1320 Bishop Randall Drive, Lander, Wyoming, Zip 82520–3996; tel. 307/332–4420; Stephen M Erixon, Chief Executive Officer), (Nonreporting) **A**1 10 20 **F**3 11 13 15 18 20 22 28 29 34 35 39 40 43 45 50 57 59 68 70 74 75 76 77 79 81 85 87 93 97 107 108 110 111 114 115 119 129 130 146 147 148 149 **S** LifePoint Health, Brentwood, TN
Primary Contact: John Ferrelli, Chief Executive Officer
COO: Derrick Brumfield, Chief Operating Officer
CFO: Jennifer Hamilton, Chief Financial Officer
CMO: Cielette Karn, M.D., Chief of Staff
CIO: Linda Tice, Director Information Systems
CHR: Dawn Nelson, Director Human Resources
CNO: Vickie Bessey, MSN, R.N., Chief Nursing Officer
Web address: www.sagewesthealthcare.com
**Control**: Corporation, Investor–owned (for–profit) **Service**: General medical and surgical

| Staffed Beds: 93 Admissions: 2476 Census: 20 |
| --- |

## ROCK SPRINGS—Sweetwater County

⇑ **ASPEN MOUNTAIN MEDICAL CENTER (530035)**, 4401 College Drive, Zip 82901–3507; tel. 307/352–8900, (Nonreporting) **A**21
Primary Contact: Cody Barnhart, Chief Executive Officer
Web address: www.aspenmountainmc.com
**Control**: Partnership, Investor–owned (for–profit) **Service**: General medical and surgical

| Staffed Beds: 16 |
| --- |

**WY**

☒ **MEMORIAL HOSPITAL OF SWEETWATER COUNTY (530011)**, 1200 College Drive, Zip 82901–5868, Mailing Address: P.O. Box 1359, Zip 82902–1359; tel. 307/362–3711, (Nonreporting) **A**1 10 20 **F**3 11 13 15 28 29 30 31 34 35 40 43 48 57 59 60 64 68 70 75 76 77 78 79 81 82 87 93 96 97 107 110 111 114 115 118 119 120 121 122 123 129 130 131 132 135 146 147 148 154 **P**6
Primary Contact: Irene Richardson, Chief Executive Officer
COO: Mandeep Gill, Chief Operating Officer
CFO: Tami Love, Chief Financial Officer
CMO: Sigsbee Duck, M.D., President, Medical Staff
CHR: Amber Fisk, Director Human Resources
CNO: Kallie Mikkelsen, Vice President Nursing
Web address: www.sweetwatermemorial.com/default.aspx
**Control**: County, Government, Nonfederal **Service**: General medical and surgical

**Staffed Beds: 58 Admissions: 1589 Census: 13 Outpatient Visits: 141406 Births: 437 Total Expense ($000): 88018 Payroll Expense ($000): 37637 Personnel: 461**

### SHERIDAN—Sheridan County

**MEM HOSP OF SHERIDAN COUNTY** See Sheridan Memorial Hospital

★ **SHERIDAN MEMORIAL HOSPITAL (530006)**, 1401 West Fifth Street, Zip 82801–2799; tel. 307/672–1000, (Nonreporting) **A**5 10 20
Primary Contact: Michael McCafferty, Chief Executive Officer
CMO: John Addlesperger, D.O., Chief Medical Officer
CIO: Nyle Morgan, Chief Information Officer
CHR: Len Gross, Chief Human Resources Officer
Web address: www.sheridanhospital.org
**Control**: County, Government, Nonfederal **Service**: General medical and surgical

**Staffed Beds: 88**

☒ **SHERIDAN VETERANS AFFAIRS MEDICAL CENTER**, 1898 Fort Road, Zip 82801–8320; tel. 307/672–3473, (Nonreporting) **A**1 **S** Department of Veterans Affairs, Washington, DC
Primary Contact: Pamela Crowell, Director
COO: Chandra Lake, Associate Director
CFO: Donna Fuerstenberg, Fiscal Chief
CMO: Wendell Robison, M.D., Chief of Staff
CIO: Anthony Giljum, Chief Information Officer
CHR: James Hardin, Human Resources Officer
Web address: www.sheridan.va.gov/
**Control**: Veterans Affairs, Government, federal **Service**: Psychiatric

**Staffed Beds: 145**

**VETERANS AFFAIRS MEDICAL CENTER** See Sheridan Veterans Affairs Medical Center

### SUNDANCE—Crook County

**CROOK CNTY MED SYSTEM DIST** See Crook County Medical Services District

★ **CROOK COUNTY MEDICAL SERVICES DISTRICT (531311)**, 713 Oak Street, Zip 82729, Mailing Address: P.O. Box 517, Zip 82729–0517; tel. 307/283–3501, (Nonreporting) **A**10 18 **F**7 40 41 44 57 59 64 65 68 75 89 107 111 114 119 127 128 130 133 143 146 148 149 150
Primary Contact: Micki Lyons, Chief Executive Officer
CFO: Betty Meyers, Chief Financial Officer
CMO: Jeremi Villano, M.D., Chief of Staff
CHR: Patricia Feist, Manager Human Resources
Web address: www.ccmsd.org/
**Control**: Hospital district or authority, Government, Nonfederal **Service**: Acute long–term care hospital

**Staffed Beds: 16 Admissions: 144 Census: 2 Births: 0**

### THERMOPOLIS—Hot Springs County

★ **HOT SPRINGS COUNTY MEMORIAL HOSPITAL (531304)**, 150 East Arapahoe Street, Zip 82443–2498; tel. 307/864–3121, (Nonreporting) **A**3 10 18 **F**3 11 13 15 28 29 31 34 35 40 43 45 50 57 59 64 68 75 76 81 82 85 89 97 107 108 110 111 115 119 127 130 133 135 145 146 **S** HealthTech Management Services, Brentwood, TN
Primary Contact: Margie Molitor, FACHE, R.N., Chief Executive Officer
CFO: Shelly Larson, Chief Financial Officer
CHR: Patti Jeunehomme, Director Human Resources
CNO: Sarah Aliff, Ph.D., Chief Nursing Officer
Web address: www.hscmh.org
**Control**: Hospital district or authority, Government, Nonfederal **Service**: General medical and surgical

**Staffed Beds: 25 Admissions: 327 Census: 3 Personnel: 129**

### TORRINGTON—Goshen County

☒ **COMMUNITY HOSPITAL (531307)**, 2000 Campbell Drive, Zip 82240–1597; tel. 307/532–4181, (Nonreporting) **A**1 10 18 **F**3 11 13 15 18 28 29 30 34 35 40 43 45 55 56 57 59 65 68 70 75 76 79 81 85 89 90 93 94 97 104 107 110 115 119 127 128 130 131 133 143 146 147 148 149 153 154 156 157 **P**8 **S** Banner Health, Phoenix, AZ
Primary Contact: Zachary T. Miller, Interim Chief Executive Officer
CMO: Bonnie Randolph, M.D., Chief of Staff
CIO: Rod Miller, Chief Information Technology
Web address: www.bannerhealth.com/Locations/Wyoming/Community+Hospital/
**Control**: Other not–for–profit (including NFP Corporation) **Service**: General medical and surgical

**Staffed Beds: 20 Admissions: 542 Census: 6 Outpatient Visits: 33149 Births: 63 Total Expense ($000): 29222 Payroll Expense ($000): 12297 Personnel: 175**

### WHEATLAND—Platte County

☒ **PLATTE COUNTY MEMORIAL HOSPITAL (531305)**, 201 14th Street, Zip 82201–3201, Mailing Address: P.O. Box 848, Zip 82201–0848; tel. 307/322–3636, (Nonreporting) **A**1 10 18 **F**3 7 13 15 29 30 32 34 35 40 45 46 47 48 50 56 57 59 65 68 70 75 76 77 79 81 85 90 93 107 108 110 115 119 127 129 133 135 146 147 148 149 150 154 156 **P**8 **S** Banner Health, Phoenix, AZ
Primary Contact: Ned Resch, Chief Executive Officer
CFO: James Cussins, Chief Financial Officer
CMO: Willard Woods, M.D., Chief Medical Officer
CIO: Robin May, Director Information Systems
Web address: www.https://www.bannerhealth.com/locations/wheatland/platte-county-memorial-hospital
**Control**: Other not–for–profit (including NFP Corporation) **Service**: General medical and surgical

**Staffed Beds: 25 Admissions: 362 Census: 4 Outpatient Visits: 20913 Births: 38 Total Expense ($000): 23410 Payroll Expense ($000): 9591 Personnel: 150**

### WORLAND—Washakie County

★ **WASHAKIE MEDICAL CENTER (531306)**, 400 South 15th Street, Zip 82401–3531, Mailing Address: P.O. Box 700, Zip 82401–0700; tel. 307/347–3221, (Nonreporting) **A**1 10 18 **F**3 8 11 13 15 28 29 31 34 37 40 43 45 53 56 59 64 68 70 75 76 78 81 85 89 93 107 110 111 115 119 133 145 146 148 149 154 **P**8 **S** Banner Health, Phoenix, AZ
Primary Contact: Jay Stallings, Chief Executive Officer
CFO: Jennifer Montgomery, Chief Financial Officer
CMO: Ryan Clifford, M.D., Chief of Staff
CHR: Jerry Clipp, Manager Human Resources
CNO: Lisa Van Brunt, Chief Nursing Officer
Web address: www.https://www.bannerhealth.com/locations/worland/washakie-medical-center
**Control**: Other not–for–profit (including NFP Corporation) **Service**: General medical and surgical

**Staffed Beds: 18 Admissions: 510 Census: 6 Outpatient Visits: 29060 Births: 24 Total Expense ($000): 25600 Payroll Expense ($000): 8513 Personnel: 132**

**WASHAKIE MEMORIAL HOSPITAL** See Washakie Medical Center

# AMERICAN SAMOA

### PAGO PAGO—Washakie County

★ **LYNDON B. JOHNSON TROPICAL MEDICAL CENTER (640001)**, Faga'alu Village, Zip 96799, Mailing Address: P.O. Box LBJ, Zip 96799; tel. 684/633–1222, (Nonreporting) **A**10
Primary Contact: Taufete's John. Faumuina, Chief Executive Officer
Web address: www.asmca.org
**Control:** State, Government, Nonfederal **Service:** General medical and surgical

| Staffed Beds: 144 |
|---|

# GUAM

### AGANA—Guam County

**U. S. NAVAL HOSPITAL** See U.S. Naval Hospital Guam

☒ **U. S. NAVAL HOSPITAL GUAM**, Building #50 Farenholt Avenue, Zip 96910, Mailing Address: PSC 490, Box 208, FPO, Zip 96540; tel. 671/344–9340, (Nonreporting) **A**1 **S** Bureau of Medicine and Surgery, Department of the Navy, Falls Church, VA
Primary Contact: Captain Daniel Cornwell, Command Officer
Web address: www.med.navy.mil/sites/usnhguam/Pages/default.aspx
**Service:** General medical and surgical

| Staffed Beds: 55 |
|---|

### DEDEDO—Guam County

☒ **GUAM REGIONAL MEDICAL CITY (650003)**, 133 Route 3, Zip 96932, Mailing Address: P.O. Box 3830, Hagatna, Zip 96932; tel. 671/645–5500, (Nonreporting) **A**1 10
Primary Contact: Alan V. Funtanilla, Executive Vice President, Chief Operating Officer
Web address: www.grmc.gu/
**Control:** Corporation, Investor–owned (for–profit) **Service:** General medical and surgical

| Staffed Beds: 130 |
|---|

### TAMUNING—Guam County

**GUAM MEMORIAL HOSPITAL AUTHORITY (650001)**, 850 Governor Carlos G Camacho Road, Zip 96913; tel. 671/647–2108, (Nonreporting) **A**10
Primary Contact: Joseph P. Verga, FACHE, Chief Executive Officer
CFO: Alan Ulrich, Chief Financial Officer
CMO: James J Stadler, M.D., Associate Administrator Medical Services
CIO: Vince Quichocho, Manager Information Systems
CHR: Elizabeth Claros, Administrator Personnel Services
Web address: www.gmha.org
**Control:** Hospital district or authority, Government, Nonfederal **Service:** General medical and surgical

| Staffed Beds: 104 |
|---|

# MARSHALL ISLANDS

### KWAJALEIN ATOLL—Guam County

**KWAJALEIN HOSPITAL**, U S Army Kwajalein Atoll, Zip 96555, Mailing Address: Ocean Road, P.O. Box 1607, APO AP, Zip 96555–5000; tel. 805/355–2225, (Nonreporting) **S** Department of the Army, Office of the Surgeon General, Falls Church, VA
Primary Contact: Elaine McMahon, Administrator
**Service:** General medical and surgical

| Staffed Beds: 14 |
|---|

**USAKA HOSPITAL** See Kwajalein Hospital

# NORTHERN MARIANA ISLANDS

### SAIPAN—Guam County

★ **COMMONWEALTH HEALTH CENTER (660001)**, Navy Hill Road, Zip 96950, Mailing Address: P.O. Box 500409, Zip 96950; tel. 670/234–8950, (Nonreporting) **A**10
Primary Contact: Esther L. Muna, FACHE, Chief Executive Officer
CFO: Priscilla Maratita Iakopo, Chief Financial Officer
CMO: John M Tudela, M.D., Director of Medical Affairs
CIO: Anthony Reyes, Information Technology Director
CHR: Clarinda Ngiraisui, Director, Human Resources
CNO: Leslie Camacho, R.N., Director of Nursing
Web address: www.chcc.gov.mp
**Control:** Corporation, Investor–owned (for–profit) **Service:** General medical and surgical

| Staffed Beds: 86 |
|---|

**COMMONWESLTH HEALTH CENTER** See Commonwealth Health Center

# PUERTO RICO

### AGUADILLA—Aguadilla County

**AGUADILLA GENERAL HOSPITAL** See Hospital Buen Samaritano

☒ **HOSPITAL BUEN SAMARITANO (400079)**, Carr #2 Km 141-1 Ave Severiano Cuevas, Zip 603, Mailing Address: P.O. Box 4055, Zip 00605–4055; tel. 787/658–0000, (Nonreporting) **A**1 10 **F**3 13 14 15 18 29 30 34 40 41 45 57 59 65 70 75 76 77 81 87 89 107 111 114 119 130 146 148 149 150 157
Primary Contact: Marilyn Morales, Chief Executive Officer
CFO: Edwin Orama Acevedo, Financial Supervisor
CMO: Arturo Cedeno Llorens, M.D., Medical Director
CHR: Jose Garcia Rivera, Director Human Resources
CNO: Eneida Alicea Perez, Interim Nursing Director
Web address: www.hbspr.org
**Control:** Other not–for–profit (including NFP Corporation) **Service:** General medical and surgical

| Staffed Beds: 145 Admissions: 4721 Census: 71 Births: 0 |
|---|

## AIBONITO—Aibonito County

See Centro De Salud Conductual Menonita-Cima

⊞ **CENTRO DE SALUD CONDUCTUAL MENONITA-CIMA (404009)**, Carretera Estatal 14 Interior, Zip 705, Mailing Address: PO Box 871, Zip 705; tel. 787/714–2462, (Nonreporting) **A**1 10
Primary Contact: Pedro Melendez, Chief Executive Officer
Web address: www.menonitacima.org
**Control**: Other not–for–profit (including NFP Corporation) **Service**: Psychiatric

**Staffed Beds:** 20

⊞ **MENNONITE GENERAL HOSPITAL (400018)**, Calle Jose C Vasquez, Zip 705, Mailing Address: P.O. Box 372800, Cayey, Zip 00737–2800; tel. 787/535–1001, (Nonreporting) **A**1 5 10
Primary Contact: Pedro Melendez, Chief Executive Officer
COO: Marta R Mercado Suro, Chief Operating Officer
CFO: Jose E Solivan, Chief Financial Officer
CMO: Victor Hernandez Miranda, M.D., Chief of Staff
CIO: Daniza Morales, Manager Information System
CHR: Evelyn Padilla Ortiz, Director Human Resources
CNO: Gloria Mercado, Director of Nursing
Web address: www.hospitalmenonita.com
**Control**: Other not–for–profit (including NFP Corporation) **Service**: General medical and surgical

**Staffed Beds:** 143

## ARECIBO—Arecibo County

**HOSPITAL DR. CAYETANO COLL Y TOSTE** See Hospital Pavia Arecibo

**HOSPITAL DR. SUSONI** See Hospital Metropolitano Dr. Susoni

⊞ **HOSPITAL METROPOLITANO DR. SUSONI (400117)**, Calle Palma #55, Zip 612, Mailing Address: P.O. Box 145200, Zip 614; tel. 787/650–1030, (Nonreporting) **A**1 10
Primary Contact: Yelitza Lucena, Executive Director
CFO: Francisco Silva, Financial Director
CMO: Ada S Miranda, M.D., Medical Director
CIO: Mayra Montano, Director Information Systems
CHR: Janira Hernandez, Coordinator Human Resources
CNO: Damaris Rios, Executive Nursing Director
Web address: www.metropavia.com/DrSusoni.cfm
**Control**: Corporation, Investor–owned (for–profit) **Service**: General medical and surgical

**Staffed Beds:** 130

⊞ **HOSPITAL PAVIA ARECIBO (400087)**, 129 San Luis Avenue, Zip 612, Mailing Address: P.O. Box 659, Zip 613; tel. 787/650–7272, (Nonreporting) **A**1 10
Primary Contact: Jose Luis Rodriguez Collazo, Executive Director
COO: Jamie Rivera, Chief Financial Officer
CFO: Agustin Gonzalez, Director Finance
CMO: Antoine Pavia, M.D., Medical Director
CIO: David Valle, Chief Information Officer
CHR: Yesenia Natal, Coordinator Human Resources
CNO: Iris Toledo, Chief Nursing Officer
Web address: www.cayetano@xsn.net
**Control**: Corporation, Investor–owned (for–profit) **Service**: General medical and surgical

**Staffed Beds:** 184

## BAYAMON—Bayamon County

⊞ **BAYAMON MEDICAL CENTER (400032)**, Route 2, KM 11-7, Zip 960, Mailing Address: P.O. Box 306, Zip 960; tel. 787/620–8181, (Includes PUERTO RICO CHILDREN'S HOSPITAL, Mailing address: P O Box 1999, Bayamon, Puerto Rico, Zip 960; tel. 787/474–1378; Tania Conde, Administrator), (Nonreporting) **A**1 5 10
Primary Contact: Richard Machado, M.D., President and Chief Executive Officer
CFO: Luz D Medina, Controller
CMO: Norma Ortiz, M.D., Medical Director
CIO: Leticia Santana, Administrator Medical Records
Web address: www.hospitalhermanosmelendez.net
**Control**: Corporation, Investor–owned (for–profit) **Service**: General medical and surgical

**Staffed Beds:** 211

★ **DOCTOR'S CENTER OF BAYAMON (400102)**, Extension Hermanas Davila, Zip 960, Mailing Address: P.O. Box 2957, Zip 960; tel. 787/622–5420, (Nonreporting) **A**10
Primary Contact: Maria Marte, Administrator
Web address: www.https://www.tuhospitalfamiliar.com
**Control**: Corporation, Investor–owned (for–profit) **Service**: General medical and surgical

**Staffed Beds:** 91

**HOSPITAL HERMANOS MELENDEZ** See Bayamon Medical Center

**HOSPITAL MATILDE BRENES** See Doctor's Center of Bayamon

⊞ **HOSPITAL SAN PABLO (400109)**, Calle Santa Cruz 70, Zip 00961–7020, Mailing Address: P.O. Box 236, Zip 00960–0236; tel. 787/740–4747, (Nonreporting) **A**1 3 5 10
Primary Contact: Claudia V. Guzman, Chief Executive Officer and Managing Director
Web address: www.sanpablo.com
**Control**: Corporation, Investor–owned (for–profit) **Service**: General medical and surgical

**Staffed Beds:** 400

⊞ **HOSPITAL UNIVERSITARIO DR. RAMON RUIZ ARNAU (400105)**, Avenue Laurel #100, Santa Juanita, Zip 956; tel. 787/787–5151, (Nonreporting) **A**1 3 5 10 **S** Puerto Rico Department of Health, San Juan, PR
Primary Contact: Prudencio A. Laureano, Chief Executive Officer
CFO: Elsie Morales, Chief Financial Officer
CMO: Hector Cintron Principe, M.D., Director
CIO: Irma Duprey, Administrator Medical Records
CHR: Aurea De Leon, Chief Human Resources Officer
Web address: www.salud.gov.pr/Dept-de-Salud/Pages/Nuestros-Hospitales.aspx
**Control**: State, Government, Nonfederal **Service**: General medical and surgical

**Staffed Beds:** 101

## CABO ROJO—Cabo Rojo County

See Hospital Psiquiatrico Metropolitano

⊞ **HOSPITAL PSIQUIATRICO METROPOLITANO (404007)**, 108 Munoz Rivera Street, Zip 00623–4060, Mailing Address: P.O. Box 910, Zip 00623–0910; tel. 787/851–2025, (Nonreporting) **A**1 10
Primary Contact: Marco Reyes, Executive Director
Web address: www.metropavia.com/CaboRojo.cfm
**Control**: Other not–for–profit (including NFP Corporation) **Service**: Psychiatric

**Staffed Beds:** 43

## CAGUAS—Caguas County

⊞ **HIMA SAN PABLO CAGUAS (400120)**, Avenida Munoz Marin, Zip 726, Mailing Address: P.O. Box 4980, Zip 726; tel. 787/653–3434, (Nonreporting) **A**1 2 3 5 10
Primary Contact: Maria E. Jacobo Moreno, Administrator
CFO: Luis A Arroyo, Chief Financial Officer
CMO: Ivan E Del Toro, M.D., Medical Director
CIO: Giovanni Piereschi, Vice President Enterprise Information and Chief Information Officer
CHR: Elena Robinson, Chief Human Resources Officer
CNO: Elenia Berrios, Chief Nursing Officer
Web address: www.himasanpablo.com
**Control**: Partnership, Investor–owned (for–profit) **Service**: General medical and surgical

**Staffed Beds:** 415

**HIMA SAN PABLO CUPEY** See Hima San Pablo Caguas

⊞ **HOSPITAL MENONITA DE CAGUAS (400104)**, P.O. Box 6660, Zip 00726–6660; tel. 787/653–0550, (Nonreporting) **A**1 5 10
Primary Contact: Pedro Melendez, Executive Director
Web address: www.sistemamenonita.com
**Control**: Other not–for–profit (including NFP Corporation) **Service**: General medical and surgical

**Staffed Beds:** 25

*Many Facility Codes have changed. Please refer to the AHA Guide Code Chart.*

## CAROLINA—Carolina County

⊞ **HOSPITAL DE LA UNIVERSIDAD DE PUERTO RICO/DR. FEDERICO TRILLA (400112)**, 65th Infanteria, KM 8 3, Zip 984, Mailing Address: P.O. Box 6021, Zip 984; tel. 787/757–1800, (Nonreporting) **A**1 3 5 10
Primary Contact: Diraida Maldonado, Chief Executive Officer
COO: Diraida Maldonado, Chief Executive Officer
CFO: Yolanda Quinonez, Chief Financial Officer
CMO: Marina Roman, M.D., Medical Director
CIO: Francisco Perez, Manager Management Information Systems
CHR: Betzaida Jimenez, Director Human Resources
Web address: www.hospitalupr.org
**Control**: Corporation, Investor–owned (for–profit) **Service**: General medical and surgical

| Staffed Beds: 250 |
|---|

**HOSPITAL DR FEDERICO TRILLA** See Hospital De La Universidad De Puerto Rico/Dr. Federico Trilla

## CASTANER—Lares County

★ **CASTANER GENERAL HOSPITAL (400010)**, KM 64-2, Route 135, Zip 631, Mailing Address: P.O. Box 1003, Zip 631; tel. 787/829–5010, (Nonreporting) **A**5 10
Primary Contact: Domingo Monroig, Executive Director
COO: Agustin Ponce, Supervisor Maintenance
CFO: Guillermo Jimenez, Director Finance
CMO: Jose O Rodriguez, M.D., Medical Director
CIO: Domingo Monroig, Executive Director
CHR: Nydimar Salcedo, Chief Human Resources Officer
CNO: Margarita Rentas, R.N., Nursing Director
Web address: www.hospitalcastaner.com
**Control**: Other not–for–profit (including NFP Corporation) **Service**: General medical and surgical

| Staffed Beds: 24 |
|---|

## CAYEY—Cayey County

⊞ **HOSPITAL MENONITA DE CAYEY (400013)**, 4 H Mendoza Street, Zip 00736–3801, Mailing Address: P.O. Box 373130, Zip 00737–3130; tel. 787/263–1001, (Nonreporting) **A**1 5 10
Primary Contact: Pedro Melendez, Chief Executive Director
COO: Leda Marta R Mercado, Chief Operating Officer
CFO: Jose E Solivan, Chief Financial Officer
CMO: Luis J Rodriquez Saenz, M.D., Medical Director
CIO: Daniza Morales, Chief Information Officer
CHR: Evelyn Padilla Ortiz, Director Human Resources
Web address: www.hospitalmenonita.com
**Control**: Other not–for–profit (including NFP Corporation) **Service**: General medical and surgical

| Staffed Beds: 242 |
|---|

## CIDRA—Cidra County

⊞ **FIRST HOSPITAL PANAMERICANO (404004)**, State Road 787 KM 1 5, Zip 739, Mailing Address: P.O. Box 1400, Zip 739; tel. 787/739–5555, (Nonreporting) **A**1 3 5 10 **S** Universal Health Services, Inc., King of Prussia, PA
Primary Contact: Astro Munoz, Executive Director
COO: Tim McCarthy, President Puerto Rico Division
CFO: Arthur Fernandez, Chief Financial Officer
CMO: William Almodavar, M.D., Director Medical
CIO: Tomas Rodriguez, Chief Information Technology Officer
CHR: Shirley Ayala, Director Human Resources
Web address: www.hospitalpanamericano.com
**Control**: Corporation, Investor–owned (for–profit) **Service**: Psychiatric

| Staffed Beds: 153 |
|---|

## COTO LAUREL—Ponce County

★ **HOSPITAL SAN CRISTOBAL (400113)**, 506 Carr Road, Zip 780; tel. 787/848–2100, (Nonreporting) **A**3 10
Primary Contact: Pedro L. Benetti-Loyola, Administrator
COO: Pedro L Benetti-Loyola, Senior Executive and Vice President
CFO: Marian Collazo, Director Finance
CMO: Ramon Rodriguez Rivas, M.D., Medical Director
CIO: Ramon Acevedo, Supervisor Information Systems
CHR: Candie Rodriguez, Director Human Resources
Web address: www.hospitalsancristobal.com
**Control**: Corporation, Investor–owned (for–profit) **Service**: Other specialty treatment

| Staffed Beds: 103 |
|---|

## FAJARDO—Fajardo County

★ **CARIBBEAN MEDICAL CENTER (400131)**, 151 Avenue Osvaldo Molina, Zip 00738–4013, Mailing Address: Call Box 70006, Zip 00738–7006; tel. 787/801–0081, (Nonreporting) **A**10
Primary Contact: Ana Oliveras Laguna, Administrator
CMO: Miguel Rodriguez, Medical Director
Web address: www.caribbeanmedicalcenter.com
**Control**: Other not–for–profit (including NFP Corporation) **Service**: General medical and surgical

| Staffed Beds: 39 |
|---|

**DR JOSE RAMOS LEBRON HOSPITAL** See Hospital San Pablo Del Este

⊞ **HOSPITAL SAN PABLO DEL ESTE (400125)**, Avenida General Valero, 404, Zip 738, Mailing Address: P.O. Box 1028, Zip 00738–1028; tel. 787/863–0505, (Nonreporting) **A**1 10
Primary Contact: Venus V. Ramirez, Executive Director
CFO: Luis A Arroyo, Chief Financial Officer
CMO: Manuel Navas, M.D., Medical Director
CHR: Vilma Rodriguez, Director Human Resources
Web address: www.sanpablo.com
**Control**: Corporation, Investor–owned (for–profit) **Service**: General medical and surgical

| Staffed Beds: 221 |
|---|

## GUAYAMA—Guayama County

**HOSPITAL EPISCOPAL CRISTO REDENTOR** See Hospital Episcopal San Lucas Guayama

⊞ **HOSPITAL EPISCOPAL SAN LUCAS GUAYAMA (400048)**, Avenue Pedro Albizu Campos, Zip 784, Mailing Address: PO Box 10011, Zip 00785–1006; tel. 787/864–4300, (Nonreporting) **A**1 5 10
Primary Contact: Elyonel Ponton, Executive Director
COO: Arnaldo Rodriguez Sanchez, M.D., Chief Operating Officer
CFO: Rosemary De La Cruz, Chief Financial Officer
CMO: Gerson Jimenez, M.D., Medical Director
CHR: Ivette Lacot, Director Human Resources
Web address: www.ssepr.com
**Control**: Church operated, Nongovernment, not–for–profit **Service**: General medical and surgical

| Staffed Beds: 115 |
|---|

## GUAYNABO—Guaynabo County

**PROFESSIONAL HOSPITAL GUAYNABO (400122)**, Carretera 199 Km 1.2 Avenue, Zip 969, Mailing Address: PO Box 1609, Zip 970; tel. 787/708–6560, (Nonreporting) **A**5 10
Primary Contact: Leonardo Valentin, Chief Executive Officer
Web address: www.professionalhospital.com
**Control**: Other not–for–profit (including NFP Corporation) **Service**: Psychiatric

| Staffed Beds: 54 |
|---|

---

| Hospital, Medicare Provider Number, Address, Telephone, Approval, Facility, and Physician Codes, Health Care System |
|---|

★ American Hospital Association (AHA) membership    ○ Healthcare Facilities Accreditation Program    ⇧ Center for Improvement in Healthcare Quality Accreditation
□ The Joint Commission accreditation    ◇ DNV Healthcare Inc. accreditation    △ Commission on Accreditation of Rehabilitation Facilities (CARF) accreditation

## HATO REY—San Juan County

✉ **I. GONZALEZ MARTINEZ ONCOLOGIC HOSPITAL (400012)**, Puerto Rico
Medical Center, Zip 935, Mailing Address: P.O. Box 191811, Zip 00919–1811;
tel. 787/765–2382, (Nonreporting) **A**1 2 3 5 10
Primary Contact: Jorge De Jesus, Executive Director
COO: Felix Ortiz Baez, Administrator
CFO: Yolanda Quinones, Director Finance
CMO: Carlos Chevere, M.D., Medical Director
CHR: Luz Maria Hernandez, Director Human Resources
**Control**: Other not-for-profit (including NFP Corporation) **Service**: Cancer

**Staffed Beds:** 57

## HUMACAO—Humacao County

**HOSPITAL DR. DOMINGUEZ** See Hospital Oriente

✉ **HOSPITAL HIMA DE HUMACAO (400005)**, 3 Font Martelo Street,
Zip 00791–3342, Mailing Address: P.O. Box 639, Zip 00792–0639;
tel. 787/656–2424, (Nonreporting) **A**1 10
Primary Contact: Aixa Irizarry, Executive Director
COO: Carlos M Pineiro, President
CFO: Luis A Arroyo, Chief Financial Officer
CMO: Francisco R. Carballo, M.D., Medical Director
CIO: Giovanni Piereschi, Vice President Management Information Systems
CHR: Iris Abreu, Supervisor Human Resources
Web address: www.himasanpablo.com
**Control**: Corporation, Investor–owned (for-profit) **Service**: General medical and
surgical

**Staffed Beds:** 64

**HOSPITAL HMA DE HUMACAO** See Hospital Hima De Humacao

★ **HOSPITAL ORIENTE (400011)**, 300 Font Martelo Street, Zip 00791–3230,
Mailing Address: P.O. Box 699, Zip 00792–0699; tel. 787/852–0505,
(Nonreporting) **A**10
Primary Contact: Efrain Pinero, Administrator
CFO: Ivonne Rivera, Director Finance
CMO: Carmelo Herrero, M.D., Medical Director
CHR: Ivonne Lopez, Director Human Resources
**Control**: Corporation, Investor–owned (for-profit) **Service**: General medical and
surgical

**Staffed Beds:** 60

★ **RYDER MEMORIAL HOSPITAL (400007)**, 355 Font Martelo Street,
Zip 00791–3249, Mailing Address: P O Box 859, Zip 00792–0859;
tel. 787/852–0768, (Nonreporting) **A**5 10
Primary Contact: Jose R. Feliciano, Chief Executive Officer
CFO: Jose O Ortiz, Chief Financial Officer
CMO: Raul Ramos Pereira, M.D., Medical Director
CIO: Joseph V Cruz, Chief Information Officer
CHR: Maria Figueroa, Director Human Resources
CNO: Aurelis Burgus, Nursing Director
Web address: www.hryder@prtc.net
**Control**: Other not-for-profit (including NFP Corporation) **Service**: General
medical and surgical

**Staffed Beds:** 227

## MANATI—Manati County

**ALEJANDRO OTERO LOPEZ HOSPITAL** See Hospital Manati Medical Center

✉ **DOCTORS CENTER (400118)**, KM 47-7, Zip 674, Mailing Address: P.O. Box
30532, Zip 674; tel. 787/854–3322, (Nonreporting) **A**1 3 5 10
Primary Contact: Belinda L. Toro Palacios, Executive Director
Web address: www.https://www.tuhospitalfamiliar.com
**Control**: Corporation, Investor–owned (for-profit) **Service**: General medical and
surgical

**Staffed Beds:** 250

★ **ENCOMPASS HEALTH REHABILITATION HOSPITAL OF MANATI (403026)**,
Carretera 2, Kilometro 47 7, Zip 674; tel. 787/621–3800, (Nonreporting) **A**10 **S**
Encompass Health Corporation, Birmingham, AL
Primary Contact: Enid Y. Gonzalez, Chief Executive Officer
CFO: Jesus M Corazon, Controller
CMO: Jamie L Marrero, M.D., Medical Director
CHR: Erika Landrau, Director Human Resources
CNO: Evelyn Diaz, R.N., Chief Nursing Officer
Web address: www.healthsouth.com
**Control**: Corporation, Investor–owned (for-profit) **Service**: Rehabilitation

**Staffed Beds:** 40

**HEALTHSOUTH HOSPITAL OF MANATI** See Encompass Health Rehabilitation
Hospital of Manati

✉ **HOSPITAL MANATI MEDICAL CENTER (400114)**, Calle Hernandez,
Carrion 668, Zip 674, Mailing Address: P.O. Box 1142, Zip 00674–1142;
tel. 787/621–3700, (Nonreporting) **A**1 3 5 10
Primary Contact: Jose S. Rosado, Executive Director
CFO: Noriselle Rivera-Pol, Vice President Finance
CMO: Luis R Rosa-Toledo, M.D., Medical Director
CIO: Alberto Medina, Information Technology Senior Consultant
CHR: Nilda Paravisini, Director Human Resources
Web address: www.manatimedical.com
**Control**: Corporation, Investor–owned (for-profit) **Service**: General medical and
surgical

**Staffed Beds:** 235

## MAYAGUEZ—Mayaguez County

✉ **BELLA VISTA HOSPITAL (400014)**, State Road 349, Zip 680, Mailing Address:
P.O. Box 1750, Zip 681; tel. 787/834–6000, (Nonreporting) **A**1 3 5 10
Primary Contact: Luis Rivera Maldonado, Executive Director
CFO: Enrique Rivera, Chief Financial Officer
CMO: Miguel Cruz, M.D., Medical Director
CHR: Benjamin Astacio, Director Human Resources
Web address: www.bvhpr.org
**Control**: Church operated, Nongovernment, not-for-profit **Service**: General
medical and surgical

**Staffed Beds:** 157

**CLINICA DOCTOR PEREA** See Hospital Perea

✉ **DR. RAMON E. BETANCES HOSPITAL-MAYAGUEZ MEDICAL CENTER
BRANCH (400103)**, 410 Hostos Avenue, Zip 00680–1501, Mailing Address: P.O.
Box 600, Zip 00681–0600; tel. 787/652–9200, (Nonreporting) **A**1 3 5 10
Primary Contact: Idelfonso Vargas, Executive Director
CMO: Milton D Carrero, M.D., Medical Director
CHR: Betsmari Medina, Director Human Resources
Web address: www.mayaguezmedical.com
**Control**: State, Government, Nonfederal **Service**: General medical and surgical

**Staffed Beds:** 189

★ **HOSPITAL PEREA (400123)**, 15 Basora Street, Zip 681, Mailing Address: P.O.
Box 170, Zip 681; tel. 787/834–0101, (Nonreporting) **A**3 10 **S** United Medical
Corporation, Windermere, FL
Primary Contact: Jorge I. Martinez, Executive Director
CFO: Joannie Garcia, CPA, Director Finance
CMO: Humberto Olivencia, M.D., Medical Director
Web address: www.paviahealth.com/perea_hospital.htm
**Control**: Corporation, Investor–owned (for-profit) **Service**: General medical and
surgical

**Staffed Beds:** 103

## MAYAGUEZ—Mataguez County

★ **HOSPITAL SAN ANTONIO (018487)**, Calle Dr Ramon Emeterio Betances N #18,
Zip 680, Mailing Address: PO Box 546, Zip 00681–0546; tel. 787/834–0050,
(Nonreporting) **A**3 10
Primary Contact: Francisco Martinez, Executive Director
Web address: www.hsaipr.com/
**Control**: Other not-for-profit (including NFP Corporation) **Service**: General
medical and surgical

**Staffed Beds:** 25

## MOCA—Moca County

★ **HOSPITAL SAN CARLOS BORROMEO (400111)**, 550 Concepcion Vera Ayala,
Zip 676, Mailing Address: PO Box 68, Zip 676; tel. 787/877–8000, (Nonreporting)
**A**10
Primary Contact: Rosaida M. Crespo, Executive Director
COO: Rosaida M Crespo, Executive Director
CFO: Irma Cabrera, Finance Director
CMO: Erick Nieves, M.D., Medical Director
CIO: Juan Carlos Soto, Director Information Systems
CHR: Migdalia Ortiz, Director Human Resources
CNO: Luz M Velez, Director-Administration of Nursing Services
Web address: www.hscbpr.org
**Control**: Other not-for-profit (including NFP Corporation) **Service**: General
medical and surgical

**Staffed Beds:** 106

## PONCE—Ponce County

☒ **DR. PILA'S HOSPITAL (400003)**, Avenida Las Americas, Zip 731, Mailing Address: P.O. Box 1910, Zip 00733–1910; tel. 787/848–5600, (Nonreporting) **A**1 10
Primary Contact: Rafael Alvarado, Chief Executive Officer
Web address: www.drpila.com
**Control:** Other not–for–profit (including NFP Corporation) **Service:** General medical and surgical

**Staffed Beds:** 143

☒ **HOSPITAL DE DAMAS (400022)**, 2213 Ponce Bypass, Zip 717; tel. 787/840–8686, (Nonreporting) **A**1 3 5 10
Primary Contact: Maria Mercedes Torres. Bernal, Administrator
CFO: Julio Colon, Financial Director
CMO: Pedro Benitez, M.D., Medical Director
CIO: Bienvenido Ortiz, Coordinator Information Systems
CHR: Gilberto Cuevas, Director Human Resources
CNO: Sandra Dominicci, Nursing Director
Web address: www.hospitaldamas.com/
**Control:** Other not–for–profit (including NFP Corporation) **Service:** General medical and surgical

**Staffed Beds:** 201

**HOSPITAL DE PSIQUIATRIA FORENSE**, Road 14, Zip 731; tel. 787/844–0210, (Nonreporting)
Primary Contact: Nemuel O. Artiles, FACHE, Administrator
Web address: www.bestmentalhealthfacilities.com/hospital-psiquiatria-forenseponce-in-ponce-pr-731/
**Control:** State, Government, Nonfederal **Service:** Psychiatric

**Staffed Beds:** 25

★ **INSPIRA PONCE (404008)**, Calle Guadalupe, #184, Piso2, Zip 730; tel. 787/709–4130, (Nonreporting) **A**10
Primary Contact: Alberto M. Varela, M.D., President
Web address: www.inspirapr.com
**Control:** Corporation, Investor–owned (for–profit) **Service:** Psychiatric

**Staffed Beds:** 30

**PONCE REGIONAL HOSPITAL** See St. Luke's Episcopal Hospital

☒ **ST. LUKE'S EPISCOPAL HOSPITAL (400044)**, 917 Tito Castro Avenue, Zip 00731–4717, Mailing Address: P.O. Box 336810, Zip 00733–6810; tel. 787/844–2080, (Nonreporting) **A**1 3 10
Primary Contact: Jose M. Torres, Executive Director
CFO: Carlos Valentin, Chief Financial Officer
CMO: Jesus Cruz Correa, Chief Medical Officer
CIO: Jose Abrams, Chief Information Officer
CHR: Hector Troche Garcin, Human Resources Director
CNO: Zoraida Vega, MSN, R.N., Chief Nursing Officer
Web address: www.sanlucaspr.com
**Control:** Church operated, Nongovernment, not–for–profit **Service:** General medical and surgical

**Staffed Beds:** 291

## RIO PIEDRAS—San Juan County

☒ **UNIVERSITY PEDIATRIC HOSPITAL (403301)**, Barrio Monacenno, Carretera 22, Zip 935, Mailing Address: P.O. Box 191079, San Juan, Zip 00910–1070; tel. 787/777–3535, (Nonreporting) **A**1 3 5 10 **S** Puerto Rico Department of Health, San Juan, PR
Primary Contact: Gloria Hernandez, Executive Director
CMO: Myrna Quinones Feliciano, M.D., Medical Director
Web address: www.md.rcm.upr.edu/pediatrics/university_pediatric_hospital.php
**Control:** State, Government, Nonfederal **Service:** Children's general medical and surgical

**Staffed Beds:** 145

## SAN GERMAN—San German County

☒ **HOSPITAL DE LA CONCEPCION (400021)**, Carr 2, Km 173, Bo Cain Alto, Zip 00683–3920, Mailing Address: P.O. Box 285, Zip 00683–0285; tel. 787/892–1860, (Nonreporting) **A**1 3 5 10
Primary Contact: Felicita Bonilla, Administrator
COO: Gustavo Almodovar, Executive Director
CFO: Lizmari Calderon, Director Finance
CMO: Ivan Acosta, M.D., Medical Director
CIO: Daniel Ferreira, Director Management Information Systems
CHR: Ada Bermudez, Director Human Resources
CNO: Amanda Caraballo, Nursing Director
Web address: www.hospitalconcepcion.org
**Control:** Church operated, Nongovernment, not–for–profit **Service:** General medical and surgical

**Staffed Beds:** 187

★ **HOSPITAL METROPOLITANO SAN GERMAN (400126)**, Calle Javilla Al Costado Parque de Bombas, Zip 683, Mailing Address: PO Box 63, Zip 683; tel. 787/892–5300, (Nonreporting) **A**10
Primary Contact: Luis A. Berdiel, Executive Director
**Control:** Corporation, Investor–owned (for–profit) **Service:** Other specialty treatment

**Staffed Beds:** 76

## SAN JUAN—San Juan County

☒ **ASHFORD PRESBYTERIAN COMMUNITY HOSPITAL (400001)**, 1451 Avenue Ashford, Zip 00907–1511, Mailing Address: P.O. Box 9020032, Zip 00902–0032; tel. 787/721–2160, (Nonreporting) **A**1 3 5 10
Primary Contact: Pedro J. Gonzalez, FACHE, Chief Executive Officer
COO: Obdulia Medina, MSN, Associate Director for Administrative Support, Clinical Management and Ambulatory Care
CFO: Mayra Torres, CPA, Chief Financial Officer
CMO: Rafael Gonzalez, M.D., Medical Director
CIO: Sigfredo Irizarry, Information Technology Director
CHR: Irma Carrillo, Director Human Resources
CNO: Berenice Perez, Chief Nursing Officer
Web address: www.presbypr.com
**Control:** Other not–for–profit (including NFP Corporation) **Service:** General medical and surgical

**Staffed Beds:** 177

☒ **AUXILIO MUTUO HOSPITAL (400016)**, Ponce De Leon Avenue, Zip 00918–1000, Mailing Address: P.O. Box 191227, Zip 00919–1227; tel. 787/758–2000, (Nonreporting) **A**1 3 5 10
Primary Contact: Jorge L Matta. Serrano, Administrator
COO: Carmen Martin, Associate Administrator
CFO: Maria L Marti, Director Fiscal Services
CMO: Jose Isado, M.D., Medical Director
CIO: Edgardo Rodriguez, Director Management Information Systems
CHR: Maria Vega, Director Human Resources
Web address: www.auxiliomutuo.com
**Control:** Other not–for–profit (including NFP Corporation) **Service:** General medical and surgical

**Staffed Beds:** 483

☒ **CARDIOVASCULAR CENTER OF PUERTO RICO AND THE CARIBBEAN (400124)**, Americo Miranda Centro Medico, Zip 936, Mailing Address: P.O. Box 366528, Zip 00936–6528; tel. 787/754–8500, (Nonreporting) **A**1 3 5 10 **F**3 17 18 19 20 21 22 23 24 25 26 27 29 30 34 45 46 57 60 65 69 70 74 75 77 87 88 107 108 109 114 115 130 135 137 146 148 149 **S** Puerto Rico Department of Health, San Juan, PR
Primary Contact: Carlos Cabrera, Executive Director
COO: Wilfredo Rabelo Millan, Chief Operating Officer
CFO: Arthur J Fernandez del Valle, Chief Financial Officer
CMO: Jose E Novoa Loyola, M.D., Medical Director
CIO: Eugenio Torres Ayala, Director Information Systems
CHR: Myriam T Rodriguez Schmidt, Director Human Resources
CNO: Pedro Laureano Cantre, Chief Nursing Officer
Web address: www.cardiovascular.gobierno.pr
**Control:** State, Government, Nonfederal **Service:** Heart

**Staffed Beds:** 164 **Admissions:** 3498 **Census:** 80 **Outpatient Visits:** 16177 **Births:** 0 **Total Expense ($000):** 78171 **Payroll Expense ($000):** 17613

---

**Hospital, Medicare Provider Number, Address, Telephone, Approval, Facility, and Physician Codes, Health Care System**

★ American Hospital Association (AHA) membership
□ The Joint Commission accreditation
○ Healthcare Facilities Accreditation Program
◇ DNV Healthcare Inc. accreditation
⇑ Center for Improvement in Healthcare Quality Accreditation
△ Commission on Accreditation of Rehabilitation Facilities (CARF) accreditation

**CARIBBEAN PED & SURGERY HOSP** See Hospital San Francisco

**CENTRO CARDIOVASCULAR DE PR** See Cardiovascular Center of Puerto Rico and The Caribbean

**SAN JUAN—Moca County**

**CENTRO DE TRAUMA** See Hospital Cuidado Agudo Especializado En Pacientes Politraumatizados

**SAN JUAN—San Juan County**

**CUPEY HOSPITAL & NRSG HOME** See Hospital San Gerardo

**DOCTORS CENTER HOSPITAL** See Doctors' Center Hospital San Juan

★ **DOCTORS' CENTER HOSPITAL SAN JUAN (400006)**, 1395 San Rafael Street, Zip 00909–2518, Mailing Address: Box 11338, Santurce Station, Zip 00910–3428; tel. 787/999-7620, (Nonreporting) **A**10
Primary Contact: Norma Marrero, Executive Administrator
COO: Norma Marrero, Executive Administrator
CFO: Alejandro Santiago, Director Finance
CMO: Ubaldo Santiago, M.D., Chairman
CIO: Luis Alicea, Chief Information Officer
CHR: Carmen Perez, Director Human Resources
CNO: Lesbia Lopez, Chief Nursing Officer
Web address: www.tuhospitalfamiliar.com
**Control**: Corporation, Investor–owned (for–profit) **Service**: General medical and surgical

**Staffed Beds**: 133

★ **ENCOMPASS HEALTH REHABILITATION HOSPITAL OF SAN JUAN (403025)**, University Hospital, 3rd Floor, Zip 923, Mailing Address: P.O. Box 70344, Zip 923; tel. 787/274-5100, (Nonreporting) **A**3 5 10 **S** Encompass Health Corporation, Birmingham, AL
Primary Contact: Daniel Del Castillo, Chief Executive Officer
CFO: Jesus M Corazon, Controller
CMO: Eduardo Ramos, M.D., Medical Director
CHR: Frances Fuentes, Coordinator Human Resources
CNO: Zamarys Rivera, R.N., Chief Nursing Officer
Web address: www.healthsouthsanjuan.com
**Control**: Corporation, Investor–owned (for–profit) **Service**: Rehabilitation

**Staffed Beds**: 32

**FUNDACION HOSP METROPOLITAN** See Hospital Metropolitan

**HATO REY COMMUNITY HOSPITAL** See Hospital Pavia-Hato Rey

**HEALTHSOUTH REHABILITATION HOSPITAL OF SAN JUAN** See Encompass Health Rehabilitation Hospital of San Juan

**SAN JUAN—Moca County**

**HOSPITAL CUIDADO AGUDO ESPECIALIZADO EN PACIENTES POLITRAUMATIZADOS (400127)**, Carr. Num. 22 BO. Monacillos, Centro Medico, Zip 00922–2129, Mailing Address: PO Box 2129, Zip 00922–2129; tel. 787/777-3535, (Nonreporting) **A**10
Primary Contact: Victor L. Medina Cruz, M.D., Administrator
Web address: www.asempr.org
**Control**: Other not–for–profit (including NFP Corporation) **Service**: General medical and surgical

**Staffed Beds**: 25

**SAN JUAN—San Juan County**

⊞ **HOSPITAL DE PSIQUIATRIA (404006)**, Dr. Ramon Fernandez Marina, P O Box 2100, Zip 936; tel. 787/766-4646, (Nonreporting) **A**1 3 5 10
Primary Contact: Elizabeth De Santiago, Executive Director
CMO: Brunilda Vazquez, Medical Director
CHR: Idalia Garcia, Chief Human Resources Officer
**Control**: State, Government, Nonfederal **Service**: Psychiatric

**Staffed Beds**: 141

⊞ **HOSPITAL DEL MAESTRO (400004)**, 550 Sergio Cuevas, Zip 00918–3741, Mailing Address: P.O. Box 364708, Zip 00936–4708; tel. 787/758-8383, (Nonreporting) **A**1 10 **F**3 15 17 18 20 29 30 40 41 45 70 80 81 87 89 93 107 110 111 115 119 130 146 147 148 149
Primary Contact: Jorge Torres. Otero, Executive Director
CFO: Marisol Vargas, Director Finance
CMO: Jose Montalvo, M.D., Medical Director
CIO: Laura Rodriguez, Director Medical Records
CHR: Orlando Santiago, Human Resources Officer
Web address: www.hospitaldelmaestro.org
**Control**: Other not–for–profit (including NFP Corporation) **Service**: General medical and surgical

**Staffed Beds**: 125 **Admissions**: 2810 **Census**: 47 **Births**: 0 **Total Expense ($000)**: 23026 **Payroll Expense ($000)**: 8594 **Personnel**: 304

⊞ **HOSPITAL METROPOLITAN (400106)**, 1785 Carr 21, Zip 00921–3399, Mailing Address: P.O. Box 11981, Zip 922; tel. 787/782-9999, (Nonreporting) **A**1 3 10
Primary Contact: Domingo Nevarez, Chief Executive Officer
CFO: Maritza Rodriguez, Chief Financial Officer
CMO: Maria de los Angeles Correa, M.D., Medical Director
CIO: Manuel Santiago, Chief Information Officer
**Control**: Corporation, Investor–owned (for–profit) **Service**: General medical and surgical

**Staffed Beds**: 127

**HOSPITAL PAVIA** See Hospital Pavia-Santurce

⊞ **HOSPITAL PAVIA-HATO REY (400128)**, 435 Ponce De Leon Avenue, Zip 00917–3428, Mailing Address: PO Box 190828, Zip 00917–3428; tel. 787/641-2323, (Nonreporting) **A**1 5 10 **S** United Medical Corporation, Windermere, FL
Primary Contact: Guillermo Pastrana, Executive Director
Web address: www.paviahealth.com
**Control**: Corporation, Investor–owned (for–profit) **Service**: General medical and surgical

**Staffed Beds**: 180

⊞ **HOSPITAL PAVIA-SANTURCE (400019)**, 1462 Asia Street, Zip 00909–2143, Mailing Address: Box 11137, Santurce Station, Zip 00910–1137; tel. 787/727-6060, (Nonreporting) **A**1 3 10 **S** United Medical Corporation, Windermere, FL
Primary Contact: Jose Luis. Rodriguez, Chief Executive Officer
CFO: Francisco Espina, Director Finance
Web address: www.paviahealth.com
**Control**: Corporation, Investor–owned (for–profit) **Service**: General medical and surgical

**Staffed Beds**: 197

★ **HOSPITAL PSIQUIATRICO CORRECCIONAL**, PMB 302 P O Box 70344, Zip 936; tel. 939/225-2400, (Nonreporting)
Primary Contact: Felicita E. Alvarado, Administrator
Web address: www.www2.pr.gov/Directorios/Pages/InfoAgencia.aspx?PRIFA=220
**Control**: State, Government, Nonfederal **Service**: General medical and surgical

**Staffed Beds**: 25

⊞ **HOSPITAL SAN FRANCISCO (400098)**, 371 Avenida De Diego, Zip 00923–1711, Mailing Address: P.O. Box 29025, Zip 00929–0025; tel. 787/767-5100, (Nonreporting) **A**1 10 **S** United Medical Corporation, Windermere, FL
Primary Contact: Marcos Aguila, Chief Executive Officer
CFO: Lizzette Rodriguez, Director Finance
CMO: Hector L Cotto, M.D., Medical Director
CIO: Deborah Nieves, Director Management Information Systems
CHR: Sugehi Santiago, Director
Web address: www.metropavia.com/SanFrancisco.cfm
**Control**: Corporation, Investor–owned (for–profit) **Service**: General medical and surgical

**Staffed Beds**: 133

★ **HOSPITAL SAN GERARDO (400121)**, 138 Avenue Winston Churchill, Zip 00926–6013; tel. 787/761-8383, (Nonreporting)
Primary Contact: Henry Ruberte, Administrator
Web address: www.https://hospitales.cybo.com/PR-biz/hospital-san-gerardo_2P
**Control**: Other not–for–profit (including NFP Corporation) **Service**: Chronic disease

**Staffed Beds**: 60

**HOSPITAL SAN JUAN CAPESTRANO** See San Juan Capestrano Hospital

★ **INDUSTRIAL HOSPITAL**, Puerto Rico Medical Center, Zip 936, Mailing Address: P.O. Box 365028, Zip 936; tel. 787/754–2525, (Nonreporting)
Primary Contact: Jane Vega, Executive Director
CFO: Robert Bernier Casanova, Chief Financial Officer
CMO: Carmen Carrasquillo, M.D., Medical Director
CHR: Sonia M Lebron, Human Resources Specialist
**Control**: State, Government, Nonfederal **Service**: General medical and surgical

**Staffed Beds: 108**

✚ **SAN JUAN CAPESTRANO HOSPITAL (404005)**, Rural Route 2, Box 11, Zip 926; tel. 787/625–2900, (Nonreporting) **A**1 5 10 **S** Acadia Healthcare Company, Inc., Franklin, TN
Primary Contact: Marta Rivera. Plaza, Chief Executive Officer and Managing Director
CFO: Julia Cruz, Chief Financial Officer
CMO: Jose' Alonso, M.D., Medical Director
CIO: Ana Morandeira, Director Marketing
CHR: Luis Rivera, Director Human Resources
Web address: www.sjcapestrano.com
**Control**: Corporation, Investor–owned (for–profit) **Service**: Psychiatric

**Staffed Beds: 158**

✚ **SAN JUAN CITY HOSPITAL (400015)**, Puerto Rico Medical Center, Zip 928, Mailing Address: PMB 79, P O Box 70344, Zip 00936–8344; tel. 787/766–2222, (Nonreporting) **A**1 3 5 10
Primary Contact: James F. Nieves, Executive Director
COO: Norma Marcano, Chief Operating Officer
CFO: Jaime Rodriguez, Chief Financial Officer
CMO: Raul Reyes, M.D., Medical Director
CIO: Gustavo Mesa, Chief Information Officer
CHR: Jose Garcia, Chief Human Resources Officer
Web address: www.massalud.com
**Control**: City, Government, Nonfederal **Service**: General medical and surgical

**Staffed Beds: 267**

**SAN JUAN MUNICIPAL HOSPITAL** See San Juan City Hospital

**STATE PSYCHIATRIC HOSPITAL** See Hospital De Psiquiatria

✚ **UNIVERSITY HOSPITAL (400061)**, Nineyas 869 Rio Piedras, Zip 922, Mailing Address: P.O. Box 2116, Zip 922; tel. 787/754–0101, (Nonreporting) **A**1 3 5 10 **S** Puerto Rico Department of Health, San Juan, PR
Primary Contact: Jorge Matta. Gonzalez, Executive Director
CFO: Janet Baez, Director
CMO: Ricardo Moscoso, M.D., Medical Director
CIO: Josue Martinez, Coordinator Information Systems
CHR: Ramomita Navarro, Director Human Resources
**Control**: State, Government, Nonfederal **Service**: General medical and surgical

**Staffed Beds: 220**

✚ △ **VETERANS AFFAIRS CARIBBEAN HEALTHCARE SYSTEM**, 10 Casia Street, Zip 00921–3201; tel. 787/641–7582, (Nonreporting) **A**1 2 3 5 7 8 **S** Department of Veterans Affairs, Washington, DC
Primary Contact: Carlos R. Escobar, FACHE, Director
CFO: Oscar Rodriguez, Chief Fiscal Officer
CIO: Manuel Negron, Chief Information Technology Service
CHR: Omar Ahmed, Acting Manager Human Resources
CNO: Kathleen Ruiz, M.D., Associate Director Patient Care Services
Web address: www.caribbean.va.gov/
**Control**: Veterans Affairs, Government, federal **Service**: General medical and surgical

**Staffed Beds: 422**

**VETERANS AFFAIRS MEDICAL CENTER** See Veterans Affairs Caribbean Healthcare System

★ ⇑ **SAN JORGE CHILDREN'S HOSPITAL (400134)**, 258 San Jorge Street, Santurce, Zip 00912–3310, Mailing Address: PO Box 6308, San Juan, Zip 00912–3310; tel. 787/727–1000, (Nonreporting) **A**3 5 10 21 **S** United Medical Corporation, Windermere, FL
Primary Contact: Domingo Cruz, Senior Vice President Operations
CFO: Jose Marrero, Director Finance
CMO: Luis Clavell, M.D., Medical Director
CIO: Rogelio Caballero, Chief Information Systems
CHR: Odette Burgos, Supervisor Human Resources
CNO: Leticia Fuentes, Nursing Director
Web address: www.sanjorgechildrenshospital.com
**Control**: Corporation, Investor–owned (for–profit) **Service**: Children's general medical and surgical

**Staffed Beds: 167**

⇑ **SAN JORGE HOSPITAL** See San Jorge Children's Hospital

★ **METROPOLITANO DE LA MONTANA (400130)**, Calle Issac Gonzalez Martinez, Zip 641, Mailing Address: P.O. Box 2600, Zip 641; tel. 787/933–1100, (Nonreporting) **A**3 5 10
Primary Contact: Yelitza Sanchez. Rodriguez, Executive Director
Web address: www.metropavia.com/DeLaMontana.cfm
**Control**: Corporation, Investor–owned (for–profit) **Service**: General medical and surgical

**Staffed Beds: 25**

★ **WILMA N. VAZQUEZ MEDICAL CENTER (400115)**, KM 39 1/2 Road 2, Call Box 7001, Zip 694; tel. 787/858–1580, (Nonreporting) **A**10
Primary Contact: Ramon J. Vilar, Administrator
COO: Jose O Pabon, Director Operations
CFO: Youdie Reynolds-Gossette, Controller
CMO: Jorge Feria, M.D., President Medical Staff
CIO: Miguel Aponte, Supervisor Management Information Systems
CHR: Aymette Garcia, Manager Human Resources
**Control**: Corporation, Investor–owned (for–profit) **Service**: General medical and surgical

**Staffed Beds: 150**

**HOSPITAL METROPOLITANO DR. TITO MATTEI** See Hospital Pavia Yauco

✚ **HOSPITAL PAVIA YAUCO (400110)**, Carretera 128 KM 1.0, Zip 698, Mailing Address: P.O. Box 5643, Zip 698; tel. 787/856–1000, (Nonreporting) **A**1 10
Primary Contact: Dinorah Hernandez Esq, Executive Director
CFO: Elizabeth Gonzalez, CPA, Financial Director
CMO: Juan Pillot, M.D., EsqMedical Director
CIO: Edson Ortiz, Chief Information Officer
Web address: www.metropavia.com/facilities/hospitals/pavia-yauco/?lang=en/
**Control**: Corporation, Investor–owned (for–profit) **Service**: General medical and surgical

**Staffed Beds: 115**

---

**Hospital, Medicare Provider Number, Address, Telephone, Approval, Facility, and Physician Codes, Health Care System**

★ American Hospital Association (AHA) membership
☐ The Joint Commission accreditation
◯ Healthcare Facilities Accreditation Program
◇ DNV Healthcare Inc. accreditation
⇑ Center for Improvement in Healthcare Quality Accreditation
△ Commission on Accreditation of Rehabilitation Facilities (CARF) accreditation

# VIRGIN ISLANDS

## CHRISTIANSTED—St. Croix County

**GOVERNOR JUAN F. LOUIS HOSPITAL** See Governor Juan F. Luis Hospital

**GOVERNOR JUAN F. LUIS HOSPITAL (480002)**, 4007 Estate Diamond Ruby,
Zip 00820–4421; tel. 340/778–6311, (Nonreporting) **A**10
Primary Contact: Darice S. Plaskett, R.N., FACHE, Interim Chief Executive Officer
CFO: Rosalie Javois, Chief Financial Officer
CMO: Robert Centeno, M.D., Chief Medical Officer
CIO: Reuben D Molloy, Chief Information Officer
CHR: Joan Jean-Baptiste, Vice President Human Resources
Web address: www.jflusvi.org
**Control:** State, Government, Nonfederal **Service:** General medical and surgical

**Staffed Beds:** 165

## SAINT THOMAS—St. Thomas County

**ROY LESTER SCHNEIDER HOSPITAL** See Schneider Regional Medical Center

☐ **SCHNEIDER REGIONAL MEDICAL CENTER (480001)**, 9048 Sugar Estate,
Charlotte Amalie, Zip 802; tel. 340/776–8311, (Nonreporting) **A**1 10
Primary Contact: Bernard Wheatley, FACHE, Chief Executive Officer
CMO: Thelma Ruth Watson, M.D., Medical Director
CIO: J C Creque, Director Management Information Systems
CHR: Marlene J Adams, Director Human Resources
Web address: www.rlshospital.org
**Control:** State, Government, Nonfederal **Service:** General medical and surgical

**Staffed Beds:** 86

*Many Facility Codes have changed. Please refer to the AHA Guide Code Chart.*   © 2021 AHA Guide

# U.S. Government Hospitals
# Outside the United States, by Area

## GERMANY

**Heidelberg:** ★ Heidelberg Army Community Hospital, APO, CMR 242, AE 09042

**Landstuhl:** ★ Landstuhl Army Regional Medical Center, APO, CMR 402, AE 09180

**Wuerzburg:** ★ Wuerzburg Army Community Hospital, APO, USAMEDDAC Wuerzburg, Ut 26610, AE 09244

## ITALY

**Naples:** ★ U. S. Naval Hospital, FPO, none, AE 09619

## JAPAN

**Yokosuka:** ★ U. S. Naval Hospital, Box 1487, UNIT 96350

## SOUTH KOREA

Seoul: ★ Brian Allgood Army Community Hospital, 121st General Hospital, UNIT 96205

## SPAIN

**Rota:** ★ U. S. Naval Hospital, Rota, FPO, PSC 819, Box 18, AE 09645–2500

## TAIWAN

**Taipei:** ★ U. S. Naval Hospital Taipei, No 300 Shin–Pai Road, Sec 2

This section is an index of all hospitals in alphabetical order by hospital name, followed by the city, state, and page reference to the hospital's listing in Section A.

# A

ABBEVILLE AREA MEDICAL CENTER, ABBEVILLE, SC, p. A615
ABBEVILLE COUNTY MEM HOSPITAL, ABBEVILLE, SC, p. A615
ABBEVILLE GENERAL HOSPITAL, ABBEVILLE, LA, p. A295
ABBOTT NORTHWESTERN HOSPITAL, MINNEAPOLIS, MN, p. A380
ABBOTT-NORTHWESTERN HOSPITAL, MINNEAPOLIS, MN, p. A380
ABILENE REGIONAL MEDICAL CENTER, ABILENE, TX, p. A651
ABINGTON HEALTH LANSDALE HOSPITAL, LANSDALE, PA, p. A594
ABINGTON JEFFERSON HEALTH, ABINGTON, PA, p. A583
ABINGTON-LANSDALE HOSPITAL JEFFERSON HEALTH, LANSDALE, PA, p. A594
ABINGTON MEMORIAL HOSPITAL, ABINGTON, PA, p. A583
ABRAHAM LINCOLN MEMORIAL HOSPITAL, LINCOLN, IL, p. A210
ABRAZO ARROWHEAD CAMPUS, GLENDALE, AZ, p. A32
ABRAZO CENTRAL CAMPUS, PHOENIX, AZ, p. A35
ABRAZO SCOTTSDALE CAMPUS, PHOENIX, AZ, p. A35
ABRAZO WEST CAMPUS, GOODYEAR, AZ, p. A32
ABROM KAPLAN MEMORIAL HOSPITAL, KAPLAN, LA, p. A304
ACADIA GENERAL, CROWLEY, LA, p. A300
ACADIA GENERAL HOSPITAL, CROWLEY, LA, p. A300
ACADIA HOSPITAL, BANGOR, ME, p. A318
ACADIA-ST. LANDRY HOSPITAL, CHURCH POINT, LA, p. A299
ACCEL REHABILITATION HOSPITAL OF PLANO, PLANO, TX, p. A706
ACCESS HOSPITAL DAYTON, DAYTON, OH, p. A538
ACCORD REHABILIATION HOSPITAL, PLAQUEMINE, LA, p. A313
ACMH, KITTANNING, PA, p. A593
ACMH HOSPITAL, KITTANNING, PA, p. A593
ACOMA-CANONCITO-LAGUNA HOSPITAL, ACOMA, NM, p. A467
ACUITY SPECIALTY HOSPITAL OF NEW JERSEY, ATLANTIC CITY, NJ, p. A452
ACUITY SPECIALTY HOSPITAL OF SOUTHERN NEW JERSEY, WILLINGBORO, NJ, p. A466
ACUITY SPECIALTY HOSPITALS OHIO VALLEY, STEUBENVILLE, OH, p. A549
ACUTE CARE SPECIALTY HOSPITAL OF AULTMAN, CANTON, OH, p. A530
AD HOSPITAL EAST, HOUSTON, TX, p. A684
ADA WILSON HOSP OF PHYS MED, CORPUS CHRISTI, TX, p. A665
ADAIR COUNTY HEALTH SYSTEM, GREENFIELD, IA, p. A250
ADAIR COUNTY MEMORIAL HOSPITAL, GREENFIELD, IA, p. A250
ADAMS COUNTY HOSPITAL, SEAMAN, OH, p. A549
ADAMS COUNTY MEMORIAL HOSPITAL, DECATUR, IN, p. A226
ADAMS COUNTY REGIONAL MEDICAL CENTER, SEAMAN, OH, p. A549
ADAMS MEMORIAL HOSPITAL, DECATUR, IN, p. A226
ADCARE HOSPITAL OF WORCESTER, WORCESTER, MA, p. A346
ADDISON COMMUNITY HOSPITAL, YPSILANTI, MI, p. A370
ADDISON GILBERT HOSPITAL, GLOUCESTER, MA, p. A339
ADENA GREENFIELD MEDICAL CENTER, GREENFIELD, OH, p. A541
ADENA HEALTH SYSTEM, CHILLICOTHE, OH, p. A531
ADENA MEDICAL CENTER, CHILLICOTHE, OH, p. A531
ADENA PIKE MEDICAL CENTER, WAVERLY, OH, p. A552
ADIRONDACK HEALTH, SARANAC LAKE, NY, p. A497
ADIRONDACK MEDICAL CENTER, SARANAC LAKE, NY, p. A497
ADVANCED CARE HOSPITAL OF MONTANA, BILLINGS, MT, p. A421
ADVANCED CARE HOSPITAL OF SOUTHERN NEW MEXICO, LAS CRUCES, NM, p. A470
ADVANCED CARE HOSPITAL OF WHITE COUNTY, SEARCY, AR, p. A52

ADVANCED DIAGNOSTICS HOSPITAL, HOUSTON, TX, p. A684
ADVANCED SPECIALTY HOSPITAL, TOLEDO, OH, p. A550
ADVANCED SPECIALTY HOSPITAL OF TOLEDO, TOLEDO, OH, p. A550
ADVANCED SURGICAL HOSPITAL, WASHINGTON, PA, p. A609
ADVENTHEALTH ALTAMONTE SPRINGS, ALTAMONTE SPRINGS, FL, p. A131
ADVENTHEALTH APOPKA, APOPKA, FL, p. A131
ADVENTHEALTH CARROLLWOOD, TAMPA, FL, p. A159
ADVENTHEALTH CELEBRATION, CELEBRATION, FL, p. A134
ADVENTHEALTH CENTRAL TEXAS, KILLEEN, TX, p. A693
ADVENTHEALTH CHIPPEWA, DURAND, WI, p. A782
ADVENTHEALTH CONNERTON, LAND O'LAKES, FL, p. A143
ADVENTHEALTH DADE CITY, DADE CITY, FL, p. A135
ADVENTHEALTH DAYTONA BEACH, DAYTONA BEACH, FL, p. A136
ADVENTHEALTH DELAND, DELAND, FL, p. A136
ADVENTHEALTH DURAND, DURAND, WI, p. A782
ADVENTHEALTH FISH MEMORIAL, ORANGE CITY, FL, p. A150
ADVENTHEALTH GORDON, CALHOUN, GA, p. A168
ADVENTHEALTH HEART OF FLORIDA, DAVENPORT, FL, p. A135
ADVENTHEALTH HENDERSONVILLE, HENDERSONVILLE, NC, p. A512
ADVENTHEALTH KISSIMMEE, KISSIMMEE, FL, p. A142
ADVENTHEALTH LAKE WALES, LAKE WALES, FL, p. A143
ADVENTHEALTH MANCHESTER, MANCHESTER, KY, p. A289
ADVENTHEALTH MURRAY, CHATSWORTH, GA, p. A168
ADVENTHEALTH NEW SMYRNA BEACH, NEW SMYRNA BEACH, FL, p. A149
ADVENTHEALTH NORTH PINELLAS, TARPON SPRINGS, FL, p. A160
ADVENTHEALTH OCALA, OCALA, FL, p. A149
ADVENTHEALTH ORLANDO, ORLANDO, FL, p. A151
ADVENTHEALTH OTTAWA, OTTAWA, KS, p. A273
ADVENTHEALTH PALM COAST, PALM COAST, FL, p. A152
ADVENTHEALTH ROLLINS BROOK, LAMPASAS, TX, p. A694
ADVENTHEALTH SEBRING, SEBRING, FL, p. A157
ADVENTHEALTH SHAWNEE MISSION, SHAWNEE MISSION, KS, p. A276
ADVENTHEALTH TAMPA, TAMPA, FL, p. A159
ADVENTHEALTH WATERMAN, TAVARES, FL, p. A160
ADVENTHEALTH WAUCHULA, WAUCHULA, FL, p. A161
ADVENTHEALTH WESLEY CHAPEL, WESLEY CHAPEL, FL, p. A161
ADVENTHEALTH WINTER PARK, WINTER PARK, FL, p. A162
ADVENTHEALTH ZEPHYRHILLS, ZEPHYRHILLS, FL, p. A162
ADVENTIST BEHAVIORAL HEALTH ROCKVILLE, ROCKVILLE, MD, p. A332
ADVENTIST HEALTH—TULARE, TULARE, CA, p. A102
ADVENTIST HEALTH AND RIDEOUT, MARYSVILLE, CA, p. A77
ADVENTIST HEALTH BAKERSFIELD, BAKERSFIELD, CA, p. A57
ADVENTIST HEALTH CASTLE, KAILUA, HI, p. A185
ADVENTIST HEALTH CLEAR LAKE, CLEARLAKE, CA, p. A60
ADVENTIST HEALTH GLENDALE, GLENDALE, CA, p. A66
ADVENTIST HEALTH HANFORD, HANFORD, CA, p. A67
ADVENTIST HEALTH HOWARD MEMORIAL, WILLITS, CA, p. A105
ADVENTIST HEALTH LODI, LODI, CA, p. A71
ADVENTIST HEALTH LODI MEMORIAL, LODI, CA, p. A71
ADVENTIST HEALTH MEDICAL CENTER—TEHACHAPI VALLEY, TEHACHAPI, CA, p. A100
ADVENTIST HEALTH PORTLAND, PORTLAND, OR, p. A579
ADVENTIST HEALTH REEDLEY, REEDLEY, CA, p. A88
ADVENTIST HEALTH SIMI VALLEY, SIMI VALLEY, CA, p. A98
ADVENTIST HEALTH SONORA, SONORA, CA, p. A99
ADVENTIST HEALTH ST. HELENA, SAINT HELENA, CA, p. A90
ADVENTIST HEALTH ST. HELENA, VALLEJO, CA, p. A103
ADVENTIST HEALTH TEHACHAPI VALLEY, TEHACHAPI, CA, p. A100
ADVENTIST HEALTH UKIAH VALLEY, UKIAH, CA, p. A102
ADVENTIST HEALTH WHITE MEMORIAL, LOS ANGELES, CA, p. A73
ADVENTIST HEALTHCARE PHYSICAL HEALTH AND REHABILITATION, ROCKVILLE, MD, p. A332
ADVENTIST HEALTHCARE SHADY GROVE MEDICAL CENTER, ROCKVILLE, MD, p. A332
ADVENTIST HEALTHCARE WHITE OAK MEDICAL CENTER, SILVER SPRING, MD, p. A332

ADVENTIST HEALTHTILLAMOOK, TILLAMOOK, OR, p. A582
ADVENTIST MEDICAL CENTER—HANFORD, HANFORD, CA, p. A67
ADVENTIST MEDICAL CENTER—HINSDALE, HINSDALE, IL, p. A208
ADVENTIST MEDICAL CENTER BOLINGBROOK, BOLINGBROOK, IL, p. A196
ADVENTIST MEDICAL CENTER GLENOAKS, GLENDALE HEIGHTS, IL, p. A206
ADVENTIST MEDICAL CENTER LAGRANGE, LA GRANGE, IL, p. A210
ADVENTIST MEDICAL CENTER-PORTLAND, PORTLAND, OR, p. A579
ADVENTIST MEDICAL CENTER-REEDLEY, REEDLEY, CA, p. A88
ADVENTIST REHABILITATION HOSPITAL OF MARYLAND, ROCKVILLE, MD, p. A332
ADVOCATE BETHANY HOSPITAL, CHICAGO, IL, p. A197
ADVOCATE BROMENN REGIONAL MEDICAL CENTER, NORMAL, IL, p. A214
ADVOCATE CHRIST MEDICAL CENTER, OAK LAWN, IL, p. A215
ADVOCATE CHRIST MEDICAL CTR, OAK LAWN, IL, p. A215
ADVOCATE CONDELL MEDICAL CENTER, LIBERTYVILLE, IL, p. A210
ADVOCATE GOOD SAMARITAN HOSPITAL, DOWNERS GROVE, IL, p. A203
ADVOCATE GOOD SHEPHERD HOSPITAL, BARRINGTON, IL, p. A195
ADVOCATE ILLINOIS MASONIC MEDICAL CENTER, CHICAGO, IL, p. A197
ADVOCATE LUTHERAN GENERAL HOSPITAL, PARK RIDGE, IL, p. A216
ADVOCATE NORTH SIDE HEALTH, CHICAGO, IL, p. A197
ADVOCATE SHERMAN HOSPITAL, ELGIN, IL, p. A203
ADVOCATE SOUTH SUBURBAN HOSPITAL, HAZEL CREST, IL, p. A207
ADVOCATE TRINITY HOSPITAL, CHICAGO, IL, p. A197
AGNESIAN HEALTHCARE, FOND DU LAC, WI, p. A783
AGUADILLA GENERAL HOSPITAL, AGUADILLA, PR, p. A805
AHMC ANAHEIM REGIONAL MEDICAL CENTER, ANAHEIM, CA, p. A55
AHN GROVE CITY, GROVE CITY, PA, p. A591
AHN/JEFFERSON HOSPITAL, JEFFERSON HILLS, PA, p. A593
AIKEN REGIONAL MEDICAL CENTER, AIKEN, SC, p. A615
AIKEN REGIONAL MEDICAL CENTERS, AIKEN, SC, p. A615
AKRON CHILDREN'S HOSPITAL, AKRON, OH, p. A527
AKRON CITY HOSPITAL, AKRON, OH, p. A527
AKRON GENERAL MEDICAL CENTER, AKRON, OH, p. A527
ALAMANCE HEALTH SERVICES, BURLINGTON, NC, p. A505
ALAMANCE REGIONAL MEDICAL CENTER, BURLINGTON, NC, p. A506
ALAMEDA COUNTY MEDICAL CENTER-FAIRMONT CAMPUS, SAN LEANDRO, CA, p. A95
ALAMEDA HEALTH SYSTEM, OAKLAND, CA, p. A82
ALAMEDA HOSPITAL, ALAMEDA, CA, p. A55
ALASKA NATIVE MEDICAL CENTER, ANCHORAGE, AK, p. A27
ALASKA PSYCHIATRIC HOSPITAL, ANCHORAGE, AK, p. A27
ALASKA PSYCHIATRIC INSTITUTE, ANCHORAGE, AK, p. A27
ALASKA REGIONAL HOSPITAL, ANCHORAGE, AK, p. A27
ALBANY GENERAL HOSPITAL, ALBANY, OR, p. A573
ALBANY MEDICAL CENTER, ALBANY, NY, p. A474
ALBANY STRATTON VETERANS AFFAIRS MEDICAL CENTER, ALBANY, NY, p. A474
ALBEMARLE HEALTH, ELIZABETH CITY, NC, p. A509
ALBERT EINSTEIN MEDICAL CENTER, PHILADELPHIA, PA, p. A599
ALBERT J. SOLNIT PSYCHIATRIC CENTER—SOUTH CAMPUS, MIDDLETOWN, CT, p. A123
ALCOHOLISM TREATMENT CENTER, WINFIELD, IL, p. A222
ALEDA E. LUTZ VETERANS AFFAIRS MEDICAL CENTER, SAGINAW, MI, p. A365
ALEGENT CREIGHTON HEALTH COMMUNITY MEMORIAL HOSPITAL, MISSOURI VALLEY, IA, p. A254
ALEGENT CREIGHTON HEALTH IMMANUEL MEDICAL CENTER, OMAHA, NE, p. A436
ALEGENT CREIGHTON HEALTH LAKESIDE HOSPITAL, OMAHA, NE, p. A436
ALEGENT CREIGHTON HEALTH MERCY HOSPITAL, CORNING, IA, p. A246

ALEGENT CREIGHTON HEALTH MERCY HOSPITAL, COUNCIL BLUFFS, IA, p. A247
ALEGENT CREIGHTON HEALTH MIDLANDS HOSPITAL, PAPILLION, NE, p. A438
ALEGENT CREIGHTON HEALTH PLAINVIEW HOSPITAL, PLAINVIEW, NE, p. A439
ALEGENT CREIGHTON HEALTH-MEMORIAL HOSPITAL, SCHUYLER, SCHUYLER, NE, p. A439
ALEXANDRIA COMM BEHAV HOSPITAL, ALEXANDRIA, MN, p. A371
ALEXANDRIA HOSPITAL, ALEXANDRIA, VA, p. A738
ALEXANDRIA VETERANS AFFAIRS HEALTH CARE SYSTEM, PINEVILLE, LA, p. A312
ALEXIAN BROTHERS BEHAVIORAL HEALTH HOSPITAL, HOFFMAN ESTATES, IL, p. A208
ALEXIAN BROTHERS MEDICAL CENTER, ELK GROVE VILLAGE, IL, p. A203
ALEXIAN BROTHERS WOMEN & CHILDREN'S HOSPITAL, HOFFMAN ESTATES, IL, p. A208
ALEXIAN REHABILITATION HOSPITAL, ELK GROVE VILLAGE, IL, p. A204
ALFRED I. DUPONT HOSPITAL FOR CHILDREN, WILMINGTON, DE, p. A128
ALHAMBRA HOSPITAL, ALHAMBRA, CA, p. A55
ALHAMBRA HOSPITAL, ROSEMEAD, CA, p. A88
ALHAMBRA HOSPITAL MEDICAL CENTER, ALHAMBRA, CA, p. A55
ALICE HYDE MEDICAL CENTER, MALONE, NY, p. A487
ALICE PECK DAY MEMORIAL HOSPITAL, LEBANON, NH, p. A449
ALLE KISKI MEDICAL CENTER, NATRONA HEIGHTS, PA, p. A598
ALLE-KISKI MEDICAL CENTER, NATRONA HEIGHTS, PA, p. A598
ALLEGAN GENERAL HOSPITAL, ALLEGAN, MI, p. A348
ALLEGHANY CNTY MEM HOSPITAL, SPARTA, NC, p. A518
ALLEGHANY MEMORIAL HOSPITAL, SPARTA, NC, p. A518
ALLEGHANY REGIONAL HOSPITAL, LOW MOOR, VA, p. A745
ALLEGHENY GENERAL HOSPITAL, PITTSBURGH, PA, p. A602
ALLEGHENY UNIVERSITY HOSPITALS, PITTSBURGH, PA, p. A602
ALLEGHENY VALLEY HOSPITAL, NATRONA HEIGHTS, PA, p. A598
ALLEGIANCE BEHAVIORAL HEALTH CENTER OF PLAINVIEW, PLAINVIEW, TX, p. A706
ALLEGIANCE BEHAVIORAL HEALTH CENTERS, MONROE, LA, p. A309
ALLEGIANCE BEHAVIORAL HEALTH CENTERS OF MONROE, RUSTON, LA, p. A313
ALLEGIANCE BEHAVIORAL HEALTH CENTERS OF RUSTON, RUSTON, LA, p. A313
ALLEGIANCE HEALTH, JACKSON, MI, p. A358
ALLEGIANCE SPECIALTY HOSPITAL OF GREENVILLE, GREENVILLE, MS, p. A392
ALLEN COMMUNITY HOSPITAL, OBERLIN, OH, p. A546
ALLEN COUNTY HOSPITAL, IOLA, KS, p. A267
ALLEN COUNTY REGIONAL HOSPITAL, IOLA, KS, p. A267
ALLEN COUNTY WAR MEM HOSPITAL, SCOTTSVILLE, KY, p. A293
ALLEN MEMORIAL HOSPITAL, MOAB, UT, p. A729
ALLEN PARISH COMMUNITY HEALTHCARE, KINDER, LA, p. A305
ALLEN PARISH HOSPITAL, KINDER, LA, p. A305
ALLENDALE COUNTY HOSPITAL, FAIRFAX, SC, p. A619
ALLENMORE HOSPITAL, TACOMA, WA, p. A766
ALLENTOWN HOSP-LEHIGH CTR, ALLENTOWN, PA, p. A583
ALLENTOWN OSTEOPATHIC MED CTR, ALLENTOWN, PA, p. A583
ALLIANCE COMMUNITY HOSPITAL, ALLIANCE, OH, p. A527
ALLIANCE HEALTH CENTER, MERIDIAN, MS, p. A397
ALLIANCE HEALTHCARE SYSTEM, HOLLY SPRINGS, MS, p. A394
ALLIANCE-LAIRD HOSPITAL, UNION, MS, p. A400
ALLIANCEHEALTH BLACKWELL, BLACKWELL, OK, p. A556
ALLIANCEHEALTH CLINTON, CLINTON, OK, p. A557
ALLIANCEHEALTH DEACONESS, OKLAHOMA CITY, OK, p. A563
ALLIANCEHEALTH DURANT, DURANT, OK, p. A558
ALLIANCEHEALTH MADILL, MADILL, OK, p. A561
ALLIANCEHEALTH MIDWEST, MIDWEST CITY, OK, p. A562
ALLIANCEHEALTH PONCA CITY, PONCA CITY, OK, p. A567
ALLIANCEHEALTH PRYOR, PRYOR, OK, p. A567
ALLIANCEHEALTH SEMINOLE, SEMINOLE, OK, p. A568
ALLIANCEHEALTH WOODWARD, WOODWARD, OK, p. A572
ALLIED SERVICES REHABILITATION HOSPITAL, SCRANTON, PA, p. A606
ALLIED SERVS INST REHAB HOSP, SCRANTON, PA, p. A607
ALOMERE HEALTH, ALEXANDRIA, MN, p. A371
ALPENA REGIONAL MEDICAL CENTER, ALPENA, MI, p. A348

ALTA BATE SUMMIT MED CENTER, OAKLAND, CA, p. A82
ALTA BATES SUMMIT MEDICAL CENTER—SUMMIT CAMPUS, OAKLAND, CA, p. A82
ALTA BATES SUMMIT MEDICAL CENTER, BERKELEY, CA, p. A58
ALTA BATES SUMMIT MEDICAL CENTER-ALTA BATES CAMPUS, BERKELEY, CA, p. A58
ALTA VIEW HOSPITAL, SANDY, UT, p. A733
ALTA VISTA REGIONAL HOSPITAL, LAS VEGAS, NM, p. A470
ALTON MEMORIAL HOSPITAL, ALTON, IL, p. A194
ALTON MENTAL HEALTH CENTER, ALTON, IL, p. A194
ALTON MENTAL HLTH & DEV CTR, ALTON, IL, p. A194
ALTOONA REGIONAL HEALTH SYSTEM, ALTOONA, PA, p. A583
ALTRU HEALTH SYSTEM, GRAND FORKS, ND, p. A523
ALTRU REHAB CENTER, GRAND FORKS, ND, p. A523
ALTUS BAYTOWN HOSPITAL, BAYTOWN, TX, p. A657
ALTUS HOUSTON HOSPITAL, HOUSTON, TX, p. A684
ALUTMAN HOSPITAL PEDIATRIC SERVICES, CANTON, OH, p. A530
ALVARADO HOSPITAL MEDICAL CENTER, SAN DIEGO, CA, p. A91
ALVARADO MEDICAL CENTER, SAN DIEGO, CA, p. A91
ALVARADO PARKWAY INSTITUTE BEHAVIORAL HEALTH SYSTEM, LA MESA, CA, p. A70
ALVIN C. YORK CAMPUS, MURFREESBORO, TN, p. A646
ALVIN C. YORK VETERANS AFFAIRS MEDICAL CENTER, MURFREESBORO, TN, p. A646
ALVIN DIAGNOSTIC AND URGENT CARE CENTER, ALVIN, TX, p. A652
ALVIN MEDICAL CENTER, ALVIN, TX, p. A652
AMADOR HOSPITAL, JACKSON, CA, p. A69
AMARILLO VETERANS AFFAIRS HEALTH CARE SYSTEM, AMARILLO, TX, p. A652
AMERICAN FORK HOSPITAL, AMERICAN FORK, UT, p. A727
AMERICAN INTERNATIONAL HOSP, ZION, IL, p. A222
AMERICAN ONCOLOGIC HOSPITAL, PHILADELPHIA, PA, p. A599
AMERY HOSPITAL AND CLINIC, AMERY, WI, p. A779
AMERY REGIONAL MEDICAL CENTER, AMERY, WI, p. A779
AMG MERCY, OKLAHOMA CITY, OK, p. A563
AMG PHYSICAL REHABILITATION HOSPITAL, COVINGTON, LA, p. A300
AMG SPECIALTY HOSPITAL—LAFAYETTE, LAFAYETTE, LA, p. A305
AMG SPECIALTY HOSPITAL—LAS VEGAS, LAS VEGAS, NV, p. A443
AMG SPECIALTY HOSPITAL—MUNCIE, MUNCIE, IN, p. A237
AMG SPECIALTY HOSPITAL, LAS VEGAS, NV, p. A443
AMG SPECIALTY HOSPITAL-ALBUQUERQUE, ALBUQUERQUE, NM, p. A467
AMG SPECIALTY HOSPITAL-HOUMA, HOUMA, LA, p. A303
AMG SPECIALTY HOSPITAL-LAFAYETTE, LAFAYETTE, LA, p. A305
AMG SPECIALTY HOSPITAL-WICHITA, WICHITA, KS, p. A278
AMG SPECIALTY HOSPITAL-ZACHARY, ZACHARY, LA, p. A317
AMI ARROYO GRANDE COMM HOSP, ARROYO GRANDE, CA, p. A56
AMI CENTRAL CAROLINA HOSPITAL, SANFORD, NC, p. A518
AMI DEL AMO HOSPITAL, TORRANCE, CA, p. A101
AMI DOCTORS' HOSPITAL, LANHAM, MD, p. A330
AMI MEMORIAL HOSPITAL OF TAMPA, TAMPA, FL, p. A159
AMI NACOGDOCHES MEDICAL CENTER, NACOGDOCHES, TX, p. A702
AMI PALM BEACH GARDENS MED CTR, PALM BEACH GARDENS, FL, p. A152
AMI PALMETTO GENERAL HOSPITAL, HIALEAH, FL, p. A139
AMI PEMBROKE HOSPITAL, PEMBROKE, MA, p. A343
AMITA HEALTH ADVENTIST MEDICAL CENTER—HINSDALE, HINSDALE, IL, p. A208
AMITA HEALTH ADVENTIST MEDICAL CENTER BOLINGBROOK, BOLINGBROOK, IL, p. A196
AMITA HEALTH ADVENTIST MEDICAL CENTER GLENOAKS, GLENDALE HEIGHTS, IL, p. A206
AMITA HEALTH ADVENTIST MEDICAL CENTER LA GRANGE, LA GRANGE, IL, p. A210
AMITA HEALTH ALEXIAN BROTHERS BEHAVIORAL HEALTH HOSPITAL, HOFFMAN ESTATES, IL, p. A208
AMITA HEALTH ELK GROVE VILLAGE, ELK GROVE VILLAGE, IL, p. A204
AMITA HEALTH HOFFMAN ESTATES, HOFFMAN ESTATES, IL, p. A208
AMITA HEALTH HOLY FAMILY MEDICAL CENTER, DES PLAINES, IL, p. A202
AMITA HEALTH MERCY MEDICAL CENTER, AURORA, IL, p. A195
AMITA HEALTH RESURRECTION MEDICAL CENTER, CHICAGO, IL, p. A197
AMITA HEALTH SAINT FRANCIS HOSPITAL EVANSTON, EVANSTON, IL, p. A204

AMITA HEALTH SAINT JOSEPH HOSPITAL, CHICAGO, IL, p. A197
AMITA HEALTH SAINT JOSEPH HOSPITAL, ELGIN, IL, p. A203
AMITA HEALTH SAINT JOSEPH MEDICAL CENTER, JOLIET, IL, p. A209
AMITA HEALTH SAINTS MARY & ELIZABETH MEDICAL CENTER, CHICAGO, IL, p. A198
AMITA HEALTH ST. MARY'S HOSPITAL, KANKAKEE, IL, p. A209
ANADARKO MUNICIPAL HOSPITAL, ANADARKO, OK, p. A555
ANAHEIM GLOBAL MEDICAL CENTER, ANAHEIM, CA, p. A55
ANAHEIM REGIONAL MEDICAL CENTER, ANAHEIM, CA, p. A55
ANCHOR HOSPITAL, ATLANTA, GA, p. A164
ANCORA PSYCHIATRIC HOSPITAL, HAMMONTON, NJ, p. A456
ANDALUSIA HEALTH, ANDALUSIA, AL, p. A13
ANDALUSIA REGIONAL HOSPITAL, ANDALUSIA, AL, p. A13
ANDERSON COUNTY HOSPITAL, GARNETT, KS, p. A265
ANDERSON HOSPITAL, MARYVILLE, IL, p. A211
ANDERSON REGIONAL HEALTH SYSTEM, MERIDIAN, MS, p. A397
ANDERSON REGIONAL HEALTH SYSTEM SOUTH, MERIDIAN, MS, p. A397
ANDERSON REGIONAL MEDICAL CENTER, MERIDIAN, MS, p. A397
ANDERSON REGIONAL MEDICAL CENTER-SOUTH CAMPUS, MERIDIAN, MS, p. A397
ANDREW MCFARLAND MENTAL HEALTH CENTER, SPRINGFIELD, IL, p. A220
ANDROSCOGGIN VALLEY HOSPITAL, BERLIN, NH, p. A448
ANDRUS PAVILION, YONKERS, NY, p. A502
ANGEL COMMUNITY HOSPITAL, FRANKLIN, NC, p. A510
ANGEL MEDICAL CENTER, FRANKLIN, NC, p. A510
ANGLETON DANBURY MEDICAL CENTER, ANGLETON, TX, p. A653
ANIMAS SURGICAL HOSPITAL, DURANGO, CO, p. A111
ANMED HEALTH CANNON, PICKENS, SC, p. A623
ANMED HEALTH MEDICAL CENTER, ANDERSON, SC, p. A615
ANMED HEALTH REHAB HOSP, ANDERSON, SC, p. A615
ANMED HEALTH REHABILITATION HOSPITAL, ANDERSON, SC, p. A615
ANN & ROBERT H. LURIE CHILDREN'S HOSPITAL OF CHICAGO, CHICAGO, IL, p. A198
ANNA JAQUES HOSPITAL, NEWBURYPORT, MA, p. A342
ANNANDALE COMM BEHAV HOSPITAL, ANNANDALE, MN, p. A371
ANNE ARUNDEL MEDICAL CENTER, ANNAPOLIS, MD, p. A324
ANNIE JEFFREY MEM CNTY HOSP, OSCEOLA, NE, p. A438
ANNIE JEFFREY MEMORIAL COUNTY HEALTH CENTER, OSCEOLA, NE, p. A438
ANNIE PENN HOSPITAL, REIDSVILLE, NC, p. A517
ANNIE PENN MEMORIAL HOSPITAL, REIDSVILLE, NC, p. A517
ANOKA METRO REGIONAL TREATMENT CENTER, ANOKA, MN, p. A371
ANOKA-METROPOLITAN REGIONAL TREATMENT CENTER, ANOKA, MN, p. A371
ANSON GENERAL HOSPITAL, ANSON, TX, p. A653
ANTELOPE MEMORIAL HOSPITAL, NELIGH, NE, p. A435
ANTELOPE VALLEY HOSP, LANCASTER, CA, p. A71
ANTELOPE VALLEY HOSPITAL, LANCASTER, CA, p. A71
ANTIOCH MEDICAL CENTER, ANTIOCH, CA, p. A56
APACHE JUNCTION HOSPITAL, APACHE JUNCTION, AZ, p. A30
APOLLO BEHAVIORAL HEALTH HOSPITAL, BATON ROUGE, LA, p. A296
APPALACHIAN BEHAVIORAL HEALTHCARE, ATHENS, OH, p. A528
APPALACHIAN PSYCHIATRIC HLTH, ATHENS, OH, p. A528
APPLETON AREA HEALTH SERVICES, APPLETON, MN, p. A371
APPLETON MEDICAL CENTER, APPLETON, WI, p. A779
APPLETON MUNICIPAL HOSPITAL AND NURSING HOME, APPLETON, MN, p. A371
APPLING GENERAL HOSPITAL, BAXLEY, GA, p. A166
APPLING HEALTHCARE SYSTEM, BAXLEY, GA, p. A167
ARBOR HEALTH, MORTON HOSPITAL, MORTON, WA, p. A760
ARBOUR H. R. I. HOSPITAL, BROOKLINE, MA, p. A337
ARBOUR HOSPITAL, BOSTON, MA, p. A334
ARBOUR-FULLER HOSPITAL, ATTLEBORO, MA, p. A334
ARBUCKLE MEMORIAL HOSPITAL, SULPHUR, OK, p. A568
ARCHBOLD HOSPITAL, ARCHBOLD, OH, p. A528
ARH OUR LADY OF THE WAY, MARTIN, KY, p. A289
ARH REGIONAL MEDICAL CENTER, HAZARD, KY, p. A284
ARISE AUSTIN MEDICAL CENTER, AUSTIN, TX, p. A654
ARIZONA CHILDREN'S CENTER MARICOPA MEDICAL CENTER, PHOENIX, AZ, p. A35
ARIZONA HEART HOSPITAL, PHOENIX, AZ, p. A35
ARIZONA ORTHOPEDIC SURGICAL HOSPITAL, CHANDLER, AZ, p. A30

ARIZONA SPINE AND JOINT HOSPITAL, MESA, AZ, p. A33
ARIZONA STATE HOSPITAL, PHOENIX, AZ, p. A35
ARKANSAS CHILDREN'S HOSPITAL, LITTLE ROCK, AR, p. A48
ARKANSAS CHILDREN'S NORTHWEST, SPRINGDALE, AR, p. A53
ARKANSAS CONTINUED CARE HOSPITAL, JONESBORO, AR, p. A47
ARKANSAS HEART HOSPITAL, LITTLE ROCK, AR, p. A48
ARKANSAS METHODIST HOSPITAL, PARAGOULD, AR, p. A51
ARKANSAS METHODIST MEDICAL CENTER, PARAGOULD, AR, p. A51
ARKANSAS STATE HOSPITAL, LITTLE ROCK, AR, p. A48
ARKANSAS SURGICAL HOSPITAL, NORTH LITTLE ROCK, AR, p. A51
ARKANSAS VALLEY REGIONAL MEDICAL CENTER, LA JUNTA, CO, p. A115
ARLINGTON MEMORIAL HOSPITAL, ARLINGTON, TX, p. A653
ARMS ACRES, CARMEL, NY, p. A481
ARNOLD MEMORIAL HOSPITAL, ADRIAN, MN, p. A371
ARNOLD PALMER CHILDREN'S HOSPITAL, ORLANDO, FL, p. A151
ARNOLD PALMER HOSPITAL FOR CHILDREN, ORLANDO, FL, p. A151
ARNOT OGDEN MEDICAL CENTER, ELMIRA, NY, p. A483
ARNOT-OGDEN MEDICAL HOSPITAL, ELMIRA, NY, p. A483
AROOSTOOK HEALTH CENTER, MARS HILL, ME, p. A321
AROOSTOOK MEDICAL CENTER, PRESQUE ISLE, ME, p. A322
ARROWHEAD BEHAVIORAL HEALTH HOSPITAL, MAUMEE, OH, p. A544
ARROWHEAD HOSPITAL, GLENDALE, AZ, p. A32
ARROWHEAD REGIONAL MEDICAL CENTER, COLTON, CA, p. A60
ARROYO GRANDE COMMUNITY HOSPITAL, ARROYO GRANDE, CA, p. A56
ARTESIA GENERAL HOSPITAL, ARTESIA, NM, p. A468
ASANTE ASHLAND COMMUNITY HOSPITAL, ASHLAND, OR, p. A573
ASANTE ROGUE REGIONAL MEDICAL CENTER, MEDFORD, OR, p. A577
ASANTE THREE RIVERS MEDICAL CENTER, GRANTS PASS, OR, p. A575
ASBURY-SALINA REG MEDICAL CTR, SALINA, KS, p. A275
ASCENSION ALL SAINTS, RACINE, WI, p. A794
ASCENSION ALLEGAN HOSPITAL, ALLEGAN, MI, p. A348
ASCENSION BORGESS HOSPITAL, KALAMAZOO, MI, p. A359
ASCENSION BORGESS-LEE HOSPITAL, DOWAGIAC, MI, p. A353
ASCENSION BRIGHTON CENTER FOR RECOVERY, BRIGHTON, MI, p. A350
ASCENSION CALUMET HOSPITAL, CHILTON, WI, p. A781
ASCENSION COLUMBIA ST. MARY'S HOSPITAL MILWAUKEE, MILWAUKEE, WI, p. A790
ASCENSION COLUMBIA ST. MARY'S HOSPITAL OZAUKEE, MEQUON, WI, p. A790
ASCENSION COLUMBIA ST. MARY'S MILWAUKEE HOSPITAL, MILWAUKEE, WI, p. A790
ASCENSION CRITTENTON HOSPITAL MEDICAL CENTER, ROCHESTER, MI, p. A365
ASCENSION EAGLE RIVER HOSPITAL, EAGLE RIVER, WI, p. A782
ASCENSION GENESYS HOSPITAL, GRAND BLANC, MI, p. A355
ASCENSION GONZALES REHABILITATION HOSPITAL, GONZALES, LA, p. A302
ASCENSION GOOD SAMARITAN HOSPITAL, MERRILL, WI, p. A790
ASCENSION MACOMB-OAKLAND HOSPITAL, WARREN, MI, p. A368
ASCENSION NORTHEAST WISCONSIN MERCY HOSPITAL, OSHKOSH, WI, p. A793
ASCENSION NORTHEAST WISCONSIN ST. ELIZABETH HOSPITAL, APPLETON, WI, p. A779
ASCENSION NORTHEAST WISCONSON MERCY HOSPITAL, OSHKOSH, WI, p. A793
ASCENSION OF PROVIDENCE HOSPITAL, SOUTHFIELD CAMPUS, SOUTHFIELD, MI, p. A367
ASCENSION OUR LADY OF VICTORY HOSPITAL, STANLEY, WI, p. A796
ASCENSION PROVIDENCE, WACO, TX, p. A723
ASCENSION RIVER DISTRICT HOSPITAL, EAST CHINA, MI, p. A353
ASCENSION SACRED HEART HOSPITAL, TOMAHAWK, WI, p. A797
ASCENSION SAINT MARY'S HOSPITALS, RHINELANDER, WI, p. A795
ASCENSION SETON BASTROP, BASTROP, TX, p. A657
ASCENSION SETON EDGAR B. DAVIS HOSPITAL, LULING, TX, p. A699
ASCENSION SETON HAYS, KYLE, TX, p. A694

ASCENSION SETON HIGHLAND LAKES, BURNET, TX, p. A662
ASCENSION SETON MEDICAL CENTER AUSTIN, AUSTIN, TX, p. A654
ASCENSION SETON NORTHWEST, AUSTIN, TX, p. A655
ASCENSION SETON SHOAL CREEK, AUSTIN, TX, p. A655
ASCENSION SETON SMITHVILLE, SMITHVILLE, TX, p. A716
ASCENSION SETON SOUTHWEST, AUSTIN, TX, p. A655
ASCENSION SETON WILLIAMSON, ROUND ROCK, TX, p. A709
ASCENSION SOUTHEAST WISCONSIN HOSPITAL— ELMBROOK CAMPUS, BROOKFIELD, WI, p. A781
ASCENSION SOUTHEAST WISCONSIN HOSPITAL—FRANKLIN CAMPUS, FRANKLIN, WI, p. A784
ASCENSION SOUTHEAST WISCONSIN HOSPITAL—ST. FRANCIS CAMPUS, MILWAUKEE, WI, p. A790
ASCENSION SOUTHEAST WISCONSIN HOSPITAL—ST. JOSEPH'S CAMPUS, MILWAUKEE, WI, p. A790
ASCENSION ST. ELIZABETH HOSPITAL, APPLETON, WI, p. A779
ASCENSION ST. JOHN, DETROIT, MI, p. A352
ASCENSION ST. JOHN HOSPITAL, DETROIT, MI, p. A352
ASCENSION ST. JOHN JANE PHILLIPS, BARTLESVILLE, OK, p. A556
ASCENSION ST. JOSEPH HOSPITAL, TAWAS CITY, MI, p. A367
ASCENSION ST. MARY'S HOSPITAL, RHINELANDER, WI, p. A795
ASCENSION ST. MARY'S OF MICHIGAN, SAGINAW, MI, p. A365
ASCENSION ST. MICHAEL'S HOSPITAL, STEVENS POINT, WI, p. A796
ASCENSION ST. VINCENT ANDERSON, ANDERSON, IN, p. A223
ASCENSION ST. VINCENT CARMEL HOSPITAL, CARMEL, IN, p. A225
ASCENSION ST. VINCENT CLAY HOSPITAL, BRAZIL, IN, p. A224
ASCENSION ST. VINCENT DUNN, BEDFORD, IN, p. A224
ASCENSION ST. VINCENT DUNN HOSPITAL, BEDFORD, IN, p. A224
ASCENSION ST. VINCENT EVANSVILLE, EVANSVILLE, IN, p. A227
ASCENSION ST. VINCENT FISHERS, FISHERS, IN, p. A228
ASCENSION ST. VINCENT HEART CENTER, INDIANAPOLIS, IN, p. A231
ASCENSION ST. VINCENT INDIANAPOLIS HOSPITAL, INDIANAPOLIS, IN, p. A231
ASCENSION ST. VINCENT JENNINGS, NORTH VERNON, IN, p. A238
ASCENSION ST. VINCENT KOKOMO, KOKOMO, IN, p. A234
ASCENSION ST. VINCENT MERCY, ELWOOD, IN, p. A227
ASCENSION ST. VINCENT RANDOLPH, WINCHESTER, IN, p. A242
ASCENSION ST. VINCENT SALEM, SALEM, IN, p. A240
ASCENSION ST. VINCENT SETON SPECIALTY HOSPITAL, INDIANAPOLIS, IN, p. A231
ASCENSION ST. VINCENT WARRICK, BOONVILLE, IN, p. A224
ASCENSION ST. VINCENT WILLIAMSPORT, WILLIAMSPORT, IN, p. A242
ASCENSION STANDISH HOSPITAL, STANDISH, MI, p. A367
ASCENSION VIA CHRISTI HOSPITAL, MANHATTAN, KS, p. A270
ASCENSION VIA CHRISTI HOSPITAL, PITTSBURG, KS, p. A274
ASCENSION VIA CHRISTI HOSPITAL ON ST. TERESA, WICHITA, KS, p. A278
ASCENSION VIA CHRISTI HOSPITAL ST. FRANCIS, MULVANE, KS, p. A271
ASCENSION VIA CHRISTI HOSPITAL ST. FRANCIS, WICHITA, KS, p. A278
ASCENSION VIA CHRISTI HOSPITAL, MANHATTAN, MANHATTAN, KS, p. A270
ASCENSION VIA CHRISTI HOSPITAL, PITTSBURG, PITTSBURG, KS, p. A274
ASCENSION VIA CHRISTI REHABILITATION HOSPITAL, WICHITA, KS, p. A278
ASCENSION VIA CHRISTI ST. FRANCIS, MULVANE, KS, p. A271
ASHE MEMORIAL HOSPITAL, JEFFERSON, NC, p. A513
ASHEVILLE SPECIALTY HOSPITAL, ASHEVILLE, NC, p. A504
ASHFORD PRESBYTERIAN COMMUNITY HOSPITAL, SAN JUAN, PR, p. A809
ASHLAND COMMUNITY HOSPITAL, ASHLAND, OR, p. A573
ASHLAND DISTRICT HOSPITAL, ASHLAND, KS, p. A261
ASHLAND HEALTH CENTER, ASHLAND, KS, p. A261
ASHLEY COUNTY MEDICAL CENTER, CROSSETT, AR, p. A44
ASHLEY MEDICAL CENTER, ASHLEY, ND, p. A521
ASHLEY MEMORIAL HOSPITAL, CROSSETT, AR, p. A44
ASHLEY REGIONAL MEDICAL CENTER, VERNAL, UT, p. A734
ASHLEY VALLEY MEDICAL CENTER, VERNAL, UT, p. A734
ASHTABULA COUNTY MEDICAL CENTER, ASHTABULA, OH, p. A528

ASPEN MOUNTAIN MEDICAL CENTER, ROCK SPRINGS, WY, p. A803
ASPEN VALLEY HOSPITAL, ASPEN, CO, p. A107
ASPEN VALLEY HOSPITAL DISTRICT, ASPEN, CO, p. A107
ASPIRE BEHAVIORAL HEALTH OF CONROE, CONROE, TX, p. A665
ASPIRE HEALTH PARTNERS, ORLANDO, FL, p. A151
ASPIRE HOSPITAL, CONROE, TX, p. A665
ASPIRUS IRON RIVER HOSPITALS & CLINICS, IRON RIVER, MI, p. A358
ASPIRUS IRON RIVER HOSPITALS & CLINICS, INC., IRON RIVER, MI, p. A358
ASPIRUS IRONWOOD HOSITAL & CLINICS, INC., IRONWOOD, MI, p. A358
ASPIRUS IRONWOOD HOSPITALS & CLINICS, INC., IRONWOOD, MI, p. A358
ASPIRUS KEWEENAW HOSPITAL, LAURIUM, MI, p. A360
ASPIRUS KEWEENAW HOSPITAL, INC., LAURIUM, MI, p. A360
ASPIRUS LANGLADE HOSPITAL, ANTIGO, WI, p. A779
ASPIRUS MEDFORD HOSPITAL & CLINICS, INC., MEDFORD, WI, p. A789
ASPIRUS MEDFORD HOSPITAL, MEDFORD, WI, p. A789
ASPIRUS ONTONAGON HOSPITAL, ONTONAGON, MI, p. A363
ASPIRUS ONTONAGON HOSPITAL, INC., ONTONAGON, MI, p. A363
ASPIRUS RIVERVIEW HOSPITAL AND CLINICS, INC., WISCONSIN RAPIDS, WI, p. A800
ASPIRUS WAUSAU HOSPITAL, WAUSAU, WI, p. A798
ASPIRUS WAUSAU HOSPITAL, INC., WAUSAU, WI, p. A798
ASSUMPTION COMMUNITY HOSPITAL, NAPOLEONVILLE, LA, p. A309
ASTRIA SUNNYSIDE HOSPITAL, SUNNYSIDE, WA, p. A766
ASTRIA TOPPENISH HOSPITAL, TOPPENISH, WA, p. A768
ATASCADERO STATE HOSPITAL, ATASCADERO, CA, p. A56
ATCHISON HOSPITAL, ATCHISON, KS, p. A261
ATHENS REGIONAL MEDICAL CENTER, ATHENS, GA, p. A163
ATHENS REGIONAL MEDICAL CENTER, ATHENS, TN, p. A634
ATHENS-LIMESTONE HOSPITAL, ATHENS, AL, p. A14
ATHOL HOSPITAL, ATHOL, MA, p. A334
ATHOL MEMORIAL HOSPITAL, ATHOL, MA, p. A334
ATLANTA MEDICAL CENTER—SOUTH CAMPUS, ATLANTA, GA, p. A164
ATLANTA MEDICAL CENTER, ATLANTA, GA, p. A164
ATLANTA VETERANS AFFAIRS MEDICAL CENTER, DECATUR, GA, p. A170
ATLANTIC CITY MEDICAL CENTER-MAINLAND DIVISION, POMONA, NJ, p. A461
ATLANTIC GENERAL HOSPITAL, BERLIN, MD, p. A327
ATLANTICARE REGIONAL MEDICAL CENTER, ATLANTIC CITY, NJ, p. A452
ATLANTICARE REGIONAL MEDICAL CENTER-MAINLAND DIVISION, POMONA, NJ, p. A461
ATMORE COMMUNITY HOSPITAL, ATMORE, AL, p. A14
ATOKA COUNTY MEDICAL CENTER, ATOKA, OK, p. A556
ATOKA MEMORIAL HOSPITAL, ATOKA, OK, p. A556
ATRIUM HEALTH ANSON, WADESBORO, NC, p. A519
ATRIUM HEALTH CABARRUS, CONCORD, NC, p. A508
ATRIUM HEALTH CLEVELAND, SHELBY, NC, p. A518
ATRIUM HEALTH LINCOLN, LINCOLNTON, NC, p. A514
ATRIUM HEALTH PINEVILLE, CHARLOTTE, NC, p. A506
ATRIUM HEALTH STANLY, ALBEMARLE, NC, p. A504
ATRIUM HEALTH UNION, MONROE, NC, p. A514
ATRIUM HEALTH UNIVERSITY CITY, CHARLOTTE, NC, p. A506
ATRIUM HEALTH'S CAROLINAS MEDICAL CENTER, CHARLOTTE, NC, p. A506
ATRIUM HEALTH'S CAROLINAS REHABILITATION, CHARLOTTE, NC, p. A507
ATRIUM MEDICAL CENTER, MIDDLETOWN, OH, p. A545
ATRIUM MEDICAL CENTER, STAFFORD, TX, p. A716
AUBURN COMMUNITY HOSPITAL, AUBURN, NY, p. A475
AUBURN FAITH COMMUNITY HOSP, AUBURN, CA, p. A56
AUBURN MEMORIAL HOSPITAL, AUBURN, NY, p. A475
AUDIE L MURPHY MEM HOSPITAL, SAN ANTONIO, TX, p. A710
AUDRAIN MEDICAL CENTER, MEXICO, MO, p. A412
AUDUBON BEHAVIORAL HOSPITAL LONGVIEW, LONGVIEW, TX, p. A696
AUDUBON COUNTY MEMORIAL HOSPITAL, AUDUBON, IA, p. A243
AUDUBON COUNTY MEMORIAL HOSPITAL AND CLINICS, AUDUBON, IA, p. A243
AUDUBON HOSPITAL, LOUISVILLE, KY, p. A287
AUGUSTA HEALTH, FISHERSVILLE, VA, p. A742
AUGUSTA MEDICAL CENTER, FISHERSVILLE, VA, p. A742
AUGUSTA MENTAL HLTH INSTITUTE, AUGUSTA, ME, p. A318
AUGUSTA UNIVERSITY MEDICAL CENTER, AUGUSTA, GA, p. A165
AULTMAN HOSPITAL, CANTON, OH, p. A530
AULTMAN ORRVILLE HOSPITAL, ORRVILLE, OH, p. A547
AULTMAN SPECIALTY HOSPITAL, CANTON, OH, p. A531

AURELIA OSBORN FOX MEMORIAL HOSPITAL, ONEONTA, NY, p. A494
AURELIA OXBORN FOX MEM HOSP, ONEONTA, NY, p. A494
AURORA BAYCARE MEDICAL CENTER, GREEN BAY, WI, p. A785
AURORA BEHAVIORAL HEALTH SYSTEM EAST, TEMPE, AZ, p. A39
AURORA BEHAVIORAL HEALTH SYSTEM WEST, GLENDALE, AZ, p. A32
AURORA BEHAVIORAL HEALTHCARE, COVINA, CA, p. A61
AURORA BEHAVIORAL HEALTHCARE SAN DIEGO, SAN DIEGO, CA, p. A91
AURORA CHARTER OAK HOSPITAL, COVINA, CA, p. A61
AURORA LAKELAND MEDICAL CENTER, ELKHORN, WI, p. A783
AURORA LAS ENCINAS HOSPITAL, PASADENA, CA, p. A85
AURORA MEDICAL CENTER—BAY AREA, MARINETTE, WI, p. A788
AURORA MEDICAL CENTER—MANITOWOC COUNTY, TWO RIVERS, WI, p. A797
AURORA MEDICAL CENTER, KENOSHA, WI, p. A786
AURORA MEDICAL CENTER BURLINGTON, BURLINGTON, WI, p. A781
AURORA MEDICAL CENTER GRAFTON, GRAFTON, WI, p. A784
AURORA MEDICAL CENTER IN WASHINGTON COUNTY, HARTFORD, WI, p. A786
AURORA MEDICAL CENTER KENOSHA, KENOSHA, WI, p. A786
AURORA MEDICAL CENTER OF OSHKOSH, OSHKOSH, WI, p. A793
AURORA MEDICAL CENTER OF WASHINGTON COUNTY, HARTFORD, WI, p. A786
AURORA MEDICAL CENTER SUMMIT, SUMMIT, WI, p. A797
AURORA MEMORIAL HOSPITAL OF BURLINGTON, BURLINGTON, WI, p. A781
AURORA PHOENIX HOSPITAL, GLENDALE, AZ, p. A32
AURORA PSYCHIATRIC HOSPITAL, WAUWATOSA, WI, p. A799
AURORA REGIONAL MEDICAL CENTER, AURORA, CO, p. A107
AURORA SAN DIEGO HOSPITAL, SAN DIEGO, CA, p. A91
AURORA SANTA ROSA HOSPITAL, SANTA ROSA, CA, p. A98
AURORA SHEBOYGAN MEMORIAL MEDICAL CENTER, SHEBOYGAN, WI, p. A796
AURORA SINAI MEDICAL CENTER, MILWAUKEE, WI, p. A790
AURORA ST. LUKE'S MEDICAL CENTER, MILWAUKEE, WI, p. A790
AURORA ST. LUKE'S SOUTH SHORE, CUDAHY, WI, p. A782
AURORA TEMPE HOSPITAL, TEMPE, AZ, p. A39
AURORA VISTA DEL MAR HOSPITAL, VENTURA, CA, p. A103
AURORA WEST ALLIS MEDICAL CENTER, WEST ALLIS, WI, p. A799
AUSTEN RIGGS CENTER, STOCKBRIDGE, MA, p. A345
AUSTIN LAKES HOSPITAL, AUSTIN, TX, p. A655
AUSTIN OAKS HOSPITAL, AUSTIN, TX, p. A655
AUSTIN STATE HOSPITAL, AUSTIN, TX, p. A655
AUSTIN SURGICAL HOSPITAL, AUSTIN, TX, p. A655
AUXILIO MUTUO HOSPITAL, SAN JUAN, PR, p. A809
AVAIL HEALTH LAKE CHARLES HOSPITAL, LAKE CHARLES, LA, p. A306
AVALA, COVINGTON, LA, p. A300
AVALON MUNICIPAL HOSPITAL, AVALON, CA, p. A56
AVENIR BEHAVIORAL HEALTH CENTER, SURPRISE, AZ, p. A39
AVENTURA HOSPITAL AND MEDICAL CENTER, AVENTURA, FL, p. A131
AVERA ANTHONY'S HOSPITAL, O'NEILL, NE, p. A438
AVERA CREIGHTON HOSPITAL, CREIGHTON, NE, p. A431
AVERA DE SMET MEMORIAL HOSPITAL, DE SMET, SD, p. A627
AVERA DELLS AREA HEALTH CENTER, DELL RAPIDS, SD, p. A627
AVERA DELLS AREA HOSPITAL, DELL RAPIDS, SD, p. A627
AVERA FLANDREAU HOSPITAL, FLANDREAU, SD, p. A628
AVERA FLANDREAU MEDICAL CENTER, FLANDREAU, SD, p. A628
AVERA GETTYSBURG HOSPITAL, GETTYSBURG, SD, p. A628
AVERA GRANITE FALLS HEALTH CENTER, GRANITE FALLS, MN, p. A377
AVERA GREGORY HEALTHCARE CENTER, GREGORY, SD, p. A628
AVERA GREGORY HOSPITAL, GREGORY, SD, p. A628
AVERA HAND COUNTY MEMORIAL HOSPITAL & CLINIC, MILLER, SD, p. A629
AVERA HAND COUNTY MEMORIAL HOSPITAL, MILLER, SD, p. A629
AVERA HEART HOSPITAL OF SOUTH DAKOTA, SIOUX FALLS, SD, p. A631
AVERA HOLY FAMILY HEALTH, ESTHERVILLE, IA, p. A249
AVERA HOLY FAMILY HOSPITAL, ESTHERVILLE, IA, p. A249
AVERA MARSHALL REGIONAL MEDICAL CENTER, MARSHALL, MN, p. A380

AVERA MCKENNAN HOSPITAL AND UNIVERSITY HEALTH CENTER, SIOUX FALLS, SD, p. A631
AVERA MERRILL PIONEER HOSPITAL, ROCK RAPIDS, IA, p. A257
AVERA MILBANK AREA HOSPITAL, MILBANK, SD, p. A629
AVERA QUEEN OF PEACE, MITCHELL, SD, p. A629
AVERA QUEEN OF PEACE HOSPITAL, MITCHELL, SD, p. A629
AVERA SACRED HEART, YANKTON, SD, p. A633
AVERA SACRED HEART HOSPITAL, YANKTON, SD, p. A633
AVERA ST. ANTHONY'S HOSPITAL, O'NEILL, NE, p. A438
AVERA ST. BENEDICT HEALTH CENTER, PARKSTON, SD, p. A630
AVERA ST. BENEDICT HOSPITAL, PARKSTON, SD, p. A630
AVERA ST. LUKE'S, ABERDEEN, SD, p. A626
AVERA ST. LUKE'S HOSPITAL, ABERDEEN, SD, p. A626
AVERA ST. MARY'S HOSPITAL, PIERRE, SD, p. A630
AVERA TYLER HOSPITAL, TYLER, MN, p. A387
AVERA WESKOTA MEMORIAL HOSPITAL, WESSINGTON SPRINGS, SD, p. A633
AVERA WESKOTA MEMORIAL MEDICAL CENTER, WESSINGTON SPRINGS, SD, p. A633
AVISTA ADVENTIST HOSPITAL, LOUISVILLE, CO, p. A116
AVITA ONTARIO HOSPITAL, ONTARIO, OH, p. A547
AVOYELLES HOSPITAL, MARKSVILLE, LA, p. A308

# B

BABIES AND CHILDREN'S HOSPITAL, CLEVELAND, OH, p. A534
BACHARACH INSTITUTE FOR REHABILITATION, POMONA, NJ, p. A461
BACHARACH REHAB HOSPITAL, POMONA, NJ, p. A461
BACON COUNTY HOSPITAL, ALMA, GA, p. A163
BACON COUNTY HOSPITAL AND HEALTH SYSTEM, ALMA, GA, p. A163
BAILEY MEDICAL CENTER, OWASSO, OK, p. A566
BAILEY MEMORIAL HOSPITAL, CLINTON, SC, p. A617
BAKERSFIELD BEHAVIORAL HEALTHCARE HOSPITAL, BAKERSFIELD, CA, p. A57
BAKERSFIELD HEART HOSPITAL, BAKERSFIELD, CA, p. A57
BAKERSFIELD MEMORIAL HOSPITAL, BAKERSFIELD, CA, p. A57
BALDPATE HOSPITAL, GEORGETOWN, MA, p. A339
BALDWIN AREA MEDICAL CENTER, BALDWIN, WI, p. A780
BALDWIN PARK MEDICAL CENTER, BALDWIN PARK, CA, p. A57
BALL MEMORIAL HOSPITAL, MUNCIE, IN, p. A237
BALLARD COMMUNITY HOSPITAL, SEATTLE, WA, p. A763
BALLARD REHABILITATION HOSPITAL, SAN BERNARDINO, CA, p. A91
BALLINGER MEMORIAL HOSPITAL, BALLINGER, TX, p. A657
BALTIMORE WASHINGTON MEDICAL CENTER, GLEN BURNIE, MD, p. A330
BANGOR MENTAL HEALTH INSTITUTE, BANGOR, ME, p. A318
BANNER—UNIVERSITY MEDICAL CENTER PHOENIX, PHOENIX, AZ, p. A35
BANNER—UNIVERSITY MEDICAL CENTER SOUTH, TUCSON, AZ, p. A39
BANNER—UNIVERSITY MEDICAL CENTER TUCSON, TUCSON, AZ, p. A39
BANNER—UNIVERSITY MEDICAL CENTER TUCSON BANNER—UNIVERSITY MEDICAL CENTER SOUTH, TUCSON, AZ, p. A40
BANNER—UNIVERSITY OF ARIZONA MEDICAL CENTER—SOUTH CAMPUS, TUCSON, AZ, p. A40
BANNER BAYWOOD HEART HOSPITAL, MESA, AZ, p. A33
BANNER BAYWOOD MEDICAL CENTER, MESA, AZ, p. A33
BANNER BEHAVIORAL HEALTH HOSPITAL—SCOTTSDALE, SCOTTSDALE, AZ, p. A38
BANNER BEHAVIORAL HLTH CTR, SCOTTSDALE, AZ, p. A38
BANNER BOSWELL HOSPITAL, SUN CITY, AZ, p. A39
BANNER BOSWELL MEDICAL CENTER, SUN CITY, AZ, p. A39
BANNER CASA GRANDE MEDICAL CENTER, CASA GRANDE, AZ, p. A30
BANNER CHILDREN'S HOSPITAL, MESA, AZ, p. A33
BANNER CHURCHILL COMMUNITY HOSPITAL, FALLON, NV, p. A442
BANNER DEL E WEBB HOSPITAL, SUN CITY WEST, AZ, p. A39
BANNER DEL E. WEBB MEDICAL CENTER, SUN CITY WEST, AZ, p. A39
BANNER DESERT MEDICAL CENTER, MESA, AZ, p. A33
BANNER ESTRELLA MEDICAL, PHOENIX, AZ, p. A35
BANNER ESTRELLA MEDICAL CENTER, PHOENIX, AZ, p. A35

BANNER FORT COLLINS MEDICAL CENTER, FORT COLLINS, CO, p. A112
BANNER GATEWAY MEDICAL CENTER, GILBERT, AZ, p. A32
BANNER GOLDFIELD MEDICAL CENTER, APACHE JUNCTION, AZ, p. A30
BANNER GOOD SAMARITAN MEDICAL CENTER, PHOENIX, AZ, p. A35
BANNER HEART HOSPITAL, MESA, AZ, p. A34
BANNER IRONWOOD MEDICAL CENTER, SAN TAN VALLEY, AZ, p. A38
BANNER LASSEN MEDICAL CENTER, SUSANVILLE, CA, p. A100
BANNER PAYSON MEDICAL CENTER, PAYSON, AZ, p. A34
BANNER THUNDERBIRD MEDICAL CENTER, GLENDALE, AZ, p. A32
BAPTIST EASLEY HOSPITAL, EASLEY, SC, p. A619
BAPTIST EMERGENCY HOSPITAL—THOUSAND OAKS, SAN ANTONIO, TX, p. A710
BAPTIST EMERGENCY HOSPITAL, SAN ANTONIO, TX, p. A710
BAPTIST HEALTH—FORT SMITH, FORT SMITH, AR, p. A46
BAPTIST HEALTH—VAN BUREN, VAN BUREN, AR, p. A54
BAPTIST HEALTH BAPTIST MEM CTR, NORTH LITTLE ROCK, AR, p. A51
BAPTIST HEALTH CORBIN, CORBIN, KY, p. A282
BAPTIST HEALTH EXTENDED CARE HOSPITAL, LITTLE ROCK, AR, p. A48
BAPTIST HEALTH FLOYD, NEW ALBANY, IN, p. A237
BAPTIST HEALTH LA GRANGE, LA GRANGE, KY, p. A285
BAPTIST HEALTH LEXINGTON, LEXINGTON, KY, p. A286
BAPTIST HEALTH LOUISVILLE, LOUISVILLE, KY, p. A287
BAPTIST HEALTH MADISONVILLE, MADISONVILLE, KY, p. A289
BAPTIST HEALTH MEDICAL CENTER—CONWAY, CONWAY, AR, p. A43
BAPTIST HEALTH MEDICAL CENTER—NORTH LITTLE ROCK, NORTH LITTLE ROCK, AR, p. A51
BAPTIST HEALTH MEDICAL CENTER-ARKADELPHIA, ARKADELPHIA, AR, p. A42
BAPTIST HEALTH MEDICAL CENTER-HEBER SPRINGS, HEBER SPRINGS, AR, p. A46
BAPTIST HEALTH MEDICAL CENTER-HOT SPRING COUNTY, MALVERN, AR, p. A50
BAPTIST HEALTH MEDICAL CENTER-LITTLE ROCK, LITTLE ROCK, AR, p. A49
BAPTIST HEALTH MEDICAL CENTER-STUTTGART, STUTTGART, AR, p. A53
BAPTIST HEALTH PADUCAH, PADUCAH, KY, p. A291
BAPTIST HEALTH REHABILITATION INSTITUTE, LITTLE ROCK, AR, p. A49
BAPTIST HEALTH RICHMOND, RICHMOND, KY, p. A292
BAPTIST HEALTH SOUTH FLORIDA, BAPTIST HOSPITAL OF MIAMI, MIAMI, FL, p. A146
BAPTIST HEALTH SOUTH FLORIDA, DOCTORS HOSPITAL, CORAL GABLES, FL, p. A135
BAPTIST HEALTH SOUTH FLORIDA, HOMESTEAD HOSPITAL, HOMESTEAD, FL, p. A140
BAPTIST HEALTH SOUTH FLORIDA, MARINERS HOSPITAL, TAVERNIER, FL, p. A160
BAPTIST HEALTH SOUTH FLORIDA, SOUTH MIAMI HOSPITAL, MIAMI, FL, p. A146
BAPTIST HEALTH SOUTH FLORIDA, WEST KENDALL BAPTIST HOSPITAL, MIAMI, FL, p. A146
BAPTIST HEALTH SYSTEM, SAN ANTONIO, TX, p. A711
BAPTIST HEALTH SYSTEMS ATTALA, KOSCIUSKO, MS, p. A395
BAPTIST HOSPITAL, NASHVILLE, TN, p. A646
BAPTIST HOSPITAL, PENSACOLA, FL, p. A153
BAPTIST HOSPITAL, WINNER, SD, p. A633
BAPTIST HOSPITAL EAST, LOUISVILLE, KY, p. A287
BAPTIST HOSPITAL NORTHEAST, LA GRANGE, KY, p. A285
BAPTIST HOSPITAL, WORTH COUNTY, SYLVESTER, GA, p. A181
BAPTIST HOSPITALS OF SOUTHEAST TEXAS, BEAUMONT, TX, p. A658
BAPTIST MED CTR ARKADELPHIA, ARKADELPHIA, AR, p. A42
BAPTIST MEDICAL CENTER, CUMMING, GA, p. A170
BAPTIST MEDICAL CENTER, HEBER SPRINGS, AR, p. A46
BAPTIST MEDICAL CENTER, JACKSONVILLE, FL, p. A140
BAPTIST MEDICAL CENTER, LITTLE ROCK, AR, p. A49
BAPTIST MEDICAL CENTER, MONTGOMERY, AL, p. A22
BAPTIST MEDICAL CENTER, SAN ANTONIO, TX, p. A711
BAPTIST MEDICAL CENTER ATTALA, KOSCIUSKO, MS, p. A395
BAPTIST MEDICAL CENTER BEACHES, JACKSONVILLE BEACH, FL, p. A142
BAPTIST MEDICAL CENTER EAST, MONTGOMERY, AL, p. A22
BAPTIST MEDICAL CENTER JACKSONVILLE, JACKSONVILLE, FL, p. A140
BAPTIST MEDICAL CENTER LEAKE, CARTHAGE, MS, p. A390

BAPTIST MEDICAL CENTER NASSAU, FERNANDINA BEACH, FL, p. A137
BAPTIST MEDICAL CENTER SOUTH, MONTGOMERY, AL, p. A22
BAPTIST MEDICAL CENTER YAZOO, YAZOO CITY, MS, p. A401
BAPTIST MEDICAL CENTER-NASSAU, FERNANDINA BEACH, FL, p. A137
BAPTIST MEM HOSP-NORTH MISS, OXFORD, MS, p. A398
BAPTIST MEMORIAL HOSP-OSCEOLA, OSCEOLA, AR, p. A51
BAPTIST MEMORIAL HOSPITAL—CALHOUN, CALHOUN CITY, MS, p. A390
BAPTIST MEMORIAL HOSPITAL—CRITTENDEN, INC., WEST MEMPHIS, AR, p. A54
BAPTIST MEMORIAL HOSPITAL—MEMPHIS, MEMPHIS, TN, p. A643
BAPTIST MEMORIAL HOSPITAL, BLYTHEVILLE, AR, p. A43
BAPTIST MEMORIAL HOSPITAL, BOONEVILLE, MS, p. A390
BAPTIST MEMORIAL HOSPITAL, GADSDEN, AL, p. A19
BAPTIST MEMORIAL HOSPITAL EAST, MEMPHIS, TN, p. A643
BAPTIST MEMORIAL HOSPITAL FOR WOMEN, MEMPHIS, TN, p. A644
BAPTIST MEMORIAL HOSPITAL-BOONEVILLE, BOONEVILLE, MS, p. A390
BAPTIST MEMORIAL HOSPITAL-CARROLL COUNTY, HUNTINGDON, TN, p. A639
BAPTIST MEMORIAL HOSPITAL-COLLIERVILLE, COLLIERVILLE, TN, p. A636
BAPTIST MEMORIAL HOSPITAL-DESOTO, SOUTHAVEN, MS, p. A400
BAPTIST MEMORIAL HOSPITAL-GOLDEN TRIANGLE, COLUMBUS, MS, p. A391
BAPTIST MEMORIAL HOSPITAL-HUNTINGDON, HUNTINGDON, TN, p. A639
BAPTIST MEMORIAL HOSPITAL-NORTH MISSISSIPPI, OXFORD, MS, p. A398
BAPTIST MEMORIAL HOSPITAL-TIPTON, COVINGTON, TN, p. A637
BAPTIST MEMORIAL HOSPITAL-UNION CITY, UNION CITY, TN, p. A650
BAPTIST MEMORIAL HOSPITAL-UNION COUNTY, NEW ALBANY, MS, p. A398
BAPTIST MEMORIAL REHABILITATION HOSPITAL, GERMANTOWN, TN, p. A638
BAPTIST MEMORIAL RESTORATIVE CARE HOSPITAL, MEMPHIS, TN, p. A644
BAPTIST MERIWETHER HOSPITAL, WARM SPRINGS, GA, p. A182
BAPTIST PERRY COMMUNITY HOSP, LINDEN, TN, p. A642
BAPTIST PRINCETON, BIRMINGHAM, AL, p. A14
BAPTIST REGIONAL MEDICAL CENTER, CORBIN, KY, p. A282
BAPTIST REHAB INSTITUTE, LITTLE ROCK, AR, p. A49
BAPTIST ST VINCENT'S BEACHES, JACKSONVILLE BEACH, FL, p. A142
BAPTIST ST. ANTHONY HEALTH SYSTEM, AMARILLO, TX, p. A652
BAPTIST THREE RIVERS HOSPITAL, WAVERLY, TN, p. A650
BARAGA COUNTY MEMORIAL HOSPITAL, L'ANSE, MI, p. A359
BARBARA KARMANOS CANCER INST, DETROIT, MI, p. A352
BARBOURVILLE ARH, BARBOURVILLE, KY, p. A280
BARBOURVILLE ARH HOSPITAL, BARBOURVILLE, KY, p. A280
BARIX CLINICS OF PENNSYLVANIA, LANGHORNE, PA, p. A594
BARLOW HOSPITAL, LOS ANGELES, CA, p. A73
BARLOW RESPIRATORY HOSPITAL, LOS ANGELES, CA, p. A73
BARNES HOSPITAL, SAINT LOUIS, MO, p. A415
BARNES ST PETERS HOSPITAL, SAINT PETERS, MO, p. A418
BARNES WEST COUNTY HOSPITAL, SAINT LOUIS, MO, p. A415
BARNES-JEWISH HOSPITAL, SAINT LOUIS, MO, p. A415
BARNES-JEWISH ST. PETERS HOSPITAL, SAINT PETERS, MO, p. A418
BARNES-JEWISH WEST COUNTY HOSPITAL, SAINT LOUIS, MO, p. A415
BARNES-KASSON COUNTY HOSPITAL, SUSQUEHANNA, PA, p. A608
BARNESVILLE HOSPITAL, BARNESVILLE, OH, p. A528
BARRETT HOSPITAL & HEALTHCARE, DILLON, MT, p. A423
BARRETT MEMORIAL HOSPITAL, DILLON, MT, p. A423
BARROW REGIONAL MEDICAL CENTER, WINDER, GA, p. A183
BARSTOW COMMUNITY HOSPITAL, BARSTOW, CA, p. A58
BARTHOLOMEW COUNTY HOSPITAL, COLUMBUS, IN, p. A225
BARTLETT MEM MEDICAL CENTER, SAPULPA, OK, p. A567
BARTLETT MEMORIAL HOSPITAL, JUNEAU, AK, p. A28
BARTLETT REGIONAL HOSPITAL, JUNEAU, AK, p. A28
BARTON COUNTY MEMORIAL HOSPITAL, LAMAR, MO, p. A410
BARTON HEALTHCARE SYSTEM, SOUTH LAKE TAHOE, CA, p. A99

BARTON MEMORIAL HOSPITAL, SOUTH LAKE TAHOE, CA, p. A99
BARTOW MEMORIAL HOSPITAL, BARTOW, FL, p. A131
BARTOW REGIONAL MEDICAL CENTER, BARTOW, FL, p. A131
BASIN HEALTHCARE CENTER, ODESSA, TX, p. A703
BASSETT ARMY COMMUNITY HOSPITAL, FORT WAINWRIGHT, AK, p. A28
BASSETT HOSP OF SCHOHARIE CNTY, COBLESKILL, NY, p. A481
BASSETT MEDICAL CENTER, COOPERSTOWN, NY, p. A481
BASTROP REHABILITATION HOSPITAL, MONROE, LA, p. A309
BATES COUNTY MEMORIAL HOSPITAL, BUTLER, MO, p. A403
BATES MEDICAL CENTER, BENTONVILLE, AR, p. A42
BATH COMMUNITY HOSPITAL, HOT SPRINGS, VA, p. A744
BATH COUNTY COMMUNITY HOSPITAL, HOT SPRINGS, VA, p. A744
BATH VETERANS AFFAIRS MEDICAL CENTER, BATH, NY, p. A475
BATON ROUGE BEHAVIORAL HOSPITAL, BATON ROUGE, LA, p. A296
BATON ROUGE GEN HEALTH CENTER, BATON ROUGE, LA, p. A296
BATON ROUGE GENERAL MEDICAL CENTER, BATON ROUGE, LA, p. A296
BATON ROUGE REHABILITATION HOSPITAL, BATON ROUGE, LA, p. A296
BATTLE CREEK ADVENTIST HOSP, BATTLE CREEK, MI, p. A349
BATTLE CREEK VETERANS AFFAIRS MEDICAL CENTER, BATTLE CREEK, MI, p. A349
BATTLE MOUNTAIN GENERAL HOSPITAL, BATTLE MOUNTAIN, NV, p. A441
BAXTER COMMUNITY BEHAV HOSP, BAXTER, MN, p. A372
BAXTER COUNTY REGIONAL HOSP, MOUNTAIN HOME, AR, p. A50
BAXTER REGIONAL MEDICAL CENTER, MOUNTAIN HOME, AR, p. A50
BAY AREA HOSPITAL, COOS BAY, OR, p. A574
BAY AREA MEDICAL CENTER, MARINETTE, WI, p. A788
BAY MEDICAL CENTER SACRED HEART HEALTH SYSTEM, PANAMA CITY, FL, p. A152
BAY MEDICAL SACRED HEART, PANAMA CITY, FL, p. A152
BAY PARK COMMUNITY HOSPITAL, OREGON, OH, p. A547
BAY PINES VETERANS AFFAIRS HEALTHCARE SYSTEM, BAY PINES, FL, p. A131
BAY PINES VETERANS AFFAIRS MEDICAL CENTER, BAY PINES, FL, p. A131
BAY REGIONAL MEDICAL CENTER, BAY CITY, MI, p. A349
BAY REGIONAL MEDICAL CENTER-WEST CAMPUS, BAY CITY, MI, p. A349
BAY SPECIAL CARE HOSPITAL, BAY CITY, MI, p. A349
BAYAMON MEDICAL CENTER, BAYAMON, PR, p. A806
BAYCARE ALLIANT HOSPITAL, DUNEDIN, FL, p. A136
BAYFRONT HEALTH BROOKSVILLE, BROOKSVILLE, FL, p. A133
BAYFRONT HEALTH PORT CHARLOTTE, PORT CHARLOTTE, FL, p. A154
BAYFRONT HEALTH PUNTA GORDA, PUNTA GORDA, FL, p. A155
BAYFRONT HEALTH ST. PETERSBURG, SAINT PETERSBURG, FL, p. A156
BAYFRONT MEDICAL CENTER, SAINT PETERSBURG, FL, p. A156
BAYHEALTH MEDICAL CENTER, DOVER, DE, p. A127
BAYHEALTH MEDICAL CENTER, MILFORD MEMORIAL HOSPITAL, MILFORD, DE, p. A127
BAYLOR ALL SAINTS MEDICAL CENTER AT FORT WORTH, FORT WORTH, TX, p. A677
BAYLOR COLLEGE OF MEDICINE MEDICAL CENTER, HOUSTON, TX, p. A684
BAYLOR EMERGENCY MEDICAL CENTERS—BURLESON, BURLESON, TX, p. A661
BAYLOR INSTITUTE FOR REHABILITATION, DALLAS, TX, p. A667
BAYLOR INSTITUTE FOR REHABILITATION AT FORT WORTH, FORT WORTH, TX, p. A677
BAYLOR INSTITUTE FOR REHABILITATION AT FRISCO, FRISCO, TX, p. A680
BAYLOR JACK AND JANE HAMILTON HEART AND VASCULAR HOSPITAL, DALLAS, TX, p. A667
BAYLOR MEDICAL CENTER AT FRISCO, FRISCO, TX, p. A680
BAYLOR MEDICAL CENTER AT IRVING, IRVING, TX, p. A690
BAYLOR MEDICAL CENTER AT MCKINNEY, MCKINNEY, TX, p. A700
BAYLOR MEDICAL CENTER AT TROPHY CLUB, TROPHY CLUB, TX, p. A721
BAYLOR MEDICAL CENTER AT UPTOWN, DALLAS, TX, p. A667
BAYLOR ORTHOPEDIC AND SPINE HOSPITAL AT ARLINGTON, ARLINGTON, TX, p. A653

BAYLOR REGIONAL MEDICAL CENTER AT GRAPEVINE, GRAPEVINE, TX, p. A682
BAYLOR REGIONAL MEDICAL CENTER AT PLANO, PLANO, TX, p. A706
BAYLOR SCOTT & WHITE ALL SAINTS MEDICAL CENTER—FORT WORTH, FORT WORTH, TX, p. A678
BAYLOR SCOTT & WHITE CONTINUING CARE HOSPITAL-TEMPLE, TEMPLE, TX, p. A718
BAYLOR SCOTT & WHITE EMERGENCY HOSPIOTAL—GRAND PRAIRIE, GRAND PRAIRIE, TX, p. A682
BAYLOR SCOTT & WHITE EMERGENCY HOSPITAL—GRAND PRAIRIE, GRAND PRAIRIE, TX, p. A682
BAYLOR SCOTT & WHITE EMERGENCY HOSPITAL—ROCKWALL, ROCKWALL, TX, p. A709
BAYLOR SCOTT & WHITE EMERGENCY HOSPITAL—AUBREY, AUBREY, TX, p. A654
BAYLOR SCOTT & WHITE EMERGENCY HOSPITAL—BURLESON, BURLESON, TX, p. A662
BAYLOR SCOTT & WHITE EMERGENCY HOSPITAL—ROCKWALL, ROCKWALL, TX, p. A709
BAYLOR SCOTT & WHITE EMERGENCY HOSPITAL- CEDAR PARK, CEDAR PARK, TX, p. A663
BAYLOR SCOTT & WHITE EMERGENCY HOSPITALS—AUBREY, AUBREY, TX, p. A654
BAYLOR SCOTT & WHITE EMERGENCY MEDICAL CENTER-CEDAR PARK, CEDAR PARK, TX, p. A663
BAYLOR SCOTT & WHITE HEART & VASCULAR HOSPITAL-DALLAS, DALLAS, TX, p. A667
BAYLOR SCOTT & WHITE HILLCREST MEDICAL CENTER, WACO, TX, p. A724
BAYLOR SCOTT & WHITE HOSPITAL MEDICAL CENTER—COLLEGE STATION, COLLEGE STATION, TX, p. A664
BAYLOR SCOTT & WHITE INSTITUTE FOR REHABILITATION—DALLAS, DALLAS, TX, p. A667
BAYLOR SCOTT & WHITE INSTITUTE FOR REHABILITATION—LAKEWAY, LAKEWAY, TX, p. A694
BAYLOR SCOTT & WHITE INSTITUTE FOR REHABILITATION-FORT WORTH, FORT WORTH, TX, p. A678
BAYLOR SCOTT & WHITE INSTITUTE FOR REHABILITATION-FRISCO, FRISCO, TX, p. A680
BAYLOR SCOTT & WHITE MEDICAL CENTER—AUSTIN, AUSTIN, TX, p. A655
BAYLOR SCOTT & WHITE MEDICAL CENTER—BRENHAM, BRENHAM, TX, p. A660
BAYLOR SCOTT & WHITE MEDICAL CENTER—BUDA, BUDA, TX, p. A661
BAYLOR SCOTT & WHITE MEDICAL CENTER—CARROLLTON, CARROLLTON, TX, p. A662
BAYLOR SCOTT & WHITE MEDICAL CENTER—CENTENNIAL, FRISCO, TX, p. A680
BAYLOR SCOTT & WHITE MEDICAL CENTER—GRAPEVINE, GRAPEVINE, TX, p. A682
BAYLOR SCOTT & WHITE MEDICAL CENTER—HILLCREST, WACO, TX, p. A724
BAYLOR SCOTT & WHITE MEDICAL CENTER—LAKE POINTE, ROWLETT, TX, p. A710
BAYLOR SCOTT & WHITE MEDICAL CENTER—LLANO, LLANO, TX, p. A696
BAYLOR SCOTT & WHITE MEDICAL CENTER—MARBLE FALLS, MARBLE FALLS, TX, p. A699
BAYLOR SCOTT & WHITE MEDICAL CENTER—PFLUGERVILLE, PFLUGERVILLE, TX, p. A706
BAYLOR SCOTT & WHITE MEDICAL CENTER—PLANO, PLANO, TX, p. A706
BAYLOR SCOTT & WHITE MEDICAL CENTER—ROUND ROCK, ROUND ROCK, TX, p. A709
BAYLOR SCOTT & WHITE MEDICAL CENTER—SUNNYVALE, SUNNYVALE, TX, p. A718
BAYLOR SCOTT & WHITE MEDICAL CENTER—TAYLOR, TAYLOR, TX, p. A718
BAYLOR SCOTT & WHITE MEDICAL CENTER—TEMPLE, TEMPLE, TX, p. A719
BAYLOR SCOTT & WHITE MEDICAL CENTER—TROPHY CLUB, TROPHY CLUB, TX, p. A721
BAYLOR SCOTT & WHITE MEDICAL CENTER—WHITE ROCK, DALLAS, TX, p. A667
BAYLOR SCOTT & WHITE MEDICAL CENTER AT—MCKINNEY, MCKINNEY, TX, p. A700
BAYLOR SCOTT & WHITE MEDICAL CENTER—FRISCO, FRISCO, TX, p. A680
BAYLOR SCOTT & WHITE MEDICAL CENTER—WAXAHACHIE, WAXAHACHIE, TX, p. A724
BAYLOR SCOTT & WHITE MEDICAL CENTER-IRVING, IRVING, TX, p. A690
BAYLOR SCOTT & WHITE MEDICAL CENTER-UPTOWN, DALLAS, TX, p. A667
BAYLOR SCOTT & WHITE MEDICAL CENTER-WAXAHACHIE, WAXAHACHIE, TX, p. A724
BAYLOR SCOTT & WHITE SURGICAL HOSPITAL AT SHERMAN, SHERMAN, TX, p. A715

BAYLOR SCOTT & WHITE SURGICAL HOSPITAL FORT WORTH, FORT WORTH, TX, p. A678
BAYLOR SCOTT & WHITE SURGICAL HOSPITAL-SHERMAN, SHERMAN, TX, p. A715
BAYLOR SCOTT & WHITE TEXAS SPINE & JOINT HOSPITAL, TYLER, TX, p. A721
BAYLOR SCOTT & WHITE TEXAS SPINE & JOINT HOSPITAL-TYLER, TYLER, TX, p. A721
BAYLOR SCOTT & WHITE THE HEART HOSPITAL DENTON, DENTON, TX, p. A671
BAYLOR SCOTT & WHITE THE HEART HOSPITAL PLANO, PLANO, TX, p. A706
BAYLOR SCOTT & WHITE THE HEART HOSPITAL—DENTON, DENTON, TX, p. A671
BAYLOR SCOTT & WHITEMEDICAL CENTER—BRENHAM, BRENHAM, TX, p. A660
BAYLOR SCOTT AND WHITE CONTINUING CARE HOSPITAL, TEMPLE, TX, p. A719
BAYLOR ST. LUKE'S MEDICAL CENTER, HOUSTON, TX, p. A684
BAYLOR ST. LUKE'S MEDICAL CENTER MCNAIR CAMPUS, HOUSTON, TX, p. A684
BAYLOR SURGICAL HOSPITAL AT LAS COLINAS, IRVING, TX, p. A690
BAYLOR UNIVERSITY MEDICAL CENTER, DALLAS, TX, p. A668
BAYNE-JONES ARMY COMMUNITY HOSPITAL, FORT POLK, LA, p. A301
BAYONNE MEDICAL CENTER, BAYONNE, NJ, p. A452
BAYPOINTE BEHAVIORAL HEALTH, MOBILE, AL, p. A21
BAYSHORE COMMUNITY HOSPITAL, HOLMDEL, NJ, p. A456
BAYSHORE MEDICAL CENTER, PASADENA, TX, p. A704
BAYSIDE COMMUNITY HOSPITAL, ANAHUAC, TX, p. A653
BAYSTATE FRANKLIN MEDICAL CENTER, GREENFIELD, MA, p. A339
BAYSTATE MEDICAL CENTER, SPRINGFIELD, MA, p. A344
BAYSTATE NOBLE HOSPITAL, WESTFIELD, MA, p. A346
BAYSTATE WING HOSPITAL, PALMER, MA, p. A343
BAYVIEW HOSP & MENTAL SYSTEM, CHULA VISTA, CA, p. A60
BCA STONECREST HOSPITAL, DETROIT, MI, p. A352
BEACHAM MEMORIAL HOSPITAL, MAGNOLIA, MS, p. A396
BEACON BEHAVIORAL HOSPITAL—NEW ORLEANS, NEW ORLEANS, LA, p. A310
BEACON BEHAVIORAL HOSPITAL—NORTHSHORE, LACOMBE, LA, p. A305
BEACON BEHAVIORAL HOSPITAL, BUNKIE, LA, p. A299
BEACON BEHAVIORAL HOSPITAL, LUTCHER, LA, p. A307
BEACON BEHAVIORAL HOSPITAL NORTHSHORE, LACOMBE, LA, p. A305
BEACON CHILDREN'S HOSPITAL, LUVERNE, AL, p. A20
BEACON HOSPITAL AND REHABILITATION OF POCATELLO, POCATELLO, ID, p. A192
BEACON SPECIALTY HOSPITAL, SHENANDOAH, TX, p. A715
BEAR LAKE MEMORIAL HOSPITAL, MONTPELIER, ID, p. A191
BEAR RIVER VALLEY HOSPITAL, TREMONTON, UT, p. A734
BEAR VALLEY COMMUNITY HOSPITAL, BIG BEAR LAKE, CA, p. A58
BEARTOOTH BILLINGS CLINIC, RED LODGE, MT, p. A427
BEARTOOTH HOSPITAL AND HEALTH CENTER, RED LODGE, MT, p. A427
BEATRICE COMM HOSP & HLTH CNTR, BEATRICE, NE, p. A430
BEATRICE COMMUNITY HOSPITAL AND HEALTH CENTER, BEATRICE, NE, p. A430
BEAUFORT COUNTY MEDICAL CENTER, WASHINGTON, NC, p. A519
BEAUFORT MEMORIAL HOSPITAL, BEAUFORT, SC, p. A615
BEAUMONT HOSP—ROYAL OAK, ROYAL OAK, MI, p. A365
BEAUMONT HOSPITAL—DEARBORN, DEARBORN, MI, p. A352
BEAUMONT HOSPITAL—FARMINGTON HILLS, FARMINGTON HILLS, MI, p. A354
BEAUMONT HOSPITAL—GROSSE POINTE, GROSSE POINTE, MI, p. A357
BEAUMONT HOSPITAL—ROYAL OAK, ROYAL OAK, MI, p. A365
BEAUMONT HOSPITAL—TAYLOR, TAYLOR, MI, p. A367
BEAUMONT HOSPITAL—TRENTON, TRENTON, MI, p. A368
BEAUMONT HOSPITAL—TROY, TROY, MI, p. A368
BEAUMONT HOSPITAL—WAYNE, WAYNE, MI, p. A369
BEAUMONT HOSPITAL GROSSE POINTE, GROSSE POINTE, MI, p. A357
BEAUMONT HOSPITAL, WAYNE, WAYNE, MI, p. A369
BEAUMONT HOSPITAL-DEARBORN, DEARBORN, MI, p. A352
BEAUMONT HOSPITAL-SOUTHSHORE, TRENTON, MI, p. A368
BEAUMONT HOSPITALS—TROY, TROY, MI, p. A368
BEAUMONT MEDICAL & SURG HOSP, BEAUMONT, TX, p. A658
BEAUREGARD HEALTH SYSTEM, DE RIDDER, LA, p. A300

BEAUREGARD MEMORIAL HOSPITAL, DE RIDDER, LA, p. A300
BEAVER COUNTY MEMORIAL HOSPITAL, BEAVER, OK, p. A556
BEAVER VALLEY HOSPITAL, BEAVER, UT, p. A727
BECKETT SPRINGS, WEST CHESTER, OH, p. A552
BECKLEY APPALACHIAN REGIONAL HOSPITAL, BECKLEY, WV, p. A770
BECKLEY ARH HOSPITAL, BECKLEY, WV, p. A770
BECKLEY VETERANS AFFAIRS MEDICAL CENTER, BECKLEY, WV, p. A770
BEDFORD MEMORIAL HOSPITAL, BEDFORD, VA, p. A739
BEDFORD REGIONAL MEDICAL CENTER, BEDFORD, IN, p. A224
BEDFORD VETERANS AFFAIRS MEDICAL CENTER, EDITH NOURSE ROGERS MEMORIAL VETERANS HOSPITAL, BEDFORD, MA, p. A334
BEEBE HEALTHCARE, LEWES, DE, p. A127
BEEBE MEDICAL CENTER, LEWES, DE, p. A127
BEHAVIORAL CENTER OF MICHIGAN, WARREN, MI, p. A369
BEHAVIORAL HEALTH CENTER OF THE PERMIAN BASIN, MIDLAND, TX, p. A701
BEHAVIORAL HEALTH OF ROCKY TOP, ROCKY TOP, TN, p. A648
BEHAVIORAL HEALTHCARE CENTER AT CLARKSVILLE, CLARKSVILLE, TN, p. A636
BEHAVIORAL HEALTHCARE CENTER AT COLUMBIA, COLUMBIA, TN, p. A636
BEHAVIORAL HEALTHCARE CENTER AT HUNTSVILLE, HUNTSVILLE, AL, p. A20
BEHAVIORAL HEALTHCARE CENTER AT MARTIN, MARTIN, TN, p. A643
BEHAVIORAL HLTHCARE OF INDIANA, PLYMOUTH, IN, p. A239
BEHAVIORAL HOSPITAL—LUTCHER, GONZALES, LA, p. A302
BEHAVIORAL HOSPITAL OF BATON ROUGE, BATON ROUGE, LA, p. A296
BEHAVIORAL HOSPITAL OF BELLAIRE, HOUSTON, TX, p. A684
BEHAVIORAL HOSPITAL OF LONGVIEW, LONGVIEW, TX, p. A696
BELLA VISTA HOSPITAL, MAYAGUEZ, PR, p. A808
BELLEVUE HOSPITAL, BELLEVUE, OH, p. A529
BELLEVUE MEDICAL CENTER, BELLEVUE, NE, p. A430
BELLEVUE WOMAN'S HOSPITAL, SCHENECTADY, NY, p. A498
BELLIN HEALTH OCONTO HOSPITAL, OCONTO, WI, p. A793
BELLIN HOSPITAL, GREEN BAY, WI, p. A785
BELLIN MEMORIAL HOSPITAL, GREEN BAY, WI, p. A785
BELLIN PSYCHIATRIC CENTER, GREEN BAY, WI, p. A785
BELLVILLE MEDICAL CENTER, BELLVILLE, TX, p. A659
BELMOND MEDICAL CENTER, BELMOND, IA, p. A244
BELMONT BEHAVIORAL HOSPITAL, PHILADELPHIA, PA, p. A599
BELMONT CENTER FOR COMPREHENSIVE TREATMENT, PHILADELPHIA, PA, p. A599
BELMONT PINES HOSPITAL, YOUNGSTOWN, OH, p. A553
BELOIT HEALTH SYSTEM, BELOIT, WI, p. A781
BELOIT MEMORIAL HOSPITAL, BELOIT, WI, p. A781
BELTON REGIONAL MEDICAL CENTER, BELTON, MO, p. A402
BEN TAUB GENERAL HOSPITAL, HOUSTON, TX, p. A684
BENEDICTINE HOSPITAL, KINGSTON, NY, p. A486
BENEFIS HEALTH CARE-EAST CAMP, GREAT FALLS, MT, p. A424
BENEFIS HEALTH CARE-WEST CAMP, GREAT FALLS, MT, p. A424
BENEFIS HEALTH SYSTEM, GREAT FALLS, MT, p. A424
BENEFIS HOSPITALS, GREAT FALLS, MT, p. A424
BENEFIS TETON MEDICAL CENTER, CHOTEAU, MT, p. A422
BENEWAH COMMUNITY HOSPITAL, SAINT MARIES, ID, p. A193
BENNETT CNTY HEALTHCARE CENTER, MARTIN, SD, p. A629
BENNETT COUNTY HOSPITAL AND NURSING HOME, MARTIN, SD, p. A629
BENSON HOSPITAL, BENSON, AZ, p. A30
BERGEN NEW BRIDGE MEDICAL CENTER, PARAMUS, NJ, p. A460
BERGER HEALTH SYSTEM, CIRCLEVILLE, OH, p. A533
BERKELEY MEDICAL CENTER, MARTINSBURG, WV, p. A774
BERKELEY REGIONAL MEDICAL CENTER, MONCKS CORNER, SC, p. A622
BERKSHIRE MEDICAL CENTER, PITTSFIELD, MA, p. A343
BERNARD MITCHELL HOSPITAL, CHICAGO, IL, p. A198
BERNARD PARISH HOSPITAL, CHALMETTE, LA, p. A299
BERRIEN COUNTY HOSPITAL, NASHVILLE, GA, p. A178
BERTIE MEMORIAL HOSPITAL, WINDSOR, NC, p. A520
BERTRAND CHAFFEE HOSPITAL, SPRINGVILLE, NY, p. A498
BERWICK HOSPITAL CENTER, BERWICK, PA, p. A584
BETH ABRAHAM HOSPITAL, BRONX, NY, p. A476
BETH ISRAEL DEACONESS HOSPITAL PLYMOUTH, PLYMOUTH, MA, p. A343
BETH ISRAEL DEACONESS HOSPITAL-MILTON, MILTON, MA, p. A342

BETH ISRAEL DEACONESS HOSPITAL-NEEDHAM CAMPUS, NEEDHAM, MA, p. A342
BETH ISRAEL DEACONESS HOSPITAL-PLYMOUTH, PLYMOUTH, MA, p. A343
BETH ISRAEL DEACONESS MEDICAL CENTER, BOSTON, MA, p. A335
BETH ISRAEL MEDICAL CENTER, NEW YORK, NY, p. A489
BETH ISRAEL MEDICAL CENTER-KINGS HIGHWAY DIVISION, BROOKLYN, NY, p. A477
BETHANIA REGIONAL HEALTH CNTR, WICHITA FALLS, TX, p. A725
BETHESDA HOSPITAL, SAINT PAUL, MN, p. A385
BETHESDA HOSPITAL EAST, BOYNTON BEACH, FL, p. A132
BETHESDA MEMORIAL HOSPITAL, BOYNTON BEACH, FL, p. A132
BETHESDA NORTH HOSPITAL, CINCINNATI, OH, p. A532
BETHESDA REHABILITATION HOSPITAL, BATON ROUGE, LA, p. A296
BEVERLY HOSPITAL, BEVERLY, MA, p. A334
BEVERLY HOSPITAL, MONTEBELLO, CA, p. A79
BEXAR COUNTY HOSPITAL DISTRICT, SAN ANTONIO, TX, p. A711
BHC ALHAMBRA HOSPITAL, ROSEMEAD, CA, p. A88
BHC BELMONT PINES HOSPITAL, YOUNGSTOWN, OH, p. A553
BHC CANYON RIDGE HOSPITAL, CHINO, CA, p. A60
BHC FREMONT HOSPITAL, FREMONT, CA, p. A65
BHC HERITAGE OAKS HOSPITAL, SACRAMENTO, CA, p. A89
BHC INTERMOUNTAIN HOSPITAL, BOISE, ID, p. A188
BHC MESILLA VALLEY HOSPITAL, LAS CRUCES, NM, p. A470
BHC MILLWOOD HOSPITAL, ARLINGTON, TX, p. A653
BHC MONTEVISTA HOSPITAL, LAS VEGAS, NV, p. A443
BHC PINNACLE POINTE HOSPITAL, LITTLE ROCK, AR, p. A49
BHC SIERRA VISTA HOSPITAL, SACRAMENTO, CA, p. A89
BHC WEST HILLS HOSPITAL, RENO, NV, p. A445
BIBB MEDICAL CENTER, CENTREVILLE, AL, p. A16
BIENVILLE MEDICAL CENTER, ARCADIA, LA, p. A296
BIG BEND REGIONAL MEDICAL CENTER, ALPINE, TX, p. A652
BIG FORK VALLEY HOSPITAL, BIGFORK, MN, p. A372
BIG HORN COUNTY MEMORIAL HOSPITAL, HARDIN, MT, p. A424
BIG HORN HOSPITAL ASSOCIAITON, HARDIN, MT, p. A424
BIG SANDY MEDICAL CENTER, BIG SANDY, MT, p. A421
BIG SKY MEDICAL CENTER, BIG SKY, MT, p. A421
BIG SOUTH FORK MEDICAL CENTER, ONEIDA, TN, p. A648
BIG SPRING STATE HOSPITAL, BIG SPRING, TX, p. A659
BIGFORK VALLEY HOSPITAL, BIGFORK, MN, p. A372
BIGGS-GRIDLEY MEMORIAL HOSPITAL, GRIDLEY, CA, p. A67
BILLINGS CLINIC, BILLINGS, MT, p. A421
BILOXI REGIONAL MEDICAL CENTER, BILOXI, MS, p. A389
BINGHAM MEMORIAL HOSPITAL, BLACKFOOT, ID, p. A188
BINGHAMTON GENERAL HOSPITAL, BINGHAMTON, NY, p. A475
BINGHAMTON PSYCHIATRIC CENTER, BINGHAMTON, NY, p. A475
BIRMINGHAM VETERANS AFFAIRS MEDICAL CENTER, BIRMINGHAM, AL, p. A14
BIXBY MEDICAL CENTER, ADRIAN, MI, p. A348
BJC MEDICAL CENTER, COMMERCE, GA, p. A169
BLACK HILLS SURGERY HOSPITAL, RAPID CITY, SD, p. A630
BLACK HILLS SURGICAL HOSPITAL, RAPID CITY, SD, p. A630
BLACK RIVER MEMORIAL HOSPITAL, BLACK RIVER FALLS, WI, p. A781
BLACKFEET COMMUNITY HOSPITAL, SAINT MARY, MT, p. A427
BLACKFORD COMMUNITY HOSPITAL, HARTFORD CITY, IN, p. A230
BLACKWELL REGIONAL HOSPITAL, BLACKWELL, OK, p. A556
BLADEN COUNTY HOSPITAL, ELIZABETHTOWN, NC, p. A509
BLAKE MEDICAL CENTER, BRADENTON, FL, p. A132
BLANCHARD VALLEY HEALTH SYSTEM, FINDLAY, OH, p. A540
BLANCHARD VALLEY HOSPITAL, FINDLAY, OH, p. A540
BLANCHARD VALLEY REG HLTH CTR, BLUFFTON, OH, p. A529
BLANCHARD VALLEY REG HLTH CTR, FINDLAY, OH, p. A540
BLANK CHILDREN'S HOSPITAL, DES MOINES, IA, p. A248
BLECKLEY MEMORIAL HOSPITAL, COCHRAN, GA, p. A169
BLEDSOE COMMUNITY MEDICAL CTR, PIKEVILLE, TN, p. A648
BLESSING HOSPITAL, QUINCY, IL, p. A218
BLIANT SPECIALTY HOSPITAL, NEW ORLEANS, LA, p. A310
BLODGETT MEMORIAL MEDICAL CTR, GRAND RAPIDS, MI, p. A355
BLOOMINGTON HOSPITAL, BLOOMINGTON, IN, p. A224
BLOOMINGTON HOSPITAL OF ORANGE COUNTY, PAOLI, IN, p. A238
BLOOMINGTON MEADOWS HOSPITAL, BLOOMINGTON, IN, p. A224
BLOOMSBURG HOSPITAL, BLOOMSBURG, PA, p. A585

BLOUNT MEMORIAL HOSPITAL, MARYVILLE, TN, p. A643
BLOWING ROCK HOSPITAL, BLOWING ROCK, NC, p. A505
BLUE HILL MEMORIAL HOSPITAL, BLUE HILL, ME, p. A319
BLUE MOUNTAIN HOSPITAL, BLANDING, UT, p. A727
BLUE MOUNTAIN HOSPITAL, JOHN DAY, OR, p. A576
BLUE MOUNTAIN HOSPITAL DISTRICT, JOHN DAY, OR, p. A576
BLUE MOUNTAIN HOSPITAL PALMERTON CAMPUS, PALMERTON, PA, p. A599
BLUE RIDGE REGIONAL HOSPITAL, SPRUCE PINE, NC, p. A518
BLUEGRASS COMMUNITY HOSPITAL, VERSAILLES, KY, p. A294
BLUFFTON HOSPITAL, BLUFFTON, OH, p. A529
BLUFFTON REGIONAL MEDICAL CENTER, BLUFFTON, IN, p. A224
BLYTHEDALE CHILDREN'S HOSPITAL, VALHALLA, NY, p. A500
BOAZ-ALBERTVILLE MEDICAL CTR, BOAZ, AL, p. A16
BOB WILSON MEMORIAL GRANT COUNTY HOSPITAL, ULYSSES, KS, p. A278
BOCA RATON COMMUNITY HOSPITAL, BOCA RATON, FL, p. A132
BOCA RATON REGIONAL HOSPITAL, BOCA RATON, FL, p. A132
BOISE BEHAVIORAL HEALTH HOSPITAL, BOISE, ID, p. A188
BOISE VETERANS AFFAIRS MEDICAL CENTER, BOISE, ID, p. A188
BOLDEN PLAINS COMM HOSPITAL, BORGER, TX, p. A660
BOLIVAR COUNTY HOSPITAL, CLEVELAND, MS, p. A391
BOLIVAR GENERAL HOSPITAL, BOLIVAR, TN, p. A634
BOLIVAR MEDICAL CENTER, BOLIVAR, TN, p. A634
BOLIVAR MEDICAL CENTER, CLEVELAND, MS, p. A391
BON SECOUR-DEPAUL MEDICAL CTR, NORFOLK, VA, p. A747
BON SECOURS BALTIMORE HEALTH SYSTEM, BALTIMORE, MD, p. A324
BON SECOURS COMMUNITY HOSPITAL, PORT JERVIS, NY, p. A495
BON SECOURS MARY IMMACULATE HOSPITAL, NEWPORT NEWS, VA, p. A746
BON SECOURS MARYVIEW MEDICAL CENTER, PORTSMOUTH, VA, p. A749
BON SECOURS MEMORIAL REGIONAL MEDICAL CENTER, MECHANICSVILLE, VA, p. A746
BON SECOURS ST MARY'S HOSPITAL, NORTON, VA, p. A748
BON SECOURS ST. FRANCIS EASTSIDE, GREENVILLE, SC, p. A620
BON SECOURS ST. FRANCIS HEALTH SYSTEM, GREENVILLE, SC, p. A620
BON SECOURS ST. FRANCIS HOSPITAL, CHARLESTON, SC, p. A616
BON SECOURS ST. FRANCIS MEDICAL CENTER, MIDLOTHIAN, VA, p. A746
BON SECOURS ST. FRANCIS XAVIER HOSPITAL, CHARLESTON, SC, p. A616
BON SECOURS ST. MARY'S HOSPITAL, RICHMOND, VA, p. A749
BON SECOURS-DEPAUL MEDICAL CENTER, NORFOLK, VA, p. A747
BON SECOURS-RICHMOND COMMUNITY HOSPITAL, RICHMOND, VA, p. A749
BONE AND JOINT HOSPITAL, OKLAHOMA CITY, OK, p. A563
BONNER GENERAL HEALTH, SANDPOINT, ID, p. A193
BOONE COUNTY COMM HOSPITAL, ALBION, NE, p. A429
BOONE COUNTY HEALTH CENTER, ALBION, NE, p. A429
BOONE COUNTY HOSPITAL, BOONE, IA, p. A244
BOONE HOSPITAL CENTER, COLUMBIA, MO, p. A405
BOONE MEMORIAL HOSPITAL, MADISON, WV, p. A774
BOONEVILLE COMMUNITY HOSPITAL, BOONEVILLE, AR, p. A43
BORGESS MEDICAL CENTER, KALAMAZOO, MI, p. A359
BORGESS-LEE MEMORIAL HOSPITAL, DOWAGIAC, MI, p. A353
BORGESS-PIPP HEALTH CENTER, PLAINWELL, MI, p. A364
BOSTON CHILDREN'S HOSPITAL, BOSTON, MA, p. A335
BOSTON MEDICAL CENTER, BOSTON, MA, p. A335
BOTHWELL REGIONAL HEALTH CENTER, SEDALIA, MO, p. A418
BOTSFORD HOSPITAL, FARMINGTON HILLS, MI, p. A354
BOULDER CITY HOSPITAL, BOULDER CITY, NV, p. A441
BOULDER COMMUNITY HEALTH, BOULDER, CO, p. A108
BOULDER COMMUNITY HOSPITAL, BOULDER, CO, p. A108
BOUNDARY COMMUNITY HOSPITAL, BONNERS FERRY, ID, p. A189
BOURBON COMMUNITY HOSPITAL, PARIS, KY, p. A292
BOURNEWOOD HEALTH SYSTEMS, BROOKLINE, MA, p. A337
BOURNEWOOD HOSPITAL, BROOKLINE, MA, p. A337
BOWDLE HOSPITAL, BOWDLE, SD, p. A626
BOX BUTTE GENERAL HOSPITAL, ALLIANCE, NE, p. A429
BOYS TOWN NATIONAL RESEARCH HOSPITAL, OMAHA, NE, p. A436

BOYS TOWN NATL INST FOR CHILD, OMAHA, NE, p. A436
BOZEMAN HEALTH, BOZEMAN, MT, p. A422
BOZEMAN HEALTH BIG SKY MEDICAL CENTER, BIG SKY, MT, p. A421
BOZEMAN HEALTH DEACONESS HOSPITAL, BOZEMAN, MT, p. A422
BRADFORD HEALTH SERVICES AT BIRMINGHAM LODGE, WARRIOR, AL, p. A25
BRADFORD HEALTH SERVICES AT HUNTSVILLE, MADISON, AL, p. A21
BRADFORD HEALTH SERVICES AT WARRIOR LODGE, WARRIOR, AL, p. A25
BRADFORD HOSPITAL, BRADFORD, PA, p. A585
BRADFORD PARKSIDE AT MADISON, MADISON, AL, p. A21
BRADLEY CENTER, COLUMBUS, GA, p. A169
BRADLEY CENTER OF ST. FRANCIS, COLUMBUS, GA, p. A169
BRADLEY COUNTY MEDICAL CENTER, WARREN, AR, p. A54
BRADLEY COUNTY MEM HOSPITAL, WARREN, AR, p. A54
BRADLEY MEMORIAL, SOUTHINGTON, CT, p. A125
BRADLEY MEMORIAL HOSPITAL AND HEALTH CENTER, SOUTHINGTON, CT, p. A125
BRADY-GREEN COMM HEALTH CENTER, SAN ANTONIO, TX, p. A711
BRANDON REGIONAL HOSPITAL, BRANDON, FL, p. A133
BRANDON REGIONAL MEDICAL CTR, BRANDON, FL, p. A133
BRANDYWINE HOSP & TRAUMA CNTR, COATESVILLE, PA, p. A587
BRANDYWINE HOSPITAL, COATESVILLE, PA, p. A587
BRATTLEBORO MEMORIAL HOSPITAL, BRATTLEBORO, VT, p. A735
BRATTLEBORO RETREAT, BRATTLEBORO, VT, p. A735
BRAXTON COUNTY MEMORIAL HOSPITAL, GASSAWAY, WV, p. A772
BRAZOSPORT REGIONAL HEALTH SYSTEM, LAKE JACKSON, TX, p. A694
BRECKINRIDGE MEMORIAL HOSPITAL, HARDINSBURG, KY, p. A284
BRENNER CHILDREN'S HOSPITAL & HEALTH SERVICES, WINSTON SALEM, NC, p. A520
BRENTWOOD BEHAVIORAL CARE, JACKSON, MS, p. A394
BRENTWOOD BEHAVIORAL COMPANY, SHREVEPORT, LA, p. A313
BRENTWOOD BEHAVIORAL HEALTHCARE OF MISSISSIPPI, JACKSON, MS, p. A394
BRENTWOOD HOSPITAL, SHREVEPORT, LA, p. A314
BRENTWOOD MEADOWS, NEWBURGH, IN, p. A238
BRENTWOOD SPRINGS, NEWBURGH, IN, p. A238
BREWSTER MEMORIAL HOSPITAL, ALPINE, TX, p. A652
BRIDGEPOINT CONTINUING CARE HOSPITAL, MARRERO, LA, p. A308
BRIDGEPOINT HOSPITAL CAPITOL HILL, WASHINGTON, DC, p. A129
BRIDGEPOINT HOSPITAL NATIONAL HARBOR, WASHINGTON, DC, p. A129
BRIDGEPOINT HOSPITAL-CAPITOL HILL, WASHINGTON, DC, p. A129
BRIDGEPOINT HOSPITAL-NATIONAL HARBOR, WASHINGTON, DC, p. A129
BRIDGEPORT HOSPITAL, BRIDGEPORT, CT, p. A121
BRIDGETON HEALTH CENTER, BRIDGETON, NJ, p. A453
BRIDGETON HOSPITAL, BRIDGETON, NJ, p. A453
BRIDGEWATER STATE HOSPITAL, BRIDGEWATER, MA, p. A336
BRIDGEWAY, NORTH LITTLE ROCK, AR, p. A51
BRIDGTON HOSPITAL, BRIDGTON, ME, p. A319
BRIGHAM AND WOMEN'S FAULKNER HOSPITAL, BOSTON, MA, p. A335
BRIGHAM AND WOMEN'S HOSPITAL, BOSTON, MA, p. A335
BRIGHAM CITY COMMUNITY HOSPITAL, BRIGHAM CITY, UT, p. A727
BRIGHTON CAMPUS-MAINE MED CTR, PORTLAND, ME, p. A322
BRIGHTON CENTER FOR RECOVERY, BRIGHTON, MI, p. A350
BRISTOL BAY AREA HEALTH CORPORATION, DILLINGHAM, AK, p. A8
BRISTOL HEALTH, BRISTOL, CT, p. A121
BRISTOL HOSPITAL, BRISTOL, CT, p. A121
BRISTOL REGIONAL MEDICAL CENTER, BRISTOL, TN, p. A634
BRISTOW MEDICAL CENTER, BRISTOW, OK, p. A556
BRISTOW MEMORIAL HOSPITAL, BRISTOW, OK, p. A556
BROADDUS HOSPITAL, PHILIPPI, WV, p. A775
BROADLAWNS MEDICAL CENTER, DES MOINES, IA, p. A248
BROADWATER HEALTH CENTER, TOWNSEND, MT, p. A428
BROCKTON HOSPITAL, BROCKTON, MA, p. A337
BROCKTON VETERANS AFFAIRS MEDICAL CENTER, BROCKTON, MA, p. A337
BRODSTONE MEM HOSP, SUPERIOR, NE, p. A440
BRODSTONE MEMORIAL HOSPITAL, SUPERIOR, NE, p. A440

BROMENN MEDICAL CENTER, NORMAL, IL, p. A214
BROMENN REGIONAL MEDICAL CENTER, NORMAL, IL, p. A214
BRONSON BATTLE CREEK, BATTLE CREEK, MI, p. A349
BRONSON BATTLE CREEK HOSPITAL, BATTLE CREEK, MI, p. A349
BRONSON LAKEVIEW HOSPITAL, PAW PAW, MI, p. A363
BRONSON METHODIST HOSPITAL, KALAMAZOO, MI, p. A359
BRONSON SOUTH HAVEN HOSPITAL, SOUTH HAVEN, MI, p. A367
BRONX HEALTH CARE SYSTEM, BRONX, NY, p. A476
BRONX PSYCHIATRIC CENTER, BRONX, NY, p. A476
BRONXCARE HEALTH SYSTEM, BRONX, NY, p. A476
BROOK LANE HEALTH SERVICES, HAGERSTOWN, MD, p. A330
BROOK LANE PSYCHIATRIC CENTER, HAGERSTOWN, MD, p. A330
BROOKDALE HOSPITAL MEDICAL CENTER, NEW YORK, NY, p. A489
BROOKE ARMY MEDICAL CENTER, FORT SAM HOUSTON, TX, p. A677
BROOKE GLEN BEHAVIORAL HOSPITAL, FORT WASHINGTON, PA, p. A590
BROOKHAVEN HOSPITAL, TULSA, OK, p. A569
BROOKHAVEN MEMORIAL HOSPITAL MEDICAL CENTER, PATCHOGUE, NY, p. A494
BROOKINGS HEALTH SYSTEM, BROOKINGS, SD, p. A626
BROOKINGS HOSPITAL, BROOKINGS, SD, p. A626
BROOKLYN HOSP-CALEDONIAN HOSP, BROOKLYN, NY, p. A477
BROOKLYN HOSPITAL CENTER, BROOKLYN, NY, p. A477
BROOKS COUNTY HOSPITAL, QUITMAN, GA, p. A178
BROOKS MEMORIAL HOSPITAL, DUNKIRK, NY, p. A482
BROOKS REHABILITATION HOSP, JACKSONVILLE, FL, p. A140
BROOKS REHABILITATION HOSPITAL, JACKSONVILLE, FL, p. A141
BROOKSVILLE REGIONAL HOSPITAL, BROOKSVILLE, FL, p. A133
BROOKVILLE HOSPITAL, BROOKVILLE, PA, p. A585
BROOKWOOD BAPTIST MEDICAL CENTER, BIRMINGHAM, AL, p. A14
BROOKWOOD MEDICAL CENTER, BIRMINGHAM, AL, p. A14
BROTMAN MEDICAL CENTER, CULVER CITY, CA, p. A62
BROUGHTON HOSPITAL, MORGANTON, NC, p. A515
BROWARD GENERAL MEDICAL CENTER, FORT LAUDERDALE, FL, p. A137
BROWARD HEALTH CORAL SPRINGS, CORAL SPRINGS, FL, p. A135
BROWARD HEALTH IMPERIAL POINT, FORT LAUDERDALE, FL, p. A137
BROWARD HEALTH MEDICAL CENTER, FORT LAUDERDALE, FL, p. A137
BROWARD HEALTH NORTH, DEERFIELD BEACH, FL, p. A136
BROWN COUNTY COMMUNITY TREATMENT CENTER, GREEN BAY, WI, p. A785
BROWN COUNTY HOSPITAL, AINSWORTH, NE, p. A429
BROWN COUNTY HUMAN SERVICES MENTAL HEALTH CENTER, GREEN BAY, WI, p. A785
BROWNFIELD REGIONAL MEDICAL CENTER, BROWNFIELD, TX, p. A660
BROWNSVILLE MEDICAL CENTER, BROWNSVILLE, TX, p. A660
BROWNWOOD REGIONAL MEDICAL CENTER, BROWNWOOD, TX, p. A661
BRUNSWICK HOUSE ALCOHOLISM TREATMENT CENTER, AMITYVILLE, NY, p. A474
BRUNSWICK NOVANT MEDICAL CENTER, BOLIVIA, NC, p. A505
BRUNSWICK PSYCH CENTER, AMITYVILLE, NY, p. A474
BRYAN COMMUNITY HOSPITAL, BRYAN, OH, p. A530
BRYAN MEDICAL CENTER, LINCOLN, NE, p. A434
BRYAN W. WHITFIELD MEMORIAL HOSPITAL, DEMOPOLIS, AL, p. A17
BRYANLGH MEDICAL CENTER, LINCOLN, NE, p. A434
BRYANLGH MEDICAL CENTER-EAST, LINCOLN, NE, p. A434
BRYANLGH MEDICAL CENTER-WEST, LINCOLN, NE, p. A434
BRYCE HOSPITAL, TUSCALOOSA, AL, p. A25
BRYLIN HOSPITALS, BUFFALO, NY, p. A479
BRYN MAWR HOSPITAL, BRYN MAWR, PA, p. A585
BRYN MAWR REHABILITATION HOSPITAL, MALVERN, PA, p. A596
BRYNN MARR BEHAVIORAL SYSTEM, JACKSONVILLE, NC, p. A512
BRYNN MARR HOSPITAL, JACKSONVILLE, NC, p. A512
BSA HOSPITAL, LLC, AMARILLO, TX, p. A652
BSA-PANHANDLE SURGICAL HOSP, AMARILLO, TX, p. A652
BUCHANAN COUNTY HEALTH CENTER, INDEPENDENCE, IA, p. A251
BUCHANAN GENERAL HOSPITAL, GRUNDY, VA, p. A743
BUCK COUNTY CAMPUS, LANGHORNE, PA, p. A594

BUCKS COUNTY CAMPUS, LANGHORNE, PA, p. A594
BUCKTAIL MEDICAL CENTER, RENOVO, PA, p. A606
BUCYRUS COMMUNITY HOSPITAL, BUCYRUS, OH, p. A530
BUCYRUS HOSPITAL, BUCYRUS, OH, p. A530
BUENA VISTA COUNTY HOSPITAL, STORM LAKE, IA, p. A258
BUENA VISTA REGIONAL MEDICAL CENTER, STORM LAKE, IA, p. A258
BUFFALO HOSPITAL, BUFFALO, MN, p. A373
BUFFALO PSYCHIATRIC CENTER, BUFFALO, NY, p. A479
BULLHEAD COMMUNITY HOSPITAL, BULLHEAD CITY, AZ, p. A30
BULLOCH MEMORIAL HOSPITAL, STATESBORO, GA, p. A181
BULLOCK COUNTY HOSPITAL, UNION SPRINGS, AL, p. A25
BUNKIE GENERAL HOSPITAL, BUNKIE, LA, p. A299
BURBON COMMUNITY HOSPITAL, PARIS, KY, p. A292
BURDETT BIRTH CENTER, TROY, NY, p. A500
BURDICK WEST MEDICAL CENTER, HALEYVILLE, AL, p. A20
BURGESS HEALTH CENTER, ONAWA, IA, p. A255
BURGESS MEMORIAL HOSPITAL, ONAWA, IA, p. A255
BURKE COUNTY HOSPITAL, WAYNESBORO, GA, p. A183
BURKE MEDICAL CENTER, WAYNESBORO, GA, p. A183
BURKE REHABILITATION CENTER, WHITE PLAINS, NY, p. A502
BURKE REHABILITATION HOSPITAL, WHITE PLAINS, NY, p. A502
BURLESON ST. JOSEPH HEALTH CENTER, CALDWELL, TX, p. A662
BURNETT GENERAL HOSPITAL, GRANTSBURG, WI, p. A784
BURNETT MEDICAL CENTER, GRANTSBURG, WI, p. A785
BUTLER COUNTY HEALTH CARE CENTER, DAVID CITY, NE, p. A431
BUTLER COUNTY HEALTH CARE CNTR, DAVID CITY, NE, p. A431
BUTLER COUNTY MEDICAL CENTER, HAMILTON, OH, p. A541
BUTLER HEALTH SYSTEM, BUTLER, PA, p. A585
BUTLER HOSPITAL, PROVIDENCE, RI, p. A613
BUTLER MEMORIAL HOSPITAL, BUTLER, PA, p. A585
BUTTONWOOD HOSPITAL OF BURLINGTON, NEW LISBON, NJ, p. A459
BYERLY HOSPITAL, HARTSVILLE, SC, p. A621
BYRD MEMORIAL HOSPITAL, LEESVILLE, LA, p. A307
BYRD REGIONAL HOSPITAL, LEESVILLE, LA, p. A307

# C

CABELL HUNTINGTON HOSPITAL, HUNTINGTON, WV, p. A772
CABINET PEAKS MEDICAL CENTER, LIBBY, MT, p. A425
CACHE VALLEY HOSPITAL, NORTH LOGAN, UT, p. A729
CACHE VALLEY SPECIALTY HOSPITAL, NORTH LOGAN, UT, p. A729
CALAIS REGIONAL HOSPITAL, CALAIS, ME, p. A319
CALDWELL COUNTY HOSPITAL, PRINCETON, KY, p. A292
CALDWELL MEDICAL CENTER, PRINCETON, KY, p. A292
CALDWELL MEMORIAL HOSPITAL, COLUMBIA, LA, p. A299
CALDWELL MEMORIAL HOSPITAL, LENOIR, NC, p. A513
CALDWELL UNC HEALTH CARE, LENOIR, NC, p. A513
CALHOUN GENERAL HOSPITAL, GRANTSVILLE, WV, p. A772
CALHOUN HEALTH SERVICES, CALHOUN CITY, MS, p. A390
CALHOUN-LIBERTY HOSIPTAL, BLOUNTSTOWN, FL, p. A132
CALHOUN-LIBERTY HOSPITAL, BLOUNTSTOWN, FL, p. A132
CALIF MED CENTER-LOS ANGELES, LOS ANGELES, CA, p. A73
CALIFORNIA HEART AND SURGICAL HOSPITAL, LOMA LINDA, CA, p. A71
CALIFORNIA HOSPITAL MEDICAL CENTER, LOS ANGELES, CA, p. A73
CALIFORNIA MEDICAL FACILITY, VACAVILLE, CA, p. A102
CALIFORNIA MENS COLONY CORRECTIONAL TREATMENT CENTER, SAN LUIS OBISPO, CA, p. A95
CALIFORNIA MENS COLONY HOSPITAL, SAN LUIS OBISPO, CA, p. A95
CALIFORNIA PACIFIC MEDICAL CENTER, SAN FRANCISCO, CA, p. A93
CALIFORNIA PACIFIC MEDICAL CENTER-DAVIES CAMPUS, SAN FRANCISCO, CA, p. A93
CALIFORNIA PACIFIC MEDICAL CENTER-ST. LUKE'S CAMPUS, SAN FRANCISCO, CA, p. A93
CALIFORNIA REHABILITATION INSTITUTE, LOS ANGELES, CA, p. A73
CALLAWAY COMMUNITY HOSPITAL, FULTON, MO, p. A407
CALLAWAY DISTRICT HOSPITAL, CALLAWAY, NE, p. A430
CALUMET MEDICAL CENTER, CHILTON, WI, p. A781
CALVARY HOSPITAL, BRONX, NY, p. A476
CALVERT MEMORIAL HOSPITAL, PRINCE FREDERICK, MD, p. A331

CALVERTHEALTH MEDICAL CENTER, PRINCE FREDERICK, MD, p. A331
CAMBRIDGE HEALTH ALLIANCE, CAMBRIDGE, MA, p. A337
CAMBRIDGE MEDICAL CENTER, CAMBRIDGE, MN, p. A373
CAMBRIDGE MEMORIAL HOSPITAL, CAMBRIDGE, MN, p. A373
CAMBRIDGE MEMOtRIAL HOSPITAL, CAMBRIDGE, NE, p. A430
CAMBRIDGE PUB HLTH COMMISSION, CAMBRIDGE, MA, p. A337
CAMC MEMORIAL HOSPITAL, CHARLESTON, WV, p. A771
CAMC WOMEN AND CHILDREN'S HOSPITAL, CHARLESTON, WV, p. A771
CAMDEN CLARK MEDICAL CENTER, PARKERSBURG, WV, p. A775
CAMDEN GENERAL HOSPITAL, CAMDEN, TN, p. A634
CAMDEN-CLARK MEMORIAL HOSPITAL, PARKERSBURG, WV, p. A775
CAMERON COMMUNITY HOSPITAL, CAMERON, MO, p. A403
CAMERON HOSPITAL, CAMERON, TX, p. A662
CAMERON MEMORIAL COMMUNITY HOSPITAL, ANGOLA, IN, p. A223
CAMERON REGIONAL MEDICAL CENTER, CAMERON, MO, p. A403
CAMINO HEALTHCARE, MOUNTAIN VIEW, CA, p. A80
CAMPBELL COUNTY HEALTH, GILLETTE, WY, p. A802
CAMPBELL COUNTY MEMORIAL HOSPITAL, GILLETTE, WY, p. A802
CANANDAIGUA VETERANS AFFAIRS MEDICAL CENTER, CANANDAIGUA, NY, p. A480
CANCER TREATMENT CENTER, TULSA, OK, p. A569
CANCER TREATMENT CENTERS OF AMERICA-EASTERN REGIONAL MEDICAL CENTER, PHILADELPHIA, PA, p. A599
CANDLER COUNTY HOSPITAL, METTER, GA, p. A176
CANDLER HOSPITAL, SAVANNAH, GA, p. A179
CANNON FALLS MEDICAL CENTER, CANNON FALLS, MN, p. A374
CANNON MEMORIAL HOSPITAL, PICKENS, SC, p. A623
CANONSBURG GENERAL HOSPITAL, CANONSBURG, PA, p. A586
CANONSBURG HOSPITAL, CANONSBURG, PA, p. A586
CANTON-POTSDAM HOSPITAL, POTSDAM, NY, p. A495
CANYON RIDGE HOSPITAL, CHINO, CA, p. A60
CANYON VISTA MEDICAL CENTER, SIERRA VISTA, AZ, p. A38
CAPE CANAVERAL HOSPITAL, COCOA BEACH, FL, p. A134
CAPE COD & ISLAND COMMUNITY MENTAL HEALTH CENTER, POCASSET, MA, p. A343
CAPE COD HOSPITAL, HYANNIS, MA, p. A340
CAPE CORAL HOSPITAL, CAPE CORAL, FL, p. A134
CAPE FEAR MEMORIAL HOSPITAL, WILMINGTON, NC, p. A520
CAPE FEAR VALLEY—BLADEN COUNTY HOSPITAL, ELIZABETHTOWN, NC, p. A509
CAPE FEAR VALLEY HEALTH SYSTEM, FAYETTEVILLE, NC, p. A510
CAPE FEAR VALLEY MEDICAL CENTER, FAYETTEVILLE, NC, p. A510
CAPE REGIONAL HEALTH SYSTEM, CAPE MAY COURT HOUSE, NJ, p. A453
CAPE REGIONAL MEDICAL CENTER, CAPE MAY COURT HOUSE, NJ, p. A453
CAPITAL DISTRICT PSYCHIATRIC CENTER, ALBANY, NY, p. A474
CAPITAL HEALTH—FULD CAMPUS, TRENTON, NJ, p. A464
CAPITAL HEALTH—MERCER CAMPUS, PENNINGTON, NJ, p. A461
CAPITAL HEALTH MEDICAL CENTER-HOPEWELL, PENNINGTON, NJ, p. A461
CAPITAL HEALTH REGIONAL MEDICAL CENTER, TRENTON, NJ, p. A464
CAPITAL HOSPICE, ARLINGTON, VA, p. A738
CAPITAL MEDICAL CENTER, OLYMPIA, WA, p. A761
CAPITAL REGION MEDICAL CENTER, JEFFERSON CITY, MO, p. A408
CAPITAL REGIONAL MEDICAL CENTER, TALLAHASSEE, FL, p. A158
CAPROCK HOSPITAL, BRYAN, TX, p. A661
CAPTAIN JAMES A. LOVELL FEDERAL HEALTH CARE CENTER, NORTH CHICAGO, IL, p. A214
CARDINAL CUSHING GEN HOSPITAL, BROCKTON, MA, p. A337
CARDINAL HILL HOSPITAL, LEXINGTON, KY, p. A286
CARDINAL HILL REHABILITATION HOSPITAL, LEXINGTON, KY, p. A286
CARDINAL HILL SPECIALTY HOSPITAL, FORT THOMAS, KY, p. A283
CARDIOVASCULAR CENTER OF PUERTO RICO AND THE CARIBBEAN, SAN JUAN, PR, p. A809
CARDON CHILDREN'S MEDICAL CENTER, MESA, AZ, p. A34
CARE ONE AT HACKSENSACK UNIVERSITY MEDICAL CENTER AT PASCACK VALLEY, WESTWOOD, NJ, p. A465

CARE ONE AT TRINITAS REGIONAL MEDICAL CENTER, ELIZABETH, NJ, p. A454
CARELINK OF JACKSON, JACKSON, MI, p. A358
CAREONE AT HACKSENSACK UNIVERSITY MEDICAL CENTER AT PASCACK VALLEY, WESTWOOD, NJ, p. A465
CAREONE AT TRINITAS REGIONAL MEDICAL CENTER, ELIZABETH, NJ, p. A454
CAREPARTNERS HEALTH SERVICES, ASHEVILLE, NC, p. A504
CAREPARTNERS REHABILITATION HOSPITAL, ASHEVILLE, NC, p. A504
CAREPOINT HEALTH -CHRIST HOSPITAL, JERSEY CITY, NJ, p. A456
CAREPOINT HEALTH BAYONNE MEDICAL CENTER, BAYONNE, NJ, p. A452
CAREPOINT HEALTH CHRIST HOSPITAL, JERSEY CITY, NJ, p. A456
CAREPOINT HEALTH HOBOKEN UNIVERSITY MEDICAL CENTER, HOBOKEN, NJ, p. A456
CARIBBEAN MEDICAL CENTER, FAJARDO, PR, p. A807
CARIBBEAN PED & SURGERY HOSP, SAN JUAN, PR, p. A810
CARIBOU MEM HOSPITAL & NSG HM, SODA SPRINGS, ID, p. A193
CARIBOU MEMORIAL HOSPITAL AND LIVING CENTER, SODA SPRINGS, ID, p. A193
CARILION FRANKLIN MEMORIAL HOSPITAL, ROCKY MOUNT, VA, p. A751
CARILION GILES COMMUNITY HOSPITAL, PEARISBURG, VA, p. A748
CARILION GILES MEMORIAL HOSPITAL, PEARISBURG, VA, p. A748
CARILION MEDICAL CENTER, ROANOKE, VA, p. A751
CARILION NEW RIVER VALLEY MEDICAL CENTER, CHRISTIANSBURG, VA, p. A740
CARILION RADFORD COMM HOSP, CHRISTIANSBURG, VA, p. A740
CARILION ROANOKE COMM HOSP, ROANOKE, VA, p. A751
CARILION ROANOKE MEMORIAL HOSPITAL, ROANOKE, VA, p. A751
CARILION SAINT ALBANS HOSPITAL, CHRISTIANSBURG, VA, p. A740
CARILION STONEWALL JACKSON HOSPITAL, LEXINGTON, VA, p. A744
CARILION TAZEWELL COMMUNITY HOSPITAL, TAZEWELL, VA, p. A752
CARITAS CARNEY HOSPITAL, BOSTON, MA, p. A335
CARITAS GOOD SAMARITAN MEDICAL CENTER, BROCKTON, MA, p. A337
CARITAS HOLY FAMILY HOSPITAL AND MEDICAL CENTER, METHUEN, MA, p. A341
CARITAS MEDICAL CENTER, LOUISVILLE, KY, p. A287
CARITAS NORWOOD HOSPITAL, NORWOOD, MA, p. A343
CARITAS ST. ELIZABETH'S MEDICAL CENTER, BRIGHTON, MA, p. A336
CARL ALBERT COMMUNITY MENTAL HEALTH CENTER, MCALESTER, OK, p. A561
CARL R. DARNALL ARMY MEDICAL CENTER, FORT HOOD, TX, p. A677
CARL T HAYDEN VET AFFAIRS CTR, PHOENIX, AZ, p. A35
CARL VINSON VETERANS AFFAIRS MEDICAL CENTER, DUBLIN, GA, p. A171
CARLE FOUNDATION HOSPITAL, URBANA, IL, p. A221
CARLE HOOPESTON REGIONAL HEALTH CENTER, HOOPESTON, IL, p. A208
CARLE PAVILION, CHAMPAIGN, IL, p. A197
CARLE RICHLAND MEMORIAL HOSPITAL, OLNEY, IL, p. A215
CARLINVILLE AREA HOSPITAL, CARLINVILLE, IL, p. A196
CARLSBAD MEDICAL CENTER, CARLSBAD, NM, p. A468
CARNEGIE TRI-COUNTY MUNICIPAL HOSPITAL, CARNEGIE, OK, p. A557
CARNEY HOSPITAL, BOSTON, MA, p. A335
CARO CENTER, CARO, MI, p. A350
CARO COMMUNITY HOSPITAL, CARO, MI, p. A350
CARO REG MENTAL HLTH CENTER, CARO, MI, p. A350
CAROLINA CENTER FOR BEHAVIORAL HEALTH, GREER, SC, p. A621
CAROLINA PINES REGIONAL MEDICAL CENTER, HARTSVILLE, SC, p. A621
CAROLINAEAST HEALTH SYSTEM, NEW BERN, NC, p. A515
CAROLINAEAST MEDICAL CENTER, NEW BERN, NC, p. A515
CAROLINAS CONTINUECARE HOSPITAL AT PINEVILLE, CHARLOTTE, NC, p. A507
CAROLINAS CONTINUECARE HOSPITAL AT UNIVERSITY, CHARLOTTE, NC, p. A507
CAROLINAS HEALTHCARE SYSTEM—BLUE RIDGE MORGANTON, MORGANTON, NC, p. A515
CAROLINAS HEALTHCARE SYSTEM ANSON, WADESBORO, NC, p. A519
CAROLINAS HEALTHCARE SYSTEM BLUE RIDGE, MORGANTON, NC, p. A515
CAROLINAS HEALTHCARE SYSTEM CLEVELAND, SHELBY, NC, p. A518

CAROLINAS HEALTHCARE SYSTEM KINGS MOUNTAIN, KINGS MOUNTAIN, NC, p. A513

CAROLINAS HEALTHCARE SYSTEM LINCOLN, LINCOLNTON, NC, p. A514

CAROLINAS HEALTHCARE SYSTEM NORTHEAST, CONCORD, NC, p. A508

CAROLINAS HEALTHCARE SYSTEM PINEVILLE, CHARLOTTE, NC, p. A507

CAROLINAS HEALTHCARE SYSTEM STANLY, ALBEMARLE, NC, p. A504

CAROLINAS HEALTHCARE SYSTEM UNION, MONROE, NC, p. A514

CAROLINAS HEALTHCARE SYSTEM UNIVERSITY, CHARLOTTE, NC, p. A507

CAROLINAS HOSP SYST-KINGSTREE, KINGSTREE, SC, p. A621

CAROLINAS HOSP SYST-LAKE CITY, LAKE CITY, SC, p. A622

CAROLINAS HOSPITAL SYSTEM, FLORENCE, SC, p. A619

CAROLINAS HOSPITAL SYSTEM MARION, MULLINS, SC, p. A623

CAROLINAS MED CENTER-PINEVILLE, CHARLOTTE, NC, p. A507

CAROLINAS MEDICAL CENTER, CHARLOTTE, NC, p. A507

CAROLINAS REHABILITATION, CHARLOTTE, NC, p. A507

CAROMONT REGIONAL MEDICAL CENTER, GASTONIA, NC, p. A510

CARONDELET BEHAVIORAL HLTH CTR, RICHLAND, WA, p. A763

CARONDELET HOLY CROSS HOSPITAL, NOGALES, AZ, p. A34

CARONDELET ST. JOSEPH'S HOSPITAL, TUCSON, AZ, p. A40

CARONDELET ST. MARY'S HOSPITAL, TUCSON, AZ, p. A40

CARONDOLET HOLY CROSS HOSPITAL, NOGALES, AZ, p. A34

CARRIER CLINIC, BELLE MEAD, NJ, p. A452

CARRIS HEALTH—REDWOOD, REDWOOD FALLS, MN, p. A383

CARROLL COUNTY MEMORIAL HOSPITAL, CARROLLTON, KY, p. A281

CARROLL COUNTY MEMORIAL HOSPITAL, CARROLLTON, MO, p. A404

CARROLL COUNTY REG MED CENTER, CARROLLTON, KY, p. A281

CARROLL HOSPITAL, WESTMINSTER, MD, p. A333

CARROLL HOSPITAL CENTER, WESTMINSTER, MD, p. A333

CARROLLTON REGIONAL MEDICAL CENTER, CARROLLTON, TX, p. A663

CARROLLTON SPRINGS, CARROLLTON, TX, p. A663

CARRUS REHABILITATION HOSPITAL, SHERMAN, TX, p. A715

CARRUS SPECIALTY HOSPITAL, SHERMAN, TX, p. A715

CARSON HEALTH, CARSON CITY, MI, p. A350

CARSON TAHOE CONTINUING CARE HOSPITAL, CARSON CITY, NV, p. A441

CARSON TAHOE HEALTH, CARSON CITY, NV, p. A441

CARSON TAHOE REGIONAL HEALTHCARE, CARSON CITY, NV, p. A441

CARSON VALLEY MEDICAL CENTER, GARDNERVILLE, NV, p. A442

CARTERET HEALTH CARE, MOREHEAD CITY, NC, p. A514

CARTERSVILLE MEDICAL CENTER, CARTERSVILLE, GA, p. A168

CARTHAGE AREA HOSPITAL, CARTHAGE, NY, p. A481

CARY MEDICAL CENTER, CARIBOU, ME, p. A320

CASA COLINA HOSPITAL AND CENTERS FOR HEALTHCARE, POMONA, CA, p. A86

CASA COLINA HOSPITAL AND HEALTH SYSTEMS, POMONA, CA, p. A86

CASA GRANDE REGIONAL MEDICAL CENTER, CASA GRANDE, AZ, p. A30

CASCADE BEHAVIORAL HOSPITAL, TUKWILA, WA, p. A768

CASCADE GENERAL HOSPITAL, LEAVENWORTH, WA, p. A760

CASCADE MEDICAL CENTER, CASCADE, ID, p. A189

CASCADE MEDICAL CENTER, LEAVENWORTH, WA, p. A760

CASCADE VALLEY HOSPITAL, ARLINGTON, WA, p. A755

CASCADE VALLEY HOSPITAL AND CLINICS, ARLINGTON, WA, p. A755

CASEY COUNTY HOSPITAL, LIBERTY, KY, p. A287

CASEY COUNTY WAR MEM HOSPITAL, LIBERTY, KY, p. A287

CASS COUNTY HEALTH SYSTEM, ATLANTIC, IA, p. A243

CASS COUNTY MEMORIAL HOSPITAL, ATLANTIC, IA, p. A243

CASS MEDICAL CENTER, HARRISONVILLE, MO, p. A407

CASS REGIONAL MEDICAL CENTER, HARRISONVILLE, MO, p. A407

CASSIA REGIONAL HOSPITAL, BURLEY, ID, p. A189

CASSIA REGIONAL MEDICAL CENTER, BURLEY, ID, p. A189

CASTANER GENERAL HOSPITAL, CASTANER, PR, p. A807

CASTLE MEDICAL CENTER, KAILUA, HI, p. A185

CASTLE ROCK ADVENTIST HOSPITAL, CASTLE ROCK, CO, p. A108

CASTLEVIEW HOSPITAL, PRICE, UT, p. A731

CATALINA ISLAND MEDICAL CENTER, AVALON, CA, p. A56

CATAWBA HOSPITAL, CATAWBA, VA, p. A739

CATAWBA MEMORIAL HOSPITAL, HICKORY, NC, p. A512

CATAWBA VALLEY MEDICAL CENTER, HICKORY, NC, p. A512

CATHERINE MCAULEY MANOR, KENMORE, NY, p. A486

CATHOLIC MEDICAL CENTER, MANCHESTER, NH, p. A450

CATSKILL REGIONAL MEDICAL CENTER, HARRIS, NY, p. A485

CAVALIER COUNTY MEMORIAL HOSPITAL, LANGDON, ND, p. A524

CAVALIER COUNTY MEMORIAL HOSPITAL AND CLINICS, LANGDON, ND, p. A524

CAYUGA MEDICAL CENTER AT ITHACA, ITHACA, NY, p. A485

CAYUGAMEDICAL CENTER, ITHACA, NY, p. A485

CCC AT PINEVIEW HOSPITAL, LAKESIDE, AZ, p. A33

CCM HEALTH, MONTEVIDEO, MN, p. A381

CEDAR CITY HOSPITAL, CEDAR CITY, UT, p. A727

CEDAR COUNTY MEMORIAL HOSPITAL, EL DORADO SPRINGS, MO, p. A405

CEDAR CREEK HOSPITAL OF MICHIGAN, SAINT JOHNS, MI, p. A366

CEDAR CREST HOSPITAL, BELTON, TX, p. A659

CEDAR CREST HOSPITAL AND RESIDENTIAL TREATMENT CENTER, BELTON, TX, p. A659

CEDAR HILLS HOSPITAL, PORTLAND, OR, p. A579

CEDAR PARK REGIONAL MEDICAL CENTER, CEDAR PARK, TX, p. A663

CEDAR RIDGE HOSPITAL, OKLAHOMA CITY, OK, p. A563

CEDAR SPRINGS BEHAVIORAL HEALTH SYSTEM, COLORADO SPRINGS, CO, p. A109

CEDAR SPRINGS HOSPITAL, COLORADO SPRINGS, CO, p. A109

CEDAR VISTA HOSPITAL, FRESNO, CA, p. A65

CEDARS HOSPITAL, DESOTO, TX, p. A672

CEDARS MEDICAL CENTER, MIAMI, FL, p. A146

CEDARS-SINAI MEDICAL CENTER, LOS ANGELES, CA, p. A73

CENTEGRA HOSPITAL—HUNTLEY, HUNTLEY, IL, p. A208

CENTENNIAL HILLS HOSPITAL MEDICAL CENTER, LAS VEGAS, NV, p. A443

CENTENNIAL MEDICAL CENTER, FRISCO, TX, p. A680

CENTENNIAL PEAKS HEALTH, LOUISVILLE, CO, p. A116

CENTENNIAL PEAKS HOSPITAL, LOUISVILLE, CO, p. A116

CENTER FOR BEHAVIORAL MEDICINE, KANSAS CITY, MO, p. A408

CENTER FOR FORENSIC PSYCHIATRY, SALINE, MI, p. A366

CENTER FOR RESTORATIVE CARE AND REHABILITATION, LYNCHBURG, VA, p. A745

CENTER FOR SPINAL SURGERY, NASHVILLE, TN, p. A646

CENTERPOINT MEDICAL CENTER, INDEPENDENCE, MO, p. A407

CENTERPOINTE HOSPITAL, SAINT CHARLES, MO, p. A414

CENTERPOINTE HOSPITAL OF COLUMBIA, COLUMBIA, MO, p. A405

CENTERSTONE HOSPITAL, BRADENTON, FL, p. A132

CENTINELA FREEMAN MED CENTER, INGLEWOOD, CA, p. A69

CENTINELA FREEMAN REGIONAL MEDICAL CENTER, MARINA CAMPUS, MARINA DEL REY, CA, p. A77

CENTINELA HOSPITAL MEDICAL CENTER, INGLEWOOD, CA, p. A69

CENTINELA MAMMOTH HOSPITAL, MAMMOTH LAKES, CA, p. A77

CENTRA BEDFORD MEMORIAL HOSPITAL, BEDFORD, VA, p. A739

CENTRA HEALTH, LYNCHBURG, VA, p. A745

CENTRA LYNCHBURG GENERAL HOSPITAL, LYNCHBURG, VA, p. A745

CENTRA SOUTHSIDE COMMUNITY HOSPITAL, FARMVILLE, VA, p. A742

CENTRA SPECIALTY HOSPITAL, LYNCHBURG, VA, p. A745

CENTRACARE—LONG PRAIRIE, LONG PRAIRIE, MN, p. A379

CENTRACARE—MELROSE, MELROSE, MN, p. A380

CENTRACARE—MONTICELLO, MONTICELLO, MN, p. A381

CENTRACARE HEALTH-LONG PRAIRIE, LONG PRAIRIE, MN, p. A379

CENTRACARE HEALTH-MELROSE, MELROSE, MN, p. A380

CENTRACARE HEALTH-MONTICELLO, MONTICELLO, MN, p. A381

CENTRACARE HEALTH-PAYNESVILLE, PAYNESVILLE, MN, p. A383

CENTRACARE HEALTH-SAUK CENTRE, SAUK CENTRE, MN, p. A386

CENTRAL ALABAMA MED CENTER, WETUMPKA, AL, p. A26

CENTRAL ALABAMA VA HEALTH CARE SYSTEM-MONTGOMERY DIVISION, MONTGOMERY, AL, p. A22

CENTRAL ALABAMA VA HLTH CARE, MONTGOMERY, AL, p. A22

CENTRAL ALABAMA VETERANS AFFAIRS HEALTH CARE SYSTEM-TUSKEGEE DIVISION, TUSKEGEE, AL, p. A25

CENTRAL ALABAMA VETERANS HEALTH CARE SYSTEM, MONTGOMERY, AL, p. A22

CENTRAL ARKANSAS VETERANS AFFAIRS HEALTHCARE SYSTEM, EUGENE TOWBIN HEALTHCARE CENTER, NORTH LITTLE ROCK, AR, p. A51

CENTRAL ARKANSAS VETERANS HEALTHCARE SYSTEM, LITTLE ROCK, AR, p. A49

CENTRAL BAPTIST HOSPITAL, LEXINGTON, KY, p. A286

CENTRAL CAROLINA HOSPITAL, SANFORD, NC, p. A518

CENTRAL COMMUNITY HOSPITAL, ELKADER, IA, p. A249

CENTRAL DUPAGE HOSPITAL, WINFIELD, IL, p. A222

CENTRAL FLORIDA BEHAVIORAL HOSPITAL, ORLANDO, FL, p. A151

CENTRAL FLORIDA REGIONAL HOSPITAL, SANFORD, FL, p. A156

CENTRAL GEORGIA REHABILITATION HOSPITAL, MACON, GA, p. A176

CENTRAL INDIANA AMG SPECIALTY HOSPITAL, MUNCIE, IN, p. A237

CENTRAL IOWA HEALTHCARE, MARSHALLTOWN, IA, p. A254

CENTRAL LOUISIANA STATE HOSPITAL, PINEVILLE, LA, p. A313

CENTRAL LOUISIANA SURGICAL HOSPITAL, ALEXANDRIA, LA, p. A295

CENTRAL MAINE MEDICAL CENTER, LEWISTON, ME, p. A321

CENTRAL MICHIGAN COMMUNITY HOSPITAL, MOUNT PLEASANT, MI, p. A362

CENTRAL MISSISSIPPI MEDICAL CENTER, JACKSON, MS, p. A394

CENTRAL MONTANA MED CTR, LEWISTOWN, MT, p. A425

CENTRAL MONTANA MEDICAL CENTER, LEWISTOWN, MT, p. A425

CENTRAL NEW YORK PSYCHIATRIC CENTER, MARCY, NY, p. A488

CENTRAL PENINSULA GENERAL HOSPITAL, SOLDOTNA, AK, p. A29

CENTRAL PENINSULA HOSPITAL, SOLDOTNA, AK, p. A29

CENTRAL PRISON HOSPITAL, RALEIGH, NC, p. A516

CENTRAL REGIONAL HOSPITAL, BUTNER, NC, p. A506

CENTRAL STATE HOSPITAL, LOUISVILLE, KY, p. A288

CENTRAL STATE HOSPITAL, MILLEDGEVILLE, GA, p. A177

CENTRAL STATE HOSPITAL, PETERSBURG, VA, p. A748

CENTRAL SUFFOLK HOSPITAL, RIVERHEAD, NY, p. A496

CENTRAL TEXAS MEDICAL CENTER, SAN MARCOS, TX, p. A714

CENTRAL TEXAS REHABILITATION HOSPITAL, AUSTIN, TX, p. A655

CENTRAL TEXAS VETERANS AFFAIRS HEALTH CARE SYSTEM, OLIN E. TEAGUE VETERANS CENTER, TEMPLE, TX, p. A719

CENTRAL TEXAS VETERANS AFFAIRS HEALTH CARE SYSTEM, OLIN E. TEAGUE VETERANS MEDICAL CENTER, TEMPLE, TX, p. A719

CENTRAL TEXAS VETERANS HEALTH CARE SYSTEM, TEMPLE, TX, p. A719

CENTRAL TEXAS VETERANS HEALTH CARE SYSTEM, DORIS MILLER VETERANS MEDICAL CENTER, WACO, TX, p. A724

CENTRAL TEXAS VETERANS HEALTHCARE SYSTEM, TEMPLE, TX, p. A719

CENTRAL VALLEY GENERAL HOSPITAL, HANFORD, CA, p. A68

CENTRAL VALLEY MEDICAL CENTER, NEPHI, UT, p. A729

CENTRAL VALLEY SPECIALTY HOSPITAL, MODESTO, CA, p. A78

CENTRAL VERMONT MEDICAL CENTER, BERLIN, VT, p. A735

CENTRAL VIRGINIA TRAINING CENTER, MADISON HEIGHTS, VA, p. A745

CENTRAL WASHINGTON HOSPITAL, WENATCHEE, WA, p. A768

CENTRASTATE HEALTHCARE SYSTEM, FREEHOLD, NJ, p. A455

CENTRASTATE MEDICAL CENTER, FREEHOLD, NJ, p. A455

CENTRO CARDIOVASCULAR DE PR, SAN JUAN, PR, p. A810

CENTRO DE SALUD CONDUCTUAL MENONITA-CIMA, AIBONITO, PR, p. A806

CENTRO DE TRAUMA, SAN JUAN, PR, p. A810

CGH MEDICAL CENTER, STERLING, IL, p. A221

CHADRON COMMUNITY HOSPITAL AND HEALTH SERVICES, CHADRON, NE, p. A431

CHAMBERS COUNTY PUBLIC HOSPITAL DISTRICT NO. 1, ANAHUAC, TX, p. A653

CHAMBERS MEMORIAL HOSPITAL, DANVILLE, AR, p. A44

CHAMBERSBURG HOSPITAL, CHAMBERSBURG, PA, p. A586

CHAN SOON-SHIONG MEDICAL CENTER, WINDBER, PA, p. A611

CHANDLER REGIONAL HOSPITAL, CHANDLER, AZ, p. A30

CHANDLER REGIONAL MEDICAL CENTER, CHANDLER, AZ, p. A30

CHAPMAN GLOBAL MEDICAL CENTER, ORANGE, CA, p. A82

CHAPMAN MEDICAL CENTER, ORANGE, CA, p. A83

CHARLES A. CANNON JR. MEMORIAL HOSPITAL, NEWLAND, NC, p. A515

CHARLES A. CANNON MEMORIAL HOSPITAL, NEWLAND, NC, p. A515

CHARLES A. DEAN MEMORIAL HOSPITAL, GREENVILLE, ME, p. A320

CHARLES F KETTERING MEM CENTER, KETTERING, OH, p. A542

CHARLES GEORGE VETERANS AFFAIRS MEDICAL CENTER, ASHEVILLE, NC, p. A504

CHARLESTON AREA MEDICAL CENTER, CHARLESTON, WV, p. A771

CHARLESTON GENERAL HOSPITAL, CHARLESTON, WV, p. A771

CHARLESTON SURGICAL HOSPITAL, CHARLESTON, WV, p. A771

CHARLEVOIX AREA HOSPITAL, CHARLEVOIX, MI, p. A350

CHARLIE NORWOOD VETERANS AFFAIRS MEDICAL CENTER, AUGUSTA, GA, p. A166

CHARLOTTE HUNGERFORD HOSPITAL, TORRINGTON, CT, p. A125

CHARLOTTE REGIONAL MEDICAL CENTER, PUNTA GORDA, FL, p. A155

CHARLTON MEMORIAL HOSPITAL, FALL RIVER, MA, p. A338

CHARLTON METHODIST HOSPITAL, DALLAS, TX, p. A668

CHARTER ANCHOR HOSPITAL, ATLANTA, GA, p. A164

CHARTER BEHAVIORAL HEALTH SYSTEM OF MILWAUKEE/ WEST ALLIS, WEST ALLIS, WI, p. A799

CHARTER BEHAVIORAL HLTH SYSTEM, ATLANTA, GA, p. A164

CHARTER BEHAVIORAL HLTH SYSTEM, SAVANNAH, GA, p. A180

CHARTER CHARLESTON BEHAV HLTH, CHARLESTON, SC, p. A616

CHARTER FAIRMOUNT BEHAVIORAL, PHILADELPHIA, PA, p. A599

CHARTER GREENSBORO HEALTH SYST, GREENSBORO, NC, p. A511

CHARTER GREENVILLE HLTH SYST, GREER, SC, p. A621

CHARTER HOSPITAL OF TOLEDO, MAUMEE, OH, p. A545

CHARTER LAKESIDE HLTH SYSTEM, MEMPHIS, TN, p. A644

CHARTER NORTHBROOKE BEHAVIORAL HEALTH SYSTEM OF MILWAUKEE/BROWN DEER, BROWN DEER, WI, p. A781

CHARTER PARKWOOD HLTH SYSTEM, OLIVE BRANCH, MS, p. A398

CHARTER RIDGE BEHAVIORAL HLTH, LEXINGTON, KY, p. A286

CHASE COUNTY COMMUNITY HOSPITAL, IMPERIAL, NE, p. A433

CHATHAM HOSPITAL, SILER CITY, NC, p. A518

CHATUGE REGIONAL HOSPITAL AND NURSING HOME, HIAWASSEE, GA, p. A173

CHELSEA COMMUNITY HOSPITAL, CHELSEA, MI, p. A351

CHENANGO MEMORIAL HOSPITAL, NORWICH, NY, p. A493

CHEROKEE INDIAN HOSPITAL, CHEROKEE, NC, p. A507

CHEROKEE INDIAN HOSPITAL AUTHORITY, CHEROKEE, NC, p. A507

CHEROKEE MEDICAL CENTER, CENTRE, AL, p. A16

CHEROKEE MEDICAL CENTER, GAFFNEY, SC, p. A620

CHEROKEE MENTAL HEALTH INSTITUTE, CHEROKEE, IA, p. A245

CHEROKEE NATION W.W. HASTINGS INDIAN HOSPITAL, TAHLEQUAH, OK, p. A569

CHEROKEE REGIONAL MED CTR, CHEROKEE, IA, p. A245

CHEROKEE REGIONAL MEDICAL CENTER, CHEROKEE, IA, p. A245

CHERRY COUNTY HOSPITAL, VALENTINE, NE, p. A440

CHERRY HOSPITAL, GOLDSBORO, NC, p. A510

CHESAPEAKE REGIONAL HEALTHCARE, CHESAPEAKE, VA, p. A740

CHESAPEAKE REGIONAL MEDICAL CENTER, CHESAPEAKE, VA, p. A740

CHESHIRE MEDICAL CENTER, KEENE, NH, p. A449

CHESTER COUNTY HOSPITAL, WEST CHESTER, PA, p. A610

CHESTER MENTAL HEALTH CENTER, CHESTER, IL, p. A197

CHESTER REGIONAL MEDICAL CENTER, CHESTER, SC, p. A617

CHESTER RIVER HEALTH SYSTEM, CHESTERTOWN, MD, p. A328

CHESTERFIELD GENERAL HOSPITAL, CHERAW, SC, p. A617

CHESTNUT HILL HEALTH SYSTEM, PHILADELPHIA, PA, p. A599

CHESTNUT HILL HOSPITAL, PHILADELPHIA, PA, p. A599

CHESTNUT RIDGE HOSPITAL, MORGANTOWN, WV, p. A774

CHEYENNE COUNTY HOSPITAL, CHEYENNE WELLS, CO, p. A108

CHEYENNE COUNTY HOSPITAL, SAINT FRANCIS, KS, p. A275

CHEYENNE REGIONAL MEDICAL CENTER, CHEYENNE, WY, p. A801

CHEYENNE VETERANS AFFAIRS MEDICAL CENTER, CHEYENNE, WY, p. A802

CHG CORNERSTONE HOSPITAL CONROE, CONROE, TX, p. A665

CHG HOSPITAL TUCSON, LLC, TUCSON, AZ, p. A40

CHI CARRINGTON HEALTH, CARRINGTON, ND, p. A522

CHI FLAGET MEMORIAL HOSPITAL, BARDSTOWN, KY, p. A280

CHI FRANCISCAN REHABILITATION, TACOMA, WA, p. A766

CHI HEALTH BERGAN MERCY, OMAHA, NE, p. A436

CHI HEALTH CREIGHTON UNIVERSITY MEDICAL CENTER— BERGAN MERCY, OMAHA, NE, p. A436

CHI HEALTH GOOD SAMARITAN, KEARNEY, NE, p. A433

CHI HEALTH IMMANUEL, OMAHA, NE, p. A436

CHI HEALTH LAKESIDE, OMAHA, NE, p. A436

CHI HEALTH MERCY CORNING, CORNING, IA, p. A246

CHI HEALTH MERCY COUNCIL BLUFFS, COUNCIL BLUFFS, IA, p. A247

CHI HEALTH MIDLANDS, PAPILLION, NE, p. A438

CHI HEALTH MISSOURI VALLEY, MISSOURI VALLEY, IA, p. A254

CHI HEALTH NEBRASKA HEART, LINCOLN, NE, p. A434

CHI HEALTH PLAINVIEW, PLAINVIEW, NE, p. A439

CHI HEALTH SAINT FRANCIS, GRAND ISLAND, NE, p. A433

CHI HEALTH SCHUYLER, SCHUYLER, NE, p. A439

CHI HEALTH ST ELIZABETH, LINCOLN, NE, p. A434

CHI HEALTH ST. MARY'S, NEBRASKA CITY, NE, p. A435

CHI LAKEWOOD HEALTH, BAUDETTE, MN, p. A372

CHI LISBON HEALTH, LISBON, ND, p. A525

CHI MEMORIAL, CHATTANOOGA, TN, p. A635

CHI MEMORIAL HOSPITAL—GEORGIA, FORT OGLETHORPE, GA, p. A173

CHI MERCY HEALTH, VALLEY CITY, ND, p. A526

CHI MERCY HOSPITAL, DEVILS LAKE, ND, p. A522

CHI OAKES HOSPITAL, OAKES, ND, p. A525

CHI OUR LADY OF PEACE, LOUISVILLE, KY, p. A288

CHI SAINT JOSEPH BEREA, BEREA, KY, p. A280

CHI SAINT JOSEPH EAST, LEXINGTON, KY, p. A286

CHI SAINT JOSEPH HEALTH, LEXINGTON, KY, p. A286

CHI SAINT JOSEPH LONDON, LONDON, KY, p. A287

CHI ST ALEXIUS HEALTH CARRINGTON MEDICAL CENTER, CARRINGTON, ND, p. A522

CHI ST. ALEXIUS HEALTH—DICKINSON MEDICAL CENTER, DICKINSON, ND, p. A522

CHI ST. ALEXIUS HEALTH—WILLISTON MEDICAL CENTER, WILLISTON, ND, p. A526

CHI ST. ALEXIUS HEALTH, BISMARCK, ND, p. A521

CHI ST. ALEXIUS HEALTH DEVILS LAKE HOSPITAL, DEVILS LAKE, ND, p. A522

CHI ST. ALEXIUS HEALTH GARRISON, GARRISON, ND, p. A523

CHI ST. ALEXIUS HEALTH-GARRISON MEMORIAL HOSPITAL, GARRISON, ND, p. A523

CHI ST. ALEXIUS HEALTH-TURTLE LAKE HOSPITAL, TURTLE LAKE, ND, p. A526

CHI ST. ANTHONY HOSPITAL, PENDLETON, OR, p. A578

CHI ST. FRANCIS HEALTH, BRECKENRIDGE, MN, p. A373

CHI ST. GABRIEL'S HEALTH, LITTLE FALLS, MN, p. A379

CHI ST. JOSEPH COLLEGE STATION HOSPITAL, COLLEGE STATION, TX, p. A664

CHI ST. JOSEPH HEALTH BELLVILLE HOSPITAL, BELLVILLE, TX, p. A659

CHI ST. JOSEPH HEALTH BURLESON HOSPITAL, CALDWELL, TX, p. A662

CHI ST. JOSEPH HEALTH GRIMES HOSPITAL, NAVASOTA, TX, p. A703

CHI ST. JOSEPH HEALTH MADISON HOSPITAL, MADISONVILLE, TX, p. A699

CHI ST. JOSEPH HEALTH REHABILITATION HOSPITAL, AN AFFILIATE OF ENCOMPASS HEALTH, BRYAN, TX, p. A661

CHI ST. JOSEPH REGIONAL HEALTH CENTER, BRYAN, TX, p. A661

CHI ST. JOSEPH'S HEALTH, PARK RAPIDS, MN, p. A382

CHI ST. LUKE'S HEALTH—PATIENTS MEDICAL CENTER, PASADENA, TX, p. A705

CHI ST. LUKE'S HEALTH BRAZOSPORT, LAKE JACKSON, TX, p. A694

CHI ST. LUKE'S HEALTH MEMORIAL LIVINGSTON, LIVINGSTON, TX, p. A696

CHI ST. LUKE'S HEALTH MEMORIAL LUFKIN, LUFKIN, TX, p. A698

CHI ST. LUKE'S HEALTH MEMORIAL SAN AUGUSTINE, SAN AUGUSTINE, TX, p. A714

CHI ST. LUKE'S HEALTH-LAKESIDE HOSPITAL, THE WOODLANDS, TX, p. A720

CHI ST. LUKE'S HEALTH-MEMORIAL LUFKIN, LUFKIN, TX, p. A698

CHI ST. LUKE'S HEALTH-THE WOODLANDS HOSPITAL, THE WOODLANDS, TX, p. A720

CHI ST. LUKE'S HOSPITAL—THE VINTAGE HOSPITAL, HOUSTON, TX, p. A685

CHI ST. VINCENT HOT SPRINGS, HOT SPRINGS, AR, p. A47

CHI ST. VINCENT HOT SPRINGS REHABILITATION HOSPITAL, HOT SPRINGS, AR, p. A47

CHI ST. VINCENT INFIRMARY MEDICAL CENTER, LITTLE ROCK, AR, p. A49

CHI ST. VINCENT MEDICAL CENTER-NORTH, SHERWOOD, AR, p. A53

CHI ST. VINCENT MORRILTON, MORRILTON, AR, p. A50

CHI ST. VINCENT SHERWOOD REHABILITATION HOSPITAL, SHERWOOD, AR, p. A53

CHICAGO BEHAVIORAL HOSPITAL, DES PLAINES, IL, p. A202

CHICAGO LYING-IN (CLI), CHICAGO, IL, p. A198

CHICAGO LYING-IN HOSPITAL, CHICAGO, IL, p. A198

CHICAGO-READ MENTAL HEALTH CENTER, CHICAGO, IL, p. A198

CHICKASAW NATION HEALTH SYSTEM, ADA, OK, p. A555

CHICKASAW NATION MEDICAL CENTER, ADA, OK, p. A555

CHICO COMMUNITY HOSPITAL, CHICO, CA, p. A60

CHICOT MEMORIAL HOSPITAL, LAKE VILLAGE, AR, p. A48

CHICOT MEMORIAL MEDICAL CENTER, LAKE VILLAGE, AR, p. A48

CHILD AND ADOLESCENT BEHAVIORAL HEALTH SERVICES, WILLMAR, MN, p. A388

CHILDREN INST OF PITTSBURGH, PITTSBURGH, PA, p. A602

CHILDRENS CARE HOSPITAL AND SCHOOL, SIOUX FALLS, SD, p. A631

CHILDRENS HOSP LOS ANGELES, LOS ANGELES, CA, p. A73

CHILDRENS HOSP OF ORANGE CNTY, ORANGE, CA, p. A83

CHILDREN'S CENTER, BETHANY, OK, p. A556

CHILDREN'S CENTER AT WESLEY, WICHITA, KS, p. A278

CHILDREN'S HEALTH CARE, MINNEAPOLIS, MN, p. A380

CHILDREN'S HEALTH CENTER ST. JOSEPH'S HOSPITAL AND MEDICAL CENTER, PHOENIX, AZ, p. A35

CHILDREN'S HEALTH SYSTEM OF TEXAS, DALLAS, TX, p. A668

CHILDREN'S HEALTHCARE OF ATLANTA, ATLANTA, GA, p. A164

CHILDREN'S HOSP MEDICAL CENTER, AKRON, OH, p. A527

CHILDREN'S HOSP MEDICAL CENTER, CINCINNATI, OH, p. A532

CHILDREN'S HOSP OF NEW YORK, NEW YORK, NY, p. A489

CHILDREN'S HOSP OF WI-FOX VLY, NEENAH, WI, p. A792

CHILDREN'S HOSPITAL & CLINICS, SAINT PAUL, MN, p. A385

CHILDREN'S HOSPITAL, BUFFALO, NY, p. A479

CHILDREN'S HOSPITAL, COLUMBUS, OH, p. A536

CHILDREN'S HOSPITAL, GREENVILLE, SC, p. A620

CHILDREN'S HOSPITAL, MACON, GA, p. A176

CHILDREN'S HOSPITAL, NEW ORLEANS, LA, p. A310

CHILDREN'S HOSPITAL AND MEDICAL CENTER, OMAHA, NE, p. A437

CHILDREN'S HOSPITAL AND REGIONAL MEDICAL CENTER, SEATTLE, WA, p. A763

CHILDREN'S HOSPITAL AT DARTMOUTH, LEBANON, NH, p. A449

CHILDREN'S HOSPITAL AT MISSION, MISSION VIEJO, CA, p. A78

CHILDREN'S HOSPITAL AT PROVIDENCE, EL PASO, TX, p. A674

CHILDREN'S HOSPITAL AT SCOTT & WHITE, TEMPLE, TX, p. A719

CHILDREN'S HOSPITAL AT ST. MARY'S MEDICAL CENTER, WEST PALM BEACH, FL, p. A162

CHILDREN'S HOSPITAL BOSTON, BOSTON, MA, p. A335

CHILDREN'S HOSPITAL COLORADO, AURORA, CO, p. A107

CHILDREN'S HOSPITAL LOS ANGELES, LOS ANGELES, CA, p. A74

CHILDREN'S HOSPITAL OF AUSTIN, AUSTIN, TX, p. A655

CHILDREN'S HOSPITAL OF MICHIGAN, DETROIT, MI, p. A352

CHILDREN'S HOSPITAL OF OKLAHOMA, OKLAHOMA CITY, OK, p. A563

CHILDREN'S HOSPITAL OF ORANGE COUNTY, ORANGE, CA, p. A83

CHILDREN'S HOSPITAL OF PHILADE, PHILADELPHIA, PA, p. A599

CHILDREN'S HOSPITAL OF PHILADELPHIA, PHILADELPHIA, PA, p. A599

CHILDREN'S HOSPITAL OF PITTSBURGH OF UPMC, PITTSBURGH, PA, p. A602

CHILDREN'S HOSPITAL OF RICHMOND, RICHMOND, VA, p. A749

CHILDREN'S HOSPITAL OF RICHMOND AT VCU-BROOK ROAD CAMPUS, RICHMOND, VA, p. A750

CHILDREN'S HOSPITAL OF SAN ANTONIO, SAN ANTONIO, TX, p. A711

CHILDREN'S HOSPITAL OF SANTA ROSA, SAN ANTONIO, TX, p. A711

CHILDREN'S HOSPITAL OF SOUTHWEST FLORIDA, FORT MYERS, FL, p. A138

CHILDREN'S HOSPITAL OF THE KING'S DAUGHTERS, NORFOLK, VA, p. A747

CHILDREN'S HOSPITAL OF WISCONSIN, MILWAUKEE, WI, p. A791

CHILDREN'S HOSPITAL OF WISCONSIN-FOX VALLEY, NEENAH, WI, p. A792

CHILDREN'S HOSPITALS AND CLINICS OF MINNESOTA, MINNEAPOLIS, MN, p. A380

CHILDREN'S MEDICAL CENTER, DAYTON, OH, p. A538

CHILDREN'S MEDICAL CENTER AT WINTHROP UNIVERSITY HOSPITAL, MINEOLA, NY, p. A488

CHILDREN'S MEDICAL CENTER DALLAS, DALLAS, TX, p. A668

CHILDREN'S MEDICAL CENTER PLANO, PLANO, TX, p. A706

CHILDREN'S MEMORIAL HOSPITAL, CHICAGO, IL, p. A198

CHILDREN'S MEMORIAL HOSPITAL, OMAHA, NE, p. A437

CHILDREN'S MERCY HOSPITAL KANSAS, OVERLAND PARK, KS, p. A273

CHILDREN'S MERCY HOSPITAL KANSAS CITY, KANSAS CITY, MO, p. A408

CHILDREN'S MERCY KANSAS CITY, KANSAS CITY, MO, p. A408

CHILDREN'S MERCY SOUTH, OVERLAND PARK, KS, p. A273

CHILDREN'S NATIONAL HEALTH SYSTEM, WASHINGTON, DC, p. A129

CHILDREN'S NATIONAL HOSPITAL, WASHINGTON, DC, p. A129

CHILDREN'S OF ALABAMA, BIRMINGHAM, AL, p. A15

CHILDREN'S SPECIALIZED HOSPITAL, NEW BRUNSWICK, NJ, p. A459

CHILDREN'S SPECIALIZED HOSPITAL-PSE&G, NEW BRUNSWICK, NJ, p. A459

CHILDRESS GENERAL HOSPITAL, CHILDRESS, TX, p. A663

CHILDRESS REGIONAL MEDICAL CENTER, CHILDRESS, TX, p. A663

CHILD'S HOSPITAL, ALBANY, NY, p. A474

CHILLICOTHE VETERANS AFFAIRS MEDICAL CENTER, CHILLICOTHE, OH, p. A531

CHILTON HOSPITAL, POMPTON PLAINS, NJ, p. A462

CHILTON MEDICAL CENTER, POMPTON PLAINS, NJ, p. A462

CHINESE HOSPITAL, SAN FRANCISCO, CA, p. A93

CHINLE COMPREHENSIVE HEALTH CARE FACILITY, CHINLE, AZ, p. A31

CHINO VALLEY HOSPITAL, CHINO, CA, p. A60

CHINO VALLEY MEDICAL CENTER, CHINO, CA, p. A60

CHIPPENHAM HOSPITAL, RICHMOND, VA, p. A750

CHIPPEWA CNTY WAR MEM HOSPITAL, SAULT SAINTE MARIE, MI, p. A366

CHIPPEWA COUNTY-MONTEVIDEO HOSPITAL, MONTEVIDEO, MN, p. A381

CHOATE MENTAL HEALTH CENTER, ANNA, IL, p. A194

CHOATE MENTAL HLTH & DEV CTR, ANNA, IL, p. A194

CHOC CHILDREN'S AT MISSION HOSPITAL, MISSION VIEJO, CA, p. A78

CHOCTAW COUNTY HOSPITAL, ACKERMAN, MS, p. A389

CHOCTAW GENERAL HOSPITAL, BUTLER, AL, p. A16

CHOCTAW HEALTH CENTER, PHILADELPHIA, MS, p. A398

CHOCTAW MEMORIAL HOSPITAL, HUGO, OK, p. A560

CHOCTAW NATION HEALTH CARE CENTER, TALIHINA, OK, p. A569

CHOCTAW NATION INDIAN HOSPITAL, TALIHINA, OK, p. A569

CHOCTAW REGIONAL MEDICAL CENTER, ACKERMAN, MS, p. A389

CHOUTEAU CNTY DIST HOSPITAL, FORT BENTON, MT, p. A423

CHOWAN HOSPITAL, EDENTON, NC, p. A509

CHOWCHILLA DISTRICT MEMORIAL HOSPITAL, CHOWCHILLA, CA, p. A60

CHRIST HOSPITAL, CINCINNATI, OH, p. A532

CHRISTIAN HEALTH CARE CENTER, WYCKOFF, NJ, p. A466

CHRISTIAN HOSPITAL, SAINT LOUIS, MO, p. A415

CHRISTIAN HOSPITAL NE-NW, SAINT LOUIS, MO, p. A415

CHRISTIANA CARE HEALTH SYSTEM, NEWARK, DE, p. A128

CHRISTIANACARE, NEWARK, DE, p. A128

CHRISTUS COUSHATTA HEALTH CARE, COUSHATTA, LA, p. A299

CHRISTUS COUSHATTA HEALTH CARE CENTER, COUSHATTA, LA, p. A299

CHRISTUS DUBUIS HOSPITAL OF ALEXANDRIA, ALEXANDRIA, LA, p. A295

CHRISTUS DUBUIS HOSPITAL OF BEAUMONT, BEAUMONT, TX, p. A658

CHRISTUS DUBUIS HOSPITAL OF FORT SMITH, FORT SMITH, AR, p. A46

CHRISTUS DUBUIS HOSPITAL OF HOT SPRINGS, HOT SPRINGS NATIONAL PARK, AR, p. A47

CHRISTUS DUBUIS HOSPITAL OF PORT ARTHUR, PORT ARTHUR, TX, p. A707

CHRISTUS GOOD SHEPHERD MEDICAL CENTER-MARSHALL, MARSHALL, TX, p. A700

CHRISTUS HEALTH SHREVEPORT-BOSSIER, SHREVEPORT, LA, p. A314

CHRISTUS HIGHLAND MEDICAL CENTER, SHREVEPORT, LA, p. A314

CHRISTUS LAKE AREA HOSPITAL, LAKE CHARLES, LA, p. A306

CHRISTUS MOTHER FRANCES HOSPITAL—JACKSONVILLE, JACKSONVILLE, TX, p. A691

CHRISTUS MOTHER FRANCES HOSPITAL—SULPHUR SPRINGS, SULPHUR SPRINGS, TX, p. A718

CHRISTUS MOTHER FRANCES HOSPITAL—TYLER, TYLER, TX, p. A721

CHRISTUS MOTHER FRANCES HOSPITAL—WINNSBORO, WINNSBORO, TX, p. A726

CHRISTUS OCHSNER LAKE AREA HOSPITAL, LAKE CHARLES, LA, p. A306

CHRISTUS OCHSNER ST. PATRICK, LAKE CHARLES, LA, p. A306

CHRISTUS OCHSNER ST. PATRICK HOSPITAL SOUTHWEST LOUISIANA, LAKE CHARLES, LA, p. A306

CHRISTUS ORTHOPEDIC SPECIALTY CENTER—ST. ELIZABETH, BEAUMONT, TX, p. A658

CHRISTUS SANTA ROSA HEALTH CARE, SAN ANTONIO, TX, p. A711

CHRISTUS SANTA ROSA HEALTH SYSTEM, SAN ANTONIO, TX, p. A711

CHRISTUS SANTA ROSA HOSPITAL—NEW BRAUNFELS, NEW BRAUNFELS, TX, p. A703

CHRISTUS SANTA ROSA HOSPITAL—SAN MARCOS, SAN MARCOS, TX, p. A714

CHRISTUS SANTA ROSA REHABILITATION HOSPITAL, SAN ANTONIO, TX, p. A711

CHRISTUS SCHUMPERT HIGHLAND, SHREVEPORT, LA, p. A314

CHRISTUS SOUTHEAST TEXAS HOSPITAL—ST. ELIZABETH, BEAUMONT, TX, p. A658

CHRISTUS SOUTHEAST TEXAS HOSPITAL, BEAUMONT, TX, p. A658

CHRISTUS SOUTHEAST TEXAS JASPER MEMORIAL, JASPER, TX, p. A691

CHRISTUS SOUTHEAST TEXAS JASPER MEMORIALA, JASPER, TX, p. A691

CHRISTUS SOUTHEAST TEXAS ORTHOPEDIC SPECIALTY CENTER, BEAUMONT, TX, p. A658

CHRISTUS SPOHN HOSP KLEBERG, KINGSVILLE, TX, p. A693

CHRISTUS SPOHN HOSP SHORELINE, CORPUS CHRISTI, TX, p. A665

CHRISTUS SPOHN HOSPITAL, BEEVILLE, TX, p. A659

CHRISTUS SPOHN HOSPITAL ALICE, ALICE, TX, p. A651

CHRISTUS SPOHN HOSPITAL BEEVILLE, BEEVILLE, TX, p. A659

CHRISTUS SPOHN HOSPITAL CORPUS CHRISTI, CORPUS CHRISTI, TX, p. A665

CHRISTUS SPOHN HOSPITAL CORPUS CHRISTI MEMORIAL, CORPUS CHRISTI, TX, p. A665

CHRISTUS SPOHN HOSPITAL KLEBERG, KINGSVILLE, TX, p. A693

CHRISTUS ST FRANCES HOSPITAL, ALEXANDRIA, LA, p. A295

CHRISTUS ST JOSEPH HOSP NORTH, PARIS, TX, p. A704

CHRISTUS ST JOSEPH HOSPITAL, HOUSTON, TX, p. A685

CHRISTUS ST MICHAEL HLTH SYST, TEXARKANA, TX, p. A719

CHRISTUS ST MICHAEL REHAB HOSP, TEXARKANA, TX, p. A719

CHRISTUS ST. FRANCES CABRINI HOSPITAL, ALEXANDRIA, LA, p. A295

CHRISTUS ST. MICHAEL HEALTH SYSTEM, TEXARKANA, TX, p. A719

CHRISTUS ST. MICHAEL REHABILITATION HOSPITAL, TEXARKANA, TX, p. A719

CHRISTUS ST. MICHAEL'S HEALTH SYSTEM, ATLANTA, TX, p. A654

CHRISTUS ST. VINCENT REGIONAL MEDICAL CENTER, SANTA FE, NM, p. A472

CHRISTUS TRINITY MOTHER FRANCES REHABILITATION HOSPITAL, TYLER, TX, p. A721

CHRISTUS TRINITY MOTHER FRANCES REHABILITATION HOSPITAL, A PARTNER OF ENCOMPASS HEALTH, TYLER, TX, p. A721

CHURCHILL COMMUNITY HOSPITAL, FALLON, NV, p. A442

CIBOLA GENERAL HOSPITAL, GRANTS, NM, p. A469

CIMARRON MEMORIAL HOSPITAL, BOISE CITY, OK, p. A556

CINCINNATI CHILDREN'S HOSPITAL MEDICAL CENTER, CINCINNATI, OH, p. A532

CINCINNATI VETERANS AFFAIRS MEDICAL CENTER, CINCINNATI, OH, p. A532

CIRCLE CITY MEDICAL CENTER, CORONA, CA, p. A61

CIRCLES OF CARE, MELBOURNE, FL, p. A145

CITIZENS BAPTIST MED CTR, TALLADEGA, AL, p. A24

CITIZENS BAPTIST MEDICAL CENTER, TALLADEGA, AL, p. A24

CITIZENS MEDICAL CENTER, COLBY, KS, p. A263

CITIZENS MEDICAL CENTER, COLUMBIA, LA, p. A299

CITIZENS MEDICAL CENTER, VICTORIA, TX, p. A723

CITIZENS MEMORIAL HOSPITAL, BOLIVAR, MO, p. A402

CITRUS MEMORIAL HEALTH SYSTEM, INVERNESS, FL, p. A140

CITRUS MEMORIAL HOSPITAL, INVERNESS, FL, p. A140

CITRUS VALLEY MEDICAL CENTER-INTER COMMUNITY CAMPUS, COVINA, CA, p. A61

CITY HOSPITAL, MARTINSBURG, WV, p. A774

CITY HOSPITAL AT WHITE ROCK, DALLAS, TX, p. A668

CITY OF HOPE NATIONAL MEDICAL CENTER, DUARTE, CA, p. A62

CITY OF HOPE'S HELFORD CLINICAL RESEARCH HOSPITAL, DUARTE, CA, p. A62

CITY OF MILAN HOSPITAL, MILAN, TN, p. A645

CIVISTA HEALTH, LA PLATA, MD, p. A330

CJW MEDICAL CENTER, RICHMOND, VA, p. A750

CLAGETT MEMORIAL HOSPITAL, RIFLE, CO, p. A118

CLAIBORNE COUNTY HOSPITAL, TAZEWELL, TN, p. A650

CLAIBORNE COUNTY MEDICAL CENTER, PORT GIBSON, MS, p. A399

CLAIBORNE MEDICAL CENTER, TAZEWELL, TN, p. A650

CLAIBORNE MEMORIAL MEDICAL CENTER, HOMER, LA, p. A303

CLARA BARTON HOSPITAL, HOISINGTON, KS, p. A266

CLARA MAASS HEALTH SYSTEM, BELLEVILLE, NJ, p. A452

CLARA MAASS MEDICAL CENTER, BELLEVILLE, NJ, p. A452

CLAREMORE INDIAN HOSPITAL, CLAREMORE, OK, p. A557

CLAREMORE REGIONAL HOSPITAL, CLAREMORE, OK, p. A557

CLARENDON HEALTH SYSTEM, MANNING, SC, p. A622

CLARIAN ARNETT HOSPITAL, LAFAYETTE, IN, p. A234

CLARIAN HEALTH PARTNERS, INDIANAPOLIS, IN, p. A231

CLARIAN NORTH MEDICAL CENTER, CARMEL, IN, p. A225

CLARIAN WEST MEDICAL CENTER, AVON, IN, p. A223

CLARINDA MUNICIPAL HOSPITAL, CLARINDA, IA, p. A246

CLARINDA REGIONAL HEALTH CENTER, CLARINDA, IA, p. A246

CLARION HOSPITAL, CLARION, PA, p. A586

CLARION PSYCHIATRIC CENTER, CLARION, PA, p. A586

CLARITY CHILD GUIDANCE CENTER, SAN ANTONIO, TX, p. A711

CLARK FORK VALLEY HOSPITAL, PLAINS, MT, p. A426

CLARK MEMORIAL HEALTH, JEFFERSONVILLE, IN, p. A233

CLARK MEMORIAL HOSPITAL, JEFFERSONVILLE, IN, p. A233

CLARK REGIONAL MEDICAL CENTER, WINCHESTER, KY, p. A294

CLARKE COUNTY HOSPITAL, OSCEOLA, IA, p. A256

CLARKS SUMMIT STATE HOSPITAL, CLARKS SUMMIT, PA, p. A586

CLAXTON-HEPBURN MEDICAL CENTER, OGDENSBURG, NY, p. A493

CLAY COUNTY HOSPITAL & NRSG HM, ASHLAND, AL, p. A14

CLAY COUNTY HOSPITAL, ASHLAND, AL, p. A14

CLAY COUNTY HOSPITAL, CLAY CENTER, KS, p. A262

CLAY COUNTY HOSPITAL, FLORA, IL, p. A205

CLAY COUNTY MEDICAL CENTER, CLAY CENTER, KS, p. A262

CLAY COUNTY MEDICAL CENTER, WEST POINT, MS, p. A401

CLAY COUNTY MEMORIAL HOSPITAL, HENRIETTA, TX, p. A684

CLAYTON GENERAL HOSPITAL, RIVERDALE, GA, p. A178

CLEAR BROOK LODGE, SHICKSHINNY, PA, p. A608

CLEAR LAKE REGIONAL MEDICAL CENTER, LEAGUE CITY, TX, p. A695

CLEAR VIEW BEHAVIORAL HEALTH, JOHNSTOWN, CO, p. A114

CLEARFIELD HOSPITAL, CLEARFIELD, PA, p. A586

CLEARSKY REHABILITATION HOSPITAL OF LEESVILLE, LEESVILLE, LA, p. A307

CLEARSKY REHABILITATION HOSPITAL OF ROSEPINE, LEESVILLE, LA, p. A307

CLEARSKY REHABILITATION HOSPITAL OF WEATHERFORD, WEATHERFORD, TX, p. A724

CLEARVIEW REGIONAL MEDICAL CENTER, MONROE, GA, p. A177

CLEARVISTA HEALTH AND WELLNESS, LORAIN, OH, p. A543

CLEARWATER HEALTH SERVICES, BAGLEY, MN, p. A372

CLEARWATER VALLEY HOSPITAL AND CLINICS, OROFINO, ID, p. A192

CLEMENT J. ZABLOCKI VETERANS AFFAIRS MEDICAL CENTER, MILWAUKEE, WI, p. A791

CLEVELAND AREA HOSPITAL, CLEVELAND, OK, p. A557

CLEVELAND CLINIC, CLEVELAND, OH, p. A534

CLEVELAND CLINIC AKRON GENERAL, AKRON, OH, p. A527

CLEVELAND CLINIC AKRON GENERAL LODI HOSPITAL, LODI, OH, p. A543

CLEVELAND CLINIC AVON HOSPITAL, AVON, OH, p. A528

CLEVELAND CLINIC CHILD HOSPITA, CLEVELAND, OH, p. A534

CLEVELAND CLINIC CHILDREN'S HOSPITAL FOR REHABILITATION, CLEVELAND, OH, p. A534

CLEVELAND CLINIC FAIRVIEW HOSPITAL, CLEVELAND, OH, p. A534
CLEVELAND CLINIC FLORIDA, WESTON, FL, p. A162
CLEVELAND CLINIC FOUNDATION, CLEVELAND, OH, p. A534
CLEVELAND CLINIC HOSPITAL, WESTON, FL, p. A162
CLEVELAND CLINIC INDIAN RIVER HOSPITAL, VERO BEACH, FL, p. A161
CLEVELAND CLINIC MARTIN NORTH HOSPITAL, STUART, FL, p. A158
CLEVELAND CLINIC REHABILITATION HOSPITAL, AVON, OH, p. A528
CLEVELAND CLINIC UNION HOSPITAL, DOVER, OH, p. A539
CLEVELAND CLINIC, MEDINA HOSPITAL, MEDINA, OH, p. A545
CLEVELAND COMMUNITY HOSPITAL, CLEVELAND, TN, p. A636
CLEVELAND EMERGENCY HOSPITAL, CLEVELAND, TX, p. A664
CLIFTON SPRINGS HOSPITAL AND CLINIC, CLIFTON SPRINGS, NY, p. A481
CLIFTON T. PERKINS HOSPITAL CENTER, JESSUP, MD, p. A330
CLIFTON-FINE HOSPITAL, STAR LAKE, NY, p. A498
CLINCH MEMORIAL HOSPITAL, HOMERVILLE, GA, p. A174
CLINCH VALLEY MEDICAL CENTER, RICHLANDS, VA, p. A749
CLINICA DOCTOR PEREA, MAYAGUEZ, PR, p. A808
CLINTON COUNTY HOSPITAL, ALBANY, KY, p. A280
CLINTON HOSPITAL, CLINTON, MA, p. A338
CLINTON MEMORIAL HOSPITAL, SAINT JOHNS, MI, p. A366
CLINTON MEMORIAL HOSPITAL, WILMINGTON, OH, p. A553
CLINTON REGIONAL HOSPITAL, CLINTON, OK, p. A557
CLOQUET COMMUNITY MEM HOSPITAL, CLOQUET, MN, p. A374
CLOUD COUNTY HEALTH CENTER, CONCORDIA, KS, p. A263
CLOVIS COMMUNITY MEDICAL CENTER, CLOVIS, CA, p. A60
CMH REGIONAL HEALTH SYSTEM, WILMINGTON, OH, p. A553
COAL COUNTY GENERAL HOSPITAL, COALGATE, OK, p. A558
COAST PLAZA DOCTORS HOSPITAL, NORWALK, CA, p. A81
COAST PLAZA HOSPITAL, NORWALK, CA, p. A81
COASTAL CAROLINA HOSPITAL, HARDEEVILLE, SC, p. A621
COASTAL CAROLINA MEDICAL CTR, HARDEEVILLE, SC, p. A621
COASTAL COMMUNITIES HOSPITAL, SANTA ANA, CA, p. A96
COASTAL HARBOR TREATMENT CENTER, SAVANNAH, GA, p. A180
COASTAL VIRGINIA REHABILITATION, NEWPORT NEWS, VA, p. A746
COATESVILLE VETERANS AFFAIRS MEDICAL CENTER, COATESVILLE, PA, p. A587
COBALT REHABILITATION HOSPITAL, FARGO, ND, p. A522
COBALT REHABILITATION HOSPITAL, SURPRISE, AZ, p. A39
COBALT REHABILITATION HOSPITAL EL PASO, EL PASO, TX, p. A674
COBALT REHABILITATION HOSPITAL OF NEW ORLEANS, NEW ORLEANS, LA, p. A310
COBALT REHABILITATION HOUSTON HEIGHTS, HOUSTON, TX, p. A685
COBLESKILL REGIONAL HOSPITAL, COBLESKILL, NY, p. A481
COBRE VALLEY COMMUNITY HOSPITAL, GLOBE, AZ, p. A32
COBRE VALLEY REGIONAL MEDICAL CENTER, GLOBE, AZ, p. A32
COCHRAN MEMORIAL HOSPITAL, MORTON, TX, p. A702
COFFEE REGIONAL HOSPITAL, DOUGLAS, GA, p. A171
COFFEE REGIONAL MEDICAL CENTER, DOUGLAS, GA, p. A171
COFFEY COUNTY HOSPITAL, BURLINGTON, KS, p. A262
COFFEYVILLE REGIONAL MEDICAL CENTER, COFFEYVILLE, KS, p. A262
COGDELL MEMORIAL HOSPITAL, SNYDER, TX, p. A716
COLE MEMORIAL, COUDERSPORT, PA, p. A587
COLEMAN COUNTY COMMUNITY HOSP, COLEMAN, TX, p. A664
COLEMAN COUNTY MEDICAL CENTER, COLEMAN, TX, p. A664
COLER MEMORIAL HOSPITAL, NEW YORK, NY, p. A489
COLISEUM MEDICAL CENTERS, MACON, GA, p. A176
COLISEUM NORTHSIDE HOSPITAL, MACON, GA, p. A176
COLISEUM PSYCHIATRIC CENTER, MACON, GA, p. A176
COLLEGE HOSPITAL, CERRITOS, CA, p. A59
COLLEGE HOSPITAL CERRITOS, CERRITOS, CA, p. A59
COLLEGE HOSPITAL COSTA MESA, COSTA MESA, CA, p. A61
COLLEGE MEDICAL CENTER, LONG BEACH, CA, p. A72
COLLEGE STATION MEDICAL CENTER, COLLEGE STATION, TX, p. A664
COLLETON MEDICAL CENTER, WALTERBORO, SC, p. A625
COLLINGSWORTH GENERAL HOSPITAL, WELLINGTON, TX, p. A724
COLMERY-O'NEIL VETERANS AFFAIRS MEDICAL CENTER, TOPEKA, KS, p. A277
COLONEL FLORENCE A. BLANCHFIELD ARMY COMMUNITY HOSPITAL, FORT CAMPBELL, KY, p. A283

COLONIAL HOSPITAL, TERRELL, TX, p. A719
COLORADO ACUTE LONG TERM HOSPITAL, DENVER, CO, p. A110
COLORADO CANYONS HOSPITAL AND MEDICAL CENTER, FRUITA, CO, p. A113
COLORADO MENTAL HEALTH INSTITUTE AT FORT LOGAN, DENVER, CO, p. A110
COLORADO MENTAL HEALTH INSTITUTE AT PUEBLO, PUEBLO, CO, p. A117
COLORADO PLAINS MEDICAL CENTER, FORT MORGAN, CO, p. A112
COLORADO RIVER MEDICAL CENTER, NEEDLES, CA, p. A81
COLORADO STATE HOSPITAL, PUEBLO, CO, p. A117
COLORADO WEST PSYCHIATRIC HOSPITAL, GRAND JUNCTION, CO, p. A113
COLQUITT REGIONAL MEDICAL CENTER, MOULTRIE, GA, p. A177
COLUMBIA ALASKA REGIONAL HOSP, ANCHORAGE, AK, p. A27
COLUMBIA AVENTURA HOSPITAL, AVENTURA, FL, p. A131
COLUMBIA BASIN HOSPITAL, EPHRATA, WA, p. A758
COLUMBIA BLAKE MEDICAL CENTER, BRADENTON, FL, p. A132
COLUMBIA BRIGHAM CITY HOSP, BRIGHAM CITY, UT, p. A727
COLUMBIA BROWNWOOD MED CTR, BROWNWOOD, TX, p. A661
COLUMBIA CAPITAL MEDICAL CTR, OLYMPIA, WA, p. A761
COLUMBIA CLINCH VALLEY MED CTR, RICHLANDS, VA, p. A749
COLUMBIA COLISEUM MED CTRS, MACON, GA, p. A176
COLUMBIA COLLETON MEDICAL CTR, WALTERBORO, SC, p. A625
COLUMBIA COUNTY HEALTH SYSTEM, DAYTON, WA, p. A757
COLUMBIA DOCTORS HOSPITAL, LAREDO, TX, p. A695
COLUMBIA DOCTORS HOSPITAL, SARASOTA, FL, p. A157
COLUMBIA DOCTORS REG MED CTR, CORPUS CHRISTI, TX, p. A665
COLUMBIA EAST RIDGE HOSPITAL, EAST RIDGE, TN, p. A637
COLUMBIA EASTERN IDAHO REG MED, IDAHO FALLS, ID, p. A190
COLUMBIA ENGLEWOOD COMM HOSP, ENGLEWOOD, FL, p. A137
COLUMBIA FAIRVIEW PARK HOSP, DUBLIN, GA, p. A172
COLUMBIA FAWCETT MEM HOSP, PORT CHARLOTTE, FL, p. A154
COLUMBIA FORT WALTON BEACH MED, FORT WALTON BEACH, FL, p. A138
COLUMBIA GARDEN PARK HOSPITAL, GULFPORT, MS, p. A393
COLUMBIA GOOD SAMARITAN HOSP, SAN JOSE, CA, p. A94
COLUMBIA HOSPITAL FRANKFORT, FRANKFORT, KY, p. A283
COLUMBIA HOSPITAL GEORGETOWN, GEORGETOWN, KY, p. A284
COLUMBIA JOHN RANDOLPH MED CTR, HOPEWELL, VA, p. A744
COLUMBIA LAKE CITY MEDICAL CTR, LAKE CITY, FL, p. A143
COLUMBIA LAKE CUMBERLAND HOSP, SOMERSET, KY, p. A293
COLUMBIA LAKEVIEW REG MED CTR, COVINGTON, LA, p. A300
COLUMBIA LARGO MEDICAL CENTER, LARGO, FL, p. A143
COLUMBIA LEWIS-GALE MED CTR, BOONES MILL, VA, p. A739
COLUMBIA LIVINGSTON REG HOSP, LIVINGSTON, TN, p. A642
COLUMBIA LOGAN MEMORIAL HOSP, RUSSELLVILLE, KY, p. A293
COLUMBIA LONGVIEW REG MED CTR, LONGVIEW, TX, p. A696
COLUMBIA MAINLAND MEDICAL CTR, TEXAS CITY, TX, p. A720
COLUMBIA MED CTR OF CARLSBAD, CARLSBAD, NM, p. A468
COLUMBIA MED CTR OF HUNTSVILLE, HUNTSVILLE, AL, p. A20
COLUMBIA MED CTR-PORT ST LUCIE, PORT ST LUCIE, FL, p. A155
COLUMBIA MEDICAL CENTER, PAMPA, TX, p. A704
COLUMBIA MEDICAL CENTER, SAN ANGELO, TX, p. A710
COLUMBIA MEDICAL CENTER-EAST, EL PASO, TX, p. A674
COLUMBIA MEDICAL CTR SANFORD, SANFORD, FL, p. A156
COLUMBIA MEMORIAL HOSPITAL, ASTORIA, OR, p. A573
COLUMBIA MEMORIAL HOSPITAL, HUDSON, NY, p. A485
COLUMBIA MERCY MEDICAL CENTER, CANTON, OH, p. A531
COLUMBIA METROWEST MEDICAL CTR, FRAMINGHAM, MA, p. A339
COLUMBIA MONTGOMERY MED CTR, MONTGOMERY, AL, p. A22
COLUMBIA NAVARRO REGIONAL HOSP, CORSICANA, TX, p. A666

COLUMBIA NORTH FL REG MED CTR, GAINESVILLE, FL, p. A138
COLUMBIA NORTHWEST MEDICAL CTR, MARGATE, FL, p. A144
COLUMBIA OCALA REG MED CTR, OCALA, FL, p. A149
COLUMBIA OGDEN REG MED CTR, OGDEN, UT, p. A730
COLUMBIA ORANGE PARK MED CTR, ORANGE PARK, FL, p. A150
COLUMBIA OVERLAND PARK REG CTR, OVERLAND PARK, KS, p. A273
COLUMBIA PALMS WEST HOSPITAL, LOXAHATCHEE, FL, p. A144
COLUMBIA PARKRIDGE MEDICAL CTR, CHATTANOOGA, TN, p. A635
COLUMBIA PLANTATION GEN HOSP, PLANTATION, FL, p. A154
COLUMBIA POLK GENERAL HOSPITAL, CEDARTOWN, GA, p. A168
COLUMBIA PRESBY-ST LUKE'S CTR, DENVER, CO, p. A110
COLUMBIA PRESBYTERIAN MED CTR, AURORA, CO, p. A107
COLUMBIA PRESBYTERIAN MED CTR, NEW YORK, NY, p. A489
COLUMBIA PUTNAM MEDICAL CENTER, PALATKA, FL, p. A152
COLUMBIA RAULERSON HOSPITAL, OKEECHOBEE, FL, p. A150
COLUMBIA REDMOND REG MED CTR, ROME, GA, p. A179
COLUMBIA REGIONAL HOSPITAL, COLUMBIA, MO, p. A405
COLUMBIA REGIONAL MED CTR, BROOKSVILLE, FL, p. A133
COLUMBIA RIO GRANDE REG HOSP, MCALLEN, TX, p. A700
COLUMBIA RIVER PARK HOSPITAL, HUNTINGTON, WV, p. A772
COLUMBIA RIVEREDGE HOSPITAL, FOREST PARK, IL, p. A205
COLUMBIA ROSE MEDICAL CENTER, DENVER, CO, p. A110
COLUMBIA SAN LEANDRO HOSP, SAN LEANDRO, CA, p. A95
COLUMBIA SOUTH BAY HOSPITAL, SUN CITY CENTER, FL, p. A158
COLUMBIA SOUTHWESTERN MED CTR, LAWTON, OK, p. A561
COLUMBIA SPRINGHILL MED CTR, SPRINGHILL, LA, p. A315
COLUMBIA ST DAVID'S HOSPITAL, AUSTIN, TX, p. A655
COLUMBIA ST MARK'S HOSPITAL, SALT LAKE CITY, UT, p. A732
COLUMBIA ST MARY'S-COLUMBIA, MILWAUKEE, WI, p. A791
COLUMBIA ST MARY'S-MILWAUKEE, MILWAUKEE, WI, p. A791
COLUMBIA ST. MARY'S HOSPITAL MILWAUKEE, MILWAUKEE, WI, p. A791
COLUMBIA ST. MARY'S HOSPITAL OZAUKEE, MEQUON, WI, p. A790
COLUMBIA ST. MARY'S MILWAUKEE HOSPITAL, MILWAUKEE, WI, p. A791
COLUMBIA SUNRISE HOSPITAL, LAS VEGAS, NV, p. A443
COLUMBIA SWEDISH MEDICAL CTR, ENGLEWOOD, CO, p. A112
COLUMBIA SYCAMORE SHOALS HOSP, ELIZABETHTON, TN, p. A637
COLUMBIA TERRE HAUTE REG HOSP, TERRE HAUTE, IN, p. A241
COLUMBIA TEXAS ORTHOPEDIC HOSP, HOUSTON, TX, p. A685
COLUMBIA TRIDENT MEDICAL CTR, CHARLESTON, SC, p. A616
COLUMBIA TWIN CITIES HOSPITAL, NICEVILLE, FL, p. A149
COLUMBIA UNIVERSITY HOSPITAL, TAMARAC, FL, p. A159
COLUMBIA VALLEY REG MED CTR, BROWNSVILLE, TX, p. A660
COLUMBIA WAGONER HOSPITAL, WAGONER, OK, p. A571
COLUMBIA WEST ANAHEIM MED CTR, ANAHEIM, CA, p. A55
COLUMBIA WESTSIDE REG MED CTR, PLANTATION, FL, p. A154
COLUMBIA WOODLAND HEIGHTS CTR, LUFKIN, TX, p. A698
COLUMBIA-GREENE LONG TERM CARE, CATSKILL, NY, p. A481
COLUMBIA-GREENE MEDICAL CENTER, HUDSON, NY, p. A485
COLUMBUS COMMUNITY HOSPITAL, COLUMBUS, NE, p. A431
COLUMBUS COMMUNITY HOSPITAL, COLUMBUS, TX, p. A664
COLUMBUS COUNTY HOSPITAL, WHITEVILLE, NC, p. A519
COLUMBUS DUBLIN SPRINGS, DUBLIN, OH, p. A539
COLUMBUS HOSPITAL LTACH, NEWARK, NJ, p. A459
COLUMBUS REGIONAL HEALTHCARE SYSTEM, WHITEVILLE, NC, p. A519
COLUMBUS REGIONAL HOSPITAL, COLUMBUS, IN, p. A225
COLUMBUS SPECIALTY HOSPITAL, COLUMBUS, GA, p. A169
COMANCHE COMMUNITY HOSPITAL, COMANCHE, TX, p. A664
COMANCHE COUNTY HOSPITAL, COLDWATER, KS, p. A263
COMANCHE COUNTY MEDICAL CENTER, COMANCHE, TX, p. A665

COMANCHE COUNTY MEMORIAL HOSPITAL, LAWTON, OK, p. A561
COMER CHILDREN'S HOSPITAL, CHICAGO, IL, p. A198
COMM HLTH SYSTEM STATE ISLAND, STATEN ISLAND, NY, p. A498
COMM HOSP FDN, MONTEREY, CA, p. A79
COMM HOSP IN NELSON CNTY, MCVILLE, ND, p. A525
COMM HOSP OF CHULA VISTA, CHULA VISTA, CA, p. A60
COMM HOSPS OF WILLIAMS CNTY, BRYAN, OH, p. A530
COMM KIMBALL HLTH CARE SYSTEM, TOMS RIVER, NJ, p. A464
COMMONWEALTH CENTER FOR CHILDREN AND ADOLESCENTS, STAUNTON, VA, p. A752
COMMONWEALTH HEALTH CENTER, SAIPAN, MP, p. A805
COMMONWEALTH REGIONAL SPECIALTY HOSPITAL, BOWLING GREEN, KY, p. A280
COMMONWESLTH HEALTH CENTER, SAIPAN, MP, p. A805
COMMUNITY AND MISSION HOSPITALS OF HUNTINGTON PARK, HUNTINGTON PARK, CA, p. A68
COMMUNITY BEHAVIORAL HEALTH CENTER, FRESNO, CA, p. A65
COMMUNITY BEHAVIORAL HEALTH HOSPITAL—ALEXANDRIA, ALEXANDRIA, MN, p. A371
COMMUNITY BEHAVIORAL HEALTH HOSPITAL—ANNANDALE, ANNANDALE, MN, p. A371
COMMUNITY BEHAVIORAL HEALTH HOSPITAL—BAXTER, BAXTER, MN, p. A372
COMMUNITY BEHAVIORAL HEALTH HOSPITAL—BEMIDJI, BEMIDJI, MN, p. A372
COMMUNITY BEHAVIORAL HEALTH HOSPITAL—FERGUS FALLS, FERGUS FALLS, MN, p. A376
COMMUNITY BEHAVIORAL HEALTH HOSPITAL—ROCHESTER, ROCHESTER, MN, p. A384
COMMUNITY CARE HOSPITAL, NEW ORLEANS, LA, p. A310
COMMUNITY FIRST MEDICAL CENTER, CHICAGO, IL, p. A198
COMMUNITY GENERAL HEALTH CENTER, FORT FAIRFIELD, ME, p. A320
COMMUNITY GENERAL HOSPITAL, FORT FAIRFIELD, ME, p. A320
COMMUNITY HEALTH CENTER OF BRANCH COUNTY, COLDWATER, MI, p. A351
COMMUNITY HEALTH PARTNERS REGIONAL MEDICAL CENTER, LORAIN, OH, p. A543
COMMUNITY HEALTHCARE SYSTEM, ONAGA, KS, p. A273
COMMUNITY HLTH CARE SYST INC, ONAGA, KS, p. A273
COMMUNITY HOSP OF NOBLE COUNTY, KENDALLVILLE, IN, p. A233
COMMUNITY HOSP SOUTH, INDIANAPOLIS, IN, p. A231
COMMUNITY HOSPITAL, BONNERS FERRY, ID, p. A189
COMMUNITY HOSPITAL, ELK CITY, OK, p. A558
COMMUNITY HOSPITAL, GRAND JUNCTION, CO, p. A113
COMMUNITY HOSPITAL, HARRISBURG, PA, p. A591
COMMUNITY HOSPITAL, MCCOOK, NE, p. A435
COMMUNITY HOSPITAL, MUNSTER, IN, p. A237
COMMUNITY HOSPITAL, OKLAHOMA CITY, OK, p. A564
COMMUNITY HOSPITAL, POPLAR, MT, p. A427
COMMUNITY HOSPITAL, TALLASSEE, AL, p. A24
COMMUNITY HOSPITAL, TORRINGTON, WY, p. A804
COMMUNITY HOSPITAL, TRINITY, FL, p. A161
COMMUNITY HOSPITAL ANDERSON, ANDERSON, IN, p. A223
COMMUNITY HOSPITAL ASSOCIATION, FAIRFAX, MO, p. A406
COMMUNITY HOSPITAL AT DOBBS FERRY, DOBBS FERRY, NY, p. A482
COMMUNITY HOSPITAL EAST, INDIANAPOLIS, IN, p. A231
COMMUNITY HOSPITAL NORTH, INDIANAPOLIS, IN, p. A231
COMMUNITY HOSPITAL OF ANACONDA, ANACONDA, MT, p. A421
COMMUNITY HOSPITAL OF ANDERSON & MADISON COUNTY, INC., ANDERSON, IN, p. A223
COMMUNITY HOSPITAL OF BREMEN, BREMEN, IN, p. A225
COMMUNITY HOSPITAL OF HUNTINGTON PARK, HUNTINGTON PARK, CA, p. A68
COMMUNITY HOSPITAL OF LOS GATOS, LOS GATOS, CA, p. A76
COMMUNITY HOSPITAL OF SAN BERNARDINO, SAN BERNARDINO, CA, p. A91
COMMUNITY HOSPITAL OF STAUNTON, STAUNTON, IL, p. A221
COMMUNITY HOSPITAL OF THE MONTEREY PENINSULA, MONTEREY, CA, p. A79
COMMUNITY HOSPITAL SOUTH, INDIANAPOLIS, IN, p. A231
COMMUNITY HOSPITAL-FAIRFAX, FAIRFAX, MO, p. A406
COMMUNITY HOSPITALS AND WELLNESS CENTERS, BRYAN, OH, p. A530
COMMUNITY HOSPITALS AND WELLNESS CENTERS, MONTPELIER, OH, p. A546
COMMUNITY HOSPITALS AND WELLNESS CENTERS-MONTPELIER, MONTPELIER, OH, p. A546
COMMUNITY HOWARD REGIONAL HEALTH, KOKOMO, IN, p. A234

COMMUNITY HOWARD REGIONAL HOSPITAL, KOKOMO, IN, p. A234
COMMUNITY HSPS OF INDIANAPOLIS, INDIANAPOLIS, IN, p. A231
COMMUNITY MEDICAL CENTER, FALLS CITY, NE, p. A432
COMMUNITY MEDICAL CENTER, FRESNO, CA, p. A65
COMMUNITY MEDICAL CENTER, MISSOULA, MT, p. A426
COMMUNITY MEDICAL CENTER, MONMOUTH, IL, p. A212
COMMUNITY MEDICAL CENTER, TOMS RIVER, NJ, p. A464
COMMUNITY MEDICAL CENTER HEALTHCARE SYSTEM, SCRANTON, PA, p. A607
COMMUNITY MEDICAL CENTER OF IZARD COUNTY, CALICO ROCK, AR, p. A43
COMMUNITY MEDICAL CENTER, INC., FALLS CITY, NE, p. A432
COMMUNITY MEDICAL CTR-CLOVIS, CLOVIS, CA, p. A60
COMMUNITY MEMORIAL HEALTH SYSTEM, VENTURA, CA, p. A103
COMMUNITY MEMORIAL HEALTHCARE, MARYSVILLE, KS, p. A270
COMMUNITY MEMORIAL HOSPITAL, BURKE, SD, p. A626
COMMUNITY MEMORIAL HOSPITAL, CLOQUET, MN, p. A374
COMMUNITY MEMORIAL HOSPITAL, HAMILTON, NY, p. A485
COMMUNITY MEMORIAL HOSPITAL, HICKSVILLE, OH, p. A542
COMMUNITY MEMORIAL HOSPITAL, MARYSVILLE, KS, p. A270
COMMUNITY MEMORIAL HOSPITAL, OCONTO FALLS, WI, p. A793
COMMUNITY MEMORIAL HOSPITAL, REDFIELD, SD, p. A630
COMMUNITY MEMORIAL HOSPITAL, SIDNEY, MT, p. A428
COMMUNITY MEMORIAL HOSPITAL, STAUNTON, IL, p. A221
COMMUNITY MEMORIAL HOSPITAL, SUMNER, IA, p. A259
COMMUNITY MEMORIAL HOSPITAL, SYRACUSE, NE, p. A440
COMMUNITY MEMORIAL HOSPITAL, TURTLE LAKE, ND, p. A526
COMMUNITY MEMORIAL HOSPITAL, VENTURA, CA, p. A103
COMMUNITY MENTAL HEALTH CENTER, LAWRENCEBURG, IN, p. A235
COMMUNITY METHODIST HOSPITAL, HENDERSON, KY, p. A285
COMMUNITY REGIONAL MEDICAL CENTER, FRESNO, CA, p. A65
COMMUNITY-GENERAL HOSPITAL OF GREATER SYRACUSE, SYRACUSE, NY, p. A499
COMPASS BEHAVIORAL CENTER OF ALEXANDRIA, ALEXANDRIA, LA, p. A295
COMPASS BEHAVIORAL CENTER OF HOUMA, HOUMA, LA, p. A303
COMPASS BEHAVIORAL CENTER OF HOUMA, INC., HOUMA, LA, p. A303
COMPASS BEHAVIORAL CENTER OF LAFAYETTE, LAFAYETTE, LA, p. A305
COMPASS BEHAVIORAL CENTER OF MARKSVILLE, MARKSVILLE, LA, p. A308
COMPASS MEMORIAL HEALTHCARE, MARENGO, IA, p. A253
COMPLEX CARE HOSPITAL AT RIDGELAKE, SARASOTA, FL, p. A157
COMPLEX CARE HOSPITAL AT TENAYA, LAS VEGAS, NV, p. A443
COMPLEX CARE HOSPITAL OF IDAHO, BOISE, ID, p. A188
CONCHO COUNTY HOSPITAL, EDEN, TX, p. A673
CONCHO VALLEY REGIONAL HOSP, SAN ANGELO, TX, p. A710
CONCORD HOSPITAL, CONCORD, NH, p. A448
CONCOURSE DIVISION, BRONX, NY, p. A476
CONCOURSE NURSING HOME, BRONX, NY, p. A476
CONDELL MEDICAL CENTER, LIBERTYVILLE, IL, p. A210
CONE HEALTH, GREENSBORO, NC, p. A511
CONEJOS COUNTY HOSPITAL, LA JARA, CO, p. A114
CONEMAUGH MEMORIAL MEDICAL CENTER, JOHNSTOWN, PA, p. A593
CONEMAUGH MEYERSDALE MEDICAL CENTER, MEYERSDALE, PA, p. A597
CONEMAUGH MINERS MEDICAL CENTER, HASTINGS, PA, p. A592
CONEMAUGH NASON MEDICAL CENTER, ROARING SPRING, PA, p. A606
CONEY ISLAND HOSPITAL, BROOKLYN, NY, p. A477
CONFLUENCE HEALTH/CENTRAL WASHINGTON HOSPITAL, WENATCHEE, WA, p. A768
CONFLUENCE HEALTH/WENATCHEE VALLEY HOSPITAL, WENATCHEE, WA, p. A768
CONIFER PARK, GLENVILLE, NY, p. A484
CONNALLY MEDICAL CENTER, FLORESVILLE, TX, p. A677
CONNALLY MEMORIAL MEDICAL CENTER, FLORESVILLE, TX, p. A677
CONNECTICUT CHILDREN'S MEDICAL CENTER, HARTFORD, CT, p. A122
CONNECTICUT DEPARTMENT OF CORRECTION'S HOSPITAL, SOMERS, CT, p. A125

CONNECTICUT MENTAL HEALTH CENTER, NEW HAVEN, CT, p. A124
CONNECTICUT VALLEY HOSPITAL, MIDDLETOWN, CT, p. A123
CONNECTICUT VETERANS HOME AND HOSPITAL, ROCKY HILL, CT, p. A125
CONROE REGIONAL MEDICAL CENTER, CONROE, TX, p. A665
CONTINUE CARE HOSPITAL AT HENDRICK MEDICAL CENTER, ABILENE, TX, p. A651
CONTINUECARE HOSPITAL, PADUCAH, KY, p. A291
CONTINUECARE HOSPITAL AT BAPTIST HEALTH CORBIN, CORBIN, KY, p. A282
CONTINUECARE HOSPITAL AT BAPTIST HEALTH PADUCAH, PADUCAH, KY, p. A291
CONTINUECARE HOSPITAL AT HENDRICK MEDICAL CENTER, ABILENE, TX, p. A651
CONTINUECARE HOSPITAL AT MADISONVILLE, MADISONVILLE, KY, p. A289
CONTINUECARE HOSPITAL AT MEDICAL CENTER (ODESSA), ODESSA, TX, p. A703
CONTINUECARE HOSPITAL AT PALMETTO HEALTH BAPTIST, COLUMBIA, SC, p. A617
CONTINUECARE HOSPITAL OF CARSON TAHOE, CARSON CITY, NV, p. A441
CONTINUING CARE HOSPITAL, LEXINGTON, KY, p. A286
CONTINUUM REHABILITATION HOSPITAL OF NORTH TEXAS, FLOWER MOUND, TX, p. A677
CONTRA COSTA REGIONAL MEDICAL CENTER, MARTINEZ, CA, p. A77
CONVERSE COUNTY MEM HOSPITAL, DOUGLAS, WY, p. A802
CONWAY BEHAVIORAL HEALTH HOSPITAL, CONWAY, AR, p. A43
CONWAY HOSPITAL, CONWAY, SC, p. A618
CONWAY MEDICAL CENTER, CONWAY, SC, p. A618
CONWAY REGIONAL HOSPITAL, CONWAY, AR, p. A44
CONWAY REGIONAL MEDICAL CENTER, CONWAY, AR, p. A44
CONWAY REGIONAL REHAB HOSPITAL, CONWAY, AR, p. A44
CONWAY REGIONAL REHABILITATION HOSPITAL, CONWAY, AR, p. A44
COOK CHILDREN'S MEDICAL CENTER, FORT WORTH, TX, p. A678
COOK COUNTY NORTH SHORE HOSPITAL, GRAND MARAIS, MN, p. A377
COOK HOSPITAL & CARE CENTER, COOK, MN, p. A374
COOK HOSPITAL AND CARE CENTER, COOK, MN, p. A374
COOK MEDICAL CENTER-A CAMPUS OF TIFT REGIONAL MEDICAL CENTER, ADEL, GA, p. A163
COOK-FORT WORTH CHILD MED CTR, FORT WORTH, TX, p. A678
COOKEVILLE GENERAL HOSPITAL, COOKEVILLE, TN, p. A637
COOKEVILLE REGIONAL MEDICAL CENTER, COOKEVILLE, TN, p. A637
COOLEY DICKINSON HOSPITAL, NORTHAMPTON, MA, p. A342
COON MEMORIAL HOSPITAL, DALHART, TX, p. A667
COON MEMORIAL HOSPITAL AND HOME, DALHART, TX, p. A667
COOPER HEALTH SYSTEM, CAMDEN, NJ, p. A453
COOPER UNIVERSITY HEALTH CARE, CAMDEN, NJ, p. A453
COOPERSTOWN MEDICAL CENTER, COOPERSTOWN, ND, p. A522
COORDINATED HEALTH-BETHLEHEM, BETHLEHEM, PA, p. A584
COOSA VALLEY BAPTIST MED CTR, SYLACAUGA, AL, p. A24
COOSA VALLEY MEDICAL CENTER, SYLACAUGA, AL, p. A24
COPIAH COUNTY MEDICAL CENTER, HAZLEHURST, MS, p. A394
COPLEY HOSPITAL, MORRISVILLE, VT, p. A736
COPPER QUEEN COMMUNITY HOSPITAL, BISBEE, AZ, p. A30
COPPER SPRINGS HOSPITAL, AVONDALE, AZ, p. A30
COQUILLE VALLEY HOSPITAL, COQUILLE, OR, p. A574
CORAL GABLES HOSPITAL, CORAL GABLES, FL, p. A135
CORAL SPRINGS MEDICAL CENTER, CORAL SPRINGS, FL, p. A135
CORDELL MEMORIAL HOSPITAL, CORDELL, OK, p. A558
CORDOVA COMMUNITY HOSPITAL, CORDOVA, AK, p. A28
CORDOVA COMMUNITY MEDICAL CENTER, CORDOVA, AK, p. A28
CORNERSTONE BEHAVIORAL HEALTH HOSPITAL OF UNION COUNTY, BERKELEY HEIGHTS, NJ, p. A452
CORNERSTONE HOSPITAL OF AUSTIN, AUSTIN, TX, p. A655
CORNERSTONE HOSPITAL OF BOSSIER CITY, BOSSIER CITY, LA, p. A298
CORNERSTONE HOSPITAL OF CENTRAL TEXAS, AUSTIN, TX, p. A655
CORNERSTONE HOSPITAL OF HOUSTON AT CLEARLAKE, WEBSTER, TX, p. A724

CORNERSTONE HOSPITAL OF HUNTINGTON, HUNTINGTON, WV, p. A773
CORNERSTONE HOSPITAL OF LITTLE ROCK, LITTLE ROCK, AR, p. A49
CORNERSTONE HOSPITAL OF NORTH LITTLE ROCK, LITTLE ROCK, AR, p. A49
CORNERSTONE HOSPITAL OF OKLAHOMA-MUSKOGEE, MUSKOGEE, OK, p. A562
CORNERSTONE HOSPITAL OF OKLAHOMA-SHAWNEE, SHAWNEE, OK, p. A568
CORNERSTONE HOSPITAL OF SOUTH HOUSTON, HOUSTON, TX, p. A685
CORNERSTONE HOSPITAL OF SOUTHEAST ARIZONA, TUCSON, AZ, p. A40
CORNERSTONE HOSPITAL OF SOUTHWEST LOUISIANA, LAKE CHARLES, LA, p. A306
CORNERSTONE HOSPITAL-MEDICAL CENTER OF HOUSTON, HOUSTON, TX, p. A685
CORNERSTONE HOSPITAL-WEST MONROE, WEST MONROE, LA, p. A316
CORNERSTONE HOSPITALS BOSSIER CITY, BOSSIER CITY, LA, p. A298
CORNERSTONE HOSPITALS SOUTHWEST LOUISIANA, LAKE CHARLES, LA, p. A306
CORNERSTONE HOSPITALS WEST MONROE, WEST MONROE, LA, p. A316
CORNERSTONE MEDICAL CENTER, FORT OGLETHORPE, GA, p. A173
CORNERSTONE OF MEDICAL ARTS CENTER HOSPITAL, FRESH MEADOWS, NY, p. A484
CORNERSTONE REGIONAL HOSPITAL, EDINBURG, TX, p. A673
CORNERSTONE SPECIALTY HOSPITALS AUSTIN, AUSTIN, TX, p. A655
CORNING HOSPITAL, CORNING, NY, p. A481
CORNWALL HOSPITAL, CORNWALL, NY, p. A482
CORONA REGIONAL MEDICAL CENTER, CORONA, CA, p. A61
CORONADO HOSPITAL, CORONADO, CA, p. A61
CORPUS CHRISTI MEDICAL CENTER, CORPUS CHRISTI, TX, p. A666
CORPUS CHRUSTI MEDICAL CENTER, CORPUS CHRISTI, TX, p. A666
CORRY MEMORIAL HOSPITAL, CORRY, PA, p. A587
CORTLAND REGIONAL MEDICAL CENTER, CORTLAND, NY, p. A482
CORYELL HEALTH, GATESVILLE, TX, p. A681
CORYELL MEMORIAL HOSPITAL, GATESVILLE, TX, p. A681
COSHOCTON COUNTY MEMORIAL HOSPITAL, COSHOCTON, OH, p. A537
COSHOCTON REGIONAL MEDICAL CENTER, COSHOCTON, OH, p. A538
COTEAU DES PRAIRIES HOSPITAL, SISSETON, SD, p. A632
COTTAGE GROVE COMMUNITY HOSPITAL, COTTAGE GROVE, OR, p. A574
COTTAGE HOSPITAL, WOODSVILLE, NH, p. A451
COTTAGE REHABILITATION HOSPITAL, SANTA BARBARA, CA, p. A96
COTTONWOOD HOSPITAL MED CNTR, MURRAY, UT, p. A729
COTTONWOOD SPRINGS HOSPITAL, OLATHE, KS, p. A272
COULEE COMMUNITY HOSPITAL, GRAND COULEE, WA, p. A759
COULEE MEDICAL CENTER, GRAND COULEE, WA, p. A759
COVENANT CHILDREN'S HOSPITAL, LUBBOCK, TX, p. A697
COVENANT HEALTHCARE, SAGINAW, MI, p. A365
COVENANT HOSPITAL PLAINVIEW, PLAINVIEW, TX, p. A706
COVENANT HOSPITAL-LEVELLAND, LEVELLAND, TX, p. A695
COVENANT MEDICAL CENTER, LUBBOCK, TX, p. A697
COVENANT MEDICAL CENTER, SAGINAW, MI, p. A365
COVENANT MEDICAL CENTER, WATERLOO, IA, p. A259
COVENANT SPECIALTY HOSPITAL, LUBBOCK, TX, p. A697
COVINGTON BEHAVIORAL HEALTH, COVINGTON, LA, p. A300
COVINGTON BEHAVIORAL HEALTH, COVINGTON, LA, p. A300
COVINGTON COUNTY HOSPITAL, COLLINS, MS, p. A391
COX BARTON COUNTY MEMORIAL HOSPITAL, LAMAR, MO, p. A410
COX MEDICAL CENTERS BRANSON, BRANSON, MO, p. A403
COX MEDICAL CENTERS, SPRINGFIELD, MO, p. A418
COX MONETT, MONETT, MO, p. A412
COX MONETT HOSPITAL, MONETT, MO, p. A412
COZAD COMMUNITY HEALTH SYSTEM, COZAD, NE, p. A431
COZAD COMMUNITY HOSPITAL, COZAD, NE, p. A431
CRAIG GENERAL HOSPITAL, VINITA, OK, p. A571
CRAIG HOSPITAL, ENGLEWOOD, CO, p. A112
CRANE MEMORIAL HOSPITAL, CRANE, TX, p. A666
CRANFORD HEALTH AND EC CENTER, CRANFORD, NJ, p. A453
CRAWFORD COUNTY MEMORIAL HOSPITAL, DENISON, IA, p. A248
CRAWFORD MEMORIAL HOSPITAL, ROBINSON, IL, p. A218
CREEDMOOR PSYCHIATRIC CENTER, JAMAICA, NY, p. A486

CREEK NATION COMMUNITY HOSPITAL, OKEMAH, OK, p. A563
CREEKSIDE BEHAVIORAL HEALTH, KINGSPORT, TN, p. A640
CREIGHTON AREA HEALTH SERVICES, CREIGHTON, NE, p. A431
CRENSHAW BAPTIST HOSPITAL, LUVERNE, AL, p. A21
CRENSHAW COMMUNITY HOSPITAL, LUVERNE, AL, p. A21
CRESCENT MEDICAL CENTER LANCASTER, LANCASTER, TX, p. A695
CREST MEDICAL CENTER-PERRY, PERRY, FL, p. A154
CRESTVIEW HOSPITAL, CASPER, WY, p. A801
CRESTWOOD MEDICAL CENTER, HUNTSVILLE, AL, p. A20
CRESTWYN BEHAVIORAL HEALTH, MEMPHIS, TN, p. A644
CRETE AREA MEDICAL CENTER, CRETE, NE, p. A431
CRETE MUNICIPAL HOSPITAL, CRETE, NE, p. A431
CRISP COUNTY HOSPITAL, CORDELE, GA, p. A170
CRISP REGIONAL HOSPITAL, CORDELE, GA, p. A170
CRITTENDEN COUNTY HOSPITAL, MARION, KY, p. A289
CRITTENTON CHILDREN'S CENTER, KANSAS CITY, MO, p. A408
CRITTENTON HOSPITAL MEDICAL CENTER, ROCHESTER, MI, p. A365
CROCKETT HOSPITAL, LAWRENCEBURG, TN, p. A642
CROCKETT MEDICAL CENTER, CROCKETT, TX, p. A666
CROOK CNTY MED SYSTEM DIST, SUNDANCE, WY, p. A804
CROOK COUNTY MEDICAL SERVICES DISTRICT, SUNDANCE, WY, p. A804
CROSBY MEMORIAL HOSPITAL, PICAYUNE, MS, p. A398
CROSBYTON CLINIC HOSPITAL, CROSBYTON, TX, p. A666
CROSS CREEK HOSPITAL, AUSTIN, TX, p. A655
CROSSBRIDGE COMMUNITY HOSPITAL, WYNNE, AR, p. A54
CROSSGATES RIVER OAKS HOSPITAL, BRANDON, MS, p. A390
CROSSING RIVERS HEALTH MEDICAL CENTER, PRAIRIE DU CHIEN, WI, p. A794
CROSSRIDGE COMMUNITY HOSPITAL, WYNNE, AR, p. A54
CROSSROADS COMMUNITY HOSPITAL, MOUNT VERNON, IL, p. A213
CROSSROADS REGIONAL HOSPITAL, ALEXANDRIA, LA, p. A295
CROUSE HEALTH, SYRACUSE, NY, p. A499
CROUSE HOSPITAL, SYRACUSE, NY, p. A499
CROW/NORTHERN CHEYENNE HOSPITAL, CROW AGENCY, MT, p. A422
CROW/NORTHERN CHEYENNE INDIAN HOSPITAL, CROW AGENCY, MT, p. A422
CROZER-CHESTER MEDICAL CENTER, UPLAND, PA, p. A609
C.S. MOTT CHILDREN'S HOSPITAL, ANN ARBOR, MI, p. A348
CUBA CITY MEDICAL CENTER, CUBA CITY, WI, p. A782
CUBA MEMORIAL HOSPITAL, CUBA, NY, p. A482
CUERO COMMUNITY HOSPITAL, CUERO, TX, p. A666
CUERO REGIONAL HOSPITAL, CUERO, TX, p. A667
CULBERSON HOSPITAL, VAN HORN, TX, p. A722
CULBERSON HOSPITAL DISTRICT, VAN HORN, TX, p. A722
CULLMAN MEDICAL CENTER, CULLMAN, AL, p. A17
CULLMAN REGIONAL MEDICAL CENTER, CULLMAN, AL, p. A17
CUMBERLAND COUNTY HOSPITAL, BURKESVILLE, KY, p. A281
CUMBERLAND HALL HOSPITAL, HOPKINSVILLE, KY, p. A285
CUMBERLAND HEALTHCARE, CUMBERLAND, WI, p. A782
CUMBERLAND HOSPITAL, FAYETTEVILLE, NC, p. A510
CUMBERLAND HOSPITAL, NEW KENT, VA, p. A746
CUMBERLAND HOSPITAL FOR CHILDREN AND ADOLESCENTS, NEW KENT, VA, p. A746
CUMBERLAND MEDICAL CENTER, CROSSVILLE, TN, p. A637
CUMBERLAND MEMORIAL HOSPITAL, CUMBERLAND, WI, p. A782
CUPEY HOSPITAL & NRSG HOME, SAN JUAN, PR, p. A810
CURAHEALTH HERITAGE VALLEY, BEAVER, PA, p. A584
CURAHEALTH HOSPITAL OKLAHOMA CITY, OKLAHOMA CITY, OK, p. A564
CURAHEALTH HOSPITAL STOUGHTON, STOUGHTON, MA, p. A345
CURAHEALTH JACKSONVILLE, JACKSONVILLE, FL, p. A141
CURAHEALTH NASHVILLE, NASHVILLE, TN, p. A646
CURAHEALTH NEW ORLEANS, NEW ORLEANS, LA, p. A310
CURAHEALTH OKLAHOMA, OKLAHOMA CITY, OK, p. A564
CURAHEALTH PHOENIX, PEORIA, AZ, p. A35
CURAHEALTH PHOENIX, PHOENIX, AZ, p. A35
CURAHEALTH PITTSBURGH, OAKDALE, PA, p. A598
CURAHEALTH STOUGHTON, STOUGHTON, MA, p. A345
CURAHEALTH TUCSON, TUCSON, AZ, p. A40
CURRY GENERAL HOSPITAL, GOLD BEACH, OR, p. A575
CUSHING MEMORIAL HOSPITAL, LEAVENWORTH, KS, p. A269
CUSHING REGIONAL HOSPITAL, CUSHING, OK, p. A558
CUSTER REGIONAL HOSPITAL, CUSTER, SD, p. A627
CUYUNA RANGE DISTRICT HOSPITAL, CROSBY, MN, p. A374

CUYUNA REGIONAL MEDICAL CENTER, CROSBY, MN, p. A374
CYPRESS CREEK HOSPITAL, HOUSTON, TX, p. A685
CYPRESS FAIRBANKS MEDICAL CENTER, HOUSTON, TX, p. A685
CYPRESS GROVE BEHAVIORAL HEALTH, BASTROP, LA, p. A296
CYPRESS POINTE HOSPITAL EAST, SLIDELL, LA, p. A315
CYPRESS POINTE SURGICAL HOSPITAL, HAMMOND, LA, p. A302

# D

DAHL MEMORIAL HEALTHCARE ASSOCIATION, EKALAKA, MT, p. A423
DAHL MEMORIAL MAF, EKALAKA, MT, p. A423
DAKOTA PLAINS SURGICAL CENTER, ABERDEEN, SD, p. A626
DALE COUNTY HOSPITAL, OZARK, AL, p. A23
DALE MEDICAL CENTER, OZARK, AL, p. A23
DALLAS BEHAVIORAL HEALTHCARE HOSPITAL, DESOTO, TX, p. A672
DALLAS COUNTY HOSPITAL, FORDYCE, AR, p. A45
DALLAS COUNTY HOSPITAL, PERRY, IA, p. A256
DALLAS COUNTY HOSPITAL DIST, DALLAS, TX, p. A668
DALLAS COUNTY MEDICAL CENTER, FORDYCE, AR, p. A45
DALLAS MEDICAL CENTER, DALLAS, TX, p. A668
DALLAS REGIONAL MEDICAL CENTER, MESQUITE, TX, p. A700
DAMERON HOSPITAL, STOCKTON, CA, p. A99
DANA-FARBER CANCER INSTITUTE, BOSTON, MA, p. A335
DANBURY HOSPITAL, DANBURY, CT, p. A121
DANIEL DRAKE CENTER FOR POST ACUTE CARE, CINCINNATI, OH, p. A532
DANIELS MEMORIAL HEALTHCARE CENTER, SCOBEY, MT, p. A427
DANIELS MEMORIAL HOSPITAL, SCOBEY, MT, p. A427
DANVILLE REGIONAL MEDICAL CENTER, DANVILLE, VA, p. A741
DANVILLE STATE HOSPITAL, DANVILLE, PA, p. A587
DARDANELLE HOSPITAL YELL COUNTY, DARDANELLE, AR, p. A44
DARDANELLE REGIONAL MEDICAL CENTER, DARDANELLE, AR, p. A44
DARNALL ARMY COMM HOSPITAL, FORT HOOD, TX, p. A677
DARTMOUTH-HITCHCOCK MEDICAL CENTER, LEBANON, NH, p. A449
DAVID GRANT MEDICAL CENTER, TRAVIS AFB, CA, p. A101
DAVID GRANT USAF MEDICAL CENTER, TRAVIS AFB, CA, p. A101
DAVIES MEDICAL CENTER, SAN FRANCISCO, CA, p. A93
DAVIESS COMMUNITY HOSPITAL, WASHINGTON, IN, p. A242
DAVIESS COUNTY HOSPITAL, WASHINGTON, IN, p. A242
DAVIS COUNTY HOSPITAL, BLOOMFIELD, IA, p. A244
DAVIS COUNTY HOSPITAL AND CLINICS, BLOOMFIELD, IA, p. A244
DAVIS HOSPITAL & MEDICAL CNTR, LAYTON, UT, p. A728
DAVIS HOSPITAL AND MEDICAL CENTER, LAYTON, UT, p. A728
DAVIS MEDICAL CENTER, ELKINS, WV, p. A772
DAVIS MEMORIAL HOSPITAL, ELKINS, WV, p. A772
DAVIS REGIONAL MEDICAL CENTER, STATESVILLE, NC, p. A519
DAVIS REGIONAL MEDICAL CTR, STATESVILLE, NC, p. A519
DAY KIMBALL HOSPITAL, PUTNAM, CT, p. A124
DAYTON CHILDREN'S HOSPITAL, DAYTON, OH, p. A538
DAYTON GENERAL HOSPITAL, DAYTON, WA, p. A757
DAYTON VETERANS AFFAIRS MEDICAL CENTER, DAYTON, OH, p. A538
DCH REGIONAL MEDICAL CENTER, TUSCALOOSA, AL, p. A25
DE GRAFF MEMORIAL HOSPITAL, NORTH TONAWANDA, NY, p. A493
DE JARNETTE CENTER, STAUNTON, VA, p. A752
DE SMET MEMORIAL HOSPITAL, DE SMET, SD, p. A627
DE SOTO GENERAL HOSPITAL, MANSFIELD, LA, p. A308
DE SOTO REGIONAL HEALTH SYSTEM, MANSFIELD, LA, p. A308
DEACONESS BILLINGS CLINIC, BILLINGS, MT, p. A421
DEACONESS HOSPITAL, EVANSVILLE, IN, p. A227
DEACONESS MIDTOWN HOSPITAL, EVANSVILLE, IN, p. A227
DEACONESS-GLOVER HOSPITAL CORP, NEEDHAM, MA, p. A342
DEACONESS-NASHOBA HOSPITAL, AYER, MA, p. A334
DEAF SMITH GENERAL HOSPITAL, HEREFORD, TX, p. A684

DEARBORN COUNTY HOSPITAL, LAWRENCEBURG, IN, p. A235
DEBORAH HEART AND LUNG CENTER, BROWNS MILLS, NJ, p. A453
DECATUR COUNTY HOSPITAL, LEON, IA, p. A253
DECATUR COUNTY HOSPITAL AND CEDAR LIVING CENTER, OBERLIN, KS, p. A272
DECATUR COUNTY MEMORIAL HOSPITAL, GREENSBURG, IN, p. A230
DECATUR GENERAL HOSPITAL, DECATUR, AL, p. A17
DECATUR GENERAL HOSPITAL-WEST, DECATUR, AL, p. A17
DECATUR HEALTH SYSTEMS, OBERLIN, KS, p. A272
DECATUR MEMORIAL HOSPITAL, DECATUR, IL, p. A202
DECATUR MORGAN HOSPITAL, DECATUR, AL, p. A17
DECKERVILLE COMMUNITY HOSPITAL, DECKERVILLE, MI, p. A352
DEER LODGE MEDICAL CENTER, DEER LODGE, MT, p. A423
DEER RIVER HEALTHCARE CENTER, DEER RIVER, MN, p. A375
DEER VALLEY MEDICAL CENTER, PHOENIX, AZ, p. A35
DEERING HOSPITAL, MIAMI, FL, p. A146
DEER'S HEAD HOSPITAL CENTER, SALISBURY, MD, p. A332
DEER'S HEAD HOSPITASL CENTER, SALISBURY, MD, p. A332
DEFIANCE REGIONAL MEDICAL CENTER, DEFIANCE, OH, p. A539
DEKALB COMMUNITY HOSPITAL, SMITHVILLE, TN, p. A649
DEKALB HEALTH, AUBURN, IN, p. A223
DEKALB MEDICAL AT DOWNTOWN DECATUR, DECATUR, GA, p. A171
DEKALB MEDICAL AT HILLANDALE, LITHONIA, GA, p. A175
DEKALB MEDICAL AT NORTH DECATUR, DECATUR, GA, p. A171
DEKALB MEDICAL CENTER, FORT PAYNE, AL, p. A19
DEKALB REGIONAL MEDICAL CENTER, FORT PAYNE, AL, p. A19
DEL AMO HOSPITAL, TORRANCE, CA, p. A101
DEL SOL REHABILITATION HOSP, EL PASO, TX, p. A674
DEL VLY MENTAL HLTH FOUNDATION, DOYLESTOWN, PA, p. A588
DELANO REGIONAL MEDICAL CENTER, DELANO, CA, p. A62
DELAWARE COUNTY MEM HOSPITAL, MANCHESTER, IA, p. A253
DELAWARE COUNTY MEMORIAL HOSPITAL, DREXEL HILL, PA, p. A588
DELAWARE PSYCHIATRIC CENTER, NEW CASTLE, DE, p. A127
DELAWARE STATE HOSPITAL, NEW CASTLE, DE, p. A127
DELAWARE VALLEY HOSPITAL, WALTON, NY, p. A501
DELL CHILDREN'S MEDICAL CENTER OF CENTRAL TEXAS, AUSTIN, TX, p. A656
DELL SETON MEDICAL CENTER AT THE UNIVERSITY OF TEXAS, AUSTIN, TX, p. A656
DELNOR HOSPITAL, GENEVA, IL, p. A206
DELRAY MEDICAL CENTER, DELRAY BEACH, FL, p. A136
DELTA COMMUNITY MEDICAL CENTER, DELTA, UT, p. A727
DELTA COUNTY MEMORIAL HOSPITAL, DELTA, CO, p. A110
DELTA MEDICAL CENTER, MEMPHIS, TN, p. A644
DELTA MEMORIAL HOSPITAL, DUMAS, AR, p. A44
DELTA REGIONAL MEDICAL CENTER, GREENVILLE, MS, p. A392
DELTA SPECIALTY HOSPITAL, MEMPHIS, TN, p. A644
DENTON COMMUNITY HOSPITAL, DENTON, TX, p. A671
DENTON REGIONAL MEDICAL CENTER, DENTON, TX, p. A671
DENVER HEALTH, DENVER, CO, p. A110
DENVER HEALTH MEDICAL CENTER, DENVER, CO, p. A110
DENVER SPRINGS, ENGLEWOOD, CO, p. A112
DEPARTMENT OF STATE HOSPITALS-NAPA, NAPA, CA, p. A80
DEPT OF VETERANS AFF MED CTR, DES MOINES, IA, p. A248
DEPT OF VETERANS AFF MED CTR, KNOXVILLE, IA, p. A253
DEQUINCY MEMORIAL HOSPITAL, DEQUINCY, LA, p. A301
DES MOINES DIVISION, DES MOINES, IA, p. A248
DES PERES HOSPITAL, SAINT LOUIS, MO, p. A415
DESERT PARKWAY BEHAVIORAL HEALTHCARE HOSPITAL, LAS VEGAS, NV, p. A443
DESERT REGIONAL MEDICAL CENTER, PALM SPRINGS, CA, p. A83
DESERT REGIONAL MEDICAL CTR, PALM SPRINGS, CA, p. A83
DESERT SAMARITAN MEDICAL CTR, MESA, AZ, p. A34
DESERT SPRINGS HOSPITAL, LAS VEGAS, NV, p. A443
DESERT SPRINGS HOSPITAL MEDICAL CENTER, LAS VEGAS, NV, p. A443
DESERT VALLEY HOSPITAL, VICTORVILLE, CA, p. A104
DESERT VIEW HOSPITAL, PAHRUMP, NV, p. A445
DESERT VIEW REGIONAL MEDICAL CENTER, PAHRUMP, NV, p. A445
DESERT WILLOW TREATMENT CENTER, LAS VEGAS, NV, p. A443

DESOTO MEMORIAL HOSPITAL, ARCADIA, FL, p. A131
DETAR HEALTHCARE SYSTEM, VICTORIA, TX, p. A723
DETAR HOSPITAL NAVARRO, VICTORIA, TX, p. A723
DETROIT RECEIVING HOSPITAL/UNIVERSITY HEALTH CENTER, DETROIT, MI, p. A352
DEVEREUX ADVANCED BEHAVIORAL HEALTH GEORGIA, KENNESAW, GA, p. A174
DEVEREUX CHILDREN'S BEHAVIORAL HEALTH CENTER, MALVERN, PA, p. A596
DEVEREUX GEORGIA TREATMENT NETWORK, KENNESAW, GA, p. A174
DEVEREUX HOSPITAL, LEAGUE CITY, TX, p. A695
DEVEREUX HOSPITAL AND CHILDREN'S CENTER OF FLORIDA, MELBOURNE, FL, p. A145
DEVEREUX MAPLETON PSYCH INST, MALVERN, PA, p. A596
DEVEREUX TEXAS TREATMENT NETWORK, LEAGUE CITY, TX, p. A695
DEWITT ARMY COMMUNITY HOSPITAL, FORT BELVOIR, VA, p. A742
DEWITT CITY HOSPITAL, DEWITT, AR, p. A44
DEWITT COMMUNITY HOSPITAL, DE WITT, IA, p. A248
DEWITT HOSPITAL, DEWITT, AR, p. A44
DICKENSON COMMUNITY HOSPITAL, CLINTWOOD, VA, p. A740
DICKINSON CNTY MEM HOSP SYSTEM, IRON MOUNTAIN, MI, p. A358
DICKINSON COUNTY HEALTHCARE SYSTEM, IRON MOUNTAIN, MI, p. A358
DICKINSON COUNTY MEM HOSPITAL, SPIRIT LAKE, IA, p. A258
DIGNITY HEALTH ARIZONA GENERAL HOSPITAL, LAVEEN, AZ, p. A33
DIGNITY HEALTH EAST VALLEY REHABILITATION HOSPITAL, CHANDLER, AZ, p. A31
DIGNITY HEALTH REHABILITATION HOSPITAL, HENDERSON, NV, p. A442
DILEY RIDGE MEDICAL CENTER, CANAL WINCHESTER, OH, p. A530
DIMMIT COUNTY MEMORIAL HOSPITAL, CARRIZO SPRINGS, TX, p. A662
DIMMIT REGIONAL HOSPITAL, CARRIZO SPRINGS, TX, p. A662
DISTRICT ONE HOSPITAL, FARIBAULT, MN, p. A376
DIVINE SAVIOR HEALTHCARE, PORTAGE, WI, p. A794
DIVINE SAVIOR HOSPITAL, PORTAGE, WI, p. A794
DIXIE MEDICAL CENTER, SAINT GEORGE, UT, p. A732
DIXIE REGIONAL MEDICAL CENTER, SAINT GEORGE, UT, p. A732
D. M. COGDELL MEMORIAL HOSPITAL, SNYDER, TX, p. A716
DMC—CHILDREN'S HOSPITAL OF MICHIGAN, DETROIT, MI, p. A352
DMC—DETROIT RECEIVING HOSPITAL, DETROIT, MI, p. A352
DMC—REHABILITATION INSTITUTE OF MICHIGAN, DETROIT, MI, p. A352
DMC—SINAI-GRACE HOSPITAL, DETROIT, MI, p. A352
DMC HARPER UNIVERSITY HOSPITAL, DETROIT, MI, p. A353
DMC HURON VALLEY-SINAI HOSPITAL, COMMERCE TOWNSHIP, MI, p. A351
DOCTORS CENTER, MANATI, PR, p. A808
DOCTORS CENTER HOSPITAL, SAN JUAN, PR, p. A810
DOCTORS COMMUNITY HOSPITAL, LANHAM, MD, p. A330
DOCTORS HOSP OF JEFFERSON, METAIRIE, LA, p. A308
DOCTORS HOSPITAL, AUGUSTA, GA, p. A166
DOCTORS HOSPITAL, COLUMBUS, OH, p. A536
DOCTORS HOSPITAL MEDICAL CTR, MONTCLAIR, CA, p. A79
DOCTORS HOSPITAL OF AUGUSTA, AUGUSTA, GA, p. A166
DOCTORS HOSPITAL OF LAKEWOOD, LAKEWOOD, CA, p. A71
DOCTORS HOSPITAL OF LAREDO, LAREDO, TX, p. A695
DOCTORS HOSPITAL OF LODI, LODI, CA, p. A71
DOCTORS HOSPITAL OF MANTECA, MANTECA, CA, p. A77
DOCTORS HOSPITAL OF SARASOTA, SARASOTA, FL, p. A157
DOCTORS HOSPITAL OF TATTNALL, REIDSVILLE, GA, p. A178
DOCTORS HOSPITAL OF WEST COVINA, WEST COVINA, CA, p. A104
DOCTORS MEDICAL CENTER, MODESTO, CA, p. A78
DOCTORS MEDICAL CENTER OF MODESTO, MODESTO, CA, p. A78
DOCTORS MEMORIAL HOSPITAL, BONIFAY, FL, p. A132
DOCTORS NEUROPSYCHIATRIC HOSPITAL AND RESEARCH INSTITUTE, BREMEN, IN, p. A225
DOCTORS SPECIALTY HOSPITAL, COLUMBUS, GA, p. A169
DOCTORS' CENTER HOSPITAL SAN JUAN, SAN JUAN, PR, p. A810
DOCTORS' HOSPITAL, CORAL GABLES, FL, p. A135
DOCTORS' HOSPITAL OF MICHIGAN, PONTIAC, MI, p. A364
DOCTOR'S CENTER OF BAYAMON, BAYAMON, PR, p. A806
DOCTOR'S HOSPITAL, LEAWOOD, KS, p. A269
DOCTOR'S HOSPITAL AT RENAISSANCE, EDINBURG, TX, p. A674

DOCTOR'S MEMORIAL HOSPITAL, PERRY, FL, p. A154
DODGE COUNTY HOSPITAL, EASTMAN, GA, p. A172
DOMINICAN HOSPITAL, SANTA CRUZ, CA, p. A97
DOMINICAN SANTA CRUZ HOSPITAL, SANTA CRUZ, CA, p. A97
DOMINION HOSPITAL, FALLS CHURCH, VA, p. A741
DONALSONVILLE HOSPITAL, DONALSONVILLE, GA, p. A171
DOOR COUNTY MEDICAL CENTER, STURGEON BAY, WI, p. A797
DOR-A-LIN OF SOUTH BEND, SOUTH BEND, IN, p. A240
DORCHESTER GENERAL HOSPITAL, CAMBRIDGE, MD, p. A328
DORMINY MEDICAL CENTER, FITZGERALD, GA, p. A172
DORN VETERANS HOSPITAL, COLUMBIA, SC, p. A617
DOROTHEA DIX PSYCHIATRIC CENTER, BANGOR, ME, p. A318
DOUGLAS COUNTY COMMUNITY MENTAL HEALTH CENTER, OMAHA, NE, p. A437
DOUGLAS COUNTY HOSPITAL, ALEXANDRIA, MN, p. A371
DOUGLAS COUNTY HOSPITAL, OMAHA, NE, p. A437
DOUGLAS COUNTY MEMORIAL HOSPITAL, ARMOUR, SD, p. A626
DOVER BEHAVIORAL HEALTH SYSTEM, DOVER, DE, p. A127
DOWN EAST COMMUNITY HOSPITAL, MACHIAS, ME, p. A321
DOWNEY MEDICAL CENTER, DOWNEY, CA, p. A62
DOWNEY REGIONAL MEDICAL CENTER, DOWNEY, CA, p. A62
DOYLESTOWN HOSPITAL, DOYLESTOWN, PA, p. A588
DR J CORRIGAN MENTAL HLTH CNTR, FALL RIVER, MA, p. A338
DR JOHN M MEADOWS MEM HOSPITAL, VIDALIA, GA, p. A182
DR JOSE RAMOS LEBRON HOSPITAL, FAJARDO, PR, p. A807
DR. DAN C. TRIGG MEMORIAL HOSPITAL, TUCUMCARI, NM, p. A473
DR. J. CORRIGAN MENTAL HEALTH CENTER, FALL RIVER, MA, p. A338
DR. JOHN WARNER HOSPITAL, CLINTON, IL, p. A201
DR. PILA'S HOSPITAL, PONCE, PR, p. A809
DR. RAMON E. BETANCES HOSPITAL-MAYAGUEZ MEDICAL CENTER BRANCH, MAYAGUEZ, PR, p. A808
DR. SOLOMON CARTER FULLER MENTAL HEALTH CENTER, BOSTON, MA, p. A335
DRAKE CENTER, CINCINNATI, OH, p. A532
DREW MEMORIAL HEALTH SYSTEM, MONTICELLO, AR, p. A50
DREW MEMORIAL HOSPITAL, MONTICELLO, AR, p. A50
DRISCOLL CHILDREN'S HOSPITAL, CORPUS CHRISTI, TX, p. A666
DRISCOLL FDN CHILDREN'S HOSP, CORPUS CHRISTI, TX, p. A666
DRUMRIGHT REGIONAL HOSPITAL, DRUMRIGHT, OK, p. A558
DSH METROPOLITAN, NORWALK, CA, p. A81
DSH PATTON, PATTON, CA, p. A85
DUANE L. WATERS HOSPITAL, JACKSON, MI, p. A358
DUBLIN METHODIST HOSPITAL, DUBLIN, OH, p. A539
DUBLIN SPRINGS, DUBLIN, OH, p. A539
DUBOIS REGIONAL MEDICAL CENTER, DUBOIS, PA, p. A588
DUBUIS HOSPITAL OF ALEXANDRIA, ALEXANDRIA, LA, p. A295
DUBUIS HOSPITAL OF BEAUMONT, BEAUMONT, TX, p. A658
DUCHESNE COUNTY HOSPITAL, ROOSEVELT, UT, p. A731
DUKE HEALTH RALEIGH HOSPITAL, RALEIGH, NC, p. A516
DUKE RALEIGH HOSPITAL, RALEIGH, NC, p. A516
DUKE REGIONAL HOSPITAL, DURHAM, NC, p. A508
DUKE UNIVERSITY HOSPITAL, DURHAM, NC, p. A508
DUKE UNIVERSITY MEDICAL CENTER, DURHAM, NC, p. A508
DUKES MEMORIAL HOSPITAL, PERU, IN, p. A239
DUNCAN REGIONAL HOSPITAL, DUNCAN, OK, p. A558
DUNDY COUNTY HEALTH SYSTEM, BENKELMAN, NE, p. A430
DUNDY COUNTY HOSPITAL, BENKELMAN, NE, p. A430
DUNES SURGICAL HOSPITAL, DAKOTA DUNES, SD, p. A627
DUNLAP COMMUNITY HOSPITAL, ORRVILLE, OH, p. A547
DUPLIN GENERAL HOSPITAL, KENANSVILLE, NC, p. A513
DUPONT HOSPITAL, FORT WAYNE, IN, p. A228
DUPONT HOSPITAL FOR CHILDREN, WILMINGTON, DE, p. A128
DURHAM REGIONAL HOSPITAL, DURHAM, NC, p. A508
DURHAM VETERANS AFFAIRS MEDICAL CENTER, DURHAM, NC, p. A509
D. W. MCMILLAN MEMORIAL HOSPITAL, BREWTON, AL, p. A16

DWIGHT D. EISENHOWER VETERANS AFFAIRS MEDICAL CENTER, LEAVENWORTH, KS, p. A269
DWIGHT DAVID EISENHOWER ARMY MEDICAL CENTER, FORT GORDON, GA, p. A173

# E

EAGLEVILLE HOSPITAL, EAGLEVILLE, PA, p. A588
EARLE E. MORRIS ALCOHOL AND DRUG TREATMENT CENTER, COLUMBIA, SC, p. A617
EAST ADAMS RURAL HEALTHCARE, RITZVILLE, WA, p. A763
EAST ADAMS RURAL HOSPITAL, RITZVILLE, WA, p. A763
EAST ALABAMA MEDICAL CENTER, OPELIKA, AL, p. A23
EAST CARROLL PARISH HOSPITAL, LAKE PROVIDENCE, LA, p. A307
EAST CENTRAL REGIONAL HOSP, GRACEWOOD, GA, p. A173
EAST CENTRAL REGIONAL HOSPITAL, AUGUSTA, GA, p. A166
EAST CENTRAL REGIONAL HOSPITAL, GRACEWOOD, GA, p. A173
EAST COOPER MEDICAL CENTER, MOUNT PLEASANT, SC, p. A622
EAST COOPER REGIONAL MEDICAL CENTER, MOUNT PLEASANT, SC, p. A622
EAST GEORGIA REGIONAL MEDICAL CENTER, STATESBORO, GA, p. A181
EAST JEFFERSON GENERAL HOSPITAL, METAIRIE, LA, p. A308
EAST LIVERPOOL CITY HOSPITAL, EAST LIVERPOOL, OH, p. A539
EAST LOS ANGELES DOCTORS HOSPITAL, LOS ANGELES, CA, p. A74
EAST LOUISIANA STATE HOSPITAL, JACKSON, LA, p. A303
EAST MISSISSIPPI STATE HOSPITAL, MERIDIAN, MS, p. A397
EAST MORGAN COUNTY HOSPITAL, BRUSH, CO, p. A108
EAST ORANGE GENERAL HOSPITAL, EAST ORANGE, NJ, p. A454
EAST POINTE HOSPITAL, LEHIGH ACRES, FL, p. A144
EAST RIDGE HOSPITAL, EAST RIDGE, TN, p. A637
EAST TENNESSEE CHILDREN'S HOSPITAL, KNOXVILLE, TN, p. A641
EAST TEXAS MEDICAL CENTER ATHENS, ATHENS, TX, p. A654
EAST TEXAS MEDICAL CENTER BEHAVIORAL HEALTH CENTER, TYLER, TX, p. A722
EAST TEXAS MEDICAL CENTER CARTHAGE, CARTHAGE, TX, p. A663
EAST TEXAS MEDICAL CENTER HENDERSON, HENDERSON, TX, p. A683
EAST TEXAS MEDICAL CENTER JACKSONVILLE, JACKSONVILLE, TX, p. A691
EAST TEXAS MEDICAL CENTER PITTSBURG, PITTSBURG, TX, p. A706
EAST TEXAS MEDICAL CENTER SPECIALTY HOSPITAL, TYLER, TX, p. A722
EAST TEXAS MEDICAL CENTER TYLER, TYLER, TX, p. A722
EAST TEXAS MEDICAL CENTER-QUITMAN, QUITMAN, TX, p. A708
EAST VALLEY HOSPITAL MEDICAL CENTER, GLENDORA, CA, p. A67
EASTAR HEALTH SYSTEM, MUSKOGEE, OK, p. A562
EASTAR HEALTH SYSTEM, EAST CAMPUS, MUSKOGEE, OK, p. A562
EASTERN IDAHO REGIONAL MEDICAL CENTER, IDAHO FALLS, ID, p. A190
EASTERN LONG ISLAND HOSPITAL, GREENPORT, NY, p. A485
EASTERN LOUISIANA MENTAL HEALTH SYSTEM, JACKSON, LA, p. A303
EASTERN MAINE MEDICAL CENTER, BANGOR, ME, p. A318
EASTERN NEW MEXICO MEDICAL CENTER, ROSWELL, NM, p. A471
EASTERN NIAGARA HEALTH SYSTEM, LOCKPORT, NY, p. A487
EASTERN NIAGARA HOSPITAL, LOCKPORT, NY, p. A487
EASTERN OKLAHOMA MEDICAL CENTER, POTEAU, OK, p. A567
EASTERN PLUMAS HEALTH CARE, PORTOLA, CA, p. A86
EASTERN PLUMAS HEALTH CARE DISTRICT, PORTOLA, CA, p. A86
EASTERN REGIONAL MEDICAL CENTER, PHILADELPHIA, PA, p. A599
EASTERN SHORE HOSPITAL CENTER, CAMBRIDGE, MD, p. A328
EASTERN STATE HOSPITAL, LEXINGTON, KY, p. A286

EASTERN STATE HOSPITAL, MEDICAL LAKE, WA, p. A760
EASTERN STATE HOSPITAL, VINITA, OK, p. A571
EASTERN STATE HOSPITAL, WILLIAMSBURG, VA, p. A753
EASTLAND MEMORIAL HOSPITAL, EASTLAND, TX, p. A673
EASTPOINTE HOSPITAL, DAPHNE, AL, p. A17
EASTSIDE MEDICAL CENTER, SNELLVILLE, GA, p. A180
EASTSIDE PSYCHIATRIC HOSPITAL, TALLAHASSEE, FL, p. A158
EATON RAPIDS COMM HOSPITAL, EATON RAPIDS, MI, p. A354
EATON RAPIDS MEDICAL CENTER, EATON RAPIDS, MI, p. A354
ED FRASER MEMORIAL HOSPITAL, MACCLENNY, FL, p. A144
ED FRASER MEMORIAL HOSPITAL AND BAKER COMMUNITY HEALTH CENTER, MACCLENNY, FL, p. A144
EDEN MEDICAL CENTER, CASTRO VALLEY, CA, p. A59
EDEN SPRINGS HEALTH CARE CENTER, GREEN SPRINGS, OH, p. A541
EDGE REGIONAL MEDICAL CENTER, TROY, AL, p. A25
EDGEFIELD COUNTY HEALTHCARE, EDGEFIELD, SC, p. A619
EDGEFIELD COUNTY HOSPITAL, EDGEFIELD, SC, p. A619
EDGERTON HOSPITAL AND HEALTH SERVICES, EDGERTON, WI, p. A783
EDGEWOOD SURGICAL HOSPITAL, TRANSFER, PA, p. A609
EDINBURG REGIONAL HOSPITAL, EDINBURG, TX, p. A674
EDITH NOURSE ROGERS MEMORIAL VETERANS HOSPITAL, BEDFORD, MA, p. A334
EDMOND MEDICAL CENTER, EDMOND, OK, p. A558
EDWARD HINES, JR. VETERANS AFFAIRS HOSPITAL, HINES, IL, p. A207
EDWARD HOSPITAL, NAPERVILLE, IL, p. A213
EDWARD HOSPITAL ASSOCIATION, NAPERVILLE, IL, p. A213
EDWARD JOHN NOBLE HOSPITAL OF GOUVERNEUR, GOUVERNEUR, NY, p. A485
EDWARDS COUNTY HOSPITAL AND HEALTHCARE CENTER, KINSLEY, KS, p. A268
EDWARDS COUNTY MEDICAL CENTER, KINSLEY, KS, p. A268
EDWIN SHAW HOSPITAL, COPLEY, OH, p. A537
EDWIN SHAW REHAB, COPLEY, OH, p. A537
EFFINGHAM COUNTY HOSP & ECF, SPRINGFIELD, GA, p. A180
EFFINGHAM HOSPITAL, SPRINGFIELD, GA, p. A180
EGLESTON CHILDREN'S HOSPITAL, ATLANTA, GA, p. A164
EINSTEIN MEDICAL CENTER MONTGOMERY, EAST NORRITON, PA, p. A589
EINSTEIN MEDICAL CENTER PHILADELPHIA, PHILADELPHIA, PA, p. A600
EINSTEIN-WEILER HOSPITAL, BRONX, NY, p. A476
EISENHOWER HEALTH, RANCHO MIRAGE, CA, p. A86
EISENHOWER MEDICAL CENTER, RANCHO MIRAGE, CA, p. A87
E J NOBLE HOSPITAL SAMARITAN, ALEXANDRIA BAY, NY, p. A474
EL CAMINO HOSPITAL, MOUNTAIN VIEW, CA, p. A80
EL CAMPO MEMORIAL HOSPITAL, EL CAMPO, TX, p. A674
EL CENTRO REGIONAL MEDICAL CENTER, EL CENTRO, CA, p. A63
EL PASO BEHAVIORAL HEALTH SYSTEM, EL PASO, TX, p. A674
EL PASO CHILDREN'S HOSPITAL, EL PASO, TX, p. A674
EL PASO LTAC HOSPITAL, EL PASO, TX, p. A675
EL PASO PSYCHIATRIC CENTER, EL PASO, TX, p. A675
ELBERT MEMORIAL HOSPITAL, ELBERTON, GA, p. A172
ELEAH MEDICAL CENTER, ELBOW LAKE, MN, p. A376
ELEANOR SLATER HOSPITAL, CRANSTON, RI, p. A613
ELECTRA MEMORIAL HOSPITAL, ELECTRA, TX, p. A676
ELGIN MENTAL HEALTH CENTER, ELGIN, IL, p. A203
ELIZA COFFEE MEMORIAL HOSPITAL, FLORENCE, AL, p. A18
ELIZABETH SETON PEDIATRIC CENTER, YONKERS, NY, p. A502
ELIZABETHTOWN COMMUNITY HOSPITAL, ELIZABETHTOWN, NY, p. A483
ELK REGIONAL HEALTH CENTER, SAINT MARYS, PA, p. A606
ELKHART GENERAL HEALTHCARE SYSTEM, ELKHART, IN, p. A227
ELKHART GENERAL HOSPITAL, ELKHART, IN, p. A227
ELKHORN VALLEY REHABILITATION HOSPITAL, CASPER, WY, p. A801
ELKO GENERAL HOSPITAL, ELKO, NV, p. A441
ELKS REHAB HOSPITAL, BOISE, ID, p. A188
ELKVIEW GENERAL HOSPITAL, HOBART, OK, p. A560
ELLENVILLE COMMUNITY HOSPITAL, ELLENVILLE, NY, p. A483
ELLENVILLE REGIONAL HOSPITAL, ELLENVILLE, NY, p. A483
ELLETT MEMORIAL HOSPITAL, APPLETON CITY, MO, p. A402
ELLINWOOD DISTRICT HOSPITAL, ELLINWOOD, KS, p. A264
ELLIOT HOSPITAL, MANCHESTER, NH, p. A450
ELLIS FISCHEL CANCER CENTER, COLUMBIA, MO, p. A405
ELLIS FISCHEL CANCER CTR, COLUMBIA, MO, p. A405
ELLIS HOSPITAL, SCHENECTADY, NY, p. A498

ELLIS HOSPITAL HEALTH CENTER, SCHENECTADY, NY, p. A498
ELLIS HOSPITAL MCCLELLAN CAMPUS, SCHENECTADY, NY, p. A498
ELLSWORTH COUNTY HOSPITAL, ELLSWORTH, KS, p. A264
ELLSWORTH COUNTY MEDICAL CENTER, ELLSWORTH, KS, p. A264
ELLSWORTH MUNICIPAL HOSPITAL, IOWA FALLS, IA, p. A252
ELMHURST HOSPITAL, ELMHURST, IL, p. A204
ELMHURST HOSPITAL CENTER, ELMHURST, NY, p. A483
ELMHURST MEMORIAL HOSPITAL, ELMHURST, IL, p. A204
ELMIRA PSYCHIATRIC CENTER, ELMIRA, NY, p. A483
ELMORE COMMUNITY HOSPITAL, WETUMPKA, AL, p. A26
ELMORE MEDICAL CENTER, MOUNTAIN HOME, ID, p. A191
ELMWOOD HEALTHCARE CENTER AT THE SPRINGS, GREEN SPRINGS, OH, p. A541
ELY-BLOOMENSON COMMUNITY HOSPITAL, ELY, MN, p. A376
EMANATE HEALTH FOOTHILL PRESBYTERIAN HOSPITAL, GLENDORA, CA, p. A67
EMANATE HEALTH INTER-COMMUNITY HOSPITAL, COVINA, CA, p. A61
EMANUEL MEDICAL CENTER, SWAINSBORO, GA, p. A181
EMANUEL MEDICAL CENTER, TURLOCK, CA, p. A102
EMANUEL MEDICAL HOSPITAL, SWAINSBORO, GA, p. A181
EMCOMPASS HEALTH REHABILITATION HOSPITAL OF ALEXANDRIA, ALEXANDRIA, LA, p. A295
EMCOMPASS HEALTH SCOTTSDALE REHABILITATION HOSPITAL, SCOTTSDALE, AZ, p. A38
EMERALD COAST BEHAVIORAL HOSPITAL, PANAMA CITY, FL, p. A152
EMERALD COAST HOSPITAL, APALACHICOLA, FL, p. A131
EMERALD-HODGSON HOSPITAL, SEWANEE, TN, p. A649
EMERSON HOSPITAL, CONCORD, MA, p. A338
EMERUS HOSPITAL—SUGAR LAND, SUGAR LAND, TX, p. A717
EMINENT MEDICAL CENTER, RICHARDSON, TX, p. A708
EMMA PENDLETON BRADLEY HOSPITAL, EAST PROVIDENCE, RI, p. A613
EMORY CARTERSVILLE MEDICAL CTR, CARTERSVILLE, GA, p. A168
EMORY CRAWFORD LONG HOSPITAL, ATLANTA, GA, p. A164
EMORY DECATUR HOSPITAL, DECATUR, GA, p. A171
EMORY DUNWOODY MEDICAL CTR, JOHNS CREEK, GA, p. A174
EMORY EASTSIDE MEDICAL CENTER, SNELLVILLE, GA, p. A180
EMORY HILLANDALE HOSPITAL, LITHONIA, GA, p. A175
EMORY JOHNS CREEK HOSPITAL, JOHNS CREEK, GA, p. A174
EMORY LONG-TERM ACUTE CARE, DECATUR, GA, p. A171
EMORY REHABILITATION HOSPITAL, ATLANTA, GA, p. A164
EMORY SAINT JOSEPH'S HOSPITAL OF ATLANTA, ATLANTA, GA, p. A164
EMORY UNIVERSITY HOSPITAL, ATLANTA, GA, p. A164
EMORY UNIVERSITY HOSPITAL MIDTOWN, ATLANTA, GA, p. A164
ENCINO HOSPITAL MEDICAL CENTER, ENCINO, CA, p. A63
ENCINO-TARZANA REG MED CENTER, ENCINO, CA, p. A63
ENCINO-TARZANA REG MED CENTER, TARZANA, CA, p. A100
ENCOMPASS HEALTH DEACONESS REHABILITATION HOSPITAL, NEWBURGH, IN, p. A238
ENCOMPASS HEALTH HARMARVILLE REHABILITATION HOSPITAL, PITTSBURGH, PA, p. A602
ENCOMPASS HEALTH LAKESHORE REHABILITATION HOSPITAL, BIRMINGHAM, AL, p. A15
ENCOMPASS HEALTH NITTANY VALLEY REHABILITATION HOSPITAL, PLEASANT GAP, PA, p. A605
ENCOMPASS HEALTH READING REHABILITATION HOSPITAL, READING, PA, p. A606
ENCOMPASS HEALTH REHABILITATION HOSPITAL AN AFFILIATE OF MARTIN HEALTH, STUART, FL, p. A158
ENCOMPASS HEALTH REHABILITATION HOSPITAL AT CINCINNATI, CINCINNATI, OH, p. A532
ENCOMPASS HEALTH REHABILITATION HOSPITAL MIDLAND ODESSA, MIDLAND, TX, p. A701
ENCOMPASS HEALTH REHABILITATION HOSPITAL OF ABILENE, ABILENE, TX, p. A651
ENCOMPASS HEALTH REHABILITATION HOSPITAL OF ALBUQUERQUE, ALBUQUERQUE, NM, p. A467
ENCOMPASS HEALTH REHABILITATION HOSPITAL OF ALEXANDRIA, ALEXANDRIA, LA, p. A295
ENCOMPASS HEALTH REHABILITATION HOSPITAL OF ALTAMONTE SPRINGS, ALTAMONTE SPRINGS, FL, p. A131
ENCOMPASS HEALTH REHABILITATION HOSPITAL OF ALTOONA, ALTOONA, PA, p. A583
ENCOMPASS HEALTH REHABILITATION HOSPITAL OF ARLINGTON, ARLINGTON, TX, p. A653
ENCOMPASS HEALTH REHABILITATION HOSPITAL OF AUSTIN, AUSTIN, TX, p. A656

ENCOMPASS HEALTH REHABILITATION HOSPITAL OF BAKERSFIELD, BAKERSFIELD, CA, p. A57
ENCOMPASS HEALTH REHABILITATION HOSPITAL OF BRAINTREE, BRAINTREE, MA, p. A336
ENCOMPASS HEALTH REHABILITATION HOSPITAL OF CHARLESTON, CHARLESTON, SC, p. A616
ENCOMPASS HEALTH REHABILITATION HOSPITAL OF CHATTANOOGA, CHATTANOOGA, TN, p. A635
ENCOMPASS HEALTH REHABILITATION HOSPITAL OF CITY VIEW, FORT WORTH, TX, p. A678
ENCOMPASS HEALTH REHABILITATION HOSPITAL OF COLORADO SPRINGS, COLORADO SPRINGS, CO, p. A109
ENCOMPASS HEALTH REHABILITATION HOSPITAL OF COLUMBIA, COLUMBIA, SC, p. A617
ENCOMPASS HEALTH REHABILITATION HOSPITAL OF CONCORD, CONCORD, NH, p. A448
ENCOMPASS HEALTH REHABILITATION HOSPITAL OF CYPRESS, HOUSTON, TX, p. A685
ENCOMPASS HEALTH REHABILITATION HOSPITAL OF DALLAS, DALLAS, TX, p. A668
ENCOMPASS HEALTH REHABILITATION HOSPITAL OF DESERT CANYON, LAS VEGAS, NV, p. A443
ENCOMPASS HEALTH REHABILITATION HOSPITAL OF DOTHAN, DOTHAN, AL, p. A17
ENCOMPASS HEALTH REHABILITATION HOSPITAL OF EAST, MESA, AZ, p. A34
ENCOMPASS HEALTH REHABILITATION HOSPITAL OF EAST VALLEY, MESA, AZ, p. A34
ENCOMPASS HEALTH REHABILITATION HOSPITAL OF ERIE, ERIE, PA, p. A589
ENCOMPASS HEALTH REHABILITATION HOSPITAL OF FLORENCE, FLORENCE, SC, p. A619
ENCOMPASS HEALTH REHABILITATION HOSPITAL OF FRANKLIN, FRANKLIN, TN, p. A638
ENCOMPASS HEALTH REHABILITATION HOSPITAL OF FREDERICKSBURG, FREDERICKSBURG, VA, p. A742
ENCOMPASS HEALTH REHABILITATION HOSPITAL OF GADSDEN, GADSDEN, AL, p. A19
ENCOMPASS HEALTH REHABILITATION HOSPITAL OF GULFPORT, GULFPORT, MS, p. A393
ENCOMPASS HEALTH REHABILITATION HOSPITAL OF HAMARVILLE, PITTSBURGH, PA, p. A603
ENCOMPASS HEALTH REHABILITATION HOSPITAL OF HENDERSON, HENDERSON, NV, p. A442
ENCOMPASS HEALTH REHABILITATION HOSPITAL OF HUMBLE, HUMBLE, TX, p. A689
ENCOMPASS HEALTH REHABILITATION HOSPITAL OF HUNTINGTON, HUNTINGTON, WV, p. A773
ENCOMPASS HEALTH REHABILITATION HOSPITAL OF JONESBORO, JONESBORO, AR, p. A47
ENCOMPASS HEALTH REHABILITATION HOSPITAL OF KATY, KATY, TX, p. A691
ENCOMPASS HEALTH REHABILITATION HOSPITAL OF KINGSPORT, KINGSPORT, TN, p. A640
ENCOMPASS HEALTH REHABILITATION HOSPITAL OF LARGO, LARGO, FL, p. A143
ENCOMPASS HEALTH REHABILITATION HOSPITAL OF LAS VEGAS, LAS VEGAS, NV, p. A443
ENCOMPASS HEALTH REHABILITATION HOSPITAL OF LITTLETON, LITTLETON, CO, p. A115
ENCOMPASS HEALTH REHABILITATION HOSPITAL OF MANATI, MANATI, PR, p. A808
ENCOMPASS HEALTH REHABILITATION HOSPITAL OF MECHANICSBURG, MECHANICSBURG, PA, p. A596
ENCOMPASS HEALTH REHABILITATION HOSPITAL OF MEMPHIS, MEMPHIS, TN, p. A644
ENCOMPASS HEALTH REHABILITATION HOSPITAL OF MIAMI, CUTLER BAY, FL, p. A135
ENCOMPASS HEALTH REHABILITATION HOSPITAL OF MIDDLETOWN, MIDDLETOWN, DE, p. A127
ENCOMPASS HEALTH REHABILITATION HOSPITAL OF MODESTO, MODESTO, CA, p. A78
ENCOMPASS HEALTH REHABILITATION HOSPITAL OF MONTGOMERY, MONTGOMERY, AL, p. A22
ENCOMPASS HEALTH REHABILITATION HOSPITAL OF MORGANTOWN, MORGANTOWN, WV, p. A774
ENCOMPASS HEALTH REHABILITATION HOSPITAL OF NEW ENGLAND, WOBURN, MA, p. A346
ENCOMPASS HEALTH REHABILITATION HOSPITAL OF NEWNAN, NEWNAN, GA, p. A178
ENCOMPASS HEALTH REHABILITATION HOSPITAL OF NORTH MEMPHIS, MEMPHIS, TN, p. A644
ENCOMPASS HEALTH REHABILITATION HOSPITAL OF NORTH MEMPHIS-NORTH, MEMPHIS, TN, p. A644
ENCOMPASS HEALTH REHABILITATION HOSPITAL OF NORTHERN KENTUCKY, EDGEWOOD, KY, p. A282
ENCOMPASS HEALTH REHABILITATION HOSPITAL OF NORTHERN VIRGINIA, ALDIE, VA, p. A738
ENCOMPASS HEALTH REHABILITATION HOSPITAL OF NORTHWEST TUCSON, TUCSON, AZ, p. A40

ENCOMPASS HEALTH REHABILITATION HOSPITAL OF OCALA, OCALA, FL, p. A150
ENCOMPASS HEALTH REHABILITATION HOSPITAL OF PANAMA CITY, PANAMA CITY, FL, p. A153
ENCOMPASS HEALTH REHABILITATION HOSPITAL OF PARKERSBURG, PARKERSBURG, WV, p. A775
ENCOMPASS HEALTH REHABILITATION HOSPITAL OF PEARLAND, PEARLAND, TX, p. A705
ENCOMPASS HEALTH REHABILITATION HOSPITAL OF PETERSBURG, PETERSBURG, VA, p. A748
ENCOMPASS HEALTH REHABILITATION HOSPITAL OF PLANO, PLANO, TX, p. A707
ENCOMPASS HEALTH REHABILITATION HOSPITAL OF PRINCETON, PRINCETON, WV, p. A776
ENCOMPASS HEALTH REHABILITATION HOSPITAL OF RICHARDSON, RICHARDSON, TX, p. A708
ENCOMPASS HEALTH REHABILITATION HOSPITAL OF RICHMOND, RICHMOND, VA, p. A750
ENCOMPASS HEALTH REHABILITATION HOSPITAL OF ROCK HILL, ROCK HILL, SC, p. A623
ENCOMPASS HEALTH REHABILITATION HOSPITAL OF ROUND ROCK, ROUND ROCK, TX, p. A709
ENCOMPASS HEALTH REHABILITATION HOSPITAL OF SALISBURY, SALISBURY, MD, p. A332
ENCOMPASS HEALTH REHABILITATION HOSPITAL OF SAN ANTONIO (RIOSA), SAN ANTONIO, TX, p. A711
ENCOMPASS HEALTH REHABILITATION HOSPITAL OF SAN ANTONIO, SAN ANTONIO, TX, p. A711
ENCOMPASS HEALTH REHABILITATION HOSPITAL OF SAN JUAN, SAN JUAN, PR, p. A810
ENCOMPASS HEALTH REHABILITATION HOSPITAL OF SARASOTA, SARASOTA, FL, p. A157
ENCOMPASS HEALTH REHABILITATION HOSPITAL OF SAVANNAH, SAVANNAH, GA, p. A180
ENCOMPASS HEALTH REHABILITATION HOSPITAL OF SCOTTSDALE, SCOTTSDALE, AZ, p. A38
ENCOMPASS HEALTH REHABILITATION HOSPITAL OF SEWICKLEY, SEWICKLEY, PA, p. A607
ENCOMPASS HEALTH REHABILITATION HOSPITAL OF SHELBY COUNTY, PELHAM, AL, p. A23
ENCOMPASS HEALTH REHABILITATION HOSPITAL OF SIOUX FALLS, SIOUX FALLS, SD, p. A631
ENCOMPASS HEALTH REHABILITATION HOSPITAL OF SPRING HILL, BROOKSVILLE, FL, p. A133
ENCOMPASS HEALTH REHABILITATION HOSPITAL OF SUGAR LAND, SUGAR LAND, TX, p. A717
ENCOMPASS HEALTH REHABILITATION HOSPITAL OF SUNRISE, SUNRISE, FL, p. A158
ENCOMPASS HEALTH REHABILITATION HOSPITAL OF TALLAHASSEE, TALLAHASSEE, FL, p. A158
ENCOMPASS HEALTH REHABILITATION HOSPITAL OF TEXARKANA, TEXARKANA, TX, p. A720
ENCOMPASS HEALTH REHABILITATION HOSPITAL OF THE MID-CITIES, BEDFORD, TX, p. A658
ENCOMPASS HEALTH REHABILITATION HOSPITAL OF TINTON FALLS, TINTON FALLS, NJ, p. A464
ENCOMPASS HEALTH REHABILITATION HOSPITAL OF TOMS RIVER, TOMS RIVER, NJ, p. A464
ENCOMPASS HEALTH REHABILITATION HOSPITAL OF TREASURE COAST, VERO BEACH, FL, p. A161
ENCOMPASS HEALTH REHABILITATION HOSPITAL OF TUSTIN, TUSTIN, CA, p. A102
ENCOMPASS HEALTH REHABILITATION HOSPITAL OF UTAH, SANDY, UT, p. A733
ENCOMPASS HEALTH REHABILITATION HOSPITAL OF VINELAND, VINELAND, NJ, p. A465
ENCOMPASS HEALTH REHABILITATION HOSPITAL OF VIRGINIA, RICHMOND, VA, p. A750
ENCOMPASS HEALTH REHABILITATION HOSPITAL OF WESTERN MASSACHUSETTS, LUDLOW, MA, p. A341
ENCOMPASS HEALTH REHABILITATION HOSPITAL OF WICHITA FALLS, WICHITA FALLS, TX, p. A725
ENCOMPASS HEALTH REHABILITATION HOSPITAL OF YORK, YORK, PA, p. A612
ENCOMPASS HEALTH REHABILITATION HOSPITAL THE VINTAGE, HOUSTON, TX, p. A685
ENCOMPASS HEALTH REHABILITATION HOSPITAL THE WOODLANDS, CONROE, TX, p. A665
ENCOMPASS HEALTH REHABILITATION HOSPITAL VISION PARK, SHENANDOAH, TX, p. A715
ENCOMPASS HEALTH REHABILITATION HOSPITAL, A PARTNER OF WASHINGTON REGIONAL, FAYETTEVILLE, AR, p. A45
ENCOMPASS HEALTH REHABILITATION INSTITUTE OF TUCSON, TUCSON, AZ, p. A40
ENCOMPASS HEALTH VALLEY OF THE SUN REHABILITATION HOSPITAL, GLENDALE, AZ, p. A32
ENCOMPASS REHABILITATION HOSPITAL OF LAKEVIEW, ELIZABETHTOWN, KY, p. A282
ENCOMPASS REHABILITATION HOSPITAL OF NORTH ALABAMA, HUNTSVILLE, AL, p. A20

ENCOMPASS VALLEY OF THE SUN REHABILITATION HOSPITAL, GLENDALE, AZ, p. A32
ENCOMPASS HEALTH REHABILITATION HOSPITAL OF FORT SMITH, FORT SMITH, AR, p. A46
ENDLESS MOUNTAIN HEALTH SYSTEMS, MONTROSE, PA, p. A597
ENGLEWOOD COMMUNITY HOSPITAL, ENGLEWOOD, FL, p. A137
ENGLEWOOD HEALTH, ENGLEWOOD, NJ, p. A455
ENGLEWOOD HOSPITAL AND MEDICAL CENTER, ENGLEWOOD, NJ, p. A455
ENLOE MEDICAL CENTER, CHICO, CA, p. A60
ENNIS REGIONAL MEDICAL CENTER, ENNIS, TX, p. A677
ENUMCLAW REGIONAL HOSPITAL, ENUMCLAW, WA, p. A758
EPHRAIM MCDOWELL FORT LOGAN HOSPITAL, STANFORD, KY, p. A293
EPHRAIM MCDOWELL JAMES B. HAGGIN MEMORIAL HOSPITAL, HARRODSBURG, KY, p. A284
EPHRAIM MCDOWELL REGIONAL MEDICAL CENTER, DANVILLE, KY, p. A282
EPHRATA COMMUNITY HOSPITAL, EPHRATA, PA, p. A589
EPISCOPAL HOSPITAL, PHILADELPHIA, PA, p. A600
ERIE COUNTY MEDICAL CENTER, BUFFALO, NY, p. A479
ERIE VETERANS AFFAIRS MEDICAL CENTER, ERIE, PA, p. A589
ERLANGER BEHAVIORAL HOSPITAL, CHATTANOOGA, TN, p. A635
ERLANGER BLEDSOE HOSPITAL, PIKEVILLE, TN, p. A648
ERLANGER HEALTH SYSTEM, CHATTANOOGA, TN, p. A635
ERLANGER MEDICAL CENTER, CHATTANOOGA, TN, p. A635
ERLANGER MURPHY MEDICAL CENTER, MURPHY, NC, p. A515
ERLANGER WESTERN CAROLINA HOSPITAL, MURPHY, NC, p. A515
ERLANGER WOMEN'S EAST HOSPITAL, CHATTANOOGA, TN, p. A635
ESKENAZI HEALTH, INDIANAPOLIS, IN, p. A231
ESPANOLA HOSPITAL, ESPANOLA, NM, p. A469
ESSENTIA HEALTH—ST. JOSEPH'S MEDICAL CENTER, BRAINERD, MN, p. A373
ESSENTIA HEALTH, FARGO, ND, p. A522
ESSENTIA HEALTH ADA, ADA, MN, p. A371
ESSENTIA HEALTH DULUTH, DULUTH, MN, p. A375
ESSENTIA HEALTH FARGO, FARGO, ND, p. A522
ESSENTIA HEALTH FOSSTON, FOSSTON, MN, p. A376
ESSENTIA HEALTH MOOSE LAKE, MOOSE LAKE, MN, p. A381
ESSENTIA HEALTH NORTHERN PINES, AURORA, MN, p. A372
ESSENTIA HEALTH NORTHERN PINES MEDICAL CENTER, AURORA, MN, p. A372
ESSENTIA HEALTH SANDSTONE, SANDSTONE, MN, p. A385
ESSENTIA HEALTH ST. MARY'S—DETROIT LAKES, DETROIT LAKES, MN, p. A375
ESSENTIA HEALTH ST. MARY'S HOSPITAL—DETROIT LAKES, DETROIT LAKES, MN, p. A375
ESSENTIA HEALTH ST. MARY'S HOSPITAL OF SUPERIOR, SUPERIOR, WI, p. A797
ESSENTIA HEALTH ST. MARY'S MEDICAL CENTER, DULUTH, MN, p. A375
ESSENTIA HEALTH-ADA, ADA, MN, p. A371
ESSENTIA HEALTH-DEER RIVER, DEER RIVER, MN, p. A375
ESSENTIA HEALTH-FOSSTON, FOSSTON, MN, p. A376
ESSENTIA HEALTH-GRACEVILLE, GRACEVILLE, MN, p. A377
ESSENTIA HEALTH-HOLY TRINITY HOSPITAL, GRACEVILLE, MN, p. A377
ESSENTIA HEALTH-ST. JOSEPH'S MEDICAL CENTER, BRAINERD, MN, p. A373
ESSENTIA HEALTH-VIRGINIA, VIRGINIA, MN, p. A387
ESSEX COUNTY HOSPITAL CENTER, CEDAR GROVE, NJ, p. A453
ESTES PARK MEDICAL CENTER, ESTES PARK, CO, p. A112
EUCLID HOSPITAL, EUCLID, OH, p. A540
EUNICE COMMUNITY MEDICAL CTR, EUNICE, LA, p. A301
EUREKA COMMUNITY HEALTH SERVICES AVERA, EUREKA, SD, p. A628
EUREKA COMMUNITY HOSPITAL, EUREKA, IL, p. A204
EUREKA COMMUNITY HOSPITAL, EUREKA, SD, p. A628
EUREKA HOSPITAL, EUREKA, IL, p. A204
EUREKA SPRINGS HOSPITAL, EUREKA SPRINGS, AR, p. A45
EVANGELICAL COMMUNITY HOSPITAL, LEWISBURG, PA, p. A595
EVANS MEMORIAL HOSPITAL, CLAXTON, GA, p. A168
EVANS U. S. ARMY COMMUNITY HOSPITAL, FORT CARSON, CO, p. A112
EVANSTON HOSPITAL, EVANSTON, IL, p. A204
EVANSTON REGIONAL HOSPITAL, EVANSTON, WY, p. A802
EVANSVILLE PSYCH CHILDREN CNTR, EVANSVILLE, IN, p. A227
EVANSVILLE PSYCHIATRIC CHILDREN CENTER, EVANSVILLE, IN, p. A227

EVANSVILLE STATE HOSPITAL, EVANSVILLE, IN, p. A227
EVAN'S U S ARMY COMM HOSPITAL, FORT CARSON, CO, p. A112
EVENDALE MEDICAL CENTER, CINCINNATI, OH, p. A532
EVEREST REHABILITATION HOSPITAL LONGVIEW, LONGVIEW, TX, p. A696
EVEREST REHABILITATION HOSPITAL TEMPLE, TEMPLE, TX, p. A719
EVERETT TOWER, OKLAHOMA CITY, OK, p. A564
EVERGREEN HOSPITAL MEDICAL CENTER, KIRKLAND, WA, p. A759
EVERGREEN MED CTR, EVERGREEN, AL, p. A18
EVERGREEN MEDICAL CENTER, EVERGREEN, AL, p. A18
EVERGREENHEALTH, KIRKLAND, WA, p. A759
EVERGREENHEALTH MONROE, MONROE, WA, p. A760
EXCELA FRICK HOSPITAL, MOUNT PLEASANT, PA, p. A598
EXCELA HEALTH WESTMORELAND HOSPITAL, GREENSBURG, PA, p. A591
EXCELA LATROBE AREA HOSPITAL, LATROBE, PA, p. A594
EXCELA WESTMORELAND REGIONAL HOSPITAL, GREENSBURG, PA, p. A591
EXCELSIOR SPRINGS HOSPITAL, EXCELSIOR SPRINGS, MO, p. A406
EXCELSIOR SPRINGS MEDICAL CENTER, EXCELSIOR SPRINGS, MO, p. A406
EXEMPLA GOOD SAMARITAN MEDICAL CENTER, LAFAYETTE, CO, p. A115
EXEMPLA LUTHERAN MEDICAL CENTER, WHEAT RIDGE, CO, p. A119
EXEMPLA SAINT JOSEPH HOSPITAL, DENVER, CO, p. A110
EXETER HOSPITAL, EXETER, NH, p. A449
EXTENDED CARE HOSPITAL, NEW ORLEANS, LA, p. A310
EYE AND EAR CLINIC OF CHARLESTON, CHARLESTON, WV, p. A771
EYE AND EAR HOSPITAL OF PITTSBURGH, PITTSBURGH, PA, p. A603

# F

FAIR OAKS HOSPITAL, DELRAY BEACH, FL, p. A136
FAIR OAKS HOSPITAL, FAIRFAX, VA, p. A741
FAIRBANKS, INDIANAPOLIS, IN, p. A232
FAIRBANKS HOSPITAL, INDIANAPOLIS, IN, p. A232
FAIRBANKS MEMORIAL HOSPITAL, FAIRBANKS, AK, p. A28
FAIRCHILD MEDICAL CENTER, YREKA, CA, p. A106
FAIRFAX BEHAVIORAL HEALTH, KIRKLAND, WA, p. A759
FAIRFAX COMMUNITY HOSPITAL, FAIRFAX, OK, p. A559
FAIRFAX HOSPITAL, FALLS CHURCH, VA, p. A741
FAIRFAX HOSPITAL, KIRKLAND, WA, p. A759
FAIRFAX MEMORIAL HOSPITAL, FAIRFAX, OK, p. A559
FAIRFIELD MEDICAL CENTER, LANCASTER, OH, p. A542
FAIRFIELD MEDICAL CENTER, YREKA, CA, p. A106
FAIRFIELD MEMORIAL HOSPITAL, FAIRFIELD, IL, p. A205
FAIRLAWN REHABILITATION HOSPITAL, WORCESTER, MA, p. A346
FAIRMONT HOSPITAL, SAN LEANDRO, CA, p. A95
FAIRMONT MEDICAL CENTER-MAYO HEALTH SYSTEM, FAIRMONT, MN, p. A376
FAIRMOUNT BEHAVIORAL HEALTH SYSTEM, PHILADELPHIA, PA, p. A600
FAIRVIEW DEVELOPMENTAL CENTER, COSTA MESA, CA, p. A61
FAIRVIEW HOSPITAL, CLEVELAND, OH, p. A534
FAIRVIEW HOSPITAL, FAIRVIEW, OK, p. A559
FAIRVIEW HOSPITAL, GREAT BARRINGTON, MA, p. A339
FAIRVIEW LAKES HEALTH SERVICES, WYOMING, MN, p. A388
FAIRVIEW LAKES REGIONAL HEALTH CARE, WYOMING, MN, p. A388
FAIRVIEW NORTHLAND HEALTH SERV, PRINCETON, MN, p. A383
FAIRVIEW NORTHLAND MEDICAL CENTER, PRINCETON, MN, p. A383
FAIRVIEW PARK HOSPITAL, DUBLIN, GA, p. A172
FAIRVIEW RANGE MEDICAL CENTER, HIBBING, MN, p. A378
FAIRVIEW RED WING MEDICAL CENTER, RED WING, MN, p. A383
FAIRVIEW REGIONAL MEDICAL CENTER, FAIRVIEW, OK, p. A559
FAIRVIEW RIDGES HOSPITAL, BURNSVILLE, MN, p. A373
FAIRVIEW RIVERSIDE HOSPITAL, MINNEAPOLIS, MN, p. A380
FAIRVIEW SOUTHDALE HOSPITAL, EDINA, MN, p. A376
FAIRVIEW-UNIVERSITY MED CENTER, MINNEAPOLIS, MN, p. A380
FAIRWAY MEDICAL SURGICAL HOSPITAL, COVINGTON, LA, p. A300

FAITH COMMUNITY HOSPITAL, JACKSBORO, TX, p. A691
FAITH REGIONAL HEALTH SERVICES, NORFOLK, NE, p. A435
FALL RIVER HOSPITAL, HOT SPRINGS, SD, p. A628
FALLON MEDICAL COMPLEX, BAKER, MT, p. A421
FALLS COMM HOSP & CLINIC, MARLIN, TX, p. A699
FALLS COMMUNITY HOSPITAL AND CLINIC, MARLIN, TX, p. A699
FALMOUTH HOSPITAL, FALMOUTH, MA, p. A339
FAMILY HEALTH WEST, FRUITA, CO, p. A113
FANNIN REGIONAL HOSPITAL, BLUE RIDGE, GA, p. A167
FANNY ALLEN CAMPUS, COLCHESTER, VT, p. A736
FARGO NURSING HOME, FARGO, ND, p. A522
FARGO VETERANS AFFAIRS HEALTH CARE SYSTEM, FARGO, ND, p. A523
FARREN MEMORIAL HOSPITAL, TURNERS FALLS, MA, p. A345
FAULK COUNTY MEMORIAL HOSPITAL, FAULKTON, SD, p. A628
FAULKNER HOSPITAL, BOSTON, MA, p. A335
FAULKTON AREA MEDICAL CENTER, FAULKTON, SD, p. A628
FAUQUIER HOSPITAL, WARRENTON, VA, p. A753
FAWCETT MEMORIAL HOSPITAL, PORT CHARLOTTE, FL, p. A155
FAXTON ST. LUKE'S HEALTHCARE, UTICA, NY, p. A500
FAXTON-ST LUKE'S HEALTHCARE, UTICA, NY, p. A500
FAXTON-ST. LUKE'S HEALTHCARE, UTICA, NY, p. A500
FAYETTE COMMUNITY HOSPITAL, FAYETTEVILLE, GA, p. A172
FAYETTE COUNTY HOSPITAL & HOME, FAYETTE, AL, p. A18
FAYETTE COUNTY HOSPITAL & LTC, VANDALIA, IL, p. A222
FAYETTE COUNTY HOSPITAL, VANDALIA, IL, p. A222
FAYETTE COUNTY MEMORIAL HOSPITAL, WASHINGTON COURT HOUSE, OH, p. A552
FAYETTE MEDICAL CENTER, FAYETTE, AL, p. A18
FAYETTE MEMORIAL HOSPITAL, LA GRANGE, TX, p. A694
FAYETTEVILLE VETERANS AFFAIRS MEDICAL CENTER, FAYETTEVILLE, NC, p. A510
FEDERAL CORRECTIONAL INSTITUTE HOSPITAL, LITTLETON, CO, p. A116
FEDERAL MEDICAL CENTER, LEXINGTON, KY, p. A286
FERGUS FALLS COMM BEHAV HOSP, FERGUS FALLS, MN, p. A376
FERRELL HOSPITAL, ELDORADO, IL, p. A203
FERRELL HOSPITAL COMMUNITY FDN, ELDORADO, IL, p. A203
FERRY COUNTY MEMORIAL HOSPITAL, REPUBLIC, WA, p. A763
F. F. THOMPSON HOSPITAL, CANANDAIGUA, NY, p. A481
FHN MEMORIAL HOSPITAL, FREEPORT, IL, p. A205
FIELD MEMORIAL COMMUNITY HOSPITAL, CENTREVILLE, MS, p. A390
FILLMORE COMMUNITY HOSPITAL, FILLMORE, UT, p. A728
FILLMORE COMMUNITY MEDICAL CENTER, FILLMORE, UT, p. A728
FILLMORE COUNTY HOSPITAL, GENEVA, NE, p. A432
FINGER LAKES HOSPITAL, GENEVA, NY, p. A484
FIRELANDS COMMUNITY HOSPITAL, SANDUSKY, OH, p. A548
FIRELANDS REGIONAL HEALTH SYSTEM, SANDUSKY, OH, p. A549
FIRELANDS REGIONAL MEDICAL CTR, SANDUSKY, OH, p. A549
FIRST BAPTIST MEDICAL CENTER, DALLAS, TX, p. A668
FIRST CARE HEALTH CENTER, PARK RIVER, ND, p. A525
FIRST HOSPITAL PANAMERICANO, CIDRA, PR, p. A807
FIRST HOSPITAL WYOMING VALLEY, KINGSTON, PA, p. A593
FIRST STREET HOSPITAL, BELLAIRE, TX, p. A659
FIRST SURGICAL HOSPITAL, BELLAIRE, TX, p. A659
FIRSTHEALTH MONTGOMERY HOSP, TROY, NC, p. A519
FIRSTHEALTH MONTGOMERY MEMORIAL HOSPITAL, TROY, NC, p. A519
FIRSTHEALTH MOORE REG HOSP, PINEHURST, NC, p. A516
FIRSTHEALTH MOORE REGIONAL HOSPITAL, PINEHURST, NC, p. A516
FIRSTHEALTH RICHMOND MEMORIAL HOSPITAL, ROCKINGHAM, NC, p. A517
FIRSTLIGHT HEALTH SYSTEM, MORA, MN, p. A381
FISHER COUNTY HOSPITAL DISTRICT, ROTAN, TX, p. A709
FISHER-TITUS MEDICAL CENTER, NORWALK, OH, p. A546
FISHERMEN'S HOSPITAL, MARATHON, FL, p. A144
FITZGERALD MERCY HOSPITAL, DARBY, PA, p. A588
FITZGIBBON HOSPITAL, MARSHALL, MO, p. A411
FIVE RIVERS MEDICAL CENTER, POCAHONTAS, AR, p. A52
FLAGET MEMORIAL HOSPITAL, BARDSTOWN, KY, p. A280
FLAGLER HOSPITAL, SAINT AUGUSTINE, FL, p. A155
FLAGSTAFF MEDICAL CENTER, FLAGSTAFF, AZ, p. A31
FLAMBEAU HOSPITAL, PARK FALLS, WI, p. A794
FLAMBEAU MEDICAL CENTER, PARK FALLS, WI, p. A794
FLEMING COUNTY HOSPITAL, FLEMINGSBURG, KY, p. A283
FLINT RIVER COMMUNITY HOSPITAL, MONTEZUMA, GA, p. A177

FLORIDA HOSPITAL, ORLANDO, FL, p. A151
FLORIDA HOSPITAL AT CONNERTON LONG TERM ACUTE CARE, LAND O'LAKES, FL, p. A143
FLORIDA HOSPITAL CARROLLWOOD, TAMPA, FL, p. A159
FLORIDA HOSPITAL CELEBRATION HEALTH, CELEBRATION, FL, p. A134
FLORIDA HOSPITAL DADE CITY, DADE CITY, FL, p. A135
FLORIDA HOSPITAL DELAND, DELAND, FL, p. A136
FLORIDA HOSPITAL EAST ORLANDO, ORLANDO, FL, p. A151
FLORIDA HOSPITAL FISH MEMORIAL, ORANGE CITY, FL, p. A150
FLORIDA HOSPITAL FLAGLER, PALM COAST, FL, p. A152
FLORIDA HOSPITAL FOR CHILDREN-WALT DISNEY PAVILION, ORLANDO, FL, p. A151
FLORIDA HOSPITAL HEARTLAND MEDICAL CENTER, SEBRING, FL, p. A157
FLORIDA HOSPITAL KISSIMMEE, KISSIMMEE, FL, p. A142
FLORIDA HOSPITAL MEMORIAL MEDICAL CENTER, DAYTONA BEACH, FL, p. A136
FLORIDA HOSPITAL NEW SMYRNA, NEW SMYRNA BEACH, FL, p. A149
FLORIDA HOSPITAL NORTH PINELLAS, TARPON SPRINGS, FL, p. A160
FLORIDA HOSPITAL OCALA, OCALA, FL, p. A150
FLORIDA HOSPITAL TAMPA, TAMPA, FL, p. A159
FLORIDA HOSPITAL WATERMAN, TAVARES, FL, p. A160
FLORIDA HOSPITAL WAUCHULA, WAUCHULA, FL, p. A161
FLORIDA HOSPITAL WESLEY CHAPEL, WESLEY CHAPEL, FL, p. A162
FLORIDA HOSPITAL ZEPHYRHILLS, ZEPHYRHILLS, FL, p. A162
FLORIDA HOSPITAL-ALTAMONTE, ALTAMONTE SPRINGS, FL, p. A131
FLORIDA HOSPITAL-APOPKA, APOPKA, FL, p. A131
FLORIDA STATE HOSPITAL, CHATTAHOOCHEE, FL, p. A134
FLOWER HOSPITAL, SYLVANIA, OH, p. A550
FLOWERS HOSPITAL, DOTHAN, AL, p. A17
FLOYD CHEROKEE MEDICAL CENTER, CENTRE, AL, p. A16
FLOYD COUNTY MEDICAL CENTER, CHARLES CITY, IA, p. A245
FLOYD COUNTY MEMORIAL HOSPITAL, CHARLES CITY, IA, p. A245
FLOYD MEDICAL CENTER, ROME, GA, p. A179
FLOYD MEMORIAL HOSPITAL AND HEALTH SERVICES, NEW ALBANY, IN, p. A237
FLOYD VALLEY HEALTHCARE, LE MARS, IA, p. A253
FLOYD VALLEY HOSPITAL, LE MARS, IA, p. A253
FLUSHING HOSP MEDICAL CENTER, FLUSHING, NY, p. A484
FLUSHING HOSPITAL MEDICAL CENTER, FLUSHING, NY, p. A484
FOCUS BY-THE-SEA, SAINT SIMONS ISLAND, GA, p. A179
FOND DU LAC CNTY MENTAL HLTH, FOND DU LAC, WI, p. A783
FOND DU LAC COUNTY MENTAL HEALTH CENTER, FOND DU LAC, WI, p. A784
FONTANA MEDICAL CENTER, FONTANA, CA, p. A64
FOOTHILL PRESBYTERIAN HOSPITAL, GLENDORA, CA, p. A67
FOOTHILL REGIONAL MEDICAL CENTER, TUSTIN, CA, p. A102
FORBES HOSPITAL, MONROEVILLE, PA, p. A597
FORBES REGIONAL HOSPITAL, MONROEVILLE, PA, p. A597
FOREST GROVE COMM HOSPITAL, FOREST GROVE, OR, p. A575
FOREST HEALTH MEDICAL CENTER, YPSILANTI, MI, p. A370
FOREST HILLS HOSPITAL, FOREST HILLS, NY, p. A484
FOREST PARK MEDICAL CENTER, FORT WORTH, TX, p. A678
FOREST PARK MEDICAL CENTER-SOUTHLAKE, SOUTHLAKE, TX, p. A716
FOREST SPRINGS HOSPITAL, HOUSTON, TX, p. A685
FOREST VIEW HOSPITAL, GRAND RAPIDS, MI, p. A355
FOREST VIEW PSYCHIATRIC HOSPITAL, GRAND RAPIDS, MI, p. A355
FORKS COMMUNITY HOSPITAL, FORKS, WA, p. A758
FORREST CITY MED CENTER, FORREST CITY, AR, p. A45
FORREST CITY MEDICAL CENTER, FORREST CITY, AR, p. A45
FORREST COUNTY GEN HOSPITAL, HATTIESBURG, MS, p. A393
FORREST GENERAL HOSPITAL, HATTIESBURG, MS, p. A393
FORSYTH MEDICAL CENTER, WINSTON, NC, p. A520
FORT BELKNAP SERVICE UNIT, HARLEM, MT, p. A424
FORT BELKNAP U. S. PUBLIC HEALTH SERVICE INDIAN HOSPITAL, HARLEM, MT, p. A424
FORT BELVOIR COMMUNITY HOSPITAL, FORT BELVOIR, VA, p. A742
FORT DEFIANCE INDIAN HEALTH SERVICE HOSPITAL, FORT DEFIANCE, AZ, p. A31
FORT DUNCAN MEDICAL CENTER, EAGLE PASS, TX, p. A673
FORT DUNCAN REGIONAL MEDICAL CENTER, EAGLE PASS, TX, p. A673
FORT HAMILTON HOSPITAL, HAMILTON, OH, p. A542

FORT HAMILTON-HUGHES MEM HOSP, HAMILTON, OH, p. A542

FORT HEALTHCARE, FORT ATKINSON, WI, p. A784

FORT LAUDERDALE BEHAVIORAL HEALTH CENTER, OAKLAND PARK, FL, p. A149

FORT LAUDERDALE HOSPITAL, OAKLAND PARK, FL, p. A149

FORT LOGAN HOSPITAL, STANFORD, KY, p. A293

FORT LOGAN MENTAL HLTH CENTER, DENVER, CO, p. A110

FORT LOUDOUN MEDICAL CENTER, LENOIR CITY, TN, p. A642

FORT MADISON COMMUNITY HOSPITAL, FORT MADISON, IA, p. A250

FORT MORGAN COMMUNITY HOSPITAL, FORT MORGAN, CO, p. A112

FORT SANDERS LOUDON MED CENTER, LENOIR CITY, TN, p. A642

FORT SANDERS REG MEDICAL CNTR, KNOXVILLE, TN, p. A641

FORT SANDERS REGIONAL MEDICAL CENTER, KNOXVILLE, TN, p. A641

FORT SANDERS-SEVIER MEDICAL CENTER, SEVIERVILLE, TN, p. A649

FORT WALTON BEACH MEDICAL CENTER, FORT WALTON BEACH, FL, p. A138

FORT WASHINGTON HOSPITAL, OXEN HILL, MD, p. A331

FORT WASHINGTON MEDICAL CENTER, OXEN HILL, MD, p. A331

FORUM HEALTH TRUMBULL MEMORIAL HOSPITAL, WARREN, OH, p. A551

FORUM HILLSIDE REHABILITATION HOSPITAL, WARREN, OH, p. A551

FOSTORIA COMMUNITY HOSPITAL, FOSTORIA, OH, p. A540

FOUNDATION BARIATRIC HOSPITAL OF OKLAHOMA, EDMOND, OK, p. A558

FOUNDATION BARIATRIC HOSPITAL OF SAN ANTONIO, SAN ANTONIO, TX, p. A711

FOUNDATION SURGICAL HOSPITAL OF EL PASO, EL PASO, TX, p. A675

FOUNDATION SURGICAL HOSPITAL OF SAN ANTONIO, SAN ANTONIO, TX, p. A711

FOUNDATIONS BEHAVIORAL HEALTH, DOYLESTOWN, PA, p. A588

FOUNTAIN VALLEY REGIONAL HOSPITAL AND MEDICAL CENTER, FOUNTAIN VALLEY, CA, p. A64

FOUNTAIN VLY REG HOSP, FOUNTAIN VALLEY, CA, p. A64

FOUR COUNTY COUNSELING CENTER, LOGANSPORT, IN, p. A235

FOUR WINDS HOSPITAL, KATONAH, NY, p. A486

FOUR WINDS HOSPITAL, SARATOGA SPRINGS, NY, p. A497

FOX CHASE CANCER CENTER-AMERICAN ONCOLOGIC HOSPITAL, PHILADELPHIA, PA, p. A600

FRAMINGTON UNION HOSPITAL, FRAMINGHAM, MA, p. A339

FRANCES MAHON DEACONESS HOSPITAL, GLASGOW, MT, p. A424

FRANCIS SCOTT KEY MED CENTER, BALTIMORE, MD, p. A324

FRANCISCAN—MOORESVILLE, MOORESVILLE, IN, p. A237

FRANCISCAN CHILDREN'S, BRIGHTON, MA, p. A336

FRANCISCAN HEALTH—CARMEL, CARMEL, IN, p. A225

FRANCISCAN HEALTH—INDIANAPOLIS, INDIANAPOLIS, IN, p. A232

FRANCISCAN HEALTH—LAFAYETTE CENTRAL, LAFAYETTE, IN, p. A234

FRANCISCAN HEALTH—MICHIGAN CITY, MICHIGAN CITY, IN, p. A236

FRANCISCAN HEALTH CARMEL, CARMEL, IN, p. A225

FRANCISCAN HEALTH CRAWFORDSVILLE, CRAWFORDSVILLE, IN, p. A226

FRANCISCAN HEALTH CROWN POINT, CROWN POINT, IN, p. A226

FRANCISCAN HEALTH DYER, DYER, IN, p. A226

FRANCISCAN HEALTH HAMMOND, HAMMOND, IN, p. A230

FRANCISCAN HEALTH INDIANAPOLIS, INDIANAPOLIS, IN, p. A232

FRANCISCAN HEALTH LAFAYETTE EAST, LAFAYETTE, IN, p. A234

FRANCISCAN HEALTH MICHIGAN CITY, MICHIGAN CITY, IN, p. A236

FRANCISCAN HEALTH MOORESVILLE, MOORESVILLE, IN, p. A237

FRANCISCAN HEALTH OLYMPIA FIELDS, OLYMPIA FIELDS, IL, p. A215

FRANCISCAN HEALTH RENSSELEAR, RENSSELAER, IN, p. A239

FRANCISCAN HEALTHCARE—MUNSTER, MUNSTER, IN, p. A237

FRANCISCAN HEALTHCARE MUNSTER, MUNSTER, IN, p. A237

FRANCISCAN HOSPITAL FOR CHILDREN, BRIGHTON, MA, p. A336

FRANCISCAN SKEMP HEALTHCARE-LA CROSSE CAMPUS, LA CROSSE, WI, p. A787

FRANCISCAN SKEMP HEALTHCARE-SPARTA CAMPUS, SPARTA, WI, p. A796

FRANCISCAN ST. ANTHONY HEALTH—CROWN POINT, CROWN POINT, IN, p. A226

FRANCISCAN ST. ELIZABETH HEALTH—CRAWFORDSVILLE, CRAWFORDSVILLE, IN, p. A226

FRANCISCAN ST. ELIZABETH HEALTH—LAFAYETTE EAST, LAFAYETTE, IN, p. A234

FRANCISCAN ST. JAMES HOSPITAL AND HEALTH CENTERS, OLYMPIA FIELDS, IL, p. A215

FRANCISCAN ST. MARGARET HEALTH—DYER, DYER, IN, p. A226

FRANCISCAN ST. MARGARET HEALTH—HAMMOND, HAMMOND, IN, p. A230

FRANK R. HOWARD MEMORIAL HOSPITAL, WILLITS, CA, p. A105

FRANKFORT REGIONAL MEDICAL CENTER, FRANKFORT, KY, p. A283

FRANKLIN COUNTY MED CENTER, PRESTON, ID, p. A192

FRANKLIN COUNTY MEDICAL CENTER, PRESTON, ID, p. A192

FRANKLIN COUNTY MEMORIAL HOSPITAL, FRANKLIN, NE, p. A432

FRANKLIN COUNTY MEMORIAL HOSPITAL, MEADVILLE, MS, p. A396

FRANKLIN FOUNDATION HOSPITAL, FRANKLIN, LA, p. A301

FRANKLIN GENERAL HOSPITAL, HAMPTON, IA, p. A251

FRANKLIN HOSPITAL, BENTON, IL, p. A195

FRANKLIN HOSPITAL, VALLEY STREAM, NY, p. A501

FRANKLIN HOSPITAL DISTRICT, BENTON, IL, p. A195

FRANKLIN MEDICAL CENTER, GREENFIELD, MA, p. A339

FRANKLIN MEDICAL CENTER, WINNSBORO, LA, p. A317

FRANKLIN MEMORIAL HOSPITAL, FARMINGTON, ME, p. A320

FRANKLIN MEMORIAL HOSPITAL, ROCKY MOUNT, VA, p. A751

FRANKLIN PARISH HOSPITAL, WINNSBORO, LA, p. A317

FRANKLIN REGIONAL HOSPITAL, FRANKLIN, NH, p. A449

FRANKLIN WOODS COMMUNITY HOSPITAL, JOHNSON CITY, TN, p. A640

FRAZIER INSTITUTE, LOUISVILLE, KY, p. A288

FREDERICK HEALTH, FREDERICK, MD, p. A329

FREDERICK REGIONAL HEALTH SYSTEM, FREDERICK, MD, p. A329

FREDONIA REGIONAL HOSPITAL, FREDONIA, KS, p. A264

FREEMAN COMMUNITY HOSPITAL, FREEMAN, SD, p. A628

FREEMAN HEALTH SYSTEM, JOPLIN, MO, p. A408

FREEMAN HOSPITAL WEST, JOPLIN, MO, p. A408

FREEMAN NEOSHO HOSPITAL, NEOSHO, MO, p. A412

FREEMAN REGIONAL HEALTH SERVICES, FREEMAN, SD, p. A628

FREEPORT MEMORIAL HOSPITAL, FREEPORT, IL, p. A205

FREESTON MEDICAL CENTER, FAIRFIELD, TX, p. A677

FREESTONE MEDICAL CENTER, FAIRFIELD, TX, p. A677

FREMONT HEALTH, FREMONT, NE, p. A432

FREMONT HOSPITAL, FREMONT, CA, p. A65

FREMONT MEDICAL CENTER, FREMONT, CA, p. A65

FREMONT MEDICAL CENTER, YUBA CITY, CA, p. A106

FRENCH HOSPITAL MEDICAL CENTER, SAN LUIS OBISPO, CA, p. A95

FRESNO HEART AND SURGICAL HOSPITAL, FRESNO, CA, p. A65

FRESNO HEART HOSPITAL, FRESNO, CA, p. A65

FRESNO MEDICAL CENTER, FRESNO, CA, p. A65

FRESNO SURGERY CENTER, FRESNO, CA, p. A65

FRESNO SURGICAL HOSPITAL, FRESNO, CA, p. A65

FRICK HOSPITAL, MOUNT PLEASANT, PA, p. A598

FRIEND COMMUNITY HEALTHCARE SYSTEM, FRIEND, NE, p. A432

FRIENDS BEHAVIORAL HEALTH SYSTEM, PHILADELPHIA, PA, p. A600

FRIENDS HOSPITAL, PHILADELPHIA, PA, p. A600

FRIO HOSPITAL, PEARSALL, TX, p. A705

FRIO REGIONAL HOSPITAL, PEARSALL, TX, p. A705

FRISBIE MEMORIAL HOSPITAL, ROCHESTER, NH, p. A451

FROEDTERT & THE MEDICAL COLLEGE OF WISCONSIN FROEDTERT HOSPITAL, MILWAUKEE, WI, p. A791

FROEDTERT AND THE MEDICAL COLLEGE OF WISCONSIN FROEDTERT HOSPITAL, MILWAUKEE, WI, p. A791

FROEDTERT MENOMONEE FALLS HOSPITAL, MENOMONEE FALLS, WI, p. A789

FROEDTERT SOUTH—KENOSHA MEDICAL CENTER, KENOSHA, WI, p. A786

FROEDTERT WEST BEND HOSPITAL, WEST BEND, WI, p. A799

FRYE REGIONAL MED CENTER, HICKORY, NC, p. A512

FRYE REGIONAL MEDICAL CENTER, HICKORY, NC, p. A512

FULLER MEMORIAL HOSPITAL, ATTLEBORO, MA, p. A334

FULTON COUNTY HEALTH CENTER, WAUSEON, OH, p. A552

FULTON COUNTY HOSPITAL, SALEM, AR, p. A52

FULTON COUNTY MEDICAL CENTER, MC CONNELLSBURG, PA, p. A596

FULTON DIVISION, BRONX, NY, p. A476

FULTON MEDICAL CENTER, FULTON, MO, p. A407

FULTON STATE HOSPITAL, FULTON, MO, p. A407

FUNDACION HOSP METROPOLITAN, SAN JUAN, PR, p. A810

F. W. HUSTON MEDICAL CENTER, WINCHESTER, KS, p. A279

# G

G. WERBER BRYAN PSYCHIATRIC HOSPITAL, COLUMBIA, SC, p. A617

GADSDEN REGIONAL MEDICAL CENTER, GADSDEN, AL, p. A19

GAINESVILLE MEMORIAL HOSPITAL, GAINESVILLE, TX, p. A680

GALENA-STAUSS HOSPITAL, GALENA, IL, p. A205

GALESBURG COTTAGE HOSPITAL, GALESBURG, IL, p. A205

GALICHIA HEART HOSPITAL, WICHITA, KS, p. A278

GALION COMMUNITY HOSPITAL, GALION, OH, p. A541

GALION HOSPITAL, GALION, OH, p. A541

GALLUP INDIAN MEDICAL CENTER, GALLUP, NM, p. A469

GARDEN CITY HOSPITAL, GARDEN CITY, MI, p. A355

GARDEN CITY OSTEO HOSPITAL, GARDEN CITY, MI, p. A355

GARDEN COUNTY HEALTH SERVICES, OSHKOSH, NE, p. A438

GARDEN GROVE HOSP & MED CTR, GARDEN GROVE, CA, p. A66

GARDEN GROVE HOSPITAL AND MEDICAL CENTER, GARDEN GROVE, CA, p. A66

GARDEN PARK MEDICAL CENTER, GULFPORT, MS, p. A393

GARFIELD COUNTY HEALTH CENTER, JORDAN, MT, p. A425

GARFIELD COUNTY HOSP DISTRICT, POMEROY, WA, p. A762

GARFIELD COUNTY PUBLIC HOSPITAL DISTRICT, POMEROY, WA, p. A762

GARFIELD MEDICAL CENTER, MONTEREY PARK, CA, p. A79

GARFIELD MEMORIAL HOSPITAL, PANGUITCH, UT, p. A730

GARFIELD MEMORIAL HOSPITAL AND CLINICS, PANGUITCH, UT, p. A730

GARFIELD PARK HOSPITAL, CHICAGO, IL, p. A198

GARLAND BEHAVIORAL HOSPITAL, GARLAND, TX, p. A681

GARNET HEALTH MEDICAL CENTER—CATSKILLS, HARRIS, NY, p. A485

GARNET HEALTH MEDICAL CENTER—CATSKILLS, MIDDLETOWN, NY, p. A488

GARNETT HEALTH MEDICAL CENTER—CATSKILLS, CALLICOON, NY, p. A480

GARRETT COUNTY MEMORIAL HOSPITAL, OAKLAND, MD, p. A331

GARRETT REGIONAL MEDICAL CENTER, OAKLAND, MD, p. A331

GARY MEMORIAL HOSPITAL, BREAUX BRIDGE, LA, p. A298

GATEWAY MEDICAL CENTER, CLARKSVILLE, TN, p. A636

GATEWAY REGIONAL HEALTH SYSTEM, MOUNT STERLING, KY, p. A290

GATEWAY REGIONAL MEDICAL CENTER, GRANITE CITY, IL, p. A206

GATEWAY REHABILITATION HOSPITA, FLORENCE, KY, p. A283

GATEWAY REHABILITATION HOSPITAL, FLORENCE, KY, p. A283

GATEWAYS HOSP & MNTL HLTH CNTR, LOS ANGELES, CA, p. A74

GATEWAYS HOSPITAL AND MENTAL HEALTH CENTER, LOS ANGELES, CA, p. A74

GAYLORD HOSPITAL, WALLINGFORD, CT, p. A125

GAYLORD SPECIALTY HEALTHCARE, WALLINGFORD, CT, p. A126

GEARY COMMUNITY HOSPITAL, JUNCTION CITY, KS, p. A267

GEISINGER ENCOMPASS HEALTH REHABILITATION HOSPITAL, DANVILLE, PA, p. A587

GEISINGER HEALTHSOUTH REHABILITATION HOSPITAL, DANVILLE, PA, p. A587

GEISINGER HOLY SPIRIT, CAMP HILL, PA, p. A585

GEISINGER JERSEY SHORE HOSPITAL, JERSEY SHORE, PA, p. A593

GEISINGER MEDICAL CENTER, DANVILLE, PA, p. A588

GEISINGER SHAMOKIN AREA COMMUNITY HOSPITAL, COAL TOWNSHIP, PA, p. A587

GEISINGER WYOMING VALLEY MEDICAL CENTER, WILKES BARRE, PA, p. A611

GEISINGER-BLOOMSBURG HOSPITAL, BLOOMSBURG, PA, p. A585

GEISINGER-COMMUNITY MEDICAL CENTER, SCRANTON, PA, p. A607

GEISINGER-LEWISTOWN HOSPITAL, LEWISTOWN, PA, p. A595
GENERAL HOSPITAL, CHARLESTON, WV, p. A771
GENERAL JOHN J. PERSHING MEMORIAL HOSPITAL, BROOKFIELD, MO, p. A403
GENERAL LEONARD WOOD ARMY COMMUNITY HOSPITAL, FORT LEONARD WOOD, MO, p. A406
GENESEE MEMORIAL HOSPITAL, BATAVIA, NY, p. A475
GENESIS BEHAVIORAL HOSPITAL, BREAUX BRIDGE, LA, p. A298
GENESIS HEALTHCARE SYSTEM, ZANESVILLE, OH, p. A554
GENESIS MEDICAL CENTER—DAVENPORT, DAVENPORT, IA, p. A247
GENESIS MEDICAL CENTER, DAVENPORT, DAVENPORT, IA, p. A247
GENESIS MEDICAL CENTER, DEWITT, DE WITT, IA, p. A248
GENESIS MEDICAL CENTER, ILLINI CAMPUS, SILVIS, IL, p. A220
GENESIS MEDICAL CENTER, SILVIS, SILVIS, IL, p. A220
GENESIS MEDICAL CENTER-ALEDO, ALEDO, IL, p. A194
GENESIS SPECIALTY HOSPITAL, NATCHITOCHES, LA, p. A309
GENESYS REGIONAL MEDICAL CENTER, GRAND BLANC, MI, p. A355
GENEVA GENERAL HOSPITAL, GENEVA, NY, p. A484
GENOA COMMUNITY HOSPITAL, GENOA, NE, p. A432
GENOA MEDICAL FACILITIES, GENOA, NE, p. A432
GEORGE AND MARIE BACKUS CHILDREN'S HOSPITAL, SAVANNAH, GA, p. A180
GEORGE C GRAPE COMMUNITY HOSPITAL, HAMBURG, IA, p. A251
GEORGE C. GRAPE COMMUNITY HOSPITAL, HAMBURG, IA, p. A251
GEORGE COUNTY HOSPITAL, LUCEDALE, MS, p. A396
GEORGE E. WEEMS MEMORIAL HOSPITAL, APALACHICOLA, FL, p. A131
GEORGE L. MEE MEMORIAL HOSPITAL, KING CITY, CA, p. A69
GEORGE REGIONAL HOSPITAL, LUCEDALE, MS, p. A396
GEORGE WASHINGTON UNIVERSITY HOSPITAL, WASHINGTON, DC, p. A129
GEORGETOWN BEHAVIORAL HEALTH INSTITUTE, GEORGETOWN, TX, p. A681
GEORGETOWN BEHAVIORAL HOSPITAL, GEORGETOWN, OH, p. A541
GEORGETOWN COMMUNITY HOSPITAL, GEORGETOWN, KY, p. A284
GEORGETOWN HEALTHCARE SYSTEM, GEORGETOWN, TX, p. A681
GEORGETOWN MEMORIAL HOSPITAL, GEORGETOWN, SC, p. A620
GEORGIA REG HOSP AT AUGUSTA, AUGUSTA, GA, p. A166
GEORGIA REGENTS MEDICAL CENTER, AUGUSTA, GA, p. A166
GEORGIA REGIONAL HOSPITAL AT ATLANTA, DECATUR, GA, p. A171
GEORGIA REGIONAL HOSPITAL AT SAVANNAH, SAVANNAH, GA, p. A180
GERALD CHAMPION MEM HOSPITAL, ALAMOGORDO, NM, p. A467
GERALD CHAMPION REGIONAL MEDICAL CENTER, ALAMOGORDO, NM, p. A467
GERBER MEMORIAL HEALTH SERVICES, FREMONT, MI, p. A355
GETTYSBURG MEMORIAL HOSPITAL, GETTYSBURG, SD, p. A628
GHS GREENVILLE MEMORIAL HOSPITAL, GREENVILLE, SC, p. A620
GIBSON AREA HOSPITAL AND HEALTH SERVICES, GIBSON CITY, IL, p. A206
GIBSON COMMUNITY HOSPITAL, GIBSON CITY, IL, p. A206
GIBSON GENERAL HOSPITAL, PRINCETON, IN, p. A239
GIFFORD MEDICAL CENTER, RANDOLPH, VT, p. A736
GIFFORD MEMORIAL HOSPITAL, RANDOLPH, VT, p. A736
GILA REGIONAL MEDICAL CENTER, SILVER CITY, NM, p. A472
GILA REGIONAL MEDICAL CTR, SILVER CITY, NM, p. A472
GILLETTE CHILDREN'S SPEC CARE, SAINT PAUL, MN, p. A385
GILLETTE CHILDREN'S SPECIALTY HEALTHCARE, SAINT PAUL, MN, p. A385
GILMORE MEMORIAL HOSPITAL, AMORY, MS, p. A389
GIRARD MEDICAL CENTER, GIRARD, KS, p. A265
GLACIAL RIDGE HEALTH SYSTEM, GLENWOOD, MN, p. A377
GLACIAL RIDGE HOSPITAL, GLENWOOD, MN, p. A377
GLACIER COUNTY MEDICAL CENTER, CUT BANK, MT, p. A423
GLACIER VIEW HOSPITAL, KALISPELL, MT, p. A425
GLADES GENERAL HOSPITAL, BELLE GLADE, FL, p. A132
GLEN COVE HOSPITAL, GLEN COVE, NY, p. A484
GLEN OAKS HOSPITAL, GREENVILLE, TX, p. A682
GLEN ROSE MEDICAL CENTER, GLEN ROSE, TX, p. A681

GLENBEIGH HEALTH SOURCES, ROCK CREEK, OH, p. A548
GLENBEIGH HOSPITAL AND OUTPATIENT CENTERS, ROCK CREEK, OH, p. A548
GLENCOE REGIONAL HEALTH, GLENCOE, MN, p. A377
GLENCOE REGIONAL HEALTH SERVICES, GLENCOE, MN, p. A377
GLENDALE ADVENTIST MEDICAL CENTER, GLENDALE, CA, p. A67
GLENDALE MEMORIAL HOSPITAL AND HEALTH CENTER, GLENDALE, CA, p. A67
GLENDIVE MEDICAL CENTER, GLENDIVE, MT, p. A424
GLENDORA COMMUNITY HOSPITAL, GLENDORA, CA, p. A67
GLENMORE FOUNDATION, CROOKSTON, MN, p. A374
GLENN GENERAL HOSPITAL, WILLOWS, CA, p. A105
GLENN MEDICAL CENTER, WILLOWS, CA, p. A105
GLENS FALLS HOSPITAL, GLENS FALLS, NY, p. A484
GLENWOOD REGIONAL MEDICAL CENTER, WEST MONROE, LA, p. A316
GLOBALREHAB HOSPITAL—SAN ANTONIO, SAN ANTONIO, TX, p. A711
GOLDEN PLAINS COMMUNITY HOSPITAL, BORGER, TX, p. A660
GOLDEN TRIANGLE REG MED CENTER, COLUMBUS, MS, p. A391
GOLDEN VALLEY HEALTH CENTER, GOLDEN VALLEY, MN, p. A377
GOLDEN VALLEY MEMORIAL HEALTHCARE, CLINTON, MO, p. A405
GOLDEN VALLEY MEMORIAL HOSPITAL, CLINTON, MO, p. A405
GOLDWATER MEMORIAL HOSPITAL, NEW YORK, NY, p. A489
GOLETA VALLEY COMM HOSPITAL, SANTA BARBARA, CA, p. A96
GOLETA VALLEY COTTAGE HOSPITAL, SANTA BARBARA, CA, p. A96
GOLISANO CHILDREN'S HOSPITAL OF SOUTHWEST FLORIDA, FORT MYERS, FL, p. A138
GONZALES HEALTHCARE SYSTEMS, GONZALES, TX, p. A681
GOOD SAMARITAN HOSP CORVALLIS, CORVALLIS, OR, p. A574
GOOD SAMARITAN HOSPITAL, BAKERSFIELD, CA, p. A57
GOOD SAMARITAN HOSPITAL, CINCINNATI, OH, p. A532
GOOD SAMARITAN HOSPITAL, DOWNERS GROVE, IL, p. A203
GOOD SAMARITAN HOSPITAL, GREENSBORO, GA, p. A173
GOOD SAMARITAN HOSPITAL, KEARNEY, NE, p. A433
GOOD SAMARITAN HOSPITAL, LOS ANGELES, CA, p. A74
GOOD SAMARITAN HOSPITAL, SAN JOSE, CA, p. A94
GOOD SAMARITAN HOSPITAL, SUFFERN, NY, p. A499
GOOD SAMARITAN HOSPITAL, VINCENNES, IN, p. A242
GOOD SAMARITAN HOSPITAL, WATERTOWN, NY, p. A502
GOOD SAMARITAN HOSPITAL, WEST ISLIP, NY, p. A502
GOOD SAMARITAN HOSPITAL, WEST PALM BEACH, FL, p. A162
GOOD SAMARITAN HOSPITAL AND MEDICAL CENTER, PORTLAND, OR, p. A579
GOOD SAMARITAN HOSPITAL MEDICAL CENTER, WEST ISLIP, NY, p. A502
GOOD SAMARITAN HOSPITAL OF MARYLAND, BALTIMORE, MD, p. A324
GOOD SAMARITAN HOSPITAL-NORTH, BAKERSFIELD, CA, p. A57
GOOD SAMARITAN MEDICAL CENTER, BROCKTON, MA, p. A337
GOOD SAMARITAN MEDICAL CENTER, LAFAYETTE, CO, p. A115
GOOD SAMARITAN MEDICAL CENTER, WEST PALM BEACH, FL, p. A162
GOOD SAMARITAN REGIONAL HEALTH CENTER, MOUNT VERNON, IL, p. A213
GOOD SAMARITAN REGIONAL MEDICAL CENTER, CORVALLIS, OR, p. A574
GOOD SAMARITAN REGIONAL MEDICAL CENTER, SUFFERN, NY, p. A499
GOOD SHEPHERD HEALTH CARE SYSTEM, HERMISTON, OR, p. A576
GOOD SHEPHERD HEALTHCARE SYSTEM, HERMISTON, OR, p. A576
GOOD SHEPHERD HOSPITAL, BARRINGTON, IL, p. A195
GOOD SHEPHERD MEDICAL CENTER, LONGVIEW, TX, p. A696
GOOD SHEPHERD MEDICAL CENTER-MARSHALL, MARSHALL, TX, p. A700
GOOD SHEPHERD PENN PARTNERS SPECIALTY HOSPITAL AT RITTENHOUSE, PHILADELPHIA, PA, p. A600
GOOD SHEPHERD REHABILITATION HOSPITAL, ALLENTOWN, PA, p. A583
GOOD SHEPHERD REHABILITATION HOSPITAL-ALLENTOWN, ALLENTOWN, PA, p. A583
GOOD SHEPHERD SPECIALTY HOSPITAL, BETHLEHEM, PA, p. A584

GOODALL-WITCHER HOSPITAL, CLIFTON, TX, p. A664
GOODALL-WITCHER HOSPITAL AUTHORITY, CLIFTON, TX, p. A664
GOODING COUNTY MEMORIAL HOSPITAL, GOODING, ID, p. A190
GOODLAND REGIONAL MEDICAL CENTER, GOODLAND, KS, p. A265
GORDON HOSPITAL, CALHOUN, GA, p. A168
GORDON MEMORIAL HEALTH SERVICES, GORDON, NE, p. A432
GORDON MEMORIAL HOSPITAL, GORDON, NE, p. A432
GOSHEN HEALTH, GOSHEN, IN, p. A229
GOSHEN HOSPITAL, GOSHEN, IN, p. A229
GOTHENBURG HEALTH, GOTHENBURG, NE, p. A432
GOTHENBURG MEMORIAL HOSPITAL, GOTHENBURG, NE, p. A432
GOTTLIEB MEMORIAL HOSPITAL, MELROSE PARK, IL, p. A212
GOUVERNEUR HOSPITAL, GOUVERNEUR, NY, p. A485
GOUVERNEUR HOSPITAL, NEW YORK, NY, p. A489
GOVE COUNTY HOSPITAL, QUINTER, KS, p. A275
GOVE COUNTY MEDICAL CENTER, QUINTER, KS, p. A275
GOVERNOR JUAN F. LOUIS HOSPITAL, CHRISTIANSTED, VI, p. A812
GOVERNOR JUAN F. LUIS HOSPITAL, CHRISTIANSTED, VI, p. A812
GRACE COTTAGE HOSPITAL, TOWNSHEND, VT, p. A737
GRACE HOSPITAL, CLEVELAND, OH, p. A534
GRACE HOSPITAL, MORGANTON, NC, p. A515
GRACE MEDICAL CENTER, BALTIMORE, MD, p. A324
GRACE MEDICAL CENTER, LUBBOCK, TX, p. A697
GRACIE SQUARE HOSPITAL, NEW YORK, NY, p. A489
GRADY GENERAL HOSPITAL, CAIRO, GA, p. A167
GRADY MEMORIAL HOSPITAL, ATLANTA, GA, p. A164
GRADY MEMORIAL HOSPITAL, CHICKASHA, OK, p. A557
GRADY MEMORIAL HOSPITAL, DELAWARE, OH, p. A539
GRAFTON CITY HOSPITAL, GRAFTON, WV, p. A772
GRAHAM COUNTY HOSPITAL, HILL CITY, KS, p. A266
GRAHAM GENERAL HOSPITAL, GRAHAM, TX, p. A681
GRAHAM HOSPITAL, CANTON, IL, p. A196
GRAHAM HOSPITAL ASSOCIATION, CANTON, IL, p. A196
GRAHAM REGIONAL MEDICAL CENTER, GRAHAM, TX, p. A681
GRAND ITASCA CLINIC AND HOSPITAL, GRAND RAPIDS, MN, p. A377
GRAND JUNCTION VETERANS AFFAIRS MEDICAL CENTER, GRAND JUNCTION, CO, p. A113
GRAND JUNCTION VETERANS HEALTH CARE SYSTEM, GRAND JUNCTION, CO, p. A113
GRAND RIVER HOSPITAL DISTRICT, RIFLE, CO, p. A118
GRAND STRAND MEDICAL CENTER, MYRTLE BEACH, SC, p. A623
GRAND STRAND REGIONAL MEDICAL CENTER, MYRTLE BEACH, SC, p. A623
GRAND VALLEY NURSING CENTRE, GRAND RAPIDS, MI, p. A356
GRAND VIEW HEALTH, SELLERSVILLE, PA, p. A607
GRAND VIEW HOSPITAL, SELLERSVILLE, PA, p. A607
GRANDE RONDE HOSPITAL, LA GRANDE, OR, p. A576
GRANDVIEW HOSPITAL AND MEDICAL CENTER, DAYTON, OH, p. A538
GRANDVIEW MEDICAL CENTER, BIRMINGHAM, AL, p. A15
GRANDVIEW MEDICAL CENTER, DAYTON, OH, p. A538
GRANDVIEW MEDICAL CENTER, JASPER, TN, p. A640
GRANITE COUNTY MEDICAL CENTER, PHILIPSBURG, MT, p. A426
GRANITE COUNTY MEM HOSPITAL, PHILIPSBURG, MT, p. A426
GRANITE FALLS HEALTH, GRANITE FALLS, MN, p. A377
GRANT MEDICAL CENTER, COLUMBUS, OH, p. A536
GRANT MEMORIAL HOSPITAL, PETERSBURG, WV, p. A775
GRANT REGIONAL HEALTH CENTER, LANCASTER, WI, p. A787
GRANT-BLACKFORD MENTAL HEALTH CENTER, MARION, IN, p. A236
GRANVILLE HEALTH SYSTEM, OXFORD, NC, p. A516
GRANVILLE MEDICAL CENTER, OXFORD, NC, p. A516
GRATIOT MEDICAL CENTER, ALMA, MI, p. A348
GRAYS HARBOR COMMUNITY HOSPITAL, ABERDEEN, WA, p. A755
GRAYSON COUNTY HOSPITAL, LEITCHFIELD, KY, p. A286
GREAT BEND REGIONAL HOSPITAL, GREAT BEND, KS, p. A265
GREAT FALLS CLINIC HOSPITAL, GREAT FALLS, MT, p. A424
GREAT FALLS CLINIC MEDICAL CENTER, GREAT FALLS, MT, p. A424
GREAT LAKES SPECIALTY HOSPITAL-MUSKEGON, MUSKEGON, MI, p. A362
GREAT PLAINS HEALTH, NORTH PLATTE, NE, p. A436
GREAT PLAINS HOSP & HEALTH CTR, GARDNER, KS, p. A265

GREAT PLAINS REGIONAL MEDICAL CENTER, ELK CITY, OK, p. A558

GREAT PLAINS REGIONAL MEDICAL CENTER, NORTH PLATTE, NE, p. A436

GREAT RIVER HEALTH SYSTEM, WEST BURLINGTON, IA, p. A260

GREAT RIVER MEDICAL CENTER, BLYTHEVILLE, AR, p. A43

GREAT RIVER MEDICAL CENTER, WEST BURLINGTON, IA, p. A260

GREATER BALTIMORE MEDICAL CENTER, BALTIMORE, MD, p. A324

GREATER BINGHAMTON HEALTH CENTER, BINGHAMTON, NY, p. A475

GREATER COMMUNITY HOSPITAL, CRESTON, IA, p. A247

GREATER EL MONTE COMMUNITY HOSPITAL, SOUTH EL MONTE, CA, p. A99

GREATER PEORIA SPECIALTY HOSPITAL, PEORIA, IL, p. A216

GREATER REGIONAL MEDICAL CENTER, CRESTON, IA, p. A247

GREATER SOUTHEAST COMM HOSP, WASHINGTON, DC, p. A129

GREATER STAPLES HOSPITAL, STAPLES, MN, p. A386

GREELEY COUNTY HEALTH SERVICES, TRIBUNE, KS, p. A278

GREELEY COUNTY HOSPITAL, TRIBUNE, KS, p. A278

GREEN HOSP OF SCRIPPS CLINIC, LA JOLLA, CA, p. A69

GREEN OAKS HOSPITAL, DALLAS, TX, p. A668

GREEN VALLEY HOSPITAL, GREEN VALLEY, AZ, p. A33

GREENBRIER HOSPITAL, BROOKSVILLE, FL, p. A133

GREENBRIER VALLEY MEDICAL CENTER, RONCEVERTE, WV, p. A776

GREENE COUNTY GENERAL HOSPITAL, LINTON, IN, p. A235

GREENE COUNTY HEALTH SYSTEM, EUTAW, AL, p. A18

GREENE COUNTY HOSPITAL, EUTAW, AL, p. A18

GREENE COUNTY HOSPITAL, LEAKESVILLE, MS, p. A396

GREENE COUNTY MEDICAL CENTER, JEFFERSON, IA, p. A252

GREENE MEMORIAL HOSPITAL, XENIA, OH, p. A553

GREENEVILLE COMMUNITY HOSPITAL WEST, GREENEVILLE, TN, p. A638

GREENFIELD AREA MEDICAL CENTER, GREENFIELD, OH, p. A541

GREENLAWN HOSPITAL, ATMORE, AL, p. A14

GREENLEAF BEHAVIORAL HEALTH HOSPITAL, VALDOSTA, GA, p. A182

GREENLEAF CENTER, VALDOSTA, GA, p. A182

GREENSBORO HOSPITAL, GREENSBORO, NC, p. A511

GREENSVILLE MEMORIAL HOSPITAL, EMPORIA, VA, p. A741

GREENVIEW REGIONAL HOSPITAL, BOWLING GREEN, KY, p. A280

GREENVILLE REGIONAL HOSPITAL, GREENVILLE, IL, p. A206

GREENVILLE REGIONAL HOSPITAL, GREENVILLE, PA, p. A591

GREENWICH HOSPITAL, GREENWICH, CT, p. A122

GREENWOOD COUNTY HOSPITAL, EUREKA, KS, p. A264

GREENWOOD LEFLORE HOSPITAL, GREENWOOD, MS, p. A392

GREENWOOD REGIONAL REHABILITATION HOSPITAL, GREENWOOD, SC, p. A621

GREER MEMORIAL HOSPITAL, GREER, SC, p. A621

GRENADA LAKE MEDICAL CENTER, GRENADA, MS, p. A393

GREYSTONE PARK PSYCHIATRIC HOSPITAL, MORRIS PLAINS, NJ, p. A458

GRIFFIN HOSPITAL, DERBY, CT, p. A122

GRIFFIN MEM HOSP, NORMAN, OK, p. A563

GRIFFIN MEMORIAL HOSPITAL, NORMAN, OK, p. A563

GRIGGS CNTY HOSPITAL & NRSG HM, COOPERSTOWN, ND, p. A522

GRIMES ST. JOSEPH HEALTH CENTER, NAVASOTA, TX, p. A703

GRINNELL REGIONAL MEDICAL CENTER, GRINNELL, IA, p. A250

GRISELL MEMORIAL HOSPITAL DISTRICT ONE, RANSOM, KS, p. A275

GRITMAN MEDICAL CENTER, MOSCOW, ID, p. A191

GRITMAN MEMORIAL HOSPITAL, MOSCOW, ID, p. A191

GROSSMONT HOSPITAL, LA MESA, CA, p. A70

GROTTA CENTER FOR SENIOR CARE, WEST ORANGE, NJ, p. A465

GROUP HEALTH COOPERATIVE CENTRAL HOSPITAL, SEATTLE, WA, p. A763

GROVE HILL MEMORIAL HOSPITAL, GROVE HILL, AL, p. A19

GROVER C. DILS MEDICAL CENTER, CALIENTE, NV, p. A441

GROVER M. HERMANN HOSPITAL, CALLICOON, NY, p. A480

GRTR BRIDGEPORT COMM HLTH CTR, BRIDGEPORT, CT, p. A121

GRUNDY COUNTY MEMORIAL HOSPITAL, GRUNDY CENTER, IA, p. A250

GUADALUPE COUNTY HOSPITAL, SANTA ROSA, NM, p. A472

GUADALUPE REGIONAL MEDICAL CENTER, SEGUIN, TX, p. A714

GUADALUPE VALLEY HOSPITAL, SEGUIN, TX, p. A714

GUAM MEMORIAL HOSPITAL AUTHORITY, TAMUNING, GU, p. A805

GUAM REGIONAL MEDICAL CITY, DEDEDO, GU, p. A805

GUERNSEY MEMORIAL HOSPITAL, CAMBRIDGE, OH, p. A530

GUIDANCE CENTER, FLAGSTAFF, AZ, p. A31

GULF BREEZE HOSPITAL, GULF BREEZE, FL, p. A139

GULF COAST MEDICAL CENTER, FORT MYERS, FL, p. A138

GULF COAST MEDICAL CENTER, PANAMA CITY, FL, p. A153

GULF COAST REGIONAL MEDICAL CENTER, PANAMA CITY, FL, p. A153

GULFPORT BEHAVIORAL HEALTH SYSTEM, GULFPORT, MS, p. A393

GUMMERVILLE MEDICAL CENTER, SUMMERVILLE, SC, p. A624

GUNDERSEN BOSCOBEL AREA HEALTH CARE AND CLINICS, BOSCOBEL, WI, p. A781

GUNDERSEN BOSCOBEL AREA HOSPITAL AND CLINICS, BOSCOBEL, WI, p. A781

GUNDERSEN HEALTH SYSTEM, LA CROSSE, WI, p. A787

GUNDERSEN LUTHERAN MEDICAL CENTER, LA CROSSE, WI, p. A787

GUNDERSEN MOUNDVIEW HOSPITAL & CLINICS, FRIENDSHIP, WI, p. A784

GUNDERSEN MOUNDVIEW MEMORIAL HOSPITAL & CLINICS, FRIENDSHIP, WI, p. A784

GUNDERSEN PALMER LUTHERAN HOSPITAL AND CLINICS, WEST UNION, IA, p. A260

GUNDERSEN ST. JOSEPH'S HOSPITAL AND CLINICS, HILLSBORO, WI, p. A786

GUNDERSEN TRI-COUNTY HOSPITAL AND CLINICS, WHITEHALL, WI, p. A799

GUNNISON VALLEY HOSPITAL, GUNNISON, CO, p. A114

GUNNISON VALLEY HOSPITAL, GUNNISON, UT, p. A728

GUNTERSVILLE-ARAB MED CENTER, GUNTERSVILLE, AL, p. A19

GUTHRIE CORNING HOSPITAL, CORNING, NY, p. A481

GUTHRIE CORTLAND REGIONAL MEDICAL CENTER, CORTLAND, NY, p. A482

GUTHRIE COUNTY HOSPITAL, GUTHRIE CENTER, IA, p. A250

GUTHRIE ROBERT PACKER HOSPITAL, SAYRE, PA, p. A606

GUTHRIE TOWANDA MEMORIAL HOSPITAL, TOWANDA, PA, p. A609

GUTHRIE TROY COMMUNITY HOSPITAL, TROY, PA, p. A609

GUTTENBERG MUNICIPAL HOSPITAL, GUTTENBERG, IA, p. A250

GUTTENBERG MUNICIPAL HOSPITAL AND CLINICS, GUTTENBERG, IA, p. A250

G.V. (SONNY) MONTGOMERY VETERANS AFFAIRS MEDICAL CENTER, JACKSON, MS, p. A394

GWINNETT MEDICAL CENTER-DULUTH, DULUTH, GA, p. A172

# H

H. LEE MOFFITT CANCER CENTER AND RESEARCH INSTITUTE, TAMPA, FL, p. A159

HABERSHAM COUNTY MEDICAL CENTER, DEMOREST, GA, p. A171

HABERSHAM MEDICAL CENTER, DEMOREST, GA, p. A171

HACKENSACK MERIDIAN HEALTH BAYSHORE COMMUNITY HOSPITAL, HOLMDEL, NJ, p. A456

HACKENSACK MERIDIAN HEALTH CARRIER CLINIC, BELLE MEAD, NJ, p. A452

HACKENSACK MERIDIAN HEALTH HACKENSACK UNIVERSITY MEDICAL CENTER, HACKENSACK, NJ, p. A455

HACKENSACK MERIDIAN HEALTH JERSEY SHORE UNIVERSITY MEDICAL CENTER, NEPTUNE, NJ, p. A459

HACKENSACK MERIDIAN HEALTH JFK MEDICAL CENTER, EDISON, NJ, p. A454

HACKENSACK MERIDIAN HEALTH MOUNTAINSIDE MEDICAL CENTER, MONTCLAIR, NJ, p. A458

HACKENSACK MERIDIAN HEALTH OCEAN MEDICAL CENTER, BRICK TOWNSHIP, NJ, p. A453

HACKENSACK MERIDIAN HEALTH PALISADES MEDICAL CENTER, NORTH BERGEN, NJ, p. A460

HACKENSACK MERIDIAN HEALTH PASCACK VALLEY MEDICAL CENTER, WESTWOOD, NJ, p. A465

HACKENSACK MERIDIAN HEALTH RARITAN BAY MEDICAL CENTER, PERTH AMBOY, NJ, p. A461

HACKENSACK MERIDIAN HEALTH RIVERVIEW MEDICAL CENTER, RED BANK, NJ, p. A462

HACKENSACK MERIDIAN HEALTH SHORE REHABILITATION INSTITUTE, BRICK, NJ, p. A452

HACKENSACK MERIDIAN HEALTH SOUTHERN OCEAN MEDICAL CENTER, MANAHAWKIN, NJ, p. A458

HACKENSACK UNIVERSITY MEDICAL CENTER, HACKENSACK, NJ, p. A455

HACKENSACK UNIVERSITY MEDICAL CENTER MOUNTAINSIDE, MONTCLAIR, NJ, p. A458

HACKENSACKUMC PALISADES, NORTH BERGEN, NJ, p. A460

HACKETTSTOWN MEDICAL CENTER, HACKETTSTOWN, NJ, p. A456

HACKETTSTOWN REGIONAL MEDICAL CENTER, HACKETTSTOWN, NJ, p. A456

HALE COUNTY HOSPITAL, GREENSBORO, AL, p. A19

HALE HO'OLA HAMAKUA, HONOKAA, HI, p. A184

HALE MAKUA, KAHULUI, HI, p. A185

HALIFAX BEHAVIORAL CENTER, DAYTONA BEACH, FL, p. A136

HALIFAX COMMUNITY HEALTH SYST, DAYTONA BEACH, FL, p. A136

HALIFAX HEALTH MEDICAL CENTER OF DAYTONA BEACH, DAYTONA BEACH, FL, p. A136

HALIFAX HOSPITAL PORT ORANGE, PORT ORANGE, FL, p. A155

HALIFAX REGIONAL HEALTH SYSTEM, SOUTH BOSTON, VA, p. A751

HALIFAX REGIONAL MEDICAL CENTER, ROANOKE RAPIDS, NC, p. A517

HALL-BROOKE HOSPITAL, A DIVISION OF HALL-BROOKE BEHAVIORAL HEALTH SERVICES, WESTPORT, CT, p. A126

HALLMARK HEALTH SYSTEM, MELROSE, MA, p. A341

HAMILTON CENTER, TERRE HAUTE, IN, p. A241

HAMILTON COUNTY HOSPITAL, SYRACUSE, KS, p. A277

HAMILTON GENERAL HOSPITAL, HAMILTON, TX, p. A682

HAMILTON HOSPITAL, HAMILTON, NJ, p. A456

HAMILTON HOSPITAL, OLNEY, TX, p. A704

HAMILTON HOSPITAL, WEBSTER CITY, IA, p. A260

HAMILTON MEDICAL CENTER, DALTON, GA, p. A170

HAMILTON MEMORIAL HOSPITAL, MCLEANSBORO, IL, p. A212

HAMILTON MEMORIAL HOSPITAL DISTRICT, MCLEANSBORO, IL, p. A212

HAMMOND-HENRY HOSPITAL, GENESEO, IL, p. A205

HAMOT MEDICAL CENTER, ERIE, PA, p. A589

HAMPSHIRE MEMORIAL HOSPITAL, ROMNEY, WV, p. A776

HAMPSTEAD HOSPITAL, HAMPSTEAD, NH, p. A449

HAMPTON BEHAVIORAL HEALTH CENTER, WESTAMPTON, NJ, p. A465

HAMPTON GENERAL HOSPITAL, VARNVILLE, SC, p. A625

HAMPTON HOSPITAL, WESTAMPTON, NJ, p. A465

HAMPTON REGIONAL MEDICAL CENTER, VARNVILLE, SC, p. A625

HAMPTON ROADS SPECIALTY HOSPITAL, NEWPORT NEWS, VA, p. A746

HAMPTON VETERANS AFFAIRS MEDICAL CENTER, HAMPTON, VA, p. A743

HANCOCK COUNTY HEALTH SYSTEM, BRITT, IA, p. A244

HANCOCK COUNTY HOSPITAL, SNEEDVILLE, TN, p. A649

HANCOCK COUNTY MEMORIAL HOSPITAL, BRITT, IA, p. A244

HANCOCK MEDICAL CENTER, BAY SAINT LOUIS, MS, p. A389

HANCOCK MEMORIAL HOSPITAL, GREENFIELD, IN, p. A230

HANCOCK REGIONAL HOSPITAL, GREENFIELD, IN, p. A230

HANNA HOUSE, CLEVELAND, OH, p. A534

HANNIBAL REG HEALTHCARE SYST, HANNIBAL, MO, p. A407

HANNIBAL REGIONAL HOSPITAL, HANNIBAL, MO, p. A407

HANOVER HOSPITAL, HANOVER, KS, p. A265

HANS P. PETERSON MEMORIAL HOSPITAL, PHILIP, SD, p. A630

HANSEN FAMILY HOSPITAL, IOWA FALLS, IA, p. A252

HANSFORD HOSPITAL, SPEARMAN, TX, p. A716

HARBOR BEACH COMMUNITY HOSPITAL, HARBOR BEACH, MI, p. A357

HARBOR OAKS HOSPITAL, NEW BALTIMORE, MI, p. A362

HARBOR-UCLA MEDICAL CENTER, TORRANCE, CA, p. A101

HARBORVIEW MEDICAL CENTER, SEATTLE, WA, p. A763

HARBOUR SHORES OF LAWNWOOD, FORT PIERCE, FL, p. A138

HARDEMAN COUNTY MEMORIAL HOSPITAL, QUANAH, TX, p. A708

HARDEMAN MEMORIAL HOSPITAL, QUANAH, TX, p. A708

HARDIN COUNTY GENERAL HOSPITAL, ROSICLARE, IL, p. A219

HARDIN COUNTY GENERAL HOSPITAL, SAVANNAH, TN, p. A649

HARDIN MEDICAL CENTER, SAVANNAH, TN, p. A649

HARDIN MEMORIAL HEALTH, ELIZABETHTOWN, KY, p. A282

HARDIN MEMORIAL HOSPITAL, ELIZABETHTOWN, KY, p. A282

HARDIN MEMORIAL HOSPITAL, KENTON, OH, p. A542

HARDTNER MEDICAL CENTER, OLLA, LA, p. A312

HARDY WILSON MEMORIAL HOSPITAL, HAZLEHURST, MS, p. A394

HARFORD MEMORIAL HOSPITAL, HAVRE DE GRACE, MD, p. A330
HARLAN ARH HOSPITAL, HARLAN, KY, p. A284
HARLAN COUNTY HEALTH SYSTEM, ALMA, NE, p. A429
HARLAN COUNTY HOSPITAL, ALMA, NE, p. A429
HARLEM HOSPITAL CENTER, NEW YORK, NY, p. A489
HARLINGEN MEDICAL CENTER, HARLINGEN, TX, p. A683
HARMON MEDICAL AND REHABILITATION HOSPITAL, LAS VEGAS, NV, p. A443
HARMON MEMORIAL HOSPITAL, HOLLIS, OK, p. A560
HARMS MEMORIAL HOSPITAL DISTRICT, AMERICAN FALLS, ID, p. A188
HARNETT HEALTH SYSTEM, DUNN, NC, p. A508
HARNEY COUNTY HOSPITAL, BURNS, OR, p. A574
HARNEY DISTRICT HOSPITAL, BURNS, OR, p. A574
HARPER COUNTY COMMUNITY HOSPITAL, BUFFALO, OK, p. A557
HARPER UNIVERSITY HOSPITAL/HUTZEL WOMEN'S HOSPITAL, DETROIT, MI, p. A353
HARRIMAN CITY HOSPITAL, HARRIMAN, TN, p. A638
HARRINGTON HOSPITAL, SOUTHBRIDGE, MA, p. A344
HARRINGTON MEMORIAL HOSPITAL, SOUTHBRIDGE, MA, p. A344
HARRIS CONTINUED CARE HOSPITAL, FORT WORTH, TX, p. A678
HARRIS COUNTY HOSPITAL DISTRICT, HOUSTON, TX, p. A685
HARRIS HEALTH SYSTEM, HOUSTON, TX, p. A685
HARRIS HOSPITAL, NEWPORT, AR, p. A51
HARRIS METHODIST FORT WORTH, FORT WORTH, TX, p. A678
HARRIS METHODIST NORTHWEST, AZLE, TX, p. A657
HARRIS METHODIST SOUTHLAKE CENTER FOR DIAGNOSTICS AND SURGERY, SOUTHLAKE, TX, p. A716
HARRIS METHODIST SOUTHWEST, FORT WORTH, TX, p. A678
HARRIS METHODIST-ERATH COUNTY, STEPHENVILLE, TX, p. A717
HARRIS METHODIST-GLEN ROSE, GLEN ROSE, TX, p. A681
HARRIS METHODIST-HEB, BEDFORD, TX, p. A658
HARRIS METHODIST-MEXIA, MEXIA, TX, p. A701
HARRIS REGIONAL HOSPITAL, SYLVA, NC, p. A519
HARRISBURG HOSPITAL, HARRISBURG, PA, p. A591
HARRISBURG MEDICAL CENTER, HARRISBURG, IL, p. A206
HARRISON COMMUNITY HOSPITAL, CADIZ, OH, p. A530
HARRISON COUNTY COMMUNITY HOSPITAL, BETHANY, MO, p. A402
HARRISON COUNTY HOSPITAL, CORYDON, IN, p. A226
HARRISON MEDICAL CENTER, BREMERTON, WA, p. A756
HARRISON MEMORIAL HOSPITAL, CYNTHIANA, KY, p. A282
HARRY S. TRUMAN MEMORIAL VETERANS HOSPITAL, COLUMBIA, MO, p. A405
HARSHA BEHAVIORAL CENTER, TERRE HAUTE, IN, p. A241
HARTFORD HOSPITAL, HARTFORD, CT, p. A122
HARTGROVE HOSPITAL, CHICAGO, IL, p. A198
HARTNETT HEALTH SYSTEM, DUNN, NC, p. A508
HARTON REGIONAL MEDICAL CENTER, TULLAHOMA, TN, p. A650
HARTSVILLE MEDICAL CENTER, HARTSVILLE, TN, p. A639
HASKELL COUNTY COMMUNITY HOSPITAL, STIGLER, OK, p. A568
HASKELL COUNTY HEALTHCARE SYSTEM, STIGLER, OK, p. A568
HASKELL MEMORIAL HOSPITAL, HASKELL, TX, p. A683
HATO REY COMMUNITY HOSPITAL, SAN JUAN, PR, p. A810
HAVASU REGIONAL MEDICAL CENTER, LAKE HAVASU CITY, AZ, p. A33
HAVASU SAMARITAN REG HOSP, LAKE HAVASU CITY, AZ, p. A33
HAVEN BEHAVIORAL HEALTH OF EASTERN PENNSYLVANIA, READING, PA, p. A606
HAVEN BEHAVIORAL HOSPITAL OF EASTERN PENNSYLVANIA, READING, PA, p. A606
HAVEN BEHAVIORAL HOSPITAL OF FRISCO, FRISCO, TX, p. A680
HAVEN BEHAVIORAL HOSPITAL OF PHILADELPHIA, PHILADELPHIA, PA, p. A600
HAVEN BEHAVIORAL HOSPITAL OF PHOENIX, PHOENIX, AZ, p. A35
HAVEN BEHAVIORAL SENIOR CARE OF ALBUQUERQUE, ALBUQUERQUE, NM, p. A467
HAVEN BEHAVIORAL SENIOR CARE OF DAYTON, DAYTON, OH, p. A538
HAVEN SENIOR HORIZONS, PHOENIX, AZ, p. A36
HAVENWYCK HOSPITAL, AUBURN HILLS, MI, p. A349
HAWAII MEDICAL CENTER-WEST, EWA BEACH, HI, p. A184
HAWAII STATE HOSPITAL, KANEOHE, HI, p. A186
HAWARDEN COMMUNITY HOSPITAL, HAWARDEN, IA, p. A251
HAWARDEN REGIONAL HEALTHCARE, HAWARDEN, IA, p. A251

HAWKINS COUNTY MEMORIAL HOSPITAL, ROGERSVILLE, TN, p. A648
HAWTHORN CENTER, NORTHVILLE, MI, p. A363
HAWTHORN CHILDREN PSYCHIATRIC HOSPITAL, SAINT LOUIS, MO, p. A415
HAWTHORNE CHILD PSYCH HOSPITAL, SAINT LOUIS, MO, p. A415
HAXTUN HOSPITAL DISTRICT, HAXTUN, CO, p. A114
HAYES GREEN BEACH MEMORIAL HOSPITAL, CHARLOTTE, MI, p. A351
HAYS MEDICAL CENTER, HAYS, KS, p. A265
HAYWARD AREA MEMORIAL HOSPITAL AND NURSING HOME, HAYWARD, WI, p. A786
HAYWARD AREA MEMORIAL HOSPITAL AND WATER'S EDGE, HAYWARD, WI, p. A786
HAYWOOD REGIONAL MEDICAL CENTER, CLYDE, NC, p. A507
HAZARD ARH REGIONAL MEDICAL CENTER, HAZARD, KY, p. A284
HAZEL HAWKINS MEMORIAL HOSPITAL, HOLLISTER, CA, p. A68
H. B. MAGRUDER MEMORIAL HOSPITAL, PORT CLINTON, OH, p. A548
H. C. WATKINS MEMORIAL HOSPITAL, QUITMAN, MS, p. A399
HCA CHIPPENHAM MEDICAL CENTER, RICHMOND, VA, p. A750
HCA DOMINION HOSPITAL, FALLS CHURCH, VA, p. A741
HCA HOUSTON HEALTHCARE CLEAR LAKE, LEAGUE CITY, TX, p. A695
HCA HOUSTON HEALTHCARE CONROE, CONROE, TX, p. A665
HCA HOUSTON HEALTHCARE KINGWOOD, KINGWOOD, TX, p. A693
HCA HOUSTON HEALTHCARE MEDICAL CENTER, HOUSTON, TX, p. A685
HCA HOUSTON HEALTHCARE NORTHWEST, HOUSTON, TX, p. A685
HCA HOUSTON HEALTHCARE PEARLAND, PEARLAND, TX, p. A705
HCA HOUSTON HEALTHCARE SOUTHEAST, PASADENA, TX, p. A705
HCA HOUSTON HEALTHCARE TOMBALL, TOMBALL, TX, p. A721
HCA HOUSTON HEALTHCARE WEST, HOUSTON, TX, p. A686
HCA JOHNSTON-WILLIS HOSPITAL, RICHMOND, VA, p. A750
HCA PARKLAND MEDICAL CENTER, DERRY, NH, p. A448
HCA POPLAR SPRINGS HOSPITAL, PETERSBURG, VA, p. A748
HCA WESLEY REHABILITATION HOSP, WICHITA, KS, p. A278
HEALDSBURG DISTRICT HOSPITAL, HEALDSBURG, CA, p. A68
HEALDTON MERCY HOSPITAL, HEALDTON, OK, p. A560
HEALTH ALLIANCE HOSPITAL—BROADWAY CAMPUS, KINGSTON, NY, p. A486
HEALTH ALLIANCE HOSPITAL—MARY'S AVENUE CAMPUS, KINGSTON, NY, p. A487
HEALTH CENTRAL, OCOEE, FL, p. A150
HEALTH CENTRAL HOSPITAL, OCOEE, FL, p. A150
HEALTH FIRST CAPE CANAVERAL HOSPITAL, COCOA BEACH, FL, p. A134
HEALTH FIRST HOLMES REGIONAL MEDICAL CENTER, MELBOURNE, FL, p. A145
HEALTH FIRST PALM BAY HOSPITAL, PALM BAY, FL, p. A152
HEALTH FIRST VIERA HOSPITAL, MELBOURNE, FL, p. A145
HEALTH ONE BUFFALO HOSPITAL, BUFFALO, MN, p. A373
HEALTH ONE MERCY HOSPITAL, COON RAPIDS, MN, p. A374
HEALTH ONE OWATONNA HOSPITAL, OWATONNA, MN, p. A382
HEALTHBRIDGE CHILDRENS REHABILITATION HOSPITAL, ORANGE, CA, p. A83
HEALTHBRIDGE CHILDREN'S HOSPITAL, ORANGE, CA, p. A83
HEALTHBRIDGE CHILDREN'S HOSPITAL OF HOUSTON, HOUSTON, TX, p. A686
HEALTHCENTER NORTHWEST, KALISPELL, MT, p. A425
HEALTHEAST BETHESDA HOSPITAL, SAINT PAUL, MN, p. A385
HEALTHEAST ST JOHN'S HOSPITAL, MAPLEWOOD, MN, p. A380
HEALTHEAST ST JOSEPH'S HOSP, SAINT PAUL, MN, p. A385
HEALTHMARK REGIONAL MEDICAL CENTER, DEFUNIAK SPRINGS, FL, p. A136
HEALTHSOURCE SAGINAW, SAGINAW, MI, p. A365
HEALTHSOURCE SAGINAW, INC., SAGINAW, MI, p. A365
HEALTHSOUTH BAKERSFIELD REHABILITATION HOSPITAL, BAKERSFIELD, CA, p. A57
HEALTHSOUTH CHATTANOOGA REHABILITATION HOSPITAL, CHATTANOOGA, TN, p. A635
HEALTHSOUTH CHESAPEAKE REHABILITATION HOSPITAL, SALISBURY, MD, p. A332

HEALTHSOUTH CITY VIEW REHABILITATION HOSPITAL, FORT WORTH, TX, p. A678
HEALTHSOUTH DEACONESS REHABILITATION HOSPITAL, NEWBURGH, IN, p. A238
HEALTHSOUTH DESERT CANYON REHABILITATION HOSPITAL, LAS VEGAS, NV, p. A443
HEALTHSOUTH EMERALD COAST REHABILITATION HOSPITAL, PANAMA CITY, FL, p. A153
HEALTHSOUTH HOSPITAL OF MANATI, MANATI, PR, p. A808
HEALTHSOUTH HUNTINGTON REHABILITATION HOSPITAL, HUNTINGTON, WV, p. A773
HEALTHSOUTH LAKESHORE REHABILITATION HOSPITAL, BIRMINGHAM, AL, p. A15
HEALTHSOUTH LAKEVIEW REHABILITATION HOSPITAL, ELIZABETHTOWN, KY, p. A282
HEALTHSOUTH MEDICAL CENTER, BIRMINGHAM, AL, p. A15
HEALTHSOUTH MEDICAL CENTER, RICHMOND, VA, p. A750
HEALTHSOUTH MOUNTAINVIEW REGIONAL REHABILITATION HOSPITAL, MORGANTOWN, WV, p. A774
HEALTHSOUTH NEW ENGLAND REHABILITATION HOSPITAL, WOBURN, MA, p. A346
HEALTHSOUTH NITTANY VALLEY REHABILITATION HOSPITAL, PLEASANT GAP, PA, p. A605
HEALTHSOUTH NORTHERN KENTUCKY REHABILITATION HOSPITAL, EDGEWOOD, KY, p. A282
HEALTHSOUTH PLANO REHABILITATION HOSPITAL, PLANO, TX, p. A707
HEALTHSOUTH READING REHABILITATION HOSPITAL, READING, PA, p. A606
HEALTHSOUTH REHAB HOSPITAL, PORTLAND, ME, p. A322
HEALTHSOUTH REHABILITATION HOSPITAL—ABILENE, ABILENE, TX, p. A651
HEALTHSOUTH REHABILITATION HOSPITAL—DALLAS, DALLAS, TX, p. A668
HEALTHSOUTH REHABILITATION HOSPITAL—HENDERSON, HENDERSON, NV, p. A442
HEALTHSOUTH REHABILITATION HOSPITAL—MID-CITIES, BEDFORD, TX, p. A658
HEALTHSOUTH REHABILITATION HOSPITAL, CONCORD, NH, p. A448
HEALTHSOUTH REHABILITATION HOSPITAL, DOTHAN, AL, p. A17
HEALTHSOUTH REHABILITATION HOSPITAL, FAYETTEVILLE, AR, p. A45
HEALTHSOUTH REHABILITATION HOSPITAL, KINGSPORT, TN, p. A641
HEALTHSOUTH REHABILITATION HOSPITAL AT DRAKE, CINCINNATI, OH, p. A532
HEALTHSOUTH REHABILITATION HOSPITAL AT MARTIN HEALTH, STUART, FL, p. A158
HEALTHSOUTH REHABILITATION HOSPITAL MIDLAND-ODESSA, MIDLAND, TX, p. A701
HEALTHSOUTH REHABILITATION HOSPITAL NORTH TEXAS, RICHARDSON, TX, p. A708
HEALTHSOUTH REHABILITATION HOSPITAL OF ALTAMONTE SPRINGS, ALTAMONTE SPRINGS, FL, p. A131
HEALTHSOUTH REHABILITATION HOSPITAL OF ALTOONA, ALTOONA, PA, p. A583
HEALTHSOUTH REHABILITATION HOSPITAL OF ARLINGTON, ARLINGTON, TX, p. A653
HEALTHSOUTH REHABILITATION HOSPITAL OF AUSTIN, AUSTIN, TX, p. A656
HEALTHSOUTH REHABILITATION HOSPITAL OF BATON ROUGE, BATON ROUGE, LA, p. A296
HEALTHSOUTH REHABILITATION HOSPITAL OF BEAUMONT, BEAUMONT, TX, p. A658
HEALTHSOUTH REHABILITATION HOSPITAL OF CHARLESTON, CHARLESTON, SC, p. A616
HEALTHSOUTH REHABILITATION HOSPITAL OF CINCINNATI AT NORWOOD, CINCINNATI, OH, p. A532
HEALTHSOUTH REHABILITATION HOSPITAL OF COLORADO SPRINGS, COLORADO SPRINGS, CO, p. A109
HEALTHSOUTH REHABILITATION HOSPITAL OF COLUMBIA, COLUMBIA, SC, p. A617
HEALTHSOUTH REHABILITATION HOSPITAL OF CYPRESS, HOUSTON, TX, p. A686
HEALTHSOUTH REHABILITATION HOSPITAL OF DAYTON, DAYTON, OH, p. A538
HEALTHSOUTH REHABILITATION HOSPITAL OF ERIE, ERIE, PA, p. A589
HEALTHSOUTH REHABILITATION HOSPITAL OF FLORENCE, FLORENCE, SC, p. A619
HEALTHSOUTH REHABILITATION HOSPITAL OF FORT SMITH, FORT SMITH, AR, p. A46
HEALTHSOUTH REHABILITATION HOSPITAL OF FRANKLIN, FRANKLIN, TN, p. A638
HEALTHSOUTH REHABILITATION HOSPITAL OF FREDERICKSBURG, FREDERICKSBURG, VA, p. A742
HEALTHSOUTH REHABILITATION HOSPITAL OF GULFPORT, GULFPORT, MS, p. A393

HEALTHSOUTH REHABILITATION HOSPITAL OF HUMBLE, LLC, HUMBLE, TX, p. A689
HEALTHSOUTH REHABILITATION HOSPITAL OF JONESBORO, JONESBORO, AR, p. A48
HEALTHSOUTH REHABILITATION HOSPITAL OF LARGO, LARGO, FL, p. A143
HEALTHSOUTH REHABILITATION HOSPITAL OF LITTLETON, LITTLETON, CO, p. A116
HEALTHSOUTH REHABILITATION HOSPITAL OF MECHANICSBURG, MECHANICSBURG, PA, p. A596
HEALTHSOUTH REHABILITATION HOSPITAL OF MEMPHIS, MEMPHIS, TN, p. A644
HEALTHSOUTH REHABILITATION HOSPITAL OF MIAMI, CUTLER BAY, FL, p. A135
HEALTHSOUTH REHABILITATION HOSPITAL OF MIDDLETOWN, MIDDLETOWN, DE, p. A127
HEALTHSOUTH REHABILITATION HOSPITAL OF MODESTO, MODESTO, CA, p. A79
HEALTHSOUTH REHABILITATION HOSPITAL OF MONTGOMERY, MONTGOMERY, AL, p. A22
HEALTHSOUTH REHABILITATION HOSPITAL OF NEW MEXICO, ALBUQUERQUE, NM, p. A467
HEALTHSOUTH REHABILITATION HOSPITAL OF NORTH ALABAMA, HUNTSVILLE, AL, p. A20
HEALTHSOUTH REHABILITATION HOSPITAL OF NORTHERN VIRGINIA, ALDIE, VA, p. A738
HEALTHSOUTH REHABILITATION HOSPITAL OF OCALA, OCALA, FL, p. A150
HEALTHSOUTH REHABILITATION HOSPITAL OF PETERSBURG, PETERSBURG, VA, p. A748
HEALTHSOUTH REHABILITATION HOSPITAL OF ROCK HILL, ROCK HILL, SC, p. A623
HEALTHSOUTH REHABILITATION HOSPITAL OF SAN JUAN, SAN JUAN, PR, p. A810
HEALTHSOUTH REHABILITATION HOSPITAL OF SARASOTA, SARASOTA, FL, p. A157
HEALTHSOUTH REHABILITATION HOSPITAL OF SEWICKLEY, SEWICKLEY, PA, p. A607
HEALTHSOUTH REHABILITATION HOSPITAL OF SOUTHERN ARIZONA, TUCSON, AZ, p. A40
HEALTHSOUTH REHABILITATION HOSPITAL OF SPRING HILL, BROOKSVILLE, FL, p. A133
HEALTHSOUTH REHABILITATION HOSPITAL OF TALLAHASSEE, TALLAHASSEE, FL, p. A158
HEALTHSOUTH REHABILITATION HOSPITAL OF TEXARKANA, TEXARKANA, TX, p. A720
HEALTHSOUTH REHABILITATION HOSPITAL OF TINTON FALLS, TINTON FALLS, NJ, p. A464
HEALTHSOUTH REHABILITATION HOSPITAL OF TOMS RIVER, TOMS RIVER, NJ, p. A464
HEALTHSOUTH REHABILITATION HOSPITAL OF UTAH, SANDY, UT, p. A733
HEALTHSOUTH REHABILITATION HOSPITAL OF VINELAND, VINELAND, NJ, p. A465
HEALTHSOUTH REHABILITATION HOSPITAL OF WESTERN MASSACHUSETTS, LUDLOW, MA, p. A341
HEALTHSOUTH REHABILITATION HOSPITAL OF YORK, YORK, PA, p. A612
HEALTHSOUTH REHABILITATION HOSPITAL ROUND ROCK, ROUND ROCK, TX, p. A709
HEALTHSOUTH REHABILITATION HOSPITAL THE VINTAGE, HOUSTON, TX, p. A686
HEALTHSOUTH REHABILITATION HOSPITAL THE WOODLANDS, CONROE, TX, p. A665
HEALTHSOUTH REHABILITATION HOSPITAL VISION PARK, SHENANDOAH, TX, p. A715
HEALTHSOUTH REHABILITATION HOSPITAL-LAS VEGAS, LAS VEGAS, NV, p. A443
HEALTHSOUTH REHABILITATION HOSPITAL-WICHITA FALLS, WICHITA FALLS, TX, p. A725
HEALTHSOUTH REHABILITATION INSTITUTE OF TUCSON, TUCSON, AZ, p. A40
HEALTHSOUTH REHABILITATION OF GADSDEN, GADSDEN, AL, p. A19
HEALTHSOUTH SEA PINES REHABILITATION HOSPITAL, MELBOURNE, FL, p. A145
HEALTHSOUTH SOUTHERN HILLS REHABILITATION HOSPITAL, PRINCETON, WV, p. A776
HEALTHSOUTH SUGAR LAND REHABILITATION HOSPITAL, SUGAR LAND, TX, p. A717
HEALTHSOUTH SUNRISE REHABILITATION HOSPITAL, SUNRISE, FL, p. A158
HEALTHSOUTH TREASURE COAST REHABILITATION HOSPITAL, VERO BEACH, FL, p. A161
HEALTHSOUTH TREASURE VLY HOSP, BOISE, ID, p. A188
HEALTHSOUTH TUSTIN REHABILITATION HOSPITAL, TUSTIN, CA, p. A102
HEALTHSOUTH WALTON REHABILITATION HOSPITAL, AUGUSTA, GA, p. A166

HEALTHSOUTH WESTERN HILLS REGIONAL REHABILITATION HOSPITAL, PARKERSBURG, WV, p. A775
HEALTHSOUTHBRAINTREE REHABILITATION HOSPITAL, BRAINTREE, MA, p. A336
HEART HOSPITAL OF LAFAYETTE, LAFAYETTE, LA, p. A305
HEART HOSPITAL OF SOUTH DAKOTA, SIOUX FALLS, SD, p. A631
HEART OF AMERICA MEDICAL CENTER, RUGBY, ND, p. A525
HEART OF AMERICAN MEDICAL CNTR, RUGBY, ND, p. A525
HEART OF FLORIDA REGIONAL MEDICAL CENTER, DAVENPORT, FL, p. A135
HEART OF TEXAS MEMORIAL HOSPITAL, BRADY, TX, p. A660
HEART OF THE ROCKIES REGIONAL MEDICAL CENTER, SALIDA, CO, p. A118
HEARTLAND BEHAVIORAL HEALTH SERVICES, NEVADA, MO, p. A412
HEARTLAND BEHAVIORAL HEALTHCARE, MASSILLON, OH, p. A544
HEARTLAND HOSPITAL, NEVADA, MO, p. A412
HEARTLAND LONG TERM ACUTE CARE HOSPITAL, SAINT JOSEPH, MO, p. A415
HEARTLAND REGIONAL MEDICAL CENTER, MARION, IL, p. A211
HEARTLAND SURGICAL SPECIALTY HOSPITAL, OVERLAND PARK, KS, p. A273
HEATHERHILL CARE COMMUNITIES, CHARDON, OH, p. A531
HEBER VALLEY HOSPITAL, HEBER CITY, UT, p. A728
HEBER VALLEY MEDICAL CENTER, HEBER CITY, UT, p. A728
HEBREW CENTER FOR HEALTH REHABILITATION, WEST HARTFORD, CT, p. A126
HEBREW HOME FOR AGED-RIVERDALE, BRONX, NY, p. A476
HEBREW HOSP FOR CHRONIC SICK, BRONX, NY, p. A476
HEBREW REHABILITATION CENTER, ROSLINDALE, MA, p. A344
HEBREW REHABILITATION CENTER FOR AGED, ROSLINDALE, MA, p. A344
HEBREW SENIOR CARE, WEST HARTFORD, CT, p. A126
HEDRICK MEDICAL CENTER, CHILLICOTHE, MO, p. A404
HEGG HEALTH CENTER AVERA, ROCK VALLEY, IA, p. A257
HEGG MEMORIAL HEALTH CENTER AVERA, ROCK VALLEY, IA, p. A257
HELEN HAYES HOSPITAL, WEST HAVERSTRAW, NY, p. A502
HELEN KELLER HOSPITAL, SHEFFIELD, AL, p. A24
HELEN KELLER MEMORIAL HOSPITAL, SHEFFIELD, AL, p. A24
HELEN M. SIMPSON REHABILITATION HOSPITAL, HARRISBURG, PA, p. A591
HELEN NEWBERRY JOY HOSPITAL, NEWBERRY, MI, p. A363
HELENA REGIONAL MEDICAL CENTER, HELENA, AR, p. A46
HEMET VALLEY MEDICAL CENTER, HEMET, CA, p. A68
HEMPHILL COUNTY HOSPITAL, CANADIAN, TX, p. A662
HENDERSON COMMUNITY HOSPITAL, HENDERSON, NE, p. A433
HENDERSON COUNTY COMMUNITY HOSPITAL, LEXINGTON, TN, p. A642
HENDERSON HEALTH CARE SERVICES, HENDERSON, NE, p. A433
HENDERSON HOSPITAL, HENDERSON, NV, p. A442
HENDERSONVILLE MEDICAL CENTER, HENDERSONVILLE, TN, p. A639
HENDRICK HEALTH SYSTEM, ABILENE, TX, p. A651
HENDRICK MEDICAL CENTER, ABILENE, TX, p. A651
HENDRICKS COMM HOSPITAL, DANVILLE, IN, p. A226
HENDRICKS COMMUNITY HOSPITAL, HENDRICKS, MN, p. A378
HENDRICKS COMMUNITY HOSPITAL ASSOCIATION, HENDRICKS, MN, p. A378
HENDRICKS REGIONAL HEALTH, DANVILLE, IN, p. A226
HENDRY REGIONAL MED CENTER, CLEWISTON, FL, p. A134
HENDRY REGIONAL MEDICAL CENTER, CLEWISTON, FL, p. A134
HENNEPIN COUNTY MEDICAL CENTER, MINNEAPOLIS, MN, p. A380
HENNEPIN HEALTHCARE, MINNEAPOLIS, MN, p. A380
HENRICO DOCTORS' HOSPITAL, RICHMOND, VA, p. A750
HENRICO DOCTOR'S HOSPITAL, RICHMOND, VA, p. A750
HENRY COMMUNITY HEALTH, NEW CASTLE, IN, p. A238
HENRY COUNTY HEALTH CENTER, MOUNT PLEASANT, IA, p. A254
HENRY COUNTY HOSPITAL, NAPOLEON, OH, p. A546
HENRY COUNTY HOSPITAL, NEW CASTLE, IN, p. A238
HENRY COUNTY MEDICAL CENTER, PARIS, TN, p. A648
HENRY FORD ALLEGIANCE HEALTH, JACKSON, MI, p. A359
HENRY FORD ALLEGIANCE SPECIALTY HOSPITAL, JACKSON, MI, p. A359
HENRY FORD HOSPITAL, DETROIT, MI, p. A353
HENRY FORD KINGSWOOD HOSPITAL, FERNDALE, MI, p. A354
HENRY FORD MACOMB HOSPITAL, CLINTON TOWNSHIP, MI, p. A351

HENRY FORD MACOMB HOSPITALS, CLINTON TOWNSHIP, MI, p. A351
HENRY FORD MEDICAL CENTER, WEST BLOOMFIELD, MI, p. A369
HENRY FORD WEST BLOOMFIELD HOSPITAL, WEST BLOOMFIELD, MI, p. A369
HENRY FORD WYANDOTTE HOSP, WYANDOTTE, MI, p. A369
HENRY FORD WYANDOTTE HOSPITAL, WYANDOTTE, MI, p. A370
HENRY HEYWOOD MEM HOSPITAL, GARDNER, MA, p. A339
HENRY J. CARTER SPECIALTY HOSPITAL & NURSING FACILITY, NEW YORK, NY, p. A489
HENRY MAYO NEWHALL HOSPITAL, VALENCIA, CA, p. A103
HENRY MAYO NEWHALL MEMORIAL HOSPITAL, VALENCIA, CA, p. A103
HENRY MEDICAL CENTER, STOCKBRIDGE, GA, p. A181
HENRYETTA MEDICAL CENTER, HENRYETTA, OK, p. A560
HEPBURN MEDICAL CENTER, OGDENSBURG, NY, p. A493
HEREFORD REGIONAL MEDICAL CENTER, HEREFORD, TX, p. A684
HERINGTON MUNICIPAL HOSPITAL, HERINGTON, KS, p. A266
HERITAGE HOSPITAL, TARBORO, NC, p. A519
HERITAGE MEDICAL CENTER, SHELBYVILLE, TN, p. A649
HERITAGE OAKS HOSPITAL, SACRAMENTO, CA, p. A89
HERITAGE VALLEY BEAVER, BEAVER, PA, p. A584
HERITAGE VALLEY HEALTH SYSTEM, BEAVER, PA, p. A584
HERITAGE VALLEY KENNEDY, MCKEES ROCKS, PA, p. A596
HERMANN AREA DISTRICT HOSPITAL, HERMANN, MO, p. A407
HERRICK HOSPITAL & HLTH CENTER, BERKELEY, CA, p. A58
HERRICK MEDICAL CENTER, TECUMSEH, MI, p. A368
HERRIN HOSPITAL, HERRIN, IL, p. A207
HESS MEMORIAL HOSPITAL, MAUSTON, WI, p. A789
HEYWOOD HOSPITAL, GARDNER, MA, p. A339
HI-DESERT MEDICAL CENTER, JOSHUA TREE, CA, p. A69
HIALEAH HOSPITAL, HIALEAH, FL, p. A139
HIAWATHA COMMUNITY HOSPITAL, HIAWATHA, KS, p. A266
HICKMAN COMMUNITY HOSPITAL, CENTERVILLE, TN, p. A635
HICKORY TRAIL HOSPITAL, DESOTO, TX, p. A672
HIGGINS GENERAL HOSPITAL, BREMEN, GA, p. A167
HIGH POINT MEDICAL CENTER, HIGH POINT, NC, p. A512
HIGH POINT REGIONAL HEALTH SYSTEM, HIGH POINT, NC, p. A512
HIGHLAND COMMUNITY HOSPITAL, LUBBOCK, TX, p. A697
HIGHLAND COMMUNITY HOSPITAL, PICAYUNE, MS, p. A398
HIGHLAND DISTRICT HOSP, HILLSBORO, OH, p. A542
HIGHLAND DISTRICT HOSPITAL, HILLSBORO, OH, p. A542
HIGHLAND HOSPITAL, CHARLESTON, WV, p. A771
HIGHLAND HOSPITAL, OAKLAND, CA, p. A82
HIGHLAND HOSPITAL, ROCHESTER, NY, p. A496
HIGHLAND HOSPITAL OF ROCHESTER, ROCHESTER, NY, p. A496
HIGHLAND PARK HOSPITAL, MIAMI, FL, p. A146
HIGHLAND RIDGE HOSPITAL, MIDVALE, UT, p. A728
HIGHLAND SPRINGS HOSPITAL, HIGHLAND HILLS, OH, p. A542
HIGHLAND-CLARKSBURG HOSPITAL, CLARKSBURG, WV, p. A771
HIGHLANDS ARH REGIONAL MEDICAL CENTER, PRESTONSBURG, KY, p. A292
HIGHLANDS BEHAVIORAL HEALTH SYSTEM, LITTLETON, CO, p. A116
HIGHLANDS HOSPITAL & HLTH CTR, CONNELLSVILLE, PA, p. A587
HIGHLANDS HOSPITAL, CONNELLSVILLE, PA, p. A587
HIGHLANDS MEDICAL CENTER, SCOTTSBORO, AL, p. A24
HIGHLANDS MEDICAL CENTER, SPARTA, TN, p. A649
HIGHLANDS REGIONAL MEDICAL CENTER, PRESTONSBURG, KY, p. A292
HIGHLANDS REGIONAL MEDICAL CENTER, SEBRING, FL, p. A157
HIGHLANDS REHABILITATION HOSPITAL, EL PASO, TX, p. A675
HIGHLANDS-CASHIERS HOSPITAL, HIGHLANDS, NC, p. A512
HIGHLINE MEDICAL CENTER, BURIEN, WA, p. A756
HIGHPOINT HEALTH, LAWRENCEBURG, IN, p. A235
HIGHSMITH-RAINEY MEMORIAL HOSPITAL, FAYETTEVILLE, NC, p. A510
HIGHSMITH-RAINEY SPECIALTY HOSPITAL, FAYETTEVILLE, NC, p. A510
HILL COUNTRY MEMORIAL HOSPITAL, FREDERICKSBURG, TX, p. A679
HILL CREST BEHAVIORAL HEALTH SERVICES, BIRMINGHAM, AL, p. A15
HILL CREST HOSPITAL, BIRMINGHAM, AL, p. A15
HILL HOSPITAL OF SUMTER COUNTY, YORK, AL, p. A26
HILL HOSPITAL OF YORK, YORK, AL, p. A26
HILL REGIONAL HOSPITAL, HILLSBORO, TX, p. A684
HILLCREST HEALTHCARE SYSTEM, TULSA, OK, p. A569

HILLCREST HOSPITAL—SOUTH, TULSA, OK, p. A569
HILLCREST HOSPITAL, CLEVELAND, OH, p. A534
HILLCREST HOSPITAL, SIMPSONVILLE, SC, p. A624
HILLCREST HOSPITAL CLAREMORE, CLAREMORE, OK, p. A557
HILLCREST HOSPITAL CUSHING, CUSHING, OK, p. A558
HILLCREST HOSPITAL HENRYETTA, HENRYETTA, OK, p. A560
HILLCREST HOSPITAL PRYOR, PRYOR, OK, p. A567
HILLCREST MEDICAL CENTER, TULSA, OK, p. A569
HILLS & DALES GENERAL HOSPITAL, CASS CITY, MI, p. A350
HILLS AND DALES GENERAL HOSPITAL, CASS CITY, MI, p. A350
HILLSBORO AREA HOSPITAL, HILLSBORO, IL, p. A207
HILLSBORO COMMUNITY HOSPITAL, HILLSBORO, KS, p. A266
HILLSBORO COMMUNITY MEDICAL CENTER, HILLSBORO, KS, p. A266
HILLSBORO HOSPITAL, HILLSBORO, IL, p. A207
HILLSBORO MEDICAL CENTER, HILLSBORO, ND, p. A524
HILLSBORO NURSING HOME, HILLSBORO, ND, p. A524
HILLSDALE COMMUNITY HEALTH CENTER, HILLSDALE, MI, p. A357
HILLSDALE HOSPITAL, HILLSDALE, MI, p. A357
HILLSIDE REHABILITATION HOSPITAL, WARREN, OH, p. A551
HILO HOSPITAL, HILO, HI, p. A184
HILO MEDICAL CENTER, HILO, HI, p. A184
HILTON HEAD HOSPITAL, HILTON HEAD ISLAND, SC, p. A621
HILTON HEAD REGIONAL MED CTR, HILTON HEAD ISLAND, SC, p. A621
HIMA SAN PABLO CAGUAS, CAGUAS, PR, p. A806
HIMA SAN PABLO CUPEY, CAGUAS, PR, p. A806
HIRAM W. DAVIS MEDICAL CENTER, PETERSBURG, VA, p. A748
HOAG MEMORIAL HOSPITAL PRESBYTERIAN, NEWPORT BEACH, CA, p. A81
HOAG ORTHOPEDIC INSTITUTE, IRVINE, CA, p. A69
HOBOKEN UNIVERSITY MEDICAL CENTER, HOBOKEN, NJ, p. A456
HOCKING VALLEY COMMUNITY HOSPITAL, LOGAN, OH, p. A543
HODGEMAN COUNTY HEALTH CENTER, JETMORE, KS, p. A267
HOISINGTON LUTHERAN HOSPITAL, HOISINGTON, KS, p. A266
HOKE HOSPITAL, RAEFORD, NC, p. A516
HOLDENVILLE GENERAL HOSPITAL, HOLDENVILLE, OK, p. A560
HOLLAND COMMUNITY HOSPITAL, HOLLAND, MI, p. A357
HOLLAND HOSPITAL, HOLLAND, MI, p. A357
HOLLY HILL HOSPITAL, RALEIGH, NC, p. A516
HOLLY HILL/ CHARTER BEHAVIORAL, RALEIGH, NC, p. A516
HOLLYWOOD COMMUNITY HOSPITAL, LOS ANGELES, CA, p. A74
HOLLYWOOD COMMUNITY HOSPITAL OF VAN NUYS, VAN NUYS, CA, p. A103
HOLLYWOOD MEDICAL CENTER, HOLLYWOOD, FL, p. A139
HOLLYWOOD PAVILION, HOLLYWOOD, FL, p. A139
HOLLYWOOD PRESBYTERIAN MEDICAL CENTER, LOS ANGELES, CA, p. A74
HOLMES COUNTY HOSPITAL AND CLINICS, LEXINGTON, MS, p. A396
HOLMES REGIONAL MEDICAL CENTER, MELBOURNE, FL, p. A145
HOLSTON VALLEY MEDICAL CENTER, KINGSPORT, TN, p. A641
HOLTON CITY HOSPITAL, HOLTON, KS, p. A266
HOLTON COMMUNITY HOSPITAL, HOLTON, KS, p. A266
HOLTZ CHILDREN'S HOSPITAL JACKSON MEMORIAL HOSPITAL, MIAMI, FL, p. A146
HOLY CROSS GERMANTOWN HOSPITAL, GERMANTOWN, MD, p. A329
HOLY CROSS HEALTH, SILVER SPRING, MD, p. A332
HOLY CROSS HOSPITAL, CHICAGO, IL, p. A198
HOLY CROSS HOSPITAL, FORT LAUDERDALE, FL, p. A137
HOLY CROSS HOSPITAL, SALT LAKE CITY, UT, p. A732
HOLY CROSS HOSPITAL, SILVER SPRING, MD, p. A332
HOLY CROSS HOSPITAL, TAOS, NM, p. A473
HOLY CROSS MEDICAL CENTER, MISSION HILLS, CA, p. A78
HOLY FAMILY HOME FOR THE AGED, BROOKLYN, NY, p. A477
HOLY FAMILY HOPSITAL AT MERRIMACK VALLEY, HAVERHILL, MA, p. A340
HOLY FAMILY HOSPITAL, METHUEN, MA, p. A341
HOLY FAMILY HOSPITAL, SPOKANE, WA, p. A765
HOLY FAMILY MEMORIAL, MANITOWOC, WI, p. A788
HOLY FAMILY MEMORIAL MEDICAL CENTER, MANITOWOC, WI, p. A788
HOLY NAME HOSPITAL, TEANECK, NJ, p. A464
HOLY NAME MEDICAL CENTER, TEANECK, NJ, p. A464
HOLY NAME OF JESUS MED CTR, GADSDEN, AL, p. A19
HOLY REDEEMER HOSPITAL, MEADOWBROOK, PA, p. A596

HOLY REDEEMER HOSPITAL AND MEDICAL CENTER, MEADOWBROOK, PA, p. A596
HOLY ROSARY HEALTH CENTER, MILES CITY, MT, p. A426
HOLY ROSARY HEALTHCARE, MILES CITY, MT, p. A426
HOLY ROSARY MEDICAL CENTER, ONTARIO, OR, p. A578
HOLY SPIRIT—A GEISINGER AFFILIATE, CAMP HILL, PA, p. A585
HOLYOKE HOSPITAL, HOLYOKE, MA, p. A340
HOLYOKE MEDICAL CENTER, HOLYOKE, MA, p. A340
HOLZER MEDICAL CENTER—JACKSON, JACKSON, OH, p. A542
HOLZER MEDICAL CENTER, GALLIPOLIS, OH, p. A541
HOMER MEMORIAL HOSPITAL, HOMER, LA, p. A303
HONOKAA HOSPITAL, HONOKAA, HI, p. A184
HONORHEALTH DEER VALLEY MEDICAL CENTER, PHOENIX, AZ, p. A36
HONORHEALTH JOHN C. LINCOLN MEDICAL CENTER, PHOENIX, AZ, p. A36
HONORHEALTH REHABILITATION HOSPITAL, SCOTTSDALE, AZ, p. A38
HONORHEALTH SCOTTSDALE OSBORN MEDICAL CENTER, SCOTTSDALE, AZ, p. A38
HONORHEALTH SCOTTSDALE SHEA MEDICAL CENTER, SCOTTSDALE, AZ, p. A38
HONORHEALTH SCOTTSDALE THOMPSON PEAK MEDICAL CENTER, SCOTTSDALE, AZ, p. A38
HOOD GENERAL HOSPITAL, GRANBURY, TX, p. A682
HOOD MEMORIAL HOSPITAL, AMITE, LA, p. A296
HOOD RIVER MEMORIAL HOSPITAL, HOOD RIVER, OR, p. A576
HOOPESTON REGIONAL HEALTH CENTER, HOOPESTON, IL, p. A208
HOPEDALE HOSPITAL, HOPEDALE, IL, p. A208
HOPEDALE MEDICAL COMPLEX, HOPEDALE, IL, p. A208
HOPI HEALTH CARE CENTER, KEAMS CANYON, AZ, p. A33
HOPKINS COUNTY MEMORIAL HOSPITAL, SULPHUR SPRINGS, TX, p. A718
HORIZON MEDICAL CENTER, DENTON, TX, p. A671
HORIZON MEDICAL CENTER, DICKSON, TN, p. A637
HORIZON MEDICAL CENTER, LLC, DENTON, TX, p. A672
HORIZON SPECIALTY HOSPITAL, LAS VEGAS, NV, p. A443
HORN MEMORIAL HOSPITAL, IDA GROVE, IA, p. A251
HORSHAM CLINIC, AMBLER, PA, p. A584
HOSP AUTHORITY OF TOWNS CNTY, HIAWASSEE, GA, p. A173
HOSPICE OF NORTHERN VIRGINIA, ARLINGTON, VA, p. A738
HOSPITAL BUEN SAMARITANO, AGUADILLA, PR, p. A805
HOSPITAL CUIDADO AGUDO ESPECIALIZADO EN PACIENTES POLITRAUMATIZADOS, SAN JUAN, PR, p. A810
HOSPITAL DE DAMAS, PONCE, PR, p. A809
HOSPITAL DE LA CONCEPCION, SAN GERMAN, PR, p. A809
HOSPITAL DE LA UNIVERSIDAD DE PUERTO RICO/DR. FEDERICO TRILLA, CAROLINA, PR, p. A807
HOSPITAL DE PSIQUIATRIA, SAN JUAN, PR, p. A810
HOSPITAL DE PSIQUIATRIA FORENSE, PONCE, PR, p. A809
HOSPITAL DEL MAESTRO, SAN JUAN, PR, p. A810
HOSPITAL DISTRICT 6—PATTERSON HEALTH CENTER, ANTHONY, KS, p. A261
HOSPITAL DISTRICT 6, ANTHONY, KS, p. A261
HOSPITAL DISTRICT NO 1 OF RICE COUNTY, LYONS, KS, p. A270
HOSPITAL DISTRICT NUMBER 1 OF CRAWFORD COUNTY, GIRARD, KS, p. A265
HOSPITAL DISTRICT ONE OF RICE COUNTY, LYONS, KS, p. A270
HOSPITAL DR FEDERICO TRILLA, CAROLINA, PR, p. A807
HOSPITAL DR. CAYETANO COLL Y TOSTE, ARECIBO, PR, p. A806
HOSPITAL DR. DOMINGUEZ, HUMACAO, PR, p. A808
HOSPITAL DR. SUSONI, ARECIBO, PR, p. A806
HOSPITAL EPISCOPAL CRISTO REDENTOR, GUAYAMA, PR, p. A807
HOSPITAL EPISCOPAL SAN LUCAS GUAYAMA, GUAYAMA, PR, p. A807
HOSPITAL FOR BEHAVIORAL MEDICINE, WORCESTER, MA, p. A346
HOSPITAL FOR EXTENDED RECOVERY, NORFOLK, VA, p. A748
HOSPITAL FOR SICK CHILDREN, WASHINGTON, DC, p. A129
HOSPITAL FOR SPECIAL CARE, NEW BRITAIN, CT, p. A123
HOSPITAL FOR SPECIAL SURGERY, NEW YORK, NY, p. A490
HOSPITAL HERMANOS MELENDEZ, BAYAMON, PR, p. A806
HOSPITAL HIMA DE HUMACAO, HUMACAO, PR, p. A808
HOSPITAL HMA DE HUMACAO, HUMACAO, PR, p. A808
HOSPITAL MANATI MEDICAL CENTER, MANATI, PR, p. A808
HOSPITAL MATILDE BRENES, BAYAMON, PR, p. A806
HOSPITAL MENONITA DE CAGUAS, CAGUAS, PR, p. A806
HOSPITAL MENONITA DE CAYEY, CAYEY, PR, p. A807
HOSPITAL METROPOLITAN, SAN JUAN, PR, p. A810

HOSPITAL METROPOLITANO DR. SUSONI, ARECIBO, PR, p. A806
HOSPITAL METROPOLITANO DR. TITO MATTEI, YAUCO, PR, p. A811
HOSPITAL METROPOLITANO SAN GERMAN, SAN GERMAN, PR, p. A809
HOSPITAL OF SAINT RAPHAEL, NEW HAVEN, CT, p. A124
HOSPITAL OF THE GOOD SAMARITAN, LOS ANGELES, CA, p. A74
HOSPITAL OF THE UNIV OF PENN, PHILADELPHIA, PA, p. A600
HOSPITAL OF THE UNIVERSITY OF PENNSYLVANIA, PHILADELPHIA, PA, p. A600
HOSPITAL ORIENTE, HUMACAO, PR, p. A808
HOSPITAL PAVIA, SAN JUAN, PR, p. A810
HOSPITAL PAVIA ARECIBO, ARECIBO, PR, p. A806
HOSPITAL PAVIA YAUCO, YAUCO, PR, p. A811
HOSPITAL PAVIA-HATO REY, SAN JUAN, PR, p. A810
HOSPITAL PAVIA-SANTURCE, SAN JUAN, PR, p. A810
HOSPITAL PEREA, MAYAGUEZ, PR, p. A808
HOSPITAL PSIQUIATRICO CORRECCIONAL, SAN JUAN, PR, p. A810
HOSPITAL PSIQUIATRICO METROPOLITANO, CABO ROJO, PR, p. A806
HOSPITAL SAN ANTONIO, MAYAGUEZ, PR, p. A808
HOSPITAL SAN CARLOS BORROMEO, MOCA, PR, p. A808
HOSPITAL SAN CRISTOBAL, COTO LAUREL, PR, p. A807
HOSPITAL SAN FRANCISCO, SAN JUAN, PR, p. A810
HOSPITAL SAN GERARDO, SAN JUAN, PR, p. A810
HOSPITAL SAN JUAN CAPESTRANO, SAN JUAN, PR, p. A810
HOSPITAL SAN PABLO, BAYAMON, PR, p. A806
HOSPITAL SAN PABLO DEL ESTE, FAJARDO, PR, p. A807
HOSPITAL UNIVERSITARIO DR. RAMON RUIZ ARNAU, BAYAMON, PR, p. A806
HOT SPRINGS COUNTY MEMORIAL HOSPITAL, THERMOPOLIS, WY, p. A804
HOULTON REGIONAL HOSPITAL, HOULTON, ME, p. A321
HOUSTON BEHAVIORAL HEALTHCARE HOSPITAL, HOUSTON, TX, p. A686
HOUSTON COMMUNITY HOSPITAL, HOUSTON, MS, p. A394
HOUSTON COUNTY COMMUNITY HOSPITAL, ERIN, TN, p. A638
HOUSTON MEDICAL CENTER, WARNER ROBINS, GA, p. A183
HOUSTON METHODIST BAYTOWN HOSPITAL, BAYTOWN, TX, p. A657
HOUSTON METHODIST CLEAR LAKE HOSPITAL, NASSAU BAY, TX, p. A702
HOUSTON METHODIST CONTINUING CARE HOSPITAL, KATY, TX, p. A692
HOUSTON METHODIST HOSPITAL, HOUSTON, TX, p. A686
HOUSTON METHODIST SAN JACINTO HOSPITAL, BAYTOWN, TX, p. A657
HOUSTON METHODIST ST. CATHERINE HOSPITAL, KATY, TX, p. A692
HOUSTON METHODIST ST. JOHN HOSPITAL, NASSAU BAY, TX, p. A702
HOUSTON METHODIST SUGAR LAND HOSPITAL, SUGAR LAND, TX, p. A717
HOUSTON METHODIST THE WOODLANDS HOSPITAL, THE WOODLANDS, TX, p. A720
HOUSTON METHODIST WEST HOSPITAL, HOUSTON, TX, p. A686
HOUSTON METHODIST WILLOWBROOK HOSPITAL, HOUSTON, TX, p. A686
HOUSTON NORTHWEST MEDICAL CENTER, HOUSTON, TX, p. A686
HOUSTON PHYSICIANS HOSPITAL, WEBSTER, TX, p. A724
HOWARD A. RUSK REHABILITATION CENTER, COLUMBIA, MO, p. A405
HOWARD COUNTY COMMUNITY HOSPITAL, SAINT PAUL, NE, p. A439
HOWARD COUNTY GENERAL HOSPITAL, COLUMBIA, MD, p. A328
HOWARD COUNTY HOSPITAL, CRESCO, IA, p. A247
HOWARD COUNTY MEDICAL CENTER, SAINT PAUL, NE, p. A439
HOWARD MEMORIAL HOSPITAL, NASHVILLE, AR, p. A51
HOWARD UNIVERSITY HOSPITAL, WASHINGTON, DC, p. A129
HOWARD YOUNG MEDICAL CENTER, WOODRUFF, WI, p. A800
H R I HOSPITAL, BROOKLINE, MA, p. A337
H.S.C. MEDICAL CENTER, MALVERN, AR, p. A50
HSHS GOOD SHEPHERD HOSPITAL, SHELBYVILLE, IL, p. A220
HSHS HOLY FAMILY HOSPITAL IN GREENVILLE, GREENVILLE, IL, p. A206
HSHS SACRED HEART HOSPITAL, EAU CLAIRE, WI, p. A783
HSHS ST. ANTHONY'S MEMORIAL HOSPITAL, EFFINGHAM, IL, p. A203
HSHS ST. CLARE MEMORIAL HOSPITAL, OCONTO FALLS, WI, p. A793

HSHS ST. ELIZABETH'S HOSPITAL, O'FALLON, IL, p. A215
HSHS ST. FRANCIS HOSPITAL, LITCHFIELD, IL, p. A210
HSHS ST. JOHN'S HOSPITAL, SPRINGFIELD, IL, p. A220
HSHS ST. JOSEPH'S HOSPITAL, BREESE, IL, p. A196
HSHS ST. JOSEPH'S HOSPITAL, CHIPPEWA FALLS, WI, p. A781
HSHS ST. JOSEPH'S HOSPITAL, HIGHLAND, IL, p. A207
HSHS ST. MARY'S HOSPITAL, DECATUR, IL, p. A202
HSHS ST. MARY'S HOSPITAL MEDICAL CENTER, GREEN BAY, WI, p. A785
HSHS ST. NICHOLAS HOSPITAL, SHEBOYGAN, WI, p. A796
HSHS ST. VINCENT HOSPITAL, GREEN BAY, WI, p. A785
HUDSON COUNTY MEADOWVIEW PSYCHIATRIC HOSPITAL, SECAUCUS, NJ, p. A462
HUDSON HOSPITAL AND CLINIC, HUDSON, WI, p. A786
HUDSON HOSPITAL AND CLINICS, HUDSON, WI, p. A786
HUDSON REGIONAL HOSPITAL, SECAUCUS, NJ, p. A463
HUDSON VALLEY HOSPITAL CENTER, CORTLANDT MANOR, NY, p. A482
HUERFANO MEDICAL CENTER, WALSENBURG, CO, p. A119
HUGGINS HOSPITAL, WOLFEBORO, NH, p. A451
HUGH CHATHAM MEMORIAL HOSPITAL, ELKIN, NC, p. A509
HUGULEY MEMORIAL MEDICAL CENTER, BURLESON, TX, p. A662
HUHUKAM MEMORIAL HOSPITAL, SACATON, AZ, p. A37
HUMANA HOSP-GREENBRIER VALLEY, RONCEVERTE, WV, p. A776
HUMANA HOSPITAL-ABILENE, ABILENE, TX, p. A651
HUMANA HOSPITAL-ENTERPRISE, ENTERPRISE, AL, p. A18
HUMANA HOSPITAL-LOUISA, LOUISA, KY, p. A287
HUMANA HOSPITAL-MARKSVILLE, MARKSVILLE, LA, p. A308
HUMANA HOSPITAL-OAKDALE, OAKDALE, LA, p. A312
HUMANA HOSPITAL-TACOMA, TACOMA, WA, p. A766
HUMANA HOSPITAL-UNIVERSITY, LOUISVILLE, KY, p. A288
HUMANA HOSPITAL-WINN PARISH, WINNFIELD, LA, p. A317
HUMBOLDT COUNTY MEMORIAL HOSPITAL, HUMBOLDT, IA, p. A251
HUMBOLDT COUNTY MENTAL HEALTH, EUREKA, CA, p. A63
HUMBOLDT GENERAL HOSPITAL, WINNEMUCCA, NV, p. A447
HUNT MEMORIAL HOSPITAL DISTRICT, GREENVILLE, TX, p. A682
HUNT REGIONAL MEDICAL CENTER, GREENVILLE, TX, p. A682
HUNTER HOLMES MCGUIRE VETERANS AFFAIRS MEDICAL CENTER-RICHMOND, RICHMOND, VA, p. A750
HUNTER HOLMES MCGUIRE VETERANS AFFAIRS MEDICAL CENTER-RICHMOND, VA, RICHMOND, VA, p. A750
HUNTERDON HEALTHCARE, FLEMINGTON, NJ, p. A455
HUNTERDON MEDICAL CENTER, FLEMINGTON, NJ, p. A455
HUNTINGTON BEACH HOSPITAL, HUNTINGTON BEACH, CA, p. A68
HUNTINGTON BEACH MEDICAL CTR, HUNTINGTON BEACH, CA, p. A68
HUNTINGTON CREEK RECOVERY CENTER, SHICKSHINNY, PA, p. A608
HUNTINGTON HOSPITAL, HUNTINGTON, NY, p. A485
HUNTINGTON HOSPITAL, PASADENA, CA, p. A85
HUNTINGTON MEMORIAL HOSPITAL, HUNTINGTON, IN, p. A230
HUNTINGTON MEMORIAL HOSPITAL, PASADENA, CA, p. A85
HUNTINGTON VETERANS AFFAIRS MEDICAL CENTER, HUNTINGTON, WV, p. A773
HUNTSVILLE HOSPITAL, HUNTSVILLE, AL, p. A20
HUNTSVILLE HOSPITAL EAST, HUNTSVILLE, AL, p. A20
HUNTSVILLE MEMORIAL HOSPITAL, HUNTSVILLE, TX, p. A690
HURLEY HEALTH CENTER, COALGATE, OK, p. A558
HURLEY MEDICAL CENTER, FLINT, MI, p. A354
HURON MEDICAL CENTER, BAD AXE, MI, p. A349
HURON REGIONAL MEDICAL CENTER, HURON, SD, p. A629
HURON VALLEY-SINAI HOSPITAL, COMMERCE TOWNSHIP, MI, p. A351
HUTCHINSON AREA HEALTH CARE, HUTCHINSON, MN, p. A378
HUTCHINSON HEALTH, HUTCHINSON, MN, p. A378
HUTCHINSON REGIONAL MEDICAL CENTER, HUTCHINSON, KS, p. A266
HUTZEL WOMEN'S HOSPITAL, DETROIT, MI, p. A353

I

I. GONZALEZ MARTINEZ ONCOLOGIC HOSPITAL, HATO REY, PR, p. A808
IBERIA GENERAL HOSP & MED CTR, NEW IBERIA, LA, p. A310

IBERIA MEDICAL CENTER, NEW IBERIA, LA, p. A310
IBERIA REHABILITATION HOSPITAL, NEW IBERIA, LA, p. A310
ICARE REHABILITATION HOSPITAL, FLOWER MOUND, TX, p. A677
ICON HOSPITAL, HUMBLE, TX, p. A689
IDAHO DOCTOR'S HOSPITAL, BLACKFOOT, ID, p. A188
IHC EVANSTON REGIONAL HOSPITAL, EVANSTON, WY, p. A802
ILLINI COMMUNITY HOSPITAL, PITTSFIELD, IL, p. A217
ILLINOIS VALLEY COMMUNITY HOSPITAL, PERU, IL, p. A217
IMMANUEL ST. JOSEPH'S-MAYO HEALTH SYSTEM, MANKATO, MN, p. A379
IMPERIAL POINT MEDICAL CENTER, FORT LAUDERDALE, FL, p. A137
INCLINE VILLAGE COMMUNITY HOSPITAL, INCLINE VILLAGE, NV, p. A442
INDEPENDENCE MENTAL HEALTH INSTITUTE, INDEPENDENCE, IA, p. A251
INDIAN HEALTH SERV HOSP, RAPID CITY, SD, p. A630
INDIAN HEALTH SERVICE—QUENTIN N. BURDICK MEMORIAL HEALTH CARE FACILITY, BELCOURT, ND, p. A521
INDIAN HEALTH SERVICE HOSPITAL, RAPID CITY, SD, p. A630
INDIAN PATH COMMUNITY HOSPITAL, KINGSPORT, TN, p. A641
INDIAN PATH MEDICAL CENTER, KINGSPORT, TN, p. A641
INDIAN RIVER MEDICAL CENTER, VERO BEACH, FL, p. A161
INDIANA HEART HOSPITAL, INDIANAPOLIS, IN, p. A232
INDIANA HOSPITAL, INDIANA, PA, p. A592
INDIANA ORTHOPAEDIC HOSPITAL, INDIANAPOLIS, IN, p. A232
INDIANA REGIONAL MEDICAL CENTER, INDIANA, PA, p. A592
INDIANA SPINE HOSPITAL, CARMEL, IN, p. A225
INDIANA UNIVERSITY HEALTH ARNETT HOSPITAL, LAFAYETTE, IN, p. A234
INDIANA UNIVERSITY HEALTH BALL MEMORIAL HOSPITAL, MUNCIE, IN, p. A237
INDIANA UNIVERSITY HEALTH BEDFORD HOSPITAL, BEDFORD, IN, p. A224
INDIANA UNIVERSITY HEALTH BLACKFORD HOSPITAL, HARTFORD CITY, IN, p. A230
INDIANA UNIVERSITY HEALTH BLOOMINGTON HOSPITAL, BLOOMINGTON, IN, p. A224
INDIANA UNIVERSITY HEALTH FRANKFORT, FRANKFORT, IN, p. A229
INDIANA UNIVERSITY HEALTH JAY HOSPITAL, PORTLAND, IN, p. A239
INDIANA UNIVERSITY HEALTH LA PORTE HOSPITAL, LA PORTE, IN, p. A234
INDIANA UNIVERSITY HEALTH METHODIST HOSPITAL, FRANKFORT, IN, p. A229
INDIANA UNIVERSITY HEALTH NORTH HOSPITAL, CARMEL, IN, p. A225
INDIANA UNIVERSITY HEALTH PAOLI HOSPITAL, PAOLI, IN, p. A238
INDIANA UNIVERSITY HEALTH TIPTON HOSPITAL, TIPTON, IN, p. A241
INDIANA UNIVERSITY HEALTH UNIVERSITY HOSPITAL, INDIANAPOLIS, IN, p. A232
INDIANA UNIVERSITY HEALTH WEST HOSPITAL, AVON, IN, p. A223
INDIANA UNIVERSITY HEALTH WHITE MEMORIAL HOSPITAL, MONTICELLO, IN, p. A236
INDIANA UNIVERSITY HOSPITAL, INDIANAPOLIS, IN, p. A232
INDIANA UNIVERSITY MED CENTER, INDIANAPOLIS, IN, p. A232
INDIANHEAD MEDICAL CENTER, SHELL LAKE, WI, p. A796
INDUSTRIAL HOSPITAL, SAN JUAN, PR, p. A811
INFIRMARY LONG TERM ACUTE CARE HOSPITAL, MOBILE, AL, p. A22
INGALLS HOSPITAL, HARVEY, IL, p. A207
INGALLS MEMORIAL HOSPITAL, HARVEY, IL, p. A207
INGHAM REGIONAL MEDICAL CENTER, LANSING, MI, p. A360
INGHAM REGIONAL MEDICAL CENTER, GREENLAWN CAMPUS, LANSING, MI, p. A360
INGHAM REGIONAL ORTHOPEDIC HOSPITAL, PENNSYLVANIA CAMPUS, LANSING, MI, p. A360
INLAND HOSPITAL, WATERVILLE, ME, p. A323
INLAND NORTHWEST BEHAVIORAL HEALTH, SPOKANE, WA, p. A765
INLAND VALLEY REG MEDICAL CTR, WILDOMAR, CA, p. A105
INNER HARBOUR, DOUGLASVILLE, GA, p. A171
INOVA ALEXANDRIA HOSPITAL, ALEXANDRIA, VA, p. A738
INOVA FAIR OAKS HOSPITAL, FAIRFAX, VA, p. A741
INOVA FAIRFAX HOSPITAL, FALLS CHURCH, VA, p. A741
INOVA LOUDOUN HOSPITAL, LEESBURG, VA, p. A744
INOVA MOUNT VERNON HOSPITAL, ALEXANDRIA, VA, p. A738
INSPIRA MEDICAL CENTER-ELMER, ELMER, NJ, p. A455
INSPIRA MEDICAL CENTER-VINELAND, VINELAND, NJ, p.A465

INSPIRA MEDICAL CENTER-WOODBURY, WOODBURY, NJ, p. A466
INSPIRA PONCE, PONCE, PR, p. A809
INSPIRE SPECIALTY HOSPITAL, MIDWEST CITY, OK, p. A562
INSTITUTE FOR ORTHOPAEDIC SURGERY, LIMA, OH, p. A543
INSTITUTE OF PSYCHIATRY, CHICAGO, IL, p. A198
INTEGRIS BAPTIST MEDICAL CENTER, OKLAHOMA CITY, OK, p. A564
INTEGRIS BAPTIST REGIONAL HEALTH CENTER, MIAMI, OK, p. A562
INTEGRIS BASS BAPTIST HEALTH CENTER, ENID, OK, p. A559
INTEGRIS BASS BAPTIST HOSPITAL, ENID, OK, p. A559
INTEGRIS BASS BEHAVIORAL HEALTH SYSTEM, ENID, OK, p. A559
INTEGRIS CANADIAN VALLEY HOSPITAL, YUKON, OK, p. A572
INTEGRIS CANADIAN VALLEY REGIONAL HOSPITAL, YUKON, OK, p. A572
INTEGRIS COMMUNITY HOSPITAL AT COUNCIL CROSSING, OKLAHOMA CITY, OK, p. A564
INTEGRIS DEACONESS, OKLAHOMA CITY, OK, p. A564
INTEGRIS GROVE HOSPITAL, GROVE, OK, p. A559
INTEGRIS HEALTH EDMOND, EDMOND, OK, p. A558
INTEGRIS MENTAL HEALTH SYSTEM-SPENCER, SPENCER, OK, p. A568
INTEGRIS MIAMI HOSPITAL, MIAMI, OK, p. A562
INTEGRIS SOUTHWEST MEDICAL CENTER, OKLAHOMA CITY, OK, p. A564
INTER-COMMUNITY MED CENTER, COVINA, CA, p. A61
INTERFAITH MEDICAL CENTER, BROOKLYN, NY, p. A478
INTERIM LSU PUBLIC HOSPITAL, NEW ORLEANS, LA, p. A310
INTERMEDICAL HOSPITAL OF SOUTH CAROLINA, COLUMBIA, SC, p. A617
INTERMOUNTAIN HOSPITAL, BOISE, ID, p. A188
INTERMOUNTAIN MEDICAL CENTER, MURRAY, UT, p. A729
INTERNATIONAL FALLS MEM HOSP, INTERNATIONAL FALLS, MN, p. A378
INTRACARE NORTH HOSPITAL, HOUSTON, TX, p. A686
IOANNIS A LOUGARIS VA MED CTR, RENO, NV, p. A445
IONIA COUNTY MEMORIAL HOSPITAL, IONIA, MI, p. A358
IOWA CITY VA HEALTH CARE SYSTEM, IOWA CITY, IA, p. A252
IOWA CITY VETERANS AFFAIRS HEALTH CARE SYSTEM, IOWA CITY, IA, p. A252
IOWA MEDICAL AND CLASSIFICATION CENTER, CORALVILLE, IA, p. A246
IOWA METHODIST MEDICAL CENTER, DES MOINES, IA, p. A248
IOWA SPECIALTY HOSPITAL-BELMOND, BELMOND, IA, p. A244
IOWA SPECIALTY HOSPITAL-CLARION, CLARION, IA, p. A246
IRA DAVENPORT MEMORIAL HOSPITAL, BATH, NY, p. A475
IRAAN GENERAL HOSPITAL, IRAAN, TX, p. A690
IREDELL HEALTH SYSTEM, STATESVILLE, NC, p. A519
IREDELL MEMORIAL HOSPITAL, STATESVILLE, NC, p. A519
IRON COUNTY HOSPITAL, PILOT KNOB, MO, p. A413
IRON COUNTY MEDICAL CENTER, PILOT KNOB, MO, p. A413
IROQUOIS MEMORIAL HOSPITAL AND RESIDENT HOME, WATSEKA, IL, p. A222
IRVING COPPELL SURGICAL HOSPITAL, IRVING, TX, p. A690
IRWIN ARMY COMMUNITY HOSPITAL, JUNCTION CITY, KS, p. A267
IRWIN COUNTY HOSPITAL, OCILLA, GA, p. A178
ISLAND HEALTH NORTHWEST, ANACORTES, WA, p. A755
ISLAND HOSPITAL, ANACORTES, WA, p. A755
ITASCA MEDICAL CENTER, GRAND RAPIDS, MN, p. A377
IU HEALTH SAXONY HOSPITAL, FISHERS, IN, p. A228
IU HEALTH WHITE MEMORIAL HOSPITAL, MONTICELLO, IN, p. A236
IUKA HOSPITAL, IUKA, MS, p. A394
IVINSON MEMORIAL HOSPITAL, LARAMIE, WY, p. A803
IZARD COUNTY MEDICAL CENTER, CALICO ROCK, AR, p. A43

J

J. ARTHUR DOSHER MEMORIAL HOSPITAL, SOUTHPORT, NC, p. A518
JACK C. MONTGOMERY VETERAN AFFAIRS MEDICAL CENTER, MUSKOGEE, OK, p. A562
JACK C. MONTGOMERY VETERANS AFFAIRS MEDICAL CENTER, MUSKOGEE, OK, p. A562
JACK COUNTY HOSPITAL, JACKSBORO, TX, p. A691
JACK D WEILER HOSPITAL OF ALBERT EINSTEIN COLLEGE OF MEDICINE, BRONX, NY, p. A476
JACK HUGHSTON MEMORIAL HOSPITAL, PHENIX CITY, AL, p. A23

JACKSON BEHAVIORAL HEALTH HOSPITAL, MIAMI, FL, p. A146
JACKSON BROOK INSTITUTE, WESTBROOK, ME, p. A323
JACKSON COUNTY HOSPITAL, EDNA, TX, p. A674
JACKSON COUNTY HOSPITAL, SCOTTSBORO, AL, p. A24
JACKSON COUNTY HOSPITAL DISTRICT, EDNA, TX, p. A674
JACKSON COUNTY MEMORIAL HOSPITAL, ALTUS, OK, p. A555
JACKSON COUNTY PUBLIC HOSPITAL, MAQUOKETA, IA, p. A253
JACKSON COUNTY REGIONAL HEALTH CENTER, MAQUOKETA, IA, p. A253
JACKSON GENERAL HOSPITAL, RIPLEY, WV, p. A776
JACKSON HEALTH SYSTEM, MIAMI, FL, p. A146
JACKSON HOSPITAL, MARIANNA, FL, p. A145
JACKSON HOSPITAL AND CLINIC, MONTGOMERY, AL, p. A22
JACKSON MEDICAL CENTER, JACKSON, AL, p. A20
JACKSON MEMORIAL HOSPITAL, MIAMI, FL, p. A146
JACKSON NORTH MEDICAL CENTER, NORTH MIAMI BEACH, FL, p. A149
JACKSON PARISH HOSPITAL, JONESBORO, LA, p. A304
JACKSON PARK HOSPITAL, CHICAGO, IL, p. A198
JACKSON PARK HOSPITAL AND MEDICAL CENTER, CHICAGO, IL, p. A198
JACKSON PURCHASE MEDICAL CENTER, MAYFIELD, KY, p. A290
JACKSON SOUTH COMMUNITY HOSPITAL, MIAMI, FL, p. A146
JACKSON-MADISON COUNTY GENERAL HOSPITAL, JACKSON, TN, p. A639
JACOBI MEDICAL CENTER, BRONX, NY, p. A476
JACOBSON MEMORIAL HOSPITAL CARE CENTER, ELGIN, ND, p. A522
JAMAICA HOSPITAL, JAMAICA, NY, p. A486
JAMAICA HOSPITAL MEDICAL CENTER, JAMAICA, NY, p. A486
JAMES A. HALEY VETERANS' HOSPITAL, TAMPA, FL, p. A159
JAMES A. HALEY VETERANS' HOSPITAL-TAMPA, TAMPA, FL, p. A159
JAMES B. HAGGIN MEMORIAL HOSPITAL, HARRODSBURG, KY, p. A284
JAMES CANCER HOSPITAL AND SOLOVE RESEARCH INSTITUTE, COLUMBUS, OH, p. A536
JAMES E. VAN ZANDT VETERANS AFFAIRS MEDICAL CENTER, ALTOONA, PA, p. A584
JAMES H & CECILE C QUILLEN, JOHNSON CITY, TN, p. A640
JAMES H. QUILLEN VETERANS AFFAIRS MEDICAL CENTER, MOUNTAIN HOME, TN, p. A646
JAMES J. PETERS VETERANS AFFAIRS MEDICAL CENTER, BRONX, NY, p. A476
JAMES M JACKSON MEMORIAL HOSP, MIAMI, FL, p. A146
JAMESTOWN HOSPITAL, JAMESTOWN, ND, p. A524
JAMESTOWN REGIONAL MEDICAL CENTER, JAMESTOWN, ND, p. A524
JAMESTOWN REGIONAL MEDICAL CENTER, JAMESTOWN, TN, p. A640
JANE PHILLIPS MEDICAL CENTER, BARTLESVILLE, OK, p. A556
JANE PHILLIPS NOWATA HEALTH CENTER, NOWATA, OK, p. A563
JANE TODD CRAWFORD HOSPITAL, GREENSBURG, KY, p. A284
JANE TODD CRAWFORD MEM HOSP, GREENSBURG, KY, p. A284
JASPER COUNTY HOSPITAL, RENSSELAER, IN, p. A239
JASPER GENERAL HOSPITAL, BAY SPRINGS, MS, p. A389
JASPER MEMORIAL HOSPITAL, MONTICELLO, GA, p. A177
JAVON BEA HOSPITAL-ROCKTON, ROCKFORD, IL, p. A218
JAY COUNTY HOSPITAL, PORTLAND, IN, p. A239
JAY HOSPITAL, JAY, FL, p. A142
J. C. BLAIR MEMORIAL HOSPITAL, HUNTINGDON, PA, p. A592
J D MCCARTHY CTR FOR CHILDREN, NORMAN, OK, p. A563
J. D. MCCARTY CENTER FOR CHILDREN WITH DEVELOPMENTAL DISABILITIES, NORMAN, OK, p. A563
JEFF DAVIS HOSPITAL, HAZLEHURST, GA, p. A173
JEFFERSON COMMUNITY HEALTH AND LIFE, FAIRBURY, NE, p. A431
JEFFERSON COMMUNITY HEALTH CENTER, FAIRBURY, NE, p. A431
JEFFERSON COUNTY HEALTH CENTER, FAIRFIELD, IA, p. A250
JEFFERSON COUNTY HOSPITAL, FAIRFIELD, IA, p. A250
JEFFERSON COUNTY HOSPITAL, FAYETTE, MS, p. A392
JEFFERSON COUNTY HOSPITAL, WAURIKA, OK, p. A571
JEFFERSON COUNTY MEMORIAL HOSPITAL, WINCHESTER, KS, p. A279
JEFFERSON DAVIS COMMUNITY HOSPITAL, PRENTISS, MS, p. A399
JEFFERSON DAVIS HOSPITAL, HOUSTON, TX, p. A686
JEFFERSON GENERAL HOSPITAL, PORT TOWNSEND, WA, p. A762

JEFFERSON HEALTH NORTHEAST, PHILADELPHIA, PA, p. A600
JEFFERSON HEALTH NORTHEST, PHILADELPHIA, PA, p. A600
JEFFERSON HEALTHCARE, PORT TOWNSEND, WA, p. A762
JEFFERSON HOSPITAL, JEFFERSON HILLS, PA, p. A593
JEFFERSON HOSPITAL, LOUISVILLE, GA, p. A175
JEFFERSON MEDICAL CENTER, RANSON, WV, p. A776
JEFFERSON MEMORIAL HOSPITAL, RANSON, WV, p. A776
JEFFERSON METHODIST HOSPITAL, PHILADELPHIA, PA, p. A600
JEFFERSON REGIONAL MEDICAL CENTER, FESTUS, MO, p. A406
JEFFERSON REGIONAL MEDICAL CENTER, PINE BLUFF, AR, p. A52
JEFFERSON STRATFORD HOSPITAL, STRATFORD, NJ, p. A463
JEFFERSON WASHINGTON TOWNSHIP HOSPITAL, TURNERSVILLE, NJ, p. A464
JELLICO COMMUNITY HOSPITAL, JELLICO, TN, p. A640
JENKINS COUNTY MEDICAL CENTER, MILLEN, GA, p. A177
JENNERSVILLE HOSPITAL, WEST GROVE, PA, p. A610
JENNERSVILLE REGIONAL HOSPITAL, WEST GROVE, PA, p. A610
JENNIE EDMUNDSON HOSPITAL, COUNCIL BLUFFS, IA, p. A247
JENNIE M. MELHAM MEMORIAL MEDICAL CENTER, BROKEN BOW, NE, p. A430
JENNIE STUART MEDICAL CENTER, HOPKINSVILLE, KY, p. A285
JENNINGS AMERICAN LEGION HOSPITAL, JENNINGS, LA, p. A304
JENNINGS SENIOR CARE HOSPITAL, JENNINGS, LA, p. A304
JEROLD PHELPS COMMUNITY HOSPITAL, GARBERVILLE, CA, p. A66
JEROME GOLDEN CENTER FOR BEHAVIORAL HEALTH, INC., WEST PALM BEACH, FL, p. A162
JERRY L. PETTIS MEMORIAL VETERANS MEDICAL CENTER, LOMA LINDA, CA, p. A71
JERSEY CITY MEDICAL CENTER, JERSEY CITY, NJ, p. A456
JERSEY COMMUNITY HOSPITAL, JERSEYVILLE, IL, p. A209
JERSEY SHORE HOSPITAL, JERSEY SHORE, PA, p. A593
JERSEY SHORE UNIVERSITY MEDICAL CENTER, NEPTUNE, NJ, p. A459
JESSE BROWN VETERANS AFFAIRS CHICAGO HEALTH CARE SYSTEM, CHICAGO, IL, p. A198
JESSE BROWN VETERANS AFFAIRS MEDICAL CENTER, CHICAGO, IL, p. A198
JEWELL COUNTY HOSPITAL, MANKATO, KS, p. A270
JEWISH HOME & HOSP FOR AGED, MIAMI, FL, p. A146
JEWISH HOME FOR THE AGED, LONGMEADOW, MA, p. A340
JEWISH HOME OF SAN FRANCISCO, SAN FRANCISCO, CA, p. A93
JFK JOHNSON REHABILITATION INSTITUTE, EDISON, NJ, p. A454
JFK JOHNSON REHABILITATION INSTITUTE AT HACKENSACK MERIDIAN HEALTH, EDISON, NJ, p. A454
J. F. K. MEDICAL CENTER, ATLANTIS, FL, p. A131
JFK MEDICAL CENTER, ATLANTIS, FL, p. A131
JFK MEDICAL CENTER, EDISON, NJ, p. A454
JFK MEMORIAL HOSPITAL, INDIO, CA, p. A68
JIM TALIAFERRO COMMUNITY MENTAL HEALTH, LAWTON, OK, p. A561
JOHN AND MARY KIRBY HOSPITAL, MONTICELLO, IL, p. A212
JOHN C FREMONT DISTRICT HEALTH, MARIPOSA, CA, p. A77
JOHN C. FREMONT HEALTHCARE DISTRICT, MARIPOSA, CA, p. A77
JOHN C. LINCOLN MEDICAL CENTER, PHOENIX, AZ, p. A36
JOHN C. STENNIS MEMORIAL HOSPITAL, DE KALB, MS, p. A391
JOHN D ARCHBOLD MEMRIAL HOSP, THOMASVILLE, GA, p. A182
JOHN D. ARCHBOLD MEMORIAL HOSPITAL, THOMASVILLE, GA, p. A182
JOHN D. DINGELL VETERANS AFFAIRS MEDICAL CENTER, DETROIT, MI, p. A353
JOHN F. KENNEDY MEMORIAL HOSPITAL, INDIO, CA, p. A68
JOHN FITZGIBBON MEM HOSPITAL, MARSHALL, MO, p. A411
JOHN H. STROGER JR. HOSPITAL OF COOK COUNTY, CHICAGO, IL, p. A199
JOHN HEINZ INSTITUTE OF REHABILITATION MEDICINE, WILKES-BARRE, PA, p. A611
JOHN J MADDEN MENTAL HLTH CNTR, HINES, IL, p. A208
JOHN J PERSHING VA MED CNTR, POPLAR BLUFF, MO, p. A413
JOHN J. MADDEN MENTAL HEALTH CENTER, HINES, IL, p. A208
JOHN J. PERSHING VETERANS AFFAIRS MEDICAL CENTER, POPLAR BLUFF, MO, p. A413
JOHN MACOMB-OAKLAND HOSPITAL, WARREN, MI, p. A369
JOHN MUIR BEHAVIORAL HEALTH CENTER, CONCORD, CA, p. A61

JOHN MUIR BEHAVIORAL HLTH, CONCORD, CA, p. A61
JOHN MUIR MEDICAL CENTER, CONCORD, CONCORD, CA, p. A61
JOHN MUIR MEDICAL CENTER, WALNUT CREEK, WALNUT CREEK, CA, p. A104
JOHN PETER SMITH HOSPITAL, FORT WORTH, TX, p. A678
JOHN RANDOLPH MEDICAL CENTER, HOPEWELL, VA, p. A744
JOHN REHABILITATION HOSPITAL, BROKEN ARROW, OK, p. A556
JOHN STODDARD CANCER CENTER, DES MOINES, IA, p. A248
JOHNS HOPKINS ALL CHILDREN'S HOSPITAL, SAINT PETERSBURG, FL, p. A156
JOHNS HOPKINS ALL CHILDREN'S HOSPITALA, SAINT PETERSBURG, FL, p. A156
JOHNS HOPKINS BAYVIEW MEDICAL CENTER, BALTIMORE, MD, p. A324
JOHNS HOPKINS HOSPITAL, BALTIMORE, MD, p. A324
JOHNSON CITY MED CENTER, JOHNSON CITY, TN, p. A640
JOHNSON CITY MEDICAL CENTER, JOHNSON CITY, TN, p. A640
JOHNSON COUNTY COMMUNITY HOSPITAL, MOUNTAIN CITY, TN, p. A645
JOHNSON COUNTY HEALTCARE CTR, BUFFALO, WY, p. A801
JOHNSON COUNTY HEALTH CENTER, MOUNTAIN CITY, TN, p. A645
JOHNSON COUNTY HEALTHCARE CENTER, BUFFALO, WY, p. A801
JOHNSON COUNTY HOSPITAL, TECUMSEH, NE, p. A440
JOHNSON MEM HOSPITAL & HOME, DAWSON, MN, p. A375
JOHNSON MEMORIAL HEALTH SERVICES, DAWSON, MN, p. A375
JOHNSON MEMORIAL HOSPITAL, FRANKLIN, IN, p. A229
JOHNSON MEMORIAL HOSPITAL, STAFFORD SPRINGS, CT, p. A125
JOHNSON MEMORIAL MEDICAL CENTER, STAFFORD SPRINGS, CT, p. A125
JOHNSON REGIONAL HOSPITAL, CLARKSVILLE, AR, p. A43
JOHNSON REGIONAL MEDICAL CENTER, CLARKSVILLE, AR, p. A43
JOHNSTON HEALTH, SMITHFIELD, NC, p. A518
JOHNSTON MEMORIAL HOSPITAL, ABINGDON, VA, p. A738
JOHNSTON MEMORIAL HOSPITAL, TISHOMINGO, OK, p. A569
JOHNSTON R. BOWMAN HEALTH CENTER, CHICAGO, IL, p. A199
JOHNSTON UNC HEALTH CARE, SMITHFIELD, NC, p. A518
JOHNSTON-WILLIS HOSPITAL, RICHMOND, VA, p. A750
JOINT TOWNSHIP DISTRICT MEMORIAL HOSPITAL, SAINT MARYS, OH, p. A548
JONES MEMORIAL HOSPITAL, WELLSVILLE, NY, p. A502
JONES REGIONAL MEDICAL CENTER, ANAMOSA, IA, p. A243
JORDAN VALLEY MED CENTER, WEST JORDAN, UT, p. A734
JORDAN VALLEY MEDICAL CENTER, WEST JORDAN, UT, p. A734
JORDAN VALLEY MEDICAL CENTER WEST VALLEY CAMPUS, WEST VALLEY CITY, UT, p. A734
JOSEPH'S HOSPITAL -NORTH, LUTZ, FL, p. A144
JOSEPH'S HOSPITAL SOUTH, RIVERVIEW, FL, p. A155
JOYCE EISENBERG-KEEFER MEDICAL CENTER, RESEDA, CA, p. A88
JPS HEALTH NETWORK, FORT WORTH, TX, p. A678
JULIAN F. KEITH ALCOHOL AND DRUG ABUSE TREATMENT CENTER, BLACK MOUNTAIN, NC, p. A505
JULIAN K KEITH ALCOHOL CENTER, BLACK MOUNTAIN, NC, p. A505
JUPITER HOSPITAL, JUPITER, FL, p. A142
JUPITER MEDICAL CENTER, JUPITER, FL, p. A142

# K

KADLEC MEDICAL CENTER, RICHLAND, WA, p. A763
KADLEC REGIONAL MEDICAL CENTER, RICHLAND, WA, p. A763
KAHI MOHALA BEHAVIORAL HEALTH, EWA BEACH, HI, p. A184
KAHUKU HOSPITAL, KAHUKU, HI, p. A185
KAHUKU MEDICAL CENTER, KAHUKU, HI, p. A185
KAISER FOUNDATION HOSPITAL—ORANGE COUNTY, IRVINE, CA, p. A69
KAISER FOUNDATION HOSPITAL, HONOLULU, HI, p. A184
KAISER FOUNDATION HOSPITAL, MARTINEZ, CA, p. A77
KAISER FOUNDATION HOSPITAL, MODESTO, CA, p. A79
KAISER FOUNDATION HOSPITAL WESTSIDE MEDICAL CENTER, HILLSBORO, OR, p. A576

KAISER FOUNDATION MENTAL HEALTH CENTER, LOS ANGELES, CA, p. A74
KAISER PERMANENTE ANAHEIM MEDICAL CENTER, ANAHEIM, CA, p. A55
KAISER PERMANENTE ANTIOCH MEDICAL CENTER, ANTIOCH, CA, p. A56
KAISER PERMANENTE BALDWIN PARK MEDICAL CENTER, BALDWIN PARK, CA, p. A57
KAISER PERMANENTE CAPITOL HILL CAMPUS, SEATTLE, WA, p. A763
KAISER PERMANENTE DOWNEY MEDICAL CENTER, DOWNEY, CA, p. A62
KAISER PERMANENTE FONTANA MEDICAL CENTER, FONTANA, CA, p. A64
KAISER PERMANENTE FREMONT MEDICAL CENTER, FREMONT, CA, p. A65
KAISER PERMANENTE FRESNO MEDICAL CENTER, FRESNO, CA, p. A65
KAISER PERMANENTE LOS ANGELES MEDICAL CENTER, LOS ANGELES, CA, p. A74
KAISER PERMANENTE MANTECA MEDICAL CENTER, MANTECA, CA, p. A77
KAISER PERMANENTE MEDICAL CENTER, HONOLULU, HI, p. A184
KAISER PERMANENTE MEDICAL CNTR, MARTINEZ, CA, p. A77
KAISER PERMANENTE MORENO VALLEY MEDICAL CENTER, MORENO VALLEY, CA, p. A80
KAISER PERMANENTE OAKLAND MEDICAL CENTER, OAKLAND, CA, p. A82
KAISER PERMANENTE ORANGE COUNTY ANAHEIM MEDICAL CENTER, ANAHEIM, CA, p. A55
KAISER PERMANENTE PANORAMA CITY MEDICAL CENTER, PANORAMA CITY, CA, p. A84
KAISER PERMANENTE REDWOOD CITY MEDICAL CENTER, REDWOOD CITY, CA, p. A87
KAISER PERMANENTE RICHMOND MEDICAL CENTER, RICHMOND, CA, p. A88
KAISER PERMANENTE RIVERSIDE MEDICAL CENTER, RIVERSIDE, CA, p. A88
KAISER PERMANENTE ROSEVILLE MEDICAL CENTER, ROSEVILLE, CA, p. A89
KAISER PERMANENTE SACRAMENTO MEDICAL CENTER, SACRAMENTO, CA, p. A89
KAISER PERMANENTE SAN DIEGO MEDICAL CENTER, SAN DIEGO, CA, p. A91
KAISER PERMANENTE SAN FRANCISCO MEDICAL CENTER, SAN FRANCISCO, CA, p. A93
KAISER PERMANENTE SAN JOSE MEDICAL CENTER, SAN JOSE, CA, p. A94
KAISER PERMANENTE SAN LEANDRO MEDICAL CENTER, SAN LEANDRO, CA, p. A95
KAISER PERMANENTE SAN RAFAEL MEDICAL CENTER, SAN RAFAEL, CA, p. A96
KAISER PERMANENTE SANTA CLARA MEDICAL CENTER, SANTA CLARA, CA, p. A97
KAISER PERMANENTE SANTA ROSA MEDICAL CENTER, SANTA ROSA, CA, p. A98
KAISER PERMANENTE SOUTH BAY MEDICAL CENTER, HARBOR CITY, CA, p. A68
KAISER PERMANENTE SOUTH SACRAMENTO MEDICAL CENTER, SACRAMENTO, CA, p. A89
KAISER PERMANENTE SOUTH SAN FRANCISCO, SOUTH SAN FRANCISCO, CA, p. A99
KAISER PERMANENTE SUNNYSIDE MEDICAL CENTER, CLACKAMAS, OR, p. A574
KAISER PERMANENTE VACAVILLE MEDICAL CENTER, VACAVILLE, CA, p. A102
KAISER PERMANENTE VALLEJO MEDICAL CENTER, VALLEJO, CA, p. A103
KAISER PERMANENTE WALNUT CREEK MEDICAL CENTER, WALNUT CREEK, CA, p. A104
KAISER PERMANENTE WEST LOS ANGELES MEDICAL CENTER, LOS ANGELES, CA, p. A74
KAISER PERMANENTE WOODLAND HILLS MEDICAL CENTER, WOODLAND HILLS, CA, p. A105
KAISER SUNNYSIDE MEDICAL CENTER, CLACKAMAS, OR, p. A574
KAISER WESTSIDE MEDICAL CENTER, HILLSBORO, OR, p. A576
KALAMAZOO PSYCHIATRIC HOSPITAL, KALAMAZOO, MI, p. A359
KALAMAZOO REG PSYCHIATRIC HOSP, KALAMAZOO, MI, p. A359
KALEIDA HEALTH, BUFFALO, NY, p. A480
KALISPELL REGIONAL HEALTHCARE, KALISPELL, MT, p. A425
KALISPELL REGIONAL MEDICAL CENTER, KALISPELL, MT, p. A425
KALKASKA MEMORIAL HEALTH CENTER, KALKASKA, MI, p. A359

KALKASKA MEMORIAL HLTH CTR, KALKASKA, MI, p. A359
KANAKANAK HOSPITAL, DILLINGHAM, AK, p. A28
KANE COMMUNITY HOSPITAL, KANE, PA, p. A593
KANE COUNTY HOSPITAL, KANAB, UT, p. A728
KANSAS CITY ORTHOPAEDIC INSTITUTE, LEAWOOD, KS, p. A269
KANSAS CITY VETERANS AFFAIRS MEDICAL CENTER, KANSAS CITY, MO, p. A408
KANSAS HEART HOSPITAL, WICHITA, KS, p. A278
KANSAS MEDICAL CENTER, ANDOVER, KS, p. A261
KANSAS NEUROLOGICAL INSTITUTE, TOPEKA, KS, p. A277
KANSAS REHABILITATION HOSPITAL, TOPEKA, KS, p. A277
KANSAS SPINE & SPECIALTY HOSPITAL, WICHITA, KS, p. A279
KANSAS SPINE AND SPECIALTY HOSPITAL, WICHITA, KS, p. A279
KANSAS SURGERY AND RECOVERY CENTER, WICHITA, KS, p. A279
KAPIOLANI MEDICAL CENTER AT PALI MOMI, AIEA, HI, p. A184
KAPIOLANI MEDICAL CENTER FOR WOMEN & CHILDREN, HONOLULU, HI, p. A184
KARMANOS CANCER CENTER, DETROIT, MI, p. A353
KASEMAN PRESBYTERIAN HOSPITAL, ALBUQUERQUE, NM, p. A467
KATE DISHMAN REHABILITATION HOSPITAL, BEAUMONT, TX, p. A658
KATHERINE SHAW BETHEA HOSPITAL, DIXON, IL, p. A202
KATY MEDICAL CENTER, KATY, TX, p. A692
KATY REHABILITATION HOSPITAL, KATY, TX, p. A692
KAU HOSPITAL, PAHALA, HI, p. A186
KAUAI VETERANS MEMORIAL HOSPITAL, WAIMEA, HI, p. A187
KAWEAH DELTA HEALTH CARE DISTRICT, VISALIA, CA, p. A104
KAWEAH DELTA MEDICAL CENTER, VISALIA, CA, p. A104
KA'U HOSPITAL, PAHALA, HI, p. A186
KEARNEY COUNTY COMM HOSPITAL, MINDEN, NE, p. A435
KEARNEY COUNTY HEALTH SERVICES, MINDEN, NE, p. A435
KEARNEY REGIONAL MEDICAL CENTER, KEARNEY, NE, p. A434
KEARNY COUNTY HOSPITAL, LAKIN, KS, p. A268
KECK HOSPITAL OF USC, LOS ANGELES, CA, p. A74
KEDREN COMMUNITY MENTAL HEALTH CENTER, LOS ANGELES, CA, p. A75
KEEFE MEMORIAL HOSPITAL, CHEYENNE WELLS, CO, p. A109
KELL WEST REGIONAL HOSPITAL, WICHITA FALLS, TX, p. A725
KELLER ARMY COMMUNITY HOSPITAL, WEST POINT, NY, p. A502
KEMPSVILLE CENTER FOR BEHAVIORAL HEALTH, NORFOLK, VA, p. A748
KENDALL MEDICAL CENTER, MIAMI, FL, p. A146
KENDALL REGIONAL MEDICAL CENTER, MIAMI, FL, p. A146
KENMARE COMMUNITY HOSPITAL, KENMARE, ND, p. A524
KENMORE MERCY HOSPITAL, KENMORE, NY, p. A486
KENNEDY HEALTH SYSTEM, STRATFORD, NJ, p. A463
KENNEDY KRIEGER CHILDREN'S HSP, BALTIMORE, MD, p. A324
KENNEDY KRIEGER INSTITUTE, BALTIMORE, MD, p. A324
KENNEDY UNIVERSITY HOSPITAL—STRATFORD, STRATFORD, NJ, p. A463
KENNEDY UNIVERSITY HOSPITAL—WASHINGTON TOWNSHIP, TURNERSVILLE, NJ, p. A464
KENNER REGIONAL MEDICAL CENTER, KENNER, LA, p. A304
KENNEWICK GENERAL HOSPITAL, KENNEWICK, WA, p. A759
KENSINGTON HOSPITAL, PHILADELPHIA, PA, p. A601
KENT COUNTY MEMORIAL HOSPITAL, WARWICK, RI, p. A614
KENT GENERAL HOSPITAL, DOVER, DE, p. A127
KENTFIELD HOSPITAL, KENTFIELD, CA, p. A69
KENTFIELD REHABILITATION AND SPECIALTY HOSPITAL, KENTFIELD, CA, p. A69
KENTUCKY RIVER MEDICAL CENTER, JACKSON, KY, p. A285
KEOKUK AREA HOSPITAL, KEOKUK, IA, p. A252
KEOKUK COUNTY HEALTH CENTER, SIGOURNEY, IA, p. A257
KERN HOSPITAL & MEDICAL CENTER, WARREN, MI, p. A369
KERN MEDICAL, BAKERSFIELD, CA, p. A57
KERN MEDICAL CENTER, BAKERSFIELD, CA, p. A57
KERN VALLEY HEALTHCARE DISTRICT, LAKE ISABELLA, CA, p. A70
KERN VALLEY HOSPITAL DISTRICT, LAKE ISABELLA, CA, p. A70
KERNAN ORTHOPAEDICS AND REHABILITATION, BALTIMORE, MD, p. A324
KERRVILLE DIVISION, KERRVILLE, TX, p. A692
KERRVILLE STATE HOSPITAL, KERRVILLE, TX, p. A692
KERSHAW COUNTY MEDICAL CENTER, CAMDEN, SC, p. A615
KERSHAWHEALTH, CAMDEN, SC, p. A615

KESSLER INSTITUTE FOR REHABILITATION, CHESTER, NJ, p. A453
KESSLER INSTITUTE FOR REHABILITATION, SADDLE BROOK, NJ, p. A462
KESSLER INSTITUTE FOR REHABILITATION, WEST ORANGE, NJ, p. A465
KESSLER MARLTON REHABILITATION, MARLTON, NJ, p. A458
KESWICK-HOME FOR INCURABLES, BALTIMORE, MD, p. A324
KETCHIKAN GENERAL HOSPITAL, KETCHIKAN, AK, p. A28
KETTERING HEALTH NETWORK TROY HOSPITAL, TROY, OH, p. A551
KETTERING MEDICAL CENTER, KETTERING, OH, p. A542
KETTERING MEDICAL CENTER-SYCAMORE, MIAMISBURG, OH, p. A545
KETTERING YOUTH SERVICES, DAYTON, OH, p. A538
KEWANEE HOSPITAL, KEWANEE, IL, p. A209
KEYSTONE NEWPORT NEWS, NEWPORT NEWS, VA, p. A746
KIDSPEACE CHILDREN'S HOSPITAL, OREFIELD, PA, p. A599
KIMBALL COUNTY HOSPITAL, KIMBALL, NE, p. A434
KIMBALL HEALTH SERVICES, KIMBALL, NE, p. A434
KIMBLE HOSPITAL, JUNCTION, TX, p. A691
KINDRED CHICAGO LAKESHORE, CHICAGO, IL, p. A199
KINDRED CHICAGO-CENTRAL HOSPITAL, CHICAGO, IL, p. A199
KINDRED HOSP-FORT LAUDERDALE, FORT LAUDERDALE, FL, p. A137
KINDRED HOSP-FORT WORTH SW, FORT WORTH, TX, p. A678
KINDRED HOSPITAL—LAKESHORE, CHICAGO, IL, p. A199
KINDRED HOSPITAL, ARLINGTON, TX, p. A653
KINDRED HOSPITAL ARIZONA-NORTHWEST PHOENIX, PEORIA, AZ, p. A35
KINDRED HOSPITAL ARIZONA-PHOENIX, PHOENIX, AZ, p. A36
KINDRED HOSPITAL BAY AREA, SAINT PETERSBURG, FL, p. A156
KINDRED HOSPITAL BAY AREA-TAMPA, TAMPA, FL, p. A159
KINDRED HOSPITAL CENTRAL TAMPA, TAMPA, FL, p. A159
KINDRED HOSPITAL CHICAGO NORTH, CHICAGO, IL, p. A199
KINDRED HOSPITAL CHICAGO-NORTHLAKE, NORTHLAKE, IL, p. A214
KINDRED HOSPITAL CLEAR LAKE, WEBSTER, TX, p. A724
KINDRED HOSPITAL CLEVELAND-GATEWAY, CLEVELAND, OH, p. A534
KINDRED HOSPITAL DALLAS CENTRAL, DALLAS, TX, p. A668
KINDRED HOSPITAL EL PASO, EL PASO, TX, p. A675
KINDRED HOSPITAL FARGO, FARGO, ND, p. A523
KINDRED HOSPITAL HOUSTON MEDICAL CENTER, HOUSTON, TX, p. A686
KINDRED HOSPITAL INDIANAPOLIS NORTH, INDIANAPOLIS, IN, p. A232
KINDRED HOSPITAL LAS VEGAS-SAHARA, HENDERSON, NV, p. A442
KINDRED HOSPITAL LIMA, LIMA, OH, p. A543
KINDRED HOSPITAL LOUISVILLE AT JEWISH HOSPITAL, LOUISVILLE, KY, p. A288
KINDRED HOSPITAL MELBOURNE, MELBOURNE, FL, p. A145
KINDRED HOSPITAL NEW JERSEY—RAHWAY, RAHWAY, NJ, p. A462
KINDRED HOSPITAL NEW JERSEY—WAYNE, WAYNE, NJ, p. A465
KINDRED HOSPITAL NORTH FLORIDA, GREEN COVE SPRINGS, FL, p. A139
KINDRED HOSPITAL NORTHLAKE, NORTHLAKE, IL, p. A214
KINDRED HOSPITAL NORTHLAND, KANSAS CITY, MO, p. A409
KINDRED HOSPITAL NORTHWEST INDIANA, HAMMOND, IN, p. A230
KINDRED HOSPITAL OCALA, OCALA, FL, p. A150
KINDRED HOSPITAL OF CLEVELAND, CLEVELAND, OH, p. A534
KINDRED HOSPITAL OF RIVERSIDE, PERRIS, CA, p. A85
KINDRED HOSPITAL OF SOUTH BAY, GARDENA, CA, p. A66
KINDRED HOSPITAL PARAMOUNT, PARAMOUNT, CA, p. A84
KINDRED HOSPITAL PARK VIEW, SPRINGFIELD, MA, p. A344
KINDRED HOSPITAL PARK VIEW-CENTRAL MASSACHUSETTS, ROCHDALE, MA, p. A343
KINDRED HOSPITAL PEORIA, PEORIA, IL, p. A216
KINDRED HOSPITAL RANCHO, RANCHO CUCAMONGA, CA, p. A86
KINDRED HOSPITAL RICHMOND, RICHMOND, VA, p. A750
KINDRED HOSPITAL RIVERSIDE, PERRIS, CA, p. A85
KINDRED HOSPITAL SAN ANTONIO CENTRAL, SAN ANTONIO, TX, p. A711
KINDRED HOSPITAL SEATTLE-FIRST HILL, SEATTLE, WA, p. A763
KINDRED HOSPITAL SOUTH BAY, GARDENA, CA, p. A66
KINDRED HOSPITAL SOUTH FLORIDA-FORT LAUDERDALE, FORT LAUDERDALE, FL, p. A137
KINDRED HOSPITAL ST. LOUIS-ST. ANTHONY'S, SAINT LOUIS, MO, p. A415
KINDRED HOSPITAL SUGAR LAND, SUGAR LAND, TX, p. A717

KINDRED HOSPITAL TARRANT COUNTY-ARLINGTON, ARLINGTON, TX, p. A653
KINDRED HOSPITAL THE PALM BEACHES, RIVIERA BEACH, FL, p. A155
KINDRED HOSPITAL TULSA, TULSA, OK, p. A569
KINDRED HOSPITAL-ALBUQUERQUE, ALBUQUERQUE, NM, p. A467
KINDRED HOSPITAL-AMARILLO, AMARILLO, TX, p. A652
KINDRED HOSPITAL-ATLANTA, ATLANTA, GA, p. A164
KINDRED HOSPITAL-AURORA, AURORA, CO, p. A107
KINDRED HOSPITAL-BALDWIN PARK, BALDWIN PARK, CA, p. A58
KINDRED HOSPITAL-BREA, BREA, CA, p. A58
KINDRED HOSPITAL-CENTRAL DAKOTAS, MANDAN, ND, p. A525
KINDRED HOSPITAL-CENTRAL TAMPA, TAMPA, FL, p. A159
KINDRED HOSPITAL-CHATTANOOGA, CHATTANOOGA, TN, p. A635
KINDRED HOSPITAL-CHICAGO NORTH, CHICAGO, IL, p. A199
KINDRED HOSPITAL-DAYTON, DAYTON, OH, p. A538
KINDRED HOSPITAL-DENVER, DENVER, CO, p. A110
KINDRED HOSPITAL-GREENSBORO, GREENSBORO, NC, p. A511
KINDRED HOSPITAL-HERITAGE VALLEY, BEAVER, PA, p. A584
KINDRED HOSPITAL-HOLLYWOOD, HOLLYWOOD, FL, p. A139
KINDRED HOSPITAL-HOUSTON, HOUSTON, TX, p. A686
KINDRED HOSPITAL-HOUSTON NORTHWEST, HOUSTON, TX, p. A686
KINDRED HOSPITAL-INDIANAPOLIS, INDIANAPOLIS, IN, p. A232
KINDRED HOSPITAL-LA MIRADA, LA MIRADA, CA, p. A70
KINDRED HOSPITAL-LAS VEGAS, HENDERSON, NV, p. A442
KINDRED HOSPITAL-LOS ANGELES, LOS ANGELES, CA, p. A75
KINDRED HOSPITAL-LOUISVILLE, LOUISVILLE, KY, p. A288
KINDRED HOSPITAL-MANSFIELD, MANSFIELD, TX, p. A699
KINDRED HOSPITAL-NASHVILLE, NASHVILLE, TN, p. A646
KINDRED HOSPITAL-NEW JERSEY MORRIS COUNTY, DOVER, NJ, p. A454
KINDRED HOSPITAL-NEW ORLEANS, NEW ORLEANS, LA, p. A310
KINDRED HOSPITAL-NORTH FLORIDA, GREEN COVE SPRINGS, FL, p. A139
KINDRED HOSPITAL-OKLAHOMA CITY SOUTH, OKLAHOMA CITY, OK, p. A564
KINDRED HOSPITAL-ONTARIO, ONTARIO, CA, p. A82
KINDRED HOSPITAL-ORANGE COUNTY, WESTMINSTER, CA, p. A105
KINDRED HOSPITAL-PHILADELPHIA, PHILADELPHIA, PA, p. A601
KINDRED HOSPITAL-PITTSBURGH, OAKDALE, PA, p. A598
KINDRED HOSPITAL-SACRAMENTO, FOLSOM, CA, p. A64
KINDRED HOSPITAL-SAN ANTONIO, SAN ANTONIO, TX, p. A711
KINDRED HOSPITAL-SAN DIEGO, SAN DIEGO, CA, p. A91
KINDRED HOSPITAL-SAN FRANCISCO BAY AREA, SAN LEANDRO, CA, p. A95
KINDRED HOSPITAL-SAN LEANDRO, SAN LEANDRO, CA, p. A95
KINDRED HOSPITAL-ST. LOUIS, SAINT LOUIS, MO, p. A416
KINDRED HOSPITAL-SYCAMORE, SYCAMORE, IL, p. A221
KINDRED HOSPITAL-TAMPA, TAMPA, FL, p. A159
KINDRED HOSPITAL-TUCSON, TUCSON, AZ, p. A40
KINDRED HOSPITAL-WESTMINSTER, WESTMINSTER, CA, p. A105
KINDRED REHABILITATION HOSPITAL AMARILLO, AMARILLO, TX, p. A652
KINGFISHER REGIONAL HOSPITAL, KINGFISHER, OK, p. A560
KINGMAN COMMUNITY HOSPITAL, KINGMAN, KS, p. A268
KINGMAN REGIONAL MEDICAL CENTER, KINGMAN, AZ, p. A33
KINGS COUNTY HOSPITAL CENTER, BROOKLYN, NY, p. A478
KINGS DAUGHTERS MEDICAL CENTER OHIO, PORTSMOUTH, OH, p. A548
KINGSBORO PSYCHIATRIC CENTER, BROOKLYN, NY, p. A478
KINGSBROOK JEWISH MEDICAL CENTER, BROOKLYN, NY, p. A478
KINGSBROOK JEWISH MEDICAL CNTR, BROOKLYN, NY, p. A478
KINGSTON HOSPITAL, KINGSTON, NY, p. A487
KINGSWOOD HOSPITAL, FERNDALE, MI, p. A354
KINGWOOD EMERGENCY HOSPITAL, KINGWOOD, TX, p. A693
KINGWOOD HEALTH CENTER, KINGWOOD, TX, p. A693
KINGWOOD MEDICAL CENTER, KINGWOOD, TX, p. A693
KINGWOOD PINES HOSPITAL, KINGWOOD, TX, p. A693
KINGWOOD SPECIALTY HOSPITAL, KINGWOOD, TX, p. A693
KING'S DAUGHTERS HOSPITAL, BROOKHAVEN, MS, p. A390
KING'S DAUGHTERS HOSPITAL, TEMPLE, TX, p. A719
KING'S DAUGHTERS HOSPITAL, YAZOO CITY, MS, p. A401
KING'S DAUGHTERS MEDICAL CENTER, ASHLAND, KY, p. A280

KING'S DAUGHTERS MEDICAL CENTER, BROOKHAVEN, MS, p. A390
KING'S DAUGHTERS MEDICAL CENTER OHIO, PORTSMOUTH, OH, p. A548
KING'S DAUGHTERS' HEALTH, MADISON, IN, p. A236
KING'S DAUGHTERS' HOSPITAL AND HEALTH SERVICES, MADISON, IN, p. A236
KING'S DAUGHTERS' MEDICAL CTR, ASHLAND, KY, p. A280
KIOWA COUNTY MEMORIAL HOSPITAL, GREENSBURG, KS, p. A265
KIOWA DISTRICT HEALTHCARE, KIOWA, KS, p. A268
KIOWA DISTRICT HOSPITAL AND MANOR, KIOWA, KS, p. A268
KIRBY FORENSIC PSYCHIATRIC CENTER, NEW YORK, NY, p. A490
KIRBY MEDICAL CENTER, MONTICELLO, IL, p. A212
KIRKSVILLE OSTEO MED CENTER, KIRKSVILLE, MO, p. A410
KISHWAUKEE HOSPITAL, DEKALB, IL, p. A202
KIT CARSON COUNTY HEALTH SERVICE DISTRICT, BURLINGTON, CO, p. A108
KIT CARSON COUNTY MEMORIAL HOSPITAL, BURLINGTON, CO, p. A108
KITTITAS VALLEY COMMUNITY HOSPITAL, ELLENSBURG, WA, p. A757
KITTITAS VALLEY HEALTHCARE, ELLENSBURG, WA, p. A757
KITTSON MEMORIAL HEALTHCARE CENTER, HALLOCK, MN, p. A377
KITTSON MEMORIAL HOSPITAL, HALLOCK, MN, p. A377
KLICKITAT VALLEY HEALTH, GOLDENDALE, WA, p. A759
KLICKITAT VALLEY HEALTH SERVS, GOLDENDALE, WA, p. A759
KNAPP MEDICAL CENTER, WESLACO, TX, p. A725
KNOX COMMUNITY HOSPITAL, MOUNT VERNON, OH, p. A546
KNOX COUNTY HOSPITAL, KNOX CITY, TX, p. A694
KNOXVILLE AREA COMMUNITY HOSP, KNOXVILLE, IA, p. A253
KNOXVILLE DIVISION, KNOXVILLE, IA, p. A253
KNOXVILLE HOSPITAL & CLINICS, KNOXVILLE, IA, p. A253
KOHALA HOSPITAL, KOHALA, HI, p. A186
KONA COMMUNITY HOSPITAL, KEALAKEKUA, HI, p. A186
KONA HOSPITAL, KEALAKEKUA, HI, p. A186
KOOTENAI HEALTH, COEUR D'ALENE, ID, p. A190
KOOTENAI MEDICAL CENTER, COEUR D'ALENE, ID, p. A190
KOSAIR CHILDREN'S HOSPITAL, LOUISVILLE, KY, p. A288
KOSCIUSKO COMMUNITY HOSPITAL, WARSAW, IN, p. A242
KOSSUTH REGIONAL HEALTH CENTER, ALGONA, IA, p. A243
KOSSUTH RGIONAL HEALTH CENTER, ALGONA, IA, p. A243
KPC PROMISE HOSPITAL OF BATON ROUGE, BATON ROUGE, LA, p. A297
KPC PROMISE HOSPITAL OF DALLAS, DALLAS, TX, p. A668
KPC PROMISE HOSPITAL OF OVERLAND PARK, OVERLAND PARK, KS, p. A274
KPC PROMISE HOSPITAL OF PHOENIX, MESA, AZ, p. A34
KPC PROMISE HOSPITAL OF SALT LAKE, SALT LAKE CITY, UT, p. A732
KPC PROMISE HOSPITAL OF VICKSBURG, VICKSBURG, MS, p. A400
KPC PROMISE HOSPITAL OF WICHITA FALLS, WICHITA FALLS, TX, p. A725
KPC PROMISE OF VICKSBURG, VICKSBURG, MS, p. A400
KUAKINI MEDICAL CENTER, HONOLULU, HI, p. A184
KULA HOSPITAL, KULA, HI, p. A186
KVC PRAIRIE RIDGE PSYCHIATRIC HOSPITAL, KANSAS CITY, KS, p. A267
KVC PSYCHIATRIC HOSPITAL, KANSAS CITY, KS, p. A267
KWAJALEIN HOSPITAL, KWAJALEIN ATOLL, MH, p. A805

## L

LA DOWNTOWN MEDICAL CENTER, LLC, LOS ANGELES, CA, p. A75
LA PALMA INTERCOMMUNITY HOSPITAL, LA PALMA, CA, p. A70
LA PAZ REGIONAL HOSPITAL, PARKER, AZ, p. A34
LA PORTE HOSPITAL, LA PORTE, IN, p. A234
LA RABIDA CHILDREN'S HOSPITAL, CHICAGO, IL, p. A199
LA SALLE GENERAL HOSPITAL, JENA, LA, p. A304
LABETTE COUNTY MEDICAL CENTER, PARSONS, KS, p. A274
LABETTE HEALTH, PARSONS, KS, p. A274
LAC+USC MEDICAL CENTER, LOS ANGELES, CA, p. A75
LAC-HARBOR-UNIVERSITY OF CALIFORNIA AT LOS ANGELES MEDICAL CENTER, TORRANCE, CA, p. A101
LAC-OLIVE VIEW-UCLA MEDICAL CENTER, SYLMAR, CA, p. A100

LAC-RANCHO LOS AMIGOS CENTER, DOWNEY, CA, p. A62
LAC/UNIVERSITY OF SOUTHERN CALIFORNIA MEDICAL CENTER, LOS ANGELES, CA, p. A75
LACKEY MEMORIAL HOSPITAL, FOREST, MS, p. A392
LADD MEMORIAL HOSPITAL, OSCEOLA, WI, p. A793
LADY OF THE SEA GENERAL HOSPITAL, CUT OFF, LA, p. A300
LAFAYETTE GENERAL MEDICAL CENTER, LAFAYETTE, LA, p. A305
LAFAYETTE GENERAL SOUTHWEST, LAFAYETTE, LA, p. A305
LAFAYETTE PHYSICAL REHABILITATION HOSPITAL, LAFAYETTE, LA, p. A305
LAFAYETTE REGIONAL HEALTH CENTER, LEXINGTON, MO, p. A411
LAFAYETTE REGIONAL HEALTH CNTR, LEXINGTON, MO, p. A411
LAFAYETTE REGIONAL REHABILITATION HOSPITAL, LAFAYETTE, IN, p. A234
LAFOLLETTE MEDICAL CENTER, LA FOLLETTE, TN, p. A641
LAGRANGE COMMUNITY HOSPITAL, LAGRANGE, IN, p. A235
LAGUNA HONDA HOSP & REHAB CNTR, SAN FRANCISCO, CA, p. A93
LAGUNA HONDA HOSPITAL AND REHABILITATION CENTER, SAN FRANCISCO, CA, p. A93
LAHEY CLINIC HOSPITAL, BURLINGTON, MA, p. A337
LAHEY HOSPITAL & MEDICAL CENTER, BURLINGTON, MA, p. A337
LAIRD HOSPITAL, UNION, MS, p. A400
LAKE BEHAVIORAL HOSPITAL, WAUKEGAN, IL, p. A222
LAKE BUTLER HOSPITAL, LAKE BUTLER, FL, p. A142
LAKE BUTLER HOSPITAL HAND SURGERY CENTER, LAKE BUTLER, FL, p. A143
LAKE CHARLES MEMORIAL HOSPITAL, LAKE CHARLES, LA, p. A307
LAKE CHELAN COMMUNITY HOSPITAL, CHELAN, WA, p. A756
LAKE CHELAN COMMUNITY HOSPITAL AND CLINICS, CHELAN, WA, p. A756
LAKE CITY COMMUNITY HOSPITAL, LAKE CITY, SC, p. A622
LAKE CITY MEDICAL CENTER, LAKE CITY, FL, p. A143
LAKE CITY MEDICAL CENTER-MAYO, LAKE CITY, MN, p. A378
LAKE CUMBERLAND REGIONAL HOSPITAL, SOMERSET, KY, p. A293
LAKE DISTRICT HOSPITAL, LAKEVIEW, OR, p. A577
LAKE GRANBURY MEDICAL CENTER, GRANBURY, TX, p. A682
LAKE HEALTH, CONCORD TOWNSHIP, OH, p. A537
LAKE HEALTH BEACHWOOD MEDICAL CENTER, BEACHWOOD, OH, p. A529
LAKE HOSPITAL SYSTEM, INC, CONCORD TOWNSHIP, OH, p. A537
LAKE HURON MEDICAL CENTER, PORT HURON, MI, p. A364
LAKE MARTIN COMMUNITY HOSPITAL, DADEVILLE, AL, p. A17
LAKE MEAD HOSP MEDICAL CTR, NORTH LAS VEGAS, NV, p. A445
LAKE NORMAN REGIONAL MEDICAL CENTER, MOORESVILLE, NC, p. A514
LAKE PINES HOSPITAL, KENNER, LA, p. A304
LAKE POINTE MEDICAL CENTER, ROWLETT, TX, p. A710
LAKE REGION HEALTHCARE, FERGUS FALLS, MN, p. A376
LAKE REGION HEALTHCARE CORPORATION, FERGUS FALLS, MN, p. A376
LAKE REGIONAL HEALTH SYSTEM, OSAGE BEACH, MO, p. A413
LAKE REGIONAL HOSPITAL, OSAGE BEACH, MO, p. A413
LAKE TAYLOR HOSPITAL, NORFOLK, VA, p. A748
LAKE TAYLOR TRANSITIONAL CARE HOSPITAL, NORFOLK, VA, p. A748
LAKE VIEW HOSPITAL, TWO HARBORS, MN, p. A386
LAKE VIEW MEMORIAL HOSPITAL, TWO HARBORS, MN, p. A386
LAKE WALES MEDICAL CENTER, LAKE WALES, FL, p. A143
LAKELAND BEHAVIORAL HEALTH SYSTEM, SPRINGFIELD, MO, p. A418
LAKELAND COMMUNITY HOSPITAL, HALEYVILLE, AL, p. A20
LAKELAND COMMUNITY HOSPITAL WATERVLIET, WATERVLIET, MI, p. A369
LAKELAND HOSPITAL, WATERVLIET, WATERVLIET, MI, p. A369
LAKELAND MEDICAL CENTER, ELKHORN, WI, p. A783
LAKELAND REGIONAL HEALTH, LAKELAND, FL, p. A143
LAKELAND REGIONAL HEALTH MEDICAL CENTER, LAKELAND, FL, p. A143
LAKELAND REGIONAL HOSPITAL, SPRINGFIELD, MO, p. A418
LAKES REGION GENERAL HOSPITAL, LACONIA, NH, p. A449
LAKES REGIONAL HEALTHCARE, SPIRIT LAKE, IA, p. A258
LAKESHORE COMMUNITY HOSPITAL, DADEVILLE, AL, p. A17
LAKESIDE BEHAVIORAL HEALTH SYSTEM, MEMPHIS, TN, p. A644

LAKESIDE BEHAVIORAL HEALTHCARE-PRINCETON PLAZA, ORLANDO, FL, p. A151
LAKESIDE COMMUNITY HOSPITAL, INCLINE VILLAGE, NV, p. A442
LAKESIDE COMMUNITY HOSPITAL, LAKEPORT, CA, p. A71
LAKESIDE HOSPITAL, METAIRIE, LA, p. A308
LAKESIDE MEDICAL CENTER, BELLE GLADE, FL, p. A132
LAKESIDE WOMEN'S HOSPITAL, OKLAHOMA CITY, OK, p. A564
LAKEVIEW BEHAVIORAL HEALTH, NORCROSS, GA, p. A178
LAKEVIEW COMMUNITY HOSPITAL, EUFAULA, AL, p. A18
LAKEVIEW COMMUNITY HOSPITAL, PAW PAW, MI, p. A363
LAKEVIEW HOSPITAL, BOUNTIFUL, UT, p. A727
LAKEVIEW HOSPITAL, STILLWATER, MN, p. A386
LAKEVIEW MEDICAL CENTER, RICE LAKE, WI, p. A795
LAKEVIEW MEMORIAL HOSPITAL, STILLWATER, MN, p. A386
LAKEVIEW SPECIALTY HOSPITAL AND REHAB, WATERFORD, WI, p. A798
LAKEVIEW SPECIALTY HOSPITAL AND REHABILITATION CENTER, WATERFORD, WI, p. A798
LAKEWAY REGIONAL MEDICAL CENTER, LAKEWAY, TX, p. A694
LAKEWOOD HEALTH CENTER, BAUDETTE, MN, p. A372
LAKEWOOD HEALTH SYSTEM, STAPLES, MN, p. A386
LAKEWOOD QUARTERS REHAB HOSP, BATON ROUGE, LA, p. A297
LAKEWOOD RANCH MEDICAL CENTER, BRADENTON, FL, p. A133
LAKEWOOD REGIONAL MEDICAL CENTER, LAKEWOOD, CA, p. A71
LALLIE KEMP MEDICAL CENTER, INDEPENDENCE, LA, p. A303
LALLIE KEMP REGIONAL MED CTR, INDEPENDENCE, LA, p. A303
LAMB HEALTHCARE CENTER, LITTLEFIELD, TX, p. A696
LANAI COMMUNITY HOSPITAL, LANAI CITY, HI, p. A186
LANCASTER COMMUNITY HOSPITAL, PALMDALE, CA, p. A84
LANCASTER GENERAL HOSPITAL, LANCASTER, PA, p. A594
LANCASTER MEMORIAL HOSPITAL, LANCASTER, WI, p. A787
LANCASTER REHABILITATION HOSPITAL, LANCASTER, PA, p. A594
LANCASTER-FAIRFIELD COMM HOSP, LANCASTER, OH, p. A542
LANDMANN-JUNGMAN MEMORIAL HOSPITAL, SCOTLAND, SD, p. A631
LANDMANN-JUNGMAN MEMORIAL HOSPITAL AVERA, SCOTLAND, SD, p. A631
LANDMARK HOSP OF JOPLIN, JOPLIN, MO, p. A408
LANDMARK HOSPITAL, CAPE GIRARDEAU, MO, p. A403
LANDMARK HOSPITAL OF ATHENS, ATHENS, GA, p. A163
LANDMARK HOSPITAL OF CAPE GIRARDEAU, CAPE GIRARDEAU, MO, p. A403
LANDMARK HOSPITAL OF COLUMBIA, COLUMBIA, MO, p. A405
LANDMARK HOSPITAL OF JOPLIN, JOPLIN, MO, p. A408
LANDMARK HOSPITAL OF SAVANNAH, SAVANNAH, GA, p. A180
LANDMARK HOSPITAL OF SOUTHWEST FLORIDA, NAPLES, FL, p. A148
LANDMARK MEDICAL CENTER, WOONSOCKET, RI, p. A614
LANDMARK MEDICAL CENTER-FOGARTY UNIT, NORTH SMITHFIELD, RI, p. A613
LANE COUNTY HOSPITAL, DIGHTON, KS, p. A263
LANE MEMORIAL HOSPITAL, ZACHARY, LA, p. A317
LANE REGIONAL MEDICAL CENTER, ZACHARY, LA, p. A317
LANGLADE HOSPITAL, ANTIGO, WI, p. A779
LANIER HEALTH SERVICES, VALLEY, AL, p. A25
LANKENAU HOSPITAL, WYNNEWOOD, PA, p. A611
LANKENAU MEDICAL CENTER, WYNNEWOOD, PA, p. A612
LAPEER REGIONAL MEDICAL CENTER, LAPEER, MI, p. A360
LARABIDA CHILDREN'S HOSPITAL, CHICAGO, IL, p. A199
LAREDO HEALTH CENTER, LAREDO, TX, p. A695
LAREDO MEDICAL CENTER, LAREDO, TX, p. A695
LAREDO REHABILITATION HOSPITAL, LAREDO, TX, p. A695
LAREDO SPECIALTY HOSPITAL, LAREDO, TX, p. A695
LARGO MEDICAL CENTER, LARGO, FL, p. A143
LARKIN COMMUNITY HOSPITAL, HIALEAH, FL, p. A139
LARKIN COMMUNITY HOSPITAL, SOUTH MIAMI, FL, p. A157
LARKIN COMMUNITY HOSPITAL BEHAVIORAL HEALTH SERVICES, HOLLYWOOD, FL, p. A140
LARKIN COMMUNITY HOSPITAL-PALM SPRINGS CAMPUS, HIALEAH, FL, p. A139
LARKIN COMMUNITY HOSPITAL-SOUTH MIAMI CAMPUS, SOUTH MIAMI, FL, p. A157
LARNED STATE HOSPITAL, LARNED, KS, p. A268
LARRY B. ZIEVERINK, SR. ALCOHOLISM TREATMENT CENTER, RALEIGH, NC, p. A516
LARUE D. CARTER MEMORIAL HOSPITAL, INDIANAPOLIS, IN, p. A232
LAS COLINAS MEDICAL CENTER, IRVING, TX, p. A690

LAS ENCINAS HOSPITAL, PASADENA, CA, p. A85
LAS PALMAS DEL SOL HEALTHCARE, EL PASO, TX, p. A675
LAS PALMAS MEDICAL CENTER, EL PASO, TX, p. A675
LAS VEGAS MEDICAL CENTER, LAS VEGAS, NM, p. A470
LASALLE GENERAL HOSPITAL, JENA, LA, p. A304
LASSEN COMMUNITY HOSPITAL, SUSANVILLE, CA, p. A100
LATROBE AREA HOSPITAL, LATROBE, PA, p. A594
LAUGHLIN MEMORIAL HOSPITAL, GREENEVILLE, TN, p. A638
LAUREATE PSYCHIATRIC CLINIC AND HOSPITAL, TULSA, OK, p. A569
LAUREL OAKS BEHAVIORAL HEALTH CENTER, DOTHAN, AL, p. A17
LAUREL RIDGE HOSPITAL, SAN ANTONIO, TX, p. A711
LAUREL RIDGE TREATMENT CENTER, SAN ANTONIO, TX, p. A712
LAUREL WOOD CENTER, MERIDIAN, MS, p. A397
LAURELWOOD HOSPITAL, WILLOUGHBY, OH, p. A553
LAURENS COUNTY HOSPITAL, CLINTON, SC, p. A617
LAVACA MEDICAL CENTER, HALLETTSVILLE, TX, p. A682
LAWNWOOD REGIONAL MEDICAL CENTER & HEART INSTITUTE, FORT PIERCE, FL, p. A138
LAWNWOOD REGIONAL MEDICAL CENTER, FORT PIERCE, FL, p. A138
LAWRENCE & MEMORIAL HOSPITAL, NEW LONDON, CT, p. A124
LAWRENCE + MEMORIAL HOSPITAL, NEW LONDON, CT, p. A124
LAWRENCE COUNTY HOSPITAL, MONTICELLO, MS, p. A397
LAWRENCE COUNTY MEMORIAL HOSPITAL, LAWRENCEVILLE, IL, p. A210
LAWRENCE GENERAL HOSPITAL, LAWRENCE, MA, p. A340
LAWRENCE HOSPITAL CENTER, BRONXVILLE, NY, p. A477
LAWRENCE MEDICAL CENTER, MOULTON, AL, p. A22
LAWRENCE MEDICAL CTR, MOULTON, AL, p. A22
LAWRENCE MEMORIAL HOSPITAL, LAWRENCE, KS, p. A269
LAWRENCE MEMORIAL HOSPITAL, WALNUT RIDGE, AR, p. A54
LAWRENCE MEMORIAL HOSPITAL OF MEDFORD, MEDFORD, MA, p. A341
LAWTON INDIAN HOSPITAL, LAWTON, OK, p. A561
LAYTON HOSPITAL, LAYTON, UT, p. A728
LDS HOSPITAL, SALT LAKE CITY, UT, p. A732
LE BONHEUR CHILDREN'S HOSPITAL, MEMPHIS, TN, p. A644
LE BONHEUR CHILDREN'S MEDICAL CENTER, MEMPHIS, TN, p. A644
LEA REGIONAL HOSPITAL, HOBBS, NM, p. A470
LEA REGIONAL MEDICAL CENTER, HOBBS, NM, p. A470
LEAD-DEADWOOD REGIONAL HOSPITAL, DEADWOOD, SD, p. A627
LEAHI HOSPITAL, HONOLULU, HI, p. A184
LEAKE MEMORIAL HOSPITAL, CARTHAGE, MS, p. A390
LEBANON COMMUNITY HOSPITAL, LEBANON, OR, p. A577
LEBANON VETERANS AFFAIRS MEDICAL CENTER, LEBANON, PA, p. A594
LECOM CORRY MEMORIAL HOSPITAL, CORRY, PA, p. A587
LECOM HEALTH MILLCREEK COMMUNITY HOSPITAL, ERIE, PA, p. A590
LECONTE MEDICAL CENTER, SEVIERVILLE, TN, p. A649
LEE MEMORIAL HEALTH SYSTEM, FORT MYERS, FL, p. A138
LEE MEMORIAL HOSPITAL, FORT MYERS, FL, p. A138
LEESBURG REGIONAL MEDICAL CENTER, LEESBURG, FL, p. A144
LEESVILLE REHABILITATION HOSPITAL, LEESVILLE, LA, p. A307
LEE'S SUMMIT HOSPITAL, LEE'S SUMMIT, MO, p. A410
LEE'S SUMMIT MEDICAL CENTER, LEE'S SUMMIT, MO, p. A410
LEGACY EMANUEL CHILDREN'S HOSPITAL, PORTLAND, OR, p. A579
LEGACY EMANUEL HOSPITAL AND HEALTH CENTER, PORTLAND, OR, p. A579
LEGACY EMANUEL MEDICAL CENTER, PORTLAND, OR, p. A579
LEGACY GOOD SAMARITAN HOSPITAL AND MEDICAL CENTER, PORTLAND, OR, p. A579
LEGACY GOOD SAMARITAN MEDICAL CENTER, PORTLAND, OR, p. A579
LEGACY MERIDIAN PARK HOSPITAL, TUALATIN, OR, p. A582
LEGACY MERIDIAN PARK MEDICAL CENTER, TUALATIN, OR, p. A582
LEGACY MOUNT HOOD MEDICAL CENTER, GRESHAM, OR, p. A575
LEGACY SALMON CREEK HOSPITAL, VANCOUVER, WA, p. A768
LEGACY SALMON CREEK MEDICAL CENTER, VANCOUVER, WA, p. A768
LEGACY SILVERTON MEDICAL CENTER, SILVERTON, OR, p. A581
LEGENT HOSPITAL FOR SPECIAL SURGERY, PLANO, TX, p. A707

LEGENT HOSPITAL OF EL PASO, EL PASO, TX, p. A675
LEGENT ORTHOPEDIC & SPINE HOSPITAL, SAN ANTONIO, TX, p. A712
LEGENT ORTHOPEDIC + SPINE HOSPITAL, SAN ANTONIO, TX, p. A712
LEGENT ORTHOPEDIC HOSPITAL CARROLLTON, CARROLLTON, TX, p. A663
LEHIGH REGIONAL MEDICAL CENTER, LEHIGH ACRES, FL, p. A144
LEHIGH VALLEY HEALTH NETWORK AT COORDINATED HEALTH, ALLENTOWN, PA, p. A583
LEHIGH VALLEY HEALTH NETWORK PEDIATRICS, ALLENTOWN, PA, p. A583
LEHIGH VALLEY HOSPITAL—HAZLETON, HAZLETON, PA, p. A592
LEHIGH VALLEY HOSPITAL—POCONO, EAST STROUDSBURG, PA, p. A589
LEHIGH VALLEY HOSPITAL—SCHUYLKILL, POTTSVILLE, PA, p. A605
LEHIGH VALLEY HOSPITAL—SCHUYLKILL SOUTH JACKSON STREET, POTTSVILLE, PA, p. A605
LEHIGH VALLEY HOSPITAL, ALLENTOWN, PA, p. A583
LEIGH VALLEY HOSPITAL—HAZLETON, HAZLETON, PA, p. A592
LEMUEL SHATTUCK HOSPITAL, JAMAICA PLAIN, MA, p. A340
LENOIR MEMORIAL HOSPITAL, KINSTON, NC, p. A513
LENOX HILL HOSPITAL, NEW YORK, NY, p. A490
LEONARD J. CHABERT MEDICAL CENTER, HOUMA, LA, p. A303
LEONARD MORSE HOSPITAL, NATICK, MA, p. A342
LESTER E. COX MEDICAL CENTER NORTH, SPRINGFIELD, MO, p. A418
LESTER E. COX MEDICAL CENTER SOUTH, SPRINGFIELD, MO, p. A418
LESTER E. COX MEDICAL CENTERS, SPRINGFIELD, MO, p. A418
LEVI ARTHRITIS HOSPITAL, HOT SPRINGS NATIONAL PARK, AR, p. A47
LEVI HOSPITAL, HOT SPRINGS NATIONAL PARK, AR, p. A47
LEVINDALE HEBREW GERIATRIC CENTER AND HOSPITAL, BALTIMORE, MD, p. A325
LEVINDALE HEBREW HOSPITAL AND NURSING, BALTIMORE, MD, p. A325
LEWIS AND CLARK SPECIALTY HOSPITAL, YANKTON, SD, p. A633
LEWIS COUNTY GENERAL HOSPITAL, LOWVILLE, NY, p. A487
LEWIS-GALE MEDICAL CENTER, BOONES MILL, VA, p. A739
LEWIS-GALE PSYCHIATRIC CENTER, SALEM, VA, p. A751
LEWISBURG COMMUNITY HOSPITAL, LEWISBURG, TN, p. A642
LEWISGALE HOSPITAL ALLEGHANY, LOW MOOR, VA, p. A745
LEWISGALE HOSPITAL AT PULASKI, PULASKI, VA, p. A749
LEWISGALE HOSPITAL MONTGOMERY, BLACKSBURG, VA, p. A739
LEWISGALE HOSPITAL PULASKI, PULASKI, VA, p. A749
LEWISTOWN HOSPITAL, LEWISTOWN, PA, p. A595
LEXINGTON MEDICAL CENTER, WEST COLUMBIA, SC, p. A625
LEXINGTON MEMORIAL HOSPITAL, LEXINGTON, NC, p. A514
LEXINGTON REGIONAL HEALTH CENTER, LEXINGTON, NE, p. A434
LEXINGTON VETERANS AFFAIRS MEDICAL CENTER, LEXINGTON, KY, p. A286
LI JEWISH-HILLSIDE MED CENTER, GLEN OAKS, NY, p. A484
LIBERTY COUNTY HOSPITAL, CHESTER, MT, p. A422
LIBERTY DAYTON REGIONAL MEDICAL CENTER, LIBERTY, TX, p. A696
LIBERTY HEALTHCARE SYSTEMS, BASTROP, LA, p. A296
LIBERTY HEALTHCARE SYSTEMS, RUSTON, LA, p. A313
LIBERTY HOSPITAL, LIBERTY, MO, p. A411
LIBERTY MEDICAL CENTER, CHESTER, MT, p. A422
LIBERTY MEMORIAL HOSPITAL, HINESVILLE, GA, p. A174
LIBERTY REGIONAL MEDICAL CENTER, HINESVILLE, GA, p. A174
LIBERTY-DAYTON REGIONAL MEDICAL CENTER, LIBERTY, TX, p. A696
LIBERTYHEALTH-JERSEY CITY MEDICAL CENTER, JERSEY CITY, NJ, p. A456
LICKING MEMORIAL HOSPITAL, NEWARK, OH, p. A546
LIFE CENTER, WILMINGTON, NC, p. A520
LIFE LINE HOSPITAL, STEUBENVILLE, OH, p. A549
LIFEBRITE COMMUNITY HOSPITAL OF EARLY, BLAKELY, GA, p. A167
LIFEBRITE COMMUNITY HOSPITAL OF STOKES, DANBURY, NC, p. A508
LIFECARE BEHAVIORAL HEALTH HOSPITAL, PITTSBURGH, PA, p. A603
LIFECARE HOSP OF FORT WORTH, FORT WORTH, TX, p. A678
LIFECARE HOSPITAL OF DAYTON, MIAMISBURG, OH, p. A545

LIFECARE HOSPITALS OF DALLAS, DALLAS, TX, p. A669
LIFECARE HOSPITALS OF NORTH CAROLINA, ROCKY MOUNT, NC, p. A517
LIFECARE HOSPITALS OF NORTH TEXAS, DALLAS, TX, p. A669
LIFECARE HOSPITALS OF PITTSBURGH—SUBURBAN CAMPUS, PITTSBURGH, PA, p. A603
LIFECARE HOSPITALS OF PITTSBURGH, PITTSBURGH, PA, p. A603
LIFECARE HOSPITALS OF PLANO, PLANO, TX, p. A707
LIFECARE HOSPITALS OF SAN ANTONIO, SAN ANTONIO, TX, p. A712
LIFECARE HOSPITALS OF SHREVEPORT—NORTH CAMPUS, SHREVEPORT, LA, p. A314
LIFECARE HOSPITALS OF SHREVEPORT-WILLIS KNIGHTON, SHREVEPORT, LA, p. A314
LIFECARE MEDICAL CENTER, ROSEAU, MN, p. A384
LIFECARE SPECIALTY HOSPITAL OF NORTH LOUISIANA, RUSTON, LA, p. A313
LIFECOURSE REHABILITATION HOSP, FARMINGTON, NM, p. A469
LIFESCAPE, SIOUX FALLS, SD, p. A631
LIFESTREAM BEHAVIORAL CENTER, LEESBURG, FL, p. A144
LIGHTHOUSE BEHAVIORAL HEALTH HOSPITAL, CONWAY, SC, p. A618
LIGHTHOUSE CARE CENTER OF CONWAY, CONWAY, SC, p. A618
LILLIAN M. HUDSPETH MEMORIAL HOSPITAL, SONORA, TX, p. A716
LIMA MEMORIAL HEALTH SYSTEM, LIMA, OH, p. A543
LIMA MEMORIAL HOSPITAL, LIMA, OH, p. A543
LIMESTONE MEDICAL CENTER, GROESBECK, TX, p. A682
LINCOLN CNTY HOSP DISTRICT 3, DAVENPORT, WA, p. A757
LINCOLN COMMUNITY HOSPITAL AND NURSING HOME, HUGO, CO, p. A114
LINCOLN COUNTY HEALTH SYSTEM, FAYETTEVILLE, TN, p. A638
LINCOLN COUNTY HEALTH SYSTEMS, FAYETTEVILLE, TN, p. A638
LINCOLN COUNTY HOSPITAL, LINCOLN, KS, p. A269
LINCOLN COUNTY MEDICAL CENTER, RUIDOSO, NM, p. A471
LINCOLN COUNTY MEDICAL CENTER, TROY, MO, p. A419
LINCOLN DIVISION, LINCOLN, NE, p. A434
LINCOLN GENERAL HOSPITAL, RUSTON, LA, p. A313
LINCOLN HEALTH, DAMARISCOTTA, ME, p. A320
LINCOLN HOSPITAL, DAVENPORT, WA, p. A757
LINCOLN MEDICAL AND MENTAL HEALTH CENTER, BRONX, NY, p. A477
LINCOLN PRAIRIE BEHAVIORAL HEALTH CENTER, SPRINGFIELD, IL, p. A220
LINCOLN REGIONAL CENTER, LINCOLN, NE, p. A434
LINCOLN SURGICAL HOSPITAL, LINCOLN, NE, p. A434
LINCOLN TRAIL BEHAVIORAL HEALTH SYSTEM, RADCLIFF, KY, p. A292
LINCOLN TRAIL HOSPITAL, RADCLIFF, KY, p. A292
LINCOLNHEALTH, DAMARISCOTTA, ME, p. A320
LINDEN OAKS HOSPITAL, NAPERVILLE, IL, p. A214
LINDEN OAKS HOSPITAL AT EDWARD, NAPERVILLE, IL, p. A214
LINDNER CENTER OF HOPE, MASON, OH, p. A544
LINDSAY MUNICIPAL HOSPITAL, LINDSAY, OK, p. A561
LINDSBORG COMMUNITY HOSPITAL, LINDSBORG, KS, p. A270
LINTON HOSPITAL, LINTON, ND, p. A524
LISBON AREA HEALTH SERVICES, LISBON, ND, p. A525
LITTLE COLORADO MEDICAL CENTER, WINSLOW, AZ, p. A41
LITTLE FALLS HOSPITAL, LITTLE FALLS, NY, p. A487
LITTLE RIVER CAMERON HOSPITAL, CAMERON, TX, p. A662
LITTLE RIVER MEMORIAL HOSPITAL, ASHDOWN, AR, p. A42
LITTLETON ADVENTIST HOSPITAL, LITTLETON, CO, p. A116
LITTLETON REGIONAL HEALTHCARE, LITTLETON, NH, p. A450
LITTLETON REGIONAL HOSPITAL, LITTLETON, NH, p. A450
LITZENBERG MEMORIAL COUNTY HOSPITAL, CENTRAL CITY, NE, p. A430
LIVENGRIN FOUNDATION, BENSALEM, PA, p. A584
LIVINGSTON COUNTY HOSPITAL, SALEM, KY, p. A293
LIVINGSTON HEALTHCARE, LIVINGSTON, MT, p. A426
LIVINGSTON HOSPITAL AND HEALTHCARE SERVICES, SALEM, KY, p. A293
LIVINGSTON MEMORIAL HOSPITAL, LIVINGSTON, MT, p. A426
LIVINGSTON REGIONAL HOSPITAL, LIVINGSTON, TN, p. A642
LMH HEALTH, LAWRENCE, KS, p. A269
LOCK HAVEN HOSPITAL, LOCK HAVEN, PA, p. A595
LOCKNEY GENERAL HOSPITAL, LOCKNEY, TX, p. A696
LOCKPORT MEMORIAL HOSPITAL, LOCKPORT, NY, p. A487
LODI COMMUNITY HOSPITAL, LODI, OH, p. A543
LOGAN COUNTY HOSPITAL, OAKLEY, KS, p. A272
LOGAN GENERAL HOSPITAL, LOGAN, WV, p. A774

LOGAN MEDICAL CENTER, GUTHRIE, OK, p. A559
LOGAN MEMORIAL HOSPITAL, RUSSELLVILLE, KY, p. A293
LOGAN REGIONAL HOSPITAL, LOGAN, UT, p. A728
LOGAN REGIONAL MEDICAL CENTER, LOGAN, WV, p. A774
LOGANSPORT MEMORIAL HOSPITAL, LOGANSPORT, IN, p. A235
LOGANSPORT STATE HOSPITAL, LOGANSPORT, IN, p. A235
LOMA LINDA UNIV COMM MED CTR, LOMA LINDA, CA, p. A71
LOMA LINDA UNIVERSITY BEHAVIORAL MEDICINE CENTER, REDLANDS, CA, p. A87
LOMA LINDA UNIVERSITY CHILDREN'S HOSPITAL, LOMA LINDA, CA, p. A71
LOMA LINDA UNIVERSITY HEART & SURGICAL HOSPITAL, LOMA LINDA, CA, p. A71
LOMA LINDA UNIVERSITY MEDICAL CENTER, LOMA LINDA, CA, p. A72
LOMA LINDA UNIVERSITY MEDICAL CENTER-MURRIETA, MURRIETA, CA, p. A80
LOMPOC HEALTHCARE DISTRICT, LOMPOC, CA, p. A72
LOMPOC VALLEY MEDICAL CENTER, LOMPOC, CA, p. A72
LONE PEAK HOSPITAL, DRAPER, UT, p. A728
LONE STAR BEHAVIORAL HEALTH, CYPRESS, TX, p. A667
LONESOME PINE HOSPITAL, BIG STONE GAP, VA, p. A739
LONG BEACH MEDICAL CENTER, LONG BEACH, CA, p. A72
LONG BEACH MEMORIAL MEDICAL CENTER, LONG BEACH, CA, p. A72
LONG ISLAND COMMUNITY HOSPITAL, PATCHOGUE, NY, p. A494
LONG ISLAND JEWISH MEDICAL CENTER, NEW HYDE PARK, NY, p. A489
LONG TERM CARE HOSPITAL, MONTGOMERY, AL, p. A22
LONG TERM HOSPITAL OF ANNISTON, ANNISTON, AL, p. A13
LONG TERM HOSPITAL OF BIRMINGHAM, BIRMINGHAM, AL, p. A15
LONG TERM HOSPITAL OF DOTHAN, DOTHAN, AL, p. A17
LONG TERM HOSPITAL OF TUSCALOOSA, TUSCALOOSA, AL, p. A25
LONG-TERM ACUTE CARE HOSPITAL, MOSAIC LIFE CARE AT ST. JOSEPH, SAINT JOSEPH, MO, p. A415
LONGLEAF HOSPITAL, ALEXANDRIA, LA, p. A295
LONGMONT UNITED HOSPITAL, LONGMONT, CO, p. A116
LONGVIEW REGIONAL MEDICAL CENTER, LONGVIEW, TX, p. A697
LORETTO HOSPITAL, CHICAGO, IL, p. A199
LORING HOSPITAL, SAC CITY, IA, p. A257
LOS ALAMITOS MEDICAL CENTER, LOS ALAMITOS, CA, p. A73
LOS ALAMOS MEDICAL CENTER, LOS ALAMOS, NM, p. A470
LOS ANGELES COMMUNITY HOSPITAL, LOS ANGELES, CA, p. A75
LOS ANGELES COMMUNITY HOSPITAL AT LOS ANGELES, LOS ANGELES, CA, p. A75
LOS ANGELES COMMUNITY HOSPITAL OF NORWALK, NORWALK, CA, p. A81
LOS ANGELES COUNTY CENTRAL JAIL HOSPITAL, LOS ANGELES, CA, p. A75
LOS ANGELES MEDICAL CENTER, LOS ANGELES, CA, p. A75
LOS BANOS COMMUNITY HOSPITAL, LOS BANOS, CA, p. A76
LOS NINOS HOSPITAL, PHOENIX, AZ, p. A36
LOS ROBLES HOSPITAL AND MEDICAL CENTER, THOUSAND OAKS, CA, p. A101
LOS ROBLES REGIONAL MED CENTER, THOUSAND OAKS, CA, p. A101
LOST RIVERS DISTRICT HOSPITAL, ARCO, ID, p. A188
LOST RIVERS MEDICAL CENTER, ARCO, ID, p. A188
LOUDOUN HOSPITAL CENTER, LEESBURG, VA, p. A744
LOUIS A JOHNSON VETERANS CNTR, CLARKSBURG, WV, p. A771
LOUIS A. JOHNSON VETERANS AFFAIRS MEDICAL CENTER, CLARKSBURG, WV, p. A772
LOUIS A. WEISS MEMORIAL HOSPITAL, CHICAGO, IL, p. A199
LOUIS SMITH MEMORIAL HOSPITAL, LAKELAND, GA, p. A175
LOUIS STOKES CLEVELAND VETERANS AFFAIRS MEDICAL CENTER, CLEVELAND, OH, p. A534
LOUISE OBICI MEMORIAL HOSPITAL, SUFFOLK, VA, p. A752
LOUISIANA CONTINUING CARE HOSPITAL, MARRERO, LA, p. A308
LOUISIANA EXTENDED CARE HOSPITAL OF LAFAYETTE, LAFAYETTE, LA, p. A305
LOUISIANA EXTENDED CARE HOSPITAL OF NATCHITOCHES, NATCHITOCHES, LA, p. A309
LOUISIANA EXTENDED CARE HOSPITAL OF WEST MONROE, WEST MONROE, LA, p. A316
LOUISIANA EXTENDED CARE HOSPITAL WEST MONROE, WEST MONROE, LA, p. A316
LOURDES COUNSELING CENTER, RICHLAND, WA, p. A763
LOURDES HOSPITAL, PADUCAH, KY, p. A291
LOURDES MEDICAL CENTER, PASCO, WA, p. A762
LOURDES MEDICAL CENTER OF BURLINGTON COUNTY, WILLINGBORO, NJ, p. A466

LOURDES SPECIALTY HOSPITAL OF SOUTHERN NEW JERSEY, WILLINGBORO, NJ, p. A466
LOVE COUNTY HEALTH CENTER, MARIETTA, OK, p. A561
LOVELACE MEDICAL CENTER, ALBUQUERQUE, NM, p. A467
LOVELACE MEDICAL CENTER-DOWNTOWN, ALBUQUERQUE, NM, p. A467
LOVELACE REGIONAL HOSPITAL—ROSWELL, ROSWELL, NM, p. A471
LOVELACE REGIONAL HOSPITAL, ROSWELL, NM, p. A471
LOVELACE REHABILITATION HOSPITAL, ALBUQUERQUE, NM, p. A467
LOVELACE UNM REHABILITATION HOSPITAL, ALBUQUERQUE, NM, p. A467
LOVELACE WESTSIDE HOSPITAL, ALBUQUERQUE, NM, p. A467
LOVELACE WOMEN'S HOSPITAL, ALBUQUERQUE, NM, p. A468
LOWELL GENERAL HOSPITAL, LOWELL, MA, p. A341
LOWER BUCKS HOSPITAL, BRISTOL, PA, p. A585
LOWER FLORIDA KEYS HEALTH SYST, KEY WEST, FL, p. A142
LOWER KEYS MEDICAL CENTER, KEY WEST, FL, p. A142
LOWER UMPQUA HOSPITAL DISTRICT, REEDSPORT, OR, p. A580
LOYOLA UNIV MEDICAL CENTER, MAYWOOD, IL, p. A211
LOYOLA UNIVERSITY MEDICAL CENTER, MAYWOOD, IL, p. A211
LTAC OF WICHITA, WICHITA, KS, p. A279
LUBBOCK GEN HOSPITAL, LUBBOCK, TX, p. A697
LUBBOCK HEART & SURGICAL HOSPITAL, LUBBOCK, TX, p. A697
LUBBOCK HEART HOSPITAL, LUBBOCK, TX, p. A697
LUCAS COUNTY HEALTH CENTER, CHARITON, IA, p. A245
LUCILE PACKARD CHILDREN'S HOSPITAL STANFORD, PALO ALTO, CA, p. A84
LUCILE SALTER PACKARD CHILDREN'S HOSPITAL STANFORD, PALO ALTO, CA, p. A84
LUTHER HOSPITAL, EAU CLAIRE, WI, p. A783
LUTHER MIDELFORT CHIPPEWA VALLEY, BLOOMER, WI, p. A781
LUTHER MIDELFORT NORTHLAND, BARRON, WI, p. A781
LUTHER MIDELFORT OAKRIDGE, OSSEO, WI, p. A793
LUTHERAN GENERAL HOSPITAL, PARK RIDGE, IL, p. A216
LUTHERAN HOSP OF INDIANA, FORT WAYNE, IN, p. A228
LUTHERAN HOSPITAL, CLEVELAND, OH, p. A534
LUTHERAN HOSPITAL OF INDIANA, FORT WAYNE, IN, p. A228
LUTHERAN MEDICAL CENTER, CLEVELAND, OH, p. A534
LUTHERAN MEDICAL CENTER, SAINT LOUIS, MO, p. A416
LUTHERAN MEDICAL CENTER, WHEAT RIDGE, CO, p. A120
L. V. STABLER MEMORIAL HOSPITAL, GREENVILLE, AL, p. A19
LYNDON B JOHNSON GENERAL HOSPITAL, HOUSTON, TX, p. A686
LYNDON B. JOHNSON TROPICAL MEDICAL CENTER, PAGO PAGO, AS, p. A805
LYNN COUNTY HOSPITAL DISTRICT, TAHOKA, TX, p. A718
LYONS DIVISION, LYONS, NJ, p. A457

# M

MACDONALD HOSPITAL FOR WOMEN, CLEVELAND, OH, p. A534
MACKINAC STRAITS HEALTH SYSTEM, SAINT IGNACE, MI, p. A366
MACKINAC STRAITS HEALTH SYSTEM, INC., SAINT IGNACE, MI, p. A366
MACNEAL HOSPITAL, BERWYN, IL, p. A195
MACON COMMUNITY HOSPITAL, LAFAYETTE, TN, p. A642
MACON COUNTY GENERAL HOSPITAL, LAFAYETTE, TN, p. A642
MACON NORTHSIDE HOSPITAL, MACON, GA, p. A176
MAD RIVER COMMUNITY HOSPITAL, ARCATA, CA, p. A56
MADELIA COMMUNITY HOSPITAL, MADELIA, MN, p. A379
MADERA COMMUNITY HOSPITAL, MADERA, CA, p. A76
MADIGAN ARMY MEDICAL CENTER, TACOMA, WA, p. A767
MADIGAN HEALTHCARE SYSTEM, TACOMA, WA, p. A767
MADISON COMMUNITY HOSPITAL D/B/A MADISON REGIONAL HEALTH SYSTEM, MADISON, SD, p. A629
MADISON COUNTY HEALTH CARE SYSTEM (DKA MADISON COUNTY MEMORIAL HOSPITAL), WINTERSET, IA, p. A260
MADISON COUNTY HEALTH CARE SYSTEM, WINTERSET, IA, p. A260
MADISON COUNTY HOSPITAL, LONDON, OH, p. A543
MADISON COUNTY MEMORIAL HOSPITAL, MADISON, FL, p. A144
MADISON HEALTH, LONDON, OH, p. A543

MADISON HEALTHCARE SERVICES, MADISON, MN, p. A379
MADISON HOSPITAL, MADISON, MN, p. A379
MADISON MEDICAL CENTER, FREDERICKTOWN, MO, p. A406
MADISON MEMORIAL HOSPITAL, FREDERICKTOWN, MO, p. A406
MADISON MEMORIAL HOSPITAL, REXBURG, ID, p. A192
MADISON PARISH HOSPITAL, TALLULAH, LA, p. A316
MADISON REGIONAL HEALTH SYSTEM, MADISON, SD, p. A629
MADISON RIVER OAKS MEDICAL CENTER, CANTON, MS, p. A390
MADISON ST. JOSEPH HEALTH CENTER, MADISONVILLE, TX, p. A699
MADISON STATE HOSPITAL, MADISON, IN, p. A236
MADISON VALLEY HOSPITAL, ENNIS, MT, p. A423
MADISON VALLEY MEDICAL CENTER, ENNIS, MT, p. A423
MADONNA CENTERS, LINCOLN, NE, p. A434
MADONNA REHABILITATION HOSPITAL, LINCOLN, NE, p. A434
MADONNA REHABILITATION HOSPITAL, OMAHA, NE, p. A437
MADONNA REHABILITATION SPECIALTY HOSPITAL, OMAHA, NE, p. A437
MAGEE GENERAL HOSPITAL, MAGEE, MS, p. A396
MAGEE REHABILITATION HOSPITAL, PHILADELPHIA, PA, p. A601
MAGEE-WOMENS HOSPITAL OF UPMC, PITTSBURGH, PA, p. A603
MAGNOLIA BEHAVIORAL HOSPITAL OF EAST TEXAS, LONGVIEW, TX, p. A697
MAGNOLIA HOSPITAL, CORINTH, MS, p. A391
MAGNOLIA HOSPITAL, MAGNOLIA, AR, p. A49
MAGNOLIA REGIONAL HEALTH CENTER, CORINTH, MS, p. A391
MAGNOLIA REGIONAL MEDICAL CENTER, MAGNOLIA, AR, p. A49
MAGRUDER MEMORIAL HOSPITAL, PORT CLINTON, OH, p. A548
MAHASKA COUNTY HOSPITAL, OSKALOOSA, IA, p. A256
MAHASKA HEALTH PARTNERSHIP, OSKALOOSA, IA, p. A256
MAHNOMEN COUNTY & VILLAGE HOSP, MAHNOMEN, MN, p. A379
MAHNOMEN HEALTH CENTER, MAHNOMEN, MN, p. A379
MAHONING VALLEY HOSPITAL, BOARDMAN, OH, p. A529
MAIMONIDES MEDICAL CENTER, BROOKLYN, NY, p. A478
MAINE MEDICAL CENTER, PORTLAND, ME, p. A322
MAINE VETERANS AFFAIRS MEDICAL CENTER, AUGUSTA, ME, p. A318
MAINEGENERAL MEDICAL CENTER, AUGUSTA, ME, p. A318
MAINEGENERAL MEDICAL CENTER-AUGUSTA CAMPUS, AUGUSTA, ME, p. A318
MAINEGENERAL MEDICAL CENTER-WATERVILLE CAMPUS, AUGUSTA, ME, p. A318
MAJOR HOSPITAL, SHELBYVILLE, IN, p. A240
MALCOLM BLISS MENTAL HLTH CTR, SAINT LOUIS, MO, p. A416
MALCOM RANDALL VETERANS AFFAIRS MEDICAL CENTER, GAINESVILLE, FL, p. A138
MALVERN INSTITUTE, MALVERN, PA, p. A596
MAMMOTH HOSPITAL, MAMMOTH LAKES, CA, p. A77
MANATEE GLENS HOSPITAL AND ADDICTION CENTER, BRADENTON, FL, p. A133
MANATEE MEMORIAL HOSPITAL, BRADENTON, FL, p. A133
MANATEE PALMS YOUTH SERVICES, BRADENTON, FL, p. A133
MANCHESTER MEMORIAL HOSPITAL, MANCHESTER, CT, p. A122
MANCHESTER MEMORIAL HOSPITAL, MANCHESTER, KY, p. A289
MANCHESTER VETERANS AFFAIRS MEDICAL CENTER, MANCHESTER, NH, p. A450
MANGUM CITY HOSPITAL, MANGUM, OK, p. A561
MANGUM REGIONAL MEDICAL CENTER, MANGUM, OK, p. A561
MANHASSET AMBULATORY CARE CTR, MANHASSET, NY, p. A487
MANHATTAN EET HOSPITAL, NEW YORK, NY, p. A490
MANHATTAN PSYCH CENTER, NEW YORK, NY, p. A490
MANHATTAN PSYCHIATRIC CENTER-WARD'S ISLAND, NEW YORK, NY, p. A490
MANHATTAN SURGICAL, MANHATTAN, KS, p. A270
MANHATTAN SURGICAL CENTER, MANHATTAN, KS, p. A270
MANIILAQ HEALTH CENTER, KOTZEBUE, AK, p. A29
MANIILAQ MEDICAL CENTER, KOTZEBUE, AK, p. A29
MANN-GRANDSTAFF VETERANS AFFAIRS MEDICAL CENTER, SPOKANE, WA, p. A765
MANNING GENERAL HOSPITAL, MANNING, IA, p. A253
MANNING REGIONAL HEALTHCARE CENTER, MANNING, IA, p. A253
MANSFIELD GENERAL HOSPITAL, MANSFIELD, OH, p. A544
MANTECA MEDICAL CENTER, MANTECA, CA, p. A77

MAPLE GROVE HOSPITAL, MAPLE GROVE, MN, p. A380
MARCUM AND WALLACE MEMORIAL HOSPITAL, IRVINE, KY, p. A285
MARCUS DALY MEMORIAL HOSPITAL, HAMILTON, MT, p. A424
MARCUS J LAWRENCE MED CENTER, COTTONWOOD, AZ, p. A31
MARENGO MEMORIAL HOSPITAL, MARENGO, IA, p. A253
MARGARET MARY COMMUNITY HOSPITAL, BATESVILLE, IN, p. A223
MARGARET MARY HEALTH, BATESVILLE, IN, p. A223
MARGARET R. PARDEE MEMORIAL HOSPITAL, HENDERSONVILLE, NC, p. A512
MARGARET TIETZ CNTR FOR NRSG, JAMAICA, NY, p. A486
MARGARETVILLE HOSPITAL, MARGARETVILLE, NY, p. A488
MARGARETVILLE MEM HOSPITAL, MARGARETVILLE, NY, p. A488
MARIA PARHAM HOSPITAL, HENDERSON, NC, p. A511
MARIA PARHAM MEDICAL CENTER, HENDERSON, NC, p. A511
MARIAN CENTER, SALT LAKE CITY, UT, p. A732
MARIAN MEDICAL CENTER, SANTA MARIA, CA, p. A97
MARIAN REGIONAL MEDICAL CENTER, SANTA MARIA, CA, p. A97
MARIANJOY REHABILITATION HOSPITAL, WHEATON, IL, p. A222
MARIAS MEDICAL CENTER, SHELBY, MT, p. A427
MARICOPA INTEGRATED HEALTH SYSTEM, PHOENIX, AZ, p. A36
MARIETTA MEMORIAL HOSPITAL, MARIETTA, OH, p. A544
MARIN GENERAL HOSPITAL, GREENBRAE, CA, p. A67
MARINA DEL REY HOSPITAL, MARINA DEL REY, CA, p. A77
MARINHEALTH MEDICAL CENTER, GREENBRAE, CA, p. A67
MARION GENERAL HOSPITAL, COLUMBIA, MS, p. A391
MARION GENERAL HOSPITAL, MARION, IN, p. A236
MARION GENERAL HOSPITAL, MARION, OH, p. A544
MARION MEMORIAL HOSPITAL, BUENA VISTA, GA, p. A167
MARION MEMORIAL HOSPITAL, MARION, IL, p. A211
MARION REGIONAL MEDICAL CENTER, HAMILTON, AL, p. A20
MARION VETERANS AFFAIRS MEDICAL CENTER, MARION, IL, p. A211
MARK REED HEALTH CARE DISTRICT, ELMA, WA, p. A757
MARK TWAIN MEDICAL CENTER, SAN ANDREAS, CA, p. A90
MARK TWAIN ST. JOSEPH'S HOSPITAL, SAN ANDREAS, CA, p. A90
MARLETTE COMMUNITY HOSPITAL, MARLETTE, MI, p. A361
MARLETTE REGIONAL HOSPITAL, MARLETTE, MI, p. A361
MARLTON REHABILITATION HOSPITAL, MARLTON, NJ, p. A458
MARQUETTE GENERAL HOSPITAL, MARQUETTE, MI, p. A361
MARSHALL BROWNING HOSPITAL, DU QUOIN, IL, p. A203
MARSHALL COUNTY HEALTHCARE CENTER AVERA, BRITTON, SD, p. A626
MARSHALL COUNTY HOSPITAL, BENTON, KY, p. A280
MARSHALL COUNTY MEDICAL CENTER, HOLLY SPRINGS, MS, p. A394
MARSHALL COUNTY MEDICAL CENTER, MADILL, OK, p. A561
MARSHALL COUNTY MEM HOSPITAL, BRITTON, SD, p. A626
MARSHALL HOSPITAL CENTER, PLACERVILLE, CA, p. A85
MARSHALL MEDICAL CENTER, LEWISBURG, TN, p. A642
MARSHALL MEDICAL CENTER, PLACERVILLE, CA, p. A85
MARSHALL MEDICAL CENTER NORTH, GUNTERSVILLE, AL, p. A19
MARSHALL MEDICAL CENTER SOUTH, BOAZ, AL, p. A16
MARSHFIELD MEDICAL CENTER—BEAVER DAM, BEAVER DAM, WI, p. A781
MARSHFIELD MEDICAL CENTER—EAU CLAIRE HOSPITAL, EAU CLAIRE, WI, p. A783
MARSHFIELD MEDICAL CENTER—LADYSMITH, LADYSMITH, WI, p. A787
MARSHFIELD MEDICAL CENTER—MINOCQUA, MINOCQUA, WI, p. A791
MARSHFIELD MEDICAL CENTER—NEILLSVILLE, NEILLSVILLE, WI, p. A792
MARSHFIELD MEDICAL CENTER—RICE LAKE, RICE LAKE, WI, p. A795
MARSHFIELD MEDICAL CENTER—WESTON, WESTON, WI, p. A799
MARSHFIELD MEDICAL CENTER, MARSHFIELD, WI, p. A789
MARTHA JEFFERSON HOSPITAL, CHARLOTTESVILLE, VA, p. A739
MARTHA'S VINEYARD HOSPITAL, OAK BLUFFS, MA, p. A343
MARTIN ARMY COMMUNITY HOSPITAL, FORT BENNING, GA, p. A172
MARTIN COUNTY HOSPITAL DISTRICT, STANTON, TX, p. A717
MARTIN GENERAL HOSPITAL, WILLIAMSTON, NC, p. A520
MARTIN HEALTH SYSTEM, STUART, FL, p. A158

MARTIN LUTHER KING, JR. COMMUNITY HOSPITAL, LOS ANGELES, CA, p. A75
MARTIN MEMORIAL HOSPITAL SOUTH, STUART, FL, p. A158
MARTINSBURG VETERANS AFFAIRS MEDICAL CENTER, MARTINSBURG, WV, p. A774
MARWOOD MANOR, PORT HURON, MI, p. A364
MARY BLACK HEALTH SYSTEM—GAFFNEY, GAFFNEY, SC, p. A620
MARY BLACK HEALTH SYSTEM-SPARTANBURG, SPARTANBURG, SC, p. A624
MARY BRECKINRIDGE ARH HOSPITAL, HYDEN, KY, p. A285
MARY BRECKINRIDGE HOSPITAL, HYDEN, KY, p. A285
MARY BRIDGE CHILDREN'S HOSPITAL AND HEALTH CENTER, TACOMA, WA, p. A767
MARY FREE BED HOSP & REHAB CTR, GRAND RAPIDS, MI, p. A356
MARY FREE BED REHABILITATION HOSPITAL, GRAND RAPIDS, MI, p. A356
MARY GREELEY MEDICAL CENTER, AMES, IA, p. A243
MARY HITCHCOCK MEM HOSPITAL, LEBANON, NH, p. A449
MARY IMMACULATE HOSPITAL, NEWPORT NEWS, VA, p. A746
MARY IMOGENE BASSETT HOSPITAL, COOPERSTOWN, NY, p. A481
MARY LANNING HEALTHCARE, HASTINGS, NE, p. A433
MARY LANNING MEMORIAL HOSPITAL, HASTINGS, NE, p. A433
MARY REHABILITATION HOSPITAL, LANGHORNE, PA, p. A594
MARY RUTAN HOSPITAL, BELLEFONTAINE, OH, p. A529
MARY S HARPER GERIATRIC PSYCHIATRIC CENTER, TUSCALOOSA, AL, p. A25
MARY S HARPER GERIATRIC PSYCHIATRY CENTER, TUSCALOOSA, AL, p. A25
MARY SHERMAN HOSPITAL, SULLIVAN, IN, p. A240
MARY WASHINGTON HOSPITAL, FREDERICKSBURG, VA, p. A742
MARYLAND GENERAL HOSPITAL, BALTIMORE, MD, p. A325
MARYMOUNT HOSPITAL, GARFIELD HEIGHTS, OH, p. A541
MARYVIEW MEDICAL CENTER, PORTSMOUTH, VA, p. A749
MARYVILLE BEHAVIORAL HEALTH HOSPITAL, DES PLAINES, IL, p. A202
MASON DISTRICT HOSPITAL, HAVANA, IL, p. A207
MASON GENERAL HOSPITAL, SHELTON, WA, p. A765
MASON GENERAL HOSPITAL AND FAMILY OF CLINICS, SHELTON, WA, p. A765
MASONIC HEALTHCARE CENTER, WALLINGFORD, CT, p. A126
MASONICARE HEALTH CENTER, WALLINGFORD, CT, p. A126
MASSAC MEMORIAL HOSPITAL, METROPOLIS, IL, p. A212
MASSACHUSETTS EYE AND EAR, BOSTON, MA, p. A336
MASSACHUSETTS EYE AND EAR INFIRMARY, BOSTON, MA, p. A336
MASSACHUSETTS GENERAL HOSPITAL, BOSTON, MA, p. A336
MASSACHUSETTS HOSPITAL SCHOOL, CANTON, MA, p. A338
MASSENA HOSPITAL, INC., MASSENA, NY, p. A488
MASSENA MEMORIAL HOSPITAL, MASSENA, NY, p. A488
MASSILLON PSYCHIATRIC CENTER, MASSILLON, OH, p. A544
MAT-SU REGIONAL MEDICAL CENTER, PALMER, AK, p. A29
MATAGORDA COUNTY HOSPITAL DISTRICT, BAY CITY, TX, p. A657
MATAGORDA REGIONAL MEDICAL CENTER, BAY CITY, TX, p. A657
MATHENY MEDICAL AND EDUCATIONAL CENTER, PEAPACK, NJ, p. A460
MATHENY SCHOOL AND HOSPITAL, PEAPACK, NJ, p. A460
MATHER HOSPITAL, PORT JEFFERSON, NY, p. A495
MAUI MEDICAL MEMORIAL CENTER, WAILUKU, HI, p. A187
MAUI MEMORIAL MEDICAL CENTER, WAILUKU, HI, p. A187
MAURY REGIONAL HOSPITAL, COLUMBIA, TN, p. A636
MAYERS MEMORIAL HOSPITAL DISTRICT, FALL RIVER MILLS, CA, p. A64
MAYHILL HOSPITAL, DENTON, TX, p. A672
MAYO CLINIC—SAINT MARYS HOSPITAL, ROCHESTER, MN, p. A384
MAYO CLINIC HEALTH SYSTEM—ALBERT LEA & AUSTIN, ALBERT LEA, MN, p. A371
MAYO CLINIC HEALTH SYSTEM—ALBERT LEA AND AUSTIN, ALBERT LEA, MN, p. A371
MAYO CLINIC HEALTH SYSTEM—CHIPPEWA VALLEY IN BLOOMER, BLOOMER, WI, p. A781
MAYO CLINIC HEALTH SYSTEM—FRANCISCAN HEALTHCARE IN LA CROSSE, LA CROSSE, WI, p. A787
MAYO CLINIC HEALTH SYSTEM—FRANCISCAN HEALTHCARE IN SPARTA, SPARTA, WI, p. A796
MAYO CLINIC HEALTH SYSTEM—NORTHLAND IN BARRON, BARRON, WI, p. A781

MAYO CLINIC HEALTH SYSTEM—OAKRIDGE IN OSSEO, OSSEO, WI, p. A793
MAYO CLINIC HEALTH SYSTEM—RED CEDAR, MENOMONIE, WI, p. A789
MAYO CLINIC HEALTH SYSTEM—RED CEDAR IN MENOMONIE, MENOMONIE, WI, p. A789
MAYO CLINIC HEALTH SYSTEM IN CANNON FALLS, CANNON FALLS, MN, p. A374
MAYO CLINIC HEALTH SYSTEM IN EAU CLAIRE, EAU CLAIRE, WI, p. A783
MAYO CLINIC HEALTH SYSTEM IN FAIRMONT, FAIRMONT, MN, p. A376
MAYO CLINIC HEALTH SYSTEM IN LAKE CITY, LAKE CITY, MN, p. A378
MAYO CLINIC HEALTH SYSTEM IN MANKATO, MANKATO, MN, p. A379
MAYO CLINIC HEALTH SYSTEM IN NEW PRAGUE, NEW PRAGUE, MN, p. A382
MAYO CLINIC HEALTH SYSTEM IN PRAGUE, NEW PRAGUE, MN, p. A382
MAYO CLINIC HEALTH SYSTEM IN RED WING, RED WING, MN, p. A383
MAYO CLINIC HEALTH SYSTEM IN SAINT JAMES, SAINT JAMES, MN, p. A384
MAYO CLINIC HEALTH SYSTEM IN WASECA, WASECA, MN, p. A387
MAYO CLINIC HEALTH SYSTEM-ALBERT LEA AND AUSTIN, AUSTIN, MN, p. A372
MAYO CLINIC HOSPITAL—ROCHESTER, ROCHESTER, MN, p. A384
MAYO CLINIC HOSPITAL, PHOENIX, AZ, p. A36
MAYO CLINIC HOSPITAL IN FLORIDA, JACKSONVILLE, FL, p. A141
MAYO CLINIC JACKSONVILLE, JACKSONVILLE, FL, p. A141
MAYO REGIONAL HOSPITAL, DOVER–FOXCROFT, ME, p. A320
MCALESTER REGIONAL HEALTH CENTER, MCALESTER, OK, p. A562
MCBRIDE CLINIC ORTHOPEDIC HOSPITAL, OKLAHOMA CITY, OK, p. A564
MCBRIDE ORTHOPEDIC HOSPITAL, OKLAHOMA CITY, OK, p. A564
MCCAMEY COUNTY HOSPITAL DISTRICT, MCCAMEY, TX, p. A700
MCCAMEY HOSPITAL, MCCAMEY, TX, p. A700
MCCONE COUNTY HEALTH CENTER, CIRCLE, MT, p. A422
MCCONE COUNTY MAF, CIRCLE, MT, p. A422
MCCREADY FOUNDATION, CRISFIELD, MD, p. A329
MCCULLOUGH-HYDE MEMORIAL HOSPITAL, OXFORD, OH, p. A547
MCCULLOUGH-HYDE MEMORIAL HOSPITAL/TRIHEALTH, OXFORD, OH, p. A547
MCCURTAIN MEMORIAL HOSPITAL, IDABEL, OK, p. A560
MCDONOUGH DISTRICT HOSPITAL, MB, IL, p. A211
MCDOWELL ARH HOSPITAL, MCDOWELL, KY, p. A290
MCDOWELL HOSPITAL, MARION, NC, p. A514
MCDUFFIE REGIONAL MEDICAL CENTER, THOMSON, GA, p. A182
MCG CHILDREN'S MEDICAL CENTER, AUGUSTA, GA, p. A166
MCGEHEE HOSPITAL, MCGEHEE, AR, p. A50
MCGEHEE-DESHA COUNTY HOSPITAL, MCGEHEE, AR, p. A50
MCKAY-DEE HOSPITAL, OGDEN, UT, p. A730
MCKAY-DEE HOSPITAL CENTER, OGDEN, UT, p. A730
MCKEE MEDICAL CENTER, LOVELAND, CO, p. A117
MCKEESPORT HOSPITAL, MCKEESPORT, PA, p. A596
MCKENNAN HOSPITAL, SIOUX FALLS, SD, p. A631
MCKENZIE COUNTY HEALTHCARE SYSTEM, WATFORD CITY, ND, p. A526
MCKENZIE COUNTY MEM HOSPITAL, WATFORD CITY, ND, p. A526
MCKENZIE HEALTH SYSTEM, SANDUSKY, MI, p. A366
MCKENZIE MEMORIAL HOSPITAL, SANDUSKY, MI, p. A366
MCKENZIE-WILLAMETTE HOSPITAL, SPRINGFIELD, OR, p. A581
MCKENZIE-WILLAMETTE MEDICAL CENTER, SPRINGFIELD, OR, p. A581
MCLANE CHILDREN'S HOSPITAL SCOTT & WHITE, TEMPLE, TX, p. A719
MCLAREN BAY REGION, BAY CITY, MI, p. A349
MCLAREN BAY SPECIAL CARE, BAY CITY, MI, p. A349
MCLAREN CARO REGION, CARO, MI, p. A350
MCLAREN CENTRAL MICHIGAN, MOUNT PLEASANT, MI, p. A362
MCLAREN FLINT, FLINT, MI, p. A354
MCLAREN GREATER LANSING, LANSING, MI, p. A360
MCLAREN LAPEER REGION, LAPEER, MI, p. A360
MCLAREN MACOMB, MOUNT CLEMENS, MI, p. A362
MCLAREN NORTHERN MICHIGAN, PETOSKEY, MI, p. A363
MCLAREN OAKLAND, PONTIAC, MI, p. A364
MCLAREN PORT HURON, PORT HURON, MI, p. A364
MCLAREN REGIONAL MEDICAL CENTER, FLINT, MI, p. A354

MCLAREN THUMB REGION, BAD AXE, MI, p. A349
MCLEAN HOSPITAL, BELMONT, MA, p. A334
MCLEOD HEALTH, FLORENCE, SC, p. A619
MCLEOD HEALTH CHERAW, CHERAW, SC, p. A617
MCLEOD HEALTH CLARENDON, MANNING, SC, p. A622
MCLEOD HEALTH DARLINGTON, DARLINGTON, SC, p. A618
MCLEOD HEALTH DILLON, DILLON, SC, p. A619
MCLEOD HEALTH LORIS, LORIS, SC, p. A622
MCLEOD LORIS HEALTH, LORIS, SC, p. A622
MCLEOD MEDICAL CENTER DARLINGTON, DARLINGTON, SC, p. A618
MCLEOD MEDICAL CENTER DILLON, DILLON, SC, p. A619
MCLEOD REGIONAL MEDICAL CENTER, FLORENCE, SC, p. A619
MCPHERSON HOSPITAL, HOWELL, MI, p. A357
MCPHERSON HOSPITAL, MCPHERSON, KS, p. A270
MEADE DISTRICT HOSPITAL, MEADE, KS, p. A271
MEADOVIEW REGIONAL MEDICAL CTR, MAYSVILLE, KY, p. A290
MEADOW WOOD BEHAVIORAL HEALTH SYSTEM, NEW CASTLE, DE, p. A127
MEADOW WOOD HOSPITAL, NEW CASTLE, DE, p. A127
MEADOWBROOK REHAB HOSPITAL, MIAMI, FL, p. A146
MEADOWBROOK REHABILITATION HOSPITAL, GARDNER, KS, p. A265
MEADOWCREST HOSPITAL, GRETNA, LA, p. A302
MEADOWLANDS HOSPITAL MEDICAL CENTER, SECAUCUS, NJ, p. A463
MEADOWS HOSPITAL, BLOOMINGTON, IN, p. A224
MEADOWS PSYCHIATRIC CENTER, CENTRE HALL, PA, p. A586
MEADOWS REGIONAL MEDICAL CENTER, VIDALIA, GA, p. A182
MEADOWVIEW REGIONAL MEDICAL CENTER, MAYSVILLE, KY, p. A290
MEADVILLE MEDICAL CENTER, MEADVILLE, PA, p. A596
MEASE COUNTRYSIDE HOSPITAL, SAFETY HARBOR, FL, p. A155
MEASE DUNEDIN HOSPITAL, DUNEDIN, FL, p. A137
MEASE HOSPITAL COUNTRYSIDE, SAFETY HARBOR, FL, p. A155
MEASE HOSPITAL DUNEDIN, DUNEDIN, FL, p. A137
MECOSTA COUNTY MEDICAL CENTER, BIG RAPIDS, MI, p. A349
MEDCENTRAL—MANSFIELD HOSPITAL, MANSFIELD, OH, p. A544
MEDCENTRAL—SHELBY HOSPITAL, SHELBY, OH, p. A549
MEDICAL ARTS CENTER HOSPITAL, FRESH MEADOWS, NY, p. A484
MEDICAL ARTS HOSPITAL, LAMESA, TX, p. A694
MEDICAL BEHAVIORAL HOSPITAL OF MISHAWAKA, KNOX, IN, p. A234
MEDICAL CENTER ALLIANCE, FORT WORTH, TX, p. A678
MEDICAL CENTER ARLINGTON, ARLINGTON, TX, p. A653
MEDICAL CENTER AT BOWLING GREEN, BOWLING GREEN, KY, p. A281
MEDICAL CENTER AT CAVERNA, HORSE CAVE, KY, p. A285
MEDICAL CENTER AT FRANKLIN, FRANKLIN, KY, p. A283
MEDICAL CENTER AT SCOTTSVILLE, SCOTTSVILLE, KY, p. A293
MEDICAL CENTER BARBOUR, EUFAULA, AL, p. A18
MEDICAL CENTER BLOUNT, ONEONTA, AL, p. A23
MEDICAL CENTER EAST, BIRMINGHAM, AL, p. A15
MEDICAL CENTER ENTERPRISE, ENTERPRISE, AL, p. A18
MEDICAL CENTER FRISCO, FRISCO, TX, p. A680
MEDICAL CENTER HEALTH SYSTEM, ODESSA, TX, p. A703
MEDICAL CENTER HOSPITAL, ODESSA, TX, p. A703
MEDICAL CENTER HOSPITAL, SAN ANTONIO, TX, p. A712
MEDICAL CENTER MCKINNEY, MCKINNEY, TX, p. A700
MEDICAL CENTER OF AURORA, AURORA, CO, p. A107
MEDICAL CENTER OF AURORA-SOUTH, AURORA, CO, p. A107
MEDICAL CENTER OF CENTRAL GEORGIA, MACON, GA, p. A176
MEDICAL CENTER OF LEWISVILLE, LEWISVILLE, TX, p. A696
MEDICAL CENTER OF PEACH COUNTY, NAVICENT HEALTH, BRYON, GA, p. A167
MEDICAL CENTER OF PLANO, PLANO, TX, p. A707
MEDICAL CENTER OF SOUTH ARKANSAS, EL DORADO, AR, p. A44
MEDICAL CENTER OF SOUTHEAST TEXAS, BEAUMONT, TX, p. A658
MEDICAL CENTER OF SOUTHEASTERN OKLAHOMA, DURANT, OK, p. A558
MEDICAL CENTER OF THE ROCKIES, LOVELAND, CO, p. A117
MEDICAL CENTER OF TRINITY, TRINITY, FL, p. A161
MEDICAL CENTER SHOALS, MUSCLE SHOALS, AL, p. A22
MEDICAL CENTER, NAVICENT HEALTH, MACON, GA, p. A176
MEDICAL CENTRE SURGICAL HOSP, FORT WORTH, TX, p. A678

MEDICAL CITY ALLIANCE, FORT WORTH, TX, p. A678
MEDICAL CITY ARLINGTON, ARLINGTON, TX, p. A653
MEDICAL CITY DALLAS, DALLAS, TX, p. A669
MEDICAL CITY DALLAS HOSPITAL, DALLAS, TX, p. A669
MEDICAL CITY DENTON, DENTON, TX, p. A672
MEDICAL CITY FORT WORTH, FORT WORTH, TX, p. A678
MEDICAL CITY GREEN OAKS HOSPITAL, DALLAS, TX, p. A669
MEDICAL CITY LAS COLINAS, IRVING, TX, p. A690
MEDICAL CITY LEWISVILLE, LEWISVILLE, TX, p. A696
MEDICAL CITY MCKINNEY, MCKINNEY, TX, p. A700
MEDICAL CITY NORTH HILLS, NORTH RICHLAND HILLS, TX, p. A703
MEDICAL CITY PLANO, PLANO, TX, p. A707
MEDICAL CITY WEATHERFORD, WEATHERFORD, TX, p. A724
MEDICAL PARK HOSPITAL, HOPE, AR, p. A47
MEDICAL PARK HOSPITAL, WINSTON, NC, p. A520
MEDICAL UNIVERSITY OF OHIO, TOLEDO, OH, p. A550
MEDICAL WEST, BESSEMER, AL, p. A14
MEDICINE LODGE MEMORIAL HOSPITAL, MEDICINE LODGE, KS, p. A271
MEDINA COMMUNITY HOSPITAL, HONDO, TX, p. A684
MEDINA HOSPITAL, MEDINA, OH, p. A545
MEDINA MEMORIAL HOSPITAL, MEDINA, NY, p. A488
MEDINA REGIONAL HOSPITAL, HONDO, TX, p. A684
MEDIPLEX REHABILITATION HOSP, BOWLING GREEN, KY, p. A281
MEDSTAR FRANKLIN SQUARE MEDICAL CENTER, BALTIMORE, MD, p. A325
MEDSTAR GEORGETOWN UNIVERSITY HOSPITAL, WASHINGTON, DC, p. A129
MEDSTAR GOOD SAMARITAN HOSPITAL, BALTIMORE, MD, p. A325
MEDSTAR HARBOR HOSPITAL, BALTIMORE, MD, p. A325
MEDSTAR MONTGOMERY MEDICAL CENTER, OLNEY, MD, p. A331
MEDSTAR NATIONAL REHABILITATION HOSPITAL, WASHINGTON, DC, p. A130
MEDSTAR NATIONAL REHABILITATION NETWORK, WASHINGTON, DC, p. A130
MEDSTAR SOUTHERN MARYLAND HOSPITAL CENTER, CLINTON, MD, p. A328
MEDSTAR ST. MARY'S HOSPITAL, LEONARDTOWN, MD, p. A331
MEDSTAR UNION MEMORIAL HOSPITAL, BALTIMORE, MD, p. A325
MEDSTAR WASHINGTON HOSPITAL CENTER, WASHINGTON, DC, p. A130
MEDWEST—HARRIS, SYLVA, NC, p. A519
MEDWEST—HAYWOOD, CLYDE, NC, p. A507
MEE MEMORIAL HOSPITAL, KING CITY, CA, p. A69
MEEKER COUNTY MEM HOSPITAL, LITCHFIELD, MN, p. A379
MEEKER MEMORIAL HOSPITAL, LITCHFIELD, MN, p. A379
MELBOURNE REGIONAL MEDICAL CENTER, MELBOURNE, FL, p. A145
MELISSA MEMORIAL HOSPITAL, HOLYOKE, CO, p. A114
MELROSEWAKEFIELD HEALTHCARE, MELROSE, MA, p. A341
MEM HERMANN CHILDREN'S HOSP, HOUSTON, TX, p. A686
MEM HERMANN FORT BEND HOSP, SUGAR LAND, TX, p. A717
MEM HOSP OF SHERIDAN COUNTY, SHERIDAN, WY, p. A804
MEM HOSPITAL OF BEDFORD COUNTY, EVERETT, PA, p. A590
MEM MED CTR LEE CAMPUS, JOHNSTOWN, PA, p. A593
MEMORIAL BEHAVIORAL HEALTH, GULFPORT, MS, p. A393
MEMORIAL CENTER, BAKERSFIELD, CA, p. A57
MEMORIAL CHILDREN'S HOSPITAL, SOUTH BEND, IN, p. A240
MEMORIAL COMMUNITY HEALTH, AURORA, NE, p. A429
MEMORIAL COMMUNITY HOSPITAL, BLAIR, NE, p. A430
MEMORIAL COMMUNITY HOSPITAL, EDGERTON, WI, p. A783
MEMORIAL COMMUNITY HOSPITAL AND HEALTH SYSTEM, BLAIR, NE, p. A430
MEMORIAL DIVISION, CHARLESTON, WV, p. A771
MEMORIAL GENERAL HOSPITAL, LAS CRUCES, NM, p. A470
MEMORIAL HEALTH, MARYSVILLE, OH, p. A544
MEMORIAL HEALTH, SAVANNAH, GA, p. A180
MEMORIAL HEALTH CARE SYSTEM, CHATTANOOGA, TN, p. A635
MEMORIAL HEALTH CARE SYSTEM, SEWARD, NE, p. A439
MEMORIAL HEALTH CARE SYSTEMS, SEWARD, NE, p. A439
MEMORIAL HEALTH CENTER, SIDNEY, NE, p. A439
MEMORIAL HEALTH SYSTEM, ABILENE, KS, p. A261
MEMORIAL HEALTH SYSTEM, SAVANNAH, GA, p. A180
MEMORIAL HEALTHCARE, OWOSSO, MI, p. A363
MEMORIAL HEALTHCARE CENTER, OWOSSO, MI, p. A363
MEMORIAL HERMAN HOSPITAL CYPRESS, CYPRESS, TX, p. A667
MEMORIAL HERMANN—TEXAS MEDICAL CENTER, HOUSTON, TX, p. A687

MEMORIAL HERMANN—THE INSTITUTE FOR REHABILITATION AND RESEARCH, HOUSTON, TX, p. A687
MEMORIAL HERMANN BAPTIST FANNIN BEHAVIORAL HEALTH CENTER, BEAUMONT, TX, p. A658
MEMORIAL HERMANN FIRST COLONY HOSPITAL, SUGAR LAND, TX, p. A717
MEMORIAL HERMANN GREATER HEIGHTS HOSPITAL, HOUSTON, TX, p. A687
MEMORIAL HERMANN HOSPITAL, HOUSTON, TX, p. A687
MEMORIAL HERMANN HOUSTON ORTHOPEDIC AND SPINE HOSPITAL, BELLAIRE, TX, p. A659
MEMORIAL HERMANN KATY HOSPITAL, KATY, TX, p. A692
MEMORIAL HERMANN MEMORIAL CITY HOSPITAL, HOUSTON, TX, p. A687
MEMORIAL HERMANN MEMORIAL CITY MEDICAL CENTER, HOUSTON, TX, p. A687
MEMORIAL HERMANN NORTHEAST, HUMBLE, TX, p. A690
MEMORIAL HERMANN NORTHWEST HOSPITAL, HOUSTON, TX, p. A687
MEMORIAL HERMANN REHABILITATION HOSPITAL—KATY, KATY, TX, p. A692
MEMORIAL HERMANN SOUTHEAST, HOUSTON, TX, p. A687
MEMORIAL HERMANN SOUTHEAST HOSPITAL, HOUSTON, TX, p. A687
MEMORIAL HERMANN SOUTHWEST HOSPITAL, HOUSTON, TX, p. A687
MEMORIAL HERMANN SUGAR LAND HOSPITAL, SUGAR LAND, TX, p. A717
MEMORIAL HERMANN SURGICAL HOSPITAL KINGWOOD, KINGWOOD, TX, p. A693
MEMORIAL HERMANN THE WOODLANDS HOSPITAL, THE WOODLANDS, TX, p. A720
MEMORIAL HOSP OF JACKSONVILLE, JACKSONVILLE, FL, p. A141
MEMORIAL HOSPITAL & MED CENTER, MIDLAND, TX, p. A701
MEMORIAL HOSPITAL, ABILENE, KS, p. A261
MEMORIAL HOSPITAL, ALBANY, NY, p. A474
MEMORIAL HOSPITAL, AURORA, NE, p. A429
MEMORIAL HOSPITAL, BELLEVILLE, IL, p. A195
MEMORIAL HOSPITAL, CARTHAGE, IL, p. A196
MEMORIAL HOSPITAL, CHESTER, IL, p. A197
MEMORIAL HOSPITAL, DUMAS, TX, p. A673
MEMORIAL HOSPITAL, FREMONT, OH, p. A540
MEMORIAL HOSPITAL, GONZALES, TX, p. A681
MEMORIAL HOSPITAL, GUYMON, OK, p. A559
MEMORIAL HOSPITAL, HOLLYWOOD, FL, p. A140
MEMORIAL HOSPITAL, KERMIT, TX, p. A692
MEMORIAL HOSPITAL, LOGANSPORT, IN, p. A235
MEMORIAL HOSPITAL, MARTINSVILLE, VA, p. A746
MEMORIAL HOSPITAL, MCPHERSON, KS, p. A270
MEMORIAL HOSPITAL, NACOGDOCHES, TX, p. A702
MEMORIAL HOSPITAL, NORTH CONWAY, NH, p. A451
MEMORIAL HOSPITAL, OCONOMOWOC, WI, p. A792
MEMORIAL HOSPITAL, SEMINOLE, TX, p. A714
MEMORIAL HOSPITAL, SEYMOUR, IN, p. A240
MEMORIAL HOSPITAL, SOUTH BEND, IN, p. A240
MEMORIAL HOSPITAL, THE WOODLANDS, TX, p. A720
MEMORIAL HOSPITAL, TOWANDA, PA, p. A609
MEMORIAL HOSPITAL, WEISER, ID, p. A193
MEMORIAL HOSPITAL AND HEALTH CARE CENTER, JASPER, IN, p. A233
MEMORIAL HOSPITAL AND MANOR, BAINBRIDGE, GA, p. A166
MEMORIAL HOSPITAL AT EASTON MARYLAND, EASTON, MD, p. A329
MEMORIAL HOSPITAL AT GULFPORT, GULFPORT, MS, p. A393
MEMORIAL HOSPITAL EAST, SHILOH, IL, p. A220
MEMORIAL HOSPITAL FOR CANCER, NEW YORK, NY, p. A490
MEMORIAL HOSPITAL FOR CHILDREN, COLORADO SPRINGS, CO, p. A109
MEMORIAL HOSPITAL JACKSONVILLE, JACKSONVILLE, FL, p. A141
MEMORIAL HOSPITAL LOS BANOS, LOS BANOS, CA, p. A76
MEMORIAL HOSPITAL MIRAMAR, MIRAMAR, FL, p. A148
MEMORIAL HOSPITAL NORTH, COLORADO SPRINGS, CO, p. A109
MEMORIAL HOSPITAL OF CARBON COUNTY, RAWLINS, WY, p. A803
MEMORIAL HOSPITAL OF CARBONDALE, CARBONDALE, IL, p. A196
MEMORIAL HOSPITAL OF CONVERSE COUNTY, DOUGLAS, WY, p. A802
MEMORIAL HOSPITAL OF GARDENA, GARDENA, CA, p. A66
MEMORIAL HOSPITAL OF LAFAYETTE COUNTY, DARLINGTON, WI, p. A782
MEMORIAL HOSPITAL OF SALEM COUNTY, SALEM, NJ, p. A462
MEMORIAL HOSPITAL OF SOUTH BEND, SOUTH BEND, IN, p. A240

MEMORIAL HOSPITAL OF STILWELL, STILWELL, OK, p. A568
MEMORIAL HOSPITAL OF SWEETWATER COUNTY, ROCK SPRINGS, WY, p. A804
MEMORIAL HOSPITAL OF TAMPA, TAMPA, FL, p. A159
MEMORIAL HOSPITAL OF TEXAS COUNTY, GUYMON, OK, p. A560
MEMORIAL HOSPITAL OF UNION COUNTY, MARYSVILLE, OH, p. A544
MEMORIAL HOSPITAL PEMBROKE, PEMBROKE PINES, FL, p. A153
MEMORIAL HOSPITAL SOUTHWEST, HOUSTON, TX, p. A687
MEMORIAL HOSPITAL WEST, PEMBROKE PINES, FL, p. A153
MEMORIAL HOSPITAL-EL CAMPO, EL CAMPO, TX, p. A674
MEMORIAL HOSPITALS ASSOCIATION, MODESTO, CA, p. A79
MEMORIAL MEDICAL CENTER—ASHLAND, ASHLAND, WI, p. A779
MEMORIAL MEDICAL CENTER—LEE CAMPUS, JOHNSTOWN, PA, p. A593
MEMORIAL MEDICAL CENTER—LIVINGSTON, LIVINGSTON, TX, p. A696
MEMORIAL MEDICAL CENTER—LUFKIN, LUFKIN, TX, p. A698
MEMORIAL MEDICAL CENTER—NEILLSVILLE, NEILLSVILLE, WI, p. A792
MEMORIAL MEDICAL CENTER—SAN AUGUSTINE, SAN AUGUSTINE, TX, p. A714
MEMORIAL MEDICAL CENTER, JOHNSTOWN, PA, p. A593
MEMORIAL MEDICAL CENTER, LAS CRUCES, NM, p. A470
MEMORIAL MEDICAL CENTER, MODESTO, CA, p. A79
MEMORIAL MEDICAL CENTER, NEW ORLEANS, LA, p. A310
MEMORIAL MEDICAL CENTER, PORT LAVACA, TX, p. A707
MEMORIAL MEDICAL CENTER, SPRINGFIELD, IL, p. A221
MEMORIAL MEDICAL CENTER OF ASHLAND, ASHLAND, WI, p. A779
MEMORIAL MEDICAL CENTER OF WEST MICHIGAN, LUDINGTON, MI, p. A361
MEMORIAL MISSION HOSPITAL, ASHEVILLE, NC, p. A504
MEMORIAL NORTH PARK HOSPITAL, HIXSON, TN, p. A639
MEMORIAL REGIONAL HEALTH, CRAIG, CO, p. A110
MEMORIAL REGIONAL HOSPITAL, HOLLYWOOD, FL, p. A140
MEMORIAL REGIONAL MEDICAL CENTER, MECHANICSVILLE, VA, p. A746
MEMORIAL SATILLA HEALTH, WAYCROSS, GA, p. A183
MEMORIAL SLOAN-KETTERING CANCER CENTER, NEW YORK, NY, p. A490
MEMORIALCARE, MILLER CHILDREN'S & WOMEN'S HOSPITAL LONG BEACH, LONG BEACH, CA, p. A72
MEMORIALCARE, ORANGE COAST MEMORIAL MEDICAL CENTER, FOUNTAIN VALLEY, CA, p. A64
MEMPHIS MENTAL HEALTH INSTITUTE, MEMPHIS, TN, p. A644
MEMPHIS VETERANS AFFAIRS MEDICAL CENTER, MEMPHIS, TN, p. A644
MENA MEDICAL CENTER, MENA, AR, p. A50
MENA REGIONAL HEALTH SYSTEM, MENA, AR, p. A50
MENDOCINO COAST DISTRICT HOSPITAL, FORT BRAGG, CA, p. A64
MENDOTA COMMUNITY HOSPITAL, MENDOTA, IL, p. A212
MENDOTA MENTAL HEALTH INSTITUTE, MADISON, WI, p. A787
MENIFEE VALLEY MEDICAL CENTER, SUN CITY, CA, p. A100
MENLO PARK SURGICAL HOSPITAL, MENLO PARK, CA, p. A77
MENNINGER CLINIC, HOUSTON, TX, p. A687
MENNONITE GENERAL HOSPITAL, AIBONITO, PR, p. A806
MENORAH MEDICAL CENTER, OVERLAND PARK, KS, p. A274
MENTAL HEALTH INSTITUTE, CHEROKEE, IA, p. A245
MENTAL HEALTH INSTITUTE, INDEPENDENCE, IA, p. A251
MENTAL HEALTH SERVICES FOR CLARK AND MADISON COUNTIES, SPRINGFIELD, OH, p. A549
MERCER COUNTY HOSPITAL, ALEDO, IL, p. A194
MERCER COUNTY JOINT TOWNSHIP COMMUNITY HOSPITAL, COLDWATER, OH, p. A535
MERCER HEALTH, COLDWATER, OH, p. A535
MERCY ALLEN HOSPITAL, OBERLIN, OH, p. A547
MERCY CARE CENTER, OMAHA, NE, p. A437
MERCY CATHOLIC MEDICAL CENTER—MERCY FITZGERALD CAMPUS, DARBY, PA, p. A588
MERCY COMMUNITY HOSPITAL, PORT JERVIS, NY, p. A495
MERCY FITZGERALD HOSPITAL, DARBY, PA, p. A588
MERCY GENERAL HOSPITAL, SACRAMENTO, CA, p. A89
MERCY GILBERT MEDICAL CENTER, GILBERT, AZ, p. A32
MERCY HEALTH—ANDERSON HOSPITAL, CINCINNATI, OH, p. A532
MERCY HEALTH—CLERMONT HOSPITAL, BATAVIA, OH, p. A528
MERCY HEALTH—FAIRFIELD HOSPITAL, FAIRFIELD, OH, p. A540
MERCY HEALTH—MARCUM AND WALLACE, IRVINE, KY, p. A285
MERCY HEALTH—ST. CHARLES HOSPITAL, OREGON, OH, p. A547

MERCY HEALTH—ST. ELIZABETH BOARDMAN HOSPITAL, BOARDMAN, OH, p. A529
MERCY HEALTH—ST. ELIZABETH YOUNGSTOWN HOSPITAL, YOUNGSTOWN, OH, p. A554
MERCY HEALTH—ST. JOSEPH WARREN HOSPITAL, WARREN, OH, p. A551
MERCY HEALTH—ST. RITA'S MEDICAL CENTER, LIMA, OH, p. A543
MERCY HEALTH—WEST HOSPITAL, CINCINNATI, OH, p. A533
MERCY HEALTH—WILLARD HOSPITAL, WILLARD, OH, p. A553
MERCY HEALTH CENTER, OKLAHOMA CITY, OK, p. A564
MERCY HEALTH HACKLEY CAMPUS, MUSKEGON, MI, p. A362
MERCY HEALTH LOVE COUNTY, MARIETTA, OK, p. A561
MERCY HEALTH PARTNERS, LAKESHORE CAMPUS, SHELBY, MI, p. A366
MERCY HEALTH PARTNERS, MERCY CAMPUS, MUSKEGON, MI, p. A362
MERCY HEALTH PARTNERS-MUSKEGON GENERAL CAMPUS, MUSKEGON, MI, p. A362
MERCY HEALTH SAINT MARY'S, GRAND RAPIDS, MI, p. A356
MERCY HEALTH, HACKLEY CAMPUS, MUSKEGON, MI, p. A362
MERCY HEALTH, LAKESHORE CAMPUS, SHELBY, MI, p. A366
MERCY HOSPITAL, BAKERSFIELD, CA, p. A57
MERCY HOSPITAL, BUFFALO, NY, p. A480
MERCY HOSPITAL, COON RAPIDS, MN, p. A374
MERCY HOSPITAL, DAVENPORT, IA, p. A247
MERCY HOSPITAL, MIAMI, FL, p. A146
MERCY HOSPITAL, MOUNDRIDGE, KS, p. A271
MERCY HOSPITAL, OWENSBORO, KY, p. A291
MERCY HOSPITAL, ROCKVILLE CENTRE, NY, p. A497
MERCY HOSPITAL, SPRINGFIELD, MA, p. A344
MERCY HOSPITAL, VALLEY CITY, ND, p. A526
MERCY HOSPITAL ADA, ADA, OK, p. A555
MERCY HOSPITAL AND HEALTH CARE CENTER, MOOSE LAKE, MN, p. A381
MERCY HOSPITAL AND MEDICAL CENTER, CHICAGO, IL, p. A199
MERCY HOSPITAL AND TRAUMA CENTER, JANESVILLE, WI, p. A786
MERCY HOSPITAL ANDERSON, CINCINNATI, OH, p. A533
MERCY HOSPITAL ARDMORE, ARDMORE, OK, p. A556
MERCY HOSPITAL AURORA, AURORA, MO, p. A402
MERCY HOSPITAL BERRYVILLE, BERRYVILLE, AR, p. A42
MERCY HOSPITAL BOONEVILLE, BOONEVILLE, AR, p. A43
MERCY HOSPITAL CADILLAC, CADILLAC, MI, p. A350
MERCY HOSPITAL CARTHAGE, CARTHAGE, MO, p. A404
MERCY HOSPITAL CASSVILLE, CASSVILLE, MO, p. A404
MERCY HOSPITAL CLERMONT, BATAVIA, OH, p. A528
MERCY HOSPITAL COLUMBUS, COLUMBUS, KS, p. A263
MERCY HOSPITAL FAIRFIELD, FAIRFIELD, OH, p. A540
MERCY HOSPITAL FORT SMITH, FORT SMITH, AR, p. A46
MERCY HOSPITAL GRAYLING, GRAYLING, MI, p. A356
MERCY HOSPITAL HEALDTON, HEALDTON, OK, p. A560
MERCY HOSPITAL INC., MOUNDRIDGE, KS, p. A271
MERCY HOSPITAL JEFFERSON, FESTUS, MO, p. A406
MERCY HOSPITAL JOPLIN, JOPLIN, MO, p. A408
MERCY HOSPITAL KINGFISHER, KINGFISHER, OK, p. A560
MERCY HOSPITAL LEBANON, LEBANON, MO, p. A410
MERCY HOSPITAL LINCOLN, TROY, MO, p. A419
MERCY HOSPITAL LOGAN COUNTY, GUTHRIE, OK, p. A559
MERCY HOSPITAL OF DEFIANCE, DEFIANCE, OH, p. A539
MERCY HOSPITAL OF FOLSOM, FOLSOM, CA, p. A64
MERCY HOSPITAL OF FRANCISCAN SISTERS, OELWEIN, IA, p. A255
MERCY HOSPITAL OF PITTSBURGH, PITTSBURGH, PA, p. A603
MERCY HOSPITAL OF PORTLAND, PORTLAND, ME, p. A322
MERCY HOSPITAL OF SCOTT COUNTY, WALDRON, AR, p. A54
MERCY HOSPITAL OF SCRANTON, SCRANTON, PA, p. A607
MERCY HOSPITAL OF TIFFIN, TIFFIN, OH, p. A550
MERCY HOSPITAL OKLAHOMA CITY, OKLAHOMA CITY, OK, p. A564
MERCY HOSPITAL OZARK, OZARK, AR, p. A51
MERCY HOSPITAL PARIS, PARIS, AR, p. A51
MERCY HOSPITAL ROGERS, ROGERS, AR, p. A52
MERCY HOSPITAL SOUTH, SAINT LOUIS, MO, p. A416
MERCY HOSPITAL SPRINGFIELD, SPRINGFIELD, MO, p. A419
MERCY HOSPITAL ST. LOUIS, SAINT LOUIS, MO, p. A416
MERCY HOSPITAL TISHOMINGO, TISHOMINGO, OK, p. A569
MERCY HOSPITAL WALDRON, WALDRON, AR, p. A54
MERCY HOSPITAL WASHINGTON, WASHINGTON, MO, p. A420
MERCY HOSPITAL WATONGA, WATONGA, OK, p. A571
MERCY HOSPITAL-TURNER MEMORIAL, OZARK, AR, p. A51
MERCY HOSPITALS OF BAKERSFIELD, BAKERSFIELD, CA, p. A57
MERCY IOWA CITY, IOWA CITY, IA, p. A252

MERCY MAUDE NORTON HOSPITAL, COLUMBUS, KS, p. A263

MERCY MCCUNE-BROOKS HOSPITAL, CARTHAGE, MO, p. A404

MERCY MED CTR MERCED, DOWNTOWN, MERCED, CA, p. A78

MERCY MEDICAL CENTER—CEDAR RAPIDS, CEDAR RAPIDS, IA, p. A245

MERCY MEDICAL CENTER—WEST LAKES, WEST DES MOINES, IA, p. A260

MERCY MEDICAL CENTER, BALTIMORE, MD, p. A325

MERCY MEDICAL CENTER, CANTON, OH, p. A531

MERCY MEDICAL CENTER, CEDAR RAPIDS, IA, p. A245

MERCY MEDICAL CENTER, DURANGO, CO, p. A111

MERCY MEDICAL CENTER, NAMPA, ID, p. A191

MERCY MEDICAL CENTER, REDDING, CA, p. A87

MERCY MEDICAL CENTER, ROCKVILLE CENTRE, NY, p. A497

MERCY MEDICAL CENTER, ROGERS, AR, p. A52

MERCY MEDICAL CENTER, ROSEBURG, OR, p. A580

MERCY MEDICAL CENTER, SPRINGFIELD, MA, p. A344

MERCY MEDICAL CENTER, WILLISTON, ND, p. A526

MERCY MEDICAL CENTER MERCED, MERCED, CA, p. A78

MERCY MEDICAL CENTER MOUNT SHASTA, MOUNT SHASTA, CA, p. A80

MERCY MEDICAL CENTER MT SHASTA, MOUNT SHASTA, CA, p. A80

MERCY MEDICAL CENTER REDDING, REDDING, CA, p. A87

MERCY MEDICAL CENTER-CENTERVILLE, CENTERVILLE, IA, p. A245

MERCY MEDICAL CENTER-CLINTON, CLINTON, IA, p. A246

MERCY MEDICAL CENTER-DES MOINES, DES MOINES, IA, p. A248

MERCY MEDICAL CENTER-DUBUQUE, DUBUQUE, IA, p. A249

MERCY MEDICAL CENTER-DYERSVILLE, DYERSVILLE, IA, p. A249

MERCY MEDICAL CENTER-NEW HAMPTON, NEW HAMPTON, IA, p. A255

MERCY MEDICAL CENTER-NORTH IOWA, MASON CITY, IA, p. A254

MERCY MEDICAL CENTER-SIOUX CITY, SIOUX CITY, IA, p. A258

MERCY MEMORIAL HEALTH CENTER, ARDMORE, OK, p. A556

MERCY MEMORIAL HOSPITAL, URBANA, OH, p. A551

MERCY MEMORIAL HOSPITAL SYSTEM, MONROE, MI, p. A362

MERCY REGIONAL MEDICAL CENTER, DURANGO, CO, p. A111

MERCY REGIONAL MEDICAL CENTER, LORAIN, OH, p. A544

MERCY REGIONAL MEDICAL CENTER, VILLE PLATTE, LA, p. A316

MERCY REHABILITATION HOSPITAL, CHESTERFIELD, MO, p. A404

MERCY REHABILITATION HOSPITAL, CLIVE, IA, p. A246

MERCY REHABILITATION HOSPITAL OKLAHOMA CITY, OKLAHOMA CITY, OK, p. A564

MERCY REHABILITATION HOSPITAL ST. LOUIS, CHESTERFIELD, MO, p. A404

MERCY REHABILITION HOSPITAL SPRINGFIELD, SPRINGFIELD, MO, p. A419

MERCY SAN JUAN HOSPITAL, CARMICHAEL, CA, p. A59

MERCY SAN JUAN MEDICAL CENTER, CARMICHAEL, CA, p. A59

MERCY ST. ANNE HOSPITAL, TOLEDO, OH, p. A550

MERCY ST. CHARLES HOSPITAL, OREGON, OH, p. A547

MERCY ST. FRANCIS HOSPITAL, MOUNTAIN VIEW, MO, p. A412

MERCY ST. VINCENT MEDICAL CENTER, TOLEDO, OH, p. A550

MERCY SUBURBAN HOSPITAL, EAST NORRITON, PA, p. A589

MERCY TIFFIN HOSPITAL, TIFFIN, OH, p. A550

MERCY TYLER HOSPITAL, TUNKHANNOCK, PA, p. A609

MERCY WALWORTH HOSPITAL AND MEDICAL CENTER, LAKE GENEVA, WI, p. A787

MERCY WILLARD HOSPITAL, WILLARD, OH, p. A553

MERCYHEALTH HOSPITAL—ROCKTON AVENUE, ROCKFORD, IL, p. A218

MERCYHEALTH HOSPITAL AND MEDICAL CENTER—HARVARD, HARVARD, IL, p. A207

MERCYHEALTH HOSPITAL AND MEDICAL CENTER—WALWORTH, LAKE GENEVA, WI, p. A787

MERCYHEALTH HOSPITAL AND MEDICAL CENTER, HARVARD, IL, p. A207

MERCYHEALTH HOSPITAL AND TRAUMA CENTER—JANESVILLE, JANESVILLE, WI, p. A786

MERCYONE CEDAR FALLS MEDICAL CENTER, CEDAR FALLS, IA, p. A244

MERCYONE CENTERVILLE MEDICAL CENTER, CENTERVILLE, IA, p. A245

MERCYONE CLINTON MEDICAL CENTER, CLINTON, IA, p. A246

MERCYONE CLIVE REHABILITATION HOSPITAL, CLIVE, IA, p. A246

MERCYONE DES MOINES MEDICAL CENTER, DES MOINES, IA, p. A248

MERCYONE DUBUQUE MEDICAL CENTER, DUBUQUE, IA, p. A249

MERCYONE DYERSVILLE MEDICAL CENTER, DYERSVILLE, IA, p. A249

MERCYONE ELKADER MEDICAL CENTER, ELKADER, IA, p. A249

MERCYONE IOWA CITY MEDICAL CENTER, IOWA CITY, IA, p. A252

MERCYONE NEW HAMPTON MEDICAL CENTER, NEW HAMPTON, IA, p. A255

MERCYONE NEWTON MEDICAL CENTER, NEWTON, IA, p. A255

MERCYONE NORTH IOWA MEDICAL CENTER, MASON CITY, IA, p. A254

MERCYONE OAKLAND MEDICAL CENTER, OAKLAND, NE, p. A436

MERCYONE OELWEIN MEDICAL CENTER, OELWEIN, IA, p. A255

MERCYONE PRIMGHAR, PRIMGHAR, IA, p. A256

MERCYONE PRIMGHAR MEDICAL CENTER, PRIMGHAR, IA, p. A256

MERCYONE SIOUXLAND MEDICAL CENTER, SIOUX CITY, IA, p. A258

MERCYONE WATERLOO MEDICAL CENTER, WATERLOO, IA, p. A259

MERIDIA EUCLID HOSPITAL, EUCLID, OH, p. A540

MERIDIA HILLCREST HOSPITAL, CLEVELAND, OH, p. A534

MERIDIA SOUTH POINTE HOSPITAL, WARRENSVILLE HEIGHTS, OH, p. A552

MERIDIAN HEALTH SERVICES, MUNCIE, IN, p. A237

MERIT HEALTH BATESVILLE, BATESVILLE, MS, p. A389

MERIT HEALTH BILOXI, BILOXI, MS, p. A389

MERIT HEALTH CENTRAL, JACKSON, MS, p. A394

MERIT HEALTH MADISON, CANTON, MS, p. A390

MERIT HEALTH NATCHEZ, NATCHEZ, MS, p. A397

MERIT HEALTH NORTHWEST MISSISSIPPI, CLARKSDALE, MS, p. A391

MERIT HEALTH RANKIN, BRANDON, MS, p. A390

MERIT HEALTH RIVER OAKS, FLOWOOD, MS, p. A392

MERIT HEALTH RIVER REGION, VICKSBURG, MS, p. A401

MERIT HEALTH WESLEY, HATTIESBURG, MS, p. A393

MERIT HEALTH WOMAN'S HOSPITAL, FLOWOOD, MS, p. A392

MERITCARE MEDICAL CENTER, FARGO, ND, p. A523

MERITCARE SOUTH UNIVERSITY, FARGO, ND, p. A523

MERITER UNITYPOINT HEALTH, MADISON, WI, p. A787

MERITUS MEDICAL CENTER, HAGERSTOWN, MD, p. A330

MERLE WEST MEDICAL CENTER, KLAMATH FALLS, OR, p. A576

MERRICK MEDICAL CENTER, CENTRAL CITY, NE, p. A430

MERRITHEW MEMORIAL HOSPITAL, MARTINEZ, CA, p. A77

MESA HILLS SPECIALTY HOSPITAL, EL PASO, TX, p. A675

MESA SPRINGS, FORT WORTH, TX, p. A679

MESA VIEW REGIONAL HOSPITAL, MESQUITE, NV, p. A445

MESA VISTA HOSPITAL, SAN DIEGO, CA, p. A91

MESCALERO PUBLIC HEALTH SERVICE INDIAN HOSPITAL, MESCALERO, NM, p. A471

MESILLA VALLEY HOSPITAL, LAS CRUCES, NM, p. A470

MESQUITE REHABILITATION HOSPITAL, MESQUITE, TX, p. A700

MESQUITE REHABILITATION INSTITUTE, MESQUITE, TX, p. A701

MESQUITE SPECIALTY HOSPITAL, MESQUITE, TX, p. A701

METH HEALTHCARE—SOUTH HOSP, MEMPHIS, TN, p. A644

METHODIST AMBULATORY SURGERY HOSPITAL—NORTHWEST, SAN ANTONIO, TX, p. A712

METHODIST AMBULATORY SURGERY HOSPITAL, SAN ANTONIO, TX, p. A712

METHODIST BEHAVIORAL HOSPITAL OF ARKANSAS, MAUMELLE, AR, p. A50

METHODIST CHARLTON MEDICAL CENTER, DALLAS, TX, p. A669

METHODIST CHILDREN'S HOSPITAL, LUBBOCK, TX, p. A697

METHODIST DALLAS MEDICAL CENTER, DALLAS, TX, p. A669

METHODIST FREMONT HEALTH, FREMONT, NE, p. A432

METHODIST HEALTHCARE MEMPHIS HOSPITALS, MEMPHIS, TN, p. A644

METHODIST HEALTHCARE OLIVE BRANCH HOSPITAL, OLIVE BRANCH, MS, p. A398

METHODIST HEALTHCARE-LEXINGTON, LEXINGTON, TN, p. A642

METHODIST HLTHCARE-GERMANTOWN, GERMANTOWN, TN, p. A638

METHODIST HOSP OF MARION CNTY, COLUMBIA, MS, p. A391

METHODIST HOSPITAL & REHAB CTR, JACKSON, MS, p. A394

METHODIST HOSPITAL, ARCADIA, CA, p. A56

METHODIST HOSPITAL, FRANKFORT, IN, p. A229

METHODIST HOSPITAL, HENDERSON, KY, p. A285

METHODIST HOSPITAL, LUBBOCK, TX, p. A697

METHODIST HOSPITAL, OMAHA, NE, p. A437

METHODIST HOSPITAL, PHILADELPHIA, PA, p. A601

METHODIST HOSPITAL, SACRAMENTO, CA, p. A89

METHODIST HOSPITAL, SAINT LOUIS PARK, MN, p. A384

METHODIST HOSPITAL, SAN ANTONIO, TX, p. A712

METHODIST HOSPITAL FOR SURGERY, ADDISON, TX, p. A651

METHODIST HOSPITAL OF CHICAGO, CHICAGO, IL, p. A199

METHODIST HOSPITAL OF SACRAMENTO, SACRAMENTO, CA, p. A89

METHODIST HOSPITAL OF SOUTHERN CALIFORNIA, ARCADIA, CA, p. A56

METHODIST HOSPITAL PLAINVIEW, PLAINVIEW, TX, p. A706

METHODIST HOSPITAL SOUTH, JOURDANTON, TX, p. A691

METHODIST HOSPITAL STONE OAK REHABILITATION CENTER, SAN ANTONIO, TX, p. A712

METHODIST HOSPITAL UNION COUNTY, MORGANFIELD, KY, p. A290

METHODIST HOSPITAL-LEVELLAND, LEVELLAND, TX, p. A695

METHODIST HOSPITALS, GARY, IN, p. A229

METHODIST HOSPITALS, INC, GARY, IN, p. A229

METHODIST JENNIE EDMUNDSON HOSPITAL, COUNCIL BLUFFS, IA, p. A247

METHODIST LE BONHEUR GERMANTOWN HOSPITAL, GERMANTOWN, TN, p. A638

METHODIST MANSFIELD MEDICAL CENTER, MANSFIELD, TX, p. A699

METHODIST MCKINNEY HOSPITAL, MCKINNEY, TX, p. A700

METHODIST MEDICAL CENTER, DALLAS, TX, p. A669

METHODIST MEDICAL CENTER OF OAK RIDGE, OAK RIDGE, TN, p. A648

METHODIST NORTH-J HARRIS HSP, MEMPHIS, TN, p. A644

METHODIST OLIVE BRANCH HOSPITAL, OLIVE BRANCH, MS, p. A398

METHODIST REHABILITATION CENTER, JACKSON, MS, p. A394

METHODIST REHABILITATION HOSPITAL, DALLAS, TX, p. A669

METHODIST RICHARDSON MEDICAL CENTER, RICHARDSON, TX, p. A708

METHODIST SOUTHLAKE HOSPITAL, SOUTHLAKE, TX, p. A716

METHODIST STONE OAK HOSPITAL, SAN ANTONIO, TX, p. A712

METHODIST SUGAR LAND HOSPITAL, SUGAR LAND, TX, p. A717

METHODIST UNIVERSITY HOSPITAL, MEMPHIS, TN, p. A645

METHODIST WEST HOSPITAL, WEST DES MOINES, IA, p. A260

METHODIST WEST HOUSTON HOSPITAL, HOUSTON, TX, p. A687

METHODIST WILLOWBROOK HOSPITAL, HOUSTON, TX, p. A687

METHODIST WOMEN'S & CHILD HOSP, SAN ANTONIO, TX, p. A712

METHODIST WOMEN'S HOSPITAL, ELKHORN, NE, p. A431

METRO HEALTH—UNIVERSITY OF MICHIGAN HEALTH, WYOMING, MI, p. A370

METRO HEALTH HOSPITAL, WYOMING, MI, p. A370

METRO HOSP-SPRINGFIELD DIV, SPRINGFIELD, PA, p. A608

METRO NASHVILLE GEN HOSPITAL, NASHVILLE, TN, p. A646

METROHEALTH CTR FOR NRSG CARE, CLEVELAND, OH, p. A534

METROHEALTH MEDICAL CENTER, CLEVELAND, OH, p. A535

METROPLEX ADVENTIST HOSPITAL, KILLEEN, TX, p. A693

METROPOLITAN HOSPITAL, SAN ANTONIO, TX, p. A712

METROPOLITAN MEDICAL CENTER, NEW YORK, NY, p. A490

METROPOLITAN ST. LOUIS PSYCHIATRIC CENTER, SAINT LOUIS, MO, p. A416

METROPOLITAN STATE HOSPITAL, NORWALK, CA, p. A81

METROPOLITANO DE LA MONTANA, UTUADO, PR, p. A811

METROWEST MEDICAL CENTER, FRAMINGHAM, MA, p. A339

METROWEST MEDICAL CENTER, NATICK, MA, p. A342

MEYERSDALE MEDICAL CENTER, MEYERSDALE, PA, p. A597

MIAMI CHILDREN'S HOSPITAL, MIAMI, FL, p. A146

MIAMI COUNTY HOSPITAL, PAOLA, KS, p. A274

MIAMI COUNTY MEDICAL CENTER, PAOLA, KS, p. A274

MIAMI HEART CAMPUS AT MOUNT SINAI MEDICAL CENTER, MIAMI BEACH, FL, p. A147

MIAMI HEART INST & MED CTR, MIAMI BEACH, FL, p. A147

MIAMI JEWISH HOME AND HOSPITAL FOR AGED, MIAMI, FL, p. A146

MIAMI VALLEY HOSPITAL, DAYTON, OH, p. A538

MIAMI VETERANS AFFAIRS HEALTHCARE SYSTEM, MIAMI, FL, p. A147

MICHAEL E. DEBAKEY VETERANS AFFAIRS MEDICAL CENTER, HOUSTON, TX, p. A687

MICHAEL'S ELITE HOSPITAL, SUGAR LAND, TX, p. A717
MICHIANA BEHAVIORAL HEALTH CENTER, PLYMOUTH, IN, p. A239
MICHIGAN MEDICINE, ANN ARBOR, MI, p. A348
MID COAST HOSPITAL, BRUNSWICK, ME, p. A319
MID—AMERICA REHABILITATION HOSPITAL, SHAWNEE MISSION, KS, p. A276
MID-COLUMBIA MEDICAL CENTER, THE DALLES, OR, p. A582
MID-HUDSON FORENSIC PSYCHIATRIC CENTER, NEW HAMPTON, NY, p. A489
MID-HUDSON PSYCHIATRIC CENTER, NEW HAMPTON, NY, p. A489
MID-JEFFERSON EXTENDED CARE HOSPITAL OF BEAUMONT, BEAUMONT, TX, p. A658
MID-MAINE GENERAL MEDICAL CTR, AUGUSTA, ME, p. A318
MID-VALLEY HOSPITAL, OMAK, WA, p. A761
MIDDLE PARK HEALTH-KREMMLING, KREMMLING, CO, p. A114
MIDDLE PARK MEDICAL CENTER-KREMMLING, KREMMLING, CO, p. A114
MIDDLE TENNESSEE MEDICAL CENTER, MURFREESBORO, TN, p. A646
MIDDLE TENNESSEE MENTAL HEALTH INSTITUTE, NASHVILLE, TN, p. A646
MIDDLESBORO APPALACHIAN REGIONAL HOSPITAL, MIDDLESBORO, KY, p. A290
MIDDLESBORO ARH HOSPITAL, MIDDLESBORO, KY, p. A290
MIDDLESEX HOSPITAL, MIDDLETOWN, CT, p. A123
MIDDLESEX MEMORIAL HOSPITAL, MIDDLETOWN, CT, p. A123
MIDDLETOWN REGIONAL HOSPITAL, MIDDLETOWN, OH, p. A545
MIDLAND MEM HOSP WEST CAMPUS, MIDLAND, TX, p. A701
MIDLAND MEMORIAL HOSPITAL, MIDLAND, TX, p. A701
MIDMICHIGAN MEDICAL CENTER—ALPENA, ALPENA, MI, p. A348
MIDMICHIGAN MEDICAL CENTER—WEST BRANCH, WEST BRANCH, MI, p. A369
MIDMICHIGAN MEDICAL CENTER-CLARE, CLARE, MI, p. A351
MIDMICHIGAN MEDICAL CENTER-GLADWIN, GLADWIN, MI, p. A355
MIDMICHIGAN MEDICAL CENTER-GRATIOT, ALMA, MI, p. A348
MIDMICHIGAN MEDICAL CENTER-MIDLAND, MIDLAND, MI, p. A361
MIDMICHIGAN REG CTR-GLADWIN, GLADWIN, MI, p. A355
MIDMICHIGAN REG MED CTR-CLARE, CLARE, MI, p. A351
MIDMICHIGAN REG MEDICAL CENTER, MIDLAND, MI, p. A361
MIDSTATE MEDICAL CENTER, MERIDEN, CT, p. A123
MIDWAY HOSPITAL MEDICAL CENTER, LOS ANGELES, CA, p. A75
MIDWEST CITY SPECIALTY HOSPITAL, MIDWEST CITY, OK, p. A562
MIDWEST MEDICAL CENTER, GALENA, IL, p. A205
MIDWEST ORTHOPEDIC SPECIALTY HOSPITAL, FRANKLIN, WI, p. A784
MIDWEST REGIONAL MEDICAL CENTER, MIDWEST CITY, OK, p. A562
MIDWEST SURGICAL HOSPITAL, OMAHA, NE, p. A437
MIDWESTERN REGIONAL MEDICAL CENTER, ZION, IL, p. A222
MIKE O'CALLAGHAN FEDERAL HOSPITAL, NELLIS AFB, NV, p. A445
MILAN GENERAL HOSPITAL, MILAN, TN, p. A645
MILBANK AREA HOSPITAL AVERA, MILBANK, SD, p. A629
MILDRED MITCHELL BATEMAN HOSP, HUNTINGTON, WV, p. A773
MILDRED MITCHELL-BATEMAN HOSPITAL, HUNTINGTON, WV, p. A773
MILE BLUFF MEDICAL CENTER, MAUSTON, WI, p. A789
MILFORD MEMORIAL HOSPITAL, MILFORD, DE, p. A127
MILFORD REGIONAL MEDICAL CENTER, MILFORD, MA, p. A341
MILFORD VALLEY MEMORIAL HOSPITAL, MILFORD, UT, p. A729
MILFORD-WHITINSVILLE REG HOSP, MILFORD, MA, p. A341
MILLARD FILLMORE SUBURBAN HOSPITAL, WILLIAMSVILLE, NY, p. A502
MILLCREEK COMMUNITY HOSPITAL, ERIE, PA, p. A590
MILLE LACS HEALTH SYSTEM, ONAMIA, MN, p. A382
MILLE LACS HOSPITAL, ONAMIA, MN, p. A382
MILLER CHILDREN'S & WOMEN'S HOSPITAL LONG BEACH, LONG BEACH, CA, p. A72
MILLER COUNTY HOSPITAL, COLQUITT, GA, p. A169
MILLINOCKET REGIONAL HOSPITAL, MILLINOCKET, ME, p. A321
MILLS HEALTH CENTER, SAN MATEO, CA, p. A96
MILLS HOSPITAL, SAN MATEO, CA, p. A96
MILLS-PENINSULA HEALTH SERVICE, BURLINGAME, CA, p. A59
MILLS-PENINSULA HEALTH SERVICES, BURLINGAME, CA, p. A59

MILLWOOD HOSPITAL, ARLINGTON, TX, p. A653
MILTON HOSPITAL, MILTON, MA, p. A342
MILTON S HERSHEY MEDICAL CTR, HERSHEY, PA, p. A592
MILWAUKEE COUNTY BEHAVIORAL HEALTH DIVISION, MILWAUKEE, WI, p. A791
MILWAUKEE MENTAL HLTH DIVISION, MILWAUKEE, WI, p. A791
MILWAUKEE PSYCHIATRIC HOSPITAL, WAUWATOSA, WI, p. A799
MIMBRES MEMORIAL HOSPITAL, DEMING, NM, p. A469
MINDEN MEDICAL CENTER, MINDEN, LA, p. A309
MINERAL COMMUNITY HOSPITAL, SUPERIOR, MT, p. A428
MINERAL COUNTY HOSPITAL, SUPERIOR, MT, p. A428
MINERS MEDICAL CENTER, HASTINGS, PA, p. A592
MINERS' COLFAX MEDICAL CENTER, RATON, NM, p. A471
MINERS' HOSPITAL OF NEW MEXICO, RATON, NM, p. A471
MINIDOKA MEMORIAL HOSPITAL, RUPERT, ID, p. A193
MINIDOKA MEMORIAL HOSPITAL AND EXTENDED CARE FACILITY, RUPERT, ID, p. A193
MINIMALLY INVASIVE SURGERY CENTER, LENEXA, KS, p. A269
MINIMALLY INVASIVE SURGERY HOSPITAL, LENEXA, KS, p. A269
MINISTRY DOOR COUNTY MEDICAL CENTER, STURGEON BAY, WI, p. A797
MINISTRY EAGLE RIVER MEMORIAL HOSPITAL, EAGLE RIVER, WI, p. A782
MINISTRY GOOD SAMARITAN HEALTH CENTER, MERRILL, WI, p. A790
MINISTRY GOOD SAMARITAN HEALTH CENTER, WESTON, WI, p. A799
MINISTRY OUR LADY OF VICTORY HOSPITAL, STANLEY, WI, p. A796
MINISTRY SACRED HEART HOSPITAL, TOMAHAWK, WI, p. A797
MINISTRY SAINT JOSEPH'S HOSPITAL, MARSHFIELD, WI, p. A789
MINISTRY SAINT MICHAEL'S HOSPITAL, STEVENS POINT, WI, p. A796
MINNEAPOLIS VETERANS AFFAIRS HEALTH CARE SYSTEM, MINNEAPOLIS, MN, p. A381
MINNEOLA DISTRICT HOSPITAL, MINNEOLA, KS, p. A271
MINNIE HAMILTON HEALTHCARE CENTER, GRANTSVILLE, WV, p. A772
MIRACLE MILE MEDICAL CENTER, LOS ANGELES, CA, p. A75
MIRIAM HOSPITAL, PROVIDENCE, RI, p. A613
MISHAWAKA MEDICAL CENTER, MISHAWAKA, IN, p. A236
MISSION COMMUNITY HOSPITAL, PANORAMA CITY, CA, p. A84
MISSION HOSPITAL, ASHEVILLE, NC, p. A504
MISSION HOSPITAL, MISSION, TX, p. A701
MISSION HOSPITAL, MISSION VIEJO, CA, p. A78
MISSION HOSPITAL MISSION VIEJO, MISSION VIEJO, CA, p. A78
MISSION HOSPITALS, ASHEVILLE, NC, p. A504
MISSION REGIONAL MEDICAL CENTER, MISSION, TX, p. A701
MISSISSIPPI BAPTIST HLTH SYST, JACKSON, MS, p. A394
MISSISSIPPI BAPTIST MEDICAL CENTER, JACKSON, MS, p. A395
MISSISSIPPI HOSPITAL FOR RESTORATIVE CARE, JACKSON, MS, p. A395
MISSISSIPPI STATE HOSPITAL, WHITFIELD, MS, p. A401
MISSOURI BAPT HOSP-SULLIVAN, SULLIVAN, MO, p. A419
MISSOURI BAPTIST MEDICAL CENTER, SAINT LOUIS, MO, p. A416
MISSOURI BAPTIST MEDICAL CNTR, SAINT LOUIS, MO, p. A416
MISSOURI BAPTIST SULLIVAN HOSPITAL, SULLIVAN, MO, p. A419
MISSOURI DELTA MEDICAL CENTER, SIKESTON, MO, p. A418
MISSOURI RIVER MEDICAL CENTER, FORT BENTON, MT, p. A423
MISSOURI SOUTHERN HEALTHCARE, DEXTER, MO, p. A405
MITCHELL CNTY REG HLTH CTR, OSAGE, IA, p. A255
MITCHELL COUNTY HOSPITAL, BELOIT, KS, p. A262
MITCHELL COUNTY HOSPITAL, CAMILLA, GA, p. A168
MITCHELL COUNTY HOSPITAL, COLORADO CITY, TX, p. A664
MITCHELL COUNTY HOSPITAL HEALTH SYSTEMS, BELOIT, KS, p. A262
MITCHELL COUNTY REGIONAL HEALTH CENTER, OSAGE, IA, p. A255
MIZELL MEMORIAL HOSPITAL, OPP, AL, p. A23
MMO REHABILITATION AND WELLNESS CENTER, PLAQUEMINE, LA, p. A313
MOAB REGIONAL HOSPITAL, MOAB, UT, p. A729
MOBERLY REGIONAL MEDICAL CENTER, MOBERLY, MO, p. A412
MOBERLY REGIONAL MEDICAL CNTR, MOBERLY, MO, p. A412
MOBILE INFIRMARY MEDICAL CENTER, MOBILE, AL, p. A22

MOBRIDGE REGIONAL HOSPITAL, MOBRIDGE, SD, p. A629
MOCCASIN BEND MENTAL HEALTH INSTITUTE, CHATTANOOGA, TN, p. A635
MODESTO MEDICAL CENTER, MODESTO, CA, p. A79
MODOC MEDICAL CENTER, ALTURAS, CA, p. A55
MOHAWK VALLEY PSYCHIATRIC CENTER, UTICA, NY, p. A500
MOLOKAI GENERAL HOSPITAL, KAUNAKAKAI, HI, p. A186
MON HEALTH MEDICAL CENTER, MORGANTOWN, WV, p. A774
MONADNOCK COMMUNITY HOSPITAL, PETERBOROUGH, NH, p. A451
MONCRIEF ARMY COMMUNITY HOSPITAL, FORT JACKSON, SC, p. A620
MONMOUTH MEDICAL CENTER—SOUTHERN CAMPUS, LAKEWOOD, NJ, p. A457
MONMOUTH MEDICAL CENTER, LONG BRANCH, NJ, p. A457
MONMOUTH MEDICAL CENTER, LONG BRANCH CAMPUS, LONG BRANCH, NJ, p. A457
MONMOUTH MEDICAL CENTER, SOUTHERN CAMPUS, LAKEWOOD, NJ, p. A457
MONONGAHELA VALLEY HOSPITAL, MONONGAHELA, PA, p. A597
MONONGALIA GENERAL HOSPITAL, MORGANTOWN, WV, p. A774
MONROE CARELL JR. CHILDREN'S HOSPITAL AT VANDERBILT, NASHVILLE, TN, p. A646
MONROE CLINIC, MONROE, WI, p. A792
MONROE CLINIC HOSPITAL, MONROE, WI, p. A792
MONROE COUNTY HOSPITAL, ALBIA, IA, p. A243
MONROE COUNTY HOSPITAL, FORSYTH, GA, p. A172
MONROE COUNTY HOSPITAL, MONROEVILLE, AL, p. A22
MONROE COUNTY HOSPITAL AND CLINICS, ALBIA, IA, p. A243
MONROE COUNTY MEDICAL CENTER, TOMPKINSVILLE, KY, p. A293
MONROE HOSPITAL, BLOOMINGTON, IN, p. A224
MONROE REGIONAL HOSPITAL, ABERDEEN, MS, p. A389
MONROE SURGICAL HOSPITAL, MONROE, LA, p. A309
MONROVIA COMMUNITY HOSPITAL, MONROVIA, CA, p. A79
MONROVIA MEMORIAL HOSPITAL, MONROVIA, CA, p. A79
MONTANA STATE HOSPITAL, WARM SPRINGS, MT, p. A428
MONTCLAIR HOSPITAL MEDICAL CENTER, MONTCLAIR, CA, p. A79
MONTEFIORE HOSPITAL, PITTSBURGH, PA, p. A603
MONTEFIORE MEDICAL CENTER, BRONX, NY, p. A477
MONTEFIORE MOUNT VERNON, MOUNT VERNON, NY, p. A489
MONTEFIORE NEW ROCHELLE, NEW ROCHELLE, NY, p. A489
MONTEFIORE NYACK HOSPITAL, NYACK, NY, p. A493
MONTEFIORE ST. LUKE'S CORNWALL, NEWBURGH, NY, p. A492
MONTEREY PARK HOSPITAL, MONTEREY PARK, CA, p. A79
MONTEVISTA HOSPITAL, LAS VEGAS, NV, p. A443
MONTGOMERY COUNTY EMERGENCY SERVICE, NORRISTOWN, PA, p. A598
MONTGOMERY COUNTY MEMORIAL HOSPITAL, RED OAK, IA, p. A256
MONTGOMERY DIVISION, MONTGOMERY, AL, p. A22
MONTGOMERY GENERAL HOSPITAL, MONTGOMERY, WV, p. A774
MONTGOMERY REGIONAL HOSPITAL, BLACKSBURG, VA, p. A739
MONTPELIER HOSPITAL, MONTPELIER, OH, p. A546
MONTROSE GENERAL HOSPITAL, MONTROSE, PA, p. A597
MONTROSE MEMORIAL HOSPITAL, MONTROSE, CO, p. A117
MONUMENT HEALTH CUSTER HOSPITAL, CUSTER, SD, p. A627
MONUMENT HEALTH LEAD-DEADWOOD HOSPITAL, DEADWOOD, SD, p. A627
MONUMENT HEALTH RAPID CITY HOSPITAL, RAPID CITY, SD, p. A630
MONUMENT HEALTH SPEARFISH HOSPITAL, SPEARFISH, SD, p. A632
MONUMENT HEALTH STURGIS HOSPITAL, STURGIS, SD, p. A632
MOORE COUNTY HOSPITAL DISTRICT, DUMAS, TX, p. A673
MOORE MEDICAL CENTER, MOORE, OK, p. A562
MOREHEAD MEMORIAL HOSPITAL, EDEN, NC, p. A509
MOREHOUSE GENERAL HOSPITAL, BASTROP, LA, p. A296
MORENO VALLEY COMMUNITY HOSPITAL, MORENO VALLEY, CA, p. A80
MORGAN COUNTY APPALACHIAN REGIONAL HOSPITAL, WEST LIBERTY, KY, p. A294
MORGAN COUNTY ARH HOSPITAL, WEST LIBERTY, KY, p. A294
MORGAN MEMORIAL HOSPITAL, MADISON, GA, p. A176
MORGAN STANLEY CHILDREN'S HOSPITAL OF NEW YORK-PRESBYTERIAN, NEW YORK, NY, p. A490
MORRILL COUNTY COMMUNITY HOSPITAL, BRIDGEPORT, NE, p. A430

MORRIS COUNTY HOSPITAL, COUNCIL GROVE, KS, p. A263
MORRIS HOSPITAL & HEALTHCARE CENTERS, MORRIS, IL, p. A213
MORRIS HOSPITAL, MORRIS, IL, p. A213
MORRIS VILLAGE ALCOHOL AND DRUG ADDICTION TREATMENT CENTER, COLUMBIA, SC, p. A617
MORRISON COMMUNITY HOSPITAL, MORRISON, IL, p. A213
MORRISTOWN MEDICAL CENTER, MORRISTOWN, NJ, p. A458
MORRISTOWN MEMORIAL HOSPITAL, MORRISTOWN, NJ, p. A458
MORRISTOWN-HAMBLEN HEALTHCARE SYSTEM, MORRISTOWN, TN, p. A645
MORRISTOWN-HAMBLEN HOSPITAL, MORRISTOWN, TN, p. A645
MORROW COUNTY HOSPITAL, MOUNT GILEAD, OH, p. A546
MORTON COUNTY HEALTH SYSTEM, ELKHART, KS, p. A264
MORTON COUNTY HOSPITAL, ELKHART, KS, p. A264
MORTON F PLANT HOSPITAL, CLEARWATER, FL, p. A134
MORTON GENERAL HOSPITAL, MORTON, WA, p. A760
MORTON HOSPITAL AND MEDICAL CENTER, TAUNTON, MA, p. A345
MORTON PLANT HOSPITAL, CLEARWATER, FL, p. A134
MORTON PLANT NORTH BAY HOSPITAL, NEW PORT RICHEY, FL, p. A149
MORTON PLANT REHAB & NRSG CNTR, BELLEAIR, FL, p. A132
MORTON PLANT-MEASE-NORTH BAY, NEW PORT RICHEY, FL, p. A149
MOSAIC LIFE CARE, SAINT JOSEPH, MO, p. A415
MOSAIC LIFE CARE AT ST. JOSEPH—MEDICAL CENTER, SAINT JOSEPH, MO, p. A415
MOSAIC MEDICAL CENTER—ALBANY, ALBANY, MO, p. A402
MOSAIC MEDICAL CENTER—MARYVILLE, MARYVILLE, MO, p. A411
MOSES H. CONE MEMORIAL HOSPITAL, GREENSBORO, NC, p. A511
MOSES TAYLOR HOSPITAL, SCRANTON, PA, p. A607
MOSS REHAB, EINSTEIN AT ELKINS PARK, ELKINS PARK, PA, p. A589
MOTHER FRANCES HOSPITAL—JACKSONVILLE, JACKSONVILLE, TX, p. A691
MOTHER FRANCES HOSPITAL—TYLER, TYLER, TX, p. A722
MOTHER FRANCES HOSPITAL—WINNSBORO, WINNSBORO, TX, p. A726
MOTION PICTURE AND TELEVISION FUND HOSPITAL AND RESIDENTIAL SERVICES, WOODLAND HILLS, CA, p. A105
MOUNT AUBURN HOSPITAL, CAMBRIDGE, MA, p. A338
MOUNT CARMEL, COLUMBUS, OH, p. A536
MOUNT CARMEL HOSPITAL, COLVILLE, WA, p. A757
MOUNT CARMEL MEDICAL CENTER, COLUMBUS, OH, p. A536
MOUNT CARMEL NEW ALBANY SURGICAL HOSPITAL, NEW ALBANY, OH, p. A546
MOUNT CARMEL REHABILITATION HOSPITAL, WESTERVILLE, OH, p. A552
MOUNT CARMEL ST. ANN'S, WESTERVILLE, OH, p. A553
MOUNT CARMEL WEST, COLUMBUS, OH, p. A536
MOUNT CLEMENS REGIONAL MEDICAL CENTER, MOUNT CLEMENS, MI, p. A362
MOUNT DESERT ISLAND HOSPITAL, BAR HARBOR, ME, p. A318
MOUNT DIABLO MEDICAL CENTER, CONCORD, CA, p. A61
MOUNT GRANT GENERAL HOSPITAL, HAWTHORNE, NV, p. A442
MOUNT HOOD MEDICAL CENTER, GRESHAM, OR, p. A575
MOUNT NITTANY HEALTH, STATE COLLEGE, PA, p. A608
MOUNT NITTANY MEDICAL CENTER, STATE COLLEGE, PA, p. A608
MOUNT PLEASANT HOSPITAL, MOUNT PLEASANT, SC, p. A622
MOUNT SAN RAFAEL HOSPITAL, TRINIDAD, CO, p. A119
MOUNT SINAI BETH ISRAEL, NEW YORK, NY, p. A490
MOUNT SINAI HOSP MED CENTER, CHICAGO, IL, p. A199
MOUNT SINAI HOSPITAL, CHICAGO, IL, p. A199
MOUNT SINAI HOSPITAL OF QUEENS, LONG ISLAND CITY, NY, p. A487
MOUNT SINAI MEDICAL CENTER, MIAMI BEACH, FL, p. A148
MOUNT SINAI MEDICAL CENTER, NEW YORK, NY, p. A490
MOUNT SINAI MORNINGSIDE, NEW YORK, NY, p. A490
MOUNT SINAI REHABILITATION HOSPITAL, HARTFORD, CT, p. A122
MOUNT SINAI ROOSEVELT HOSPITAL, NEW YORK, NY, p. A490
MOUNT SINAI SOUTH NASSAU, OCEANSIDE, NY, p. A493
MOUNT SINAI WEST HOSPITAL, NEW YORK, NY, p. A490
MOUNT ST. MARY'S HOSPITAL AND HEALTH CENTER, LEWISTON, NY, p. A487
MOUNT VERNON HOSPITAL, ALEXANDRIA, VA, p. A738
MOUNT VERNON HOSPITAL, MOUNT VERNON, NY, p. A489

MOUNTAIN COMMUNITY MED SERVS, WEAVERVILLE, CA, p. A104
MOUNTAIN LAKES MEDICAL CENTER, CLAYTON, GA, p. A168
MOUNTAIN VALLEY REGIONAL REHABILITATION HOSPITAL, PRESCOTT VALLEY, AZ, p. A37
MOUNTAIN VIEW BAPTIST HOSPITAL, GADSDEN, AL, p. A19
MOUNTAIN VIEW HOSPITAL, GADSDEN, AL, p. A19
MOUNTAIN VIEW HOSPITAL, IDAHO FALLS, ID, p. A190
MOUNTAIN VIEW HOSPITAL, PAYSON, UT, p. A730
MOUNTAIN VIEW HOSPITAL DISTRICT, MADRAS, OR, p. A577
MOUNTAIN VIEW REGIONAL MED CTR, LAS CRUCES, NM, p. A470
MOUNTAIN VIEW REGIONAL MEDICAL CENTER, NORTON, VA, p. A748
MOUNTAIN VISTA MEDICAL CENTER, MESA, AZ, p. A34
MOUNTAIN WEST MEDICAL CENTER, TOOELE, UT, p. A733
MOUNTAINS COMMUNITY HOSPITAL, LAKE ARROWHEAD, CA, p. A70
MOUNTAINVIEW HOSPITAL, LAS VEGAS, NV, p. A443
MOUNTAINVIEW MEDICAL CENTER, WHITE SULPHUR SPRINGS, MT, p. A428
MOUNTAINVIEW MEMORIAL HOSPITAL, WHITE SULPHUR SPRINGS, MT, p. A428
MOUNTAINVIEW REGIONAL MEDICAL CENTER, LAS CRUCES, NM, p. A470
MOUNTAIN'S EDGE HOSPITAL, LAS VEGAS, NV, p. A443
MOUNTRAIL COUNTY MEDICAL CENTER, STANLEY, ND, p. A526
MT ASCUTNEY HOSP AND HLTH CTR, WINDSOR, VT, p. A737
MT GRAHAM COMMUNITY HOSPITAL, SAFFORD, AZ, p. A37
MT. ASCUTNEY HOSPITAL AND HEALTH CENTER, WINDSOR, VT, p. A737
MT. GRAHAM REGIONAL MEDICAL CENTER, SAFFORD, AZ, p. A37
MT. SAN RAFAEL HOSPITAL, TRINIDAD, CO, p. A119
MT. WASHINGTON PEDIATRIC HOSPITAL, BALTIMORE, MD, p. A326
MUENSTER HOSPITAL DISTRICT, MUENSTER, TX, p. A702
MUENSTER MEMORIAL HOSPITAL, MUENSTER, TX, p. A702
MUHLENBERG COMMUNITY HOSPITAL, GREENVILLE, KY, p. A284
MUHLENBERG HOSPITAL CENTER, BETHLEHEM, PA, p. A584
MULESHOE AREA MEDICAL CENTER, MULESHOE, TX, p. A702
MULTICARE AUBURN MEDICAL CENTER, AUBURN, WA, p. A755
MULTICARE COVINGTON MEDICAL CENTER, COVINGTON, WA, p. A757
MULTICARE DEACONESS HOSPITAL, SPOKANE, WA, p. A765
MULTICARE GOOD SAMARITAN HOSPITAL, PUYALLUP, WA, p. A762
MULTICARE MARY BRIDGE CHILDREN'S HOSPITAL AND HEALTH CENTER, TACOMA, WA, p. A767
MULTICARE TACOMA GENERAL HOSPITAL, TACOMA, WA, p. A767
MULTICARE VALLEY HOSPITAL, SPOKANE VALLEY, WA, p. A766
MUNCY VALLEY HOSPITAL, MUNCY, PA, p. A598
MUNISING MEMORIAL HOSPITAL, MUNISING, MI, p. A362
MUNSON HEALTHCARE CADILLAC HOSPITAL, CADILLAC, MI, p. A350
MUNSON HEALTHCARE CHARLEVOIX HOSPITAL, CHARLEVOIX, MI, p. A350
MUNSON HEALTHCARE GRAYLING HOSPITAL, GRAYLING, MI, p. A356
MUNSON HEALTHCARE MANISTEE HOSPITAL, MANISTEE, MI, p. A361
MUNSON HEALTHCARE OTSEGO MEMORIAL HOSPITAL, GAYLORD, MI, p. A355
MUNSON MEDICAL CENTER, TRAVERSE CITY, MI, p. A368
MURRAY COUNTY MEDICAL CENTER, SLAYTON, MN, p. A386
MURRAY COUNTY MEM HOSPITAL, SLAYTON, MN, p. A386
MURRAY MEDICAL CENTER, CHATSWORTH, GA, p. A168
MURRAY-CALLOWAY COUNTY HOSPITAL, MURRAY, KY, p. A291
MUSC CHILDREN'S HOSPITAL, CHARLESTON, SC, p. A616
MUSC HEALTH CHESTER MEDICAL CENTER, CHESTER, SC, p. A617
MUSC HEALTH FLORENCE MEDICAL CENTER, FLORENCE, SC, p. A619
MUSC HEALTH LANCASTER MEDICAL CENTER, LANCASTER, SC, p. A622
MUSC HEALTH MARION MEDICAL CENTER, MULLINS, SC, p. A623
MUSC HEALTH OF MEDICAL UNIVERSITY OF SOUTH CAROLINA, CHARLESTON, SC, p. A616
MUSC MEDICAL CENTER OF MEDICAL UNIVERSITY OF SOUTH CAROLINA, CHARLESTON, SC, p. A616
MUSCOGEE CREEK NATION MEDICAL CENTER, OKMULGEE, OK, p. A566

MUSCOGEE CREEK NATION PHYSICAL REHABILITATION CENTER, OKMULGEE, OK, p. A566
MUSKOGEE COMMUNITY HOSPITAL, MUSKOGEE, OK, p. A562
MYRTUE MEDICAL CENTER, HARLAN, IA, p. A251

## N

NACOGDOCHES MEDICAL CENTER, NACOGDOCHES, TX, p. A702
NACOGDOCHES MEMORIAL HOSPITAL, NACOGDOCHES, TX, p. A702
NANTUCKET COTTAGE HOSPITAL, NANTUCKET, MA, p. A342
NAPA STATE HOSPITAL, NAPA, CA, p. A80
NASH HEALTH CARE SYSTEMS, ROCKY MOUNT, NC, p. A517
NASH UNC HEALTH CARE, ROCKY MOUNT, NC, p. A517
NASHOBA VALLEY MEDICAL CENTER, AYER, MA, p. A334
NASHVILLE GENERAL HOSPITAL, NASHVILLE, TN, p. A646
NASON HOSPITAL, ROARING SPRING, PA, p. A606
NASSAU COUNTY MEDICAL CENTER, EAST MEADOW, NY, p. A483
NASSAU UNIVERSITY MEDICAL CENTER, EAST MEADOW, NY, p. A483
NATCHAUG HOSPITAL, MANSFIELD CENTER, CT, p. A123
NATCHEZ REGIONAL MEDICAL CENTER, NATCHEZ, MS, p. A397
NATCHITOCHES PARISH HOSPITAL, NATCHITOCHES, LA, p. A309
NATCHITOCHES REGIONAL MEDICAL CENTER, NATCHITOCHES, LA, p. A310
NATHAN LITTAUER HOSPITAL AND NURSING HOME, GLOVERSVILLE, NY, p. A485
NATIONAL HOSPITAL FOR KIDS, OREFIELD, PA, p. A599
NATIONAL INSTITUTES OF HEALTH CLINICAL CENTER, BETHESDA, MD, p. A327
NATIONAL JEWISH HEALTH, DENVER, CO, p. A110
NATIONAL NAVAL MEDICAL CENTER, BETHESDA, MD, p. A327
NATIONAL PARK MEDICAL CENTER, HOT SPRINGS, AR, p. A47
NATIONAL PARK MEDICAL CTR, HOT SPRINGS, AR, p. A47
NATIONWIDE CHILDREN'S HOSPITAL, COLUMBUS, OH, p. A536
NATIVIDAD MEDICAL CENTER, SALINAS, CA, p. A90
NATL JEWISH MED & RES CTR, DENVER, CO, p. A110
NATLIONAL INSTITUTES OF HEALTH, BETHESDA, MD, p. A327
NAVAL HOSPITAL, BEAUFORT, SC, p. A615
NAVAL HOSPITAL, BREMERTON, WA, p. A756
NAVAL HOSPITAL, CAMP LEJEUNE, NC, p. A506
NAVAL HOSPITAL, CAMP PENDLETON, CA, p. A59
NAVAL HOSPITAL, JACKSONVILLE, FL, p. A141
NAVAL HOSPITAL, LEMOORE, CA, p. A71
NAVAL HOSPITAL, OAK HARBOR, WA, p. A761
NAVAL HOSPITAL, PENSACOLA, FL, p. A153
NAVAL HOSPITAL, PORTSMOUTH, VA, p. A749
NAVAL HOSPITAL, TWENTYNINE PALMS, CA, p. A102
NAVAL HOSPITAL BEAUFORT, BEAUFORT, SC, p. A615
NAVAL HOSPITAL BREMERTON, BREMERTON, WA, p. A756
NAVAL HOSPITAL CAMP LEJEUNE, CAMP LEJEUNE, NC, p. A506
NAVAL HOSPITAL CAMP PENDLETON, CAMP PENDLETON, CA, p. A59
NAVAL HOSPITAL JACKSONVILLE, JACKSONVILLE, FL, p. A141
NAVAL HOSPITAL LEMOORE, LEMOORE, CA, p. A71
NAVAL HOSPITAL OAK HARBOR, OAK HARBOR, WA, p. A761
NAVAL HOSPITAL PENSACOLA, PENSACOLA, FL, p. A153
NAVAL MEDICAL CENTER, PORTSMOUTH, VA, p. A749
NAVAL MEDICAL CENTER, SAN DIEGO, CA, p. A91
NAVAL MEDICAL CENTER SAN DIEGO, SAN DIEGO, CA, p. A91
NAVAPACHE REGIONAL MED CENTER, SHOW LOW, AZ, p. A38
NAVARRO REGIONAL HOSPITAL, CORSICANA, TX, p. A666
NAVICENT HEALTH BALDWIN, MILLEDGEVILLE, GA, p. A177
NAVOS, SEATTLE, WA, p. A763
NAVOS INPATIENT SERVICES, SEATTLE, WA, p. A763
NAZARETH HOSPITAL, PHILADELPHIA, PA, p. A601
NAZARETH NURSING HOME, BUFFALO, NY, p. A480
NCH BAKER HOSPITAL, NAPLES, FL, p. A148
NCH DOWNTOWN NAPLES HOSPITAL, NAPLES, FL, p. A148
NEA BAPTIST MEMORIAL HOSPITAL, JONESBORO, AR, p. A48
NEA MEDICAL CENTER, JONESBORO, AR, p. A48
NEBRASKA HEART HOSPITAL, LINCOLN, NE, p. A434

NEBRASKA MEDICINE—BELLEVUE, BELLEVUE, NE, p. A430
NEBRASKA MEDICINE—NEBRASKA MEDICAL CENTER,
    OMAHA, NE, p. A437
NEBRASKA MEDICINE, OMAHA, NE, p. A437
NEBRASKA METHODIST HOSPITAL, OMAHA, NE, p. A437
NEBRASKA ORTHOPAEDIC HOSPITAL, OMAHA, NE, p. A437
NEBRASKA PENAL AND CORRECTIONAL HOSPITAL,
    LINCOLN, NE, p. A435
NEBRASKA SPINE HOSPITAL, OMAHA, NE, p. A437
NEEDLES-DESERT COMMUNITIES HSP, NEEDLES, CA, p. A81
NELL J. REDFIELD MEMORIAL HOSPITAL, MALAD CITY, ID,
    p. A191
NELLIS FEDERAL HOSPITAL, NELLIS AFB, NV, p. A445
NELSON COUNTY HEALTH SYSTEM, MCVILLE, ND, p. A525
NEMAHA COUNTY HOSPITAL, AUBURN, NE, p. A429
NEMAHA VALLEY COMMUNITY HOSPITAL, SENECA, KS,
    p. A276
NEMOURS CHILDREN'S HOSPITAL, ORLANDO, FL, p. A151
NEOSHO MEMORIAL REG MED CNTR, CHANUTE, KS, p. A262
NEOSHO MEMORIAL REGIONAL MEDICAL CENTER,
    CHANUTE, KS, p. A262
NESHOBA COUNTY GENERAL HOSPITAL, PHILADELPHIA,
    MS, p. A398
NESS COUNTY HOSPITAL, NESS CITY, KS, p. A272
NESS COUNTY HOSPITAL DISTRICT NO 2, NESS CITY, KS,
    p. A272
NEUROBEHAVIORAL HOSPITAL OF NW INDIANA, CROWN
    POINT, IN, p. A226
NEURODIAGNOSTIC INSTITUTE AND ADVANCED TREATMENT
    CENTER, INDIANAPOLIS, IN, p. A232
NEUROMEDICAL CENTER REHABILITATION HOSPITAL, BATON
    ROUGE, LA, p. A297
NEUROPSYCHIATRIC HOSPITAL OF INDIANAPOLIS,
    INDIANAPOLIS, IN, p. A232
NEVADA CITY HOSPITAL, NEVADA, MO, p. A412
NEVADA MENTAL HEALTH INSTITUTE, SPARKS, NV, p. A446
NEVADA REGIONAL MEDICAL CENTER, NEVADA, MO,
    p. A413
NEW ALBANY SURGICAL HOSPITAL, NEW ALBANY, OH,
    p. A546
NEW BEDFORD REHABILITATION HOSPITAL, NEW BEDFORD,
    MA, p. A342
NEW BRAUNFELS REGIONAL REHABILITATION HOSPITAL,
    NEW BRAUNFELS, TX, p. A703
NEW BRIDGE MEDICAL CENTER, PARAMUS, NJ, p. A460
NEW BRITAIN GENERAL HOSPITAL, NEW BRITAIN, CT,
    p. A123
NEW BRITAIN MEMORIAL HOSPITAL, NEW BRITAIN, CT,
    p. A123
NEW ENGLAND BAPTIST HOSPITAL, BOSTON, MA, p. A336
NEW ENGLAND REHABILITATION HOSPITAL OF PORTLAND,
    PORTLAND, ME, p. A322
NEW ENGLAND SINAI HOSPITAL AND REHABILITATION
    CENTER, STOUGHTON, MA, p. A345
NEW HAMPSHIRE HOSPITAL, CONCORD, NH, p. A448
NEW HANOVER REGIONAL MEDICAL CENTER, WILMINGTON,
    NC, p. A520
NEW HORIZON HOSPITAL, HOUSTON, TX, p. A687
NEW ISLAND HOSPITAL, BETHPAGE, NY, p. A475
NEW LONDON FAMILY MEDICAL CENTER, NEW LONDON,
    WI, p. A792
NEW LONDON HOSPITAL, NEW LONDON, NH, p. A450
NEW MEXICO BEHAVIORAL HEALTH INSTITUTE AT LAS
    VEGAS, LAS VEGAS, NM, p. A470
NEW MEXICO REHAB CTR, ROSWELL, NM, p. A471
NEW MEXICO REHABILITATION CENTER, ROSWELL, NM,
    p. A471
NEW MEXICO VETERANS AFFAIRS HEALTH CARE SYSTEM—
    RAYMOND G. MURPHY MEDICAL CENTER, ALBUQUERQUE,
    NM, p. A468
NEW ORLEANS EAST HOSPITAL, NEW ORLEANS, LA,
    p. A310
NEW ULM MEDICAL CENTER, NEW ULM, MN, p. A382
NEW YORK CITY CHILDREN'S CENTER, JAMAICA, NY, p. A486
NEW YORK COMM HOSP OF BROOKLYN, BROOKLYN, NY,
    p. A478
NEW YORK COMMUNITY HOSPITAL, BROOKLYN, NY, p. A478
NEW YORK DOWNTOWN HOSPITAL, NEW YORK, NY, p. A490
NEW YORK EYE AND EAR INFIRMARY, NEW YORK, NY,
    p. A490
NEW YORK EYE AND EAR INFIRMARY OF MOUNT SINAI, NEW
    YORK, NY, p. A490
NEW YORK FOUNDLING HOSPITAL, NEW YORK, NY, p. A491
NEW YORK METHODIST HOSPITAL, BROOKLYN, NY, p. A478
NEW YORK PRESBYTERIAN HOSPITAL, NEW YORK, NY,
    p. A491
NEW YORK STATE PSYCHIATRIC INSTITUTE, NEW YORK, NY,
    p. A491
NEW YORK WEILL CORNELL MED CTR, NEW YORK, NY,
    p. A491

NEW YORK-PRESBYTERIAN HOSPITAL, NEW YORK, NY,
    p. A491
NEW YORK-PRESBYTERIAN HOSPITAL, WESTCHESTER
    DIVISION, WHITE PLAINS, NY, p. A502
NEW YORK-PRESBYTERIAN QUEENS, FLUSHING, NY, p. A484
NEW YORK-PRESBYTERIAN/HUDSON VALLEY HOSPITAL,
    CORTLANDT MANOR, NY, p. A482
NEW YORK-PRESBYTERIAN/QUEENS, FLUSHING, NY, p. A484
NEWARK BETH ISRAEL MEDICAL CENTER, NEWARK, NJ,
    p. A459
NEWARK-WAYNE COMMUNITY HOSPITAL, NEWARK, NY,
    p. A492
NEWBERRY COUNTY MEMORIAL HOSPITAL, NEWBERRY, SC,
    p. A623
NEWINGTON CHILDREN'S HOSPITAL, HARTFORD, CT,
    p. A122
NEWMAN MEM CNTY HOSPITAL, EMPORIA, KS, p. A264
NEWMAN MEMORIAL HOSPITAL, SHATTUCK, OK, p. A568
NEWMAN REGIONAL HEALTH, EMPORIA, KS, p. A264
NEWNAN HOSPITAL, NEWNAN, GA, p. A178
NEWPORT BAY HOSPITAL, NEWPORT BEACH, CA, p. A81
NEWPORT COMMUNITY HOSPITAL, NEWPORT, WA, p. A761
NEWPORT HOSPITAL, NEWPORT, RI, p. A613
NEWPORT HOSPITAL AND HEALTH SERVICES, NEWPORT,
    WA, p. A761
NEWPORT MEDICAL CENTER, NEWPORT, TN, p. A647
NEWPORT NEWS BEHAVIORAL HEALTH CENTER, NEWPORT
    NEWS, VA, p. A747
NEWPORT SPECIALTY HOSPITAL, TUSTIN, CA, p. A102
NEWTON MEDICAL CENTER, COVINGTON, GA, p. A170
NEWTON MEDICAL CENTER, NEWTON, KS, p. A272
NEWTON MEDICAL CENTER, NEWTON, NJ, p. A460
NEWTON MEMORIAL HOSPITAL, NEWTON, NJ, p. A460
NEWTON-WELLESLEY HOSPITAL, NEWTON LOWER FALLS,
    MA, p. A342
NEWYORK-PRESBYTERIAN BROOKLYN METHODIST
    HOSPITAL, BROOKLYN, NY, p. A478
NEXUS CHILDREN'S HOSPITAL HOUSTON, HOUSTON, TX,
    p. A688
NEXUS SPECIALTY HOSPITAL, SHENANDOAH, TX, p. A715
NEXUS SPECIALTY HOSPITAL THE WOODLANDS, THE
    WOODLANDS, TX, p. A720
NIAGARA FALLS MEM MED CNTR, NIAGARA FALLS, NY,
    p. A493
NIAGARA FALLS MEMORIAL MEDICAL CENTER, NIAGARA
    FALLS, NY, p. A493
NICHOLAS H. NOYES MEMORIAL HOSPITAL, DANSVILLE,
    NY, p. A482
NICKLAUS CHILDREN'S HOSPITAL, MIAMI, FL, p. A147
NINNESCAH VALLEY HEALTH SYSTEM, KINGMAN, KS,
    p. A268
NIOBRARA COMMUNITY HOSPITAL, LUSK, WY, p. A803
NIOBRARA COUNTY HOSPITAL DIST, LUSK, WY, p. A803
NIOBRARA VALLEY HOSPITAL, LYNCH, NE, p. A435
NOBLE HOSPITAL, WESTFIELD, MA, p. A346
NOCONA GENERAL HOSPITAL, NOCONA, TX, p. A703
NOLAND HOSPITAL ANNISTON, ANNISTON, AL, p. A13
NOLAND HOSPITAL BIRMINGHAM, BIRMINGHAM, AL, p. A15
NOLAND HOSPITAL DOTHAN, DOTHAN, AL, p. A17
NOLAND HOSPITAL MONTGOMERY, MONTGOMERY, AL,
    p. A22
NOLAND HOSPITAL SHELBY, ALABASTER, AL, p. A13
NOLAND HOSPITAL TUSCALOOSA, TUSCALOOSA, AL, p. A25
NOLL MEMORIAL HOSPITAL, BETHANY, MO, p. A402
NOR-LEA GENERAL HOSPITAL, LOVINGTON, NM, p. A470
NOR-LEA HOSPITAL DISTRICT, LOVINGTON, NM, p. A470
NORMAN REGIONAL HEALTH SYSTEM, NORMAN, OK,
    p. A563
NORMAN REGIONAL MOORE, MOORE, OK, p. A562
NORRISTOWN STATE HOSPITAL, NORRISTOWN, PA, p. A598
NORTH ALABAMA MEDICAL CENTER, FLORENCE, AL,
    p. A18
NORTH ALABAMA SPECIALTY HOSPITAL, ATHENS, AL, p. A14
NORTH ARKANSAS MEDICAL CENTER, HARRISON, AR,
    p. A46
NORTH ARKANSAS REGIONAL MEDICAL CENTER, HARRISON,
    AR, p. A46
NORTH AUSTIN MEDICAL CENTER, AUSTIN, TX, p. A656
NORTH BALDWIN HOSPITAL, BAY MINETTE, AL, p. A14
NORTH BALDWIN INFIRMARY, BAY MINETTE, AL, p. A14
NORTH BAY HOSPITAL, NEWPORT BEACH, CA, p. A81
NORTH BIG HORN HOSPITAL, LOVELL, WY, p. A803
NORTH BIG HORN HOSPITAL DISTRICT, LOVELL, WY, p. A803
NORTH BROWARD MEDICAL CENTER, DEERFIELD BEACH,
    FL, p. A136
NORTH CADDO MEDICAL CENTER, VIVIAN, LA, p. A316
NORTH CADDO MEMORIAL HOSPITAL, VIVIAN, LA, p. A316
NORTH CANYON MEDICAL CENTER, GOODING, ID, p. A190
NORTH CAROLINA BAPTIST HOSPITAL, WINSTON, NC,
    p. A520

NORTH CAROLINA MEM HOSPITAL, CHAPEL HILL, NC,
    p. A506
NORTH CAROLINA SPECIALTY HOSPITAL, DURHAM, NC,
    p. A509
NORTH CENTRAL BRONX HOSPITAL, BRONX, NY, p. A477
NORTH CENTRAL HEALTH CARE, WAUSAU, WI, p. A798
NORTH CENTRAL HEALTH CARE FACILITIES, WAUSAU, WI,
    p. A798
NORTH CENTRAL SURGICAL CENTER, DALLAS, TX, p. A669
NORTH COLORADO MEDICAL CENTER, GREELEY, CO,
    p. A113
NORTH COUNTRY HOSPITAL AND HEALTH CENTER,
    NEWPORT, VT, p. A736
NORTH COUNTRY REGIONAL HOSPITAL, BEMIDJI, MN,
    p. A372
NORTH CREST MEDICAL CENTER, SPRINGFIELD, TN,
    p. A649
NORTH CYPRESS MEDICAL CENTER, CYPRESS, TX, p. A667
NORTH DAKOTA STATE HOSPITAL, JAMESTOWN, ND,
    p. A524
NORTH FL RECEPTION CTR HOSP, LAKE BUTLER, FL,
    p. A143
NORTH FLORIDA REGIONAL MEDICAL CENTER, GAINESVILLE,
    FL, p. A138
NORTH FLORIDA/SOUTH GEORGIA VETERAN'S HEALTH
    SYSTEM, GAINESVILLE, FL, p. A138
NORTH FULTON REGIONAL HOSPITAL, ROSWELL, GA,
    p. A179
NORTH GREENVILLE HOSPITAL, TRAVELERS REST, SC,
    p. A625
NORTH HAWAII COMMUNITY HOSPITAL, KAMUELA, HI,
    p. A186
NORTH HILLS HOSPITAL, NORTH RICHLAND HILLS, TX,
    p. A703
NORTH IDAHO BEHAVIORAL HEALTH, DIVISION OF KOOTENAI
    MEDICAL CENTER, COEUR D'ALENE, ID, p. A190
NORTH KANSAS CITY HOSPITAL, NORTH KANSAS CITY, MO,
    p. A413
NORTH KNOXVILLE MEDICAL CENTER, POWELL, TN, p. A648
NORTH LINCOLN HOSPITAL, LINCOLN CITY, OR, p. A577
NORTH LITTLE ROCK DIVISION, NORTH LITTLE ROCK, AR,
    p. A51
NORTH LOGAN MERCY HOSPITAL, PARIS, AR, p. A51
NORTH MEMORIAL HEALTH, ROBBINSDALE, MN, p. A383
NORTH MEMORIAL HEALTH HOSPITAL, ROBBINSDALE, MN,
    p. A383
NORTH MISSISSIPPI HEALTH SERVICES, INC., TUPELO, MI,
    p. A368
NORTH MISSISSIPPI MEDICAL CENTER GILMORE-AMORY,
    AMORY, MS, p. A389
NORTH MISSISSIPPI MEDICAL CENTER-EUPORA, EUPORA,
    MS, p. A392
NORTH MISSISSIPPI MEDICAL CENTER-HAMILTON,
    HAMILTON, AL, p. A20
NORTH MISSISSIPPI MEDICAL CENTER-IUKA, IUKA, MS,
    p. A394
NORTH MISSISSIPPI MEDICAL CENTER-PONTOTOC,
    PONTOTOC, MS, p. A399
NORTH MISSISSIPPI MEDICAL CENTER-PONTOTOC HOSPITAL
    AND NURSING HOME, PONTOTOC, MS, p. A399
NORTH MISSISSIPPI MEDICAL CENTER-WEST POINT, WEST
    POINT, MS, p. A401
NORTH MISSISSIPPI STATE HOSPITAL, TUPELO, MS, p. A400
NORTH OAK REGIONAL MEDICAL CENTER, SENATOBIA, MS,
    p. A400
NORTH OAKS HEALTH SYSTEM, HAMMOND, LA, p. A302
NORTH OAKS MEDICAL CENTER, HAMMOND, LA, p. A302
NORTH OAKS REHABILITATION HOSPITAL, HAMMOND, LA,
    p. A302
NORTH OKALOOSA MEDICAL CENTER, CRESTVIEW, FL,
    p. A135
NORTH OKALOOSA MEDICAL CTR, CRESTVIEW, FL,
    p. A135
NORTH OTTAWA COMMUNITY HOSPITAL, GRAND HAVEN,
    MI, p. A355
NORTH PHILADELPHIA HEALTH SYST, PHILADELPHIA, PA,
    p. A601
NORTH PHILADELPHIA HEALTH SYSTEM, PHILADELPHIA, PA,
    p. A601
NORTH RUNNELS HOSPITAL, WINTERS, TX, p. A726
NORTH SHORE CHILDREN'S HOSPITAL, SALEM, MA, p. A344
NORTH SHORE HEALTH, GRAND MARAIS, MN, p. A377
NORTH SHORE LONG ISLAND MED CT, NEW HYDE PARK,
    NY, p. A489
NORTH SHORE MEDICAL CENTER, MIAMI, FL, p. A147
NORTH SHORE MEDICAL CENTER, SALEM, MA, p. A344
NORTH SHORE MEDICAL CENTER, FLORIDA MEDICAL
    CENTER CAMPUS, FORT LAUDERDALE, FL, p. A137
NORTH SHORE UNIV HSP GLEN COVE, GLEN COVE, NY,
    p. A484

NORTH SHORE UNIVERSITY HOSPITAL, MANHASSET, NY, p. A487

NORTH SHORE UNIVERSITY HOSPITAL AT PLAINVIEW, PLAINVIEW, NY, p. A495

NORTH SHORE UNIVERSITY HOSPITAL AT SYOSSET, SYOSSET, NY, p. A499

NORTH SIDE HOSPITAL, JOHNSON CITY, TN, p. A640

NORTH SONOMA COUNTY HEALTHCARE DISTRICT, HEALDSBURG, CA, p. A68

NORTH STAR BEHAVIORAL HEALTH SYSTEM, ANCHORAGE, AK, p. A27

NORTH STAR BEHAVIORAL HLTH SYS, ANCHORAGE, AK, p. A27

NORTH STAR HLTH SYST, ANCHORAGE, AK, p. A27

NORTH SUBURBAN MEDICAL CENTER, THORNTON, CO, p. A119

NORTH SUBURBAN MEDICALCENTER, THORNTON, CO, p. A119

NORTH SUNFLOWER CNTY HOSPITAL, RULEVILLE, MS, p. A400

NORTH SUNFLOWER MEDICAL CENTER, RULEVILLE, MS, p. A400

NORTH TAMPA BEHAVIORAL HEALTH, WESLEY CHAPEL, FL, p. A162

NORTH TEXAS MEDICAL CENTER, GAINESVILLE, TX, p. A680

NORTH TEXAS STATE HOSPITAL, VERNON, TX, p. A723

NORTH TEXAS STATE HOSPITAL, WICHITA FALLS CAMPUS, WICHITA FALLS, TX, p. A725

NORTH VALLEY HEALTH CENTER, WARREN, MN, p. A387

NORTH VALLEY HOSPITAL, TONASKET, WA, p. A767

NORTH VALLEY HOSPITAL, WHITEFISH, MT, p. A428

NORTH VISTA HOSPITAL, NORTH LAS VEGAS, NV, p. A445

NORTHBAY MEDICAL CENTER, FAIRFIELD, CA, p. A63

NORTHBAY VACAVALLEY HOSPITAL, VACAVILLE, CA, p. A102

NORTHBROOK BEHAVIORAL HEALTH HOSPITAL, BLACKWOOD, NJ, p. A452

NORTHCOAST BEHAVIORAL HEALTHCARE, NORTHFIELD, OH, p. A546

NORTHCOAST BEHAVIORAL HEALTHCARE SYSTEM, NORTHFIELD, OH, p. A546

NORTHCREST MEDICAL CENTER, SPRINGFIELD, TN, p. A650

NORTHEAST GEORGIA MEDICAL CENTER, GAINESVILLE, GA, p. A173

NORTHEAST GEORGIA MEDICAL CENTER BARROW, WINDER, GA, p. A183

NORTHEAST GEORGIA MEDICAL CENTER BRASELTON, BRASELTON, GA, p. A167

NORTHEAST GEORGIA MEDICAL CENTER LUMPKIN, DAHLONEGA, GA, p. A170

NORTHEAST GEORGIA MEDICAL CENTER-LUMPKIN, DAHLONEGA, GA, p. A170

NORTHEAST MEDICAL CENTER HOSP, HUMBLE, TX, p. A690

NORTHEAST REGIONAL MEDICAL CENTER, KIRKSVILLE, MO, p. A410

NORTHEAST REHABILITATION HOSPITAL, SALEM, NH, p. A451

NORTHEASTERN CENTER, AUBURN, IN, p. A223

NORTHEASTERN HEALTH SYSTEM, TAHLEQUAH, OK, p. A569

NORTHEASTERN HEALTH SYSTEM SEQUOYAH, SALLISAW, OK, p. A567

NORTHEASTERN NEVADA REGIONAL HOSPITAL, ELKO, NV, p. A441

NORTHEASTERN REGIONAL HOSPITAL, LAS VEGAS, NM, p. A470

NORTHEASTERN VERMONT REGIONAL HOSPITAL, SAINT JOHNSBURY, VT, p. A736

NORTHERN ARIZONA VA HEALTH CARE SYSTEM, PRESCOTT, AZ, p. A37

NORTHERN ARIZONA VETERANS AFFAIRS HEALTH CARE SYSTEM, PRESCOTT, AZ, p. A37

NORTHERN CALIFORNIA REHABILITATION HOSPITAL, REDDING, CA, p. A87

NORTHERN COCHISE COMMUNITY HOSPITAL, WILLCOX, AZ, p. A41

NORTHERN COLORADO LONG TERM ACUTE HOSPITAL, JOHNSTOWN, CO, p. A114

NORTHERN COLORADO REHABILITATION HOSPITAL, JOHNSTOWN, CO, p. A114

NORTHERN CUMBERLAND MEM HOSP, BRIDGTON, ME, p. A319

NORTHERN DUTCHESS HOSPITAL, RHINEBECK, NY, p. A496

NORTHERN HOSPITAL OF SURRY COUNTY, MOUNT AIRY, NC, p. A515

NORTHERN IDAHO ADVANCED CARE HOSPITAL, POST FALLS, ID, p. A192

NORTHERN INYO HOSPITAL, BISHOP, CA, p. A58

NORTHERN LIGHT BLUE HILL HOSPITAL, BLUE HILL, ME, p. A319

NORTHERN LIGHT CA DEAN HOSPITAL, GREENVILLE, ME, p. A320

NORTHERN LIGHT EASTERN MAINE MEDICAL CENTER, BANGOR, ME, p. A318

NORTHERN LIGHT INLAND HOSPITAL, WATERVILLE, ME, p. A323

NORTHERN LIGHT MAINE COAST HOSPITAL, ELLSWORTH, ME, p. A320

NORTHERN LIGHT MERCY HOSPITAL, PORTLAND, ME, p. A322

NORTHERN LIGHT SEBASTICOOK VALLEY HOSPITAL, PITTSFIELD, ME, p. A322

NORTHERN LOUISIANA MEDICAL CENTER, RUSTON, LA, p. A313

NORTHERN MAINE MEDICAL CENTER, FORT KENT, ME, p. A320

NORTHERN MICHIGAN REGIONAL HOSPITAL, PETOSKEY, MI, p. A363

NORTHERN MONTANA HEALTH CARE, HAVRE, MT, p. A425

NORTHERN MONTANA HOSPITAL, HAVRE, MT, p. A425

NORTHERN NAVAJO MEDICAL CENTER, SHIPROCK, NM, p. A472

NORTHERN NEVADA ADULT MENTAL HEALTH SERVICES, SPARKS, NV, p. A446

NORTHERN NEVADA MEDICAL CENTER, SPARKS, NV, p. A446

NORTHERN REGIONAL HOSPITAL, MOUNT AIRY, NC, p. A515

NORTHERN ROCKIES MEDICAL CENTER, CUT BANK, MT, p. A423

NORTHERN UTAH REHABILITATION HOSPITAL, SOUTH OGDEN, UT, p. A733

NORTHERN VIRGINIA MENTAL HEALTH INSTITUTE, FALLS CHURCH, VA, p. A741

NORTHERN WESTCHESTER HOSP CTR, MOUNT KISCO, NY, p. A488

NORTHERN WESTCHESTER HOSPITAL, MOUNT KISCO, NY, p. A488

NORTHFIELD HOSPITAL, NORTHFIELD, MN, p. A382

NORTHFIELD HOSPITAL AND CLINICS, NORTHFIELD, MN, p. A382

NORTHLAKE BEHAVIORAL HEALTH SYSTEM, MANDEVILLE, LA, p. A308

NORTHLAKE BEHAVIORAL HOSPITAL SYSTEM, MANDEVILLE, LA, p. A308

NORTHLAND LTAC HOSPITAL, KANSAS CITY, MO, p. A409

NORTHLIGHT SEBASTICOOK VALLEY HOSPITAL, PITTSFIELD, ME, p. A322

NORTHPORT HOSPITAL-DCH, NORTHPORT, AL, p. A23

NORTHPORT VETERANS AFFAIRS MEDICAL CENTER, NORTHPORT, NY, p. A493

NORTHRIDGE HOSPITAL MEDICAL CENTER, NORTHRIDGE, CA, p. A81

NORTHRIDGE HOSPITAL MEDICAL CENTER-ROSCOE BOULEVARD CAMPUS, NORTHRIDGE, CA, p. A81

NORTHRIDGE MEDICAL CENTER, COMMERCE, GA, p. A169

NORTHRIDGE MEDICAL CENTER, PRATTVILLE, AL, p. A24

NORTHSHORE GLENBROOK HOSPITAL, GLENVIEW, IL, p. A206

NORTHSHORE HIGHLAND PARK HOSPITAL, HIGHLAND PARK, IL, p. A207

NORTHSHORE REGIONAL MEDICAL CENTER, SLIDELL, LA, p. A315

NORTHSHORE REHABILITATION HOSPITAL, LACOMBE, LA, p. A305

NORTHSHORE SPECIALTY HOSPITAL, COVINGTON, LA, p. A300

NORTHSHORE UNIVERSITY HEALTH SYSTEM, EVANSTON, IL, p. A204

NORTHSHORE UNIVERSITY HEALTH SYSTEM EVANSTON HOSPITAL, EVANSTON, IL, p. A204

NORTHSHORE UNIVERSITY HEALTH SYSTEM SKOKIE HOSPITAL, SKOKIE, IL, p. A220

NORTHSHORE UNIVERSITY HEALTHSYSTEM-GLENBROOK HOSPITAL, GLENVIEW, IL, p. A206

NORTHSHORE UNIVERSITY HEALTHSYSTEM-HIGHLAND PARK HOSPITAL, HIGHLAND PARK, IL, p. A207

NORTHSIDE HOSPITAL—DULUTH, DULUTH, GA, p. A172

NORTHSIDE HOSPITAL—GWINNETT, LAWRENCEVILLE, GA, p. A175

NORTHSIDE HOSPITAL, ATLANTA, GA, p. A165

NORTHSIDE HOSPITAL, SAINT PETERSBURG, FL, p. A156

NORTHSIDE HOSPITAL AND HEART INSTITUTE, SAINT PETERSBURG, FL, p. A156

NORTHSIDE HOSPITAL GWINNETT, LAWRENCEVILLE, GA, p. A175

NORTHSIDE HOSPITAL-CHEROKEE, CANTON, GA, p. A168

NORTHSIDE HOSPITAL-FORSYTH, CUMMING, GA, p. A170

NORTHSIDE MEDICAL CENTER, COLUMBUS, GA, p. A169

NORTHWEST CENTER FOR BEHAVIORAL HEALTH, FORT SUPPLY, OK, p. A559

NORTHWEST COMMUNITY HEALTHCARE, ARLINGTON HEIGHTS, IL, p. A194

NORTHWEST COMMUNITY HOSPITAL, ARLINGTON HEIGHTS, IL, p. A194

NORTHWEST FLORIDA COMMUNITY HOSPITAL, CHIPLEY, FL, p. A134

NORTHWEST HEALTH PHYSICIANS' SPECIALTY HOSPITAL, FAYETTEVILLE, AR, p. A45

NORTHWEST HILLS SURGICAL HOSPITAL, AUSTIN, TX, p. A656

NORTHWEST HOSPITAL & MEDICAL CENTER, SEATTLE, WA, p. A763

NORTHWEST HOSPITAL, RANDALLSTOWN, MD, p. A331

NORTHWEST HOSPITAL, TUCSON, AZ, p. A40

NORTHWEST HOSPITAL CENTER, RANDALLSTOWN, MD, p. A331

NORTHWEST IOWA HEALTH CENTER, SHELDON, IA, p. A257

NORTHWEST KANSAS REG MED CTR, GOODLAND, KS, p. A265

NORTHWEST MEDICAL CENTER—SPRINGDALE, SPRINGDALE, AR, p. A53

NORTHWEST MEDICAL CENTER, ALBANY, MO, p. A402

NORTHWEST MEDICAL CENTER, MARGATE, FL, p. A145

NORTHWEST MEDICAL CENTER, SPRINGDALE, AR, p. A53

NORTHWEST MEDICAL CENTER, TUCSON, AZ, p. A40

NORTHWEST MEDICAL CENTER, WINFIELD, AL, p. A26

NORTHWEST MEDICAL CENTER, ORO VALLEY, ORO VALLEY, AZ, p. A34

NORTHWEST MEDICAL CTR, WINFIELD, AL, p. A26

NORTHWEST MISSISSIPPI MEDICAL CENTER, CLARKSDALE, MS, p. A391

NORTHWEST MISSOURI PSYCHIATRIC REHABILITATION CENTER, SAINT JOSEPH, MO, p. A415

NORTHWEST OHIO PSYCHIATRIC HOSPITAL, TOLEDO, OH, p. A550

NORTHWEST SPECIALTY HOSPITAL, POST FALLS, ID, p. A192

NORTHWEST SURGICAL HOSPITAL, OKLAHOMA CITY, OK, p. A565

NORTHWEST TEXAS HEALTHCARE SYSTEM, AMARILLO, TX, p. A652

NORTHWEST TEXAS HOSPITAL, AMARILLO, TX, p. A652

NORTHWESTERN INSTITUTE, FORT WASHINGTON, PA, p. A590

NORTHWESTERN LAKE FOREST HOSPITAL, LAKE FOREST, IL, p. A210

NORTHWESTERN MEDICAL CENTER, SAINT ALBANS, VT, p. A736

NORTHWESTERN MEDICINE CENTRAL DUPAGE HOSPITAL, WINFIELD, IL, p. A222

NORTHWESTERN MEDICINE DELNOR HOSPITAL, GENEVA, IL, p. A206

NORTHWESTERN MEDICINE KISHWAUKEE HOSPITAL, DEKALB, IL, p. A202

NORTHWESTERN MEDICINE LAKE FOREST HOSPITAL, LAKE FOREST, IL, p. A210

NORTHWESTERN MEDICINE MARIANJOY REHABILITATION HOSPITAL, WHEATON, IL, p. A222

NORTHWESTERN MEDICINE MCHENRY, MCHENRY, IL, p. A212

NORTHWESTERN MEDICINE VALLEY WEST HOSPITAL, SANDWICH, IL, p. A219

NORTHWESTERN MEMORIAL HOSPITAL, CHICAGO, IL, p. A200

NORTHWESTERN WOODSTOCK, WOODSTOCK, IL, p. A222

NORTHWOOD DEACONESS HEALTH CENTER, NORTHWOOD, ND, p. A525

NORTON CHILDREN'S HOSPITAL, LOUISVILLE, KY, p. A288

NORTON COMMUNITY HOSPITAL, NORTON, VA, p. A748

NORTON COUNTY HOSPITAL, NORTON, KS, p. A272

NORTON HEALTHCARE, LOUISVILLE, KY, p. A288

NORTON HEALTHCARE PAVILION, LOUISVILLE, KY, p. A288

NORTON HOSPITAL, LOUISVILLE, KY, p. A288

NORTON MEDICAL PAVILION, LOUISVILLE, KY, p. A288

NORTON SOUND REGIONAL HOSPITAL, NOME, AK, p. A29

NORTON SOUTHWEST HOSPITAL, LOUISVILLE, KY, p. A288

NORTON SPRING VIEW HOSPITAL, LEBANON, KY, p. A286

NORTON WOMEN'S AND KOSAIR CHILDREN'S HOSPITAL, LOUISVILLE, KY, p. A288

NORWALK COMMUNITY HOSPITAL, NORWALK, CA, p. A81

NORWALK HOSPITAL, NORWALK, CT, p. A124

NORWEGIAN AMERICAN HOSPITAL, CHICAGO, IL, p. A200

NORWEGIAN-AMERICAN HOSPITAL, CHICAGO, IL, p. A200

NORWOOD HEALTH CENTER, MARSHFIELD, WI, p. A789

NORWOOD HOSPITAL, NORWOOD, MA, p. A343

NOVANT HEALTH BRUNSWICK MEDICAL CENTER, BOLIVIA, NC, p. A505

NOVANT HEALTH CHARLOTTE ORTHOPAEDIC HOSPITAL, CHARLOTTE, NC, p. A507

NOVANT HEALTH FORSYTH MEDICAL CENTER, WINSTON, NC, p. A520

NOVANT HEALTH HAYMARKET MEDICAL CENTER, HAYMARKET, VA, p. A744

NOVANT HEALTH HUNTERSVILLE MEDICAL CENTER, HUNTERSVILLE, NC, p. A512
NOVANT HEALTH MATTHEWS MEDICAL CENTER, MATTHEWS, NC, p. A514
NOVANT HEALTH MEDICAL PARK HOSPITAL, WINSTON, NC, p. A520
NOVANT HEALTH MINT HILL MEDICAL CENTER, CHARLOTTE, NC, p. A507
NOVANT HEALTH PRESBYTERIAN MEDICAL CENTER, CHARLOTTE, NC, p. A507
NOVANT HEALTH PRINCE WILLIAM MEDICAL CENTER, MANASSAS, VA, p. A745
NOVANT HEALTH ROWAN MEDICAL CENTER, SALISBURY, NC, p. A518
NOVANT HEALTH THOMASVILLE MEDICAL CENTER, THOMASVILLE, NC, p. A519
NOVANT HEALTH UVA HEALTH SYSTEM CULPEPER MEDICAL CENTER, CULPEPER, VA, p. A740
NOVANT HEALTH UVA HEALTH SYSTEM HAYMARKET MEDICAL CENTER, HAYMARKET, VA, p. A744
NOVANT HEALTH UVA HEALTH SYSTEM PRINCE WILLIAM MEDICAL CENTER, MANASSAS, VA, p. A745
NOVATO COMMUNITY HOSPITAL, NOVATO, CA, p. A81
NOXUBEE GENERAL HOSPITAL, MACON, MS, p. A396
NYC HEALTH & HOSPITALS / BELLEVUE, NEW YORK, NY, p. A491
NYC HEALTH + HOSPITALS / BELLEVUE, NEW YORK, NY, p. A491
NYC HEALTH + HOSPITALS / CARTER, NEW YORK, NY, p. A491
NYC HEALTH + HOSPITALS / CONEY ISLAND, BROOKLYN, NY, p. A478
NYC HEALTH + HOSPITALS / ELMHURST, ELMHURST, NY, p. A483
NYC HEALTH + HOSPITALS / HARLEM, NEW YORK, NY, p. A491
NYC HEALTH + HOSPITALS / HENRY J CARTER SPECIALTY HOSPITAL AND MEDICAL CENTER, NEW YORK, NY, p. A491
NYC HEALTH + HOSPITALS / JACOBI, BRONX, NY, p. A477
NYC HEALTH + HOSPITALS / KINGS COUNTY, BROOKLYN, NY, p. A478
NYC HEALTH + HOSPITALS / LINCOLN, BRONX, NY, p. A477
NYC HEALTH + HOSPITALS / METROPOLITAN, NEW YORK, NY, p. A491
NYC HEALTH + HOSPITALS / NORTH CENTRAL BRONX, BRONX, NY, p. A477
NYC HEALTH + HOSPITALS / QUEENS, JAMAICA, NY, p. A486
NYC HEALTH + HOSPITALS / WOODHULL, BROOKLYN, NY, p. A479
NYU CHILDREN'S HOSPITAL, NEW YORK, NY, p. A492
NYU LANGONE HOSPITALS, NEW YORK, NY, p. A492
NYU LANGONE MEDICAL CENTER, NEW YORK, NY, p. A492
NYU LANGONE MEDICAL CENTER'S HOSPITAL FOR JOINT DISEASES, NEW YORK, NY, p. A492
NYU LUTHERAN (NYU HOSPITALS CENTER), BROOKLYN, NY, p. A479

# O

OAK HILL HOSPITAL, BROOKSVILLE, FL, p. A133
OAK HILL HOSPITAL, JOPLIN, MO, p. A408
OAK HILLS BEHAVIORAL CENTER, JACKSON, TN, p. A639
OAK PARK HOSPITAL, OAK PARK, IL, p. A215
OAK VALLEY HOSPITAL, OAKDALE, CA, p. A82
OAK VALLEY HOSPITAL DISTRICT, OAKDALE, CA, p. A82
OAKBEND MEDICAL CENTER, RICHMOND, TX, p. A708
OAKDALE COMMUNITY HOSPITAL, OAKDALE, LA, p. A312
OAKES COMMUNITY HOSPITAL, OAKES, ND, p. A525
OAKLAND MEDICAL CENTER, OAKLAND, CA, p. A82
OAKLAND MERCY HOSPITAL, OAKLAND, NE, p. A436
OAKLAND REGIONAL HOSPITAL, SOUTHFIELD, MI, p. A367
OAKLAWN HOSPITAL, GOSHEN, IN, p. A229
OAKLAWN HOSPITAL, MARSHALL, MI, p. A361
OAKLAWN PSYCHIATRIC CENTER, GOSHEN, IN, p. A229
OAKLEAF SURGICAL CENTER, ALTOONA, WI, p. A779
OAKLEAF SURGICAL HOSPITAL, ALTOONA, WI, p. A779
OAKWOOD CENTER OF THE PALM BEACHES, INC., WEST PALM BEACH, FL, p. A162
OAKWOOD HOSPITAL, WINDSOR, MO, p. A420
OAKWOOD HOSPITAL-TAYLOR, TAYLOR, MI, p. A367
OAKWOOD SPRINGS, OKLAHOMA CITY, OK, p. A565
OASIS BEHAVIORAL HEALTH—CHANDLER, CHANDLER, AZ, p. A31
OASIS HOSPITAL, PHOENIX, AZ, p. A36

OASIS REHAB HOSP OF LAFAYETTE, LAFAYETTE, LA, p. A305
O'BLENESS MEMORIAL HOSPITAL, ATHENS, OH, p. A528
OCALA REGIONAL MEDICAL CENTER, OCALA, FL, p. A150
OCEAN BEACH HOSPITAL, ILWACO, WA, p. A759
OCEAN MEDICAL CENTER, BRICK TOWNSHIP, NJ, p. A453
OCEAN SPRINGS HOSPITAL, OCEAN SPRINGS, MS, p. A398
OCEANS BEHAVIORAL HEALTH CENTER PERMIAN BASIN, MIDLAND, TX, p. A701
OCEANS BEHAVIORAL HOSPITAL, LUFKIN, TX, p. A698
OCEANS BEHAVIORAL HOSPITAL ABILENE, ABILENE, TX, p. A651
OCEANS BEHAVIORAL HOSPITAL BILOXI, BILOXI, MS, p. A389
OCEANS BEHAVIORAL HOSPITAL FORT WORTH, FORT WORTH, TX, p. A679
OCEANS BEHAVIORAL HOSPITAL KATY, KATY, TX, p. A692
OCEANS BEHAVIORAL HOSPITAL LONGVIEW, LONGVIEW, TX, p. A697
OCEANS BEHAVIORAL HOSPITAL LUFKIN, LUFKIN, TX, p. A698
OCEANS BEHAVIORAL HOSPITAL OF ALEXANDRIA, ALEXANDRIA, LA, p. A295
OCEANS BEHAVIORAL HOSPITAL OF BATON ROUGE, BATON ROUGE, LA, p. A297
OCEANS BEHAVIORAL HOSPITAL OF BROSSARD, BROUSSARD, LA, p. A299
OCEANS BEHAVIORAL HOSPITAL OF DE RIDDER, DERIDDER, LA, p. A301
OCEANS BEHAVIORAL HOSPITAL OF DERIDDER, DERIDDER, LA, p. A301
OCEANS BEHAVIORAL HOSPITAL OF GREATER NEW ORLEANS, KENNER, LA, p. A304
OCEANS BEHAVIORAL HOSPITAL OF LAKE CHARLES, LAKE CHARLES, LA, p. A307
OCEANS BEHAVIORAL HOSPITAL OF OPELOUSAS, OPELOUSAS, LA, p. A312
OCEANS BEHAVIORAL HOSPITAL OF PASADENA, PASADENA, TX, p. A705
OCEANS BEHAVIORAL HOSPITAL PLANO, PLANO, TX, p. A707
OCEANS BEHAVIORAL HOSPITAL SAN MARCOS, SAN MARCOS, TX, p. A714
OCH REGIONAL MEDICAL CENTER, STARKVILLE, MS, p. A400
OCHILTREE GENERAL HOSPITAL, PERRYTON, TX, p. A705
OCHSNER CLINIC FOUNDATION, NEW ORLEANS, LA, p. A311
OCHSNER EXTENDED CARE HOSPITAL, NEW ORLEANS, LA, p. A311
OCHSNER LSU HEALTH SHREVEPORT—ACADEMIC MEDICAL CENTER, SHREVEPORT, LA, p. A314
OCHSNER LSU HEALTH SHREVEPORT—MONROE MEDICAL CENTER, MONROE, LA, p. A309
OCHSNER LSU HEALTH SHREVPORT—ACADEMIC MEDICAL CENTER, SHREVEPORT, LA, p. A314
OCHSNER MEDICAL CENTER—BATON ROUGE, BATON ROUGE, LA, p. A297
OCHSNER MEDICAL CENTER—KENNER, KENNER, LA, p. A304
OCHSNER MEDICAL CENTER—NORTH SHORE, SLIDELL, LA, p. A315
OCHSNER MEDICAL CENTER, NEW ORLEANS, LA, p. A311
OCHSNER MEDICAL CENTER-BATON ROUGE, BATON ROUGE, LA, p. A297
OCHSNER REHABILITATON HOSPITAL WEST CAMPUS, JEFFERSON, LA, p. A304
OCHSNER ST. ANNE GENERAL HOSPITAL, RACELAND, LA, p. A313
OCHSNER ST. MARY, MORGAN CITY, LA, p. A309
OCONEE MEMORIAL HOSPITAL, SENECA, SC, p. A624
OCONEE REGIONAL MEDICAL CENTER, MILLEDGEVILLE, GA, p. A177
O'CONNOR HOSPITAL, DELHI, NY, p. A482
O'CONNOR HOSPITAL, SAN JOSE, CA, p. A95
O'CONNOR HOSPITAL DIVISION, DELHI, NY, p. A482
OCONOMOWOC MEMORIAL HOSPITAL, OCONOMOWOC, WI, p. A792
OCONTO HOSPITAL & MEDICAL CENTER, OCONTO, WI, p. A793
ODESSA MEMORIAL HEALTHCARE CENTER, ODESSA, WA, p. A761
ODESSA MEMORIAL HOSPITAL, ODESSA, WA, p. A761
ODESSA REGIONAL HOSPITAL, ODESSA, TX, p. A704
ODESSA REGIONAL MEDICAL CENTER, ODESSA, TX, p. A704
ODESSA REGIONAL MEDICAL CENTER SOUTH CAMPUS, ODESSA, TX, p. A704
OGALLALA COMMUNITY HOSPITAL, OGALLALA, NE, p. A436
OGDEN REGIONAL MEDICAL CENTER, OGDEN, UT, p. A730
OHIO COUNTY HOSPITAL, HARTFORD, KY, p. A284
OHIO HOSPITAL FOR CHILD AND ADOLESCENT PSYCHIATRY, COLUMBUS, OH, p. A536
OHIO HOSPITAL FOR PSYCHIATRY, COLUMBUS, OH, p. A536

OHIO STATE UNIVERSITY MEDICAL CENTER, COLUMBUS, OH, p. A536
OHIO STATE UNIVERSITY WEXNER MEDICAL CENTER, COLUMBUS, OH, p. A536
OHIO VALLEY HOSPITAL, MCKEES ROCKS, PA, p. A596
OHIO VALLEY HOSPITAL, STEUBENVILLE, OH, p. A549
OHIO VALLEY MEDICAL CENTER, SPRINGFIELD, OH, p. A549
OHIO VALLEY SURGICAL HOSPITAL, SPRINGFIELD, OH, p. A549
OHIOHEALTH BERGER HOSPITAL, CIRCLEVILLE, OH, p. A533
OHIOHEALTH DOCTORS HOSPITAL, COLUMBUS, OH, p. A536
OHIOHEALTH DUBLIN METHODIST HOSPITAL, DUBLIN, OH, p. A539
OHIOHEALTH GRADY MEMORIAL HOSPITAL, DELAWARE, OH, p. A539
OHIOHEALTH GRANT MEDICAL CENTER, COLUMBUS, OH, p. A536
OHIOHEALTH HARDIN MEMORIAL HOSPITAL, KENTON, OH, p. A542
OHIOHEALTH MARION GENERAL HOSPITAL, MARION, OH, p. A544
OHIOHEALTH MEDCENTRAL MANSFIELD HOSPITAL, MANSFIELD, OH, p. A544
OHIOHEALTH MEDCENTRAL SHELBY HOSPITAL, SHELBY, OH, p. A549
OHIOHEALTH REHABILITATION HOSPITAL, COLUMBUS, OH, p. A536
OHIOHEALTH RIVERSIDE METHODIST HOSPITAL, COLUMBUS, OH, p. A537
OHSU HOSPITAL, PORTLAND, OR, p. A579
OJAI VALLEY COMMUNITY HOSPITAL, OJAI, CA, p. A82
OKANOGAN DOUGLAS DISTRICT HOSPITAL, BREWSTER, WA, p. A756
OKC-AMG SPECIALTY HOSPITAL, OKLAHOMA CITY, OK, p. A565
OKEENE MUNICIPAL HOSPITAL, OKEENE, OK, p. A563
OKLAHOMA CENTER FOR ORTHOPEDIC AND MULTI-SPECIALTY SURGERY, OKLAHOMA CITY, OK, p. A565
OKLAHOMA CITY VETERANS AFFAIRS MEDICAL CENTER, OKLAHOMA CITY, OK, p. A565
OKLAHOMA CTR FOR ORTHOPAEDIC, OKLAHOMA CITY, OK, p. A565
OKLAHOMA FORENSIC CENTER, VINITA, OK, p. A571
OKLAHOMA HEART HOSPITAL, OKLAHOMA CITY, OK, p. A565
OKLAHOMA HEART HOSPITAL SOUTH CAMPUS, OKLAHOMA CITY, OK, p. A565
OKLAHOMA SPINE HOSPITAL, OKLAHOMA CITY, OK, p. A565
OKLAHOMA STATE UNIVERSITY MEDICAL CENTER, TULSA, OK, p. A570
OKLAHOMA SURGICAL HOSPITAL, TULSA, OK, p. A570
OKMULGEE MEMORIAL HOSPITAL, OKMULGEE, OK, p. A566
OKTIBBEHA COUNTY HOSPITAL, STARKVILLE, MS, p. A400
OLATHE MEDICAL CENTER, OLATHE, KS, p. A272
OLD VINEYARD BEHAVIORAL HEALTH SERVICES, WINSTON, NC, p. A520
OLD VINEYARD YOUTH SERVICES, WINSTON, NC, p. A520
OLEAN GENERAL HOSPITAL, OLEAN, NY, p. A494
OLIVE VIEW-UCLA MEDICAL CTR, SYLMAR, CA, p. A100
OLIVER ANDERSON HOSPITAL, MARYVILLE, IL, p. A211
OLMSTED COMMUNITY HOSPITAL, ROCHESTER, MN, p. A384
OLMSTED MEDICAL CENTER, ROCHESTER, MN, p. A384
OLYMPIA MEDICAL CENTER, LOS ANGELES, CA, p. A75
OLYMPIC MEDICAL CENTER, PORT ANGELES, WA, p. A762
OLYMPIC MEMORIAL HOSPITAL, PORT ANGELES, WA, p. A762
OMEGA HOSPITAL, METAIRIE, LA, p. A308
OMEGA INST OF HEALTH & HOSP, METAIRIE, LA, p. A308
ONECORE HEALTH, OKLAHOMA CITY, OK, p. A565
ONEIDA COUNTY HOSPITAL, MALAD CITY, ID, p. A191
ONEIDA HEALTHCARE, ONEIDA, NY, p. A494
ONEIDA HEALTHCARE CENTER, ONEIDA, NY, p. A494
ONSLOW MEMORIAL HOSPITAL, JACKSONVILLE, NC, p. A513
ONTARIO MEDICAL CENTER, ONTARIO, CA, p. A82
OPELOUSAS GENERAL HEALTH STSTEM-SOUTH CAMPUS, OPELOUSAS, LA, p. A312
OPELOUSAS GENERAL HEALTH SYSTEM, OPELOUSAS, LA, p. A312
OPELOUSAS GENERAL HOSPITAL, OPELOUSAS, LA, p. A312
OPTIM MEDICAL CENTER—JENKINS, MILLEN, GA, p. A177
OPTIM MEDICAL CENTER—SCREVEN, SYLVANIA, GA, p. A181
OPTIM MEDICAL CENTER—TATTNALL, REIDSVILLE, GA, p. A178
OPTIONS BEHAVIORAL HEALTH SYSTEM, INDIANAPOLIS, IN, p. A232
ORANGE CITY AREA HEALTH SYSTEM, ORANGE CITY, IA, p. A255
ORANGE CITY HEALTH SYSTEM, ORANGE CITY, IA, p. A255

ORANGE COAST MEMORIAL MEDICAL CENTER, FOUNTAIN VALLEY, CA, p. A64
ORANGE COUNTY GLOBAL MEDICAL CENTER, INC., SANTA ANA, CA, p. A96
ORANGE COUNTY IRVINE MEDICAL CENTER, IRVINE, CA, p. A69
ORANGE PARK MEDICAL CENTER, ORANGE PARK, FL, p. A150
ORANGE REGIONAL MEDICAL CENTER, MIDDLETOWN, NY, p. A488
ORCHARD HOSPITAL, GRIDLEY, CA, p. A67
ORCHARD PARK NURSING HOME, ORCHARD PARK, NY, p. A494
OREGON HLTH SCIENCES UNIV HOSP, PORTLAND, OR, p. A579
OREGON STATE HOSPITAL, SALEM, OR, p. A581
OREM COMMUNITY HOSPITAL, OREM, UT, p. A730
ORLANDO REGIONAL MEDICAL CENTER, ORLANDO, FL, p. A151
ORLANDO REGIONAL MEDICAL CNTR, ORLANDO, FL, p. A151
ORLANDO REGIONAL SOUTH SEMINOLE HOSPITAL, LONGWOOD, FL, p. A144
ORLANDO VA MEDICAL CENTER, ORLANDO, FL, p. A151
ORLEANS COMMUNITY HEALTH, MEDINA, NY, p. A488
ORO VALLEY HOSPITAL, ORO VALLEY, AZ, p. A34
OROVILLE HOSPITAL, OROVILLE, CA, p. A83
ORTHOCOLORADO HOSPITAL, LAKEWOOD, CO, p. A115
ORTHOINDY HOSPITAL, INDIANAPOLIS, IN, p. A232
ORTHONEBRASKA HOSPITAL, OMAHA, NE, p. A437
ORTHOPAEDIC HOSPITAL AT PARKVIEW NORTH, FORT WAYNE, IN, p. A228
ORTHOPAEDIC HOSPITAL OF LUTHERAN HEALTH, FORT WAYNE, IN, p. A228
ORTHOPAEDIC HOSPITAL OF LUTHERAN HEALTH NETWORK, FORT WAYNE, IN, p. A228
ORTHOPAEDIC HOSPITAL OF WISCONSIN—GLENDALE, GLENDALE, WI, p. A784
ORTHOPAEDIC HOSPITAL OF WISCONSIN, GLENDALE, WI, p. A784
ORTHOPEDIC HOSPITAL, OKLAHOMA CITY, OK, p. A565
ORTHOPEDIC SPECIALTY HOSPITAL OF NEVADA, LAS VEGAS, NV, p. A443
ORTHOPEDIC SURGICAL HOSPITAL, TULSA, OK, p. A570
ORTONVILLE AREA HEALTH SERVICES, ORTONVILLE, MN, p. A382
OSAGE BEACH CENTER FOR COGNITIVE DISORDERS, OSAGE BEACH, MO, p. A413
OSAWATOMIE STATE HOSPITAL, OSAWATOMIE, KS, p. A273
OSAWATOMIE STATE HOSPITAL AT ADAIR ACUTE CARE, OSAWATOMIE, KS, p. A273
OSBORNE COUNTY MEMORIAL HOSPITAL, OSBORNE, KS, p. A273
OSCAR G. JOHNSON VETERANS AFFAIRS MEDICAL CENTER, IRON MOUNTAIN, MI, p. A358
OSCEOLA COMMUNITY HOSPITAL DBA OSCEOLA REGIONAL HEALTH CENTER, SIBLEY, IA, p. A257
OSCEOLA MEDICAL CENTER, KISSIMMEE, FL, p. A142
OSCEOLA MEDICAL CENTER, OSCEOLA, WI, p. A793
OSCEOLA REGIONAL HEALTH CENTER, SIBLEY, IA, p. A257
OSCEOLA REGIONAL MEDICAL CENTER, KISSIMMEE, FL, p. A142
OSF HEALTHCARE LITTLE COMPANY OF MARY MEDICAL, EVERGREEN PARK, IL, p. A204
OSF HEALTHCARE LITTLE COMPANY OF MARY MEDICAL CENTER, EVERGREEN PARK, IL, p. A204
OSF HEALTHCARE SAINT ANTHONY'S HEALTH CENTER, ALTON, IL, p. A194
OSF HEART OF MARY MEDICAL CENTER, URBANA, IL, p. A222
OSF HOLY FAMILY MEDICAL CENTER, MONMOUTH, IL, p. A212
OSF SACRED HEART MEDICAL CENTER, DANVILLE, IL, p. A202
OSF SACRED HEART MEDICAL CENTER, URBANA, IL, p. A222
OSF SAINT ANTHONY MEDICAL CENTER, ROCKFORD, IL, p. A219
OSF SAINT ANTHONY'S HEALTH CENTER, ALTON, IL, p. A194
OSF SAINT CLARE'S HOSPITAL, ALTON, IL, p. A194
OSF SAINT ELIZABETH MEDICAL CENTER, OTTAWA, IL, p. A216
OSF SAINT FRANCIS MEDICAL CENTER, PEORIA, IL, p. A217
OSF SAINT JAMES—JOHN W. ALBRECHT MEDICAL CENTER, PONTIAC, IL, p. A217
OSF SAINT JAMES HOSPITAL, PONTIAC, IL, p. A217
OSF SAINT LUKE MEDICAL CENTER, KEWANEE, IL, p. A209
OSF SAINT PAUL MEDICAL CENTER, MENDOTA, IL, p. A212
OSF ST. FRANCIS HOSPITAL AND MEDICAL, ESCANABA, MI, p. A354
OSF ST. FRANCIS HOSPITAL AND MEDICAL GROUP, ESCANABA, MI, p. A354

OSF ST. JOSEPH MEDICAL CENTER, BLOOMINGTON, IL, p. A195
OSF ST. MARY MEDICAL CENTER, GALESBURG, IL, p. A205
OSMOND GENERAL HOSPITAL, OSMOND, NE, p. A438
OSS HEALTH, YORK, PA, p. A612
OSS ORTHOPAEDIC SPECIALTY HOSPITAL, YORK, PA, p. A612
OSSINING CORRECTIONAL FACILITIES HOSPITAL, OSSINING, NY, p. A494
OSU JAMES CANCER HOSPITAL, COLUMBUS, OH, p. A537
OSWEGO HOSPITAL, OSWEGO, NY, p. A494
OTHELLO COMMUNITY HOSPITAL, OTHELLO, WA, p. A761
OTIS R. BOWEN CENTER FOR HUMAN SERVICES, WARSAW, IN, p. A242
OTSEGO MEMORIAL HOSPITAL, GAYLORD, MI, p. A355
OTTAWA COUNTY HEALTH CENTER, MINNEAPOLIS, KS, p. A271
OTTAWA COUNTY HOSPITAL, MINNEAPOLIS, KS, p. A271
OTTAWA REGIONAL HOSPITAL AND HEALTHCARE CENTER, OTTAWA, IL, p. A216
OTTO KAISER MEMORIAL HOSPITAL, KENEDY, TX, p. A692
OTTUMWA REGIONAL HEALTH CENTER, OTTUMWA, IA, p. A256
OU MED CTR, OKLAHOMA CITY, OK, p. A565
OU MEDICAL CENTER, OKLAHOMA CITY, OK, p. A565
OU MEDICAL CENTER EDMOND, EDMOND, OK, p. A558
OUACHITA COMMUNITY HOSPITAL, WEST MONROE, LA, p. A316
OUACHITA COUNTY MEDICAL CENTER, CAMDEN, AR, p. A43
OUACHITA MEDICAL CENTER, CAMDEN, AR, p. A43
OUR CHILDREN'S HOUSE, DALLAS, TX, p. A670
OUR CHILDREN'S HOUSE AT BAYLOR, DALLAS, TX, p. A670
OUR LADY OF ANGELS HOSPITAL, BOGALUSA, LA, p. A298
OUR LADY OF LOURDES HEALTH CTR, PASCO, WA, p. A762
OUR LADY OF LOURDES MED CENTER, LAFAYETTE, LA, p. A305
OUR LADY OF LOURDES MEDICAL CENTER, CAMDEN, NJ, p. A453
OUR LADY OF LOURDES MEMORIAL HOSPITAL, BINGHAMTON, NY, p. A476
OUR LADY OF LOURDES MEMORIAL HOSPITAL, INC., BINGHAMTON, NY, p. A476
OUR LADY OF LOURDES REGIONAL MEDICAL CENTER, LAFAYETTE, LA, p. A306
OUR LADY OF MERCY MED CENTER, BRONX, NY, p. A477
OUR LADY OF THE ANGELS HOSPITAL, BOGALUSA, LA, p. A298
OUR LADY OF THE LAKE, NAPOLEONVILLE, LA, p. A309
OUR LADY OF THE LAKE REGIONAL MEDICAL CENTER, BATON ROUGE, LA, p. A297
OVERLAKE HOSPITAL MEDICAL CENTER, BELLEVUE, WA, p. A755
OVERLAKE MEDICAL CENTER, BELLEVUE, WA, p. A755
OVERLAND PARK REGIONAL MEDICAL CENTER, OVERLAND PARK, KS, p. A274
OVERLOOK HOSPITAL, SUMMIT, NJ, p. A463
OVERLOOK MEDICAL CENTER, SUMMIT, NJ, p. A463
OVERTON BROOKS VETERANS AFFAIRS MEDICAL CENTER, SHREVEPORT, LA, p. A314
OVIEDO MEDICAL CENTER, OVIEDO, FL, p. A152
OWATONNA HOSPITAL, OWATONNA, MN, p. A382
OWENSBORO HEALTH MUHLENBERG COMMUNITY HOSPITAL, GREENVILLE, KY, p. A284
OWENSBORO HEALTH REGIONAL HOSPITAL, OWENSBORO, KY, p. A291
OWENSBORO MEDICAL HEALTH SYSTEM, OWENSBORO, KY, p. A291
OZARK HEALTH MEDICAL CENTER, CLINTON, AR, p. A43
OZARKS COMMUNITY HOSPITAL, GRAVETTE, AR, p. A46
OZARKS MEDICAL CENTER, WEST PLAINS, MO, p. A420

## P

PACIFIC GROVE HOSPITAL, RIVERSIDE, CA, p. A88
PACIFIC HOSPITAL OF LONG BEACH, LONG BEACH, CA, p. A72
PACIFICA HOSPITAL OF THE VALLEY, SUN VALLEY, CA, p. A100
PADRE BEHAVIORAL HOSPITAL, CORPUS CHRISTI, TX, p. A666
PAGE HOSPITAL, PAGE, AZ, p. A34
PAGE MEMORIAL HOSPITAL, LURAY, VA, p. A745
PAGOSA MOUNTAIN HOSPITAL, PAGOSA SPRINGS, CO, p. A117
PAGOSA SPRINGS MEDICAL CENTER, PAGOSA SPRINGS, CO, p. A117

PALACIOS COMMUNITY MEDICAL CENTER, PALACIOS, TX, p. A704
PALESTINE REGIONAL MEDICAL CENTER-EAST, PALESTINE, TX, p. A704
PALESTINE REGIONAL REHABILITATION CENTER, PALESTINE, TX, p. A704
PALI MOMI MEDICAL CENTER, AIEA, HI, p. A184
PALM BAY HOSPITAL, PALM BAY, FL, p. A152
PALM BEACH GARDENS MEDICAL CENTER, PALM BEACH GARDENS, FL, p. A152
PALM DRIVE HOSPITAL, SEBASTOPOL, CA, p. A98
PALM POINT BEHAVIORAL HEALTH, TITUSVILLE, FL, p. A160
PALMDALE REGIONAL MEDICAL CENTER, PALMDALE, CA, p. A84
PALMER LUTHERAN HEALTH CENTER, WEST UNION, IA, p. A260
PALMETTO GENERAL HOSPITAL, HIALEAH, FL, p. A139
PALMETTO HEALTH BAPTIST PARKRIDGE, COLUMBIA, SC, p. A617
PALMETTO HEALTH CHILDREN'S HOSPITAL, COLUMBIA, SC, p. A617
PALMETTO HEALTH RICHLAND, COLUMBIA, SC, p. A617
PALMETTO HEALTH TUOMEY, SUMTER, SC, p. A624
PALMETTO LOWCOUNTRY BEHAVIORAL HEALTH, CHARLESTON, SC, p. A616
PALMS OF PASADENA HOSPITAL, SAINT PETERSBURG, FL, p. A156
PALMS WEST HOSPITAL, LOXAHATCHEE, FL, p. A144
PALMYRA MEDICAL CENTERS, ALBANY, GA, p. A163
PALO ALTO COUNTY HEALTH SYSTEM, EMMETSBURG, IA, p. A249
PALO ALTO COUNTY HOSPITAL, EMMETSBURG, IA, p. A249
PALO PINTO GENERAL HOSPITAL, MINERAL WELLS, TX, p. A701
PALO VERDE BEHAVIORAL HEALTH, TUCSON, AZ, p. A40
PALO VERDE HOSPITAL, BLYTHE, CA, p. A58
PALO VERDE MENTAL HEALTH SERVICES, TUCSON, AZ, p. A40
PALOMAR MEDICAL CENTER, ESCONDIDO, CA, p. A63
PALOMAR MEDICAL CENTER ESCONDIDO, ESCONDIDO, CA, p. A63
PALOMAR MEDICAL CENTER POWAY, POWAY, CA, p. A86
PALOS COMMUNITY HOSPITAL, PALOS HEIGHTS, IL, p. A216
PALOS HEALTH, PALOS HEIGHTS, IL, p. A216
PAM REHABILITATION HOSPITAL OF ALLEN, ALLEN, TX, p. A651
PAM REHABILITATION HOSPITAL OF BEAUMONT, BEAUMONT, TX, p. A658
PAM REHABILITATION HOSPITAL OF CENTENNIAL HILLS, LAS VEGAS, NV, p. A444
PAM REHABILITATION HOSPITAL OF CLEAR LAKE, WEBSTER, TX, p. A724
PAM REHABILITATION HOSPITAL OF CORPUS CHRISTI, CORPUS CHRISTI, TX, p. A666
PAM REHABILITATION HOSPITAL OF DOVER, DOVER, DE, p. A127
PAM REHABILITATION HOSPITAL OF HUMBLE, HUMBLE, TX, p. A690
PAM REHABILITATION HOSPITAL OF ROUND ROCK, ROUND ROCK, TX, p. A709
PAM REHABILITATION HOSPITAL OF TULSA, TULSA, OK, p. A570
PAM REHABILITATION HOSPITAL OF VICTORIA, VICTORIA, TX, p. A723
PAM SPECIALTY HOSPITAL OF COVINGTON, COVINGTON, LA, p. A300
PAM SPECIALTY HOSPITAL OF DAYTON, MIAMISBURG, OH, p. A545
PAM SPECIALTY HOSPITAL OF DENVER, DENVER, CO, p. A110
PAM SPECIALTY HOSPITAL OF HAMMOND, HAMMOND, LA, p. A302
PAM SPECIALTY HOSPITAL OF LAS VEGAS, LAS VEGAS, NV, p. A444
PAM SPECIALTY HOSPITAL OF LUFKIN, LUFKIN, TX, p. A698
PAM SPECIALTY HOSPITAL OF LULING, LULING, TX, p. A699
PAM SPECIALTY HOSPITAL OF NEW BRAUNFELS, NEW BRAUNFELS, TX, p. A703
PAM SPECIALTY HOSPITAL OF ROCKY MOUNT, ROCKY MOUNT, NC, p. A517
PAM SPECIALTY HOSPITAL OF SAN ANTONIO CENTER, SAN ANTONIO, TX, p. A712
PAM SPECIALTY HOSPITAL OF SARASOTA, SARASOTA, FL, p. A157
PAM SPECIALTY HOSPITAL OF SHREVEPORT SOUTH, SHREVEPORT, LA, p. A314
PAM SPECIALTY HOSPITAL OF SPARKS, SPARKS, NV, p. A447
PAM SPECIALTY HOSPITAL OF VICTORIA NORTH, VICTORIA, TX, p. A723

PAM SPECIALTY HOSPITAL OF VICTORIA SOUTH, VICTORIA, TX, p. A723
PAM SPECIALTY HOSPITAL OF WILKES-BARRE, WILKES BARRE, PA, p. A611
PAMPA REGIONAL MEDICAL CENTER, PAMPA, TX, p. A704
PANA COMMUNITY HOSPITAL, PANA, IL, p. A216
PANOLA MEDICAL CENTER, BATESVILLE, MS, p. A389
PANORAMA CITY MEDICAL CENTER, PANORAMA CITY, CA, p. A84
PAOLI HOSPITAL, PAOLI, PA, p. A599
PAOLI MEMORIAL HOSPITAL, PAOLI, PA, p. A599
PAPPAS REHABILITATION HOSPITAL FOR CHILDREN, CANTON, MA, p. A338
PARADISE VALLEY HOSPITAL, NATIONAL CITY, CA, p. A81
PARIS COMMUNITY HOSPITAL, PARIS, IL, p. A216
PARIS REGIONAL MEDICAL CENTER, PARIS, TX, p. A704
PARK CITY HOSPITAL, PARK CITY, UT, p. A730
PARK CITY MEDICAL CENTER, PARK CITY, UT, p. A730
PARK MEDICAL CENTER, COLUMBUS, OH, p. A537
PARK NICOLLET METHODIST HOSPITAL, SAINT LOUIS PARK, MN, p. A385
PARK PLACE SURGERY CENTER, LAFAYETTE, LA, p. A306
PARK PLACE SURGICAL HOSPITAL, LAFAYETTE, LA, p. A306
PARK PLAZA HOSPITAL, HOUSTON, TX, p. A688
PARK RIDGE HEALTH, HENDERSONVILLE, NC, p. A512
PARK ROYAL HOSPITAL, FORT MYERS, FL, p. A138
PARKER ADVENTIST HOSPITAL, PARKER, CO, p. A117
PARKER COMMUNITY HOSPITAL, PARKER, AZ, p. A34
PARKLAND HEALTH & HOSPITAL SYSTEM, DALLAS, TX, p. A670
PARKLAND HEALTH CENTER—FARMINGTON COMMUNITY, FARMINGTON, MO, p. A406
PARKLAND HEALTH CENTER—LIBERTY STREET, FARMINGTON, MO, p. A406
PARKLAND HEALTH CENTER-BONNE TERRE, BONNE TERRE, MO, p. A402
PARKLAND HLYH CTR-BOONE TERRE, BONNE TERRE, MO, p. A402
PARKLAND MEDICAL CENTER, DERRY, NH, p. A448
PARKRIDGE MEDICAL CENTER, CHATTANOOGA, TN, p. A636
PARKRIDGE VALLEY HOSPTIAL, CHATTANOOGA, TN, p. A636
PARKSIDE HOSPITAL, TULSA, OK, p. A570
PARKSIDE PSYCHIATRIC HOSPITAL AND CLINIC, TULSA, OK, p. A570
PARKVIEW COMM HOSP & MED CTR, RIVERSIDE, CA, p. A88
PARKVIEW COMMUNITY HOSPITAL MEDICAL CENTER, RIVERSIDE, CA, p. A88
PARKVIEW DEKALB HOSPITAL, AUBURN, IN, p. A223
PARKVIEW EPISCOPAL MED CENTER, PUEBLO, CO, p. A117
PARKVIEW HOSPITAL, FORT WAYNE, IN, p. A228
PARKVIEW HOSPITAL, WHEELER, TX, p. A725
PARKVIEW HUNTINGTON HOSPITAL, HUNTINGTON, IN, p. A230
PARKVIEW LAGRANGE HOSPITAL, LAGRANGE, IN, p. A235
PARKVIEW MEDICAL CENTER, PUEBLO, CO, p. A118
PARKVIEW NOBLE HOSPITAL, KENDALLVILLE, IN, p. A233
PARKVIEW NORTH HOSPITAL, FORT WAYNE, IN, p. A228
PARKVIEW ORTHO HOSPITAL, FORT WAYNE, IN, p. A228
PARKVIEW REGIONAL HOSPITAL, MEXIA, TX, p. A701
PARKVIEW REGIONAL MEDICAL CENTER, FORT WAYNE, IN, p. A228
PARKVIEW WABASH COUNTY HOSPITAL, WABASH, IN, p. A242
PARKVIEW WABASH HOSPITAL, WABASH, IN, p. A242
PARKVIEW WHITLEY HOSPITAL, COLUMBIA CITY, IN, p. A225
PARKWAY REGIONAL MED CENTER, NORTH MIAMI BEACH, FL, p. A149
PARKWAY SURGICAL & CARDIOVASCULAR HOSPITAL, FORT WORTH, TX, p. A679
PARKWEST MED CTR, KNOXVILLE, TN, p. A641
PARKWEST MEDICAL CENTER, KNOXVILLE, TN, p. A641
PARKWOOD BEHAVIORAL HEALTH SYSTEM, OLIVE BRANCH, MS, p. A398
PARMA COMMUNITY GENERAL HOSPITAL, PARMA, OH, p. A547
PARMER COUNTY COMMUNITY HOSPITAL, FRIONA, TX, p. A679
PARMER MEDICAL CENTER, FRIONA, TX, p. A680
PARRISH MEDICAL CENTER, TITUSVILLE, FL, p. A160
PARSONS STATE HOSP & TRNG CNTR, PARSONS, KS, p. A274
PARSONS STATE HOSPITAL AND TRAINING CENTER, PARSONS, KS, p. A274
PASCACK VALLEY MEDICAL CENTER, WESTWOOD, NJ, p. A466
PASSAVANT AREA HOSPITAL, JACKSONVILLE, IL, p. A209
PATEWOOD HOSPITAL, GREENVILLE, SC, p. A620
PATHWAY REHABILITATION HOSPITAL, BOSSIER CITY, LA, p. A298
PATHWAY REHABILITATION HOSPITAL OF BOSSIER, BOSSIER CITY, LA, p. A298

PATHWAYS, JACKSON, TN, p. A639
PATHWAYS OF TENNESSEE, JACKSON, TN, p. A639
PATIENTS CHOICE MEDICAL CENTER OF SMITH COUNTY, RALEIGH, MS, p. A399
PATIENTS' CHOICE MEDICAL CENTER OF ERIN, ERIN, TN, p. A638
PATIENTS' HOSPITAL OF REDDING, REDDING, CA, p. A87
PATIENT'S CHOICE MEDICAL CENTER OF CLAIBORNE COUNTY, PORT GIBSON, MS, p. A399
PATRICK B. HARRIS PSYCHIATRIC HOSPITAL, ANDERSON, SC, p. A615
PATTERSON HOSPITAL, CUTHBERT, GA, p. A170
PATTIE A. CLAY REGIONAL MEDICAL CENTER, RICHMOND, KY, p. A292
PATTON STATE HOSPITAL, PATTON, CA, p. A85
PAUL B. HALL REGIONAL MEDICAL CENTER, PAINTSVILLE, KY, p. A292
PAUL OLIVER MEMORIAL HOSPITAL, FRANKFORT, MI, p. A355
PAULDING COUNTY HOSPITAL, PAULDING, OH, p. A547
PAULINE WARFIELD LEWIS CENTER, CINCINNATI, OH, p. A533
PAWHUSKA HOSPITAL, PAWHUSKA, OK, p. A566
PAWNEE COUNTY MEMORIAL HOSPITAL, PAWNEE CITY, NE, p. A438
PAWNEE COUNTY MEMORIAL HOSPITAL AND RURAL HEALTH CLINIC, PAWNEE CITY, NE, p. A438
PAWNEE VALLEY COMMUNITY HOSPITAL, LARNED, KS, p. A268
PAYNE WHITNEY PSYCHIATRIC CLINIC, NEW YORK, NY, p. A492
PAYNESVILLE AREA HEALTH CARE SYSTEM, PAYNESVILLE, MN, p. A383
PAYSON REGIONAL MEDICAL CENTER, PAYSON, AZ, p. A34
PEACE HARBOR HOSPITAL, FLORENCE, OR, p. A575
PEACE RIVER REGIONAL MEDICAL CENTER, PORT CHARLOTTE, FL, p. A155
PEACEHEALTH COTTAGE GROVE COMMUNITY MEDICAL CENTER, COTTAGE GROVE, OR, p. A574
PEACEHEALTH KETCHIKAN MEDICAL CENTER, KETCHIKAN, AK, p. A28
PEACEHEALTH PEACE HARBOR MEDICAL CENTER, FLORENCE, OR, p. A575
PEACEHEALTH PEACE ISLAND MEDICAL CENTER, FRIDAY HARBOR, WA, p. A758
PEACEHEALTH SACRED HEART MEDICAL CENTER AT RIVERBEND, SPRINGFIELD, OR, p. A581
PEACEHEALTH SACRED HEART MEDICAL CENTER UNIVERSITY DISTRICT, EUGENE, OR, p. A575
PEACEHEALTH SACRED HEART MEDICAL CENTER, UNIVERSITY DISTRICT, EUGENE, OR, p. A575
PEACEHEALTH SOUTHWEST MEDICAL CENTER, VANCOUVER, WA, p. A768
PEACEHEALTH ST. JOHN MEDICAL CENTER, LONGVIEW, WA, p. A760
PEACEHEALTH ST. JOSEPH HOSPITAL, BELLINGHAM, WA, p. A755
PEACEHEALTH ST. JOSEPH MEDICAL CENTER, BELLINGHAM, WA, p. A755
PEACEHEALTH UNITED GENERAL MEDICAL CENTER, SEDRO, WA, p. A765
PEACEHEALTH UNITED MEDICAL CENTER, SEDRO, WA, p. A765
PEACH REGIONAL MEDICAL CENTER, BRYON, GA, p. A167
PEACHFORD BEHAVIORAL HEALTH SYSTEM, ATLANTA, GA, p. A165
PEAK BEHAVIORAL HEALTH SERVICES, SANTA TERESA, NM, p. A472
PEAK PSYCHIACTRIC HOSPITAL, SANTA TERESA, NM, p. A472
PEAK VIEW BEHAVIORAL HEALTH, COLORADO SPRINGS, CO, p. A109
PEARL RIVER COUNTY HOSPITAL, POPLARVILLE, MS, p. A399
PEARLAND MEDICAL CENTER, PEARLAND, TX, p. A705
PECONIC BAY MEDICAL CENTER, RIVERHEAD, NY, p. A496
PECOS COUNTY GENERAL HOSPITAL, IRAAN, TX, p. A690
PECOS COUNTY MEMORIAL HOSPITAL, FORT STOCKTON, TX, p. A677
PELHAM MEDICAL CENTER, GREER, SC, p. A621
PELLA COMMUNITY HOSPITAL, PELLA, IA, p. A256
PELLA REGIONAL HEALTH CENTER, PELLA, IA, p. A256
PEMBINA COUNTY MEMORIAL HOSPITAL AND WEDGEWOOD MANOR, CAVALIER, ND, p. A522
PEMBROKE HOSPITAL, PEMBROKE, MA, p. A343
PEMBROKE PINES HOSPITAL, PEMBROKE PINES, FL, p. A153
PEMISCOT MEMORIAL HEALTH SYSTEM, HAYTI, MO, p. A407
PEMISCOT MEMORIAL HLTH SYSTEMS, HAYTI, MO, p. A407
PEN BAY MEDICAL CENTER, ROCKPORT, ME, p. A322
PENDER COMMUNITY HOSPITAL, PENDER, NE, p. A439
PENDER MEMORIAL HOSPITAL, BURGAW, NC, p. A505

PENINSULA BEHAVIORAL CENTER, HAMPTON, VA, p. A743
PENINSULA HOSPITAL, BURLINGAME, CA, p. A59
PENINSULA REGIONAL HEALTH SYSTEM, SALISBURY, MD, p. A332
PENN HIGHLANDS BROOKVILLE, BROOKVILLE, PA, p. A585
PENN HIGHLANDS CLEARFIELD, CLEARFIELD, PA, p. A586
PENN HIGHLANDS DUBOIS, DUBOIS, PA, p. A588
PENN HIGHLANDS ELK, SAINT MARYS, PA, p. A606
PENN HIGHLANDS HUNTINGDON, HUNTINGDON, PA, p. A592
PENN MEDICINE LANCASTER GENERAL HOSPITAL, LANCASTER, PA, p. A594
PENN MEDICINE PRINCETON MEDICAL CENTER, PLAINSBORO, NJ, p. A461
PENN PRESBYTERIAN MEDICAL CENTER, PHILADELPHIA, PA, p. A601
PENN STATE GEISINGER WYOMING, WILKES BARRE, PA, p. A611
PENN STATE HEALTH ST. JOSEPH, READING, PA, p. A606
PENN STATE HERSEY REHAB, HUMMELSTOWN, PA, p. A592
PENN STATE HERSHEY REHABILITATION HOSPITAL, HUMMELSTOWN, PA, p. A592
PENN STATE MILTON S. HERSHEY MEDICAL CENTER, HERSHEY, PA, p. A592
PENNOCK HEALTH SERVICES, HASTINGS, MI, p. A357
PENNSYLVANIA HOSPITAL, PHILADELPHIA, PA, p. A601
PENNSYLVANIA PSYCHIATRIC HOSPITAL, HARRISBURG, PA, p. A591
PENNSYLVANIA PSYCHIATRIC INSTITUTE, HARRISBURG, PA, p. A591
PENOBSCOT BAY MEDICAL CENTER, ROCKPORT, ME, p. A322
PENOBSCOT VALLEY HOSPITAL, LINCOLN, ME, p. A321
PENROSE HOSPITALS, COLORADO SPRINGS, CO, p. A109
PENROSE-ST FRANCIS HLTH SYSTEM, COLORADO SPRINGS, CO, p. A109
PENROSE-ST. FRANCIS HEALTH SERVICES, COLORADO SPRINGS, CO, p. A109
PEOPLE'S MEMORIAL HOSPITAL, INDEPENDENCE, IA, p. A251
PERHAM HEALTH, PERHAM, MN, p. A383
PERHAM MEMORIAL HOSPITAL AND HOME, PERHAM, MN, p. A383
PERIMETER BEHAVIORAL HOSPITAL OF ARLINGTON, ARLINGTON, TX, p. A653
PERIMETER BEHAVIORAL HOSPITAL OF DALLAS, GARLAND, TX, p. A681
PERIMETER BEHAVIORAL HOSPITAL OF JACKSON, JACKSON, TN, p. A639
PERIMETER BEHAVIORAL HOSPITAL OF NEW ORLEANS, KENNER, LA, p. A304
PERIMETER BEHAVIORAL HOSPITAL OF SPRINGFIELD, SPRINGFIELD, MO, p. A419
PERIMETER BEHAVIORAL HOSPITAL OF WEST MEMPHIS, WEST MEMPHIS, AR, p. A54
PERIMETER BEHAVIORAL HOSPTIAL OF SPRINGFIELD, SPRINGFIELD, MO, p. A419
PERKINS COUNTY COMM HOSPITAL, GRANT, NE, p. A433
PERKINS COUNTY HEALTH SERVICES, GRANT, NE, p. A433
PERMIAN GENERAL HOSPITAL, ANDREWS, TX, p. A653
PERMIAN REGIONAL MEDICAL CENTER, ANDREWS, TX, p. A653
PERRY COMMUNITY HOSPITAL, LINDEN, TN, p. A642
PERRY COUNTY GENERAL HOSPITAL, RICHTON, MS, p. A399
PERRY COUNTY MEMORIAL HOSPITAL, PERRYVILLE, MO, p. A413
PERRY COUNTY MEMORIAL HOSPITAL, TELL CITY, IN, p. A241
PERRY HOSPITAL, PERRY, GA, p. A178
PERRY MEMORIAL HOSPITAL, PERRY, OK, p. A566
PERRY MEMORIAL HOSPITAL, PRINCETON, IL, p. A218
PERSHING GENERAL HOSPITAL, LOVELOCK, NV, p. A445
PERSHING MEMORIAL HOSPITAL, BROOKFIELD, MO, p. A403
PERSON COUNTY MEM HOSPITAL, ROXBORO, NC, p. A517
PERSON MEMORIAL HOSPITAL, ROXBORO, NC, p. A517
PETALUMA VALLEY HOSPITAL, PETALUMA, CA, p. A85
PETERSBURG GENERAL MED CTR, PETERSBURG, AK, p. A29
PETERSBURG MEDICAL CENTER, PETERSBURG, AK, p. A29
PETERSON HEALTH, KERRVILLE, TX, p. A693
PETERSON HEALTHCARE AND REHABILITATION HOSPITAL, WHEELING, WV, p. A778
PETERSON REGIONAL MEDICAL CENTER, KERRVILLE, TX, p. A693
PETERSON REHABILITATION HOSPITAL, WHEELING, WV, p. A778
PHELPS COUNTY REGIONAL MEDICAL CENTER, ROLLA, MO, p. A414
PHELPS HEALTH, ROLLA, MO, p. A414
PHELPS MEMORIAL HEALTH CENTER, HOLDREGE, NE, p. A433

PHELPS MEMORIAL HOSPITAL CENTER, SLEEPY HOLLOW, NY, p. A498
PHILADELPHIA VETERANS AFFAIRS MEDICAL CENTER, PHILADELPHIA, PA, p. A601
PHILADEPHIA VETERANS AFFAIRS MEDICAL CENTER, PHILADELPHIA, PA, p. A601
PHILHAVEN, MOUNT GRETNA, PA, p. A597
PHILIP HEALTH SERVICES, PHILIP, SD, p. A630
PHILLIPS COUNTY HEALTH SYSTEMS, PHILLIPSBURG, KS, p. A274
PHILLIPS COUNTY HOSPITAL, MALTA, MT, A426
PHILLIPS COUNTY HOSPITAL, PHILLIPSBURG, KS, p. A274
PHILLIPS COUNTY MEDICAL CENTER, MALTA, MT, p. A426
PHOEBE PUTNEY MEMORIAL HOSPITAL, ALBANY, GA, p. A163
PHOEBE SUMTER MEDICAL CENTER, AMERICUS, GA, p. A163
PHOEBE WORTH MEDICAL CENTER, SYLVESTER, GA, p. A181
PHOENIX BAPTIST HOSPITAL, PHOENIX, AZ, p. A36
PHOENIX CHILDREN'S HOSPITAL, PHOENIX, AZ, p. A36
PHOENIX VETERANS AFFAIRS HEALTH CARE SYSTEM, PHOENIX, AZ, p. A36
PHOENIXVILLE HOSPITAL, PHOENIXVILLE, PA, p. A602
PHS ALASKA NATIVE HOSPITAL, BARROW, AK, p. A27
PHS ALASKA NATIVE MED CENTER, ANCHORAGE, AK, p. A27
PHS COMP INDIAN HLTH FACILITY, CLAREMORE, OK, p. A557
PHS INDIAN HOSPITAL, LAWTON, OK, p. A561
PHS INDIAN HOSPITAL, MESCALERO, NM, p. A471
PHS INDIAN HOSPITAL, PARKER, AZ, p. A34
PHS INDIAN HOSPITAL, SACATON, AZ, p. A37
PHS INDIAN HOSPITAL, SELLS, AZ, p. A38
PHS SANTA FE INDIAN HOSPITAL, SANTA FE, NM, p. A472
PHS YUKON-KUSKOKWIM DELTA HOSP, BETHEL, AK, p. A27
PHYSICIANS ALLIANCE HOSPITAL OF HOUMA, HOUMA, LA, p. A303
PHYSICIANS BEHAVIORAL HOSPITAL, SHREVEPORT, LA, p. A314
PHYSICIANS CARE SURGICAL HOSPITAL, ROYERSFORD, PA, p. A606
PHYSICIANS CENTRE, BRYAN, TX, p. A661
PHYSICIANS HOSPITAL, OKLAHOMA CITY, OK, p. A565
PHYSICIANS MEDICAL CENTER, HOUMA, LA, p. A303
PHYSICIANS MEDICAL CENTER OF SANTA FE HOSPITAL, SANTA FE, NM, p. A472
PHYSICIANS REGIONAL—PINE RIDGE, NAPLES, FL, p. A149
PHYSICIANS REGIONAL MEDICAL CENTER—PINE RIDGE, NAPLES, FL, p. A149
PHYSICIANS REGIONAL MEDICAL CENTER, NAPLES, FL, p. A149
PHYSICIANS SURG SPEC HOSPITAL, HOUMA, LA, p. A303
PHYSICIANS SURGICAL HOSPITAL—QUAIL CREEK, AMARILLO, TX, p. A652
PHYSICIANS' HOSPITAL IN ANADARKO, ANADARKO, OK, p. A555
PHYSICIANS' MEDICAL CENTER, NEW ALBANY, IN, p. A237
PHYSICIANS' SPECIALTY HOSPITAL, FAYETTEVILLE, AR, p. A45
PIEDMONT ATHENS REGIONAL MEDICAL CENTER, ATHENS, GA, p. A163
PIEDMONT COLUMBUS REGIONAL, COLUMBUS, GA, p. A169
PIEDMONT COLUMBUS REGIONAL MIDTOWN, COLUMBUS, GA, p. A169
PIEDMONT COLUMBUS REGIONAL NORTHSIDE, COLUMBUS, GA, p. A169
PIEDMONT FAYETTE HOSPITAL, FAYETTEVILLE, GA, p. A172
PIEDMONT GERIATRIC HOSPITAL, BURKEVILLE, VA, p. A739
PIEDMONT HEALTHCARE SYSTEM, ROCK HILL, SC, p. A623
PIEDMONT HENRY HOSPITAL, STOCKBRIDGE, GA, p. A181
PIEDMONT HOSPITAL, ATLANTA, GA, p. A165
PIEDMONT MEDICAL CENTER, ROCK HILL, SC, p. A624
PIEDMONT MOUNTAINSIDE HOSP, JASPER, GA, p. A174
PIEDMONT MOUNTAINSIDE HOSPITAL, JASPER, GA, p. A174
PIEDMONT NEWNAN HOSPITAL, NEWNAN, GA, p. A178
PIEDMONT NEWTON HOSPITAL, COVINGTON, GA, p. A170
PIEDMONT ROCKDALE HOSPITAL, CONYERS, GA, p. A170
PIEDMONT WALTON HOSPITAL, MONROE, GA, p. A177
PIGGOTT COMMUNITY HOSPITAL, PIGGOTT, AR, p. A52
PIH HEALTH HOSPITAL—DOWNEY, DOWNEY, CA, p. A62
PIH HEALTH HOSPITAL—WHITTIER, WHITTIER, CA, p. A105
PIH HEALTH HOSPITAL-WHITTIER, WHITTIER, CA, p. A105
PIKE COMMUNITY HOSPITAL, WAVERLY, OH, p. A552
PIKE COUNTY MEMORIAL HOSPITAL, LOUISIANA, MO, p. A411
PIKES PEAK REGIONAL HOSPITAL, WOODLAND PARK, CO, p. A120
PIKEVILLE MEDICAL CENTER, PIKEVILLE, KY, p. A292
PIKEVILLE METHODIST HOSPITAL, PIKEVILLE, KY, p. A292
PILGRIM PSYCHIATRIC CENTER, BRENTWOOD, NY, p. A476

PINCKNEYVILLE COMMUNITY HOSPITAL, PINCKNEYVILLE, IL, p. A217
PINE CREEK MEDICAL CENTER, DALLAS, TX, p. A670
PINE MEDICAL CENTER, SANDSTONE, MN, p. A385
PINE REST CHRISTIAN HLTH, GRAND RAPIDS, MI, p. A356
PINE REST CHRISTIAN MENTAL HEALTH SERVICES, GRAND RAPIDS, MI, p. A356
PINELAKE REGIONAL HOSPITAL, MAYFIELD, KY, p. A290
PINEVILLE COMMUNITY HEALTH CENTER, PINEVILLE, KY, p. A292
PINEWOOD SPRINGS, COLUMBIA, TN, p. A636
PINNACLE HOSPITAL, CROWN POINT, IN, p. A226
PINNACLE POINTE HOSPITAL, LITTLE ROCK, AR, p. A49
PINNACLE REHABILITATION HOSP, OKLAHOMA CITY, OK, p. A565
PINNACLEHEALTH AT COMMUNITY GENERAL OSTEOPATHIC HOSPITAL, HARRISBURG, PA, p. A591
PIONEER COMMUNITY HOSPITAL OF ABERDEEN, ABERDEEN, MS, p. A389
PIONEER COMMUNITY HOSPITAL OF EARLY, BLAKELY, GA, p. A167
PIONEER COMMUNITY HOSPITAL OF STOKES, DANBURY, NC, p. A508
PIONEER MEDICAL CENTER, BIG TIMBER, MT, p. A421
PIONEER MEMORIAL HOSPITAL, HEPPNER, OR, p. A575
PIONEER MEMORIAL HOSPITAL, PRINEVILLE, OR, p. A580
PIONEER MEMORIAL HOSPITAL AND HEALTH SERVICES, VIBORG, SD, p. A632
PIONEER SPECIALTY HOSPITAL, PONTIAC, MI, p. A364
PIONEER VALLEY HOSPITAL, WEST VALLEY CITY, UT, p. A734
PIONEERS HOSP OF RIO BLANCO, MEEKER, CO, p. A117
PIONEERS MEDICAL CENTER, MEEKER, CO, p. A117
PIONEERS MEMORIAL HEALTHCARE DISTRICT, BRAWLEY, CA, p. A58
PIONEERS MEMORIAL HOSPITAL, BRAWLEY, CA, p. A58
PIPESTONE COUNTY MEDICAL CENTER AVERA, PIPESTONE, MN, p. A383
PIPESTONE COUNTY MEDICAL CENTER/AVERA HEALTH, PIPESTONE, MN, p. A383
PITT COUNTY MEMORIAL HOSPITAL, GREENVILLE, NC, p. A511
PLACENTIA LINDA HOSPITAL, PLACENTIA, CA, p. A85
PLACENTIA-LINDA HOSPITAL, PLACENTIA, CA, p. A85
PLAINS MEMORIAL HOSPITAL, DIMMITT, TX, p. A673
PLAINS REGIONAL MEDICAL CENTER, CLOVIS, NM, p. A469
PLAINVIEW HOSPITAL, PLAINVIEW, NY, p. A495
PLAINVILLE RURAL HOSP DIST ONE, PLAINVILLE, KS, p. A274
PLANTATION GENERAL HOSPITAL, PLANTATION, FL, p. A154
PLATEAU MEDICAL CENTER, OAK HILL, WV, p. A775
PLATEAU MEDICAL CENTER INC, OAK HILL, WV, p. A775
PLATTE COUNTY MEMORIAL HOSPITAL, WHEATLAND, WY, p. A804
PLATTE HEALTH CENTER, PLATTE, SD, p. A630
PLATTE HEALTH CENTER AVERA, PLATTE, SD, p. A630
PLATTE VALLEY MEDICAL CENTER, BRIGHTON, CO, p. A108
PLAZA MEDICAL CENTER OF FORT WORTH, FORT WORTH, TX, p. A679
PLAZA SPECIALTY HOSPITAL, HOUSTON, TX, p. A688
PLEASANT VALLEY HOSPITAL, CAMARILLO, CA, p. A59
PLEASANT VALLEY HOSPITAL, POINT PLEASANT, WV, p. A776
PLUMAS DISTRICT HOSPITAL, QUINCY, CA, p. A86
PLYMOUTH MEDICAL CENTER, PLYMOUTH, IN, p. A239
PMH MEDICAL CENTER, PROSSER, WA, p. A762
POCAHONTAS COMMUNITY HOSPITAL, POCAHONTAS, IA, p. A256
POCAHONTAS MEMORIAL HOSPITAL, BUCKEYE, WV, p. A770
POCASSET MENTAL HEALTH CENTER, POCASSET, MA, p. A343
POCONO MEDICAL CENTER, EAST STROUDSBURG, PA, p. A589
POH REGIONAL MEDICAL CENTER, PONTIAC, MI, p. A364
POINCIANA MEDICAL CENTER, KISSIMMEE, FL, p. A142
POINTE COUPEE GENERAL HOSPITAL, NEW ROADS, LA, p. A312
POLK MEDICAL CENTER, CEDARTOWN, GA, p. A168
POMERADO HOSPITAL, POWAY, CA, p. A86
POMERENE HOSPITAL, MILLERSBURG, OH, p. A545
POMERENE MEMORIAL HOSPITAL, MILLERSBURG, OH, p. A545
POMONA VALLEY HOSPITAL MEDICAL CENTER, POMONA, CA, p. A84
PONCA CITY MEDICAL CENTER, PONCA CITY, OK, p. A567
PONCE REGIONAL HOSPITAL, PONCE, PR, p. A809
PONDERA MEDICAL CENTER, CONRAD, MT, p. A422
PONTIAC GENERAL HOSPITAL, PONTIAC, MI, p. A364
POPLAR BLUFF REGIONAL MEDICAL CENTER, POPLAR BLUFF, MO, p. A414
POPLAR COMMUNITY HOSPITAL, POPLAR, MT, p. A427

POPLAR SPRINGS HOSPITAL, PETERSBURG, VA, p. A748
PORT HURON HOSPITAL, PORT HURON, MI, p. A364
PORT SAINT LUCIE HOSPITAL, PORT ST LUCIE, FL, p. A155
PORT ST. LUCIE HOSPITAL, PORT ST LUCIE, FL, p. A155
PORTAGE HEALTH, HANCOCK, MI, p. A357
PORTER ADVENTIST HOSPITAL, DENVER, CO, p. A111
PORTER CARE HOSPITAL, DENVER, CO, p. A111
PORTER CARE HOSPITAL-LITTLETON, LITTLETON, CO, p. A116
PORTER HOSPITAL, MIDDLEBURY, VT, p. A736
PORTER MEDICAL CENTER, MIDDLEBURY, VT, p. A736
PORTER REGIONAL HOSPITAL, VALPARAISO, IN, p. A241
PORTER-STARKE SERVICES, VALPARAISO, IN, p. A241
PORTER-VALPARAISO HOSPITAL CAMPUS, VALPARAISO, IN, p. A241
PORTERCARE HOSPITAL—AVISTA, LOUISVILLE, CO, p. A116
PORTERVILLE DEVELOPMENTAL CENTER, PORTERVILLE, CA, p. A86
PORTNEUF MEDICAL CENTER, POCATELLO, ID, p. A192
PORTSMOUTH REGIONAL HOSP, PORTSMOUTH, NH, p. A451
PORTSMOUTH REGIONAL HOSPITAL, PORTSMOUTH, NH, p. A451
POST ACUTE MEDICAL SPECIALTY HOSPITAL OF CORPUS CHRISTI—NORTH, CORPUS CHRISTI, TX, p. A666
POST ACUTE MEDICAL SPECIALTY HOSPITAL OF CORPUS CHRISTI, CORPUS CHRISTI, TX, p. A666
POST ACUTE MEDICAL SPECIALTY HOSPITAL OF TEXARKANA—NORTH, TEXARKANA, TX, p. A720
POST ACUTE MEDICAL SPECIALTY HOSPITAL OF TEXARKANA, TEXARKANA, TX, p. A720
POST ACUTE MEDICAL SPECIALTY HOSPITAL OF TULSA, TULSA, OK, p. A570
POST ACUTE MEDICAL SPECIALTY HOSPITAL OF VICTORIA, VICTORIA, TX, p. A723
POST ACUTE REHABILITATION HOSPITAL OF ALLEN, ALLEN, TX, p. A651
POST ACUTE SPECIALTY HOSPITAL OF HAMMOND, HAMMOND, LA, p. A302
POST ACUTE/WARM SPRINGS REHABILITATION HOSPITAL OF SAN ANTONIO, SAN ANTONIO, TX, p. A712
POST ACUTE/WARM SPRINGS SPECIALTY HOSPITAL OF LULING, LULING, TX, p. A699
POST ACUTE/WARM SPRINGS SPECIALTY HOSPITAL OF NEW BRAUNFELS, NEW BRAUNFELS, TX, p. A703
POST ACUTE/WARM SPRINGS SPECIALTY HOSPITAL OF SAN ANTONIO, SAN ANTONIO, TX, p. A713
POST ACUTE/WARM SPRINGS SPECIALTY HOSPITAL OF VICTORIA, VICTORIA, TX, p. A723
POTOMAC VALLEY HOSPITAL, KEYSER, WV, p. A773
POTTSTOWN HOSPITAL, POTTSTOWN, PA, p. A605
POTTSTOWN MEMORIAL MEDICAL CENTER, POTTSTOWN, PA, p. A605
POUDRE VALLEY HOSPITAL, FORT COLLINS, CO, p. A112
POWELL COUNTY MEDICAL CENTER, DEER LODGE, MT, p. A423
POWELL HOSPITAL, POWELL, WY, p. A803
POWELL VALLEY HEALTHCARE, POWELL, WY, p. A803
POWER COUNTY HOSPITAL DISTRICT, AMERICAN FALLS, ID, p. A188
PRAGUE COMMUNITY HOSPITAL, PRAGUE, OK, p. A567
PRAGUE MUNICIPAL HOSPITAL, PRAGUE, OK, p. A567
PRAIRIE AT ST JOHN'S, FARGO, ND, p. A523
PRAIRIE COMMUNITY HEALTH CENTER, TERRY, MT, p. A428
PRAIRIE COMMUNITY HOSPITAL, TERRY, MT, p. A428
PRAIRIE DU CHIEN MEMORIAL HOSPITAL, PRAIRIE DU CHIEN, WI, p. A794
PRAIRIE LAKES HEALTHCARE SYSTEM, WATERTOWN, SD, p. A633
PRAIRIE LAKES HOSP & CARE CTR, WATERTOWN, SD, p. A633
PRAIRIE RIDGE HEALTH, COLUMBUS, WI, p. A781
PRAIRIE RIDGE HEALTH, INC., COLUMBUS, WI, p. A782
PRAIRIE RIDGE HOSPITAL AND HEALTH SERVICES, ELBOW LAKE, MN, p. A376
PRAIRIE ST. JOHN'S, FARGO, ND, p. A523
PRAIRIE VIEW, NEWTON, KS, p. A272
PRAIRIE VIEW MENTAL HLTH CNTR, NEWTON, KS, p. A272
PRAIRIECARE—BROOKLYN PARK, BROOKLYN PARK, MN, p. A373
PRAIRIECARE, BROOKLYN PARK, MN, p. A373
PRAIRIEVILLE FAMILY HOSPITAL, PRAIRIEVILLE, LA, p. A313
PRATT REGIONAL MEDICAL CENTER, PRATT, KS, p. A275
PRATTVILLE BAPTIST HOSPITAL, PRATTVILLE, AL, p. A24
PREMIER SPECIALTY HOSPITAL OF EL PASO, EL PASO, TX, p. A675
PREMIER SURGICAL INSTITUTE, GALENA, KS, p. A264
PRENTICE WOMEN'S HOSPITAL, CHICAGO, IL, p. A200
PRENTISS REG HOSP & CARE FACIL, PRENTISS, MS, p. A399
PRESBYTERIAN ESPANOLA HOSPITAL, ESPANOLA, NM, p. A469

PRESBYTERIAN HEALTHCARE SERVS, ALBUQUERQUE, NM, p. A468
PRESBYTERIAN HOSP OF KAUFMAN, KAUFMAN, TX, p. A692
PRESBYTERIAN HOSPITAL, ALBUQUERQUE, NM, p. A468
PRESBYTERIAN HOSPITAL, CHARLOTTE, NC, p. A507
PRESBYTERIAN HOSPITAL, OKLAHOMA CITY, OK, p. A565
PRESBYTERIAN HOSPITAL DALLAS, DALLAS, TX, p. A670
PRESBYTERIAN HOSPITAL HUNTERSVILLE, HUNTERSVILLE, NC, p. A512
PRESBYTERIAN HOSPITAL MATTHEWS, MATTHEWS, NC, p. A514
PRESBYTERIAN HOSPITAL OF ALLEN, ALLEN, TX, p. A651
PRESBYTERIAN HOSPITAL OF PLANO, PLANO, TX, p. A707
PRESBYTERIAN HOSPITAL OF ROCKWALL, ROCKWALL, TX, p. A709
PRESBYTERIAN MEDICAL CENTER OF THE UNIVERSITY OF PENNSYLVANIA HEALTH SYSTEM, PHILADELPHIA, PA, p. A601
PRESBYTERIAN PLANO CENTER FOR DIAGNOSTIC & SURGERY, PLANO, TX, p. A707
PRESBYTERIAN SANTA FE MEDICAL CENTER, SANTA FE, NM, p. A472
PRESBYTERIAN TOWER, OKLAHOMA CITY, OK, p. A565
PRESBYTERIAN-ORTHOPAEDIC HOSPITAL, CHARLOTTE, NC, p. A507
PRESBYTERIAN/ST. LUKE'S MEDICAL CENTER, DENVER, CO, p. A111
PRESENCE HOLY FAMILY MEDICAL CENTER, DES PLAINES, IL, p. A202
PRESENCE MERCY MEDICAL CENTER, AURORA, IL, p. A195
PRESENCE OUR LADY OF THE RESURRECTION MEDICAL CENTER, CHICAGO, IL, p. A200
PRESENCE RESURRECTION MEDICAL CENTER, CHICAGO, IL, p. A200
PRESENCE SAINT FRANCIS HOSPITAL, EVANSTON, IL, p. A204
PRESENCE SAINT JOSEPH HOSPITAL, CHICAGO, IL, p. A200
PRESENCE SAINT JOSEPH HOSPITAL, ELGIN, IL, p. A203
PRESENCE SAINT JOSEPH MEDICAL CENTER, JOLIET, IL, p. A209
PRESENCE SAINTS MARY & ELIZABETH MEDICAL CENTER, CHICAGO, IL, p. A200
PRESENCE ST. MARY'S HOSPITAL, KANKAKEE, IL, p. A209
PRESENCE UNITED SAMARITANS MEDICAL CENTER, DANVILLE, IL, p. A202
PRESENTATION MED CENTER, ROLLA, ND, p. A525
PRESENTATION MEDICAL CENTER, ROLLA, ND, p. A525
PRESTON MEMORIAL HOSPITAL, KINGWOOD, WV, p. A773
PREVOST MEMORIAL HOSPITAL, DONALDSONVILLE, LA, p. A301
PRIMARY CHILDREN'S HOSPITAL, SALT LAKE CITY, UT, p. A732
PRIMARY CHILDREN'S MEDICAL CENTER, SALT LAKE CITY, UT, p. A732
PRINCE GEORGE'S HOSPITAL CENTER, CHEVERLY, MD, p. A328
PRINCETON BAPTIST MEDICAL CENTER, BIRMINGHAM, AL, p. A15
PRINCETON COMMUNITY HOSPITAL, PRINCETON, WV, p. A776
PRISMA HEALTH BAPTIST, COLUMBIA, SC, p. A617
PRISMA HEALTH BAPTIST EASLEY HOSPITAL, EASLEY, SC, p. A619
PRISMA HEALTH BAPTIST HOSPITAL, COLUMBIA, SC, p. A618
PRISMA HEALTH BAPTIST PARKRIDGE HOSPITAL, COLUMBIA, SC, p. A618
PRISMA HEALTH GREENVILLE MEMORIAL HOSPITAL, GREENVILLE, SC, p. A620
PRISMA HEALTH GREER MEMORIAL HOSPITAL, GREER, SC, p. A621
PRISMA HEALTH HILLCREST HOSPITAL, SIMPSONVILLE, SC, p. A624
PRISMA HEALTH LAURENS COUNTY HOSPITAL, CLINTON, SC, p. A617
PRISMA HEALTH NORTH GREENVILLE, TRAVELERS REST, SC, p. A625
PRISMA HEALTH OCONEE MEMORIAL HOSPITAL, SENECA, SC, p. A624
PRISMA HEALTH PATEWOOD HOSPITAL, GREENVILLE, SC, p. A620
PRISMA HEALTH RICHLAND HOSPITAL, COLUMBIA, SC, p. A618
PRISMA HEALTH TUOMEY HOSPITAL, SUMTER, SC, p. A624
PROFESSIONAL HOSPITAL GUAYNABO, GUAYNABO, PR, p. A807
PROGRESS WEST HEALTHCARE CENTER, O'FALLON, MO, p. A413
PROGRESS WEST HOSPITAL, O'FALLON, MO, p. A413
PROMEDICA BAY PARK HOSPITAL, OREGON, OH, p. A547
PROMEDICA BIXBY HOSPITAL, ADRIAN, MI, p. A348

PROMEDICA COLDWATER REGIONAL HOSPITAL, COLDWATER, MI, p. A351
PROMEDICA DEFIANCE REGIONAL HOSPITAL, DEFIANCE, OH, p. A539
PROMEDICA FOSTORIA COMMUNITY HOSPITAL, FOSTORIA, OH, p. A540
PROMEDICA HERRICK HOSPITAL, TECUMSEH, MI, p. A368
PROMEDICA MEMORIAL HOSPITAL, FREMONT, OH, p. A540
PROMEDICA MONROE REGIONAL HOSPITAL, MONROE, MI, p. A362
PROMEDICA ST. LUKE'S HOSPITAL, MAUMEE, OH, p. A545
PROMEDICA TOLEDO HOSPITAL, TOLEDO, OH, p. A550
PROMINA COBB HOSPITAL, AUSTELL, GA, p. A166
PROMINA DOUGLAS HOSPITAL, DOUGLASVILLE, GA, p. A171
PROMINA PAULDING MEM MED CTR, HIRAM, GA, p. A174
PROMINA WINDY HILL HOSPITAL, MARIETTA, GA, p. A176
PROMINA-KENNESTONE HOSPITAL, MARIETTA, GA, p. A176
PROMISE HOSPITAL BATON ROUGE, BATON ROUGE, LA, p. A297
PROMISE HOSPITAL OF BOSSIER CITY, BOSSIER CITY, LA, p. A298
PROMISE HOSPITAL OF DALLAS, DALLAS, TX, p. A670
PROMISE HOSPITAL OF EAST LOS ANGELES, SUBURBAN MEDICAL CENTER CAMPUS, PARAMOUNT, CA, p. A84
PROMISE HOSPITAL OF FLORIDA AT THE VILLAGES, OXFORD, FL, p. A152
PROMISE HOSPITAL OF FORT MYERS, FORT MYERS, FL, p. A138
PROMISE HOSPITAL OF LOUISIANA—SHREVEPORT CAMPUS, SHREVEPORT, LA, p. A314
PROMISE HOSPITAL OF MIAMI, MIAMI LAKES, FL, p. A148
PROMISE HOSPITAL OF MISS LOU, VIDALIA, LA, p. A316
PROMISE HOSPITAL OF OVERLAND PARK, OVERLAND PARK, KS, p. A274
PROMISE HOSPITAL OF PHOENIX, MESA, AZ, p. A34
PROMISE HOSPITAL OF SALT LAKE, SALT LAKE CITY, UT, p. A732
PROMISE HOSPITAL OF WICHITA FALLS, WICHITA FALLS, TX, p. A725
PROMISE REGIONAL MEDICAL CENTER-HUTCHINSON, HUTCHINSON, KS, p. A267
PROMISE SPECIALTY HOSPITAL OF SHREVEPORT, SHREVEPORT, LA, p. A314
PROMISE SPECIALTY HOSPITAL OF SOUTHEAST TEXAS, NEDERLAND, TX, p. A703
PROSSER MEMORIAL HEALTH, PROSSER, WA, p. A762
PROVIDENCE—PROVIDENCE PARK HOSPITAL, NOVI CAMPUS, NOVI, MI, p. A363
PROVIDENCE ALASKA MEDICAL CENTER, ANCHORAGE, AK, p. A27
PROVIDENCE CENTRALIA HOSPITAL, CENTRALIA, WA, p. A756
PROVIDENCE EVERETT MEDICAL CTR, EVERETT, WA, p. A758
PROVIDENCE GENERAL MEDICAL CTR, EVERETT, WA, p. A758
PROVIDENCE HEALTH SYSTEM, PORTLAND, OR, p. A579
PROVIDENCE HEALTHCARE NETWORK, WACO, TX, p. A724
PROVIDENCE HOLY CROSS MEDICAL CENTER, MISSION HILLS, CA, p. A78
PROVIDENCE HOLY FAMILY HOSPITAL, SPOKANE, WA, p. A766
PROVIDENCE HOOD RIVER MEMORIAL HOSPITAL, HOOD RIVER, OR, p. A576
PROVIDENCE HOSP & MEDICAL CTR, MEDFORD, OR, p. A577
PROVIDENCE HOSPITAL, ANCHORAGE, AK, p. A27
PROVIDENCE HOSPITAL, CENTRALIA, WA, p. A756
PROVIDENCE HOSPITAL, COLUMBIA, SC, p. A618
PROVIDENCE HOSPITAL, MOBILE, AL, p. A22
PROVIDENCE HOSPITAL, SANDUSKY, OH, p. A549
PROVIDENCE HOSPITAL NORTHEAST, COLUMBIA, SC, p. A618
PROVIDENCE KODIAK ISLAND HOSP, KODIAK, AK, p. A28
PROVIDENCE KODIAK ISLAND MEDICAL CENTER, KODIAK, AK, p. A28
PROVIDENCE LITTLE COMPANY OF MARY MEDICAL CENTER—TORRANCE, TORRANCE, CA, p. A101
PROVIDENCE LITTLE COMPANY OF MARY MEDICAL CENTER, TORRANCE, CA, p. A101
PROVIDENCE LITTLE COMPANY OF MARY MEDICAL CENTER SAN PEDRO, SAN PEDRO, CA, p. A96
PROVIDENCE LITTLE COMPANY OF MARY MEDICAL CENTER SAN PEDRO HOSPITAL, SAN PEDRO, CA, p. A96
PROVIDENCE MEDFORD MEDICAL CENTER, MEDFORD, OR, p. A578
PROVIDENCE MEDICAL CENTER, KANSAS CITY, KS, p. A267
PROVIDENCE MEDICAL CENTER, WAYNE, NE, p. A440
PROVIDENCE MEMORIAL HOSPITAL, EL PASO, TX, p. A675
PROVIDENCE MILWAUKIE HOSPITAL, MILWAUKIE, OR, p. A578
PROVIDENCE MOUNT CARMEL HOSPITAL, COLVILLE, WA, p. A757
PROVIDENCE NEWBERG HOSPITAL, NEWBERG, OR, p. A578

PROVIDENCE NEWBERG MEDICAL CENTER, NEWBERG, OR, p. A578
PROVIDENCE PARK HOSPITAL, NOVI, MI, p. A363
PROVIDENCE PORTLAND MED CTR, PORTLAND, OR, p. A579
PROVIDENCE PORTLAND MEDICAL CENTER, PORTLAND, OR, p. A579
PROVIDENCE REGIONAL MEDICAL CENTER EVERETT, EVERETT, WA, p. A758
PROVIDENCE SACRED HEART MEDICAL CENTER & CHILDREN'S HOSPITAL, SPOKANE, WA, p. A766
PROVIDENCE SACRED HEART MEDICAL CENTER, SPOKANE, WA, p. A766
PROVIDENCE SAINT JOHN'S HEALTH CENTER, SANTA MONICA, CA, p. A97
PROVIDENCE SAINT JOSEPH MEDICAL CENTER, BURBANK, CA, p. A59
PROVIDENCE SEASIDE HOSPITAL, SEASIDE, OR, p. A581
PROVIDENCE SEWARD MEDICAL CENTER, SEWARD, AK, p. A29
PROVIDENCE ST. JOSEPH MEDICAL CENTER, POLSON, MT, p. A427
PROVIDENCE ST. JOSEPH'S HOSPITAL, CHEWELAH, WA, p. A756
PROVIDENCE ST. MARY MEDICAL CENTER, WALLA WALLA, WA, p. A768
PROVIDENCE ST. PATRICK HOSPITAL, MISSOULA, MT, p. A426
PROVIDENCE ST. PETER HOSPITAL, OLYMPIA, WA, p. A761
PROVIDENCE ST. VINCENT MEDICAL CENTER, PORTLAND, OR, p. A580
PROVIDENCE TARZANA MEDICAL CENTER, TARZANA, CA, p. A100
PROVIDENCE VALDEZ MEDICAL CENTER, VALDEZ, AK, p. A29
PROVIDENCE VETERANS AFFAIRS MEDICAL CENTER, PROVIDENCE, RI, p. A613
PROVIDENCE WILLAMETTE FALLS HOSPITAL, OREGON CITY, OR, p. A578
PROVIDENCE WILLAMETTE FALLS MEDICAL CENTER, OREGON CITY, OR, p. A578
PROVIDENCE-PROVIDENCE PARK HOSPITALS, SOUTHFIELD, MI, p. A367
PROVIDENCE-ST MARGARET CENTER, KANSAS CITY, KS, p. A267
PROVIDENT HOSPITAL OF COOK COUNTY, CHICAGO, IL, p. A200
PROVIDENT MEDICAL CENTER, CHICAGO, IL, p. A200
PROVO CANYON BEHAVIORAL HOSPITAL, OREM, UT, p. A730
PROWERS MEDICAL CENTER, LAMAR, CO, p. A115
PSYCHIATRIC CENTER OF MICHIGAN, NEW BALTIMORE, MI, p. A362
PSYCHIATRIC HOSP OF FLORIDA, CLEARWATER, FL, p. A134
PSYCHIATRIC HOSPITAL AT VANDERBILT, NASHVILLE, TN, p. A646
PSYCHIATRIC INSTITUTE OF WASHINGTON, WASHINGTON, DC, p. A130
PSYCHIATRIC PAVILION NEW ORLEANS, NEW ORLEANS, LA, p. A311
PUB HOSP OF THE TOWN OF SALEM, SALEM, IL, p. A219
PUBLIC HEALTH SERVICE INDIAN HOSPITAL—QUENTIN N. BURDICK MEMORIAL HEALTH FACILITY, BELCOURT, ND, p. A521
PULASKI MEMORIAL HOSPITAL, WINAMAC, IN, p. A242
PULLMAN MEMORIAL HOSPITAL, PULLMAN, WA, p. A762
PULLMAN REGIONAL HOSPITAL, PULLMAN, WA, p. A762
PUNXSUTAWNEY AREA HOSPITAL, PUNXSUTAWNEY, PA, p. A605
PURCELL MUNICIPAL HOSPITAL, PURCELL, OK, p. A567
PUSHMATAHA HOSPITAL & HOME HEALTH, ANTLERS, OK, p. A555
PUSHMATAHA HOSPITAL, ANTLERS, OK, p. A555
PUTNAM COMMUNITY MEDICAL CENTER, PALATKA, FL, p. A152
PUTNAM COUNTY HOSPITAL, GREENCASTLE, IN, p. A229
PUTNAM COUNTY MEMORIAL HOSPITAL, UNIONVILLE, MO, p. A420
PUTNAM GENERAL HOSPITAL, EATONTON, GA, p. A172
PUTNAM HOSPITAL CENTER, CARMEL, NY, p. A481

# Q

QUAIL RUN BEHAVIORAL HEALTH, PHOENIX, AZ, p. A36
QUEEN OF ANGELS-HOLLYWOOD CTR, LOS ANGELES, CA, p. A75
QUEEN OF THE VALLEY HOSPITAL, NAPA, CA, p. A80

QUEEN OF THE VALLEY HOSPITAL, WEST COVINA, CA, p. A104
QUEEN OF THE VALLEY MEDICAL CENTER, NAPA, CA, p. A80
QUEENS CHILDREN'S PSYCHIATRIC CENTER, JAMAICA, NY, p. A486
QUEENS HOSPITAL CENTER, JAMAICA, NY, p. A486
QUEEN'S MEDICAL CENTER, HONOLULU, HI, p. A184
QUEEN'S NORTH HAWAII COMMUNITY HOSPITAL, KAMUELA, HI, p. A186
QUILLEN REHABILITATION HOSPITAL, JOHNSON CITY, TN, p. A640
QUINCY VALLEY HOSPITAL, QUINCY, WA, p. A762
QUINCY VALLEY MEDICAL CENTER, QUINCY, WA, p. A762

# R

RABUN COUNTY HOSPITAL, CLAYTON, GA, p. A168
RADY CHILDREN'S HOSPITAL—SAN DIEGO, SAN DIEGO, CA, p. A91
RADY CHILDREN'S HOSPITAL AND HEALTH CENTER, SAN DIEGO, CA, p. A91
RAINBOW BABIES AND CHILDREN'S HOSPITAL, CLEVELAND, OH, p. A535
RAINIER SPRINGS HOSPITAL, VANCOUVER, WA, p. A768
RAINY LAKE MEDICAL CENTER, INTERNATIONAL FALLS, MN, p. A378
RALEIGH GENERAL HOSPITAL, BECKLEY, WV, p. A770
RALPH H. JOHNSON VETERANS AFFAIRS MEDICAL CENTER, CHARLESTON, SC, p. A616
RAMAPO RIDGE PSYCHIATRIC HOSP, WYCKOFF, NJ, p. A466
RANCHO LOS AMIGOS NATIONAL REHABILITATION CENTER, DOWNEY, CA, p. A62
RANCHO SPECIALTY HOSPITAL, RANCHO CUCAMONGA, CA, p. A86
RANDOLPH HOSPITAL, ASHEBORO, NC, p. A504
RANGE REGIONAL HEALTH SERVICES, HIBBING, MN, p. A378
RANGELY DISTRICT HOSPITAL, RANGELY, CO, p. A118
RANKEN JORDAN—A PEDIATRIC SPECIALTY HOSPITAL, MARYLAND HEIGHTS, MO, p. A411
RANKEN JORDAN PEDIATRIC BRIDGE HOSPITAL, MARYLAND HEIGHTS, MO, p. A411
RANKIN COUNTY HOSPITAL DISTRICT, RANKIN, TX, p. A708
RANKIN HOSPITAL DISTRICT, RANKIN, TX, p. A708
RANSOM MEMORIAL HOSPITAL, OTTAWA, KS, p. A273
RAPID CITY REGIONAL HOSPITAL, RAPID CITY, SD, p. A630
RAPIDES REGIONAL MEDICAL CENTER, ALEXANDRIA, LA, p. A295
RAPPAHANNOCK GENERAL HOSPITAL, KILMARNOCK, VA, p. A744
RARITAN BAY MEDICAL CENTER, PERTH AMBOY, NJ, p. A461
RAULERSON HOSPITAL, OKEECHOBEE, FL, p. A150
RAWLINS COUNTY HEALTH CENTER, ATWOOD, KS, p. A262
RAWLINS COUNTY HOSPITAL, ATWOOD, KS, p. A262
RAY COUNTY MEMORIAL HOSPITAL, RICHMOND, MO, p. A414
RC HOSPITAL AND CLINICS, OLIVIA, MN, p. A382
R E THOMASON GENERAL HOSPITAL, EL PASO, TX, p. A675
READING HEALTH, WEST READING, PA, p. A610
READING HEALTH REHABILITATION HOSPITAL, WYOMISSING, PA, p. A612
READING HOSPITAL, WEST READING, PA, p. A610
READING HOSPITAL REHABILITATION AT WYOMISSING, WYOMISSING, PA, p. A612
REAGAN MEMORIAL HOSPITAL, BIG LAKE, TX, p. A659
REBOUND BEHAVIORAL HEALTH, LANCASTER, SC, p. A622
RECEPTION AND MEDICAL CENTER, LAKE BUTLER, FL, p. A143
RECOVERY INN OF MENLO PARK, MENLO PARK, CA, p. A77
RED BAY HOSPITAL, RED BAY, AL, p. A24
RED BUD REGIONAL HOSPITAL, RED BUD, IL, p. A218
RED LAKE INDIAN HEALTH SERVICE HOSPITAL, RED LAKE, MN, p. A383
RED RIVER BEHAVIORAL CENTER, BOSSIER CITY, LA, p. A298
RED RIVER BEHAVIORAL HEALTH SYSTEM, GRAND FORKS, ND, p. A524
RED RIVER HOSPITAL, WICHITA FALLS, TX, p. A725
RED RIVER HOSPITAL, LLC, WICHITA FALLS, TX, p. A725
RED RIVER REGIONAL HOSPITAL, BONHAM, TX, p. A660
REDBUD REGIONAL HOSPITAL, RED BUD, IL, p. A218
REDDING MEDICAL CENTER, REDDING, CA, p. A87
REDINGTON-FAIRVIEW GENERAL HOSPITAL, SKOWHEGAN, ME, p. A323
REDLANDS COMMUNITY HOSPITAL, REDLANDS, CA, p. A87
REDMOND REGIONAL MEDICAL CENTER, ROME, GA, p. A179
REDWOOD AREA HOSPITAL, REDWOOD FALLS, MN, p. A383

REDWOOD CITY MEDICAL CENTER, REDWOOD CITY, CA, p. A87
REDWOOD MEMORIAL HOSPITAL, FORTUNA, CA, p. A64
REEDSBURG AREA MEDICAL CENTER, REEDSBURG, WI, p. A795
REEDSBURG MEMORIAL HOSPITAL, REEDSBURG, WI, p. A795
REEVES COUNTY HOSPITAL, PECOS, TX, p. A705
REEVES COUNTY HOSPITAL DISTRICT, PECOS, TX, p. A705
REEVES MEMORIAL MEDICAL CENTER, BERNICE, LA, p. A298
REFUGIO COUNTY MEMORIAL HOSPITAL, REFUGIO, TX, p. A708
REGENCY HOSPITAL, FLORENCE, SC, p. A619
REGENCY HOSPITAL CLEVELAND EAST, WARRENSVILLE HEIGHTS, OH, p. A552
REGENCY HOSPITAL OF CENTRAL GEORGIA, MACON, GA, p. A176
REGENCY HOSPITAL OF CINCINNATI, CINCINNATI, OH, p. A533
REGENCY HOSPITAL OF COLUMBUS, COLUMBUS, OH, p. A537
REGENCY HOSPITAL OF FLORENCE, FLORENCE, SC, p. A619
REGENCY HOSPITAL OF GREENVILLE, GREENVILLE, SC, p. A620
REGENCY HOSPITAL OF MERIDIAN, MERIDIAN, MS, p. A397
REGENCY HOSPITAL OF MINNEAPOLIS, GOLDEN VALLEY, MN, p. A377
REGENCY HOSPITAL OF NORTHWEST ARKANSAS— SPRINGDALE, SPRINGDALE, AR, p. A53
REGENCY HOSPITAL OF NORTHWEST INDIANA, EAST CHICAGO, IN, p. A226
REGENCY HOSPITAL OF SOUTH ATLANTA, EAST POINT, GA, p. A172
REGENCY HOSPITAL OF SPRINGDALE, SPRINGDALE, AR, p. A53
REGENCY HOSPITAL OF TOLEDO, SYLVANIA, OH, p. A550
REGINA HOSPITAL, HASTINGS, MN, p. A378
REGINA MEDICAL CENTER, HASTINGS, MN, p. A378
REGIONAL HEALTH SERVICES OF HOWARD COUNTY, CRESCO, IA, p. A247
REGIONAL HOSPITAL OF SCRANTON, SCRANTON, PA, p. A607
REGIONAL MEDICAL CENTER—ANNISTON, ANNISTON, AL, p. A13
REGIONAL MEDICAL CENTER, MANCHESTER, IA, p. A253
REGIONAL MEDICAL CENTER, ORANGEBURG, SC, p. A623
REGIONAL MEDICAL CENTER, VICTORIA, TX, p. A723
REGIONAL MEDICAL CENTER AT MEMPHIS, MEMPHIS, TN, p. A645
REGIONAL MEDICAL CENTER BAYONET POINT, HUDSON, FL, p. A140
REGIONAL MEDICAL CENTER OF CENTRAL ALABAMA, GREENVILLE, AL, p. A19
REGIONAL MEDICAL CENTER OF HOPKINS COUNTY, MADISONVILLE, KY, p. A289
REGIONAL MEDICAL CENTER OF ORANGEBURG AND CALHOUN COUNTIES, ORANGEBURG, SC, p. A623
REGIONAL MEDICAL CENTER OF SAN JOSE, SAN JOSE, CA, p. A95
REGIONAL MEDICAL CENTER-BAYONET POINT, HUDSON, FL, p. A140
REGIONAL MENTAL HEALTH CENTER, MERRILLVILLE, IN, p. A236
REGIONAL ONE HEALTH, MEMPHIS, TN, p. A645
REGIONAL ONE HEALTH EXTENDED CARE HOSPITAL, MEMPHIS, TN, p. A645
REGIONAL REHABILITATION CENTER, SALEM, OR, p. A581
REGIONAL REHABILITATION HOSPITAL, PHENIX CITY, AL, p. A23
REGIONAL WEST GARDEN COUNTY, OSHKOSH, NE, p. A438
REGIONAL WEST MEDICAL CENTER, SCOTTSBLUFF, NE, p. A439
REGIONS BEHAVIORAL HOSPITAL, BATON ROUGE, LA, p. A297
REGIONS HOSPITAL, SAINT PAUL, MN, p. A385
REHAB HOSP OF CONNECTICUT, HARTFORD, CT, p. A122
REHAB INST AT SANTA BARBARA, SANTA BARBARA, CA, p. A96
REHAB INSTTITUTE OF ST LOUIS, SAINT LOUIS, MO, p. A416
REHABILITATION HOSPITAL OF BRISTOL, BRISTOL, VA, p. A739
REHABILITATION HOSPITAL OF FORT WAYNE, FORT WAYNE, IN, p. A228
REHABILITATION HOSPITAL OF INDIANA, INDIANAPOLIS, IN, p. A233
REHABILITATION HOSPITAL OF JENNINGS, JENNINGS, LA, p. A304
REHABILITATION HOSPITAL OF NORTHERN ARIZONA, FLAGSTAFF, AZ, p. A31

REHABILITATION HOSPITAL OF NORTHWEST OHIO, TOLEDO, OH, p. A550
REHABILITATION HOSPITAL OF OVERLAND PARK, OVERLAND PARK, KS, p. A274
REHABILITATION HOSPITAL OF RHODE ISLAND, NORTH SMITHFIELD, RI, p. A613
REHABILITATION HOSPITAL OF SAVANNAH, SAVANNAH, GA, p. A180
REHABILITATION HOSPITAL OF SOUTHERN NEW MEXICO, LAS CRUCES, NM, p. A470
REHABILITATION HOSPITAL OF SOUTHWEST VIRGINIA, BRISTOL, VA, p. A739
REHABILITATION HOSPITAL OF THE CAPE AND ISLANDS, EAST SANDWICH, MA, p. A338
REHABILITATION HOSPITAL OF THE NORTHWEST, POST FALLS, ID, p. A192
REHABILITATION HOSPITAL OF THE PACIFIC, HONOLULU, HI, p. A185
REHABILITATION HOSPITAL OF WISCONSIN, WAUKESHA, WI, p. A798
REHABILITATION HOSPITAL, NAVICENT HEALTH, MACON, GA, p. A176
REHABILITATION INSTITUTE OF CHICAGO, CHICAGO, IL, p. A200
REHABILITATION INSTITUTE OF MICHIGAN, DETROIT, MI, p. A353
REHABILITATION INSTITUTE OF OREGON, PORTLAND, OR, p. A580
REHABILITATION INSTITUTE OF WEST FLORIDA, PENSACOLA, FL, p. A153
REHOBOTH MCKINLEY CHRISTIAN HEALTH CARE SERVICES, GALLUP, NM, p. A469
REHOBOTH MCKINLEY HOSPITAL, GALLUP, NM, p. A469
REID HEALTH, RICHMOND, IN, p. A239
REID HOSPITAL AND HEALTH CARE SERVICES, RICHMOND, IN, p. A239
RENO BEHAVIORAL HEALTHCARE HOSPITAL, RENO, NV, p. A445
RENOWN REGIONAL MEDICAL CENTER, RENO, NV, p. A446
RENOWN REHABILITATION HOSPITAL, RENO, NV, p. A446
RENOWN SOUTH MEADOWS MEDICAL CENTER, RENO, NV, p. A446
RENVILLE COUNTY HOSPITAL, OLIVIA, MN, p. A382
REPUBLIC COUNTY HOSPITAL, BELLEVILLE, KS, p. A262
RESEARCH BELTON HOSPITAL, BELTON, MO, p. A402
RESEARCH MEDICAL CENTER, KANSAS CITY, MO, p. A409
RESOLUTE HEALTH, NEW BRAUNFELS, TX, p. A703
RESTON HOSPITAL CENTER, RESTON, VA, p. A749
RESTON HOSPITAL CTR, RESTON, VA, p. A749
RETREAT DOCTORS' HOSPITAL, RICHMOND, VA, p. A750
REYNOLDS MEMORIAL HOSPITAL, GLEN DALE, WV, p. A772
RHEA COUNTY MEDICAL CENTER, DAYTON, TN, p. A637
RHEA MEDICAL CENTER, DAYTON, TN, p. A637
RHODE ISLAND HOSPITAL, PROVIDENCE, RI, p. A614
RICE CNTY DISTRICT ONE HOSP, FARIBAULT, MN, p. A376
RICE DISTRICT COMMUNITY HOSP, EAGLE LAKE, TX, p. A673
RICE MEDICAL CENTER, EAGLE LAKE, TX, p. A673
RICE MEMORIAL HOSPITAL, WILLMAR, MN, p. A388
RICELAND MEDICAL CENTER, WINNIE, TX, p. A726
RICHARD H HUTCHINGS PSYCH CNTR, SYRACUSE, NY, p. A499
RICHARD H. HUTCHINGS PSYCHIATRIC CENTER, SYRACUSE, NY, p. A499
RICHARD H. YOUNG HOSPITAL, KEARNEY, NE, p. A434
RICHARD L. ROUDEBUSH VETERANS AFFAIRS MEDICAL CENTER, INDIANAPOLIS, IN, p. A233
RICHARD P. STADTER PSYCHIATRIC CENTER, GRAND FORKS, ND, p. A524
RICHARDSON MEDICAL CENTER, RAYVILLE, LA, p. A313
RICHARDSON REGIONAL MEDICAL CENTER, RICHARDSON, TX, p. A708
RICHLAND HOSPITAL, RICHLAND CENTER, WI, p. A795
RICHLAND MEMORIAL HOSPITAL, OLNEY, IL, p. A215
RICHLAND PARISH HOSP-RAYVILLE, RAYVILLE, LA, p. A313
RICHLAND PARISH HOSPITAL, DELHI, LA, p. A300
RICHLAND PARISH HOSPITAL-DELHI, DELHI, LA, p. A300
RICHMOND COMMUNITY HOSPITAL, RICHMOND, VA, p. A750
RICHMOND MEDICAL CENTER, RICHMOND, CA, p. A88
RICHMOND STATE HOSPITAL, RICHMOND, IN, p. A239
RICHMOND UNIVERSITY MEDICAL CENTER, STATEN ISLAND, NY, p. A498
RIDDLE HOSPITAL, MEDIA, PA, p. A597
RIDDLE MEMORIAL HOSPITAL, MEDIA, PA, p. A597
RIDEOUT MEMORIAL HOSPITAL, MARYSVILLE, CA, p. A77
RIDGE BEHAVIORAL HEALTH SYSTEM, LEXINGTON, KY, p. A287
RIDGECREST COMMUNITY HOSPITAL, RIDGECREST, CA, p. A88
RIDGECREST REGIONAL HOSPITAL, RIDGECREST, CA, p. A88

RIDGEVIEW BEHAVIORAL HOSPITAL, MIDDLE POINT, OH, p. A545

RIDGEVIEW INSTITUTE, MONROE, GA, p. A177

RIDGEVIEW INSTITUTE, SMYRNA, GA, p. A180

RIDGEVIEW LE SEUR MEDICAL CENTER, LE SUEUR, MN, p. A378

RIDGEVIEW LE SUEUR MEDICAL CENTER, LE SUEUR, MN, p. A378

RIDGEVIEW MEDICAL CENTER, WACONIA, MN, p. A387

RIDGEVIEW PSYCHIATRIC HOSPITAL AND CENTER, OAK RIDGE, TN, p. A648

RIDGEVIEW SIBLEY MEDICAL CENTER, ARLINGTON, MN, p. A372

RILEY HOSPITAL FOR CHILDREN, INDIANAPOLIS, IN, p. A233

RILEY HOSPITAL FOR CHILDREN AT INDIANA UNIVERSITY HEALTH, INDIANAPOLIS, IN, p. A233

RINGGOLD COUNTY HOSPITAL, MOUNT AYR, IA, p. A254

RIO BRAVO BEHAVIORAL HEALTH, EL PASO, TX, p. A675

RIO GRANDE HOSPITAL, DEL NORTE, CO, p. A110

RIO GRANDE REGIONAL HOSPITAL, MCALLEN, TX, p. A700

RIO GRANDE STATE CENTER/SOUTH TEXAS HEALTH CARE SYSTEM, HARLINGEN, TX, p. A683

RIO VISTA BEHAVIORAL HEALTH, EL PASO, TX, p. A675

RIPON MEDICAL CENTER, RIPON, WI, p. A795

RIPON MEMORIAL HOSPITAL, RIPON, WI, p. A795

RIVENDELL BEHAVIORAL HEALTH, BENTON, AR, p. A42

RIVENDELL BEHAVIORAL HEALTH, BOWLING GREEN, KY, p. A281

RIVENDELL BEHAVIORAL HEALTH SERVICES OF ARKANSAS, BENTON, AR, p. A42

RIVER BEND HOSPITAL, WEST LAFAYETTE, IN, p. A242

RIVER CREST HOSPITAL, SAN ANGELO, TX, p. A710

RIVER FALLS AREA HOSPITAL, RIVER FALLS, WI, p. A795

RIVER HOSPITAL, ALEXANDRIA BAY, NY, p. A474

RIVER OAKS HOSPITAL, FLOWOOD, MS, p. A392

RIVER OAKS HOSPITAL, NEW ORLEANS, LA, p. A311

RIVER OAKS PSYCH HOSPITAL, NEW ORLEANS, LA, p. A311

RIVER PARK HOSPITAL, HUNTINGTON, WV, p. A773

RIVER PARK HOSPITAL, MC MINNVILLE, TN, p. A643

RIVER PLACE BEHAVIORAL HEALTH, LA PLACE, LA, p. A305

RIVER POINT BEHAVIORAL HEALTH, JACKSONVILLE, FL, p. A141

RIVER REGION MEDICAL CENTER, VICKSBURG, MS, p. A401

RIVERBEND REHABILITATION HOSPITAL, MONROE, LA, p. A309

RIVERBRIDGE SPECIALTY HOSPITAL, VIDALIA, LA, p. A316

RIVERCREST SPECIALTY HOSPITAL, KNOX, IN, p. A234

RIVEREDGE HOSPITAL, FOREST PARK, IL, p. A205

RIVERLAND MEDICAL CENTER, FERRIDAY, LA, p. A301

RIVERSIDE CENTER FOR BEHAVIORAL MEDICINE, RIVERSIDE, CA, p. A88

RIVERSIDE COMMUNITY HOSPITAL, RIVERSIDE, CA, p. A88

RIVERSIDE COUNTY REGIONAL MEDICAL CENTER, MORENO VALLEY, CA, p. A80

RIVERSIDE DOCTORS' HOSPITAL, WILLIAMSBURG, VA, p. A753

RIVERSIDE DOCTORS' HOSPITAL WILLIAMSBURG, WILLIAMSBURG, VA, p. A753

RIVERSIDE HEALTHCARE, KANKAKEE, IL, p. A209

RIVERSIDE HOSP—SKILLED CARE, RENO, NV, p. A446

RIVERSIDE HOSPITAL, ALEXANDRIA, LA, p. A296

RIVERSIDE HOSPITAL OF LOUISIANA, ALEXANDRIA, LA, p. A296

RIVERSIDE MEDICAL CENTER, FRANKLINTON, LA, p. A302

RIVERSIDE MEDICAL CENTER, KANKAKEE, IL, p. A209

RIVERSIDE MEDICAL CENTER, RIVERSIDE, CA, p. A88

RIVERSIDE MEDICAL CENTER, WAUPACA, WI, p. A798

RIVERSIDE METHODIST HOSPITAL, COLUMBUS, OH, p. A537

RIVERSIDE MIDDLE PENINSULA HSP, GLOUCESTER, VA, p. A743

RIVERSIDE REGIONAL MED CTR, NEWPORT NEWS, VA, p. A747

RIVERSIDE REGIONAL MEDICAL CENTER, NEWPORT NEWS, VA, p. A747

RIVERSIDE REHABILITATION INSTITUTE, NEWPORT NEWS, VA, p. A747

RIVERSIDE SHORE MEMORIAL HOSPITAL, ONANCOCK, VA, p. A748

RIVERSIDE TAPPAHANNOCK HOSPITAL, TAPPAHANNOCK, VA, p. A752

RIVERSIDE UNIVERSITY HEALTH SYSTEM-MEDICAL CENTER, MORENO VALLEY, CA, p. A80

RIVERSIDE WALTER REED HOSPITAL, GLOUCESTER, VA, p. A743

RIVERTON HOSPITAL, RIVERTON, UT, p. A731

RIVERTON HOSPITAL, TUKWILA, WA, p. A768

RIVERTON MEMORIAL HOSPITAL, RIVERTON, WY, p. A803

RIVERVALLEY BEHAVIORAL HEALTH HOSPITAL, OWENSBORO, KY, p. A291

RIVERVIEW BEHAVIORAL HEALTH, TEXARKANA, AR, p. A53

RIVERVIEW HEALTH, CROOKSTON, MN, p. A374

RIVERVIEW HEALTH, NOBLESVILLE, IN, p. A238

RIVERVIEW HEALTHCARE ASSOCIATION, CROOKSTON, MN, p. A374

RIVERVIEW HOSPITAL, NOBLESVILLE, IN, p. A238

RIVERVIEW HOSPITAL ASSOCIATION, WISCONSIN RAPIDS, WI, p. A800

RIVERVIEW HOSPITAL FOR CHILDREN AND YOUTH, MIDDLETOWN, CT, p. A123

RIVERVIEW MEDICAL CENTER, RED BANK, NJ, p. A462

RIVERVIEW PSYCHIATRIC CENTER, AUGUSTA, ME, p. A318

RIVERVIEW REGIONAL MEDICAL CENTER, CARTHAGE, TN, p. A635

RIVERVIEW REGIONAL MEDICAL CENTER, GADSDEN, AL, p. A19

RIVERVIEW REGIONAL MEDICAL CENTER NORTH, CARTHAGE, TN, p. A635

RIVERWOOD HEALTHCARE CENTER, AITKIN, MN, p. A371

RIVERWOODS BEHAVIORAL HEALTH SYSTEM, RIVERDALE, GA, p. A178

RIVER'S EDGE HOSPITAL AND CLINIC, SAINT PETER, MN, p. A385

R M SPECIALTY HOSPITAL, HINSDALE, IL, p. A208

RMC ANNISTON, ANNISTON, AL, p. A13

RMC-STRINGFELLOW MEMORIAL HOSPITAL, ANNISTON, AL, p. A13

RML SPECIALTY HOSPITAL, HINSDALE, IL, p. A208

ROANE GENERAL HOSPITAL, SPENCER, WV, p. A777

ROANE MEDICAL CENTER, HARRIMAN, TN, p. A639

ROANOKE-CHOWAN HOSPITAL, AHOSKIE, NC, p. A504

ROBERT E. BUSH NAVAL HOSPITAL, TWENTYNINE PALMS, CA, p. A102

ROBERT H. BALLARD REHABILITATION HOSPITAL, SAN BERNARDINO, CA, p. A91

ROBERT J. DOLE VETERANS AFFAIRS MEDICAL CENTER, WICHITA, KS, p. A279

ROBERT PACKER HOSPITAL, SAYRE, PA, p. A606

ROBERT W JOHNSON UNIV HOSP, RAHWAY, NJ, p. A462

ROBERT WOOD JOHNSON UNIVERSITY HOSPITAL, NEW BRUNSWICK, NJ, p. A459

ROBERT WOOD JOHNSON UNIVERSITY HOSPITAL AT HAMILTON, HAMILTON, NJ, p. A456

ROBERT WOOD JOHNSON UNIVERSITY HOSPITAL RAHWAY, RAHWAY, NJ, p. A462

ROBERT WOOD JOHNSON UNIVERSITY HOSPITAL SOMERSET, SOMERVILLE, NJ, p. A463

ROBLEY REX VETERANS AFFAIRS MEDICAL CENTER, LOUISVILLE, KY, p. A288

ROCHELLE COMMUNITY HOSPITAL, ROCHELLE, IL, p. A218

ROCHESTER COMM BEHAV HOSPITAL, ROCHESTER, MN, p. A384

ROCHESTER GENERAL HOSPITAL, ROCHESTER, NY, p. A496

ROCHESTER METHODIST HOSPITAL, ROCHESTER, MN, p. A384

ROCHESTER PSYCHIATRIC CENTER, ROCHESTER, NY, p. A496

ROCK COUNTY HOSPITAL, BASSETT, NE, p. A429

ROCK PRAIRIE BEHAVIORAL HEALTH, COLLEGE STATION, TX, p. A664

ROCK REGIONAL HOSPITAL, DERBY, KS, p. A263

ROCK SPRINGS, GEORGETOWN, TX, p. A681

ROCK SPRINGS, LLC, GEORGETOWN, TX, p. A681

ROCKCASTLE HOSPITAL AND RESPIRATORY CARE CENTER, MOUNT VERNON, KY, p. A291

ROCKCASTLE REGIONAL HOSPITAL AND RESPIRATORY CARE CENTER, MOUNT VERNON, KY, p. A291

ROCKDALE MEDICAL CENTER, CONYERS, GA, p. A170

ROCKEFELLER UNIVERSITY HOSPITAL, NEW YORK, NY, p. A492

ROCKFORD CENTER, NEWARK, DE, p. A128

ROCKINGHAM MEMORIAL HOSPITAL, HARRISONBURG, VA, p. A743

ROCKLAND CHILDREN'S PSYCH CNTR, ORANGEBURG, NY, p. A494

ROCKLAND CHILDREN'S PSYCHIATRIC CENTER, ORANGEBURG, NY, p. A494

ROCKLAND PSYCHIATRIC CENTER, ORANGEBURG, NY, p. A494

ROCKLEDGE REGIONAL MEDICAL CENTER, ROCKLEDGE, FL, p. A155

ROCKVILLE GENERAL HOSPITAL, VERNON, CT, p. A125

ROGER MILLS MEMORIAL HOSPITAL, CHEYENNE, OK, p. A557

ROGER WILLIAMS MEDICAL CENTER, PROVIDENCE, RI, p. A614

ROGER WILLIAMS MEDICAL CNTR, PROVIDENCE, RI, p. A614

ROGERS MEMORIAL HOSPITAL, OCONOMOWOC, WI, p. A792

ROGERS MEMORIAL HOSPITAL, INC., OCONOMOWOC, WI, p. A793

ROGUE VALLEY MEDICAL CENTER, MEDFORD, OR, p. A578

ROLLING HILLS HOSPITAL, ADA, OK, p. A555

ROLLING HILLS HOSPITAL, FRANKLIN, TN, p. A638

ROLLING PLAINS MEMORIAL HOSPITAL, SWEETWATER, TX, p. A718

ROLLINS BROOK COMMUNITY HOSPITAL, LAMPASAS, TX, p. A694

ROME HOSP AND MURPHY MEM HOSP, ROME, NY, p. A497

ROME MEMORIAL HOSPITAL, ROME, NY, p. A497

RONALD REAGAN UCLA MEDICAL CENTER, LOS ANGELES, CA, p. A75

ROOKS COUNTY HEALTH CENTER, PLAINVILLE, KS, p. A274

ROOSEVELT GENERAL HOSPITAL, PORTALES, NM, p. A471

ROOSEVELT HOSPITAL, EDISON, NJ, p. A454

ROOSEVELT MEDICAL CENTER, CULBERTSON, MT, p. A422

ROOSEVELT MEMORIAL MEDICAL CTR, CULBERTSON, MT, p. A422

ROOSEVELT WARM SPRINGS REHABILITATION AND SPECIALTY HOSPITALS—LTAC, WARM SPRINGS, GA, p. A182

ROOSEVELT WARM SPRINGS REHABILITATION AND SPECIALTY HOSPITALS—REHAB, WARM SPRINGS, GA, p. A183

ROOSEVELT WARM SPRINGS REHABILITATION AND SPECIALTY HOSPITALS, WARM SPRINGS, GA, p. A182

ROOSEVELT WARM SPRINGS REHABILITATION HOSPITAL—REHAB, WARM SPRINGS, GA, p. A183

ROPER HOSPITAL, CHARLESTON, SC, p. A616

ROPER ST. FRANCIS, CHARLESTON, SC, p. A616

ROPER ST. FRANCIS HOSPITAL-BERKELEY, SUMMERVILLE, SC, p. A624

ROPER ST. FRANCIS MOUNT PLEASANT HOSPITAL, MOUNT PLEASANT, SC, p. A622

ROSE MEDICAL CENTER, DENVER, CO, p. A111

ROSEAU AREA HOSPITAL & HOMES, ROSEAU, MN, p. A384

ROSEBUD HEALTH CARE CENTER, FORSYTH, MT, p. A423

ROSELAND COMMUNITY HOSPITAL, CHICAGO, IL, p. A200

ROSEVILLE HOSPITAL, ROSEVILLE, CA, p. A89

ROSEVILLE MEDICAL CENTER, ROSEVILLE, CA, p. A89

ROSWELL PARK CANCER INSTITUTE, BUFFALO, NY, p. A480

ROSWELL PARK COMPREHENSIVE CANCER CENTER, BUFFALO, NY, p. A480

ROTARY REHABILITATION HOSPITAL, MOBILE, AL, p. A22

ROTHMAN SPECIALTY HOSPITAL, BENSALEM, PA, p. A584

ROUND ROCK MEDICAL CENTER, ROUND ROCK, TX, p. A709

ROUNDUP MEMORIAL HEALTHCARE, ROUNDUP, MT, p. A427

ROUNDUP MEMORIAL HOSPITAL, ROUNDUP, MT, p. A427

ROWAN REGIONAL MEDICAL CENTER, SALISBURY, NC, p. A518

ROXBOROUGH MEMORIAL HOSPITAL, PHILADELPHIA, PA, p. A601

ROXBURY TREATMENT CENTER, SHIPPENSBURG, PA, p. A608

ROY LESTER SCHNEIDER HOSPITAL, SAINT THOMAS, VI, p. A812

ROYAL C. JOHNSON VETERANS MEMORIAL MEDICAL CENTER, SIOUX FALLS, SD, p. A631

ROYAL OAKS HOSPITAL, WINDSOR, MO, p. A420

R T JONES HOSPITAL, CANTON, GA, p. A168

RUBY VALLEY HOSPITAL, SHERIDAN, MT, p. A427

RUBY VALLEY MEDICAL CENTER, SHERIDAN, MT, p. A428

RUMFORD COMMUNITY HOSPITAL, RUMFORD, ME, p. A323

RUMFORD HOSPITAL, RUMFORD, ME, p. A323

RUNNELLS SPECIALIZED HOSPITAL OF UNION COUNTY, BERKELEY HEIGHTS, NJ, p. A452

RUSH COUNTY HEALTHCARE CENTER, LA CROSSE, KS, p. A268

RUSH COUNTY MEMORIAL HOSPITAL, LA CROSSE, KS, p. A268

RUSH FOUNDATION HOSPITAL, MERIDIAN, MS, p. A397

RUSH MEMORIAL HOSPITAL, RUSHVILLE, IN, p. A240

RUSH OAK PARK HOSPITAL, OAK PARK, IL, p. A215

RUSH UNIVERSITY MEDICAL CENTER, CHICAGO, IL, p. A200

RUSH-COPLEY MEDICAL CENTER, AURORA, IL, p. A195

RUSH-COPLEY MEMORIAL HOSPITAL, AURORA, IL, p. A195

RUSH-PRESBY-ST LUKE'S MED CTR, CHICAGO, IL, p. A200

RUSK COUNTY MEMORIAL HOSPITAL, LADYSMITH, WI, p. A787

RUSK INSTITUTE, NEW YORK, NY, p. A492

RUSK REHABILITATION HOSPITAL, COLUMBIA, MO, p. A405

RUSK STATE HOSPITAL, RUSK, TX, p. A710

RUSSELL CNTY MEDICAL CENTER, LEBANON, VA, p. A744

RUSSELL COUNTY HOSPITAL, RUSSELL SPRINGS, KY, p. A292

RUSSELL COUNTY MEDICAL CENTER, LEBANON, VA, p. A744

RUSSELL MEDICAL, ALEXANDER CITY, AL, p. A13

RUSSELL MEDICAL CENTER, ALEXANDER CITY, AL, p. A13

RUSSELL REGIONAL HOSPITAL, RUSSELL, KS, p. A275

RUSSELLVILLE HOSPITAL, RUSSELLVILLE, AL, p. A24

RUSSELLVILLE MEDICAL CENTER, RUSSELLVILLE, AL, p. A24

RUSTON REGIONAL SPECIALTY HOSPITAL, RUSTON, LA, p. A313
RUTGERS UNIVERSITY BEHAVIORAL HEALTHCARE, PISCATAWAY, NJ, p. A461
RUTHERFORD REGIONAL HEALTH SYSTEM, RUTHERFORDTON, NC, p. A517
RUTHERFORD REGIONAL MEDICAL CENTER, RUTHERFORDTON, NC, p. A517
RUTLAND REGIONAL MEDICAL CENTER, RUTLAND, VT, p. A736
RWJBARNABAS HEALTH BEHAVIORAL HEALTH CENTER, TOMS RIVER, NJ, p. A464
RWJBARNABAS HEALTH BEHAVIORAL HEALTH CENTER AND NETWORK, TOMS RIVER, NJ, p. A464
RYDER MEMORIAL HOSPITAL, HUMACAO, PR, p. A808

# S

S JOSEPH MEDICAL CENTER, KANSAS CITY, MO, p. A409
SABETHA COMMUNITY HOSPITAL, SABETHA, KS, p. A275
SABINE COUNTY HOSPITAL, HEMPHILL, TX, p. A683
SABINE MEDICAL CENTER, MANY, LA, p. A308
SACRAMENTO MEDICAL CENTER, SACRAMENTO, CA, p. A89
SACRED HEART CHILDREN'S HOSPITAL, SPOKANE, WA, p. A766
SACRED HEART HOSP & CNTR, HANFORD, CA, p. A68
SACRED HEART HOSPITAL, ALLENTOWN, PA, p. A583
SACRED HEART HOSPITAL, EAU CLAIRE, WI, p. A783
SACRED HEART HOSPITAL OF PENSACOLA, PENSACOLA, FL, p. A153
SACRED HEART HOSPITAL ON THE EMERALD COAST, MIRAMAR BEACH, FL, p. A148
SACRED HEART HOSPITAL ON THE GULF, PORT ST JOE, FL, p. A155
SACRED HEART HOSPITAL PENSACOLA, PENSACOLA, FL, p. A154
SACRED HEART MEDICAL CENTER AT RIVERBEND, SPRINGFIELD, OR, p. A581
SACRED OAK MEDICAL CENTER, HOUSTON, TX, p. A688
SADDLEBACK MEDICAL CENTER, LAGUNA HILLS, CA, p. A70
SADDLEBACK MEMORIAL MEDICAL CENTER, LAGUNA HILLS, CA, p. A70
SAFE HAVEN HOSPITAL OF POCATELLO, POCATELLO, ID, p. A192
SAFE HAVEN HOSPITAL OF TREASURE VALLEY, BOISE, ID, p. A188
SAGAMORE CHILDREN'S PSYCHIATRIC CENTER, DIX HILLS, NY, p. A482
SAGE MEMORIAL HOSPITAL, GANADO, AZ, p. A31
SAGE REHABILITATION HOSPITAL, BATON ROUGE, LA, p. A297
SAGE SPECIALTY HOSPITAL (LTAC), DENHAM SPRINGS, LA, p. A301
SAGE SPECIALTY HOSPITAL, DENHAM SPRINGS, LA, p. A301
SAGECREST HOSPITAL, CARROLLTON, TX, p. A663
SAGEWEST HEALTH CARE, RIVERTON, WY, p. A803
SAGEWEST HEALTHCARE-LANDER, LANDER, WY, p. A802
SAGINAW GENERAL HOSPITAL, SAGINAW, MI, p. A366
SAINT AGNES HEALTHCARE, BALTIMORE, MD, p. A326
SAINT AGNES HOSPITAL, BALTIMORE, MD, p. A326
SAINT AGNES MEDICAL CENTER, FRESNO, CA, p. A65
SAINT ALPHONSUS MEDICAL CENTER—BAKER CITY, BAKER CITY, OR, p. A573
SAINT ALPHONSUS MEDICAL CENTER—NAMPA, NAMPA, ID, p. A192
SAINT ALPHONSUS MEDICAL CENTER—ONTARIO, ONTARIO, OR, p. A578
SAINT ALPHONSUS REGIONAL MEDICAL CENTER, BOISE, ID, p. A188
SAINT ALPHONSUS REGIONAL REHABILITATION HOSPITAL—AN AFFILIATE OF ENCOMPASS HEALTH, BOISE, ID, p. A189
SAINT ANNE'S HOSPITAL, FALL RIVER, MA, p. A339
SAINT ANTHONY HOSPITAL, CHICAGO, IL, p. A200
SAINT ANTHONY MEDICAL CENTER, ROCKFORD, IL, p. A219
SAINT BARNABAS MEDICAL CENTER, LIVINGSTON, NJ, p. A457
SAINT BERNARD HOSPITAL, CHICAGO, IL, p. A200
SAINT CAMILLUS MEDICAL CENTER, HURST, TX, p. A690
SAINT CLAIRE HOME, PEORIA HEIGHTS, IL, p. A217
SAINT CLARE'S DENVILLE HOSPITAL, DENVILLE, NJ, p. A454
SAINT CLARE'S HEALTH SYSTEM, DENVILLE, NJ, p. A454
SAINT CLARE'S HOSPITAL/BOONTON TOWNSHIP, BOONTON TOWNSHIP, NJ, p. A452
SAINT CLARE'S HOSPITAL/DENVILLE, DENVILLE, NJ, p. A454
SAINT ELIZABETH HOSPITAL, CHICAGO, IL, p. A200

SAINT ELIZABETH REGIONAL MEDICAL CENTER, LINCOLN, NE, p. A435
SAINT ELIZABETHS HOSPITAL, WASHINGTON, DC, p. A130
SAINT ELIZABETH'S MEDICAL CENTER, WABASHA, MN, p. A387
SAINT FRANCIS HEALTH SYSTEM, TULSA, OK, p. A570
SAINT FRANCIS HEALTHCARE SYSTEM, CAPE GIRARDEAU, MO, p. A403
SAINT FRANCIS HEART HOSPITAL, TULSA, OK, p. A570
SAINT FRANCIS HOSPITAL, CHARLESTON, WV, p. A771
SAINT FRANCIS HOSPITAL, MEMPHIS, TN, p. A645
SAINT FRANCIS HOSPITAL, TULSA, OK, p. A570
SAINT FRANCIS HOSPITAL AND HEALTH CENTERS, POUGHKEEPSIE, NY, p. A495
SAINT FRANCIS HOSPITAL AND MEDICAL CENTER, HARTFORD, CT, p. A122
SAINT FRANCIS HOSPITAL MUSKOGEE, MUSKOGEE, OK, p. A562
SAINT FRANCIS HOSPITAL SOUTH, TULSA, OK, p. A570
SAINT FRANCIS HOSPITAL VINITA, VINITA, OK, p. A571
SAINT FRANCIS HOSPITAL-BARTLETT, BARTLETT, TN, p. A634
SAINT FRANCIS MEDICAL CENTER, CAPE GIRARDEAU, MO, p. A403
SAINT FRANCIS MEDICAL CENTER, GRAND ISLAND, NE, p. A433
SAINT FRANCIS MEDICAL CENTER, PEORIA, IL, p. A217
SAINT FRANCIS MEMORIAL HEALTH CENTER, GRAND ISLAND, NE, p. A433
SAINT FRANCIS MEMORIAL HOSPITAL, SAN FRANCISCO, CA, p. A94
SAINT JOHN HOSPITAL, LEAVENWORTH, KS, p. A269
SAINT JOHN'S HEALTH CENTER, SANTA MONICA, CA, p. A97
SAINT JOSEPH—MARTIN, MARTIN, KY, p. A289
SAINT JOSEPH BEREA, BEREA, KY, p. A280
SAINT JOSEPH EAST, LEXINGTON, KY, p. A287
SAINT JOSEPH HEALTH SYSTEM, MISHAWAKA, IN, p. A236
SAINT JOSEPH HOSPITAL, DENVER, CO, p. A111
SAINT JOSEPH HOSPITAL, LEXINGTON, KY, p. A287
SAINT JOSEPH LONDON, LONDON, KY, p. A287
SAINT JOSEPH MEDICAL CENTER, BURBANK, CA, p. A59
SAINT JOSEPH MOUNT STERLING, MOUNT STERLING, KY, p. A290
SAINT JOSEPH REGIONAL MEDICAL CENTER-PLYMOUTH CAMPUS, PLYMOUTH, IN, p. A239
SAINT JOSEPH'S CHILDREN'S HOSPITAL, MARSHFIELD, WI, p. A789
SAINT JOSEPH'S HOSPITAL OF ATLANTA, ATLANTA, GA, p. A165
SAINT JOSEPH'S MEDICAL CENTER, YONKERS, NY, p. A502
SAINT LOUIS UNIVERSITY HOSPITAL, SAINT LOUIS, MO, p. A416
SAINT LUKE INSTITUTE, SILVER SPRING, MD, p. A332
SAINT LUKE'S CUSHING HOSPITAL, LEAVENWORTH, KS, p. A269
SAINT LUKE'S EAST HOSPITAL, LEE'S SUMMIT, MO, p. A411
SAINT LUKE'S EAST-LEE'S SUMMIT, LEE'S SUMMIT, MO, p. A411
SAINT LUKE'S HOSPITAL OF KANSAS CITY, KANSAS CITY, MO, p. A409
SAINT LUKE'S NORTH HOSPITAL—BARRY ROAD, KANSAS CITY, MO, p. A409
SAINT LUKE'S NORTHLAND HOSPITAL—BARRY ROAD, KANSAS CITY, MO, p. A409
SAINT LUKE'S NORTHLAND HOSPITAL-SMITHVILLE CAMPUS, SMITHVILLE, MO, p. A418
SAINT LUKE'S SOUTH, OVERLAND PARK, KS, p. A274
SAINT LUKE'S SOUTH HOSPITAL, OVERLAND PARK, KS, p. A274
SAINT MARGARET HOSP & HLTH CTR, HAMMOND, IN, p. A230
SAINT MARY HOSPITAL, LANGHORNE, PA, p. A594
SAINT MARY'S HEALTH CARE, GRAND RAPIDS, MI, p. A356
SAINT MARY'S HOSPITAL, WATERBURY, CT, p. A126
SAINT MARY'S REGIONAL MEDICAL CENTER, RENO, NV, p. A446
SAINT MARY'S REGIONAL MEDICAL CENTER, RUSSELLVILLE, AR, p. A52
SAINT MICHAEL'S MEDICAL CENTER, NEWARK, NJ, p. A460
SAINT PETER'S UNIVERSITY HOSPITAL, NEW BRUNSWICK, NJ, p. A459
SAINT SIMONS BY-THE-SEA HOSPITAL, SAINT SIMONS ISLAND, GA, p. A179
SAINT THOMAS DEKALB HOSPITAL, SMITHVILLE, TN, p. A649
SAINT THOMAS HICKMAN HOSPITAL, CENTERVILLE, TN, p. A635
SAINT THOMAS HIGHLANDS HOSPITAL, SPARTA, TN, p. A649
SAINT THOMAS HOSPITAL, AKRON, OH, p. A527
SAINT THOMAS HOSPITAL, NASHVILLE, TN, p. A646

SAINT THOMAS HOSPITAL FOR SPINAL SURGERY, NASHVILLE, TN, p. A646
SAINT THOMAS RIVER PARK HOSPITAL, MC MINNVILLE, TN, p. A643
SAINT THOMAS RUTHERFORD HOSPITAL, MURFREESBORO, TN, p. A646
SAINT THOMAS STONES RIVER HOSPITAL, WOODBURY, TN, p. A650
SAINT THOMAS WEST HOSPITAL, NASHVILLE, TN, p. A646
SAINT VINCENT HEALTH CENTER, ERIE, PA, p. A590
SAINT VINCENT HOSPITAL, BILLINGS, MT, p. A421
SAINT VINCENT HOSPITAL, ERIE, PA, p. A590
SAINT VINCENT HOSPITAL, WORCESTER, MA, p. A346
SAINT VINCENT HOSPITAL AT WORCESTER MEDICAL CENTER, WORCESTER, MA, p. A346
SAINTS MEDICAL CENTER, LOWELL, MA, p. A341
SAKAKAWEA MEDICAL CENTER, HAZEN, ND, p. A524
SALE HOSPITAL, NEOSHO, MO, p. A412
SALEM COMMUNITY HOSPITAL, SALEM, OH, p. A548
SALEM HEALTH WEST VALLEY, DALLAS, OR, p. A574
SALEM HOSPITAL, SALEM, MA, p. A344
SALEM HOSPITAL, SALEM, OR, p. A581
SALEM MEDICAL CENTER, SALEM, NJ, p. A462
SALEM MEMORIAL DISTRICT HOSPITAL, SALEM, MO, p. A418
SALEM REGIONAL MEDICAL CENTER, SALEM, OH, p. A548
SALEM TOWNSHIP HOSPITAL, SALEM, IL, p. A219
SALEM VETERANS AFFAIRS MEDICAL CENTER, SALEM, VA, p. A751
SALINA REGIONAL HEALTH CENTER, SALINA, KS, p. A275
SALINA SURGICAL HOSPITAL, SALINA, KS, p. A276
SALINAS VALLEY MEM HOSPITAL, SALINAS, CA, p. A90
SALINAS VALLEY MEMORIAL HEALTHCARE SYSTEM, SALINAS, CA, p. A90
SALINE MEMORIAL HOSPITAL, BENTON, AR, p. A42
SALT LAKE BEHAVIORAL HEALTH, SALT LAKE CITY, UT, p. A732
SALT LAKE REGIONAL MEDICAL CENTER, SALT LAKE CITY, UT, p. A732
SAM RAYBURN MEMORIAL VETERANS CENTER, BONHAM, TX, p. A660
SAMARITAN ALBANY GENERAL HOSPITAL, ALBANY, OR, p. A573
SAMARITAN BEHAVELBACK HOSPITAL, MESA, AZ, p. A34
SAMARITAN BEHAVIORAL HEALTH CENTER-DESERT SAMARITAN MEDICAL CENTER, MESA, AZ, p. A34
SAMARITAN BEHAVIORAL HLTH CTR, GLENDALE, AZ, p. A32
SAMARITAN HEALTHCARE, MOSES LAKE, WA, p. A760
SAMARITAN HOSPITAL—MAIN CAMPUS, TROY, NY, p. A500
SAMARITAN HOSPITAL, MACON, MO, p. A411
SAMARITAN HOSPITAL, MOSES LAKE, WA, p. A760
SAMARITAN HOSPITAL, TROY, NY, p. A500
SAMARITAN LEBANON COMMUNITY HOSPITAL, LEBANON, OR, p. A577
SAMARITAN MEDICAL CENTER, WATERTOWN, NY, p. A502
SAMARITAN MEMORIAL HOSPITAL, MACON, MO, p. A411
SAMARITAN NORTH LINCOLN HOSPITAL, LINCOLN CITY, OR, p. A577
SAMARITAN PACIFIC COMM HOSPITA, NEWPORT, OR, p. A578
SAMARITAN PACIFIC COMMUNITIES HOSPITAL, NEWPORT, OR, p. A578
SAMARITAN SERVICES FOR AGING, CLINTON, IA, p. A246
SAME DAY SURGERY CENTER, RAPID CITY, SD, p. A630
SAMPSON COUNTY MEM HOSPITAL, CLINTON, NC, p. A507
SAMPSON REGIONAL MEDICAL CENTER, CLINTON, NC, p. A507
SAMUEL MAHELONA MEMORIAL HOSPITAL, KAPAA, HI, p. A186
SAMUEL SIMMONDS MEMORIAL HOSPITAL, BARROW, AK, p. A27
SAN ANGELO COMMUNITY MEDICAL CENTER, SAN ANGELO, TX, p. A710
SAN ANTONIO BEHAVIORAL HEALTHCARE HOSPITAL, SAN ANTONIO, TX, p. A713
SAN ANTONIO COMMUNITY HOSPITAL, SAN ANTONIO, TX, p. A713
SAN ANTONIO COMMUNITY HOSPITAL, UPLAND, CA, p. A102
SAN ANTONIO MILITARY MEDICAL CENTER, FORT SAM HOUSTON, TX, p. A677
SAN ANTONIO REGIONAL HOSPITAL, UPLAND, CA, p. A102
SAN ANTONIO STATE HOSPITAL, SAN ANTONIO, TX, p. A713
SAN BENITO HOSPITAL DISTRICT, HOLLISTER, CA, p. A68
SAN BERNARDINO CNTY MED CENTER, COLTON, CA, p. A60
SAN BERNARDINO COMMUNITY HOSP, SAN BERNARDINO, CA, p. A91
SAN BERNARDINO MOUNTAINS COMMUNITY HOSPITAL DISTRICT, LAKE ARROWHEAD, CA, p. A70
SAN CARLOS APACHE HEALTHCARE CORPORATION, PERIDOT, AZ, p. A35
SAN DIEGO COUNTY PSYCHIATRIC HOSPITAL, SAN DIEGO, CA, p. A92

SAN DIEGO MEDICAL CENTER, SAN DIEGO, CA, p. A92
SAN DIMAS COMM HOSPITAL, SAN DIMAS, CA, p. A93
SAN DIMAS COMMUNITY HOSPITAL, SAN DIMAS, CA, p. A93
SAN FERNANDO COMMUNITY HOSP, PANORAMA CITY, CA, p. A84
SAN FRANCISCO GENERAL HOSPITAL AND TRAUMA CENTER, SAN FRANCISCO, CA, p. A94
SAN FRANCISCO MEDICAL CENTER, SAN FRANCISCO, CA, p. A94
SAN FRANCISCO VA MEDICAL CENTER, SAN FRANCISCO, CA, p. A94
SAN FRANCISO VA MEDICAL CENTER, SAN FRANCISCO, CA, p. A94
SAN GABRIEL VALLEY MEDICAL CENTER, SAN GABRIEL, CA, p. A94
SAN GORGONIO MEMORIAL HOSPITAL, BANNING, CA, p. A58
SAN GORGONIO MEMORIAL HOSPTIAL, BANNING, CA, p. A58
SAN JOAQUIN COMMUNITY HOSPITAL, BAKERSFIELD, CA, p. A57
SAN JOAQUIN GENERAL HOSPITAL, FRENCH CAMP, CA, p. A65
SAN JOAQUIN VALLEY REHABILITATION HOSPITAL, FRESNO, CA, p. A66
SAN JORGE CHILDREN'S HOSPITAL, SANTURCE, PR, p. A811
SAN JORGE HOSPITAL, SANTURCE, PR, p. A811
SAN JOSE BEHAVORIAL HEALTH, SAN JOSE, CA, p. A95
SAN JOSE MEDICAL CENTER, SAN JOSE, CA, p. A95
SAN JOSE REGIONAL MEDICAL CTR, SAN JOSE, CA, p. A95
SAN JUAN CAPESTRANO HOSPITAL, SAN JUAN, PR, p. A811
SAN JUAN CITY HOSPITAL, SAN JUAN, PR, p. A811
SAN JUAN HEALTH SERVICE DISTRICT, MONTICELLO, UT, p. A729
SAN JUAN HEALTH SERVICES DISTRICT, MONTICELLO, UT, p. A729
SAN JUAN MUNICIPAL HOSPITAL, SAN JUAN, PR, p. A811
SAN JUAN REGIONAL MEDICAL CENTER, FARMINGTON, NM, p. A469
SAN JUAN REGIONAL MEDICAL CNTR, FARMINGTON, NM, p. A469
SAN LEANDRO HOSPITAL, SAN LEANDRO, CA, p. A95
SAN LUIS VALLEY HEALTH, ALAMOSA, CO, p. A107
SAN LUIS VALLEY HEALTH CONEJOS COUNTY HOSPITAL, LA JARA, CO, p. A115
SAN LUIS VALLEY HEALTH REGIONAL MEDICAL CENTER, ALAMOSA, CO, p. A107
SAN MATEO COUNTY GENERAL HOSP, SAN MATEO, CA, p. A96
SAN MATEO MEDICAL CENTER, SAN MATEO, CA, p. A96
SAN RAFAEL MEDICAL CENTER, SAN RAFAEL, CA, p. A96
SAN RAMON REGIONAL MEDICAL CENTER, SAN RAMON, CA, p. A96
SANA BEHAVIORAL HOSPITAL, LAS VEGAS, NV, p. A444
SANFORD ABERDEEN MEDICAL CENTER, ABERDEEN, SD, p. A626
SANFORD BAGLEY MEDICAL CENTER, BAGLEY, MN, p. A372
SANFORD BEMIDJI MEDICAL CENTER, BEMIDJI, MN, p. A372
SANFORD BISMARCK, BISMARCK, ND, p. A521
SANFORD CANBY MEDICAL CENTER, CANBY, MN, p. A374
SANFORD CANTON-INWOOD MEDICAL CENTER, CANTON, SD, p. A626
SANFORD CHAMBERLAIN MEDICAL CENTER, CHAMBERLAIN, SD, p. A627
SANFORD CLEAR LAKE MEDICAL CENTER, CLEAR LAKE, SD, p. A627
SANFORD DEUEL COUNTY MEDICAL CENTER, CLEAR LAKE, SD, p. A627
SANFORD HILLSBORO MEDICAL CENTER, HILLSBORO, ND, p. A524
SANFORD HOSPITAL CANTON-INWOOD, CANTON, SD, p. A626
SANFORD HOSPITAL LUVERNE, LUVERNE, MN, p. A379
SANFORD JACKSON MED CENTER, JACKSON, MN, p. A378
SANFORD JACKSON MEDICAL CENTER, JACKSON, MN, p. A378
SANFORD LUVERNE MEDICAL CENTER, LUVERNE, MN, p. A379
SANFORD MAYVILLE MEDICAL CENTER, MAYVILLE, ND, p. A525
SANFORD MEDICAL CENTER ABERDEEN, ABERDEEN, SD, p. A626
SANFORD MEDICAL CENTER BISMARCK, BISMARCK, ND, p. A521
SANFORD MEDICAL CENTER CANBY, CANBY, MN, p. A374
SANFORD MEDICAL CENTER CHAMBERLAIN, CHAMBERLAIN, SD, p. A627
SANFORD MEDICAL CENTER FARGO, FARGO, ND, p. A523
SANFORD MEDICAL CENTER MAYVILLE, MAYVILLE, ND, p. A525
SANFORD MEDICAL CENTER THIEF RIVER FALLS, THIEF RIVER FALLS, MN, p. A386

SANFORD MEDICAL CENTER WEBSTER, WEBSTER, SD, p. A633
SANFORD MEDICAL CENTER WORTHINGTON, WORTHINGTON, MN, p. A388
SANFORD NORTHWOOD DEACONESS HEALTH CENTER, NORTHWOOD, ND, p. A525
SANFORD SHELDON MEDICAL CENTER, SHELDON, IA, p. A257
SANFORD THIEF RIVER FALLS BEHAVIORAL HEALTH CENTER, THIEF RIVER FALLS, MN, p. A386
SANFORD THIEF RIVER FALLS MEDICAL CENTER, THIEF RIVER FALLS, MN, p. A386
SANFORD TRACY MED CTR, TRACY, MN, p. A386
SANFORD TRACY MEDICAL CENTER, TRACY, MN, p. A386
SANFORD USD MED CTR, SIOUX FALLS, SD, p. A631
SANFORD USD MEDICAL CENTER, SIOUX FALLS, SD, p. A631
SANFORD VERMILLION MEDICAL CENTER, VERMILLION, SD, p. A632
SANFORD WEBSTER MEDICAL CENTER, WEBSTER, SD, p. A633
SANFORD WESTBROOK MEDICAL CENTER, WESTBROOK, MN, p. A387
SANFORD WHEATON MEDICAL CENTER, WHEATON, MN, p. A388
SANFORD WORTHINGTON MEDICAL CENTER, WORTHINGTON, MN, p. A388
SANPETE VALLEY HOSPITAL, MOUNT PLEASANT, UT, p. A729
SANTA BARBARA COTTAGE HOSP, SANTA BARBARA, CA, p. A96
SANTA BARBARA COTTAGE HOSPITAL, SANTA BARBARA, CA, p. A97
SANTA BARBARA COUNTY PSYCHIATRIC HEALTH FACILITY, SANTA BARBARA, CA, p. A97
SANTA CLARA MEDICAL CENTER, SANTA CLARA, CA, p. A97
SANTA CLARA VALLEY MEDICAL CENTER, SAN JOSE, CA, p. A95
SANTA CLARA VLY HLTH SYSTEM, SAN JOSE, CA, p. A95
SANTA CRUZ COUNTY PSYCHIATRIC HEALTH FACILITY, SANTA CRUZ, CA, p. A97
SANTA CRUZ VALLEY REGIONAL HOSPITAL, GREEN VALLEY, AZ, p. A33
SANTA FE USPHS-IHS HOSPITAL, SANTA FE, NM, p. A472
SANTA MONICA-UCLA MEDICAL CENTER AND ORTHOPAEDIC HOSPITAL, SANTA MONICA, CA, p. A97
SANTA ROSA MEDICAL CENTER, MILTON, FL, p. A148
SANTA ROSA MEDICAL CENTER, SANTA ROSA, CA, p. A98
SANTA ROSA MEMORIAL HOSPITAL, SANTA ROSA, CA, p. A98
SANTA YNEZ VALLEY COTTAGE HOSPITAL, SOLVANG, CA, p. A99
SANTA YNEZ VALLEY HOSPITAL, SOLVANG, CA, p. A99
SANTIAM HOSPITAL, STAYTON, OR, p. A582
SANTIAM MEMORIAL HOSPITAL, STAYTON, OR, p. A582
SARAH BUSH LINCOLN HEALTH CENTER, MATTOON, IL, p. A211
SARAH BUSH LINCOLN HEALTH SYST, MATTOON, IL, p. A211
SARAH D. CULBERTSON MEMORIAL HOSPITAL, RUSHVILLE, IL, p. A219
SARASOTA MEMORIAL HEALTH CARE SYSTEM, SARASOTA, FL, p. A157
SARASOTA MEMORIAL HOSPITAL, SARASOTA, FL, p. A157
SARATOGA HOSPITAL, SARATOGA SPRINGS, NY, p. A497
SARTORI MEMORIAL HOSPITAL, CEDAR FALLS, IA, p. A244
SATANTA DISTRICT HOSPITAL, SATANTA, KS, p. A276
SATANTA DISTRICT HOSPITAL AND LONG TERM CARE, SATANTA, KS, p. A276
SATILLA REGIONAL MEDICAL CENTER, WAYCROSS, GA, p. A183
SAUK PRAIRIE HEALTHCARE, PRAIRIE DU SAC, WI, p. A794
SAUK PRAIRIE MEMORIAL HOSPITAL & CLINICS, PRAIRIE DU SAC, WI, p. A794
SAUNDERS COUNTY HLTH SERVICES, WAHOO, NE, p. A440
SAUNDERS MEDICAL CENTER, WAHOO, NE, p. A440
SAVOY MEDICAL CENTER, MAMOU, LA, p. A307
SCENIC MOUNTAIN MEDICAL CENTER, BIG SPRING, TX, p. A659
SCHEIE INSTITUTE OF THE HOSPITAL OF THE UNIVERSITY OF PENNSYLVANIA, PHILADELPHIA, PA, p. A601
SCHEURER HEALTH, PIGEON, MI, p. A363
SCHEURER HOSPITAL, PIGEON, MI, p. A363
SCHICK SHADEL HOSPITAL, SEATTLE, WA, p. A763
SCHLEICHER COUNTY MEDICAL CENTER, ELDORADO, TX, p. A676
SCHLEICHER COUNTY MEDICAL CNTR, ELDORADO, TX, p. A676
SCHNECK MEDICAL CENTER, SEYMOUR, IN, p. A240
SCHNEIDER CHILDREN'S HOSPITAL, NEW HYDE PARK, NY, p. A489

SCHNEIDER REGIONAL MEDICAL CENTER, SAINT THOMAS, VI, p. A812
SCHOOLCRAFT MEMORIAL HOSPITAL, MANISTIQUE, MI, p. A361
SCHUYLER HOSPITAL, MONTOUR FALLS, NY, p. A488
SCHUYLKILL MEDICAL CENTER—EAST NORWEGIAN STREET, POTTSVILLE, PA, p. A605
SCHWAB REHABILITATION CENTER, CHICAGO, IL, p. A200
SCHWAB REHABILITATION HOSPITAL, CHICAGO, IL, p. A200
SCOTLAND COUNTY HOSPITAL, MEMPHIS, MO, p. A412
SCOTLAND COUNTY MEMORIAL HOSPITAL, MEMPHIS, MO, p. A412
SCOTLAND HEALTH CARE SYSTEM, LAURINBURG, NC, p. A513
SCOTLAND MEMORIAL HOSPITAL, LAURINBURG, NC, p. A513
SCOTT & WHITE HOSPITAL—LLANO, LLANO, TX, p. A696
SCOTT & WHITE HOSPITAL—MARBLE FALLS, MARBLE FALLS, TX, p. A699
SCOTT & WHITE HOSPITAL—TAYLOR, TAYLOR, TX, p. A718
SCOTT & WHITE HOSPITAL AT ROUND ROCK, ROUND ROCK, TX, p. A709
SCOTT & WHITE MEDICAL CENTER—TEMPLE, TEMPLE, TX, p. A719
SCOTT COUNTY HOSPITAL, SCOTT CITY, KS, p. A276
SCOTT MEMORIAL HEALTH, SCOTTSBURG, IN, p. A240
SCOTT MEMORIAL HOSPITAL, SCOTTSBURG, IN, p. A240
SCOTT REGIONAL HOSPITAL, MORTON, MS, p. A397
SCOTTISH RITE CHILDREN'S CTR, ATLANTA, GA, p. A165
SCOTTSDALE HEALTHCARE REHABILITATION HOSPITAL, SCOTTSDALE, AZ, p. A38
SCOTTSDALE OSBORN MEDICAL CENTER, SCOTTSDALE, AZ, p. A38
SCOTTSDALE SHEA MEDICAL CENTER, SCOTTSDALE, AZ, p. A38
SCOTTSDALE THOMPSON PEAK MEDICAL CENTER, SCOTTSDALE, AZ, p. A38
SCREVEN COUNTY HOSPITAL, SYLVANIA, GA, p. A181
SCRIPPS GREEN HOSPITAL, LA JOLLA, CA, p. A69
SCRIPPS MEM HOSP—LA JOLLA, LA JOLLA, CA, p. A69
SCRIPPS MEMORIAL HOSPITAL, CHULA VISTA, CA, p. A60
SCRIPPS MEMORIAL HOSPITAL-ENCINITAS, ENCINITAS, CA, p. A63
SCRIPPS MEMORIAL HOSPITAL-LA JOLLA, LA JOLLA, CA, p. A70
SCRIPPS MERCY HOSPITAL, SAN DIEGO, CA, p. A92
SCRIPPS MERCY HOSPITAL CHULA VISTA, CHULA VISTA, CA, p. A60
SCRIPPS MERCY MEDICAL CENTER, SAN DIEGO, CA, p. A92
SCRIPPS OCEANVIEW CONV HOSP, ENCINITAS, CA, p. A63
SCRIPPS TORREY PINES CONV HOSP, LA JOLLA, CA, p. A70
S. E. LACKEY MEMORIAL HOSPITAL, FOREST, MS, p. A392
SE TEXAS ER & HOSPITAL, HUMBLE, TX, p. A690
SEA PINES REHABILITATION HOSPITAL, MELBOURNE, FL, p. A145
SEA VIEW HOSPITAL REHABILITATION CENTER AND HOME, STATEN ISLAND, NY, p. A498
SEARHC MT EDGECUMBE HOSPITAL, SITKA, AK, p. A29
SEARHC MT. EDGECUMBE HOSPITAL, SITKA, AK, p. A29
SEASIDE BEHAVIORAL CENTER—NEW ORLEANS, NEW ORLEANS, LA, p. A311
SEASIDE BEHAVIORAL CENTER, NEW ORLEANS, LA, p. A311
SEASIDE GENERAL HOSPITAL, SEASIDE, OR, p. A581
SEASIDE HEALTH SYSTEM—BATON ROUGE, BATON ROUGE, LA, p. A297
SEASIDE HEALTH SYSTEM, BATON ROUGE, LA, p. A297
SEATTLE CANCER CARE ALLIANCE, SEATTLE, WA, p. A764
SEATTLE CHILDREN'S HOSPITAL, SEATTLE, WA, p. A764
SEBASTIAN HOSPITAL, SEBASTIAN, FL, p. A157
SEBASTIAN RIVER MEDICAL CENTER, SEBASTIAN, FL, p. A157
SEDAN CITY HOSPITAL, SEDAN, KS, p. A276
SEDGWICK COUNTY HEALTH CENTER, JULESBURG, CO, p. A114
SEDGWICK COUNTY MEM HOSPITAL, JULESBURG, CO, p. A114
SEILING MUNICIPAL HOSPITAL, SEILING, OK, p. A568
SEILING REGIONAL MEDICAL CENTER, SEILING, OK, p. A568
SELBY GENERAL HOSPITAL, MARIETTA, OH, p. A544
SELECT REHABILITATION HOSPITAL OF DENTON, DENTON, TX, p. A672
SELECT SPEC HOSP-WYANDOTTE, WYANDOTTE, MI, p. A370
SELECT SPECIAL HOSPITAL—DALLAS DOWNTOWN, DALLAS, TX, p. A670
SELECT SPECIALTY HOSP—KANSAS, KANSAS CITY, KS, p. A267
SELECT SPECIALTY HOSP—YORK, YORK, PA, p. A612
SELECT SPECIALTY HOSP OF MIAMI, MIAMI, FL, p. A147
SELECT SPECIALTY HOSP-DANVILLE, DANVILLE, PA, p. A588
SELECT SPECIALTY HOSP-FLINT, FLINT, MI, p. A354

SELECT SPECIALTY HOSP-JACKSON, JACKSON, MS, p. A395

SELECT SPECIALTY HOSP-SAGINAW, SAGINAW, MI, p. A366

SELECT SPECIALTY HOSPITAL—BELHAVEN, JACKSON, MS, p. A395

SELECT SPECIALTY HOSPITAL—BOARDMAN, BOARDMAN, OH, p. A529

SELECT SPECIALTY HOSPITAL—CINCINNATI NORTH, CINCINNATI, OH, p. A533

SELECT SPECIALTY HOSPITAL—CLEVELAND FAIRHILL, CLEVELAND, OH, p. A535

SELECT SPECIALTY HOSPITAL—CLEVELAND GATEWAY, CLEVELAND, OH, p. A535

SELECT SPECIALTY HOSPITAL—DALLAS DOWNTOWN, DALLAS, TX, p. A670

SELECT SPECIALTY HOSPITAL—LINCOLN, LINCOLN, NE, p. A435

SELECT SPECIALTY HOSPITAL—SAN DIEGO, SAN DIEGO, CA, p. A92

SELECT SPECIALTY HOSPITAL—SPECTRUM HEALTH, GRAND RAPIDS, MI, p. A356

SELECT SPECIALTY HOSPITAL—YOUNGSTOWN, BOARDMAN, OH, p. A529

SELECT SPECIALTY HOSPITAL, AUGUSTA, GA, p. A166

SELECT SPECIALTY HOSPITAL, CANTON, OH, p. A531

SELECT SPECIALTY HOSPITAL, ERIE, PA, p. A590

SELECT SPECIALTY HOSPITAL DAYTONA BEACH, DAYTONA BEACH, FL, p. A136

SELECT SPECIALTY HOSPITAL HAMPTON ROADS, NEWPORT NEWS, VA, p. A747

SELECT SPECIALTY HOSPITAL MIDTOWN ATLANTA, ATLANTA, GA, p. A165

SELECT SPECIALTY HOSPITAL OF SOUTHEAST OHIO, NEWARK, OH, p. A546

SELECT SPECIALTY HOSPITAL-AKRON, AKRON, OH, p. A527

SELECT SPECIALTY HOSPITAL-ANN ARBOR, YPSILANTI, MI, p. A370

SELECT SPECIALTY HOSP-AUGUSTA, AUGUSTA, GA, p. A166

SELECT SPECIALTY HOSPITAL-BATTLE CREEK, BATTLE CREEK, MI, p. A349

SELECT SPECIALTY HOSPITAL-BELLEVILLE, ROCHELLE PARK, NJ, p. A462

SELECT SPECIALTY HOSPITAL-BIRMINGHAM, BIRMINGHAM, AL, p. A15

SELECT SPECIALTY HOSPITAL-CAMP HILL, CAMP HILL, PA, p. A586

SELECT SPECIALTY HOSPITAL-CANTON, CANTON, OH, p. A531

SELECT SPECIALTY HOSPITAL-CENTRAL PENNSYLVANIA, CAMP HILL, PA, p. A586

SELECT SPECIALTY HOSPITAL-CHARLESTON, CHARLESTON, WV, p. A771

SELECT SPECIALTY HOSPITAL-CINCINNATI, CINCINNATI, OH, p. A533

SELECT SPECIALTY HOSPITAL-COLUMBUS, COLUMBUS, OH, p. A537

SELECT SPECIALTY HOSPITAL-DALLAS, CARROLLTON, TX, p. A663

SELECT SPECIALTY HOSPITAL-DANVILLE, DANVILLE, PA, p. A588

SELECT SPECIALTY HOSPITAL-DES MOINES, DES MOINES, IA, p. A248

SELECT SPECIALTY HOSPITAL-DOWNRIVER, WYANDOTTE, MI, p. A370

SELECT SPECIALTY HOSPITAL-DURHAM, DURHAM, NC, p. A509

SELECT SPECIALTY HOSPITAL-ERIE, ERIE, PA, p. A590

SELECT SPECIALTY HOSPITAL-EVANSVILLE, EVANSVILLE, IN, p. A228

SELECT SPECIALTY HOSPITAL-FLINT, FLINT, MI, p. A354

SELECT SPECIALTY HOSPITAL-FORT SMITH, FORT SMITH, AR, p. A46

SELECT SPECIALTY HOSPITAL-GAINESVILLE, GAINESVILLE, FL, p. A139

SELECT SPECIALTY HOSPITAL-GREENSBORO, GREENSBORO, NC, p. A511

SELECT SPECIALTY HOSPITAL-GROSSE POINTE, GROSSE POINTE, MI, p. A357

SELECT SPECIALTY HOSPITAL-GULF COAST, GULFPORT, MS, p. A393

SELECT SPECIALTY HOSPITAL-GULFPORT, GULFPORT, MS, p. A393

SELECT SPECIALTY HOSPITAL-HARRISBURG, HARRISBURG, PA, p. A591

SELECT SPECIALTY HOSPITAL-INDIANAPOLIS, INDIANAPOLIS, IN, p. A233

SELECT SPECIALTY HOSPITAL-JACKSON, JACKSON, MS, p. A395

SELECT SPECIALTY HOSPITAL-JOHNSTOWN, JOHNSTOWN, PA, p. A593

SELECT SPECIALTY HOSPITAL-KALAMAZOO, BATTLE CREEK, MI, p. A349

SELECT SPECIALTY HOSPITAL-KANSAS CITY, KANSAS CITY, KS, p. A267

SELECT SPECIALTY HOSPITAL-LAUREL HIGHLANDS, LATROBE, PA, p. A594

SELECT SPECIALTY HOSPITAL-LEXINGTON, LEXINGTON, KY, p. A287

SELECT SPECIALTY HOSPITAL-LONGVIEW, LONGVIEW, TX, p. A697

SELECT SPECIALTY HOSPITAL-MACOMB COUNTY, MOUNT CLEMENS, MI, p. A362

SELECT SPECIALTY HOSPITAL-MADISON, MADISON, WI, p. A787

SELECT SPECIALTY HOSPITAL-MCKEESPORT, MCKEESPORT, PA, p. A596

SELECT SPECIALTY HOSPITAL-MEMPHIS, MEMPHIS, TN, p. A645

SELECT SPECIALTY HOSPITAL-MIAMI, MIAMI, FL, p. A147

SELECT SPECIALTY HOSPITAL-MIAMI LAKES, MIAMI LAKES, FL, p. A148

SELECT SPECIALTY HOSPITAL-MIDTOWN, TULSA, OK, p. A570

SELECT SPECIALTY HOSPITAL-MILWAUKEE, MILWAUKEE, WI, p. A791

SELECT SPECIALTY HOSPITAL-MILWAUKEE ST. LUKES, MILWAUKEE, WI, p. A791

SELECT SPECIALTY HOSPITAL-MUSKEGON, MUSKEGON, MI, p. A362

SELECT SPECIALTY HOSPITAL-NASHVILLE, NASHVILLE, TN, p. A646

SELECT SPECIALTY HOSPITAL-NORTH DALLAS, CARROLLTON, TX, p. A663

SELECT SPECIALTY HOSPITAL-NORTH KNOXVILLE, POWELL, TN, p. A648

SELECT SPECIALTY HOSPITAL-NORTHEAST NEW JERSEY, ROCHELLE PARK, NJ, p. A462

SELECT SPECIALTY HOSPITAL-NORTHERN KENTUCKY, FORT THOMAS, KY, p. A283

SELECT SPECIALTY HOSPITAL-OKLAHOMA CITY, OKLAHOMA CITY, OK, p. A566

SELECT SPECIALTY HOSPITAL-OMAHA, OMAHA, NE, p. A438

SELECT SPECIALTY HOSPITAL-ORLANDO, ORLANDO, FL, p. A152

SELECT SPECIALTY HOSPITAL-ORLANDO NORTH, ORLANDO, FL, p. A152

SELECT SPECIALTY HOSPITAL-PALM BEACH, LAKE WORTH, FL, p. A143

SELECT SPECIALTY HOSPITAL-PANAMA CITY, PANAMA CITY, FL, p. A153

SELECT SPECIALTY HOSPITAL-PENSACOLA, PENSACOLA, FL, p. A154

SELECT SPECIALTY HOSPITAL-PHOENIX, PHOENIX, AZ, p. A36

SELECT SPECIALTY HOSPITAL-PHOENIX DOWNTOWN, PHOENIX, AZ, p. A36

SELECT SPECIALTY HOSPITAL-PITTSBURGH/UPMC, PITTSBURGH, PA, p. A603

SELECT SPECIALTY HOSPITAL-PONTIAC, PONTIAC, MI, p. A364

SELECT SPECIALTY HOSPITAL-QUAD CITIES, DAVENPORT, IA, p. A247

SELECT SPECIALTY HOSPITAL-SAGINAW, SAGINAW, MI, p. A366

SELECT SPECIALTY HOSPITAL-SAN ANTONIO, SAN ANTONIO, TX, p. A713

SELECT SPECIALTY HOSPITAL-SAVANNAH, SAVANNAH, GA, p. A180

SELECT SPECIALTY HOSPITAL-SIOUX FALLS, SIOUX FALLS, SD, p. A631

SELECT SPECIALTY HOSPITAL-SPRINGFIELD, SPRINGFIELD, MO, p. A419

SELECT SPECIALTY HOSPITAL-ST. LOUIS, SAINT CHARLES, MO, p. A414

SELECT SPECIALTY HOSPITAL-TALLAHASSEE, TALLAHASSEE, FL, p. A158

SELECT SPECIALTY HOSPITAL-TRI CITIES, BRISTOL, TN, p. A634

SELECT SPECIALTY HOSPITAL-TRICITIES, BRISTOL, TN, p. A634

SELECT SPECIALTY HOSPITAL-TULSA MIDTOWN, TULSA, OK, p. A570

SELECT SPECIALTY HOSPITAL-UPMC, PITTSBURGH, PA, p. A603

SELECT SPECIALTY HOSPITAL-WICHITA, WICHITA, KS, p. A279

SELECT SPECIALTY HOSPITAL-WILMINGTON, WILMINGTON, DE, p. A128

SELECT SPECIALTY HOSPITAL-YORK, YORK, PA, p. A612

SELECT SPECIALTY HOSPITAL-YOUNGSTOWN, YOUNGSTOWN, OH, p. A554

SELECT SPECIALTY HOSPITAL-YOUNGSTOWN-BOARDMAN, YOUNGSTOWN, OH, p. A554

SELECT SPECIALTY HOSPITAL-ZANESVILLE, NEWARK, OH, p. A546

SELF MEMORIAL HOSPITAL, GREENWOOD, SC, p. A621

SELF REGIONAL HEALTHCARE, GREENWOOD, SC, p. A621

SELMA COMMUNITY HOSPITAL, SELMA, CA, p. A98

SELMA REGIONAL MEDICAL CENTER, SELMA, AL, p. A24

SEMINOLE MEDICAL CENTER, SEMINOLE, OK, p. A568

SEMPERVIRENS PSYCHIATRIC HEALTH FACILITY, EUREKA, CA, p. A63

SENATOBIA COMMUNITY HOSPITAL, SENATOBIA, MS, p. A400

SENECA DISTRICT HOSPITAL, CHESTER, CA, p. A60

SENECA HEALTHCARE DISTRICT, CHESTER, CA, p. A60

SENTARA ALBEMARLE MEDICAL CENTER, ELIZABETH CITY, NC, p. A509

SENTARA BAYSIDE HOSPITAL, VIRGINIA BEACH, VA, p. A753

SENTARA CAREPLEX HOSPITAL, HAMPTON, VA, p. A743

SENTARA HALIFAX REGIONAL HOSPITAL, SOUTH BOSTON, VA, p. A751

SENTARA HAMPTON GEN HOSPITAL, HAMPTON, VA, p. A743

SENTARA LEIGH HOSPITAL, NORFOLK, VA, p. A748

SENTARA MARTHA JEFFERSON HOSPITAL, CHARLOTTESVILLE, VA, p. A739

SENTARA NORFOLK GEN HOSP, NORFOLK, VA, p. A748

SENTARA NORFOLK GENERAL HOSPITAL, NORFOLK, VA, p. A748

SENTARA NORTHERN VIRGINIA MEDICAL CENTER, WOODBRIDGE, VA, p. A754

SENTARA OBICI HOSPITAL, SUFFOLK, VA, p. A752

SENTARA POTOMAC HOSPITAL, WOODBRIDGE, VA, p. A754

SENTARA PRINCESS ANNE HOSPITAL, VIRGINIA BEACH, VA, p. A753

SENTARA RMH MEDICAL CENTER, HARRISONBURG, VA, p. A743

SENTARA VIRGINIA BEACH GENERAL HOSPITAL, VIRGINIA BEACH, VA, p. A753

SENTARA WILLIAMSBURG COMM HOSP, WILLIAMSBURG, VA, p. A753

SENTARA WILLIAMSBURG REGIONAL MEDICAL CENTER, WILLIAMSBURG, VA, p. A753

SEQUEL POMEGRANATE HEALTH SYSTEMS, COLUMBUS, OH, p. A537

SEQUOIA DISTRICT HOSPITAL, REDWOOD CITY, CA, p. A87

SEQUOIA HOSPITAL, REDWOOD CITY, CA, p. A88

SEQUOYAH MEMORIAL HOSPITAL, SALLISAW, OK, p. A567

SERENITY SPRINGS SPECIALTY HOSPITAL, RUSTON, LA, p. A313

SETON EDGAR B. DAVIS HOSPITAL, LULING, TX, p. A699

SETON HEALTH ST. MARY'S HOSPITAL, TROY, NY, p. A500

SETON HIGHLAND LAKES, BURNET, TX, p. A662

SETON HLTH SYST-ST MARY'S, TROY, NY, p. A500

SETON MEDICAL CENTER, DALY CITY, CA, p. A62

SETON MEDICAL CENTER AUSTIN, AUSTIN, TX, p. A656

SETON MEDICAL CENTER HARKER HEIGHTS, HARKER HEIGHTS, TX, p. A683

SETON MEDICAL CENTER HAYS, KYLE, TX, p. A694

SETON MEDICAL CENTER WILLIAMSON, ROUND ROCK, TX, p. A709

SETON NORTHWEST HOSPITAL, AUSTIN, TX, p. A656

SETON SHOAL CREEK HOSPITAL, AUSTIN, TX, p. A656

SETON SMITHVILLE REGIONAL HOSPITAL, SMITHVILLE, TX, p. A716

SETON SOUTHWEST HEALTHCARE CENTER, AUSTIN, TX, p. A656

SEVEN HILLS BEHAVIORAL INSTITUTE, HENDERSON, NV, p. A442

SEVEN HILLS HOSPITAL, HENDERSON, NV, p. A442

SEVEN RIVERS COMMUNITY HOSP, CRYSTAL RIVER, FL, p. A135

SEVEN RIVERS REGIONAL MEDICAL CENTER, CRYSTAL RIVER, FL, p. A135

SEVIER VALLEY HOSPITAL, RICHFIELD, UT, p. A731

SEVIER VALLEY MEDICAL CENTER, RICHFIELD, UT, p. A731

SEWARD GENERAL HOSPITAL, SEWARD, AK, p. A29

SEWICKLEY VALLEY HOSPITAL, SEWICKLEY, PA, p. A607

SEWICKLEY VALLEY HOSPITAL, (A DIVISION OF VALLEY MEDICAL FACILITIES), SEWICKLEY, PA, p. A608

SEYMOUR HOSPITAL, SEYMOUR, TX, p. A715

SEYMOUR HOSPITAL AUTHORITY, SEYMOUR, TX, p. A715

SHADY GROVE ADVENTIST HOSPITAL, ROCKVILLE, MD, p. A332

SHADYSIDE HOSPITAL, PITTSBURGH, PA, p. A603

SHAMROCK GENERAL HOSPITAL, SHAMROCK, TX, p. A715

SHANDS AT THE UNIVERSITY OF FLORIDA, GAINESVILLE, FL, p. A139

SHANDS AT VISTA, GAINESVILLE, FL, p. A139

SHANDS CHILDRENS HOSPITAL, GAINESVILLE, FL, p. A139

SHANDS JACKSONVILLE MEDICAL CENTER, JACKSONVILLE, FL, p. A141
SHANDS REHAB HOSPITAL, GAINESVILLE, FL, p. A139
SHANNON MEDICAL CENTER, SAN ANGELO, TX, p. A710
SHARE MEDICAL CENTER, ALVA, OK, p. A555
SHARKEY-ISSAQUENA COMMUNITY HOSPITAL, ROLLING FORK, MS, p. A400
SHARON HOSPITAL, SHARON, CT, p. A125
SHARON REGIONAL HEALTH SYSTEM, SHARON, PA, p. A608
SHARON REGIONAL MEDICAL CENTER, SHARON, PA, p. A608
SHARP CHULA VISTA MEDICAL CENTER, CHULA VISTA, CA, p. A60
SHARP CORONADO HOSPITAL AND HEALTHCARE CENTER, CORONADO, CA, p. A61
SHARP GROSSMONT HOSPITAL, LA MESA, CA, p. A70
SHARP HEALTHCARE MURRIETA, MURRIETA, CA, p. A80
SHARP MARY BIRCH HOSPITAL FOR WOMEN, SAN DIEGO, CA, p. A92
SHARP MARY BIRCH HOSPITAL FOR WOMEN AND NEWBORNS, SAN DIEGO, CA, p. A92
SHARP MEMORIAL HOSP, SAN DIEGO, CA, p. A92
SHARP MEMORIAL HOSPITAL, SAN DIEGO, CA, p. A92
SHARP MESA VISTA HOSPITAL, SAN DIEGO, CA, p. A92
SHARPE HOSPITAL, WESTON, WV, p. A777
SHASTA REGIONAL MEDICAL CENTER, REDDING, CA, p. A87
SHAWANO MEDICAL CENTER, SHAWANO, WI, p. A795
SHAWNEE MISSION MEDICAL CENTER, SHAWNEE MISSION, KS, p. A276
SHEBOYGAN MEMORIAL MEDICAL CTR, SHEBOYGAN, WI, p. A796
SHELBY BAPTIST MEDICAL CENTER, ALABASTER, AL, p. A13
SHELBY COUNTY MYRTUE MEM HOSP, HARLAN, IA, p. A251
SHELBY MEDICAL CENTER, ALABASTER, AL, p. A13
SHELBY MEMORIAL HOSPITAL, SHELBYVILLE, IL, p. A220
SHELTERING ARMS HOSPITAL SOUTH, MIDLOTHIAN, VA, p. A746
SHELTERING ARMS REHABILITATION HOSPITAL, MECHANICSVILLE, VA, p. A746
SHENANDOAH MEDICAL CENTER, SHENANDOAH, IA, p. A257
SHENANDOAH MEMORIAL HOSPITAL, SHENANDOAH, IA, p. A257
SHENANGO VALLEY CAMPUS, FARRELL, PA, p. A590
SHENANGO VALLEY MEDICAL CENTER, FARRELL, PA, p. A590
SHEPHERD CENTER, ATLANTA, GA, p. A165
SHEPHERD SPINAL CENTER, ATLANTA, GA, p. A165
SHEPPARD AND ENOCH PRATT HOSPITAL, BALTIMORE, MD, p. A326
SHEPPARD PRATT HEALTH SYSTEM, BALTIMORE, MD, p. A326
SHERIDAN COMMUNITY HOSPITAL, SHERIDAN, MI, p. A366
SHERIDAN COUNTY HEALTH COMPLEX, HOXIE, KS, p. A266
SHERIDAN COUNTY HOSPITAL, HOXIE, KS, p. A266
SHERIDAN MEMORIAL HOSPITAL, PLENTYWOOD, MT, p. A426
SHERIDAN MEMORIAL HOSPITAL, SHERIDAN, WY, p. A804
SHERIDAN VETERANS AFFAIRS MEDICAL CENTER, SHERIDAN, WY, p. A804
SHERMAN HOSPITAL, ELGIN, IL, p. A203
SHERMAN OAKS HOSP, SHERMAN OAKS, CA, p. A98
SHERMAN OAKS HOSPITAL, SHERMAN OAKS, CA, p. A98
SHIPROCK INDIAN HOSPITAL, SHIPROCK, NM, p. A472
SHIRLEY RYAN ABILITYLAB, CHICAGO, IL, p. A200
SHOALS HOSPITAL, MUSCLE SHOALS, AL, p. A22
SHODAIR CHILDREN'S HOSPITAL, HELENA, MT, p. A425
SHORE MEDICAL CENTER, SOMERS POINT, NJ, p. A463
SHORE MEMORIAL HOSPITAL, ONANCOCK, VA, p. A748
SHORE MEMORIAL HOSPITAL, SOMERS POINT, NJ, p. A463
SHORE REHABILITATION INSTITUTE, BRICK, NJ, p. A452
SHOSHONE MEDICAL CENTER, KELLOGG, ID, p. A191
SHRINERS HOSP FOR CHILDREN, CHICAGO, IL, p. A200
SHRINERS HOSPITALS FOR CHILDREN—CINCINNATI, CINCINNATI, OH, p. A533
SHRINERS HOSPITALS FOR CHILDREN, PORTLAND, PORTLAND, OR, p. A580
SHRINERS HOSPITALS FOR CHILDREN, SHREVEPORT, SHREVEPORT, LA, p. A314
SHRINERS HOSPITALS FOR CHILDREN, SPRINGFIELD, SPRINGFIELD, MA, p. A344
SHRINERS HOSPITALS FOR CHILDREN, ST. LOUIS, SAINT LOUIS, MO, p. A416
SHRINERS HOSPITALS FOR CHILDREN-BOSTON, BOSTON, MA, p. A336
SHRINERS HOSPITALS FOR CHILDREN-BOSTON BURNS HOSPITAL, BOSTON, MA, p. A336
SHRINERS HOSPITALS FOR CHILDREN-CHICAGO, CHICAGO, IL, p. A201

SHRINERS HOSPITALS FOR CHILDREN-CINCINNATI BURNS HOSPITAL, CINCINNATI, OH, p. A533
SHRINERS HOSPITALS FOR CHILDREN-GALVESTON, GALVESTON, TX, p. A680
SHRINERS HOSPITALS FOR CHILDREN-GALVESTON BURNS HOSPITAL, GALVESTON, TX, p. A680
SHRINERS HOSPITALS FOR CHILDREN-GREENVILLE, GREENVILLE, SC, p. A620
SHRINERS HOSPITALS FOR CHILDREN-HONOLULU, HONOLULU, HI, p. A185
SHRINERS HOSPITALS FOR CHILDREN-HOUSTON, HOUSTON, TX, p. A688
SHRINERS HOSPITALS FOR CHILDREN-INTERMOUNTAIN, SALT LAKE CITY, UT, p. A732
SHRINERS HOSPITALS FOR CHILDREN-NORTHERN CALIFORNIA, SACRAMENTO, CA, p. A89
SHRINERS HOSPITALS FOR CHILDREN-PHILADELPHIA, PHILADELPHIA, PA, p. A602
SHRINERS HOSPITALS FOR CHILDREN-PORTLAND, PORTLAND, OR, p. A580
SHRINERS HOSPITALS FOR CHILDREN-SALT LAKE CITY, SALT LAKE CITY, UT, p. A732
SHRINERS HOSPITALS FOR CHILDREN-SHREVEPORT, SHREVEPORT, LA, p. A314
SHRINERS HOSPITALS FOR CHILDREN-SPOKANE, SPOKANE, WA, p. A766
SHRINERS HOSPITALS FOR CHILDREN-SPRINGFIELD, SPRINGFIELD, MA, p. A345
SHRINERS HOSPITALS FOR CHILDREN-ST. LOUIS, SAINT LOUIS, MO, p. A416
SHRINERS HOSPITALS FOR CHILDREN-TAMPA, TAMPA, FL, p. A159
SHRINERS HOSPS FOR CHILD, PHILADELPHIA, PA, p. A602
SHRINERS HOSPS FOR CHILD, SACRAMENTO, CA, p. A89
SHRINERS HOSPS FOR CRPLD CHILD, GREENVILLE, SC, p. A620
SHRINERS HOSPS FOR CRPLD CHILD, HONOLULU, HI, p. A185
SHRINERS HOSPS FOR CRPLD CHILD, HOUSTON, TX, p. A688
SHRINERS HOSPS FOR CRPLD CHILD, SPOKANE, WA, p. A766
SHRINERS HOSPS FOR CRPLD CHILD, TAMPA, FL, p. A160
SIBLEY MEDICAL CENTER, ARLINGTON, MN, p. A372
SIBLEY MEMORIAL HOSPITAL, WASHINGTON, DC, p. A130
SIDNEY HEALTH CENTER, SIDNEY, MT, p. A428
SIDNEY REGIONAL MEDICAL CENTER, SIDNEY, NE, p. A439
SIERRA MEDICAL CENTER, EL PASO, TX, p. A675
SIERRA NEVADA MEMORIAL HOSPITAL, GRASS VALLEY, CA, p. A67
SIERRA REGIONAL HOSPITAL, TRUTH OR CONSEQUENCES, NM, p. A473
SIERRA TUCSON, TUCSON, AZ, p. A40
SIERRA VIEW DISTRICT HOSPITAL, PORTERVILLE, CA, p. A86
SIERRA VIEW MEDICAL CENTER, PORTERVILLE, CA, p. A86
SIERRA VISTA HOSPITAL, SACRAMENTO, CA, p. A90
SIERRA VISTA HOSPITAL, TRUTH OR CONSEQUENCES, NM, p. A473
SIERRA VISTA REG MED CTR, SAN LUIS OBISPO, CA, p. A95
SIERRA VISTA REGIONAL HEALTH CENTER, SIERRA VISTA, AZ, p. A38
SIERRA VISTA REGIONAL MEDICAL CENTER, SAN LUIS OBISPO, CA, p. A96
SIGNATURE HEALTHCARE BROCKTON HOSPITAL, BROCKTON, MA, p. A337
SIGNATURE PSYCHIATRIC HOSPITAL, KANSAS CITY, MO, p. A409
SILOAM SPRINGS MEMORIAL HOSPITAL, SILOAM SPRINGS, AR, p. A53
SILOAM SPRINGS REGIONAL HOSPITAL, SILOAM SPRINGS, AR, p. A53
SILVER CROSS HOSPITAL, NEW LENOX, IL, p. A214
SILVER HILL FOUNDATION HOSP, NEW CANAAN, CT, p. A123
SILVER HILL HOSPITAL, NEW CANAAN, CT, p. A124
SILVER LAKE MEDICAL CENTER, LOS ANGELES, CA, p. A76
SILVER LAKE MEDICAL CENTER-INGLESIDE HOSPITAL, ROSEMEAD, CA, p. A88
SILVER OAKS BEHAVIORAL HOSPITAL, NEW LENOX, IL, p. A214
SILVERTON HOSPITAL, SILVERTON, OR, p. A581
SIMI VALLEY HOSPITAL, SIMI VALLEY, CA, p. A98
SIMPSON GENERAL HOSPITAL, MENDENHALL, MS, p. A396
SINAI HOSPITAL OF BALTIMORE, BALTIMORE, MD, p. A326
SINAI SAMARITAN MEDICAL CENTER, MILWAUKEE, WI, p. A791
SINAI-GRACE HOSPITAL, DETROIT, MI, p. A353
SINGING RIVER HEALTH SYSTEM, PASCAGOULA, MS, p. A398
SINGING RIVER HOSPITAL SYSTEM, PASCAGOULA, MS, p. A398

SIOUX CENTER COMMUNITY HOSPITAL AND HEALTH CENTER AVERA, SIOUX CENTER, IA, p. A258
SIOUX CENTER HEALTH, SIOUX CENTER, IA, p. A258
SIOUX FALLS SPECIALTY HOSPITAL, SIOUX FALLS, SD, p. A631
SIOUX FALLS SURGICAL CENTER, SIOUX FALLS, SD, p. A631
SIOUX FALLS VETERANS AFFAIRS HEALTH CARE SYSTEM, SIOUX FALLS, SD, p. A632
SIOUX VALLEY HOSPITAL, NEW ULM, MN, p. A382
SIOUX VALLEY VERMILLION MED, VERMILLION, SD, p. A632
SIOUXLAND SURGERY CENTER, DAKOTA DUNES, SD, p. A627
SISKIN HOSPITAL FOR PHYSICAL REHABILITATION, CHATTANOOGA, TN, p. A636
SISTER KENNY INSTITUTE, MINNEAPOLIS, MN, p. A381
SISTER KENNY REHABILITATION INSTITUTE, MINNEAPOLIS, MN, p. A381
SISTERS OF CHARITY HOSPITAL OF BUFFALO, BUFFALO, NY, p. A480
SISTERS OF CHARITY PROVIDENCE HOSPITALS, COLUMBIA, SC, p. A618
SISTERSVILLE GENERAL HOSPITAL, SISTERSVILLE, WV, p. A776
SKAGGS REGIONAL MEDICAL CENTER, BRANSON, MO, p. A403
SKAGIT REGIONAL HEALTH, MOUNT VERNON, WA, p. A760
SKAGIT VALLEY HOSPITAL, MOUNT VERNON, WA, p. A761
SKIFF MEDICAL CENTER, NEWTON, IA, p. A255
SKY LAKES MEDICAL CENTER, KLAMATH FALLS, OR, p. A576
SKY RIDGE MEDICAL CENTER, LONE TREE, CO, p. A116
SKYLINE HOSPITAL, WHITE SALMON, WA, p. A769
SKYLINE MADISON CAMPUS, MADISON, TN, p. A643
SKYLINE MEDICAL CENTER, NASHVILLE, TN, p. A646
SKYRIDGE MEDICAL CENTER, CLEVELAND, TN, p. A636
SLEEPY EYE MEDICAL CENTER, SLEEPY EYE, MN, p. A386
SLEEPY EYE MUNICIPAL HOSPITAL, SLEEPY EYE, MN, p. A386
SLIDELL MEMORIAL HOSPITAL, SLIDELL, LA, p. A315
SLIDELL MEMORIAL HSP & MED CTR, SLIDELL, LA, p. A315
SMDC MEDICAL CENTER, DULUTH, MN, p. A375
SMH HOMESTEAD HOSPITAL, HOMESTEAD, FL, p. A140
SMITH COUNTY MEMORIAL HOSPITAL, SMITH CENTER, KS, p. A276
SMITH HOSPITAL, VALDOSTA, GA, p. A182
SMOKEY POINT BEHAVIORAL HOSPITAL, MARYSVILLE, WA, p. A760
SMYTH COUNTY COMMUNITY HOSPITAL, MARION, VA, p. A745
SNOQUALMIE VALLEY HOSPITAL, SNOQUALMIE, WA, p. A765
SNOQUALMIE VALLEY HOSPITAL DISTRICT, SNOQUALMIE, WA, p. A765
SO HUMBOLDT COMM HLTHCARE DIST, GARBERVILLE, CA, p. A66
SOCORRO GENERAL HOSPITAL, SOCORRO, NM, p. A472
SOIN MEDICAL CENTER, BEAVERCREEK, OH, p. A529
SOJOURN AT SENECA SENIOR BEHAVIORAL HEALTH, TIFFIN, OH, p. A550
SOLARA HOSPITAL CONROE, CONROE, TX, p. A665
SOLARA HOSPITAL HARLINGEN, HARLINGEN, TX, p. A683
SOLARA HOSPITAL HARLINGEN-BROWNSVILLE CAMPUS, BROWNSVILLE, TX, p. A660
SOLARA HOSPITAL MCALLEN, MCALLEN, TX, p. A700
SOLARA HOSPITAL OF MUSKOGEE, MUSKOGEE, OK, p. A562
SOLARA HOSPITAL OF SHAWNEE, SHAWNEE, OK, p. A568
SOLDIERS AND SAILORS MEMORIAL HOSPITAL, PENN YAN, NY, p. A495
SOMERSET MEDICAL CENTER, SOMERVILLE, NJ, p. A463
SOMERVILLE HOSPITAL, SOMERVILLE, MA, p. A344
SONOMA DEVELOPMENTAL CENTER, ELDRIDGE, CA, p. A63
SONOMA VALLEY HOSPITAL, SONOMA, CA, p. A99
SONOMA WEST MEDICAL CENTER, SEBASTOPOL, CA, p. A98
SONORA BEHAVIORAL HEALTH HOSPITAL, TUCSON, AZ, p. A40
SONORA REGIONAL MEDICAL CENTER, SONORA, CA, p. A99
SOUND SHORE MEDICAL CENTER OF WESTCHESTER, NEW ROCHELLE, NY, p. A489
SOUTH BALDWIN HOSPITAL, FOLEY, AL, p. A18
SOUTH BALDWIN REGIONAL MEDICAL CENTER, FOLEY, AL, p. A18
SOUTH BAY HOSPITAL, SUN CITY CENTER, FL, p. A158
SOUTH BAY MEDICAL CENTER, HARBOR CITY, CA, p. A68
SOUTH BEACH PSYCHIATRIC CENTER, STATEN ISLAND, NY, p. A498
SOUTH BIG HORN COUNTY HOSPITAL, BASIN, WY, p. A801
SOUTH CAMERON MEMORIAL HOSPITAL, CAMERON, LA, p. A299
SOUTH CAROLINA DEPARTMENT OF CORRECTIONS HOSPITAL, COLUMBIA, SC, p. A618

SOUTH CENTRAL HEALTH, WISHEK, ND, p. A526
SOUTH CENTRAL KANSAS MEDICAL CENTER, ARKANSAS CITY, KS, p. A261
SOUTH CENTRAL KANSAS REGIONAL MEDICAL CENTER, ARKANSAS CITY, KS, p. A261
SOUTH CENTRAL REGIONAL MEDICAL CENTER, LAUREL, MS, p. A395
SOUTH COAST GLOBAL MEDICAL CENTER, SANTA ANA, CA, p. A96
SOUTH COAST MEDICAL CENTER, LAGUNA BEACH, CA, p. A70
SOUTH COUNTY HOSPITAL, WAKEFIELD, RI, p. A614
SOUTH DAVIS COMMUNITY HOSPITAL, BOUNTIFUL, UT, p. A727
SOUTH FLORIDA BAPTIST HOSPITAL, PLANT CITY, FL, p. A154
SOUTH FLORIDA STATE HOSPITAL, HOLLYWOOD, FL, p. A140
SOUTH GEORGIA MEDICAL CENTER, VALDOSTA, GA, p. A182
SOUTH GEORGIA MEDICAL CENTER BERRIEN CAMPUS, NASHVILLE, GA, p. A178
SOUTH GEORGIA MEDICAL CENTER LANIER CAMPUS, LAKELAND, GA, p. A175
SOUTH HAVEN HEALTH SYSTEM, SOUTH HAVEN, MI, p. A367
SOUTH JERSEY HEALTHCARE—ELMER HOSPITAL, ELMER, NJ, p. A455
SOUTH JERSEY HEALTHCARE—REGIONAL MEDICAL CENTER, VINELAND, NJ, p. A465
SOUTH LAKE HOSPITAL, CLERMONT, FL, p. A134
SOUTH LAKE MEMORIAL HOSPITAL, CLERMONT, FL, p. A134
SOUTH LIMESTONE HOSPITAL, GROESBECK, TX, p. A682
SOUTH LINCOLN MEDICAL CENTER, KEMMERER, WY, p. A802
SOUTH LOUISIANA MEDICAL CENTER, HOUMA, LA, p. A303
SOUTH LYON MED CENTER, YERINGTON, NV, p. A447
SOUTH LYON MEDICAL CENTER, YERINGTON, NV, p. A447
SOUTH MISSISSIPPI COUNTY REGIONAL MEDICAL CENTER, OSCEOLA, AR, p. A51
SOUTH MISSISSIPPI STATE HOSPITAL, PURVIS, MS, p. A399
SOUTH OAKS HOSPITAL, AMITYVILLE, NY, p. A474
SOUTH PENINSULA HOSPITAL, HOMER, AK, p. A28
SOUTH PLAINS REHABILITATION HOSPITAL, LUBBOCK, TX, p. A698
SOUTH POINTE HOSPITAL, WARRENSVILLE HEIGHTS, OH, p. A552
SOUTH SACRAMENTO MEDICAL CENTER, SACRAMENTO, CA, p. A90
SOUTH SAN FRANCISCO MEDICAL CENTER, SOUTH SAN FRANCISCO, CA, p. A99
SOUTH SHORE HOSPITAL, CHICAGO, IL, p. A201
SOUTH SHORE HOSPITAL, SOUTH WEYMOUTH, MA, p. A344
SOUTH SUBURBAN HOSPITAL, HAZEL CREST, IL, p. A207
SOUTH SUNFLOWER COUNTY HOSPITAL, INDIANOLA, MS, p. A394
SOUTH TEXAS HEALTH SYSTEM, EDINBURG, TX, p. A674
SOUTH TEXAS HOSPITAL, HARLINGEN, TX, p. A683
SOUTH TEXAS REGIONAL MEDICAL CENTER, JOURDANTON, TX, p. A691
SOUTH TEXAS REHABILITATION HOSPITAL, BROWNSVILLE, TX, p. A661
SOUTH TEXAS SPINE AND SURGICAL HOSPITAL, SAN ANTONIO, TX, p. A713
SOUTH TEXAS SURGICAL HOSPITAL, CORPUS CHRISTI, TX, p. A666
SOUTH TEXAS VETERANS HEALTH CARE SYSTEM, SAN ANTONIO, TX, p. A713
SOUTHAMPTON MEMORIAL HOSPITAL, FRANKLIN, VA, p. A742
SOUTHCOAST BEHAVIORAL HEALTH, DARTMOUTH, MA, p. A338
SOUTHCOAST HOSPITALS GROUP, FALL RIVER, MA, p. A339
SOUTHCREST HOSPITAL, TULSA, OK, p. A570
SOUTHEAST ALABAMA MEDICAL CENTER, DOTHAN, AL, p. A18
SOUTHEAST BAPTIST HOSPITAL, SAN ANTONIO, TX, p. A713
SOUTHEAST COLORADO HOSPITAL, SPRINGFIELD, CO, p. A118
SOUTHEAST COLORADO HOSPITAL DISTRICT, SPRINGFIELD, CO, p. A118
SOUTHEAST GA HLTH SYST CAMDEN, SAINT MARYS, GA, p. A179
SOUTHEAST GEORGIA HEALTH SYSTEM BRUNSWICK CAMPUS, BRUNSWICK, GA, p. A167
SOUTHEAST GEORGIA HEALTH SYSTEM CAMDEN CAMPUS, SAINT MARYS, GA, p. A179
SOUTHEAST GEORGIA REG MED CTR, BRUNSWICK, GA, p. A167
SOUTHEAST HEALTH CENTER OF STODDARD COUNTY, DEXTER, MO, p. A405
SOUTHEAST HOSPITAL, CAPE GIRARDEAU, MO, p. A404

SOUTHEAST MICHIGAN SURGICAL HOSPITAL, WARREN, MI, p. A369
SOUTHEAST MISSOURI HOSPITAL, CAPE GIRARDEAU, MO, p. A404
SOUTHEAST MISSOURI MENTAL HEALTH CENTER, FARMINGTON, MO, p. A406
SOUTHEAST REGIONAL MEDICAL CENTER, KENTWOOD, LA, p. A304
SOUTHEAST REHABILITATION HOSPITAL, LAKE VILLAGE, AR, p. A48
SOUTHEASTERN HEALTH, LUMBERTON, NC, p. A514
SOUTHEASTERN KENTUCKY MEDICAL CENTER, PINEVILLE, KY, p. A292
SOUTHEASTERN OHIO REGIONAL MEDICAL CENTER, CAMBRIDGE, OH, p. A530
SOUTHEASTERN REGIONAL MEDICAL CENTER, LUMBERTON, NC, p. A514
SOUTHEASTERN REGIONAL MEDICAL CENTER, NEWNAN, GA, p. A178
SOUTHEASTERN REGIONAL REHABILITATION CENTER, FAYETTEVILLE, NC, p. A510
SOUTHERN ARIZONA VA HEALTHCARE, TUCSON, AZ, p. A41
SOUTHERN ARIZONA VETERANS AFFAIRS HEALTH CARE SYSTEM, TUCSON, AZ, p. A41
SOUTHERN CALIFORNIA HOSPITAL AT CULVER CITY, CULVER CITY, CA, p. A62
SOUTHERN CALIFORNIA HOSPITAL AT HOLLYWOOD, LOS ANGELES, CA, p. A76
SOUTHERN CALIFORNIA HOSPITAL AT VAN NUYS, VAN NUYS, CA, p. A103
SOUTHERN COOS GENERAL HOSPITAL, BANDON, OR, p. A573
SOUTHERN COOS HOSPITAL AND HEALTH CENTER, BANDON, OR, p. A573
SOUTHERN HILLS GEN HOSPITAL, HOT SPRINGS, SD, p. A628
SOUTHERN HILLS HOSPITAL AND MEDICAL CENTER, LAS VEGAS, NV, p. A444
SOUTHERN HILLS MEDICAL CENTER, NASHVILLE, TN, p. A646
SOUTHERN INDIANA REHABILITATION HOSPITAL, NEW ALBANY, IN, p. A238
SOUTHERN INYO HEALTHCARE DIST, LONE PINE, CA, p. A72
SOUTHERN INYO HEALTHCARE DISTRICT, LONE PINE, CA, p. A72
SOUTHERN KENTUCKY REHABILITATION HOSPITAL, BOWLING GREEN, KY, p. A281
SOUTHERN MAINE HEALTH CARE—BIDDEFORD MEDICAL CENTER, BIDDEFORD, ME, p. A319
SOUTHERN MAINE HEALTH CARE—BIDDEFORD MEDICAL CTR, BIDDEFORD, ME, p. A319
SOUTHERN MAINE HEALTHCARE—BIDDEFORD CAMPUS, BIDDEFORD, ME, p. A319
SOUTHERN MARYLAND HOSPITAL CENTER, CLINTON, MD, p. A328
SOUTHERN NEVADA ADULT MENTAL HEALTH SERVICES, LAS VEGAS, NV, p. A444
SOUTHERN NEW HAMPSHIRE MEDICAL CENTER, NASHUA, NH, p. A450
SOUTHERN NH REGIONAL MED CTR, NASHUA, NH, p. A450
SOUTHERN OCEAN MEDICAL CENTER, MANAHAWKIN, NJ, p. A458
SOUTHERN OHIO MEDICAL CENTER, PORTSMOUTH, OH, p. A548
SOUTHERN REGIONAL MEDICAL CENTER, RIVERDALE, GA, p. A178
SOUTHERN SURGICAL HOSPITAL, SLIDELL, LA, p. A315
SOUTHERN TENNESSEE MEDICAL CENTER, WINCHESTER, TN, p. A650
SOUTHERN TENNESSEE REGIONAL HEALTH SYSTEM-LAWRENCEBURG, LAWRENCEBURG, TN, p. A642
SOUTHERN TENNESSEE REGIONAL HEALTH SYSTEM-PULASKI, PULASKI, TN, p. A648
SOUTHERN TENNESSEE REGIONAL HEALTH SYSTEM-SEWANEE, SEWANEE, TN, p. A649
SOUTHERN TENNESSEE REGIONAL HEALTH SYSTEM-WINCHESTER, WINCHESTER, TN, p. A650
SOUTHERN TENNESSESS REGIONAL HEALTH SYSTEM-PULASKI, PULASKI, TN, p. A648
SOUTHERN VIRGINIA MENTAL HEALTH INSTITUTE, DANVILLE, VA, p. A741
SOUTHERN VIRGINIA REGIONAL MEDICAL CENTER, EMPORIA, VA, p. A741
SOUTHERN WINDS HOSPITAL, HIALEAH, FL, p. A139
SOUTHLAKE CAMPUS, MERRILLVILLE, IN, p. A236
SOUTHLAKE CENTER FOR MENTAL HEALTH, MERRILLVILLE, IN, p. A236
SOUTHSIDE COMMUNITY HOSPITAL, FARMVILLE, VA, p. A742
SOUTHSIDE HOSPITAL, BAY SHORE, NY, p. A475
SOUTHSIDE REGIONAL MEDICAL CENTER, PETERSBURG, VA, p. A749

SOUTHWELL MEDICAL, ADEL, GA, p. A163
SOUTHWEST COMM HLTH SYSTEM, MIDDLEBURG HEIGHTS, OH, p. A545
SOUTHWEST CONNECTICUT MENTAL HEALTH SYSTEM, BRIDGEPORT, CT, p. A121
SOUTHWEST GENERAL HEALTH CENTER, MIDDLEBURG HEIGHTS, OH, p. A545
SOUTHWEST GENERAL HOSPITAL, SAN ANTONIO, TX, p. A713
SOUTHWEST GEORGIA REGIONAL MEDICAL CENTER, CUTHBERT, GA, p. A170
SOUTHWEST HEALTH, PLATTEVILLE, WI, p. A794
SOUTHWEST HEALTH CENTER, PLATTEVILLE, WI, p. A794
SOUTHWEST HEALTH CENTER NURSING HOME, CUBA CITY, WI, p. A782
SOUTHWEST HEALTH SYSTEM, CORTEZ, CO, p. A109
SOUTHWEST HEALTHCARE SERVICES, BOWMAN, ND, p. A521
SOUTHWEST HEALTHCARE SYSTEM, MURRIETA, CA, p. A80
SOUTHWEST MEDICAL CENTER, LIBERAL, KS, p. A269
SOUTHWEST MEMORIAL HOSPITAL, CORTEZ, CO, p. A109
SOUTHWEST MENTAL HEALTH CENTER, SAN ANTONIO, TX, p. A713
SOUTHWEST MISSISSIPPI REGIONAL MEDICAL CENTER, MCCOMB, MS, p. A396
SOUTHWEST REGIONAL MEDICAL CENTER, WAYNESBURG, PA, p. A610
SOUTHWEST TEXAS METHODIST HOSP, SAN ANTONIO, TX, p. A713
SOUTHWEST WASHINGTON MEDICAL CENTER, VANCOUVER, WA, p. A768
SOUTHWESTERN MEDICAL CENTER, LAWTON, OK, p. A561
SOUTHWESTERN MEMORIAL HOSPITAL, WEATHERFORD, OK, p. A572
SOUTHWESTERN REGIONAL MEDICAL CENTER, TULSA, OK, p. A570
SOUTHWESTERN STATE HOSPITAL, MARION, VA, p. A745
SOUTHWESTERN VERMONT MEDICAL CENTER, BENNINGTON, VT, p. A735
SOUTHWESTERN VIRGINIA MENTAL HEALTH INSTITUTE, MARION, VA, p. A745
SOUTHWOOD PSYCHIATRIC HOSPITAL, PITTSBURGH, PA, p. A603
SOVAH HEALTH-DANVILLE, DANVILLE, VA, p. A741
SOVAH HEALTH-MARTINSVILLE, MARTINSVILLE, VA, p. A746
SPALDING REGIONAL HOSPITAL, GRIFFIN, GA, p. A173
SPALDING REHABILITATION HOSPITAL, AURORA, CO, p. A107
SPANISH PEAKS REGIONAL HEALTH CENTER, WALSENBURG, CO, p. A119
SPARKS FAMILY HOSPITAL, SPARKS, NV, p. A447
SPARKS MEDICAL CENTER—VAN BUREN, VAN BUREN, AR, p. A54
SPARKS REGIONAL MEDICAL CENTER, FORT SMITH, AR, p. A46
SPARROW CARSON HOSPITAL, CARSON CITY, MI, p. A350
SPARROW CLINTON HOSPITAL, SAINT JOHNS, MI, p. A366
SPARROW EATON HOSPITAL, CHARLOTTE, MI, p. A351
SPARROW HEALTH SYSTEM, LANSING, MI, p. A360
SPARROW HOSPITAL, LANSING, MI, p. A360
SPARROW IONIA HOSPITAL, IONIA, MI, p. A358
SPARROW REGIONAL CHILDREN'S CENTER, LANSING, MI, p. A360
SPARROW SPECIALTY HOSPITAL, LANSING, MI, p. A360
SPARTA COMMUNITY HOSPITAL, SPARTA, IL, p. A220
SPARTANBURG HOSPITAL FOR RESTORATIVE CARE, SPARTANBURG, SC, p. A624
SPARTANBURG MEDICAL CENTER—CHURCH STREET CAMPUS, SPARTANBURG, SC, p. A624
SPARTANBURG MEDICAL CENTER—MARY BLACK, SPARTANBURG, SC, p. A624
SPARTANBURG MEDICAL CENTER, SPARTANBURG, SC, p. A624
SPAULDING HOSPITAL CAMBRIDGE, CAMBRIDGE, MA, p. A338
SPAULDING HOSPITAL FOR CONTINUING MEDICAL CARE CAMBRIDGE, CAMBRIDGE, MA, p. A338
SPAULDING REHABILITATION HOSPITAL, CHARLESTOWN, MA, p. A338
SPAULDING REHABILITATION HOSPITAL CAPE COD, EAST SANDWICH, MA, p. A338
SPEARE MEMORIAL HOSPITAL, PLYMOUTH, NH, p. A451
SPEARFISH REGIONAL HOSPITAL, SPEARFISH, SD, p. A632
SPEARFISH SURGERY CENTER, SPEARFISH, SD, p. A632
SPECIALISTS HOSPITAL—SHREVEPORT, SHREVEPORT, LA, p. A314
SPECIALISTS HOSPITAL SHREVEPORT, SHREVEPORT, LA, p. A314
SPECIALTY EXTENDED CARE HOSPITAL OF MONROE, MONROE, LA, p. A309
SPECIALTY HOSP OF SANTA ANA, SANTA ANA, CA, p. A96

SPECIALTY HOSPITAL, MONROE, LA, p. A309
SPECIALTY HOSPITAL, WEST COVINA, CA, p. A104
SPECIALTY HOSPITAL AT KIMBALL, LAKEWOOD, NJ, p. A457
SPECIALTY HOSPITAL JACKSONVILLE, JACKSONVILLE, FL, p. A141
SPECIALTY HOSPITAL OF ALBUQUERQUE, ALBUQUERQUE, NM, p. A468
SPECIALTY HOSPITAL OF CENTRAL JERSEY, LAKEWOOD, NJ, p. A457
SPECIALTY HOSPITAL OF HOUSTON, HOUSTON, TX, p. A688
SPECIALTY HOSPITAL OF LORAIN, AMHERST, OH, p. A527
SPECIALTY HOSPITAL OF MERIDIAN, MERIDIAN, MS, p. A397
SPECIALTY REHABILITATION HOSPITAL, COUSHATTA, LA, p. A299
SPECIALTY REHABILITATION HOSPITAL, LULING, LA, p. A307
SPECIALTY REHABILITATION HOSPITAL OF COUSHATTA, COUSHATTA, LA, p. A299
SPECTRUM HEALTH—BUTTERWORTH, GRAND RAPIDS, MI, p. A356
SPECTRUM HEALTH—BUTTERWORTH HOSPITAL, GRAND RAPIDS, MI, p. A356
SPECTRUM HEALTH—GRAND RAPIDS, GRAND RAPIDS, MI, p. A356
SPECTRUM HEALTH BIG RAPIDS HOSPITAL, BIG RAPIDS, MI, p. A349
SPECTRUM HEALTH GERBER MEMORIAL, FREMONT, MI, p. A355
SPECTRUM HEALTH KELSEY HOSPITAL, LAKEVIEW, MI, p. A359
SPECTRUM HEALTH LAKELAND, SAINT JOSEPH, MI, p. A366
SPECTRUM HEALTH LUDINGTON HOSPITAL, LUDINGTON, MI, p. A361
SPECTRUM HEALTH PENNOCK, HASTINGS, MI, p. A357
SPECTRUM HEALTH REED CITY HOSPITAL, REED CITY, MI, p. A364
SPECTRUM HEALTH UNITED HOSPITAL, GREENVILLE, MI, p. A356
SPECTRUM HEALTH ZEELAND COMMUNITY HOSPITAL, ZEELAND, MI, p. A370
SPECTRUM HEALTH-REED CITY, REED CITY, MI, p. A364
SPECTRUM HLTH KELSEY CAMPUS, LAKEVIEW, MI, p. A359
SPENCER HOSPITAL, SPENCER, IA, p. A258
SPENCER MUNICIPAL HOSPITAL, SPENCER, IA, p. A258
SPINE HOSP OF SOUTH TEXAS, SAN ANTONIO, TX, p. A713
SPINE HOSPITAL OF LOUISIANA (FORMALLY THE NEUROMEDICAL CENTER SURGICAL HOSPITAL), BATON ROUGE, LA, p. A297
SPIRE CANE CREEK REHABILITATION HOSPITAL, MARTIN, TN, p. A643
SPIRIT OF ST LOUIS HOSPITAL, SAINT CHARLES, MO, p. A414
SPOKANE VETERANS AFFAIRS MEDICAL CENTER, SPOKANE, WA, p. A766
SPOONER HEALTH, SPOONER, WI, p. A796
SPOONER HEALTH SYSTEM, SPOONER, WI, p. A796
SPOTSYLVANIA REGIONAL MEDICAL CENTER, FREDERICKSBURG, VA, p. A742
SPRING GROVE HOSPITAL CENTER, BALTIMORE, MD, p. A326
SPRING HARBOR HOSPITAL, WESTBROOK, ME, p. A323
SPRING HILL REGIONAL HOSPITAL, SPRING HILL, FL, p. A158
SPRING MOUNTAIN SAHARA, LAS VEGAS, NV, p. A444
SPRING MOUNTAIN TREATMENT CENTER, LAS VEGAS, NV, p. A444
SPRING VALLEY HOSPITAL MEDICAL CENTER, LAS VEGAS, NV, p. A444
SPRING VIEW HOSPITAL, LEBANON, KY, p. A286
SPRINGBROOK AUTISM BEHAVIORAL HEALTH SYSTEM, TRAVELERS REST, SC, p. A625
SPRINGBROOK BEHAVIORAL HEALTH, TRAVELERS REST, SC, p. A625
SPRINGBROOK HOSPITAL, BROOKSVILLE, FL, p. A133
SPRINGFIELD HOSPITAL, SPRINGFIELD, PA, p. A608
SPRINGFIELD HOSPITAL, SPRINGFIELD, VT, p. A736
SPRINGFIELD HOSPITAL CENTER, SYKESVILLE, MD, p. A333
SPRINGFIELD REGIONAL MEDICAL CENTER—HIGH STREET CAMPUS, SPRINGFIELD, OH, p. A549
SPRINGFIELD REGIONAL MEDICAL CENTER, SPRINGFIELD, OH, p. A549
SPRINGHILL MEDICAL CENTER, SPRINGHILL, LA, p. A315
SPRINGHILL MEMORIAL HOSPITAL, MOBILE, AL, p. A22
SPRINGS MEMORIAL HOSPITAL, LANCASTER, SC, p. A622
SPRINGWOODS BEHAVIORAL HEALTH HOSPITAL, FAYETTEVILLE, AR, p. A45
SPRUCE PINE COMMUNITY HOSPITAL, SPRUCE PINE, NC, p. A518
SSM CARDINAL GLENNON CHILDREN'S HOSPITAL, SAINT LOUIS, MO, p. A416
SSM CARDINAL GLENNON CHILDREN'S MEDICAL CENTER, SAINT LOUIS, MO, p. A416

SSM DEPAUL HEALTH CENTER, BRIDGETON, MO, p. A403
SSM HEALTH DEPAUL HOSPITAL—ST. LOUIS, BRIDGETON, MO, p. A403
SSM HEALTH GOOD SAMARITAN HOSPITAL, MOUNT VERNON, IL, p. A213
SSM HEALTH SAINT LOUIS UNIVERSITY HOSPITAL—SOUTH CAMPUS, SAINT LOUIS, MO, p. A417
SSM HEALTH SAINT LOUIS UNIVERSITY HOSPITAL, SAINT LOUIS, MO, p. A417
SSM HEALTH ST. ANTHONY HOSPITAL—OKLAHOMA CITY, OKLAHOMA CITY, OK, p. A566
SSM HEALTH ST. ANTHONY HOSPITAL—SHAWNEE, SHAWNEE, OK, p. A568
SSM HEALTH ST. CLARE HOSPITAL—FENTON, FENTON, MO, p. A406
SSM HEALTH ST. CLARE HOSPITAL-BARABOO, BARABOO, WI, p. A780
SSM HEALTH ST. FRANCIS HOSPITAL—MARYVILLE, MARYVILLE, MO, p. A411
SSM HEALTH ST. JOSEPH—ST. CHARLES, SAINT CHARLES, MO, p. A414
SSM HEALTH ST. JOSEPH—WENTZVILLE, WENTZVILLE, MO, p. A420
SSM HEALTH ST. JOSEPH HOSPITAL—LAKE SAINT LOUIS, LAKE SAINT LOUIS, MO, p. A410
SSM HEALTH ST. MARY'S HOSPITAL—AUDRAIN, MEXICO, MO, p. A412
SSM HEALTH ST. MARY'S HOSPITAL—JEFFERSON CITY, JEFFERSON CITY, MO, p. A408
SSM HEALTH ST. MARY'S HOSPITAL—ST. LOUIS, SAINT LOUIS, MO, p. A417
SSM HEALTH ST. MARY'S HOSPITAL, MADISON, WI, p. A788
SSM HEALTH ST. MARY'S HOSPITAL CENTRALIA, CENTRALIA, IL, p. A196
SSM HEALTH ST. MARY'S HOSPITAL JANESVILLE, JANESVILLE, WI, p. A786
SSM REHABILITATION HOSPITAL, BRIDGETON, MO, p. A403
SSM SELECT REHABILITATION HOSPITAL, RICHMOND HEIGHTS, MO, p. A414
SSM ST. CLARE HOSPITAL, FENTON, MO, p. A406
SSM ST. JOSEPH—WENTZVILLE, WENTZVILLE, MO, p. A420
SSM ST. JOSEPH HEALTH CENTER, SAINT CHARLES, MO, p. A414
SSM ST. JOSEPH HOSPITAL WEST, LAKE SAINT LOUIS, MO, p. A410
SSM ST. MARY'S HEALTH CENTER, SAINT LOUIS, MO, p. A417
ST AGNES MEDICAL CENTER, FRESNO, CA, p. A66
ST ANDREW'S MEDICAL CENTER, BOTTINEAU, ND, p. A521
ST ANNE GENERAL HOSPITAL, RACELAND, LA, p. A313
ST ANNE'S HOSPITAL, FALL RIVER, MA, p. A339
ST ANN'S HOSPITAL, WESTERVILLE, OH, p. A553
ST ANSGAR'S HEALTH CENTER, PARK RIVER, ND, p. A525
ST ANTHONY CONTINUING CARE CTR, ROCK ISLAND, IL, p. A218
ST ANTHONY HOSPITAL, CHICAGO, IL, p. A201
ST BARNABAS MEDICAL CENTER, LIVINGSTON, NJ, p. A457
ST BERNARDS REGIONAL MED CTR, JONESBORO, AR, p. A48
ST CATHERINE HOSP OF CHICAGO, EAST CHICAGO, IN, p. A226
ST CATHERINE HOSP ON HALF MOON, MOSS BEACH, CA, p. A80
ST CHARLES HOSP & REHAB CENTER, PORT JEFFERSON, NY, p. A495
ST CHARLES HOSPITAL, LULING, LA, p. A307
ST CLAIR REGIONAL HOSPITAL, PELL CITY, AL, p. A23
ST CLARE HOSPITAL, LAKEWOOD, WA, p. A760
ST CLARE'S HOSPITAL/BOONTON, BOONTON TOWNSHIP, NJ, p. A452
ST CLARE'S HOSPITAL/DENVILLE, DENVILLE, NJ, p. A454
ST CLOUD HOSPITAL, SAINT CLOUD, FL, p. A156
ST CROIX VALLEY MEM HOSPITAL, ST CROIX FALLS, WI, p. A796
ST DAVID'S PAVILION, AUSTIN, TX, p. A656
ST DAVID'S REHAB HOSPITAL, AUSTIN, TX, p. A656
ST ELIZABETH HOSPITAL, UTICA, NY, p. A500
ST ELIZABETH HOSPITAL, WABASHA, MN, p. A387
ST ELIZABETH MED CENTER, LAFAYETTE, IN, p. A234
ST ELIZABETH MEDICAL CENTER, GRANITE CITY, IL, p. A206
ST FRANCIS COMM HOSPITAL, FEDERAL WAY, WA, p. A758
ST FRANCIS HEALTH CENTER, COLORADO SPRINGS, CO, p. A109
ST FRANCIS HEALTH SYSTEM, GREENVILLE, SC, p. A620
ST FRANCIS HOME, WILLIAMSVILLE, NY, p. A502
ST FRANCIS HOSPITAL, CHARLESTON, WV, p. A771
ST FRANCIS HOSPITAL, MEMPHIS, TN, p. A645
ST FRANCIS HOSPITAL CRANBERRY, CRANBERRY, PA, p. A587
ST FRANCIS HOSPITAL OF BUFFALO, BUFFALO, NY, p. A480

ST FRANCIS HOSPITAL, INC, COLUMBUS, GA, p. A169
ST FRANCIS MEDICAL CENTER, MIDLOTHIAN, VA, p. A746
ST FRANCIS MEMORIAL HOSPITAL, SAN FRANCISCO, CA, p. A94
ST JAMES COMMUNITY HOSPITAL, BUTTE, MT, p. A422
ST JEROME HOSPITAL, BATAVIA, NY, p. A475
ST JOHN HOSPITAL, LEAVENWORTH, KS, p. A269
ST JOHN MEDICAL CENTER, STEUBENVILLE, OH, p. A549
ST JOHNS RIVER HOSPITAL, JACKSONVILLE, FL, p. A141
ST JOHN'S EPISCOPAL HOME, BROOKLYN, NY, p. A479
ST JOHN'S EPISCOPAL HOSPITAL, SMITHTOWN, NY, p. A498
ST JOHN'S HOSP & LIVING CTR, JACKSON, WY, p. A802
ST JOHN'S REGIONAL HEALTH CTR, SALINA, KS, p. A276
ST JOHN'S RIVERSIDE HOSPTIAL, YONKERS, NY, p. A502
ST JOSEPH HEALTH SYSTEM, FORT WAYNE, IN, p. A228
ST JOSEPH HEALTHCARE, NASHUA, NH, p. A450
ST JOSEPH HOSP & HLTH CARE CTR, TACOMA, WA, p. A767
ST JOSEPH HOSP OF RHODE ISLAND, NORTH PROVIDENCE, RI, p. A613
ST JOSEPH HOSPITAL, CONCORDIA, KS, p. A263
ST JOSEPH MEDICAL CENTER, BLOOMINGTON, IL, p. A195
ST JOSEPH MERCY-OAKLAND, PONTIAC, MI, p. A364
ST JOSEPH'S HOSP & HLTH CTR, TUCSON, AZ, p. A41
ST JOSEPH'S HOSPITAL, BUCKHANNON, WV, p. A771
ST JOSEPH'S HOSPITAL HLTH CNTR, SYRACUSE, NY, p. A499
ST JOSEPH'S MERCY HOSP-EAST, MOUNT CLEMENS, MI, p. A362
ST JOSEPH'S MERCY HOSPITAL, CLINTON TOWNSHIP, MI, p. A351
ST JOSEPH'S PARKSIDE HOSPITAL, STOCKTON, CA, p. A99
ST JOSEPH'S-TRI COUNTY HOSP, ROMEO, MI, p. A365
ST JUDE HOSP & REHAB CENTER, FULLERTON, CA, p. A66
ST LOUIS STATE PSYCH REHAB CTR, SAINT LOUIS, MO, p. A417
ST LOUISE REGIONAL HOSPITAL, GILROY, CA, p. A66
ST LUKE HOSPITAL, MARION, KS, p. A270
ST LUKES REHAB INSTITUTE, SPOKANE, WA, p. A766
ST LUKE'S HOSP OF NEW BEDFORD, NEW BEDFORD, MA, p. A342
ST LUKE'S HOSPITAL—ALLENTOWN CAMPUS, ALLENTOWN, PA, p. A583
ST LUKE'S HOSPITAL, DAVENPORT, IA, p. A247
ST LUKE'S HOSPITAL, KANSAS CITY, MO, p. A409
ST LUKE'S HOSPITAL, SAGINAW, MI, p. A366
ST LUKE'S LUTHERAN HOSPITAL, SAN ANTONIO, TX, p. A713
ST LUKE'S MEDICAL CENTER, MILWAUKEE, WI, p. A791
ST LUKE'S MEM HOSPITAL CENTER, UTICA, NY, p. A500
ST LUKE'S SOUTH SHORE, CUDAHY, WI, p. A782
ST LUKE'S SUGAR LAND HOSPITAL, SUGAR LAND, TX, p. A717
ST LUKE'S TRI-STATE HOSPITAL, BOWMAN, ND, p. A521
ST MARY HOSPITAL, LIVONIA, MI, p. A360
ST MARY HOSPITAL, QUINCY, IL, p. A218
ST MARY MEDICAL CENTER, GALESBURG, IL, p. A205
ST MARY OF THE PLAINS HOSPITAL, LUBBOCK, TX, p. A698
ST MARY-CORWIN REG MED CENTER, PUEBLO, CO, p. A118
ST MARY'S GENERAL HOSPITAL, LEWISTON, ME, p. A321
ST MARY'S HOSP OF BLUE SPRINGS, BLUE SPRINGS, MO, p. A402
ST MARY'S HOSPITAL, ATHENS, GA, p. A164
ST MARY'S HOSPITAL, HUNTINGTON, WV, p. A773
ST MARY'S HOSPITAL, RICHMOND, VA, p. A750
ST MARY'S HOSPITAL, WATERBURY, CT, p. A126
ST MARY'S HOSPITAL, WEST PALM BEACH, FL, p. A162
ST MARY'S HOSPITAL AND HOME, WINSTED, MN, p. A388
ST MARY'S MEDICAL CENTER, SAN FRANCISCO, CA, p. A94
ST MARY'S MERCY HOSPITAL, ENID, OK, p. A559
ST MARY'S REGIONAL MED CENTER, RENO, NV, p. A446
ST MARY'S REGIONAL MEDICAL CTR, RUSSELLVILLE, AR, p. A52
ST PAUL-RAMSEY MEDICAL CENTER, SAINT PAUL, MN, p. A385
ST PETER COMMUNITY HOSPITAL, SAINT PETER, MN, p. A385
ST PETER HOSPITAL, OLYMPIA, WA, p. A761
ST PETERSBURG MEDICAL CENTER, SAINT PETERSBURG, FL, p. A156
ST PETER'S COMMUNITY HOSPITAL, HELENA, MT, p. A425
ST PETER'S UNIVERSITY HOSPITAL, NEW BRUNSWICK, NJ, p. A459
ST THOMAS BENEDICTINE HLTH CTR, CANON CITY, CO, p. A108
ST VINCENT CHILDREN'S HOSPITAL, INDIANAPOLIS, IN, p. A233
ST VINCENT GENERAL HOSPITAL, LEADVILLE, CO, p. A115
ST VINCENT MEMORIAL HOSPITAL, TAYLORVILLE, IL, p. A221
ST VINCENT'S HOSPITAL, BIRMINGHAM, AL, p. A15

ST VINCENT'S HOSPITAL, STATEN ISLAND, NY, p. A498

ST. AGNES HOSPITAL, FOND DU LAC, WI, p. A784

ST. ALBANS PRIMARY AND EXTENDED CARE CENTER, JAMAICA, NY, p. A486

ST. ALEXIUS HOSPITAL—BROADWAY CAMPUS, SAINT LOUIS, MO, p. A417

ST. ALEXIUS HOSPITAL, SAINT LOUIS, MO, p. A417

ST. ALEXIUS MEDICAL CENTER, BISMARCK, ND, p. A521

ST. ALEXIUS MEDICAL CENTER, HOFFMAN ESTATES, IL, p. A208

ST. ALOISIUS MEDICAL CENTER, HARVEY, ND, p. A524

ST. ANDREW'S HEALTH CENTER, BOTTINEAU, ND, p. A521

ST. ANNE HOSPITAL, BURIEN, WA, p. A756

ST. ANNE MERCY HOSPITAL, TOLEDO, OH, p. A550

ST. ANTHONY CENTRAL HOSPITAL, LAKEWOOD, CO, p. A115

ST. ANTHONY COMMUNITY HOSPITAL, WARWICK, NY, p. A501

ST. ANTHONY HOSPITAL, GIG HARBOR, WA, p. A758

ST. ANTHONY HOSPITAL, LAKEWOOD, CO, p. A115

ST. ANTHONY HOSPITAL, OKLAHOMA CITY, OK, p. A566

ST. ANTHONY HOSPITAL, PENDLETON, OR, p. A578

ST. ANTHONY NORTH HEALTH CAMPUS, WESTMINSTER, CO, p. A119

ST. ANTHONY NORTH HOSPITAL, WESTMINSTER, CO, p. A119

ST. ANTHONY REGIONAL HOSPITAL, CARROLL, IA, p. A244

ST. ANTHONY SHAWNEE HOSPITAL, SHAWNEE, OK, p. A568

ST. ANTHONY SOUTH, OKLAHOMA CITY, OK, p. A566

ST. ANTHONY SUMMIT MEDICAL CENTER, FRISCO, CO, p. A113

ST. ANTHONY'S HOSPITAL, SAINT PETERSBURG, FL, p. A156

ST. ANTHONY'S MEMORIAL HOSPITAL, EFFINGHAM, IL, p. A203

ST. ANTHONY'S MERCY, SAINT LOUIS, MO, p. A417

ST. ANTHONY'S REHABILITATION HOSPITAL, LAUDERDALE LAKES, FL, p. A144

ST. BARNABAS HOSPITAL, BRONX, NY, p. A477

ST. BENEDICTS FAMILY MEDICAL CENTER, JEROME, ID, p. A190

ST. BERNARD HOSPITAL AND HEALTH CARE CENTER, CHICAGO, IL, p. A201

ST. BERNARD PARISH HOSPITAL, CHALMETTE, LA, p. A299

ST. BERNARDINE MEDICAL CENTER, SAN BERNARDINO, CA, p. A91

ST. BERNARDS FIVE RIVERS, POCAHONTAS, AR, p. A52

ST. BERNARDS MEDICAL CENTER, JONESBORO, AR, p. A48

ST. CATHERINE HOSPITAL, EAST CHICAGO, IN, p. A227

ST. CATHERINE HOSPITAL, GARDEN CITY, KS, p. A264

ST. CATHERINE OF SIENA MEDICAL CENTER, SMITHTOWN, NY, p. A498

ST. CATHERINE'S REHABILITATION HOSPITAL, NORTH MIAMI, FL, p. A149

ST. CHARLES BEND, BEND, OR, p. A573

ST. CHARLES HEALTH SYSTEM-BEND, BEND, OR, p. A573

ST. CHARLES HOSPITAL, PORT JEFFERSON, NY, p. A495

ST. CHARLES MADRAS, MADRAS, OR, p. A577

ST. CHARLES MEDICAL CENTER—REDMOND, REDMOND, OR, p. A580

ST. CHARLES PARISH HOSPITAL, LULING, LA, p. A307

ST. CHARLES PRINEVILLE, PRINEVILLE, OR, p. A580

ST. CHARLES REDMOND, REDMOND, OR, p. A580

ST. CHARLES SURGICAL HOSPITAL, NEW ORLEANS, LA, p. A311

ST. CHRISTOPHER'S HOSPITAL FOR CHILDREN, PHILADELPHIA, PA, p. A602

ST. CLAIR HOSPITAL, PITTSBURGH, PA, p. A603

ST. CLAIR MEMORIAL HOSPITAL, PITTSBURGH, PA, p. A603

ST. CLAIRE HEALTHCARE, MOREHEAD, KY, p. A290

ST. CLAIRE REGIONAL MEDICAL CENTER, MOREHEAD, KY, p. A290

ST. CLARE HOSPITAL, BARABOO, WI, p. A780

ST. CLARE HOSPITAL, LAKEWOOD, WA, p. A760

ST. CLARE'S HOSPITAL/DOVER, DOVER, NJ, p. A454

ST. CLOUD HOSPITAL, SAINT CLOUD, MN, p. A384

ST. CLOUD REGIONAL MEDICAL CENTER, SAINT CLOUD, FL, p. A156

ST. CLOUD VETERANS AFFAIRS HEALTH CARE SYSTEM, SAINT CLOUD, MN, p. A384

ST. CROIX REGIONAL MEDICAL CENTER, ST CROIX FALLS, WI, p. A796

ST. DAVID'S MEDICAL CENTER, AUSTIN, TX, p. A656

ST. DAVID'S NORTH AUSTIN MEDICAL CENTER, AUSTIN, TX, p. A656

ST. DAVID'S ROUND ROCK MEDICAL CENTER, ROUND ROCK, TX, p. A710

ST. DAVID'S SOUTH AUSTIN HOSPITAL, AUSTIN, TX, p. A656

ST. DAVID'S SOUTH AUSTIN MEDICAL CENTER, AUSTIN, TX, p. A656

ST. DOMINIC-JACKSON MEMORIAL HOSPITAL, JACKSON, MS, p. A395

ST. EDWARD MERCY MEDICAL CENTER, FORT SMITH, AR, p. A46

ST. ELIAS SPECIALTY HOSPITAL, ANCHORAGE, AK, p. A27

ST. ELIZABETH BOARDMAN HEALTH CENTER, BOARDMAN, OH, p. A529

ST. ELIZABETH COMMUNITY HOSPITAL, RED BLUFF, CA, p. A87

ST. ELIZABETH EDGEWOOD, EDGEWOOD, KY, p. A282

ST. ELIZABETH FLORENCE, FLORENCE, KY, p. A283

ST. ELIZABETH FORT THOMAS, FORT THOMAS, KY, p. A283

ST. ELIZABETH GRANT, WILLIAMSTOWN, KY, p. A294

ST. ELIZABETH HEALTH CENTER, YOUNGSTOWN, OH, p. A554

ST. ELIZABETH HEALTH SERVICES, BAKER CITY, OR, p. A573

ST. ELIZABETH HEALTHCARE FLORENCE, FLORENCE, KY, p. A283

ST. ELIZABETH HEALTHCARE FORT THOMAS, FORT THOMAS, KY, p. A283

ST. ELIZABETH HEALTHCARE-EDGEWOOD, EDGEWOOD, KY, p. A282

ST. ELIZABETH HOSPITAL, ENUMCLAW, WA, p. A758

ST. ELIZABETH HOSPITAL, GONZALES, LA, p. A302

ST. ELIZABETH MEDICAL CENTER, UTICA, NY, p. A500

ST. ELIZABETH MEDICAL CENTER-GRANT COUNTY, WILLIAMSTOWN, KY, p. A294

ST. ELIZABETH MEDICAL CENTER-NORTH, COVINGTON, KY, p. A282

ST. ELIZABETH TOLUCA LAKE CONVALESCENT HOSPITAL, NORTH HOLLYWOOD, CA, p. A81

ST. ELIZABETHS HOSPITAL, WASHINGTON, DC, p. A130

ST. ELIZABETH'S HOSPITAL, O'FALLON, IL, p. A215

ST. ELIZABETH'S MEDICAL CENTER, BRIGHTON, MA, p. A337

ST. FRANCIS HEALTH, TOPEKA, KS, p. A277

ST. FRANCIS HEALTHCARE CAMPUS, BRECKENRIDGE, MN, p. A373

ST. FRANCIS HOSPITAL, COLUMBUS, GA, p. A169

ST. FRANCIS HOSPITAL, FEDERAL WAY, WA, p. A758

ST. FRANCIS HOSPITAL, LITCHFIELD, IL, p. A210

ST. FRANCIS HOSPITAL, ROSLYN, NY, p. A497

ST. FRANCIS HOSPITAL, WILMINGTON, DE, p. A128

ST. FRANCIS HOSPITAL, THE HEART CENTER, ROSLYN, NY, p. A497

ST. FRANCIS MEDICAL CENTER, LYNWOOD, CA, p. A76

ST. FRANCIS MEDICAL CENTER, MONROE, LA, p. A309

ST. FRANCIS MEDICAL CENTER, TRENTON, NJ, p. A464

ST. FRANCIS MEMORIAL HOSPITAL, WEST POINT, NE, p. A440

ST. FRANCIS REGIONAL MEDICAL CENTER, SHAKOPEE, MN, p. A386

ST. GABRIEL'S HOSPITAL, LITTLE FALLS, MN, p. A379

ST. HELENA HOSPITAL CENTER FOR BEHAVIORAL HEALTH, VALLEJO, CA, p. A103

ST. HELENA HOSPITAL CLEAR LAKE, CLEARLAKE, CA, p. A60

ST. HELENA HOSPITAL NAPA VALLEY, SAINT HELENA, CA, p. A90

ST. HELENA PARISH HOSPITAL, GREENSBURG, LA, p. A302

ST. JAMES BEHAVIORAL HEALTH HOSPITAL, GONZALES, LA, p. A302

ST. JAMES HEALTHCARE, BUTTE, MT, p. A422

ST. JAMES HOSPITAL, HORNELL, NY, p. A485

ST. JAMES HOSPITALS AND HEALTH CENTERS—OLYMPIA FIELDS CAMPUS, OLYMPIA FIELDS, IL, p. A215

ST. JAMES MEDICAL CENTER, SAINT JAMES, MN, p. A384

ST. JAMES MERCY HOSPITAL, HORNELL, NY, p. A485

ST. JAMES PARISH HOSPITAL, LUTCHER, LA, p. A307

ST. JOHN BROKEN ARROW, BROKEN ARROW, OK, p. A556

ST. JOHN MACOMB-OAKLAND HOSPITAL, WARREN, MI, p. A369

ST. JOHN MEDICAL CENTER, LONGVIEW, WA, p. A760

ST. JOHN MEDICAL CENTER, TULSA, OK, p. A571

ST. JOHN MEDICAL CENTER, WESTLAKE, OH, p. A553

ST. JOHN OWASSO, OWASSO, OK, p. A566

ST. JOHN PROVIDENCE MACOMB-OAKLAND HOSPITAL, OAKLAND CENTER, MADISON HEIGHTS, MI, p. A361

ST. JOHN REHABILITATION HOSPITAL, BROKEN ARROW, OK, p. A557

ST. JOHN RIVER DISTRICT HOSPITAL, EAST CHINA, MI, p. A353

ST. JOHN SAPULPA, SAPULPA, OK, p. A567

ST. JOHN VIANNEY HOSPITAL, DOWNINGTOWN, PA, p. A588

ST. JOHN'S CHILDREN'S HOSPITAL, SPRINGFIELD, MO, p. A419

ST. JOHN'S EPISCOPAL HOSPITAL, FAR ROCKAWAY, NY, p. A483

ST. JOHN'S HEALTH, JACKSON, WY, p. A802

ST. JOHN'S HOSPITAL—AURORA, AURORA, MO, p. A402

ST. JOHN'S HOSPITAL—CASSVILLE, CASSVILLE, MO, p. A404

ST. JOHN'S HOSPITAL—LEBANON, LEBANON, MO, p. A410

ST. JOHN'S HOSPITAL, MAPLEWOOD, MN, p. A380

ST. JOHN'S HOSPITAL, SPRINGFIELD, IL, p. A221

ST. JOHN'S HOSPITAL, SPRINGFIELD, MO, p. A419

ST. JOHN'S HOSPITAL-BERRYVILLE, BERRYVILLE, AR, p. A42

ST. JOHN'S LUTHERAN HOSPITAL, LIBBY, MT, p. A425

ST. JOHN'S MERCY CHILDREN'S HOSPITAL, SAINT LOUIS, MO, p. A417

ST. JOHN'S MERCY HOSPITAL, WASHINGTON, MO, p. A420

ST. JOHN'S MERCY MEDICAL CENTER, SAINT LOUIS, MO, p. A417

ST. JOHN'S PLEASANT VALLEY HOSPITAL, CAMARILLO, CA, p. A59

ST. JOHN'S REGIONAL MEDICAL CENTER, JOPLIN, MO, p. A408

ST. JOHN'S REGIONAL MEDICAL CENTER, OXNARD, CA, p. A83

ST. JOHN'S RIVERSIDE HOSPITAL, YONKERS, NY, p. A503

ST. JOHN'S ST. FRANCIS HOSPITAL, MOUNTAIN VIEW, MO, p. A412

ST. JOSEPH HEALTH CENTER, WARREN, OH, p. A551

ST. JOSEPH HEALTH SERVICES OF RHODE ISLAND, NORTH PROVIDENCE, RI, p. A613

ST. JOSEPH HEALTH ST. MARY, APPLE VALLEY, CA, p. A56

ST. JOSEPH HEALTH SYSTEM, TAWAS CITY, MI, p. A367

ST. JOSEPH HOSPITAL, BANGOR, ME, p. A318

ST. JOSEPH HOSPITAL, BETHPAGE, NY, p. A475

ST. JOSEPH HOSPITAL, EUREKA, CA, p. A63

ST. JOSEPH HOSPITAL, FORT WAYNE, IN, p. A228

ST. JOSEPH HOSPITAL, NASHUA, NH, p. A450

ST. JOSEPH HOSPITAL, ORANGE, CA, p. A83

ST. JOSEPH HOSPITAL, POLSON, MT, p. A427

ST. JOSEPH HOSPITAL EUREKA, EUREKA, CA, p. A63

ST. JOSEPH HOSPITAL FOR SPECIALTY CARE, PROVIDENCE, RI, p. A614

ST. JOSEPH HOSPITAL ORANGE, ORANGE, CA, p. A83

ST. JOSEPH MEDICAL CENTER, HOUSTON, TX, p. A688

ST. JOSEPH MEDICAL CENTER, KANSAS CITY, MO, p. A409

ST. JOSEPH MEDICAL CENTER, TACOMA, WA, p. A767

ST. JOSEPH MEDICAL CENTER, TOWSON, MD, p. A333

ST. JOSEPH MEDICAL CENTER-DOWNTOWN READING, READING, PA, p. A606

ST. JOSEPH MEMORIAL HOSPITAL, MURPHYSBORO, IL, p. A213

ST. JOSEPH MERCY ANN ARBOR, YPSILANTI, MI, p. A370

ST. JOSEPH MERCY CHELSEA, CHELSEA, MI, p. A351

ST. JOSEPH MERCY HOSPITAL ANN ARBOR, YPSILANTI, MI, p. A370

ST. JOSEPH MERCY LIVINGSTON HOSPITAL, HOWELL, MI, p. A358

ST. JOSEPH MERCY OAKLAND, PONTIAC, MI, p. A364

ST. JOSEPH MERCY PORT HURON, PORT HURON, MI, p. A364

ST. JOSEPH REGIONAL HEALTH CENTER, BRYAN, TX, p. A661

ST. JOSEPH REGIONAL HEALTH NETWORK, READING, PA, p. A606

ST. JOSEPH REGIONAL MEDICAL CENTER, LEWISTON, ID, p. A191

ST. JOSEPH'S AREA HEALTH SERVICES, PARK RAPIDS, MN, p. A382

ST. JOSEPH'S BEHAVIORAL HEALTH CENTER, STOCKTON, CA, p. A100

ST. JOSEPH'S CANDLER HOSPITAL, SAVANNAH, GA, p. A180

ST. JOSEPH'S CHILDREN'S HOSPITAL OF TAMPA, TAMPA, FL, p. A160

ST. JOSEPH'S HEALTH SERVICES-GUNDERSEN LUTHERAN, HILLSBORO, WI, p. A786

ST. JOSEPH'S HEALTHCARE SYSTEM, PATERSON, NJ, p. A460

ST. JOSEPH'S HOSPITAL, ASHEVILLE, NC, p. A504

ST. JOSEPH'S HOSPITAL, BREESE, IL, p. A196

ST. JOSEPH'S HOSPITAL, CHEWELAH, WA, p. A756

ST. JOSEPH'S HOSPITAL, CHIPPEWA FALLS, WI, p. A781

ST. JOSEPH'S HOSPITAL, HIGHLAND, IL, p. A207

ST. JOSEPH'S HOSPITAL, SAINT PAUL, MN, p. A385

ST. JOSEPH'S HOSPITAL, SAVANNAH, GA, p. A180

ST. JOSEPH'S HOSPITAL, TAMPA, FL, p. A160

ST. JOSEPH'S HOSPITAL, WEST BEND, WI, p. A799

ST. JOSEPH'S HOSPITAL AND HEALTH CENTER, DICKINSON, ND, p. A522

ST. JOSEPH'S HOSPITAL AND MEDICAL CENTER, PHOENIX, AZ, p. A36

ST. JOSEPH'S HOSPITAL HEALTH CENTER, SYRACUSE, NY, p. A499

ST. JOSEPH'S HOSPITAL OF BUCKHANNON, BUCKHANNON, WV, p. A771

ST. JOSEPH'S MEDICAL CENTER, STOCKTON, CA, p. A100

ST. JOSEPH'S MEDICAL CENTER, YONKERS, NY, p. A503

ST. JOSEPH'S MERCY-NORTH, ROMEO, MI, p. A365

ST. JOSEPH'S UNIVERSITY MEDICAL CENTER, PATERSON, NJ, p. A460

ST. JOSEPH'S WOMEN'S HOSPITAL—TAMPA, TAMPA, FL, p. A160
ST. JOSEPH'S/CANDLER, ST. JOSEPH'S HOSPITAL, SAVANNAH, GA, p. A180
ST. JUDE CHILDREN'S RESEARCH HOSPITAL, MEMPHIS, TN, p. A645
ST. JUDE MEDICAL CENTER, FULLERTON, CA, p. A66
ST. LANDRY EXTENDED CARE HOSPITAL, OPELOUSAS, LA, p. A312
ST. LAWRENCE PSYCHIATRIC CENTER, OGDENSBURG, NY, p. A493
ST. LAWRENCE REHABILITATION CENTER, LAWRENCEVILLE, NJ, p. A457
ST. LOUIS CHILDREN'S HOSPITAL, SAINT LOUIS, MO, p. A417
ST. LOUIS PSYCHIATRIC REHABILITATION CENTER, SAINT LOUIS, MO, p. A417
ST. LOUIS REGIONAL PSYCHIATRIC STABILIZATION CENTER, SAINT LOUIS, MO, p. A417
ST. LOUISE REGIONAL HOSPITAL, GILROY, CA, p. A66
ST. LUCIE MEDICAL CENTER, PORT ST LUCIE, FL, p. A155
ST. LUKE COMMUNITY HEALTHCARE, RONAN, MT, p. A427
ST. LUKE COMMUNITY HOSPITAL, RONAN, MT, p. A427
ST. LUKE HOSPITAL AND LIVING CENTER, MARION, KS, p. A270
ST. LUKE'S—GNADEN HUETTEN CAMPUS, LEHIGHTON, PA, p. A595
ST. LUKE'S—LEHIGHTON CAMPUS, LEHIGHTON, PA, p. A595
ST. LUKE'S BAPTIST HOSPITAL, SAN ANTONIO, TX, p. A713
ST. LUKE'S BEHAVIORAL HEALTH CENTER, PHOENIX, AZ, p. A36
ST. LUKE'S CAMPUS, UTICA, NY, p. A500
ST. LUKE'S CORNWALL HOSPITAL—CORNWALL CAMPUS, CORNWALL, NY, p. A482
ST. LUKE'S CORNWALL HOSPITAL, NEWBURGH, NY, p. A492
ST. LUKE'S DES PERES HOSPITAL, CHESTERFIELD, MO, p. A404
ST. LUKE'S DES PERES HOSPITAL, SAINT LOUIS, MO, p. A417
ST. LUKE'S EASTON CAMPUS, EASTON, PA, p. A589
ST. LUKE'S ELMORE, MOUNTAIN HOME, ID, p. A191
ST. LUKE'S EPISCOPAL HOSPITAL, PONCE, PR, p. A809
ST. LUKE'S HOSPITAL—ANDERSON CAMPUS, EASTON, PA, p. A589
ST. LUKE'S HOSPITAL—BETHLEHEM CAMPUS, BETHLEHEM, PA, p. A584
ST. LUKE'S HOSPITAL—MINERS CAMPUS, COALDALE, PA, p. A587
ST. LUKE'S HOSPITAL—QUAKERTOWN CAMPUS, QUAKERTOWN, PA, p. A605
ST. LUKE'S HOSPITAL—THE VINTAGE HOSPITAL, HOUSTON, TX, p. A688
ST. LUKE'S HOSPITAL—WARREN CAMPUS, PHILLIPSBURG, NJ, p. A461
ST. LUKE'S HOSPITAL, CHESTERFIELD, MO, p. A404
ST. LUKE'S HOSPITAL, COLUMBUS, NC, p. A508
ST. LUKE'S HOSPITAL, CROSBY, ND, p. A522
ST. LUKE'S HOSPITAL, DULUTH, MN, p. A375
ST. LUKE'S HOSPITAL, JACKSONVILLE, FL, p. A141
ST. LUKE'S HOSPITAL, MAUMEE, OH, p. A545
ST. LUKE'S HOSPITAL, NEW BEDFORD, MA, p. A342
ST. LUKE'S HOSPITAL, NEWBURGH, NY, p. A492
ST. LUKE'S HOSPITAL, SAN FRANCISCO, CA, p. A94
ST. LUKE'S JEROME, JEROME, ID, p. A190
ST. LUKE'S LAKESIDE HOSPITAL, THE WOODLANDS, TX, p. A720
ST. LUKE'S MAGIC VALLEY MEDICAL CENTER, TWIN FALLS, ID, p. A193
ST. LUKE'S MAGIC VALLEY REGIONAL MEDICAL CENTER, TWIN FALLS, ID, p. A193
ST. LUKE'S MCCALL, MCCALL, ID, p. A191
ST. LUKE'S MCCALL HOSPITAL, MCCALL, ID, p. A191
ST. LUKE'S MEDICAL CENTER, CROSBY, ND, p. A522
ST. LUKE'S MEDICAL CENTER, HOUSTON, TX, p. A688
ST. LUKE'S MERIDIAN MEDICAL CENTER, MERIDIAN, ID, p. A191
ST. LUKE'S MINERS MEMORIAL HOSPITAL, COALDALE, PA, p. A587
ST. LUKE'S MONROE, STROUDSBURG, PA, p. A608
ST. LUKE'S NAMPA, NAMPA, ID, p. A192
ST. LUKE'S PATIENTS MEDICAL CENTER, PASADENA, TX, p. A705
ST. LUKE'S QUAKERTOWN HOSPITAL, QUAKERTOWN, PA, p. A605
ST. LUKE'S REGIONAL MEDICAL CENTER, BOISE, ID, p. A189
ST. LUKE'S REHABILITATION HOSPITAL, BOISE, ID, p. A189
ST. LUKE'S REHABILITATION HOSPITAL, CHESTERFIELD, MO, p. A404
ST. LUKE'S REHABILITATION INSTITUTE, SPOKANE, WA, p. A766

ST. LUKE'S SACRED HEART CAMPUS, ALLENTOWN, PA, p. A583
ST. LUKE'S SUGAR LAND HOSPITAL, SUGAR LAND, TX, p. A717
ST. LUKE'S THE WOODLANDS HOSPITAL, THE WOODLANDS, TX, p. A720
ST. LUKE'S UNIVERSITY HOSPITAL—BETHLEHEM CAMPUS, BETHLEHEM, PA, p. A585
ST. LUKE'S WOOD RIVER MEDICAL CENTER, KETCHUM, ID, p. A191
ST. MARGARET'S HOSPITAL, SPRING VALLEY, IL, p. A220
ST. MARK'S HOSPITAL, SALT LAKE CITY, UT, p. A733
ST. MARK'S MEDICAL CENTER, LA GRANGE, TX, p. A694
ST. MARTIN HOSPITAL, BREAUX BRIDGE, LA, p. A298
ST. MARY MEDICAL CENTER, APPLE VALLEY, CA, p. A56
ST. MARY MEDICAL CENTER, HOBART, IN, p. A230
ST. MARY MEDICAL CENTER, LANGHORNE, PA, p. A594
ST. MARY MEDICAL CENTER, LONG BEACH, CA, p. A72
ST. MARY MEDICAL CENTER, WALLA WALLA, WA, p. A768
ST. MARY MEDICAL CENTER LONG BEACH, LONG BEACH, CA, p. A72
ST. MARY MERCY HOSPITAL, LIVONIA, MI, p. A360
ST. MARY REHABILITATION HOSPITAL, LANGHORNE, PA, p. A594
ST. MARY-CORWIN MEDICAL CENTER, PUEBLO, CO, p. A118
ST. MARYS HEALTH CENTER, JEFFERSON CITY, MO, p. A408
ST. MARY'S COMMUNITY HOSPITAL, NEBRASKA CITY, NE, p. A435
ST. MARY'S GENERAL HOSPITAL, PASSAIC, NJ, p. A460
ST. MARY'S GOOD SAMARITAN HOSPITAL, GREENSBORO, GA, p. A173
ST. MARY'S HEALTH CARE SYSTEM, ATHENS, GA, p. A164
ST. MARY'S HEALTHCARE, AMSTERDAM, NY, p. A474
ST. MARY'S HEALTHCARE CENTER, PIERRE, SD, p. A630
ST. MARY'S HOSPITAL, AMSTERDAM, NY, p. A474
ST. MARY'S HOSPITAL, CENTRALIA, IL, p. A196
ST. MARY'S HOSPITAL, COTTONWOOD, ID, p. A190
ST. MARY'S HOSPITAL, DECATUR, IL, p. A202
ST. MARY'S HOSPITAL, MADISON, WI, p. A788
ST. MARY'S HOSPITAL, PASSAIC, NJ, p. A460
ST. MARY'S HOSPITAL AMSTERDAM, AMSTERDAM, NY, p. A474
ST. MARY'S HOSPITAL AND MEDICAL CENTER, GRAND JUNCTION, CO, p. A113
ST. MARY'S HOSPITAL AND REHABILITATION CENTER, MINNEAPOLIS, MN, p. A381
ST. MARY'S HOSPITAL MEDICAL CENTER, GREEN BAY, WI, p. A785
ST. MARY'S HOSPITAL OF SUPERIOR, SUPERIOR, WI, p. A797
ST. MARY'S JANESVILLE HOSPITAL, JANESVILLE, WI, p. A786
ST. MARY'S MEDICAL CENTER, BLUE SPRINGS, MO, p. A402
ST. MARY'S MEDICAL CENTER, DULUTH, MN, p. A375
ST. MARY'S MEDICAL CENTER, GRAND JUNCTION, CO, p. A113
ST. MARY'S MEDICAL CENTER, HUNTINGTON, WV, p. A773
ST. MARY'S MEDICAL CENTER, SAN FRANCISCO, CA, p. A94
ST. MARY'S MEDICAL CENTER, WEST PALM BEACH, FL, p. A162
ST. MARY'S OF MICHIGAN, SAGINAW, MI, p. A366
ST. MARY'S OF MICHIGAN STANDISH HOSPITAL, STANDISH, MI, p. A367
ST. MARY'S REGIONAL MEDICAL CENTER, ENID, OK, p. A559
ST. MARY'S REGIONAL MEDICAL CENTER, LEWISTON, ME, p. A321
ST. MARY'S SACRED HEART HOSPITAL, LAVONIA, GA, p. A175
ST. MICHAEL MEDICAL CENTER, BREMERTON, WA, p. A756
ST. MICHAEL'S ELITE HOSPITAL, SUGAR LAND, TX, p. A718
ST. MICHAEL'S HOSPITAL, TYNDALL, SD, p. A632
ST. MICHAEL'S HOSPITAL AND NURSING HOME, SAUK CENTRE, MN, p. A386
ST. MICHAEL'S HOSPITAL AVERA, TYNDALL, SD, p. A632
ST. NICHOLAS HOSPITAL, SHEBOYGAN, WI, p. A796
ST. PATRICK HOSPITAL, MISSOULA, MT, p. A426
ST. PETERSBURG GENERAL HOSPITAL, SAINT PETERSBURG, FL, p. A156
ST. PETER'S HOSPITAL, ALBANY, NY, p. A474
ST. PETER'S HOSPITAL, HELENA, MT, p. A425
ST. RITA'S MEDICAL CENTER, LIMA, OH, p. A543
ST. ROSE DOMINCIAN HOSPITALS—SAN MARTIN CAMPUS, LAS VEGAS, NV, p. A444
ST. ROSE DOMINICAN HOSPITALS—ROSE DE LIMA CAMPUS, HENDERSON, NV, p. A442
ST. ROSE DOMINICAN HOSPITALS—SAN MARTIN CAMPUS, LAS VEGAS, NV, p. A444
ST. ROSE DOMINICAN HOSPITALS—SIENA CAMPUS, HENDERSON, NV, p. A442
ST. ROSE HOSPITAL, HAYWARD, CA, p. A68
ST. TAMMANY HEALTH SYSTEM, COVINGTON, LA, p. A300
ST. TAMMANY PARISH HOSPITAL, COVINGTON, LA, p. A300

ST. THERESA SPECIALTY HOSPITAL, NEW ORLEANS, LA, p. A311
ST. THOMAS MORE HOSPITAL, CANON CITY, CO, p. A108
ST. VINCENT ANDERSON, ANDERSON, IN, p. A223
ST. VINCENT CARMEL HOSPITAL, CARMEL, IN, p. A225
ST. VINCENT CHARITY HOSPITAL, CLEVELAND, OH, p. A535
ST. VINCENT CHARITY MEDICAL CENTER, CLEVELAND, OH, p. A535
ST. VINCENT CLAY HOSPITAL, BRAZIL, IN, p. A224
ST. VINCENT EVANSVILLE, EVANSVILLE, IN, p. A228
ST. VINCENT FISHERS HOSPITAL, FISHERS, IN, p. A228
ST. VINCENT FRANKFORT HOSPITAL, FRANKFORT, IN, p. A229
ST. VINCENT GENERAL HOSPITAL DISTRICT, LEADVILLE, CO, p. A115
ST. VINCENT HEALTHCARE, BILLINGS, MT, p. A421
ST. VINCENT HEART CENTER, INDIANAPOLIS, IN, p. A233
ST. VINCENT HOSPITAL, GREEN BAY, WI, p. A785
ST. VINCENT HOSPITAL HOT SPRINGS, HOT SPRINGS, AR, p. A47
ST. VINCENT INDIANAPOLIS HOSPITAL, INDIANAPOLIS, IN, p. A233
ST. VINCENT INFIRMARY MEDICAL CENTER, LITTLE ROCK, AR, p. A49
ST. VINCENT JENNINGS HOSPITAL, NORTH VERNON, IN, p. A238
ST. VINCENT KOKOMO, KOKOMO, IN, p. A234
ST. VINCENT MEDICAL CENTER-NORTH, SHERWOOD, AR, p. A53
ST. VINCENT MERCY HOSPITAL, ELWOOD, IN, p. A227
ST. VINCENT MERCY MEDICAL CENTER, TOLEDO, OH, p. A550
ST. VINCENT MORRILTON, MORRILTON, AR, p. A50
ST. VINCENT PEDIATRIC REHABILITATION CENTER, INDIANAPOLIS, IN, p. A233
ST. VINCENT RANDOLPH HOSPITAL, WINCHESTER, IN, p. A242
ST. VINCENT REHABILITATION HOSPITAL, SHERWOOD, AR, p. A53
ST. VINCENT SALEM HOSPITAL, SALEM, IN, p. A240
ST. VINCENT SETON SPECIALTY HOSPITAL, INDIANAPOLIS, IN, p. A233
ST. VINCENT WARRICK, BOONVILLE, IN, p. A224
ST. VINCENT WILLIAMSPORT HOSPITAL, WILLIAMSPORT, IN, p. A242
ST. VINCENT'S BEHAVIORAL HEALTH, WESTPORT, CT, p. A126
ST. VINCENT'S BIRMINGHAM, BIRMINGHAM, AL, p. A15
ST. VINCENT'S BLOUNT, ONEONTA, AL, p. A23
ST. VINCENT'S CHILTON HOSPITAL, CLANTON, AL, p. A16
ST. VINCENT'S EAST, BIRMINGHAM, AL, p. A15
ST. VINCENT'S MEDICAL CENTER, BRIDGEPORT, CT, p. A121
ST. VINCENT'S MEDICAL CENTER, JACKSONVILLE, FL, p. A141
ST. VINCENT'S MEDICAL CENTER CLAY COUNTY, MIDDLEBURG, FL, p. A148
ST. VINCENT'S MEDICAL CENTER RIVERSIDE, JACKSONVILLE, FL, p. A141
ST. VINCENT'S MEDICAL CENTER SOUTHSIDE, JACKSONVILLE, FL, p. A141
ST. VINCENT'S ST. CLAIR, PELL CITY, AL, p. A23
ST.LUKE'S MONROE, STROUDSBURG, PA, p. A608
STAFFORD COUNTY HOSPITAL, STAFFORD, KS, p. A277
STAFFORD DISTRICT HOSPITAL 4, STAFFORD, KS, p. A277
STAFFORD HOSPITAL, STAFFORD, VA, p. A752
STAFFORD HOSPITAL CENTER, STAFFORD, VA, p. A752
STAMFORD HEALTH SYSTEM, STAMFORD, CT, p. A125
STAMFORD HOSPITAL, STAMFORD, CT, p. A125
STANDING ROCK SERVICE UNIT, FORT YATES HOSPITAL, INDIAN HEALTH SERVICE, DHHS, FORT YATES, ND, p. A523
STANFORD HEALTH CARE—VALLEYCARE, PLEASANTON, CA, p. A85
STANFORD HEALTH CARE, PALO ALTO, CA, p. A84
STANFORD HOSPITAL AND CLINICS, PALO ALTO, CA, p. A84
STANISLAUS SURGERY CENTER, MODESTO, CA, p. A79
STANISLAUS SURGICAL HOSPITAL, MODESTO, CA, p. A79
STANLEY COMMUNITY HOSPITAL, STANLEY, ND, p. A526
STANTON COUNTY HEALTH CARE FACILITY, JOHNSON, KS, p. A267
STANTON COUNTY HOSPITAL, JOHNSON, KS, p. A267
STAR MEDICAL CENTER, PLANO, TX, p. A707
STAR VALLEY HEALTH, AFTON, WY, p. A801
STAR VALLEY MEDICAL CENTER, AFTON, WY, p. A801
STARKE HOSPITAL, KNOX, IN, p. A234
STARR COUNTY MEMORIAL HOSPITAL, RIO GRANDE CITY, TX, p. A709
STARR REGIONAL MEDICAL CENTER, ATHENS, TN, p. A634
STATE CORRECTIONAL INSTITUTION AT CAMP HILL, CAMP HILL, PA, p. A586

STATE HOSPITAL NORTH, OROFINO, ID, p. A192
STATE HOSPITAL SOUTH, BLACKFOOT, ID, p. A188
STATE PENITENTIARY HOSPITAL, WALLA WALLA, WA, p. A768
STATE PSYCHIATRIC HOSPITAL, SAN JUAN, PR, p. A811
STATEN ISLAND UNIVERSITY HOSPITAL, STATEN ISLAND, NY, p. A499
STE. GENEVIEVE COUNTY MEMORIAL HOSPITAL, STE GENEVIEVE, MO, p. A419
STEELE MEMORIAL HOSPITAL, SALMON, ID, p. A193
STEELE MEMORIAL MEDICAL CENTER, SALMON, ID, p. A193
STEPHENS COUNTY HOSPITAL, TOCCOA, GA, p. A182
STEPHENS MEMORIAL HOSPITAL, BRECKENRIDGE, TX, p. A660
STEPHENS MEMORIAL HOSPITAL, NORWAY, ME, p. A321
STERLING REGIONAL MEDCENTER, STERLING, CO, p. A118
STERLING REGIONAL MEDCENTER, STERLING, CO, p. A119
STERLING SURGICAL HOSPITAL, SLIDELL, LA, p. A315
STERLINGTON REHABILITATION HOSPITAL, BASTROP, LA, p. A296
STEVEN AND ALEXANDRA COHEN CHILDREN'S MEDICAL CENTER OF NEW YORK, NEW HYDE PARK, NY, p. A489
STEVENS COMM MEMORIAL HOSPITAL, MORRIS, MN, p. A381
STEVENS COMMUNITY MEDICAL CENTER, MORRIS, MN, p. A381
STEVENS COUNTY HOSPITAL, HUGOTON, KS, p. A266
STEVENS HEALTHCARE, EDMONDS, WA, p. A757
STEWART & LYNDA RESNICK NEUROPSYCHIATRIC HOSPITAL AT UCLA, LOS ANGELES, CA, p. A76
STEWART MEMORIAL COMMUNITY HOSPITAL, LAKE CITY, IA, p. A253
STILLWATER BILLINGS CLINIC, COLUMBUS, MT, p. A422
STILLWATER COMMUNITY HOSPITAL, COLUMBUS, MT, p. A422
STILLWATER MEDICAL CENTER, STILLWATER, OK, p. A568
STILLWATER MEDICAL PERRY, PERRY, OK, p. A567
STILWELL MEMORIAL HOSPITAL, STILWELL, OK, p. A568
STONE CNTY MEDICAL CENTER, MOUNTAIN VIEW, AR, p. A50
STONE COUNTY HOSPITAL, WIGGINS, MS, p. A401
STONE COUNTY MEDICAL CENTER, MOUNTAIN VIEW, AR, p. A50
STONECREST CENTER, DETROIT, MI, p. A353
STONECREST MEDICAL CENTER, SMYRNA, TN, p. A649
STONES RIVER HOSPITAL, WOODBURY, TN, p. A650
STONESPRINGS HOSPITAL CENTER, DULLES, VA, p. A741
STONEWALL JACKSON HOSPITAL, LEXINGTON, VA, p. A744
STONEWALL JACKSON MEMORIAL HOSPITAL, WESTON, WV, p. A777
STONEWALL MEMORIAL HOSPITAL, ASPERMONT, TX, p. A654
STONY BROOK UNIVERSITY HOSPITAL, STONY BROOK, NY, p. A499
STONY BROOK UNIVERSITY MEDICAL CENTER, STONY BROOK, NY, p. A499
STONY BROOK CHILDREN'S HOSPITAL, STONY BROOK, NY, p. A499
STORMONT VAIL HEALTH, TOPEKA, KS, p. A277
STORMONT-VAIL HEALTHCARE, TOPEKA, KS, p. A277
STORY COUNTY HOSPITAL & LTC, NEVADA, IA, p. A254
STORY COUNTY MEDICAL CENTER, NEVADA, IA, p. A254
STOUGHTON HOSPITAL ASSOCIATION, STOUGHTON, WI, p. A797
STRAITH HOSPITAL FOR SPECIAL SURGERY, SOUTHFIELD, MI, p. A367
STRATEGIC BEHAVIORAL HEALTH—RALEIGH, GARNER, NC, p. A510
STRATEGIC BEHAVIORAL HEALTH—WILMINGTON, LELAND, NC, p. A513
STRAUB CLINIC & HOSPITAL, HONOLULU, HI, p. A185
STRAUB MEDICAL CENTER, HONOLULU, HI, p. A185
STREAMWOOD BEHAVIORAL HEALTH CENTER, STREAMWOOD, IL, p. A221
STREAMWOOD HOSPITAL, STREAMWOOD, IL, p. A221
STRINGFELLOW MEMORIAL HOSPITAL, ANNISTON, AL, p. A13
STROGER HOSP OF COOK COUNTY, CHICAGO, IL, p. A201
STRONG MEMORIAL HOSPITAL OF THE UNIVERSITY OF ROCHESTER, ROCHESTER, NY, p. A496
STURDY MEMORIAL HOSPITAL, ATTLEBORO, MA, p. A334
STURGIS HOSPITAL, STURGIS, MI, p. A367
STURGIS REGIONAL HOSPITAL, STURGIS, SD, p. A632
STUTTGART MEMORIAL HOSPITAL, STUTTGART, AR, p. A53
SUBURBAN COMMUNITY HOSPITAL, EAST NORRITON, PA, p. A589
SUBURBAN HOSP HEALTHCARE SYST, BETHESDA, MD, p. A327
SUBURBAN HOSPITAL, BETHESDA, MD, p. A327

SULLIVAN COUNTY COMMUNITY HOSPITAL, SULLIVAN, IN, p. A241
SULLIVAN COUNTY MEMORIAL HOSPITAL, MILAN, MO, p. A412
SUMMA AKRON CITY HOSPITAL, AKRON, OH, p. A527
SUMMA BARBERTON CITIZENS HOSPITAL, BARBERTON, OH, p. A528
SUMMA HEALTH SYSTEM, AKRON, OH, p. A527
SUMMA REHAB HOSPITAL, AKRON, OH, p. A527
SUMMA SAINT THOMAS HOSPITAL, AKRON, OH, p. A527
SUMMA WESTERN RESERVE HOSPITAL, CUYAHOGA FALLS, OH, p. A538
SUMMERLIN HOSPITAL MEDICAL CENTER, LAS VEGAS, NV, p. A444
SUMMERLIN MEDICAL CENTER, LAS VEGAS, NV, p. A444
SUMMERS COUNTY APPALACHIAN REGIONAL HOSPITAL, HINTON, WV, p. A772
SUMMERS COUNTY ARH HOSPITAL, HINTON, WV, p. A772
SUMMERSVILLE MEMORIAL HOSPITAL, SUMMERSVILLE, WV, p. A777
SUMMERSVILLE REGIONAL MEDICAL CENTER, SUMMERSVILLE, WV, p. A777
SUMMIT BEHAVIORAL HEALTHCARE, CINCINNATI, OH, p. A533
SUMMIT HEALTHCARE REGIONAL MEDICAL CENTER, SHOW LOW, AZ, p. A38
SUMMIT HOSPITAL, PHENIX CITY, AL, p. A23
SUMMIT HOSPITAL, SUMMIT, NJ, p. A463
SUMMIT MEDICAL CENTER, CASPER, WY, p. A801
SUMMIT MEDICAL CENTER, EDMOND, OK, p. A558
SUMMIT MEDICAL CENTER, HERMITAGE, TN, p. A639
SUMMIT OAKS HOSPITAL, SUMMIT, NJ, p. A463
SUMMIT PACIFIC MEDICAL CENTER, ABERDEEN, WA, p. A755
SUMMIT PACIFIC MEDICAL CENTER, ELMA, WA, p. A757
SUMMIT SURGICAL, HUTCHINSON, KS, p. A267
SUMMIT SURGICAL, LLC, HUTCHINSON, KS, p. A267
SUMMITRIDGE HOSPITAL, LAWRENCEVILLE, GA, p. A175
SUMMITT MEDICAL CENTER, CASPER, WY, p. A801
SUMNER COUNTY HOSPITAL DISTRICT 1, CALDWELL, KS, p. A262
SUMNER COUNTY HOSPITAL DISTRICT ONE, CALDWELL, KS, p. A262
SUMNER MEMORIAL HOSPITAL, GALLATIN, TN, p. A638
SUMNER REGIONAL MEDICAL CENTER, GALLATIN, TN, p. A638
SUMTER REGIONAL HOSPITAL EAST, AMERICUS, GA, p. A163
SUN BEHAVIORAL COLUMBUS, COLUMBUS, OH, p. A537
SUN BEHAVIORAL DELAWARE, GEORGETOWN, DE, p. A127
SUN BEHAVIORAL DELEWARE, GEORGETOWN, DE, p. A127
SUN BEHAVIORAL HEALTH, ERLANGER, KY, p. A283
SUN BEHAVIORAL HOUSTON, HOUSTON, TX, p. A688
SUN BEHAVIORAL KENTUCKY, ERLANGER, KY, p. A283
SUN COAST HOSPITAL, LARGO, FL, p. A143
SUNCOAST BEHAVIORAL HEALTH CENTER, BRADENTON, FL, p. A133
SUNNYSIDE COMMUNITY HOSPITAL AND CLINICS, SUNNYSIDE, WA, p. A766
SUNNYVIEW HOSP & REHAB CENTER, SCHENECTADY, NY, p. A498
SUNNYVIEW REHABILITATION HOSPITAL, SCHENECTADY, NY, p. A498
SUNRISE CANYON HOSPITAL, LUBBOCK, TX, p. A698
SUNRISE HOSPITAL AND MEDICAL CENTER, LAS VEGAS, NV, p. A444
SUNY DOWNSTATE-UNIVERSITY HOSPITAL OF BROOKLYN, BROOKLYN, NY, p. A479
SURGEONS CHOICE MEDICAL CENTER, SOUTHFIELD, MI, p. A367
SURGERY SPECIALTY HOSPITALS OF AMERICA, PASADENA, TX, p. A705
SURGICAL ARTS CENTER, WEBSTER, TX, p. A724
SURGICAL HOSPITAL AT SOUTHWOODS, YOUNGSTOWN, OH, p. A554
SURGICAL HOSPITAL OF AUSTIN, AUSTIN, TX, p. A656
SURGICAL HOSPITAL OF OKLAHOMA, OKLAHOMA CITY, OK, p. A566
SURGICAL INSTITUTE OF READING, WYOMISSING, PA, p. A612
SURGICAL SPECIALTY CENTER OF BATON ROUGE, BATON ROUGE, LA, p. A297
SURGICAL SPECIALTY CENTRE, BATON ROUGE, LA, p. A297
SURPRISE VALLEY HEALTH CARE DISTRICT, CEDARVILLE, CA, p. A59
SURPRISE VALLEY HEALTHCARE DISTRICT, CEDARVILLE, CA, p. A59
SUSAN B. ALLEN MEMORIAL HOSPITAL, EL DORADO, KS, p. A264
SUTTER AMADOR HOSPITAL, JACKSON, CA, p. A69
SUTTER AUBURN FAITH HOSPITAL, AUBURN, CA, p. A56

SUTTER CENTER FOR PSYCHIATRY, SACRAMENTO, CA, p. A90
SUTTER COAST HOSPITAL, CRESCENT CITY, CA, p. A62
SUTTER COMMUNITY HOSPITALS, SACRAMENTO, CA, p. A90
SUTTER DAVIS HOSPITAL, DAVIS, CA, p. A62
SUTTER DELTA MEDICAL CENTER, ANTIOCH, CA, p. A56
SUTTER DELTA MEMORIAL HOSPITAL, ANTIOCH, CA, p. A56
SUTTER HEALTH KAHI MOHALA, EWA BEACH, HI, p. A184
SUTTER LAKESIDE HOSPITAL, LAKEPORT, CA, p. A71
SUTTER MATERNITY AND SURGERY CENTER OF SANTA CRUZ, SANTA CRUZ, CA, p. A97
SUTTER MEDICAL CENTER OF SANTA ROSA, CHANATE CAMPUS, SANTA ROSA, CA, p. A98
SUTTER MEDICAL CENTER, SACRAMENTO, SACRAMENTO, CA, p. A90
SUTTER ROSEVILLE MEDICAL CENTER, ROSEVILLE, CA, p. A89
SUTTER SANTA ROSA REGIONAL HOSPITAL, SANTA ROSA, CA, p. A98
SUTTER SOLANO MEDICAL CENTER, VALLEJO, CA, p. A103
SUTTER SURGICAL HOSPITAL—NORTH VALLEY, YUBA CITY, CA, p. A106
SUTTER TRACY COMMUNITY HOSPITAL, TRACY, CA, p. A101
SWAIN COMMUNITY HOSPITAL, BRYSON CITY, NC, p. A505
SWAIN COUNTY HOSPITAL, BRYSON CITY, NC, p. A505
SWEDISH COVENANT HOSPITAL, CHICAGO, IL, p. A201
SWEDISH HEALTH SERVICES, SEATTLE, WA, p. A764
SWEDISH MED CTR PROVIDENCE CMP, SEATTLE, WA, p. A764
SWEDISH MEDICAL CENTER, ENGLEWOOD, CO, p. A112
SWEDISH MEDICAL CENTER-CHERRY HILL CAMPUS, SEATTLE, WA, p. A764
SWEDISH MEDICAL CENTER-FIRST HILL, SEATTLE, WA, p. A764
SWEDISH/EDMONDS, EDMONDS, WA, p. A757
SWEDISH/ISSAQUAH, ISSAQUAH, WA, p. A759
SWEDISHAMERICAN—A DIVISION OF UW HEALTH, ROCKFORD, IL, p. A219
SWEDISHAMERICAN HOSPITAL, A DIVISION OF UW HEALTH, ROCKFORD, IL, p. A219
SWEENY COMMUNITY HOSPITAL, SWEENY, TX, p. A718
SWEETWATER HOSPITAL, SWEETWATER, TN, p. A650
SWIFT COUNTY—BENSON HEALTH SERVICES, BENSON, MN, p. A372
SWIFT COUNTY-BENSON HOSPITAL, BENSON, MN, p. A372
SWISHER MEMORIAL HEALTHCARE SYSTEM, TULIA, TX, p. A721
SWISHER MEMORIAL HOSPITAL DISTRICT, TULIA, TX, p. A721
SYCAMORE MEDICAL CENTER, MIAMISBURG, OH, p. A545
SYCAMORE SHOALS HOSPITAL, ELIZABETHTON, TN, p. A637
SYCAMORE SPRINGS, LAFAYETTE, IN, p. A234
SYLVAN GROVE HOSPITAL, JACKSON, GA, p. A174
SYRACUSE AREA HEALTH, SYRACUSE, NE, p. A440
SYRACUSE VETERANS AFFAIRS MEDICAL CENTER, SYRACUSE, NY, p. A500
SYRINGA GENERAL HOSPITAL, GRANGEVILLE, ID, p. A190
SYRINGA HOSPITAL AND CLINICS, GRANGEVILLE, ID, p. A190

# T

TACOMA GENERAL HOSPITAL, TACOMA, WA, p. A767
TAHLEQUAH CITY HOSPITAL, TAHLEQUAH, OK, p. A569
TAHOE FOREST HOSPITAL DISTRICT, TRUCKEE, CA, p. A102
TAHOE PACIFIC HOSPITALS, SPARKS, NV, p. A447
TAKOMA REGIONAL HOSPITAL, GREENEVILLE, TN, p. A638
TALLAHASSEE COMMUNITY HOSPITAL, TALLAHASSEE, FL, p. A158
TALLAHASSEE MEM REG MED CENTER, TALLAHASSEE, FL, p. A158
TALLAHASSEE MEMORIAL HEALTHCARE, TALLAHASSEE, FL, p. A158
TALLAHATCHIE GENERAL HOSPITAL, CHARLESTON, MS, p. A391
TAMPA GENERAL HEALTHCARE, TAMPA, FL, p. A160
TAMPA GENERAL HOSPITAL, TAMPA, FL, p. A160
TANNER HIGGINS GENERAL HOSPITAL, BREMEN, GA, p. A167
TANNER MEDICAL CENTER, CARROLLTON, GA, p. A168
TANNER MEDICAL CENTER-CARROLLTON, CARROLLTON, GA, p. A168
TANNER MEDICAL CENTER-VILLA RICA, VILLA RICA, GA, p. A182
TANNER MEDICAL CENTER/EAST ALABAMA, WEDOWEE, AL, p. A25
TARRANT COUNTY HOSP DISTRICT, FORT WORTH, TX, p. A679

TAUNTON STATE HOSPITAL, TAUNTON, MA, p. A345

TAYLOR COUNTY HOSPITAL, CAMPBELLSVILLE, KY, p. A281

TAYLOR HARDIN SECURE MEDICAL FACILITY, TUSCALOOSA, AL, p. A25

TAYLOR HOSPITAL, RIDLEY PARK, PA, p. A606

TAYLOR REGIONAL HOSPITAL, CAMPBELLSVILLE, KY, p. A281

TAYLOR REGIONAL HOSPITAL, HAWKINSVILLE, GA, p. A173

TAYLORVILLE MEMORIAL HOSPITAL, TAYLORVILLE, IL, p. A221

TAZEWELL COMMUNITY HOSPITAL, TAZEWELL, VA, p. A752

T. C. THOMPSON CHILDREN'S HOSPITAL, CHATTANOOGA, TN, p. A636

TEAYS VALLEY HOSPITAL, HURRICANE, WV, p. A773

TECHE REGIONAL MEDICAL CENTER, MORGAN CITY, LA, p. A309

TELECARE HERITAGE PSYCHIATRIC HEALTH CENTER, OAKLAND, CA, p. A82

TEMECULA VALLEY HOSPITAL, TEMECULA, CA, p. A100

TEMPE ST. LUKE'S HOSPITAL, TEMPE, AZ, p. A39

TEMPLE LOWER BUCKS HOSPITAL, BRISTOL, PA, p. A585

TEMPLE UNIVERSITY HOSPITAL—JEANES CAMPUS, PHILADELPHIA, PA, p. A602

TEMPLE UNIVERSITY HOSPITAL, PHILADELPHIA, PA, p. A602

TEMPLE UNIVERSITYHOSPITAL—JEANES CAMPUS, PHILADELPHIA, PA, p. A602

TEN BROECK DUPONT, LOUISVILLE, KY, p. A288

TEN BROECK HOSPITAL, HICKORY, NC, p. A512

TEN BROECK HOSPITAL, LOUISVILLE, KY, p. A288

TEN BROECK HOSPITAL-OCALA, OCALA, FL, p. A150

TENNESSEE VALLEY HEALTHCARE SYSTEM, NASHVILLE, TN, p. A647

TENNOVA HEALTHCARE—CLEVELAND, CLEVELAND, TN, p. A636

TENNOVA HEALTHCARE DYERSBURG REGIONAL MEDICAL CENTER, DYERSBURG, TN, p. A637

TENNOVA HEALTHCARE REGIONAL HOSPITAL OF JACKSON, JACKSON, TN, p. A639

TENNOVA HEALTHCARE VOLUNTEER COMMUNITY HOSPITAL, MARTIN, TN, p. A643

TENNOVA HEALTHCARE-CLARKSVILLE, CLARKSVILLE, TN, p. A636

TENNOVA HEALTHCARE-HARTON, TULLAHOMA, TN, p. A650

TENNOVA HEALTHCARE-JAMESTOWN, JAMESTOWN, TN, p. A640

TENNOVA HEALTHCARE-JEFFERSON MEMORIAL HOSPITAL, JEFFERSON CITY, TN, p. A640

TENNOVA HEALTHCARE-LAFOLLETTE MEDICAL CENTER, LA FOLLETTE, TN, p. A642

TENNOVA HEALTHCARE-LEBANON, LEBANON, TN, p. A642

TENNOVA HEALTHCARE-LEBANON MCFARLAND CAMPUS, LEBANON, TN, p. A642

TENNOVA HEALTHCARE-SHELBYVILLE, SHELBYVILLE, TN, p. A649

TENNOVA NEWPORT MEDICAL CENTER, NEWPORT, TN, p. A647

TENNOVA NORTH KNOXVILLE MEDICAL CENTER, POWELL, TN, p. A648

TENNOVA-JEFFERSON MEMORIAL HOSPITAL, JEFFERSON CITY, TN, p. A640

TERENCE CARDINAL COOKE HEALTH CARE CENTER, NEW YORK, NY, p. A492

TERRE HAUTE REGIONAL HOSPITAL, TERRE HAUTE, IN, p. A241

TERREBONNE GENERAL MEDICAL CENTER, HOUMA, LA, p. A303

TERRELL STATE HOSPITAL, TERRELL, TX, p. A719

TETON MEDICAL CENTER, CHOTEAU, MT, p. A422

TETON VALLEY HEALTH CARE, DRIGGS, ID, p. A190

TETON VALLEY HOSPITAL AND SURGICENTER, DRIGGS, ID, p. A190

TEWKSBURY HOSPITAL, TEWKSBURY, MA, p. A345

TEXAS CENTER FOR INFECTIOUS DISEASE, SAN ANTONIO, TX, p. A713

TEXAS CHILDREN'S HOSPITAL, HOUSTON, TX, p. A688

TEXAS COUNTY MEMORIAL HOSPITAL, HOUSTON, MO, p. A407

TEXAS GENERAL HOSPITAL, GRAND PRAIRIE, TX, p. A682

TEXAS HEALTH ARLINGTON MEMORIAL HOSPITAL, ARLINGTON, TX, p. A654

TEXAS HEALTH CENTER FOR DIAGNOSTIC & SURGERY, PLANO, TX, p. A707

TEXAS HEALTH FRISCO, FRISCO, TX, p. A680

TEXAS HEALTH HARRIS METHODIST HOSPITAL ALLIANCE, FORT WORTH, TX, p. A679

TEXAS HEALTH HARRIS METHODIST HOSPITAL AZLE, AZLE, TX, p. A657

TEXAS HEALTH HARRIS METHODIST HOSPITAL CLEBURNE, CLEBURNE, TX, p. A663

TEXAS HEALTH HARRIS METHODIST HOSPITAL FORT WORTH, FORT WORTH, TX, p. A679

TEXAS HEALTH HARRIS METHODIST HOSPITAL HURST-EULESS-BEDFORD, BEDFORD, TX, p. A659

TEXAS HEALTH HARRIS METHODIST HOSPITAL SOUTHLAKE, SOUTHLAKE, TX, p. A716

TEXAS HEALTH HARRIS METHODIST HOSPITAL SOUTHWEST FORT WORTH, FORT WORTH, TX, p. A679

TEXAS HEALTH HARRIS METHODIST HOSPITAL STEPHENVILLE, STEPHENVILLE, TX, p. A717

TEXAS HEALTH HEART & VASCULAR HOSPITAL ARLINGTON, ARLINGTON, TX, p. A654

TEXAS HEALTH HUGULEY HOSPITAL FORT WORTH SOUTH, BURLESON, TX, p. A662

TEXAS HEALTH PRESBYTERIAN HOSPITAL ALLEN, ALLEN, TX, p. A652

TEXAS HEALTH PRESBYTERIAN HOSPITAL DALLAS, DALLAS, TX, p. A670

TEXAS HEALTH PRESBYTERIAN HOSPITAL DENTON, DENTON, TX, p. A672

TEXAS HEALTH PRESBYTERIAN HOSPITAL FLOWER MOUND, FLOWER MOUND, TX, p. A677

TEXAS HEALTH PRESBYTERIAN HOSPITAL KAUFMAN, KAUFMAN, TX, p. A692

TEXAS HEALTH PRESBYTERIAN HOSPITAL OF ROCKWALL, ROCKWALL, TX, p. A709

TEXAS HEALTH PRESBYTERIAN HOSPITAL PLANO, PLANO, TX, p. A707

TEXAS HEALTH PRESBYTERIAN HOSPITAL-WNJ, SHERMAN, TX, p. A715

TEXAS HEALTH SPECIALTY HOSPITAL, FORT WORTH, TX, p. A679

TEXAS HEALTH SPRINGWOOD, BEDFORD, TX, p. A659

TEXAS HOSPITAL FOR ADVANCED MEDICINE, DALLAS, TX, p. A670

TEXAS INSTITUTE FOR SURGERY AT PRESBYTERIAN HOSPITAL OF DALLAS, DALLAS, TX, p. A670

TEXAS INSTITUTE FOR SURGERY AT TEXAS HEALTH PRESBYTERIAN DALLAS, DALLAS, TX, p. A670

TEXAS NEURO REHAB CENTER, AUSTIN, TX, p. A656

TEXAS NEUROREHAB CENTER, AUSTIN, TX, p. A657

TEXAS ORTHOPEDIC HOSPITAL, HOUSTON, TX, p. A688

TEXAS REGIONAL MEDICAL CENTER AT SUNNYVALE, SUNNYVALE, TX, p. A718

TEXAS REHABILITATION HOSPITAL OF ARLINGTON, ARLINGTON, TX, p. A654

TEXAS REHABILITATION HOSPITAL OF FORT WORTH, FORT WORTH, TX, p. A679

TEXAS REHABILITATION OF FORT WORTH, FORT WORTH, TX, p. A679

TEXAS SCOTTISH RITE HOSPITAL FOR CHILDREN, DALLAS, TX, p. A670

TEXAS STAR RECOVERY, AUSTIN, TX, p. A657

TEXAS WEST OAKS HOSPITAL, HOUSTON, TX, p. A688

TEXOMA HEALTHCARE SYSTEM, DENISON, TX, p. A671

TEXOMA MEDICAL CENTER, DENISON, TX, p. A671

TEXOMA MEDICAL CENTER RESTORATIVE CARE HOSPITAL, SHERMAN, TX, p. A715

TEXSAN HEART HOSPITAL, SAN ANTONIO, TX, p. A713

THAYER COUNTY HEALTH SERVICES, HEBRON, NE, p. A433

THAYER COUNTY MEM HOSPITAL, HEBRON, NE, p. A433

THE ACADIA HOSPITAL, BANGOR, ME, p. A318

THE ALLEN PAVILION, NEW YORK, NY, p. A492

THE AROOSTOOK MEDICAL CENTER, PRESQUE ISLE, ME, p. A322

THE BARBARA BUSH CHILDREN'S HOSPITAL, PORTLAND, ME, p. A322

THE BLACKBERRY CENTER, SAINT CLOUD, FL, p. A156

THE BRIDGEWAY, NORTH LITTLE ROCK, AR, p. A51

THE BRISTOL-MYERS SQUIBB CHILDREN'S HOSPITAL, NEW BRUNSWICK, NJ, p. A459

THE BROOK AT DUPONT, LOUISVILLE, KY, p. A288

THE BROOK HOSPITAL—KMI, LOUISVILLE, KY, p. A288

THE CHARLOTTE HUNGERFORD HOSPITAL, TORRINGTON, CT, p. A125

THE CHILDEN'S REGIONAL HOSPITAL AT COOPER, CAMDEN, NJ, p. A453

THE CHILDREN'S CENTER REHABILITATION HOSPITAL, BETHANY, OK, p. A556

THE CHILDREN'S HOME OF PITTSBURGH, PITTSBURGH, PA, p. A603

THE CHILDREN'S HOSPITAL, AMARILLO, TX, p. A652

THE CHILDREN'S HOSPITAL, AURORA, CO, p. A107

THE CHILDREN'S HOSPITAL AT BRONSON, KALAMAZOO, MI, p. A359

THE CHILDREN'S HOSPITAL AT MONMOUTH MEDICAL CENTER, LONG BRANCH, NJ, p. A457

THE CHILDREN'S HOSPITAL AT PROVIDENCE, ANCHORAGE, AK, p. A27

THE CHILDREN'S HOSPITAL AT SAINT FRANCIS, TULSA, OK, p. A571

THE CHILDREN'S HOSPITAL OF ALABAMA, BIRMINGHAM, AL, p. A16

THE CHILDREN'S HOSPITAL OF MONTEFIORE, BRONX, NY, p. A477

THE CHILDREN'S INN AT NIH, BETHESDA, MD, p. A327

THE CHILDREN'S INSTITUTE OF PITTSBURGH, PITTSBURGH, PA, p. A603

THE COLONY ER HOSPITAL, THE COLONY, TX, p. A720

THE CONNECTICUT HOSPICE, BRANFORD, CT, p. A121

THE CORE INSTITUTE SPECIALTY HOSPITAL, PHOENIX, AZ, p. A37

THE GENERAL, BATON ROUGE, LA, p. A297

THE GOOD SAMARITAN HOSPITAL, LEBANON, PA, p. A594

THE HCMC DEPARTMENT OF PEDIATRICS, MINNEAPOLIS, MN, p. A381

THE HEALTHCENTER, KALISPELL, MT, p. A425

THE HEART HOSPITAL AT DEACONESS GATEWAY, NEWBURGH, IN, p. A238

THE HEART HOSPITAL BAYLOR PLANO, PLANO, TX, p. A707

THE HOSPITAL AT WESTLAKE MEDICAL CENTER, AUSTIN, TX, p. A657

THE HOSPITAL OF CENTRAL CONNECTICUT, NEW BRITAIN, CT, p. A123

THE HOSPITALS OF PROVIDENCE EAST CAMPUS, EL PASO, TX, p. A676

THE HOSPITALS OF PROVIDENCE MEMORIAL CAMPUS, EL PASO, TX, p. A676

THE HOSPITALS OF PROVIDENCE SIERRA CAMPUS, EL PASO, TX, p. A676

THE HOSPITALS OF PROVIDENCE TRANSMOUNTAIN CAMPUS, EL PASO, TX, p. A676

THE HOSPITALS OF SIERRA PROVIDENCE EAST CAMPUS, EL PASO, TX, p. A676

THE HSC PEDIATRIC CENTER, WASHINGTON, DC, p. A130

THE JEWISH HOSPITAL—MERCY HEALTH, CINCINNATI, OH, p. A533

THE JEWISH HOSPITAL, CINCINNATI, OH, p. A533

THE LINDNER CENTER OF HOPE, MASON, OH, p. A544

THE MEDICAL CENTER ALBANY, ALBANY, NY, p. A280

THE MEDICAL CENTER AT BOWLING GREEN, BOWLING GREEN, KY, p. A281

THE MEDICAL CENTER AT CAVERNA, HORSE CAVE, KY, p. A285

THE MEDICAL CENTER AT FRANKLIN, FRANKLIN, KY, p. A283

THE MEDICAL CENTER OF SOUTHEAST TEXAS, PORT ARTHUR, TX, p. A707

THE MEMORIAL HOSPITAL AT CRAIG, CRAIG, CO, p. A110

THE METHODIST HOSPITAL, HOUSTON, TX, p. A688

THE METROHEALTH SYSTEM, CLEVELAND, OH, p. A535

THE MOUNT SINAI HOSPITAL, NEW YORK, NY, p. A492

THE NEUROMEDICAL CENTER REHABILITATION HOSPITAL, BATON ROUGE, LA, p. A297

THE ORTHOPEDIC SPECIALTY HOSP, MURRAY, UT, p. A729

THE ORTHOPEDIC SPECIALTY HOSPITAL, MURRAY, UT, p. A729

THE OUTER BANKS HOSPITAL, NAGS HEAD, NC, p. A515

THE PAVILION, CHAMPAIGN, IL, p. A197

THE PAVILION AT WILLIAMSBURG PLACE, WILLIAMSBURG, VA, p. A753

THE PHYSICIANS CENTRE HOSPITAL, BRYAN, TX, p. A661

THE QUEEN'S MEDICAL CENTER, HONOLULU, HI, p. A185

THE REHABILITATION HOSPITAL OF MONTANA, BILLINGS, MT, p. A422

THE REHABILITATION INSTITUTE OF ST. LOUIS, SAINT LOUIS, MO, p. A417

THE SPINE HOSPITAL OF LOUISIANA AT THE NEUROMEDICAL CENTER, BATON ROUGE, LA, p. A298

THE SURGICAL HOSPITAL OF PHOENIX, PHOENIX, AZ, p. A37

THE UNIVERSITY OF KANSAS HEALTH SYSTEM, KANSAS CITY, KS, p. A268

THE UNIVERSITY OF KANSAS HOSPITAL, KANSAS CITY, KS, p. A268

THE UNIVERSITY OF TOLEDO MEDICAL CENTER, TOLEDO, OH, p. A551

THE UNIVERSITY OF VERMONT HEALTH NETWORK—ALICE HYDE MEDICAL CENTER, MALONE, NY, p. A487

THE UNIVERSITY OF VERMONT HEALTH NETWORK CENTRAL VERMONT MEDICAL CENTER, BERLIN, VT, p. A735

THE UNIVERSITY OF VERMONT HEALTH NETWORK CHAMPLAIN VALLEY PHYSICIANS HOSPITAL MEDICAL CENTER, PLATTSBURGH, NY, p. A495

THE UNIVERSITY OF VERMONT HEALTH NETWORK ELIZABETHTOWN COMMUNITY HOSPITAL, ELIZABETHTOWN, NY, p. A483

THE UNIVERSITY OF VERMONT HEALTH NETWORK UNIVERSITY OF VERMONT MEDICAL CENTER, BURLINGTON, VT, p. A735

THE UNIVERSITY OF VERMONT HEALTH NETWORK-CHAMPLAIN VALLEY PHYSICIANS HOSPITAL, PLATTSBURGH, NY, p. A495

THE VILLAGES HEALTH SYSTEM, THE VILLAGES, FL, p. A160

THE VILLAGES REGIONAL HOSPITAL, THE VILLAGES, FL, p. A160

THE VINES, OCALA, FL, p. A150

THE WILLIAM W. BACKUS HOSPITAL, NORWICH, CT, p. A124

THE WILLOUGH AT NAPLES, NAPLES, FL, p. A149

THE WOMAN'S HOSPITAL OF TEXAS, HOUSTON, TX, p. A688

THE WOMEN'S HOSPITAL, NEWBURGH, IN, p. A238

THE WOODS AT PARKSIDE, GAHANNA, OH, p. A540

THEDA CARE MEDICAL CENTER—WILD ROSE, WILD ROSE, WI, p. A799

THEDA CLARK MEDICAL CENTER, NEENAH, WI, p. A792

THEDACARE MEDICAL CENTER-BERLIN, BERLIN, WI, p. A781

THEDACARE MEDICAL CENTER-NEW LONDON, NEW LONDON, WI, p. A792

THEDACARE MEDICAL CENTER-SHAWANO, SHAWANO, WI, p. A795

THEDACARE MEDICAL CENTER-WAUPACA, WAUPACA, WI, p. A798

THEDACARE REGIONAL MEDICAL CENTER-APPLETON, APPLETON, WI, p. A779

THEDACARE REGIONAL MEDICAL CENTER-BERLIN, BERLIN, WI, p. A781

THEDACARE REGIONAL MEDICAL CENTER-NEENAH, NEENAH, WI, p. A792

THIBODAUX REGIONAL HEALTH CENTER, THIBODAUX, LA, p. A316

THIBODAUX REGIONAL HEALTH SYSTEM, THIBODAUX, LA, p. A316

THOMAS B. FINAN CENTER, CUMBERLAND, MD, p. A329

THOMAS H. BOYD MEMORIAL HOSPITAL, CARROLLTON, IL, p. A196

THOMAS HOSPITAL, FAIRHOPE, AL, p. A18

THOMAS JEFFERSON UNIVERSITY HOSPITALS, PHILADELPHIA, PA, p. A602

THOMAS MEMORIAL HOSPITAL, SOUTH CHARLESTON, WV, p. A777

THOMASVILLE MEDICAL CENTER, THOMASVILLE, NC, p. A519

THOMPSON HEALTH, CANANDAIGUA, NY, p. A481

THOREK HOSPITAL AND MED CENTER, CHICAGO, IL, p. A201

THOREK MEMORIAL HOSPITAL, CHICAGO, IL, p. A201

THREE GABLES SURGERY CENTER, PROCTORVILLE, OH, p. A548

THREE RIVERS AREA HOSPITAL, THREE RIVERS, MI, p. A368

THREE RIVERS BEHAVIORAL HEALTH, WEST COLUMBIA, SC, p. A625

THREE RIVERS CENTER FOR HEALTH, WEST COLUMBIA, SC, p. A625

THREE RIVERS HEALTH, THREE RIVERS, MI, p. A368

THREE RIVERS HEALTHCARE, POPLAR BLUFF, MO, p. A414

THREE RIVERS HOSPITAL, BREWSTER, WA, p. A756

THREE RIVERS HOSPITAL, WAVERLY, TN, p. A650

THREE RIVERS MEDICAL CENTER, GRANTS PASS, OR, p. A575

THREE RIVERS MEDICAL CENTER, LOUISA, KY, p. A287

THROCKMORTON COUNTY MEMORIAL HOSPITAL, THROCKMORTON, TX, p. A721

THUNDERBIRD SAMARITAN MED CTR, GLENDALE, AZ, p. A32

TIDALHEALTH NANTICOKE, SEAFORD, DE, p. A128

TIDALHEALTH PENINSULA, SALISBURY, MD, p. A332

TIDELANDS GEORGETOWN MEMORIAL HOSPITAL, GEORGETOWN, SC, p. A620

TIDELANDS WACCAMAW COMMUNITY HOSPITAL, MURRELLS INLET, SC, p. A623

TIDEWATER PSYCH INST-NORFOLK, NORFOLK, VA, p. A748

TIFT REGIONAL HEALTH SYSTEM, TIFTON, GA, p. A182

TIFT REGIONAL MEDICAL CENTER, TIFTON, GA, p. A182

TILLAMOOK REGIONAL MEDICAL CENTER, TILLAMOOK, OR, p. A582

TIMPANOGOS REGIONAL HOSPITAL, OREM, UT, p. A730

TIOGA COMMUNITY HOSPITAL, TIOGA, ND, p. A526

TIOGA MEDICAL CENTER, TIOGA, ND, p. A526

TIPPAH COUNTY HOSPITAL, RIPLEY, MS, p. A399

TIPTON HOSPITAL, TIPTON, IN, p. A241

TIRR MEMORIAL HERMANN, HOUSTON, TX, p. A688

TITUS REGIONAL MEDICAL CENTER, MOUNT PLEASANT, TX, p. A702

TITUS REGIONAL MEDICAL CTR, MOUNT PLEASANT, TX, p. A702

TITUSVILLE AREA HOSPITAL, TITUSVILLE, PA, p. A608

T.J. HEALTH COLUMBIA, COLUMBIA, KY, p. A281

TJ HEALTH COLUMBIA, COLUMBIA, KY, p. A281

T. J. SAMSON COMMUNITY HOSPITAL, GLASGOW, KY, p. A284

TMC BONHAM HOSPITAL, BONHAM, TX, p. A660

TMC FOR CHILDREN, TUCSON, AZ, p. A41

TMC HEALTHCARE, TUCSON, AZ, p. A41

TOBEY HOSPITAL, WAREHAM, MA, p. A345

TOLEDO CHILDREN'S HOSPITAL, TOLEDO, OH, p. A551

TOMAH HEALTH, TOMAH, WI, p. A797

TOMAH MEMORIAL HOSPITAL, TOMAH, WI, p. A797

TOMAH VETERANS AFFAIRS MEDICAL CENTER, TOMAH, WI, p. A797

TOMBALL REGIONAL MEDICAL CENTER, TOMBALL, TX, p. A721

TOOELE VALLEY REG MED CTR, TOOELE, UT, p. A733

TOOLE COUNTY HOSP & NRSG HOME, SHELBY, MT, p. A427

TOPPENISH COMMUNITY HOSPITAL, TOPPENISH, WA, p. A768

TOPS SURGICAL SPECIALTY HOSP, HOUSTON, TX, p. A688

TOPS SURGICAL SPECIALTY HOSPITAL, HOUSTON, TX, p. A689

TORRANCE MEMORIAL MEDICAL CENTER, TORRANCE, CA, p. A101

TORRANCE STATE HOSPITAL, TORRANCE, PA, p. A608

TOTALLY KIDS REHABILITATION HOSPITAL, LOMA LINDA, CA, p. A72

TOUCHETTE REGIONAL HOSPITAL, CENTREVILLE, IL, p. A197

TOUCHETTE REGIONAL HOSPITALS, CENTREVILLE, IL, p. A197

TOURO INFIRMARY, NEW ORLEANS, LA, p. A311

TOWN AND COUNTRY HOSPITAL, TAMPA, FL, p. A160

TOWNER COUNTY MEDICAL CENTER, CANDO, ND, p. A521

TOWNER COUNTY MEMORIAL HOSP, CANDO, ND, p. A521

TRACE REGIONAL HOSPITAL, HOUSTON, MS, p. A394

TRACY COMM MEMORIAL HOSPITAL, TRACY, CA, p. A101

TRADITION MEDICAL CENTER, PORT ST LUCIE, FL, p. A155

TRANSITIONAL CARE HOSPITAL, CHARLOTTESVILLE, VA, p. A739

TRANSYLVANIA COMM HOSPITAL, BREVARD, NC, p. A505

TRANSYLVANIA REGIONAL HOSPITAL, BREVARD, NC, p. A505

TREASURE VALLEY HOSPITAL, BOISE, ID, p. A189

TREGO COUNTY-LEMKE MEMORIAL HOSPITAL, WAKEENEY, KS, p. A274

TRENTON PSYCHIATRIC HOSPITAL, TRENTON, NJ, p. A464

TRI PARISH REHABILITATION HOSPITAL, LEESVILLE, LA, p. A307

TRI VALLEY HEALTH SYSTEM, CAMBRIDGE, NE, p. A430

TRI-CITY MEDICAL CENTER, OCEANSIDE, CA, p. A82

TRI-COUNTY AREA HOSPITAL, LEXINGTON, NE, p. A434

TRI-COUNTY HOSPITAL, WADENA, MN, p. A387

TRI-COUNTY MEMORIAL HOSPITAL, WHITEHALL, WI, p. A799

TRI-STATE MEMORIAL HOSPITAL, CLARKSTON, WA, p. A756

TRI-WARD GENERAL HOSPITAL, BERNICE, LA, p. A298

TRIANGLE SPRINGS HOSPITAL, RALEIGH, NC, p. A516

TRIDENT MEDICAL CENTER, CHARLESTON, SC, p. A616

TRIGG COUNTY HOSPITAL, CADIZ, KY, p. A281

TRIHEALTH EVENDALE HOSPITAL, CINCINNATI, OH, p. A533

TRIHEALTH REHABILITATION HOSPITAL, CINCINNATI, OH, p. A533

TRINITAS HOSPITAL—JERSEY STREET CAMPUS, ELIZABETH, NJ, p. A454

TRINITAS HOSPITAL—NEW POINT CAMPUS, ELIZABETH, NJ, p. A454

TRINITAS HOSPITAL-WILLIAMSON STREET CAMPUS, ELIZABETH, NJ, p. A454

TRINITAS REGIONAL MEDICAL CENTER, ELIZABETH, NJ, p. A455

TRINITY BETTENDORF, BETTENDORF, IA, p. A244

TRINITY HEALTH, MINOT, ND, p. A525

TRINITY HEALTH SYSTEM, STEUBENVILLE, OH, p. A550

TRINITY HOSPITAL, CHICAGO, IL, p. A201

TRINITY HOSPITAL, WEAVERVILLE, CA, p. A104

TRINITY HOSPITAL, WOLF POINT, MT, p. A428

TRINITY HOSPITAL OF AUGUSTA, AUGUSTA, GA, p. A166

TRINITY HOSPITAL TWIN CITY, DENNISON, OH, p. A539

TRINITY MEDICAL CENTER, BIRMINGHAM, AL, p. A16

TRINITY MEDICAL CENTER, STEUBENVILLE, OH, p. A550

TRINITY MOLINE, MOLINE, IL, p. A212

TRINITY MUSCATINE, MUSCATINE, IA, p. A254

TRINITY REGIONAL MEDICAL CENTER, FORT DODGE, IA, p. A250

TRINITY ROCK ISLAND, ROCK ISLAND, IL, p. A218

TRINITY SPRINGS PAVILION-EAST, FORT WORTH, TX, p. A679

TRINITY VALLEY MEDICAL CENTER, PALESTINE, TX, p. A704

TRIOS HEALTH, KENNEWICK, WA, p. A759

TRIPLER ARMY MEDICAL CENTER, HONOLULU, HI, p. A185

TRISTAR ASHLAND CITY MEDICAL CENTER, ASHLAND CITY, TN, p. A634

TRISTAR CENTENNIAL MEDICAL CENTER, NASHVILLE, TN, p. A647

TRISTAR CENTENNIAL MEDICAL CENTER AT ASHLAND CITY, ASHLAND CITY, TN, p. A634

TRISTAR GREENVIEW REGIONAL HOSPITAL, BOWLING GREEN, KY, p. A281

TRISTAR HENDERSONVILLE MEDICAL CENTER, HENDERSONVILLE, TN, p. A639

TRISTAR HORIZON MEDICAL CENTER, DICKSON, TN, p. A637

TRISTAR SKYLINE MEDICAL CENTER, NASHVILLE, TN, p. A647

TRISTAR SOUTHERN HILLS MEDICAL CENTER, NASHVILLE, TN, p. A647

TRISTAR STONECREST MEDICAL CENTER, SMYRNA, TN, p. A649

TRISTAR SUMMIT MEDICAL CENTER, HERMITAGE, TN, p. A639

TRIUMPH HOSPITAL AURORA, AURORA, CO, p. A107

TRIUMPH HOSPITAL CLEAR LAKE, WEBSTER, TX, p. A724

TRIUMPH HOSPITAL DALLAS, DALLAS, TX, p. A670

TRIUMPH HOSPITAL EL PASO, EL PASO, TX, p. A676

TRIUMPH HOSPITAL LIMA, LIMA, OH, p. A543

TRIUMPH HOSPITAL NORTHWEST INDIANA, HAMMOND, IN, p. A230

TRIUMPH HOSPITAL SOUTHWEST, SUGAR LAND, TX, p. A718

TROUSDALE MEDICAL CENTER, HARTSVILLE, TN, p. A639

TROY COMMUNITY HOSPITAL, TROY, PA, p. A609

TROY REGIONAL MEDICAL CENTER, TROY, AL, p. A25

TRUMAN MEDICAL CENTER, KANSAS CITY, MO, p. A409

TRUMAN MEDICAL CENTER-EAST, KANSAS CITY, MO, p. A409

TRUMAN MEDICAL CENTER-HOSPITAL HILL, KANSAS CITY, MO, p. A410

TRUMAN MEDICAL CENTER-LAKEWOOD, KANSAS CITY, MO, p. A410

TRUMBULL MEMORIAL HOSPITAL, WARREN, OH, p. A551

TRUSTED MEDICAL CENTERS-MANSFIELD, MANSFIELD, TX, p. A699

TRUSTPOINT HOSPITAL, LUBBOCK, TX, p. A698

TRUSTPOINT HOSPITAL, MURFREESBORO, TN, p. A646

TRUSTPOINT REHABILITATION HOSPITAL OF LUBBOCK, LUBBOCK, TX, p. A698

TSEHOOTSOOI MEDICAL CENTER, FORT DEFIANCE, AZ, p. A31

TUALITY FOREST GROVE HOSPITAL, FOREST GROVE, OR, p. A575

TUALITY HEALTHCARE, HILLSBORO, OR, p. A576

TUBA CITY INDIAN MEDICAL CTR, TUBA CITY, AZ, p. A39

TUBA CITY REGIONAL HEALTH CARE CORPORATION, TUBA CITY, AZ, p. A39

TUFTS MEDICAL CENTER, BOSTON, MA, p. A336

TUFTS-NEW ENGLAND MED CENTER, BOSTON, MA, p. A336

TUG VALLEY ARH REGIONAL MEDICAL CENTER, SOUTH WILLIAMSON, KY, p. A293

TULANE HEALTH SYSTEM, NEW ORLEANS, LA, p. A311

TULANE MEDICAL CENTER, NEW ORLEANS, LA, p. A311

TULARE REGIONAL MEDICAL CENTER, TULARE, CA, p. A102

TULSA CENTER FOR BEHAVIORAL HEALTH, TULSA, OK, p. A571

TULSA REGIONAL MEDICAL CENTER, TULSA, OK, p. A571

TULSA SPINE AND SPECIALTY HOSPITAL, TULSA, OK, p. A571

TULSA SPINE HOSPITAL, TULSA, OK, p. A571

TURKEY CREEK MEDICAL CENTER, KNOXVILLE, TN, p. A641

TURNING POINT CARE CENTER, MOULTRIE, GA, p. A177

TURNING POINT HOSPITAL, MOULTRIE, GA, p. A177

TURQUOISE LODGE, ALBUQUERQUE, NM, p. A468

TURQUOISE LODGE HOSPITAL, ALBUQUERQUE, NM, p. A468

TUSCALOOSA VETERANS AFFAIRS MEDICAL CENTER, TUSCALOOSA, AL, p. A25

TUSKEGEE DIVISION, TUSKEGEE, AL, p. A25

TWEETEN LUTHERAN HLTH CARE CTR, SPRING GROVE, MN, p. A386

TWELVE CLANS UNITY HOSPITAL, WINNEBAGO, NE, p. A440

TWIN CITIES COMMUNITY HOSPITAL, TEMPLETON, CA, p. A101

TWIN CITIES HOSPITAL, NICEVILLE, FL, p. A149

TWIN CITY HOSPITAL, DENNISON, OH, p. A539

TWIN COUNTY REGIONAL HEALTHCARE, GALAX, VA, p. A743

TWIN COUNTY REGIONAL HOSPITAL, GALAX, VA, p. A743

TWIN LAKES REGIONAL MEDICAL CENTER, LEITCHFIELD, KY, p. A286

TWIN VALLEY BEHAVIORAL HEALTHCARE, COLUMBUS, OH, p. A537

TWIN VALLEY PSYCHIATRIC SYSTEM, COLUMBUS, OH, p. A537

TWINBROOK NURSING & CONV HOME, ERIE, PA, p. A590

TWO RIVERS COMMUNITY HOSPITAL, TWO RIVERS, WI, p. A797

TX CTR FOR INFECTIOUS DESEASE, SAN ANTONIO, TX, p. A713

TY COBB REGIONAL MEDICAL CENTER, LAVONIA, GA, p. A175

TYLER CONTINUECARE HOSPITAL, TYLER, TX, p. A722

TYLER COUNTY HOSPITAL, WOODVILLE, TX, p. A726

TYLER HEALTHCARE CENTER AVERA, TYLER, MN, p. A387

TYLER HOLMES MEMORIAL HOSPITAL, WINONA, MS, p. A401

TYLER MEMORIAL HOSPITAL, TUNKHANNOCK, PA, p. A609

TYRONE HOSPITAL, TYRONE, PA, p. A609

**U**

UAB HIGHLANDS, BIRMINGHAM, AL, p. A16
UAB MEDICAL WEST, BESSEMER, AL, p. A14
UAMS MEDICAL CENTER, LITTLE ROCK, AR, p. A49
UC IRVINE MEDICAL CENTER, ORANGE, CA, p. A83
UC SAN DIEGO HEALTH, SAN DIEGO, CA, p. A92
UC SAN DIEGO MEDICAL CENTER—HILLCREST, SAN DIEGO, CA, p. A92
UC SAN DIEGO SHILEY EYE CENTER, LA JOLLA, CA, p. A70
UCHEALTH BROOMFIELD HOSPITAL, BROOMFIELD, CO, p. A108
UCHEALTH GRANDVIEW HOSPITAL, COLORADO SPRINGS, CO, p. A109
UCHEALTH GREELEY, GREELEY, CO, p. A114
UCHEALTH HIGHLANDS RANCH HOSPITAL, HIGHLANDS RANCH, CO, p. A114
UCHEALTH LONGS PEAK HOSPITAL, LONGMONT, CO, p. A116
UCHEALTH MEDICAL CENTER OF THE ROCKIES, LOVELAND, CO, p. A117
UCHEALTH MEMORIAL, COLORADO SPRINGS, CO, p. A109
UCHEALTH MEMORIAL HOSPITAL, COLORADO SPRINGS, CO, p. A109
UCHEALTH PIKES PEAK REGIONAL HOSPITAL, WOODLAND PARK, CO, p. A120
UCHEALTH POUDRE VALLEY HOSPITAL, FORT COLLINS, CO, p. A112
UCHEALTH YAMPA VALLEY MEDICAL CENTER, STEAMBOAT SPRINGS, CO, p. A118
UCI MEDICAL CENTER, ORANGE, CA, p. A83
UCLA MEDICAL CENTER-SANTA MONICA, SANTA MONICA, CA, p. A98
UCONN, JOHN DEMPSEY HOSPITAL, FARMINGTON, CT, p. A122
UCSF BENIOFF CHILDREN'S HOSPITAL OAKLAND, OAKLAND, CA, p. A82
UCSF CHILDREN'S HOSPITAL, SAN FRANCISCO, CA, p. A94
UCSF MEDICAL CENTER, SAN FRANCISCO, CA, p. A94
UF HEALTH JACKSONVILLE, JACKSONVILLE, FL, p. A142
UF HEALTH REHAB HOSPITAL, GAINESVILLE, FL, p. A139
UF HEALTH SHANDS HOSPITAL, GAINESVILLE, FL, p. A139
UH AHUJA MEDICAL CENTER, BEACHWOOD, OH, p. A529
UH AVON REHABILITATION HOSPITAL, AVON, OH, p. A528
UH CLEVELAND MEDICAL CENTER, CLEVELAND, OH, p. A535
UH CONNEAUT MEDICAL CENTER, CONNEAUT, OH, p. A537
UH ELYRIA MEDICAL CENTER, ELYRIA, OH, p. A540
UH GEAUGA MEDICAL CENTER, CHARDON, OH, p. A531
UH GENEVA MEDICAL CENTER, GENEVA, OH, p. A541
UH PORTAGE MEDICAL CENTER, RAVENNA, OH, p. A548
UH REGIONAL HOSPITALS, CLEVELAND, OH, p. A535
UH REHABILITATION HOSPITAL, BEACHWOOD, OH, p. A529
UH ROBINSON MEDICAL CENTER, RAVENNA, OH, p. A548
UH SAMARITAN MEDICAL CENTER, ASHLAND, OH, p. A528
UH ST. JOHN MEDICAL CENTER, WESTLAKE, OH, p. A553
UHS CHENANGO MEMORIAL HOSPITAL, NORWICH, NY, p. A493
UHS DELAWARE VALLEY HOSPITAL, WALTON, NY, p. A501
UINTAH BASIN MEDICAL CENTER, ROOSEVELT, UT, p. A731
UK HEALTHCARE GOOD SAMARITAN, LEXINGTON, KY, p. A287
UKIAH VALLEY MEDICAL CENTER, UKIAH, CA, p. A102
UMASS MEMORIAL HEALTH CARE, WORCESTER, MA, p. A346
UMASS MEMORIAL HEALTHALLIANCE-CLINTON HOSPITAL—LEOMINSTER CAMPUS, LEOMINSTER, MA, p. A340
UMASS MEMORIAL HEALTHALLIANCE-CLINTON HOSPITAL, LEOMINSTER, MA, p. A340
UMASS MEMORIAL MEDICAL CENTER, WORCESTER, MA, p. A347
UMASS MEMORIAL-MARLBOROUGH HOSPITAL, MARLBOROUGH, MA, p. A341
UMASS-MEM MARLBOROUGH HOSP, MARLBOROUGH, MA, p. A341
UMPC HORIZON, FARRELL, PA, p. A590
UNC LENOIR HEALTHCARE, KINSTON, NC, p. A513
UNC REX HEALTH CARE, RALEIGH, NC, p. A517
UNC REX HEALTHCARE, RALEIGH, NC, p. A517
UNC ROCKINGHAM HEALTH CARE, EDEN, NC, p. A509
UNDERWOOD-MEMORIAL HOSPITAL, WOODBURY, NJ, p. A466
UNICOI COUNTY MEMORIAL HOSPITAL, ERWIN, TN, p. A638
UNIMED MEDICAL CENTER, MINOT, ND, p. A525
UNION CAMPUS, LYNN, MA, p. A341
UNION CNTY METHODIST HOSPITAL, MORGANFIELD, KY, p. A290

UNION COUNTY GENERAL HOSPITAL, CLAYTON, NM, p. A468
UNION COUNTY HOSPITAL, ANNA, IL, p. A194
UNION COUNTY HOSPITAL DISTRICT, ANNA, IL, p. A194
UNION GENERAL HOSPITAL, BLAIRSVILLE, GA, p. A167
UNION GENERAL HOSPITAL, FARMERVILLE, LA, p. A301
UNION HOSPITAL, DOVER, OH, p. A539
UNION HOSPITAL, ELKTON, MD, p. A329
UNION HOSPITAL, LYNN, MA, p. A341
UNION HOSPITAL, TERRE HAUTE, IN, p. A241
UNION HOSPITAL CLINTON, CLINTON, IN, p. A225
UNION HOSPITAL OF CECIL COUNTY, ELKTON, MD, p. A329
UNION MEDICAL CENTER, UNION, SC, p. A625
UNIONTOWN HOSPITAL, UNIONTOWN, PA, p. A609
UNITED COMMUNITY HOSPITAL, GROVE CITY, PA, p. A591
UNITED HEALTH SERVICES, BINGHAMTON, NY, p. A476
UNITED HEALTH SERVICES, GRAND FORKS, ND, p. A524
UNITED HEALTH SERVICES HOSPITALS-BINGHAMTON, BINGHAMTON, NY, p. A476
UNITED HOME, NEW ROCHELLE, NY, p. A489
UNITED HOSPITAL, GRAND FORKS, ND, p. A524
UNITED HOSPITAL, SAINT PAUL, MN, p. A385
UNITED HOSPITAL CENTER, BRIDGEPORT, WV, p. A770
UNITED HOSPITAL DISTRICT, BLUE EARTH, MN, p. A373
UNITED HOSPITAL SYSTEM, ST. CATHERINE'S MEDICAL CENTER CAMPUS, PLEASANT PRAIRIE, WI, p. A794
UNITED HOSPITAL SYSTEM-KENOSHA CAMPUS, KENOSHA, WI, p. A786
UNITED MEDICAL CENTER, CHEYENNE, WY, p. A802
UNITED MEDICAL CENTER, WASHINGTON, DC, p. A130
UNITED MEDICAL CTR-SHELBYVILLE, SHELBYVILLE, KY, p. A293
UNITED MEDICAL HEALTHWEST NEW ORLEANS, LLC, GRETNA, LA, p. A302
UNITED MEDICAL REHABILITATION HOSPITAL, GRETNA, LA, p. A302
UNITED MEDICAL REHABILITATION HOSPITAL, HAMMOND, LA, p. A302
UNITED MEMORIAL HEALTH CENTER, GREENVILLE, MI, p. A356
UNITED MEMORIAL MEDICAL CARE, HOUSTON, TX, p. A689
UNITED MEMORIAL MEDICAL CENTER, BATAVIA, NY, p. A475
UNITED MEMORIAL MEDICAL CENTER, HOUSTON, TX, p. A689
UNITED REGIONAL HEALTH CARE SYSTEM, WICHITA FALLS, TX, p. A725
UNITED REGIONAL MEDICAL CENTER, MANCHESTER, TN, p. A643
UNITY HEALTH WHITE COUNTY MEDICAL CENTER, SEARCY, AR, p. A52
UNITY HOSPITAL, FRIDLEY, MN, p. A376
UNITY HOSPITAL, GRAFTON, ND, p. A523
UNITY HOSPITAL, ROCHESTER, NY, p. A496
UNITY MEDICAL & SURGICAL HOSPITAL, MISHAWAKA, IN, p. A236
UNITY MEDICAL CENTER, GRAFTON, ND, p. A523
UNITY MEDICAL CENTER, MANCHESTER, TN, p. A643
UNITY POINT HEALTH-PEKIN HOSPITAL, PEKIN, IL, p. A216
UNITY PSYCH CARE-MEMPHIS, MEMPHIS, TN, p. A645
UNITY PSYCHIATRIC CARE-CLARKSVILLE, CLARKSVILLE, TN, p. A636
UNITY PSYCHIATRIC CARE-COLUMBIA, COLUMBIA, TN, p. A637
UNITY PSYCHIATRIC CARE-HUNTSVILLE, HUNTSVILLE, AL, p. A20
UNITY PSYCHIATRIC CARE-MARTIN, MARTIN, TN, p. A643
UNITYHEALTH MACNEAL HOSPITAL, BERWYN, IL, p. A195
UNITYPOINT HEALTH—ALLEN HOSPITAL, WATERLOO, IA, p. A259
UNITYPOINT HEALTH—DES MOINES, DES MOINES, IA, p. A248
UNITYPOINT HEALTH—FINLEY, DUBUQUE, IA, p. A249
UNITYPOINT HEALTH—FINLEY HOSPITAL, DUBUQUE, IA, p. A249
UNITYPOINT HEALTH—GRINNELL REGIONAL MEDICAL CENTER, GRINNELL, IA, p. A250
UNITYPOINT HEALTH—IOWA METHODIST MEDICAL CENTER, DES MOINES, IA, p. A248
UNITYPOINT HEALTH—JONES REGIONAL MEDICAL CENTER, ANAMOSA, IA, p. A243
UNITYPOINT HEALTH—MARSHALLTOWN, MARSHALLTOWN, IA, p. A254
UNITYPOINT HEALTH—METHODIST PROCTOR, PEORIA, IL, p. A217
UNITYPOINT HEALTH—PEORIA, PEORIA, IL, p. A217
UNITYPOINT HEALTH—PROCTOR, PEORIA, IL, p. A217
UNITYPOINT HEALTH—ST. LUKES'S SIOUX CITY, SIOUX CITY, IA, p. A258
UNITYPOINT HEALTH—ST. LUKE'S, CEDAR RAPIDS, IA, p. A245

UNITYPOINT HEALTH—ST. LUKE'S, SIOUX CITY, IA, p. A258
UNITYPOINT HEALTH—ST. LUKE'S HOSPITAL, CEDAR RAPIDS, IA, p. A245
UNITYPOINT HEALTH—TRINITY BETTENDORF, BETTENDORF, IA, p. A244
UNITYPOINT HEALTH—TRINITY MOLINE, MOLINE, IL, p. A212
UNITYPOINT HEALTH—TRINITY MUSCATINE, MUSCATINE, IA, p. A254
UNITYPOINT HEALTH—TRINITY REGIONAL MEDICAL CENTER, FORT DODGE, IA, p. A250
UNITYPOINT HEALTH—TRINITY ROCK ISLAND, ROCK ISLAND, IL, p. A218
UNITYPOINT HEALTH—WATERLOO, WATERLOO, IA, p. A259
UNITYPOINT HEALTH MERITER, MADISON, WI, p. A788
UNITYPOINT HEALTH-KEOKUK, KEOKUK, IA, p. A252
UNITYPOINT HEALTH-PEKIN HOSPITAL, PEKIN, IL, p. A216
UNITYPOINT HEALTH-PROCTOR, PEORIA, IL, p. A217
UNIV BEHAVIORAL HEALTH CENTER, DENTON, TX, p. A672
UNIV MED CTR, LAS VEGAS, NV, p. A444
UNIV MEDICAL CENTER-PASSAVANT, PITTSBURGH, PA, p. A603
UNIV OF CA SAN FRANCISCO, SAN FRANCISCO, CA, p. A94
UNIV OF CALIF, DAVIS MED CTR, SACRAMENTO, CA, p. A90
UNIV OF COLORADO HOSPITAL, AURORA, CO, p. A108
UNIV OF CONN HEALTH CENTER, FARMINGTON, CT, p. A122
UNIV OF MARYLAND MED SYSTEM, BALTIMORE, MD, p. A326
UNIV OF NEW MEXICO HOSPITAL, ALBUQUERQUE, NM, p. A468
UNIV OF TN MEM HOSPITAL, KNOXVILLE, TN, p. A641
UNIVERSITY BEHAVIORAL HEALTH OF DENTON, DENTON, TX, p. A672
UNIVERSITY BEHAVIORAL HEALTH OF EL PASO, EL PASO, TX, p. A676
UNIVERSITY BEHAVIORAL HEALTHCARE, PISCATAWAY, NJ, p. A461
UNIVERSITY EVERETT TOWER, OKLAHOMA CITY, OK, p. A566
UNIVERSITY HEALTH CARE SYSTEM, AUGUSTA, GA, p. A166
UNIVERSITY HEALTH CONWAY, MONROE, LA, p. A309
UNIVERSITY HEALTH SYSTEM, SAN ANTONIO, TX, p. A714
UNIVERSITY HOSP OF ARKANSAS, LITTLE ROCK, AR, p. A49
UNIVERSITY HOSPITAL & CLINICS, LAFAYETTE, LA, p. A306
UNIVERSITY HOSPITAL, ALBUQUERQUE, NM, p. A468
UNIVERSITY HOSPITAL, AUGUSTA, GA, p. A166
UNIVERSITY HOSPITAL, CINCINNATI, OH, p. A533
UNIVERSITY HOSPITAL, JACKSON, MS, p. A395
UNIVERSITY HOSPITAL, MADISON, WI, p. A788
UNIVERSITY HOSPITAL, NEWARK, NJ, p. A460
UNIVERSITY HOSPITAL, SAN JUAN, PR, p. A811
UNIVERSITY HOSPITAL AND CLINICS, LAFAYETTE, LA, p. A306
UNIVERSITY HOSPITAL AND MEDICAL CENTER, TAMARAC, FL, p. A159
UNIVERSITY HOSPITAL MCDUFFIE, THOMSON, GA, p. A182
UNIVERSITY HOSPITAL RICHMOND, CLEVELAND, OH, p. A535
UNIVERSITY HOSPITAL SCHOOL, IOWA CITY, IA, p. A252
UNIVERSITY HOSPITALS AHUJA MEDICAL CENTER, BEACHWOOD, OH, p. A529
UNIVERSITY HOSPITALS AVON REHABILITATION HOSPITALS, AVON, OH, p. A528
UNIVERSITY HOSPITALS BEDFORD, CLEVELAND, OH, p. A535
UNIVERSITY HOSPITALS CLEVELAND MEDICAL CENTER, CLEVELAND, OH, p. A535
UNIVERSITY HOSPITALS CONNEAUT MEDICAL CENTER, CONNEAUT, OH, p. A537
UNIVERSITY HOSPITALS ELYRIA MEDICAL CENTER, ELYRIA, OH, p. A540
UNIVERSITY HOSPITALS EXTENDED CARE CAMPUS, CHARDON, OH, p. A531
UNIVERSITY HOSPITALS GEAUGA MEDICAL CENTER, CHARDON, OH, p. A531
UNIVERSITY HOSPITALS GENEVA MEDICAL CENTER, GENEVA, OH, p. A541
UNIVERSITY HOSPITALS PARMA MEDICAL CENTER, PARMA, OH, p. A547
UNIVERSITY HOSPITALS SAMARITAN MEDICAL CENTER, ASHLAND, OH, p. A528
UNIVERSITY MEDICAL CENTER, LAS VEGAS, NV, p. A444
UNIVERSITY MEDICAL CENTER, LUBBOCK, TX, p. A698
UNIVERSITY MEDICAL CENTER, NEW ORLEANS, LA, p. A312
UNIVERSITY MEDICAL CENTER OF EL PASO, EL PASO, TX, p. A676
UNIVERSITY MEDICAL CENTER OF PRINCETON AT PLAINSBORO, PLAINSBORO, NJ, p. A461
UNIVERSITY MEDICAL CENTER-PSYCHIATRIC UNIT, LAFAYETTE, LA, p. A306
UNIVERSITY OF ALA HOSPITAL, BIRMINGHAM, AL, p. A16
UNIVERSITY OF ALABAMA HOSPITAL, BIRMINGHAM, AL, p. A16

UNIVERSITY OF CALIFORNIA LOS ANGELES MEDICAL CENTER, LOS ANGELES, CA, p. A76
UNIVERSITY OF CALIFORNIA LOS ANGELES NEUROPSYCHIATRIC HOSPITAL, LOS ANGELES, CA, p. A76
UNIVERSITY OF CALIFORNIA, DAVIS MEDICAL CENTER, SACRAMENTO, CA, p. A90
UNIVERSITY OF CHICAGO COMER CHILDREN'S HOSPITAL, CHICAGO, IL, p. A201
UNIVERSITY OF CHICAGO HOSP, CHICAGO, IL, p. A201
UNIVERSITY OF CHICAGO MEDICAL CENTER, CHICAGO, IL, p. A201
UNIVERSITY OF CINCINNATI MEDICAL CENTER, CINCINNATI, OH, p. A533
UNIVERSITY OF COLORADO HOSPITAL, AURORA, CO, p. A108
UNIVERSITY OF ILLINOIS HOSPITAL & HEALTH SCIENCES SYSTEM, CHICAGO, IL, p. A201
UNIVERSITY OF ILLINOIS MEDICAL CENTER AT CHICAGO, CHICAGO, IL, p. A201
UNIVERSITY OF IOWA CHILDREN'S HOSPITAL, IOWA CITY, IA, p. A252
UNIVERSITY OF IOWA HOSPITALS AND CLINICS, IOWA CITY, IA, p. A252
UNIVERSITY OF KANSAS HEALTH SYSTEM GREAT BEND CAMPUS, GREAT BEND, KS, p. A265
UNIVERSITY OF KANSAS HEALTH SYSTEM PAWNEE VALLEY CAMPUS, LARNED, KS, p. A268
UNIVERSITY OF KANSAS HEALTH SYSTEM ST. FRANCIS CAMPUS, TOPEKA, KS, p. A277
UNIVERSITY OF KENTUCKY ALBERT B. CHANDLER HOSPITAL, LEXINGTON, KY, p. A287
UNIVERSITY OF KENTUCKY HOSPITAL, LEXINGTON, KY, p. A287
UNIVERSITY OF MARYLAND BALTIMORE WASHINGTON MEDICAL CENTER, GLEN BURNIE, MD, p. A331
UNIVERSITY OF MARYLAND CAPITAL REGION HEALTH AT LAUREL REGIONAL MEDICAL CENTER, LAUREL, MD, p. A331
UNIVERSITY OF MARYLAND CAPITAL REGION HEALTH PRINCE GEORGE'S HOSPITAL CENTER, CHEVERLY, MD, p. A328
UNIVERSITY OF MARYLAND CHARLES REGIONAL MEDICAL CENTER, LA PLATA, MD, p. A330
UNIVERSITY OF MARYLAND HARFORD MEMORIAL HOSPITAL, HAVRE DE GRACE, MD, p. A330
UNIVERSITY OF MARYLAND MEDICAL CENTER, BALTIMORE, MD, p. A326
UNIVERSITY OF MARYLAND MEDICAL CENTER MIDTOWN CAMPUS, BALTIMORE, MD, p. A326
UNIVERSITY OF MARYLAND REHABILITATION & ORTHOPAEDIC INSTITUTE, BALTIMORE, MD, p. A327
UNIVERSITY OF MARYLAND SHORE MEDICAL CENTER AT CHESTERTOWN, CHESTERTOWN, MD, p. A328
UNIVERSITY OF MARYLAND SHORE MEDICAL CENTER AT DORCHESTER, CAMBRIDGE, MD, p. A328
UNIVERSITY OF MARYLAND SHORE MEDICAL CENTER AT EASTON, EASTON, MD, p. A329
UNIVERSITY OF MARYLAND ST. JOSEPH MEDICAL CENTER, TOWSON, MD, p. A333
UNIVERSITY OF MARYLAND UPPER CHESAPEAKE MEDICAL CENTER, BEL AIR, MD, p. A327
UNIVERSITY OF MEDICINE AND DENTISTRY OF NEW JERSEY-UNIVERSITY HOSPITAL, NEWARK, NJ, p. A460
UNIVERSITY OF MIAMI HOSPITAL AND CLINICS, MIAMI, FL, p. A147
UNIVERSITY OF MICHIGAN HEALTH SYSTEM, ANN ARBOR, MI, p. A348
UNIVERSITY OF MINNESOTA, MINNEAPOLIS, MN, p. A381
UNIVERSITY OF MINNESOTA CHILDREN'S HOSPITAL, FAIRVIEW, MINNEAPOLIS, MN, p. A381
UNIVERSITY OF MINNESOTA HOSPITAL AND CLINIC, MINNEAPOLIS, MN, p. A381
UNIVERSITY OF MISSISSIPPI MEDICAL CENTER, JACKSON, MS, p. A395
UNIVERSITY OF MISSISSIPPI MEDICAL CENTER GRENADA, GRENADA, MS, p. A393
UNIVERSITY OF MISSISSIPPI MEDICAL CENTER HOLMES COUNTY, LEXINGTON, MS, p. A396
UNIVERSITY OF MISSOURI HEALTH CARE, COLUMBIA, MO, p. A405
UNIVERSITY OF MISSOURI HOSPITALS AND CLINICS, COLUMBIA, MO, p. A405
UNIVERSITY OF MN HOSPITAL, MINNEAPOLIS, MN, p. A381
UNIVERSITY OF NEW MEXICO HOSPITALS, ALBUQUERQUE, NM, p. A468
UNIVERSITY OF NORTH CAROLINA HOSPITALS, CHAPEL HILL, NC, p. A506
UNIVERSITY OF SOUTH ALABAMA MEDICAL CENTER, MOBILE, AL, p. A22
UNIVERSITY OF SOUTHERN CALIFORNIA-NORRIS CANCER HOSPITAL, LOS ANGELES, CA, p. A76

UNIVERSITY OF TENNESSEE MEDICAL CENTER, KNOXVILLE, TN, p. A641
UNIVERSITY OF TEXAS HARRIS COUNTY PSYCHIATRIC CENTER, HOUSTON, TX, p. A689
UNIVERSITY OF TEXAS HEALTH NORTHEAST, TYLER, TX, p. A722
UNIVERSITY OF TEXAS M. D. ANDERSON CANCER CENTER, HOUSTON, TX, p. A689
UNIVERSITY OF TEXAS M.D. ANDERSON CANCER CENTER, HOUSTON, TX, p. A689
UNIVERSITY OF TEXAS MEDICAL BRANCH, GALVESTON, TX, p. A680
UNIVERSITY OF TEXAS MEDICAL BRANCH HOSPITALS, GALVESTON, TX, p. A680
UNIVERSITY OF TEXAS SOUTHWESTERN MEDICAL CENTER, DALLAS, TX, p. A671
UNIVERSITY OF UTAH HEALTH, SALT LAKE CITY, UT, p. A733
UNIVERSITY OF UTAH HEALTH CARE—HOSPITAL AND CLINICS, SALT LAKE CITY, UT, p. A733
UNIVERSITY OF VERMONT MEDICAL CENTER, BURLINGTON, VT, p. A735
UNIVERSITY OF VIRGINIA HOSPS, CHARLOTTESVILLE, VA, p. A740
UNIVERSITY OF VIRGINIA MEDICAL CENTER, CHARLOTTESVILLE, VA, p. A740
UNIVERSITY OF WASHINGTON MEDICAL CENTER, SEATTLE, WA, p. A764
UNIVERSITY OF WISCONSIN HOSPITALS AND CLINICS AUTHORITY, MADISON, WI, p. A788
UNIVERSITY PEDIATRIC HOSPITAL, RIO PIEDRAS, PR, p. A809
UNIVERSITY POINTE SURGICAL HOSPITAL, WEST CHESTER, OH, p. A552
UNM CHILDREN'S PSYCH HOSPITAL, ALBUQUERQUE, NM, p. A468
UNM SANDOVAL REGIONAL MEDICAL CENTER, RIO RANCHO, NM, p. A471
UNM SANDOVAL REGIONAL MEDICAL CENTER, INC., RIO RANCHO, NM, p. A471
UOFL HEALTH—JEWISH HOSPITAL, LOUISVILLE, KY, p. A288
UOFL HEALTH—MARY AND ELIZABETH HOSPITAL, LOUISVILLE, KY, p. A289
UOFL HEALTH—PEACE HOSPITAL, LOUISVILLE, KY, p. A289
UOFL HEALTH—SHELBYVILLE HOSPITAL, SHELBYVILLE, KY, p. A293
UOFL HEALTH—UOFL HOSPITAL, LOUISVILLE, KY, p. A289
UP HEALTH SYSTEM-BELL, ISHPEMING, MI, p. A358
UP HEALTH SYSTEM-BELL HOSPITAL, ISHPEMING, MI, p. A358
UP HEALTH SYSTEM-MARQUETTE, MARQUETTE, MI, p. A361
UP HEALTH SYSTEM-PORTAGE, HANCOCK, MI, p. A357
UPLAND HILLS HEALTH, DODGEVILLE, WI, p. A782
UPLAND HILLS HEALTH, INC, DODGEVILLE, WI, p. A782
UPMC ALTOONA, ALTOONA, PA, p. A584
UPMC BEDFORD, EVERETT, PA, p. A590
UPMC CARLISLE, CARLISLE, PA, p. A586
UPMC CHAUTAUQUA, JAMESTOWN, NY, p. A486
UPMC CHAUTAUQUA WCA, JAMESTOWN, NY, p. A486
UPMC CHILDREN'S HOSPITAL OF PITTSBURGH, PITTSBURGH, PA, p. A603
UPMC COLE, COUDERSPORT, PA, p. A587
UPMC EAST, MONROEVILLE, PA, p. A597
UPMC HAMOT, ERIE, PA, p. A590
UPMC HANOVER, HANOVER, PA, p. A591
UPMC HORIZON, FARRELL, PA, p. A590
UPMC JAMESON, NEW CASTLE, PA, p. A598
UPMC JAMESON HOSPITAL, NEW CASTLE, PA, p. A598
UPMC KANE, KANE, PA, p. A593
UPMC LITITZ, LITITZ, PA, p. A595
UPMC LOCK HAVEN, LOCK HAVEN, PA, p. A595
UPMC MAGEE-WOMENS HOSPITAL, PITTSBURGH, PA, p. A604
UPMC MCKEESPORT, MCKEESPORT, PA, p. A596
UPMC MEMORIAL, YORK, PA, p. A612
UPMC MERCY, PITTSBURGH, PA, p. A604
UPMC MONTEFIORE, PITTSBURGH, PA, p. A604
UPMC MUNCY, MUNCY, PA, p. A598
UPMC NORTHWEST, SENECA, PA, p. A607
UPMC NORTHWEST MEDICAL CENTER, SENECA, PA, p. A607
UPMC PASSAVANT, PITTSBURGH, PA, p. A604
UPMC PASSAVANT CRANBERRY, CRANBERRY, PA, p. A587
UPMC PINNACLE CARLISLE, CARLISLE, PA, p. A586
UPMC PINNACLE HANOVER, HANOVER, PA, p. A591
UPMC PINNACLE HARRISBURG, HARRISBURG, PA, p. A591
UPMC PINNACLE HARRISBURG CAMPUS, HARRISBURG, PA, p. A591
UPMC PINNACLE LITITZ, LITITZ, PA, p. A595
UPMC PMEMORIAL, YORK, PA, p. A612
UPMC PRESBYTERIAN, PITTSBURGH, PA, p. A604
UPMC PRESBYTERIAN SHADYSIDE, PITTSBURGH, PA, p. A604

UPMC SOMERSET, SOMERSET, PA, p. A608
UPMC SOMERSET HOSPITAL, SOMERSET, PA, p. A608
UPMC ST. MARGARET, PITTSBURGH, PA, p. A604
UPMC SUSQUEHANNA DIVINE PROVIDENCE, WILLIAMSPORT, PA, p. A611
UPMC SUSQUEHANNA SOLDIERS + SAILORS, WELLSBORO, PA, p. A610
UPMC SUSQUEHANNA WILLIAMSPORT REGIONAL MEDICAL CENTER, WILLIAMSPORT, PA, p. A611
UPMC WELLSBORO, WELLSBORO, PA, p. A610
UPMC WILLIAMSPORT, WILLIAMSPORT, PA, p. A611
UPMC-PRESBYTERIAN HOSPITAL, PITTSBURGH, PA, p. A604
UPMC-ST MARGARET, PITTSBURGH, PA, p. A604
UPPER CHESAPEAKE MEDICAL CENTER, BEL AIR, MD, p. A327
UPPER CONNECTICUT VALLEY HOSPITAL, COLEBROOK, NH, p. A448
UPPER VALLEY MEDICAL CENTER, TROY, OH, p. A551
UPSON REGIONAL MED CTR, THOMASTON, GA, p. A181
UPSON REGIONAL MEDICAL CENTER, THOMASTON, GA, p. A181
UPSTATE MEDICAL UNIVERSITY, SYRACUSE, NY, p. A500
UPSTATE UNIVERSITY HOSPITAL, SYRACUSE, NY, p. A500
U. S. AIR FORCE HOSPITAL, HAMPTON, VA, p. A743
U. S. AIR FORCE MEDICAL CENTER KEESLER, KEESLER AFB, MS, p. A395
U S AIR FORCE REGIONAL HOSP, HAMPTON, VA, p. A743
U. S. AIR FORCE REGIONAL HOSPITAL, EGLIN AFB, FL, p. A137
U. S. AIR FORCE REGIONAL HOSPITAL, ELMENDORF AFB, AK, p. A28
U S HLTH CORP OF SOUTHERN OHIO, PORTSMOUTH, OH, p. A548
U. S. NAVAL HOSPITAL, AGANA, GU, p. A805
U. S. NAVAL HOSPITAL GUAM, AGANA, GU, p. A805
U S PENITENTIARY HOSPITAL, LEWISBURG, PA, p. A595
U. S. PENITENTIARY INFIRMARY, LEWISBURG, PA, p. A595
U. S. PUBLIC HEALTH SERVICE BLACKFEET COMMUNITY HOSPITAL, SAINT MARY, MT, p. A427
U. S. PUBLIC HEALTH SERVICE INDIAN HOSPITAL, CASS LAKE, MN, p. A374
U. S. PUBLIC HEALTH SERVICE INDIAN HOSPITAL, CROWNPOINT, NM, p. A469
U. S. PUBLIC HEALTH SERVICE INDIAN HOSPITAL, EAGLE BUTTE, SD, p. A627
U. S. PUBLIC HEALTH SERVICE INDIAN HOSPITAL, FORT YATES, ND, p. A523
U. S. PUBLIC HEALTH SERVICE INDIAN HOSPITAL, PARKER, AZ, p. A34
U. S. PUBLIC HEALTH SERVICE INDIAN HOSPITAL, PERIDOT, AZ, p. A35
U. S. PUBLIC HEALTH SERVICE INDIAN HOSPITAL, PINE RIDGE, SD, p. A630
U. S. PUBLIC HEALTH SERVICE INDIAN HOSPITAL, ROSEBUD, SD, p. A631
U. S. PUBLIC HEALTH SERVICE INDIAN HOSPITAL, WINNEBAGO, NE, p. A440
U. S. PUBLIC HEALTH SERVICE INDIAN HOSPITAL, ZUNI, NM, p. A473
U.S. PUBLIC HEALTH SERVICE INDIAN HOSPITAL, RED LAKE, MN, p. A383
U. S. PUBLIC HEALTH SERVICE INDIAN HOSPITAL-SELLS, SELLS, AZ, p. A38
U. S. PUBLIC HEALTH SERVICE INDIAN HOSPITAL-WHITERIVER, WHITERIVER, AZ, p. A41
U. S. PUBLIC HEALTH SERVICE PHOENIX INDIAN MEDICAL CENTER, PHOENIX, AZ, p. A37
USA CHILDREN'S AND WOMEN'S HOSPITAL, MOBILE, AL, p. A22
USA HEALTH CHILDREN'S & WOMEN'S HOSPITAL, MOBILE, AL, p. A22
USA HEALTH UNIVERSITY HOSPITAL, MOBILE, AL, p. A22
USAF MED CTR WRIGHT-PATTERSON, WRIGHT, OH, p. A553
USAKA HOSPITAL, KWAJALEIN ATOLL, MH, p. A805
USC NORRIS COMPREHENSIVE CANCER CENTER, LOS ANGELES, CA, p. A76
USC UNIVERSITY HOSPITAL, LOS ANGELES, CA, p. A76
USC VERDUGO HILLS HOSPITAL, GLENDALE, CA, p. A67
USCF BENIOFF CHILDREN'S HOSPITAL OAKLAND, OAKLAND, CA, p. A82
USMD HOSPITAL AT ARLINGTON, ARLINGTON, TX, p. A654
USPHS INDIAN HOSPITAL, KEAMS CANYON, AZ, p. A33
USPHS INDIAN HOSPITAL, WHITERIVER, AZ, p. A41
USPHS PHOENIX INDIAN MED CTR, PHOENIX, AZ, p. A37
UT HEALTH ATHENS, ATHENS, TX, p. A654
UT HEALTH CARTHAGE, CARTHAGE, TX, p. A663
UT HEALTH EAST TEXAS REHABILITATION HOSPITAL, TYLER, TX, p. A722
UT HEALTH HENDERSON, HENDERSON, TX, p. A683
UT HEALTH JACKSONVILLE, JACKSONVILLE, TX, p. A691

UT HEALTH NORTH CAMPUS TYLER, TYLER, TX, p. A722
UT HEALTH PITTSBURG, PITTSBURG, TX, p. A706
UT HEALTH QUITMAN, QUITMAN, TX, p. A708
UT HEALTH REHABILITATION HOSPITAL, TYLER, TX, p. A722
UT HEALTH SPECIALTY HOSPITAL, TYLER, TX, p. A722
UT HEALTH TYLER, TYLER, TX, p. A722
UTAH NEUROPSYCHIATRIC INST, SALT LAKE CITY, UT, p. A733
UTAH STATE HOSPITAL, PROVO, UT, p. A731
UTAH VALLEY HOSPITAL, PROVO, UT, p. A731
UTAH VALLEY REGIONAL MEDICAL CENTER, PROVO, UT, p. A731
UTAH VALLEY SPECIALTY HOSPITAL, PROVO, UT, p. A731
UTHEALTH HARRIS COUNTY PSYCHIATRIC CENTER, HOUSTON, TX, p. A689
UVA CULPEPER HOSPITAL, CULPEPER, VA, p. A740
UVA ENCOMPASS HEALTH REHABILITATION HOSPITAL, CHARLOTTESVILLE, VA, p. A740
UVA TRANSITIONAL CARE HOSPITAL, CHARLOTTESVILLE, VA, p. A740
UVA-HEALTHSOUTH REHABILITATION HOSPITAL, CHARLOTTESVILLE, VA, p. A740
UVALDE COUNTY HOSPITAL AUTHORITY, UVALDE, TX, p. A722
UVALDE MEMORIAL HOSPITAL, UVALDE, TX, p. A722
UW HEALTH REHABILITATION HOSPITAL, MADISON, WI, p. A788
UW MEDICINE/HARBORVIEW MEDICAL CENTER, SEATTLE, WA, p. A764
UW MEDICINE/NORTHWEST HOSPITAL & MEDICAL CENTER, SEATTLE, WA, p. A764
UW MEDICINE/VALLEY MEDICAL CENTER, RENTON, WA, p. A763

# V

VA CENTRAL IOWA HEALTH CARE SYSTEM, DES MOINES, IA, p. A249
VA CENTRAL WESTERN MASSACHUSETTS HEALTHCARE SYSTEM, LEEDS, MA, p. A340
VA GREATER LOS ANGELES HEALTHCARE SYSTEM, LOS ANGELES, CA, p. A76
VA GULF COAST VETERANS HLTH, BILOXI, MS, p. A389
VA LONG BEACH HEALTHCARE SYSTEM, LONG BEACH, CA, p. A73
VA MEDICAL CENTER, TOMAH, WI, p. A797
VA MONTANA HEALTHCARE SYSTEM, FORT HARRISON, MT, p. A423
VA PALO ALTO HEALTH CARE SYSTEM, PALO ALTO, CA, p. A84
VA PALO ALTO HEALTH CARE SYSTEM-LIVERMORE DIVISION, LIVERMORE, CA, p. A71
VA PORTLAMD HEALTHCARE SYSTEM, PORTLAND, OR, p. A580
VA PORTLAND HEALTHCARE SYSTEM, PORTLAND, OR, p. A580
VA ROSEBURG HLTH CARE SYSTEM, ROSEBURG, OR, p. A580
VA SAN DIEGO HEALTHCARE SYSTEM, SAN DIEGO, CA, p. A93
VA SOUTHERN NEVADA HEALTCARE, NORTH LAS VEGAS, NV, p. A445
VACAVILLE MEDICAL CENTER, VACAVILLE, CA, p. A102
VAIL HEALTH, VAIL, CO, p. A119
VAIL VALLEY HEALTH HOSPITAL, VAIL, CO, p. A119
VAL VERDE MEMORIAL HOSPITAL, DEL RIO, TX, p. A671
VAL VERDE REGIONAL MEDICAL CENTER, DEL RIO, TX, p. A671
VALDESE GENERAL HOSPITAL, VALDESE, NC, p. A519
VALDEZ COMMUNITY HOSPITAL, VALDEZ, AK, p. A29
VALIR REHABILITATION HOSPITAL, OKLAHOMA CITY, OK, p. A566
VALLE VISTA HEALTH SYSTEM, GREENWOOD, IN, p. A230
VALLE VISTA HOSPITAL, GREENWOOD, IN, p. A230
VALLEJO MEDICAL CENTER, VALLEJO, CA, p. A103
VALLEY BAPTIST HEALTH SYSTEM, HARLINGEN, TX, p. A683
VALLEY BAPTIST MEDICAL CENTER-BROWNSVILLE, BROWNSVILLE, TX, p. A661
VALLEY BAPTIST MEDICAL CENTER-HARLINGEN, HARLINGEN, TX, p. A683
VALLEY BEHAVIORAL HEALTH SYSTEM, BARLING, AR, p. A42
VALLEY CHILDREN'S HEALTHCARE, MADERA, CA, p. A76
VALLEY CHILDREN'S HOSPITAL, MADERA, CA, p. A76
VALLEY COUNTY HEALTH SYSTEM, ORD, NE, p. A438
VALLEY COUNTY HOSPITAL, CASCADE, ID, p. A189

VALLEY COUNTY HOSPITAL, ORD, NE, p. A438
VALLEY FORGE MED CNTR & HOSP, NORRISTOWN, PA, p. A598
VALLEY FORGE MEDICAL CENTER AND HOSPITAL, NORRISTOWN, PA, p. A598
VALLEY GENERAL HOSPITAL, MONROE, WA, p. A760
VALLEY HEALTH—HAMPSHIRE MEMORIAL HOSPITAL, ROMNEY, WV, p. A776
VALLEY HEALTH—PAGE MEMORIAL HOSPITAL, LURAY, VA, p. A745
VALLEY HEALTH—SHENANDOAH MEMORIAL HOSPITAL, WOODSTOCK, VA, p. A754
VALLEY HEALTH—WAR MEMORIAL HOSPITAL, BERKELEY SPRINGS, WV, p. A770
VALLEY HEALTH—WARREN MEMORIAL HOSPITAL, FRONT ROYAL, VA, p. A742
VALLEY HEALTH—WINCHESTER MEDICAL CENTER, WINCHESTER, VA, p. A754
VALLEY HEALTH SHENANDOAH MEMORIAL HOSPITAL, WOODSTOCK, VA, p. A754
VALLEY HOSPITAL, OWENSBORO, KY, p. A291
VALLEY HOSPITAL, PALMER, AK, p. A29
VALLEY HOSPITAL, PHOENIX, AZ, p. A37
VALLEY HOSPITAL, RIDGEWOOD, NJ, p. A462
VALLEY HOSPITAL MEDICAL CENTER, LAS VEGAS, NV, p. A445
VALLEY HOSPITAL PHOENIX, PHOENIX, AZ, p. A37
VALLEY LUTHERAN MEDICAL CENTER, MESA, AZ, p. A34
VALLEY MEDICAL CENTER, RENTON, WA, p. A763
VALLEY MEMORIAL, LIVERMORE, CA, p. A71
VALLEY PRESBYTERIAN HOSPITAL, VAN NUYS, CA, p. A103
VALLEY REGIONAL HOSPITAL, CAMDEN, TN, p. A634
VALLEY REGIONAL HOSPITAL, CLAREMONT, NH, p. A448
VALLEY REGIONAL MEDICAL CENTER, BROWNSVILLE, TX, p. A661
VALLEY VIEW HOSPITAL, GLENWOOD SPRINGS, CO, p. A113
VALLEY VIEW MEDICAL CENTER, CEDAR CITY, UT, p. A727
VALLEY VIEW MEDICAL CENTER, FORT MOHAVE, AZ, p. A31
VALLEY VIEW REGIONAL HOSPITAL, ADA, OK, p. A555
VALLEY WEST HEALTH CENTER, EUGENE, OR, p. A575
VALLEY WEST HOSPITAL, SANDWICH, IL, p. A219
VALLEYCARE MEDICAL CENTER, LIVERMORE, CA, p. A71
VALLEYCARE MEDICAL CENTER, PLEASANTON, CA, p. A85
VALLEYWISE HEALTH, PHOENIX, AZ, p. A37
VALOR HEALTH, EMMETT, ID, p. A190
VAN BUREN COUNTY HOSPITAL, KEOSAUQUA, IA, p. A252
VAN BUREN COUNTY MEM HOSPITAL, CLINTON, AR, p. A43
VAN BUREN COUNTY MEM HOSPITAL, KEOSAUQUA, IA, p. A252
VAN DIEST MEDICAL CENTER, WEBSTER CITY, IA, p. A260
VAN MATRE ENCOMPASS HEALTH, ROCKFORD, IL, p. A219
VAN MATRE ENCOMPASS HEALTH REHABILITATION HOSPITAL, ROCKFORD, IL, p. A219
VAN WERT COUNTY HOSPITAL, VAN WERT, OH, p. A551
VANCE JOHNSON RECOVERY CENTER, LAS VEGAS, NV, p. A445
VANCOUVER MEMORIAL HOSPITAL, VANCOUVER, WA, p. A768
VANDERBILT HOSPITAL AND CLINICS, NASHVILLE, TN, p. A647
VANDERBILT PSYCHIATRIC HOSPITAL, NASHVILLE, TN, p. A647
VANDERBILT STALLWORTH REHABILITATION HOSPITAL, NASHVILLE, TN, p. A647
VANDERBILT UNIVERSITY MEDICAL CENTER, NASHVILLE, TN, p. A647
VANDERBILT WILSON COUNTY HOSPITAL, LEBANON, TN, p. A642
VANTAGE POINT OF NORTHWEST ARKANSAS, FAYETTEVILLE, AR, p. A45
VASSAR BROTHERS HOSPITAL, POUGHKEEPSIE, NY, p. A495
VASSAR BROTHERS MEDICAL CENTER, POUGHKEEPSIE, NY, p. A495
VAUGHAN REGIONAL MEDICAL CENTER, SELMA, AL, p. A24
VAUGHN JACKSON MEDICAL CTR, JACKSON, AL, p. A20
VCU COMMUNITY MEMORIAL HOSPITAL, SOUTH HILL, VA, p. A752
VCU HEALTH COMMUNITY MEMORIAL HOSPITAL, SOUTH HILL, VA, p. A752
VCU HEALTH SYSTEM, RICHMOND, VA, p. A750
VCU HEALTH SYSTEM CHILDREN'S MEDICAL CENTER, RICHMOND, VA, p. A750
VCU MEDICAL CENTER, RICHMOND, VA, p. A751
VEGAS VALLEY REHABILITATION HOSPITAL, LAS VEGAS, NV, p. A445
VENCOR HOSP-CHICAGO CENTRAL, CHICAGO, IL, p. A201
VENCOR HOSP-HOUSTON NORTHWEST, HOUSTON, TX, p. A689
VENCOR HOSPITAL—ALBUQUERQUE, ALBUQUERQUE, NM, p. A468

VENCOR HOSPITAL-BREA, BREA, CA, p. A58
VENCOR HOSPITAL-CHATTANOOGA, CHATTANOOGA, TN, p. A636
VENCOR HOSPITAL-CORAL GABLES, CORAL GABLES, FL, p. A135
VENCOR HOSPITAL-DENVER, DENVER, CO, p. A111
VENCOR HOSPITAL-GREENSBORO, GREENSBORO, NC, p. A511
VENCOR HOSPITAL-INDIANAPOLIS, INDIANAPOLIS, IN, p. A233
VENCOR HOSPITAL-LOS ANGELES, LOS ANGELES, CA, p. A76
VENCOR HOSPITAL-LOUISVILLE, LOUISVILLE, KY, p. A289
VENCOR HOSPITAL-MANSFIELD, MANSFIELD, TX, p. A699
VENCOR HOSPITAL-ONTARIO, ONTARIO, CA, p. A82
VENCOR HOSPITAL-PHILADELPHIA, PHILADELPHIA, PA, p. A602
VENCOR HOSPITAL-SAN ANTONIO, SAN ANTONIO, TX, p. A714
VENCOR HOSPITAL-SAN DIEGO, SAN DIEGO, CA, p. A93
VENCOR HOSPITAL-ST LOUIS, SAINT LOUIS, MO, p. A417
VENCOR HOSPITAL-SYCAMORE, SYCAMORE, IL, p. A221
VENICE REGIONAL BAYFRONT HEALTH, VENICE, FL, p. A161
VENICE REGIONAL MEDICAL CENTER, VENICE, FL, p. A161
VENTURA COUNTY MEDICAL CENTER, VENTURA, CA, p. A103
VERDE VALLEY MEDICAL CENTER, COTTONWOOD, AZ, p. A31
VERDUGO HILLS HOSPITAL, GLENDALE, CA, p. A67
VERITAS COLLABORATIVE, ATLANTA, GA, p. A165
VERITAS COLLABORATIVE, DURHAM, NC, p. A509
VERMILION BEHAVIORAL HEALTH SYSTEMS—NORTH CAMPUS, LAFAYETTE, LA, p. A306
VERMILION BEHAVIORAL HEALTH SYSTEMS, LAFAYETTE, LA, p. A306
VERMILION BEHAVIORAL HEALTH SYSTEMS SOUTH, LAFAYETTE, LA, p. A306
VERMONT PSYCHIATRIC CARE HOSPITAL, BERLIN, VT, p. A735
VERNON MEMORIAL HEALTHCARE, ELK MOUND, WI, p. A783
VERNON MEMORIAL HOSPITAL, ELK MOUND, WI, p. A783
VERNON STATE HOSPITAL, VERNON, TX, p. A723
VET AFF NORTHERN IN HLTH CARE, FORT WAYNE, IN, p. A228
VETERAN AFFAIRS HUDSON VALLEY HEALTH CARE SYSTEM-CASTLE POINT CAMPUS, WAPPINGERS, NY, p. A501
VETERAN AFFAIRS HUDSON VALLEY HEALTH CARE SYSTEM-CASTLE POINT DIVISION, WAPPINGERS, NY, p. A501
VETERANS ADM MEDICAL CENTER, EAST ORANGE, NJ, p. A454
VETERANS ADM MEDICAL CENTER, FAYETTEVILLE, AR, p. A45
VETERANS ADM MEDICAL CENTER, NASHVILLE, TN, p. A647
VETERANS ADM MEDICAL CENTER, PITTSBURGH, PA, p. A604
VETERANS ADMINISTRATION NEW YORK HARBOR HEALTHCARE SYSTEM, BROOKLYN, NY, p. A479
VETERANS AFF MEDICAL CENTER, PITTSBURGH, PA, p. A604
VETERANS AFFAIRS—WESTERN IOWA HEALTHCARE SYSTEM, OMAHA, NE, p. A438
VETERANS AFFAIRS ANN ARBOR HEALTHCARE SYSTEM, ANN ARBOR, MI, p. A348
VETERANS AFFAIRS BLACK HILLS HEALTH CARE SYSTEM, FORT MEADE, SD, p. A628
VETERANS AFFAIRS BOSTON HEALTHCARE SYSTEM, WEST ROXBURY, MA, p. A345
VETERANS AFFAIRS BOSTON HEALTHCARE SYSTEM BROCKTON DIVISION, BROCKTON, MA, p. A337
VETERANS AFFAIRS CARIBBEAN HEALTHCARE SYSTEM, SAN JUAN, PR, p. A811
VETERANS AFFAIRS CENTRAL CALIFORNIA HEALTH CARE SYSTEM, FRESNO, CA, p. A66
VETERANS AFFAIRS CENTRAL IOWA HEALTH CARE SYSTEM, DES MOINES, IA, p. A249
VETERANS AFFAIRS CENTRAL WESTERN MASSACHUSETTS HEALTHCARE SYSTEM, LEEDS, MA, p. A340
VETERANS AFFAIRS CONNECTICUT HEALTHCARE SYSTEM, WEST HAVEN, CT, p. A126
VETERANS AFFAIRS CONNECTICUT HEALTHCARE SYSTEM-NEW HAVEN DIVISION, WEST HAVEN, CT, p. A126
VETERANS AFFAIRS DOMICILIARY, WHITE CITY, OR, p. A582
VETERANS AFFAIRS EASTERN COLORADO HEALTH CARE SYSTEM, DENVER, CO, p. A111
VETERANS AFFAIRS EASTERN KANSAS HEALTH CARE SYSTEM, TOPEKA, KS, p. A277
VETERANS AFFAIRS EASTERN KANSAS HEALTH CARE SYSTEM-COLMERY-O'NEIL VETERANS AFFAIRS MEDICAL CENTER, TOPEKA, KS, p. A277

VETERANS AFFAIRS EASTERN KANSAS HEALTH CARE SYSTEM-DWIGHT D. EISENHOWER VETERANS AFFAIRS MEDICAL CENTER, LEAVENWORTH, KS, p. A269
VETERANS AFFAIRS EDWARD HINES, JR. HOSPITAL, HINES, IL, p. A208
VETERANS AFFAIRS GREATER LOS ANGELES HEALTHCARE SYSTEM, LOS ANGELES, CA, p. A76
VETERANS AFFAIRS GULF COAST VETERANS HEALTH CARE SYSTEM, BILOXI, MS, p. A390
VETERANS AFFAIRS HEALTH CARE SYSTEM, FARGO, ND, p. A523
VETERANS AFFAIRS HUDSON VALLEY HEALTH CARE SYSTEM, MONTROSE, NY, p. A488
VETERANS AFFAIRS HUDSON VALLEY HEALTH CARE SYSTEM-F.D. ROOSEVELT HOSPITAL, MONTROSE, NY, p. A488
VETERANS AFFAIRS HUDSON VALLEY HEALTH CARE SYSTEM-MONTROSE DIVISION, MONTROSE, NY, p. A488
VETERANS AFFAIRS ILLIANA HEALTH CARE SYSTEM, DANVILLE, IL, p. A202
VETERANS AFFAIRS LOMA LINDA HEALTHCARE SYSTEM, LOMA LINDA, CA, p. A72
VETERANS AFFAIRS LONG BEACH HEALTHCARE SYSTEM, LONG BEACH, CA, p. A73
VETERANS AFFAIRS MARYLAND HEALTH CARE SYSTEM-BALTIMORE DIVISION, BALTIMORE, MD, p. A327
VETERANS AFFAIRS MARYLAND HEALTH CARE SYSTEM-PERRY POINT DIVISION, PERRY POINT, MD, p. A331
VETERANS AFFAIRS MED & REG CTR, WICHITA, KS, p. A279
VETERANS AFFAIRS MED CENTER, AMARILLO, TX, p. A652
VETERANS AFFAIRS MED CENTER, ANN ARBOR, MI, p. A348
VETERANS AFFAIRS MED CENTER, BALTIMORE, MD, p. A327
VETERANS AFFAIRS MED CENTER, BATAVIA, NY, p. A475
VETERANS AFFAIRS MED CENTER, BUFFALO, NY, p. A480
VETERANS AFFAIRS MED CENTER, CHARLESTON, SC, p. A616
VETERANS AFFAIRS MED CENTER, DANVILLE, IL, p. A202
VETERANS AFFAIRS MED CENTER, DENVER, CO, p. A111
VETERANS AFFAIRS MED CENTER, DETROIT, MI, p. A353
VETERANS AFFAIRS MED CENTER, DURHAM, NC, p. A509
VETERANS AFFAIRS MED CENTER, FRESNO, CA, p. A66
VETERANS AFFAIRS MED CENTER, HOUSTON, TX, p. A689
VETERANS AFFAIRS MED CENTER, JACKSON, MS, p. A395
VETERANS AFFAIRS MED CENTER, KERRVILLE, TX, p. A693
VETERANS AFFAIRS MED CENTER, LAS ANIMAS, CO, p. A115
VETERANS AFFAIRS MED CENTER, LINCOLN, NE, p. A435
VETERANS AFFAIRS MED CENTER, LITTLE ROCK, AR, p. A49
VETERANS AFFAIRS MED CENTER, MARION, IN, p. A236
VETERANS AFFAIRS MED CENTER, MILWAUKEE, WI, p. A791
VETERANS AFFAIRS MED CENTER, PALO ALTO, CA, p. A84
VETERANS AFFAIRS MED CENTER, PERRY POINT, MD, p. A331
VETERANS AFFAIRS MED CENTER, SAGINAW, MI, p. A366
VETERANS AFFAIRS MED CENTER, SALT LAKE CITY, UT, p. A733
VETERANS AFFAIRS MED CENTER, SHREVEPORT, LA, p. A315
VETERANS AFFAIRS MED CENTER, TACOMA, WA, p. A767
VETERANS AFFAIRS MED CENTER, WEST ROXBURY, MA, p. A345
VETERANS AFFAIRS MEDICAL CENTER—ALEXANDRIA, PINEVILLE, LA, p. A313
VETERANS AFFAIRS MEDICAL CENTER, ALBANY, NY, p. A474
VETERANS AFFAIRS MEDICAL CENTER, ALBUQUERQUE, NM, p. A468
VETERANS AFFAIRS MEDICAL CENTER, ASHEVILLE, NC, p. A504
VETERANS AFFAIRS MEDICAL CENTER, AUGUSTA, GA, p. A166
VETERANS AFFAIRS MEDICAL CENTER, AUGUSTA, ME, p. A318
VETERANS AFFAIRS MEDICAL CENTER, BATH, NY, p. A475
VETERANS AFFAIRS MEDICAL CENTER, BATTLE CREEK, MI, p. A349
VETERANS AFFAIRS MEDICAL CENTER, BECKLEY, WV, p. A770
VETERANS AFFAIRS MEDICAL CENTER, BIRMINGHAM, AL, p. A16
VETERANS AFFAIRS MEDICAL CENTER, BOISE, ID, p. A189
VETERANS AFFAIRS MEDICAL CENTER, BRONX, NY, p. A477
VETERANS AFFAIRS MEDICAL CENTER, CANANDAIGUA, NY, p. A481
VETERANS AFFAIRS MEDICAL CENTER, CHEYENNE, WY, p. A802
VETERANS AFFAIRS MEDICAL CENTER, CHILLICOTHE, OH, p. A531
VETERANS AFFAIRS MEDICAL CENTER, CINCINNATI, OH, p. A533
VETERANS AFFAIRS MEDICAL CENTER, CLEVELAND, OH, p. A535
VETERANS AFFAIRS MEDICAL CENTER, COATESVILLE, PA, p. A587

VETERANS AFFAIRS MEDICAL CENTER, DAYTON, OH, p. A538
VETERANS AFFAIRS MEDICAL CENTER, DECATUR, GA, p. A171
VETERANS AFFAIRS MEDICAL CENTER, ERIE, PA, p. A590
VETERANS AFFAIRS MEDICAL CENTER, FAYETTEVILLE, NC, p. A510
VETERANS AFFAIRS MEDICAL CENTER, HAMPTON, VA, p. A743
VETERANS AFFAIRS MEDICAL CENTER, HOT SPRINGS, SD, p. A628
VETERANS AFFAIRS MEDICAL CENTER, HUNTINGTON, WV, p. A773
VETERANS AFFAIRS MEDICAL CENTER, IRON MOUNTAIN, MI, p. A358
VETERANS AFFAIRS MEDICAL CENTER, KANSAS CITY, MO, p. A410
VETERANS AFFAIRS MEDICAL CENTER, LAKE CITY, FL, p. A143
VETERANS AFFAIRS MEDICAL CENTER, LEBANON, PA, p. A594
VETERANS AFFAIRS MEDICAL CENTER, MANCHESTER, NH, p. A450
VETERANS AFFAIRS MEDICAL CENTER, MARION, IL, p. A211
VETERANS AFFAIRS MEDICAL CENTER, MARTINSBURG, WV, p. A774
VETERANS AFFAIRS MEDICAL CENTER, MEMPHIS, TN, p. A645
VETERANS AFFAIRS MEDICAL CENTER, MIAMI, FL, p. A147
VETERANS AFFAIRS MEDICAL CENTER, MINNEAPOLIS, MN, p. A381
VETERANS AFFAIRS MEDICAL CENTER, NORTH CHICAGO, IL, p. A214
VETERANS AFFAIRS MEDICAL CENTER, NORTHPORT, NY, p. A493
VETERANS AFFAIRS MEDICAL CENTER, OKLAHOMA CITY, OK, p. A566
VETERANS AFFAIRS MEDICAL CENTER, PROVIDENCE, RI, p. A614
VETERANS AFFAIRS MEDICAL CENTER, SAINT CLOUD, MN, p. A384
VETERANS AFFAIRS MEDICAL CENTER, SAINT LOUIS, MO, p. A417
VETERANS AFFAIRS MEDICAL CENTER, SALEM, VA, p. A751
VETERANS AFFAIRS MEDICAL CENTER, SALISBURY, NC, p. A518
VETERANS AFFAIRS MEDICAL CENTER, SAN JUAN, PR, p. A811
VETERANS AFFAIRS MEDICAL CENTER, SHERIDAN, WY, p. A804
VETERANS AFFAIRS MEDICAL CENTER, SYRACUSE, NY, p. A500
VETERANS AFFAIRS MEDICAL CENTER, TUSCALOOSA, AL, p. A25
VETERANS AFFAIRS MEDICAL CENTER, WASHINGTON, DC, p. A130
VETERANS AFFAIRS MEDICAL CENTER, WEST HAVEN, CT, p. A126
VETERANS AFFAIRS MEDICAL CENTER, WEST PALM BEACH, FL, p. A162
VETERANS AFFAIRS MEDICAL CENTER, WEST ROXBURY, MA, p. A346
VETERANS AFFAIRS MEDICAL CENTER, WHITE RIVER JUNCTION, VT, p. A737
VETERANS AFFAIRS MEDICAL CENTER, WILKES-BARRE, PA, p. A611
VETERANS AFFAIRS MEDICAL CENTER, WILMINGTON, DE, p. A128
VETERANS AFFAIRS MEDICAL CENTER HOT SPRINGS CAMPUS, HOT SPRINGS, SD, p. A628
VETERANS AFFAIRS MEDICAL CENTER WEST ROXBURY DIVISION, WEST ROXBURY, MA, p. A346
VETERANS AFFAIRS MEDICAL CENTER-LEXINGTON, LEXINGTON, KY, p. A287
VETERANS AFFAIRS MEDICAL CENTER-LOUISVILLE, LOUISVILLE, KY, p. A289
VETERANS AFFAIRS MEDICAL CTR, DUBLIN, GA, p. A172
VETERANS AFFAIRS MEDICAL CTR, MOUNTAIN HOME, TN, p. A646
VETERANS AFFAIRS MONTANA HEALTH CARE SYSTEM, FORT HARRISON, MT, p. A423
VETERANS AFFAIRS NEBRASKA-WESTERN IOWA HEALTH CARE SYSTEM—LINCOLN, LINCOLN, NE, p. A435
VETERANS AFFAIRS NEBRASKA-WESTERN IOWA HEALTH CARE SYSTEM, LINCOLN, NE, p. A435
VETERANS AFFAIRS NEBRASKA-WESTERN IOWA HEALTH CARE SYSTEM, OMAHA, NE, p. A438
VETERANS AFFAIRS NEW JERSEY HEALTH CARE SYSTEM, EAST ORANGE, NJ, p. A454

VETERANS AFFAIRS NEW JERSEY HEALTH CARE SYSTEM, LYONS, NJ, p. A457
VETERANS AFFAIRS NEW YORK HARBOR HEALTHCARE SYSTEM, BROOKLYN, NY, p. A479
VETERANS AFFAIRS NORTH TEXAS HEALTH CARE SYSTEM, DALLAS, TX, p. A671
VETERANS AFFAIRS NORTHERN INDIANA HEALTH CARE SYSTEM, FORT WAYNE, IN, p. A229
VETERANS AFFAIRS NORTHERN INDIANA HEALTH CARE SYSTEM-MARION CAMPUS, MARION, IN, p. A236
VETERANS AFFAIRS NY HARBOR HEALTHCARE SYSTEM—MANHATTAN CAMPUS, NEW YORK, NY, p. A492
VETERANS AFFAIRS PALO ALTO HEALTH CARE SYSTEM, LIVERMORE DIVISION, LIVERMORE, CA, p. A71
VETERANS AFFAIRS PITTSBURGH HEALTHCARE SYSTEM, PITTSBURGH, PA, p. A604
VETERANS AFFAIRS PUGET SOUND HEALTH CARE SYSTEM, SEATTLE, WA, p. A764
VETERANS AFFAIRS PUGET SOUND HEALTH CARE SYSTEM-AMERICAN LAKE DIVISION, TACOMA, WA, p. A767
VETERANS AFFAIRS ROSEBURG HEALTHCARE SYSTEM, ROSEBURG, OR, p. A581
VETERANS AFFAIRS SALT LAKE CITY HEALTH CARE SYSTEM, SALT LAKE CITY, UT, p. A733
VETERANS AFFAIRS SAN DIEGO HEALTHCARE SYSTEM, SAN DIEGO, CA, p. A93
VETERANS AFFAIRS SIERRA NEVADA HEALTH CARE SYSTEM, RENO, NV, p. A446
VETERANS AFFAIRS SOUTHERN NEVADA HEALTHCARE SYSTEM, NORTH LAS VEGAS, NV, p. A445
VETERANS AFFAIRS ST. LOUIS HEALTH CARE SYSTEM, SAINT LOUIS, MO, p. A418
VETERANS AFFAIRS TENNESSEE VALLEY HEALTHCARE SYSTEM, NASHVILLE, TN, p. A647
VETERANS AFFAIRS WESTERN NEW YORK HEALTHCARE SYSTEM-BATAVIA DIVISION, BATAVIA, NY, p. A475
VETERANS AFFAIRS WESTERN NEW YORK HEALTHCARE SYSTEM-BUFFALO DIVISION, BUFFALO, NY, p. A480
VETERANS AFFARIS PALO ALTO HEALTH CARE SYSTEM, PALO ALTO, CA, p. A84
VETERANS HEALTH CARE SYSTEM OF THE OZARKS, FAYETTEVILLE, AR, p. A45
VETERANS HOME AND HOSPITAL, ROCKY HILL, CT, p. A125
VETERANS MEMORIAL HOSPITAL, WAUKON, IA, p. A259
VETERANS MEMORIAL MED CENTER, MERIDEN, CT, p. A123
VIA CHRISTI BEHAVIORAL HEALTH CENTER, WICHITA, KS, p. A279
VIA CHRISTI HOSPITAL ON ST. TERESA, WICHITA, KS, p. A279
VIA CHRISTI REHABILITATION HOSPITAL, WICHITA, KS, p. A279
VIA CHRISTI ST. JOSEPH, WICHITA, KS, p. A279
VIA HLTH WAYNE-NEWARK COMM HSP, NEWARK, NY, p. A492
VIBRA HIGHLANDS REHABILITATION HOSPITAL OF EL PASO, EL PASO, TX, p. A676
VIBRA HOSPITAL DENVER, THORNTON, CO, p. A119
VIBRA HOSPITAL OF AMARILLO, AMARILLO, TX, p. A652
VIBRA HOSPITAL OF BOISE, BOISE, ID, p. A189
VIBRA HOSPITAL OF CENTRAL DAKOTAS, MANDAN, ND, p. A525
VIBRA HOSPITAL OF CHARLESTON, MT. PLEASANT, SC, p. A622
VIBRA HOSPITAL OF CHARLESTON-TCU, MT. PLEASANT, SC, p. A622
VIBRA HOSPITAL OF DENVER, THORNTON, CO, p. A119
VIBRA HOSPITAL OF FARGO, FARGO, ND, p. A523
VIBRA HOSPITAL OF MAHONING VALLEY, BOARDMAN, OH, p. A530
VIBRA HOSPITAL OF NORTHERN CALIFORNIA, REDDING, CA, p. A87
VIBRA HOSPITAL OF NORTHWESTERN INDIANA, CROWN POINT, IN, p. A226
VIBRA HOSPITAL OF RICHMOND, RICHMOND, VA, p. A751
VIBRA HOSPITAL OF SACRAMENTO, FOLSOM, CA, p. A64
VIBRA HOSPITAL OF SAN DIEGO, SAN DIEGO, CA, p. A93
VIBRA HOSPITAL OF SOUTHEASTERN MASSACHUSETTS, NEW BEDFORD, MA, p. A342
VIBRA HOSPITAL OF SOUTHEASTERN MICHIGAN, LINCOLN PARK, MI, p. A360
VIBRA HOSPITAL OF SOUTHEASTERN MICHIGAN, LLC, LINCOLN PARK, MI, p. A360
VIBRA HOSPITAL OF WESTERN MASSACHUSETTS, SPRINGFIELD, MA, p. A345
VIBRA HOSPITAL OF WESTERN MASSACHUSETTS-CENTRAL CAMPUS, ROCHDALE, MA, p. A343
VIBRA REHABILITATION HOSPITAL LAKE TRAVIS, LAKEWAY, TX, p. A694
VIBRA REHABILITATION HOSPITAL OF AMARILLO, Amarillo, TX, p. A652

VIBRA REHABILITATION HOSPITAL OF DENVER, THORNTON, CO, p. A119
VIBRA REHABILITATION HOSPITAL RANCHO MIRAGE, RANCHO MIRAGE, CA, p. A87
VIBRA SPECIALTY HOSPITAL AT DESOTO, DESOTO, TX, p. A673
VIBRA SPECIALTY HOSPITAL OF DALLAS, DESOTO, TX, p. A673
VIBRA SPECIALTY HOSPITAL OF PORTLAND, PORTLAND, OR, p. A580
VICKSBURG MEDICAL CENTER, VICKSBURG, MS, p. A401
VICTOR VALLEY COMMUNITY HOSPITAL, VICTORVILLE, CA, p. A104
VICTOR VALLEY GLOBAL MEDICAL CENTER, VICTORVILLE, CA, p. A104
VICTORY MEDICAL CENTER BEAUMONT, BEAUMONT, TX, p. A658
VICTORY SURGICAL HOSPITAL EAST HOUSTON, HOUSTON, TX, p. A689
VIDANT BEAUFORT HOSPITAL, WASHINGTON, NC, p. A519
VIDANT BERTIE HOSPITAL, WINDSOR, NC, p. A520
VIDANT CHOWAN HOSPITAL, EDENTON, NC, p. A509
VIDANT DUPLIN HOSPITAL, KENANSVILLE, NC, p. A513
VIDANT EDGECOMBE HOSPITAL, TARBORO, NC, p. A519
VIDANT MEDICAL CENTER, GREENVILLE, NC, p. A511
VIDANT NORTH HOSPITAL, ROANOKE RAPIDS, NC, p. A517
VIDANT ROANOKE-CHOWAN HOSPITAL, AHOSKIE, NC, p. A504
VIERA HOSPITAL, MELBOURNE, FL, p. A145
VILLA FELICIANA CHRON DIS HOSP, JACKSON, LA, p. A303
VILLA FELICIANA MEDICAL COMPLEX, JACKSON, LA, p. A303
VILLA MARIA HOSPITAL, NORTH MIAMI, FL, p. A149
VILLA ST JOHN VIANNEY HOSPITAL, DOWNINGTOWN, PA, p. A588
VILLAGE HOSPITAL, GREER, SC, p. A621
VILLAGE OAKS MEDICAL CENTER, LIVE OAK, TX, p. A696
VIRGINIA BAPTIST HOSPITAL, LYNCHBURG, VA, p. A745
VIRGINIA BEACH GEN HOSPITAL, VIRGINIA BEACH, VA, p. A753
VIRGINIA BEACH PSYCHIATRIC CENTER, VIRGINIA BEACH, VA, p. A753
VIRGINIA GAY HOSPITAL, VINTON, IA, p. A259
VIRGINIA HOSPITAL CENTER—ARLINGTON, ARLINGTON, VA, p. A738
VIRGINIA HOSPITAL CENTER, ARLINGTON, VA, p. A738
VIRGINIA MASON HOSPITAL, SEATTLE, WA, p. A764
VIRGINIA MASON MEDICAL CENTER, SEATTLE, WA, p. A765
VIRGINIA MASON MEMORIAL, YAKIMA, WA, p. A769
VIRGINIA REGIONAL MEDICAL CENTER, VIRGINIA, MN, p. A387
VIRTUA MARLTON, MARLTON, NJ, p. A458
VIRTUA MEMORIAL, MOUNT HOLLY, NJ, p. A458
VIRTUA MEMORIAL HOSPITAL BURLINGTON COUNTY, MOUNT HOLLY, NJ, p. A458
VIRTUA OUR LADY OF LOURDES HOSPITAL, CAMDEN, NJ, p. A453
VIRTUA VOORHEES, VOORHEES, NJ, p. A465
VIRTUA WEST JERSEY HOSPITAL-MARLTON, MARLTON, NJ, p. A458
VIRTUA WEST JERSEY HOSPITAL-VOORHEES, VOORHEES, NJ, p. A465
VIRTUA WILLINGBORO HOSPITAL, WILLINGBORO, NJ, p. A466
VISALIA COMMUNITY HOSPITAL, VISALIA, CA, p. A104
VISTA DEL MAR HOSPITAL, VENTURA, CA, p. A103
VISTA HEALTH, FAYETTEVILLE, AR, p. A45
VISTA HEALTH, WAUKEGAN, IL, p. A222
VISTA HEALTH OF FORT SMITH, BARLING, AR, p. A42
VISTA HEALTH TEXARKANA, TEXARKANA, AR, p. A53
VISTA HOSPITAL OF SAN GABRIEL VALLEY, BALDWIN PARK, CA, p. A58
VISTA MEDICAL CENTER EAST, WAUKEGAN, IL, p. A222
VISTA MEDICAL CENTER HOSPITAL, PASADENA, TX, p. A705

# W

WABASH GENERAL HOSPITAL, MOUNT CARMEL, IL, p. A213
WABASH GENERAL HOSPITAL DISTRICT, MOUNT CARMEL, IL, p. A213
WABASH VALLEY HOSPITAL, WEST LAFAYETTE, IN, p. A242
WACCAMAW COMMUNITY HOSPITAL, MURRELLS INLET, SC, p. A623
WACO VETERANS AFFAIRS HOSPITAL, WACO, TX, p. A724
WACONIA RIDGEVIEW HOSPITAL, WACONIA, MN, p. A387
WADLEY REGIONAL MEDICAL CENTER, TEXARKANA, TX, p. A720

WADLEY REGIONAL MEDICAL CENTER AT HOPE, HOPE, AR, p. A47
WAGNER COMMUNITY MEMORIAL HOSPITAL AVERA, WAGNER, SD, p. A632
WAGNER GENERAL HOSPITAL, PALACIOS, TX, p. A704
WAGONER COMMUNITY HOSPITAL, WAGONER, OK, p. A571
WAHIAWA GENERAL HOSPITAL, WAHIAWA, HI, p. A187
WAKE CNTY ALCOHOLISM TREAT CTR, RALEIGH, NC, p. A517
WAKE FOREST BAPTIST HEALTH—WILKES MEDICAL CENTER, NORTH WILKESBORO, NC, p. A516
WAKE FOREST BAPTIST HEALTH-DAVIE HOSPITAL, BERMUDA RUN, NC, p. A505
WAKE FOREST BAPTIST HEALTH-DAVIE MEDICAL CENTER, BERMUDA RUN, NC, p. A505
WAKE FOREST BAPTIST HEALTH-LEXINGTON MEDICAL CENTER, LEXINGTON, NC, p. A514
WAKE FOREST BAPTIST MEDICAL CENTER, WINSTON, NC, p. A520
WAKEMED CARY HOSPITAL, CARY, NC, p. A506
WAKEMED NEW BERN CAMPUS, RALEIGH, NC, p. A517
WAKEMED NORTH FAMILY HEALTH & WOMEN'S HOSPITAL, RALEIGH, NC, p. A517
WAKEMED RALEIGH CAMPUS, RALEIGH, NC, p. A517
WALDEN BEHAVIORAL CARE, WALTHAM, MA, p. A345
WALDEN PSYCHIATRIC CARE, WALTHAM, MA, p. A345
WALDO COUNTY GENERAL HOSPITAL, BELFAST, ME, p. A319
WALDO COUNTY GENERAL HOSPITAL MAINE HEALTH, BELFAST, ME, p. A319
WALKER BAPTIST MEDICAL CENTER, JASPER, AL, p. A20
WALKER REGIONAL MEDICAL CENTER, JASPER, AL, p. A20
WALLACE THOMSON HOSPITAL, UNION, SC, p. A625
WALLOWA MEMORIAL HOSPITAL, ENTERPRISE, OR, p. A574
WALLS REGIONAL HOSPITAL, CLEBURNE, TX, p. A663
WALNUT CREEK MEDICAL CENTER, WALNUT CREEK, CA, p. A104
WALTER B. JONES ALCOHOL AND DRUG ABUSE TREATMENT CENTER, GREENVILLE, NC, p. A511
WALTER KNOX MEMORIAL HOSPITAL, EMMETT, ID, p. A190
WALTER P. REUTHER PSYCHIATRIC HOSPITAL, WESTLAND, MI, p. A369
WALTER REED NATIONAL MILITARY MEDICAL CENTER, BETHESDA, MD, p. A328
WALTHALL COUNTY GENERAL HOSPITAL, TYLERTOWN, MS, p. A400
WALTON REHABILITATION HOSPITAL, AUGUSTA, GA, p. A166
WAMEGO CITY HOSPITAL, WAMEGO, KS, p. A278
WAMEGO HEALTH CENTER, WAMEGO, KS, p. A278
WAR MEMORIAL HOSPITAL, BERKELEY SPRINGS, WV, p. A770
WAR MEMORIAL HOSPITAL, SAULT SAINTE MARIE, MI, p. A366
WARD MEMORIAL HOSPITAL, MONAHANS, TX, p. A702
WARM SPRINGS MEDICAL CENTER, WARM SPRINGS, GA, p. A183
WARM SPRINGS REHABILITATION HOSPITAL OF KYLE, KYLE, TX, p. A694
WARM SPRINGS REHABILITATION HOSPITAL OF SAN ANTONIO, SAN ANTONIO, TX, p. A714
WARM SPRINGS SPECIALTY HOSPITAL OF SAN ANTONIO, SAN ANTONIO, TX, p. A714
WARNER HOSPITAL AND HEALTH SERVICES, CLINTON, IL, p. A201
WARRACK HOSPITAL CAMPUS, SANTA ROSA, CA, p. A98
WARREN COMMUNITY HOSPITAL, WARREN, MN, p. A387
WARREN GENERAL HOSPITAL, WARREN, PA, p. A609
WARREN HOSPITAL, PHILLIPSBURG, NJ, p. A461
WARREN MEMORIAL HOSPITAL, FRIEND, NE, p. A432
WARREN MEMORIAL HOSPITAL, FRONT ROYAL, VA, p. A742
WARREN STATE HOSPITAL, WARREN, PA, p. A609
WASECA MEDICAL CENTER, WASECA, MN, p. A387
WASHAKIE MEDICAL CENTER, WORLAND, WY, p. A804
WASHAKIE MEMORIAL HOSPITAL, WORLAND, WY, p. A804
WASHINGTON ADVENTIST HOSPITAL, TAKOMA PARK, MD, p. A333
WASHINGTON CNTY HOSP DIST 1, HANOVER, KS, p. A265
WASHINGTON COUNTY HEALTH SYSTEM, HAGERSTOWN, MD, p. A330
WASHINGTON COUNTY HOSPITAL, CHATOM, AL, p. A16
WASHINGTON COUNTY HOSPITAL, NASHVILLE, IL, p. A214
WASHINGTON COUNTY HOSPITAL, PLYMOUTH, NC, p. A516
WASHINGTON COUNTY HOSPITAL, WASHINGTON, IA, p. A259
WASHINGTON COUNTY HOSPITAL, WASHINGTON, KS, p. A278
WASHINGTON COUNTY HOSPITAL AND CLINICS, WASHINGTON, IA, p. A259
WASHINGTON COUNTY HOSPITAL AND NURSING HOME, CHATOM, AL, p. A16

WASHINGTON COUNTY MEMORIAL HOSPITAL, POTOSI, MO, p. A414
WASHINGTON COUNTY REG HOSP, SANDERSVILLE, GA, p. A179
WASHINGTON COUNTY REGIONAL MEDICAL CENTER, SANDERSVILLE, GA, p. A179
WASHINGTON DC VETERANS AFFAIRS MEDICAL CENTER, WASHINGTON, DC, p. A130
WASHINGTON HEALTH CARE DIST, FREMONT, CA, p. A65
WASHINGTON HEALTH SYSTEM GREENE, WAYNESBURG, PA, p. A610
WASHINGTON HOSPITAL, WASHINGTON, PA, p. A610
WASHINGTON HOSPITAL HEALTHCARE SYSTEM, FREMONT, CA, p. A65
WASHINGTON REGIONAL MEDICAL CENTER, FAYETTEVILLE, AR, p. A45
WASHOE MED CTR REHAB HOSPITAL, RENO, NV, p. A446
WASHOE MEDICAL CENTER, RENO, NV, p. A446
WATAUGA COUNTY HOSPITAL, BOONE, NC, p. A505
WATAUGA MEDICAL CENTER, BOONE, NC, p. A505
WATERBURY HOSPITAL, WATERBURY, CT, p. A126
WATERTOWN MEMORIAL HOSPITAL, WATERTOWN, WI, p. A798
WATERTOWN REGIONAL MEDICAL CENTER, WATERTOWN, WI, p. A798
WATONGA MUNICIPAL HOSPITAL, WATONGA, OK, p. A571
WATSONVILLE COMMUNITY HOSPITAL, WATSONVILLE, CA, p. A104
WAUKESHA COUNTY MENTAL HEALTH CENTER, WAUKESHA, WI, p. A798
WAUKESHA MEMORIAL HOSPITAL, WAUKESHA, WI, p. A798
WAUPUN MEMORIAL HOSPITAL, WAUPUN, WI, p. A798
WAVERLY HEALTH CENTER, WAVERLY, IA, p. A259
WAVERLY MUNICIPAL HOSPITAL, WAVERLY, IA, p. A259
WAYNE COUNTY GENERAL HOSPITAL, WAYNESBORO, TN, p. A650
WAYNE COUNTY HOSPITAL, CORYDON, IA, p. A246
WAYNE COUNTY HOSPITAL, MONTICELLO, KY, p. A290
WAYNE COUNTY MEMORIAL HOSPITAL, HONESDALE, PA, p. A592
WAYNE GENERAL HOSPITAL, WAYNE, NJ, p. A465
WAYNE GENERAL HOSPITAL, WAYNESBORO, MS, p. A401
WAYNE HEALTHCARE, GREENVILLE, OH, p. A541
WAYNE HOSPITAL, GREENVILLE, OH, p. A541
WAYNE MEDICAL CENTER, WAYNESBORO, TN, p. A650
WAYNE MEMORIAL HOSPITAL, GOLDSBORO, NC, p. A510
WAYNE MEMORIAL HOSPITAL, HONESDALE, PA, p. A592
WAYNE MEMORIAL HOSPITAL, JESUP, GA, p. A174
WAYNE UNC HEALTH CARE, GOLDSBORO, NC, p. A511
WAYNESBORO HOSPITAL, WAYNESBORO, PA, p. A610
W B JONES ALCOHOLIC REBHAB CTR, GREENVILLE, NC, p. A511
WEATHERFORD REGIONAL HOSPITAL, WEATHERFORD, OK, p. A572
WEATHERFORD REGIONAL MEDICAL CENTER, WEATHERFORD, TX, p. A724
WEATHERFORD REHABILITATION HOSPITAL, WEATHERFORD, TX, p. A724
WEBSTER COUNTY COMMUNITY HOSPITAL, RED CLOUD, NE, p. A439
WEBSTER COUNTY MEMORIAL HOSPITAL, WEBSTER SPRINGS, WV, p. A777
WEBSTER HEALTH SERVICES, EUPORA, MS, p. A392
WEDOWEE HOSPITAL, WEDOWEE, AL, p. A25
WEED ARMY COMMUNITY HOSPITAL, FORT IRWIN, CA, p. A64
WEEKS MEDICAL CENTER, LANCASTER, NH, p. A449
WEEKS MEDICAL HOSPITAL, LANCASTER, NH, p. A449
WEINER MEMORIAL MEDICAL CENTER, MARSHALL, MN, p. A380
WEIRTON MEDICAL CENTER, WEIRTON, WV, p. A777
WEISBROD MEMORIAL COUNTY HOSPITAL, EADS, CO, p. A112
WEISBROD MEMORIAL HOSPITAL, EADS, CO, p. A112
WEISER MEMORIAL HOSPITAL, WEISER, ID, p. A193
WEISMAN CHILDREN'S REHABILITATION HOSPITAL, MARLTON, NJ, p. A458
WEKIVA SPRINGS, JACKSONVILLE, FL, p. A142
WEKIVA SPRINGS CENTER FOR WOMEN, JACKSONVILLE, FL, p. A142
WELCH COMMUNITY HOSPITAL, WELCH, WV, p. A777
WELCH EMERGENCY HOSPITAL, WELCH, WV, p. A777
WELIA HEALTH, MORA, MN, p. A381
WELKIND FACILITY, CHESTER, NJ, p. A453
WELLBRIDGE HEALTHCARE GREATER DALLAS, PLANO, TX, p. A707
WELLBRIDGE HEALTHCARE OF FORT WORTH, FORT WORTH, TX, p. A679
WELLBRIDGE HEATLHCARE OF SAN MARCOS, SAN MARCOS, TX, p. A714

WELLFOUND BEHAVIORAL HEALTH HOSPITAL, TACOMA, WA, p. A767

WELLINGTON REGIONAL MEDICAL CENTER, WELLINGTON, FL, p. A161

WELLMONT BRISTOL REGIONAL MEDICAL CENTER, BRISTOL, TN, p. A634

WELLMONT HANCOCK COUNTY HOSPITAL, SNEEDVILLE, TN, p. A649

WELLMONT HAWKINS COUNTY MEMORIAL HOSPITAL, ROGERSVILLE, TN, p. A648

WELLMONT HOLSTON VALLEY MEDICAL CENTER, KINGSPORT, TN, p. A641

WELLMONT LONESOME PINE HOSPITAL, BIG STONE GAP, VA, p. A739

WELLSPAN CHAMBERSBURG HOSPITAL, CHAMBERSBURG, PA, p. A586

WELLSPAN EPHRATA COMMUNITY HOSPITAL, EPHRATA, PA, p. A589

WELLSPAN GETTYSBURG HOSPITAL, GETTYSBURG, PA, p. A590

WELLSPAN GOOD SAMARITAN HOSPITAL, LEBANON, PA, p. A595

WELLSPAN PHILHAVEN, MOUNT GRETNA, PA, p. A597

WELLSPAN SURGERY AND REHABILLITATION HOSPITAL, YORK, PA, p. A612

WELLSPAN WAYNESBORO HOSPITAL, WAYNESBORO, PA, p. A610

WELLSPAN YORK HOSPITAL, YORK, PA, p. A612

WELLSPANGETTYSBURG HOSPITAL, GETTYSBURG, PA, p. A590

WELLSTAR ATLANTA MEDICAL CENTER, ATLANTA, GA, p. A165

WELLSTAR COBB HOSPITAL, AUSTELL, GA, p. A166

WELLSTAR DOUGLAS HOSPITAL, DOUGLASVILLE, GA, p. A171

WELLSTAR KENNESTONE HOSPITAL, MARIETTA, GA, p. A176

WELLSTAR NORTH FULTON HOSPITAL, ROSWELL, GA, p. A179

WELLSTAR PAULDING HOSPITAL, HIRAM, GA, p. A174

WELLSTAR SPALDING REGIONAL HOSPITAL, GRIFFIN, GA, p. A173

WELLSTAR SYLVAN GROVE HOSPITAL, JACKSON, GA, p. A174

WELLSTAR WEST GEORGIA MEDICAL CENTER, LAGRANGE, GA, p. A175

WELLSTAR WINDY HILL HOSPITAL, MARIETTA, GA, p. A176

WELLSTONE REGIONAL HOSPITAL, JEFFERSONVILLE, IN, p. A233

WENATCHEE VALLEY HOSPITAL, WENATCHEE, WA, p. A768

WENTWORTH-DOUGLASS HOSPITAL, DOVER, NH, p. A448

WERNERSVILLE STATE HOSPITAL, WERNERSVILLE, PA, p. A610

WESLACO REGIONAL REHABILITATION HOSPITAL, WESLACO, TX, p. A725

WESLACO REHABILITATION HOSPITAL, WESLACO, TX, p. A725

WESLEY HEALTHCARE CENTER, WICHITA, KS, p. A279

WESLEY MEDICAL CENTER, HATTIESBURG, MS, p. A393

WESLEY MEDICAL CENTER, WICHITA, KS, p. A279

WESLEY REHABILITATION HOSPITAL, WICHITA, KS, p. A279

WESLEY WOODS CENTER, ATLANTA, GA, p. A165

WESLEY WOODS GERIATRIC HOSPITAL OF EMORY UNIVERSITY, ATLANTA, GA, p. A165

WEST ALLIS MEMORIAL HOSPITAL, WEST ALLIS, WI, p. A799

WEST ANAHEIM MEDICAL CENTER, ANAHEIM, CA, p. A55

WEST BOCA MEDICAL CENTER, BOCA RATON, FL, p. A132

WEST BRANCH REGIONAL MEDICAL CENTER, WEST BRANCH, MI, p. A369

WEST CALCASIEU CAMERON HOSPITAL, SULPHUR, LA, p. A315

WEST CALCASIEU-CAMERON HOSP, SULPHUR, LA, p. A315

WEST CARROLL MEMORIAL HOSPITAL, OAK GROVE, LA, p. A312

WEST CENTRAL COMMUNITY HOSPITAL, CLINTON, IN, p. A225

WEST CENTRAL GEORGIA REGIONAL HOSPITAL, COLUMBUS, GA, p. A169

WEST CHESTER HOSPITAL, WEST CHESTER, OH, p. A552

WEST COVINA MEDICAL CENTER, WEST COVINA, CA, p. A104

WEST FELICIANA HOSPITAL, SAINT FRANCISVILLE, LA, p. A313

WEST FELICIANA PARISH HOSPITAL, SAINT FRANCISVILLE, LA, p. A313

WEST FLORIDA COMMUNITY CARE CENTER, MILTON, FL, p. A148

WEST FLORIDA HOSPITAL, PENSACOLA, FL, p. A154

WEST FLORIDA REG MED CENTER, PENSACOLA, FL, p. A154

WEST FLORIDA REHABILITATION INSTITUTE, PENSACOLA, FL, p. A154

WEST GABLES REHABILITATION HOSPITAL, MIAMI, FL, p. A147

WEST GEORGIA HEALTH, LAGRANGE, GA, p. A175

WEST HILLS HOSPITAL, RENO, NV, p. A446

WEST HILLS HOSPITAL AND MEDICAL CENTER, WEST HILLS, CA, p. A104

WEST HILLS MEDICAL CENTER, WEST HILLS, CA, p. A104

WEST HOLT MEDICAL SERVICES, ATKINSON, NE, p. A429

WEST HOLT MEMORIAL HOSPITAL, ATKINSON, NE, p. A429

WEST HOUSTON MEDICAL CENTER, HOUSTON, TX, p. A689

WEST JEFFERSON MEDICAL CENTER, MARRERO, LA, p. A308

WEST LOS ANGELES MEDICAL CENTER, LOS ANGELES, CA, p. A76

WEST MESA MEDICAL CENTER, ALBUQUERQUE, NM, p. A468

WEST OAKS AT CYPRESS CREEK, HOUSTON, TX, p. A689

WEST OAKS HOSPITAL, HOUSTON, TX, p. A689

WEST PALM BEACH VETERANS AFFAIRS MEDICAL CENTER, WEST PALM BEACH, FL, p. A162

WEST PALM HOSPITAL, WEST PALM BEACH, FL, p. A162

WEST PARK HOSPITAL, CODY, WY, p. A802

WEST PENN HOSPITAL, PITTSBURGH, PA, p. A605

WEST PINES AT LUTHERAN MED CTR, WHEAT RIDGE, CO, p. A120

WEST RIVER REGIONAL MEDICAL CENTER, HETTINGER, ND, p. A524

WEST SHORE MEDICAL CENTER, MANISTEE, MI, p. A361

WEST SPRINGS HOSPITAL, GRAND JUNCTION, CO, p. A113

WEST SUBURBAN HOSP MED CENTER, OAK PARK, IL, p. A215

WEST SUBURBAN MEDICAL CENTER, OAK PARK, IL, p. A215

WEST TENNESSEE HEALTHCARE DYERSBURG HOSPITAL, DYERSBURG, TN, p. A637

WEST TENNESSEE HEALTHCARE REHABILITATION HOSPITAL JACKSON, JACKSON, TN, p. A640

WEST TENNESSEE HEALTHCARE VOLUNTEER HOSPITAL, MARTIN, TN, p. A643

WEST TENNESSEE REHABILITATION HOSPITAL CANE CREEK, MARTIN, TN, p. A643

WEST TEXAS VA HEALTH CARE SYSTEM, BIG SPRING, TX, p. A659

WEST TEXAS VETERANS AFFAIRS HEALTH CARE SYSTEM, BIG SPRING, TX, p. A660

WEST VALLEY HOSPITAL, DALLAS, OR, p. A574

WEST VALLEY HOSPITAL, GOODYEAR, AZ, p. A32

WEST VALLEY MED CTR, CALDWELL, ID, p. A189

WEST VALLEY MEDICAL CENTER, CALDWELL, ID, p. A189

WEST VIRGINIA UNIVERSITY HOSPITALS, MORGANTOWN, WV, p. A775

WESTBOROUGH BEHAVIORAL HEALTHCARE HOSPITAL, WESTBOROUGH, MA, p. A346

WESTBROOK HEALTH CENTER, WESTBROOK, MN, p. A387

WESTCHESTER COUNTY MED CENTER, VALHALLA, NY, p. A500

WESTCHESTER GENERAL HOSPITAL, MIAMI, FL, p. A147

WESTCHESTER MEDICAL CENTER, VALHALLA, NY, p. A501

WESTERLY HOSPITAL, WESTERLY, RI, p. A614

WESTERN ARIZONA REGIONAL MEDICAL CENTER, BULLHEAD CITY, AZ, p. A30

WESTERN BAPTIST HOSPITAL, PADUCAH, KY, p. A291

WESTERN MARYLAND CENTER, HAGERSTOWN, MD, p. A330

WESTERN MARYLAND HOSPITAL CENTER, HAGERSTOWN, MD, p. A330

WESTERN MARYLAND REGIONAL MEDICAL CENTER, CUMBERLAND, MD, p. A329

WESTERN MASSACHUSETTS HOSPITAL, WESTFIELD, MA, p. A346

WESTERN MEDICAL CENTER ANAHEIM, ANAHEIM, CA, p. A55

WESTERN MEDICAL CENTER-SANTA ANA, SANTA ANA, CA, p. A96

WESTERN MENTAL HEALTH INSTITUTE, BOLIVAR, TN, p. A634

WESTERN MISSOURI MEDICAL CENTER, WARRENSBURG, MO, p. A420

WESTERN MISSOURI MENTAL HEALTH CENTER, KANSAS CITY, MO, p. A410

WESTERN NEW YORK CHILDREN'S PSYCHIATRIC CENTER, WEST SENECA, NY, p. A502

WESTERN PENNSYLVANIA HOSPITAL, PITTSBURGH, PA, p. A605

WESTERN PLAINS MEDICAL COMPLEX, DODGE CITY, KS, p. A263

WESTERN PLAINS REGIONAL HOSP, DODGE CITY, KS, p. A263

WESTERN PSYCHIATRIC INSTITUTE AND CLINIC, PITTSBURGH, PA, p. A605

WESTERN REGIONAL MEDICAL CENTER, GOODYEAR, AZ, p. A32

WESTERN RESERVE HOSPITAL, CUYAHOGA FALLS, OH, p. A538

WESTERN STATE HOSPITAL, HOPKINSVILLE, KY, p. A285

WESTERN STATE HOSPITAL, STAUNTON, VA, p. A752

WESTERN STATE HOSPITAL, TACOMA, WA, p. A767

WESTERN STATE PSYCHIATRIC CTR, FORT SUPPLY, OK, p. A559

WESTERN WAKE MED CENTER, CARY, NC, p. A506

WESTERN WISCONSIN HEALTH, BALDWIN, WI, p. A780

WESTFIELD MEMORIAL HOSPITAL, WESTFIELD, NY, p. A502

WESTFIELDS HOSPITAL, NEW RICHMOND, WI, p. A792

WESTFIELDS HOSPITAL AND CLINIC, NEW RICHMOND, WI, p. A792

WESTON COUNTY HEALTH SERVICES, NEWCASTLE, WY, p. A803

WESTON COUNTY MEM HOSPITAL, NEWCASTLE, WY, p. A803

WESTPARK SPRINGS, RICHMOND, TX, p. A708

WESTPARK SURGERY CENTER, MCKINNEY, TX, p. A700

WESTSIDE REGIONAL MEDICAL CENTER, PLANTATION, FL, p. A154

WESTSIDE SURGICAL HOSPITAL, HOUSTON, TX, p. A689

WETZEL COUNTY HOSPITAL, NEW MARTINSVILLE, WV, p. A775

W. G. (BILL) HEFFNER VETERANS AFFAIRS MEDICAL CENTER, SALISBURY, NC, p. A518

WHEATLAND MEMORIAL HEALTHCARE, HARLOWTON, MT, p. A424

WHEATLAND MEMORIAL HOSPITAL, HARLOWTON, MT, p. A424

WHEATON COMMUNITY HOSPITAL, WHEATON, MN, p. A388

WHEATON FRANCISCAN—ELMBROOK MEMORIAL CAMPUS, BROOKFIELD, WI, p. A781

WHEATON FRANCISCAN HEALTHCARE—ALL SAINTS, RACINE, WI, p. A794

WHEATON FRANCISCAN HEALTHCARE—FRANKLIN, FRANKLIN, WI, p. A784

WHEATON FRANCISCAN HEALTHCARE—ST. FRANCIS, MILWAUKEE, WI, p. A791

WHEATON FRANCISCAN HEALTHCARE—ST. JOSEPH'S, MILWAUKEE, WI, p. A791

WHEELING HOSPITAL, WHEELING, WV, p. A778

WHIDBEY GENERAL HOSPITAL, COUPEVILLE, WA, p. A757

WHIDBEYHEALTH, COUPEVILLE, WA, p. A757

WHIDDEN MEMORIAL HOSPITAL, EVERETT, MA, p. A338

WHITE COUNTY MEDICAL CENTER—SOUTH CAMPUS, SEARCY, AR, p. A52

WHITE COUNTY MEDICAL CENTER, SEARCY, AR, p. A52

WHITE MEMORIAL MEDICAL CENTER, LOS ANGELES, CA, p. A76

WHITE MOUNTAIN COMM HOSPITAL, SPRINGERVILLE, AZ, p. A39

WHITE MOUNTAIN REGIONAL MEDICAL CENTER, SPRINGERVILLE, AZ, p. A39

WHITE PLAINS HOSPITAL CENTER, WHITE PLAINS, NY, p. A502

WHITE PLAINS HOSPITAL CTR, WHITE PLAINS, NY, p. A502

WHITE RIVER JUNCTION VETERANS AFFAIRS MEDICAL CENTER, WHITE RIVER JUNCTION, VT, p. A737

WHITE RIVER MEDICAL CENTER, BATESVILLE, AR, p. A42

WHITESBURG APPALACHIAN REGIONAL HOSPITAL, WHITESBURG, KY, p. A294

WHITESBURG ARH HOSPITAL, WHITESBURG, KY, p. A294

WHITING FORENSIC DIVISION OF CONNECTICUT VALLEY HOSPITAL, MIDDLETOWN, CT, p. A123

WHITING FORENSIC HOSPITAL, MIDDLETOWN, CT, p. A123

WHITINSVILLE HOSPITAL, WHITINSVILLE, MA, p. A346

WHITINSVILLE MEDICAL CENTER, WHITINSVILLE, MA, p. A346

WHITLEY MEMORIAL HOSPITAL, COLUMBIA CITY, IN, p. A225

WHITMAN HOSPITAL, COLFAX, WA, p. A756

WHITMAN HOSPITAL AND MEDICAL CENTER, COLFAX, WA, p. A757

WHITTIER HOSPITAL MEDICAL CENTER, WHITTIER, CA, p. A105

WHITTIER PAVILION, HAVERHILL, MA, p. A340

WHITTIER PAVILLION, HAVERHILL, MA, p. A340

WHITTIER REHABILITATION HOSPITAL, BRADFORD, MA, p. A336

WHITTIER REHABILITATION HOSPITAL, WESTBOROUGH, MA, p. A346

WICHITA COUNTY HEALTH CENTER, LEOTI, KS, p. A269

WICHITA COUNTY HOSPITAL, LEOTI, KS, p. A269

WICHITA FALLS STATE HOSPITAL, WICHITA FALLS, TX, p. A725

WICKENBURG COMMUNITY HOSPITAL, WICKENBURG, AZ, p. A41

WICKENBURG REGIONAL MED CTR, WICKENBURG, AZ, p. A41

WILBARGER GENERAL HOSPITAL, VERNON, TX, p. A723

WILCOX MEDICAL CENTER, LIHUE, HI, p. A186

WILCOX MEMORIAL HOSPITAL, LIHUE, HI, p. A186

WILD ROSE COMMUNITY MEMORIAL HOSPITAL, WILD ROSE, WI, p. A799
WILKES REGIONAL MEDICAL CENTER, NORTH WILKESBORO, NC, p. A516
WILKES-BARRE GENERAL HOSPITAL, WILKES-BARRE, PA, p. A611
WILKES-BARRE VETERANS AFFAIRS MEDICAL CENTER, WILKES-BARRE, PA, p. A611
WILLAMETTE VALLEY MEDICAL CENTER, MCMINNVILLE, OR, p. A577
WILLAPA HARBOR HOSPITAL, SOUTH BEND, WA, p. A765
WILLIAM BEAUMONT ARMY MEDICAL CENTER, EL PASO, TX, p. A676
WILLIAM BEE RIRIE HOSPITAL, ELY, NV, p. A441
WILLIAM J. MCCORD ADOLESCENT AND TREATMENT CENTER, ORANGEBURG, SC, p. A623
WILLIAM J. MCCORD ADOLESCENT TREATMENT FACILITY, ORANGEBURG, SC, p. A623
WILLIAM NEWTON HOSPITAL, WINFIELD, KS, p. A279
WILLIAM NEWTON MEM HOSPITAL, WINFIELD, KS, p. A279
WILLIAM R. SHARPE, JR. HOSPITAL, WESTON, WV, p. A777
WILLIAM S. HALL PSYCHIATRIC INSTITUTE, COLUMBIA, SC, p. A618
WILLIAM S. MIDDLETON MEMORIAL VETERANS HOSPITAL, MADISON, WI, p. A788
WILLIAM W. HASTINGS INDIAN HOSPITAL, TAHLEQUAH, OK, p. A569
WILLIAMETTE VALLEY MEDICAL CTR, MCMINNVILLE, OR, p. A577
WILLIAMS COUNTY GEN HOSPITAL, MONTPELIER, OH, p. A546
WILLIAMSBURG REGIONAL HOSPITAL, KINGSTREE, SC, p. A622
WILLIAMSON ARH HOSPITAL, SOUTH WILLIAMSON, KY, p. A293
WILLIAMSON MEDICAL CENTER, FRANKLIN, TN, p. A638
WILLINGWAY HOSPITAL, STATESBORO, GA, p. A181
WILLIS-KNIGHTON SOUTH, SHREVEPORT, LA, p. A315
WILLIS-KNIGHTON BOSSIER HEALTH CENTER, BOSSIER CITY, LA, p. A298
WILLIS-KNIGHTON MEDICAL CENTER, SHREVEPORT, LA, p. A315
WILLOUGH HEALTHCARE SYSTEM, NAPLES, FL, p. A149
WILLOW CREEK BEHAVIORAL HEALTH, GREEN BAY, WI, p. A785
WILLOW CREST HOSPITAL, MIAMI, OK, p. A562
WILLOW ROCK CENTER, SAN LEANDRO, CA, p. A95
WILLOW SPRINGS HOSPITAL, RENO, NV, p. A446
WILLOW SPRINGS RES TREATMENT, RENO, NV, p. A446
WILLOW VIEW MENTAL HLTH SYSTEM, SPENCER, OK, p. A568
WILLS MEMORIAL HOSPITAL, WASHINGTON, GA, p. A183
WILMA N. VAZQUEZ MEDICAL CENTER, VEGA BAJA, PR, p. A811
WILMED NURSING CARE CENTER, WILSON, NC, p. A520
WILMINGTON TREATMENT CENTER, WILMINGTON, NC, p. A520
WILMINGTON VETERANS AFFAIRS MEDICAL CENTER, WILMINGTON, DE, p. A128
WILSON COUNTY HOSPITAL, NEODESHA, KS, p. A271
WILSON MEDICAL CENTER, NEODESHA, KS, p. A271
WILSON MEDICAL CENTER, WILSON, NC, p. A520
WILSON MEMORIAL CENTER, WILSON, NC, p. A520
WILSON MEMORIAL HOSPITAL, SIDNEY, OH, p. A549
WILSON MEMORIAL REG MED CTR, JOHNSON CITY, NY, p. A486
WILSON MEMORIAL REGIONAL MEDICAL CENTER, JOHNSON CITY, NY, p. A486
WILSON N. JONES REGIONAL MEDICAL CENTER, SHERMAN, TX, p. A716
WINCHESTER HOSPITAL, WINCHESTER, MA, p. A346
WINCHESTER MEDICAL CENTER, WINCHESTER, VA, p. A754
WINDBER MEDICAL CENTER, WINDBER, PA, p. A611
WINDHAM COMMUNITY MEMORIAL HOSPITAL, WILLIMANTIC, CT, p. A126
WINDHAM HOSPITAL, WILLIMANTIC, CT, p. A126
WINDHAVEN PSYCHIATRIC HOSPITAL, PRESCOTT VALLEY, AZ, p. A37
WINDMOOR HEALTHCARE OF CLEARWATER, CLEARWATER, FL, p. A134
WINDOM AREA HEALTH, WINDOM, MN, p. A388
WINDOM AREA HOSPITAL, WINDOM, MN, p. A388
WINDSOR-LAURELWOOD CENTER FOR BEHAVIORAL MEDICINE, WILLOUGHBY, OH, p. A553

WING MEMORIAL HOSPITAL AND MEDICAL CENTERS, PALMER, MA, p. A343
WINKLER COUNTY MEMORIAL HOSPITAL, KERMIT, TX, p. A692
WINN ARMY COMMUNITY HOSPITAL, HINESVILLE, GA, p. A174
WINN PARISH MEDICAL CENTER, WINNFIELD, LA, p. A317
WINNEBAGO MENTAL HEALTH INSTITUTE, WINNEBAGO, WI, p. A800
WINNER REGIONAL HEALTHCARE CENTER, WINNER, SD, p. A633
WINNESHIEK COUNTY MEM HOSPITAL, DECORAH, IA, p. A248
WINNESHIEK MEDICAL CENTER, DECORAH, IA, p. A248
WINNIE COMMUNITY HOSPITAL, WINNIE, TX, p. A726
WINNIE PALMER HOSPITAL FOR WOMEN AND BABIES, ORLANDO, FL, p. A152
WINONA COMM MEMORIAL HOSPITAL, WINONA, MN, p. A388
WINONA HEALTH, WINONA, MN, p. A388
WINSLOW MEMORIAL HOSPITAL, WINSLOW, AZ, p. A41
WINSTON CNTY COMM HOSP, LOUISVILLE, MS, p. A396
WINSTON MEDICAL CENTER, LOUISVILLE, MS, p. A396
WINTER HAVEN HOSPITAL, WINTER HAVEN, FL, p. A162
WINTER PARK MEMORIAL HOSPITAL, WINTER PARK, FL, p. A162
WINTHROP-UNIVERSITY HOSPITAL, MINEOLA, NY, p. A488
WIREGRASS HOSPITAL, GENEVA, AL, p. A19
WIREGRASS MEDICAL CENTER, GENEVA, AL, p. A19
WISE HEALTH SURGICAL HOSPITAL AT PARKWAY, FORT WORTH, TX, p. A679
WISE HEALTH SYSTEM, DECATUR, TX, p. A671
WISE REGIONAL HEALTH SYSTEM, DECATUR, TX, p. A671
WISHARD-ESKENAZI HEALTH, INDIANAPOLIS, IN, p. A233
WISHEK COMMUNITY HOSPITAL AND CLINICS, WISHEK, ND, p. A526
WITHAM HEALTH SERVICES, LEBANON, IN, p. A235
WITHAM MEMORIAL HOSPITAL, LEBANON, IN, p. A235
W. J. MANGOLD MEMORIAL HOSPITAL, LOCKNEY, TX, p. A696
WM S MIDDLETON MEM VET HOSP, MADISON, WI, p. A788
WM. JENNINGS BRYAN DORN VETERANS AFFAIRS MEDICAL CENTER, COLUMBIA, SC, p. A618
WOMACK ARMY COMMUNITY HOSPITAL, FORT BRAGG, NC, p. A510
WOMACK ARMY MEDICAL CENTER, FORT BRAGG, NC, p. A510
WOMAN'S HOSPITAL, BATON ROUGE, LA, p. A298
WOMAN'S HOSPITAL, FLOWOOD, MS, p. A392
WOMAN'S HOSPITAL FOUNDATION, BATON ROUGE, LA, p. A298
WOMAN'S HOSPITAL OF TEXAS, HOUSTON, TX, p. A689
WOMEN & INFANTS HOSPITAL OF RHODE ISLAND, PROVIDENCE, RI, p. A614
WOMEN AND CHILDREN'S HOSP, CHARLESTON, WV, p. A771
WOMEN AND CHILDREN'S HOSPITAL, BUFFALO, NY, p. A480
WOMEN'S AND CHILDREN'S HOSPITAL, LAFAYETTE, LA, p. A306
WOMEN'S HOSPITAL, ALBUQUERQUE, NM, p. A468
WOMEN'S HOSPITAL, LOS ANGELES, CA, p. A76
WOMEN'S HOSPITAL-INDIANAPOLIS, INDIANAPOLIS, IN, p. A233
WOOD COUNTY HOSPITAL, BOWLING GREEN, OH, p. A530
WOOD RIVER MEDICAL CENTER, KETCHUM, ID, p. A191
WOODFORD HOSPITAL, VERSAILLES, KY, p. A294
WOODHULL MEDICAL AND MENTAL HEALTH CENTER, BROOKLYN, NY, p. A479
WOODLAND HEALTHCARE, WOODLAND, CA, p. A105
WOODLAND HEIGHTS MEDICAL CENTER, LUFKIN, TX, p. A698
WOODLAND HILLS MEDICAL CENTER, WOODLAND HILLS, CA, p. A105
WOODLAND MEMORIAL HOSPITAL, WOODLAND, CA, p. A105
WOODLAND SPRINGS HOSPITAL, CONROE, TX, p. A665
WOODLANDS SPECIALTY HOSPITAL, THE, WOODLANDS, TX, p. A721
WOODLANS SPECIALTY HOSPITAL, THE WOODLANDS, TX, p. A721
WOODLAWN HOSPITAL, ROCHESTER, IN, p. A240
WOODWARD REGIONAL HOSPITAL, WOODWARD, OK, p. A572
WOODWINDS HEALTH, WOODBURY, MN, p. A388
WOODWINDS HEALTH CAMPUS, WOODBURY, MN, p. A388
WOOSTER COMMUNITY HOSPITAL, WOOSTER, OH, p. A553
WORCESTER HAHNEMANN HOSPITAL, WORCESTER, MA, p. A347

WORCESTER MEMORIAL HOSPITAL, WORCESTER, MA, p. A347
WORCESTER RECOVERY CENTER AND HOSPITAL, WORCESTER, MA, p. A347
WORCESTER STATE HOSPITAL, WORCESTER, MA, p. A347
WRANGELL GENERAL HOSPITAL, WRANGELL, AK, p. A29
WRANGELL MEDICAL CENTER, WRANGELL, AK, p. A29
WRAY COMMUNITY DISTRICT HOSPITAL, WRAY, CO, p. A120
WRIGHT MEDICAL CENTER, CLARION, IA, p. A246
WRIGHT MEMORIAL HOSPITAL, TRENTON, MO, p. A419
WRIGHT PATTERSON MEDICAL CENTER, WRIGHT, OH, p. A553
WUESTHOFF MEDICAL CENTER—MELBOURNE, MELBOURNE, FL, p. A145
WUESTHOFF MEDICAL CENTER—ROCKLEDGE, ROCKLEDGE, FL, p. A155
WVU MEDICINE—BARNESVILLE HOSPITAL, BARNESVILLE, OH, p. A528
WVU MEDICINE UNITED HOSPITAL CENTER, BRIDGEPORT, WV, p. A770
WYANDOT MEMORIAL HOSPITAL, UPPER SANDUSKY, OH, p. A551
WYCKOFF HEIGHTS HOSPITAL, BROOKLYN, NY, p. A479
WYCKOFF HEIGHTS MEDICAL CENTER, BROOKLYN, NY, p. A479
WYOMING BEHAVIORAL INSTITUTE, CASPER, WY, p. A801
WYOMING COUNTY COMMUNITY HOSPITAL, WARSAW, NY, p. A501
WYOMING MEDICAL CENTER, CASPER, WY, p. A801
WYOMING STATE HOSPITAL, EVANSTON, WY, p. A802
WYOMING VALLEY HEALTH CARE SYSTEM, WILKES-BARRE, PA, p. A611
WYTHE COUNTY COMMUNITY HOSPITAL, WYTHEVILLE, VA, p. A754

# Y

YAKIMA VALLEY MEMORIAL HOSPITAL, YAKIMA, WA, p. A769
YALE PSYCHIATRIC INSTITUTE, NEW HAVEN, CT, p. A124
YALE-NEW HAVEN HOSPITAL, NEW HAVEN, CT, p. A124
YALOBUSHA GENERAL HOSPITAL, WATER VALLEY, MS, p. A401
YAMPA VALLEY MEDICAL CENTER, STEAMBOAT SPRINGS, CO, p. A118
YANCEY COMMUNITY MEDICAL CENTER, BURNSVILLE, NC, p. A506
YAVAPAI REGIONAL MEDICAL CENTER, PRESCOTT, AZ, p. A37
YELL COUNTY HOSPITAL, DANVILLE, AR, p. A44
YOAKUM COMMUNITY HOSPITAL, YOAKUM, TX, p. A726
YOAKUM COUNTY HOSPITAL, DENVER CITY, TX, p. A672
YONKERS GENERAL HOSPITAL, YONKERS, NY, p. A503
YORK GENERAL, YORK, NE, p. A440
YORK GENERAL HOSPITAL, YORK, NE, p. A440
YORK HOSPITAL, YORK, ME, p. A323
YORK HOSPITAL, YORK, PA, p. A612
YOUTH VILLAGES INNER HARBOUR CAMPUS, DOUGLASVILLE, GA, p. A171
YUKON-KUSKOKWIM DELTA REGIONAL HOSPITAL, BETHEL, AK, p. A27
YUMA DISTRICT HOSPITAL, YUMA, CO, p. A120
YUMA REGIONAL MEDICAL CENTER, YUMA, AZ, p. A41
YUMA REHABILITATION HOSPITAL, YUMA, AZ, p. A41
YUMA REHABILITATION HOSPITAL, A PARTNERSHIP OF ENCOMPASS HEALTH AND YRMC, YUMA, AZ, p. A41

# Z

ZALE LIPSHY UNIV HOSPITAL, DALLAS, TX, p. A671
ZEELAND COMMUNITY HOSPITAL, ZEELAND, MI, p. A370
ZUCKER HILLSIDE HOSPITAL, GLEN OAKS, NY, p. A484
ZUCKERBERG SAN FRANCISCO GENERAL HOSPITAL AND TRAUMA CENTER, SAN FRANCISCO, CA, p. A94

# Index of Health Care Professionals

This section is an index of the key health care professionals for the hospitals and/or health care systems listed in this publication. The index is in alphabetical order, by individual, followed by the title, institutional affiliation, city, state and page reference to the hospital and/or health care system listing in section A and/or B.

## A

AAGARD, Kim, Chief Financial Officer, Tri-County Hospital, Wadena, MN, p. A387

AALBORG, Chase, Vice President and Chief Financial Officer, Amita Health Adventist Medical Center Glenoaks, Glendale Heights, IL, p. A206

AASVED, Craig E., Chief Executive Officer, Shodair Children's Hospital, Helena, MT, p. A425

ABAD, Ann, President, Barnes-Jewish West County Hospital, Saint Louis, MO, p. A415

ABAIR, Cynthia, Associate Director, Va San Diego Healthcare System, San Diego, CA, p. A93

ABAN, Chona, Controller, Kindred Hospital Chicago-Northlake, Northlake, IL, p. A214

ABANG, Toni, M.D., Medical Director, Encompass Rehabilitation Hospital Of Lakeview, Elizabethtown, KY, p. A282

ABBATE, Anthony, Director of Information Services, San Ramon Regional Medical Center, San Ramon, CA, p. A96

ABBATIELLO, Michael, Chief Financial Officer, Spring Harbor Hospital, Westbrook, ME, p. A323

ABBEY, Kurt, Chief Nursing Officer and Chief Operating Officer, Ozarks Medical Center, West Plains, MO, p. A420

ABBOTT, Ed, Vice President Finance, Methodist Richardson Medical Center, Richardson, TX, p. A708

ABBOTT, Justin, M.D., Medical Director, Sevier Valley Hospital, Richfield, UT, p. A731

ABBOTT, Michael, Chief Operating Officer, Lewis-Gale Medical Center, Boones Mill, VA, p. A739

ABBOTT, Peggy L., President and Chief Executive Officer, Ouachita County Medical Center, Camden, AR, p. A43

ABBOTT, Rhonda
Interim Chief Executive Officer, Memorial Hermann Rehabilitation Hospital - Katy, Katy, TX, p. A692
Interim Chief Executive Officer, Tirr Memorial Hermann, Houston, TX, p. A688

ABBOUD, Josie, R.N., FACHE, President and Chief Executive Officer, Nebraska Methodist Hospital, Omaha, NE, p. A437

ABDA, William, Chief Human Resources Officer, Clarks Summit State Hospital, Clarks Summit, PA, p. A586

ABDELKARIM, Riad, M.D., Vice President and Chief Medical Officer, St. Mary Medical Center, Apple Valley, CA, p. A56

ABDELNASER, Mohammad, Chief Nursing Officer, Centinela Hospital Medical Center, Inglewood, CA, p. A69

ABDO, Abed, Chief Financial Officer, St. Jude Children's Research Hospital, Memphis, TN, p. A645

ABE, Ann
Administrator and Chief Operating Officer, Orange County Global Medical Center, Inc., Santa Ana, CA, p. A96
Interim Chief Executive Officer, Orange County Global Medical Center, Inc., Santa Ana, CA, p. A96

ABEL, Danielle, Vice President of Patient Care Services, Chi Lakewood Health, Baudette, MN, p. A372

ABEL, Jeffrey, M.D., Chief Medical Officer, Ogden Regional Medical Center, Ogden, UT, p. A730

ABEL, Kevin, Chief Executive Officer, North Valley Hospital, Whitefish, MT, p. A428

ABEL, Stacy, Vice President People and Culture, Craig Hospital, Englewood, CO, p. A112

ABELLERA, Roland, Vice President and Chief Operating Officer, St. Bernard Hospital And Health Care Center, Chicago, IL, p. A201

ABELY, Susan
Chief Information Officer, St. Josep. Health Services Of Rhode Island, North Providence, RI, p. A613
Vice President and Chief Information Officer, Roger Williams Medical Center, Providence, RI, p. A614

ABERCROMBIE, David
Controller, Baptist Health South Florida, Homestead Hospital, Homestead, FL, p. A140
Controller, Baptist Health South Florida, Mariners Hospital, Tavernier, FL, p. A160

ABERCROMBIE, David E., Chief Executive Officer, Montgomery County Memorial Hospital, Red Oak, IA, p. A256

ABERCROMBIE, Zach, Chief Financial Officer, Citizens Baptist Medical Center, Talladega, AL, p. A24

ABERNATHY, Clint, President, Texas Health Harris Methodist Hospital Alliance, Fort Worth, TX, p. A679

ABERNETHY, Allen, Interim Chief Executive Officer, Williamsburg Regional Hospital, Kingstree, SC, p. A622

ABEY, Michelle, Chief Financial Officer, Stoughton Hospital Association, Stoughton, WI, p. A797

ABLA, Mike, Director of Nursing, Griffin Memorial Hospital, Norman, OK, p. A563

ABNEY, Stuart, Controller, Jasper Memorial Hospital, Monticello, GA, p. A177

ABOUD, Al, CPA, Chief Financial Officer, Hackensack Meridian Health Mountainside Medical Center, Montclair, NJ, p. A458

ABRAHAM, Akram, M.D., Chief of Staff, Harmon Memorial Hospital, Hollis, OK, p. A560

ABRAHAM, Brian, Chief Executive Officer, Clearsky Rehabilitation Hospital Of Weatherford, Weatherford, TX, p. A724

ABRAHAM, JiJi
Area Chief Financial Officer, Kaiser Permanente Moreno Valley Medical Center, Moreno Valley, CA, p. A80
Chief Financial Officer, Kaiser Permanente Riverside Medical Center, Riverside, CA, p. A88

ABRAHAMSON-BATY, Sherri, Director Patient Care Services, Cambridge Medical Center, Cambridge, MN, p. A373

ABRAHAMY, Ran, M.D., Chief of Staff, University Hospital And Medical Center, Tamarac, FL, p. A159

ABRAMS, Jose, Chief Information Officer, St. Luke's Episcopal Hospital, Ponce, PR, p. A809

ABREU, Iris, Supervisor Human Resources, Hospital Hima De Humacao, Humacao, PR, p. A808

ABREU, John, Vice President and Chief Financial Officer, Portneuf Medical Center, Pocatello, ID, p. A192

ABRINA, Sofia
R.N., Administrator, Montclair Hospital Medical Center, Montclair, CA, p. A79
R.N., Chief Executive Officer, Glendora Community Hospital, Glendora, CA, p. A67

ABRUTZ, Josep. F. Jr, Administrator, Cameron Regional Medical Center, Cameron, MO, p. A403

ABSALON, Jeffrey
M.D., Chief Physician Officer, St. Charles Bend, Bend, OR, p. A573
M.D., Chief Physician Officer, St. Charles Redmond, Redmond, OR, p. A580

ABSHIER, Trey, Chief Executive Officer, Central Florida Regional Hospital, Sanford, FL, p. A156

ABUNDO, Manuel, M.D., Chief of Staff, Wahiawa General Hospital, Wahiawa, HI, p. A187

ACCASHIAN, Chris
Chief Executive Officer, Bon Secours St. Francis Medical Center, Midlothian, VA, p. A746
Chief Executive Officer, Rappahannock General Hospital, Kilmarnock, VA, p. A744

ACETO, Anthony, Vice President Human Resources, Norwalk Hospital, Norwalk, CT, p. A124

ACEVEDO, Edwin, Financial Supervisor, Hospital Buen Samaritano, Aguadilla, PR, p. A805

ACEVEDO, Elizabeth, Director Human Resources, Houston Methodist Willowbrook Hospital, Houston, TX, p. A686

ACEVEDO, Jose
M.D., President and Chief Executive Officer, Geneva General Hospital, Geneva, NY, p. A484
M.D., President and Chief Executive Officer, Soldiers And Sailors Memorial Hospital, Penn Yan, NY, p. A495

ACEVEDO, Ramon, Supervisor Information Systems, Hospital San Cristobal, Coto Laurel, PR, p. A807

ACHARYA, Vik, M.P.H., Chief Executive Officer, Brandywine Hospital, Coatesville, PA, p. A587

ACHEBE, James, M.D., President Medical Staff, South Shore Hospital, Chicago, IL, p. A201

ACHTER, Dick, Chief Financial Officer, Barrett Hospital & Healthcare, Dillon, MT, p. A423

ACHURY, Dario, Director of Information Management, St. Anthony's Rehabilitation Hospital, Lauderdale Lakes, FL, p. A144

ACKER, David B., FACHE, President and Chief Executive Officer, Canton-Potsdam Hospital, Potsdam, NY, p. A495

ACKERMAN, Kenneth F., FACHE, Hospital Administrator, Mayo Clinic Hospital - Rochester, Rochester, MN, p. A384

ACKERSON, David, Chief Information Officer, Seattle Cancer Care Alliance, Seattle, WA, p. A764

ACKERT, Sara, Associate Director, Sioux Falls Veterans Affairs Health Care System, Sioux Falls, SD, p. A632

ACKLAND, Jeanne, Director of Finance, Fillmore County Hospital, Geneva, NE, p. A432

ACKLEY, Michael
Chief Financial Officer, Kentucky River Medical Center, Jackson, KY, p. A285
Chief Financial Officer, Three Rivers Medical Center, Louisa, KY, p. A287

ACKLIN, Traci, M.D., Chief of Staff, Montgomery General Hospital, Montgomery, WV, p. A774

ACKMAN, Jeffrey, M.D., Chief of Staff, Shriners Hospitals For Children-Chicago, Chicago, IL, p. A201

ACKMAN, Laura, Chief Operating Officer and Administrator, Essentia Health Northern Pines Medical Center, Aurora, MN, p. A372

ACOSTA, Ivan, M.D., Medical Director, Hospital De La Concepcion, San German, PR, p. A809

ACOSTA, Louis, M.D., Chief of Staff, La Downtown Medical Center, Llc, Los Angeles, CA, p. A75

ACOSTA, Todd, R.N., Chief Nursing Officer, Hood Memorial Hospital, Amite, LA, p. A296

ACOSTA-CARLSON, Francisca, M.D., Chief of Staff, Lexington Regional Health Center, Lexington, NE, p. A434

ACOSTA-CRUZ, Maridel, Chief Executive Officer, Lubbock Heart & Surgical Hospital, Lubbock, TX, p. A697

ACREE, Charis, Vice President and Chief Operating Officer, Wellstar West Georgia Medical Center, Lagrange, GA, p. A175

ADAIR, Dale, M.D., Chief Medical Officer, Wernersville State Hospital, Wernersville, PA, p. A610

ADAIR, Julie, Interim Corporate Chief Human Resources Officer, Fresno Heart And Surgical Hospital, Fresno, CA, p. A65

ADAIR-TRIPLETT, Alonna, Chief Nurse Executive, Claremore Indian Hospital, Claremore, OK, p. A557

ADAM, Sheryl, Chief Financial Officer, Hanover Hospital, Hanover, KS, p. A265

ADAM, Suzanne, D.O., Medical Director, Encompass Health Reading Rehabilitation Hospital, Reading, PA, p. A606

ADAMO, James, M.D., Medical Director, Harbor Oaks Hospital, New Baltimore, MI, p. A362

ADAMOLEKUN, Michelle
Chief Human Resource Officer, St. Vincent's Medical Center Riverside, Jacksonville, FL, p. A141
Vice President Human Resource Market Lead Florida/ Alabama Ministry Market, Sacred Heart Hospital Pensacola, Pensacola, FL, p. A154

ADAMS, Aaron
President, St. Charles Bend, Bend, OR, p. A573
President, St. Charles Redmond, Redmond, OR, p. A580

ADAMS, Alan L., Administrator, Memorial Hospital Of Stilwell, Stilwell, OK, p. A568

ADAMS, Amy Lynn, Chief Executive Officer, Encompass Health Nittany Valley Rehabilitation Hospital, Pleasant Gap. PA, p. A605

ADAMS, Bob, Director Information Services, Bay Area Hospital, Coos Bay, OR, p. A574

ADAMS, Brian
Chief Executive Officer, Adventhealth Heart Of Florida, Davenport, FL, p. A135
Chief Executive Officer, Adventhealth Lake Wales, Lake Wales, FL, p. A143

ADAMS, Bryan D., Chief Executive Officer, Greenleaf Behavioral Health Hospital, Valdosta, GA, p. A182

ADAMS, Carla, Chief Nursing Officer, Northern Nevada Medical Center, Sparks, NV, p. A446

ADAMS, Cathleen, Chief Nursing Officer, Carepartners Health Services, Asheville, NC, p. A504

ADAMS, Charlotte, Director of Human Resources, Carolina Pines Regional Medical Center, Hartsville, SC, p. A621

ADAMS, Chris, Vice President Patient Care Services, Ssm Health Good Samaritan Hospital, Mount Vernon, IL, p. A213

ADAMS, Cynthia, Vice President Human Resources, Tristar Stonecrest Medical Center, Smyrna, TN, p. A649

ADAMS, Denise, Human Resources Generalist, Hancock County Hospital, Sneedville, TN, p. A649

ADAMS, Elizabeth, R.N., Chief Nursing Officer, Oak Hill Hospital, Brooksville, FL, p. A133

ADAMS, Emmy
Chief Financial Officer, Mayhill Hospital, Denton, TX, p. A672
Chief Financial Officer, Provo Canyon Behavioral Hospital, Orem, UT, p. A730

ADAMS, Essie, Director of Nursing, Kedren Community Mental Health Center, Los Angeles, CA, p. A75

ADAMS, Felicia, MS, Chief Nursing Officer, Mid-Columbia Medical Center, The Dalles, OR, p. A582

ADAMS, Gini, Director Employee and Public Relations, Yuma District Hospital, Yuma, CO, p. A120

ADAMS, Gregory A., Chief Executive Officer and Chairman, Kaiser Permanente Roseville Medical Center, Roseville, CA, p. A89

ADAMS, Heather, Chief Nursing Officer, Jfk Memorial Hospital, Indio, CA, p. A68

ADAMS, Jason
M.D., Medical Staff President, Forest Health Medical Center, Ypsilanti, MI, p. A370
Chief Operating Officer, Chi Saint Josep. East, Lexington, KY, p. A286
Chief Operating Officer, Chi Saint Josep. Health, Lexington, KY, p. A286

ADAMS, Jason M., President, Chi Saint Josep. East, Lexington, KY, p. A286

ADAMS, Jennifer, Chief Operating Officer and Chief Financial Officer, Lake City Medical Center, Lake City, FL, p. A143

ADAMS, Jo, Director Human Resources, Donalsonville Hospital, Donalsonville, GA, p. A171

ADAMS, John, Chief Hospital Executive, Integris Southwest Medical Center, Oklahoma City, OK, p. A564

ADAMS, J'Dee, Chief Executive Officer, North Canyon Medical Center, Gooding, ID, p. A190

ADAMS, Karen, Vice President Human Resources, Baxter Regional Medical Center, Mountain Home, AR, p. A50

ADAMS, Kelly, Chief Executive Officer, Santa Cruz Valley Regional Hospital, Green Valley, AZ, p. A33

ADAMS, Kimberly, Manager Human Resources, Carroll County Memorial Hospital, Carrollton, KY, p. A281

ADAMS, Leslie, Chief Nursing Executive, Chi Saint Josep. Berea, Berea, KY, p. A280

ADAMS, Mark, M.D., Chief Medical Officer, El Camino Hospital, Mountain View, CA, p. A80

ADAMS, Mark A., President and Chief Executive Officer, Methodist Rehabilitation Center, Jackson, MS, p. A394

ADAMS, Mark B., Chief Executive Officer, Ogden Regional Medical Center, Ogden, UT, p. A730

ADAMS, Marlene, Director Human Resources, Schneider Regional Medical Center, Saint Thomas, VI, p. A812

ADAMS, Marsha, Interim Director Human Resources, Texas Health Harris Methodist Hospital Cleburne, Cleburne, TX, p. A663

ADAMS, Martin, CPA, Vice President Finance and Chief Financial Officer, Paris Community Hospital, Paris, IL, p. A216

ADAMS, Mary Jane, R.N., MSN, Senior Vice President and Chief Nursing Officer, Uofl Health - Uofl Hospital, Louisville, KY, p. A289

ADAMS, Mike, M.D., Chief Medical Officer, Gateway Regional Medical Center, Granite City, IL, p. A206

ADAMS, Nancy, R.N., Senior Vice President and Chief Operating Officer, Western Maryland Regional Medical Center, Cumberland, MD, p. A329

ADAMS, Norma, Director Human Resources, Southern Regional Medical Center, Riverdale, GA, p. A178

ADAMS, Patsy, Vice President Human Resources, Redmond Regional Medical Center, Rome, GA, p. A179

ADAMS, Renee, Director Information Technology, Chan Soon-Shiong Medical Center, Windber, PA, p. A611

ADAMS, Robert, Vice President Operations, Hackensack Meridian Health Jersey Shore University Medical Center, Neptune, NJ, p. A459

ADAMS, Robert H.
President, Western Region, Hackettstown Medical Center, Hackettstown, NJ, p. A456
President, Western Region, Newton Medical Center, Newton, NJ, p. A460

ADAMS, Robin, Director Human Resources, Reeves Memorial Medical Center, Bernice, LA, p. A298

ADAMS, Russell, M.D., Chief Medical Officer, Unitypoint Health - Marshalltown, Marshalltown, IA, p. A254

ADAMS, Scott K., FACHE, Chief Executive Officer, Pullman Regional Hospital, Pullman, WA, p. A762

ADAMS, Shannon, Chief Financial Officer, Avera Holy Family Hospital, Estherville, IA, p. A249

ADAMS, Sharon
Chief Nursing Officer, Danbury Hospital, Danbury, CT, p. A121
Chief Operating Officer, Danbury Hospital, Danbury, CT, p. A121
President, Danbury Hospital, Danbury, CT, p. A121

ADAMS, Shaun, Chief Financial Officer, Tennova Healthcare-Harton, Tullahoma, TN, p. A650

ADAMS, Shawn, Chief Financial Officer, Christus Southeast Texas Hospital - St. Elizabeth, Beaumont, TX, p. A658

ADAMS, Sheila, MSN, R.N., Chief Operating Officer and Chief Nursing Officer, Legent Hospital Of El Paso, El Paso, TX, p. A675

ADAMS, Susan, Chief Nursing Officer and Chief Operating Officer, Specialty Hospital Of Lorain, Amherst, OH, p. A527

ADAMS, T, M.D., Chief of Staff, Mclaren Caro Region, Caro, MI, p. A350

ADAMS, Tim, Interim Chief Executive Officer and President, H. Lee Moffitt Cancer Center And Research Institute, Tampa, FL, p. A159

ADAMS, Tony, President, Barix Clinics Of Pennsylvania, Langhorne, PA, p. A594

ADAMSKI, Joseph, Chief Nursing Officer, Encompass Health Rehabilitation Hospital Of Concord, Concord, NH, p. A448

ADAMSON, James, Chief Executive Officer, Mountain View Hospital, Idaho Falls, ID, p. A190

ADAMSON, Nancy, Chief Nursing Officer, Banner Del E. Webb Medical Center, Sun City West, AZ, p. A39

ADCOCK, Tanya M., President, St. Mary's Good Samaritan Hospital, Greensboro, GA, p. A173

ADCOCK, William, Chief Financial Officer, Union General Hospital, Farmerville, LA, p. A301

ADDINGTON, Tom, Chief Information Officer, Saint Michael's Medical Center, Newark, NJ, p. A460

ADDISON, Holland, M.D., Medical Director, Select Specialty Hospital - Belhaven, Jackson, MS, p. A395

ADDISON, John, D.O., Chief Medical Officer, Mccamey County Hospital District, Mccamey, TX, p. A700

ADDISON, Lenora, Vice President Patient Care and Nursing, Medstar Harbor Hospital, Baltimore, MD, p. A325

ADDISON, Lewis, Senior Vice President and Chief Financial Officer, Centra Lynchburg General Hospital, Lynchburg, VA, p. A745

ADDLESPERGER, John, D.O., Chief Medical Officer, Sheridan Memorial Hospital, Sheridan, WY, p. A804

ADDO, Deborah, Chief Executive Officer, Inova Loudoun Hospital, Leesburg, VA, p. A744

ADEEL, Mohammed, Medical Director, Encompass Health Deaconess Rehabilitation Hospital, Newburgh, IN, p. A238

ADELEKAN, Ade, Chief Nursing Officer, Continuecare Hospital At Medical Center (Odessa), Odessa, TX, p. A703

ADEMA, Carolyn, Senior Vice President, St. Tammany Health System, Covington, LA, p. A300

ADEN, Susie, Director of IP Services, Pocahontas Community Hospital, Pocahontas, IA, p. A256

ADER, Michael, M.D., Vice President Medical Affairs, Upmc Hanover, Hanover, PA, p. A591

ADERS, Deb, MS, R.N., Vice President Patient Care Services, Chief Nursing Officer, Yuma Regional Medical Center, Yuma, AZ, p. A41

ADESSO, Patrick
Director Information Technology and Systems, Curahealth Jacksonville, Jacksonville, FL, p. A141
Director Information Technology and Systems, Memorial Hospital Jacksonville, Jacksonville, FL, p. A141

ADKINS, Gary, Chief Executive Officer, Parkview Noble Hospital, Kendallville, IN, p. A233

ADKINS, Gary W., President, Parkview Noble Hospital, Kendallville, IN, p. A233

ADKINS, Kedrick, Chief Financial Officer, Mayo Clinic Hospital - Rochester, Rochester, MN, p. A384

ADKINS, Kevin, Director Human Resources, Medical City Green Oaks Hospital, Dallas, TX, p. A669

ADKINS, Melisa, Chief Executive Officer, Uofl Health - Mary And Elizabeth Hospital, Louisville, KY, p. A289

ADKINS, Michael, Chief Operating Officer, Hca Houston Healthcare Northwest, Houston, TX, p. A685

ADKINS, Paige, Chief Financial Officer, Greenbrier Valley Medical Center, Ronceverte, WV, p. A776

ADKINS, Raymond, Chief Information Officer, Tidalhealth Peninsula, Salisbury, MD, p. A332

ADKINS, Scott, Manager Information Technology, Vernon Memorial Healthcare, Elk Mound, WI, p. A783

ADKINS, Tyler, Chief Financial Officer, Vaughan Regional Medical Center, Selma, AL, p. A24

ADLER, Josh, M.D., Chief Medical Officer, Ucsf Medical Center, San Francisco, CA, p. A94

ADLER, Kenneth, M.D., Medical Director, Arrowhead Behavioral Health Hospital, Maumee, OH, p. A544

ADLER, Maurita, Director Information Services, Gottlieb Memorial Hospital, Melrose Park, IL, p. A212

ADMA, Vishal, M.D., Medical Director, Kvc Prairie Ridge Psychiatric Hospital, Kansas City, KS, p. A267

ADORNATO, Sara F., Executive Director, Barnes-Kasson County Hospital, Susquehanna, PA, p. A608

ADORNETTO-GARCIA, Debra, MSN, R.N., Chief Nursing Officer, Banner Gateway Medical Center, Gilbert, AZ, p. A32

ADREAN, Christina
Chief Executive Officer, Pam Specialty Hospital Of Victoria North, Victoria, TX, p. A723
Chief Executive Officer, Pam Specialty Hospital Of Victoria South, Victoria, TX, p. A723

ADRIAANSE, Steven, Vice President and Chief Human Resources Officer, Tallahassee Memorial Healthcare, Tallahassee, FL, p. A158

ADUDDELL, Chad S., Market Chief Executive Officer, Chi St. Vincent Infirmary Medical Center, Little Rock, AR, p. A49

ADVEY, Linda, Manager Information Systems, Glenbeigh Hospital And Outpatient Centers, Rock Creek, OH, p. A548

AFENYA, Kenneth, M.D., Chief of Staff, Baptist Memorial Hospital-Tipton, Covington, TN, p. A637

AFLAK, Ziba, Chief Financial Officer, Kindred Hospital-San Francisco Bay Area, San Leandro, CA, p. A95

AFZAL, Muhammed, M.D., Chief of Staff, Sutter Medical Center, Sacramento, Sacramento, CA, p. A90

AGANA, Ben, M.D., Medical Director, Encompass Health Rehabilitation Hospital The Woodlands, Conroe, TX, p. A665

AGEE, Joan
Chief Operating Officer and Chief Nursing Officer, St. Luke's Nampa, Nampa, ID, p. A192
Vice President Patient Care Services, St. Josep. Regional Medical Center, Lewiston, ID, p. A191

AGENBROAD, Connie, Chief Executive Officer, Othello Community Hospital, Othello, WA, p. A761

AGLIECO, Fabio, D.O., Chief of Staff, Sweeny Community Hospital, Sweeny, TX, p. A718

AGLOINGA, Roy, Chief Administrative Officer, Norton Sound Regional Hospital, Nome, AK, p. A29

AGNEW, James, Chief Executive Officer, Prisma Health Greenville Memorial Hospital, Greenville, SC, p. A620

AGOSTINI, Irene, M.D., Chief Medical Officer, University Of New Mexico Hospitals, Albuquerque, NM, p. A468

AGOSTO, Paula, R.N., MSN, Senior Vice President and Chief Nursing Officer, Children's Hospital Of Philadelphia, Philadelphia, PA, p. A599

AGRELA, Ramona, Associate Chancellor & Chief Human Resources Executive, Uci Medical Center, Orange, CA, p. A83

AGRESTI, Katie, R.N., Director Patient Care Services, Lecom Health Millcreek Community Hospital, Erie, PA, p. A590

AGUAS, Hugo, Vice President Human Resources, Inova Alexandria Hospital, Alexandria, VA, p. A738

AGUERO, Samuel, Chief Operating Officer, Adventhealth Deland, Deland, FL, p. A136

AGUILA, Marcos, Chief Executive Officer, Hospital San Francisco, San Juan, PR, p. A810

AGUILAR, Gretchen, Director Patient Care and Chief Nursing Officer, Three Rivers Hospital, Brewster, WA, p. A756

AGUILAR, Marisa
Chief Operating Officer, Valley Baptist Medical Center-Brownsville, Brownsville, TX, p. A661
Interim Chief Nursing Officer, Valley Baptist Medical Center-Brownsville, Brownsville, TX, p. A661

AGUILERA, Louie, Director Information Technology, Legent Hospital Of El Paso, El Paso, TX, p. A675

AGUILLARD, Clay, R.N., Administrator, Baton Rouge Behavioral Hospital, Baton Rouge, LA, p. A296

AGUILLARD, Kristopher, Chief Executive Officer, Mercy Regional Medical Center, Ville Platte, LA, p. A316

AGUILLARD, Shelly, Vice President Human Resources, Christus Ochsner St. Patrick, Lake Charles, LA, p. A306

AGUINAGA, Miguel, M.D., FACS, Medical Director, Advanced Care Hospital Of White County, Searcy, AR, p. A52

AGUIRRE, Jose, M.D., Medical Director, Carson Tahoe Continuing Care Hospital, Carson City, NV, p. A441

AGWUNOBI, Andrew, M.D., Chief Executive Officer, Uconn, John Dempsey Hospital, Farmington, CT, p. A122

AHAINE, Israel, Chief Nursing Officer, West Oaks Hospital, Houston, TX, p. A689

AHEARN, Patrick
Chief Executive Officer, Community Medical Center, Toms River, NJ, p. A464
Chief Operating Officer and Senior Vice President, Saint Barnabas Medical Center, Livingston, NJ, p. A457

AHL, Dennis, Director Information Technology, Jefferson Community Health And Life, Fairbury, NE, p. A431

AHLERS, Tim, Chief Executive Officer, Guttenberg Municipal Hospital And Clinics, Guttenberg, IA, p. A250

AHMAD, Shariq, M.D., Chief of Staff, Baptist Hospitals Of Southeast Texas, Beaumont, TX, p. A658

AHMED, Ashraf, M.D., Senior Vice President Physician and Hospital Services, Alliance Community Hospital, Alliance, OH, p. A527

AHMED, Imtiaz, Chief of Staff, Mercy Hospital Ada, Ada, OK, p. A555

AHMED, Mohammed, M.D., Vice President of Medical Affairs and Chief Medical Officer, Howard County General Hospital, Columbia, MD, p. A328

AHMED, Omar, Acting Manager Human Resources, Veterans Affairs Caribbean Healthcare System, San Juan, PR, p. A811

AHMED, Sajid, Chief Information and Innovation Officer, Martin Luther King, Jr. Community Hospital, Los Angeles, CA, p. A75

AHMED, Shabeer, M.D., Clinical Director, Community Behavioral Health Hospital - Annandale, Annandale, MN, p. A371

AHNER, Dawn
Chief Operating Officer Acute Services, Renown Regional Medical Center, Reno, NV, p. A446
Chief Operating Officer Acute Services, Renown Rehabilitation Hospital, Reno, NV, p. A446
Chief Operating Officer Acute Services, Renown South Meadows Medical Center, Reno, NV, p. A446

AHRENS, C Todd., President and Chief Executive Officer, Hannibal Regional Hospital, Hannibal, MO, p. A407

AHUJA, Teena, Interim Chief Executive Officer and Regional Vice President of Operations, Willow Creek Behavioral Health, Green Bay, WI, p. A785

AIELLO, Louis
Chief Financial Officer, St. Elizabeth Medical Center, Utica, NY, p. A500
Senior Vice President and Chief Financial Officer, Faxton St. Luke's Healthcare, Utica, NY, p. A500

AIKEN, Avery, Chief Financial Officer, Smith County Memorial Hospital, Smith Center, KS, p. A276

AIKEN, Patsy, Coordinator Human Resource, Monument Health Spearfish Hospital, Spearfish, SD, p. A632

AIKEN, Richard, M.D., Medical Director, Lakeland Behavioral Health System, Springfield, MO, p. A418

AILOR, Lorie, Chief Executive Officer, Chief Administrative Officer, Network Vice President Orthopedics and Sports, Orthopaedic Hospital Of Lutheran Health Network, Fort Wayne, IN, p. A228

AINTABLIAN, Susan, Chief Information Officer, Lac-Olive View-Ucla Medical Center, Sylmar, CA, p. A100

AIONA, Michael, M.D., Chief of Staff, Shriners Hospitals For Children-Portland, Portland, OR, p. A580

AIRHART, Steven
Chief Executive Officer, Garfield Park Hospital, Chicago, IL, p. A198
Chief Executive Officer, Hartgrove Hospital, Chicago, IL, p. A198

AIROSUS, Diane
Chief Financial Officer, Arbour H. R. I. Hospital, Brookline, MA, p. A337
Chief Financial Officer, Pembroke Hospital, Pembroke, MA, p. A343

AISEN, Mindy, M.D., Chief Medical Officer, Rancho Los Amigos National Rehabilitation Center, Downey, CA, p. A62

AISENBREY, Lisa, Administrator Human Resources and Support Services, Sidney Health Center, Sidney, MT, p. A428

AIYELAWO, Pius, Chief Operating Officer, National Institutes Of Health Clinical Center, Bethesda, MD, p. A327

AJANAH, Muhammad, M.D., Clinical Director, Clifton T. Perkins Hospital Center, Jessup. MD, p. A330

AJMAL, Farooq, Vice President and Chief Information Officer, Nassau University Medical Center, East Meadow, NY, p. A483

AKENBERGER, Gary, Chief Operating Officer, Promedica Toledo Hospital, Toledo, OH, p. A550

AKENS, Rick, Director Human Resources and Labor Relations, Methodist Medical Center Of Oak Ridge, Oak Ridge, TN, p. A648

AKERS, Earl, Supervisor Information Technology, Salina Surgical Hospital, Salina, KS, p. A276

AKERSON, Jeffrey, M.D., Chief Medical Officer, Nebraska Medicine - Bellevue, Bellevue, NE, p. A430

AKHRAS, Omar, M.D., Chief of Staff, Putnam General Hospital, Eatonton, GA, p. A172

AKHTAR, M., Chief Operating Officer, St. John's Hospital, Maplewood, MN, p. A380

AKIF, Joe, Chief Clinical Officer and Chief Nursing Officer, Warren General Hospital, Warren, PA, p. A609

AKIN, Pam, R.N., MSN, Chief Nursing Officer, Whitman Hospital And Medical Center, Colfax, WA, p. A757

AKINS, Tina, Director Human Resources, Lost Rivers Medical Center, Arco, ID, p. A188

AKIYOSHI, Derek, Chief Executive Officer, Leahi Hospital, Honolulu, HI, p. A184

AKKUB, Laura, Director Human Resources, Magnolia Regional Medical Center, Magnolia, AR, p. A49

AKOPYAN, George, Director Human Resources, Centinela Hospital Medical Center, Inglewood, CA, p. A69

AL RAYES, Rachid, Chief Operating Officer, Atrium Medical Center, Stafford, TX, p. A716

AL-HASHMI, Samer, M.D., Chief Medical Staff, Stevens County Hospital, Hugoton, KS, p. A266

ALAGAR, Ravi, M.D., Medical Director, Curahealth Pittsburgh, Oakdale, PA, p. A598

ALAM, Md
Chief Information Officer, Nyc Health + Hospitals / Jacobi, Bronx, NY, p. A477
Chief Information Officer, Nyc Health + Hospitals / Metropolitan, New York, NY, p. A491

ALAM, Muhammad, M.D., Medical Director, Turning Point Hospital, Moultrie, GA, p. A177

ALAMEDDINE, Hala, Chief Nursing Executive, Kindred Hospital Sugar Land, Sugar Land, TX, p. A717

ALASZEWSKI, Lydia, Chief Nursing Officer, Select Specialty Hospital-Macomb County, Mount Clemens, MI, p. A362

ALBANY, Karen, Chief Information Officer, Naval Medical Center, Portsmouth, VA, p. A749

ALBAUM, Michael, M.D., Senior Vice President and Chief Medical Officer, Southern Maine Health Care - Biddeford Medical Center, Biddeford, ME, p. A319

ALBERS, Craig, President and Chief Operating Officer, Mercy Health - St. Charles Hospital, Oregon, OH, p. A547

ALBERS, Mary, Chief Operating Officer, Billings Clinic, Billings, MT, p. A421

ALBERT, Shannon, Chief Operating Officer, Carson Valley Medical Center, Gardnerville, NV, p. A442

ALBERT, Todd, M.D., Surgeon-in-Chief and Medical Director, Hospital For Special Surgery, New York, NY, p. A490

ALBERTS, Patrick, Senior Vice President and Chief Operating Officer, Monongahela Valley Hospital, Monongahela, PA, p. A597

ALBERTSON, Chris
Chief Executive Officer and President, Presentation Medical Center, Rolla, ND, p. A525
Director Human Resources, Presentation Medical Center, Rolla, ND, p. A525

ALBERTSON, Robert, M.D., Chief Medical Officer, Henry Ford Allegiance Specialty Hospital, Jackson, MI, p. A359

ALBIETZ, Minta, Resource Chief Executive Officer, Kindred Hospital Seattle-First Hill, Seattle, WA, p. A763

ALBIN, James
Chief Information Officer, Baylor St. Luke's Medical Center, Houston, TX, p. A684
Chief Information Officer, Theda Care Medical Center - Wild Rose, Wild Rose, WI, p. A799

ALBOSTA, Kevin, Vice President, Chief Financial Officer, Covenant Healthcare, Saginaw, MI, p. A365

ALBRECHT, David L.
President, District One Hospital, Faribault, MN, p. A376
President, Owatonna Hospital, Owatonna, MN, p. A382

ALBRECHT, John, Chief of Staff, Union Hospital Clinton, Clinton, IN, p. A225

ALBRECHT, Sandra, Interim Chief Financial Officer, Singing River Health System, Pascagoula, MS, p. A398

ALBRIGHT, Bill, Director Human Resources, Stewart Memorial Community Hospital, Lake City, IA, p. A253

ALBRIGHT, Leslie, Vice President Information Systems, Bethesda Hospital East, Boynton Beach, FL, p. A132

ALBRIGHT, Sara, Vice President Human Resources, Bassett Medical Center, Cooperstown, NY, p. A481

ALBRIGHT, Tammy, Chief Executive Officer, Greeneville Community Hospital West, Greeneville, TN, p. A638

ALBRIGHT, Tina, Director Human Resources, National Park Medical Center, Hot Springs, AR, p. A47

ALCOCER, Deborah, Chief Information Officer, South Texas Rehabilitation Hospital, Brownsville, TX, p. A661

ALDANA, Eladio, Manager Information Systems, College Hospital Costa Mesa, Costa Mesa, CA, p. A61

ALDER, Cal, Director Information Technology, Rock County Hospital, Bassett, NE, p. A429

ALDERFER, Jennifer, President, Good Samaritan Medical Center, Lafayette, CO, p. A115

ALDERMAN, Una, Chief Executive Officer, Northern Idaho Advanced Care Hospital, Post Falls, ID, p. A192

ALDRED, Linda, Senior Vice President, Texas Children's Hospital, Houston, TX, p. A688

ALDREDGE, Sarah, M.D., Chief Medical Officer, Essentia Health Sandstone, Sandstone, MN, p. A385

ALDRICH, Alan, Chief Financial Officer, Central Montana Medical Center, Lewistown, MT, p. A425

ALDRICH, Jim, Chief Executive Officer, Select Specialty Hospital - Spectrum Health, Grand Rapids, MI, p. A356

ALDRIDGE, Cassandra, Chief Human Resources Officer, Phoebe Sumter Medical Center, Americus, GA, p. A163

ALDRIDGE, Kenneth, M.D., Vice President Medical Affairs, Dch Regional Medical Center, Tuscaloosa, AL, p. A25

ALEEM, Asaf, M.D., Medical Director, Peachford Behavioral Health System, Atlanta, GA, p. A165

ALEXAITIS, Irene, R.N., Vice President of Nursing and Patient Services and Chief Nursing Officer, Uf Health Shands Hospital, Gainesville, FL, p. A139

ALEXANDA, Lisa, M.D., Vice President Medical Affairs, Parrish Medical Center, Titusville, FL, p. A160

ALEXANDER, Alan B., FACHE, Vice President and Administrator, The Medical Center At Caverna, Horse Cave, KY, p. A285

ALEXANDER, Amy, Chief Executive Officer, Ridgeview Institute, Monroe, GA, p. A177

ALEXANDER, Angie, Chief Executive Officer, Allegiance Behavioral Health Centers Of Ruston, Ruston, LA, p. A313

ALEXANDER, April, Director Human Resources, Nyc Health + Hospitals / Metropolitan, New York, NY, p. A491

ALEXANDER, Bobby, R.N., Chief Nursing Officer, Pinnacle Pointe Hospital, Little Rock, AR, p. A49

ALEXANDER, Brenda, System Vice President, Human Resources, Ssm Health St. Mary's Hospital Centralia, Centralia, IL, p. A196

ALEXANDER, Brian, Chief Executive Officer, Sutter Roseville Medical Center, Roseville, CA, p. A89

ALEXANDER, Craig, Chief Operating Officer, Thomas B. Finan Center, Cumberland, MD, p. A329

ALEXANDER, David, Senior Vice President and Chief Financial Officer, St. Joseph's University Medical Center, Paterson, NJ, p. A460

ALEXANDER, Dean, President and Chief Executive Officer, Christus Santa Rosa Health System, San Antonio, TX, p. A711

ALEXANDER, Debra, Chief Information Officer, Safe Haven Hospital Of Treasure Valley, Boise, ID, p. A188

ALEXANDER, Drew, Chief Nursing Officer, Cedar County Memorial Hospital, El Dorado Springs, MO, p. A405

ALEXANDER, Fred, M.D., Medical Director, Kaiser Permanente West Los Angeles Medical Center, Los Angeles, CA, p. A74

ALEXANDER, Jane, Director Facility Administrative Services, Sagamore Children's Psychiatric Center, Dix Hills, NY, p. A482

ALEXANDER, Jeffrey, Chief Executive Officer, Encompass Health Rehabilitation Hospital Of Spring Hill, Brooksville, FL, p. A133

ALEXANDER, Jeremy, Chief Financial Officer, Great River Medical Center, West Burlington, IA, p. A260

ALEXANDER, Josette, Director, Human Resources, Ohiohealth Rehabilitation Hospital, Columbus, OH, p. A536

ALEXANDER, Lisa, Vice President Patient Services and Chief Nursing Officer, University Of Kansas Health System St. Francis Campus, Topeka, KS, p. A277

ALEXANDER, Michael D., MS, Chief Executive Officer, Jamestown Regional Medical Center, Jamestown, TN, p. A640

ALEXANDER-HINES, Joyce, R.N., MSN, Associate Director, Patient Care Services, Fayetteville Veterans Affairs Medical Center, Fayetteville, NC, p. A510

ALEXIADES, Nikolas, Chief Financial Officer, Monmouth Medical Center, Southern Campus, Lakewood, NJ, p. A457

ALFANO, Alan, M.D., Medical Director, Uva Encompass Health Rehabilitation Hospital, Charlottesville, VA, p. A740

ALFANO, Anthony, Vice President Executive Director, Montefiore New Rochelle, New Rochelle, NY, p. A489

ALFORD, Charles, Vice President Financial Services, Vidant Edgecombe Hospital, Tarboro, NC, p. A519

ALFORD, Karla, Chief Information Officer, Greater Regional Medical Center, Creston, IA, p. A247

ALFORD, Michelle, R.N., MSN, Director of Nursing, Washington County Hospital, Chatom, AL, p. A16

ALFRED, Lorrie, Director Human Resources, Southern Surgical Hospital, Slidell, LA, p. A315

ALGER, Steve, Senior Vice President and Chief Financial Officer, Lakes Regional Healthcare, Spirit Lake, IA, p. A258

ALI, Irfan, Director Information Services, Saint Agnes Medical Center, Fresno, CA, p. A65

ALI, Mirza, M.D., Chief of Staff, Wilkes-Barre Veterans Affairs Medical Center, Wilkes-Barre, PA, p. A611

ALI, Muhammad, M.D., Chief Medical Officer, Sanford Tracy Medical Center, Tracy, MN, p. A386

ALI, Syed, M.D., Chief Medical Officer, Aurora Medical Center - Bay Area, Marinette, WI, p. A788
M.D., Chief of Staff, Syracuse Veterans Affairs Medical Center, Syracuse, NY, p. A500

Ali-Khan, Mir, M.D., Medical Director, Canyon Ridge Hospital, Chino, CA, p. A60

ALI-KHAN, Mujtaba, D.O., Chief Medical Officer, Hca Houston Healthcare Conroe, Conroe, TX, p. A665

ALICE, Patricia K., Chief Executive Officer, Arizona Orthopedic Surgical Hospital, Chandler, AZ, p. A30

ALICEA, Luis, Chief Information Officer, Doctors' Center Hospital San Juan, San Juan, PR, p. A810

ALICEA PEREZ, Eneida, Interim Nursing Director, Hospital Buen Samaritano, Aguadilla, PR, p. A805

ALIFF, Sarah, Ph.D., Chief Nursing Officer, Hot Springs County Memorial Hospital, Thermopolis, WY, p. A804

ALKHOULI, Hassan
  M.D., Chief Medical Officer, Garden Grove Hospital And Medical Center, Garden Grove, CA, p. A66
  M.D., Chief Medical Officer, West Anaheim Medical Center, Anaheim, CA, p. A55
  M.D., Medical Director, Huntington Beach Hospital, Huntington Beach, CA, p. A68

ALLA, Vamseedhar, M.D., Director Medical Staff, Connecticut Veterans Home And Hospital, Rocky Hill, CT, p. A125

ALLARD, Joan, Director Human Resources, Adventhealth Heart Of Florida, Davenport, FL, p. A135

ALLARD, Marie, Finance Manager, Ascension Brighton Center For Recovery, Brighton, MI, p. A350

ALLATT, Richard, M.D., Medical Director, Encompass Health Nittany Valley Rehabilitation Hospital, Pleasant Gap. PA, p. A605

ALLDREDGE, Kim, Director Human Resources, Lawrence County Memorial Hospital, Lawrenceville, IL, p. A210

ALLEMAN, Scott, Senior Vice President Patient Care Services and Chief Nursing Officer, Uw Medicine/Valley Medical Center, Renton, WA, p. A763

ALLEMAN, Tara, Chief Financial Officer, Ochsner Medical Center - Kenner, Kenner, LA, p. A304

ALLEN, Audrey, Coordinator Benefits, Dallas County Medical Center, Fordyce, AR, p. A45

ALLEN, Brian, M.D., President Medical Staff, Georgetown Community Hospital, Georgetown, KY, p. A284

ALLEN, Candice, Director of Nursing, Rio Grande Hospital, Del Norte, CO, p. A110

ALLEN, Carolyn
  Chief Financial Officer, Saint Michael's Medical Center, Newark, NJ, p. A460
  Vice President and Chief Financial Officer, Camden Clark Medical Center, Parkersburg, WV, p. A775

ALLEN, Dawn, R.N., Chief Clinical Officer, Carris Health - Redwood, Redwood Falls, MN, p. A383

ALLEN, Devon, M.D., Chief of Medical Staff, Samuel Simmonds Memorial Hospital, Barrow, AK, p. A27

ALLEN, Donald, Chief Operating Officer, Unity Medical & Surgical Hospital, Mishawaka, IN, p. A236

ALLEN, Janel, Senior Vice President and Chief Human Resources Officer, Children's Hospital And Medical Center, Omaha, NE, p. A437

ALLEN, Jason
  Chief Operating Officer, Brook Lane Health Services, Hagerstown, MD, p. A330
  Director Patient Care Services, Brook Lane Health Services, Hagerstown, MD, p. A330

ALLEN, Jean, Human Resources Director, Bleckley Memorial Hospital, Cochran, GA, p. A169

ALLEN, Jennifer, Vice President Human Resources, Plantation General Hospital, Plantation, FL, p. A154

ALLEN, John
  Chief Information Officer, Holzer Medical Center, Gallipolis, OH, p. A541
  Interim Chief Executive Officer, Vice President, Population Health, St. Luke's Regional Medical Center, Boise, ID, p. A189

ALLEN, Judy, Human Resource Specialist, Carl Albert Community Mental Health Center, Mcalester, OK, p. A561

ALLEN, Kandice K., R.N., Chief Executive Officer, Share Medical Center, Alva, OK, p. A555

ALLEN, Karen, R.N., Chief Nursing Officer, Butler Health System, Butler, PA, p. A585

ALLEN, Keith
  Senior Vice President and Chief Human Resources Officer, Froedtert And The Medical College Of Wisconsin Froedtert Hospital, Milwaukee, WI, p. A791
  Senior Vice President and Chief Human Resources Officer, Froedtert Menomonee Falls Hospital, Menomonee Falls, WI, p. A789

ALLEN, Kent, Director Human Resources, Midmichigan Medical Center - West Branch, West Branch, MI, p. A369

ALLEN, Linda, Vice President Human Resources, The Children's Institute Of Pittsburgh, Pittsburgh, PA, p. A603

ALLEN, Lori, Chief Financial Officer, Hospital District 6 - Patterson Health Center, Anthony, KS, p. A261

ALLEN, Lucretia, Director Human Resources, Sweetwater Hospital, Sweetwater, TN, p. A650

ALLEN, Lyndon, Director Information Systems, Canton-Potsdam Hospital, Potsdam, NY, p. A495

ALLEN, Mark, Chief Operating Officer, Marian Regional Medical Center, Santa Maria, CA, p. A97

ALLEN, Mike
  Director Information Services, Adventhealth Shawnee Mission, Shawnee Mission, KS, p. A276
  Director Information Services, Shriners Hospitals For Children-Spokane, Spokane, WA, p. A766
  Director Information Technology, Shriners Hospitals For Children-Salt Lake City, Salt Lake City, UT, p. A732

ALLEN, Myrna, R.N., MS, Chief Operating and Nursing Officer, Martin Luther King, Jr. Community Hospital, Los Angeles, CA, p. A75

ALLEN, Nancy, R.N., MS, Director, Patient Services and Chief Nursing Executive, Eureka Hospital, Eureka, IL, p. A204

ALLEN, Nikki, Patient Care Executive, Sutter Amador Hospital, Jackson, CA, p. A69

ALLEN, Patty, St. John's Vice President Finance, Hshs St. John's Hospital, Springfield, IL, p. A220

ALLEN, R, Senior Vice President Human Resources, University Of Maryland Medical Center, Baltimore, MD, p. A326

ALLEN, Richard
  Chief Executive Officer, Palmdale Regional Medical Center, Palmdale, CA, p. A84
  Chief Executive Officer, Warren General Hospital, Warren, PA, p. A609

ALLEN, Robert
  M.D., Chief Medical Officer, Mercy Hospital Of Folsom, Folsom, CA, p. A64
  President and Chief Executive Officer, Hollywood Presbyterian Medical Center, Los Angeles, CA, p. A74

ALLEN, Timothy, Vice President Human Resources, United Hospital Center, Bridgeport, WV, p. A770

ALLEN, Timothy J.
  FACHE, Chief Executive Officer, Leonard J. Chabert Medical Center, Houma, LA, p. A303
  FACHE, Chief Executive Officer, Ochsner St. Anne General Hospital, Raceland, LA, p. A313

ALLEN, Vicki
  R.N., MS, Vice President Patient Care Services and Chief Nursing Officer, Harnett Health System, Dunn, NC, p. A508
  Chief Financial Officer, Chicot Memorial Medical Center, Lake Village, AR, p. A48

ALLEN, Wayne, Interim Chief Executive Officer, Mendocino Coast District Hospital, Fort Bragg, CA, p. A64

ALLEN, Zac, CPA, Chief Financial Officer, Floyd Cherokee Medical Center, Centre, AL, p. A16

ALLEN-DAVIS, Jandel, President and Chief Executive Officer, Craig Hospital, Englewood, CO, p. A112

ALLENDE RUIZ, Luis R., Chief Executive Officer, Encompass Health Rehabilitation Hospital Of Miami, Cutler Bay, FL, p. A135

ALLENSWORTH, Ed, M.D., Medical Director, Saint Francis Hospital Vinita, Vinita, OK, p. A571

ALLENSWORTH, Kenneth W., Interim Medical Center Director, Martinsburg Veterans Affairs Medical Center, Martinsburg, WV, p. A774

ALLEX, Carnie, Administrator, Carris Health - Redwood, Redwood Falls, MN, p. A383

ALLEY, David, Chief Financial Officer, Starr Regional Medical Center, Athens, TN, p. A634

ALLEY, John L., Chief Executive Officer, Woodlawn Hospital, Rochester, IN, p. A240

ALLEY, Jon, D.O., President Medical Staff, Cameron Memorial Community Hospital, Angola, IN, p. A223

ALLEY, Steve, M.D., Chief of Staff, Crosbyton Clinic Hospital, Crosbyton, TX, p. A666

ALLGOOD, Libby, Chief Financial Officer, Kittitas Valley Healthcare, Ellensburg, WA, p. A757

ALLICON, Keary, Vice President Finance and Chief Financial Officer, Baystate Wing Hospital, Palmer, MA, p. A343

ALLINSON, Randy, R.N., Chief Nursing Officer, Central Valley Medical Center, Nephi, UT, p. A729

ALLISON, Lorraine, Human Resource Partner, Peacehealth Peace Island Medical Center, Friday Harbor, WA, p. A758

ALLISON, Steve, Director Human Resources, Logan County Hospital, Oakley, KS, p. A272

ALLISON, William, Senior Vice President and Chief Operating Officer, Administration, Mount Sinai South Nassau, Oceanside, NY, p. A493

ALLMAN, Rex, M.D., President Medical Staff, Pulaski Memorial Hospital, Winamac, IN, p. A242

ALLORE, Gary, President, Mercy Health Hackley Campus, Muskegon, MI, p. A362

ALLPHIN, Allan, M.D., Chief of Staff, Mercy Hospital Springfield, Springfield, MO, p. A419

ALLPORT, Jeff, Vice President, Chief Information Officer, Valley Presbyterian Hospital, Van Nuys, CA, p. A103

ALLRED, Al, Chief Financial Officer, Adventhealth New Smyrna Beach, New Smyrna Beach, FL, p. A149

ALLRED, B, M.D., President Medical Staff, Jordan Valley Medical Center, West Jordan, UT, p. A734

ALLRED, Lowell, M.D., Chief of Staff, Columbia Basin Hospital, Ephrata, WA, p. A758

ALLRED, William, M.D., Vice President Medical Affairs, St. John Medical Center, Tulsa, OK, p. A571

ALLSOP, Brian, Director Human Resources, Central Valley Medical Center, Nephi, UT, p. A729

ALLSTOTT, Patti, Administrative Coordinator Human Resources and Grant Writer, Pioneer Memorial Hospital, Heppner, OR, p. A575

ALLUSON, Valerie, M.D., Chief Medical Officer, Hackensack Meridian Health Mountainside Medical Center, Montclair, NJ, p. A458

ALMAUHY, Deborah, R.N., Chief Nursing Officer, Emory Rehabilitation Hospital, Atlanta, GA, p. A164

ALMEIDA, Sergio, Director Information Systems, Hca Houston Healthcare West, Houston, TX, p. A686

ALMEIDA-SUAREZ, Mario, M.D., Chief of Staff, Larkin Community Hospital-South Miami Campus, South Miami, FL, p. A157

ALMENDINGER, J Todd., President and Chief Executive Officer, Magruder Memorial Hospital, Port Clinton, OH, p. A548

ALMETER, Connie, Chief Nursing Officer, Wyoming County Community Hospital, Warsaw, NY, p. A501

ALMETER, Marilyn, Chief Nursing Officer, United Memorial Medical Center, Batavia, NY, p. A475

ALMODAVAR, William, M.D., Director Medical, First Hospital Panamericano, Cidra, PR, p. A807

ALMODOVAR, Gustavo, Executive Director, Hospital De La Concepcion, San German, PR, p. A809

ALMOHAMMED, Salah, Chief of Staff, Ut Health Carthage, Carthage, TX, p. A663

ALO, Kathleen, Chief Nursing Officer, Mammoth Hospital, Mammoth Lakes, CA, p. A77

ALONSO, Gwen, Chief Nursing Officer, Adventhealth Zephyrhills, Zephyrhills, FL, p. A162

ALONSO, Jose', M.D., Medical Director, San Juan Capestrano Hospital, San Juan, PR, p. A811

ALONZO, Patti, Manager Human Resources, Pacifica Hospital Of The Valley, Sun Valley, CA, p. A100

ALPERT, Jeffrey, M.D., Medical Director, Wichita County Health Center, Leoti, KS, p. A269

ALPERT, Len, Director Human Resources, Larkin Community Hospital Behavioral Health Services, Hollywood, FL, p. A140

ALRASHEDY, Farhad, M.D., Chief Medical Officer, Ferry County Memorial Hospital, Republic, WA, p. A763

ALSADON, Danielle, Clinic/Hospital Manager, Kenmare Community Hospital, Kenmare, ND, p. A524

ALSIP, Bryan, M.D., Executive Vice President, Chief Medical Officer, University Health System, San Antonio, TX, p. A714

ALSTAD, Nancy, Director Human Resources, Fort Healthcare, Fort Atkinson, WI, p. A784

ALT, Melinda, Chief Financial Officer, Audubon County Memorial Hospital And Clinics, Audubon, IA, p. A243

ALTENBURGER, Andy, Chief Information Officer, Johnson Regional Medical Center, Clarksville, AR, p. A43

ALTENDORF, Amanda, Chief Human Resources and Quality Management, Red River Behavioral Health System, Grand Forks, ND, p. A524

ALTHOEN, David, Director Financial Planning and Analysis, Forest Health Medical Center, Ypsilanti, MI, p. A370

ALTHOUSE, Douglas, Chief Medical Staff, Kearney County Health Services, Minden, NE, p. A435

ALTMAN, Alexander Chief Financial Officer, Union County General Hospital, Clayton, NM, p. A468

ALTMAN, Brett, FACHE, Chief Executive Officer, Cass County Health System, Atlantic, IA, p. A243

ALTMAN, Deana, Interim Chief Nursing Officer, Harney District Hospital, Burns, OR, p. A574

ALTMAN, Harold, M.D., Chief Medical Officer, Acmh Hospital, Kittanning, PA, p. A593

ALTMILLER, Steve, President and Chief Executive Officer, Camden Clark Medical Center, Parkersburg, WV, p. A775

ALTOM, Andy, President and Chief Executive Officer, Methodist Behavioral Hospital Of Arkansas, Maumelle, AR, p. A50

ALTOSE, Murray, M.D., Chief of Staff, Louis Stokes Cleveland Veterans Affairs Medical Center, Cleveland, OH, p. A534

ALTSHULER, Keith, President and Chief Administrative Officer, Fort Sanders Regional Medical Center, Knoxville, TN, p. A641

ALUISE, Tony, Chief Executive Officer, Three Gables Surgery Center, Proctorville, OH, p. A548

ALURI, Bapu, M.D., Chief Medical Officer, Yuma Rehabilitation Hospital, A Partnership Of Encompass Health And Yrmc, Yuma, AZ, p. A41

ALVARADO, Felicita E., Administrator, Hospital Psiquiatrico Correccional, San Juan, PR, p. A810

ALVARADO, Rafael, Chief Executive Officer, Dr. Pila's Hospital, Ponce, PR, p. A809

ALVARADO, Ramona, Interim Manager Human Resources, Adventist Health Reedley, Reedley, CA, p. A88

ALVAREZ, Dena, R.N., COO & Chief Compliance Officer, Brodstone Memorial Hospital, Superior, NE, p. A440

ALVAREZ, Janie, Accounting Director, Cornerstone Regional Hospital, Edinburg, TX, p. A673

ALVAREZ, Jose, M.D., Chief Medical Staff, Circles Of Care, Melbourne, FL, p. A145

ALVAREZ, Maria, M.D., Chief of Staff, Sheridan Community Hospital, Sheridan, MI, p. A366

ALVAREZ, Valerie, Executive Assistant, Adventist Health Reedley, Reedley, CA, p. A88

ALVEY, Raymond, Chief Financial Officer, Ssm Health Saint Louis University Hospital, Saint Louis, MO, p. A417

ALVIS, Kimberly, CPA, Chief Financial Officer, Kirby Medical Center, Monticello, IL, p. A212

ALWARD, Dale, Chief Executive Officer, Twin County Regional Healthcare, Galax, VA, p. A743

ALWIN-POPP, Sue, Chief Clinical Officer, Edgerton Hospital And Health Services, Edgerton, WI, p. A783

ALWINE, Steven, Chief Executive Officer, Highlands Rehabilitation Hospital, El Paso, TX, p. A675

ALZEIN, Bashar, M.D., President Medical Staff, Illini Community Hospital, Pittsfield, IL, p. A217

AMADO, Mitchell, Senior Vice President Finance and Chief Financial Officer, Glens Falls Hospital, Glens Falls, NY, p. A484

AMANTEA, Paul, Director Finance, Uh Geauga Medical Center, Chardon, OH, p. A531

AMARANTOS, Stacie, Chief Operating Officer, Catalina Island Medical Center, Avalon, CA, p. A56

AMBROSE, Sherie, Chief Nurse Executive, Sequoia Hospital, Redwood City, CA, p. A88

AMBROSIANI, Michael, Chief Financial Officer, Knox Community Hospital, Mount Vernon, OH, p. A546

AMBROSINI, Joseph, Director Human Resources, Olympia Medical Center, Los Angeles, CA, p. A75

AMEEN, David J., Interim President and Chief Executive Officer, St. Francis Memorial Hospital, West Point, NE, p. A440

AMENT, Rick, Medical Center Director, Jesse Brown Veterans Affairs Medical Center, Chicago, IL, p. A198

AMERSON, Jeff, Director Information System, West Florida Hospital, Pensacola, FL, p. A154

AMES, Becky, Chief Executive Officer, Medical Center Of Southeast Texas, Beaumont, TX, p. A658

AMES, Lance, Chief Executive Officer, South Texas Health System, Edinburg, TX, p. A674

AMIN, Saad, Medical Director Hospital, Kindred Hospital-Greensboro, Greensboro, NC, p. A511

AMITRANO, Catherine, MSN, R.N., Vice President and Chief Nursing Officer, Christus Santa Rosa Hospital - San Marcos, San Marcos, TX, p. A714

AMMONS, Angela, Administrator, Clinch Memorial Hospital, Homerville, GA, p. A174

AMMONS, Eric, President, Mercy Hospital Jefferson, Festus, MO, p. A406

AMODO, Mitch, Vice President and Chief Financial Officer, Garnet Health Medical Center - Catskills, Middletown, NY, p. A488

AMOH, Eric, Chief Executive Officer, Behavioral Hospital Of Bellaire, Houston, TX, p. A684

AMONS, Gene, R.N., Chief Executive Officer, Oakdale Community Hospital, Oakdale, LA, p. A312

AMOROSE, Carl, Vice President Finance, Norton Hospital, Louisville, KY, p. A288

AMOROSO, Mitze, Chief Information Officer, Terence Cardinal Cooke Health Care Center, New York, NY, p. A492

AMOS, John R., President and Chief Executive Officer, Yavapai Regional Medical Center, Prescott, AZ, p. A37

AMOS, Michael, Chief Operating Officer, Lakewood Regional Medical Center, Lakewood, CA, p. A71

AMOS, Robert, Vice President and Chief Financial Officer, Valley Health - Winchester Medical Center, Winchester, VA, p. A754

AMOX, Mark, Chief Operating Officer, Sunrise Hospital And Medical Center, Las Vegas, NV, p. A444

AMSBERRY, Shelly, Director of Nursing, Jennie M. Melham Memorial Medical Center, Broken Bow, NE, p. A430

AMSTUTZ, Charles, Director of Information Technology, Cascade Medical Center, Leavenworth, WA, p. A760

AMSTUTZ, Terry Lee., FACHE, Chief Executive Officer, Mcgehee Hospital, Mcgehee, AR, p. A50

AMYX, Maleigha, Chief Information Officer, Rockcastle Regional Hospital And Respiratory Care Center, Mount Vernon, KY, p. A291

ANASTASI, Frank, Chief Financial Officer, Pennsylvania Hospital, Philadelphia, PA, p. A601

ANAYA, Sandra J., R.N., Chief Executive Officer, Palo Verde Hospital, Blythe, CA, p. A58

ANCHONDO, Laura, Administrator Human Resources, Kindred Hospital El Paso, El Paso, TX, p. A675

ANCZAK, Deb, Interim Chief Executive Officer, Livingston Healthcare, Livingston, MT, p. A426

ANDERER, Tammy, Acting President, Geisinger Jersey Shore Hospital, Jersey Shore, PA, p. A593

ANDERS, Anna, R.N., MSN, Vice President and Chief Nursing Officer, Carson Tahoe Health, Carson City, NV, p. A441

ANDERS, Robert, Chief Financial Officer, Ouachita County Medical Center, Camden, AR, p. A43

ANDERS JR, JamesAdministrator and Chief Operating Officer, Kennedy Krieger Institute, Baltimore, MD, p. A324

ANDERSEN, Connie, R.N., MS, Chief Nursing Officer, Sarasota Memorial Health Care System, Sarasota, FL, p. A157

ANDERSEN, Donia, Director of Nursing, Centennial Peaks Hospital, Louisville, CO, p. A116

ANDERSEN, Frank, Interim Chief Medical Officer, Providence Regional Medical Center Everett, Everett, WA, p. A758

ANDERSEN, Janet
Chief Financial Officer, Ut Health Pittsburg, Pittsburg, TX, p. A706
Chief Financial Officer, Ut Health Quitman, Quitman, TX, p. A708

ANDERSEN, John, Manager Information Systems, Astria Sunnyside Hospital, Sunnyside, WA, p. A766

ANDERSEN, Michelle, R.N., Chief Nursing Officer, Manning Regional Healthcare Center, Manning, IA, p. A253

ANDERSEN, Sue
Chief Executive Officer, Arroyo Grande Community Hospital, Arroyo Grande, CA, p. A56
Vice President and Service Area and Chief Financial Officer, Marian Regional Medical Center, Santa Maria, CA, p. A97

ANDERSEN, Tracy, Chief Information Officer, St. Mary's Regional Medical Center, Enid, OK, p. A559

ANDERSEN, Travis, Chief Executive Officer, Ascension Columbia St. Mary's Hospital Milwaukee, Milwaukee, WI, p. A790

ANDERSEN, Wendy, Director Human Resources, Eastern Idaho Regional Medical Center, Idaho Falls, ID, p. A190

ANDERSON, Alison, Chief Nursing Officer, Select Specialty Hospital-Sioux Falls, Sioux Falls, SD, p. A631

ANDERSON, Allen, Administrator, Avera Tyler Hospital, Tyler, MN, p. A387

ANDERSON, Angela, Manager Human Resource, Kansas Spine & Specialty Hospital, Wichita, KS, p. A279

ANDERSON, Angie, Director Information Technology, Crawford County Memorial Hospital, Denison, IA, p. A248

ANDERSON, Brad
Chief Executive Officer, Rehabilitation Hospital Of Wisconsin, Waukesha, WI, p. A798
Chief Financial Officer, Community Memorial Hospital, Cloquet, MN, p. A374

ANDERSON, Braden, Chief Executive Officer, Caprock Hospital, Bryan, TX, p. A661

ANDERSON, Brady, Chief Human Resource Officer, Utah Valley Hospital, Provo, UT, p. A731

ANDERSON, Brian
Chief Financial Officer, Adventist Health Simi Valley, Simi Valley, CA, p. A98
Chief Financial Officer, Capital Medical Center, Olympia, WA, p. A761

ANDERSON, Calandra, Vice President Patient Care and Chief Nursing Officer, Mclaren Oakland, Pontiac, MI, p. A364

ANDERSON, Charles, M.D., Chief Medical Officer, Desert Regional Medical Center, Palm Springs, CA, p. A83

ANDERSON, Cherri, Chief Nursing Officer, Banner Behavioral Health Hospital - Scottsdale, Scottsdale, AZ, p. A38

ANDERSON, Christine, Chief Nursing Officer and Vice President of Patient Care Services, Lincolnhealth, Damariscotta, ME, p. A320

ANDERSON, Conde, M.D., Chief of Staff, Detar Healthcare System, Victoria, TX, p. A723

ANDERSON, Craig, Director Management Information Systems, River Bend Hospital, West Lafayette, IN, p. A242

ANDERSON, Dale, Chief Executive Officer, Sabine Medical Center, Many, LA, p. A308

ANDERSON, Dana, R.N., Administrator, Long-Term Acute Care Hospital, Mosaic Life Care At St. Joseph, Saint Joseph, MO, p. A415

ANDERSON, Darla, Chief Financial Officer, Ridgeview Sibley Medical Center, Arlington, MN, p. A372

ANDERSON, Dave

FACHE, Vice President Administration, Atrium Health Union, Monroe, NC, p. A514

FACHE, Vice President and Administrator, Atrium Health Anson, Wadesboro, NC, p. A519

ANDERSON, David, Chief Executive Officer, Jackson Purchase Medical Center, Mayfield, KY, p. A290

ANDERSON, Derek, Executive Director, Northern Westchester Hospital, Mount Kisco, NY, p. A488

ANDERSON, DeVry, Chief Medical Officer, St. David's South Austin Medical Center, Austin, TX, p. A656

ANDERSON, Donna
R.N., MSN, Vice President Clinical Support and Chief Nursing Officer, Bassett Medical Center, Cooperstown, NY, p. A481
R.N., Chief Nursing Officer, Anmed Health Cannon, Pickens, SC, p. A623

ANDERSON, Edward, Chief Executive Officer, Ed Fraser Memorial Hospital, Macclenny, FL, p. A144

ANDERSON, Edwin, M.D., Chief of Staff and Chief Medical Officer, Bigfork Valley Hospital, Bigfork, MN, p. A372

ANDERSON, Gaynell, M.D., Medical Director, Ssm Health St. Anthony Hospital - Shawnee, Shawnee, OK, p. A568

ANDERSON, Gina, Human Resources Officer, Riverview Regional Medical Center, Carthage, TN, p. A635

ANDERSON, Heidi
Chief Executive Officer, Forks Community Hospital, Forks, WA, p. A758
Chief Nursing Officer, Arbor Health, Morton Hospital, Morton, WA, p. A760

ANDERSON, Jay
President, Northwestern Medicine Kishwaukee Hospital, Dekalb, IL, p. A202
President, Northwestern Medicine Valley West Hospital, Sandwich, IL, p. A219

ANDERSON, Jeremy, M.D., Medical Staff President, Good Shepherd Health Care System, Hermiston, OR, p. A576

ANDERSON, Joann, President and Chief Executive Officer, Southeastern Health, Lumberton, NC, p. A514

ANDERSON, John D., FACHE, Interim Chief Executive Officer, Highlands Medical Center, Scottsboro, AL, p. A24

ANDERSON, John G., FACHE, President and Chief Executive Officer, Anderson Regional Health System, Meridian, MS, p. A397

ANDERSON, Jonathan, Medical Director, Western State Hospital, Staunton, VA, p. A752

ANDERSON, Kathleen, Director, Acute Clinical Systems, Prisma Health Laurens County Hospital, Clinton, SC, p. A617

ANDERSON, Kenneth, M.D., Vice President and Chief Medical Officer, Baptist Health Louisville, Louisville, KY, p. A287

ANDERSON, Kimball S., FACHE, Chief Executive Officer, Timpanogos Regional Hospital, Orem, UT, p. A730

ANDERSON, Kristin, Director, Human Resources, California Hospital Medical Center, Los Angeles, CA, p. A73

ANDERSON, Leslie, Chief Operating Officer, Cary Medical Center, Caribou, ME, p. A320

ANDERSON, Libby, Chief Financial Officer, Satanta District Hospital And Long Term Care, Satanta, KS, p. A276

ANDERSON, Louis, Chief Financial Officer, Mcleod Health Cheraw, Cheraw, SC, p. A617

ANDERSON, Lucia, Senior Vice President Operations and Chief Nurse Executive, Lake Region Healthcare, Fergus Falls, MN, p. A376

ANDERSON, Mark
Chief Financial Officer, North Oaks Medical Center, Hammond, LA, p. A302
Chief Financial Officer, North Oaks Rehabilitation Hospital, Hammond, LA, p. A302
Chief Financial Officer, Sovah Health-Danville, Danville, VA, p. A741

ANDERSON, Michael
M.D., Chief Medical Officer, St. Josep. Medical Center, Tacoma, WA, p. A767
M.D., President, Ucsf Benioff Children's Hospital Oakland, Oakland, CA, p. A82
Ph.D., Chief Operating Officer, Metropolitan St. Louis Psychiatric Center, Saint Louis, MO, p. A416

ANDERSON, Mickey, M.D., Vice President Medical Affairs, Chi Flaget Memorial Hospital, Bardstown, KY, p. A280

ANDERSON, Patricia, Chief Nursing Officer, Riverview Regional Medical Center, Carthage, TN, p. A635

ANDERSON, Patrick
Chief Information Officer and Senior Vice President, Hoag Memorial Hospital Presbyterian, Newport Beach, CA, p. A81
Chief Information Officer, Memorial Medical Center, Modesto, CA, p. A79

ANDERSON, Paula, Administrative Director Human Resources, Endless Mountain Health Systems, Montrose, PA, p. A597

ANDERSON, Rhena
Chief Nursing Officer, Nexus Specialty Hospital The Woodlands, The Woodlands, TX, p. A720
Chief Nursing Officer, Nexus Specialty Hospital, Shenandoah, TX, p. A715

ANDERSON, Rhonda
Executive Vice President Finance and Chief Financial Officer, Ascension Columbia St. Mary's Hospital Milwaukee, Milwaukee, WI, p. A790
Executive Vice President Finance and Chief Financial Officer, Ascension Columbia St. Mary's Hospital Ozaukee, Mequon, WI, p. A790
Executive Vice President Finance and Chief Financial Officer, Ascension Columbia St. Mary's Milwaukee Hospital, Milwaukee, WI, p. A790

ANDERSON, Rick, M.D., Senior Vice President and Chief Medical Officer, Tmc Healthcare, Tucson, AZ, p. A41

ANDERSON, Rob J., Chief Executive Officer, The Hospitals Of Providence Sierra Campus, El Paso, TX, p. A676

ANDERSON, Robert, Interim Chief Financial Officer, Alameda Hospital, Alameda, CA, p. A55

ANDERSON, Robert G. Jr, President, Osf Saint Francis Medical Center, Peoria, IL, p. A217

ANDERSON, Rohan, Chief Information Officer, Doctors Memorial Hospital, Bonifay, FL, p. A132

ANDERSON, Rosemary, Administrator, Ccc At Pineview Hospital, Lakeside, AZ, p. A33

ANDERSON, Sandy, Interim President, Hshs Sacred Heart Hospital, Eau Claire, WI, p. A783

ANDERSON, Scott, Chief Medical Officer, Banner Del E. Webb Medical Center, Sun City West, AZ, p. A39

ANDERSON, Sharla, Chief Executive Officer, Christus Trinity Mother Frances Rehabilitation Hospital, A Partner Of Encompass Health, Tyler, TX, p. A721

ANDERSON, Shawn D., Chief Executive Officer, Houlton Regional Hospital, Houlton, ME, p. A321

ANDERSON, Sims, Manager Facility Automation, Terrell State Hospital, Terrell, TX, p. A719

ANDERSON, Stephanie, Executive Vice President and Chief Operating Officer, Woman's Hospital, Baton Rouge, LA, p. A298

ANDERSON, Stephen, M.D., Chief Medical Officer, Plymouth Medical Center, Plymouth, IN, p. A239

ANDERSON, Steven, Chief Executive Officer, University Of Kansas Health System St. Francis Campus, Topeka, KS, p. A277

ANDERSON, Susan, Director Information Systems, Texas Health Presbyterian Hospital Plano, Plano, TX, p. A707

ANDERSON, Suzanne
Nurse Administrator, Intermountain Medical Center, Murray, UT, p. A729
President, Virginia Mason Medical Center, Seattle, WA, p. A765

ANDERSON, Terry, R.N., Director of Nursing Services, Ccm Health, Montevideo, MN, p. A381

ANDERSON, Thomas
M.D., Vice President Medical Affairs, Wellspan Chambersburg Hospital, Chambersburg, PA, p. A586
M.D., Vice President Medical Affairs, Wellspan Waynesboro Hospital, Waynesboro, PA, p. A610
Vice President Medical Affairs, Lakeview Hospital, Stillwater, MN, p. A386

ANDERSON, Traci, Chief Financial Officer, Memorial Hospital, Seminole, TX, p. A714

ANDERSON, Valerie, Chief Nursing Officer, Select Specialty Hospital-Tri Cities, Bristol, TN, p. A634

ANDERSON, William, Medical Director, Rosebud Health Care Center, Forsyth, MT, p. A423

ANDERT, Nancy, Director Human Resources, Murray County Medical Center, Slayton, MN, p. A386

ANDERTON, Scott, Chief Financial Officer, Coliseum Medical Centers, Macon, GA, p. A176

ANDRADA, Sally, Chief Information Officer, Los Alamitos Medical Center, Los Alamitos, CA, p. A73

ANDRADE, Marisa, Controller, Southern Inyo Healthcare District, Lone Pine, CA, p. A72

ANDRAE, Andrea, Chief Financial Officer, St. Luke's - Lehighton Campus, Lehighton, PA, p. A595

ANDRE, Katelyn, Human Resource Coordinator, Select Specialty Hospital-Macomb County, Mount Clemens, MI, p. A362

ANDREAS, Ginger, Coordinator Personnel and Credentialing, El Camp. Memorial Hospital, El Campo, TX, p. A674

ANDREAS, Lori, Chief Executive Officer and Administrator, Appleton Area Health Services, Appleton, MN, p. A371

ANDREASEN, Raymond, M.D., Chief Medical Officer-Inpatient, California Medical Facility, Vacaville, CA, p. A102

ANDRES, Chad, Chief Information Officer, Desert View Hospital, Pahrump, NV, p. A445

ANDRES, Elizabeth, Director Human Resources, Atascadero State Hospital, Atascadero, CA, p. A56

ANDRES, Leonidas, M.D., Chief of Staff, Riceland Medical Center, Winnie, TX, p. A726

ANDRESEN, Daniel, Chief information Officer, Mercy Medical Center Merced, Merced, CA, p. A78

ANDREW, Sigrid, Director, James E. Van Zandt Veterans Affairs Medical Center, Altoona, PA, p. A584

ANDREWS, Callie, President, Wellstar Cobb Hospital, Austell, GA, p. A166

ANDREWS, Carolle, Vice President, Interim Human Resources Officer, Uconn, John Dempsey Hospital, Farmington, CT, p. A122

ANDREWS, Charles, Director Information Technology, West Springs Hospital, Grand Junction, CO, p. A113

ANDREWS, David, Manager Information Systems, Chicot Memorial Medical Center, Lake Village, AR, p. A48

ANDREWS, Fred, Director of Nursing, North Shore Health, Grand Marais, MN, p. A377

ANDREWS, Jade, Chief Financial Officer, Dallas Medical Center, Dallas, TX, p. A668

ANDREWS, Jim, Chief Financial Officer, North Okaloosa Medical Center, Crestview, FL, p. A135

ANDREWS, John, M.D., Chief of Staff, Ut Health Tyler, Tyler, TX, p. A722

ANDREWS, Kathy, Chief Financial Officer, Kindred Hospital-Philadelphia, Philadelphia, PA, p. A601

ANDREWS, Lisa, Director Human Resources, Lancaster Rehabilitation Hospital, Lancaster, PA, p. A594

ANDREWS, Michael, Coordinator Information Systems, Harlan County Health System, Alma, NE, p. A429

ANDREWS, Mike, Associate Administrator and Chief Operating Officer, Och Regional Medical Center, Starkville, MS, p. A400

ANDREWS, Paul
Chief Executive Officer, The Brook At Dupont, Louisville, KY, p. A288
Chief Executive Officer, The Brook Hospital - Kmi, Louisville, KY, p. A288

ANDREWS, Rebecca, Chief Financial Officer, Vibra Hospital Of Northern California, Redding, CA, p. A87

ANDREWS, Ryan, M.D., Chief Medical Officer, Aspirus Wausau Hospital, Inc., Wausau, WI, p. A798

ANDREWS, Steve, Chief Financial Officer, Three Rivers Health, Three Rivers, MI, p. A368

ANDREWS, Sue, Chief Financial Officer, O'Connor Hospital, Delhi, NY, p. A482

ANDREWS, Terri, Director Information Technology, Alamance Regional Medical Center, Burlington, NC, p. A506

ANDRO, Ronald J., R.N., MS, President and Chief Executive Officer, West Penn Hospital, Pittsburgh, PA, p. A605

ANDRUS, Helen
Chief Financial Officer, Providence Mount Carmel Hospital, Colville, WA, p. A757
Chief Financial Officer, Providence St. Joseph's Hospital, Chewelah, WA, p. A756
Chief Financial Officer, St. Luke's Rehabilitation Institute, Spokane, WA, p. A766

ANDRUS, Jonathon, Chief Executive Officer, Fairchild Medical Center, Yreka, CA, p. A106

ANDURSKY, John S., President and Chief Executive Officer, Highlands Hospital, Connellsville, PA, p. A587

ANFINSON, Julie, Director Human Resources, Mercyone Siouxland Medical Center, Sioux City, IA, p. A258

ANGELI, Maribeth, Chief Nursing Officer, Berwick Hospital Center, Berwick, PA, p. A584

ANGELL, Deborah, Chief Financial Officer, Syracuse Veterans Affairs Medical Center, Syracuse, NY, p. A500

ANGELL, Nancy, Associate Administrator Personnel, Sagamore Children's Psychiatric Center, Dix Hills, NY, p. A482

ANGELO, Gregory, Chief Fiscal Program, James J. Peters Veterans Affairs Medical Center, Bronx, NY, p. A476

ANGELO, Thomas, Chief Executive Officer, Centra Southside Community Hospital, Farmville, VA, p. A742

ANGELUCCI, Patricia, MS, R.N., Director Patient Care Services, Thedacare Medical Center-Shawano, Shawano, WI, p. A795

ANGERAMI, Deborah
Chief Operating Officer, Health First Community Hospitals, Health First Cap. Canaveral Hospital, Cocoa Beach, FL, p. A134
Chief Operating Officer, Health First Community Hospitals, Health First Palm Bay Hospital, Palm Bay, FL, p. A152
Chief Operating Officer, Health First Viera Hospital, Melbourne, FL, p. A145

ANGERMEIER, Elizabeth, Director of Nursing, Evansville Psychiatric Children Center, Evansville, IN, p. A227

ANGLE, Mary Ann, R.N., FACHE, Chief Nursing Officer, Tristar Summit Medical Center, Hermitage, TN, p. A639

ANGLIM, John, Human Resources Client Manager, Providence Seaside Hospital, Seaside, OR, p. A581

ANGLIN, Jason, Chief Executive Officer, Memorial Medical Center, Port Lavaca, TX, p. A707

ANGLIN, Kristine, Human Resources Manager, Willow Springs Center, Reno, NV, p. A446

ANHALT, Jacqueline, Chief Nursing Officer, Theda Care Medical Center - Wild Rose, Wild Rose, WI, p. A799

ANMUTH, Craig, M.D., Medical Director, Bacharach Institute For Rehabilitation, Pomona, NJ, p. A461

ANNECHARICO, Mary
System Vice President and Chief Information Officer, Henry Ford Hospital, Detroit, MI, p. A353
System Vice President and Chief Information Officer, Henry Ford West Bloomfield Hospital, West Bloomfield, MI, p. A369
System Vice President and Chief Information Officer, Henry Ford Wyandotte Hospital, Wyandotte, MI, p. A370

ANNESSER, Sue, Director Information Systems, Freeman Neosho Hospital, Neosho, MO, p. A412

ANSALDO, Luanne, Chief Operating Officer, Aventura Hospital And Medical Center, Aventura, FL, p. A131

ANSHUTZ, Margie, Chief Development Officer, Hamilton Center, Terre Haute, IN, p. A241

ANSI, Azena, Manager Health Information Management, Horizon Specialty Hospital, Las Vegas, NV, p. A443

ANSLEY, Pamela, Director Finance, Sutter Center For Psychiatry, Sacramento, CA, p. A90

ANTCZAK, Brett, Chief Executive Officer, Palo Alto County Health System, Emmetsburg, IA, p. A249

ANTCZAK, Kenneth, Vice President Human Resources, St. Mary Mercy Hospital, Livonia, MI, p. A360

ANTES, John, President, Missouri Baptist Medical Center, Saint Louis, MO, p. A416

ANTHONY, Ashley, R.N., Chief Executive Officer, Delta Memorial Hospital, Dumas, AR, p. A44

ANTHONY, Harry, M.D., Chief Medical Officer, Tidalhealth Nanticoke, Seaford, DE, p. A128

ANTHONY, Jean, R.N., President and Chief Executive Officer, Hills & Dales General Hospital, Cass City, MI, p. A350

ANTHONY, Kim, Director Human Resources, Burke Medical Center, Waynesboro, GA, p. A183

ANTHONY, Mark, Executive Vice President and Chief Operating Officer, Ascension Borgess Hospital, Kalamazoo, MI, p. A359

ANTHONY, Michelle, Chief Nursing Officer, Encompass Health Rehabilitation Hospital Of Richmond, Richmond, VA, p. A750

ANTHONY, Paula
Vice President Information Services, Ut Health Pittsburg, Pittsburg, TX, p. A706
Vice President Information Services, Ut Health Specialty Hospital, Tyler, TX, p. A722
Vice President Information Services, Ut Health Tyler, Tyler, TX, p. A722

ANTILL, Theunette, Chief Financial Officer, Thibodaux Regional Health System, Thibodaux, LA, p. A316

ANTINELLI, Mark, Manager Human Resources, Syracuse Veterans Affairs Medical Center, Syracuse, NY, p. A500

ANTINORI, James, M.D., Chief of Staff, Mountain West Medical Center, Tooele, UT, p. A733

ANTLE, Sue, Director of Nursing, Casey County Hospital, Liberty, KY, p. A287

ANTOINE, Greg, M.D., Chief of Staff, Fayetteville Veterans Affairs Medical Center, Fayetteville, NC, p. A510

ANTON, Lourdes, Director Human Resources, Larkin Community Hospital-Palm Springs Campus, Hialeah, FL, p. A139

ANTONACCI, Amy, MSN, R.N., Vice President Nursing Services, Alliance Community Hospital, Alliance, OH, p. A527

ANTONECCHIA, Paul, M.D., Vice President Medical Affairs and Chief Medical Officer, St. John's Riverside Hospital, Yonkers, NY, p. A503

ANTONSON, Pete, Chief Executive Officer, Northwood Deaconess Health Center, Northwood, ND, p. A525

ANTONUCCI, Lawrence
M.D., President and Chief Executive Officer, Cap. Coral Hospital, Cap. Coral, FL, p. A134
M.D., President and Chief Executive Officer, Gulf Coast Medical Center, Fort Myers, FL, p. A138
M.D., President and Chief Executive Officer, Lee Memorial Hospital, Fort Myers, FL, p. A138

ANTRUM, Sheila, R.N., President, Ucsf Medical Center, San Francisco, CA, p. A94

ANUSZKIEWICZ, Dawn, Chief Operating Officer, Reading Hospital, West Reading, PA, p. A610

ANWAR, Muhammad, M.D., Chief Medical Officer, Encino Hospital Medical Center, Encino, CA, p. A63

ANYEBE, Abiola, Interim Chief Executive Officer, Kindred Hospital-San Antonio, San Antonio, TX, p. A711

ANZALDUA, Brandon, Chief Financial Officer, Riverside Medical Center, Franklinton, LA, p. A302

ANZURES, Rosey, Acting Chief Financial Officer, Central Texas Veterans Health Care System, Temple, TX, p. A719

APIKI, Zessica, Accountant, Molokai General Hospital, Kaunakakai, HI, p. A186

APLAND, Wendy, Interim Chief Financial Officer, Peacehealth Sacred Heart Medical Center University District, Eugene, OR, p. A575

APODACA, Mark, Chief Executive Officer, Kindred Hospital Paramount, Paramount, CA, p. A84

APOLINAR, Adam, Chief Nursing Officer, Uvalde Memorial Hospital, Uvalde, TX, p. A722

APOLIONA, Nicole, M.D., Medical Director, Kula Hospital, Kula, HI, p. A186

APONTE, Miguel, Supervisor Management Information Systems, Wilma N. Vazquez Medical Center, Vega Baja, PR, p. A811

APPLEBAUM, Jon D., President and Chief Operating Officer, Novant Health Thomasville Medical Center, Thomasville, NC, p. A519

APPLEGEET, Carol, MSN, R.N., Vice President and Chief Nursing Officer, Fort Hamilton Hospital, Hamilton, OH, p. A542

APPLETON, Joe, M.D., Chief of Surgery, Milan General Hospital, Milan, TN, p. A645

APPLEWOOD, David, Chief Financial Officer, Grant Memorial Hospital, Petersburg, WV, p. A775

APRILE, Patricia, Chief Operating Officer, Southern Maine Health Care - Biddeford Medical Center, Biddeford, ME, p. A319

AQUILINA, Anthony, D.O., Chief Medical Officer, Geisinger-Community Medical Center, Scranton, PA, p. A607

AQUILINA, Joanne, Vice President Finance and Chief Financial Officer, Bethesda Hospital East, Boynton Beach, FL, p. A132

AQUINO, Jonathon F., Chief Executive Officer, San Gabriel Valley Medical Center, San Gabriel, CA, p. A94

ARA, Farideh, Interim Chief Nursing Officer, Hollywood Presbyterian Medical Center, Los Angeles, CA, p. A74

ARABIT, Aleen Davis., Chief Executive Officer, San Antonio Behavioral Healthcare Hospital, San Antonio, TX, p. A713

ARAD, Lana
Chief Financial Officer, Good Samaritan Hospital, San Jose, CA, p. A94
Chief Financial Officer, Mountainview Hospital, Las Vegas, NV, p. A443

ARAGON, Juliette, Finance Director, Turquoise Lodge Hospital, Albuquerque, NM, p. A468

ARAKELIAN, Armen
Chief Information Officer, Fulton County Medical Center, Mc Connellsburg, PA, p. A596
Chief Information Officer, Penn Highlands Huntingdon, Huntingdon, PA, p. A592

ARANDA, Heather, R.N., MSN, Chief Nursing Officer, F. W. Huston Medical Center, Winchester, KS, p. A279

ARANIO, Lani, Regional Director Human Resources, Samuel Mahelona Memorial Hospital, Kapaa, HI, p. A186

ARATOW, Michael, M.D., Chief Information Officer, San Mateo Medical Center, San Mateo, CA, p. A96

ARAUJO, Marianne, R.N., Ph.D., FACHE, Vice President Nursing and Chief Nurse Executive, Advocate Good Shepherd Hospital, Barrington, IL, p. A195

ARAUJO, Markeeta, Chief Nursing Officer, Desert View Hospital, Pahrump. NV, p. A445

ARBAUGH, Ronnie, Director Human Resources, Grant Memorial Hospital, Petersburg, WV, p. A775

ARBON, Terron, R.N., Chief Nursing Officer, Salt Lake Regional Medical Center, Salt Lake City, UT, p. A732

ARCANGELI, Barbara, Vice President Human Resources, Newport Hospital, Newport, RI, p. A613

ARCE, Daisy, President Medical Staff, Weslaco Regional Rehabilitation Hospital, Weslaco, TX, p. A725

ARCENEAUX, Larrie, Chief Clinical Officer, Kp. Promise Hospital Of Baton Rouge, Baton Rouge, LA, p. A297

ARCENEAUX, Trina, Assistant Chief Financial Officer, Kp. Promise Hospital Of Baton Rouge, Baton Rouge, LA, p. A297

ARCH, Chrissy, Chief Financial Officer, Cherokee Indian Hospital, Cherokee, NC, p. A507

ARCHAMBEAULT, Shirley, Chief Information Officer, Medical City Lewisville, Lewisville, TX, p. A696

ARCHER, David, Director Information Systems, Tristar Ashland City Medical Center, Ashland City, TN, p. A634

ARCHER, Doug
Administrator, Memorial Hospital Los Banos, Los Banos, CA, p. A76

President and Chief Executive Officer, Mark Twain Medical Center, San Andreas, CA, p. A90

ARCHER, Joe, Chief Information Officer, Victor Valley Global Medical Center, Victorville, CA, p. A104

ARCHER, Stuart
Chief Executive Officer, Oceans Healthcare, Oceans Behavioral Hospital Of Deridder, Deridder, LA, p. A301
Chief Executive Officer, Oceans Behavioral Hospital Katy, Katy, TX, p. A692

ARCHER-DUSTE, Helen, Chief Operating Officer, Kaiser Permanente San Francisco Medical Center, San Francisco, CA, p. A93

ARCHEY, Eugene, Chief Information Technology, Va Greater Los Angeles Healthcare System, Los Angeles, CA, p. A76

ARCHIBOLD, Robert, Director, Human Resources, St. Anthony North Health Campus, Westminster, CO, p. A119

ARCHIBONG, Henry, Vice President, Information Services and Technology, University Of Maryland Capital Region Health Prince George's Hospital Center, Cheverly, MD, p. A328

ARCHULETA, Michael, Chief Information Technology Officer, Mt. San Rafael Hospital, Trinidad, CO, p. A119

ARCIDI, Alfred J.
M.D., Chief Executive Officer, Whittier Pavilion, Haverhill, MA, p. A340
M.D., Senior Vice President, Whittier Rehabilitation Hospital, Bradford, MA, p. A336
M.D., Senior Vice President, Whittier Rehabilitation Hospital, Westborough, MA, p. A346

ARD, Sheila, Chief Nursing Officer, Huntsville Memorial Hospital, Huntsville, TX, p. A690

ARDEMAGNI, Jeff, Chief Financial Officer, Medical City Arlington, Arlington, TX, p. A653

ARDESHNA, Harish, Pulmonologist & Chief Medical Officer, Bluffton Regional Medical Center, Bluffton, IN, p. A224

ARDION, Doug, M.D., Chief Medical Officer, Nch Baker Hospital, Naples, FL, p. A148

ARDOIN, Cody, Director Human Resources, Mercy Regional Medical Center, Ville Platte, LA, p. A316

ARDOLIC, Brahim, M.D., Chief Executive Officer, Staten Island University Hospital, Staten Island, NY, p. A499

AREAUX, Rene, Vice President and Chief Operating Officer, Springhill Memorial Hospital, Mobile, AL, p. A22

ARELLANO, Edgar, Chief Information Technologist, Three Rivers Hospital, Brewster, WA, p. A756

ARENDS, Candace, R.N., Chief Nursing Officer, United Hospital District, Blue Earth, MN, p. A373

ARETINO, Sandi, M.D., Chief Executive Officer, Tsehootsooi Medical Center, Fort Defiance, AZ, p. A31

ARGUELLO-VASQUEZ, Mabel, R.N., Executive Nurse Administrator, New Mexico Behavioral Health Institute At Las Vegas, Las Vegas, NM, p. A470

ARGYROS, Gregory J., M.D., Senior Vice President and President, Medstar Washington Hospital Center, Washington, DC, p. A130

ARIGAN, Helen, Director Human Resources, Encompass Health Rehabilitation Hospital Of Huntington, Huntington, WV, p. A773

ARISPE, Joe, Director Information Systems, Wise Health System, Decatur, TX, p. A671

ARIZMENDEZ, Maria, M.D., Medical Director, Baylor Scott & White Institute For Rehabilitation - Lakeway, Lakeway, TX, p. A694

ARIZPE, Robert C., Superintendent, San Antonio State Hospital, San Antonio, TX, p. A713

ARKEMA, Ashley, Director of Human Resources, Pella Regional Health Center, Pella, IA, p. A256

ARLEDGE, Denton, Vice President and Chief Information Officer, Wakemed Cary Hospital, Cary, NC, p. A506

ARLEDGE, William, Administrator and Chief Financial Officer, Genesis Behavioral Hospital, Breaux Bridge, LA, p. A298

ARLIEN, Dana, M.D., Chief Medical Officer, Willow Springs Center, Reno, NV, p. A446

ARMBRUSTER, Kent, M.D., Vice President Medical Affairs, Osf Healthcare Little Company Of Mary Medical Center, Evergreen Park, IL, p. A204

ARMBRUSTER, Rebecca, M.D., Chief Medical Officer, Temple University Hospital - Jeanes Campus, Philadelphia, PA, p. A602

ARMENTOR, Lance, Chief Executive Officer, Avail Health Lake Charles Hospital, Lake Charles, LA, p. A306

ARMFIELD, Ben
Associate Administrator, Fresno Heart And Surgical Hospital, Fresno, CA, p. A65
Chief Financial Officer, Fresno Heart And Surgical Hospital, Fresno, CA, p. A65

ARMOUR, Dale, Chief Financial Officer, Melbourne Regional Medical Center, Melbourne, FL, p. A145

ARMOUR, John, Chief Financial Officer, Hca Houston Healthcare Southeast, Pasadena, TX, p. A705

ARMSTRONG, Alan, M.D., Chief Medical Officer, Pine Rest Christian Mental Health Services, Grand Rapids, MI, p. A356

ARMSTRONG, Caroline, D.O., M.D., Chief of Staff, Grant Memorial Hospital, Petersburg, WV, p. A775

ARMSTRONG, Eleze, Chief Operating Officer, Sierra Vista Regional Medical Center, San Luis Obispo, CA, p. A96

ARMSTRONG, Gary, Executive Vice President, Methodist Rehabilitation Center, Jackson, MS, p. A394

ARMSTRONG, Jeffery, CPA, Chief Financial Officer, Granville Health System, Oxford, NC, p. A516

ARMSTRONG, Jeremy, FACHE, Chief Executive Officer, Mitchell County Hospital Health Systems, Beloit, KS, p. A262

ARMSTRONG, Kim, Chief Financial Officer, Windom Area Health, Windom, MN, p. A388

ARMSTRONG, Kyle, Chief Operating Officer, Baylor University Medical Center, Dallas, TX, p. A668

ARMSTRONG, Mark, M.D., Medical Director, Baylor Scott & White Medical Center-Uptown, Dallas, TX, p. A667

ARMSTRONG, Paula, Chief Financial Officer, Kaiser Permanente Fresno Medical Center, Fresno, CA, p. A65

ARMSTRONG, Robert, M.D., Chief Medical Officer, Sanpete Valley Hospital, Mount Pleasant, UT, p. A729
Senior Vice President and Chief Operating Officer, Lima Memorial Health System, Lima, OH, p. A543

ARMSTRONG, Roger, Interim Chief Financial Officer, Pioneers Memorial Healthcare District, Brawley, CA, p. A58
Vice President Finance and Chief Financial Officer, Unitypoint Health - Proctor, Peoria, IL, p. A217

ARMSTRONG, William, Senior Vice President and Chief Financial Officer, Mercy Medical Center, Rockville Centre, NY, p. A497
Vice President and Chief Financial Officer, St. Francis Hospital, The Heart Center, Roslyn, NY, p. A497

ARMSTRONG-HUFF, Glenda, Assistant Superintendent, Texas Center For Infectious Disease, San Antonio, TX, p. A713

ARNDELL, Scott, Chief Financial Officer, Twin Lakes Regional Medical Center, Leitchfield, KY, p. A286

ARNER, Steven, Executive Vice President of Administration, Carilion Franklin Memorial Hospital, Rocky Mount, VA, p. A751
President, Carilion Roanoke Memorial Hospital, Roanoke, VA, p. A751

ARNER, Steven C., President, Carilion Roanoke Memorial Hospital, Roanoke, VA, p. A751

ARNESON, Brenda, Administrative Assistant, St. Andrew's Health Center, Bottineau, ND, p. A521

ARNESON, Garrett, FACHE, R.N., Chief Executive Officer, Acuity Specialty Hospital Of Southern New Jersey, Willingboro, NJ, p. A466

ARNETT, Jacob, Chief Information Technology Officer, Lakeside Behavioral Health System, Memphis, TN, p. A644

ARNETT, James, Vice President Human Resources, Unitypoint Health Meriter, Madison, WI, p. A788

ARNETT, Randal M., President and Chief Executive Officer, Southern Ohio Medical Center, Portsmouth, OH, p. A548

ARNETT, Sallie, Vice President Information Systems, Licking Memorial Hospital, Newark, OH, p. A546

ARNETT, Stuart, Regional Vice President Finance, Aurora Lakeland Medical Center, Elkhorn, WI, p. A783
Vice President Finance and Chief Financial Officer, Aurora Medical Center Burlington, Burlington, WI, p. A781

ARNHART, Carol, Vice President Finance and Chief Financial Officer, Siskin Hospital For Physical Rehabilitation, Chattanooga, TN, p. A636

ARNO, Michael J., President, Astria Toppenish Hospital, Toppenish, WA, p. A768

ARNOLD, Ann, M.D., Medical Director, Medical City Plano, Plano, TX, p. A707

ARNOLD, Dustin, D.O., Chief Medical Officer, Unitypoint Health - St. Luke's Hospital, Cedar Rapids, IA, p. A245

ARNOLD, Jeffrey, M.D., Chief Medical Officer, Santa Clara Valley Medical Center, San Jose, CA, p. A95

ARNOLD, Kimberly, R.N., Chief Nursing Officer and Interim Chief Quality Officer, Alliancehealth Woodward, Woodward, OK, p. A572

ARNOLD, Leslie, Chief Executive Officer and Administrator, Chi St. Vincent Morrilton, Morrilton, AR, p. A50

ARNOLD, Scott, Senior Vice President Information Systems, Tamp. General Hospital, Tampa, FL, p. A160

ARNTZ, Mary, Manager Business Office and Executive Assistant, Physicians' Medical Center, New Albany, IN, p. A237

AROCHA, Joe, Chief of Staff, Alleghany Memorial Hospital, Sparta, NC, p. A518

AROCHO, Jacqueline, Administrator, Baycare Alliant Hospital, Dunedin, FL, p. A136

ARORA, Pamela, Senior Vice President and Chief Information Officer, Children's Medical Center Plano, Plano, TX, p. A706

Senior Vice President Information Systems, Children's Medical Center Dallas, Dallas, TX, p. A668

ARORA, Sat, M.D., President Medical and Dental Staff, Crozer-Chester Medical Center, Upland, PA, p. A609

ARQUETTE, Darrin, President, Promedica Monroe Regional Hospital, Monroe, MI, p. A362

ARQUILLA, Thomas J., Chief Strategy Officer, Thedacare Regional Medical Center-Appleton, Appleton, WI, p. A779

ARRANTS, Diane, Chief Information Officer, Kershawhealth, Camden, SC, p. A615

ARROGANTE, Revelyn, M.D., Medical Director, Northern Colorado Rehabilitation Hospital, Johnstown, CO, p. A114

ARROWOOD, Melina, Interim President and Chief Nursing Officer, Transylvania Regional Hospital, Brevard, NC, p. A505

ARROYO, Luis, Chief Financial Officer, Hima San Pablo Caguas, Caguas, PR, p. A806

Chief Financial Officer, Hospital Hima De Humacao, Humacao, PR, p. A808

Chief Financial Officer, Hospital San Pablo Del Este, Fajardo, PR, p. A807

ARSENAULT, Lisa, Vice President Human Resources and Compliance, Millinocket Regional Hospital, Millinocket, ME, p. A321

ARSLANPAY, Robin, Director Human Resources, Lifecare Behavioral Health Hospital, Pittsburgh, PA, p. A603

ARSURA, Edward, M.D., Chief Medical Officer, Richmond University Medical Center, Staten Island, NY, p. A498

ARTENSTEIN, Andrew, M.D., Chief Physician Executive, Chief Academic Officer and President, Baystate Medical Practices, Baystate Medical Center, Springfield, MA, p. A344

ARTERBURN, Catherine, R.N., Vice President Human Resources, Sidney Regional Medical Center, Sidney, NE, p. A439

ARTHUR, Cynthia, Fiscal Director, Piedmont Geriatric Hospital, Burkeville, VA, p. A739

ARTHUR, John, Chief Financial Officer, Ascension St. Vincent Mercy, Elwood, IN, p. A227

Chief Financial Officer, Ascension St. Vincent Randolph, Winchester, IN, p. A242

ARTHUR, Rita, Director Human Resources, Littleton Adventist Hospital, Littleton, CO, p. A116

ARTILES, Nemuel O., FACHE, Administrator, Hospital De Psiquiatria Forense, Ponce, PR, p. A809

ARTMAN, David, Chief Operating Officer, Weirton Medical Center, Weirton, WV, p. A777

ARTS-STRENKE, Cindy, R.N., Chief Operating Officer and Chief Nursing Officer, Marshfield Medical Center - Rice Lake, Rice Lake, WI, p. A795

ARUNAMATA, Peti, Interim Area Director Information Technology, Kaiser Permanente San Francisco Medical Center, San Francisco, CA, p. A93

ARVIDSON, Betty, Chief Financial Officer, Riverview Health, Crookston, MN, p. A374

ARVIN, Jon, M.D., Chief Medical Officer, Rockcastle Regional Hospital And Respiratory Care Center, Mount Vernon, KY, p. A291

ARVON, Christina, Administrator and Chief Executive Officer, Charleston Surgical Hospital, Charleston, WV, p. A771

ARZOUMANIAN, Aimee, Chief Operating Officer, Baptist Health - Fort Smith, Fort Smith, AR, p. A46

ASADA, Bonnie, Chief Nursing Officer, Alvarado Parkway Institute Behavioral Health System, La Mesa, CA, p. A70

ASAFTEI, Laura, Administrative Director, Adventhealth Zephyrhills, Zephyrhills, FL, p. A162

ASAOKA, Danny, Executive Director Information Systems, Long Beach Medical Center, Long Beach, CA, p. A72

Executive Director Information Systems, Miller Children's & Women's Hospital Long Beach, Long Beach, CA, p. A72

ASBURY, Wesley, M.D., President Medical Staff, Princeton Community Hospital, Princeton, WV, p. A776

ASCHOFF, Jodi, Chief Financial Officer, Osmond General Hospital, Osmond, NE, p. A438

ASH, Michael, Chief Transformation Officer, Nebraska Medicine - Nebraska Medical Center, Omaha, NE, p. A437

ASH, Richard M., Chief Executive Officer, United Hospital District, Blue Earth, MN, p. A373

ASHBY, F, M.D., Vice President and Medical Director, Sentara Martha Jefferson Hospital, Charlottesville, VA, p. A739

ASHBY, Fred, Director Information Technology, Fort Washington Medical Center, Oxen Hill, MD, p. A331

ASHBY, Kim, Vice President of Finance, Baptist Health Madisonville, Madisonville, KY, p. A289

ASHBY, Natalie, Chief Nursing Officer, Dixie Regional Medical Center, Saint George, UT, p. A732

ASHBY, Pamela, Vice President Human Resources, Medstar National Rehabilitation Hospital, Washington, DC, p. A130

ASHBY, Rae, Director Human Resources, Sullivan County Memorial Hospital, Milan, MO, p. A412

ASHCOM, Thomas L., M.D., Ph.D., Chief Executive Officer, Kansas Heart Hospital, Wichita, KS, p. A278

ASHENFELTER, Kathy, Chief Financial Officer, Swedish Medical Center, Englewood, CO, p. A112

ASHKENASE, Donald, Executive Vice President and Chief Operating Officer, Nassau University Medical Center, East Meadow, NY, p. A483

ASHLEY, Ada, HIM Director, Lifebrite Community Hospital Of Stokes, Danbury, NC, p. A508

ASHLEY, Dennis, Vice President Human Resources, Montefiore Mount Vernon, Mount Vernon, NY, p. A489

ASHLEY, Kent, Chief Financial Officer, Mesa Springs, Fort Worth, TX, p. A679

ASHLEY, Sharon, MSN, Chief Nursing Officer, Adams County Regional Medical Center, Seaman, OH, p. A549

ASHLEY, Stanley, M.D., Senior Vice President Medical Affairs and Chief Medical Officer, Brigham And Women's Hospital, Boston, MA, p. A335

ASHMENT, Kerry, Chief Executive Officer, Kindred Hospital-San Diego, San Diego, CA, p. A91

ASHWORTH, Fred, Chief Financial Officer, Regional Medical Center Of San Jose, San Jose, CA, p. A95

ASHWORTH, Jerry, Senior Vice President and Chief Executive Officer, Memorial Hermann Katy Hospital, Katy, TX, p. A692

ASIC, Jason, Chief Operating Officer, Mercy Health - West Hospital, Cincinnati, OH, p. A533

ASKEW, Pam, R.N., Vice President Patient Care Services, Unitypoint Health - Trinity Muscatine, Muscatine, IA, p. A254

ASKINS, Stephen, M.D., Chief of Staff, Lake City Community Hospital, Lake City, SC, p. A622

ASLIN, Judy, MSN, R.N., Vice President and Chief Nursing Officer, Southeast Hospital, Cap. Girardeau, MO, p. A404

ASMUS, Trevor, Chief Executive Officer, Las Encinas Hospital, Pasadena, CA, p. A85

ASP, Josh, Chief Financial Officer, Welia Health, Mora, MN, p. A381

ASPEL, Tracy, Chief Nursing Officer, Northern Inyo Hospital, Bishop. CA, p. A58

ASPLIN, Iain, Chief Medical Officer, Multicare Mary Bridge Children's Hospital And Health Center, Tacoma, WA, p. A767

ASPLUND, David, Chief Operating Officer, Motion Picture And Television Fund Hospital And Residential Services, Woodland Hills, CA, p. A105

ASSAAD, Haney, Vice President Medical Affairs, North Ottawa Community Hospital, Grand Haven, MI, p. A355

ASSAVAPISITKUL, MSN, RN, HCAP, Colleen, R.N., Patient Care Executive, Adventist Health Clear Lake, Clearlake, CA, p. A60

ASTACIO, Benjamin, Director Human Resources, Bella Vista Hospital, Mayaguez, PR, p. A808

ASTLEFORD, Daniel, Vice President Operations, Lafayette Regional Health Center, Lexington, MO, p. A411

ATADERO, Robyn, R.N., Chief Nursing Officer, Pioneers Memorial Healthcare District, Brawley, CA, p. A58

ATCHISON, Garfield, Chief Executive Officer, Up Health System-Marquette, Marquette, MI, p. A361

ATCHISON, Marcie, Vice President Human Resources, Long Beach Medical Center, Long Beach, CA, p. A72

Vice President Human Resources, Miller Children's & Women's Hospital Long Beach, Long Beach, CA, p. A72

ATCHLEY, Mark, Vice President and Chief Financial Officer, Medical City Dallas, Dallas, TX, p. A669

ATHERTON, Dorie, Manager Human Resources, University Behavioral Health Of Denton, Denton, TX, p. A672

ATHEY, Alycia, Director of Nursing, Prairie Ridge Hospital And Health Services, Elbow Lake, MN, p. A376

ATKINS, Christa, Administrator, Commonwealth Regional Specialty Hospital, Bowling Green, KY, p. A280

ATKINS, James, PharmD, Chief Operating Officer, Piedmont Henry Hospital, Stockbridge, GA, p. A181

ATKINS, Jim, Director Employee Services, St. Luke's Rehabilitation Hospital, Boise, ID, p. A189

ATKINS, Melissa, CPA, Chief Executive Officer, Graham County Hospital, Hill City, KS, p. A266

ATKINS, Tracy, Chief Operating and Nursing Officer, Orchard Hospital, Gridley, CA, p. A67

ATKINSON, Andrew, Chief Operating Officer, Fulton State Hospital, Fulton, MO, p. A407

ATKINSON, James, M.D., Medical Director, Ucla Medical Center-Santa Monica, Santa Monica, CA, p. A98

ATKINSON, Johnie, Chief Human Resources Officer, Saint Vincent Hospital, Erie, PA, p. A590

ATTEBURY, Mary, Chief Operating Officer, Northwest Missouri Psychiatric Rehabilitation Center, Saint Joseph, MO, p. A415

ATTENBURY, Kristen, Commanding Officer, Naval Hospital Lemoore, Lemoore, CA, p. A71

ATTERBERG, Linda, Chief Information Officer, Unitypoint Health-Keokuk, Keokuk, IA, p. A252

ATTLESEY-PRIES, Jacqueline, MS, R.N., Chief Nursing Officer, Vice President, Boulder Community Health, Boulder, CO, p. A108

ATTRIDGE, Scott, Chief Financial Officer, Chi St. Anthony Hospital, Pendleton, OR, p. A578

Chief Financial Officer, Mid-Valley Hospital, Omak, WA, p. A761

ATTY, James, Chief Executive Officer, Waverly Health Center, Waverly, IA, p. A259

ATWAL, Money, Chief Information Officer, Hilo Medical Center, Hilo, HI, p. A184

ATWOOD, Brian, M.D., Associate Medical Director, Carle Richland Memorial Hospital, Olney, IL, p. A215

ATWOOD, Julie, Director Human Resources, Mountains Community Hospital, Lake Arrowhead, CA, p. A70

ATWOOD, Linda, Chief Nursing Officer, Merit Health Woman's Hospital, Flowood, MS, p. A392

AUBEL, Eugenia, President, St. Elizabeth Boardman Hospital, Mercy Health - St. Elizabeth Boardman Hospital, Boardman, OH, p. A529

AUBRY, Michael, Director Information Systems, Adventist Health Hanford, Hanford, CA, p. A67

AUBUCHON, Christy, Director Personnel, Washington County Memorial Hospital, Potosi, MO, p. A414

AUCKER, Kendra, Vice President Operations, Evangelical Community Hospital, Lewisburg, PA, p. A595

AUCKER, Kendra A., President and Chief Executive Officer, Evangelical Community Hospital, Lewisburg, PA, p. A595

AUCKERMAN, Graydon, Chief Nursing Officer, Ohiohealth Rehabilitation Hospital, Columbus, OH, p. A536

AUD, Pam, Chief Clinical Officer, Andalusia Health, Andalusia, AL, p. A13

AUDETT, John, M.D., Medical Director Clinical Affairs, Overlook Medical Center, Summit, NJ, p. A463

AUERBACH, Lorraine P., FACHE, President and Chief Executive Officer, Dameron Hospital, Stockton, CA, p. A99

AUGSBURGER, Marc, R.N., President and Chief Executive Officer, Mclaren Caro Region, Caro, MI, p. A350

AUGSBURGER, Tod, FACHE, President and Chief Executive Officer, Lexington Medical Center, West Columbia, SC, p. A625

AUGUST, Brad, Director Information Systems, Fairfield Memorial Hospital, Fairfield, IL, p. A205

AUGUST, Prudence, Chief Information Officer, Palomar Medical Center Escondido, Escondido, CA, p. A63

AUGUSTIN, Robert, Director Human Resources, Southern Tennessee Regional Health System-Lawrenceburg, Lawrenceburg, TN, p. A642

AUGUSTIN, W, CPA, IIIVice President Financial Services and Chief Financial Officer, University Of Maryland Rehabilitation & Orthopaedic Institute, Baltimore, MD, p. A327

AUGUSTINE, David, Chief Executive Officer, Trego County-Lemke Memorial Hospital, Wakeeney, KS, p. A278

AUGUSTUS, Richard, M.D., Chief Medical Officer, West Valley Medical Center, Caldwell, ID, p. A189

AUGUSTYNIAK, Becky, Director Human Resources, Piedmont Columbus Regional Northside, Columbus, GA, p. A169

AURAND, Brendan, Director, Human Resources, Fairmount Behavioral Health System, Philadelphia, PA, p. A600

AURILIO, Lisa, R.N., MSN, Chief Operating Officer, Akron Children's Hospital, Akron, OH, p. A527

AUSMAN, Dan F., President and Chief Executive Officer, Methodist Hospital Of Southern California, Arcadia, CA, p. A56

AUSTIN, Aaron, Division Vice President Human Resources Administration, Chi Health Creighton University Medical Center - Bergan Mercy, Omaha, NE, p. A436

Division Vice President, Human Resources, Chi Health Good Samaritan, Kearney, NE, p. A433

AUSTIN, Bill, Senior Vice President of Finance, Coastal Virginia Rehabilitation, Newport News, VA, p. A746

AUSTIN, Dan, Director Information Technology, Arkansas Methodist Medical Center, Paragould, AR, p. A51

Manager Data Processing, Ashley County Medical Center, Crossett, AR, p. A44

AUSTIN, Donnica, Vice President, Operations, Holy Cross Hospital, Chicago, IL, p. A198

AUSTIN, Geoff, Chief Operating Officer, University Of Washington Medical Center, Seattle, WA, p. A764

AUSTIN, Joe, Executive Vice President and Chief Operating Officer, Phoebe Putney Memorial Hospital, Albany, GA, p. A163

AUSTIN, Pam, Senior Vice-President, Chief Information Officer, Bristol Regional Medical Center, Bristol, TN, p. A634

AUSTIN, Sherri, MSN, R.N., Chief Nursing Officer, Wrangell Medical Center, Wrangell, AK, p. A29

AUSTIN, Tommye, Ph.D., R.N., MSN, Chief Nursing Executive, University Health System, San Antonio, TX, p. A714

AUSTIN, Warren, M.D., Vice President Medical Affairs, Bon Secours Maryview Medical Center, Portsmouth, VA, p. A749

AUSTIN JR, WSenior Vice President Finance, Riverside Shore Memorial Hospital, Onancock, VA, p. A748

AUSTIN-MOORE, Gale, Director Area Technology, Kaiser Permanente Vallejo Medical Center, Vallejo, CA, p. A103

AUSTRIA, Ramon, R.N., Chief Nursing Officer, Baylor Scott & White Institute For Rehabilitation - Lakeway, Lakeway, TX, p. A694

AUTELLI, Oscar, Chief Information Officer, Lac+Usc Medical Center, Los Angeles, CA, p. A75

AUTHUR, Tanya, Chief Information Officer, Summa Health System, Akron, OH, p. A527

AUTLER, Tracy, R.N., Chief Nursing and Quality Officer, Bonner General Health, Sandpoint, ID, p. A193

AUTREY, Pamela, R.N., Ph.D., MSN, Chief Nursing Officer, Medical West, Bessemer, AL, p. A14

AUTRY, Paula R., FACHE, President and Chief Executive Officer, Henry Ford Allegiance Health, Jackson, MI, p. A359

AVANT, Andre, Facility Automation Manager, Texas Center For Infectious Disease, San Antonio, TX, p. A713

AVATO, Rich, Director, St. Mary's Medical Center, West Palm Beach, FL, p. A162

AVELINO, Joseph, Chief Executive Officer, College Medical Center, Long Beach, CA, p. A72

AVERILL, Clark, Director Information Technology, St. Luke's Hospital, Duluth, MN, p. A375

AVERNA, Russell, Vice President Human Resources, Spaulding Rehabilitation Hospital, Charlestown, MA, p. A338

Vice President of Human Resources, Spaulding Rehabilitation Hospital Cap. Cod, East Sandwich, MA, p. A338

AVERY, Danny, Chief Financial Officer and Chief Operating Officer, Mangum Regional Medical Center, Mangum, OK, p. A561

AVERY, Donald R., FACHE, President and Chief Executive Officer, Fairview Park Hospital, Dublin, GA, p. A172

AVERY, Jonathan, President, Legacy Good Samaritan Medical Center, Portland, OR, p. A579

AVERY, Scott, Chief Operating Officer, Paris Regional Medical Center, Paris, TX, p. A704

AVERY III, John B., Administrator, Perry Community Hospital, Linden, TN, p. A642

AVIADO, Gail, Chief Nursing Officer, Montclair Hospital Medical Center, Montclair, CA, p. A79

AVIGDOR, Lauren, Director Human Resources, Advanced Specialty Hospital Of Toledo, Toledo, OH, p. A550

AVILA, Brandi, Chief Nursing Officer, Martin County Hospital District, Stanton, TX, p. A717

AVILA, Patrick, President and Chief Executive Officer, Merrick Medical Center, Central City, NE, p. A430

AVVISATO, Michael, Senior Vice President and Chief Financial Officer, Allied Services Rehabilitation Hospital, Scranton, PA, p. A606

AVVISATO, Mike, Vice President and Chief Financial Officer, John Heinz Institute Of Rehabilitation Medicine, Wilkes-Barre, PA, p. A611

AWALD, Tamara, Chief Nursing Officer and Chief Operating Officer, Plymouth Medical Center, Plymouth, IN, p. A239

AWALT, Scott, Chief Financial Officer, Sanford Hillsboro Medical Center, Hillsboro, ND, p. A524

AWAN, Naveed, FACHE, Chief Executive Officer, St. Helena Parish Hospital, Greensburg, LA, p. A302

AWOLOWO, Yinusa, Business Officer, Kingsboro Psychiatric Center, Brooklyn, NY, p. A478

AWWAD, Emad, Director Care Delivery Sites Information Systems and Technology, Lakeview Hospital, Stillwater, MN, p. A386

AXTELL, Vicki, Director Human Resources, Livingston Healthcare, Livingston, MT, p. A426

AYALA, Jose, M.D., Chief Medical Officer, Valley Baptist Medical Center-Brownsville, Brownsville, TX, p. A661

AYALA, Lisa, R.N., Director Human Resources, Curahealth Jacksonville, Jacksonville, FL, p. A141

AYALA, Shirley, Director Human Resources, First Hospital Panamericano, Cidra, PR, p. A807

AYCOCK, Mark, Chief Operating Officer, Spartanburg Medical Center - Church Street Campus, Spartanburg, SC, p. A624

AYERS, Jessi, Chief Financial Officer, Person Memorial Hospital, Roxboro, NC, p. A517

AYERS, Matthew, Chief Administrative Officer, Norton Hospital, Louisville, KY, p. A288

AYERS, Pam, Chief Nursing Officer, North Oak Regional Medical Center, Senatobia, MS, p. A400

AYOUB, John J., FACHE, Chief Executive Officer, Mobridge Regional Hospital, Mobridge, SD, p. A629

AYRES, Robert, Director Information Systems, Firelands Regional Health System, Sandusky, OH, p. A549

AYRES, Shane, Chief Financial Officer, Sanford Wheaton Medical Center, Wheaton, MN, p. A388

AZAR, Richard, Chief Operating Officer, Ucla Medical Center-Santa Monica, Santa Monica, CA, p. A98

Chief Operation Officer, Ronald Reagan Ucla Medical Center, Los Angeles, CA, p. A75

AZAR, Robert, Chief Operating Officer, Ucla Medical Center-Santa Monica, Santa Monica, CA, p. A98

AZCONA, Alain, Chief Executive Officer, Aurora Behavioral Healthcare San Diego, San Diego, CA, p. A91

Director Business Development, Aurora Behavioral Healthcare San Diego, San Diego, CA, p. A91

AZCUY, Karla, Acting Chief Human Resources Officer, Va Portland Healthcare System, Portland, OR, p. A580

AZEEM, Sohail, Chief Executive Officer, Kindred Hospital Northwest Indiana, Hammond, IN, p. A230

AZEVEDO, Michael, M.D., Medical Director, San Joaquin Valley Rehabilitation Hospital, Fresno, CA, p. A66

AZIZ, Samir, M.D., Medical Director, Fairfax Behavioral Health, Kirkland, WA, p. A759

# B

BAAS, Dina, Director Financial Services, Orange City Area Health System, Orange City, IA, p. A255

BABAKANIAN, Ed, Chief Information Officer, Uc San Diego Medical Center—Hillcrest, San Diego, CA, p. A92

BABB, A., Vice President, Operations, Duke Regional Hospital, Durham, NC, p. A508

BABB, Cindy, Executive Director Human Resources and Organizational Effectiveness, Ascension St. Vincent Kokomo, Kokomo, IN, p. A234

BABB, Dan, Chief Financial Officer, Dmc - Rehabilitation Institute Of Michigan, Detroit, MI, p. A352

BABB, Kathy, Manager Human Resources, Clifton Springs Hospital And Clinic, Clifton Springs, NY, p. A481

BABB, Tamie, Chief Medical Officer, Tristar Hendersonville Medical Center, Hendersonville, TN, p. A639

BABCOCK, Daniel, Chief Executive Officer, Marlette Regional Hospital, Marlette, MI, p. A361

BABCOCK, Jordon, Chief Executive Officer, Springwoods Behavioral Health Hospital, Fayetteville, AR, p. A45

BABCOCK, Kimberly, Administrative Director of Operations, Kalkaska Memorial Health Center, Kalkaska, MI, p. A359

BABCOCK, Paul, Chief Financial Officer, Coulee Medical Center, Grand Coulee, WA, p. A759

BABCOCK, Robert, Interim Chief of Staff, Bath Veterans Affairs Medical Center, Bath, NY, p. A475

BABE, Heather, M.D., Chief of Staff, Shenandoah Medical Center, Shenandoah, IA, p. A257

BABER, Jonathan, Director Information Technology, Central State Hospital, Petersburg, VA, p. A748

BABICH, Eli, Chief Nursing Officer, Select Specialty Hospital-Pittsburgh/Upmc, Pittsburgh, PA, p. A603

BABUSCIO, Cathy, Director Human Resources, Mat-Su Regional Medical Center, Palmer, AK, p. A29

BACH, Dawn, MS, Chief Clinical Officer, Buena Vista Regional Medical Center, Storm Lake, IA, p. A258

BACHA, Fadi, M.D., Chief Medical Officer, Select Specialty Hospital-Lexington, Lexington, KY, p. A287

BACHELDOR, H, D.O., Chief Medical Officer, Ascension River District Hospital, East China, MI, p. A353

BACHELIER, Erin, Human Resource Administrator, Ranken Jordan Pediatric Bridge Hospital, Maryland Heights, MO, p. A411

BACHER, Beth, Chief Executive Officer, Encompass Health Valley Of The Sun Rehabilitation Hospital, Glendale, AZ, p. A32

BACHMAN, John, Corporate Vice President, St. John Medical Center, Tulsa, OK, p. A571

BACHMAN, Judith, Chief Operating Officer, Fox Chase Cancer Center-American Oncologic Hospital, Philadelphia, PA, p. A600

Chief Operating Officer, Temple University Hospital - Jeanes Campus, Philadelphia, PA, p. A602

BACHMAN, Roberta, Director Human Resources, Riverview Behavioral Health, Texarkana, AR, p. A53

BACHMEIER, Susan, MSN, R.N., Chief Nursing Officer, Wake Forest Baptist Health-Davie Medical Center, Bermuda Run, NC, p. A505

BACK, Barbara, Manager Human Resources, Encino Hospital Medical Center, Encino, CA, p. A63

BACKUS, Michael, Executive Vice President and Chief Operating Officer, Oswego Hospital, Oswego, NY, p. A494

BACON, Jeff, D.O., Chief Medical Officer, Sterling Regional Medcenter, Sterling, CO, p. A119

BADEN, Robert, Chief Financial Officer, Lompoc Valley Medical Center, Lompoc, CA, p. A72

BADEN JR, ThomasChief Information Officer, Community Behavioral Health Hospital - Rochester, Rochester, MN, p. A384

BADER, Destiny, Director of Nursing, Saunders Medical Center, Wahoo, NE, p. A440

BADGER, Jeff, Chief Financial Officer, Ascension Calumet Hospital, Chilton, WI, p. A781

Chief Financial Officer, Ascension Northeast Wisconsin Mercy Hospital, Oshkosh, WI, p. A793

Chief Financial Officer, Ascension Northeast Wisconsin St. Elizabeth Hospital, Appleton, WI, p. A779

BADINGER, Sandy, Chief Executive Officer, Ochsner Medical Center - North Shore, Slidell, LA, p. A315

Chief Executive Officer, Slidell Memorial Hospital, Slidell, LA, p. A315

BAENEN, Sharla, MSN, R.N., President Mental Well Being, Vice President Emergency Medicine, Hospitalists & Medical Subspecialist, Bellin Psychiatric Center, Green Bay, WI, p. A785

BAER, Douglas M., Chief Executive Officer, Brooks Rehabilitation Hospital, Jacksonville, FL, p. A141

BAEZ, Janet, Director, University Hospital, San Juan, PR, p. A811

BAEZ, Juan, M.D., President Medical Staff, Robert Wood Johnson University Hospital Rahway, Rahway, NJ, p. A462

BAFFONE, Karen, R.N., Chief Nursing Officer, Tahoe Forest Hospital District, Truckee, CA, p. A102

BAGGERLY, Karen, Chief Nursing Officer and Vice President, Covenant Medical Center, Lubbock, TX, p. A697

BAGGETT, Al, M.D., Interim Chief of Staff, Taylor Regional Hospital, Hawkinsville, GA, p. A173

BAGGETT, Margarita, MSN, R.N., Chief Nursing Officer, Uc San Diego Medical Center—Hillcrest, San Diego, CA, p. A92

MSN, R.N., Interim Chief Operating Officer, Uc San Diego Medical Center—Hillcrest, San Diego, CA, p. A92

BAGLEY, Brenda, Director Human Resources, Tmc Bonham Hospital, Bonham, TX, p. A660

BAGLEY, Lisa, Chief Nursing Officer, The Orthopedic Specialty Hospital, Murray, UT, p. A729

BAGNELL, Kelly, M.D., Chief of Staff, Providence St. Josep. Medical Center, Polson, MT, p. A427

BAHL, Barry, Director, St. Cloud Veterans Affairs Health Care System, Saint Cloud, MN, p. A384

BAHLS, Fredrick, M.D., Chief of Staff, Va Central Iowa Health Care System, Des Moines, IA, p. A249

BAIG, Mirza, M.D., Medical Director, Uh Rehabilitation Hospital, Beachwood, OH, p. A529

BAILEY, Ann, Assistant Director Administration, Central State Hospital, Petersburg, VA, p. A748

BAILEY, Becky, R.N., Director Nursing, Kansas Surgery And Recovery Center, Wichita, KS, p. A279

Director Human Resources, Lincoln Hospital, Davenport, WA, p. A757

BAILEY, Bruce P., Chief Executive Officer, Tidelands Georgetown Memorial Hospital, Georgetown, SC, p. A620

Chief Executive Officer, Tidelands Waccamaw Community Hospital, Murrells Inlet, SC, p. A623

BAILEY, Cori, Accountant, Tyler Holmes Memorial Hospital, Winona, MS, p. A401

BAILEY, Dan, Director Information Systems, Norton Sound Regional Hospital, Nome, AK, p. A29

BAILEY, David, FACHE, Chief Executive Officer, Community Hospital Of Bremen, Bremen, IN, p. A225

BAILEY, Dawn, R.N., Vice President Nursing and Chief Nursing Officer, Euclid Hospital, Euclid, OH, p. A540

BAILEY, Dianne, Chief Information Officer, Pana Community Hospital, Pana, IL, p. A216

BAILEY, Heather, Chief Human Resources Officer, Jefferson Healthcare, Port Townsend, WA, p. A762

BAILEY, Jodi, Human Resources Director, Odessa Memorial Healthcare Center, Odessa, WA, p. A761

BAILEY, John, Chief Financial Officer, Moore County Hospital District, Dumas, TX, p. A673

BAILEY, Jonathan, Chief Operating Officer, Stamford Hospital, Stamford, CT, p. A125

BAILEY, Jonathan D., Chief Executive Officer and Administrator, Hansford Hospital, Spearman, TX, p. A716

BAILEY, Jordana, Chief Operating Officer, Nyc Health + Hospitals / Jacobi, Bronx, NY, p. A477

BAILEY, Joy, Director Information Technology, Sutter Amador Hospital, Jackson, CA, p. A69

BAILEY, Joyce, Vice President Patient Care, Chi St. Anthony Hospital, Pendleton, OR, p. A578

BAILEY, Kathy C., President and Chief Executive Officer, Carolinas Healthcare System Blue Ridge, Morganton, NC, p. A515

BAILEY, Larry, President, Indiana University Health Paoli Hospital, Paoli, IN, p. A238

BAILEY, Leisa, M.D., Chief of Staff, Doctors Memorial Hospital, Bonifay, FL, p. A132

BAILEY, Lilicia, Senior Vice President and Chief People Officer, Wake Forest Baptist Health-Lexington Medical Center, Lexington, NC, p. A514

BAILEY, Lori, R.N., Vice President and Chief Nursing Officer, Ottumwa Regional Health Center, Ottumwa, IA, p. A256

BAILEY, Mikeana, Director Human Resources, Brownwood Regional Medical Center, Brownwood, TX, p. A661

BAILEY, Rachel, Chief Executive Officer, Kp. Promise Hospital Of Wichita Falls, Wichita Falls, TX, p. A725

BAILEY, Robert, Chief Information Officer, Hawthorn Center, Northville, MI, p. A363

BAILEY, Ron, Chief Financial Officer, Franklin Foundation Hospital, Franklin, LA, p. A301

BAILEY, Scott, Chief Financial Officer, Saint Francis Hospital Muskogee, Muskogee, OK, p. A562
Chief Operating Officer, Saint Mary's Regional Medical Center, Russellville, AR, p. A52

BAILEY, Susan P., R.N., Chief Executive Officer, Landmark Hospital Of Southwest Florida, Naples, FL, p. A148

BAILEY, Thomas, Chief Operating Officer, Bothwell Regional Health Center, Sedalia, MO, p. A418

BAILEY-NEWELL, Susan, Vice President Human Resources, Baylor St. Luke's Medical Center, Houston, TX, p. A684

BAILEY-OETKER, Jessica, Director Quality and Medical Staff, Providence Willamette Falls Medical Center, Oregon City, OR, p. A578

BAILLARGEON, Stephanie, R.N., Chief Nursing Officer, Down East Community Hospital, Machias, ME, p. A321

BAIN, Joel, Director Information Services, Tristar Summit Medical Center, Hermitage, TN, p. A639

BAIN, Mark, Chief Human Resources, Veterans Affairs Connecticut Healthcare System, West Haven, CT, p. A126

BAIN, Pat, Chief Nursing Officer, Lower Bucks Hospital, Bristol, PA, p. A585

BAIO, Katie, Human Resource Director, Amita Health Adventist Medical Center Bolingbrook, Bolingbrook, IL, p. A196

BAIR, Ada, Chief Executive Officer, Memorial Hospital, Carthage, IL, p. A196

BAIR, Andrew P., Chief Executive Officer, Ellsworth County Medical Center, Ellsworth, KS, p. A264

BAIRD, David, Chief Information Officer, Lds Hospital, Salt Lake City, UT, p. A732
Chief Information Officer, The Orthopedic Specialty Hospital, Murray, UT, p. A729

BAIRD, Donna, Vice President Corporate Services, Bay Medical Sacred Heart, Panama City, FL, p. A152

BAIRD, Glen, M.D., Chief of Staff, Shriners Hospitals For Children-Spokane, Spokane, WA, p. A766

BAIRD, James D., President, Amita Health Saint Josep. Hospital, Chicago, IL, p. A197

BAISCH, Kim, R.N., Associate Vice President Patient Care Services, St. Anne Hospital, Burien, WA, p. A756

BAISDEN, Monica, Director Human Resources, Memorial Hermann Northeast, Humble, TX, p. A690

BAJ-WRIGHT, Irena, Director Human Resources, Southwest Connecticut Mental Health System, Bridgeport, CT, p. A121

BAJAJ, Samyukt, Chief Operating Officer, Kaiser Permanente San Jose Medical Center, San Jose, CA, p. A94

BAJAK, Sally, Chief Financial Officer, St. Croix Regional Medical Center, St Croix Falls, WI, p. A796

BAJAK, Tony, Chief Operating Officer, Good Samaritan Medical Center, West Palm Beach, FL, p. A162

BAJARI, Pamela, R.N., Nurse Executive MHSATS, Community Behavioral Health Hospital - Rochester, Rochester, MN, p. A384

BAKAR, Anne L., President and Chief Executive Officer, Telecare Heritage Psychiatric Health Center, Oakland, CA, p. A82
President and Chief Executive Officer, Willow Rock Center, San Leandro, CA, p. A95

BAKER, Alison, M.D., Chief of Staff, Missouri Baptist Sullivan Hospital, Sullivan, MO, p. A419

BAKER, Bonnie, M.D., Chief Medical Services, Veterans Health Care System Of The Ozarks, Fayetteville, AR, p. A45
Vice President Finance and Chief Financial Officer, Butler Hospital, Providence, RI, p. A613

BAKER, Brenda, Chief Financial Officer, Riverview Health, Noblesville, IN, p. A238

BAKER, Christina, Chief Nursing Officer, Fairfield Memorial Hospital, Fairfield, IL, p. A205

BAKER, Cindi, Chief Operating Officer, Riverwood Healthcare Center, Aitkin, MN, p. A371

BAKER, Damon, D.O., Chief Medical Officer, Oklahoma State University Medical Center, Tulsa, OK, p. A570

BAKER, Deborah, Vice President, Nursing, Johns Hopkins Hospital, Baltimore, MD, p. A324
Vice President, Patient Care Services, Mount Auburn Hospital, Cambridge, MA, p. A338

BAKER, Denis, Chief Information Officer, Sarasota Memorial Health Care System, Sarasota, FL, p. A157

BAKER, Erin, Chief Nursing Officer, Eminent Medical Center, Richardson, TX, p. A708

BAKER, Frank, Chief Information Officer, Mary Breckinridge Arh Hospital, Hyden, KY, p. A285

BAKER, Gary E., Chief Executive Officer, Honorhealth John C. Lincoln Medical Center, Phoenix, AZ, p. A36
Senior Vice President and Chief Executive Officer, Honorhealth Scottsdale Shea Medical Center, Scottsdale, AZ, p. A38

BAKER, Harlan, Chief Information Officer, Mcdonough District Hospital, Mb, IL, p. A211

BAKER, J, M.D., President Medical Staff, Bertrand Chaffee Hospital, Springville, NY, p. A498

BAKER, Jason, Administrator, Christus Dubuis Hospital Of Beaumont, Beaumont, TX, p. A658

BAKER, Joann, Administrator, Doctors Memorial Hospital, Bonifay, FL, p. A132

BAKER, Joel, D.O., Chief Medical Officer, Wayne County Hospital, Corydon, IA, p. A246

BAKER, Judy, Chief Financial Officer, Kindred Hospital-Mansfield, Mansfield, TX, p. A699

BAKER, Maia, MSN, Chief Nurse Executive, Rio Grande State Center/South Texas Health Care System, Harlingen, TX, p. A683

BAKER, Mark A., Chief Executive Officer, Jack Hughston Memorial Hospital, Phenix City, AL, p. A23

BAKER, Melissa, Director, Human Resources, Providence Little Company Of Mary Medical Center - Torrance, Torrance, CA, p. A101
Director, Human Resources, Providence Little Company Of Mary Medical Center San Pedro, San Pedro, CA, p. A96

BAKER, Michelle, Director Information Systems, Indiana University Health White Memorial Hospital, Monticello, IN, p. A236

BAKER, Nichelle, Chair Human Resources, Mayo Clinic Hospital, Phoenix, AZ, p. A36

BAKER, Paige, MSN, R.N., Chief Nursing Officer, Lee's Summit Medical Center, Lee's Summit, MO, p. A410

BAKER, Paula F., President and Chief Executive Officer, Freeman Health System, Joplin, MO, p. A408

BAKER, Peter, Senior Vice President and Administrator, Loma Linda University Medical Center-Murrieta, Murrieta, CA, p. A80

BAKER, R, M.D., Vice President and Chief Information Officer, Wellspan York Hospital, York, PA, p. A612

BAKER, Reese, Director Information Systems, Crittenden County Hospital, Marion, KY, p. A289

BAKER, Roni, Director of Nursing, Herington Municipal Hospital, Herington, KS, p. A266

BAKER, Sharon, Director Support Services, Fairbanks, Indianapolis, IN, p. A232

BAKER, Steve, Vice President and Chief Technology and Information Officer, Columbus Regional Hospital, Columbus, IN, p. A225

BAKER, Vanya, Director, Wake Forest Baptist Health - Wilkes Medical Center, North Wilkesboro, NC, p. A516

BAKER-WITT, Francine, R.N., Chief Executive Officer, Effingham Hospital, Springfield, GA, p. A180

BAKEWELL, Nancy, Administrator, Monroe Hospital, Bloomington, IN, p. A224
Chief Nursing Officer, Monroe Hospital, Bloomington, IN, p. A224

BAKHTIER, Hasan, M.D., Medical Director, Community Mental Health Center, Lawrenceburg, IN, p. A235

BAKICH, Sandy, Director Information Management, Delano Regional Medical Center, Delano, CA, p. A62

BAKKEN, Mary, Executive Vice President and Chief Operating Officer, Silver Cross Hospital, New Lenox, IL, p. A214

BAKKUM, Kyle, Chief Executive Officer and Administrator, Vernon Memorial Healthcare, Elk Mound, WI, p. A783

BALASIA, Tim, Chief Financial Officer, Johnson Memorial Hospital, Franklin, IN, p. A229

BALASUBRAMONY, Suresh, M.D., Chief Medical Officer, Minnie Hamilton Healthcare Center, Grantsville, WV, p. A772

BALASUNDARAM, Anusuya, M.D., Medical Director, Hampton Behavioral Health Center, Westampton, NJ, p. A465

BALAZY, Thomas, M.D., Medical Director, Craig Hospital, Englewood, CO, p. A112

BALCAVAGE, Thomas, Vice President Chief Patient Safety and Quality Officer, Jefferson Stratford Hospital, Stratford, NJ, p. A463

BALCEZAK, Thomas, M.D., Senior Vice President Medical Affairs and Chief Medical Officer, Yale-New Haven Hospital, New Haven, CT, p. A124

BALDAUF, Mary-Lyn, Chief Executive Officer, Kindred Hospital-Greensboro, Greensboro, NC, p. A511

BALDAUF, Robb, Coordinator Information Systems, Cleveland Clinic Akron General Lodi Hospital, Lodi, OH, p. A543

BALDERRAMA, Jose, Vice President Human Resources, Valley Hospital, Ridgewood, NJ, p. A462

BALDOSARO, Thomas, Chief Financial Officer, Inspira Medical Center-Elmer, Elmer, NJ, p. A455
Chief Financial Officer, Inspira Medical Center-Vineland, Vineland, NJ, p. A465

BALDRIDGE, Dava, R.N., Chief Nursing Officer, Hillcrest Hospital - South, Tulsa, OK, p. A569

BALDWIN, Barbara, Chief Information Officer, Anne Arundel Medical Center, Annapolis, MD, p. A324

BALDWIN, Bruce A., Chief Executive Officer, Newberry County Memorial Hospital, Newberry, SC, p. A623

BALDWIN, Chad, Interim Chief Executive Officer, Westside Surgical Hospital, Houston, TX, p. A689

BALDWIN, Ellen, R.N., Chief Nursing Officer, Texas Health Center For Diagnostic & Surgery, Plano, TX, p. A707

BALDWIN, Erin, M.P.H., Chief Operating Officer, Mahaska Health Partnership. Oskaloosa, IA, p. A256

BALDWIN, Linda, Chief Nursing Officer, Ogallala Community Hospital, Ogallala, NE, p. A436

BALDWIN, Nathan, M.D., President Medical Staff, Baptist Memorial Hospital-Booneville, Booneville, MS, p. A390

BALDWIN, Stephen, Chief Operating Officer, Touro Infirmary, New Orleans, LA, p. A311

BALDWIN, Steve, Manager Information Technology, Wyoming State Hospital, Evanston, WY, p. A802
Vice President Finance, The Willough At Naples, Naples, FL, p. A149

BALDWIN, William, Chief Information Officer, Ashe Memorial Hospital, Jefferson, NC, p. A513

BALES, Alicia, Senior Director, Chief Executive Officer and Chief Nursing Officer, Carilion Tazewell Community Hospital, Tazewell, VA, p. A752

BALES, Brian, Director Plant Operations, Encompass Health Rehabilitation Hospital Of Princeton, Princeton, WV, p. A776

BALES, Glenn, Chief Financial Officer, Providence Saint Josep. Medical Center, Burbank, CA, p. A59

BALES-CHUBB, Denyse, Chief Executive Officer, Adventhealth Tampa, Tampa, FL, p. A159
President and Chief Executive Officer, Adventhealth Connerton, Land O'Lakes, FL, p. A143

BALKO, Tom, Manager Information Systems, Carris Health - Redwood, Redwood Falls, MN, p. A383

BALL, Cassie, Chief Financial Officer, Colleton Medical Center, Walterboro, SC, p. A625

BALL, Charlie, Chief Operating Officer, Specialty Rehabilitation Hospital Of Coushatta, Coushatta, LA, p. A299

BALL, Connie, Chief Financial Officer, Specialty Rehabilitation Hospital Of Coushatta, Coushatta, LA, p. A299

BALL, Craig, Chief Executive Officer, Specialty Rehabilitation Hospital Of Coushatta, Coushatta, LA, p. A299

BALL, James, Chief Operating Officer, Executive, St. Anthony's Rehabilitation Hospital, Lauderdale Lakes, FL, p. A144

BALL, Jim, Chief Operating Officer, St. Catherine's Rehabilitation Hospital, North Miami, FL, p. A149

BALL, Kelly, Vice President of Clinical Operations, Calais Regional Hospital, Calais, ME, p. A319

BALL, Rodney, Vice President Finance, Atrium Health Cabarrus, Concord, NC, p. A508

BALLANCE, William, Chief of Medical Staff, Vidant Bertie Hospital, Windsor, NC, p. A520

BALLARD, Jerry, Director Information Systems, Central Florida Regional Hospital, Sanford, FL, p. A156

BALLARD, John, Ph.D., FACHE, Chief Executive Officer, Forrest City Medical Center, Forrest City, AR, p. A45

BALLARD, Lorraine, Director Human Resources, St. Helena Parish Hospital, Greensburg, LA, p. A302

BALLARD, Terri, Chief Nursing Officer, Encompass Health Rehabilitation Hospital Of Northern Kentucky, Edgewood, KY, p. A282

BALLESTERO, Susan, Vice President and Chief Human Resources Officer, Saint Peter's University Hospital, New Brunswick, NJ, p. A459

BALLEW, Cheryl, Human Resources Director, Encompass Health Rehabilitation Hospital Of Las Vegas, Las Vegas, NV, p. A443

BALLIETT, Matt, Chief Information Officer, Coal County General Hospital, Coalgate, OK, p. A558

BALLIN, Daniel, Administrator, Coastal Virginia Rehabilitation, Newport News, VA, p. A746

BALLINGHOFF, James, MSN, R.N., Chief Nursing Officer and Associate Executive Director, Penn Presbyterian Medical Center, Philadelphia, PA, p. A601

BALLMAN, Patricia, Director, Westfield Memorial Hospital, Westfield, NY, p. A502

BALLOU, Michele, M.D., Chief Medical Staff, Lewisgale Hospital Alleghany, Low Moor, VA, p. A745

BALOGA-ALTIERI, Bonnie, Ph.D., R.N., Vice President Patient Care Services and Chief Nursing Officer, Children's Specialized Hospital, New Brunswick, NJ, p. A459

BALSANO, Tony, Vice President Finance, Saint Francis Medical Center, Cap. Girardeau, MO, p. A403

BALSAR, Jeffrey R., President and Chief Executive Officer Vanderbilt Medical Center and Dean, Vanderbilt University Scho, Vanderbilt University Medical Center, Nashville, TN, p. A647

BALT, David, D.O., Chief Medical Officer, Avera Queen Of Peace Hospital, Mitchell, SD, p. A629

BALTIERRA, David, M.D., President Medical Staff, Jefferson Medical Center, Ranson, WV, p. A776

BALTZ, Phyllis, Chief Executive Officer, Methodist Hospital Of Sacramento, Sacramento, CA, p. A89

BALUKOFF, Sam E., Hospital Administrator, Kaiser Permanente Medical Center, Honolulu, HI, p. A184

BALULGA, Josefina, M.D., Clinical Director, Florida State Hospital, Chattahoochee, FL, p. A134

BALUNTANSKI, Brian, Chief Financial Officer, Mclaren Macomb, Mount Clemens, MI, p. A362

BALZ, Pat, Vice President Operations Human Resources, Baylor Scott & White Medical Center - Temple, Temple, TX, p. A719

BAMAN, Raj, D.O., President Medical Staff, Samaritan North Lincoln Hospital, Lincoln City, OR, p. A577

BAMBERGER, John, Administrator, Cornerstone Behavioral Health Hospital of Union County, Berkeley Heights, NJ, p. A452

BAMBURG, Jeanna, FACHE, Chief Executive Officer, Hca Houston Healthcare Southeast, Pasadena, TX, p. A705

BAME, Jeremiah, R.N., Chief Nursing Officer, Piedmont Newton Hospital, Covington, GA, p. A170

BAMFORD, Jaime, M.D., Director, Commonwealth Center For Children And Adolescents, Staunton, VA, p. A752

BAMMEL, Paul, Vice President, Mayo Clinic Health System - Northland In Barron, Barron, WI, p. A781

BANAS, Mark, M.D., Chief Medical Officer, Ascension St. Mary's Hospital, Rhinelander, WI, p. A795

BANBURY, Brian, Director Site Information Systems, Advocate Christ Medical Center, Oak Lawn, IL, p. A215

BANCHY, Pamela, Chief Information Officer, Western Reserve Hospital, Cuyahoga Falls, OH, p. A538

BANDEH, Jamal, Interim Chief Executive Officer, Prague Community Hospital, Prague, OK, p. A567

BANDFIELD-KEOUGH, Kathryn, Vice President Patient Care Services, Munson Healthcare Cadillac Hospital, Cadillac, MI, p. A350

BANDLA, H., M.D., Chief Clinical Affairs, Walter P. Reuther Psychiatric Hospital, Westland, MI, p. A369

BANDS, James Chief Financial Officer, Ivinson Memorial Hospital, Laramie, WY, p. A803

BANDY, Dawn, Chief Financial Officer, Grant Regional Health Center, Lancaster, WI, p. A787

BANDY, Don, Director Information Technology, Integris Deaconess, Oklahoma City, OK, p. A564

BANDY, Jennifer, Human Resource Business Partner, Wake Forest Baptist Health-Davie Medical Center, Bermuda Run, NC, p. A505

BANDY, P, M.D., Chief Medical Officer and Chief of Staff, Levi Hospital, Hot Springs National Park, AR, p. A47

BANE, Brian, Vice President Human Resources, Rush Memorial Hospital, Rushville, IN, p. A240

BANE, Harrison, President, Good Samaritan Medical Center, Brockton, MA, p. A337

BANE, William, Chief Financial Officer, Inova Loudoun Hospital, Leesburg, VA, p. A744

BANGA, Alok, M.D., Medical Director, Sierra Vista Hospital, Sacramento, CA, p. A90

BANIEWICZ, John, M.D., Chief Medical Officer, Lake Health, Concord Township, OH, p. A537

BANK, Carol, Vice President Human Resources, Divine Savior Healthcare, Portage, WI, p. A794

BANKER, Julie, R.N., MSN, Chief Nursing Officer, Lehigh Regional Medical Center, Lehigh Acres, FL, p. A144

BANKERS, Diane, Chief Nursing Officer, Welia Health, Mora, MN, p. A381

BANKS, Chester, Director Human Resources, East Orange General Hospital, East Orange, NJ, p. A454

BANKS, Elizabeth, Chief Executive Officer, Summit Behavioral Healthcare, Cincinnati, OH, p. A533

BANKS, Matthew, Chief Executive Officer, Merit Health Wesley, Hattiesburg, MS, p. A393

BANKS, Maureen, Chief Nursing Officer, Spaulding Rehabilitation Hospital, Charlestown, MA, p. A338
Chief Operating Officer, Spaulding Rehabilitation Hospital, Charlestown, MA, p. A338
President, Spaulding Hospital For Continuing Medical Care Cambridge, Cambridge, MA, p. A338

President, Spaulding Rehabilitation Hospital Cap. Cod, East Sandwich, MA, p. A338

BANKS, Patti, Chief Operating Officer, Ely-Bloomenson Community Hospital, Ely, MN, p. A376
Interim Chief Executive Officer, Ely-Bloomenson Community Hospital, Ely, MN, p. A376

BANKS, Penny, R.N., Administrator, St. Charles Surgical Hospital, New Orleans, LA, p. A311

BANKS, Robbi, Vice President, Human Resources, Medical Center Health System, Odessa, TX, p. A703

BANKS, Walter, Director Human Resources, Baptist Memorial Hospital-Desoto, Southaven, MS, p. A400

BANKSTON, Doug, Director Technical Services, North Oaks Medical Center, Hammond, LA, p. A302

BANKTSON, Julie, Manager Human Resources, Paul Oliver Memorial Hospital, Frankfort, MI, p. A355

BANNA, Shannon, Chief Financial Officer, Northside Hospital - Gwinnett, Lawrenceville, GA, p. A175

BANNER, Fred, Chief Information Officer, Shore Medical Center, Somers Point, NJ, p. A463

BANSAL, Rina, M.D., President, Inova Alexandria Hospital, Alexandria, VA, p. A738

BANTZ, Steve, Manager Information Technology, Grundy County Memorial Hospital, Grundy Center, IA, p. A250

BANUEDOS, Jorge, Director Human Resources, Dsh Metropolitan, Norwalk, CA, p. A81

BAQUET, Shawn, Chief of Staff, Iberia Medical Center, New Iberia, LA, p. A310

BARAKAT, Tawfik, M.D., President, Medical Staff, Mercyhealth Hospital And Medical Center - Harvard, Harvard, IL, p. A207

BARANSKI, Kenneth, Chief Financial Officer, Hills & Dales General Hospital, Cass City, MI, p. A350

BARANSKI, Monica, MS, R.N., President, Mclaren Bay Special Care, Bay City, MI, p. A349

BARBADIAN, John, Vice President Human Resources, Adventist Health - Tulare, Tulare, CA, p. A102

BARBAREE, Jerry, Director Human Resources, Baptist Memorial Hospital - Memphis, Memphis, TN, p. A643

BARBARIN, LaSharndra, Chief Executive Officer, Medical City Lewisville, Lewisville, TX, p. A696

BARBAROTTA, Ann Marie., Executive Director, Creedmoor Psychiatric Center, Jamaica, NY, p. A486

BARBEE, Daniel, Chief Executive Officer, The University Of Toledo Medical Center, Toledo, OH, p. A551

BARBER, Eric A., President and Chief Executive Officer, Mary Lanning Healthcare, Hastings, NE, p. A433

BARBER, Karen, R.N., Chief Executive Officer, Yoakum Community Hospital, Yoakum, TX, p. A726

BARBER, Keith, CPA, Chief Executive Officer, Houston Methodist Willowbrook Hospital, Houston, TX, p. A686

BARBER, Michael, Chief Operating Officer, Chester County Hospital, West Chester, PA, p. A610

BARBER, Richard, M.D., Chief Medical Officer, Wake Forest Baptist Health - Wilkes Medical Center, North Wilkesboro, NC, p. A516

BARBER, Roxann, Regional Ambulatory Care and Ancillary Services Officer, Amita Health Mercy Medical Center, Aurora, IL, p. A195

BARBER, Scott, Administrator, Camden General Hospital, Camden, TN, p. A634
Interim Chief Executive Officer, West Tennessee Healthcare Dyersburg Hospital, Dyersburg, TN, p. A637

BARBINI, Gerald J., Interim Chief Executive Officer, Northwestern Medical Center, Saint Albans, VT, p. A736

BARBO, Steve, R.N., Chief Executive Officer, Citizens Medical Center, Columbia, LA, p. A299

BARBOUR, Alexis, Director Finance, Columbus Dublin Springs, Dublin, OH, p. A539

BARBOUR, Michael, Chief Nursing Officer, Emerald Coast Behavioral Hospital, Panama City, FL, p. A152

BARCHI, Daniel, Senior Vice President, Technical Services and Chief Information Officer, Bridgeport Hospital, Bridgeport, CT, p. A121

BARCLAY, Duane, D.O., Chief Medical Officer, Emory Hillandale Hospital, Lithonia, GA, p. A175

BARCLAY, Jeremy, Chief Executive Officer, St. David's Round Rock Medical Center, Round Rock, TX, p. A710

BARCLAY, Rick, Vice President Support Services, Mercy Hospital Rogers, Rogers, AR, p. A52

BARCUS, Krista, Human Resources Leader, Mosaic Medical Center - Maryville, Maryville, MO, p. A411

BARDEN, Sean, Executive Vice President and Chief Financial Officer, Mary Washington Hospital, Fredericksburg, VA, p. A742
Executive Vice President and Chief Financial Officer, Stafford Hospital, Stafford, VA, p. A752

BARDIER, Catherine, Vice President, Human Resources, Elliot Hospital, Manchester, NH, p. A450

BARDWELL, Carol, R.N., MSN, Chief Nurse Executive, Martha's Vineyard Hospital, Oak Bluffs, MA, p. A343

BARDWELL, Sheila, Director Information Systems, Baptist Memorial Hospital-Golden Triangle, Columbus, MS, p. A391

BAREFOOT, Denise, Director of Information Technology, Carolina Pines Regional Medical Center, Hartsville, SC, p. A621

BAREIS, Charles, M.D., Medical Director, Macneal Hospital, Berwyn, IL, p. A195

BARELA, Barbara, Director Human Resources, Gila Regional Medical Center, Silver City, NM, p. A472

BARFIELD, Donna, Chief Nursing Officer, West Tennessee Healthcare Volunteer Hospital, Martin, TN, p. A643
Interim Chief Executive Officer, West Tennessee Healthcare Volunteer Hospital, Martin, TN, p. A643

BARGEN, Jim, Chief Operating Officer, Box Butte General Hospital, Alliance, NE, p. A429

BARHAM, Ed, M.D., Chief of Staff, Merit Health Woman's Hospital, Flowood, MS, p. A392

BARIOLA, Christopher L., Chief Executive Officer, Baptist Memorial Rehabilitation Hospital, Germantown, TN, p. A638

BARKER, Alanna, Director of Human Resources, Hartgrove Hospital, Chicago, IL, p. A198

BARKER, James, Chief Executive Officer, Munson Healthcare Manistee Hospital, Manistee, MI, p. A361
President and Chief Executive Officer, Paul Oliver Memorial Hospital, Frankfort, MI, p. A355

BARKER, Karen, Vice President and Chief Information Officer, Sinai Hospital Of Baltimore, Baltimore, MD, p. A326

BARKER, Kathryn, Chief Human Resources Management, Veterans Health Care System Of The Ozarks, Fayetteville, AR, p. A45

BARKER, Louise, R.N., Chief Executive Officer, Central Louisiana Surgical Hospital, Alexandria, LA, p. A295

BARKER, Richard, Administrator and Chief Executive Officer, Mercy Health Love County, Marietta, OK, p. A561

BARKER, Russell, Community Chief Executive Officer, Mcdowell Arh Hospital, Mcdowell, KY, p. A290
Information Officer, U. S. Public Health Service Indian Hospital-Whiteriver, Whiteriver, AZ, p. A41

BARKER JR, William Vice President Administration, Pleasant Valley Hospital, Point Pleasant, WV, p. A776

BARKHYMER, Mary, R.N., MSN, Vice President Patient Care Services and Chief Nursing Officer, Upmc St. Margaret, Pittsburgh, PA, p. A604

BARKMAN, Joseph, Vice President Financial Services, Oaklawn Psychiatric Center, Goshen, IN, p. A229

BARKSDALE, Mary, Director Human Resources, Person Memorial Hospital, Roxboro, NC, p. A517

BARLAGE, Seth, Associate Medical Center Director, John J. Pershing Veterans Affairs Medical Center, Poplar Bluff, MO, p. A411

BARLEY, Tammy, Director, Human Resources, Encompass Health Rehabilitation Hospital Of Jonesboro, Jonesboro, AR, p. A47

BARLIS, Ellen, Chief Financial Officer, Nyc Health + Hospitals / Jacobi, Bronx, NY, p. A477

BARLOW, Carol, Chief Financial Officer, Bailey Medical Center, Owasso, OK, p. A566

BARLOW, Mark, M.D., Chief Medical Officer and President Medical Staff, Cornerstone Hospital Of Houston At Clearlake, Webster, TX, p. A724

BARLOW, Roddex, Chief Operating Officer, The Hospitals Of Providence Memorial Campus, El Paso, TX, p. A676

BARLOW, Sereka, Chief Operating Officer, The Hospitals Of Providence Sierra Campus, El Paso, TX, p. A676

BARMECHA, Jitendra, M.D., M.P.H., Senior Vice President and Chief Information Officer, St. Barnabas Hospital, Bronx, NY, p. A477

BARNARD, Kerri, Director Human Resources, Larned State Hospital, Larned, KS, p. A268

BARNARD, Lawrence, President and Chief Executive Officer, St. Rose Dominican Hospitals - Siena Campus, Henderson, NV, p. A442

BARNCORD, Sharon, Human Resource Business Partner, Kaiser Permanente South San Francisco, South San Francisco, CA, p. A99

BARND, Kristi, Chief Operating Officer, Henry County Hospital, Napoleon, OH, p. A546
Interim Chief Executive Officer, Henry County Hospital, Napoleon, OH, p. A546

BARNELL, Phil, Chief Medical Officer, Hshs St. Mary's Hospital, Decatur, IL, p. A202

BARNER, Wiley B., Chief Executive Officer, Wellbridge Heathcare Of San Marcos, San Marcos, TX, p. A714

BARNES, Alan, Chief Financial Officer, North Star Behavioral Health System, Anchorage, AK, p. A27
Interim Chief Executive Officer, North Star Behavioral Health System, Anchorage, AK, p. A27

BARNES, Becky, Chief Operating Officer, St. David's North Austin Medical Center, Austin, TX, p. A656

BARNES, Betty, Director Human Resources, Chicago Behavioral Hospital, Des Plaines, IL, p. A202

BARNES, Bridget, Vice President and Chief Information Officer, Ohsu Hospital, Portland, OR, p. A579

BARNES, Deborah, Vice President and Chief Information Officer, Children's Hospital Of The King's Daughters, Norfolk, VA, p. A747

BARNES, Douglas, M.D., Chief of Staff, Shriners Hospitals For Children-Houston, Houston, TX, p. A688

BARNES, Elbert, M.D., Chief Medical Officer, Medical Center Of Trinity, Trinity, FL, p. A161

BARNES, Gary, Senior Vice President, Chief Information Officer, Medical Center Health System, Odessa, TX, p. A703

BARNES, Gloria, MSN, Assistant Vice President Patient Care Services, Southeastern Regional Medical Center, Newnan, GA, p. A178

BARNES, Jacqueline, Manager Health Information, Select Specialty Hospital-Jackson, Jackson, MS, p. A395

BARNES, Jeff, Director Information Technology, Girard Medical Center, Girard, KS, p. A265

BARNES, Karen, Interim Chief Nursing Officer, Logan Regional Medical Center, Logan, WV, p. A774

BARNES, Larry, Vice President Information Technology, Salina Regional Health Center, Salina, KS, p. A275

BARNES, Leslie, Chief Executive Officer, Parkview Medical Center, Pueblo, CO, p. A118
Chief Financial Officer, Parkview Medical Center, Pueblo, CO, p. A118

BARNES, Marla, Director of Nursing, Pushmataha Hospital, Antlers, OK, p. A555

BARNES, Michael, Chief Information Officer, North Valley Hospital, Whitefish, MT, p. A428

BARNES, P., Director, Human Resources, North Mississipp. Medical Center-Pontotoc, Pontotoc, MS, p. A399

BARNES, Shannon, Chief Human Resource Officer, Bonner General Health, Sandpoint, ID, p. A193

BARNES, Sherry, Director Health Information and Quality Management, Rolling Hills Hospital, Ada, OK, p. A555

BARNETT, DeLynn, Director Human Resources, Lake Chelan Community Hospital And Clinics, Chelan, WA, p. A756

BARNETT, Frederick, M.D., Chief of Staff, Adventhealth Central Texas, Killeen, TX, p. A693

BARNETT, Julia, Chief Nursing Officer, Union General Hospital, Blairsville, GA, p. A167

BARNETT, Kelly, Human Resource Officer, Brownfield Regional Medical Center, Brownfield, TX, p. A660

BARNETT, Laura, Executive Director, Human Resources, Brigham And Women's Faulkner Hospital, Boston, MA, p. A335

BARNETT, Lori, R.N., MSN, President and Chief Operating Officer, Guthrie Troy Community Hospital, Troy, PA, p. A609

BARNETT, Pam, R.N., Director of Nursing, Highland District Hospital, Hillsboro, OH, p. A542

BARNETT, Shawn, President and Chief Executive Officer, Chi St. Vincent Medical Center-North, Sherwood, AR, p. A53
Senior Vice President and Chief Financial Officer, Chi St. Vincent Hot Springs, Hot Springs, AR, p. A47
Senior Vice President and Chief Financial Officer, Chi St. Vincent Infirmary Medical Center, Little Rock, AR, p. A49
Senior Vice President and Chief Financial Officer, Chi St. Vincent Medical Center-North, Sherwood, AR, p. A53
Senior Vice President and Chief Financial Officer, Chi St. Vincent Morrilton, Morrilton, AR, p. A50

BARNETT, Steve, President and Chief Executive Officer, Mckenzie Health System, Sandusky, MI, p. A366

BARNETT, Tom, Chief Information Officer, Highland Hospital, Rochester, NY, p. A496

BARNETTE, Brian, Chief Information Officer, Shepherd Center, Atlanta, GA, p. A165

BARNHARDT, Bonnie, Executive Director Human Resources, Ridgeview Le Sueur Medical Center, Le Sueur, MN, p. A378

BARNHART, Cody, Chief Executive Officer, Aspen Mountain Medical Center, Rock Springs, WY, p. A803

BARNHART, David, Director Information Systems, Rockledge Regional Medical Center, Rockledge, FL, p. A155

BARNHART, J. T., Chief Executive Officer, Tennova Healthcare - Cleveland, Cleveland, TN, p. A636

BARNHART, Jeff, FACHE, Chief Executive Officer, Hereford Regional Medical Center, Hereford, TX, p. A684

BARNO, Jill, M.D., Chief Medical Officer, Ohiohealth Berger Hospital, Circleville, OH, p. A533

BARNOSKI, Phillip. Administrator, Creek Nation Community Hospital, Okemah, OK, p. A563

BARONE, Richard, M.D., Medical Director, Montefiore New Rochelle, New Rochelle, NY, p. A489

BARR, Ann, Chief Information Officer - Bay Area, California Pacific Medical Center-St. Luke's Campus, San Francisco, CA, p. A93

Chief Information Officer - Bay Area, California Pacific Medical Center, San Francisco, CA, p. A93
Chief Information Officer, Sutter Health Bay Area, Sutter Maternity And Surgery Center Of Santa Cruz, Santa Cruz, CA, p. A97
Interim Chief Financial Officer, Adventhealth Dade City, Dade City, FL, p. A135

BARR, Brent, Chief Information Officer, Minnie Hamilton Healthcare Center, Grantsville, WV, p. A772

BARR, Bret A., President and Chief Executive Officer, Conway Medical Center, Conway, SC, p. A618

BARR, Francine, R.N., MS, Chief Executive Officer, Bon Secours St. Mary's Hospital, Richmond, VA, p. A749
R.N., MS, Vice President and Chief Operating Officer, Bon Secours St. Mary's Hospital, Richmond, VA, p. A749

BARR, Kristine, Vice President Communication Services, O'Bleness Memorial Hospital, Athens, OH, p. A528

BARR, Kyle, Senior Vice President, Chief Team Resources Officer, Mease Countryside Hospital, Safety Harbor, FL, p. A155
Senior Vice President, Chief Team Resources Officer, Mease Dunedin Hospital, Dunedin, FL, p. A137
Senior Vice President, Chief Team Resources Officer, Morton Plant North Bay Hospital, New Port Richey, FL, p. A149

BARR, Mary Beth, R.N., Chief Executive Officer, Pocahontas Memorial Hospital, Buckeye, WV, p. A770

BARRA, Jon, Director Human Resources, Wyoming Behavioral Institute, Casper, WY, p. A801

BARRACLOUGH, Grant, R.N., Chief Nursing Officer, Castleview Hospital, Price, UT, p. A731

BARRALL, Audrey, Director Human Resources, Adventist Health Clear Lake, Clearlake, CA, p. A60
Director Human Resources, Adventist Health St. Helena, Saint Helena, CA, p. A90

BARRERA, Edward, Director Communications, Encino Hospital Medical Center, Encino, CA, p. A63

BARRERA, Liflor, Manager Human Resources, Wahiawa General Hospital, Wahiawa, HI, p. A187

BARRERA-RICHARDS, Ursula, Human Resource Director, Northwest Ohio Psychiatric Hospital, Toledo, OH, p. A550

BARRERE, Davie Ann, Coordinator Information Technology, Dahl Memorial Healthcare Association, Ekalaka, MT, p. A423

BARRETT, Anne, Associate Executive Director Human Resources, Southside Hospital, Bay Shore, NY, p. A475

BARRETT, Bill, Manager Human Resources, Wilson N. Jones Regional Medical Center, Sherman, TX, p. A716

BARRETT, Cindy, Administrative Assistant, Dsh Patton, Patton, CA, p. A85

BARRETT, Hannah, Director of Nursing, North Sunflower Medical Center, Ruleville, MS, p. A400

BARRETT, James W., Chief Executive Officer, Richardson Medical Center, Rayville, LA, p. A313

BARRETT, Jason P., Chief Executive Officer, Flagler Hospital, Saint Augustine, FL, p. A155

BARRETT, John, Regional Director Human Resources, Franciscan Health Michigan City, Michigan City, IN, p. A236

BARRETT, Kristen, Chief Executive Officer, Meadowbrook Rehabilitation Hospital, Gardner, KS, p. A265

BARRETT, Lynn, Chief Nursing Officer, Centerpoint Medical Center, Independence, MO, p. A407

BARRETT, Nichole, R.N., Interim Administrator, Mercy Hospital Healdton, Healdton, OK, p. A560

BARRETT, Pam, Human Resources Director, Colorado River Medical Center, Needles, CA, p. A81

BARRICK, Lisa, Controller, Encompass Health Rehabilitation Hospital Of Scottsdale, Scottsdale, AZ, p. A38

BARRIENT, Mac, Administrator, North Oaks Rehabilitation Hospital, Hammond, LA, p. A302

BARRILLEAUX, Scott G., FACHE, Chief Executive Officer, Drew Memorial Health System, Monticello, AR, p. A50

BARRIO, Gabe, M.D., Chief of Staff, Whidbeyhealth, Coupeville, WA, p. A757

BARRIOS, Luis, Chief Information Officer, Veterans Affairs New York Harbor Healthcare System, Brooklyn, NY, p. A479

BARROCAS, Albert, M.D., Chief Medical Officer, Wellstar Atlanta Medical Center, Atlanta, GA, p. A165

BARRON, Steven R. Esq, Chief Executive Officer, San Gorgonio Memorial Hospital, Banning, CA, p. A58

BARROW, Robert, Chief Executive Officer, Pontiac General Hospital, Pontiac, MI, p. A364

BARROW, William F. II, Chief Executive Officer, Beauregard Health System, De Ridder, LA, p. A300

BARROWS, Cheryl, Vice President Human Resources, Sturdy Memorial Hospital, Attleboro, MA, p. A334

BARRY, Rick, Director Information Systems, Baylor Scott & White Medical Center—Frisco, Frisco, TX, p. A680

BARRY, Thomas, Chief Executive Officer, Pulaski Memorial Hospital, Winamac, IN, p. A242

BARSOM, Michael, M.D., Executive Director, Dsh Metropolitan, Norwalk, CA, p. A81

BARSOUM, Wael, M.D., President, Cleveland Clinic Florida, Weston, FL, p. A162

BARSTAD, Stacy, Chief Executive Officer, Sanford Tracy Medical Center, Tracy, MN, p. A386
Chief Executive Officer, Sanford Westbrook Medical Center, Westbrook, MN, p. A387

BARTA, Brian, Assistant Administrator and Chief Financial Officer, William Newton Hospital, Winfield, KS, p. A279

BARTAL, Ely, M.D., Chief Executive Officer and Medical Director, Kansas Surgery And Recovery Center, Wichita, KS, p. A279
M.D., Chief Executive Officer, Kansas Surgery And Recovery Center, Wichita, KS, p. A279

BARTELL, Michael, Chief Executive Officer, Encompass Health Lakeshore Rehabilitation Hospital, Birmingham, AL, p. A15

BARTELS, Bruce J., Chief Executive Officer, Lafayette Physical Rehabilitation Hospital, Lafayette, LA, p. A305

BARTELS, Dara, Chief Financial Officer, Gundersen Lutheran Medical Center, La Crosse, WI, p. A787

BARTELS, Jennifer, Director Human Resources, Pawnee County Memorial Hospital And Rural Health Clinic, Pawnee City, NE, p. A438

BARTH, Andrew J., Executive Director, Aspirus Langlade Hospital, Antigo, WI, p. A779

BARTH, Marci, Chief Nursing Officer, Fayette County Hospital, Vandalia, IL, p. A222

BARTHEL, Gayle, Coordinator Human Resources, Select Specialty Hospital-Flint, Flint, MI, p. A354

BARTHOLOMEW, Brenda, Chief Nursing Officer, Gunnison Valley Hospital, Gunnison, UT, p. A728

BARTHOLOMEW, K, M.D., Medical Director, Faulkton Area Medical Center, Faulkton, SD, p. A628

BARTILSON, Jim, Manager Information Systems, South Peninsula Hospital, Homer, AK, p. A28

BARTKOSKI, Tony, M.D., Chief of Medical Staff, Nemaha Valley Community Hospital, Seneca, KS, p. A276

BARTLETT, Beth, MSN, R.N., Vice President Nursing, Chi Health Saint Francis, Grand Island, NE, p. A433

BARTLETT, Freda, Director of Nursing, Crosbyton Clinic Hospital, Crosbyton, TX, p. A666

BARTLETT, Karolyn, Assistant Administrator, Mayo Clinic Health System - Northland In Barron, Barron, WI, p. A781

BARTLETT, Regina, Chief Executive Officer, Tristar Hendersonville Medical Center, Hendersonville, TN, p. A639

BARTLETT, Richard, M.D., Chief Medical Officer, Odessa Regional Medical Center South Campus, Odessa, TX, p. A704

BARTLETT, Ronald, Chief Financial Officer, Boston Medical Center, Boston, MA, p. A335

BARTLETT, Wayne, Director Information Systems, Alvarado Hospital Medical Center, San Diego, CA, p. A91

BARTLETT III, Thomas G., Administrator, Laird Hospital, Union, MS, p. A400

BARTLEY, Tracy, Manager Information Technology, Bath Community Hospital, Hot Springs, VA, p. A744

BARTOLETTI, Freddy, M.D., Chief of Staff, Community Hospital Of Anaconda, Anaconda, MT, p. A421

BARTOLOTTA, Carmen, R.N., Vice President, Patient Care Services and Chief Nursing Officer, Missouri Baptist Sullivan Hospital, Sullivan, MO, p. A419

BARTON, Douglas, M.D., Chief Medical Officer, Ssm Health St. Josep. - St. Charles, Saint Charles, MO, p. A414

BARTON, Josiah, Director Information Technology, Mobridge Regional Hospital, Mobridge, SD, p. A629

BARTON, Michelle, Chief Operating Officer, Milford Valley Memorial Hospital, Milford, UT, p. A729

BARTON, Thomas, M.D., Medical Director, Top. Surgical Specialty Hospital, Houston, TX, p. A689

BARTON, Vikki, R.N., Chief Nursing Officer, Collingsworth General Hospital, Wellington, TX, p. A724

BARTOW, Byran, Director, Winnebago Mental Health Institute, Winnebago, WI, p. A800

BARUT, Jennifer, Chief Executive Officer, Haven Behavioral Senior Care Of Albuquerque, Albuquerque, NM, p. A467

BARWIS, Kurt A., FACHE, President and Chief Executive Officer, Bristol Health, Bristol, CT, p. A121

BARYLSKE, Ben, Chief Financial Officer, St. Bernards Medical Center, Jonesboro, AR, p. A48

BASA, Rhea, Director Human Resources, Morrill County Community Hospital, Bridgeport, NE, p. A430

BASA-REYES, Fiona, Chief Executive Officer, Kindred Hospital-Los Angeles, Los Angeles, CA, p. A75

BASALAY, Erin, PsyD, Director Clinical Services, Rock Springs, Georgetown, TX, p. A681

BASEY, Marjorie, Chief Financial Officer, Rehabilitation Hospital Of Indiana, Indianapolis, IN, p. A233

BASH, Camille, Chief Financial Officer, Doctors Community Hospital, Lanham, MD, p. A330

BASHAM, Mark, M.D., Chief Medical Officer, Greenwood County Hospital, Eureka, KS, p. A264

BASILE, Michele S., Chief Executive Officer, Kindred Hospital-Philadelphia, Philadelphia, PA, p. A601

BASQUE, Tonya, Chief Nursing Officer, Freestone Medical Center, Fairfield, TX, p. A677

BASQUILL, Debra, Director Human Resources, Jennersville Hospital, West Grove, PA, p. A610

BASRA, Amandeep, Chief Administrative Officer, Good Samaritan Hospital, Bakersfield, CA, p. A57

BASRIA, Deborah, Human Resources Payroll Administrator, Kindred Hospital Bay Area-Tampa, Tampa, FL, p. A159

BASS, Darren, President, Cox Monett Hospital, Monett, MO, p. A412

BASS, Louis A., Chief Executive Officer, Rmc Anniston, Anniston, AL, p. A13

BASS, Sonya, MS, Chief Nursing Officer, Colorado Plains Medical Center, Fort Morgan, CO, p. A112

BASSETT, Keri, Human Resources Business Partner, Florida State Hospital, Chattahoochee, FL, p. A134

BASSETT, Kimberly S., R.N., President, St. Josep. Medical Center, Houston, TX, p. A688

BASSO, Amanda J., Chief Executive Officer, Crossroads Community Hospital, Mount Vernon, IL, p. A213

BASSO, Marty, Chief Financial Officer, Sibley Memorial Hospital, Washington, DC, p. A130
Senior Vice President Finance, Suburban Hospital, Bethesda, MD, p. A327

BASTARACHE, Maurice, Chief Information Officer, Chesapeake Regional Medical Center, Chesapeake, VA, p. A740

BASTIANELLO, Carol, Director Human Resources, Aspirus Iron River Hospitals & Clinics, Inc., Iron River, MI, p. A358

BASTIEN, Samuel A. IV, Ph.D., Chief Executive Officer, Four Winds Hospital, Saratoga Springs, NY, p. A497

BASTING, Gregory, M.D., Vice President Medical Affairs, Allied Services Rehabilitation Hospital, Scranton, PA, p. A606
M.D., Vice President Medical Affairs, John Heinz Institute Of Rehabilitation Medicine, Wilkes-Barre, PA, p. A611

BATA, Katie, Vice President Human Resources, Advocate Illinois Masonic Medical Center, Chicago, IL, p. A197
Vice President Human Resources, Advocate Lutheran General Hospital, Park Ridge, IL, p. A216

BATAL, Lucille M., Administrator, Baldpate Hospital, Georgetown, MA, p. A339

BATCHELOR, Dale, M.D., Chief Medical Officer, Saint Thomas West Hospital, Nashville, TN, p. A646

BATCHLOR, Daniela, Director Human Resources, Springhill Memorial Hospital, Mobile, AL, p. A22

BATCHLOR, Elaine, M.D., M.P.H., Chief Executive Officer, Martin Luther King, Jr. Community Hospital, Los Angeles, CA, p. A75

BATDORF, Karyn, Director of Human Resources, Monroe Hospital, Bloomington, IN, p. A224

BATEMAN, Bryan S., Chief Executive Officer, Poplar Bluff Regional Medical Center, Poplar Bluff, MO, p. A414

BATEMAN, Devin, M.D., Chief Medical Officer, Parker Adventist Hospital, Parker, CO, p. A117

BATEMAN, Gary, Chief Information Technology, Adair County Health System, Greenfield, IA, p. A250

BATEMAN, Jana, R.N., Chief Nursing Officer, Ut Health Jacksonville, Jacksonville, TX, p. A691

BATEMAN, Kenneth, CPA, President and Chief Executive Officer, Southeast Hospital, Cap. Girardeau, MO, p. A404

BATEMAN, Mark, Interim Chief Operating Officer, Saint Agnes Medical Center, Fresno, CA, p. A65

BATES, Christine, Chief Nursing Officer, Shodair Children's Hospital, Helena, MT, p. A425

BATES, Don, Chief Executive Officer, Golden Plains Community Hospital, Borger, TX, p. A660

BATES, Earl, Director Information Technology, Western Mental Health Institute, Bolivar, TN, p. A634

BATES, Joe, M.D., Clinical Director, Rusk State Hospital, Rusk, TX, p. A710

BATES, Margaret, Chief of Staff, Good Samaritan Hospital, Los Angeles, CA, p. A74

BATES, Ondrea, Senior Vice President, Operations and Continuum of Care, Henry Ford Allegiance Health, Jackson, MI, p. A359

BATES, Robert, Chief Financial Officer, Ascension St. Vincent Carmel Hospital, Carmel, IN, p. A225

BATES, Victoria, Director Human Resources, Salem Medical Center, Salem, NJ, p. A462

BATH, Harneet, M.D., Vice President, Chief Medicine Officer, Osf Saint Anthony Medical Center, Rockford, IL, p. A219

BATISTE, Michele, Director Human Resources, Preston Memorial Hospital, Kingwood, WV, p. A773

BATKE, Miriam, Interim Chief Human Resource Officer, Fisher-Titus Medical Center, Norwalk, OH, p. A546

BATORY, Robert, Vice President Human Resources, Wellspan York Hospital, York, PA, p. A612

BATRASH, Ahmad, Chief of Staff, Kansas City Veterans Affairs Medical Center, Kansas City, MO, p. A408

BATSHAW, Mark, M.D., Physician-in-Chief, Executive Vice President and Chief Academic Officer, Children's National Hospital, Washington, DC, p. A129

BATTEY, Patrick M., FACS, M.D., Chief Executive Officer, Piedmont Hospital, Atlanta, GA, p. A165

BATTISTA, Edward, Vice President Human Resources, California Pacific Medical Center-St. Luke's Campus, San Francisco, CA, p. A93
Vice President Human Resources, California Pacific Medical Center, San Francisco, CA, p. A93
Vice President Human Resources, Good Samaritan Hospital, San Jose, CA, p. A94

BATTLE, Joe, Director, James A. Haley Veterans' Hospital-Tampa, Tampa, FL, p. A159

BATTLES, Lindsay, Director Human Resources, Encompass Health Rehabilitation Hospital Of Dallas, Dallas, TX, p. A668

BATTS, Kayla, Manager Human Resources, Baptist Health La Grange, La Grange, KY, p. A285

BATTY, Jill, Chief Financial Officer, Cambridge Health Alliance, Cambridge, MA, p. A337

BATTY, Mark, Chief Operating Officer, Mason General Hospital And Family Of Clinics, Shelton, WA, p. A765

BATY, Krista, R.N., Chief Nursing Officer, Cedar Park Regional Medical Center, Cedar Park, TX, p. A663

BATZEL, Linnane, M.D., Senior Vice President Quality and Medical Affairs and Chief Medical Officer, Upmc Altoona, Altoona, PA, p. A584

BAUER, Denise, Director of Human Resources, Rochelle Community Hospital, Rochelle, IL, p. A218

BAUER, Jeremy, Director of Finance, West Holt Medical Services, Atkinson, NE, p. A429

BAUER, Jessica, President, Aurora Medical Center In Washington County, Hartford, WI, p. A786
President, Aurora Medical Center Summit, Summit, WI, p. A797

BAUER, John, Chief Operating Officer, Pam Specialty Hospital Of Covington, Covington, LA, p. A300

BAUER, Jonathan, Vice President Information Systems and Chief Information Officer, Atlantic General Hospital, Berlin, MD, p. A327

BAUER, Kyle, Chief Executive Officer, Cuyuna Regional Medical Center, Crosby, MN, p. A374

BAUER, Lafe, Vice President, Post Acute Care Services and Chief Administrative Officer, Daniel Drake Center For Post Acute Care, Cincinnati, OH, p. A532

BAUER, Roberta, M.D., Acting Chair Medical Staff, Cleveland Clinic Children's Hospital For Rehabilitation, Cleveland, OH, p. A534

BAUER, Sandra, Director Human Resources, Jefferson Community Health And Life, Fairbury, NE, p. A431

BAUER, Shar, Executive Secretary, South Central Health, Wishek, ND, p. A526

BAUER, Tracy, Chief Executive Officer, Midwest Medical Center, Galena, IL, p. A205

BAUER, William, M.D., Medical Director, Montevista Hospital, Las Vegas, NV, p. A443
Vice President Finance and Chief Financial Officer, Lehigh Valley Hospital - Hazleton, Hazleton, PA, p. A592

BAUGHMAN, Nathan, Chief Nursing Officer, Putnam County Memorial Hospital, Unionville, MO, p. A420

BAUM, David, M.D., Senior Vice President Medical Services, F. F. Thompson Hospital, Canandaigua, NY, p. A481

BAUM, Judy, Chief Executive Officer, Mountain Valley Regional Rehabilitation Hospital, Prescott Valley, AZ, p. A37

BAUMAN, Chris, Director of Nursing, Ballard Rehabilitation Hospital, San Bernardino, CA, p. A91

BAUMAN, Jonathan, M.D., Chief Medical Officer, Four Winds Hospital, Katonah, NY, p. A486

BAUMAN, Stephen R., Medical Center Director, Veterans Affairs Central California Health Care System, Fresno, CA, p. A66

BAUMBERGER, Sandra, M.D., President Medical Staff, Memorial Community Hospital And Health System, Blair, NE, p. A430

BAUMERT, Steven P., President and Chief Executive Officer, Methodist Jennie Edmundson Hospital, Council Bluffs, IA, p. A247

BAUMGARDNER, David, Director Information Management, Cleveland Clinic Union Hospital, Dover, OH, p. A539

BAUMGARTNER, David, M.D., Interim President, Mercy Health Saint Mary's, Grand Rapids, MI, p. A356

BAUMGARTNER, Jennifer, Chief Information Officer, Perkins County Health Services, Grant, NE, p. A433

BAUMGARTNER, Michael A., President, Ssm Health St. Mary's Hospital - Audrain, Mexico, MO, p. A412
President, Ssm Health St. Mary's Hospital - Jefferson City, Jefferson City, MO, p. A408

BAUNCHALK, James, Deputy Chief Clinical Services, Dwight David Eisenhower Army Medical Center, Fort Gordon, GA, p. A173

BAUSCHKA, Martha, R.N., Vice President and Chief Nursing Officer, Southwest General Health Center, Middleburg Heights, OH, p. A545

BAUTE, Corey, Vice President Human Resources, Franciscan Health Indianapolis, Indianapolis, IN, p. A232
Vice President of Human Resource, Franciscan Health Carmel, Carmel, IN, p. A225

BAVA, Michele, Director Human Resources, Doctors Medical Center Of Modesto, Modesto, CA, p. A78

BAVERSO, Lou, President, Upmc Carlisle, Carlisle, PA, p. A586
Vice President Operations, Upmc Magee-Womens Hospital, Pittsburgh, PA, p. A604

BAW, Joseph, Chief Operating Officer, Riveredge Hospital, Forest Park, IL, p. A205

BAWA, Balraj, M.D., Assistant Director Medical Services, Central Virginia Training Center, Madison Heights, VA, p. A745

BAXA, Erin, M.D., Chief Medical Officer, Osborne County Memorial Hospital, Osborne, KS, p. A273

BAXLEY III, Edmond Russell., President and Chief Executive Officer, Beaufort Memorial Hospital, Beaufort, SC, p. A615

BAXTER, Greg, M.D., President, Elliot Hospital, Manchester, NH, p. A450
M.D., Senior Vice President Medical Affairs and Chief Medical Officer, Elliot Hospital, Manchester, NH, p. A450

BAXTER, Joshua, Director, Information Systems, Powell Valley Healthcare, Powell, WY, p. A803

BAXTER, Kyle, Chief Operating Officer, Musc Health Florence Medical Center, Florence, SC, p. A619

BAYARDO, Fernando, M.D., Chief Medical Officer, Presbyterian Espanola Hospital, Espanola, NM, p. A469

BAYER, Brian, Information Technology Site Leader, Kalamazoo Psychiatric Hospital, Kalamazoo, MI, p. A359

BAYOUMY, Sam, Chief Executive Officer, Cleveland Clinic Rehabilitation Hospital, Avon, OH, p. A528

BAYTOS, David G., President, Methodist Healthcare Olive Branch Hospital, Olive Branch, MS, p. A398

BAYUS, Robin, Chief Financial Officer, Rancho Los Amigos National Rehabilitation Center, Downey, CA, p. A62

BAZELEY, Stephen, M.D., Vice President Medical Affairs, St. Luke's Hospital, Maumee, OH, p. A545

BAZEMORE, Webster Carl., M.D., Interim Medical Director, Fayetteville Veterans Affairs Medical Center, Fayetteville, NC, p. A510

BEA, Javon R., Chief Executive Officer, Mercyhealth Hospital And Medical Center - Harvard, Harvard, IL, p. A207
President and Chief Executive Officer, Javon Bea Hospital-Rockton, Rockford, IL, p. A218
President and Chief Executive Officer, Mercyhealth Hospital And Medical Center - Walworth, Lake Geneva, WI, p. A787
President and Chief Executive Officer, Mercyhealth Hospital And Trauma Center - Janesville, Janesville, WI, p. A786

BEACH, Karrie, Vice President Finance, Syracuse Area Health, Syracuse, NE, p. A440

BEACH, Sarah, Director of Nursing, Jerold Phelp. Community Hospital, Garberville, CA, p. A66

BEAGLE, Ashley, Director of Nursing, Doctor's Memorial Hospital, Perry, FL, p. A154

BEAL, Christopher, M.D., Chief of Staff, Sparrow Clinton Hospital, Saint Johns, MI, p. A366

BEAL, Dwight, Chief Fiscal Services, Jack C. Montgomery Veterans Affairs Medical Center, Muskogee, OK, p. A562

BEAL, Rachel, Chief Operating Officer, Poplar Springs Hospital, Petersburg, VA, p. A748

BEAL, Walter Edwin., Chief Executive Officer, Central Regional Hospital, Butner, NC, p. A506

BEALES, Julie, M.D., Chief of Staff, Hunter Holmes Mcguire Veterans Affairs Medical Center-Richmond, Richmond, VA, p. A750

BEALS, Susie, Chief Nursing Officer, Northern Rockies Medical Center, Cut Bank, MT, p. A423

BEAM, William, M.D., Chief of Staff, Cornerstone Hospital Of Huntington, Huntington, WV, p. A773

BEAMAN, Frank, Chief Executive Officer, Faith Community Hospital, Jacksboro, TX, p. A691

BEAMES, Bo, Interim Chief Executive Officer, Miners' Colfax Medical Center, Raton, NM, p. A471

BEAMON, Ron, Chief Financial Officer, St. Joseph's Hospital, Tampa, FL, p. A160

Vice President, Chief Financial Officer, Winter Haven Hospital, Winter Haven, FL, p. A162

BEAN, Howard, M.D., Chief Medical Officer, Spartanburg Medical Center - Mary Black, Spartanburg, SC, p. A624

BEAN, Roberta, R.N., Associate Chief Nursing Officer, Banner Fort Collins Medical Center, Fort Collins, CO, p. A112

BEAN, Todd, Chief Medical Officer, Cass County Health System, Atlantic, IA, p. A243

BEAR, John, Hospital Administrator Officer and Supervisor Human Resources, Lawton Indian Hospital, Lawton, OK, p. A561

BEARD, Angie, R.N., Chief Nursing Officer, Northcrest Medical Center, Springfield, TN, p. A650

BEARD, Bert, Chief Executive Officer, Maria Parham Medical Center, Henderson, NC, p. A511

BEARD, Bradley, Chief Operating Officer, Essentia Health Duluth, Duluth, MN, p. A375

BEARD, Chris, Chief Nursing Officer, Brownfield Regional Medical Center, Brownfield, TX, p. A660

BEARD, Edward L., R.N., President and Chief Executive Officer, Catawba Valley Medical Center, Hickory, NC, p. A512

BEARD, Gerald, Chief Operating Officer, Healthmark Regional Medical Center, Defuniak Springs, FL, p. A136

BEARD, Joan, Chief Nursing Officer, Northwest Florida Community Hospital, Chipley, FL, p. A134

BEARD, Rhonda, Director Human Resources, Palestine Regional Medical Center-East, Palestine, TX, p. A704

BEARD, Robert, Chief Clinical Officer, Vibra Hospital Of Northwestern Indiana, Crown Point, IN, p. A226

BEARD, Tim, Chief Executive Officer, Cimarron Memorial Hospital, Boise City, OK, p. A556

Director, Information Technology, Cimarron Memorial Hospital, Boise City, OK, p. A556

BEARDEN, Amy, R.N., MSN, Vice President Patient Care Services and Chief Nursing Officer, St. Luke's Magic Valley Medical Center, Twin Falls, ID, p. A193

BEARDEN, Stephen, Chief Financial Officer, Tristar Hendersonville Medical Center, Hendersonville, TN, p. A639

BEARS, Tiffany, Chief Nursing Officer, Layton Hospital, Layton, UT, p. A728

BEASLEY, Carla, Director of Nursing, Mitchell County Hospital, Camilla, GA, p. A168

BEASLEY, Craig, M.D., Chief Medical Officer, Throckmorton County Memorial Hospital, Throckmorton, TX, p. A721

BEASLEY, Jared, R.N., Vice President Patient Care, Parkview Lagrange Hospital, Lagrange, IN, p. A235

BEASLEY, Ruth, Director Human Resources, Vanderbilt Stallworth Rehabilitation Hospital, Nashville, TN, p. A647

BEASLEY, Tareka, Director Human Resources, Riverwoods Behavioral Health System, Riverdale, GA, p. A178

BEATTIE, Kathryn, M.D., Senior Vice President and Chief Medical Officer, Uw Medicine/Valley Medical Center, Renton, WA, p. A763

BEATTIE, Mac, Computer Network Specialist, Deer's Head Hospital Center, Salisbury, MD, p. A332

BEATTY, Alan, Vice President Human Resources, Shore Medical Center, Somers Point, NJ, p. A463

BEATTY, Ann, Director Human Resources, Cleveland Clinic Fairview Hospital, Cleveland, OH, p. A534

BEATTY, James, President and Chief Operating Officer, Multicare Good Samaritan Hospital, Puyallup. WA, p. A762

BEATTY, Robert, Chief Operating Officer, Highland Ridge Hospital, Midvale, UT, p. A728

BEATY, Holly, Chief Financial Officer, South Central Kansas Medical Center, Arkansas City, KS, p. A261

BEAUBIEN, Troy, Director Information Services, Manatee Memorial Hospital, Bradenton, FL, p. A133

BEAUCHAMP, Bill, Chief Financial Officer, St. Luke's Sugar Land Hospital, Sugar Land, TX, p. A717

BEAUCHANE, Nichole, Director Information Technology, Riverview Health, Crookston, MN, p. A374

BEAUDOIN, Dale, Vice President Human Resources, Lewis-Gale Medical Center, Boones Mill, VA, p. A739

BEAUDOIN, Paul, Chief Financial Officer, Day Kimball Hospital, Putnam, CT, p. A124

BEAUDRY, Carl (Bo), Chief Executive Officer, Cedar Park Regional Medical Center, Cedar Park, TX, p. A663

BEAULAC, Gary, Chief Operating Officer, Henry Ford Macomb Hospitals, Clinton Township. MI, p. A351

BEAULIEU, Brent, Chief Financial Officer, Baptist Health Extended Care Hospital, Little Rock, AR, p. A48

BEAULIEU, Jennifer, Director of Nursing, Intermountain Hospital, Boise, ID, p. A188

BEAULIEU, Lynn, Chief Nursing Officer, Walton Rehabilitation Hospital, Augusta, GA, p. A166

BEAULIEU, Michael, M.D., Chief Medical Officer, Helen Newberry Joy Hospital, Newberry, MI, p. A363

BEAUPRE', Paul, M.D., Chief Executive Officer, St. John's Health, Jackson, WY, p. A802

BEAVER, Patrick, MSN, R.N., Chief Nursing Officer, East Cooper Medical Center, Mount Pleasant, SC, p. A622

BEAVER, Rhonda, Chief Operating Officer, Creek Nation Community Hospital, Okemah, OK, p. A563

BECHAMPS, Gerald, M.D., Vice President Medical Affairs, Valley Health - Hampshire Memorial Hospital, Romney, WV, p. A776

M.D., Vice President Medical Affairs, Valley Health - War Memorial Hospital, Berkeley Springs, WV, p. A770

BECHTEL, Kathleen, MSN, R.N., Vice President Patient Care Services and Chief Nursing Officer, Froedtert And The Medical College Of Wisconsin Froedtert Hospital, Milwaukee, WI, p. A791

BECHTLE, Mavis, MSN, R.N., FACHE, Chief Executive Officer, Select Specialty Hospital-Northern Kentucky, Fort Thomas, KY, p. A283

BECK, Allan, Chief Executive Officer, Baylor Orthopedic And Spine Hospital At Arlington, Arlington, TX, p. A653

BECK, Ann, Chief Financial Officer, Renown Rehabilitation Hospital, Reno, NV, p. A446

Chief Financial Officer, Renown South Meadows Medical Center, Reno, NV, p. A446

Vice President and Chief Financial Officer, Carson Tahoe Continuing Care Hospital, Carson City, NV, p. A441

Vice President Finance, Carson Tahoe Health, Carson City, NV, p. A441

BECK, Brody, Director Information Technology, Minidoka Memorial Hospital, Rupert, ID, p. A193

BECK, Brynn, Chief Executive Officer, Utah Valley Specialty Hospital, Provo, UT, p. A731

BECK, David, Chief Operating Officer, Lane Regional Medical Center, Zachary, LA, p. A317

BECK, Debbie, Manager Human Resource and Payroll, Ochiltree General Hospital, Perryton, TX, p. A705

BECK, Howard, M.D., Chief of Staff, Grace Medical Center, Lubbock, TX, p. A697

BECK, J, D.O., President Medical Staff, Aspen Valley Hospital, Aspen, CO, p. A107

BECK, Rebecca, President, Hancock County Hospital, Sneedville, TN, p. A649

BECK, Robert, Chief Executive Officer, Kp. Promise Hospital Of Overland Park, Overland Park, KS, p. A274

BECK, Steve, MS, Chief Human Resource Officer, Kearney Regional Medical Center, Kearney, NE, p. A434

BECK,PHR,MHROD, Brian, Vice President Human Resources, Oak Valley Hospital, Oakdale, CA, p. A82

BECKER, Brian, Vice President Medical Affairs and Chief Medical Officer, Ascension Providence, Waco, TX, p. A723

BECKER, Cindy, Vice President and Chief Operating Officer, Highland Hospital, Rochester, NY, p. A496

BECKER, Colleen, Chief Nursing Officer, Osf Healthcare Saint Anthony's Health Center, Alton, IL, p. A194

BECKER, Donald, Chief Executive Officer, Vibra Hospital Of Charleston, Mt. Pleasant, SC, p. A622

BECKER, Eric, Chief Executive Officer, Texas Orthopedic Hospital, Houston, TX, p. A688

Chief Operating Officer, Research Medical Center, Kansas City, MO, p. A409

BECKER, Frank, Chief Financial Officer, Lourdes Counseling Center, Richland, WA, p. A763

Chief Financial Officer, Lourdes Medical Center, Pasco, WA, p. A762

BECKER, Kathleen R., M.P.H., JD, Chief Executive Officer, University Of New Mexico Hospitals, Albuquerque, NM, p. A468

BECKER, Kathy, Ph.D., R.N., Vice President and Chief Nursing Officer, Aurora West Allis Medical Center, West Allis, WI, p. A799

BECKER, Preston, Chief Executive Officer, Boundary Community Hospital, Bonners Ferry, ID, p. A189

BECKER, Ralph, Vice President, Chief Financial Officer, Saint Mary's Hospital, Waterbury, CT, p. A126

BECKER, Sherri, Chief Executive Officer, Select Specialty Hospital-Canton, Canton, OH, p. A531

BECKES, Hap. Director Information Systems, Sullivan County Community Hospital, Sullivan, IN, p. A241

BECKHAM, Blue, Interim Chief Information Officer, Wickenburg Community Hospital, Wickenburg, AZ, p. A41

BECKHAM, Steve, Director Human Resources, Magee General Hospital, Magee, MS, p. A396

BECKHAM, Steward, Director, Chief Operating Officer, Saint Elizabeths Hospital, Washington, DC, p. A130

BECKLUN, Megan, Director Human Resources, Antelop. Memorial Hospital, Neligh, NE, p. A435

BECKMANN, Gregory, Regional President, Chi Health Plainview, Plainview, NE, p. A439

BECKMANN, Lauren, Vice President Patient Services and Chief Nursing Officer, Barnes-Jewish St. Peters Hospital, Saint Peters, MO, p. A418

BECKNER, Jana, Director Human Resources, Lewisgale Hospital Pulaski, Pulaski, VA, p. A749

BECKSVOORT, Jennifer, Senior Human Resource Business Partner, Spectrum Health Zeeland Community Hospital, Zeeland, MI, p. A370

BECKWITH, Jami, Director Human Resources, Choctaw Nation Health Care Center, Talihina, OK, p. A569

BEDELL, Mikael, M.D., Medical Director, Cascade Medical Center, Cascade, ID, p. A189

BEDFORD, Tim, Chief Executive Officer, Emerald Coast Behavioral Hospital, Panama City, FL, p. A152

BEDGER, Kathy, Chief Nursing Officer, Penn Highlands Clearfield, Clearfield, PA, p. A586

BEDI, Andrew, Chief Operating Officer, Tristar Greenview Regional Hospital, Bowling Green, KY, p. A281

BEDICK, Jennifer, Deputy Commander Nursing, Tripler Army Medical Center, Honolulu, HI, p. A185

BEDNAR, Jan, R.N., MS, Chief Nursing Officer, Saint Clare's Denville Hospital, Denville, NJ, p. A454

BEDSOLE, Jessica, Director, Human Resources, Wellstar Paulding Hospital, Hiram, GA, p. A174

BEDZYK, J., Deputy Director Administration, Elmira Psychiatric Center, Elmira, NY, p. A483

BEEBE, Chris, Director Human Resources, Raleigh General Hospital, Beckley, WV, p. A770

BEEBY, Lori, Director Information Systems, Community Hospital, Mccook, NE, p. A435

BEECHY, Andrew, Manager Information Technology Systems, Lee's Summit Medical Center, Lee's Summit, MO, p. A410

BEED, Donna, Chief Information Management Division, Tripler Army Medical Center, Honolulu, HI, p. A185

BEEDLE, Chester, Chief Financial Officer, Kern Valley Healthcare District, Lake Isabella, CA, p. A70

Interim Chief Financial Officer, Adventist Health Tehachap. Valley, Tehachapi, CA, p. A100

BEEDY, Scott, Chief Financial Officer, Hansford Hospital, Spearman, TX, p. A716

BEEG, Gregg M., FACHE, Interim President and Chief Executive Officer, Oaklawn Hospital, Marshall, MI, p. A361

BEEHN, Holly, Director Human Resources, Southwest Health, Platteville, WI, p. A794

BEELER, Janelle, Human Resource Manager, Baraga County Memorial Hospital, L'Anse, MI, p. A359

BEER, Nicole, Chief Nursing Officer, The Pavilion At Williamsburg Place, Williamsburg, VA, p. A753

BEER, Ronald R., FACHE, Chief Administrative Officer, Geisinger Wyoming Valley Medical Center, Wilkes Barre, PA, p. A611

FACHE, Chief Administrative Officer, Geisinger-Community Medical Center, Scranton, PA, p. A607

BEESON, John, M.D., Chief Medical Officer, Christus St. Vincent Regional Medical Center, Santa Fe, NM, p. A472

BEGALSKE, Kathy, Chief Nursing Officer, Gundersen Palmer Lutheran Hospital And Clinics, West Union, IA, p. A260

BEGAN, Victoria D., R.N., MS, President and Chief Executive Officer, San Carlos Apache Healthcare Corporation, Peridot, AZ, p. A35

BEGAY, Trudy, Human Resources Specialist, Hop. Health Care Center, Keams Canyon, AZ, p. A33

BEGAYE, Lorraine, Supervisory Human Resource Specialist, Chinle Comprehensive Health Care Facility, Chinle, AZ, p. A31

BEGG, William, M.D., IIIVice President Medical Affairs, Vassar Brothers Medical Center, Poughkeepsie, NY, p. A495

BEGGANE, Thomas, Manager Human Resources, Lac-Olive View-Ucla Medical Center, Sylmar, CA, p. A100

BEGGS, Shawn, Administrator, Finance, Beaumont Hospital - Trenton, Trenton, MI, p. A368

BEHAN, Lawrence, Vice President Administration and Finance, Chief Financial Officer, Walden Behavioral Care, Waltham, MA, p. A345

BEHM, Anthony, D.O., Chief of Staff, Erie Veterans Affairs Medical Center, Erie, PA, p. A589

BEHNER, Bruce, Chief Operating Officer, Knox Community Hospital, Mount Vernon, OH, p. A546

BEHNKEN, Nick, IT Director, Red Bud Regional Hospital, Red Bud, IL, p. A218

BEHRENDT, Darcy, R.N., Vice President, Patient Care Services, Chi Health Missouri Valley, Missouri Valley, IA, p. A254

BEHRENDTSEN, Ole, M.D., Interim Director, Santa Barbara County Psychiatric Health Facility, Santa Barbara, CA, p. A97

M.D., Medical Director, Santa Barbara County Psychiatric Health Facility, Santa Barbara, CA, p. A97

BEHRENS, Karen, Director Technology Services, Perry Memorial Hospital, Princeton, IL, p. A218

BEIDELSCHIES, Sandra, MSN, R.N., Vice President Patient Services, Wood County Hospital, Bowling Green, OH, p. A530

BEIERMAN, Jennifer, Director Human Resources, Boone County Health Center, Albion, NE, p. A429

BEIGHLE, John, Flight Chief Medical Information Systems, Wright Patterson Medical Center, Wright, OH, p. A553

BEIGI, Richard, M.D., President, Upmc Magee-Womens Hospital, Pittsburgh, PA, p. A604

BEIKMAN, Sara, Director of Nursing, Clay County Medical Center, Clay Center, KS, p. A262

BEILER, Jeffrey, Chief Operating Officer, Horsham Clinic, Ambler, PA, p. A584

BEINDIT, Dawn, Labor Relations Partner, Ascension River District Hospital, East China, MI, p. A353

BEIRL, Luke, PharmD, Chief Executive Officer, Hayward Area Memorial Hospital And Water's Edge, Hayward, WI, p. A786

BEISSEL, Rachel, Chief Nursing Officer, Southern Coos Hospital And Health Center, Bandon, OR, p. A573

BEISWENGER, Joel, Chief Executive Officer, Tri-County Hospital, Wadena, MN, p. A387

BEITCHER, Bob, Chief Executive Officer, Motion Picture And Television Fund Hospital And Residential Services, Woodland Hills, CA, p. A105

BEITEL, Suzanne, Senior Vice President and Chief Financial Officer, Seattle Children's Hospital, Seattle, WA, p. A764

BEITING, Mark, Vice President Human Resources, Alta Bates Summit Medical Center - Summit Campus, Oakland, CA, p. A82

BEITZEL, Mark, Director Information Systems, Advocate Lutheran General Hospital, Park Ridge, IL, p. A216

BEJNAR, Darla, M.D., Chief Medical Officer, Socorro General Hospital, Socorro, NM, p. A472

BELAIR, Norman, Senior Vice President and Chief Financial Officer, Southern Maine Health Care - Biddeford Medical Center, Biddeford, ME, p. A319

BELANGER, Robert, Administrator Director, Sanford Bagley Medical Center, Bagley, MN, p. A372

BELCASTRO, Marc, D.O., Chief Medical Officer, Miami Valley Hospital, Dayton, OH, p. A538

BELCHER, Debbie, Director Human Resource, Baylor Scott & White Institute For Rehabilitation - Lakeway, Lakeway, TX, p. A694

BELCHER, Laura, Administrator, The Medical Center Albany, Albany, KY, p. A280

BELDECOS, Athena, M.D., Medical Director, Vibra Hospital Of Charleston, Mt. Pleasant, SC, p. A622

BELEC, Tim, Chief Information Officer, Owensboro Health Regional Hospital, Owensboro, KY, p. A291

BELGARDE, Donna, Human Resources Specialist, Indian Health Service - Quentin N. Burdick Memorial Health Care Facility, Belcourt, ND, p. A521

BELHASEN, F, M.D., Medical Director, Paul B. Hall Regional Medical Center, Paintsville, KY, p. A292

BELJIN, Dawn, R.N., Chief Nursing Officer, Venice Regional Bayfront Health, Venice, FL, p. A161

BELKOSKI, Dave, Chief Financial Officer, University Hospital Mcduffie, Thomson, GA, p. A182

BELKOSKI, David, Senior Vice President and Chief Financial Officer, University Hospital, Augusta, GA, p. A166

BELL, Billie, Chief Nursing Officer, Medina Regional Hospital, Hondo, TX, p. A684

BELL, Brian, Associate Administrator and Chief Operating Officer, National Park Medical Center, Hot Springs, AR, p. A47

BELL, Cindy, Director Finance, Willow Crest Hospital, Miami, OK, p. A562

BELL, Gary C., LFACHE, Chief Executive Officer, Lehigh Regional Medical Center, Lehigh Acres, FL, p. A144

BELL, Heath, Vice President, Information Services, Northwestern Medicine Valley West Hospital, Sandwich, IL, p. A219

BELL, Hollis, M.D., Medical Director, Mercy Rehabilitation Hospital Springfield, Springfield, MO, p. A419

BELL, Kae, Chief Financial Officer, Brentwood Hospital, Shreveport, LA, p. A314

BELL, Kenneth, Chief Executive Officer, Encompass Health Rehabilitation Hospital Of Scottsdale, Scottsdale, AZ, p. A38

BELL, Madeline, President and Chief Executive Officer, Children's Hospital Of Philadelphia, Philadelphia, PA, p. A599

BELL, Michael J., Chief Executive Officer, Hialeah Hospital, Hialeah, FL, p. A139

BELL, Randall, M.D., Medical Director, Pam Specialty Hospital Of San Antonio Center, San Antonio, TX, p. A712

BELL, Roderick, Chief Financial Officer, College Hospital Cerritos, Cerritos, CA, p. A59

BELL, Roseanna, Chief Nurse Executive, Multicare Auburn Medical Center, Auburn, WA, p. A755

BELL, Scot, Chief Medical Officer, Anderson Regional Health System, Meridian, MS, p. A397

BELL, Sonja, Coordinator Human Resources, Sedgwick County Health Center, Julesburg, CO, p. A114

BELL, Stuart, M.D., Vice President, Medical Affairs, Medstar Union Memorial Hospital, Baltimore, MD, p. A325

BELL, Talana, Chief Financial Officer, Flowers Hospital, Dothan, AL, p. A17

BELL, Tammie, Director Human Resources, West Tennessee Healthcare Volunteer Hospital, Martin, TN, p. A643

BELL, W, M.D., Chief Medical Officer, Rush Foundation Hospital, Meridian, MS, p. A397

BELL JR, SammieChief Financial Officer, Tallahatchie General Hospital, Charleston, MS, p. A391

BELLAMY, David, Chief Financial Officer, Mclaren Northern Michigan, Petoskey, MI, p. A363

BELLATTY, Christine, Acting Director of Nursing, Dorothea Dix Psychiatric Center, Bangor, ME, p. A318

BELLEAU, Christopher, M.D., Medical Director, Sage Rehabilitation Hospital, Baton Rouge, LA, p. A297

BELLEAU, Donella, Director Human Resources, Graham County Hospital, Hill City, KS, p. A266

BELLUCCI, Alessandro, M.D., Executive Director, North Shore University Hospital, Manhasset, NY, p. A487

BELLUCY, Regina, Vice President Human Resources, Bethesda Hospital East, Boynton Beach, FL, p. A132

BELMONT, Chris, Chief Information Officer and Vice President, University Of Texas M.D. Anderson Cancer Center, Houston, TX, p. A689

BELMONT, James, Associate Director, Northern Arizona Veterans Affairs Health Care System, Prescott, AZ, p. A37 Interim Director, Lexington Veterans Affairs Medical Center, Lexington, KY, p. A286

BELONGEA, M. Anselma, Chief Operating Officer, Osf Healthcare Saint Anthony's Health Center, Alton, IL, p. A194

BELTRAN, Grace, Director Human Resources, Legent Hospital Of El Paso, El Paso, TX, p. A675

BELTZ, John, Chief Financial Officer, Hendry Regional Medical Center, Clewiston, FL, p. A134

BELZER, Leslie, Director Human Resources, Howard County Medical Center, Saint Paul, NE, p. A439

BEMBAS, Jill, Executive Assistant, Dmc - Children's Hospital Of Michigan, Detroit, MI, p. A352

BEMENT, Douglas, Chief Financial Officer, Kosciusko Community Hospital, Warsaw, IN, p. A242

BEN, Sabrina, Director Human Resources, North Star Behavioral Health System, Anchorage, AK, p. A27

BENAQUISTA, Kathleen, Executive Vice President and Chief Financial Officer, Valleywise Health, Phoenix, AZ, p. A37

BENAVIDES, Christina, Director Employee Services, Otto Kaiser Memorial Hospital, Kenedy, TX, p. A692

BENCITO ACAAC, Norie Lee, R.N., MS, Executive Director, Loma Linda University Behavioral Medicine Center, Redlands, CA, p. A87

BENDER, Bob, Vice-President Hospital Finance and Operations, Northeast Market, Bristol Regional Medical Center, Bristol, TN, p. A634

BENDER, Brad, M.D., Chief of Staff, North Florida/South Georgia Veteran's Health System, Gainesville, FL, p. A138

BENDER, Daniel, Chief Executive Officer, South Bay Hospital, Sun City Center, FL, p. A158

BENDER, David, M.D., Chief Medical Staff, Grafton City Hospital, Grafton, WV, p. A772 Chief Executive Officer, Massena Hospital, Inc., Massena, NY, p. A488

BENDINELLI, Emily, Director of Nurses, Ashley County Medical Center, Crossett, AR, p. A44

BENDING, Tammy, Vice President, Critical Access Hospital, Thedacare Medical Center-Berlin, Berlin, WI, p. A781 Vice President, Theda Care Medical Center - Wild Rose, Wild Rose, WI, p. A799

BENEDICT, Brian, Director of Information Technology, Murray-Calloway County Hospital, Murray, KY, p. A291

BENEDICT, Eva, R.N., President and Chief Executive Officer, Jones Memorial Hospital, Wellsville, NY, p. A502

BENEDICT, Joy, Director Human Resources, Baptist Health Richmond, Richmond, KY, p. A292

BENEFIELD, Marlene, Director Human Resources, Floyd Cherokee Medical Center, Centre, AL, p. A16

BENEPAL, Jaspreet, Chief Nursing Officer, Contra Costa Regional Medical Center, Martinez, CA, p. A77

BENET, Miguel, M.D., Chief Medical Officer, Medical City Las Colinas, Irving, TX, p. A690

BENETTI-LOYOLA, Pedro, Senior Executive and Vice President, Hospital San Cristobal, Coto Laurel, PR, p. A807

BENETTI-LOYOLA, Pedro L., Administrator, Hospital San Cristobal, Coto Laurel, PR, p. A807

BENFIELD, Angie, Director Human Resources, Cherokee Medical Center, Gaffney, SC, p. A620 Human Resources Generalist, Union Medical Center, Union, SC, p. A625

BENFIELD, Justin, Southern Region Chief Operating Officer, Prisma Health Laurens County Hospital, Clinton, SC, p. A617

BENFIELD, Ronald, Chief Financial Officer, Peacehealth Southwest Medical Center, Vancouver, WA, p. A768

Chief Financial Officer, Peacehealth St. John Medical Center, Longview, WA, p. A760

BENGSTON, Jennifer, M.D., Chief Medical Officer, Valley County Health System, Ord, NE, p. A438

BENGYAK, Daniel, Vice President, Administrative Services, Montefiore St. Luke's Cornwall, Newburgh, NY, p. A492

BENHAM, D'Linda, Director of Nursing, Fisher County Hospital District, Rotan, TX, p. A709

BENHAM, Rebecca, Interim Chief Executive Officer, Drumright Regional Hospital, Drumright, OK, p. A558

BENINK, Eric, M.D., Chief Medical Officer, Medical City Arlington, Arlington, TX, p. A653

BENITEZ, Pedro, M.D., Medical Director, Hospital De Damas, Ponce, PR, p. A809

BENJAMIN, Christian, USAF, MC, Commander, Mike O'Callaghan Federal Hospital, Nellis Afb, NV, p. A445

BENJAMIN, Lucia, Chief Nursing Officer, West Gables Rehabilitation Hospital, Miami, FL, p. A147

BENNER, Brenda, Director Human Resources, Encompass Health Rehabilitation Hospital Of Sarasota, Sarasota, FL, p. A157

BENNETT, Angela, Chief Nursing Officer, Dekalb Regional Medical Center, Fort Payne, AL, p. A19

BENNETT, Anthony, M.D., Chief Clinical Affairs, Baptist Health Medical Center-Little Rock, Little Rock, AR, p. A49

BENNETT, Bart, Chief Financial Officer, Springbrook Behavioral Health, Travelers Rest, SC, p. A625 Chief Information Technology Officer, Springbrook Behavioral Health, Travelers Rest, SC, p. A625

BENNETT, Courtney, Human Resource Manager, Alleghany Memorial Hospital, Sparta, NC, p. A518

BENNETT, Dan, President and Chief Executive Officer, Gifford Medical Center, Randolph, VT, p. A736

BENNETT, Darnell, Director Finance, Horizon Specialty Hospital, Las Vegas, NV, p. A443

BENNETT, E Kyle., President and Chief Executive Officer, Memorial Hospital And Health Care Center, Jasper, IN, p. A233

BENNETT, Edwin, Controller, Turning Point Hospital, Moultrie, GA, p. A177

BENNETT, Fay, Vice President Employee Services, Guadalup. Regional Medical Center, Seguin, TX, p. A714

BENNETT, Gary, M.D., Chief of Medical Staff, Chapman Global Medical Center, Orange, CA, p. A82

BENNETT, James, Chief Executive Officer, Surgical Institute Of Reading, Wyomissing, PA, p. A612

BENNETT, Kay, System Director Human Resources, Baptist Medical Center South, Montgomery, AL, p. A22 Vice President Human Resources, Baptist Medical Center East, Montgomery, AL, p. A22

BENNETT, Kimberly, R.N., Director of Nursing, Christus Dubuis Hospital Of Alexandria, Alexandria, LA, p. A295

BENNETT, Laura, Chief Executive Officer, Central Montana Medical Center, Lewistown, MT, p. A425

BENNETT, Laurie, Director Human Resources, Sarasota Memorial Health Care System, Sarasota, FL, p. A157

BENNETT, Leo, M.D., Deputy Commander Clinical Services, Bassett Army Community Hospital, Fort Wainwright, AK, p. A28

BENNETT, Lisa, Chief Financial Officer, Waverly Health Center, Waverly, IA, p. A259

BENNETT, Mary Ann, Chief Nursing Officer, Glendora Community Hospital, Glendora, CA, p. A67 Chief Operating Officer and Chief Nursing Officer, Springbrook Behavioral Health, Travelers Rest, SC, p. A625 Director of Nursing, Springbrook Behavioral Health, Travelers Rest, SC, p. A625

BENNETT, Melissa, Chief Nursing Officer, Trumbull Memorial Hospital, Warren, OH, p. A551

BENNETT, Patti, Chief Nursing Officer, Nacogdoches Medical Center, Nacogdoches, TX, p. A702

BENNETT, Randall, Assistant Administrator, Uintah Basin Medical Center, Roosevelt, UT, p. A731

BENNETT, Richard, Senior Vice President and Chief Financial Officer, Delaware County Memorial Hospital, Drexel Hill, PA, p. A588

BENNETT, Richard G., M.D., President, Johns Hopkins Bayview Medical Center, Baltimore, MD, p. A324

BENNETT, Rick, Director, The Blackberry Center, Saint Cloud, FL, p. A156

BENNETT, Robert, M.D., Medical Director, Millwood Hospital, Arlington, TX, p. A653

BENNETT, Sharon, Manager Information Systems, Cobre Valley Regional Medical Center, Globe, AZ, p. A32

BENNETT, Sheila, R.N., Vice President & Chief Nursing Officer, Floyd Medical Center, Rome, GA, p. A179

BENNETT, Tony N., Chief Executive Officer, Encompass Health Rehabilitation Hospital Of Panama City, Panama City, FL, p. A153

BENNETT, Wayne, Chief Financial Officer, Franklin Memorial Hospital, Farmington, ME, p. A320

BENNETT, Will, Chief Financial Officer, Candler County Hospital, Metter, GA, p. A176

BENOIT, Linda, Human Resource Officer, Cavalier County Memorial Hospital And Clinics, Langdon, ND, p. A524

BENOIT, Paul, Associate Administrator, Central Louisiana State Hospital, Pineville, LA, p. A313

BENOIT, William, President, Uh Portage Medical Center, Ravenna, OH, p. A548

BENSEN, Carol, MSN, R.N., Chief Nursing Officer, Providence St. Patrick Hospital, Missoula, MT, p. A426

BENSON, Cheryl, Chief Operating Officer, Wernersville State Hospital, Wernersville, PA, p. A610

BENSON, Karla, Executive Assistant, Throckmorton County Memorial Hospital, Throckmorton, TX, p. A721

BENSON, Kathryn, Human Resources Partner, Avera St. Anthony's Hospital, O'Neill, NE, p. A438

BENSON, Kevin, Chief Financial Officer, Bartlett Regional Hospital, Juneau, AK, p. A28

BENSON, Michael, M.D., President Medical Staff, Wilson N. Jones Regional Medical Center, Sherman, TX, p. A716

BENTLEY, Scott, Chief Financial Officer, Woman's Hospital Of Texas, Houston, TX, p. A689

BENTON, Edred, Chief Executive Officer and Chief Operating Officer, Cleveland Area Hospital, Cleveland, OK, p. A557

BENTON, Nancy, Assistant Director Patient Care Services, Mann-Grandstaff Veterans Affairs Medical Center, Spokane, WA, p. A765

BENTZ, Douglas E., Chief Executive Officer, Roane General Hospital, Spencer, WV, p. A777

BENVENUTTI, Cathy, Human Resource Director, Hancock Medical Center, Bay Saint Louis, MS, p. A389

BENWARE, Joel, Vice President Information Technology and Compliance, Northwestern Medical Center, Saint Albans, VT, p. A736

BENZ, Robert, M.D., Chief Medical Officer, Lankenau Medical Center, Wynnewood, PA, p. A612

BENZEL, Cindy, Manager Human Resources, Sanford Vermillion Medical Center, Vermillion, SD, p. A632

BEPLER, Gerold, M.D., Ph.D., President and Chief Executive Officer, Karmanos Cancer Center, Detroit, MI, p. A353

BERARDI, Paula, Manager Human Resources, Bournewood Health Systems, Brookline, MA, p. A337

BERCHER, Richard, M.D., Chief Medical Officer, Paris Regional Medical Center, Paris, TX, p. A704

BERCI, Haya, Executive Director of Nursing, Joyce Eisenberg-Keefer Medical Center, Reseda, CA, p. A88

BERCIER, Paula, M.D., Chief Medical Officer, Indian Health Service - Quentin N. Burdick Memorial Health Care Facility, Belcourt, ND, p. A521

BERDAL, Ritche, Chief Nursing Officer, Chg Hospital Tucson, Llc, Tucson, AZ, p. A40

BERDAN, Barclay E., FACHE, Chief Executive Officer, Texas Health Specialty Hospital, Fort Worth, TX, p. A679

BERDIEL, Luis A., Executive Director, Hospital Metropolitano San German, San German, PR, p. A809

BERENS, Jeff, MS, Chief Nursing Officer, Sanford Vermillion Medical Center, Vermillion, SD, p. A632

BERENTES, Amy, R.N., MSN, Executive Vice President and Chief Operating Officer, Mercyone Clinton Medical Center, Clinton, IA, p. A246

R.N., MSN, Vice President Patient Care Services, Mercyone Clinton Medical Center, Clinton, IA, p. A246

BERETTA, Dante, M.D., Chief of Staff, Centracare - Melrose, Melrose, MN, p. A380

BERG, Gary, D.O., Chief Medical Officer, Ascension Macomb-Oakland Hospital, Warren, MI, p. A368

BERG, Jon, M.D., Chief of Staff, Northwood Deaconess Health Center, Northwood, ND, p. A525

BERG, Katie, Chief Financial Officer, Cuyuna Regional Medical Center, Crosby, MN, p. A374

BERG, Tony, M.D., Chief of Staff, Winner Regional Healthcare Center, Winner, SD, p. A633

BERG, William, Chief Information Officer, Naval Hospital Pensacola, Pensacola, FL, p. A153

BERGE, Ron, Executive Vice President and Chief Operating Officer, National Jewish Health, Denver, CO, p. A110

BERGEAUX, Scott, M.D., Chief Medical Staff, Abrom Kaplan Memorial Hospital, Kaplan, LA, p. A304

BERGEMANN, John, Director Human Resources, Crouse Health, Syracuse, NY, p. A499

BERGEN, Jan L., President and Chief Executive Officer, Penn Medicine Lancaster General Hospital, Lancaster, PA, p. A594

BERGEN, Lorinda, Chief Executive Officer, Willamette Valley Medical Center, Mcminnville, OR, p. A577

BERGER, David, M.D., Senior Vice President and Chief Operating Officer, Leesburg Regional Medical Center, Leesburg, FL, p. A144

BERGER, George, Controller, Encompass Health Rehabilitation Hospital Of Altoona, Altoona, PA, p. A583

BERGER, Kathy, R.N., Medical Center Director, Chillicothe Veterans Affairs Medical Center, Chillicothe, OH, p. A531

BERGER, Robert, M.D., Medical Director, Southwest Connecticut Mental Health System, Bridgeport, CT, p. A121

BERGERON, Pierre, Information Services Director, Wellington Regional Medical Center, Wellington, FL, p. A161

BERGERSEN, Jennifer, Interim Chief Operating Officer, Milwaukee County Behavioral Health Division, Milwaukee, WI, p. A791

BERGERSON, Melissa, R.N., Chief Nursing Officer, Black River Memorial Hospital, Black River Falls, WI, p. A781

BERGES, Iris, Chief Executive Officer, Larkin Community Hospital Behavioral Health Services, Hollywood, FL, p. A140

BERGFORT, Joe, Chief Information Officer, Ucsf Medical Center, San Francisco, CA, p. A94

BERGHOLM, Brenda, MSN, R.N., Chief Nursing Officer, Caribou Memorial Hospital And Living Center, Soda Springs, ID, p. A193

BERGMAN, Angela, Director of Quality, Risk and Health Information Management, Van Matre Encompass Health Rehabilitation Hospital, Rockford, IL, p. A219

BERGMAN, Chris, Chief Financial Officer, Dayton Children's Hospital, Dayton, OH, p. A538

BERGMAN, Jim, Director Human Resources, Northeast Regional Medical Center, Kirksville, MO, p. A410

BERGMAN-EVANS, Brenda, Chief Nursing Officer, Chi Health Midlands, Papillion, NE, p. A438

BERGMANN, Peter U., President and Chief Executive Officer, Ascension Borgess Hospital, Kalamazoo, MI, p. A359

President, Ascension Allegan Hospital, Allegan, MI, p. A348

President, Ascension Borgess-Lee Hospital, Dowagiac, MI, p. A353

BERGQUIST, Susan, Human Resources Generalist, Kindred Hospital-La Mirada, La Mirada, CA, p. A70

BERGSTEDT, Sharon, Director of Nursing, Alaska Psychiatric Institute, Anchorage, AK, p. A27

BERGSTROM, Jenny, Project Manager Information Technology, Cloud County Health Center, Concordia, KS, p. A263

BERGSTROM, Michael, Chief Financial Officer, Harlingen Medical Center, Harlingen, TX, p. A683

BERINI, Deborah, President, Penn State Milton S. Hershey Medical Center, Hershey, PA, p. A592

BERKOWITZ, David, Vice President and Chief Operating Officer, Hackensack Meridian Health Palisades Medical Center, North Bergen, NJ, p. A460

BERKRAM, Treasure, Chief Financial Officer, Northern Rockies Medical Center, Cut Bank, MT, p. A423

BERLINGHOFF, Kathleen, Director Human Resources, Sharon Hospital, Sharon, CT, p. A125

BERLOT, Alvin, M.D., Medical Director, Bucktail Medical Center, Renovo, PA, p. A606

BERLOWITZ, Dan, M.D., M.P.H., Acting Chief of Staff, Bedford Veterans Affairs Medical Center, Edith Nourse Rogers Memorial Veterans Hospital, Bedford, MA, p. A334

BERLUCCHI, Scott A., FACHE, President and Chief Executive Officer, Auburn Community Hospital, Auburn, NY, p. A475

BERLYN, Maria, Assistant Vice President Nursing Services, John Heinz Institute Of Rehabilitation Medicine, Wilkes-Barre, PA, p. A611

BERMAN, Alan, M.D., Medical Director, Mountain Valley Regional Rehabilitation Hospital, Prescott Valley, AZ, p. A37

BERMUDEZ, Ada, Director Human Resources, Hospital De La Concepcion, San German, PR, p. A809

BERMUDEZ, Armand, M.D., Medical Director, Select Specialty Hospital Of Southeast Ohio, Newark, OH, p. A546

BERMUDEZ, Yuri, M.D., Chief of Staff, South Texas Health System, Edinburg, TX, p. A674

BERNAL, Hector, Chief Executive Officer, Pam Rehabilitation Hospital Of Corpus Christi, Corpus Christi, TX, p. A666

Chief Executive Officer, Post Acute Medical Specialty Hospital Of Corpus Christi - North, Corpus Christi, TX, p. A666

BERNAL, Maria Mercedes Torres., Administrator, Hospital De Damas, Ponce, PR, p. A809

BERNARD, David P., FACHE, Chief Executive Officer, Houston Methodist Baytown Hospital, Baytown, TX, p. A657

BERNARD, Donald, Chief Financial Officer, St. John's Pleasant Valley Hospital, Camarillo, CA, p. A59

Chief Financial Officer, St. John's Regional Medical Center, Oxnard, CA, p. A83

BERNARD, Doug, M.D., Chief Medical Officer, White River Medical Center, Batesville, AR, p. A42

BERNARD, Mark L., Chief Executive Officer, Resolute Health, New Braunfels, TX, p. A703

BERNARD, Robert, M.D., Chief of Staff, Alexandria Veterans Affairs Health Care System, Pineville, LA, p. A312

BERNARD, Traci, R.N., President, Chief Executive Officer and Chief Operating Officer, Texas Health Harris Methodist Hospital Southlake, Southlake, TX, p. A716

BERNARDO, Maria, M.D., Chief of Staff, Bullock County Hospital, Union Springs, AL, p. A25

BERNASEK, Robert, M.D., Chief Medical Officer, Southeast Georgia Health System Camden Campus, Saint Marys, GA, p. A179

BERNATIS, Terry D., Director Human Resources, Community Healthcare System, Onaga, KS, p. A273

BERND, Jason, President and Chief Operating Officer, Novant Health Matthews Medical Center, Matthews, NC, p. A514

BERNERT-YAP, Kellie, Director Human Resources, Vibra Specialty Hospital Of Portland, Portland, OR, p. A580

BERNEY, Bernadette, Director Human Resources, Pullman Regional Hospital, Pullman, WA, p. A762

BERNHARDT, Alison, Chief Financial Officer, Upmc Carlisle, Carlisle, PA, p. A586

Chief Financial Officer, Upmc Pinnacle Harrisburg, Harrisburg, PA, p. A591

BERNHARDT-KADLEC, Peggy, Chief Human Resources Officer, Searhc Mt. Edgecumbe Hospital, Sitka, AK, p. A29

BERNICK, Michael, Executive Vice President and Chief Financial Officer, Clarity Child Guidance Center, San Antonio, TX, p. A711

BERNIER, Justin, R.N., Director of Nursing, Seaside Behavioral Center - New Orleans, New Orleans, LA, p. A311

BERNIER, Stephanie, Chief Executive Officer, Canyon Ridge Hospital, Chino, CA, p. A60

BERNS, Erin, Director Human Resources, Veterans Memorial Hospital, Waukon, IA, p. A259

BERNSEN, Tina, Chief Nursing Officer, Othello Community Hospital, Othello, WA, p. A761

BERNSTEIN, Lee, Regional Executive Vice President and Chief Operating Officer, Ssm Health St. Clare Hospital - Fenton, Fenton, MO, p. A406

Regional Executive Vice President of Hospital and Chief Operating Officer, Ssm Health St. Josep. Hospital - Lake Saint Louis, Lake Saint Louis, MO, p. A410

BERNSTEIN, Les, Chief Information Officer, Cookeville Regional Medical Center, Cookeville, TN, p. A637

BERNSTEIN, Michael, Chief Financial Officer, Adventist Health - Tulare, Tulare, CA, p. A102

BERNSTEIN, Paul, M.D., Area Medical Director, Kaiser Permanente San Diego Medical Center, San Diego, CA, p. A91

BERRIOS, Elenia, Chief Nursing Officer, Hima San Pablo Caguas, Caguas, PR, p. A806

BERRY, Carlos, M.D., Acting Chief of Staff, Tuscaloosa Veterans Affairs Medical Center, Tuscaloosa, AL, p. A25

BERRY, David T., President, System Clinical Operations, Our Children's House, Dallas, TX, p. A670

President, Children's Medical Center Dallas, Dallas, TX, p. A668

BERRY, Greg, Chief Financial Officer, Doctors Medical Center Of Modesto, Modesto, CA, p. A78

BERRY, James T., FACHE, Executive Vice President and Administrator, Northeastern Health System, Tahlequah, OK, p. A569

BERRY, Julie, Chief Information Officer, Saint Anne's Hospital, Fall River, MA, p. A339

BERRY, Linda, Vice President Human Resources, Guthrie Towanda Memorial Hospital, Towanda, PA, p. A609

BERRY, Rebecca, Senior Director Human Resources, St. Charles Prineville, Prineville, OR, p. A580

Vice President Human Resources, St. Charles Bend, Bend, OR, p. A573

Vice President Human Resources, St. Charles Redmond, Redmond, OR, p. A580

BERRYMAN, John, M.D., Chief of Staff, Beckley Veterans Affairs Medical Center, Beckley, WV, p. A770

BERRYMAN, William, M.D., Chief of Staff, Grand Junction Veterans Health Care System, Grand Junction, CO, p. A113

BERSHAD, Joshua, M.D., Senior Vice President Medical Affairs and Chief Medical Officer, Robert Wood Johnson University Hospital, New Brunswick, NJ, p. A459

BERSINGER, David, M.D., Chief of Staff, Mcleod Health Cheraw, Cheraw, SC, p. A617

BERTANY, Kathryn, M.D., President, Bozeman Health, Bozeman, MT, p. A422

BERTAPELLE, Andrew, Chief Nursing Officer, Gunnison Valley Hospital, Gunnison, CO, p. A114

BERTHIL, Emmanuel, Chief Clinical Officer, Vibra Hospital Of Southeastern Massachusetts, New Bedford, MA, p. A342

BERTKE, Bradley J., President and Chief Operating Officer, Mercy St. Anne Hospital, Toledo, OH, p. A550

BERTRAND, Joan, Vice President Human Resources, Adcare Hospital Of Worcester, Worcester, MA, p. A346

BERTRAND, Neil, Interim Chief Financial Officer, Cheyenne Regional Medical Center, Cheyenne, WY, p. A801

BERTSCH, Darrold, Chief Executive Officer, Sakakawea Medical Center, Hazen, ND, p. A524

BERTSCH, John, M.D., Chief of Staff, Euclid Hospital, Euclid, OH, p. A540

BERZ, Derek, Chief Operating Officer, Kaiser Permanente Los Angeles Medical Center, Los Angeles, CA, p. A74

BESCOE, Bradley, Chief Financial Officer, Straith Hospital For Special Surgery, Southfield, MI, p. A367

BESIO, Adam, Chief Information Officer, Memorial Medical Center, Port Lavaca, TX, p. A707

BESPALEC, Jason, M.D., Chief of Staff, Fillmore County Hospital, Geneva, NE, p. A432

BESS, Amy, Chief Financial Officer, Mizell Memorial Hospital, Opp. AL, p. A23

BESS, Charles, M.D., Medical Director, Potomac Valley Hospital, Keyser, WV, p. A773

BESSE, Kim, Executive Vice President and Chief Human Resource Officer, Children's Medical Center Dallas, Dallas, TX, p. A668

Executive Vice President and Chief Human Resource Officer, Children's Medical Center Plano, Plano, TX, p. A706

BESSEY, Kerry, Senior Vice President and Chief Human Resources Officer, Memorial Sloan-Kettering Cancer Center, New York, NY, p. A490

BESSEY, Vickie, MSN, R.N., Chief Nursing Officer, Sagewest Health Care, Riverton, WY, p. A803

BESSLER, Christine, Vice President Information Services, Oconomowoc Memorial Hospital, Oconomowoc, WI, p. A792

BESSLER, September, Director, Human Resources, Brookings Health System, Brookings, SD, p. A626

BESSON, Kathleen, Executive Vice President and Chief Operating Officer, Caromont Regional Medical Center, Gastonia, NC, p. A510

BESST, Kara, President and Chief Executive Officer, Gritman Medical Center, Moscow, ID, p. A191

BESTEN, Robert, Chief Financial Officer, Mary Breckinridge Arh Hospital, Hyden, KY, p. A285

BESTGEN, Pat, Manager Human Resources, Cameron Regional Medical Center, Cameron, MO, p. A403

BESWICK, Elizabeth, Vice President Human Resources and Public Relations, Carteret Health Care, Morehead City, NC, p. A514

BETANCES, Luis, Chief Executive Officer, Anchor Hospital, Atlanta, GA, p. A164

BETANCOURT, Erika, Coordinator Human Resources, Cornerstone Regional Hospital, Edinburg, TX, p. A673

BETTCHER, Sue, R.N., Vice President of Nursing Services, Community Hospital Of Bremen, Bremen, IN, p. A225

BETTINELLI, Stephanie, Vice President of Human Resources, Winchester Hospital, Winchester, MA, p. A346

BETTS, Brooks, Director Information Systems and Chief Information Officer, Pen Bay Medical Center, Rockport, ME, p. A322

BETTS, Crystal, Chief Financial Officer, Incline Village Community Hospital, Incline Village, NV, p. A442

Chief Financial Officer, Tahoe Forest Hospital District, Truckee, CA, p. A102

BETTS, Kris, Director Team Resources, St. Joseph's Hospital, Tampa, FL, p. A160

BETTS, Kristen, Director Team Resources, St. Anthony's Hospital, Saint Petersburg, FL, p. A156

BETTS, Tracy, Chief Financial Officer, Hardeman County Memorial Hospital, Quanah, TX, p. A708

BETZ, Paul, FACHE, Administrator, Dch Regional Medical Center, Tuscaloosa, AL, p. A25

BEUCLER, MSN, RN, BS-NE, FACHE, Lori, R.N., Vice President and Chief Nursing Officer, Upmc Williamsport, Williamsport, PA, p. A611

BEUERLEIN, Jennifer, Chief Executive Officer, Pam Rehabilitation Hospital Of Allen, Allen, TX, p. A651

BEUS, Lance, Chief Executive Officer, Cmh Regional Health System, Wilmington, OH, p. A553

BEUTKE, Kenneth, President, Osf Saint Elizabeth Medical Center, Ottawa, IL, p. A216

BEVARD, Julie, Vice President Human Resources, Perkins County Health Services, Grant, NE, p. A433

BEVEL, John, Manager Information Systems, Shriners Hospitals For Children-Northern California, Sacramento, CA, p. A89

BEVERLY, Douglas H., Chief Executive Officer, Encompass Rehabilitation Hospital Of North Alabama, Huntsville, AL, p. A20

BEVERLY, Esther, Vice President Human Resources, Tri-City Medical Center, Oceanside, CA, p. A82

BEVIER, Mary, Chief Financial Officer, Rehoboth Mckinley Christian Health Care Services, Gallup. NM, p. A469

BEYER, Jim, Administrative Director Human Resources, Norman Regional Health System, Norman, OK, p. A563

BEYER, Laurie, Senior Vice President and Chief Financial Officer, Union Hospital, Elkton, MD, p. A329

BEYER, Teri, Chief Information Officer, Quality, Rice Memorial Hospital, Willmar, MN, p. A388

BEYER, Tommy, Director of Operations, Pam Rehabilitation Hospital Of Victoria, Victoria, TX, p. A723

BHAGAT, Sarah, Chief Operating Officer and Vice President of Organizational Effectiveness, Lakeland Regional Health Medical Center, Lakeland, FL, p. A143

BHAMBI, Brijesh, M.D., Chief Medical Officer, Bakersfield Heart Hospital, Bakersfield, CA, p. A57

BHAMBRA, Jody, Chief Nursing Officer, Hartgrove Hospital, Chicago, IL, p. A198

BHARUCHA, Bomi, Chief Financial Officer, Reeves County Hospital District, Pecos, TX, p. A705

BHATEJA, Renu, M.D., President Medical Staff, Ridgeview Psychiatric Hospital And Center, Oak Ridge, TN, p. A648

BHATIA, Sanjay, Chief Medical Officer, Lower Bucks Hospital, Bristol, PA, p. A585

BHAYANI, Sam, M.D., Chief Medical Officer, Barnes-Jewish West County Hospital, Saint Louis, MO, p. A415

BHIMANI, Meenesh, M.D., Hospital Executive, O'Connor Hospital, San Jose, CA, p. A95

BHOORASINGH, Merlene, Administrator, Kindred Hospital Ocala, Ocala, FL, p. A150

BHUCHAR, Subodh, M.D., Chief of Staff, Kindred Hospital Sugar Land, Sugar Land, TX, p. A717

BIAGIONI, Donna, R.N., MSN, Director of Nursing, Maniilaq Health Center, Kotzebue, AK, p. A29

BIALORUCKI, Tom, Chief Information Officer, Adena Pike Medical Center, Waverly, OH, p. A552

BIAS, Richard, Chief Operating Officer, Lahey Hospital & Medical Center, Burlington, Burlington, MA, p. A337

BIBAL, Antoinette, Director Human Resources, Kindred Hospital-Baldwin Park, Baldwin Park, CA, p. A58

BIBB, Jeff, Chief Operating Officer, Oklahoma Center For Orthopedic And Multi-Specialty Surgery, Oklahoma City, OK, p. A565

BIBB, Lisa, Director Human Resources, San Angelo Community Medical Center, San Angelo, TX, p. A710

BIBER, Carl, Chief Financial Officer, Columbus Regional Healthcare System, Whiteville, NC, p. A519

BIBLO, Lee, M.D., Chief Medical Officer, Froedtert And The Medical College Of Wisconsin Froedtert Hospital, Milwaukee, WI, p. A791

BIBY, Thomas, Chief Executive Officer, Pam Rehabilitation Hospital Of Tulsa, Tulsa, OK, p. A570

BICE, Doug, Administrator, Cypress Grove Behavioral Health, Bastrop. LA, p. A296

BICKEL, George, Director, Information Systems, Merit Health Biloxi, Biloxi, MS, p. A389

BICKEL, Jim, President and Chief Executive Officer, Columbus Regional Hospital, Columbus, IN, p. A225

BICKERSTAFF, Detra, Vice President, Human Resources, Wellstar Atlanta Medical Center, Atlanta, GA, p. A165

BICKFORD, Carmel, Chief Financial Officer, Wyoming Behavioral Institute, Casper, WY, p. A801

BICKFORD, David, Chief Information Officer, Melissa Memorial Hospital, Holyoke, CO, p. A114

BIDDLE, Kenneth, Controller, Kensington Hospital, Philadelphia, PA, p. A601

BIDES, Adrienne, Assistant Chief Financial Officer and Budget Analyst, Big Spring State Hospital, Big Spring, TX, p. A659

BIDLEMAN, Angie, Chief Nursing Officer, Ascension St. John Jane Phillips, Bartlesville, OK, p. A556

BIE, Gary, CPA, Chief Financial Officer, Stony Brook University Hospital, Stony Brook, NY, p. A499

BIEBER, Courtney, Director Information Systems, Mercy Regional Medical Center, Ville Platte, LA, p. A316

BIEBER, Judi, Senior Vice President Human Resources, Beth Israel Deaconess Medical Center, Boston, MA, p. A335

BIEBER, Julie, Vice President, Bellin Health Oconto Hospital, Oconto, WI, p. A793

BIEDIGER, Daniel, Vice President Human Resources, Firsthealth Moore Regional Hospital, Pinehurst, NC, p. A516

BIEGERT, Dara, Vice President Human Resources, Medical City Lewisville, Lewisville, TX, p. A696

BIEGLER, Elizabeth, R.N., Chief Nursing Officer, Ohiohealth Dublin Methodist Hospital, Dublin, OH, p. A539

R.N., Chief Nursing Officer, Ohiohealth Grady Memorial Hospital, Delaware, OH, p. A539

BIEHL, Albert, M.D., Vice President Medical Affairs, Bethesda Hospital East, Boynton Beach, FL, p. A132

BIEHL, Benjamin, M.D., Chief Medical Officer, Johnson County Hospital, Tecumseh, NE, p. A440

BIEKER, Jeff, Director Human Resource, Trego County-Lemke Memorial Hospital, Wakeeney, KS, p. A278

BIELECKI, Thomas, Chief Financial Officer, Geisinger Wyoming Valley Medical Center, Wilkes Barre, PA, p. A611

BIEN, John, Vice President Finance, United Hospital, Saint Paul, MN, p. A385

BIERI, Bryan, Manager Finance, Kansas City Veterans Affairs Medical Center, Kansas City, MO, p. A408

BIERLE, Dennis, Chief Operating Officer, Nebraska Medicine - Nebraska Medical Center, Omaha, NE, p. A437

BIERMAN, Debra, Associate Executive Director Human Resources, North Shore University Hospital, Manhasset, NY, p. A487

BIERMAN, Joan, Vice President Finance, Cherokee Regional Medical Center, Cherokee, IA, p. A245

BIERMAN, Marcia, M.D., Chief of Staff, North Shore Medical Center, Miami, FL, p. A147

BIERMAN, Ronald L., President, Sebastian River Medical Center, Sebastian, FL, p. A157

BIERSACK, Matt, Chief Medical Officer, Mercy Health Saint Mary's, Grand Rapids, MI, p. A356

BIERSCHENK, Cindy, Director of Financial Services, Jenkins County Medical Center, Millen, GA, p. A177

BIERSCHENK, Kevin, Chief Executive Officer, Union General Hospital, Blairsville, GA, p. A167

BIERUT, Barbara, Chief Financial Officer, Encompass Health Rehabilitation Hospital Of Sarasota, Sarasota, FL, p. A157

BIGANDO, Kelli, Chief Nursing Officer, Mercy Hospital Joplin, Joplin, MO, p. A408

BIGELOW, Timothy, Director Human Resources, Butler Hospital, Providence, RI, p. A613

BIGGAR, Carrie, Chief Financial Officer, Osceola Regional Medical Center, Kissimmee, FL, p. A142

BIGGERSTAFF, David, Chief Operating Officer, Children's Hospital Colorado, Aurora, CO, p. A107

BIGGS, Daniel, Chief Operating Officer, Valley View Hospital, Glenwood Springs, CO, p. A113

BIGGS, Jeremy, President and Chief Administrative Officer, Methodist Medical Center Of Oak Ridge, Oak Ridge, TN, p. A648

BIGGS, Kelly, M.D., Chief Medical Officer, Tyrone Hospital, Tyrone, PA, p. A609

BIGGS, Lee, M.D., Chief Medical Officer, Trident Medical Center, Charleston, SC, p. A616

BIGGS, R., M.D., Chief Medical Officer, Eastern Idaho Regional Medical Center, Idaho Falls, ID, p. A190

BIGLER, Pamela, R.N., Senior Vice President of Clinical Partnership. and Programs, Carle Foundation Hospital, Urbana, IL, p. A221

BIGLEY, John, M.D., Medical Director, Kaiser Permanente Baldwin Park Medical Center, Baldwin Park, CA, p. A57

BIGNAULT, Jon, M.D., Chief of Staff, Athens-Limestone Hospital, Athens, AL, p. A14

BIGONEY, Rebecca, Executive Vice President and Chief Medical Officer, Mary Washington Hospital, Fredericksburg, VA, p. A742

Executive Vice President and Chief Medical Officer, Stafford Hospital, Stafford, VA, p. A752

BIGOS, Ardelle, Vice President Nursing, Geneva General Hospital, Geneva, NY, p. A484

BIHUNIAK, Peter, Vice President Finance, Robert Wood Johnson University Hospital Rahway, Rahway, NJ, p. A462

BILELLO, Rene, Manager Information System, Ochsner St. Mary, Morgan City, LA, p. A309

BILES, Lauren, Administrator, Access Hospital Dayton, Dayton, OH, p. A538

BILL, Charles E., Chief Executive Officer, Bartlett Regional Hospital, Juneau, AK, p. A28

BILLECI, Theresa, Executive Director, Porterville Developmental Center, Porterville, CA, p. A86

BILLIG, Samantha, Chief Executive Officer, Pam Rehabilitation Hospital Of Centennial Hills, Las Vegas, NV, p. A444

BILLINGS, Cathy, Interim Executive Director, Northwest Center For Behavioral Health, Fort Supply, OK, p. A559

BILLINGS, Mark, Chief Operating Officer, Halifax Health Medical Center Of Daytona Beach, Daytona Beach, FL, p. A136

BILLINGS, Mary, Director of Nursing, Potomac Valley Hospital, Keyser, WV, p. A773

BILLINGSLEA, Anidra, Health Insurance Management, Encompass Health Rehabilitation Hospital Of Montgomery, Montgomery, AL, p. A22

BILLINGTON, Carole, R.N., MSN, Vice President Operations, Chief Nursing Officer, Saint Anne's Hospital, Fall River, MA, p. A339

BILLMEYER, Joe, Director, Information Services, Mercyone Dubuque Medical Center, Dubuque, IA, p. A249

BILLS, James, Chief Executive Officer, Logan Memorial Hospital, Russellville, KY, p. A293

BILLY, Frank, Chief Financial Officer, Kindred Hospital Bay Area-Tampa, Tampa, FL, p. A159

BILUNKA, Dianne, Director Human Resources, Clarion Psychiatric Center, Clarion, PA, p. A586

BINDER, Dore, M.D., Chief Medical Officer, Woman's Hospital, Baton Rouge, LA, p. A298

BINDERMAN, Judi, Chief Information Technology Officer and Chief Medical Informatics Officer, St. Francis Medical Center, Lynwood, CA, p. A76

BINDERMAN, Warren, Chief Financial Officer, Lifebrite Community Hospital Of Stokes, Danbury, NC, p. A508

BINDL, Karen, CPA, Controller, Uw Health Rehabilitation Hospital, Madison, WI, p. A788

BINGHAM, Julie, IT Supervisor, San Juan Health Service District, Monticello, UT, p. A729

BINGHAM, Leslie, Senior Vice President and Chief Executive Officer, Valley Baptist Medical Center-Brownsville, Brownsville, TX, p. A661

BINGHAM, Paulette, Director Nursing Services, Heritage Valley Kennedy, Mckees Rocks, PA, p. A596

BINGMAN, Ryan, Director Operations, Grundy County Memorial Hospital, Grundy Center, IA, p. A250

BINKLEY, Sharon, Director Human Resources, Fairfax Community Hospital, Fairfax, OK, p. A559

BINTZ, Marilu, M.D., Chief of Staff, Gundersen Boscobel Area Hospital And Clinics, Boscobel, WI, p. A781

BIRCH, Misty, Director Human Resources, Castleview Hospital, Price, UT, p. A731

BIRCHFIELD, Patrick T., Commanding Officer, Colonel Florence A. Blanchfield Army Community Hospital, Fort Campbell, KY, p. A283

BIRCHMEIER, Kevin, Director Human Resources, Covenant Healthcare, Saginaw, MI, p. A365

BIRD, Alan, Chief Executive Officer, Adams County Regional Medical Center, Seaman, OH, p. A549

BIRD, Jace, M.D., Chief Medical Officer, Missouri River Medical Center, Fort Benton, MT, p. A423

BIRD, Jeffrey C., M.D., President, Indiana University Health Ball Memorial Hospital, Muncie, IN, p. A237

BIRD, Lindsay, Director Finance, South Pointe Hospital, Warrensville Heights, OH, p. A552

BIRD, Michele, Chief Human Resources Officer, Hemet Valley Medical Center, Hemet, CA, p. A68
  Chief Human Resources Officer, Menifee Valley Medical Center, Sun City, CA, p. A100

BIRENBERG, Allan, Vice President Medical Affairs, Medstar Harbor Hospital, Baltimore, MD, p. A325

BIRI, Abel, Chief Executive Officer, Adventhealth Waterman, Tavares, FL, p. A160

BIRKEL, Sue, R.N., Director of Nursing, Butler County Health Care Center, David City, NE, p. A431

BIRKHOFER, Colleen, Chief Nursing Officer, Trenton Psychiatric Hospital, Trenton, NJ, p. A464

BIRMINGHAM, Karen, Director Human Resources, West Springs Hospital, Grand Junction, CO, p. A113

BIRSCHBACH, Nancy, Vice President and Chief Information Officer, Ripon Medical Center, Ripon, WI, p. A795
  Vice President and Chief Information Officer, St. Agnes Hospital, Fond Du Lac, WI, p. A784
  Vice President and Chief Information Officer, Waupun Memorial Hospital, Waupun, WI, p. A798

BISCO-FLORA, Nancy, Chief Nursing Officer, Saint Michael's Medical Center, Newark, NJ, p. A460

BISDORF, Jonathan, Director Information Technology, Ohio Valley Surgical Hospital, Springfield, OH, p. A549

BISH, Carol, Human Resources Coordinator, Prisma Health North Greenville, Travelers Rest, SC, p. A625

BISHARA, Reemon, M.D., Medical Director, Coastal Harbor Treatment Center, Savannah, GA, p. A180

BISHOP, Amy, Director Human Resources, Red Bay Hospital, Red Bay, AL, p. A24

BISHOP, Bill, Chief Information Officer, Colquitt Regional Medical Center, Moultrie, GA, p. A177

BISHOP, Elizabeth, Business Office Manager, Salina Surgical Hospital, Salina, KS, p. A276

BISHOP, Glenda, Interim Chief Executive Officer, Quincy Valley Medical Center, Quincy, WA, p. A762

BISHOP, Janice, R.N., Chief Nursing Officer, Tewksbury Hospital, Tewksbury, MA, p. A345

BISHOP, Jim, Chief Financial Officer, Sullivan County Community Hospital, Sullivan, IN, p. A241

BISHOP, Jody, Chief Nursing Officer, Bon Secours St. Mary's Hospital, Richmond, VA, p. A749

BISHOP, John, Chief Executive Officer, Long Beach Medical Center, Long Beach, CA, p. A72
  Chief Executive Officer, Marcus Daly Memorial Hospital, Hamilton, MT, p. A424
  Chief Executive Officer, Miller Children's & Women's Hospital Long Beach, Long Beach, CA, p. A72

BISHOP, Regina L., Administrator, Providence Kodiak Island Medical Center, Kodiak, AK, p. A28

BISHOP, Steve, Chief Financial Officer, Up Health System-Portage, Hancock, MI, p. A357

BISHOP-MCWAIN, Toni, Chief Nursing Officer, Osf St. Josep. Medical Center, Bloomington, IL, p. A195

BISIG, John, Chief Nursing Officer, The Brook Hospital - Kmi, Louisville, KY, p. A288

BISIGNANI, Thomas, Chief Financial Officer, Moses Taylor Hospital, Scranton, PA, p. A607

BISPHAM, Stuart, Director, Information Technology and Security Officer, Madera Community Hospital, Madera, CA, p. A76

BISSENDEN, Chris, Director Human Resources, Ogden Regional Medical Center, Ogden, UT, p. A730

BISSET, George, M.D., IiiChief Medical Officer, Children's Hospital, New Orleans, LA, p. A310

BISSONETTE, Christine, R.N., Service Line Director for Acute Services, Kalkaska Memorial Health Center, Kalkaska, MI, p. A359

BISSONNETTE, Andre, Chief Financial Officer, Brattleboro Memorial Hospital, Brattleboro, VT, p. A735

BISTERFELDT, Joanne, Chief Information Officer, Ascension All Saints, Racine, WI, p. A794

BITAR, Adib, M.D., Medical Director, Aurora Charter Oak Hospital, Covina, CA, p. A61

BITAR, Ali, M.D., Vice President Medical Affairs, Dmc - Rehabilitation Institute Of Michigan, Detroit, MI, p. A352

BITHER, Dean, Chief Financial Officer, Northern Light Inland Hospital, Waterville, ME, p. A323

BITNER, Janet, Chief Operating Officer, Texas Neurorehab Center, Austin, TX, p. A657

BITSILLY, Christina, Human Resource Specialist, U. S. Public Health Service Indian Hospital, Crownpoint, NM, p. A469

BITSOLI, Deborah, CPA, President, Mercy Medical Center, Springfield, MA, p. A344

BITTEL, Rayna, Chief Financial Officer, Grisell Memorial Hospital District One, Ransom, KS, p. A275
  Co-Chief Executive Officer and Chief Financial Officer, Grisell Memorial Hospital District One, Ransom, KS, p. A275

BITTNER, Augustine, Chief Information Officer, Robley Rex Veterans Affairs Medical Center, Louisville, KY, p. A288

BITTNER, David, Chief Financial Officer, Mount Sinai Rehabilitation Hospital, Hartford, CT, p. A122

BITZ, Joan, Chief Nursing Officer, Meeker Memorial Hospital, Litchfield, MN, p. A379

BIUSO, Joseph, M.D., Vice President and Chief of Medical Affairs, Floyd Medical Center, Rome, GA, p. A179

BIVANS, Michelle, Director Human Resources, Duncan Regional Hospital, Duncan, OK, p. A558

BIVINS, Tera, Chief Human Resources Officer, Iroquois Memorial Hospital And Resident Home, Watseka, IL, p. A222

BIXLER, David, Chief Executive Officer, Rhea Medical Center, Dayton, TN, p. A637

BJARNASON, Dana, Ph.D., R.N., Vice President and Chief Nursing Officer, Ohsu Hospital, Portland, OR, p. A579

BJELLAND ESQ, TimPhysician, Mile Bluff Medical Center, Mauston, WI, p. A789

BJERKE, Carolyn, Director Human Resources, Mercy Hospital Kingfisher, Kingfisher, OK, p. A560

BJERKE, Erik, Chief Executive Officer, Madison Healthcare Services, Madison, MN, p. A379

BJERKNES, Dan, Director Human Resources, Chi St. Alexius Health - Williston Medical Center, Williston, ND, p. A526
  President, Chi St. Alexius Health - Williston Medical Center, Williston, ND, p. A526

BJORDAHL, Kevin, M.D., Chief Medical Officer, Milbank Area Hospital Avera, Milbank, SD, p. A629

BJORNSTAD, Brad, M.D., Vice President and Chief Medical Officer, Adventhealth Tampa, Tampa, FL, p. A159

BLACK, Amy, R.N., MSN, Chief Operating Officer, Sentara Martha Jefferson Hospital, Charlottesville, VA, p. A739

BLACK, Douglas, Vice President of Operations, Christian Hospital, Saint Louis, MO, p. A415

BLACK, Jessica, Chief Executive Officer, Copper Springs Hospital, Avondale, AZ, p. A30

BLACK, Marcey, Chief Financial Officer, Northwest Florida Community Hospital, Chipley, FL, p. A134

BLACK, Maria, Chief Nursing Officer, Utah Valley Hospital, Provo, UT, p. A731

BLACK, Marilynn, Chief Information Officer, Northern Arizona Healthcare, Flagstaff Medical Center, Flagstaff, AZ, p. A31
  Chief Information Officer, Northern Arizona Healthcare, Verde Valley Medical Center, Cottonwood, AZ, p. A31

BLACK, Michael, Director Human Resources, East Georgia Regional Medical Center, Statesboro, GA, p. A181

BLACK, Paul, Chief Financial Officer, Scott Regional Hospital, Morton, MS, p. A397

Controller, H. C. Watkins Memorial Hospital, Quitman, MS, p. A399

BLACK, Paul S., Chief Executive Officer, Winston Medical Center, Louisville, MS, p. A396

BLACK, Robert O., Chief Executive Officer, Linton Hospital, Linton, ND, p. A524

BLACK, Ronald, M.D., Chief Medical Officer, Clark Fork Valley Hospital, Plains, MT, p. A426

BLACK, Stephen, MS, Health Care System Director, St. Cloud Veterans Affairs Health Care System, Saint Cloud, MN, p. A384

BLACK, Terri, Network Manager, Lucas County Health Center, Chariton, IA, p. A245

BLACK, Tim, Director Human Resources, Timpanogos Regional Hospital, Orem, UT, p. A730

BLACK ESQ, JasonVice President and Chief Nursing Officer, Glendale Memorial Hospital And Health Center, Glendale, CA, p. A67

BLACK JR, CharlesChief Financial Officer, Rockcastle Regional Hospital And Respiratory Care Center, Mount Vernon, KY, p. A291

BLACKBEAR, Annabelle, Human Resources Specialist, U. S. Public Health Service Indian Hospital, Pine Ridge, SD, p. A630

BLACKBURN, Donovan, Chief Executive Officer and Vice President of Board of Directors, Pikeville Medical Center, Pikeville, KY, p. A292

BLACKBURN, Lisa, Director Human Resources, St. Margaret's Hospital, Spring Valley, IL, p. A220

BLACKBURN, Mary, Vice President Operations and Chief Practice Officer, Hugh Chatham Memorial Hospital, Elkin, NC, p. A509

BLACKBURN, Susan, Chief Administrative Officer, Providence St. Mary Medical Center, Walla Walla, WA, p. A768
  Chief Operating Officer, Providence St. Mary Medical Center, Walla Walla, WA, p. A768

BLACKFORD, Nate, President, Mosaic Medical Center - Maryville, Maryville, MO, p. A411

BLACKHAM, Cami, R.N., Nurse Administrator, Sevier Valley Hospital, Richfield, UT, p. A731

BLACKHURST, Kristi, Interim Vice President Operations, Asante Rogue Regional Medical Center, Medford, OR, p. A577

BLACKMON, Jenean, Assistant Vice President and Chief Information Officer, Mcleod Health Dillon, Dillon, SC, p. A619
  Associate Vice President and Chief Information Officer, Mcleod Regional Medical Center, Florence, SC, p. A619

BLACKWELL, David, Vice President Operations, Baylor Scott & White Medical Center - Hillcrest, Waco, TX, p. A724

BLACKWELL, James, President and Chief Executive Officer, Clara Barton Hospital, Hoisington, KS, p. A266

BLACKWELL, Kelsie, Chief Financial Officer, Placentia-Linda Hospital, Placentia, CA, p. A85

BLACKWELL, Lenore, Director Human Resources, Tennova Healthcare-Harton, Tullahoma, TN, p. A650

BLACKWELL, Timothy, Manager Human Resources, Rolling Hills Hospital, Ada, OK, p. A555

BLACKWOOD, Jim, Chief Executive Officer, Tallahatchie General Hospital, Charleston, MS, p. A391

BLACKWOOD, Mark, M.D., Chief of Staff, Bolivar Medical Center, Cleveland, MS, p. A391

BLAD, Nathan, Chief Executive Officer, Rc Hospital And Clinics, Olivia, MN, p. A382
  Chief Financial Officer, Rc Hospital And Clinics, Olivia, MN, p. A382

BLADEN, Anthony, Vice President Human Resources, Calverthealth Medical Center, Prince Frederick, MD, p. A331

BLAHA, Bill, Manager Information Technology, Tri-County Hospital, Wadena, MN, p. A387

BLAHNIK, David, Chief Operating Officer, Twin Valley Behavioral Healthcare, Columbus, OH, p. A537

BLAIN, Brenda, MSN, Senior Vice President and Chief Nursing Executive, Bayhealth Medical Center, Dover, DE, p. A127

BLAIR, Diane, Human Resources and Admissions, Chi Health Plainview, Plainview, NE, p. A439

BLAIR, Erin, Interim Chief Executive Officer, Baylor Scott & White Medical Center At - Mckinney, Mckinney, TX, p. A700

BLAIR, Heidi, Vice President Administration, Centerstone Hospital, Bradenton, FL, p. A132

BLAIR, Jan, Director Human Resources, Cmh Regional Health System, Wilmington, OH, p. A553

BLAIR, Mark, M.D., Medical Director, Columbus Dublin Springs, Dublin, OH, p. A539

BLAIR, Melinda, Vice President and Chief Nursing Officer, Baptist Health Richmond, Richmond, KY, p. A292

BLAIR, Robert D., Chief Executive Officer, The Spine Hospital Of Louisiana At The Neuromedical Center, Baton Rouge, LA, p. A298

BLAKE, Alan, M.D., President Medical Staff, Samaritan Lebanon Community Hospital, Lebanon, OR, p. A577

BLAKE, Daphne, R.N., MSN, Chief Nursing Officer, Guadalup. Regional Medical Center, Seguin, TX, p. A714

BLAKE, Diane, Chief Executive Officer, Cascade Medical Center, Leavenworth, WA, p. A760

BLAKE, Jean, Chief Nursing Officer, Uh Cleveland Medical Center, Cleveland, OH, p. A535

BLAKE, Kelly, Chief Executive Officer, Select Specialty Hospital-Johnstown, Johnstown, PA, p. A593

BLAKE, Robert, Chief Human Resources Officer Southwest Market, Memorial Hermann Sugar Land Hospital, Sugar Land, TX, p. A717

BLAKE, Skylier, R.N., Chief Executive Officer, El Paso Ltac Hospital, El Paso, TX, p. A675

BLAKE, Steven, Corporate Chief Financial Officer, East Los Angeles Doctors Hospital, Los Angeles, CA, p. A74

BLAKELY, Michelle, FACHE, Ph.D., Associate Director, Jesse Brown Veterans Affairs Medical Center, Chicago, IL, p. A198

FACHE, Ph.D., Chief Operating Officer, Norwegian American Hospital, Chicago, IL, p. A200

BLAKEMORE, Caanan, Chief Executive Officer, Cedar Crest Hospital And Residential Treatment Center, Belton, TX, p. A659

BLAKENEY, Dell, Vice President and Chief Information Officer, South Central Regional Medical Center, Laurel, MS, p. A395

BLAKEY GORMAN, Mary, Director Human Resources, Northwest Missouri Psychiatric Rehabilitation Center, Saint Joseph, MO, p. A415

BLALOCK, Tracey, MSN, R.N., Chief Nurse Executive, Medical Center, Navicent Health, Macon, GA, p. A176

BLANC, Linda, R.N., Administrative Director of Nursing, Jefferson Medical Center, Ranson, WV, p. A776

BLANCHARD, Charmaine, Chief Nursing Officer, Encompass Health Rehabilitation Hospital An Affiliate Of Martin Health, Stuart, FL, p. A158

BLANCHARD, Jeremy, M.D., Chief Medical Officer, North Mississipp. Health Services, Inc., Tupelo, MI, p. A368

BLANCHARD, Susan, R.N., Chief Nursing Officer, Encompass Health Rehabilitation Hospital Of Albuquerque, Albuquerque, NM, p. A467

BLANCHARD, Timothy, Chief Financial Officer, Kingman Regional Medical Center, Kingman, AZ, p. A33

BLANCHAT, Tim, Chief Information Officer, Catawba Valley Medical Center, Hickory, NC, p. A512

BLANCHETTE, Edward A., M.D., Director, Connecticut Department Of Correction's Hospital, Somers, CT, p. A125

BLANCO, Andres, Director Management Information Systems, Westside Regional Medical Center, Plantation, FL, p. A154

BLAND, Andrew, M.D., Vice President and Chief Medical Officer, Hamilton Medical Center, Dalton, GA, p. A170

BLAND, Casey, Director of Nursing, Rush Foundation Hospital, Meridian, MS, p. A397

BLAND, David, Chief Executive Officer, South Davis Community Hospital, Bountiful, UT, p. A727

BLAND, Douglas, Manager Information Services, Spring View Hospital, Lebanon, KY, p. A286

BLANEY, Gerard, Vice President Finance and Interim Chief Financial Officer, Einstein Medical Center Philadelphia, Philadelphia, PA, p. A600

Vice President, Finance, Einstein Medical Center Montgomery, East Norriton, PA, p. A589

BLANK, Arthur J., President and Chief Executive Officer, Mount Desert Island Hospital, Bar Harbor, ME, p. A318

BLANK, Kim, Director Human Resources, Lake Region Healthcare, Fergus Falls, MN, p. A376

Director Human Resources, Prairie Ridge Hospital And Health Services, Elbow Lake, MN, p. A376

BLANKE, Kerry, Chief Financial Officer, Thedacare Medical Center-Shawano, Shawano, WI, p. A795

Director Financial Services, Thedacare Medical Center-Waupaca, Waupaca, WI, p. A798

BLANKENHORN, Ann, Chief Nursing Officer, Pottstown Hospital, Pottstown, PA, p. A605

BLANKENSHIP, Diana, Director Human Resources, Welch Community Hospital, Welch, WV, p. A777

BLANKENSHIP, Jeff, CPA, Chief Financial Officer, Pathways Of Tennessee, Jackson, TN, p. A639

CPA, Vice President and Chief Financial Officer, Jackson-Madison County General Hospital, Jackson, TN, p. A639

BLANSKY, Richard, M.D., Chief Medical Officer, Our Lady Of Lourdes Memorial Hospital, Inc., Binghamton, NY, p. A476

BLANTON, Forest, Chief Information Officer, Memorial Hospital Pembroke, Pembroke Pines, FL, p. A153

Chief Information Officer, Memorial Hospital West, Pembroke Pines, FL, p. A153

Senior VP and Chief Information Officer, Memorial Hospital Miramar, Miramar, FL, p. A148

BLANTON, James, Chief Financial Officer, Ut Health East Texas Rehabilitation Hospital, Tyler, TX, p. A722

Chief Financial Officer, Ut Health Specialty Hospital, Tyler, TX, p. A722

BLANTON, Kevin, D.O., Chief of Staff, Goodall-Witcher Hospital, Clifton, TX, p. A664

BLANTON, Ron, Chief Fiscal Services, Boise Veterans Affairs Medical Center, Boise, ID, p. A188

BLANTON, Sherry, Human Resource Director, Doctor's Memorial Hospital, Perry, FL, p. A154

BLASER, Joseph, Chief Medical Officer, Fayette County Hospital, Vandalia, IL, p. A222

BLASER, Karla, Director Human Resources, Unitypoint Health - Trinity Muscatine, Muscatine, IA, p. A254

BLASING, Amy, Chief Executive Officer, Lovelace Westside Hospital, Albuquerque, NM, p. A467

BLASIUS, Rita, Assistant Administrator and Chief Financial Officer, Avera St. Benedict Health Center, Parkston, SD, p. A630

President and Chief Executive Officer, Avera St. Benedict Health Center, Parkston, SD, p. A630

BLASKO, Edward, Chief of Staff, Atrium Health Anson, Wadesboro, NC, p. A519

BLASY, Christopher, D.O., Chief of Staff, Carl Vinson Veterans Affairs Medical Center, Dublin, GA, p. A171

BLAUER, Michael, Chief Executive Officer, Bear Lake Memorial Hospital, Montpelier, ID, p. A191

BLAUSTEIN, Ron, Chief Financial Officer, Ann & Robert H. Lurie Children's Hospital Of Chicago, Chicago, IL, p. A198

BLAUWET, Judy, M.P.H., R.N., Senior Vice President of Hospital Operations and Chief Nursing Officer, Avera Mckennan Hospital And University Health Center, Sioux Falls, SD, p. A631

M.P.H., R.N., Senior Vice President Operations and Chief Nursing Officer, Avera Mckennan Hospital And University Health Center, Sioux Falls, SD, p. A631

BLAYLOCK, Darrell, Chief Executive Officer, Lincoln County Health System, Fayetteville, TN, p. A638

BLAYLOCK, Kevin, Chief Executive Officer, Oklahoma Spine Hospital, Oklahoma City, OK, p. A565

BLAYLOCK, L Dwayne., Chief Executive Officer, Merit Health River Oaks, Flowood, MS, p. A392

BLAZAKIS, Shelly, Director Human Resources Services, Scripp. Memorial Hospital-La Jolla, La Jolla, CA, p. A70

BLAZEK, Dennis, Chief Information Officer, Clarke County Hospital, Osceola, IA, p. A256

BLAZEK, Robert, System Director, Human Resources Business Partners, Elmhurst Hospital, Elmhurst, IL, p. A204

BLAZIER, Patty, Chief Nursing Officer, Hamilton Memorial Hospital District, Mcleansboro, IL, p. A212

BLEAK, Jason, Chief Executive Officer, Battle Mountain General Hospital, Battle Mountain, NV, p. A441

BLECHA, Timothy, M.D., Medical Director, Brodstone Memorial Hospital, Superior, NE, p. A440

BLEECKER, Leigh, Chief Financial Officer, Duke Raleigh Hospital, Raleigh, NC, p. A516

Interim President, Duke Raleigh Hospital, Raleigh, NC, p. A516

BLENDERMAN, Robert, Senior Vice President and Chief Operating Officer, New York-Presbyterian Queens, Flushing, NY, p. A484

BLESI, Michael, Director Information Technology, Rainy Lake Medical Center, International Falls, MN, p. A378

BLESSING, Brian, Chief Financial Officer, Texas Health Harris Methodist Hospital Azle, Azle, TX, p. A657

BLEVINS, Bonnie, R.N., Chief Financial Officer, Faith Community Hospital, Jacksboro, TX, p. A691

BLEVINS, Denzil, Director Information Systems, Montgomery General Hospital, Montgomery, WV, p. A774

BLEVINS, Matthew, Chief Operating Officer, Flowers Hospital, Dothan, AL, p. A17

BLEVINS, Pam, R.N., Director Information Technology Member Hospitals Mission, Mcdowell Hospital, Marion, NC, p. A514

R.N., Director, Clinical Informatics, Blue Ridge Regional Hospital, Spruce Pine, NC, p. A518

BLIGHTON, Gordon, Director Resource Management, Naval Hospital Camp Pendleton, Camp Pendleton, CA, p. A59

BLINCO, Lynne, Chief Executive Officer, Healthsouth Rehabilitation Hospital Of Dayton, Dayton, OH, p. A538

BLISS, Howard, Director of Information Systems, Helen Newberry Joy Hospital, Newberry, MI, p. A363

BLIVEN, Donna, Vice President Patient Care Services and Chief Nursing Officer, Jones Memorial Hospital, Wellsville, NY, p. A502

BLOB, Burchkhard, Manager Human Resources, Central Virginia Training Center, Madison Heights, VA, p. A745

BLOCHLINGER, Pamela, Acting Vice President Finance, Cloud County Health Center, Concordia, KS, p. A263

BLOCK, Annie, Director Human Resources, Poplar Community Hospital, Poplar, MT, p. A427

BLOCK, Deborah, Vice President Nursing and Chief Nursing Officer, Navicent Health Baldwin, Milledgeville, GA, p. A177

BLOCK, Linn, R.N., Chief Executive Officer, Manning Regional Healthcare Center, Manning, IA, p. A253

BLODGETT, Debbie, Director Fiscal Services, Ochiltree General Hospital, Perryton, TX, p. A705

BLOEMER, Brad, Vice President Finance and Chief Financial Officer, Arkansas Methodist Medical Center, Paragould, AR, p. A51

BLOMBERG, Emily, Chief Operating Officer, Hennepin Healthcare, Minneapolis, MN, p. A380

BLOMQUIST, David, Director Information Technology, Mckenzie-Willamette Medical Center, Springfield, OR, p. A581

BLOMSTEDT, Jason, Chief of Staff, Community Hospital, Mccook, NE, p. A435

BLOOD, Barbara, Director Human Resources, Lourdes Counseling Center, Richland, WA, p. A763

Executive Director Human Resources, Lourdes Medical Center, Pasco, WA, p. A762

BLOOM, Barry, Chief Executive Officer, Jeff Davis Hospital, Hazlehurst, GA, p. A173

BLOOM, Laura, Director Human Resources, Coffee Regional Medical Center, Douglas, GA, p. A171

BLOOM, Rob, Chief Financial Officer, Carthage Area Hospital, Carthage, NY, p. A481

BLOUGH, Daniel D. Jr, Chief Executive Officer, Punxsutawney Area Hospital, Punxsutawney, PA, p. A605

BLOW, Osbert, M.D., Ph.D., FACS, President and Chief Medical Officer, Christus Spohn Hospital Corpus Christi Memorial, Corpus Christi, TX, p. A665

BLUE, Jan, Vice President Human Resources, Hoag Memorial Hospital Presbyterian, Newport Beach, CA, p. A81

BLUE, Lee, MSN, R.N., Chief Nursing Officer and Executive Vice President Patient Care Services, Eskenazi Health, Indianapolis, IN, p. A231

BLUHM, Tom, Director Information Systems, Island Hospital, Anacortes, WA, p. A755

BLUM, Daniel, President and Chief Operating Officer, Senior Vice President LifeBridge Health, Sinai Hospital Of Baltimore, Baltimore, MD, p. A326

President, Grace Medical Center, Baltimore, MD, p. A324

BLUM, Donald, M.D., Chief of Staff, Wetzel County Hospital, New Martinsville, WV, p. A775

BLUM, Gavin, Chief Financial Officer, Kearney County Health Services, Minden, NE, p. A435

BLUM, Walter, M.D., Chief of Staff, Mcleod Health Dillon, Dillon, SC, p. A619

BLUNK, Jim, D.O., Chief Medical Officer, Sumner County Hospital District 1, Caldwell, KS, p. A262

BLURTON, SPHR,SHRM-SCP, Cheri, Director Human Resources, HIPAA Privacy Officer, Great River Medical Center, Blytheville, AR, p. A43

Director Human Resources, South Mississipp. County Regional Medical Center, Osceola, AR, p. A51

BLYE, Colleen, Executive Vice President and Chief Financial Officer, Montefiore Medical Center, Bronx, NY, p. A477

BLYTHE, Thomas, System Vice President Human Resources, Ssm Health Good Samaritan Hospital, Mount Vernon, IL, p. A213

BOAL, Jeremy, M.D., President, Mount Sinai Beth Israel, New York, NY, p. A490

BOARD, Pat, Chief Administrative Officer, Marshfield Medical Center, Marshfield, WI, p. A789

BOARD, Patricia, Vice President Human Resources, Community Hospital Of Bremen, Bremen, IN, p. A225

BOATMAN, Robert, Director Information Technology, Richmond State Hospital, Richmond, IN, p. A239

BOBBITT, James, Vice President Human Resources, Group Ministry Market, Saint Agnes Healthcare, Baltimore, MD, p. A326

BOBEK, Bruce, President Professional Staff, Columbia Memorial Hospital, Astoria, OR, p. A573

BOBO, Matt, Chief Information Officer, Meade District Hospital, Meade, KS, p. A271

BOCCELLATO, Judy, R.N., MSN, Chief Nursing Officer, Specialty Hospital Of Central Jersey, Lakewood, NJ, p. A457

BOCKENEK, William, M.D., Chief Medical Officer, Atrium Health's Carolinas Rehabilitation, Charlotte, NC, p. A507

BODE, Edwin, Chief Financial Officer, Mid-Columbia Medical Center, The Dalles, OR, p. A582

BODENHAM, Steve, Senior Manager Clinical Engineering, Indiana University Health North Hospital, Carmel, IN, p. A225

BODENNER, Nancy, Director Human Resources, Ascension St. Josep. Hospital, Tawas City, MI, p. A367

BODENSTEINER, Kim, Chief Financial Officer, Essentia Health-Fosston, Fosston, MN, p. A376

BODIN, Donna, Vice President, Woman's Hospital, Baton Rouge, LA, p. A298

BODINE, Maureen, Chief Clinical Officer, Kindred Hospital-San Diego, San Diego, CA, p. A91

BODLOVIC, Kirk, Vice President and Chief Financial Officer, Providence St. Josep. Medical Center, Polson, MT, p. A427
WMSA Chief Financial Officer, Providence St. Patrick Hospital, Missoula, MT, p. A426

BODNAR, Darrell, Director Information, Weeks Medical Center, Lancaster, NH, p. A449

BOECKMANN, Patricia, R.N., Chief Operating Officer and Chief Nursing Officer, Straub Medical Center, Honolulu, HI, p. A185

BOEHMER, Bernard, M.D., Medical Director, Cassia Regional Hospital, Burley, ID, p. A189

BOEMER, Sally, Chief Financial Officer, North Shore Medical Center, Salem, MA, p. A344
Senior Vice President Finance, Massachusetts General Hospital, Boston, MA, p. A336

BOEMMEL, Michael, Vice President and Chief Financial Officer, Medstar National Rehabilitation Hospital, Washington, DC, p. A130

BOEN, Stefanie, Chief Nursing Officer, Skyline Hospital, White Salmon, WA, p. A769

BOER, Jeff, Director Information Technology, Pulaski Memorial Hospital, Winamac, IN, p. A242

BOERGER, Kathy, Director Human Resources, Upper Valley Medical Center, Troy, OH, p. A551

BOERSCHEL, Viva, Director of Nursing, Floyd County Medical Center, Charles City, IA, p. A245

BOERSMA, Wendy, Vice President, Nursing and Chief Nursing Officer, Henry Ford Allegiance Health, Jackson, MI, p. A359

BOESE, Chris, Vice President and Chief Nursing Officer, Regions Hospital, Saint Paul, MN, p. A385

BOGARD, Tim, Manager Information Technology, Highland District Hospital, Hillsboro, OH, p. A542

BOGARDUS, Tim, Chief Executive Officer, Oasis Hospital, Phoenix, AZ, p. A36

BOGEN, Mark, CPA, Senior Vice President, Finance, Mount Sinai South Nassau, Oceanside, NY, p. A493

BOGERS, Christina, Chief Clinical Officer, North Valley Hospital, Whitefish, MT, p. A428

BOGGESS, Carrie, Human Resource Generalist, Carilion Giles Community Hospital, Pearisburg, VA, p. A748
Human Resources Generalist, Carilion Tazewell Community Hospital, Tazewell, VA, p. A752

BOGGESS, Jack, Chief Executive Officer, Cobalt Rehabilitation Hospital El Paso, El Paso, TX, p. A674

BOGGUS, Bradley, Chief Financial Officer, Cmh Regional Health System, Wilmington, OH, p. A553

BOGLE, William, Director Information Systems, North Arkansas Regional Medical Center, Harrison, AR, p. A46

BOGOLIN, Lore, MSN, R.N., Vice President Patient Care Services and Chief Nursing Officer, Vassar Brothers Medical Center, Poughkeepsie, NY, p. A495

BOHACH, Christopher, DPM, Chief of Staff, Mercy Health - Willard Hospital, Willard, OH, p. A553

BOHALL, Karen, Director Human Resources, Upmc Chautauqua, Jamestown, NY, p. A486

BOHATY, Richard, Director Information Technology, Chi Health St Elizabeth, Lincoln, NE, p. A434

BOHLIN, Sarah, Human Resources Director, North Carolina Specialty Hospital, Durham, NC, p. A509

BOHN, Terry, Director, Human Resources, Orange County Global Medical Center, Inc., Santa Ana, CA, p. A96

BOHNEN, Christa, Director Human Resources, Ellsworth County Medical Center, Ellsworth, KS, p. A264

BOHNENKAMP, Russ, Chief Financial Officer, Chadron Community Hospital And Health Services, Chadron, NE, p. A431

BOIK, Reyne, Director Human Resources, Cascade Medical Center, Leavenworth, WA, p. A760

BOIKE, Darlene, Chief Financial Officer, Ccm Health, Montevideo, MN, p. A381

BOILEAU, Michel, M.D., Chief Clinical Officer, St. Charles Prineville, Prineville, OR, p. A580

BOILY, Cindy, MSN, R.N., Senior Vice President and Chief Nursing Officer, Wakemed Cary Hospital, Cary, NC, p. A506
MSN, R.N., Senior Vice President and Chief Nursing Officer, Wakemed Raleigh Campus, Raleigh, NC, p. A517

BOIS, Alain, R.N., Director of Nursing, Northern Maine Medical Center, Fort Kent, ME, p. A320

BOISVERT, Gerald, Vice President and Chief Financial Officer, Connecticut Children's Medical Center, Hartford, CT, p. A122

BOJO, Rolland, R.N., Administrator, Garnett Health Medical Center - Catskills, Callicoon, NY, p. A480

R.N., Chief Nursing Officer, Administrator Patient Care and Services, Garnet Health Medical Center - Catskills, Harris, NY, p. A485

BOKON, Mark, Chief Information Officer, Northwest Medical Center - Springdale, Springdale, AR, p. A53

BOKOVITZ, Beverly, R.N., Chief Nursing Officer, University Of Cincinnati Medical Center, Cincinnati, OH, p. A533

BOLAND, Albert, Vice President Operations, Upmc Jameson, New Castle, PA, p. A598

BOLAND, E. Kay, R.N., MS, Vice President and Chief Nursing Officer, United Health Services Hospitals-Binghamton, Binghamton, NY, p. A476

BOLANDER, Patrick, Chief Financial Officer, East Cooper Medical Center, Mount Pleasant, SC, p. A622
Chief Financial Officer, Georgetown Community Hospital, Georgetown, KY, p. A284

BOLCAVAGE, Ted, Vice President Division Controller, Inpatient, Ohiohealth Rehabilitation Hospital, Columbus, OH, p. A536

BOLDA, Craig, Chief Operating Officer, St. Catherine Hospital, East Chicago, IN, p. A227

BOLDT, Stephanie, President and Chief Executive Officer, Crete Area Medical Center, Crete, NE, p. A431

BOLDUC, Tiana, Chief Information Officer, Mercy Hospital Ozark, Ozark, AR, p. A51

BOLEN, Shannon, Director Human Resources, Baptist Memorial Hospital-Booneville, Booneville, MS, p. A390

BOLES, Glen, Vice President and Chief Financial Officer, Christus St. Michael Health System, Texarkana, TX, p. A719
Vice President and Chief Financial Officer, Christus St. Michael Rehabilitation Hospital, Texarkana, TX, p. A719

BOLES, Lee, Assistant Administrator and Chief Financial Officer, Hunt Regional Medical Center, Greenville, TX, p. A682

BOLEWARE, Mike, Administrator, Franklin County Memorial Hospital, Meadville, MS, p. A396

BOLEY, Jason, M.D., Medical Director, Rock Prairie Behavioral Health, College Station, TX, p. A664

BOLEY, Sarah, Director Human Resources, Wetzel County Hospital, New Martinsville, WV, p. A775

BOLIN, Cris, Chief Financial Officer, Grand River Hospital District, Rifle, CO, p. A118

BOLIN, Kari, Chief Nursing Officer, Putnam Community Medical Center, Palatka, FL, p. A152

BOLIN, Paul, Vice President and Chief Human Resources Officer, The Acadia Hospital, Bangor, ME, p. A318

BOLINE, Steve, Acting Administrator and Chief Executive Officer, Seneca Healthcare District, Chester, CA, p. A60

BOLINGER, John, M.D., Vice President Medical Affairs, Union Hospital, Terre Haute, IN, p. A241

BOLISH, Cameron, Chief Executive Officer, Rebound Behavioral Health, Lancaster, SC, p. A622

BOLLARD, Robert, Chief Financial Officer, Encompass Health Rehabilitation Hospital Of Henderson, Henderson, NV, p. A442

BOLLICH, Mary, Director of Nurses, Amg Specialty Hospital-Lafayette, Lafayette, LA, p. A305

BOLLIER, Sheila A., Chief Executive Officer, Encompass Health Rehabilitation Hospital Of Cypress, Houston, TX, p. A685

BOLLINGER, Bill, Chief Information Officer, Carroll County Memorial Hospital, Carrollton, MO, p. A404

BOLLINGER, Bruce, M.D., Medical Director, Baylor Scott & White Surgical Hospital Fort Worth, Fort Worth, TX, p. A678

BOLLMAN, Brooke, Chief Executive Officer and Administrator, Sumner County Hospital District 1, Caldwell, KS, p. A262

BOLLMANN, Brett, Administrator, Memorial Hospital, Chester, IL, p. A197

BOLLU, Prabhu, Director Information Technology, Wilson N. Jones Regional Medical Center, Sherman, TX, p. A716

BOLOGNA, Monica, R.N., Chief Nursing Officer, West Jefferson Medical Center, Marrero, LA, p. A308

BOLOGNANI, Laurie, Human Resources Officer, Speare Memorial Hospital, Plymouth, NH, p. A451

BOLOR, Erlinda, R.N., Chief Nursing Officer, San Joaquin General Hospital, French Camp. CA, p. A65

BOLTER, Cindy, Chief Nursing and Operations Officer, John Muir Behavioral Health Center, Concord, CA, p. A61

BOLTON, Jeffrey, Chief Administrative Officer, Mayo Clinic Hospital - Rochester, Rochester, MN, p. A384

BOMAR, Jacob, Director Information Technology, Hardin Medical Center, Savannah, TN, p. A649

BOMGAARS, Scott, M.D., Vice President Medical Affairs, Methodist Jennie Edmundson Hospital, Council Bluffs, IA, p. A247

BOMSTAD, Heather, MSN, R.N., Vice President Patient Care Services and Chief Nursing Officer, Osf Saint Paul Medical Center, Mendota, IL, p. A212
MSN, R.N., Vice President, Chief Nursing Officer, Osf Saint Elizabeth Medical Center, Ottawa, IL, p. A216

BONACORSO, Donna, R.N., Chief Nursing Officer, Community Medical Center, Toms River, NJ, p. A464

BONACQUISTI, Gary, M.D., Chief Medical Officer, Texas Health Presbyterian Hospital Of Rockwall, Rockwall, TX, p. A709

BONAR, Carrie, Chief Information Officer, Southern California Hospital At Culver City, Culver City, CA, p. A62

BONAR, Lynette, FACHE, R.N., Chief Executive Officer, Tuba City Regional Health Care Corporation, Tuba City, AZ, p. A39

BONASORO, Cheryl, MSN, R.N., Vice President of Nursing and Chief Operating Officer, Nashoba Valley Medical Center, Ayer, MA, p. A334

BONAZZOLA, Michael, M.D., Interim Chief Medical Officer, Ohsu Hospital, Portland, OR, p. A579

BONCZEK, Mary Ellen, R.N., Chief Nursing Executive, New Hanover Regional Medical Center, Wilmington, NC, p. A520

BOND, Lee, Chief Executive Officer, Singing River Health System, Pascagoula, MS, p. A398

BOND, Rodney, Director of Information Technology, Northern Regional Hospital, Mount Airy, NC, p. A515

BOND, Sharon, Director Human Resources, Chi St. Josep. College Station Hospital, College Station, TX, p. A664

BONDEROFF, Scott, President, O'Connor Hospital, Delhi, NY, p. A482

BONDI, Blaise, Chief Financial Officer, Baylor Scott & White Medical Center - Centennial, Frisco, TX, p. A680

BONDS, Cyrilla, R.N., Administrator, United Medical Rehabilitation Hospital, Hammond, LA, p. A302

BONDS, Juanita Bates., M.D., President and Chief Executive Officer, Bliant Specialty Hospital, New Orleans, LA, p. A310

BONDURANT, Barry, Administrator and Chief Executive Officer, Baptist Memorial Hospital-Union City, Union City, TN, p. A650

BONDURANT, Charles, Chief Information Officer, Meadows Regional Medical Center, Vidalia, GA, p. A182

BONE, Janice, Human Resources, Marshall County Hospital, Benton, KY, p. A280

BONEY, Rebecca, R.N., Chief Nursing Officer, Encompass Health Rehabilitation Hospital Of Middletown, Middletown, DE, p. A127

BONFILIO, Nicholas, M.D., Chief of Staff, Great Falls Clinic Hospital, Great Falls, MT, p. A424

BONI, Shirley, Administrative Officer, San Carlos Apache Healthcare Corporation, Peridot, AZ, p. A35

BONIFAY, Shawn, Chief Human Resource Officer, The Orthopedic Specialty Hospital, Murray, UT, p. A729

BONILLA, Felicita, Administrator, Hospital De La Concepcion, San German, PR, p. A809

BONJOUR, Richard, Chief Information Officer, Sauk Prairie Healthcare, Prairie Du Sac, WI, p. A794

BONK, Daniel J., Chief Executive Officer, Bellville Medical Center, Bellville, TX, p. A659

BONNECARRERE, Anthony, Controller, St. Bernard Parish Hospital, Chalmette, LA, p. A299

BONNER, Brad, Executive Director, Human Resources and General Counsel, Crawford County Memorial Hospital, Denison, IA, p. A248

BONNER, Gwen, Chief Operating Officer, Saint Francis Hospital-Bartlett, Bartlett, TN, p. A634

BONNER, Jason, Interim Chief Financial, Accounting Analyst, Morehouse General Hospital, Bastrop. LA, p. A296

BONNER, Kimber, R.N., Vice President Patient Care Services, Chi Health Good Samaritan, Kearney, NE, p. A433

BONNER, Lenne, President, Clearwater Valley Hospital And Clinics, Orofino, ID, p. A192
President, St. Mary's Hospital, Cottonwood, ID, p. A190

BONNER, Robert, Chief Financial Officer, Glendora Community Hospital, Glendora, CA, p. A67
Chief Financial Officer, Montclair Hospital Medical Center, Montclair, CA, p. A79

BONO JR, AnthonyChief Nursing Officer, Ahn Grove City, Grove City, PA, p. A591

BONOMO, Carrie, M.D., Chief of Staff, Riverland Medical Center, Ferriday, LA, p. A301

BONTHRON, Rikki, Chief Financial Officer, Franklin Hospital District, Benton, IL, p. A195

BONTRAGER, Mandy, Director Nursing, Holton Community Hospital, Holton, KS, p. A266

BONZO, Kelly, Director, Baptist Health Richmond, Richmond, KY, p. A292

BOOKER, Angela, Director of Nursing Services, Teton Valley Health Care, Driggs, ID, p. A190

BOOKER, Carolyn, Chief Nursing Officer, Northside Hospital-Forsyth, Cumming, GA, p. A170

BOONE, Donna, MS, R.N., Chief Nursing Officer, Medical City Weatherford, Weatherford, TX, p. A724

BOONE, Richard, Chief Financial Officer, Johnson City Medical Center, Johnson City, TN, p. A640

BOONE III, Elwood Bernard., FACHE, President, Sentara Virginia Beach General Hospital, Virginia Beach, VA, p. A753

BOORAS, Laura, Vice President Human Resources, Coliseum Medical Centers, Macon, GA, p. A176

BOORNAZIAN, John, M.D., Chief Medical Officer, Huggins Hospital, Wolfeboro, NH, p. A451

BOOTH, Christy, Chief Human Resources Officer, Doctors Memorial Hospital, Bonifay, FL, p. A132

BOOTH, Daniel, Vice President Operations and Chief Human Resources Officer, Northern Light Inland Hospital, Waterville, ME, p. A323
Vice President Operations, Northern Light Inland Hospital, Waterville, ME, p. A323

BOOTH, Donny, Chief Executive Officer, Permian Regional Medical Center, Andrews, TX, p. A653

BOOTH, Leslie, Human Resources Director, Houston County Community Hospital, Erin, TN, p. A638

BORCHERS, Jonathan, M.D., Chief Medical Officer, Washington County Memorial Hospital, Potosi, MO, p. A414

BORCHERT, Barry, Vice President Finance, Reedsburg Area Medical Center, Reedsburg, WI, p. A795

BORCHI, Daniel, Chief Information Officer, Carilion New River Valley Medical Center, Christiansburg, VA, p. A740

BORDELON, James, M.D., JrChief of Staff, Avoyelles Hospital, Marksville, LA, p. A308

BORDEN, Eric, Chief Operating Officer and Chief Financial Officer, Jewell County Hospital, Mankato, KS, p. A270

BORDEN, Sandy, Chief Financial Officer, Brodstone Memorial Hospital, Superior, NE, p. A440

BORDERS, James, M.D., Chief Medical Officer, Baptist Health Lexington, Lexington, KY, p. A286

BORDO, David, M.D., Chief Medical Officer, Amita Health Holy Family Medical Center, Des Plaines, IL, p. A202
M.D., Regional Chief Medical Officer and AMITA Health Chief Clinical Reliability Officer, Amita Health Resurrection Medical Center, Chicago, IL, p. A197
M.D., Vice President and Chief Medical Officer, Community First Medical Center, Chicago, IL, p. A198

BOREL, Patricia, Chief Financial Officer, Mercyone Elkader Medical Center, Elkader, IA, p. A249

BOREN, Kevin, Chief Financial Officer, Essentia Health Duluth, Duluth, MN, p. A375
Chief Financial Officer, Essentia Health Northern Pines Medical Center, Aurora, MN, p. A372

BORENS, Dwan, Chief Nursing Officer, St. John Broken Arrow, Broken Arrow, OK, p. A556

BORER, Tom, Vice President Operations, Promedica Fostoria Community Hospital, Fostoria, OH, p. A540

BORGERSON, Carol, Chief Financial Officer, Madison Healthcare Services, Madison, MN, p. A379

BORGSTROM, Christopher, Associate Administrator, Coastal Carolina Hospital, Hardeeville, SC, p. A621

BORGSTROM, Marna P., Chief Executive Officer, Yale-New Haven Hospital, New Haven, CT, p. A124

BORING, Ron, Senior Vice President and Chief Operating Officer, Mcleod Regional Medical Center, Florence, SC, p. A619

BORIS, Diane, Chief Financial Officer, Lehigh Valley Hospital - Schuylkill, Pottsville, PA, p. A605

BORIS, Jamie, M.D., President Medical Staff, Washington Health System Greene, Waynesburg, PA, p. A610

BORJA, Catherine, M.D., Chairman Executive Committee Medical Staff, Naval Hospital Oak Harbor, Oak Harbor, WA, p. A761

BORNICK, Brian, Chief Information Officer, Minneapolis Veterans Affairs Health Care System, Minneapolis, MN, p. A381

BORNMANN, Debora, Chief Executive Officer, Chg Hospital Tucson, Llc, Tucson, AZ, p. A40

BOROWSKI, Thomas, FACHE, President, Hudson Hospital And Clinic, Hudson, WI, p. A786

BORRENPOHL, James, Market Site Director, Community Hospital Of San Bernardino, San Bernardino, CA, p. A91

BORSOS, Dean B., Medical Center Director, James H. Quillen Veterans Affairs Medical Center, Mountain Home, TN, p. A646

BORTEL, Karol, Vice President Financial Services, Wood County Hospital, Bowling Green, OH, p. A530

BORTKE, Todd, Director Information Systems, Chi St. Alexius Health, Bismarck, ND, p. A521

BORTZ, Tammy, Director of Finance, Peterson Healthcare And Rehabilitation Hospital, Wheeling, WV, p. A778

BORUS, Zachary, M.D., Medical Chief of Staff, Lakes Regional Healthcare, Spirit Lake, IA, p. A258

BORYSZAK, Martin W., President, Sisters Of Charity Hospital Of Buffalo, Buffalo, NY, p. A480

BOS, Robbi, Vice President Human Resources, Sauk Prairie Healthcare, Prairie Du Sac, WI, p. A794

BOSCIA, Michael, Chief Financial Officer, Bartow Regional Medical Center, Bartow, FL, p. A131

BOSCO, John, Senior Vice President and Chief Information Officer, Long Island Jewish Medical Center, New Hyde Park, NY, p. A489

BOSCO, Maureen, Executive Director, Central New York Psychiatric Center, Marcy, NY, p. A488

BOSHUT, Sami, Chief Information Officer, Jamaica Hospital Medical Center, Jamaica, NY, p. A486

BOSLEY, Elizabeth, R.N., FACHE, Vice President Patient Services and Chief Nursing Officer, St. Mary's Medical Center, Huntington, WV, p. A773

BOSO, William, Executive Director, Administrator, Southern Indiana Rehabilitation Hospital, New Albany, IN, p. A238

BOSSARD, Neva, Chief Nursing Officer, Lewis County General Hospital, Lowville, NY, p. A487

BOSSE, Patrick, Chief Administrative Officer, Roper St. Francis Hospital-Berkeley, Summerville, SC, p. A624

BOST, Cecelia, Chief Operating Officer, Alliance Healthcare System, Holly Springs, MS, p. A394

BOST, Marcus, Director Information Services and Chief Information Officer, Adena Greenfield Medical Center, Greenfield, OH, p. A541

BOSTER, Brian, M.D., Medical Director, Select Specialty Hospital-Cincinnati, Cincinnati, OH, p. A533

BOSTIC, Deborah, R.N., Chief Nursing Officer, Texas Health Presbyterian Hospital Denton, Denton, TX, p. A672
Chief Operating Officer, Owensboro Health Regional Hospital, Owensboro, KY, p. A291

BOSTIC, William, Administrative Assistant Human Resources, Surprise Valley Health Care District, Cedarville, CA, p. A59
Interim Administrator, Surprise Valley Health Care District, Cedarville, CA, p. A59

BOSTON, Scott, R.N., MS, President and Chief Executive Officer, Passavant Area Hospital, Jacksonville, IL, p. A209

BOSTON-LEARY, Katie, Vice President and Chief Nursing Officer, UMPGHC, University Of Maryland Capital Region Health Prince George's Hospital Center, Cheverly, MD, p. A328

BOSTROM, Brenda, Director of Nursing, Coteau Des Prairies Hospital, Sisseton, SD, p. A632

BOSTROM, Gary, Chief Executive Officer and Chief Financial Officer, East Adams Rural Healthcare, Ritzville, WA, p. A763

BOSTROM, Stuart, M.D., Director Medical Affairs, Sutter Roseville Medical Center, Roseville, CA, p. A89

BOSTWICK, John, Interim Chief Financial Officer, Henderson County Community Hospital, Lexington, TN, p. A642

BOSTWICK, Monte J., Market Chief Executive Officer, Chi St. Luke's Health Memorial Lufkin, Lufkin, TX, p. A698

BOSTWICK, Shari, Director Human Resources, New London Hospital, New London, NH, p. A450

BOSWELL, Debbie, Chief Operating Officer and Chief Nursing Officer, Mercy Medical Center, Roseburg, OR, p. A580

BOSWELL, Diane, Director Human Resources and Marketing, Salem Township Hospital, Salem, IL, p. A219

BOSWELL, John, Chief Human Resources Officer, University Of Virginia Medical Center, Charlottesville, VA, p. A740

BOSWELL, William, M.D., JrChief Medical Officer, City Of Hope's Helford Clinical Research Hospital, Duarte, CA, p. A62

BOSWINKEL, Jan, M.D., Vice President Medical Operations and Chief Safety Officer, Children's Hospital Of Philadelphia, Philadelphia, PA, p. A599

BOSWORTH, Dawn, Director Human Resources, Arrowhead Behavioral Health Hospital, Maumee, OH, p. A544

BOTAK, Geoff, Chief Executive Officer, Malvern Institute, Malvern, PA, p. A596

BOTHNER, Joan, M.D., Chief Medical Officer, Children's Hospital Colorado, Aurora, CO, p. A107

BOTHUN, Crystal, Chief Financial Officer, Johnson Memorial Health Services, Dawson, MN, p. A375

BOTINE, Gary, Vice President, Chief Financial Officer, Mary Greeley Medical Center, Ames, IA, p. A243

BOTLER, Joel, M.D., Chief Medical Officer, Maine Medical Center, Portland, ME, p. A322

BOTNEY, Mitchell, M.D., Vice President Medical Affairs and Chief Medical Officer, Missouri Baptist Medical Center, Saint Louis, MO, p. A416

BOTTENFIELD, Dana, Vice President Human Resources, St. Jude Children's Research Hospital, Memphis, TN, p. A645

BOTTGER, Barry, Chief Financial Officer, Republic County Hospital, Belleville, KS, p. A262

BOTTOM, Paige, Director Operations, Wilmington Treatment Center, Wilmington, NC, p. A520

BOUCHER, Christopher, Director of Information Services, Grace Cottage Hospital, Townshend, VT, p. A737

BOUCHER, Travis, Chief Financial Officer, Speare Memorial Hospital, Plymouth, NH, p. A451

BOUCK, Nancy, Senior Director of Human Resources, Mclaren Thumb Region, Bad Axe, MI, p. A349

BOUCOT, Mark G., FACHE, President and Chief Executive Officer, Garrett Regional Medical Center, Oakland, MD, p. A331
FACHE, President and Chief Executive Officer, Potomac Valley Hospital, Keyser, WV, p. A773

BOUDREAUX, Angela, Director Information Technology, St. Charles Parish Hospital, Luling, LA, p. A307

BOUDREAUX, Scott, Chief Executive Officer, Avala, Covington, LA, p. A300

BOUE, Lourdes, Chief Executive Officer, Baptist Health South Florida, West Kendall Baptist Hospital, Miami, FL, p. A146

BOUFFARD, Rodney, Superintendent, Riverview Psychiatric Center, Augusta, ME, p. A318

BOUGHAL, Ginni, Director Health Information and Information Technology, Peacehealth Peace Harbor Medical Center, Florence, OR, p. A575

BOUHAROUN, Khalil, Chief Information Officer, The Hsc Pediatric Center, Washington, DC, p. A130

BOULA, Rodney, Chief Executive Officer, Calais Regional Hospital, Calais, ME, p. A319

BOUQUET RONSONET, Sheena, Vice President Human Resources, University Hospital & Clinics, Lafayette, LA, p. A306
Vice President, Lafayette General Medical Center, Lafayette, LA, p. A305

BOUQUIO, George, Director Human Resources, South Beach Psychiatric Center, Staten Island, NY, p. A498

BOURGEOIS, Jeff A., President and Chief Executive Officer, San Juan Regional Medical Center, Farmington, NM, p. A469

BOURLAND, Don, Vice President Human Resources, Peacehealth Peace Harbor Medical Center, Florence, OR, p. A575

BOURLAND, Renee, Human Resources Specialist, San Antonio State Hospital, San Antonio, TX, p. A713

BOURLAND, Trent, Chief Executive Officer, Coal County General Hospital, Coalgate, OK, p. A558

BOURN, Jennifer, Director, Health Information Services and Medical Staff Services, Centerpointe Hospital, Saint Charles, MO, p. A414

BOURNE, Kara, R.N., MSN, Chief Nursing Officer and Chief Operating Officer, Foothill Regional Medical Center, Tustin, CA, p. A102

BOURNE, Kimberly L., President and Chief Executive Officer, Taylorville Memorial Hospital, Taylorville, IL, p. A221

BOURQUE, Teresa, Sr. Administrator for Nursing/Chief Nurse, Hurley Medical Center, Flint, MI, p. A354

BOUTAIN, Thomas, Information Services Executive, North Central Health Care, Wausau, WI, p. A798

BOUTIN, Anthony, M.D., Chief Medical Officer, Nassau University Medical Center, East Meadow, NY, p. A483
M.D., Interim President and Chief Executive Officer, Nassau University Medical Center, East Meadow, NY, p. A483

BOUTROS, Akram, M.D., FACHE, President and Chief Executive Officer, Metrohealth Medical Center, Cleveland, OH, p. A535

BOUTWELL, Wayne B., Chief Executive Officer, Continuecare Hospital At Palmetto Health Baptist, Columbia, SC, p. A617
Chief Executive Officer, Regency Hospital Of Central Georgia, Macon, GA, p. A176

BOUYEA, Lawanda, Director Human Resources, Natividad Medical Center, Salinas, CA, p. A90

BOVA, Sheila, Chief Financial Officer, Kindred Hospital-Albuquerque, Albuquerque, NM, p. A467

BOVIO, Ernest L. Jr, President, Unc Rex Health Care, Raleigh, NC, p. A517

BOWE, Christopher, M.D., Chief Medical Officer, Medical Affairs, St. Mary's Regional Medical Center, Lewiston, ME, p. A321

BOWEN, Aaron, Chief Executive Officer, Arizona State Hospital, Phoenix, AZ, p. A35

BOWEN, Christine, R.N., Chief Nursing Officer, Dmc Harper University Hospital, Detroit, MI, p. A353

BOWEN, John, Chief Operating Officer, Parkview Regional Medical Center, Fort Wayne, IN, p. A228

BOWEN, Rodger, M.P.H., Chief Financial Officer, Scenic Mountain Medical Center, Big Spring, TX, p. A659

BOWEN, Stephen, Administrator, Lavaca Medical Center, Hallettsville, TX, p. A682

BOWEN, Tim, Vice President and Administrator, Baptist Health Medical Center - Conway, Conway, AR, p. A43

BOWER, David, M.D., Chief of Staff, Atlanta Veterans Affairs Medical Center, Decatur, GA, p. A170

BOWER, James, M.D., Chief Medical Officer, Research Medical Center, Kansas City, MO, p. A409

BOWER, Kay, Associate Director for Patient Care Services, Battle Creek Veterans Affairs Medical Center, Battle Creek, MI, p. A349

BOWERMAN, Stephen, Senior Vice President, Chief Financial Officer, Midland Memorial Hospital, Midland, TX, p. A701

BOWERS, Daniel, Chief Operating Officer, Riverside Community Hospital, Riverside, CA, p. A88

BOWERS, David, M.D., Medical Director, Siskin Hospital For Physical Rehabilitation, Chattanooga, TN, p. A636

BOWERS, Dusty A., Chief Executive Officer, Acuity Specialty Hospitals Ohio Valley, Steubenville, OH, p. A549

BOWERS, Melodee, Director Human Resources, Carle Hoopeston Regional Health Center, Hoopeston, IL, p. A208

BOWERS, Michael, Head Human Resources, Naval Hospital Oak Harbor, Oak Harbor, WA, p. A761

Interim Director for Administration, Naval Hospital Oak Harbor, Oak Harbor, WA, p. A761

Regional Executive Vice President and Chief Operating Officer, Ssm Health St. Josep. - St. Charles, Saint Charles, MO, p. A414

BOWERS, Sharon, R.N., Manager of Community, Public and Employee Relations, Sheridan Community Hospital, Sheridan, MI, p. A366

BOWERS, Tracy, Vice President Human Resources and Administrative Services, Novant Health Uva Health System Haymarket Medical Center, Haymarket, VA, p. A744

Vice President Human Resources and Administrative Services, Novant Health Uva Health System Prince William Medical Center, Manassas, VA, p. A745

BOWERY, Leslie, Director of Standards and Compliance, Cumberland Hospital For Children And Adolescents, New Kent, VA, p. A746

BOWES, Arthur, Senior Vice President Human Resources, North Shore Medical Center, Salem, MA, p. A344

BOWES, William, Chief Financial Officer, Uams Medical Center, Little Rock, AR, p. A49

BOWIE, John, Chief Operating Officer, Morehouse General Hospital, Bastrop. LA, p. A296

BOWIE, Joshua, Chief Executive Officer, Vibra Rehabilitation Hospital Rancho Mirage, Rancho Mirage, CA, p. A87

BOWLEG, Teresa, R.N., Chief Nursing Officer, Erlanger Western Carolina Hospital, Murphy, NC, p. A515

BOWLES, Patrica, R.N., Chief Nursing Officer, Franklin County Medical Center, Preston, ID, p. A192

BOWLES, Tara, Employee Relations Director, Rawlins County Health Center, Atwood, KS, p. A262

BOWLINE, Brandon, Chief Operating Officer, Claxton-Hepburn Medical Center, Ogdensburg, NY, p. A493

BOWLING, Donald, M.D., Chief Medical Staff, Southampton Memorial Hospital, Franklin, VA, p. A742

BOWLING, Karen, Chief Information Officer, St. Mary's Regional Medical Center, Lewiston, ME, p. A321

BOWLING, Karen L., MSN, R.N., Interim Chief Executive Officer, Braxton County Memorial Hospital, Gassaway, WV, p. A772

MSN, R.N., Interim Chief Executive Officer, Summersville Regional Medical Center, Summersville, WV, p. A777

BOWLING, Kay, Chief Executive Officer, Centra Specialty Hospital, Lynchburg, VA, p. A745

BOWLING, Kelli, Chief Culture Officer, Door County Medical Center, Sturgeon Bay, WI, p. A797

BOWLING, Nancy, Director Human Resources, Shoals Hospital, Muscle Shoals, AL, p. A22

BOWMAN, Dyan, Director Human Resources, Newberry County Memorial Hospital, Newberry, SC, p. A623

BOWMAN, Erin, Director, Julian F. Keith Alcohol And Drug Abuse Treatment Center, Black Mountain, NC, p. A505

BOWMAN, Jeff, Chief Executive Officer, South Central Kansas Medical Center, Arkansas City, KS, p. A261

BOWMAN, Joe, Chief Financial Officer, Tristar Ashland City Medical Center, Ashland City, TN, p. A634

BOWMAN, Joseph, Chief Financial Officer, Tristar Stonecrest Medical Center, Smyrna, TN, p. A649

BOWMAN, Julie, Senior Vice President, Patient Care and Chief Nursing Officer, Phoenix Children's Hospital, Phoenix, AZ, p. A36

BOWMAN, Mark, M.D., President Medical Staff, Adventist Healthtillamook, Tillamook, OR, p. A582

BOWMAN, Scott, Administrator, Sweetwater Hospital, Sweetwater, TN, p. A650

BOWMAN, William, M.D., Vice President Medical Affairs, Moses H. Cone Memorial Hospital, Greensboro, NC, p. A511

BOWSER, John, Vice President, Chief Financial Officer, Osf Saint Luke Medical Center, Kewanee, IL, p. A209

BOX, Darrel, Chief Executive Officer, Lafayette Regional Health Center, Lexington, MO, p. A411

BOX, Justin, Senior Vice President & Chief Information Officer, Mary Washington Hospital, Fredericksburg, VA, p. A742

Senior Vice President and Chief Information Officer, Stafford Hospital, Stafford, VA, p. A752

BOXELL, Shelley, R.N., Chief Nursing Officer, Rehabilitation Hospital Of Fort Wayne, Fort Wayne, IN, p. A228

R.N., Interim Chief Operating Officer, Rehabilitation Hospital Of Fort Wayne, Fort Wayne, IN, p. A228

BOYCE, Charlotte, Chief Nursing Officer, Encompass Health Rehabilitation Hospital Of North Memphis, Memphis, TN, p. A644

BOYD, Aaron, M.D., Chief Medical Officer, Norman Regional Health System, Norman, OK, p. A563

BOYD, Andre Sr, Executive Vice President, Hospital Division, New Hanover Regional Medical Center, Wilmington, NC, p. A520

BOYD, Cathy, Chief Nursing Officer, Select Specialty Hospital-Pontiac, Pontiac, MI, p. A364

BOYD, Christopher L., Senior Vice President and Area Manager, Kaiser Permanente Santa Clara Medical Center, Santa Clara, CA, p. A97

BOYD, Cody, Chief Executive Officer, Ut Health North Campus Tyler, Tyler, TX, p. A722

BOYD, Diana, Vice President Nursing, Cleveland Clinic Union Hospital, Dover, OH, p. A539

BOYD, Donald, Executive Vice President and Chief Operating Officer, Kaleida Health, Buffalo, NY, p. A480

BOYD, Jason E., Chief Executive Officer, Tristar Horizon Medical Center, Dickson, TN, p. A637

BOYD, John W., PsyD, Chief Executive Officer, Sutter Center For Psychiatry, Sacramento, CA, p. A90

BOYD, Kenneth, Chief Operating Officer, Maury Regional Hospital, Columbia, TN, p. A636

BOYD, Kim, Chief Financial Officer, Buchanan General Hospital, Grundy, VA, p. A743

BOYD, Lance, Chief Executive Officer, Merit Health Natchez, Natchez, MS, p. A397

BOYD, Roy, Chief Financial Officer, Wilkes-Barre General Hospital, Wilkes-Barre, PA, p. A611

BOYD, Steven, R.N., Nurse Executive, Levi Hospital, Hot Springs National Park, AR, p. A47

BOYD, Travis, Manager, Information Technology, Mercy Hospital Lincoln, Troy, MO, p. A419

BOYER, Aurelia, Senior Vice President and Chief Information Officer, New York-Presbyterian Hospital, New York, NY, p. A491

BOYER, Charlene, Chief Nursing Officer, Kaiser Permanente Oakland Medical Center, Oakland, CA, p. A82

BOYER, Cheryl, Vice President Human Resources, Levindale Hebrew Hospital And Nursing, Baltimore, MD, p. A325

Vice President Human Resources, Sinai Hospital Of Baltimore, Baltimore, MD, p. A326

BOYER, Craig, Chief Financial Officer, The Healthcenter, Kalispell, MT, p. A425

BOYER, Jim, Vice President Information Technology and Chief Information Officer, Rush Memorial Hospital, Rushville, IN, p. A240

BOYER, Roderick, M.D., Medical Director, Select Specialty Hospital-Downriver, Wyandotte, MI, p. A370

BOYER, Steve, M.D., Chief Medical Officer, Regional West Garden County, Oshkosh, NE, p. A438

BOYER, William, Chief Financial Officer, Community Memorial Hospital, Redfield, SD, p. A630

BOYETTE, Jon, Chief Financial Officer, Pocahontas Memorial Hospital, Buckeye, WV, p. A770

BOYLE, James, M.D., Chief Medical Officer, Upmc Passavant, Pittsburgh, PA, p. A604

BOYLE, Kathy, R.N., Ph.D., Chief Nursing Officer, Denver Health, Denver, CO, p. A110

BOYLE, Linda Lake, R.N., MSN, Director, Central Alabama Veterans Health Care System, Montgomery, AL, p. A22

BOYLE, Lisa, M.D., Vice President Medical Affairs and Medical Director, Medstar Georgetown University Hospital, Washington, DC, p. A129

BOYLE, Patrick, Vice President Human Resources, Geneva General Hospital, Geneva, NY, p. A484

Vice President Human Resources, Soldiers And Sailors Memorial Hospital, Penn Yan, NY, p. A495

BOYLE, Thomas, Chief Financial Officer, St. Lawrence Rehabilitation Center, Lawrenceville, NJ, p. A457

BOYLES, Clay, Director Human Resources, Peachford Behavioral Health System, Atlanta, GA, p. A165

Executive Director, Human Resources, Piedmont Newnan Hospital, Newnan, GA, p. A178

BOYLES, George C., Interim President and Chief Administrative Officer, Grafton City Hospital, Grafton, WV, p. A772

BOYLES, Lee, Chief Executive Officer, St. Anthony Summit Medical Center, Frisco, CO, p. A113

BOYLES, Mary, Chief Nursing Officer, Encompass Health Rehabilitation Hospital Of Altoona, Altoona, PA, p. A583

BOYLES, Robert, Director of Human Resources, Highland-Clarksburg Hospital, Clarksburg, WV, p. A771

BOYNTON, Kimberly, President and Chief Executive Officer, Crouse Health, Syracuse, NY, p. A499

BOYNTON, Stephanie, Administrator, Erlanger Bledsoe Hospital, Pikeville, TN, p. A648

BOYNTON JR, JamesChief Financial Officer, Carolina Center For Behavioral Health, Greer, SC, p. A621

BOYO, Tosan, Chief Operating Officer, Zuckerberg San Francisco General Hospital And Trauma Center, San Francisco, CA, p. A94

BOYSEN, Doug, Chief Legal Counsel and Vice President Human Resources, Good Samaritan Regional Medical Center, Corvallis, OR, p. A574

BOYSEN, James, M.D., Executive Medical Director, Texas Neurorehab Center, Austin, TX, p. A657

BOZZUTO, Elizabeth, R.N., Chief Nursing Officer and Vice President, Saint Mary's Hospital, Waterbury, CT, p. A126

BRAAM, Richard, Vice President, Operations and Chief Financial Officer, Bristol Health, Bristol, CT, p. A121

BRAASCH, David A., President, Alton Memorial Hospital, Alton, IL, p. A194

BRABANT, Christopher, President and Chief Executive Officer, Hshs St. Clare Memorial Hospital, Oconto Falls, WI, p. A793

BRABY, Heath, Director Fiscal Services, Shriners Hospitals For Children-Salt Lake City, Salt Lake City, UT, p. A732

BRACEY, Donny, Director Information Services, Marion General Hospital, Columbia, MS, p. A391

BRACK, Nancy, Vice President Human Resources, Syracuse Area Health, Syracuse, NE, p. A440

BRACKEEN, Steven, Chief Nursing Officer, Helena Regional Medical Center, Helena, AR, p. A46

BRACKEN, Thomas, M.D., Vice President Medical Affairs, Mille Lacs Health System, Onamia, MN, p. A382

BRACKETT, Lori, Director Human Resources, Encompass Health Rehabilitation Hospital Of Bakersfield, Bakersfield, CA, p. A57

BRACKLEY, Donna, R.N., MSN, Senior Vice President Patient Care Services, John Muir Medical Center, Concord, Concord, CA, p. A61

BRACKS, Adam, Chief Executive Officer, Siloam Springs Regional Hospital, Siloam Springs, AR, p. A53

BRACY, Dale, Chief Financial Officer, College Hospital Costa Mesa, Costa Mesa, CA, p. A61

BRADBURY, Monica, Chief Executive Officer, Clarks Summit State Hospital, Clarks Summit, PA, p. A586

BRADDOCK, Mary, Director Human Resources, Palo Pinto General Hospital, Mineral Wells, TX, p. A701

BRADFORD, Beth, Director Human Resources, Floyd Medical Center, Rome, GA, p. A179

BRADFORD, Jeremy, President, Ssm Health Good Samaritan Hospital, Mount Vernon, IL, p. A213

BRADFORD, John, Chief Financial Officer, Murray-Calloway County Hospital, Murray, KY, p. A291

BRADFORD, Randy L., Chief Executive Officer, Eastern Shore Hospital Center, Cambridge, MD, p. A328

BRADFORD, Scot, Chief Information Officer, Baylor Scott & White Medical Center - Trophy Club, Trophy Club, TX, p. A721

BRADFORD, Susan, Director Nursing, Kansas Heart Hospital, Wichita, KS, p. A278

BRADICK, Joe, Chief Financial Officer, Forks Community Hospital, Forks, WA, p. A758

BRADLEY, Betsy, Coordinator Performance Improvement, Central State Hospital, Milledgeville, GA, p. A177

BRADLEY, Connie, R.N., MSN, FACHE, Chief Nursing Officer, Health First Cap. Canaveral Hospital, Cocoa Beach, FL, p. A134

R.N., MSN, FACHE, Chief Nursing Officer, Health First Palm Bay Hospital, Palm Bay, FL, p. A152

R.N., MSN, FACHE, Senior Vice President and Chief Nursing Officer, Health First Viera Hospital, Melbourne, FL, p. A145

BRADLEY, Constance, FACHE, R.N., Vice President and Chief Operating Officer, Wellstar Kennestone Hospital, Marietta, GA, p. A176

BRADLEY, Deidre, Vice President Human Resources, Clark Regional Medical Center, Winchester, KY, p. A294

BRADLEY, Eric, Director Computer Information Services, Summit Behavioral Healthcare, Cincinnati, OH, p. A533

BRADLEY, Linda, Chief Executive Officer, Centinela Hospital Medical Center, Inglewood, CA, p. A69

BRADLEY, Melody, Chief Nursing Officer, Miracle Mile Medical Center, Los Angeles, CA, p. A75

BRADLEY, Michelle, Director Health Information Management, Amg Specialty Hospital-Wichita, Wichita, KS, p. A278

BRADLEY, Sara, Chief Financial Officer, Oklahoma State University Medical Center, Tulsa, OK, p. A570

BRADLEY, Stacye, R.N., Chief Nursing Officer, Union County General Hospital, Clayton, NM, p. A468

BRADLY, Vivian, Chief Nursing Officer, Atrium Medical Center, Stafford, TX, p. A716

BRADSHAW, Benjamin, M.D., President Medical Staff, Texas Health Presbyterian Hospital Kaufman, Kaufman, TX, p. A692

BRADSHAW, David, Chief Information Officer, Memorial Hermann - Texas Medical Center, Houston, TX, p. A687
Chief Information Officer, Memorial Hermann Greater Heights Hospital, Houston, TX, p. A687
Chief Information, Planning and Marketing Officer, Memorial Hermann Memorial City Medical Center, Houston, TX, p. A687

BRADSHAW, Jeremy, Chief Executive Officer, Mountain View Hospital, Gadsden, AL, p. A19
Chief Executive Officer, Mountainview Hospital, Las Vegas, NV, p. A443

BRADSHAW, Pamela, R.N., Vice President, Chief Operating Officer and Chief Nursing Officer, Shannon Medical Center, San Angelo, TX, p. A710

BRADSHAW, Rita, Director Human Resources, Chatuge Regional Hospital And Nursing Home, Hiawassee, GA, p. A173

BRADSHAW, Thomas, Vice President Operations, Wayne Unc Health Care, Goldsboro, NC, p. A511

BRADTMILLER DNP, RN, Theresa, MSN, R.N., Chief Nursing Officer, Adams Memorial Hospital, Decatur, IN, p. A226

BRADY, Dan, Chief Financial Officer, Lds Hospital, Salt Lake City, UT, p. A732
Chief Financial Officer, The Orthopedic Specialty Hospital, Murray, UT, p. A729

BRADY, James, Area Information Officer, Kaiser Permanente Orange County Anaheim Medical Center, Anaheim, CA, p. A55

BRADY, Jeff, Chief Information Officer, Tug Valley Arh Regional Medical Center, South Williamson, KY, p. A293
Director Information Systems, Hazard Arh Regional Medical Center, Hazard, KY, p. A284
Director Information Systems, Mcdowell Arh Hospital, Mcdowell, KY, p. A290
Director Information Systems, Morgan County Arh Hospital, West Liberty, KY, p. A294

BRADY, John, Vice President Physician Services and Organizational Planning, Northwestern Medicine Marianjoy Rehabilitation Hospital, Wheaton, IL, p. A222

BRADY, Karen, R.N., MSN, Vice President, Chief Nursing Officer, Legacy Silverton Medical Center, Silverton, OR, p. A581

BRADY, Kit, Vice President Human Resources, Education and Guest Experience, Gillette Children's Specialty Healthcare, Saint Paul, MN, p. A385

BRADY, Lisa, Senior Vice President and Chief Operating Officer, St. Joseph's University Medical Center, Paterson, NJ, p. A460

BRADY, Mike, Director Information Technology, Up Health System-Bell, Ishpeming, MI, p. A358

BRADY, Tim, Director Information Systems, Mt. Washington Pediatric Hospital, Baltimore, MD, p. A326

BRAGDON, Carol, Director Human Resources, Saint Thomas Rutherford Hospital, Murfreesboro, TN, p. A646

BRAGG, Craig, Chief Executive Officer, Trustpoint Rehabilitation Hospital Of Lubbock, Lubbock, TX, p. A698

BRAGG, Deborah, Senior Vice President, Finance, Decatur Memorial Hospital, Decatur, IL, p. A202

BRAGG, Krista, MSN, Chief Operating Officer, Allegheny Valley Hospital, Natrona Heights, PA, p. A598
MSN, Chief Operating Officer, Forbes Hospital, Monroeville, PA, p. A597

BRAGG, Lisa, Vice President Human Resources, Knox Community Hospital, Mount Vernon, OH, p. A546

BRAHM, Victoria, R.N., MSN, Medical Center Director, Va Medical Center, Tomah, WI, p. A797

BRAIN, David, Interim Vice President Finance, St. James Healthcare, Butte, MT, p. A422

BRAITHWAITE, Robert, President and Chief Executive Officer, Hoag Memorial Hospital Presbyterian, Newport Beach, CA, p. A81

BRAKENHOFF, Jason, Director Information Services, Presbyterian/St. Luke's Medical Center, Denver, CO, p. A111

BRALY, Cindy, MAAL, R.N., Chief Nursing Officer, Surgical Hospital Of Oklahoma, Oklahoma City, OK, p. A566

BRANCH, Terrance, Chief Information Management, Fort Belvoir Community Hospital, Fort Belvoir, VA, p. A742

BRANCHICK, James, R.N., MS, Senior Vice President and Area Manager, Kaiser Permanente Downey Medical Center, Downey, CA, p. A62

BRANDENBURG, Ronald, Vice President and Chief Financial Officer, Holy Cross Hospital, Fort Lauderdale, FL, p. A137

BRANDIS, Destin, Chief Information Officer, William Bee Ririe Hospital, Ely, NV, p. A441

BRANDNER, Nicholas R., Chief Executive Officer, Freeman Regional Health Services, Freeman, SD, p. A628

BRANDON, Deborah, Director Total Quality Management, Eastern Louisiana Mental Health System, Jackson, LA, p. A303

BRANDON, Heather, Vice President of Finance, Grant, Ohiohealth Grant Medical Center, Columbus, OH, p. A536

BRANDOS, Orla, Vice President of Patient Care Services and Chief Nursing Officer, Newport Hospital, Newport, RI, p. A613

BRANDSTATER, Ronda, Vice President Patient Care, Grandview Medical Center, Dayton, OH, p. A538

BRANDT, Debbie, Director Human Resources, Community Hospital, Munster, IN, p. A237

BRANDT, Lauren, Chief Clinical Officer, Central Texas Rehabilitation Hospital, Austin, TX, p. A655

BRANDT, Nolan, Chief Finance Officer, Madigan Army Medical Center, Tacoma, WA, p. A767

BRANDT, Rob, Chief Executive Officer, Mountainview Medical Center, White Sulphur Springs, MT, p. A428

BRANDT, Steve, M.D., Chief of Staff, Dale Medical Center, Ozark, AL, p. A23

BRANDT ESQ, MelanieChief Nursing Officer, Grays Harbor Community Hospital, Aberdeen, WA, p. A755

BRANN, Terry, Chief Financial Officer, Mainegeneral Medical Center, Augusta, ME, p. A318

BRANNAN, Debbie, Chief Financial Officer, George Regional Hospital, Lucedale, MS, p. A396
Chief Financial Officer, Greene County Hospital, Leakesville, MS, p. A396

BRANNEN, Charles, Senior Vice President and Chief Operating Officer, Southeast Alabama Medical Center, Dothan, AL, p. A18

BRANNIGAN, Timothy, Director Information Services, Platte Valley Medical Center, Brighton, CO, p. A108

BRANNON, Jeffrey M., Chief Executive Officer, Flowers Hospital, Dothan, AL, p. A17
Chief Executive Officer, Wiregrass Medical Center, Geneva, AL, p. A19

BRANNON, Jim, Vice President Human Resources, Atlantic General Hospital, Berlin, MD, p. A327

BRANNON, Linda, Vice President Human Resources, Circles Of Care, Melbourne, FL, p. A145

BRANNON, Rebecca, R.N., Chief Nursing Officer, Thomas Memorial Hospital, South Charleston, WV, p. A777
R.N., Senior Vice President and Chief Nursing Officer, Saint Francis Hospital, Charleston, WV, p. A771

BRANSCUM, Suzette, Director of Nursing, Vantage Point Of Northwest Arkansas, Fayetteville, AR, p. A45

BRANSTETTER, Steve, Chief Executive Officer, Nevada Regional Medical Center, Nevada, MO, p. A413

BRANT, Johnny, Chief Financial Officer, Welch Community Hospital, Welch, WV, p. A777

BRANT, Mick, FACHE, Chief Executive Officer, Gothenburg Health, Gothenburg, NE, p. A432

BRANT-LUCICH, Kim, Director, Information Systems, Providence Little Company Of Mary Medical Center San Pedro, San Pedro, CA, p. A96

BRASEL, James, Chief Financial Officer, Ascension St. John Jane Phillips, Bartlesville, OK, p. A556

BRASS, Steven, Medical Officer, Adventist Health Glendale, Glendale, CA, p. A66

BRASSER, Brian, Chief Operating Officer, Spectrum Health - Butterworth Hospital, Grand Rapids, MI, p. A356

BRASSINGER, Cindy, Chief Operating Officer, Vibra Hospital Of Southeastern Michigan, Llc, Lincoln Park, MI, p. A360

BRATCHER, Tammy, Director Information Technology, South Mississipp. County Regional Medical Center, Osceola, AR, p. A51
Director System Information Technology, Great River Medical Center, Blytheville, AR, p. A43

BRATKO, Eddie, President, Mercy Hospital, Buffalo, NY, p. A480

BRATTON, Michael, R.N., Market Chief Nursing and Quality Officer, Bon Secours-Depaul Medical Center, Norfolk, VA, p. A747

BRAUDT, Theresa, Chief Nursing Officer, Gundersen Boscobel Area Hospital And Clinics, Boscobel, WI, p. A781

BRAUGHTON, David, Chief Operating Officer, Lifestream Behavioral Center, Leesburg, FL, p. A144

BRAUN, James R., Chief Administrative Officer and Chief Financial Officer, Flambeau Hospital, Park Falls, WI, p. A794

BRAUN, Peggy, R.N., Vice President Patient Care Services and Chief Nurse Executive, Sentara Virginia Beach General Hospital, Virginia Beach, VA, p. A753

BRAUN, Richard, CPA, JrChief Operating Officer, Olean General Hospital, Olean, NY, p. A494

BRAUN, Tim, Chief Operation Officer, Carroll County Memorial Hospital, Carrollton, MO, p. A404

BRAVERMAN, Kelly, President, Indiana University Health Frankfort, Frankfort, IN, p. A229

BRAVERMAN, Steven E., M.D., Director, Edward Hines, Jr. Veterans Affairs Hospital, Hines, IL, p. A207
M.D., Director, Va Greater Los Angeles Healthcare System, Los Angeles, CA, p. A76

BRAVO, Stacey, Vice President Human Resources, Medical City Denton, Denton, TX, p. A672

BRAWLEY, Carrie, Administrator, Unity Psychiatric Care-Martin, Martin, TN, p. A643

BRAXL-COLE, Kim, Chief Financial Officer, Broward Health North, Deerfield Beach, FL, p. A136

BRAXTON, Edwin, Director Human Resources, Lompoc Valley Medical Center, Lompoc, CA, p. A72

BRAY, Jason, Chief Information Officer, Mcalester Regional Health Center, Mcalester, OK, p. A562

BRAY, John, M.D., Medical Director, Select Specialty Hospital-Pensacola, Pensacola, FL, p. A154

BRAY, Karen, R.N., MSN, Vice President Patient Care Services, Washington Hospital, Washington, PA, p. A610

BRAY, Pam, Director of Nursing and Director Inpatient Services, Upmc Kane, Kane, PA, p. A593

BRAYFORD, Amy, Chief Human Resources Officer, Geisinger Medical Center, Danville, PA, p. A588

BRAYTON, Jackie, Vice President Human Resources, Portsmouth Regional Hospital, Portsmouth, NH, p. A451

BRAYTON, Ranee C., FACHE, MSN, R.N., Chief Executive Officer, Northeast Regional Medical Center, Kirksville, MO, p. A410

BRAZ, Marcus, Chief Executive Officer, Encompass Health Rehabilitation Hospital Of Sarasota, Sarasota, FL, p. A157

BRAZEL, Gary, M.D., Chief Medical Officer, Ascension St. Vincent Mercy, Elwood, IN, p. A227

BRAZIL, Wendy, Chief Operating Officer, Neosho Memorial Regional Medical Center, Chanute, KS, p. A262

BREA, Christie, Manager Human Resources, Kp. Promise Hospital Of Phoenix, Mesa, AZ, p. A34

BREADY, Sharon, R.N., Chief Executive Officer, Careone At Hacksensack University Medical Center At Pascack Valley, Westwood, NJ, p. A465
R.N., Chief Executive Officer, Careone At Trinitas Regional Medical Center, Elizabeth, NJ, p. A454

BREAKWELL, Michael, R.N., Nurse Executive, Twin Valley Behavioral Healthcare, Columbus, OH, p. A537

BREAZEALE, Scott, Chief Nursing Officer, Neshoba County General Hospital, Philadelphia, MS, p. A398

BREDESON, Christopher, Chief Operating Officer, Evergreenhealth, Kirkland, WA, p. A759

BREDTHAUER, Vicki, R.N., Director of Nursing, Valley County Health System, Ord, NE, p. A438

BREEDEN, Patricia, M.D., Chief of Staff, Lexington Veterans Affairs Medical Center, Lexington, KY, p. A286

BREEDEN, Susan M., Administrator and Chief Executive Officer, Baptist Memorial Hospital-Carroll County, Huntingdon, TN, p. A639

BREEDLOVE, Stacey, Chief Nursing Officer, Christus St. Michael Rehabilitation Hospital, Texarkana, TX, p. A719

BREEDVELD, Stacey, R.N., MSN, Associate Director for Patient Care, Veterans Affairs Ann Arbor Healthcare System, Ann Arbor, MI, p. A348

BREEN, Charles, M.D., Medical Director, Sanford Hillsboro Medical Center, Hillsboro, ND, p. A524

BREEN, Sue, Chief Financial Officer, Western State Hospital, Tacoma, WA, p. A767

BREEN, Thomas, Vice President and Chief Financial Officer, South County Hospital, Wakefield, RI, p. A614

BREHMER, Jennifer, Director Patient Care, New Ulm Medical Center, New Ulm, MN, p. A382

BREIDENBACH, Kim, Medical Director, Gundersen Tri-County Hospital And Clinics, Whitehall, WI, p. A799

BREIDSTER, Cara, Chief Financial Officer, Indiana University Health Arnett Hospital, Lafayette, IN, p. A234

BREITBACH, Dave, Chief Financial Officer, Crossing Rivers Health Medical Center, Prairie Du Chien, WI, p. A794

BREITENBACH, Ray, M.D., Chief of Staff, Pontiac General Hospital, Pontiac, MI, p. A364

BREITFELDER, Michelle, Chief Nursing Officer, Piedmont Mountainside Hospital, Jasper, GA, p. A174

BREITLING, Bryan, Administrator, Avera Hand County Memorial Hospital, Miller, SD, p. A629

BREKKE, Erin, Director Human Resources, Burgess Health Center, Onawa, IA, p. A255

BRELAND, Kelly, CPA, Director Support Services, Mississipp. State Hospital, Whitfield, MS, p. A401

BREMER, David, D.O., Chief of Staff, Midmichigan Medical Center-Clare, Clare, MI, p. A351

BRENDEN, Stephanie, Vice President Finance, Columbia Memorial Hospital, Astoria, OR, p. A573

BRENDLER, Stephen, Director Information Systems, Hilton Head Hospital, Hilton Head Island, SC, p. A621

BRENHOLT, Craig, Division Director People Services, Hshs Sacred Heart Hospital, Eau Claire, WI, p. A783

BRENKLE, George, Chief Information Officer, Umass Memorial Medical Center, Worcester, MA, p. A347

BRENN, Andrea, R.N., Chief Nursing Officer, Texoma Medical Center, Denison, TX, p. A671

BRENNAN, Angela, M.D., Chief of Staff, Howard County Medical Center, Saint Paul, NE, p. A439

BRENNAN, Kevin, CPA, Executive Vice President and Chief Financial Officer, Geisinger Medical Center, Danville, PA, p. A588

BRENNAN, Lina, Site Administrator, Soldiers And Sailors Memorial Hospital, Penn Yan, NY, p. A495

BRENNAN, Noreen, Chief Nursing Officer, Nyc Health + Hospitals / Metropolitan, New York, NY, p. A491

BRENNAN, Patrick, M.D., Senior Vice President and Chief Medical Officer, Hospital Of The University Of Pennsylvania, Philadelphia, PA, p. A600
    Director Information System Technology, Ssm Health Saint Louis University Hospital, Saint Louis, MO, p. A417

BRENNAN, Theresa, M.D., Chief Medical Officer, University Of Iowa Hospitals And Clinics, Iowa City, IA, p. A252

BRENNER, Pattie, R.N., Chief Nursing Officer, Encompass Health Rehabilitation Hospital Of Largo, Largo, FL, p. A143

BRENNER, William, Chief Financial Officer, Kindred Hospital-Indianapolis, Indianapolis, IN, p. A232

BRES, Thomas, Senior Vice President and Chief Administrative Officer, Sparrow Hospital, Lansing, MI, p. A360

BRESCIA, Michael, M.D., Executive Medical Director, Calvary Hospital, Bronx, NY, p. A476

BRESLIN, Susan, R.N., MSN, Vice President Patient Care Services and Chief Nursing Officer, Emory Decatur Hospital, Decatur, GA, p. A171

BRESNAHAN, Patti, Director Human Resources, Mercy Medical Center, Canton, OH, p. A531

BRESSLER, Kathy, Division Senior Vice President and Chief Operating Officer, Chi Health Lakeside, Omaha, NE, p. A436

BRETT, Mark, Chief Executive Officer, Sparrow Hospital, Lansing, MI, p. A360

BRETTNER, Eric, Chief Financial Officer, Marinhealth Medical Center, Greenbrae, CA, p. A67

BREUDER, Andrew, M.D., Chief of Staff, Manchester Veterans Affairs Medical Center, Manchester, NH, p. A450

BREUER, Rick, Chief Executive Officer and Administrator, Community Memorial Hospital, Cloquet, MN, p. A374

BREUM, Linda, R.N., MSN, Chief Nursing Officer, Adventhealth New Smyrna Beach, New Smyrna Beach, FL, p. A149

BREVING, Joel, M.D., Medical Director, Central Louisiana State Hospital, Pineville, LA, p. A313

BREVING, Robert, M.D., Chief of Staff, National Park Medical Center, Hot Springs, AR, p. A47

BREWER, Aimee, President, NorthBay Healthcare Group. Northbay Medical Center, Fairfield, CA, p. A63

BREWER, Becca, Chief Operations Officer, Falls Community Hospital And Clinic, Marlin, TX, p. A699

BREWER, Douglas, M.D., Chief Medical Officer, Navicent Health Baldwin, Milledgeville, GA, p. A177

BREWER, Douglas L., Chief Executive Officer, Bryan W. Whitfield Memorial Hospital, Demopolis, AL, p. A17

BREWER, Glenn, Chief Financial Officer, The Brook Hospital - Kmi, Louisville, KY, p. A288

BREWER, Jackie, Director, Human Resources, Lake Behavioral Hospital, Waukegan, IL, p. A222

BREWER, Jennifer, Chief Executive Officer, Encompass Health Rehabilitation Hospital The Woodlands, Conroe, TX, p. A665
    Chief Executive Officer, Encompass Health Rehabilitation Hospital Vision Park, Shenandoah, TX, p. A715

BREWER, Jim, M.P.H., Chief Financial Officer, Healthmark Regional Medical Center, Defuniak Springs, FL, p. A136

BREWER, Kaye, Chief Human Resources Officer, Maury Regional Medical Center, Columbia, TN, p. A636

BREWER, Kelley, R.N., MSN, President, Lakeside Women's Hospital, Oklahoma City, OK, p. A564

BREWER, Luke, Acting Chief Executive Officer, Swisher Memorial Healthcare System, Tulia, TX, p. A721

BREWER, Peter G., Administrator, Shriners Hospitals For Children-Spokane, Spokane, WA, p. A766

BREWER, Rebecca, FACHE, Chief Operating Officer, Adventhealth Lake Wales, Lake Wales, FL, p. A143

BREWER, Ruby Senior Vice President, Chief Nursing and Quality Officer, East Jefferson General Hospital, Metairie, LA, p. A308

BREWER, Sarah, President, Legacy Silverton Medical Center, Silverton, OR, p. A581

BREWER, Traci, R.N., Chief Clinical Officer, Kindred Hospital Dallas Central, Dallas, TX, p. A668

BREXLER, James L., President and Chief Executive Officer, Doylestown Hospital, Doylestown, PA, p. A588

BREYFOGLE, Cynthia, FACHE, Director, Charles George Veterans Affairs Medical Center, Asheville, NC, p. A504

BREZA, Lisa, R.N., Vice President and Chief Nursing Officer, Robert Wood Johnson University Hospital At Hamilton, Hamilton, NJ, p. A456

BREZNY, Angie, Director Human Resources, Prague Community Hospital, Prague, OK, p. A567

BRIA, Susan, Chief Nursing Officer, Shelby Baptist Medical Center, Alabaster, AL, p. A13

BRIAN, David, Chief Information Officer, Shriners Hospitals For Children - Cincinnati, Cincinnati, OH, p. A533

BRICE ROSHELL, Jade, M.D., Chief Medical Officer, Shelby Baptist Medical Center, Alabaster, AL, p. A13

BRICHER, Joan, Senior Vice President Finance and Chief Financial Officer, Goleta Valley Cottage Hospital, Santa Barbara, CA, p. A96
    Senior Vice President Finance and Chief Financial Officer, Santa Barbara Cottage Hospital, Santa Barbara, CA, p. A97

BRICKER, Jan, R.N., Chief Nursing Officer, Mount Carmel Rehabilitation Hospital, Westerville, OH, p. A552

BRICKHOUSE, Jerimiah, Chief Information Officer, St. Charles Bend, Bend, OR, p. A573
    Chief Information Officer, St. Charles Redmond, Redmond, OR, p. A580

BRICKNER, Derek, President Medical Staff, Jamestown Regional Medical Center, Jamestown, ND, p. A524

BRIDEAU, Donald, M.D., Chief Executive Officer, Inova Fair Oaks Hospital, Fairfax, VA, p. A741

BRIDEN, David, Chief Information Officer, Exeter Hospital, Exeter, NH, p. A449

BRIDGE, Lauren, R.N., Chief Nursing Officer, Kaiser Sunnyside Medical Center, Clackamas, OR, p. A574

BRIDGELAND, Aaron, Director Finance, Ascension Southeast Wisconsin Hospital - Franklin Campus, Franklin, WI, p. A784
    Director Finance, Ascension Southeast Wisconsin Hospital - St. Francis Campus, Milwaukee, WI, p. A790
    Director Finance, Midwest Orthopedic Specialty Hospital, Franklin, WI, p. A784

BRIDGES, Alan, M.D., Chief of Staff, William S. Middleton Memorial Veterans Hospital, Madison, WI, p. A788

BRIDGES, Angela, R.N., Chief Executive Officer, Mount Carmel Rehabilitation Hospital, Westerville, OH, p. A552

BRIDGES, Barbara, R.N., Chief Nursing Officer, Indiana Spine Hospital, Carmel, IN, p. A225

BRIDGES, Carol, M.D., Medical Director, Broadwater Health Center, Townsend, MT, p. A428

BRIDGES, James, Executive Vice President and Chief Operating Officer, Prisma Health Baptist Hospital, Columbia, SC, p. A618

BRIDGES, Jane Ann, Chief Financial Officer, Nacogdoches Memorial Hospital, Nacogdoches, TX, p. A702

BRIDGES, Mary, Director Human Resources, Ouachita County Medical Center, Camden, AR, p. A43

BRIDGES, Richard, M.D., Chief of Staff, Hood Memorial Hospital, Amite, LA, p. A296

BRIDGES-KEE, Lorinnsa, Vice President Human Resources, Carolinas Healthcare System Blue Ridge, Morganton, NC, p. A515

BRIDGEWATER, Melinda, Director, Information Services, Montana State Hospital, Warm Springs, MT, p. A428

BRIESEMEISTER, Eric, Chief Executive Officer, Unitypoint Health - Jones Regional Medical Center, Anamosa, IA, p. A243

BRIETE, Mark, M.D., Vice President Medical Affairs, Mercy Hospital Jefferson, Festus, MO, p. A406

BRIGGS, Deborah, Vice President Human Resources, Marketing, Volunteer Services and Community Relations, Ellenville Regional Hospital, Ellenville, NY, p. A483

BRIGGS, Gary, Vice President Human Resources, Tristar Southern Hills Medical Center, Nashville, TN, p. A647

BRIGGS, Michael, M.D., Chief Medical Officer, Essentia Health Fargo, Fargo, ND, p. A522

BRIGGS, Sharlet, Ph.D., Chief Operating Officer, Adventist Health Bakersfield, Bakersfield, CA, p. A57
    Ph.D., Market Chief Executive Officer and President, Adventist Health Bakersfield, Bakersfield, CA, p. A57

BRIGGS, Thomas, Chief Financial Officer, Alliancehealth Madill, Madill, OK, p. A561

BRIGGS, Vicki R., Chief Executive Officer, Ut Health Tyler, Tyler, TX, p. A722

BRIGHAM, Randy, Chief Human Resource Officer, Estes Park Medical Center, Estes Park, CO, p. A112

BRIGHT, Cheryl, Executive Director, Fairview Developmental Center, Costa Mesa, CA, p. A61

BRIGHT, Kim, M.D., Clinical Director, Springfield Hospital Center, Sykesville, MD, p. A333

BRIGHT, Shawn, Chief Executive Officer, Encompass Health Rehabilitation Hospital Of Newnan, Newnan, GA, p. A178

BRILL, Beth, Senior Director Human Resources, Wvu Medicine - Barnesville Hospital, Barnesville, OH, p. A528

BRILL, Karen, R.N., Chief Nursing Officer, Vice President Care, Gillette Children's Specialty Healthcare, Saint Paul, MN, p. A385

BRILLI, Richard, M.D., Chief Medical Officer, Nationwide Children's Hospital, Columbus, OH, p. A536

BRILLIANT, Lawrence, M.D., Vice President and Chief Medical Officer, St. Mary Medical Center, Langhorne, PA, p. A594

BRILLIANT, Steven, M.D., Chief of Staff, Veterans Affairs Sierra Nevada Health Care System, Reno, NV, p. A446

BRIM, Celena, Chief Financial Officer, Palestine Regional Medical Center-East, Palestine, TX, p. A704

BRINDLE, Charles, M.D., Chief Medical Staff, Iowa Specialty Hospital-Belmond, Belmond, IA, p. A244

BRINER, Junior, Chief Operating Officer, Lawrence Memorial Hospital, Walnut Ridge, AR, p. A54

BRINKERHOFF, Douglas, M.D., Clinical Director, San Carlos Apache Healthcare Corporation, Peridot, AZ, p. A35

BRINKERHOFF, Kenley, Chief Information Officer, Dixie Regional Medical Center, Saint George, UT, p. A732

BRINKHAUS, Theresa, Chief Financial Officer, St. Helena Parish Hospital, Greensburg, LA, p. A302

BRINKMAN, Dan, R.N., Chief Executive Officer, Hilo Medical Center, Hilo, HI, p. A184
    R.N., Chief Operating Officer, Hilo Medical Center, Hilo, HI, p. A184

BRINKMAN, Janet, Director Human Resources, Colorado Plains Medical Center, Fort Morgan, CO, p. A112

BRINSON, Pam, Nurse Executive, South Mississipp. State Hospital, Purvis, MS, p. A399

BRIONES, Melba, M.D., Medical Director, Evansville State Hospital, Evansville, IN, p. A227

BRISBOE, Mark, VP and Chief Financial Officer, Sparrow Clinton Hospital, Saint Johns, MI, p. A366
    VP and Chief Financial Officer, Sparrow Ionia Hospital, Ionia, MI, p. A358

BRISCOE, Betsy, Chief Executive Officer, Pecos County Memorial Hospital, Fort Stockton, TX, p. A677

BRISCOE, Charles, FACHE, Chief Operating Officer, Houston Medical Center, Warner Robins, GA, p. A183
    FACHE, Chief Operating Officer, Perry Hospital, Perry, GA, p. A178

BRISCOE, Charles G., FACHE, Interim President and Chief Executive Officer, Houston Medical Center, Warner Robins, GA, p. A183

BRISCOE, Janell, Chief Executive Officer, Encompass Health Rehabilitation Hospital Of City View, Fort Worth, TX, p. A678

BRISENDINE, Chad, Chief Information Officer, St. Luke's Hospital - Quakertown Campus, Quakertown, PA, p. A605
    Chief Information Officer, St. Luke's University Hospital - Bethlehem Campus, Bethlehem, PA, p. A585
    Vice President and Chief Information Officer, St. Luke's Hospital - Miners Campus, Coaldale, PA, p. A587

BRISSE, Thomas M., President and Chief Executive Officer, Mclaren Macomb, Mount Clemens, MI, p. A362

BRISTER, Kim, Director Human Resources, Wellspan Gettysburg Hospital, Gettysburg, PA, p. A590

BRISTER, Marilyn, M.D., Chief of Staff, Texas Health Harris Methodist Hospital Stephenville, Stephenville, TX, p. A717

BRISTOW, Clyde, R.N., IIIChief Nursing Officer, Network Hospital, Wake Forest Baptist Health-Lexington Medical Center, Lexington, NC, p. A514

BRITO, Manuela, Chief Financial Officer Post Acute Care, Nyc Health + Hospitals / Henry J Carter Specialty Hospital And Medical Center, New York, NY, p. A491

BRITT, Kevin, Chief Operating Officer, Reynolds Memorial Hospital, Glen Dale, WV, p. A772

BRITT, Key, Associate Director, Greenwood Leflore Hospital, Greenwood, MS, p. A392

BRITT, Linda, Director Information Systems, Baptist Memorial Hospital-North Mississippi, Oxford, MS, p. A398

BRITT, Suzanne, Director Human Resources, Samaritan Hospital, Macon, MO, p. A411

BRITT, Tommy, Vice President of Human Resources, Wellstar West Georgia Medical Center, Lagrange, GA, p. A175

BRITTAIN, Libby, Director Human Resources, Steele Memorial Medical Center, Salmon, ID, p. A193

BRITTON, Natalie, Manager Employee Relations, Legacy Silverton Medical Center, Silverton, OR, p. A581

BRITTON, William, Associate Administrator Finance, Alfred I. Dupont Hospital For Children, Wilmington, DE, p. A128

BRIX, Hsiu-chin, R.N., Director of Nursing, St. Lawrence Rehabilitation Center, Lawrenceville, NJ, p. A457

BROADWAY, Chris, Manager Information Technology, Mayers Memorial Hospital District, Fall River Mills, CA, p. A64

BROBERG, John, Chief Executive Officer, Hiawatha Community Hospital, Hiawatha, KS, p. A266

BROBST, Mary, R.N., MSN, Senior Vice President Patient Care Services and Chief Nursing Officer, Mercy Medical Center - Cedar Rapids, Cedar Rapids, IA, p. A245

BROCATO, Ray, Chief Financial Officer, Rolling Hills Hospital, Franklin, TN, p. A638

BROCCARD, Alain, M.D., Chief Medical Officer, Ascension St. Vincent Seton Specialty Hospital, Indianapolis, IN, p. A231

BROCK, B. J., Nursing Director, Higgins General Hospital, Bremen, GA, p. A167

BROCK, Jamie, Vice President Human Resources, Chan Soon-Shiong Medical Center, Windber, PA, p. A611

BROCK, Lisa, Chief Human Resource Officer, Overlake Medical Center, Bellevue, WA, p. A755

BROCK, Melinda, Director Human Resources, Alliancehealth Woodward, Woodward, OK, p. A572

BROCK, Nancy, Chief Financial Officer, Houston Methodist Continuing Care Hospital, Katy, TX, p. A692

BROCK, Paul, Administrator, East Central Regional Hospital, Augusta, GA, p. A166

BROCK, Robert, Chief Financial Officer and Vice President, Adventhealth Rollins Brook, Lampasas, TX, p. A694
Vice President Finance, Arh Our Lady Of The Way, Martin, KY, p. A289

BROCK, Shea, Chief Financial Officer, Navarro Regional Hospital, Corsicana, TX, p. A666

BROCK, Steve, Chief Financial Officer, Lynn County Hospital District, Tahoka, TX, p. A718

BROCK, Tammy, MSN, R.N., Chief Nursing Officer, Rockcastle Regional Hospital And Respiratory Care Center, Mount Vernon, KY, p. A291

BROCK, Theresa, Vice President Nursing, Good Shepherd Health Care System, Hermiston, OR, p. A576

BROCK, William, Chief Information Officer, Atlanta Veterans Affairs Medical Center, Decatur, GA, p. A170

BROCKERT, Nicholas, President, Saint Luke's Cushing Hospital, Leavenworth, KS, p. A269

BROCKETTE, Darby, Chief Executive Officer, Rehabilitation Hospital Of The Northwest, Post Falls, ID, p. A192

BROCKHAUS, Jennifer, Chief Information Officer, Sidney Regional Medical Center, Sidney, NE, p. A439

BROCKHOUSE, Dena, Director Human Resources, Mercyone Iowa City Medical Center, Iowa City, IA, p. A252

BROCKMAN, Vicki, R.N., Chief Nursing Officer, Texas Health Harris Methodist Hospital Cleburne, Cleburne, TX, p. A663

BROCKMEYER, Heather, Human Resource Administrative Officer, Nevada Regional Medical Center, Nevada, MO, p. A413

BROCKMEYER, JoEllyn, Director Human Resources, Indiana University Health White Memorial Hospital, Monticello, IN, p. A236

BROCKUS, Harry, Chief Executive Officer, Carle Hoopeston Regional Health Center, Hoopeston, IL, p. A208
Chief Executive Officer, Carle Richland Memorial Hospital, Olney, IL, p. A215

BRODBECK, Kathleen Chief Nursing Officer, St. James Hospital, Hornell, NY, p. A485

BRODBECK, Lisa, Chief Financial Officer, Medical City Lewisville, Lewisville, TX, p. A696

BRODERSEN, Benjamin, Chief Operating Officer, Venice Regional Bayfront Health, Venice, FL, p. A161

BRODHEAD, Roderick, Chief Medical Officer, Ascension Eagle River Hospital, Eagle River, WI, p. A782

BRODHEAD, Ross, Manager Human Resources, Ascension St. Vincent Mercy, Elwood, IN, p. A227
Senior Director, Human Resource, Ascension St. Vincent Anderson, Anderson, IN, p. A223
Senior Director, Human Resources, Ascension St. Vincent Carmel Hospital, Carmel, IN, p. A225

BRODIAN, Craig, Vice President Human Resources, Johns Hopkins Bayview Medical Center, Baltimore, MD, p. A324

BRODY, Anne Marie, Director Information Systems Customer Service, Providence Saint Josep. Medical Center, Burbank, CA, p. A59

BROEKHUIS, Arlyn, Chief Information Officer, Sanford Medical Center Fargo, Fargo, ND, p. A523
Vice President and Chief Information Officer, Sanford Usd Medical Center, Sioux Falls, SD, p. A631

BROERMANN, Robert, Senior Vice President and Chief Financial Officer, Sentara Leigh Hospital, Norfolk, VA, p. A748
Senior Vice President and Chief Financial Officer, Sentara Norfolk General Hospital, Norfolk, VA, p. A748
Senior Vice President and Chief Financial Officer, Sentara Princess Anne Hospital, Virginia Beach, VA, p. A753

BROHAWN, Bill, Chief of Staff, Trace Regional Hospital, Houston, MS, p. A394

BROKAW, Sara, Vice President Patient Care Services, Bellevue Hospital, Bellevue, OH, p. A529

BROMAN, Craig J., FACHE, President, St. Cloud Hospital, Saint Cloud, MN, p. A384

BROMLEY, Trudy, Vice President Human Resources, Jfk Medical Center, Atlantis, FL, p. A131

BRONHARD, John, CPA, Corporate Vice President, Chief Financial Officer and Treasurer, Umass Memorial Healthalliance-Clinton Hospital, Leominster, MA, p. A340

BRONSON, Becki, Chief Information Officer, Cedar City Hospital, Cedar City, UT, p. A727

BROOCKS, Kelli, Director Human Resources, Public Relations and Physician Recruitment, Beauregard Health System, De Ridder, LA, p. A300

BROOKER, Doug, Chief Financial Officer, Bryan W. Whitfield Memorial Hospital, Demopolis, AL, p. A17

BROOKER, Paula, Director Information Services, Pleasant Valley Hospital, Point Pleasant, WV, p. A776

BROOKER, Susan, R.N., Chief Clinical Officer, Vibra Specialty Hospital Of Portland, Portland, OR, p. A580

BROOKES, Jeffrey, M.D., Chief Medical Officer, Parkview Lagrange Hospital, Lagrange, IN, p. A235
M.D., Medical Director, Parkview Whitley Hospital, Columbia City, IN, p. A225

BROOKMAN, Mark, Chief Information Officer, Medical Center At Bowling Green, Bowling Green, KY, p. A281
Chief Information Officer, Medical Center At Scottsville, Scottsville, KY, p. A293
Chief Information Officer, The Medical Center Albany, Albany, KY, p. A280
Vice President and Chief Information Officer, Medical Center At Franklin, Franklin, KY, p. A283
Vice President, Chief Information Officer, The Medical Center At Caverna, Horse Cave, KY, p. A285

BROOKS, Albert, M.D., Chief Medical Staff Services, Washington Hospital Healthcare System, Fremont, CA, p. A65

BROOKS, Anthony, Chief Information Officer, Miami Veterans Affairs Healthcare System, Miami, FL, p. A147

BROOKS, April, Chief Nursing Officer, Encompass Health Rehabilitation Hospital Of Columbia, Columbia, SC, p. A617

BROOKS, Barbara, Interim Chief Financial Officer, St. Mark's Medical Center, La Grange, TX, p. A694

BROOKS, Brian, Information Manager, Dewitt Hospital, Dewitt, AR, p. A44

BROOKS, Cheri, R.N., Chief Nursing Officer, King's Daughters Medical Center, Brookhaven, MS, p. A390

BROOKS, Clint, Chief Operating Officer, Fairbanks Memorial Hospital, Fairbanks, AK, p. A28

BROOKS, Colin, Chief Financial Officer, Southwest General Hospital, San Antonio, TX, p. A713

BROOKS, David, M.D., Chief Medical Officer, Valley View Hospital, Glenwood Springs, CO, p. A113

BROOKS, Decha, Chief Operations Officer, Horizon Medical Center, Llc, Denton, TX, p. A672

BROOKS, Gary, Chief Executive Officer, Pam Specialty Hospital Of Sparks, Sparks, NV, p. A447
Chief Operating Officer, Pam Specialty Hospital Of Sparks, Sparks, NV, p. A447

BROOKS, J, M.D., Chief Medical Officer, Calverthealth Medical Center, Prince Frederick, MD, p. A331

BROOKS, Jeffrey, M.D., Chief Medical Officer, Parkview Huntington Hospital, Huntington, IN, p. A230

BROOKS, Kevin, Chief Operating Officer, Swedish Medical Center-First Hill, Seattle, WA, p. A764

BROOKS, Lisa, Administrator, Comanche County Hospital, Coldwater, KS, p. A263

BROOKS, Lori, Director Human Resources, Red Bud Regional Hospital, Red Bud, IL, p. A218

BROOKS, Nick, Director of Information Systems, Citrus Memorial Health System, Inverness, FL, p. A140

BROOKS, Patrice Gay., Chief Executive Officer, Cumberland Hospital For Children And Adolescents, New Kent, VA, p. A746

BROOKS, Steven, Vice President Human Resources, Southeastern Ohio Regional Medical Center, Cambridge, OH, p. A530

BROOKS, Troy, Chief Financial Officer, Conway Regional Medical Center, Conway, AR, p. A44

BROOKSHIRE, Tim, Chief Operating Officer, Prisma Health Patewood Hospital, Greenville, SC, p. A620

BROOKSHIRE-HEAVIN, Keri, Senior Vice President and Chief Nursing Officer, Phelp. Health, Rolla, MO, p. A414

BROOM, Matthew, Vice President of Medical Affairs and Chief Medical Officer, Ssm Health Saint Louis University Hospital, Saint Louis, MO, p. A417

BROOME, J. Scott, Chief Executive Officer, Musc Health Chester Medical Center, Chester, SC, p. A617
Chief Executive Officer, Musc Health Lancaster Medical Center, Lancaster, SC, p. A622

BROPHY, Beth, Interim VP for Human Resources, Hurley Medical Center, Flint, MI, p. A354

BROSE, Tamara, Director Human Resources, Thayer County Health Services, Hebron, NE, p. A433

BROSIUS, William, Chief Financial Officer, University Of Maryland Capital Region Health Prince George's Hospital Center, Cheverly, MD, p. A328

BROSNAHAN, Jan, Chief Financial Officer, Winona Health, Winona, MN, p. A388

BROSNAN, Kimberly, Director Human Resources, Norwood Hospital, Norwood, MA, p. A343

BROTEN, Kurt, Chief Financial Officer, Palmdale Regional Medical Center, Palmdale, CA, p. A84
Chief Financial Officer, Vista Del Mar Hospital, Ventura, CA, p. A103

BROTHMAN, Joe, Assistant Vice President, Information Systems, Medstar Washington Hospital Center, Washington, DC, p. A130

BROUGHMAN, Robin, R.N., Ph.D., Chief Nursing Officer, Lewisgale Hospital Alleghany, Low Moor, VA, p. A745

BROUGHMAN, Wade, Chief Financial Officer, Southcoast Hospitals Group. Fall River, MA, p. A339
Executive Vice President and Chief Financial Officer, Riverside Regional Medical Center, Newport News, VA, p. A747

BROUILLETTE, Blaine, Director Information Technology, Avoyelles Hospital, Marksville, LA, p. A308

BROUK, Jonathan, Chief Operating Officer, Children's Hospital, New Orleans, LA, p. A310

BROUSSARD, Heidi, Chief Nursing Officer, Abbeville General Hospital, Abbeville, LA, p. A295

BROUWER, Heath, Administrator, Douglas County Memorial Hospital, Armour, SD, p. A626

BROVOLD, Diana, Chief Nurse Executive, Multicare Mary Bridge Children's Hospital And Health Center, Tacoma, WA, p. A767

BROVOLD, Nathan, Chief Nursing Officer, Lifecare Medical Center, Roseau, MN, p. A384

BROW, Benjamin, Vice President of Finance, Mclaren Lapeer Region, Lapeer, MI, p. A360

BROWDER, Renate, R.N., Director of Nursing, Lake City Community Hospital, Lake City, SC, p. A622

BROWER, Laura, R.N., MSN, Chief Nursing Officer, Augusta University Medical Center, Augusta, GA, p. A165

BROWN, Alisa, Administrative Assistant, Dewitt Hospital, Dewitt, AR, p. A44

BROWN, Angel, Director Human Resources, Morton Plant Hospital, Clearwater, FL, p. A134

BROWN, Ann R., M.D., Director, Atlanta Veterans Affairs Medical Center, Decatur, GA, p. A170

BROWN, Austin, Chief Operating Officer, Bayfront Health St. Petersburg, Saint Petersburg, FL, p. A156

BROWN, B, Vice President and General Counsel, Prattville Baptist Hospital, Prattville, AL, p. A24

BROWN, Barbra, MS, R.N., Interim Chief Nursing Officer and Vice President of Nursing, Alice Peck Day Memorial Hospital, Lebanon, NH, p. A449

BROWN, Bartley, D.O., Chief of Staff, St. Joseph's Hospital Of Buckhannon, Buckhannon, WV, p. A771

BROWN, Benjamin, Chief Operating Officer, Stonesprings Hospital Center, Dulles, VA, p. A741

BROWN, Bobby, Chief Executive Officer, Behavioral Health Of Rocky Top. Rocky Top. TN, p. A648

BROWN, Bryan, Executive Director, Mercy Hospital Fort Smith, Fort Smith, AR, p. A46

BROWN, Chad J., M.P.H., FACHE, President, Wake Forest Baptist Health - Wilkes Medical Center, North Wilkesboro, NC, p. A516
M.P.H., FACHE, President, Wake Forest Baptist Health-Davie Medical Center, Bermuda Run, NC, p. A505

BROWN, Charna, Chief Nursing Officer, Cullman Regional Medical Center, Cullman, AL, p. A17

BROWN, Cheryl, Chief Executive Officer, Henderson Health Care Services, Henderson, NE, p. A433

BROWN, Chistiane, Assistant Vice President, Medstar Montgomery Medical Center, Olney, MD, p. A331

BROWN, Christi, Director Human Resources, Our Lady Of The Angels Hospital, Bogalusa, LA, p. A298

BROWN, Crystal, M.D., Medical Director, Medical Center Of Peach County, Navicent Health, Bryon, GA, p. A167

BROWN, Cullen, Chief Operating Officer, Southern Hills Hospital And Medical Center, Las Vegas, NV, p. A444

BROWN, Cynthia, Director of Nursing, Hill Hospital Of Sumter County, York, AL, p. A26

BROWN, Damon, Interim Chief Executive Officer, Alliancehealth Seminole, Seminole, OK, p. A568

BROWN, Darin, Chief Financial Officer, Henry Community Health, New Castle, IN, p. A238

BROWN, David, Human Resources Director, Crestwood Medical Center, Huntsville, AL, p. A20

BROWN, Deana, Director Administrative Services, Franciscan Health Rensselaer, Rensselaer, IN, p. A239

BROWN, DeAnn, Chief Nursing Officer, Garfield Memorial Hospital, Panguitch, UT, p. A730

BROWN, Deborah, Chief Nursing Officer, Logan Memorial Hospital, Russellville, KY, p. A293

BROWN, Debra, Area Financial Officer, Kaiser Permanente Manteca Medical Center, Manteca, CA, p. A77

BROWN, Debra M., Vice President Patient Care and Chief Operating Officer, Dell Children's Medical Center Of Central Texas, Austin, TX, p. A656

BROWN, Denise, Vice President Human Resources, Amita Health Saint Josep. Hospital, Chicago, IL, p. A197

BROWN, Derek, Chief Information Officer, Jellico Community Hospital, Jellico, TN, p. A640

BROWN, Doris, Chief Executive Officer, Gordon Memorial Health Services, Gordon, NE, p. A432

BROWN, Douglas, Chief Financial Officer, Northridge Hospital Medical Center, Northridge, CA, p. A81

BROWN, Ed, Chief Financial Officer, Cibola General Hospital, Grants, NM, p. A460

Chief Information Officer, Medical Center, Navicent Health, Macon, GA, p. A176

BROWN, Eric, M.D., Physician Executive, Prisma Health Richland Hospital, Columbia, SC, p. A618

BROWN, Geoffrey, Chief Information Officer, Piedmont Fayette Hospital, Fayetteville, GA, p. A172

Chief Information Officer, Piedmont Mountainside Hospital, Jasper, GA, p. A174

Vice President Information Systems, Inova Fairfax Hospital, Falls Church, VA, p. A741

BROWN, Howard, Chief Financial Officer, North Shore Medical Center, Miami, FL, p. A147

BROWN, James, Chief Financial Officer, Centerpoint Medical Center, Independence, MO, p. A407

BROWN, Janice, Chief Financial Officer, Coosa Valley Medical Center, Sylacauga, AL, p. A24

BROWN, Jason, M.D., Chief Medical Officer, Banner Goldfield Medical Center, Apache Junction, AZ, p. A30

Director Information Systems, Sanford Sheldon Medical Center, Sheldon, IA, p. A257

BROWN, Jay, Senior Vice President, Chief Information Officer, West Chester Hospital, West Chester, OH, p. A552

Vice President and Chief Information Officer, University Of Cincinnati Medical Center, Cincinnati, OH, p. A533

BROWN, Jayma, R.N., Director of Nursing, Mercyone Oakland Medical Center, Oakland, NE, p. A436

BROWN, Jeffrey, M.D., Chief Medical Officer, Indiana University Health Arnett Hospital, Lafayette, IN, p. A234

BROWN, Jenny, Director of Human Resources, Vidant Beaufort Hospital, Washington, NC, p. A519

BROWN, Jill, Chief Financial Officer, Miller County Hospital, Colquitt, GA, p. A169

BROWN, Jim, Director Information Technology, Lynn County Hospital District, Tahoka, TX, p. A718

BROWN, Jon, Chief Information Officer, Mission Hospital, Asheville, NC, p. A504

BROWN, Joni, Director Human Resources, Rehabilitation Hospital Of Indiana, Indianapolis, IN, p. A233

BROWN, Joseph, Vice President Operations, Baylor Scott & White Medical Center - Plano, Plano, TX, p. A706

Vice President Operations, Baylor Scott & White Medical Center - Round Rock, Round Rock, TX, p. A709

BROWN, Judy, Chief Nursing Officer, Mitchell County Regional Health Center, Osage, IA, p. A255

BROWN, Karen, Manager Information Technology, Guthrie Towanda Memorial Hospital, Towanda, PA, p. A609

Vice President Chief Operating Officer, Osf Saint Anthony Medical Center, Rockford, IL, p. A219

BROWN, Katie, Coordinator Human Resources, Pocahontas Memorial Hospital, Buckeye, WV, p. A770

BROWN, Kendra, MSN, R.N., Chief Nursing Officer, Kearney County Health Services, Minden, NE, p. A435

Job Requisition Coordinator, Rusk State Hospital, Rusk, TX, p. A710

BROWN, Kenneth, Vice President and Chief Human Resource Officer, Pratt Regional Medical Center, Pratt, KS, p. A275

BROWN, Kevin, Chief Executive Officer, La Paz Regional Hospital, Parker, AZ, p. A34

BROWN, Kris, Associate Director, Bay Pines Veterans Affairs Healthcare System, Bay Pines, FL, p. A131

BROWN, LaRay, President and Chief Executive Officer, Interfaith Medical Center, Brooklyn, NY, p. A478

BROWN, LaTonya, Interim Chief Operating Officer and Chief Financial Officer, Unc Rockingham Health Care, Eden, NC, p. A509

BROWN, Lewis, Director Information Technology, Bsa Hospital, Llc, Amarillo, TX, p. A652

BROWN, Lisa, Director of Nursing, Pearl River County Hospital, Poplarville, MS, p. A399

BROWN, Lorenzo, Chief Executive Officer, Adventhealth Deland, Deland, FL, p. A136

BROWN, Lori, R.N., FACHE, Chief Nursing Officer, Hennepin Healthcare, Minneapolis, MN, p. A380

Chief Nursing Officer, Baptist Memorial Hospital-Union City, Union City, TN, p. A650

BROWN, Margaret, Director Medical Records, Vantage Point Of Northwest Arkansas, Fayetteville, AR, p. A45

BROWN, Mark, Chief Nursing Officer, Seton Medical Center, Daly City, CA, p. A62

BROWN, Markham, M.D., Chief Medical Staff, Mike O'Callaghan Federal Hospital, Nellis Afb, NV, p. A445

BROWN, Marlon, Human Resources, Essex County Hospital Center, Cedar Grove, NJ, p. A453

BROWN, Martin, Vice President Information Services and Chief Information Officer, Nathan Littauer Hospital And Nursing Home, Gloversville, NY, p. A485

BROWN, Mary, Director Human Resources, Bertrand Chaffee Hospital, Springville, NY, p. A498

BROWN, Michael, D.O., Chief of Staff, Tmc Bonham Hospital, Bonham, TX, p. A466

BROWN, Michael L., Chief Executive Officer, Regional Hospital Of Scranton, Scranton, PA, p. A607

President and Chief Executive Officer, Moses Taylor Hospital, Scranton, PA, p. A607

BROWN, Mike, Chief Financial Officer, Carlinville Area Hospital, Carlinville, IL, p. A196

BROWN, Molly, Chief Operating Officer, University Of Mississipp. Medical Center Grenada, Grenada, MS, p. A393

BROWN, Natalie, Chief Human Resources Management Services, Memphis Veterans Affairs Medical Center, Memphis, TN, p. A644

BROWN, Pam, Human Resources Manager, Unity Psychiatric Care-Columbia, Columbia, TN, p. A637

BROWN, Pat, R.N., Chief Nursing Officer, San Gorgonio Memorial Hospital, Banning, CA, p. A58

BROWN, Patsy, Site Coordinator Human Resources, Erlanger Bledsoe Hospital, Pikeville, TN, p. A648

BROWN, Penny, Human Resource Representative, Broaddus Hospital, Philippi, WV, p. A775

BROWN, Philip. D.O., Vice President Medical Affairs, The University Of Vermont Health Network Central Vermont Medical Center, Berlin, VT, p. A735

BROWN, Phyllis, Chief Executive Officer, Marshall Medical Center, Lewisburg, TN, p. A642

BROWN, Randal, M.D., Chief of Medical Staff, Guadalup. County Hospital, Santa Rosa, NM, p. A472

BROWN, Regenia, Vice President Human Resources, Magnolia Regional Health Center, Corinth, MS, p. A391

BROWN, Rex H., President and Chief Executive Officer, Hillsboro Area Hospital, Hillsboro, IL, p. A207

BROWN, Rickie, Chief Financial Officer, Monroe County Medical Center, Tompkinsville, KY, p. A293

BROWN, Rita, Director Human Resources, Richardson Medical Center, Rayville, LA, p. A313

BROWN, Robert, Chief Operating Officer, Parkview Community Hospital Medical Center, Riverside, CA, p. A88

BROWN, Roberta, Chief Nursing Officer, Community Hospital Of Staunton, Staunton, IL, p. A221

BROWN, Robin, Chief Information Officer and Compliance Officer, St. Josep. Medical Center, Houston, TX, p. A688

BROWN, Scott, Chief Financial Officer, Valir Rehabilitation Hospital, Oklahoma City, OK, p. A566

BROWN, Sharon, Deputy Commander Nursing, Winn Army Community Hospital, Hinesville, GA, p. A174

Vice President Human Resources, Sierra View Medical Center, Porterville, CA, p. A86

Vice President Patient Care and Chief Nursing Officer, St. Mary Medical Center, Langhorne, PA, p. A594

BROWN, Sherry, Director Human Resources, Cleveland Area Hospital, Cleveland, OK, p. A557

BROWN, Stacey L., Chief Executive Officer, Odessa Regional Medical Center South Campus, Odessa, TX, p. A704

Chief Executive Officer, Odessa Regional Medical Center, Odessa, TX, p. A704

President, Scenic Mountain Medical Center, Big Spring, TX, p. A659

BROWN, Stephen, Chief Financial Officer, Grace Cottage Hospital, Townshend, VT, p. A737

BROWN, Steve, M.D., Chief Quality Officer, Saint Alphonsus Regional Medical Center, Boise, ID, p. A188

Chief Information Officer, Wellstar Sylvan Grove Hospital, Jackson, GA, p. A174

Director Information Systems, Wellstar Spalding Regional Hospital, Griffin, GA, p. A173

Health Services Director, U. S. Penitentiary Infirmary, Lewisburg, PA, p. A595

BROWN, Steven, M.D., Medical Director, Wyoming Behavioral Institute, Casper, WY, p. A801

Vice President Finance, Anderson Regional Health System South, Meridian, MS, p. A397

Vice President Finance, Anderson Regional Health System, Meridian, MS, p. A397

Vice President Fiscal Affairs, Mary Rutan Hospital, Bellefontaine, OH, p. A529

BROWN, Susan, Chief Human Resources Officer, Wellstar North Fulton Hospital, Roswell, GA, p. A179

Chief Nursing Officer, El Paso Behavioral Health System, El Paso, TX, p. A674

BROWN, Terry, Chief Financial Officer, Raulerson Hospital, Okeechobee, FL, p. A150

BROWN, Theodore, Chief Operating Officer, Community Howard Regional Health, Kokomo, IN, p. A234

Vice President Financial Services, Community Howard Regional Health, Kokomo, IN, p. A234

BROWN, Thomas W., Chief Executive Officer, Brookhaven Hospital, Tulsa, OK, p. A569

BROWN, Todd, M.D., Medical Director, Logan Regional Hospital, Logan, UT, p. A728

BROWN, Traci, Director Human Resources, Medical Arts Hospital, Lamesa, TX, p. A694

BROWN, Wendy, M.D., M.P.H., Chief of Staff, Jesse Brown Veterans Affairs Medical Center, Chicago, IL, p. A198

BROWN, Willie, Director Administration, Naval Hospital Beaufort, Beaufort, SC, p. A615

BROWN, Winfield S., FACHE, President and Chief Executive Officer, Athol Hospital, Athol, MA, p. A334

FACHE, President and Chief Executive Officer, Heywood Hospital, Gardner, MA, p. A339

BROWN-ROBERTS, Bonita, Director Information Systems, Advocate Trinity Hospital, Chicago, IL, p. A197

BROWN-SMITH, Clarissa, Director Fiscal Services, Shriners Hospitals For Children-Shreveport, Shreveport, LA, p. A314

BROWN-TEZERA, Belina, MSN, Associate Director Patient Care Services, John D. Dingell Veterans Affairs Medical Center, Detroit, MI, p. A353

BROWNE, Colleen, Vice President and Chief People Officer, Lmh Health, Lawrence, KS, p. A269

BROWNE, John, Assistant Administrator Finance, Kindred Hospital-Brea, Brea, CA, p. A58

Senior Chief Financial Officer, Kindred Hospital Riverside, Perris, CA, p. A85

BROWNE, Mark, M.D., Chief Medical Officer, Roane Medical Center, Harriman, TN, p. A639

M.D., Covenant Health, Senior Vice President and Chief Medical Officer, Methodist Medical Center Of Oak Ridge, Oak Ridge, TN, p. A648

BROWNER, Warren S., M.D., M.P.H., Chief Executive Officer, California Pacific Medical Center-St. Luke's Campus, San Francisco, CA, p. A93

M.D., M.P.H., Chief Executive Officer, California Pacific Medical Center, San Francisco, CA, p. A93

BROWNEWELL, Victoria, Chief Nursing Officer, Houston Methodist West Hospital, Houston, TX, p. A686

BROWNING, Douglas, Chief Financial Officer, Texas Health Center For Diagnostic & Surgery, Plano, TX, p. A707

BROWNING, Michael, Chief Financial Officer, Madison Health, London, OH, p. A543

BROWNLEE, Tamarah, Vice President, Human Resources, Indiana University Health West Hospital, Avon, IN, p. A223

BROWNSTEIN, Richard, M.D., Chief of Staff, Northwest Mississipp. Medical Center, Clarksdale, MS, p. A391

BROYLES, Susan, Director Human Resources and Safety, Unicoi County Memorial Hospital, Erwin, TN, p. A638

BRUBAKER, Kathy, R.N., MSN, Vice President and Chief Nursing Officer, St. Josep. Mercy Chelsea, Chelsea, MI, p. A351

BRUBAKER, Margaret, Senior Vice President Human Resources, Brookdale Hospital Medical Center, New York, NY, p. A489

BRUCE, Blackhart, M.D., Chief of Staff, Oak Valley Hospital, Oakdale, CA, p. A82

BRUCE, Caleigh, Director of Human Resources/Chief Compliance Officer, Ferrell Hospital, Eldorado, IL, p. A203

BRUCE, Jordan, Administrator, Norwood Health Center, Marshfield, WI, p. A789

BRUCE, Karen, Director of Nursing, Newport News Behavioral Health Center, Newport News, VA, p. A747

BRUCE, Michael, Chief Executive Officer, Elmore Community Hospital, Wetumpka, AL, p. A26

Chief Financial Officer, Elmore Community Hospital, Wetumpka, AL, p. A26

BRUCE, Michael D., Chief Executive Officer, Lake Martin Community Hospital, Dadeville, AL, p. A17

BRUCE, Scott, President, St. Mary's Healthcare, Amsterdam, NY, p. A474

BRUCKNER, Alison, Chief Operating Officer, Cass County Health System, Atlantic, IA, p. A243

BRUDNICKI, Gary, Senior Executive Vice President, Chief Operating Officer and Chief Financial Officer, Westchester Medical Center, Valhalla, NY, p. A501

BRUEGGEMANN, Marty, Chief Medical Officer, Virginia Mason Memorial, Yakima, WA, p. A769

BRUENING, Teri, MSN, Chief Nursing Officer and Vice President Patient Care Services, Nebraska Methodist Hospital, Omaha, NE, p. A437

BRUENS, Dennis, Vice President Operations, St. Thomas More Hospital, Canon City, CO, p. A108

BRUFF, Edward, President and Chief Executive Officer, Covenant Healthcare, Saginaw, MI, p. A365

BRUGGEMAN, Chris, Chief Operating Officer, Riverview Health, Crookston, MN, p. A374

BRUHL, Lisa, Chief Operating Officer, Lallie Kemp Medical Center, Independence, LA, p. A303

BRUHL, Steven, Chief Medical Officer, Mercy Tiffin Hospital, Tiffin, OH, p. A550

BRUHN, Julie, R.N., MS, Associate Director Patient Care and Nurse Executive, Fargo Veterans Affairs Health Care System, Fargo, ND, p. A523

BRUI, Thomas, Director Resource Management, Naval Hospital Lemoore, Lemoore, CA, p. A71

BRUINS, Melanie, Chief Talent Officer, Marshfield Medical Center - Beaver Dam, Beaver Dam, WI, p. A781

BRUMFIELD, Derrick, Chief Operating Officer, Sagewest Health Care, Riverton, WY, p. A803

BRUMFIELD, Rita, R.N., MSN, Chief Nursing Officer, Ste. Genevieve County Memorial Hospital, Ste Genevieve, MO, p. A419

BRUMMER, Amy, MSN, Chief Nursing Officer, Saint Luke's North Hospital - Barry Road, Kansas City, MO, p. A409

BRUMMETT, Vincent, Chief Executive Officer, Parkwood Behavioral Health System, Olive Branch, MS, p. A398

BRUNDAGE, Kelsey, Director Human Resources, Arkansas Valley Regional Medical Center, La Junta, CO, p. A115

BRUNDISE, Cynthia, Vice President Human Resources, Ssm Health St. Anthony Hospital - Oklahoma City, Oklahoma City, OK, p. A566

BRUNELLE, Diane, MSN, R.N., Director Patient Care Services and Chief Nursing Officer, Shriners Hospitals For Children-Springfield, Springfield, MA, p. A345

BRUNER, Deborah, Chief Executive Officer and Administrator, Minneola District Hospital, Minneola, KS, p. A271

BRUNER, Kristy C., Chief Executive Officer, Select Specialty Hospital-Evansville, Evansville, IN, p. A228

BRUNING, Troy, Director Information Technology, Meeker Memorial Hospital, Litchfield, MN, p. A379

BRUNKE, Renea, Vice President Human Resources, Chandler Regional Medical Center, Chandler, AZ, p. A30

BRUNN, Mary E., R.N., Acting Associate Director Nursing, Clement J. Zablocki Veterans Affairs Medical Center, Milwaukee, WI, p. A791

BRUNO, Catherine, FACHE, Chief Information Officer, Northern Light Eastern Maine Medical Center, Bangor, ME, p. A318

BRUNO, John, Senior Vice President Human Resources, St. Joseph's University Medical Center, Paterson, NJ, p. A460

BRUNO, Judy, President, Vidant Roanoke-Chowan Hospital, Ahoskie, NC, p. A504

BRUNS, Susan, Chief Nursing Officer, Phoebe Sumter Medical Center, Americus, GA, p. A163

BRUNSCHEON, Keagan, Manager, Human Resources, Grundy County Memorial Hospital, Grundy Center, IA, p. A250

BRUNSING, Alisa, Chief Financial Officer, St. Francis Memorial Hospital, West Point, NE, p. A440

BRUNSON, Pamela, Director Human Resources, South Baldwin Regional Medical Center, Foley, AL, p. A18

BRUNT, C, M.D., Medical Director, Lakeside Behavioral Health System, Memphis, TN, p. A644

BRUNTON, Hope, Chief Manpower Branch, Irwin Army Community Hospital, Junction City, KS, p. A267

BRUNTZ, Troy, CPA, President and Chief Executive Officer, Community Hospital, Mccook, NE, p. A435

BRUSCO, Louis, M.D., Chief Medical Officer, Hackensack Meridian Health Raritan Bay Medical Center, Perth Amboy, NJ, p. A461

BRUTON, Christine, Chief Financial Officer, Baptist Medical Center East, Montgomery, AL, p. A22

BRUTON, Jeff, Director Human Resources, Fairview Park Hospital, Dublin, GA, p. A172

BRYAN, Darlene, R.N., Chief Nursing Officer, Humboldt General Hospital, Winnemucca, NV, p. A447

BRYAN, Jason, Director Human Resources, Middle Park Health-Kremmling, Kremmling, CO, p. A114

BRYAN, Kenneth, FACHE, President and Chief Executive Officer, Harnett Health System, Dunn, NC, p. A508

BRYAN, Linda, Vice President Human Resources, Fawcett Memorial Hospital, Port Charlotte, FL, p. A155

BRYAN, Lynda, Vice President Human Resources, Northwest Medical Center, Margate, FL, p. A145

BRYAN, Margaret, Administrator, Shriners Hospitals For Children-Northern California, Sacramento, CA, p. A89

BRYAN-SMITH, Lissa, Chief Administrative Officer, Geisinger-Bloomsburg Hospital, Bloomsburg, PA, p. A585

BRYANT, Amy, Chief Financial Officer, Cornerstone Hospitals Southwest Louisiana, Lake Charles, LA, p. A306

BRYANT, Dawn, Vice President Human Resources, North Kansas City Hospital, North Kansas City, MO, p. A413

BRYANT, Gary, Chief Financial Officer, Carepoint Health Bayonne Medical Center, Bayonne, NJ, p. A452 Executive Vice President and Chief Financial Officer, Carepoint Health Christ Hospital, Jersey City, NJ, p. A456

BRYANT, Gerald, R.N., Chief Nursing Officer, Baylor Scott & White Medical Center - Temple, Temple, TX, p. A719

BRYANT, Justin, Chief Operating Officer, Grandview Medical Center, Birmingham, AL, p. A15

BRYANT, Karen L., Chief Executive Officer, Prowers Medical Center, Lamar, CO, p. A115

BRYANT, Lidia, Director Human Resources, Ottumwa Regional Health Center, Ottumwa, IA, p. A256

BRYANT, Lisa, Director Human Resources, Anmed Health Cannon, Pickens, SC, p. A623

BRYANT, Marcia, R.N., Vice President, Clinical Operations, The Outer Banks Hospital, Nags Head, NC, p. A515

BRYANT, Maureen A., FACHE, President, Northwestern Medicine Delnor Hospital, Geneva, IL, p. A206

BRYANT, Pam, Director Human Resources, Helen Keller Hospital, Sheffield, AL, p. A24

BRYANT, Ronald, President, Baystate Franklin Medical Center, Greenfield, MA, p. A339 President, Baystate Noble Hospital, Westfield, MA, p. A346

BRYANT, Rusty, Director Information Technology, Drew Memorial Health System, Monticello, AR, p. A50

BRYANT, Samantha, Chief Nursing Officer, Rhea Medical Center, Dayton, TN, p. A637

BRYANT-MOBLEY, Phyllis, M.D., Director Medical Services, William S. Hall Psychiatric Institute, Columbia, SC, p. A618

BRYCE, Keith, Vice President Finance and Chief Financial Officer, Mt. Graham Regional Medical Center, Safford, AZ, p. A37

BRYER, Alex, Director Information Management, Los Robles Hospital And Medical Center, Thousand Oaks, CA, p. A101

BRYNER, Jennifer, Director Nursing, Petersburg Medical Center, Petersburg, AK, p. A29

BRYNES, Jeremy M., Chief Executive Officer, Kingwood Emergency Hospital, Kingwood, TX, p. A693

BRYSON, Kellie, Director Human Resources, The Hospital At Westlake Medical Center, Austin, TX, p. A657

BRZEZINSKI, Christina, Chief Nursing Officer, Coastal Carolina Hospital, Hardeeville, SC, p. A621

BUCCELLATO, Vito, Chief Hospital Executive, Hackensack Meridian Health Jersey Shore University Medical Center, Neptune, NJ, p. A459

BUCCI, Annette, Vice President Human Resources, Burke Rehabilitation Hospital, White Plains, NY, p. A502

BUCCIARELLI, Brant, Chief Information Officer, Riverview Health, Noblesville, IN, p. A238

BUCCOLO, Martin A., Ph.D., Chief Executive Officer, Four Winds Hospital, Katonah, NY, p. A486

BUCH, Naishadh, Chief Operating Officer, Lompoc Valley Medical Center, Lompoc, CA, p. A72

BUCHANAN, Anna, Vice President Finance and Chief Financial Officer, Berkeley Medical Center, Martinsburg, WV, p. A774 Vice President Finance and Chief Financial Officer, Jefferson Medical Center, Ranson, WV, p. A776

BUCHANAN, Herbert, President, Amita Health Saint Josep. Medical Center, Joliet, IL, p. A209

BUCHANAN, Jean, Director Human Resources, Broughton Hospital, Morganton, NC, p. A515

BUCHANAN, Kyle, President, Helen Keller Hospital, Sheffield, AL, p. A24

BUCHANAN, Robert, Chief Information Officer, Anna Jaques Hospital, Newburyport, MA, p. A342

BUCHANAN, Toni, Chief Financial Officer, Unicoi County Memorial Hospital, Erwin, TN, p. A638

BUCHANAN, Tracy, Chief Executive Officer and President, Carepartners Health Services, Asheville, NC, p. A504

BUCHART, Phyllis, Chief Operating Officer, Marina Del Rey Hospital, Marina Del Rey, CA, p. A77

BUCHE, Karen, Chief Human Resource Officer, Douglas County Community Mental Health Center, Omaha, NE, p. A437

BUCHELE, Paula, Chief Human Resources, Bay Pines Veterans Affairs Healthcare System, Bay Pines, FL, p. A131

BUCHER, Ben, Chief Executive Officer, Towner County Medical Center, Cando, ND, p. A521 Interim Chief Executive Officer, Mountrail County Medical Center, Stanley, ND, p. A526

BUCHHEIT, Anne, Coordinator Mental Health Local Information Systems, Buffalo Psychiatric Center, Buffalo, NY, p. A479

BUCHHOLZ, Kari, Director Health Information Management, South Central Health, Wishek, ND, p. A526

BUCK, Catherine, MSN, R.N., President, Froedtert And The Medical College Of Wisconsin Froedtert Hospital, Milwaukee, WI, p. A791

BUCK, Cindy, Interim Chief Executive Officer, Abbeville Area Medical Center, Abbeville, SC, p. A615

BUCK, Linda, Vice President Human Resources, Unitypoint Health - Proctor, Peoria, IL, p. A217

BUCK, Nathan, R.N., Nursing Manager, Idaho Doctor's Hospital, Blackfoot, ID, p. A188

BUCK, Phylis, Controller, Encompass Health Rehabilitation Hospital Of Texarkana, Texarkana, TX, p. A720

BUCK, Shelly, President, Riddle Hospital, Media, PA, p. A597

BUCK, Tavia, Chief Administrative Officer, Roper St. Francis Mount Pleasant Hospital, Mount Pleasant, SC, p. A622

BUCKLEY, David, Acting Chief Information Management Services, Oklahoma City Veterans Affairs Medical Center, Oklahoma City, OK, p. A565

BUCKLEY, John, M.D., President Medical Staff, Vibra Hospital Of Denver, Thornton, CO, p. A119

BUCKLEY, Kalvin, Director Information Systems, Woodland Heights Medical Center, Lufkin, TX, p. A698

BUCKLEY, Karen, R.N., Chief Nursing Officer, Community Behavioral Health Center, Fresno, CA, p. A65

BUCKLEY, Martha, Chief Medical Informatics Officer, Fairfield Medical Center, Lancaster, OH, p. A542

BUCKMAN, Janet, Chief Financial Officer, Hedrick Medical Center, Chillicothe, MO, p. A404

BUCKMINSTER, Joe, Manager Information Technology, Community Medical Center, Inc., Falls City, NE, p. A432

BUCKNER, Marlys, Chief Nursing Officer, Cox Barton County Memorial Hospital, Lamar, MO, p. A410

BUCKNER, Twila, R.N., Chief Nursing Officer, Cass Regional Medical Center, Harrisonville, MO, p. A407

BUCKNOR, Jermaine, Chief Financial Officer, Northwest Health Physicians' Specialty Hospital, Fayetteville, AR, p. A45

BUCKWORTH, Ben, Human Resources Administrative Director, Primary Children's Hospital, Salt Lake City, UT, p. A732

BUDA, Jeff, Chief Information Officer, Floyd Medical Center, Rome, GA, p. A179

BUDD, Edward, President and Chief Executive Officer, Thorek Memorial Hospital, Chicago, IL, p. A201

BUDGE, Nathanael, Administrator, Jordan Valley Medical Center West Valley Campus, West Valley City, UT, p. A734

BUDZINSKI, Anthony, R.N., Executive Vice President and Chief Financial Officer, Wellstar Kennestone Hospital, Marietta, GA, p. A176

BUDZINSKY, Chris, Vice President Nursing and Chief Nursing Officer Alexian Brothers Acute Care Ministries, Amita Health Hoffman Estates, Hoffman Estates, IL, p. A208 Vice President, Nursing and Chief Nursing Officer, Amita Health Elk Grove Village, Elk Grove Village, IL, p. A204

BUE, Cheryl, Health Information Transcriptionist, Faulkton Area Medical Center, Faulkton, SD, p. A628

BUEGLER, Carisa, Director of Operations, New Ulm Medical Center, New Ulm, MN, p. A382

BUEHLER, Bonnie, Chief Information Officer, St. Mary Medical Center, Langhorne, PA, p. A594 Chief Information Technology, Nazareth Hospital, Philadelphia, PA, p. A601

BUEHRLE, Char, Interim Chief Executive Officer, West Hills Hospital, Reno, NV, p. A446

BUEHRLE, Jeff, Chief Financial Officer, Banner - University Medical Center South, Tucson, AZ, p. A39

BUELL, Jack, Director Information Services, Sutter Lakeside Hospital, Lakeport, CA, p. A71

BUENAVIDEZ, Nanette, Chief Nursing Officer, Arrowhead Regional Medical Center, Colton, CA, p. A60

BUER, Shane, Vice President, Human Resources, Mercyone Clinton Medical Center, Clinton, IA, p. A246

BUFFENBARGER, Andrew, FACHE, Chief Compliance Officer, Director of Human Resources & Risk Management, Kirby Medical Center, Monticello, IL, p. A212

BUFFINGTON, John, Chief Operating Officer, San Juan Regional Medical Center, Farmington, NM, p. A469

BUFFINGTON, Mike, Manager Information Technology, Kansas Medical Center, Andover, KS, p. A261

BUFKIN, Ben, Human Resource Director, Bolivar Medical Center, Cleveland, MS, p. A391

BUGALLO-MUROS, Mariana, Vice President Chief Human Resources Officer, H. Lee Moffitt Cancer Center And Research Institute, Tampa, FL, p. A159

BUGAYONG, Carol, Human Resources Director, Encompass Health Rehabilitation Hospital Of Tallahassee, Tallahassee, FL, p. A158

BUGNA, Eric, M.D., Chief of Staff, Eastern Plumas Health Care, Portola, CA, p. A86

BUHLKE, Brian, M.D., Medical Director, Genoa Medical Facilities, Genoa, NE, p. A432

BUI, Steven, M.D., Chief of Staff, Orange County Global Medical Center, Inc., Santa Ana, CA, p. A96

BUICE, Johnathan, Chief Information Officer, Upson Regional Medical Center, Thomaston, GA, p. A181

BUIT, Timothy, President and Chief Executive Officer, Bellevue Hospital, Bellevue, OH, p. A529

BUKAC, Amy, M.D., Medical Director, Providence Seward Medical Center, Seward, AK, p. A29

BULAU, Chris, Manager Information Technology, Ridgeview Sibley Medical Center, Arlington, MN, p. A372

BULEN, Susan, M.D., Medical Director, Encompass Health Rehabilitation Hospital Of Northwest Tucson, Tucson, AZ, p. A40

BULLARD, Brandon, Chief Executive Officer, Hamilton County Hospital, Syracuse, KS, p. A277

BULLARD, John, Director Information Technology, St. Mary's Hospital And Medical Center, Grand Junction, CO, p. A113

BULLARD, Patrick, Chief Financial Officer, Fayetteville Veterans Affairs Medical Center, Fayetteville, NC, p. A510

BULLER, Lisa, Regional Vice President and Chief Information Officer, Cascade Valley Hospital, Arlington, WA, p. A755

BULLINGTON, Benjamin, M.D., Chief of Staff, Pioneer Medical Center, Big Timber, MT, p. A421

BULLINGTON, Gina, Chief Nursing Officer, Tristar Horizon Medical Center, Dickson, TN, p. A637

BULLOCK, David, Director Information Services, Northwest Medical Center, Tucson, AZ, p. A40

BULLOCK, Deann, M.D., Chief Medical Officer, Nashville General Hospital, Nashville, TN, p. A646

BULLOCK, Lance, M.D., Medical Director, St. James Behavioral Health Hospital, Gonzales, LA, p. A302

BULLOCK, Scott, Director Information Systems, Barstow Community Hospital, Barstow, CA, p. A58

BULMAN, Laurie, Director Human Resources, Winneshiek Medical Center, Decorah, IA, p. A248

BULMASH, Jack, M.D., Chief of Staff, Edward Hines, Jr. Veterans Affairs Hospital, Hines, IL, p. A207

BUMAN, Karen, MSN, Chief Nursing Officer, Myrtue Medical Center, Harlan, IA, p. A251

BUMGARDNER, Charles, Director Information Systems, Southeast Georgia Health System Brunswick Campus, Brunswick, GA, p. A167
Director, Southeast Georgia Health System Camden Campus, Saint Marys, GA, p. A179

BUMGARNER, William J., President, Spencer Hospital, Spencer, IA, p. A258

BUMP, Cathy, R.N., Chief Nursing Officer, Methodist Ambulatory Surgery Hospital - Northwest, San Antonio, TX, p. A712

BUNCH, David V., President and Chief Administrative Officer, Cumberland Medical Center, Crossville, TN, p. A637

BUNCH, Elicia, Chief Executive Officer, Highlands Behavioral Health System, Littleton, CO, p. A116

BUNCH, Mark, Director Finance, Othello Community Hospital, Othello, WA, p. A761

BUNCH, Michael, Chief Financial Officer, Caldwell Unc Health Care, Lenoir, NC, p. A513

BUNCH, Mike, Executive Vice President, Chief Operating Officer and Chief Financial Officer, Kershawhealth, Camden, SC, p. A615

BUNCH, Rita, M.P.H., FACHE, Vice President of Operations, Sentara Careplex Hospital, Hampton, VA, p. A743

BUNCH, Terri, MSN, R.N., MSN, Chief Nursing Officer, Stone County Medical Center, Mountain View, AR, p. A50
MSN, R.N., MSN, Chief Nursing Officer, White River Medical Center, Batesville, AR, p. A42

BUND, Linda, Chief Information Officer and Director Education, James J. Peters Veterans Affairs Medical Center, Bronx, NY, p. A476

BUNDY, Michael N., Chief Operating Officer, Prisma Health Baptist Hospital, Columbia, SC, p. A618
Chief Operating Officer, Prisma Health Baptist Parkridge Hospital, Columbia, SC, p. A618

BUNKER, Marla, Vice President Nursing and Chief Operating Officer, War Memorial Hospital, Sault Sainte Marie, MI, p. A366

BUNN, Barry, M.D., Chief of Staff, Vidant Edgecombe Hospital, Tarboro, NC, p. A519

BUNNELL, Craig, Chief Medical Officer, Dana-Farber Cancer Institute, Boston, MA, p. A335

BUNNELL, Emily, Chief Nurse Executive, Senior Director of Acute Care, Upmc Cole, Coudersport, PA, p. A587

BUNNELL, Kimberly Lynn, Chief Executive Officer, Garland Behavioral Hospital, Garland, TX, p. A681

BUNNER, Blake, Chief Executive Officer, Encompass Health Deaconess Rehabilitation Hospital, Newburgh, IN, p. A238

BUNSELMEYER, Becky, Director Information Services, Memorial Hospital, Chester, IL, p. A197

BUNTEN, Sherry, Director Patient Care Services, Aspirus Langlade Hospital, Antigo, WI, p. A779

BUNTING, Katherine Esq, Chief Executive Officer, Fairfield Memorial Hospital, Fairfield, IL, p. A205

BUNTYN, Diane, MSN, R.N., Vice President Patient Care Services, Southeast Alabama Medical Center, Dothan, AL, p. A18

BUNYARD, Steve, President, Ohiohealth Dublin Methodist Hospital, Dublin, OH, p. A539
President, Ohiohealth Grady Memorial Hospital, Delaware, OH, p. A539

BUONGIORNO, Michael, Executive Vice President Finance and Chief Financial Officer, Bryn Mawr Hospital, Bryn Mawr, PA, p. A585
Vice President Finance, Lankenau Medical Center, Wynnewood, PA, p. A612

BUPP, Steven, M.D., Medical Director, Sonora Behavioral Health Hospital, Tucson, AZ, p. A40

BURBANK, Jimmy, Chief Information Officer, U. S. Public Health Service Indian Hospital, Crownpoint, NM, p. A469

BURCH, Debra, Chief Nursing Officer, Burke Medical Center, Waynesboro, GA, p. A183

BURCH, Eric, Chief Operating Officer, Canton-Potsdam Hospital, Potsdam, NY, p. A495

BURCH, Eric R., Chief Executive Officer, Gouverneur Hospital, Gouverneur, NY, p. A485

BURCH, Lee, Director Management Information Systems, Bayfront Health Brooksville, Brooksville, FL, p. A133

BURCH, Todd, Chief Executive Officer, Aspirus Riverview Hospital And Clinics, Inc., Wisconsin Rapids, WI, p. A800

BURCHELL, Pam, Director Human Resources, Lawnwood Regional Medical Center & Heart Institute, Fort Pierce, FL, p. A138

BURCHETT, Claudia, R.N., Vice President of Patient Services, Southern Ohio Medical Center, Portsmouth, OH, p. A548

BURCHETT, Shelby, Chief Executive Officer, Fort Madison Community Hospital, Fort Madison, IA, p. A250

BURCHETT, Travis, Troop Commander Human Resources, Colonel Florence A. Blanchfield Army Community Hospital, Fort Campbell, KY, p. A283

BURCZEUSKI, Jason, Controller, Arms Acres, Carmel, NY, p. A481
Controller, Conifer Park, Glenville, NY, p. A484

BURD, David, Senior Vice President, Operations, Methodist Jennie Edmundson Hospital, Council Bluffs, IA, p. A247

BURDEN, Jennifer, Human Resources Director, Tristar Centennial Medical Center, Nashville, TN, p. A647

BURDEN, Matthew J., President and Chief Executive Officer, Porter-Starke Services, Valparaiso, IN, p. A241

BURDETTE, Marie, Chief Nursing Officer, East Georgia Regional Medical Center, Statesboro, GA, p. A181

BURDICK, Ginny, Senior Vice President and Chief Human Resources Officer, Clovis Community Medical Center, Clovis, CA, p. A60
Vice President Human Resources, Community Behavioral Health Center, Fresno, CA, p. A65
Vice President Human Resources, Community Regional Medical Center, Fresno, CA, p. A65

BURDICK, Hoyt, M.D., Vice President Medical Affairs, Cabell Huntington Hospital, Huntington, WV, p. A772

BURG, Sherry, Chief Nursing Officer, Fairview Range Medical Center, Hibbing, MN, p. A378

BURGE, Eugene H. Jr, Chief Executive Officer, Savoy Medical Center, Mamou, LA, p. A307

BURGER, Janice, Chief Executive, Providence St. Vincent Medical Center, Portland, OR, p. A580

BURGESS, Angela, Chief Information Officer, Randolp. Hospital, Asheboro, NC, p. A504

BURGESS, Daniel, Chief Information Officer, Mainegeneral Medical Center, Augusta, ME, p. A318

BURGESS, John, Director Information Services, Hocking Valley Community Hospital, Logan, OH, p. A543

BURGESS, Steven, Administrator Human Resources, Henrico Doctors' Hospital, Richmond, VA, p. A750

BURGHART, Steven, President, Ssm Cardinal Glennon Children's Hospital, Saint Louis, MO, p. A416

BURGOS, Odette, Supervisor Human Resources, San Jorge Children's Hospital, Santurce, PR, p. A811

BURGUS, Aurelis, Nursing Director, Ryder Memorial Hospital, Humacao, PR, p. A808

BURICK, Adam, M.D., Chief Medical Officer, Pam Specialty Hospital Of Covington, Covington, LA, p. A300
M.D., Chief Medical Officer, Pam Specialty Hospital Of Victoria North, Victoria, TX, p. A723
M.D., Chief Medical Officer, Pam Specialty Hospital Of Victoria South, Victoria, TX, p. A723

BURICK, Marsha, Chief Financial Officer, Central Florida Behavioral Hospital, Orlando, FL, p. A151

BURINGRUD, Duane, Chief Medical and Quality Officer, Palomar Medical Center Escondido, Escondido, CA, p. A63

BURISH, Brent, Chief Executive Officer, St. Cloud Regional Medical Center, Saint Cloud, FL, p. A156

BURK, Kaye, Administrator, Noland Hospital Dothan, Dothan, AL, p. A17

BURK, Thomas, Chief Operating Officer, Danville State Hospital, Danville, PA, p. A587

BURKE, Brian, M.D., President Medical Staff, Fairview Hospital, Great Barrington, MA, p. A339

BURKE, Brigid, Chief Financial Officer, Pondera Medical Center, Conrad, MT, p. A422

BURKE, Christopher D., Ph.D., Chief Executive Officer, Smokey Point Behavioral Hospital, Marysville, WA, p. A760

BURKE, David, Director Finance and Chief Financial Officer, Nantucket Cottage Hospital, Nantucket, MA, p. A342

BURKE, Dennis E., President and Chief Executive Officer, Good Shepherd Health Care System, Hermiston, OR, p. A576

BURKE, Dorothy, Chief Financial Officer, Southeast Colorado Hospital District, Springfield, CO, p. A118

BURKE, Greg, M.D., Medical Director, Geisinger Encompass Health Rehabilitation Hospital, Danville, PA, p. A587

BURKE, Jack, MS, R.N., Chief Operating Officer and Chief Nursing Officer, Antelop. Valley Hospital, Lancaster, CA, p. A71

BURKE, James, M.D., Senior Vice President and Chief Medical Officer, Honorhealth Scottsdale Osborn Medical Center, Scottsdale, AZ, p. A38
M.D., Senior Vice President and Chief Medical Officer, Honorhealth Scottsdale Shea Medical Center, Scottsdale, AZ, p. A38
Vice President Finance, Chief Nursing Executive Medical Surgical Hospitals, Kent County Memorial Hospital, Warwick, RI, p. A614

BURKE, Jeff, Chief Information Officer, Bon Secours-Richmond Community Hospital, Richmond, VA, p. A749

BURKE, John, Chief Financial Officer, Montefiore Nyack Hospital, Nyack, NY, p. A493

BURKE, Julie, Director Human Resources, New England Sinai Hospital And Rehabilitation Center, Stoughton, MA, p. A345

BURKE, Marsha, Senior Vice President and Chief Financial Officer, Wellstar Windy Hill Hospital, Marietta, GA, p. A176

BURKE, Paul, Administrator, Schleicher County Medical Center, Eldorado, TX, p. A676

BURKE, Rebecca, R.N., MS, Senior Vice President and Chief Nursing Officer, Kent County Memorial Hospital, Warwick, RI, p. A614

BURKE, Richard, M.D., Chief Medical Officer, Community Hospital-Fairfax, Fairfax, MO, p. A406

BURKE, Rose, Associate Director Patient Care Services, Marion Veterans Affairs Medical Center, Marion, IL, p. A211

BURKE, Timothy, M.D., Medical Director, The Brook Hospital - Kmi, Louisville, KY, p. A288

BURKE ESQ, RyanVice President, Human Resources, Emanate Health Inter-Community Hospital, Covina, CA, p. A61

BURKEL, Greg, Chief Financial Officer, Regional Health Services Of Howard County, Cresco, IA, p. A247

BURKEL, Gregory, Chief Financial Officer, Mitchell County Regional Health Center, Osage, IA, p. A255

BURKET, Mark, Chief Executive Officer, Platte Health Center Avera, Platte, SD, p. A630

BURKETT, Doug, Manager Information Technology, Regional Medical Center Of Central Alabama, Greenville, AL, p. A19

BURKETT, Eric, M.D., Vice President Medical Affairs, Monmouth Medical Center, Long Branch Campus, Long Branch, NJ, p. A457

BURKETT, Evan, Chief Human Resource Officer, Sanford Usd Medical Center, Sioux Falls, SD, p. A631

BURKEY, Brent, M.D., President and Chief Executive Officer, Fisher-Titus Medical Center, Norwalk, OH, p. A546

BURKEY, Kathleen, R.N., MSN, Vice President, Patient Care Service and Chief Nursing Officer, Grand View Health, Sellersville, PA, p. A607

BURKHARDT, Jennifer, Chief Human Resources Officer, Olympic Medical Center, Port Angeles, WA, p. A762

BURKHARDT, Raye, Chief Nurse Executive, Kaiser Permanente Fontana Medical Center, Fontana, CA, p. A64

BURKHART, Brad, Assistant Administrator, Harlan Arh Hospital, Harlan, KY, p. A284

BURKHART, Steven, M.D., Chief Medical Officer, Crittenden County Hospital, Marion, KY, p. A289

BURKHART, Tracy, Vice President Information Services, St. Luke's Sacred Heart Campus, Allentown, PA, p. A583

BURKHOLDER, Adrienne, Director Human Resources, Amg Specialty Hospital-Wichita, Wichita, KS, p. A278

BURKS, Felicia, Chief Financial Officer, U. S. Air Force Regional Hospital, Elmendorf Afb, AK, p. A28

BURKS, Matt, Director Information Technology, Unity Medical Center, Manchester, TN, p. A643

BURKS, Melvin, Chief Executive Officer, Hamilton Center, Terre Haute, IN, p. A241

BURKS, Tami, Chief Fiscal Services, Iraan General Hospital, Iraan, TX, p. A690
Comptroller, Rankin County Hospital District, Rankin, TX, p. A708

BURLESON, Linda, Administrative Secretary, Clay County Memorial Hospital, Henrietta, TX, p. A684

BURLESON, Stan, M.D., Chief Medical Staff, Dewitt Hospital, Dewitt, AR, p. A44

BURLING, Chris, M.D., Chief of Staff, Titus Regional Medical Center, Mount Pleasant, TX, p. A702

BURLINGAME DEAL, Penney, FACHE, R.N., Chief Executive Officer, Onslow Memorial Hospital, Jacksonville, NC, p. A513

BURMAN, Don, Director, Veterans Affairs Nebraska-Western Iowa Health Care System - Lincoln, Lincoln, NE, p. A435
Director, Veterans Affairs Nebraska-Western Iowa Health Care System, Omaha, NE, p. A438

BURMESTER, Mark, Vice President Strategy and Communications, Kaiser Sunnyside Medical Center, Clackamas, OR, p. A574

BURNAM, Gregg, Chief Information Officer and Manager Business Office, Mangum Regional Medical Center, Mangum, OK, p. A561

BURNELL, Lori, R.N., Ph.D., Senior Vice President and Chief Nursing Officer, Valley Presbyterian Hospital, Van Nuys, CA, p. A103

BURNETT, Anthony, M.D., Medical Director, Julian F. Keith Alcohol And Drug Abuse Treatment Center, Black Mountain, NC, p. A505

BURNETT, Brad, Chief Financial Officer, Heart Of Texas Memorial Hospital, Brady, TX, p. A660

BURNETT, Brenda, R.N., Vice President Patient Care Services and Chief Nursing Officer, Titusville Area Hospital, Titusville, PA, p. A608

BURNETT, Cindi, Chief Human Resources Officer, Madison County Memorial Hospital, Madison, FL, p. A144

BURNETT, David Mark., President and Chief Executive Officer, Scott County Hospital, Scott City, KS, p. A276

BURNETT, Michael, Chief Executive Officer, Piedmont Athens Regional Medical Center, Athens, GA, p. A163

BURNETT, Rob, Director Human Resources, Jordan Valley Medical Center West Valley Campus, West Valley City, UT, p. A734

BURNETT, Tasha, Director of Nursing, Falls Community Hospital And Clinic, Marlin, TX, p. A699

BURNETTE, Peg, Chief Financial Officer, Denver Health, Denver, CO, p. A110

BURNETTE, Sheri, R.N., Chief Executive Officer, Cornerstone Hospitals Bossier City, Bossier City, LA, p. A298

BURNETTE, W Scott., Chief Executive Officer, Vcu Health Community Memorial Hospital, South Hill, VA, p. A752

BURNEY, Sibte, M.D., Senior Vice President Medical Affairs and Chief Medical Officer, Kingsbrook Jewish Medical Center, Brooklyn, NY, p. A478

BURNHAM, Natalie, Chief Operating Officer, Carthage Area Hospital, Carthage, NY, p. A481

BURNHAM, Sharon, Director of Nursing, Simpson General Hospital, Mendenhall, MS, p. A396

BURNS, Barry, Vice President, Methodist Ambulatory Surgery Hospital - Northwest, San Antonio, TX, p. A712

BURNS, Becky, Manager Health Information Management, Ellinwood District Hospital, Ellinwood, KS, p. A264

BURNS, Bruce, Chief Financial Officer, Concord Hospital, Concord, NH, p. A448

BURNS, Helen, Ph.D., R.N., Senior Vice President and Chief Nursing Officer, Excela Frick Hospital, Mount Pleasant, PA, p. A598
Ph.D., R.N., Senior Vice President and Chief Nursing Officer, Excela Health Westmoreland Hospital, Greensburg, PA, p. A591
Ph.D., R.N., Senior Vice President and Chief Nursing Officer, Excela Latrobe Area Hospital, Latrobe, PA, p. A594

BURNS, Helene, R.N., Senior Vice President and Chief Nursing Officer, Jefferson Stratford Hospital, Stratford, NJ, p. A463

BURNS, Jeff, Manager of Information Technology, Mary Free Bed Rehabilitation Hospital, Grand Rapids, MI, p. A356

BURNS, Jon, Chief Information Officer, University Of Maryland Medical Center, Baltimore, MD, p. A326
Senior Vice President and Chief Information Officer, University Of Maryland Baltimore Washington Medical Center, Glen Burnie, MD, p. A330
Senior Vice President and Chief Information Officer, University Of Maryland Medical Center Midtown Campus, Baltimore, MD, p. A326

BURNS, Katherine, Vice President Human Resources, High Point Medical Center, High Point, NC, p. A512

BURNS, Kathryn I., R.N., Director of Nursing, Medicine Lodge Memorial Hospital, Medicine Lodge, KS, p. A271

BURNS, Lori, Administrator, Victor Valley Global Medical Center, Victorville, CA, p. A104

BURNS, Patrick, Vice President Finance, Acmh Hospital, Kittanning, PA, p. A593

BURNS, Rhonda, Director Human Resources, Caldwell Medical Center, Princeton, KY, p. A292

BURNS, Steve, Chief Operating Officer, Cumberland County Hospital, Burkesville, KY, p. A281

BURNS, Steven, Director Fiscal Services, Summit Behavioral Healthcare, Cincinnati, OH, p. A533

BURNS, Terry M., President, Kettering Medical Center, Kettering, OH, p. A542

BURNS, Tom, M.D., Chief of Staff, The Hospital At Westlake Medical Center, Austin, TX, p. A657
Chief Operating Officer and Chief Nurse Executive, St. Rose Dominican Hospitals - Rose De Lima Campus, Henderson, NV, p. A442

BURNS JR, LarryChief Operating Officer, Yavapai Regional Medical Center, Prescott, AZ, p. A37

BURNS-CHISTENSON, Katherine, Human Resource Director, Grand Itasca Clinic And Hospital, Grand Rapids, MN, p. A377

BURNS-TISDALE, Susan, Senior Vice President Clinical Operations, Interim CNO, Exeter Hospital, Exeter, NH, p. A449

BURRELL, Carol H., Chief Executive Officer, Northeast Georgia Medical Center Braselton, Braselton, GA, p. A167
Chief Executive Officer, Northeast Georgia Medical Center Lumpkin, Dahlonega, GA, p. A170
Chief Executive Officer, Northeast Georgia Medical Center, Gainesville, GA, p. A173

BURRESS, Lori, Vice President Patient Services and Chief Nursing Officer, Mt. Graham Regional Medical Center, Safford, AZ, p. A37

BURRIS, Bradley D., Chief Executive Officer, Pipestone County Medical Center Avera, Pipestone, MN, p. A383

BURRIS, Lisa, Director Human Resources, Southern Indiana Rehabilitation Hospital, New Albany, IN, p. A238

BURRIS, Olga, Human Resource/Executive Assistant, North Oak Regional Medical Center, Senatobia, MS, p. A400

BURRISS, Jessica, Chief Financial Officer, Encompass Health Rehabilitation Hospital Of Columbia, Columbia, SC, p. A617

BURROUGHS, Shawn, Director of Information Services, Northeastern Vermont Regional Hospital, Saint Johnsbury, VT, p. A736

BURROUGHS, Steven, Chief Financial Officer, Palms West Hospital, Loxahatchee, FL, p. A144

BURROUGHS, Susan, FACHE, Chief Operating Officer, Kershawhealth, Camden, SC, p. A615

BURROUGHS, Valentine, M.D., Chief Medical Officer, East Orange General Hospital, East Orange, NJ, p. A454

BURROWS, Susan, Vice President Human Resources, Martin Luther King, Jr. Community Hospital, Los Angeles, CA, p. A75

BURRUS, Gary, Director Information Technology, Winner Regional Healthcare Center, Winner, SD, p. A633

BURT, Alan, Director Information Services, Sunrise Hospital And Medical Center, Las Vegas, NV, p. A444

BURT, Linda, Corporate Vice President Finance, Nebraska Methodist Hospital, Omaha, NE, p. A437

BURT, Noel, Ph.D., Chief Human Resources Officer, Moses H. Cone Memorial Hospital, Greensboro, NC, p. A511

BURT, Suzanne, Director Human Resources, Mercyone Cedar Falls Medical Center, Cedar Falls, IA, p. A244
Director Human Resources, Mercyone Waterloo Medical Center, Waterloo, IA, p. A259

BURTCH, Gloria, Director Human Resources, Cornerstone Of Medical Arts Center Hospital, Fresh Meadows, NY, p. A484

BURTCHELL, Scott, Director Information Systems, Northern Light Maine Coast Hospital, Ellsworth, ME, p. A320

BURTON, Angela, Privacy Officer, Wayne County Hospital, Monticello, KY, p. A290

BURTON, Charles, Chief Human Resources, Carl R. Darnall Army Medical Center, Fort Hood, TX, p. A677

BURTON, James, Vice President and Chief Information Officer, Valley Health, Valley Health - Shenandoah Memorial Hospital, Woodstock, VA, p. A754

BURTON, Luanne, Director Human Resources, Encompass Health Rehabilitation Hospital Of Columbia, Columbia, SC, p. A617

BURTON, Robert, Manager Finance, Utah State Hospital, Provo, UT, p. A731

BURTON, Stacey, Director Human Resources, Muscogee Creek Nation Medical Center, Okmulgee, OK, p. A566

BURY, Peter, Vice President Finance, Ohiohealth Riverside Methodist Hospital, Columbus, OH, p. A537

BUSBY, Jay, M.D., President Medical Staff, Franklin Medical Center, Winnsboro, LA, p. A317

BUSCH, Rebecca, Chief Financial Officer, Spooner Health, Spooner, WI, p. A796

BUSCH, Steve, Chief Operating Officer, Midwest Medical Center, Galena, IL, p. A205

BUSH, Amy, Vice President Operations, Upmc Mckeesport, Mckeesport, PA, p. A596

BUSH, Bruce, M.D., Interim Chief Medical Officer, Indiana Regional Medical Center, Indiana, PA, p. A592

BUSH, Doug, President, Promedica Defiance Regional Hospital, Defiance, OH, p. A539

BUSH, Michael, M.D., Chief Medical Officer, Holy Rosary Healthcare, Miles City, MT, p. A426
M.D., Chief Medical Officer, St. Vincent Healthcare, Billings, MT, p. A421

BUSH, Stephen, Chief Financial Officer, Tmc Healthcare, Tucson, AZ, p. A41

BUSH, Steven, Chief Medical Officer, Crossing Rivers Health Medical Center, Prairie Du Chien, WI, p. A794

BUSH, Wayne, M.D., Chief of Staff, Tristar Greenview Regional Hospital, Bowling Green, KY, p. A281

BUSHART, Phyllis, R.N., Chief Operating Officer, Providence Tarzana Medical Center, Tarzana, CA, p. A100

BUSHART, Stephanie, Chief Financial Officer, Ochsner Medical Center - Baton Rouge, Baton Rouge, LA, p. A297

BUSHELL, Michael, President, Saint Anne's Hospital, Fall River, MA, p. A339

BUSHEY, Dale, Chief Financial Officer, Oss Health, York, PA, p. A612

BUSHEY, Melissa, Director, Human Resources, Madera Community Hospital, Madera, CA, p. A76

BUSHMAN, Jerry, Chief Nursing Officer, Brigham City Community Hospital, Brigham City, UT, p. A727

BUSHNELL, Andrew, M.D., Interim Chief Medical Officer, Rome Memorial Hospital, Rome, NY, p. A497

BUSHNELL, Kim, R.N., Vice President, Patient Care Services and Chief Nursing Officer, Northwest, Northwest Hospital, Randallstown, MD, p. A331
R.N., Vice President, Patient Care Services, Mercy Medical Center, Baltimore, MD, p. A325

BUSINELLE, Denise, Chief Financial Officer, Avala, Covington, LA, p. A300

BUSKEY, Dawn M., President, Promedica Toledo Hospital, Toledo, OH, p. A550

BUSKEY, Irene, Director Human Resources, Southside Regional Medical Center, Petersburg, VA, p. A749

BUSS, Theresa, Regional Vice President Human Resources, Windham Hospital, Willimantic, CT, p. A126

BUSSELL, Walter, Chief Financial Officer, Memorial Hospital West, Pembroke Pines, FL, p. A153
Chief Financial Officer, Memorial Regional Hospital, Hollywood, FL, p. A140

BUSSIERE, Mark, Administrator Human Resources, New Hampshire Hospital, Concord, NH, p. A448

BUSSINGER, Brandy, Director of Nursing, Brown County Hospital, Ainsworth, NE, p. A429

BUSSLER, David, Chief Information Officer, Sheridan Community Hospital, Sheridan, MI, p. A366

BUTCHER, Gina, Chief Financial Officer, Garden City Hospital, Garden City, MI, p. A355

BUTCHER, Kay, Director Health Information Management, Stonewall Jackson Memorial Hospital, Weston, WV, p. A777

BUTE, Phil, Manager Information Technology, Clay County Hospital, Flora, IL, p. A205

BUTERBAUGH, Roger, Chief Human Resources Officer, Charlie Norwood Veterans Affairs Medical Center, Augusta, GA, p. A166

BUTKER, Jeff, Chief Information Officer, Sovah Health-Martinsville, Martinsville, VA, p. A746

BUTLER, Brad, Network Administrator, Cox Barton County Memorial Hospital, Lamar, MO, p. A410

BUTLER, Carol, R.N., MSN, VP Patient Care Services & Operations, St. Anthony North Health Campus, Westminster, CO, p. A119

BUTLER, Catherine, M.D., Chief Medical Staff, Hancock County Health System, Britt, IA, p. A244

BUTLER, Chris, Chief Information Officer, Monmouth Medical Center, Long Branch Campus, Long Branch, NJ, p. A457

BUTLER, Dana, M.D., Medical Director, Sunrise Canyon Hospital, Lubbock, TX, p. A698

BUTLER, David, Chief Executive Officer, Delano Regional Medical Center, Delano, CA, p. A62
Chief Financial Officer, Specialty Hospital Of Meridian, Meridian, MS, p. A397

BUTLER, Debby, Director Human Resources, Wadley Regional Medical Center At Hope, Hope, AR, p. A47
Director Human Resources, Wadley Regional Medical Center, Texarkana, TX, p. A720

BUTLER, Keith L., Chief Executive Officer, Iraan General Hospital, Iraan, TX, p. A690

BUTLER, Linda, M.D., Chief Medical Officer, Unc Rex Health Care, Raleigh, NC, p. A517

BUTLER, Margaret, Vice President Human Resources, Abbott Northwestern Hospital, Minneapolis, MN, p. A380

BUTLER, Matt, Chief Financial Officer, Abilene Regional Medical Center, Abilene, TX, p. A651

BUTLER, Monique, Chief Medical Officer, Swedish Medical Center, Englewood, CO, p. A112

BUTLER, Randy, Chief Financial Officer, West Florida Hospital, Pensacola, FL, p. A154

BUTLER, Rosemary, R.N., MSN, Chief Nurse Executive, Kaiser Permanente Riverside Medical Center, Riverside, CA, p. A88

BUTLER, Stuart, Director Information Technology, Sweeny Community Hospital, Sweeny, TX, p. A718

BUTLER ESQ, LaDonnaChief Nursing Officer, Encompass Health Rehabilitation Hospital Of Tustin, Tustin, CA, p. A102

BUTT, Shiraz, M.D., Medical Director, Chicago Behavioral Hospital, Des Plaines, IL, p. A202

BUTT, Zaahra, Chief Executive Officer, Select Specialty Hospital-Grosse Pointe, Grosse Pointe, MI, p. A357

BUTTELL, Phil, Chief Executive Officer, Menorah Medical Center, Overland Park, KS, p. A274

BUTTER, Hazel, Manager Human Resources, Hammond-Henry Hospital, Geneseo, IL, p. A205

BUTTERFIELD, Cindy, Director, Fiscal and Administrative Services, Connecticut Valley Hospital, Middletown, CT, p. A123

BUTTERFIELD, Jon, Administrator and Chief Executive Officer, Jordan Valley Medical Center, West Jordan, UT, p. A734

BUTTERMORE, Bruce, Director Human Resources, Parkview Lagrange Hospital, Lagrange, IN, p. A235

Manager Human Resources, Parkview Noble Hospital, Kendallville, IN, p. A233

BUTTON, Charlie, Chief Executive Officer, Regional Medical Center, Manchester, IA, p. A253

BUTTS, Cody, President, Cherokee Medical Center, Gaffney, SC, p. A620

BUTTS, Paula, Chief Nursing Officer, Piedmont Henry Hospital, Stockbridge, GA, p. A181

BUTTS, Ursula, FACHE, Vice President of Patient Care Services, Vcu Health Community Memorial Hospital, South Hill, VA, p. A752

BUTZINE, Bart, Director Information Technology, Community Hospital, Grand Junction, CO, p. A113

BUTZLER, Hilary, Director Human Resources, Cumberland Healthcare, Cumberland, WI, p. A782

BUUCK, Brian, Chief Executive Officer, Ridgeview Psychiatric Hospital And Center, Oak Ridge, TN, p. A648

BUURMAN, Rita K., Interim Chief Executive Officer, Republic County Hospital, Belleville, KS, p. A262

BUZACHERO, Victor, Corporate Senior Vice President for Innovation, Human Resources and Performance Management, Scripp. Green Hospital, La Jolla, CA, p. A69

BUZZAS, G., M.D., Chief Medical Officer, St. Rose Dominican Hospitals - Siena Campus, Henderson, NV, p. A442

BYARS, Stephanie, Chief Nursing Officer, Unity Medical Center, Manchester, TN, p. A643

BYDA, Jeff, Vice President Information Technology, Mercy Catholic Medical Center - Mercy Fitzgerald Campus, Darby, PA, p. A588

BYERS, Grant, Senior Vice President and Chief Financial Officer, South Georgia Medical Center, Valdosta, GA, p. A182

BYERS, John, M.D., Medical Director, Select Specialty Hospital-Tri Cities, Bristol, TN, p. A634

BYERS, Suzann, Director of Nursing, Southern Indiana Rehabilitation Hospital, New Albany, IN, p. A238

BYERS, William, Chief Information Officer, Western Maryland Regional Medical Center, Cumberland, MD, p. A329

BYLER, Karen, Information Technology Generalist, Warren State Hospital, Warren, PA, p. A609

BYNUM, Justin, Chief Financial Officer, Saint Anthony Hospital, Chicago, IL, p. A200

BYORICK, Joseph, Senior Vice President and Chief Financial Officer, Penn Medicine Lancaster General Hospital, Lancaster, PA, p. A594

BYRD, Catherine, Vice President Patient Services, Parkview Noble Hospital, Kendallville, IN, p. A233

BYRD, David, Chief Financial Officer, The Hospitals Of Providence Transmountain Campus, El Paso, TX, p. A676

Chief Operating Officer, The Hospitals Of Providence Transmountain Campus, El Paso, TX, p. A676

BYRD, Greg, Vice President Medical Affairs, Valley Health - Shenandoah Memorial Hospital, Woodstock, VA, p. A754

BYRD, Lu, R.N., MSN, Vice President Hospital Operations and Chief Nursing Officer, Billings Clinic, Billings, MT, p. A421

BYRD, O, M.D., Chief of Staff, H. C. Watkins Memorial Hospital, Quitman, MS, p. A399

BYRD-PELAEZ, Brenda, Chief Human Resources Management Office, Martinsburg Veterans Affairs Medical Center, Martinsburg, WV, p. A774

BYRNE, Bobbie, M.D., Chief Information Officer, Aurora Medical Center - Manitowoc County, Two Rivers, WI, p. A797

BYRNE, Frank, Vice President Finance, Newport Hospital, Newport, RI, p. A613

BYRNE, John, M.D., Vice President and Chief Medical Officer, Baylor St. Luke's Medical Center, Houston, TX, p. A684

BYRNES, Matthew, M.D., Chief Medical Officer, St. Catherine Hospital, Garden City, KS, p. A264

BYROM, David, Chief Executive Officer, Coryell Health, Gatesville, TX, p. A681

## C

CAAMANO, Tero, Director Information Technology, Saint Clare's Denville Hospital, Denville, NJ, p. A454

CABALLERO, Rogelio, Chief Information Systems, San Jorge Children's Hospital, Santurce, PR, p. A811

CABE, Jacque, Chief Financial Officer, University Of Washington Medical Center, Seattle, WA, p. A764

CABIBBO, Tiffany, Executive Vice President and Chief Nursing Officer, Mount Nittany Medical Center, State College, PA, p. A608

CABIGAO, Edwin, Chief Nursing Officer, Jewish Home Of San Francisco, San Francisco, CA, p. A93

CABIRO, Michael, Chief Executive Officer, Encompass Health Rehabilitation Hospital Of Pearland, Pearland, TX, p. A705

CABLE, Cammie, Chief Human Resource Officer, Intermountain Medical Center, Murray, UT, p. A729

CABRERA, Ana, Interim Chief Nursing Officer, Baptist Health South Florida, Homestead Hospital, Homestead, FL, p. A140

CABRERA, Carlos, Executive Director, Cardiovascular Center Of Puerto Rico And The Caribbean, San Juan, PR, p. A809

CABRERA, Irma, Finance Director, Hospital San Carlos Borromeo, Moca, PR, p. A808

CABRERA, Sheelah, Chief Information Officer, La Rabida Children's Hospital, Chicago, IL, p. A199

CABUNOC, Brenda, Chief Human Resources, Va Greater Los Angeles Healthcare System, Los Angeles, CA, p. A76

CACCAMISE, Chad, Director Information Services, United Memorial Medical Center, Batavia, NY, p. A475

CACCAMO, Michael, M.D., Chief Medical Officer, Greene Memorial Hospital, Xenia, OH, p. A553

M.D., Chief Medical Officer, Soin Medical Center, Beavercreek, OH, p. A529

CACCIAMANI, John D., M.D., Chief Executive Officer, Chestnut Hill Hospital, Philadelphia, PA, p. A599

CADE, Paul, Administrator and Chief Executive Officer, Baptist Memorial Hospital-Golden Triangle, Columbus, MS, p. A391

CADIEUX, Marc, Corporate Vice President and Chief Financial Officer, Children's Hospital Of Wisconsin-Fox Valley, Neenah, WI, p. A792

Corporate Vice President and Chief Financial Officer, Children's Hospital Of Wisconsin, Milwaukee, WI, p. A791

CADIGAN, Elizabeth, R.N., MSN, Senior Vice President Patient Care Services and Chief Nursing Officer, Cambridge Health Alliance, Cambridge, MA, p. A337

CADOGAN, David, Chief Medical Officer, Alaska Regional Hospital, Anchorage, AK, p. A27

CADORETTE, Brenda, Chief Nursing Officer, Berkshire Medical Center, Pittsfield, MA, p. A343

CADWELL, Carrie, PsyD, Chief Executive Officer, Four County Counseling Center, Logansport, IN, p. A235

CADWELL, Jason, Chief Financial Officer, Four County Counseling Center, Logansport, IN, p. A235

CADWELL, Maureen K., Chief Executive Officer, Weston County Health Services, Newcastle, WY, p. A803

CADY, Kathy, Coordinator Human Resources, Accounts Payable and Payroll, Safe Haven Hospital Of Treasure Valley, Boise, ID, p. A188

CADY, Thomas, Vice President Human Resources, Heywood Hospital, Gardner, MA, p. A339

CADY, Tina, Controller, The Women's Hospital, Newburgh, IN, p. A238

CAFASSO, Michael, Chief Executive Officer, St. Mary-Corwin Medical Center, Pueblo, CO, p. A118

Chief Operating Officer, St. Mary-Corwin Medical Center, Pueblo, CO, p. A118

CAGLE, Jennifer, Director of Nursing, North Mississipp. Medical Center-Hamilton, Hamilton, AL, p. A20

CAGLE, Karen, Chief Nursing Officer, Select Specialty Hospital-Nashville, Nashville, TN, p. A646

CAGLE, LaDonna, HIM Appeals Coordinator III, Monroe Hospital, Bloomington, IN, p. A224

CAGLE, Lynn, Chief Nursing Officer, Parkwest Medical Center, Knoxville, TN, p. A641

CAGNA, Ralph, Director Information Technology Operations, Cleveland Clinic Health System South Market, Marymount Hospital, Garfield Heights, OH, p. A541

Director Information Technology, South Pointe Hospital, Warrensville Heights, OH, p. A552

CAHALAN, Jay P., President and Chief Executive Officer, Columbia Memorial Hospital, Hudson, NY, p. A485

CAHILL, Joseph, Executive Vice President and Chief Operating Officer, South Shore Hospital, South Weymouth, MA, p. A344

CAHILL, Marty, Chief Executive Officer, Samaritan Lebanon Community Hospital, Lebanon, OR, p. A577

CAHILL, Patricia, Vice President, Patient Care Services and Chief Nursing Officer, Bronxcare Health System, Bronx, NY, p. A476

CAHO-MOONEY, Linda, Chief Financial Officer, Claiborne County Medical Center, Port Gibson, MS, p. A399

CAHOJ, Lindsey, Chief Nursing Officer, Select Specialty Hospital-Wichita, Wichita, KS, p. A279

CAIN, Mark, Chief Executive Officer, Tennova Healthcare-Lafollette Medical Center, La Follette, TN, p. A642

CAIN, Roxie, Chief Financial Officer, Big Horn County Memorial Hospital, Hardin, MT, p. A424

CAIN, William, Controller, Penn Highlands Clearfield, Clearfield, PA, p. A586

CAINE, Jamie, Director of Human Resources, Multicare Valley Hospital, Spokane Valley, WA, p. A766

CAIRNS, Craig, M.D., Vice President Medical Affairs, Licking Memorial Hospital, Newark, OH, p. A546

CALAIS, C, Senior Vice President and Chief Information Officer, Legacy Good Samaritan Medical Center, Portland, OR, p. A579

CALAIS, Daniel Jr, Superintendent, Bridgewater State Hospital, Bridgewater, MA, p. A336

CALAMARI, Frank A., President and Chief Executive Officer, Calvary Hospital, Bronx, NY, p. A476

CALAMARI, Jacquelyn, MSN, MS, Chief Nursing Officer and Vice President, Patient Care Services, Middlesex Hospital, Middletown, CT, p. A123

CALANDRELLA, Paul, Chief Operating Officer, Mt. Ascutney Hospital And Health Center, Windsor, VT, p. A737

CALANDRIELLO, John, Vice President and Chief Financial Officer, Hackensack Meridian Health Palisades Medical Center, North Bergen, NJ, p. A460

CALARCO, Marge, Chief Nursing Executive, Michigan Medicine, Ann Arbor, MI, p. A348

CALAWAY, Shearmaine, Director Human Resources, East Mississipp. State Hospital, Meridian, MS, p. A397

CALBONE, Angelo G., President and Chief Executive Officer, Saratoga Hospital, Saratoga Springs, NY, p. A497

CALBY, Elizabeth, Vice President Human Resources, Advocate Good Samaritan Hospital, Downers Grove, IL, p. A203

CALDARI, Patricia, Vice President, Richmond University Medical Center, Staten Island, NY, p. A498

CALDEIRA, Amy, Director Information Technology and Systems, Fort Walton Beach Medical Center, Fort Walton Beach, FL, p. A138

CALDERA, Ken, Director Human Resources, Kessler Institute For Rehabilitation, West Orange, NJ, p. A465

CALDERON, Lizmari, Director Finance, Hospital De La Concepcion, San German, PR, p. A809

CALDWELL, Carolyn P., FACHE, President and Chief Executive Officer, St. Mary Medical Center Long Beach, Long Beach, CA, p. A72

CALDWELL, Charles, M.D., Chief of Staff, Byrd Regional Hospital, Leesville, LA, p. A307

CALDWELL, Dari, R.N., Ph.D., FACHE, President and Chief Operating Officer, Novant Health Rowan Medical Center, Salisbury, NC, p. A518

CALDWELL, Eric, Director Finance, Northside Hospital-Forsyth, Cumming, GA, p. A170

CALDWELL, Lisa, Chief Nursing Officer, Encompass Health Rehabilitation Hospital Of Huntington, Huntington, WV, p. A773

CALDWELL, Marita, Chief Financial Officer, Twin County Regional Healthcare, Galax, VA, p. A743

CALDWELL, Matthew T., President and Chief Executive Officer, Mercy Memorial Hospital, Urbana, OH, p. A551

President, Bon Secours St. Francis Health System, Greenville, SC, p. A620

CALDWELL, Nesa, Chief Nursing Officer, Solara Hospital Harlingen, Harlingen, TX, p. A683

CALDWELL, Noah, Vice President and Chief Information Officer, Mount Sinai South Nassau, Oceanside, NY, p. A493

CALDWELL, Paul, Facility Coordinator Information Technology Customer Relations, Page Hospital, Page, AZ, p. A34

CALDWELL, Steve, Vice President Finance and Chief Financial Officer, Ssm Health St. Mary's Hospital, Madison, WI, p. A788

CALDWELL, William E. Jr, FACHE, Chief Executive Officer, Conemaugh Memorial Medical Center, Johnstown, PA, p. A593

CALEY, Carl, Chief Financial Officer, Forest View Psychiatric Hospital, Grand Rapids, MI, p. A355
Chief Financial Officer, Spring Valley Hospital Medical Center, Las Vegas, NV, p. A444
Chief Financial Officer, St. Cloud Regional Medical Center, Saint Cloud, FL, p. A156

CALEYO, Kristy, MSN, R.N., Chief Executive Officer, Curahealth New Orleans, New Orleans, LA, p. A310

CALHOUN, Cathy, Director Human Resources, River Point Behavioral Health, Jacksonville, FL, p. A141

CALHOUN, Joshua, M.D., Medical Director, Hawthorn Children Psychiatric Hospital, Saint Louis, MO, p. A415

CALHOUN, Rob, President and Chief Executive Officer, West Jefferson Medical Center, Marrero, LA, p. A308

CALHOUN, Timothy, Vice President Finance and Chief Financial Officer, Spectrum Health Lakeland, Saint Joseph, MI, p. A366
Vice President Finance, Chief Financial Officer, Lakeland Hospital, Watervliet, Watervliet, MI, p. A369

CALHOUN, William, FACHE, Chief Executive Officer, Kearney Regional Medical Center, Kearney, NE, p. A434

CALIA, Christopher, Vice President Human Resources, Chi St. Luke's Health Brazosport, Lake Jackson, TX, p. A694

CALIFORNIA, Randy, Chief Operating Officer, Warren General Hospital, Warren, PA, p. A609

CALIME, Erica, Director Human Resources, Carrollton Regional Medical Center, Carrollton, TX, p. A663

CALIVA, Todd, FACHE, Chief Executive Officer, Hca Houston Healthcare Clear Lake, League City, TX, p. A695

CALKIN, Steven, D.O., Vice President Medical Affairs, Mclaren Oakland, Pontiac, MI, p. A364

CALKINS, Megan, R.N., Chief Nursing Officer, T. J. Samson Community Hospital, Glasgow, KY, p. A284

CALKINS, Paul, M.D., Chief Medical Officer, Indiana University Health North Hospital, Carmel, IN, p. A225

CALL, Stacie, R.N., Vice President Patient Care and Chief Nursing Officer, East Liverpool City Hospital, East Liverpool, OH, p. A539
Chief Nursing Officer, Mercy Health - St. Elizabeth Boardman Hospital, Boardman, OH, p. A529

CALLAGHAN, Peter, President and Chief Executive Officer, Columbus Hospital Ltach, Newark, NJ, p. A459

CALLAGHAN III, James, M.D., President and Chief Executive Officer, Franciscan Health Indianapolis, Indianapolis, IN, p. A232

CALLAHAN, Ame, Acting Manager Resource Management Service, Northern Arizona Veterans Affairs Health Care System, Prescott, AZ, p. A37

CALLAHAN, Charles D., Ph.D., President and Chief Executive Officer, Memorial Medical Center, Springfield, IL, p. A221

CALLAHAN, Christopher, Vice President Human Resources, Exeter Hospital, Exeter, NH, p. A449

CALLAHAN, Kelly, Public Information Officer, Elgin Mental Health Center, Elgin, IL, p. A203

CALLAHAN, Kevin J., President and Chief Executive Officer, Exeter Hospital, Exeter, NH, p. A449

CALLAHAN, Larry, Senior Vice President Human Resources, Grady Memorial Hospital, Atlanta, GA, p. A164

CALLAHAN, Mark, Chief Operating Officer, Mary Lanning Healthcare, Hastings, NE, p. A433

CALLAHAN, Neil, Chief Executive Officer, Brooke Glen Behavioral Hospital, Fort Washington, PA, p. A590

CALLAHAN, Robert W. Jr, Interim Director, Wilmington Veterans Affairs Medical Center, Wilmington, DE, p. A128

CALLAHAN, William, Chief Information Management Division, Bayne-Jones Army Community Hospital, Fort Polk, LA, p. A301

CALLAN, Michael, Executive Vice President and Chief Financial Officer, Kidspeace Children's Hospital, Orefield, PA, p. A599

CALLAS, Robin, Human Resource Director, Springbrook Behavioral Health, Travelers Rest, SC, p. A625
Vice President Human Resources, Rutherford Regional Health System, Rutherfordton, NC, p. A517

CALLAWAY, Blair, Chief Financial Officer, Texas Orthopedic Hospital, Houston, TX, p. A688

CALLENS, Don, M.D., Chief Medical Officer, Liberty Dayton Regional Medical Center, Liberty, TX, p. A696

CALLENS, Paul A., Ph.D., Director, North Mississipp. State Hospital, Tupelo, MS, p. A400

CALLISTE, Gregory, Ph.D., FACHE, Chief Executive Officer, Nyc Health + Hospitals / Woodhull, Brooklyn, NY, p. A479

CALLMAN, Mark, M.D., Chief Medical Officer, Fawcett Memorial Hospital, Port Charlotte, FL, p. A155

CALLOWAY, Maria, R.N., MSN, Chief Nursing Officer, Central Florida Regional Hospital, Sanford, FL, p. A156

CALUBAQUIB, Evelyn, Chief Nursing Officer, Greater El Monte Community Hospital, South El Monte, CA, p. A99

CALVARUSO, Gaspare, President, Capital Region Medical Center, Jefferson City, MO, p. A408

CALVERT, Mandy, Director Information Systems, Southern Coos Hospital And Health Center, Bandon, OR, p. A573

CALVERT, Sarah, Chief Nursing Officer, Mcgehee Hospital, Mcgehee, AR, p. A50

CALVIN, Irene, Vice President Human Resources, South Oaks Hospital, Amityville, NY, p. A474

CALVIN, Jeff, Chief Financial Officer, Michiana Behavioral Health Center, Plymouth, IN, p. A239

CAMACHO, Leslie, R.N., Director of Nursing, Commonwealth Health Center, Saipan, MP, p. A805

CAMARDELLO, Heidi, Vice President Patient Care Services and Chief Nursing Officer, Little Falls Hospital, Little Falls, NY, p. A487

CAMARENA, Elizabeth, Chief Human Resource Officer, Palmetto General Hospital, Hialeah, FL, p. A139

CAMERON, Carl, Director Information Systems, Holyoke Medical Center, Holyoke, MA, p. A340

CAMERON, Don, Chief Operating Officer, Allegiance Behavioral Health Center Of Plainview, Plainview, TX, p. A706

CAMERON, Kim, Manager Health Information Services, Patients' Hospital Of Redding, Redding, CA, p. A87

CAMMACK, Geri, R.N., Director of Nursing, Lost Rivers Medical Center, Arco, ID, p. A188

CAMMENGA, Randall, M.D., Vice President Medical Affairs, Goshen Health, Goshen, IN, p. A229

CAMP, David, Director Human Resources, St. Mary's Regional Medical Center, Enid, OK, p. A559

CAMP, Kendra, R.N., Chief Executive Officer, Amg Specialty Hospital-Albuquerque, Albuquerque, NM, p. A467

CAMPA, Melissa, Controller, Kindred Hospital El Paso, El Paso, TX, p. A675

CAMPANA, Thomas, M.D., Chief of Staff, Spectrum Health Reed City Hospital, Reed City, MI, p. A364

CAMPANELLA, Alfred, Chief Information Officer, Virtua Voorhees, Voorhees, NJ, p. A465

CAMPAS, Janice, Chief Financial Officer, Wichita County Health Center, Leoti, KS, p. A269

CAMPBELL, Al, Senior Vice President and Chief Operating Officer, Fort Washington Medical Center, Oxen Hill, MD, p. A331

CAMPBELL, Alicia, Vice President, Facility Executive, Atrium Health Pineville, Charlotte, NC, p. A506

CAMPBELL, Amy, Chief Financial Officer, Community Hospital North, Indianapolis, IN, p. A231

CAMPBELL, Andrew, Associate Executive Director, Nyc Health + Hospitals / Coney Island, Brooklyn, NY, p. A478

CAMPBELL, April, Director Human Resources, Broadwater Health Center, Townsend, MT, p. A428

CAMPBELL, Bernard, Administrator Human Resources, Lewisgale Hospital Alleghany, Low Moor, VA, p. A745

CAMPBELL, Brian, Director Professional Services, U. S. Public Health Service Indian Hospital-Whiteriver, Whiteriver, AZ, p. A41

CAMPBELL, Christine, Controller, Vanderbilt Stallworth Rehabilitation Hospital, Nashville, TN, p. A647

CAMPBELL, Cinthia, Chief Nursing Officer, Encompass Health Rehabilitation Hospital Of Chattanooga, Chattanooga, TN, p. A635

CAMPBELL, David, Administrator, Perry Hospital, Perry, GA, p. A178

CAMPBELL, Dean, Vice President Information Services and Chief Information Officer, Good Samaritan Hospital, Los Angeles, CA, p. A74

CAMPBELL, Deborah, Administrator, Thomas H. Boyd Memorial Hospital, Carrollton, IL, p. A196

CAMPBELL, Emily, Assistant Vice President People and Patient Experience, The University Of Vermont Health Network - Alice Hyde Medical Center, Malone, NY, p. A487

CAMPBELL, Eric, Chief Financial Officer, Oswego Hospital, Oswego, NY, p. A494

CAMPBELL, Gary, Chief Executive Officer, St. Vincent General Hospital District, Leadville, CO, p. A115

CAMPBELL, Ivy, Director of Nursing, Community Medical Center, Inc., Falls City, NE, p. A432

CAMPBELL, Jennie, Chief Financial Officer, Baylor Scott & White Medical Center - Llano, Llano, TX, p. A696

CAMPBELL, John, Chief Information Officer, Spaulding Hospital For Continuing Medical Care Cambridge, Cambridge, MA, p. A338
Chief Information Officer, Spaulding Rehabilitation Hospital Cap. Cod, East Sandwich, MA, p. A338
Chief Information Officer, Spaulding Rehabilitation Hospital, Charlestown, MA, p. A338

CAMPBELL, Kathy, Interim Chief Nursing Officer, Holston Valley Medical Center, Kingsport, TN, p. A641

CAMPBELL, Kevin, Chief Executive Officer, Saint Thomas Hickman Hospital, Centerville, TN, p. A635

CAMPBELL, Matthew J. Esq, Chief Executive Officer, Select Specialty Hospital-Saginaw, Saginaw, MI, p. A366

CAMPBELL, Melissa, Chief Financial Officer and Controller, Mercy Rehabilitation Hospital Springfield, Springfield, MO, p. A419

CAMPBELL, Melvin, M.D., Medical Staff Chairman, Brown County Hospital, Ainsworth, NE, p. A429

CAMPBELL, Pamela, M.D., Medical Director, Lincoln Prairie Behavioral Health Center, Springfield, IL, p. A220

CAMPBELL, Paul, Director Technology Support and Operations, Ut Health East Texas Rehabilitation Hospital, Tyler, TX, p. A722

CAMPBELL, Philip. Vice President Information Services, Calverthealth Medical Center, Prince Frederick, MD, p. A331

CAMPBELL, Sandra, R.N., Chief Nursing Officer, Dodge County Hospital, Eastman, GA, p. A172

CAMPBELL, Scott, Chief Executive Officer, Ut Health Athens, Athens, TX, p. A654

CAMPBELL, Shari, Chief Operating Officer, Kearny County Hospital, Lakin, KS, p. A268

CAMPBELL, Sharon, Director, Human Resources, Adventhealth Hendersonville, Hendersonville, NC, p. A512

CAMPBELL, Sherry, Director of Human Resources, Medical Records, Seaside Behavioral Center - New Orleans, New Orleans, LA, p. A311

CAMPBELL, Stephen, Chief Operating Officer, Pioneers Memorial Healthcare District, Brawley, CA, p. A58

CAMPBELL, Susie, Chief Executive Officer, Community Hospital Of Staunton, Staunton, IL, p. A221

CAMPBELL, Suzannah, President, St. Vincent's Blount, Oneonta, AL, p. A23
President, St. Vincent's East, Birmingham, AL, p. A15
President, St. Vincent's St. Clair, Pell City, AL, p. A23

CAMPBELL, Suzanne, R.N., Director Patient Services, Monument Health Spearfish Hospital, Spearfish, SD, p. A632

CAMPBELL, Teresa, R.N., Chief Nursing Executive, Sutter Lakeside Hospital, Lakeport, CA, p. A71

CAMPBELL, Todd, Chief Executive Officer, St. Mary's Medical Center, Huntington, WV, p. A773

CAMPEAU, Arleen, R.N., Vice President of Patient Care Services, Chief Nursing Officer, Powell Valley Healthcare, Powell, WY, p. A803

CAMPO, Mary Beth, MS, R.N., Director of Nursing, Eastern Niagara Hospital, Lockport, NY, p. A487

CAMPOS, Christina, Administrator, Guadalup. County Hospital, Santa Rosa, NM, p. A472

CAMPOS, Emilio, Department Head Information Technology, Guadalup. County Hospital, Santa Rosa, NM, p. A472

CAMPOVERDE, Jacqueline, Business Manager, Essex County Hospital Center, Cedar Grove, NJ, p. A453

CAMPS, Lourdes, Chief Operating Officer, Hialeah Hospital, Hialeah, FL, p. A139

CANADY, Carolyn, Chief Financial Officer, Sierra Nevada Memorial Hospital, Grass Valley, CA, p. A67

CANADY, Michael R., M.D., Chief Executive Officer, Holzer Medical Center - Jackson, Jackson, OH, p. A542
M.D., Interim Chief Executive Officer, Holzer Medical Center, Gallipolis, OH, p. A541

CANALE, Joseph, Acting Chief Executive Officer, Ancora Psychiatric Hospital, Hammonton, NJ, p. A456
Business Manager, Trenton Psychiatric Hospital, Trenton, NJ, p. A464

CANALES, Joe, Director Human Resources, Ascension Seton Edgar B. Davis Hospital, Luling, TX, p. A699
Director Human Resources, Ascension Seton,Shoal Creek, Austin, TX, p. A655
Vice President Human Resources, Ministry Market Texas, Dell Seton Medical Center At The University Of Texas, Austin, TX, p. A656
Vice President Human Resources, Ascension Seton Medical Center Austin, Austin, TX, p. A654
Vice President, Ascension and Human Resources Officer, Texas Market, Ascension Seton Northwest, Austin, TX, p. A655

CANARD, Robert Shannon., Chief Executive Officer, Select Specialty Hospital - Belhaven, Jackson, MS, p. A395

CANCEL, Diana, Director Human Resources, Glendora Community Hospital, Glendora, CA, p. A67

CANDELA, Chris, President and Chief Executive Officer, Mclaren Lapeer Region, Lapeer, MI, p. A360

CANDILIS, Phillip. M.D., Director, Medical Affairs, Saint Elizabeths Hospital, Washington, DC, p. A130

CANDILL, James, M.D., President Medical Staff, Charleston Surgical Hospital, Charleston, WV, p. A771

CANDULLO, Carl, Chief Information Officer, Adventhealth Ocala, Ocala, FL, p. A149

CANEDO, Jim, Chief Financial Officer, College Medical Center, Long Beach, CA, p. A72

CANFIELD, Brian, Chief Operating Officer, Firsthealth Moore Regional Hospital, Pinehurst, NC, p. A516

CANFIELD, Michael, Chief Information Officer, Augusta Health, Fishersville, VA, p. A742

CANIZARO, Tom, Vice President and Chief Financial Officer, South Central Regional Medical Center, Laurel, MS, p. A395

CANLAS, Emma, Chief Financial Officer, Valley View Medical Center, Fort Mohave, AZ, p. A31

CANNIFF, Christopher, Executive Director, Human Resources, Harrington Hospital, Southbridge, MA, p. A344

CANNING, John, Chief Financial Officer, Blythedale Children's Hospital, Valhalla, NY, p. A500

CANNINGTON, H, Interim Chief Financial Officer, Fishermen's Hospital, Marathon, FL, p. A144

CANNON, Don, Chief Financial Officer, Dixie Regional Medical Center, Saint George, UT, p. A732

CANNON, Gayle, Director Human Resources, Childress Regional Medical Center, Childress, TX, p. A663

CANNON, Heather, M.D., Medical Director, Neshoba County General Hospital, Philadelphia, MS, p. A398

CANNON, Linda, Chief Medical Records Services, San Diego County Psychiatric Hospital, San Diego, CA, p. A92

CANNON, Lorraine, Chief Financial Officer, Olympic Medical Center, Port Angeles, WA, p. A762

CANNON, William, M.D., Medical Director, Fort Healthcare, Fort Atkinson, WI, p. A784

CANO, Daniel, M.D., Chief Medical Officer, Citizens Medical Center, Victoria, TX, p. A723

CANSLER, Vicki, Chief Human Resource Officer, Piedmont Hospital, Atlanta, GA, p. A165

CANTLEY, J Scott., President and Chief Executive Officer, Marietta Memorial Hospital, Marietta, OH, p. A544

CANTRE, Pedro, Chief Nursing Officer, Cardiovascular Center Of Puerto Rico And The Caribbean, San Juan, PR, p. A809

CANTRELL, David, CPA, Vice President and Chief Financial Officer, West Hills Hospital And Medical Center, West Hills, CA, p. A104

CANTRELL, Dedra, Chief Information Officer, Emory University Hospital Midtown, Atlanta, GA, p. A164

CANTRELL, Eric, Chief Executive Officer, Nexus Specialty Hospital The Woodlands, The Woodlands, TX, p. A720
Chief Executive Officer, Nexus Specialty Hospital, Shenandoah, TX, p. A715

CANTU, Andrew, Chief Financial Officer, Kern Medical, Bakersfield, CA, p. A57

CANTU, Janie, Director Human Resources, Crosbyton Clinic Hospital, Crosbyton, TX, p. A666

CAPECE, Vincent G. Jr, M.D., President and Chief Executive Officer, Middlesex Hospital, Middletown, CT, p. A123

CAPERS, Travis, FACHE, President, Ssm Health St. Mary's Hospital - St. Louis, Saint Louis, MO, p. A417

CAPILI, Anthony, M.D., Chief of Staff, Bayside Community Hospital, Anahuac, TX, p. A653

CAPIOLA, Richard, M.D., Chief Medical Officer, Baton Rouge Behavioral Hospital, Baton Rouge, LA, p. A296

CAPITELLI, Robert, M.D., Senior Vice President and Chief Medical Officer, St. Tammany Health System, Covington, LA, p. A300

CAPITULO, Kathleen, Ph.D., R.N., Chief Nurse Executive, James J. Peters Veterans Affairs Medical Center, Bronx, NY, p. A476

CAPIZZI, Thomas, Vice President Human Resources, Choc Children's At Mission Hospital, Mission Viejo, CA, p. A78

CAPLAN, Margaret B., Director, James J. Peters Veterans Affairs Medical Center, Bronx, NY, p. A476

CAPLES, Greg, Chief Executive Officer, Coliseum Northside Hospital, Macon, GA, p. A176

CAPO, Ann Marie, R.N., Chief Nursing Officer, Vice President, Quality and Patient Services, Uconn, John Dempsey Hospital, Farmington, CT, p. A122

CAPOROSO, Robyn, Chief Executive Officer, Trenton Psychiatric Hospital, Trenton, NJ, p. A464

CAPOTE, Henry, Interim Chief Financial Officer, Coral Gables Hospital, Coral Gables, FL, p. A135

CAPPEL, Blaine, Director Information Systems, Memorial Health System, Abilene, KS, p. A261

CAPPLEMAN, Troy, M.D., Chief of Staff, Tippah County Hospital, Ripley, MS, p. A399

CAPPS, Anita, R.N., Chief Nursing Executive, Community Hospital South, Indianapolis, IN, p. A231

CAPPS, Jeremy D., R.N., Chief Executive Officer, St. Bernards Five Rivers, Pocahontas, AR, p. A52

CAPPS, Kim, Chief Financial Officer, Sparrow Eaton Hospital, Charlotte, MI, p. A351

CAPPS, Melissa, Site Leader Information Technology, St. Luke's Magic Valley Medical Center, Twin Falls, ID, p. A193

CAPPS, Rick, Chief Financial Officer, Cumberland County Hospital, Burkesville, KY, p. A281

CAPRICO, Rick, Chief Financial Officer, Garnet Health Medical Center - Catskills, Harris, NY, p. A485

CAPSHAW, Marcia, Chief Operating Officer, West Central Georgia Regional Hospital, Columbus, GA, p. A169

CAPUANO, Rebecca, Director Human Resources, St. Francis Medical Center, Trenton, NJ, p. A464

CAPUANO, Terry Ann, R.N., MSN, FACHE, Executive Vice President and Chief Operating Officer, Lehigh Valley Hospital, Allentown, PA, p. A583

CAPUANO, Tony, Chief Operating Officer, Saint Francis Hospital Muskogee, Muskogee, OK, p. A562

CAPUTO, Louis, Chief Executive Officer, Tristar Stonecrest Medical Center, Smyrna, TN, p. A649

CARABALLO, Amanda, Nursing Director, Hospital De La Concepcion, San German, PR, p. A809

CARACCIOLO, Kevin, Chief Human Resources Officer, Palm Beach Gardens Medical Center, Palm Beach Gardens, FL, p. A152

CARACCIOLO, Mary Jo, Human Resource Director, Wellington Regional Medical Center, Wellington, FL, p. A161

CARBALLO, Francisco, M.D., Medical Director, Hospital Hima De Humacao, Humacao, PR, p. A808

CARBONE, Davide M., FACHE, Chief Executive Officer, Osceola Regional Medical Center, Kissimmee, FL, p. A142

CARBONE, Dominick, M.D., Chief of Staff, Hugh Chatham Memorial Hospital, Elkin, NC, p. A509

CARD, Dean, Chief Financial Officer, Kindred Hospital South Florida-Fort Lauderdale, Fort Lauderdale, FL, p. A137
Chief Financial Officer, Kindred Hospital The Palm Beaches, Riviera Beach, FL, p. A155

CARD, Edwin, President Medical Staff, Mcdonough District Hospital, Mb, IL, p. A211

CARDA, Greg, Vice President Finance, Missouri Delta Medical Center, Sikeston, MO, p. A418

CARDA, Vern, Chief Executive Officer, Estes Park Medical Center, Estes Park, CO, p. A112

CARDELL, Melinda, Interim Chief Information Officer, Roper St. Francis Mount Pleasant Hospital, Mount Pleasant, SC, p. A622
Interim Vice President and Chief Information Officer, Roper Hospital, Charleston, SC, p. A616

CARDENAS, Lydia, Director Human Resources, River Crest Hospital, San Angelo, TX, p. A710

CARDENAS, Mark, Director Plant Operations, Vibra Hospital Of Northern California, Redding, CA, p. A87

CARDENAS, Mitzi, Chief Administrative Officer, Truman Medical Center-Hospital Hill, Kansas City, MO, p. A410
Chief Administrative Officer, Truman Medical Center-Lakewood, Kansas City, MO, p. A410

CARDIFF, Michael, Systems Supervisor, Abrom Kaplan Memorial Hospital, Kaplan, LA, p. A304

CARDLE, Lori, Senior Vice President, Chief Operating Officer, Valley Presbyterian Hospital, Van Nuys, CA, p. A103

CARDOZA, Phuong, Chief Executive Officer, El Paso Behavioral Health System, El Paso, TX, p. A674

CARDWELL, Marian, Chief Financial Officer, Potomac Valley Hospital, Keyser, WV, p. A773

CAREY, Ann, Chief Information Officer, St. Vincent's Medical Center Southside, Jacksonville, FL, p. A141
Vice President and Chief Information Officer, St. Vincent's Medical Center Riverside, Jacksonville, FL, p. A141

CAREY, Calvin, Chief Financial Officer, Mt. San Rafael Hospital, Trinidad, CO, p. A119
Chief Financial Officer, Summit Medical Center, Casper, WY, p. A801

CAREY, Debra D., Interim Chief Executive Officer, John H. Stroger Jr. Hospital Of Cook County, Chicago, IL, p. A199
Interim Chief Executive Officer, Provident Hospital Of Cook County, Chicago, IL, p. A200

CAREY, Eric, Vice President Information Systems and Chief Information Officer, Valley Hospital, Ridgewood, NJ, p. A462

CAREY, Herschel, Chief Executive Officer, Lafayette Regional Rehabilitation Hospital, Lafayette, IN, p. A234

CAREY, Robin, Director of Nursing, Jasper Memorial Hospital, Monticello, GA, p. A177

CARIGSON, John, Chief Financial Officer, Covenant Specialty Hospital, Lubbock, TX, p. A697

CARIKER, Kelly, Chief Information Officer, North Valley Hospital, Tonasket, WA, p. A767

CARISSIMO-HARRIS, Amy, Chief Nursing Officer, Rome Memorial Hospital, Rome, NY, p. A497

CARLE, Chris, Senior Vice President and Chief Operating Officer, St. Elizabeth Florence, Florence, KY, p. A283

CARLETON, David, Chief Information Officer, Heritage Valley Health System, Beaver, PA, p. A584

Chief Information Officer, Sewickley Valley Hospital, (A Division Of Valley Medical Facilities), Sewickley, PA, p. A608

CARLIN, Diane, FACHE, Chief Executive Officer, Antelop. Memorial Hospital, Neligh, NE, p. A435

CARLISLE, Charles, Director, East Mississipp. State Hospital, Meridian, MS, p. A397

CARLISLE, Sandy, Manager Human Resources, Holzer Medical Center - Jackson, Jackson, OH, p. A542

CARLOCK, Carey, Chief Executive Officer, Riveredge Hospital, Forest Park, IL, p. A205

CARLOS, Ilona, M.D., President Medical Staff, Thorek Memorial Hospital, Chicago, IL, p. A201

CARLSON, Beth, R.N., Chief Nurse Executive, St. Rose Dominican Hospitals - Siena Campus, Henderson, NV, p. A442

CARLSON, Brian J., FACHE, Chief Executive Officer, Sanford Thief River Falls Behavioral Health Center, Thief River Falls, MN, p. A386
FACHE, Executive Director, Sanford Medical Center Thief River Falls, Thief River Falls, MN, p. A386

CARLSON, Daniel, M.D., Chief Medical Officer, Holston Valley Medical Center, Kingsport, TN, p. A641

CARLSON, Kellie, Director Human Resources, Coastal Harbor Treatment Center, Savannah, GA, p. A180

CARLSON, Kim, Director Human Resources, Essentia Health Northern Pines Medical Center, Aurora, MN, p. A372

CARLSON, Kurt, Chief Executive Officer, Otis R. Bowen Center For Human Services, Warsaw, IN, p. A242

CARLSON, Lisa, Chief Financial Officer, Adena Pike Medical Center, Waverly, OH, p. A552

CARLSON, Nancy, Chief Financial Officer, Burgess Health Center, Onawa, IA, p. A255

CARLSON, Peter, President, Behavioral Health Services, Aurora Psychiatric Hospital, Wauwatosa, WI, p. A799

CARLSON, Richard, Chief Financial Officer, Crawford Memorial Hospital, Robinson, IL, p. A218

CARLSON, Sandee, Director of Nursing, Essentia Health Duluth, Duluth, MN, p. A375

CARLSON, Sarah, Director Human Resources, Essentia Health-St. Joseph's Medical Center, Brainerd, MN, p. A373

CARLSON, Scott, Director, Mary Greeley Medical Center, Ames, IA, p. A243

CARLSON, Shannon, Chief Operating Officer, Lifecare Medical Center, Roseau, MN, p. A384

CARLSON, Wendie, Chief Human Resources Officer, Jackson-Madison County General Hospital, Jackson, TN, p. A639

CARLSON, Wendy, Director Human Resources, Pathways Of Tennessee, Jackson, TN, p. A639

CARLTON, Roy, Chief Financial Officer, Walter B. Jones Alcohol And Drug Abuse Treatment Center, Greenville, NC, p. A511

CARLTON, Terrie, R.N., Vice President & Chief Nursing Officer, Prisma Health Tuomey Hospital, Sumter, SC, p. A624

CARLYLE, Dave, Director Human Resources, Wayne County Hospital, Corydon, IA, p. A246

CARMAN, Susan, Chief Information Officer, United Health Services Hospitals-Binghamton, Binghamton, NY, p. A476

CARMAN, Thomas H., President and Chief Executive Officer, Samaritan Medical Center, Watertown, NY, p. A502

CARMELLINI, Tracy, M.D., Chief of Staff, Jennersville Hospital, West Grove, PA, p. A610

CARMEN, Lee, Associate Vice President Health Care Information Systems, University Of Iowa Hospitals And Clinics, Iowa City, IA, p. A252

CARMICHAEL, Craig, President and Chief Operating Officer, Senior Vice President, LifeBridge Health, Northwest Hospital, Randallstown, MD, p. A331

CARMICHAEL, Gavin, FACHE, Chief Operating Officer, Alaska Psychiatric Institute, Anchorage, AK, p. A27

CARMODY, James, Vice President Human Resources, Wilkes-Barre General Hospital, Wilkes-Barre, PA, p. A611

CARNAHAN, David, Chief Executive Officer, Quail Run Behavioral Health, Phoenix, AZ, p. A36

CARNAHAN, Robert H. II, R.N., Chief Executive Officer, Banner Churchill Community Hospital, Fallon, NV, p. A442

CARNES, Ruth, Manager Human Resources, Jennings American Legion Hospital, Jennings, LA, p. A304

CARNEY, Adrienne, R.N., Director Nursing and Surgical Services, Kearney Regional Medical Center, Kearney, NE, p. A434

CARNEY, Eric, Chief Executive Officer, Monmouth Medical Center, Long Branch Campus, Long Branch, NJ, p. A457
Chief Executive Officer, Monmouth Medical Center, Southern Campus, Lakewood, NJ, p. A457

CARNEY, Judi, M.D., President Medical Staff, Baptist Memorial Hospital For Women, Memphis, TN, p. A644

CARNEY, Kevin, Senior Information Systems Analyst, Pine Creek Medical Center, Dallas, TX, p. A670

CARNEY, Michael J., Chief Executive Officer, Brentwood Behavioral Healthcare Of Mississippi, Jackson, MS, p. A394

CARO, Vique, Chief Information Officer, Cincinnati Veterans Affairs Medical Center, Cincinnati, OH, p. A532

CAROLINA, Dorinda, Chief Human Resources Officer, Jefferson Health Northeast, Philadelphia, PA, p. A600

CARON, Jacqueline, Chief Human Resources, Birmingham Veterans Affairs Medical Center, Birmingham, AL, p. A14

CARON, William J., Chief Executive Officer, Veterans Affairs Southern Nevada Healthcare System, North Las Vegas, NV, p. A445

CAROSELLI, Cynthia, R.N., Ph.D., Chief Nursing Officer, Veterans Affairs New York Harbor Healthcare System, Brooklyn, NY, p. A479

CAROZZA, Sally, Director Human Resources, West Penn Hospital, Pittsburgh, PA, p. A605

CARPENTER, Curt, Manager Information Technology, Coquille Valley Hospital, Coquille, OR, p. A574

CARPENTER, Deb, Director Information Technology, Lourdes Medical Center, Pasco, WA, p. A762

CARPENTER, Garen, Chief Executive Officer, Van Buren County Hospital, Keosauqua, IA, p. A252

CARPENTER, Jackie, Office Manager, Rock County Hospital, Bassett, NE, p. A429

CARPENTER, Leah A., Administrator and Chief Executive Officer, Memorial Hospital West, Pembroke Pines, FL, p. A153

CARPENTER, Stephanie, Director of Nursing Services, Columbia County Health System, Dayton, WA, p. A757

CARPER, Joleen, Vice President Quality and Risk, Tri-State Memorial Hospital, Clarkston, WA, p. A756

CARR, Ann, R.N., Chief Nursing Officer, Saint Francis Hospital Vinita, Vinita, OK, p. A571

CARR, David, M.D., Physician Medical Director, The Rehabilitation Institute Of St. Louis, Saint Louis, MO, p. A417

CARR, Deborah, Vice President Human Resources, Garnet Health Medical Center - Catskills, Middletown, NY, p. A488

CARR, Desiree, Director Human Resources, Minidoka Memorial Hospital, Rupert, ID, p. A193

CARR, Diane, Chief Information Officer, Nyc Health + Hospitals / North Central Bronx, Bronx, NY, p. A477

CARR, George, Chief Information Officer, Bryan Medical Center, Lincoln, NE, p. A434

CARR, James, Chief Information Officer, Nyc Health + Hospitals / Bellevue, New York, NY, p. A491
Chief Information Officer, Nyc Health + Hospitals / Lincoln, Bronx, NY, p. A477

CARR, Julie, Chief Nursing Officer, Roane General Hospital, Spencer, WV, p. A777

CARR, Kay, Chief Information Officer, Bryn Mawr Hospital, Bryn Mawr, PA, p. A585
Chief Information Officer, Bryn Mawr Rehabilitation Hospital, Malvern, PA, p. A596
Chief Information Officer, Lankenau Medical Center, Wynnewood, PA, p. A612
Senior Vice President and Chief Information Officer, Paoli Hospital, Paoli, PA, p. A599

CARR, Randall, Director Human Resources, Roane Medical Center, Harriman, TN, p. A639

CARR, Sheila, Chief Executive Officer, Wekiva Springs, Jacksonville, FL, p. A142

CARR, Tim, Chief Financial Officer, Methodist Ambulatory Surgery Hospital - Northwest, San Antonio, TX, p. A712

CARRADINE, Damon, Director Information Technology, Highland Hospital, Charleston, WV, p. A771

CARRANZA, Diana, Associate Director, Veterans Affairs Illiana Health Care System, Danville, IL, p. A202
Interim Director, Veterans Affairs Illiana Health Care System, Danville, IL, p. A202

CARRASCO, Carlos, Chief Operating Officer, Orlando Regional Medical Center, Orlando, FL, p. A151

CARRASCO, Michelle, Director Human Resources, Palo Verde Behavioral Health, Tucson, AZ, p. A40

CARRASQUILLO, Carmen, M.D., Medical Director, Industrial Hospital, San Juan, PR, p. A811

CARREJO, Angela, Director Human Resources, Nor-Lea Hospital District, Lovington, NM, p. A470

CARRELLI, Bobbie, Director Human Resources, Summit Behavioral Healthcare, Cincinnati, OH, p. A533

CARREON, Aleana, Executive Director, Sonoma Developmental Center, Eldridge, CA, p. A63

CARRERO, Milton, M.D., Medical Director, Dr. Ramon E. Betances Hospital-Mayaguez Medical Center Branch, Mayaguez, PR, p. A808

CARRICO, Tom, Vice President of Operations, Hardin Memorial Health, Elizabethtown, KY, p. A282

CARRIER, Craig, Chief Financial Officer, American Fork Hospital, American Fork, UT, p. A727

Chief Financial Officer, Orem Community Hospital, Orem, UT, p. A730

CARRIER, Jeffrey, R.N., MS, FACHE, Chief Clinical Officer, Freeman Health System, Joplin, MO, p. A408

CARRIERE, Archie, Information Technology Technician, Northlake Behavioral Health System, Mandeville, LA, p. A308

CARRIGG, John, Executive Vice President and Chief Operating Officer, United Health Services Hospitals-Binghamton, Binghamton, NY, p. A476

CARRIGG, John M., President and Chief Executive Officer, United Health Services Hospitals-Binghamton, Binghamton, NY, p. A476

CARRIKER, Burton, Chief Executive Officer, Avenir Behavioral Health Center, Surprise, AZ, p. A39

CARRILLO, Irma, Director Human Resources, Ashford Presbyterian Community Hospital, San Juan, PR, p. A809

CARRILLO, Todd, Chief Information Officer, Yoakum County Hospital, Denver City, TX, p. A672

CARRILLO, Zulema, Superintendent, El Paso Psychiatric Center, El Paso, TX, p. A675

CARRINGER, Rick, Vice President and Chief Financial Officer, Methodist Medical Center Of Oak Ridge, Oak Ridge, TN, p. A648

CARRINGTON, Ebone', Chief Executive Officer and Chief Operating Officer, Nyc Health + Hospitals / Harlem, New York, NY, p. A491

CARRION, Gloria, Chief Financial Offricer, Atrium Medical Center, Stafford, TX, p. A716

CARROCINO, Joanne, FACHE, President and Chief Executive Officer, Cap. Regional Health System, Cap. May Court House, NJ, p. A453

CARROLL, Candice, Nurse Executive, Riverside Regional Medical Center, Newport News, VA, p. A747

CARROLL, Eric, Chief Executive Officer, Unicoi County Memorial Hospital, Erwin, TN, p. A638

CARROLL, Ginger, Chief Executive Officer, Citrus Memorial Health System, Inverness, FL, p. A140

CARROLL, Jack, Director Human Resources, Spaulding Hospital For Continuing Medical Care Cambridge, Cambridge, MA, p. A338

CARROLL, Jacqueline, Director Human Resources, Los Alamos Medical Center, Los Alamos, NM, p. A470

CARROLL, Jaime, R.N., Vice President Nursing, Sentara Albemarle Medical Center, Elizabeth City, NC, p. A509
Department Head, Walter Reed National Military Medical Center, Bethesda, MD, p. A328

CARROLL, James, Chief Information Officer, Uh St. John Medical Center, Westlake, OH, p. A553

CARROLL, Jan, MSN, M.P.H., R.N., Chief Nursing Officer, Canton-Potsdam Hospital, Potsdam, NY, p. A495

CARROLL, John, M.D., Chief Medical Officer, St. James Hospital, Hornell, NY, p. A485

CARROLL, Jonathan, Chief Information Officer, Uconn, John Dempsey Hospital, Farmington, CT, p. A122

CARROLL, Karen, R.N., Vice President Patient Care Services, Beaufort Memorial Hospital, Beaufort, SC, p. A615

CARROLL, Kristen, M.D., Chief of Staff, Shriners Hospitals For Children-Salt Lake City, Salt Lake City, UT, p. A732

CARROLL, Leonard, M.D., Chief of Staff, Hendry Regional Medical Center, Clewiston, FL, p. A134

CARROLL, Michael W., Administrator, Richland Parish Hospital-Delhi, Delhi, LA, p. A300

CARROLL, Patrick, M.D., Chief Medical Officer, Dixie Regional Medical Center, Saint George, UT, p. A732

CARROLL, Peggy, Chief Information Officer, Palos Health, Palos Heights, IL, p. A216

CARROLL, Richard, M.D., Chief Medical officer, Amita Health Adventist Medical Center Bolingbrook, Bolingbrook, IL, p. A196
M.D., Vice President and Chief Medical Officer, Amita Health Adventist Medical Center Glenoaks, Glendale Heights, IL, p. A206

CARROLL, Susan T., FACHE, Acting President, Inova Fairfax Hospital, Falls Church, VA, p. A741

CARROLL, Terri, Vice President Financial Services, Hillsboro Area Hospital, Hillsboro, IL, p. A207

CARROLL, William, M.D., Chief Medical Executive, Sutter Santa Rosa Regional Hospital, Santa Rosa, CA, p. A98

CARRON, Patrick E., FACHE, President and Chief Executive Officer, Perry County Memorial Hospital, Perryville, MO, p. A413

CARRUTH, Gregory, Head Information Management, Naval Hospital Oak Harbor, Oak Harbor, WA, p. A761

CARRUTH, Keith, Market Chief Executive Officer, Bridgepoint Continuing Care Hospital, Marrero, LA, p. A308

CARSON, Carole, Director of Nursing Operations, Rehabilitation Hospital Of Southern New Mexico, Las Cruces, NM, p. A470

CARSON, Chad, Director of Nursing, Lake Behavioral Hospital, Waukegan, IL, p. A222

CARSON, Debbie, Director Human Resources, Kp. Promise Hospital Of Vicksburg, Vicksburg, MS, p. A400

CARSON, Kara, Chief Financial Officer, Pinckneyville Community Hospital, Pinckneyville, IL, p. A217

CARSON, Stacy, Chief Executive Officer, Select Specialty Hospital-Laurel Highlands, Latrobe, PA, p. A594

CARSON, Whisper, Manager Human Resource, Scott County Hospital, Scott City, KS, p. A276

CARSTENS, Craig, Chief Financial Officer, Osceola Regional Health Center, Sibley, IA, p. A257

CARSTENS, Cynthia L., R.N., Chief Executive Officer, Stewart Memorial Community Hospital, Lake City, IA, p. A253

CARSTENSEN, Karla, Director Patient Care, Avera Dells Area Hospital, Dell Rapids, SD, p. A627

CARTAGENA, Maria, M.D., Chief Medical Officer, Brylin Hospitals, Buffalo, NY, p. A479

CARTER, Andrea, M.D., Chief Medical Officer, Samaritan Healthcare, Moses Lake, WA, p. A760

CARTER, Barbara, Chief Nursing Officer, Cimarron Memorial Hospital, Boise City, OK, p. A556

CARTER, Billie, Chief Executive Officer, Stonewall Memorial Hospital, Aspermont, TX, p. A654

CARTER, Bob, Interim Chief Executive Officer, Eastern Oklahoma Medical Center, Poteau, OK, p. A567

CARTER, Carolyn, Chief Nursing Officer, Broward Health Coral Springs, Coral Springs, FL, p. A135

CARTER, Christen, Director Public Relations, Roosevelt Warm Springs Rehabilitation Hospital - Rehab, Warm Springs, GA, p. A183

CARTER, D. Montez., Chief Executive Officer, St. Mary's Health Care System, Athens, GA, p. A164

CARTER, Dennis, M.D., Chief of Staff, Eastern Oklahoma Medical Center, Poteau, OK, p. A567

CARTER, Donna, MSN, R.N., Chief Nursing Officer, Minden Medical Center, Minden, LA, p. A309
Chief Information Officer and Security Officer, Russell Medical, Alexander City, AL, p. A13

CARTER, Douglas, M.D., Vice President and Chief Medical Officer, Major Hospital, Shelbyville, IN, p. A240

CARTER, Gloria, Chief Nurse Executive Officer, St. Mary Medical Center Long Beach, Long Beach, CA, p. A72

CARTER, Gregory, M.D., Chief Medical Officer, St. Luke's Rehabilitation Institute, Spokane, WA, p. A766

CARTER, Jessica, Chief Financial Officer, Crisp Regional Hospital, Cordele, GA, p. A170

CARTER, Jim, Chief Operating Officer, Grady General Hospital, Cairo, GA, p. A167

CARTER, Josh, Chief Executive Officer, Memphis Mental Health Institute, Memphis, TN, p. A644

CARTER, Leonard, Chief Human Resources Officer, Fhn Memorial Hospital, Freeport, IL, p. A205

CARTER, Leslia, Administrator, North Mississipp. Medical Center-Pontotoc, Pontotoc, MS, p. A399

CARTER, Malinda, Vice President Human Resources, Saint Anthony Hospital, Chicago, IL, p. A200

CARTER, Marcia, Director Human Resources, Bluegrass Community Hospital, Versailles, KY, p. A294

CARTER, Michael, M.D., Chief Medical Officer, Houston County Community Hospital, Erin, TN, p. A638
Administrator Information Technology, Northwest Ohio Psychiatric Hospital, Toledo, OH, p. A550

CARTER, Misty, Chief Human Resource Officer and Ancillary Services, Great Plains Regional Medical Center, Elk City, OK, p. A558

CARTER, Priscilla, Chief Financial Officer, Premier Specialty Hospital Of El Paso, El Paso, TX, p. A675

CARTER, Rebecca W., MSN, R.N., FACHE, President, Firsthealth Montgomery Memorial Hospital, Troy, NC, p. A519

CARTER, Richard, M.D., Chief Medical Director, Hamilton County Hospital, Syracuse, KS, p. A277
M.D., Chief of Staff, Tennova Healthcare-Jefferson Memorial Hospital, Jefferson City, TN, p. A640
District Chief Executive Officer, Hunt Regional Medical Center, Greenville, TX, p. A682

CARTER, Steve, Chief Information Officer, Mon Health Medical Center, Morgantown, WV, p. A774

CARTER, Teresa, Vice President Patient Care Services, Onecore Health, Oklahoma City, OK, p. A565

CARTER, Tomika, Chief Executive Officer, Greystone Park Psychiatric Hospital, Morris Plains, NJ, p. A458

CARTER, Vickie, Information Systems Director, Sumner Regional Medical Center, Gallatin, TN, p. A638

CARTWRIGHT, Bryan, Chief Information Technology Officer, Missouri River Medical Center, Fort Benton, MT, p. A423

CARTWRIGHT, David, Director Management Information Systems, Sovah Health-Danville, Danville, VA, p. A741

---

CARTWRIGHT, Debra, Chief Financial Officer, St. Josep. Medical Center, Kansas City, MO, p. A409

CARTWRIGHT, Michelle, Chief Financial Officer, St. Mary's Medical Center, West Palm Beach, FL, p. A162

CARUCCI, Dean, Chief Executive Officer, Portsmouth Regional Hospital, Portsmouth, NH, p. A451

CARUGATI, Diane, Chief Operating Officer, Friends Hospital, Philadelphia, PA, p. A600

CARUSO, Diane, MSN, Chief Nursing Officer, Encompass Health Rehabilitation Hospital Of Scottsdale, Scottsdale, AZ, p. A38

CARUSO, Don, M.D., Chief Executive Officer and President, Cheshire Medical Center, Keene, NH, p. A449
M.D., Chief Medical Officer, Cheshire Medical Center, Keene, NH, p. A449

CARUSO, Maria, Chief Financial Officer, Palms Of Pasadena Hospital, Saint Petersburg, FL, p. A156

CARVER, Carol, MSN, R.N., Vice President Patient Services, Clarity Child Guidance Center, San Antonio, TX, p. A711

CARVER, Deborah, Chief Nursing Officer, Providence Tarzana Medical Center, Tarzana, CA, p. A100

CARVER, Gary, M.D., Chief Medical Officer, Coshocton Regional Medical Center, Coshocton, OH, p. A538

CARVETH, Barbara, Chief Financial Officer, University Of Colorado Hospital, Aurora, CO, p. A108

CARYER, Steve, Chief Financial Officer, Community Memorial Hospital, Hicksville, OH, p. A542

CARYNSKI, Paula A., MS, R.N., President, Osf Saint Anthony Medical Center, Rockford, IL, p. A219

CASANO, Jayleen, Ph.D., FACHE, President, Chi Health Creighton University Medical Center - Bergan Mercy, Omaha, NE, p. A436

CASANOVA, Robert, Chief Financial Officer, Industrial Hospital, San Juan, PR, p. A811

CASAREZ, Margaret, Chief Financial Officer, San Joaquin Valley Rehabilitation Hospital, Fresno, CA, p. A66

CASDORPH, Michael, Ph.D., Chief Information Officer, Augusta University Medical Center, Augusta, GA, p. A165

CASE, Cliff, Chief Financial Officer, Mineral Community Hospital, Superior, MT, p. A428

CASE, Ed, Executive Vice President and Chief Financial Officer, Shirley Ryan Abilitylab, Chicago, IL, p. A200

CASE, Harvey, President, Carteret Health Care, Morehead City, NC, p. A514

CASE, Helen, Chief Nursing Officer, Nemours Children's Hospital, Orlando, FL, p. A151

CASE, Matthew, MSC, USN, Commanding Officer, Naval Hospital Jacksonville, Jacksonville, FL, p. A141

CASE, Nancy, Chief Nursing Officer, Daviess Community Hospital, Washington, IN, p. A242

CASERTA, Kevin, M.D., Chief Medical Officer, Providence Centralia Hospital, Centralia, WA, p. A756
M.D., Chief Medical Officer, Providence St. Peter Hospital, Olympia, WA, p. A761

CASEY, Allison, Director, Gadsden Regional Medical Center, Gadsden, AL, p. A19

CASEY, Dina, Human Resources Officer, Lane County Hospital, Dighton, KS, p. A263

CASEY, Joseph, Interim President and Chief Executive Officer, Sturdy Memorial Hospital, Attleboro, MA, p. A334

CASEY, Kevin, M.D., Chief Clinical Officer, Mercy Health - St. Rita's Medical Center, Lima, OH, p. A543

CASEY, Kevin John., President, Rochester General Hospital, Rochester, NY, p. A496

CASH, Jeff, Senior Vice President and Chief Information Officer, Mercy Medical Center - Cedar Rapids, Cedar Rapids, IA, p. A245

CASHEN CHACON, Chanda, Executive Vice President and Chief Operating Officer, Arkansas Children's Hospital, Little Rock, AR, p. A48

CASHMAN, Tim, Chief Financial Officer, Estes Park Medical Center, Estes Park, CO, p. A112

CASHWELL, David, Chief Executive Officer, Encompass Health Rehabilitation Hospital Of Fredericksburg, Fredericksburg, VA, p. A742

CASIANO, Manuel, M.D., Senior Vice President Medical Affairs, Frederick Health, Frederick, MD, p. A329

CASILLAS, Rosalind, Chief Nursing Officer, Lawrence Memorial Hospital, Walnut Ridge, AR, p. A54

CASNER, Trina, President and Chief Executive Officer, Pana Community Hospital, Pana, IL, p. A216

CASOLA, Frances, Senior Vice President Operations, Saint Joseph's Medical Center, Yonkers, NY, p. A502

CASON, Amy, MSN, Chief Nursing Officer, Tristar Stonecrest Medical Center, Smyrna, TN, p. A649

CASON, Cathy, Chief Financial Officer, Jeff Davis Hospital, Hazlehurst, GA, p. A173

CASON, Diane, Chief Information Officer, Controller and Director Human Resources, Lake Butler Hospital, Lake Butler, FL, p. A142

CASON, Randall R., FACHE, Senior Administrator, Ascension Via Christi Hospital, Pittsburg, KS, p. A274

CASON, Will, Vice President Human Resources, Mercy Health - St. Rita's Medical Center, Lima, OH, p. A543

CASPERSON, William, M.D., Vice President Medical Affairs, Memorial Hospital, Belleville, IL, p. A195
Vice President Medical Affairs, Memorial Hospital East, Shiloh, IL, p. A220

CASS, Julene, R.N., Director of Nursing, Community Memorial Hospital, Redfield, SD, p. A630

CASS, Paul, D.O., Chief Medical & Clinical Integration Officer, Wentworth-Douglass Hospital, Dover, NH, p. A448

CASSADY, Perry, M.D., Medical Director, Physicians' Medical Center, New Albany, IN, p. A237

CASSEDY, Ryan, Chief Administrative Officer, Rehabilitation Hospital Of Fort Wayne, Fort Wayne, IN, p. A228

CASSEL, Asenath, Chief Nursing Officer, Wellington Regional Medical Center, Wellington, FL, p. A161

CASSEL, Kari, Senior Vice President and Chief Information Officer, Uf Health Jacksonville, Jacksonville, FL, p. A142

CASSELL, Sally, Manager Human Resources, Ozark Health Medical Center, Clinton, AR, p. A43

CASSIDY, Donna, Chief Nursing Executive, Bronson South Haven Hospital, South Haven, MI, p. A367

CASSIDY, Joseph, Vice President, Holy Redeemer Hospital, Meadowbrook, PA, p. A596

CASSINGHAM, Brandi, Chief Nursing Officer, Saddleback Medical Center, Laguna Hills, CA, p. A70

CASSLE, Susie, R.N., MSN, Vice President Nursing Services, Hendrick Health System, Abilene, TX, p. A651

CASTALDO, Jennifer, R.N., Vice President, Patient Care and Chief Nursing Officer, Henry Mayo Newhall Hospital, Valencia, CA, p. A103

CASTANEDA, Edmundo, President and Chief Executive Officer, Woodland Healthcare, Woodland, CA, p. A105
President, Mercy General Hospital, Sacramento, CA, p. A89

CASTANEDA, Marissa, Chief Operating Officer and Director Marketing, Doctor's Hospital At Renaissance, Edinburg, TX, p. A674

CASTANEDA, Trevor, Chief Executive Officer, Baylor Scott & White Medical Center—Frisco, Frisco, TX, p. A680

CASTEEL, Brian, Information Technology Technician, Hardin County General Hospital, Rosiclare, IL, p. A219

CASTEEL, Lisa, Chief Executive Officer, Henry County Medical Center, Paris, TN, p. A648

CASTEEL, Rick, Vice President Management Information Systems and Chief Information Officer, University Of Maryland Harford Memorial Hospital, Havre De Grace, MD, p. A330
Vice President Management Information Systems and Chief Information Officer, University Of Maryland Upper Chesapeake Medical Center, Bel Air, MD, p. A327

CASTELBERRY, Lindsey, Vice President Human Resources and General Counsel, White River Medical Center, Batesville, AR, p. A42

CASTILLO, Carlos, R.N., Chief Nursing Officer, The Hospitals Of Providence Sierra Campus, El Paso, TX, p. A676

CASTILLO, Carol, Medical Director, Sonoma Developmental Center, Eldridge, CA, p. A63

CASTILLO, Edgar, Chief Financial Officer, Larkin Community Hospital-South Miami Campus, South Miami, FL, p. A157

CASTILLO, Paul, Chief Financial Officer, Michigan Medicine, Ann Arbor, MI, p. A348

CASTILLO, Ralp. A., CPA, Chief Executive Officer, Morgan Memorial Hospital, Madison, GA, p. A176

CASTILLO, Randall, Chief Executive Officer, St. Mary Medical Center, Apple Valley, CA, p. A56

CASTILLO, Renee, Chief Nursing Officer, Plains Memorial Hospital, Dimmitt, TX, p. A673

CASTILLO, Rita, R.N., Vice President, Quality, Risk and Safety, Methodist Hospital South, Jourdanton, TX, p. A691

CASTLE, Eric, Director Information Services, Lawnwood Regional Medical Center & Heart Institute, Fort Pierce, FL, p. A138

CASTLE, Samantha, Chief Executive Officer, Carrollton Springs, Carrollton, TX, p. A663

CASTLEBERRY, Ginger, Corporate Risk Manager, Quality and Patient Safety, Valir Rehabilitation Hospital, Oklahoma City, OK, p. A566

CASTLEMAN, Pam, MSN, Chief Nursing Officer, Regional One Health, Memphis, TN, p. A645

CASTON, David, Chief Executive Officer, Reeves Memorial Medical Center, Bernice, LA, p. A298

CASTOR, Susan, Chief Nursing Officer, Encompass Health Rehabilitation Hospital Of Toms River, Toms River, NJ, p. A464

CASTRO, Ana, Director Information Technology, Gerald Champion Regional Medical Center, Alamogordo, NM, p. A467

CASTRO, Craig, Chief Executive Officer, Clovis Community Medical Center, Clovis, CA, p. A60
Chief Information Officer, Community Regional Medical Center, Fresno, CA, p. A65

CASTRO, Darcy, Director Human Resources, Garfield Medical Center, Monterey Park, CA, p. A79

CASTRO, Jill, M.D., Medical Director, Encompass Health Rehabilitation Hospital Of Littleton, Littleton, CO, p. A115

CASTRO, Pete, D.O., Chief of Staff, Heart Of Texas Memorial Hospital, Brady, TX, p. A660

CASTRO, Richard, Chief Executive Officer, Ahmc Anaheim Regional Medical Center, Anaheim, CA, p. A55
Chief Executive Officer, Whittier Hospital Medical Center, Whittier, CA, p. A105

CASTRODALE, Andrew, M.D., Chief Medical Officer, Coulee Medical Center, Grand Coulee, WA, p. A759

CASTRONUEVO, Joseph, Director Information Management, St. Lawrence Rehabilitation Center, Lawrenceville, NJ, p. A457

CASWELL, Lori, Director Information Technology, Good Samaritan Medical Center, Brockton, MA, p. A337

CASWELL, Penny, Director of Nursing, Bloomington Meadows Hospital, Bloomington, IN, p. A224

CATALA, Lucy, Vice President Finance, Baylor Scott & White All Saints Medical Center - Fort Worth, Fort Worth, TX, p. A678

CATALDO, Linda, Human Resources Secretary, Prevost Memorial Hospital, Donaldsonville, LA, p. A301

CATALDO, Vincent A., Administrator, Prevost Memorial Hospital, Donaldsonville, LA, p. A301

CATANIA, Josep. M., Chief Executive Officer, St. Anthony's Rehabilitation Hospital, Lauderdale Lakes, FL, p. A144

CATAUDELLA, Mary, Corporate Director Human Resources, Jersey City Medical Center, Jersey City, NJ, p. A456

CATENA, Cornelio R., President and Chief Executive Officer, Wilkes-Barre General Hospital, Wilkes-Barre, PA, p. A611

CATES, Brett, Director Information Services, Medical City Weatherford, Weatherford, TX, p. A724

CATES, Jessica, Fiscal Manager, Western State Hospital, Hopkinsville, KY, p. A285

CATHEY, Michele, Interim Chief Financial officer, Martin County Hospital District, Stanton, TX, p. A717

CATHEY, Walt, Chief Executive Officer, Covenant Medical Center, Lubbock, TX, p. A697

CATINO, Anne, MS, R.N., Vice President and Chief Nursing Officer, Holy Redeemer Hospital, Meadowbrook, PA, p. A596

CATTALANI, Mark, M.D., Clinical Director, Richard H. Hutchings Psychiatric Center, Syracuse, NY, p. A499

CATTELL, JoAnne, Chief Nursing Officer, St. Petersburg General Hospital, Saint Petersburg, FL, p. A156

CATTELL, Nancy, Vice President Human Resources, Liberty Hospital, Liberty, MO, p. A411

CATTON, Carolyn, Interim Chief Patient Care Officer, Marshfield Medical Center - Beaver Dam, Beaver Dam, WI, p. A781

CATTON, Jane, R.N., Chief Operating Officer and Chief Nursing Officer, Northwestern Medical Center, Saint Albans, VT, p. A736

CAUBLE, David, Executive Vice President and Chief Financial Officer, Children's Mercy Hospital Kansas City, Kansas City, MO, p. A408
Executive Vice President and Chief Financial Officer, Children's Mercy Hospital Kansas, Overland Park, KS, p. A273

CAUDILL, Allan, M.D., Chief of Staff, Bronson South Haven Hospital, South Haven, MI, p. A367

CAUDILL, David, Chief Executive Officer, Gove County Medical Center, Quinter, KS, p. A275

CAUGHELL, David, M.D., Chief of Staff, Jane Phillip. Nowata Health Center, Nowata, OK, p. A563

CAUGHEY, Michelle, M.D., Physician in Chief, Kaiser Permanente South San Francisco, South San Francisco, CA, p. A99

CAUGHMAN, Katie, Chief Financial Officer, St. John Broken Arrow, Broken Arrow, OK, p. A556
Chief Financial Officer, St. John Owasso, Owasso, OK, p. A566

CAUSEY, Cynthia, Associate Administrator Human and Mission Services, Mcleod Health Dillon, Dillon, SC, p. A619

CAUSEY, Jack M., Chief Executive Officer, Clearsky Rehabilitation Hospital Of Leesville, Leesville, LA, p. A307

CAUSEY, Jennifer, Chief Executive Officer, Select Specialty Hospital-Nashville, Nashville, TN, p. A646

CAUWENBERG, Jude, M.D., Chief of Staff, Ashtabula County Medical Center, Ashtabula, OH, p. A528

CAVA, Anthony V., MS, FACHE, President and Chief Executive Officer, Robert Wood Johnson University Hospital Somerset, Somerville, NJ, p. A463

CAVACOS, Mike, MSN, Chief Nursing Officer, Methodist Medical Center Of Oak Ridge, Oak Ridge, TN, p. A648

CAVAGNARO, Charles, M.D., IllInterim Chief Medical officer, Umass Memorial Medical Center, Worcester, MA, p. A347

CAVANAUGH, Cheryl, Senior Director Human Resources, Valley Regional Hospital, Claremont, NH, p. A448

CAVANAUGH, Paul, Director Human Resources, Friends Hospital, Philadelphia, PA, p. A600

CAVANAUGH, Steven, Chief Financial Officer, Promedica Toledo Hospital, Toledo, OH, p. A550

CAVAZOS, David-Paul, Interim Chief Executive Officer, Fulton Medical Center, Fulton, MO, p. A407

CAVEN, Tom, M.D., Vice President, Medical Director, Dell Seton Medical Center At The University Of Texas, Austin, TX, p. A656

CAVENEY, Timothy, President, South Shore Hospital, Chicago, IL, p. A201

CAVERNO, John, Chief Human Resources Officer, Excela Frick Hospital, Mount Pleasant, PA, p. A598
Chief Human Resources Officer, Excela Health Westmoreland Hospital, Greensburg, PA, p. A591

CAVES, Chandler, M.D., Chief Medical Officer, Theda Care Medical Center - Wild Rose, Wild Rose, WI, p. A799

CAWLEY, Karen, Chief Executive Officer, Curahealth Phoenix, Phoenix, AZ, p. A35
Chief Executive Officer, Select Specialty Hospital-Phoenix, Phoenix, AZ, p. A36

CAWLEY, Kevin, Interim Chief Financial Officer, Mclaren Thumb Region, Bad Axe, MI, p. A349

CAWLEY, Patrick J., Chief Executive Officer, MUSC Health and Vice President for Health Affairs, University, Musc Health Of Medical University Of South Carolina, Charleston, SC, p. A616

CAYER, Gerald, Chief Executive Officer, Lewis County General Hospital, Lowville, NY, p. A487

CAYTON, Mical, Area Information Officer, Kaiser Permanente Antioch Medical Center, Antioch, CA, p. A56

CAZAYOUX, John, Chief Financial Officer, Pointe Coupee General Hospital, New Roads, LA, p. A312

CAZES, Anna, Interim Chief Nursing Officer, Senior Vice President and Chief Operating Officer, Lake Charles Memorial Hospital, Lake Charles, LA, p. A307
Interim Chief Nursing Officer, Senior Vice President, Chief Operating Officer, Lake Charles Memorial Hospital, Lake Charles, LA, p. A307

CECAVA, Eric, Chief Operating Officer, Adena Medical Center, Chillicothe, OH, p. A531
Chief Operating Officer, Adena Pike Medical Center, Waverly, OH, p. A552

CECCHINI, Marina T., Administrator, Uf Health Rehab Hospital, Gainesville, FL, p. A139

CECH, Bob, Regional Finance Officer, Amita Health Saints Mary & Elizabeth Medical Center, Chicago, IL, p. A198

CECIL, Bruce, Chief Financial Officer, Fresno Surgical Hospital, Fresno, CA, p. A65

CECIL, Janell, R.N., MSN, Senior Vice President and Chief Nursing Officer, University Of Tennessee Medical Center, Knoxville, TN, p. A641

CECIL, Jason, Vice President, Information, Capital Region Medical Center, Jefferson City, MO, p. A408

CECIL, Jon, Chief Human Resource Officer, Cap. Coral Hospital, Cap. Coral, FL, p. A134
Chief Human Resource Officer, Gulf Coast Medical Center, Fort Myers, FL, p. A138
Chief Human Resource Officer, Lee Memorial Hospital, Fort Myers, FL, p. A138

CEDENO LLORENS, Arturo, M.D., Medical Director, Hospital Buen Samaritano, Aguadilla, PR, p. A805

CEDILLO, Alaina, Administrator, Jefferson Davis Community Hospital, Prentiss, MS, p. A399
Administrator, Marion General Hospital, Columbia, MS, p. A391

CEDOTAL, Kiley P., FACHE, Chief Executive Officer, Kp. Promise Hospital Of Baton Rouge, Baton Rouge, LA, p. A297
FACHE, Chief Executive Officer, Kp. Promise Hospital Of Dallas, Dallas, TX, p. A668
FACHE, Chief Executive Officer, Kp. Promise Hospital Of Vicksburg, Vicksburg, MS, p. A400

CEJA, Daniel, Interim Chief Financial Officer, North Sunflower Medical Center, Ruleville, MS, p. A400

CELLA, Ann, R.N., Senior Vice President, Patient Care Services, St. Francis Hospital, The Heart Center, Roslyn, NY, p. A497

CELLA, Robert, M.D., Chief Medical Officer, St. Peter's Hospital, Albany, NY, p. A474

CELSOR, Reba, Chief Executive Officer, Spring View Hospital, Lebanon, KY, p. A286

CELUCH, Paul, Chief Human Resource Officer, East Los Angeles Doctors Hospital, Los Angeles, CA, p. A74

Corporate Human Resources Director, Community Hospital Of Huntington Park, Huntington Park, CA, p. A68

CEMENO, Michael, Chief Information Officer, Waterbury Hospital, Waterbury, CT, p. A126

CENTENO, Robert, M.D., Chief Medical Officer, Governor Juan F. Luis Hospital, Christiansted, VI, p. A812

CEPEDA, Aaron, Director Nursing Operations, South Texas Rehabilitation Hospital, Brownsville, TX, p. A661

CERALDI, Christopher, M.D., Chief of Staff, Abbeville Area Medical Center, Abbeville, SC, p. A615

CERFOLIO, Robert, M.D., Chief Operating Officer, Nyu Langone Hospitals, New York, NY, p. A492

CERIMELE, Joseph, D.O., Medical Director, Hillside Rehabilitation Hospital, Warren, OH, p. A551

CERIMELE, Leeann, Vice President Human Resources, West Virginia University Hospitals, Morgantown, WV, p. A775

CERISE, Fred, M.D., Chief Executive Officer, Parkland Health & Hospital System, Dallas, TX, p. A670

CERNAVA, Joanne, Director Human Resources, Kessler Marlton Rehabilitation, Marlton, NJ, p. A458

CERNAVA, Tia, Chief Financial Officer, Pomerene Hospital, Millersburg, OH, p. A545

CERNEY, Ryan D., Administrator, Community Behavioral Health Hospital - Baxter, Baxter, MN, p. A372

CERNOCH, Desiree, Director of Nurses, El Camp. Memorial Hospital, El Campo, TX, p. A674

CERRA, Jane, Market Nurse Executive and Chief Nursing Officer, Select Specialty Hospital-Milwaukee, Milwaukee, WI, p. A791

CERVANTES, Jason, Chief Information Officer, East Los Angeles Doctors Hospital, Los Angeles, CA, p. A74
Corporate Chief Information Officer, Community Hospital Of Huntington Park, Huntington Park, CA, p. A68

CERVINO, Noel A., President and Chief Executive Officer, University Of Maryland Charles Regional Medical Center, La Plata, MD, p. A330

CESAREZ, Margaret, Chief Financial Officer, Gateway Rehabilitation Hospital, Florence, KY, p. A283

CESCA, Ken, Vice President Human Resources, Midstate Medical Center, Meriden, CT, p. A123

CESKO, David, M.D., Chief of Staff, Memorial Hospital Of Carbon County, Rawlins, WY, p. A803

CHA, Wontae, Chief Operating Officer, Hollywood Presbyterian Medical Center, Los Angeles, CA, p. A74

CHA BRIDIER, Vicky, Chief Operating Officer, Chi St. Josep. College Station Hospital, College Station, TX, p. A664

CHABALOWSKI, Edward, Chief Financial Officer, Phoenixville Hospital, Phoenixville, PA, p. A602

CHABOT, Judy, Chief Nursing Officer, Los Alamitos Medical Center, Los Alamitos, CA, p. A73

CHACKO, Benson, Vice President, Operations, Baylor Scott & White Medical Center - Lake Pointe, Rowlett, TX, p. A710

CHACON, Barbara, Chief Financial Officer, The Core Institute Specialty Hospital, Phoenix, AZ, p. A37

CHACON, Chanda, President and Chief Executive Officer, Children's Hospital And Medical Center, Omaha, NE, p. A437

CHADEK, Richard, M.D., Clinical Director, Lawton Indian Hospital, Lawton, OK, p. A561

CHADHA, Beenu, Chief Financial Officer, San Ramon Regional Medical Center, San Ramon, CA, p. A96

CHADOCK, Brandon, Director of Operations, Sistersville General Hospital, Sistersville, WV, p. A776
Interim Chief Executive Officer, Sistersville General Hospital, Sistersville, WV, p. A776

CHADWICK, LeeAnn, Chief Nursing Officer, Midmichigan Medical Center-Gratiot, Alma, MI, p. A348

CHADWICK, Sharon, Director Human Resources, Abrazo Arrowhead Campus, Glendale, AZ, p. A32

CHAFFIN, Linda, Director Medical Review, Baptist Memorial Hospital-Booneville, Booneville, MS, p. A390

CHAHANOVICH, Jen, President and Chief Executive Officer, Wilcox Medical Center, Lihue, HI, p. A186

CHALFANT, Cathie, Director Human Resources, Harrison County Community Hospital, Bethany, MO, p. A402

CHALIAN, Christopher, M.D., Medical Director, Casa Colina Hospital And Centers For Healthcare, Pomona, CA, p. A86

CHALK, Jackie, Director Human Resources, Encompass Health Rehabilitation Hospital Of Largo, Largo, FL, p. A143

CHALKE, Dennis, Senior Vice President, Chief Financial Officer and Treasurer, Baystate Medical Center, Springfield, MA, p. A344

CHALPHANT, Steve, Director Information Management Service Line, Wm. Jennings Bryan Dorn Veterans Affairs Medical Center, Columbia, SC, p. A618

CHALTRY, Richard, M.D., Director Medical Staff, Aspirus Ontonagon Hospital, Inc., Ontonagon, MI, p. A363

CHALUPA, Rebecca, MSN, R.N., Chief Nursing Officer, Houston Methodist Baytown Hospital, Baytown, TX, p. A657

CHAMBERLAIN, Denise, Executive Vice President, Chief Financial Officer, Edward Hospital, Naperville, IL, p. A213

CHAMBERLAIN, Diana, Director Human Resources, Carthage Area Hospital, Carthage, NY, p. A481

CHAMBERLIN, Brad, Director of Finance, Osf Saint Elizabeth Medical Center, Ottawa, IL, p. A216

CHAMBERLIN, Kim, Vice President Patient Services and Chief Nursing Officer, Mercyone North Iowa Medical Center, Mason City, IA, p. A254

CHAMBERS, Bradley, President and Senior Vice President, MedStar Health, Medstar Good Samaritan Hospital, Baltimore, MD, p. A325
President, Medstar Union Memorial Hospital, Baltimore, MD, p. A325

CHAMBERS, Gwen, Executive Director Human Resources, Methodist Hospital Of Southern California, Arcadia, CA, p. A56

CHAMBERS, Matthew, Chief Information Officer, Baylor Scott & White Medical Center - Round Rock, Round Rock, TX, p. A709
Chief Information Officer, Baylor Scott & White Medical Center - Temple, Temple, TX, p. A719

CHAMBERS, Regina, Vice President Human Resource, Rome Memorial Hospital, Rome, NY, p. A497

CHAMBLEE, Jane, Manager Human Resources, North Mississipp. Medical Center-Iuka, Iuka, MS, p. A394

CHAMBLESS, Lesley, Assistant Vice President Human Resources, Atrium Health Lincoln, Lincolnton, NC, p. A514
Assistant Vice President Workforce Relations, Atrium Health Cabarrus, Concord, NC, p. A508

CHAMBLISS, James, Chief of Staff, Magnolia Regional Medical Center, Magnolia, AR, p. A49

CHAMPAGNE, Charles, Chief Financial Officer, Northeast Rehabilitation Hospital, Salem, NH, p. A451

CHAMPAGNE, Laurie, Controller, Curahealth New Orleans, New Orleans, LA, p. A310

CHAMPAVANNARATH, Vilakon, Director Information Systems, Bartow Regional Medical Center, Bartow, FL, p. A131

CHAMPION, Joshua, Director, Adventhealth Palm Coast, Palm Coast, FL, p. A152

CHAN, Eric, M.D., Chief Executive Officer, Surgery Specialty Hospitals Of America, Pasadena, TX, p. A705

CHAN, Fred, Chief Financial Officer, Intracare North Hospital, Houston, TX, p. A686

CHAN, Joyce, Chief Human Resources Officer, Centracare - Melrose, Melrose, MN, p. A380

CHAN, Thomas, Chief Financial Officer, Meritus Medical Center, Hagerstown, MD, p. A330

CHANAA, Ziad, M.D., Chief of Staff, Boone Memorial Hospital, Madison, WV, p. A774

CHANAGA, Luis, Chief Financial Officer, Grandview Medical Center, Dayton, OH, p. A538

CHANCE, Andre, Chief Financial Officer, Veterans Affairs New York Harbor Healthcare System, Brooklyn, NY, p. A479

CHANDIO, Adam, Administrator, The Orthopedic Specialty Hospital, Murray, UT, p. A729

CHANDLER, Carla, Vice President and Chief Financial Officer, Emory University Hospital, Atlanta, GA, p. A164

CHANDLER, Christopher, Chief Executive Officer, Monroe Regional Hospital, Aberdeen, MS, p. A389

CHANDLER, Laurie, Chairman, Prairie Community Hospital, Terry, MT, p. A428
Financial Officer, Prairie Community Hospital, Terry, MT, p. A428

CHANDLER, Loren, President, Mount Sinai Hospital, Chicago, IL, p. A199

CHANDLER, Mike, Administrator, Willis-Knighton Medical Center, Shreveport, LA, p. A315

CHANDLER, Ryan, Chief Executive Officer, Northwest Texas Healthcare System, Amarillo, TX, p. A652

CHANDLER, Vincent, Director Information Services, Porterville Developmental Center, Porterville, CA, p. A86

CHANDLER, Wendy, Regional Vice President Human Resources, Christus St. Frances Cabrini Hospital, Alexandria, LA, p. A295
Vice President Human Resources, Christus Health Shreveport-Bossier, Shreveport, LA, p. A314
Vice President Human Resources, Christus St. Michael Health System, Texarkana, TX, p. A719

CHANDRAN, Kutty, M.D., Regional Medical Officer, Broward Health Coral Springs, Coral Springs, FL, p. A135

CHANDRASENA, Anita, M.D., Vice President Medical Affairs, Sequoia Hospital, Redwood City, CA, p. A88

CHANDY, Joseph, Administrator, Methodist Hospital Of Chicago, Chicago, IL, p. A199

CHANEY, Cindy, Chief Executive Officer, Pam Specialty Hospital Of Denver, Denver, CO, p. A110

CHANEY, Martin, M.D., Chief Medical Officer, Maury Regional Hospital, Columbia, TN, p. A636

CHANG, Alex, Chief Operating Officer, Englewood Community Hospital, Englewood, FL, p. A137

CHANG, Jason, Executive Vice President and Chief Operating Officer, The Queen's Medical Center, Honolulu, HI, p. A185

CHANG, Michael, M.D., Chief Medical Officer, Usa Health Children's & Women's Hospital, Mobile, AL, p. A22

CHANG, Sang-ick, M.D., M.P.H., Chief Medical Officer, Highland Hospital, Oakland, CA, p. A82

CHANNELL, Lesley, Vice President Human Resources, Reston Hospital Center, Reston, VA, p. A749
Vice President Human Resources, Dominion Hospital, Falls Church, VA, p. A741

CHAPDELAINE, Debora, Manager Information Technology, Aurora Medical Center Kenosha, Kenosha, WI, p. A786

CHAPITAL, Alyssa, M.D., Medical Director, Mayo Clinic Hospital, Mayo Clinic Hospital, Phoenix, AZ, p. A36

CHAPLIN, Steven, M.D., Medical Director, Sutter Health Kahi Mohala, Ewa Beach, HI, p. A184

CHAPMAN, Bradley, President, Penn Highlands Elk, Saint Marys, PA, p. A606

CHAPMAN, Cully, Chief Financial Officer, Lutheran Hospital Of Indiana, Fort Wayne, IN, p. A228

CHAPMAN, Donna, R.N., Chief Nursing Officer, Mckay-Dee Hospital, Ogden, UT, p. A730

CHAPMAN, Emily, Chief Medical Officer, Children's Hospitals And Clinics Of Minnesota, Minneapolis, MN, p. A380

CHAPMAN, Jeffrey, M.D., Chief Medical Officer, Cheyenne Regional Medical Center, Cheyenne, WY, p. A801

CHAPMAN, Jerry, Chief Executive Officer, Carolina Center For Behavioral Health, Greer, SC, p. A621

CHAPMAN, John, Chief Operative Officer, San Antonio Regional Hospital, Upland, CA, p. A102

CHAPMAN, John T., Interim President and Chief Executive Officer, San Antonio Regional Hospital, Upland, CA, p. A102

CHAPMAN, Jon, Fiscal Officer, Western State Hospital, Staunton, VA, p. A752

CHAPMAN, Judy, Interim Director Information Systems, Upmc Lock Haven, Lock Haven, PA, p. A595

CHAPMAN, Karen, Director Human Resources, Musc Health Chester Medical Center, Chester, SC, p. A617
Human Resources Director, Musc Health Lancaster Medical Center, Lancaster, SC, p. A622

CHAPMAN, Kathy, R.N., Chief Clinical Officer and Vice President of Patient Services, Ascension Allegan Hospital, Allegan, MI, p. A348

CHAPMAN, Patrick, Ed.D., Chief Executive Officer, Tippah County Hospital, Ripley, MS, p. A399

CHAPMAN, Rachel, Nurse Manager, Noland Hospital Birmingham, Birmingham, AL, p. A15

CHAPMAN, Rick, Chief Information Officer, Kindred Hospital North Florida, Green Cove Springs, FL, p. A139

CHAPMAN, Roland, Chief Information Officer, Northern Navajo Medical Center, Shiprock, NM, p. A472

CHAPMAN, Teresa, Vice President Human Resources, Northwestern Medicine Marianjoy Rehabilitation Hospital, Wheaton, IL, p. A222

CHAPMAN, Terina, Director of Nursing, Northern Utah Rehabilitation Hospital, South Ogden, UT, p. A733

CHAPMAN CIANCI, Sergio, Chief Executive Officer, Valle Vista Health System, Greenwood, IN, p. A230

CHAPMAN ESQ, KathleenDeputy Director, Patient Care Services, Va Portland Healthcare System, Portland, OR, p. A580

CHAPPEL, Blaine, Director Information Technology, Martin General Hospital, Williamston, NC, p. A520

CHAPPELL, Pamela, R.N., Assistant Administrator, Louisiana Extended Care Hospital Of West Monroe, West Monroe, LA, p. A316
R.N., Assistant Administrator, Specialty Hospital, Monroe, LA, p. A309

CHAPPELL, Robert, M.D., Chief Medical Officer and Chief Quality Officer, Huntsville Hospital, Huntsville, AL, p. A20

CHAPPELL, Teresa, Chief Information Officer, Johnston Health, Smithfield, NC, p. A518

CHAPPLE, Scott, Chief Operating Officer, Oroville Hospital, Oroville, CA, p. A83

CHARARA, Kassem, Chief Medical Officer, Beaumont Hospital - Taylor, Taylor, MI, p. A367

CHARBENEAU, Ryan, M.D., Chief Medical Officer, St. David's North Austin Medical Center, Austin, TX, p. A656

CHARDAVOYNE, Alan, Chief Financial Officer, The University Of Vermont Health Network Elizabethtown Community Hospital, Elizabethtown, NY, p. A483

CHARLAT, Richard, Chief of Staff, Iowa City Va Health Care System, Iowa City, IA, p. A252

CHARLES, Charlotte, Director Acute Patient Services, Madison Regional Health System, Madison, SD, p. A629

CHARLES, John, M.D., Chief Medical Officer, Mcleod Health Loris, Loris, SC, p. A622

CHARLES, Sally, Coordinator Human Resources, Grace Medical Center, Lubbock, TX, p. A697

CHARLES, Timothy L., President and Chief Executive Officer, Mercy Medical Center - Cedar Rapids, Cedar Rapids, IA, p. A245

CHARLIER, Brian, President and Chief Executive Officer, Hshs St. Mary's Hospital Medical Center, Green Bay, WI, p. A785
President and Chief Executive Officer, Hshs St. Vincent Hospital, Green Bay, WI, p. A785

CHARLTON, Beth, Vice President Patient Services and Chief Nursing Officer, Covenant Healthcare, Saginaw, MI, p. A365

CHARLTON, Francis, M.D., JrChief Medical Staff, St. Mary's Medical Center, San Francisco, CA, p. A94

CHARLTON, Judie, M.D., Chief Medical Officer, West Virginia University Hospitals, Morgantown, WV, p. A775

CHARMEL, Patrick, President and Chief Executive Officer, Griffin Hospital, Derby, CT, p. A122

CHARTIER, Bridgett, Director of Nursing, Beartooth Billings Clinic, Red Lodge, MT, p. A427

CHARTIER, Terry, Director, Information Systems, Mercyone New Hampton Medical Center, New Hampton, IA, p. A255
Director, Information Systems, Mercyone North Iowa Medical Center, Mason City, IA, p. A254

CHARVAT, Peter, M.D., Chief Medical Officer, St. Joseph's Hospital, Tampa, FL, p. A160

CHASE, Amy, Chief Financial Officer, Wyoming County Community Hospital, Warsaw, NY, p. A501

CHASE, Jean, Regional Manager Information Services, Aurora Lakeland Medical Center, Elkhorn, WI, p. A783
Regional Manager Information Services, Aurora Medical Center Burlington, Burlington, WI, p. A781

CHASE, Kyle, Chief Financial Officer, Glacial Ridge Health System, Glenwood, MN, p. A377

CHASE, Layla, Interim Chief Financial Officer, Bunkie General Hospital, Bunkie, LA, p. A299

CHASE, Linda, Ph.D., R.N., Division Senior Vice President and Chief Nursing Officer, Chi Health Lakeside, Omaha, NE, p. A436

CHASE, Pansy, Director Human Resources, Vidant Duplin Hospital, Kenansville, NC, p. A513

CHASE, Robert, M.D., Physician Advisor, West Suburban Medical Center, Oak Park, IL, p. A215

CHASE, Susan, Vice President, Atrium Health's Carolinas Rehabilitation, Charlotte, NC, p. A507

CHASSE, Floyd, Vice President Human Resources, Erlanger Medical Center, Chattanooga, TN, p. A635

CHASTAIN, James G., FACHE, Director, Mississipp. State Hospital, Whitfield, MS, p. A401

CHASTAIN, Stephen, M.D., Chief Medical Officer, Encompass Health Rehabilitation Hospital An Affiliate Of Martin Health, Stuart, FL, p. A158

CHASTANG, Mark J., M.P.H., Chief Executive Officer, Saint Elizabeths Hospital, Washington, DC, p. A130

CHASTANT III, Lee J., Chief Executive Officer, West Feliciana Hospital, Saint Francisville, LA, p. A313

CHATANI, Kumar, Chief Information Officer, Mount Sinai Health System, Mount Sinai Morningside, New York, NY, p. A490
Chief Information Officer, Mount Sinai Health System, New York Eye And Ear Infirmary Of Mount Sinai, New York, NY, p. A490
Senior Vice President and Chief Information Officer Mount Sinai Health System, Mount Sinai Beth Israel, New York, NY, p. A490
Senior Vice President and Chief Information Officer Mount Sinai Health System, The Mount Sinai Hospital, New York, NY, p. A492

CHATELAIN, Alicia, Director Human Resource, Hood Memorial Hospital, Amite, LA, p. A296

CHATELAIN, Vincent, Director Business Development, River Oaks Hospital, New Orleans, LA, p. A311

CHATLEY, Alice, R.N., MSN, Vice President Acute Care Services, Ssm Health St. Mary's Hospital - Jefferson City, Jefferson City, MO, p. A408

CHATMAN, Hubert, Chief Civilian Personnel, Wright Patterson Medical Center, Wright, OH, p. A553

CHATMAN, Jim, Chief Financial Officer, Maria Parham Medical Center, Henderson, NC, p. A511

CHATMAN, Mary, Ph.D., R.N., Chief Executive Officer, Wellstar Windy Hill Hospital, Marietta, GA, p. A176
Ph.D., R.N., Senior Vice President and President, Wellstar Kennestone Hospital, Marietta, GA, p. A176

CHATTERJEE, Kanan, M.D., Chief of Staff, Lebanon Veterans Affairs Medical Center, Lebanon, PA, p. A594

CHAUDHARY, Shahid, M.D., Chief Medical Officer, Avera St. Luke's Hospital, Aberdeen, SD, p. A626

CHAUDHRY, Riaz, M.D., Chief Medical Officer, Mercy Health - St. Charles Hospital, Oregon, OH, p. A547

CHAUDHURI, Sumanta, M.D., Chief Medical Officer, Hemet Valley Medical Center, Hemet, CA, p. A68
M.D., Chief Medical Officer, Menifee Valley Medical Center, Sun City, CA, p. A100

CHAUDRY, Ramesh, M.D., Medical Director, Piedmont Geriatric Hospital, Burkeville, VA, p. A739

CHAUDRY, Zafar, M.D., Senior Vice President and Chief Information Officer, Seattle Children's Hospital, Seattle, WA, p. A764

CHAUHAN, Varun, Chief Executive Officer, Kentfield Hospital, Kentfield, CA, p. A69

CHAUSSARD, David, Chief Executive Officer, Hillcrest Hospital Claremore, Claremore, OK, p. A557

CHAVARRIA, Annmarie, Senior Vce President Patient Care Services, Chief Nursing Officer, Abington Jefferson Health, Abington, PA, p. A583

CHAVEZ, Irene, Senior Vice President and Area Manager, Kaiser Permanente San Jose Medical Center, San Jose, CA, p. A94

CHAVEZ, Kevin, Chief Executive Officer, Kindred Hospital-Brea, Brea, CA, p. A58

CHAVEZ, Shari, Chief Nursing Officer, Swedish Medical Center, Englewood, CO, p. A112

CHAVEZ, Steven, Vice President Finance and Operations, Kettering Medical Center, Kettering, OH, p. A542

CHAVEZ, Virgil, Director Information Technology, Tsehootsooi Medical Center, Fort Defiance, AZ, p. A31

CHAVIS, Anthony, M.D., Vice President Enterprise Medical Officer, Community Hospital Foundation, Community Hospital Of The Monterey Peninsula, Monterey, CA, p. A79

CHAWLA, Nikki, M.D., Medical Director, Alliancehealth Seminole, Seminole, OK, p. A568

CHAYER, Olivia, Director, Human Resources, York Hospital, York, ME, p. A323

CHECK, Arthur, M.D., Chief Medical Officer, Story County Medical Center, Nevada, IA, p. A254

CHECKETTS, Lannie, Chief Financial Officer, Saint Alphonsus Medical Center - Nampa, Nampa, ID, p. A192
Chief Financial Officer, Saint Alphonsus Medical Center - Ontario, Ontario, OR, p. A578

CHEE, Darlene, Acting Chief Executive Officer, Chinle Comprehensive Health Care Facility, Chinle, AZ, p. A31

CHEEK, Collin, Administrator, Baptist Memorial Hospital - Calhoun, Calhoun City, MS, p. A390

CHEEK, Michael, Chief Financial Officer, Christus Good Shepherd Medical Center-Marshall, Marshall, TX, p. A700

CHEEK, Ramona, MS, R.N., Chief Nursing Officer, Mercy Health - Fairfield Hospital, Fairfield, OH, p. A540

CHEEMA, Linde, Vice President Human Resources, Sequoia Hospital, Redwood City, CA, p. A88

CHEESEMAN, Karen, Chief Executive Officer, Mackinac Straits Health System, Inc., Saint Ignace, MI, p. A366

CHEEVER, Liz, Administrator, Miracle Mile Medical Center, Los Angeles, CA, p. A75

CHEKURU, Naidu, M.D., Chief Medical Officer, Covenant Specialty Hospital, Lubbock, TX, p. A697

CHELLAPPA, Sheila, M.D., Chief of Staff, Coatesville Veterans Affairs Medical Center, Coatesville, PA, p. A587

CHEN, Bonny, M.D., Vice President and Chief Medical Officer, Amita Health Adventist Medical Center - Hinsdale, Hinsdale, IL, p. A208

CHEN, David, M.D., Chief Medical Officer, Multicare Deaconess Hospital, Spokane, WA, p. A765
M.D., Chief Medical Officer, Multicare Valley Hospital, Spokane Valley, WA, p. A766

CHEN, Helen, M.D., Chief Medical Officer, Hebrew Rehabilitation Center, Roslindale, MA, p. A344

CHEN, Stephen, M.D., Chief Medicare, Alhambra Hospital Medical Center, Alhambra, CA, p. A55

CHEN, Van, M.D., Medical Director, Ballard Rehabilitation Hospital, San Bernardino, CA, p. A91

CHENEY, David, Chief Executive Officer, Sutter Medical Center, Sacramento, Sacramento, CA, p. A90

CHENG, Alice, President and Chief Executive Officer, Beverly Hospital, Montebello, CA, p. A79

CHENG, Rebecca, Chief Financial Officer, California Hospital Medical Center, Los Angeles, CA, p. A73
Chief Financial Officer, Glendale Memorial Hospital And Health Center, Glendale, CA, p. A67

CHENG, Ringo, Director Information Technology, Surgery Specialty Hospitals Of America, Pasadena, TX, p. A705

CHENNAULT, Paula, Administrator, Unity Psychiatric Care-Columbia, Columbia, TN, p. A637

CHENOWETH, Judy, Chief Nursing Officer, Russell County Hospital, Russell Springs, KY, p. A292

CHERAMIE, Bennett, Vice President Information Technology, Baton Rouge General Medical Center, Baton Rouge, LA, p. A296

CHERAY, James, M.D., Chief Medical Officer, Menorah Medical Center, Overland Park, KS, p. A274

CHERMSIDE, Paula, Chief Executive Officer, Aspirus Ironwood Hospitals & Clinics, Inc., Ironwood, MI, p. A358

CHERMSIDE, Paula L., Chief Executive Officer, Aspirus Ironwood Hospitals & Clinics, Inc., Ironwood, MI, p. A358

CHERRY, Deano, Chief Information Officer, Upmc Kane, Kane, PA, p. A593

CHERRY, Jean, Executive Vice President, Commonwealth Regional Specialty Hospital, Bowling Green, KY, p. A280

CHERRY, Jonathan M., President and Chief Executive Officer, Lifestream Behavioral Center, Leesburg, FL, p. A144

CHERRY, Michael, Chief Financial Officer, Tennova Healthcare-Lafollette Medical Center, La Follette, TN, p. A642

CHERRY, Robert, M.D., Chief Medical and Quality Officer, Ronald Reagan Ucla Medical Center, Los Angeles, CA, p. A75

CHERRY, Troy, Chief Financial Officer, Schick Shadel Hospital, Seattle, WA, p. A763

CHESLEK, Ingrid, R.N., Chief Nursing Officer, Mary Free Bed Rehabilitation Hospital, Grand Rapids, MI, p. A356

CHESLEY, Jeanine, Chief Executive Officer, New England Rehabilitation Hospital Of Portland, Portland, ME, p. A322

CHESLEY, Judy, M.D., Chief of Staff, Sanford Luverne Medical Center, Luverne, MN, p. A379

CHESLEY, Randy, Director Information Technology, Copley Hospital, Morrisville, VT, p. A736

CHESLEY, Walter, Senior Vice President Human Resources, Hennepin Healthcare, Minneapolis, MN, p. A380

CHESNOS, Richard, Senior Vice President Finance and Chief Financial Officer, St. Clair Hospital, Pittsburgh, PA, p. A603

CHESSARE, John B., M.D., M.P.H., FACHE, President and Chief Executive Officer, Greater Baltimore Medical Center, Baltimore, MD, p. A324

CHESSON, Andrew, Chief Medical Officer, Catawba Valley Medical Center, Hickory, NC, p. A512

CHESSUM, George, Senior Vice President and Chief Information Officer, Community First Medical Center, Chicago, IL, p. A198

Senior Vice President Information Systems and Chief Information Officer, Amita Health Saint Josep. Hospital, Chicago, IL, p. A197

Vice President Information Systems, Amita Health Saint Francis Hospital Evanston, Evanston, IL, p. A204

CHESTER, Julie, Vice President Human Resources, Uh Cleveland Medical Center, Cleveland, OH, p. A535

CHESTER, Linnes, USAF, MSC, Administrator, Mike O'Callaghan Federal Hospital, Nellis Afb, NV, p. A445

CHESTER, William, Manager Human Resources, Grand Junction Veterans Health Care System, Grand Junction, CO, p. A113

CHESTNUT-RAULS, Monica, Vice President Human Resources, Peconic Bay Medical Center, Riverhead, NY, p. A496

CHEUNG, Alan, M.D., Vice President Medical Affairs, Adventist Health Castle, Kailua, HI, p. A185

CHEUNG, Marilou, Assistant Administrator Finance, Kaiser Permanente Woodland Hills Medical Center, Woodland Hills, CA, p. A105

CHEVERE, Carlos, M.D., Medical Director, I. Gonzalez Martinez Oncologic Hospital, Hato Rey, PR, p. A808

CHHABRA, Ankit, Director Finance, Cleveland Clinic Fairview Hospital, Cleveland, OH, p. A534

CHIACCHIARO, Peter, Vice President Human Resources, St. Josep. Hospital, Bethpage, NY, p. A475

CHIANESE, Charles, Vice President, Chief Operating Officer, Children's Specialized Hospital, New Brunswick, NJ, p. A459

CHIANTELLA, Christopher, M.D., Chief Medical Officer, Inova Loudoun Hospital, Leesburg, VA, p. A744

CHIAVETTA, Robert, Vice President Finance, United Memorial Medical Center, Batavia, NY, p. A475

CHIBAYA, Daniel, Chief Information Officer, Adventist Health And Rideout, Marysville, CA, p. A77

CHICK, Melanie, Chief Executive Officer, Baylor Scott & White Medical Center - Trophy Club, Trophy Club, TX, p. A721

CHICKEN, Kurt, Director Support Services, Gundersen Palmer Lutheran Hospital And Clinics, West Union, IA, p. A260

CHIDESTER, Annamarie, R.N., Vice President, Patient Care Services, St. Joseph's Hospital Of Buckhannon, Buckhannon, WV, p. A771

CHIEDA, Katie, Chief Nursing Officer, Fisher-Titus Medical Center, Norwalk, OH, p. A546

CHIEFFO, Ron, Chief Information Officer, Colorado River Medical Center, Needles, CA, p. A81

CHILCOTT, Stephen, Associate Director Human Resources, University Of California, Davis Medical Center, Sacramento, CA, p. A90

CHILD, Clint, R.N., Chief Nursing Officer, Saint Alphonsus Medical Center - Nampa, Nampa, ID, p. A192

CHILDERS, Bethany, Director Human Resources, Methodist Fremont Health, Fremont, NE, p. A432

CHILDERS, Linda, Director Human Resources, Wallowa Memorial Hospital, Enterprise, OR, p. A574

CHILDS, Joe, M.D., Vice President Medical Services, East Tennessee Children's Hospital, Knoxville, TN, p. A641

CHILDS, Michelle, Chief Human Resources Officer, Salinas Valley Memorial Healthcare System, Salinas, CA, p. A90

CHILES, Kevin, Vice President Human Resources, Hutchinson Regional Medical Center, Hutchinson, KS, p. A266

CHILES, Morton, M.D., Chief Medical Officer, Novant Health Uva Health System Culpeper Medical Center, Culpeper, VA, p. A740

CHILESE, Melody, Chief Nurse Executive, Hawthorn Children Psychiatric Hospital, Saint Louis, MO, p. A415

CHILESKI, Andy, Chief Information Officer and Vice President Facilities, Ohiohealth Berger Hospital, Circleville, OH, p. A533

CHILL, Martha, Interim Chief Information Officer, Hancock County Hospital, Sneedville, TN, p. A649

CHILSON, Terrance, Chief of Staff, Tyler Memorial Hospital, Tunkhannock, PA, p. A609

CHILTON, Bryan, Director Information Systems, Navarro Regional Hospital, Corsicana, TX, p. A666

CHILTON, Hal, Senior Vice President and Chief Operating Officer, Adventist Health St. Helena, Saint Helena, CA, p. A90

CHIN, Ellyn, Vice President Finance, Gottlieb Memorial Hospital, Melrose Park, IL, p. A212

CHINBURG, Paul, M.D., Medical Director, Lane County Hospital, Dighton, KS, p. A263

CHING, Angelica, Director Information Systems, Garfield Medical Center, Monterey Park, CA, p. A79

Director Information Systems, Monterey Park Hospital, Monterey Park, CA, p. A79

CHINN, Jeff, Interim Chief Executive Officer, Bakersfield Behavioral Healthcare Hospital, Bakersfield, CA, p. A57

CHINN, Tammie, Director Marketing and Public Relations, Plateau Medical Center, Oak Hill, WV, p. A775

CHINN, Terri, Vice President Finance, St. Mary's Hospital And Medical Center, Grand Junction, CO, p. A113

CHINNOCK, Richard, Chief Medical Officer, LLUCH, Loma Linda University Children's Hospital, Loma Linda, CA, p. A71

CHIOLO, Denise, Chief Human Resources Officer, Phoenixville Hospital, Phoenixville, PA, p. A602

CHIPMAN, Glen, Chief Financial Officer, Healthsource Saginaw, Inc., Saginaw, MI, p. A365

CHIRICHELLA, Joseph, President and Chief Executive Officer, Deborah Heart And Lung Center, Browns Mills, NJ, p. A453

CHISHOLM, Sharon, Entity Human Resource Officer, Texas Health Presbyterian Hospital Allen, Allen, TX, p. A652

CHISOLM, Troy, Chief Executive Officer, Pinewood Springs, Columbia, TN, p. A636

CHISSELL, Herbert, M.D., Chief Medical Officer, Torrance State Hospital, Torrance, PA, p. A608

CHITCHYAN, Ara, M.D., Medical Director, Roosevelt Warm Springs Rehabilitation Hospital - Rehab, Warm Springs, GA, p. A183

CHITESTER, Jamie, Director Information Systems, Poplar Bluff Regional Medical Center, Poplar Bluff, MO, p. A414

CHIUSANO, Jennifer, R.N., Chief Nursing Officer, Saint Francis Hospital, Memphis, TN, p. A645

CHIVERS, John, Chief Financial Officer, Ridgecrest Regional Hospital, Ridgecrest, CA, p. A88

Senior Vice President Finance, Sierra View Medical Center, Porterville, CA, p. A86

CHMURA, David, Chief Information Officer, Copper Queen Community Hospital, Bisbee, AZ, p. A30

CHOATE, Matthew, Chief Nursing Officer, The University Of Vermont Health Network Central Vermont Medical Center, Berlin, VT, p. A735

CHOCKLETT, Wyatt, Chief Operating Officer, Largo Medical Center, Largo, FL, p. A143

CHOINIERE, Leon, Vice President, Chief Financial Officer, St. Mary Medical Center Long Beach, Long Beach, CA, p. A72

CHOINKA, Keith, Vice President Information Systems and Chief Information Officer, St. Josep. Hospital, Nashua, NH, p. A450

CHONG, Johnnette, Chief Financial Officer, Los Angeles Community Hospital At Los Angeles, Los Angeles, CA, p. A75

CHORD, Ginger, Coordinator Human Resources, Monument Health Sturgis Hospital, Sturgis, SD, p. A632

CHOU, David, Vice President, Chief Information and Digital Officer, Children's Mercy Hospital Kansas City, Kansas City, MO, p. A408

CHOU, Rebecca, Director Information Systems, Palestine Regional Medical Center-East, Palestine, TX, p. A704

CHOUDHURY, Golam, Chief of Staff, Desert Springs Hospital Medical Center, Las Vegas, NV, p. A443

CHOUDHURY, Seleem, R.N., MSN, President and Chief Operating Officer, Porter Medical Center, Middlebury, VT, p. A736

CHOY, Ann, Manager Human Resources and Payroll, Kuakini Medical Center, Honolulu, HI, p. A184

CHOZINSKI, Joseph, M.D., Deputy Commander Clinical Services, Brooke Army Medical Center, Fort Sam Houston, TX, p. A677

CHRISTENSEN, Carl, Senior Vice President and Chief Information Officer, Northwestern Memorial HealthCare, Northwestern Memorial Hospital, Chicago, IL, p. A200

Senior Vice President, Chief Information Officer, Northwestern Medicine Kishwaukee Hospital, Dekalb, IL, p. A202

CHRISTENSEN, Claudia, Director, Human Resources, Mills-Peninsula Health Services, Burlingame, CA, p. A59

CHRISTENSEN, Connie, Chief Financial Officer, Morrill County Community Hospital, Bridgeport, NE, p. A430

CHRISTENSEN, David, M.D., Senior Vice President and Chief Medical Officer, Valley Children's Healthcare, Madera, CA, p. A76

CHRISTENSEN, Elizabeth, Director Human Resources, Northern Light Mercy Hospital, Portland, ME, p. A322

CHRISTENSEN, G, M.D., Chief Medical Officer, William Bee Ririe Hospital, Ely, NV, p. A441

CHRISTENSEN, Gwen, Vice President, Finance, Aurora Baycare Medical Center, Green Bay, WI, p. A785

CHRISTENSEN, Jay, FACHE, Chief Financial Officer, Lucas County Health Center, Chariton, IA, p. A245

FACHE, Interim Chief Executive Officer, Lucas County Health Center, Chariton, IA, p. A245

CHRISTENSEN, Jeffrey, Chief Executive Officer, Encompass Health Rehabilitation Hospital Of Northwest Tucson, Tucson, AZ, p. A40

Chief Executive Officer, Encompass Health Rehabilitation Institute Of Tucson, Tucson, AZ, p. A40

CHRISTENSEN, Kim, Interim Chief Nursing Executive, Sheridan Community Hospital, Sheridan, MI, p. A366

CHRISTENSEN, Mark, Chief Financial Officer, Weiser Memorial Hospital, Weiser, ID, p. A193

CHRISTENSEN, Marti, Director of Psychiatric Nursing, Douglas County Community Mental Health Center, Omaha, NE, p. A437

CHRISTENSEN, Ryan, Chief Operatng Officer, St. Rose Dominican Hospitals - Siena Campus, Henderson, NV, p. A442

CHRISTENSEN, Scott, FACHE, Chief Executive Officer, Delta Regional Medical Center, Greenville, MS, p. A392

CHRISTENSEN, Todd, Vice President, Finance, Grand Itasca Clinic And Hospital, Grand Rapids, MN, p. A377

CHRISTENSEN, Troy, Chief Financial Officer, Madison Memorial Hospital, Rexburg, ID, p. A192

CHRISTENSEN, W, M.D., Chief of Staff, Ut Health Pittsburg, Pittsburg, TX, p. A706

CHRISTENSON, Erik, Chief Executive Officer, Heart Of America Medical Center, Rugby, ND, p. A525

CHRISTENSON, Ron, Chief Financial Officer, Morris County Hospital, Council Grove, KS, p. A263

CHRISTENSON, Shannon, Director Human Resources, Aurora West Allis Medical Center, West Allis, WI, p. A799

CHRISTIAN, Bruce C., Chief Executive Officer, Amita Health Adventist Medical Center Bolingbrook, Bolingbrook, IL, p. A196

President and Chief Executive Officer, Amita Health Adventist Medical Center Glenoaks, Glendale Heights, IL, p. A206

CHRISTIAN, Greg, Senior Vice President, Area Manager - San Bernardino County Area, Kaiser Permanente Fontana Medical Center, Fontana, CA, p. A64

CHRISTIAN, Karolyne, Director Human Resources, Byrd Regional Hospital, Leesville, LA, p. A307

CHRISTIAN, Lynn, MSN, R.N., Senior Director Acute Care Nursing, Centracare - Monticello, Monticello, MN, p. A381

CHRISTIAN, Michael, Chief Operating Officer, St. John Sapulpa, Sapulpa, OK, p. A567

CHRISTIANO, Barbara, Vice President, Patient Care Services and Chief Nursing Officer, Penn Medicine Princeton Medical Center, Plainsboro, NJ, p. A461

CHRISTIANSEN, Anne, Chief Financial Officer, Pioneer Memorial Hospital And Health Services, Viborg, SD, p. A632

CHRISTIANSEN, Hilary, Chief Financial Officer, George C. Grap. Community Hospital, Hamburg, IA, p. A251

CHRISTIANSEN, Keith, Chief Nursing Officer, Select Specialty Hospital-Erie, Erie, PA, p. A590

CHRISTIANSEN, Lia, Chief Operating Officer, Acute Care Hospitals, Fairview Lakes Health Services, Wyoming, MN, p. A388

Chief Operating Officer, Acute Care Hospitals, Fairview Northland Medical Center, Princeton, MN, p. A383

Chief Operating Officer, Acute Care Hospitals, St. John's Hospital, Maplewood, MN, p. A380

Chief Operating Officer, Acute Care Hospitals, St. Joseph's Hospital, Saint Paul, MN, p. A385

Chief Operating Officer, Acute Care Hospitals, Woodwinds Health Campus, Woodbury, MN, p. A388

CHRISTIANSEN, Sara, Interim Director Human Resources, Ridgeview Sibley Medical Center, Arlington, MN, p. A372

CHRISTIANSON, Chad, Chief Executive Officer, Ocala Regional Medical Center, Ocala, FL, p. A150

CHRISTIANSON, Delano, Administrator, Centracare Health-Sauk Centre, Sauk Centre, MN, p. A386

CHRISTIE, Janet, Senior Vice President Human Resources, Uf Health Shands Hospital, Gainesville, FL, p. A139

CHRISTINE, Gerald, Chief Financial Officer, Lakewood Ranch Medical Center, Bradenton, FL, p. A133

CHRISTION, Lydia, Director Human Resources, Encompass Health Rehabilitation Hospital Of Dothan, Dothan, AL, p. A17

CHRISTISON, George, M.D., Medical Director, Dsh Patton, Patton, CA, p. A85

CHRISTMAN, Lawrence, Chief Financial Officer and Chief Operating Officer, Riverview Health, Noblesville, IN, p. A238

CHRISTMAN, Thomas, Director Plant Operations, Kindred Hospital-St. Louis, Saint Louis, MO, p. A416

CHRISTNER, Jane, Chief Nursing Officer, Mclaren Thumb Region, Bad Axe, MI, p. A349

CHRISTOPH, Rebecca, Director Nursing and Patient Care Services, Mid-Valley Hospital, Omak, WA, p. A761

CHRISTOPHEL, Randal, President and Chief Executive Officer, Goshen Health, Goshen, IN, p. A229

CHRISTOPHER, Candi, CPA, Chief Financial Officer, Stonesprings Hospital Center, Dulles, VA, p. A741

CHRISTOPHERSEN, Kristin, Chief Nursing Officer, Fountain Valley Regional Hospital And Medical Center, Fountain Valley, CA, p. A64

CHRISTY, Richard, Information Technology Manager, Houston County Community Hospital, Erin, TN, p. A638

CHRISTY, Rose, Executive Director of Medical Services, Hamilton Center, Terre Haute, IN, p. A241

CHU, Betty, M.D., Chief Medical Officer and Vice President of Medical Affairs, Henry Ford West Bloomfield Hospital, West Bloomfield, MI, p. A369

CHU, Edward, Chief Financial Officer, Leahi Hospital, Honolulu, HI, p. A184

CHUA, Catherine, M.D., Chief Medical Officer, Davis Medical Center, Elkins, WV, p. A772

CHUA, Jesus, M.D., Chief of Staff, Franklin Foundation Hospital, Franklin, LA, p. A301

CHUE, Bevins, M.D., Medical Director, Encompass Health Rehabilitation Hospital Of Desert Canyon, Las Vegas, NV, p. A443

CHUGDEN, Robert, M.D., Chief Medical Officer, West Jefferson Medical Center, Marrero, LA, p. A308

CHUKWUMA, Lilian, Chief Financial Officer, United Medical Center, Washington, DC, p. A130

CHULICK, Michele, President and Chief Executive Officer, Wyoming Medical Center, Casper, WY, p. A801

CHUN, Ryan, Information Resources Management, San Francisco Va Medical Center, San Francisco, CA, p. A94

CHUNG, Esther, Chief Operating Officer, St. David's Medical Center, Austin, TX, p. A656

CHUNG, Maria, CPA, Director Fiscal Services, Shriners Hospitals For Children-Boston, Boston, MA, p. A336

CHUNG, Michael, Chief Financial Officer, Greater El Monte Community Hospital, South El Monte, CA, p. A99

CHUNG, William, M.D., Chief of Staff, Chinese Hospital, San Francisco, CA, p. A93

CHURCH, Brian, Senior Vice President and Chief Financial Officer, Phoebe Putney Memorial Hospital, Albany, GA, p. A163

CHURCH, Kim, Manager Human Resources, G. Werber Bryan Psychiatric Hospital, Columbia, SC, p. A617

Manager Human Resources, William S. Hall Psychiatric Institute, Columbia, SC, p. A618

CHURCH, Rhonda, Director Human Resources, Riverbend Rehabilitation Hospital, Monroe, LA, p. A309

CHURCHILL, Brigitte, Director of Human Resources, Memorial Satilla Health, Waycross, GA, p. A183

CHURCHILL, Larry, Director Information Services, Alliancehealth Woodward, Woodward, OK, p. A572

CHURCHILL, Sandi, Vice President Business Development and Operations, Professional Services, Advocate Good Samaritan Hospital, Downers Grove, IL, p. A203

CHURCHILL, Timothy A., President, Stephens Memorial Hospital, Norway, ME, p. A321

CHURCHWELL, Kevin, M.D., President and Chief Operating Officer, Boston Children's Hospital, Boston, MA, p. A335

CIAMPA, Amy, Chief Financial Officer, Park Royal Hospital, Fort Myers, FL, p. A138

CIAMPA, Steve, Vice President Finance, Porter Medical Center, Middlebury, VT, p. A736

CIANCIOTTO CROYLE, Allison, Vice President of Human Resources, Mercy Medical Center, Rockville Centre, NY, p. A497

CIANFLONE, Laura, Director Human Resources, Kenmore Mercy Hospital, Kenmore, NY, p. A486

CIAREFELLA, Donna, Director Human Resources, Vibra Hospital Of Western Massachusetts, Springfield, MA, p. A345

CICCARELLI, John, Director Information Technology, Parkview Community Hospital Medical Center, Riverside, CA, p. A88

CICCARELLI, Thomas, Chief Information Officer, East Orange General Hospital, East Orange, NJ, p. A454

CICCHELLI, Duane, Director, Information Technology Services, San Gorgonio Memorial Hospital, Banning, CA, p. A58

CICCONE, Josie, Director, Human Resources, Garden City Hospital, Garden City, MI, p. A355

CICERI, David, M.D., Chief Medical Officer, Baylor Scott & White Continuing Care Hospital-Temple, Temple, TX, p. A718

CICIRETTI, Mary, Director Human Resources, Riddle Hospital, Media, PA, p. A597

CIHA, Clayton, President and Chief Executive Officer, Amita Health Alexian Brothers Behavioral Health Hospital, Hoffman Estates, IL, p. A208

CIHAK, Scott A., President and Chief Executive Officer, Tristar Centennial Medical Center, Nashville, TN, p. A647

CIMA, Robert, M.D., Medical Director, Hospital Operations, Mayo Clinic Hospital - Rochester, Rochester, MN, p. A384

CIMALA, Derek W., Chief Executive Officer, Kentucky River Medical Center, Jackson, KY, p. A285

CIMINO JR, MichaelChief Financial Officer, Banner Behavioral Health Hospital - Scottsdale, Scottsdale, AZ, p. A38

CIMMINO, Denise, MSN, R.N., Assistant Vice President, Nursing and Patient Care Services, Carepoint Health Christ Hospital, Jersey City, NJ, p. A456

CINTRON, Jacob, FACHE, President and Chief Executive Officer, University Medical Center Of El Paso, El Paso, TX, p. A676

CIOFFI, Cheryl, R.N., Senior Vice President, Chief Operating Officer and Chief Nursing Officer, Frederick Health, Frederick, MD, p. A329

CIRALDO, Lou, Information Services Representative, Uh Geauga Medical Center, Chardon, OH, p. A531

CIRBA, Michael, Chief Information Officer, Good Shepherd Specialty Hospital, Bethlehem, PA, p. A584

CIRO, Maria, Director Human Resources, Acuity Specialty Hospital Of New Jersey, Atlantic City, NJ, p. A452

CIROCCO, Anthony, Chief Financial Officer, Dignity Health Arizona General Hospital, Laveen, AZ, p. A33

CITA, Bob, Chief Information Officer, Searhc Mt. Edgecumbe Hospital, Sitka, AK, p. A29

CITAK, Michael, M.D., Chief Medical Officer, Lake Cumberland Regional Hospital, Somerset, KY, p. A293

CITARA, Frank, Chief Hospital Executive, Hackensack Meridian Health Bayshore Community Hospital, Holmdel, NJ, p. A456

CITRO, Tina, R.N., Chief Nursing Officer, Vice President, Patient Services, Wellspan Ephrata Community Hospital, Ephrata, PA, p. A589

CIUFO, Donna, R.N., Vice President and Chief Nurse Executive, Hackensack Meridian Health Southern Ocean Medical Center, Manahawkin, NJ, p. A458

CIVIC, Dave, M.D., Associate Director Clinical Services, U. S. Public Health Service Phoenix Indian Medical Center, Phoenix, AZ, p. A37

CIVITELLO, Dean, Vice President Human Resources, Saint Joseph's Medical Center, Yonkers, NY, p. A502

Vice President, Human Resources, Public Relations and Development, The University Of Vermont Health Network-Champlain Valley Physicians Hospital, Plattsburgh, NY, p. A495

CLAASSENS, Nicolise, Nurse Executive, West Central Georgia Regional Hospital, Columbus, GA, p. A169

CLABAUGH, John, Director Human Resources, Saint Luke's East Hospital, Lee's Summit, MO, p. A411

CLABUESCH, Paul, President and Chief Executive Officer, Harbor Beach Community Hospital, Harbor Beach, MI, p. A357

CLACK, Deborah, Chief Nursing Officer, Hunt Regional Medical Center, Greenville, TX, p. A682

CLAEYS, David, FACHE, Chief Executive Officer, Beaumont Hospital - Dearborn, Dearborn, MI, p. A352

CLANCY, Mikki, Chief Operating Officer, Miami Valley Hospital, Dayton, OH, p. A538

CLANCY, Patricia, M.D., Director Medical Services, Maniilaq Health Center, Kotzebue, AK, p. A29

CLAPP, Ann, Director Human Resources, Encompass Health Rehabilitation Hospital Of Texarkana, Texarkana, TX, p. A720

CLAPP, Denise, Chief Nursing Officer, Lourdes Counseling Center, Richland, WA, p. A763

Chief Nursing Officer, Lourdes Medical Center, Pasco, WA, p. A762

CLAPP, William, M.D., Chief of Medical Staff, Methodist Hospital Union County, Morganfield, KY, p. A290

CLARK, Allan, M.D., Medical Director, Southwood Psychiatric Hospital, Pittsburgh, PA, p. A603

CLARK, Ashley, Coordinator Human Resources, Noland Hospital Birmingham, Birmingham, AL, p. A15

CLARK, Ben, Vice President and Chief Information Officer, Centra Lynchburg General Hospital, Lynchburg, VA, p. A745

CLARK, Christopher, D.O., President and Chief Executive Officer, Saint Vincent Hospital, Erie, PA, p. A590

CLARK, Dale, Chief Operating Officer, Holston Valley Medical Center, Kingsport, TN, p. A641

Chief Operating Officer, Indian Path Community Hospital, Kingsport, TN, p. A641

CLARK, David D., FACHE, Chief Executive Officer, Alta Bates Summit Medical Center - Summit Campus, Oakland, CA, p. A82

FACHE, Chief Executive Officer, Alta Bates Summit Medical Center-Alta Bates Campus, Berkeley, CA, p. A58

CLARK, Debra, Chief Nursing Officer, Bayfront Health Port Charlotte, Port Charlotte, FL, p. A154

CLARK, Denise, Chief Nursing Officer, Holy Cross Hospital, Taos, NM, p. A473

CLARK, Eileen, Vice President Information Services, Charleston Area Medical Center, Charleston, WV, p. A771

CLARK, Janice, Manager Human Resources, Garfield Park Hospital, Chicago, IL, p. A198

CLARK, Jason, Director Information Systems, Greenwood County Hospital, Eureka, KS, p. A264

CLARK, Jeff, Director Information Systems, Graham Regional Medical Center, Graham, TX, p. A681

CLARK, Jeffrey, Chief Nursing Officer, Cornerstone Hospitals Southwest Louisiana, Lake Charles, LA, p. A306

CLARK, Jeremy L., Market Chief Executive Officer, Hilton Head Hospital, Hilton Head Island, SC, p. A621

CLARK, Jimmy, Administrator, Ut Health Specialty Hospital, Tyler, TX, p. A722

CLARK, Karen, MS, R.N., Vice President Operations, Advocate South Suburban Hospital, Hazel Crest, IL, p. A207

Director Administrative Services, Sonoma Developmental Center, Eldridge, CA, p. A63

Vice President Patient Care Services, St. Mary's Regional Medical Center, Lewiston, ME, p. A321

CLARK, Kent, M.D., Chief Medical Affairs and Quality, Waldo County General Hospital, Belfast, ME, p. A319

CLARK, Lisa, Director Human Resources, Willamette Valley Medical Center, Mcminnville, OR, p. A577

CLARK, Mark, Human Resources Liaison, U. S. Air Force Regional Hospital, Elmendorf Afb, AK, p. A28

Vice President Operations, Ssm Health Good Samaritan Hospital, Mount Vernon, IL, p. A213

CLARK, Michael, Chief Operating Officer, Mckay-Dee Hospital, Ogden, UT, p. A730

Executive Vice President and Chief Financial Officer, Fhn Memorial Hospital, Freeport, IL, p. A205

Fiscal Administrative Manager, Connecticut Veterans Home And Hospital, Rocky Hill, CT, p. A125

CLARK, Michael A., Administrator, Mckay-Dee Hospital, Ogden, UT, p. A730

CLARK, N. Travis., President, Valley Health - Page Memorial Hospital, Luray, VA, p. A745

President, Valley Health - Shenandoah Memorial Hospital, Woodstock, VA, p. A754

CLARK, Nancy, Vice President Human Resources, Regional Medical Center Of San Jose, San Jose, CA, p. A95

CLARK, Patrick, Manager Information Technology, Sunnyview Rehabilitation Hospital, Schenectady, NY, p. A498

CLARK, Paulette, Chief Human Resource Officer, Roseland Community Hospital, Chicago, IL, p. A200

CLARK, Randal, Vice President Finance, Northern Light Sebasticook Valley Hospital, Pittsfield, ME, p. A322

CLARK, Rebecca, Chief Nursing Officer, Indiana University Health Jay Hospital, Portland, IN, p. A239

CLARK, Renee, M.D., Executive Vice President and Chief Operating Officer, Southcoast Hospitals Group. Fall River, MA, p. A339

CLARK, Rhonda, Interim Chief Nursing Officer, Alta Vista Regional Hospital, Las Vegas, NM, p. A470

CLARK, Robert J., President and Chief Executive Officer, Bristol Bay Area Health Corporation, Dillingham, AK, p. A28

CLARK, Robin, Chief Nursing Officer, Select Specialty Hospital-Greensboro, Greensboro, NC, p. A511

CLARK, Rodney, Chief Operating Officer, North Sunflower Medical Center, Ruleville, MS, p. A400

CLARK, Ron, M.D., Interim Chief Executive Officer, Vcu Medical Center, Richmond, VA, p. A751

M.D., Vice President Clinical Activities and Chief Medical Officer, Vcu Medical Center, Richmond, VA, p. A751

CLARK, Sharon, Director Human Resources, Hillsboro Area Hospital, Hillsboro, IL, p. A207

CLARK, Shawn, Director Information Systems, The Physicians Centre Hospital, Bryan, TX, p. A661

CLARK, Stella, MSN, R.N., Chief Nursing Officer, Hshs St. Joseph's Hospital, Chippewa Falls, WI, p. A781

CLARK, Teresa, R.N., MS, Chief Nursing Officer, Cook Children's Medical Center, Fort Worth, TX, p. A678

Chief Executive Officer and Administrator, Wichita County Health Center, Leoti, KS, p. A269

CLARK, Theo, Director Financial Services, Kp. Promise Hospital Of Phoenix, Mesa, AZ, p. A34

CLARK, Troy, Chief Executive Officer, Encompass Health Rehabilitation Hospital Of Kingsport, Kingsport, TN, p. A640

Chief Executive Officer, Rehabilitation Hospital Of Bristol, Bristol, VA, p. A739

CLARK, William, M.D., Chief Clinical Affairs, Caro Center, Caro, MI, p. A350

Chief Financial Officer, Caldwell Memorial Hospital, Columbia, LA, p. A299

CLARKE, Clifton, Vice President Medical Management, Advocate Illinois Masonic Medical Center, Chicago, IL, p. A197

CLARKE, James, M.D., Vice President Medical Affairs and Clinical Effectiveness, Hackensack Meridian Health Ocean Medical Center, Brick Township. NJ, p. A453

CLAROS, Elizabeth, Administrator Personnel Services, Guam Memorial Hospital Authority, Tamuning, GU, p. A805

CLARY, Brandon, President and Chief Executive Officer, Anmed Health Cannon, Pickens, SC, p. A623

CLARY, Robert, M.D., Medical Director, Northern Rockies Medical Center, Cut Bank, MT, p. A423

CLATANOFF, Kris, Director Human Resources, St. Josep. Medical Center, Houston, TX, p. A688

CLAUDY, Frank, M.D., Vice President Medical Staff Affairs, Genesis Medical Center - Davenport, Davenport, IA, p. A247

CLAUNCH, Jeremy, Chief Financial Officer, Power County Hospital District, American Falls, ID, p. A188

CLAUSEN, Patricia, R.N., Chief Nurse Executive, Kaiser Permanente Downey Medical Center, Downey, CA, p. A62

CLAUSSEN, Denise, R.N., MSN, Chief Nursing Officer, Texas Health Presbyterian Hospital Kaufman, Kaufman, TX, p. A692

CLAUSSEN, Tammy, Chief Human Resource Officer, Tri Valley Health System, Cambridge, NE, p. A430

CLAVELL, Luis, M.D., Medical Director, San Jorge Children's Hospital, Santurce, PR, p. A811

CLAWSON, Tonya, Manager Human Resources, Mercyone Centerville Medical Center, Centerville, IA, p. A245

CLAXTON, Tracey, Chief Financial Officer, Jennersville Hospital, West Grove, PA, p. A610

Chief Financial Officer, Musc Health Chester Medical Center, Chester, SC, p. A617

CLAY, David, Chief Executive Officer, Lower Keys Medical Center, Key West, FL, p. A142

CLAY, Elysia, Chief Nursing Officer, Encompass Health Rehabilitation Hospital Of Dallas, Dallas, TX, p. A668

CLAYMORE, Krystal, Chief Financial Officer, Great Plains Health, North Platte, NE, p. A436

CLAYTON, Edward, Chief Executive Officer, Phelp. Health, Rolla, MO, p. A414

CLAYTON, Julie, Chief Nursing Officer, Barton Memorial Hospital, South Lake Tahoe, CA, p. A99

CLAYTON, Kent G., Chief Executive Officer, Los Alamitos Medical Center, Los Alamitos, CA, p. A73

CLEARY, Gerard, M.D., Senior Vice President, Chief of Staff and Chief Medical Officer, Abington Jefferson Health, Abington, PA, p. A583

CLEARY, Mary Elizabeth., President, Gottlieb Memorial Hospital, Melrose Park, IL, p. A212

President, Macneal Hospital, Berwyn, IL, p. A195

CLEARY, Steven, Chief Financial Officer, Overland Park Regional Medical Center, Overland Park, KS, p. A274

CLEAVER, Chuck, Vice President and Chief Financial Officer, Cleveland Clinic Martin North Hospital, Stuart, FL, p. A158

CLECKLER, Jason, Chief Executive Officer, Middle Park Health-Kremmling, Kremmling, CO, p. A114

CLEGG, Travis, Vice President, Operations, Adventist Health Castle, Kailua, HI, p. A185

CLELAND, Dub, Chief Financial Officer, Oklahoma Surgical Hospital, Tulsa, OK, p. A570

CLELAND, William, M.D., Chief Medical Officer, University Of Mississipp. Medical Center, Jackson, MS, p. A395

CLEMEN, Linda, Vice President and Chief Nursing Officer, Katherine Shaw Bethea Hospital, Dixon, IL, p. A202

CLEMENT, Bernie, Chief Information Officer, Thibodaux Regional Health System, Thibodaux, LA, p. A316

CLEMENT, Charles, Chief Executive Officer, Searhc Mt. Edgecumbe Hospital, Sitka, AK, p. A29

CLEMENT, Kevin J., Chief Executive Officer, Encompass Health Rehabilitation Hospital, A Partner Of Washington Regional, Fayetteville, AR, p. A45

CLEMENT, Mark C., President, Bethesda North Hospital, Cincinnati, OH, p. A532

CLEMENTS, James, Chief Executive Officer, Cullman Regional Medical Center, Cullman, AL, p. A17

CLEMENTS, John, Chief Financial Officer, Mccullough-Hyde Memorial Hospital/Trihealth, Oxford, OH, p. A547

CLEMENTS, Morgan, Director of Human Resources, Anmed Health Rehabilitation Hospital, Anderson, SC, p. A615

CLEMMENSEN, Scott, Vice President Human Resources and Leadership Enhancement, Capital Health Medical Center-Hopewell, Pennington, NJ, p. A461

Vice President Human Resources and Leadership Enhancement, Capital Health Regional Medical Center, Trenton, NJ, p. A464

CLEMMER, Deb, Vice President Human Resources, Bothwell Regional Health Center, Sedalia, MO, p. A418

CLEMONS, Deneace, Chief Operating Officer, Twin Lakes Regional Medical Center, Leitchfield, KY, p. A286

CLER, Leslie, M.D., Chief Medical Officer, Methodist Dallas Medical Center, Dallas, TX, p. A669

CLEVELAND, Cynthia, Ph.D., R.N., Associate Director for Patient Care Services and Nurse Executive, Birmingham Veterans Affairs Medical Center, Birmingham, AL, p. A14

CLEVENGER, Erin, Chief Nursing Officer and Director of Quality, Memorial Medical Center, Port Lavaca, TX, p. A707

CLEVINGER, Betty, Chief Nursing Officer, Community Memorial Hospital, Hicksville, OH, p. A542

CLEWS, Donna, Ph.D., R.N., Vice President Patient Care Services, Berkeley Medical Center, Martinsburg, WV, p. A774

CLIFFORD, Joan, R.N., FACHE, Medical Center Director and Chief Executive Officer, Bedford Veterans Affairs Medical Center, Edith Nourse Rogers Memorial Veterans Hospital, Bedford, MA, p. A334

CLIFFORD, Michael, Director Finance, Wayne Memorial Hospital, Honesdale, PA, p. A592

CLIFFORD, Ryan, M.D., Chief of Staff, Washakie Medical Center, Worland, WY, p. A804

CLINE, Carl T., Vice President, Carilion Clinic and Hospital Administrator, Carilion Franklin Memorial Hospital, Rocky Mount; VA, p. A751

CLINE, Vickie, Director Human Resources, Mosaic Medical Center - Albany, Albany, MO, p. A402

CLINGENPEEL, Jeremy, Administrator, Satanta District Hospital And Long Term Care, Satanta, KS, p. A276

CLINGER, Dallas, Administrator, Power County Hospital District, American Falls, ID, p. A188

CLINITE, Ed, D.O., Chief of Staff, Adventist Health Sonora, Sonora, CA, p. A99

CLINTON, Lee M., FACHE, President and Chief Executive Officer, Titusville Area Hospital, Titusville, PA, p. A608

CLINTON, Lori, Chief Nursing Officer, Sparta Community Hospital, Sparta, IL, p. A220

CLIPP, Jerry, Manager Human Resources, Washakie Medical Center, Worland, WY, p. A804

CLISTER, Martha, Director Human Resources, Canonsburg Hospital, Canonsburg, PA, p. A586

CLOHSEY, Maria, Director of Nursing, Hackensack Meridian Health Shore Rehabilitation Institute, Brick, NJ, p. A452

CLONCH, Les, Chief Information Officer, Texas Scottish Rite Hospital For Children, Dallas, TX, p. A670

CLONTS, Jolene, Director Human Resources, Logan Regional Hospital, Logan, UT, p. A728

CLOSE, Debra, Chief Executive Officer, Dukes Memorial Hospital, Peru, IN, p. A239

CLOUD, Avery, Vice President and Chief Information Officer, New Hanover Regional Medical Center, Wilmington, NC, p. A520

CLOUD, Sylvia, Director Human Resources, La Downtown Medical Center, Llc, Los Angeles, CA, p. A75

CLOUGH, Jeanette G., President and Chief Executive Officer, Mount Auburn Hospital, Cambridge, MA, p. A338

CLOUGH, Sheila, Chief Executive Officer, Asante Ashland Community Hospital, Ashland, OR, p. A573

CLOUGH-BERRY, Cherie, Vice President, Finance, Hampstead Hospital, Hampstead, NH, p. A449

CLOUSE, Joseph, Chief Administrative Officer, Newport Hospital And Health Services, Newport, WA, p. A761

CLOUSE DAY, Sherry, Vice President Finance, Mercy Hospital Berryville, Berryville, AR, p. A42

CLOUTIER, Jonathan, Manager, Information Services, Buffalo Hospital, Buffalo, MN, p. A373

CLOUTIER, Michael, Director Information Services, Trios Health, Kennewick, WA, p. A759

CLOVER, Robert, Interim Superintendent, Larue D. Carter Memorial Hospital, Indianapolis, IN, p. A232

Superintendent and Chief Executive Officer, Logansport State Hospital, Logansport, IN, p. A235

Superintendent, Neurodiagnostic Institute And Advanced Treatment Center, Indianapolis, IN, p. A232

CLOWARD, Mitchell, Administrator, Dixie Regional Medical Center, Saint George, UT, p. A732

CLOWES, Jennifer, Chief Financial Officer, Broadwater Health Center, Townsend, MT, p. A428

CLUCK, Robert, M.D., Vice President and Medical Director, Texas Health Arlington Memorial Hospital, Arlington, TX, p. A654

CLUNN, Amy, M.D., Medical Director, Encompass Health Rehabilitation Hospital Of Ocala, Ocala, FL, p. A150

CLUTE, Gerald B., Chief Executive Officer, East Los Angeles Doctors Hospital, Los Angeles, CA, p. A74

CLUTTS, Kathaleen, Chief Human Resources Officer, St. Luke's Des Peres Hospital, Saint Louis, MO, p. A417

CLYNE, Mary Ellen, Ph.D., President and Chief Executive Officer, Clara Maass Medical Center, Belleville, NJ, p. A452

COATES, Jennifer, Coordinator Information Technology, Purcell Municipal Hospital, Purcell, OK, p. A567

COATES, Robert, M.D., Vice President, Medical Affairs, Hunterdon Healthcare, Flemington, NJ, p. A455

COATS, Daniel J., Chief Executive Officer, Oklahoma Center For Orthopedic And Multi-Specialty Surgery, Oklahoma City, OK, p. A565

COATS, John, M.D., Chief Medical Staff, Morehouse General Hospital, Bastrop. LA, p. A296

COATS, Kevin, Chief Financial Officer, Baylor Scott & White Medical Center—Frisco, Frisco, TX, p. A680

Chief Operating Officer and Chief Financial Officer, Baylor Scott & White Medical Center—Frisco, Frisco, TX, p. A680

COBARRUBIAS, Samuel, M.D., Chief of Staff, Clinch Memorial Hospital, Homerville, GA, p. A174

COBB, April, Chief Nursing Officer, Encompass Health Lakeshore Rehabilitation Hospital, Birmingham, AL, p. A15

COBB, Janice, R.N., Chief Nursing Officer, Tennessee Valley Healthcare System, Nashville, TN, p. A647

COBB, Jason E., FACHE, Chief Executive Officer, Rapides Regional Medical Center, Alexandria, LA, p. A295

COBB, Jeff, Information Technologist, Guthrie County Hospital, Guthrie Center, IA, p. A250

COBB, Lindsay, Director Human Resources, Cypress Grove Behavioral Health, Bastrop. LA, p. A296

COBB, Stephen, M.D., Chief Medical Officer, Presbyterian/St. Luke's Medical Center, Denver, CO, p. A111

COBB, Tammy, Chief Financial Officer, Tennova Healthcare-Shelbyville, Shelbyville, TN, p. A649

COBURN, Brad, Vice President, Human Resources, Orange Park Medical Center, Orange Park, FL, p. A150

COBURN, Meridith, Vice President Information Services, Saint Francis Hospital, Tulsa, OK, p. A570

Vice President, Information Systems, Saint Francis Hospital South, Tulsa, OK, p. A570

COBURN, Paul, Chief Financial Officer, Cypress Grove Behavioral Health, Bastrop. LA, p. A296

COBURN, Thomas, M.D., Chief Medical Officer, Middle Park Health-Kremmling, Kremmling, CO, p. A114

COCCA, Lisa, Chief Executive Officer, Belmont Pines Hospital, Youngstown, OH, p. A553

COCCHI, Dean, Chief Financial Officer, Kindred Hospital Ocala, Ocala, FL, p. A150

COCHRAN, Avril, R.N., Vice President Patient Care Services, North Country Hospital And Health Center, Newport, VT, p. A736

COCHRAN, Dan, Chief Operating Officer, Idaho Doctor's Hospital, Blackfoot, ID, p. A188

COCHRAN, Daniel, Vice President and Chief Financial Officer, Adventist Healthcare Shady Grove Medical Center, Rockville, MD, p. A332

COCHRAN, Jennifer, Director Human Relations, Northern Cochise Community Hospital, Willcox, AZ, p. A41

COCHRAN, Kenneth J., R.N., FACHE, President and Chief Executive Officer, Opelousas General Health System, Opelousas, LA, p. A312

COCHRAN, Lena, Director of Finance, Highlands-Cashiers Hospital, Highlands, NC, p. A512

COCHRAN, Liz, Operations Executive, Adventist Health Glendale, Glendale, CA, p. A66

COCHRAN, Lynn, R.N., System Vice President Operations, Chief Nursing Officer, Edward Hospital, Naperville, IL, p. A213

COCHRAN, Sherry, Manager Human Resources, Cascade Behavioral Hospital, Tukwila, WA, p. A768

COCHRAN, Willie, M.D., JrChief of Staff, Southern Regional Medical Center, Riverdale, GA, p. A178

COCHRANE, Andrew S., Chief Executive Officer, Maple Grove Hospital, Maple Grove, MN, p. A380

COCHRANE, Donna, Chief Nursing Officer, Liberty Regional Medical Center, Hinesville, GA, p. A174

COCHRANE, Robert, Vice President Finance and Chief Financial Officer, Frisbie Memorial Hospital, Rochester, NH, p. A451

COCKAYNE, Heather, Chief Financial Officer, Clifton-Fine Hospital, Star Lake, NY, p. A498

COCKFIELD, Costa, Chief Nursing Officer, Musc Health Florence Medical Center, Florence, SC, p. A619

COCKING, Kathy, R.N., Director of Clinical Services, Carson Valley Medical Center, Gardnerville, NV, p. A442

COCKRELL, Christopher, Executive Director Human Resources, Providence Hospital, Mobile, AL, p. A22

COCKRELL, Tim, Chief Executive Officer, Patients Choice Medical Center Of Smith County, Raleigh, MS, p. A399

CODER, Charles, Vice President, Novant Health Uva Health System Haymarket Medical Center, Haymarket, VA, p. A744
　Vice President, Novant Health Uva Health System Prince William Medical Center, Manassas, VA, p. A745

CODER, Denise, Chief Human Resource Officer, Cass County Health System, Atlantic, IA, p. A243

CODY, Karla, Chief Executive Officer, Pam Specialty Hospital Of Dayton, Miamisburg, OH, p. A545

COE, Jason, M.D., Medical Director, Covington Behavioral Health, Covington, LA, p. A300

COE, Susan, Regional Vice President Human Resources, University Of Maryland Shore Medical Center At Dorchester, Cambridge, MD, p. A328
　Regional Vice President Human Resources, University Of Maryland Shore Medical Center At Easton, Easton, MD, p. A329
　Vice President Human Resources, University Of Maryland Shore Medical Center At Chestertown, Chestertown, MD, p. A328

COEN, Vickie, Chief Clinical Officer and Nurse Executive, Pana Community Hospital, Pana, IL, p. A216

COFFEE, Paula, Director Human Resources, Ascension St. Mary's Of Michigan, Saginaw, MI, p. A365

COFFEE, Robert, Chief Information Officer, Creek Nation Community Hospital, Okemah, OK, p. A563

COFFELL, Randy, Manager Human Resources, Mid-Valley Hospital, Omak, WA, p. A761

COFFEY, Douglas, R.N., MSN, Chief Nursing Officer, St. Mary's Regional Medical Center, Enid, OK, p. A559

COFFEY, Joseph, Director Facility Administration, Rochester Psychiatric Center, Rochester, NY, p. A496

COFFEY, Kevin, Chief Executive Officer, Winner Regional Healthcare Center, Winner, SD, p. A633

COFFEY, M., Vice President and Chief Information Officer, Medical Director Center for Brain Stimulation, Menninger Clinic, Houston, TX, p. A687

COFFING, Sylvia, R.N., MSN, Chief Nursing and Compliance Officer, Unity Medical & Surgical Hospital, Mishawaka, IN, p. A236

COFFMAN, Brian, Director Information System, National Park Medical Center, Hot Springs, AR, p. A47

COFFMAN, Courtney, Vice President, Finance and Chief Financial Officer, Penn State Health St. Joseph, Reading, PA, p. A606

COFFMAN, Joan M., FACHE, President and Chief Executive Officer, St. Tammany Health System, Covington, LA, p. A300

COFFMAN BARNES, Julie, M.D., Chief Medical Officer, Redmond Regional Medical Center, Rome, GA, p. A179

COFIELD, Robert, Dr.PH, Chief Executive Officer, Prisma Health Richland Hospital, Columbia, SC, p. A618

COGGINS, David, MS, Chief Executive Officer, Encompass Health Rehabilitation Hospital Of New England, Woburn, MA, p. A346

COGGINS, Lisa, Chief Nursing Officer, Morton Hospital And Medical Center, Taunton, MA, p. A345

COGGINS, Parkes, Vice President Hospital Integration, Spartanburg Medical Center - Mary Black, Spartanburg, SC, p. A624

COHEE, Thomas, M.D., Chief of Staff, St. Francis Memorial Hospital, West Point, NE, p. A440

COHEN, Jason, M.D., Chief Medical Officer, North Valley Hospital, Whitefish, MT, p. A428

COHEN, Kathleena, MSN, R.N., Director of Nursing, Hampton Behavioral Health Center, Westampton, NJ, p. A465

COHEN, Kenneth, M.D., Medical Director, Beverly Hospital, Montebello, CA, p. A79

COHEN, Larry, Chief Executive Officer, Ocean Beach Hospital, Ilwaco, WA, p. A759

COHEN, Lisa, Chief Financial Officer, New London Hospital, New London, NH, p. A450

COHEN, Mark, M.D., Chief Medical Officer, Piedmont Hospital, Atlanta, GA, p. A165

COHEN, Philip A., Chief Executive Officer, Monterey Park Hospital, Monterey Park, CA, p. A79

COHEN, Susan, Director Human Resources, Montefiore New Rochelle, New Rochelle, NY, p. A489

COKER, Cindy, Vice President, Patient Care Services, Vidant Chowan Hospital, Edenton, NC, p. A509

COKER, Robert, M.D., Medical Director, Deer's Head Hospital Center, Salisbury, MD, p. A332

COKER, Tina, MSN, Chief Nursing Officer, Henderson Hospital, Henderson, NV, p. A442

COLADONATO, Angela, R.N., MSN, Chief Nursing Officer, Chester County Hospital, West Chester, PA, p. A610

COLAMARIA, James, Director of Nursing, Four Winds Hospital, Saratoga Springs, NY, p. A497

COLAS, Chuck, M.D., Medical Director, Surprise Valley Health Care District, Cedarville, CA, p. A59

COLBURN, Douglas, Chief Information Officer, Piedmont Columbus Regional Northside, Columbus, GA, p. A169

COLBURN, Tim A., President and Chief Executive Officer, Ohiohealth Berger Hospital, Circleville, OH, p. A533

COLBY, Dennis, M.D., Chief of Staff, Iowa Specialty Hospital-Clarion, Clarion, IA, p. A246

COLBY, Karen, MS, Chief Nursing Officer, Shirley Ryan Abilitylab, Chicago, IL, p. A200

COLBY, Ruth A., President and Chief Executive Officer, Silver Cross Hospital, New Lenox, IL, p. A214

COLBY, Scott, President and Chief Executive Officer, Upper Connecticut Valley Hospital, Colebrook, NH, p. A448

COLCHER, Robert, M.D., Medical Director, Valley Forge Medical Center And Hospital, Norristown, PA, p. A598

COLE, Annette, R.N., MSN, Vice President and Chief Nursing Officer, Sky Lakes Medical Center, Klamath Falls, OR, p. A576

COLE, Bernadette, R.N., Chief Nursing Officer, Munson Healthcare Charlevoix Hospital, Charlevoix, MI, p. A350

COLE, Beth, Director Information Services, Lewis-Gale Medical Center, Boones Mill, VA, p. A739

COLE, Cal, Director Information Systems, Winter Haven Hospital, Winter Haven, FL, p. A162

COLE, Carlene, Manager Human Resources, Kittson Memorial Healthcare Center, Hallock, MN, p. A377

COLE, Dale, Director, Human Resources, Corona Regional Medical Center, Corona, CA, p. A61

COLE, David, Assistant Director of Administration, Chief Financial Officer, Department of Behavioral Health and D, Central Virginia Training Center, Madison Heights, VA, p. A745

COLE, Donas, FACHE, President, Baylor Scott & White Medical Center - Lake Pointe, Rowlett, TX, p. A710

COLE, Dylan, Chief Medical Officer, Moab Regional Hospital, Moab, UT, p. A729

COLE, F., M.D., Chief Medical Officer, St. Louis Children's Hospital, Saint Louis, MO, p. A417

COLE, James B., President and Chief Executive Officer, Virginia Hospital Center, Arlington, VA, p. A738

COLE, Jason, Regional Chief Financial Officer, Baylor Scott & White Medical Center - Round Rock, Round Rock, TX, p. A709
　Senior Director, Management Information Systems, Suburban Hospital, Bethesda, MD, p. A327

COLE, Karen S., MS, FACHE, Interim Chief Executive Officer, Humboldt General Hospital, Winnemucca, NV, p. A447

COLE, Kristin, R.N., Chief Nursing Officer, Springhill Medical Center, Springhill, LA, p. A315

COLE, Lori, Director Information Technology, Wayne Unc Health Care, Goldsboro, NC, p. A511

COLE, Nancye, MS, R.N., FACHE, Chief Nursing Officer, Lovelace Medical Center, Albuquerque, NM, p. A467

COLE, Robert, Chief Operating Officer, Connecticut Mental Health Center, New Haven, CT, p. A124

COLE, Sherry, Chief Nursing Officer, Grandview Medical Center, Birmingham, AL, p. A15

COLE, William, M.D., Chief of Staff, Leconte Medical Center, Sevierville, TN, p. A649

COLEMAN, Alisa, Chief Executive Officer, Ferrell Hospital, Eldorado, IL, p. A203

COLEMAN, Connie, R.N., Chief Nursing Officer, Wyoming Medical Center, Casper, WY, p. A801

COLEMAN, Curt, FACHE, Critical Access Hospitals President, Genesis Medical Center, Dewitt, De Witt, IA, p. A248
　FACHE, President, Jackson County Regional Health Center, Maquoketa, IA, p. A253

COLEMAN, D., M.D., Medical Director, Livingston Healthcare, Livingston, MT, p. A426

COLEMAN, Donna, Coordinator Human Resources, Jackson County Hospital District, Edna, TX, p. A674

COLEMAN, Edie, Chief Financial Officer, Nyc Health + Hospitals / Metropolitan, New York, NY, p. A491

COLEMAN, Karen, Director of Nursing, Grove Hill Memorial Hospital, Grove Hill, AL, p. A19

COLEMAN, Kevin, M.D., Chief Medical Officer, Grand River Hospital District, Rifle, CO, p. A118

COLEMAN, Linda, Chief Nursing Officer, Candler County Hospital, Metter, GA, p. A176

COLEMAN, Melissa, Director Human Resources, Encompass Health Rehabilitation Hospital Of Sewickley, Sewickley, PA, p. A607

COLEMAN, Robert, Chief Executive Officer, Baptist Medical Center Attala, Kosciusko, MS, p. A395
　Chief Executive Officer, Baptist Medical Center Yazoo, Yazoo City, MS, p. A401

COLEMAN, Shane, Chief Operating Officer, Palo Pinto General Hospital, Mineral Wells, TX, p. A701

COLEMAN, Stanley, Director Human Resources, Texas Rehabilitation Hospital Of Arlington, Arlington, TX, p. A654

COLERICK, Steven, Chief Executive Officer, Buena Vista Regional Medical Center, Storm Lake, IA, p. A258

COLETTA, Antonio, Vice President Human Resources, Bromenn Medical Center, Normal, IL, p. A214
　Vice President Human Resources, Eureka Hospital, Eureka, IL, p. A204

COLETTA, Diane, Vice President Human Resources, Royal Oaks Hospital, Windsor, MO, p. A420

COLETTI, Edmund, Chief Executive Officer, Helen Hayes Hospital, West Haverstraw, NY, p. A502

COLEY, Aaron, Chief Financial Officer, Orange County, Saddleback Medical Center, Laguna Hills, CA, p. A70

COLEY, Brenda, Executive Director, Adventhealth Central Texas, Killeen, TX, p. A693
　Executive Director, Adventhealth Rollins Brook, Lampasas, TX, p. A694

COLGAN, Teresa, Vice President Nursing, Great River Medical Center, West Burlington, IA, p. A260

COLGLAZIER, Garrett, Director Health Information Management, Sabetha Community Hospital, Sabetha, KS, p. A275

COLINERI, Lori, R.N., Senior Vice President Nursing and Chief Nursing Officer, Robert Wood Johnson University Hospital, New Brunswick, NJ, p. A459

COLL, Shawni, D.O., Chief Medical Officer, Tahoe Forest Hospital District, Truckee, CA, p. A102

COLL, Tammy L., Chief Executive Officer, Mountain Lakes Medical Center, Clayton, GA, p. A168

COLLADO, Raquel, Vice President Human Resources, New York Community Hospital, Brooklyn, NY, p. A478

COLLAZO, Marian, Director Finance, Hospital San Cristobal, Coto Laurel, PR, p. A807

COLLETT, John, Vice President and Chief Financial Officer, Cayuga Medical Center At Ithaca, Ithaca, NY, p. A485

COLLETT, Josh, Director Human Resources, Pineville Community Health Center, Pineville, KY, p. A292

COLLETTI, Teresa, Director Patient Services, South Florida Baptist Hospital, Plant City, FL, p. A154

COLLEY, Sarah, Senior Vice President Human Resources, Regional One Health, Memphis, TN, p. A645

COLLIER, Brad, Director, Piedmont Newton Hospital, Covington, GA, p. A170

COLLIER, Jack, M.D., Chief of Staff, Mountainview Hospital, Las Vegas, NV, p. A443

COLLIER, Louis, Chief Executive Officer, Uva Encompass Health Rehabilitation Hospital, Charlottesville, VA, p. A740

COLLIER, Margaret P., Chief Executive Officer, Ridgeview Institute, Smyrna, GA, p. A180

COLLIER, Shari, Chief Financial Officer, Presbyterian/St. Luke's Medical Center, Denver, CO, p. A111

COLLINI, M., M.D., President Medical Staff, Usmd Hospital At Arlington, Arlington, TX, p. A654

COLLINS, Alesha, MSN, R.N., Chief Nursing Officer, Howard Memorial Hospital, Nashville, AR, p. A51

COLLINS, Ava, FACHE, Chief Operating Officer, Saint Vincent Hospital, Worcester, MA, p. A346

COLLINS, Bobby, Director Human Resources, Lonesome Pine Hospital, Big Stone Gap. VA, p. A739
　Director Human Resources, Mountain View Regional Medical Center, Norton, VA, p. A748

COLLINS, Chauncey, Chief Operating Officer and Chief Financial Officer, Austen Riggs Center, Stockbridge, MA, p. A345

COLLINS, Daniel, M.D., Clinical Director, New Mexico Behavioral Health Institute At Las Vegas, Las Vegas, NM, p. A470

COLLINS, Edmund, Chief Information Officer, Cleveland Clinic Martin North Hospital, Stuart, FL, p. A158

COLLINS, Ethan, R.N., Chief Nursing Officer, Smyth County Community Hospital, Marion, VA, p. A745

COLLINS, Frances, Director of Nursing, Andrew Mcfarland Mental Health Center, Springfield, IL, p. A220

COLLINS, Harold, JD, Chief Financial Officer, Franciscan Healthcare Munster, Munster, IN, p. A237

COLLINS, James M., President and Chief Executive Officer, St. Clair Hospital, Pittsburgh, PA, p. A603

COLLINS, Jeff, Chief Medical Officer, Providence St. Joseph's Hospital, Chewelah, WA, p. A756

COLLINS, Jeffrey A., M.D., Senior Vice President and Area Manager, Kaiser Permanente Oakland Medical Center, Oakland, CA, p. A82

COLLINS, John, Corporate Chief Financial Officer, Chapman Global Medical Center, Orange, CA, p. A82
  Chief Financial Officer, Anaheim Global Medical Center, Anaheim, CA, p. A55
  Chief Financial Officer, Hemet Valley Medical Center, Hemet, CA, p. A68
  Chief Financial Officer, Orange County Global Medical Center, Inc., Santa Ana, CA, p. A96
  Chief Financial Officer, South Coast Global Medical Center, Santa Ana, CA, p. A96

COLLINS, John P., FACHE, Medical Center Director, Veterans Affairs Central Western Massachusetts Healthcare System, Leeds, MA, p. A340

COLLINS, Karen S., Chief Executive Officer, Lady Of The Sea General Hospital, Cut Off, LA, p. A300

COLLINS, Kevin, M.D., Medical Director, Chi St. Vincent Sherwood Rehabilitation Hospital, Sherwood, AR, p. A53

COLLINS, Kimberly, M.D., Chief of Staff, Saint Thomas Dekalb Hospital, Smithville, TN, p. A649

COLLINS, Lainie, Human Resources Partner, Ascension St. Vincent Clay Hospital, Brazil, IN, p. A224

COLLINS, Leonora, Chief Nursing Officer, Nashville General Hospital, Nashville, TN, p. A646

COLLINS, Pam, Director Human Resources, Avala, Covington, LA, p. A300

COLLINS, Pamela, Vice President Chief Patient Services Officer, Mccullough-Hyde Memorial Hospital/Trihealth, Oxford, OH, p. A547

COLLINS, Richard, M.D., Executive Vice President and Chief Medical Officer, Jefferson Hospital, Jefferson Hills, PA, p. A593

COLLINS, Ricky, M.D., Chief of Staff, Whitesburg Arh Hospital, Whitesburg, KY, p. A294

COLLINS, Ronald, Chief Financial Officer, Pamp. Regional Medical Center, Pampa, TX, p. A704

COLLINS, Sharon, Chief Executive Officer, Russell Regional Hospital, Russell, KS, p. A275
  Chief Information Officer, Salem Veterans Affairs Medical Center, Salem, VA, p. A751

COLLINS, Teresa, R.N., Interim Chief Executive Officer, Rock Regional Hospital, Derby, KS, p. A263

COLLINS, Thomas M., President, Chairman and Chief Executive Officer, Medical City Green Oaks Hospital, Dallas, TX, p. A669

COLLIPP, Dan, M.D., Chief of Staff, Wayne Memorial Hospital, Jesup. GA, p. A174

COLLISON, June, President, Community Hospital Of San Bernardino, San Bernardino, CA, p. A91

COLLOM, Bobbie, Nursing Director, North Runnels Hospital, Winters, TX, p. A726

COLMAN, Gerard, Chief Operating Officer, Aurora West Allis Medical Center, West Allis, WI, p. A799

COLMENARES, Derek, M.D., Chief Medical Officer, Ripon Medical Center, Ripon, WI, p. A795
  M.D., Chief Medical Officer, St. Agnes Hospital, Fond Du Lac, WI, p. A784
  M.D., Chief Medical Officer, Waupun Memorial Hospital, Waupun, WI, p. A798

COLOMBO, Armando, Chief Executive Officer, Menninger Clinic, Houston, TX, p. A687

COLOMBO, Maria Carmen, R.N., Chief Nursing Officer, Sharp Mary Birch Hospital For Women And Newborns, San Diego, CA, p. A92
  R.N., Chief Nursing Officer, Sharp Mesa Vista Hospital, San Diego, CA, p. A92

COLON, Julio, Financial Director, Hospital De Damas, Ponce, PR, p. A809

COLON, Omar, M.D., Medical Director, Encompass Health Rehabilitation Hospital Of Plano, Plano, TX, p. A707

COLONES, Robert L., President and Chief Executive Officer, Mcleod Regional Medical Center, Florence, SC, p. A619

COLONNELLI, Kimberly, Chief Operating Officer and Chief Nurse Executive, Kaiser Permanente San Rafael Medical Center, San Rafael, CA, p. A96

COLORADO, Judy, R.N., Chief Nursing Officer, Monmouth Medical Center, Southern Campus, Lakewood, NJ, p. A457

COLPITTS, Robert, Chief Human Resource Service, Bedford Veterans Affairs Medical Center, Edith Nourse Rogers Memorial Veterans Hospital, Bedford, MA, p. A334

COLSDEN, Kristen, Director of Nursing, Osmond General Hospital, Osmond, NE, p. A438

COLSON, Wayne, Chief Financial Officer, Southwestern Medical Center, Lawton, OK, p. A561

COLTHARP, Missy, Director, Baptist Memorial Hospital-Union County, New Albany, MS, p. A398

COLTON, Jan, M.D., Acting Clinical Director, U. S. Public Health Service Indian Hospital, Pine Ridge, SD, p. A630

COLUCCI, Eugene, Vice President Finance, Greenwich Hospital, Greenwich, CT, p. A122

COLVARD, Dusty, Manager Information Technology, Adventist Health Tehachap. Valley, Tehachapi, CA, p. A100

COLVERT, Richard, Chief Information Officer, Royal Oaks Hospital, Windsor, MO, p. A420

COLVIN, Garren, Chief Executive Officer, St. Elizabeth Edgewood, Edgewood, KY, p. A282
  Chief Executive Officer, St. Elizabeth Florence, Florence, KY, p. A283
  Chief Executive Officer, St. Elizabeth Fort Thomas, Fort Thomas, KY, p. A283
  Chief Executive Officer, St. Elizabeth Grant, Williamstown, KY, p. A294

COLVIN, William, Human Resources Officer, Claiborne Memorial Medical Center, Homer, LA, p. A300

COLWELL, Dean, D.O., Vice President Medical Affairs, Ohiohealth Doctors Hospital, Columbus, OH, p. A536

COLWELL, Melodie, Chief Financial Officer, Drew Memorial Health System, Monticello, AR, p. A50

COLYER, Valeri, Director Human Resources, Dickenson Community Hospital, Clintwood, VA, p. A740
  Director Human Resources, Norton Community Hospital, Norton, VA, p. A748

COMAIANNI, Sheri, Vice President Human Resources, Bakersfield Memorial Hospital, Bakersfield, CA, p. A57

COMBEST, Felton, M.D., Vice President Medical Affairs, Magnolia Regional Health Center, Corinth, MS, p. A391

COMBETTA, Jeffery, M.D., Medical Director, Riverbend Rehabilitation Hospital, Monroe, LA, p. A309

COMBS, Jennifer, Chief Financial Officer, Jackson County Memorial Hospital, Altus, OK, p. A555

COMBS, Mark, Chief Information Security Officer, Jefferson Medical Center, Ranson, WV, p. A776
  Interim Director System Information Technology, Berkeley Medical Center, Martinsburg, WV, p. A774

COMBS, Mike, Manager Information Technology, Holdenville General Hospital, Holdenville, OK, p. A560

COMBS, Will, Director Information Technology, Harrison Community Hospital, Cadiz, OH, p. A530

COMEAUX, Heather, R.N., Director of Nursing, Oceans Behavioral Hospital Of Opelousas, Opelousas, LA, p. A312

COMER, Fannessa, Chief Executive Officer, Northern Navajo Medical Center, Shiprock, NM, p. A472

COMER, Jennifer, M.D., Medical Director, Valle Vista Health System, Greenwood, IN, p. A230

COMER, Randy, Chief Financial Officer, Athens-Limestone Hospital, Athens, AL, p. A14
  Chief Operating Officer, Athens-Limestone Hospital, Athens, AL, p. A14

COMER, Scott, Vice President Human Resources, Marshall Medical Center, Placerville, CA, p. A85

COMER, William J., President, Mountain Vista Medical Center, Mesa, AZ, p. A34

COMERFORD, Jennifer, Manager Information Services, Midstate Medical Center, Meriden, CT, p. A123

COMITO, Arthur, Chief Financial Officer, St. Luke's Easton Campus, Easton, PA, p. A589

COMITTO, Judy, Vice President Information Services and Chief Information Officer, Trinitas Regional Medical Center, Elizabeth, NJ, p. A455

COMP, Susan, Senior Vice President and Chief Nursing Officer, Upmc Pinnacle Harrisburg, Harrisburg, PA, p. A591

COMPTON, Brenda, Manager Information Technology, Plumas District Hospital, Quincy, CA, p. A86

COMPTON, Carri, Administrative Officer, Heartland Behavioral Health Services, Nevada, MO, p. A412

COMPTON, Randy, Information Technology and System Director, Logan Memorial Hospital, Russellville, KY, p. A293

CONABOY, William P., Chief Executive Officer, Allied Services Rehabilitation Hospital, Scranton, PA, p. A606

CONANT, Cathy, Chief Human Resources and Personnel, Eastern Plumas Health Care, Portola, CA, p. A86

CONANT, Merrill, M.D., Chief of Staff, Western Plains Medical Complex, Dodge City, KS, p. A263

CONANT, Sonya, Senior Director Human Resources, Alaska Native Medical Center, Anchorage, AK, p. A27

CONAWAY, E, M.D., Vice President Medical Affairs and Chief Medical Officer, Southeastern Ohio Regional Medical Center, Cambridge, OH, p. A530

CONCANNON, Laura, M.D., Regional Chief Medical Officer, Amita Health Saints Mary & Elizabeth Medical Center, Chicago, IL, p. A198

CONCEPCION, Walter, Chief Executive Officer, West Gables Rehabilitation Hospital, Miami, FL, p. A147

CONDIT, Brian, M.D., Chief Medical Officer, Johnston Memorial Hospital, Abingdon, VA, p. A738
  M.D., Vice President Chief Medical Officer, Virginia Operations Medical Staff Services, Russell County Medical Center, Lebanon, VA, p. A744

CONDIT, Edward, President and Chief Executive Officer, St. Mary's General Hospital, Passaic, NJ, p. A460

CONDOLUCI, David, M.D., Senior Vice President and Chief Medical Officer, Jefferson Stratford Hospital, Stratford, NJ, p. A463

CONDRY, Donna, Director Human Resources, Unitypoint Health - Jones Regional Medical Center, Anamosa, IA, p. A243

CONE, Maryann, Chief Operating Officer, Sharp Grossmont Hospital, La Mesa, CA, p. A70

CONFALONE, Daniel, Chief Financial Officer and Vice President Finance, St. Mary Medical Center, Langhorne, PA, p. A594

CONFER, James, Manager Information Systems, Clarion Hospital, Clarion, PA, p. A586

CONGDON, James, M.D., Medical Director, Horsham Clinic, Ambler, PA, p. A584

CONGER, Sue, Chief Operating Officer, Eastside Psychiatric Hospital, Tallahassee, FL, p. A158

CONKLIN, Maggie, M.P.H., Interim Chief Nurse Officer, Novant Health Uva Health System Prince William Medical Center, Manassas, VA, p. A745
  M.P.H., Interim Chief Nursing Officer, Novant Health Uva Health System Haymarket Medical Center, Haymarket, VA, p. A744

CONKLIN, Robin, R.N., Chief Nursing Officer, Carondelet St. Joseph's Hospital, Tucson, AZ, p. A40

CONKLIN, Stacey, Chief Nursing Officer, Mount Sinai South Nassau, Oceanside, NY, p. A493

CONKLIN JR, MichaelChief Financial Officer, St. Josep. Health Services Of Rhode Island, North Providence, RI, p. A613

CONKLING, Victoria, Vice President, Patient Services and Chief Nursing Officer, Uhs Delaware Valley Hospital, Walton, NY, p. A501

CONLEE, Josh, President, Lawrence Memorial Hospital, Walnut Ridge, AR, p. A54

CONLEY, Christopher, M.D., President of the Medical Staff, Tristar Skyline Medical Center, Nashville, TN, p. A647

CONLEY, Joanna J., FACHE, Chief Executive Officer, Tristar Southern Hills Medical Center, Nashville, TN, p. A647

CONLEY, Kenneth, Chief Financial Officer, Baptist Memorial Hospital - Calhoun, Calhoun City, MS, p. A390

CONLEY, Kirkpatrick, President, Sentara Careplex Hospital, Hampton, VA, p. A743

CONLEY, Melissa, Director Human Resources, Midwest Medical Center, Galena, IL, p. A205

CONLEY, Michelle, R.N., Chief Nursing Officer, Jefferson Health Northeast, Philadelphia, PA, p. A600

CONLEY, Teressa, Vice President and Chief Operating Officer, St. Rose Dominican Hospitals - Rose De Lima Campus, Henderson, NV, p. A442

CONLEY, Theresa, Manager Human Resources, Cherokee Regional Medical Center, Cherokee, IA, p. A245

CONLEY, Thomas, Vice President, Human Resources and Organizational Development, Northwestern Medical Center, Saint Albans, VT, p. A736

CONLIN, Elizabeth, PsyD, Chief Executive Officer, Friends Hospital, Philadelphia, PA, p. A600

CONLON, John, M.D., Chief Medical Officer, Saint Anne's Hospital, Fall River, MA, p. A339

CONN, Chris, Chief Financial Officer, Poinciana Medical Center, Kissimmee, FL, p. A142

CONN, Stephanie, Administrator and Chief Nursing Officer, Coshocton Regional Medical Center, Coshocton, OH, p. A538

CONNAWAY, Jessica, Director Human Resources, Crossroads Community Hospital, Mount Vernon, IL, p. A213

CONNEL, Lorene, Chief Human Resources Management Service, Veterans Affairs Eastern Colorado Health Care System, Denver, CO, p. A111

CONNELL, Eric, Chief Executive Officer, Daniels Memorial Healthcare Center, Scobey, MT, p. A427

CONNELL, Lawrence B., Director, Providence Veterans Affairs Medical Center, Providence, RI, p. A613

CONNELL, Pam, Manager Human Resources, Windsor-Laurelwood Center For Behavioral Medicine, Willoughby, OH, p. A553

CONNELLEY, Bertha, Director Human Resources, Austen Riggs Center, Stockbridge, MA, p. A345

CONNELLY, Jac, Chief Financial Officer, Rose Medical Center, Denver, CO, p. A111

CONNELLY, Manager Information Technology, Connecticut Valley Hospital, Middletown, CT, p. A123

CONNELLY, Michael, CPA, FACHE, Executive Vice President and Chief Financial Officer, Melrosewakefield Healthcare, Melrose, MA, p. A341

CONNELLY, Steven, M.D., President and Chief Medical Officer, Park Nicollet Methodist Hospital, Saint Louis Park, MN, p. A385

CONNER, Jeff, M.D., Chief Medical Staff, Loma Linda University Medical Center-Murrieta, Murrieta, CA, p. A80

CONNER, Laurie A., FACHE, President, Mercyone Newton Medical Center, Newton, IA, p. A255

CONNER, Stacey, Human Resources Director, Ed Fraser Memorial Hospital, Macclenny, FL, p. A144

CONNERTON, Kathryn, President and Chief Executive Officer, Our Lady Of Lourdes Memorial Hospital, Inc., Binghamton, NY, p. A476

CONNOLLY, Christine, M.D., Chief of Staff, Keefe Memorial Hospital, Cheyenne Wells, CO, p. A109

CONNOLLY, Seam, Commissioner, Connecticut Veterans Home And Hospital, Rocky Hill, CT, p. A125

CONNOLLY, Teresa, R.N., Chief Nursing Officer, Mayo Clinic Hospital, Phoenix, AZ, p. A36

CONNOR, William, Assistant Administrator and Director Human Resources, River Hospital, Alexandria Bay, NY, p. A474

CONNORS, Alfred, M.D., Executive Vice President and Chief Quality Officer and Interim Chief Medical Officer, Metrohealth Medical Center, Cleveland, OH, p. A535

CONNORS, Lawrence, Chief Operating Officer, Hshs St. Mary's Hospital Medical Center, Green Bay, WI, p. A785

CONNORS, Michael, Senior Vice President and Chief Financial Officer, Cap. Cod Hospital, Hyannis, MA, p. A340
Senior Vice President and Chief Financial Officer, Falmouth Hospital, Falmouth, MA, p. A339

CONNOVICH, Ron, Chief Financial Officer and Chief Operating Officer, Soin Medical Center, Beavercreek, OH, p. A529
Chief Financial Officer, Greene Memorial Hospital, Xenia, OH, p. A553

CONNY, Sophia, Deputy Administrative Officer, U. S. Public Health Service Indian Hospital, Pine Ridge, SD, p. A630

CONRAD, Elizabeth, Senior Vice President and Chief Human Resource Officer, Lahey Hospital & Medical Center, Burlington, Burlington, MA, p. A337

CONRAD, Heidi, Vice President and Chief Financial Officer, Regions Hospital, Saint Paul, MN, p. A385

CONRAD, Matthew, Chief Operating Officer, Abilene Regional Medical Center, Abilene, TX, p. A651

CONRATH, Mark, Chief Financial Officer, Drumright Regional Hospital, Drumright, OK, p. A558

CONROW-VERVERIS, Stacy, Director Human Resources, Mineral Community Hospital, Superior, MT, p. A428

CONROY, Joanne M., M.D., President and Chief Executive Officer, Dartmouth-Hitchcock Medical Center, Lebanon, NH, p. A449

CONROY, Michael, Chief Financial Officer, Pine Creek Medical Center, Dallas, TX, p. A670

CONROY, Mike, Chief Financial Officer, Methodist Mckinney Hospital, Mckinney, TX, p. A700

CONROY, Tracy, Chief Executive Officer, Daviess Community Hospital, Washington, IN, p. A242

CONSBRUCK, Todd, Chief Executive Officer, Avera Creighton Hospital, Creighton, NE, p. A431
President and Chief Executive Officer, Avera St. Anthony's Hospital, O'Neill, NE, p. A438

CONSIGLIO, Gayle, Chief Information Officer, Mclaren Lapeer Region, Lapeer, MI, p. A360

CONSIGNEY, Ginger, Vice President Human Resources, Lake Charles Memorial Hospital, Lake Charles, LA, p. A307

CONSOLVER, Roberta, Chief Information Officer, Healthbridge Children's Hospital, Orange, CA, p. A83

CONSTANT, Jean-Charles, Administrator, Dover Behavioral Health System, Dover, DE, p. A127

CONSTANTINE-CASTILLO, Candida, MSN, R.N., Chief Nursing Officer, South Texas Health System, Edinburg, TX, p. A674

CONTE, John, Director Facility Services and Real Estate, Wayne Memorial Hospital, Honesdale, PA, p. A592

CONTE, Thomas, M.D., President, Medical Staff, Van Wert County Hospital, Van Wert, OH, p. A551

CONTI, John, Director Finance, Shriners Hospitals For Children-Greenville, Greenville, SC, p. A620

CONTRERAS, Cristina, Executive Director, Nyc Health + Hospitals / North Central Bronx, Bronx, NY, p. A477

CONTRERAS, Theresa, Chief Executive Officer, Arrowhead Behavioral Health Hospital, Maumee, OH, p. A544

CONTRERAS ESQ, AmyChief Nursing Officer, Milford Valley Memorial Hospital, Milford, UT, p. A729

CONVERY, Luanne, Vice President Patient Care Services, Putnam Hospital Center, Carmel, NY, p. A481

CONWAY, Jimmy, M.D., President Medical Staff, Northwest Surgical Hospital, Oklahoma City, OK, p. A565

CONWAY, Kevin, Chief Information Officer, Upmc Mercy, Pittsburgh, PA, p. A604

CONWILL, Michael, Director Human Resources, Corpus Christi Medical Center, Corpus Christi, TX, p. A666

COOGAN, Ben, Chief Operating Officer, Medical City Arlington, Arlington, TX, p. A653

COOK, Aaron, Director Information Services, Christus Ochsner Lake Area Hospital, Lake Charles, LA, p. A306

COOK, Alan, Chief Medical Officer, Central Regional Hospital, Butner, NC, p. A506

COOK, Anthony, M.D., Chief of Staff, Avera Holy Family Hospital, Estherville, IA, p. A249

COOK, Brooke, Director of Nursing, Strategic Behavioral Health - Wilmington, Leland, NC, p. A513

COOK, Carla, Director of Nursing, Scotland County Hospital, Memphis, MO, p. A412

COOK, Daniel, Director of Finance, Aurora Medical Center - Bay Area, Marinette, WI, p. A788

COOK, Darrin, Chief Executive Officer and Administrator, Horizon Specialty Hospital, Las Vegas, NV, p. A448

COOK, David, Manager Information Systems, Christus Dubuis Hospital Of Hot Springs, Hot Springs National Park, AR, p. A47
Vice President and Chief Financial Officer, Uh Elyria Medical Center, Elyria, OH, p. A540

COOK, Elizabeth, Chief Information Officer, Mizell Memorial Hospital, Opp. AL, p. A23

COOK, G., M.D., Medical Director, Hemphill County Hospital, Canadian, TX, p. A662

COOK, Greg, Chief Executive Officer, Castleview Hospital, Price, UT, p. A731

COOK, Heidi, Chief Nursing Officer, Warner Hospital And Health Services, Clinton, IL, p. A201

COOK, Jana, Vice President and Chief Financial Officer, Phelp. Health, Rolla, MO, p. A414

COOK, John, Interim Chief Information Officer, University Of California, Davis Medical Center, Sacramento, CA, p. A90
Senior Vice President & Chief Financial Officer, Javon Bea Hospital-Rockton, Rockford, IL, p. A218
Vice President and Chief Financial Officer, Mercyhealth Hospital And Trauma Center - Janesville, Janesville, WI, p. A786

COOK, Kathy, FACHE, MSN, President, Mercy Health - St. Josep. Warren Hospital, Warren, OH, p. A551

COOK, Kim, Interim Clinical Applications Services Manager, Tri-City Medical Center, Oceanside, CA, p. A82

COOK, LaMont, Administrator, F. W. Huston Medical Center, Winchester, KS, p. A279

COOK, Linda, Vice President Human Resources, St. Josep. Hospital Eureka, Eureka, CA, p. A63

COOK, Marcia, Director Information Technology, Bates County Memorial Hospital, Butler, MO, p. A403

COOK, Mary, R.N., Director of Nursing, Red Lake Indian Health Service Hospital, Red Lake, MN, p. A383

COOK, Natalie, Administrative Director of Human Resources, Manchester Memorial Hospital, Manchester, CT, p. A122
Administrative Director, Human Resources, Rockville General Hospital, Vernon, CT, p. A125

COOK, Pamela, Chief Financial Officer, Trace Regional Hospital, Houston, MS, p. A394

COOK, Patrick, Vice President Support Services, Morgan Memorial Hospital, Madison, GA, p. A176

COOK, Paul, M.D., Chief Medical Officer, Baylor Scott & White Medical Center - Llano, Llano, TX, p. A696

COOK, Robert, Chief Nursing Officer, Twin Cities Community Hospital, Templeton, CA, p. A101

COOK, Scott, Chief Financial Officer, Garland Behavioral Hospital, Garland, TX, p. A681

COOK, Sheliah, Director Human Resources, Boone Memorial Hospital, Madison, WV, p. A774

COOK, Sherry, R.N., MSN, Chief Nursing Executive, Merit Health River Oaks, Flowood, MS, p. A392

COOK, Stacey, MS, Vice President, Human Resources, University Of Maryland Charles Regional Medical Center, La Plata, MD, p. A330

COOK, Thomas, Chief Financial Officer, Good Samaritan Hospital, Vincennes, IN, p. A242

COOK, Wendy, Chief Financial Officer, Piedmont Athens Regional Medical Center, Athens, GA, p. A163

COOK, William, Associate Warden Business Service, California Mens Colony Correctional Treatment Center, San Luis Obispo, CA, p. A95
Director, Southern Virginia Mental Health Institute, Danville, VA, p. A741
President and Chief Executive Officer, Vail Health, Vail, CO, p. A119

COOKE, Barbara, Director Health Information Systems, Montefiore Mount Vernon, Mount Vernon, NY, p. A489

COOKE, David, R.N., Chief Nursing Officer, Sutter Surgical Hospital - North Valley, Yuba City, CA, p. A106
R.N., Chief Operating Officer, Hi-Desert Medical Center, Joshua Tree, CA, p. A69

COOKE, Nancy, Chief Executive Officer, Martin County Hospital District, Stanton, TX, p. A717

COOKE, Rebecca, Director Human Resources, Kearney County Health Services, Minden, NE, p. A435

COOKE, Timothy J., Medical Center Director and Chief Executive Officer, Orlando Va Medical Center, Orlando, FL, p. A151

COOKE, William, M.D., Chief of Staff, Gundersen St. Joseph's Hospital And Clinics, Hillsboro, WI, p. A786

COOKSON, Diane M., President, Uchealth Highlands Ranch Hospital, Highlands Ranch, CO, p. A114

COOL, Megan, Chief Operating Officer, Methodist Ambulatory Surgery Hospital - Northwest, San Antonio, TX, p. A712

COOLEY, Andrew, M.D., Chief Medical Officer, Eastern State Hospital, Lexington, KY, p. A286

COOLEY, Jennifer, Director of Nursing, Rock Springs, Georgetown, TX, p. A681

COOLEY, Richard, M.D., Chief Physician Executive, Hshs St. Clare Memorial Hospital, Oconto Falls, WI, p. A793
M.D., Chief Physician Executive, Hshs St. Nicholas Hospital, Sheboygan, WI, p. A796

COOMBS, James, Chief Executive Officer, Grand River Hospital District, Rifle, CO, p. A118

COOMBS, Jodi, R.N., Executive Vice President, Chief Operating Officer, Children's Mercy Hospital Kansas, Overland Park, KS, p. A273

COOMBS, Teri, R.N., Director Nursing Services, Cascade Medical Center, Cascade, ID, p. A189

COOMES, Larry, Chief Executive Officer, Queen Of The Valley Medical Center, Napa, CA, p. A80

COOMLER, Mimi, R.N., Vice President and Chief Nursing Officer, Tmc Healthcare, Tucson, AZ, p. A41

COONER, Suzanne, MSN, R.N., Chief Executive Officer, Audubon County Memorial Hospital And Clinics, Audubon, IA, p. A243

COONEY, Lauri, Director Nursing, Wheatland Memorial Healthcare, Harlowton, MT, p. A424

COONEY, Marina, Medical Director, Montgomery County Emergency Service, Norristown, PA, p. A598

COOPER, Alisa, Manager Financial Resources, Michael E. Debakey Veterans Affairs Medical Center, Houston, TX, p. A687

COOPER, Alison, Chief Financial Officer, Ward Memorial Hospital, Monahans, TX, p. A702

COOPER, Allison, Administrator, Physicians Behavioral Hospital, Shreveport, LA, p. A314

COOPER, Brenda, Director Quality and Human Resources, Lecom Corry Memorial Hospital, Corry, PA, p. A587

COOPER, Casey, Chief Executive Officer, Cherokee Indian Hospital, Cherokee, NC, p. A507

COOPER, Curtis, Manager Information Systems, Pioneers Medical Center, Meeker, CO, p. A117

COOPER, Donald, Director Information Systems, Tennova Healthcare-Harton, Tullahoma, TN, p. A650

COOPER, Douglas, M.D., Chief Medical Officer, Grundy County Memorial Hospital, Grundy Center, IA, p. A250

COOPER, Jerry, Manager Data Processing, Richland Hospital, Richland Center, WI, p. A795

COOPER, Michael, Chief Executive Officer, Rush County Memorial Hospital, La Crosse, KS, p. A268

COOPER, Misty, Chief Financial Officer, Specialists Hospital Shreveport, Shreveport, LA, p. A314

COOPER, Pamela, Director Finance, Providence Seaside Hospital, Seaside, OR, p. A581

COOPER, Robert, M.D., Chief Medical Officer, Faith Community Hospital, Jacksboro, TX, p. A691

COOPER, Tim, Chief Financial Officer, Prosser Memorial Health, Prosser, WA, p. A762

COOPER-LEHKI, Christi, Chief Clinical Officer, Highland-Clarksburg Hospital, Clarksburg, WV, p. A771

COOPER-LOHR, Willie, Chief Financial Officer, Wvu Medicine - Barnesville Hospital, Barnesville, OH, p. A528

COOPERMAN, Todd, M.D., Medical Director, Encompass Health Rehabilitation Hospital Of Tinton Falls, Tinton Falls, NJ, p. A464

COOPWOOD, Reginald W., M.D., President and Chief Executive Officer, Regional One Health, Memphis, TN, p. A645

COOTS, Aaron, Information Technology Director, Mason District Hospital, Havana, IL, p. A207

COPE, Dave, Director Information Systems, Marshall County Hospital, Benton, KY, p. A280

COPE, Mary, R.N., Chief Clinical Officer, Spanish Peaks Regional Health Center, Walsenburg, CO, p. A119

COPE, Yvette, Chief Nurse Executive, Lompoc Valley Medical Center, Lompoc, CA, p. A72

COPELAND, Carolyn, Business Administrator, Madison State Hospital, Madison, IN, p. A236

COPELAND, Darlinda, Chief Operating Officer, Adventhealth Daytona Beach, Daytona Beach, FL, p. A136

COPELAND, Gail, Director Management Information Systems, Crossridge Community Hospital, Wynne, AR, p. A54

COPELAND, Gearline, R.N., Chief Nursing Officer, Saint Thomas Highlands Hospital, Sparta, TN, p. A649

COPELAND, Kristie, Interim Chief Nursing Officer, Claiborne Memorial Medical Center, Homer, LA, p. A303

COPELAND, Stephen, Chief Financial Officer, Cypress Creek Hospital, Houston, TX, p. A685

COPELAND, Willie, Chief Financial Officer, Harmon Memorial Hospital, Hollis, OK, p. A560

COPELAND, Yolanda, R.N., Senior Vice President Patient Care Services and Chief Nursing Officer, Saint Agnes Healthcare, Baltimore, MD, p. A326

COPEN, Greg, Chief Information Officer, Haywood Regional Medical Center, Clyde, NC, p. A507

COPENHAVER, Kathy, Director Human Resources, Haven Behavioral Hospital Of Eastern Pennsylvania, Reading, PA, p. A606

COPES, Tammy, Director Information Systems, Ascension Standish Hospital, Standish, MI, p. A367

COPPEDGE, Mitch, M.D., Chief Medical Officer, Grady Memorial Hospital, Chickasha, OK, p. A557

COPPLE, Brad, Vice President Operations, Northwestern Medicine Valley West Hospital, Sandwich, IL, p. A219
Vice President, Operations, Northwestern Medicine Kishwaukee Hospital, Dekalb, IL, p. A202

COPPLE, Robert C., FACHE, Senior Administrator, Ascension Via Christi Hospital, Manhattan, Manhattan, KS, p. A270

CORAZON, Jesus, Controller, Encompass Health Rehabilitation Hospital Of Manati, Manati, PR, p. A808
Controller, Encompass Health Rehabilitation Hospital Of San Juan, San Juan, PR, p. A810

CORBEIL, John, Chief Executive Officer, Hca Houston Healthcare Kingwood, Kingwood, TX, p. A693

CORBET, Mark, Interim Chief Financial Officer, Lac+Usc Medical Center, Los Angeles, CA, p. A75

CORBETT, David, M.D., Chief of Staff, Northwest Medical Center, Winfield, AL, p. A26

CORBIN, Loren, Chief Nursing Officer, Hillsdale Hospital, Hillsdale, MI, p. A357

CORBIN, Michelle, M.D., Chief of Staff, Deer Lodge Medical Center, Deer Lodge, MT, p. A423

CORCIMIGLIA, Michael, Chief Operating Officer, Wyoming County Community Hospital, Warsaw, NY, p. A501

CORCORAN, Frank, R.N., Chief Executive Officer, Geary Community Hospital, Junction City, KS, p. A267

CORCORAN, John, Vice President Medical Affairs, South County Hospital, Wakefield, RI, p. A614

CORCORAN, Joseph, D.O., Chief Medical Officer, Brandon Regional Hospital, Brandon, FL, p. A133
D.O., Chief Medical Officer, South Bay Hospital, Sun City Center, FL, p. A158
D.O., Division Chief Medical Officer, Southern Hills Hospital And Medical Center, Las Vegas, NV, p. A444

CORCORAN, Kevin, Chief Financial Officer, Westside Regional Medical Center, Plantation, FL, p. A154

CORCORAN, Nancy, Senior Vice President Human Resources and Quality Service, Hackensack Meridian Health Hackensack University Medical Center, Hackensack, NJ, p. A455

CORCORAN, Rose, R.N., Chief Nursing Executive, Sutter Coast Hospital, Crescent City, CA, p. A62

CORD, Jennifer, R.N., Chief Nursing Officer, Mission Hospital Mission Viejo, Mission Viejo, CA, p. A78

CORDEAU, Peter, President, Norwalk Hospital, Norwalk, CT, p. A124

CORDER, Earline, Chief Fiscal, Charlie Norwood Veterans Affairs Medical Center, Augusta, GA, p. A166

CORDER, Scott, Controller, Encompass Health Rehabilitation Hospital At Cincinnati, Cincinnati, OH, p. A532

CORDERO, Edwin, Chief Financial Officer, Valley Baptist Medical Center-Brownsville, Brownsville, TX, p. A661

CORDES, Debra, Chief Nursing Officer, Rehabilitation Hospital Of Indiana, Indianapolis, IN, p. A233

CORDIA, Jennifer, Vice President and Chief Nursing Executive, Christian Hospital, Saint Louis, MO, p. A415

CORDOVA, Mandelyn, R.N., Director of Nurses, Guadalup. County Hospital, Santa Rosa, NM, p. A472

CORDOVA, Martin, Director Information Services, Centinela Hospital Medical Center, Inglewood, CA, p. A69

CORDOVA, Sheila, Chief Operating Officer and Chief Nursing Officer, Aurora Charter Oak Hospital, Covina, CA, p. A61
Director Clinical Services and Chief Operating Officer, Aurora Charter Oak Hospital, Covina, CA, p. A61

CORDOVES, America, Controller, Jerome Golden Center For Behavioral Health, Inc., West Palm Beach, FL, p. A162

CORDUM, Shelly, MSN, R.N., Vice President Nursing and Chief Nursing Officer, Ssm Health Depaul Hospital - St. Louis, Bridgeton, MO, p. A403

CORDY, Roy, M.D., President Medical Staff, Presentation Medical Center, Rolla, ND, p. A525

COREA, Rohan, Director Healthcare Information Technology, College Medical Center, Long Beach, CA, p. A72

COREY, Mark, Chief Financial Officer, Behavioral Center Of Michigan, Warren, MI, p. A369

CORKERY, Thomas, D.O., Chief Medical Officer, Canonsburg Hospital, Canonsburg, PA, p. A586

CORLEY, Becky, Director Human Resources, Tyler Holmes Memorial Hospital, Winona, MS, p. A401

CORLEY, Craig, Chief Financial Officer, Bhc Alhambra Hospital, Rosemead, CA, p. A88

CORLEY, Janet, Accountant, Malvern Institute, Malvern, PA, p. A596

CORLEY, Juli, Chief Financial Officer, Edgefield County Healthcare, Edgefield, SC, p. A619

CORLEY, Lesa, Director of Nursing, Broaddus Hospital, Philippi, WV, p. A775

CORMIER, Debbie, Chief Executive Officer, New Horizon Hospital, Houston, TX, p. A687

CORMIER, Philip M., Chief Executive Officer, Beverly Hospital, Beverly, MA, p. A334

CORN, Rick, Chief Information Officer, Huntsville Hospital, Huntsville, AL, p. A20

CORNEJO, C, Chief Financial Officer, Sacred Heart Hospital Pensacola, Pensacola, FL, p. A154
Chief Operating Officer, Providence Hospital, Mobile, AL, p. A22

CORNELIUS, David, Director Information Systems, Parkridge Medical Center, Chattanooga, TN, p. A636

CORNELIUS, Margaret, Vice President Human Resources, Wyckoff Heights Medical Center, Brooklyn, NY, p. A479

CORNELIUS, Michelle, Director Human Resources for Northern Region, Ascension Eagle River Hospital, Eagle River, WI, p. A782
Director Human Resources for the Northern Region, Ascension St. Mary's Hospital, Rhinelander, WI, p. A795
Director Human Resources, Ascension Sacred Heart Hospital, Tomahawk, WI, p. A797
Director Human Resources, Howard Young Medical Center, Woodruff, WI, p. A800

CORNELIUS, Senta, Director Human Resources, West Valley Medical Center, Caldwell, ID, p. A189

CORNELIUS, Teresa, R.N., Interim Chief Nursing Officer, Hshs St. Joseph's Hospital, Highland, IL, p. A207

CORNET, Trina, JD, Vice President Human Resources, Jamaica Hospital Medical Center, Jamaica, NY, p. A486

CORNETT, Sheila, Manager Human Resources, Hazard Arh Regional Medical Center, Hazard, KY, p. A284

CORNETT, Suzanne, Director Human Resources, Southern Kentucky Rehabilitation Hospital, Bowling Green, KY, p. A281

CORNICELLI, Kari, Chief Financial Officer, Sharp Grossmont Hospital, La Mesa, CA, p. A70
Chief Financial Officer, Sharp Mary Birch Hospital For Women And Newborns, San Diego, CA, p. A92
Chief Financial Officer, Sharp Memorial Hospital, San Diego, CA, p. A92

CORNWALL, Rick, HIT Site Coordinator, Advocate Condell Medical Center, Libertyville, IL, p. A210

CORNWALL, Thomas, M.D., Medical Director, Holly Hill Hospital, Raleigh, NC, p. A516

CORNWELL, Cheryl, Chief Financial Officer, Great Falls Clinic Hospital, Great Falls, MT, p. A424
Chief Financial Officer, Lake District Hospital, Lakeview, OR, p. A577

CORNWELL, Daniel, Command Officer, U. S. Naval Hospital Guam, Agana, GU, p. A805

CORONA JR., Robert J., Chief Executive Officer, Upstate University Hospital, Syracuse, NY, p. A500

CORONEL, Jorge, Chief Information Officer, Regional Hospital Of Scranton, Scranton, PA, p. A607

CORPORA, Don, Executive Vice President and Chief Human Resources Officer, Cleveland Clinic Akron General, Akron, OH, p. A527

CORRA, Michelle, Administrator, Human Resources, Beaumont Hospital - Trenton, Trenton, MI, p. A368

CORRADO, Bob, Chief Information Officer, Canandaigua Veterans Affairs Medical Center, Canandaigua, NY, p. A480

CORRADO, Theresa, Director Finance, St. Luke's Hospital - Quakertown Campus, Quakertown, PA, p. A605

CORREA, Elizabeth, Director Information Management, Big Spring State Hospital, Big Spring, TX, p. A659

CORREA, Leo, Chief Executive Officer and Administrator, St. Catherine Hospital, East Chicago, IN, p. A227

CORREA, Maria, M.D., Medical Director, Hospital Metropolitan, San Juan, PR, p. A810

CORREA, Omar, Chief Financial Officer, Texas Neurorehab Center, Austin, TX, p. A657

CORREA, Sharon, Chief Information Officer, Adventist Health Glendale, Glendale, CA, p. A66

CORRELL, Anne, Chief Clinical Officer, Kindred Hospital-Greensboro, Greensboro, NC, p. A511

CORRIGAN, Jeffrey, Vice President Human Resources, Brattleboro Retreat, Brattleboro, VT, p. A735
Vice President Human Resources, Day Kimball Hospital, Putnam, CT, p. A124

CORRIGAN, Paula, Vice President and Chief Financial Officer, Osf Saint James - John W. Albrecht Medical Center, Pontiac, IL, p. A217

CORRY, Craig, Chief Financial Officer, Cedar City Hospital, Cedar City, UT, p. A727
Chief Financial Officer, Garfield Memorial Hospital, Panguitch, UT, p. A730

CORS, William, M.D., Senior Medical Director, Lehigh Valley Hospital - Pocono, East Stroudsburg, PA, p. A589

CORSO, David, Vice President Critical Access Hospitals, Thedacare Medical Center-Waupaca, Waupaca, WI, p. A798

CORTES, Anais, Chief of Staff, Palmetto General Hospital, Hialeah, FL, p. A139

CORTI, Ronald J., President and Chief Executive Officer, St. John's Riverside Hospital, Yonkers, NY, p. A503

CORUM, Sharon, Chief Financial Officer, Kingwood Pines Hospital, Kingwood, TX, p. A693

CORWIN, Nancy, Chief Nursing Officer, Summit Surgical, Hutchinson, KS, p. A267
Chief Operating Officer, Summit Surgical, Hutchinson, KS, p. A267

CORWIN, Steven J., M.D., President and Chief Executive Officer, New York-Presbyterian Hospital, New York, NY, p. A491

CORZINE, Judy, Administrative Director and Chief Information Officer, Stormont Vail Health, Topeka, KS, p. A277

COSBY, Christopher, Chief Executive Officer, Poinciana Medical Center, Kissimmee, FL, p. A142

COSBY, Dwan, Manager Human Resources, Mclaren Oakland, Pontiac, MI, p. A364

COSBY, Ernestine, Vice President Clinical Services and Chief Nursing Officer, Sheppard Pratt Health System, Baltimore, MD, p. A326

COSLETT, John, R.N., Chief Nursing Officer, Kansas Spine & Specialty Hospital, Wichita, KS, p. A279

COSTA, Christopher, M.D., Chief of Staff, Gordon Memorial Health Services, Gordon, NE, p. A432

COSTA, Joe, Acting Chief Fiscal Officer, Veterans Affairs Boston Healthcare System Brockton Division, Brockton, MA, p. A337
Chief Financial Officer, Veterans Affairs Boston Healthcare System, West Roxbury, MA, p. A345

COSTA, Mark E., Executive Director, Kaiser Permanente Orange County Anaheim Medical Center, Anaheim, CA, p. A55

COSTA, Michael, Vice President Human Resources, Chi St. Josep. Regional Health Center, Bryan, TX, p. A661

COSTAKIS, Angie, Chief Information Officer, Claiborne Memorial Medical Center, Homer, LA, p. A303

COSTANTINO, Vincent, Vice President Operations and Human Resources, Hackensack Meridian Health Raritan Bay Medical Center, Perth Amboy, NJ, p. A461

COSTANZO, Kristin, Direct-In-Market Lead Human Relations Partner, St. Vincent's Blount, Oneonta, AL, p. A23

COSTELLA, Jeane, Vice President, New York-Presbyterian/ Hudson Valley Hospital, Cortlandt Manor, NY, p. A482

COSTELLO, Jeff, Chief Financial Officer, Beacon Health System, Memorial Hospital Of South Bend, South Bend, IN, p. A240
Chief Financial Officer, Elkhart General Hospital, Elkhart, IN, p. A227

COSTELLO, Jodi, Chief Executive Officer, Select Specialty Hospital - Boardman, Boardman, OH, p. A529
Chief Executive Officer, Select Specialty Hospital-Youngstown, Youngstown, OH, p. A554

COSTELLO, Karen, President, Holy Rosary Healthcare, Miles City, MT, p. A426

COSTIC, Andrew, Vice President of Regional Finance, Aspirus Keweenaw Hospital, Inc., Laurium, MI, p. A360

COSTNER, Marc, Chief Financial Officer, Chestnut Hill Hospital, Philadelphia, PA, p. A599

COTA, Scott, M.D., Director Medical Services, Naval Hospital Lemoore, Lemoore, CA, p. A71

COTE, Gerri, Chief Operating Officer, Brattleboro Retreat, Brattleboro, VT, p. A735

COTE, Mary, Director Human Resources, New England Rehabilitation Hospital Of Portland, Portland, ME, p. A322

COTT, Gary, M.D., Executive Vice President Medical and Clinical Services, National Jewish Health, Denver, CO, p. A110

COTTEN, Brandon, Chief Financial Officer, Dewitt Hospital, Dewitt, AR, p. A44

COTTER, Bonny, Chief Nursing Officer, Baraga County Memorial Hospital, L'Anse, MI, p. A359

COTTER, Brian, Chief Operating Officer, Southern Inyo Healthcare District, Lone Pine, CA, p. A72

COTTER, Carole, Senior Vice President and Chief Information Officer, Emma Pendleton Bradley Hospital, East Providence, RI, p. A613

Senior Vice President and Chief Information Officer, Rhode Island Hospital, Providence, RI, p. A614

Vice President and Chief Information Officer, Miriam Hospital, Providence, RI, p. A613

COTTERILL, Allison, Chief Nursing Officer, Mercy General Hospital, Sacramento, CA, p. A89

COTTERMAN, Rob, Chief Executive Officer, Middle Tennessee Mental Health Institute, Nashville, TN, p. A646

COTTINGHAM, Jerod, Director Information Systems, Carlinville Area Hospital, Carlinville, IL, p. A196

COTTLE, Jeremy, Ph.D., Chief Executive Officer, Provo Canyon Behavioral Hospital, Orem, UT, p. A730

COTTLE, Mike, Chief Information Officer, Newton Medical Center, Newton, KS, p. A272

COTTO, Hector, M.D., Medical Director, Hospital San Francisco, San Juan, PR, p. A810

COTTON, C, Interim Chief Operating Officer, Baptist Medical Center Leake, Carthage, MS, p. A390

COTTON, Michael, Chief Financial Officer, Grandview Medical Center, Birmingham, AL, p. A15

COTTON, Toni, R.N., Chief Nursing Officer, Harris Health System, Houston, TX, p. A685

COTTRILL, Brian, Chief Information Officer, United Hospital Center, Bridgeport, WV, p. A770

COUBAL, Steve, Manager Information Technology and Systems, Johnson Memorial Health Services, Dawson, MN, p. A375

COUCH, Beulah, Director Human Resources, Mary Breckinridge Arh Hospital, Hyden, KY, p. A285

COUCH, Bill, Chief Financial Officer, Ashley County Medical Center, Crossett, AR, p. A44

COUCH, Chad, M.D., Chief Medical Officer, Northeast Market, Bristol Regional Medical Center, Bristol, TN, p. A634

M.D., Interim Chief Executive Officer, Bristol Regional Medical Center, Bristol, TN, p. A634

COUCHMAN, Diane, Vice President Patient Care Services and Chief Nursing Executive, Calverthealth Medical Center, Prince Frederick, MD, p. A331

COUGHLIN, Ann, Director Human Resources, Boundary Community Hospital, Bonners Ferry, ID, p. A189

COUGHLIN, Cynthia, MS, R.N., Chief Nursing Officer, Cheshire Medical Center, Keene, NH, p. A449

COUGHLIN, Kevin B., President and Chief Executive Officer, Beth Israel Deaconess Hospital Plymouth, Plymouth, MA, p. A343

COULE, Phillip. M.D., Chief Medical Officer, Augusta University Medical Center, Augusta, GA, p. A165

COULTER, Barbara, Director Information Systems, Franciscan Health Indianapolis, Indianapolis, IN, p. A232

Director Information Systems, Franciscan Health Mooresville, Mooresville, IN, p. A237

COUNTRYMAN, Cory, Chief Executive Officer, Wilson N. Jones Regional Medical Center, Sherman, TX, p. A716

COUNTS, Virginia, Manager Human Resources, Baylor Scott & White Medical Center - Brenham, Brenham, TX, p. A660

COUNTY-TEEMER, Vickie, Coordinator Human Resources, Mitchell County Hospital, Camilla, GA, p. A168

COURIS, John D., Chief Executive Officer, Tamp. General Hospital, Tampa, FL, p. A160

COURREGE, Gary, Chief Information Officer, Jennings American Legion Hospital, Jennings, LA, p. A304

COURTOIS, Harold, Chief Executive Officer, Memorial Health System, Abilene, KS, p. A261

COURTOIS, Robert, Vice President Finance, Munson Healthcare Otsego Memorial Hospital, Gaylord, MI, p. A355

COURY, Justin, Chief Operating Officer, Tristar Centennial Medical Center, Nashville, TN, p. A647

COURY, Tiffany, Chief Executive Officer, Saint Mary's Regional Medical Center, Reno, NV, p. A446

COUSAR, Myra, Director Human Resources, Baptist Memorial Hospital-Tipton, Covington, TN, p. A637

COUSINEAU, Cathy, Director Human Resources, Kaiser Permanente Woodland Hills Medical Center, Woodland Hills, CA, p. A105

COUTURE, Maureen, Chief Nursing Officer and Vice President Nursing, Cardinal Hill Rehabilitation Hospital, Lexington, KY, p. A286

COUVILLON, Larry, M.D., Chief Medical Officer, Memorial Hospital At Gulfport, Gulfport, MS, p. A393

COVAULT, Julie, Vice President Finance, Wilson Memorial Hospital, Sidney, OH, p. A549

COVAULT, Myra, Associate Vice President of Human Resources, Hardin Memorial Health, Elizabethtown, KY, p. A282

COVELL, Nancy, Director Human Resources, Cameron Memorial Community Hospital, Angola, IN, p. A223

COVELLI, Margaret, R.N., Chief Nursing Officer, Spring Valley Hospital Medical Center, Las Vegas, NV, p. A444

COVERT, David G., Chief Executive Officer, South Texas Surgical Hospital, Corpus Christi, TX, p. A666

COVERT, Kathy, MSN, Vice President Workforce Development and Organizational Development, Schneck Medical Center, Seymour, IN, p. A240

COVERT, Terri, Vice President Human Resources, Mission Hospital Mission Viejo, Mission Viejo, CA, p. A78

COVINGTON, Casey, M.D., President Elect, Medical Staff, Jennie Stuart Medical Center, Hopkinsville, KY, p. A285

COVINGTON, Jerome, M.D., Chief Medical Officer, Lower Keys Medical Center, Key West, FL, p. A142

COVONE, Ann Marie, Senior Vice President and Chief Financial Officer, Terence Cardinal Cooke Health Care Center, New York, NY, p. A492

COWAN, Christopher, Senior Vice President and Chief Human Resources Officer, Christianacare, Newark, DE, p. A128

COWAN, J W., Administrator, Choctaw General Hospital, Butler, AL, p. A16.

COWAN, Ronald, Vice President Information Systems, Geisinger-Lewistown Hospital, Lewistown, PA, p. A595

COWART, Mark, Facility Chief Information Officer, Carl Vinson Veterans Affairs Medical Center, Dublin, GA, p. A171

COWLES, John, Chief Financial Officer, La Downtown Medical Center, Llc, Los Angeles, CA, p. A75

COWLING, Phyllis A., CPA, President and Chief Executive Officer, United Regional Health Care System, Wichita Falls, TX, p. A725

COX, Amber, Director Human Resources, Ut Health Carthage, Carthage, TX, p. A663

COX, Brian, Director Information Systems, Baptist Health Floyd, New Albany, IN, p. A237

COX, Carla, Chief Nursing Officer, Indiana University Health Ball Memorial Hospital, Muncie, IN, p. A237

COX, Chandler, Director Human Resources, Mena Regional Health System, Mena, AR, p. A50

COX, Christopher, Chief Nursing Officer, Baptist Health Extended Care Hospital, Little Rock, AR, p. A48

COX, Debbie, Administrative Director Human Resources, Christus Santa Rosa Hospital - San Marcos, San Marcos, TX, p. A714

COX, Dianne, Vice President of Human Resources, Kaweah Delta Medical Center, Visalia, CA, p. A104

COX, Dina, Director Human Resources, Kansas Rehabilitation Hospital, Topeka, KS, p. A277

COX, Dorothy, Manager Information Systems, Hackettstown Medical Center, Hackettstown, NJ, p. A456

COX, Gwen, Director Nursing Services, Klickitat Valley Health, Goldendale, WA, p. A759

COX, Jeffrey, Chief Information Officer, Glendora Community Hospital, Glendora, CA, p. A67

Director Information Technology, San Dimas Community Hospital, San Dimas, CA, p. A93

COX, Kenneth, Interim Chief Financial Officer, Mckenzie County Healthcare System, Watford City, ND, p. A526

COX, Leigh, Chief Information Officer, Wellstar Windy Hill Hospital, Marietta, GA, p. A176

COX, Lynna, Director Health Information Services, Anson General Hospital, Anson, TX, p. A653

COX, Randy, Chief Information Officer, Ascension St. Vincent Indianapolis Hospital, Indianapolis, IN, p. A231

COX, Sandra, Controller, Permian Regional Medical Center, Andrews, TX, p. A653

COX, Sheila, Director Human Resources, Cibola General Hospital, Grants, NM, p. A469

COX, Steven, M.D., Chief Medical Officer, Ut Health North Campus Tyler, Tyler, TX, p. A722

COYE, Ed, Director Information Technology Mission Health System Hospitals, Angel Medical Center, Franklin, NC, p. A510

Director Information Technology, Transylvania Regional Hospital, Brevard, NC, p. A505

COYLE, Michael F., Chief Executive Officer, Veterans Memorial Hospital, Waukon, IA, p. A259

COYNE, Rose, Interim CFO, Haywood Regional Medical Center, Clyde, NC, p. A507

COZART, Adrienne, Senior Vice President Human Resources, University Medical Center, Lubbock, TX, p. A698

CRABB, David, M.D., Chief Medical Officer, Eskenazi Health, Indianapolis, IN, p. A231

CRABB, Ian, M.D., Chief Medical Officer, Orthonebraska Hospital, Omaha, NE, p. A437

CRABBE, Amy, Senior Vice President Human Resources, Watauga Medical Center, Boone, NC, p. A505

Vice President People Services, Charles A. Cannon Memorial Hospital, Newland, NC, p. A515

CRABTREE, Gordon, Chief Financial Officer, University Of Utah Health, Salt Lake City, UT, p. A733

Interim Chief Executive Officer, University Of Utah Health, Salt Lake City, UT, p. A733

CRABTREE, John, M.D., Chief of Staff, Tennova Healthcare-Harton, Tullahoma, TN, p. A650

CRABTREE, Robert, M.D., Chief of Staff and Medical Director, Physicians Surgical Hospital - Quail Creek, Amarillo, TX, p. A652

CRABTREE, Susan, Director Human Resources, Adventist Health Simi Valley, Simi Valley, CA, p. A98

CRACROFT, Davis, M.D., Senior Director Medical Affairs, Scripp. Mercy Hospital, San Diego, CA, p. A92

CRAFT, Brian, Group Finance Officer, Texas Health Presbyterian Hospital Dallas, Dallas, TX, p. A670

CRAFT, Christina, Director Information Systems, Washington County Hospital, Plymouth, NC, p. A516

CRAFT, Kirby, Chief Information Officer, Magee General Hospital, Magee, MS, p. A396

CRAGGS, Chris, Deputy Director, Winnebago Mental Health Institute, Winnebago, WI, p. A800

CRAIG, Alan, M.D., Chief Medical Officer, Princeton Baptist Medical Center, Birmingham, AL, p. A15

CRAIG, Celine, Chief Human Resources Officer, King's Daughters Medical Center, Brookhaven, MS, p. A390

CRAIG, Donnette, Director Human Resources, Christus Coushatta Health Care Center, Coushatta, LA, p. A299

CRAIG, Elizabeth, MSN, Chief Nursing Officer and Vice President Patient Services, Temple University Hospital, Philadelphia, PA, p. A602

CRAIG, Emmett, Chief Human Resources Officer, Knap. Medical Center, Weslaco, TX, p. A725

Director Human Resources, Harlingen Medical Center, Harlingen, TX, p. A683

CRAIG, Jeff, Chief Human Resource Management, Veterans Affairs Maryland Health Care System-Baltimore Division, Baltimore, MD, p. A327

CRAIG, Mike, Chief Financial Officer, Indiana University Health Bloomington Hospital, Bloomington, IN, p. A224

Vice President, Chief Financial Officer, Indiana University Health Bedford Hospital, Bedford, IN, p. A224

CRAIG, Pamela, R.N., Chief Nursing Officer, Seton Medical Center Harker Heights, Harker Heights, TX, p. A683

CRAIG, Patrice, Manager Human Resources, Southern Arizona Veterans Affairs Health Care System, Tucson, AZ, p. A41

CRAIG, Rebecca, Vice President and Chief Financial Officer, Wayne Unc Health Care, Goldsboro, NC, p. A511

CRAIG, Scott, M.D., Medical Director, Encompass Health Rehabilitation Hospital Of Franklin, Franklin, TN, p. A638

CRAIG, Sherry, Director Human Resources, Trace Regional Hospital, Houston, MS, p. A394

CRAIG, Steven, Ph.D., Chief Operating Officer and Acting Chief Executive Officer, Surgeons Choice Medical Center, Southfield, MI, p. A367

CRAIG, William, CPA, Chief Financial Officer, Howard Memorial Hospital, Nashville, AR, p. A51

CRAIN, Greg, FACHE, Senior Vice President and Administrator, Baptist Health Medical Center-Little Rock, Little Rock, AR, p. A49

CRAMBES, Terry, Manager Finance, Warren State Hospital, Warren, PA, p. A609

CRAMER, Brian J., Chief Executive Officer, Orthopaedic Hospital of Wisconsin, Glendale, WI, p. A784

CRAMER, James, Vice President and Chief Information Officer, Honorhealth Scottsdale Osborn Medical Center, Scottsdale, AZ, p. A38

Vice President and Chief Information Officer, Honorhealth Scottsdale Shea Medical Center, Scottsdale, AZ, p. A38

CRAMER, Lonnie, Chief Operating Officer, Penrose-St. Francis Health Services, Colorado Springs, CO, p. A109

President, Uchealth Broomfield Hospital, Broomfield, CO, p. A108

President, Uchealth Longs Peak Hospital, Longmont, CO, p. A116

CRANDELL, Kristy, M.D., Medical Staff President, Red Bay Hospital, Red Bay, AL, p. A24

CRANE, Aaron, Executive Vice President, Seattle Cancer Care Alliance, Seattle, WA, p. A764

CRANFORD, Melvin, Chief Fiscal Services, Cheyenne Veterans Affairs Medical Center, Cheyenne, WY, p. A802

CRANKER, John, Chief Information Officer, Carthage Area Hospital, Carthage, NY, p. A481

CRATON, Deborah, M.D., Chief Medical Officer, Ascension St. Vincent Dunn, Bedford, IN, p. A224

CRATTY, Michael, M.D., Chief Medical Officer, Heritage Valley Health System, Beaver, PA, p. A584
M.D., Chief Medical Officer, Sewickley Valley Hospital, (A Division Of Valley Medical Facilities), Sewickley, PA, p. A608
CRAVEY, Lavonda, Chief Financial Officer, Coffee Regional Medical Center, Douglas, GA, p. A171
CRAW, David, Coordinator Information Technology, Dundy County Hospital, Benkelman, NE, p. A430
CRAWFORD, Allen, Chief Nursing Officer, Jeff Davis Hospital, Hazlehurst, GA, p. A173
CRAWFORD, Angie, Chief Executive Officer, Haven Behavioral Hospital Of Frisco, Frisco, TX, p. A680
CRAWFORD, Arnita, Director Human Resources, Woman's Hospital Of Texas, Houston, TX, p. A689
CRAWFORD, Jeff, Chief Executive Officer, Cobalt Rehabilitation Houston Heights, Houston, TX, p. A685
CRAWFORD, Jim, Chief Financial Officer, Lawrence Medical Center, Moulton, AL, p. A22
CRAWFORD, John, Chief Financial Officer, Muscogee Creek Nation Medical Center, Okmulgee, OK, p. A566
Chief Financial Officer, St. John Sapulpa, Sapulpa, OK, p. A567
CRAWFORD, Linda, R.N., MSN, Chief Nursing Officer, Cookeville Regional Medical Center, Cookeville, TN, p. A637
CRAWFORD, Lucinda, Vice President Financial Services, Vidant Duplin Hospital, Kenansville, NC, p. A513
Vice President of Patient Care Services, Vidant Beaufort Hospital, Washington, NC, p. A519
CRAWFORD, Marc, Chief Operating Officer, Regions Behavioral Hospital, Baton Rouge, LA, p. A297
CRAWFORD, Pam, R.N., Ph.D., Vice President of Nursing and Chief Nursing Officer, Ohiohealth Medcentral Mansfield Hospital, Mansfield, OH, p. A544
CRAWFORD, Randy, Chief Executive Officer, Appling Healthcare System, Baxley, GA, p. A167
CRAWFORD, Ryan, Director Talent, Southwestern Regional Medical Center, Tulsa, OK, p. A570
CRAWFORD, Susan, Manager Human Resources, Fayette County Hospital, Vandalia, IL, p. A222
CRAWFORD, Thomas, Chicago Market Chief Information Officer, Louis A. Weiss Memorial Hospital, Chicago, IL, p. A199
CRAWFORD, Tom, Vice President Human Resources, Emory Hillandale Hospital, Lithonia, GA, p. A175
Vice President Human Resources, Emory Long-Term Acute Care, Decatur, GA, p. A171
CRAWFORD, Traci, R.N., Commander, Moncrief Army Community Hospital, Fort Jackson, SC, p. A620
CRAWFORD, Wendy, Chief Human Resource Officer, Honorhealth Scottsdale Thompson Peak Medical Center, Scottsdale, AZ, p. A38
CRAYTON, Cory, Director Information Systems, Northeast Georgia Medical Center Barrow, Winder, GA, p. A183
Director of Information Systems, Piedmont Walton Hospital, Monroe, GA, p. A177
CRAYTON, Karen, Administrator, Sage Rehabilitation Hospital, Baton Rouge, LA, p. A297
CREAL, Sharon, Vice President Financial Operations, Scripp. Memorial Hospital-Encinitas, Encinitas, CA, p. A63
CREAMER, Julie L., President, Northwestern Memorial Hospital and Senior Vice President Northwestern Memorial HealthCare, Northwestern Memorial Hospital, Chicago, IL, p. A200
President, Northwestern Medicine Marianjoy Rehabilitation Hospital, Wheaton, IL, p. A222
CREAMER, Ken, Chief Human Resource, Amarillo Veterans Affairs Health Care System, Amarillo, TX, p. A652
CREASMAN, Ginny, Associate Director, Richard L. Roudebush Veterans Affairs Medical Center, Indianapolis, IN, p. A233
CREEL, Keith, Vice President Operations, Christus Good Shepherd Medical Center-Marshall, Marshall, TX, p. A700
CREEL, Mary, Chief Information Resource Management, Martinsburg Veterans Affairs Medical Center, Martinsburg, WV, p. A774
CREIGHTON, Peggy, R.N., Director of Nursing, Methodist Hospital Union County, Morganfield, KY, p. A290
CRENSHAW, Neville, D.O., Chief of Staff, Unitypoint Health-Keokuk, Keokuk, IA, p. A252
CRENSHAW, Rachel, Chief Operating Officer, Jack Hughston Memorial Hospital, Phenix City, AL, p. A23
CRENSHAW, William, M.D., Chief of Staff, Lady Of The Sea General Hospital, Cut Off, LA, p. A300
CREPEAU, Diana, Director Human Resources, Encompass Health Rehabilitation Hospital Of Colorado Springs, Colorado Springs, CO, p. A109
CREPS, Barbara, Director Human Resources and Accounting, Okeene Municipal Hospital, Okeene, OK, p. A563

CREQUE, J, Director Management Information Systems, Schneider Regional Medical Center, Saint Thomas, VI, p. A812
CRESPO, Rosaida, Executive Director, Hospital San Carlos Borromeo, Moca, PR, p. A808
CRESPO, Rosaida M., Executive Director, Hospital San Carlos Borromeo, Moca, PR, p. A808
CREVLING, Charles, Chief Financial Officer, Valley View Hospital, Glenwood Springs, CO, p. A113
CREWS, Carol, Chief Financial Officer, Higgins General Hospital, Bremen, GA, p. A167
Chief Financial Officer, Tanner Medical Center-Carrollton, Carrollton, GA, p. A168
Senior Vice President and Chief Financial Officer, Tanner Medical Center-Villa Rica, Villa Rica, GA, p. A182
CREWS, Kimberly, Vice President and Chief Financial Officer, Catawba Valley Medical Center, Hickory, NC, p. A512
CREWS, Paul, Director, Durham Veterans Affairs Medical Center, Durham, NC, p. A509
CREWSE, Britt, Chief Executive Officer, University Of Mississipp. Medical Center, Jackson, MS, p. A395
CRIBBS, Sammie, Vice President Clinical Services and Chief Nursing Officer, North Arkansas Regional Medical Center, Harrison, AR, p. A46
CRIBBS, Susan, D.O., Chief of Staff, Adventist Health Tehachap. Valley, Tehachapi, CA, p. A100
CRIDER, Terry, Information Technology Site Manager, Nea Baptist Memorial Hospital, Jonesboro, AR, p. A48
CRIGER, Sara J., President, Mercy Hospital, Coon Rapids, MN, p. A374
CRILLY, Tom, Executive Vice President and Chief Financial Officer, Unity Hospital, Rochester, NY, p. A496
Executive Vice President, Chief Financial Officer, Rochester Regional Health, Newark-Wayne Community Hospital, Newark, NY, p. A492
CRIM, Marcia, R.N., MSN, Chief Executive Officer, Usmd Hospital At Arlington, Arlington, TX, p. A654
R.N., MSN, Chief Nursing Officer and Chief Executive Officer, Usmd Hospital At Arlington, Arlington, TX, p. A654
CRINER, Mark, Director Information Technology, Memorial Health Care Systems, Seward, NE, p. A439
CRINION, Shannon, Chief Executive Officer, Baptist Emergency Hospital, San Antonio, TX, p. A710
CRINOLE, Shannon, Chief Executive Officer, Integris Community Hospital At Council Crossing, Oklahoma City, OK, p. A564
CRIPE, Kimberly C., President and Chief Executive Officer, Children's Hospital Of Orange County, Orange, CA, p. A83
President and Chief Executive Officer, Choc Children's At Mission Hospital, Mission Viejo, CA, p. A78
CRIST, Claudia, Chief Executive Officer, Sutter Health Kahi Mohala, Ewa Beach, HI, p. A184
CRISTY, Kirk, Vice President Finance, Sanford Medical Center Bismarck, Bismarck, ND, p. A521
CRISWELL, Jodie, Vice President of Fiscal Services, Hammond-Henry Hospital, Geneseo, IL, p. A205
CRITCHLEY, Dan, Chief Information Officer, Banner - University Medical Center Tucson, Tucson, AZ, p. A39
CRITTENDEN, Shana, Chief Operating Officer, North Shore Medical Center, Miami, FL, p. A147
CROCE, Martin, M.D., Senior Vice President and Chief Medical Officer, Regional One Health, Memphis, TN, p. A645
CROCKER, Daniel, M.D., Chief Medical Officer, Pam Specialty Hospital Of Rocky Mount, Rocky Mount, NC, p. A517
CROCKETT, James, M.D., Chief of Staff, Falls Community Hospital And Clinic, Marlin, TX, p. A699
CROCKETT, John, Chief Information Officer, Guidance Center, Flagstaff, AZ, p. A31
CROCKETT, Mandy, Director Human Resources, San Luis Valley Health Conejos County Hospital, La Jara, CO, p. A115
Director Human Resources, San Luis Valley Health, Alamosa, CO, p. A107
CROCKETT, Matt, Chief Executive Officer, Wellfound Behavioral Health Hospital, Tacoma, WA, p. A767
CROCKETT, Richard, Director, Overton Brooks Veterans Affairs Medical Center, Shreveport, LA, p. A314
CROCKETT, Timothy, Chief Financial Officer, Breckinridge Memorial Hospital, Hardinsburg, KY, p. A284
CROFFUT, Tom, Chief Financial Officer, Centerpointe Hospital, Saint Charles, MO, p. A414
CROFT, Kim, R.N., Executive Director Human Resources, Pomerene Hospital, Millersburg, OH, p. A545
CROFTON, Michael, Chief Financial Officer, Good Samaritan Hospital, Cincinnati, OH, p. A532
Chief Financial Officer, Trihealth Evendale Hospital, Cincinnati, OH, p. A533
Senior Vice President and Chief Financial Officer, Bethesda North Hospital, Cincinnati, OH, p. A532

CROKER, James, Director Information Systems, St. Bernardine Medical Center, San Bernardino, CA, p. A91
CROLEY, John, Chief Executive Officer and Chief Financial Officer, Texas Institute For Surgery At Texas Health Presbyterian Dallas, Dallas, TX, p. A670
CROLEY, John S., Chief Executive Officer and Chief Financial Officer, Texas Institute For Surgery At Texas Health Presbyterian Dallas, Dallas, TX, p. A670
CROMWELL, Andre, Chief Executive Officer, Delta Specialty Hospital, Memphis, TN, p. A644
CRONER, Robert, Senior Vice President and Chief Human Resources Officer, Children's Hospital Of Philadelphia, Philadelphia, PA, p. A599
CRONIN, David, Regional Vice President Human Resources, Good Samaritan Medical Center, Brockton, MA, p. A337
CRONIN-WAELDE, Deborah, MSN, R.N., Senior Vice President Clinical Operations and Chief Nursing Officer, Melrosewakefield Healthcare, Melrose, MA, p. A341
CROOKS, John, Chair Information Services, Mayo Clinic Hospital In Florida, Jacksonville, FL, p. A141
CROOM, Jon-Paul, President, Wellstar North Fulton Hospital, Roswell, GA, p. A179
CROPPER, Ronnie, Chief Operating Officer, Warren State Hospital, Warren, PA, p. A609
CROSBY, Evalie, CPA, Vice President Finance and Chief Financial Officer, Alice Peck Day Memorial Hospital, Lebanon, NH, p. A449
CROSBY, Robert, Chief Financial Officer, Athol Hospital, Athol, MA, p. A334
Senior Vice President and Chief Financial Officer, Heywood Hospital, Gardner, MA, p. A339
CROSHAW, Diane, Vice President Human Resources, Bacharach Institute For Rehabilitation, Pomona, NJ, p. A461
CROSS, Carol, CPA, Chief Financial Officer, Northeast Regional Medical Center, Kirksville, MO, p. A410
CROSS, John D., Chief Executive Officer, Kindred Hospital Sugar Land, Sugar Land, TX, p. A717
CROSS, Lynda, R.N., Director of Nurses, Nemaha Valley Community Hospital, Seneca, KS, p. A276
CROSS, Patricia, Chief Executive Officer, Life Line Hospital, Steubenville, OH, p. A549
CROSS, Renee, Senior Vice President and Chief Financial Officer, Saint Francis Hospital, Charleston, WV, p. A771
CROSSAN, Eric, Chief Executive Officer, Walton Rehabilitation Hospital, Augusta, GA, p. A166
CROSSLAND, Jeanne, Director of Nursing, Shamrock General Hospital, Shamrock, TX, p. A715
CROSSLEY, Kent, M.D., Chief of Staff, Minneapolis Veterans Affairs Health Care System, Minneapolis, MN, p. A381
CROSSMAN, Margaret, M.D., Chief Medical Officer, Halifax Health Medical Center Of Daytona Beach, Daytona Beach, FL, p. A136
CROTEAU, Gary, Assistant Vice President and Chief Information Officer, South County Hospital, Wakefield, RI, p. A614
CROTTY, Glenn, M.D., JrExecutive Vice President and Chief Operating Officer, Charleston Area Medical Center, Charleston, WV, p. A771
CROTTY, Renee, Coordinator Marketing and Public Relations, Capital Medical Center, Olympia, WA, p. A761
CROUCH, Amy, Chief Financial Officer, Promedica Coldwater Regional Hospital, Coldwater, MI, p. A351
CROUCH, James, Vice President Technical Services, Mosaic Medical Center - Albany, Albany, MO, p. A402
CROUCH, Matthew, Chief Executive Officer and Managing Director, Peachford Behavioral Health System, Atlanta, GA, p. A165
CROUSE, Autumn, Chief Financial Officer, Behavioral Hospital Of Bellaire, Houston, TX, p. A684
CROUT, Tom, MS, Director Human Resources, Central Louisiana State Hospital, Pineville, LA, p. A313
CROW, Angie, Director Finance, Saint Thomas Hospital For Spinal Surgery, Nashville, TN, p. A646
CROW, Regina, Chief Nursing Officer, Bothwell Regional Health Center, Sedalia, MO, p. A418
CROW, Ronda, Chief Nursing Officer, Moore County Hospital District, Dumas, TX, p. A673
CROWDER, Andy, Chief Information Officer and Corporate Senior Vice President, Scripp. Green Hospital, La Jolla, CA, p. A69
CROWDER, Lonna, Director of Nursing, Phillip. County Hospital, Malta, MT, p. A426
CROWE, Arthur, Director Information Systems, Peconic Bay Medical Center, Riverhead, NY, p. A496
CROWE, Danny, Chief Financial Officer, Decatur Morgan Hospital, Decatur, AL, p. A17
CROWE, Darren, Chief Executive Officer, Crow/Northern Cheyenne Hospital, Crow Agency, MT, p. A422

CROWELL, Lynn, Chief Executive Officer, Arkansas Valley Regional Medical Center, La Junta, CO, p. A115

CROWELL, Pamela, Director, Sheridan Veterans Affairs Medical Center, Sheridan, WY, p. A804

CROWELL, Robin, Chief Nursing Officer and Chief Operating Officer, Saint Thomas Hickman Hospital, Centerville, TN, p. A635

CROWL, Steve, Director of Information Services, Davis Medical Center, Elkins, WV, p. A772

CROWLEY, Thomas, President and Chief Executive Officer, Saint Elizabeth's Medical Center, Wabasha, MN, p. A387

CRUIKSHANK, Jennifer, R.N., Chief Executive Officer, Riverside University Health System-Medical Center, Moreno Valley, CA, p. A80

CRUM, Aaron, M.D., Chief Medical Officer, Assistant Chief Executive Officer and Senior Vice President, Pikeville Medical Center, Pikeville, KY, p. A292

CRUM, Dennis, Senior Vice President and Chief Financial Officer, Tift Regional Medical Center, Tifton, GA, p. A182

CRUM, Jarett, Hospital Director, Baypointe Behavioral Health, Mobile, AL, p. A21

CRUMB, Robert, MS, Chief Executive Officer, Schoolcraft Memorial Hospital, Manistique, MI, p. A361

CRUMLEY, Vickie, Chief Human Resources Officer, Mary Rutan Hospital, Bellefontaine, OH, p. A529

CRUMP, John, M.D., Medical Staff President, Howard Young Medical Center, Woodruff, WI, p. A800

CRUMP, Rick, Chief Financial Officer, Lakeland Behavioral Health System, Springfield, MO, p. A418

CRUMPLER, John, R.N., Director of Nursing, Red River Behavioral Center, Bossier City, LA, p. A298

CRUMPTON, Patsy, R.N., Chief Nursing Officer, National Park Medical Center, Hot Springs, AR, p. A47

CRUSE, Ray, Chief Executive Officer, Lakeland Hospital, Watervliet, Watervliet, MI, p. A369

CRUSON, Jim, Chief Information Officer, Riverview Behavioral Health, Texarkana, AR, p. A53

CRUTCHFIELD, David, Vice President, Information Services & Chief Information Officer, Conway Medical Center, Conway, SC, p. A618

CRUZ, Arlene, Director, Rush Oak Park Hospital, Oak Park, IL, p. A215

CRUZ, Domingo, Senior Vice President Operations, San Jorge Children's Hospital, Santurce, PR, p. A811

CRUZ, Jorge, Interim Chief Executive Officer, Plains Regional Medical Center, Clovis, NM, p. A469

CRUZ, Joseph, Chief Information Officer, Ryder Memorial Hospital, Humacao, PR, p. A808

CRUZ, Julia, Chief Financial Officer, San Juan Capestrano Hospital, San Juan, PR, p. A811

CRUZ, Michael, Senior Vice President Operations, Bsa Hospital, Llc, Amarillo, TX, p. A652

CRUZ, Miguel, M.D., Medical Director, Bella Vista Hospital, Mayaguez, PR, p. A808
Medical Staff Credentialing Coordinator, Encompass Health Rehabilitation Hospital Of Miami, Cutler Bay, FL, p. A135

CRUZ, Obed, Vice President and Chief Nursing Officer, Amita Health Adventist Medical Center Bolingbrook, Bolingbrook, IL, p. A196

CRUZ, Randi, Chief Nursing Officer, Encompass Health Rehabilitation Hospital Of Round Rock, Round Rock, TX, p. A709

CRUZ CORREA, Jesus, Chief Medical Officer, St. Luke's Episcopal Hospital, Ponce, PR, p. A809

CRYER, Betty, R.N., Administrator, Anderson Regional Health System South, Meridian, MS, p. A397

CRYER, Selena, Director Human Resources, Ennis Regional Medical Center, Ennis, TX, p. A677

CUBELLIS, Guido J., Chief Executive Officer, Cornerstone Hospital-Medical Center Of Houston, Houston, TX, p. A685

CUELLAR, Eddie, Vice President Information Systems, Methodist Hospital, San Antonio, TX, p. A712

CUELLAR, Jacob, M.D., Chief Executive Officer, Laurel Ridge Treatment Center, San Antonio, TX, p. A712

CUENCA, Derrick, Chief Executive Officer, Mountainview Regional Medical Center, Las Cruces, NM, p. A470

CUEVAS, Gilberto, Director Human Resources, Hospital De Damas, Ponce, PR, p. A809

CUEVAS, Jacki, Director Health Information Services, Regional Rehabilitation Hospital, Phenix City, AL, p. A23

CUFF, Randy, Chief Operating Officer, Central Valley Medical Center, Nephi, UT, p. A729

CULBERSON, David K., Chief Executive Officer, San Joaquin General Hospital, French Camp, CA, p. A65

CULBERT, Devon, Controller, The Hospital At Westlake Medical Center, Austin, TX, p. A657

CULLEN, Barry, Chief Executive Officer, Southeast Michigan Surgical Hospital, Warren, MI, p. A369

CULLEN, John, M.D., Chief of Staff and Medical Director Long Term Care, Providence Valdez Medical Center, Valdez, AK, p. A29

Chief Executive Officer, Thomas B. Finan Center, Cumberland, MD, p. A329

CULLEN, Kelly, R.N., Executive Vice President and Chief Operating Officer, Tamp. General Hospital, Tampa, FL, p. A160

CULLEN, Michael, Senior Vice President and Chief Financial Officer, South Shore Hospital, South Weymouth, MA, p. A344

CULLEN, Neil, Director Human Resources, Encompass Health Rehabilitation Hospital Of Northwest Tucson, Tucson, AZ, p. A40

CULLOM, Christopher, President, Mercy Catholic Medical Center - Mercy Fitzgerald Campus, Darby, PA, p. A588

CULP, Judy, Chief Financial Officer, Hill Regional Hospital, Hillsboro, TX, p. A684

CULVER, Douglas, Chief Financial Officer, Mercy Hospital Carthage, Carthage, MO, p. A404

CULVER, Shawna, Director Information Systems, Western Plains Medical Complex, Dodge City, KS, p. A263

CUMBEE, Lib, Director Information Systems, Providence Hospital, Columbia, SC, p. A618

CUMBIE, Dan, Chief Nursing Officer, Flowers Hospital, Dothan, AL, p. A17

CUMBO, Adam, Chief Financial Officer, Dukes Memorial Hospital, Peru, IN, p. A239

CUMING, Richard, R.N., MSN, Ed.D., Chief Nurse Executive, Christianacare, Newark, DE, p. A128

CUMMINGS, Allana, Chief Information Officer, Children's Healthcare Of Atlanta, Atlanta, GA, p. A164

CUMMINGS, Brooke, Chief Financial Officer, Our Lady Of The Angels Hospital, Bogalusa, LA, p. A298

CUMMINGS, Greg, Chief Financial Officer, Baylor Scott & White Texas Spine & Joint Hospital-Tyler, Tyler, TX, p. A721

CUMMINGS, Jerry, Chief Operating Officer, Putnam County Memorial Hospital, Unionville, MO, p. A420

CUMMINGS, Kelly, Chief Nursing Officer, Abington-Lansdale Hospital Jefferson Health, Lansdale, PA, p. A594

CUMMINGS, Rae, Chief Operating Officer, Boulder City Hospital, Boulder City, NV, p. A441

CUMMINGS, Steve, M.D., Chief of Medical Staff, Stillwater Medical Center, Stillwater, OK, p. A568

CUMMINGS, Steven, Chief Operating Officer and Chief Information Officer, Baystate Noble Hospital, Westfield, MA, p. A346

CUMMINGS, Tyler, Administrator and Chief Executive Officer, Kindred Hospital-Mansfield, Mansfield, TX, p. A699

CUMMINGS, Vickie, Vice President of Human Resources, Trident Medical Center, Charleston, SC, p. A616

CUMMINS, Frank, Vice President Human Resources, Honorhealth Deer Valley Medical Center, Phoenix, AZ, p. A36

CUNNINGHAM, Becky, Controller, Salem Memorial District Hospital, Salem, MO, p. A418

CUNNINGHAM, Brian, Chief Executive Officer, Wahiawa General Hospital, Wahiawa, HI, p. A187

CUNNINGHAM, Carol, Administrative Assistant, Highland Ridge Hospital, Midvale, UT, p. A728

CUNNINGHAM, Dennis, M.D., Chief Medical Officer, Mclaren Macomb, Mount Clemens, MI, p. A362

CUNNINGHAM, Gail, Interim Chief Medical Officer, University Of Maryland St. Josep. Medical Center, Towson, MD, p. A333

CUNNINGHAM, James, M.D., Chief Medical Officer, Cook Children's Medical Center, Fort Worth, TX, p. A678

CUNNINGHAM, Julie, Associate Administrator and Chief Human Resources Officer, Pioneers Memorial Healthcare District, Brawley, CA, p. A58

CUNNINGHAM, Keith, M.D., Medical Director, Encompass Health Rehabilitation Hospital Of Scottsdale, Scottsdale, AZ, p. A38

CUNNINGHAM, M Edward., Chief Executive Officer, Heartland Regional Medical Center, Marion, IL, p. A211

CUNNINGHAM, Michelle P., Chief Executive Officer, Encompass Health Rehabilitation Hospital Of Hamarville, Pittsburgh, PA, p. A603

CUNNINGHAM, Regina, Ph.D., R.N., Chief Executive Officer, Hospital Of The University Of Pennsylvania, Philadelphia, PA, p. A600

CUNNINGHAM, Robert, Chief Operations Officer, Olmsted Medical Center, Rochester, MN, p. A384

CUPPS, Cheryl, Director Finance, Griffin Memorial Hospital, Norman, OK, p. A563

CURD, R Blake., M.D., Chief Executive Officer, Sioux Falls Specialty Hospital, Sioux Falls, SD, p. A631

CURLING, Susan, M.D., Chief Medical Officer, Memorial Hermann Northeast, Humble, TX, p. A690

CURNEL, Robin, MSN, Chief Operating Officer and Chief Nursing Officer, Crittenden County Hospital, Marion, KY, p. A289

CURNUTT, Melody, CPA, Chief Financial Officer, Greenwood County Hospital, Eureka, KS, p. A264

CURPHY, Rona, Chief Executive Officer, The Core Institute Specialty Hospital, Phoenix, AZ, p. A37

CURRAN, Dezerae, Director Human Resources, Osawatomie State Hospital At Adair Acute Care, Osawatomie, KS, p. A273

CURRAN, Maria, Vice President Human Resources, Vcu Medical Center, Richmond, VA, p. A751

CURRAN, Michael, President, Crozer-Chester Medical Center, Upland, PA, p. A609

CURRAN, Todd, M.D., President Medical Staff, Oss Health, York, PA, p. A612

CURRAN-MEULI, Jane, Chief Operating Officer, Holy Family Memorial, Manitowoc, WI, p. A788

CURRANS, Sheila, Chief Executive Officer, Harrison Memorial Hospital, Cynthiana, KY, p. A282

CURREN, Robert, Director Information Technology, Center For Behavioral Medicine, Kansas City, MO, p. A408
Western Region Chief Information Technology Officer, Northwest Missouri Psychiatric Rehabilitation Center, Saint Joseph, MO, p. A415

CURRIE, Michelle, Chief Financial Officer, Red River Behavioral Health System, Grand Forks, ND, p. A524

CURRIE, Peggy M., R.N., Chief Operating Officer, Providence Holy Family Hospital, Spokane, WA, p. A766
R.N., Chief Operating Officer, Providence Sacred Heart Medical Center & Children's Hospital, Spokane, WA, p. A766

CURRIE, Scott, Vice President and Chief Financial Officer, Midmichigan Medical Center-Midland, Midland, MI, p. A361

CURRIN, Randy, Chief Executive Officer, Blake Medical Center, Bradenton, FL, p. A132

CURRY, Cheryl, Chief Financial Officer, Littleton Adventist Hospital, Littleton, CO, p. A116

CURRY, Christopher, Chief Executive Officer, Kindred Hospital Peoria, Peoria, IL, p. A216

CURRY, Jeffrey, Executive Vice President and Chief Financial Officer, Excela Frick Hospital, Mount Pleasant, PA, p. A598
Executive Vice President and Chief Financial Officer, Excela Health Westmoreland Hospital, Greensburg, PA, p. A591

CURRY, Robert H., President and Chief Executive Officer, Emanate Health Foothill Presbyterian Hospital, Glendora, CA, p. A67
President and Chief Executive Officer, Emanate Health Inter-Community Hospital, Covina, CA, p. A61

CURRY, Stephen, Director Information Services, Princeton Community Hospital, Princeton, WV, p. A776

CURRY, Steve, Regional Director Human Resources, Four County Counseling Center, Logansport, IN, p. A235

CURRY, Timothey, Chief Executive Officer, Avoyelles Hospital, Marksville, LA, p. A308

CURRY-PELYAK, Mary Jane, R.N., Vice President and Chief Clinical Officer, The Villages Regional Hospital, The Villages, FL, p. A160

CURTI, Tate, Senior Vice President and Chief Operating Officer, Southern New Hampshire Medical Center, Nashua, NH, p. A450

CURTIS, Bryan, Chief Information Officer, Memorial Regional Health, Craig, CO, p. A110

CURTIS, George, Chief Information Officer, Houston Medical Center, Warner Robins, GA, p. A183

CURTIS, Gregory, M.D., Chief Medical Officer, New London Hospital, New London, NH, p. A450

CURTIS, Joy, Senior Vice President Human Resources, Cambridge Health Alliance, Cambridge, MA, p. A337

CURTIS, Michael, Chief Administrative Officer, Mckenzie County Healthcare System, Watford City, ND, p. A526

CURTIS, Tracie, Business Partner Human Resources, Cleveland Clinic, Medina Hospital, Medina, OH, p. A545

CURTRIGHT, Jonathan W., Chief Executive Officer, University Of Missouri Health Care, Columbia, MO, p. A405

CURVIN, Thomas, M.D., Chief of Staff, Rankin County Hospital District, Rankin, TX, p. A708

CUSA, Philip L., Hospital Director, Eastpointe Hospital, Daphne, AL, p. A17

CUSACK, Michele, Senior Vice President and Chief Financial Officer, Southside Hospital, Bay Shore, NY, p. A475

CUSACK-MCGUIRK, Joan, President and Chief Executive Officer, Montefiore St. Luke's Cornwall, Newburgh, NY, p. A492

CUSANO, Susan, Director Human Resources, Four Winds Hospital, Katonah, NY, p. A486

CUSENZ, Bruce, M.D., Medical Director, Eastern Niagara Hospital, Lockport, NY, p. A487

CUSHING, Ginger, Chief Executive Officer, Lifebrite Community Hospital Of Early, Blakely, GA, p. A167

CUSHING, Heidi, Chief Financial Officer, Harlan County Health System, Alma, NE, p. A429

CUSHING, Herbert, M.D., Chief Medical Officer, Temple University Hospital, Philadelphia, PA, p. A602

CUSHMAN, Bonnie, Chief Financial Officer, Northern Colorado Rehabilitation Hospital, Johnstown, CO, p. A114

CUSSINS, James, Chief Financial Officer, Platte County Memorial Hospital, Wheatland, WY, p. A804

CUSTER, Joshua, Director Finance, St. Luke's Magic Valley Medical Center, Twin Falls, ID, p. A193

CUSTER, Lindsey, Director Human Resources, Riverside Tappahannock Hospital, Tappahannock, VA, p. A752

CUSTER, Patrick, Interim Chief Executive Officer, Morton County Health System, Elkhart, KS, p. A264

CUSTER-MITCHELL, Marilyn J., President, Parkview Wabash Hospital, Wabash, IN, p. A242

CUSTIN, Melinda, Chief Information Officer, Jp. Health Network, Fort Worth, TX, p. A678

CUSTODIO, David, M.D., President Summa Akron City and St. Thomas Campuses, Summa Health System, Akron, OH, p. A527

CUSUMANO, Margaret, R.N., MSN, Vice President Patient Care Services and Chief Nursing Officer, Saint Joseph's Medical Center, Yonkers, NY, p. A502

CUTHRELL, Rob, Director of Human Resources, Coastal Virginia Rehabilitation, Newport News, VA, p. A746

CUTLIFF, Bryan, Chief Executive Officer, Select Specialty Hospital-Ann Arbor, Ypsilanti, MI, p. A370

CUTOLO, Edward, M.D., JrChief of Staff, James A. Haley Veterans' Hospital-Tampa, Tampa, FL, p. A159

CUTRELL, Carrie, Chief Nursing Officer, Arkansas Valley Regional Medical Center, La Junta, CO, p. A115

CUTRIGHT, Bruce, MS, Vice President Human Resources, Mary Lanning Healthcare, Hastings, NE, p. A433

CUTSFORTH, Shawn, Information Systems Officer, Pioneer Memorial Hospital, Heppner, OR, p. A575

CUTTER, Elise, Chief Financial Officer, Island Hospital, Anacortes, WA, p. A755

CUTTS, Jennifer, M.D., Chief Medical Officer, York Hospital, York, ME, p. A323
M.D., Interim Chief Executive Officer, York Hospital, York, ME, p. A323

CUZZOLA, Anthony, Vice President Operations, Jfk Johnson Rehabilitation Institute At Hackensack Meridian Health, Edison, NJ, p. A454

CYBORON, Abigail, Chief Executive Officer, Chase County Community Hospital, Imperial, NE, p. A433

CYR, Kristin, R.N., MSN, Senior Nursing Executive and Vice President of Patient Care Services, Northern Light Maine Coast Hospital, Ellsworth, ME, p. A320

CYTLAK, David, Chief Financial Officer, Blanchard Valley Hospital, Findlay, OH, p. A540
Vice President Finance, Bluffton Hospital, Bluffton, OH, p. A529

CZAJKOWSKI, Cheryl, Associate Director Patient and Nursing Services, Syracuse Veterans Affairs Medical Center, Syracuse, NY, p. A500

CZAPLINSKI, Cindy, MSN, R.N., Vice President Operations, Vassar Brothers Medical Center, Poughkeepsie, NY, p. A495

CZEREW, Jane, Vice President Clinical Services and Quality, Spectrum Health Zeeland Community Hospital, Zeeland, MI, p. A370

CZYMBOR, Mary, Chief Medical Officer, Milford Regional Medical Center, Milford, MA, p. A341

CZYZ, AnneMarie, R.N., Ed.D., Chief Operating Officer and Chief Nursing Officer, St. Joseph's Hospital Health Center, Syracuse, NY, p. A499

# D

DAANE, John, Information Systems Officer, Crossing Rivers Health Medical Center, Prairie Du Chien, WI, p. A794

DABNEY, Ann, Manager Human Resources, Spring View Hospital, Lebanon, KY, p. A286

DADD, Steven, Flight Commander Resource Management, U. S. Air Force Hospital, Hampton, VA, p. A743

DADO, Joe, Chief Information Officer, Conemaugh Memorial Medical Center, Johnstown, PA, p. A593
Chief Information Officer, Conemaugh Miners Medical Center, Hastings, PA, p. A592

DAEGER, Brian, Chief Financial Officer and Vice President Financial Services, Margaret Mary Health, Batesville, IN, p. A223

DAFFRON, Eric, Division Director, Information Systems, Southeast Alabama Medical Center, Dothan, AL, p. A18

DAGENBACH, Pete, Chief Financial Officer, Adams County Regional Medical Center, Seaman, OH, p. A549

DAGGETT, Jake, Chief Executive Officer, Texas Rehabilitation Hospital Of Fort Worth, Fort Worth, TX, p. A679

DAHDUL, Adnan, M.D., Medical Director, Encompass Health Rehabilitation Hospital Of Western Massachusetts, Ludlow, MA, p. A341

DAHER, Amyra, MSN, R.N., Chief Nursing Officer, University Medical Center Of El Paso, El Paso, TX, p. A676

DAHL, Robert, President and Chief Executive Officer, Amita Health Saints Mary & Elizabeth Medical Center, Chicago, IL, p. A198

DAHLBERG, Connie, Director Business and Employee, Sleep. Eye Medical Center, Sleep. Eye, MN, p. A386

DAHLHAUSEN, Daniel, M.D., President of Medical Staff/ Chief Medical Officer, Anmed Health Cannon, Pickens, SC, p. A623

DAHLING, James D., President and Chief Executive Officer, Children's Hospital Of The King's Daughters, Norfolk, VA, p. A747

DAHLQUIST, Clay, M.D., Chief Medical Officer, Waverly Health Center, Waverly, IA, p. A259

DAHLSTRAND, David, Chief, OI&T, Hunter Holmes Mcguire Veterans Affairs Medical Center-Richmond, Richmond, VA, p. A750

DAHLSTROM, Sheri, R.N., Chief Nursing Officer, Banner Estrella Medical Center, Phoenix, AZ, p. A35

DAIGLE, Charles D., Chief Executive Officer, Ochsner Lsu Health Shreveport - Academic Medical Center, Shreveport, LA, p. A314
Chief Executive Officer, Ochsner Lsu Health Shreveport - Monroe Medical Center, Monroe, LA, p. A309

DAIGLE, Cindy, Chief Financial Officer, Northern Maine Medical Center, Fort Kent, ME, p. A320

DAIGLE, Jennifer, R.N., Director of Nursing and Utilization Review, Carolina Center For Behavioral Health, Greer, SC, p. A621

DAIGLE, Richard, Chief Information Officer, Manchester Memorial Hospital, Manchester, CT, p. A122
Chief Information Officer, Rockville General Hospital, Vernon, CT, p. A125

DAIKER, David, Chief Information Resource Management, Veterans Affairs Nebraska-Western Iowa Health Care System - Lincoln, Lincoln, NE, p. A435

DAILEY, Gina, Chief Financial Officer, Pinnacle Pointe Hospital, Little Rock, AR, p. A49

DAILEY, Glenn, Chief Executive Officer, St. Martin Hospital, Breaux Bridge, LA, p. A298

DAILEY, Jacqueline, Chief Information Officer, West Penn Hospital, Pittsburgh, PA, p. A605

DAILEY, James, Director Information Services, Good Samaritan Medical Center, West Palm Beach, FL, p. A162

DAILEY, Richard, D.O., President Medical Staff, Ellett Memorial Hospital, Appleton City, MO, p. A402

DAISE, Travis, M.D., Chief Medical Officer, Goodland Regional Medical Center, Goodland, KS, p. A265

DAISLEY, Samuel, D.O., Vice President Medical Affairs, Upmc Horizon, Farrell, PA, p. A590

DAJCZAK, Stanislaw, M.D., Chief of Staff, Promedica Defiance Regional Hospital, Defiance, OH, p. A539

DALBY, William, Director Fiscal Services, Shriners Hospitals For Children-Northern California, Sacramento, CA, p. A89

DALE, Jackson, Director Management Information Services, Johnston Memorial Hospital, Abingdon, VA, p. A738

DALE, Jae, Chief Executive Officer, Kosciusko Community Hospital, Warsaw, IN, p. A242

DALEY, Robert, CPA, Chief Financial Officer, Black River Memorial Hospital, Black River Falls, WI, p. A781
CPA, Vice President Fiscal and Information Technology Services, Black River Memorial Hospital, Black River Falls, WI, p. A781

DALGAI, Netrisha, Director of Operations, Sage Memorial Hospital, Ganado, AZ, p. A31

DALL, Jamie, Chief Financial Officer, New Hampshire Hospital, Concord, NH, p. A448

DALLER, Sue, R.N., Assistant Administrator Nursing, Hermann Area District Hospital, Hermann, MO, p. A407

DALLEY, Mark F., Administrator, Gunnison Valley Hospital, Gunnison, UT, p. A728

DALLIS, Donna, R.N., Vice President Patient Care, Northeastern Health System, Tahlequah, OK, p. A569

DALPOAS, Dolan, President and Chief Executive Officer, Abraham Lincoln Memorial Hospital, Lincoln, IL, p. A210

DALTON, Dana, Vice President and Chief Nursing Officer, Regional Medical Center, Orangeburg, SC, p. A623

DALTON, Deana, Human Resources, San Juan Health Service District, Monticello, UT, p. A729

DALTON, Eric, Administrator, Tanner Medical Center-Villa Rica, Villa Rica, GA, p. A182
Chief Financial Officer, Memorial Medical Center, Modesto, CA, p. A79

Chief Financial Officer, Sutter Tracy Community Hospital, Tracy, CA, p. A101

DALTON, Leigh, Director of Nursing and Patient Care Services, Highland Hospital, Charleston, WV, p. A771

DALTON, Nissi, Manager Human Resources, Baylor Scott & White Institute For Rehabilitation-Fort Worth, Fort Worth, TX, p. A678

DALTON, Valerie, R.N., Administrator, Oceans Behavioral Hospital Of Baton Rouge, Baton Rouge, LA, p. A297

DALTON, Wayne, Chief Financial Officer, Lakeview Hospital, Bountiful, UT, p. A727

DALY, Cindy, R.N., Director of Nursing, Syringa Hospital And Clinics, Grangeville, ID, p. A190

DALY, Derek, Chief Executive Officer, Blue Mountain Hospital District, John Day, OR, p. A576

DALY, Linda, Vice President Human Resources, Auburn Community Hospital, Auburn, NY, p. A475

DALY, Thomas, CPA, Chief Financial Officer, University Hospital, Newark, NJ, p. A460

DAMA, Sunil, M.D., Medical Director, Select Specialty Hospital - Cincinnati North, Cincinnati, OH, p. A533

DAMBOISE, Robin, Director Human Resources, Northern Maine Medical Center, Fort Kent, ME, p. A320

DAMIANO, Louis, M.D., President, Holy Cross Hospital, Silver Spring, MD, p. A332

DAMM, Julie, Chief Financial Officer, Hancock County Health System, Britt, IA, p. A244

DAMMEYER, Matt, Ph.D., Chief Executive Officer, Memorial Hospital Of Converse County, Douglas, WY, p. A802

DAMODARAN, A, M.D., President Medical Staff, Starke Hospital, Knox, IN, p. A234

DAMON, Chad, Contractor, Ascension St. Vincent Dunn, Bedford, IN, p. A224

DAMON, Kerry, Director Human Resources, Baystate Franklin Medical Center, Greenfield, MA, p. A339

DAMRON, Paul, Chief Financial Officer, Highlands Regional Medical Center, Sebring, FL, p. A157

DAMRON, Tony, Senior Vice President and Chief Information Officer, Pikeville Medical Center, Pikeville, KY, p. A292

DAMSCHRODER, Robin, Chief Operating Officer, St. Josep. Mercy Livingston Hospital, Howell, MI, p. A358

DANBDALA, Kayyan, M.D., Medical Director, Schick Shadel Hospital, Seattle, WA, p. A763

DANCY, Peter C. Jr, FACHE, Director, Alexandria Veterans Affairs Health Care System, Pineville, LA, p. A312

DANE, Brenda, Director, Human Resources, Highlands Regional Medical Center, Sebring, FL, p. A157

DANE, Jeff, Executive Vice President and Chief Financial Officer, University Medical Center, Lubbock, TX, p. A698

DANEFF, Jeffrey, Chief Financial Officer, Porter Regional Hospital, Valparaiso, IN, p. A241

DANELLO, Sherry, MSN, R.N., Vice President and Chief Nursing Officer, Candler Hospital, Savannah, GA, p. A179
MSN, R.N., Vice President and Chief Nursing Officer, St. Joseph's Hospital, Savannah, GA, p. A180

DANESHMAND, Alex, D.O., Chief Patient Safety Officer, Lee Memorial Hospital, Fort Myers, FL, p. A138

DANG, Cynthia, Vice President Human Resources, Medical City North Hills, North Richland Hills, TX, p. A703

DANGERFIELD, Wesley, Community Chief Executive Officer, Summers County Arh Hospital, Hinton, WV, p. A772

DANIEL, Colene Y., MS, M.P.H., FACHE, Chief Executive Officer, United Medical Center, Washington, DC, p. A130

DANIEL, Dena, Chief Administrative Officer, Harmon Memorial Hospital, Hollis, OK, p. A560

DANIEL, Karen, Chief Executive Officer, Warm Springs Medical Center, Warm Springs, GA, p. A183
Director Human Resources, Bibb Medical Center, Centreville, AL, p. A16

DANIEL, Ron, Manager Information Systems, Matheny Medical And Educational Center, Peapack, NJ, p. A460

DANIEL, S., M.D., Chief Medical Officer, Spring Valley Hospital Medical Center, Las Vegas, NV, p. A444

DANIELS, Alex, Chief Nurse Executive, U. S. Public Health Service Indian Hospital, Crownpoint, NM, p. A469

DANIELS, Andrew J., Chief Executive Officer, Memorial Regional Health, Craig, CO, p. A110

DANIELS, Betty, M.D., Chief of Staff, St. Bernardine Medical Center, San Bernardino, CA, p. A91

DANIELS, Buddy, Chief Executive Officer, Lovelace Regional Hospital - Roswell, Roswell, NM, p. A471

DANIELS, Christine, R.N., Chief Nursing Officer, Camden Clark Medical Center, Parkersburg, WV, p. A775

DANIELS, Craig, Chief Financial Officer, Moab Regional Hospital, Moab, UT, p. A729

DANIELS, D. Jeffery., Chief Executive Officer, Idaho Doctor's Hospital, Blackfoot, ID, p. A188

DANIELS, Don, M.D., Chief Medical Officer, Adventhealth Rollins Brook, Lampasas, TX, p. A694

Executive Vice President and Chief Operating Officer, Swedishamerican - A Division Of Uw Health, Rockford, IL, p. A219

DANIELS, Janette, Chief Executive Officer, Chi St. Vincent Hot Springs Rehabilitation Hospital, Hot Springs, AR, p. A47

DANIELS, Kristin, Manager Human Resources, Sutter Center For Psychiatry, Sacramento, CA, p. A90

DANIELS, Mark, M.D., Vice President/Chief Medical Officer, Northwestern Medicine Delnor Hospital, Geneva, IL, p. A206

DANIELS, S, Director Human Resources, Encompasss Health Rehabilitation Hospital Of Fort Smith, Fort Smith, AR, p. A46

DANIELS, Sarah, Vice President, Information Technology, Mayo Clinic Health System In Mankato, Mankato, MN, p. A379

DANIELS, Todd, M.D., Medical Director, Encompass Health Rehabilitation Hospital Of Arlington, Arlington, TX, p. A653

DANIELS, Troy, Chief Human Resources Officer, Forrest General Hospital, Hattiesburg, MS, p. A393

DANIELYAN, Arman, M.D., Chief of Staff, John Muir Behavioral Health Center, Concord, CA, p. A61

DANN, Doreen, R.N., Chief Operating Officer, Victor Valley Global Medical Center, Victorville, CA, p. A104

DANNA, Denise Chief Nursing Officer, University Medical Center, New Orleans, LA, p. A312

DANNENBERG, Walt, Director, Va Long Beach Healthcare System, Long Beach, CA, p. A73

DANOWSKI, Dale, R.N., Vice President, Patient Care Services, St. Vincent's Medical Center, Bridgeport, CT, p. A121

DANSBY, Tommy, Chief Medical Officer, Cypress Grove Behavioral Health, Bastrop. LA, p. A296

DANSIE, Kimberly, Chief Human Resource Officer, Riverton Hospital, Riverton, UT, p. A731

DANT, Joseph, President and Chief Executive Officer, Edward Hospital, Naperville, IL, p. A213

DANUSER, James, Chief Information Officer, Va Central Iowa Health Care System, Des Moines, IA, p. A249

DAOUD, Joudat, M.D., Chief of Staff, Promedica Coldwater Regional Hospital, Coldwater, MI, p. A351

DARBONNE, Tina, Chief Financial Officer, Central Louisiana State Hospital, Pineville, LA, p. A313

DARBY, Kristin, Chief Information Officer, Cancer Treatment Centers Of America-Eastern Regional Medical Center, Philadelphia, PA, p. A599

DARBY, Sharon, R.N., FACHE, Vice President, Clinical Operations, Children's Hospital Of Richmond At Vcu-Brook Road Campus, Richmond, VA, p. A750

DARCY, Deborah, Human Resources, Chg Hospital Tucson, Llc, Tucson, AZ, p. A40

DARDANO, Anthony, M.D., Chief Medical Officer, Delray Medical Center, Delray Beach, FL, p. A136

DARDEAU, Sean T., FACHE, Chief Executive Officer, Porter Regional Hospital, Valparaiso, IN, p. A241

DAREY, Roland, M.D., Medical Director, Wamego Health Center, Wamego, KS, p. A278

DARLING, Cory, Chief Operating Officer, Memorial Hospital Jacksonville, Jacksonville, FL, p. A141

DARMELIO, Matthew, Chief of Staff, Mon Health Medical Center, Morgantown, WV, p. A774

DARNAUER, Kristina, M.D., Chief of Staff, Hospital District No 1 Of Rice County, Lyons, KS, p. A270

DARNELL, Linda, Director Management Information Systems, King's Daughters' Health, Madison, IN, p. A236

DARRINGTON, Gilbert, Director Human Resources, Jackson Hospital And Clinic, Montgomery, AL, p. A22

DASARO, Lynda, Director Human Resources, Sutter Roseville Medical Center, Roseville, CA, p. A89

DASCENZO, Douglas, MSN, R.N., Chief Nursing Officer, St. Josep. Mercy Oakland, Pontiac, MI, p. A364

DASCOULIAS, Kristine, Chief Nursing Officer, Memorial Hospital, North Conway, NH, p. A451

DASHIELD, Luanne, Chief Operating Officer, Deer's Head Hospital Center, Salisbury, MD, p. A332

DASKALAKIS, Tom G., Chief Administrative Officer, West Chester Hospital, West Chester, OH, p. A552

DASKEVICH, Cris, Chief Executive Officer, Children's Hospital Of San Antonio, San Antonio, TX, p. A711

DASSENKO, Dennis, Chief Information Officer, Essentia Health Duluth, Duluth, MN, p. A375

DAUBERT, Stephanie, Chief Financial Officer, Nebraska Medicine - Bellevue, Bellevue, NE, p. A430
Chief Financial Officer, Nebraska Medicine - Nebraska Medical Center, Omaha, NE, p. A437

DAUBY, Randall W., Chief Executive Officer, Pinckneyville Community Hospital, Pinckneyville, IL, p. A217

DAUERMAN, Rebecca, R.N., Vice President, Administrator Mental Health Services and Chief Nursing Officer, Christian Health Care Center, Wyckoff, NJ, p. A466

DAUGHDRILL, Diane, Director Human Resources, Jefferson Davis Community Hospital, Prentiss, MS, p. A399

DAUGHDRILL, Richard P., R.N., Administrator, Greene County Hospital, Leakesville, MS, p. A396

DAUGHERTY, Beth Ann, M.P.H., R.N., President, Sparrow Clinton Hospital, Saint Johns, MI, p. A366

DAUGHERTY, Don, Director Information Systems, Fleming County Hospital, Flemingsburg, KY, p. A283

DAUGHERTY, Marney, Worklife Services Consultant, Ascension Brighton Center For Recovery, Brighton, MI, p. A350

DAUGHERTY, Stephen J., Chief Executive Officer, Coliseum Medical Centers, Macon, GA, p. A176

DAUGHTRY, Chris, Chief Executive Officer, Encompass Health Rehabilitation Hospital Of Columbia, Columbia, SC, p. A617

DAUTERIVE, F, M.D., Vice President Medical Affairs, Ochsner Medical Center - Baton Rouge, Baton Rouge, LA, p. A297

DAVACHI, Khosrow, Chief Medical Officer, Bridgepoint Hospital National Harbor, Washington, DC, p. A129

DAVE, Bhasker, M.D., Superintendent, Independence Mental Health Institute, Independence, IA, p. A251

DAVE, Bhasker J., M.D., Superintendent, Independence Mental Health Institute, Independence, IA, p. A251

DAVENPORT, Allison, Chief Executive Officer, Brynn Marr Hospital, Jacksonville, NC, p. A512

DAVENPORT, Douglas, Interim Chief Financial Officer, Mercyone Iowa City Medical Center, Iowa City, IA, p. A252

DAVENPORT, Ginger, Director Human Resources, Kp. Promise Hospital Of Dallas, Dallas, TX, p. A668

DAVENPORT, Michael, D.O., President, Medical Staff, Saint Luke's South Hospital, Overland Park, KS, p. A274

DAVENPORT, Paula, Chief Nursing Officer, Princeton Baptist Medical Center, Birmingham, AL, p. A15

DAVENPORT, Polly J., FACHE, R.N., President and Chief Executive Officer, Amita Health Hoffman Estates, Hoffman Estates, IL, p. A208
FACHE, R.N., President and Chief Executive Officer, Amita Health Saint Josep. Hospital, Elgin, IL, p. A203

DAVES, Ronnie, Chief Executive Officer, North Okaloosa Medical Center, Crestview, FL, p. A135

DAVE', Rajesh, M.D., Executive Vice President and Chief Medical Officer, United Health Services Hospitals-Binghamton, Binghamton, NY, p. A476

DAVID, Biff, R.N., Administrator, St. Landry Extended Care Hospital, Opelousas, LA, p. A312

DAVID, Daphne G., President and Chief Executive Officer, North Suburban Medical Center, Thornton, CO, p. A119

DAVID, Robert G., President, Uh St. John Medical Center, Westlake, OH, p. A553

DAVIDOFF, Ravin, M.D., Chief Medical Officer, Boston Medical Center, Boston, MA, p. A335

DAVIDOW, Daniel, M.D., Medical Director, Cumberland Hospital For Children And Adolescents, New Kent, VA, p. A746

DAVIDSON, Camille, Director Human Resources, Stanton County Hospital, Johnson, KS, p. A267

DAVIDSON, Diane, Senior Vice President Human Resources, Essentia Health Duluth, Duluth, MN, p. A375

DAVIDSON, Dianne, Chief Operating Officer, Union General Hospital, Farmerville, LA, p. A301

DAVIDSON, Elizabeth, R.N., Vice President, Patient Care Services, Osf Saint James - John W. Albrecht Medical Center, Pontiac, IL, p. A217

DAVIDSON, Gary, M.D., Medical Director, Select Specialty Hospital-Johnstown, Johnstown, PA, p. A593
Senior Vice President and Chief Information Officer, Penn Medicine Lancaster General Hospital, Lancaster, PA, p. A594

DAVIDSON, James, Director of Information Services, Ferry County Memorial Hospital, Republic, WA, p. A763
Troop Commander, Tripler Army Medical Center, Honolulu, HI, p. A185

DAVIDSON, Judy, R.N., Chief Nursing Officer, Porter Regional Hospital, Valparaiso, IN, p. A241

DAVIDSON, Rocky, Chief Financial Officer, Larkin Community Hospital Behavioral Health Services, Hollywood, FL, p. A140

DAVIDSON, Stephen, Director Human Resources, Lafayette Regional Health Center, Lexington, MO, p. A411

DAVIDSON, Stuart, M.D., Chief Medical Officer, Mount Desert Island Hospital, Bar Harbor, ME, p. A318

DAVIDSON, Tim, M.D., Chief Executive Physician Services, Providence St. Mary Medical Center, Walla Walla, WA, p. A768

DAVIDSON, Tori, R.N., Chief Nursing Officer, Tsehootsooi Medical Center, Fort Defiance, AZ, p. A31

DAVILA, Susan, Chief Executive Officer, Desert View Hospital, Pahrump. NV, p. A445

DAVIN, Joni, Director Information and Business Management Service Line, Veterans Affairs Eastern Kansas Health Care System, Topeka, KS, p. A277

DAVINI, John, Vice President, St. Rose Hospital, Hayward, CA, p. A68

DAVIS, Amelia, Director of Nursing, Crossridge Community Hospital, Wynne, AR, p. A54

DAVIS, Andy, Chief Executive Officer, Ascension Seton Bastrop. Bastrop. TX, p. A657
Chief Executive Officer, Ascension Seton Smithville, Smithville, TX, p. A716
Chief Operating Officer, St. Vincent's Birmingham, Birmingham, AL, p. A15

DAVIS, Anne, Director Human Resources, Mason District Hospital, Havana, IL, p. A207

DAVIS, Astrid, R.N., Chief Nursing Officer, Wellspan York Hospital, York, PA, p. A612

DAVIS, Autherine, Director Human Resources, D. W. Mcmillan Memorial Hospital, Brewton, AL, p. A16

DAVIS, Barry L., FACHE, President and Chief Executive Officer, Arkansas Methodist Medical Center, Paragould, AR, p. A51

DAVIS, Ben, Chief Executive Officer, Osceola Regional Health Center, Sibley, IA, p. A257

DAVIS, Betty, Director Administrative Services, Porterville Developmental Center, Porterville, CA, p. A86

DAVIS, Brent, Chief Financial Officer, Central Valley Medical Center, Nephi, UT, p. A729

DAVIS, Brian, Chief Executive Officer, Pam Specialty Hospital Of Covington, Covington, LA, p. A300

DAVIS, Charissa, Chief Nursing Officer and Director of Nursing, Oasis Behavioral Health - Chandler, Chandler, AZ, p. A31

DAVIS, Charlotte, Director Human Resources, Lincoln Trail Behavioral Health System, Radcliff, KY, p. A292

DAVIS, Cheryl, M.D., Chief Medical Officer, Scotland Health Care System, Laurinburg, NC, p. A513

DAVIS, Christopher, Vice President, Finance, De Soto Regional Health System, Mansfield, LA, p. A308

DAVIS, Cynthia, Interim Chief Financial Officer, Loyola University Medical Center, Maywood, IL, p. A211

DAVIS, Dan, Managing Director and Chief Financial Officer, Integris Southwest Medical Center, Oklahoma City, OK, p. A564

DAVIS, Daniel, Chief Financial Officer, Hca Houston Healthcare Kingwood, Kingwood, TX, p. A693

DAVIS, Darcy, Chief Financial Officer, Lakeside Medical Center, Belle Glade, FL, p. A132

DAVIS, David, Chief Operating Officer, Western Maryland Hospital Center, Hagerstown, MD, p. A330

DAVIS, Debra, Director of Operations, Winner Regional Healthcare Center, Winner, SD, p. A633

DAVIS, Deland, Chief Financial Officer, Indian Health Service - Quentin N. Burdick Memorial Health Care Facility, Belcourt, ND, p. A521

DAVIS, Dell, Director Information Systems, United Memorial Medical Center, Houston, TX, p. A689

DAVIS, Dustin, Chief Executive Officer, Woodland Springs Hospital, Conroe, TX, p. A665
Market Chief Executive Officer, Westpark Springs, Richmond, TX, p. A708

DAVIS, Dustin Lee., Administrator, Wise Health Surgical Hospital At Parkway, Fort Worth, TX, p. A679

DAVIS, Elaine, Chief Nursing Officer and Vice President Patient Services, Rmc Anniston, Anniston, AL, p. A13

DAVIS, Evan, Director Technology and Environmental Services, Barbourville Arh Hospital, Barbourville, KY, p. A280

DAVIS, Gannon, Director Human Resources, Medical West, Bessemer, AL, p. A14

DAVIS, Gary, Vice President Information Systems, Baptist Medical Center, San Antonio, TX, p. A711

DAVIS, Heather, M.D., Chief of Staff, Pender Memorial Hospital, Burgaw, NC, p. A505
Administrator, Scott Regional Hospital, Morton, MS, p. A397

DAVIS, Howard, M.D., Chief Medical Officer, Providence Tarzana Medical Center, Tarzana, CA, p. A100

DAVIS, Jack, Vice President Human Resources, Faxton St. Luke's Healthcare, Utica, NY, p. A500

DAVIS, James R., Chief Executive Officer, University Hospital, Augusta, GA, p. A166

DAVIS, Janet, R.N., MS, Senior Vice President and Chief Nursing Officer, Tamp. General Hospital, Tampa, FL, p. A160

DAVIS, Janice, Interim Director Human Resources, Gifford Medical Center, Randolph, VT, p. A736

DAVIS, Jeff, Chief Financial Officer, Harrison County Hospital, Corydon, IN, p. A226

DAVIS, Jeffrey, D.O., Chief Medical Officer, St. Mary's Medical Center, West Palm Beach, FL, p. A162

DAVIS, Jeremy P., President and Chief Executive Officer, Grande Ronde Hospital, La Grande, OR, p. A576

DAVIS, John, Chief Human Resources Officer, Bristol Bay Area Health Corporation, Dillingham, AK, p. A28

DAVIS, Johnnie, Director Human Resources, Medicine Lodge Memorial Hospital, Medicine Lodge, KS, p. A271

DAVIS, Jon, Chief Financial Officer, Community Hospital-Fairfax, Fairfax, MO, p. A406

DAVIS, Jonathan S., FACHE, President, Sentara Martha Jefferson Hospital, Charlottesville, VA, p. A739

DAVIS, Karen, Chief Nursing Officer and Vice President, Nursing, Howard County General Hospital, Columbia, MD, p. A328

DAVIS, Kassi, Director Patient Care Services, Willow Crest Hospital, Miami, OK, p. A562

DAVIS, Kelli, Interim Chief Executive Officer, Northern Inyo Hospital, Bishop. CA, p. A58

DAVIS, Kelly, Chief Nursing Officer, Anmed Health Rehabilitation Hospital, Anderson, SC, p. A615

DAVIS, Kenneth, M.D., Chief Medical Officer, Christus Santa Rosa Health System, San Antonio, TX, p. A711
Assistant Vice President Information Systems, Kennedy Krieger Institute, Baltimore, MD, p. A324

DAVIS, LaKeitha, Director Human Resources, Medical Center Of South Arkansas, El Dorado, AR, p. A44

DAVIS, Lance, PharmD, Associate Director, Miami Veterans Affairs Healthcare System, Miami, FL, p. A147

DAVIS, Lora, FACHE, Chief Executive Officer, Regional Rehabilitation Hospital, Phenix City, AL, p. A23

DAVIS, Lorraine, Vice President Human Resources, Horn Memorial Hospital, Ida Grove, IA, p. A251

DAVIS, Malene S., R.N., President and Chief Executive Officer, Capital Hospice, Arlington, VA, p. A738

DAVIS, Margaret, Chief Operating Officer, Pecos County Memorial Hospital, Fort Stockton, TX, p. A677

DAVIS, Mark, M.D., Chief of Staff, Newberry County Memorial Hospital, Newberry, SC, p. A623
M.D., President Medical Staff, Galesburg Cottage Hospital, Galesburg, IL, p. A205
Director Information Systems, Lake Taylor Transitional Care Hospital, Norfolk, VA, p. A748

DAVIS, Marla, Interim Chief Nursing Officer, Prosser Memorial Health, Prosser, WA, p. A762

DAVIS, Matt, FACHE, Chief Executive Officer, Hca Houston Healthcare Conroe, Conroe, TX, p. A665

DAVIS, Michael, Administrator, Baylor Scott & White Continuing Care Hospital-Temple, Temple, TX, p. A718

DAVIS, Myra, Senior Vice President and Chief Information Officer, Texas Children's Hospital, Houston, TX, p. A688

DAVIS, Myrna, Manager Human Resources, Palo Verde Hospital, Blythe, CA, p. A58

DAVIS, Natalie, R.N., Interim Chief Nursing Officer, Mcleod Health Clarendon, Manning, SC, p. A622

DAVIS, Pam, Chief Nursing Officer, Galesburg Cottage Hospital, Galesburg, IL, p. A205

DAVIS, Patricia, Chief Nursing Officer, South Central Kansas Medical Center, Arkansas City, KS, p. A261

DAVIS, Paula, Chief Human Resources Officer, Sonoma Valley Hospital, Sonoma, CA, p. A99

DAVIS, Rachel, Director, Sharp Coronado Hospital And Healthcare Center, Coronado, CA, p. A61

DAVIS, Randy, Chief Executive Officer, Northcrest Medical Center, Springfield, TN, p. A650
Vice President and Chief Information Officer, Cgh Medical Center, Sterling, IL, p. A221

DAVIS, Regana, Vice President Human Resources, Tri-State Memorial Hospital, Clarkston, WA, p. A756

DAVIS, Richard, Chief Executive Officer, Central Peninsula Hospital, Soldotna, AK, p. A29
Chief Financial Officer, George Washington University Hospital, Washington, DC, p. A129
Chief Financial Officer, Saint Barnabas Medical Center, Livingston, NJ, p. A457

DAVIS, Rick, Chief Operating Officer and Support Services, Coshocton Regional Medical Center, Coshocton, OH, p. A538

DAVIS, Robert, Chief Nursing Officer, Adventhealth Palm Coast, Palm Coast, FL, p. A152

DAVIS, Roger, Director Human Resources, Bourbon Community Hospital, Paris, KY, p. A292

DAVIS, Ronald, Chief Financial Officer - UCLA Hospital System, Stewart & Lynda Resnick Neuropsychiatric Hospital At Ucla, Los Angeles, CA, p. A76

DAVIS, Roy, M.D., Chief Medical Officer, Providence Alaska Medical Center, Anchorage, AK, p. A27

DAVIS, Scott, Chief Executive Officer, Hca Houston Healthcare Northwest, Houston, TX, p. A685
Manager Information Technology, Arkansas Surgical Hospital, North Little Rock, AR, p. A51

DAVIS, Shawn, Chief Information Officer, Tuba City Regional Health Care Corporation, Tuba City, AZ, p. A39

DAVIS, Sondra, Vice President Human Resources & System Development, Harnett Health System, Dunn, NC, p. A508

DAVIS, Stephanie, Controller, Encompass Health Rehabilitation Hospital Of Colorado Springs, Colorado Springs, CO, p. A109

DAVIS, Steven T., Chief Executive Officer, Clarion Hospital, Clarion, PA, p. A586

DAVIS, Takeisha C., M.D., M.P.H., President and Chief Executive Officer, New Orleans East Hospital, New Orleans, LA, p. A310

DAVIS, Tamara, R.N., Chief Nurse Executive Officer, Sutter Davis Hospital, Davis, CA, p. A62

DAVIS, Tammy, Director Human Resources, Union County Hospital, Anna, IL, p. A194

DAVIS, Terry, Manager Information Systems, Atchison Hospital, Atchison, KS, p. A261

DAVIS, Teshia, Chief Clinical Officer, Carolinas Continuecare Hospital At Pineville, Charlotte, NC, p. A507

DAVIS, Toby, Chief Nursing Officer, Good Samaritan Hospital, Bakersfield, CA, p. A57

DAVIS, Todd, M.D., Executive Vice President, Chief Medical Officer, Caromont Regional Medical Center, Gastonia, NC, p. A510
Executive Director of Information Systems, Hendricks Regional Health, Danville, IN, p. A226

DAVIS, Tommy, M.D., Chief of Staff, Oakdale Community Hospital, Oakdale, LA, p. A312

DAVIS, Tracy, Chief Executive Officer, Neuropsychiatric Hospital Of Indianapolis, Indianapolis, IN, p. A232

DAVIS, Tracye B., Medical Center Director, Maine Veterans Affairs Medical Center, Augusta, ME, p. A318

DAVIS, Trish, Chief Nursing Officer, Santa Rosa Medical Center, Milton, FL, p. A148

DAVIS, Tyler, Chief Executive Officer and Chief Nursing Officer, Erlanger Behavioral Hospital, Chattanooga, TN, p. A634

DAVIS, Tyson, Chief Financial Officer, Adventhealth Tampa, Tampa, FL, p. A159

DAVIS, Verlene, Director Human Resources, Blue Mountain Hospital District, John Day, OR, p. A576

DAVIS, Wayne, Manager Human Resources, Jesse Brown Veterans Affairs Medical Center, Chicago, IL, p. A198

DAVIS, Wendy, Associate Vice President and Chief Human Resource Officer, The University Of Toledo Medical Center, Toledo, OH, p. A551

DAVIS III, Boyd, Chief Executive Officer, Encompass Health Rehabilitation Hospital Of Wichita Falls, Wichita Falls, TX, p. A725

DAVIS JR, AndrewChief Operating Officer, Erie County Medical Center, Buffalo, NY, p. A479

DAVIS, MSN, Dan, R.N., Nurse Administrator, Park City Hospital, Park City, UT, p. A730

DAVIS-HAGENS, Patricia, R.N., Central Market Leader and President, The Jewish Hospital - Mercy Health, Cincinnati, OH, p. A533

DAVISON, Katie, Vice President, Human Resources, Nash Unc Health Care, Rocky Mount, NC, p. A517

DAVISON, Trish, R.N., Chief Nursing Officer, Regional West Garden County, Oshkosh, NE, p. A438

DAVISSON, Deborah, MSN, Chief Nursing Officer and Vice President, Patient Care Services, Holy Cross Hospital, Chicago, IL, p. A198

DAVY, Larry, Chief Executive Officer, Wallowa Memorial Hospital, Enterprise, OR, p. A574

DAWE, Jacqueline, R.N., Chief Nursing Officer, Oneida Healthcare, Oneida, NY, p. A494

DAWSON, Brian, Senior Vice President and Chief Medical Officer, South Georgia Medical Center, Valdosta, GA, p. A182

DAWSON, Cindy, MSN, R.N., Chief Nursing Executive, University Of Iowa Hospitals And Clinics, Iowa City, IA, p. A252

DAWSON, Kane A., Chief Executive Officer, Mission Regional Medical Center, Mission, TX, p. A701

DAWSON, Theresa, MSN, R.N., Chief Nursing Officer, Oaklawn Hospital, Marshall, MI, p. A361

DAWSON, Trang, Chief Information Officer, Baylor Scott & White Emergency Hospitals—Aubrey, Aubrey, TX, p. A654

DAX, Jennifer, Director Human Resources, Gundersen Boscobel Area Hospital And Clinics, Boscobel, WI, p. A781

DAY, Gordy, M.D., Medical Director, Schleicher County Medical Center, Eldorado, TX, p. A676

DAY, Mark, Chief Financial Officer, Twin Cities Hospital, Niceville, FL, p. A149

DAY, Regina, Chief Executive Officer, Hawkins County Memorial Hospital, Rogersville, TN, p. A648
Director of Finance, Hancock County Hospital, Sneedville, TN, p. A649

Executive Director Finance, Mountain View Regional Medical Center, Norton, VA, p. A748

Executive Vice President of Finance, Lonesome Pine Hospital, Big Stone Gap. VA, p. A739

DAY, Scott, Vice President Human Resources, Lutheran Medical Center, Wheat Ridge, CO, p. A120

DAY, Sherry, CPA, Chief Financial Officer, Mercy Hospital Cassville, Cassville, MO, p. A404
CPA, Chief Financial Officer, Mercy St. Francis Hospital, Mountain View, MO, p. A412
CPA, Vice President Finance and Regional Chief Financial Officer, Mercy Hospital Aurora, Aurora, MO, p. A402

DAY, Therese, Chief Financial Officer, Umass Memorial Medical Center, Worcester, MA, p. A347

DAY, Victoria, Chief Financial Officer and Vice President of Ancillary Services, Sharp Coronado Hospital And Healthcare Center, Coronado, CA, p. A61

DAYAO, Jerome, Chief Nursing Officer, Uw Medicine/ Harborview Medical Center, Seattle, WA, p. A764

DE BOND, Virginia, Chief Financial Officer, Woodlands Specialty Hospital, The Woodlands, TX, p. A721

DE BRUYCKER, Allison, Chief Executive Officer, Riverview Behavioral Health, Texarkana, AR, p. A53

DE FARIA, Ludmila, M.D., Chief Medical Officer, Eastside Psychiatric Hospital, Tallahassee, FL, p. A158

DE JESUS, Alexander, M.D., Medical Director, Encompass Health Rehabilitation Hospital Of Sarasota, Sarasota, FL, p. A157

DE JESUS, Jorge, Executive Director, I. Gonzalez Martinez Oncologic Hospital, Hato Rey, PR, p. A808

DE LA CRUZ, Rosemary, Chief Financial Officer, Hospital Episcopal San Lucas Guayama, Guayama, PR, p. A807

DE LA GARZA, Josiah, Chief Operating Officer, Baylor Scott & White Medical Center - Sunnyvale, Sunnyvale, TX, p. A718

DE LA PAZ, Christine, Director Human Resources, Aurora Charter Oak Hospital, Covina, CA, p. A61

DE LEON, Aurea, Chief Human Resources Officer, Hospital Universitario Dr. Ramon Ruiz Arnau, Bayamon, PR, p. A806

DE LEON, Darcy, Executive Director, Human Resources, Adventist Health Howard Memorial, Willits, CA, p. A105

DE LEON, Dennis, M.D., Associate Chief Medical Officer and Vice President Medical Affairs, St. Anne Hospital, Burien, WA, p. A756

DE LOS SANTOS, Conrad, President Medical Staff, Medical West, Bessemer, AL, p. A14

DE LOS SANTOS, Ruben, M.D., Chief Medical Officer, Fort Duncan Regional Medical Center, Eagle Pass, TX, p. A673

DE MELO, Dennis, Chief Information Officer, Heber Valley Hospital, Heber City, UT, p. A728

DE NESHEREA, Alexander, M.D., Chief Medical Officer, Dartmouth-Hitchcock Medical Center, Lebanon, NH, p. A449

DE ONIS, Luis, Interim Chief Human Resources Officer, Stony Brook University Hospital, Stony Brook, NY, p. A499

DE PIANO, Linda, Ph.D., Chief Executive Officer, Jerome Golden Center For Behavioral Health, Inc., West Palm Beach, FL, p. A162

DE SANTIAGO, Elizabeth, Executive Director, Hospital De Psiquiatria, San Juan, PR, p. A810

DE SHAZO, Sheri, R.N., President, Advocate Sherman Hospital, Elgin, IL, p. A203

DE SIMON JOHNSON, Lauren, Senior Vice President, Chief Human Resources Officer, Southcoast Hospitals Group. Fall River, MA, p. A339

DEAK, Terry, Chief Financial Officer, Adventist Health Lodi Memorial, Lodi, CA, p. A71

DEAKYNE, John, Chief Financial Officer, Saint Mary's Regional Medical Center, Reno, NV, p. A446

DEAL, Lisa, Budget Analyst, U. S. Public Health Service Indian Hospital, Eagle Butte, SD, p. A627

DEAL, Roy, Chief Medical Officer, Emerald Coast Behavioral Hospital, Panama City, FL, p. A152

DEAN, Douglas, Chief Human Resources Officer, Children's Of Alabama, Birmingham, AL, p. A15

DEAN, Joel, Director Information Services, Piedmont Medical Center, Rock Hill, SC, p. A624

DEAN, Laura, Director Human Resources, Wilson Medical Center, Neodesha, KS, p. A271

DEAN, Ronald, Chief Executive Officer, South Georgia Medical Center, Valdosta, GA, p. A182

DEAN, Sam, Administrator, Usa Health University Hospital, Mobile, AL, p. A22

DEAN, Thomas, M.D., Chief of Staff, Avera Weskota Memorial Hospital, Wessington Springs, SD, p. A633

DEANGELIS, Lisa, M.D., Acting Physician-in-Chief, Memorial Sloan-Kettering Cancer Center, New York, NY, p. A490

DEARDORFF, Chad, Chief Financial Officer, Curahealth Heritage Valley, Beaver, PA, p. A584

DEARDORFF, John A., President and Chief Executive, Northern Virginia Market, Reston Hospital Center, Reston, VA, p. A749

DEARY, Shirley, Director Human Resources, Glenbeigh Hospital And Outpatient Centers, Rock Creek, OH, p. A548

DEATER, Gary, Vice President Administration, Human Resources and Risk Management, Witham Health Services, Lebanon, IN, p. A235

DEATON, Dan, Executive Director Human Resources, Valley View Hospital, Glenwood Springs, CO, p. A113

DEATON, David, FACHE, Chief Executive Officer, Ozark Health Medical Center, Clinton, AR, p. A43

DEATON, Eric, Executive Vice President, Chief Operating Officer and Corporate Operating, Hancock County Hospital, Sneedville, TN, p. A649

DEATON, Mike, Chief Financial Officer, Ozark Health Medical Center, Clinton, AR, p. A43

DEATON, Susan, Human Resources Director, Logan Memorial Hospital, Russellville, KY, p. A293

DEATRICK, Steve, Administrator, Riceland Medical Center, Winnie, TX, p. A726

DEBBAS, Elias, M.D., President Medical Staff, Fort Washington Medical Center, Oxen Hill, MD, p. A331

DEBEVEC, Teresa, Chief Executive Officer and Administrator, Cook Hospital & Care Center, Cook, MN, p. A374

DEBLANC, Hunt, M.D., Chief of Staff, Opelousas General Health System, Opelousas, LA, p. A312

DEBLASIS, John, Vice President, Harrison Community Hospital, Cadiz, OH, p. A530

DEBLIEUX, Dawna, Vice President Patient Care Services and Chief Nurse Executive, Natchitoches Regional Medical Center, Natchitoches, LA, p. A310

DEBLOIS, Georgean, M.D., Chairman Medical Staff, Chippenham Hospital, Richmond, VA, p. A750

DEBLOUW, Christina, Chief Executive Officer, Select Specialty Hospital-Flint, Flint, MI, p. A354

DEBOER, Cynthia, Chief Financial Officer, Cedar Springs Hospital, Colorado Springs, CO, p. A109

DEBOER, K. C., President and Chief Executive Officer, Prairie Lakes Healthcare System, Watertown, SD, p. A633

DEBOLT, Larry, Chief Financial Officer, Bluffton Regional Medical Center, Bluffton, IN, p. A224

DEBONA, Paul, Chief Executive Officer, Baylor Scott & White Surgical Hospital Fort Worth, Fort Worth, TX, p. A678

DEBONO, Julie, Director, Human Resources, Umass Memorial Healthalliance-Clinton Hospital, Leominster, MA, p. A340

DEBORD, Thomas, Chief Operating Officer, Overlake Medical Center, Bellevue, WA, p. A755

DEBRUYCKER, Allison, Administrator, Magnolia Behavioral Hospital Of East Texas, Longview, TX, p. A697

DECARLO, Donald, M.D., President, Uh Geauga Medical Center, Chardon, OH, p. A531

DECASPERIS, Ilyssa, Director of Human Resources, Parkview Community Hospital Medical Center, Riverside, CA, p. A88

DECEAULT, David, Chief Executive Officer, Pemiscot Memorial Health System, Hayti, MO, p. A407

DECELIS, Lori, Director Human Resources, Hampton Behavioral Health Center, Westampton, NJ, p. A465

DECELL, Daniela, Chief Executive Officer, Medical City Las Colinas, Irving, TX, p. A690

DECHABERT, Rebecca, Acting Director Personnel, New York State Psychiatric Institute, New York, NY, p. A491

DECHANT, David, Chief Human Resources Officer, Va Medical Center, Tomah, WI, p. A797

DECKARD, Rick, Chief Fiscal Service, Chillicothe Veterans Affairs Medical Center, Chillicothe, OH, p. A531

DECKARD, Steven, Vice President Human Resources, Indiana University Health Bloomington Hospital, Bloomington, IN, p. A224

DECKER, Chad, Director Human Resources, Winona Health, Winona, MN, p. A388

DECKER, Diann, Chief Human Resource Officer, Provo Canyon Behavioral Hospital, Orem, UT, p. A730

DECKER, Janet, Assistant Vice President, Information Systems, Medstar Union Memorial Hospital, Baltimore, MD, p. A325

DECKER, Jeanine, Manager Human Resources, Arizona State Hospital, Phoenix, AZ, p. A35

DECKER, Michael, President and Chief Executive Officer, Divine Savior Healthcare, Portage, WI, p. A794

DECORTE, Raymond, M.D., Chief Medical Officer, East Jefferson General Hospital, Metairie, LA, p. A308

DECREMER, Dean, Information Systems Manager, Dickinson County Healthcare System, Iron Mountain, MI, p. A358

DECUBELLIS, Jennifer, Chief Executive Officer, Hennepin Healthcare, Minneapolis, MN, p. A380

DEDOMINICO, Tony, Chief Operating Officer, Ascension Seton Northwest, Austin, TX, p. A655

DEE, Thomas A., President and Chief Executive Officer, Southwestern Vermont Medical Center, Bennington, VT, p. A735

DEEN ESQ, CeceliaChief Nursing Officer, Southeast Colorado Hospital District, Springfield, CO, p. A118

DEERING, Lisa, Administrator, Heatherhill Care Communities, Chardon, OH, p. A531
Chief Executive Officer, Regency Hospital Cleveland East, Warrensville Heights, OH, p. A552

DEETER, Joe, MS, Director Information Systems, Clifton-Fine Hospital, Star Lake, NY, p. A498

DEFIGUIEREDO, Kathy, Director, Information Technology, Chi St. Luke's Health Memorial Livingston, Livingston, TX, p. A696

DEFILLIPO, Emily, Chief Executive Officer, Vibra Hospital Of Northern California, Redding, CA, p. A87

DEFOE, Mike, Chief Financial Officer, Perry Memorial Hospital, Princeton, IL, p. A218

DEFORD, Drexel, Chief Information Officer, Scripp. Mercy Hospital, San Diego, CA, p. A92

DEFRANCESCO, Anthony, Associate Director, Va Long Beach Healthcare System, Long Beach, CA, p. A73

DEFREECE, Daniel, M.D., Interim President, Chi Health St. Mary's, Nebraska City, NE, p. A435

DEFREECE, Todd, Vice President Operations, Chi Health Creighton University Medical Center - Bergan Mercy, Omaha, NE, p. A436

DEFURIO, Anthony, Executive Vice President Chief Financial Officer, Atrium Health's Carolinas Medical Center, Charlotte, NC, p. A506

DEFURIO, Ken, President and Chief Executive Officer, Butler Health System, Butler, PA, p. A585

DEGEAR, David, M.D., Vice President Medical Affairs, Westfields Hospital And Clinic, New Richmond, WI, p. A792

DEGENNARO, Melanie, Vice President of Human Resources, Emory University Hospital, Atlanta, GA, p. A164

DEGENNARO, Vincent, M.D., Chief of Staff, Miami Veterans Affairs Healthcare System, Miami, FL, p. A147

DEGENSTEIN-GARTMAN, Katherine, MSN, R.N., Chief Nursing Officer, Abilene Regional Medical Center, Abilene, TX, p. A651

DEGNAN, William, Vice President Finance, Jefferson Health Northeast, Philadelphia, PA, p. A600

DEGRAVELLE, Eric, Vice President Professional Services, Thibodaux Regional Health System, Thibodaux, LA, p. A316

DEGROOD, Robert, M.D., Chief Medical Staff, Musc Health Marion Medical Center, Mullins, SC, p. A623

DEGROOT, Daniel, President and Chief Executive Officer, Stoughton Hospital Association, Stoughton, WI, p. A797

DEGROOT, Randy, President and Chief Executive Officer, Promedica Coldwater Regional Hospital, Coldwater, MI, p. A351

DEHAAI, Sarah, R.N., Director of Nursing, Avera Hand County Memorial Hospital, Miller, SD, p. A629

DEHART, Kristen, Chief Executive Officer, Excelsior Springs Hospital, Excelsior Springs, MO, p. A406

DEHAVEN, Bryce, Chief Financial Officer, Medical Center Of Aurora, Aurora, CO, p. A107

DEHERRERA, Barbara, Chief Nursing Officer, Garfield County Public Hospital District, Pomeroy, WA, p. A762

DEHNING, Cielo, M.D., Medical Director, Mid—America Rehabilitation Hospital, Shawnee Mission, KS, p. A276

DEIBEL, Justin, Senior Vice President and Chief Financial Officer, Mercy Medical Center, Baltimore, MD, p. A323

DEININGER, Robert, Chief Executive Officer, Adventhealth Fish Memorial, Orange City, FL, p. A150

DEIS, Terrence G., CPA, FACHE, President, Chi Saint Josep. Berea, Berea, KY, p. A280
CPA, FACHE, President, Chi Saint Josep. London, London, KY, p. A287
CPA, FACHE, President, Saint Josep. Mount Sterling, Mount Sterling, KY, p. A290

DEITRICK, Diana, Director Information Services, Devereux Hospital And Children's Center Of Florida, Melbourne, FL, p. A145

DEJACO, Lynn, Chief Financial Officer, Firsthealth Moore Regional Hospital, Pinehurst, NC, p. A516

DEJONG, Tyler, Vice President, Operational Finance, Chi Health Midlands, Papillion, NE, p. A438
Vice President, Operational Finance, Chi Health St Elizabeth, Lincoln, NE, p. A434

DEJOSEPH, Anthony M., PsyD, Chief Executive Officer, Chicago Behavioral Hospital, Des Plaines, IL, p. A202

DEKEYZER, Ron, Regional Director Information Systems, Christus St. Vincent Regional Medical Center, Santa Fe, NM, p. A472

DEKEZEL, Lisa, President, Osf St. Mary Medical Center, Galesburg, IL, p. A205

DEKOK, Joni, Chief Nursing Officer, Sanford Sheldon Medical Center, Sheldon, IA, p. A257

DEKONING, Bernard, M.D., Chief of Staff, Wm. Jennings Bryan Dorn Veterans Affairs Medical Center, Columbia, SC, p. A618

DEKREY, Dale, MS, Associate Director Operations and Resources, Fargo Veterans Affairs Health Care System, Fargo, ND, p. A523

DEKREY, Daniel, M.D., Chief of Staff, Sanford Bemidji Medical Center, Bemidji, MN, p. A372

DEKRUSE, Jet L., Administrator, Humboldt County Mental Health, Eureka, CA, p. A63

DEL CASTILLO, Daniel, Chief Executive Officer, Encompass Health Rehabilitation Hospital Of San Juan, San Juan, PR, p. A810

DEL GAUDIO, Frank J., Department and Hospital Center Director, Essex County Hospital Center, Cedar Grove, NJ, p. A453

DEL RIO, R, M.D., Medical Director, Northern Virginia Mental Health Institute, Falls Church, VA, p. A741

DEL TORO, Gustavo, M.D., Chief Medical Officer, Wyckoff Heights Medical Center, Brooklyn, NY, p. A479

DEL TORO, Ivan, M.D., Medical Director, Hima San Pablo Caguas, Caguas, PR, p. A806

DELA TORRE, Victor, Command Legal Officer, Naval Hospital Lemoore, Lemoore, CA, p. A71

DELAGARDELLE, Pamela K., President and Chief Executive Officer, Unitypoint Health - Allen Hospital, Waterloo, IA, p. A259

DELAHANTY, Paula, Regional Chief Nursing Officer, Pen Bay Medical Center, Rockport, ME, p. A322
Regional Chief Nursing Officer, Waldo County General Hospital, Belfast, ME, p. A319

DELAHOUSSAYE, Renee, R.N., Vice President, Chief Nursing Officer, Lafayette General Medical Center, Lafayette, LA, p. A305

DELANCEY, Darlene, Interim Director, Albany Stratton Veterans Affairs Medical Center, Albany, NY, p. A474

DELANEY, Bryan, Director Information Technology, Crossroads Community Hospital, Mount Vernon, IL, p. A213

DELANEY, Kristi, Director, Human Resources, Siskin Hospital For Physical Rehabilitation, Chattanooga, TN, p. A636

DELANEY, Patrick, Vice President, Operations, Robert Wood Johnson University Hospital Somerset, Somerville, NJ, p. A463

DELANO, John, Chief Information Officer, Southwest Region, Texas Health Huguley Hospital Fort Worth South, Burleson, TX, p. A662

DELATTE, Sandra, Director Human Resources, Villa Feliciana Medical Complex, Jackson, LA, p. A303

DELAVAN, Karen, Interim Director Human Resources, Comanche County Medical Center, Comanche, TX, p. A665

DELEON, Arsenio, M.D., Chief Medical Officer, Select Specialty Hospital-Macomb County, Mount Clemens, MI, p. A362

DELEON, Dennis, M.D., Chief Medical Officer, King Region, St. Francis Hospital, Federal Way, WA, p. A758

DELEON, John, Chief Executive Officer, Methodist Hospital Stone Oak Rehabilitation Center, San Antonio, TX, p. A712

DELEON, Joseph, President, Texas Health Harris Methodist Hospital Fort Worth, Fort Worth, TX, p. A679

DELEON, Sherilene, Chief Financial Officer, Spring Mountain Treatment Center, Las Vegas, NV, p. A444

DELFS, Michael, President and Chief Executive Officer, Jamestown Regional Medical Center, Jamestown, ND, p. A524

DELGADO, Eric, Chief Financial Officer, Lakewood Regional Medical Center, Lakewood, CA, p. A71

DELGADO, Lupe, Coordinator Human Resources, Kindred Hospital Sugar Land, Sugar Land, TX, p. A717

DELGADO, Pete, President and Chief Executive Officer, Salinas Valley Memorial Healthcare System, Salinas, CA, p. A90

DELGRECO, Trish, Director of Nursing, Ohiohealth Medcentral Shelby Hospital, Shelby, OH, p. A549

DELIEN, Rudie, Director of Human Resources, Devereux Advanced Behavioral Health Georgia, Kennesaw, GA, p. A174

DELLA FLORA, Thomas, Vice President and Chief Information Officer, Catholic Medical Center, Manchester, NH, p. A450

DELLEA, Eugene A., President, Fairview Hospital, Great Barrington, MA, p. A339

DELLER, Jerry, Chief Executive Officer, Curahealth Jacksonville, Jacksonville, FL, p. A141

DELLICKER, Sandra, Director of Human Resources, Saint Anne's Hospital, Fall River, MA, p. A339

DELLOCONO, John, Senior Vice President and Chief Financial Officer, Centrastate Healthcare System, Freehold, NJ, p. A455

DELOACH, Stephen, Regional Information Management Executive, Christus St. Michael Health System, Texarkana, TX, p. A719

DELONG, Patricia, Chief Nursing Officer, Essentia Health-St. Joseph's Medical Center, Brainerd, MN, p. A373

DELORENZO, David, Senior Director Human Resources, Sisters Of Charity Hospital Of Buffalo, Buffalo, NY, p. A480

DELORME, Robert, Vice President Medical Affairs, Community Memorial Hospital, Hamilton, NY, p. A485

DELVEAUX, Joe, Manager Information Services, St. Francis Regional Medical Center, Shakopee, MN, p. A386

DEMARCO, Cindy, Chief Operating Officer, Lake Behavioral Hospital, Waukegan, IL, p. A222

DEMARCO, Victor, Chief Financial Officer, Bronxcare Health System, Bronx, NY, p. A476

DEMAREST, Pamela, MSN, R.N., Chief Nursing Officer, Unm Sandoval Regional Medical Center, Inc., Rio Rancho, NM, p. A471

MSN, R.N., Chief Operating Officer, Unm Sandoval Regional Medical Center, Inc., Rio Rancho, NM, p. A471

DEMASIE, Dennis, Vice President Information Systems and Chief Information Officer, Rush-Copley Medical Center, Aurora, IL, p. A195

DEMATTEO, Kathleen, Chief Information Officer, Danbury Hospital, Danbury, CT, p. A121

DEMBLA, Preeti, Chief Medical Officer and Medical Director, Rehabilitation Hospital Of Fort Wayne, Fort Wayne, IN, p. A228

DEMERICH, Lois, Director Human Resources, Sentara Williamsburg Regional Medical Center, Williamsburg, VA, p. A753

DEMERS, Becky, R.N., Chief Nursing Officer, Samaritan Healthcare, Moses Lake, WA, p. A760

DEMETRIADES, James, Vice President, Operations, Penn Medicine Princeton Medical Center, Plainsboro, NJ, p. A461

DEMING, Mark, Administrator, Finance and Support, Beaumont Hospital - Taylor, Taylor, MI, p. A367

DEMING, Peggy, Executive Vice President and Chief Financial Officer, University Health System, San Antonio, TX, p. A714

DEMING, Terra, Director Human Resources, Munson Healthcare Otsego Memorial Hospital, Gaylord, MI, p. A355

DEMLAKIAN, Vahan, Director of Human Resources, Gateways Hospital And Mental Health Center, Los Angeles, CA, p. A74

DEMMEL, Ruth, M.D., Chief Medical Officer, Perkins County Health Services, Grant, NE, p. A433

DEMOE, Sara, Chief Financial Officer, North Canyon Medical Center, Gooding, ID, p. A190

DEMORLIS, John, M.D., Chief Medical Staff, Salem Memorial District Hospital, Salem, MO, p. A418

DEMORROW, Dawn, Chief Human Resources Service, Wilkes-Barre Veterans Affairs Medical Center, Wilkes-Barre, PA, p. A611

DEMOSS, Jill, Finance Manager, Guttenberg Municipal Hospital And Clinics, Guttenberg, IA, p. A250

DEMPSEY, Jeffrey, President, Mercy St. Vincent Medical Center, Toledo, OH, p. A550

DEMPSEY, John J., Chief Executive Officer, Little Colorado Medical Center, Winslow, AZ, p. A41

DEMPSEY, Melanie, Vice President and Chief Financial Officer, Davis Medical Center, Elkins, WV, p. A772

DEMURO, Rob, M.D., Chief Medical Officer, The University Of Vermont Health Network Elizabethtown Community Hospital, Elizabethtown, NY, p. A483

DENEFF, Randall, Vice President Finance, Mary Free Bed Rehabilitation Hospital, Grand Rapids, MI, p. A356

DENEGRI, David, Chief Financial Officer, Parkwood Behavioral Health System, Olive Branch, MS, p. A398

DENG, Mei, Chief Financial Officer, T. J. Samson Community Hospital, Glasgow, KY, p. A284

DENHAM, Stephanie, Chief Financial Officer and Human Resources Officer, Phillip County Hospital, Malta, MT, p. A426

DENIGRIS, Deborah, Chief Nursing Officer, Kingsboro Psychiatric Center, Brooklyn, NY, p. A478

DENIKE, Michael, D.O., Vice President, Medical Affairs, Blanchard Valley Hospital, Findlay, OH, p. A540

DENIO, Arthur, Vice President and Chief Financial Officer, Northbay Medical Center, Fairfield, CA, p. A63

DENIRO, Lori, Regional Chief Nursing Officer, Mercy Health - St. Elizabeth Youngstown Hospital, Youngstown, OH, p. A554

DENISIENKO, Mary, Vice President Human Resources, Palos Health, Palos Heights, IL, p. A216

DENISON, Rita, Director of Information Systems, Sturgis Hospital, Sturgis, MI, p. A367

DENKER, Jill, Executive Director Human Resources, Lexington Regional Health Center, Lexington, NE, p. A434

DENMARK, Donald, M.D., Chief Medical Officer, Carondelet St. Joseph's Hospital, Tucson, AZ, p. A40

DENNETT, Bryan, M.D., Chief of Staff, William Newton Hospital, Winfield, KS, p. A279

DENNIS, Kera, Assistant Administrator, Finance, Uw Medicine/Harborview Medical Center, Seattle, WA, p. A764

DENNIS, Michael, Director, William J. Mccord Adolescent Treatment Facility, Orangeburg, SC, p. A623

DENNISON, Cynthia, Chief Financial Officer, Mercy Allen Hospital, Oberlin, OH, p. A547

DENNY, Donald, M.D., Senior Vice President, Medical Affairs, Penn Medicine Princeton Medical Center, Plainsboro, NJ, p. A461

DENO, Mark S., Chief Executive Officer, Medical City North Hills, North Richland Hills, TX, p. A703

DENSON, Anna, Human Resources Specialist, Choctaw Health Center, Philadelphia, MS, p. A398

DENSON, Paula, M.D., President, Tyler County Hospital, Woodville, TX, p. A726

DENT, Bruce, Human Resources Director, Heber Valley Hospital, Heber City, UT, p. A728

DENTEN, Jane, MSN, R.N., Chief Nurse Executive, Advocate Lutheran General Hospital, Park Ridge, IL, p. A216

DENTON, Brian, Administrator, Mercy Hospital Kingfisher, Kingfisher, OK, p. A560

DENTON, Christopher, Chief Financial Officer, Henrico Doctors' Hospital, Richmond, VA, p. A750

DENTON, Genise, Manager Human Resources, John J. Pershing Veterans Affairs Medical Center, Poplar Bluff, MO, p. A413

DENTON, Joe, Executive Vice President and Chief Financial Officer, Mobile Infirmary Medical Center, Mobile, AL, p. A22

DENTON, Renee, Chief Operating Officer, Freeman Neosho Hospital, Neosho, MO, p. A412

DENTON, Roy, M.D., Chief Medical Officer, Conway Regional Rehabilitation Hospital, Conway, AR, p. A44

DENTON, Tony, JD, Senior Vice President and Chief Operating Officer, University of Michigan Health System, Michigan Medicine, Ann Arbor, MI, p. A348

DENTONI, Terry, Chief Nursing Officer, Zuckerberg San Francisco General Hospital And Trauma Center, San Francisco, CA, p. A94

DENUCCI, Alex, Chief Financial Officer, Franciscan Children's, Brighton, MA, p. A336

DEPAULIS, Hugh, Interim Vice President and Chief Financial Officer, Mercyone Siouxland Medical Center, Sioux City, IA, p. A258

DEPKO, Mike, Director Information Technology, Brown County Hospital, Ainsworth, NE, p. A429

DEPLONTY, Sandy, Senior Director Clinical Services, War Memorial Hospital, Sault Sainte Marie, MI, p. A366

DEPOMPEI, Patricia, President, Rainbow Babies And Children's Hospital, Cleveland, OH, p. A535

DEPOOTER, Stephen, Chief Information Officer, Norwegian American Hospital, Chicago, IL, p. A200

DEPPERMAN, Kristi, Chief Financial Officer, Memphis Veterans Affairs Medical Center, Memphis, TN, p. A644

DEPPERT, Eric, M.D., Chief Medical Officer, Manatee Memorial Hospital, Bradenton, FL, p. A133

DEPRATO, Jeremy, Director Information Technology, The Spine Hospital Of Louisiana At The Neuromedical Center, Baton Rouge, LA, p. A298

DERAMUS, Brenda, Manager Human Resources, Sutter Lakeside Hospital, Lakeport, CA, p. A71

DERKS, Jenny, Chief Administrative Officer, Ascension Calumet Hospital, Chilton, WI, p. A781

DEROCHE, Richard, Manager Information Technology, Multicare Deaconess Hospital, Spokane, WA, p. A765

DERONCEREY, Josiane, Director Human Resources, Carepoint Health Christ Hospital, Jersey City, NJ, p. A456

DERONDE, Kevin, Chief Executive Officer, Mahaska Health Partnership. Oskaloosa, IA, p. A256

DEROSSETTE, Stephanie, Human Resources Business Partner, Eastern State Hospital, Lexington, KY, p. A286

DEROSSITT, James, M.D., Chief of Staff, Forrest City Medical Center, Forrest City, AR, p. A45

DEROUEN, Jason, Director Management Information Systems, Grace Medical Center, Lubbock, TX, p. A697

DERRICO, Patricia, FACHE, R.N., Chief Nursing Officer, Coliseum Northside Hospital, Macon, GA, p. A176

DERSCH, Stephen, M.D., President Medical Staff, Regency Hospital Of Florence, Florence, SC, p. A619

DERUS, Charles, M.D., Vice President Medical Management, Advocate Good Samaritan Hospital, Downers Grove, IL, p. A203

DERUYTER, David, M.D., President Medical Staff, Select Specialty Hospital Midtown Atlanta, Atlanta, GA, p. A165

DERYNCK, Dodie, Chief Nursing Officer, Avera Marshall Regional Medical Center, Marshall, MN, p. A380

DESAI, Colleen, Chief Nursing Officer, Holyoke Medical Center, Holyoke, MA, p. A340

DESAI, Nimesh, M.D., Medical Director, Massena Hospital, Inc., Massena, NY, p. A488

DESAI, Shailesh, M.D., Chief of Staff, Mercyone Primghar Medical Center, Primghar, IA, p. A256

DESALVO, Susan, Manager Human Resources, Bath Veterans Affairs Medical Center, Bath, NY, p. A475

DESANTIS, John, Interim Chief Financial Officer, Glenwood Regional Medical Center, West Monroe, LA, p. A316

DESANTIS, Vincent, Vice President Finance, Phelp. Memorial Hospital Center, Sleep. Hollow, NY, p. A498

DESART, Amy, Vice President, Chief Financial Officer, Missouri Baptist Medical Center, Saint Louis, MO, p. A416

DESCHAMBEAU, Wayne G., President and Chief Executive Officer, Wayne Healthcare, Greenville, OH, p. A541

DESCHRYVER, Joseph, Chief Executive Officer, Good Samaritan Hospital, San Jose, CA, p. A94

DESEI, Nitin, M.D., Medical Director, Regional Rehabilitation Hospital, Phenix City, AL, p. A23

DESIMINI, Esther Muscari., Interim Administrator, Riverside Walter Reed Hospital, Gloucester, VA, p. A743

DESIMONE, Maureen, Chief Operating Officer, Blythedale Children's Hospital, Valhalla, NY, p. A500

DESIMONE, Shane, M.D., Chief of Staff, Jane Todd Crawford Hospital, Greensburg, KY, p. A284

DESJARDINS, Isabelle, M.D., Chief Medical Officer, University Of Vermont Medical Center, Burlington, VT, p. A735

DESJEUNES, Carol, Vice President and Chief Operating Officer, Psychiatric Institute Of Washington, Washington, DC, p. A130

DESMARTEAU, Lisa Jo, Chief Financial Officer, Miami Jewish Home And Hospital For Aged, Miami, FL, p. A146

DESMOND, Debbie, Director Human Resources, Sentara Martha Jefferson Hospital, Charlottesville, VA, p. A739

DESMOND, Heather, Chief Financial Officer, Bibb Medical Center, Centreville, AL, p. A16

DESMOND, Jeffrey, M.D., Chief Medical Officer, Michigan Medicine, Ann Arbor, MI, p. A348

DESMOND, Matthew, Chief Administrative Officer, Roper Hospital, Charleston, SC, p. A616

DESMOND, Phillip Craig., Chief Executive Officer, The Medical Center Of Southeast Texas, Port Arthur, TX, p. A707

DESOTELLE, Robert C., President and Chief Executive Officer, Continuing Care Hospital, Lexington, KY, p. A286

DESOTO, James, M.D., Vice President Medical Affairs, Mercy Medical Center Redding, Redding, CA, p. A87

M.D., Vice President Medical Affairs, St. Elizabeth Community Hospital, Red Bluff, CA, p. A87

DESOUZA-VAN BLARICUM, Jacqueline, President and Chief Executive Officer, Riverside Community Hospital, Riverside, CA, p. A88

DESROCHES, Jeff, Director Information Systems, Ahmc Anaheim Regional Medical Center, Anaheim, CA, p. A55

DESROSIERS, Chelsea, Chief Financial Officer, Cary Medical Center, Caribou, ME, p. A320

DESTEFANO, Stephen, Chief Financial Officer, Magee Rehabilitation Hospital, Philadelphia, PA, p. A601

DETILLIO, Joshua, Chief Executive Officer, Palms West Hospital, Loxahatchee, FL, p. A144

DETTERMAN, B Lynn., President and Chief Executive Officer, Mercy Health - Willard Hospital, Willard, OH, p. A553

President and Chief Executive Officer, Mercy Hospital Of Defiance, Defiance, OH, p. A539

President and Chief Executive Officer, Mercy Tiffin Hospital, Tiffin, OH, p. A550

DETTMER, Brantley, Chief Operating Officer, Kaiser Westside Medical Center, Hillsboro, OR, p. A576

DETWILER, Eric, Director Information Technology, Barnes-Kasson County Hospital, Susquehanna, PA, p. A608

DEURMIER, Carol, Chief Executive Officer, St. Michael's Hospital Avera, Tyndall, SD, p. A632

DEUTSCH, Stephen, Vice President Operations and Support, Spencer Hospital, Spencer, IA, p. A258

DEVANATHAN, Raja, M.D., Chief Medical Officer, Vibra Hospital Of Northwestern Indiana, Crown Point, IN, p. A226

DEVARAJ, Kiran, Chief Medical Officer and Chief Clinical Officer, Highland Hospital, Charleston, WV, p. A771

DEVARAJAN, Vadakkipalayam, Chief Medical Staff, St. Charles Parish Hospital, Luling, LA, p. A307

DEVAULT, Jennifer, Vice President Associate Services, F. F. Thompson Hospital, Canandaigua, NY, p. A481

DEVAULT, Rosanne, Chief Financial Officer, Mckenzie-Willamette Medical Center, Springfield, OR, p. A581

DEVAULT, Roseann, Chief Financial Officer, Tennova Healthcare-Jefferson Memorial Hospital, Jefferson City, TN, p. A640

DEVAUX, Sheri, Information Technology Manager, Connecticut Veterans Home And Hospital, Rocky Hill, CT, p. A125

DEVERA, Rozelle, Director of Information Systems, Gateways Hospital And Mental Health Center, Los Angeles, CA, p. A74

DEVEREUX, Chris, Human Resources Director, Business Partner, Edward Hospital, Naperville, IL, p. A213

DEVILLE, Linda F., Chief Executive Officer, Bunkie General Hospital, Bunkie, LA, p. A299

DEVIN, Brian V., Chief Executive Officer, Pappas Rehabilitation Hospital For Children, Canton, MA, p. A338

DEVIN, Joseph, Chief Financial Officer, Boone County Hospital, Boone, IA, p. A244

DEVINE, Kathryn, Vice President Human Resources, Upmc Presbyterian, Pittsburgh, PA, p. A604

DEVINE, Sarah, M.D., Chief of Staff, Myrtue Medical Center, Harlan, IA, p. A251

DEVITA, James, M.D., Chief Medical Officer, Tewksbury Hospital, Tewksbury, MA, p. A345

DEVITO, Joseph, Vice President Finance and Chief Operating Officer, Geisinger-Bloomsburg Hospital, Bloomsburg, PA, p. A585

DEVLIN, James, Director Information Systems, St. Cloud Regional Medical Center, Saint Cloud, FL, p. A156

DEVORE, Druery, Chief of Medical Staff, Northern Regional Hospital, Mount Airy, NC, p. A515

DEVORE, Kathy, R.N., Administrator, Christus Dubuis Hospital Of Hot Springs, Hot Springs National Park, AR, p. A47

DEVORSETZ, Marc, Chief Executive Officer, Baylor Scott & White Surgical Hospital-Sherman, Sherman, TX, p. A715

DEW, Douglas, M.D., President Medical Staff, Flagler Hospital, Saint Augustine, FL, p. A155

DEWAN, Vijay, M.D., Clinical Director, Lincoln Regional Center, Lincoln, NE, p. A434

DEWANE, Patti, Vice President Finance and Treasurer, Swedishamerican - A Division Of Uw Health, Rockford, IL, p. A219

DEWAR, William, M.D., Chief of Staff, Wayne Memorial Hospital, Honesdale, PA, p. A592

DEWBERRY, Robbie, Chief Executive Officer, Mitchell County Hospital, Colorado City, TX, p. A664

DEWISPELARE, Cheryl, Chief Human Resources Officer, Veterans Affairs Nebraska-Western Iowa Health Care System, Omaha, NE, p. A438

DEWITT, Alan, Chief Medical Officer, Summit Healthcare Regional Medical Center, Show Low, AZ, p. A38

DEWITT, Jocelyn, Ph.D., Vice President and Chief Information Officer, University Hospital, Madison, WI, p. A788

DEWORTH, Gerald, Associate Director, Carl Vinson Veterans Affairs Medical Center, Dublin, GA, p. A171

DEWS, Teresa, M.D., President, Euclid Hospital, Euclid, OH, p. A540

DEXTER, Heather, Chief Executive Officer, Emory Saint Joseph's Hospital Of Atlanta, Atlanta, GA, p. A164

DEYARMIN, James, Controller, Children's Hospital Of Richmond At Vcu-Brook Road Campus, Richmond, VA, p. A750

DEYO-ALLERS, Margaret, Vice President, Chief Nursing Officer, Montefiore St. Luke's Cornwall, Newburgh, NY, p. A492

DEYOUNG, Keith, M.D., Chief Medical Staff, Wallowa Memorial Hospital, Enterprise, OR, p. A574

DEYOUNG, Peter, M.D., Chief Medical Officer, Methodist Stone Oak Hospital, San Antonio, TX, p. A712

DHAWAN, Ajay, M.D., Chief of Staff, Veterans Affairs Northern Indiana Health Care System, Fort Wayne, IN, p. A229

DHAWAN, Rahul, M.D., Chief Medical Officer, St. Francis Medical Center, Lynwood, CA, p. A76

DHILLON, Avtar, M.D., Medical Director, Newport News Behavioral Health Center, Newport News, VA, p. A747

M.D., Medical Director, The Pavilion At Williamsburg Place, Williamsburg, VA, p. A753

DHULIPALA, Vasudeva, M.D., Medical Director, Encompass Health Rehabilitation Hospital Of Alexandria, Alexandria, LA, p. A295

DHUPER, Aman, President and Chief Executive Officer, St. Rose Hospital, Hayward, CA, p. A68

DI BERNARDO, Deborah, Chief Information Officer, Saint Joseph's Medical Center, Yonkers, NY, p. A502

DI PIETRO, Rose, MSN, R.N., Interim Chief Executive Officer, South Shore Hospital, South Weymouth, MA, p. A344

DIAL, Jeffery, Interim President, Vidant Duplin Hospital, Kenansville, NC, p. A513

DIAL, Jody, Chief Financial Officer, Timpanogos Regional Hospital, Orem, UT, p. A730

DIAL, Ray, Director of Nursing, Nebraska Medicine - Bellevue, Bellevue, NE, p. A430

DIALTO, Margaret, Regional Chief Human Resource Officer, Staten Island University Hospital, Staten Island, NY, p. A499

DIAMOND, Anne, President, Bridgeport Hospital, Bridgeport, CT, p. A121

DIAMOND, Kevin, M.D., Chief Medical Officer, Lawrence Memorial Hospital, Walnut Ridge, AR, p. A54

DIAMOND, Lester K., President, St. Dominic-Jackson Memorial Hospital, Jackson, MS, p. A395

DIAMOND, Robert, Senior Vice President and Chief Operating Officer, Kaleida Health, Buffalo, NY, p. A480

DIAMOND, Timothy, Chief Information Officer, Methodist Hospitals, Gary, IN, p. A229

DIAMOND, Victoria, R.N., MS, President, Wellspan Surgery And Rehabilitation Hospital, York, PA, p. A612

R.N., MS, President, Wellspan York Hospital, York, PA, p. A612

DIANDA-MARTIN, Barb, Chief Nursing Officer, Mercy St. Anne Hospital, Toledo, OH, p. A550

DIASIO, Anthony, Chief Financial Officer, Fox Chase Cancer Center-American Oncologic Hospital, Philadelphia, PA, p. A600

DIATI, Raquel, Chief Executive Officer, Sacred Oak Medical Center, Houston, TX, p. A688

DIAZ, Evelyn, R.N., Chief Nursing Officer, Encompass Health Rehabilitation Hospital Of Manati, Manati, PR, p. A808

DIAZ, Janine, Human Resources Manager, Emory Rehabilitation Hospital, Atlanta, GA, p. A164

DIAZ, Jesse, Chief Information Officer, Phoebe Putney Memorial Hospital, Albany, GA, p. A163

DIAZ, Jimmy, Director Information Technology, Odessa Regional Medical Center, Odessa, TX, p. A704

DIAZ, Jose, Director Information Systems, Ascension St. Vincent Evansville, Evansville, IN, p. A227

DIAZ, Ron, Manager Operations, Albany Stratton Veterans Affairs Medical Center, Albany, NY, p. A474

DIBATTISTA, Vincent, Senior Vice President, Fairfield Region President, St. Vincent's Medical Center, Bridgeport, CT, p. A121

DIBBLE, Lynn, Vice President Patient Care Services, Guthrie Towanda Memorial Hospital, Towanda, PA, p. A609

DICESARE, Jan, Vice President Financial Operations, St. Vincent's East, Birmingham, AL, p. A15

DICICCO, Marilyn, Director Human Resources, Chestnut Hill Hospital, Philadelphia, PA, p. A599

DICK, Andy, Director Information Services, Saline Memorial Hospital, Benton, AR, p. A42

DICK, Deanna, Chief Executive Officer, U. S. Public Health Service Phoenix Indian Medical Center, Phoenix, AZ, p. A37

DICK, Lynette, Director of Support Services, Ellsworth County Medical Center, Ellsworth, KS, p. A264

DICK, Mollie, Coordinator Human Resources, Wayne County Hospital, Monticello, KY, p. A290

DICK, Myra, Manager Business Office, Amg Specialty Hospital-Wichita, Wichita, KS, p. A278

DICK ESQ, MandyChief Nursing Officer, Wilson N. Jones Regional Medical Center, Sherman, TX, p. A716

DICKE, Timothy, M.D., Chief Executive Officer, Orthoindy Hospital, Indianapolis, IN, p. A232

DICKENS, Betty, Director Human Resources, Sierra Tucson, Tucson, AZ, p. A40

DICKENS, Shelby, Director, Patient Care Services, Fort Madison Community Hospital, Fort Madison, IA, p. A250

DICKERSON, Gene, M.D., Vice President Medical Affairs, Prisma Health Tuomey Hospital, Sumter, SC, p. A624

DICKERSON, Kathy, Chief Financial Officer, Encompass Health Rehabilitation Hospital Of Arlington, Arlington, TX, p. A653

DICKERSON, Melody, R.N., MSN, Senior Vice President, Chief Nursing Officer, Virginia Hospital Center, Arlington, VA, p. A738

DICKERSON, Michelle, Chief Nursing Officer, Frye Regional Medical Center, Hickory, NC, p. A512

DICKERSON, Sandra, Chief Executive Officer, Greenwood County Hospital, Eureka, KS, p. A264

DICKERSON, Taylor, Chief Information Officer, Lake City Medical Center, Lake City, FL, p. A143

DICKERSON, Toby, Chief Information Resources Management Services, Durham Veterans Affairs Medical Center, Durham, NC, p. A520

DICKEY, Ashley, Director Human Resources, Benson Hospital, Benson, AZ, p. A30

DICKEY, John, Chief Administrative Officer, Mayo Clinic Health System In Eau Claire, Eau Claire, WI, p. A783

DICKEY, Mark, Director Business Development, Valir Rehabilitation Hospital, Oklahoma City, OK, p. A566

DICKEY, Sarah, Executive Director, Human Resource People and Culture, Mahaska Health Partnership. Oskaloosa, IA, p. A256

Human Resource Director, Marshall Browning Hospital, Du Quoin, IL, p. A203

DICKINSON, Ashley, Chief Executive Officer, La Porte Hospital, La Porte, IN, p. A234

Chief Executive Officer, Starke Hospital, Knox, IN, p. A234

DICKINSON, Cathy, Chief Human Resources, Baptist Health Extended Care Hospital, Little Rock, AR, p. A48

Vice President Human Resources, Baptist Health Medical Center - North Little Rock, North Little Rock, AR, p. A51

DICKINSON, Lani, Chief Executive Officer, Emanuel Medical Center, Turlock, CA, p. A102

DICKLICH-COBB, Cristy, Chief Nursing Officer, Memorial Hospital Of Converse County, Douglas, WY, p. A802

DICKMAN, Kathy, Director of Information Systems, Highpoint Health, Lawrenceburg, IN, p. A235

DICKS, Mandy, Director of Nursing, Lake Butler Hospital, Lake Butler, FL, p. A142

DICKSON, Anita, Director Human Resources, St. Bernards Five Rivers, Pocahontas, AR, p. A52

DICKSON, Scott, Director Information Technology, Reeves Memorial Medical Center, Bernice, LA, p. A298

DICKSON, Thomas C., Chief Executive Officer, Sutter Amador Hospital, Jackson, CA, p. A69

DICKSON, William, Executive Director, Capital District Psychiatric Center, Albany, NY, p. A474

DIDDLE, Derrick, Chief Information Officer, Colorado Canyons Hospital And Medical Center, Fruita, CO, p. A113

DIDERRICH, Mary Kay., R.N., Chief Executive Officer, Uw Health Rehabilitation Hospital, Madison, WI, p. A788

DIDRIKSON, Lynne, M.D., Chief Medical Officer, Cavalier County Memorial Hospital And Clinics, Langdon, ND, p. A524

DIEBLING, Tara, Chief Executive Officer, Cardinal Hill Rehabilitation Hospital, Lexington, KY, p. A286

DIEDERICH, John, Senior Vice President Operations and Chief Operating Officer, Rush-Copley Medical Center, Aurora, IL, p. A195

DIEDRICH, Michele, R.N., Chief Nursing Officer, Vice President Patient Care, Baptist Health Medical Center-Little Rock, Little Rock, AR, p. A49

DIENER, D Michael., Chief Executive Officer, Fayette County Memorial Hospital, Washington Court House, OH, p. A552

DIERKENS, Janelle, Chief Administration Officer, New York State Psychiatric Institute, New York, NY, p. A491

DIERKER, Anne, Vice President Hospital Services, Unitypoint Health-Pekin Hospital, Pekin, IL, p. A216

DIERS, Suzanne, R.N., Director Patient Care Services, Shriners Hospitals For Children-Portland, Portland, OR, p. A580

DIESTEL, Peter, Senior Vice President and Chief Operating Officer, Valley Hospital, Ridgewood, NJ, p. A462

DIETER, Brian, President and Chief Executive Officer, Mary Greeley Medical Center, Ames, IA, p. A243

DIETERICH, Kevin, Director Information Services, Northern Light Inland Hospital, Waterville, ME, p. A323

DIETLIN, Steve, Chief Executive Officer, Tri-City Medical Center, Oceanside, CA, p. A82

DIETRICH, Brenda, Chief Human Resources Officer, Banner Boswell Medical Center, Sun City, AZ, p. A39

DIETRICH, Jill, JD, FACHE, Executive Director, Louis Stokes Cleveland Veterans Affairs Medical Center, Cleveland, OH, p. A534

DIETRICK, Brian, Director Information Systems, Wilson Medical Center, Wilson, NC, p. A520

DIETSCH, Barry, Chief Financial Officer, Virginia Gay Hospital, Vinton, IA, p. A259

DIETSCHE, Jim, Chief Financial Officer, Bellin Hospital, Green Bay, WI, p. A785

DIETZ, Brian E., FACHE, President and Chief Executive Officer, Mcdonough District Hospital, Mb, IL, p. A211

DIETZ, Michael, Administrator, U. S. Air Force Hospital, Hampton, VA, p. A743

DIEUVEUIL, Harry, Vice President Human Resources, Wellspan Chambersburg Hospital, Chambersburg, PA, p. A586

DIFRANCO, Vincent, Chief Executive Officer, W. J. Mangold Memorial Hospital, Lockney, TX, p. A696

DIGIAMARINO, Edward, M.D., President of Medical Staff, San Antonio Regional Hospital, Upland, CA, p. A102

DIGUILIO, Jason, Controller, Uh Avon Rehabilitation Hospital, Avon, OH, p. A528

DIIESO, Nicholas, R.N., Chief Operating Officer, Mount Auburn Hospital, Cambridge, MA, p. A338

DIKE, Charles, M.D., Chief of Staff, Sanford Worthington Medical Center, Worthington, MN, p. A388

DIKOS, Julie A., President and Chief Executive Officer, Asheville Specialty Hospital, Asheville, NC, p. A504

DILALLO, Kevin, Chief Executive Officer, Manatee Memorial Hospital, Bradenton, FL, p. A133

DILISI, Jeffrey, M.D., Senior Vice President, Chief Medical Officer, Virginia Hospital Center, Arlington, VA, p. A738

DILLARD, Sharon, Chief Nursing Officer, Poinciana Medical Center, Kissimmee, FL, p. A142

DILLEHUNT, David, Chief Information Officer, Firsthealth Montgomery Memorial Hospital, Troy, NC, p. A519

Chief Information Officer, Firsthealth Moore Regional Hospital, Pinehurst, NC, p. A516

DILLIE, Codie, Chief Executive Officer, Select Specialty Hospital-Quad Cities, Davenport, IA, p. A247

DILLION, Tim, Vice President of Human Resources, Devereux Hospital And Children's Center Of Florida, Melbourne, FL, p. A145

DILLON, Jim, Chief Financial Officer, Rangely District Hospital, Rangely, CO, p. A118

DILLON, Lorie, Chief Executive Officer, Geisinger Encompass Health Rehabilitation Hospital, Danville, PA, p. A587

DILORETO, David, M.D., Executive Vice President and Chief Medical Officer, Amita Health Saint Francis Hospital Evanston, Evanston, IL, p. A204

DIMAMBRO, Christina, Chief Financial Officer, Havasu Regional Medical Center, Lake Havasu City, AZ, p. A33

DIMARCO, Lisa, Chief Nursing Officer, Ssm Health St. Mary's Hospital Centralia, Centralia, IL, p. A196
Vice President Patient Care Service and Chief Nursing Officer, Osf Healthcare Little Company Of Mary Medical Center, Evergreen Park, IL, p. A204

DIMARE, John, M.D., Medical Director, Emanate Health Foothill Presbyterian Hospital, Glendora, CA, p. A67

DIMEK, Carolyn, Acting Superintendent, Dorothea Dix Psychiatric Center, Bangor, ME, p. A318

DIMICHELE, Maria, Administrative Assistant, Kensington Hospital, Philadelphia, PA, p. A601

DIMITROVA, Gergana, M.D., Medical Director, Carolina Center For Behavioral Health, Greer, SC, p. A621

DIMM, Adam, Chief Executive Officer, Penn Highlands Huntingdon, Huntingdon, PA, p. A592

DIMMICK, Scott, Senior Vice President and Chief Human Resources Officer, Lakeland Regional Health Medical Center, Lakeland, FL, p. A143

DIMOND, Margaret, Ph.D., President and Chief Executive Officer, Mclaren Oakland, Pontiac, MI, p. A364

DIMURIA, Asja, Chief Financial Officer, Abrazo West Campus, Goodyear, AZ, p. A32

DINARDO, Mark, Chief Nursing Officer, Encompass Health Rehabilitation Hospital Of Modesto, Modesto, CA, p. A78

DINEEN, C., Chief Nursing Officer, Northern Cochise Community Hospital, Willcox, AZ, p. A41

DINGER, Bradley, Chief Financial Officer, Upmc Chautauqua, Jamestown, NY, p. A486
Chief Financial Officer, Upmc Hamot, Erie, PA, p. A590
Chief Financial Officer, Upmc Kane, Kane, PA, p. A593
Chief Financial Officer, Upmc Northwest, Seneca, PA, p. A607

DINGILIAN, John, M.D., Chief Medical Officer, Adventist Health Simi Valley, Simi Valley, CA, p. A98

DINGLEDINE, Jon, Chief Financial Officer and Chief Operating Officer, Mercer Health, Coldwater, OH, p. A535

DINGLER, Chance, M.D., Chief Medical Officer, Nocona General Hospital, Nocona, TX, p. A703

DINHAM, Vilma, R.N., Chief Nursing Officer, Encino Hospital Medical Center, Encino, CA, p. A63

DINKHA, Duncan, M.D., Chief of Staff, Morrison Community Hospital, Morrison, IL, p. A213

DINKINS, Vicki, Director Human Resources, South Georgia Medical Center Lanier Campus, Lakeland, GA, p. A175

DION, Jeffrey, Vice President and Chief Financial Officer, Holy Family Hospital, Methuen, MA, p. A341

DIONNE, Andrew, M.D., Chief Medical Officer, Mainegeneral Medical Center, Augusta, ME, p. A318

DIPALMA, Maureen, Chief Financial Officer, Tewksbury Hospital, Tewksbury, MA, p. A345

DIPIETRO, Sandra, Chief Financial Officer, St. Tammany Health System, Covington, LA, p. A300

DIPPEL, Doug, R.N., MSN, Chief Executive Officer, Rolling Plains Memorial Hospital, Sweetwater, TX, p. A718

DISANTE, Ginger, Chief Nursing Executive, Christus Health Shreveport-Bossier, Shreveport, LA, p. A314
Chief Nursing Officer, Christus Ochsner St. Patrick, Lake Charles, LA, p. A306

DISHMAN, Kevin, M.D., Chief Medical Officer, Stormont Vail Health, Topeka, KS, p. A277

DISLER, Jordi K., President, Parkview Lagrange Hospital, Lagrange, IN, p. A235

DISPOTO, Martha, R.N., Chief Nurse Executive, Anaheim Medical Center, Kaiser Permanente Orange County Anaheim Medical Center, Anaheim, CA, p. A55

DISWOOD, Lavenia, R.N., Chief Nurse Executive, Northern Navajo Medical Center, Shiprock, NM, p. A472

DITMANSON, Paul, M.D., Clinical Director, Red Lake Indian Health Service Hospital, Red Lake, MN, p. A383

DITMAR, Angela, R.N., President, Spectrum Health Pennock, Hastings, MI, p. A357

DITTBENNER, Beth, Regional Director, Human Resources, Mayo Clinic Health System In Mankato, Mankato, MN, p. A379

DITTBERNER, Deborah, M.D., Chief Medical Officer, Alomere Health, Alexandria, MN, p. A371

DITTO, Debbie, CPA, Controller, Lincoln Trail Behavioral Health System, Radcliff, KY, p. A292

DITURO, Beth, Divisional Chief Information Officer, Lenox Hill Hospital, New York, NY, p. A490

DITZLER, Andru, Chief Information Officer, Lebanon Veterans Affairs Medical Center, Lebanon, PA, p. A594

DIVELLO, Douglas F., FACHE, M.P.H., President and Chief Executive Officer, Grace Cottage Hospital, Townshend, VT, p. A737

DIVINS, Brooke, Director Human Resources, Clarion Hospital, Clarion, PA, p. A586

DIX, Roger, Vice President Finance, Hannibal Regional Hospital, Hannibal, MO, p. A407

DIX, Theresa, R.N., Chief Nursing Officer, Wythe County Community Hospital, Wytheville, VA, p. A754

DIXON, Christy, Chief Human Resources Officer, Encompass Health Rehabilitation Hospital Of Humble, Humble, TX, p. A689

DIXON, Debbie, Director Human Resources, Pamp. Regional Medical Center, Pampa, TX, p. A704

DIXON, Del, Chief Information Officer, South Shore Hospital, South Weymouth, MA, p. A344

DIXON, Florine, Chief Operating Officer, Memorial Hospital, Carthage, IL, p. A196

DIXON, Gregg, Chief Financial Officer, Asheville Specialty Hospital, Asheville, NC, p. A504
Chief Financial Officer, Carepartners Health Services, Asheville, NC, p. A504

DIXON, John, Chief Medical Officer, Mobile Infirmary Medical Center, Mobile, AL, p. A22

DIXON, Lisa, Business Partner and Human Resource Director, Linden Oaks Hospital, Naperville, IL, p. A214

DIXON, Mary, MSN, R.N., Interim Chief Nursing Officer, University Of Virginia Medical Center, Charlottesville, VA, p. A740

DIXON, Michael, Vice President of Human Resources, Self Regional Healthcare, Greenwood, SC, p. A621
Vice President, Human Resources, Beaumont Hospital - Royal Oak, Royal Oak, MI, p. A365

DIXON, Shannon, Manager Business Office, Weisbrod Memorial County Hospital, Eads, CO, p. A112

DIXON, Todd, R.N., Chief Executive Officer, Navicent Health Baldwin, Milledgeville, GA, p. A177

DOAK, Scott, System Vice President, Human Resources, University Of North Carolina Hospitals, Chapel Hill, NC, p. A506
Vice President, Human Resources, Unc Rex Health Care, Raleigh, NC, p. A517

DOAN, Angela, Chief Financial Officer, Scott Memorial Health, Scottsburg, IN, p. A240

DOANE, Peter, M.D., Chief Medical Officer, Franklin Regional Hospital, Franklin, NH, p. A449
M.D., Chief Medical Officer, Lakes Region General Hospital, Laconia, NH, p. A449

DOBBINS, Jim, Vice President and Chief Human Resources Officer, Unc Lenoir Healthcare, Kinston, NC, p. A513

DOBBS, Jacee, Chief Information Officer, Citizens Medical Center, Colby, KS, p. A263

DOBBS, Stephanie, Chief Nursing Officer, Sanford Clear Lake Medical Center, Clear Lake, SD, p. A627

DOBIE, Linda, R.N., JD, Vice President, Legal Affairs, Torrance Memorial Medical Center, Torrance, CA, p. A101

DOBIN, Jennifer, Executive Vice President Human Resources, Carepoint Health Bayonne Medical Center, Bayonne, NJ, p. A452

DOBIZL, Howard, Director Information Services for the Northern Region, Ascension St. Mary's Hospital, Rhinelander, WI, p. A795
Director Information Technology Services, Ascension Eagle River Hospital, Eagle River, WI, p. A782
Director Information Technology Services, Ascension Sacred Heart Hospital, Tomahawk, WI, p. A797
Director Information Technology Services, Howard Young Medical Center, Woodruff, WI, p. A800

DOBKIN, Eric, M.D., Vice President Medical Affairs, Suburban Hospital, Bethesda, MD, p. A327

DOBOSENSKI, David, Chief Executive Officer, St. Croix Regional Medical Center, St Croix Falls, WI, p. A796

DOBOSH JR, JosephVice President and Chief Financial Officer, Children's Specialized Hospital, New Brunswick, NJ, p. A459

DOBRAWA, Stanley, Area Information Officer, Kaiser Permanente San Rafael Medical Center, San Rafael, CA, p. A96
Area Information Officer, Kaiser Permanente Santa Rosa Medical Center, Santa Rosa, CA, p. A98

DOBRINSKI, Sandra, Director of Nursing, Comanche County Hospital, Coldwater, KS, p. A263

DOBROVICH, Michael, M.D., Chief Medical Officer, Uh St. John Medical Center, Westlake, OH, p. A553

DOBSON, Glenda, R.N., Chief Executive Officer, Cypress Pointe Surgical Hospital, Hammond, LA, p. A302

DOBSON, Glenn, Vice President, Finance and Chief Financial Officer, Aspirus Iron River Hospitals & Clinics, Inc., Iron River, MI, p. A358

DOBSON, Trey, M.D., Chief Medical Officer, Southwestern Vermont Medical Center, Bennington, VT, p. A735

DODD, John, Vice President Human Resources, Central Peninsula Hospital, Soldotna, AK, p. A29

DODD, Kathy, Director of Nursing, Southern Virginia Mental Health Institute, Danville, VA, p. A741

DODD, Pam, Chief Operating Officer, Harper County Community Hospital, Buffalo, OK, p. A557

DODD, Randy, President, Adventist Health - Tulare, Tulare, CA, p. A102

DODDS, George, M.D., Medical Director, Gouverneur Hospital, Gouverneur, NY, p. A485

DODDS, Rick A., President, Greene Memorial Hospital, Xenia, OH, p. A553
President, Soin Medical Center, Beavercreek, OH, p. A529

DODDS, Sheryl, Chief Clinical Officer, Adventhealth Orlando, Orlando, FL, p. A151

DODERER, Marcella, FACHE, President and Chief Executive Officer, Arkansas Children's Hospital, Little Rock, AR, p. A48

DODGE, Terry, M.D., Chief of Staff, Musc Health Chester Medical Center, Chester, SC, p. A617

DODSON, Carrie, Director of Nursing, Wellstone Regional Hospital, Jeffersonville, IN, p. A233

DODSON, Louise, R.N., Chief Nursing Officer, Wagoner Community Hospital, Wagoner, OK, p. A571
R.N., Chief Operating Officer and Chief Nursing Officer, Wagoner Community Hospital, Wagoner, OK, p. A571

DODSON, Paige, M.D., M.P.H., Chief Medical Officer, Susan B. Allen Memorial Hospital, El Dorado, KS, p. A264

DOEHRING, Christopher, M.D., Vice President Medical Affairs, Franciscan Health Indianapolis, Indianapolis, IN, p. A232
M.D., Vice President of Medical Affairs, Franciscan Health Carmel, Carmel, IN, p. A225

DOEHRMANN, Melissa, Director Patient Care Services, Mercyone Newton Medical Center, Newton, IA, p. A255

DOELING, Mariann, R.N., President, Chi St Alexius Health Carrington Medical Center, Carrington, ND, p. A522

DOELLING, James, Executive Director, Battle Creek Veterans Affairs Medical Center, Battle Creek, MI, p. A349

DOERFLER, Mary, Chief Human Resources Officer, Central Texas Veterans Health Care System, Temple, TX, p. A719

DOERGE, Jean, MS, R.N., Chief Nursing Executive, Unitypoint Health - Trinity Bettendorf, Bettendorf, IA, p. A244
R.N., MSN, Nurse Executive, Swedish/Edmonds, Edmonds, WA, p. A757

DOERING, Dean, Chief Executive Officer, Central Prison Hospital, Raleigh, NC, p. A516

DOERR, Brian, Chief Information Officer, Continuecare Hospital At Baptist Health Corbin, Corbin, KY, p. A282

DOGGETT, Geri, Director Business, East Mississipp. State Hospital, Meridian, MS, p. A397

DOGGETT, Sherri, Vice President Patient Services, Mercyone Centerville Medical Center, Centerville, IA, p. A245

DOHERTY, Allison, Chief Financial Officer, The Spine Hospital Of Louisiana At The Neuromedical Center, Baton Rouge, LA, p. A298

DOHERTY, Bryan, Management Information Technology Services I, Sagamore Children's Psychiatric Center, Dix Hills, NY, p. A482

DOHERTY, Dan, Vice President, Operations, Advocate Trinity Hospital, Chicago, IL, p. A197

DOHERTY, Donna R., Vice President of Nursing and Chief Nursing Officer, Beth Israel Deaconess Hospital Plymouth, Plymouth, MA, p. A343

DOHERTY, John, Co-President, M Health, University Of Minnesota, Minneapolis, MN, p. A381
Vice President Finance, University Of Minnesota, Minneapolis, MN, p. A381

DOHERTY, Randy, CPA, Chief Executive Officer, Encompass Health Rehabilitation Hospital Of Braintree, Braintree, MA, p. A336

DOHERTY, Ray, Director Information Technology, Cmh Regional Health System, Wilmington, OH, p. A553

DOHMANN, Eileen, R.N., Senior Vice President and Chief Nursing Officer, Mary Washington Hospital, Fredericksburg, VA, p. A742
R.N., Senior Vice President and Chief Nursing Officer, Stafford Hospital, Stafford, VA, p. A752

DOIDGE, John, Vice President Finance, Glencoe Regional Health, Glencoe, MN, p. A377

DOKKEN, Susan, Chief Human Resources, St. Josep. Regional Medical Center, Lewiston, ID, p. A191

DOKSUM, Kathryn, Director Finance, Samaritan North Lincoln Hospital, Lincoln City, OR, p. A577

DOLAN, Lisa, Interim Chief Executive Officer, St. Josep. Hospital, Fort Wayne, IN, p. A228

DOLAN, Mary, Regional Director Information Services and HIPAA Security Official, Shriners Hospitals For Children-Boston, Boston, MA, p. A336

DOLAN, Steve, Chief Information Officer, Eastpointe Hospital, Daphne, AL, p. A17

DOLBEE, Hilary, Chief Financial Officer, Monroe Hospital, Bloomington, IN, p. A224

DOLBIN, Kathy, Director of Human Resources, Mercy Allen Hospital, Oberlin, OH, p. A547

DOLEN, Cassie, Vice President Finance and Chief Financial Officer, Hutchinson Regional Medical Center, Hutchinson, KS, p. A266

DOLORESCO, Laureen, R.N., Associate Director for Patient Care and Nursing Services, James A. Haley Veterans' Hospital-Tampa, Tampa, FL, p. A159

DOMALESKI, Vareen, MS, R.N., Vice Patient Care Services and Chief Nursing Officer, Emma Pendleton Bradley Hospital, East Providence, RI, p. A613

DOMANICO, Lee, Chief Executive Officer, Marinhealth Medical Center, Greenbrae, CA, p. A67

DOMANN, Debbie, Director of Operations, Fillmore County Hospital, Geneva, NE, p. A432

DOMANSKY, John, Vice President Operations, Rutherford Regional Health System, Rutherfordton, NC, p. A517

DOMAYER, Cory, Chief Financial Officer, Adventhealth Palm Coast, Palm Coast, FL, p. A152

DOMBROUSKI, Joyce, R.N., Chief Executive Officer, Providence St. Patrick Hospital, Missoula, MT, p. A426

DOMEIER, Sandy, Director Patient Care Services, Ridgeview Sibley Medical Center, Arlington, MN, p. A372

DOMINGO, Connie, M.D., Medical Director, Weisman Children's Rehabilitation Hospital, Marlton, NJ, p. A458

DOMINGUEZ, Brenda, Director Human Resources, Cypress Creek Hospital, Houston, TX, p. A685

DOMINGUEZ, Ed, President Medical Staff, Vibra Specialty Hospital At Desoto, Desoto, TX, p. A673

DOMINGUEZ, Marie, Commander, Martin Army Community Hospital, Fort Benning, GA, p. A172

DOMINICCI, Sandra, Nursing Director, Hospital De Damas, Ponce, PR, p. A809

DOMINIQUE, Ravon, Chief Nursing Officer, Brentwood Hospital, Shreveport, LA, p. A314

DOMINSKI, Paul, Vice President Human Resources, Park Nicollet Methodist Hospital, Saint Louis Park, MN, p. A385

DOMMER, Matthew, M.D., Vice President for Medical Affairs, Bronson Lakeview Hospital, Paw Paw, MI, p. A363

DOMON, Steven, M.D., Medical Director, Arkansas State Hospital, Little Rock, AR, p. A48

DONAHEY, Kenneth C., Chief Executive Officer, Oviedo Medical Center, Oviedo, FL, p. A152

DONAHUE, Edward, M.D., Chief Medical Officer, St. Joseph's Hospital And Medical Center, Phoenix, AZ, p. A36

DONAHUE, Kristine, Administrator, Clinical Operations, Beaumont Hospital - Taylor, Taylor, MI, p. A367

DONAHUE, Michael, M.D., Medical Director, Select Specialty Hospital-Pittsburgh/Upmc, Pittsburgh, PA, p. A603

DONAHUE, Ruth, R.N., Chief Nursing Officer, Harrison County Hospital, Corydon, IN, p. A226

DONAHUE, Samantha, Director Human Resources, Crossing Rivers Health Medical Center, Prairie Du Chien, WI, p. A794

DONALD, Steve, M.D., Chief of Staff, Washington County Hospital, Chatom, AL, p. A16

DONALDSON, Brooke, Assistant Administrator Human Resources, Jackson Hospital, Marianna, FL, p. A145

DONALDSON, Jill, President, Medstar Harbor Hospital, Baltimore, MD, p. A325

DONALDSON, Les, M.D., Chief of Staff, Roosevelt General Hospital, Portales, NM, p. A471

DONALDSON, Lori, Chief Financial Officer, Uc San Diego Medical Center—Hillcrest, San Diego, CA, p. A92

DONALDSON, Nesha, Chief Operating Officer, Cullman Regional Medical Center, Cullman, AL, p. A17

DONATELLE, Lawrence, M.D., Vice President Medical Affairs, Ascension Northeast Wisconsin St. Elizabeth Hospital, Appleton, WI, p. A779

DONATO, Cyndy, Vice President, Human Resources, Missouri Baptist Medical Center, Saint Louis, MO, p. A416

DONAWAY, Duane, Director Information Technology, Hendrick Health System, Abilene, TX, p. A651

DONELAN, Matthias, M.D., Chief of Staff, Shriners Hospitals For Children-Boston, Boston, MA, p. A336

DONENWIRTH, Karl, Vice President Information Services, Northcoast Behavioral Healthcare, Northfield, OH, p. A546

DONGILLI, Paul Jr, Ph.D., FACHE, President and Chief Executive Officer, Madonna Rehabilitation Hospital, Lincoln, NE, p. A434

Jr, Ph.D., FACHE, President and Chief Executive Officer, Madonna Rehabilitation Hospital, Omaha, NE, p. A437

Jr, Ph.D., FACHE, President and Chief Executive Officer, Madonna Rehabilitation Specialty Hospital, Omaha, NE, p. A437

DONHAM, Guyle, M.D., Chief of Staff, Comanche County Medical Center, Comanche, TX, p. A665

DONICA, Joanna, Director Human Resource, Pam Rehabilitation Hospital Of Beaumont, Beaumont, TX, p. A658

DONLEY, Linda, Vice President Operations, Ira Davenport Memorial Hospital, Bath, NY, p. A475

DONLIN, John, Director Human Resources, Shriners Hospitals For Children-Springfield, Springfield, MA, p. A345

Regional Director Human Resources - Boston, Erie, and Springfield, Shriners Hospitals For Children-Boston, Boston, MA, p. A336

DONNELLY, James, Chief Nursing Officer and Vice President Patient Care Services, Upmc Hamot, Erie, PA, p. A590

DONNELLY, Sheryl, Human Resources Specialist, State Hospital South, Blackfoot, ID, p. A188

DONNELY, Lisa, Controller II, Central Texas Rehabilitation Hospital, Austin, TX, p. A655

DONOFRIO, Kathryn, Chief Nursing Officer, Swedish Covenant Hospital, Chicago, IL, p. A201

DONOGHUE, Alicia, Director Human Resources, Eastpointe Hospital, Daphne, AL, p. A17

DONOHUE, Mary Ann, Ph.D., R.N., Chief Patient Care Services Officer, Stony Brook University Hospital, Stony Brook, NY, p. A499

DONOHUE, Vince, Chief Financial Officer, Delta Community Medical Center, Delta, UT, p. A727

Chief Financial Officer, Fillmore Community Hospital, Fillmore, UT, p. A728

Chief Financial Officer, Sanpete Valley Hospital, Mount Pleasant, UT, p. A729

DONOVAN, Andrew, Director Information Technology, Ascension Southeast Wisconsin Hospital - Elmbrook Campus, Brookfield, WI, p. A781

Regional Director Information Services, Ascension Southeast Wisconsin Hospital - St. Joseph's Campus, Milwaukee, WI, p. A790

DONOVAN, James W., President, Lincolnhealth, Damariscotta, ME, p. A320

DONOVAN, Jenny, Director Human Resources, Wright Memorial Hospital, Trenton, MO, p. A419

DONOVAN, Kevin, FACHE, President and Chief Executive Officer, Franklin Regional Hospital, Franklin, NH, p. A449

FACHE, President and Chief Executive Officer, Lakes Region General Hospital, Laconia, NH, p. A449

DONOVAN, Mary, Controller, Encompass Health Rehabilitation Institute Of Tucson, Tucson, AZ, p. A40

DONOVAN, Mike, Chief Financial Officer, Lemuel Shattuck Hospital, Jamaica Plain, MA, p. A340

DONSON, Elliott, Chief Information Specialist, Lincoln Hospital, Davenport, WA, p. A757

DONZE, Richard, D.O., Senior Vice President Medical Affairs, Chester County Hospital, West Chester, PA, p. A610

DOODY, Kris A., R.N., Chief Executive Officer, Cary Medical Center, Caribou, ME, p. A320

DOOKEERAM, David, Chief Operating Officer, Porter Adventist Hospital, Denver, CO, p. A111

DOOLEY, Jerry, Interim Chief Executive Officer, Western Plains Medical Complex, Dodge City, KS, p. A263

DOOLEY, Mark J., Chief Executive Officer, Putnam Community Medical Center, Palatka, FL, p. A152

DOOLEY, Paige, R.N., MSN, Chief Nursing Executive, Community Hospital East, Indianapolis, IN, p. A231

DOOLING, Edward, Vice President, Human Resources, Masonicare Health Center, Wallingford, CT, p. A126

DOOLITTLE, Doak, M.D., Chief of Staff, Phillip. County Health Systems, Phillipsburg, KS, p. A274

DOOLITTLE, Jon D., Regional President, Mosaic Medical Center - Albany, Albany, MO, p. A402

DOOM, Stephanie, Chief Financial Officer, Baptist Health Lexington, Lexington, KY, p. A286

DOORENBOS, Pamela, M.D., Vice President, Medical Affairs, Maple Grove Hospital, Maple Grove, MN, p. A380

DOORN, Douglas, Chief Executive Officer, Lewis And Clark Specialty Hospital, Yankton, SD, p. A633

DOPERAK, Martin, Commander, Tripler Army Medical Center, Honolulu, HI, p. A185

DORAIN, Debbie, Chief Financial Officer, Copley Hospital, Morrisville, VT, p. A736

DORAK, John, Director, Information Systems, Nicholas H. Noyes Memorial Hospital, Dansville, NY, p. A482

DORAN, Judy, Vice President of Hospital Services and Chief Nurse Executive, Atrium Health Stanly, Albemarle, NC, p. A504

DORAN, T, M.D., Chief of Staff, Perry Memorial Hospital, Princeton, IL, p. A218

DORIA, Thomas, Vice President and Patient Services - West, Morton Plant North Bay Hospital, New Port Richey, FL, p. A149

Vice President and Patient Services West, St. Anthony's Hospital, Saint Petersburg, FL, p. A156

Vice President Patient Services - West, Morton Plant Hospital, Clearwater, FL, p. A134

Vice President, Patient Services and Chief Nursing Officer, Mease Countryside Hospital, Safety Harbor, FL, p. A155

Vice President, Patient Services and Chief Nursing Officer, Mease Dunedin Hospital, Dunedin, FL, p. A137

DORION, Heath, Physician Administrator, Mercy Health - St. Elizabeth Boardman Hospital, Boardman, OH, p. A529

DORITY, Paula, Director Human Resources, Martin County Hospital District, Stanton, TX, p. A717

DORMAN, Christopher, Chief Executive Officer, Southwell Medical, Adel, GA, p. A163

President and Chief Executive Officer, Tift Regional Medical Center, Tifton, GA, p. A182

DORMAN, Doug, Vice President Human Resources, Prisma Health Greenville Memorial Hospital, Greenville, SC, p. A620

DORMAN, Julie, Human Resources Director, Parkwood Behavioral Health System, Olive Branch, MS, p. A398

DORNOFF, Edward, Associate Director, Battle Creek Veterans Affairs Medical Center, Battle Creek, MI, p. A349

DOROGY, Sharon, Chief Information Officer, The Children's Institute Of Pittsburgh, Pittsburgh, PA, p. A603

DOROTHY, Jonnie, Senior Director Human Resources, Massena Hospital, Inc., Massena, NY, p. A488

DORR, Amy, Vice President Human Resources, Mclaren Greater Lansing, Lansing, MI, p. A360

Vice President Human Resources, Mclaren Lapeer Region, Lapeer, MI, p. A360

DORSCH, Anthony, Chief Financial Officer, Providence Alaska Medical Center, Anchorage, AK, p. A27

DORSEY, Bob, Human Resources Coordinator, Select Specialty Hospital - Lincoln, Lincoln, NE, p. A435

DORSEY, John, M.D., Vice President Physician Services and Chief Medical Officer, Javon Bea Hospital-Rockton, Rockford, IL, p. A218

DORSEY, Michael A., FACHE, Chief Executive Officer, Johnson Regional Medical Center, Clarksville, AR, p. A43

DORSEY, William, M.D., Board Chairman and Chief Executive Officer, Jackson Park Hospital And Medical Center, Chicago, IL, p. A198

DORST, Jake, Chief Information Officer, Tahoe Forest Hospital District, Truckee, CA, p. A102

DORTON, Patty, Director of Nursing, Buchanan General Hospital, Grundy, VA, p. A743

DOSCHER, Suzanne, FACHE, Chief Executive Officer, Optim Medical Center - Screven, Sylvania, GA, p. A181

DOSHI, Nikunj, D.O., Chief Medical Officer, Banner Gateway Medical Center, Gilbert, AZ, p. A32

DOSI, Abhishek, Chief Executive Officer, Sutter Solano Medical Center, Vallejo, CA, p. A103

DOSS, Delilah, Director, Human Resources, Mountainview Regional Medical Center, Las Cruces, NM, p. A470

DOSS, Mounir, Executive Vice President and Chief Financial Officer, Flushing Hospital Medical Center, Flushing, NY, p. A484

Executive Vice President and Chief Financial Officer, Jamaica Hospital Medical Center, Jamaica, NY, p. A486

DOSSETT, Jeffrey, Chief Operating Officer, Abrazo West Campus, Goodyear, AZ, p. A32

DOSSETT, Phyllis, Director of Clinical Services, Hancock County Hospital, Sneedville, TN, p. A649

DOTTS-MCCOOL, Michelle, Chief Nursing Officer, Ascension St. Vincent Dunn, Bedford, IN, p. A224

DOTY, Jennifer, Chief Executive Officer, Sidney Health Center, Sidney, MT, p. A428

DOTY, Lisa, Manager Human Resources, Desert View Hospital, Pahrump. NV, p. A445

DOUBLE, Ron, Chief Information Officer, Parkview Huntington Hospital, Huntington, IN, p. A230

Chief Information Officer, Parkview Noble Hospital, Kendallville, IN, p. A233

Chief Information Technology Officer, Parkview Lagrange Hospital, Lagrange, IN, p. A235

DOUCETTE, Diane, R.N., President, Mount Carmel New Albany Surgical Hospital, New Albany, OH, p. A546

DOUCETTE, Elmer, Chief Financial Officer, Redington-Fairview General Hospital, Skowhegan, ME, p. A323

DOUCETTE, Michael J., Senior Vice President and Administrator, Riverside Regional Medical Center, Newport News, VA, p. A747

DOUCETTE, Nick, Chief Executive Officer, Niobrara Community Hospital, Lusk, WY, p. A803

DOUD, Tony, Controller, Ascension St. Josep. Hospital, Tawas City, MI, p. A367

Controller, Ascension Standish Hospital, Standish, MI, p. A367

DOUGHERTY, Chuck, Chief Information Officer, Shenandoah Medical Center, Shenandoah, IA, p. A257

DOUGHERTY, David, Chief Information Management Officer, Irwin Army Community Hospital, Junction City, KS, p. A267

DOUGHERTY, James, Commander, U. S. Air Force Medical Center Keesler, Keesler Afb, MS, p. A395

DOUGHERTY, Terry, Director Human Resources, Bryn Mawr Hospital, Bryn Mawr, PA, p. A585

DOUGHTY, Cathy, Vice President Human Resources, Sheppard Pratt Health System, Baltimore, MD, p. A326

DOUGHTY, Linda, Chief Nursing Officer, Alaska Regional Hospital, Anchorage, AK, p. A27

DOUGHTY, Stephanie, Chief Financial Officer, Uchealth Medical Center Of The Rockies, Loveland, CO, p. A117
Chief Financial Officer, Uchealth Poudre Valley Hospital, Fort Collins, CO, p. A112

DOUGLAS, Andy, Manager Information Technology, Burnett Medical Center, Grantsburg, WI, p. A785

DOUGLAS, Debbie, Director Human Resources, Putnam County Memorial Hospital, Unionville, MO, p. A420

DOUGLAS, Doug, Interim Vice President Human Resources, Beaufort Memorial Hospital, Beaufort, SC, p. A615

DOUGLAS, Errol, MS, Vice President, Human Resources, Roswell Park Comprehensive Cancer Center, Buffalo, NY, p. A480

DOUGLAS, Jason T., Chief Executive Officer, Memorial Medical Center Of Ashland, Ashland, WI, p. A779

DOUGLAS, Johnna, Human Resources Manager, Massac Memorial Hospital, Metropolis, IL, p. A212

DOUGLAS, Kay, Human Resources Director, Musc Health Florence Medical Center, Florence, SC, p. A619

DOUGLAS, Pam, Chief Nursing Officer, Putnam General Hospital, Eatonton, GA, p. A172

DOUGLAS, Paul, Vice President Human Resources, Baton Rouge General Medical Center, Baton Rouge, LA, p. A296

DOUVILLE, Arthur, M.D., Chief Medical Officer, O'Connor Hospital, San Jose, CA, p. A95
M.D., Chief Medical Officer, St. Louise Regional Hospital, Gilroy, CA, p. A66

DOVER, Chris, CPA, Chief Financial Officer, Wilbarger General Hospital, Vernon, TX, p. A723

DOVER, Deborah, Senior Vice-President of Human Resources, Bristol Regional Medical Center, Bristol, TN, p. A634

DOW, Alan, Chief Financial Officer, Southern Coos Hospital And Health Center, Bandon, OR, p. A573

DOW, Korry, President, Nashoba Valley Medical Center, Ayer, MA, p. A334

DOW, Laura, Chief Financial Officer, Memorial Health, Savannah, GA, p. A180

DOWDLE, Paula, Chief Operating Officer, Jefferson Healthcare, Port Townsend, WA, p. A762

DOWELL, James, Administrator and Chief Executive Officer, Little River Memorial Hospital, Ashdown, AR, p. A42

DOWERS, Christopher, Chief Executive Officer, Bloomington Meadows Hospital, Bloomington, IN, p. A224

DOWERS, Cindy, Chief Nursing Officer, Harsha Behavioral Center, Terre Haute, IN, p. A241

DOWLING, Deanna, R.N., Chief Nursing Officer, Kp. Promise Hospital Of Wichita Falls, Wichita Falls, TX, p. A725

DOWLING, Lisa, Manager Finance, Mercy Hospital Tishomingo, Tishomingo, OK, p. A569

DOWLING, Sally, M.D., Vice President Medical Affairs, Atlantic General Hospital, Berlin, MD, p. A327

DOWN, Melanie, Site Manager, Crow/Northern Cheyenne Hospital, Crow Agency, MT, p. A422

DOWNARD, Diane, Chief Financial Officer, Coal County General Hospital, Coalgate, OK, p. A558

DOWNES, Patrick, Chief Executive Officer, East Cooper Medical Center, Mount Pleasant, SC, p. A622

DOWNEY, William, Chief Operating Officer, Riverside Regional Medical Center, Newport News, VA, p. A747
President and Chief Executive Officer, Coastal Virginia Rehabilitation, Newport News, VA, p. A746

DOWNIE, Beth, Chief Information Officer, Newton-Wellesley Hospital, Newton Lower Falls, MA, p. A342

DOWNING, James R., M.D., Chief Executive Officer, St. Jude Children's Research Hospital, Memphis, TN, p. A645

DOWNING, Jeff, R.N., MS, Chief Nursing Officer, National Jewish Health, Denver, CO, p. A110

DOWNS, Bryan, Director Information Systems, Central Peninsula Hospital, Soldotna, AK, p. A29

DOWNS, Kenny, Chief Executive Officer, Cordell Memorial Hospital, Cordell, OK, p. A558

DOWNS, Lisa, R.N., Chief Nursing Officer, Sarah D. Culbertson Memorial Hospital, Rushville, IL, p. A219

DOWNS, Patricia, Director Human Resources, Northern Nevada Medical Center, Sparks, NV, p. A446

DOWNS, Ray, Senior Staff Accountant, Healthmark Regional Medical Center, Defuniak Springs, FL, p. A136

DOWNS, Steven, Chief Financial Officer, St. Luke's Des Peres Hospital, Saint Louis, MO, p. A417

DOWNS, Stuart, R.N., Vice President and Chief Operating Officer, Wellstar Atlanta Medical Center, Atlanta, GA, p. A165

DOWNS, Stuart D., R.N., Interim President, Wellstar Atlanta Medical Center, Atlanta, GA, p. A165

DOYLE, Christopher, Chief Executive Officer, Physicians Care Surgical Hospital, Royersford, PA, p. A606

DOYLE, Craig, Director and Chief Information Officer, St. Tammany Health System, Covington, LA, p. A300

DOYLE, Jay, President and Chief Executive Officer, St. James Healthcare, Butte, MT, p. A422

DOYLE, John, Chief Financial Officer, Confluence Health/Central Washington Hospital, Wenatchee, WA, p. A768
Chief Financial Officer, Confluence Health/Wenatchee Valley Hospital, Wenatchee, WA, p. A768
Vice President Finance, Paoli Hospital, Paoli, PA, p. A599

DOYLE, Kelly, Chief Executive Officer, Rothman Specialty Hospital, Bensalem, PA, p. A584

DOYLE, Mark, President and Chief Executive Officer, Holy Cross Hospital, Fort Lauderdale, FL, p. A137

DOYLE, Matt, Chief Executive Officer, Strategic Behavioral Health - Raleigh, Garner, NC, p. A510

DOYLE, Matthew, CPA, President and Chief Executive Officer, Methodist Hospitals, Gary, IN, p. A229

DOYLE, Michael, M.D., Executive Director and Chief Medical Officer, Health Alliance Hospital - Broadway Campus, Kingston, NY, p. A486
M.D., Executive Director and Chief Medical Officer, Health Alliance Hospital - Mary's Avenue Campus, Kingston, NY, p. A487

DOZIER, Carol, Chief Financial Officer, Lifestream Behavioral Center, Leesburg, FL, p. A144
President and Chief Executive Officer, King's Daughters' Health, Madison, IN, p. A236

DOZIER, Michael, Senior Vice President, Chief Information Officer, University Hospital & Clinics, Lafayette, LA, p. A306
Vice President, Chief Information Officer, Lafayette General Medical Center, Lafayette, LA, p. A305

DOZIER, Mike, Chief Information Officer, Southeast Hospital, Cap. Girardeau, MO, p. A404

DRAEGER, Anne, Chief Nursing Officer, Owatonna Hospital, Owatonna, MN, p. A382

DRAEGER, Trish, Chief Nursing Officer, Encompass Health Deaconess Rehabilitation Hospital, Newburgh, IN, p. A238

DRAGO, Susan, R.N., Chief Executive Officer, Kindred Hospital North Florida, Green Cove Springs, FL, p. A139

DRAIME, D., Vice President and Chief Financial Officer, Avita Ontario Hospital, Ontario, OH, p. A547
Vice President and Chief Financial Officer, Galion Hospital, Galion, OH, p. A541

DRAKE, Carolyn, Director of Nursing, Milan General Hospital, Milan, TN, p. A645

DRAKE, Megan, Chief Operating Officer, Shelby Baptist Medical Center, Alabaster, AL, p. A13

DRANEY, Randall, Chief Executive Officer and Chief Financial Officer, Cordova Community Medical Center, Cordova, AK, p. A28

DRANSFIELD, Darin, Chief Executive Officer, Franklin County Medical Center, Preston, ID, p. A192

DRAPER, Jason, Chief Financial Officer, West Tennessee Healthcare Volunteer Hospital, Martin, TN, p. A643
Vice President and Chief Support Officer, Parkwest Medical Center, Knoxville, TN, p. A641

DRAPER, Vivian, Chief Financial Officer, U. S. Public Health Service Indian Hospital-Sells, Sells, AZ, p. A38

DREGNEY, James, Vice President Finance and Operations, Chief Financial Officer, Sauk Prairie Healthcare, Prairie Du Sac, WI, p. A794

DREHER, Craig, Chief Information Officer, Northern Light Mercy Hospital, Portland, ME, p. A322

DREHER, Ronald, Finance Director, Robert J. Dole Veterans Affairs Medical Center, Wichita, KS, p. A279

DREHR, Sammie, Chief Nursing Officer, Detar Healthcare System, Victoria, TX, p. A723

DRENTH, Nancy, R.N., Director Ancillary Services, Sanford Luverne Medical Center, Luverne, MN, p. A379

DRESSER, Paula, Chief Nursing Officer, Orleans Community Health, Medina, NY, p. A488

DRESSLER, Kaeli, R.N., MSN, Chief Nursing Officer, Peterson Health, Kerrville, TX, p. A693

DREW, Jeff, Fiscal Officer, Aleda E. Lutz Veterans Affairs Medical Center, Saginaw, MI, p. A365

DREW, Laura, Chief Operating Officer, Piedmont Columbus Regional Northside, Columbus, GA, p. A169

DREW, Peter, Chief Executive Officer, Warm Springs Rehabilitation Hospital Of San Antonio, San Antonio, TX, p. A714

DREWS, Manty, Chief Information Officer, Adventist Health Sonora, Sonora, CA, p. A99

DREXLER, Diane, R.N., Chief Nursing Officer, Yavapai Regional Medical Center, Prescott, AZ, p. A37

DRIEMEYER, Jed, Director of Human Resources, Hshs St. Joseph's Hospital, Breese, IL, p. A196

DRIESSNACK, Hans, Chief Executive Officer, Northwest Medical Center - Springdale, Springdale, AR, p. A53

DRIGGERS, Steve, M.D., Chief Medical Officer, Holy Family Memorial, Manitowoc, WI, p. A788

DRINKWATER, Jinia, R.N., Director Patient Care Services, Encompass Health Rehabilitation Hospital Of Braintree, Braintree, MA, p. A336

DRINKWATER, Linda, Chief Financial Officer, Waldo County General Hospital, Belfast, ME, p. A319

DRINKWITZ, Jeremy, President and Chief Executive Officer, Mercy Hospital Joplin, Joplin, MO, p. A408

DRISCOLL, Kelly, R.N., FACHE, President and Chief Executive Officer, Faith Regional Health Services, Norfolk, NE, p. A435

DRISCOLL, Laureen, President, Multicare Tacoma General Hospital, Tacoma, WA, p. A767

DRISCOLL, Mark, Chief Information Officer, Jackson County Memorial Hospital, Altus, OK, p. A555

DRISKILL, Chris, M.D., Chief of Staff, Lea Regional Medical Center, Hobbs, NM, p. A470

DRONE, Marilyn, R.N., MSN, Vice President, CNO, St. Mary Medical Center, Apple Valley, CA, p. A56

DROZD, Carol, Chief Operating Officer, St. Mark's Medical Center, La Grange, TX, p. A694

DRUSKOVICH, Gary, M.D., President, Ascension Macomb-Oakland Hospital, Warren, MI, p. A368

DRVARIC, David, M.D., Chief of Staff, Shriners Hospitals For Children-Springfield, Springfield, MA, p. A345

DRY, Laurence, Chief Operating Officer, Acute Care Hospitals Northern Region, Amita Health Elk Grove Village, Elk Grove Village, IL, p. A204
Chief Operating Officer, Acute Care Hospitals Northern Region, Amita Health Hoffman Estates, Hoffman Estates, IL, p. A208

DRYMON, Lisa, Manager, Fairfax Community Hospital, Fairfax, OK, p. A559

DRZEWIECKI-BURGER, Mary, Administrative Manager, Caro Center, Caro, MI, p. A350

DU PONT, Karen, Chief Human Resource Officer, Casa Colina Hospital And Centers For Healthcare, Pomona, CA, p. A86

DUANE, Paul, Chief Financial Officer and Office of Health Reform, Prisma Health Baptist Hospital, Columbia, SC, p. A618
Chief Financial Officer and Office of Health Reform, Prisma Health Richland Hospital, Columbia, SC, p. A618

DUARTE, Ray, Director, Information Technology and Services, Monmouth Medical Center, Southern Campus, Lakewood, NJ, p. A457

DUBOIS, Brady, Chief Executive Officer, Lutheran Hospital Of Indiana, Fort Wayne, IN, p. A228

DUBROW, Melissa, Vice President and Chief Operating Officer, Wellspan Waynesboro Hospital, Waynesboro, PA, p. A610

DUBRUYNE, Sharon, Director Human Resources, College Hospital Costa Mesa, Costa Mesa, CA, p. A61

DUCHARME, Adele, MSN, R.N., Chief Executive Officer, Saint Luke's Cushing Hospital, Leavenworth, KS, p. A269
MSN, R.N., Chief Executive Officer, Saint Luke's North Hospital - Barry Road, Kansas City, MO, p. A409

DUCHARME, Maria, R.N., Senior Vice President Patient Care Services and Chief Nursing Officer, Miriam Hospital, Providence, RI, p. A613

DUCHEMIN, MaDena, Assistant Administrator Human Resources, John Randolp. Medical Center, Hopewell, VA, p. A744

DUCHENE, Pamela, R.N., Vice President Patient Care Services and Chief Nursing Officer, Southwestern Vermont Medical Center, Bennington, VT, p. A735

DUCHESNEAU, Angy, Senior Director Human Resources, Lakeview Hospital, Stillwater, MN, p. A386

DUCK, Sandra, R.N., MSN, Mental Hospital Administrator 2, Central Louisiana State Hospital, Pineville, LA, p. A313

DUCK, Sigsbee, M.D., President, Medical Staff, Memorial Hospital Of Sweetwater County, Rock Springs, WY, p. A804

DUCKERT, Jon, FACHE, Chief Executive Officer, Baylor Scott & White Medical Center - Sunnyvale, Sunnyvale, TX, p. A718

DUCKWORTH, Bob, Director Information Systems, Medical West, Bessemer, AL, p. A14

DUDEK, Michelle, President and Chief Executive Officer, Summa Rehab Hospital, Akron, OH, p. A527

DUDLEY, Edward Executive Vice President and Chief Financial Officer, Catholic Medical Center, Manchester, NH, p. A450

DUDLEY, Heather, Director Administrative Services, Brookhaven Hospital, Tulsa, OK, p. A569

DUDLEY, W., CPA, Chief Financial Officer, Ed Fraser Memorial Hospital, Macclenny, FL, p. A144

DUET, Kendrick, Chief Operating Officer, Leonard J. Chabert Medical Center, Houma, LA, p. A303

DUFF, James, M.D., Chief Medical Officer, Cox Medical Center Branson, Branson, MO, p. A403

DUFF, Jim, Chief Financial Officer, Colorado Mental Health Institute At Pueblo, Pueblo, CO, p. A117

DUFF, Mary, CPA, Chief Financial Officer, Ridgeview Psychiatric Hospital And Center, Oak Ridge, TN, p. A648

DUFFEE, Patrick, Director Medical Information Systems, Delta Specialty Hospital, Memphis, TN, p. A644

DUFFEY, DNP, RN, NEA-BC, Pamela, MSN, R.N., Chief Nursing Officer, Texas Health Specialty Hospital, Fort Worth, TX, p. A679

DUFFIN, Kelly, Operations Officer, Intermountain Medical Center, Murray, UT, p. A729

DUFFORD, Shawn, M.D., Vice President Medical Affairs and Chief Medical Officer, Saint Josep. Hospital, Denver, CO, p. A111

DUFFY, Beth, Chief Operating Officer, Einstein Medical Center Montgomery, East Norriton, PA, p. A589

DUFFY, Daniel, D.O., Chief Medical Director, Healthsource Saginaw, Inc., Saginaw, MI, p. A365

DUFFY, Kenneth, M.D., Medical Director, Seiling Regional Medical Center, Seiling, OK, p. A568

DUFFY, Marie Theresa, Chief Hospital Executive, Carepoint Health Christ Hospital, Jersey City, NJ, p. A456
Chief Operating Officer, Carepoint Health Christ Hospital, Jersey City, NJ, p. A456

DUFFY, Pamela, MSN, R.N., Vice President Operations and Chief Nursing Executive, Northwestern Medicine Valley West Hospital, Sandwich, IL, p. A219
MSN, R.N., Vice President Operations and Chief Nursing Officer, Northwestern Medicine Kishwaukee Hospital, Dekalb, IL, p. A202

DUFFY, William, Interim Chief Nursing Officer, Norwegian American Hospital, Chicago, IL, p. A200

DUFRAYNE, Francis, M.D., Chief Medical Officer, Owensboro Health Regional Hospital, Owensboro, KY, p. A291

DUFRESNE, Joshua, Chief of Practice Operations, Springfield Hospital, Springfield, VT, p. A736

DUFT, Ryan, R.N., Chief Nursing Officer, Fredonia Regional Hospital, Fredonia, KS, p. A264

DUGAI, Jody L., Commanding Officer, Bayne-Jones Army Community Hospital, Fort Polk, LA, p. A301

DUGAN, Elizabeth, Ph.D., R.N., MSN, Chief Nursing Officer, Inova Loudoun Hospital, Leesburg, VA, p. A744

DUGAN, Gary, M.D., Vice President Medical Affairs, Penn Highlands Dubois, Dubois, PA, p. A588

DUGGAL, Harpreet, M.D., Medical Director, Department of Health and Human Services, Humboldt County Mental Health, Eureka, CA, p. A63

DUGGAN, James, Director Human Resources, Western Massachusetts Hospital, Westfield, MA, p. A346

DUGGAN, Margaret, M.D., Chief Medical Officer, Brigham And Women's Faulkner Hospital, Boston, MA, p. A335

DUGGAN, Stephanie J., M.D., President, Ascension St. Josep. Hospital, Tawas City, MI, p. A367
'M.D., President, Ascension St. Mary's Of Michigan, Saginaw, MI, p. A365
M.D., President, Ascension Standish Hospital, Standish, MI, p. A367

DUGGAN, Tonya, Director Human Resources, Northern Louisiana Medical Center, Ruston, LA, p. A313

DUGGAR, Susan, MSN, Vice President Nursing, Spartanburg Medical Center - Church Street Campus, Spartanburg, SC, p. A624

DUGGER, Curtis, Chief Financial Officer, Memorial Hospital Of Converse County, Douglas, WY, p. A802

DUGGER, Sandy, Chief Executive Officer, Banner Lassen Medical Center, Susanville, CA, p. A100

DUHAIME, Robert, R.N., Senior Vice President Clinical Operations and Chief Nursing Officer, Catholic Medical Center, Manchester, NH, p. A450

DUHANEY-WEST, Aphreikah, Chief Executive Officer, Clark Regional Medical Center, Winchester, KY, p. A294

DUHE, Louis, Executor Director, Information Services, Piedmont Athens Regional Medical Center, Athens, GA, p. A163
Senior Director Information Technology, George Washington University Hospital, Washington, DC, p. A129

DUKE, Ezekiel, M.D., Chief of Staff, Knox County Hospital, Knox City, TX, p. A694

DUKE, Kelly, Chief Executive Officer, Select Specialty Hospital-Oklahoma City, Oklahoma City, OK, p. A566

DUKE, Lee, M.D., Senior Vice President and Chief Physician Executive, Penn Medicine Lancaster General Hospital, Lancaster, PA, p. A594

DUKE, Scott A., Interim Chief Executive Officer, Phillip. County Hospital, Malta, MT, p. A426

DUKES, Brenda, Director Human Resources, Sonoma Developmental Center, Eldridge, CA, p. A63

DUKOFF, Ruth, M.D., Medical Director, North Star Behavioral Health System, Anchorage, AK, p. A27

DULANEY, Paul, M.D., Chief of Staff, Troy Regional Medical Center, Troy, AL, p. A25

DULIN, Misty, CAH, Director, Mercyone Primghar Medical Center, Primghar, IA, p. A256

DULING, Ruth, Chief Executive Officer, Girard Medical Center, Girard, KS, p. A265

DULL, David, M.D., Chief Medical Officer, Penrose-St. Francis Health Services, Colorado Springs, CO, p. A109

DULL, Kevin, Senior Vice President Human Potential, Multicare Auburn Medical Center, Auburn, WA, p. A755
Senior Vice President Human Potential, Multicare Good Samaritan Hospital, Puyallup. WA, p. A762
Senior Vice President Human Potential, Multicare Mary Bridge Children's Hospital And Health Center, Tacoma, WA, p. A767
Senior Vice President Human Potential, Multicare Tacoma General Hospital, Tacoma, WA, p. A767

DULNY, David, Chief Financial Officer, Providence Medical Center, Kansas City, KS, p. A267
Chief Financial Officer, Saint John Hospital, Leavenworth, KS, p. A269

DUMAIS, Mark, M.D., Chief Medical Officer, Northridge Hospital Medical Center, Northridge, CA, p. A81

DUMAL, Jennifer, R.N., Chief Operating Officer of Clinical and Chief Nursing Officer, Memorial Hospital At Gulfport, Gulfport, MS, p. A393

DUMKE, Steve, FACHE, Executive Vice President and Chief Operating Officer, Christian Health Care Center, Wyckoff, NJ, p. A466

DUMONSEAU, Kent, Vice President Finance and Information Services, Hayward Area Memorial Hospital And Water's Edge, Hayward, WI, p. A786
Vice President Finance and Information Services, Memorial Medical Center Of Ashland, Ashland, WI, p. A779

DUNAVAN, Chad, R.N., Vice President, Chief Nursing Officer, Medical Center Health System, Odessa, TX, p. A703

DUNCAN, Allison, Chief Financial Officer, Arrowhead Behavioral Health Hospital, Maumee, OH, p. A544

DUNCAN, Barbara, Chief Financial Officer, Habersham Medical Center, Demorest, GA, p. A171

DUNCAN, Charles, M.D., Medical Director, Kindred Hospital-San Antonio, San Antonio, TX, p. A711

DUNCAN, Cindy, Director Human Resources, Roosevelt General Hospital, Portales, NM, p. A471
Manager Human Resources, Plains Regional Medical Center, Clovis, NM, p. A469

DUNCAN, Cynthia, Chief Executive Officer, Roger Mills Memorial Hospital, Cheyenne, OK, p. A557

DUNCAN, Erika, Vice President Human Resources, St. Joseph's Hospital Health Center, Syracuse, NY, p. A499

DUNCAN, Jeremy, Director Information Systems, Lawrence Medical Center, Moulton, AL, p. A22

DUNCAN, Jimmy, Senior Vice President and Chief People Officer, Arkansas Children's Hospital, Little Rock, AR, p. A48

DUNCAN, Joani, Chief Human Resource Officer, Ann & Robert H. Lurie Children's Hospital Of Chicago, Chicago, IL, p. A198

DUNCAN, Leeann, Director Patient Care Services, Harbor Oaks Hospital, New Baltimore, MI, p. A362

DUNCAN, Linda, Director Human Resources, Lee's Summit Medical Center, Lee's Summit, MO, p. A410

DUNCAN, Lyman, Chief Financial Officer, San Juan Health Service District, Monticello, UT, p. A729

DUNCAN, Michael J., President and Chief Executive Officer, Chester County Hospital, West Chester, PA, p. A610

DUNCAN, Nathan, Chief Executive Officer, Lakeland Behavioral Health System, Springfield, MO, p. A418

DUNCAN, Thomas, Executive Vice President and Chief Financial Officer, Miami Valley Hospital, Dayton, OH, p. A538

DUNCAN, Traci, R.N., Vice President, Chief Nursing Officer, Northbay Medical Center, Fairfield, CA, p. A63

DUNFORD, Bill, Manager, Northside Hospital-Cherokee, Canton, GA, p. A168

DUNHAM, Cathy, Vice President Human Resources, Mcpherson Hospital, Mcpherson, KS, p. A270

DUNHAM, Shelly, Chief Executive Officer, Okeene Municipal Hospital, Okeene, OK, p. A563

DUNIO, Gina, Chief Human Resources, James E. Van Zandt Veterans Affairs Medical Center, Altoona, PA, p. A584

DUNKEL, Jason, President and Chief Executive Officer, Adventhealth North Pinellas, Tarpon Springs, FL, p. A160

DUNKER, Karla, Chief Financial Officer, Sedgwick County Health Center, Julesburg, CO, p. A114

DUNKIEL, Barbara, Director Human Resources, Encompass Health Rehabilitation Hospital Of Sunrise, Sunrise, FL, p. A158

DUNKIN, Jackie, Director Human Resources, Platte Valley Medical Center, Brighton, CO, p. A108

DUNKLE, David, Vice President Medical Affairs, Johnson Memorial Hospital, Franklin, IN, p. A229

DUNLAP, Cyndy, R.N., FACHE, Chief Nursing Officer, Ascension Providence, Waco, TX, p. A723

DUNLEAVY, Christopher, Senior Vice President Finance and Chief Financial Officer, Brigham And Women's Hospital, Boston, MA, p. A335

DUNLEY, Pamela L., MS, R.N., Chief Executive Officer, Elmhurst Hospital, Elmhurst, IL, p. A204

DUNLOP, James, CPA, JrChief Financial Officer, Sisters Of Charity Hospital Of Buffalo, Buffalo, NY, p. A480
CPA, JrExecutive Vice President and Chief Financial Officer, Kenmore Mercy Hospital, Kenmore, NY, p. A486
CPA, JrSenior Vice President Finance and Chief Financial Officer, Mercy Hospital, Buffalo, NY, p. A480

DUNN, Denise, R.N., Chief Nursing Officer, Baptist Health Madisonville, Madisonville, KY, p. A289

DUNN, E, Vice President Human Resources, Virtua Memorial, Mount Holly, NJ, p. A458

DUNN, Hope, Chief Nursing Officer, Encompass Health Rehabilitation Hospital Of East Valley, Mesa, AZ, p. A34

DUNN, Jack, M.D., Chief of Staff, La Paz Regional Hospital, Parker, AZ, p. A34

DUNN, Janice, Chief Financial Officer, Plymouth Medical Center, Plymouth, IN, p. A239

DUNN, Jim, Ph.D., Chief Human Resource Officer, Atrium Health's Carolinas Medical Center, Charlotte, NC, p. A506

DUNN, Leonard, M.D., Chief Medical Officer, Baycare Alliant Hospital, Dunedin, FL, p. A136

DUNN, Marcy, Vice President Information Services and Chief Information Officer, Good Samaritan Hospital Medical Center, West Islip. NY, p. A502
Vice President Information Services and Chief Information Officer, Mercy Medical Center, Rockville Centre, NY, p. A497
Vice President Information Services and Chief Information Officer, St. Francis Hospital, The Heart Center, Roslyn, NY, p. A497

DUNN, Margie, Director Human Resources, Middle Tennessee Mental Health Institute, Nashville, TN, p. A646

DUNN, Nicholas, Director Information Systems, Mena Regional Health System, Mena, AR, p. A50

DUNN, Richard, M.D., Chief Medical Officer, Riverside Tappahannock Hospital, Tappahannock, VA, p. A752

DUNN, Rosemary, R.N., Chief Nursing Officer, Cap. Regional Health System, Cap. May Court House, NJ, p. A453

DUNN, Sheila, Assistant Administrator Human Resources, Dale Medical Center, Ozark, AL, p. A23

DUNN, Tandra, Director of Nursing, San Luis Valley Health Conejos County Hospital, La Jara, CO, p. A115

DUNN, Terry, Director Information Technology, Battle Mountain General Hospital, Battle Mountain, NV, p. A441

DUNNING, David K., Medical Center Director and Chief Executive Officer, Memphis Veterans Affairs Medical Center, Memphis, TN, p. A644

DUNNING, Nan, Human Resources Manager, Paris Community Hospital, Paris, IL, p. A216

DUNPHY-ALEXANDER, Shannon, Director, Mercyhealth Hospital And Medical Center - Harvard, Harvard, IL, p. A207

DUNWOODY, Robert, Chief Financial Officer, Lawnwood Regional Medical Center & Heart Institute, Fort Pierce, FL, p. A138

DUPONT, Laurel, Chief Executive Officer, Northshore Rehabilitation Hospital, Lacombe, LA, p. A305

DUPPER, Harold, Chief Financial Officer, Platte Valley Medical Center, Brighton, CO, p. A108

DUPRE, Charlotte W., Chief Executive Officer, Southern Regional Medical Center, Riverdale, GA, p. A178

DUPREE, Eric, M.D., Chief of Staff, Winn Parish Medical Center, Winnfield, LA, p. A317

DUPREE, Lucy, Director Human Resources, Columbia Memorial Hospital, Astoria, OR, p. A573

DUPREY, Irma, Administrator Medical Records, Hospital Universitario Dr. Ramon Ruiz Arnau, Bayamon, PR, p. A806

DUQUETTE, Connie, Director Human Resources, Sharp Mary Birch Hospital For Women And Newborns, San Diego, CA, p. A92
Director Human Resources, Sharp Memorial Hospital, San Diego, CA, p. A92

DUQUETTE, William M., Chief Executive Officer, Baptist Health South Florida, South Miami Hospital, Miami, FL, p. A146

DURAN, Jody, Manager Information Systems, Livingston Healthcare, Livingston, MT, p. A426

DURAND, Crista F., President, Newport Hospital, Newport, RI, p. A613

DURAND, Mark, Assistant Administrator Operations, Christus Southeast Texas Jasper Memorial, Jasper, TX, p. A691

DURBAK, Ivan, Chief Information Officer, Bronxcare Health System, Bronx, NY, p. A476

DURBIN, Melissa, R.N., MSN, Chief Nursing Officer, Boca Raton Regional Hospital, Boca Raton, FL, p. A132

DURFLINGER, Kathy, Vice President and Chief Nursing Officer, Avita Ontario Hospital, Ontario, OH, p. A547

Vice President and Chief Nursing Officer, Galion Hospital, Galion, OH, p. A541

DURGIN, Manal, Network Medical Director, Devereux Hospital And Children's Center Of Florida, Melbourne, FL, p. A145

DURHAM, Karla, Director of Information Systems, Baptist Health Madisonville, Madisonville, KY, p. A289

DURHAM, Linda, Director Human Resources, Henderson County Community Hospital, Lexington, TN, p. A642

DURHAM, Thomas, Chief Nursing Officer, Ferry County Memorial Hospital, Republic, WA, p. A763

DURIS, Deb, Director of Nursing, Northwest Ohio Psychiatric Hospital, Toledo, OH, p. A550

DURNEY, Gerry, Chief Operating Officer, Good Samaritan Regional Medical Center, Suffern, NY, p. A499

DURNIAT-SUSHRSTEDT, Karen, Nurse Executive, Appalachian Behavioral Healthcare, Athens, OH, p. A528

DURNIOK, Brian, President, Upmc Chautauqua, Jamestown, NY, p. A486

President, Upmc Northwest, Seneca, PA, p. A607

Vice President Operations, Upmc Northwest, Seneca, PA, p. A607

DURON, Kety, Vice President Human Resources, Stanford Health Care, Palo Alto, CA, p. A84

DURRENCE, Liz, Chief Operating Officer, Brandon Regional Hospital, Brandon, FL, p. A133

DURRETT, Johnathan, Chief Executive Officer, Fredonia Regional Hospital, Fredonia, KS, p. A264

DURST, Geoff, Vice President Finance, Avera St. Luke's Hospital, Aberdeen, SD, p. A626

DURST, Sue, R.N., MS, Vice President Plant Operations, Mclaren Macomb, Mount Clemens, MI, p. A362

DURSTELER, Courtney, Chief Human Resources Officer, Franklin County Medical Center, Preston, ID, p. A192

DURYEE, Edward, Director Information Systems, Saint Francis Medical Center, Cap. Girardeau, MO, p. A403

DUSANG, Nina, Vice President Finance and Chief Financial Officer, Dch Regional Medical Center, Tuscaloosa, AL, p. A25

DUSENBERY, Jack, President and Chief Executive Officer, Mercyone Waterloo Medical Center, Waterloo, IA, p. A259

DUTCHER, Phillip. Chief Operating Officer, Nch Baker Hospital, Naples, FL, p. A148

DUTHE, Robert, Director Information Systems and Chief Information Officer, Guthrie Cortland Regional Medical Center, Cortland, NY, p. A482

DUTLA, Nimal, M.D., Chief Medical Staff, Holzer Medical Center - Jackson, Jackson, OH, p. A542

DUTMERS, David, Manager, Information Services, Spectrum Health United Hospital, Greenville, MI, p. A356

DUTTON, Angela, Chief Human Resources Management Service, Robley Rex Veterans Affairs Medical Center, Louisville, KY, p. A288

DUTTON, Michelle, Human Resources, Galesburg Cottage Hospital, Galesburg, IL, p. A205

DUTTON, Rebecca, Director Human Resources, Larue D. Carter Memorial Hospital, Indianapolis, IN, p. A232

DUTTON, Teresa, R.N., Chief Nursing Officer, Baylor Scott & White Surgical Hospital-Sherman, Sherman, TX, p. A715

DUVAL, Rob, Chief Human Resources Officer, Emma Pendleton Bradley Hospital, East Providence, RI, p. A613

DUVALL, Richard, Chief Executive Officer, Carthage Area Hospital, Carthage, NY, p. A481

President and Chief Executive Officer, Claxton-Hepburn Medical Center, Ogdensburg, NY, p. A493

DUVALL, Wendy, Chief Financial Officer, Heartland Behavioral Health Services, Nevada, MO, p. A412

DUVVURI, Vikas, M.D., Medical Director, Fremont Hospital, Fremont, CA, p. A65

DWIGHT, John, Regional Vice President and Chief Information Officer, Skagit Valley Hospital, Mount Vernon, WA, p. A761

DWORAK, Paige, FACHE, Chief Executive Officer, East Orange General Hospital, East Orange, NJ, p. A454

DWORKIN, Darren, Senior Vice President Enterprise Information Systems and Chief Information Officer, Cedars-Sinai Medical Center, Los Angeles, CA, p. A73

DWORKIN, Jack, M.D., Vice President Medical Affairs and Chief Medical Officer, Centrastate Healthcare System, Freehold, NJ, p. A455

DWORKIN, Paul, M.D., Physician-in-Chief, Connecticut Children's Medical Center, Hartford, CT, p. A122

DWYER, Amy, R.N., MSN, Chief Nursing Officer, Hshs Sacred Heart Hospital, Eau Claire, WI, p. A783

DWYER, Cathy, Senior Administrator Information Systems, Burke Rehabilitation Hospital, White Plains, NY, p. A502

DWYER, James, D.O., Executive Vice President and Chief Medical Officer, Virtua Memorial, Mount Holly, NJ, p. A458

D.O., Executive Vice President and Chief Medical Officer, Virtua Voorhees, Voorhees, NJ, p. A465

DWYER, Mark, FACHE, Chief Executive Officer, The Rehabilitation Institute Of St. Louis, Saint Louis, MO, p. A417

DWYER, Susan, Vice President Finance, Aurora Psychiatric Hospital, Wauwatosa, WI, p. A799

DWYER, William, Vice President and Chief Human Resources Officer, Children's Specialized Hospital, New Brunswick, NJ, p. A459

DYBDAL, Landon, Chief Executive Officer, Ruby Valley Medical Center, Sheridan, MT, p. A428

DYCHE, Ginny, Director Community Relations, Aspen Valley Hospital, Aspen, CO, p. A107

DYCUS, Steve, Director Marketing and Public Relations, Williamson Medical Center, Franklin, TN, p. A638

DYE, Chris, Director Information Systems, Arh Our Lady Of The Way, Martin, KY, p. A289

DYE, Dana, R.N., Vice President, Baptist Memorial Hospital - Memphis, Memphis, TN, p. A643

DYE, David, M.D., Chief Medical Officer, Purcell Municipal Hospital, Purcell, OK, p. A567

DYE, Emily, Vice President Human Resources, Tristar Summit Medical Center, Hermitage, TN, p. A639

DYE, Leslie, Chief Executive Officer, Phs Santa Fe Indian Hospital, Santa Fe, NM, p. A472

DYKEHOUSE, Rodney, Senior Vice President Information Services, Waukesha Memorial Hospital, Waukesha, WI, p. A798

DYKES, Bradford W., President, Indiana University Health Bedford Hospital, Bedford, IN, p. A224

DYKSTERHOUSE, Trevor J., President, Forest Health Medical Center, Ypsilanti, MI, p. A370

DYKSTRA, Lisa, Senior Vice President and Chief Information Officer, Ann & Robert H. Lurie Children's Hospital Of Chicago, Chicago, IL, p. A198

DYLE, Amanda, Chief Financial Officer, Princeton Baptist Medical Center, Birmingham, AL, p. A15

Chief Financial Officer, Walker Baptist Medical Center, Jasper, AL, p. A20

DYRKACZ, Anna, Chief Financial Officer, Vibra Hospital Of Western Massachusetts, Springfield, MA, p. A345

DYSART-CREDEUR, Amy, Administrator, Oceans Behavioral Hospital Of Broussard, Broussard, LA, p. A299

DZIEDZICKI, Ron, R.N., Chief Operating Officer, Uh Cleveland Medical Center, Cleveland, OH, p. A535

DZIESINSKI, Ray, Vice President and Chief Financial Officer, Sheppard Pratt Health System, Baltimore, MD, p. A326

D'ACCURZIO, Albert, M.D., Medical Director, St. Elizabeth Medical Center, Utica, NY, p. A500

D'AGOSTINO, Christopher, Chief Medical Officer, Amita Health Alexian Brothers Behavioral Health Hospital, Hoffman Estates, IL, p. A208

D'AMBROSIO, Matthew, MSN, R.N., Chief Nursing Officer, Encompass Health Rehabilitation Hospital Of San Antonio, San Antonio, TX, p. A711

D'AMICO, David, St. Anthony's Rehabilitation Hospital, Lauderdale Lakes, FL, p. A144

D'AMICO, Paul, M.D., Chief of Staff, Atrium Health Stanly, Albemarle, NC, p. A504

D'AMORE, Seanna, Director Human Resources, Penn Highlands Elk, Saint Marys, PA, p. A606

D'ANGINA, Joseph, Chief Financial Officer, Mercy Medical Center Redding, Redding, CA, p. A87

D'APOLLO, Julie, R.N., Director of Nursing, Hampstead Hospital, Hampstead, NH, p. A449

D'AURIA, Joseph, Director Finance, Morristown Medical Center, Morristown, NJ, p. A458

D'ELIA, Peter, Chief Financial Officer, Saint Vincent Hospital, Worcester, MA, p. A346

D'ERAMO, John, Chief Operating Officer, Connecticut Valley Hospital, Middletown, CT, p. A123

D'ORTENZIO, Gabe, Director of Human Resources, Weirton Medical Center, Weirton, WV, p. A777

D'sOUZA, Carol, Chief Human Resources Officer, Banner Casa Grande Medical Center, Casa Grande, AZ, p. A30

D'sOUZA, Gladys, Chief Nursing Officer, Barlow Respiratory Hospital, Los Angeles, CA, p. A73

# E

EADS, Barry, R.N., Chief Nursing Officer, Encompass Health Rehabilitation Hospital Of Gadsden, Gadsden, AL, p. A19

R.N., Chief Nursing Officer, Medical Center Enterprise, Enterprise, AL, p. A18

EADS, Ted, Interim Chief Nursing Officer, Ascension St. Vincent Carmel Hospital, Carmel, IN, p. A225

EADY, Bruce, Chief Executive Officer, Select Specialty Hospital-St. Louis, Saint Charles, MO, p. A414

EAGAR, Troy, Director Human Resources, Mountain Valley Regional Rehabilitation Hospital, Prescott Valley, AZ, p. A37

EAKER, Blake, Interim Director Information Services, Uvalde Memorial Hospital, Uvalde, TX, p. A722

EAMRANOND, Pracha, M.D., Senior Vice President Population Health and Medical Affairs, Lawrence General Hospital, Lawrence, MA, p. A340

EANES, Janine, Senior Human Resources Business Partner, Unc Rockingham Health Care, Eden, NC, p. A509

EARDLEY, Robert, Senior Vice President and Chief Information Officer, Houston Methodist Hospital, Houston, TX, p. A686

EARL, Mindy, Health Information Manager, Power County Hospital District, American Falls, ID, p. A188

EARLEY, Robert, President and Chief Executive Officer, Jp. Health Network, Fort Worth, TX, p. A678

EARLEY, Tom, Chief Financial Officer, Alliancehealth Woodward, Woodward, OK, p. A572

EARLY, David T., FACHE, Chief Executive Officer, Floyd Cherokee Medical Center, Centre, AL, p. A16

EARLY, Drew, President and Chief Executive Officer, Decatur Memorial Hospital, Decatur, IL, p. A202

EARLY, Elfie, Manager Data Services, Georgia Regional Hospital At Atlanta, Decatur, GA, p. A171

EARLY, Gerald, M.D., Chief Medical Officer, Pullman Regional Hospital, Pullman, WA, p. A762

EARNSHAW, Dallas, Superintendent, Utah State Hospital, Provo, UT, p. A731

EASLEY, Evan, M.D., Chief Medical Officer, Carson Valley Medical Center, Gardnerville, NV, p. A442

EASLEY, Mike, Vice President and Chief Operating Officer, Sabine County Hospital, Hemphill, TX, p. A683

EAST, Becky, CPA, Senior Vice President, Chief Financial Officer, Bronson Lakeview Hospital, Paw Paw, MI, p. A363

EASTBURG, Mark C., Ph.D., President and Chief Executive Officer, Pine Rest Christian Mental Health Services, Grand Rapids, MI, p. A356

EASTER, Susan, Chief Nursing Officer, Palacios Community Medical Center, Palacios, TX, p. A704

EASTERLING, Jamie, Executive Director, Operations, Good Samaritan Hospital, Cincinnati, OH, p. A532

EASTERWOOD, Diane, Human Resources Business Partner, Kaiser Permanente San Francisco Medical Center, San Francisco, CA, p. A93

EASTHOPE, Kerry, Area Finance Officer, Kaiser Permanente Antioch Medical Center, Antioch, CA, p. A56

EASTMAN, David, Interim Chief Executive Officer, Adventist Health Tehachap. Valley, Tehachapi, CA, p. A100

EASTON, Laura, President and Chief Executive Officer, Caldwell Unc Health Care, Lenoir, NC, p. A513

EASTON, Laura J., President and Chief Executive Officer, Caldwell Unc Health Care, Lenoir, NC, p. A513

EATHERLY, Theresa, Chief Financial Officer, United Memorial Medical Center, Houston, TX, p. A689

EATON, Lisa, R.N., Chief Nursing Officer, Grace Cottage Hospital, Townshend, VT, p. A737

EATON, Philip. Chief Executive Officer, Mountain West Medical Center, Tooele, UT, p. A733

EAVENSON, Steve, Vice President Finance, Mercy Health Saint Mary's, Grand Rapids, MI, p. A356

EAVES, Dan, Chief Executive Officer, Marshall Browning Hospital, Du Quoin, IL, p. A203

EBBETT, Patricia, Chief Human Resources Officer, Catawba Hospital, Catawba, VA, p. A739

EBELING, April, Chief Executive Officer, Amg Specialty Hospital-Lafayette, Lafayette, LA, p. A305

EBENAL, Shelley, Chief Executive Officer, Fairbanks Memorial Hospital, Fairbanks, AK, p. A28

EBERHARDT, Lisa, Chief Nursing Officer, Clark Fork Valley Hospital, Plains, MT, p. A426

EBERS, Layne, Director Human Resources and Marketing, Pike County Memorial Hospital, Louisiana, MO, p. A411

EBERSOLE, Nathan, Controller, Calhoun-Liberty Hospital, Blountstown, FL, p. A132

EBERT, Larry W. Jr, Chief Executive Officer, Piedmont Walton Hospital, Monroe, GA, p. A177

EBERT, Michael, M.D., Chief of Staff, Veterans Affairs Connecticut Healthcare System, West Haven, CT, p. A126

EBERT-LOOMIS, Cynthia, R.N., Chief Nursing Officer, Summit Healthcare Regional Medical Center, Show Low, AZ, p. A38

EBKE, Russell, M.D., Chief of Staff, Crete Area Medical Center, Crete, NE, p. A431

EBLIN, Steven E., Interim President and Chief Executive Officer, Unc Rockingham Health Care, Eden, NC, p. A509

EBNER, Joseph, M.D., Chief Medical Officer, Speare Memorial Hospital, Plymouth, NH, p. A451

EBRIGHT, Brian, Chief Financial Officer, Salt Lake Regional Medical Center, Salt Lake City, UT, p. A732

ECKELS, Dan, Chief Financial Officer, Washington Regional Medical Center, Fayetteville, AR, p. A45

ECKENFELS, Susan, Chief Financial Officer, Ste. Genevieve County Memorial Hospital, Ste Genevieve, MO, p. A419

ECKERT, Mary L., President and Chief Executive Officer, Lecom Health Millcreek Community Hospital, Erie, PA, p. A590

ECKERT, Susan, R.N., MSN, Senior Vice President and Chief Nursing Officer, Medstar Washington Hospital Center, Washington, DC, p. A130

ECKFORD, Marjorie, Chief Nursing Officer, Menlo Park Surgical Hospital, Menlo Park, CA, p. A77

ECKLAND, Christopher, M.D., Chief Medical Officer, Miami County Medical Center, Paola, KS, p. A274

ECKLER, Patrick, Administrator, Villa Feliciana Medical Complex, Jackson, LA, p. A303

ECKSTEIN, Becca, Executive Director, Veritas Collaborative, Durham, NC, p. A509

ECKSTEIN, William, Chief Executive Officer and Chief Financial Officer, Columbus Specialty Hospital, Columbus, GA, p. A169

EDALATI, David, M.D., Medical Director, Meadowbrook Rehabilitation Hospital, Gardner, KS, p. A265

EDDEY, Gary, M.D., Medical Director, Matheny Medical And Educational Center, Peapack, NJ, p. A460

EDDINGTON, Paul, CPA, Affiliate Vice President and Chief Financial Officer, Passavant Area Hospital, Jacksonville, IL, p. A209

EDDINGTON, Tonya, Coordinator Human Resources, Select Specialty Hospital-Springfield, Springfield, MO, p. A419

EDDLEMAN, Patricia, Fiscal Officer, Heartland Behavioral Healthcare, Massillon, OH, p. A544

EDDY, Lee Anne, Senior Vice President and Chief Nursing Officer, Arkansas Children's Hospital, Little Rock, AR, p. A48

EDELSTEIN, Tracy, MSN, R.N., Vice President and Chief Nursing Officer, Bethesda Hospital East, Boynton Beach, FL, p. A132

EDEN, Tina, Director of Nursing, Virginia Gay Hospital, Vinton, IA, p. A259

EDENFIELD, Janet, Director Financial Services, Georgia Regional Hospital At Savannah, Savannah, GA, p. A180

EDENS, Melanie, Chief Operating Officer, Nea Baptist Memorial Hospital, Jonesboro, AR, p. A48

EDGAR, Joseph, Senior Vice President Operations, Wellspan Gettysburg Hospital, Gettysburg, PA, p. A590

EDGAR, Nancy, Vice President Human Resources, Methodist Hospital, San Antonio, TX, p. A712

EDGAR, Steven, FACHE, President and Chief Executive Officer, Medical City Denton, Denton, TX, p. A672

EDGE, Jeffery, Chief Operating Officer, Ochsner Medical Center - Kenner, Kenner, LA, p. A304

EDGE, Lee, Administrator, Oceans Behavioral Hospital Of Alexandria, Alexandria, LA, p. A295

EDIN, Scott, Vice President, Finance and Chief Financial Officer, Northfield Hospital And Clinics, Northfield, MN, p. A382

EDINGTON, Brent, Director Information Services, Pomerene Hospital, Millersburg, OH, p. A545

EDLER, Susie, R.N., Chief Nursing Officer, Dallas Behavioral Healthcare Hospital, Desoto, TX, p. A672

EDMINSTER, Sue, Vice President Human Resources, Ripon Medical Center, Ripon, WI, p. A795
Vice President Human Resources, St. Agnes Hospital, Fond Du Lac, WI, p. A784
Vice President Human Resources, Waupun Memorial Hospital, Waupun, WI, p. A798

EDMISTEN, Cathy, Chief Operating Officer, Memorial Hospital Of Tampa, Tampa, FL, p. A159

EDMONDS, Kelly, Chief Financial Officer, Western Maryland Hospital Center, Hagerstown, MD, p. A330

EDMONDSON, Bobby, Controller, Regional Rehabilitation Hospital, Phenix City, AL, p. A23

EDMONDSON, Cory, President and Chief Executive Officer, Peterson Health, Kerrville, TX, p. A693

EDMONDSON, James H., Chief Executive Officer, Southern Tennessee Regional Health System-Pulaski, Pulaski, TN, p. A648

EDMUNDS, Liza, Director Human Resources, Tennova Healthcare-Clarksville, Clarksville, TN, p. A636

EDNEY, Daniel, M.D., Chief of Staff, Kp. Promise Hospital Of Vicksburg, Vicksburg, MS, p. A400

EDWARD, Adolphe, Chief Executive Officer, El Centro Regional Medical Center, El Centro, CA, p. A63

EDWARDS, Aaron, Chief Executive Officer, Ferry County Memorial Hospital, Republic, WA, p. A763

EDWARDS, Angela, R.N., Chief Nurse Executive, Nyc Health + Hospitals / Woodhull, Brooklyn, NY, p. A479

EDWARDS, Annette, Chief Financial Officer, Odessa Memorial Healthcare Center, Odessa, WA, p. A761

EDWARDS, Becky, Manager Human Resources, Irwin County Hospital, Ocilla, GA, p. A178

EDWARDS, Bruce, Vice President Human Resources, Heritage Valley Health System, Beaver, PA, p. A584

Vice President Human Resources, Sewickley Valley Hospital, (A Division Of Valley Medical Facilities), Sewickley, PA, p. A608

EDWARDS, Chris, M.D., Chief Medical Officer, Piedmont Columbus Regional Midtown, Columbus, GA, p. A169
M.D., Chief Medical Officer, Piedmont Columbus Regional Northside, Columbus, GA, p. A169

EDWARDS, Dana, Chief Financial Officer, Sea Pines Rehabilitation Hospital, Melbourne, FL, p. A145

EDWARDS, Dennis, M.D., Vice President Medical Affairs, Chi Health Good Samaritan, Kearney, NE, p. A433

EDWARDS, Gregg, Chief People Officer, Asante Rogue Regional Medical Center, Medford, OR, p. A577
Chief People Officer, Asante Three Rivers Medical Center, Grants Pass, OR, p. A575
Vice President Human Resources, Asante Ashland Community Hospital, Ashland, OR, p. A573

EDWARDS, Jeff, Manager Information Services, Mendocino Coast District Hospital, Fort Bragg, CA, p. A64

EDWARDS, Jonita, Director Human Resources, Dmc - Children's Hospital Of Michigan, Detroit, MI, p. A352

EDWARDS, Kathleen, Manager Information Systems Operation, Encompass Health Rehabilitation Hospital Of Altoona, Altoona, PA, p. A583

EDWARDS, Marti, MSN, R.N., Chief Nursing Officer, Rml Specialty Hospital, Hinsdale, IL, p. A208

EDWARDS, Matt, Vice President Nursing Services and Chief Nursing Officer, Anderson Regional Health System, Meridian, MS, p. A397

EDWARDS, Michelle, Chief Information Officer, Regional Medical Center, Orangeburg, SC, p. A623
Executive Vice President Information Technology, Prisma Health Baptist Hospital, Columbia, SC, p. A618

EDWARDS, Nicki, Ph.D., R.N., Interim Chief Nursing Officer, Sierra Vista Regional Medical Center, San Luis Obispo, CA, p. A96

EDWARDS, Paul, President and Chief Executive Officer, Thayer County Health Services, Hebron, NE, p. A433

EDWARDS, Rebecca, Chief Human Resources Officer, Penn Highlands Brookville, Brookville, PA, p. A585
Director Human Resources, Martin General Hospital, Williamston, NC, p. A520

EDWARDS, Rick, Vice President and Chief Financial Officer, Hancock Regional Hospital, Greenfield, IN, p. A230

EDWARDS, Robert, Administrator, Unity Psych Care-Memphis, Memphis, TN, p. A645
Chief Nursing Officer, Lakeside Behavioral Health System, Memphis, TN, p. A644

EDWARDS, Samuel, M.D., Chief of Staff, Adventhealth Deland, Deland, FL, p. A136

EDWARDS, Scott, Chief Operating Officer, Scott Memorial Health, Scottsburg, IN, p. A240

EDWARDS, Steven D., President and Chief Executive Officer, Cox Medical Centers, Springfield, MO, p. A418

EDWARDS, Susan, Vice President Human Resources, Novant Health Uva Health System Culpeper Medical Center, Culpeper, VA, p. A740

EDWARDS, Susan A., President and Chief Executive Officer, Oconomowoc Memorial Hospital, Oconomowoc, WI, p. A792
President and Chief Executive Officer, Waukesha Memorial Hospital, Waukesha, WI, p. A798

EDWARDS, Todd, Director Information Management Systems, Chi St. Luke's Health Brazosport, Lake Jackson, TX, p. A694

EDWARDS, William, Information Technology Generalist, Wernersville State Hospital, Wernersville, PA, p. A610

EGAN, Carol, R.N., MSN, Chief Nursing Officer, Rutland Regional Medical Center, Rutland, VT, p. A736

EGAN, Eileen Esq, Executive Director, Phelp. Memorial Hospital Center, Sleep. Hollow, NY, p. A498

EGAN, Timothy, President and Chief Executive Officer, Roseland Community Hospital, Chicago, IL, p. A200

EGBERT, James, Chief of Staff, Vidant Beaufort Hospital, Washington, NC, p. A519

EGBERT, Jeff, Interim Chief Executive Officer, Susan B. Allen Memorial Hospital, El Dorado, KS, p. A264

EGERTON, W, M.D., Chief Medical Officer, University Of Maryland Medical Center Midtown Campus, Baltimore, MD, p. A326

EGGEN, Caity, Chief Human Resource Officer, Cuyuna Regional Medical Center, Crosby, MN, p. A374

EGGERS, Judy, Manager Human Resources, Alliance Healthcare System, Holly Springs, MS, p. A394

EGGLESTON, Brett, Chief Executive Officer, Callaway District Hospital, Callaway, NE, p. A430

EGGLESTON, Kirk W., Commanding Officer, Winn Army Community Hospital, Hinesville, GA, p. A174

EGGLESTON, Lara, Finance Manager, Uh Conneaut Medical Center, Conneaut, OH, p. A537
Finance Manager, Uh Geneva Medical Center, Geneva, OH, p. A541

EGGLESTON, Ryan, Chief Financial Officer, Desert View Hospital, Pahrump. NV, p. A445

EGYUD, Amber, R.N., Chief Nursing Officer and Chief Operating Officer, Chesapeake Regional Medical Center, Chesapeake, VA, p. A740

EHASZ, James, Chief Financial Officer, Copper Queen Community Hospital, Bisbee, AZ, p. A30

EHLEBRACHT, Jeanne, Senior Vice President and Chief Financial Officer, Wyoming Medical Center, Casper, WY, p. A801

EHLER, Phyllis, Director Human Resources, Avera St. Benedict Health Center, Parkston, SD, p. A630

EHLERS, Jeffrey, Chief Financial Officer, Memorial Health, Marysville, OH, p. A544

EHLINGER, Forrest, System Chief Financial Officer, Benefis Health System, Great Falls, MT, p. A424

EHLKE, Ranae, Administrative Secretary and Coordinator Risk Management and Human Resources, Kenmare Community Hospital, Kenmare, ND, p. A524

EHLY, Ronda, R.N., Chief Nursing Officer, Mary Lanning Healthcare, Hastings, NE, p. A433

EHN, Jerry, Chief Operating Officer, Northfield Hospital And Clinics, Northfield, MN, p. A382

EHN, Nicole, M.D., Chief of Staff, Van Diest Medical Center, Webster City, IA, p. A260

EHRAT, Michael, Chief Executive Officer, Englewood Community Hospital, Englewood, FL, p. A137
Interim Chief Executive Officer, Fawcett Memorial Hospital, Port Charlotte, FL, p. A155

EHRENBERGER, David, M.D., Chief Medical Officer, Avista Adventist Hospital, Louisville, CO, p. A116

EHRICH, Laurie, Chief Communications Officer, Wayne County Hospital, Corydon, IA, p. A246

EHRLICH, Frank, M.D., Chief Medical Officer, Health Alliance Hospital - Broadway Campus, Kingston, NY, p. A486
M.D., Chief Medical Officer, Health Alliance Hospital - Mary's Avenue Campus, Kingston, NY, p. A487

EHRLICH, Susan P., M.D., Chief Executive Officer, Zuckerberg San Francisco General Hospital And Trauma Center, San Francisco, CA, p. A94

EICHER, Natasha, President and Chief Executive Officer, Parkview Dekalb Hospital, Auburn, IN, p. A223

EICHORN, Aaron, Interim Chief Financial Officer, Eskenazi Health, Indianapolis, IN, p. A231

EIDE, Tom, Chief Financial Officer, Prairie St. John's, Fargo, ND, p. A523

EIDE, Trevor, M.D., Chief Medical Officer, Frisbie Memorial Hospital, Rochester, NH, p. A451

EIG, Blair, M.D., Senior Vice President Medical Affairs, Holy Cross Hospital, Silver Spring, MD, p. A332
M.D., Vice President and Chief Medical Officer, Medical Affairs, Holy Cross Germantown Hospital, Germantown, MD, p. A329

EIKE, Gail, Chief Financial Officer, Sanford Jackson Medical Center, Jackson, MN, p. A378

EILBRACHT, Hans, Chief Information Officer, Hamilton Center, Terre Haute, IN, p. A241

EIMERS, Katy, Human Resources Officer, Syringa Hospital And Clinics, Grangeville, ID, p. A190

EIPE, Joseph, M.D., Chief Medical Officer, Pacifica Hospital Of The Valley, Sun Valley, CA, p. A100

EISCHENS, Shelby, Chief Medical Officer, Brookings Health System, Brookings, SD, p. A626

EISELE, Karla, M.D., Clinical Director, State Hospital North, Orofino, ID, p. A192

EISEN, Robert, Vice President Human Resources, Northern California Region, Queen Of The Valley Medical Center, Napa, CA, p. A80

EISENMAN, Edward, Chief Executive Officer, Sunnyview Rehabilitation Hospital, Schenectady, NY, p. A498

EISENMANN, Claudia A., President and Chief Executive Officer, Gibson General Hospital, Princeton, IN, p. A239

EISENTRAGER, Steve, President, Ohio Valley Surgical Hospital, Springfield, OH, p. A549

EISMAN, Michael, M.D., Medical Director, Schuyler Hospital, Montour Falls, NY, p. A488

EISNER, Nina W., Chief Executive Officer and Managing Director, Ridge Behavioral Health System, Lexington, KY, p. A287

EITZEN, Tamara, Chief Nursing Officer, Fairview Regional Medical Center, Fairview, OK, p. A559

EKENGREN, Francie, M.D., Chief Medical Officer, Wesley Healthcare Center, Wichita, KS, p. A279

EKEREN, Douglas R., FACHE, Interim Regional President and Chief Executive Officer, Avera Queen Of Peace Hospital, Mitchell, SD, p. A629
FACHE, Regional President and Chief Executive Officer, Administration, Avera Sacred Heart Hospital, Yankton, SD, p. A633

EKUNDAYO, Adedayo, Ph.D., Director of Nursing, Bridgepoint Hospital Capitol Hill, Washington, DC, p. A129

EL KHALILI, Nizar, M.D., Medical Director, Sycamore Springs, Lafayette, IN, p. A234

EL-DALATI, Sam, M.D., Chief Medical Officer, Mercy Regional Medical Center, Lorain, OH, p. A544

EL-MELIGI, Christi J., Chief Executive Officer, Sage Memorial Hospital, Ganado, AZ, p. A31

EL-SOLH, Ali, M.D., Interim Chief of Staff, Veterans Affairs Western New York Healthcare System-Buffalo Division, Buffalo, NY, p. A480

ELAM, Lora, R.N., Chief Nursing Officer, Wayne County Hospital, Monticello, KY, p. A290

ELAM, Moses, M.D., Physician-in-Chief, Kaiser Permanente Manteca Medical Center, Manteca, CA, p. A77

ELARBEE, Vernon, Director of Human Resources, Adventhealth North Pinellas, Tarpon Springs, FL, p. A160

ELBERT, Darlene, R.N., MS, Assistant Administrator and Chief Nursing Officer, Kossuth Regional Health Center, Algona, IA, p. A243

ELBERT, Darlene M., R.N., MS, Chief Executive Officer and Chief Nursing Officer, Kossuth Regional Health Center, Algona, IA, p. A243

ELBERT, Lee, Chief Financial Officer, Franklin General Hospital, Hampton, IA, p. A251

ELDER, Deborah, Director Human Resources, Scenic Mountain Medical Center, Big Spring, TX, p. A659

ELDIDY, Rene, M.D., Chief of Staff, Centracare - Long Prairie, Long Prairie, MN, p. A379

ELDRED, Jamie, Controller, Klickitat Valley Health, Goldendale, WA, p. A759

ELDRIDGE, Janet, Director Human Resources and Personnel, Brooks County Hospital, Quitman, GA, p. A178

ELDRIDGE, Jim, Area Financial Officer, Kaiser Permanente Sacramento Medical Center, Sacramento, CA, p. A89

ELDRIDGE, Laurie, Chief Financial Officer, Marshall Medical Center, Placerville, CA, p. A85

ELDRIDGE, Lisa, Human Resources Officer, Thomas H. Boyd Memorial Hospital, Carrollton, IL, p. A196

ELEGANT, Bruce M., FACHE, President and Chief Executive Officer, Rush Oak Park Hospital, Oak Park, IL, p. A215

ELFERT, Mike, Director Information Services, Virtua Willingboro Hospital, Willingboro, NJ, p. A466

ELGARICO, David, Chief Executive Officer, Mckenzie-Willamette Medical Center, Springfield, OR, p. A581

ELI, Bev, Chief Nursing Officer, Cox Monett Hospital, Monett, MO, p. A412

ELIAS, Jose, Director Information Technology, Fort Duncan Regional Medical Center, Eagle Pass, TX, p. A673

ELICH, Elizabeth, Chief Human Resources Officer, Piedmont Medical Center, Rock Hill, SC, p. A624

ELIOT, Jason, Vice President Human Resources, Integris Baptist Medical Center, Oklahoma City, OK, p. A564

ELKINGTON, Bruce, Regional Chief Information Officer, St. Clare Hospital, Lakewood, WA, p. A760

ELKINGTON, Mark, M.D., Chief Medical Officer, Willow Crest Hospital, Miami, OK, p. A562

ELKINS, Carl, Director Information Technology, Adventhealth Rollins Brook, Lampasas, TX, p. A694

ELKINS, James N., FACHE, Director, Texas Center For Infectious Disease, San Antonio, TX, p. A713

ELKINS, Kelly, President and Chief Executive Officer, Ascension Columbia St. Mary's Hospital Ozaukee, Mequon, WI, p. A790
President and Chief Executive Officer, Ascension Columbia St. Mary's Milwaukee Hospital, Milwaukee, WI, p. A790

ELKINS, Wendy, Director Operations, Dundy County Hospital, Benkelman, NE, p. A430

ELLARD, Samuel, Chief Executive Officer, Riverland Medical Center, Ferriday, LA, p. A301

ELLEDGE, David, Controller, Select Specialty Hospital-North Knoxville, Powell, TN, p. A648

ELLEN, Jonathan, M.D., Medical Director, Encompass Health Rehabilitation Hospital Of Memphis, Memphis, TN, p. A644

ELLENBURG, Cynthia, Director Health Information Services, Prisma Health Baptist Easley Hospital, Easley, SC, p. A619

ELLER, Bill, Director Information Technology, El Camp. Memorial Hospital, El Campo, TX, p. A674

ELLER, Steven, Chief Human Resources Officer, Memorial Hospital of South Bend, South Bend, IN, p. A240
Vice President Human Resources, Elkhart General Hospital, Elkhart, IN, p. A227

ELLER, Troy, Chief Financial Officer, Guthrie County Hospital, Guthrie Center, IA, p. A250

ELLERSON, Thomas, Chief Information Officer, Our Lady Of Lourdes Memorial Hospital, Inc., Binghamton, NY, p. A476

ELLERT, William, M.D., Medical Director, Carondelet St. Mary's Hospital, Tucson, AZ, p. A40

ELLINGTON, Christopher, Executive Vice President and Chief Financial Officer, University Of North Carolina Hospitals, Chapel Hill, NC, p. A506

ELLIOTT, Amy, M.D., Director Medical Affairs, District One Hospital, Faribault, MN, p. A376

ELLIOTT, Barb, Chief Financial Officer, Fairbanks, Indianapolis, IN, p. A232
Interim President and Chief Executive Officer, Fairbanks, Indianapolis, IN, p. A232

ELLIOTT, Jim, Director Human Resources, Bryce Hospital, Tuscaloosa, AL, p. A25
Director Human Resources, Mary S Harper Geriatric Psychiatry Center, Tuscaloosa, AL, p. A25

ELLIOTT, Kimberly, Chief Nursing Officer, Holy Cross Germantown Hospital, Germantown, MD, p. A329

ELLIOTT, Laura, Director Human Resources, Northeastern Nevada Regional Hospital, Elko, NV, p. A441

ELLIOTT, Lee Ann, R.N., Director of Nursing, Select Rehabilitation Hospital Of Denton, Denton, TX, p. A672

ELLIOTT, Michael, M.D., Chief Medical Officer and Senior Vice President of Medical Affairs, Avera Mckennan Hospital And University Health Center, Sioux Falls, SD, p. A631
Acting Chief Executive Officer, Centra Lynchburg General Hospital, Lynchburg, VA, p. A745
Controller, Indianhead Medical Center, Shell Lake, WI, p. A796

ELLIOTT, Peyton, Chief Executive Officer, Hca Houston Healthcare Medical Center, Houston, TX, p. A685
Chief Executive Officer, Plaza Specialty Hospital, Houston, TX, p. A688

ELLIOTT, R, Vice President Human Resources, Charlotte Hungerford Hospital, Torrington, CT, p. A125

ELLIOTT, Randi, MSN, Chief Nursing Officer, Baylor Scott & White Medical Center—Frisco, Frisco, TX, p. A680

ELLIOTT, Rhonda, Director Information Technology and Meaningful Use, Person Memorial Hospital, Roxboro, NC, p. A517

ELLIOTT, Robin, Personnel Officer, Community Memorial Hospital, Sumner, IA, p. A259

ELLIOTT, Shane, Associate Director Administration, Veterans Affairs Loma Linda Healthcare System, Loma Linda, CA, p. A72

ELLIOTT, Thomas, President, Mercy Rehabilitation Hospital Oklahoma City, Oklahoma City, OK, p. A564

ELLIOTT, Wendy C., President and Chief Executive Officer, Southeastern Ohio Regional Medical Center, Cambridge, OH, p. A530

ELLIS, Amanda, Chief Financial Officer, Barbourville Arh Hospital, Barbourville, KY, p. A280

ELLIS, Angela, R.N., Chief Nursing Officer, Terre Haute Regional Hospital, Terre Haute, IN, p. A241

ELLIS, Bob, Director of Nursing, D. W. Mcmillan Memorial Hospital, Brewton, AL, p. A16

ELLIS, Cynthia, Chief Nursing Officer, Merit Health Rankin, Brandon, MS, p. A390

ELLIS, Deb, Director Human Resource, Blackwell Regional Hospital, Blackwell, OK, p. A556
Director Human Resources, Stillwater Medical Perry, Perry, OK, p. A567

ELLIS, Kristin, Controller, Munson Healthcare Cadillac Hospital, Cadillac, MI, p. A350

ELLIS, Lisa, Chief Operating Officer, Alliancehealth Midwest, Midwest City, OK, p. A562

ELLIS, Mark, Director Information Technology, Lakeview Hospital, Bountiful, UT, p. A727

ELLIS, Michael, M.D., Chief Medical Officer, The University Of Toledo Medical Center, Toledo, OH, p. A551

ELLIS, Michael J., FACHE, Chief Executive Officer, Hill Regional Hospital, Hillsboro, TX, p. A684

ELLIS, Michelle, Director Human Resources, Whitman Hospital And Medical Center, Colfax, WA, p. A757

ELLIS, Mike, Chief Financial Officer, Lake Chelan Community Hospital And Clinics, Chelan, WA, p. A756
Chief Financial Officer, Mendocino Coast District Hospital, Fort Bragg, CA, p. A64

ELLIS, Nichole, Chief Medical Officer, Hillsdale Hospital, Hillsdale, MI, p. A357

ELLIS, Paula, Administrator, Saint John Hospital, Leavenworth, KS, p. A269

ELLIS, Richard, Chief Executive Officer, Tennova Healthcare-Harton, Tullahoma, TN, p. A650

ELLIS, Scott, D.O., Chief Medical Officer, Memorial Regional Health, Craig, CO, p. A110

ELLIS, Susan, R.N., MSN, Community Chief Nursing Officer, Highlands Arh Regional Medical Center, Prestonsburg, KY, p. A292

ELLIS, Tammy, FACHE, R.N., Vice President Patient Services, Texas Health Huguley Hospital Fort Worth South, Burleson, TX, p. A662

ELLIS, Thomas, Vice President Human Resources, Mt. Washington Pediatric Hospital, Baltimore, MD, p. A326

ELLIS, Wendel, D.O., Chief Medical Staff, Greeley County Health Services, Tribune, KS, p. A278

ELLISON, Darcy, R.N., MSN, Senior Vice President, Chief Nursing Officer and Inpatient Flow, Ascension St. Vincent Evansville, Evansville, IN, p. A227

ELLISON, Keith, Chief Nursing Officer, Big Bend Regional Medical Center, Alpine, TX, p. A652

ELLISON, Mike, Information Systems Lead, Summersville Regional Medical Center, Summersville, WV, p. A777

ELLISON, Patricia, Chief Financial Officer, Wellstone Regional Hospital, Jeffersonville, IN, p. A233

ELLNER, Scott J., D.O., M.P.H., FACS, Chief Executive Officer, Billings Clinic, Billings, MT, p. A421

ELLSWORTH, Anthon, Director Information Technology, Mt. Graham Regional Medical Center, Safford, AZ, p. A37

ELMORE, Kevin, Chief Information Officer, Covenant Hospital-Levelland, Levelland, TX, p. A695

ELMORE, Nadine, Chief Executive Officer, Dahl Memorial Healthcare Association, Ekalaka, MT, p. A423

ELMOUCHI, Daryl, M.D., President, Spectrum Health West Michigan, Spectrum Health - Butterworth Hospital, Grand Rapids, MI, p. A356

ELNAHAL, Shereef, M.D., President and Chief Executive Officer, University Hospital, Newark, NJ, p. A460

ELROD, Emily, R.N., Chief Nursing Officer, Saint Thomas Dekalb Hospital, Smithville, TN, p. A649
R.N., Director of Nursing, Saint Thomas Stones River Hospital, Woodbury, TN, p. A650

ELROD, James K., LFACHE, Chief Executive Officer, Willis-Knighton Medical Center, Shreveport, LA, p. A315

ELSBERRY, Kevin, Senior Vice President Human Resources, Mercyone Des Moines Medical Center, Des Moines, IA, p. A248

ELSBREE, Heidi, Vice President People and Culture, Javon Bea Hospital-Rockton, Rockford, IL, p. A218

ELSE, Ryan, M.D., Vice President Medical Affairs, Mercy Hospital, Coon Rapids, MN, p. A374

ELSESSER, William, Administrator, Noland Hospital Montgomery, Montgomery, AL, p. A22

ELSWICK, Beth, Administrative Assistant, Summers County Arh Hospital, Hinton, WV, p. A772

ELWELL, Richard, Senior Vice President and Chief Financial Officer, Elliot Hospital, Manchester, NH, p. A450

ELWELL, Russell, M.D., Medical Director, Westfield Memorial Hospital, Westfield, NY, p. A502

ELY, Thomas, D.O., Chief Medical Officer, Tennova Healthcare-Clarksville, Clarksville, TN, p. A636

EMAMGHORAISHI, Anna, Human Resources, Inspire Specialty Hospital, Midwest City, OK, p. A562

EMANUEL, Kate, Director Human Resources, Clarke County Hospital, Osceola, IA, p. A256

EMANUEL, Sandra, Chief Executive Officer, Peak Behavioral Health Services, Santa Teresa, NM, p. A472

EMBREE, Steve, Chief Financial Officer, Up Health System-Marquette, Marquette, MI, p. A361

EMBREY, Jeffrey, M.D., Chief Medical Officer, Baylor Scott & White Medical Center-Irving, Irving, TX, p. A690

EMBREY, Richard, M.D., Chief Medical Officer, Augusta Health, Fishersville, VA, p. A742

EMBURY, Stuart, M.D., Chief Medical Officer, Phelp. Memorial Health Center, Holdrege, NE, p. A433

EMDUR, Larry, D.O., Chief Medical Officer, Alvarado Hospital Medical Center, San Diego, CA, p. A91

EMEOTT, Sandra, R.N., Chief Nursing Officer, Northwest Medical Center, Margate, FL, p. A145

EMERSON, Leah, Director of Nursing, St. Luke Community Healthcare, Ronan, MT, p. A427

EMERSON, Sherri, Chief Operating Officer, Texas Health Heart & Vascular Hospital Arlington, Arlington, TX, p. A654

EMERSON, Sherri Leigh., Chief Executive Officer, Texas Health Heart & Vascular Hospital Arlington, Arlington, TX, p. A654

EMERY, Andrew, Chief Executive Officer, Woodland Heights Medical Center, Lufkin, TX, p. A698

EMERY SHEA, Emily, Interim Chief Financial Officer, Geary Community Hospital, Junction City, KS, p. A267

EMGE, Joann, Chief Executive Officer, Sparta Community Hospital, Sparta, IL, p. A220

EMIG, Laura, Director Marketing Operations, Encompass Health Rehabilitation Hospital Of York, York, PA, p. A612

EMMINGER, Dianne, Vice President Information Services, Acmh Hospital, Kittanning, PA, p. A593

EMPEDRAD, Globert, Chief Clinical Officer, Curahealth Tucson, Tucson, AZ, p. A40

EMPEY, Dennis, Chief Financial Officer, Kenmare Community Hospital, Kenmare, ND, p. A524
Chief Financial Officer, Trinity Health, Minot, ND, p. A525

EMPEY, Nathan, Chief Finanial Officer, Utah Valley Hospital, Provo, UT, p. A731

ENCAPERA, Kimberly, M.D., Medical Director, Rehabilitation Hospital Of Southern New Mexico, Las Cruces, NM, p. A470

ENCE, Michael, Computer Specialist, Sanpete Valley Hospital, Mount Pleasant, UT, p. A729

ENCKE, Faye, Director Information Management, Encompass Health Rehabilitation Hospital Of Richmond, Richmond, VA, p. A750

ENDEN, Jay, M.D., Medical Director, Southside Hospital, Bay Shore, NY, p. A475

ENDERS, Robert A. Jr, President and Chief Executive Officer, Unc Lenoir Healthcare, Kinston, NC, p. A513

ENDERSON, Dan, Chief Operating Officer and Chief Financial Officer, Swift County - Benson Health Services, Benson, MN, p. A372

   Co-Chief Executive Officer, Swift County - Benson Health Services, Benson, MN, p. A372

ENDOM, Beth, R.N., MSN, Vice President and Chief Nursing Officer, South Central Regional Medical Center, Laurel, MS, p. A395

ENDSLEY, Scott, Chief Financial Officer, Fisher-Titus Medical Center, Norwalk, OH, p. A546

ENG, Bland, Chief Executive Officer, Brandon Regional Hospital, Brandon, FL, p. A133

ENG, Jeffrey, M.D., Medical Director, Encompass Health Rehabilitation Hospital Of Montgomery, Montgomery, AL, p. A22

ENGBERS, Jon, M.D., President, Hegg Health Center Avera, Rock Valley, IA, p. A257

ENGBRECHT, Chad, Chief Financial Officer, Alvarado Parkway Institute Behavioral Health System, La Mesa, CA, p. A70

ENGEL, David, Chief Executive Officer and Administrator, Southeast Colorado Hospital District, Springfield, CO, p. A118

ENGELKE, Brian, Chief Financial Officer, Community Hospital Of Staunton, Staunton, IL, p. A221

ENGESSER, Edward, Chief Financial Officer and Chief Information Officer, Barlow Respiratory Hospital, Los Angeles, CA, p. A73

ENGFEHR, Tricia, Chief Human Resources, Selby General Hospital, Marietta, OH, p. A544

ENGLAND, Dave, Director Human Resources, Lakeland Behavioral Health System, Springfield, MO, p. A418

ENGLAND, Leslie, Chief of Staff, Merit Health Natchez, Natchez, MS, p. A397

ENGLAND, Mary Ann, Chief Nurse Executive, Wilcox Medical Center, Lihue, HI, p. A186

ENGLAND, Richard, Chief Financial Officer, Palo Verde Behavioral Health, Tucson, AZ, p. A40

ENGLAND, Teresa, R.N., Ph.D., Nurse Executive, Salem Veterans Affairs Medical Center, Salem, VA, p. A751

ENGLE, Dana E., Chief Executive Officer, Madison Health, London, OH, p. A543

ENGLE, Lisa, Director Information Technology, Texoma Medical Center, Denison, TX, p. A671

ENGLE, Sharon, Director Clinical Services, Noland Hospital Birmingham, Birmingham, AL, p. A15

ENGLE-RAMIREZ, Jeanette, Chief Executive Officer, Menlo Park Surgical Hospital, Menlo Park, CA, p. A77

ENGLEHART, Jay, M.D., Medical Director, Southeast Missouri Mental Health Center, Farmington, MO, p. A406

ENGLERTH, LaDonna, Administrator and Chief Executive Officer, East Carroll Parish Hospital, Lake Providence, LA, p. A307

ENGLISH, Anne, Director Human Resources, Uhs Chenango Memorial Hospital, Norwich, NY, p. A493

ENGLISH, Brett, Chief Financial Officer, Spartanburg Medical Center - Mary Black, Spartanburg, SC, p. A624

ENGLISH, Dennis, M.D., Vice President Medical Affairs, Upmc Magee-Womens Hospital, Pittsburgh, PA, p. A604

ENGLISH, Jeff, President, St. Mary's Sacred Heart Hospital, Lavonia, GA, p. A175

   Vice President Human Resources, St. Mary's Health Care System, Athens, GA, p. A164

ENGLISH, Julene, Director Human Resources, Kentfield Hospital, Kentfield, CA, p. A69

ENGLISH, Kathy, R.N., MSN, Executive Vice President and Chief Nursing Officer, Children's Hospital And Medical Center, Omaha, NE, p. A437

   R.N., MSN, Executive Vice President and Chief Operating Officer, Children's Hospital And Medical Center, Omaha, NE, p. A437

ENGLISH, Laurie, Senior Vice President and Chief Human Resource Officer, Excela Latrobe Area Hospital, Latrobe, PA, p. A594

ENGSTROM, Chad, Director Human Resources, Westfields Hospital And Clinic, New Richmond, WI, p. A792

ENGSTROM, Frederick, M.D., Chief Medical Officer, Brattleboro Retreat, Brattleboro, VT, p. A735

ENJADY, Rainey, Administrative Officer, Mescalero Public Health Service Indian Hospital, Mescalero, NM, p. A471

ENNEN, Mark, Director of Finance, Hshs Holy Family Hospital In Greenville, Greenville, IL, p. A206

ENNIS, Debra, Vice President and Chief Nursing Officer, Texas Health Harris Methodist Hospital Southlake, Southlake, TX, p. A716

ENNIS, Virgil, Chief Information Officer, Helen Hayes Hospital, West Haverstraw, NY, p. A502

ENOCHS, Darren, Director Human Resources, Kp. Promise Hospital Of Overland Park, Overland Park, KS, p. A274

ENOKA, Christina, Director Human Resources and Risk Management, Sutter Health Kahi Mohala, Ewa Beach, HI, p. A184

ENRICO-SIMON, Agnes, M.D., President Medical Staff, Pleasant Valley Hospital, Point Pleasant, WV, p. A776

ENRIQUEZ, Michael, Chief Executive Officer, Oss Health, York, PA, p. A612

ENSEY, Jeremy, Chief Executive Officer, St. Luke Hospital And Living Center, Marion, KS, p. A270

ENSLEY, Terrasina, Director Human Resources, Fannin Regional Hospital, Blue Ridge, GA, p. A167

ENSMINGER, Jennifer, Chief Operating Officer, College Medical Center, Long Beach, CA, p. A72

ENSRUDE, Layne, Chief Financial Officer, First Care Health Center, Park River, ND, p. A525

ENTIN, Ari, Chief Information Officer, Natividad Medical Center, Salinas, CA, p. A90

ENTLER, Paul, D.O., Medical Director, Sparrow Specialty Hospital, Lansing, MI, p. A360

ENTWISTLE, David, President and Chief Executive Officer, Stanford Health Care, Palo Alto, CA, p. A84

ENTZMINGER, Julie, Manager Human Resources, Chi Oakes Hospital, Oakes, ND, p. A525

EOLOFF, Eric J., President, Mercy Hospital Washington, Washington, MO, p. A420

EPPERSON, Elysia, Director Human Resources, Ut Health Jacksonville, Jacksonville, TX, p. A691

EPPERSON, Jeff, Chief Financial Officer, Millwood Hospital, Arlington, TX, p. A653

EPPERSON, Joel, M.D., Chief of Staff, Arkansas Methodist Medical Center, Paragould, AR, p. A42

EPPLER, Todd, FACHE, Chief Executive Officer, De Soto Regional Health System, Mansfield, LA, p. A308

EPPLEY, Colette, Chief Human Resource Officer, Dixie Regional Medical Center, Saint George, UT, p. A732

EPPS, Donna, Vice President and Chief Human Resources Officer, Lawrence + Memorial Hospital, New London, CT, p. A124

   Vice President, Chief Human Resource Officer, Westerly Hospital, Westerly, RI, p. A614

EPPS, Jerry, M.D., Senior Vice President and Chief Medical Officer, University Of Tennessee Medical Center, Knoxville, TN, p. A641

EPPS, Michelle, MSN, R.N., Chief Nursing Officer, Stonesprings Hospital Center, Dulles, VA, p. A741

EPSTEIN, Michael, M.D., Senior Vice President Medical Affairs, Johns Hopkins All Children's Hospital, Saint Petersburg, FL, p. A156

ERDMAN, Beth, Chief Financial Officer, Unitypoint Health Meriter, Madison, WI, p. A788

ERDMAN, Donja, Chief Financial Officer, Shoshone Medical Center, Kellogg, ID, p. A191

ERDMAN, John, M.D., Chief of Staff, Chi Memorial Hospital - Georgia, Fort Oglethorpe, GA, p. A173

ERDMANN, Michael, M.D., Chief of Staff, Clement J. Zablocki Veterans Affairs Medical Center, Milwaukee, WI, p. A791

ERDOS, Joseph, M.D., Chief Information Officer, Veterans Affairs Connecticut Healthcare System, West Haven, CT, p. A126

ERDRICH, Louis P., Acting Chief Executive Officer, U. S. Public Health Service Indian Hospital, Cass Lake, MN, p. A374

EREMAN, Melissa, R.N., Chief Nursing Officer, Coleman County Medical Center, Coleman, TX, p. A664

ERGLE, Jeanine, Chief Financial Officer, Bay Pines Veterans Affairs Healthcare System, Bay Pines, FL, p. A131

ERICKSON, Ashley M., Chief Executive Officer, Sanford Aberdeen Medical Center, Aberdeen, SD, p. A626

ERICKSON, Brent, Administrator, Wright Patterson Medical Center, Wright, OH, p. A553

ERICKSON, Doug, Chief Financial Officer, Prague Community Hospital, Prague, OK, p. A567

ERICKSON, Jake, Chief Executive Officer, Bingham Memorial Hospital, Blackfoot, ID, p. A188

ERICKSON, Karyn, Director Human Resources, Delta Specialty Hospital, Memphis, TN, p. A644

ERICKSON, Laura, R.N., Chief Nursing Officer, Pondera Medical Center, Conrad, MT, p. A422

ERICKSON, Nancy, Administrator Information Systems, Kossuth Regional Health Center, Algona, IA, p. A243

   Human Resource Director, Southern Inyo Healthcare District, Lone Pine, CA, p. A72

ERICKSON, Robert J., President and Chief Executive Officer, Unitypoint Health - Trinity Bettendorf, Bettendorf, IA, p. A244

   President and Chief Executive Officer, Unitypoint Health - Trinity Muscatine, Muscatine, IA, p. A254

   President and Chief Executive Officer, Unitypoint Health - Trinity Rock Island, Rock Island, IL, p. A218

ERICKSON, Sue, President and Chief Executive Officer, Unitypoint Health Meriter, Madison, WI, p. A788

ERICKSON, Vonnie, Human Resource Manager, Ccm Health, Montevideo, MN, p. A381

ERICSON, Allen, Chief Operating Officer, Community Hospital Division and President, St. Joseph's Hospital, Froedtert Menomonee Falls Hospital, Menomonee Falls, WI, p. A789

   President, Froedtert West Bend Hospital, West Bend, WI, p. A799

ERICSON, Bob, Chief Financial Officer, Hemphill County Hospital, Canadian, TX, p. A662

ERKEN, Carole, Human Resources Leader, Kaiser Permanente Panorama City Medical Center, Panorama City, CA, p. A84

ERLING, Brian, M.D., Chief Executive Officer, Penrose-St. Francis Health Services, Colorado Springs, CO, p. A109

   M.D., Group Chief Medical Officer, St. Anthony Hospital, Lakewood, CO, p. A115

ERNST, William E., Chief Executive Officer, Allegiance Behavioral Health Center Of Plainview, Plainview, TX, p. A706

ERTEL, Matthew, Chief Financial Officer, Gibson Area Hospital And Health Services, Gibson City, IL, p. A206

ERUKHIMOU, Jeffrey, M.D., Medical Director, Curahealth Heritage Valley, Beaver, PA, p. A584

ERVIN, Joan, Administrator, Mcleod Health Dillon, Dillon, SC, p. A619

ERVIN, Paul, Chief Financial Officer, Valley Behavioral Health System, Barling, AR, p. A42

ERVIN, Richard, Chief Financial Officer, Hca Houston Healthcare Tomball, Tomball, TX, p. A721

ERVIN, Samuel Chief Financial Officer, Mcleod Regional Medical Center, Florence, SC, p. A619

   Senior Vice President and Chief Financial Officer, Mcleod Health Dillon, Dillon, SC, p. A619

ERVING-MENGEL, Tammi, R.N., MSN, Vice President, Chief Nursing Officer, High Point Medical Center, High Point, NC, p. A512

ERWAY, Robert, Director for Administration, Bronx Psychiatric Center, Bronx, NY, p. A476

ERWIN, Connie, Manager, Samaritan Lebanon Community Hospital, Lebanon, OR, p. A577

ESCARDA, Ron, Interim Chief Executive Officer, Fairfax Behavioral Health, Kirkland, WA, p. A759

ESCHENBRENNER, Wade, Chief Financial Officer, Lexington Regional Health Center, Lexington, NE, p. A434

ESCOBAR, Carlos R., FACHE, Director, Veterans Affairs Caribbean Healthcare System, San Juan, PR, p. A811

ESHLEMAN, James, D.O., President Medical Staff, Stephens Memorial Hospital, Norway, ME, p. A321

ESKER, Jerry, President and Chief Executive Officer, Sarah Bush Lincoln Health Center, Mattoon, IL, p. A211

ESLAVA, Lee, Chief Medical Officer, South Baldwin Regional Medical Center, Foley, AL, p. A18

ESPARZA, Becky, Human Resources, Crane Memorial Hospital, Crane, TX, p. A666

ESPARZA, Caroline, R.N., Senior Vice President, Chief Operating Officer and Chief Nurse Officer, Adventist Health Simi Valley, Simi Valley, CA, p. A98

   R.N., Sr. VP, COO & CNO, Adventist Health Simi Valley, Simi Valley, CA, p. A98

ESPELAND, Darryl, D.O., Chief Medical Staff, Fallon Medical Complex, Baker, MT, p. A421

   D.O., Medical Director, Dahl Memorial Healthcare Association, Ekalaka, MT, p. A423

ESPELAND, David, Chief Executive Officer, Fallon Medical Complex, Baker, MT, p. A421

ESPINA, Francisco, Director Finance, Hospital Pavia-Santurce, San Juan, PR, p. A810

ESPINOZA, Judy, Chief Human Resources Officer, Ascension Via Christi St. Francis, Mulvane, KS, p. A271

ESPOSITO, Mary, Assistant Executive Director, Devereux Advanced Behavioral Health Georgia, Kennesaw, GA, p. A174

ESPOSITO, Pamela, Director Administration, Buffalo Psychiatric Center, Buffalo, NY, p. A479

ESPY, Christine, Division Director, Mid-Columbia Medical Center, The Dalles, OR, p. A582

ESROCK, Brett A., FACHE, Chief Executive Officer, Health First Holmes Regional Medical Center, Melbourne, FL, p. A145

   FACHE, President, Health First Cap. Canaveral Hospital, Cocoa Beach, FL, p. A134

   FACHE, President, Health First Palm Bay Hospital, Palm Bay, FL, p. A152

   FACHE, President, Health First Viera Hospital, Melbourne, FL, p. A145

ESSELMAN, Charlotte, Director Finance, Marshfield Medical Center - Weston, Weston, WI, p. A799

ESSMYER, Dale, M.D., Chief of Staff, Sullivan County Memorial Hospital, Milan, MO, p. A412

ESTAY, Mike, Chief Financial Officer, Hood Memorial Hospital, Amite, LA, p. A296

ESTES, Benton, Materials Management, Baptist Medical Center Yazoo, Yazoo City, MS, p. A401

ESTES, Mary, Director Information Systems, St. Luke's Des Peres Hospital, Saint Louis, MO, p. A417

ESTES, Stephen A., Chief Executive Officer, Rockcastle Regional Hospital And Respiratory Care Center, Mount Vernon, KY, p. A291

ESTEVEZ, Aurora, M.D., Chief Medical Officer, Texas Health Presbyterian Hospital Dallas, Dallas, TX, p. A670

ESTEVEZ, Mercy, Chief Executive Officer, Springbrook Hospital, Brooksville, FL, p. A133

ESTRADA, Jack, Chief Administrative Officer, Peacehealth Peace Island Medical Center, Friday Harbor, WA, p. A758

ESTRADA, Luis, Director Multifacility Information Systems, North Shore Medical Center, Miami, FL, p. A147

ESTRADA, Marina, Director Human Resources, El Paso Children's Hospital, El Paso, TX, p. A674

ETCHASON, Barbara, HR Manager, West Gables Rehabilitation Hospital, Miami, FL, p. A147

ETCITTY, Ronnye, Director Human Resources, Rehoboth Mckinley Christian Health Care Services, Gallup. NM, p. A469

ETHERIDGE, Darold, Vice President and Chief Financial Officer, Wellstar Cobb Hospital, Austell, GA, p. A166

ETHERINGTON, Rosalie, Superintendent and Chief Executive Officer, North Dakota State Hospital, Jamestown, ND, p. A524

ETHRIDGE, Sandy, Interim Chief Operating Officer, Baptist Medical Center, San Antonio, TX, p. A711

ETTER, Carl J., Chief Executive and Senior Vice President, Scripp. Memorial Hospital-Encinitas, Encinitas, CA, p. A63
    Chief Executive Officer, Scripp. Green Hospital, La Jolla, CA, p. A69
    Chief Executive Officer, Scripp. Memorial Hospital-La Jolla, La Jolla, CA, p. A70

ETTESTAD, Donita, R.N., MS, Chief Nursing Officer, Rainy Lake Medical Center, International Falls, MN, p. A378

ETTIEN, Joann, R.N., MS, Interim Chief Executive Officer, National Park Medical Center, Hot Springs, AR, p. A47

ETZEL, Glen, M.D., Chief of Staff, Castleview Hospital, Price, UT, p. A731

ETZLER, Randal, Chief Human Resources Officer, Yuma Regional Medical Center, Yuma, AZ, p. A41

EUBANKS, Bill, Senior Vice President and Chief Information Officer, University Medical Center, Lubbock, TX, p. A698

EUBANKS, Susan, Chief Executive Officer, Page Hospital, Page, AZ, p. A34

EUCLIDE, Jeff, R.N., Chief Administrative Officer, Marshfield Medical Center - Ladysmith, Ladysmith, WI, p. A787

EULIARTE, Mary Ann, R.N., Chief Nursing Officer, Memorial Hermann Rehabilitation Hospital - Katy, Katy, TX, p. A692
    R.N., Chief Operating Officer, Memorial Hermann Rehabilitation Hospital - Katy, Katy, TX, p. A692

EUSEBIO, Barbara, R.N., JD, Vice President, Chief Nurse Executive, St. Mary's Medical Center, San Francisco, CA, p. A94

EUSTACE, Scott, Director Health Information Technology, Trenton Psychiatric Hospital, Trenton, NJ, p. A464

EVANCHO, Timothy, Chief Financial Officer, Southeastern Ohio Regional Medical Center, Cambridge, OH, p. A530

EVANDER, Justin, Chief Financial Officer, Kaiser Sunnyside Medical Center, Clackamas, OR, p. A574

EVANS, Bonnie A., Chief Executive Officer, Kessler Institute For Rehabilitation, West Orange, NJ, p. A465

EVANS, Brian Esq, M.D., President and Chief Executive Officer, Sierra Nevada Memorial Hospital, Grass Valley, CA, p. A67

EVANS, Brian G., FACHE, Chief Executive Officer, Clarke County Hospital, Osceola, IA, p. A259

EVANS, Cindy, R.N., MS, Chief Nursing Officer, Legacy Good Samaritan Medical Center, Portland, OR, p. A579

EVANS, Dave, Chief Financial Officer, Community Hospital Of San Bernardino, San Bernardino, CA, p. A91

EVANS, Dawn, Manager Information Technology, Ssm Health St. Mary's Hospital - Audrain, Mexico, MO, p. A412

EVANS, Dwight, M.D., Chief of Staff, Veterans Affairs Loma Linda Healthcare System, Loma Linda, CA, p. A72

EVANS, Eric, Chief Executive Officer, Corpus Christi Medical Center, Corpus Christi, TX, p. A666

EVANS, George, Vice President and Chief Information Officer, Candler Hospital, Savannah, GA, p. A179

EVANS, Heath, President, Bay Medical Sacred Heart, Panama City, FL, p. A152

EVANS, Janice, Chief Financial Officer, John J. Madden Mental Health Center, Hines, IL, p. A208

EVANS, Jeff, Vice President Information and Technology, Hannibal Regional Hospital, Hannibal, MO, p. A407

EVANS, Jeremy, Vice President Operations, Kootenai Health, Coeur D'Alene, ID, p. A190

EVANS, Kelley, Chief Administrative Officer, Beartooth Billings Clinic, Red Lodge, MT, p. A427

EVANS, Lola, Director of Nursing, Surgeons Choice Medical Center, Southfield, MI, p. A367

EVANS, Lorrie, Director Human Resources, Laurel Oaks Behavioral Health Center, Dothan, AL, p. A17

EVANS, Melinda, Vice President Finance, Chi Saint Josep. East, Lexington, KY, p. A286
    Vice President Finance, Chi Saint Josep. Health, Lexington, KY, p. A286

EVANS, Michael, Chief Executive Officer and Deputy Director of Finance and Administration, Santa Barbara County Psychiatric Health Facility, Santa Barbara, CA, p. A97

EVANS, Rod, Chief Information Officer, Community Healthcare System, Onaga, KS, p. A273

EVANS, Ronald, M.D., Chief Medical Officer, Citizens Memorial Hospital, Bolivar, MO, p. A402

EVANS, Sam, Chief Human Resources Management, G.V. (Sonny) Montgomery Veterans Affairs Medical Center, Jackson, MS, p. A394

EVANS, Scott, PharmD, FACHE, Senior Vice President and Chief Executive Officer, Sharp Grossmont Hospital, La Mesa, CA, p. A70

EVANS, Sharon, R.N., Assistant Chief Nursing Officer, Jenkins County Medical Center, Millen, GA, p. A177
    R.N., Assistant Chief Nursing Officer, Optim Medical Center - Screven, Sylvania, GA, p. A181

EVANS, Susan, Chief Nursing Officer, Old Vineyard Behavioral Health Services, Winston, NC, p. A520

EVANS, Tim, Assistant Financial Director, Devereux Children's Behavioral Health Center, Malvern, PA, p. A596

EVANS, Timothy, Vice President and Chief Financial Officer, Self Regional Healthcare, Greenwood, SC, p. A621

EVANS-HARRISON, Martina, R.N., MSN, Chief Nurse Executive, Methodist Hospital Of Sacramento, Sacramento, CA, p. A89

EVE, John, Vice President Human Resources and Education, Wilson Memorial Hospital, Sidney, OH, p. A549

EVELIUS, Karen, Director Human Resources, Medstar Harbor Hospital, Baltimore, MD, p. A325

EVELYN, David, M.D., Vice President Medical Affairs, Cayuga Medical Center At Ithaca, Ithaca, NY, p. A485

EVENS, James, Executive Director, Human Resources and General Services, Upmc Cole, Coudersport, PA, p. A587

EVENSON, Laura, Chief Nursing Officer, Mayo Clinic Health System In Mankato, Mankato, MN, p. A379

EVENSON, Margie, Manager Human Resources, Osceola Medical Center, Osceola, WI, p. A793

EVERDING, Dawn, President and Chief Financial Officer, Community Memorial Hospital, Sumner, IA, p. A259

EVERETT, Curren, Chief Executive Officer, Fulton County Hospital, Salem, AR, p. A52

EVERETT, John, Chief Financial Officer, Cogdell Memorial Hospital, Snyder, TX, p. A716

EVERETT, Leianne, Chief Executive Officer, Arbor Health, Morton Hospital, Morton, WA, p. A760

EVERETT, Neil, Vice President Human Resources, Uh Portage Medical Center, Ravenna, OH, p. A548

EVERHART, Martin, Senior Vice President Human Resources, Robert Wood Johnson University Hospital, New Brunswick, NJ, p. A459

EVERLY, Nanette, Manager Human Resources and Administrative Assistant, Jefferson County Health Center, Fairfield, IA, p. A250

EVERS, Andrea, Director Information Technology, Haxtun Hospital District, Haxtun, CO, p. A114

EVERS-MANLY, Shirley, Chief Nursing Officer, Howard University Hospital, Washington, DC, p. A129

EVERSOLE, Matt, Regional Vice President Information Services, Mercy Health - Anderson Hospital, Cincinnati, OH, p. A532

EVERT, Barbara, M.D., Vice President Medical Affairs, Ohiohealth Dublin Methodist Hospital, Dublin, OH, p. A539
    M.D., Vice President Medical Affairs, Ohiohealth Grady Memorial Hospital, Delaware, OH, p. A539

EVINS, Starling, M.D., Chief of Staff, Williamson Medical Center, Franklin, TN, p. A638

EVISCHI, Deland, Regional Chief Financial Officer, Southern Illinois, Ssm Health Good Samaritan Hospital, Mount Vernon, IL, p. A213

EVOLGA, Nancy, Director Human Resources, Adventhealth New Smyrna Beach, New Smyrna Beach, FL, p. A149

EWALD, Ronald, Chief Financial Officer, Inova Fairfax Hospital, Falls Church, VA, p. A741

EWELL, Dorene, Director of Human Resources and Development, Harrisburg Medical Center, Harrisburg, IL, p. A206

EWELL, Sandy, Chief Nursing Officer, Timpanogos Regional Hospital, Orem, UT, p. A730

EWING, Catherine, M.D., Chief Nursing Officer, Baylor Scott & White Institute For Rehabilitation-Fort Worth, Fort Worth, TX, p. A678

EWING, Chandler, Chief Executive Officer, Select Specialty Hospital-Jackson, Jackson, MS, p. A395

EWING, Corey, Chief Executive Officer, Gadsden Regional Medical Center, Gadsden, AL, p. A19

EWING, Hella, Vice President Patient Care Services and Chief Nursing Officer, East Tennessee Children's Hospital, Knoxville, TN, p. A641

EWING, Steven, Chief Financial Officer, San Angelo Community Medical Center, San Angelo, TX, p. A710

EWING, Thomas, Director Information Technology, Sentara Careplex Hospital, Hampton, VA, p. A743
    Director Information Technology, Sentara Northern Virginia Medical Center, Woodbridge, VA, p. A754

EXLINE, Michael, Chief Financial Officer, Carrus Rehabilitation Hospital, Sherman, TX, p. A715
    Chief Financial Officer, Carrus Specialty Hospital, Sherman, TX, p. A715

EYE, Jeffrey, R.N., Vice President Patient Care Services, Murray-Calloway County Hospital, Murray, KY, p. A291

EYLER, Sandra, MS, Chief Nursing Officer, Sheltering Arms Hospital South, Midlothian, VA, p. A746
    MS, Chief Nursing Officer, Sheltering Arms Rehabilitation Hospital, Mechanicsville, VA, p. A746

EZZIE, Michael, Director of Medical Education and Interim Vice President of Medical Affairs, Ohiohealth Grant Medical Center, Columbus, OH, p. A536

# F

FABER, Chris, Human Resources Analyst, Stanford Health Care - Valleycare, Pleasanton, CA, p. A85

FABER, Tammy, Director Human Resources, Hegg Health Center Avera, Rock Valley, IA, p. A257

FABIAN, Alan J., Chief Executive Officer, Lewisgale Hospital Montgomery, Blacksburg, VA, p. A739

FABIANO, Tom, Director Human Resources, Mount Auburn Hospital, Cambridge, MA, p. A338

FABIN, Peggy, Director Human Resources, Phillip. County Health Systems, Phillipsburg, KS, p. A274

FABRICK, Peter, Vice President Clinical Operations, Mountain View Hospital, Idaho Falls, ID, p. A190

FABRY, Joseph, D.O., Chief of Staff, Sutter Maternity And Surgery Center Of Santa Cruz, Santa Cruz, CA, p. A97

FACKRELL, Sherlyn, Finance Controller, Grover C. Dils Medical Center, Caliente, NV, p. A441

FACTEAU, Patrick, Chief Financial Officer, Massena Hospital, Inc., Massena, NY, p. A488

FADALE, Sean, President and Chief Executive Officer, Community Memorial Hospital, Hamilton, NY, p. A485

FADLER, Jeannie, R.N., Vice President Patient Care Services, Saint Francis Medical Center, Cap. Girardeau, MO, p. A403

FAERBER, Craig, Interim Chief Financial Officer, Altru Health System, Grand Forks, ND, p. A523

FAGAN, Erin, Manager Human Resources, George Washington University Hospital, Washington, DC, p. A129

FAGAN, Mary, MSN, R.N., Chief Nursing Officer, Rady Children's Hospital - San Diego, San Diego, CA, p. A91

FAGAN, Michael, Senior Vice President Finance, Newyork-Presbyterian Brooklyn Methodist Hospital, Brooklyn, NY, p. A478

FAGBONGBE, Eniola, M.D., Chief Medical Staff, Grove Hill Memorial Hospital, Grove Hill, AL, p. A19

FAGERBERG, Lesley, Vice President Fiscal Services, Heart Of The Rockies Regional Medical Center, Salida, CO, p. A118

FAGERHAUG, Larry, Carson Tahoe Continuing Care Hospital, Carson City, NV, p. A441

FAGERSTROM, Joel, Executive Vice President and Chief Operating Officer, St. Luke's Hospital - Miners Campus, Coaldale, PA, p. A587

FAGG, Cindy, Fiscal Officer, Battle Mountain General Hospital, Battle Mountain, NV, p. A441

FAHERTY, Jay, Chief Executive Officer, Select Specialty Hospital-Tallahassee, Tallahassee, FL, p. A158

FAHEY, Dana, Manager Management Information Systems, Santa Barbara County Psychiatric Health Facility, Santa Barbara, CA, p. A97

FAHEY, Patrick, M.D., Chief Medical Officer, Rml Specialty Hospital, Hinsdale, IL, p. A208

FAHEY, Stephen, Executive Director, Sierra Tucson, Tucson, AZ, p. A40

FAHEY, Walter, Chief Information Officer, Maimonides Medical Center, Brooklyn, NY, p. A478

FAIN, Marilyn, R.N., MSN, Chief Operating Officer, Banner Fort Collins Medical Center, Fort Collins, CO, p. A112

FAIN, Nona, Ph.D., R.N., Director of Nursing, Belmont Behavioral Hospital, Philadelphia, PA, p. A599

FAIRBANKS, Bruce, Vice President and Chief Financial Officer, Southeast Hospital, Cap. Girardeau, MO, p. A404

FAIRBANKS, Trish, R.N., Associate Vice President and Chief Nursing Officer, Linden Oaks Hospital, Naperville, IL, p. A214

FAIRCHILD, David, M.D., Chief Medical Officer, Tufts Medical Center, Boston, MA, p. A336

FAIRCLOTH, Karen, Chief Financial Officer, Memorial Hospital And Manor, Bainbridge, GA, p. A166

FAIRFAX, Tom, Director Information Systems, Bothwell Regional Health Center, Sedalia, MO, p. A418

FAIRFAX, Walter, M.D., Chief Medical Officer, Kootenai Health, Coeur D'Alene, ID, p. A190

FAIRLEY, Dawn, M.D., Chief of Staff, Putnam County Memorial Hospital, Unionville, MO, p. A420

FAIRLEY, Michelle, R.N., Chief Nursing Officer, Iroquois Memorial Hospital And Resident Home, Watseka, IL, p. A222

FALCONE, Lynn, Chief Executive Officer, Cuero Regional Hospital, Cuero, TX, p. A667

FALGOUT, Charlene, Chief Nursing Officer, St. Francis Hospital, Columbus, GA, p. A169

FALGOUT, Meagan, Chief Executive Officer, Amg Specialty Hospital-Zachary, Zachary, LA, p. A317

FALIVENA, Richard, D.O., M.P.H., Vice President and Chief Medical Officer, Saratoga Hospital, Saratoga Springs, NY, p. A497

FALK, Chelsie, Senior Director, Sanford Wheaton Medical Center, Wheaton, MN, p. A388

FALKENBERRY, Jody, Director Information Systems, Monroe County Hospital, Monroeville, AL, p. A22

FALL, J Mark., Chief Executive Officer, Henry Ford Allegiance Specialty Hospital, Jackson, MI, p. A359

FALLIS, Susan, Chief Nursing Officer, Buffalo Psychiatric Center, Buffalo, NY, p. A479

FALLON, Laurence, JD, JD, Executive Vice President, Chief Legal and Human Resources Officer, Carle Foundation Hospital, Urbana, IL, p. A221

FALO, Carol, R.N., Chief Executive Officer, Curahealth Heritage Valley, Beaver, PA, p. A584
R.N., Chief Executive Officer, Curahealth Pittsburgh, Oakdale, PA, p. A598

FALTERMAN, James, M.D., JrMedical Director, University Hospital & Clinics, Lafayette, LA, p. A306

FANALE, Linda, Chief Financial Officer, Conemaugh Miners Medical Center, Hastings, PA, p. A592

FANKHAUSER, John, M.D., Chief Executive Officer, Ventura County Medical Center, Ventura, CA, p. A103

FANNIN, Allyson, Human Resources Officer, Lasalle General Hospital, Jena, LA, p. A304

FANTANO, Gene, Chief Financial Officer, Aurora Behavioral Healthcare San Diego, San Diego, CA, p. A91

FARAH, Tony, M.D., President Medical Staff, Allegheny General Hospital, Pittsburgh, PA, p. A602

FARBER, Bobbi, M.D., Chief Medical Officer, St. Francis Hospital, Columbus, GA, p. A169

FARBER, Niceta, Chief Executive Officer, Sheridan County Health Complex, Hoxie, KS, p. A266

FARBER, Stephen, Chief Financial Officer, Kindred Hospital-New Jersey Morris County, Dover, NJ, p. A454

FARBERMAN, Daniel, Director Human Resource, Wyoming County Community Hospital, Warsaw, NY, p. A501

FARELL, Clay, Chief Operation Officer, Los Alamitos Medical Center, Los Alamitos, CA, p. A73

FARGASON, Crayton, M.D., Medical Director, Children's Of Alabama, Birmingham, AL, p. A15

FARGUSON, Jack, Director Information Technology, Tmc Bonham Hospital, Bonham, TX, p. A660

FARINA, Albert, Chief Financial Officer, Montefiore Mount Vernon, Mount Vernon, NY, p. A489

FARINA, Jonathan, Chief Information Officer, Brattleboro Memorial Hospital, Brattleboro, VT, p. A735

FARKAS, Laura, Director Human Resources, Fairview Hospital, Great Barrington, MA, p. A339

FARLEY, Chris, Chief Financial Officer, Willow Springs Center, Reno, NV, p. A446

FARMER, Kathleen, Assistant Administrator Finance and Chief Financial Officer, El Centro Regional Medical Center, El Centro, CA, p. A63

FARMER, Pat, Coordinator Human Resources and Safety Officer, Institute For Orthopaedic Surgery, Lima, OH, p. A543

FARMER, William, M.D., Chief of Staff, Evergreen Medical Center, Evergreen, AL, p. A18

FARNHAM, Diane, Acting Director Human Resources, Lallie Kemp Medical Center, Independence, LA, p. A303

FARNHAM, Krista, Chief Executive, Providence Portland Medical Center, Portland, OR, p. A579

FARO, Joan, M.D., Chief Medical Officer, Mather Hospital, Port Jefferson, NY, p. A495

FARR, Lorraine, Manager Human Resources, Georgia Regional Hospital At Atlanta, Decatur, GA, p. A171

FARR, Ronald, Chief Financial Officer, Uofl Health - Jewish Hospital, Louisville, KY, p. A288

FARR, William, M.D., Chief Medical Officer, University Hospital, Augusta, GA, p. A166

FARRAGE, Jim, M.D., Medical Director, Southern Kentucky Rehabilitation Hospital, Bowling Green, KY, p. A281

FARRAR, William, M.D., Interim Chief Executive Officer, James Cancer Hospital And Solove Research Institute, Columbus, OH, p. A536

FARRAUTO, Joseph, Director Human Resources, Eastern Niagara Hospital, Lockport, NY, p. A487

FARRELL, Brenda, Vice President Finance, Long Island Community Hospital, Patchogue, NY, p. A494

FARRELL, Coleen, Vice President Human Resources, Mid Coast Hospital, Brunswick, ME, p. A319

FARRELL, George, M.D., Chief Medical Officer, Clinch Valley Medical Center, Richlands, VA, p. A749
M.D., Chief of Staff, Wythe County Community Hospital, Wytheville, VA, p. A754

FARRELL, Roy, M.D., Chief Medical Officer, Carondelet Holy Cross Hospital, Nogales, AZ, p. A34

FARRELL, Steven, M.D., Chief Medical Officer, Forrest General Hospital, Hattiesburg, MS, p. A393

FARRELL, Terence, President, Mercy Hospital Ada, Ada, OK, p. A555

FARRELL, Teresa, Chief Human Resources Officer, Nacogdoches Medical Center, Nacogdoches, TX, p. A702

FARRELL, Timothy, Executive Director, St. Lawrence Psychiatric Center, Ogdensburg, NY, p. A493

FARRELLY, Irene, Vice President and Chief Information Officer, Brooklyn Hospital Center, Brooklyn, NY, p. A477

FARRER, Brandy, R.N., Chief Nursing Officer, Medical City Denton, Denton, TX, p. A672

FARRINGTON, Robyn, Chief Nursing Officer, Broward Health Medical Center, Fort Lauderdale, FL, p. A137

FARRIS, James R., FACHE, Chief Executive Officer, Union County Hospital, Anna, IL, p. A194

FARRIS, Jason, Chief Nursing Officer, Inspire Specialty Hospital, Midwest City, OK, p. A562

FARRISH, John, Health Information Director, University Of Mississipp. Medical Center Grenada, Grenada, MS, p. A393

FARROW, Diane, Manager Information Technology and Systems, Willamette Valley Medical Center, Mcminnville, OR, p. A577

FARROW, Rachel, Chief Operations Officer, Seiling Regional Medical Center, Seiling, OK, p. A568

FARSHAO, Nosratian, M.D., Chief Medical Staff, Memorial Hospital Of Gardena, Gardena, CA, p. A66

FARWELL, Brenda, Director Human Resources, Providence Medical Center, Kansas City, KS, p. A267
Director Human Resources, Saint John Hospital, Leavenworth, KS, p. A269

FASANO, Philip. Chief Information Officer, Kaiser Permanente Sacramento Medical Center, Sacramento, CA, p. A89

FASHINA, Olawale, M.D., Chief of Staff, Central Texas Veterans Health Care System, Temple, TX, p. A719

FAST, Gary, M.D., Medical Director, Prairie View, Newton, KS, p. A272

FASTHORSE, Lena, Supervisor Human Resource, U. S. Public Health Service Indian Hospital-Whiteriver, Whiteriver, AZ, p. A41

FATCH, Casey, Chief Executive Officer, Shasta Regional Medical Center, Redding, CA, p. A87

FATTIG, Marty, Chief Executive Officer, Nemaha County Hospital, Auburn, NE, p. A429

FATULA, Suzette, Chief Financial Officer, Oakdale Community Hospital, Oakdale, LA, p. A312
Chief Financial Officer, Winn Parish Medical Center, Winnfield, LA, p. A317

FAUBION, Matthew, M.D., Clinical Director, Kerrville State Hospital, Kerrville, TX, p. A692

FAUCETT, Michael, Chief Operating Officer, Lake City Community Hospital, Lake City, SC, p. A622

FAUCHEAUX, Patrick, R.N., Chief Nursing Officer, Ochsner Rehabilitaton Hospital West Campus, Jefferson, LA, p. A304

FAUCHER, Kimberly, M.D., Chief Medical Officer, Adventist Health Howard Memorial, Willits, CA, p. A105

FAUCHEUX, Lisa, Director Human Resources, St. James Parish Hospital, Lutcher, LA, p. A307

FAUL, Jennifer, Chief Operating Officer, Prairie St. John's, Fargo, ND, p. A523

FAULIS, Karen, Chief Executive Officer, Hi-Desert Medical Center, Joshua Tree, CA, p. A69

FAULK, Robin, Senior Vice President, Chief Human Resources Officer, Children's Mercy Hospital Kansas, Overland Park, KS, p. A273

FAULKNER, Cheryl, Director of Nursing, Mckenzie County Healthcare System, Watford City, ND, p. A526

FAULKNER, Cynthia, R.N., Chief Nursing Executive, Pender Memorial Hospital, Burgaw, NC, p. A505

FAULKNER, David, Interim Chief Executive Officer, Sierra Vista Hospital, Truth Or Consequences, NM, p. A473

FAULKNER, Kristi, Vice President Organizational Growth, United Regional Health Care System, Wichita Falls, TX, p. A725

FAULKNER, Laura, Chief Human Resource Management Service, Lexington Veterans Affairs Medical Center, Lexington, KY, p. A286

FAULKNER, Sharon, R.N., Administrator, Sage Specialty Hospital (Ltac), Denham Springs, LA, p. A301
R.N., Chief Nursing Officer, Sage Specialty Hospital (Ltac), Denham Springs, LA, p. A301

FAUMUINA, Taufete's John., Chief Executive Officer, Lyndon B. Johnson Tropical Medical Center, Pago Pago, AS, p. A805

FAUS, Doug, FACHE, Chief Executive Officer, Ivinson Memorial Hospital, Laramie, WY, p. A803

FAUST, Cheryl, Chief Nursing Officer, Edgefield County Healthcare, Edgefield, SC, p. A619

FAUTHEREE, Greg, M.D., Medical Director, The Spine Hospital Of Louisiana At The Neuromedical Center, Baton Rouge, LA, p. A298

FAVATA, Valerie, R.N., MS, Chief Nursing Officer, Oswego Hospital, Oswego, NY, p. A494

FAY, Brian, Director Information Systems, Sidney Health Center, Sidney, MT, p. A428

FAYEN, Edward, Associate Administrator Operations and Support, Washington Hospital Healthcare System, Fremont, CA, p. A65

FAYRE, Gail, M.D., Medical Director, Anna Jaques Hospital, Newburyport, MA, p. A342

FAZIO, Charles, Chief Health Officer and Medical Director Health Plan, Regions Hospital, Saint Paul, MN, p. A385

FAZIO, Corey, M.D., Chief Medical Officer, Bellevue Hospital, Bellevue, OH, p. A529

FEAGIN, Bridgett, Chief Financial Officer, Dmc - Detroit Receiving Hospital, Detroit, MI, p. A352
Chief Financial Officer, Dmc Harper University Hospital, Detroit, MI, p. A353

FEASEL, Jeff, President and Chief Executive Officer, Halifax Health Medical Center Of Daytona Beach, Daytona Beach, FL, p. A136

FEATHER, Leroy, Vice President Finance, Community Hospitals And Wellness Centers, Bryan, OH, p. A530

FEAZELL, Kayla, Chief Executive Officer, Encompass Health Rehabilitation Hospital Of Gadsden, Gadsden, AL, p. A19

FEBRY, Ricardo, M.D., Medical Director, Bliant Specialty Hospital, New Orleans, LA, p. A310

FEBUS, Steven, Chief Financial Officer, Pullman Regional Hospital, Pullman, WA, p. A762

FEDDERS, Neil, Interim Chief Executive Officer, Ochsner Rehabilitaton Hospital West Campus, Jefferson, LA, p. A304

FEDER, Diane, R.N., FACHE, Senior Vice President and Chief Operating Officer, Witham Health Services, Lebanon, IN, p. A235

FEDERICO, Skip. Director Information Systems, Avala, Covington, LA, p. A300

FEDIE, Corey J., Chief Executive Officer, East Adams Rural Healthcare, Ritzville, WA, p. A763

FEDORA, Deborah, Director Human Resources, Paoli Hospital, Paoli, PA, p. A599

FEEBACK, Kristin, Superintendent, Osawatomie State Hospital At Adair Acute Care, Osawatomie, KS, p. A273

FEELEY, Daniel, Interim Chief Financial Officer, Medstar Southern Maryland Hospital Center, Clinton, MD, p. A328

FEEMAN, Kimberly, Interim Chief Executive Officer, Pennsylvania Psychiatric Institute, Harrisburg, PA, p. A591
Senior Vice President and Chief Operating Officer, Wellspan Good Samaritan Hospital, Lebanon, PA, p. A595

FEEN, Jim, Senior Vice President and Chief Information Officer, Southcoast Hospitals Group. Fall River, MA, p. A339

FEENEY, Daniel, M.D., Medical Director, Brentwood Hospital, Shreveport, LA, p. A314

FEENEY, Sheri, Chief Financial Officer, Providence Regional Medical Center Everett, Everett, WA, p. A758

FEESS, David, CPA, President and Chief Executive Officer, Liberty Hospital, Liberty, MO, p. A411

FEGAN, Claudia, M.D., Chief Medical Officer, John H. Stroger Jr. Hospital Of Cook County, Chicago, IL, p. A199

FEGHALI, Georges, M.D., Senior Vice President Quality and Chief Medical Officer, Bethesda North Hospital, Cincinnati, OH, p. A532
    M.D., Senior Vice President Quality and Chief Medical Officer, Good Samaritan Hospital, Cincinnati, OH, p. A532

FEHR, Daniel, Chief Financial Officer, Community Memorial Healthcare, Marysville, KS, p. A270

FEHRING, Marcia, Chief Financial Officer, Horn Memorial Hospital, Ida Grove, IA, p. A251

FEICKERT, Brent, Chief Financial Officer, Unitypoint Health - Trinity Regional Medical Center, Fort Dodge, IA, p. A250

FEIDT, Leslie, Chief Information Officer, Erie County Medical Center, Buffalo, NY, p. A479

FEIGENBAUM, Avi, Chief Executive Officer, Northbrook Behavioral Health Hospital, Blackwood, NJ, p. A452

FEIKE, Jeffrey, President and Chief Administrative Officer, Fort Loudoun Medical Center, Lenoir City, TN, p. A642

FEILNER, Margaret, Director Information Services, Ssm Health St. Josep. - St. Charles, Saint Charles, MO, p. A414

FEINBERG, Daniel, M.D., Chief Medical Officer, Pennsylvania Hospital, Philadelphia, PA, p. A601

FEINBERG, Jason, M.D., Vice President Medical Affairs and Chief Medical Officer, Geneva General Hospital, Geneva, NY, p. A484
    M.D., Vice President Medical Affairs and Chief Medical Officer, Soldiers And Sailors Memorial Hospital, Penn Yan, NY, p. A495

FEINOUR, Jamie, Interim President, Novant Health Charlotte Orthopaedic Hospital, Charlotte, NC, p. A507

FEISAL, J Philip., President and Chief Executive Officer, Spartanburg Medical Center - Church Street Campus, Spartanburg, SC, p. A624

FEIST, Patricia, Manager Human Resources, Crook County Medical Services District, Sundance, WY, p. A804

FEISTRITZER, Nancye, Chief Nursing Officer, Emory University Hospital, Atlanta, GA, p. A164

FELDMAN, David, Executive Vice President and Treasurer, Circles Of Care, Melbourne, FL, p. A145

FELDMAN, David L., President and Chief Executive Officer, Circles Of Care, Melbourne, FL, p. A145

FELDMAN, Deborah A., President and Chief Executive Officer, Dayton Children's Hospital, Dayton, OH, p. A538

FELDSTEIN, Charles, M.D., Vice President Medical Affairs, St. Rose Hospital, Hayward, CA, p. A68

FELICE, Michael, Chief Financial Officer, Poplar Springs Hospital, Petersburg, VA, p. A748

FELICETTI, Jacqueline, Chief Human Resource Officer, Chester County Hospital, West Chester, PA, p. A610

FELICIANO, Jose R., Chief Executive Officer, Ryder Memorial Hospital, Humacao, PR, p. A808

FELICIANO, Myrna, M.D., Medical Director, University Pediatric Hospital, Rio Piedras, PR, p. A809

FELICIANO, Pablo, Manager Human Resources, Veterans Affairs Central Western Massachusetts Healthcare System, Leeds, MA, p. A340

FELIZ, Miriam, M.D., Medical Director, St. Catherine's Rehabilitation Hospital, North Miami, FL, p. A149

FELKNER, Joseph, Chief Financial Officer, Health First Viera Hospital, Melbourne, FL, p. A145
    Executive Vice President and Chief Financial Officer, Health First Palm Bay Hospital, Palm Bay, FL, p. A152
    Executive Vice President/Chief Financial Officer, Health First Holmes Regional Medical Center, Melbourne, FL, p. A145
    Senior Vice President Finance and Chief Financial Officer, Health First Cap. Canaveral Hospital, Cocoa Beach, FL, p. A134

FELL, David, M.D., Chief Medical Officer, Tulsa Spine And Specialty Hospital, Tulsa, OK, p. A571

FELLER, Alicia, Chief Executive Officer, Southwest Connecticut Mental Health System, Bridgeport, CT, p. A121

FELLER, Julie, Executive Director Human Resources, Grays Harbor Community Hospital, Aberdeen, WA, p. A755

FELLOWS, Rhonda, R.N., Chief Nursing Officer, Van Buren County Hospital, Keosauqua, IA, p. A252

FELLOWS, Steven, Executive Vice President and Chief Operating Officer, Goleta Valley Cottage Hospital, Santa Barbara, CA, p. A96
    Executive Vice President and Chief Operating Officer, Santa Barbara Cottage Hospital, Santa Barbara, CA, p. A97
    Executive Vice President and Chief Operating Officer, Santa Ynez Valley Cottage Hospital, Solvang, CA, p. A99

FELMLEE, Charles, Assistant Director Fiscal Services, Central Virginia Training Center, Madison Heights, VA, p. A745

FELTMAN, Steven, CPA, Chief Financial Officer, Essentia Health-Virginia, Virginia, MN, p. A387

FELTON, David, Manager Information Systems, Waldo County General Hospital, Belfast, ME, p. A319

Regional Chief Information Officer, Lincolnhealth, Damariscotta, ME, p. A320

FELTS, Dave, Chief Information Systems, Logan Regional Hospital, Logan, UT, p. A728

FELTZ, Stacy, Manager Human Resource, Hillsdale Hospital, Hillsdale, MI, p. A357

FENDER, Tamra, Chief Nursing Officer, Marias Medical Center, Shelby, MT, p. A427

FENDT, Phil, Chief Financial Officer, Memorial Community Health, Aurora, NE, p. A429

FENELLO, Michael A., Vice President Population Health, St. Luke's Magic Valley Medical Center, Twin Falls, ID, p. A193

FENER, Michael, Executive Director, Plainview Hospital, Plainview, NY, p. A495

FENN, Mark, Director Human Resources, Pulaski Memorial Hospital, Winamac, IN, p. A242

FENNELL, Charles, Vice President Information Management, St. Joseph's Hospital Health Center, Syracuse, NY, p. A499

FENNELL, Colin, M.D., Chief Medical Officer, Riverview Health, Crookston, MN, p. A374

FENNELL, David, M.D., Acting Medical Director, Atascadero State Hospital, Atascadero, CA, p. A56

FENOUGHTY, Michelle, M.D., Chief Medical Officer, Vice President of Medical Affairs, Hendricks Regional Health, Danville, IN, p. A226

FENSKE, Bill, Chief Financial Officer, Rice Memorial Hospital, Willmar, MN, p. A388

FENSTERLE, Chris, Interim Chief Executive Officer, Haywood Regional Medical Center, Clyde, NC, p. A507

FENWICK, Sandra L., M.P.H., Chief Executive Officer, Boston Children's Hospital, Boston, MA, p. A335

FEOLA, Ferd, Chief Information Officer, Lehigh Valley Hospital - Pocono, East Stroudsburg, PA, p. A589

FERCH, Wayne, President and Chief Executive Officer, Adventist Health Hanford, Hanford, CA, p. A67
    President and Chief Executive Officer, Adventist Health Reedley, Reedley, CA, p. A88
    President and Chief Executive Officer, Central Valley General Hospital, Hanford, CA, p. A68

FERDOUS, Riza, Health Services Director, Ossining Correctional Facilities Hospital, Ossining, NY, p. A494

FERGUS, Janie, Director and Chief Information Officer, Chi Saint Josep. East, Lexington, KY, p. A286
    Director and Chief Information Officer, Chi Saint Josep. Health, Lexington, KY, p. A286

FERGUS, Linda, Manager Information Technology, Allegheny Valley Hospital, Natrona Heights, PA, p. A598

FERGUSON, Allison, Director Human Resources, Avoyelles Hospital, Marksville, LA, p. A308

FERGUSON, Cathy, R.N., MSN, Vice President and Chief Nursing Officer, Hamilton Medical Center, Dalton, GA, p. A170

FERGUSON, Cheryl, Associate Administrator, Sanford Canby Medical Center, Canby, MN, p. A374

FERGUSON, Clifford, Director Information Technology and Systems, Hca Houston Healthcare Southeast, Pasadena, TX, p. A705

FERGUSON, Daniel, Chief of Staff, Ahn Grove City, Grove City, PA, p. A591

FERGUSON, Deborah, Director, Human Resources, Sentara Albemarle Medical Center, Elizabeth City, NC, p. A509
    Human Resources Consultant, Sentara Obici Hospital, Suffolk, VA, p. A752

FERGUSON, Denise, Chief Nursing Officer, Baptist Memorial Hospital-Collierville, Collierville, TN, p. A636

FERGUSON, G, Senior Vice President and Chief Human Resources Officer, New York-Presbyterian Hospital, New York, NY, p. A491

FERGUSON, Gordon B., President and Chief Executive Officer, Saint Thomas Rutherford Hospital, Murfreesboro, TN, p. A646

FERGUSON, Karen, Director Human Resources, Johnson County Healthcare Center, Buffalo, WY, p. A801

FERGUSON, Michael, Chief Financial Officer, Harbor Oaks Hospital, New Baltimore, MI, p. A362

FERGUSON, Nina, Director Human Resources, Little Colorado Medical Center, Winslow, AZ, p. A41

FERGUSON, Randy, Information Systems Manager, Fairchild Medical Center, Yreka, CA, p. A106

FERGUSON, Rick, Chief Executive Officer, Oklahoma Surgical Hospital, Tulsa, OK, p. A570

FERGUSON, Tonya, Director Human Resources, Encompass Health Rehabilitation Hospital Of Richmond, Richmond, VA, p. A750

FERGUSON, Zeta, Chief Human Resources, Atlanta Veterans Affairs Medical Center, Decatur, GA, p. A170

FERIA, Jorge, M.D., President Medical Staff, Wilma N. Vazquez Medical Center, Vega Baja, PR, p. A811

FERNANDES, Roxanne, R.N., Chief Nursing Officer, Children's Hospitals And Clinics Of Minnesota, Minneapolis, MN, p. A380

FERNANDEZ, Alexander, Chief Financial Officer, Broward Health Medical Center, Fort Lauderdale, FL, p. A137

FERNANDEZ, Arthur, Chief Financial Officer, First Hospital Panamericano, Cidra, PR, p. A807

FERNANDEZ, Benigno, M.D., Executive Medical Director, Laurel Ridge Treatment Center, San Antonio, TX, p. A712

FERNANDEZ, Darlene, Chief Financial Officer, Unm Sandoval Regional Medical Center, Inc., Rio Rancho, NM, p. A471

FERNANDEZ, Jaime, Chief Executive Officer, Kempsville Center For Behavioral Health, Norfolk, VA, p. A748

FERNANDEZ, Jean, Chief Information Officer, Beth Israel Deaconess Hospital-Milton, Milton, MA, p. A342

FERNANDEZ, John, Chief Operating Officer, United Hospital Center, Bridgeport, WV, p. A770

FERNANDEZ, John R., President and Chief Executive Officer, Massachusetts Eye And Ear, Boston, MA, p. A336

FERNANDEZ, Mark, M.D., Chief of Staff and President Medical Staff, Illinois Valley Community Hospital, Peru, IL, p. A217

FERNANDEZ, Miguel, Chief Operating Officer, Fort Lauderdale Behavioral Health Center, Oakland Park, FL, p. A149

FERNANDEZ, Richard W., President and Chief Executive Officer, Beth Israel Deaconess Hospital-Milton, Milton, MA, p. A342

FERNANDEZ, Ruben, R.N., Vice President and Chief Nursing Officer, Hackensack Meridian Health Palisades Medical Center, North Bergen, NJ, p. A460

FERNANDEZ, Tracey, Chief Financial Officer, St. Mary Medical Center, Apple Valley, CA, p. A56

FERNANDEZ DEL VALLE, Arthur, Chief Financial Officer, Cardiovascular Center Of Puerto Rico And The Caribbean, San Juan, PR, p. A809

FERNANDEZ-BRAVO, Grisel, R.N., Administrator and Chief Executive Officer, Memorial Hospital Miramar, Miramar, FL, p. A148

FERNYAK, Susan, M.D., Interim Chief Medical Officer & Chief Quality Officer, San Mateo Medical Center, San Mateo, CA, p. A96

FERRACANE, Tony, Vice President Human Resources, St. Mary Medical Center, Hobart, IN, p. A230

FERRANTI, Jeffrey, M.D., Chief Information Officer, Duke University Hospital, Durham, NC, p. A508

FERRARA, Carol, Director Human Resources, Saint Luke's South Hospital, Overland Park, KS, p. A274

FERRARO, Lisa, Senior Vice President and Chief Operating Officer, Virtua Marlton, Marlton, NJ, p. A458

FERRAROTTI, Gianna, Director Human Resources North Region, Ohiohealth Marion General Hospital, Marion, OH, p. A544

FERREIRA, Daniel, Director Management Information Systems, Hospital De La Concepcion, San German, PR, p. A809

FERRELL, Angie, Director Human Resources, Mercy Health - Anderson Hospital, Cincinnati, OH, p. A532
    Director Human Resources, Mercy Health - Clermont Hospital, Batavia, OH, p. A528

FERRELL, Eileen, MS, R.N., Vice President and Chief Nursing Officer, Medstar Georgetown University Hospital, Washington, DC, p. A129

FERRELL, Jennifer, Chief Nursing Officer, Encompass Health Rehabilitation Hospital Of Memphis, Memphis, TN, p. A644

FERRELL, Leslie, Chief Nursing Officer, Harrisburg Medical Center, Harrisburg, IL, p. A206

FERRELL, Ronald, Chief Information Officer, New Mexico Veterans Affairs Health Care System - Raymond G. Murphy Medical Center, Albuquerque, NM, p. A468

FERRELLI, John, Chief Executive Officer, Sagewest Health Care, Riverton, WY, p. A803

FERREN, Alison, Interim President and Chief Operating Officer, Abington Jefferson Health, Abington, PA, p. A583
    President, Abington-Lansdale Hospital Jefferson Health, Lansdale, PA, p. A594

FERRIS, David, Chief Nursing Officer and Vice President Patient Care Services, Claxton-Hepburn Medical Center, Ogdensburg, NY, p. A493

FERRIS, Joseph, Chief Financial Officer, Veterans Affairs Black Hills Health Care System, Fort Meade, SD, p. A628

FERRIS, Michael, M.D., Chief Medical Officer, Chi Health St Elizabeth, Lincoln, NE, p. A434

FERRIS, Norma, R.N., MS, Chief Nursing Officer, Spring Mountain Treatment Center, Las Vegas, NV, p. A444

FERRONI, Karen, M.D., Medical Director, Holyoke Medical Center, Holyoke, MA, p. A340

FERRY, Jane, M.D., Vice President Medical Affairs, Grand View Health, Sellersville, PA, p. A607

FERRY, Jennilyn, Chief Financial Officer, Heber Valley Hospital, Heber City, UT, p. A728
    Chief Financial Officer, Park City Hospital, Park City, UT, p. A730

FERTIG, Ashley, Chief Nursing Officer, Uh Conneaut Medical Center, Conneaut, OH, p. A537

Chief Nursing Officer, Uh Geneva Medical Center, Geneva, OH, p. A541

FESSER, James, Chief Nursing Officer, Palo Pinto General Hospital, Mineral Wells, TX, p. A701

FESSLER, Paula, MSN, R.N., Chief Nursing Executive, Westchester Medical Center, Valhalla, NY, p. A501

FETTO, Julie, R.N., Chief Nursing Officer, Cleveland Clinic, Medina Hospital, Medina, OH, p. A545

FEUCHT, Jason, Chief Financial Officer, Kossuth Regional Health Center, Algona, IA, p. A243

FEUNNING, Charles, M.D., Chief Medical Officer, Western Reserve Hospital, Cuyahoga Falls, OH, p. A538

FIBIYI, Abayomi, Chief Human Resources Officer, North Vista Hospital, North Las Vegas, NV, p. A445

FICCHI, Adrienne, Vice President Information Management, Philadelphia Veterans Affairs Medical Center, Philadelphia, PA, p. A601

FICICCHY, Teri, R.N., MSN, Chief Nursing Officer, Bon Secours St. Francis Health System, Greenville, SC, p. A620

FICK, Beverly, Chief Nursing Officer, Desert Regional Medical Center, Palm Springs, CA, p. A83
Chief Nursing Officer, Doctors Hospital Of Manteca, Manteca, CA, p. A77

FIDLER, Soniya, MS, President, Uchealth Yamp. Valley Medical Center, Steamboat Springs, CO, p. A118

FIELD, Clifford, M.D., Medical Director, Ka'U Hospital, Pahala, HI, p. A186

FIELD, Edward, Administrator, Loma Linda University Behavioral Medicine Center, Redlands, CA, p. A87

FIELD, Kori, Director of Nursing, Brodstone Memorial Hospital, Superior, NE, p. A440

FIELD, Laurie, Director Human Resources, Eaton Rapids Medical Center, Eaton Rapids, MI, p. A354

FIELDER, Barb, Vice President Finance, St. Josep. Mercy Chelsea, Chelsea, MI, p. A351

FIELDING, Colene, Manager Business Office, Baylor Scott & White Medical Center-Uptown, Dallas, TX, p. A667

FIELDING, Laura, Administrative Director Organizational Development, Holy Family Memorial, Manitowoc, WI, p. A788

FIELDS, Donald R., Community Chief Executive Officer, Harlan Arh Hospital, Harlan, KY, p. A284

FIELDS, Greg, Director Information Technology, Elbert Memorial Hospital, Elberton, GA, p. A172

FIERER, Jonathan, M.D., Chief of Staff, Martinsburg Veterans Affairs Medical Center, Martinsburg, WV, p. A774

FIERRO, Barbara, Director, Human Resources, St. Francis Hospital, The Heart Center, Roslyn, NY, p. A497

FIETEK, Denise, Information Technology, Rio Grande Hospital, Del Norte, CO, p. A110

FIFE, Stephen, Chief Financial Officer, Cap. Fear Valley - Bladen County Hospital, Elizabethtown, NC, p. A509
Interim Chief Executive Officer, Cap. Fear Valley - Bladen County Hospital, Elizabethtown, NC, p. A509

FIFIELD, Michael, Vice President Human Resources, Oneida Healthcare, Oneida, NY, p. A494

FIGGINS, Tara, Director Human Resources, Davis Hospital And Medical Center, Layton, UT, p. A728

FIGUEROA, Maria, Director Human Resources, Ryder Memorial Hospital, Humacao, PR, p. A808

FIGUEROA, Roseann, Director Human Resources, Doctors Hospital Of Laredo, Laredo, TX, p. A695

FIGUERORA PERALTA, Wanda, President and Chief Executive Officer, Rivervalley Behavioral Health Hospital, Owensboro, KY, p. A291

FIKE, Ruthita, Chief Executive Officer, Loma Linda University Behavioral Medicine Center, Redlands, CA, p. A87

FILER, Christine, Director Human Resources, Encompass Health Rehabilitation Hospital Of Altoona, Altoona, PA, p. A583

FILES, Ashley, Director Human Resources, Public Relations and Marketing, Winn Parish Medical Center, Winnfield, LA, p. A317

FILES, Carol, Chief Financial Officer, Advanced Diagnostics Hospital, Houston, TX, p. A684

FILIPINI, Alfred, Manager Human Resources, Ancora Psychiatric Hospital, Hammonton, NJ, p. A456

FILIPOWICZ, Thomas, M.D., Medical Director, St. Luke's Hospital - Quakertown Campus, Quakertown, PA, p. A605

FILLER, Richard, Chief Financial Officer, Ohiohealth Berger Hospital, Circleville, OH, p. A533

FILLER, Scott, Chief Executive Officer, Encompass Health Rehabilitation Hospital Of Altoona, Altoona, PA, p. A583

FILLINGIM, Jed, Acting Chief Operating Officer and Associate Director, G.V. (Sonny) Montgomery Veterans Affairs Medical Center, Jackson, MS, p. A394

FILLIPO, Brian, M.D., Chief Medical Officer, Guthrie Robert Packer Hospital, Sayre, PA, p. A606

FILLMAN, Donald, M.D., Chief Medical Officer, Guthrie County Hospital, Guthrie Center, IA, p. A250

FILOSA, Frank, Fiscal Manager, Washington Dc Veterans Affairs Medical Center, Washington, DC, p. A130

FILSON, Debbie, Chief Financial Officer, Ashland Health Center, Ashland, KS, p. A261

FINCH, John, Chief Information and Community Officer, Health Alliance Hospital - Mary's Avenue Campus, Kingston, NY, p. A487
Vice President Information Services, Health Alliance Hospital - Broadway Campus, Kingston, NY, p. A486

FINCH, Kim, Chief Nursing Officer, Kosciusko Community Hospital, Warsaw, IN, p. A242

FINCH, Robert, Director, Human Resources, Piedmont Athens Regional Medical Center, Athens, GA, p. A163

FINCH, Roy, Chief Executive Officer, Palestine Regional Medical Center-East, Palestine, TX, p. A704
Chief Operating Officer, Longview Regional Medical Center, Longview, TX, p. A697

FINCH, Sally, Chief Nursing Officer, Atoka County Medical Center, Atoka, OK, p. A556

FINCH, Steve, Chief Financial Officer, Guidance Center, Flagstaff, AZ, p. A31

FINCHER, Jodi, R.N., Administrator, St. Josep. Medical Center, Kansas City, MO, p. A409
R.N., Vice President Patient Care Services, Saint John Hospital, Leavenworth, KS, p. A269

FINDLAY, Andrew, Deputy Commander Clinical Services, Tripler Army Medical Center, Honolulu, HI, p. A185

FINDLAY, Kelly, Director of Nurses, Pawnee County Memorial Hospital And Rural Health Clinic, Pawnee City, NE, p. A438

FINDLEY, Amber, Senior Director Nursing Services and NRC Administrator, Pleasant Valley Hospital, Point Pleasant, WV, p. A776

FINE, Mathew, M.D., Chief Medical Officer, Oroville Hospital, Oroville, CA, p. A83

FINEGAN, Michael S., President, Acute Care, Samaritan Hospital - Main Campus, Troy, NY, p. A500
President, Acute Care, St. Peter's Hospital, Albany, NY, p. A474

FINELLI, Frederick, M.D., Vice President Medical Affairs, Medstar Montgomery Medical Center, Olney, MD, p. A331

FINELLI, Peter, Chief Financial Officer, Banner Payson Medical Center, Payson, AZ, p. A34

FINESTEIN, Brian, Chief Executive Officer, Saint Clare's Denville Hospital, Denville, NJ, p. A454

FINETTI, Yoany, R.N., Vice President Patient Care Services Chief Nurse Officer, Barnes-Jewish West County Hospital, Saint Louis, MO, p. A415

FINK, Renee, CPA, Chief Financial Officer, Dundy County Hospital, Benkelman, NE, p. A430

FINK, Tom, Vice President Regional Finance Officer, Fairview Range Medical Center, Hibbing, MN, p. A378

FINK, Walter, Chief Medical Officer, Multicare Good Samaritan Hospital, Puyallup. WA, p. A762

FINKEL, Naomi, Nurse Executive, Montgomery County Emergency Service, Norristown, PA, p. A598

FINKENBINER, Joy, Vice President, Operations, Ascension Genesys Hospital, Grand Blanc, MI, p. A355

FINLAYSON, Susan, MSN, R.N., Senior Vice President of MMC Operations, Mercy Medical Center, Baltimore, MD, p. A325

FINLEY, Alan, Chief Executive Officer, Dardanelle Regional Medical Center, Dardanelle, AR, p. A44
Chief Operating Officer, Conway Regional Medical Center, Conway, AR, p. A44

FINLEY, Delvecchio, Chief Executive Officer, Alameda Hospital, Alameda, CA, p. A55
Chief Executive Officer, Highland Hospital, Oakland, CA, p. A82

FINLEY, Jane, Senior Vice President & Area Manager, Kaiser Permanente San Diego Medical Center, San Diego, CA, p. A91

FINLEY, Kelly, Customer Site Executive, Mclaren Oakland, Pontiac, MI, p. A364

FINLEY, Kevan, Chief Executive Officer, Oklahoma Forensic Center, Vinita, OK, p. A571

FINLEY, Mike, M.D., Chief Medical Officer, Christus St. Michael Health System, Texarkana, TX, p. A719

FINLEY, Tommy, Chief Information Officer, Rutherford Regional Health System, Rutherfordton, NC, p. A517

FINLEY-HAZLE, Gabrielle, President and Chief Executive Officer, St. Joseph's Hospital And Medical Center, Phoenix, AZ, p. A36

FINN, Barry C., President and Chief Executive Officer, Rush-Copley Medical Center, Aurora, IL, p. A195

FINN, Patricia, Chief Executive Officer, Fulton County Health Center, Wauseon, OH, p. A552

FINNEGAN, Jay, Chief Executive Officer, St. Lucie Medical Center, Port St Lucie, FL, p. A155

FINNEGAN, Mary Jane, Chief Nursing Officer, St. Catherine Of Siena Medical Center, Smithtown, NY, p. A498

FINNERTY, Kimberley, MSN, R.N., Chief Nursing Officer, Jefferson Hospital, Jefferson Hills, PA, p. A593

FINNEY, David, R.N., Vice President Nursing, Uhs Chenango Memorial Hospital, Norwich, NY, p. A493

FINNEY, Michele, Chief Executive Officer, Desert Regional Medical Center, Palm Springs, CA, p. A83

FINSTAD, Gary, M.D., Chief of Staff, Kern Valley Healthcare District, Lake Isabella, CA, p. A70

FIORE-LOPEZ, Nicolette, R.N., Chief Nursing Officer, St. Charles Hospital, Port Jefferson, NY, p. A495

FIORET, Phil, M.D., Vice President Medical Affairs, King's Daughters Medical Center, Ashland, KY, p. A280

FIORICA, James, M.D., Chief Medical Officer, Sarasota Memorial Health Care System, Sarasota, FL, p. A157

FIRES, Wiley, Administrator, Shamrock General Hospital, Shamrock, TX, p. A715

FIRES, Wiley M., Administrator, Shamrock General Hospital, Shamrock, TX, p. A715

FIRMAN, Russell, M.D., Chief Medical Officer, Guthrie Cortland Regional Medical Center, Cortland, NY, p. A482

FIRMINGER, Barbara, Chief Administrative Officer, Verde Valley Medical Center, Cottonwood, AZ, p. A31

FIRTCH, William, M.D., Physician in Chief, Kaiser Permanente Redwood City Medical Center, Redwood City, CA, p. A87

FISCHBACH, John, Vice President of Finance, Chief Financial Officer, Lima Memorial Health System, Lima, OH, p. A543

FISCHELS, Diane, Senior Vice President and Chief Operating Officer, Mercyone North Iowa Medical Center, Mason City, IA, p. A254

FISCHER, Jason, Chief Information Officer, Pih Health Hospital - Downey, Downey, CA, p. A62
Chief Information Officer, Pih Health Hospital - Whittier, Whittier, CA, p. A105

FISCHER, JC, Director Human Resources, Mercy Regional Medical Center, Lorain, OH, p. A544

FISCHER, Lisa, Director Human Resources, Brown County Hospital, Ainsworth, NE, p. A429

FISCHER, Patricia, FACHE, R.N., President and Chief Executive Officer, Hshs St. Elizabeth's Hospital, O'Fallon, IL, p. A215

FISCHER, Rebecca, Chief Financial Officer, Nyc Health + Hospitals / Bellevue, New York, NY, p. A491

FISCHER, Robert, M.D., Medical Center Director, Mann-Grandstaff Veterans Affairs Medical Center, Spokane, WA, p. A765
M.D., Medical Director, Methodist Hospital For Surgery, Addison, TX, p. A651

FISCHER, Rochelle M., Hospital Administrator, Anoka Metro Regional Treatment Center, Anoka, MN, p. A371

FISCHER, Sandra, Director Human Resources, W. G. (Bill) Heffner Veterans Affairs Medical Center, Salisbury, NC, p. A518

FISCHER, Steven, Chief Financial Officer, Beth Israel Deaconess Medical Center, Boston, MA, p. A335

FISCHER, Tamara, Chief Nursing Officer, Okeene Municipal Hospital, Okeene, OK, p. A563

FISER, David, Vice President and Chief Information Officer, Cleveland Clinic Akron General, Akron, OH, p. A527

FISH, Carolyn, Director Human Resources, Mission Community Hospital, Panorama City, CA, p. A84

FISH, Elizabeth, Chief Information Officer, University Of Maryland Shore Medical Center At Dorchester, Cambridge, MD, p. A328
Chief Information Officer, University Of Maryland Shore Medical Center At Easton, Easton, MD, p. A329
Information Technology Site Executive, University Of Maryland Charles Regional Medical Center, La Plata, MD, p. A330
Senior Director Site Executive and Information Technology, University Of Maryland Shore Medical Center At Chestertown, Chestertown, MD, p. A328

FISH, Eric, M.D., President and Chief Executive Officer, Schneck Medical Center, Seymour, IN, p. A240
M.D., Vice President of Medical Affairs and Chief Medical Officers, Schneck Medical Center, Seymour, IN, p. A240

FISH, Francis, Vice President and Chief Financial Officer, Mile Bluff Medical Center, Mauston, WI, p. A789

FISHBAUGHER, David, Chief Medical Information, Mercyone Iowa City Medical Center, Iowa City, IA, p. A252

FISHEL, Stephanie, Vice President Patient Care Services and Chief Nursing Officer, Nathan Littauer Hospital And Nursing Home, Gloversville, NY, p. A485

FISHER, Alan, Chief Executive Officer, Mid-Valley Hospital, Omak, WA, p. A761

FISHER, Charles, Chief Executive Officer, U. S. Public Health Service Indian Hospital, Eagle Butte, SD, p. A627

FISHER, David, Director Information Systems, Upmc Lititz, Lititz, PA, p. A595
Vice President Human Resources, Signature Healthcare Brockton Hospital, Brockton, MA, p. A337

FISHER, Diane, R.N., VP, Patient Care Services, Munson Healthcare Otsego Memorial Hospital, Gaylord, MI, p. A355

FISHER, J., Chief Financial Officer, Russell Medical, Alexander City, AL, p. A13

FISHER, Jan, Executive Vice President, Chief Operating Officer and Chief Administrative Officer, Upmc Williamsport, Williamsport, PA, p. A611

FISHER, Jan E., President, Upmc Altoona, Altoona, PA, p. A584
President, Upmc Bedford, Everett, PA, p. A590

FISHER, Jeannie, Coordinator Information Technology, Webster County Memorial Hospital, Webster Springs, WV, p. A777

FISHER, Jennifer, Manager Human Resources, Henry County Hospital, Napoleon, OH, p. A546

FISHER, Jessica Marie., Chief Executive Officer, Tri Valley Health System, Cambridge, NE, p. A430

FISHER, John, M.D., Chief Medical Officer, Martin Luther King, Jr. Community Hospital, Los Angeles, CA, p. A75

FISHER, Jonathan, Chief Financial Officer, Parker Adventist Hospital, Parker, CO, p. A117

FISHER, Kerry, M.D., Medical Director, Lds Hospital, Salt Lake City, UT, p. A732

FISHER, Lynn, M.D., Chief of Staff, Rooks County Health Center, Plainville, KS, p. A274

FISHER, Mahana, M.D., Medical Director, Blue Mountain Hospital, Blanding, UT, p. A727

FISHER, Mark, Chief Human Resources Officer, Los Alamitos Medical Center, Los Alamitos, CA, p. A73

FISHER, Mathew, M.D., Medical Director, Springbrook Behavioral Health, Travelers Rest, SC, p. A625

FISHER, Michael, President and Chief Executive Officer, Cincinnati Children's Hospital Medical Center, Cincinnati, OH, p. A532

FISHER, Michael W., Director, Va Portland Healthcare System, Portland, OR, p. A580

FISHER, Richard, M.D., President and Chief Executive Officer, Fox Chase Cancer Center-American Oncologic Hospital, Philadelphia, PA, p. A600

FISHER, Robert, Chief Financial Officer, Coquille Valley Hospital, Coquille, OR, p. A574

FISHER, Ryan, Director Human Resources, Bluffton Hospital, Bluffton, OH, p. A529
Director of Human Resources, Blanchard Valley Hospital, Findlay, OH, p. A540

FISHER, Sharon, M.D., Chief of Staff, Bartlett Regional Hospital, Juneau, AK, p. A28
R.N., Chief Nursing Officer, Tyrone Hospital, Tyrone, PA, p. A609

FISHER, Teresa, R.N., Chief Nursing Officer, Fort Loudoun Medical Center, Lenoir City, TN, p. A642
Chief Nursing Officer, Lakewood Health System, Staples, MN, p. A386

FISHER, Thomas, Senior Vice President and Chief Financial Officer, University Of Tennessee Medical Center, Knoxville, TN, p. A641

FISHER, Vicky, Ph.D., R.N., Chief Nurse Executive, Catawba Hospital, Catawba, VA, p. A739

FISHER-FORD, Karen, Director of Health Information Management, West Central Georgia Regional Hospital, Columbus, GA, p. A169

FISHKIN, Edward, M.D., Medical Director, Nyc Health + Hospitals / Woodhull, Brooklyn, NY, p. A479

FISK, Amber, Director Human Resources, Memorial Hospital Of Sweetwater County, Rock Springs, WY, p. A804

FISK, Anita, Director Human Resources, Three Rivers Hospital, Brewster, WA, p. A756

FISK, Kathryn, Chief Human Resources Officer, El Camino Hospital, Mountain View, CA, p. A80

FISK, Kellee, Chief People and Strategy Officer, Altru Health System, Grand Forks, ND, p. A523

FISLER, Eileen, Chief Financial Officer, Pacifica Hospital Of The Valley, Sun Valley, CA, p. A100

FISLER, Elyse, Chief Nursing Officer, Wellspan Chambersburg Hospital, Chambersburg, PA, p. A586
Chief Nursing Officer, Wellspan Waynesboro Hospital, Waynesboro, PA, p. A610

FITCH, Andrew, Chief Financial Officer, St. Elias Specialty Hospital, Anchorage, AK, p. A27

FITCH, James, Director Human Resources, Houston Methodist Continuing Care Hospital, Katy, TX, p. A692

FITCH, John, Vice President Human Resources, Campbell County Health, Gillette, WY, p. A802

FITCH, Ron, Chief Executive Officer, Uchealth Pikes Peak Regional Hospital, Woodland Park, CO, p. A120

FITE, David, Director Information Technology, Towner County Medical Center, Cando, ND, p. A521

FITE, Theresa, R.N., Chief Financial Officer, Fleming County Hospital, Flemingsburg, KY, p. A283

FITTERMAN, Nick, M.D., Executive Director, Huntington Hospital, Huntington, NY, p. A485

FITTS, Barry, Chief Information Officer, Hillside Rehabilitation Hospital, Warren, OH, p. A551
Chief Information Officer, Trumbull Memorial Hospital, Warren, OH, p. A551

FITZGERALD, Amy, Human Resources Manager, Copley Hospital, Morrisville, VT, p. A736

FITZGERALD, Kerri, Executive Director, Hackensack Meridian Health Shore Rehabilitation Institute, Brick, NJ, p. A452

FITZGERALD, Michelle, R.N., Chief Executive Officer, Encompass Health Rehabilitation Hospital Of York, York, PA, p. A612

FITZGERALD, Mike, Chief Financial Officer, St. Clare Hospital, Lakewood, WA, p. A760
Chief Financial Officer, St. Francis Hospital, Federal Way, WA, p. A758
Chief Financial Officer, St. Josep. Medical Center, Tacoma, WA, p. A767
Chief Financial Officer, St. Michael Medical Center, Bremerton, WA, p. A756

FITZGERALD, Patty, Staff Services, Munson Healthcare Charlevoix Hospital, Charlevoix, MI, p. A350

FITZGERALD III, Thomas J., Director, Va Palo Alto Health Care System, Palo Alto, CA, p. A84

FITZMAURICE, Dennis, Vice President, Professional Services, Community First Medical Center, Chicago, IL, p. A198

FITZPATRICK, Anna, Director Human Resources, St. Anthony Regional Hospital, Carroll, IA, p. A244

FITZPATRICK, Daniel, Director Human Resources, Whitesburg Arh Hospital, Whitesburg, KY, p. A294

FITZPATRICK, James, M.D., Vice President Medical Affairs, Kenmore Mercy Hospital, Kenmore, NY, p. A486

FITZPATRICK, Leigh Ann, Superintendent, Kerrville State Hospital, Kerrville, TX, p. A692

FITZSIMMONS, Shaun, Director Information Technology Services, Community Medical Center, Toms River, NJ, p. A464

FITZSIMONS, Patricia, R.N., Ph.D., Senior Vice President Patient Services, Yale-New Haven Hospital, New Haven, CT, p. A124

FLACH, Shannan, Chief Executive Officer, Kingman Community Hospital, Kingman, KS, p. A268

FLACK, Charles, Interim Chief Information Officer, Orange County Global Medical Center, Inc., Santa Ana, CA, p. A96

FLAHERTY, John, Chief Financial Officer, Encompass Health Rehabilitation Hospital Of Western Massachusetts, Ludlow, MA, p. A341
Controller, Fairlawn Rehabilitation Hospital, Worcester, MA, p. A346

FLAHERTY, Linda, R.N., Senior Vice President, Patient Care Services, Mclean Hospital, Belmont, MA, p. A334

FLAHERTY, Patrick, Director Management Information, Naval Hospital Bremerton, Bremerton, WA, p. A756

FLAHERTY, Tom, Assistant Administrator, Los Angeles County Central Jail Hospital, Los Angeles, CA, p. A75

FLAHERTY-OXLER, Karen Ann., MSN, R.N., Director, Philadelphia Veterans Affairs Medical Center, Philadelphia, PA, p. A601

FLAKE, Leslie, Senior Vice President, Finance, Spectrum Health - Butterworth Hospital, Grand Rapids, MI, p. A356

FLAMING, Patrick, R.N., Director Inpatient Operations, Prairie View, Newton, KS, p. A272

FLAMM, Cindy, Manager Quality, Choate Mental Health Center, Anna, IL, p. A194

FLANAGAN, Carl, Chief Financial Officer, La Paz Regional Hospital, Parker, AZ, p. A34

FLANAGAN, Craig, Chief Financial Officer, Unitypoint Health - Allen Hospital, Waterloo, IA, p. A259

FLANAGAN, Michael, Senior Vice President and Chief Operating Officer, St. Clair Hospital, Pittsburgh, PA, p. A603

FLANAGAN, Thomas, M.D., Medical Director, Aurora Behavioral Healthcare San Diego, San Diego, CA, p. A91

FLANAGAN, Tom, Chief Executive Officer, Osage Beach Center For Cognitive Disorders, Osage Beach, MO, p. A413

FLANARY, Tresha, R.N., Chief Clinical Services Officer, Wamego Health Center, Wamego, KS, p. A278

FLANDERS, David, Chief Operating Officer, Candler County Hospital, Metter, GA, p. A176

FLANIGAN, Erin, Vice President Human Resources, Wentworth-Douglass Hospital, Dover, NH, p. A448

FLANNERY, Lindsay, R.N., Vice President Patient Care Services, Avera Sacred Heart Hospital, Yankton, SD, p. A633

FLANNERY, Maureen, Vice President Clinic Operations, Straub Medical Center, Honolulu, HI, p. A185

FLANNERY, Patrick, Administrator, Christus St. Michael Rehabilitation Hospital, Texarkana, TX, p. A719

FLANNERY, Robert, Chief Financial Officer, University Hospital, Madison, WI, p. A788

FLANZ, Bruce J., President and Chief Executive Officer, Flushing Hospital Medical Center, Flushing, NY, p. A484
President and Chief Executive Officer, Jamaica Hospital Medical Center, Jamaica, NY, p. A486

FLASCHENRIEM, Julie, Chief Information Officer, Park Nicollet Methodist Hospital, Saint Louis Park, MN, p. A385

FLASHER, Sara, Chief Nurse Executive, Warren State Hospital, Warren, PA, p. A609

FLATT, G, D.O., Chief Medical Director, Pushmataha Hospital, Antlers, OK, p. A555

FLATTERY, William, Vice President and Administrator Western Division, Carilion Giles Community Hospital, Pearisburg, VA, p. A748
Vice President and Administrator Western Division, Carilion New River Valley Medical Center, Christiansburg, VA, p. A740

FLECHLER, Leslie, Chief Executive Officer, Lincoln Trail Behavioral Health System, Radcliff, KY, p. A292

FLECK, Julie, Chief Operating Officer, Parkview Ortho Hospital, Fort Wayne, IN, p. A228

FLECKENSTEIN, Casey, Nurse Manager, Monroe County Hospital, Forsyth, GA, p. A172

FLEEGEL, Monica, Director Human Resources, Mayo Clinic Health System - Albert Lea And Austin, Albert Lea, MN, p. A371

FLEENOR, Dennis, R.N., Administrator, Muleshoe Area Medical Center, Muleshoe, TX, p. A702

FLEET, Aaron, R.N., Chief Nursing Officer, Baylor Scott & White Texas Spine & Joint Hospital-Tyler, Tyler, TX, p. A721

FLEISCHMANN, Craig, Vice President Finance, University Of Maryland Medical Center Midtown Campus, Baltimore, MD, p. A326

FLEISCHMANN, Tim, Chief Financial Officer, Tuality Healthcare, Hillsboro, OR, p. A576

FLEISHMAN, Samuel, M.D., Chief Medical Officer, Cap. Fear Valley Medical Center, Fayetteville, NC, p. A510

FLEITES, Fernando, Senior Vice President Human Resources, Bon Secours St. Francis Health System, Greenville, SC, p. A620

FLEMING, Jared, Director, Information Services, Lourdes Counseling Center, Richland, WA, p. A763

FLEMING, Joshua, Vice President Chief Clinical Officer, Leesburg Regional Medical Center, Leesburg, FL, p. A144

FLEMING, Michael, Chief People Officer, Banner - University Medical Center Phoenix, Phoenix, AZ, p. A35

FLEMING, Shane, Chief Financial Officer, Capital Health Medical Center-Hopewell, Pennington, NJ, p. A461
Chief Financial Officer, Capital Health Regional Medical Center, Trenton, NJ, p. A464

FLEMING, William, Chief Operating Officer, Norwood Hospital, Norwood, MA, p. A343

FLEMMING, Libby, Controller and Chief Information Officer, South Georgia Medical Center Lanier Campus, Lakeland, GA, p. A175

FLESNER, Lynn, Director of Nursing, Glacial Ridge Health System, Glenwood, MN, p. A377

FLETCHALL, Terry L., President and Chief Executive Officer, Santiam Hospital, Stayton, OR, p. A582

FLETCHER, Chris, Director of Human Resources, Fishermen's Hospital, Marathon, FL, p. A144

FLETCHER, James, M.D., Medical Staff President, Cascade Valley Hospital, Arlington, WA, p. A755

FLETCHER, Jennifer, Chief of Staff, Decatur County Memorial Hospital, Greensburg, IN, p. A230

FLETCHER, John R., President, Lehigh Valley Hospital - Hazleton, Hazleton, PA, p. A592

FLETCHER, Kathy, R.N., MSN, Interim Chief Nursing Officer, Val Verde Regional Medical Center, Del Rio, TX, p. A671

FLETCHER, Kevin, Director Information Systems, Medical City Mckinney, Mckinney, TX, p. A700

FLETCHER, Michael, M.D., Vice President and Chief Medical Officer, Hancock Regional Hospital, Greenfield, IN, p. A230

FLETCHER, Stephanie, CPA, Chief Financial Officer, Union General Hospital, Blairsville, GA, p. A167

FLETT, Will, Vice President Finance and Chief Financial Officer, Avera Queen Of Peace Hospital, Mitchell, SD, p. A629

FLICEK, David, President and Chief Executive Officer, Avera Mckennan Hospital And University Health Center, Sioux Falls, SD, p. A631

FLICKEMA, James, Vice President Market Development, Munson Healthcare Otsego Memorial Hospital, Gaylord, MI, p. A355

FLICKINGER, Kenneth, Chief Financial Officer, Chester County Hospital, West Chester, PA, p. A610

FLINN, Charles, Vice President, Chief Operating Officer, Saint Mary's Hospital, Waterbury, CT, p. A126

FLINT, Dan, Director Healthcare Information Systems, Wyoming County Community Hospital, Warsaw, NY, p. A501

FLINT, Jennifer, Chief Financial Officer, Laird Hospital, Union, MS, p. A400

FLINT, Ruth, Chief Nursing Officer, St. Josep. Medical Center, Tacoma, WA, p. A767

FLIPPO, Mary, R.N., MSN, Vice President and Chief Nursing Officer, Cleveland Clinic Martin North Hospital, Stuart, FL, p. A158

FLIS, James, Chief Financial Officer, Livengrin Foundation, Bensalem, PA, p. A584

FLITTON, Emileh, Administrator, Oceans Behavioral Health Center Permian Basin, Midland, TX, p. A701

FLOOD, James, Director Information Systems, Claxton-Hepburn Medical Center, Ogdensburg, NY, p. A493

FLOREN, Joshua, President, Texas Health Presbyterian Hospital Plano, Plano, TX, p. A707

FLORENTINE, Erich, Chief People Officer, Inspira Medical Center-Elmer, Elmer, NJ, p. A455
Chief People Officer, Inspira Medical Center-Vineland, Vineland, NJ, p. A465

FLORES, Andrea, Director, Information Systems, Providence Little Company of Mary Medical Center - Torrance, Torrance, CA, p. A101

FLORES, Debbie, Chief Executive Officer, Banner Thunderbird Medical Center, Glendale, AZ, p. A32

FLORES, Debra, R.N., MS, President and Chief Operating Officer, Valley Children's Healthcare, Madera, CA, p. A76

FLORES, Jacob, Chief Information Officer, Frio Regional Hospital, Pearsall, TX, p. A705

FLORES, Jerome, Chief Financial Officer and Chief Operating Officer, Kahuku Medical Center, Kahuku, HI, p. A185
Chief Financial Officer, Sunrise Canyon Hospital, Lubbock, TX, p. A698

FLORES, Linda, R.N., MSN, Vice President Nursing Services, Parkview Medical Center, Pueblo, CO, p. A118

FLORES, Rick, Interim Chief Executive Officer, Big Bend Regional Medical Center, Alpine, TX, p. A652

FLORKOWSKI, Douglas, Chief Executive Officer, Crawford Memorial Hospital, Robinson, IL, p. A218

FLORKOWSKI, Jessica, Administrator, Good Shepherd Specialty Hospital, Bethlehem, PA, p. A584

FLOURA, Kamal, M.D., Medical Director, Eastern State Hospital, Medical Lake, WA, p. A760

FLOWE, Kenneth, M.D., Chief Medical Officer, Rice Memorial Hospital, Willmar, MN, p. A388

FLOWERS, Amy, Controller, Encompass Health Rehabilitation Hospital Of Princeton, Princeton, WV, p. A776

FLOWERS, Deborah, Director Human Resources, Monroe County Hospital, Forsyth, GA, p. A172

FLOWERS, Frank, M.D., Area Medical Director, Kaiser Permanente Moreno Valley Medical Center, Moreno Valley, CA, p. A80
M.D., Area Medical Director, Kaiser Permanente Riverside Medical Center, Riverside, CA, p. A88

FLOWERS, Michael, Director Information Management, Calhoun-Liberty Hospital, Blountstown, FL, p. A132

FLOWERS, Susan, MSN, R.N., Chief Nursing Officer, Cumberland County Hospital, Burkesville, KY, p. A281

FLOWERS, Taylor, Senior Vice President Human Resources, Onslow Memorial Hospital, Jacksonville, NC, p. A513

FLOYD, Dorothy, Ph.D., Superintendent, Terrell State Hospital, Terrell, TX, p. A719

FLOYD, Duane, Vice President Human Resources and Professional Services, Watertown Regional Medical Center, Watertown, WI, p. A798

FLOYD, Kiley, Chief Executive Officer, Nemaha Valley Community Hospital, Seneca, KS, p. A276

FLOYD, Miranda, R.N., Chief Nursing Officer, Mosaic Medical Center - Albany, Albany, MO, p. A402

FLOYD, Robert, D.O., Chief Medical Staff, Davis County Hospital And Clinics, Bloomfield, IA, p. A244

FLOYD, Terri, Chief Financial Officer, Bates County Memorial Hospital, Butler, MO, p. A403

FLOYD, William Brian., President, Vidant Medical Center, Greenville, NC, p. A511

FLUGUM, Aaron, Chief Executive Officer, Mercyone New Hampton Medical Center, New Hampton, IA, p. A255

FLUKE, Cinda, R.N., Chief Nursing Officer, Saint Josep. Mount Sterling, Mount Sterling, KY, p. A290

FLUTY, Lisa, Director Information Services, Baptist Health Lexington, Lexington, KY, p. A286

FLYGARE, Matthew, Director Human Resources, Mountain West Medical Center, Tooele, UT, p. A733

FLYNN, Brian, Chief Human Resources Officer, Veterans Affairs Northern Indiana Health Care System, Fort Wayne, IN, p. A229

FLYNN, Chanda, R.N., MSN, Chief Nursing Officer, Spartanburg Medical Center - Mary Black, Spartanburg, SC, p. A624

FLYNN, Julianne, M.D., Chief of Staff, South Texas Veterans Health Care System, San Antonio, TX, p. A713

FLYNN, Kristin, Chief Human Resources Officer, Sierra Vista Regional Medical Center, San Luis Obispo, CA, p. A96

FLYNN, Matt, Vice President/Chief Finanicial Officer, Northwestern Medicine Delnor Hospital, Geneva, IL, p. A206

FLYNN, Matthew, Chief Financial Officer West Region, Northwestern Medicine Valley West Hospital, Sandwich, IL, p. A219

FLYNN, Patrick, Chief Financial Officer, Warm Springs Medical Center, Warm Springs, GA, p. A183

FOARD, Mesa, Director Information technology, William S. Hall Psychiatric Institute, Columbia, SC, p. A618

FOGARTY, John M., President and Chief Executive Officer, Beth Israel Deaconess Hospital-Needham Campus, Needham, MA, p. A342

FOGELSON, Julia, R.N., Chief Operating Officer and Chief Nursing Executive, French Hospital Medical Center, San Luis Obispo, CA, p. A95

FOGG, Jay, Chief Nursing Officer, Western Plains Medical Complex, Dodge City, KS, p. A263

FOGG, Robert, Director Finance, Lake Taylor Transitional Care Hospital, Norfolk, VA, p. A748

FOLDS, Jesse, Director of Information Technologies, Merit Health Wesley, Hattiesburg, MS, p. A393

FOLEY, Chris, Chief of Medicine, Children's Hospital Of The King's Daughters, Norfolk, VA, p. A747

FOLEY, James, CPA, Vice President and Chief Financial Officer, Shore Medical Center, Somers Point, NJ, p. A463

FOLEY, Jay, President and Chief Executive Officer, Southwestern Regional Medical Center, Tulsa, OK, p. A570

FOLEY, John, Chief Information Officer, Allegheny General Hospital, Pittsburgh, PA, p. A602

FOLEY, Michael, M.D., Chief Medical Officer, North Okaloosa Medical Center, Crestview, FL, p. A135

FOLEY, Regina, R.N., FACHE, Vice President Nursing and Operations, Hackensack Meridian Health Ocean Medical Center, Brick Township. NJ, p. A453

FOLK, Jeffrey, M.D., Vice President Medical Affairs and Chief Medical Officer, Piedmont Newnan Hospital, Newnan, GA, p. A178

FOLKENBERG, Todd, Chief Executive Officer, Porter Adventist Hospital, Denver, CO, p. A111

FOLL, Gary, Chief Financial Officer, Atchison Hospital, Atchison, KS, p. A261

FOLLETT, Traci, Director Clinical Informatics, Sierra View Medical Center, Porterville, CA, p. A86

FOLSKE, Lance, Chief Executive Officer, Sun Behavioral Columbus, Columbus, OH, p. A537

FOLSOM, Lori, Assistant Vice President Human Resources, Tift Regional Medical Center, Tifton, GA, p. A182

FOLTZ, Merri, Director of Human Resources, Mount Carmel Rehabilitation Hospital, Westerville, OH, p. A552

FONDESSY, Terrence, M.D., Vice President Medical Affairs, Promedica Fostoria Community Hospital, Fostoria, OH, p. A540

FONDREN, Shay, Administrator, Hale County Hospital, Greensboro, AL, p. A19

FONKEN, Paul, M.D., Chief of Staff, Estes Park Medical Center, Estes Park, CO, p. A112

FONTAINE, Barbara, Vice President, Nursing, Sacred Heart Hospital On The Emerald Coast, Miramar Beach, FL, p. A148

FONTAINE-WESTHART, Mark, Associate Director, Bedford Veterans Affairs Medical Center, Edith Nourse Rogers Memorial Veterans Hospital, Bedford, MA, p. A334

FONTENAULT, Richard, Director Information Systems, Medical City Green Oaks Hospital, Dallas, TX, p. A669

FONTENELLE, Mary, Executive Nurse Director, Eastern Louisiana Mental Health System, Jackson, LA, p. A303

FONTENOT, Michael, Regional Chief Financial Officer, Mercy Regional Medical Center, Ville Platte, LA, p. A316

FONTENOT, Robert, Director Human Resources, Kingwood Pines Hospital, Kingwood, TX, p. A693

FONZIE, Juril, Director Human Resources, Helena Regional Medical Center, Helena, AR, p. A46

FOOTE, Donald, Fiscal Officer, Wilkes-Barre Veterans Affairs Medical Center, Wilkes-Barre, PA, p. A611

FOOTE, John, Chief Information Officer, Manchester Veterans Affairs Medical Center, Manchester, NH, p. A450

FOOTE, Mark, Chief Financial Officer, Madera Community Hospital, Madera, CA, p. A76

FORBES, Brenda, Controller, Encompasss Health Rehabilitation Hospital Of Fort Smith, Fort Smith, AR, p. A46

FORBES, Dan, Vice President Human Resources, Ohsu Hospital, Portland, OR, p. A579

FORBES, Jonathan, Director Human Resources, Ashtabula County Medical Center, Ashtabula, OH, p. A528

FORBES, Ronald, M.D., Medical Director, Central State Hospital, Petersburg, VA, p. A748

FORBORT, Gordy, Interim Chief Financial Officer, Burnett Medical Center, Grantsburg, WI, p. A785

FORD, Alisa, Vice President Human Resources, The University Of Kansas Hospital, Kansas City, KS, p. A268

FORD, Angelique, Administrator Human Resources, Spring Valley Hospital Medical Center, Las Vegas, NV, p. A444

FORD, Cora, Vice President Human Resources, Our Lady Of The Lake Regional Medical Center, Baton Rouge, LA, p. A297

FORD, Frank, President, St. Luke's Sacred Heart Campus, Allentown, PA, p. A583

FORD, James, Director Human Resources, Baptist Health - Van Buren, Van Buren, AR, p. A54

FORD, Jessica, Interim Chief Executive Officer, Falls Community Hospital And Clinic, Marlin, TX, p. A699

FORD, John, Information Technology Director, The Brook Hospital - Kmi, Louisville, KY, p. A288

FORD, Karen, Chief Nursing Officer, Sabine Medical Center, Many, LA, p. A308

FORD, LeeAnn, Director Human Resources and Imaging, The Physicians Centre Hospital, Bryan, TX, p. A661

FORD, Marcia, Chief Operating Officer, Hawthorn Children Psychiatric Hospital, Saint Louis, MO, p. A415

FORD, Mary, Chief Information Officer, Einstein Medical Center Montgomery, East Norriton, PA, p. A589

FORD, Michael, Vice President Patient Services, Wood County Hospital, Bowling Green, OH, p. A530

FORD, Nathan, Chief Executive Officer, Encompass Health Rehabilitation Hospital Of Shelby County, Pelham, AL, p. A23

FORD, Veronica, Vice President Human Resources, University Of Maryland Capital Region Health Prince George's Hospital Center, Cheverly, MD, p. A328

FORDE, Steve, Chief Executive Officer, Nelson County Health System, Mcville, ND, p. A525

FORDYCE, Brian, Director Information Technology, Roosevelt Medical Center, Culbertson, MT, p. A422

FOREMAN, Christopher, Director Human Resources, Santa Rosa Medical Center, Milton, FL, p. A148

FOREMAN, Kim, M.D., Chief of Staff, Baylor Scott & White Texas Spine & Joint Hospital-Tyler, Tyler, TX, p. A721

FOREMAN, Lee Ann, Vice President Human Resources, Mississipp. Baptist Medical Center, Jackson, MS, p. A395
Vice President Human Resources, Select Specialty Hospital - Belhaven, Jackson, MS, p. A395

FOREMAN, Nena, Chief Nursing Officer, Palo Verde Hospital, Blythe, CA, p. A58

FORESE, Laura, M.D., M.P.H., Executive Assistant to the Chief Operating Officer, New York-Presbyterian Hospital, New York, NY, p. A491
M.D., M.P.H., Executive Vice President and Chief Medical Officer, New York-Presbyterian Hospital, New York, NY, p. A491

FORET, Chris, M.D., Chief of Staff, Riverside Medical Center, Franklinton, LA, p. A302

FORET, Robert, Chief Financial Officer, Yoakum Community Hospital, Yoakum, TX, p. A726

FORGE, Brenda, Vice President, Human Resources, Regional West Medical Center, Scottsbluff, NE, p. A439

FORKEL, Todd, President and Chief Executive Officer, Avera St. Luke's Hospital, Aberdeen, SD, p. A626

FORKNER, Christine, Executive Vice President and Chief Financial Officer, National Jewish Health, Denver, CO, p. A110

FORNIER-JOHNSON, Michelle, Group Vice President Human Resources, St. Anthony Hospital, Lakewood, CO, p. A115

FORREST, Brian, Vice President Human Resources, Cayuga Medical Center At Ithaca, Ithaca, NY, p. A485

FORREST, LaDessa, Administrator, Encompass Health Rehabilitation Hospital Of Richardson, Richardson, TX, p. A708

FORREST, Mary Helen, R.N., Chief Nursing Officer, Uams Medical Center, Little Rock, AR, p. A49

FORREST, Molly, President and Chief Executive Officer, Joyce Eisenberg-Keefer Medical Center, Reseda, CA, p. A88

FORRESTER, John, Director Information Services, Hamilton Medical Center, Dalton, GA, p. A170

FORSCH, Randall, M.D., M.P.H., Chief Medical Officer, St. Josep. Mercy Chelsea, Chelsea, MI, p. A351

FORSTER, Sean, Interim Chief Executive Officer, Centennial Peaks Hospital, Louisville, CO, p. A116

FORSTER, Tracy, R.N., Senior Director of Nursing, Novant Health Matthews Medical Center, Matthews, NC, p. A514

FORSTNER, Jim, Chief Executive Officer, Emory Decatur Hospital, Decatur, GA, p. A171
Chief Executive Officer, Emory Hillandale Hospital, Lithonia, GA, p. A175

Chief Executive Officer, Emory Long-Term Acute Care, Decatur, GA, p. A171

FORSYTH, Beth, Chief Operating Officer, Good Samaritan Medical Center, Lafayette, CO, p. A115

FORSYTH, Kurt, Administrator, Delta Community Medical Center, Delta, UT, p. A727
Administrator, Fillmore Community Hospital, Fillmore, UT, p. A728

FORSYTH, Larry, Director Information Services, Ou Medical Center, Oklahoma City, OK, p. A565

FORT, Claudio D., President and Chief Executive Officer, Rutland Regional Medical Center, Rutland, VT, p. A736

FORT, Glenn, Chief Medical Officer, Landmark Medical Center, Woonsocket, RI, p. A614

FORTENBERRY, Denise, Chief Nursing Officer and Chief Compliance Officer, Cypress Pointe Surgical Hospital, Hammond, LA, p. A302

FORTENBERRY, Doris, Coordinator Human Resources, Delta Memorial Hospital, Dumas, AR, p. A44

FORTENBERRY, Rob, Chief Information Officer, Mann-Grandstaff Veterans Affairs Medical Center, Spokane, WA, p. A765

FORTIN, Amanda, Manager Finance, Decatur Health Systems, Oberlin, KS, p. A272

FORTIN, Laura, R.N., Chief Operating Officer, St. Josep. Medical Center, Houston, TX, p. A688

FORTNEY, John, Chief Medical Officer, Adena Pike Medical Center, Waverly, OH, p. A552
Senior System Medical Advisor, Adena Medical Center, Chillicothe, OH, p. A531

FORTNEY, Robert, MS, R.N., Chief Nursing Officer and Vice President of Patient Care, Illinois Valley Community Hospital, Peru, IL, p. A217

FORTUNE, Michelle, R.N., Chief Executive Officer, St. Luke's Hospital, Columbus, NC, p. A508

FOSBERG, Renee, Chief Information Officer, Emerson Hospital, Concord, MA, p. A338

FOSNESS, Nick, Chief Executive Officer, Marshall County Healthcare Center Avera, Britton, SD, p. A626

FOSNOCHT, Kevin, M.D., Chief Medical Officer and Associate Executive Director, Penn Presbyterian Medical Center, Philadelphia, PA, p. A601

FOSS, Coleman, Chief Executive Officer, Wellstar West Georgia Medical Center, Lagrange, GA, p. A175

FOSS, David, Chief Information Officer, New London Hospital, New London, NH, p. A450

FOSS, John T., Vice President, Operations, Mercy Health, Lakeshore Campus, Shelby, MI, p. A366

FOSTER, Angelia, Chief Administrative Officer, Marshfield Medical Center - Beaver Dam, Beaver Dam, WI, p. A781

FOSTER, Barbara, Regional Human Resources Director, Select Specialty Hospital-Wilmington, Wilmington, DE, p. A128

FOSTER, Becky, Employee Relations Specialist, Sanford Tracy Medical Center, Tracy, MN, p. A386
Employee Relations Specialist, Sanford Westbrook Medical Center, Westbrook, MN, p. A387

FOSTER, Beverly, Chief Executive Officer, Kindred Hospital-Sycamore, Sycamore, IL, p. A221

FOSTER, Bob, Chief Information Officer, South Georgia Medical Center, Valdosta, GA, p. A182

FOSTER, Brian, Chief Information Officer, Vail Health, Vail, CO, p. A119

FOSTER, Carolyn, Chief Financial Officer, Peacehealth Peace Island Medical Center, Friday Harbor, WA, p. A758

FOSTER, Charles, Regional Director Human Resources, Christus Southeast Texas Hospital - St. Elizabeth, Beaumont, TX, p. A658

FOSTER, Chris, Director Health Information Management, Deer Lodge Medical Center, Deer Lodge, MT, p. A423

FOSTER, Daniel, Chief Financial Officer, Northern Utah Rehabilitation Hospital, South Ogden, UT, p. A733

FOSTER, Gary, R.N., Associate Administrator, Banner Estrella Medical Center, Phoenix, AZ, p. A35
R.N., Chief Operating Officer, Peacehealth Southwest Medical Center, Vancouver, WA, p. A768
Vice President and Chief Financial Officer, Saratoga Hospital, Saratoga Springs, NY, p. A497

FOSTER, Kennetha, Chief Nursing Officer, Mission Regional Medical Center, Mission, TX, p. A701

FOSTER, Larry, R.N., MSN, Chief Executive Officer, Kindred Hospital-Baldwin Park, Baldwin Park, CA, p. A58

FOSTER, Michael, Director Information Systems, East Cooper Medical Center, Mount Pleasant, SC, p. A622

FOSTER, Mickey W., Chief Executive Officer, Firsthealth Moore Regional Hospital, Pinehurst, NC, p. A516

FOSTER, Mike, Manager Information Systems, Moab Regional Hospital, Moab, UT, p. A729

FOSTER, Mitzi, Director Information Services, Southern Tennessee Regional Health System-Pulaski, Pulaski, TN, p. A648

FOSTER, Nancy, Vice President, Human Resources, Hendricks Regional Health, Danville, IN, p. A226

FOSTER, Rebecca, MSN, R.N., Chief Nursing Officer, Cumberland Medical Center, Crossville, TN, p. A637

FOSTER, Robert, Director Human Resources, Regional Medical Center Of Central Alabama, Greenville, AL, p. A19

FOSTER, Stephanie, MSN, R.N., Chief Nursing Officer, Longview Regional Medical Center, Longview, TX, p. A697

FOSTER, Steven, Chief Executive Officer, Chi St. Luke's Health - Patients Medical Center, Pasadena, TX, p. A705
President and Interim Chief Executive Officer, St. Luke's Sugar Land Hospital, Sugar Land, TX, p. A717

FOSTER, Terri, Hospital Finance Officer, Baylor Scott & White Medical Center - Grapevine, Grapevine, TX, p. A682

FOSTER, Timothy, Acting Chief Medical Officer, Newton-Wellesley Hospital, Newton Lower Falls, MA, p. A342

FOSTER, Wanda, Vice President Nursing, Mcdonough District Hospital, Mb, IL, p. A211

FOTIADIS, George, M.D., Chief of Staff, Clarke County Hospital, Osceola, IA, p. A256

FOTTER, Robert, Chief Financial Officer, Pennsylvania Psychiatric Institute, Harrisburg, PA, p. A591

FOUCH, Loren, Chief Executive Officer, Mayhill Hospital, Denton, TX, p. A672

FOUGHT, Scott, Vice President Finance, Promedica Bay Park Hospital, Oregon, OH, p. A547

FOULKE, Elvia, Executive Vice President and Chief Operating Officer, Emanate Health Foothill Presbyterian Hospital, Glendora, CA, p. A67

FOUNTAIN, Aaron, Chief Information Officer, Brandon Regional Hospital, Brandon, FL, p. A133

FOUNTAIN, Wesley, Chief Financial Officer, St. David's South Austin Medical Center, Austin, TX, p. A656

FOURRE, Mark, President, Pen Bay Medical Center, Rockport, ME, p. A322
President, Waldo County General Hospital, Belfast, ME, p. A319

FOUSE, Carla, Administrator and Chief Nursing Officer, Ascension St. Vincent Randolph, Winchester, IN, p. A242
Chief Nursing Officer, Ascension St. Vincent Randolph, Winchester, IN, p. A242

FOUSE, Sarah, Associate Director of Patient Services, Captain James A. Lovell Federal Health Care Center, North Chicago, IL, p. A214

FOUST, Lisa, Senior Vice President Human Resources, John Muir Behavioral Health Center, Concord, CA, p. A61
Senior Vice President Human Resources, John Muir Medical Center, Concord, Concord, CA, p. A61
Senior Vice President, Human Resources, John Muir Medical Center, Walnut Creek, Walnut Creek, CA, p. A104

FOUST-COFIELD, Misti, R.N., Vice President and Chief Nursing Officer, Reid Health, Richmond, IN, p. A239

FOUTS, Kyle, Interim Administrator, Montana State Hospital, Warm Springs, MT, p. A428

FOUTS, Phillip. Chief Financial Officer, Dekalb Regional Medical Center, Fort Payne, AL, p. A19
Chief Financial Officer, Fannin Regional Hospital, Blue Ridge, GA, p. A167

FOUTZ, Patricia, Director Human Resources, Bath Community Hospital, Hot Springs, VA, p. A744

FOWLER, Barry, Director Human and System Resources, Clark Fork Valley Hospital, Plains, MT, p. A426

FOWLER, Brian, Information Technology Director, Jeff Davis Hospital, Hazlehurst, GA, p. A173

FOWLER, Jennifer, Central State Hospital, Louisville, KY, p. A288

FOWLER, Kate, Chief Financial Officer, West Valley Medical Center, Caldwell, ID, p. A189

FOWLER, Kevin, Chief Financial Officer, Ferrell Hospital, Eldorado, IL, p. A203
Director Finance, Putnam County Hospital, Greencastle, IN, p. A229

FOWLER, Kevin N., President and Chief Executive Officer, Cabell Huntington Hospital, Huntington, WV, p. A772

FOWLER, Marcia, Chief Executive Officer, Bournewood Health Systems, Brookline, MA, p. A337

FOWLER, Maureen, Director Human Resources, Conifer Park, Glenville, NY, p. A484

FOWLER, Ruth, Senior Vice President and Chief Financial Officer, Children's Healthcare Of Atlanta, Atlanta, GA, p. A164

FOWLER, Ryan, Chief Administrative Officer, Lower Umpqua Hospital District, Reedsport, OR, p. A580

FOWLER, Sean, Chief Executive Officer, Watsonville Community Hospital, Watsonville, CA, p. A104

FOWLER, Steven, M.D., President Medical Staff, Genesis Medical Center, Dewitt, De Witt, IA, p. A248

FOX, Alan, Chief Financial Officer, Saint Francis Memorial Hospital, San Francisco, CA, p. A94

FOX, Carol, M.D., Senior Vice President and Chief Medical Officer, Excela Latrobe Area Hospital, Latrobe, PA, p. A594

FOX, David, Vice President and Chief Operating Officer, Baxter Regional Medical Center, Mountain Home, AR, p. A50

FOX, Debra, Chief Nursing Officer, University Medical Center, Las Vegas, NV, p. A444

FOX, Devin, M.D., Vice President Medical Operations, Chi Health Creighton University Medical Center - Bergan Mercy, Omaha, NE, p. A436

FOX, Jay, Chief Executive Officer, Baylor Scott & White Medical Center - Austin, Austin, TX, p. A655
Chief Executive Officer, Baylor Scott & White Medical Center - Pflugerville, Pflugerville, TX, p. A706
Chief Executive Officer, Baylor Scott & White Medical Center - Taylor, Taylor, TX, p. A718
President, Baylor Scott & White Medical Center - Buda, Buda, TX, p. A661

FOX, Jessica, Director of Human Resources, Aspirus Riverview Hospital And Clinics, Inc., Wisconsin Rapids, WI, p. A800

FOX, John, M.D., Medical Director, Select Specialty Hospital - San Diego, San Diego, CA, p. A92

FOX, Judi, Chief Financial Officer, Rutland Regional Medical Center, Rutland, VT, p. A736

FOX, Leana, Interim Chief Nurse Executive, Bon Secours Maryview Medical Center, Portsmouth, VA, p. A749

FOX, Randy, Director Performance Improvement and Risk Management, Lakeland Behavioral Health System, Springfield, MO, p. A418

FOX, Starla, Director of Nursing, Bristol Bay Area Health Corporation, Dillingham, AK, p. A28

FOX, Susan, President and Chief Executive Officer, White Plains Hospital Center, White Plains, NY, p. A502

FOX, William, Chief Executive Officer, Baptist Memorial Restorative Care Hospital, Memphis, TN, p. A644

FOX JR, JerryChief Information Officer, Alton Memorial Hospital, Alton, IL, p. A194

FOXX, Randy, Chief Financial Officer, Boone Memorial Hospital, Madison, WV, p. A774

FOY, Gregory, Risk Manager, Scheurer Health, Pigeon, MI, p. A363

FRACHISEUR, Kenny, Chief Information Officer, Ouachita County Medical Center, Camden, AR, p. A43

FRACICA, Philip. M.D., Chief Medical Officer, Bothwell Regional Health Center, Sedalia, MO, p. A418

FRACK, Darla, MSN, Vice President, Patient Services, St. Luke's Hospital - Anderson Campus, Easton, PA, p. A589

FRACK, Gina, Chief Executive Officer, Norton County Hospital, Norton, KS, p. A272

FRAGEN, Andrew, M.D., Chief Medical Officer, Community Hospital Of San Bernardino, San Bernardino, CA, p. A91

FRAHER, Francis, Vice President, Finance, Northwestern Memorial Hospital, Northwestern Memorial Hospital, Chicago, IL, p. A200

FRAIOLA, Anthony, Associate Administrator Administrative and Support Services, Hawaii State Hospital, Kaneohe, HI, p. A186

FRAKER, Steve, Chief Financial Officer, Banner Churchill Community Hospital, Fallon, NV, p. A442

FRALICKER, Tammy, MS, R.N., Chief Nursing Officer, Crawford Memorial Hospital, Robinson, IL, p. A218

FRAME, Angela, Chief Financial Officer, Jackson General Hospital, Ripley, WV, p. A776

FRAME, Ken, Chief Nursing Officer, Ashtabula County Medical Center, Ashtabula, OH, p. A528

FRANCE, Cheryl, M.D., Chief Medical Officer, William R. Sharpe, Jr. Hospital, Weston, WV, p. A777

FRANCE, James, M.D., Chief of Staff, Conway Regional Medical Center, Conway, AR, p. A44

FRANCE, Larry O., Commander, Weed Army Community Hospital, Fort Irwin, CA, p. A64

FRANCETICH, Kane, Chief Information Officer, Gritman Medical Center, Moscow, ID, p. A191

FRANCIOLI, Carl, Vice President Finance, Johns Hopkins Bayview Medical Center, Baltimore, MD, p. A324

FRANCIS, Carolyn, R.N., MSN, Director of Nursing, Lasalle General Hospital, Jena, LA, p. A304

FRANCIS, Christy, Chief Executive Officer, Hemphill County Hospital, Canadian, TX, p. A662

FRANCIS, Jeff, Vice President Finance and Chief Financial Officer, Methodist Jennie Edmundson Hospital, Council Bluffs, IA, p. A247
Vice President, Chief Financial Officer, Methodist Fremont Health, Fremont, NE, p. A432

FRANCIS, Lana B., Chief Executive Officer, Lasalle General Hospital, Jena, LA, p. A304

FRANCIS, Perry, Supervisory Information Technology Specialist, Chinle Comprehensive Health Care Facility, Chinle, AZ, p. A31

FRANCIS, Rebekah, JD, Chief Financial Officer, Aurora Behavioral Health System East, Tempe, AZ, p. A39
JD, Chief Financial Officer, Aurora Behavioral Health System West, Glendale, AZ, p. A32

FRANCISCO, Gerard, M.D., Chief Medical Officer, Tirr Memorial Hermann, Houston, TX, p. A688

FRANCKOWIAK, Debra, Executive Director, Children's Hospital Of Wisconsin-Fox Valley, Neenah, WI, p. A792

FRANCO, Glenda, Director, Human Resources, Vibra Hospital Of Sacramento, Folsom, CA, p. A64

FRANCO, Luis, M.D., Medical Director, United Medical Rehabilitation Hospital, Hammond, LA, p. A302

FRANCO, Richard, Chief Financial Officer, Community First Medical Center, Chicago, IL, p. A198
Vice President and Chief Financial Officer, Northwestern Medicine Lake Forest Hospital, Lake Forest, IL, p. A210

FRANCO, Roger, Director Human Resources, St. John's Episcopal Hospital, Far Rockaway, NY, p. A483

FRANCO, Rosemary, Chief Nursing Officer, Cochran Memorial Hospital, Morton, TX, p. A702

FRANCOIS, Brennan, Chief Executive Officer, Sun Behavioral Houston, Houston, TX, p. A688

FRANCOIS, Fritz, M.D., Chief Medical Officer, Nyu Langone Hospitals, New York, NY, p. A492

FRANI, Christopher M., Interim Director, Syracuse Veterans Affairs Medical Center, Syracuse, NY, p. A500

FRANK, Anthony, M.D., Senior Vice President and Chief Medical Officer, Carolinas Healthcare System Blue Ridge, Morganton, NC, p. A515

FRANK, Barbara, Human Resource Specialist, Caro Center, Caro, MI, p. A350

FRANK, Cathrine, M.D., Chairperson, Henry Ford Kingswood Hospital, Ferndale, MI, p. A354

FRANK, Daniel, Chief Financial Officer, Craig Hospital, Englewood, CO, p. A112

FRANK, Debra, Chief Financial Officer, Ness County Hospital District No 2, Ness City, KS, p. A272

FRANK, James, CPA, Chief Executive Officer, Providence Medical Center, Wayne, NE, p. A440

FRANK, Joseph, Interim President, Penn State Health St. Joseph, Reading, PA, p. A606

FRANK, Kim, Chief Human Resources Officer, Virginia Gay Hospital, Vinton, IA, p. A259

FRANK, Patricia, Chief Nursing Officer, Henry County Hospital, Napoleon, OH, p. A546

FRANK, Robert, Senior Vice President of Operations, University Of Maryland Shore Medical Center At Chestertown, Chestertown, MD, p. A328
Senior Vice President of Operations, University Of Maryland Shore Medical Center At Easton, Easton, MD, p. A329
Senior Vice President Operations, University Of Maryland Shore Medical Center At Dorchester, Cambridge, MD, p. A328

FRANK, Thomas, Chief Operating Officer, North Country Hospital And Health Center, Newport, VT, p. A736

FRANK-LIGHTFOOT, Loraine, Vice President and Market Chief Nursing Officer, Novant Health Forsyth Medical Center, Winston, NC, p. A520

FRANKE, Paul, M.D., Chief Medical Officer, Alaska Native Medical Center, Anchorage, AK, p. A27

FRANKEL, Harris, M.D., Interim Chief Medical Officer, Nebraska Medicine - Nebraska Medical Center, Omaha, NE, p. A437

FRANKEL, Michele, Associate Executive Director Finance, Glen Cove Hospital, Glen Cove, NY, p. A484

FRANKEN, Stephanie, Vice President Operational Finance, Chi St. Alexius Health - Dickinson Medical Center, Dickinson, ND, p. A522

FRANKL, Angie, Director Human Resources, Adair County Health System, Greenfield, IA, p. A250

FRANKLIN, Chuck, M.D., Chief Medical Staff, Weston County Health Services, Newcastle, WY, p. A803

FRANKLIN, Clay, Chief Executive Officer, Alliancehealth Midwest, Midwest City, OK, p. A562

FRANKLIN, David, Chief Executive Officer, Cedar Springs Hospital, Colorado Springs, CO, p. A109

FRANKLIN, Ed, Chief Human Resources Officer, Page Hospital, Page, AZ, p. A34

FRANKLIN, Jennifer, R.N., Chief Clinical Officer, Yoakum Community Hospital, Yoakum, TX, p. A726

FRANKLIN, Matthew, Director Human Resources, Warren General Hospital, Warren, PA, p. A609

FRANKLIN, Michael A., FACHE, President and Chief Executive Officer, Atlantic General Hospital, Berlin, MD, p. A327

FRANKLIN, Michelle, Chief Executive Officer, Sullivan County Community Hospital, Sullivan, IN, p. A241

FRANKLIN, Tammy, Manager Personnel and Marketing, Covenant Hospital-Levelland, Levelland, TX, p. A695

FRANKO, Stephen, Vice President Finance and Chief Financial Officer, Regional Hospital Of Scranton, Scranton, PA, p. A607

FRANKOVITCH, John C., President and Chief Executive Officer, Weirton Medical Center, Weirton, WV, p. A777

FRANKS, Cathy Chief Operating Officer, Izard County Medical Center, Calico Rock, AR, p. A43

FRANKS, Charles, Chief Human Resources, Louis Stokes Cleveland Veterans Affairs Medical Center, Cleveland, OH, p. A534

FRANKS, Dennis, FACHE, Chief Executive Officer, Neosho Memorial Regional Medical Center, Chanute, KS, p. A262
Interim Chief Financial Officer, Pontiac General Hospital, Pontiac, MI, p. A364
Vice President Operations, Pontiac General Hospital, Pontiac, MI, p. A364

FRANSEN, Mitchell, Chief Financial Officer, Mesa View Regional Hospital, Mesquite, NV, p. A445

FRANSON, John, M.D., Chief Medical Staff, Caribou Memorial Hospital And Living Center, Soda Springs, ID, p. A193

FRANTZ, Vincent, M.D., Chief of Staff, Plumas District Hospital, Quincy, CA, p. A86

FRANZ, Eric, Vice President, Finance and Chief Financial Officer, Graham Hospital Association, Canton, IL, p. A196

FRANZ, Staci, Director Human Resources, St. Luke's Rehabilitation Institute, Spokane, WA, p. A766

FRARDO, Virgil, M.D., Medical Director, Encompass Health Rehabilitation Hospital Of Wichita Falls, Wichita Falls, TX, p. A725

FRASCA, Edith, Controller and Chief Financial Officer, The Pavilion, Champaign, IL, p. A197

FRASCH, Sara, Chief Human Resource Officer, University Of New Mexico Hospitals, Albuquerque, NM, p. A468

FRASER, Cathryn, Chief Human Resources Officer, Mayo Clinic Health System - Franciscan Healthcare In Sparta, Sparta, WI, p. A796
Chief Human Resources Officer, Mayo Clinic Hospital - Rochester, Rochester, MN, p. A384

FRASER, James, Administrator Finance, Ascension Via Christi Hospital, Manhattan, Manhattan, KS, p. A270

FRASIER, Nora, R.N., FACHE, Chief Nursing Officer, Methodist Mansfield Medical Center, Mansfield, TX, p. A699

FRASURE, Jane, Human Resources, Baylor Scott & White Medical Center - Llano, Llano, TX, p. A696

FRATZKE, Jason, Chief Nursing Officer, Mayo Clinic Health System - Franciscan Healthcare In Sparta, Sparta, WI, p. A796

FRATZKE, Mark, R.N., President and Chief Executive Officer, Seton Medical Center, Daly City, CA, p. A62

FRAUENHOFER, Chris, Chief Financial Officer, Northern Light Maine Coast Hospital, Ellsworth, ME, p. A320

FRAZIER, Amy, Supervisor Management Information Systems, Wetzel County Hospital, New Martinsville, WV, p. A775

FRAZIER, Brandon, Chief Financial Officer, River Oaks Hospital, New Orleans, LA, p. A311

FRAZIER, Derrick A., FACHE, Chief Executive Officer, Morehouse General Hospital, Bastrop. LA, p. A296

FRAZIER, Joel, M.D., Medical Director, Onecore Health, Oklahoma City, OK, p. A565

FRAZIER, Kimberly, R.N., Chief Nursing Officer, East Los Angeles Doctors Hospital, Los Angeles, CA, p. A74

FRAZIER, Shane, Chief Executive Officer, Pinnacle Pointe Hospital, Little Rock, AR, p. A49

FREAS, Mary, Senior Vice President and Chief Financial Officer, Southwest General Health Center, Middleburg Heights, OH, p. A545

FRED, Mark, R.N., Chief Operating Officer, Kirby Medical Center, Monticello, IL, p. A212
R.N., Chief Operating Offier, Chief Information Officer, Kirby Medical Center, Monticello, IL, p. A212

FREDEBOELLING, Elizabeth, Chief Nursing Officer, Dell Children's Medical Center Of Central Texas, Austin, TX, p. A656

FREDERICK, Brenda, Director Human Resources, Laurel Ridge Treatment Center, San Antonio, TX, p. A712

FREDERICK, Dessa, Manager Human Resources, St. James Behavioral Health Hospital, Gonzales, LA, p. A302

FREDERICK, Gretchen, R.N., Director Patient Care Services, Buffalo Hospital, Buffalo, MN, p. A373

FREDERICK, John, Chief Financial Officer, West Central Georgia Regional Hospital, Columbus, GA, p. A169

FREDERICK, Ryannon, Chief Nursing Officer, Mayo Clinic Hospital In Florida, Jacksonville, FL, p. A141

FREDERICKSON, Kathy, Information Systems Site Lead, Sutter Delta Medical Center, Antioch, CA, p. A56

FREDETTE, Beth, Chief Information Officer, Dayton Children's Hospital, Dayton, OH, p. A538

FREDRICK, Joyce, Associate Director, Veterans Affairs Central Western Massachusetts Healthcare System, Leeds, MA, p. A340

FREDRICK, Rick, Director Information Technology, Cottage Hospital, Woodsville, NH, p. A451

FREDRICKSON, Kelley, Director Information Services, Medical City Fort Worth, Fort Worth, TX, p. A678

FREDRICKSON, Mark, M.D., Medical Director, Encompass Health Rehabilitation Hospital Midland Odessa, Midland, TX, p. A701

FREEBORN, Fawn, Human Resources Generalist, Schoolcraft Memorial Hospital, Manistique, MI, p. A361

FREEBURG, Rick, Chief Executive Officer, Baptist Health South Florida, Mariners Hospital, Tavernier, FL, p. A160
Chief Executive Officer, Fishermen's Hospital, Marathon, FL, p. A144

FREEBURN, Mark, Chief Executive Officer, Helen M. Simpson Rehabilitation Hospital, Harrisburg, PA, p. A591

FREED, Nancy, Chief Financial Officer, Seiling Regional Medical Center, Seiling, OK, p. A568

FREED, Stuart, M.D., Chief Medical Officer, Confluence Health/Central Washington Hospital, Wenatchee, WA, p. A768
M.D., Medical Director, Confluence Health/Wenatchee Valley Hospital, Wenatchee, WA, p. A768

FREED-SIGURDSSON, Anna, M.D., Medical Director, Encompass Health Rehabilitation Hospital Of Dallas, Dallas, TX, p. A668

FREEDMAN, Kenneth, M.D., Chief Medical Officer, Lemuel Shattuck Hospital, Jamaica Plain, MA, p. A340

FREEDMAN, Rick, Commanding Officer, Naval Hospital Camp Lejeune, Camp Lejeune, NC, p. A506

FREEHILL, Sarah, Chief Nursing Officer, Arbuckle Memorial Hospital, Sulphur, OK, p. A568

FREEHOF, Leonard, Chief Executive Officer and Managing Director, Spring Valley Hospital Medical Center, Las Vegas, NV, p. A444

FREELAND, R, M.D., Chief Clinical Officer, Twin Valley Behavioral Healthcare, Columbus, OH, p. A537

FREEMAN, Brian, President, Atrium Health Stanly, Albemarle, NC, p. A504

FREEMAN, Diane, R.N., Assistant Vice President and Chief Nursing Officer, Chi St. Luke's Health-Lakeside Hospital, The Woodlands, TX, p. A720

FREEMAN, Gail, Chief Nursing Officer, San Gabriel Valley Medical Center, San Gabriel, CA, p. A94

FREEMAN, Jerry, Chief, Human Resources Management Services, Durham Veterans Affairs Medical Center, Durham, NC, p. A509

FREEMAN, Kimberlee, Vice President of Patient Care Services/Chief Nursing Officer, Wayne Healthcare, Greenville, OH, p. A541
Vice President Patient Care Services and Chief Nursing Officer, Wayne Healthcare, Greenville, OH, p. A541

FREEMAN, Marianne, Vice President Human Resources, Piedmont Rockdale Hospital, Conyers, GA, p. A170

FREEMAN, Michael, Director Human Resources, Alta Vista Regional Hospital, Las Vegas, NM, p. A470
Director Human Resources, Huhukam Memorial Hospital, Sacaton, AZ, p. A37

FREEMAN, Mike, Director Information Technology, Sentara Williamsburg Regional Medical Center, Williamsburg, VA, p. A753

FREEMAN, Peggy, Chief Physicians Services Officer, Dickinson County Healthcare System, Iron Mountain, MI, p. A358

FREEMAN, Richard, FACS, M.D., Chief Clinical Officer, Loyola University Medical Center, Maywood, IL, p. A211
President and Chief Executive Officer, Robert Wood Johnson University Hospital At Hamilton, Hamilton, NJ, p. A456

FREEMAN, Robert, Director Human Resources, Baptist Health - Fort Smith, Fort Smith, AR, p. A46

FREEMAN-BROWN, Samantha, Assistant Administrator, Respiratory Director, Lifebrite Community Hospital Of Stokes, Danbury, NC, p. A508

FREGOLI, Fabian, M.D., Chief Medical Officer, St. Josep. Mercy Oakland, Pontiac, MI, p. A364

FREID-SCHEPPKE, Denise, Chief Accounting Officer, Oakleaf Surgical Hospital, Altoona, WI, p. A779

FREIER, Toby, President, New Ulm Medical Center, New Ulm, MN, p. A382

FREIJ, Walid, M.D., Chief of Staff, Vaughan Regional Medical Center, Selma, AL, p. A24

FREILICH, Josh, Vice President and Chief Nurse Executive, Mercy Hospital Of Folsom, Folsom, CA, p. A64

FREIMARK, Jeffrey P., Chief Executive Officer, Miami Jewish Home And Hospital For Aged, Miami, FL, p. A146

FREITAG, Donald, M.D., Chief Medical Officer, Lynn County Hospital District, Tahoka, TX, p. A718

FRELING, Eric, M.D., Director Medical Staff Affairs, Memorial Hospital West, Pembroke Pines, FL, p. A153

FRENCH, Chad, Chief Executive Officer, Regional Medical Center Of Central Alabama, Greenville, AL, p. A19

FRENCH, Dean, M.D., Chief Executive Officer, Community Medical Center, Missoula, MT, p. A426

M.D., Chief of Staff, Faith Regional Health Services, Norfolk, NE, p. A435

FRENCH, Holly, Chief Financial Officer, Newman Regional Health, Emporia, KS, p. A264

FRENCH, Lori, Manager Human Resources, Fulton State Hospital, Fulton, MO, p. A407

FRENCH, Toni, Manager Human Resources, Callaway District Hospital, Callaway, NE, p. A430

FRENCH, Tracy, Chief Financial Officer, Banner Goldfield Medical Center, Apache Junction, AZ, p. A30

Chief Financial Officer, Banner Ironwood Medical Center, San Tan Valley, AZ, p. A38

FRENGLE, Kelley, Director, Human Resources, Peacehealth St. John Medical Center, Longview, WA, p. A760

Senior Director, Human Resources, Peacehealth Southwest Medical Center, Vancouver, WA, p. A768

FRENIER, Karen, Chief Human Resources Officer, Health Central Hospital, Ocoee, FL, p. A150

FRERER, Mary, Chief Human Resources Officer, Freeman Health System, Joplin, MO, p. A408

Chief Human Resources Officer, Freeman Neosho Hospital, Neosho, MO, p. A412

FRERICHS, Craig, Chief Information Technology Service, Grand Junction Veterans Health Care System, Grand Junction, CO, p. A113

FRESQUEZ, Juan, President, Methodist Mansfield Medical Center, Mansfield, TX, p. A699

FREUDENBERG, Liz, Chief Financial Officer, Encompass Health Rehabilitation Hospital Of Littleton, Littleton, CO, p. A115

FREUDENBERGER, Joe, Chief Executive Officer, Oakbend Medical Center, Richmond, TX, p. A708

FREY, Jack, Acting Business Manager, Greystone Park Psychiatric Hospital, Morris Plains, NJ, p. A458

FREY, Jeff, Business Administrator, Andrew Mcfarland Mental Health Center, Springfield, IL, p. A220

FREY, Paul, Director Information Technology Applications, Orthoindy Hospital, Indianapolis, IN, p. A232

FREY, Rachel, Director Human Resources, Athens-Limestone Hospital, Athens, AL, p. A14

FREY JR, JamesActing Manager Human Resources, Greystone Park Psychiatric Hospital, Morris Plains, NJ, p. A458

FREYER, Mary, Chief Operating Officer, Osf Healthcare Little Company Of Mary Medical Center, Evergreen Park, IL, p. A204

FREYER, Sharon, R.N., Chief Nursing Officer, Baptist Health Paducah, Paducah, KY, p. A291

FREYMULLER, Robert S., Chief Executive Officer, Summerlin Hospital Medical Center, Las Vegas, NV, p. A444

FREYSINGER, Edward E., Chief Executive Officer, Up Health System-Portage, Hancock, MI, p. A357

FRIARTE, Pedro, Director of Physician Services, Coral Gables Hospital, Coral Gables, FL, p. A135

FRIAS, Patricio A., M.D., President and Chief Executive Officer, Rady Children's Hospital - San Diego, San Diego, CA, p. A91

FRICK, Mary Jo, Director Finance, St. Catherine's Rehabilitation Hospital, North Miami, FL, p. A149

FRICKE, Rhett D., Chief Executive Officer, Ballinger Memorial Hospital, Ballinger, TX, p. A657

FRIDAY, Lisa, Director Human Resources, Christus Ochsner Lake Area Hospital, Lake Charles, LA, p. A306

FRIDKIN, Marjorie, M.D., Chief Medical Officer, Garrett Regional Medical Center, Oakland, MD, p. A331

FRIED, Guy, M.D., Chief Medical Officer, Magee Rehabilitation Hospital, Philadelphia, PA, p. A601

FRIED, Tera, Manager Human Resources, West River Regional Medical Center, Hettinger, ND, p. A524

FRIEDEN, Robert, Vice President Information Systems, Genesis Medical Center - Davenport, Davenport, IA, p. A247

Vice President Information Systems, Genesis Medical Center, Silvis, IL, p. A220

Vice President, Information Services and Chief Information Officer, Genesis Medical Center-Aledo, Aledo, IL, p. A194

FRIEDENBACH, Daryl, Director Fiscal Services, Floyd Valley Healthcare, Le Mars, IA, p. A253

FRIEDLY, Jennifer, Chief Operating Officer and Vice President, Unitypoint Health - Allen Hospital, Waterloo, IA, p. A259

President, Unitypoint Health - Marshalltown, Marshalltown, IA, p. A254

FRIEDMAN, Jonathan, Public Affairs Officer, Captain James A. Lovell Federal Health Care Center, North Chicago, IL, p. A214

FRIEDMAN, Ross, Chief Executive Officer, Summit Oaks Hospital, Summit, NJ, p. A463

FRIEL, Donald, Executive Vice President, Holy Redeemer Hospital, Meadowbrook, PA, p. A596

FRIEL, John P., Chief Executive Officer, Bear Valley Community Hospital, Big Bear Lake, CA, p. A58

FRIELING, Jeff, Chief Information Officer, Pathways Of Tennessee, Jackson, TN, p. A639

Vice President and Chief Information Officer, Jackson-Madison County General Hospital, Jackson, TN, p. A639

Vice President Information Systems, Camden General Hospital, Camden, TN, p. A634

FRIEND, Chad, Director, T. J. Samson Community Hospital, Glasgow, KY, p. A284

FRIEND, Lori, Human Resources Director, Alliancehealth Seminole, Seminole, OK, p. A568

FRIERSON, Cathy, Chief Human Resource Officer, Danbury Hospital, Danbury, CT, p. A121

FRIES, Richard, Vice President Finance, Ahn Grove City, Grove City, PA, p. A591

Vice President Finance, Allegheny General Hospital, Pittsburgh, PA, p. A602

FRIESEL, Dawn, Director of Finance, Pawnee County Memorial Hospital And Rural Health Clinic, Pawnee City, NE, p. A438

FRIESEN, Dale, Chief Financial Officer, Henry Ford Allegiance Specialty Hospital, Jackson, MI, p. A359

FRIESEN, John, President and Chief Operating Officer, Methodist Hospital For Surgery, Addison, TX, p. A651

FRIESEN, Lorie, Director of Nursing, Mercy Hospital Inc., Moundridge, KS, p. A271

FRIESEN, Lynette, Manager Human Resources, Henderson Health Care Services, Henderson, NE, p. A433

FRIGO, Dave, Vice President Financial Planning and Treasury, Cleveland Clinic Akron General, Akron, OH, p. A527

Chief Financial Officer, Edwin Shaw Rehab, Copley, OH, p. A537

Director Finance and Controller, Cleveland Clinic Akron General Lodi Hospital, Lodi, OH, p. A543

FRIGY, Alan, M.D., President Medical Staff, Pana Community Hospital, Pana, IL, p. A216

FRIMODIG, Mindy, D.O., President Medical Staff ThedaCare Physicians Shawano, Thedacare Medical Center-Shawano, Shawano, WI, p. A795

FRISBEE, Kent, Director Human Resources, Saint Thomas Highlands Hospital, Sparta, TN, p. A649

FRISINA, Marcy, Chief Nursing Officer, South Bay Hospital, Sun City Center, FL, p. A158

FRITSCH, William, M.D., Medical Director, Landmark Hospital Of Cap. Girardeau, Cap. Girardeau, MO, p. A403

FRITTON, Amy, Controller, Sierra Tucson, Tucson, AZ, p. A40

FRITTS, Doris, R.N., Executive Director, Same Day Surgery Center, Rapid City, SD, p. A630

FRITTS, Robert, Chief Financial Officer and Senior Vice President, Carolinas Healthcare System Blue Ridge, Morganton, NC, p. A515

FRITZ, Brian, Chief Financial Officer, Upmc Horizon, Farrell, PA, p. A590

Chief Financial Officer, Upmc Jameson, New Castle, PA, p. A598

Chief Financial Officer, Upmc Passavant, Pittsburgh, PA, p. A604

Chief Financial Officer, Upmc St. Margaret, Pittsburgh, PA, p. A604

FRITZ, Howard, M.D., Vice President, Medical Affairs and Chief Medical Officer, Glens Falls Hospital, Glens Falls, NY, p. A484

FRITZ, Robert, Chief Information Officer, Brook Lane Health Services, Hagerstown, MD, p. A330

FROCHTZWAJG, Stanley, M.D., Chief Medical Officer, Community Memorial Hospital, Ventura, CA, p. A103

FROEMKE, Janet, Human Resources Officer, Chi Lisbon Health, Lisbon, ND, p. A525

FROESE, Kristi, R.N., Chief Nursing Officer, Chi St. Luke's Health Memorial Livingston, Livingston, TX, p. A696

R.N., Vice President Clinical Operations, Chi St. Luke's Health Memorial Livingston, Livingston, TX, p. A696

FROH, Chris, Senior Coordinator Human Resources, Select Specialty Hospital-Milwaukee, Milwaukee, WI, p. A791

FROHNHOFER, Erin, Director Human Resources, Southwood Psychiatric Hospital, Pittsburgh, PA, p. A603

Vice President Human Resources, Heritage Valley Kennedy, Mckees Rocks, PA, p. A596

FROISLAND, Jeffrey, Chief Financial Officer, Mayo Clinic Hospital, Phoenix, AZ, p. A36

FROMM, Daniel, Chief Financial Officer, North Memorial Health Hospital, Robbinsdale, MN, p. A383

FROMME, Richard, Chief Financial Officer, Cavalier County Memorial Hospital And Clinics, Langdon, ND, p. A524

FROMMELT, William, Director Operations and Finance, River Falls Area Hospital, River Falls, WI, p. A795

FROSCH, Kevin, Chief Financial Officer, Medina Regional Hospital, Hondo, TX, p. A684

FROST, Eric, Associate Vice President Human Resources, Upstate University Hospital, Syracuse, NY, p. A500

FROST, Joan, R.N., Chief Operating Officer, Mercy Hospital Washington, Washington, MO, p. A420

FROST, Mark, M.D., Senior Vice President Medical Affairs, Saint Francis Health System, Saint Francis Hospital, Tulsa, OK, p. A570

M.D., Senior Vice President Medical Affairs, Laureate Psychiatric Clinic And Hospital, Tulsa, OK, p. A569

M.D., Senior Vice President Medical Affairs, Saint Francis Hospital South, Tulsa, OK, p. A570

FROST, Sarah, Chief Executive Officer, Banner - University Medical Center South, Tucson, AZ, p. A39

Chief Executive Officer, Banner - University Medical Center Tucson, Tucson, AZ, p. A39

FROWNFELTER, Penny, Chief Nursing Officer, Encompass Health Nittany Valley Rehabilitation Hospital, Pleasant Gap, PA, p. A605

FRUGE, Janie D., FACHE, Chief Executive Officer, West Calcasieu Cameron Hospital, Sulphur, LA, p. A315

FRUM, Judy, Chief Nursing Officer, Memorial Hospital Pembroke, Pembroke Pines, FL, p. A153

Chief Operating Officer, Memorial Regional Hospital, Hollywood, FL, p. A140

Interim Chief Executive Officer, Memorial Regional Hospital, Hollywood, FL, p. A140

FRY, Kenneth, Chief Financial Officer, Saint Alphonsus Regional Medical Center, Boise, ID, p. A188

FRY, Robin, CPA, Market Controller, Kindred Hospital Dallas Central, Dallas, TX, p. A668

FRY, Terry, R.N., Chief Nursing Officer, Upper Valley Medical Center, Troy, OH, p. A551

FRYE, Kelly, Director Human Resources, Montgomery General Hospital, Montgomery, WV, p. A774

FRYE, Terri, Information Technology Officer, Weston County Health Services, Newcastle, WY, p. A803

FRYFOGLE, Anthoney, Chief Information Officer, George Regional Hospital, Lucedale, MS, p. A396

FRYSZTAK, Christopher, CPA, Chief Financial Officer, Western Arizona Regional Medical Center, Bullhead City, AZ, p. A30

FUCHS, Mary Ann, R.N., Vice President Patient Care and System Chief Nurse Executive, Duke University Hospital, Durham, NC, p. A508

FUENTES, Frances, Coordinator Human Resources, Encompass Health Rehabilitation Hospital Of San Juan, San Juan, PR, p. A810

FUENTES, Leticia, Nursing Director, San Jorge Children's Hospital, Santurce, PR, p. A811

FUENTES, Michelle, President, Adventist Health Sonora, Sonora, CA, p. A99

FUENTES, Miguel A. Jr, President and Chief Executive Officer, Bronxcare Health System, Bronx, NY, p. A476

FUERSTENBERG, Donna, Fiscal Chief, Sheridan Veterans Affairs Medical Center, Sheridan, WY, p. A804

FUGATTE, Cheryl, MSN, Vice President and Chief Nursing Officer, Uofl Health - Jewish Hospital, Louisville, KY, p. A288

FUGITT, Jacki, Director Employee Relations, Osf Saint Francis Medical Center, Peoria, IL, p. A217

FUGLER, Shawna, R.N., Chief Nursing Officer, Memorial Hermann Surgical Hospital Kingwood, Kingwood, TX, p. A693

FUHRMAN, Bradley, M.D., Physician in Chief, El Paso Children's Hospital, El Paso, TX, p. A674

FUHRMAN, Dennis, Vice President Finance, Essentia Health Fargo, Fargo, ND, p. A522

FUHRO, Mary, Chief Nursing Officer, Newark Beth Israel Medical Center, Newark, NJ, p. A459

FUHS, Veronica, Chief Executive Officer, Davis County Hospital And Clinics, Bloomfield, IA, p. A244

Chief Executive Officer, Monroe County Hospital And Clinics, Albia, IA, p. A243

FUJINAKA, Jason, Manager Information System, Wahiawa General Hospital, Wahiawa, HI, p. A187

FULBRIGHT, Gary D., CPA, Chief Executive Officer, Citizens Memorial Hospital, Bolivar, MO, p. A402

FULCHER, Kimberly, Chief Human Resources Officer, Halifax Health Medical Center Of Daytona Beach, Daytona Beach, FL, p. A136

FULKERSON, Judy, Director Human Resources, Tristar Greenview Regional Hospital, Bowling Green, KY, p. A281

FULKERSON, Kimberly, Chief Nursing Officer, Dupont Hospital, Fort Wayne, IN, p. A228

FULKERSON, Richard, Director Fiscal Services, Shriners Hospitals For Children-Springfield, Springfield, MA, p. A345

FULKERSON, William, Chief Operating Officer, University Of Virginia Medical Center, Charlottesville, VA, p. A740

FULKROD, Ray, Chief Nursing Officer, Tidalhealth Nanticoke, Seaford, DE, p. A128

FULKS, Chris, Vice President Finance, Lake Huron Medical Center, Port Huron, MI, p. A364

FULLER, Cara, Vice President Human Resources, Unitypoint Health - Trinity Bettendorf, Bettendorf, IA, p. A244
Vice President Human Resources, Unitypoint Health - Trinity Rock Island, Rock Island, IL, p. A218

FULLER, Cheryl, Director Information Resources, Kansas Neurological Institute, Topeka, KS, p. A277

FULLER, Dale, Vice President and Chief Information Officer, Upmc Altoona, Altoona, PA, p. A584
Vice President, Chief Information Officer, Upmc Somerset, Somerset, PA, p. A608

FULLER, David, Vice President of Human Resources, Porter Medical Center, Middlebury, VT, p. A736

FULLER, Harrington, Information Technology Director, Hendry Regional Medical Center, Clewiston, FL, p. A134

FULLER, Jane, Vice President Human Resources, North Florida Regional Medical Center, Gainesville, FL, p. A138

FULLER, Jeremy, Director Information Systems, Hca Houston Healthcare Conroe, Conroe, TX, p. A665

FULLER, Marion, Chief of Staff, Munson Healthcare Manistee Hospital, Manistee, MI, p. A361

FULLER, Scott O., President and Chief Executive Officer, Ascension Seton Edgar B. Davis Hospital, Luling, TX, p. A699
President and Chief Executive Officer, Ascension Seton Highland Lakes, Burnet, TX, p. A662

FULLER SPENCER, Carrie, Chief Financial Officer, Highland Hospital, Rochester, NY, p. A496

FULLER-WILLIAMS, Vonetta, Director Human Resources Strategic and Business Services, Baylor Scott & White Medical Center-Irving, Irving, TX, p. A690

FULLUM, Jane, Vice President Patient Care Services, East Alabama Medical Center, Opelika, AL, p. A23

FULTON, Lynn, President, Osf St. Josep. Medical Center, Bloomington, IL, p. A195

FUNDERBURG, Michelle, Director Human Resources, Stephens Memorial Hospital, Breckenridge, TX, p. A660

FUNDERBURK, Mark, President and Chief Executive Officer, University Medical Center, Lubbock, TX, p. A698

FUNG, Adrian, Director Information Systems, Vanderbilt Wilson County Hospital, Lebanon, TN, p. A642

FUNK, Luann, Administrative Assistant and Manager Human Resources, Pana Community Hospital, Pana, IL, p. A216

FUNKHOUSER, Krisy, Manager Human Resources, Willap. Harbor Hospital, South Bend, WA, p. A765

FUNTANILLA, Alan V., Executive Vice President, Chief Operating Officer, Guam Regional Medical City, Dededo, GU, p. A805

FUQUA, David, Director Human Resources Management, Ochsner Lsu Health Shreveport - Academic Medical Center, Shreveport, LA, p. A314

FUQUA, David G., Chief Executive Officer, Marshall County Hospital, Benton, KY, p. A280

FUQUA, Leon, Chief Operating Officer, Wise Health System, Decatur, TX, p. A671

FURER, Darnell, MS, R.N., Vice President Patient Care Services and Chief Nursing Officer, Lehigh Valley Hospital - Schuylkill, Pottsville, PA, p. A605

FURGURSON, Carol, Chief Operating Officer, St. Louise Regional Hospital, Gilroy, CA, p. A66

FURLANI, Thomas, M.D., Chief Information Officer, Roswell Park Comprehensive Cancer Center, Buffalo, NY, p. A480

FURLOW, Pete, Chief Information Officer, Rmc Anniston, Anniston, AL, p. A13

FURNAS, David, Chief Information Officer, Gila Regional Medical Center, Silver City, NM, p. A472

FURNEY, June, R.N., Director of Nursing, Brooks County Hospital, Quitman, GA, p. A178

FURNISS, Scott, Vice President and Chief Financial Officer, Saint Agnes Healthcare, Baltimore, MD, p. A326

FURR, Robert, Director Information Services, Anmed Health Cannon, Pickens, SC, p. A623

FUSCHILLO, Ronald, Chief Information Officer, Renown Regional Medical Center, Reno, NV, p. A446
Chief Information Officer, Renown Rehabilitation Hospital, Reno, NV, p. A446
Chief Information Officer, Renown South Meadows Medical Center, Reno, NV, p. A446

FUSCO, Gina, M.D., Chief Executive Officer, Foundations Behavioral Health, Doylestown, PA, p. A588

FUSELIER, Gerald, Chief Operating Officer, Savoy Medical Center, Mamou, LA, p. A307

FUSELIER, Michael, FACHE, CPA, R.N., Chief Financial Officer, Central Louisiana Surgical Hospital, Alexandria, LA, p. A295

FUSILERO, Jane, Vice President Chief Nursing Officer, H. Lee Moffitt Cancer Center And Research Institute, Tampa, FL, p. A159

FUSTON, Kathie, Director Human Resources, Moore County Hospital District, Dumas, TX, p. A673

FUTCH, Margaret A., Chief Executive Officer, Encompass Health Rehabilitation Hospital Of Dothan, Dothan, AL, p. A17

FUTRAL, Cindy, Director Human Resources, Elmore Community Hospital, Wetumpka, AL, p. A26

FUTRELL, Bradley, Chief Operating Officer, Pinckneyville Community Hospital, Pinckneyville, IL, p. A217

FUTRELL, Cynthia, MSN, R.N., Chief Nursing Officer, Marion General Hospital, Marion, IN, p. A236

# G

GAAL, James, M.D., Chief of Medical Staff, Jackson General Hospital, Ripley, WV, p. A776

GAASCH, Andrew, Chief Financial Officer, Porter Adventist Hospital, Denver, CO, p. A111

GABALDON, Karen, Chief Management Information Systems, West Palm Beach Veterans Affairs Medical Center, West Palm Beach, FL, p. A162

GABEL, Christopher, Chief Operating Officer, Larkin Community Hospital Behavioral Health Services, Hollywood, FL, p. A140

GABEL, Kelly, Chief of Staff, Citizens Medical Center, Colby, KS, p. A263

GABEL, Marcia, Chief Financial Officer and Co-Chief Executive Officer, Lane County Hospital, Dighton, KS, p. A263
Chief Financial Officer, Lane County Hospital, Dighton, KS, p. A263

GABLE, Beth, Administrative Assistant, Jasper General Hospital, Bay Springs, MS, p. A389

GABLENZ, Gordon, Vice President Finance, Ridgeview Medical Center, Waconia, MN, p. A387

GABORIAULT, Randall, Chief Information Officer, Christianacare, Newark, DE, p. A128

GABRIEL, Scott, President, Parkview Whitley Hospital, Columbia City, IN, p. A225

GABRIEL, Scott F., President, Parkview Whitley Hospital, Columbia City, IN, p. A225

GABRIEL, Shirley, Vice President and Chief Information Officer, University Hospital, Augusta, GA, p. A166

GABRIEL, Stacey, R.N., President and Chief Executive Officer, Hocking Valley Community Hospital, Logan, OH, p. A543

GABRIELE, Joan, Deputy Executive Director, Nyc Health + Hospitals / Queens, Jamaica, NY, p. A486

GABRYEL, Timothy, M.D., Vice President Medical Affairs and Medical Director, Mercy Hospital, Buffalo, NY, p. A480

GABUAT, Jesse, Chief Nursing Officer, Aventura Hospital And Medical Center, Aventura, FL, p. A131
Chief Nursing Officer, Plantation General Hospital, Plantation, FL, p. A154

GAC, Deborah, Vice President Human Resources, Valley Presbyterian Hospital, Van Nuys, CA, p. A103

GADALLAH, Yousri, M.D., Chief Medical Officer, Pershing General Hospital, Lovelock, NV, p. A445

GADDAM, Sumalatha, Senior Vice President and Chief Information Officer, Kent County Memorial Hospital, Warwick, RI, p. A614

GADDAM, Summa, Chief Information Officer, Butler Hospital, Providence, RI, p. A613

GADDIS, Cathryn, Director Human Resources, Rivervalley Behavioral Health Hospital, Owensboro, KY, p. A291

GADDY, Pam, Director, Patient Care Services and Chief Nursing Officer, Firsthealth Montgomery Memorial Hospital, Troy, NC, p. A519

GADE, Swami, M.D., Medical Director, Tioga Medical Center, Tioga, ND, p. A526

GADEN, Paul, Chief Executive Officer, Bon Secours Maryview Medical Center, Portsmouth, VA, p. A747
Chief Executive Officer, Bon Secours-Depaul Medical Center, Norfolk, VA, p. A747
Chief Executive Officer, Sentara Princess Anne Hospital, Virginia Beach, VA, p. A753

GAEDE, John, Director Information Systems, El Centro Regional Medical Center, El Centro, CA, p. A63

GAFFOLI, Jill, Director Human Resources, Physicians Regional - Pine Ridge, Naples, FL, p. A149

GAFFORD, Deborah, Chief Financial Officer, Menorah Medical Center, Overland Park, KS, p. A274

GAFFORD, Grady, Chief Financial Officer, Brownfield Regional Medical Center, Brownfield, TX, p. A660

GAGE, Bobby, Director Information Technology, Wabash General Hospital, Mount Carmel, IL, p. A213

GAGE, Kevin, Chief Financial Officer, Stamford Hospital, Stamford, CT, p. A125

GAGE, Mark, D.O., Medical Director, Brookhaven Hospital, Tulsa, OK, p. A569

GAGE, Susan, Financial Manager, Veterans Affairs Western New York Healthcare System-Buffalo Division, Buffalo, NY, p. A480

GAGE, Weldon, Chief Financial Officer, University Of Texas M.D. Anderson Cancer Center, Houston, TX, p. A689

GAGLIARDI, Teresa, R.N., Chief Nursing Officer, Trinity Hospital Twin City, Dennison, OH, p. A539
R.N., Vice President of Hospital Operations and Site Administrator, Trinity Hospital Twin City, Dennison, OH, p. A539

GAGLIO, Anthony, CPA, Senior Vice President and Chief Financial Officer, Menninger Clinic, Houston, TX, p. A687

GAGNE, Cheryl Vice President Patient Care Services and Chief Nursing Officer, Southern New Hampshire Medical Center, Nashua, NH, p. A450

GAGNE, Margaret, R.N., MS, Interim Chief Nursing Officer, University Of Vermont Medical Center, Burlington, VT, p. A735

GAGNON, Andy, Manager Information Technology, Ascension Via Christi Hospital, Manhattan, Manhattan, KS, p. A270

GAILLARD, Timothy, Chief Operating Officer, Augusta University Medical Center, Augusta, GA, p. A165

GAINES, April, Chief Nursing Officer, Crete Area Medical Center, Crete, NE, p. A431

GAINES, Jared, M.D., Chief Medical Officer, Fort Lauderdale Behavioral Health Center, Oakland Park, FL, p. A149

GAINES, Jeffrey, M.D., Vice President and Chief Medical Officer, Newport Hospital, Newport, RI, p. A613

GAINEY, Rachel, Administrator, Mcleod Health Clarendon, Manning, SC, p. A622

GAINEY, Shari, Chief Human Resource Officer, Tanner Medical Center-Villa Rica, Villa Rica, GA, p. A182
Human Resource Director, Higgins General Hospital, Bremen, GA, p. A167

GAJ, Steve, Facility Chief Information Officer, Louis Stokes Cleveland Veterans Affairs Medical Center, Cleveland, OH, p. A534

GAJARAJ, Krishnaswamy, M.D., Medical Director, Arbour H. R. I. Hospital, Brookline, MA, p. A337

GAJEWSKI, Christie, Director Human Resources, Pinckneyville Community Hospital, Pinckneyville, IL, p. A217

GALANG, Michael, M.D., Chief Information Officer, Mercy Hospital, Buffalo, NY, p. A480
M.D., Chief Information Officer, Sisters Of Charity Hospital Of Buffalo, Buffalo, NY, p. A480

GALARNEAU, Ciprian, Director Information Systems, Tri Valley Health System, Cambridge, NE, p. A430

GALARNEAU, Gerard, M.D., Regional Chief Medical Officer, Garnet Health Medical Center - Catskills, Harris, NY, p. A485

GALAVIZ, Veronica, Chief Financial Officer, Lovelace Regional Hospital - Roswell, Roswell, NM, p. A471

GALBRAITH, Kathleen B., FACHE, President, Duke Regional Hospital, Durham, NC, p. A508

GALDIERI, Lou, R.N., President, Morton Plant Hospital, Clearwater, FL, p. A134

GALE, Gabrielle, Chief Financial Officer, Lighthouse Behavioral Health Hospital, Conway, SC, p. A618

GALE, Melissa, Chief Executive Officer, Landmann-Jungman Memorial Hospital Avera, Scotland, SD, p. A631

GALE, Michael, Chief Financial Officer, Bournewood Health Systems, Brookline, MA, p. A337

GALEY, John, M.D., Chief Medical Officer, Schoolcraft Memorial Hospital, Manistique, MI, p. A361

GALIANA, Amy, Chief Human Resource Officer, Highland Hospital, Rochester, NY, p. A496

GALIPEAU, Michelle, Director Human Resources, St. Vincent's Birmingham, Birmingham, AL, p. A15

GALKOWSKI, James, Associate Director for Operations, Fayetteville Veterans Affairs Medical Center, Fayetteville, NC, p. A510

GALLAGHER, Chris, M.D., Chief Medical Officer, Christus Mother Frances Hospital - Sulphur Springs, Sulphur Springs, TX, p. A718

GALLAGHER, Deborah, Manager Human Resources, Ojai Valley Community Hospital, Ojai, CA, p. A82

GALLAGHER, Doug, Director Human Resources, Carolinas Continuecare Hospital At Pineville, Charlotte, NC, p. A507

GALLAGHER, J. P., President and Chief Executive Officer, Northshore University Health System, Evanston, IL, p. A204

GALLAGHER, James, Chief Executive Officer, Centerpointe Hospital Of Columbia, Columbia, MO, p. A405
Chief Executive Officer, Oasis Behavioral Health - Chandler, Chandler, AZ, p. A31

GALLAGHER, Jeannie, Chief Human Resource Officer, North Colorado Medical Center, Greeley, CO, p. A113 Mckee Medical Center, Loveland, CO, p. A117

GALLAGHER, Karen, MSN, Chief Nursing Office, Vice President Operations, Amita Health St. Mary's Hospital, Kankakee, IL, p. A209 Vice President Human Resources and Learning, Brooks Rehabilitation Hospital, Jacksonville, FL, p. A141

GALLAGHER, Pamela, Chief Financial Officer, Providence Hospital, Columbia, SC, p. A618

GALLAGHER, Regen, D.O., Chief Medical Officer, Cary Medical Center, Caribou, ME, p. A320

GALLAGHER, Sherry, Director Nursing, Department of Health and Human Services, Humboldt County Mental Health, Eureka, CA, p. A63

GALLAHOM, Gerty, Director Human Resources, Maniilaq Health Center, Kotzebue, AK, p. A29

GALLARDO, Kathleen, Chief Nursing Officer, Select Specialty Hospital-Flint, Flint, MI, p. A354

GALLARDO, Laura, Chief Operating Officer, Kaiser Permanente Panorama City Medical Center, Panorama City, CA, p. A84

GALLARDO, Ysidro, Associate Administrator Human Resources, Hazel Hawkins Memorial Hospital, Hollister, CA, p. A68

GALLATI, Todd, FACHE, President and Chief Executive Officer, Trident Medical Center, Charleston, SC, p. A616

GALLAY, Emily, Vice President and Chief Information Officer, Spectrum Health Lakeland, Saint Joseph, MI, p. A366

GALLEGO, Janeen, Chief Nursing Officer, West Hills Hospital And Medical Center, West Hills, CA, p. A104

GALLEGOS, Colleen, Director Human Resources, Guadalup. County Hospital, Santa Rosa, NM, p. A472

GALLEGOS, Enrique, Chief Executive Officer, Laredo Medical Center, Laredo, TX, p. A695

GALLEGOS, Kelly, Administrator, San Luis Valley Health Conejos County Hospital, La Jara, CO, p. A115

GALLEGOS, Ken, Director Support Services and Information Technology, Medina Regional Hospital, Hondo, TX, p. A684

GALLI, Jodi, R.N., Chief Nursing Officer, Kaiser Permanente Redwood City Medical Center, Redwood City, CA, p. A87

GALLIART, Mark, Chief Executive Officer, Mcbride Orthopedic Hospital, Oklahoma City, OK, p. A564

GALLIK, Becky, Information Systems Manager, Welia Health, Mora, MN, p. A381

GALLO, Carrie, Chief Nursing Officer, Western Reserve Hospital, Cuyahoga Falls, OH, p. A538

GALLO, Ronald, Director Human Resources, Blythedale Children's Hospital, Valhalla, NY, p. A500

GALLOGLY-SIMON, Catherine, R.N., MS, Chief Nursing Officer, Wyckoff Heights Medical Center, Brooklyn, NY, p. A479

GALLUCCI, Vince, Senior Vice President Human Resources, Ascension Northeast Wisconsin Mercy Hospital, Oshkosh, WI, p. A793 Senior Vice President Human Resources, Ascension Northeast Wisconsin St. Elizabeth Hospital, Appleton, WI, p. A779

GALLUP, Jared, Chief Information Officer, Cassia Regional Hospital, Burley, ID, p. A189

GALT, Nick, Chief Financial Officer, Medical City Las Colinas, Irving, TX, p. A690 Chief Financial Officer, Medical City North Hills, North Richland Hills, TX, p. A703

GALUP, Richard, President, Jefferson Health Northeast, Philadelphia, PA, p. A600

GALUSHA, Fred, Chief Information Officer, St. Luke's Rehabilitation Institute, Spokane, WA, p. A766

GALYON, Darlene, Director Human Resources, Choctaw Memorial Hospital, Hugo, OK, p. A560

GAMACHE, Cynde, R.N., Vice President and Chief Nursing Officer, Baptist Hospital, Pensacola, FL, p. A153

GAMB, Pamela, Manager Human Resources, Aurora Psychiatric Hospital, Wauwatosa, WI, p. A799

GAMBLA, Kurt, D.O., Chief Medical Officer, Beaufort Memorial Hospital, Beaufort, SC, p. A615

GAMBLE, Allen J., Interim Chief Executive Officer, Regional West Garden County, Oshkosh, NE, p. A438

GAMBLE, Brian, Chief Financial Officer, Karmanos Cancer Center, Detroit, MI, p. A353

GAMBLE, Kathleen, Fiscal Officer, Dsh Patton, Patton, CA, p. A85

GAMBLE, Mike, M.D., Chief Medical Officer, Greene County General Hospital, Linton, IN, p. A235

GAMBLE, Troy, M.D., JrChief Medical Staff, Williamsburg Regional Hospital, Kingstree, SC, p. A622

GAMBOA, Eileen, Vice President Human Resources, HCA Houston Healthcare Southeast, Oakbend Medical Center, Richmond, TX, p. A708

GAMBRELL, Titus, Vice President and Chief Nursing Officer, St. Mary's Health Care System, Athens, GA, p. A164

GAMET, Nicki, R.N., Administrator, Mercy Hospital Aurora, Aurora, MO, p. A402 R.N., Administrator, Mercy Hospital Cassville, Cassville, MO, p. A404 R.N., Administrator, Mercy Hospital Lebanon, Lebanon, MO, p. A404

GAMEZ, Kriss, Director Human Resources, Baylor Scott & White Medical Center - Plano, Plano, TX, p. A706

GAMINO, Randall, Director Perot Site, St. Joseph's Medical Center, Stockton, CA, p. A100

GAMMIERE, Thomas A., Chief Executive, Senior Vice President, Scripp. Mercy Hospital, San Diego, CA, p. A92

GANDHI, Tejas, Ph.D., Chief Operating Officer, Baystate Medical Center, Springfield, MA, p. A344

GANDY, Galina, Vice President Information Technology, Columbia Memorial Hospital, Astoria, OR, p. A573

GANDY, Patrick W. Jr, CPA, Executive Vice President and Chief Executive Officer, Lafayette General Medical Center, Lafayette, LA, p. A305

GANGULY, Indranil, Vice President and Chief Information Officer, Hackensack Meridian Health Jfk Medical Center, Edison, NJ, p. A454

GANGULY, Neal, Chief Information Officer, Jfk Johnson Rehabilitation Institute At Hackensack Meridian Health, Edison, NJ, p. A454

GANN, Michele, Vice President Patient Services, Mercy Hospital Berryville, Berryville, AR, p. A42

GANNON, Ronnie, Director Information Services, Tristar Southern Hills Medical Center, Nashville, TN, p. A647

GANS, Bruce, M.D., Executive Vice President and Chief Medical Officer, Kessler Institute For Rehabilitation, West Orange, NJ, p. A465

GANSEMER, Sheila, R.N., Vice President Patient Care Services and Chief Nursing Officer, Ascension Southeast Wisconsin Hospital - Franklin Campus, Franklin, WI, p. A784

GANSKE, Jary, Chief Financial Officer, Methodist Mansfield Medical Center, Mansfield, TX, p. A699

GANSZ, Phil, Director Information Technology, Colleton Medical Center, Walterboro, SC, p. A625

GANT, Curtis, Chief Financial Officer, New Mexico Rehabilitation Center, Roswell, NM, p. A471

GANTNER, John J., President and Chief Executive Officer, Robert Wood Johnson University Hospital, New Brunswick, NJ, p. A459

GANTT, Cynthia, Chief of Staff, Naval Medical Center, Portsmouth, VA, p. A749

GANTZER, Ann, Ph.D., R.N., Vice President Patient Services and Chief Nursing Officer, Swedishamerican - A Division Of Uw Health, Rockford, IL, p. A219

GARAY, Kenneth, M.D., Chief Medical Officer, Jersey City Medical Center, Jersey City, NJ, p. A456

GARBANZOS, Del, Director Human Resources, Delano Regional Medical Center, Delano, CA, p. A62

GARBARINO, James, Chief Financial Officer, Clay County Medical Center, Clay Center, KS, p. A262

GARBER, Mary, Vice President Finance, Mercy Hospital Ada, Ada, OK, p. A555

GARCIA, Antonio, Chief Nursing Officer, Miller Children's & Women's Hospital Long Beach, Long Beach, CA, p. A72

GARCIA, Ara, Manager Human Resources, Milwaukee County Behavioral Health Division, Milwaukee, WI, p. A791

GARCIA, Aymette, Manager Human Resources, Wilma N. Vazquez Medical Center, Vega Baja, PR, p. A811

GARCIA, Charla, Human Resource Officer, Uvalde Memorial Hospital, Uvalde, TX, p. A722

GARCIA, Danette, Director Human Resources, Encompass Health Valley Of The Sun Rehabilitation Hospital, Glendale, AZ, p. A32

GARCIA, Estevan, M.D., Chief Medical Officer, Cooley Dickinson Hospital, Northampton, MA, p. A342

GARCIA, Evangeline, M.D., Clinical Director, Eastern Shore Hospital Center, Cambridge, MD, p. A328

GARCIA, Georgina R., R.N., Executive Director, Kaiser Permanente West Los Angeles Medical Center, Los Angeles, CA, p. A74

GARCIA, Gerard, Chief Human Resource Officer, University Hospital, Newark, NJ, p. A460

GARCIA, Idalia, Chief Human Resources Officer, Hospital De Psiquiatria, San Juan, PR, p. A810

GARCIA, Iris, Director, Information Services, Jerome Golden Center For Behavioral Health, Inc., West Palm Beach, FL, p. A162

GARCIA, Irma, Job Coordinator, Rio Grande State Center/ South Texas Health Care System, Harlingen, TX, p. A683

GARCIA, Jacob, Chief Information Officer, Little Colorado Medical Center, Winslow, AZ, p. A41

GARCIA, Jannina, Director of Human Resources, Adventhealth Fish Memorial, Orange City, FL, p. A150

GARCIA, Joanne, Chief Operating Officer, Kindred Chicago-Central Hospital, Chicago, IL, p. A199

GARCIA, Joannie, CPA, Director Finance, Hospital Perea, Mayaguez, PR, p. A808

GARCIA, Jose, M.D., Chief Medical Staff, Dundy County Hospital, Benkelman, NE, p. A430 Chief Human Resources Officer, San Juan City Hospital, San Juan, PR, p. A811

GARCIA, Karen, MSN, R.N., Chief Nursing Officer, Baptist Hospitals Of Southeast Texas, Beaumont, TX, p. A658

GARCIA, Kathleen, Controller, St. John's Episcopal Hospital, Far Rockaway, NY, p. A483

GARCIA, Margaret, Manager Human Resources, Baylor Scott & White Medical Center—Frisco, Frisco, TX, p. A680

GARCIA, Michael, Vice President and Chief Information Officer, Jackson Health System, Miami, FL, p. A146

GARCIA, Orlando, M.D., Chief Medical Officer, Hialeah Hospital, Hialeah, FL, p. A139

GARCIA, Robert, M.D., Chief Medical Officer, Iraan General Hospital, Iraan, TX, p. A690

GARCIA, Rodolfo R., Chief Executive Officer, Westchester General Hospital, Miami, FL, p. A147

GARCIA, Roland, Senior Vice President and Chief Information Officer, Baptist Medical Center Beaches, Jacksonville Beach, FL, p. A142 Senior Vice President and Chief Information Officer, Baptist Medical Center Jacksonville, Jacksonville, FL, p. A140

GARCIA, Sharon, Human Resources Representative, Medina Regional Hospital, Hondo, TX, p. A684

GARCIA, Shawn, Manager Human Resources, Memorial Hospital Los Banos, Los Banos, CA, p. A76

GARCIA, Sylvia, Chief Accounting Officer, South Texas Spine And Surgical Hospital, San Antonio, TX, p. A713

GARCIA, Tracy, MS, Chief Nursing Officer, Cheyenne Regional Medical Center, Cheyenne, WY, p. A801

GARCIA JR, LuisDirector Human Resources, Houston Methodist Sugar Land Hospital, Sugar Land, TX, p. A717

GARCIN, Hector, Human Resources Director, St. Luke's Episcopal Hospital, Ponce, PR, p. A809

GARD, Emily, Chief Clinical Officer, Kindred Hospital-San Francisco Bay Area, San Leandro, CA, p. A95

GARDEPE, Cynthia, Director, Human Resources, Uhs Delaware Valley Hospital, Walton, NY, p. A501

GARDINER, Greg, Chief Clinical Officer, Ashley Regional Medical Center, Vernal, UT, p. A734

GARDINER, Karen, Human Resources Director, Bayfront Health Port Charlotte, Port Charlotte, FL, p. A154

GARDNER, Carla, Director of Nursing, Munson Healthcare Grayling Hospital, Grayling, MI, p. A356

GARDNER, Greg, Senior Vice President and Chief Financial Officer, Cleveland Clinic Indian River Hospital, Vero Beach, FL, p. A161

GARDNER, Jacque, Administrative Assistant, Clinic Manager, Co-Chief Financial Officer and Chief Human Resources, Mccone County Health Center, Circle, MT, p. A422

GARDNER, James, M.D., Vice President and Chief Medical Officer, Waukesha Memorial Hospital, Waukesha, WI, p. A798

GARDNER, Kristin, Chief Nursing Officer, Ohiohealth Berger Hospital, Circleville, OH, p. A533

GARDNER, Michelle, M.D., Clinical Director, Dorothea Dix Psychiatric Center, Bangor, ME, p. A318

GARDNER, Patrick, M.D., Associate Vice President, Medical Affairs, St. Joseph's Hospital, Froedtert West Bend Hospital, West Bend, WI, p. A799

GARDNER, Robb, Chief Executive Officer, Henry County Health Center, Mount Pleasant, IA, p. A254

GARDNER, Robert, Chief Executive Officer, Banner Goldfield Medical Center, Apache Junction, AZ, p. A30 Chief Executive Officer, Banner Ironwood Medical Center, San Tan Valley, AZ, p. A38

GARDNER, Sharon, Manager Information Systems, Ssm Health St. Josep. Hospital - Lake Saint Louis, Lake Saint Louis, MO, p. A410

GARDNER, William, Chief Clinical Officer, Bartlett Regional Hospital, Juneau, AK, p. A28

GARDNER, Zoe, Manager Human Resources, Sharp Chula Vista Medical Center, Chula Vista, CA, p. A60

GARES, Donna, R.N., FACHE, MSN, Chief Executive Officer, Select Specialty Hospital-Wilmington, Wilmington, DE, p. A128

GARISON, Jerri, R.N., President, Baylor Scott & White Medical Center - Plano, Plano, TX, p. A706

GARLAND, Pamela, R.N., Chief Nursing Officer, Northside Hospital - Gwinnett, Lawrenceville, GA, p. A175

GARMAN, Denise, Director Human Resources, Wellspan Good Samaritan Hospital, Lebanon, PA, p. A595

GARMAN, Michael, Chief Financial Officer, Avera St. Anthony's Hospital, O'Neill, NE, p. A438

GARMAN, Patrick M., Commander, Evans U. S. Army Community Hospital, Fort Carson, CO, p. A112

GARMANY, Kandi, Interim Chief Financial Officer, Gadsden Regional Medical Center, Gadsden, AL, p. A19

GARNAS, David, Administrator, Cloud County Health Center, Concordia, KS, p. A263

GARNER, Douglas, Vice President, Thomas Hospital, Fairhope, AL, p. A18

GARNER, John, D.O., Medical Director, Culberson Hospital, Van Horn, TX, p. A722

GARNER, Mario J., Ed.D., FACHE, Chief Executive Officer, Chi St. Luke's Hospital - The Vintage Hospital, Houston, TX, p. A685

GARNER, Stephen, Chief Operating Officer, Delray Medical Center, Delray Beach, FL, p. A136

GARNETT, Mark, M.D., Chief of Staff, Hansford Hospital, Spearman, TX, p. A716

GAROFOLA, Aaron, Chief Executive Officer, Uofl Health - Shelbyville Hospital, Shelbyville, KY, p. A293

GARONE, Marlene, M.D., Vice President Medical Affairs and Medical Director, Upmc Chautauqua, Jamestown, NY, p. A486

GARRARD, Michael Eric., FACHE, Chief Executive Officer, Emory Rehabilitation Hospital, Atlanta, GA, p. A164

GARRED, John, M.D., Chief Medical Officer, Burgess Health Center, Onawa, IA, p. A255

GARREN-OSTER, Cynthia, Human Resource Manager, South Coast Global Medical Center, Santa Ana, CA, p. A96
Human Resources Manager, Chapman Global Medical Center, Orange, CA, p. A82

GARRETT, Alan H., Chief Executive Officer, Carson Tahoe Health, Carson City, NV, p. A441

GARRETT, Courtney, CPA, Senior Vice President, Chief Financial Officer, Children's Hospital, New Orleans, LA, p. A310

GARRETT, Dana, R.N., Nursing Services Administrator, Taylor Regional Hospital, Campbellsville, KY, p. A281

GARRETT, David, Senior Vice President and Chief Information Officer, Novant Health Brunswick Medical Center, Bolivia, NC, p. A505
Senior Vice President and Chief Information Officer, Novant Health Charlotte Orthopaedic Hospital, Charlotte, NC, p. A507
Senior Vice President and Chief Information Officer, Novant Health Forsyth Medical Center, Winston, NC, p. A520
Senior Vice President and Chief Information Officer, Novant Health Huntersville Medical Center, Huntersville, NC, p. A512
Senior Vice President and Chief Information Officer, Novant Health Matthews Medical Center, Matthews, NC, p. A514
Senior Vice President and Chief Information Officer, Novant Health Medical Park Hospital, Winston, NC, p. A520
Senior Vice President and Chief Information Officer, Novant Health Rowan Medical Center, Salisbury, NC, p. A518
Senior Vice President and Chief Information Officer, Novant Health Thomasville Medical Center, Thomasville, NC, p. A519
Senior Vice President and Chief Information Officer, Novant Health Uva Health System Haymarket Medical Center, Haymarket, VA, p. A744
Senior Vice President and Chief Information Officer, Novant Health Uva Health System Prince William Medical Center, Manassas, VA, p. A745
Senior Vice President Information Technology, Novant Health Presbyterian Medical Center, Charlotte, NC, p. A507

GARRETT, Josh, Chief of Staff, Habersham Medical Center, Demorest, GA, p. A171

GARRETT, Kevin, M.D., Medical Executive East Region, St. Joseph's Hospital, Saint Paul, MN, p. A385
M.D., Medical Executive, East Region, Woodwinds Health Campus, Woodbury, MN, p. A388

GARRETT, Matthew, Director Information Systems, Flowers Hospital, Dothan, AL, p. A17

GARRETT, Nancy, Chief Analytics and Information Technology Officer, Hennepin Healthcare, Minneapolis, MN, p. A380

GARRETT, Scott, Director of IS, Ottumwa Regional Health Center, Ottumwa, IA, p. A256

GARRICK, Renee, M.D., Executive Medical Director, Westchester Medical Center, Valhalla, NY, p. A501

GARRIOTT, Edie, Director Human Resources, Community Hospital South, Indianapolis, IN, p. A231

GARRISON, Christopher, M.D., Medical Director, Central Texas Rehabilitation Hospital, Austin, TX, p. A655

GARRISON, Tina, President, Ssm Health St. Clare Hospital - Fenton, Fenton, MO, p. A406

GARRISON, Wes, St. Luke's Sugar Land Hospital, Sugar Land, TX, p. A717

GARRITY, Elizabeth, Director Human Resources, Hudson Regional Hospital, Secaucus, NJ, p. A463

GARRITY, Nerissa, Chief Financial Officer, Kula Hospital, Kula, HI, p. A186

GARROW, Dina, Chief Nursing Officer and Chief Operating Officer, Kindred Hospital-Baldwin Park, Baldwin Park, CA, p. A58

GARTMAN, Kathy, Chief Nursing Officer, Medical Center Of South Arkansas, El Dorado, AR, p. A44

GARTNER, Katie, Director Health Information Management, Chi Health Good Samaritan, Kearney, NE, p. A433

GARTON, Debra, R.N., Chief Nursing Officer, Oss Health, York, PA, p. A612

GARVEY, James, Senior Vice President Hospital Practice, Essentia Health East, Essentia Health St. Mary's Medical Center, Duluth, MN, p. A375

GARVEY, Rita, Chief Nursing Officer, Lawrence County Memorial Hospital, Lawrenceville, IL, p. A210

GARVEY, Thomas, Senior Vice President Operations and Chief Financial Officer, Swedish Covenant Hospital, Chicago, IL, p. A201

GARY, Al, COO, Simpson General Hospital, Mendenhall, MS, p. A396

GARZA, Art, FACHE, Chief Executive Officer, Valley Regional Medical Center, Brownsville, TX, p. A661

GARZA, Ismelda, Director Information Systems, Comanche County Medical Center, Comanche, TX, p. A665

GARZA, Laura, Manager Information Technology, Hereford Regional Medical Center, Hereford, TX, p. A684

GARZA, Leo, Chief Executive Officer, South Texas Rehabilitation Hospital, Brownsville, TX, p. A661

GARZA, Oscar, M.D., Chief Medical Staff, Frio Regional Hospital, Pearsall, TX, p. A705

GARZA, Ruben, Chief Executive Officer, Dallas Medical Center, Dallas, TX, p. A668

GARZA, Teri, Director Health Information Services, Knap. Medical Center, Weslaco, TX, p. A725

GARZA, Tom, Director Fiscal and Support, Rio Grande State Center/South Texas Health Care System, Harlingen, TX, p. A683

GASBARRE, Christopher, D.O., Community Medical Director, Monument Health Spearfish Hospital, Spearfish, SD, p. A632

GASH, Deborah, Chief Information Officer, Saint Luke's Hospital Of Kansas City, Kansas City, MO, p. A409
Chief Information Officer, Saint Luke's South Hospital, Overland Park, KS, p. A274

GASKILL, Paulette, Executive Director of Nursing, Ascension St. Vincent Clay Hospital, Brazil, IN, p. A224

GASKILL III, Harold V., M.D., Chief Executive Officer, First Baptist Medical Center, Dallas, TX, p. A668

GASKILL-HAMES, Michelle, R.N., Senior Vice President & Area Manager, Kaiser Permanente Redwood City Medical Center, Redwood City, CA, p. A87

GASKINS, Michael, Director Information Technology, Lincoln Community Hospital And Nursing Home, Hugo, CO, p. A114

GASKINS, Michael W., President, Upmc Hanover, Hanover, PA, p. A591
President, Upmc Memorial, York, PA, p. A612

GASPAR, Gabrielle, M.D., Chief Medical Officer, Doctors Medical Center Of Modesto, Modesto, CA, p. A78

GASPAR-YOO, Vicenta, M.D., Director and Chief Executive Officer, Allegheny Valley Hospital, Natrona Heights, PA, p. A598

GASQUE, James, M.D., Chief Hospital Services, U. S. Air Force Medical Center Keesler, Keesler Afb, MS, p. A395

GASSELING, Cassie, Chief Financial Officer, Kimball Health Services, Kimball, NE, p. A434

GASTINEAU, Trent, Chief Executive Officer, Tulsa Spine And Specialty Hospital, Tulsa, OK, p. A571

GASTON, Jan, Administrator, Jasper Memorial Hospital, Monticello, GA, p. A177

GASTON, Tammy, Chief Information Officer, Smith County Memorial Hospital, Smith Center, KS, p. A276

GATES, Misty, Chief Financial Officer, Forrest City Medical Center, Forrest City, AR, p. A45

GATES, Rose, Director Human Resources, Hayward Area Memorial Hospital And Water's Edge, Hayward, WI, p. A786

GATES, Tracy, Vice President Operations and Chief Operating Officer, Guthrie Cortland Regional Medical Center, Cortland, NY, p. A482

GATHERS, Mary, Director Information Systems, Mckay-Dee Hospital, Ogden, UT, p. A730
Director Information Systems, Utah Valley Hospital, Provo, UT, p. A731
Manager Information Systems, American Fork Hospital, American Fork, UT, p. A727

GATLIFF, Peggy, Chief Financial Officer, Northside Hospital, Saint Petersburg, FL, p. A156

GATLIFF, Rob, Chief of Medical Staff, Washington County Regional Medical Center, Sandersville, GA, p. A179

GATO, Carlos, Director of Human Resources, Fort Lauderdale Behavioral Health Center, Oakland Park, FL, p. A149

GATRELL, Kristi, Chief Executive Officer, Big Horn County Memorial Hospital, Hardin, MT, p. A424

GATTO, Tony, Director Management Information Systems, Flushing Hospital Medical Center, Flushing, NY, p. A484

GATTO, Vincent, M.D., Chief Medical Officer, Winter Haven Hospital, Winter Haven, FL, p. A162

GAUER, Natalie, Administrator, Milbank Area Hospital Avera, Milbank, SD, p. A629

GAUG, Mathew, Executive Director of Information Technology, Lima Memorial Health System, Lima, OH, p. A543
Vice President Information Systems and Chief Information Officer, Memorial Hospital And Health Care Center, Jasper, IN, p. A233

GAUGHAN, Thomas, M.D., Chief Medical Officer, Kingman Regional Medical Center, Kingman, AZ, p. A33

GAUL, Mike, Director Information Technology, Golden Valley Memorial Healthcare, Clinton, MO, p. A405

GAULT, Cindy, Chief Financial Officer, Union Medical Center, Union, SC, p. A625

GAURON, Patricia, Director Human Resources, Holy Family Hospital, Methuen, MA, p. A341

GAUSE, Levi, M.D., Chief Information Officer and Vice President Health System Informatics, Great River Medical Center, West Burlington, IA, p. A260

GAUTHIER, Paul, Chief Information Resources Management, Veterans Affairs Montana Health Care System, Fort Harrison, MT, p. A423

GAUTNEY, Steven, Chief Executive Officer, Crisp Regional Hospital, Cordele, GA, p. A170

GAVALCHIK, Stephen M., FACHE, Community Chief Executive Officer, Morgan County Arh Hospital, West Liberty, KY, p. A294

GAVIN, Andrea, M.D., Chief Medical officer, Aurora Sheboygan Memorial Medical Center, Sheboygan, WI, p. A796

GAVIN, Donald, Chief Financial Officer, Southern Tennessee Regional Health System-Pulaski, Pulaski, TN, p. A648

GAVIN, Patrick J., M.P.H., President and Chief Executive Officer, Hunterdon Healthcare, Flemington, NJ, p. A455

GAVIN, Todd, Chief Medical Officer, Madelia Community Hospital, Madelia, MN, p. A379

GAVORA, George, Director Program Evaluation, Kingsboro Psychiatric Center, Brooklyn, NY, p. A478

GAVULIC, Melany, President & Chief Executive Officer, Hurley Medical Center, Flint, MI, p. A354
Senior Vice President Operations & COO, Hurley Medical Center, Flint, MI, p. A354

GAW, Kris, Executive Vice President and Chief Operating Officer, Valleywise Health, Phoenix, AZ, p. A37

GAWALUCK, David, Vice President and Chief Information Officer, Excela Frick Hospital, Mount Pleasant, PA, p. A598
Vice President and Chief Information Officer, Excela Health Westmoreland Hospital, Greensburg, PA, p. A591
Vice President and Chief Information Officer, Excela Latrobe Area Hospital, Latrobe, PA, p. A594

GAWITH, Marlene, Director of Nursing, Ottawa County Health Center, Minneapolis, KS, p. A271

GAWLER, William, Chief Information Officer, Chillicothe Veterans Affairs Medical Center, Chillicothe, OH, p. A531

GAWNE, Bernard, M.D., Vice President and Chief Medical Officer, Christ Hospital, Cincinnati, OH, p. A532

GAY, Christophe, M.D., Chief of Staff, Bellville Medical Center, Bellville, TX, p. A659

GAY, Don, Director Human Resources, West Hills Hospital, Reno, NV, p. A446

GAY, Heywood, M.D., Physician, Optim Medical Center - Screven, Sylvania, GA, p. A181

GAY, Kent, M.D., Chief of Medical Staff, Arkansas Valley Regional Medical Center, La Junta, CO, p. A115

GAY, Kristi, Chief Financial Officer, Chi St. Luke's Health Memorial Lufkin, Lufkin, TX, p. A698
Chief Financial Officer, Chi St. Luke's Health Memorial San Augustine, San Augustine, TX, p. A714

GAY, Michael, Chief Operating Officer, Habersham Medical Center, Demorest, GA, p. A171

GAY, Perry, President and Chief Executive Officer, Logansport Memorial Hospital, Logansport, IN, p. A235

GAY, Vickie Lynn., Chief Executive Officer, Montgomery General Hospital, Montgomery, WV, p. A774

GAYNE, William, Chief Financial Officer, Medstar Washington Hospital Center, Washington, DC, p. A130

GAYTKO, Caren, Chief Nursing Officer, Regency Hospital Of Minneapolis, Golden Valley, MN, p. A377

GAZAWAY, William, Information Technology Security Officer, Alliancehealth Ponca City, Ponca City, OK, p. A567

GAZECKI, Cindy, Senior Vice President, Hospital Operations, Seattle Children's Hospital, Seattle, WA, p. A764

GEARHART, Danielle, FACHE, Chief Executive Officer, Cozad Community Health System, Cozad, NE, p. A431

GEARHART, Heidi, Director Information Systems, Arkansas Valley Regional Medical Center, La Junta, CO, p. A115

GEARY, David, Chief Financial Officer, Cache Valley Hospital, North Logan, UT, p. A729

GEARY, Herb, Chief Nursing Officer, Santa Ynez Valley Cottage Hospital, Solvang, CA, p. A99

Vice President Patient Care Services and Chief Nursing Officer, Santa Barbara Cottage Hospital, Santa Barbara, CA, p. A97

GEBAUER, Laurie, Director Patient Care, Orange City Area Health System, Orange City, IA, p. A255

GEBHARD, Scott, Chief Operating Officer, Jfk Johnson Rehabilitation Institute At Hackensack Meridian Health, Edison, NJ, p. A454

Executive VP and Chief Operating Officer, Hackensack Meridian Health Jfk Medical Center, Edison, NJ, p. A454

GEBHART, Cheryl, Chief Human Resources Officer, Tuality Healthcare, Hillsboro, OR, p. A576

Director Human Resources Providence Health Plan and Providence Medical Group. Providence Newberg Medical Center, Newberg, OR, p. A578

GEBHART, Jim Jr, FACHE, President, Mercy Hospital Oklahoma City, Oklahoma City, OK, p. A564

GEBHART, Ronald, M.D., Chief of Staff, Veterans Affairs Salt Lake City Health Care System, Salt Lake City, UT, p. A733

GEBHART, Ryan, President, Baylor Scott & White Medical Center - Centennial, Frisco, TX, p. A680

GECKLE, Rachel, Chief Human Resource Officer, Fulton County Health Center, Wauseon, OH, p. A552

GEDDINGS, Toni, Director Human Resources, Cullman Regional Medical Center, Cullman, AL, p. A17

GEDIES, Lucille, Chief Financial Officer, Mildred Mitchell-Bateman Hospital, Huntington, WV, p. A773

GEE, Kyle, Chief Financial Officer, Beartooth Billings Clinic, Red Lodge, MT, p. A427

Chief Financial Officer, Pioneer Medical Center, Big Timber, MT, p. A421

Regional Vice President Financial Operations, Roundup Memorial Healthcare, Roundup. MT, p. A427

GEERTS, Jodi, Chief Nursing Officer, Henry County Health Center, Mount Pleasant, IA, p. A254

GEESEY, Wanda, Director Human Resources, Pennsylvania Psychiatric Institute, Harrisburg, PA, p. A591

GEHA, Andrew, D.O., President Medical Staff, Floyd Valley Healthcare, Le Mars, IA, p. A253

GEHLAUF, Dee Ann, Senior Vice President Business and Organization Development, Marietta Memorial Hospital, Marietta, OH, p. A544

GEHLHAUSEN, Sherri, Chief Financial Officer, Logansport Memorial Hospital, Logansport, IN, p. A235

GEHRIG, Ryan T., FACHE, President, Mercy Hospital Fort Smith, Fort Smith, AR, p. A46

GEHRING, Betty, Finance Director, Operations, Thedacare Medical Center-New London, New London, WI, p. A792

GEHRING, Jay, Director Information Systems, Kingman Community Hospital, Kingman, KS, p. A268

GEHRING, Mikaela, Chief Operating Officer, Compass Memorial Healthcare, Marengo, IA, p. A253

GEHRING, Samuel, M.D., Chief of Staff, Fleming County Hospital, Flemingsburg, KY, p. A283

GEHRING, Terri, President and Chief Executive Officer, Mcpherson Hospital, Mcpherson, KS, p. A270

Vice President Operations, Mcpherson Hospital, Mcpherson, KS, p. A270

GEIB, Ryan, Chief Operating Officer, Mercy Hospital Fort Smith, Fort Smith, AR, p. A46

GEIER, Joyce, Director Nursing, Girard Medical Center, Girard, KS, p. A265

GEIER, Kathy, Director of Nursing, Chase County Community Hospital, Imperial, NE, p. A433

GEIGER, Deb, Executive Director of Acute Care, Harbor Beach Community Hospital, Harbor Beach, MI, p. A357

GEIGER, Ralph, M.D., Chief of Staff, Sebastian River Medical Center, Sebastian, FL, p. A157

GEIGLE, Joseph, Director Human Resources, Fort Hamilton Hospital, Hamilton, OH, p. A542

GEIL, Kristie, Vice President, Chief Nursing Officer, Cgh Medical Center, Sterling, IL, p. A221

GEISLER, Linda, R.N., FACHE, Vice President Patient Services, Centrastate Healthcare System, Freehold, NJ, p. A455

GEISSLER, Bonnie, R.N., Chief Nursing Officer, Vice President Patient Care Services, Clara Maass Medical Center, Belleville, NJ, p. A452

GEIST, Jim, Executive Vice President and Chief Operating Officer, Skagit Valley Hospital, Mount Vernon, WA, p. A761

GEISTER, Bennett, Chief Executive Officer, Hillcrest Hospital - South, Tulsa, OK, p. A569

GEITZ, Cheri, Director Human Resources, Hansen Family Hospital, Iowa Falls, IA, p. A252

GEIVER, Betsy, Chief Human Resources Officer, Sioux Falls Veterans Affairs Health Care System, Sioux Falls, SD, p. A632

GELDHOF, Jay, Director Information Systems, Greater El Monte Community Hospital, South El Monte, CA, p. A99

Director Information Systems, Whittier Hospital Medical Center, Whittier, CA, p. A105

GELFAND, Andrew, M.D., Medical Director, Our Children's House, Dallas, TX, p. A670

GELLASCH, Tara, Chief Medical Officer, United Memorial Medical Center, Batavia, NY, p. A475

GELLER, Harold S., Chief Executive Officer, Chi St. Anthony Hospital, Pendleton, OR, p. A578

GELLER, Mark, M.D., President and Chief Executive Officer, Montefiore Nyack Hospital, Nyack, NY, p. A493

GELLER, Warren, President and Chief Executive Officer, Englewood Health, Englewood, NJ, p. A455

GEMBOL, Leslie, MSN, R.N., Chief Nursing Officer, Baylor Scott & White Medical Center - Round Rock, Round Rock, TX, p. A709

GEMENY, Anna, Regional Director Human Resources, Baylor Scott & White The Heart Hospital Denton, Denton, TX, p. A671

Regional Director Human Resources, Baylor Scott & White The Heart Hospital Plano, Plano, TX, p. A706

GENESIO, Sabina, Finance Officer for Institutes, Colorado Mental Health Institute At Fort Logan, Denver, CO, p. A110

GENEVRO, Thomas, Vice President Human Resources, Butler Health System, Butler, PA, p. A585

GENGLE, Tim, Director Human Resources, North Ottawa Community Hospital, Grand Haven, MI, p. A355

GENGLER, Laraine, Chief Financial Officer, Lindsborg Community Hospital, Lindsborg, KS, p. A270

GENNA, Nick, Administrator, Treasure Valley Hospital, Boise, ID, p. A189

GENNARO, John, FACHE, Director, Erie Veterans Affairs Medical Center, Erie, PA, p. A589

GENOVESE, Vincent, M.D., President Medical Staff, Owensboro Health Muhlenberg Community Hospital, Greenville, KY, p. A284

GENSERT, Kurt, FACHE, R.N., Vice President Operations, Platte Valley Medical Center, Brighton, CO, p. A108

GENTILE, John, M.D., Vice President Medical Affairs, Alta Bates Summit Medical Center - Summit Campus, Oakland, CA, p. A82

M.D., Vice President Medical Affairs, Alta Bates Summit Medical Center-Alta Bates Campus, Berkeley, CA, p. A58

GENTNER, Kim, Chief Financial Officer, Deckerville Community Hospital, Deckerville, MI, p. A352

GENTNER, Rocky, Chief Financial Officer, Newport Bay Hospital, Newport Beach, CA, p. A81

GENTRY, Jeanine, Chief Executive Officer, Steele Memorial Medical Center, Salmon, ID, p. A193

GENTRY, Jennifer, R.N., Chief Nursing Officer, Christus Spohn Hospital Corpus Christi Memorial, Corpus Christi, TX, p. A665

GENTRY, Laura, Administrator, Medical Center Of Peach County, Navicent Health, Bryon, GA, p. A167

GENTRY, Lee, FACHE, Chief Executive Officer, Continuecare Hospital At Baptist Health Paducah, Paducah, KY, p. A291

GENTRY, Margie, Controller, T. J. Samson Community Hospital, Glasgow, KY, p. A284

GEOGHEGAN, Jeffrey, Chief Financial Officer, Uconn, John Dempsey Hospital, Farmington, CT, p. A122

GEORGE, Alan, Chief Operating Officer, St. Francis Hospital, Columbus, GA, p. A169

GEORGE, Brad, Director Information Systems, Parkland Medical Center, Derry, NH, p. A448

GEORGE, Dana, Chief Human Resources Officer, Abrazo Central Campus, Phoenix, AZ, p. A35

GEORGE, Daniel, Executive Vice President, Operations, Covenant Healthcare, Saginaw, MI, p. A365

GEORGE, Denise, R.N., President, Northern Dutchess Hospital, Rhinebeck, NY, p. A496

GEORGE, Eric, M.D., Chief Executive Officer, Omega Hospital, Metairie, LA, p. A308

GEORGE, Gary, Senior Vice President Human Resources, Mercy St. Vincent Medical Center, Toledo, OH, p. A550

GEORGE, P, M.D., Chief of Staff, Madison Medical Center, Fredericktown, MO, p. A406

GEORGE, Saju, Chief Executive Officer, Garden City Hospital, Garden City, MI, p. A355

GEORGE, Shayne, Chief Executive Officer, Memorial Health, Savannah, GA, p. A180

GEORGE, Susan, R.N., M.P.H., Associate Director Patient Care Services, Martinsburg Veterans Affairs Medical Center, Martinsburg, WV, p. A774

GEORGE, Tracy, Chief Financial Officer, St. James Parish Hospital, Lutcher, LA, p. A307

GEORGE, William, M.D., Chief of Staff, Beartooth Billings Clinic, Red Lodge, MT, p. A427

GEORGES, Angelo, M.D., President Medical and Dental Staff, Wheeling Hospital, Wheeling, WV, p. A778

GEORGOFF, Julie, Vice President of Finance and Chief Financial Officer, Magruder Memorial Hospital, Port Clinton, OH, p. A548

GEPFORD, John, Director Information Systems, Evergreenhealth Monroe, Monroe, WA, p. A760

GERACI, Nichole, Chief Operating Officer, Acmh Hospital, Kittanning, PA, p. A593

GERARD, Greg Donavan., President, Baptist Health Richmond, Richmond, KY, p. A292

GERARD, Jennifer, R.N., Chief Nursing Officer, Abrom Kaplan Memorial Hospital, Kaplan, LA, p. A304

GERBER, Allen, M.D., Chief of Staff, Baptist Health Medical Center-Hot Spring County, Malvern, AR, p. A50

GERBER, Andrew, M.D., Ph.D., President and Medical Director, Silver Hill Hospital, New Canaan, CT, p. A124

GERBER, Andrew J., M.D., Ph.D., President and Chief Executive Officer, Silver Hill Hospital, New Canaan, CT, p. A124

GERBER, Greg, M.D., Chief Medical Officer, Aurora Lakeland Medical Center, Elkhorn, WI, p. A783

GERBERRY, Amy, Chief Executive Officer, Haven Behavioral Hospital Of Phoenix, Phoenix, AZ, p. A35

GERDES, Isaac, Chief Executive Officer, Sanford Webster Medical Center, Webster, SD, p. A633

GERDTS, Elizabeth, Chief Nursing Officer, Nyc Health + Hospitals / North Central Bronx, Bronx, NY, p. A477

GERE, Zsaber, Chief Human Resource Officer, Banner Behavioral Health Hospital - Scottsdale, Scottsdale, AZ, p. A38

GERETY, Meghan, M.D., Chief of Staff, New Mexico Veterans Affairs Health Care System - Raymond G. Murphy Medical Center, Albuquerque, NM, p. A468

GERHART, Paul, Chief Financial Officer, Sanford Canton-Inwood Medical Center, Canton, SD, p. A626

GERING, Paul, M.D., Vice President Medical Affairs, Saint Alphonsus Medical Center - Ontario, Ontario, OR, p. A578

GERKE, Daniel, Chief Nursing Officer, Wright Patterson Medical Center, Wright, OH, p. A553

GERKE, Sarah, Manager Human Resources, Warner Hospital And Health Services, Clinton, IL, p. A201

GERKEN, Jennifer, R.N., Chief Financial Officer, Kansas Spine & Specialty Hospital, Wichita, KS, p. A279

GERLACH, Carl, Chief Financial Officer, Curry General Hospital, Gold Beach, OR, p. A575

GERLACH, Matthew, Chief Operating Officer, Children's Hospital Of Orange County, Orange, CA, p. A83

Chief Operating Officer, Choc Children's At Mission Hospital, Mission Viejo, CA, p. A78

GERMANY, Alan, Chief Operating Officer, Adventist Health - Tulare, Tulare, CA, p. A102

GERNDT, Angie, Human Resources Manager, Mercyone Elkader Medical Center, Elkader, IA, p. A249

GERNHART, Diana, Senior Vice President and Hospital Chief Financial Officer, Ohsu Hospital, Portland, OR, p. A579

GERRIOR, Marilyn, R.N., MSN, Chief Nursing Executive, St. Louise Regional Hospital, Gilroy, CA, p. A66

GERRITS, Brad, Director Information Systems, Marshfield Medical Center - Rice Lake, Rice Lake, WI, p. A795

GERSON, Elaine, Chief Clinical Officer and General Counsel, Aspen Valley Hospital, Aspen, CO, p. A107

GERSTENBERGER, Linda, Vice President Human Resources, St. Rose Dominican Hospitals - San Martin Campus, Las Vegas, NV, p. A444

Vice President Human Resources, St. Rose Dominican Hospitals - Siena Campus, Henderson, NV, p. A442

GERSTNER, Nancy, Manager Human Resources, Robert J. Dole Veterans Affairs Medical Center, Wichita, KS, p. A279

GERVELER, Patrick, Vice President Finance and Chief Financial Officer, Blessing Hospital, Quincy, IL, p. A218

GESME, Barbara, MSN, Vice President Patient Care Services & Chief Nurse Executive, Bon Secours St. Francis Medical Center, Midlothian, VA, p. A746

GESSLER, Kevin, Chief Financial Officer, Preston Memorial Hospital, Kingwood, WV, p. A773

Interim Chief Financial Officer, Grafton City Hospital, Grafton, WV, p. A772

GESSLING, Heather, M.D., Chief Medical Officer, Moberly Regional Medical Center, Moberly, MO, p. A412

GESSNER, Christopher A., President and Chief Executive Officer, University Of Colorado Hospital, Aurora, CO, p. A108

GETCHIUS, Joseph, Director Information Technology, Benewah Community Hospital, Saint Maries, ID, p. A193

GETMAN, Sylvia, President and Chief Executive Officer, Adirondack Health, Saranac Lake, NY, p. A497

GETSAY, Timothy, Chief Information Officer, Vice President of Performance & Information Mgmt, Gillette Children's Specialty Healthcare, Saint Paul, MN, p. A385

GETTINGER, Thomas, Executive Vice President and Chief Operating Officer, Mary Washington Hospital, Fredericksburg, VA, p. A742

Executive Vice President and Chief Operating Officer, Stafford Hospital, Stafford, VA, p. A752

GETTINGS, Scott, M.D., Senior Vice President and Chief Medical Officer, Health First Viera Hospital, Melbourne, FL, p. A145

GETTYS, Sky, Chief Financial Officer, Fairfield Medical Center, Lancaster, OH, p. A542

GETZ, Liz, Chief Information Officer, Aultman Hospital, Canton, OH, p. A530

GEUDER, Denise, Vice President Patient Care Service and Chief Nursing Officer, Southwestern Regional Medical Center, Tulsa, OK, p. A570

GEURTS, Chuck, Manager Information Technology Client Services, Aurora Baycare Medical Center, Green Bay, WI, p. A785

GEWECKE, Tyler, Information Technology Technician, Fillmore County Hospital, Geneva, NE, p. A432

GFELLER, Michael, Director Information Systems, Medical City Plano, Plano, TX, p. A707

GHAEMMAGHAMI, Chris, M.D., Chief Medical Officer, University Of Virginia Medical Center, Charlottesville, VA, p. A740

GHAFFARI, Bahram, President, Delano Regional Medical Center, Delano, CA, p. A62

GHAFOOR, Tariq, Medical Director, Aurora Behavioral Health System East, Tempe, AZ, p. A39

GHALI, Sara, Chief Financial Officer, Santa Cruz Valley Regional Hospital, Green Valley, AZ, p. A33

GHERINGHELLI, Thomas, Senior Vice President, Chief Financial Officer, New England Baptist Hospital, Boston, MA, p. A336

GHERKE, Sheila, Director Human Resources, Minnie Hamilton Healthcare Center, Grantsville, WV, p. A772

GHIDOTTI, Craig, Vice President Human Resources, Lake Health, Concord Township. OH, p. A537

GHINASSI, Frank A., Ph.D., President and Chief Executive Officer, Rutgers University Behavioral Healthcare, Piscataway, NJ, p. A461

GHION, christopher, Vice President and Chief Information Officer, Adventist Healthcare Shady Grove Medical Center, Rockville, MD, p. A332

GHULUM, Evelyn, Chief Financial Officer, Jellico Community Hospital, Jellico, TN, p. A640

GIAGUINTO, Shelly, Chief Financial Officer, Highland-Clarksburg Hospital, Clarksburg, WV, p. A771

GIAMPA, Patricia, Chief Nursing Officer, Searhc Mt. Edgecumbe Hospital, Sitka, AK, p. A29

GIANELLI, Arthur A., M.P.H., President, Mount Sinai Morningside, New York, NY, p. A490

GIANG, Vernon, M.D., Chief Medical Executive, California Pacific Medical Center-St. Luke's Campus, San Francisco, CA, p. A93
M.D., Chief Medical Executive, California Pacific Medical Center, San Francisco, CA, p. A93

GIANGARDELLA, Mike, Vice President Finance and Administration, Salem Regional Medical Center, Salem, OH, p. A548

GIANNINI, Fran, Associate Director, Southwest Connecticut Mental Health System, Bridgeport, CT, p. A121

GIANNONE, John, M.D., Delaware Valley Hospital Medical Director, Uhs Delaware Valley Hospital, Walton, NY, p. A501

GIANNOSA, Amy, Director Human Resources, Havenwyck Hospital, Auburn Hills, MI, p. A349

GIANNUZZI, Donna, R.N., Chief Nursing Officer, Lee Memorial Hospital, Fort Myers, FL, p. A138

GIANSANTE, Joseph, Vice President Human Resources, Ellis Hospital, Schenectady, NY, p. A498

GIARDINA, Deborah, Director Human Resources and Medical Staff Services, Rehabilitation Hospital Of Fort Wayne, Fort Wayne, IN, p. A228

GIARDINO, Angelo, M.D., Chief Medical Officer, Primary Children's Hospital, Salt Lake City, UT, p. A732

GIBB, Matthew, M.D., Executive Vice President and System Chief Medical Officer, Carle Foundation Hospital, Urbana, IL, p. A221

GIBBENS, Lori, Controller, Encompass Health Rehabilitation Hospital Of Erie, Erie, PA, p. A589

GIBBERMAN, Val, M.D., Acting Chief of Staff, Hampton Veterans Affairs Medical Center, Hampton, VA, p. A743

GIBBES, Gregg, Chief Executive Officer, Covington County Hospital, Collins, MS, p. A391
Chief Executive Officer, Magee General Hospital, Magee, MS, p. A396

GIBBONS, Barbara, Vice President Patient Care Services, St. Josep. Hospital, Bethpage, NY, p. A475

GIBBONS, Brian P. Jr, Chief Executive Officer, Astria Sunnyside Hospital, Sunnyside, WA, p. A766

GIBBONS, David, President, Upmc Hamot, Erie, PA, p. A590

GIBBONS, Jason, Chief Financial Officer, Minidoka Memorial Hospital, Rupert, ID, p. A193

GIBBS, Christopher, Director Information Management Systems, Taylor Regional Hospital, Campbellsville, KY, p. A281

GIBBS, Jeffrey, M.D., Regional Vice President Medical Affairs, Skagit Valley Hospital, Mount Vernon, WA, p. A761

GIBBS, Kenneth, President and Chief Executive Officer, Maimonides Medical Center, Brooklyn, NY, p. A478

GIBBS, Michael, President, Avera Heart Hospital Of South Dakota, Sioux Falls, SD, p. A631

GIBBS, Parker, M.D., Chief Medical Officer, Uf Health Shands Hospital, Gainesville, FL, p. A139

GIBBS, Tim, Director of Information Technology, Information Security Officer, Children's Hospital Of Richmond At Vcu-Brook Road Campus, Richmond, VA, p. A750

GIBBS, Vickie, Director Nursing, Phillip. County Health Systems, Phillipsburg, KS, p. A274

GIBBS-MCELVY, Shelana, M.D., Medical Director, Encompass Health Rehabilitation Hospital Of Sewickley, Sewickley, PA, p. A607

GIBNEY, Thomas, Senior Vice President and Chief Financial Officer, Montefiore St. Luke's Cornwall, Newburgh, NY, p. A492

GIBSON, Armetria, Human Resources Generalist, Select Specialty Hospital Midtown Atlanta, Atlanta, GA, p. A165

GIBSON, Belinda, R.N., Senior Vice President Patient Services, Bsa Hospital, Llc, Amarillo, TX, p. A652

GIBSON, Elizabeth, Chief Executive Officer, Encompass Health Rehabilitation Hospital Of East Valley, Mesa, AZ, p. A34
Director Human Resources, Mid—America Rehabilitation Hospital, Shawnee Mission, KS, p. A276

GIBSON, Jack, Administrator, Noland Hospital Tuscaloosa, Tuscaloosa, AL, p. A25

GIBSON, Joel, Vice President Human Resources, Henry Ford Macomb Hospitals, Clinton Township. MI, p. A341

GIBSON, Mary, Director Human Resources, Floyd Valley Healthcare, Le Mars, IA, p. A253

GIBSON, Matt, Chief Executive Officer, Siskin Hospital For Physical Rehabilitation, Chattanooga, TN, p. A636

GIBSON, Megan, Nurse Manager, River Bend Hospital, West Lafayette, IN, p. A242

GIBSON, Todd, Chief Financial Officer, Medical City Denton, Denton, TX, p. A672

GICCA, Ron, Chief Executive Officer, Melbourne Regional Medical Center, Melbourne, FL, p. A145

GICZI, Mary Beth, Director Human Resources, Encompass Health Rehabilitation Hospital Of Scottsdale, Scottsdale, AZ, p. A38

GIDDINGS, Carleen, Information Technology System Leader, Scheurer Health, Pigeon, MI, p. A363

GIDEON, Daniel L., FACHE, Chief Executive Officer, Pine Creek Medical Center, Dallas, TX, p. A670

GIEGER, Julie, Chief Financial Officer, Lackey Memorial Hospital, Forest, MS, p. A392
Chief Financial Officer, Monroe Regional Hospital, Aberdeen, MS, p. A389

GIER, Jennifer, Director Human Resources, Brynn Marr Hospital, Jacksonville, NC, p. A512

GIERTUGA, Garry, Site Manager Human Resources, Amita Health Adventist Medical Center La Grange, La Grange, IL, p. A210

GIESE, Kristine, Chief Operating Officer, Providence Medical Center, Wayne, NE, p. A440

GIESIE, Pamela, R.N., Chief Nursing Officer, Roswell Park Comprehensive Cancer Center, Buffalo, NY, p. A480

GIFFORD, Ellen, Director Human Resources, Integris Deaconess, Oklahoma City, OK, p. A564

GIGLIO, Aimee, Chief Human Resources Officer, Dartmouth-Hitchcock Medical Center, Lebanon, NH, p. A449

GIGLIOTTI, Vicki, Chief Clinical Officer, Moab Regional Hospital, Moab, UT, p. A729

GIL, Julio, Manager Information Services, Hazel Hawkins Memorial Hospital, Hollister, CA, p. A68

GILBERT, Alicia, Vice President, Regions Hospital, Saint Paul, MN, p. A385

GILBERT, Andrea F., FACHE, President, Bryn Mawr Hospital, Bryn Mawr, PA, p. A585

GILBERT, Carla, Director Finance, Cedar County Memorial Hospital, El Dorado Springs, MO, p. A405

GILBERT, Christy, Interim Chief Executive Officer, Doctors Neuropsychiatric Hospital And Research Institute, Bremen, IN, p. A225
President and Chief Operating Officer, Medical Behavioral Hospital Of Mishawaka, Knox, IN, p. A234

GILBERT, Jack, Vice President Finance and Facilities, Advocate Illinois Masonic Medical Center, Chicago, IL, p. A197

GILBERT, Kevin, R.N., Vice President, Confluence Health/ Wenatchee Valley Hospital, Wenatchee, WA, p. A768

GILBERT, Kim, R.N., Chief Nursing Officer, Electra Memorial Hospital, Electra, TX, p. A676

GILBERT, Thomas, Director Information Technology Services, Lake Cumberland Regional Hospital, Somerset, KY, p. A293

GILBERT, Thomas D., FACHE, Chief Executive Officer, Wadley Regional Medical Center At Hope, Hope, AR, p. A47
FACHE, Chief Executive Officer, Wadley Regional Medical Center, Texarkana, TX, p. A720

GILBERT, Tim J., President and Administrator, Maniilaq Health Center, Kotzebue, AK, p. A29

GILBERT, William L., Hospital Director, Arrowhead Regional Medical Center, Colton, CA, p. A60

GILBERTSON, Gerry, FACHE, Administrator, Centracare - Melrose, Melrose, MN, p. A380

GILCHRIST, Doug, Chief Operating Officer, Summit Healthcare Regional Medical Center, Show Low, AZ, p. A38

GILDON, Lisa, Group Financial Officer, Texas Health Presbyterian Hospital Allen, Allen, TX, p. A652
Vice President and Chief Financial Officer, Texas Health Presbyterian Hospital Plano, Plano, TX, p. A707

GILES, Charles, M.D., President Medical Staff, T.J. Health Columbia, Columbia, KY, p. A281

GILES, Dolly, Chief Nursing Officer, Pike County Memorial Hospital, Louisiana, MO, p. A411

GILES, Jared, Chief Operating Officer, Southwest Healthcare System, Murrieta, CA, p. A80

GILES, Steve, Chief Information Officer, Hollywood Presbyterian Medical Center, Los Angeles, CA, p. A74

GILG, Ronald, Assistant Vice President Talent, Cancer Treatment Centers Of America-Eastern Regional Medical Center, Philadelphia, PA, p. A599

GILGEN, Steve, Chief Financial Officer, Erlanger Western Carolina Hospital, Murphy, NC, p. A515

GILJUM, Anthony, Chief Information Officer, Sheridan Veterans Affairs Medical Center, Sheridan, WY, p. A804

GILKEY, Edward, M.D., Vice President Medical Affairs, St. Luke's Hospital - Warren Campus, Phillipsburg, NJ, p. A461

GILL, Brian, Chief Executive Officer, Millwood Hospital, Arlington, TX, p. A653

GILL, Jon, Chief Operating Officer, Great Plains Regional Medical Center, Elk City, OK, p. A558

GILL, Mandeep. Chief Operating Officer, Memorial Hospital Of Sweetwater County, Rock Springs, WY, p. A804

GILL, Margaret, Chief Executive Officer, Delray Medical Center, Delray Beach, FL, p. A136

GILL, Mark, Vice President Finance and Chief Financial Officer, Cap. Regional Health System, Cap. May Court House, NJ, p. A453

GILLAM, Sally, R.N., Chief Nursing Officer, St. David's South Austin Medical Center, Austin, TX, p. A656

GILLARD, Austin M., Chief Executive Officer, Clay County Medical Center, Clay Center, KS, p. A262

GILLELAND, Dana, Chief Financial Officer, Iroquois Memorial Hospital And Resident Home, Watseka, IL, p. A222

GILLEN, Mark, Director Finance and Operations, Owatonna Hospital, Owatonna, MN, p. A382
Director of Operations, Owatonna Hospital, Owatonna, MN, p. A382

GILLES, Ken, Associate Chief Information Officer, Essentia Health St. Mary's - Detroit Lakes, Detroit Lakes, MN, p. A375
Chief Information Officer, Essentia Health Fargo, Fargo, ND, p. A522

GILLESPIE, Anne, R.N., Associate Director Patient Care and Nursing Services, Veterans Affairs Loma Linda Healthcare System, Loma Linda, CA, p. A72

GILLESPIE, Bob, Chief Executive Officer, Connally Memorial Medical Center, Floresville, TX, p. A677
Chief Operating Officer, Connally Memorial Medical Center, Floresville, TX, p. A677

GILLESPIE, Christina L., Chief Executive Officer, Harrison County Community Hospital, Bethany, MO, p. A402

GILLESPIE, Curt, Chief Executive Officer, Mental Health Services For Clark And Madison Counties, Springfield, OH, p. A549

GILLESPIE, Eileen, Chief Nursing Officer, Northwest Community Healthcare, Arlington Heights, IL, p. A194

GILLESPIE, Karen, Director Human Resources, Anderson County Hospital, Garnett, KS, p. A265

GILLESPIE, Lisa, M.D., Chief Medical Officer, Piedmont Rockdale Hospital, Conyers, GA, p. A170

GILLESPIE, Rebekah, Chief Financial Officer, Madison County Health Care System, Winterset, IA, p. A260

GILLESPIE, Richard, President, Jefferson County Hospital, Waurika, OK, p. A571

GILLESPIE, Tim, Manager Information Systems, Carle Richland Memorial Hospital, Olney, IL, p. A215

GILLETTE, Karen, Associate Director Patient Care Services, Memphis Veterans Affairs Medical Center, Memphis, TN, p. A644

GILLETTE, Nicole, R.N., Chief Nursing Officer, Midmichigan Medical Center - West Branch, West Branch, MI, p. A369

GILLETTE, Robert, Chief Information Officer, St. Elizabeth Medical Center, Utica, NY, p. A500

GILLETTE, Tom, Senior Vice President and Chief Information Officer, Mount Sinai Medical Center, Miami Beach, FL, p. A148

GILLIAM, David, M.D., Medical Director, Bloomington Meadows Hospital, Bloomington, IN, p. A224

GILLIAM, Leslie, Director Health Information Management, Dominion Hospital, Falls Church, VA, p. A741

GILLIAN, Tom, Chief Operating Officer, River Bend Hospital, West Lafayette, IN, p. A242

GILLILAND, Michael, M.D., Chief of Staff, Chi St. Luke's Health Brazosport, Lake Jackson, TX, p. A694

GILLILAND, Michelle, Director of Nursing, River Park Hospital, Huntington, WV, p. A773

GILLILAND, Sharon, Chief of Staff, Baraga County Memorial Hospital, L'Anse, MI, p. A359

GILLILAND, Terry, M.D., Chief Medical Officer, Sentara Leigh Hospital, Norfolk, VA, p. A748

M.D., Senior Vice President and Chief Medical Officer, Sentara Princess Anne Hospital, Virginia Beach, VA, p. A753

GILLIS, Anne, Chief Financial Officer, Holy Cross Hospital, Silver Spring, MD, p. A332

GILLMAN, Kreg, Chief Executive Officer, Salt Lake Behavioral Health, Salt Lake City, UT, p. A732

GILLY, Mike, Chief Information Officer, Our Lady Of The Angels Hospital, Bogalusa, LA, p. A298

GILMAN, James K., M.D., Chief Executive Officer, National Institutes Of Health Clinical Center, Bethesda, MD, p. A327

GILMAN, Kim, Chief Executive Officer and Chief Nursing Officer, Southwest Georgia Regional Medical Center, Cuthbert, GA, p. A170

Chief Executive Officer, Phoebe Worth Medical Center, Sylvester, GA, p. A181

Chief Nursing Officer, Phoebe Worth Medical Center, Sylvester, GA, p. A181

GILMORE, BJ, Chief Nursing Officer, St. Vincent Healthcare, Billings, MT, p. A421

GILMORE, Hugh, M.D., Vice President Medical Affairs, Ascension Seton Williamson, Round Rock, TX, p. A709

GILMORE, Joshua, Chief Executive Officer, Iron County Medical Center, Pilot Knob, MO, p. A413

GILMORE, Phillip K., Ph.D., FACHE, Chief Executive Officer, Ashley County Medical Center, Crossett, AR, p. A44

GILMORE, Stephen, Chief Financial Officer, Piedmont Medical Center, Rock Hill, SC, p. A624

GILPIN, Michael, Vice President Human Resources, Sampson Regional Medical Center, Clinton, NC, p. A507

GILSON, Sheila, R.N., Chief Operating Officer, Kaiser Permanente Redwood City Medical Center, Redwood City, CA, p. A87

GILTNER, Michelle, Interim Chief Nursing Officer, Uh Regional Hospitals, Cleveland, OH, p. A535

GIN, Nancy, M.D., Area Associate Medical Director, Kaiser Permanente Orange County Anaheim Medical Center, Anaheim, CA, p. A55

GINDER, Phil, Chief Executive Officer, Hodgeman County Health Center, Jetmore, KS, p. A267

GINGRAS, Sean, CPA, Chief Financial Officer, Centerstone Hospital, Bradenton, FL, p. A132

GINGRICH, Curtis, M.D., Chief Operating Officer, Ohiohealth Marion General Hospital, Marion, OH, p. A544

GINGRICH, Joye, Director Patient Care Services and Chief Nursing Officer, Penn Highlands Huntingdon, Huntingdon, PA, p. A592

GINGRICH, Mary, Director Health Care Services, Kansas Neurological Institute, Topeka, KS, p. A277

GINN, Bobby, Chief Operating Officer, Crestwood Medical Center, Huntsville, AL, p. A20

GINN, Doug, Executive Vice President Operations, Peak Behavioral Health Services, Santa Teresa, NM, p. A472

GINNATY, Rayn, Vice President Nursing, Benefis Health System, Great Falls, MT, p. A424

GINSBERG, Jo-Ann M., R.N., MSN, Director, Marion Veterans Affairs Medical Center, Marion, IL, p. A211

GINTER, Gary, System Vice President and Chief Information Officer, Miami Valley Hospital, Dayton, OH, p. A538

GINTZIG, Donald R., President and Chief Executive Officer, Wakemed Cary Hospital, Cary, NC, p. A506

President and Chief Executive Officer, Wakemed Raleigh Campus, Raleigh, NC, p. A517

GIOIA, Anthony, Chief Financial Officer, Orthoindy Hospital, Indianapolis, IN, p. A232

GIORDANO, Paul, Senior Vice President, Human Resources, Mount Sinai South Nassau, Oceanside, NY, p. A493

GIORDANO, Peter, Senior Director Human Resources, Harrison Community Hospital, Cadiz, OH, p. A530

GIORDANO, Roger, M.D., Medical Director, Encompass Health Rehabilitation Hospital Of Richmond, Richmond, VA, p. A750

GIORDANO, Susan, Chief Nursing Officer, Hackensack Meridian Health Pascack Valley Medical Center, Westwood, NJ, p. A465

GIPP, Jana, Chief Executive Officer, Standing Rock Service Unit, Fort Yates Hospital, Indian Health Service, Dhhs, Fort Yates, ND, p. A523

GIPSON, Hilary, Director of Nursing, Rolling Hills Hospital, Franklin, TN, p. A638

GIPSON, Linda, MSN, Ph.D., Chief Nursing Officer, Whidbeyhealth, Coupeville, WA, p. A757

GIRARD, Thomas, Vice President Human Resources, Lincolnhealth, Damariscotta, ME, p. A320

Vice President Human Resources, Pen Bay Medical Center, Rockport, ME, p. A322

GIRARDEAU, Brian, Director Information System, East Georgia Regional Medical Center, Statesboro, GA, p. A181

GIRARDIER, Cheryl, Director Information Technology, Lecom Health Millcreek Community Hospital, Erie, PA, p. A590

GIRARDY, James, M.D., Vice President, Chief Surgical Officer, Osf Saint Anthony Medical Center, Rockford, IL, p. A219

GIRTY, Tara, Director Human Resources, Kiowa District Healthcare, Kiowa, KS, p. A268

GISH, Kevin, Administrator and Vice President, Essentia Health-Fosston, Fosston, MN, p. A376

GISI, Dale, President, Mercy Health - St. Rita's Medical Center, Lima, OH, p. A543

GISLER, Greg, Chief Financial Officer, Mcbride Orthopedic Hospital, Oklahoma City, OK, p. A564

GISLESON, Joni, Director Finance, Gundersen Palmer Lutheran Hospital And Clinics, West Union, IA, p. A260

GITMAN, Michael, M.D., Medical Director, North Shore University Hospital, Manhasset, NY, p. A487

GITTLER, Michelle, M.D., Medical Director, Schwab Rehabilitation Hospital, Chicago, IL, p. A200

GITZINGER, Matthew, Director of Operations, Vidant Duplin Hospital, Kenansville, NC, p. A513

GIUDICE, William, Vice President and Chief Financial Officer, Tallahassee Memorial Healthcare, Tallahassee, FL, p. A158

GIVEN, Christopher, Regional Vice President, Finance, St. Vincent's Medical Center, Bridgeport, CT, p. A121

GIVENS, Michael K., FACHE, Administrator, St. Bernards Medical Center, Jonesboro, AR, p. A48

GIVENS, Patricia, R.N., Chief Nursing Officer, Children's Hospital Colorado, Aurora, CO, p. A107

GIVENS, Seth, Chief Human Resource Officer, Drew Memorial Health System, Monticello, AR, p. A50

GIVENS, Stephen K., Assistant Vice President and Administrator, Russell County Medical Center, Lebanon, VA, p. A744

GIZZI, Jason, Controller, Encompass Health Rehabilitation Hospital Of Morgantown, Morgantown, WV, p. A774

GJOLBERG, Skip. FACHE, Administrator, St. Joseph's Hospital Of Buckhannon, Buckhannon, WV, p. A771

GLADEN, Tracy, Chief Financial Officer, Twin Valley Behavioral Healthcare, Columbus, OH, p. A537

GLADSTONE, Art, R.N., Chief Executive Officer, Straub Medical Center, Honolulu, HI, p. A185

GLANVILLE, Tristan, Chief Financial Officer, Adirondack Health, Saranac Lake, NY, p. A497

GLANZER, Elgin, Chief Financial Officer, Memorial Health System, Abilene, KS, p. A261

GLASBERG, Michael, Senior Vice President, Chief Operating Officer, Dameron Hospital, Stockton, CA, p. A99

GLASER, Ruth, President, Pender Memorial Hospital, Burgaw, NC, p. A505

GLASGO, Leah, Chief Executive Officer, Unitypoint Health - Trinity Regional Medical Center, Fort Dodge, IA, p. A250

GLASNAPP, Sherry L., Director, Douglas County Community Mental Health Center, Omaha, NE, p. A437

GLASS, Ian, M.D., Chief Medical Officer, Hca Houston Healthcare Tomball, Tomball, TX, p. A721

GLASS, Ina, MSN, Administrator, Ephraim Mcdowell Fort Logan Hospital, Stanford, KY, p. A293

GLASS, Ina Louise, MSN, Administrator, Ephraim Mcdowell Fort Logan Hospital, Stanford, KY, p. A293

GLASS, Kyle, Chief Financial Officer, Adventhealth Deland, Deland, FL, p. A136

GLASS, Steven, Chief Financial Officer, Cleveland Clinic, Cleveland, OH, p. A534

GLASSBURN, Zach, Chief Executive Officer, Michiana Behavioral Health Center, Plymouth, IN, p. A239

GLASSCOCK, Sheryl, Chief Nursing Officer, Lake Cumberland Regional Hospital, Somerset, KY, p. A293

GLAUBKE, Nancy, Chief Executive Officer, Valley County Health System, Ord, NE, p. A438

GLAVIN, Jolene, R.N., MSN, Director Nursing, Salina Surgical Hospital, Salina, KS, p. A276

GLAZIER, Stephen, Chief Operating Officer, Uthealth Harris County Psychiatric Center, Houston, TX, p. A689

GLEASON, Jeffrey, M.D., Chief Medical Officer, Cookeville Regional Medical Center, Cookeville, TN, p. A637

GLEASON, Joe, Chief Operating Officer, Tristar Stonecrest Medical Center, Smyrna, TN, p. A649

GLEASON, Jonathan, Chief Executive Officer, Crittenden County Hospital, Marion, KY, p. A289

GLEASON, Vallerie L., President and Chief Executive Officer, Newton Medical Center, Newton, KS, p. A272

GLEN, Diane, Assistant Administrator, Barnes-Jewish West County Hospital, Saint Louis, MO, p. A415

GLENN, Chris, Chief Financial Officer, Orange Park Medical Center, Orange Park, FL, p. A150

GLENN, Daphne, Chief Executive Officer, Trihealth Rehabilitation Hospital, Cincinnati, OH, p. A533

GLENN, Gary, Director Information Technology, Carrus Rehabilitation Hospital, Sherman, TX, p. A715

Director Information Technology, Carrus Specialty Hospital, Sherman, TX, p. A715

GLENN, Jeannette, Vice President Human Resources, Education and Training, Mcleod Regional Medical Center, Florence, SC, p. A619

GLENN, Michael, M.D., Chief Medical Officer, Virginia Mason Medical Center, Seattle, WA, p. A765

GLENN, Mike, Chief Executive Officer, Jefferson Healthcare, Port Townsend, WA, p. A762

GLENN, Wil, Director Communications, Larry B. Zieverink, Sr. Alcoholism Treatment Center, Raleigh, NC, p. A516

GLENNING, Robert, Executive Vice President Finance and Chief Financial Officer, Hackensack Meridian Health Hackensack University Medical Center, Hackensack, NJ, p. A455

GLESSNER, Theresa, Chief Nursing Officer, Eastern Region, Newark-Wayne Community Hospital, Newark, NY, p. A492

GLICK, Jennifer, Manager Clinical Informatics, Oaklawn Psychiatric Center, Goshen, IN, p. A229

GLIDDEN, Nancy, Chief Financial Officer and Vice President Finance, Mayo Regional Hospital, Dover—Foxcroft, ME, p. A320

GLIHA, Jennie, Chief Human Resource Officer, Aurelia Osborn Fox Memorial Hospital, Oneonta, NY, p. A494

GLIMCHER, Laurie H., President and Chief Executive Officer, Dana-Farber Cancer Institute, Boston, MA, p. A335

GLIMP, Richard, M.D., Chief Medical Officer, Providence Little Company Of Mary Medical Center - Torrance, Torrance, CA, p. A101

M.D., Chief Medical Officer, Providence Little Company Of Mary Medical Center San Pedro, San Pedro, CA, p. A96

GLINES, Grant, Vice President Operation Finance, Mercy Medical Center, Roseburg, OR, p. A580

GLODOWSKI, Brenda, Chief Financial Officer, North Central Health Care, Wausau, WI, p. A798

GLOGGNER, Peter, Chief Human Resources Officer, Jupiter Medical Center, Jupiter, FL, p. A142

GLONER, James, Senior Vice President, North Philadelphia Health System, Philadelphia, PA, p. A601

GLORIA-BARRAZA, Patricia, Coordinator Human Resources, Mayhill Hospital, Denton, TX, p. A672

GLOTZBACK, Lee, Director Human Resources, Citrus Memorial Health System, Inverness, FL, p. A140

GLOVER, Cynthia, R.N., Vice President and Chief Nursing Officer, Reston Hospital Center, Reston, VA, p. A749

GLOVER, Doug, Controller, William S. Hall Psychiatric Institute, Columbia, SC, p. A618

GLOWA, Meghan, Director Human Resources, Sunnyview Rehabilitation Hospital, Schenectady, NY, p. A498

GLOWCZEWSKI, Jason, Chief Operating Officer, Uh Conneaut Medical Center, Conneaut, OH, p. A537

Chief Operating Officer, Uh Geneva Medical Center, Geneva, OH, p. A541

GLUCHOWSKI, Jeanne, Executive Director, Conifer Park, Glenville, NY, p. A484

GLUECK, Dane, M.D., Chief of Staff, Progress West Hospital, O'Fallon, MO, p. A413

GLYER, David, Vice President Finance, Community Memorial Hospital, Ventura, CA, p. A103

Vice President Finance, Ojai Valley Community Hospital, Ojai, CA, p. A82

GLYNN, Cindy, Director Human Resources, Regional Rehabilitation Hospital, Phenix City, AL, p. A23

GLYNN, John, Chief Information Officer, Rochester General Hospital, Rochester, NY, p. A496

Executive Vice President, Chief Information Officer, Rochester Regional Health, Newark-Wayne Community Hospital, Newark, NY, p. A492

Senior Vice President and Chief Information Officer, Unity Hospital, Rochester, NY, p. A496

GLYNN, Margaret, M.D., Chief Medical Officer, North Mississipp. Medical Center-Iuka, Iuka, MS, p. A394

GLYNN, Shari, Vice President Finance and Chief Financial Officer, Eaton Rapids Medical Center, Eaton Rapids, MI, p. A354

GNAGEY, Keith, Chief Executive Officer, Teton Valley Health Care, Driggs, ID, p. A190

GNAM, Gwen, R.N., MSN, Chief Nursing Officer, Henry Ford Hospital, Detroit, MI, p. A353

GNANN, Andrew, President, St. Vincent's Birmingham, Birmingham, AL, p. A15

President, St. Vincent's Chilton Hospital, Clanton, AL, p. A16

GNEGY, David, M.D., Vice President of Medical Affairs, Camden Clark Medical Center, Parkersburg, WV, p. A775

GOACHER, Brad, Vice President Administration, Alton Memorial Hospital, Alton, IL, p. A194

GOAD, Pat, Director Human Resources, Hillcrest Hospital Claremore, Claremore, OK, p. A557

GOBEL, Bret, Chief Financial Officer, Sierra Vista Hospital, Truth Or Consequences, NM, p. A473

GOBELL, James, Chief Financial Officer, Unitypoint Health - St. Lukes's Sioux City, Sioux City, IA, p. A258

GOBER, Dennis, Interim Chief Executive Officer, Rolling Hills Hospital, Ada, OK, p. A555

GOBER, Kirby, M.D., Chief Executive Officer, Throckmorton County Memorial Hospital, Throckmorton, TX, p. A721

GOBLE, Mandy C., President and Chief Executive Officer, Mary Rutan Hospital, Bellefontaine, OH, p. A529

GOCHENOUR, Julia, Manager Information Systems, West River Regional Medical Center, Hettinger, ND, p. A524

GOCHNOUR, Eric, Chief Human Resource Officer, Cassia Regional Hospital, Burley, ID, p. A189

GODAMUNNE, Karim, M.D., Chief Medical Officer, Wellstar North Fulton Hospital, Roswell, GA, p. A179

GODBEE, Mitchell, Chief of Staff, Capital Region Medical Center, Jefferson City, MO, p. A408

GODBOLD, Steven, Vice President Operations and Chief Operating Officer, East Tennessee Children's Hospital, Knoxville, TN, p. A641

GODDARD, Mark, M.D., Medical Director, Encompass Health Rehabilitation Hospital At Cincinnati, Cincinnati, OH, p. A532

GODDARD, Nichole, Chief Operating Officer, South Region, Community Hospital South, Indianapolis, IN, p. A231

GODFREY, John, M.D., Vice President and Chief Executive Officer, Hardin Memorial Health, Elizabethtown, KY, p. A282

GODFREY, Katrina, Director Human Resources, Mercy Hospital Ada, Ada, OK, p. A555

GODFREY, Kristine, Director Human Resources, Tennova Healthcare - Cleveland, Cleveland, TN, p. A636

GODINA, Gabriel, M.D., Chief of Staff, Ogallala Community Hospital, Ogallala, NE, p. A436

GODLEY, James, Vice President of Human Resources, Mayo Regional Hospital, Dover—Foxcroft, ME, p. A320

GODLEY, Patrick, Chief Financial Officer, Contra Costa Regional Medical Center, Martinez, CA, p. A77

GODWIN, Herman, M.D., JrSenior Vice President and Medical Director, Watauga Medical Center, Boone, NC, p. A505

GODWIN, Robin, MSN, Vice President of Nursing, Sacred Heart Hospital On The Gulf, Port St Joe, FL, p. A155

GOEB-BURKETT, Michele, R.N., MSN, Chief Nursing Officer, Adventhealth Daytona Beach, Daytona Beach, FL, p. A136

GOEBEL, Bret, Chief Financial Officer, Guadalup. County Hospital, Santa Rosa, NM, p. A472

GOEBEL, Cecilia, R.N., Chief Nursing Officer, Susan B. Allen Memorial Hospital, El Dorado, KS, p. A264

GOEBEL, Donna, M.D., Chief Nursing Officer, Mitchell County Hospital, Colorado City, TX, p. A664

GOEBEL, Michael, Chief Executive Officer, Parker Adventist Hospital, Parker, CO, p. A117

GOEDDE, Ronald, Chief Executive Officer, Paulding County Hospital, Paulding, OH, p. A547

GOEHRING, Jennifer, R.N., Assistant Chief Nursing Officer, Ascension Via Christi Hospital, Manhattan, Manhattan, KS, p. A270

GOEL, Amitabh, M.D., Chief Medical Officer, Uh Geneva Medical Center, Geneva, OH, p. A541

GOEL, Ash, Senior Vice President Information Technology and Chief Information/Medical Informatics Officer, Bronson Lakeview Hospital, Paw Paw, MI, p. A363

GOEL, Vineet, Chief Medical Officer, Atrium Health Lincoln, Lincolnton, NC, p. A514

GOELZER, Mark, M.D., Director Medical Affairs, Mercyhealth Hospital And Trauma Center - Janesville, Janesville, WI, p. A786

GOERINGER, Dawn, Chief Clinical Care Officer, O'Connor Hospital, San Jose, CA, p. A95

GOETTSCH, Barry, FACHE, Chief Executive Officer, Compass Memorial Healthcare, Marengo, IA, p. A253

GOFF, Gary, M.D., Medical Director, Kp. Promise Hospital Of Dallas, Dallas, TX, p. A668

GOFF, Vivian, R.N., Chief Executive Officer, Landmark Hospital Of Athens, Athens, GA, p. A163

GOGGIN, Daniel, Senior Vice President and Chief Financial Officer, Chi St. Josep. Health Burleson Hospital, Caldwell, TX, p. A662

Senior Vice President and Chief Financial Officer, Chi St. Josep. Health Grimes Hospital, Navasota, TX, p. A703

GOGGIN, Kathy, Director of Finance, Devereux Advanced Behavioral Health Georgia, Kennesaw, GA, p. A174

GOING, Rita, Director of Critical Access Hospitals, Mercyone Oakland Medical Center, Oakland, NE, p. A436

GOINS, Rick, Chief Executive Officer, Massac Memorial Hospital, Metropolis, IL, p. A212

GOLAN, Marc, Chief Financial Officer, Franciscan Health Crown Point, Crown Point, IN, p. A226

Chief Financial Officer, Franciscan Health Hammond, Hammond, IN, p. A230

Regional Chief Financial Officer, Franciscan Health Michigan City, Michigan City, IN, p. A236

GOLANOWSKI, Marie, R.N., MS, President, Aurora St. Luke's Medical Center, Milwaukee, WI, p. A790

GOLBIN, Jason, M.D., Chief Medical Officer, St. Catherine Of Siena Medical Center, Smithtown, NY, p. A498

GOLD, Barbara, M.D., Chief Medical Officer, University Of Minnesota, Minneapolis, MN, p. A381

GOLD, Joseph, M.D., Chief Medical Officer, Mclean Hospital, Belmont, MA, p. A334

GOLD, Larry, Vice President, Information Services, Southern Virginia Regional Medical Center, Emporia, VA, p. A741

GOLDA, David, Vice President Hospital and Administrator, St. Charles Madras, Madras, OR, p. A577

GOLDAMMER, Kyle, Chief Financial Officer, Sioux Falls Specialty Hospital, Sioux Falls, SD, p. A631

GOLDBERG, David, M.D., Vice President Medical Affairs and Chief Medical Officer, Froedtert Menomonee Falls Hospital, Menomonee Falls, WI, p. A789

President and Chief Executive Officer, Mon Health Medical Center, Morgantown, WV, p. A774

GOLDBERG, Frederick, M.D., Vice President Medical Affairs and Chief Medical Officer, Nathan Littauer Hospital And Nursing Home, Gloversville, NY, p. A485

GOLDBERG, Gary, M.D., Chief Medical Officer, Queen's North Hawaii Community Hospital, Kamuela, HI, p. A186

GOLDBERG, Jonathan, Senior Vice President and Chief Information Officer, Arkansas Children's Hospital, Little Rock, AR, p. A48

GOLDBERG, Michael, Executive Director, Long Island Jewish Medical Center, New Hyde Park, NY, p. A489

GOLDBERG, Paul, Chief Financial Officer, Jersey City Medical Center, Jersey City, NJ, p. A456

GOLDBERG, Stephanie, MSN, R.N., Senior Vice President and Chief Nursing Officer, Hospital For Special Surgery, New York, NY, p. A490

GOLDEN, Joy, Chief Executive Officer, Lakeside Behavioral Health System, Memphis, TN, p. A644

GOLDEN, William, M.D., Chief Medical Officer, East Alabama Medical Center, Opelika, AL, p. A23

GOLDENSTEIN, Rachel, R.N., Chief Nursing Officer, Buchanan County Health Center, Independence, IA, p. A251

GOLDESBERRY-CURRY, Christine, Director of Strategic Finance-CAH, Taylorville Memorial Hospital, Taylorville, IL, p. A221

GOLDFARB, I, Chief Medical Officer, West Penn Hospital, Pittsburgh, PA, p. A605

GOLDFRACH, Andrew, Chief Executive Officer, Uh Avon Rehabilitation Hospital, Avon, OH, p. A528

GOLDHAGEN, Michele, M.D., Chief Medical Officer, Russell Medical, Alexander City, AL, p. A13

GOLDIS, Glenn, Chief Medical Officer, Kern Medical, Bakersfield, CA, p. A57

GOLDMAN, Eric, Chief Executive Officer, Lawnwood Regional Medical Center & Heart Institute, Fort Pierce, FL, p. A138

GOLDMAN, Kris, Director Human Resources, Shriners Hospitals For Children-Salt Lake City, Salt Lake City, UT, p. A732

GOLDSMITH, Cheri, Director Financial Services, Parkland Health Center - Farmington Community, Farmington, MO, p. A406

Director Financial Services, Parkland Health Center-Bonne Terre, Bonne Terre, MO, p. A402

GOLDSMITH, Dana, M.D., Vice President Medical Affairs, Pen Bay Medical Center, Rockport, ME, p. A322

GOLDSTEIN, Allan, M.D., Medical Director and Chief of Staff, Select Specialty Hospital-Birmingham, Birmingham, AL, p. A15

GOLDSTEIN, David, M.D., Chief Medical Officer, Contra Costa Regional Medical Center, Martinez, CA, p. A77

GOLDSTEIN, Gerald, M.D., Senior Vice President and Chief Medical Officer, Western Maryland Regional Medical Center, Cumberland, MD, p. A329

GOLDSTEIN, Lawrence, M.D., Chief Medical Officer, Vibra Hospital Of Mahoning Valley, Boardman, OH, p. A530

GOLDSTEIN, Lisa, Executive Vice President and Chief Operating Officer, Hospital For Special Surgery, New York, NY, p. A490

GOLDSTEIN, Mark L., President and Chief Executive Officer, Anna Jaques Hospital, Newburyport, MA, p. A342

GOLDSTEIN, Steven I., President and Chief Executive Officer, Highland Hospital, Rochester, NY, p. A496

President and Chief Executive Officer, Strong Memorial Hospital Of The University Of Rochester, Rochester, NY, p. A496

GOLDSZER, Robert, M.D., Senior Vice President and Chief Medical Officer, Mount Sinai Medical Center, Miami Beach, FL, p. A148

GOLIGHTLY, Beverly, Director Information Technology, St. Vincent's East, Birmingham, AL, p. A15

GOLKE, Rynae, Director Human Resources, Jacobson Memorial Hospital Care Center, Elgin, ND, p. A522

GOLLAHER, Jeffrey, Chief Executive Officer, Hendricks Community Hospital Association, Hendricks, MN, p. A378

GOLLINGER, Mary, MS, R.N., Director of Nursing, Schwab Rehabilitation Hospital, Chicago, IL, p. A200

GOLOLOBOV, Alexey, Chief Financial Officer, Columbus Hospital Ltach, Newark, NJ, p. A459

GOLOVAN, Ronald, M.D., Vice President Medical Operations, Lutheran Hospital, Cleveland, OH, p. A534

GOMBAR, Greg, Chief Financial Officer, Atrium Health University City, Charlotte, NC, p. A506

GOMBERG, Sandra, Chief Operating Officer, Jefferson Health Northeast, Philadelphia, PA, p. A600

GOMES, Bob, FACHE, President and Chief Executive Officer, Canyon Vista Medical Center, Sierra Vista, AZ, p. A38

GOMES, Carol, FACHE, Chief Executive Officer and Chief Operating Officer, Stony Brook University Hospital, Stony Brook, NY, p. A499

GOMEZ, Carmen, Director Human Resources, North Shore Medical Center, Miami, FL, p. A147

GOMEZ, Denise, Assistant Vice President Information Systems, Unitypoint Health Meriter, Madison, WI, p. A788

GOMEZ, Dianna, Controller, Uva Encompass Health Rehabilitation Hospital, Charlottesville, VA, p. A740

GOMEZ, Dolores, R.N., Chief Operating Officer, Mills-Peninsula Health Services, Burlingame, CA, p. A59

GOMEZ, Gloria, M.D., Medical Director, East Mississipp. State Hospital, Meridian, MS, p. A397

GOMEZ, Jay, Chief Financial Officer, Memorial Hermann Surgical Hospital Kingwood, Kingwood, TX, p. A693

GOMEZ, Jesse, Vice President Human Resources, Ut Health North Campus Tyler, Tyler, TX, p. A722

GOMEZ, Nico, Chief Executive Officer, The Children's Center Rehabilitation Hospital, Bethany, OK, p. A556

GOMEZ, Omar, M.D., Chief of Staff, Cornerstone Regional Hospital, Edinburg, TX, p. A673

GOMEZ, Richard, Assistant Vice President Information Technology Division, Hillcrest Medical Center, Tulsa, OK, p. A569

GOMEZ, Robin, R.N., MSN, Administrator, Alvarado Hospital Medical Center, San Diego, CA, p. A91

GOMEZ, Tad A., President, Loyola University Medical Center, Maywood, IL, p. A211

GOMILLION, Suzann, Interim Chief Executive Officer, Landmark Hospital Of Joplin, Joplin, MO, p. A408

GOMPF, Shelly, Director Human Resources, Alomere Health, Alexandria, MN, p. A371

GONCZ, Gray, Vice President of Medical Affairs, Trinity Health System, Steubenville, OH, p. A550

GONGAWARE, Robert, Chief Financial Officer, Indiana Regional Medical Center, Indiana, PA, p. A592

GONYO, Katelyn, Director of Human Resources, Rehabilitation Hospital Of Wisconsin, Waukesha, WI, p. A798

GONZALES, Amy, Director of Human Resources, Mckenzie County Healthcare System, Watford City, ND, p. A526

GONZALES, Angela, Manager Human Resources, San Mateo Medical Center, San Mateo, CA, p. A96

GONZALES, Ed, Vice President Human Resources, Marian Regional Medical Center, Santa Maria, CA, p. A97

Vice President Human Resources, St. John's Pleasant Valley Hospital, Camarillo, CA, p. A59

Vice President Human Resources, St. John's Regional Medical Center, Oxnard, CA, p. A83

GONZALES, Jan, Director Human Resources, North Valley Hospital, Tonasket, WA, p. A767

GONZALES, Mike, Chief Financial Officer, Select Specialty Hospital - San Diego, San Diego, CA, p. A92

GONZALES, Mindy, Chief Human Resources Officer, Othello Community Hospital, Othello, WA, p. A761

GONZALES, Rachel Ann., Chief Executive Officer, Madison Memorial Hospital, Rexburg, ID, p. A192

GONZALEZ, Agustin, Director Finance, Hospital Pavia Arecibo, Arecibo, PR, p. A806

GONZALEZ, Alan, Chief Operating Officer, Fort Duncan Regional Medical Center, Eagle Pass, TX, p. A673

GONZALEZ, Aurelio, Chief Financial Officer, University Hospital And Medical Center, Tamarac, FL, p. A159

GONZALEZ, David, M.D., Medical Director, Brook Lane Health Services, Hagerstown, MD, p. A330
  Chief Clinical Officer, Advanced Diagnostics Hospital, Houston, TX, p. A684

GONZALEZ, Dinah, Chief Financial Officer, Knap. Medical Center, Weslaco, TX, p. A725

GONZALEZ, Elizabeth, CPA, Financial Director, Hospital Pavia Yauco, Yauco, PR, p. A811

GONZALEZ, Enid Y., Chief Executive Officer, Encompass Health Rehabilitation Hospital Of Manati, Manati, PR, p. A808

GONZALEZ, Jacqueline, Senior Vice President and Chief Nursing Officer, Nicklaus Children's Hospital, Miami, FL, p. A147

GONZALEZ, Jaime, Administrator, St. Catherine's Rehabilitation Hospital, North Miami, FL, p. A149

GONZALEZ, Jerry, Interim Chief Nursing Officer, Las Palmas Medical Center, El Paso, TX, p. A675

GONZALEZ, Jorge, M.D., Chief Medical Officer, Adventhealth Sebring, Sebring, FL, p. A157
  M.D., Vice President and Chief Nursing Officer, Adventhealth Wauchula, Wauchula, FL, p. A161

GONZALEZ, Jorge Matta, Executive Director, University Hospital, San Juan, PR, p. A811

GONZALEZ, Laura, Interim Chief Nurse Executive, South Shore Hospital, Chicago, IL, p. A201

GONZALEZ, Pedro J., FACHE, Chief Executive Officer, Ashford Presbyterian Community Hospital, San Juan, PR, p. A809

GONZALEZ, Rafael, M.D., Medical Director, Ashford Presbyterian Community Hospital, San Juan, PR, p. A809

GONZALEZ, Roberto, Executive Director Human Resources, Carepoint Health Hoboken University Medical Center, Hoboken, NJ, p. A456

GONZALEZ, Susan, Director of Clinical Services, Stanislaus Surgical Hospital, Modesto, CA, p. A79

GOOCH, Mathew, Chief Executive Officer, Encompass Health Rehabilitation Hospital Of Middletown, Middletown, DE, p. A127

GOOD, Jo, Director of Nursing, Palmetto Lowcountry Behavioral Health, Charleston, SC, p. A616

GOOD, Vance, M.D., Chief Medical Staff, Guthrie Troy Community Hospital, Troy, PA, p. A609

GOODALL, David, M.D., Chief Medical Staff, Essentia Health-Deer River, Deer River, MN, p. A375

GOODBALIAN, Terry, Regional Chief Financial Officer, Henry Ford West Bloomfield Hospital, West Bloomfield, MI, p. A369
  Vice President Finance and Chief Financial Officer, Henry Ford Macomb Hospitals, Clinton Township. MI, p. A351
  Vice President, Finance and Chief Financial Officer, Henry Ford Wyandotte Hospital, Wyandotte, MI, p. A370

GOODE, Jennifer, Director Human Resources, Russell County Hospital, Russell Springs, KY, p. A292

GOODE, Lori, Director Human Resources, Baptist Memorial Hospital-Union County, New Albany, MS, p. A398

GOODE, Richard, Executive Vice President and Chief Financial Officer, Children's Medical Center Dallas, Dallas, TX, p. A668

GOODE, Vicky, Director Human Resources, Pam Specialty Hospital Of Rocky Mount, Rocky Mount, NC, p. A517

GOODIN, Scott, Interim Chief Financial Officer, Delta Regional Medical Center, Greenville, MS, p. A392

GOODING, Lari, Chief Executive Officer, Allendale County Hospital, Fairfax, SC, p. A619

GOODLETT, Lisa, Administrator Finance and Support Services, Musc Health Of Medical University Of South Carolina, Charleston, SC, p. A616

GOODMAN, Brenda, Chief Nursing Officer, Medical Center Of Peach County, Navicent Health, Bryon, GA, p. A167

GOODMAN, Darrell, Chief Information Officer, Hi-Desert Medical Center, Joshua Tree, CA, p. A69

GOODMAN, David, Ph.D., Chief Information Officer, Veterans Affairs Boston Healthcare System, West Roxbury, MA, p. A345

GOODMAN, Doug, Vice President Human Resources, Brandon Regional Hospital, Brandon, FL, p. A133

GOODMAN, Josie, Hospital Director, Central State Hospital, Louisville, KY, p. A288

GOODMAN, Mary, Chief Operating Officer, Hca Houston Healthcare Medical Center, Houston, TX, p. A685

GOODMAN, Steven, Chief Operating Officer, Willow Crest Hospital, Miami, OK, p. A562

GOODMAN, William, Vice President Medical Affairs, Chief Medical Officer, Catholic Medical Center, Manchester, NH, p. A450

GOODNER, Beth, Chief Executive Officer, Trustpoint Hospital, Murfreesboro, TN, p. A646

GOODNO, Janell, Chief Executive Officer, Kiowa District Healthcare, Kiowa, KS, p. A268

GOODNOW, John H., Chief Executive Officer, Benefis Health System, Great Falls, MT, p. A424

GOODPASTER, Amber, Chief Financial Officer, Clark Regional Medical Center, Winchester, KY, p. A294

GOODRICH, C, Vice President and Chief Information Officer, Midmichigan Medical Center-Midland, Midland, MI, p. A361

GOODRICH, Craig, Chief Financial Officer, Virginia Mason Medical Center, Seattle, WA, p. A765

GOODROW, Darrin, Chief Information Officer, The University Of Vermont Health Network Elizabethtown Community Hospital, Elizabethtown, NY, p. A483

GOODSON, David, Chief Executive Officer, Encompass Health Rehabilitation Hospital Of Alexandria, Alexandria, LA, p. A295

GOODSTEIN, Ruth, Controller, Encompass Health Rehabilitation Hospital Of Sunrise, Sunrise, FL, p. A158

GOODWIN, Jeremy, M.D., President, Medical Staff, Monroe County Hospital, Forsyth, GA, p. A172

GOODWIN, Jeronica, Senior Director Human Resources, Howard University Hospital, Washington, DC, p. A129

GOODWIN, Linda, Chief Operating Officer and Chief Nursing Executive, Mercyone Des Moines Medical Center, Des Moines, IA, p. A248

GOODWIN, W, M.D., Director, University Of Miami Hospital And Clinics, Miami, FL, p. A147

GOPALAKRISHNAN, Paari, M.D., Chief Medical Officer, Kent County Memorial Hospital, Warwick, RI, p. A614

GOPALAM, Gopinath, Administrator and Chief Executive Officer, Apollo Behavioral Health Hospital, Baton Rouge, LA, p. A296

GOPINATH, Anil, FACHE, M.D., Regional Chief Medical Officer, Amita Health Mercy Medical Center, Aurora, IL, p. A195

GORAB, Robert, M.D., Chief Medical Officer, Hoag Orthopedic Institute, Irvine, CA, p. A69

GORANSON, Ken, Chief Financial Officer, Benson Hospital, Benson, AZ, p. A30

GORBY, Cherie, Chief Operations Officer, Uchealth Memorial Hospital, Colorado Springs, CO, p. A109

GORBY, Karen J., R.N., MSN, FACHE, Chief Executive Officer and Chief Nursing Officer, Angel Medical Center, Franklin, NC, p. A510

GORCZYCA, Julie, R.N., Chief Nursing Officer, Ascension Genesys Hospital, Grand Blanc, MI, p. A355

GORDIN, Peggy, Vice President, Patient Care Services and Chief Nursing Officer, St. Louis Children's Hospital, Saint Louis, MO, p. A417

GORDON, Alyson, Chief Human Resources Officer, Duke Raleigh Hospital, Raleigh, NC, p. A516

GORDON, Cyndy, Chief Operating Officer, Adventist Health And Rideout, Marysville, CA, p. A77

GORDON, Kevin, M.D., Chief of Staff, Alliancehealth Durant, Durant, OK, p. A558

GORDON, Mandy, Human Resource Coordinator, Phoebe Worth Medical Center, Sylvester, GA, p. A181

GORDON, Mark, Chief Nursing Officer, Kern Valley Healthcare District, Lake Isabella, CA, p. A70

GORDON, Michael, M.D., Chief Medical Officer, Carthage Area Hospital, Carthage, NY, p. A481

GORDON, Robert, Manager, Information Services, Vidant North Hospital, Roanoke Rapids, NC, p. A517

GORDON, Steve, Chief Operating Officer, Osceola Regional Medical Center, Kissimmee, FL, p. A142
  Director Human Resources, Lake City Medical Center, Lake City, FL, p. A143

GORDON, Steven R., President and Chief Executive Officer, Brattleboro Memorial Hospital, Brattleboro, VT, p. A735

GORDON, Susan, R.N., Chief Nursing Officer, Upmc Memorial, York, PA, p. A612

GORDON, Thomas, Chief Information Officer, Virtua Marlton, Marlton, NJ, p. A458

GORDON, Wayne, Chief Financial Officer, Memorial Hermann Rehabilitation Hospital - Katy, Katy, TX, p. A692
  Chief Financial Officer, Tirr Memorial Hermann, Houston, TX, p. A688

GORE, Carol, MSN, R.N., Chief Nursing Officer, Saint Mary's Regional Medical Center, Russellville, AR, p. A52

GORE, Lesley, Human Resources Director, North Mississipp. Medical Center-Eupora, Eupora, MS, p. A392

GORE, Tim, Chief Financial Officer, Rivendell Behavioral Health, Bowling Green, KY, p. A281

GORE, Vincent, Chief Executive Officer, Arkansas Continued Care Hospital, Jonesboro, AR, p. A47

GOREAU, Judy, R.N., Director of Nursing, Eastside Psychiatric Hospital, Tallahassee, FL, p. A158

GORELICK, Marc, M.D., President and Chief Executive Officer, Children's Hospitals And Clinics Of Minnesota, Minneapolis, MN, p. A380

GOREY, Peter, Administrative Coordinator, Rockland Children's Psychiatric Center, Orangeburg, NY, p. A494

GORLEWSKI, Todd, Senior Vice President and Chief Financial Officer, St. Barnabas Hospital, Bronx, NY, p. A477

GORMAN, Brandon, Chief Financial Officer, Bradley County Medical Center, Warren, AR, p. A54

GORMAN, Deitrick, M.D., Chief of Staff, Reeves County Hospital District, Pecos, TX, p. A705

GORMAN, Jodie, Director Human Resources, Salem Memorial District Hospital, Salem, MO, p. A448

GORMAN, Kathleen, MSN, R.N., Executive Vice President Patient Care Services and Chief Operating Officer, Children's National Hospital, Washington, DC, p. A129

GORMLEY, Ann, Senior Vice President Human Resources, Upmc Pinnacle Harrisburg, Harrisburg, PA, p. A591

GORMSEN, David, D.O., Senior Vice President and Chief Medical Officer, Mercy Medical Center, Canton, OH, p. A531

GORN, Angela, Vice President, Norton Sound Regional Hospital, Nome, AK, p. A29

GORSUCH, Penelope, Associate Director Patient Care Services, Dayton Veterans Affairs Medical Center, Dayton, OH, p. A538

GOSEY, J, M.D., Medical Director, Southern Surgical Hospital, Slidell, LA, p. A315

GOSHE, Nick, Chief Executive Officer, Sedgwick County Health Center, Julesburg, CO, p. A114

GOSHIA, Rob, Chief Financial Officer, Paulding County Hospital, Paulding, OH, p. A547

GOSLEE, Belle, Chief Nursing Officer, Encompass Health Rehabilitation Hospital Of Salisbury, Salisbury, MD, p. A332

GOSNEY, Brett, Chief Executive Officer, Animas Surgical Hospital, Durango, CO, p. A111

GOSS, Darin, FACHE, Chief Executive Officer, Providence St. Peter Hospital, Olympia, WA, p. A761
  FACHE, Site Administrator, Providence Centralia Hospital, Centralia, WA, p. A756

GOSS, Ella M., MSN, R.N., Chief Executive Officer, Providence Alaska Medical Center, Anchorage, AK, p. A27

GOSS, J., M.D., Medical Director, Uw Medicine/Harborview Medical Center, Seattle, WA, p. A764

GOSS, Norma, R.N., Chief Nursing Officer, Chi Flaget Memorial Hospital, Bardstown, KY, p. A280

GOSS, Roger, Chief Information Officer, North Sunflower Medical Center, Ruleville, MS, p. A400

GOSSELIN, Gail, Director Human Resources, Landmark Medical Center, Woonsocket, RI, p. A614
  Director Human Resources, Rehabilitation Hospital Of Rhode Island, North Smithfield, RI, p. A613

GOSSENS, Kevin, Director Human Resources, Thedacare Medical Center-Waupaca, Waupaca, WI, p. A798

GOSSETT, Lisa, MSN, R.N., Chief Nursing Officer, Ohiohealth Riverside Methodist Hospital, Columbus, OH, p. A537

GOTSOULIAS, Kostas, Interim Chief Executive Officer, Aspire Hospital, Conroe, TX, p. A665

GOTTI, Sreekant, Director Information Systems, Desert Valley Hospital, Victorville, CA, p. A104

GOTTLE, L. Gill, Senior Vice President and Chief Financial Officer, Robert Wood Johnson University Hospital At Hamilton, Hamilton, NJ, p. A456

GOTTLIEB, Harold, M.D., Chief Medical Officer, Memorial Hermann Memorial City Medical Center, Houston, TX, p. A687

GOTTLIEB, Jonathan, M.D., Senior Vice President and Chief Medical Officer, University Of Maryland Medical Center, Baltimore, MD, p. A326

GOTTSCHALK, Amy, M.D., Chief Medical Officer, Verde Valley Medical Center; Vice President Quality, Northern Arizona Healthcare, Verde Valley Medical Center, Cottonwood, AZ, p. A31

GOTTSCHALL, Dan, Vice President, Medical Officer, St. Vincent's Medical Center, Bridgeport, CT, p. A121

GOUGEON, Michele, Executive Vice President and Chief Operating Officer, Mclean Hospital, Belmont, MA, p. A334

GOUGH, Galal, M.D., Chief of Staff, Coast Plaza Hospital, Norwalk, CA, p. A81

GOUGH, Michelle Chief Nursing Officer, Southwest Mississipp. Regional Medical Center, Mccomb, MS, p. A396

GOULD, Christine, Director Human Resources, Martha's Vineyard Hospital, Oak Bluffs, MA, p. A343

GOULD, Dana L., Chief Executive Officer, Broaddus Hospital, Philippi, WV, p. A775

GOULD, Jacquelyn, MS, R.N., Vice President Patient Care Services and Chief Nursing Officer, Wellspan Good Samaritan Hospital, Lebanon, PA, p. A595

GOULD, Rebecca, President and Chief Financial Officer, Schuyler Hospital, Montour Falls, NY, p. A488

GOULD, Robert, President and Chief Executive Officer, Western Regional Medical Center, Goodyear, AZ, p. A32

GOULD, Tamara, R.N., Vice President Clinical Services and Chief Nursing Officer, Wabash General Hospital, Mount Carmel, IL, p. A213

GOULD, William, Vice President Human Resources, Saint Josep. Hospital, Denver, CO, p. A111

GOULET, James, Vice President Operations, Columbus Community Hospital, Columbus, NE, p. A431

GOURLEY, Paul, M.D., Chief Hospital Services, U. S. Air Force Hospital, Hampton, VA, p. A743

GOUTHRO, Robert, M.D., Chief Medical Officer, North Central Health Care, Wausau, WI, p. A798

GOVE, Cynthia, Chief Operating Officer, Hampstead Hospital, Hampstead, NH, p. A449

GOVERO, Chris, Director of Operations, Hshs St. Joseph's Hospital, Highland, IL, p. A207

GOVINDAIAH, Rajesh, M.D., Chief Medical Officer, Memorial Medical Center, Springfield, IL, p. A221

GOVORCHIN, Pete, Senior Vice President Operations, Midwestern Regional Medical Center, Zion, IL, p. A222

GOWEN, Tina, System Controller, Westfield Memorial Hospital, Westfield, NY, p. A502

GOWER, Gary, Chief Information Officer, Appling Healthcare System, Baxley, GA, p. A167

GOWLER, Barbara, Human Resources Manager, Washington County Hospital, Nashville, IL, p. A214

GOWSKI, Bill, M.D., Chief Medical Officer, The Orthopedic Specialty Hospital, Murray, UT, p. A729

GOYAL, Deepak, M.D., Chief of Staff, Jacobson Memorial Hospital Care Center, Elgin, ND, p. A522

GOYKOVICH, Stephen, D.O., Chief Medical Officer, Geisinger Jersey Shore Hospital, Jersey Shore, PA, p. A593

GOZA, Brian, Chief Information Officer, Hemphill County Hospital, Canadian, TX, p. A662

GRABER, Donald, M.D., Medical Director, Richmond State Hospital, Richmond, IN, p. A239

GRABOSO, Rebecca, Vice President and Chief Nurse Executive, Hackensack Meridian Health Riverview Medical Center, Red Bank, NJ, p. A462

GRABOWSKI, David, Chief Executive Officer, Meadows Psychiatric Center, Centre Hall, PA, p. A586

GRACE, Jeffery, M.D., Clinical Director, Buffalo Psychiatric Center, Buffalo, NY, p. A479

GRACE, Michael A., President, Upmc Mercy, Pittsburgh, PA, p. A604

GRACE, Richard, Chief Administrative Officer, Mayo Clinic Health System In Saint James, Saint James, MN, p. A384

GRACE, Robert, Chief Financial Officer, Kendall Regional Medical Center, Miami, FL, p. A146

GRACIE, Michael, Chief Information Officer, Veterans Health Care System Of The Ozarks, Fayetteville, AR, p. A45

GRADDY, Steve, Chief Financial Officer, Freeman Health System, Joplin, MO, p. A408
Chief Financial Officer, Freeman Neosho Hospital, Neosho, MO, p. A412

GRADNEY, Angel, Chief Executive Officer, Kindred Hospital Clear Lake, Webster, TX, p. A724

GRADY, John, Associate Director, Veterans Affairs Hudson Valley Health Care System, Montrose, NY, p. A488

GRADY, Kevin, M.D., President, Ascension River District Hospital, East China, MI, p. A353
M.D., President, Ascension St. John Hospital, Detroit, MI, p. A352

GRAEBER, Tod, Administrator, Chi St. Alexius Health-Garrison Memorial Hospital, Garrison, ND, p. A523
Administrator, Chi St. Alexius Health-Turtle Lake Hospital, Turtle Lake, ND, p. A526

GRAEBNER, David, President, Aurora Medical Center Grafton, Grafton, WI, p. A784
President, Aurora Sheboygan Memorial Medical Center, Sheboygan, WI, p. A796

GRAEBNER, Nancy Kay., President and Chief Executive Officer, St. Josep. Mercy Chelsea, Chelsea, MI, p. A351

GRAF, John, Senior Vice President, Watertown Regional Medical Center, Watertown, WI, p. A798

GRAGG, Connie, Director Human Resources, Saint Mary's Regional Medical Center, Russellville, AR, p. A52

GRAH, John A., FACHE, Chief Executive Officer, Lakewood Regional Medical Center, Lakewood, CA, p. A71

GRAHAM, Bill, President, Sequoia Hospital, Redwood City, CA, p. A88

GRAHAM, Bonnie S., Director, San Francisco Va Medical Center, San Francisco, CA, p. A94

GRAHAM, Brenda, Chief Nursing Officer, Barbourville Arh Hospital, Barbourville, KY, p. A280

GRAHAM, Brooke, Human Resources Manager, Franklin Woods Community Hospital, Johnson City, TN, p. A640

GRAHAM, Christopher, Chief Financial Officer, Community Memorial Hospital, Hamilton, NY, p. A485

GRAHAM, Connie, Public Information Officer, Mercy Health Love County, Marietta, OK, p. A561

GRAHAM, Gail L., Director, Va Central Iowa Health Care System, Des Moines, IA, p. A249

GRAHAM, Jeff, President and Chief Executive Officer, Adena Medical Center, Chillicothe, OH, p. A531

GRAHAM, John, M.D., Vice President Medical Affairs, Day Kimball Hospital, Putnam, CT, p. A124
Chief Financial Officer, Jefferson Hospital, Louisville, GA, p. A175

GRAHAM, Jon, Chief Finance Officer, Vidant Roanoke-Chowan Hospital, Ahoskie, NC, p. A504

GRAHAM, Kathryn, Director Communications and Community Relations, Novato Community Hospital, Novato, CA, p. A81

GRAHAM, Larry M., FACHE, President and Chief Executive Officer, Lake Charles Memorial Hospital, Lake Charles, LA, p. A307

GRAHAM, Michelle, M.D., Vice President Medical Affairs, Ascension Southeast Wisconsin Hospital - Franklin Campus, Franklin, WI, p. A784
M.D., Vice President Medical Affairs, Ascension Southeast Wisconsin Hospital - St. Francis Campus, Milwaukee, WI, p. A790

GRAHAM, Scott, Chief Executive Officer, North Valley Hospital, Tonasket, WA, p. A767
Chief Executive Officer, Three Rivers Hospital, Brewster, WA, p. A756

GRAHAM, Shauna, Director of Professional Services Human Resources, Marketing Foundation, Merrick Medical Center, Central City, NE, p. A430

GRAHAM, Susan, R.N., Nurse Executive, Healthsource Saginaw, Inc., Saginaw, MI, p. A365

GRAHAM, Yolanda, M.D., Medical Director, Devereux Advanced Behavioral Health Georgia, Kennesaw, GA, p. A174

GRAMER, Johanna, Director Human Resources, Mimbres Memorial Hospital, Deming, NM, p. A469

GRAMS, Shannon, Chief Executive Officer, Select Specialty Hospital-Fort Smith, Fort Smith, AR, p. A46

GRAMZA, Jeanne, Director Finance, Ascension All Saints, Racine, WI, p. A794

GRANADO-VILLAR, Deise, M.D., Chief Medical Officer and Senior Vice President Medical Affairs, Nicklaus Children's Hospital, Miami, FL, p. A147

GRANATH, Brad, M.D., Chief of Staff, Humboldt General Hospital, Winnemucca, NV, p. A447

GRANATO, Jerome, M.D., Senior Vice President and Chief Medical Officer, Excela Frick Hospital, Mount Pleasant, PA, p. A598
M.D., Senior Vice President and Chief Medical Officer, Excela Health Westmoreland Hospital, Greensburg, PA, p. A591

GRAND, Lawrence, MS, R.N., Chief Operating Officer, Hunterdon Healthcare, Flemington, NJ, p. A455

GRAND, Michael, Director of Finance, New Ulm Medical Center, New Ulm, MN, p. A382

GRANNELL, James, Chief Medical Officer, Sturgis Hospital, Sturgis, MI, p. A367

GRANT, Chad M., President and Chief Executive Officer, Mclaren Flint, Flint, MI, p. A354

GRANT, Cheryl, Director Information Systems, Coastal Carolina Hospital, Hardeeville, SC, p. A621

GRANT, Gail, Director Human Resources, Chi St. Francis Health, Breckenridge, MN, p. A373

GRANT, Mikki, Chief Information Officer, Fort Belknap Service Unit, Harlem, MT, p. A424

GRANT, Timothy, M.D., Chief Medical Officer, Parkridge Medical Center, Chattanooga, TN, p. A636

GRANT, Tonya, Director Human Resources, T.J. Health Columbia, Columbia, KY, p. A281

GRANT, Will, Chief Financial Officer, Anmed Health Cannon, Pickens, SC, p. A623
Interim Chief Financial Officer, Clarion Hospital, Clarion, PA, p. A586
Interim Chief Financial Officer, Lane Regional Medical Center, Zachary, LA, p. A317

GRANTHAM, Charlie, Manager Information Systems, Musc Health Marion Medical Center, Mullins, SC, p. A623

GRANTHAM, James, Administrator and Chief Executive Officer, Baptist Memorial Hospital-Booneville, Booneville, MS, p. A390
Administrator and Chief Executive Officer, Baptist Memorial Hospital-Union County, New Albany, MS, p. A398

GRANVILLE, Sabrina, Senior Vice President and Chief Human Resources Officer, Lowell General Hospital, Lowell, MA, p. A341

GRASER, David, Vice President and Chief Information Officer, Hillcrest Hospital - South, Tulsa, OK, p. A569

GRASS, Linda J., President, St. Luke's Easton Campus, Easton, PA, p. A589

GRASSER, Tierney, Senior Vice President and Chief Financial Officer, Olathe Medical Center, Olathe, KS, p. A272

GRATCH, Amie, Director Financial Services, Lifecare Hospitals Of Dallas, Dallas, TX, p. A669

GRATE, Anthony, Controller, Kindred Hospital-Greensboro, Greensboro, NC, p. A511

GRATRIX, Katie, Administrative Assistant III, Alaska Psychiatric Institute, Anchorage, AK, p. A27

GRATZ, Silvia, D.O., Chief Medical Officer, Fairmount Behavioral Health System, Philadelphia, PA, p. A600

GRAU, Leah, Director Human Resources, Tulane Health System, New Orleans, LA, p. A311

GRAUMANN, Julie, Director, Alliancehealth Clinton, Clinton, OK, p. A557

GRAVES, Amanda, Chief Information Systems, Washington Dc Veterans Affairs Medical Center, Washington, DC, p. A130

GRAVES, Bruce, M.D., Chief of Staff, Hale Ho'Ola Hamakua, Honokaa, HI, p. A184

GRAVES, Buddy, Chief Information Officer, Southern Surgical Hospital, Slidell, LA, p. A315

GRAVES, Deborah, R.N., President and Chief Operating Officer, Levindale Hebrew Hospital And Nursing, Baltimore, MD, p. A325

GRAVES, Jared, Chief Financial Officer, Byrd Regional Hospital, Leesville, LA, p. A307

GRAVES, John A., Chief Executive Officer, Dimmit Regional Hospital, Carrizo Springs, TX, p. A662

GRAVES III, Kenneth F., Chief Executive Officer, Continuecare Hospital At Madisonville, Madisonville, KY, p. A289

GRAY, Amy, Chief Executive Officer, Chi St. Josep. Health Rehabilitation Hospital, An Affiliate Of Encompass Health, Bryan, TX, p. A661

GRAY, Anthony, Chief Financial Officer, Lac-Olive View-Ucla Medical Center, Sylmar, CA, p. A100

GRAY, Bob, Chief Financial Officer, Aspire Hospital, Conroe, TX, p. A665

GRAY, Carrie, Director of Nursing, Riverview Behavioral Health, Texarkana, AR, p. A53

GRAY, Clarence, Chief Financial Officer, Tristar Horizon Medical Center, Dickson, TN, p. A637

GRAY, Cynthia, Interim Chief Financial Officer, Alliancehealth Midwest, Midwest City, OK, p. A562

GRAY, Eric, Chief Financial Officer, Encompass Health Rehabilitation Hospital Of Memphis, Memphis, TN, p. A644

GRAY, Gary, D.O., Chief Executive Officer, Natividad Medical Center, Salinas, CA, p. A90

GRAY, Janis, Chief Information Officer, Dupont Hospital, Fort Wayne, IN, p. A228
Chief Information Officer, Rehabilitation Hospital Of Fort Wayne, Fort Wayne, IN, p. A228

GRAY, Jason, M.D., Chief Medical Officer, Mercy Medical Center, Roseburg, OR, p. A580

GRAY, Judy, Vice President Human Resources, St. Peter's Hospital, Albany, NY, p. A474

GRAY, Karen, Director Human Resources, Vibra Hospital Of Southeastern Michigan, Llc, Lincoln Park, MI, p. A360

GRAY, Kris, Chief Medical Officer, Adventhealth Daytona Beach, Daytona Beach, FL, p. A136

GRAY, Larry, Chief Executive Officer, Memorial Hospital, Seminole, TX, p. A714

GRAY, Larry W., President, Baptist Health Louisville, Louisville, KY, p. A287

GRAY, Marty, R.N., Director of Nursing, Wyandot Memorial Hospital, Upper Sandusky, OH, p. A551

GRAY, Mary, Director Human Resources, Lehigh Regional Medical Center, Lehigh Acres, FL, p. A144

GRAY, Mike, Corporate Vice President Human Resources, Ut Health Tyler, Tyler, TX, p. A722

GRAY, Patricia, Director Health Information Management, Cumberland Hall Hospital, Hopkinsville, KY, p. A285

GRAY, Richard, M.D., Vice President Operations, Mayo Clinic Hospital, Phoenix, AZ, p. A36

GRAY, Rick, Chief Executive Officer, Culberson Hospital, Van Horn, TX, p. A722

GRAY, Roshanda, Assistant Administrator, Memorial Medical Center, Port Lavaca, TX, p. A707

GRAY, Sarah, Vice President Information Services, East Alabama Medical Center, Opelika, AL, p. A23

GRAY, Tami, Chief Financial Officer, Irwin County Hospital, Ocilla, GA, p. A178

GRAY, Teresa, President, Integris Canadian Valley Hospital, Yukon, OK, p. A572

GRAY, Thomas, M.D., Medical Director, Montana State Hospital, Warm Springs, MT, p. A428

GRAY, Tracy, Chief Information Officer, Grady General Hospital, Cairo, GA, p. A167
Chief Information Officer, Mitchell County Hospital, Camilla, GA, p. A168
Senior Vice President Information Services, John D. Archbold Memorial Hospital, Thomasville, GA, p. A182

GRAYBEAL, Phillip, CPA, Chief Financial Officer, Valley Health - Page Memorial Hospital, Luray, VA, p. A745

CPA, Chief Financial Officer, Valley Health - Warren Memorial Hospital, Front Royal, VA, p. A742

CPA, Vice President, Finance, Valley Health - Shenandoah Memorial Hospital, Woodstock, VA, p. A754

GRAYBILL, Matthew, Vice President, Human Resources and Chief Administrative Officer, Dayton Children's Hospital, Dayton, OH, p. A538

GRAYSON, Barbara, Vice President Human Resources, Mercy Hospital Washington, Washington, MO, p. A420

GREAKER, Mark, Chief Information Officer, New York-Presbyterian Queens, Flushing, NY, p. A484

GREAR, Esther, Director Hospital Social Work and Assistant Hospital Administrator, Windhaven Psychiatric Hospital, Prescott Valley, AZ, p. A37

GREASON, Linda, Vice President Human Resources, Milford Regional Medical Center, Milford, MA, p. A341

GREBOSKY, Jamie, M.D., Vice President of Medical Affairs, Asante Rogue Regional Medical Center, Medford, OR, p. A577

GRECCO, Jamie, Chief Human Resource Executive, Nyc Health + Hospitals / Jacobi, Bronx, NY, p. A477

Director Human Resources Post Acute, Nyc Health + Hospitals / Henry J Carter Specialty Hospital And Medical Center, New York, NY, p. A491

GRECO, Andrew, Chief Financial Officer, Calvary Hospital, Bronx, NY, p. A476

GRECO, Margaret, Chief Human Resources, Keller Army Community Hospital, West Point, NY, p. A502

GREEAR, Joy, President, Novant Health Mint Hill Medical Center, Charlotte, NC, p. A507

GREELEY, Donna, Director Human Resources, Spalding Rehabilitation Hospital, Aurora, CO, p. A107

GREELEY, Gerald, Chief Information Officer, Signature Healthcare Brockton Hospital, Brockton, MA, p. A337

GREEN, Amber, R.N., Chief Operating Officer and Chief Nursing Officer, St. Luke's Mccall, Mccall, ID, p. A191

GREEN, Barbara, Director Human Resources, O'Connor Hospital, Delhi, NY, p. A482

GREEN, Brenda, Director of Nursing, Ruby Valley Medical Center, Sheridan, MT, p. A428

GREEN, Bridget, Chief Human Resources Officer, Northside Hospital - Gwinnett, Lawrenceville, GA, p. A175

GREEN, Calvin, Interim Chief Executive Officer, Dequincy Memorial Hospital, Dequincy, LA, p. A301

GREEN, Christopher, Chief Financial Officer, Citrus Memorial Health System, Inverness, FL, p. A140

GREEN, Dante, Assistant Vice President Operations, New Orleans East Hospital, New Orleans, LA, p. A310

GREEN, David, M.D., Chief Medical Officer, Concord Hospital, Concord, NH, p. A448

Chief Human Resources, West Palm Beach Veterans Affairs Medical Center, West Palm Beach, FL, p. A162

Manager Information Technology, W. J. Mangold Memorial Hospital, Lockney, TX, p. A696

GREEN, Debra, R.N., Director of Nursing, Turquoise Lodge Hospital, Albuquerque, NM, p. A468

GREEN, Elizabeth, Chief Human Resources Officer, Cooper University Health Care, Camden, NJ, p. A453

GREEN, Garry Kim., FACHE, Administrator, Shriners Hospitals For Children-Shreveport, Shreveport, LA, p. A314

GREEN, Gayle, Director of Nursing, Hale Ho'Ola Hamakua, Honokaa, HI, p. A184

GREEN, John, Chief Operating Officer, Iredell Health System, Statesville, NC, p. A519

President and Chief Executive Officer, Iredell Health System, Statesville, NC, p. A519

Vice President Finance, St. Peter's Hospital, Helena, MT, p. A425

GREEN, Jon, R.N., Chief Executive Officer, Bleckley Memorial Hospital, Cochran, GA, p. A169

R.N., Chief Executive Officer, Taylor Regional Hospital, Hawkinsville, GA, p. A173

GREEN, Julie, Vice President Human Resources, Cheshire Medical Center, Keene, NH, p. A449

GREEN, Karen, Chief Information Officer, Brooks Rehabilitation Hospital, Jacksonville, FL, p. A141

GREEN, Kaye, FACHE, Chief Executive Officer, Roosevelt General Hospital, Portales, NM, p. A471

GREEN, Ladonna, Director Human Resources, Glen Rose Medical Center, Glen Rose, TX, p. A681

GREEN, Marsha, Administrator and Chief Operating Officer, Essentia Health-Deer River, Deer River, MN, p. A375

GREEN, Meredith, Senior Vice President and Chief Nursing Officer, Washington Regional Medical Center, Fayetteville, AR, p. A45

GREEN, Patrick, FACHE, President and Chief Executive Officer, Lawrence + Memorial Hospital, New London, CT, p. A124

FACHE, President and Chief Executive Officer, Westerly Hospital, Westerly, RI, p. A614

GREEN, Paul, Chief Clinical Officer, Kindred Hospital-Aurora, Aurora, CO, p. A107

GREEN, Rhonda G., R.N., Administrator, Lallie Kemp Medical Center, Independence, LA, p. A303

GREEN, Rose, Director Human Resources, Humboldt General Hospital, Winnemucca, NV, p. A447

GREEN, Steve, Comptroller, Jasper General Hospital, Bay Springs, MS, p. A389

GREEN, Susan, Senior Vice President Finance, Chief Financial Officer, Lowell General Hospital, Lowell, MA, p. A341

GREEN, Trent, President, Legacy Emanuel Medical Center, Portland, OR, p. A579

GREEN, Vince, Chief Operating Officer, St. Josep. Hospital, Fort Wayne, IN, p. A228

GREEN, Vincent, Medical Director, Prisma Health Laurens County Hospital, Clinton, SC, p. A617

GREEN-CHEATWOOD, Toni, M.D., Chief Medical Offider, Billings Clinic, Billings, MT, p. A421

GREENBERG, Mark, M.D., Chief Medical Officer, Cap. Coral Hospital, Cap. Coral, FL, p. A134

M.D., Medical Director, Gulf Coast Medical Center, Fort Myers, FL, p. A138

GREENBLATT, James, M.D., Chief Medical Officer, Vice President Medical Clinical Services, Walden Behavioral Care, Waltham, MA, p. A345

GREENE, Arthur, M.D., Vice President Medical Affairs, Sentara Careplex Hospital, Hampton, VA, p. A743

GREENE, Beth, Chief Operating Officer, Cherokee Indian Hospital, Cherokee, NC, p. A507

GREENE, Bradley, Chief Financial Officer, Wellstar Douglas Hospital, Douglasville, GA, p. A171

GREENE, Casey, Vice President and Chief Operating Officer, Unitypoint Health - St. Luke's Hospital, Cedar Rapids, IA, p. A245

GREENE, Charles, Chief Information Technology Officer, Och Regional Medical Center, Starkville, MS, p. A400

GREENE, Chelsea, Manager Human Resources, Guttenberg Municipal Hospital And Clinics, Guttenberg, IA, p. A250

GREENE, Cora, Senior Director, Chief Nursing Officer, Novant Health Rowan Medical Center, Salisbury, NC, p. A518

GREENE, Dustin, Chief Executive Officer, Tristar Skyline Medical Center, Nashville, TN, p. A647

GREENE, Erin, Coordinator Human Resources, Kindred Hospital-San Francisco Bay Area, San Leandro, CA, p. A95

GREENE, Jana, Chief Executive Officer, Jefferson County Hospital, Fayette, MS, p. A392

GREENE, Melodi, R.N., MS, Chief Nursing Officer, Community Howard Regional Health, Kokomo, IN, p. A234

GREENE, Palmer, R.N., Chief Nursing Officer, Sierra Vista Hospital, Truth Or Consequences, NM, p. A473

GREENE, Robert, Director Information Technology, Riverbridge Specialty Hospital, Vidalia, LA, p. A316

GREENE, Scott, Chief Information Officer, Tennova Healthcare-Clarksville, Clarksville, TN, p. A636

GREENE, Todd, Chief Executive Officer, Arizona Spine And Joint Hospital, Mesa, AZ, p. A33

Chief Executive Officer, Physicians Surgical Hospital - Quail Creek, Amarillo, TX, p. A652

GREENE, Tracie, Director Human Resources, Brigham City Community Hospital, Brigham City, UT, p. A727

GREENFIELD, Tadd S., Chief Executive Officer, South Big Horn County Hospital, Basin, WY, p. A801

GREENMAN, Sharon, Director Human Resources, Melissa Memorial Hospital, Holyoke, CO, p. A114

GREENSLIT, Mark, M.D., Chief Medical Staff, Colleton Medical Center, Walterboro, SC, p. A625

GREENSPAN, Jay S., M.D., Chief Executive Officer, Alfred I. Dupont Hospital For Children, Wilmington, DE, p. A128

GREENWALD, Derek, Chief Nursing Officer, Star Valley Health, Afton, WY, p. A801

Chief Nursing Officer, Syracuse Area Health, Syracuse, NE, p. A440

GREENWOOD, Annette, Chief Nursing Officer, Riverside Community Hospital, Riverside, CA, p. A88

GREENWOOD, Les, M.D., President, Medical Staff, Davis Hospital And Medical Center, Layton, UT, p. A728

GREER, Jinger, CPA, Chief Financial Officer, Richland Parish Hospital-Delhi, Delhi, LA, p. A300

GREGG, Richard, M.D., Medical Director, Pam Specialty Hospital Of Dayton, Miamisburg, OH, p. A545

GREGG, Shawna, Director Human Resources, Porterville Developmental Center, Porterville, CA, p. A86

GREGG, Sherry, Chief Information Technology Officer, Beckley Veterans Affairs Medical Center, Beckley, WV, p. A770

GREGG, Tom, Vice President Human Resources, Chi St. Alexius Health, Bismarck, ND, p. A521

GREGG, Travis, Chief Strategy Officer, Kearney Regional Medical Center, Kearney, NE, p. A434

GREGGAIN, Don, M.D., Physician Network Director, Tri-State Memorial Hospital, Clarkston, WA, p. A756

GREGONIS, Michael, Comptroller, Naval Hospital Jacksonville, Jacksonville, FL, p. A141

GREGOR, Brian, Manager Information Technology Operations, Glendale Memorial Hospital And Health Center, Glendale, CA, p. A67

GREGORIAN, Myra, Vice President and Chief Human Resources Officer, Children's Hospital Los Angeles, Los Angeles, CA, p. A74

GREGORICH, Miki, Director Human Resources, Pioneer Medical Center, Big Timber, MT, p. A421

GREGORY, Adina, Chief Nursing Officer, University Of Kansas Health System Great Bend Campus, Great Bend, KS, p. A265

Chief Operating Officer, University Of Kansas Health System Great Bend Campus, Great Bend, KS, p. A265

GREGORY, Ben, Chief Executive Officer, Walter B. Jones Alcohol And Drug Abuse Treatment Center, Greenville, NC, p. A511

GREGORY, Cody, Comptroller, Beaver County Memorial Hospital, Beaver, OK, p. A556

GREGORY, Jan, Chief of Human Resources, Crittenden County Hospital, Marion, KY, p. A289

GREGORY, Jay, M.D., Chief Medical Officer, Saint Francis Hospital Muskogee, Muskogee, OK, p. A562

GREGORY, Jim, Controller, Methodist Hospital Of Chicago, Chicago, IL, p. A199

GREGORY, Jody, R.N., Chief Nursing Officer, Encompass Health Rehabilitation Hospital Of Wichita Falls, Wichita Falls, TX, p. A725

GREGORY, Phyllis, Registered Health Information Administrator, Southern Inyo Healthcare District, Lone Pine, CA, p. A72

GREGORY, Sean, Chief Executive, Peacehealth Southwest Medical Center, Vancouver, WA, p. A768

GREGORY, Shawn, Chief Financial Officer, St. Petersburg General Hospital, Saint Petersburg, FL, p. A156

GREGORY, Trip. Senior Vice President Human Resources, Prisma Health Baptist Hospital, Columbia, SC, p. A618

GREGOS, Ruth, Director Finance, Shriners Hospitals For Children-Tampa, Tampa, FL, p. A159

GREGSON, Jennifer, Chief Nursing Officer, Red Bud Regional Hospital, Red Bud, IL, p. A218

GREIMAN, Alan W., Chief Executive Officer and President, Royal Oaks Hospital, Windsor, MO, p. A420

GREINER, Walter, Chief Financial Officer, Atlanticare Regional Medical Center, Atlantic City, NJ, p. A452

GREINER, William, M.D., Chief of Staff, F. W. Huston Medical Center, Winchester, KS, p. A279

GRENALDO, Paul, President, Doctors Community Hospital, Lanham, MD, p. A330

GRENDON, M, M.D., President Medical Staff, Amita Health Saint Josep. Hospital, Chicago, IL, p. A197

GRENIER, Raymond, Chief Financial Officer, Memorial Medical Center, Las Cruces, NM, p. A470

GREW, Kate, MSN, R.N., Vice President/Chief Nurse Executive, Atrium Health Cabarrus, Concord, NC, p. A508

GREW, Terry, Chief Business Office, Hampton Veterans Affairs Medical Center, Hampton, VA, p. A743

GREY, Michael, M.D., Interim Chief Medical Officer, Saint Francis Hospital And Medical Center, Hartford, CT, p. A122

GREY, Mitzi, Chief Operating Officer, Bath Community Hospital, Hot Springs, VA, p. A744

GRIBBIN, John, FACHE, President and Chief Executive Officer, Centrastate Healthcare System, Freehold, NJ, p. A455

GRICE, William N., Executive Director, Kaiser Permanente Los Angeles Medical Center, Los Angeles, CA, p. A74

GRICUS, Peggy, R.N., Vice President, Patient Care Services and Chief Nursing Officer, Silver Cross Hospital, New Lenox, IL, p. A214

GRIDLEY, Mark, FACHE, President and Chief Executive Officer, Fhn Memorial Hospital, Freeport, IL, p. A205

GRIEP, John, M.D., Chief Medical Director, St. Catherine Hospital, East Chicago, IN, p. A227

GRIEST, Mary, Vice President Finance and Chief Financial Officer, Uh Samaritan Medical Center, Ashland, OH, p. A528

GRIFFES, Carol, Administrator, Duane L. Waters Hospital, Jackson, MI, p. A358

GRIFFEY, Jennifer, Vice President of Finance, Calais Regional Hospital, Calais, ME, p. A319

GRIFFIN, Amy, Vice President Patient Care Services, John D. Archbold Memorial Hospital, Thomasville, GA, p. A182

GRIFFIN, Anthony, M.D., Chief Medical Officer, Passavant Area Hospital, Jacksonville, IL, p. A209

GRIFFIN, Barbara, MSN, R.N., Chief Nursing Officer, Rapides Regional Medical Center, Alexandria, LA, p. A295

GRIFFIN, Betty, Interim Chief Nursing Officer, Musc Health Chester Medical Center, Chester, SC, p. A617

GRIFFIN, Brad, Chief Executive Officer, Gulf Coast Regional Medical Center, Panama City, FL, p. A153

GRIFFIN, Brian, Director Information Services, Springhill Medical Center, Springhill, LA, p. A315
Director of Medical Affairs, Houlton Regional Hospital, Houlton, ME, p. A321
GRIFFIN, Charles, Director of Nursing, Clay County Hospital, Ashland, AL, p. A14
GRIFFIN, Cindy, Chief Nursing Officer, Liberty Dayton Regional Medical Center, Liberty, TX, p. A696
Director Human Resources, Medical Center Barbour, Eufaula, AL, p. A18
GRIFFIN, Dean A., Chief Executive Officer, Lawrence Medical Center, Moulton, AL, p. A22
GRIFFIN, Douglas, M.D., Vice President Medical Officer, Sanford Medical Center Fargo, Fargo, ND, p. A523
GRIFFIN, Holly, R.N., Chief Nursing Officer, Lady Of The Sea General Hospital, Cut Off, LA, p. A300
GRIFFIN, Jarvis, Assistant Director Administration and Chief Operating Officer, Piedmont Geriatric Hospital, Burkeville, VA, p. A739
GRIFFIN, Jeannine, M.D., Chief of Staff, Memorial Medical Center, Port Lavaca, TX, p. A707
GRIFFIN, Jeff, Assistant Vice President Finance, Atrium Health Anson, Wadesboro, NC, p. A519
GRIFFIN, Joe, Controller, Encompass Health Rehabilitation Hospital Of Round Rock, Round Rock, TX, p. A709
GRIFFIN, Kathryn, Chief Nurse Executive, Terrell State Hospital, Terrell, TX, p. A719
GRIFFIN, Matthew, M.D., Chief Medical Officer, St. Mary Mercy Hospital, Livonia, MI, p. A360
GRIFFIN, Philip. Director of Operations, Rochester Psychiatric Center, Rochester, NY, p. A496
GRIFFIN, Wes, Division Human Resources Manager, Ut Health East Texas Rehabilitation Hospital, Tyler, TX, p. A722
GRIFFIN-JONES, Christie, R.N., Chief Nursing Officer, Encompass Health Rehabilitation Hospital Of Humble, Humble, TX, p. A689
GRIFFIN-MAHON, Selena, Assistant Vice President Human Resources, Bronxcare Health System, Bronx, NY, p. A476
GRIFFIS, Daniel, M.D., Chief Medical Officer, Syringa Hospital And Clinics, Grangeville, ID, p. A190
GRIFFITH, Barbara, M.D., Chief Executive Officer, Woman's Hospital, Baton Rouge, LA, p. A298
Vice President Human Resources, St. Anthony's Rehabilitation Hospital, Lauderdale Lakes, FL, p. A144
GRIFFITH, David, M.D., Medical Director, Texas Center For Infectious Disease, San Antonio, TX, p. A713
GRIFFITH, H., Chief Financial Officer, Tennova Healthcare - Cleveland, Cleveland, TN, p. A636
GRIFFITH, James, Chief Operating Officer, El Camino Hospital, Mountain View, CA, p. A80
GRIFFITH, Jeanne, Chief Nursing Officer, Coryell Health, Gatesville, TX, p. A681
GRIFFITH, John, R.N., Associate Director, Veterans Affairs New Jersey Health Care System, East Orange, NJ, p. A454
GRIFFITH, John H., Ph.D., President and Chief Executive Officer, Kedren Community Mental Health Center, Los Angeles, CA, p. A75
GRIFFITH, Joshua, Manager Human Resources, Presbyterian Espanola Hospital, Espanola, NM, p. A469
GRIFFITH, Leah, Chief Executive Officer, Big Sandy Medical Center, Big Sandy, MT, p. A421
GRIFFITH, Maria, Director Human Resources, Signature Psychiatric Hospital, Kansas City, MO, p. A409
GRIFFITH, Patti, R.N., MS, Chief Nursing Officer, Methodist Hospital For Surgery, Addison, TX, p. A651
GRIFFITH, Susan, Finance Business Partner Specialist, Eastern State Hospital, Lexington, KY, p. A286
GRIFFITHS, Mark, Director Management Information Systems, Incline Village Community Hospital, Incline Village, NV, p. A442
GRIGG, Dan, Chief Executive Officer, Harney District Hospital, Burns, OR, p. A574
GRIGG, William, Senior Vice President and Chief Financial Officer, Methodist Hospital Of Southern California, Arcadia, CA, p. A56
GRIGGS, Stacie, MIS Analyst, North Mississippi Medical Center-West Point, West Point, MS, p. A401
GRIGSBY, Jan, Vice President and Chief Financial Officer, Springhill Memorial Hospital, Mobile, AL, p. A22
GRIGSON, John, Vice President and Chief Financial Officer, Covenant Medical Center, Lubbock, TX, p. A697
GRILL, Laura D., R.N., Chief Executive Officer, East Alabama Medical Center, Opelika, AL, p. A23
GRILLS, Kathy, Director Human Resources, Encompass Health Rehabilitation Hospital Of Hamarville, Pittsburgh, PA, p. A603
GRIM, Andrew, Chief Financial Officer, San Gabriel Valley Medical Center, San Gabriel, CA, p. A94
GRIM, Charles, D.D.S., Secretary of Health, Chickasaw Nation Medical Center, Ada, OK, p. A555

GRIMES, Paula, R.N., MSN, Chief Nursing Officer, Nea Baptist Memorial Hospital, Jonesboro, AR, p. A48
GRIMES, Teresa G., Chief Executive Officer, Washington County Hospital, Chatom, AL, p. A16
GRIMES, Walter, Director Information Technology, Christus Good Shepherd Medical Center-Marshall, Marshall, TX, p. A700
GRIMLEY, Karen, Chief Nursing Executive, Ronald Reagan Ucla Medical Center, Los Angeles, CA, p. A75
GRIMM, Debra, MS, R.N., Vice President and Chief Nursing Officer, Long Island Community Hospital, Patchogue, NY, p. A494
GRIMM, Tamara, R.N., Chief Clinical Officer and Chief Nursing Officer, Cornerstone Hospitals Bossier City, Bossier City, LA, p. A298
GRIMM, William, Chief Information Officer, Henry County Hospital, Napoleon, OH, p. A546
GRIMMER, Michael, Chief Operating Officer, Athol Hospital, Athol, MA, p. A334
GRIMSHAW, Bruce P., FACHE, Chief Executive Officer, Southern California Hospital At Hollywood, Los Angeles, CA, p. A76
GRIMSHAW, Matthew, Market Chief Executive Officer, Trinity Health System, Steubenville, OH, p. A550
GRIMSLEY, Denise, R.N., Vice President and Administrator, Adventhealth Wauchula, Wauchula, FL, p. A161
GRINER, Alisa, Director, Human Resources, Memorial Health, Savannah, GA, p. A180
GRINER, Ginny, Director Human Resources, George E. Weems Memorial Hospital, Apalachicola, FL, p. A131
GRIPPI, Michael, M.D., Chief Medical Officer, Good Shepherd Penn Partners Specialty Hospital At Rittenhouse, Philadelphia, PA, p. A600
GRISH, John, Chief Financial Officer, Johnson Memorial Hospital, Stafford Springs, CT, p. A125
GRISHOW, Cathy, Director Human Resources, Ellett Memorial Hospital, Appleton City, MO, p. A402
GRISIER, Douglas, D.O., Medical Director, Encompass Health Rehabilitation Hospital Of Erie, Erie, PA, p. A589
GRISNAK, Karen, R.N., Chief Operating Officer and Assistant Administrator Quality Services, Kaiser Permanente Vallejo Medical Center, Vallejo, CA, p. A103
GRISPINO, Frank, Vice President Operations, Mosaic Medical Center - Maryville, Maryville, MO, p. A411
GRISSOM, Robyn, Director of Human Resources, Osf Healthcare Saint Anthony's Health Center, Alton, IL, p. A194
GRISSOM, Tina, Chief Information Technology Officer, Arkansas State Hospital, Little Rock, AR, p. A48
GRIZZARD, David, CPA, Chief Financial Officer, Slidell Memorial Hospital, Slidell, LA, p. A315
GROCE, Vicky, Chief Nursing Officer, Lincoln County Health System, Fayetteville, TN, p. A638
GROCHALA, Eugene, Vice President Information Systems, Capital Health Medical Center-Hopewell, Pennington, NJ, p. A461
Vice President Information Systems, Capital Health Regional Medical Center, Trenton, NJ, p. A464
GROENIG, Matt, Vice President Finance, St. Luke's Mccall, Mccall, ID, p. A191
GROEPER, William, Vice President Finance, Beloit Health System, Beloit, WI, p. A781
GROEPPER, Ronald, Senior Vice President and Area Manager, Kaiser Permanente San Francisco Medical Center, San Francisco, CA, p. A93
Senior Vice President and Area Manager, Kaiser Permanente South San Francisco, South San Francisco, CA, p. A99
GRONERT, Thomas, Chief Information Officer, University Of Maryland St. Josep. Medical Center, Towson, MD, p. A333
GRONOW, Thomas, Chief Operating Officer, University Of Colorado Hospital, Aurora, CO, p. A108
GROOMS, Kim, Administrator, King's Daughters Medical Center Ohio, Portsmouth, OH, p. A548
GROS, Mark, Director Human Resources, United Medical Rehabilitation Hospital, Hammond, LA, p. A302
GROSECLOSE, Cathy, Vice President Patient Care Services, Grady Memorial Hospital, Chickasha, OK, p. A557
GROSETH, Bradley D., Chief Administrative Officer, Marshfield Medical Center - Rice Lake, Rice Lake, WI, p. A795
GROSHANS, Adam, President, Springfield Regional Medical Center, Springfield, OH, p. A549
GROSKREUTZ, Kevin, Chief Information Officer, Hshs Sacred Heart Hospital, Eau Claire, WI, p. A783
Division Chief Information Officer, Ancillary Systems, Hshs St. Joseph's Hospital, Chippewa Falls, WI, p. A781
GROSS, Anne, Senior Vice President, Patient Care Services and Chief Nursing Officer, Dana-Farber Cancer Institute, Boston, MA, p. A335
GROSS, Barry, M.D., Executive Vice President and Chief Medical Officer, Riverside Regional Medical Center, Newport News, VA, p. A747

GROSS, Cathy, Director Health Information Management Systems, Wrangell Medical Center, Wrangell, AK, p. A29
GROSS, Cindy, Director of Finance, Barnes-Jewish St. Peters Hospital, Saint Peters, MO, p. A418
GROSS, Denton, Director Information Services, Larue D. Carter Memorial Hospital, Indianapolis, IN, p. A232
GROSS, Kristin, Director Information Technology Center, Avera Mckennan Hospital And University Health Center, Sioux Falls, SD, p. A631
GROSS, Len, Chief Human Resources Officer, Sheridan Memorial Hospital, Sheridan, WY, p. A804
GROSS, Mark, Chief Finance Officer, Hillsdale Hospital, Hillsdale, MI, p. A357
Executive Vice President and Chief Financial Officer, Bronson South Haven Hospital, South Haven, MI, p. A367
Vice President Finance and Chief Financial Officer, North Ottawa Community Hospital, Grand Haven, MI, p. A355
GROSS, Paul, Human Services and Finance Officer, Larry B. Zieverink, Sr. Alcoholism Treatment Center, Raleigh, NC, p. A516
GROSS, Peter, M.D., Senior Vice President and Chief Medical Officer, Hackensack Meridian Health Hackensack University Medical Center, Hackensack, NJ, p. A455
GROSS, Randy, Chief Executive Officer, Broward Health Imperial Point, Fort Lauderdale, FL, p. A137
GROSS, Tina, MSN, R.N., Chief Nursing Officer, Sparrow Specialty Hospital, Lansing, MI, p. A360
GROSSER, Joy, Chief Information Officer, University Of Washington Medical Center, Seattle, WA, p. A764
Chief Information Officer, Uw Medicine/Harborview Medical Center, Seattle, WA, p. A764
GROSSMAN, Drew, Chief Executive Officer, St. Mary's Medical Center, Blue Springs, MO, p. A402
GROSSMAN, Hannah, M.D., Chief Medical Officer, Los Robles Hospital And Medical Center, Thousand Oaks, CA, p. A101
GROSSMAN, Rick, Senior Vice President and General Counsel, Sharp Mesa Vista Hospital, San Diego, CA, p. A92
GROSSMAN, Robert I., M.D., Chief Executive Officer, Nyu Langone Hospitals, New York, NY, p. A492
GROSSO, Michael, M.D., Senior Vice President Medical Affairs, Huntington Hospital, Huntington, NY, p. A485
GROTE, Brad, Chief Operating Officer, Glendale Memorial Hospital And Health Center, Glendale, CA, p. A67
GROTELUSCHEN, Ronald, Chief Financial Officer, Coastal Carolina Hospital, Hardeeville, SC, p. A621
GROTH, Jill, Site Administrator, Mercyone Oelwein Medical Center, Oelwein, IA, p. A255
GROTH, McGarrett, Chief of Staff, Atchison Hospital, Atchison, KS, p. A261
GROVE, Gene, M.D., Chief of Staff, Elkhart General Hospital, Elkhart, IN, p. A227
GROVE, Jeri, Chief Nursing Officer, Scott County Hospital, Scott City, KS, p. A276
GROVE, Julia, Chief Nursing Officer, Jackson Purchase Medical Center, Mayfield, KY, p. A290
GROVE, Sarah, M.D., Medical Director, Mount Carmel Rehabilitation Hospital, Westerville, OH, p. A552
GROVER, James, Manager Data Processing, Atascadero State Hospital, Atascadero, CA, p. A56
GROVES, Ned, Executive Vice President and Administrator, Memorial Sloan-Kettering Cancer Center, New York, NY, p. A490
GROVES, Tandy, Director Human Resources, Bailey Medical Center, Owasso, OK, p. A566
GROW, Heidi, Director Human Resources, Aurora Sinai Medical Center, Milwaukee, WI, p. A790
GROW, Julie, Chief Financial Officer, Hocking Valley Community Hospital, Logan, OH, p. A543
GROWSE, Michael, M.D., Clinical Director, Federal Medical Center, Lexington, KY, p. A286
GRUBB, Michael, Chief Financial Officer, Bridgepoint Hospital National Harbor, Washington, DC, p. A129
Senior Chief Financial Officer, Bridgepoint Hospital Capitol Hill, Washington, DC, p. A129
GRUBB, Nora, Chief Financial Officer, Big Sandy Medical Center, Big Sandy, MT, p. A421
GRUBER, Scott, M.D., Chief of Staff, John D. Dingell Veterans Affairs Medical Center, Detroit, MI, p. A353
GRUEN, Jeremy, Director Information Systems, Pike County Memorial Hospital, Louisiana, MO, p. A411
GRUHONJIC, Osman, Chief Financial Officer, Lehigh Regional Medical Center, Lehigh Acres, FL, p. A144
GRUN, Joseph, Chief Information Officer, New York State Psychiatric Institute, New York, NY, p. A491
GRUNDIG, Kevin, Chief Human Resource Officer, Veterans Affairs New York Harbor Healthcare System, Brooklyn, NY, p. A479
GRUNHOVD, April, Vice President of Patient Care Services and Chief Nursing Officer, Riverview Health, Crookston, MN, p. A374

GRUNWALD, Pat, MSN, Chief Nursing Officer, Unitypoint Health Meriter, Madison, WI, p. A788

GRUVER, Laquita, Fiscal Officer, Grand Junction Veterans Health Care System, Grand Junction, CO, p. A113

GRZYBOWSKI, John, M.D., Medical Director, Mayo Clinic Health System - Albert Lea And Austin, Albert Lea, MN, p. A371

GUACCIO, Anthony, President and Chief Executive Officer, Swedish Covenant Hospital, Chicago, IL, p. A201

GUADAGNOLI, Donald, M.D., Chief Medical Officer, Cap. Cod Hospital, Hyannis, MA, p. A340

GUAJARDO, Carlos, Chief Financial Officer, South Texas Health System, Edinburg, TX, p. A674

GUAJARDO, Michael, Director Finance, Christus Spohn Hospital Alice, Alice, TX, p. A651

GUARINO, Celia, R.N., MSN, Vice President and Chief Nursing Officer, Holy Cross Hospital, Silver Spring, MD, p. A332

GUARINO, Rick, M.D., Vice President Medical Affairs, Wilson Medical Center, Wilson, NC, p. A520

GUARNESCHELLI, Philip, President and Chief Executive Officer, Upmc Pinnacle Harrisburg, Harrisburg, PA, p. A591

GUARNI, Andrew, Chief Financial Officer, Hoag Memorial Hospital Presbyterian, Newport Beach, CA, p. A81

GUARNIERI, Candace, Chief Financial Officer, Phoebe Worth Medical Center, Sylvester, GA, p. A181
Chief Financial Officer, Southwest Georgia Regional Medical Center, Cuthbert, GA, p. A170

GUARRACINO, Joseph, Senior Vice President and Chief Financial Officer, White Plains Hospital Center, White Plains, NY, p. A502

GUARRERA, Frank, Executive Vice President and Chief Financial Officer, Motion Picture And Television Fund Hospital And Residential Services, Woodland Hills, CA, p. A105

GUAY, Amy, Chief Financial Officer, Spaulding Rehabilitation Hospital, Charlestown, MA, p. A338

GUBERMAN, Wayne, Director Finance, Matheny Medical And Educational Center, Peapack, NJ, p. A460

GUDAHL, Shanna, Manager Human Resources, United Hospital District, Blue Earth, MN, p. A373

GUEHLSTORF, Daniel, M.D., Chief of Staff, Midwest Orthopedic Specialty Hospital, Franklin, WI, p. A784

GUELKER, Rhonda, Senior Director Finance, Rolling Plains Memorial Hospital, Sweetwater, TX, p. A718

GUERRA, Tony, Chief Financial Officer, Sharp Mesa Vista Hospital, San Diego, CA, p. A92

GUERRERO, Bonnie, Director Human Resources, Valley View Medical Center, Fort Mohave, AZ, p. A31

GUERRERO, Kerrie, R.N., MSN, Vice President and Chief Nursing Officer, Houston Methodist The Woodlands Hospital, The Woodlands, TX, p. A720

GUERRERO, Lori, Chief Executive Officer, Trusted Medical Centers-Mansfield, Mansfield, TX, p. A699

GUERRERO, Marisa, Director Human Resources, Laredo Specialty Hospital, Laredo, TX, p. A695

GUERRIERO, John, D.O., IIIChief of Staff, Berwick Hospital Center, Berwick, PA, p. A584

GUESMAN, Kim, R.N., Chief Nursing Officer, Beaumont Hospital - Farmington Hills, Farmington Hills, MI, p. A354

GUEST, William, M.D., Senior Vice President and Chief Medical Officer, Tift Regional Medical Center, Tifton, GA, p. A182

GUEVARA, Al Jr, FACHE, President, Chi St. Luke's Health Brazosport, Lake Jackson, TX, p. A694

GUGEL, Paul, Manager Information Technology, Marlette Regional Hospital, Marlette, MI, p. A361

GUGLIELMI, Diane, Vice President, Human Resources, Ohiohealth Berger Hospital, Circleville, OH, p. A533

GUGLIELMO, Elaine, Vice President Human Resources and Organizational Development, Stamford Hospital, Stamford, CT, p. A125

GUIDO, Kathleen, Chief Nursing Officer, Palmetto General Hospital, Hialeah, FL, p. A139

GUIDO-ALLEN, Debra, Chief Operating Officer, Beaumont Hospital - Royal Oak, Royal Oak, MI, p. A365

GUIDRY, Charles, Network Development Executive, Director Information Technology, Abbeville General Hospital, Abbeville, LA, p. A295

GUIDRY, Linda, Human Resources Generalist, Abrom Kaplan Memorial Hospital, Kaplan, LA, p. A304

GUIDRY, Lloyd, Chief Operating Officer, Lady Of The Sea General Hospital, Cut Off, LA, p. A300

GUIDRY, Stephanie A., Chief Executive Officer, Franklin Foundation Hospital, Franklin, LA, p. A301

GUIDRY, Trisha, Administrator, Baton Rouge Rehabilitation Hospital, Baton Rouge, LA, p. A296

GUIGNIER, Liz, Vice President Human Resources, Eisenhower Health, Rancho Mirage, CA, p. A86

GUILD, Anthony, Chief Executive Officer, Conway Behavioral Health Hospital, Conway, AR, p. A43

GUILFOIL, Thomas, Director Human Resources, Baystate Wing Hospital, Palmer, MA, p. A343

GUILLAUME, Kristen, Vice President and Chief Information Officer, North Kansas City Hospital, North Kansas City, MO, p. A413

GUILLORY, Larry, Chief Human Resources Officer, Baylor Scott & White Emergency Hospitals—Aubrey, Aubrey, TX, p. A654

GUILLORY, Pamela, Chief Operating Officer and Chief Nursing Officer, Methodist Hospital South, Jourdanton, TX, p. A691

GUIMARAES, Antonio, M.D., Clinical Director, U. S. Public Health Service Indian Hospital, Cass Lake, MN, p. A374

GUIMENTO, Robert, President, Newyork-Presbyterian Brooklyn Methodist Hospital, Brooklyn, NY, p. A478

GUINA, Michelle, Manager Human Resources, Sutter Surgical Hospital - North Valley, Yuba City, CA, p. A106

GUINANE, Gerard, Vice President Human Resources, Swedishamerican - A Division Of Uw Health, Rockford, IL, p. A219

GUIRL, Nadine, Senior Vice President Human Resources, Waukesha Memorial Hospital, Waukesha, WI, p. A798

GUISE, Linda, Senior Human Resource Consultant, Indiana University Health Jay Hospital, Portland, IN, p. A239

GUITTAP, Taylor, Chief Financial Officer, Good Samaritan Medical Center, West Palm Beach, FL, p. A162

GULL, Joann, Chief Nursing Officer, Nyc Health + Hospitals / Elmhurst, Elmhurst, NY, p. A483

GULLATT, Thomas, M.D., Chief Medical Officer, St. Francis Medical Center, Monroe, LA, p. A309

GULLINGSRUD, Timothy, Chief Executive Officer, Ogallala Community Hospital, Ogallala, NE, p. A436

GULRICH, Erica, Chief Executive Officer, Northwest Medical Center, Margate, FL, p. A145

GUM, Jessica, Controller, Encompass Health Rehabilitation Hospital Of Parkersburg, Parkersburg, WV, p. A775

GUMATO, Sixta, M.D., Chief Medical Officer, Crane Memorial Hospital, Crane, TX, p. A666

GUMBEL, Wendy, Director of Human Resources, Encompass Health Deaconess Rehabilitation Hospital, Newburgh, IN, p. A238

GUMBS, Milton, M.D., Vice President and Medical Director, Bronxcare Health System, Bronx, NY, p. A476

GUMMADI, Subhaker, M.D., Chief Medical Staff, Kp. Promise Hospital Of Baton Rouge, Baton Rouge, LA, p. A297

GUMP, Linda, Chief Clinical Services Officer, Aurora Medical Center Kenosha, Kenosha, WI, p. A786

GUNABALAN, Ryan, Chief Executive Officer, Behavioral Center Of Michigan, Warren, MI, p. A369

GUNASEKARAN, Suresh, Chief Executive Officer, University Of Iowa Hospitals And Clinics, Iowa City, IA, p. A252

GUNDLAPALLI, Madhu, M.D., Clinical Director, Utah State Hospital, Provo, UT, p. A731

GUNKEL, Jeff, Chief Information Officer, Jamestown Regional Medical Center, Jamestown, ND, p. A524

GUNN, Deborah, Chief Information Officer, W. G. (Bill) Heffner Veterans Affairs Medical Center, Salisbury, NC, p. A518

GUNN, Terry, FACHE, Chief Executive Officer, Providence Hospital, Columbia, SC, p. A618

GUNNELL, Nancy, Chief Human Resource Officer, West Suburban Medical Center, Oak Park, IL, p. A215

GUNNERSEN, Nils, Administrator, Bertrand Chaffee Hospital, Springville, NY, p. A498

GUNTLOW, Ann, Chief Nursing Officer, Ellenville Regional Hospital, Ellenville, NY, p. A483

GUNUKULA, Srinivas, M.D., Chief of Staff, Dallas Regional Medical Center, Mesquite, TX, p. A700

GUOYAVATIN, Kora, Chief Financial Officer, Garden Grove Hospital And Medical Center, Garden Grove, CA, p. A66
Chief Financial Officer, West Anaheim Medical Center, Anaheim, CA, p. A55

GUPTA, Anil, M.D., Chief of Staff, Kindred Hospital-Baldwin Park, Baldwin Park, CA, p. A58

GUPTA, Arun, M.D., Vice President Medical Affairs, South Pointe Hospital, Warrensville Heights, OH, p. A552

GUPTA, Ashok, M.D., Chief of Staff, Eaton Rapids Medical Center, Eaton Rapids, MI, p. A354

GUPTA, John, Executive Vice President and Chief Operating Officer, Brooklyn Hospital Center, Brooklyn, NY, p. A477

GUPTA, Saurabh, Chief Medical Officer, Rockford Center, Newark, DE, p. A128

GUPTA, Vijay, M.D., President and Chief Executive Officer, Franciscan Healthcare Munster, Munster, IN, p. A237

GURGA, Jean J., Medical Center Director, Northern Arizona Veterans Affairs Health Care System, Prescott, AZ, p. A37

GURR, Lory, Chief Human Resources Division, Evans U. S. Army Community Hospital, Fort Carson, CO, p. A112

GURRAD, Trece, Vice President Patient Care Services, Columbia Memorial Hospital, Astoria, OR, p. A573

GURROLA, Jose, Administrator, New Mexico Rehabilitation Center, Roswell, NM, p. A471

GURULE, Eric, Chief Information Officer, Turquoise Lodge Hospital, Albuquerque, NM, p. A468

GURUNG, Anju, M.D., Chief Medical Officer, Mahnomen Health Center, Mahnomen, MN, p. A379

GUSHEE, Dean, M.D., Medical Director, Mason General Hospital And Family Of Clinics, Shelton, WA, p. A765

GUSHO, Michael, Chief Financial Officer, St. Josep. Mercy Oakland, Pontiac, MI, p. A364

GUSMANO, Jane, Interim Vice President Finance, Memorial Hospital East, Shiloh, IL, p. A220
Interim Vice President Finance, Memorial Hospital, Belleville, IL, p. A195

GUSTAFSON, Brian, Chief Financial Officer, Veterans Affairs Montana Health Care System, Fort Harrison, MT, p. A423

GUSTAFSON, Connie, Director of Nursing, Jacobson Memorial Hospital Care Center, Elgin, ND, p. A522

GUSTAFSON, Michael, M.D., President, Umass Memorial Medical Center, Worcester, MA, p. A347

GUSTER, Cherie, R.N., MSN, Senior Vice President and Chief Nursing Officer, Cleveland Clinic Akron General, Akron, OH, p. A527

GUSTILO, Maria, M.D., Medical Director, Osawatomie State Hospital At Adair Acute Care, Osawatomie, KS, p. A273

GUSTIN, Michael, Information Technology, John J. Pershing Veterans Affairs Medical Center, Poplar Bluff, MO, p. A413

GUTHMILLER, Martin W., Chief Executive Officer, Orange City Area Health System, Orange City, IA, p. A255

GUTHRIE, Pamela, Chief Human Resources Officer, Hillcrest Hospital Pryor, Pryor, OK, p. A567

GUTIERREZ, Lori, Chief Financial Officer, Rochelle Community Hospital, Rochelle, IL, p. A218

GUTIERREZ, Michelle, Executive Director Human Resources, Orange County, Saddleback Medical Center, Laguna Hills, CA, p. A70
Executive Director Human Resources, Memorialcare, Orange Coast Memorial Medical Center, Fountain Valley, CA, p. A64

GUTIERREZ, Noe, Chief Financial Officer, Lake Granbury Medical Center, Granbury, TX, p. A682

GUTIERREZ, Santiago, M.D., Chief Medical Officer, Doctors Hospital Of Laredo, Laredo, TX, p. A695

GUTIERREZ, Vickie, Chief Executive, Dr. Dan C. Trigg Memorial Hospital, Tucumcari, NM, p. A473
Director of Patient Care, Dr. Dan C. Trigg Memorial Hospital, Tucumcari, NM, p. A473

GUTIERREZ, Victor, M.D., Medical Director, Allegiance Behavioral Health Center Of Plainview, Plainview, TX, p. A706

GUTJAHR, Susan, Reimbursement Specialist, Sparta Community Hospital, Sparta, IL, p. A220

GUTNICK, Michael, Executive Vice President and Chief Financial Officer, Memorial Sloan-Kettering Cancer Center, New York, NY, p. A490

GUTOW, Andrew, M.D., Medical Director, Menlo Park Surgical Hospital, Menlo Park, CA, p. A77

GUTOWSKI, Jennifer S., FACHE, Director, Southern Arizona Veterans Affairs Health Care System, Tucson, AZ, p. A41

GUTSCH, Michael, Chief Executive Officer and Administrator, Cumberland Healthcare, Cumberland, WI, p. A782

GUTSCHENRITTER, John, Chief Financial Officer, Wilson Medical Center, Neodesha, KS, p. A271

GUTTENBERG, Ellen, Chief Operating Officer, Frances Mahon Deaconess Hospital, Glasgow, MT, p. A424

GUTTIN, Enrique, M.D., FACS, Chief of Staff, Wilmington Veterans Affairs Medical Center, Wilmington, DE, p. A128

GUTTMACHER, Laurence, M.D., Clinical Director, Rochester Psychiatric Center, Rochester, NY, p. A496

GUTZEIT, Michael, M.D., Chief Medical Officer, Children's Hospital Of Wisconsin, Milwaukee, WI, p. A791

GUY, Kimberly, President, St. Joseph's Hospital, Tampa, FL, p. A160

GUYETTE, William, M.D., President Medical Staff, Livingston Hospital And Healthcare Services, Salem, KY, p. A293

GUZ, Andrew, Chief Executive Officer, Lakewood Ranch Medical Center, Bradenton, FL, p. A133

GUZMAN, Claudia V., Chief Executive Officer and Managing Director, Hospital San Pablo, Bayamon, PR, p. A806

GUZMAN, David, Chief Financial Officer, Nyc Health + Hospitals / Elmhurst, Elmhurst, NY, p. A483

GUZMAN, Lisa, Human Resource Vice President, Redlands Community Hospital, Redlands, CA, p. A87

GWATKIN, Elizabeth, Vice President Human Resources, Northeastern Vermont Regional Hospital, Saint Johnsbury, VT, p. A736

GWYN, Andrea, Chief Operating Officer, Terre Haute Regional Hospital, Terre Haute, IN, p. A241

GWYN, Brian, West Market President- Atrium Health, Atrium Health Cleveland, Shelby, NC, p. A518

GYIMAH, Ed, Chief Financial Officer, Howard University Hospital, Washington, DC, p. A129

GYNTHER, Tracy, R.N., Vice President and Chief Nursing Officer, Wellstar West Georgia Medical Center, Lagrange, GA, p. A175

**H**

HAACK, Sally, Vice President and Director of Human Resources, St. Francis Regional Medical Center, Shakopee, MN, p. A386

HAACK, Wanda, MSN, R.N., Chief Nursing Officer, Genesis Medical Center, Dewitt, De Witt, IA, p. A248

HAAG, Adam, Manager Information Technology, Coffey County Hospital, Burlington, KS, p. A262

HAAGENSON, Deb, R.N., Vice President of Patient Care, Chi St. Joseph's Health, Park Rapids, MN, p. A382

HAAK, Karen, R.N., MSN, Chief Nursing Officer, Good Samaritan Hospital, Vincennes, IN, p. A242

HAAS, Christine, Chief Information Officer, Geisinger Jersey Shore Hospital, Jersey Shore, PA, p. A593

HAAS, Robert, M.D., Chief Medical Officer, Liberty Hospital, Liberty, MO, p. A411

HAAS, Steven, Chief Financial Officer, Health Alliance Hospital - Broadway Campus, Kingston, NY, p. A486
Chief Financial Officer, Health Alliance Hospital - Mary's Avenue Campus, Kingston, NY, p. A487

HAAS, Susan, Director Human Resources, Aurora Behavioral Healthcare San Diego, San Diego, CA, p. A91

HAASE, Patricia, Director Information Technology and Communications, Marian Regional Medical Center, Santa Maria, CA, p. A97

HAASE, Ronald, Chief Human Resources Officer, Northern Arizona Healthcare, Flagstaff Medical Center, Flagstaff, AZ, p. A31
Chief Human Resources Officer, Northern Arizona Healthcare, Verde Valley Medical Center, Cottonwood, AZ, p. A31

HAASE, Russ, Director Human Resources, Aurora Medical Center Of Oshkosh, Oshkosh, WI, p. A793

HAASKEN, Timothy, Chief Financial Officer, Lewisgale Hospital Montgomery, Blacksburg, VA, p. A739

HABIB, Noel, M.D., Chief Medical Officer, Huhukam Memorial Hospital, Sacaton, AZ, p. A37

HABIS, Saba, M.D., Chief Medical Officer, Freeman Health System, Joplin, MO, p. A408

HABOWSKI, Michael J., President and Chief Executive Officer, Ashtabula County Medical Center, Ashtabula, OH, p. A528

HACHEY, Michael, Senior Vice President and Chief Financial Officer, Emerson Hospital, Concord, MA, p. A338
Senior Vice President and Chief Financial Officer, Northern Light Mercy Hospital, Portland, ME, p. A322

HACKBARTH, John, CPA, Senior Vice President Finance and Chief Financial Officer, Owensboro Health Regional Hospital, Owensboro, KY, p. A291

HACKER, Leanne, Chief Financial Officer, Eastern New Mexico Medical Center, Roswell, NM, p. A471

HACKER, Mary Dee, R.N., Vice President, Patient Care Services and Chief Nursing Officer, Children's Hospital Los Angeles, Los Angeles, CA, p. A74

HACKER, Phillip, Chief Financial Officer, Stone County Medical Center, Mountain View, AR, p. A50

HACKETT, Leslie, Chief Nursing Officer, Covenant Hospital Plainview, Plainview, TX, p. A706

HACKSTEDDE, Anita, M.D., President and Chief Executive Officer, Salem Regional Medical Center, Salem, OH, p. A548
M.D., Vice President Medical Affairs, Salem Regional Medical Center, Salem, OH, p. A548

HADAWAY, Krystal, Director Human Resources, Healthsource Saginaw, Inc., Saginaw, MI, p. A365

HADDAD, Housam, M.D., Chief of Staff, Casey County Hospital, Liberty, KY, p. A287

HADDADIN, Maen, M.D., President Medical Staff, Chi Health Mercy Corning, Corning, IA, p. A246

HADDEN, Scott, M.D., Medical Staff President, Santiam Hospital, Stayton, OR, p. A582

HADDIX, Parker, Chief Executive Officer, William R. Sharpe, Jr. Hospital, Weston, WV, p. A777

HADDOX, Melissa, Controller, Encompass Health Rehabilitation Hospital Of Cypress, Houston, TX, p. A685

HADEN, Meg, Chief Operating Officer, Austin Oaks Hospital, Austin, TX, p. A655

HADLEY, Gerard, Vice President Finance for Brigham & Women's Faulkner Hospital and Vice President Finance and Controller, Brigham And Women's Faulkner Hospital, Boston, MA, p. A335

HADLEY, H, M.D., Vice President, Medical Affairs, Loma Linda University Medical Center, Loma Linda, CA, p. A72

HADLEY, Steven, Chief Financial Officer, Kansas Medical Center, Andover, KS, p. A261

HADLEY, Susan, MS, Chief Nursing Officer, Dickinson County Healthcare System, Iron Mountain, MI, p. A358

HAEHN, Debra, Chief Financial Officer, Clay County Memorial Hospital, Henrietta, TX, p. A684

HAENELT, Michael, Chief Information Management, Weed Army Community Hospital, Fort Irwin, CA, p. A64

HAESEMEYER, Allan, M.D., Chief of Staff, Indianhead Medical Center, Shell Lake, WI, p. A796

HAESEMEYER, Christa, Chief Nursing Officer, Lincoln County Hospital, Lincoln, KS, p. A269

HAFEMAN, Paula, Chief Nursing Officer, Hshs St. Clare Memorial Hospital, Oconto Falls, WI, p. A793
Chief Nursing Officer, Hshs St. Mary's Hospital Medical Center, Green Bay, WI, p. A785

HAFFEY, Robert, R.N., President and Chief Operating Officer, Kent County Memorial Hospital, Warwick, RI, p. A614

HAFFNER, John, M.D., Chief Medical Officer, St. Anthony's Hospital, Saint Petersburg, FL, p. A156

HAFIZ, Irfan, Vice President Medical Affairs, Northwestern Medicine Mchenry, Mchenry, IL, p. A212

HAGAN, Donald, Chief Financial Officer, Detar Healthcare System, Victoria, TX, p. A723

HAGAN, Eric, R.N., Executive Vice President and Administrator, Medical Center At Scottsville, Scottsville, KY, p. A293

HAGAN, Frank, Senior Vice President Finance, Saint Joseph's Medical Center, Yonkers, NY, p. A502

HAGEDORN, Tammy, Chief Human Resource Officer, Genesis Medical Center-Aledo, Aledo, IL, p. A194

HAGEL, Bonnie, Chief Financial Officer, Logan County Hospital, Oakley, KS, p. A272

HAGELBERG, Robbi, Vice President Nursing Services and Chief Nursing Officer, Lakeview Hospital, Stillwater, MN, p. A386

HAGELTHORN, Diane, Human Resources Generalist, Modoc Medical Center, Alturas, CA, p. A55

HAGEN, Mary, R.N., MSN, VP and Chief Nursing Officer, Unitypoint Health - Allen Hospital, Waterloo, IA, p. A259

HAGEN, Paulette, Human Resources and Administrative Services Director, Centracare Health-Paynesville, Paynesville, MN, p. A383

HAGEN, SHRM-CP, Lynne, Human Resources Officer, Avera Mckennan Hospital And University Health Center, Sioux Falls, SD, p. A631

HAGENS, Paul, Vice President Human Resources, Doctors Community Hospital, Lanham, MD, p. A330

HAGERSTROM, Paige, System Director of Talent Management, St. Josep. Hospital, Bangor, ME, p. A318

HAGERTY, Cindy, Assistant Chief Nurse Officer and Administrator of Operations, Ascension Via Christi Rehabilitation Hospital, Wichita, KS, p. A278

HAGGARD, Tommy, Chief Executive Officer, Bluegrass Community Hospital, Versailles, KY, p. A294

HAGGERTY, Cheryl, Chief Nursing Officer, Assistant Chief Executive Officer, Mercyone New Hampton Medical Center, New Hampton, IA, p. A255

HAGLER, Dan, M.D., Vice President and Chief Medical Officer, Atrium Health Cabarrus, Concord, NC, p. A508

HAGLUND, Nicole, Vice President of Nursing Services, Providence Medical Center, Wayne, NE, p. A440

HAGOOD, Teena, Chief Nursing Officer, Kimble Hospital, Junction, TX, p. A691

HAGWELL, Mick, Chief Financial Officer, Aspirus Ironwood Hospitals & Clinics, Inc., Ironwood, MI, p. A358

HAGY, Kelly, Director Human Resources, Cumberland Hall Hospital, Hopkinsville, KY, p. A285

HAGY, Michelle, Senior Vice President and Chief Financial Officer, Pikeville Medical Center, Pikeville, KY, p. A292

HAHEY, Joanne, Senior Vice President and Chief Financial Officer, University Of Maryland Shore Medical Center At Dorchester, Cambridge, MD, p. A328
Senior Vice President and Chief Financial Officer, University Of Maryland Shore Medical Center At Easton, Easton, MD, p. A329
Vice President Finance and Chief Financial Officer, University Of Maryland Shore Medical Center At Chestertown, Chestertown, MD, p. A328

HAHN, Donna, R.N., Vice President Acute Care and Chief Nurse Executive, Sentara Rmh Medical Center, Harrisonburg, VA, p. A743

HAHN, Jen, Finance Manager, Uh Portage Medical Center, Ravenna, OH, p. A548

HAHN, Joseph, M.D., Chief of Staff, Cleveland Clinic, Cleveland, OH, p. A534

HAHN, Kurt, M.D., Acting Clinical Director, Elmira Psychiatric Center, Elmira, NY, p. A483

HAHN, Lisa, R.N., Chief Nursing Officer, Ahmc Anaheim Regional Medical Center, Anaheim, CA, p. A55

HAHN, Lori, Vice President Nursing Services, Chi St. Alexius Health - Williston Medical Center, Williston, ND, p. A526

HAHN, Peter, M.D., President and Chief Executive Officer, Metro Health - University Of Michigan Health, Wyoming, MI, p. A370

HAHN, Stephen, Deputy to the President and Chief Operating Officer, University Of Texas M.D. Anderson Cancer Center, Houston, TX, p. A689

HAIGH, Sara, Associate Director, Durham Veterans Affairs Medical Center, Durham, NC, p. A509

HAIL, Brian, Deputy Executive Director of External Operations, Cherokee Nation W.W. Hastings Indian Hospital, Tahlequah, OK, p. A569

HAIN, Jim, Chief Operating Officer, Lexington Regional Health Center, Lexington, NE, p. A434

HAINES, Christopher, D.O., Vice President and Chief Medical Officer, Children's Specialized Hospital, New Brunswick, NJ, p. A459

HAIR, Denise, Vice President of Nursing Services and Chief Nursing Officer, Dameron Hospital, Stockton, CA, p. A99

HAIR, Troy, Chief Financial Officer, Abbeville General Hospital, Abbeville, LA, p. A295

HAISLIP, Heidi, M.D., Chief of Staff, Alliancehealth Madill, Madill, OK, p. A561

HAISLIP, Wendy, Chief Nursing Officer, Indiana Regional Medical Center, Indiana, PA, p. A592

HAIZLIP, Thomas, M.D., JrChief of Staff, Charles A. Cannon Memorial Hospital, Newland, NC, p. A515

HAJEK, Julie, Director Human Resources, St. David's Medical Center, Austin, TX, p. A656

HAKENSON, Diana, Director of Patient Care Services, Newport Bay Hospital, Newport Beach, CA, p. A81

HALAMA, George, Vice President Finance, Mcpherson Hospital, Mcpherson, KS, p. A270

HALBROOK, Gerrie, Chief Financial Officer, Good Samaritan Hospital, Bakersfield, CA, p. A57

HALDEMAN, Larry, M.D., Executive Vice President and Chief Medical Officer, Wellstar Windy Hill Hospital, Marietta, GA, p. A176

HALDER, Ranjay, M.D., Chief Medical Director, Centerstone Hospital, Bradenton, FL, p. A132

HALE, Becky, Director Human Resources, Hill Regional Hospital, Hillsboro, TX, p. A684

HALE, Byron, Chief Financial Officer, Ut Health Tyler, Tyler, TX, p. A722

HALE, Danny, Director Human Resources, Southwestern Medical Center, Lawton, OK, p. A561

HALE, Donna, Director of Nursing, Baptist Memorial Rehabilitation Hospital, Germantown, TN, p. A638

HALE, Ken, Executive Director of Operations, Mercy Allen Hospital, Oberlin, OH, p. A547

HALE, Kirsten, Coordinator Health Information Services, Uh Conneaut Medical Center, Conneaut, OH, p. A537
Coordinator Health Information Systems and Coding, Uh Geneva Medical Center, Geneva, OH, p. A541

HALE, Margie, R.N., MSN, Chief Executive Officer, Baraga County Memorial Hospital, L'Anse, MI, p. A359

HALE, Renae, Chief Nursing Officer, Lincoln Prairie Behavioral Health Center, Springfield, IL, p. A220

HALE, Ron, Superintendent, Colorado Mental Health Institute At Pueblo, Pueblo, CO, p. A117

HALE, Steven D., FACHE, Chief Executive Officer, Weiser Memorial Hospital, Weiser, ID, p. A193

HALE, Tonia, R.N., Chief Executive Officer and Chief Nursing Officer, Blue Ridge Regional Hospital, Spruce Pine, NC, p. A518

HALEN, Catherine, Vice President Human Resources, Beebe Healthcare, Lewes, DE, p. A127

HALES, Brent, Chief Financial Officer, Uintah Basin Medical Center, Roosevelt, UT, p. A731

HALES, Joe, Chief Information Officer, Primary Children's Hospital, Salt Lake City, UT, p. A732

HALEY, DeLeigh, Chief Executive Officer, Ut Health Jacksonville, Jacksonville, TX, p. A691

HALEY, James, M.D., Senior Vice President and Chief Medical Officer, Unity Hospital, Rochester, NY, p. A496

HALEY, Leon L. Jr, M.D., Chief Executive Officer, Uf Health Jacksonville, Jacksonville, FL, p. A142

HALEY, Thomas, Information Technology Services Site Director, Chi Health Mercy Council Bluffs, Council Bluffs, IA, p. A247
Information Technology Systems Site Director, Chi Health Lakeside, Omaha, NE, p. A436
Information Technology Systems Site Director, Chi Health Midlands, Papillion, NE, p. A438

HALFEN, John, M.D., Medical Director, Lakewood Health System, Staples, MN, p. A386

HALIMI, Hamid, M.D., Medical Director, Select Specialty Hospital-Ann Arbor, Ypsilanti, MI, p. A370

HALL, Becky, R.N., Director Nursing, Rumford Hospital, Rumford, ME, p. A323

HALL, Catherine, Manager Human Resources, Jefferson Hospital, Louisville, GA, p. A175

HALL, Charles, Chief Executive Officer, Island Hospital, Anacortes, WA, p. A755

HALL, Dan, R.N., Chief Operating Officer, St. John Owasso, Owasso, OK, p. A566

HALL, David, Chief Information Officer, Pineville Community Health Center, Pineville, KY, p. A292
   Senior Vice President and Chief Operating Officer, University Of Tennessee Medical Center, Knoxville, TN, p. A641

HALL, Gary, Vice President of Information Technology, Estes Park Medical Center, Estes Park, CO, p. A112

HALL, Geoffrey, Chief Executive Officer, Edwin Shaw Rehab, Copley, OH, p. A537

HALL, George, M.D., Vice President Medical Affairs, St. Elizabeth Florence, Florence, KY, p. A283
   M.D., Vice President Medical Affairs, St. Elizabeth Fort Thomas, Fort Thomas, KY, p. A283

HALL, Ginger, Chief Nursing Officer, Emanuel Medical Center, Swainsboro, GA, p. A181

HALL, James, M.D., Chief Medical Officer, Pamp. Regional Medical Center, Pampa, TX, p. A704

HALL, Jeanne, Director Information Systems, Shriners Hospitals For Children-St. Louis, Saint Louis, MO, p. A416

HALL, Jeffrey, DPM, Chief Medical Officer, St. Croix Regional Medical Center, St Croix Falls, WI, p. A796

HALL, Jim, Acting Chief Information Officer, Central Arkansas Veterans Healthcare System, Little Rock, AR, p. A49

HALL, Joy, Chief Executive Officer, Winn Parish Medical Center, Winnfield, LA, p. A317
   Interim Chief Executive Officer, Eureka Springs Hospital, Eureka Springs, AR, p. A45

HALL, Kenneth, R.N., Chief Nursing Officer, Saint Josep. Health System, Mishawaka, IN, p. A236

HALL, Kent, M.D., Chief Medical Officer, The University Of Vermont Health Network - Alice Hyde Medical Center, Malone, NY, p. A487
   M.D., Vice President and Chief Medical Officer, The University Of Vermont Health Network-Champlain Valley Physicians Hospital, Plattsburgh, NY, p. A495

HALL, Margaret, M.D., Chief Medical Officer, Lakeside Women's Hospital, Oklahoma City, OK, p. A564

HALL, Mary, Chief Medical Staff, Mcdowell Arh Hospital, Mcdowell, KY, p. A290

HALL, Melissa, Chief Executive Officer, Munising Memorial Hospital, Munising, MI, p. A362
   Chief Nursing Officer, Coffey County Hospital, Burlington, KS, p. A262

HALL, Michael Daines., Interim Chief Executive Officer, Tmc Bonham Hospital, Bonham, TX, p. A660

HALL, Morrison, Chief Financial Officer, Pender Memorial Hospital, Burgaw, NC, p. A505

HALL, Patricia, MSN, Ph.D., R.N., Medical Center Director, Harry S. Truman Memorial Veterans Hospital, Columbia, MO, p. A405

HALL, Richard, Chief Executive Officer, Samuel Simmonds Memorial Hospital, Barrow, AK, p. A27

HALL, Sally, Manager Human Resources, South Texas Spine And Surgical Hospital, San Antonio, TX, p. A713

HALL, Stephanie, M.D., Chief Medical Officer, Keck Hospital Of Usc, Los Angeles, CA, p. A74
   M.D., Chief Medical Officer, Usc Verdugo Hills Hospital, Glendale, CA, p. A67
   M.D., Medical Director, Usc Norris Comprehensive Cancer Center, Los Angeles, CA, p. A76

HALL, Steve, Chief Financial Officer, Unitypoint Health-Pekin Hospital, Pekin, IL, p. A216

HALL, Terry, Chief of Staff, Harrison County Community Hospital, Bethany, MO, p. A402

HALL, Veronica, R.N., Interim President and Chief Executive Officer, Henry Ford Hospital, Detroit, MI, p. A353

HALL-OLSEN, Kathy, Administrator, Weisman Children's Rehabilitation Hospital, Marlton, NJ, p. A458

HALLAL, Joseph, M.D., Chief Medical Officer, Inova Fairfax Hospital, Falls Church, VA, p. A741

HALLATT, Jennifer, Chief Operating Officer, Mercyhealth Hospital And Medical Center - Harvard, Harvard, IL, p. A207
   Vice President, Mercyhealth Hospital And Medical Center - Walworth, Lake Geneva, WI, p. A787

HALLEY, Andrea, Vice President of Non-Clinical Operations/ Director Human Resources, Hopedale Medical Complex, Hopedale, IL, p. A208

HALLEY, Lisa, Vice President Human Resources, Holzer Medical Center, Gallipolis, OH, p. A541

HALLIDAY, Lisa, Director Accounting Services, Taylor Regional Hospital, Hawkinsville, GA, p. A173

HALLIWILL, Donald, Chief Financial Officer, Carilion Franklin Memorial Hospital, Rocky Mount, VA, p. A751
   Executive Vice President and Chief Financial Officer, Carilion Roanoke Memorial Hospital, Roanoke, VA, p. A751

HALLMARK, Todd, Chief Executive Officer, Choctaw Nation Health Care Center, Talihina, OK, p. A569
   Chief Operating Officer, Choctaw Nation Health Care Center, Talihina, OK, p. A569

HALLOCK, Mirya, Administrator, Webster County Community Hospital, Red Cloud, NE, p. A439

HALLORAN, Teresa, Ph.D., R.N., Vice President Nursing Services, Memorial Hospital East, Shiloh, IL, p. A220
   Ph.D., R.N., Vice President Nursing Services, Memorial Hospital, Belleville, IL, p. A195

HALPIN, Kim, Director Human Resources, Arms Acres, Carmel, NY, p. A481

HALSELL, David, Senior Vice President and Chief Financial Officer, Lake Regional Health System, Osage Beach, MO, p. A413

HALSTEAD, Lisa, Chief Nursing Officer, Integris Miami Hospital, Miami, OK, p. A562

HALSTEAD, Rhonda, President, Penn Highlands Clearfield, Clearfield, PA, p. A586

HALTER, Bev, Director Human Resources and Payroll, Liberty Medical Center, Chester, MT, p. A422

HALTERMAN, Mary, R.N., Chief Nursing Officer, Trident Medical Center, Charleston, SC, p. A616

HALTOM, Shannon, Vice President, Patient Care Services, Chi St. Luke's Health Brazosport, Lake Jackson, TX, p. A694

HALVORSEN, Lisa, Chief Nurse Executive, Providence Milwaukie Hospital, Milwaukie, OR, p. A578

HALVORSON, Marla, Director Human Resources, St. Luke's Hospital, Duluth, MN, p. A375

HAMAN, Timothy, M.D., Vice President Medical Affairs, Christus Ochsner St. Patrick, Lake Charles, LA, p. A306

HAMATY, Edward, D.O., Chief Medical Officer, Acuity Specialty Hospital Of Southern New Jersey, Willingboro, NJ, p. A466

HAMB, Aaron, M.D., Chief Medical Officer, Provident Hospital Of Cook County, Chicago, IL, p. A200

HAMBLIN, Garth, Chief Financial Officer, Bear Valley Community Hospital, Big Bear Lake, CA, p. A58

HAMBLIN, James, Chief Financial Officer, White Mountain Regional Medical Center, Springerville, AZ, p. A39

HAMBLIN, Scott, M.D., President Medical Staff, White Mountain Regional Medical Center, Springerville, AZ, p. A39

HAMBRIDGE, Mark, Director Information Systems, Livingston Regional Hospital, Livingston, TN, p. A642

HAMBY, Kelley, Vice President Patient Care, Baptist Health Medical Center - North Little Rock, North Little Rock, AR, p. A51

HAMEL, Loren, M.D., President and Chief Executive Officer, Spectrum Health Lakeland, Saint Joseph, MI, p. A366

HAMEL, Susan, Chief Nursing Officer, St. Luke's Hospital, Duluth, MN, p. A375

HAMILL, Dave H., President and Chief Executive Officer, Hampton Regional Medical Center, Varnville, SC, p. A625

HAMILTON, Adriana, Chief Human Resources Officer, Hunter Holmes Mcguire Veterans Affairs Medical Center-Richmond, Richmond, VA, p. A750

HAMILTON, Aggie, Chief Human Resources, Veterans Affairs Montana Health Care System, Fort Harrison, MT, p. A423

HAMILTON, Brandy, Chief Executive Officer, Suncoast Behavioral Health Center, Bradenton, FL, p. A133

HAMILTON, Catherine, MSN, Chief Nursing Officer, Hedrick Medical Center, Chillicothe, MO, p. A404

HAMILTON, Chanda, Chief Information Officer, Clifton T. Perkins Hospital Center, Jessup. MD, p. A330

HAMILTON, Dan, Chief Operating Officer, Nor-Lea Hospital District, Lovington, NM, p. A470

HAMILTON, David, Chief Information Officer, Southwest Mississipp. Regional Medical Center, Mccomb, MS, p. A396

HAMILTON, Geoff, Interim Chief Financial Officer, Arbor Health, Morton Hospital, Morton, WA, p. A760

HAMILTON, Jennifer, Chief Financial Officer, Sagewest Health Care, Riverton, WY, p. A803
   COO - Mary Bridge, Multicare Mary Bridge Children's Hospital And Health Center, Tacoma, WA, p. A767

HAMILTON, Kevin, M.D., Chief Medical Officer, Tristar Summit Medical Center, Hermitage, TN, p. A639

HAMILTON, Marci, Chief Nursing Officer, Orthopaedic Hospital Of Lutheran Health Network, Fort Wayne, IN, p. A228

HAMILTON, Marilyn, Director Human Resources, Kp. Promise Hospital Of Baton Rouge, Baton Rouge, LA, p. A297

HAMILTON, Michelle, Human Resource Manager, Turning Point Hospital, Moultrie, GA, p. A177

HAMILTON, Nancy, Chief Human and Learning Resources, Veterans Affairs New Jersey Health Care System, East Orange, NJ, p. A454

HAMILTON, Patricia, R.N., Director of Nursing, Mildred Mitchell-Bateman Hospital, Huntington, WV, p. A773
   Chief Executive Officer, Riverwoods Behavioral Health System, Riverdale, GA, p. A178

HAMILTON, Peggy, Chief Financial Officer, Bayside Community Hospital, Anahuac, TX, p. A653

HAMILTON, Phil, R.N., Chief Executive Officer, Pershing Memorial Hospital, Brookfield, MO, p. A403

HAMILTON, Randal S., Chief Executive Officer, Select Specialty Hospital-Panama City, Panama City, FL, p. A153

HAMILTON, Scott, Vice President and Chief Financial Officer, Parkwest Medical Center, Knoxville, TN, p. A641

HAMILTON, Sharon, Chief Nursing Officer, Encompass Health Rehabilitation Hospital Of Panama City, Panama City, FL, p. A153

HAMILTON-BEYER, Maggie, Chief Financial Officer, Knoxville Hospital & Clinics, Knoxville, IA, p. A253

HAMLIN, Faye, Manager Human Resources, Julian F. Keith Alcohol And Drug Abuse Treatment Center, Black Mountain, NC, p. A505

HAMM, Sonja, Vice President Human and Foundation Resources, Lakes Regional Healthcare, Spirit Lake, IA, p. A258

HAMMAKER, Barry, M.D., Chief Medical Officer and Chief Clinical Officer, Vail Health, Vail, CO, p. A119

HAMMAN, Baron, M.D., Chief Medical Officer, Texas Health Heart & Vascular Hospital Arlington, Arlington, TX, p. A654

HAMMEL, Leah, Acting Administrator, Chester Mental Health Center, Chester, IL, p. A197

HAMMERAN, Kevin R., Chief Executive Officer and Administrator, Baptist Memorial Hospital For Women, Memphis, TN, p. A644

HAMMES, Paul, Chief Executive Officer, Hugh Chatham Memorial Hospital, Elkin, NC, p. A509

HAMMETT, Doran, Chief Financial Officer, Petersburg Medical Center, Petersburg, AK, p. A29

HAMMOCK, Preston W., President, Moses H. Cone Memorial Hospital, Greensboro, NC, p. A511

HAMMOND, Flora, M.D., Chief Medical Affairs, Rehabilitation Hospital Of Indiana, Indianapolis, IN, p. A233

HAMMOND, Michael, Chief Financial Officer, Virtua Our Lady Of Lourdes Hospital, Camden, NJ, p. A453
   Chief Financial Officer, Virtua Willingboro Hospital, Willingboro, NJ, p. A466

HAMMOND, Nancy, M.D., Vice President, Chief Medical Officer, Saint Agnes Healthcare, Baltimore, MD, p. A326

HAMMOND, Patti, Chief Operating Officer, Adirondack Health, Saranac Lake, NY, p. A497

HAMMOND, Reed, Chief Executive Officer, Frankfort Regional Medical Center, Frankfort, KY, p. A283

HAMMONDS, Janie, Human Resources Officer, Columbus Community Hospital, Columbus, TX, p. A664

HAMMONDS, Kim, R.N., Chief Nursing Officer, Scotland Health Care System, Laurinburg, NC, p. A513

HAMNER, Candy, Vice President and Chief Nursing Officer, Levindale Hebrew Hospital And Nursing, Baltimore, MD, p. A325

HAMNER, James, Regional Information Technology Director, Ssm Health Depaul Hospital - St. Louis, Bridgeton, MO, p. A403

HAMON, Eric, Executive Vice President and Chief Financial Officer, Driscoll Children's Hospital, Corpus Christi, TX, p. A666
   Interim President and Chief Executive Officer, Driscoll Children's Hospital, Corpus Christi, TX, p. A666

HAMPF, Carl, M.D., Chief Medical Officer, Saint Thomas Hospital For Spinal Surgery, Nashville, TN, p. A646

HAMPTON, Angie, Director Human Resources, Porter Regional Hospital, Valparaiso, IN, p. A241

HAMPTON, Connie, R.N., Associate Director for Patient Care Services, Carl Vinson Veterans Affairs Medical Center, Dublin, GA, p. A171

HAMPTON, Jeff, Director Information Systems, Lehigh Regional Medical Center, Lehigh Acres, FL, p. A144

HAMPTON, Mary Ann, MSN, R.N., Chief Nursing Officer, St. Luke's Des Peres Hospital, Saint Louis, MO, p. A417

HAMRICK, Jan, Chief Financial Officer, Dodge County Hospital, Eastman, GA, p. A172

HAMSTRA, Nancy, Chief Operating Officer, University Hospital, Newark, NJ, p. A460

HAMULA, Michelle, Director of Nursing and Quality, Chan Soon-Shiong Medical Center, Windber, PA, p. A611

HANCOCK, J, M.D., Chief of Staff, Fargo Veterans Affairs Health Care System, Fargo, ND, p. A523

HANCOCK, Katherine, R.N., Executive Chief Nursing Officer, Cleveland Clinic, Cleveland, OH, p. A534

HANCOCK, Kerry, Director Human Resources, Bacon County Hospital And Health System, Alma, GA, p. A163

HANCOCK, Lori, Chief Business Officer, West Palm Beach Veterans Affairs Medical Center, West Palm Beach, FL, p. A162

HANCOCK, Melinda, Chief Financial Officer, Vcu Medical Center, Richmond, VA, p. A751

HANCOCK, Myrna, Director Financial Services, Choctaw Health Center, Philadelphia, MS, p. A398

HANCOCK, Sharon, Chief Human Resources Officer, Mcculloiough-Hyde Memorial Hospital/Trihealth, Oxford, OH, p. A547

HANCOCK, Todd, President and Chief Executive Officer, Christus Good Shepherd Medical Center-Marshall, Marshall, TX, p. A700

HANDEL, Daniel, M.D., Chief Medical Officer, Indiana University Health Bedford Hospital, Bedford, IN, p. A224
M.D., Chief Medical Officer, Musc Health Of Medical University Of South Carolina, Charleston, SC, p. A616
M.D., Vice President, Chief Medical Officer, Indiana University Health Bloomington Hospital, Bloomington, IN, p. A224

HANDLER, Michael, M.D., Vice President Medical Affairs and Chief Medical Officer, Ssm Health St. Josep. Hospital - Lake Saint Louis, Lake Saint Louis, MO, p. A410

HANDLEY, Charles, Chief Financial Officer, Plaza Specialty Hospital, Houston, TX, p. A688
Chief Financial Officer, The Hospitals Of Providence Memorial Campus, El Paso, TX, p. A676
Chief Financial Officer, The Hospitals Of Providence Sierra Campus, El Paso, TX, p. A676

HANDLEY, Donna, President, The William W. Backus Hospital, Norwich, CT, p. A124
President, Windham Hospital, Willimantic, CT, p. A126

HANDLEY, Jack, M.D., Chief Medical Officer, Evergreenhealth Monroe, Monroe, WA, p. A760

HANDLEY, Rhonda, Chief Financial Officer, Columbia Basin Hospital, Ephrata, WA, p. A758

HANDOL, Nelson, M.D., Medical Director, Laurel Oaks Behavioral Health Center, Dothan, AL, p. A17

HANDWERK, Ashley, Director, Human Resources, Medstar Union Memorial Hospital, Baltimore, MD, p. A325

HANDY, Steven P., CPA, Chief Executive Officer, Uniontown Hospital, Uniontown, PA, p. A609

HANEFELD, Darlene, Chief Human Resources Officer, Banner Churchill Community Hospital, Fallon, NV, p. A442

HANENBURG, Thomas S., Senior Vice President and Area Manager, Kaiser Permanente San Leandro Medical Center, San Leandro, CA, p. A95

HANEY, Kathryn, Controller, Encompass Health Valley Of The Sun Rehabilitation Hospital, Glendale, AZ, p. A32

HANEY, Lisa, Chief Executive Officer, St. Mary Rehabilitation Hospital, Langhorne, PA, p. A594

HANGER, Kelvin, Chief Executive Officer, Trihealth Evendale Hospital, Cincinnati, OH, p. A533

HANIGAN, Hank, FACHE, Chief Executive Officer, Whitman Hospital And Medical Center, Colfax, WA, p. A757
FACHE, Interim Chief Financial Officer, Whitman Hospital And Medical Center, Colfax, WA, p. A757

HANISCH, Denise, M.D., Chief of Staff, Avera St. Mary's Hospital, Pierre, SD, p. A630

HANKINS, Brad, Chief Operating Quality Officer, Lake Chelan Community Hospital And Clinics, Chelan, WA, p. A756

HANKINS, Steven, Chief Operating Officer, Evans U. S. Army Community Hospital, Fort Carson, CO, p. A112

HANKS, John, Director Information Systems, East Tennessee Children's Hospital, Knoxville, TN, p. A641

HANKS, Susan, Chief Information Officer, Riverton Hospital, Riverton, UT, p. A731

HANLEY, Bob, Senior Vice President and Chief Human Resources Officer, University Of Chicago Medical Center, Chicago, IL, p. A201

HANLEY, Darlene S., R.N., FACHE, President and Chief Executive Officer, St. Lawrence Rehabilitation Center, Lawrenceville, NJ, p. A457

HANLEY, Mathew, Chief Financial Officer, Osf Healthcare Saint Anthony's Health Center, Alton, IL, p. A194

HANLEY, Patrick, D.O., Interim Vice President Medical Affairs, St. Luke's - Lehighton Campus, Lehighton, PA, p. A595

HANLON, Jerad, Chief Operating Officer, Southside Regional Medical Center, Petersburg, VA, p. A749

HANNA, Casey, M.D., Chief of Staff, Wagoner Community Hospital, Wagoner, OK, p. A571

HANNA, Mitchell J., Chief Executive Officer, Sutter Auburn Faith Hospital, Auburn, CA, p. A56
Chief Executive Officer, Sutter Coast Hospital, Crescent City, CA, p. A62

HANNA, Philip S., Chief Executive Officer, North Oak Regional Medical Center, Senatobia, MS, p. A400

HANNA, Robb, Executive Director Information Technology, Lexington Regional Health Center, Lexington, NE, p. A434

HANNAH, Jill, Director Human Resources, James Cancer Hospital And Solove Research Institute, Columbus, OH, p. A536

HANNAPEL, Andrew, Chief Medical Officer, Chatham Hospital, Siler City, NC, p. A518

HANNERS, Brandy, Chief Financial Officer, Sovah Health-Martinsville, Martinsville, VA, p. A746

HANNERS, Rodney B., Chief Executive Officer, Keck Hospital Of Usc, Los Angeles, CA, p. A74
Chief Executive Officer, Usc Norris Comprehensive Cancer Center, Los Angeles, CA, p. A76

HANNON, Edward J., FACHE, President, Chi Health Saint Francis, Grand Island, NE, p. A433

HANNON, Patricia, Chief Nursing Officer, Vaughan Regional Medical Center, Selma, AL, p. A24

HANOLD, Cindy, Chief Nursing Officer, Richland Hospital, Richland Center, WI, p. A795

HANS, Christopher, Chief Financial Officer, Riverside University Health System-Medical Center, Moreno Valley, CA, p. A80

HANSCOM, Kristine, Chief Financial Officer, Tufts Medical Center, Boston, MA, p. A336

HANSCOME, Joyce, Chief Information Officer, Doctors Community Hospital, Lanham, MD, p. A330

HANSEL, Jimmie W., Ph.D., Chief Executive Officer, Edwards County Medical Center, Kinsley, KS, p. A268

HANSEN, Carolyn, Chief Nursing Officer, Bingham Memorial Hospital, Blackfoot, ID, p. A188

HANSEN, Chris, Senior Vice President and Chief Information Officer, The University Of Kansas Hospital, Kansas City, KS, p. A268

HANSEN, Gayle, R.N., Chief Integration Officer, Mayo Clinic Health System In Saint James, Saint James, MN, p. A384
R.N., Chief Operating Officer, Mayo Clinic Health System In Fairmont, Fairmont, MN, p. A376

HANSEN, James, Chief Financial Officer, Summit Pacific Medical Center, Elma, WA, p. A757

HANSEN, Jay, Director Information Services, Prisma Health Oconee Memorial Hospital, Seneca, SC, p. A624

HANSEN, Julie, Chief Financial Officer, Mayo Clinic Health System - Franciscan Healthcare In Sparta, Sparta, WI, p. A796

HANSEN, Karen, Vice President and Chief Operating Officer, Memorial Medical Center Of Ashland, Ashland, WI, p. A779

HANSEN, Kristy, CPA, Chief Financial Officer, Myrtue Medical Center, Harlan, IA, p. A251

HANSEN, Kyle, Corporate Director Information Systems, Riverside Medical Center, Kankakee, IL, p. A209

HANSEN, Kyle A., Chief Executive Officer, Utah Valley Hospital, Provo, UT, p. A731

HANSEN, Laurie, Director of Administration, Johnson County Healthcare Center, Buffalo, WY, p. A801
Vice President of Operations, Emory Johns Creek Hospital, Johns Creek, GA, p. A174

HANSEN, Linda, Director Human Resources, Bakersfield Heart Hospital, Bakersfield, CA, p. A57

HANSEN, Michael T., FACHE, President and Chief Executive Officer, Columbus Community Hospital, Columbus, NE, p. A431

HANSEN, Misty, Chief Financial Officer, Banner - University Medical Center Tucson, Tucson, AZ, p. A39

HANSEN, Steven, Director Information Technology, Healdsburg District Hospital, Healdsburg, CA, p. A68

HANSEN, Tim, Interim Chief Human Resource Officer, Denver Health, Denver, CO, p. A110

HANSERT, Benjamin K., Administrator, North Baldwin Infirmary, Bay Minette, AL, p. A14

HANSON, Brent, Chief Executive Officer, Select Specialty Hospital-Des Moines, Des Moines, IA, p. A248

HANSON, Denise, Information Technology Specialist, St. Cloud Veterans Affairs Health Care System, Saint Cloud, MN, p. A384

HANSON, Emily, M.D., President, Medical Staff, St. Josep. Memorial Hospital, Murphysboro, IL, p. A213

HANSON, Gregory S., M.D., Chief Executive Officer, Clark Fork Valley Hospital, Plains, MT, p. A426

HANSON, Jacqueline, Chief Executive Officer, Red River Behavioral Health System, Grand Forks, ND, p. A524

HANSON, Jane E., R.N., Chief Executive Officer, Dignity Health Arizona General Hospital, Laveen, AZ, p. A33

HANSON, Jesica, Vice President and Chief Financial Officer, Bakersfield Memorial Hospital, Bakersfield, CA, p. A57

HANSON, Jim, Director Information Systems, Avera Queen Of Peace Hospital, Mitchell, SD, p. A629

HANSON, Karen, Vice President Patient Care Services, Advocate Condell Medical Center, Libertyville, IL, p. A210

HANSON, Lesley, Director Human Resources, Lake District Hospital, Lakeview, OR, p. A577

HANSON, Mary Ann, Director Personnel, Cherokee Mental Health Institute, Cherokee, IA, p. A245

HANSON, Paul A., FACHE, President, Sanford Usd Medical Center, Sioux Falls, SD, p. A631

HANSON, Rhonda, Director Human Resources, Huron Regional Medical Center, Huron, SD, p. A629

HANSON, Rita, M.D., Vice President Medical Affairs, Ascension Southeast Wisconsin Hospital - Elmbrook Campus, Brookfield, WI, p. A781
M.D., Vice President Medical Affairs, Ascension Southeast Wisconsin Hospital - St. Joseph's Campus, Milwaukee, WI, p. A790

HANSON, Samantha, Chief Human Resources Officer, Children's Hospitals And Clinics Of Minnesota, Minneapolis, MN, p. A380

HANSON, Tamra, Human Resource Manager, Dorothea Dix Psychiatric Center, Bangor, ME, p. A318

HANYAK, Diana, Chief Executive Officer, Encompass Health Rehabilitation Hospital Of Tustin, Tustin, CA, p. A102

HANZLIK, Debra, R.N., Director of Nursing, Niobrara Valley Hospital, Lynch, NE, p. A435

HAPPEL, Terry, M.D., Vice President and Chief Medical Officer, Chandler Regional Medical Center, Chandler, AZ, p. A30

HAQQANI, Rahim, M.D., Medical Director, Dallas Behavioral Healthcare Hospital, Desoto, TX, p. A672

HAQUE, Syed, Vice President and Chief Information Officer, Loretto Hospital, Chicago, IL, p. A199

HARA, Karen, Personnel Management Specialist, Hawaii State Hospital, Kaneohe, HI, p. A186

HARALDSON, Richard, CPA, FACHE, Chief Executive Officer, Beatrice Community Hospital And Health Center, Beatrice, NE, p. A430

HARALSON, Gregory, FACHE, Senior Vice President and Chief Executive Officer, Memorial Hermann - Texas Medical Center, Houston, TX, p. A687

HARARI, Jack, M.D., Chief Medical Officer, West Boca Medical Center, Boca Raton, FL, p. A132

HARBAUGH, Charles, Director Human Resources, Mountain Lakes Medical Center, Clayton, GA, p. A168

HARBAUGH, Ken, Vice President and Chief Financial Officer, Osf Saint Francis Medical Center, Peoria, IL, p. A217

HARBERTS, Jerry, Information Technologist, Madison Healthcare Services, Madison, MN, p. A379

HARBESON, Mary, R.N., Chief Executive Officer, Nexus Children's Hospital Houston, Houston, TX, p. A688

HARBIN, Cathy, Chief Nursing Officer, Roosevelt Warm Springs Rehabilitation And Specialty Hospitals - Ltac, Warm Springs, GA, p. A182
Chief Nursing Officer, Roosevelt Warm Springs Rehabilitation Hospital - Rehab, Warm Springs, GA, p. A183

HARBIN, Jason, Director of Nursing, Ward Memorial Hospital, Monahans, TX, p. A702

HARBISON, Damon R., President, Ssm Health St. Mary's Hospital Centralia, Centralia, IL, p. A196

HARCHENKO, Vern, M.D., Chief of Staff, Chi St. Alexius Health-Garrison Memorial Hospital, Garrison, ND, p. A523

HARCLERODE, Timothy, Chief Executive Officer, Conemaugh Miners Medical Center, Hastings, PA, p. A592
Chief Executive Officer, Conemaugh Nason Medical Center, Roaring Spring, PA, p. A606

HARCOURT, Jenifer, Chief Operating Officer, Riverwoods Behavioral Health System, Riverdale, GA, p. A178

HARDACRE, Jerry, M.D., Chief of Staff, Ascension All Saints, Racine, WI, p. A794

HARDAGE, Tony, PharmD, Assistant Vice President and Administrator, Baptist Health Medical Center-Arkadelphia, Arkadelphia, AR, p. A42
PharmD, Interim Chief Executive Officer, Baptist Health Medical Center-Hot Spring County, Malvern, AR, p. A50

HARDAN, Terry, Director Human Resources, Longview Regional Medical Center, Longview, TX, p. A697

HARDCASTLE, Brad, Chief Financial Officer, South Baldwin Regional Medical Center, Foley, AL, p. A18

HARDCASTLE, Kathy, Director Human Resources, Texas Health Presbyterian Hospital Denton, Denton, TX, p. A672

HARDEE, Gary, M.D., Medical Director, Plains Memorial Hospital, Dimmitt, TX, p. A673

HARDEE, Virginia, Administrator, Mcleod Health Darlington, Darlington, SC, p. A618
Interim Administrator, Mcleod Health Cheraw, Cheraw, SC, p. A617

HARDEMAN, Diane, Director Personnel, Stephens County Hospital, Toccoa, GA, p. A182

HARDEN, Diane, Chief Financial Officer, Leesburg Regional Medical Center, Leesburg, FL, p. A144
Senior Vice President and Chief Financial Officer, The Villages Regional Hospital, The Villages, FL, p. A160

HARDEN, Jeffrey, Chief Nursing Officer, Meadows Regional Medical Center, Vidalia, GA, p. A182

HARDESTY, Keith, Chief Financial Officer, Springfield Hospital Center, Sykesville, MD, p. A333

HARDICK, Cindy, Human Resources Coordinator, Select Specialty Hospital-Ann Arbor, Ypsilanti, MI, p. A370

HARDIE, Rebecca, Chief Nursing Officer, Baylor Scott & White Medical Center - Hillcrest, Waco, TX, p. A724

HARDIE, Rebecca Kay., Interim President, Baylor Scott & White Medical Center - Hillcrest, Waco, TX, p. A724

HARDIN, Cecil, CPA, Chief Financial Officer, Catawba Hospital, Catawba, VA, p. A739

HARDIN, James, Human Resources Officer, Sheridan Veterans Affairs Medical Center, Sheridan, WY, p. A804

HARDIN, Leslie, Chief Executive Officer and Chief Financial Officer, Seymour Hospital, Seymour, TX, p. A715

HARDIN, Marci, Manager Information Technology, Nevada Regional Medical Center, Nevada, MO, p. A413

HARDIN, Mark, M.D., Medical Director, Ed Fraser Memorial Hospital, Macclenny, FL, p. A144

HARDIN, Nicholas, FACHE, Chief Executive Officer, Encompass Health Rehabilitation Hospital Of Katy, Katy, TX, p. A691

HARDING, Andrew D., R.N., Chief Executive Officer, Metrowest Medical Center, Framingham, MA, p. A339

HARDING, Barry, Interim Chief Executive Officer, St. Mark's Medical Center, La Grange, TX, p. A694

HARDING, Denise, Director Human Resources, Plumas District Hospital, Quincy, CA, p. A86

HARDING, Edward A., FACHE, President, Aurora Medical Center - Bay Area, Marinette, WI, p. A788

HARDING, Geoff, Chief Clinical Officer, Kp. Promise Hospital Of Salt Lake, Salt Lake City, UT, p. A732

HARDING, Gwen, Site Manager Information Systems, Bon Secours Memorial Regional Medical Center, Mechanicsville, VA, p. A746

HARDING, Helen, Chief Nursing Officer, Fairfield Medical Center, Lancaster, OH, p. A542

HARDING, John, Chief Operating Officer, Children's Hospital Of The King's Daughters, Norfolk, VA, p. A747

HARDISON, Randall, M.D., Chief Medical Officer, Arizona Orthopedic Surgical Hospital, Chandler, AZ, p. A30

HARDMAN, Danny, FACHE, R.N., Chief Executive Officer, University Medical Center, New Orleans, LA, p. A312

HARDMAN, Joe, M.D., Chief Medical Officer, Tuality Healthcare, Hillsboro, OR, p. A576

HARDWICK, Garry, R.N., Chief Operating Officer, Newport Bay Hospital, Newport Beach, CA, p. A81

HARDY, Bob, Chief Operating Officer, Opelousas General Health System, Opelousas, LA, p. A312

HARDY, Geoff, Administrator, South Georgia Medical Center Lanier Campus, Lakeland, GA, p. A175

HARDY, James, D.O., Chief of Staff, Dayton Veterans Affairs Medical Center, Dayton, OH, p. A538

HARDY, Janice, Chief Human Resource Management Service, Central Alabama Veterans Health Care System, Montgomery, AL, p. A22

HARDY, Kevin, Chief Financial Officer, Encompass Health Rehabilitation Hospital Of Treasure Coast, Vero Beach, FL, p. A161

HARDY, LaBon, Chief Information Officer, Ralp. H. Johnson Veterans Affairs Medical Center, Charleston, SC, p. A616

HARDY, Melanie, D.O., Chief of Staff, Marias Medical Center, Shelby, MT, p. A427

HARDY, Raymond, Controller, Encompass Health Rehabilitation Hospital Of Las Vegas, Las Vegas, NV, p. A443

HARDY, Valonia, Chief Healthy Living Officer, Tsehootsooi Medical Center, Fort Defiance, AZ, p. A31

HARESNAPE, Julie, Coordinator Human Resources, Smith County Memorial Hospital, Smith Center, KS, p. A276

HARFF, Christine K., UP Regional President, Aspirus Keweenaw Hospital, Inc., Laurium, MI, p. A360

HARFORD, Todd, President, Uh Samaritan Medical Center, Ashland, OH, p. A528

HARGENS, Scott James., Administrator and Chief Executive Officer, Avera Dells Area Hospital, Dell Rapids, SD, p. A627
Administrator and Chief Executive Officer, Avera Flandreau Hospital, Flandreau, SD, p. A628

HARGER, Anita, Chief Human Resource Officer, Kingman Regional Medical Center, Kingman, AZ, p. A33
Director Human Resources, Mercy Gilbert Medical Center, Gilbert, AZ, p. A32

HARGETT, Fred, Executive Vice President and Chief Financial Officer, Novant Health Brunswick Medical Center, Bolivia, NC, p. A505
Executive Vice President and Chief Financial Officer, Novant Health Charlotte Orthopaedic Hospital, Charlotte, NC, p. A507
Executive Vice President and Chief Financial Officer, Novant Health Forsyth Medical Center, Winston, NC, p. A520

Executive Vice President and Chief Financial Officer, Novant Health Huntersville Medical Center, Huntersville, NC, p. A512
Executive Vice President and Chief Financial Officer, Novant Health Matthews Medical Center, Matthews, NC, p. A514
Executive Vice President and Chief Financial Officer, Novant Health Medical Park Hospital, Winston, NC, p. A520
Executive Vice President and Chief Financial Officer, Novant Health Presbyterian Medical Center, Charlotte, NC, p. A507
Executive Vice President and Chief Financial Officer, Novant Health Rowan Medical Center, Salisbury, NC, p. A518
Executive Vice President and Chief Financial Officer, Novant Health Thomasville Medical Center, Thomasville, NC, p. A519

HARGETT, Stephen, Senior Vice President and Chief Financial Officer, Marina Del Rey Hospital, Marina Del Rey, CA, p. A77

HARGRAVE, Dallas, Human Resources Director, Bartlett Regional Hospital, Juneau, AK, p. A28

HARGRAVE, David, Chief Information Officer, Ward Memorial Hospital, Monahans, TX, p. A702

HARGRAVE-THOMAS, Anne, Chief Executive Officer, Oakleaf Surgical Hospital, Altoona, WI, p. A779

HARGRODER, Ty, M.D., Chief of Staff, Acadia-St. Landry Hospital, Church Point, LA, p. A299

HARGROVE, Ben, Human Resources Director, Lifestream Behavioral Center, Leesburg, FL, p. A144

HARGROVE, Jeno, R.N., Director of Nursing, Columbus Community Hospital, Columbus, TX, p. A664

HARGROVE, Tressa, Director Human Resources, Jackson Purchase Medical Center, Mayfield, KY, p. A290

HARIHARAN, Parma, M.D., Chief of Staff, Mercy Health - Clermont Hospital, Batavia, OH, p. A528

HARKER, Jodie, Director Human Resources, Van Diest Medical Center, Webster City, IA, p. A260

HARKEY, Shirley, M.D., R.N., FACHE, Interim Vice President and Chief Nursing Officer, Unc Lenoir Healthcare, Kinston, NC, p. A513

HARKINS, Shelly, M.D., Chief Medical Officer, Hshs St. Elizabeth's Hospital, O'Fallon, IL, p. A215
M.D., Chief Medical Officer, St. Peter's Hospital, Helena, MT, p. A425

HARKLEROAD, Rod, R.N., Chief Executive Officer, Frye Regional Medical Center, Hickory, NC, p. A512

HARKNESS, Charles, D.O., Vice President Medical Affairs, Southeast Alabama Medical Center, Dothan, AL, p. A18

HARLAN, Kevin W., President, Joint Township District Memorial Hospital, Saint Marys, OH, p. A548

HARLESS, Andrea, Director Information Services, Wythe County Community Hospital, Wytheville, VA, p. A754

HARLESS, Cheryl, Chief Nursing Officer, Doctors Medical Center Of Modesto, Modesto, CA, p. A78

HARLIN, Timothy J., M.D., Chief Executive Officer and Executive Vice President, University Of Texas Medical Branch, Galveston, TX, p. A680

HARLING, Roxanne, Chief Nursing Officer, Abraham Lincoln Memorial Hospital, Lincoln, IL, p. A210

HARLOVIC, Michael, R.N., President and Chief Executive Officer, Oswego Hospital, Oswego, NY, p. A494

HARLOW, Donald, Director of Information Services, Mountainview Regional Medical Center, Las Cruces, NM, p. A470

HARLOW, Tammy, Chief Nursing Officer, Elbert Memorial Hospital, Elberton, GA, p. A172

HARLOW, Thomas R., FACHE, President, Wellspan Good Samaritan Hospital, Lebanon, PA, p. A595

HARLOWE, Michael, President and Chief Executive Officer, Indiana University Health Tipton Hospital, Tipton, IN, p. A241

HARMAN, Kenneth, Chief Executive Officer, Memorial Hospital Of Carbon County, Rawlins, WY, p. A803

HARMAN, Kimberly, Regional Manager Human Resources, Western State Hospital, Staunton, VA, p. A752

HARMATZ, Alan, M.D., Chief Medical Officer, Blake Medical Center, Bradenton, FL, p. A132

HARMON, Andre, Chief Human Resource Officer, Deer's Head Hospital Center, Salisbury, MD, p. A332

HARMON, Connie, Director of Nursing, Lakeland Hospital, Watervliet, Watervliet, MI, p. A369

HARMON, David, D.O., Vice President Medical Services, Rivervalley Behavioral Health Hospital, Owensboro, KY, p. A291

HARMON, James, Information Technology, Cypress Creek Hospital, Houston, TX, p. A685
Network Administrator, West Oaks Hospital, Houston, TX, p. A689

HARMON, Jennifer, Director of Human Resources, St. Cloud Regional Medical Center, Saint Cloud, FL, p. A156

HARMON, Thomas, M.D., Vice President Medical Affairs, Ohiohealth Riverside Methodist Hospital, Columbus, OH, p. A537

HARMS, Arlene, Chief Executive Officer, Rio Grande Hospital, Del Norte, CO, p. A110

HARMS, George, Chief Financial Officer, Hays Medical Center, Hays, KS, p. A265
Chief Financial Officer, University Of Kansas Health System Pawnee Valley Campus, Larned, KS, p. A268

HARNED, Barbara, R.N., MSN, Chief Nursing Officer, Monroe County Hospital, Monroeville, AL, p. A22

HARNESS, Phil, Chief Executive Officer, Doctor's Hospital, Leawood, KS, p. A269

HARNEY, Geraldine, Chief Financial Officer, U. S. Public Health Service Phoenix Indian Medical Center, Phoenix, AZ, p. A37

HARNEY, Sean, Chief Medical Officer, Employed Provider Clinics, Lewis County General Hospital, Lowville, NY, p. A487

HARPER, Cindy, Manager Patient Data, Westfield Memorial Hospital, Westfield, NY, p. A502

HARPER, Corwin, Senior Vice President and Area Manager, Kaiser Permanente Manteca Medical Center, Manteca, CA, p. A77

HARPER, Corwin N., Senior Vice President and Area Manager, Kaiser Permanente Manteca Medical Center, Manteca, CA, p. A77
Senior Vice President and Area Manager, Kaiser Permanente Vallejo Medical Center, Vallejo, CA, p. A103

HARPER, David, Chief Information Officer, Wills Memorial Hospital, Washington, GA, p. A183
Director, Site Information Systems, Eureka Hospital, Eureka, IL, p. A204

HARPER, Eric, Chief Information Officer, Southeastern Health, Lumberton, NC, p. A514

HARPER, James, Senior Vice President and Chief Human Resources Officer, Tidelands Georgetown Memorial Hospital, Georgetown, SC, p. A620

HARPER, Kirk, R.N., Chief Operating Officer and Chief Nursing Officer, Kadlec Regional Medical Center, Richland, WA, p. A763
R.N., Chief Operating Officer/Chief Nursing Officer, Kadlec Regional Medical Center, Richland, WA, p. A763

HARPER, R, M.D., Medical Director, Uthealth Harris County Psychiatric Center, Houston, TX, p. A689

HARPER, Ryan, Chief Operating Officer, Carondelet St. Mary's Hospital, Tucson, AZ, p. A40

HARPER, Wally, Vice President Human Resources, Gaylord Specialty Healthcare, Wallingford, CT, p. A126

HARPER, William, M.D., Chief of Staff, Birmingham Veterans Affairs Medical Center, Birmingham, AL, p. A14

HARR, Donald, Controller, Ray County Memorial Hospital, Richmond, MO, p. A414

HARREL, Mark, Chief Executive Officer, Phelp. Memorial Health Center, Holdrege, NE, p. A433

HARRELL, Aaron, Director, Grove Hill Memorial Hospital, Grove Hill, AL, p. A19

HARRELL, Jason, MSN, R.N., Vice President, Patient Care Services, Vidant North Hospital, Roanoke Rapids, NC, p. A517

HARRELL, Joy, R.N., Chief Nursing Officer, Mimbres Memorial Hospital, Deming, NM, p. A469

HARRELL, Michael, R.N., Chief Executive Officer, Riverbridge Specialty Hospital, Vidalia, LA, p. A316

HARRELL, Paula, Chief Nursing Officer, Regional One Health Extended Care Hospital, Memphis, TN, p. A645

HARRELL, Steven, FACHE, Chief Operating Officer, Adventhealth New Smyrna Beach, New Smyrna Beach, FL, p. A149

HARRELL, Thomas, M.D., Commander, U. S. Air Force Medical Center Keesler, Keesler Afb, MS, p. A395

HARRER, Seth, M.D., Chief of Staff, Buena Vista Regional Medical Center, Storm Lake, IA, p. A258

HARRIER, Margie, MSN, R.N., Medical Center Chief Operations Officer, Kaiser Permanente Orange County Anaheim Medical Center, Anaheim, CA, p. A55
MSN, R.N., Senior Vice President and Area Manager, Kaiser Permanente South Bay Medical Center, Harbor City, CA, p. A68

HARRIGER, Richard, Director of Emergency Services, Kimball Health Services, Kimball, NE, p. A434

HARRILSON, Annette, Chief Clinical Officer, Select Specialty Hospital Midtown Atlanta, Atlanta, GA, p. A165

HARRINGTON, Dan, Chief Operating Officer and Director Human Resources, Williamsburg Regional Hospital, Kingstree, SC, p. A622

HARRINGTON, Dawn, Chief Information Officer, University Of New Mexico Hospitals, Albuquerque, NM, p. A468

HARRINGTON, Hal, Vice President Human Resources, Merit Health River Region, Vicksburg, MS, p. A401

HARRINGTON, Jason, FACHE, President and Chief Executive Officer, Lakes Regional Healthcare, Spirit Lake, IA, p. A258

HARRINGTON, Jeff, Chief Financial Officer, Children's Hospital Colorado, Aurora, CO, p. A107

HARRINGTON, Kathleen, Vice President Human Resources, Beth Israel Deaconess Hospital-Milton, Milton, MA, p. A342

HARRINGTON, Lane, Chief Nursing Officer, Upson Regional Medical Center, Thomaston, GA, p. A181

HARRIS, Alicia, Director Fiscal Services, Mississipp. State Hospital, Whitfield, MS, p. A401

HARRIS, Allen, M.D., Clinical Director, South Mississipp. State Hospital, Purvis, MS, p. A399

HARRIS, Angela, Chief Executive Officer, River Crest Hospital, San Angelo, TX, p. A710

HARRIS, Ben, Chief Executive Officer, University Hospital And Medical Center, Tamarac, FL, p. A159

HARRIS, Betty, Director Human Resources, Southern California Hospital At Culver City, Culver City, CA, p. A62

HARRIS, Burt, Chief Financial Officer, Canyon Ridge Hospital, Chino, CA, p. A60
Chief Financial Officer, Fort Lauderdale Behavioral Health Center, Oakland Park, FL, p. A149

HARRIS, C, M.D., Chief Information Officer, Cleveland Clinic Children's Hospital For Rehabilitation, Cleveland, OH, p. A534
M.D., Chief Information Officer, Cleveland Clinic Fairview Hospital, Cleveland, OH, p. A534
M.D., Chief Information Officer, Lutheran Hospital, Cleveland, OH, p. A534

HARRIS, Denise, R.N., MSN, Chief Nursing Officer, Baptist Health South Florida, West Kendall Baptist Hospital, Miami, FL, p. A146

HARRIS, Donna, Chief Executive Officer, Encompass Health Rehabilitation Hospital Of Jonesboro, Jonesboro, AR, p. A47

HARRIS, Dory, Director Human Resource, Teton Valley Health Care, Driggs, ID, p. A190

HARRIS, Ethan, Manager Information Systems, Mid-Valley Hospital, Omak, WA, p. A761

HARRIS, Jan, R.N., Director of Nursing, Stonewall Memorial Hospital, Aspermont, TX, p. A654

HARRIS, Janice, Director Human Resources, University Medical Center Of El Paso, El Paso, TX, p. A676

HARRIS, Jen, Director Health Information Management, Chase County Community Hospital, Imperial, NE, p. A433

HARRIS, Jerald, Chief Information Officer, Cornerstone Hospital Of Houston At Clearlake, Webster, TX, p. A724

HARRIS, Jim, Director Information Technology, Grafton City Hospital, Grafton, WV, p. A772

HARRIS, Jo ell, R.N., Chief Nursing Officer, Forest View Psychiatric Hospital, Grand Rapids, MI, p. A355

HARRIS, John, Chief Executive Officer, Memorial Medical Center, Las Cruces, NM, p. A470
Vice President Finance and Chief Financial Officer, Community Hospital Anderson, Anderson, IN, p. A223

HARRIS, Julie, Chief Financial Officer, Riceland Medical Center, Winnie, TX, p. A726
Controller, Anmed Health Rehabilitation Hospital, Anderson, SC, p. A615

HARRIS, Justin, Chief Operating Officer, Highlands Arh Regional Medical Center, Prestonsburg, KY, p. A292

HARRIS, Karen, R.N., Chief Nursing and Operations Officer, Henry Ford West Bloomfield Hospital, West Bloomfield, MI, p. A369

HARRIS, Kathy, Vice President, Mercyhealth Hospital And Trauma Center - Janesville, Janesville, WI, p. A786

HARRIS, Kevin, Director Information Systems, Titus Regional Medical Center, Mount Pleasant, TX, p. A702

HARRIS, Kristin, Chief Executive Officer, Kingwood Pines Hospital, Kingwood, TX, p. A693

HARRIS, Laci, Chief Executive Officer, Continuecare Hospital At Medical Center (Odessa), Odessa, TX, p. A703

HARRIS, Laurie, Chief Accountant, Kerrville State Hospital, Kerrville, TX, p. A692

HARRIS, Lee, Assistant Administrator Support Services, Memorial Hospital And Manor, Bainbridge, GA, p. A166

HARRIS, Leslie, MSN, R.N., Chief Nursing Officer, Forrest City Medical Center, Forrest City, AR, p. A45

HARRIS, Lisa E., M.D., Chief Executive Officer, Eskenazi Health, Indianapolis, IN, p. A231

HARRIS, Madeline, R.N., Vice President and Chief Nursing Officer, The Queen's Medical Center, Honolulu, HI, p. A185

HARRIS, Marianna, Administrator, Osborne County Memorial Hospital, Osborne, KS, p. A273

HARRIS, Mark, Deputy Commander Clinical Services, Fort Belvoir Community Hospital, Fort Belvoir, VA, p. A742

HARRIS, Merilyn, Administrator, Ka'U Hospital, Pahala, HI, p. A186

HARRIS, Miriam, Director Finance, Oklahoma Forensic Center, Vinita, OK, p. A571

HARRIS, Parker, Chief Executive Officer and Administrator, Baptist Memorial Hospital-Tipton, Covington, TN, p. A637

HARRIS, R, M.D., Chief of Staff, Reeves Memorial Medical Center, Bernice, LA, p. A298

HARRIS, Robert, M.D., President Medical and Dental Staff, Bergen New Bridge Medical Center, Paramus, NJ, p. A460

HARRIS, Shelly, Chief Executive Officer, Indian Health Service - Quentin N. Burdick Memorial Health Care Facility, Belcourt, ND, p. A521

HARRIS, Shirley, M.D., President Medical Staff, Mosaic Medical Center - Maryville, Maryville, MO, p. A411

HARRIS, Spencer, Chief Financial Officer, Kadlec Regional Medical Center, Richland, WA, p. A763

HARRIS, Stuart, M.D., Chief of Staff, Trigg County Hospital, Cadiz, KY, p. A281

HARRIS, Susan, R.N., Chief Operating Officer, Medical Center, Navicent Health, Macon, GA, p. A176
Director Fiscal Services, Shriners Hospitals For Children - Cincinnati, Cincinnati, OH, p. A533

HARRIS, Sylvia, Fiscal Director, Moccasin Bend Mental Health Institute, Chattanooga, TN, p. A635

HARRIS, Timothy, M.D., Chief Quality Officer, Texas Health Presbyterian Hospital Denton, Denton, TX, p. A672

HARRIS, Vena, Director Human Resources, Minneola District Hospital, Minneola, KS, p. A271

HARRIS, William, Chief Information Officer, Lawton Indian Hospital, Lawton, OK, p. A561

HARRISON, Charles, Chief Executive Officer, Mountains Community Hospital, Lake Arrowhead, CA, p. A70

HARRISON, Chris, Manager Information Systems, Campbell County Health, Gillette, WY, p. A802

HARRISON, Denise, Associate Director, Veterans Affairs Nebraska-Western Iowa Health Care System, Omaha, NE, p. A438

HARRISON, Douglass, Chief Executive Officer, Wheeling Hospital, Wheeling, WV, p. A778

HARRISON, Dyan, Manager Health Information, Ochiltree General Hospital, Perryton, TX, p. A705

HARRISON, George, M.D., Chief Medical Officer, Fairview Park Hospital, Dublin, GA, p. A172

HARRISON, Jo, Vice President of Patient Care Services, Southwest Medical Center, Liberal, KS, p. A269

HARRISON, Marva, R.N., Vice President and Chief Nursing Officer, Integris Southwest Medical Center, Oklahoma City, OK, p. A564

HARRISON, Randy, Chief Financial Officer, Raleigh General Hospital, Beckley, WV, p. A770

HARRON, Rick, Chief Financial Officer, Dominican Hospital, Santa Cruz, CA, p. A97

HARROP, Elizabeth, Director, Human Resources, Flambeau Hospital, Park Falls, WI, p. A794

HARSHAWAT, Paras, M.D., Medical Director, Harsha Behavioral Center, Terre Haute, IN, p. A241

HARSHAWAT, Roopam, President and Chief Executive Officer, Harsha Behavioral Center, Terre Haute, IN, p. A241

HARSHBARGER, Catherine S., R.N., Interim Chief Executive Officer, Melissa Memorial Hospital, Holyoke, CO, p. A114

HARSY, Brice, Chief Financial Officer, Marshall Browning Hospital, Du Quoin, IL, p. A203

HART, Amy, Chief Operating Officer, Cuyuna Regional Medical Center, Crosby, MN, p. A374

HART, Betsy, Chief Operating Officer, Northridge Hospital Medical Center, Northridge, CA, p. A81

HART, Denise, Director Human Resources, Sullivan County Community Hospital, Sullivan, IN, p. A241

HART, Donna, Chief Information Officer, Provident Hospital Of Cook County, Chicago, IL, p. A200

HART, Elizabeth, R.N., MSN, Chief Nursing Officer, Providence Saint Josep. Medical Center, Burbank, CA, p. A59

HART, Gary, M.D., Chief Medical Officer, West Park Hospital, Cody, WY, p. A802

HART, James, M.D., Medical Director, Rolling Hills Hospital, Franklin, TN, p. A638

HART, John, Chief Executive Officer, Wray Community District Hospital, Wray, CO, p. A120

HART, Joline, Vice President Human Resources, Franklin Memorial Hospital, Farmington, ME, p. A320

HART, Joseph, Director Finance and Support Services, Putnam Hospital Center, Carmel, NY, p. A481

HART, Kenneth, President, Saint Alphonsus Medical Center - Ontario, Ontario, OR, p. A578

HART, Lisa, Chief Executive Officer, Elkview General Hospital, Hobart, OK, p. A560

HART, Monique, Chief Financial Officer, Baptist Memorial Hospital-Tipton, Covington, TN, p. A637

HART, Pat, Director Human Resources, Three Rivers Medical Center, Louisa, KY, p. A287

HART, Randy, Manager, Information Technology Regional Operations, Indian Path Community Hospital, Kingsport, TN, p. A641

HART, Richard, Chief Financial Officer, Stanislaus Surgical Hospital, Modesto, CA, p. A79

HART, Scott, Controller, Encompass Rehabilitation Hospital Of Lakeview, Elizabethtown, KY, p. A282

HART-FLYNN, Wilma, Ph.D., R.N., Chief Nursing Officer, Morristown-Hamblen Healthcare System, Morristown, TN, p. A645

HARTBERG, David, Chief Executive Officer, Gundersen Boscobel Area Hospital And Clinics, Boscobel, WI, p. A781

HARTE, Brian J., M.D., President, Cleveland Clinic Akron General, Akron, OH, p. A527

HARTGRAVES, Steve L., President and Chief Executive Officer, Jackson County Memorial Hospital, Altus, OK, p. A555

HARTKE, Michael, Executive Vice President, Chief Operating Officer, Northwest Community Healthcare, Arlington Heights, IL, p. A194

HARTLEY, Barbara, Chief Medical Officer, Benson Hospital, Benson, AZ, p. A30

HARTLEY, Diane, Director of Patient Care Services, Beaumont Hospital, Wayne, Wayne, MI, p. A369

HARTLEY, Melinda, R.N., Vice President Patient Care Services, Perry Hospital, Perry, GA, p. A178

HARTLEY, Michael, MS, Chief Nursing Officer, Holly Hill Hospital, Raleigh, NC, p. A516

HARTLEY, Randall, Chief Operating Officer, Nemours Children's Hospital, Orlando, FL, p. A151

HARTLEY, Randall W., Interim President, Nemours Children's Hospital, Orlando, FL, p. A151

HARTLEY, Shauna, Administrator, Turquoise Lodge Hospital, Albuquerque, NM, p. A468

HARTLEY, Shawn, Chief Financial Officer, Nash Unc Health Care, Rocky Mount, NC, p. A517

HARTLEY, Wannah, Controller, Winkler County Memorial Hospital, Kermit, TX, p. A692

HARTMAN, Daphane, Director Information Systems, Chi St. Josep. College Station Hospital, College Station, TX, p. A664

HARTMAN, Don, Director Human Resources, Sutter Davis Hospital, Davis, CA, p. A62

HARTMAN, Mark, Interim Chief Financial Officer, St. Josep. Medical Center, Houston, TX, p. A688

HARTMAN, Sally, Senior Vice President, Riverside Regional Medical Center, Newport News, VA, p. A747

HARTMANN, Doreen, Chief Financial Officer, St. Joseph's Behavioral Health Center, Stockton, CA, p. A100

HARTMANN, Peter, M.D., Vice President Medical Affairs, Wellspan York Hospital, York, PA, p. A612

HARTMANN, Rob, Assistant Director Human Resources Management, Ochsner Lsu Health Shreveport - Monroe Medical Center, Monroe, LA, p. A309

HARTNETT, Tammy, Employee Relations Manager, Unitypoint Health - St. Lukes's Sioux City, Sioux City, IA, p. A258

HARTSELL, Henry, Ph.D., Executive Director, Griffin Memorial Hospital, Norman, OK, p. A563

HARTSELL, Scott, Chief Operating Officer, Bayfront Health Brooksville, Brooksville, FL, p. A133

HARTSOCK, Aaron, Director of Operations, Geisinger-Lewistown Hospital, Lewistown, PA, p. A595

HARTUNG, Andy, Assistant Vice President of Information Systems and Chief Information Officer, Self Regional Healthcare, Greenwood, SC, p. A621

HARTWELL, Tim, Chief Human Resources, Marion Veterans Affairs Medical Center, Marion, IL, p. A211

HARTWICK, Bryan, Vice President Human Resources, Alton Memorial Hospital, Alton, IL, p. A194
Vice President Human Resources, Christian Hospital, Saint Louis, MO, p. A415

HARTWIG, Michael, M.D., Chief of Staff, Stillwater Medical Perry, Perry, OK, p. A567

HARTZ, Kimberly, Chief Executive Officer, Washington Hospital Healthcare System, Fremont, CA, p. A65

HARTZOG, Rick, Chief Information Officer, Merit Health Madison, Canton, MS, p. A390

HARVATH, Brandon, President and Chief Operating Officer, St. Francis Hospital, Wilmington, DE, p. A128

HARVEY, Alice, Director of Nursing, Heatherhill Care Communities, Chardon, OH, p. A531

HARVEY, Alisha, Director of Finance, Houston County Community Hospital, Erin, TN, p. A638

HARVEY, Jennifer, Director Human Resources, Golden Plains Community Hospital, Borger, TX, p. A660

HARVEY, John, M.D., Chief Executive Officer, Oklahoma Heart Hospital South Campus, Oklahoma City, OK, p. A565
M.D., Chief Executive Officer, Oklahoma Heart Hospital, Oklahoma City, OK, p. A565

HARVEY, Kathy, D.O., Chief Medical Officer, Logan Regional Medical Center, Logan, WV, p. A774

HARVEY, Linda, Chief Financial Officer, West Feliciana Hospital, Saint Francisville, LA, p. A313

HARVEY, Michael, FACHE, President and Chief Executive Officer, Syracuse Area Health, Syracuse, NE, p. A440

HARVEY, Paul, Chief Executive Officer, Christus Mother Frances Hospital - Winnsboro, Winnsboro, TX, p. A726
President and Chief Executive Officer, Christus Mother Frances Hospital - Sulphur Springs, Sulphur Springs, TX, p. A718

HARVILL, Brian, President, Vidant Bertie Hospital, Windsor, NC, p. A520
President, Vidant Chowan Hospital, Edenton, NC, p. A509

HARVIN, Schley, Information Technology Technician, Hood Memorial Hospital, Amite, LA, p. A296

HARWOOD, Daniel, M.D., Chief of Staff, Trinity Hospital, Weaverville, CA, p. A104

HASBROUCK, Matthew, Chief Operating Officer, Memorial Health, Savannah, GA, p. A180

HASHMI, Mubashir, Chief Information Officer, Pacifica Hospital Of The Valley, Sun Valley, CA, p. A100

HASHMI, Suleman, President and Chief Executive Officer, Texas General Hospital, Grand Prairie, TX, p. A682

HASKELL, Jeffrey, M.D., Chief Medical Staff, Lost Rivers Medical Center, Arco, ID, p. A188

HASKINS, Don, Administrative Director Human Resources, Southwest Mississipp. Regional Medical Center, Mccomb, MS, p. A396

HASLETT, Tom, Interim Chief Information Officer, Macneal Hospital, Berwyn, IL, p. A195

HASNI, Kamran, M.D., Chief of Medical Staff, Barbourville Arh Hospital, Barbourville, KY, p. A280

HASS, Roxanne, Director of Nursing, Chi St. Josep. Health Madison Hospital, Madisonville, TX, p. A699

HASSAN, Tariq, M.D., Associate Director of Patient Care, Captain James A. Lovell Federal Health Care Center, North Chicago, IL, p. A214

HASSANI, Dahlia, Vice President of Medical Affairs, Baylor Scott & White All Saints Medical Center - Fort Worth, Fort Worth, TX, p. A678

HASSELBRACK, Jeni, Director Human Resources, Adventhealth Gordon, Calhoun, GA, p. A168

HAST, Anne, R.N., Director of Nursing, Advanced Surgical Hospital, Washington, PA, p. A609

HAST, Anne S., R.N., Chief Executive Officer, Advanced Surgical Hospital, Washington, PA, p. A609

HASTIN-HULSEY, Kathy, Administrative Assistant Human Resources, Dardanelle Regional Medical Center, Dardanelle, AR, p. A44

HASTINGS, Clare, R.N., Ph.D., Chief Nurse Officer, National Institutes Of Health Clinical Center, Bethesda, MD, p. A327

HASTINGS, Elaine, MSN, R.N., Chief Nursing Officer, Piedmont Medical Center, Rock Hill, SC, p. A624

HASTINGS, Sarah, Executive Director, Ridgeview Medical Center, Waconia, MN, p. A387

HATCH, Brooke, Director Human Resource, Bradley County Medical Center, Warren, AR, p. A54

HATCH, Tammy, Manager, Northern Light Sebasticook Valley Hospital, Pittsfield, ME, p. A322

HATCHEL, Kimberly, Chief Nursing Officer, Blake Medical Center, Bradenton, FL, p. A132

HATCHER, Amy, Executive Vice President and Chief Financial Officer, Children's Hospital And Medical Center, Omaha, NE, p. A437

HATCHER, Julie, Vice President Human Resources, O'Connor Hospital, San Jose, CA, p. A95

HATCHES, Ann, Director, Human Resources, Holy Cross Hospital, Chicago, IL, p. A198
Interim Director Human Resources, Mount Sinai Hospital, Chicago, IL, p. A199

HATFIELD, Chad, Chief Executive Officer, Northeast Georgia Medical Center Barrow, Winder, GA, p. A183

HATFIELD, Jonathan, Supervisor Information Technology, Klickitat Valley Health, Goldendale, WA, p. A759

HATFIELD, Rhonda, Chief Nursing Officer and Vice President of Clinical Operations, Chi Memorial, Chattanooga, TN, p. A635

HATFIELD, Timothy A., Community Chief Executive Officer, Highlands Arh Regional Medical Center, Prestonsburg, KY, p. A292
Community Chief Executive Officer, Tug Valley Arh Regional Medical Center, South Williamson, KY, p. A293

HATHAWAY, William, M.D., Chief Medical Officer, Mission Hospital, Asheville, NC, p. A504

HATHCOCK, Claudette, Administrative Director Human Resources, University Of Mississipp. Medical Center Grenada, Grenada, MS, p. A393
Human Resources Director, University Of Mississippi. Medical Center Holmes County, Lexington, MS, p. A396

HATIC, Safet, M.D., President Medical Staff, Wayne Healthcare, Greenville, OH, p. A541

HATIRAS, Spiros, FACHE, President and Chief Executive Officer, Holyoke Medical Center, Holyoke, MA, p. A340

HATLESTAD, Jill, Vice President Human Resources and Marketing, Glencoe Regional Health, Glencoe, MN, p. A377

HATMAKER, Michael, Vice President Support Services and Admin Nursing Home, Leconte Medical Center, Sevierville, TN, p. A649

HATSFELT, Annette, R.N., Chief Nursing Officer, St. Martin Hospital, Breaux Bridge, LA, p. A298

HATTEM-SCHIFFMAN, Marita, President, Midmichigan Medical Center-Gratiot, Alma, MI, p. A348

HATTER, Jason, Chief Human Resource Officer, Princeton Baptist Medical Center, Birmingham, AL, p. A15

HATTERER-HOAG, Dawn, Director Human Resources, Psychiatric Institute Of Washington, Washington, DC, p. A130

HATTON, Tad, Vice President Chief Operating Officer, Ascension Seton Medical Center Austin, Austin, TX, p. A654

HAUBL, Eileen, Senior Vice President and Chief Financial Officer, Mission Hospital Mission Viejo, Mission Viejo, CA, p. A78

HAUG, Darin, D.O., Chief Medical Officer, Fitzgibbon Hospital, Marshall, MO, p. A411

HAUGE, Meri, R.N., MSN, Associate Director of Patient Care Services and Nurse Executive, St. Cloud Veterans Affairs Health Care System, Saint Cloud, MN, p. A384

HAUGER, Clint, Chief Executive Officer, North Tamp. Behavioral Health, Wesley Chapel, FL, p. A162

HAUGH, William, Administrator, Georgetown Community Hospital, Georgetown, KY, p. A284

HAUGHEY, Tracie, Chief Executive Officer and Chief Financial Officer, Wills Memorial Hospital, Washington, GA, p. A183

HAUK, Julie, Chief Executive Officer, The Rehabilitation Hospital Of Montana, Billings, MT, p. A422

HAULER, Jennifer, D.O., Chief Medical Officer, Upper Valley Medical Center, Troy, OH, p. A551

HAUN, Lindsay, Chief Financial Officer, Greeneville Community Hospital West, Greeneville, TN, p. A638

HAUPERT, John M., FACHE, President and Chief Executive Officer, Grady Memorial Hospital, Atlanta, GA, p. A164

HAUPT, Carolyn, Chief Financial Officer, Peacehealth United General Medical Center, Sedro, WA, p. A765

HAUSAUER, Patricia, Director Finance, Baptist Medical Center Nassau, Fernandina Beach, FL, p. A137

HAUSER, Claudia, Chief Executive Officer, Pam Rehabilitation Hospital Of Clear Lake, Webster, TX, p. A724

HAUSER, Mark, M.D., Chief Medical Officer, Baptist Health South Florida, Baptist Hospital Of Miami, Miami, FL, p. A146

HAUSER, Megan, Director Human Resources, Shriners Hospitals For Children-Philadelphia, Philadelphia, PA, p. A602

HAUSHALTER, Brandon, Chief Executive Officer, Kendall Regional Medical Center, Miami, FL, p. A146

HAUSHALTER, Richard, Senior Vice President Operations and Chief Operating Officer, Sentara Rmh Medical Center, Harrisonburg, VA, p. A743

HAUSMANN, Jena, President and Chief Executive Officer, Children's Hospital Colorado, Aurora, CO, p. A107

HAVARD, Greg, Chief Executive Officer, George Regional Hospital, Lucedale, MS, p. A396

HAVEN, Adrian, Site Manager, Gallup Indian Medical Center, Gallup. NM, p. A469

HAVENS, Jennifer, Chief Executive Officer, Unitypoint Health - Grinnell Regional Medical Center, Grinnell, IA, p. A250

HAVERICAK, Heather, Chief Executive Officer, Broward Health Medical Center, Fort Lauderdale, FL, p. A137

HAVERSTOCK, Loren, Manager Human Resources, Harrison County Hospital, Corydon, IN, p. A226

HAVICAN, Gary C., President, Midstate Medical Center, Meriden, CT, p. A123
President, The Hospital Of Central Connecticut, New Britain, CT, p. A123

HAVRILLA, David, Chief Financial Officer, Medstar Montgomery Medical Center, Olney, MD, p. A331

HAWIG, Scott, Senior Vice President Finance, Chief Financial Officer and Treasurer, Froedtert And The Medical College Of Wisconsin Froedtert Hospital, Milwaukee, WI, p. A791
Senior Vice President of Finance, Chief Financial Officer and Treasurer, Froedtert Menomonee Falls Hospital, Menomonee Falls, WI, p. A789
Senior Vice President of Finance, Chief Financial Officer and Treasurer, Froedtert West Bend Hospital, West Bend, WI, p. A799

HAWKEY, Tammy, Manager Information Technology Client Services, Marshfield Medical Center - Weston, Weston, WI, p. A799

HAWKINS, Bryan, Controller, Firsthealth Montgomery Memorial Hospital, Troy, NC, p. A519

HAWKINS, Ellis, FACHE, President, Ssm Health Depaul Hospital - St. Louis, Bridgeton, MO, p. A403

HAWKINS, Hillary, M.D., Medical Director, Sheltering Arms Rehabilitation Hospital, Mechanicsville, VA, p. A746

HAWKINS, Jason F., Chief Administrative Officer, Peacehealth Peace Harbor Medical Center, Florence, OR, p. A575

HAWKINS, Kidada, Chief Executive Officer, Shoals Hospital, Muscle Shoals, AL, p. A22

HAWKINS, Sheri, Chief Nursing Officer, Adventhealth Shawnee Mission, Shawnee Mission, KS, p. A276

HAWKINS, Tami, R.N., MSN, Vice President Patient Care and Chief Nursing Officer, Texas Health Presbyterian Hospital Of Rockwall, Rockwall, TX, p. A709

HAWKINSON, Curtis R., Chief Executive Officer, Community Memorial Healthcare, Marysville, KS, p. A270

HAWLEY, Jason, Director of Information Services and Security, Yuma District Hospital, Yuma, CO, p. A120

HAWS, Bradley, Chief Financial Officer, University Of Iowa Hospitals And Clinics, Iowa City, IA, p. A252

HAWTHORNE, Caryn, Vice President Finance and Chief Finance Officer, East Tennessee Children's Hospital, Knoxville, TN, p. A641

HAWTOF, Jeffrey, M.D., Vice President Medical Operations and Informatics, Beebe Healthcare, Lewes, DE, p. A127

HAY, Fraser, President, Texas Health Harris Methodist Hospital Hurst-Euless-Bedford, Bedford, TX, p. A659

HAYDEN, Crystal, FACHE, R.N., Executive Vice President, Chief Operating Officer and Chief Nursing Officer, Nash Unc Health Care, Rocky Mount, NC, p. A517

HAYDEN, James, M.D., Chief Medical Officer, Penn Highlands Huntingdon, Huntingdon, PA, p. A592

HAYDEN, Jamie, Chief Financial Officer, Eastland Memorial Hospital, Eastland, TX, p. A673

HAYDEN, John, Senior Vice President and Chief Human Resources Officer, Bronson Lakeview Hospital, Paw Paw, MI, p. A363
Senior Vice President and Human Resources Officer, Bronson Battle Creek Hospital, Battle Creek, MI, p. A349
Vice President and Chief Human Resources Officer, Bronson Methodist Hospital, Kalamazoo, MI, p. A359

HAYDEN, Karen, Director Health Information Services, Performance Improvement and Risk Management, Valle Vista Health System, Greenwood, IN, p. A230

HAYDEN-PUGH, Beverly, R.N., Senior Vice President and Chief Nursing Officer, Valley Children's Healthcare, Madera, CA, p. A76

HAYEK, Anthony, D.O., Medical Director, Edwin Shaw Rehab, Copley, OH, p. A537

HAYES, David, Chief Financial Officer, T.J. Health Columbia, Columbia, KY, p. A281

HAYES, Deborah, R.N., MS, MSN, Chief Operating Officer, Christ Hospital, Cincinnati, OH, p. A532

HAYES, Elaine, Controller, Uofl Health - Mary And Elizabeth Hospital, Louisville, KY, p. A289

HAYES, Farrell, Chief Financial Officer, Chi Memorial Hospital - Georgia, Fort Oglethorpe, GA, p. A173

HAYES, James, Director Human Resources, Western State Hospital, Hopkinsville, KY, p. A285

HAYES, Jo, Chief Nursing Officer, Horn Memorial Hospital, Ida Grove, IA, p. A251

HAYES, June, Chief Financial Officer, Harrisburg Medical Center, Harrisburg, IL, p. A206

HAYES, Kathe, Executive Director, Western New York Children's Psychiatric Center, West Seneca, NY, p. A502

HAYES, Kelly, Chief Financial Officer, Methodist Hospital For Surgery, Addison, TX, p. A651

HAYES, Kevin, M.D., Chief of Staff, Monroe Regional Hospital, Aberdeen, MS, p. A389

HAYES, Lisa, Chief Clinical Officer, Central Indiana Amg Specialty Hospital, Muncie, IN, p. A237

HAYES, Lynnette, Chief Nursing Officer, Golden Valley Memorial Healthcare, Clinton, MO, p. A405

HAYES, Paul, R.N., Executive Director, Uw Medicine/ Harborview Medical Center, Seattle, WA, p. A764

HAYES, Sharon, Chief Executive Officer, Bayfront Health St. Petersburg, Saint Petersburg, FL, p. A156

HAYES, Stacy, R.N., Chief Nursing Officer, Arizona Spine And Joint Hospital, Mesa, AZ, p. A33

HAYES, Susan, Director Human Resources, Southeastern Health, Lumberton, NC, p. A514

HAYES, Tammy, R.N., MS, Chief Nurse Executive and Long Term Care Administrator, Northfield Hospital And Clinics, Northfield, MN, p. A382

HAYES, Thomas P., Chief Executive Officer, Eastern Plumas Health Care, Portola, CA, p. A86

HAYES, Warren, Chief of Staff, Montgomery County Memorial Hospital, Red Oak, IA, p. A256

HAYES, William M., Chief Executive Officer, Northside Hospital-Cherokee, Canton, GA, p. A168

HAYGOOD, Rachel, Director Information Technology, Tyler County Hospital, Woodville, TX, p. A726

HAYHURST, Leslie, Director Information Systems, Washington Health System Greene, Waynesburg, PA, p. A610

HAYMAN, Judy A., Ph.D., Director, Veterans Affairs Montana Health Care System, Fort Harrison, MT, p. A423

HAYN, Jed, Chief Information Officer, Walter B. Jones Alcohol And Drug Abuse Treatment Center, Greenville, NC, p. A511

HAYNES, Deatosha, Interim Associates Director for Patient, Veterans Affairs Gulf Coast Veterans Health Care System, Biloxi, MS, p. A390

HAYNES, Elaine, R.N., MSN, Vice President Patient Services and Chief Nursing Executive, Atrium Health Lincoln, Lincolnton, NC, p. A514

HAYNES, Jamil, Regional Director Human Resources, Integris Miami Hospital, Miami, OK, p. A562

HAYNES, Jill, Financial Coach, Bath Veterans Affairs Medical Center, Bath, NY, p. A475

HAYNES, John, M.D., JrChief of Medical Staff, North Caddo Medical Center, Vivian, LA, p. A316

HAYNES, Laurie, Chief Financial Officer, Gulf Coast Regional Medical Center, Panama City, FL, p. A153

HAYNES, Mark, M.D., Chief of Staff, Claiborne Memorial Medical Center, Homer, LA, p. A303

HAYNES, Robert Gerard., FACHE, Chief Executive Officer, Guadalup. Regional Medical Center, Seguin, TX, p. A714

HAYNES, Tina, Interim Chief Executive Officer, Claiborne Memorial Medical Center, Homer, LA, p. A303

HAYNES, William, Director Information Technology, Central Louisiana State Hospital, Pineville, LA, p. A313

HAYREH, Davinder, M.D., Medical Director, Metropolitan St. Louis Psychiatric Center, Saint Louis, MO, p. A416

HAYS, Cheryl, FACHE, Chief Operating Officer, Marshall Medical Center North, Guntersville, AL, p. A19

HAYS, Cheryl M., FACHE, Chief Executive Officer, Marshall Medical Center North, Guntersville, AL, p. A19
FACHE, Chief Executive Officer, Marshall Medical Center South, Boaz, AL, p. A16

HAYS, Chuck, President and Chief Executive Officer, Mainegeneral Medical Center, Augusta, ME, p. A318

HAYS, Harry, Chief Executive Officer, Carroll County Memorial Hospital, Carrollton, KY, p. A281

HAYS, Kathie, MSN, R.N., Chief Nursing Officer, West Chester Hospital, West Chester, OH, p. A552

HAYS, Larry, Director Information Technology, Southern Virginia Mental Health Institute, Danville, VA, p. A741

HAYS, Richard, M.D., Chief Medical Officer, Wellington Regional Medical Center, Wellington, FL, p. A161
Chief Fiscal Service, Veterans Affairs Southern Nevada Healthcare System, North Las Vegas, NV, p. A445

HAYS, Timothy, Regional Vice President Human Resources, Johnston Health, Smithfield, NC, p. A518

HAYTAIAN, Mike, Head Director Information Resources Management, Naval Hospital Jacksonville, Jacksonville, FL, p. A141

HAYWOOD, Nancy, Chief Financial Officer, Ascension Genesys Hospital, Grand Blanc, MI, p. A355
Chief Financial Officer, Ascension St. Mary's Of Michigan, Saginaw, MI, p. A365

HAYWOOD, Stephanie, Director Human Resources, Southern Virginia Mental Health Institute, Danville, VA, p. A741

HAZELBAKER, Matthew, M.D., President Medical Staff, Memorial Health, Marysville, OH, p. A544

HEAD, David, M.D., Chief Medical Staff, Norton Sound Regional Hospital, Nome, AK, p. A29

HEAD, Susan, Director Nursing Services, Blackfeet Community Hospital, Saint Mary, MT, p. A427

HEALEY, Lauren, Human Resources Director, Encompass Health Rehabilitation Hospital Of New England, Woburn, MA, p. A346

HEALY, John, Manager Information Technology, Friends Hospital, Philadelphia, PA, p. A600

HEALY, Peter J., President and Chief Executive Officer, Beth Israel Deaconess Medical Center, Boston, MA, p. A335

HEALY-COLLIER, Kathy, Chief Operating Officer, Brookwood Baptist Medical Center, Birmingham, AL, p. A14

HEARD, Alex, M.D., Chief Medical Officer, Falmouth Hospital, Falmouth, MA, p. A339

HEARD, Charles, M.D., Chief of Staff, Orlando Regional Medical Center, Orlando, FL, p. A151

HEARD, Heather, Director Human Resources, Holdenville General Hospital, Holdenville, OK, p. A560

HEARD, M, Director Business Services, North Mississipp. Medical Center-Pontotoc, Pontotoc, MS, p. A399

HEARING, Tim, Associate Information Technology Director, Raulerson Hospital, Okeechobee, FL, p. A150

HEARNE, Diane, Director Human Resources, Arizona Spine And Joint Hospital, Mesa, AZ, p. A33

HEARNSBERGER, John, M.D., Chief of Staff, Howard Memorial Hospital, Nashville, AR, p. A51

HEATER, Floyd, President, Valley Health - Warren Memorial Hospital, Front Royal, VA, p. A742

HEATH, Ed, FACHE, Chief Executive Officer, Owensboro Health Muhlenberg Community Hospital, Greenville, KY, p. A284

HEATH, Marsha, Human Resources Manager, Carle Richland Memorial Hospital, Olney, IL, p. A215

HEATH, Megan, Chief Nursing Officer, Gordon Memorial Health Services, Gordon, NE, p. A432

HEATH, Merry, Chief Nursing Officer, Piedmont Fayette Hospital, Fayetteville, GA, p. A172

HEATH, Susan, R.N., Senior Vice President and Chief Nursing Officer, Seattle Children's Hospital, Seattle, WA, p. A764

HEATH, William, Chief Executive Officer, Regency Hospital Of Meridian, Meridian, MS, p. A397

HEATHERLY, Neil, Chief Executive Officer, Parkwest Medical Center, Knoxville, TN, p. A641

HEATHERLY, Steve, Chief Executive Officer, Harris Regional Hospital, Sylva, NC, p. A519
Chief Executive Officer, Swain Community Hospital, Bryson City, NC, p. A505

HEATHERLY-LLOYD, Sara, Chief Operating Officer, Tennova Healthcare-Lafollette Medical Center, La Follette, TN, p. A642

HEATON, Crystal, Director of Finance, Ascension St. Vincent Warrick, Boonville, IN, p. A224

HEBBERD, Hilda, R.N., MSN, Senior Director Clinical Services, Marlette Regional Hospital, Marlette, MI, p. A361

HEBEL, Barbara, Vice President Human Resources, Doylestown Hospital, Doylestown, PA, p. A588

HEBERT, Bryan, Director Information Systems, The Medical Center Of Southeast Texas, Port Arthur, TX, p. A707

HEBERT, Carol, Director Human Resources, The Medical Center Of Southeast Texas, Port Arthur, TX, p. A707

HEBERT, Gerard, Chief Financial Officer, Texoma Medical Center, Denison, TX, p. A671

HEBERT, Jeffrey, Vice President Finance, Chief Financial Officer, Littleton Regional Healthcare, Littleton, NH, p. A450

HEBERT, Katherine D., MS, Chief Executive Officer, University Hospital & Clinics, Lafayette, LA, p. A306

HEBERT, Kim, Chief Financial Officer, Lafayette General Medical Center, Lafayette, LA, p. A305

HEBERT, Timothy, Director Human Resources, Ochsner St. Mary, Morgan City, LA, p. A309

HEBGEN, Lynn, MSN, R.N., Vice President of Nursing, Upland Hills Health, Dodgeville, WI, p. A782

HEBL, James, M.D., Regional Vice President, Mayo Clinic Health System In Fairmont, Fairmont, MN, p. A376
M.D., Regional Vice President, Mayo Clinic Health System In Mankato, Mankato, MN, p. A379
M.D., Regional Vice President, Mayo Clinic Health System In New Prague, New Prague, MN, p. A382
M.D., Regional Vice President, Mayo Clinic Health System In Saint James, Saint James, MN, p. A384
M.D., Regional Vice President, Mayo Clinic Health System In Waseca, Waseca, MN, p. A387

HEBRA, Andre, M.D., Chief Medical Officer, Nemours Children's Hospital, Orlando, FL, p. A151

HECHLER, Tracy, Healthcare Director Information Services, Chippenham Hospital, Richmond, VA, p. A750

HECHT, David, M.D., Chief of Staff, James H. Quillen Veterans Affairs Medical Center, Mountain Home, TN, p. A646

HECKATHORNE, Daniel, Chief Financial Officer, Memorial Hospital Of Gardena, Gardena, CA, p. A66

HECKER, Cynthia, R.N., Executive Director, University Of Washington Medical Center, Seattle, WA, p. A764
R.N., Executive Director, Uw Medicine/Northwest Hospital & Medical Center, Seattle, WA, p. A764

HECKER, Julie, Vice President, Operations, Upmc Mercy, Pittsburgh, PA, p. A604

HECKER, Lisa, Director Human Resources, Hedrick Medical Center, Chillicothe, MO, p. A404

HECKERMAN, Ray, Chief Executive Officer and Managing Director, Coastal Harbor Treatment Center, Savannah, GA, p. A180

HECKERT, Robert J. Jr, Chief Executive Officer, Gerald Champion Regional Medical Center, Alamogordo, NM, p. A467

HECKMAN, Erika, Chief Executive Officer, Westborough Behavioral Healthcare Hospital, Westborough, MA, p. A346

HEDBERG, Beth, R.N., Director Nursing, Lindsborg Community Hospital, Lindsborg, KS, p. A270

HEDDE, Charles, M.D., Chief Medical Officer, Good Samaritan Hospital, Vincennes, IN, p. A242

HEDDEN, Tyler, Chief Operating Officer, Santa Rosa Memorial Hospital, Santa Rosa, CA, p. A98

Interim Chief Executive Officer, Santa Rosa Memorial Hospital, Santa Rosa, CA, p. A98

HEDDERMAN, Michael, Vice President and Chief Financial Officer, Madonna Rehabilitation Hospital, Omaha, NE, p. A437

HEDGE, William, Chief Executive Officer, Central Indiana Amg Specialty Hospital, Muncie, IN, p. A237

HEDGES, David, Chief Financial Officer, Southwestern Regional Medical Center, Tulsa, OK, p. A570

HEDLUND, Chris, Director Information Systems, Community Hospital-Fairfax, Fairfax, MO, p. A406

HEDRIX, Michael D., Administrator and President, Essentia Health Sandstone, Sandstone, MN, p. A385

HEEMANN, John, Vice President and Chief Information Officer, Aspire Hospital, Conroe, TX, p. A665

HEETER, Colleen, R.N., Chief Executive Officer, Campbell County Health, Gillette, WY, p. A802

HEFFERNAN, Paul, Vice President Human Resources, Women & Infants Hospital Of Rhode Island, Providence, RI, p. A614

HEFFERNAN, Rebecca, Director Human Resources, Metrowest Medical Center, Framingham, MA, p. A339

HEFFERS, Margaret, Assistant Vice President Human Resources, Geisinger Wyoming Valley Medical Center, Wilkes Barre, PA, p. A611

HEFFLINGER, Larry, Chief Information Officer, Fulton County Health Center, Wauseon, OH, p. A552

HEFLIN, Clyde, M.D., Chief Medical Officer, Curahealth Nashville, Nashville, TN, p. A646

HEFLIN, Erick, R.N., Chief Executive Officer, Okc-Amg Specialty Hospital, Oklahoma City, OK, p. A565

HEFNER, Donna J., R.N., President and Chief Executive Officer, Sierra View Medical Center, Porterville, CA, p. A86

HEFNER, Katherine, MSN, Chief Nursing Officer, St. Luke's Hospital, Columbus, NC, p. A508

HEFNER, Kathy, Chief Nursing Officer, Mcdowell Hospital, Marion, NC, p. A514

HEGGEM, Mark, M.D., Chief Medical Officer, Riverwood Healthcare Center, Aitkin, MN, p. A371

HEGGEN, Steve, Administrative Director Human Resources, St. Josep. Hospital, Fort Wayne, IN, p. A228

HEGGER, John, Director Information Systems, Union County Hospital, Anna, IL, p. A194

HEGLAND, Larry, M.D., Chief Medical Officer, Decatur Memorial Hospital, Decatur, IL, p. A202

HEGSTROM, Michael, M.D., Chief Medical Officer, Geisinger-Lewistown Hospital, Lewistown, PA, p. A595

HEICHERT, Susan, Chief Information Officer, Mercy Hospital, Coon Rapids, MN, p. A374
Senior Vice President and Chief Information Officer, Abbott Northwestern Hospital, Minneapolis, MN, p. A380
Senior Vice President, United Hospital, Saint Paul, MN, p. A385

HEIDT, Robert, Director Information Systems, Pembina County Memorial Hospital And Wedgewood Manor, Cavalier, ND, p. A522

HEIFNER, Bruce, Chief Financial Officer, Pella Regional Health Center, Pella, IA, p. A256

HEIKKINEN, Todd, Manager Sports Medicine and Rehabilitation Services, Orthopaedic Hospital Of Wisconsin, Glendale, WI, p. A784

HEILMAN, Brooke, Chief Financial Officer, Bowdle Hospital, Bowdle, SD, p. A626

HEIM, Chad, Management Information System Director, Lifestream Behavioral Center, Leesburg, FL, p. A144

HEIM, Nicole, Chief Information Officer, Milford Regional Medical Center, Milford, MA, p. A341

HEIM, Richard, President, Advocate Christ Medical Center, Oak Lawn, IL, p. A215

HEIMAN, Thomas, Vice President Information Services and Chief Information Officer, Mather Hospital, Port Jefferson, NY, p. A495

HEIMBECHER, Catherine, Chief Executive Officer, Select Specialty Hospital-Madison, Madison, WI, p. A787

HEIN, Janet, Chief Executive Officer, Encompass Health Rehabilitation Hospital Of Erie, Erie, PA, p. A589

HEIN, Jodi, Chief Nursing Officer, Providence Holy Cross Medical Center, Mission Hills, CA, p. A78

HEINE, Ann, Chief Executive Officer, Surgical Specialty Center Of Baton Rouge, Baton Rouge, LA, p. A297

HEINEMANN, Don, Administrator and Chief Executive Officer, Blount Memorial Hospital, Maryville, TN, p. A643

HEINEMEIER, Robert, Interim Chief Financial Officer, Sonoma West Medical Center, Sebastopol, CA, p. A98

HEINISCH, Sheri, Compliance Officer, Chi Lisbon Health, Lisbon, ND, p. A525

HEINRICH, Bill, Chief Financial Officer, Adventhealth Zephyrhills, Zephyrhills, FL, p. A162

HEINRICH, Caleb, Chief Financial Officer, Adventhealth North Pinellas, Tarpon Springs, FL, p. A160

HEINRICH, Kerry, JD, Chief Executive Officer, Loma Linda University Children's Hospital, Loma Linda, CA, p. A71
JD, Chief Executive Officer, Loma Linda University Medical Center, Loma Linda, CA, p. A72

HEINRICH, Michael, Senior Vice President and Chief Financial Officer, Unitypoint Health - St. Luke's Hospital, Cedar Rapids, IA, p. A245

HEINRICH, Michelle, Ph.D., MS, R.N., Chief Executive Officer and Chief Nursing Officer, Se Texas Er & Hospital, Humble, TX, p. A690

HEINRICHS, Alice, CPA, Chief Financial Officer, Van Diest Medical Center, Webster City, IA, p. A260

HEINRICHS, Leann, M.D., Chief of Staff, Thayer County Health Services, Hebron, NE, p. A433

HEINS, Patrick, President, Vidant Edgecombe Hospital, Tarboro, NC, p. A519

HEINSOHN, Carmel, M.D., Medical Director, Bournewood Health Systems, Brookline, MA, p. A337

HEINZMAN, Jerry, Senior Vice President and Chief Financial Officer, Sampson Regional Medical Center, Clinton, NC, p. A507

HEINZMANN, Bill, Director Human Resources, Texoma Medical Center, Denison, TX, p. A671

HEISE, James, Chief Medical Officer, Door County Medical Center, Sturgeon Bay, WI, p. A797

HEISE, Teresa, Coordinator Management Information Systems, Pender Community Hospital, Pender, NE, p. A439

HEISEL, Diane, Acting Director, Center For Forensic Psychiatry, Saline, MI, p. A366

HEISER, Eric, Chief Information Resource Management, Sioux Falls Veterans Affairs Health Care System, Sioux Falls, SD, p. A632

HEISMEYER, Joyce, Chief Operating Officer, Kansas Heart Hospital, Wichita, KS, p. A278

HEISSER, Randy, M.D., Medical Director, Kindred Hospital-Chattanooga, Chattanooga, TN, p. A635

HEIT, Ryan, Chief Financial Officer, Northern Nevada Medical Center, Sparks, NV, p. A446

HEITHAUS, Carolyn, Chief Financial Officer, Calverthealth Medical Center, Prince Frederick, MD, p. A331

HEITMEYER, Paulette, Administrator and Chief Operating Officer, Marina Del Rey Hospital, Marina Del Rey, CA, p. A77

HEITZMAN, Cynthia, R.N., Chief Nursing Officer, Seven Rivers Regional Medical Center, Crystal River, FL, p. A135

HELD, Jeffrey, M.D., Vice President, Medical Affairs, Penn State Health St. Joseph, Reading, PA, p. A606

HELDT, Katie, Chief Nursing Officer, Greene County Medical Center, Jefferson, IA, p. A252

HELFER, Cassandra, Chief Financial Officer, Ralp. H. Johnson Veterans Affairs Medical Center, Charleston, SC, p. A616

HELGESEN, Roald, Chief Executive Officer, Alaska Native Medical Center, Anchorage, AK, p. A27

HELGESON, Heidi, M.D., Chief Medical Officer, Rio Grande Hospital, Del Norte, CO, p. A110

HELGET, Peggy, R.N., MSN, Vice President Patient Services and Chief Nursing Officer, Methodist Jennie Edmundson Hospital, Council Bluffs, IA, p. A247

HELLA, Timothy, Chief Information Officer, Munson Healthcare Otsego Memorial Hospital, Gaylord, MI, p. A355

HELLAND, Don, M.D., Chief Medical Officer, Roosevelt Medical Center, Culbertson, MT, p. A422

HELLE, Dan, Human Resources Officer, Iowa City Va Health Care System, Iowa City, IA, p. A252

HELLE, Tara, Human Resources Lead, Palo Alto County Health System, Emmetsburg, IA, p. A249

HELLELAND, Brian, Chief Executive Officer, St. Jude Medical Center, Fullerton, CA, p. A66

HELLER, Michael, Chief Financial Officer, Lecom Corry Memorial Hospital, Corry, PA, p. A587

HELLER, Tom, Vice President Operations and Human Resources, Camden Clark Medical Center, Parkersburg, WV, p. A775

HELLINGER, Jeffrey, Chief Financial Officer, Lewis County General Hospital, Lowville, NY, p. A487

HELM, Carrie, Chief Executive Officer, Arkansas Surgical Hospital, North Little Rock, AR, p. A51

HELM, Pamela E., Executive Director, Devereux Texas Treatment Network, League City, TX, p. A695

HELMERS, Richard, M.D., Regional Vice President, Mayo Clinic Health System - Chippewa Valley In Bloomer, Bloomer, WI, p. A781
M.D., Regional Vice President, Mayo Clinic Health System - Northland In Barron, Barron, WI, p. A781
M.D., Regional Vice President, Mayo Clinic Health System - Oakridge In Osseo, Osseo, WI, p. A793
M.D., Regional Vice President, Mayo Clinic Health System - Red Cedar In Menomonie, Menomonie, WI, p. A789

M.D., Regional Vice President, Mayo Clinic Health System In Eau Claire, Eau Claire, WI, p. A783

HELMES, Claudia, R.N., Chief Nursing Officer, Banner Lassen Medical Center, Susanville, CA, p. A100

HELMICKI, Soni, Chief Executive Officer, Wellbridge Healthcare Of Fort Worth, Fort Worth, TX, p. A679

HELMS, Ella Raye., Chief Executive Officer, Cogdell Memorial Hospital, Snyder, TX, p. A716

HELMS, James, Vice President Finance and Chief Financial Officer, Jones Memorial Hospital, Wellsville, NY, p. A502

HELMS, Joseph, Director Information Systems, Dekalb Regional Medical Center, Fort Payne, AL, p. A19

HELPER, Mark, Corporate Vice President and Chief Financial Officer, Munson Medical Center, Traverse City, MI, p. A368

HELSEL, David S., M.D., Chief Executive Officer, Spring Grove Hospital Center, Baltimore, MD, p. A326

HELSEL, Elizabeth, Chief Executive Officer, U. S. Public Health Service Indian Hospital, Parker, AZ, p. A34

HELSPER, Richard, Chief Operating Officer, Genesis Healthcare System, Zanesville, OH, p. A554

HELSTROM, James, Chief Medical Officer, Fox Chase Cancer Center-American Oncologic Hospital, Philadelphia, PA, p. A600

HELTON, Fay, Director Medical Records, Red River Hospital, Llc, Wichita Falls, TX, p. A725

HELTON, R.J, D.O., Chief of Staff, Coal County General Hospital, Coalgate, OK, p. A558

HELTON, Stephanie, Chief Financial Officer, Weatherford Regional Hospital, Weatherford, OK, p. A572

HELVEY, John, Chief Information Officer, Orchard Hospital, Gridley, CA, p. A67

HEMANN, Randy, M.D., Chief Medical Officer, Olmsted Medical Center, Rochester, MN, p. A384

HEMATILLAKE, M., M.D., Chief of Staff, White River Junction Veterans Affairs Medical Center, White River Junction, VT, p. A737

HEMBREE, Greg, Senior Vice President and Chief Financial Officer, St. Francis Hospital, Columbus, GA, p. A169

HEMKER, Debbie, Senior Vice President and Area Manager, Kaiser Permanente Fresno Medical Center, Fresno, CA, p. A65

HEMMER, Chris, Director Finance, Aurora West Allis Medical Center, West Allis, WI, p. A799

HEMPEL, Stephen, M.D., President Medical Staff, Spectrum Health Lakeland, Saint Joseph, MI, p. A366

HEMPHILL, Dana, Manager Human Resources, Shoshone Medical Center, Kellogg, ID, p. A191

HEMPHILL, Robyn, Chief Executive Officer and Chief Nursing Officer, Monroe Surgical Hospital, Monroe, LA, p. A309

HEMPLER, Shannan, Director Human Resources, Norton County Hospital, Norton, KS, p. A272

HEMSATH, Randolph, M.D., Medical Director, Suncoast Behavioral Health Center, Bradenton, FL, p. A133

HENDEL, Dawna, R.N., Chief Nursing Officer and Vice President Patient Care Services, Providence Saint John's Health Center, Santa Monica, CA, p. A97

HENDERSHOT, Richard, Chief Financial Officer, Casey County Hospital, Liberty, KY, p. A287
Chief Financial Officer, Jane Todd Crawford Hospital, Greensburg, KY, p. A284

HENDERSON, Claudia, Chief Human Resources, St. Elizabeth's Medical Center, Brighton, MA, p. A337

HENDERSON, David, M.D., Deputy Director Clinical Care, National Institutes Of Health Clinical Center, Bethesda, MD, p. A327
Director Human Resources, Summersville Regional Medical Center, Summersville, WV, p. A777

HENDERSON, Deborah, Acting Chief Financial Officer, Harry S. Truman Memorial Veterans Hospital, Columbia, MO, p. A405

HENDERSON, Donald G., FACHE, President and Chief Executive Officer, Leesburg Regional Medical Center, Leesburg, FL, p. A144
FACHE, President and Chief Executive Officer, The Villages Regional Hospital, The Villages, FL, p. A160

HENDERSON, Gary, Chief Information Resources Management Services, Huntington Veterans Affairs Medical Center, Huntington, WV, p. A773

HENDERSON, Jace, Chief Financial Officer, Parkview Hospital, Wheeler, TX, p. A725

HENDERSON, Jessica, Manager Human Resources, Fitzgibbon Hospital, Marshall, MO, p. A411

HENDERSON, John, M.D., Chief Medical Officer, Unity Health White County Medical Center, Searcy, AR, p. A52
Chief Human Resources Management, James H. Quillen Veterans Affairs Medical Center, Mountain Home, TN, p. A646
Chief Information Officer, Choc Children's At Mission Hospital, Mission Viejo, CA, p. A78
Vice President and Chief Information Officer, Children's Hospital Of Orange County, Orange, CA, p. A83

HENDERSON, Katherine, Regional Hospital President, Ascension Seton Hays, Kyle, TX, p. A694
Regional Hospital President, Ascension Seton Northwest, Austin, TX, p. A655
Regional Hospital President, Ascension Seton Southwest, Austin, TX, p. A655
Regional Hospital President, Ascension Seton Williamson, Round Rock, TX, p. A709

HENDERSON, Kathy, Director Human Resources, Willow Crest Hospital, Miami, OK, p. A562

HENDERSON, Lisa, Chief Operating Officer, Palacios Community Medical Center, Palacios, TX, p. A704
Chief Operations Officer, Palacios Community Medical Center, Palacios, TX, p. A704

HENDERSON, Lori, Chief Nursing Officer, Vice President Clinical, Colorado Canyons Hospital And Medical Center, Fruita, CO, p. A113

HENDERSON, Melody, Ph.D., R.N., Chief Operating Officer and Chief Nursing Officer, Golden Plains Community Hospital, Borger, TX, p. A660

HENDERSON, Mike, Human Resources Director, Forest View Psychiatric Hospital, Grand Rapids, MI, p. A355

HENDERSON, Pamela, Vice President Human Resources, Memorial Hospital Of Carbondale, Carbondale, IL, p. A196

HENDERSON, Patricia, R.N., Interim Chief Executive Officer, Glencoe Regional Health, Glencoe, MN, p. A377
R.N., Vice President Nursing and Clinical Services, Glencoe Regional Health, Glencoe, MN, p. A377

HENDERSON, Paula, Chief Human Resources Officer, University Of Mississipp. Medical Center, Jackson, MS, p. A395
Vice President Human Resources, University Of Maryland Medical Center Midtown Campus, Baltimore, MD, p. A326
Vice President Human Resources, University Of Maryland Rehabilitation & Orthopaedic Institute, Baltimore, MD, p. A327

HENDERSON, Peggy, Director Health Information, Rmc-Stringfellow Memorial Hospital, Anniston, AL, p. A13

HENDERSON, Rex, M.D., Chief of Staff, Mcdowell Hospital, Marion, NC, p. A514

HENDERSON, Sue, Human Resource Manager, Smyth County Community Hospital, Marion, VA, p. A745

HENDERSON, Travis, M.D., Chief of Staff, Mobridge Regional Hospital, Mobridge, SD, p. A629

HENDERSON, Vickie, M.D., Chief Medical Officer, Saint Mary's Regional Medical Center, Russellville, AR, p. A52

HENDERSON, Volante, Director Human Resources, Walton Rehabilitation Hospital, Augusta, GA, p. A166

HENDREN, Ken, Chief Financial Officer, Brookwood Baptist Medical Center, Birmingham, AL, p. A14

HENDRICK, Kirk, Director Information Systems, Northside Hospital, Saint Petersburg, FL, p. A156

HENDRICKS, Marcia, FACHE, R.N., Chief Executive Officer, Adair County Health System, Greenfield, IA, p. A250
FACHE, R.N., Chief Executive Officer, Madison County Health Care System, Winterset, IA, p. A260

HENDRICKS, Nicole, Chief Operating Officer, Regional Medical Center, Orangeburg, SC, p. A623

HENDRICKSEN, Sherry, R.N., MSN, Chief Nursing Officer, Continuecare Hospital At Hendrick Medical Center, Abilene, TX, p. A651

HENDRICKSON, Leslie, Director Human Resources, Coteau Des Prairies Hospital, Sisseton, SD, p. A632

HENDRICKSON, Roman, M.D., Medical Director, Ruby Valley Medical Center, Sheridan, MT, p. A428

HENDRIX, Angie, Director of Nursing, Evergreen Medical Center, Evergreen, AL, p. A18

HENDRIX, Billie, R.N., Director of Nursing, W. J. Mangold Memorial Hospital, Lockney, TX, p. A696

HENDRIX, Jamie, Vice President Patient Care Services, Prairie Ridge Health, Inc., Columbus, WI, p. A782

HENDRIX, Michael, Chief Financial Officer, St. Josep. Hospital, Bangor, ME, p. A318
Chief Financial Officer, St. Mary's Regional Medical Center, Lewiston, ME, p. A321

HENDRIXSON, Mark, M.D., Chief Medical Officer, Jamestown Regional Medical Center, Jamestown, TN, p. A640

HENDRY, Christopher, M.D., Chief Medical Officer, Medical Center, Navicent Health, Macon, GA, p. A176

HENDRYX, Joel, M.D., Chief Medical Officer, University Medical Center Of El Paso, El Paso, TX, p. A676

HENES, Jean, MSN, R.N., Director of Nursing, Avera Creighton Hospital, Creighton, NE, p. A431

HENESSEE, Nolan, Vice President and Chief Information Officer, St. Joseph's Hospital, Savannah, GA, p. A180

HENGER, Robert, Chief Executive Officer, Northwest Medical Center, Winfield, AL, p. A26

HENINGER, Bev, Director of Nursing, Kenmare Community Hospital, Kenmare, ND, p. A524

HENKE, Georgia, Operational Account Manager, Osf Healthcare Saint Anthony's Health Center, Alton, IL, p. A194

HENKE, Mark, Chief Financial Officer, Mena Regional Health System, Mena, AR, p. A50

HENKENIUS, Jim, Chief Financial Officer, Stewart Memorial Community Hospital, Lake City, IA, p. A253

HENNEBOLD, Julie, R.N., Interim Chief Nursing Officer, Winner Regional Healthcare Center, Winner, SD, p. A633

HENNELLY, John, Chief Executive Officer, St. Louise Regional Hospital, Gilroy, CA, p. A66

HENNENBERG, Shayla, Director Human Resources, Essentia Health-Ada, Ada, MN, p. A371

HENNESSEY, Ruth E, President, Good Samaritan Hospital Medical Center, West Islip, NY, p. A502

HENNESSY, John, Chief Financial Officer, Bonner General Health, Sandpoint, ID, p. A193

HENNIGAN, Michael, M.D., Medical Director, Encompass Health Rehabilitation Hospital Of Panama City, Panama City, FL, p. A153

HENNIKA, Billi Jo, Vice President Operations, Mckenzie Health System, Sandusky, MI, p. A366

HENNING, Cindy, R.N., Chief Nursing Officer, Hca Houston Healthcare Northwest, Houston, TX, p. A685

HENNING, William C., Administrator and Chief Executive Officer, Baptist Memorial Hospital-North Mississippi, Oxford, MS, p. A398

HENNIS, Michelle, Administrative Director Financial Services, Grace Hospital, Cleveland, OH, p. A534

HENRICI, Michael, Associate Administrator, Roxborough Memorial Hospital, Philadelphia, PA, p. A601

HENRICKS, William, Ph.D., Vice President and Chief Operating Officer, Ascension Seton Shoal Creek, Austin, TX, p. A655

HENRY, Andrea, Director of Nursing, Sweetwater Hospital, Sweetwater, TN, p. A650

HENRY, Anna, Chief Information Officer, Kimble Hospital, Junction, TX, p. A691

HENRY, Chris, Associate Administrator and Chief Financial Officer, Washington Hospital Healthcare System, Fremont, CA, p. A65

HENRY, Dane W., FACHE, Chief Executive Officer, Lake Regional Health System, Osage Beach, MO, p. A413

HENRY, David, President and Chief Executive Officer, Northern Montana Health Care, Havre, MT, p. A425

HENRY, Debbie, Vice President and Chief Financial Officer, Baxter Regional Medical Center, Mountain Home, AR, p. A50

HENRY, Donna, Vice President of Nursing Services, Four County Counseling Center, Logansport, IN, p. A235

HENRY, Edwina, Assistant Chief Nursing Officer, Parkview Regional Hospital, Mexia, TX, p. A701

HENRY, Hannah, Interim Vice President of Human Resources, Emory Johns Creek Hospital, Johns Creek, GA, p. A174

HENRY, Heather, Information Technology Manager, Hammond-Henry Hospital, Geneseo, IL, p. A205

HENRY, James, Director Human Resources, Sea Pines Rehabilitation Hospital, Melbourne, FL, p. A145

HENRY, Joy, R.N., Chief of Nursing, Faith Community Hospital, Jacksboro, TX, p. A691

HENRY, Joyce, Controller, Encompass Health Rehabilitation Hospital Of York, York, PA, p. A612

HENRY, Kelsea, Chief Financial Officer, Memorial Regional Health, Craig, CO, p. A110

HENRY, Peter, M.D., Chief Medical Officer, Essentia Health-St. Joseph's Medical Center, Brainerd, MN, p. A373

HENRY, Roshonda, Chief Nursing Officer, Encompass Health Rehabilitation Hospital Of Cypress, Houston, TX, p. A685

HENRY, Tim, Accountant, Chatuge Regional Hospital And Nursing Home, Hiawassee, GA, p. A173

HENRY, William, Director Human Resources, Ut Health Henderson, Henderson, TX, p. A683

Director Human Resources, Ut Health Quitman, Quitman, TX, p. A708

HENSEL, David, Director Financial Operations, Ohiohealth Grady Memorial Hospital, Delaware, OH, p. A539

HENSEL, Edward, Chief Information Officer, Va Medical Center, Tomah, WI, p. A797

HENSLEE, Maureen, Chief Financial Officer, Lower Keys Medical Center, Key West, FL, p. A142

HENSLEIGH, David, Director Medical Staff, Clay County Hospital, Ashland, AL, p. A14

HENSLEY, Angela, Director of Nursing, Pathways Of Tennessee, Jackson, TN, p. A639

HENSLEY, Anna, Chief Operating Officer, Ohiohealth Dublin Methodist Hospital, Dublin, OH, p. A539

Chief Operating Officer, Ohiohealth Grady Memorial Hospital, Delaware, OH, p. A539

HENSLEY, Barry, Director Information Systems, Logan Regional Medical Center, Logan, WV, p. A774

HENSLEY, Kristy, Director Human Resources, Orthoindy Hospital, Indianapolis, IN, p. A232

HENSON, Judith, Vice President Patient Care Services, Southeast Georgia Health System Brunswick Campus, Brunswick, GA, p. A167

Vice President, Patient Care Services, Southeast Georgia Health System Camden Campus, Saint Marys, GA, p. A179

HENSON, Lily, M.D., Chief Executive Officer, Piedmont Henry Hospital, Stockbridge, GA, p. A181

HENSON, Maureen, Vice President Human Resources, Monument Health Rapid City Hospital, Rapid City, SD, p. A630

HENSON, Pam, Executive Director, Pathways Of Tennessee, Jackson, TN, p. A639

HENSON, Steve, Chief Executive Officer, Bradley County Medical Center, Warren, AR, p. A54

HENTON, Thomas, Chief Executive Officer, Carnegie Tri-County Municipal Hospital, Carnegie, OK, p. A557

HENTZEN PAGE, Ann, M.D., Chief Executive Officer, Summit Surgical, Hutchinson, KS, p. A267

M.D., Medical Director, Summit Surgical, Hutchinson, KS, p. A267

HENZE, Rick, Chief Financial Officer, St. Mary's Healthcare, Amsterdam, NY, p. A474

HEPNER, Tim, M.D., Chief Medical Officer, St. John Owasso, Owasso, OK, p. A566

HERALD, Kathleen, Vice President and Chief Information Officer, Lexington Medical Center, West Columbia, SC, p. A625

HERB, Beth, Administrator, State Correctional Institution At Camp Hill, Camp Hill, PA, p. A586

HERBECK, Marilyn, Coordinator Human Resources, Community Hospital Of Staunton, Staunton, IL, p. A221

HERBEL, Aaron, Administrator, Mercy Hospital Inc., Moundridge, KS, p. A271

HERBER, Steven, M.D., FACS, President and Chief Executive Officer, Adventist Health St. Helena, Saint Helena, CA, p. A90

M.D., FACS, President and Chief Executive Officer, Adventist Health St. Helena, Vallejo, CA, p. A103

HERBERGER, Eva, Administrator Human Resources, Usc Verdugo Hills Hospital, Glendale, CA, p. A67

HERBERT, Daniel, M.D., Medical Administrative Officer, Millinocket Regional Hospital, Millinocket, ME, p. A321

HERBERT, Laurie, Vice President Operations, Three Rivers Health, Three Rivers, MI, p. A368

HERBERT, Teresa, M.D., Chief Medical Officer, Adventhealth Hendersonville, Hendersonville, NC, p. A512

HERBOLD, Charlotte, Manager Business Officer, Garfield County Health Center, Jordan, MT, p. A425

HERBST, Gary K., Chief Executive Officer, Kaweah Delta Medical Center, Visalia, CA, p. A104

HERD, Jacqueline, Executive Vice President and Chief Nursing Officer, Grady Memorial Hospital, Atlanta, GA, p. A164

HERDELIN, Jeffrey, Vice President Human Resources, Kindred Hospital Indianapolis North, Indianapolis, IN, p. A232

HERDER, Debbie, Controller, Kp. Promise Hospital Of Wichita Falls, Wichita Falls, TX, p. A725

HERFORT, Oliver, M.D., Chief Medical Officer, Valley Regional Hospital, Claremont, NH, p. A448

HERGET, Jordan, Chief Executive Officer, Portneuf Medical Center, Pocatello, ID, p. A192

HERING, John, M.D., Administrator, Centracare - Monticello, Monticello, MN, p. A381

HERING, Kristine, R.N., Chief Nursing Officer, Speare Memorial Hospital, Plymouth, NH, p. A451

HERINK, Philip, Administrator, Schick Shadel Hospital, Seattle, WA, p. A763

HERKIMER, Eileen, Director Human Resources, United Memorial Medical Center, Batavia, NY, p. A475

HERMAN, Jeff, Chief Executive Officer, Prairie St. John's, Fargo, ND, p. A523

HERMAN, Michael, Chief Executive Officer, Riverview Regional Medical Center, Carthage, TN, p. A635

Chief Executive Officer, Trousdale Medical Center, Hartsville, TN, p. A639

HERMAN, Susan, MSN, R.N., Chief Nursing Officer, Long Beach Medical Center, Long Beach, CA, p. A72

HERMANN, Terri, R.N., Chief Nursing Officer, Franklin Hospital District, Benton, IL, p. A195

HERMES, Cliff, Administrator, Oceans Behavioral Hospital Biloxi, Biloxi, MS, p. A389

HERMES, Dina, Chief Financial Officer, Golden Plains Community Hospital, Borger, TX, p. A660

HERMOSA, Mercy, Director of Information System, Coral Gables Hospital, Coral Gables, FL, p. A135

HERNANDEZ, Ashley, Chief Information Technology Officer, Pender Memorial Hospital, Burgaw, NC, p. A505

HERNANDEZ, Carmelo, M.D., Chief Medical Officer, San Luis Valley Health, Alamosa, CO, p. A107

HERNANDEZ, Debra T., R.N., FACHE, President, Vidant Beaufort Hospital, Washington, NC, p. A519

HERNANDEZ, Dennis, Chief Executive Officer, Adventhealth New Smyrna Beach, New Smyrna Beach, FL, p. A149

Chief Medical Officer, Adventhealth New Smyrna Beach, New Smyrna Beach, FL, p. A149

HERNANDEZ, Diane, Area Finance Officer, Kaiser Permanente San Rafael Medical Center, San Rafael, CA, p. A96

Area Finance Officer, Kaiser Permanente Santa Rosa Medical Center, Santa Rosa, CA, p. A98

HERNANDEZ, Dinorah, Executive Director, Hospital Pavia Yauco, Yauco, PR, p. A811

HERNANDEZ, George B. Jr, President and Chief Executive Officer, University Health System, San Antonio, TX, p. A714

HERNANDEZ, Gloria, Executive Director, University Pediatric Hospital, Rio Piedras, PR, p. A809

HERNANDEZ, Holly, Chief Financial Officer, Newport News Behavioral Health Center, Newport News, VA, p. A747

HERNANDEZ, Jalima, Chief Financial Officer, Aventura Hospital And Medical Center, Aventura, FL, p. A131

HERNANDEZ, Janira, Coordinator Human Resources, Hospital Metropolitano Dr. Susoni, Arecibo, PR, p. A806

HERNANDEZ, Joseph, M.D., Medical Director, San Antonio Behavioral Healthcare Hospital, San Antonio, TX, p. A713

HERNANDEZ, Kim, Chief Human Resources Officer, Sage Specialty Hospital (Ltac), Denham Springs, LA, p. A301

HERNANDEZ, Kristen, Director Human Resources, Encompass Health Rehabilitation Hospital Of Albuquerque, Albuquerque, NM, p. A467

HERNANDEZ, Leonard, Chief Executive Officer, Coffey County Hospital, Burlington, KS, p. A262

HERNANDEZ, Lilly, Human Resources Director, Catalina Island Medical Center, Avalon, CA, p. A56

HERNANDEZ, Luz, Director Human Resources, I. Gonzalez Martinez Oncologic Hospital, Hato Rey, PR, p. A808

HERNANDEZ, Mark, M.D., President Medical Staff, Baptist Health South Florida, Homestead Hospital, Homestead, FL, p. A140

HERNANDEZ, Matt, Director of Information Technology and System, Kendall Regional Medical Center, Miami, FL, p. A146

HERNANDEZ, Reyna, Chief Financial Officer, Encompass Health Rehabilitation Hospital Of Miami, Cutler Bay, FL, p. A135

HERNANDEZ, Susan, R.N., Chief Nurse Executive, University Of Texas Southwestern Medical Center, Dallas, TX, p. A671

R.N., Chief Nursing Officer, Rice Medical Center, Eagle Lake, TX, p. A673

HERNANDEZ-KEEBLE, Sonia, Superintendent, Rio Grande State Center/South Texas Health Care System, Harlingen, TX, p. A683

HERNANDEZ-LICHTL, Javier, Chief Executive Officer, Baptist Health South Florida, Doctors Hospital, Coral Gables, FL, p. A135

HERNDON, Amy, Chief Finance Officer, Morristown-Hamblen Healthcare System, Morristown, TN, p. A645

HERNDON, Lori S., R.N., President and Chief Executive Officer, Atlanticare Regional Medical Center, Atlantic City, NJ, p. A452

HERNDON, Robert, Chief Financial Officer, Ascension Seton Shoal Creek, Austin, TX, p. A655

Vice President Chief Financial Officer, Ascension Seton Medical Center Austin, Austin, TX, p. A654

HERNDON, Sandra, CPA, Chief Financial Officer, Bleckley Memorial Hospital, Cochran, GA, p. A169

HERNDON, Scott, FACHE, Chief Financial Officer, Ministry Market Texas, Dell Seton Medical Center At The University Of Texas, Austin, TX, p. A656

FACHE, Chief Financial Officer, Texas Market, Ascension Seton Northwest, Austin, TX, p. A655

HERNE, Mose, Chief Executive Officer, Hop. Health Care Center, Keams Canyon, AZ, p. A33

HEROD, Andrew, Chief Executive Officer, Willow Springs Center, Reno, NV, p. A446

HEROLD, Mary, Director Human Resources, Share Medical Center, Alva, OK, p. A555

HERPFER, Caroline, Chief Nursing Officer, Arizona Orthopedic Surgical Hospital, Chandler, AZ, p. A30

HERR, Brenda, Chief Nursing Officer, East Adams Rural Healthcare, Ritzville, WA, p. A763

HERR, Michael, Chief Operating Officer, Starr Regional Medical Center, Athens, TN, p. A634

HERRARA, Espie, Chief Financial Officer, Peak Behavioral Health Services, Santa Teresa, NM, p. A472

HERRERA, Jocelyn, Director Human Resources, Kaiser Permanente Orange County Anaheim Medical Center, Anaheim, CA, p. A55

Human Resources Director, Kaiser Permanente San Diego Medical Center, San Diego, CA, p. A91

HERRERA, Veronica, Director Human Resources, Las Encinas Hospital, Pasadena, CA, p. A85

HERRERA, Yamila, Director Human Resources, Hialeah Hospital, Hialeah, FL, p. A139

HERRERO, Carmelo, M.D., Medical Director, Hospital Oriente, Humacao, PR, p. A808

HERRICK, Brian, M.D., Chief Information Officer, Cambridge Health Alliance, Cambridge, MA, p. A337

HERRING, Davey, M.D., Chief Medical Officer, Dorminy Medical Center, Fitzgerald, GA, p. A172

HERRING, Randy, M.D., Chief of Staff, Coon Memorial Hospital, Dalhart, TX, p. A667

HERRING, Sherry, Chief Nursing Officer, Uva Encompass Health Rehabilitation Hospital, Charlottesville, VA, p. A740

HERRINGTON, Bruce, M.D., Chief Medical Officer, South Georgia Medical Center Lanier Campus, Lakeland, GA, p. A175

HERRINGTON, Kristal, Senior Director, Human Resources, Twin County Regional Healthcare, Galax, VA, p. A743

HERRMAN, Edward, R.N., FACHE, President and Chief Executive Officer, Hays Medical Center, Hays, KS, p. A265

HERRMANN, Lee, Chief Healthcare Technology Officer, Santa Clara Valley Medical Center, San Jose, CA, p. A95

HERRMANN, Tim, R.N., Administrator, Peacehealth Cottage Grove Community Medical Center, Cottage Grove, OR, p. A574

HERRON, Katherine, Director Human Resources, Richard H. Hutchings Psychiatric Center, Syracuse, NY, p. A499

HERRON, Mary Beth, Director of Human Resources, Illinois Valley Community Hospital, Peru, IL, p. A217

HERSEN, Jon, President, Legacy Salmon Creek Medical Center, Vancouver, WA, p. A768

HERSEY, Robert, Chief Financial Officer, Northeastern Vermont Regional Hospital, Saint Johnsbury, VT, p. A736

HERSHBERGER, Brandy, Chief Nursing Officer, Fawcett Memorial Hospital, Port Charlotte, FL, p. A155

HERSHBERGER, Scott, Acting Chief Information Management Services, Battle Creek Veterans Affairs Medical Center, Battle Creek, MI, p. A349

HERSHMAN, Sharon, R.N., Chief Nursing Officer, Providence Holy Family Hospital, Spokane, WA, p. A766

HERSHMANN, Michael, Medical Center Director, Veterans Affairs Northern Indiana Health Care System, Fort Wayne, IN, p. A229

HERTEL, Holly, Director Nursing, Larned State Hospital, Larned, KS, p. A268

HERTZ, Karl, Assistant Administrator, Memorial Hospital Of Converse County, Douglas, WY, p. A802

HERWIG, Brian J., President and Chief Executive Officer, Perry County Memorial Hospital, Tell City, IN, p. A241

HERZBERG, Deborah L., R.N., MS, FACHE, Administrator, Avera Holy Family Hospital, Estherville, IA, p. A249

HERZL-BETZ, Kenneth, M.D., Chief Medical Officer, Arnot Ogden Medical Center, Elmira, NY, p. A483

HERZOG, Dean, Chief Financial Officer, Kona Community Hospital, Kealakekua, HI, p. A186

HERZOG, Vearnail, Chief Executive Officer, Allegiance Specialty Hospital Of Greenville, Greenville, MS, p. A392

HESCH, Dennis, Executive Vice President Finance, System Chief Financial Officer, Carle Foundation Hospital, Urbana, IL, p. A221

HESKETT, Patrick, Director, Information Technology, Promedica Bixby Hospital, Adrian, MI, p. A348
Director, Information Technology, Promedica Herrick Hospital, Tecumseh, MI, p. A368

HESLEP, Marchelle, Human Resources Director, Perry County Memorial Hospital, Tell City, IN, p. A241

HESMAN, Tasha, R.N., Senior Executive, Patient Care Services, Beatrice Community Hospital And Health Center, Beatrice, NE, p. A430

HESS, David, M.D., President Medical Staff, Reynolds Memorial Hospital, Glen Dale, WV, p. A772

HESS, David F., M.D., Chief Executive Officer, Reynolds Memorial Hospital, Glen Dale, WV, p. A772
M.D., Chief Executive Officer, Wetzel County Hospital, New Martinsville, WV, p. A775

HESS, Heidi, Chief Nursing Officer, Genesis Medical Center-Aledo, Aledo, IL, p. A194

HESS, Jim, Chief Executive Officer, Highland Ridge Hospital, Midvale, UT, p. A728

HESS, Michael, M.D., Chief Medical Officer, Lakeview Hospital, Bountiful, UT, p. A727

HESS, Pamela, Chief Financial Officer, Saint Thomas West Hospital, Nashville, TN, p. A646

HESS, Philip. President, Wellspan Philhaven, Mount Gretna, PA, p. A597

HESS, Philip D., President, Wellspan Philhaven, Mount Gretna, PA, p. A597

HESS, Steve, Vice President & Chief Information Officer, Uchealth Medical Center Of The Rockies, Loveland, CO, p. A117
Vice President Information Services and Chief Information Officer, University Of Colorado Hospital, Aurora, CO, p. A108

HESS, Susan, Director Human Resources, Penn Highlands Huntingdon, Huntingdon, PA, p. A592

HESSE, Fred, M.D., Medical Director, Arms Acres, Carmel, NY, p. A481

HESSELRODE, Renee, Director Health Information Management, Landmark Hospital Of Cap. Girardeau, Cap. Girardeau, MO, p. A403

HESSHEIMER, Susan, Director Human Resources, Johnson County Hospital, Tecumseh, NE, p. A440

HESSING, Jeffrey, M.D., Medical Director, Treasure Valley Hospital, Boise, ID, p. A189

HESSMAN, Mary, Chief Fiscal, Northport Veterans Affairs Medical Center, Northport, NY, p. A493

HESTER, Amber, Chief Executive Officer, Encompass Health Rehabilitation Hospital Of Gulfport, Gulfport, MS, p. A393

HESTER, Charles, CPA, JrChief Financial Officer, Northwest Mississipp. Medical Center, Clarksdale, MS, p. A391

HESTER, Josh, Chief Operating Officer, Gadsden Regional Medical Center, Gadsden, AL, p. A19

HESTER, Joyce, CPA, Senior Vice President and Chief Financial Officer, Christus Mother Frances Hospital - Tyler, Tyler, TX, p. A721

HESTER, Kathy, Chief Nursing Officer, Orange Park Medical Center, Orange Park, FL, p. A150

HESTER, Michael, Chief Executive Officer, Stephens County Hospital, Toccoa, GA, p. A182

HESTON, Cathy, Chief Nursing Officer, Three Rivers Medical Center, Louisa, KY, p. A287

HETHERINGTON, Ray, Network Administrator, Wheatland Memorial Healthcare, Harlowton, MT, p. A424

HETLETVED, Beth, Director of Nurses, Chi St. Alexius Health-Garrison Memorial Hospital, Garrison, ND, p. A523

HETMANSKI, Jeff, President and Chief Operating Officer, Novant Health Uva Health System Culpeper Medical Center, Culpeper, VA, p. A740

HETT, Samantha, Manager Human Resources, Satanta District Hospital And Long Term Care, Satanta, KS, p. A276

HETTICH, E, Chief Financial Officer, Brylin Hospitals, Buffalo, NY, p. A479

HETTINGER, JoAnn, R.N., Director of Patient Care Services, Avera Weskota Memorial Hospital, Wessington Springs, SD, p. A633

HETTINGER, MaryLou, Director Quality Management, Devereux Children's Behavioral Health Center, Malvern, PA, p. A596

HETTINGER, Tiffany, Associate Chief Nursing Officer, North Colorado Medical Center, Greeley, CO, p. A113

HETU, Maureen, Chief Information Officer, Virtua Our Lady Of Lourdes Hospital, Camden, NJ, p. A453

HETZ, Mark, Chief Information Officer, Asante Ashland Community Hospital, Ashland, OR, p. A573
Chief Information Officer, Asante Rogue Regional Medical Center, Medford, OR, p. A577
Chief Information Officer, Asante Three Rivers Medical Center, Grants Pass, OR, p. A575

HEUPEL, Eric, Interim Chief Executive Officer, Ashley Medical Center, Ashley, ND, p. A521

HEURING, Ron, Director Information Systems, Perry County Memorial Hospital, Perryville, MO, p. A413

HEURTIN, John, Chief Financial Officer, Lee's Summit Medical Center, Lee's Summit, MO, p. A410

HEUSER, Keith E., Administrator, Chi Lisbon Health, Lisbon, ND, p. A525
President, Chi Mercy Health, Valley City, ND, p. A526

HEUSTON, Melanie, Chief Nursing Office, Meritus Medical Center, Hagerstown, MD, p. A330

HEWLETT, Kolton, Senior Director, Administration, Audubon County Memorial Hospital And Clinics, Audubon, IA, p. A243

HEWSTON, MaryAnn, R.N., Chief Nurse Executive, Meadville Medical Center, Meadville, PA, p. A596

HEYDON, Larry, President and Chief Executive Officer, Johnson Memorial Hospital, Franklin, IN, p. A229

HEYDON, Robert, Chief Information Officer, Madonna Rehabilitation Hospital, Omaha, NE, p. A437

HEYN, Matthew M., Chief Executive Officer, Delta County Memorial Hospital, Delta, CO, p. A110

HIATT, Tim, Chief Information Officer, Brodstone Memorial Hospital, Superior, NE, p. A440

HIBBARD, Carrie, Human Resource Business Partner, Adventist Healthcare Physical Health And Rehabilitation, Rockville, MD, p. A332

HIBSCHMAN, Kimberly, Chief Financial Officer, Conway Behavioral Health Hospital, Conway, AR, p. A43
Chief Financial Officer, Riverview Behavioral Health, Texarkana, AR, p. A53

HICK, Claire, Chief Executive Officer, Longleaf Hospital, Alexandria, LA, p. A295

HICKEY, Beth, Vice President, Finance, Advocate Lutheran General Hospital, Park Ridge, IL, p. A216

HICKEY, Christopher, Chief Financial Officer and Senior Vice President, The University Of Vermont Health Network - Alice Hyde Medical Center, Malone, NY, p. A487
Chief Financial Officer, Northwestern Medical Center, Saint Albans, VT, p. A736

HICKEY, Conner, Chief Operating Officer, Woodland Heights Medical Center, Lufkin, TX, p. A698

HICKEY, Marcia, Senior Vice President Operations, Hebrew Senior Care, West Hartford, CT, p. A126

HICKEY-BOYNTON, Meg, Chief Financial Officer, Community Hospital Of Anaconda, Anaconda, MT, p. A421
Director Human Resources and Marketing, Community Hospital Of Anaconda, Anaconda, MT, p. A421

HICKLING, Andrea, Vice President of Finance and Chief Financial Officer, Northern Regional Hospital, Mount Airy, NC, p. A515

HICKLING, Karen, Director Human Resources, Palmdale Regional Medical Center, Palmdale, CA, p. A84

HICKMAN, George, Executive Vice President and Chief Information Officer, Albany Medical Center, Albany, NY, p. A474

HICKMAN, Louise, R.N., Vice President of Patient Care Services, Jefferson Regional Medical Center, Pine Bluff, AR, p. A52

HICKMAN, Monica, Director Fiscal Services, Shriners Hospitals For Children-Spokane, Spokane, WA, p. A766

HICKMAN, Sherie C., Chief Executive Officer, Sutter Delta Medical Center, Antioch, CA, p. A56

HICKS, Christia, Vice President Human Resources, Eskenazi Health, Indianapolis, IN, p. A231

HICKS, Crystal, R.N., Chief Nursing Officer, Harrison County Community Hospital, Bethany, MO, p. A402

HICKS, Dana, Director of Nursing, Izard County Medical Center, Calico Rock, AR, p. A43

HICKS, Deborah, Senior Vice President, Chief People and Culture Officer, Dana-Farber Cancer Institute, Boston, MA, p. A335

HICKS, Janelle, R.N., Vice President Patient Services, Hocking Valley Community Hospital, Logan, OH, p. A543

HICKS, Joan, Chief Information Officer, University Of Alabama Hospital, Birmingham, AL, p. A16

HICKS, John R., President and Chief Executive Officer, Platte Valley Medical Center, Brighton, CO, p. A108

HICKS, Mary Jane, Hospital Director, William S. Hall Psychiatric Institute, Columbia, SC, p. A618

HICKS, Micah J., R.N., Chief Executive Officer, CENLA Regional, Compass Behavioral Center Of Alexandria, Alexandria, LA, p. A295

HICKS, Michael, President and Chief Executive Officer, Hshs St. Mary's Hospital, Decatur, IL, p. A202
Senior Vice President and Chief Operating Officer, Ingalls Memorial Hospital, Harvey, IL, p. A207

HICKS, Ramona, Chief Executive Officer, Coulee Medical Center, Grand Coulee, WA, p. A759

HICKS, Scott, Vice President, Clark Memorial Health, Jeffersonville, IN, p. A233

HICKS, Teresa, Chief Financial Officer, Allendale County Hospital, Fairfax, SC, p. A619

HICKS, Tim, Administrator, Muscogee Creek Nation Medical Center, Okmulgee, OK, p. A566
Administrator, Muscogee Creek Nation Physical Rehabilitation Center, Okmulgee, OK, p. A566

HICKS, William, Chief Executive Officer, Nyc Health + Hospitals / Bellevue, New York, NY, p. A491

HICKSON, Stan, FACHE, Chief Executive Officer, Johnson City Medical Center, Johnson City, TN, p. A640

HIDAY, Holly, Director Human Resources, Kalamazoo Psychiatric Hospital, Kalamazoo, MI, p. A359

HIEB, Dorothy, Director Human Resources, Sanford Chamberlain Medical Center, Chamberlain, SD, p. A627

HIEB, Laura, R.N., Chief Nursing Officer, Bellin Hospital, Green Bay, WI, p. A785

HIEBERT, Leslie, Chief Executive Officer, Klickitat Valley Health, Goldendale, WA, p. A759

HIESTAND, John, M.D., Vice President Medical Affairs, Promedica Memorial Hospital, Fremont, OH, p. A540

HIGA, Russel, JD, Regional Director Human Resources, Leahi Hospital, Honolulu, HI, p. A184

HIGDON, Kevin, Chief Financial Officer, Saint Josep. Health System, Mishawaka, IN, p. A236

HIGGINBOTHAM, G Douglas, President and Chief Executive Officer, South Central Regional Medical Center, Laurel, MS, p. A395

HIGGINBOTHAM, Lee, Chief Executive Officer, Dominion Hospital, Falls Church, VA, p. A741

HIGGINS, Alana, Regional Information Management Executive, Christus St. Michael Rehabilitation Hospital, Texarkana, TX, p. A719

HIGGINS, John, Vice President and Chief Financial Officer, Good Samaritan Medical Center, Lafayette, CO, p. A115

HIGGINS, Kevin, Chief Financial Officer, Olmsted Medical Center, Rochester, MN, p. A384

HIGGINS, Michael, Commander, David Grant Usaf Medical Center, Travis Afb, CA, p. A101

HIGGINS, Rodney, Chief Financial Officer, Multicare Deaconess Hospital, Spokane, WA, p. A765

HIGGINS, Thomas, M.D., Chief Medical Officer, Baystate Franklin Medical Center, Greenfield, MA, p. A339

HIGGINS, William, M.D., Vice President Medical Affairs, New York-Presbyterian/Hudson Valley Hospital, Cortlandt Manor, NY, p. A482

HIGGINS BOWERS, Shirley, Senior Vice President Human Resources, Hackensack Meridian Health Jfk Medical Center, Edison, NJ, p. A454

HIGGINSON, David, Executive Vice President and Chief Administrative Officer, Phoenix Children's Hospital, Phoenix, AZ, p. A36

HIGH, Kim, Chief Financial Officer, Baptist Memorial Hospital-Union County, New Albany, MS, p. A398

HIGHTOWER, Bernita, Chief Human Resources, Martin Army Community Hospital, Fort Benning, GA, p. A172

HIGHTOWER, Heather, Director of Nursing, Turning Point Hospital, Moultrie, GA, p. A177

HIGHTOWER, Skip. Chief Financial Officer, Brooks County Hospital, Quitman, GA, p. A178
Chief Financial Officer, Grady General Hospital, Cairo, GA, p. A167
Senior Vice President and Chief Financial Officer, John D. Archbold Memorial Hospital, Thomasville, GA, p. A182
Senior Vice President and Chief Financial Officer, Mitchell County Hospital, Camilla, GA, p. A168

HIJECK, Thomas, R.N., MS, Vice President Nursing Services and Chief Nursing Officer, Harrington Hospital, Southbridge, MA, p. A344

HILAMAN, Brad, M.D., JD, Chief Medical Officer, J. Arthur Dosher Memorial Hospital, Southport, NC, p. A518

HILAMAN, Brad L., M.D., JD, Chief Executive Officer, J. Arthur Dosher Memorial Hospital, Southport, NC, p. A518

HILDEBRAND, Dan, Chief Information Officer, Logansport Memorial Hospital, Logansport, IN, p. A235

HILDEBRAND, Randall, M.D., Chief Medical Officer, University Of Kansas Health System Great Bend Campus, Great Bend, KS, p. A265

HILDEBRANDT, James, D.O., Vice President Medical Affairs, Sarah Bush Lincoln Health Center, Mattoon, IL, p. A211

HILDRETH, Beth, Vice President Human Resources, Ohiohealth Medcentral Mansfield Hospital, Mansfield, OH, p. A544

HILDRETH, Joe, Director Information Technology, Three Rivers Hospital, Waverly, TN, p. A650

HILDWEIN, Robin, Chief Information Officer, Boca Raton Regional Hospital, Boca Raton, FL, p. A132

HILFIGER, Janie Marie., Chief Administrative Officer, Upmc Wellsboro, Wellsboro, PA, p. A610
President, Upmc Cole, Coudersport, PA, p. A587

HILL, Beth, Director Human Resources, Russell County Medical Center, Lebanon, VA, p. A744

HILL, Cheryl, Vice President Human Resources, Ascension Columbia St. Mary's Hospital Milwaukee, Milwaukee, WI, p. A790
Vice President Human Resources, Ascension Columbia St. Mary's Hospital Ozaukee, Mequon, WI, p. A790
Vice President Human Resources, Ascension Columbia St. Mary's Milwaukee Hospital, Milwaukee, WI, p. A790

HILL, Chris, Information Technology, Anchor Hospital, Atlanta, GA, p. A164

HILL, Herbert, Director Human Resources, Klickitat Valley Health, Goldendale, WA, p. A759

HILL, Jack, Chief Operating Officer and Administrator, The Jewish Hospital - Mercy Health, Cincinnati, OH, p. A533
Vice President and Chief Operating Officer, Union Hospital Clinton, Clinton, IN, p. A225

HILL, James, Senior Vice President Administrative Services, Medstar Washington Hospital Center, Washington, DC, p. A130

HILL, Jason, M.D., Chief Medical Officer, Choctaw Nation Health Care Center, Talihina, OK, p. A569

HILL, Jill, Director Information Technology, Utah State Hospital, Provo, UT, p. A731

HILL, Kalisha, M.D., Chief Medical Officer, Amita Health St. Mary's Hospital, Kankakee, IL, p. A209

HILL, Karen, R.N., FACHE, Chief Operating Officer and Chief Nursing Officer, Baptist Health Lexington, Lexington, KY, p. A286
Departmental Personnel Officer, Zuckerberg San Francisco General Hospital And Trauma Center, San Francisco, CA, p. A94
Director Human Resources, Baylor Scott & White Institute For Rehabilitation - Dallas, Dallas, TX, p. A667

HILL, Kerry, Chief Financial Officer, Vista Health, Waukegan, IL, p. A222

HILL, Leo, Chief Information Officer, Massachusetts Eye And Ear, Boston, MA, p. A336

HILL, M. Scott., President and Chief Executive Officer, Piedmont Columbus Regional Midtown, Columbus, GA, p. A169
President and Chief Executive Officer, Piedmont Columbus Regional Northside, Columbus, GA, p. A169

HILL, Nancy, R.N., MSN, Chief Operating Officer, Medical City North Hills, North Richland Hills, TX, p. A703
R.N., Chief Nursing Officer, Johnson Regional Medical Center, Clarksville, AR, p. A43

HILL, Ned, Chief Executive Officer, Mesa View Regional Hospital, Mesquite, NV, p. A445

HILL, Robert, M.D., Hospital Director and Chief Executive Officer, Kalamazoo Psychiatric Hospital, Kalamazoo, MI, p. A359

HILL, Ryan, Interim Administrator, Essentia Health St. Mary's - Detroit Lakes, Detroit Lakes, MN, p. A375
Senior Financial Advisor, Essentia Health St. Mary's - Detroit Lakes, Detroit Lakes, MN, p. A375

HILL, Stephen, Vice President and Chief Nursing Officer, Valley Baptist Medical Center-Harlingen, Harlingen, TX, p. A683

HILL, Stuart, Vice President and Treasurer, Unity Health White County Medical Center, Searcy, AR, p. A52

HILL, Timothy, Chief Operating Officer, Uams Medical Center, Little Rock, AR, p. A49

HILL, Tracy, M.D., Chief Medical Officer, Orem Community Hospital, Orem, UT, p. A730
M.D., Chief Medical Officer, Utah Valley Hospital, Provo, UT, p. A731

HILL-DAVIS, Nancy, Vice President Human Resources, Mercy Hospital And Medical Center, Chicago, IL, p. A199

HILLARD, Mary, MSN, R.N., Chief Nursing Officer, Longmont United Hospital, Longmont, CO, p. A116

HILLARY, Maureen, Chief Nursing Officer, Sparrow Eaton Hospital, Charlotte, MI, p. A351

HILLEGASS, Bonnie Essex., Chief Executive Officer, Harmon Medical And Rehabilitation Hospital, Las Vegas, NV, p. A443

HILLESTAD, Tammy, Chief Nursing Officer, Brookings Health System, Brookings, SD, p. A626

HILLIARD, David, D.O., Chief of Staff, Wvu Medicine - Barnesville Hospital, Barnesville, OH, p. A528

HILLIARD, Jamie, Director of Information Technology, University Of Kansas Health System St. Francis Campus, Topeka, KS, p. A277

HILLIS, David W., Chairman and Chief Executive Officer, Adcare Hospital Of Worcester, Worcester, MA, p. A346

HILLIS, Jeffrey, Chief Operating Officer, Adcare Hospital Of Worcester, Worcester, MA, p. A346

HILLIS-CLARK, Patricia, Executive Director, Devereux Children's Behavioral Health Center, Malvern, PA, p. A596

HILLMAN, Brandon, R.N., Administrator, Christus Coushatta Health Care Center, Coushatta, LA, p. A299

HILLS, Cindi, Director Human Resources, Riverwood Healthcare Center, Aitkin, MN, p. A371

HILLYER, Lisa, Human Resources Manager, Box Butte General Hospital, Alliance, NE, p. A429

HILT, Monica, President and Regional Vice President, Ascension Northeast Wisconsin St. Elizabeth Hospital, Appleton, WI, p. A779

HILTON, Craig, Chief Executive Officer and Managing Director, Hampton Behavioral Health Center, Westampton, NJ, p. A465

HILTON, Daniel, M.D., Chief of Staff, Fountain Valley Regional Hospital And Medical Center, Fountain Valley, CA, p. A64

HILTON, Lois, Director Human Resources, Desoto Memorial Hospital, Arcadia, FL, p. A131

HILTON, Neil A., FACHE, President and Chief Executive Officer, Perkins County Health Services, Grant, NE, p. A433

HILTON-SIEBERT, Stephanie, MSN, President and Chief Executive Officer, Marion General Hospital, Marion, IN, p. A236

HILTUNEN, Theresa, Entity Information Officer, Penn Presbyterian Medical Center, Philadelphia, PA, p. A601

HILTZ, Paul C., FACHE, Chief Executive Officer, Nch Baker Hospital, Naples, FL, p. A148

HIMES, Judy, MSN, R.N., Chief Nursing Officer, Penn State Milton S. Hershey Medical Center, Hershey, PA, p. A592

HINCHEY, Paul P., President and Chief Executive Officer, Candler Hospital, Savannah, GA, p. A179
President and Chief Executive Officer, St. Joseph's Hospital, Savannah, GA, p. A180

HINCKLEY, Fran, Chief Information Officer, North Shore Medical Center, Salem, MA, p. A344

HINDMAN, Robbie, Chief Nursing Officer, Brookwood Baptist Medical Center, Birmingham, AL, p. A14

HINDS, Bob, Executive Director, Bradford Health Services At Huntsville, Madison, AL, p. A21

HINE, Kristy, Associate Vice President Finance, Geisinger-Lewistown Hospital, Lewistown, PA, p. A595

HINE, Rhonda, R.N., Interim Chief Nursing Executive, Mason District Hospital, Havana, IL, p. A207

HINER, Jill, Vice President and Chief Financial Officer, Western Reserve Hospital, Cuyahoga Falls, OH, p. A538

HINER, Peggy, Director Human Resources, Wheatland Memorial Healthcare, Harlowton, MT, p. A424

HINES, Andrew, Administrator, St. James Behavioral Health Hospital, Gonzales, LA, p. A302

HINES, JeDonne, Chief Financial Officer, Intermountain Hospital, Boise, ID, p. A188

HINES, Linda, Vice President Information Technology and Information Systems, University Of Maryland Rehabilitation & Orthopaedic Institute, Baltimore, MD, p. A327

HINES, Lisa, Director of Performance Improvement, Eastern Shore Hospital Center, Cambridge, MD, p. A328

HINES, Mary Beth, D.O., Chief Medical Officer, Up Health System-Portage, Hancock, MI, p. A357

HINESLEY, Jay, FACHE, Chief Executive Officer, Vanderbilt Wilson County Hospital, Lebanon, TN, p. A642

HINKLE, Stacey, Director Information Technology, Banner Desert Medical Center, Mesa, AZ, p. A33

HINNER, William, Vice President Financial Analysis and Planning Ministry Health Care, Marshfield Medical Center, Marshfield, WI, p. A789
Vice President Financial Analysis and Planning, Ascension St. Michael's Hospital, Stevens Point, WI, p. A796

HINOJOSA, Anna, MSN, R.N., Interim Chief Nursing Officer, Knap. Medical Center, Weslaco, TX, p. A725

HINRICHS, Becky, Vice President Human Resources, Riverside Medical Center, Kankakee, IL, p. A209

HINRICHS, Sandy, Director Human Resources, Burnett Medical Center, Grantsburg, WI, p. A785

HINSHAW, Bruce, Director Human Resources, Artesia General Hospital, Artesia, NM, p. A468

HINSON, Lee, Chief Nursing Officer, Merit Health Natchez, Natchez, MS, p. A397

HINSON, Renee, Chief Executive Officer, Saint Alphonsus Regional Rehabilitation Hospital—An Affiliate Of Encompass Health, Boise, ID, p. A189

HINTZ, Lori, Coordinator Information Systems, Rochester Psychiatric Center, Rochester, NY, p. A496

HINTZE, Hartland, Chief Nursing Officer, Banner Payson Medical Center, Payson, AZ, p. A34
Chief Nursing Officer, Northern Louisiana Medical Center, Ruston, LA, p. A313

HINTZE, Paul, M.D., Vice President Medical Affairs, Mercy Hospital St. Louis, Saint Louis, MO, p. A416

HIOTT III, Jimmy O., Chief Executive Officer, Colleton Medical Center, Walterboro, SC, p. A625

HIPKISS, Tom, Vice President Finance, Forbes Hospital, Monroeville, PA, p. A597

HIRKALER, Kim, Director Human Resources, Bon Secours Community Hospital, Port Jervis, NY, p. A495

HIRKO, Mark, M.D., President, Putnam Hospital Center, Carmel, NY, p. A481
M.D., President, Sharon Hospital, Sharon, CT, p. A125

HIROMOTO, Brenda, Director of Nursing, Rehabilitation Hospital Of The Pacific, Honolulu, HI, p. A185

HIRSCH, Leslie D., FACHE, President and Chief Executive Officer, Saint Peter's University Hospital, New Brunswick, NJ, p. A459

HIRSCH, Ted, Senior Executive Director, Kalispell Regional Healthcare, Kalispell, MT, p. A425

HIRSCH, Vicki, R.N., Director of Nursing, Lallie Kemp Medical Center, Independence, LA, p. A303

HIRST, Barb, R.N., Vice President Human Resources and Chief Nursing Officer, Salem Regional Medical Center, Salem, OH, p. A548

HISE, Landon E., Chief Executive Officer, Alliancehealth Clinton, Clinton, OK, p. A557
Interim Chief Executive Officer, Alliancehealth Woodward, Woodward, OK, p. A572

HISEY, Commie, D.O., Chief of Staff, Gonzales Healthcare Systems, Gonzales, TX, p. A681

HITE DAVIS, Anissa, Vice President Human Resources, St. Joseph's Hospital Of Buckhannon, Buckhannon, WV, p. A771

HITT, John, M.D., Executive Vice President and Chief Medical Officer, Valleywise Health, Phoenix, AZ, p. A37

HITT, Melissa, Director of Nursing, Highland-Clarksburg Hospital, Clarksburg, WV, p. A771

HITT, Patricia, Associate Director, Grand Junction Veterans Health Care System, Grand Junction, CO, p. A113

HIXENBAUGH, Cynthia, Chief Executive Officer, Pershing General Hospital, Lovelock, NV, p. A445

HIXSON, Kim, Vice President of Financial Officer and Chief Financial Officer, Providence Medical Center, Wayne, NE, p. A440

HJEMBO, Philip. Chief Financial Officer, St. Elizabeth Hospital, Enumclaw, WA, p. A758

HLAHOL, Jan, Manager Human Resources, Cleveland Clinic Children's Hospital For Rehabilitation, Cleveland, OH, p. A534

HLUCHY, Nicholas, Business Analyst, Support Services Manager, Baton Rouge Rehabilitation Hospital, Baton Rouge, LA, p. A296

HO, Kingman, M.D., Senior Vice President, Chief Medical and Care Innovation Officer, Henry Mayo Newhall Hospital, Valencia, CA, p. A103

HO-SHING, Viodelda, Deputy Director Administration, Creedmoor Psychiatric Center, Jamaica, NY, p. A486

HOAG, Abby, Director, Human Resources, Uh Avon Rehabilitation Hospital, Avon, OH, p. A528

HOAGBIN, Joseph, M.D., Chief Medical Officer, Chi Health Immanuel, Omaha, NE, p. A436
M.D., Chief Quality Officer, Chi Health Mercy Council Bluffs, Council Bluffs, IA, p. A247

HOAR, Brad, Director Information and Technology, Cedar Park Regional Medical Center, Cedar Park, TX, p. A663

HOARD, Kaylee, Chief Financial Officer, Cook Hospital & Care Center, Cook, MN, p. A374

HOARD, Shelly Director of Nursing, Cypress Grove Behavioral Health, Bastrop, LA, p. A296

HOBACK, Kim, Supervisor Information Systems, Athens-Limestone Hospital, Athens, AL, p. A14

HOBAN, Donna, M.D., Senior Vice President and Chief Medical Officer, Beaumont Hospital - Grosse Pointe, Grosse Pointe, MI, p. A357

HOBAN, Douglas, Vice President and Chief Financial Officer, Mercy Hospital Lebanon, Lebanon, MO, p. A410

HOBART, Robert, Director Management Information Systems, Heartland Behavioral Healthcare, Massillon, OH, p. A544

HOBBS, Donna, Nurse Executive, U. S. Public Health Service Indian Hospital-Sells, Sells, AZ, p. A38

HOBBS, Ed, Director Information Services, Parkview Dekalb Hospital, Auburn, IN, p. A223

HOBBS, Emilie, Director Human Resources, Woodland Heights Medical Center, Lufkin, TX, p. A698

HOBBS, Keith, Chief Executive Officer, Usc Verdugo Hills Hospital, Glendale, CA, p. A67

HOBBS, Mike, Chief Financial Officer, Clay County Hospital, Flora, IL, p. A205

HOBBS, Steve, Chief Financial Officer, North Alabama Medical Center, Florence, AL, p. A18
Chief Financial Officer, Shoals Hospital, Muscle Shoals, AL, p. A22

HOBBS, Tommy, Chief Executive Officer, Illinois Valley Community Hospital, Peru, IL, p. A217

HOBDY, Amy, Vice President of Human Resources, Tristar Hendersonville Medical Center, Hendersonville, TN, p. A639

HOBGOOD, Marcus, Director Information Services, Ochsner Lsu Health Shreveport - Academic Medical Center, Shreveport, LA, p. A314

HOBSON, Christopher, Chief Operating Officer, Bristol Regional Medical Center, Bristol, TN, p. A634

HOBSON, James M., Chief Executive Officer, Magnolia Regional Health Center, Corinth, MS, p. A391

HOBSON, Jim, Chief Executive Officer, Greenbrier Valley Medical Center, Ronceverte, WV, p. A776

HOCATE, Crispin, Professional and Support Services Officer, Texas Health Presbyterian Hospital Allen, Allen, TX, p. A652

HOCHSTETLER, Amy, Chief Financial Officer, Orthopaedic Hospital Of Lutheran Health Network, Fort Wayne, IN, p. A228

HOCHSTETLER, Lisa, R.N., Chief Nursing Officer, Tristar Hendersonville Medical Center, Hendersonville, TN, p. A639

HOCK, Douglas, Executive Vice President and Chief Operating Officer, Children's Hospital Of Philadelphia, Philadelphia, PA, p. A599

HOCKADAY, Christina P., FACHE, Chief Executive Officer, Assumption Community Hospital, Napoleonville, LA, p. A309

HOCKENBERRY, Michael, Senior Vice President and Chief Operating Officer, Upmc Hanover, Hanover, PA, p. A591

HOCKERSMITH, Lisa, Vice President Human Resources, Kern Medical, Bakersfield, CA, p. A57

HOCKING, Barbara, Chief Nursing Officer, St. Luke's Regional Medical Center, Boise, ID, p. A189

HOCKING, Dale, Chief Financial Officer, Jupiter Medical Center, Jupiter, FL, p. A142

HOCKING, Patrick, Chief Financial Officer, Asante Ashland Community Hospital, Ashland, OR, p. A573
Chief Financial Officer, Asante Rogue Regional Medical Center, Medford, OR, p. A577
Chief Financial Officer, Asante Three Rivers Medical Center, Grants Pass, OR, p. A575

HOCUM, Timothy, Chief Financial Officer, Providence Kodiak Island Medical Center, Kodiak, AK, p. A28

HODGE, Ian, Chief Executive Officer, Yuma Rehabilitation Hospital, A Partnership Of Encompass Health And Yrmc, Yuma, AZ, p. A41

HODGE, Lisa, Director, Human Resources, Rolling Hills Hospital, Franklin, TN, p. A638

HODGE, Montie, Vice President Information Technology and Chief Information Officer, Regional West Medical Center, Scottsbluff, NE, p. A439

HODGE, Pamela, R.N., Chief Nursing Officer and Coordinator Performance Improvement, Jellico Community Hospital, Jellico, TN, p. A640

HODGE, Stacie, Director of Nursing, Washington County Hospital, Nashville, IL, p. A214

HODGES, Alan, Chief Executive Officer, Hancock Medical Center, Bay Saint Louis, MS, p. A389

HODGES, Calvin, Director Human Resources, Alliancehealth Ponca City, Ponca City, OK, p. A567

HODGES, Craig, Director Information Services, Hancock Medical Center, Bay Saint Louis, MS, p. A389

HODGES, Dawn, Director Human Resources, Grand River Hospital District, Rifle, CO, p. A118

HODGES, Jay, Interim Chief Executive Officer, Bayside Community Hospital, Anahuac, TX, p. A653

HODGES, Leisha, Human Resources Officer, Eastland Memorial Hospital, Eastland, TX, p. A673

HODGIN, Robin, R.N., Vice President of Patient Services and Chief Nursing Officer, Northern Regional Hospital, Mount Airy, NC, p. A515

HODGSON, Judith, Chief Nursing Officer, Cheyenne County Hospital, Saint Francis, KS, p. A275

HODNETT, Laura, Interim Chief Nursing Officer, Glen Rose Medical Center, Glen Rose, TX, p. A681

HODSHIRE, Jeremiah J., President and Chief Executive Officer, Hillsdale Hospital, Hillsdale, MI, p. A357

HODSON, Don, M.D., Chief Medical Officer, St. Luke Hospital And Living Center, Marion, KS, p. A270

HOEFER, Bill, Chief Operating Officer, Mercy Hospital South, Saint Louis, MO, p. A416

HOEFS, Dennis, Manager Information Technology, New Mexico Rehabilitation Center, Roswell, NM, p. A471

HOEG, Robin, Chief Operating Officer, Winona Health, Winona, MN, p. A388

HOEHNS, Brent, M.D., Chief of Medical Staff, Knoxville Hospital & Clinics, Knoxville, IA, p. A253

HOEKSTRA, James, M.D., President, High Point Medical Center, High Point, NC, p. A512

HOELL, Paul, M.D., President Medical Staff, Thedacare Medical Center-New London, New London, WI, p. A792

HOELSCHER, Steven, Chief Operating Officer, Valley Regional Medical Center, Brownsville, TX, p. A661

HOERTZ, Joanne, Vice President of Nursing, Brooks Rehabilitation Hospital, Jacksonville, FL, p. A141

HOESCH, Marty, Director Information Systems, North Suburban Medical Center, Thornton, CO, p. A119

HOEY, Amy, R.N., MS, Executive Vice President and Chief Operating Officer, Lowell General Hospital, Lowell, MA, p. A341

HOFER, Maggie, Human Resources Representative, Hawarden Regional Healthcare, Hawarden, IA, p. A251

HOFF, David L., Chief Executive Officer, Wayne Memorial Hospital, Honesdale, PA, p. A592

HOFF, Deanna, R.N., Director of Nursing, Bacon County Hospital And Health System, Alma, GA, p. A163

HOFF, Linda, Senior Vice President and Chief Financial Officer, Legacy Mount Hood Medical Center, Gresham, OR, p. A575

HOFF, Margaret, Account Manager, Brown County Community Treatment Center, Green Bay, WI, p. A785

HOFFER, Nolan, Senior Director, St. Luke's Rehabilitation Hospital, Boise, ID, p. A189

HOFFMAN, Brad, Administrative Director Human Resources, Adventhealth Shawnee Mission, Shawnee Mission, KS, p. A276

HOFFMAN, Brian, M.D., Chief Medical Services, Veterans Affairs Boston Healthcare System, West Roxbury, MA, p. A345

HOFFMAN, Carole, Vice President, Parkridge Medical Center, Chattanooga, TN, p. A636

HOFFMAN, Daniel, M.D., Administrative Medical Director, Ssm Health Good Samaritan Hospital, Mount Vernon, IL, p. A213

HOFFMAN, Debbie, Vice President Patient Services, Mosaic Medical Center - Maryville, Maryville, MO, p. A411

HOFFMAN, Debra, Human Resources Manager, Kern Valley Healthcare District, Lake Isabella, CA, p. A70

HOFFMAN, Howard, M.D., Medical Director, Psychiatric Institute Of Washington, Washington, DC, p. A130

HOFFMAN, Jerry, Chief Financial Officer, Platte Health Center Avera, Platte, SD, p. A630

HOFFMAN, Josep. Senior Vice President and Chief Financial Officer, University Of Maryland Medical Center, Baltimore, MD, p. A326

HOFFMAN, Marcus, Area Chief Financial Officer, Kaiser Permanente Orange County Anaheim Medical Center, Anaheim, CA, p. A55

HOFFMAN, Rex, M.D., Chief Medical Officer, Providence Holy Cross Medical Center, Mission Hills, CA, p. A78

HOFFMAN, Robert, R.N., Chief Nursing Officer, Wilkes-Barre General Hospital, Wilkes-Barre, PA, p. A611

HOFFMAN, Tom, Manager Information Systems, Wayne Memorial Hospital, Honesdale, PA, p. A592

HOFFMAN, Val, Chief Financial Officer, Avera Granite Falls Health Center, Granite Falls, MN, p. A377

HOFFMANN, Wanda, Director Human Resources, River Oaks Hospital, New Orleans, LA, p. A311

HOFIUS, Chuck, Chief Executive Officer, Perham Health, Perham, MN, p. A383

HOFLER, Linda, Ph.D., R.N., FACHE, Senior Vice President, Nurse Executive, Vidant Medical Center, Greenville, NC, p. A511

HOFMAN, William, Manager Information Technology, Wake Forest Baptist Health - Wilkes Medical Center, North Wilkesboro, NC, p. A516

HOFMEIER, Sara, Executive Director, Veritas Collaborative, Durham, NC, p. A509

HOFMEISTER, David, Chief Executive Officer, Kearny County Hospital, Lakin, KS, p. A268

HOFSTETTER, Phil A., Chief Executive Officer, Petersburg Medical Center, Petersburg, AK, p. A29

HOGAN, Brian, Chief Executive Officer, Baptist Memorial Hospital-Desoto, Southaven, MS, p. A400

HOGAN, Dan, Chief Financial Officer, Desoto Memorial Hospital, Arcadia, FL, p. A131

HOGAN, Judith, Comptroller and Director Resources and Logistics, Naval Hospital Bremerton, Bremerton, WA, p. A756

HOGAN, Michael, Chief Resource Management, General Leonard Wood Army Community Hospital, Fort Leonard Wood, MO, p. A406

HOGAN, Richard, CPA, Chief Financial Officer, Landmark Hospital Of Cap. Girardeau, Cap. Girardeau, MO, p. A403
Chief Financial Officer, Pleasant Valley Hospital, Point Pleasant, WV, p. A776

HOGAN, Sean, FACHE, President, Mercy Hospital South, Saint Louis, MO, p. A416

HOGDSON, Judy, R.N., Chief Nursing Officer, Hospital District No 1 Of Rice County, Lyons, KS, p. A270

HOGGARD GREEN, Jill, Ph.D., R.N., President and Chief Executive Officer, The Queen's Medical Center, Honolulu, HI, p. A185

HOGUE, Vicky, R.N., Vice President Patient Services and Chief Nursing Officer, Wellstar Paulding Hospital, Hiram, GA, p. A174

HOHN, Craig, Chief Executive Officer, Avera Merrill Pioneer Hospital, Rock Rapids, IA, p. A257

HOLBERT, Brandon, Director, Information Services, Ocala Regional Medical Center, Ocala, FL, p. A150

HOLBROOK, Chip. M.D., Chief of Staff, Simpson General Hospital, Mendenhall, MS, p. A396

HOLBROOK, Curtis, M.D., Chief Medical Officer, Baylor Scott & White Surgical Hospital-Sherman, Sherman, TX, p. A715

HOLBROOK, Donald, Chief Executive Officer, State Penitentiary Hospital, Walla Walla, WA, p. A768

HOLCOMB, Holly, R.N., Chie Operating Officer, Childress Regional Medical Center, Childress, TX, p. A663
R.N., Chief Operating Officer, Childress Regional Medical Center, Childress, TX, p. A663

HOLCOMB, Michelle, Human Resources, Webster County Memorial Hospital, Webster Springs, WV, p. A777

HOLDEN, Carol, Chief Financial Officer, Northern Cochise Community Hospital, Willcox, AZ, p. A41

HOLDEN, Teal A., Chief Executive Officer, Memorial Hermann Surgical Hospital Kingwood, Kingwood, TX, p. A693

HOLDER, Hal, Regional Chief Financial Officer-Hospital Operations, Ssm Health St. Clare Hospital - Fenton, Fenton, MO, p. A406
Regional Chief Financial Officer, Ssm Health St. Josep. Hospital - Lake Saint Louis, Lake Saint Louis, MO, p. A410

HOLDER, Jennifer, Chief Nursing Officer, Trousdale Medical Center, Hartsville, TN, p. A639

HOLDER, Kasey, M.D., Vice President Medical Affairs, St. Bernards Medical Center, Jonesboro, AR, p. A48

HOLDER, Michelle, Nurse Executive, Straith Hospital For Special Surgery, Southfield, MI, p. A367

HOLDER, Spencer, Chief Financial Officer, Riverland Medical Center, Ferriday, LA, p. A301

HOLDER-HOOPER, Donna, Chief Human Resource Officer, Encompass Health Rehabilitation Hospital An Affiliate Of Martin Health, Stuart, FL, p. A158

HOLEKAMP, Nicholas, M.D., Chief Medical Officer, Ranken Jordan Pediatric Bridge Hospital, Maryland Heights, MO, p. A411

HOLGUIN, Brenda, Manager Human Resources, El Paso Behavioral Health System, El Paso, TX, p. A674

HOLGUIN, Mindee, Manager Human Resources, Sierra Vista Hospital, Truth Or Consequences, NM, p. A473

HOLIFIELD, Tracy, Director Information Systems, Merit Health Central, Jackson, MS, p. A394

HOLINER, Joel, M.D., Executive Medical Director, Medical City Green Oaks Hospital, Dallas, TX, p. A669

HOLIVER, John J., Chief Executive Officer, St. Josep. Health Services Of Rhode Island, North Providence, RI, p. A613

HOLLAND, Baxter, M.D., Chief Medical Officer, Rutland Regional Medical Center, Rutland, VT, p. A736

HOLLAND, Brad D., President and Chief Executive Officer, Hendrick Health System, Abilene, TX, p. A651

HOLLAND, Charles, President and Chief Executive Officer, St. Bernard Hospital And Health Care Center, Chicago, IL, p. A201

HOLLAND, David, Chief Information Officer, Herrin Hospital, Herrin, IL, p. A207
Vice President Chief Innovation Officer, Memorial Hospital Of Carbondale, Carbondale, IL, p. A196
Vice President Information Services, St. Josep. Memorial Hospital, Murphysboro, IL, p. A213

HOLLAND, Gabrielle, Chief Financial Officer, Baylor Surgical Hospital At Las Colinas, Irving, TX, p. A690

HOLLAND, Kevin, Chief Executive Officer, CHRISTUS Southwestern Louisiana, Christus Ochsner Lake Area Hospital, Lake Charles, LA, p. A306
Chief Executive Officer, CHRISTUS Southwestern Louisiana, Christus Ochsner St. Patrick, Lake Charles, LA, p. A306

HOLLAND, Kwi, Vice President Information Services, Knox Community Hospital, Mount Vernon, OH, p. A546

HOLLAND, Megan, Chief Medical Officer and Family Practitioner, Southern Coos Hospital And Health Center, Bandon, OR, p. A573

HOLLAND, Michael, M.D., Chief Executive Officer, Rehabilitation Hospital Of Jennings, Jennings, LA, p. A304

HOLLAND, Mikel, M.D., President and Chief Medical Officer, Avera St. Mary's Hospital, Pierre, SD, p. A630

HOLLAND, Penny, Associate Director for Patient Care Services, Aleda E. Lutz Veterans Affairs Medical Center, Saginaw, MI, p. A365

HOLLAND, Shannon, R.N., MSN, Chief Nursing Officer, Multicare Valley Hospital, Spokane Valley, WA, p. A766

HOLLAND, Sharron, Chief Financial Officer, Baptist Memorial Hospital-Carroll County, Huntingdon, TN, p. A639

HOLLAND, Stephen, M.D., Vice President Chief Medical Officer and Medical Director, Gaylord Specialty Healthcare, Wallingford, CT, p. A126

HOLLEMAN, James, M.D., Chief of Staff, St. Luke's Hospital, Columbus, NC, p. A508

HOLLEMAN, Stephen, Chief Financial Officer, Shepherd Center, Atlanta, GA, p. A165

HOLLEY, Brenda, Chief Nursing Officer, Lovelace Westside Hospital, Albuquerque, NM, p. A467

HOLLIDAY, Jonathan, Manager Information Technology, Mercyone Elkader Medical Center, Elkader, IA, p. A249

HOLLIMAN, Emily L., Chief Executive Officer, Hackensack Meridian Health Pascack Valley Medical Center, Westwood, NJ, p. A465

HOLLINGS, Derrick, Chief Financial Officer, Hennepin Healthcare, Minneapolis, MN, p. A380

HOLLINGSWORTH, Carl, Chief Financial Officer, Artesia General Hospital, Artesia, NM, p. A468

HOLLINGSWORTH, Christine, Chief Financial Officer, Phoenix Veterans Affairs Health Care System, Phoenix, AZ, p. A36

HOLLINGSWORTH, Nancy, R.N., MSN, President and Chief Executive Officer, Saint Agnes Medical Center, Fresno, CA, p. A65

HOLLINGSWORTH, Sherri, Chief Human Resources Officer, Pih Health Hospital - Downey, Downey, CA, p. A62

HOLLIS, Gary, Comptroller, Arkansas State Hospital, Little Rock, AR, p. A48

HOLLIS, Lauren, Chief Human Resources Officer, North Mississipp. Medical Center-West Point, West Point, MS, p. A401

HOLLIS, Roy, Chief Executive Officer, Houston Behavioral Healthcare Hospital, Houston, TX, p. A686

HOLLISTER, Jerry, Chief Executive Officer, Northeastern Center, Auburn, IN, p. A223

HOLLISTER, Richard, President of Medical Staff, Exeter Hospital, Exeter, NH, p. A449

HOLLON, Kim Norton., FACHE, President and Chief Executive Officer, Signature Healthcare Brockton Hospital, Brockton, MA, p. A337

HOLLOWAY, Kristina, Chief Human Resources Officer, Healdsburg District Hospital, Healdsburg, CA, p. A68

HOLLOWAY, Myra, Director Human Resources Management, Central State Hospital, Milledgeville, GA, p. A177

HOLLOWAY, Whitney, Chief Financial Officer, Berwick Hospital Center, Berwick, PA, p. A584

HOLM, Mary, Office Clerk, Tioga Medical Center, Tioga, ND, p. A526

HOLM, Stan, President and Chief Executive Officer, Olathe Medical Center, Olathe, KS, p. A272

HOLMAN, Resha, Chief Nurse Executive Officer, Northridge Hospital Medical Center, Northridge, CA, p. A81

HOLMAN, Steve M., Chief Executive Officer, Union Hospital, Terre Haute, IN, p. A241

HOLMES, Dawne, Chief Financial Officer, Greenwood Leflore Hospital, Greenwood, MS, p. A392
Interim Chief Executive Officer, Greenwood Leflore Hospital, Greenwood, MS, p. A392

HOLMES, Diana, Chief Nursing Officer, Central Regional Hospital, Butner, NC, p. A506

HOLMES, Ginnie, Chief Financial Officer, Electra Memorial Hospital, Electra, TX, p. A676

HOLMES, Heather, Director Health Information Systems, Merit Health Rankin, Brandon, MS, p. A390

HOLMES, Heidi, Chief Information Officer, Oklahoma State University Medical Center, Tulsa, OK, p. A570

HOLMES, James R., President and Chief Executive Officer, Redlands Community Hospital, Redlands, CA, p. A87

HOLMES, John, Business Manager, Ancora Psychiatric Hospital, Hammonton, NJ, p. A456

HOLMES, Phillip. M.D., Chief of Staff, Prairie Ridge Hospital And Health Services, Elbow Lake, MN, p. A376

HOLMES, Terry, M.D., Clinical Director, Moccasin Bend Mental Health Institute, Chattanooga, TN, p. A635

HOLMES, Tim, President, Behavioral Health, Navos, Seattle, WA, p. A763

HOLMES, Troy, Chief Financial Officer, Advanced Specialty Hospital Of Toledo, Toledo, OH, p. A550
Interim Chief Executive Officer and Chief Financial Officer, Advanced Specialty Hospital Of Toledo, Toledo, OH, p. A550

HOLMSTROM, Rebecca, Chief Nursing Officer, Ely-Bloomenson Community Hospital, Ely, MN, p. A376

HOLMSTROM, Tallulah, M.D., Chief Medical Officer, Carolina Pines Regional Medical Center, Hartsville, SC, p. A621
M.D., Chief Medical Officer, Kershawhealth, Camden, SC, p. A615

HOLOM, Randall G., Chief Executive Officer, Frances Mahon Deaconess Hospital, Glasgow, MT, p. A424

HOLSAPPLE, Kim, Human Resource Specialist, Chester Mental Health Center, Chester, IL, p. A197

HOLSCHBACH, Dennis, Chief Financial Officer, Ruby Valley Medical Center, Sheridan, MT, p. A428

HOLSON, Debbie, R.N., MSN, Chief Operating Officer, The Hsc Pediatric Center, Washington, DC, p. A130

HOLSON, Debbie C., R.N., MSN, Chief Operating Officer, The Hsc Pediatric Center, Washington, DC, p. A130

HOLST, David, M.D., Chief of Staff, Mercy Medical Center Mount Shasta, Mount Shasta, CA, p. A80

HOLSTEN, Robyn, Human Resources Director, Salt Lake Behavioral Health, Salt Lake City, UT, p. A732

HOLT, Clayton, Chief Executive Officer, San Juan Health Service District, Monticello, UT, p. A729

HOLT, David, Chief Executive Officer, Western State Hospital, Tacoma, WA, p. A767

HOLT, Jeffrey, Chief Operating Officer, Clara Maass Medical Center, Belleville, NJ, p. A452

HOLT, Kory, Assistant Vice President for Financial Integration, Avera Flandreau Hospital, Flandreau, SD, p. A628
Division Controller Network Operations, Avera Dells Area Hospital, Dell Rapids, SD, p. A627

HOLT, Peter, M.D., Director Medical Affairs, Saint Luke's Hospital Of Kansas City, Kansas City, MO, p. A409

HOLT, Richard, R.N., Associate Director Patient Care Services, Veterans Affairs St. Louis Health Care System, Saint Louis, MO, p. A418

HOLT, Sherry, Director Human Resources, Unity Medical Center, Manchester, TN, p. A643

HOLT, Stephen R., M.D., Director, Veterans Affairs North Texas Health Care System, Dallas, TX, p. A671

HOLT, Tabetha, Director of Human Resources, Riverside Walter Reed Hospital, Gloucester, VA, p. A743

HOLT, Thomas, Chief Financial Officer, Hca Houston Healthcare Conroe, Conroe, TX, p. A665

HOLT, Will, Director Information Technology, Harrison County Community Hospital, Bethany, MO, p. A402

HOLTHAUS, Julie, Director Human Resources, Sabetha Community Hospital, Sabetha, KS, p. A275

HOLTHAUS, Monica, Chief Financial Officer, Community Healthcare System, Onaga, KS, p. A273

HOLTMAN, Jean, Vice President, Human Resources, St. Mary Medical Center, Apple Valley, CA, p. A56

HOLTZ, George, Adminstrative Director Human Resources, Beverly Hospital, Montebello, CA, p. A79

HOLTZ, Jennifer, Director Finance, Centracare Health-Paynesville, Paynesville, MN, p. A383

HOLTZ, Noel, M.D., Chief Medical Officer, Wellstar Douglas Hospital, Douglasville, GA, p. A171

HOLTZMAN, Michael, M.D., Medical Director, Kindred Hospital-St. Louis, Saint Louis, MO, p. A416

HOLUBEK, William, M.D., Chief Medical Officer, University Hospital, Newark, NJ, p. A460

HOLYFIELD, Asia, Manager Business Office, Lifecare Behavioral Health Hospital, Pittsburgh, PA, p. A603

HOLYOAK, Mark C., FACHE, Chief Executive Officer, Wilson Medical Center, Wilson, NC, p. A520

HOLZER, Traci, Chief Human Resources Officer, Doctors Hospital Of Manteca, Manteca, CA, p. A77

HOMA, Jim, Chief Executive Officer, Heatherhill Care Communities, Chardon, OH, p. A531

HOMYK, Linda, Chief Nursing Officer, Heritage Valley Health System, Beaver, PA, p. A584
Chief Nursing Officer, Sewickley Valley Hospital, (A Division Of Valley Medical Facilities), Sewickley, PA, p. A608

HONAKER, Jennifer, Chief Financial Officer, John Randolp. Medical Center, Hopewell, VA, p. A744

HONEA, Bert, M.D., Associate Chief Medical Officer Northern Colorado, Banner Fort Collins Medical Center, Fort Collins, CO, p. A112
M.D., Medical Director, Mckee Medical Center, Loveland, CO, p. A117

HONEA, Bruce, Director Information Services, Christus Coushatta Health Care Center, Coushatta, LA, p. A299

HONEA, Michael, Chief Financial Officer, Glen Rose Medical Center, Glen Rose, TX, p. A681

HONEYCUTT, Bob, Chief Executive Officer, Saint Mary's Regional Medical Center, Russellville, AR, p. A52

HONEYCUTT, Cynthia, Director Human Resources, Moccasin Bend Mental Health Institute, Chattanooga, TN, p. A635

HONSINGER, Melissa, Chief Operating Officer, St. Luke's Rehabilitation Hospital, Boise, ID, p. A189

HONTS, Gary, Chief Executive Officer, Jfk Memorial Hospital, Indio, CA, p. A68

HOOD, Brenda, Chief Executive Officer, Curahealth Hospital Oklahoma City, Oklahoma City, OK, p. A564

HOOD, Cliff, Chief Operating Officer, Central Regional Hospital, Butner, NC, p. A506

HOOD, Gary, Chief Information Officer, Fayette County Hospital, Vandalia, IL, p. A222

HOOD, Kathy, Administrative Assistant Human Resources, Union General Hospital, Blairsville, GA, p. A167

HOOD, Ron, M.D., Chief of Staff, Sutter Amador Hospital, Jackson, CA, p. A69

HOOD, Sam, Director Human Resources, Heartland Regional Medical Center, Marion, IL, p. A211

HOOD, Thomas, Chief Operating Officer, King's Daughters Medical Center, Brookhaven, MS, p. A390

HOODY, Dan, M.D., Interim Chief Medical Officer, Hennepin Healthcare, Minneapolis, MN, p. A380

HOOK, Diane, Chief Financial Officer, Wayne County Hospital, Corydon, IA, p. A246

HOOKER, Melvin, Chief Human Resources, New Mexico Veterans Affairs Health Care System - Raymond G. Murphy Medical Center, Albuquerque, NM, p. A468

HOOKER, Rita, Administrative Director Information Services, Bon Secours St. Francis Health System, Greenville, SC, p. A620

HOOKS, Kurt, Chief Executive Officer, Virginia Beach Psychiatric Center, Virginia Beach, VA, p. A753

HOOLAHAN, Susan, R.N., MSN, Vice President Patient Care Services and Chief Nursing Officer, Upmc Passavant, Pittsburgh, PA, p. A604

HOOLAHAN, Susan E., R.N., MSN, President, Upmc Passavant, Pittsburgh, PA, p. A604

HOOP, Heather, Human Resources Generalist, Adams County Regional Medical Center, Seaman, OH, p. A549

HOOPER, Grady A., Chief Executive Officer, Hamilton General Hospital, Hamilton, TX, p. A682

HOOPER, Jason R., President and Chief Executive Officer, Kvc Prairie Ridge Psychiatric Hospital, Kansas City, KS, p. A267

HOOPER, Joseph, President and Chief Executive Officer, Community Howard Regional Health, Kokomo, IN, p. A234

HOOPER, Robert, Director Human Resources, Tristar Skyline Medical Center, Nashville, TN, p. A647

HOOPINGARNER, Darrick, Chief Operating Officer, Dupont Hospital, Fort Wayne, IN, p. A228

HOOPINGARNER, Traci, R.N., Chief Nursing Officer, Lmh Health, Lawrence, KS, p. A269

HOOVER, Alvin, FACHE, Chief Executive Officer, King's Daughters Medical Center, Brookhaven, MS, p. A390

HOOVER, Craig A., Chief Executive Officer, Vibra Rehabilitation Hospital Of Denver, Thornton, CO, p. A119

HOOVER, Garrett, FACHE, President and Chief Operating Officer, Senior Vice President LifeBridge Health, Carroll Hospital Center, Westminster, MD, p. A333

HOOVER, Garrett W., FACHE, President and Chief Operating Officer, Senior Vice President LifeBridge Health, Carroll Hospital Center, Westminster, MD, p. A333

HOOVER, Jeremy, Chief Information Officer, Kiowa County Memorial Hospital, Greensburg, KS, p. A265

HOOVER, John, Chief Operating Officer, Eastside Medical Center, Snellville, GA, p. A180

HOPE, Lisa, Director Human Resources, Owensboro Health Muhlenberg Community Hospital, Greenville, KY, p. A284

HOPE, Steve, Vice President Corporate Services, Methodist Rehabilitation Center, Jackson, MS, p. A394

HOPE, William Chief of Medical Staff, Vidant Chowan Hospital, Edenton, NC, p. A509

HOPKINS, Bill, Director of Operations, Northern Cochise Community Hospital, Willcox, AZ, p. A41

HOPKINS, Frances, Chief Financial Officer, Sabine Medical Center, Many, LA, p. A308

HOPKINS, Jason, Director, Human Resources, Hamilton Medical Center, Dalton, GA, p. A170

HOPKINS, Jim, Chief Financial Officer, Cascade Medical Center, Leavenworth, WA, p. A760

HOPKINS, John, M.D., Chief of Staff, Avera Hand County Memorial Hospital, Miller, SD, p. A629

HOPKINS, Joy, Vice President Patient Care Services, Osf St. Francis Hospital And Medical Group. Escanaba, MI, p. A354

HOPKINS, Kelli, Director Human Resources, Baptist Health Medical Center-Hot Spring County, Malvern, AR, p. A50

HOPKINS, Ken, Vice President Finance and Chief Financial Officer, Norman Regional Health System, Norman, OK, p. A563

HOPKINS, Kevin, Vice President of Operations, Chi Memorial Hospital - Georgia, Fort Oglethorpe, GA, p. A173

HOPKINS, Larry, Chief Medical Officer, Indiana University Health Tipton Hospital, Tipton, IN, p. A241

HOPKINS, Paul, Interim Medical Director, John J. Pershing Veterans Affairs Medical Center, Poplar Bluff, MO, p. A413

HOPKINS, Ronald, D.O., Chief of Staff, Nor-Lea Hospital District, Lovington, NM, p. A470

HOPKINS, William, Director Finance, Atrium Health's Carolinas Rehabilitation, Charlotte, NC, p. A507

HOPP, Eva, Chief Nurse Executive, Pinckneyville Community Hospital, Pinckneyville, IL, p. A217

HOPPER, Tasha, Chief Executive Officer, The Hospitals Of Providence Transmountain Campus, El Paso, TX, p. A676

HOPPS, Deborah, R.N., FACHE, Chief Executive Officer, Baylor Scott & White Institute For Rehabilitation - Lakeway, Lakeway, TX, p. A694

HOPSON, W, M.D., Clinical Medical Director, Merit Health River Region, Vicksburg, MS, p. A401

HOPSTAD, Kyle, Chief Executive Officer, Broadwater Health Center, Townsend, MT, p. A428

HOPWOOD, James, Chief Financial Officer, Riverbridge Specialty Hospital, Vidalia, LA, p. A316

HOPWOOD, Jennifer, Chief Nursing Officer, Vice President Patient Care, Osf Saint Francis Medical Center, Peoria, IL, p. A217

HORAN, Gary S., FACHE, President and Chief Executive Officer, Trinitas Regional Medical Center, Elizabeth, NJ, p. A455

HORATH, Kevin, Vice President Human Resources, Decatur Memorial Hospital, Decatur, IL, p. A202

HORCH, David, Chief Executive, California Medical Facility, Vacaville, CA, p. A102

HORECKA, Richard, Chief Medical Officer, Swift County - Benson Health Services, Benson, MN, p. A372

HORINECK, Kim, Chief Human Resource Officer, Goodland Regional Medical Center, Goodland, KS, p. A265

HORINEK, ReChelle, Chief Financial Officer, Trego County-Lemke Memorial Hospital, Wakeeney, KS, p. A278

HORN, Debbie, Controller, Texas Rehabilitation Hospital Of Arlington, Arlington, TX, p. A654

HORN, Jon, M.D., Chief of Staff, Northeast Georgia Medical Center Barrow, Winder, GA, p. A183

HORN, LeeAnn, Chief Nurse Executive, Providence Kodiak Island Medical Center, Kodiak, AK, p. A28

HORN, Sarah, Chief Nursing Officer, Salem Health West Valley, Dallas, OR, p. A574

Chief Nursing Officer, Salem Hospital, Salem, OR, p. A581

HORN, Syndi, Director Information Systems, Memorial Hospital, Carthage, IL, p. A196

HORNBURG, Tom, Director Information Systems, Mason General Hospital And Family Of Clinics, Shelton, WA, p. A765

HORNE, Beth, System Administrator Information Technology, Preston Memorial Hospital, Kingwood, WV, p. A773

HORNE, Eilene, Manager Human Resources, Mountain View Hospital, Idaho Falls, ID, p. A190

HORNE, J, Senior Vice President, Ambulatory Services and Chief Operating Officer, Grand View Health, Sellersville, PA, p. A607

HORNE, Perry, Chief Nursing Officer, St. Cloud Regional Medical Center, Saint Cloud, FL, p. A156

HORNE, Willus, M.D., Chief Medical Officer, South Central Regional Medical Center, Laurel, MS, p. A395

HORNER, Ania, R.N., MSN, Vice President and Chief Nurse Executive, Aurora Sinai Medical Center, Milwaukee, WI, p. A790

HORNER, Cheryl, Supervisor Data Processing, Community Hospital Of Staunton, Staunton, IL, p. A221

HORNER, Eva, Assistant Executive Director Operations, Devereux Hospital And Children's Center Of Florida, Melbourne, FL, p. A145

HORNER, John M., President and Chief Executive Officer, Major Hospital, Shelbyville, IN, p. A240

HORNSBY, Donny, Director Fiscal Services, Memphis Mental Health Institute, Memphis, TN, p. A644

HORNUNG, Dona, Director Information and Technology Services, Doctors Hospital, Augusta, GA, p. A166

HORNUNG, Kurt, Director, Medical Center Of Trinity, Trinity, FL, p. A161

HORRIGAN, Timothy, M.D., Chief Quality Officer, Unitypoint Health - Allen Hospital, Waterloo, IA, p. A259

HORSLEY, Steve, Vice President and Chief Information Officer, Moses H. Cone Memorial Hospital, Greensboro, NC, p. A511

HORSMAN, Sandra, Director, Veterans Affairs Black Hills Health Care System, Fort Meade, SD, p. A628

HORST, Brad, Director Human Resources, Hca Houston Healthcare Clear Lake, League City, TX, p. A695

HORST, Joanna, MSN, R.N., Chief Nursing Officer, St. Christopher's Hospital For Children, Philadelphia, PA, p. A602

HORSTMAN, Jennifer, R.N., Chief Nursing Officer and Chief Information Officer, Fairbanks, Indianapolis, IN, p. A232

HORSTMANN, Steve, Vice President Operations, North Memorial Health Hospital, Robbinsdale, MN, p. A383

HORTON, Alan, Administrator, Putnam General Hospital, Eatonton, GA, p. A172

HORTON, Greg, Director Support Services, State Hospital South, Blackfoot, ID, p. A188

HORTON, Jerrilyn, R.N., Chief Nursing Officer, Dewitt Hospital, Dewitt, AR, p. A44

HORTON, Jim, Chief Executive Officer, Rankin County Hospital District, Rankin, TX, p. A708

HORTON, Joseph, Assistant Administrator, Middlesboro Arh Hospital, Middlesboro, KY, p. A290

HORTON, Kenny, Director Information Systems, Walker Baptist Medical Center, Jasper, AL, p. A20

HORTON, Landon, Director of Nursing, Valley Behavioral Health System, Barling, AR, p. A42

HORTON, Marie, Director Associate Relations, Bartow Regional Medical Center, Bartow, FL, p. A131

HORTON, Sammy, Chief of Staff, Brownwood Regional Medical Center, Brownwood, TX, p. A661

HORTON, Shawn, Chief Nursing Officer, Harlan County Health System, Alma, NE, p. A429

HORTON, Warren, Information Technologist, Baptist Health Medical Center-Stuttgart, Stuttgart, AR, p. A53

HORVAT, Kami, Chief Financial Officer, West Covina Medical Center, West Covina, CA, p. A104

HORVATH, Alex, Vice President and Chief Human Resources Officer, Tmc Healthcare, Tucson, AZ, p. A41

Vice President Human Resources, Methodist Hospitals, Gary, IN, p. A229

HORVATH, Holly, Director of Nursing, Jerome Golden Center For Behavioral Health, Inc., West Palm Beach, FL, p. A162

HORVATH, Joanne, Vice President Finance, Theda Care Medical Center - Wild Rose, Wild Rose, WI, p. A799

HOSS, Laurna, Human Resource Coordinator, Select Specialty Hospital-Omaha, Omaha, NE, p. A438

HOSTEENEZ, Vivie, Chief Financial Officer, San Carlos Apache Healthcare Corporation, Peridot, AZ, p. A35

HOSTETTER, Lynne, Vice President Human Resources, The Hsc Pediatric Center, Washington, DC, p. A130

HOTA, Bala, Interim Chief Information Officer, John H. Stroger Jr. Hospital Of Cook County, Chicago, IL, p. A199

HOTCHKISS, Jason, CPA, Chief Financial Officer, Ottumwa Regional Health Center, Ottumwa, IA, p. A256

CPA, Chief Financial Officer, Trios Health, Kennewick, WA, p. A759

HOTCHKISS, Kaleigh, Controller, Encompass Health Rehabilitation Hospital Of Northwest Tucson, Tucson, AZ, p. A40

HOTES, Lawrence, M.D., Chief Medical Officer, New England Sinai Hospital And Rehabilitation Center, Stoughton, MA, p. A345

HOTOVY, Patrick, M.D., Chief of Staff, York General, York, NE, p. A440

HOUCHIN, Kim, Chief Nursing Officer, Minnie Hamilton Healthcare Center, Grantsville, WV, p. A772

HOUGHTON, Roxan, Director Human Resources, Riverbridge Specialty Hospital, Vidalia, LA, p. A316

HOULE, David, Executive Vice President and Chief Financial Officer, Hebrew Senior Care, West Hartford, CT, p. A126

HOULIHAN, David, M.D., Chief of Staff, Va Medical Center, Tomah, WI, p. A797

HOULTON, Andrew, M.D., Chief Medical Officer, North Memorial Health Hospital, Robbinsdale, MN, p. A383

HOUNSHELL, Jacqueline, Chief Financial Officer, Leconte Medical Center, Sevierville, TN, p. A649

HOURANY, Joseph, Chief Medical Officer, Montclair Hospital Medical Center, Montclair, CA, p. A79

HOUSAND, Jill, Director Human Resources, Mesa Springs, Fort Worth, TX, p. A679

HOUSE, David, Vice President and Chief Information Officer, Baptist Health Medical Center - North Little Rock, North Little Rock, AR, p. A51

Vice President and Chief Information Officer, Baptist Health Medical Center-Arkadelphia, Arkadelphia, AR, p. A42

Vice President and Chief Information Officer, Baptist Health Medical Center-Little Rock, Little Rock, AR, p. A49

Vice President and Chief Information Officer, Baptist Health Rehabilitation Institute, Little Rock, AR, p. A49

Vice President, Baptist Health Extended Care Hospital, Little Rock, AR, p. A48

HOUSE, John, M.D., Chief of Staff, Eureka Springs Hospital, Eureka Springs, AR, p. A45

HOUSER, David, M.D., Vice President Medical Affairs, Monument Health Rapid City Hospital, Rapid City, SD, p. A630

HOUSER, Kurt, Chief Human Resources Officer, University Medical Center, Las Vegas, NV, p. A444

HOUSER, Robert, FACHE, Chief Executive Officer, Pioneer Memorial Hospital, Heppner, OR, p. A575

HOUSER, Sara, Chief Nursing Officer, Ashe Memorial Hospital, Jefferson, NC, p. A513

HOUSH, Joe, District Director Human Resources, Kindred Hospital-Indianapolis, Indianapolis, IN, p. A232

HOUSMAN, Bradley, M.D., Chief Medical Officer, Baptist Health Paducah, Paducah, KY, p. A291

HOUSTON, Anthony, FACHE, Chief Operating Officer, Chi Memorial, Chattanooga, TN, p. A635

HOUSTON, Jerry, Director Information Systems, Jennie Stuart Medical Center, Hopkinsville, KY, p. A285

HOUSTON, Sally, M.D., Executive Vice President and Chief Medical Officer, Tamp. General Hospital, Tampa, FL, p. A160

HOUSTON-RAASIKH, Ceonne, Chief Nursing Officer, Pih Health Hospital - Downey, Downey, CA, p. A62

HOVAN, Keith A., R.N., President and Chief Executive Officer, Southcoast Hospitals Group. Fall River, MA, p. A339

HOVDENES, Jodi, R.N., Vice President Patient Care, Chi St Alexius Health Carrington Medical Center, Carrington, ND, p. A522

HOVENS, Michael, M.D., Chief Medical Officer, Panola Medical Center, Batesville, MS, p. A389

HOWALD, Nick, Chief Operating Officer, Tristar Skyline Medical Center, Nashville, TN, p. A647

HOWARD, Cameron, Chief Operating Officer, Medical City Plano, Plano, TX, p. A707

HOWARD, Catherine, Director Human Resources, Sentara Halifax Regional Hospital, South Boston, VA, p. A751

HOWARD, Cindy, Director Financial Services, Nell J. Redfield Memorial Hospital, Malad City, ID, p. A191

HOWARD, Dan, Chief Information Officer, Usa Health Children's & Women's Hospital, Mobile, AL, p. A22

HOWARD, Daniel, Chief Financial Officer, Maine Veterans Affairs Medical Center, Augusta, ME, p. A318

HOWARD, Darcy, Interim Chief Executive Officer, Kit Carson County Health Service District, Burlington, CO, p. A108

HOWARD, Deanna S., Interim President and Chief Executive Officer, Valley Regional Hospital, Claremont, NH, p. A448

HOWARD, Gary, Senior Vice President and Chief Financial Officer, Hamilton Medical Center, Dalton, GA, p. A170

HOWARD, Greg, Director Human Resource, Health Alliance Hospital - Broadway Campus, Kingston, NY, p. A486

Vice President Human Resources, Health Alliance Hospital - Mary's Avenue Campus, Kingston, NY, p. A487

HOWARD, Gwenyth, Vice President Finance, St. Thomas More Hospital, Canon City, CO, p. A108

HOWARD, Lisa, Associate Director, Veterans Affairs Sierra Nevada Health Care System, Reno, NV, p. A446

HOWARD, Lisa M., Director, Veterans Affairs Sierra Nevada Health Care System, Reno, NV, p. A446

HOWARD, Loy M., Chief Operating Officer, Tanner Medical Center-Carrollton, Carrollton, GA, p. A168

HOWARD, Mark L., Chief Executive Officer, Fairmount Behavioral Health System, Philadelphia, PA, p. A600

HOWARD, Mary, Director Human Resources, Winnebago Mental Health Institute, Winnebago, WI, p. A800

HOWARD, Melissa, Chief Nurse Executive, ICH & FPH, Emanate Health Inter-Community Hospital, Covina, CA, p. A61

HOWARD, Mike, Chief Operating Officer, North Alabama Medical Center, Florence, AL, p. A18

HOWARD, Opal, Executive Director Human Resources, Adventhealth Daytona Beach, Daytona Beach, FL, p. A136

HOWARD, Pamela B., R.N., Chief Executive Officer, Administrator and Risk Manager, Lake Butler Hospital, Lake Butler, FL, p. A142

HOWARD, Ron, Chief Financial Officer, Holly Hill Hospital, Raleigh, NC, p. A516

HOWARD, Sabra, Manager Human Resources, Harlan Arh Hospital, Harlan, KY, p. A284

HOWARD, Teresa, Manager Human Resources, Yoakum County Hospital, Denver City, TX, p. A672

HOWARD, Tina, Manager, Team Member Relations, Winter Haven Hospital, Winter Haven, FL, p. A162

HOWARD, Tom, Chief Financial Officer, Texas Health Presbyterian Hospital Flower Mound, Flower Mound, TX, p. A677

HOWARD, Win, Chief Executive Officer, Asante Three Rivers Medical Center, Grants Pass, OR, p. A575

HOWARD-CROW, Dallis, Chief Human Resources Officer, Emory University Hospital Midtown, Atlanta, GA, p. A164
Chief Human Resources Officer, Uchealth Yamp. Valley Medical Center, Steamboat Springs, CO, p. A118

HOWAT, Greg, Vice President Human Resources, Northern Light Eastern Maine Medical Center, Bangor, ME, p. A318

HOWDEN, William, Vice President Nursing, Good Samaritan Regional Medical Center, Corvallis, OR, p. A574

HOWE, Christopher L., R.N., Chief Executive Officer, Plateau Medical Center, Oak Hill, WV, p. A775

HOWE, Debbie, Chief Executive Officer, Weatherford Regional Hospital, Weatherford, OK, p. A572

HOWE, James, Director Human Resources, Pinnacle Pointe Hospital, Little Rock, AR, p. A49

HOWE, Judson, Chief Financial Officer, Adventist Health Howard Memorial, Willits, CA, p. A105

HOWE, Vicki, Health Information Management, Ness County Hospital District No 2, Ness City, KS, p. A272

HOWELL, Amy, Director Human Resources, St. Luke's Behavioral Health Center, Phoenix, AZ, p. A36

HOWELL, Bradley C., Chief Executive Officer, Pioneer Medical Center, Big Timber, MT, p. A421

HOWELL, Carrie, Chief Financial Officer, Barstow Community Hospital, Barstow, CA, p. A58

HOWELL, Diana, Director Human Resources, Hca Houston Healthcare Conroe, Conroe, TX, p. A665

HOWELL, Jerry, Administrator, Sabine County Hospital, Hemphill, TX, p. A683

HOWELL, Jill, Chief Nursing Officer, St. Luke's Jerome, Jerome, ID, p. A190
Chief Operating Officer and Chief Nursing Officer, St. Luke's Jerome, Jerome, ID, p. A190

HOWELL, Katherine, Chief Nursing Officer, University Of Colorado Hospital, Aurora, CO, p. A108

HOWELL, Kristie, System Information Technology Director, Southampton Memorial Hospital, Franklin, VA, p. A742

HOWELL, Nathan, President, Southern Maine Health Care - Biddeford Medical Center, Biddeford, ME, p. A319

HOWELL, Ronene, Director Health Information Management, Bryce Hospital, Tuscaloosa, AL, p. A25

HOWELL, Sheri, Deputy Commander Nursing, Brooke Army Medical Center, Fort Sam Houston, TX, p. A677

HOWELL, Timothy, R.N., Senior Vice President and Chief Nursing Officer, University Medical Center, Lubbock, TX, p. A698

HOWELLS, Stephen, Chief Financial Officer, Kane County Hospital, Kanab, UT, p. A728

HOWERTER, Mark, M.D., President Medical Staff, Columbus Community Hospital, Columbus, NE, p. A431

HOWERTON, Russell, M.D., Chief Medical Officer, Wake Forest Baptist Medical Center, Winston, NC, p. A520

HOWERTON, Shawn, M.D., Chief Executive Officer and President, Medical Staff, Sampson Regional Medical Center, Clinton, NC, p. A507

HOY, Jonathan, Chief Financial Officer, Duke Regional Hospital, Durham, NC, p. A508

HOY, Sarah, Chief Nursing Officer, Coffeyville Regional Medical Center, Coffeyville, KS, p. A262

HOYER, Sara, Director Administrative Services, Kansas Neurological Institute, Topeka, KS, p. A277

HOYES, Garry W., Chief Executive Officer, Columbus Dublin Springs, Dublin, OH, p. A539

HOYING, Cheryl, Ph.D., R.N., FACHE, Chief Nurse Executive and Patient Services Officer, Ohio State University Wexner Medical Center, Columbus, OH, p. A536

HOYOS, Kent, Chief Information Officer, Pomona Valley Hospital Medical Center, Pomona, CA, p. A86

HOYT, Nancy, R.N., Vice President Operations/Clinical and Chief Nursing Officer, Mercy Regional Medical Center, Durango, CO, p. A111

HRIT, Barbara, Controller, Beaumont Hospital - Farmington Hills, Farmington Hills, MI, p. A354

HRITZ, Diane, Chief Financial Officer, Advanced Surgical Hospital, Washington, PA, p. A609

HRUBIAK, Dan, Associate Computer Program Analyst, Western New York Children's Psychiatric Center, West Seneca, NY, p. A502

HRUBY, Deidre, Director of Patient Care, Madelia Community Hospital, Madelia, MN, p. A379

HSIEH, Ketty, Senior Director Finance, Uw Medicine/ Northwest Hospital & Medical Center, Seattle, WA, p. A764

HSU, Wah Chung, Senior Vice President Finance, San Antonio Regional Hospital, Upland, CA, p. A102

HUANG, Hanna, Administrator and Chief Operating Officer, Laredo Rehabilitation Hospital, Laredo, TX, p. A695
Administrator and Chief Operating Officer, Laredo Specialty Hospital, Laredo, TX, p. A695

HUANG, Joseph, M.D., Chief Medical and Quality Officer, Legacy Silverton Medical Center, Silverton, OR, p. A581

HUBBARD, Bill, Vice President, Operations, Atrium Health Cabarrus, Concord, NC, p. A508

HUBBARD, Blake W., FACHE, Chief Executive Officer, Foundation Surgical Hospital Of San Antonio, San Antonio, TX, p. A711

HUBBARD, Brenda, Corporate Director, Human Resources, Cap. Fear Valley - Bladen County Hospital, Elizabethtown, NC, p. A509

HUBBARD, Brent, FACHE, Chief Operating Officer, Mercy Hospital Ozark, Ozark, AR, p. A51
FACHE, Chief Operating Officer, Mercy Hospital Paris, Paris, AR, p. A51
FACHE, Chief Operating Officer, Mercy Hospital Springfield, Springfield, MO, p. A419
FACHE, Chief Operating Officer, Mercy Hospital Waldron, Waldron, AR, p. A54
FACHE, President and Chief Operating Officer, Mercy Hospital Springfield, Springfield, MO, p. A419

HUBBARD, Daniel, Chief Financial Officer, Sioux Falls Veterans Affairs Health Care System, Sioux Falls, SD, p. A632

HUBBARD, Gwen, Chief Nursing Officer, Sierra Vista Hospital, Sacramento, CA, p. A90

HUBBARD, Kathy, Controller, Ocean Beach Hospital, Ilwaco, WA, p. A759
Manager Human Resources, Nell J. Redfield Memorial Hospital, Malad City, ID, p. A191

HUBBARD, Lisa, Vice President and Chief Nursing Executive, Mercy Medical Center Mount Shasta, Mount Shasta, CA, p. A80

HUBBARD, Mark, Vice President Risk Management, Loma Linda University Behavioral Medicine Center, Redlands, CA, p. A87

HUBBARD, Tyson, Director Human Resources, Stanislaus Surgical Hospital, Modesto, CA, p. A79

HUBBELL, Heather, Director of Patient Care, Avera Flandreau Hospital, Flandreau, SD, p. A628

HUBBS III, Olas A., FACHE, President and Chief Executive Officer, Memorial Health, Marysville, OH, p. A544

HUBEL, Edward T., FACHE, President, Baptist Medical Center Nassau, Fernandina Beach, FL, p. A137

HUBER, Dalton, Chief Financial Officer, Campbell County Health, Gillette, WY, p. A802

HUBER, Joseph, Chief Financial Officer, Hospital Of The University Of Pennsylvania, Philadelphia, PA, p. A600

HUBER, Patricia, Chief Nursing Officer, Sojourn At Seneca Senior Behavioral Health, Tiffin, OH, p. A550

HUBER, Timothy, Controller, Mercyone Cedar Falls Medical Center, Cedar Falls, IA, p. A244
Controller, Mercyone Waterloo Medical Center, Waterloo, IA, p. A259
Vice President and Chief Financial Officer, Mercyone Oelwein Medical Center, Oelwein, IA, p. A255

HUBER, Vicki Lynn, R.N., MSN, Chief Nursing Officer, Abrazo Scottsdale Campus, Phoenix, AZ, p. A35

HUBLEY, Grover, M.D., President Medical Staff, Chi St. Josep. Health Madison Hospital, Madisonville, TX, p. A699

HUBSCHMAN, Gary, Administrative Director Finance, Sutter Auburn Faith Hospital, Auburn, CA, p. A56
Administrative Director Finance, Sutter Roseville Medical Center, Roseville, CA, p. A89

HUCKABEE, Mike, Network Administrator, Coryell Health, Gatesville, TX, p. A681

HUCKABY, Don, Chief Information Management Service, Veterans Affairs Eastern Colorado Health Care System, Denver, CO, p. A111

HUDA, Edith, Director Human Resources, Daniels Memorial Healthcare Center, Scobey, MT, p. A427

HUDAK, Corey, Director Human Resources, Upmc Memorial, York, PA, p. A612

HUDDLESTON, Tina, R.N., Chief Nursing Officer, Baylor Scott & White Medical Center - Trophy Club, Trophy Club, TX, p. A721

HUDGENS, Roselyn, Director Human Resources, Ballinger Memorial Hospital, Ballinger, TX, p. A657

HUDGINS, Laura, Assistant Administrator, Jasper Memorial Hospital, Monticello, GA, p. A177

HUDGINS, Paul, Senior Vice President, Carilion Franklin Memorial Hospital, Rocky Mount, VA, p. A751

HUDSON, Beth, Chief Nursing Officer, Baylor Scott & White Institute For Rehabilitation - Dallas, Dallas, TX, p. A667

HUDSON, Delilah, Controller, Covington County Hospital, Collins, MS, p. A391

HUDSON, Janell, Director, Nursing and Clinical Services, Sanford Medical Center Thief River Falls, Thief River Falls, MN, p. A386

HUDSON, Jason Dan., R.N., Chief Executive Officer, Encompass Health Rehabilitation Hospital Midland Odessa, Midland, TX, p. A701

HUDSON, Kenneth, Chief Financial Officer, Veterans Affairs Puget Sound Health Care System, Seattle, WA, p. A764

HUDSON, Kent, Chief Financial Officer, Kingman Community Hospital, Kingman, KS, p. A268

HUDSON, Larry, Executive Vice President and Chief Financial Officer, Charleston Area Medical Center, Charleston, WV, p. A771

HUDSON, Maggie, Chief Financial and Operations Officer, Santiam Hospital, Stayton, OR, p. A582

HUDSON, Mike, Administrator, Federal Correctional Institute Hospital, Littleton, CO, p. A116

HUDSON, Norma, Chief Financial Officer, Del Amo Hospital, Torrance, CA, p. A101

HUDSON, Pamela, M.D., Chief Executive Officer, Crestwood Medical Center, Huntsville, AL, p. A20

HUDSON, R. Guy., Chief Executive Officer, Swedish/Issaquah, Issaquah, WA, p. A759

HUDSON, Shannon, Interim Chief Executive Officer, Beacon Children's Hospital, Luverne, AL, p. A20

HUDSON-JINKS, Therese, R.N., MSN, Chief Nursing Officer, Tufts Medical Center, Boston, MA, p. A336

HUELSKAMP, Donald, Interim Chief Financial Officer, Harrison Community Hospital, Cadiz, OH, p. A530

HUERTA, Brad, Chief Executive Officer and Administrator, Lost Rivers Medical Center, Arco, ID, p. A188

HUERTA, Guillermo, M.D., Chief Medical Officer, Select Specialty Hospital-Omaha, Omaha, NE, p. A438

HUERTA, Jose, Chief Executive Officer, Premier Specialty Hospital Of El Paso, El Paso, TX, p. A675

HUERTER, Holly, Vice President Human Resources, Methodist Jennie Edmundson Hospital, Council Bluffs, IA, p. A247
Vice President Human Resources, Nebraska Methodist Hospital, Omaha, NE, p. A437

HUESMAN, Carol, Chief Information Officer, Major Hospital, Shelbyville, IN, p. A240

HUETTL, Patricia, Vice President Finance and Chief Financial Officer, Holy Family Memorial, Manitowoc, WI, p. A788

HUFF, Jeff, Assistant Administrator Finance, Fayette Medical Center, Fayette, AL, p. A18

HUFF, Michael H., Chief Executive Officer, Hamilton Hospital, Olney, TX, p. A704

HUFF, Shelley, Regional Program Manager, Indiana University Health Tipton Hospital, Tipton, IN, p. A241

HUFFINE, Daniel, Chief Financial Officer, St. David's Medical Center, Austin, TX, p. A656

HUFFMAN, David, Vice President and Controller, Select Specialty Hospital-Wilmington, Wilmington, DE, p. A128

HUFFMAN, Joshua, M.D., Chief Medical Staff, Chi Saint Josep. Berea, Berea, KY, p. A280

HUFFMAN, Patricia, Controller, Encompass Health Rehabilitation Hospital Of Franklin, Franklin, TN, p. A638

HUFFMAN, Sherry, Administrator Human Resources, Beaumont Hospital - Dearborn, Dearborn, MI, p. A352

HUFFMAN, Teresa, Chief Executive Officer, Texas Rehabilitation Hospital Of Arlington, Arlington, TX, p. A654

HUFFMAN, Tim, Western Region Director, Information Systems Business Relationships, Baylor Scott & White Medical Center-Irving, Irving, TX, p. A690

HUFFNER, William, M.D., Chief Medical Officer, University Of Maryland Shore Medical Center At Chestertown, Chestertown, MD, p. A328

M.D., Chief Medical Officer, University Of Maryland Shore Medical Center At Easton, Easton, MD, p. A329

M.D., Vice President Medical Affairs, University Of Maryland Shore Medical Center At Dorchester, Cambridge, MD, p. A328

HUFFSTUTLER, Brandon, Chief Information Officer, Electra Memorial Hospital, Electra, TX, p. A676

HUFNAGEL, Keith, Director Human Resources, Stillwater Medical Center, Stillwater, OK, p. A568

HUGGINS, Lois, Chief Human Resources Officer and Senior Vice President Human Resources, Shirley Ryan Abilitylab, Chicago, IL, p. A200

HUGGINS, Michael, Administrator Network System, Eastern Oklahoma Medical Center, Poteau, OK, p. A567

HUGHES, April, Chief Financial Officer, Peachford Behavioral Health System, Atlanta, GA, p. A165

HUGHES, Beth, President, Mercyone Siouxland Medical Center, Sioux City, IA, p. A258

HUGHES, Bill, Chief Nursing Officer, Granville Health System, Oxford, NC, p. A516

HUGHES, Brenda, Chief Operating Officer, Ssm Select Rehabilitation Hospital, Richmond Heights, MO, p. A414

HUGHES, Chad, Chief Information Officer, North Texas State Hospital, Wichita Falls Campus, Wichita Falls, TX, p. A725 Information Officer, North Texas State Hospital, Vernon, TX, p. A723

HUGHES, Chantel, Chief Financial Officer, Seven Hills Hospital, Henderson, NV, p. A442

HUGHES, David, Chief Financial Officer, Vidant Medical Center, Greenville, NC, p. A511

HUGHES, David L., Administrator, Crenshaw Community Hospital, Luverne, AL, p. A21

HUGHES, Dustan, M.D., Vice President Medical Affairs, Saint Alphonsus Medical Center - Nampa, Nampa, ID, p. A192

HUGHES, Elisabeth, Director Human Resources and Community Relations, Fairview Regional Medical Center, Fairview, OK, p. A559

HUGHES, James, Director Human Resources, Lake Cumberland Regional Hospital, Somerset, KY, p. A293

HUGHES, Jeffrey, Chief Operating Officer, Wentworth-Douglass Hospital, Dover, NH, p. A448

HUGHES, Jessica, Director Finance, Hawarden Regional Healthcare, Hawarden, IA, p. A251

HUGHES, John, Chief Executive Officer, Rehabilitation Hospital Of Overland Park, Overland Park, KS, p. A274

HUGHES, Lee, R.N., Chief Nursing Officer, Flint River Community Hospital, Montezuma, GA, p. A177

HUGHES, Leigh Ann, Chief Financial Officer, Hardin Medical Center, Savannah, TN, p. A649

HUGHES, Lori, R.N., MSN, Chief Nursing Officer, Vice President Operations & Patient Care Services, Cottage Hospital, Woodsville, NH, p. A451

R.N., MSN, Chief Nursing Officer, Vice President Operations and Patient Care Services, Cottage Hospital, Woodsville, NH, p. A451

HUGHES, Mark, M.D., Medical Director, River Park Hospital, Huntington, WV, p. A773

HUGHES, Susan, Interim Director Human Resources, Winner Regional Healthcare Center, Winner, SD, p. A633

HUGHES, Terry, Director Information Systems, Nantucket Cottage Hospital, Nantucket, MA, p. A342

HUGHES, Veronica, Chief Nursing Officer, Mesilla Valley Hospital, Las Cruces, NM, p. A470

HUGHES-MICKEL, Leann, Chief Information Officer, Touro Infirmary, New Orleans, LA, p. A311

HUGHS, Mary, Chief Human Resources Officer, Our Lady Of Lourdes Memorial Hospital, Inc., Binghamton, NY, p. A476

HUGHSON, John R., Chief Executive Officer, Frio Regional Hospital, Pearsall, TX, p. A705

HUGO, Chris, M.D., Chief of Staff, Guttenberg Municipal Hospital And Clinics, Guttenberg, IA, p. A250

HULBERT, Kim, R.N., Chief Clinical Officer, Madison County Health Care System, Winterset, IA, p. A260

HULETT, Rachelle, Vice President Human Resources, Mclaren Flint, Flint, MI, p. A354

HULETT, Wendi, Chief Nursing Officer, Artesia General Hospital, Artesia, NM, p. A468

HULL, Brad, Chief Financial Officer, Dale Medical Center, Ozark, AL, p. A23

HULL, Debbie, Chief Financial Officer, Fisher County Hospital District, Rotan, TX, p. A709

HULL, Kathy, President and Chief Executive Officer, Illini Community Hospital, Pittsfield, IL, p. A217

HULL, Ken, Director Human Resources, Inova Fairfax Hospital, Falls Church, VA, p. A741

HULL, Lauren, Chief Operating Officer, Porter Regional Hospital, Valparaiso, IN, p. A241

HULL, Patrick, Acting Director, Grand Junction Veterans Health Care System, Grand Junction, CO, p. A113

HULLANDER, Angie, Administrator and Special Operations, Chi Memorial Hospital - Georgia, Fort Oglethorpe, GA, p. A173

HULLINGER, Scott, Chief Executive Officer, Silver Oaks Behavioral Hospital, New Lenox, IL, p. A214

HULSE, Mark, MSN, Chief Digital Officer, City Of Hope's Helford Clinical Research Hospital, Duarte, CA, p. A62

HULSEY, Cathy, Manager of Human Resources, Chi Memorial Hospital - Georgia, Fort Oglethorpe, GA, p. A173

HULSEY, Grant, Director Information Technology, Baylor Scott & White Surgical Hospital-Sherman, Sherman, TX, p. A715

HULSEY, Kelly, MSN, R.N., Chief Nursing Officer, Piedmont Hospital, Atlanta, GA, p. A165

HUMBERT, Gilbert, R.N., JrChief Nursing Officer, Our Lady Of Lourdes Regional Medical Center, Lafayette, LA, p. A306

HUMBLE, Kathryn, Senior Executive, Human Resource Services, Beatrice Community Hospital And Health Center, Beatrice, NE, p. A430

HUMBLE, Linnea, Director of Finance, Sutter Lakeside Hospital, Lakeport, CA, p. A71

HUME, Diana, Manager Human Resources, Methodist Mckinney Hospital, Mckinney, TX, p. A700

HUMES, Karen, Chief Information Officer, Titusville Area Hospital, Titusville, PA, p. A608

HUMME, Sarah, MSN, R.N., Chief Nursing Officer, Southwest General Hospital, San Antonio, TX, p. A713 MSN, R.N., Chief Operating Officer, Southwest General Hospital, San Antonio, TX, p. A713

HUMMEL, Angela, Vice President Human Resources, Evangelical Community Hospital, Lewisburg, PA, p. A595

HUMMELKE, Arlita, Manager Human Resources, Mercy Hospital Tishomingo, Tishomingo, OK, p. A569

HUMMER, Denise, R.N., Vice President Administrative Services, Community Memorial Hospital, Hamilton, NY, p. A485

HUMPHREY, Dale, Chief Executive Officer, Saint Thomas River Park Hospital, Mc Minnville, TN, p. A643

HUMPHREY, Eric, Senior Vice President, Chief Human Resources Officer, Froedtert West Bend Hospital, West Bend, WI, p. A799

HUMPHREY, James, Vice President Talent Resources and Human Resources for South Side Operating Group. Penrose-St. Francis Health Services, Colorado Springs, CO, p. A109

HUMPHREY, Randy, Chief Financial Officer, Merit Health Wesley, Hattiesburg, MS, p. A393

HUMPHREY, Richard, Executive Vice President and Chief Financial Officer, Parkland Health & Hospital System, Dallas, TX, p. A670

HUMPHREYS, Corina, Chief Executive Officer, Weslaco Regional Rehabilitation Hospital, Weslaco, TX, p. A725

HUMPHREYS, Lynn, Director Human Resources, Henry County Health Center, Mount Pleasant, IA, p. A254

HUMPHRIES, Vickie, Director Human Resources, Bon Secours Maryview Medical Center, Portsmouth, VA, p. A749 Vice President Human Resources, Bon Secours Mary Immaculate Hospital, Newport News, VA, p. A746 Vice President Human Resources, Bon Secours-Depaul Medical Center, Norfolk, VA, p. A747

HUNDAL, Ranjit, M.D., Chief Medical Executive, Mills-Peninsula Health Services, Burlingame, CA, p. A59

HUNGER, Bryan, Chief Executive Officer, Jefferson County Health Center, Fairfield, IA, p. A250

HUNGER, Dennis, Chief Operating Officer, Ottumwa Regional Health Center, Ottumwa, IA, p. A256

HUNSAKER, Mike, Chief Operating Officer, Star Valley Health, Afton, WY, p. A801

HUNSBERGER, Tom, Director Human Resources, Olmsted Medical Center, Rochester, MN, p. A384

HUNSICKER, Elizabeth, Chief Executive Officer, West Valley Medical Center, Caldwell, ID, p. A189

HUNT, Amy, Director Human Resources, Menorah Medical Center, Overland Park, KS, p. A274

HUNT, Cheri, Senior Vice President Patient Care Services, Chief Nursing Officer, Children's Mercy Hospital Kansas, Overland Park, KS, p. A273 Vice President Patient Care Services and Chief Nursing Officer, Children's Mercy Hospital Kansas City, Kansas City, MO, p. A408

HUNT, Christopher, Director, Information Technologies, FISO, Helena Regional Medical Center, Helena, AR, p. A46

HUNT, Deloris, Chief Human Resources Officer, Michigan Medicine, Ann Arbor, MI, p. A348

HUNT, Don, M.D., Vice President Patient Centered Care and Chief Nursing Officer, Ut Health North Campus Tyler, Tyler, TX, p. A722

HUNT, Jeffery, Vice President, Business Development and Support Services, Roane General Hospital, Spencer, WV, p. A777

HUNT, John R., Chief Executive Officer, Encompass Health Rehabilitation Hospital Of Western Massachusetts, Ludlow, MA, p. A341

HUNT, Julie, R.N., MS, Chief Nursing Officer, Oro Valley Hospital, Oro Valley, AZ, p. A34

HUNT, Karen, Executive Director, Harsha Behavioral Center, Terre Haute, IN, p. A241

HUNT, Lynelle, Director of Nursing, Indian Health Service - Quentin N. Burdick Memorial Health Care Facility, Belcourt, ND, p. A521

HUNT, Mary Miles., Chief Executive Officer, Ballard Rehabilitation Hospital, San Bernardino, CA, p. A91

HUNT, MaryJane, Chief Clinical Officer, Knoxville Hospital & Clinics, Knoxville, IA, p. A253

HUNT, Nick, Interim Director of Nursing, Mercy Hospital Waldron, Waldron, AR, p. A54

HUNT, Nickie, Chief Executive Officer, Landmark Hospital Of Columbia, Columbia, MO, p. A405

HUNT, Richard, M.D., Chief Operating Officer, Kaiser Sunnyside Medical Center, Clackamas, OR, p. A574

HUNT, Sharon, Chief Financial Officer, Hereford Regional Medical Center, Hereford, TX, p. A684 Interim Chief Financial Officer, Pecos County Memorial Hospital, Fort Stockton, TX, p. A677

HUNT, Vanessa, Director Human Resources, Hca Houston Healthcare Tomball, Tomball, TX, p. A721

HUNT, William, Chief Financial Officer, Reynolds Memorial Hospital, Glen Dale, WV, p. A772

HUNT ESQ, CherylChief Nursing Officer, St. Peter's Hospital, Helena, MT, p. A425

HUNTER, Bridgette, Chief Executive Officer, Select Specialty HospitalKansas City, Kansas City, KS, p. A267

HUNTER, Byron, Vice President Human Resources, Cap. Regional Health System, Cap. May Court House, NJ, p. A453

HUNTER, Diana, Director of Nursing, Fort Belknap Service Unit, Harlem, MT, p. A424

HUNTER, Fred, R.N., Chief Executive Officer, Desert Valley Hospital, Victorville, CA, p. A104

HUNTER, George, Interim Chief Human Resources Officer, Tuba City Regional Health Care Corporation, Tuba City, AZ, p. A39

HUNTER, John G., M.D., FACS, Executive Vice President and Chief Executive Officer, Ohsu Hospital, Portland, OR, p. A579

HUNTER, Ken, R.N., Chief Executive Officer, Kimball Health Services, Kimball, NE, p. A434

HUNTER, Linda, Chief Nursing Officer, Spring View Hospital, Lebanon, KY, p. A286

HUNTER, Mary Ann, Director Nursing Services, Prisma Health Baptist Easley Hospital, Easley, SC, p. A619

HUNTER, Melissa, Chief Nursing Officer, Lake Regional Health System, Osage Beach, MO, p. A413

HUNTER, Stephanie, Chief Human Resources Officer, Veterans Affairs Ann Arbor Healthcare System, Ann Arbor, MI, p. A348

HUNTER, Terri, R.N., Nurse Administrator, American Fork Hospital, American Fork, UT, p. A727

HUNTER, Tracy, Chief Human Resources Officer, East Cooper Medical Center, Mount Pleasant, SC, p. A622

HUNTLEY, Adrienne, Chief Human Resources Officer, Saint Francis Hospital-Bartlett, Bartlett, TN, p. A634 Director Human Resources, Encompass Health Rehabilitation Hospital Of North Memphis, Memphis, TN, p. A644

HUNTLEY, Devin, Chief Operating Officer, Providence St. Josep. Medical Center, Polson, MT, p. A427

HUNTON, David, M.D., Chief Medical Officer, Mercy Hospital Fort Smith, Fort Smith, AR, p. A46

HUNTSINGER, Kelli, Chief Operating Officer, Northern Inyo Hospital, Bishop. CA, p. A58

HUPP, Diane, R.N., Vice President Support Services and Patient Care Services, Upmc Children's Hospital Of Pittsburgh, Pittsburgh, PA, p. A603

HURD, Debra, MS, R.N., Vice President and Chief Nursing Officer, St. Joseph's Hospital, Saint Paul, MN, p. A385 MS, R.N., Vice President and Chief Nursing Officer, Woodwinds Health Campus, Woodbury, MN, p. A388

HURD, Ross, Chief Information Officer, Lake Chelan Community Hospital And Clinics, Chelan, WA, p. A756

HURFORD, Bill, Chief Medical Officer, University Of Cincinnati Medical Center, Cincinnati, OH, p. A533

HURLEY, Al, West Region Chief Operating Officer, Essentia Health Fargo, Fargo, ND, p. A522

HURLEY, Jeff, Vice President Human Resources, Flagler Hospital, Saint Augustine, FL, p. A155

HURLEY, William, M.D., Chief Medical Officer, Summit Pacific Medical Center, Elma, WA, p. A757

HUROWITZ, Marc P., D.O., Chief Executive Officer, Temple University Hospital - Jeanes Campus, Philadelphia, PA, p. A602

HURSH, John, Vice President Human Resources, Cox Medical Centers, Springfield, MO, p. A418

HURSHE, Josep. R., President, Ascension Of Providence Hospital, Southfield Campus, Southfield, MI, p. A367

HURST, David, Chief Nursing Officer, Alta View Hospital, Sandy, UT, p. A733

HURST, Kyle, Chief Operations Officer, Northwest Ohio Psychiatric Hospital, Toledo, OH, p. A550

HURST, Paul, M.D., Chief Medical Officer, Banner Heart Hospital, Mesa, AZ, p. A34

HURST, Steve, Information Technology Specialist, Haskell County Community Hospital, Stigler, OK, p. A568

HURT, Carol, Chief Nursing Officer, Tippah County Hospital, Ripley, MS, p. A399

HURT, Christie, M.D., Chief of Staff and Medical Director, Mercy Hospital Aurora, Aurora, MO, p. A402

HURT, Kelly, Chief Human Resources Officer Northern Colorado and Western Region, Banner Fort Collins Medical Center, Fort Collins, CO, p. A112

HURT, Todd, Administrator, State Hospital North, Orofino, ID, p. A192

HURT-DEITCH, Sally A., FACHE, R.N., MSN, Chief Executive Officer, Saint Francis Hospital, Memphis, TN, p. A645

HURWITZ, Steven, Senior Vice President Shared Services, Seattle Children's Hospital, Seattle, WA, p. A764

HUSAIN, Syed, M.D., Executive Vice President and Chief Medical Officer, Royal Oaks Hospital, Windsor, MO, p. A420

HUSEBY, Custer, Chief Executive Officer, Vibra Hospital Of Fargo, Fargo, ND, p. A523

HUSHING-KLINE, Bob, Hospital Administrator, Atascadero State Hospital, Atascadero, CA, p. A56

HUSKEY, Jeff, Chief Executive Officer and Administrator, Clay County Memorial Hospital, Henrietta, TX, p. A684

HUSS, Cathy, Chief Financial Officer, Lifecare Medical Center, Roseau, MN, p. A384

HUSS, Eric, Chief Financial Officer, Butler Health System, Butler, PA, p. A585

HUSSAIN, Iftikhar, Chief Financial Officer, El Camino Hospital, Mountain View, CA, p. A80

HUSSEY, Jamie, Chief Information Officer, Jackson Hospital, Marianna, FL, p. A145

HUSSEY, Stephen, M.D., Chief of Staff, Lake District Hospital, Lakeview, OR, p. A577

HUSSON, Charles, Regional Chief Medical Officer, Ascension Genesys Hospital, Grand Blanc, MI, p. A355

HUSTEDT, Dale, President, Aspirus Medford Hospital & Clinics, Inc., Medford, WI, p. A789

HUSTON, Jennifer, Chief Nursing Officer, Adventhealth Lake Wales, Lake Wales, FL, p. A143

HUSTON, William, Senior Vice President and Chief Financial Officer, Texas Scottish Rite Hospital For Children, Dallas, TX, p. A670

HUTCHENRIDER, E. Kenneth. Jr, FACHE, President, Methodist Richardson Medical Center, Richardson, TX, p. A708

HUTCHENS, Zachary, M.D., Chief Medical Officer, Saint Thomas Hickman Hospital, Centerville, TN, p. A635

HUTCHES, Trampas, President, Franklin Memorial Hospital, Farmington, ME, p. A320

HUTCHESON, Lorie, Vice President of Human Resources, Shepherd Center, Atlanta, GA, p. A165

HUTCHESON, Lou, M.D., Chief of Staff, Bacon County Hospital And Health System, Alma, GA, p. A163

HUTCHINGS, Lisa, Chief Financial Officer, Dmc - Children's Hospital Of Michigan, Detroit, MI, p. A352

HUTCHINS, Anne, M.D., Chief of Staff, Salem Veterans Affairs Medical Center, Salem, VA, p. A751

HUTCHINS, Michael T., Administrator, Jay Hospital, Jay, FL, p. A142

HUTCHINSON, R. Michael., Chief Executive Officer, Mee Memorial Hospital, King City, CA, p. A69

HUTCHINSON, Barbra, Director Medical Records, Richland Parish Hospital-Delhi, Delhi, LA, p. A300

HUTCHISON, Florence, M.D., Chief of Staff, Ralp. H. Johnson Veterans Affairs Medical Center, Charleston, SC, p. A616

HUTCHISON, Lewis, Vice President Operations and Quality, Ashtabula County Medical Center, Ashtabula, OH, p. A528

HUTCHSIN, Joel, M.D., Chief Medical Staff, Holton Community Hospital, Holton, KS, p. A266

HUTH, Michael, Chief Financial Officer, Sycamore Springs, Lafayette, IN, p. A234

HUTH, Richard, Administrator, South Georgia Medical Center Berrien Campus, Nashville, GA, p. A178

HUTH, Thomas, M.D., Vice President Medical Affairs, Reid Health, Richmond, IN, p. A239

HUTKA, Michael, Chief Executive Officer, Everest Rehabilitation Hospital Temple, Temple, TX, p. A719

HUTSELL, Dick, Vice President Information Technology Services, St. Louise Regional Hospital, Gilroy, CA, p. A66

HUTSELL, Richard, Vice President and Chief Information Officer, Daughters of Charity Health System, O'Connor Hospital, San Jose, CA, p. A95

HUTSON, Donald, President and Chief Executive Officer, Harrisburg Medical Center, Harrisburg, IL, p. A206

HUTSON, Joy, Director Human Resources, Merit Health Rankin, Brandon, MS, p. A390

HUTSON, Marty, Chief Financial Officer, St. Mary's Health Care System, Athens, GA, p. A164

HUTSON, Wayne, Chief Financial Officer, Union Hospital Clinton, Clinton, IN, p. A225

Executive Vice President and Chief Financial Officer, Union Hospital, Terre Haute, IN, p. A241

HUTT, Si William., Administrator, Heber Valley Hospital, Heber City, UT, p. A728

HUTTER, Elizabeth, Chief Executive Officer, Cedar Hills Hospital, Portland, OR, p. A579

HUVAL, Shadelle, Director Finance, St. Martin Hospital, Breaux Bridge, LA, p. A298

HUYNH, Thai, M.D., Chief of Medical Staff, El Camp. Memorial Hospital, El Campo, TX, p. A674

HYATT, Charlotte, MSN, R.N., Chief Operating Officer and Chief Nursing Officer, Henry Ford Allegiance Specialty Hospital, Jackson, MI, p. A359

HYATT, David W., FACHE, President - Blackford Hospital and Rural Strategy Indiana University Health, Indiana University Health Blackford Hospital, Hartford City, IN, p. A230

HYATT, Ronnie, Senior Vice President Finance and Chief Financial Officer, Bon Secours St. Francis Health System, Greenville, SC, p. A620

HYBERGER, Trey, Director Information Technology, Hardin Memorial Health, Elizabethtown, KY, p. A282

HYDE, Devon, Vice President, Chief Administrative Officer, Presbyterian Hospital, Albuquerque, NM, p. A468

HYDE, Jane E., President, Wellspan Gettysburg Hospital, Gettysburg, PA, p. A590

HYDE, Robert, Human Resources Business Partner, Kaiser Permanente Santa Clara Medical Center, Santa Clara, CA, p. A97

HYDE, Shannon, Director Human Resources, Encompass Health Rehabilitation Hospital Of Morgantown, Morgantown, WV, p. A774

HYDE, Stephanie, R.N., MSN, Chief Executive Officer, Tyler Continuecare Hospital, Tyler, TX, p. A722

HYDE, Steve, Chief Executive Officer, Paris Regional Medical Center, Paris, TX, p. A704

HYDER, LouAnn, Director Information Integrity Management, Cardinal Hill Rehabilitation Hospital, Lexington, KY, p. A286

HYDER, Sayeeda, Acting Chief Executive Officer, Gallup Indian Medical Center, Gallup. NM, p. A469

HYDER, Shiraz, M.D., Director Medical Affairs, Chi St. Alexius Health, Bismarck, ND, p. A521

HYDUKE, Kyle, Chief Executive Officer, Seaside Health System - Baton Rouge, Baton Rouge, LA, p. A297

HYLAND, Donna W., President and Chief Executive Officer, Children's Healthcare Of Atlanta, Atlanta, GA, p. A164

HYLAND, Jaquelyn, M.D., Chief Medical Officer, University Of Kansas Health System St. Francis Campus, Topeka, KS, p. A277

HYLAND-HILL, Barbara, R.N., Chief Nursing Officer, Providence Regional Medical Center Everett, Everett, WA, p. A758

HYLTON, Heather, Chief Financial Officer, Plateau Medical Center, Oak Hill, WV, p. A775

HYMAN, Bruce, M.D., Vice President Clinical Performance, Advocate Sherman Hospital, Elgin, IL, p. A203

HYMBAUGH, Mitzi, Chief Personnel, Ringgold County Hospital, Mount Ayr, IA, p. A254

HYMEL, Paul, Chief Financial Officer, Abrazo Central Campus, Phoenix, AZ, p. A35

HYNES, Kristi, Director Human Resources, Georgetown Behavioral Health Institute, Georgetown, TX, p. A681

HYNES, Mary, Manager Information Services, United Hospital District, Blue Earth, MN, p. A373

HYNOSKI, Michael, Chief Information Resource Management, James E. Van Zandt Veterans Affairs Medical Center, Altoona, PA, p. A584

HYTRY, Steven, PsyD, Chief Executive Officer, Del Amo Hospital, Torrance, CA, p. A101

## I

IACUONE, Karen, Chief Nursing Officer and Chief Operating Officer, Pioneers Medical Center, Meeker, CO, p. A117

Chief Nursing Officer, Pioneers Medical Center, Meeker, CO, p. A117

IAKOPO, Priscilla, Chief Financial Officer, Commonwealth Health Center, Saipan, MP, p. A805

IBARRA, Daniel, Chief Financial Officer, Crane Memorial Hospital, Crane, TX, p. A666

IBARRA, Kyle, Director Information Systems, Geary Community Hospital, Junction City, KS, p. A267

IBRAHIM, Tajudeen, Interim Business Administrator, Elgin Mental Health Center, Elgin, IL, p. A203

ICKOWSKI, Michael, Vice President and Chief Financial Officer, Regional West Medical Center, Scottsbluff, NE, p. A439

IDBEIS, Badr, M.D., Chief Executive Officer, Kansas Medical Center, Andover, KS, p. A261

IDOINE-FRIES, Julie, Chief Executive Officer, Select Specialty Hospital - Cleveland Gateway, Cleveland, OH, p. A535

IDSTEIN, Mary, Chief Financial Officer, Porter-Starke Services, Valparaiso, IN, p. A241

IERARDI, Josep. P., Chief Executive Officer, Wayne Memorial Hospital, Jesup. GA, p. A174

IERO, Tony, Director Management Information Systems, North Philadelphia Health System, Philadelphia, PA, p. A601

IFABIYI, Candace, Medical Center Director, Robert J. Dole Veterans Affairs Medical Center, Wichita, KS, p. A279

IFTINIUK, Alan, Chief Executive Officer, French Hospital Medical Center, San Luis Obispo, CA, p. A95

IGO, Angela, MSN, R.N., Chief Nursing Officer, Fitzgibbon Hospital, Marshall, MO, p. A411

IMHOFF, Sarah, Business Administrator, Chester Mental Health Center, Chester, IL, p. A197

IMLER, Jim, Director Human Resources, Gothenburg Health, Gothenburg, NE, p. A432

Director Human Resources, Kimball Health Services, Kimball, NE, p. A434

IMMORDINO, Jonathan, Chief Financial Officer, Rockledge Regional Medical Center, Rockledge, FL, p. A155

IMSEIS, Mikhail, M.D., Chief of Staff, Ness County Hospital District No 2, Ness City, KS, p. A272

IN, Henry, Director Human Resources, Dallas Behavioral Healthcare Hospital, Desoto, TX, p. A672

INGE, Laura, MSN, R.N., Chief Executive Officer, Kindred Hospital Northland, Kansas City, MO, p. A409

INGE, Ray, Vice President Human Resources, Pomona Valley Hospital Medical Center, Pomona, CA, p. A86

INGHAM, Raymond V., Ph.D., President and Chief Executive Officer, Witham Health Services, Lebanon, IN, p. A235

INGRAM, Karen, Director Human Resources, Baptist Memorial Hospital For Women, Memphis, TN, p. A644

INGRAM, Nathan Daniel., Chief Executive Officer and Owner, Lone Star Behavioral Health, Cypress, TX, p. A667

INHOFE, Kyle, Chief Human Resources Officer, Oklahoma City Veterans Affairs Medical Center, Oklahoma City, OK, p. A565

INMAN, Debbie, Chief Nursing Officer, Physicians Surgical Hospital - Quail Creek, Amarillo, TX, p. A652

INMAN, Joanne, President, Sentara Leigh Hospital, Norfolk, VA, p. A748

INMAN, Julie, Regional Executive Officer, Southeast Missouri Mental Health Center, Farmington, MO, p. A406

INNOCENTI, John Sr, President, Upmc Presbyterian, Pittsburgh, PA, p. A604

INO, Alan, Chief Financial Officer, Good Samaritan Hospital, Los Angeles, CA, p. A74

INOUYE, Valerie, Chief Financial Officer, Zuckerberg San Francisco General Hospital And Trauma Center, San Francisco, CA, p. A94

INSCHO, Kimberly, Vice President Human Resources and Marketing, Margaret Mary Health, Batesville, IN, p. A223

INSERRA, Toni A., Interim Administrator, South Lyon Medical Center, Yerington, NV, p. A447

INSKEEP, Johnathan, Chief Information Officer, Caribou Memorial Hospital And Living Center, Soda Springs, ID, p. A193

INZANA, Lou, Senior Vice President and Chief Financial Officer, Maine Medical Center, Portland, ME, p. A322

IQBAL, Nayyar, M.D., Director Medical Staff, Western State Hospital, Hopkinsville, KY, p. A285

IRELAND, Amy, Chief Financial Officer, Carroll County Memorial Hospital, Carrollton, MO, p. A404

IRELAND, Daniel P., FACHE, President, United Memorial Medical Center, Batavia, NY, p. A475

IRION, Val, M.D., Medical Director, Specialists Hospital Shreveport, Shreveport, LA, p. A314

IRISH, Kevin, Chief Information Officer, Franklin Regional Hospital, Franklin, NH, p. A449

Chief Information Officer, Lakes Region General Hospital, Laconia, NH, p. A449

IRISH-CLARDY, Katherine, M.D., Chief Medical Officer, Baptist Health - Fort Smith, Fort Smith, AR, p. A46

IRIZARRI, David, Director Information Technology, Northwest Medical Center, Margate, FL, p. A145

IRIZARRY, Aixa, Executive Director, Hospital Hima De Humacao, Humacao, PR, p. A808

IRIZARRY, Lourdes, M.D., Chief of Staff, Albany Stratton Veterans Affairs Medical Center, Albany, NY, p. A474

IRIZARRY, Sigfredo, Information Technology Director, Ashford Presbyterian Community Hospital, San Juan, PR, p. A809

IRVIN, Debbie, Director Health Information Management, Bhc Alhambra Hospital, Rosemead, CA, p. A88

IRVIN, Donna, Director Human Resources, Baylor Scott & White Medical Center - Trophy Club, Trophy Club, TX, p. A721

IRVIN, Mary, R.N., MSN, Senior Vice President and Chief Nursing Officer, Bethesda North Hospital, Cincinnati, OH, p. A532

IRVIN, Michael, Chief Executive Officer, Palms Of Pasadena Hospital, Saint Petersburg, FL, p. A156

IRVIN, Miriam, CNO, Encompass Health Rehabilitation Hospital, A Partner Of Washington Regional, Fayetteville, AR, p. A45

IRVING, Edith, R.N., MS, FACHE, Chief Nursing Officer, West Valley Medical Center, Caldwell, ID, p. A189

IRVING, Kelly Associate Director for Patient Care Services, Michael E. Debakey Veterans Affairs Medical Center, Houston, TX, p. A687

IRVING, Mark, Manager Management Information Systems, Osf St. Francis Hospital And Medical Group. Escanaba, MI, p. A354

IRWIN, Robert, Vice President Information Systems, Robert Wood Johnson University Hospital, New Brunswick, NJ, p. A459

IRWIN, Ruth, Associate Director Clinical Operations, Stewart & Lynda Resnick Neuropsychiatric Hospital At Ucla, Los Angeles, CA, p. A76

IRWIN, Vivian, Chief Financial Officer and Controller, Encompass Health Rehabilitation Hospital Midland Odessa, Midland, TX, p. A701

ISAAC, Lisa, Chief Nursing Officer, Choctaw Nation Health Care Center, Talihina, OK, p. A569

ISAAC, Regina, Director of Nursing, Choctaw Health Center, Philadelphia, MS, p. A398

ISAACKS, David, Medical Center Director, Kansas City Veterans Affairs Medical Center, Kansas City, MO, p. A408

ISAACKS, Scott R., FACHE, Director and Chief Executive Officer, Ralp. H. Johnson Veterans Affairs Medical Center, Charleston, SC, p. A616

ISAACS, Alicia, Superintendent and Medical Director, Madison State Hospital, Madison, IN, p. A236

ISAACS, Cynthia, Chief Executive Officer, Cornerstone Hospital Of Huntington, Huntington, WV, p. A773

ISAACS, Diane, Director of Nursing, Ouachita County Medical Center, Camden, AR, p. A43

ISAACS, Michael, Vice President Human Resources, Vista Health, Waukegan, IL, p. A222

ISAACSON, Sara, Chief Nursing Officer, Mad River Community Hospital, Arcata, CA, p. A56

ISACKSEN, Daniel, Regional Chief Financial Officer, Loyola University Medical Center, Maywood, IL, p. A211

ISADO, Jose, M.D., Medical Director, Auxilio Mutuo Hospital, San Juan, PR, p. A809

ISBELL, Samantha, R.N., Chief Nursing Officer, Hamilton Hospital, Olney, TX, p. A704

ISBELL, Sherri, Chief Information Officer, Virginia Gay Hospital, Vinton, IA, p. A259

ISBELL, Todd, R.N., MSN, Chief Nursing Officer, Memorial Health, Savannah, GA, p. A180

ISEMANN, William R., President and Chief Executive Officer, Kidspeace Children's Hospital, Orefield, PA, p. A599

ISENMANN, Debra, Human Resources Generalist, Cox Monett Hospital, Monett, MO, p. A412

ISHIZUKA, Paul, Chief Financial Officer, Skagit Valley Hospital, Mount Vernon, WA, p. A761
Regional Vice President and Chief Financial Officer, Cascade Valley Hospital, Arlington, WA, p. A755

ISHKANIAN, Gary, M.D., Vice President Medical Affairs, Montefiore Mount Vernon, Mount Vernon, NY, p. A489

ISKANDAR, Said, M.D., Chief Medical Officer, Sentara Halifax Regional Hospital, South Boston, VA, p. A751

ISLAM, Asad, M.D., Chief Medical Officer, Mayhill Hospital, Denton, TX, p. A672

ISLEY, L. Lee., FACHE, Ph.D., President and Chief Executive Officer, Nash Unc Health Care, Rocky Mount, NC, p. A517

ISMAIL, Asad, M.D., Medical Director, Wellstone Regional Hospital, Jeffersonville, IN, p. A233

ISMAIL, Hummayun, M.D., Medical Director, Select Specialty Hospital-Wilmington, Wilmington, DE, p. A128

ISOM, Julie, Director Human Resources, Lakeview Hospital, Bountiful, UT, p. A727

ISON, Tamara, Chief Financial Officer, Wellstar Sylvan Grove Hospital, Jackson, GA, p. A174

Chief Operating Officer, Wellstar Spalding Regional Hospital, Griffin, GA, p. A173
Senior Vice President and President, Wellstar Spalding Regional Hospital, Griffin, GA, p. A173
Senior Vice President and President, Wellstar Sylvan Grove Hospital, Jackson, GA, p. A174

ISON, William, Human Resources Manager, Select Specialty Hospital-Tri Cities, Bristol, TN, p. A634

ISRAEL, Corry, Director Human Resources, Western Plains Medical Complex, Dodge City, KS, p. A263

ISRAEL, Michael D., President and Chief Executive Officer, Westchester Medical Center, Valhalla, NY, p. A501

ISSAI, Alice H., President, Adventist Health Glendale, Glendale, CA, p. A66

ITO, Derek, Director Human Resources, Shriners Hospitals For Children-Honolulu, Honolulu, HI, p. A185

IVERSON, Amber, Chief Nursing Officer, Orem Community Hospital, Orem, UT, p. A730

IVERSON, Caryn, MSN, Chief Nursing Officer, Memorial Medical Center, Las Cruces, NM, p. A470

IVES, Matthew, Chief Executive Officer and Chief Financial Officer, Keokuk County Health Center, Sigourney, IA, p. A257
Interim Chief Executive Officer and Chief Financial Officer, Keokuk County Health Center, Sigourney, IA, p. A257

IVES, Shawna, CPA, Chief Financial Officer, White River Medical Center, Batesville, AR, p. A42

IVES ERICKSON, Jeanette, MS, R.N., Senior Vice President Patient Care and Chief Nurse, Massachusetts General Hospital, Boston, MA, p. A336

IVEY, Kim, Director of Human Resources, Cumberland Hospital For Children And Adolescents, New Kent, VA, p. A746

IVEY, Misty, Human Resources Manager, Washington County Regional Medical Center, Sandersville, GA, p. A179

IVIE, Brian K., President and Chief Executive Officer, Cascade Valley Hospital, Arlington, WA, p. A755
President and Chief Executive Officer, Skagit Valley Hospital, Mount Vernon, WA, p. A761

IVKOVICH, Paul J., President, Indiana University Health West Hospital, Avon, IN, p. A223

IVY, Michael, M.D., Senior Vice President for Medical Affairs and Chief Medical Officer, Bridgeport Hospital, Bridgeport, CT, p. A121

IYER, Raju, Senior Vice President and Chief Financial Officer, Ucsf Medical Center, San Francisco, CA, p. A94

IZAKOVIC, Martin, M.D., Vice President Medical Staff Affairs and Chief Medical Officer, Mercyone Iowa City Medical Center, Iowa City, IA, p. A252

IZZI, Denine, Senior Director Information Technology, Robert Wood Johnson University Hospital Rahway, Rahway, NJ, p. A462

# J

JABBARPOUR, Yad, M.D., Chief of Staff, Catawba Hospital, Catawba, VA, p. A739

JABERG, Janie, FACHE, President and Chief Executive Officer, Wayne Unc Health Care, Goldsboro, NC, p. A511

JABLONSKI, Kevin, Chief Nursing Officer, Christus Mother Frances Hospital - Winnsboro, Winnsboro, TX, p. A726
Chief Nursing Officer, Ut Health Athens, Athens, TX, p. A654

JABLONSKI, Mark, Vice President Mission Integration, St. Jude Medical Center, Fullerton, CA, p. A66

JABOUR, Leon, Regional Chief Information Officer, Wellspan Ephrata Community Hospital, Ephrata, PA, p. A589
Regional Chief Information Officer, Wellspan Good Samaritan Hospital, Lebanon, PA, p. A595

JACK, Claudia, Director Associate Relations, Bayfront Health Brooksville, Brooksville, FL, p. A133

JACK, Shannon, Administrator, Indianhead Medical Center, Shell Lake, WI, p. A796

JACKES, Frederick, Assistant Administrator and Director Human Resources, Valley Forge Medical Center And Hospital, Norristown, PA, p. A598

JACKIEWICZ, Thomas E., President, University Of Chicago Medical Center, Chicago, IL, p. A201

JACKSON, Alan, M.D., Medical Director, Roseland Community Hospital, Chicago, IL, p. A200

JACKSON, Amy L., Commander, Keller Army Community Hospital, West Point, NY, p. A502

JACKSON, Angelica, Director of Nursing, Anchor Hospital, Atlanta, GA, p. A164

JACKSON, Barbara, Ed.D., Acting Facility Director, Taylor Hardin Secure Medical Facility, Tuscaloosa, AL, p. A25

JACKSON, Carolyn, Chief Executive Officer, Saint Vincent Hospital, Worcester, MA, p. A346

JACKSON, Cindy, Chief Executive Officer, Kindred Hospital Bay Area-Tampa, Tampa, FL, p. A159
Director Human Resources, Phelp. Memorial Health Center, Holdrege, NE, p. A433

JACKSON, Collette, R.N., Director of Clinical Services, Bliant Specialty Hospital, New Orleans, LA, p. A310

JACKSON, Corey, Executive Vice President and Chief Talent Officer, Parkland Health & Hospital System, Dallas, TX, p. A670

JACKSON, Courtney, Coordinator Human Resources, Atoka County Medical Center, Atoka, OK, p. A556

JACKSON, Cynthia, Vice President Human Resources, Raulerson Hospital, Okeechobee, FL, p. A150

JACKSON, Daniel, President, Dmc - Sinai-Grace Hospital, Detroit, MI, p. A352

JACKSON, Darryl, D.O., Chief of Staff, Prague Community Hospital, Prague, OK, p. A567

JACKSON, David, Chief Financial Officer, Baptist Medical Center Leake, Carthage, MS, p. A390

JACKSON, Erin, Human Resources Specialist, Baptist Medical Center Nassau, Fernandina Beach, FL, p. A137

JACKSON, Evan, Chief Information Officer and Vice President, Planning and Business Development, Middlesex Hospital, Middletown, CT, p. A123

JACKSON, Frank Facility Chief Information Officer, Veterans Affairs Illiana Health Care System, Danville, IL, p. A202

JACKSON, Gary, D.O., Medical Director, Lincoln County Medical Center, Ruidoso, NM, p. A471

JACKSON, Gregory, Chief Executive Officer, Chi Franciscan Rehabilitation, Tacoma, WA, p. A766

JACKSON, Holly, Chief Operating Officer, Gulf Coast Regional Medical Center, Panama City, FL, p. A153

JACKSON, James, M.D., Chief of Staff, Cornerstone Hospitals Bossier City, Bossier City, LA, p. A298

JACKSON, James E T., M.P.H., Chief Administrative Officer, San Leandro Hospital, San Leandro, CA, p. A95

JACKSON, James H. Jr, Chief Executive Officer, Och Regional Medical Center, Starkville, MS, p. A400

JACKSON, Jeffrey, M.D., Medical Director, Houston Methodist Sugar Land Hospital, Sugar Land, TX, p. A717

JACKSON, Jennifer, Director Human Resources, Madison County Health Care System, Winterset, IA, p. A260

JACKSON, Joanne, Administrator Human Resources, Community Relations and Quality Improvement, Amery Hospital And Clinic, Amery, WI, p. A779

JACKSON, Jodie, Associate Director, Veterans Affairs New York Harbor Healthcare System, Brooklyn, NY, p. A479

JACKSON, Judy, Director Health Information Management and Privacy Officer, Shodair Children's Hospital, Helena, MT, p. A425

JACKSON, Kevin, Interim Chief Executive Officer, Harnett Health System, Dunn, NC, p. A508
On Site Administrator, Highsmith-Rainey Specialty Hospital, Fayetteville, NC, p. A510

JACKSON, Kiland, Chief Information Officer, Bunkie General Hospital, Bunkie, LA, p. A299

JACKSON, Lynn, Chief Operating Officer, Northside Hospital-Forsyth, Cumming, GA, p. A170

JACKSON, Margaret, R.N., Vice President Patient Care Services and Chief Nursing Officer, Suny Downstate-University Hospital Of Brooklyn, Brooklyn, NY, p. A479

JACKSON, Meg, Director Information Technology, Beauregard Health System, De Ridder, LA, p. A300

JACKSON, Melinda, Director Human Resources, Bates County Memorial Hospital, Butler, MO, p. A403

JACKSON, Melonie, Human Resource Business Partner, Spectrum Health Big Rapids Hospital, Big Rapids, MI, p. A349

JACKSON, Michael, M.D., Assistant Chief Medical Officer, Integris Bass Baptist Health Center, Enid, OK, p. A559

JACKSON, Patsy, Director of Nursing, Jay Hospital, Jay, FL, p. A142

JACKSON, Phillip E., President, Sentara Albemarle Medical Center, Elizabeth City, NC, p. A509

JACKSON, Reese, President and Chief Executive Officer, Chesapeake Regional Medical Center, Chesapeake, VA, p. A740

JACKSON, Robert, Chief Financial Officer, Alliance Health Center, Meridian, MS, p. A397
Chief Financial Officer, Longleaf Hospital, Alexandria, LA, p. A295
Chief Financial Officer, Signature Psychiatric Hospital, Kansas City, MO, p. A409

JACKSON, Robert Charles. Jr, President, Upmc Horizon, Farrell, PA, p. A590
Jr, President, Upmc Jameson, New Castle, PA, p. A598

JACKSON, Robin E., Ph.D., Interim Acting Director, Charlie Norwood Veterans Affairs Medical Center, Augusta, GA, p. A166

JACKSON, Stephanie, M.D., Vice President and Chief Medical Officer, Honorhealth Scottsdale Thompson Peak Medical Center, Scottsdale, AZ, p. A38

JACKSON, Tamara, Chief Nursing Officer, Piedmont Athens Regional Medical Center, Athens, GA, p. A163

JACKSON, Thomas W., Chief Executive Officer, St. David's North Austin Medical Center, Austin, TX, p. A656

JACKSON, Tom, Chief Financial Officer, Tristar Centennial Medical Center, Nashville, TN, p. A647

JACKSON, Vance, FACHE, Chief Executive Officer, Davis Medical Center, Elkins, WV, p. A772

JACKSON, Victor, Chief Executive Officer, Vibra Specialty Hospital Of Portland, Portland, OR, p. A580

JACKSON, William M., JrExecutive Vice President, Chief Medical Officer, Erlanger Medical Center, Chattanooga, TN, p. A635

Chief Medical Officer, Inova Alexandria Hospital, Alexandria, VA, p. A738

JACKSON, William L. Jr, M.D., President and Chief Executive Officer, Erlanger Medical Center, Chattanooga, TN, p. A635

JACO, Angela, Chief Executive Officer, Pam Specialty Hospital Of New Braunfels, New Braunfels, TX, p. A703

JACO, Mary, Administrator, Shriners Hospitals For Children-Galveston, Galveston, TX, p. A680

JACOB, Briana, Chief Executive Officer, Harbor Oaks Hospital, New Baltimore, MI, p. A362

JACOBI, Diane, Chief of Staff, Ssm Health St. Mary's Hospital - Audrain, Mexico, MO, p. A412

JACOBI, Elizabeth, Associate Director Human Resources, Rancho Los Amigos National Rehabilitation Center, Downey, CA, p. A62

Human Resources Director, Lac+Usc Medical Center, Los Angeles, CA, p. A75

JACOBO MORENO, Maria E., Administrator, Hima San Pablo Caguas, Caguas, PR, p. A806

JACOBS, Anastasia, Chief Human Resources Officer, Robert Wood Johnson University Hospital Somerset, Somerville, NJ, p. A463

JACOBS, Andrea, Chief Operating Officer, South Pointe Hospital, Warrensville Heights, OH, p. A552

JACOBS, Barbara, MSN, Vice President, Nursing and Chief Nursing Officer, Anne Arundel Medical Center, Annapolis, MD, p. A324

JACOBS, Brian, M.D., Vice President Chief Information Officer and Chief Medical Information Officer, Children's National Hospital, Washington, DC, p. A129

JACOBS, Greg, Manager, Mclaren Bay Special Care, Bay City, MI, p. A349

JACOBS, Ian, Chief, Human Resource Management Service, Louis A. Johnson Veterans Affairs Medical Center, Clarksburg, WV, p. A772

JACOBS, Jenny, Director Human Resources, Osf Holy Family Medical Center, Monmouth, IL, p. A212

Director Human Resources, Osf St. Mary Medical Center, Galesburg, IL, p. A205

JACOBS, Julie, Chief Financial Officer, Warren General Hospital, Warren, PA, p. A609

Director Human Resources, Oklahoma Forensic Center, Vinita, OK, p. A571

JACOBS, Lori, Chief Financial Officer, Edgefield County Healthcare, Edgefield, SC, p. A619

JACOBS, Richard, Vice President Finance and Chief Financial Officer, Canton-Potsdam Hospital, Potsdam, NY, p. A495

JACOBS, Robert, Regional Director Information Management, Christus Southeast Texas Hospital - St. Elizabeth, Beaumont, TX, p. A658

Regional Information Management Executive, Christus Southeast Texas Jasper Memorial, Jasper, TX, p. A691

JACOBS, Ronnie, M.D., Chief Medical Officer, Asheville Specialty Hospital, Asheville, NC, p. A504

JACOBS, Stacy, Chief Nursing Officer, Millwood Hospital, Arlington, TX, p. A653

JACOBS, Trace, Director Information Technology, Santiam Hospital, Stayton, OR, p. A582

JACOBS, Yolanda, Coordinator Human Resources, Cornerstone Hospital Of Houston At Clearlake, Webster, TX, p. A724

JACOBSEN, Barry, CPA, Chief Executive Officer, Myrtue Medical Center, Harlan, IA, p. A251

JACOBSEN, Carmen, Chief Operating Officer and Chief Nursing Officer, St. Luke's Wood River Medical Center, Ketchum, ID, p. A191

JACOBSON, Becky, Vice President Finance, Ascension St. Vincent Heart Center, Indianapolis, IN, p. A231

JACOBSON, Carlton, Vice President of Finance, Adventist Health Clear Lake, Clearlake, CA, p. A60

JACOBSON, Carolyn, Chief Human Resource Officer, St. Joseph's Hospital, Saint Paul, MN, p. A385

Chief Human Resource Officer, Woodwinds Health Campus, Woodbury, MN, p. A388

Chief Human Resources Officer, Bethesda Hospital, Saint Paul, MN, p. A385

Chief Human Resources Officer, St. John's Hospital, Maplewood, MN, p. A380

JACOBSON, Ches, Chief Nursing Officer, Delta Community Medical Center, Delta, UT, p. A727

JACOBSON, Gary, M.D., Chief Medical Officer, Pembroke Hospital, Pembroke, MA, p. A343

JACOBSON, Janet, Director Human Resources, Lakewood Health System, Staples, MN, p. A386

JACOBSON, Jenny, Manager Human Resources, Sanford Hillsboro Medical Center, Hillsboro, ND, p. A524

JACOBSON, John, Chief Financial Officer, Martin General Hospital, Williamston, NC, p. A520

Interim Chief Executive Officer, Martin General Hospital, Williamston, NC, p. A520

JACOBSON, Lisa, Director of Nursing, Community Hospital Of Huntington Park, Huntington Park, CA, p. A68

JACOBSON, Mark, D.O., Vice President Medical Affairs, Wellspan Ephrata Community Hospital, Ephrata, PA, p. A589

JACOBSON, Mary Jo, Chief Executive Officer, San Joaquin Valley Rehabilitation Hospital, Fresno, CA, p. A66

JACOBSON, Randolph, Chief Financial Officer, Hackensack Meridian Health Carrier Clinic, Belle Mead, NJ, p. A452

JACOBSON, Renae, Human Resources Officer, Ralp. H. Johnson Veterans Affairs Medical Center, Charleston, SC, p. A616

JACOBSON, Sam, Director Management Information Systems, Community Memorial Hospital, Cloquet, MN, p. A374

JACOBSON, Shirley, Chief Financial Officer, Community Behavioral Health Hospital - Alexandria, Alexandria, MN, p. A371

Chief Financial Officer, Community Behavioral Health Hospital - Rochester, Rochester, MN, p. A384

JACOBY, Jamie, Chief Financial Officer, Cimarron Memorial Hospital, Boise City, OK, p. A556

JACQUAY, Dena, Chief Human Resource Officer, Parkview Huntington Hospital, Huntington, IN, p. A230

JACQUES, Alistar, Chief Information Officer, Bethesda Hospital, Saint Paul, MN, p. A385

Chief Information Officer, St. John's Hospital, Maplewood, MN, p. A380

JACQUES, Teresa, Interim Chief Financial Officer, Adventist Health Reedley, Reedley, CA, p. A88

JADCZAK, Audrey, R.N., FACHE, Vice President Chief Nursing Officer, Virtua Our Lady Of Lourdes Hospital, Camden, NJ, p. A453

R.N., FACHE, Vice President/Chief Nursing Officer, Virtua Willingboro Hospital, Willingboro, NJ, p. A466

JADEJA, Neerav, Chief Executive Officer, Paradise Valley Hospital, National City, CA, p. A81

JADWIN, Anne, R.N., MSN, Chief Nursing Officer, Fox Chase Cancer Center-American Oncologic Hospital, Philadelphia, PA, p. A600

JAEGER, Shiuvaun, M.D., Chief of Staff, Tri Valley Health System, Cambridge, NE, p. A430

JAFFE, Richard, M.D., Medical Director, Belmont Behavioral Hospital, Philadelphia, PA, p. A599

JAFFER, Amir, M.D., Senior Vice President Medical Affairs, New York-Presbyterian Queens, Flushing, NY, p. A484

JAGER, Jonathon, Chief Information Officer, St. Francis Hospital, Columbus, IN, p. A169

JAGER, Linda, Director Finance, Avera Weskota Memorial Hospital, Wessington Springs, SD, p. A633

JAGGI, Michael, D.O., Vice President and Chief Medical Officer, Hurley Medical Center, Flint, MI, p. A354

JAGOE, Patricia, Assistant Vice President Patient Care, Johnson Memorial Hospital, Stafford Springs, CT, p. A125

JAHAN, Mohammad, M.D., Clinical Director, Middle Tennessee Mental Health Institute, Nashville, TN, p. A646

JAHN, Barbara, Chief Operating Officer, Saint Josep. Hospital, Denver, CO, p. A111

JAHN, David B., President and Chief Executive Officer, War Memorial Hospital, Sault Sainte Marie, MI, p. A366

JAHN, Gregory L., R.N., Chief Executive Officer, St. Luke's Behavioral Health Center, Phoenix, AZ, p. A36

JAHN, Kim, Chief Plant Operations and Chief Information Officer, Manning Regional Healthcare Center, Manning, IA, p. A253

JAHNIG, Jay, Chief Executive Officer, Faulkton Area Medical Center, Faulkton, SD, p. A628

JAHRE, Jeffrey, M.D., Vice President Medical and Academic Affairs, St. Luke's University Hospital - Bethlehem Campus, Bethlehem, PA, p. A585

JAIN, Anil, Chief Financial Officer, St. Francis Medical Center, Lynwood, CA, p. A76

Interim Chief Financial Officer, Emanuel Medical Center, Turlock, CA, p. A102

JAIN, Ashok, M.D., Senior Vice President and Chief Medical Officer, Beaumont Hospital, Wayne, Wayne, MI, p. A369

JAKOUBECK, Denise, Director Human Resources, Hancock County Health System, Britt, IA, p. A244

JAKUBOWSKI, Michael, M.D., Chief Medical Officer, Mary Free Bed Rehabilitation Hospital, Grand Rapids, MI, p. A356

JALOMO, Angie, Chief Nursing Officer, Lynn County Hospital District, Tahoka, TX, p. A718

JAMES, Annette, R.N., MSN, Chief Nursing Officer, Creek Nation Community Hospital, Okemah, OK, p. A563

JAMES, Brittani, R.N., Vice President Operations, Legent Orthopedic Hospital Carrollton, Carrollton, TX, p. A663

JAMES, Bruce, President and Chief Executive Officer, Cleveland Clinic Union Hospital, Dover, OH, p. A539

JAMES, Craig, President, Alleghany Memorial Hospital, Sparta, NC, p. A518

JAMES, Dixie, President and Chief Operating Officer, Einstein Medical Center Philadelphia, Philadelphia, PA, p. A600

JAMES, Donald, D.O., Senior Vice President and Chief Medical Officer, Phelp. Health, Rolla, MO, p. A414

JAMES, Douglas, Chief Nursing Officer, Caldwell Medical Center, Princeton, KY, p. A292

JAMES, Gregory, D.O., Chief Medical Officer, St. Vincent's Birmingham, Birmingham, AL, p. A15

JAMES, Jaime, Entity Finance Officer, Texas Health Harris Methodist Hospital Hurst-Euless-Bedford, Bedford, TX, p. A659

JAMES, Janet, Director Human Resources, Trigg County Hospital, Cadiz, KY, p. A281

JAMES, Jobie, Chief Financial Officer, West Calcasieu Cameron Hospital, Sulphur, LA, p. A315

JAMES, Karen, Regional Director, Human Resources, The William W. Backus Hospital, Norwich, CT, p. A124

JAMES, Ken, President and Chief Executive Officer of East Market, Mercy Health - Anderson Hospital, Cincinnati, OH, p. A532

JAMES, Michael, Chief Operating Officer, Turning Point Hospital, Moultrie, GA, p. A177

Chief Operations Officer, Jackson Hospital And Clinic, Montgomery, AL, p. A22

Information Technology Technical Support Specialist 1, Villa Feliciana Medical Complex, Jackson, LA, p. A303

JAMES, Michelle, Chief Nursing Officer, Providence St. Peter Hospital, Olympia, WA, p. A761

Regional Chief Nursing Officer, Providence Centralia Hospital, Centralia, WA, p. A756

JAMES, Robert, Director Human Resources, Beaumont Hospital, Wayne, Wayne, MI, p. A369

JAMES, Shelia, Director of Nursing, Riverland Medical Center, Ferriday, LA, p. A301

JAMES, Sherrie, R.N., Chief Executive Officer, The Bridgeway, North Little Rock, AR, p. A51

JAMES, Taya, Director, Mercy Hospital Berryville, Berryville, AR, p. A42

JAMES, Teri, Chief Financial Officer, Lafayette Regional Health Center, Lexington, MO, p. A411

JAMES, Thomas, M.D., Chief Medical Officer, Trumbull Memorial Hospital, Warren, OH, p. A551

JAMES, Wesley, Chief Financial Officer, Piedmont Henry Hospital, Stockbridge, GA, p. A181

JAMES, William B., FACHE, President, Wake Forest Baptist Health-Lexington Medical Center, Lexington, NC, p. A514

JAMES-NIELSEN, Lori, President, Tuality Healthcare, Hillsboro, OR, p. A576

JAMESON, David, M.D., Chief of Staff, Annie Jeffrey Memorial County Health Center, Osceola, NE, p. A438

JAMIESON, Donna, Ph.D., R.N., Chief Nursing Officer, Aurora Medical Center Kenosha, Kenosha, WI, p. A786

JAMIESON, Pamela, Vice President Patient Care Services and Chief Nursing Officer, University Of Maryland St. Josep. Medical Center, Towson, MD, p. A333

JAMIN, David, Chief Financial Officer, St. Mary's Regional Medical Center, Enid, OK, p. A559

JAMROSE, Todd Chief Clinical Officer, Appalachian Behavioral Healthcare, Athens, OH, p. A528

JANDIAL, Rajnish, M.D., Chief Medical Officer, San Dimas Community Hospital, San Dimas, CA, p. A93

JANEK, James D., Chief Executive Officer, Rice Medical Center, Eagle Lake, TX, p. A673

JANERELLA, Wendy, Controller, Bucktail Medical Center, Renovo, PA, p. A606

JANGDHARI, Kalautie, Director, Miami Veterans Affairs Healthcare System, Miami, FL, p. A147

Director, West Texas Veterans Affairs Health Care System, Big Spring, TX, p. A660

JANICAK, Dan, Chief Financial Officer, University Of Mississipp. Medical Center, Jackson, MS, p. A395

JANIS, Terry, Assistant Vice President, Hca Houston Healthcare Medical Center, Houston, TX, p. A685

JANKOWSKI, Stan, Vice President and Chief Information Officer, Hospital For Special Care, New Britain, CT, p. A123

JANLOO, Arman, M.D., Chief Medical Staff, Fairfax Community Hospital, Fairfax, OK, p. A559

JANOSO, John R., Chief Executive Officer, Fairfield Medical Center, Lancaster, OH, p. A542

JANSEN, David, Vice President Human Resources, Karmanos Cancer Center, Detroit, MI, p. A353

JANSEN, John, Management Information Specialist, Hawaii State Hospital, Kaneohe, HI, p. A186

JANSEN, Robert, M.D., Chief Medical Officer, Grady Memorial Hospital, Atlanta, GA, p. A164

JANSSEN, Kathy, Director Medical Records, Mountrail County Medical Center, Stanley, ND, p. A526

JANSSEN, Paul, President and Chief Executive Officer, Henry Community Health, New Castle, IN, p. A238

JANTZEN, Daniel, Chief Financial Officer, Dartmouth-Hitchcock Medical Center, Lebanon, NH, p. A449

JANTZEN, Tammi, Chief Operating Officer, Okeene Municipal Hospital, Okeene, OK, p. A563

JANUS, Tammy, Senior Vice President Human Resources, Mercy Medical Center, Baltimore, MD, p. A325

JANZEN, Wes, Chief Information Officer, Wamego Health Center, Wamego, KS, p. A278

JAQUA, Terry, Human Resources Director, Whittier Hospital Medical Center, Whittier, CA, p. A105

JAQUEZ, Jason, Director Human Resources, Greater El Monte Community Hospital, South El Monte, CA, p. A99
Human Resource Director, Ahmc Anaheim Regional Medical Center, Anaheim, CA, p. A55

JARAMILLO, Charles, Chief Operating Officer, New Mexico Behavioral Health Institute At Las Vegas, Las Vegas, NM, p. A470

JARBOE, Joe, Director Human Resources, Kosciusko Community Hospital, Warsaw, IN, p. A242

JARBOE, Lori, Chief Executive Officer, Encompass Rehabilitation Hospital Of Lakeview, Elizabethtown, KY, p. A282

JARMER, Ryan, Chief Information Officer, Naval Medical Center San Diego, San Diego, CA, p. A91

JAROPILLO, Erwin, Director Information Systems, Adventhealth Lake Wales, Lake Wales, FL, p. A143

JARREAU, Jeff, Chief Human Resources Officer, North Oaks Medical Center, Hammond, LA, p. A302
Senior Vice President, Human Resources, North Oaks Health System, North Oaks Rehabilitation Hospital, Hammond, LA, p. A302

JARREAU, Valerie, R.N., Chief Nursing Officer, Pointe Coupee General Hospital, New Roads, LA, p. A312

JARRELL, Steven, Chief Executive Officer, Lifecare Behavioral Health Hospital, Pittsburgh, PA, p. A603

JARRETT, Adam, M.D., Executive Vice President and Chief Medical Officer, Holy Name Medical Center, Teaneck, NJ, p. A464

JARRY, Patricia, Manager Human Resources, Crenshaw Community Hospital, Luverne, AL, p. A21

JARVIS, Dinah, Director of Nursing, Pineville Community Health Center, Pineville, KY, p. A292

JARVIS, Keith, Director Information Systems, Longview Regional Medical Center, Longview, TX, p. A697

JARVIS, Susan, President, Sanford Bemidji Medical Center, Bemidji, MN, p. A372

JARVIS, Tammy, Vice President Clinical Services and Chief Nursing Officer, Texas Institute For Surgery At Texas Health Presbyterian Dallas, Dallas, TX, p. A670

JASPER, Harry, Chief Financial Officer, Jerold Phelp. Community Hospital, Garberville, CA, p. A66

JASPER, Jerry, Chief Executive Officer, Brownfield Regional Medical Center, Brownfield, TX, p. A660

JAURON, Jason, Director Human Resources, Orange City Area Health System, Orange City, IA, p. A255

JAVERSACK, Dawn, Vice President and Chief Financial Officer, Boca Raton Regional Hospital, Boca Raton, FL, p. A132

JAVOIS, Laurent D., Chief Executive Officer, St. Louis Psychiatric Rehabilitation Center, Saint Louis, MO, p. A417
Regional Executive Officer, Hawthorn Children Psychiatric Hospital, Saint Louis, MO, p. A415
Regional Executive Officer, Metropolitan St. Louis Psychiatric Center, Saint Louis, MO, p. A416

JAVOIS, Rosalie, Chief Financial Officer, Governor Juan F. Luis Hospital, Christiansted, VI, p. A812

JAWORSKI, James, Chief Information Officer, Beverly Hospital, Montebello, CA, p. A79

JAY, Richard, D.O., Chief of Staff, North Big Horn Hospital District, Lovell, WY, p. A803

JEAKLE, James, Chief Medical Officer, Munson Healthcare Charlevoix Hospital, Charlevoix, MI, p. A350

JEAN-BAPTISTE, Joan, Vice President Human Resources, Governor Juan F. Luis Hospital, Christiansted, VI, p. A812

JEAN-LOUIS, Marie, R.N., Chief Nursing Officer, Creedmoor Psychiatric Center, Jamaica, NY, p. A486

JEANS, Joe, CPA, Chief Financial Officer, Johnson Regional Medical Center, Clarksville, AR, p. A43

JEANSONNE, Corey, Chief Nursing Officer, Bunkie General Hospital, Bunkie, LA, p. A299

JEDLICKA, Colleen, R.N., JD, Chief Nursing Officer, Comanche County Medical Center, Comanche, TX, p. A665

JEFFERIES, Kanika, Executive Director, New York City Children's Center, Jamaica, NY, p. A486

JEFFERSON, Glenn, Chief Medical Officer, Garfield County Public Hospital District, Pomeroy, WA, p. A762

JEFFERSON, Kelly, Vice President, Operations, Osf St. Francis Hospital And Medical Group. Escanaba, MI, p. A354

JEFFERY, Jeremy, Regional Chief Financial Officer, Jefferson Regional Medical Center, Pine Bluff, AR, p. A52

JEFFRESS, Chuck, Vice President Fiscal Services, Chi St. Luke's Health Brazosport, Lake Jackson, TX, p. A694

JEFFRIES, John, Director Finance, Hshs St. Joseph's Hospital, Breese, IL, p. A196

JEFFS, Carla, Chief Financial Officer, Cornerstone Hospital Of Huntington, Huntington, WV, p. A773

JEHAN, Sayed, M.D., Interim Medical Director, Larned State Hospital, Larned, KS, p. A268

JELALIAN, Christine, M.D., Medical Director, Montefiore St. Luke's Cornwall, Newburgh, NY, p. A492

JELDEN, Dennis, M.D., Chief of Staff, Melissa Memorial Hospital, Holyoke, CO, p. A114

JELESKY, Beth, MSN, Chief Nursing Officer, Amita Health Alexian Brothers Behavioral Health Hospital, Hoffman Estates, IL, p. A208

JELKS, Kim, Fiscal Officer, Villa Feliciana Medical Complex, Jackson, LA, p. A303

JEMJEMIAN, Norair, Senior Vice President and Area Manager, Kaiser Permanente Vacaville Medical Center, Vacaville, CA, p. A102

JENE, Suzanne, Chief Operating Officer, Tennessee Valley Healthcare System, Nashville, TN, p. A647

JENKINS, Anita L.A., FABC, Chief Executive Officer, Howard University Hospital, Washington, DC, p. A129

JENKINS, Bonnie, Chief Financial Officer, Mercy General Hospital, Sacramento, CA, p. A89
Chief Financial Officer, Methodist Hospital Of Sacramento, Sacramento, CA, p. A89

JENKINS, Brian, Director Human Resources, Arbour-Fuller Hospital, Attleboro, MA, p. A334

JENKINS, Constance, Commander, Bassett Army Community Hospital, Fort Wainwright, AK, p. A28

JENKINS, Debbie, Chief Human Resources Management Service, Veterans Affairs Sierra Nevada Health Care System, Reno, NV, p. A446

JENKINS, Denise, Chief Clinical Officer, Kindred Hospital-Brea, Brea, CA, p. A58

JENKINS, Devin, Chief Operating Officer, Specialists Hospital Shreveport, Shreveport, LA, p. A314

JENKINS, Freddie, Administrator, Wright Patterson Medical Center, Wright, OH, p. A553

JENKINS, Jimmy, M.D., Chief Medical Officer, Geary Community Hospital, Junction City, KS, p. A267

JENKINS, Keith, Director, Human Resources, Grandview Medical Center, Dayton, OH, p. A538

JENKINS, Kerri, Senior Vice President and Chief Operating Officer, North Kansas City Hospital, North Kansas City, MO, p. A413

JENKINS, Kevin, Chief Executive Officer, St. Anthony Hospital, Lakewood, CO, p. A115

JENKINS, Kris, Administrator, Altus Houston Hospital, Houston, TX, p. A684

JENKINS, Linda, R.N., Vice President Patient Care Services, St. Jude Medical Center, Fullerton, CA, p. A66

JENKINS, Maynard, Regional Vice President Human Resources, Sutter Maternity And Surgery Center Of Santa Cruz, Santa Cruz, CA, p. A97

JENKINS, Michelle, M.D., President Medical Staff, Herrin Hospital, Herrin, IL, p. A207

JENKINS, Rebecca, Director Human Resources Management, Harrison Memorial Hospital, Cynthiana, KY, p. A282

JENKINS, Ruth, Chief Financial Officer, Ridgeview Institute, Smyrna, GA, p. A180

JENKINS, Timothy, M.D., Area Medical Director and Chief of Staff, Kaiser Permanente Fontana Medical Center, Fontana, CA, p. A64

JENNER, Jody J., President and Chief Executive Officer, Broadlawns Medical Center, Des Moines, IA, p. A248

JENNETTE, Brian, Chief Financial Officer, Northside Hospital-Cherokee, Canton, GA, p. A168

JENNINGS, Jason, FACHE, President, Baylor Scott & White Hospital Medical Center - College Station, College Station, TX, p. A664
FACHE, President, Baylor Scott & White Medical Center - Brenham, Brenham, TX, p. A660

JENNINGS, Keith, Chief Information Officer, Massachusetts General Hospital, Boston, MA, p. A336

JENNINGS, Lee Ann, R.N., Vice President, Nursing Services, Wise Health System, Decatur, TX, p. A671

JENNINGS, Marilyn, Director Human Resources, Arise Austin Medical Center, Austin, TX, p. A654

JENNINGS, Mark, Chief Information Officer, Saint Anthony Hospital, Chicago, IL, p. A200

JENNINGS, Peter, M.D., Chief Medical Officer, Sacred Heart Hospital Pensacola, Pensacola, FL, p. A154

JENNINGS, Shayla, Human Resources Director, Montgomery County Memorial Hospital, Red Oak, IA, p. A256

JENNINGS, William, President and Chief Executive Officer, Reading Hospital, West Reading, PA, p. A610

JENSEMA, Christine, Chief Human Resources Officer, Hshs St. Clare Memorial Hospital, Oconto Falls, WI, p. A793
Chief Human Resources Officer, Hshs St. Vincent Hospital, Green Bay, WI, p. A785
Chief People Officer, Hshs St. Mary's Hospital Medical Center, Green Bay, WI, p. A785
Chief People Officer, Hshs St. Nicholas Hospital, Sheboygan, WI, p. A796

JENSEN, Amy, Director Human Resources, Promedica Coldwater Regional Hospital, Coldwater, MI, p. A351

JENSEN, Annelise, Vice President and Chief Nursing Officer, Methodist Healthcare Olive Branch Hospital, Olive Branch, MS, p. A398

JENSEN, Beth, Director Clinic Operations, Mobridge Regional Hospital, Mobridge, SD, p. A629

JENSEN, Christopher, Chief Financial Officer, Three Rivers Behavioral Health, West Columbia, SC, p. A625

JENSEN, Dave, Director Human Resources, Performance Improvement and Risk Management, Mountain View Hospital, Gadsden, AL, p. A19

JENSEN, Janette, Manager Human Resources, Avera Holy Family Hospital, Estherville, IA, p. A249

JENSEN, Jeff, D.O., Vice President, Medical Affairs, Morton Plant Hospital, Clearwater, FL, p. A134
D.O., Vice President, Medical Affairs, Morton Plant North Bay Hospital, New Port Richey, FL, p. A149

JENSEN, Jennifer, Chief Human Resource Officer, Layton Hospital, Layton, UT, p. A728

JENSEN, Laura J., Vice President Patient Care Services, St. Croix Regional Medical Center, St Croix Falls, WI, p. A796

JENSEN, Mary, Controller, Mountain View Hospital, Gadsden, AL, p. A19

JENSEN, Michael, Chief Executive Officer, Davis Hospital And Medical Center, Layton, UT, p. A728

JENSEN, Neal, Chief Executive Officer, Cobre Valley Regional Medical Center, Globe, AZ, p. A32

JENSEN, Pamela M., FACHE, President, Regional Acute Care, Promedica Memorial Hospital, Fremont, OH, p. A540
FACHE, President, Promedica Fostoria Community Hospital, Fostoria, OH, p. A540

JENSEN, Paul, M.D., Chief of Staff, Regional Health Services Of Howard County, Cresco, IA, p. A247

JENSEN, Ron, D.O., Chief Medical Officer and Vice President, Baylor Scott & White Medical Center - Grapevine, Grapevine, TX, p. A682

JENSEN, Ryan, Chief Executive Officer, Henrico Doctors' Hospital, Richmond, VA, p. A750

JENSEN, Sherry, Vice President, Financial Services, Vidant North Hospital, Roanoke Rapids, NC, p. A517

JENSEN, Tom, Chief Executive Officer, Grays Harbor Community Hospital, Aberdeen, WA, p. A755

JENSEN, Troy, Director Human Resources, Encompass Health Rehabilitation Hospital Of Utah, Sandy, UT, p. A733

JENSEN, Twyla, Director Human Resources, Pioneers Medical Center, Meeker, CO, p. A117

JENTZ, Amy, M.D., Chief of Staff, Sparrow Ionia Hospital, Ionia, MI, p. A358

JEPPESEN, Kelly, Chief Medical Officer, San Juan Health Service District, Monticello, UT, p. A729

JEPSEN, Christinia, R.N., Chief Nursing Executive, Memorial Community Hospital And Health System, Blair, NE, p. A430

JEPSON, Brian, President, Ohiohealth Riverside Methodist Hospital, Columbus, OH, p. A537

JEPSON, Mark, Vice President, Silver Cross Hospital, New Lenox, IL, p. A214

JERDEE, Amy L., R.N., President, St. Francis Regional Medical Center, Shakopee, MN, p. A386

JERGER, Greg, Chief Financial Officer, Memorial Health Care Systems, Seward, NE, p. A439

JERNIGAN, Pam, Chief Financial Officer, Unity Medical Center, Manchester, TN, p. A643

JEROME, Jerome, M.D., Clinic Medical Director, Cascade Medical Center, Leavenworth, WA, p. A760

JESCH, Doug, Director Human Resources, Starke Hospital, Knox, IN, p. A234

JESIOLOWSKI, Craig A., FACHE, President, Holy Family Hospital, Methuen, MA, p. A341

JESSOP, Reuben, Chief Operating Officer, Northern Utah Rehabilitation Hospital, South Ogden, UT, p. A733

JESSUP, Daniel, Chief Financial Officer, Legacy Silverton Medical Center, Silverton, OR, p. A581
Chief Financial Officer, Wallowa Memorial Hospital, Enterprise, OR, p. A574

JESTER, Denise, Chief Financial Officer, Tidalhealth Nanticoke, Seaford, DE, p. A128

JESTILA-PELTOLA, Gail, Chief Financial Officer, Baraga County Memorial Hospital, L'Anse, MI, p. A359

JESURASA, Jebashini, Vice President, Chief Information Technology Officer, Wyckoff Heights Medical Center, Brooklyn, NY, p. A479

JETER, John, Chief Executive Officer, Johnston Memorial Hospital, Abingdon, VA, p. A738

JETT, Chris, Administrator, Usa Health Children's & Women's Hospital, Mobile, AL, p. A22

JETTERGREN, Tess, Director Clinical Informatics, Essentia Health St. Mary's Medical Center, Duluth, MN, p. A375

JEUNEHOMME, Patti, Director Human Resources, Hot Springs County Memorial Hospital, Thermopolis, WY, p. A804

JEWETT, Jess, Chief Medical Officer, Cache Valley Hospital, North Logan, UT, p. A729

JEWETT, Lori, R.N., Chief Executive Officer, Falmouth Hospital, Falmouth, MA, p. A339

JEX, Kerri, R.N., Chief Nursing Officer, Bear Valley Community Hospital, Big Bear Lake, CA, p. A58

JEYAKUMAR, Panch, M.D., Chief of Staff, Olympia Medical Center, Los Angeles, CA, p. A75

JEZSU, Peggy, Chief Nursing Officer, Alvarado Hospital Medical Center, San Diego, CA, p. A91

JHA, Gautam, M.D., Chief of Staff, Salem Township Hospital, Salem, IL, p. A219

JIMENEZ, Betzaida, Director Human Resources, Hospital De La Universidad De Puerto Rico/Dr. Federico Trilla, Carolina, PR, p. A807

JIMENEZ, Cristina, Chief Executive Officer, Coral Gables Hospital, Coral Gables, FL, p. A135

JIMENEZ, Edward, Chief Executive Officer, Uf Health Shands Hospital, Gainesville, FL, p. A139

JIMENEZ, Gerson, M.D., Medical Director, Hospital Episcopal San Lucas Guayama, Guayama, PR, p. A807

JIMENEZ, Guillermo, Director Finance, Castaner General Hospital, Castaner, PR, p. A807

JIMENEZ, Ronald, M.D., Chief Executive Officer, Adventhealth Palm Coast, Palm Coast, FL, p. A152

JIMMERSON, Kevin, Business Manager, Independence Mental Health Institute, Independence, IA, p. A251

JIN, Marvin, M.D., Medical Director, Parkside Psychiatric Hospital And Clinic, Tulsa, OK, p. A570

JIRON, Feliciano, Chief Executive Officer, Valley View Medical Center, Fort Mohave, AZ, p. A31

JIROVEC, David, Director Finance, Ascension Good Samaritan Hospital, Merrill, WI, p. A790

JOBBITT, Patty, Chief Executive Officer, Dmc - Rehabilitation Institute Of Michigan, Detroit, MI, p. A352

JOBE, Kenneth, Director Human Resources, Tyler County Hospital, Woodville, TX, p. A726

JODWAY, Timothy, Chief Financial Administrator, Beaumont Hospital - Dearborn, Dearborn, MI, p. A352

JOHANNSEN, Lee, M.D., Vice President and Chief Medical Officer, Christus Santa Rosa Hospital - San Marcos, San Marcos, TX, p. A714

JOHANSON, Amanda, Chief Executive Officer, Triangle Springs Hospital, Raleigh, NC, p. A516

JOHE, David, M.D., President Medical Staff, Penn Highlands Elk, Saint Marys, PA, p. A606

JOHN, Aleyamma, R.N., Director of Nursing, Kensington Hospital, Philadelphia, PA, p. A601

JOHNS, Dale, FACHE, Chief Executive Officer, Salt Lake Regional Medical Center, Salt Lake City, UT, p. A732

JOHNS, Dawn, Director Human Resources, Colquitt Regional Medical Center, Moultrie, GA, p. A177

JOHNS, Jeffery, M.D., Medical Director, Vanderbilt Stallworth Rehabilitation Hospital, Nashville, TN, p. A647

JOHNS, Paul, Chief Operating Officer, South Lake Hospital, Clermont, FL, p. A134

JOHNS, Thomas, M.D., Medical Director, Ridgeview Institute, Smyrna, GA, p. A180

JOHNSON, Aaron, Vice President Patient Care Services and Chief Nursing Officer, Chi St. Alexius Health Devils Lake Hospital, Devils Lake, ND, p. A522

JOHNSON, Alan, Interim Chief Information Officer, United Medical Center, Washington, DC, p. A130

JOHNSON, Allen, Chief Financial Officer, Truman Medical Center-Hospital Hill, Kansas City, MO, p. A410
Chief Financial Officer, Truman Medical Center-Lakewood, Kansas City, MO, p. A410

JOHNSON, Amy, R.N., Quality Improvement Safety Officer, Star Valley Health, Afton, WY, p. A801

JOHNSON, Arlan D., Chief Executive Officer, Howard County Medical Center, Saint Paul, NE, p. A439

JOHNSON, Ashley, Chief Operations Officer, Canyon Vista Medical Center, Sierra Vista, AZ, p. A38
Director Human Resource, Mccamey County Hospital District, Mccamey, TX, p. A700

JOHNSON, Becky, Director Human Resources, Oakdale Community Hospital, Oakdale, LA, p. A312

JOHNSON, Belinda, R.N., Chief Nursing Officer/Chief Clinical Officer, Russellville Hospital, Russellville, AL, p. A24

JOHNSON, Blake, M.D., Chief of Staff, Salt Lake Regional Medical Center, Salt Lake City, UT, p. A732

JOHNSON, Bonnie, R.N., Vice President of Patient Services, Perham Health, Perham, MN, p. A383

JOHNSON, Brandi, Site Manager Technology Information Systems, Spectrum Health Reed City Hospital, Reed City, MI, p. A364

JOHNSON, Brenda, Director Human Resources, Baptist Memorial Hospital-Collierville, Collierville, TN, p. A636

JOHNSON, Bret, Chief Financial Officer, Bon Secours St. Francis Hospital, Charleston, SC, p. A616
Chief Financial Officer, Roper Hospital, Charleston, SC, p. A616
Chief Financial Officer, Roper St. Francis Mount Pleasant Hospital, Mount Pleasant, SC, p. A622

JOHNSON, Brett M., Chief Executive Officer, Northwest Ohio Psychiatric Hospital, Toledo, OH, p. A550

JOHNSON, Brian, M.D., Chief Medical Officer, Aurora Baycare Medical Center, Green Bay, WI, p. A785

JOHNSON, Bryan, M.D., Chief Medical Officer, Whitman Hospital And Medical Center, Colfax, WA, p. A757

JOHNSON, Bryan L., President, St. Mary's Hospital And Medical Center, Grand Junction, CO, p. A113

JOHNSON, C Vice President Finance and Chief Financial Officer, Southeastern Health, Lumberton, NC, p. A514

JOHNSON, Candace, Ph.D., President and Chief Executive Officer, Roswell Park Comprehensive Cancer Center, Buffalo, NY, p. A480

JOHNSON, Casey, Chief Financial Officer, Riverwood Healthcare Center, Aitkin, MN, p. A371

JOHNSON, Cheri, Senior Vice President and Chief Nursing Officer, Woman's Hospital, Baton Rouge, LA, p. A298

JOHNSON, Cheryl, Regional Chief Information Officer, St. Josep. Medical Center, Kansas City, MO, p. A409

JOHNSON, Chris, M.D., Chief of Staff, Mercy Hospital Rogers, Rogers, AR, p. A52
Chief Nursing Officer, Davis Hospital And Medical Center, Layton, UT, p. A728

JOHNSON, Christina, M.D., Chief Executive Officer, Longmont United Hospital, Longmont, CO, p. A116

JOHNSON, Collette, Chief Financial Officer, Palo Alto County Health System, Emmetsburg, IA, p. A249

JOHNSON, Craig L., FACHE, Chief Executive Officer, Vibra Hospital Of Northwestern Indiana, Crown Point, IN, p. A226

JOHNSON, Cynthia, R.N., Chief Nurse Officer, Sunrise Hospital And Medical Center, Las Vegas, NV, p. A444

JOHNSON, Danielle, Chief Operating Officer, Adventhealth Fish Memorial, Orange City, FL, p. A150

JOHNSON, Darren, M.D., Chief of Staff, West Tennessee Healthcare Dyersburg Hospital, Dyersburg, TN, p. A637

JOHNSON, David, Manager Information Services, Providence Kodiak Island Medical Center, Kodiak, AK, p. A28

JOHNSON, Deeann, Director Human Resources, Saint Thomas River Park Hospital, Mc Minnville, TN, p. A643

JOHNSON, Denise, M.D., Medical Director, Meadville Medical Center, Meadville, PA, p. A596

JOHNSON, Dennis B., President and Chief Executive Officer, Hardin Memorial Health, Elizabethtown, KY, p. A282

JOHNSON, Derek Chief Operating Officer, Franklin Hospital District, Benton, IL, p. A195
Chief Executive Officer, Laurel Oaks Behavioral Health Center, Dothan, AL, p. A17

JOHNSON, Diana, Acting Chief Human Resources Officer, Novato Community Hospital, Novato, CA, p. A81

JOHNSON, Dino, R.N., Chief Operating Officer, St. Francis Hospital, Federal Way, WA, p. A758

JOHNSON, Douglas, Chief Financial Officer, Lakeview Hospital, Stillwater, MN, p. A386
Vice President, Chief Financial Officer, Hudson Hospital And Clinic, Hudson, WI, p. A786

JOHNSON, Douglas V., Chief Executive Officer, Stanislaus Surgical Hospital, Modesto, CA, p. A79

JOHNSON, Drew, Chief Financial Officer, Holdenville General Hospital, Holdenville, OK, p. A560

JOHNSON, Earle, Area Information Officer, Kaiser Permanente Panorama City Medical Center, Panorama City, CA, p. A84
Area Information Officer, Kaiser Permanente Woodland Hills Medical Center, Woodland Hills, CA, p. A105

JOHNSON, Eddie, Chief Information Technology Officer, Kansas City Veterans Affairs Medical Center, Kansas City, MO, p. A408

JOHNSON, Eric, Director, United Medical Center, Washington, DC, p. A130

JOHNSON, Ethel, Chief Nursing Officer, Legent Hospital For Special Surgery, Plano, TX, p. A707

JOHNSON, Eunice, M.D., Chief Medical Staff, Kentucky River Medical Center, Jackson, KY, p. A285

JOHNSON, Fred, M.D., Chief Medical Officer, Dignity Health Arizona General Hospital, Laveen, AZ, p. A33

JOHNSON, Gigi, Chief Nursing Officer, Kindred Hospital-Chattanooga, Chattanooga, TN, p. A635

JOHNSON, Greg, Chief Operating Officer, Colquitt Regional Medical Center, Moultrie, GA, p. A177
IT Coordinator, North Shore Health, Grand Marais, MN, p. A377

JOHNSON, Heather, Director of Finance, Operations and Business Development, Buffalo Hospital, Buffalo, MN, p. A373

JOHNSON, Helen, R.N., MSN, Vice President Patient Services, Spectrum Health Ludington Hospital, Ludington, MI, p. A361

JOHNSON, J, M.D., Chief of Staff, Ut Health Specialty Hospital, Tyler, TX, p. A722

JOHNSON, J. Ronald., Director, Hunter Holmes Mcguire Veterans Affairs Medical Center-Richmond, Richmond, VA, p. A750

JOHNSON, James, Chief Executive Officer, Franklin Hospital District, Benton, IL, p. A195

JOHNSON, Jamie, R.N., Vice President Nursing, Community Hospital Of Anaconda, Anaconda, MT, p. A421
Director Human Resources, Miners' Colfax Medical Center, Raton, NM, p. A471

JOHNSON, Jane, Chief Nursing Officer, Cincinnati Veterans Affairs Medical Center, Cincinnati, OH, p. A532
Interim Medical Director and Chief Nursing Officer, Cincinnati Veterans Affairs Medical Center, Cincinnati, OH, p. A532

JOHNSON, Jani L., R.N., MSN, Chief Executive Officer, Saint Luke's Hospital Of Kansas City, Kansas City, MO, p. A409

JOHNSON, Jason, Controller, F. W. Huston Medical Center, Winchester, KS, p. A279

JOHNSON, Jay, Chief Financial Officer, Alliancehealth Clinton, Clinton, OK, p. A557

JOHNSON, Jay R., FACHE, President and Chief Executive Officer, Duncan Regional Hospital, Duncan, OK, p. A558

JOHNSON, Jayne, Director Human Resources, Great Plains Health, North Platte, NE, p. A436

JOHNSON, Jeff, Director Information Systems, Saint Thomas River Park Hospital, Mc Minnville, TN, p. A643

JOHNSON, Jeffrey, Commander, Brooke Army Medical Center, Fort Sam Houston, TX, p. A677
Vice President, Uchealth Memorial Hospital, Colorado Springs, CO, p. A109

JOHNSON, Jessica, Chief Financial Officer, Emanuel Medical Center, Swainsboro, GA, p. A181

JOHNSON, Jimmy, Chief Financial Officer, Blue Mountain Hospital, Blanding, UT, p. A727

JOHNSON, Joe, FACHE, Chief Executive Officer, Adventhealth Ocala, Ocala, FL, p. A149
Chief Nursing Officer, Helen Newberry Joy Hospital, Newberry, MI, p. A363

JOHNSON, Joel, M.D., Chief Medical Staff, First Care Health Center, Park River, ND, p. A525

JOHNSON, John, M.D., Chief of Staff, Greenbrier Valley Medical Center, Ronceverte, WV, p. A776
M.D., Clinical Director, U. S. Public Health Service Indian Hospital, Crownpoint, NM, p. A469

JOHNSON, Juanita, Chief of Staff, Choctaw Health Center, Philadelphia, MS, p. A398

JOHNSON, Judith, Controller, Encompass Health Rehabilitation Hospital Of Largo, Largo, FL, p. A143

JOHNSON, Juli, MSN, R.N., President, Parkview Huntington Hospital, Huntington, IN, p. A230

JOHNSON, Katherine, Ph.D., President, Sentara Northern Virginia Medical Center, Woodbridge, VA, p. A754

JOHNSON, Kathryn, Chief Nursing Officer, Casa Colina Hospital And Centers For Healthcare, Pomona, CA, p. A86
Manager Human Resources, Marketing and Public Relations, Ascension St. Vincent Jennings, North Vernon, IN, p. A238

JOHNSON, Kawanda, Vice President, Specialty Hospital Of Meridian, Meridian, MS, p. A397

JOHNSON, Kayla, R.N., Vice President Patient Care Services and Chief Nursing Officer, St. Francis Medical Center, Monroe, LA, p. A309

JOHNSON, Kelly, R.N., Chief Nursing Officer, St. John Sapulpa, Sapulpa, OK, p. A567
Chief Nursing Officer, Lucile Packard Children's Hospital Stanford, Palo Alto, CA, p. A84
Director Human Resources, Madison Healthcare Services, Madison, MN, p. A379
JOHNSON, Ken, Chief Physician Executive, Hshs St. Mary's Hospital Medical Center, Green Bay, WI, p. A785
Chief Physician Executive, Hshs St. Vincent Hospital, Green Bay, WI, p. A785
President and Chief Executive Officer, Hutchinson Regional Medical Center, Hutchinson, KS, p. A266
JOHNSON, Kendall, Chief Financial Officer, Baton Rouge General Medical Center, Baton Rouge, LA, p. A296
JOHNSON, Kenneth, Vice President, Uofl Health - Mary And Elizabeth Hospital, Louisville, KY, p. A289
JOHNSON, Kevin, Chief Executive Officer, Mountain View Hospital, Payson, UT, p. A730
JOHNSON, Kristen, Chief Nursing Officer, Southwest Healthcare System, Murrieta, CA, p. A80
JOHNSON, Kyle, Chief Information Officer, The Aroostook Medical Center, Presque Isle, ME, p. A322
Vice President Finance, East Liverpool City Hospital, East Liverpool, OH, p. A539
JOHNSON, Laurie, Director - Human Resources, Ascension Via Christi Hospital, Pittsburg, KS, p. A274
JOHNSON, Lerenda, Interim Chief Executive Officer, Kindred Hospital Rancho, Rancho Cucamonga, CA, p. A86
JOHNSON, Linda, R.N., Vice President, Patient Services Risk Management and Chief Nursing Officer, Heart Of The Rockies Regional Medical Center, Salida, CO, p. A118
JOHNSON, Margaret M., President, St. Vincent Northwest Region, Ascension St. Vincent Kokomo, Kokomo, IN, p. A234
JOHNSON, Marianne, Chief Nursing Officer, Trace Regional Hospital, Houston, MS, p. A394
JOHNSON, Marie, Chief Nursing Officer, Carrus Rehabilitation Hospital, Sherman, TX, p. A715
Chief Nursing Officer, Carrus Specialty Hospital, Sherman, TX, p. A715
JOHNSON, Marissa, Chief Human Resource Officer, Alta View Hospital, Sandy, UT, p. A733
JOHNSON, Mark, Chief Financial Officer, Norwood Hospital, Norwood, MA, p. A343
Chief Information Officer, West Holt Medical Services, Atkinson, NE, p. A429
JOHNSON, Mary, Chief Nursing Officer, Falmouth Hospital, Falmouth, MA, p. A339
JOHNSON, Matthew, President, Mercyone Centerville Medical Center, Centerville, IA, p. A245
JOHNSON, Melissa, Chief Financial Officer, Baptist Medical Center South, Montgomery, AL, p. A22
JOHNSON, Michael, CPA, Chief Financial Officer, Abrom Kaplan Memorial Hospital, Kaplan, LA, p. A304
M.D., Medical Director, Salina Surgical Hospital, Salina, KS, p. A276
Vice President, Operations, Northwestern Medicine Delnor Hospital, Geneva, IL, p. A206
JOHNSON, Monte, Vice President, Medical Affairs, St. Francis Regional Medical Center, Shakopee, MN, p. A386
JOHNSON, Nancy, Chief Nursing Officer, Select Specialty Hospital-North Knoxville, Powell, TN, p. A648
JOHNSON, Nanette, Chief Nursing Officer, Orthopaedic Hospital Of Wisconsin, Glendale, WI, p. A784
JOHNSON, Nate, Chief Information Officer, Highlands Regional Medical Center, Sebring, FL, p. A157
JOHNSON, Neil, Chief Operating Officer, Eskenazi Health, Indianapolis, IN, p. A231
JOHNSON, Nikki, Administrator and Chief Executive Officer, Cooperstown Medical Center, Cooperstown, ND, p. A522
JOHNSON, Pamela, MS, R.N., Chief Nursing Officer, Mayo Clinic Hospital - Rochester, Rochester, MN, p. A384
R.N., Chief Nursing Officer, Mccurtain Memorial Hospital, Idabel, OK, p. A560
Treasurer and Chief Financial Officer, Geneva General Hospital, Geneva, NY, p. A484
Treasurer and Chief Financial Officer, Soldiers And Sailors Memorial Hospital, Penn Yan, NY, p. A495
JOHNSON, Patrick, Director Human Resources, Pondera Medical Center, Conrad, MT, p. A422
JOHNSON, Penny, Chief Executive Officer, Texas Health Huguley Hospital Fort Worth South, Burleson, TX, p. A662
JOHNSON, Peri, Human Resources Director, West Central Georgia Regional Hospital, Columbus, GA, p. A169
JOHNSON, Peter, Interim Chief Information Officer, Monadnock Community Hospital, Peterborough, NH, p. A451
JOHNSON, Phillip, Vice President, Chief Human Resources Officer, St. Luke's Regional Medical Center, Boise, ID, p. A189

JOHNSON, Ralph, Chief Information Officer, Franklin Memorial Hospital, Farmington, ME, p. A320
Chief Information Officer, Southern Maine Health Care - Biddeford Medical Center, Biddeford, ME, p. A319
JOHNSON, Rashard, President, Advocate South Suburban Hospital, Hazel Crest, IL, p. A207
President, Advocate Trinity Hospital, Chicago, IL, p. A197
JOHNSON, Regina, Chief Nurse Executive, Piedmont Geriatric Hospital, Burkeville, VA, p. A739
JOHNSON, Ric, Associate Administrator, Mountain View Hospital, Payson, UT, p. A730
JOHNSON, Richard, M.D., Chief of Medical Staff, Chi St. Alexius Health Devils Lake Hospital, Devils Lake, ND, p. A522
JOHNSON, Rick, Chief Executive Officer, West Tennessee Rehabilitation Hospital Cane Creek, Martin, TN, p. A643
JOHNSON, Robb, Director Operations, Hamilton Center, Terre Haute, IN, p. A241
JOHNSON, Roger, M.D., Chief of Staff, Cheyenne Veterans Affairs Medical Center, Cheyenne, WY, p. A802
JOHNSON, Ronald W., FACHE, President and Chief Executive Officer, Shore Medical Center, Somers Point, NJ, p. A463
JOHNSON, Russell W., President and Chief Executive Officer, Lmh Health, Lawrence, KS, p. A269
JOHNSON, Ryan, Controller, Spectrum Health United Hospital, Greenville, MI, p. A356
JOHNSON, Sam, M.D., Chief Medical Officer, Northeast Georgia Medical Center, Gainesville, GA, p. A173
JOHNSON, Scott, Executive Vice President and Chief Financial Officer, St. Luke's Hospital, Chesterfield, MO, p. A404
JOHNSON, Sean, Chief Executive Officer, Tyler Holmes Memorial Hospital, Winona, MS, p. A401
JOHNSON, Shannon J., Commanding Officer, Naval Hospital Bremerton, Bremerton, WA, p. A756
JOHNSON, Sharon, Director Health Information Management, Western State Hospital, Staunton, VA, p. A752
JOHNSON, Shelia, Director of Nursing, St. Landry Extended Care Hospital, Opelousas, LA, p. A312
JOHNSON, Shelly, Chief Operating Officer, Spectrum Health Gerber Memorial, Fremont, MI, p. A355
JOHNSON, Sheryl, Chief Information Officer, Swedishamerican - A Division Of Uw Health, Rockford, IL, p. A219
JOHNSON, Shirley, Chief Clinical Operations Officer, Roswell Park Comprehensive Cancer Center, Buffalo, NY, p. A480
JOHNSON, Shrea, Director Human Resources, Alliance Health Center, Meridian, MS, p. A397
JOHNSON, Stacy, Chief Executive Officer, Loring Hospital, Sac City, IA, p. A257
JOHNSON, Talicia, Director Human Resources, Brentwood Hospital, Shreveport, LA, p. A314
JOHNSON, Tamatha, Director Human Resources, Rmc-Stringfellow Memorial Hospital, Anniston, AL, p. A13
JOHNSON, Thomas, Director Information Systems, Penn Highlands Brookville, Brookville, PA, p. A585
JOHNSON, Timothy, President and Chief Executive Officer, Eaton Rapids Medical Center, Eaton Rapids, MI, p. A354
JOHNSON, Todd, Chief Financial Officer, Longview Regional Medical Center, Longview, TX, p. A697
JOHNSON, Tom, Chief Human Resource Officer, Minneapolis Veterans Affairs Health Care System, Minneapolis, MN, p. A381
JOHNSON, Tommy, Chief Executive Officer, Crockett Medical Center, Crockett, TX, p. A666
JOHNSON, Tripp, Assistant Vice President Operations, Rmc Anniston, Anniston, AL, p. A13
JOHNSON, Trudy, R.N., Chief Nursing Officer, Santa Clara Valley Medical Center, San Jose, CA, p. A95
JOHNSON, Vern, Director Information Technology, Sullivan County Memorial Hospital, Milan, MO, p. A412
JOHNSON, Vernon, Administrator, Dale Medical Center, Ozark, AL, p. A23
JOHNSON, Wade C., MS, FACHE, Chief Executive Officer, St. Peter's Hospital, Helena, MT, p. A425
JOHNSON, William, Chief Medical Officer, Tennova Healthcare - Cleveland, Cleveland, TN, p. A636
Director Information Systems, Shoals Hospital, Muscle Shoals, AL, p. A22
JOHNSON-HATCHER, Dawn, Chief Financial Officer, Christus Ochsner Lake Area Hospital, Lake Charles, LA, p. A306
JOHNSON-MEKOTA, Judith, Director, Iowa City Va Health Care System, Iowa City, IA, p. A252
JOHNSON-MILLER, Kimberly, Chief Financial Officer, Carl Vinson Veterans Affairs Medical Center, Dublin, GA, p. A171
JOHNSON-THREAT, Yvette, Vice President Medical Affairs, Medstar Southern Maryland Hospital Center, Clinton, MD, p. A328

JOHNSRUD, Carolyn, Manager Human Resources, Missouri River Medical Center, Fort Benton, MT, p. A423
JOHNSRUD, Jill, Director of Nursing, Essentia Health-Graceville, Graceville, MN, p. A377
JOHNSTON, Christopher, Chief Administrative Officer, Peacehealth United General Medical Center, Sedro, WA, p. A765
JOHNSTON, Diann, R.N., MSN, Vice President of Patient Care Services, Monmouth Medical Center, Long Branch Campus, Long Branch, NJ, p. A457
JOHNSTON, Don, Chief Information Officer, San Joaquin General Hospital, French Camp, CA, p. A65
JOHNSTON, John, Chief Medical Officer, Specialty Hospital Of Meridian, Meridian, MS, p. A397
JOHNSTON, Michael, M.D., Chief Medical Officer and Senior Vice President Medical Programs, Kennedy Krieger Institute, Baltimore, MD, p. A324
JOHNSTON, Michael Eric., President and Chief Executive Officer, Mclaren Thumb Region, Bad Axe, MI, p. A349
JOHNSTON, Mike, Chief Executive Officer, Decatur County Hospital, Leon, IA, p. A253
Director Facilities Operations, Union General Hospital, Blairsville, GA, p. A167
JOHNSTON, Monte, Manager Human Resources, Coquille Valley Hospital, Coquille, OR, p. A574
JOHNSTON, Patricia, Vice President Information Services, Texas Health Harris Methodist Hospital Azle, Azle, TX, p. A657
JOHNSTON, Phyllis, Vice President, Catawba Valley Medical Center, Hickory, NC, p. A512
JOHNSTON, Scott, Chief of Staff, Onslow Memorial Hospital, Jacksonville, NC, p. A513
JOHNSTON, Susan, Vice President Human Resources, East Alabama Medical Center, Opelika, AL, p. A23
JOHNSTON, Susanne, Manager Human Resources, Lincoln County Medical Center, Ruidoso, NM, p. A471
JOHNSTON, Word, Medical Director, Covington County Hospital, Collins, MS, p. A391
JOHRENDT, JT, Information Technology Network Specialist, Edgerton Hospital And Health Services, Edgerton, WI, p. A783
JOICE, Jason, M.D., Chief Medical Staff, Hillcrest Hospital Pryor, Pryor, OK, p. A567
JOLLEY, Colby, D.O., Acting Chief of Staff, Haxtun Hospital District, Haxtun, CO, p. A114
JOLLEY, Sherry, Director of Operations and Nursing, Red Bay Hospital, Red Bay, AL, p. A24
JOLLEY GREENE, Jill, MSN, R.N., President, Spartanburg Hospital For Restorative Care, Spartanburg, SC, p. A624
JOLLY, Gaye, FACHE, President and Chief Administrative Officer, Leconte Medical Center, Sevierville, TN, p. A649
JONES, Adrienne, Director Human Resources, Creedmoor Psychiatric Center, Jamaica, NY, p. A486
JONES, Alesia, Chief Human Resources Officer, University Of Alabama Hospital, Birmingham, AL, p. A16
JONES, Allan, Controller, Encompass Health Rehabilitation Hospital Of Jonesboro, Jonesboro, AR, p. A47
JONES, America, R.N., Chief Executive Officer, Kindred Hospital El Paso, El Paso, TX, p. A675
JONES, Anetra, R.N., M.P.H., Chief Nursing Officer, La Porte Hospital, La Porte, IN, p. A234
R.N., M.P.H., Chief Nursing Officer, Starke Hospital, Knox, IN, p. A234
JONES, Anitra, Director Human Resources, Encompass Health Rehabilitation Hospital Of Middletown, Middletown, DE, p. A127
JONES, Austin, CPA, Chief Financial Officer, Physicians Surgical Hospital - Quail Creek, Amarillo, TX, p. A652
JONES, Beth, Chief Operating Officer, Reeves Memorial Medical Center, Bernice, LA, p. A298
Director of Nursing, Reeves Memorial Medical Center, Bernice, LA, p. A298
JONES, Bill, Chief Executive Officer, Jackson County Hospital District, Edna, TX, p. A674
Chief Financial Officer, Florida State Hospital, Chattahoochee, FL, p. A134
JONES, Brain, Director of Information Technology, Multicare Valley Hospital, Spokane Valley, WA, p. A766
JONES, Carol, MSN, R.N., Interim Chief Nursing Officer, Morristown Medical Center, Morristown, NJ, p. A458
Controller and Manager Business Office, Coryell Health, Gatesville, TX, p. A681
JONES, Carolyn, R.N., MSN, Chief Nursing Officer, Box Butte General Hospital, Alliance, NE, p. A429
JONES, Charlene, Chief Nursing Officer, Peterson Healthcare And Rehabilitation Hospital, Wheeling, WV, p. A778
JONES, Christian, Chief Operating Officer, Poplar Bluff Regional Medical Center, Poplar Bluff, MO, p. A414

JONES, Connie, Director Human Resources, Community Behavioral Health Hospital - Rochester, Rochester, MN, p. A384

JONES, Dana, R.N., MSN, Chief Operating Officer, Springhill Medical Center, Springhill, LA, p. A315

JONES, Darrell, Interim Chief Executive Officer, Select Specialty Hospital-Pittsburgh/Upmc, Pittsburgh, PA, p. A603

JONES, David, JD, Executive Vice President of Human Resources and Organizational Learning, Wellstar Kennestone Hospital, Marietta, GA, p. A176

M.D., Chief Medical Officer, Beauregard Health System, De Ridder, LA, p. A300

Chief Executive Officer, Encompass Health Rehabilitation Hospital Of Round Rock, Round Rock, TX, p. A709

Chief Financial Officer, Amita Health Alexian Brothers Behavioral Health Hospital, Hoffman Estates, IL, p. A208

Service Chief, Riverside Shore Memorial Hospital, Onancock, VA, p. A748

JONES, David C., Administrator, North Caddo Medical Center, Vivian, LA, p. A316

JONES, Debbie, Director of Nursing, Brookhaven Hospital, Tulsa, OK, p. A569

JONES, Derrick, Chief Executive Officer, Lovelace Unm Rehabilitation Hospital, Albuquerque, NM, p. A467

JONES, Donald J., FACHE, Administrator, Fayette Medical Center, Fayette, AL, p. A18

JONES, Douglas, Chief Operating Officer, Forrest General Hospital, Hattiesburg, MS, p. A393

JONES, Elaine, M.D., President Medical Staff, Roger Williams Medical Center, Providence, RI, p. A614

JONES, Elizabeth, Chief Executive Officer, Southwestern Medical Center, Lawton, OK, p. A561

Chief Operating Officer, Lake Cumberland Regional Hospital, Somerset, KY, p. A293

JONES, Evan, Executive Vice President and Chief Financial Officer, Lakeland Regional Health Medical Center, Lakeland, FL, p. A143

JONES, Evelyn, R.N., Vice President Nursing Services, St. Bernard Hospital And Health Care Center, Chicago, IL, p. A201

JONES, Gerry, M.D., Chief Medical Officer, Chi St. Vincent Infirmary Medical Center, Little Rock, AR, p. A49

JONES, Greg, Chief Financial Officer, Wayne Memorial Hospital, Jesup. GA, p. A174

JONES, Holly, Administrative Director Nursing Services, Illini Community Hospital, Pittsfield, IL, p. A217

JONES, Jace, Interim Chief Executive Officer, Brownwood Regional Medical Center, Brownwood, TX, p. A661

JONES, Jason L., R.N., Chief Executive Officer, Fannin Regional Hospital, Blue Ridge, GA, p. A167

JONES, Jeff, Director Human Resources, Greene Memorial Hospital, Xenia, OH, p. A553

JONES, Jeffrey, Chief Financial Officer, Moses H. Cone Memorial Hospital, Greensboro, NC, p. A511

JONES, Jeremy A., Chief Executive Officer, Arbuckle Memorial Hospital, Sulphur, OK, p. A568

JONES, Joshua, Director Human Resources, Evanston Regional Hospital, Evanston, WY, p. A802

JONES, Joyce, Director Human Resources, Encompass Health Rehabilitation Hospital Of Kingsport, Kingsport, TN, p. A640

JONES, Judy, Chief Clinical Officer, Arkansas Surgical Hospital, North Little Rock, AR, p. A51

JONES, Julie L., Chief Executive Officer, Community Hospital-Fairfax, Fairfax, MO, p. A406

JONES, Karen, Administrative Director Human Resources, Marion General Hospital, Marion, IN, p. A236

JONES, Karol, Chief Nursing Officer, Huntsville Hospital, Huntsville, AL, p. A20

JONES, Kathy, Director Human Resources, Jackson Medical Center, Jackson, AL, p. A20

JONES, Keith, Chief Information Officer, Fulton State Hospital, Fulton, MO, p. A407

JONES, Ken, Chief Operating Officer, Ucsf Medical Center, San Francisco, CA, p. A94

JONES, Kenneth, President, Amita Health Saint Francis Hospital Evanston, Evanston, IL, p. A204

JONES, Kimberly, Director Human Resources, The Spine Hospital Of Louisiana At The Neuromedical Center, Baton Rouge, LA, p. A298

JONES, Kyle, Chief Financial Officer, Marshall Medical Center, Lewisburg, TN, p. A642

JONES, Lance, Chief Executive Officer, Lewis-Gale Medical Center, Boones Mill, VA, p. A739

JONES, Liston, M.D., Medical Director, Springhill Memorial Hospital, Mobile, AL, p. A22

JONES, Louis, Director Management Information Systems, Adventhealth Heart Of Florida, Davenport, FL, p. A135

JONES, M Steven., President, Uh Conneaut Medical Center, Conneaut, OH, p. A537

President, Uh Geneva Medical Center, Geneva, OH, p. A541

JONES, Mark, Chief Financial Officer, Hill Country Memorial Hospital, Fredericksburg, TX, p. A679

JONES, Mark A., President, Orlando Regional Medical Center, Orlando, FL, p. A151

JONES, Marsha, R.N., Director Nursing, Baptist Medical Center Yazoo, Yazoo City, MS, p. A401

R.N., Director of Nursing, Baptist Medical Center Yazoo, Yazoo City, MS, p. A401

JONES, Marshall, Senior Vice President Human Resources, Valleywise Health, Phoenix, AZ, p. A37

JONES, Matthew, Chief Operating Officer and Senior Vice President, The University Of Vermont Health Network - Alice Hyde Medical Center, Malone, NY, p. A487

JONES, Maud, Manager Medical Records, Top. Surgical Specialty Hospital, Houston, TX, p. A689

JONES, MaxAnne, Director Human Resources, Rock Prairie Behavioral Health, College Station, TX, p. A664

JONES, Melinda, R.N., Chief Nursing Officer, Morehouse General Hospital, Bastrop. LA, p. A296

JONES, Mike, Executive Director, Marshall Medical Center, Placerville, CA, p. A85

JONES, Mitchell, Director Information Technology, Little River Memorial Hospital, Ashdown, AR, p. A42

JONES, Naomi, Chief Executive Officer, Seven Hills Hospital, Henderson, NV, p. A442

JONES, Pam, MSN, R.N., Associate Hospital Director and Chief Nursing Officer, Vanderbilt University Medical Center, Nashville, TN, p. A647

JONES, Pamela, Executive Director of Finance, Baptist Health Corbin, Corbin, KY, p. A282

JONES, Pat, Director Information Systems, Merit Health River Oaks, Flowood, MS, p. A392

JONES, Patrice, R.N., MSN, Vice President and Chief Nursing Officer, Uf Health Jacksonville, Jacksonville, FL, p. A142

JONES, Philip. Chief Financial Officer, Curahealth Nashville, Nashville, TN, p. A646

JONES, Phyllis, Chief Human Resources, Wm. Jennings Bryan Dorn Veterans Affairs Medical Center, Columbia, SC, p. A618

JONES, Rachel, Chief Financial Officer, Watsonville Community Hospital, Watsonville, CA, p. A104

JONES, Reginald, Business Manager, Georgia Regional Hospital At Atlanta, Decatur, GA, p. A171

JONES, Reid F., Chief Executive Officer, University Of Alabama Hospital, Birmingham, AL, p. A16

JONES, Rex, Chief Executive Officer, Magnolia Regional Medical Center, Magnolia, AR, p. A49

JONES, Richard, M.D., Medical Director, Encompass Health Rehabilitation Hospital Of Richardson, Richardson, TX, p. A708

Chief Financial Officer, Reading Hospital, West Reading, PA, p. A610

JONES, Rita A., Chief Executive Officer, Dundy County Hospital, Benkelman, NE, p. A430

JONES, Rob, Director of Nursing and Operations, Physicians' Medical Center, New Albany, IN, p. A237

JONES, Robert, Director Management Information Systems, St. Josep. Mercy Oakland, Pontiac, MI, p. A364

JONES, Roger, M.D., Interim Chief of Staff, Tennessee Valley Healthcare System, Nashville, TN, p. A647

JONES, Ruth, Chief Clinical Officer, Regency Hospital Of Northwest Arkansas - Springdale, Springdale, AR, p. A53

JONES, Ruth Ann, Ed.D., MSN, R.N., Senior Vice President, Chief Nursing Officer, University Of Maryland Shore Medical Center At Chestertown, Chestertown, MD, p. A328

Ed.D., MSN, R.N., Senior Vice President, Chief Nursing Officer, University Of Maryland Shore Medical Center At Easton, Easton, MD, p. A329

JONES, Ryan, Chief Executive Officer, Alliance Community Hospital, Alliance, OH, p. A527

JONES, Sarah, Chief Nurse Executive, Metropolitan St. Louis Psychiatric Center, Saint Louis, MO, p. A416

JONES, Scott, President and Chief Executive Officer, Midwestern Regional Medical Center, Zion, IL, p. A222

JONES, Scott R., FACHE, Chief Operating Officer, Prisma Health Hillcrest Hospital, Simpsonville, SC, p. A624

JONES, Sean, Director Human Resources, Merit Health Central, Jackson, MS, p. A394

JONES, Shannon, M.D., Medical Director and Attending Psychiatrist, Evansville Psychiatric Children Center, Evansville, IN, p. A227

JONES, Sharon, M.D., Chief Executive Officer, Evergreen Medical Center, Evergreen, AL, p. A18

JONES, Sherry, Chief Financial Officer, Crestwood Medical Center, Huntsville, AL, p. A20

JONES, Staci, R.N., Chief Nursing Officer, Methodist Mckinney Hospital, Mckinney, TX, p. A700

JONES, Stacy, Chief Nursing Officer, Encompass Health Rehabilitation Hospital Of Morgantown, Morgantown, WV, p. A774

JONES, Stephanie, R.N., Chief Nursing Officer, Redmond Regional Medical Center, Rome, GA, p. A179

JONES, Stephen, M.D., Vice President Medical Staff Affairs, St. Rose Dominican Hospitals - Rose De Lima Campus, Henderson, NV, p. A442

JONES, Steven, M.D., Medical Director, Eureka Hospital, Eureka, IL, p. A204

JONES, Theresa, Manager Human Resources, St. Luke Community Healthcare, Ronan, MT, p. A427

JONES, Tim, Chief Executive Officer, Heart Of Texas Memorial Hospital, Brady, TX, p. A660

JONES, Timothy, Chief Operating Officer, Concord Hospital, Concord, NH, p. A448

JONES, Tom, Chief Information Officer, Fitzgibbon Hospital, Marshall, MO, p. A411

JONES, Tracey, Director Human Resources, Jackson Park Hospital And Medical Center, Chicago, IL, p. A198

JONES, Traci, Chief Financial Officer, Usa Health Children's & Women's Hospital, Mobile, AL, p. A22

Chief Financial Officer, Usa Health University Hospital, Mobile, AL, p. A22

JONES, Tracie, Director Information Services, Missouri Baptist Medical Center, Saint Louis, MO, p. A416

JONES, Vera, Chief Operating Officer, Copley Hospital, Morrisville, VT, p. A736

JONES, Vernita, Site Manager, Phs Santa Fe Indian Hospital, Santa Fe, NM, p. A472

JONES, Vernon, Chief Operating Officer, Rapides Regional Medical Center, Alexandria, LA, p. A295

JONES, Vickie, Interim Chief Executive Officer, Highland-Clarksburg Hospital, Clarksburg, WV, p. A771

JONES, Wendy, Interim Chief Financial Officer, Northern Light Blue Hill Hospital, Blue Hill, ME, p. A319

JONES, William, M.D., Chief Medical Officer, Baylor Scott & White Medical Center - Sunnyvale, Sunnyvale, TX, p. A718

M.D., Chief Medical Officer, City Hospital At White Rock, Dallas, TX, p. A668

JONES, Yameeka, Chief Executive Officer, Select Specialty Hospital - San Diego, San Diego, CA, p. A92

JONES, Yvette, Health Information Management Director, Putnam Community Medical Center, Palatka, FL, p. A152

JONGSMA, Michael, R.N., Chief Nursing Officer, Providence Little Company Of Mary Medical Center - Torrance, Torrance, CA, p. A101

JONTZ, Doug, Senior Vice President Human Resources, Mercy Medical Center - Cedar Rapids, Cedar Rapids, IA, p. A245

JORDAN, Amy, Chief Financial Officer, Rock Springs, Georgetown, TX, p. A681

Chief Nursing Officer/Vice President of Nursing, Adventhealth Gordon, Calhoun, GA, p. A168

JORDAN, Andrew, M.D., Chief of Staff, Vanderbilt Wilson County Hospital, Lebanon, TN, p. A642

JORDAN, Christy, R.N., JD, Chief Operating Officer/Legal Counsel, Southeast Georgia Health System Brunswick Campus, Brunswick, GA, p. A167

JORDAN, Clay, Interim Chief Nursing Officer, Tri Valley Health System, Cambridge, NE, p. A430

JORDAN, Eric, Chief Executive Officer, Jasper General Hospital, Bay Springs, MS, p. A389

JORDAN, Gary W., FACHE, Chief Executive Officer, Cherokee Regional Medical Center, Cherokee, IA, p. A245

JORDAN, Heather, Director Human Resources, Chi St. Luke's Health Memorial Livingston, Livingston, TX, p. A696

JORDAN, Ken, Chief Financial Officer, Fountain Valley Regional Hospital And Medical Center, Fountain Valley, CA, p. A64

JORDAN, Manley, M.D., Chief Medical Officer, Lake Charles Memorial Hospital, Lake Charles, LA, p. A307

JORDAN, Marie, R.N., Senior Vice President and Chief Nursing Officer, Lehigh Valley Hospital, Allentown, PA, p. A583

JORDAN, Patrick Chief Operating Officer, Dartmouth-Hitchcock Medical Center, Lebanon, NH, p. A449

JORDAN, Quincy, M.D., Chief of Staff, Flint River Community Hospital, Montezuma, GA, p. A177

JORDAN, Rhonda, Chief Human Resources Officer, Virtua Marlton, Marlton, NJ, p. A458

JORDAN, Terry, M.D., Chief of Staff, Alliance Health Center, Meridian, MS, p. A397

JORDAN, Traci, MS, R.N., Chief Nursing Officer, Ochsner Lsu Health Shreveport - Monroe Medical Center, Monroe, LA, p. A309

JORDEN BEST, Rosemary, Director Human Resources, Tyrone Hospital, Tyrone, PA, p. A609

JORE, Bernie, Chief Nursing Officer, Ascension St. Mary's Of Michigan, Saginaw, MI, p. A365

JORGENSEN, Jacob, Chief Information Officer, Floyd Valley Healthcare, Le Mars, IA, p. A253

JORGENSEN, Steven C., President, St. Mary's Regional Medical Center, Lewiston, ME, p. A321

JORGENSON, Craig, M.D., Chief of Staff, Boulder City Hospital, Boulder City, NV, p. A441

JOSEPH, Heather, Chief Executive Officer, Cedar Ridge Hospital, Oklahoma City, OK, p. A563

JOSEPH, James, M.D., President Medical Staff, Geisinger-Bloomsburg Hospital, Bloomsburg, PA, p. A585

JOSEPH, Jason, Vice President, Information Services, Spectrum Health - Butterworth Hospital, Grand Rapids, MI, p. A356

JOSEPH-TAYLOR, Terri, Chief Human Resource Manager, Ochsner Medical Center - North Shore, Slidell, LA, p. A315

JOSEPHSON, Louis, Ph.D., President and Chief Executive Officer, Brattleboro Retreat, Brattleboro, VT, p. A735

JOSHI, Maulik, President and Chief Executive Officer, Meritus Medical Center, Hagerstown, MD, p. A330

JOSHI, Nirmal, M.D., Senior Vice President Medical Affairs and Chief Medical Officer, Upmc Pinnacle Harrisburg, Harrisburg, PA, p. A591

M.D., System Chief Medical Officer, Mount Nittany Medical Center, State College, PA, p. A608

JOSLIN, Charlie, M.D., Chief of Staff, Ellinwood District Hospital, Ellinwood, KS, p. A264

JOSLYN, E, M.D., Chief Medical Officer, Centra Bedford Memorial Hospital, Bedford, VA, p. A739

JOSLYN, J, Senior Vice President and Chief Information Officer, Saddleback Medical Center, Laguna Hills, CA, p. A70

JOUD, Mohammad, M.D., Chief of Staff, Bayfront Health Brooksville, Brooksville, FL, p. A133

JOUDEH, Jalal, M.D., Chief Medical Officer, Specialty Rehabilitation Hospital Of Coushatta, Coushatta, LA, p. A299

M.D., Chief of Staff, Dequincy Memorial Hospital, Dequincy, LA, p. A301

JOURDEN, Marti, FACHE, Chief Quality Officer, Ssm Health St. Anthony Hospital - Oklahoma City, Oklahoma City, OK, p. A566

JOY, Michelle, FACHE, Chief Operating Officer, Carson Tahoe Health, Carson City, NV, p. A441

FACHE, Vice President, Chief Operating Officer, Carson Tahoe Continuing Care Hospital, Carson City, NV, p. A441

JOY, Mike, Administrator, Finance, Ascension Via Christi Hospital, Pittsburg, KS, p. A274

JOY, Susan, Chief Nursing Officer, Hillside Rehabilitation Hospital, Warren, OH, p. A551

JOY JR, RolandVice President and Chief Nursing Officer, Adventhealth Hendersonville, Hendersonville, NC, p. A512

JOYAL, Shirley, Director Information Systems, Regional Medical Center Of San Jose, San Jose, CA, p. A95

JOYCE, Allyson, Vice President Human Resources, Mclaren Caro Region, Caro, MI, p. A350

JOYCE, Maria, Chief Financial Officer, National Institutes Of Health Clinical Center, Bethesda, MD, p. A327

JOYNER, Jeff, President, Aurelia Osborn Fox Memorial Hospital, Oneonta, NY, p. A494

JOYNER, Thomas, Chief Financial Officer, Lakeside Behavioral Health System, Memphis, TN, p. A644

JOZEFIAK, Jennifer, Information Officer, Fairlawn Rehabilitation Hospital, Worcester, MA, p. A346

JUAREZ, Edward, M.D., Chief Medical Officer, Kindred Hospital El Paso, El Paso, TX, p. A675

JUAREZ, Elizabeth, M.D., Chief Medical Officer, Harlingen Medical Center, Harlingen, TX, p. A683

JUAREZ, Rose, Chief Civilian Personnel Branch, Brooke Army Medical Center, Fort Sam Houston, TX, p. A677

JUBAS, John, Vice President Finance, The Children's Institute Of Pittsburgh, Pittsburgh, PA, p. A603

JUCHNOWICZ, Jean, Director Human Resources, Merit Health Natchez, Natchez, MS, p. A397

JUDD, Russell V., Chief Executive Officer, Kern Medical, Bakersfield, CA, p. A57

JUDLIN, Karen, Director Human Resources, St. Charles Parish Hospital, Luling, LA, p. A307

JUDYCKI-CREPEAULT, Christine, Chief Financial Officer, Adcare Hospital Of Worcester, Worcester, MA, p. A346

JUHL, Valerie, Director of Health, Madelia Community Hospital, Madelia, MN, p. A379

JULE, Janet, Chief Nurse Executive, Kaiser Permanente Antioch Medical Center, Antioch, CA, p. A56

JULIAN, Bell, Associate Executive Director and Chief Financial Officer, James Cancer Hospital And Solove Research Institute, Columbus, OH, p. A536

JULIAN, Steve, M.D., Vice President Medical Affairs, Sentara Obici Hospital, Suffolk, VA, p. A752

JULIANA, Rich, Director Human Resources, Silver Hill Hospital, New Canaan, CT, p. A124

JUMPING EAGLE, Sara, Clinical Director, Standing Rock Service Unit, Fort Yates Hospital, Indian Health Service, Dhhs, Fort Yates, ND, p. A523

JUNEAU, Cindy, Chief Nursing Officer, Avoyelles Hospital, Marksville, LA, p. A308

JUNEAU, James, Chief Financial Officer, Opelousas General Health System, Opelousas, LA, p. A312

JUNEAU, Tina, Director Human Resources, Bunkie General Hospital, Bunkie, LA, p. A299

JUNG, Darra, Director of Nursing, Union General Hospital, Farmerville, LA, p. A301

JUNGELS, Trisha, R.N., Chief Nursing Officer and Vice President Clinical Services, Jamestown Regional Medical Center, Jamestown, ND, p. A524

JUNGWIRTH, Scott, Chief Human Resources Officer, Providence Alaska Medical Center, Anchorage, AK, p. A27

JUNKINS, Curt M., Chief Executive Officer, Navarro Regional Hospital, Corsicana, TX, p. A666

JUNO, Russell, M.D., Chief of Staff, St. Mark's Medical Center, La Grange, TX, p. A694

JURCZYK, John A., FACHE, Senior Vice President and President, St. Josep. Hospital, Nashua, NH, p. A450

JURGENS, Chad, Senior Executive, Financial Services, Beatrice Community Hospital And Health Center, Beatrice, NE, p. A430

JURKUS, Patti, Director Human Resources, Carilion New River Valley Medical Center, Christiansburg, VA, p. A740

Vice President and Chief Executive Officer, Centra Bedford Memorial Hospital, Bedford, VA, p. A739

JURY, Tina, R.N., Chief Hospital Operations, Anmed Health Medical Center, Anderson, SC, p. A615

JUST, Lisa, President, Aurora Medical Center Kenosha, Kenosha, WI, p. A786

JUST, Paula, Chief Human Resources Officer, Health First Cap. Canaveral Hospital, Cocoa Beach, FL, p. A134

Chief Human Resources Officer, Health First Holmes Regional Medical Center, Melbourne, FL, p. A145

Chief Human Resources Officer, Health First Palm Bay Hospital, Palm Bay, FL, p. A152

Chief Human Resources Officer, Health First Viera Hospital, Melbourne, FL, p. A145

JUSTICE, Brandi, Interim Director, Central State Hospital, Petersburg, VA, p. A748

JUSTICE, Jay, Chief Human Resource Officer, Adena Medical Center, Chillicothe, OH, p. A531

Chief Human Resources Officer, Adena Pike Medical Center, Waverly, OH, p. A552

JUSTICE, Kansas, Senior Vice President and Chief Operating Officer, Pikeville Medical Center, Pikeville, KY, p. A292

JUSTICE, Kim, Vice President Planning and Operations, Atlantic General Hospital, Berlin, MD, p. A327

JUSTIN, Patrick, Chief Financial Officer, United Hospital District, Blue Earth, MN, p. A373

JUSTIN-TANNER, Karen, R.N., Chief Nursing Officer, Fairbanks Memorial Hospital, Fairbanks, AK, p. A28

JUSTUS, Jason, Chief Executive Officer, Pomerene Hospital, Millersburg, OH, p. A545

JUTILA, Kathy, M.D., Chief of Staff, Wheatland Memorial Healthcare, Harlowton, MT, p. A424

JYRKAS, Wade, Director Computer Information Systems, Lake Region Healthcare, Fergus Falls, MN, p. A376

# K

KABERLINE, Gene, Chief Financial Officer, Susan B. Allen Memorial Hospital, El Dorado, KS, p. A264

KABITZKE-GROTH, Terry, R.N., Chief Nursing Officer, Aurora Medical Center In Washington County, Hartford, WI, p. A786

KACHIGION, Claudia, M.D., Medical Director, Alton Mental Health Center, Alton, IL, p. A194

KADDOURI, Sami, M.D., Medical Director, Cornerstone Of Medical Arts Center Hospital, Fresh Meadows, NY, p. A484

KADIVAR, Aryan, M.D., Chief Medical Officer, Southwestern Medical Center, Lawton, OK, p. A561

KAFKA, Rich, M.D., Chief Medical Officer, Avera Gregory Hospital, Gregory, SD, p. A628

KAHL, Larry, Chief Operating Officer, Mid-Columbia Medical Center, The Dalles, OR, p. A582

KAHL, Vicky, Director Human Resources, Valley Regional Medical Center, Brownsville, TX, p. A661

KAHLE, Russ, Chief Information Officer, Logan County Hospital, Oakley, KS, p. A272

KAHLE, Ty, Assistant Vice President Human Resources, Methodist Hospital Union County, Morganfield, KY, p. A290

Vice President Human Resources, Methodist Hospital, Henderson, KY, p. A285

KAHLER, John, M.D., Radiologist, Bryan W. Whitfield Memorial Hospital, Demopolis, AL, p. A17

KAHLY-MCMAHON, Heidi, Interim Vice President Human Resources, Genesis Medical Center - Davenport, Davenport, IA, p. A247

Vice President Human Resources, Genesis Medical Center, Silvis, Silvis, IL, p. A220

KAHN, Maureen A., R.N., President and Chief Executive Officer, Blessing Hospital, Quincy, IL, p. A218

KAHO, Clint, President, Baptist Health La Grange, La Grange, KY, p. A285

Vice President, Baptist Health Louisville, Louisville, KY, p. A287

KAHRS, Amy, Director of Finance, Franklin County Memorial Hospital, Franklin, NE, p. A432

KAINO, Linda, Chief Nursing Officer, Ocean Beach Hospital, Ilwaco, WA, p. A759

KAISER, Brenda, Director Human Resources, University Of Kansas Health System Great Bend Campus, Great Bend, KS, p. A265

KAISER, James, Site Director Information Technology, Upper Valley Medical Center, Troy, OH, p. A551

KAISER, Janet, R.N., Chief Nursing Officer, Kansas Medical Center, Andover, KS, p. A261

KAISER, Ken, Coordinator Information Systems, Grant Regional Health Center, Lancaster, WI, p. A787

KAISER, Russell, Interim Chief Executive Officer and Chief Nursing Officer, The Colony Er Hospital, The Colony, TX, p. A720

KAJIWARA, Gary, President and Chief Executive Officer, Kuakini Medical Center, Honolulu, HI, p. A184

KAJIWARA, Gary K., President and Chief Executive Officer, Kuakini Medical Center, Honolulu, HI, p. A184

KAKAVAS, Connie, Chief Human Resources Officer, Summit Healthcare Regional Medical Center, Show Low, AZ, p. A38

KAKUDA, James, M.D., Chief of Staff, Pali Momi Medical Center, Aiea, HI, p. A184

KALAFUS, Lisa, MSN, R.N., Chief Nursing Officer, Gaylord Specialty Healthcare, Wallingford, CT, p. A126

KALAJAINEN, Kimberly, Vice President Operations and Chief Information Officer, Lawrence + Memorial Hospital, New London, CT, p. A124

Vice President, Operations and Information Technology, Chief Information Officer, Westerly Hospital, Westerly, RI, p. A614

KALANIHUIA, Janice, President, Molokai General Hospital, Kaunakakai, HI, p. A186

KALAVAR, Jagadeesh, M.D., Chief of Staff, Michael E. Debakey Veterans Affairs Medical Center, Houston, TX, p. A687

KALCHIK, Kevin, Chief Financial Officer, War Memorial Hospital, Sault Sainte Marie, MI, p. A366

KALE, Debra, Vice President Human Resources, Atrium Health Cleveland, Shelby, NC, p. A518

KALEEL, Reza, Chief Executive, Kadlec Regional Medical Center, Richland, WA, p. A763

Executive Vice President and Chief Operating Officer, St. Mary's Hospital And Medical Center, Grand Junction, CO, p. A113

KALINA, Andrea, Vice President External Affairs and Chief Human Resources Officer, St. Clair Hospital, Pittsburgh, PA, p. A603

KALINSKI, Cami, Director Financial Services, Frances Mahon Deaconess Hospital, Glasgow, MT, p. A424

KALKA, Gina, R.N., Chief Nursing Officer, Pecos County Memorial Hospital, Fort Stockton, TX, p. A677

KALKOWSKI, Kelly, Chief Executive Officer, Niobrara Valley Hospital, Lynch, NE, p. A435

KALKUT, Gary, M.D., Senior Vice President and Chief Medical Officer, Montefiore Medical Center, Bronx, NY, p. A477

KALLEVIG, Daryl, Chief Information Officer, Riverwood Healthcare Center, Aitkin, MN, p. A371

KALMAN, Jill, M.D., Executive Director, Lenox Hill Hospital, New York, NY, p. A490

KALSMAN, Stephen, Area Finance Officer, Kaiser Permanente San Jose Medical Center, San Jose, CA, p. A94

KALTENBACH, Gretchen, R.N., Chief Operating Officer, Genesis Behavioral Hospital, Breaux Bridge, LA, p. A298

KALUA, Patricia, Chief Nurse Executive, Kona Community Hospital, Kealakekua, HI, p. A186

KAMBER, Sean, Chief Executive Officer, Medical City Weatherford, Weatherford, TX, p. A724

KAMBEROS, Peter, Chief Operating Officer, Thorek Memorial Hospital, Chicago, IL, p. A201

KAMBEROV, Denis, M.D., Chief of Staff, De Soto Regional Health System, Mansfield, LA, p. A308

KAMBIC, Phillip M., President and Chief Executive Officer, Riverside Medical Center, Kankakee, IL, p. A209

KAMBOJ, Pradeep. M.D., Chief Medical Staff, Adventist Health - Tulare, Tulare, CA, p. A102

KAMENS, Eric, Regional Director Information Systems, Shriners Hospitals For Children-Springfield, Springfield, MA, p. A345

KAMERMAYER, Angela, MS, Chief Nursing Officer, Integris Health Edmond, Edmond, OK, p. A558

KAMGUIA, Rebecca, Administrative Director Human Resources, Bon Secours Memorial Regional Medical Center, Mechanicsville, VA, p. A746

KAMIKAWA, Cynthia, R.N., MSN, President, Queen's North Hawaii Community Hospital, Kamuela, HI, p. A186

KAMINSKI, Gene, Vice President Human Resources and Hospitality Services, Mclaren Northern Michigan, Petoskey, MI, p. A363

KAMINSKI, Tammy, Director Human Resources, Alaska Regional Hospital, Anchorage, AK, p. A27
Vice President Human Relations, Riverside Community Hospital, Riverside, CA, p. A88

KAMINSKI, Toni, Director Human Resources, Medical Center Enterprise, Enterprise, AL, p. A18

KAMINSKY, Kathleen, R.N., Senior Vice President Patient Care Services, Englewood Health, Englewood, NJ, p. A455

KAMMERER, James, Vice President Support Services, Great River Medical Center, West Burlington, IA, p. A260

KAMMERUD, Shawn, Manager Information Services, Osceola Medical Center, Osceola, WI, p. A793

KAMOWSKI, David, Vice President and Chief Information Officer, Temple University Hospital, Philadelphia, PA, p. A602

KAMPWERTH, Dennis, Director Management Information Systems, Gateway Regional Medical Center, Granite City, IL, p. A206

KANAPARTI, V.R., M.D., Director Medical Services, Kalamazoo Psychiatric Hospital, Kalamazoo, MI, p. A359

KANDOW, Casey, Chief Operating Officer, Mclaren Greater Lansing, Lansing, MI, p. A360

KANE, Addy, Chief Financial Officer, Roger Williams Medical Center, Providence, RI, p. A614

KANE, Audrey, Interim Chief Financial Officer, Prowers Medical Center, Lamar, CO, p. A115

KANE, Kelli, Director of Finance, Barnes-Kasson County Hospital, Susquehanna, PA, p. A608

KANE, Steve, Director Information Technology, Lower Bucks Hospital, Bristol, PA, p. A585

KANE, Thomas, R.N., Vice President Patient Services and Chief Nursing Officer, Munson Healthcare Manistee Hospital, Manistee, MI, p. A361

KANE, Trisha, Director Human Resources, Continuecare Hospital At Hendrick Medical Center, Abilene, TX, p. A651

KANIA, Kathy, Associate Executive Director and Chief Information Officer, Staten Island University Hospital, Staten Island, NY, p. A499

KANNADAY, Colleen, FACHE, President, Bromenn Medical Center, Normal, IL, p. A214
FACHE, President, Eureka Hospital, Eureka, IL, p. A204

KANTELAS, Sandra, Chief Nursing Officer, Uh Elyria Medical Center, Elyria, OH, p. A540

KANTOS, Craig A., Chief Executive Officer, Coteau Des Prairies Hospital, Sisseton, SD, p. A632

KANUCH, James, Vice President Finance, Allegheny Valley Hospital, Natrona Heights, PA, p. A598
Vice President Finance, West Penn Hospital, Pittsburgh, PA, p. A605

KANWAL, Neeraj, M.D., Interim President, Metro Region, Promedica Bay Park Hospital, Oregon, OH, p. A547
M.D., Vice President, Medical Affairs, Promedica Toledo Hospital, Toledo, OH, p. A550

KAPER, Jonathan, Chief Medical Officer, Beaumont Hospital - Trenton, Trenton, MI, p. A368

KAPLAN, Alan, M.D., Chief Executive Officer, University Hospital, Madison, WI, p. A788

KAPLAN, Eric, Chief Operating Officer, Bayfront Health Port Charlotte, Port Charlotte, FL, p. A154
Interim Chief Executive Officer and Chief Operating Officer, Bayfront Health Port Charlotte, Port Charlotte, FL, p. A154
Interim Chief Executive Officer, Bayfront Health Punta Gorda, Punta Gorda, FL, p. A155

KAPLAN, Ronald, Chief Financial Officer, North Philadelphia Health System, Philadelphia, PA, p. A601

KAPLAN, Tamra, PharmD, Chief Operating Officer, Miller Children's & Women's Hospital Long Beach, Long Beach, CA, p. A72

KAPLANIS, Gene, Director Information Technology, Alaska Regional Hospital, Anchorage, AK, p. A27

KAPRE, Sheela, M.D., Chief Medical Officer, San Joaquin General Hospital, French Camp. CA, p. A65

KARA, Amynah, M.D., Chief Medical Officer, Baylor Scott & White Emergency Hospitals—Aubrey, Aubrey, TX, p. A654

KARADJOFF, Peter, Interim President, Henry Ford Wyandotte Hospital, Wyandotte, MI, p. A370

KARAM, Annah, Director Human Resources, San Gorgonio Memorial Hospital, Banning, CA, p. A58

KARAM, Chris, FACHE, President and Chief Executive Officer, Senior Vice President Group Operations, Christus St. Frances Cabrini Hospital, Alexandria, LA, p. A295

KARAM, Christopher, Chief Operating Officer, Saint Josep. Health System, Mishawaka, IN, p. A236

KARAM, Christopher J., President, Plymouth Medical Center, Plymouth, IN, p. A239

KARANJA, Diana, R.N., Director of Nursing, St. John Vianney Hospital, Downingtown, PA, p. A588

KARANJAI, Rajohn, M.D., Chief Medical Officer, Sidney Health Center, Sidney, MT, p. A428

KARCZ, Chrisi, Chief Nursing Officer, Van Matre Encompass Health Rehabilitation Hospital, Rockford, IL, p. A219

KARDOW, Vivian, Chief Human Resources Officer, Memorial Hermann - Texas Medical Center, Houston, TX, p. A687
Chief Human Resources Officer, Tirr Memorial Hermann, Houston, TX, p. A688

KAREL, Thomas, Vice President Organization and Talent Effectiveness, Mercy Health Saint Mary's, Grand Rapids, MI, p. A356

KARG, Gary, Interim Vice President Finance, Christus St. Frances Cabrini Hospital, Alexandria, LA, p. A295

KARIM, Parvez, M.D., Chief Medical Officer, Allegiance Specialty Hospital Of Greenville, Greenville, MS, p. A392

KARL, Don, Chief Operating Officer, Las Palmas Medical Center, El Paso, TX, p. A675
Interim Chief Executive Officer, Las Palmas Medical Center, El Paso, TX, p. A675

KARLSEN, Brooke, MSN, R.N., Regional Vice President, Operations, St. Vincent's Medical Center, Bridgeport, CT, p. A121

KARMACH, Izabela, R.N., Administrator, San Diego County Psychiatric Hospital, San Diego, CA, p. A92

KARN, Cielette, M.D., Chief of Staff, Sagewest Health Care, Riverton, WY, p. A803

KARNER, Diana, R.N., MSN, Chief Nursing Executive, California Pacific Medical Center-St. Luke's Campus, San Francisco, CA, p. A93
R.N., MSN, Chief Nursing Officer, California Pacific Medical Center, San Francisco, CA, p. A93

KARNITZ, Susan, Chief Nursing Director, Hutchinson Health, Hutchinson, MN, p. A378

KARNS, Kristopher, Chief Executive Officer, Cornerstone Hospital Of Oklahoma-Shawnee, Shawnee, OK, p. A568

KARP, Bob, M.D., Chief Medical Officer, United Hospital District, Blue Earth, MN, p. A373

KARRE, Kris, Director Finance and Accounting, Unitypoint Health-Keokuk, Keokuk, IA, p. A252

KARSOS, Felicia, R.N., Chief Nursing Officer, Hudson Regional Hospital, Secaucus, NJ, p. A463

KARSTEN, Paul, Vice President Finance and Chief Financial Officer, Pine Rest Christian Mental Health Services, Grand Rapids, MI, p. A356

KARSTETTER, James, R.N., Vice President and Chief Nursing Officer, Western Maryland Regional Medical Center, Cumberland, MD, p. A329

KASIRYE, Yusuf, M.D., Chief of Staff, Flambeau Hospital, Park Falls, WI, p. A794.

KASITZ, Todd, Vice President Finance, Newton Medical Center, Newton, KS, p. A272

KASNIC, Tracey, Chief Nursing Officer, Confluence Health/Wenatchee Valley Hospital, Wenatchee, WA, p. A768
Senior Vice President Inpatient and Chief Nursing Officer, Confluence Health/Central Washington Hospital, Wenatchee, WA, p. A768

KASPER, Katie, Chief Clinical Officer, Uh Avon Rehabilitation Hospital, Avon, OH, p. A528

KASPER, Yobi, Chief Information Officer, Advanced Diagnostics Hospital, Houston, TX, p. A684

KASS, Andrew, M.D., Assistant Superintendent, Albert J. Solnit Psychiatric Center - South Campus, Middletown, CT, p. A123

KASSAB, Jerry, President and Chief Executive Officer, Aspire Health Partners, Orlando, FL, p. A151

KASSAB, Kelly, Chief Operating Officer, Canonsburg Hospital, Canonsburg, PA, p. A586
Chief Operating Officer, Jefferson Hospital, Jefferson Hills, PA, p. A593

KASSAHN, Kristine, Chief Executive Officer, Fresno Surgical Hospital, Fresno, CA, p. A65

KASSER, Michael, Chief Financial Officer, Herrin Hospital, Herrin, IL, p. A207
Vice President Chief Financial Officer and Treasurer, Memorial Hospital Of Carbondale, Carbondale, IL, p. A196

KASSIS, Charles, President, Mercy Medical Center Merced, Merced, CA, p. A78

KASSIS, Maher, M.D., Chief Medical Staff, Mercy Health - Marcum And Wallace, Irvine, KY, p. A285

KASTEN, Gina, Manager Human Resources, Aspirus Ontonagon Hospital, Inc., Ontonagon, MI, p. A363

KATEN-BAHENSKY, Donna, Director, West Palm Beach Veterans Affairs Medical Center, West Palm Beach, FL, p. A162

KATES, Josh, Information Technology Analyst, Andrew Mcfarland Mental Health Center, Springfield, IL, p. A220

KATHRINS, Richard J., Ph.D., President and Chief Executive Officer, Bacharach Institute For Rehabilitation, Pomona, NJ, p. A461

KATNENI, Jitendra, M.D., Medical Director, Select Specialty Hospital-Flint, Flint, MI, p. A354

KATO, Laura, Vice President Human Resources, St. Francis Medical Center, Lynwood, CA, p. A76

KATSCHKE, R, M.D., JrMedical Director, Grover C. Dils Medical Center, Caliente, NV, p. A441

KATZ, Jeffrey, M.D., Chief Medical Officer, Memorial Hermann - Texas Medical Center, Houston, TX, p. A687

KATZ, Michael, Vice President Human Resources, Canton-Potsdam Hospital, Potsdam, NY, p. A495

KATZ, Michelle, Director Human Resources, Encompass Health Nittany Valley Rehabilitation Hospital, Pleasant Gap. PA, p. A605

KATZ, Richard, M.D., Vice President Medical Affairs, Mt. Washington Pediatric Hospital, Baltimore, MD, p. A326

KATZ, Robert, M.D., Chief of Staff, Columbus Community Hospital, Columbus, TX, p. A664

KATZ, Yair, Chief Financial Officer, Long Beach Medical Center, Long Beach, CA, p. A72
Chief Financial Officer, Miller Children's & Women's Hospital Long Beach, Long Beach, CA, p. A72

KAUFFMAN, Angie, Chief Executive Officer, South Texas Spine And Surgical Hospital, San Antonio, TX, p. A713

KAUFFMAN, Gail, Director Human Resources, Berwick Hospital Center, Berwick, PA, p. A584

KAUFFMAN, Linda, R.N., Chief Nursing Officer, Nazareth Hospital, Philadelphia, PA, p. A601

KAUFMAN, Cheryl, Director Health Information Management, Adventhealth Dade City, Dade City, FL, p. A135
Information Technology Technician, Coteau Des Prairies Hospital, Sisseton, SD, p. A632

KAUFMAN, Dan, Director Information Services, Paulding County Hospital, Paulding, OH, p. A547

KAUFMAN, Irvin, M.D., Chief Medical Officer, Rady Children's Hospital - San Diego, San Diego, CA, p. A91

KAUFMAN, Robert, Director Financial Services, Central State Hospital, Petersburg, VA, p. A748
Fiscal Officer, Hiram W. Davis Medical Center, Petersburg, VA, p. A748

KAUFMAN, Samuel, Chief Executive Officer, Henderson Hospital, Henderson, NV, p. A442

KAUFMAN, Seth, M.D., Chief Medical Officer, Northbay Medical Center, Fairfield, CA, p. A63

KAUL, Kamlesh, M.D., Chief of Staff, Logansport Memorial Hospital, Logansport, IN, p. A235

KAUP, Jack, Chief Executive Officer, Black Hills Surgical Hospital, Rapid City, SD, p. A630

KAUPA, Michael, Executive Vice President and Chief Operating Officer, Park Nicollet Methodist Hospital, Saint Louis Park, MN, p. A385

KAUTZ, Terri, Manager Human Resources, Weiser Memorial Hospital, Weiser, ID, p. A193

KAUZLARICH, Sidney, M.D., Medical Director, Douglas County Community Mental Health Center, Omaha, NE, p. A437

KAVALIER, MaryJo, Administrator, Mercyone Cedar Falls Medical Center, Cedar Falls, IA, p. A244

KAVANAGH, Darina, R.N., MSN, Chief Nursing Officer, Good Samaritan Hospital, San Jose, CA, p. A94

KAVANAGH, Sean, Director Information Technology, Pondera Medical Center, Conrad, MT, p. A422

KAVANAUGH, Paul B., President and Chief Executive Officer, Community Care Hospital, New Orleans, LA, p. A310

KAVANAUGH, Samantha, Chief Financial Officer, Riverview Psychiatric Center, Augusta, ME, p. A318

KAVTARADZE, David, M.D., Chief of Staff, Crisp Regional Hospital, Cordele, GA, p. A170

KAY, Kirk, Chief Financial Officer, Veterans Affairs Nebraska-Western Iowa Health Care System, Omaha, NE, p. A438

KAY, Robert, Senior Vice President and Chief Financial Officer, Memorial Medical Center, Springfield, IL, p. A221

KAY-GARCIA, Lisa, Chief Information Officer, Kearny County Hospital, Lakin, KS, p. A268

KAYE, Jessie, Chief Executive Officer, Prairie View, Newton, KS, p. A272

KAYGA, Alicia, R.N., Chief Nursing Officer, Brownwood Regional Medical Center, Brownwood, TX, p. A661

KAYROUZ, Thomas, M.D., Chief Medical Officer, Anmed Health Medical Center, Anderson, SC, p. A615

KAYSER, Sonya, Human Resources Officer, Avera Marshall Regional Medical Center, Marshall, MN, p. A380

KAZMIERCZAK, Sara Marie, R.N., Director of Nursing, North Valley Health Center, Warren, MN, p. A387

KAZMIERCZAK, Stanley, Controller, Amita Health Saint Josep. Hospital, Chicago, IL, p. A197

KA'AKIMAKA, Holly, Director Human Resources, Hilo Medical Center, Hilo, HI, p. A184

KEANE, Dennis, Vice President Finance and Chief Financial Officer, St. John's Riverside Hospital, Yonkers, NY, p. A503

KEANE, Fran, Vice President Human Resources, Centrastate Healthcare System, Freehold, NJ, p. A455

KEANE, Valerie, FACHE, Chief Nursing Executive, Sentara Northern Virginia Medical Center, Woodbridge, VA, p. A754

KEARNEY, Elizabeth, R.N., Chief Nursing Officer, Mountain Vista Medical Center, Mesa, AZ, p. A34

KEARNEY, Karen, Vice President Inpatient Rehabilitation Services, John Heinz Institute Of Rehabilitation Medicine, Wilkes-Barre, PA, p. A611

KEARNEY, Lynn, Vice President Nursing, Robert Wood Johnson University Hospital Somerset, Somerville, NJ, p. A463

KEARNEY, M, Vice President Human Resources, Saint Mary's Hospital, Waterbury, CT, p. A126

KEARNS, Debbie, Chief Executive Officer, Community Hospital, Oklahoma City, OK, p. A564
Chief Executive Officer, Northwest Surgical Hospital, Oklahoma City, OK, p. A565

KEASTER, Lorna, Interim Chief Nursing Officer, Hshs Holy Family Hospital In Greenville, Greenville, IL, p. A206

KEATING, Todd, Chief Financial Officer, University Of Vermont Medical Center, Burlington, VT, p. A735

KEATON, Tony, Director Information Systems, Roane General Hospital, Spencer, WV, p. A777

KECK, Paul, M.D., President and Chief Executive Officer, Lindner Center Of Hope, Mason, OH, p. A544

KEDDINGTON, Richard, Chief Executive Officer, Watertown Regional Medical Center, Watertown, WI, p. A798

KEDELIS, Bob, Chief Executive Officer, Neurobehavioral Hospital Of Nw Indiana, Crown Point, IN, p. A226

KEDZIERSKI, Kelly, R.N., Director of Nursing, Cordova Community Medical Center, Cordova, AK, p. A28

KEE, Agnes, Financial Manager, Gallup Indian Medical Center, Gallup. NM, p. A469

KEE, Robert, Chief Information Officer, Nyc Health + Hospitals / Coney Island, Brooklyn, NY, p. A478

KEEF, Shaun, Chief Financial Officer, Eastern Oklahoma Medical Center, Poteau, OK, p. A567

KEEFE, Eileen, Chief Nursing Officer, Parkland Medical Center, Derry, NH, p. A448

KEEFER, Katrina, Chief Executive Officer, Augusta University Medical Center, Augusta, GA, p. A165
Interim Chief Financial Officer, Augusta University Medical Center, Augusta, GA, p. A165

KEEFER, Russ, Chief Human Resources Officer, Trios Health, Kennewick, WA, p. A759

KEEGAN, Justin, Director Support Services, Avera Gregory Hospital, Gregory, SD, p. A628

KEEL, Barry L., Administrator, North Mississipp. Medical Center-West Point, West Point, MS, p. A401

KEELE, Paula, Manager Information Systems, Osf Heart Of Mary Medical Center, Urbana, IL, p. A222
Manager Information Systems, Osf Sacred Heart Medical Center, Danville, IL, p. A202

KEELE, Ryan, Chief Executive Officer, Pam Specialty Hospital Of Las Vegas, Las Vegas, NV, p. A444

KEELER, Dave, Chief Financial Officer, Pipestone County Medical Center Avera, Pipestone, MN, p. A383

KEELER, Jason, Executive Vice President and Chief Operating Officer, University Of Chicago Medical Center, Chicago, IL, p. A201

KEELER, Jean M., President and Chief Executive Officer, Grand View Health, Sellersville, PA, p. A607

KEELER, Karl, President, Mercyone Des Moines Medical Center, Des Moines, IA, p. A248

KEELEY, Katherine, M.D., Chief of Staff, Sunrise Hospital And Medical Center, Las Vegas, NV, p. A444

KEELINE, Leah, Clinical Informatics Specialist, Catalina Island Medical Center, Avalon, CA, p. A56

KEELING, Kathy, Director of Nursing, Rehabilitation Hospital Of Rhode Island, North Smithfield, RI, p. A613

KEELING, Kevin, Chief Financial Officer, St. Lucie Medical Center, Port St Lucie, FL, p. A155

KEELING, Michele A., Vice President and Administrator, Saint Francis Hospital Muskogee, Muskogee, OK, p. A562

KEELING, Terri, Vice President Information Systems, Upmc Mckeesport, Mckeesport, PA, p. A596

KEEN, Kris, Chief Information Officer, Cameron Memorial Community Hospital, Angola, IN, p. A223

KEEN, Michael, Senior Vice President and Chief Financial Officer, Grand View Health, Sellersville, PA, p. A607

KEEN, Pamela R., Chief Executive Officer, The Children's Home Of Pittsburgh, Pittsburgh, PA, p. A603

KEEN, Scott R., Chief Executive Officer, Honorhealth Rehabilitation Hospital, Scottsdale, AZ, p. A38

KEENAN, Bob, Chief Medical Officer, H. Lee Moffitt Cancer Center And Research Institute, Tampa, FL, p. A159

KEENAN, Kevin, M.D., Physician Advisor, East Cooper Medical Center, Mount Pleasant, SC, p. A622

KEENAN, Nancy, R.N., Senior Vice President and Chief Nursing Officer, Houston Methodist Willowbrook Hospital, Houston, TX, p. A686

KEENAN, Richard, Senior Vice President Finance and Chief Financial Officer, Valley Hospital, Ridgewood, NJ, p. A462

KEENE, Emilie, FACHE, Interim Chief Operating Officer, Prisma Health Baptist Parkridge Hospital, Columbia, SC, p. A618

KEENE, Kimberly, R.N., Chief Executive Officer, St. Bernard Parish Hospital, Chalmette, LA, p. A299

KEENE, Tony, Chief Executive Officer, Sullivan County Memorial Hospital, Milan, MO, p. A412

KEENER, Jayd, Co-Chief Executive Officer, Garfield County Public Hospital District, Pomeroy, WA, p. A762

KEENER, Vicki, Administrative Assistant and Director Human Resources, Little River Memorial Hospital, Ashdown, AR, p. A42

KEEPSEAGLE, Joelle, Director of Nursing, Standing Rock Service Unit, Fort Yates Hospital, Indian Health Service, Dhhs, Fort Yates, ND, p. A523

KEESBURY, Drew, Chief Financial Officer, La Porte Hospital, La Porte, IN, p. A234
Chief Financial Officer, Starke Hospital, Knox, IN, p. A234

KEEVER, Jerry, Administrator, Sharkey-Issaquena Community Hospital, Rolling Fork, MS, p. A400

KEFALAS, George, Chief Medical Officer, Aultman Specialty Hospital, Canton, OH, p. A531

KEGLEY, Carl, System Director Information Technology, Fairbanks Memorial Hospital, Fairbanks, AK, p. A28

KEGLEY, Glen, Chief Operating Officer, Hutchinson Health, Hutchinson, MN, p. A378

KEGLEY, Shawn, Director Information Services, Research Medical Center, Kansas City, MO, p. A409

KEHIAYAN, Nancy, Director of Nursing, Colorado Mental Health Institute At Fort Logan, Denver, CO, p. A110

KEHRBERG, Mark, M.D., Chief Medical Officer, Ascension Calumet Hospital, Chilton, WI, p. A781
M.D., Senior Vice President and Chief Medical Officer, Ascension Northeast Wisconsin Mercy Hospital, Oshkosh, WI, p. A793

KEHUS, Frank, Associate Director for Operations, Marion Veterans Affairs Medical Center, Marion, IL, p. A211

KEIL, James, M.D., Chief Medical Officer, Niobrara Valley Hospital, Lynch, NE, p. A435

KEILERS, Lance W., Interim Chief Executive Officer, Lillian M. Hudspeth Memorial Hospital, Sonora, TX, p. A716

KEILMAN, Stacey, Chief Executive Officer, Torrance State Hospital, Torrance, PA, p. A608

KEIRNS, Melody, Manager Human Resources, F. W. Huston Medical Center, Winchester, KS, p. A279

KEISER, Trish, Comptroller, Avera Gregory Hospital, Gregory, SD, p. A628

KEITH, Bridgette, Director Human Resources, Encompass Health Rehabilitation Hospital Of Northern Kentucky, Edgewood, KY, p. A282

KEITH, Christopher, Chief Executive Officer, Select Specialty Hospital-Wichita, Wichita, KS, p. A279

KEITH, Darlene, Chief Information Systems, Alleghany Memorial Hospital, Sparta, NC, p. A518

KEITH, David N., FACHE, President and Chief Executive Officer, Mcalester Regional Health Center, Mcalester, OK, p. A562

KEITH, Jeannie, R.N., Nurse Executive, Shriners Hospitals For Children-Galveston, Galveston, TX, p. A680
R.N., Nurse Executive, Shriners Hospitals For Children-Houston, Houston, TX, p. A688

KEITH, Lorraine, Chief Nursing Officer, St. Vincent's Medical Center Riverside, Jacksonville, FL, p. A141
Chief Nursing Officer, St. Vincent's Medical Center Southside, Jacksonville, FL, p. A141

KEITH, Marty, Chief Human Resources Officer, Saint Francis Hospital, Memphis, TN, p. A645

KELBAUGH, Brian, Chief Financial Officer, Summersville Regional Medical Center, Summersville, WV, p. A777

KELBLY, Kevin, Senior Vice President Finance and Corporate Fiscal Affairs, Carroll Hospital Center, Westminster, MD, p. A333

KELLAR, Brian, Chief Executive Officer, Banner Casa Grande Medical Center, Casa Grande, AZ, p. A30

KELLAR, Mark, R.N., Interim Chief Nursing Officer, Our Lady Of The Angels Hospital, Bogalusa, LA, p. A298

KELLEHER, Cynthia, M.P.H., President and Chief Executive Officer, University Of Maryland Rehabilitation & Orthopaedic Institute, Baltimore, MD, p. A327

KELLEHER, Mary, Vice President Human Resources, Holyoke Medical Center, Holyoke, MA, p. A340

KELLEHER, Mary Lou, R.N., MSN, Vice President, Nursing, Franciscan Children's, Brighton, MA, p. A336

KELLEHER, Michael, Chief Medical Officer, Ann & Robert H. Lurie Children's Hospital Of Chicago, Chicago, IL, p. A198

KELLENBARGER, Lance, Site Director Information Systems, St. Catherine Hospital, Garden City, KS, p. A264

KELLER, Anita, R.N., MSN, Chief Nursing Officer, Johnson Memorial Hospital, Franklin, IN, p. A229

KELLER, Ann, Supervisor Health Information Management, Walton Rehabilitation Hospital, Augusta, GA, p. A166

KELLER, Christine, Chief Administrative Officer, Bluffton Hospital, Bluffton, OH, p. A529

KELLER, Diane R., Chief Executive Officer, Memorial Community Health, Aurora, NE, p. A429

KELLER, Gretchen, Director Health Information, Neosho Memorial Regional Medical Center, Chanute, KS, p. A262

KELLER, James, M.D., Vice President, Medical Management, Advocate Trinity Hospital, Chicago, IL, p. A197
Chief Information Officer, Ascension Borgess-Lee Hospital, Dowagiac, MI, p. A353
Director Human Resources, Nea Baptist Memorial Hospital, Jonesboro, AR, p. A48

KELLER, Jim, Site Director Information Services, Mercy Health Saint Mary's, Grand Rapids, MI, p. A356

KELLER, Justin, Chief Information Officer, Murray County Medical Center, Slayton, MN, p. A386

KELLER, Ken, President and Chief Executive Officer, Bakersfield Memorial Hospital, Bakersfield, CA, p. A57

KELLER, Marsha, Director Human Resources, Upmc Kane, Kane, PA, p. A593

KELLER, Maryalice, Vice President Brand and Talent Management, Unity Hospital, Rochester, NY, p. A496

KELLER, Patricia, MSN, R.N., Nurse Administrator, Mayo Clinic Health System - Northland In Barron, Barron, WI, p. A781

KELLER, Ruey, Acting Chief Information Officer, Va San Diego Healthcare System, San Diego, CA, p. A93

KELLER, Scott, Director Information Technology, Community Memorial Healthcare, Marysville, KS, p. A270

KELLER, Stewart, M.D., Medical Director, Mesa Springs, Fort Worth, TX, p. A679

KELLER, Thomas W., President and Chief Executive Officer, Ozarks Medical Center, West Plains, MO, p. A420

KELLERMAN, Laurie, MSN, Chief Clinical Officer, Marshall Browning Hospital, Du Quoin, IL, p. A203

KELLEY, Brent, Director Information Technology, Nor-Lea Hospital District, Lovington, NM, p. A470

KELLEY, Danny, Administrative Director, Health Information Technology, Norman Regional Health System, Norman, OK, p. A563

KELLEY, Jalinda, Secretary of Interior Services, Chickasaw Nation Medical Center, Ada, OK, p. A555

KELLEY, James, Chief Human Resources Officer, Desert Regional Medical Center, Palm Springs, CA, p. A83

KELLEY, Janice, Chief Financial Officer, Marshall County Hospital, Benton, KY, p. A280

KELLEY, Julie, M.D., Chief of Staff, Red Bud Regional Hospital, Red Bud, IL, p. A218

KELLEY, Lewis, Chief Operating Officer, Union General Hospital, Blairsville, GA, p. A167

KELLEY, Mary, Director Human Resources, The Outer Banks Hospital, Nags Head, NC, p. A515

KELLEY, Neal, Vice President and Chief Operating Officer, Ascension Seton Hays, Kyle, TX, p. A694

KELLEY, Randall, FACHE, President, Spectrum Health Gerber Memorial, Fremont, MI, p. A355
FACHE, President, Spectrum Health Ludington Hospital, Ludington, MI, p. A361

KELLEY, Sarah Jo, Executive Director of Human Resources and Support Services, Ste. Genevieve County Memorial Hospital, Ste Genevieve, MO, p. A419

KELLEY, Sharon, Chief Financial Officer, Clifton Springs Hospital And Clinic, Clifton Springs, NY, p. A481

KELLEY, Steven L., President and Chief Executive Officer, Ellenville Regional Hospital, Ellenville, NY, p. A483

KELLEY, Sue, Chief Financial Officer, Cordell Memorial Hospital, Cordell, OK, p. A558

KELLEY, Thomas, Executive Vice President and Chief Financial Officer, Froedtert South - Kenosha Medical Center, Kenosha, WI, p. A786

KELLEY, Vicky, Chief Financial Officer, Dequincy Memorial Hospital, Dequincy, LA, p. A301

KELLEY, Warren, Chief Information Officer, Reynolds Memorial Hospital, Glen Dale, WV, p. A772

KELLIHER, Brandon, Chief Information Officer, Great Plains Health, North Platte, NE, p. A436

KELLOGG, Benjamin, M.D., Chief of Staff, Rhea Medical Center, Dayton, TN, p. A637

KELLOGG, Jason, M.D., Chief of Staff, Newport Bay Hospital, Newport Beach, CA, p. A81

KELLS, Anne, Interim Chief Financial Officer, Appleton Area Health Services, Appleton, MN, p. A371

KELLUM, Craig, Director Management Information Systems, Cap. Fear Valley - Bladen County Hospital, Elizabethtown, NC, p. A509

KELLUM, Kyle, Chief Executive Officer, Cherry County Hospital, Valentine, NE, p. A440

KELLY, Brian, M.D., President Medical Staff, Saint Elizabeth's Medical Center, Wabasha, MN, p. A387
M.D., Vice President Medical Affairs and Medical Director, Sturdy Memorial Hospital, Attleboro, MA, p. A334
Acting Chief Fiscal Service, San Francisco Va Medical Center, San Francisco, CA, p. A94
Vice President Finance, Advocate South Suburban Hospital, Hazel Crest, IL, p. A207

KELLY, Charles, D.O., Vice President Medical Affairs and Chief Medical Officer, Henry Ford Macomb Hospitals, Clinton Township. MI, p. A351

KELLY, Colan, Chief Financial Officer, Pineville Community Health Center, Pineville, KY, p. A292

KELLY, Dan, R.N., Chief Nursing Officer, Memorial Hermann Memorial City Medical Center, Houston, TX, p. A687

KELLY, Daniel R., Chief Executive Officer, Mckenzie County Healthcare System, Watford City, ND, p. A526

KELLY, Diane, Chief Operating Officer, Greenwich Hospital, Greenwich, CT, p. A122

KELLY, Edward, Chief Executive Officer and President, Milford Regional Medical Center, Milford, MA, p. A341

KELLY, James P., FACHE, Administrator, Community Behavioral Health Hospital - Annandale, Annandale, MN, p. A371

KELLY, Jennifer, Chief Executive Officer, Rock Prairie Behavioral Health, College Station, TX, p. A664

KELLY, Jim, Chief Operating Officer, Nantucket Cottage Hospital, Nantucket, MA, p. A342

KELLY, John, R.N., Chief Nursing Officer and Chief Operating Officer, Umass Memorial-Marlborough Hospital, Marlborough, MA, p. A341

KELLY, Kecia, R.N., Chief Nurse Executive, Kaiser Permanente Medical Center, Honolulu, HI, p. A184

KELLY, Laurence E., President and Chief Executive Officer, Nathan Littauer Hospital And Nursing Home, Gloversville, NY, p. A485

KELLY, Leo, Vice President Medical Management, Advocate Lutheran General Hospital, Park Ridge, IL, p. A216

KELLY, Mark, Administrator, Regional One Health Extended Care Hospital, Memphis, TN, p. A645
Vice President Finance, St. Francis Medical Center, Trenton, NJ, p. A464

KELLY, Maura, Vice President Fiscal Services, Pen Bay Medical Center, Rockport, ME, p. A322

KELLY, Melissa, Chief Executive Officer and Chief Financial Officer, Pender Community Hospital, Pender, NE, p. A439

KELLY, Michael, Vice President Operations, Missouri Baptist Medical Center, Saint Louis, MO, p. A416
Vice President, Christian Hospital, Saint Louis, MO, p. A415

KELLY, Patrick J., FACHE, Director, Minneapolis Veterans Affairs Health Care System, Minneapolis, MN, p. A381

KELLY, Peter, President, Vassar Brothers Medical Center, Poughkeepsie, NY, p. A495

KELLY, Ray, R.N., MSN, Vice President Chief Nursing Officer, Texas Health Harris Methodist Hospital Hurst-Euless-Bedford, Bedford, TX, p. A659

KELLY, Shannon, Director Human Resources, Arbor Health, Morton Hospital, Morton, WA, p. A760

KELLY, Stephen, M.D., Chief Medical Officer, Ssm Health St. Mary's Hospital - St. Louis, Saint Louis, MO, p. A417

KELLY, Steve, Chief Executive Officer, Austin Oaks Hospital, Austin, TX, p. A655

KELLY, Teresa, MSN, R.N., Chief Nursing Officer, Chestnut Hill Hospital, Philadelphia, PA, p. A599

KELLY, Virginia, Chief Financial Officer, Eastside Psychiatric Hospital, Tallahassee, FL, p. A158

KELLY JR, JamesSenior Vice President and Chief Financial Officer, Uf Health Shands Hospital, Gainesville, FL, p. A139

KELMAN, Gregory, M.D., Area Medical Director, Kaiser Permanente Woodland Hills Medical Center, Woodland Hills, CA, p. A105

KELSCH, Leah, Executive Director, Sanford Medical Center Bismarck, Bismarck, ND, p. A521

KELTNER, Burt, Administrator, Prairie Community Hospital, Terry, MT, p. A428

KEM, Mark, Vice President Finance and Chief Financial Officer, Chandler Regional Medical Center, Chandler, AZ, p. A30

KEMKER, S, M.D., President Medical Staff, Ascension St. Vincent Salem, Salem, IN, p. A240

KEMMERER, Jan, Director of Nursing, Mitchell County Hospital Health Systems, Beloit, KS, p. A262

KEMP, Marlo, Vice President and Chief Financial Officer, Roseland Community Hospital, Chicago, IL, p. A200

KEMP, Susie, Chief Financial Officer, Fulton State Hospital, Fulton, MO, p. A407

KEMPF, Gary L., R.N., Administrator, Houston Methodist Continuing Care Hospital, Katy, TX, p. A692

KEMPIAK, Matthew, Director Human Resources and Administrative Services, Memorial Hospital Of Gardena, Gardena, CA, p. A66

KEMPINSKI, Paul D., Chief Executive Officer, Children's Mercy Hospital Kansas City, Kansas City, MO, p. A408
Chief Executive Officer, Children's Mercy Hospital Kansas, Overland Park, KS, p. A273

KEMPTON, Matthew, Chief Executive Officer, Willap. Harbor Hospital, South Bend, WA, p. A765

KENAGY, John, Ph.D., Senior Vice President and Chief Information Officer, Legacy Meridian Park Medical Center, Tualatin, OR, p. A582
Ph.D., Senior Vice President and Chief Information Officer, Legacy Mount Hood Medical Center, Gresham, OR, p. A575

KENAGY, Rob, M.D., President and Chief Executive Officer, Stormont Vail Health, Topeka, KS, p. A277

KENDALL, Abigail, Chief Nursing Officer, Lake Granbury Medical Center, Granbury, TX, p. A682

KENDALL, Anthony, Vice President Human Resources, Baptist Health Medical Center-Arkadelphia, Arkadelphia, AR, p. A42
Vice President Human Resources, Baptist Health Medical Center-Little Rock, Little Rock, AR, p. A49
Vice President Human Resources, Baptist Health Rehabilitation Institute, Little Rock, AR, p. A49

KENDALL, Clint, R.N., Chief Executive Officer, Andalusia Health, Andalusia, AL, p. A13

KENDALL, Dorothy, Medical Director, William J. Mccord Adolescent Treatment Facility, Orangeburg, SC, p. A623

KENDLE, Melinda, Director Fiscal Management, Evansville State Hospital, Evansville, IN, p. A227
Manager Business Office, Evansville Psychiatric Children Center, Evansville, IN, p. A227

KENDLER, Lisa, Chief Financial Officer, Memorial Hermann Memorial City Medical Center, Houston, TX, p. A687
Chief Financial Officer, Memorial Hermann Sugar Land Hospital, Sugar Land, TX, p. A717

KENDRICK, Donovan, M.D., Chief Medical Officer, Baptist Medical Center South, Montgomery, AL, p. A22

KENDRICK, Justin, Senior Vice President and Chief Executive Officer, Memorial Hermann Northeast, Humble, TX, p. A690

KENDRICK, Ray, Chief Human Resources Officer, Memorial Hospital Miramar, Miramar, FL, p. A148

KENINGER, Luke, Information Technology Client Leader, Winona Health, Winona, MN, p. A388

KENLEY, William A., Chief Executive Officer, Anmed Health Medical Center, Anderson, SC, p. A615

KENNEDY, Anita, Vice President Operations, Methodist Hospital Of Sacramento, Sacramento, CA, p. A89

KENNEDY, Carol, Chief Clinical Officer, Barrett Hospital & Healthcare, Dillon, MT, p. A423

KENNEDY, Connie, Director Human Resources, Marlette Regional Hospital, Marlette, MI, p. A361

KENNEDY, Darla, Chief Information Officer, Foothill Regional Medical Center, Tustin, CA, p. A102

KENNEDY, Diana, Director Human Resources, Meadowview Regional Medical Center, Maysville, KY, p. A290

KENNEDY, Eric, Chief Executive Officer, Arbour Hospital, Boston, MA, p. A334

KENNEDY, Jack, R.N., MS, Vice President and Chief Nursing Officer, Pratt Regional Medical Center, Pratt, KS, p. A275

KENNEDY, Jessica, D.O., Chief Medical Officer, Adair County Health System, Greenfield, IA, p. A250

KENNEDY, Jill, R.N., Vice President, Ambulatory Patient Care Services, Bon Secours Memorial Regional Medical Center, Mechanicsville, VA, p. A746

KENNEDY, John, M.D., Vice President of Medical Affairs, Mercy Health - Fairfield Hospital, Fairfield, OH, p. A540

KENNEDY, Kay, Chief Nurse Executive, Wellstar Cobb Hospital, Austell, GA, p. A166

KENNEDY, Kimberly, Manager Human Resources, Osf Saint Paul Medical Center, Mendota, IL, p. A212

KENNEDY, Larkin, Chief Executive Officer, Rush Foundation Hospital, Meridian, MS, p. A397

KENNEDY, Nancy, M.D., Chief Medical Officer, Highpoint Health, Lawrenceburg, IN, p. A235

KENNEDY, Peter, Chief Operating Officer, Northside Hospital, Saint Petersburg, FL, p. A156

KENNEDY, R., M.D., Chief Medical Officer and Safety Officer, Olympic Medical Center, Port Angeles, WA, p. A762

KENNEDY, Ryan, Chief Financial Officer, Holy Name Medical Center, Teaneck, NJ, p. A464
Chief Operating Officer, Kingman Regional Medical Center, Kingman, AZ, p. A33

KENNEDY, TaDren, Administrator, Walthall County General Hospital, Tylertown, MS, p. A400

KENNEDY, Tiffany, Chief Nursing Officer, Breckinridge Memorial Hospital, Hardinsburg, KY, p. A284

KENNEDY, Timea, Director Human Resources, St. Mary-Corwin Medical Center, Pueblo, CO, p. A118

KENNEDY, Todd S., President and Chief Executive Officer, Providence Hospital, Mobile, AL, p. A22

KENNEDY ESQ, DanielleDirector of Nursing, Montefiore New Rochelle, New Rochelle, NY, p. A489

KENNEMER, Darline, Controller, Methodist Rehabilitation Hospital, Dallas, TX, p. A669

KENNETT, Jerry, M.D., Chief Medical Officer, Boone Hospital Center, Columbia, MO, p. A405

KENNEY, Mary, Chief Human Services, Manchester Veterans Affairs Medical Center, Manchester, NH, p. A450

KENNEY, Ronda, Chief Operating Officer, Eastern State Hospital, Medical Lake, WA, p. A760

KENNEY, Stephen, Chief Financial Officer, The University Of Vermont Health Network Central Vermont Medical Center, Berlin, VT, p. A735

KENNINGTON, Lynn, Chief Financial Officer, Alaska Regional Hospital, Anchorage, AK, p. A27

KENNISON, Barbara, Director Clinical Services, Aurora Behavioral Healthcare San Diego, San Diego, CA, p. A91

KENNY, Carolyn, Executive Vice President Clinical Care, Children's Healthcare Of Atlanta, Atlanta, GA, p. A164

KENNY, Virginia, Chief Nursing Officer, Hancock Medical Center, Bay Saint Louis, MS, p. A389

KENSINGER, Brooke, Chief Executive Officer, Mercyone Elkader Medical Center, Elkader, IA, p. A249

KENT, Alan, Chief Executive Officer, Meadows Regional Medical Center, Vidalia, GA, p. A182

KENT, Blair M., Administrator, Intermountain Medical Center, Murray, UT, p. A729

KENT, Craig, Interim Chief Executive Officer, University Of Virginia Medical Center, Charlottesville, VA, p. A740

KENT, David, M.D., Chief Medical Officer, Safe Haven Hospital Of Treasure Valley, Boise, ID, p. A188
Chief Executive Officer, Piedmont Newton Hospital, Covington, GA, p. A170

KENT, Mary, Administrator, Johnson County Hospital, Tecumseh, NE, p. A440

KENT, Robert, D.O., President and Chief Executive Officer, Western Reserve Hospital, Cuyahoga Falls, OH, p. A538

KENTERA, Amy, Chief Information Officer, Conifer Park, Glenville, NY, p. A484

KENTFIELD, Melinda, R.N., Chief Nursing Officer, Methodist Fremont Health, Fremont, NE, p. A432

KENTON, Bart, Chief Financial Officer, Holton Community Hospital, Holton, KS, p. A266

KENWOOD, Linda, R.N., MSN, Chief Nursing Officer and Chief Operating Officer, Shore Medical Center, Somers Point, NJ, p. A463

KEOWN, Janet, Vice President Human Resources, Behavioral Health Network, Natchaug Hospital, Mansfield Center, CT, p. A123

KEPLINGER, Ron, Chief Information Officer, Western Maryland Hospital Center, Hagerstown, MD, p. A330

KEPNER, Donald, Chief Financial Officer, Ashtabula County Medical Center, Ashtabula, OH, p. A528

KEPPLER, Edward, M.D., Chief Medical Officer, Marion General Hospital, Marion, IN, p. A236

KEPPNER, Brandon, Administrator, Laureate Psychiatric Clinic And Hospital, Tulsa, OK, p. A569

KEPSHIRE, Bob, R.N., MS, Administrator and Chief Nursing Officer, University Hospital Mcduffie, Thomson, GA, p. A182

KERBS, Curtis, Regional Chief Information Officer, Memorial Hospital, North Conway, NH, p. A451

KERCHENSKI, Marlene, Chief Nurse, U. S. Air Force Hospital, Hampton, VA, p. A743

KERI, Alison, Director Human Resources, Hiawatha Community Hospital, Hiawatha, KS, p. A266

KERIAN-MASTERS, RN, Carol, Chief Nursing Officer, Regional Health Services Of Howard County, Cresco, IA, p. A247

KERLING, Norma, Interim Chief Executive Officer and Chief Clinical Officer, Cuba Memorial Hospital, Cuba, NY, p. A482

KERMEN, John, D.O., Chief Medical Staff, Mendocino Coast District Hospital, Fort Bragg, CA, p. A64

KERN, Douglas W., Chief Executive Officer, Northcoast Behavioral Healthcare, Northfield, OH, p. A546

KERN, Howard, Chief Operating Officer, Sentara Princess Anne Hospital, Virginia Beach, VA, p. A753

President and Chief Operating Officer, Sentara Leigh Hospital, Norfolk, VA, p. A748

KERNAN, Jackie, President, Osf Holy Family Medical Center, Monmouth, IL, p. A212

KERNAN, Jacqueline D., President, Osf Saint Luke Medical Center, Kewanee, IL, p. A209

KERNDL, John, Executive Vice President and Chief Financial Officer, Beaumont Hospital - Royal Oak, Royal Oak, MI, p. A365

KERNELL, Shane, Chief Executive Officer, Graham Regional Medical Center, Graham, TX, p. A681

KERNIVAN, Lorna, Chief Operating Officer, Palms West Hospital, Loxahatchee, FL, p. A144

KERNS, Elizabeth, Senior Vice President and Chief Information Officer, Lakeland Regional Health Medical Center, Lakeland, FL, p. A143

KERR, Jeff, M.D., Chief Medical Officer, Baylor Scott & White Medical Center At - Mckinney, Mckinney, TX, p. A700

KERR, Karen, R.N., President, Bartow Regional Medical Center, Bartow, FL, p. A131

R.N., President, South Florida Baptist Hospital, Plant City, FL, p. A154

KERR, Michael D., Chief Executive Officer, Kindred Hospital South Bay, Gardena, CA, p. A66

KERRINS, David, Vice President Information Services and Chief Information Officer, Dameron Hospital, Stockton, CA, p. A99

KERRWOOD, Patrick, President, Delaware County Memorial Hospital, Drexel Hill, PA, p. A588

KERSCHEN, Susan, MS, R.N., Vice President and Chief Nursing Officer, Good Samaritan Medical Center, Lafayette, CO, p. A115

KERSTETTER, Kathleen, MSN, R.N., Chief Executive Officer, Acuity Specialty Hospital Of New Jersey, Atlantic City, NJ, p. A452

KERSWILL, Randy, M.D., Medical Director, Winnebago Mental Health Institute, Winnebago, WI, p. A800

KERWOOD, Lori, Director Human Resources, Cooley Dickinson Hospital, Northampton, MA, p. A342

KESSEL, Jennifer, Chief Executive Officer, Aultman Orrville Hospital, Orrville, OH, p. A547

KESSLER, Alexander, M.D., Chief of Staff, Northside Hospital-Cherokee, Canton, GA, p. A168

KESSLER, Charlene, R.N., Director of Nursing, Beacon Behavioral Hospital, Bunkie, LA, p. A299

KESSLER, David, M.D., Clinical Director, U. S. Public Health Service Indian Hospital, Zuni, NM, p. A473

KESSLER, John E., Chief Executive Officer, Sarah D. Culbertson Memorial Hospital, Rushville, IL, p. A219

KESSLER, Joseph, Executive Vice President and Chief Financial Officer, Kaleida Health, Buffalo, NY, p. A480

KESSNER, Jennifer, Financial Director, Roosevelt Medical Center, Culbertson, MT, p. A422

KESTER, Bonnie, R.N., MSN, Vice President Patient Care Services and Chief Nursing Officer, Nantucket Cottage Hospital, Nantucket, MA, p. A342

KESTERSON, Matt, Director Information Services, Wadley Regional Medical Center At Hope, Hope, AR, p. A47

Director Information Services, Wadley Regional Medical Center, Texarkana, TX, p. A720

KETCH, Lynn, Human Resources Recruiter Generalist, Integris Canadian Valley Hospital, Yukon, OK, p. A572

Regional Director Integris Southwest Medical Center, Integris Southwest Medical Center, Oklahoma City, OK, p. A564

KETCHAM, Krista, Chief Financial Officer, Buena Vista Regional Medical Center, Storm Lake, IA, p. A258

KETCHAM, Michael, Chief Medical Officer, Mountain View Regional Medical Center, Norton, VA, p. A748

President, Medical Staff, Lonesome Pine Hospital, Big Stone Gap. VA, p. A739

KETCHEM, Tami, Human Resource Director, Up Health System-Bell, Ishpeming, MI, p. A358

KETERI, Dan, R.N., Chief Executive Officer, Samaritan Albany General Hospital, Albany, OR, p. A573

KETTERHAGEN, James, M.D., Senior Vice President and Chief Medical Officer, Uofl Health - Jewish Hospital, Louisville, KY, p. A288

KETTERLING, Kimberly, R.N., Vice President Patient Care Services, Chi Oakes Hospital, Oakes, ND, p. A525

KETTERMAN, Patricia P., R.N., President and Chief Administrative Officer, Claiborne Medical Center, Tazewell, TN, p. A650

KETTLER, Paul, M.D., Vice President Medical Affairs, Fairview Ridges Hospital, Burnsville, MN, p. A373

KETTNER, Mark, Chief Executive Officer, Eastern State Hospital, Medical Lake, WA, p. A760

KEY, David, Division President, Select Specialty Hospital-Northeast New Jersey, Rochelle Park, NJ, p. A462

KEY, Jennifer, Chief Nursing Officer, Piedmont Newnan Hospital, Newnan, GA, p. A178

KEY, Lora, Chief Executive Officer, Sabetha Community Hospital, Sabetha, KS, p. A275

KEYONNIE, Christine, CPA, Chief Financial Officer, Tuba City Regional Health Care Corporation, Tuba City, AZ, p. A39

KHADE, Kashmira, Coordinator Non-Clinical Services, Behavioral Center Of Michigan, Warren, MI, p. A369

KHADEMI, Allen, M.D., Vice President Medical Affairs, Christian Health Care Center, Wyckoff, NJ, p. A466

KHALEGHI, Trisha, Senior Vice President and Chief Executive Officer, Sharp Mary Birch Hospital For Women And Newborns, San Diego, CA, p. A92

Senior Vice President and Chief Executive Officer, Sharp Mesa Vista Hospital, San Diego, CA, p. A92

KHALIQUE, Tania, Director Human Resources, Select Specialty Hospital - San Diego, San Diego, CA, p. A92

KHAN, Atique, M.D., Medical Director, University Behavioral Health Of Denton, Denton, TX, p. A672

KHAN, Dan, M.D., Chief Medical Officer, Yoakum County Hospital, Denver City, TX, p. A672

KHAN, Faraz, Chief Financial Officer, Doctors Hospital Of Laredo, Laredo, TX, p. A695

KHAN, Humayun, M.D., Chief Medical Officer, Hshs Sacred Heart Hospital, Eau Claire, WI, p. A783

KHAN, Sarfraz, Medical Director, Meridian Health Services, Muncie, IN, p. A237

KHAN, Waheed, M.D., President Medical Staff, Summers County Arh Hospital, Hinton, WV, p. A772

KHANCHANDANI, Ashok, Chief Financial Officer, Oroville Hospital, Oroville, CA, p. A83

KHANDELWAL, Ashish, M.D., Medical Director, Encompass Health Rehabilitation Hospital Of Middletown, Middletown, DE, p. A127

KHANNA, Rajive, Chief Executive Officer, Grace Hospital, Cleveland, OH, p. A534

Chief Executive Officer, Specialty Hospital Of Lorain, Amherst, OH, p. A527

KHARONOV, Arthur, Vice President Nursing, Columbus Hospital Ltach, Newark, NJ, p. A459

KHATAMI, Manoochehr, M.D., Medical Director, Hickory Trail Hospital, Desoto, TX, p. A672

KHAVKIN, Lisa, Vice President Human Resources, Huntington Hospital, Huntington, NY, p. A485

KHDOUR, Adel, M.D., Chief Medical Officer, Indiana University Health White Memorial Hospital, Monticello, IN, p. A236

KHEMKA, Hemant, Chief Financial Officer, Surgery Specialty Hospitals Of America, Pasadena, TX, p. A705

Chief Operating Officer, Surgery Specialty Hospitals Of America, Pasadena, TX, p. A705

KHIAMI, Ahmad, Chief of Staff, Beckley Arh Hospital, Beckley, WV, p. A770

KHIM FUGATE, Guay, Chief Operations Officer, Kindred Hospital Riverside, Perris, CA, p. A85

KHOERL, Thomas, Vice President Finance, Spectrum Health Big Rapids Hospital, Big Rapids, MI, p. A349

KHOO, Alex, Interim Area Finance Officer, Kaiser Permanente San Francisco Medical Center, San Francisco, CA, p. A93

KIBAR, Nizar, M.D., Chief Medical Staff, Kiowa County Memorial Hospital, Greensburg, KS, p. A265

KIBBY, Rosalinda, Superintendent and Administrator, Columbia Basin Hospital, Ephrata, WA, p. A758

KIDD, David, Manager Human Resources, Sentara Careplex Hospital, Hampton, VA, p. A743

KIDD, Monica, R.N., MSN, Administrator, Parkview Hospital, Wheeler, TX, p. A725

KIDD, Sabrina, M.D., Chief Medical Officer, Sonoma Valley Hospital, Sonoma, CA, p. A99

KIDD, Thomas J., CPA, Chief Executive Officer, Macon Community Hospital, Lafayette, TN, p. A642

KIDDER, David, D.O., Chief Medical Officer, Garfield County Health Center, Jordan, MT, p. A425

KIDDER, Suzanne, Human Resources Officer, Opelousas General Health System, Opelousas, LA, p. A312

KIEBZAK, Stanley, R.N., Chief Nursing Officer, Encompass Health Rehabilitation Hospital The Vintage, Houston, TX, p. A685

KIEDROWSKI, Brian, M.D., Chief Medical Director, Miami Jewish Home And Hospital For Aged, Miami, FL, p. A146

KIEFER, Michael L., FACHE, Director, Central Texas Veterans Health Care System, Temple, TX, p. A719

KIEFER, William, Chief Nursing Officer, Tmc Bonham Hospital, Bonham, TX, p. A660

Chief Operating Officer, Rehoboth Mckinley Christian Health Care Services, Gallup. NM, p. A469

KIEFFER, Kelley, Chief Nursing Officer, Banner Baywood Medical Center, Mesa, AZ, p. A33

Chief Nursing Officer, Banner Heart Hospital, Mesa, AZ, p. A34

KIEHL, Tiffany, Chief Executive Officer, Mid—America Rehabilitation Hospital, Shawnee Mission, KS, p. A276

KIELY, Sharon, M.D., Senior Vice President Medical Affairs and Chief Medical Officer, Stamford Hospital, Stamford, CT, p. A125

KIERNAN, Richard, Regional Chief Human Resources Officer, Monmouth Medical Center, Southern Campus, Lakewood, NJ, p. A457

Vice President Human Resources, Monmouth Medical Center, Long Branch Campus, Long Branch, NJ, p. A457

KIFAIEH, Nizar, M.D., President and Chief Executive Officer, Hudson Regional Hospital, Secaucus, NJ, p. A463

KIGER, Tom, Director Information Systems, Trinity Health System, Steubenville, OH, p. A550

KIGHT, Sheila, Director Human Resources, Tristar Horizon Medical Center, Dickson, TN, p. A637

KILBORN, Mark, Director Information Systems, Springhill Memorial Hospital, Mobile, AL, p. A22

KILE, Steven, Vice President Human Resources, Indiana University Health North Hospital, Carmel, IN, p. A225

KILEY, David, M.D., Indianapolis Region President, Community Hospital North, Indianapolis, IN, p. A231

M.D., Indianapolis Region President, Community Hospital South, Indianapolis, IN, p. A231

M.D., Senior Vice President, President Indianapolis Region, Community Hospital East, Indianapolis, IN, p. A231

KILEY, Patrick, Administrator, Port St. Lucie Hospital, Port St Lucie, FL, p. A155

KILGORE, Julie, Vice President, Human Resources, Broadlawns Medical Center, Des Moines, IA, p. A248

KILLORAN, Carrie, President, Aurora Sinai Medical Center, Milwaukee, WI, p. A790

KILMER, Michael T., Director, Veterans Affairs Eastern Colorado Health Care System, Denver, CO, p. A111

KILPACK, Lee, Chief Executive Officer, Marian Center, Salt Lake City, UT, p. A732

KILPATRICK, Von, Chief Nursing Officer, South Peninsula Hospital, Homer, AK, p. A28

Chief Nursing Officer, St. Vincent General Hospital District, Leadville, CO, p. A115

KIM, Anne, Chief Financial Officer, Riveredge Hospital, Forest Park, IL, p. A205

KIM, Donald, M.D., Chief Medical Officer, Memorial Regional Hospital, Hollywood, FL, p. A140

KIM, Eric, Chief Information Officer, Las Encinas Hospital, Pasadena, CA, p. A85

KIM, Eugene, M.D., Chief Medical Officer, St. Jude Medical Center, Fullerton, CA, p. A66

KIM, Hyon, M.D., Medical Director, Northlake Behavioral Health System, Mandeville, LA, p. A308

KIM, John, Chief Financial Officer, Anchor Hospital, Atlanta, GA, p. A164

KIMBALL, Joe, D.O., Chief of Staff, Madison County Health Care System, Winterset, IA, p. A260

KIMBALL, Kevin, Director Information Technology, Brooks Memorial Hospital, Dunkirk, NY, p. A482

KIMBALL, Mark E., Chief Executive Officer, Erlanger Western Carolina Hospital, Murphy, NC, p. A515

KIMBALL, Tim, Chief Nursing Officer, Northwest Health Physicians' Specialty Hospital, Fayetteville, AR, p. A45

KIMBLE, Becky, R.N., Chief Nursing Officer, Encompass Health Rehabilitation Hospital Of Jonesboro, Jonesboro, AR, p. A47

KIMBLE, D. Gay, Chief Human Resource Officer, Susan B. Allen Memorial Hospital, El Dorado, KS, p. A264

KIMBLE, Robert, Chief Financial Officer, William R. Sharpe, Jr. Hospital, Weston, WV, p. A777

KIMBRELL, Jason, Chief Executive Officer, Highlands Regional Medical Center, Sebring, FL, p. A157

KIMBREW, Missey, Director Human Resources, Grafton City Hospital, Grafton, WV, p. A772

KIMBRO, George, Vice President Finance, Angel Medical Center, Franklin, NC, p. A510

KIMBROUGH, Pam, M.D., Vice President Medical Affairs, Mercy Hospital Ardmore, Ardmore, OK, p. A556

KIMMEL, Kyle, Chief Financial Officer, Bacon County Hospital And Health System, Alma, GA, p. A163

KIMMEL, Stephen, Chief Financial Officer, Cook Children's Medical Center, Fort Worth, TX, p. A678

KIMMES, Robert P., Chief Executive Officer, Skyline Hospital, White Salmon, WA, p. A769

KIMMET, Ashley, Human Resources, Northern Rockies Medical Center, Cut Bank, MT, p. A423

KIMMET, Jackie, Chief Human Resource Officer, River's Edge Hospital And Clinic, Saint Peter, MN, p. A385

KIMPLE, Robin, Director Information Services, Wellspan Gettysburg Hospital, Gettysburg, PA, p. A590

KIMZEY, Mike, Chief Executive Officer, Onecore Health, Oklahoma City, OK, p. A565

KINARD, Tifani, Administrator and Chief Nursing Officer, Polk Medical Center, Cedartown, GA, p. A168
Chief Nursing Officer, Floyd Cherokee Medical Center, Centre, AL, p. A16

KINCAID, Kevin, Chief Executive Officer, Knoxville Hospital & Clinics, Knoxville, IA, p. A253

KINCAID, Steve, Information Technology Manager, Eastern State Hospital, Lexington, KY, p. A286

KINDER, Barbara, R.N., Chief Clinical Officer, Clark Regional Medical Center, Winchester, KY, p. A294

KINDRED, Deanne, Vice President Finance, Baylor Scott & White Medical Center - Plano, Plano, TX, p. A706

KINDSCHI, Mark, Director Human Resources, Edgerton Hospital And Health Services, Edgerton, WI, p. A783

KING, Abner, Chief Executive Officer, Syringa Hospital And Clinics, Grangeville, ID, p. A190

KING, Alan N., FACHE, Chief Executive Officer, Covenant Hospital Plainview, Plainview, TX, p. A706

KING, Beth, Chief Executive Officer, Jersey Community Hospital, Jerseyville, IL, p. A209

KING, Brent, Chief Medical Officer and Chief Physician, Alfred I. Dupont Hospital For Children, Wilmington, DE, p. A128

KING, Chris, Director Information Services, Ohiohealth Marion General Hospital, Marion, OH, p. A544

KING, Christopher, Director Operations and Administrative Services, Matheny Medical And Educational Center, Peapack, NJ, p. A460

KING, Doug, M.D., Director Clinical Services, Western Mental Health Institute, Bolivar, TN, p. A634
Senior Vice President and Chief Information Officer, Northwestern Medicine Delnor Hospital, Geneva, IL, p. A206

KING, Glenn, R.N., MSN, Vice President and Chief Nursing Officer, Midmichigan Medical Center-Gladwin, Gladwin, MI, p. A355
R.N., MSN, Vice President, Chief Nursing Officer, Midmichigan Medical Center-Clare, Clare, MI, p. A351

KING, Janine, M.D., Chief of Staff, East Los Angeles Doctors Hospital, Los Angeles, CA, p. A74

KING, Jay, Vice President Human Resources, Mercy Hospitals Of Bakersfield, Bakersfield, CA, p. A57

KING, Jo Nell, Director of Nursing, Northlake Behavioral Health System, Mandeville, LA, p. A308

KING, Joanie, Chief Financial Officer, Carteret Health Care, Morehead City, NC, p. A514

KING, JoAnne, Chief Operating Officer, Adventhealth Palm Coast, Palm Coast, FL, p. A152

KING, Joseph, Acting Chief Executive Officer, The Pavilion, Champaign, IL, p. A197

KING, Katie, R.N., Chief Nursing Officer, Mountain View Hospital, Payson, UT, p. A730

KING, Katrina, R.N., Senior Director, Nursing, Novant Health Huntersville Medical Center, Huntersville, NC, p. A512

KING, Kim, Director Human Resources and Public Relations, Baptist Memorial Hospital-Carroll County, Huntingdon, TN, p. A639

KING, Levi, Director Human Resources, Conway Behavioral Health Hospital, Conway, AR, p. A43

KING, Louie, Chief Executive Officer, Benefis Teton Medical Center, Choteau, MT, p. A422
President, Harry Bold Nursing Home Administrator, Missouri River Medical Center, Fort Benton, MT, p. A423

KING, Micheal, Controller, Spectrum Health Pennock, Hastings, MI, p. A357

KING, Mike, Chief Financial Officer and Chief Operating Officer, Jfk Memorial Hospital, Indio, CA, p. A68

KING, Monica, Chief Information Officer, Oakdale Community Hospital, Oakdale, LA, p. A312

KING, Patrick, Administrator, Riverbend Rehabilitation Hospital, Monroe, LA, p. A309

KING, Paul, M.D., Medical Director, Parkwood Behavioral Health System, Olive Branch, MS, p. A398

KING, Paul A., President and Chief Executive Officer, Lucile Packard Children's Hospital Stanford, Palo Alto, CA, p. A84

KING, Ray, M.D., Senior Vice President, Medical Affairs and Chief Medical Officer, Henry Ford Allegiance Health, Jackson, MI, p. A359

KING, Sammy, Controller, Encompass Health Rehabilitation Hospital Of Ocala, Ocala, FL, p. A150

KING, Sandra, Chief Nursing Officer, Sagamore Children's Psychiatric Center, Dix Hills, NY, p. A482

KING, Shari, Interim Vice President of Operations, Unitypoint Health - Marshalltown, Marshalltown, IA, p. A254

KING, Tamara, R.N., MSN, Chief Nurse Executive, Shepherd Center, Atlanta, GA, p. A165

KING, Val, Chief Information Officer, Val Verde Regional Medical Center, Del Rio, TX, p. A671

KINGHAM, Darrell, CPA, Vice President Finance, Beauregard Health System, De Ridder, LA, p. A300

KINGRY, Jennifer, Chief Financial Officer, St. Vincent's Blount, Oneonta, AL, p. A23

KINGSLEY, Christi, Vice President Human Resources, West Calcasieu Cameron Hospital, Sulphur, LA, p. A315

KINGSTON, Eileen, R.N., Nurse Executive, Associate Director Patient Care, Veterans Affairs Nebraska-Western Iowa Health Care System, Omaha, NE, p. A438

KINGSTON, Mary Beth, Ph.D., R.N., MSN, Executive Vice President and Chief Nursing Officer, Aurora Medical Center Of Oshkosh, Oshkosh, WI, p. A793

KINGSTON, Mary E., FACHE, R.N., Chief Executive, Peacehealth Sacred Heart Medical Center At Riverbend, Springfield, OR, p. A581

KINGSTON, Peggy, Chief Executive Officer, Select Specialty Hospital-Pontiac, Pontiac, MI, p. A364

KINKAID, Steve, Director Information Systems, St. Luke's - Lehighton Campus, Lehighton, PA, p. A595

KINLEN, Thomas, Superintendent, Larned State Hospital, Larned, KS, p. A268

KINMAN, Amanda, Director of Finance, Saint Josep. Mount Sterling, Mount Sterling, KY, p. A290

KINNAIRD, Adriene, Chief Executive Officer, Select Specialty Hospital Midtown Atlanta, Atlanta, GA, p. A165

KINNEER, James, Chief Human Resource Officer, Indiana Regional Medical Center, Indiana, PA, p. A592

KINNEY, Janet, Chief Executive Officer, Calhoun-Liberty Hospital, Blountstown, FL, p. A132

KINNEY, Thomas, Chief Human Resource Officer, St. John's Health, Jackson, WY, p. A802

KINSALA, Edeli, Chief Executive Officer, Sonora Behavioral Health Hospital, Tucson, AZ, p. A40

KINSEL, Mike, Controller, Federal Medical Center, Lexington, KY, p. A286

KINSELLA, Daniel, Vice President and Chief Information Officer, Northwestern Medicine Central Dupage Hospital, Winfield, IL, p. A222

KINSELLA, Kathleen, President, Osf Healthcare Little Company Of Mary Medical Center, Evergreen Park, IL, p. A204

KINSELLA, Matthew, Chief Financial Officer, Ssm Health St. Mary's Hospital Centralia, Centralia, IL, p. A196

KINSEY, Daniel, M.D., Medical Director, Oaklawn Psychiatric Center, Goshen, IN, p. A229

KINSEY, Wayne, Chief Executive Officer, Kp. Promise Hospital Of Phoenix, Mesa, AZ, p. A34
Chief Executive Officer, Kp. Promise Hospital Of Salt Lake, Salt Lake City, UT, p. A732

KINTZ, Ronald, Chief Financial Officer, Ira Davenport Memorial Hospital, Bath, NY, p. A475
Vice President and Treasurer, Arnot Ogden Medical Center, Elmira, NY, p. A483

KINYON, Craig C., President and Chief Executive Officer, Reid Health, Richmond, IN, p. A239

KINYON, David, Vice President of Operations and Outpatient Services, Asante Three Rivers Medical Center, Grants Pass, OR, p. A575

KINZIC, Elizabeth, M.D., Chief of Staff, Share Medical Center, Alva, OK, p. A555

KINZIE, Wesley, M.D., Chief of Staff, Stanislaus Surgical Hospital, Modesto, CA, p. A79

KIO, Kenneth, Manager Human Resources, Albany Stratton Veterans Affairs Medical Center, Albany, NY, p. A474

KIPP, Kris, Executive Director, Patient Services and Chief Nursing Officer, James Cancer Hospital And Solove Research Institute, Columbus, OH, p. A536

KIRACOFE, Darin, Director Information Resource Management, Broughton Hospital, Morganton, NC, p. A515

KIRALY, Denise, Director, Human Resources and Organization Development, Lima Memorial Health System, Lima, OH, p. A543

KIRBOW, Keith, R.N., Vice President and Chief Nursing Officer, Christus Good Shepherd Medical Center-Marshall, Marshall, TX, p. A700

KIRBY, Brendan, M.D., Medical Director, Riverview Psychiatric Center, Augusta, ME, p. A318

KIRBY, Elizabeth, Senior Director Human Resources, Aurora Baycare Medical Center, Green Bay, WI, p. A785
Senior Director Human Resources, Aurora Medical Center - Manitowoc County, Two Rivers, WI, p. A797

KIRBY, James M. II, President and Chief Executive Officer, Margaret R. Pardee Memorial Hospital, Hendersonville, NC, p. A512

KIRBY, John, Senior Vice President and Chief Financial Officer, Virtua Memorial, Mount Holly, NJ, p. A458

KIRBY, Juliana, R.N., MSN, Chief Nursing Officer, Adventist Health Tehachap. Valley, Tehachapi, CA, p. A100

KIRBY, Penny, MSN, Chief Nursing Officer, Livingston Regional Hospital, Livingston, TN; p. A642

KIRBY, Ruby, Chief Executive Officer, Bolivar General Hospital, Bolivar, TN, p. A634

KIRBY, Tracy, Assistant Vice President Business Relationship Management, Chi St. Vincent Hot Springs, Hot Springs, AR, p. A47
Assistant Vice President Business Relationship Management, Chi St. Vincent Infirmary Medical Center, Little Rock, AR, p. A49
Assistant Vice President Business Relationship Management, Chi St. Vincent Morrilton, Morrilton, AR, p. A50

KIRCH, Cyndi, Vice President Human Resources, Mercy General Hospital, Sacramento, CA, p. A89
Vice President Human Resources, Methodist Hospital Of Sacramento, Sacramento, CA, p. A89

KIRCHER, Janelle, R.N., MSN, Chief Executive Officer, Kindred Hospital-Denver, Denver, CO, p. A110

KIRCHNER, Kent, M.D., Chief of Staff, G.V. (Sonny) Montgomery Veterans Affairs Medical Center, Jackson, MS, p. A394

KIRCHNER, Susan, Director Human Resources, Four Winds Hospital, Saratoga Springs, NY, p. A497

KIRISITS, Christopher, Chief Nursing Officer, Rochester Psychiatric Center, Rochester, NY, p. A496

KIRITANI, Tracy, Vice President and Chief Financial Officer, Clovis Community Medical Center, Clovis, CA, p. A60

KIRK, Darlene, Manager Finance, U. S. Public Health Service Indian Hospital, Crownpoint, NM, p. A469

KIRK, Donald, M.D., Chief of Staff, Star Valley Health, Afton, WY, p. A801

KIRK, H Lee. Jr, FACHE, Administrator, Shriners Hospitals For Children-Springfield, Springfield, MA, p. A345

KIRK, J., M.D., Chief Medical Officer, University Of California, Davis Medical Center, Sacramento, CA, p. A90

KIRK, Jean, Chief Financial Officer, Bennett County Hospital And Nursing Home, Martin, SD, p. A629

KIRK, Paul, Vice President, Woman's Hospital, Baton Rouge, LA, p. A298

KIRK, Peggy, Senior Vice President Clinical Operations, Shirley Ryan Abilitylab, Chicago, IL, p. A200

KIRK, Vanessa, Director of Nursing, Kiowa County Memorial Hospital, Greensburg, KS, p. A265

KIRK, Warren J., Chief Executive Officer, Doctors Medical Center Of Modesto, Modesto, CA, p. A78

KIRKBRIDE, Geri, Chief Nursing Officer (Interim), Taylorville Memorial Hospital, Taylorville, IL, p. A221

KIRKER, Donna, R.N., MS, Vice President Patient Services and Chief Nursing Officer, Glens Falls Hospital, Glens Falls, NY, p. A484

KIRKER, Lynda, Chief Financial Officer, Flagler Hospital, Saint Augustine, FL, p. A155

KIRKHAM, Brett, Chief Operating Officer, Integris Deaconess, Oklahoma City, OK, p. A564

KIRKLAND, Larry, Chief Executive Officer, Newport News Behavioral Health Center, Newport News, VA, p. A747

KIRKLAND-ROSE, Tina, Coordinator Human Resources, Select Specialty Hospital-Lexington, Lexington, KY, p. A287

KIRKLEY, Scott, M.D., BJC Chief Medical Officer Group Liaison, Parkland Health Center - Farmington Community, Farmington, MO, p. A406

KIRKPATRICK, Brett, Executive Director, Mccullough-Hyde Memorial Hospital/Trihealth, Oxford, OH, p. A547

KIRKS, Linda, Vice President and Chief Financial Officer, Christus Santa Rosa Health System, San Antonio, TX, p. A711

KIRSHNER, Arthur, Chief Information Management, Winn Army Community Hospital, Hinesville, GA, p. A174

KIRSHNER, David, Chief Financial Officer, Strong Memorial Hospital Of The University Of Rochester, Rochester, NY, p. A496

KIRSTEIN, Susan, R.N., MSN, Chief Nursing Officer, Broadlawns Medical Center, Des Moines, IA, p. A248

KIRTON, Carl, Ph.D., Chief Nursing Officer, University Hospital, Newark, NJ, p. A460

KISACKY, Christina, Vice President, Operations, Uhs Chenango Memorial Hospital, Norwich, NY, p. A493

KISER, Greg, Chief Executive Officer, Three Rivers Medical Center, Louisa, KY, p. A287

KISER, Harrison, Chief Operating Officer, Saint Thomas West Hospital, Nashville, TN, p. A646

KISER, James R. II, Chief Executive Officer, Montrose Memorial Hospital, Montrose, CO, p. A117

KISER, Pamela, R.N., MS, Chief Nursing Executive and Vice President of Nursing, St. John Medical Center, Tulsa, OK, p. A571

KISHNER, Janice, R.N., FACHE, Chief Clinical Officer, St. Bernard Parish Hospital, Chalmette, LA, p. A299

KISKADDON, Robert, M.D., Chief Medical Officer, Margaret R. Pardee Memorial Hospital, Hendersonville, NC, p. A512

KISNER, Angela, Director Human Resources and Coordinator Medical Staff, Landmark Hospital Of Cap. Girardeau, Cap. Girardeau, MO, p. A403

KISS, Meredith, Administrator, Elgin Mental Health Center, Elgin, IL, p. A203

KISSNER, Michael, Chief Executive Officer, Encompass Health Rehabilitation Hospital Of Treasure Coast, Vero Beach, FL, p. A161

KISTLER, Beckie, Director of Finance, Uofl Health - Peace Hospital, Louisville, KY, p. A289

KITCH, Barrett, M.D., Senior Vice President, Clinical Affairs and Chief Medical Officer, Emerson Hospital, Concord, MA, p. A338

KITCHEN, Steven, M.D., Chief Medical Officer, Phoebe Putney Memorial Hospital, Albany, GA, p. A163

KITTNER, Bonnie, R.N., Chief Nursing Officer, Mendocino Coast District Hospital, Fort Bragg, CA, p. A64

KITTOE, Michael, Chief Financial Officer, Katherine Shaw Bethea Hospital, Dixon, IL, p. A202

KJOSA, Ann, R.N., MSN, Chief Nursing Officer, Eastern Idaho Regional Medical Center, Idaho Falls, ID, p. A190

KLAMFOTH, William, Administrator, Christus Southeast Texas Orthopedic Specialty Center, Beaumont, TX, p. A658

KLANN, Andrew, D.O., Chief of Staff, Southwest Health, Platteville, WI, p. A794

KLAPPER, Allan, M.D., Chief Executive Officer, Ahn Grove City, Grove City, PA, p. A591

KLARKOWSKI, Troy, Administrator and Chief Executive Officer, U. S. Public Health Service Indian Hospital-Sells, Sells, AZ, p. A38

KLASEK, Chance, CPA, Chief Financial Officer, Jefferson Community Health And Life, Fairbury, NE, p. A431

KLASSEN, Brad, Information Technology Coordinator, Sanford Worthington Medical Center, Worthington, MN, p. A388

KLASSEN, Karen, Controller, Encompass Health Rehabilitation Hospital Of Chattanooga, Chattanooga, TN, p. A635

KLATT, Monica, Chief Financial Officer, Upmc Altoona, Altoona, PA, p. A584
Chief Financial Officer, Upmc Bedford, Everett, PA, p. A590
Chief Financial Officer, Upmc Somerset, Somerset, PA, p. A608

KLAUSTERMEIER, Lisa, R.N., MSN, Chief Nursing Officer, Anderson Hospital, Maryville, IL, p. A211

KLAWITTER, Brad, Chief Executive Officer, Kindred Hospital-Indianapolis, Indianapolis, IN, p. A232

KLAWITTER, Kyle, Vice President Human Resources, Summa Health System, Akron, OH, p. A527

KLAY, Chris, President and Chief Executive Officer, Hshs St. Joseph's Hospital, Breese, IL, p. A196

KLEAM, Douglas V., President, St. Bernardine Medical Center, San Bernardino, CA, p. A91

KLEEMAN, Debbie, Director Information Systems, Perry County Memorial Hospital, Tell City, IN, p. A241

KLEEN, Kathy, Chief Nursing Officer, Tri-County Hospital, Wadena, MN, p. A387

KLEFFMAN, Angela, Director of Ancillary Services, Bigfork Valley Hospital, Bigfork, MN, p. A372

KLEHN, Paul, Chief Information Technology Officer, Liberty Hospital, Liberty, MO, p. A411

KLEIN, Aron, Vice President Finance, Bromenn Medical Center, Normal, IL, p. A214
Vice President of Finance, Eureka Hospital, Eureka, IL, p. A204

KLEIN, Barbara, R.N., Director of Nursing, Arms Acres, Carmel, NY, p. A481

KLEIN, Bernard, M.D., Chief Executive, Providence Holy Cross Medical Center, Mission Hills, CA, p. A78

KLEIN, Cindy, Chief Executive Officer, Lamb Healthcare Center, Littlefield, TX, p. A696
Vice President Human Resources, Peacehealth St. Josep. Medical Center, Bellingham, WA, p. A755

KLEIN, David, M.D., President and Chief Executive Officer, St. Mary's Medical Center, San Francisco, CA, p. A94
M.D., President, Saint Francis Memorial Hospital, San Francisco, CA, p. A94
Ph.D., Vice President Operations, Behavioral Health Network, Natchaug Hospital, Mansfield Center, CT, p. A123

KLEIN, Diany, Vice President Human Resources, Community Memorial Hospital, Ventura, CA, p. A103

KLEIN, Edward, Chief Financial Officer, Johnston Health, Smithfield, NC, p. A518

KLEIN, Jacqueline, Chief Financial Officer, Marshfield Medical Center - Rice Lake, Rice Lake, WI, p. A795

KLEIN, Jillyn, Chief Operating Officer, Howard County Medical Center, Saint Paul, NE, p. A439

KLEIN, Julie, Chief Operating Officer, Mckee Medical Center, Loveland, CO, p. A117

KLEIN, Kenneth, M.D., Vice President Medical Affairs, Beloit Health System, Beloit, WI, p. A781

KLEIN, Korrey, M.D., President and Chief Executive Offricer, Colorado Canyons Hospital And Medical Center, Fruita, CO, p. A113

KLEIN, Kyle, Assistant Chief Financial Officer, Mercy Health - West Hospital, Cincinnati, OH, p. A533

KLEIN, Perry, Chief Engineering, Mann-Grandstaff Veterans Affairs Medical Center, Spokane, WA, p. A765

KLEIN, Terrence, Ph.D., Vice President and Chief Operating Officer, Franciscan Health Crawfordsville, Crawfordsville, IN, p. A226

KLEINE, Doug, IT Director, St. Mary Medical Center, Apple Valley, CA, p. A56

KLEINHANZL, Thomas A., President and Chief Executive Officer, Frederick Health, Frederick, MD, p. A329

KLEINSASSER, Dustin, Information Technology and BioMed, Fall River Hospital, Hot Springs, SD, p. A628

KLEINSMITH, Carmen, MSN, R.N., Senior Vice President, Chief Nurse Executive, Unitypoint Health - St. Luke's Hospital, Cedar Rapids, IA, p. A245

KLEINSTEUBER, Kathy, Chief Executive Officer, Encompass Health Rehabilitation Hospital Of Savannah, Savannah, GA, p. A180

KLENKE, Lisa R., R.N., Chief Executive Officer, Mercer Health, Coldwater, OH, p. A535

KLENKE, Michael, Chief Information Security Officer, West Calcasieu Cameron Hospital, Sulphur, LA, p. A315

KLEPIN, Michael R., Chief Executive Officer, Southern California Hospital At Culver City, Culver City, CA, p. A62

KLEPPEN, Roxy, Director Human Resource, Sheridan Memorial Hospital, Plentywood, MT, p. A426

KLESS, Adam, Chief Nursing Officer, Highlands Regional Medical Center, Sebring, FL, p. A157
Chief Nursing Officer, Raulerson Hospital, Okeechobee, FL, p. A150

KLESSENS, Thomas, Chief Financial Officer, Landmark Medical Center, Woonsocket, RI, p. A614
Chief Financial Officer, Rehabilitation Hospital Of Rhode Island, North Smithfield, RI, p. A613

KLEVEN, Brian, Chief Financial Officer, St. Rose Dominican Hospitals - Siena Campus, Henderson, NV, p. A442

KLIEWER, Chad, Information Technology Specialist, Mercy Hospital Kingfisher, Kingfisher, OK, p. A560

KLIMEK, David, Chief Human Resources Officer, Miami County Medical Center, Paola, KS, p. A274
Vice President Human Resources, Olathe Medical Center, Olathe, KS, p. A272

KLINE, Brian, Vice President and Chief Financial Officer, Penn Highlands Dubois, Dubois, PA, p. A588

KLINE, Burke, Chief Executive Officer, Jefferson Community Health And Life, Fairbury, NE, p. A431

KLINE, Donald E., President and Chief Executive Officer, Mercy Health - St. Elizabeth Youngstown Hospital, Youngstown, OH, p. A554

KLINE, Julie, R.N., Senior Vice President Patient Services, Adventist Health Sonora, Sonora, CA, p. A99

KLINE, Melissa, Chief Nursing Officer, Metrohealth Medical Center, Cleveland, OH, p. A535

KLINGA, Maria, Director Management Information Systems, Silver Hill Hospital, New Canaan, CT, p. A124

KLINGEMAN, Jennifer, Director of Nursing, Chester Mental Health Center, Chester, IL, p. A197

KLINGENBERG, Pat, Director Human Resources, Towner County Medical Center, Cando, ND, p. A521

KLINGLER, Stacie, R.N., Vice President of Patient Services, Franciscan Health Rensselear, Rensselaer, IN, p. A239

KLINGSEIS, Robert, Director Information Systems, Desert Regional Medical Center, Palm Springs, CA, p. A83

KLINK, Sheryl, Chief Financial Officer, Piedmont Hospital, Atlanta, GA, p. A165

KLINKNER, Donna, Chief Financial Officer, Madelia Community Hospital, Madelia, MN, p. A379

KLOCK, Kathy, R.N., Senior Vice President Clinical Operations and Human Resources, Gundersen Lutheran Medical Center, La Crosse, WI, p. A787

KLOCKMAN, Dena, Chief Financial Officer, Ogallala Community Hospital, Ogallala, NE, p. A436

KLOCKO, Daniel, Vice President Human Resources, Kootenai Health, Coeur D'Alene, ID, p. A190

KLOECKNER, Vicki, Director Human Resources, Hshs Holy Family Hospital In Greenville, Greenville, IL, p. A206

KLOEWER, Ron, Chief Information Officer, Montgomery County Memorial Hospital, Red Oak, IA, p. A256

KLOPFER, Anthony Rudy., FACHE, Director, Veterans Affairs Eastern Kansas Health Care System, Topeka, KS, p. A277

KLOPP, Amanda, Director, Innovation and Clinical Integration, Penn State Health St. Joseph, Reading, PA, p. A606

KLOSTERMAN, Mark, FACHE, President and Chief Executive Officer, Wilson Memorial Hospital, Sidney, OH, p. A549

KLOSTERMEIER, Janice, Senior Vice President and Chief Financial Officer, Valley Presbyterian Hospital, Van Nuys, CA, p. A103

KLUESNER, Kevin, Chief Administrative Officer, Ascension Southeast Wisconsin Hospital - St. Joseph's Campus, Milwaukee, WI, p. A790

KLUGE, Thomas S., President, Valley Health - Hampshire Memorial Hospital, Romney, WV, p. A776
President, Valley Health - War Memorial Hospital, Berkeley Springs, WV, p. A770

KLUGHERZ, Greg, Vice President Corporate Services and Chief Financial Officer, St. Cloud Hospital, Saint Cloud, MN, p. A384

KMETZ, Thomas D., Interim Chief Executive Officer, Johns Hopkins All Children's Hospital, Saint Petersburg, FL, p. A156

KNACKSTEDT, Cameron, D.O., Chief Medical Staff, Harlan County Health System, Alma, NE, p. A429

KNACKSTEDT, Nathan, D.O., Chief of Staff, Clara Barton Hospital, Hoisington, KS, p. A266

KNAK, Roger, Administrator and Chief Executive Officer, Fairview Regional Medical Center, Fairview, OK, p. A559

KNAPHEIDE, Debbie, MSN, Site Administrator, Chief Nursing Officer and Chief Operating Officer, Carondelet Holy Cross Hospital, Nogales, AZ, p. A34

KNAPIK, Steven, M.D., Chief of Staff, Bear Valley Community Hospital, Big Bear Lake, CA, p. A58

KNAPP, Brian, Vice President Operations, Fairview Ridges Hospital, Burnsville, MN, p. A373

KNE, Tanya, M.D., Chief Medical Officer, Banner Desert Medical Center, Mesa, AZ, p. A33

KNECHT, Brian, Chief Operating Officer, Regional Medical Center Of San Jose, San Jose, CA, p. A95

KNECHT, John, Chief Medical Staff, Linton Hospital, Linton, ND, p. A524

KNECHT, Michael, President, Adventhealth Shawnee Mission, Shawnee Mission, KS, p. A276

KNEELAND, Misty, Chief Medical Staff, Medical Center Of South Arkansas, El Dorado, AR, p. A44

KNEISEL, Kristin, Interim Director, Information Services, Alice Peck Day Memorial Hospital, Lebanon, NH, p. A449

KNEPP, Gary, D.O., Regional Chief Medical Officer and Chief Quality Officer, Unitypoint Health - Peoria, Peoria, IL, p. A217

KNEPP, Keith, M.D., President and Chief Executive Officer, Unitypoint Health - Peoria, Peoria, IL, p. A217
M.D., President and Chief Executive Officer, Unitypoint Health - Proctor, Peoria, IL, p. A217
M.D., President and Chief Executive Officer, Unitypoint Health-Pekin Hospital, Pekin, IL, p. A216

KNIEVEL, Lon, Chief Executive Officer, Osmond General Hospital, Osmond, NE, p. A438

KNIFFIN, Fred, M.D., Chief Medical Officer, Porter Medical Center, Middlebury, VT, p. A736

KNIGHT, Beth, Chief Nursing Officer, Nacogdoches Memorial Hospital, Nacogdoches, TX, p. A702

KNIGHT, Bethany, M.D., Chief of Staff, Izard County Medical Center, Calico Rock, AR, p. A43

KNIGHT, Christopher, Vice President Finance and Chief Financial Officer, Reid Health, Richmond, IN, p. A239

KNIGHT, Deana, Chief Executive Officer, Select Specialty Hospital-Greensboro, Greensboro, NC, p. A511

KNIGHT, Don, Assistant Administrator and Risk Manager, Ochsner St. Mary, Morgan City, LA, p. A309

KNIGHT, Jennifer, Manager Human Resources, Wellspan Waynesboro Hospital, Waynesboro, PA, p. A610

KNIGHT, Kimber, Chief Financial Officer, Braxton County Memorial Hospital, Gassaway, WV, p. A772

KNIGHT, Laura, Chief Nursing Officer, Merit Health Central, Jackson, MS, p. A394

KNIGHT, Mark, Executive Vice President and Chief Financial Officer, Jackson Health System, Miami, FL, p. A146

KNIGHT, Michael, M.D., Medical Director, Hampstead Hospital, Hampstead, NH, p. A449

KNIGHT, Reginald, Chief Medical Officer, Aurelia Osborn Fox Memorial Hospital, Oneonta, NY, p. A494

KNIGHT, Scott, Chief Administrative Officer, Sutter Lakeside Hospital, Lakeport, CA, p. A71

KNIGHT, Terry, Public Information Officer and Administrative Assistant, California Mens Colony Correctional Treatment Center, San Luis Obispo, CA, p. A95

KNIGHT, Warren, Chief Financial Officer, Baton Rouge Behavioral Hospital, Baton Rouge, LA, p. A296

KNIGHT, Wayne, Chief Financial Officer, Indiana University Health Frankfort, Frankfort, IN, p. A229
Director Finance, Ascension St. Vincent Clay Hospital, Brazil, IN, p. A224

KNIGHT, Wesley, Chief Financial Officer, Ut Health Henderson, Henderson, TX, p. A683

KNIPP, Cindi, Director Human Resources, Rooks County Health Center, Plainville, KS, p. A274

KNISLEY, Shane, President, Mercy Health - Clermont Hospital, Batavia, OH, p. A528

KNITT, Lori, Chief Nursing Officer, Aurora Sheboygan Memorial Medical Center, Sheboygan, WI, p. A796

KNIZLEY, Andrew, Chief Executive Officer, Physicians Medical Center, Houma, LA, p. A303

KNOBLOCH, Stanley, Director Fiscal Services, Sanford Luverne Medical Center, Luverne, MN, p. A379

KNOCKE, Michael, Chief Information Officer, Kansas Spine & Specialty Hospital, Wichita, KS, p. A279

KNODE, Scott, Chief Financial Officer, Veterans Memorial Hospital, Waukon, IA, p. A259

KNOEPFFLER, Susan, R.N., Vice President Nursing, Huntington Hospital, Huntington, NY, p. A485

KNOEPFLEIN, Susan, Chief Nurse Executive, Fulton State Hospital, Fulton, MO, p. A407

KNOEPFLER, David, M.D., Chief Medical Officer, Overlake Medical Center, Bellevue, WA, p. A755

KNOERL, Thomas, Vice President Finance, Spectrum Health Reed City Hospital, Reed City, MI, p. A364

KNOTT, Neicole, Chief Executive Officer, Beckett Springs, West Chester, OH, p. A552

KNOWLES, B, D.O., Chief of Staff, Pershing Memorial Hospital, Brookfield, MO, p. A403

KNOWLES, Christy, Chief Human Resources Officer, Coosa Valley Medical Center, Sylacauga, AL, p. A24

KNOWLES, John, Director Human Resources, Clinch Valley Medical Center, Richlands, VA, p. A749

KNOWLES, Robert, M.D., Chief of Staff, Saint Thomas Highlands Hospital, Sparta, TN, p. A649

KNOWLES-SMITH, Peter, M.D., Medical Director, Bennett County Hospital And Nursing Home, Martin, SD, p. A629

KNOX, Dennis M., Chief Executive Officer, Mid-Columbia Medical Center, The Dalles, OR, p. A582

KNOX, Jody, Chief Operating Officer, Kindred Hospital Rancho, Rancho Cucamonga, CA, p. A86

KNOX, John, Senior Vice President and Chief Information Officer, Atrium Health University City, Charlotte, NC, p. A506

KNOX, Roland, Chief Executive Officer, Mt. Graham Regional Medical Center, Safford, AZ, p. A37

KNOX, Stacey A., Administrator, Rock County Hospital, Bassett, NE, p. A429

KNUDSEN, Jessica, Chief Executive Officer, Clarity Child Guidance Center, San Antonio, TX, p. A711
    Chief Operating Officer and Director Performance Improvement and Risk Management, Holly Hill Hospital, Raleigh, NC, p. A516

KNUDSEN, Mark, Director Fiscal Services, Shriners Hospitals For Children-Portland, Portland, OR, p. A580

KNUDSEN, Matthew, Director, Information Systems, Sheppard Pratt Health System, Baltimore, MD, p. A326

KNUDSON, Jenny, Controller, Hiawatha Community Hospital, Hiawatha, KS, p. A266

KNUDTEN, Kristine, M.D., Vice President Medical Affairs, Glencoe Regional Health, Glencoe, MN, p. A377

KNUTH, Kerry, Chief Operating Officer, Mercy Hospital Of Defiance, Defiance, OH, p. A539

KNUTSON, Holly, Manager Information Technology, Kittson Memorial Healthcare Center, Hallock, MN, p. A377

KNUTSON, John, M.D., Chief Medical Staff, Delta County Memorial Hospital, Delta, CO, p. A110

KNUTSON, Larry, Director Finance, Centracare - Long Prairie, Long Prairie, MN, p. A379

KNYCH, Stephen, M.D., Chief Medical Officer, Adventhealth Fish Memorial, Orange City, FL, p. A150

KO, Dicken, M.D., Vice President of Medical Affairs and Chief Medical Officer, St. Elizabeth's Medical Center, Brighton, MA, p. A337

KO, Tommy, M.D., Chief Medical Officer, St. Josep. Medical Center, Kansas City, MO, p. A409

KOBELJA, Mark A., MC, USN, Director, Walter Reed National Military Medical Center, Bethesda, MD, p. A328

KOCH, Eric, Chief Nursing Officer, Northern Montana Health Care, Havre, MT, p. A425

KOCH, Holly, Chief Financial Officer, Girard Medical Center, Girard, KS, p. A265

KOCH, Jamie, R.N., Chief Nursing Officer, Thayer County Health Services, Hebron, NE, p. A433

KOCH, Josep. G., Chief Executive Officer, Meadowview Regional Medical Center, Maysville, KY, p. A290

KOCHIE, Daniel, CPA, Chief Financial Officer, Samaritan Hospital - Main Campus, Troy, NY, p. A500

KOCHIS, Mary Ellen, MSN, R.N., Administrator Nursing Operations, Beaumont Hospital - Dearborn, Dearborn, MI, p. A352

KOCOUREK, Cathie A., President, Aurora Medical Center - Manitowoc County, Two Rivers, WI, p. A797

KOCSIS, Dana, Vice President Nursing and Operations, Cleveland Clinic Akron General Lodi Hospital, Lodi, OH, p. A543
    Vice President, Nursing and Operations, Cleveland Clinic Akron General Lodi Hospital, Lodi, OH, p. A543

KOCSIS, Violet, Chief Human Resources Officer, Hunterdon Healthcare, Flemington, NJ, p. A455

KOCZENT, Kurt, Executive Vice President and Chief Operating Officer, F. F. Thompson Hospital, Canandaigua, NY, p. A481

KOEBKE, Troy, Director Human Resources Management, Bellin Hospital, Green Bay, WI, p. A785
    Director Human Resources, Bellin Psychiatric Center, Green Bay, WI, p. A785
    Human Resource Director, Bellin Health Oconto Hospital, Oconto, WI, p. A793

KOEHLER, Amy, Director Human Resources, Hshs Good Shepherd Hospital, Shelbyville, IL, p. A220

KOELE, Craig, Chief Executive Officer, Cornerstone Hospital Of Oklahoma-Muskogee, Muskogee, OK, p. A562

KOENIG, Donald E., Director, Veterans Affairs Pittsburgh Healthcare System, Pittsburgh, PA, p. A604

KOENIG, Lori, Assistant Finance Director, Cleveland Clinic Avon Hospital, Avon, OH, p. A528

KOENIG, Mary, Chief Financial Officer, Vernon Memorial Healthcare, Elk Mound, WI, p. A783

KOENIG JR, DonaldChief Operating Officer, Mercy Health - St. Josep. Warren Hospital, Warren, OH, p. A551
    Executive Vice President and Regional Chief Operating Officer, President, St. Elizabeth Youngstown Hospital, Mercy Health - St. Elizabeth Youngstown Hospital, Youngstown, OH, p. A554

KOEPKE, Eldon, Chief Financial Officer, Mitchell County Hospital Health Systems, Beloit, KS, p. A262

KOEPKE, Jennifer, R.N., Vice President of Patient Care Services and Chief Nursing Officer, Western Missouri Medical Center, Warrensburg, MO, p. A420

KOERNER, Jill, Manager Employee Relations, Weisman Children's Rehabilitation Hospital, Marlton, NJ, p. A458

KOERNIG, Felissa, President and Chief Operating Officer, Guthrie Towanda Memorial Hospital, Towanda, PA, p. A609

KOESSL, Brenda, R.N., Director of Nursing Services, Frances Mahon Deaconess Hospital, Glasgow, MT, p. A424

KOESTER, Jean, Manager Human Resources, Limestone Medical Center, Groesbeck, TX, p. A682

KOESTERER, Susan, Vice President, Finance, Alton Memorial Hospital, Alton, IL, p. A194

KOETTING, Edward, Chief Financial Officer, Bedford Veterans Affairs Medical Center, Edith Nourse Rogers Memorial Veterans Hospital, Bedford, MA, p. A334

KOGANTI, Ravikanth, Vice President Information Technology, Englewood Health, Englewood, NJ, p. A455

KOHANKE, Crystal, Group Vice President, Human Resources, Christus Santa Rosa Health System, San Antonio, TX, p. A711

KOHL, Randy T., M.D., Deputy Director, Health Services, Nebraska Penal And Correctional Hospital, Lincoln, NE, p. A435

KOHLER, Douglas, M.D., Vice President Medical Operations, Marymount Hospital, Garfield Heights, OH, p. A541

KOHLER, Tracy, Chief Executive Officer, Kindred Hospital-Houston Northwest, Houston, TX, p. A686

KOHR, Kathy, Chief Financial Officer, Midmichigan Medical Center - West Branch, West Branch, MI, p. A369

KOHRER, Tammy, Director of Nursing-Acute, Wahiawa General Hospital, Wahiawa, HI, p. A187

KOKJOHN, Bradley, Chief Financial Officer, Fort Madison Community Hospital, Fort Madison, IA, p. A250

KOKJOHN, Vicki, Director Employee Relations, Fort Madison Community Hospital, Fort Madison, IA, p. A250

KOLACZ, Nicole, Chief Nursing Officer, Aultman Hospital, Canton, OH, p. A530

KOLB, Edward, M.D., Medical Director, Boys Town National Research Hospital, Omaha, NE, p. A436

KOLB, Edward M., M.D., Director, Boys Town National Research Hospital, Omaha, NE, p. A436

KOLB, Pat, Manager Information Technology, Mcleod Health Clarendon, Manning, SC, p. A622

KOLHEDE, Deborah, Vice President and Chief Operating Officer, St. Mary's Medical Center, San Francisco, CA, p. A94

KOLLMEYER, Sherry, Vice President Human Resources, Youth Villages Inner Harbour Campus, Douglasville, GA, p. A171

KOLMAN, Bret, CPA, FACHE, Chief Executive Officer, Centerpoint Medical Center, Independence, MO, p. A407

KOLODZIEJCYK, Wanda, Director Human Resources, Cuero Regional Hospital, Cuero, TX, p. A667

KOLODZIEJCZYK, Clayton, Chief Financial Officer, Meadowview Regional Medical Center, Maysville, KY, p. A290

KOLOSKY, John, Executive Vice President and Chief Operating Officer, H. Lee Moffitt Cancer Center And Research Institute, Tampa, FL, p. A159

KOLSETH, Shelley, Chief Financial Officer, Memorial Hospital Of Tampa, Tampa, FL, p. A159

KOMAN, Stuart, Ph.D., President and Chief Executive Officer, Walden Behavioral Care, Waltham, MA, p. A345

KOMANDURI, Ramanujam, M.D., Chief of Staff, Veterans Affairs Southern Nevada Healthcare System, North Las Vegas, NV, p. A445

KOMAR, Ellen, R.N., Vice President Patient Care Services and Chief Nursing Officer, Stamford Hospital, Stamford, CT, p. A125

KOME, Hunter, Campus President, Prisma Health Oconee Memorial Hospital, Seneca, SC, p. A624

KOMER, Claudia, M.D., Chief Medical Officer, Saint Michael's Medical Center, Newark, NJ, p. A460

KOMINS, Jeff, M.D., Chief Medical Officer, Mercy Catholic Medical Center - Mercy Fitzgerald Campus, Darby, PA, p. A588

KONARSKI, Debbie, Chief Financial Officer, Pottstown Hospital, Pottstown, PA, p. A605

KONECNE, Robin, Manager Human Resources, Kit Carson County Health Service District, Burlington, CO, p. A108

KONG, Mei, Chief Operating Officer, Nyc Health + Hospitals / Coney Island, Brooklyn, NY, p. A478

KONGARA, Rama, Chief Financial Officer, St. James Behavioral Health Hospital, Gonzales, LA, p. A302

KONIECZEK, Raymond, Chief Human Resources Officer, Jfk Memorial Hospital, Indio, CA, p. A68

KONIG, Angie, Senior Director Human Resources, Mitchell County Regional Health Center, Osage, IA, p. A255

KONKEL, Robert, Manager Finance, James A. Haley Veterans' Hospital-Tampa, Tampa, FL, p. A159

KONSAVAGE, Christian, M.D., Chief of Staff, Cumberland County Hospital, Burkesville, KY, p. A281

KOOIMAN, Thomas, Chief Executive Officer, Avera Granite Falls Health Center, Granite Falls, MN, p. A377

KOOISTRA, Josh, M.D., Senior Vice President, Chief Medical Officer, Spectrum Health - Butterworth Hospital, Grand Rapids, MI, p. A356

KOOKEN, Kyron J., MS, Chief Executive Officer, Kindred Hospital Dallas Central, Dallas, TX, p. A668

KOON, Rion, Chief Information Management Division, William Beaumont Army Medical Center, El Paso, TX, p. A676

KOOP, Steven, M.D., Chief Medical Officer, Medical Director, Gillette Children's Specialty Healthcare, Saint Paul, MN, p. A385

KOOYMAN, James, Human Resources Manager, Seneca Healthcare District, Chester, CA, p. A60

KOPEL, Samuel, M.D., Medical Director, Maimonides Medical Center, Brooklyn, NY, p. A478

KOPFLE, Sue, Chief Human Resources Officer, University Of Missouri Health Care, Columbia, MO, p. A405

KOPIN, Jeffrey, Senior Vice President and Chief Medical Officer, Northwestern Medicine Lake Forest Hospital, Lake Forest, IL, p. A210

KOPPELMAN, Benjamin, President, Chi St. Joseph's Health, Park Rapids, MN, p. A382

KOPPENHAVER, Colleen, Interim Chief Financial Officer, Amita Health Resurrection Medical Center, Chicago, IL, p. A197

KOPPERUD, Gordon, Director Operations, Sanford Westbrook Medical Center, Westbrook, MN, p. A387

KORBEL, Tamara, Director Management Information Systems, Ridgeview Medical Center, Waconia, MN, p. A387

KORDAHL, Rebecca, R.N., Associate Director, Patient Care Services, William S. Middleton Memorial Veterans Hospital, Madison, WI, p. A788

KORDUCKI, Stanley R., President, Wood County Hospital, Bowling Green, OH, p. A530

KORDUPEL, Maureen, Director Information Technology Relationship Manager, Mercy Health - St. Elizabeth Boardman Hospital, Boardman, OH, p. A529
    Director Relationship Manager, Mercy Health - St. Elizabeth Youngstown Hospital, Youngstown, OH, p. A554

KORF, Rick, Chief Financial Officer, Yuma District Hospital, Yuma, CO, p. A120

KORKMAS, Ross, Chief Executive Officer, Palo Pinto General Hospital, Mineral Wells, TX, p. A701

KORN, Roy, M.D., Medical Director, Cobleskill Regional Hospital, Cobleskill, NY, p. A481

KORNBLATT, Lynne, Chief Human Resources Officer, Einstein Medical Center Philadelphia, Philadelphia, PA, p. A600

KORNFIELD, Lee, M.D., Medical Director, St. Luke's Rehabilitation Hospital, Boise, ID, p. A189

KOROLY, Marla, M.D., Chief Medical Officer and Senior Vice President Medical Affairs, Northern Westchester Hospital, Mount Kisco, NY, p. A488

KOROM, Nancy, Chief Nursing Officer and Vice President, Children's Hospital Of Wisconsin-Fox Valley, Neenah, WI, p. A792
Chief Nursing Officer and Vice President, Children's Hospital Of Wisconsin, Milwaukee, WI, p. A791

KORPELA, Donita, R.N., Director of Patient Care Services, Essentia Health Moose Lake, Moose Lake, MN, p. A381

KORPIEL, Michael, FACHE, Chief Executive Officer, Mercy San Juan Medical Center, Carmichael, CA, p. A59

KORRELL, Charlene, Chief Executive Officer, Weisbrod Memorial County Hospital, Eads, CO, p. A112

KORTE, Fred, Chief Financial Officer, Mclaren Flint, Flint, MI, p. A354

KORTH, Paul, Chief Executive Officer, Cookeville Regional Medical Center, Cookeville, TN, p. A637
Chief Financial Officer, Cookeville Regional Medical Center, Cookeville, TN, p. A637

KORTH-WHITE, Kirsten, President, Munson Healthcare Grayling Hospital, Grayling, MI, p. A356

KOSANOVICH, John, M.D., Executive Vice President Physician Enterprise and Chief Executive Officer, Covenant Medical Group. Covenant Healthcare, Saginaw, MI, p. A365
President, Watertown Regional Medical Center, Watertown, WI, p. A798

KOSE, William, M.D., Vice President Quality and Medical Affairs, Blufftown Hospital, Bluffton, OH, p. A529

KOSEK, Kevin, Associate Director Operations, Iowa City Va Health Care System, Iowa City, IA, p. A252

KOSIER, Douglas D., Chief Executive Officer, Mason District Hospital, Havana, IL, p. A207

KOSLOW, Howard, President and Chief Executive Officer, Riverbridge Specialty Hospital, Vidalia, LA, p. A316

KOSMAN, Beth, Director Health Information Management, Ringgold County Hospital, Mount Ayr, IA, p. A254

KOSNIK, Linda, R.N., MSN, Chief Nursing Officer and Vice President, Patient Care Services, Sinai Hospital Of Baltimore, Baltimore, MD, p. A326

KOSNOSKY, David, M.D., Chief Medical Officer, Uh Geauga Medical Center, Chardon, OH, p. A531

KOSTER, Tracy, Director Human Resources, Carlinville Area Hospital, Carlinville, IL, p. A196

KOSTERS, Gregory, D.O., Chief Medical Officer, Osceola Regional Health Center, Sibley, IA, p. A257

KOSTOK, Barbara, Manager Human Resources, Punxsutawney Area Hospital, Punxsutawney, PA, p. A605

KOSTURKO, MaryEllen, R.N., Senior Vice President Patient Care Operations and Chief Nursing Officer, Bridgeport Hospital, Bridgeport, CT, p. A121

KOSYLA, Gail, Chief Financial Officer and Senior Vice President Strategy, Hunterdon Healthcare, Flemington, NJ, p. A455

KOTIL, Drew, Director Information Technology, Crete Area Medical Center, Crete, NE, p. A431

KOTIN, Kathy, Chief Financial Officer, Banner - University Medical Center Phoenix, Phoenix, AZ, p. A35

KOTRBA, Mitchell, Chief Financial Officer, North Valley Health Center, Warren, MN, p. A387

KOTTENBROOK, Susan, Administrator, Red River Behavioral Center, Bossier City, LA, p. A298

KOTTOOR, Jose, Chief Executive Officer, Lake Huron Medical Center, Port Huron, MI, p. A364

KOUNS, Jaccel, R.N., MS, Vice President and Executive Director, Montefiore Mount Vernon, Mount Vernon, NY, p. A489

KOUNTZ, David, M.D., Senior Vice President Medical Affairs, Hackensack Meridian Health Jersey Shore University Medical Center, Neptune, NJ, p. A459

KOUSKOLEKAS, Anthony, FACHE, President, Pelham Medical Center, Greer, SC, p. A621

KOUTOUZOS, Connie L., R.N., MSN, Chief Executive Officer, Aspirus Iron River Hospitals & Clinics, Inc., Iron River, MI, p. A358

KOVAC, John, Facility Chief Information Officer, Veterans Affairs Pittsburgh Healthcare System, Pittsburgh, PA, p. A604

KOVACH, Andrew, Vice President Human Resources and Chief Administrative Officer, Newton Medical Center, Newton, NJ, p. A460

KOVACS, Tina, Chief Financial Officer, Saint Francis Hospital-Bartlett, Bartlett, TN, p. A634
Chief Financial Officer, Saint Francis Hospital, Memphis, TN, p. A645

KOVAL, Matthew, M.D., Vice President Medical Affairs, Kidspeace Children's Hospital, Orefield, PA, p. A599

KOVOLYAN, Amanda, M.D., Chief Medical Officer, Bucyrus Hospital, Bucyrus, OH, p. A530

KOVSKI, Christopher, Senior Vice President Human Resources, Monongahela Valley Hospital, Monongahela, PA, p. A597

KOWALSKI, Brad, Director Information Technology, Marcus Daly Memorial Hospital, Hamilton, MT, p. A424

KOWALSKI, David, Chief Executive Officer, Kindred Hospital-La Mirada, La Mirada, CA, p. A70

KOWALSKI, Patrick, Chief Financial Officer, Mercy Health - Anderson Hospital, Cincinnati, OH, p. A532

KOWNACKI, Dawn, Director Human Resources, Brooke Glen Behavioral Hospital, Fort Washington, PA, p. A590

KOWNACKI, Hamila, Chief Operating Officer, California Pacific Medical Center-St. Luke's Campus, San Francisco, CA, p. A93
Chief Operating Officer, California Pacific Medical Center, San Francisco, CA, p. A93

KOZAR, Michael A., Chief Executive Officer, Northwest Florida Community Hospital, Chipley, FL, p. A134

KOZEL, Kenneth D., FACHE, President and Chief Executive Officer, University Of Maryland Shore Medical Center At Chestertown, Chestertown, MD, p. A328
FACHE, President and Chief Executive Officer, University Of Maryland Shore Medical Center At Dorchester, Cambridge, MD, p. A328
FACHE, President and Chief Executive Officer, University Of Maryland Shore Medical Center At Easton, Easton, MD, p. A329

KOZEL, Mary Ann, Chief Fiscal, Wilmington Veterans Affairs Medical Center, Wilmington, DE, p. A128

KOZIK, Kelly, Director Human Resources, Encompass Health Reading Rehabilitation Hospital, Reading, PA, p. A606

KOZIKUSKI, Courtney, Chief Financial Officer, Blackwell Regional Hospital, Blackwell, OK, p. A556
Chief Financial Officer, Stillwater Medical Perry, Perry, OK, p. A567

KOZIN, Scott, M.D., Chief of Staff, Shriners Hospitals For Children-Philadelphia, Philadelphia, PA, p. A602

KOZIOL, Michael, Chief Financial Officer, Holyoke Medical Center, Holyoke, MA, p. A340

KOZOROSKY, Laurie, Chief Executive Officer, Select Specialty Hospital-Mckeesport, Mckeesport, PA, p. A596

KRABILL, Emma, Chief Executive Officer, Doctors Hospital Of Laredo, Laredo, TX, p. A695

KRABLIN, Brett, M.D., Chief of Staff, Mercy Hospital Kingfisher, Kingfisher, OK, p. A560

KRAEGER, Russell, M.D., Chief Medical Officer, St. Alexius Hospital - Broadway Campus, Saint Louis, MO, p. A417

KRAFT, Chris, Director Information Systems, York General, York, NE, p. A440

KRAFT, John, Chief Financial Officer, Woodlawn Hospital, Rochester, IN, p. A240

KRAFVE, Jake, Chief Financial Officer, Royal Oaks Hospital, Windsor, MO, p. A420

KRAHNERT, John, M.D., Chief Medical Officer, Firsthealth Moore Regional Hospital, Pinehurst, NC, p. A516

KRAJEWSKI, David, Senior Vice President and Chief Financial Officer, Sinai Hospital Of Baltimore, Baltimore, MD, p. A326

KRAJNA-MATHERLY, Anna, Human Resources Leader, Kaiser Permanente Santa Rosa Medical Center, Santa Rosa, CA, p. A98

KRAMER, Blake, Administrator, Franklin Medical Center, Winnsboro, LA, p. A317

KRAMER, Danette, Chief Financial Officer, Regional Medical Center, Manchester, IA, p. A253

KRAMER, Janie, Chief Operating Officer, Sharp Memorial Hospital, San Diego, CA, p. A92

KRAMER, Karen, R.N., Senior Vice President, Chief Hospital Officer and System Chief Nursing Officer, Cox Medical Centers, Springfield, MO, p. A418

KRAMER, Kathryn, M.D., President Medical Staff, Unitypoint Health-Pekin Hospital, Pekin, IL, p. A216

KRAMER, Kevin, Chief Executive Officer, Modoc Medical Center, Alturas, CA, p. A55

KRAMER, Kyle, Chief Executive Officer, Day Kimball Hospital, Putnam, CT, p. A124

KRAMER, Lynette, M.D., Chief Medical Officer, Boone County Health Center, Albion, NE, p. A429

KRAMER, Michael, Chief Executive Officer, Mercy Health - West Hospital, Cincinnati, OH, p. A533

KRAMER, Susan, Director of Human Resources, Levi Hospital, Hot Springs National Park, AR, p. A47

KRAMPITS, Carrie, Director Human Resources, Mckenzie Health System, Sandusky, MI, p. A366

KRASON, Jane E., R.N., Chief Executive Officer, Appalachian Behavioral Healthcare, Athens, OH, p. A528

KRASS, Todd, Chief Executive Officer, Belton Regional Medical Center, Belton, MO, p. A402

KRAUKLIS, Gene, Regional Vice President Human Resources, Aurora Lakeland Medical Center, Elkhorn, WI, p. A783
Regional Vice President Human Resources, Aurora Medical Center Burlington, Burlington, WI, p. A781

KRAUS, Jason, Director Human Resources, Magruder Memorial Hospital, Port Clinton, OH, p. A548

KRAUS, John, M.D., Chief Medical Officer, Bryn Mawr Rehabilitation Hospital, Malvern, PA, p. A596

KRAUSE, Christa, Chief Nursing Officer, Door County Medical Center, Sturgeon Bay, WI, p. A797

KRAUSE, Donna, Chief Information Officer, Harry S. Truman Memorial Veterans Hospital, Columbia, MO, p. A405

KRAUSE, Jason, R.N., Director of Nursing, River Oaks Hospital, New Orleans, LA, p. A311

KRAUSE, Jill A., Chief Executive Officer, Forest View Psychiatric Hospital, Grand Rapids, MI, p. A355

KRAUSE, Kim, Director Human Resources, Baylor Scott & White Heart & Vascular Hospital-Dallas, Dallas, TX, p. A667

KRAUSE, Steven, Manager Information Technology, Franciscan Healthcare Munster, Munster, IN, p. A237

KRAUSE, Wade, M.D., Chief Medical Officer, Connally Memorial Medical Center, Floresville, TX, p. A677

KRAUTSCHEID, Steven, Ancillary Services Administrator, Tuality Healthcare, Hillsboro, OR, p. A576

KRAVETZ, Michael, M.D., Medical Director, Encompass Health Valley Of The Sun Rehabilitation Hospital, Glendale, AZ, p. A32

KRAVETZ, Todd, Chief of Staff, Wickenburg Community Hospital, Wickenburg, AZ, p. A41

KRC, Juie, Chief Financial Officer, Ut Health North Campus Tyler, Tyler, TX, p. A722

KREATSOULAS, Nicholas, Vice President Medical Affairs, Mercy Health - St. Josep. Warren Hospital, Warren, OH, p. A551

KREBS, Christine, Director of Nursing, Ascension Sacred Heart Hospital, Tomahawk, WI, p. A797
Director or Nursing, Ascension St. Mary's Hospital, Rhinelander, WI, p. A795

KREBS, Cindy, District Director Human Resources, Matagorda Regional Medical Center, Bay City, TX, p. A657

KREBS, George, M.D., Chief Medical Officer, Broughton Hospital, Morganton, NC, p. A515

KREBS, Mary Jane, FACHE, President, Spring Harbor Hospital, Westbrook, ME, p. A323

KREELEY, Chris, Director Nursing, Kessler Marlton Rehabilitation, Marlton, NJ, p. A458

KREHBIEL, Rod, M.D., Chief of Staff, Klickitat Valley Health, Goldendale, WA, p. A759

KREIDER, David, Controller, Wellspan Ephrata Community Hospital, Ephrata, PA, p. A589

KREIDLER, Marlene, Executive Director Human Resources, Adventist Health Bakersfield, Bakersfield, CA, p. A57

KREITINGER, Tate J., Chief Executive Officer, The Healthcenter, Kalispell, MT, p. A425

KREITNER, Jason, FACHE, Chief Hospital Executive, Hackensack Meridian Health Ocean Medical Center, Brick Township. NJ, p. A453

KREITZER, Teri, Director Human Resources, Saint Francis Medical Center, Cap. Girardeau, MO, p. A403

KREJCI, Kathy, Chief Nursing Officer, Marshall Medical Center, Placerville, CA, p. A85

KRELL, G, M.D., Chief of Staff, South Lincoln Medical Center, Kemmerer, WY, p. A802

KRELSTEIN, Michael, M.D., Medical Director, San Diego County Psychiatric Hospital, San Diego, CA, p. A92

KREN, John, Chief Financial Officer, St. John's Health, Jackson, WY, p. A802

KRESHON, James, M.D., Medical Director, Encompass Health Rehabilitation Hospital Of Hamarville, Pittsburgh, PA, p. A603

KRETSCHMAN, Robin, MSN, R.N., Vice President Patient Care Services, Marshfield Medical Center, Marshfield, WI, p. A789

KRETSCHMER, Suzanne, Chief Executive Officer, Chg Cornerstone Hospital Conroe, Conroe, TX, p. A665

KRETZ, Blake, FACHE, President, Texas Health Arlington Memorial Hospital, Arlington, TX, p. A654

KRETZINGER, Curt, Chief Operating Officer, Mosaic Life Care At St. Josep. - Medical Center, Saint Joseph, MO, p. A415

KRETZSCHMER, Kendra, Patient Care System Leader, Scheurer Health, Pigeon, MI, p. A363

KREUTNER, Ron, Chief Financial Officer, San Joaquin General Hospital, French Camp. CA, p. A65

KREUTZER, Kevin, Chief Financial Officer, Russell Regional Hospital, Russell, KS, p. A275

KREUZER, Jay E., FACHE, Chief Executive Officer, Kohala Hospital, Kohala, HI, p. A186
FACHE, Chief Executive Officer, Kona Community Hospital, Kealakekua, HI, p. A186

KRIEGER, Cathy, Human Resources Director, Greene County Medical Center, Jefferson, IA, p. A252

KRIEGER, Mark, Vice President and Chief Financial Officer, Barnes-Jewish Hospital, Saint Louis, MO, p. A415

KRIEGER, Tim, Director Information Systems, Harnett Health System, Dunn, NC, p. A508

KRIER, Jennifer, Vice President Human Resources, Wesley Healthcare Center, Wichita, KS, p. A279

KRILICH, Chad, M.D., Chief Med Officer-AMC/CMC, Multicare Auburn Medical Center, Auburn, WA, p. A755
M.D., Chief Medical Officer, Santa Rosa Memorial Hospital, Santa Rosa, CA, p. A98

KRINKE, Susan, Chief Executive Officer, Kindred Hospital Lima, Lima, OH, p. A543

KRIPAKARAN, Kasturi, M.D., Medical Director, Andrew Mcfarland Mental Health Center, Springfield, IL, p. A220

KRIPINSKI, Laura, Chief Nursing Officer, Forks Community Hospital, Forks, WA, p. A758

KRISHNA, M., M.D., Chief of Medical Staff, Gibson General Hospital, Princeton, IN, p. A239

KRISHNAN, Radha, M.D., Chief Medical Officer, Antelop. Valley Hospital, Lancaster, CA, p. A71

KRODEL, Scott, Vice President Information Systems, Johnson Memorial Hospital, Franklin, IN, p. A229

KROESE, Brandi, Director Operations, West Springs Hospital, Grand Junction, CO, p. A113

KROESE, Robert, FACHE, Chief Executive Officer, Pella Regional Health Center, Pella, IA, p. A256

KROESE, Robert D., FACHE, Chief Executive Officer, Pella Regional Health Center, Pella, IA, p. A256

KROLICKI, Karen, Director, Human Resources, Beaumont Hospital - Taylor, Taylor, MI, p. A367

KROLIK, Phillip. Vice President, Finance, Mercy Hospital, Coon Rapids, MN, p. A374

KRONENBERG, Seth, M.D., Chief Medical Officer, Crouse Health, Syracuse, NY, p. A499

KROSOFF, Mary, Chief Human Resources Officer, Highlands Hospital, Connellsville, PA, p. A587

KROUSE, Michael, Chief Information Officer Information Services, Ohiohealth Grady Memorial Hospital, Delaware, OH, p. A539
Chief Information Officer, Ohiohealth Doctors Hospital, Columbus, OH, p. A536
Chief Information Officer, Ohiohealth Grant Medical Center, Columbus, OH, p. A536
Chief Information Officer, Ohiohealth Riverside Methodist Hospital, Columbus, OH, p. A537
Senior Vice President Chief Information Officer, Ohiohealth Dublin Methodist Hospital, Dublin, OH, p. A539

KRUEGER, Christine, M.D., Chief of Staff, Munising Memorial Hospital, Munising, MI, p. A362

KRUEGER, Ellen, Director Human Resources, Chadron Community Hospital And Health Services, Chadron, NE, p. A431

KRUEGER, Eric, Chief Financial Officer, Mercy Hospital And Medical Center, Chicago, IL, p. A199
Finance Officer, Adventist Health Glendale, Glendale, CA, p. A66

KRUEGER, James G., M.D., Ph.D., Chief Executive Officer, Rockefeller University Hospital, New York, NY, p. A492

KRUEGER, Justin, FACHE, President, Mercy Health - Fairfield Hospital, Fairfield, OH, p. A540

KRUG, James, Affiliate Vice President, Information Systems and Support Services, Passavant Area Hospital, Jacksonville, IL, p. A209

KRUG, Robert J., M.D., Chief Executive Officer, Mount Sinai Rehabilitation Hospital, Hartford, CT, p. A122

KRUGEL, Gary, Chief Financial Officer, Norwegian American Hospital, Chicago, IL, p. A200

KRUGER, Dale K., Chief Executive Officer, Mahnomen Health Center, Mahnomen, MN, p. A379

KRUGER, George, CPA, Chief Financial Officer, Comanche County Memorial Hospital, Lawton, OK, p. A561

KRUMMEL, Dere, Director Information Systems, Ochsner Medical Center - Kenner, Kenner, LA, p. A304

KRUPALA, Judith, R.N., Chief Nursing Officer, Cuero Regional Hospital, Cuero, TX, p. A667

KRUSE, Marcia, R.N., Director Nursing, Logan County Hospital, Oakley, KS, p. A272

KRUSE, Victoria, Manager Human Resources, Franklin General Hospital, Hampton, IA, p. A251

KRUYER-COLLINS, Emyle, Chief Human Resources Officer, Unity Medical & Surgical Hospital, Mishawaka, IN, p. A236

KRUZEL, Janet, Business Office Manager, Centracare - Melrose, Melrose, MN, p. A380

KRUZICK, Michael, Acting Chief Financial Officer, Norwalk Hospital, Norwalk, CT, p. A124

KRUZNER, Melinda, Chief Financial Officer, Lexington Medical Center, West Columbia, SC, p. A625

KRYSTOWIAK, Thomas, Chief Financial Officer, Thedacare Medical Center-Berlin, Berlin, WI, p. A781

KRZASTEK, Sue, Chief Human Resources Officer, Augusta Health, Fishersville, VA, p. A742

KUBALA, Joseph, Chief Financial Officer, Ascension St. Vincent Jennings, North Vernon, IN, p. A238

Director Financial and Support Services, Ascension St. Vincent Salem, Salem, IN, p. A240

KUBALL, Lana, Director Administrative Services, Lucas County Health Center, Chariton, IA, p. A245

KUBE, Don, M.D., Chief Medical Officer, Dickinson County Healthcare System, Iron Mountain, MI, p. A358

KUBIAK, Phillip J., President, Hampstead Hospital, Hampstead, NH, p. A449

KUBOTA, Andrea, R.N., MSN, Director Patient Care Services and Nurse Executive, Shriners Hospitals For Children-Honolulu, Honolulu, HI, p. A185

KUBOUSHEK, David, Chief, Fiscal Service, Durham Veterans Affairs Medical Center, Durham, NC, p. A509

KUCERA, Katie, interim Chief Financial Officer Acute Services, Renown Regional Medical Center, Reno, NV, p. A446

KUCERA, Kim, Chief Operating Officer, Mille Lacs Health System, Onamia, MN, p. A382

KUCICH, Vincent, FACHE, FACS, M.D., Chief Medical Officer, Osf Heart Of Mary Medical Center, Urbana, IL, p. A222
FACHE, FACS, M.D., Chief Medical Officer, Osf Sacred Heart Medical Center, Danville, IL, p. A202

KUCKEWICH, Mike, Director Information Systems, Terre Haute Regional Hospital, Terre Haute, IN, p. A241

KUCZORA, Paul, Chief Executive Officer, Grant-Blackford Mental Health Center, Marion, IN, p. A236

KUDLA, Angela, MSN, R.N., Chief Nursing Officer, Select Specialty Hospital-Downriver, Wyandotte, MI, p. A370

KUEHLER, Sheila, R.N., Director of Nursing, Knox County Hospital, Knox City, TX, p. A694

KUEHLER, Stephen A., Administrator, Knox County Hospital, Knox City, TX, p. A694

KUEHN, David, Chief Financial Officer, Marshfield Medical Center - Ladysmith, Ladysmith, WI, p. A787

KUENNEN, Patrice, Chief Executive Officer, Gundersen Palmer Lutheran Hospital And Clinics, West Union, IA, p. A260

KUENY, Patrick, Chief Operating Officer, Lee's Summit Medical Center, Lee's Summit, MO, p. A410

KUEPERS, Kathleen, Chief Executive Officer, Memorial Hospital Of Lafayette County, Darlington, WI, p. A782

KUESTERSTEFFEN, Vicki, Director and Chief Executive Officer, J. D. Mccarty Center For Children With Developmental Disabilities, Norman, OK, p. A563

KUEVEN, John, Senior Vice President and President, Wellstar Paulding Hospital, Hiram, GA, p. A174

KUHAR, Peggy, R.N., MSN, Chief Nursing Officer, Uh Geauga Medical Center, Chardon, OH, p. A531

KUHARICH, Ryan, Chief Executive Officer, Aultman Specialty Hospital, Canton, OH, p. A531

KUHLMAN, Ian, Manager Information Technology, Hshs Good Shepherd Hospital, Shelbyville, IL, p. A220

KUHN, Anita, Controller, Texas County Memorial Hospital, Houston, MO, p. A407

KUHN, Brenda, Ph.D., R.N., FACHE, Chief Nursing Officer, Greene Memorial Hospital, Xenia, OH, p. A553
Ph.D., R.N., FACHE, Chief Nursing Officer, Kettering Medical Center, Kettering, OH, p. A542

KUHN, Keith, Chief Executive Officer, Haven Behavioral Senior Care Of Dayton, Dayton, OH, p. A538

KUHN, Margueritte, M.D., Vice President Medical Affairs, Midmichigan Medical Center-Midland, Midland, MI, p. A361

KUHN, Mark, Chief Executive Officer, Hammond-Henry Hospital, Geneseo, IL, p. A205

KUHN, Steve, Chief Financial Officer, River Park Hospital, Huntington, WV, p. A773

KUHNS, Jay, Vice President Human Resources, Johns Hopkins All Children's Hospital, Saint Petersburg, FL, p. A156

KUHRT, Sharon, Chief Nursing Officer, New England Rehabilitation Hospital Of Portland, Portland, ME, p. A322

KUIPER, Evert J., President and Chief Executive Officer, Hshs St. John's Hospital, Springfield, IL, p. A220

KUKELHAN, Alison, Manager Human Resources, Adams Memorial Hospital, Decatur, IN, p. A226

KULHANEK, Linda, Chief Financial Officer, Memorial Hermann Katy Hospital, Katy, TX, p. A692

KULICK, Daniel, M.D., Chief of Staff, Marlette Regional Hospital, Marlette, MI, p. A361

KULIK, Alec, Administrator, Cleveland Clinic Children's Hospital For Rehabilitation, Cleveland, OH, p. A534

KULINK, Sherri, Chief Executive Officer, Providence Milwaukie Hospital, Milwaukie, OR, p. A578

KULISZ, Michael, D.O., Chief Medical Officer, Northwestern Medicine Kishwaukee Hospital, Dekalb, IL, p. A202
D.O., Vice President, Chief Medical Officer, Northwestern Medicine Valley West Hospital, Sandwich, IL, p. A219

KULMA, Mariarose, R.N., Vice President Patient Services, Ut Health Tyler, Tyler, TX, p. A722

KUMAR, Deborah, MSN, Chief Nursing Officer, Adventhealth Carrollwood, Tampa, FL, p. A159

KUMAR, Jaya, M.D., Chief Medical Officer, Medical City Mckinney, Mckinney, TX, p. A700

KUMAR, Nanda, M.D., Chief of Staff, Vibra Hospital Of Northern California, Redding, CA, p. A87

KUMAR, Naveen, M.D., Physician-in-Chief, Kaiser Permanente San Rafael Medical Center, San Rafael, CA, p. A96

KUMAR, Raji, Chief Executive Officer, Crescent Medical Center Lancaster, Lancaster, TX, p. A695

KUMMER, Margaret, Chief Human Resource Officer, Citizens Medical Center, Colby, KS, p. A263

KUNERT, Alicia, MS, R.N., Executive Director, Conway Regional Rehabilitation Hospital, Conway, AR, p. A44

KUNES, Courtney, Director Human Resources, Upmc Lock Haven, Lock Haven, PA, p. A595

KUNKEL, Elisabeth, M.D., Professor, Pennsylvania State College of Medicine, Pennsylvania Psychiatric Institute, Harrisburg, PA, p. A591

KUNNAPPILLY, Chester, M.D., Interim Chief Executive Officer, San Mateo Medical Center, San Mateo, CA, p. A96

KUNZ, Donna, System Director Human Resources, Saint Luke's Cushing Hospital, Leavenworth, KS, p. A269
System Director Human Resources, Saint Luke's North Hospital - Barry Road, Kansas City, MO, p. A409

KUNZA, Mary Kay, Manager Human Resources, Mercy Hospital Lincoln, Troy, MO, p. A419

KUOPUS, Lisa, Chief Nursing Officer, Legent Orthopedic + Spine Hospital, San Antonio, TX, p. A712

KUPER, Kandi, Chief Nursing Officer, Kit Carson County Health Service District, Burlington, CO, p. A108

KUPFERSTEIN, Ron, Chief Executive Officer, Monrovia Memorial Hospital, Monrovia, CA, p. A79

KUPLEN, Carol, R.N., MSN, President, St. Luke's University Hospital - Bethlehem Campus, Bethlehem, PA, p. A585

KUPPLER, Sylvia, Chief Financial Officer, Belmont Pines Hospital, Youngstown, OH, p. A553

KURAITIS, Kestutis, M.D., Chief of Staff, Pioneers Memorial Healthcare District, Brawley, CA, p. A58

KURCAB, Jeff, Chief Financial Officer, Lewisgale Hospital Pulaski, Pulaski, VA, p. A749
Chief Financial Officer, Poplar Bluff Regional Medical Center, Poplar Bluff, MO, p. A414

KURTZ, Kris, Chief Financial Officer, Metro Health - University Of Michigan Health, Wyoming, MI, p. A370

KURTZ, Maria, Director Human Resources, Lutheran Hospital Of Indiana, Fort Wayne, IN, p. A228
Director Human Resources, Orthopaedic Hospital Of Lutheran Health Network, Fort Wayne, IN, p. A228

KURTZ, Thomas M., President and Chief Executive Officer, Chan Soon-Shiong Medical Center, Windber, PA, p. A611

KURTZ, Tom, Vice President Information Services and Chief Information Officer, Memorial Healthcare, Owosso, MI, p. A363

KURTZ JR, ThomasChief Operating Officer, Georgia Regional Hospital At Savannah, Savannah, GA, p. A180

KURZ, Kenneth, M.D., Chief of Staff, Midstate Medical Center, Meriden, CT, p. A123

KUSHNER, Michael, Senior Vice President and Chief Talent Officer, Nicklaus Children's Hospital, Miami, FL, p. A147

KUSLER, Julie, Manager Information Services, Avera St. Luke's Hospital, Aberdeen, SD, p. A626

KUSNIERZ, William, Vice President and Chief Financial Officer, Springfield Regional Medical Center, Springfield, OH, p. A549

KUTCH, John M., President and Chief Executive Officer, Trinity Health, Minot, ND, p. A525

KUTILEK, Richard, Chief Operating Officer, Calvary Hospital, Bronx, NY, p. A476

KUTNER, Jean, M.D., Chief Medical Officer, University Of Colorado Hospital, Aurora, CO, p. A108

KUVSHINOFF, Boris, M.D., Chief Medical Officer, Roswell Park Comprehensive Cancer Center, Buffalo, NY, p. A480

KUYKENDALL, Jana, Chief Executive Officer, Pam Specialty Hospital Of Luling, Luling, TX, p. A699

KUZAS, Betsy, Executive Vice President and Chief Operating Officer, Phoenix Children's Hospital, Phoenix, AZ, p. A36

KUZEE, Ann, Executive Director Human Resources, Riverview Health, Noblesville, IN, p. A238

KWIESIELEWICZ, Nancy, Human Resources Manager, Ascension Good Samaritan Hospital, Merrill, WI, p. A790
Human Resources Manager, Marshfield Medical Center - Weston, Weston, WI, p. A799

KYHNELL, Koreen, Vice President Human Resources, Indiana University Health Arnett Hospital, Lafayette, IN, p. A234

KYLER, Yvonne, Director Human Resources, Texas Health Arlington Memorial Hospital, Arlington, TX, p. A654
Director Human Resources, Texas Health Heart & Vascular Hospital Arlington, Arlington, TX, p. A654

KYWI, Alberto, Chief Information Officer, Goleta Valley Cottage Hospital, Santa Barbara, CA, p. A96

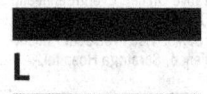

Chief Information Officer, Santa Barbara Cottage Hospital, Santa Barbara, CA, p. A97

KYZAR, Debbie, Interim Chief Financial Officer, Ochsner St. Mary, Morgan City, LA, p. A309

# L

LA CAVA, Joseph, Chief Nursing Officer and Director of Anesthesia, Desoto Memorial Hospital, Arcadia, FL, p. A131

LA CROIX, Kent, Chief Information Officer, Schoolcraft Memorial Hospital, Manistique, MI, p. A361

LABADIE, Wendy, Chief Human Resource Officer, Banner Estrella Medical Center, Phoenix, AZ, p. A35

LABAGNARA, James, M.D., Vice President Medical Affairs, St. Joseph's University Medical Center, Paterson, NJ, p. A460

LABARBERA, Sonja, President and Chief Executive Officer, Gaylord Specialty Healthcare, Wallingford, CT, p. A126

LABARCA, Laurie, President, Ascension Via Christi Hospital On St. Teresa, Wichita, KS, p. A278

President, Ascension Via Christi Rehabilitation Hospital, Wichita, KS, p. A278

LABELLE, Douglas, M.D., Chief Medical Officer, Up Health System-Bell, Ishpeming, MI, p. A358

LABELLE, James, M.D., Chief Medical Officer, Scripp. Green Hospital, La Jolla, CA, p. A69

M.D., Chief Medical Officer, Scripp. Memorial Hospital-La Jolla, La Jolla, CA, p. A70

LABER, Susan, R.N., Chief Nursing Officer, Palms Of Pasadena Hospital, Saint Petersburg, FL, p. A156

LABONTE, Karen, Chief Nursing Officer, Northwest Medical Center - Springdale, Springdale, AR, p. A53

LABONTE, Robin, Leader Financial Care, York Hospital, York, ME, p. A323

LABOUCHARDIERE, Mark, Interim Facility Administrator, Lincoln Regional Center, Lincoln, NE, p. A434

LABRIOLA, Suzanne, D.O., Chief Medical Officer, Allegheny Valley Hospital, Natrona Heights, PA, p. A598

LABRIOLA, Terri, Human Resources Officer, Sierra Nevada Memorial Hospital, Grass Valley, CA, p. A67

LABRUM, Chad, Chief Financial Officer, Ashley Regional Medical Center, Vernal, UT, p. A734

LACAZE, Todd, Chief Financial Officer, Riverside Community Hospital, Riverside, CA, p. A88

LACEFIELD, Gayla, Director Human Resources, Howard Memorial Hospital, Nashville, AR, p. A51

LACEY, Carmen, MSN, R.N., President and Director of Patient Care Services, Charles A. Cannon Memorial Hospital, Newland, NC, p. A515

MSN, R.N., President, Charles A. Cannon Memorial Hospital, Newland, NC, p. A515

LACEY, Paul, M.D., Chief Medical Staff, North Valley Hospital, Tonasket, WA, p. A767

LACHANCE, Eric, Chief Financial Officer, Adventhealth Ocala, Ocala, FL, p. A149

LACHAPELLE, Diana, CPA, Chief Executive Officer, Encompass Health Rehabilitation Hospital Of Concord, Concord, NH, p. A448

LACHER, Paula, MSN, R.N., Chief Nursing Officer, West Penn Hospital, Pittsburgh, PA, p. A605

LACHINA, Ignazio, M.D., Medical Director, Encompass Health Rehabilitation Hospital Of Cypress, Houston, TX, p. A685

LACHNEY, Cheryl, Director of Nursing, Compass Behavioral Center Of Alexandria, Alexandria, LA, p. A295

LACHOWSKY, John, M.D., Chief Medical Officer, Mercy Hospital Ozark, Ozark, AR, p. A51

LACKEY, Lori, Chief Financial Officer, Sabetha Community Hospital, Sabetha, KS, p. A275

LACKMAN, Vickie, Human Resource Director, Peninsula Region, St. Michael Medical Center, Bremerton, WA, p. A756

LACOT, Ivette, Director Human Resources, Hospital Episcopal San Lucas Guayama, Guayama, PR, p. A807

LACROSS, Erin, R.N., Chief Nursing Officer, Parkview Regional Medical Center, Fort Wayne, IN, p. A228

LACY, Julie, Chief Financial Officer, Crete Area Medical Center, Crete, NE, p. A431

LACY, Rodney, Leader Human Resources, Ssm Health Depaul Hospital - St. Louis, Bridgeton, MO, p. A403

LACY, Tyson, Chief Executive Officer and Superintendent, Lincoln Medical Center, Davenport, WA, p. A757

LADAROLA, Sandra, Chief Nursing Officer, Waterbury Hospital, Waterbury, CT, p. A126

LADD, Bill, Director Information Services, Western Missouri Medical Center, Warrensburg, MO, p. A420

LADD, Robert, M.D., Medical Director, Rush County Memorial Hospital, La Crosse, KS, p. A268

LADEVICH, Michael, FACHE, Interim Chief Executive Officer, Murray County Medical Center, Slayton, MN, p. A386

LADLEY, Herbert, M.D., Chief Medical Officer, Indian Path Community Hospital, Kingsport, TN, p. A641

LADWIG, Michael, M.D., Chief of Staff, Marion Veterans Affairs Medical Center, Marion, IL, p. A211

LADY, Brian, Administrator and Chief Executive Officer, Concho County Hospital, Eden, TX, p. A673

LAFERNEY, Jimmy, M.D., Vice President Medical Staff Affairs, Baylor Scott & White Medical Center—Frisco, Frisco, TX, p. A680

LAFFEY, Leah, R.N., Chief Executive Officer, Encompass Health Rehabilitation Hospital Of Sewickley, Sewickley, PA, p. A607

LAFLAMME, Christine, R.N., MSN, Chief Nursing Officer, Ascension Seton Smithville, Smithville, TX, p. A716

LAFONTSEE, Chris, Chief Executive Officer, Rehabilitation Hospital Of Northern Arizona, Flagstaff, AZ, p. A31

LAFRANCOIS, Gregory, President, The Aroostook Medical Center, Presque Isle, ME, p. A322

LAFRANCOIS, Mary, Vice President Human Resources, Christus Spohn Hospital Corpus Christi Memorial, Corpus Christi, TX, p. A665

LAGASSE, David, Senior Vice President Fiscal Affairs, Mclean Hospital, Belmont, MA, p. A334

LAGNESE, John, M.D., Vice President Medical Affairs, Upmc St. Margaret, Pittsburgh, PA, p. A604

LAGROU, Robert, D.O., Medical Director, Henry Ford Kingswood Hospital, Ferndale, MI, p. A354

LAGUNA-KENNEDY, Joanne, Vice President of Hospital Operations and Chief Nursing Officer, Marina Del Rey Hospital, Marina Del Rey, CA, p. A77

LAHASKY, Douglas, Chief Financial Officer, Springhill Medical Center, Springhill, LA, p. A315

LAHAYE, Daniel, Manager, Savoy Medical Center, Mamou, LA, p. A307

LAHOOD, Amy, R.N., Director of Nursing, Vermilion Behavioral Health Systems - North Campus, Lafayette, LA, p. A306

LAHOUT, Brenda, Chief Nurse Executive, Danville State Hospital, Danville, PA, p. A587

LAHTI, Molly, Director Human Resources, Parkland Medical Center, Derry, NH, p. A448

LAI, Iris, Chief Executive Officer, Alhambra Hospital Medical Center, Alhambra, CA, p. A55

LAIBINIS, Walter, M.D., Chief Medical Officer, Upmc Wellsboro, Wellsboro, PA, p. A610

LAIGN, Michael B., President and Chief Executive Officer, Holy Redeemer Hospital, Meadowbrook, PA, p. A596

LAIL, Steve, Chief Executive Officer, Down East Community Hospital, Machias, ME, p. A321

LAIOSA, Sarah, M.D., Chief Medical Staff, Harney District Hospital, Burns, OR, p. A574

LAIRD, Alan, M.D., Chief Medical Officer, Orange City Area Health System, Orange City, IA, p. A255

LAIRD, Jeff, Controller, Stephens County Hospital, Toccoa, GA, p. A182

LAIRD, Laci, Chief Executive Officer, Oceans Behavioral Hospital Lufkin, Lufkin, TX, p. A698

LAIRD, Shaw, Chief Information Officer, Musc Health Chester Medical Center, Chester, SC, p. A617

LAKE, Chandra, Associate Director, Sheridan Veterans Affairs Medical Center, Sheridan, WY, p. A804

LAKE, Nathan, Vice President Human Resources, Prairie Lakes Healthcare System, Watertown, SD, p. A633

LAKE, Peter, M.D., Chief Medical Officer, Rogers Memorial Hospital, Inc., Oconomowoc, WI, p. A793

LAKE, Ryan, Director Information Technology, Glencoe Regional Health, Glencoe, MN, p. A377

LAKEY, Travis, Chief Financial Officer, Mayers Memorial Hospital District, Fall River Mills, CA, p. A64

LALAS, Angela, Senior Vice President, Finance, Loma Linda University Children's Hospital, Loma Linda, CA, p. A71

LALIBERTE, John, Chief Information Officer, St. Vincent's Blount, Oneonta, AL, p. A23

LALIOTIS, Anna, Chief Executive Officer, Mesilla Valley Hospital, Las Cruces, NM, p. A470

LALLI, Kathleen, Chief Executive Officer, Kensington Hospital, Philadelphia, PA, p. A601

LALLY JR, RobertVice President Finance, Medstar Franklin Square Medical Center, Baltimore, MD, p. A325

LALUZERNE, Andrew, Chief Financial Officer, Door County Medical Center, Sturgeon Bay, WI, p. A797

LAM, Shiva, M.D., Executive Medical Director, Austin Lakes Hospital, Austin, TX, p. A655

LAM, Thomas, Chief Medical Officer, Garfield Medical Center, Monterey Park, CA, p. A79

LAMADELEINE, Joseph, Chief Financial Officer, Veterans Affairs Connecticut Healthcare System, West Haven, CT, p. A126

LAMANTEER, Mike, M.D., Senior Vice President Medical Affairs, Bsa Hospital, Llc, Amarillo, TX, p. A652

LAMARCHE, Maximo, M.D., Chief Medical Officer, Amg Specialty Hospital-Lafayette, Lafayette, LA, p. A305

LAMB, Andrew, M.D., Chief of Staff, Alamance Regional Medical Center, Burlington, NC, p. A506

LAMB, Cindy, Director Human Resources, Marias Medical Center, Shelby, MT, p. A427

LAMB, Deanna, Director Human Resources, Central Carolina Hospital, Sanford, NC, p. A518

LAMB, Hope, Manager Human Resources, Kimble Healthcare, Junction, TX, p. A691

LAMB, Joshua, Vice President Operations, Christus Health Shreveport-Bossier, Shreveport, LA, p. A314

LAMB, Michael, Administrator, Sterling Surgical Hospital, Slidell, LA, p. A315

LAMB-PAGONE, Jerilynn, Nurse Executive, Connecticut Valley Hospital, Middletown, CT, p. A123

LAMBERT, Amand, Director Human Resources, Allen Parish Community Healthcare, Kinder, LA, p. A305

LAMBERT, Barbara, Director Healthcare Compliance, Eastern State Hospital, Williamsburg, VA, p. A753

LAMBERT, Cheryl, Chief Financial Officer, Acuity Specialty Hospital Of New Jersey, Atlantic City, NJ, p. A452

LAMBERT, James M., FACHE, Chief Executive Officer, Memorial Hospital And Manor, Bainbridge, GA, p. A166

LAMBERT, John M., President, Baylor Scott & White Medical Center - Round Rock, Round Rock, TX, p. A709

LAMBERT, Karen A., President, Advocate Good Shepherd Hospital, Barrington, IL, p. A195

LAMBERT, Lynn, Chief Financial Officer, Harnett Health System, Dunn, NC, p. A508

LAMBERT, Paul, M.D., Chief of Staff, Boise Veterans Affairs Medical Center, Boise, ID, p. A188

LAMBERT, Suzanne, R.N., Regional Chief Nursing Officer and Support Services, Amita Health Saints Mary & Elizabeth Medical Center, Chicago, IL, p. A198

LAMBETH, Laura, Chief Executive Officer, Ashe Memorial Hospital, Jefferson, NC, p. A513

LAMBRECHT, Craig, M.D., President and Chief Executive Officer, Kalispell Regional Healthcare, Kalispell, MT, p. A425

LAMEBULL, Charlotte, Administrative Officer, Fort Belknap Service Unit, Harlem, MT, p. A424

LAMEN, Drake M., M.D., President and Chief Executive Officer, Uhs Chenango Memorial Hospital, Norwich, NY, p. A493

LAMERS, Jamon, Director Finance, Ascension Eagle River Hospital, Eagle River, WI, p. A782

Director Finance, Ascension Sacred Heart Hospital, Tomahawk, WI, p. A797

Director Finance, Ascension St. Mary's Hospital, Rhinelander, WI, p. A795

Director Finance, Howard Young Medical Center, Woodruff, WI, p. A800

LAMEY, Mark, Commander, U. S. Air Force Regional Hospital, Elmendorf Afb, AK, p. A28

LAMEY, Rebecca, Vice President Human Resources, Mainegeneral Medical Center, Augusta, ME, p. A318

LAMLE, Sandra, Chief Financial Officer, Okeene Municipal Hospital, Okeene, OK, p. A563

LAMM, Eileen, Regional Chief Financial Officer, Ssm Health Depaul Hospital - St. Louis, Bridgeton, MO, p. A403

LAMMERS, Sandra, Coordinator Human Resources and Finance, Chi Health Mercy Corning, Corning, IA, p. A246

LAMONT, Jennifer, Chief Financial Officer, West Suburban Medical Center, Oak Park, IL, p. A215

LAMOUREUX, John P., Commander, Dwight David Eisenhower Army Medical Center, Fort Gordon, GA, p. A173

LAMOUREUX, Laurie, Director of Finance, Cooley Dickinson Hospital, Northampton, MA, p. A342

LAMPE, Michael, M.D., Chief of Staff, Kossuth Regional Health Center, Algona, IA, p. A243

LAMPE, Tammy, Director Human Resources, Edwards County Medical Center, Kinsley, KS, p. A268

LAMPLEY, Danny, Chief Operating Officer, Harrisburg Medical Center, Harrisburg, IL, p. A206

LAMPLEY, Joseph, D.O., Chief of Staff, Fisher County Hospital District, Rotan, TX, p. A709

LAMPTON, Lucius, M.D., Medical Director, Beacham Memorial Hospital, Magnolia, MS, p. A396

LANCASTER, Brian, Executive Director Information Management, Nebraska Medicine - Bellevue, Bellevue, NE, p. A430

LANCASTER, Penny, Controller, Cascade Medical Center, Cascade, ID, p. A189

LAND, Steve, Senior Administrator, Wamego Health Center, Wamego, KS, p. A278

LAND, Susann, M.D., Chief Medical Officer, Texas Health Harris Methodist Hospital Hurst-Euless-Bedford, Bedford, TX, p. A659

---

LAND, Teresa, R.N., Chief Nursing Officer, Vice President Nursing, Methodist Charlton Medical Center, Dallas, TX, p. A669

LANDERS, Alice, Administrative Director Operations, Texas Health Harris Methodist Hospital Hurst-Euless-Bedford, Bedford, TX, p. A659

LANDERS, Kimberly, MS, R.N., Vice President Patient Care Services, Morris Hospital & Healthcare Centers, Morris, IL, p. A213

LANDINI, Kristin, Vice President Human Resources, Advocate South Suburban Hospital, Hazel Crest, IL, p. A207
Vice President, Human Resources, Advocate Trinity Hospital, Chicago, IL, p. A197

LANDIS, Janie, Chief Financial Officer, Russell County Hospital, Russell Springs, KY, p. A292

LANDMAN, Adam, M.D., Chief Information Officer, Brigham And Women's Hospital, Boston, MA, p. A335

LANDON, Anna, Chief Nursing Officer, Mercy Hospital Washington, Washington, MO, p. A420

LANDRAU, Erika, Director Human Resources, Encompass Health Rehabilitation Hospital Of Manati, Manati, PR, p. A808

LANDRENEAU, John Derrick., R.N., Chief Executive Officer, Amg Physical Rehabilitation Hospital, Covington, LA, p. A300

LANDRETH, Kathy, Chief Executive Officer, Bath Community Hospital, Hot Springs, VA, p. A744

LANDRETH, Sandy, Director Human Resources, Seiling Regional Medical Center, Seiling, OK, p. A568

LANDRETH, Shannan, Information Systems, Livingston Hospital And Healthcare Services, Salem, KY, p. A293

LANDRUM, David, Chief Police Services, Atascadero State Hospital, Atascadero, CA, p. A56

LANDRY, Adam, Director of Information Systems, Northern Maine Medical Center, Fort Kent, ME, p. A320

LANDRY, Candy, Chief Human Resource Officer, Eastside Psychiatric Hospital, Tallahassee, FL, p. A158

LANDRY, Crystal, R.N., Chief Executive Officer, Penobscot Valley Hospital, Lincoln, ME, p. A321

LANDRY, Donna, Chief Operating Officer, Our Lady Of Lourdes Regional Medical Center, Lafayette, LA, p. A306

LANDRY, Jeanne, Vice President Human Resources, Emory Saint Joseph's Hospital Of Atlanta, Atlanta, GA, p. A164

LANDRY, Kyle, Chief Operating Officer, St. David's South Austin Medical Center, Austin, TX, p. A656

LANDRY, Lisa, Human Resources Director, Redington-Fairview General Hospital, Skowhegan, ME, p. A323

LANDRY, Nobie, Chief Financial Officer, Prevost Memorial Hospital, Donaldsonville, LA, p. A301

LANDRY, Ray A., FACHE, Chief Executive Officer, Abbeville General Hospital, Abbeville, LA, p. A295

LANDSMAN, Joseph, President and Chief Executive Officer, University Of Tennessee Medical Center, Knoxville, TN, p. A641

LANDSTROM, John, Director Human Resources, Rml Specialty Hospital, Hinsdale, IL, p. A208

LANE, Andrea, Chief Financial Officer, Wilson N. Jones Regional Medical Center, Sherman, TX, p. A716

LANE, Andrew, Chief Financial Officer, Medical City Fort Worth, Fort Worth, TX, p. A678

LANE, Charles, Chief Medical Officer, Anderson Hospital, Maryville, IL, p. A211

LANE, Diron, Director Information Systems, Lewisgale Hospital Montgomery, Blacksburg, VA, p. A739
Director Information Systems, Lewisgale Hospital Pulaski, Pulaski, VA, p. A749

LANE, Kevin, D.O., Chief of Staff, Hardeman County Memorial Hospital, Quanah, TX, p. A708
Vice President Information Systems, Silver Cross Hospital, New Lenox, IL, p. A214

LANE, Kim, Chief Fiscal Service, Overton Brooks Veterans Affairs Medical Center, Shreveport, LA, p. A314

LANE, Mike, Chief Operating Officer, Twin Cities Community Hospital, Templeton, CA, p. A101

LANE, Richard, Chief Financial Officer, Mid—America Rehabilitation Hospital, Shawnee Mission, KS, p. A276

LANE, Sonia, Interim Chief Nursing Officer, Uci Medical Center, Orange, CA, p. A83

LANEAUX, Eleanor, Director Information Systems, Placentia-Linda Hospital, Placentia, CA, p. A85

LANER JR, RichardManager Information Systems, Miners' Colfax Medical Center, Raton, NM, p. A471

LANEY, Samuel Mark., M.D., Chief Executive Officer, Mosaic Life Care At St. Josep. - Medical Center, Saint Joseph, MO, p. A415

LANG, Cyndi, Director Information Services, French Hospital Medical Center, San Luis Obispo, CA, p. A95

LANG, Gary, M.D., Clinical Director, Claremore Indian Hospital, Claremore, OK, p. A557

LANG, Gordon, M.D., Chief of Staff, Trego County-Lemke Memorial Hospital, Wakeeney, KS, p. A278

LANG, Jeff, Chief Executive Officer, Coquille Valley Hospital, Coquille, OR, p. A574

LANG, John Christopher., FACHE, Chief Executive Officer, Cass Regional Medical Center, Harrisonville, MO, p. A407

LANG, Joseph, M.D., Chief of Staff, Carolinas Continuecare Hospital At Pineville, Charlotte, NC, p. A507

LANG, Linda, Chief Human Resources Officer, Marinhealth Medical Center, Greenbrae, CA, p. A67

LANG, Nicholas, M.D., Chief Medical Officer, Uams Medical Center, Little Rock, AR, p. A49

LANG, Richard, Ed.D., Vice President and Chief Information Officer, Doylestown Hospital, Doylestown, PA, p. A588
Chief Financial Officer, Gouverneur Hospital, Gouverneur, NY, p. A485

LANG, Robin, Vice President, Chief Information Officer, Caromont Regional Medical Center, Gastonia, NC, p. A510

LANGAN, Lynn, Chief Nursing Officer, Quillen Rehabilitation Hospital, Johnson City, TN, p. A640

LANGBEHN, Jennifer, Medical Director, Mayo Clinic Health System In Saint James, Saint James, MN, p. A384

LANGDON, Ashlee, Controller, Yalobusha General Hospital, Water Valley, MS, p. A401

LANGE, Connie, R.N., Vice President Quality, Inpatient and Community Services, Lakes Regional Healthcare, Spirit Lake, IA, p. A258

LANGENBERG, Shannon, Director Human Resources, Jackson County Regional Health Center, Maquoketa, IA, p. A253

LANGENFELD, John, Medical Records Coordinator, Arizona Orthopedic Surgical Hospital, Chandler, AZ, p. A30

LANGFORD, Scott, Administrator, Beaver Valley Hospital, Beaver, UT, p. A727
Administrator, Milford Valley Memorial Hospital, Milford, UT, p. A729

LANGFORD, Terrie, Director Human Resources, Baylor Scott & White Surgical Hospital-Sherman, Sherman, TX, p. A715

LANGLAND, Robert, Senior Vice President and Chief Financial Officer, Stormont Vail Health, Topeka, KS, p. A277

LANGLEY, Kim, Business Partner, Promedica Bixby Hospital, Adrian, MI, p. A348
Business Partner, Promedica Herrick Hospital, Tecumseh, MI, p. A368

LANGLINIAS, Amy, Chief Financial Officer, Iberia Medical Center, New Iberia, LA, p. A310

LANGLITZ, Sara, Controller, Kindred Hospital Houston Medical Center, Houston, TX, p. A686

LANGLOIS, John, Chief Executive Officer, Riverview Regional Medical Center, Gadsden, AL, p. A19

LANGMEAD, Paula A., Chief Executive Officer, Springfield Hospital Center, Sykesville, MD, p. A333

LANGSTON, David, Corporate Vice President Human Resources, Ut Health Specialty Hospital, Tyler, TX, p. A722

LANGSTON, Phillip W., Administrator, Lawrence County Hospital, Monticello, MS, p. A397

LANIER, Donna, R.N., Chief Nursing Officer, Delta Specialty Hospital, Memphis, TN, p. A644

LANIER, Mary, Vice President, Post Acute Services and Site Administrator, California Pacific Medical Center-Davies Campus, San Francisco, CA, p. A93

LANIER, Regina, MSN, R.N., Senior Vice President and Chief Nursing Officer, Onslow Memorial Hospital, Jacksonville, NC, p. A513

LANKOWICZ, Andrew, FACHE, President, Chi St. Alexius Health Devils Lake Hospital, Devils Lake, ND, p. A522

LANKOWICZ, Genevieve, M.D., Chief Medical Officer, Saint Josep. Health System, Mishawaka, IN, p. A236

LANNING, John, Chief Operating Officer, Kearney Regional Medical Center, Kearney, NE, p. A434

LANNOYE, Craig, Vice President Operations, Wilson Memorial Hospital, Sidney, OH, p. A549

LANOUE, Cheryl, Chief Financial Officer, Ottawa County Health Center, Minneapolis, KS, p. A271

LANSDOWNE, Lynn, Vice President Labor Relations and Human Resources, Lehigh Valley Hospital - Hazleton, Hazleton, PA, p. A592
Vice President Labor Relations and Human Resources, Lehigh Valley Hospital - Pocono, East Stroudsburg, PA, p. A589
Vice President Labor Relations and Human Resources, Lehigh Valley Hospital - Schuylkill, Pottsville, PA, p. A605

LANTOS, Phyllis, Executive Vice President, Corporate Chief Financial Officer and Treasurer, New York-Presbyterian Hospital, New York, NY, p. A491

LANTZY, William, Chief Financial Officer, Dmc Huron Valley-Sinai Hospital, Commerce Township. MI, p. A351

LANZA, Nicholas, Controller, St. Mary's General Hospital, Passaic, NJ, p. A460

LAPERLE, Linda, Vice President Administrative Services, Androscoggin Valley Hospital, Berlin, NH, p. A448

LAPHAM, Lisa, President and Chief Executive Officer, Healthsource Saginaw, Inc., Saginaw, MI, p. A365

LAPLANT, Dawn, Manager Health Information Management, Brown County Community Treatment Center, Green Bay, WI, p. A785

LAPLANTE, Lisa, Chief Administrative Officer, Evergreenhealth Monroe, Monroe, WA, p. A760

LAPOSTA, Mary Jo, Ph.D., R.N., Senior Vice President Patient Care and Organizational Excellence, Saratoga Hospital, Saratoga Springs, NY, p. A497

LAPPEN, Michael, Chief Executive Officer, Milwaukee County Behavioral Health Division, Milwaukee, WI, p. A791

LAPRISE, Christine, Vice President of Human Resources, Bristol Health, Bristol, CT, p. A121

LARA, Anne, Chief Information Officer, Union Hospital, Elkton, MD, p. A329

LARA, Sergio, M.D., Chief Medical Officer, Covenant Hospital Plainview, Plainview, TX, p. A706

LARABIE, Shawn, Chief Nursing Officer, San Antonio Behavioral Healthcare Hospital, San Antonio, TX, p. A713

LARAMIE, Robert, Chief Information Officer, Beverly Hospital, Beverly, MA, p. A334

LARAMIE, Wayne, Vice President Nursing, Ssm Health St. Clare Hospital - Fenton, Fenton, MO, p. A406

LARCAS, John, M.D., Acting Medical Director, Choate Mental Health Center, Anna, IL, p. A194

LAREAU, Daniel, Executive Director, Operations and Information, Ascension St. Vincent Carmel Hospital, Carmel, IN, p. A225

LARET, Mark R., Chief Executive Officer, Ucsf Medical Center, San Francisco, CA, p. A94

LARIMER, Cynthia, M.D., Chief of Staff, Lake Butler Hospital, Lake Butler, FL, p. A142

LARIMORE, Rhonda, Vice President Human Resources, Upmc Magee-Womens Hospital, Pittsburgh, PA, p. A604
Vice President, Human Resources, Upmc Children's Hospital Of Pittsburgh, Pittsburgh, PA, p. A603

LARISCY, Christopher, M.D., Chief of Staff, Davis Regional Medical Center, Statesville, NC, p. A519

LARISCY, Robin, M.D., Medical Director, Mary S Harper Geriatric Psychiatry Center, Tuscaloosa, AL, p. A25

LARIVEE, Theresa M., Chief Executive Officer, Pennsylvania Hospital, Philadelphia, PA, p. A601

LARIVIERE, Beckye, Controller, Encompass Health Rehabilitation Hospital Of Charleston, Charleston, SC, p. A616

LARKIN, Kevin, Regional Chief Financial Officer, Amita Health Mercy Medical Center, Aurora, IL, p. A195
Regional Chief Financial Officer, Amita Health Saint Josep. Hospital, Elgin, IL, p. A203

LARKIN, Kim, Chief Information Officer, Washington County Hospital, Nashville, IL, p. A214

LARKIN, Matthew, Chief Operating Officer, Portsmouth Regional Hospital, Portsmouth, NH, p. A451

LARKIN-SKINNER, Melissa, Chief Executive Officer, Centerstone Hospital, Bradenton, FL, p. A132

LARKINS, Mark, Interim Chief Information Officer, Saint Elizabeths Hospital, Washington, DC, p. A130

LARMER, Jennifer, R.N., Chief Clinical Officer, Lincoln Hospital, Davenport, WA, p. A757

LARMORE, Mark, Chief Financial Officer, Ohio State University Wexner Medical Center, Columbus, OH, p. A536

LARNER, Cheryl, Chief Financial Officer, Sentara Careplex Hospital, Hampton, VA, p. A743

LAROSA, Vincent, Director of Information Systems, Landmark Medical Center, Woonsocket, RI, p. A614
Director of Information Technology Services, Rehabilitation Hospital Of Rhode Island, North Smithfield, RI, p. A613

LAROWE, Mary E., FACHE, President and Chief Executive Officer, Brooks Memorial Hospital, Dunkirk, NY, p. A482

LARRISON, Robert G. Jr, President, Atrium Health's Carolinas Rehabilitation, Charlotte, NC, p. A507

LARSEN, Bill, Vice President Human Resources, Driscoll Children's Hospital, Corpus Christi, TX, p. A666

LARSEN, Catherine, Director Marketing, Sutter Tracy Community Hospital, Tracy, CA, p. A101

LARSEN, Donald, M.D., Chief Medical Officer, Providence Saint John's Health Center, Santa Monica, CA, p. A97

LARSEN, Kevin, Associate Vice President, Business and Ancillary Services, Uconn, John Dempsey Hospital, Farmington, CT, p. A122

LARSEN, Ryan C., FACHE, Chief Executive Officer, Community Medical Center, Inc., Falls City, NE, p. A432

LARSON, Alan, Chief Executive Officer, Sovah Health-Danville, Danville, VA, p. A741
Market President, Sovah Health-Martinsville, Martinsville, VA, p. A746

LARSON, Bill, Vice President Finance and Chief Financial Officer, Torrance Memorial Medical Center, Torrance, CA, p. A101

LARSON, Derek, Information Technology Network, Lakes Regional Healthcare, Spirit Lake, IA, p. A258

LARSON, Erick, Vice President and Chief Information Officer, Mid-Columbia Medical Center, The Dalles, OR, p. A582

LARSON, Erick J., President and Chief Executive Officer, Huron Regional Medical Center, Huron, SD, p. A629

LARSON, Jennifer, M.D., Chief of Staff, Blue Ridge Regional Hospital, Spruce Pine, NC, p. A518

LARSON, Jon, M.D., Medical Director, Encompass Health Rehabilitation Institute of Tucson, Tucson, AZ, p. A40

LARSON, Karla, Director Human Resources, Stevens Community Medical Center, Morris, MN, p. A381

LARSON, Kay, R.N., Chief Nursing Officer, Essentia Health St. Mary's - Detroit Lakes, Detroit Lakes, MN, p. A375

LARSON, Michael, Vice President Chief Information Officer, Midmichigan Medical Center-Clare, Clare, MI, p. A351

LARSON, Mike, Chief Operating Officer, Essentia Health-St. Joseph's Medical Center, Brainerd, MN, p. A373

LARSON, Pamela, Division Director Financial Services, Hutchinson Health, Hutchinson, MN, p. A378

LARSON, Rodney, M.D., Medical Director, Fall River Hospital, Hot Springs, SD, p. A628

LARSON, Ronald, Chief Financial Officer, Va San Diego Healthcare System, San Diego, CA, p. A93

LARSON, Scott, M.D., Vice President Medical Affairs and Chief Medical Officer, Bronson Methodist Hospital, Kalamazoo, MI, p. A359

LARSON, Scott C., Chief Executive Officer, Sanford Canton-Inwood Medical Center, Canton, SD, p. A626

LARSON, Shelly, Chief Financial Officer, Hot Springs County Memorial Hospital, Thermopolis, WY, p. A804

LARSON, Steve, M.D., Director Information Systems, Mercyone Siouxland Medical Center, Sioux City, IA, p. A258

LARSON, Tammy, Chief Financial Officer, Towner County Medical Center, Cando, ND, p. A521

LARSON, Tracy, MS, Vice President Patient Care Services and Chief Nursing Officer, Mercyone Siouxland Medical Center, Sioux City, IA, p. A258

LARSON, Valerie, M.D., Chief Medical Officer, Avera Dells Area Hospital, Dell Rapids, SD, p. A627

LARSON, Walt, Vice President Finance, Adventist Healthtillamook, Tillamook, OR, p. A582

LARSON, Wendy, Chief Clinical Officer, Kp. Promise Hospital Of Phoenix, Mesa, AZ, p. A34

LASATER, Laci, R.N., Chief Nursing Officer, Christus Spohn Hospital Kleberg, Kingsville, TX, p. A693

LASCANO, Terrance, Administrative Officer, U. S. Public Health Service Indian Hospital, Cass Lake, MN, p. A374

LASECKI, Cynthia, M.D., Chief Medical Officer, Bellin Hospital, Green Bay, WI, p. A785

LASELL, Jon, Chief Executive Officer, Red River Hospital, Llc, Wichita Falls, TX, p. A725

LASHBROOK, Amy, Chief Financial Officer, Community Hospital Of Bremen, Bremen, IN, p. A225

LASHER, Karen, Chief Nursing Officer, Vanderbilt Stallworth Rehabilitation Hospital, Nashville, TN, p. A647

LASHKARI, Haady, Chief Administrative Officer, Ojai Valley Community Hospital, Ojai, CA, p. A82

LASKOWSKI, Rose, R.N., Director, Caro Center, Caro, MI, p. A350

LASKY JR, JohnVice President, Chief Human Resources Officer, Temple University Hospital, Philadelphia, PA, p. A602

LASOTA, John, Assistant Finance Officer, Clement J. Zablocki Veterans Affairs Medical Center, Milwaukee, WI, p. A791

LATEEF, Omar, D.O., Chief Executive Officer, Rush University Medical Center, Chicago, IL, p. A200

LATER, Elizabeth, R.N., Chief Nursing Officer, Ogden Regional Medical Center, Ogden, UT, p. A730

LATIBEAUDIERE, Jorge, Chief Financial Officer, Lea Regional Medical Center, Hobbs, NM, p. A470

LATIMER, Kevin, Chief Executive Officer, Childress Regional Medical Center, Childress, TX, p. A663

LATIMER, Timothy, Chief Financial Officer, University Of Kansas Health System Great Bend Campus, Great Bend, KS, p. A265

LATIOLAIS, Ryan, Director Information Systems, Our Lady Of Lourdes Regional Medical Center, Lafayette, LA, p. A306

LATNEY, Cynthia, Chief Nursing Officer, Penrose-St. Francis Health Services, Colorado Springs, CO, p. A109

LATO, Barb, Chief Nursing Officer, Aspirus Medford Hospital & Clinics, Inc., Medford, WI, p. A789

LATTANZI, Katie, Chief Operating Officer, St. David's Round Rock Medical Center, Round Rock, TX, p. A710

LATTERNER, Renee, Director Human Resources, Adventhealth Lake Wales, Lake Wales, FL, p. A143

LATTO, Janet, Chief Nursing Officer and Disaster Officer, Pacifica Hospital Of The Valley, Sun Valley, CA, p. A100

LATUCHIE, Richard, Chief Information Officer, Monument Health Spearfish Hospital, Spearfish, SD, p. A632

Vice President Business Development, Monument Health Rapid City Hospital, Rapid City, SD, p. A630

LATULIPPE, Steve, President Medical Staff, East Liverpool City Hospital, East Liverpool, OH, p. A539

LAU, James, M.D., Area Medical Director, Kaiser Permanente Panorama City Medical Center, Panorama City, CA, p. A84

LAUBENTHAL, Sherrie, R.N., Chief Nursing Officer, Clarinda Regional Health Center, Clarinda, IA, p. A246

LAUDER, Lauren, Chief Executive Officer, Guidance Center, Flagstaff, AZ, p. A31

LAUDON, Larry A., Administrator, Community Behavioral Health Hospital - Bemidji, Bemidji, MN, p. A372

LAUE, Edward, M.D., Chief Medical Officer, Texas Health Huguley Hospital Fort Worth South, Burleson, TX, p. A662

LAUE, Jerry, Administrator, Ascension St. Vincent Clay Hospital, Brazil, IN, p. A224

LAUER, Bill, Chief Information Officer, Morris County Hospital, Council Grove, KS, p. A263

LAUF, Michael K., President and Chief Executive Officer, Cap. Cod Hospital, Hyannis, MA, p. A340

LAUFFER, Daniel, FACHE, President and Chief Executive Officer, Saint Francis Hospital, Charleston, WV, p. A771
FACHE, President and Chief Executive Officer, Thomas Memorial Hospital, South Charleston, WV, p. A777

LAUFLE, Chuck, Director of Information Services, San Luis Valley Health, Alamosa, CO, p. A107

LAUGHLIN, Jennifer, Chief Information Officer, Watertown Regional Medical Center, Watertown, WI, p. A798

LAUGHLIN, Paige, Chief Operating Officer, Regional Medical Center Bayonet Point, Hudson, FL, p. A140

LAUGHLIN, Thomas, Chief Executive Officer, Wesley Rehabilitation Hospital, Wichita, KS, p. A279

LAUGHLIN, Warren, Vice President Human Resources, Longmont United Hospital, Longmont, CO, p. A116

LAUKAITIS, Fran, FACHE, R.N., President, Methodist Charlton Medical Center, Dallas, TX, p. A669

LAUNIUS, Billie, Director Business Finance, Dallas County Medical Center, Fordyce, AR, p. A45

LAUREANO, Prudencio A., Chief Executive Officer, Hospital Universitario Dr. Ramon Ruiz Arnau, Bayamon, PR, p. A806

LAURENTS, W, CPA, Chief Financial Officer, Madison Parish Hospital, Tallulah, LA, p. A316

LAURETANO, Arthur, M.D., Chief Medical Officer, Lowell General Hospital, Lowell, MA, p. A341

LAURETO, Rose Ann, Chief Information Officer, Promedica Fostoria Community Hospital, Fostoria, OH, p. A540
Corporate Vice President Information Resources, Promedica Bay Park Hospital, Oregon, OH, p. A547

LAURIDSEN, Amy, Director Human Resources, Northern Colorado Rehabilitation Hospital, Johnstown, CO, p. A114

LAURIHA, Fran, Chief Nursing Officer, Pomerene Hospital, Millersburg, OH, p. A545

LAURIN, George, Interim Director Human Resources, Crisp Regional Hospital, Cordele, GA, p. A170

LAUTER, Keith, Chief Financial Officer, Franciscan Health Carmel, Carmel, IN, p. A225
Regional Chief Financial Officer, Franciscan Health Indianapolis, Indianapolis, IN, p. A232
Vice President Finance, Franciscan Health Crawfordsville, Crawfordsville, IN, p. A226

LAUTEREN, Mark, Chief Information Officer, Usa Health University Hospital, Mobile, AL, p. A22

LAUTNER, Marty, Vice President Finance and Chief Financial Officer, Cardinal Hill Rehabilitation Hospital, Lexington, KY, p. A286

LAUVE, Lisa, R.N., Regional Chief Nursing Executive and Chief Operating Officer, Christus St. Frances Cabrini Hospital, Alexandria, LA, p. A295

LAUVER, David, M.D., Chief Division Hospital Based Care, Central Maine Medical Center, Lewiston, ME, p. A321

LAVELLE, John, M.D., Chief Medical Officer, Parkview Hospital, Wheeler, TX, p. A725

LAVENDER, John, Chief Information Officer, Lincoln County Health System, Fayetteville, TN, p. A638

LAVERTY, Edward, Chief Medical Officer, Upper Connecticut Valley Hospital, Colebrook, NH, p. A448

LAVERY FRASCA, Denise Anne, MSN, R.N., Vice President Patient Care Services and Chief Nursing Officer, Temple University Hospital - Jeanes Campus, Philadelphia, PA, p. A602

LAVIGNETTE, Brooke, Director of Nursing, Sycamore Springs, Lafayette, IN, p. A234

LAVIOLETTE, Judy, M.D., Chief Medical Officer, Texas Health Harris Methodist Hospital Azle, Azle, TX, p. A657
M.D., Chief Medical Officer, Texas Health Harris Methodist Hospital Cleburne, Cleburne, TX, p. A663

LAVOIE, Brad, Chief Medical Officer, Coastal Harbor Treatment Center, Savannah, GA, p. A180

LAW, Charles, Ph.D., Chief Operating Officer, Catawba Hospital, Catawba, VA, p. A739

LAW, Johnny, Area Information Officer, Kaiser Permanente Oakland Medical Center, Oakland, CA, p. A82

LAWHORN, David, M.D., Chief Medical Officer, Shoshone Medical Center, Kellogg, ID, p. A191

LAWHORN, Renee, Director Medical Records, Ut Health Carthage, Carthage, TX, p. A663

LAWHORNE, Thomas, Chief Financial Officer, Regional Medical Center Bayonet Point, Hudson, FL, p. A140

LAWLER, Anne, Director Human Resources, North Mississipp. Medical Center-Hamilton, Hamilton, AL, p. A20

LAWLER, Kay, Business Office Manager, North Mississipp. Medical Center-West Point, West Point, MS, p. A401

LAWLER, Patrick, Chief Executive Officer, Youth Villages Inner Harbour Campus, Douglasville, GA, p. A171

LAWLESS, JoBeth, Chief Nursing Officer, Nursing Services and Director Emergency Management Services, Lucas County Health Center, Chariton, IA, p. A245

LAWLESS, Rosalie, Director Human Resources, Fairlawn Rehabilitation Hospital, Worcester, MA, p. A346

LAWONN, Kenneth, Senior Vice President and Chief Information Officer, Chi Health Mercy Corning, Corning, IA, p. A246
Senior Vice President and Chief Information Officer, Chi Health Schuyler, Schuyler, NE, p. A439
Senior Vice President and Chief Information Officer, Sharp Grossmont Hospital, La Mesa, CA, p. A70
Senior Vice President and Chief Information Officer, Sharp Memorial Hospital, San Diego, CA, p. A92
Senior Vice President Information Systems, Sharp Mesa Vista Hospital, San Diego, CA, p. A92

LAWRASON, Jock, M.D., Chief Medical Officer, Nantucket Cottage Hospital, Nantucket, MA, p. A342

LAWRENCE, Brian, Chief Executive Officer, Coffeyville Regional Medical Center, Coffeyville, KS, p. A262

LAWRENCE, Dana, Controller, Bolivar General Hospital, Bolivar, TN, p. A634

LAWRENCE, Glenda, R.N., Chief Nursing Officer, Red River Hospital, Llc, Wichita Falls, TX, p. A725

LAWRENCE, Jonathan I., President and Chief Executive Officer, Arnot Ogden Medical Center, Elmira, NY, p. A483

LAWRENCE, Kelsey, Manager Information Technology, Union County General Hospital, Clayton, NM, p. A468

LAWRENCE, Mark, Director Information Systems, Saint Francis Hospital-Bartlett, Bartlett, TN, p. A634

LAWRENCE, Michael, Chief Financial Officer, Ingalls Memorial Hospital, Harvey, IL, p. A207

LAWRENCE, Paige, Assistant Administrator, University Of Mississipp. Medical Center Holmes County, Lexington, MS, p. A396

LAWRENCE, Stephanie, Chief Financial Officer, Kentfield Hospital, Kentfield, CA, p. A69
Chief Financial Officer, Vibra Specialty Hospital Of Portland, Portland, OR, p. A580

LAWRENCE, Tiffany, Vice President of Finance, Sanford Medical Center Fargo, Fargo, ND, p. A523

LAWRENSON, Victoria, Chief Operating Officer, Bullock County Hospital, Union Springs, AL, p. A25
Chief Operating Officer, Crenshaw Community Hospital, Luverne, AL, p. A21

LAWS, Stephanie, Vice President, Administrator, Union Hospital Clinton, Clinton, IN, p. A225

LAWSON, Alvin R., JD, Chief Executive Officer, Encompass Health Rehabilitation Hospital Of Parkersburg, Parkersburg, WV, p. A775

LAWSON, Andy, Chief Human Resource Officer, Lds Hospital, Salt Lake City, UT, p. A732

LAWSON, Beth, Chief Nursing Officer, Union Medical Center, Union, SC, p. A625

LAWSON, Chad, Chief Information Officer, St. Anthony Regional Hospital, Carroll, IA, p. A244

LAWSON, Crystal, Director Human Resource, Specialists Hospital Shreveport, Shreveport, LA, p. A314

LAWSON, David, Senior Vice President Human Resources, St. Clare Hospital, Lakewood, WA, p. A760

LAWSON, Eric, Chief Executive Officer, North Florida Regional Medical Center, Gainesville, FL, p. A138

LAWSON, Jessica, Director of Nursing, Greenwood Regional Rehabilitation Hospital, Greenwood, SC, p. A621

LAWSON, Judy, Director Information Services, Norton Community Hospital, Norton, VA, p. A748

LAWSON, Kelly, Chief Nursing Officer, Williamsburg Regional Hospital, Kingstree, SC, p. A622

LAWSON, Linda, Chief Nursing Officer, The Hospitals Of Providence Transmountain Campus, El Paso, TX, p. A676

LAWSON, Michael, President and Chief Operating Officer, Ohiohealth Grant Medical Center, Columbus, OH, p. A536

LAWSON, Penny, Human Resource Director, Quillen Rehabilitation Hospital, Johnson City, TN, p. A640

LAWSON, Ralph, Executive Vice President and Chief Financial Officer, Baptist Health South Florida, Baptist Hospital Of Miami, Miami, FL, p. A146

LAWSON, Sandra, Interim Director Fiscal Services, Shriners Hospitals For Children-St. Louis, Saint Louis, MO, p. A416

LAWTON, Geoff, Vice President Operations, Littleton Adventist Hospital, Littleton, CO, p. A116

LAY, A, M.D., JrChief Medical Officer, Jasper General Hospital, Bay Springs, MS, p. A389

LAYMAN, Benjamin, President, Ssm Health St. Mary's Hospital Janesville, Janesville, WI, p. A786

LAYNE, Kristine, R.N., Chief Nursing Officer, Riverwood Healthcare Center, Aitkin, MN, p. A371

LAYUGAN, Melvin, Director Human Resources, Horizon Specialty Hospital, Las Vegas, NV, p. A443

LAZARUS, David, M.D., Medical Director Clinical Affairs, Newton Medical Center, Newton, NJ, p. A460

LAZENBY, John, M.D., Chief Medical Officer, Memorial Hospital Jacksonville, Jacksonville, FL, p. A141

LAZO, Nelson, Chief Executive Officer, Bethesda Hospital East, Boynton Beach, FL, p. A132

LAZO, Wendy, President, St. Luke's Hospital - Miners Campus, Coaldale, PA, p. A587

LAZROFF, Gary, Vice President Human Resources, Uh St. John Medical Center, Westlake, OH, p. A553

LAZZARO, Frank Chief Human Resources Officer, Phelp. Health, Rolla, MO, p. A414

LE, Emily, Director Information Technology and Services, Woman's Hospital Of Texas, Houston, TX, p. A689

LE, Jennifer, Chief Financial Officer, Southern Hills Hospital And Medical Center, Las Vegas, NV, p. A444

LE, Tuan, Chief Executive Officer, Continuecare Hospital At Baptist Health Corbin, Corbin, KY, p. A282

LEA, Hampton P. S., Chief Executive Officer, Eastern Louisiana Mental Health System, Jackson, LA, p. A303

LEA, Katie, Chief Nursing Officer, Saline Memorial Hospital, Benton, AR, p. A42

LEA, Lindsay, Chief Nursing Officer, Upper Connecticut Valley Hospital, Colebrook, NH, p. A448

LEA, Rich, Vice President Operations, Euclid Hospital, Euclid, OH, p. A540

LEACH, Craig, President and Chief Executive Officer, Torrance Memorial Medical Center, Torrance, CA, p. A101

LEACH, Dana, Director Human Resources, Alliancehealth Midwest, Midwest City, OK, p. A562

LEACH, Deonca, Director, Human Resources, Atrium Health's Carolinas Rehabilitation, Charlotte, NC, p. A507

LEACH, Ryan, Chief Information Officer, Hshs St. John's Hospital, Springfield, IL, p. A220

LEACH, Todd, Vice President and Chief Information Officer, University Of Texas Medical Branch, Galveston, TX, p. A680

LEACH, Travis, President, Saint Alphonsus Medical Center - Nampa, Nampa, ID, p. A192

LEADBETTER, Dan, Information Technology Systems Site Lead, Chi Lakewood Health, Baudette, MN, p. A372

LEADBETTER JR, RaymondRevenue Cycle Consultant, Appling Healthcare System, Baxley, GA, p. A167

LEAHY, Mary, M.D., Chief Executive Officer, Bon Secours Community Hospital, Port Jervis, NY, p. A495
M.D., Chief Executive Officer, Good Samaritan Regional Medical Center, Suffern, NY, p. A499
M.D., Chief Executive Officer, St. Anthony Community Hospital, Warwick, NY, p. A501
Regional Vice President, Chief Human Resources Officer, St. Josep. Hospital Orange, Orange, CA, p. A83

LEAHY, Rosanne, Vice President Nursing Services, Carolinaeast Health System, New Bern, NC, p. A515

LEAKE, Neta, Administrative Assistant Human Resources, West Feliciana Hospital, Saint Francisville, LA, p. A313

LEAKE, Sandy, MSN, R.N., Associate Director, Nursing and Patient Care Services, Atlanta Veterans Affairs Medical Center, Decatur, GA, p. A170

LEAKEY, Kim, R.N., Chief Nursing Officer, Lafayette Regional Health Center, Lexington, MO, p. A411

LEAL, Carlos, Director Information Technology, Valley Regional Medical Center, Brownsville, TX, p. A661

LEAL, Joseph, M.D., JrChief of Staff, Glendive Medical Center, Glendive, MT, p. A424

LEAMON, Jim, Chief Financial Officer, Jfk Medical Center, Atlantis, FL, p. A131

LEAR, Jarad, Interim Director of Information Services, Gibson General Hospital, Princeton, IN, p. A239

LEAR, Richard, Director Information Systems, St. David's Medical Center, Austin, TX, p. A656
Director Information Systems, St. David's South Austin Medical Center, Austin, TX, p. A656

LEARSON, Jerome, Manager Information Technology and Chief Security Officer, Palo Verde Hospital, Blythe, CA, p. A58

LEARY, Edward B., Chief Executive Officer, Vibra Hospital Of Southeastern Massachusetts, New Bedford, MA, p. A342
Interim Chief Executive Officer, Vibra Hospital Of Western Massachusetts, Springfield, MA, p. A345

LEASE, Faye, Chief Nursing Officer, Reeves County Hospital District, Pecos, TX, p. A705

LEASE-HOMEYER, Cheryl, Lead Information Technology Business Partner, Mercy Hospital Carthage, Carthage, MO, p. A404

LEASURE, Sandie, Senior Vice President Human Resources, O'Bleness Memorial Hospital, Athens, OH, p. A528

LEAVITT, Jared, Chief Operating Officer, Kern Medical, Bakersfield, CA, p. A57

LEBEAU, Michael, President, Sanford Medical Center Bismarck, Bismarck, ND, p. A521

LEBEAU, Michelle, President and Chief Operating Officer, The University Of Vermont Health Network-Champlain Valley Physicians Hospital, Plattsburgh, NY, p. A495
President, The University Of Vermont Health Network - Alice Hyde Medical Center, Malone, NY, p. A487

LEBER, Corey, R.N., Associate Vice President Operations, Promedica Memorial Hospital, Fremont, OH, p. A540

LEBER, Ian, M.D., Chief Medical Officer, Hackensack Meridian Health Bayshore Community Hospital, Holmdel, NJ, p. A456

LEBLANC, Fernis, Chief Operating Officer, Ochsner St. Anne General Hospital, Raceland, LA, p. A313

LEBLANC, Karen, Director, Applications, Samaritan Hospital - Main Campus, Troy, NY, p. A500

LEBOWITZ, Howard, M.D., Chief Medical Officer, Specialty Hospital Of Central Jersey, Lakewood, NJ, p. A457

LEBRON, Juan, M.D., Medical Director, Sea Pines Rehabilitation Hospital, Melbourne, FL, p. A145

LEBRON, Sonia, Human Resources Specialist, Industrial Hospital, San Juan, PR, p. A811

LECATES, William, M.D., Vice President Medical Affairs and Medical Director, Bassett Medical Center, Cooperstown, NY, p. A481

LECATES, William W., M.D., President, Bassett Medical Center, Cooperstown, NY, p. A481

LECHICH, Anthony, M.D., Chief Medical Officer, Terence Cardinal Cooke Health Care Center, New York, NY, p. A492

LECHNER, David, M.D., Chief Medical Officer and Vice President Innovation, Community Medical Center, Missoula, MT, p. A426

LECHUGA, Mario, Director Human Resources, Turquoise Lodge Hospital, Albuquerque, NM, p. A468

LECKELT, Mitchell D., Chief Executive Officer, Up Health System-Bell, Ishpeming, MI, p. A358

LECKER, Marijo, Vice President, Sentara Martha Jefferson Hospital, Charlottesville, VA, p. A739

LECKEY, Scott, Chief Financial Officer, Banner Desert Medical Center, Mesa, AZ, p. A33

LEDBETTER, Joy, Regional Chief Human Resources Officer, Unitypoint Health - Peoria, Peoria, IL, p. A217

LEDBETTER, Thomas, M.D., Chief Medical Officer, Baylor Scott & White Medical Center-Waxahachie, Waxahachie, TX, p. A724

LEDDEN, Edwin, Assistant Administrator and Director Human Resources, Henry County Medical Center, Paris, TN, p. A648

LEDELL, Michelle, Director Human Resource, Fairview Ridges Hospital, Burnsville, MN, p. A373
Director Human Resources, Fairview Southdale Hospital, Edina, MN, p. A376

LEDERER, Jane, R.N., Ed.D., Vice President and Chief Nursing Officer, Kingsbrook Jewish Medical Center, Brooklyn, NY, p. A478

LEDERMAN, Joel, Director Information Systems, Promedica Coldwater Regional Hospital, Coldwater, MI, p. A351

LEDERMAN, Mark, Chief Information Officer, Interfaith Medical Center, Brooklyn, NY, p. A478

LEDFORD, Keith, M.D., Chief of Staff, Scenic Mountain Medical Center, Big Spring, TX, p. A659

LEE, Brett D., President, Texas Health Frisco, Frisco, TX, p. A680

LEE, Byong, Chief Information Officer, Limestone Medical Center, Groesbeck, TX, p. A682

LEE, Cheryl, R.N., MSN, Vice President of Patient Care Services and Chief Nursing Officer, University Of Maryland Rehabilitation & Orthopaedic Institute, Baltimore, MD, p. A327
Human Resources Director, North Alabama Medical Center, Florence, AL, p. A18

LEE, Clare, Chief Operating Officer, Mercy General Hospital, Sacramento, CA, p. A89

LEE, Darren W., President and Chief Executive Officer, St. John's Pleasant Valley Hospital, Camarillo, CA, p. A59
President and Chief Executive Officer, St. John's Regional Medical Center, Oxnard, CA, p. A83

LEE, David, Chief Executive Officer, Otto Kaiser Memorial Hospital, Kenedy, TX, p. A692

LEE, Dennis, Vice President and Chief Information Officer, Cabell Huntington Hospital, Huntington, WV, p. A772

LEE, Eric A., President and Chief Executive Officer, Jennie Stuart Medical Center, Hopkinsville, KY, p. A285

LEE, James, M.D., Chief of Staff, Hamilton General Hospital, Hamilton, TX, p. A682

LEE, Jenny, Human Resources Generalist, Essentia Health-Graceville, Graceville, MN, p. A377

LEE, John, M.D., Chief of Staff, Lackey Memorial Hospital, Forest, MS, p. A392

LEE, John E., Interim Chief Executive Officer, Alaska Psychiatric Institute, Anchorage, AK, p. A27

LEE, Karen, Director Human Resources, Gallup Indian Medical Center, Gallup. NM, p. A469

LEE, Kenneth, Division Chair, Human Resource Advisory, Mayo Clinic Health System In Eau Claire, Eau Claire, WI, p. A783

LEE, Kim, Chief Operating Officer, Faith Community Hospital, Jacksboro, TX, p. A691

LEE, Kristina, Director Human Resources, Chi St. Josep. Health Grimes Hospital, Navasota, TX, p. A703

LEE, Kwon, Chief Information Officer, Pennsylvania Hospital, Philadelphia, PA, p. A601

LEE, Loretta, Acting Chief Nursing Officer, Baylor St. Luke's Medical Center, Houston, TX, p. A684

LEE, Michael, Chief Human Resources Officer, Adirondack Health, Saranac Lake, NY, p. A497
President, Weeks Medical Center, Lancaster, NH, p. A449

LEE, Mihi, Chief Financial Officer, Mission Community Hospital, Panorama City, CA, p. A84

LEE, Mike, R.N., Chief Nursing Officer, Matagorda Regional Medical Center, Bay City, TX, p. A657

LEE, Nancy, R.N., MSN, Vice President Patient Care Services and Chief Nursing Officer, Stanford Health Care, Palo Alto, CA, p. A84

LEE, Nathan, Chief Executive Officer, Mary Breckinridge Arh Hospital, Hyden, KY, p. A285

LEE, Randy, M.D., Senior Vice President Medical Affairs, Community Hospital South, Indianapolis, IN, p. A231

LEE, Reginald, Chief Executive Officer, Vibra Hospital Of Southeastern Michigan, Llc, Lincoln Park, MI, p. A360

LEE, Ryan, Chief Operating Officer, West Boca Medical Center, Boca Raton, FL, p. A132

LEE, S., M.D., Chief of Staff, Vibra Hospital Of Sacramento, Folsom, CA, p. A64

LEE, Sharon, Chief Executive Officer, Bullock County Hospital, Union Springs, AL, p. A25

LEE, Stacey, CPA, JD, Chief Executive Officer, Johnson Memorial Health Services, Dawson, MN, p. A375

LEE, Terri, Chief Information Officer, Higgins General Hospital, Bremen, GA, p. A167
Chief Information Officer, Tanner Medical Center-Villa Rica, Villa Rica, GA, p. A182

LEE, Thomas, Chief Financial Officer, Medicine Lodge Memorial Hospital, Medicine Lodge, KS, p. A271

LEE, Troy, Chief Executive Officer, Pam Rehabilitation Hospital Of Round Rock, Round Rock, TX, p. A709

LEE, W. Bryan., FACHE, Chief Executive Officer, Our Lady Of Lourdes Regional Medical Center, Lafayette, LA, p. A306

LEE, Wendy, Chief Nursing Officer, Regional Rehabilitation Hospital, Phenix City, AL, p. A23

LEE, William H., Chief Executive Officer, Evans Memorial Hospital, Claxton, GA, p. A168

LEEGSTRA, Ruurd, Chief Financial Officer, Silver Hill Hospital, New Canaan, CT, p. A124

LEEK, Dustin, Vice President of Enterprise Technology Services, Health First Holmes Regional Medical Center, Melbourne, FL, p. A145

LEEK, Lynn, Executive Vice President of Finance and Chief Financial Officer, Wabash General Hospital, Mount Carmel, IL, p. A213

LEEKA, Andrew B., President and Chief Executive Officer, Good Samaritan Hospital, Los Angeles, CA, p. A74

LEEMING, Rosemary, M.D., Chief Medical Officer, Uh Regional Hospitals, Cleveland, OH, p. A535

LEEPER, Doug, Chief Information Officer, Kaweah Delta Medical Center, Visalia, CA, p. A104

LEEPER, Kevin, Chief Executive Officer, Morris County Hospital, Council Grove, KS, p. A263

LEESMAN, Keenan, Director Information Systems, Abraham Lincoln Memorial Hospital, Lincoln, IL, p. A210

LEFEVRE, Denise, Chief Information Officer, Oroville Hospital, Oroville, CA, p. A83

LEFF, Marc, Vice President Human Resources, St. John's Riverside Hospital, Yonkers, NY, p. A503

LEFFLER, Stephen, M.D., President and Chief Operating Officer, University Of Vermont Medical Center, Burlington, VT, p. A735

LEFKOW, Frances, Director Human Resources, La Rabida Children's Hospital, Chicago, IL, p. A199

LEFTERIS, Chad, Chief Operating Officer, Uci Medical Center, Orange, CA, p. A83

LEFTERIS, Chad T., Chief Executive Officer, Uci Medical Center, Orange, CA, p. A83

LEFTON, Ray, Chief Financial Officer, Temple University Hospital - Jeanes Campus, Philadelphia, PA, p. A602

LEFTON, Ruth, Chief Operating Officer, Einstein Medical Center Philadelphia, Philadelphia, PA, p. A600

LEFTWICH, Hal W., FACHE, Chief Executive Officer, Big South Fork Medical Center, Oneida, TN, p. A648

LEGASPI, Johnson, Director Information Systems, Alhambra Hospital Medical Center, Alhambra, CA, p. A55

LEGAY, Jeff, Chief Financial Officer, Chatham Hospital, Siler City, NC, p. A518

LEGE, Christopher, Chief Medical Officer, Touro Infirmary, New Orleans, LA, p. A311

LEGEND, Rachel, Chief Executive Officer, Arbour-Fuller Hospital, Attleboro, MA, p. A334

LEGENDRE, Amy, Chief Financial Officer, Claiborne Memorial Medical Center, Homer, LA, p. A303

LEGER, Bernard, Chief Executive Officer, Detar Healthcare System, Victoria, TX, p. A723

LEGER, Lynn, Director Information Systems, Ridgeview Institute, Smyrna, GA, p. A180

LEGG, Alyce, Vice President Human Resources, Uh Samaritan Medical Center, Ashland, OH, p. A528

LEGG, Debra, Associate Director Patient Care Services and Nurse Executive, Beckley Veterans Affairs Medical Center, Beckley, WV, p. A770

LEGGETT, Sandra, Chief Operating Officer, Atchison Hospital, Atchison, KS, p. A261

LEGGETT III, G Raymond., President and Chief Executive Officer, Carolinaeast Health System, New Bern, NC, p. A515

LEGLEITER, Brenda, Director Quality and Human Resources, Rush County Memorial Hospital, La Crosse, KS, p. A268

LEGRAND, Kila, Chief Nursing Officer, Sanford Aberdeen Medical Center, Aberdeen, SD, p. A626

LEHMAN, Andy, Senior Vice President Technology & Analytics, Greene Memorial Hospital, Xenia, OH, p. A553

Senior Vice President Technology and Analytics, Fort Hamilton Hospital, Hamilton, OH, p. A542

Senior Vice President Technology and Analytics, Grandview Medical Center, Dayton, OH, p. A538

Senior Vice President Technology and Analytics, Kettering Medical Center, Kettering, OH, p. A542

Senior Vice President Technology and Analytics, Sycamore Medical Center, Miamisburg, OH, p. A545

Vice President Information Systems, Soin Medical Center, Beavercreek, OH, p. A529

LEHMAN, Brennan, Chief Information Officer, Mosaic Life Care At St. Josep. - Medical Center, Saint Joseph, MO, p. A415

LEHMAN, James, M.D., Vice President Medical Affairs, Mercyone Oelwein Medical Center, Oelwein, IA, p. A255

LEHMAN, Ronda, PharmD, Chief Operating Officer, SRPS, Mercy Health - St. Rita's Medical Center, Lima, OH, p. A543

LEHMAN, Sandi, Chief Financial Officer, Humboldt General Hospital, Winnemucca, NV, p. A447

LEHMAN, Travis, M.D., Medical Director, Wilbarger General Hospital, Vernon, TX, p. A723

LEHN, Toby, Director of Nurses, Concho County Hospital, Eden, TX, p. A673

LEHNHOF-WATTS, Laurie, Administrator and Chief Nursing Officer, Ut Health East Texas Rehabilitation Hospital, Tyler, TX, p. A722

Administrator and Chief Nursing Officer, Ut Health Specialty Hospital, Tyler, TX, p. A722

LEIBMAN, Maurice, M.D., Chief Medical Officer, Memorial Hermann Greater Heights Hospital, Houston, TX, p. A687

LEICHMAN, Ann Marie, MSN, R.N., Senior Vice President Patient Care Services and Chief Nursing Officer, Valley Hospital, Ridgewood, NJ, p. A462

LEIDY, R., Chief Financial Officer, Deborah Heart And Lung Center, Browns Mills, NJ, p. A453

LEIF, Sue, R.N., Director Human Resources, Annie Jeffrey Memorial County Health Center, Osceola, NE, p. A438

LEIGHTON, Martha, Senior Vice President and Chief Nursing Officer, Elliot Hospital, Manchester, NH, p. A450

LEIGHTON, Richard, Financial Application Analyst, Unity Medical & Surgical Hospital, Mishawaka, IN, p. A236

LEINEN, Rick, Chief Financial Officer, Montgomery County Memorial Hospital, Red Oak, IA, p. A256

LEININGER, Bethany, Manager Human Resource, Hillcrest Hospital Cushing, Cushing, OK, p. A558

LEISHER, Karla, Business Office Manager, Beaver County Memorial Hospital, Beaver, OK, p. A556

LEISHER JR, GeorgeChief Human Resources Officer, Antelop. Valley Hospital, Lancaster, CA, p. A71

Vice President Human Resources, Hollywood Presbyterian Medical Center, Los Angeles, CA, p. A74

LEISING, Elizabeth, Chief Nursing Officer and Vice President Patient Services, Margaret Mary Health, Batesville, IN, p. A223

LEIST, Frank, Human Resources Manager, Piedmont Mountainside Hospital, Jasper, GA, p. A174

LEIST, Vincent, President and Chief Executive Officer, North Arkansas Regional Medical Center, Harrison, AR, p. A46

LEITERMAN, Gretchen, Chief Operating Officer, Ssm Health Saint Louis University Hospital, Saint Louis, MO, p. A417

LEITNER, Mark, FACHE, Administrator, Ut Health Henderson, Henderson, TX, p. A683

FACHE, Chief Executive Officer, Ut Health Carthage, Carthage, TX, p. A663

LEJA, Loretta, M.D., Chief of Staff, Mackinac Straits Health System, Inc., Saint Ignace, MI, p. A366

LEJSEK, Shari, Administrator, Patients' Hospital Of Redding, Redding, CA, p. A87

LELAND, Joni, Director Human Resources, Gonzales Healthcare Systems, Gonzales, TX, p. A681

LEM, Alan, Vice President Finance, Fairview Ridges Hospital, Burnsville, MN, p. A373

Vice President Finance, Fairview Southdale Hospital, Edina, MN, p. A376

LEMAIRE, Joseph, Executive Vice President Finance and Partner Company Operations, Hackensack Meridian Health Bayshore Community Hospital, Holmdel, NJ, p. A456

Executive Vice President Finance, Hackensack Meridian Health Riverview Medical Center, Red Bank, NJ, p. A462

Executive Vice President, Hackensack Meridian Health Southern Ocean Medical Center, Manahawkin, NJ, p. A458

LEMANSKI, Dennis, D.O., Senior Vice President Medical Affairs and Medical Education/CMO, Henry Ford Wyandotte Hospital, Wyandotte, MI, p. A370

LEMASTERS, Ryan, Chief Operating Officer, Timpanogos Regional Hospital, Orem, UT, p. A730

LEMAY, Catherine, Vice President Finance, Millinocket Regional Hospital, Millinocket, ME, p. A321

LEMAY, Robert, R.N., Chief Nursing Officer, The Physicians Centre Hospital, Bryan, TX, p. A661

LEMBCKE, Brad, M.D., Vice President Medical Staff Affairs, Baylor University Medical Center, Dallas, TX, p. A668

LEMEL, Mark, Chief of Staff, Transylvania Regional Hospital, Brevard, NC, p. A505

LEMIEUX, Harry, Chief Information Officer, Harrington Hospital, Southbridge, MA, p. A344

LEMKE, Lynn, Chief Executive Officer, Perimeter Behavioral Hospital Of Springfield, Springfield, MO, p. A419

LEMKE, Michelle, Administrator Human Resources and Support Services, Ridgecrest Regional Hospital, Ridgecrest, CA, p. A88

LEMLE, Trent, Chief Financial Officer, Fayette County Memorial Hospital, Washington Court House, OH, p. A552

LEMMER, Donn, Chief Financial Officer and Chief Operating Officer, Munson Healthcare Manistee Hospital, Manistee, MI, p. A361

LEMMERMAN, Deborah, Chief People Officer, Hebrew Rehabilitation Center, Roslindale, MA, p. A344

LEMMON, Don, Chief Executive Officer, Providence Seaside Hospital, Seaside, OR, p. A581

LEMMONS, Joe, D.O., Chief of Staff, Lehigh Regional Medical Center, Lehigh Acres, FL, p. A144

LEMOINE, Kirk, Chief Executive Officer, Bienville Medical Center, Arcadia, LA, p. A296

LEMON, Marc, Chief Executive Officer, Kindred Hospital-Aurora, Aurora, CO, p. A107

LEMON, Rita, Director Human Resources, Avera Queen Of Peace Hospital, Mitchell, SD, p. A629

LEMON, Thomas R., Chief Executive Officer, Munson Healthcare Otsego Memorial Hospital, Gaylord, MI, p. A355

LEMONTE, David, Chief Executive Officer, Aventura Hospital And Medical Center, Aventura, FL, p. A131

Vice President and Chief Operating Officer, Christus Spohn Hospital Kleberg, Kingsville, TX, p. A693

LENA, Ela, Administrator and Vice President Operations, Bethesda Hospital East, Boynton Beach, FL, p. A132

LENAHAN, Kevin, Director Corporate Accounting, Budgets, Grants and Reimbursements, Newton Medical Center, Newton, NJ, p. A460

Vice President Finance and Chief Financial Officer, Overlook Medical Center, Summit, NJ, p. A463

LENAMOND, Kevin, Information Management Service Line Executive, Michael E. Debakey Veterans Affairs Medical Center, Houston, TX, p. A687

LENANE, Naomi, Chief Information Officer, Dana-Farber Cancer Institute, Boston, MA, p. A335

LENARZ, Sandy, Chief Nursing Officer, Grand Itasca Clinic And Hospital, Grand Rapids, MN, p. A377

LENCHUS, Joshua, Chief Medical Officer, Broward Health Medical Center, Fort Lauderdale, FL, p. A137

LENDARIS, Antonia, Chief Nursing Operations Officer, Chinese Hospital, San Francisco, CA, p. A93

LENDARIS, Nia, MS, R.N., Regional Vice President Patient Care, Adventist Health St. Helena, Saint Helena, CA, p. A90

LENFANT, Rodney, Chief Financial Officer, Oakbend Medical Center, Richmond, TX, p. A708

LENGFELDER, Valerie, M.D., Chief of Staff, Powell Valley Healthcare, Powell, WY, p. A803

LENIOR, Frank, Vice President Human Resources, St. Dominic-Jackson Memorial Hospital, Jackson, MS, p. A395

LENKO, Paul, Section Head Information Technology, Mayo Clinic Hospital, Phoenix, AZ, p. A36

LENNARTZ, Randal P., CPA, President and Chief Executive Officer, Highland District Hospital, Hillsboro, OH, p. A542

LENNON, Colin, Chief Financial Officer, Richard L. Roudebush Veterans Affairs Medical Center, Indianapolis, IN, p. A233

LENNON, Roslyn, R.N., MS, Chief Nursing Officer, West Suburban Medical Center, Oak Park, IL, p. A215

LENTENBRINK, Laura, Vice President, Human Resources, Ascension Borgess Hospital, Kalamazoo, MI, p. A359

LENTZ, Darrell, President, Aspirus Wausau Hospital, Inc., Wausau, WI, p. A798

LENZ, Jan, Chief Nursing Officer, Athens-Limestone Hospital, Athens, AL, p. A14

LEO, Elizabeth, Chief Human Resources Officer, Moses Taylor Hospital, Scranton, PA, p. A607

LEON, Daniel, Chief Financial Officer, Sherman Oaks Hospital, Sherman Oaks, CA, p. A98

LEON, Edwin, Chief Executive Officer, Pamp. Regional Medical Center, Pampa, TX, p. A704

LEON, Luis, Chief Operating Officer, Desert Valley Hospital, Victorville, CA, p. A104

LEONARD, Barry Vice President of Finance, Encompass Health Rehabilitation Hospital Of Braintree, Braintree, MA, p. A336

LEONARD, Beckie, R.N., Chief Nursing Officer, Foundation Surgical Hospital Of San Antonio, San Antonio, TX, p. A711

LEONARD, Bruce, M.D., Medical Director and Chief of Psychiatry, Colorado Mental Health Institute At Fort Logan, Denver, CO, p. A110

LEONARD, Donavan, Chief Financial Officer, Baptist Memorial Hospital-Booneville, Booneville, MS, p. A390

LEONARD, Edward, Executive Vice President and Chief Operating Officer, White Plains Hospital Center, White Plains, NY, p. A502

LEONARD, George, M.D., Chief Medical Officer, Madigan Army Medical Center, Tacoma, WA, p. A767

LEONARD, James C., M.D., President and Chief Executive Officer, Carle Foundation Hospital, Urbana, IL, p. A221

LEONARD, Jayne, M.D., Family Medicine, Ashe Memorial Hospital, Jefferson, NC, p. A513

LEONARD, Julie, Chief Financial Officer, Garfield County Public Hospital District, Pomeroy, WA, p. A762

LEONARD, Kevin, Vice President, Finance, Henry Ford Allegiance Health, Jackson, MI, p. A359

LEONARD, Mark, Vice President Finance, Beaumont Hospital - Troy, Troy, MI, p. A368

LEONARD, Mark T., Chief Executive Officer, Dickenson Community Hospital, Clintwood, VA, p. A740

Chief Executive Officer, Norton Community Hospital, Norton, VA, p. A748

Interim Chief Executive Officer, Lonesome Pine Hospital, Big Stone Gap. VA, p. A739

Interim Chief Executive Officer, Mountain View Regional Medical Center, Norton, VA, p. A748

LEONARD, Robert, Director Information Services, Sierra Vista Regional Medical Center, San Luis Obispo, CA, p. A96

LEONARD, Steven E., President and Chief Executive Officer, Tidalhealth Peninsula, Salisbury, MD, p. A332

LEONARD, William H., President, Atrium Health University City, Charlotte, NC, p. A506

LEONDAR, Kimberly, Director Human Resources, Texas Health Harris Methodist Hospital Stephenville, Stephenville, TX, p. A717

LEONELIS, Lisa, Chief Information Officer, Veterans Affairs Salt Lake City Health Care System, Salt Lake City, UT, p. A733

LEOPARD, Erik, Manager Human Resource, Methodist Hospital For Surgery, Addison, TX, p. A651

LEOPARD, Jimmy, FACHE, Chief Executive Officer, Wagoner Community Hospital, Wagoner, OK, p. A571

LEOPOLD, Michael, Chief Operating Officer, Broward Health Coral Springs, Coral Springs, FL, p. A135

LEPAK, Jason, M.D., Medical Director, St. John Broken Arrow, Broken Arrow, OK, p. A556

M.D., Medical Director, St. John Sapulpa, Sapulpa, OK, p. A567

LEPPER, Dale, Chief Information Officer, Antelop. Valley Hospital, Lancaster, CA, p. A71

LEPPKE, Ben, Chief Information Officer, Satanta District Hospital And Long Term Care, Satanta, KS, p. A276

LEQUEUX, Veronica, Vice President Human Resources, Blake Medical Center, Bradenton, FL, p. A132

LERASH, Terrance, President and Chief Executive Officer, Scheurer Health, Pigeon, MI, p. A363

LERCH, Gail, R.N., Executive Vice President Human Resources, Straub Medical Center, Honolulu, HI, p. A185
R.N., Vice President Human Resources, Pali Momi Medical Center, Aiea, HI, p. A184
R.N., Vice President, Kapiolani Medical Center For Women & Children, Honolulu, HI, p. A184

LERCH, Shawn, Chief Executive Officer, Sauk Prairie Healthcare, Prairie Du Sac, WI, p. A794

LERMA, Robert J., MS, Chief Executive Officer, Austin Lakes Hospital, Austin, TX, p. A655

LERMAN, Andrew, Interim Chief Information Officer, Arrowhead Regional Medical Center, Colton, CA, p. A60

LERNER, Jerome, M.D., Medical Director, Sierra Tucson, Tucson, AZ, p. A40

LEROY, Michael, Senior Vice President and Chief Information Officer, Dmc - Detroit Receiving Hospital, Detroit, MI, p. A352
Senior Vice President and Chief Information Officer, Dmc Harper University Hospital, Detroit, MI, p. A353

LESCH, Jason, Chief Financial Officer, Auburn Community Hospital, Auburn, NY, p. A475

LESEMANN, Julie, Chief Operating Officer and Assistant Administrator, Cook Hospital & Care Center, Cook, MN, p. A374

LESHER, Jennifer, Chief Financial Officer, Upmc Lock Haven, Lock Haven, PA, p. A595

LESIAK, Cindy, Vice President Patient Care Services and Director of Nursing, Boone County Health Center, Albion, NE, p. A429

LESINS, Ross, Chief Information Officer, Casa Colina Hospital And Centers For Healthcare, Pomona, CA, p. A86

LESKO, Joan, Director Technical Support and Services, Kidspeace Children's Hospital, Orefield, PA, p. A599

LESLIE, Andrea M., MSN, R.N., President, Spectrum Health Big Rapids Hospital, Big Rapids, MI, p. A349
MSN, R.N., President, Spectrum Health Reed City Hospital, Reed City, MI, p. A364
MSN, R.N., President, Spectrum Health United Hospital, Greenville, MI, p. A356

LESLIE, Desdemona, Finance Officer, U. S. Public Health Service Indian Hospital-Whiteriver, Whiteriver, AZ, p. A41

LESLIE, Donald, M.D., Medical Director, Shepherd Center, Atlanta, GA, p. A165

LESLIE, Kelly, Chief Financial Officer, Ferry County Memorial Hospital, Republic, WA, p. A763

LESLIE, Steve, Chief Financial Officer, Fairbanks Memorial Hospital, Fairbanks, AK, p. A28

LESMEISTER, Danielle, Chief Executive Officer, Prairie Ridge Hospital And Health Services, Elbow Lake, MN, p. A376

LESNIAK, Jacklynn, R.N., MS, Vice President Patient Care Services and Chief Nursing Officer, Midwestern Regional Medical Center, Zion, IL, p. A222

LESNICK, Kelly, Resource Manager Flight Commander, Wright Patterson Medical Center, Wright, OH, p. A553

LESNIEWSKI, Amy, Associate Director Patient Care Services, Alexandria Veterans Affairs Health Care System, Pineville, LA, p. A312

LESSARD, Greg, Chief Executive Officer, Post Acute Medical Specialty Hospital Of Texarkana - North, Texarkana, TX, p. A720

LESSMANN, Eric, Chief of Staff, South Sunflower County Hospital, Indianola, MS, p. A394

LESTER, Lisa, Chief Nursing Officer, Encompass Health Rehabilitation Hospital Of Princeton, Princeton, WV, p. A776

LESTER, Ron, Chief Human Resources, Cheyenne Veterans Affairs Medical Center, Cheyenne, WY, p. A802

LESTER, Wade K., Chief Executive Officer, Riverside Hospital, Alexandria, LA, p. A296

LESTER, William, M.D., Vice President Medical Affairs, Cardinal Hill Rehabilitation Hospital, Lexington, KY, p. A286

LETCHWORTH, Mike, Manager Information Systems, Cherry Hospital, Goldsboro, NC, p. A510

LETEXIER, Lisa, Chief Executive Officer, Pembina County Memorial Hospital And Wedgewood Manor, Cavalier, ND, p. A522

LETHI, Scott, R.N., FACHE, Chief Nursing Officer, Fort Duncan Regional Medical Center, Eagle Pass, TX, p. A673

LETT, Patrick, M.D., Medical Doctor, Medical Center Enterprise, Enterprise, AL, p. A18

LEU, Christopher, President, Texas Health Harris Methodist Hospital Stephenville, Stephenville, TX, p. A717

LEUBNER, Kristel, D.O., Chief of Staff, Chi St. Josep. Health Burleson Hospital, Caldwell, TX, p. A662

LEUDECKE, Amelia, Director Human Resources, Encompass Health Rehabilitation Hospital Of Round Rock, Round Rock, TX, p. A709

LEUNG, Lawrence, M.D., Chief of Staff, Va Palo Alto Health Care System, Palo Alto, CA, p. A84

LEURCK, Mary, Human Resources Director, Amita Health Adventist Medical Center - Hinsdale, Hinsdale, IL, p. A208

LEVANGER, Nathan, M.D., Chief of Staff, Teton Valley Health Care, Driggs, ID, p. A190

LEVECK, Dianna, Chief Human Resources Officer, Genesis Healthcare System, Zanesville, OH, p. A554

LEVEILLEE, Mary, Senior Vice President Patient Care Services and Chief Nursing Officer, Butler Hospital, Providence, RI, p. A613

LEVELING, Jim, Director Information Technology, Kansas City Orthopaedic Institute, Leawood, KS, p. A269

LEVER, Roger, M.D., President Medical Staff, The Outer Banks Hospital, Nags Head, NC, p. A515

LEVERING, Theresa, Director Human Resources, Doctors Hospital Of Sarasota, Sarasota, FL, p. A157

LEVESQUE, David, Director, Information Systems, New Hampshire Hospital, Concord, NH, p. A448

LEVI, John, Director Human Resources, St. Lawrence Rehabilitation Center, Lawrenceville, NJ, p. A457

LEVIN, Alan, MSN, R.N., Chief Nursing Officer, New York-Presbyterian Queens, Flushing, NY, p. A484

LEVINE, Larry L., President and Chief Executive Officer, Blythedale Children's Hospital, Valhalla, NY, p. A500

LEVINE, Robert, Executive Vice President and Chief Operating Officer, Flushing Hospital Medical Center, Flushing, NY, p. A484

LEVINE, Stuart M., M.D., President, Medstar Franklin Square Medical Center, Baltimore, MD, p. A325

LEVINSON, Adam, Associate Director, Information Services, Rutgers University Behavioral Healthcare, Piscataway, NJ, p. A461

LEVIS, Randolph, Chief Financial Officer, Saint Vincent Hospital, Erie, PA, p. A590

LEVISON, Julie, Director Human Resources, Providence Medford Medical Center, Medford, OR, p. A578

LEVITAN, Kenneth, Chief Administrative Officer, Einstein Medical Center Montgomery, East Norriton, PA, p. A589

LEVITOW JR, JohnVice President Patient Care Services and Chief Nursing Officer, Frisbie Memorial Hospital, Rochester, NH, p. A451

LEVITZ, Michele, Director Finance, St. Luke's Hospital - Miners Campus, Coaldale, PA, p. A587

LEVY, Becky, Chief Financial Officer, Paradise Valley Hospital, National City, CA, p. A81
Chief Financial Officer, Shasta Regional Medical Center, Redding, CA, p. A87
Chief Operating Officer, Shasta Regional Medical Center, Redding, CA, p. A87

LEVY, Dana, Chief Nursing Officer, University Of Maryland Charles Regional Medical Center, La Plata, MD, p. A330

LEVY, Jennifer, Director Human Resources, Texas Institute For Surgery At Texas Health Presbyterian Dallas, Dallas, TX, p. A670

LEVY, Scott, M.D., Vice President and Chief Medical Officer, Doylestown Hospital, Doylestown, PA, p. A588

LEVY, Susan, M.D., Vice President Medical Affairs, Levindale Hebrew Hospital And Nursing, Baltimore, MD, p. A325

LEWANDOWSKI, James, Vice President Human Resources, Perry Memorial Hospital, Princeton, IL, p. A218

LEWANDOWSKI, Jim, Interim Director of Human Resources, Carson Tahoe Health, Carson City, NV, p. A441

LEWANDOWSKI, Terri, Director Financial Services, Ascension Our Lady Of Victory Hospital, Stanley, WI, p. A796

LEWELLEN, Patsy, Interim Chief Nursing Officer, Moberly Regional Medical Center, Moberly, MO, p. A412

LEWELLEN, Thomas, D.O., Chief of Staff, Delta Memorial Hospital, Dumas, AR, p. A44

LEWERKE, Jane, Manager Human Resources, Northern Arizona Veterans Affairs Health Care System, Prescott, AZ, p. A37

LEWIS, Alene, R.N., Chief Nursing Officer, Raleigh General Hospital, Beckley, WV, p. A770

LEWIS, Alonzo T., Senior Vice President, Operations, St. Josep. Mercy Ann Arbor, Ypsilanti, MI, p. A370

LEWIS, Angela, Senior Vice President Administration, Cookeville Regional Medical Center, Cookeville, TN, p. A637

LEWIS, Barbara, Chief Nursing Officer, Alliancehealth Seminole, Seminole, OK, p. A568

LEWIS, Brandon, Director of Information Technology, Ivinson Memorial Hospital, Laramie, WY, p. A803

LEWIS, Brinsley, FACHE, Chief Executive Officer, Kindred Hospital Chicago-Northlake, Northlake, IL, p. A214

LEWIS, Caren, R.N., Chief Nursing Officer, Lawrence + Memorial Hospital, New London, CT, p. A124

LEWIS, Christine, Assistant Administrator, Finance, Hermann Area District Hospital, Hermann, MO, p. A407

LEWIS, Colleen, Director Human Resources, Texas Neurorehab Center, Austin, TX, p. A657

LEWIS, Courtney, Director Human Resources, Houston Methodist Baytown Hospital, Baytown, TX, p. A657

LEWIS, Craig, Chief Financial Officer, Sentara Albemarle Medical Center, Elizabeth City, NC, p. A509

LEWIS, Dana, Director Clinical Services, Southern Kentucky Rehabilitation Hospital, Bowling Green, KY, p. A281

LEWIS, Daniel, Chief Medical Officer, Greeneville Community Hospital West, Greeneville, TN, p. A638
Executive Vice President and Chief Operating Officer, Metrohealth Medical Center, Cleveland, OH, p. A535

LEWIS, Dave, Director Information Services, Mosaic Medical Center - Maryville, Maryville, MO, p. A411

LEWIS, Dennis, M.D., Chief of Staff, Ashley Regional Medical Center, Vernal, UT, p. A734

LEWIS, Doug, Chief Financial Officer, St. Luke's Rehabilitation Hospital, Boise, ID, p. A189
Chief Financial Officer, Wheatland Memorial Healthcare, Harlowton, MT, p. A424

LEWIS, Douglas, Chief Financial Officer, Boulder City Hospital, Boulder City, NV, p. A441

LEWIS, Gordon, Chief Executive Officer, Burnett Medical Center, Grantsburg, WI, p. A785

LEWIS, Irvan, Vice President Human Resources, Mt. Graham Regional Medical Center, Safford, AZ, p. A37

LEWIS, J, Director Finance, Youth Villages Inner Harbour Campus, Douglasville, GA, p. A171

LEWIS, Jacob, Chief Financial Officer, Mark Twain Medical Center, San Andreas, CA, p. A90

LEWIS, Jeff, Administrator, Waukesha County Mental Health Center, Waukesha, WI, p. A798

LEWIS, Jeremy, D.O., Chief of Medical Staff, Newport Hospital And Health Services, Newport, WA, p. A761

LEWIS, John I., President and Chief Executive Officer, Acmh Hospital, Kittanning, PA, p. A593

LEWIS, Kent, Director Information Services, Southwestern Medical Center, Lawton, OK, p. A561

LEWIS, Lawrence E., Chief Executive Officer, Pioneers Memorial Healthcare District, Brawley, CA, p. A58

LEWIS, Luther J., FACHE, Chief Executive Officer, Chicot Memorial Medical Center, Lake Village, AR, p. A48

LEWIS, Marcus, Chief Executive Officer, First Care Health Center, Park River, ND, p. A525

LEWIS, Marie, Human Resources Liaison, Veterans Affairs St. Louis Health Care System, Saint Louis, MO, p. A418

LEWIS, Nicholas P., Chief Executive Officer, Hardin Medical Center, Savannah, TN, p. A649

LEWIS, Pam, Chief Compliance Officer, William R. Sharpe, Jr. Hospital, Weston, WV, p. A777

LEWIS, Paul, Chief Executive Officer, Shoshone Medical Center, Kellogg, ID, p. A191

LEWIS, Paula, Interim Chief Nursing Officer, St. Bernards Five Rivers, Pocahontas, AR, p. A52

LEWIS, Rebecca, President, Grandview Medical Center, Dayton, OH, p. A538

LEWIS, Robin, Chief Financial Officer, Kiowa District Healthcare, Kiowa, KS, p. A268

LEWIS, Ron, President, Spectrum Health Zeeland Community Hospital, Zeeland, MI, p. A370

LEWIS, Rosalind, R.N., MSN, Director of Ancillary Services, Community Healthcare System, Onaga, KS, p. A273

LEWIS, Sharon, Director Information Systems, Forbes Hospital, Monroeville, PA, p. A597

LEWIS, Thomas, Chief Operating Officer, Clifton T. Perkins Hospital Center, Jessup. MD, p. A330

LEWIS, Vicki, R.N., MS, FACHE, President and Chief Executive Officer, Coffee Regional Medical Center, Douglas, GA, p. A171

LEWIS, Vickie, Chief Executive Officer, Central Florida Behavioral Hospital, Orlando, FL, p. A151

LEWIS-TAYLOR, Tracey, Chief Operating Officer, Stanford Health Care - Valleycare, Pleasanton, CA, p. A85

LEWISTON, Jamie, R.N., MSN, Chief Nursing Officer, Aurora Psychiatric Hospital, Wauwatosa, WI, p. A799

LEYDEN, Andrea Chief Nursing Officer, Washington County Hospital And Clinics, Washington, IA, p. A259

LEYHE, William, Chief Executive Officer, Carrollton Regional Medical Center, Carrollton, TX, p. A663

LI, Eric, M.D., Chief Medical Officer, United Medical Center, Washington, DC, p. A130

LI, Ronald, Vice President Management Information Systems, Bergen New Bridge Medical Center, Paramus, NJ, p. A460

LI, Stephen, Vice President Management Information Systems, Jersey City Medical Center, Jersey City, NJ, p. A456

LI, Xiao, M.D., Chief of Staff, Surgery Specialty Hospitals Of America, Pasadena, TX, p. A705

LIANG, Bonnie, Divisional Finance Officer, Sutter Maternity And Surgery Center Of Santa Cruz, Santa Cruz, CA, p. A97

LIBBY, Kenneth, Vice President Finance, Vcu Health Community Memorial Hospital, South Hill, VA, p. A752

LIBCKE, Julia, R.N., MSN, Chief Nursing Officer, Mclaren Macomb, Mount Clemens, MI, p. A362
R.N., MSN, VP Patient Care Services, Dmc - Rehabilitation Institute Of Michigan, Detroit, MI, p. A352

LIBERATORE, Kristi, Vice President and Chief Financial Officer, St. Josep. Hospital Orange, Orange, CA, p. A83

LICHIUS, Sylvia, R.N., Chief Nursing Officer, Morrill County Community Hospital, Bridgeport, NE, p. A430

LICHTENWALNER, Tom, Vice President Finance, St. Luke's University Hospital - Bethlehem Campus, Bethlehem, PA, p. A585

LICHTY, Scott, M.D., Physician, Sanford Sheldon Medical Center, Sheldon, IA, p. A257

LIDDELL, Sean, Manager Regional Service Information Technology, Unitypoint Health - Trinity Muscatine, Muscatine, IA, p. A254

LIEBER, Alan R., President, Overlook Medical Center, Vice President, Atlantic Health System, Overlook Medical Center, Summit, NJ, p. A463

LIEBERMAN, Jeffrey A., M.D., Executive Director, New York State Psychiatric Institute, New York, NY, p. A491

LIEBERMAN, Steven, M.D., Chief of Staff, Veterans Affairs New Jersey Health Care System, East Orange, NJ, p. A454

LIEBERS, David, M.D., Chief Medical Officer and Vice President Medical Affairs, Ellis Hospital, Schenectady, NY, p. A498

LIEBMAN, Jeffrey H., Chief Executive Officer, Roger Williams Medical Center, Providence, RI, p. A614

LIEFER, Alan, M.D., President Medical Staff, Memorial Hospital, Chester, IL, p. A197

LIESCHING, Timothy, M.D., Chief Medical Officer, Lahey Hospital & Medical Center, Burlington, Burlington, MA, p. A337

LIESEN, Daniel, M.D., Chief Medical Officer, Vista Health, Waukegan, IL, p. A222

LIESMANN, George, M.D., Chief Medical Officer, Blessing Hospital, Quincy, IL, p. A218

LIETTE, Cindy, Vice President Patient Care Services, Mercer Health, Coldwater, OH, p. A535

LIFFERTH, Geoffrey, M.D., Chief Medical Officer, Sumner Regional Medical Center, Gallatin, TN, p. A638

LIGHT, Asher, M.D., Medical Director, Baylor Scott & White Institute For Rehabilitation-Fort Worth, Fort Worth, TX, p. A678

LIGHT, Laura, Director Human Resources, St. David's North Austin Medical Center, Austin, TX, p. A656

LIGHTBOURNE, Olieth, Chief Nursing Officer, Streamwood Behavioral Health Center, Streamwood, IL, p. A221

LIGHTCAP, Debora, Director Human Resources, Mercy Medical Center, Roseburg, OR, p. A580

LIGHTFOOT, William, M.D., Vice President Medical Services, Providence Hospital, Mobile, AL, p. A22

LIGHTNER, Matthew, M.D., Chief Medical Staff, Scott County Hospital, Scott City, KS, p. A276

LIGON, Kim, Director Information Services, Dch Regional Medical Center, Tuscaloosa, AL, p. A25

LIGON, Lynda, Chief Nursing Officer, Warm Springs Medical Center, Warm Springs, GA, p. A183

LIKES, Randle, M.D., Chief Medical Officer, Timpanogos Regional Hospital, Orem, UT, p. A730

LILES, Jerry, D.O., Chief Medical Officer, Christus Spohn Hospital Alice, Alice, TX, p. A651

LILES, Richard, M.D., Medical Director, Encompass Health Rehabilitation Hospital Of Largo, Largo, FL, p. A143

LILLEY, Jeffrey, CPA, Chief Executive Officer, Princeton Community Hospital, Princeton, WV, p. A776

LIM, Rosemarie, M.D., Chief Medical Officer, Paradise Valley Hospital, National City, CA, p. A81

LIMA, Robert, Director Information Systems, Pappas Rehabilitation Hospital For Children, Canton, MA, p. A338

LIMBAGA, Aries, R.N., Chief Executive Officer, Rancho Los Amigos National Rehabilitation Center, Downey, CA, p. A62

LIMBAUGH, Jason, Vice President and Chief Financial Officer, Wellstar Atlanta Medical Center, Atlanta, GA, p. A165

LIMM, Whitney, M.D., Executive Vice President and Chief Physician Executive, The Queen's Medical Center, Honolulu, HI, p. A185

LIN, George, M.D., Physician Advisor, Hackensack Meridian Health Pascack Valley Medical Center, Westwood, NJ, p. A465

LIN, James, D.O., Chief of Staff, Lecom Health Millcreek Community Hospital, Erie, PA, p. A590

LINAFELTER, Robb, Chief Executive Officer, Lincoln Surgical Hospital, Lincoln, NE, p. A434

LINARES, Manuel, President and Chief Executive Officer, Touro Infirmary, New Orleans, LA, p. A311

LINCKS, Brad, Chief Executive Officer, Sun Behavioral Kentucky, Erlanger, KY, p. A283

LIND, Jonathan, Chief Operating Officer, Swedish Covenant Hospital, Chicago, IL, p. A201

LIND, Mark, Chief Information Officer, Mammoth Hospital, Mammoth Lakes, CA, p. A77

LIND, Sharon, MSN, FACHE, Chief Executive Officer, Banner Boswell Medical Center, Sun City, AZ, p. A39
MSN, FACHE, Chief Executive Officer, Banner Del E. Webb Medical Center, Sun City West, AZ, p. A39

LIND, Trent, Chief Executive Officer, Eastside Medical Center, Snellville, GA, p. A180

LINDBERG, Bob, Chief Operating Officer, Cumberland Healthcare, Cumberland, WI, p. A782

LINDBERG, Chris, Chief Information Officer, Milwaukee County Behavioral Health Division, Milwaukee, WI, p. A791

LINDBERG, Michael, M.D., Chief Medical Officer, Monadnock Community Hospital, Peterborough, NH, p. A451

LINDELL, Jonathan, Director Information Technology, Miracle Mile Medical Center, Los Angeles, CA, p. A75

LINDEMAN, Barry, Director Human Resources, Cardinal Hill Rehabilitation Hospital, Lexington, KY, p. A286

LINDEMAN, Gretchen, Director of Human Resources, Monterey Park Hospital, Monterey Park, CA, p. A79

LINDEMANN, Fran, Director Finance, Kell West Regional Hospital, Wichita Falls, TX, p. A725

LINDEMANN, Steve, Chief Financial Officer, Brookings Health System, Brookings, SD, p. A626

LINDEN, Kelly, Chief Executive Officer, Providence Saint Josep. Medical Center, Burbank, CA, p. A59

LINDER, James, M.D., Chief Executive Officer, Nebraska Medicine - Nebraska Medical Center, Omaha, NE, p. A437

LINDFORS, Teresa, Vice President Growth and Development, Stoughton Hospital Association, Stoughton, WI, p. A797

LINDQUIST, James, Chief Nursing Officer, Hackensack Meridian Health Jfk Medical Center, Edison, NJ, p. A454
Chief Nursing Officer, Jfk Johnson Rehabilitation Institute At Hackensack Meridian Health, Edison, NJ, p. A454

LINDQUIST, Peter, Vice President and Chief Nursing Officer, Providence Hospital, Mobile, AL, p. A22

LINDSAY, Kelly, Chief Operating Officer, Coliseum Medical Centers, Macon, GA, p. A176

LINDSAY-BELL, Davida, Area Human Resources Leader, Kaiser Permanente Antioch Medical Center, Antioch, CA, p. A56

LINDSAY-WOOD, Elizabeth, Interim Chief Information Officer, Overlook Medical Center, Summit, NJ, p. A463

LINDSEY, Don, Vice President and Chief Information Officer, Tallahassee Memorial Healthcare, Tallahassee, FL, p. A158

LINDSEY, Hugh, M.D., Chief Medical Officer, Sparrow Eaton Hospital, Charlotte, MI, p. A351

LINDSEY, Jay, Chief Executive Officer, Everest Rehabilitation Hospital Longview, Longview, TX, p. A696

LINDSEY, Kim, Chief Human Resources Officer, Lourdes Hospital, Paducah, KY, p. A291

LINDSEY, Robbie, Chief Information Officer, Twin Lakes Regional Medical Center, Leitchfield, KY, p. A286

LINDSEY, Tony, M.D., Chief of Staff, University Of North Carolina Hospitals, Chapel Hill, NC, p. A506

LINDSTROM, David, M.D., Vice President Medical Affairs, Promedica Bay Park Hospital, Oregon, OH, p. A547

LINE, Michael, Chief Medical Officer, Greene County Medical Center, Jefferson, IA, p. A252

LINES, Brian, Chief Executive Officer, Lone Peak Hospital, Draper, UT, p. A728
Chief Operating Officer, Ogden Regional Medical Center, Ogden, UT, p. A730

LING, Lori, Information Technician, Windom Area Health, Windom, MN, p. A388

LINGEN, Tom, M.D., Chief of Staff, Cumberland Healthcare, Cumberland, WI, p. A782

LINGLE, Dan, Chief Nursing Officer, Banner Casa Grande Medical Center, Casa Grande, AZ, p. A30

LINGLE, David, Directors Council Chairman and Chief of Staff, Vidant Roanoke-Chowan Hospital, Ahoskie, NC, p. A504

LINGO, Jessica, Human Resource Generalist, Story County Medical Center, Nevada, IA, p. A254

LINHARES, James, Chief Executive Officer, Bridgepoint Hospital Capitol Hill, Washington, DC, p. A129

LINK, Nathan, M.D., Medical Director, Nyc Health + Hospitals / Bellevue, New York, NY, p. A491

LINKENHOKER, Ellen, Chief Nursing Officer, Lewisgale Hospital Montgomery, Blacksburg, VA, p. A739

LINN, Steven, M.D., Chief Medical Officer, Inspira Medical Center-Elmer, Elmer, NJ, p. A455
M.D., Chief Medical Officer, Inspira Medical Center-Vineland, Vineland, NJ, p. A465

LINNELL, Jon E., Chief Executive Officer, North Valley Health Center, Warren, MN, p. A387

LINNINGTON, Darryl, Chief Financial Officer, Mcalester Regional Health Center, Mcalester, OK, p. A562

LINSCHEID, Carol, Vice President Human Resources, Enloe Medical Center, Chico, CA, p. A60

LINSCOTT, Jason, CPA, Chief Financial Officer, Texas Health Presbyterian Hospital Of Rockwall, Rockwall, TX, p. A709
CPA, Chief Operating Officer and Chief Financial Officer, Texas Health Presbyterian Hospital Of Rockwall, Rockwall, TX, p. A709

LINSE, Margaret, Administrative Secretary and Director Human Resources, West Holt Medical Services, Atkinson, NE, p. A429

LINSKEY, Chris, M.D., Acting Chief Medical Officer, Guidance Center, Flagstaff, AZ, p. A31

LINSTROM, Joseph, Vice President Operations, Suburban Hospital, Bethesda, MD, p. A327

LINTON, Dwight, Director Human Resources, Detar Healthcare System, Victoria, TX, p. A723

LINTZ, Gordon, President and Chief Administrative Officer, Morristown-Hamblen Healthcare System, Morristown, TN, p. A645

* LINZMAN, Rob, D.O., Chief of Staff, Jefferson County Hospital, Waurika, OK, p. A571

LIONARONS, JoAnn, Director, Burdett Birth Center, Troy, NY, p. A500

LIPE, Curt, Vice President, Chief Financial Officer, Osf St. Mary Medical Center, Galesburg, IL, p. A205

LIPINSKI, Gary, M.D., Chief Medical Officer, Amita Health Saint Josep. Medical Center, Joliet, IL, p. A209

LIPMAN, Brian, M.D., Medical Director and Medical Staff Services, Oconomowoc Memorial Hospital, Oconomowoc, WI, p. A792

LIPMAN, Henry, Senior Vice President, Financial Strategy and External Relations, Franklin Regional Hospital, Franklin, NH, p. A449

LIPNER, Zach, Vice President Human Resources, Newark Beth Israel Medical Center, Newark, NJ, p. A459

LIPPERT, Brandt, Vice President Human Resources, Adena Greenfield Medical Center, Greenfield, OH, p. A541

LIPPINCOTT, Ken, M.D., Chief of Staff, North Mississipp. State Hospital, Tupelo, MS, p. A400

LIPSCOMB, Tracy, CPA, Vice President Financial Services and Chief Financial Officer, Garrett Regional Medical Center, Oakland, MD, p. A331

LIPSON, Wayne, M.D., Chief Physician Executive, Baptist Health Madisonville, Madisonville, KY, p. A289

LIPTAK, Valenda M., Chief Executive Officer, Western Massachusetts Hospital, Westfield, MA, p. A346

LIPTON, Pat, Director Team Resources, South Florida Baptist Hospital, Plant City, FL, p. A154

LIPYANSKAYA, Svetlana, Chief Executive Officer, Nyc Health + Hospitals / Coney Island, Brooklyn, NY, p. A478

LIRAKIS, Kathy, R.N., Chief Nursing Officer, Northern Light Blue Hill Hospital, Blue Hill, ME, p. A319

LIRIO, Ruel, M.D., Clinical Physician Advisor, Spectrum Health Zeeland Community Hospital, Zeeland, MI, p. A378

LISA, Mark P., FACHE, Chief Executive Officer, Sierra Vista Regional Medical Center, San Luis Obispo, CA, p. A96
FACHE, Chief Executive Officer, Twin Cities Community Hospital, Templeton, CA, p. A101

LISKO, Stuart, Vice President, Chief Financial Officer and Compliance Officer, Levi Hospital, Hot Springs National Park, AR, p. A47

LISKOV, David, M.D., Medical Director, First Hospital Wyoming Valley, Kingston, PA, p. A593

LISS, Rita, Vice President Fiscal Services and Chief Financial Officer, Boone County Health Center, Albion, NE, p. A429

LISTER, Jack, Director Human Resources, Greeneville Community Hospital West, Greeneville, TN, p. A638

LISTI, Daniel, Chief Executive Officer, Shelby Baptist Medical Center, Alabaster, AL, p. A13

LISTON, Allison, Director, Human Resources, Cedar Crest Hospital And Residential Treatment Center, Belton, TX, p. A659

LISTON, John, Chief Operating Officer, Mclaren Port Huron, Port Huron, MI, p. A364

LITER, Jennifer, Vice President of Inpatient Services, King's Daughters' Health, Madison, IN, p. A236

LITKA, Calvin, R.N., Director of Nursing, Horsham Clinic, Ambler, PA, p. A584

LITOVITZ, Gary, M.D., Medical Director, Dominion Hospital, Falls Church, VA, p. A741

LITSINGER, James, CPA, Chief Operating Officer, Sheltering Arms Hospital South, Midlothian, VA, p. A746
CPA, Vice President and Chief Financial Officer, Sheltering Arms Rehabilitation Hospital, Mechanicsville, VA, p. A746

LITTERER, Karen, R.N., MSN, Administrator and Chief Operating Officer, Ascension Seton Highland Lakes, Burnet, TX, p. A662

LITTLE, Amy, Vice President Patient Services, Indiana University Health Bedford Hospital, Bedford, IN, p. A224

LITTLE, Chris, Chief Executive Officer, Saint Simons By-The-Sea Hospital, Saint Simons Island, GA, p. A179

LITTLE, Denise, Director Human Resources, St. Elizabeth Community Hospital, Red Bluff, CA, p. A87

LITTLE, Gary, M.D., Medical Director, George Washington University Hospital, Washington, DC, p. A129

LITTLE, James, M.D., Medical Director, Encompass Health Rehabilitation Hospital Of Kingsport, Kingsport, TN, p. A640

LITTLE, Joi, Chief Human Resources Officer, Dmc - Sinai-Grace Hospital, Detroit, MI, p. A352

LITTLE, Lou, President and Chief Executive Officer, Sparrow Specialty Hospital, Lansing, MI, p. A360

LITTLE, Suzanne, Human Resources Specialist, Columbia Basin Hospital, Ephrata, WA, p. A758

LITTLE, William, Chief Executive Officer, Carolina Pines Regional Medical Center, Hartsville, SC, p. A621

LITTLEDEER, Lenora, R.N., Chief Executive Officer and Chief Nursing Officer, Lawton Indian Hospital, Lawton, OK, p. A561

LITTLEFIELD, Karen, Director Human Resources, Waldo County General Hospital, Belfast, ME, p. A319

LITTLEJOHN, Edward, Chief Operating Officer, Fountain Valley Regional Hospital And Medical Center, Fountain Valley, CA, p. A64

LITTLEJOHN, Matthew, Chief Executive Officer, Tennova Newport Medical Center, Newport, TN, p. A647

LITTLEJOHN, Traxler, Human Resources Director, Encompass Health Rehabilitation Hospital Of Charleston, Charleston, SC, p. A616

LITTLEPAGE, Dana, Interim Chief Nursing Officer, St. John's Pleasant Valley Hospital, Camarillo, CA, p. A59

LITTLESON, Steven, FACHE, Chief Operating and Integration Officer, Penn Medicine Lancaster General Hospital, Lancaster, PA, p. A594

LITTRELL, Angela P., CPA, President and Chief Executive Officer, Fitzgibbon Hospital, Marshall, MO, p. A411

LITTRELL, Mark, Chief Executive Officer, Denver Springs, Englewood, CO, p. A112

LIUZZA, Jed, Chief Human Resources Officer, Ou Medical Center, Oklahoma City, OK, p. A565

LIVELY, Corey, Chief Executive Officer, Great Plains Regional Medical Center, Elk City, OK, p. A558

LIVERMAN, Brett, Chief Financial Officer, Alleghany Memorial Hospital, Sparta, NC, p. A518

LIVERMONT, Kristi, Administrator, Avera Gettysburg Hospital, Gettysburg, SD, p. A628

LIVESAY, William, D.O., JrMedical Director, Encompass Health Rehabilitation Hospital Of Charleston, Charleston, SC, p. A616

LIVIN, Lee, Chief Financial Officer, Yavapai Regional Medical Center, Prescott, AZ, p. A37

LIVINGSTON, Carolyn, Director Human Resources, Salt Lake Regional Medical Center, Salt Lake City, UT, p. A732

LIVINGSTON, Charles, Administrator, Dakota Plains Surgical Center, Aberdeen, SD, p. A626
Chief Executive Officer, Midwest Surgical Hospital, Omaha, NE, p. A437

LIVINGSTON, Denise, Director Human Resources, St. Mary Medical Center Long Beach, Long Beach, CA, p. A72

LIVINGSTON, Keith, Senior Vice President and Chief Information Officer, Thedacare Regional Medical Center-Appleton, Appleton, WI, p. A779
Senior Vice President and Chief Information Officer, Thedacare Regional Medical Center-Neenah, Neenah, WI, p. A792

LIVINGSTON, Richard, M.D., Medical Director, Valley Behavioral Health System, Barling, AR, p. A42

LIVINGSTON, Sam, Information Resource Consultant, G. Werber Bryan Psychiatric Hospital, Columbia, SC, p. A617

LIVSEY, Don, Vice President and Chief Information Officer, Ucsf Benioff Children's Hospital Oakland, Oakland, CA, p. A82

LIZZA, Beth, Chief Nursing Officer, Ohio Valley Surgical Hospital, Springfield, OH, p. A549

LLANO, Manuel R., Chief Executive Officer, Fort Lauderdale Behavioral Health Center, Oakland Park, FL, p. A149

LLEWELLYN, Michael, Chief Operating Officer, Laguna Honda Hospital And Rehabilitation Center, San Francisco, CA, p. A93

LLOYD, Chuck, Chief Executive Officer, Benewah Community Hospital, Saint Maries, ID, p. A193

LLOYD, Richard, D.O., Chief of Staff, Harbor Beach Community Hospital, Harbor Beach, MI, p. A357

LLOYD, Russell E., Director, Wilkes-Barre Veterans Affairs Medical Center, Wilkes-Barre, PA, p. A611

LOBBAN, Victoria, Vice President Finance, New England Sinai Hospital And Rehabilitation Center, Stoughton, MA, p. A345

LOCATELLI, Eduardo, M.D., Interim Chief Medical Officer, Holy Cross Hospital, Fort Lauderdale, FL, p. A137

LOCEY, Vicky, R.N., MSN, Chief Operating Officer and Chief Nursing Executive, Kaiser Permanente Santa Rosa Medical Center, Santa Rosa, CA, p. A98

LOCHALA, Richard, Chief of Staff, Mena Regional Health System, Mena, AR, p. A50

LOCK, Lesa, Chief Nursing Officer, Valley View Medical Center, Fort Mohave, AZ, p. A31

LOCKARD, Dennis, FACHE, Chief Financial Officer, Coshocton Regional Medical Center, Coshocton, OH, p. A538

LOCKCUFF, Todd, Chief Financial Officer, Inova Alexandria Hospital, Alexandria, VA, p. A738

LOCKE, Cheryl, Vice President and Chief Human Resource Officer, Wake Forest Baptist Medical Center, Winston, NC, p. A520

LOCKE, Christopher, Chief Executive Officer, Saint Francis Hospital-Bartlett, Bartlett, TN, p. A634

LOCKE, Marianne, R.N., MSN, Associate Director Patient Care Services, Edward Hines, Jr. Veterans Affairs Hospital, Hines, IL, p. A207

LOCKE, Stuart, Chief Executive Officer, Southern Kentucky Rehabilitation Hospital, Bowling Green, KY, p. A281

LOCKERD, Marie, M.D., Chief Medical Officer, Sanford Jackson Medical Center, Jackson, MN, p. A378

LOCKETT, Kevin, Interim Chief Financial Officer, Mayo Clinic Hospital In Florida, Jacksonville, FL, p. A141

LOCKHART, Jimmy, M.D., Medical Director, Encompass Health Rehabilitation Hospital Of Treasure Coast, Vero Beach, FL, p. A161

LOCKLEAR, Ann, Vice President, Human Resources, Scotland Health Care System, Laurinburg, NC, p. A513

LOCKRIDGE, Michael, Chief Financial Officer, Northern Louisiana Medical Center, Ruston, LA, p. A313

LOCKWOOD, Melissa, Chief Executive Officer, Preston Memorial Hospital, Kingwood, WV, p. A773

LOE, Cindy, R.N., Director of Nursing, Essentia Health Northern Pines Medical Center, Aurora, MN, p. A372

LOEB, Amy, Ed.D., R.N., Chief Nursing Officer, Peconic Bay Medical Center, Riverhead, NY, p. A496

LOEFFELHOLZ, Tim, Account Executive Information Technology, Unitypoint Health - Finley Hospital, Dubuque, IA, p. A249

LOELIGER, Eric, Vice President of Medical Affairs, Asante Three Rivers Medical Center, Grants Pass, OR, p. A575

LOEPP, Robert A. Jr, FACHE, Chief Executive Officer, Amg Specialty Hospital-Wichita, Wichita, KS, p. A278

LOERA, Arnold, M.D., Clinical Director, Bristol Bay Area Health Corporation, Dillingham, AK, p. A28

LOERINC, Albert, M.D., Medical Director, Vibra Hospital Of Southeastern Massachusetts, New Bedford, MA, p. A342

LOESCHER, Cori, R.N., Chief Nursing Officer and Vice President of Patient Care Services, Brigham And Women's Faulkner Hospital, Boston, MA, p. A335

LOEWENSTEIN, Howard, Chief Information Resource Management Services, Jesse Brown Veterans Affairs Medical Center, Chicago, IL, p. A198

LOFFING, David, Chief Operating Officer, University Of Illinois Hospital & Health Sciences System, Chicago, IL, p. A201

LOFQUIST, Barry D., Chief Executive Officer, Christus Mother Frances Hospital - Jacksonville, Jacksonville, TX, p. A691

LOFTIS, Dennis, Senior Vice President and Chief Information Officer, Riverside Regional Medical Center, Newport News, VA, p. A747
Senior Vice President of Information Systems, Coastal Virginia Rehabilitation, Newport News, VA, p. A746

LOFTIS, Michelle, Human Resources Officer, Ferry County Memorial Hospital, Republic, WA, p. A763

LOFTON, Veronica, Acting Chief Executive Officer, Twin Valley Behavioral Healthcare, Columbus, OH, p. A537

LOFTUS, Christopher, Chief Executive Officer, Desert Springs Hospital Medical Center, Las Vegas, NV, p. A443

LOFTUS, John, M.D., Chief of Staff, Kaiser Permanente Oakland Medical Center, Oakland, CA, p. A82

LOFTUS, Mary Virginia, Chief Nursing Officer, Specialists Hospital Shreveport, Shreveport, LA, p. A314

LOFTUS, Philip. Ph.D., Chief Information Officer, Aurora West Allis Medical Center, West Allis, WI, p. A799
Ph.D., Vice President and Chief Information Officer, Aurora Medical Center Of Oshkosh, Oshkosh, WI, p. A793
Ph.D., Vice President and Chief Information Officer, Aurora Psychiatric Hospital, Wauwatosa, WI, p. A799
Ph.D., Vice President and Chief Information Officer, Aurora St. Luke's Medical Center, Milwaukee, WI, p. A790

LOFTUS, Terry, M.D., Chief Medical Officer, Medical City Fort Worth, Fort Worth, TX, p. A678

LOFURNO, Justin, Director Human Resources, Providence Hospital, Columbia, SC, p. A618

LOGAN, Angela, Chief Nursing Officer, Lutheran Hospital Of Indiana, Fort Wayne, IN, p. A228

LOGAN, Ann, R.N., Ph.D., Chief Hospital Executive, Carepoint Health Hoboken University Medical Center, Hoboken, NJ, p. A456

LOGAN, Ann P., R.N., Ph.D., Chief Hospital Executive, Carepoint Health Hoboken University Medical Center, Hoboken, NJ, p. A456

LOGAN, Denise, Director Human Resources, Specialty Rehabilitation Hospital Of Coushatta, Coushatta, LA, p. A299

LOGAN, John, M.D., Chief Medical Officer, Methodist Hospital, Henderson, KY, p. A285

LOGAN, Matthew, M.D., Vice President Medical Affairs and Chief Medical Officer, Self Regional Healthcare, Greenwood, SC, p. A621

LOGAN, Renee, Chief Financial Officer, Murray County Medical Center, Slayton, MN, p. A386

LOGAN-OWENS, Michelle, Ph.D., R.N., Chief Operating Officer, Prisma Health Tuomey Hospital, Sumter, SC, p. A624

LOGAR, Michael, Assistant Superintendent, Larue D. Carter Memorial Hospital, Indianapolis, IN, p. A232

LOGDSON, David, Chief Nursing Officer, Twin Lakes Regional Medical Center, Leitchfield, KY, p. A286

LOGOZZO, Vince, Director Information Technology, Aultman Orrville Hospital, Orrville, OH, p. A547

LOGSDON, Terri, Chief Financial Officer, Hickory Trail Hospital, Desoto, TX, p. A672

LOH, Marcel C., FACHE, Chief Executive Officer, Providence Saint John's Health Center, Santa Monica, CA, p. A97

LOHMAN, Eric, M.D., Chief of Staff, Meadowview Regional Medical Center, Maysville, KY, p. A290

LOHN, Eric, Chief Financial Officer, Lake View Hospital, Two Harbors, MN, p. A386
Vice President and Chief Financial Officer, St. Luke's Hospital, Duluth, MN, p. A375

LOHR, Daniel, Regional Vice President Finance, Windham Hospital, Willimantic, CT, p. A126

LOHRMAN, Joseph, Chief Executive Officer, Annie Jeffrey Memorial County Health Center, Osceola, NE, p. A438

LOHRMAN, Josep. W., Chief Executive Officer, Annie Jeffrey Memorial County Health Center, Osceola, NE, p. A438

LOHSTRETER, Thomas, M.D., Chief of Staff, Kittson Memorial Healthcare Center, Hallock, MN, p. A377

LOKKEN, Christine, Chief Financial Officer, Bigfork Valley Hospital, Bigfork, MN, p. A372

LOLLEY, Tim, MSN, Chief Nursing Officer, Merit Health Madison, Canton, MS, p. A390

LOLLIS, Sylvia, Director Human Resources, Osceola Regional Medical Center, Kissimmee, FL, p. A142

LOLLO, Trisha, President, St. Louis Children's Hospital, Saint Louis, MO, p. A417

LOMAN, Sarah, Director Human Resources, Penobscot Valley Hospital, Lincoln, ME, p. A321

LOMBA, Maria, Medical Director, New Braunfels Regional Rehabilitation Hospital, New Braunfels, TX, p. A703

LOMBARD, Lisa, Chief Medical Officer, Ohiohealth Rehabilitation Hospital, Columbus, OH, p. A536

LOMBARDI, David, Site Chief Information Officer, Huntington Hospital, Huntington, NY, p. A485

LOMBARDO, Alan, Associate Director, Hunter Holmes Mcguire Veterans Affairs Medical Center-Richmond, Richmond, VA, p. A750

LOMEO, Jody, Chief Executive Officer, Kaleida Health, Buffalo, NY, p. A480

LONES, Malachi, Chief Nursing Officer, Hamilton County Hospital, Syracuse, KS, p. A277

LONEY, Chris, Director Personnel, Thomas B. Finan Center, Cumberland, MD, p. A329

LONG, Brian, FACHE, President and Chief Executive Officer, Memorial Healthcare, Owosso, MI, p. A363

LONG, David, Chief Executive Officer, Pam Specialty Hospital Of Wilkes-Barre, Wilkes Barre, PA, p. A611
Interim Chief Executive Officer, Hillcrest Hospital Cushing, Cushing, OK, p. A558

LONG, Dennis, Director Human Resources, Western Missouri Medical Center, Warrensburg, MO, p. A420

LONG, Erik, Controller, Baptist Health South Florida, South Miami Hospital, Miami, FL, p. A146

LONG, Floyd R., Executive Director, Nyc Health + Hospitals / Henry J Carter Specialty Hospital And Medical Center, New York, NY, p. A491

LONG, Gregory, M.D., Chief Medical Officer, Thedacare Regional Medical Center-Appleton, Appleton, WI, p. A779
M.D., Chief Medical Officer, Thedacare Regional Medical Center-Neenah, Neenah, WI, p. A792

LONG, Gretchen, Manager Human Resources, Shriners Hospitals For Children - Cincinnati, Cincinnati, OH, p. A533

LONG, Jeremy, Chief Information Officer, Ascension St. Vincent Heart Center, Indianapolis, IN, p. A231
Manager Information Systems, Ascension St. Vincent Salem, Salem, IN, p. A240

LONG, Jonathan, M.D., Chief of Staff, Weatherford Regional Hospital, Weatherford, OK, p. A572

LONG, Joseph, M.D., Medical Director, Encompass Health Rehabilitation Hospital Of Albuquerque, Albuquerque, NM, p. A467

LONG, Judy, R.N., MS, Chief Nursing Officer and Chief Operating Officer, Appling Healthcare System, Baxley, GA, p. A167

LONG, Karen, R.N., FACHE, Vice President Nursing, Bayfront Health St. Petersburg, Saint Petersburg, FL, p. A156

LONG, Kimberly C., R.N., MSN, Chief Executive Officer, Vibra Hospital Of Sacramento, Folsom, CA, p. A64

LONG, Michelle, Regional Human Resource Manager, Abraham Lincoln Memorial Hospital, Lincoln, IL, p. A210
Regional Human Resource Manager, Taylorville Memorial Hospital, Taylorville, IL, p. A221

LONG, Mike, Chief Financial Officer, National Park Medical Center, Hot Springs, AR, p. A47
Chief Financial Officer, Powell Valley Healthcare, Powell, WY, p. A803

LONG, Richard, M.D., Chief Medical Officer, Upmc Hamot, Erie, PA, p. A590

LONG, Stephanie, President and Chief Executive Officer, River Bend Hospital, West Lafayette, IN, p. A242

LONG, Steven V., FACHE, President and Chief Executive Officer, Hancock Regional Hospital, Greenfield, IN, p. A230

LONG, Theresa, Chief Executive Officer, Danville State Hospital, Danville, PA, p. A587

LONGABAUGH, James, M.D., Chief Medical Staff, Sabetha Community Hospital, Sabetha, KS, p. A275

LONGACRE, Mark, FACHE, Chief Operating Officer, Orthonebraska Hospital, Omaha, NE, p. A437

LONGDO, Derrick, Director Information Systems, Marshfield Medical Center - Neilsville, Neillsville, WI, p. A792

LONGEST, Bruce, M.D., President Medical Staff, Baptist Memorial Hospital - Calhoun, Calhoun City, MS, p. A390

LONGEST, Sonya, M.D., Chief Medical Officer, Walter B. Jones Alcohol And Drug Abuse Treatment Center, Greenville, NC, p. A511

LONGLEY, Frank, Business Partner Information Technology, Cleveland Clinic, Medina Hospital, Medina, OH, p. A545

LONGLEY, Michael, M.D., Chief Medical Officer, Adventhealth North Pinellas, Tarpon Springs, FL, p. A160

LONGMORE, David, Chief Information Officer, Wilkes-Barre Veterans Affairs Medical Center, Wilkes-Barre, PA, p. A611

LONGMUIR, Marla, M.D., Chief Medical Officer, Mountrail County Medical Center, Stanley, ND, p. A526

LONGNECKER, Stacy, Chief of Staff, Ortonville Area Health Services, Ortonville, MN, p. A382

LONGO, Joseph, Chief Information Officer, Parkland Health & Hospital System, Dallas, TX, p. A670

LONGO, Marybeth, Manager Human Resources, Trenton Psychiatric Hospital, Trenton, NJ, p. A464

LONGSTREET, Laura, Chief Executive Officer, Belmont Behavioral Hospital, Philadelphia, PA, p. A599

LONGTIN, Brett, Chief Financial Officer, Lake Region Healthcare, Fergus Falls, MN, p. A376
Chief Financial Officer, Prairie Ridge Hospital And Health Services, Elbow Lake, MN, p. A376

LONGWELL, Connie, Chief Executive Officer, Elkhorn Valley Rehabilitation Hospital, Casper, WY, p. A801

LONGWORTH, David L., M.D., Chief Executive Officer, Lahey Hospital & Medical Center, Burlington, Burlington, MA, p. A337

LONIS, Robert, CPA, Chief Financial Officer, Lincoln County Health System, Fayetteville, TN, p. A638

LOOMIS, Randy, Chief Financial Officer, Dallas County Hospital, Perry, IA, p. A256

LOONEY, Zane, Chief Information Officer, St. Bernard Parish Hospital, Chalmette, LA, p. A299

LOOS, Greg, Chief Operating Officer, Black Hills Surgical Hospital, Rapid City, SD, p. A630

LOOSBROCK, Tammy, Senior Director, Sanford Luverne Medical Center, Luverne, MN, p. A379

LOOSEMORE, Tim, Director, Franciscan Health Crown Point, Crown Point, IN, p. A226
Regional Director Information Systems, Franciscan Health Michigan City, Michigan City, IN, p. A236

LOOSLI, Angela, Assistant Administrator, Operations, State Hospital South, Blackfoot, ID, p. A188

LOPACHIN, Vicki, M.D., Chief Medical Officer, The Mount Sinai Hospital, New York, NY, p. A492

LOPAS, Mary, Chief Information Officer, Door County Medical Center, Sturgeon Bay, WI, p. A797

LOPES, Michelle, MSN, R.N., Senior Vice President, Patient Care Services & Chief Nursing Officer, John Muir Medical Center, Walnut Creek, Walnut Creek, CA, p. A104

LOPEZ, Augustine, Chief Financial Officer, Salinas Valley Memorial Healthcare System, Salinas, CA, p. A90

LOPEZ, Cesar, R.N., Director of Nurses, Chi St. Josep. Health Grimes Hospital, Navasota, TX, p. A703

LOPEZ, David, FACHE, Executive Vice President and Chief Operating Officer, Parkland Health & Hospital System, Dallas, TX, p. A670

LOPEZ, Enrique, M.D., Medical Director, Larry B. Zieverink, Sr. Alcoholism Treatment Center, Raleigh, NC, p. A516

LOPEZ, Ericca, Director Human Resources, Canyon Ridge Hospital, Chino, CA, p. A60

LOPEZ, Ivonne, Director Human Resources, Hospital Oriente, Humacao, PR, p. A808

LOPEZ, Jose, M.D., Medical Staff President, Indiana University Health Paoli Hospital, Paoli, IN, p. A238

LOPEZ, Leonard, Chief Operating Officer, Hop. Health Care Center, Keams Canyon, AZ, p. A33

LOPEZ, Leonardo, President Medical Staff, Osf Saint Paul Medical Center, Mendota, IL, p. A212

LOPEZ, Lesbia, Chief Nursing Officer, Doctors' Center Hospital San Juan, San Juan, PR, p. A810

LOPEZ, Lisa, Director Human Resources, San Joaquin General Hospital, French Camp. CA, p. A65

LOPEZ, Maritza, M.D., Chief of Staff, Sanford Canby Medical Center, Canby, MN, p. A374

LOPEZ, Rene, Chief Executive Officer, Knap. Medical Center, Weslaco, TX, p. A725

LOPEZ, Robert, Chief Medical Officer, Highland Community Hospital, Picayune, MS, p. A398

LOPEZ, Rosalio, M.D., Senior Vice President and Chief Medical Officer, Pih Health Hospital - Whittier, Whittier, CA, p. A105

LOPEZ, Steve, Chief Financial Officer, Colorado River Medical Center, Needles, CA, p. A81

LOPEZ, Steve Kelley., Chief Executive Officer, Colorado River Medical Center, Needles, CA, p. A81

LOPEZ, Steven, M.D., Chief Medical Officer, Palmetto Lowcountry Behavioral Health, Charleston, SC, p. A616

LOPEZ, Susan Nordstrom., President, Advocate Illinois Masonic Medical Center, Chicago, IL, p. A197

LOPEZ, Trish, Area Chief Financial Officer, Kaiser Permanente Fontana Medical Center, Fontana, CA, p. A64

LOPEZ, Valerie, CPA, Chief Financial Officer, Uvalde Memorial Hospital, Uvalde, TX, p. A722

LOPEZ-CEPERO, Joe, Chief Nursing Officer, Good Samaritan Medical Center, West Palm Beach, FL, p. A162

LOPP, Rhonda, Chief Executive Officer, Eminent Medical Center, Richardson, TX, p. A708

LOPREATO, Elayne, Chief Clinical Officer, Kindred Hospital The Palm Beaches, Riviera Beach, FL, p. A155
Chief Executive Officer, Kindred Hospital The Palm Beaches, Riviera Beach, FL, p. A155

LORD, David, President, Osf St. Francis Hospital And Medical Group. Escanaba, MI, p. A354

LORD, Gregory, M.D., Chief Medical Officer, Clearsky Rehabilitation Hospital Of Leesville, Leesville, LA, p. A307

LORD, Jeff, Director of Nursing, Connecticut Veterans Home And Hospital, Rocky Hill, CT, p. A125

LORD, Robert L., JD, President and Chief Executive Officer, Cleveland Clinic Martin North Hospital, Stuart, FL, p. A158

LOREN, Alan, M.D., Chief Medical Officer, Northwest Community Healthcare, Arlington Heights, IL, p. A194

LORENTZ, Derick, Chief Financial Officer, Goodland Regional Medical Center, Goodland, KS, p. A265

LORENZ, Paul E., Chief Executive Officer, Santa Clara Valley Medical Center, San Jose, CA, p. A95

LORENZ, Todd, Administrator, Pam Rehabilitation Hospital Of Beaumont, Beaumont, TX, p. A658

LORENZEN, Shelli, Chief Human Resources Officer, Manning Regional Healthcare Center, Manning, IA, p. A253

LORENZO, Heather, M.D., Vice President and Chief Medical Officer, Meritus Medical Center, Hagerstown, MD, p. A330

LORISH, Tom, M.D., Interim Chief Executive, Providence Medford Medical Center, Medford, OR, p. A578

LORMAN, William, Ph.D., Clinical Director, Livengrin Foundation, Bensalem, PA, p. A584

LORMAND, Jared, Vice President Information Technology, Opelousas General Health System, Opelousas, LA, p. A312

LORTON, Donald, Executive Vice President, Centra Bedford Memorial Hospital, Bedford, VA, p. A739

LOSITO, Glenna, R.N., MSN, Chief Nursing Officer, Cibola General Hospital, Grants, NM, p. A469

LOTHE, Eric, FACHE, Executive Vice President and Chief Operating Officer, Unitypoint Health - Iowa Methodist Medical Center, Des Moines, IA, p. A248

LOTT, Benjamin, Chief Executive Officer, Copiah County Medical Center, Hazlehurst, MS, p. A394

LOTT, Cynthia, Director Human Resources, Northern Virginia Mental Health Institute, Falls Church, VA, p. A741

LOTT, Laura, Administrative Director, Eastern Louisiana Mental Health System, Jackson, LA, p. A303

LOTT, Rodney, Director Management Information Systems and Facility Operations, Baylor Scott & White Medical Center - Llano, Llano, TX, p. A696

LOTZE, Eberhard, M.D., Chief Medical Officer, Woman's Hospital Of Texas, Houston, TX, p. A689

LOUBERT, Cheryl, M.D., Chief Medical Staff, Midmichigan Medical Center-Gladwin, Gladwin, MI, p. A355

LOUDEN CORBETT, Jeanette, Chief Human Resources Officer, Highland Hospital, Oakland, CA, p. A82

LOUGHERY, Vicki, R.N., MS, Chief Nursing Officer, Monadnock Community Hospital, Peterborough, NH, p. A451

LOUGHRAN, Lisa, Chief Nursing Officer, Steele Memorial Medical Center, Salmon, ID, p. A193

LOUGHRAN, Michael, Vice President Human Resources, Kennedy Krieger Institute, Baltimore, MD, p. A324

LOUK, Rodney, Vice President Information Systems, Washington Hospital, Washington, PA, p. A610

LOUME, Ibrahima, Controller, Mount Carmel Rehabilitation Hospital, Westerville, OH, p. A552

LOVATO, Anthony, Director Information Technology, Coon Memorial Hospital, Dalhart, TX, p. A667

LOVDAHL, Brian A., Chief Executive Officer, Ccm Health, Montevideo, MN, p. A381

LOVE, Alex, Acting Manager Human Resources, Alexandria Veterans Affairs Health Care System, Pineville, LA, p. A312

LOVE, Bianca, Assistant Administrator Human Resources, Trinity Hospital Twin City, Dennison, OH, p. A539

LOVE, E, Director Fiscal Services, Eastern State Hospital, Williamsburg, VA, p. A753

LOVE, Glenn, M.D., Medical Director, Hilton Head Hospital, Hilton Head Island, SC, p. A621

LOVE, Matthew, Interim Chief Executive Officer, Nicklaus Children's Hospital, Miami, FL, p. A147

LOVE, Tami, Chief Financial Officer, Memorial Hospital Of Sweetwater County, Rock Springs, WY, p. A804

LOVE, Tim, Director Information Services, Reid Health, Richmond, IN, p. A239

LOVE, Valerie, Manager Business Office, Heatherhill Care Communities, Chardon, OH, p. A531

LOVEJOY, David, Chief Operations Officer, Riverview Psychiatric Center, Augusta, ME, p. A318

LOVEJOY, Leslie, R.N., Ph.D., Chief Nursing and Quality Officer, Sonoma Valley Hospital, Sonoma, CA, p. A99

LOVEJOY, Rob, Chief Operating Officer, Sanford Thief River Falls Behavioral Health Center, Thief River Falls, MN, p. A386
Director, Operations, Sanford Medical Center Thief River Falls, Thief River Falls, MN, p. A386

LOVELACE, Alan, Vice President and Chief Financial Officer, Stillwater Medical Center, Stillwater, OK, p. A568

LOVELACE, Christina, Director Human Resources, Gunnison Valley Hospital, Gunnison, CO, p. A114

LOVELACE, Corey, Chief Operating Officer, Kendall Regional Medical Center, Miami, FL, p. A146

LOVELESS, Jane Doll, Vice President, Chief Information Officer, Grand View Health, Sellersville, PA, p. A607

LOVELESS, Steve, Montana Region President, St. Vincent Healthcare, Billings, MT, p. A421

LOVELL, Charles D. Jr, FACHE, Chief Executive Officer, Barbourville Arh Hospital, Barbourville, KY, p. A280

LOVELL, Mark, Vice President and Chief Financial Officer, Prisma Health Tuomey Hospital, Sumter, SC, p. A624

LOVELL, Stephanie, Vice President and General Counsel, Boston Medical Center, Boston, MA, p. A335

LOVELL, Terrence, Vice President Human Resources, Union Hospital, Elkton, MD, p. A329

LOVELLETTE, Teresa, Manager Human Resources, Herrin Hospital, Herrin, IL, p. A207

LOVERA, Carlos, Director Information Systems, Montrose Memorial Hospital, Montrose, CO, p. A117

LOVERING, Keith, Information Technician, Miller County Hospital, Colquitt, GA, p. A169

LOVERING, Richard, Corporate Vice President Human Resources and Organizational Development, Atlanticare Regional Medical Center, Atlantic City, NJ, p. A452

LOVERN, Edward, President and Chief Executive Officer, Saint Agnes Healthcare, Baltimore, MD, p. A326

LOVERSO, Felice L., Ph.D., President and Chief Executive Officer, Casa Colina Hospital And Centers For Healthcare, Pomona, CA, p. A86

LOVING, David E., FACHE, Chief Executive Officer, St. Luke's Des Peres Hospital, Saint Louis, MO, p. A417

LOVING, Tonya, Director of Human Resources, Uva Encompass Health Rehabilitation Hospital, Charlottesville, VA, p. A740

LOVINGER, Warren, M.D., Chief Medical Officer, Nevada Regional Medical Center, Nevada, MO, p. A413

LOVINGOOD, Toni, Chief Operating Officer, Erlanger Western Carolina Hospital, Murphy, NC, p. A515

LOVRICH, John, Chief Financial Officer, Catalina Island Medical Center, Avalon, CA, p. A56

Chief Financial Officer, Glenn Medical Center, Willows, CA, p. A105

LOW, Kern, M.D., Chief Medical Officer, St. Mary-Corwin Medical Center, Pueblo, CO, p. A118

M.D., Chief Medical Officer, St. Thomas More Hospital, Canon City, CO, p. A108

LOW, Lewis, M.D., Chief Medical Officer, Legacy Mount Hood Medical Center, Gresham, OR, p. A575

M.D., Senior Vice President and Chief Medical Officer, Legacy Meridian Park Medical Center, Tualatin, OR, p. A582

M.D., Senior Vice President and Chief Medical Officer, Legacy Salmon Creek Medical Center, Vancouver, WA, p. A768

LOWE, Bren, Chief Executive Officer, Star Valley Health, Afton, WY, p. A801

LOWE, E, FACHE, Operations Support Risk Management and Compliance, St. Francis Hospital, Columbus, GA, p. A169

LOWE, E Rick, FACHE, Chief Executive Officer, Select Specialty Hospital-Augusta, Augusta, GA, p. A166

LOWE, Joe, Director Management Information Systems, Cumberland Medical Center, Crossville, TN, p. A637

LOWE, Kristen, Chief Executive Officer, Post Acute/Warm Springs Specialty Hospital Of San Antonio, San Antonio, TX, p. A713

LOWE, Lavah, Chief Nursing Officer, Avista Adventist Hospital, Louisville, CO, p. A116

LOWE, Rob, Director, Healthcare Information Management, Onslow Memorial Hospital, Jacksonville, NC, p. A513

LOWE, Scott, Director Human Resource, Mcalester Regional Health Center, Mcalester, OK, p. A562

Market Chief Executive Officer, Physicians Regional - Pine Ridge, Naples, FL, p. A149

LOWELL, David, M.D., Chief Medical Officer, Spaulding Rehabilitation Hospital Cap. Cod, East Sandwich, MA, p. A338

LOWENTHAL, David, M.D., Clinical Director, New York State Psychiatric Institute, New York, NY, p. A491

LOWENTHAL, Steve, M.D., M.P.H., FACS, Senior Vice President Medical Affairs and Chief Medical Officer, Rush-Copley Medical Center, Aurora, IL, p. A195

LOWERY, Brad, Director of Operations, Atmore Community Hospital, Atmore, AL, p. A14

LOWERY, John, M.D., Deputy Commander Clinical Services, General Leonard Wood Army Community Hospital, Fort Leonard Wood, MO, p. A406

LOWERY, Josh, Director of Human Resources, Baptist Memorial Hospital-North Mississippi, Oxford, MS, p. A398

LOWMAN, LeeAnn, Director Human Resources, Lake Taylor Transitional Care Hospital, Norfolk, VA, p. A748

LOWREY, Linda, Human Resources Officer, Atmore Community Hospital, Atmore, AL, p. A14

LOWRY, David, M.D., Chief Medical Officer, Caldwell Unc Health Care, Lenoir, NC, p. A513

LOWRY, Emma L., M.D., Acting Facility Director, Chief Executive Officer, Piedmont Geriatric Hospital, Burkeville, VA, p. A739

LOY, Michael, FACHE, Chief Executive Officer, North Central Health Care, Wausau, WI, p. A798

LOYA, Velma, Administrative Human Resource Coordinator, Rice Medical Center, Eagle Lake, TX, p. A673

LOYD, Chris, Director Human Resources, Methodist Richardson Medical Center, Richardson, TX, p. A708

LOYD, Stephana, Vice President, Chief Nursing Officer, Baptist Health Medical Center - Conway, Conway, AR, p. A43

LOYKE, Christopher, Chief Medical Officer, University Hospitals Parma Medical Center, Parma, OH, p. A547

LOYO-RODRIGUEZ, Raul, Administrative Analyst III, San Diego County Psychiatric Hospital, San Diego, CA, p. A92

LOZADA, Leonardo, M.D., Chief Physician Executive, Saint Luke's North Hospital - Barry Road, Kansas City, MO, p. A409

LOZANO, Elias, Executive Officer, Tripler Army Medical Center, Honolulu, HI, p. A185

LOZANO, Melanie, Chief Financial Officer, Concho County Hospital, Eden, TX, p. A673

LOZIER, Tim, Director Human Resources, Vibra Specialty Hospital At Desoto, Desoto, TX, p. A673

LUBARSKY, Neil, Senior Vice President, Finance and Chief Financial Officer, Thomas Jefferson University Hospitals, Philadelphia, PA, p. A602

LUBINSKY, Jeanie, Chief Financial Officer, Mayo Clinic Health System - Red Cedar In Menomonie, Menomonie, WI, p. A789

LUCAS, Bob, Vice President Operations, King's Daughters Medical Center, Ashland, KY, p. A280

LUCAS, Christine, Chief of Staff, Union County Hospital, Anna, IL, p. A194

LUCAS, Jaime, Administrator, Compass Behavioral Center Of Marksville, Marksville, LA, p. A308

LUCAS, Kasey, Chief Executive Officer, Hospital Administrator, Salem Memorial District Hospital, Salem, MO, p. A418

LUCAS, Kelly, Chief Information Officer, Sampson Regional Medical Center, Clinton, NC, p. A507

LUCAS, Marshall, M.D., Medical Director, Cypress Creek Hospital, Houston, TX, p. A685

LUCAS JR, BennyChief Nursing Executive, St. Joseph's Behavioral Health Center, Stockton, CA, p. A100

LUCCHESI, Michael, M.D., Chief Medical Officer; Chair, Emergency Medicine, Suny Downstate-University Hospital Of Brooklyn, Brooklyn, NY, p. A479

LUCE, Glenda, Chief Nursing Officer, Memorial Hospital Of Gardena, Gardena, CA, p. A66

LUCE, Paul W., R.N., MSN, Vice President Operations, Miami County Medical Center, Paola, KS, p. A274

LUCENA, Ann, Chief Executive Officer, San Ramon Regional Medical Center, San Ramon, CA, p. A96

LUCENA, Yelitza, Executive Director, Hospital Metropolitano Dr. Susoni, Arecibo, PR, p. A806

LUCERO, Brenda, Chief Clinical Officer, Cornerstone Hospital Of Houston At Clearlake, Webster, TX, p. A724

LUCERO, Lupe, Manager Business Office, Presbyterian Espanola Hospital, Espanola, NM, p. A469

LUCEY, Jeffery, M.D., Clinical Director, Kingsboro Psychiatric Center, Brooklyn, NY, p. A478

LUCHSINGER, Catherine, MSN, Chief Nursing Officer, Halifax Health Medical Center Of Daytona Beach, Daytona Beach, FL, p. A136

LUCIA, Sandra, Director Health Information and Corporate Compliance Officer, Hampstead Hospital, Hampstead, NH, p. A449

LUCIANO, Lisa, D.O., Medical Director, Hackensack Meridian Health Shore Rehabilitation Institute, Brick, NJ, p. A452

LUCIER, Robbyn, Director Human Resources, Up Health System-Portage, Hancock, MI, p. A357

LUCKE, Kim, Vice President Finance, Northern Montana Health Care, Havre, MT, p. A425

LUCKETT, Douglas R., Interim Chief Executive Officer, Longview Regional Medical Center, Longview, TX, p. A697

LUCORE, Charles, M.D., President, St. Francis Hospital, The Heart Center, Roslyn, NY, p. A497

LUDFORD, Brad, Chief Financial Officer, Bozeman Health, Bozeman, MT, p. A422

LUDWIG, John A., President and Chief Operating Officer, Hshs St. Joseph's Hospital, Highland, IL, p. A207

LUDWIG, Walter, President, Kenmore Mercy Hospital, Kenmore, NY, p. A486

LUEBBERING, Tom, Vice President Finance, Capital Region Medical Center, Jefferson City, MO, p. A408

LUEBCKE, Diane, R.N., Director Nursing, Community Memorial Healthcare, Marysville, KS, p. A270

LUECHT, Jackie, Chief Human Resources Officer, Mercyone North Iowa Medical Center, Mason City, IA, p. A254

Director, Human Resources, Mercyone New Hampton Medical Center, New Hampton, IA, p. A255

LUEDDERS, Keith, Chief Operations Officer, Tri Valley Health System, Cambridge, NE, p. A430

LUEDERS, Kathy, R.N., Director of Nursing-Acute Care, Saint Elizabeth's Medical Center, Wabasha, MN, p. A387

LUEHRS, Bill, Chief Human Resources Officer, Northshore University Health System, Evanston, IL, p. A204

LUEHRS, Paul, Chief Operating Officer, Mercy San Juan Medical Center, Carmichael, CA, p. A59

LUELLEN, John, M.D., Chief Operating Officer, Heritage Valley Health System, Beaver, PA, p. A584

M.D., Chief Operating Officer, Sewickley Valley Hospital, (A Division Of Valley Medical Facilities), Sewickley, PA, p. A608

LUFF, Brian, Chief Executive Officer, Quillen Rehabilitation Hospital, Johnson City, TN, p. A640

LUFKIN, Kirk, M.D., VPMA, Mclaren Northern Michigan, Petoskey, MI, p. A363

LUGER, Gerald, M.D., President Medical Staff, Gottlieb Memorial Hospital, Melrose Park, IL, p. A212

LUGO, Cesar, Director of Nursing, Victor Valley Global Medical Center, Victorville, CA, p. A104

LUHRS, Jason, Vice President Fiscal Services, Westfields Hospital And Clinic, New Richmond, WI, p. A792

LUKE, Leslie Paul., President and Chief Executive Officer, St. Joseph's Hospital Health Center, Syracuse, NY, p. A499

LUKENS, Tammy, Director Information, Kosciusko Community Hospital, Warsaw, IN, p. A242

LUKER, Patricia A., Interim Chief Executive Officer, Perry Memorial Hospital, Princeton, IL, p. A218

LUKISH, Kris, Human Resources Officer, Chippenham Hospital, Richmond, VA, p. A750

LUKSAN, Abel, M.D., Chief Medical Officer, Mary Lanning Healthcare, Hastings, NE, p. A433

LULICH, Diane, Director Human Resources, Memorial Medical Center Of Ashland, Ashland, WI, p. A779

LULL, Todd, Director Information Technology, Southwest Health, Platteville, WI, p. A794

LULOFF, Lynn, Chief Financial Officer, Winneshiek Medical Center, Decorah, IA, p. A248

LUMPKINS, Deborah, MSN, Chief Nursing Officer, Maury Regional Hospital, Columbia, TN, p. A636

LUMPP, Karen, Senior Vice President and Chief Financial Officer, Trinitas Regional Medical Center, Elizabeth, NJ, p. A455

LUMSDEN, Chris A., President and Chief Executive Officer, Northern Regional Hospital, Mount Airy, NC, p. A515

LUNA, Raul, Chief Nurse Executive, El Paso Psychiatric Center, El Paso, TX, p. A675

LUNA, Tony, M.D., Chief of Staff, Minneola District Hospital, Minneola, KS, p. A271

LUND, Dennis, M.D., Chief Medical Officer, Lucile Packard Children's Hospital Stanford, Palo Alto, CA, p. A84

LUND, Elizabeth, M.D., Chief of Staff, West Tennessee Healthcare Volunteer Hospital, Martin, TN, p. A643

LUND, Maggie, Chief Human Resources Officer, Theda Care Medical Center - Wild Rose, Wild Rose, WI, p. A799

LUNDAL, David, Senior Vice President Information Systems and Chief Information Officer, Amita Health Holy Family Medical Center, Des Plaines, IL, p. A202

LUNDBERG, Lanetta, Vice President Culture and People, Peacehealth Ketchikan Medical Center, Ketchikan, AK, p. A28

LUNDBERG, Maggie, R.N., Chief Nursing Officer, Saint Barnabas Medical Center, Livingston, NJ, p. A457

LUNDBLAD, Jackie, Chief Financial Officer, Wickenburg Community Hospital, Wickenburg, AZ, p. A41

LUNDE, Eric E., President, Kettering Health Network Troy Hospital, Troy, OH, p. A551

LUNDE, Susan, R.N., Director of Nursing, Fallon Medical Complex, Baker, MT, p. A421

LUNDERGAN, Dan, Chief Operating Officer, University Of Utah Health, Salt Lake City, UT, p. A733

LUNDY, Kelly, Chief Information Officer, Peacehealth St. Josep. Medical Center, Bellingham, WA, p. A755

LUNDY, Marcel, Chief Information Officer, Putnam General Hospital, Eatonton, GA, p. A172

LUNDY, Noah, Director of Human Resources, Northern Light Maine Coast Hospital, Ellsworth, ME, p. A320

LUNDY-PAINE, Robert, Director Information Systems, Alameda Hospital, Alameda, CA, p. A55

LUNN, William, M.D., Chief Executive Officer, Chippenham Hospital, Richmond, VA, p. A750

LUNNEBORG, Brandi, Chief Executive Officer, Phoebe Sumter Medical Center, Americus, GA, p. A163

LUNNEY, Kathleen, MS, R.N., Vice President Patient Care Services and Chief Nursing Officer, Montefiore Nyack Hospital, Nyack, NY, p. A493

LUNSFORD, Cindy, Executive Vice President and Chief Operating Officer, Tidalhealth Peninsula, Salisbury, MD, p. A332

LUNSFORD, Kaye, System Director Human Resources, St. Vincent's Medical Center Southside, Jacksonville, FL, p. A141

LUNT, Kimberly, Controller, Encompass Health Rehabilitation Hospital Of Spring Hill, Brooksville, FL, p. A133

LUNTZ, Adam, Chief Financial Officer, Aultman Orrville Hospital, Orrville, OH, p. A547

LUOMA, Michael, M.D., Chief of Staff, Aspirus Keweenaw Hospital, Inc., Laurium, MI, p. A360

LUPINACCI, Michael, M.D., Medical Director, Encompass Health Rehabilitation Hospital Of Mechanicsburg, Mechanicsburg, PA, p. A596

LUSKIN-HAWK, Roberta, M.D., Chief Executive, Redwood Memorial Hospital, Fortuna, CA, p. A64

M.D., Chief Executive, St. Josep. Hospital Eureka, Eureka, CA, p. A63

LUSSIER, Shirley, Vice President Human Resources, Northeast Rehabilitation Hospital, Salem, NH, p. A451

LUSTERIO, Efren, Director of Nursing, Behavioral Center Of Michigan, Warren, MI, p. A369

LUTES, Adrianne, Chief Executive Officer, Select Specialty Hospital Daytona Beach, Daytona Beach, FL, p. A136

LUTHER, Lori, CPA, Chief Operating Officer, Indiana University Health Ball Memorial Hospital, Muncie, IN, p. A237

LUTHER, Tracie, Director Employee and Labor Relations, Brooks Memorial Hospital, Dunkirk, NY, p. A482

LUTHER, Vera, M.D., Chief of Staff, Sabine County Hospital, Hemphill, TX, p. A683

LUTKENHAUS, Tiffany, Chief Nursing Officer, Muenster Memorial Hospital, Muenster, TX, p. A702

LUTZ, Barbara, Vice President Human Resources, Heart Of The Rockies Regional Medical Center, Salida, CO, p. A118

LUTZ, Denise, Chief Human Resources Officer, Chi St. Alexius Health - Dickinson Medical Center, Dickinson, ND, p. A522

LUTZ, Don, Director Information Technology, St. Luke's Easton Campus, Easton, PA, p. A589

LUTZ, Kevin, DPM, Chief Operating Officer, Grant, Ohiohealth Grant Medical Center, Columbus, OH, p. A536

LUTZ, Roger, Chief Information Officer, Butler Health System, Butler, PA, p. A585

LUTZ, Terry, Chief Financial Officer, Scheurer Health, Pigeon, MI, p. A363

LUX, Teresa, President and Chief Operating Officer, Froedtert West Bend Hospital, West Bend, WI, p. A799

LUX, Teresa M., President and Chief Operating Officer, Froedtert Menomonee Falls Hospital, Menomonee Falls, WI, p. A789

LYDON, Jean, MS, R.N., System Vice President Operations, Chief Nursing Officer, Elmhurst Hospital, Elmhurst, IL, p. A204

LYLE, Janet, Chief Human Resources and Allied Health Services, Springfield Hospital, Springfield, VT, p. A736

LYMAN, Jeremy, Chief Executive Officer, Blue Mountain Hospital, Blanding, UT, p. A727

LYNAM, Sheila, M.D., Chief Medical Officer, Peacehealth St. John Medical Center, Longview, WA, p. A760

LYNCE, Danialle, Business Partner Human Resources, Uh Conneaut Medical Center, Conneaut, OH, p. A537
Business Partner Human Resources, Uh Geneva Medical Center, Geneva, OH, p. A541
Manager Human Resources, Uh Geauga Medical Center, Chardon, OH, p. A531

LYNCH, Becky, Manager Business Entity Management and Information Systems, Osf St. Mary Medical Center, Galesburg, IL, p. A205

LYNCH, Beth, MS, Chief Executive Officer, Encompass Health Rehabilitation Hospital Of Tinton Falls, Tinton Falls, NJ, p. A464

LYNCH, Cecelia, R.N., MS, Vice President Patient Care Services and Chief Nursing Officer, Lowell General Hospital, Lowell, MA, p. A341

LYNCH, Danile, Chief Operating Officer, Saint Luke Institute, Silver Spring, MD, p. A332

LYNCH, Elizabeth, Vice President Human Resources, The Hospital Of Central Connecticut, New Britain, CT, p. A123

LYNCH, G, M.D., Chief Medical Officer, Inova Fair Oaks Hospital, Fairfax, VA, p. A741

LYNCH, James, M.D., Interim Chief Executive Officer, Beaumont Hospital - Grosse Pointe, Grosse Pointe, MI, p. A357
M.D., Interim President, Beaumont Hospital - Troy, Troy, MI, p. A368
M.D., Senior Vice President and Chief Medical Officer, Beaumont Hospital - Troy, Troy, MI, p. A368

LYNCH, John, M.D., President, Barnes-Jewish Hospital, Saint Louis, MO, p. A415
Vice President and Chief Information Officer, Faxton St. Luke's Healthcare, Utica, NY, p. A500

LYNCH, Lisa, Chief Financial Officer, Illinois Valley Community Hospital, Peru, IL, p. A217

LYNCH, Marc, D.O., Chief of Staff, Kindred Hospital-Ontario, Ontario, CA, p. A82

LYNCH, Megan, Manager Human Resources, Johnson Memorial Health Services, Dawson, MN, p. A375

LYNCH, Michael, M.D., Chief Medical Officer, Alice Peck Day Memorial Hospital, Lebanon, NH, p. A449

LYNCH, Robert, M.D., Chief Executive Officer, Tulane Health System, New Orleans, LA, p. A311

LYNCH, Tim, Director of Finance, Fairview Lakes Health Services, Wyoming, MN, p. A388
Director of Finance, Fairview Northland Medical Center, Princeton, MN, p. A383

LYNCH, Torie, Manager Human Resources, Central Montana Medical Center, Lewistown, MT, p. A425

LYNCH, Tricia D., Chief Nursing Officer, First Surgical Hospital, Bellaire, TX, p. A659

LYNCH, William, Executive Vice President and Chief Operating Officer, Jamaica Hospital Medical Center, Jamaica, NY, p. A486

LYNCH III, Ernest C., FACHE, President and Chief Executive Officer, Medical City Mckinney, Mckinney, TX, p. A700

LYNCH-KILIC, Cathy, Vice President Human Resources, St. Mary's General Hospital, Passaic, NJ, p. A460

LYND, Samuel, Administrator and Chief Executive Officer, Nea Baptist Memorial Hospital, Jonesboro, AR, p. A48

LYNE, Marjorie, Associate Director for Patient Care Services, Hunter Holmes Mcguire Veterans Affairs Medical Center-Richmond, Richmond, VA, p. A750

LYNN, Christina, M.D., Medical Director, Three Rivers Behavioral Health, West Columbia, SC, p. A625

LYNN, Jason, Director Finance, St. Vincent's St. Clair, Pell City, AL, p. A23

LYNN, Michelle, Chief Executive Officer, Hospital For Behavioral Medicine, Worcester, MA, p. A346

LYNN, Priscilla, President and Chief Executive Officer, Saint Alphonsus Medical Center - Baker City, Baker City, OR, p. A573

LYNN, Samuel, Director Human Resources, Northwest Texas Healthcare System, Amarillo, TX, p. A652

LYNSKEY, Jeanne, Vice President and Chief Financial Officer, Milford Regional Medical Center, Milford, MA, p. A341

LYON, Steve, Senior Director Human Resources, Grande Ronde Hospital, La Grande, OR, p. A576

LYON, Tami, Director Human Resources, Community Memorial Hospital, Burke, SD, p. A626

LYONS, Althea, Vice President Human Resources and Development, Beverly Hospital, Beverly, MA, p. A334

LYONS, Denise, Chief Nursing Officer, Cumberland Hall Hospital, Hopkinsville, KY, p. A285

LYONS, Jim, President, Hutchinson Health, Hutchinson, MN, p. A378

LYONS, Lenny, Administrator, Orem Community Hospital, Orem, UT, p. A730

LYONS, Michael, Regional Director Information Services, Shriners Hospitals For Children-Galveston, Galveston, TX, p. A680
Regional Information Systems Director, Shriners Hospitals For Children-Shreveport, Shreveport, LA, p. A314

LYONS, Micki, Chief Executive Officer, Crook County Medical Services District, Sundance, WY, p. A804

LYONS, Rowena, Human Resource Manager, Indian Path Community Hospital, Kingsport, TN, p. A641

LYONS, Timothy, M.D., Chief Medical Officer, Adventist Health St. Helena, Saint Helena, CA, p. A90

LYREN, Joseph, Chief Financial Officer, Ohiohealth Medcentral Mansfield Hospital, Mansfield, OH, p. A544

LYSAGHT, Marcia, R.N., MSN, Associate Director Patient Care Services, Miami Veterans Affairs Healthcare System, Miami, FL, p. A147

LYSAGHT, William, Chief Financial Officer, Kindred Hospital Las Vegas-Sahara, Henderson, NV, p. A442

LYTHGOE, Derek, Chief Financial Officer, Banner Baywood Medical Center, Mesa, AZ, p. A33
Chief Financial Officer, Banner Heart Hospital, Mesa, AZ, p. A34

L'ITALIEN, Mark, Director Information Services, Salem Regional Medical Center, Salem, OH, p. A548

# M

MAAMARI, Marcela, Chief Operating Officer, United Medical Center, Washington, DC, p. A130

MAAS, Vernon, M.D., Vice President, Medical Affairs, Ascension St. Vincent Evansville, Evansville, IN, p. A227

MAASS, Judith, Chief Executive Officer, Lac-Olive View-Ucla Medical Center, Sylmar, CA, p. A100

MACAFEE, Francis, Vice President Finance and Chief Financial Officer, Guthrie Corning Hospital, Corning, NY, p. A481

MACAFFEE, Laurie, Director of Nursing, Willow Springs Center, Reno, NV, p. A446

MACARONAS, Thomas, Chief Financial Officer, Labette Health, Parsons, KS, p. A274

MACATOL, Matthew, M.D., President Medical Staff, Marietta Memorial Hospital, Marietta, OH, p. A544

MACDONALD, Joan, R.N., MSN, Chief Nursing Officer, Vice President Nursing Services, Aurelia Osborn Fox Memorial Hospital, Oneonta, NY, p. A494

MACDONALD, Laurie, Vice President Finance, Penn Highlands Elk, Saint Marys, PA, p. A606

MACDONALD, Neil, Vice President, Operations, Medstar Union Memorial Hospital, Baltimore, MD, p. A325

MACDONELL, Jean, President and Chief Executive Officer, Grand Itasca Clinic And Hospital, Grand Rapids, MN, p. A377

MACDOUGALL, David, Chief Financial Officer, United Health Services Hospitals-Binghamton, Binghamton, NY, p. A476

MACE, T., Chief Medical Officer, Garden Park Medical Center, Gulfport, MS, p. A393

MACEVOY, Bonnie, Chief of Staff, Mad River Community Hospital, Arcata, CA, p. A56

MACFADYEN, James, M.D., Medical Director, St. John Vianney Hospital, Downingtown, PA, p. A588

MACH, Robert, Chief Executive Officer, Select Specialty Hospital-Battle Creek, Battle Creek, MI, p. A349

MACHADO, James, President, St. Vincent's Medical Center Clay County, Middleburg, FL, p. A148

MACHADO, Richard, M.D., President and Chief Executive Officer, Bayamon Medical Center, Bayamon, PR, p. A806

MACHOKA, Alistair, Chief Operating Officer, Corona Regional Medical Center, Corona, CA, p. A61

MACHORRO, Vicky, R.N., Chief Nursing Officer, Kittitas Valley Healthcare, Ellensburg, WA, p. A757

MACIAG, Jeanne, Director of Nursing, Rosebud Health Care Center, Forsyth, MT, p. A423

MACIAS, Teresa, Administrator, California Mens Colony Correctional Treatment Center, San Luis Obispo, CA, p. A95

MACIEL, Maureen, M.D., Chief of Staff, Shriners Hospitals For Children-Tampa, Tampa, FL, p. A159

MACK, Charles, Vice President Finance and Chief Financial Officer, Merit Health Natchez, Natchez, MS, p. A397

MACK, Kristina, Manager, Human Resources, San Dimas Community Hospital, San Dimas, CA, p. A93

MACKAY, Cristal, Chief Operating Officer, Banner Desert Medical Center, Mesa, AZ, p. A33

MACKEN-MARBLE, Kelly, Interim President and Chief Executive Officer, Unity Medical & Surgical Hospital, Mishawaka, IN, p. A236

MACKENROTH, Robin, Chief Operating Officer, Kaiser Permanente Riverside Medical Center, Riverside, CA, p. A88

MACKETT, Charles, M.D., Senior Vice President and Chief Medical Officer, Cleveland Clinic Indian River Hospital, Vero Beach, FL, p. A161

MACKEY, Denise, Administrator, Hale Ho'Ola Hamakua, Honokaa, HI, p. A184

MACKIN, Stephen, President, Mercy Hospital St. Louis, Saint Louis, MO, p. A416

MACKINNON, Paul, MS, R.N., Chief Operating Officer, Umass Memorial Healthalliance-Clinton Hospital, Leominster, MA, p. A340

MACKSOOD, Dan, Regional Senior Vice President and Chief Financial Officer, Good Samaritan Hospital Medical Center, West Islip. NY, p. A502

MACLAUGHLIN, Jeremy, Director Human Resources, Citizens Memorial Hospital, Bolivar, MO, p. A402

MACLENNAN, Alex, Chief Human Resources Officer, Tahoe Forest Hospital District, Truckee, CA, p. A102

MACLEOD, Deborah, MS, R.N., Vice President Nursing and Patient Care Services, Mid Coast Hospital, Brunswick, ME, p. A319

MACNICOL, Daniel, Chief Executive Officer, Encompass Health Rehabilitation Hospital Of Dallas, Dallas, TX, p. A668

MACOGAY, Melissa, Vice President and Chief Nursing Officer, Johns Hopkins All Children's Hospital, Saint Petersburg, FL, p. A156

MACPHEE, Alan, Chief Executive Officer, Kahuku Medical Center, Kahuku, HI, p. A185

MACRI, Fredrick, Executive Vice President, Rhode Island Hospital, Providence, RI, p. A614

MACYK, Irene.R.N., MS, Ph.D., Chief Nursing Officer, North Shore University Hospital, Manhasset, NY, p. A487

MADAN, Sunil, M.D., Chief Medical Officer and Chief Population Health Officer, Doctors Community Hospital, Lanham, MD, p. A330

MADDEN, Ann Marie, MS, R.N., Vice President of Patient Care Services and Chief Nursing Officer, Moses H. Cone Memorial Hospital, Greensboro, NC, p. A511

MADDEN, R., Director Employee Relations, Reynolds Memorial Hospital, Glen Dale, WV, p. A772

MADDEN RICE, Ann, President, Abbott Northwestern Hospital, Minneapolis, MN, p. A380

MADDOX, Dale, Chief Financial Officer, Medical Center Of South Arkansas, El Dorado, AR, p. A44

MADDOX, Jamie, Chief Nursing Officer, Christus Mother Frances Hospital - Jacksonville, Jacksonville, TX, p. A691

MADER, Elaine, M.D., Chief of Staff, Integris Miami Hospital, Miami, OK, p. A562

MADER, Frank, Director Information Services, East Liverpool City Hospital, East Liverpool, OH, p. A539

MADER, Vikki, Director Health Information Services, Pratt Regional Medical Center, Pratt, KS, p. A275

MADIGAN, Catherine, Chief Nursing Executive, University Of North Carolina Hospitals, Chapel Hill, NC, p. A506

MADKINS, Catrina, Controller and Chief Financial Officer, Encompass Health Rehabilitation Hospital Of Plano, Plano, TX, p. A707

MADRID, Melissa, R.N., Chief Nursing Officer, Harper County Community Hospital, Buffalo, OK, p. A557

MADSEN, Greg T., Chief Executive Officer, Carilion Stonewall Jackson Hospital, Lexington, VA, p. A744

MAEKAWA, Steve, Chief Financial Officer, Garfield Medical Center, Monterey Park, CA, p. A79

MAENIUS, Linda, Chief Financial Officer, Laurel Ridge Treatment Center, San Antonio, TX, p. A712

MAERTENS, Mary B., FACHE, President and Chief Executive Officer, Avera Marshall Regional Medical Center, Marshall, MN, p. A380

MAES, Jillian, Director Marketing and Public Relations, St. Thomas More Hospital, Canon City, CO, p. A108

MAES, Stephen, Director Information Systems, Franciscan Health Olympia Fields, Olympia Fields, IL, p. A215

MAESTAS, Sadie, Interim Chief Nursing Officer, Copper Queen Community Hospital, Bisbee, AZ, p. A30

MAGDANGAL, Connie, Executive Vice President and Chief Financial Officer, Bergen New Bridge Medical Center, Paramus, NJ, p. A460

MAGEE, Becky, Chief Information Officer, Washington Regional Medical Center, Fayetteville, AR, p. A45

MAGEE, James L., Executive Director, Piggott Community Hospital, Piggott, AR, p. A52

MAGEE, Robert, Director Human Resources, Shriners Hospitals For Children-Galveston, Galveston, TX, p. A680

   Director Human Resources, Shriners Hospitals For Children-Houston, Houston, TX, p. A688

MAGEE, William, Chief Financial Officer, Alliance Healthcare System, Holly Springs, MS, p. A394

MAGER, Angela, Director, Human Resources, Kadlec Regional Medical Center, Richland, WA, p. A763

MAGER, Dan, Administrator, Vance Johnson Recovery Center, Las Vegas, NV, p. A445

MAGES, Jill, Chief Human Resource Officer, Myrtue Medical Center, Harlan, IA, p. A251

MAGESTRO, Ben, Chief Operating Officer, North Central Surgical Center, Dallas, TX, p. A669

MAGGARD, Amanda, Chief Executive Officer, Adventhealth Dade City, Dade City, FL, p. A135

   President and Chief Executive Officer, Adventhealth Zephyrhills, Zephyrhills, FL, p. A162

MAGHAZEHE, Al, Ph.D., FACHE, President and Chief Executive Officer, Capital Health Medical Center-Hopewell, Pennington, NJ, p. A461

   Ph.D., FACHE, President and Chief Executive Officer, Capital Health Regional Medical Center, Trenton, NJ, p. A464

MAGID, Philip, Director Fiscal Services, Shriners Hospitals For Children-Chicago, Chicago, IL, p. A201

MAGNER, Kile, Administrator, Ellinwood District Hospital, Ellinwood, KS, p. A264

MAGNUSON, Johna, Director Nursing, Hillsboro Community Hospital, Hillsboro, KS, p. A266

MAGRO, Michael, D.O., President, Nazareth Hospital, Philadelphia, PA, p. A601

MAGU, Bharat, M.D., Chief Medical Officer, Yuma Regional Medical Center, Yuma, AZ, p. A41

MAGUIRE, Christina, Senior Vice President, Chief Operating Officer and Chief Financial Officer, Mount Desert Island Hospital, Bar Harbor, ME, p. A318

MAGUIRE, David, M.D., Vice President Medical Affairs, Baystate Wing Hospital, Palmer, MA, p. A343

MAGUIRE, Kimberly, Chief Nursing Officer, Mercy Health Hackley Campus, Muskegon, MI, p. A362

MAGUREAN, Vickie, Chief Financial Officer, Englewood Community Hospital, Englewood, FL, p. A137

   Chief Financial Officer, Fawcett Memorial Hospital, Port Charlotte, FL, p. A155

   Chief Financial Officer, Seven Rivers Regional Medical Center, Crystal River, FL, p. A135

MAGUTA, Sam, Coordinator Information Systems, Devereux Advanced Behavioral Health Georgia, Kennesaw, GA, p. A174

MAHAN, Michelle, Senior Vice President and Chief Financial Officer, Frederick Health, Frederick, MD, p. A329

MAHAN, Vic, Chief Information Officer, Chino Valley Medical Center, Chino, CA, p. A60

   Director Information Systems, Garden Grove Hospital And Medical Center, Garden Grove, CA, p. A66

   Director Information Technology, La Palma Intercommunity Hospital, La Palma, CA, p. A70

   Director Information Technology, West Anaheim Medical Center, Anaheim, CA, p. A55

MAHAR, Priscilla, Chief Operating Officer, Spectrum Health United Hospital, Greenville, MI, p. A356

MAHER, Donna, R.N., Chief Operating Officer, Morton Hospital And Medical Center, Taunton, MA, p. A345

MAHER, John, Executive Vice President and Chief Financial Officer, Nassau University Medical Center, East Meadow, NY, p. A483

MAHER, Sean, Director Human Resources, Devereux Children's Behavioral Health Center, Malvern, PA, p. A596

MAHER, Thomas, Chief Executive Officer and Administrator, Boulder City Hospital, Boulder City, NV, p. A441

MAHERA, Tina, M.D., Chief Medical Officer, Garfield Park Hospital, Chicago, IL, p. A198

MAHESHWARI, Narendra, M.D., Chief of Staff, Broward Health North, Deerfield Beach, FL, p. A136

MAHL, Morgan, Director Human Resources, St. Luke's Hospital - Warren Campus, Phillipsburg, NJ, p. A461

MAHLE, Thomas J., Chief Executive Officer, Palm Point Behavioral Health, Titusville, FL, p. A160

MAHMOOD, Ahsan, M.D., Chief Medical Officer, Hamilton Center, Terre Haute, IN, p. A241

MAHNEKE, Suzette, Associate Vice President of Nursing, Amita Health Adventist Medical Center Glenoaks, Glendale Heights, IL, p. A206

MAHONE, William, President, Vidant North Hospital, Roanoke Rapids, NC, p. A517

MAHONEY, Bryan, Chief Financial Officer, Columbia Memorial Hospital, Hudson, NY, p. A485

MAHONEY, James, Chief Information Officer, Upmc Memorial, York, PA, p. A612

MAHONEY, Nicole, Chief Financial Officer, Pioneer Memorial Hospital, Heppner, OR, p. A575

MAHONEY, William K., FACHE, President and Senior Vice President, Community Hospital Group. Cox Medical Center Branson, Branson, MO, p. A403

MAHR, Cecile M., Chief Executive Officer, Clearvista Health And Wellness, Lorain, OH, p. A543

MAHR-CHAN, Lydia, Director of Human Resources, Chinese Hospital, San Francisco, CA, p. A93

MAIBERGER, Michael J., President, Miami Valley Hospital, Dayton, OH, p. A538

MAIDEN, Phillip. M.D., Medical Director, Belmont Pines Hospital, Youngstown, OH, p. A553

MAIER, Cindy, R.N., Director of Nursing, Ness County Hospital District No 2, Ness City, KS, p. A272

MAIER, Walter, Chief of Staff, Mountains Community Hospital, Lake Arrowhead, CA, p. A70

MAIETTA, Carol, Vice President Human Resources and Chief Learning Officer, St. Vincent's East, Birmingham, AL, p. A15

MAIJALA, Jake, Chief Human Resource Officer, Penn Highlands Dubois, Dubois, PA, p. A588

MAIN, Cleo, Finance Officer, Blackfeet Community Hospital, Saint Mary, MT, p. A427

MAINE, David N., M.D., President and Chief Executive Officer, Mercy Medical Center, Baltimore, MD, p. A325

MAINES, Stephanie, Chief Nursing Officer, Crossroads Community Hospital, Mount Vernon, IL, p. A213

MAIRE, Jeffrey, M.D., Chief of Staff, Audubon County Memorial Hospital And Clinics, Audubon, IA, p. A243

MAIZE, Makyla, Director Information Services, Washington County Hospital And Clinics, Washington, IA, p. A259

MAJAUSKAS, Joel, Chief Information Officer, Clifton Springs Hospital And Clinic, Clifton Springs, NY, p. A481

MAJCHRZAK, John, Chief Financial Officer, Touchette Regional Hospital, Centreville, IL, p. A197

MAJDALANI, Elias, Director Management Information Systems, Mildred Mitchell-Bateman Hospital, Huntington, WV, p. A773

MAJESKI, Denise, MSN, R.N., Vice President Operations and Chief Nurse Executive, Northwestern Medicine Lake Forest Hospital, Lake Forest, IL, p. A210

MAJETICH, Stephen, CPA, Chief Financial Officer, Southwestern Vermont Medical Center, Bennington, VT, p. A735

MAJHAIL, Ruby, Chief Financial Officer, St. Luke's Behavioral Health Center, Phoenix, AZ, p. A36

MAJOR, Aprille, Director Human Resources, Foothill Regional Medical Center, Tustin, CA, p. A102

MAJOR, Kerry, R.N., MSN, Chief Nursing Officer, Cleveland Clinic Florida, Weston, FL, p. A162

MAJOR, Pattie, Chief Financial Officer, Paul B. Hall Regional Medical Center, Paintsville, KY, p. A292

MAJORS, Ed, Chief Executive Officer, Newman Memorial Hospital, Shattuck, OK, p. A568

MAJORS, Valerie, Director Information Services, Western State Hospital, Hopkinsville, KY, p. A285

MAJZUN, Rick, FACHE, Chief Operating Officer, Lucile Packard Children's Hospital Stanford, Palo Alto, CA, p. A84

MAK, David, Chief Financial Officer, El Camp. Memorial Hospital, El Campo, TX, p. A674

MAKAROFF, Jason, Chief Operating Officer and Associate Vice President, Adventist Healthcare Physical Health And Rehabilitation, Rockville, MD, p. A332

MAKELA, Taylor, Director Information Technology, Baraga County Memorial Hospital, L'Anse, MI, p. A359

MAKI, Bernadette, Director Human Resources, Unm Sandoval Regional Medical Center, Inc., Rio Rancho, NM, p. A471

MAKI, Jacquelyn, Chief Nursing Officer, Oakleaf Surgical Hospital, Altoona, WI, p. A779

MAKI, Richard, R.N., Vice President Nursing and Chief Nursing Officer, Anna Jaques Hospital, Newburyport, MA, p. A342

MAKIEVSKY, Inna, Interim Chief Nursing Officer, Adventist Health And Rideout, Marysville, CA, p. A77

MAKORO, Leslie, Director Information management Systems, Merit Health Natchez, Natchez, MS, p. A397

MAKOSKY, Michael D., Chief Executive Officer, Fulton County Medical Center, Mc Connellsburg, PA, p. A596

MAKSOUD, Jane, R.N., Senior Vice President Human Resources and Labor Relations, Mount Sinai Health System, Mount Sinai Beth Israel, New York, NY, p. A490

   R.N., Senior Vice President Human Resources and Labor Relations, Mount Sinai Health System, Mount Sinai Morningside, New York, NY, p. A490

   R.N., Senior Vice President Human Resources and Labor Relations, Mount Sinai Health System, New York Eye And Ear Infirmary Of Mount Sinai, New York, NY, p. A490

   R.N., Senior Vice President Human Resources and Labor Relations, The Mount Sinai Hospital, New York, NY, p. A492

MAKSYMOW, Michael, Vice President Information Systems, Beebe Healthcare, Lewes, DE, p. A127

MAKUNDA, Beejadi, M.D., Chief Medical Officer, Heatherhill Care Communities, Chardon, OH, p. A531

MALAKAR, Crystal, Team Leader Inpatient Nursing, Bellin Psychiatric Center, Green Bay, WI, p. A785

MALAKOFF, Stacey, Executive Vice President and Chief Financial Officer, Hospital For Special Surgery, New York, NY, p. A490

MALAMED, Michael, M.D., Chief of Staff, Sherman Oaks Hospital, Sherman Oaks, CA, p. A98

MALAN, Glen, Vice President Information Technology and Chief Information Officer, Northwest Community Healthcare, Arlington Heights, IL, p. A194

MALANEY, Scott C., FACHE, President and Chief Executive Officer, Blanchard Valley Hospital, Findlay, OH, p. A540

MALCOLM, Dru, Vice President and Chief Nursing Officer, Johnson City Medical Center, Johnson City, TN, p. A640

MALCOLMSON, James, M.D., Chief of Staff, Sierra Vista Hospital, Truth Or Consequences, NM, p. A473

MALDONADO, Diraida, Chief Executive Officer, Hospital De La Universidad De Puerto Rico/Dr. Federico Trilla, Carolina, PR, p. A807

MALENSEK, Frank, M.D., Chief Medical Officer, St. Vincent's East, Birmingham, AL, p. A15

MALEY, Shelley, Director Human Resources, St. Luke's Hospital - Quakertown Campus, Quakertown, PA, p. A605

MALIK, Azfar, M.D., Chief Medical Officer, Centerpointe Hospital, Saint Charles, MO, p. A414

   M.D., Chief Medical Officer, Signature Psychiatric Hospital, Kansas City, MO, p. A409

MALIK, Chuck, Director Information Systems, Advocate Good Shepherd Hospital, Barrington, IL, p. A195

   Director Information Systems, Advocate Illinois Masonic Medical Center, Chicago, IL, p. A197

MALIN, Seth, M.D., President Medical and Dental Staff, Delaware County Memorial Hospital, Drexel Hill, PA, p. A588

MALINA, Joanne, M.D., Chief of Staff, Veterans Affairs Hudson Valley Health Care System, Montrose, NY, p. A488

MALINDZAK, Edward, Chief Human Resources Officer, Oconomowoc Memorial Hospital, Oconomowoc, WI, p. A792

MALISH, Richard, M.D., Commander, Carl R. Darnall Army Medical Center, Fort Hood, TX, p. A677

MALJOVEC, John, M.D., Medical Director, Warren General Hospital, Warren, PA, p. A609

MALLETT, Belinda, R.N., MS, Vice President, Patient Care and Clinical Services, Soin Medical Center, Beavercreek, OH, p. A529

MALLETT, Teresa, Chief Financial Officer, Madison Regional Health System, Madison, SD, p. A629

MALLIK, Subodh, M.D., Chief of Staff, Pecos County Memorial Hospital, Fort Stockton, TX, p. A677

MALLING, Timothy, M.D., Chief of Staff, Centracare Health-Paynesville, Paynesville, MN, p. A383

MALLONEE, Teresa, Director Human Resources, Angel Medical Center, Franklin, NC, p. A510

MALLORY, Brenda, M.D., Medical Director, Penn State Hershey Rehabilitation Hospital, Hummelstown, PA, p. A592

MALLOY, Patrick, M.D., Chief of Staff, Veterans Affairs New York Harbor Healthcare System, Brooklyn, NY, p. A479

MALLOY, Peter, Chief Information Officer, Cheshire Medical Center, Keene, NH, p. A449

MALM, Brad, Director Human Resources and Education, Lindsborg Community Hospital, Lindsborg, KS, p. A270

MALMSTROM, Ron, Information Research Specialist, Parsons State Hospital And Training Center, Parsons, KS, p. A274

MALONE, Donald A. Jr, M.D., President, Lutheran Hospital, Cleveland, OH, p. A534

MALONE, Ginger Chief Nursing Officer, Ssm Health St. Mary's Hospital, Madison, WI, p. A788

MALONE, Meredith, Chief Financial Officer, West Tennessee Healthcare Dyersburg Hospital, Dyersburg, TN, p. A637

MALONE, Michael, Vice President and Chief Human Resources Officer, Virginia Hospital Center, Arlington, VA, p. A738

MALONE, Patty, M.D., Chief Medical Officer, Ocean Beach Hospital, Ilwaco, WA, p. A759

MALONEY, Christopher, M.D., Senior Vice President, Medical Affairs and Chief Medical Officer, Children's Hospital And Medical Center, Omaha, NE, p. A437

MALONEY, Jay, M.D., Chief of Staff, Cabinet Peaks Medical Center, Libby, MT, p. A425

MALONEY, Patrick J., Chief Executive Officer, Franciscan Health Dyer, Dyer, IN, p. A226

   Chief Executive Officer, Franciscan Health Hammond, Hammond, IN, p. A230

   Chief Executive Officer, Franciscan Healthcare Munster, Munster, IN, p. A237

MALONEY, Paul, Vice President Finance, Behavioral Health Network, Natchaug Hospital, Mansfield Center, CT, p. A123

MALONEY JR, RobertChief Operating Officer, Mercy Health - Anderson Hospital, Cincinnati, OH, p. A532

MALOTT, Deanna, Director Human Resources, Henry Community Health, New Castle, IN, p. A238

MALOTT, Gregg, Chief Financial Officer, Pulaski Memorial Hospital, Winamac, IN, p. A242

MALSED, Brad, Area Chief Financial Officer, Kaiser Permanente Los Angeles Medical Center, Los Angeles, CA, p. A74

MALSEED, Timothy, Chief Information Officer, Keck Hospital Of Usc, Los Angeles, CA, p. A74

MALSEED, TJ, Vice President and Chief Information Officer, Children's Hospital Los Angeles, Los Angeles, CA, p. A74

MALYSZEK, Richard, M.D., Chief of Staff, Uchealth Pikes Peak Regional Hospital, Woodland Park, CO, p. A120

MANAS, Julie, Regional President, Ascension St. Vincent Carmel Hospital, Carmel, IN, p. A225

   Regional President, Ascension St. Vincent Fishers, Fishers, IN, p. A228

MANCINI, Paul, Senior Director Human Resources and Labor Relations, Beth Israel Deaconess Hospital Plymouth, Plymouth, MA, p. A343

MANDAL, Alan, Vice President Financial Operations, Scripp. Memorial Hospital-La Jolla, La Jolla, CA, p. A70

MANDAL, Konoy, M.D., Medical Director, Centennial Peaks Hospital, Louisville, CO, p. A116

MANDANAS, Renato, M.D., Chief Medical Officer, Oswego Hospital, Oswego, NY, p. A494

MANDERINO, Michelle, Chief Human Resources, North Florida/South Georgia Veteran's Health System, Gainesville, FL, p. A138

MANDHAN, Narain, M.D., Chief Medical Officer, Kirby Medical Center, Monticello, IL, p. A212

MANDI, Deepak, M.D., Chief of Staff, West Palm Beach Veterans Affairs Medical Center, West Palm Beach, FL, p. A162

MANESTRINA, Robert, Vice President Human Resources, Inspira Medical Center-Woodbury, Woodbury, NJ, p. A466

MANFREDI, Susan, R.N., Vice President and Chief Nursing Officer, Uw Medicine/Northwest Hospital & Medical Center, Seattle, WA, p. A764

MANFREDO, John, Chief Operating Officer, Norman Regional Health System, Norman, OK, p. A563

MANGAN, Melissa, Vice President of Finance and Chief Financial Officer, Prairie Ridge Health, Inc., Columbus, WI, p. A782

MANGIN, Paul, Vice President Finance, Mercyone Clinton Medical Center, Clinton, IA, p. A246

MANGINI, Susan, R.N., FACHE, Chief Nursing Officer, Metrowest Medical Center, Framingham, MA, p. A339

MANGIONE, Ellen, M.D., Chief of Staff, Veterans Affairs Eastern Colorado Health Care System, Denver, CO, p. A111

MANGONA, John, Vice President, Chief Information Officer and Compliance Officer, Saratoga Hospital, Saratoga Springs, NY, p. A497

MANGUM, Lisa, Chief Nursing Officer, North Canyon Medical Center, Gooding, ID, p. A190

MANGUM, Rozanne, Administrative Assistant and Director Human Resources, Grover C. Dils Medical Center, Caliente, NV, p. A441

MANIATIS, Theodore, M.D., Medical Director, Staten Island University Hospital, Staten Island, NY, p. A499

MANION, Martin Thomas., Chief Executive Officer, New London Hospital, New London, NH, p. A450

MANKER, Marcia, Chief Executive Officer, Memorialcare, Orange Coast Memorial Medical Center, Fountain Valley, CA, p. A64

   Chief Executive Officer, Saddleback Medical Center, Laguna Hills, CA, p. A70

MANKINS, Mark, M.D., Chief of Staff, Hamilton Hospital, Olney, TX, p. A704

MANKOSKI, Susan, Vice President Human Resources, Ssm Health St. Mary's Hospital - Jefferson City, Jefferson City, MO, p. A408

MANLAGNIT, Maybelle, Senior Accounting Officer, Dsh Metropolitan, Norwalk, CA, p. A81

MANLEY, John, Director Information Systems, Jackson General Hospital, Ripley, WV, p. A776

MANN, Brian, Chief Executive Officer, Select Specialty Hospital-Danville, Danville, PA, p. A588

MANN, Corey, Director Human Resources, Memorial Health Care Systems, Seward, NE, p. A439

MANN, Erin, R.N., Chief Nursing Officer, Mccamey County Hospital District, Mccamey, TX, p. A700

MANN, Karen, R.N., Chief Nursing Officer, Shoshone Medical Center, Kellogg, ID, p. A191

MANN, Lori, R.N., MSN, Chief Nursing Officer, Rusk Rehabilitation Hospital, Columbia, MO, p. A405

MANN, Rex, M.D., Chief Medical Officer, Ochiltree General Hospital, Perryton, TX, p. A705

MANN, Rhonda, Chief Nursing Officer, Franklin Woods Community Hospital, Johnson City, TN, p. A640

MANNI, Joseph, Executive Vice President and Chief Operating Officer, Deborah Heart And Lung Center, Browns Mills, NJ, p. A453

MANNI, Kymberlee, Chief Operating Officer, University Of Miami Hospital And Clinics, Miami, FL, p. A147

MANNI, Kymberlee Jean., Chief Executive Officer, University Of Miami Hospital And Clinics, Miami, FL, p. A147

MANNICH, Andy, Regional Administrator, Georgia Regional Hospital At Savannah, Savannah, GA, p. A180

MANNING, Angela, Director Health Information Services, Encompass Health Rehabilitation Hospital Of Sunrise, Sunrise, FL, p. A158

MANNING, Austin, Chief Operating Officer, Los Robles Hospital And Medical Center, Thousand Oaks, CA, p. A101

MANNING, Claude, Chief Financial Officer, Palacios Community Medical Center, Palacios, TX, p. A704

MANNING, Donald, M.D., Clinical Director, Georgia Regional Hospital At Savannah, Savannah, GA, p. A180

MANNING, James, Administrator, Pathway Rehabilitation Hospital Of Bossier, Bossier City, LA, p. A298

MANNING, JoAnn, Chief Financial Officer, Emory Johns Creek Hospital, Johns Creek, GA, p. A174

   Chief Financial Officer, Emory Saint Joseph's Hospital Of Atlanta, Atlanta, GA, p. A164

MANNING, Kimberly, Chief Nursing Officer, Washington County Hospital, Plymouth, NC, p. A516

MANNING, Laura, Administrative Director, Guthrie Corning Hospital, Corning, NY, p. A481

MANNING, Lori, Administrator Human Resources, Western State Hospital, Tacoma, WA, p. A767

MANNION, Stephen, Assistant Vice President Information Systems Customer Service, Medstar Franklin Square Medical Center, Baltimore, MD, p. A325

MANNIX, Mary N., FACHE, President and Chief Executive Officer, Augusta Health, Fishersville, VA, p. A742

MANNON, Jane, Vice President Human Resources, Penn State Milton S. Hershey Medical Center, Hershey, PA, p. A592

MANNY, Martin, Director, I.S., Providence St. Mary Medical Center, Walla Walla, WA, p. A768

MANRING, Shannon, Director Human Resources, Lifebrite Community Hospital Of Stokes, Danbury, NC, p. A508

MANSFIELD, Deena, Director Human Resources, Ashley Regional Medical Center, Vernal, UT, p. A734

MANSKE, Kristin, Chief Executive Officer, Greenwood Regional Rehabilitation Hospital, Greenwood, SC, p. A621

MANSKE, Lou Ann, Vice President Human Resources, Madonna Rehabilitation Hospital, Lincoln, NE, p. A434

MANSON, David, Manager Human Resources, Santa Clara Valley Medical Center, San Jose, CA, p. A95

MANSON, Kelly, Chief Financial Officer, Veterans Affairs Sierra Nevada Health Care System, Reno, NV, p. A446

MANSON, Lisa, Director Ambulatory Services, Guttenberg Municipal Hospital And Clinics, Guttenberg, IA, p. A250

MANSON, Stephanie, Chief Operating Officer, Our Lady Of The Lake Regional Medical Center, Baton Rouge, LA, p. A297

MANSTEDT, Chase, Chief Financial Officer, Saunders Medical Center, Wahoo, NE, p. A440

MANSUE, Amy B., President and Chief Executive Officer, Inspira Medical Center-Elmer, Elmer, NJ, p. A455

   President and Chief Executive Officer, Inspira Medical Center-Vineland, Vineland, NJ, p. A465

   President and Chief Executive Officer, Inspira Medical Center-Woodbury, Woodbury, NJ, p. A466

MANSUKHANI, Martin, Chief Financial Officer, Desert Valley Hospital, Victorville, CA, p. A104

MANSURE, John F., FACHE, President, Prisma Health Greer Memorial Hospital, Greer, SC, p. A621

MANTERNACH, Paul, M.D., Senior Vice President Physician Integration, Mercyone North Iowa Medical Center, Mason City, IA, p. A254

MANTOOTH, Charles, President and Chief Executive Officer, Watauga Medical Center, Boone, NC, p. A505

MANUBENS, Claudio, M.D., Chief of Staff, Adventhealth Heart Of Florida, Davenport, FL, p. A135

MANUEL, Shasta, Executive Director Finance, Ssm Health St. Anthony Hospital - Oklahoma City, Oklahoma City, OK, p. A566

MANUEL, Wendy, Vice President and Chief Financial Officer, Rehabilitation Hospital Of The Pacific, Honolulu, HI, p. A185

MANYBANSENG, Belen, R.N., Chief Nursing Officer, Trinity Hospital, Weaverville, CA, p. A104

MANZO, Arnold, Vice President Human Resources, Saint Barnabas Medical Center, Livingston, NJ, p. A457

MANZO-LUNA, Hilda, Chief Nursing Officer, La Palma Intercommunity Hospital, La Palma, CA, p. A70

MANZOOR, Amir, M.D., Medical Director, Select Specialty Hospital-Panama City, Panama City, FL, p. A153

MAPARA, Anupam, M.D., Chief of Staff, Sutter Delta Medical Center, Antioch, CA, p. A56

MAPLES, Michael, M.D., Vice President and Chief Medical Officer, Mississipp. Baptist Medical Center, Jackson, MS, p. A395

MARAAN, Sheila, Director of Nursing, Brynn Marr Hospital, Jacksonville, NC, p. A512

MARANO, Deena, Human Resources Director, Community Hospital Of San Bernardino, San Bernardino, CA, p. A91

MARANTETTE, Kay, Chief Nursing Officer, Continuecare Hospital At Madisonville, Madisonville, KY, p. A289

MARAS, Greg, Vice President Human Resources, Meadville Medical Center, Meadville, PA, p. A596

MARASA, Richard, M.D., President Medical Staff, Springfield Hospital, Springfield, VT, p. A736

MARBLE, Kevin, Director Information Technology, Oklahoma Forensic Center, Vinita, OK, p. A571

MARCANO, Norma, Chief Operating Officer, San Juan City Hospital, San Juan, PR, p. A811

MARCANTEL, Bill, Chief Information Systems, Allen Parish Community Healthcare, Kinder, LA, p. A305

MARCEAUX, Caroline, MSN, R.N., Chief Nursing Officer, Acadia General Hospital, Crowley, LA, p. A300

MARCELIN, Fitzgerald, M.D., Chief of Staff, Southern Virginia Regional Medical Center, Emporia, VA, p. A741

MARCHANT, Joseph, Administrator, Bibb Medical Center, Centreville, AL, p. A16

MARCHIK, Jeff, Chief Financial Officer, Unitypoint Health - Trinity Rock Island, Rock Island, IL, p. A218

   Vice President, Consolidated Services, UnityPoint Health and Chief Financial Officer, Trinity Regional Health System, Unitypoint Health - Trinity Muscatine, Muscatine, IA, p. A254

MARCIANO, Paolo, M.D., Chief Medical Officer, Beaumont Hospital - Dearborn, Dearborn, MI, p. A352

MARCO, Wendy, R.N., Chief Nursing Officer, Osceola Regional Health Center, Sibley, IA, p. A257

MARCO JR, JamesInterim Vice President, Human Resources, Oswego Hospital, Oswego, NY, p. A494

MARCOTTE, Eric, M.D., Chief Medical Officer, Riverview Health, Noblesville, IN, p. A238

MARCOTTE, Lynn, Chief Financial Officer, Mclaren Oakland, Pontiac, MI, p. A364

MARCOTTE, Melissa, Chief Financial Officer, Rainy Lake Medical Center, International Falls, MN, p. A378

MARCOVICI, Mia, M.D., Chief Medical Officer, Norristown State Hospital, Norristown, PA, p. A598

MARCOWITZ, David, M.D., Chief of Staff, Lucas County Health Center, Chariton, IA, p. A245

MARCUCCI, John, M.D., Vice President Medical Affairs, Baylor Scott & White Medical Center - Plano, Plano, TX, p. A706

MARCUM, Amie, Human Resources Coordinator, Continuecare Hospital At Baptist Health Corbin, Corbin, KY, p. A282

MARCUM, Laurie, MSN, R.N., Executive Director Patient Care Services, Grande Ronde Hospital, La Grande, OR, p. A576

MARCUS, Shannon, Chief Executive Officer, Three Rivers Behavioral Health, West Columbia, SC, p. A625

MARCZEWSKI, Les, M.D., Chief Medical Officer, Loring Hospital, Sac City, IA, p. A257

MARDY, Paul, Chief Information Technology Officer, Tennessee Valley Healthcare System, Nashville, TN, p. A647

MAREK, Kyle, Vice President General Services and Chief Information Officer, Carteret Health Care, Morehead City, NC, p. A514

MAREK, Rick, Vice President Medical Information Systems, Warm Springs Rehabilitation Hospital Of San Antonio, San Antonio, TX, p. A714

MARGENAU, Randall, Chief Information Officer, William S. Middleton Memorial Veterans Hospital, Madison, WI, p. A788

MARGER, Brian, Chief Executive Officer, Tristar Summit Medical Center, Hermitage, TN, p. A639

MARGOLIS, Marilyn, MSN, Chief Executive Officer, Emory Johns Creek Hospital, Johns Creek, GA, p. A174

MARGOSCHIS, Shanthi, M.D., Chief Nurse Executive, Kaiser Permanente San Jose Medical Center, San Jose, CA, p. A94

MARGULIS, Richard T., President and Chief Executive Officer, Long Island Community Hospital, Patchogue, NY, p. A494

MARIANI, Marilyn, R.N., Chief Nursing Officer, Lakeview Hospital, Bountiful, UT, p. A727

MARIANI, Meleah, Chief Nursing Officer, Spectrum Health Gerber Memorial, Fremont, MI, p. A355

MARICN, Tanya, Interim Vice President Human Resources, Mercy Hospital Springfield, Springfield, MO, p. A419

MARIETTA, John, M.D., Chief Medical Officer, St. David's Medical Center, Austin, TX, p. A656

MARIETTA, Megan, Chief Executive Officer, Hca Houston Healthcare West, Houston, TX, p. A686

MARIETTA, Richard, M.D., Medical Director, Hca Houston Healthcare Clear Lake, League City, TX, p. A695

MARIGNY, Kian, Administrator, United Medical Healthwest New Orleans, Llc, Gretna, LA, p. A302

MARIGOMEN, Nancy Ann, R.N., Director of Nursing, Milwaukee County Behavioral Health Division, Milwaukee, WI, p. A791

MARIN, Loyman, Chief Human Resources, Miami Veterans Affairs Healthcare System, Miami, FL, p. A147

MARIN, Veronica, Chief Financial Officer, Red Bud Regional Hospital, Red Bud, IL, p. A218

MARINARO, Jon, M.D., Chief Medical Officer, Kindred Hospital-Albuquerque, Albuquerque, NM, p. A467

MARINELLO, Anthony, Chief Operating Officer, University Medical Center, Las Vegas, NV, p. A444

MARINI, Frank, Senior Vice President and Chief Information Officer, Tmc Healthcare, Tucson, AZ, p. A41

MARINO, A, M.D., Senior Vice President Medical Administration, Greenwich Hospital, Greenwich, CT, p. A122

MARINO, Christopher, M.D., Chief of Staff, Memphis Veterans Affairs Medical Center, Memphis, TN, p. A644

MARINO, Joseph, Chief Financial Officer, Suburban Community Hospital, East Norriton, PA, p. A589

MARINO, Marchita, Vice President Human Resources, Rockledge Regional Medical Center, Rockledge, FL, p. A155

MARINO, Matt, Chief Financial Officer, Saint Luke's South Hospital, Overland Park, KS, p. A274

MARINOFF, Peter Jr, President, Munson Healthcare Cadillac Hospital, Cadillac, MI, p. A350

MARION, Amy, Chief Human Resource Officer, Walter B. Jones Alcohol And Drug Abuse Treatment Center, Greenville, NC, p. A511

MARION, Kristie, Chief Nurse Executive, Memorial Hospital Los Banos, Los Banos, CA, p. A76

MARIOTTI, Denise, Chief Human Resource Officer, Hospital Of The University Of Pennsylvania, Philadelphia, PA, p. A600

MARIS, Peter, Director Human Resources, Nyc Health + Hospitals / Elmhurst, Elmhurst, NY, p. A483

MARK, Joe, Interim Chief Administrator, Peacehealth Ketchikan Medical Center, Ketchikan, AK, p. A28

MARKENSON, David, M.D., Chief Medical Officer, Sky Ridge Medical Center, Lone Tree, CO, p. A116

MARKER, John, MSN, R.N., Chief Nursing Officer, Medical City North Hills, North Richland Hills, TX, p. A703

MARKESINO, Patricia, FACHE, Chief Nurse Executive and Chief Operating Officer, Providence Willamette Falls Medical Center, Oregon City, OR, p. A578

MARKGRAF, SHRM-SCP, SPHR, Janelle, Director Human Resources and Off Campus Services, Aspirus Langlade Hospital, Antigo, WI, p. A779

MARKHAM, Barbara, Chief Financial Officer, Glendive Medical Center, Glendive, MT, p. A424

MARKHAM, Chad, Chief Operating Officer, Unitypoint Health - St. Lukes's Sioux City, Sioux City, IA, p. A258

MARKHAM, Kevin, Chief Financial Officer, Eastpointe Hospital, Daphne, AL, p. A17

MARKOS, Valerie, Chief Nursing Officer, Ed Fraser Memorial Hospital, Macclenny, FL, p. A144

MARKOWITZ, Stuart, M.D., Chief Medical Officer, Hartford Hospital, Hartford, CT, p. A122

MARKOWSKI, Stan, Chief Financial Officer, Palmetto Lowcountry Behavioral Health, Charleston, SC, p. A616

MARKS, Craig J., FACHE, Chief Executive Officer, Prosser Memorial Health, Prosser, WA, p. A762

MARKS, Jerry, Vice President Finance, Decatur County Memorial Hospital, Greensburg, IN, p. A230

MARKS, Kimberly W., Chief Executive Officer, Southampton Memorial Hospital, Franklin, VA, p. A742

MARKS, Kindra, Chief Executive Officer, Regency Hospital Of Columbus, Columbus, OH, p. A537

MARKS, Marie, Chief Nursing Officer, Lake Norman Regional Medical Center, Mooresville, NC, p. A514

MARKS, Michael, M.D., Chief of Staff, Norwalk Hospital, Norwalk, CT, p. A124

MARKS, Michelle, D.O., Medical Director, Cleveland Clinic Children's Hospital For Rehabilitation, Cleveland, OH, p. A534

MARKS, Peter, Vice President & Chief Information Officer, Wakemed Raleigh Campus, Raleigh, NC, p. A517

MARKS, Stanley, M.D., FACS, Chief Medical Officer, Memorial Hospital Miramar, Miramar, FL, p. A148
M.D., FACS, Chief Medical Officer, Memorial Hospital Pembroke, Pembroke Pines, FL, p. A153

MARKSTROM, Susan, M.D., Chief of Staff, St. Cloud Veterans Affairs Health Care System, Saint Cloud, MN, p. A384

MARLATT, Pam, Business Systems Director, Essentia Health-St. Joseph's Medical Center, Brainerd, MN, p. A373

MARLATT, Trina, R.N., MSN, Administrator, Ascension St. Vincent Williamsport, Williamsport, IN, p. A242

MARLER, Ruth, Chief Nursing Officer and Chief Operating Officer, Johnston Health, Smithfield, NC, p. A518

MARLER, Steven, Assistant Administrator, Parkland Health Center - Farmington Community, Farmington, MO, p. A406

MARLETTE, Andy, Interim Chief Executive Officer, Valir Rehabilitation Hospital, Oklahoma City, OK, p. A566

MARLEY, Amelia, Chief Information Officer, Bassett Medical Center, Cooperstown, NY, p. A481

MARLEY, Charles, D.O., Vice President Medical Affairs, Wellspan Gettysburg Hospital, Gettysburg, PA, p. A590

MARLEY, Lee, VP/Information Services Chief Application Officer, Presbyterian Hospital, Albuquerque, NM, p. A468

MARLEY, Michael, Chief Information Officer, Veterans Affairs Central Western Massachusetts Healthcare System, Leeds, MA, p. A340

MARLOW, Billy, Executive Director and Administrator, North Sunflower Medical Center, Ruleville, MS, p. A400

MARMANDE, Susanne, Administrator, Infirmary Long Term Acute Care Hospital, Mobile, AL, p. A22

MARMERSTEIN, Robert, Chief Executive Officer, Hca Houston Healthcare Tomball, Tomball, TX, p. A721

MARNEY, Terri, R.N., Director of Nursing, Plains Regional Medical Center, Clovis, NM, p. A469

MARON, Michael, President and Chief Executive Officer, Holy Name Medical Center, Teaneck, NJ, p. A464

MARONEY, Gerry, Chief Information Officer and Security Officer, Gaylord Specialty Healthcare, Wallingford, CT, p. A126

MAROSTICA, Tony, Chief Compliance and Human Resource Officer, Spanish Peaks Regional Health Center, Walsenburg, CO, p. A119

MAROTTA, Diane, Vice President Human Resources, Mather Hospital, Port Jefferson, NY, p. A495

MAROUN, Christiane, M.D., Chief of Staff, Lifescape, Sioux Falls, SD, p. A631

MARQUARDT, Thomas, M.D., Interim Chief Medical Officer, Winneshiek Medical Center, Decorah, IA, p. A248

MARQUSEE, Joanne, President and Chief Executive Officer, Cooley Dickinson Hospital, Northampton, MA, p. A342

MARR, Debbie, Administrative Assistant and Director Human Resources, Fredonia Regional Hospital, Fredonia, KS, p. A264

MARRAN, Mary, MS, President and Chief Operating Officer, Butler Hospital, Providence, RI, p. A613

MARRERO, Jamie, M.D., Medical Director, Encompass Health Rehabilitation Hospital Of Manati, Manati, PR, p. A808

MARRERO, Jose, Director Finance, San Jorge Children's Hospital, Santurce, PR, p. A811

MARRERO, Norma, Executive Administrator, Doctors' Center Hospital San Juan, San Juan, PR, p. A810

MARRONI, Denise, Chief Financial Officer, Providence Centralia Hospital, Centralia, WA, p. A756
Chief Financial Officer, Providence St. Peter Hospital, Olympia, WA, p. A761

MARRUFO, Gabriel, Chief Financial Officer, Methodist Stone Oak Hospital, San Antonio, TX, p. A712

MARSEE, DeWayne, Director Information Systems, Mercer Health, Coldwater, OH, p. A535

MARSH, Amy, Chief Financial Officer, Fairfield Memorial Hospital, Fairfield, IL, p. A205

MARSH, J. Michael., President and Chief Executive Officer, Overlake Medical Center, Bellevue, WA, p. A755

MARSH, Leslie, MSN, Chief Executive Officer, Lexington Regional Health Center, Lexington, NE, p. A434

MARSH, Linda, Vice President Financial Services and Chief Financial Officer, Alhambra Hospital Medical Center, Alhambra, CA, p. A55

MARSH, Mark A., President, Health Central Hospital, Ocoee, FL, p. A150

MARSH, Mitch, Interim Executive Director, Terence Cardinal Cooke Health Care Center, New York, NY, p. A492

MARSH, Rob, Chief Executive Officer, San Jose Behavorial Health, San Jose, CA, p. A95

MARSH, Toby, MSN, R.N., Interim Chief Patient Care Services Officer, University Of California, Davis Medical Center, Sacramento, CA, p. A90

MARSH, Wallace, Director of Information Technology, Willow Springs Center, Reno, NV, p. A446

MARSHAK, Glenn, M.D., Chief of Staff, Mission Community Hospital, Panorama City, CA, p. A84

MARSHALL, David, R.N., Ph.D., Senior Vice President, Chief Nursing Executive, Cedars-Sinai Medical Center, Los Angeles, CA, p. A73

MARSHALL, Deborah, Vice President Public Relations, Good Samaritan Regional Medical Center, Suffern, NY, p. A499

MARSHALL, James I., President and Chief Executive Officer, Uintah Basin Medical Center, Roosevelt, UT, p. A731

MARSHALL, Joe, Chief Operating Officer, Lillian M. Hudspeth Memorial Hospital, Sonora, TX, p. A716

MARSHALL, Judy, Director Human Resources, Holy Cross Hospital, Taos, NM, p. A473

MARSHALL, Kenneth, Chief Operating Officer, Uofl Health - Uofl Hospital, Louisville, KY, p. A289

MARSHALL, Michael, Vice President Finance and Chief Financial Officer, Anderson Hospital, Maryville, IL, p. A211

MARSHALL, Patricia, Assistant Administrator Human Resources, Washington Health System Greene, Waynesburg, PA, p. A610

MARSHALL, Robert L. Jr, FACHE, Chief Executive Officer, Bolivar Medical Center, Cleveland, MS, p. A391

MARSHALL, Ryan, Chief Financial Officer, Doctors Hospital Of Manteca, Manteca, CA, p. A77

MARSHBURN, Deborah, Chief Nursing Executive, Cap. Fear Valley Medical Center, Fayetteville, NC, p. A510

MARSICO, Nick, Vice President and Chief Operating Officer, Magruder Memorial Hospital, Port Clinton, OH, p. A548

MARSO, Paul, Vice President Human Resources, Avera St. Mary's Hospital, Pierre, SD, p. A630

MARTANIUK, Jean, Director Human Resources, Mt. Ascutney Hospital And Health Center, Windsor, VT, p. A737

MARTE, Maria, Administrator, Doctor's Center Of Bayamon, Bayamon, PR, p. A806

MARTELL, Gustavo, M.D., Chief Medical Officer, The Hospitals Of Providence Transmountain Campus, El Paso, TX, p. A676

MARTENS, Angela, Chief Financial Officer, Cumberland Healthcare, Cumberland, WI, p. A782

MARTENS, Troy, Chief Operating Officer, Unitypoint Health - Trinity Regional Medical Center, Fort Dodge, IA, p. A250

MARTHONE, Frances, Chief Nursing Officer, Mercy Medical Center, Springfield, MA, p. A344

MARTI, Maria, Director Fiscal Services, Auxilio Mutuo Hospital, San Juan, PR, p. A809

MARTIN, Adam, Chief Executive Officer, Southern Tennessee Regional Health System-Lawrenceburg, Lawrenceburg, TN, p. A642
Chief Operating Officer, Wythe County Community Hospital, Wytheville, VA, p. A754

MARTIN, Amanda, Manager Human Resources, Ohio Valley Surgical Hospital, Springfield, OH, p. A549

MARTIN, Amy, Chief Human Resource Officer, Cedar City Hospital, Cedar City, UT, p. A727

MARTIN, Angelia, M.D., Chief of Staff, Mosaic Medical Center - Albany, Albany, MO, p. A402

MARTIN, Barbara, Chief Nursing Officer, Mercy St. Vincent Medical Center, Toledo, OH, p. A550

MARTIN, Brian, Vice President Medical Affairs, Upmc Children's Hospital Of Pittsburgh, Pittsburgh, PA, p. A603

MARTIN, Bruce, Vice President Human Resources, Carolinaeast Health System, New Bern, NC, p. A515

MARTIN, Carmen, Associate Administrator, Auxilio Mutuo Hospital, San Juan, PR, p. A809

MARTIN, Charity, Controller and Regional Business Officer Manager, Greenwood Regional Rehabilitation Hospital, Greenwood, SC, p. A621

MARTIN, Cheryl, Chief Information Officer, Prisma Health Tuomey Hospital, Sumter, SC, p. A624

MARTIN, Christine, Vice President and Chief Financial Officer, Atrium Health Cleveland, Shelby, NC, p. A518

MARTIN, Clifford, M.D., Regional Vice President and Chief Medical Officer, Osf Holy Family Medical Center, Monmouth, IL, p. A212

M.D., Regional Vice President and Chief Medical Officer, Osf Saint Luke Medical Center, Kewanee, IL, p. A209

M.D., Regional Vice President and Chief Medical Officer, Osf St. Mary Medical Center, Galesburg, IL, p. A205

MARTIN, Connie, Vice President and Chief Support Officer, Methodist Medical Center Of Oak Ridge, Oak Ridge, TN, p. A648

MARTIN, Corey, M.D., Director Medical Affairs, Buffalo Hospital, Buffalo, MN, p. A373

MARTIN, Cyndie, Director, Coal County General Hospital, Coalgate, OK, p. A558

MARTIN, David, M.D., Vice President Chief Medical Officer, Ascension Seton Medical Center Austin, Austin, TX, p. A654

Assistant Administrator, Multicare Valley Hospital, Spokane Valley, WA, p. A766

MARTIN, Deanna, Chief Executive Officer, Encompass Health Rehabilitation Hospital Of Rock Hill, Rock Hill, SC, p. A623

MARTIN, Deborah, Regional Vice President Human Resources, Cascade Valley Hospital, Arlington, WA, p. A755

Regional Vice President Human Resources, Skagit Valley Hospital, Mount Vernon, WA, p. A761

MARTIN, Debra, Chief Nursing Officer, Hamilton General Hospital, Hamilton, TX, p. A682

MARTIN, Doug, Chief Executive Officer, Houston County Community Hospital, Erin, TN, p. A638

Chief Nursing Officer, Houston County Community Hospital, Erin, TN, p. A638

MARTIN, Elizabeth J., Hospital President, Riverside Tappahannock Hospital, Tappahannock, VA, p. A752

MARTIN, Garland, M.D., Chief of Staff, Appling Healthcare System, Baxley, GA, p. A167

MARTIN, Gregg, Chief Information Officer, Arnot Ogden Medical Center, Elmira, NY, p. A483

Chief Information Officer, Ira Davenport Memorial Hospital, Bath, NY, p. A475

MARTIN, Harvey, M.D., Medical Director, Red River Hospital, Llc, Wichita Falls, TX, p. A725

MARTIN, Holly, Director Human Resource, Iowa Specialty Hospital-Belmond, Belmond, IA, p. A244

Human Resources Leader, Iowa Specialty Hospital-Clarion, Clarion, IA, p. A246

MARTIN, Jackie, Chief Financial Officer, Saint Luke's Cushing Hospital, Leavenworth, KS, p. A269

MARTIN, James, Chief Financial Officer, Hawthorn Children Psychiatric Hospital, Saint Louis, MO, p. A415

Chief Financial Officer, Metropolitan St. Louis Psychiatric Center, Saint Louis, MO, p. A416

Chief Financial Officer, St. Louis Psychiatric Rehabilitation Center, Saint Louis, MO, p. A417

Chief Information Officer, River Park Hospital, Huntington, WV, p. A773

MARTIN, Janice, R.N., Chief Nursing Officer, Davis Regional Medical Center, Statesville, NC, p. A519

MARTIN, Jason, M.D., Medical Director, Ascension Seton Northwest, Austin, TX, p. A655

MARTIN, Jeanene, M.P.H., Senior Vice President Human Resources and Chief People Officer, Wakemed Cary Hospital, Cary, NC, p. A506

M.P.H., Senior Vice President Human Resources, Wakemed Raleigh Campus, Raleigh, NC, p. A517

MARTIN, Jeffrey, M.D., Chief of Staff, Erlanger Western Carolina Hospital, Murphy, NC, p. A515

MARTIN, Jeremy, Chief Support Services Officer, St. James Parish Hospital, Lutcher, LA, p. A307

MARTIN, Jessica, Director Human Resources, Logan Regional Medical Center, Logan, WV, p. A774

MARTIN, Jessie, R.N., Chief Nursing Executive, Chi St. Alexius Health-Turtle Lake Hospital, Turtle Lake, ND, p. A526

MARTIN, Josh, Chief Executive Officer, Summit Pacific Medical Center, Elma, WA, p. A757

Chief Operating Officer, Summit Pacific Medical Center, Elma, WA, p. A757

MARTIN, Karen, R.N., MSN, Chief Nursing Officer, Marshall Medical Center, Lewisburg, TN, p. A642

Chief Nursing Officer, Musc Health Lancaster Medical Center, Lancaster, SC, p. A622

MARTIN, Keith, M.D., Chief Medical Officer, Fhn Memorial Hospital, Freeport, IL, p. A205

MARTIN, Kelly, Chief Executive Officer, Fairchild Medical Center, Yreka, CA, p. A106

Human Resource Officer, Texas Health Presbyterian Hospital Plano, Plano, TX, p. A707

MARTIN, Kenneth, M.D., Chief of Staff, Arkansas Surgical Hospital, North Little Rock, AR, p. A51

MARTIN, Kevin, M.D., Chief Medical Officer, Four Winds Hospital, Saratoga Springs, NY, p. A497

M.P.H., R.N., FACHE, Administrator, Shriners Hospitals For Children-Salt Lake City, Salt Lake City, UT, p. A732

MARTIN, Konnie, Chief Executive Officer, San Luis Valley Health, Alamosa, CO, p. A107

MARTIN, Kory, M.D., Chief of Staff, Seymour Hospital, Seymour, TX, p. A715

MARTIN, Kristina, Chief Information Officer, Curry General Hospital, Gold Beach, OR, p. A575

MARTIN, Leslee, Manager Information Technology, Hshs St. Elizabeth's Hospital, O'Fallon, IL, p. A215

MARTIN, Marlana, Director Human Resources, Benewah Community Hospital, Saint Maries, ID, p. A193

MARTIN, Mary, MSN, R.N., Chief Nursing Officer, Hshs St. Nicholas Hospital, Sheboygan, WI, p. A796

MARTIN, Matthew, Director Resource Management, Naval Hospital Oak Harbor, Oak Harbor, WA, p. A761

MARTIN, Nikki, Chief Financial Officer, Christus Southeast Texas Jasper Memorial, Jasper, TX, p. A691

MARTIN, Patrick, M.D., Medical Director, Wilmington Treatment Center, Wilmington, NC, p. A520

Director Information Systems, Calvary Hospital, Bronx, NY, p. A476

MARTIN, Patsy, Manager Human Resources, Select Rehabilitation Hospital Of Denton, Denton, TX, p. A672

MARTIN, Paul, Chief Medical Officer, Grandview Medical Center, Dayton, OH, p. A538

Director Human Resources, Kaiser Permanente Los Angeles Medical Center, Los Angeles, CA, p. A74

MARTIN, Ric, Information Specialist, Madison State Hospital, Madison, IN, p. A236

MARTIN, Richard, MSN, R.N., Senior Vice President and Chief Nursing Officer, Hoag Memorial Hospital Presbyterian, Newport Beach, CA, p. A81

MARTIN, Sabrina, Chief Executive Officer, Rehabilitation Hospital Of Southern New Mexico, Las Cruces, NM, p. A470

MARTIN, Sharon, M.D., Ph.D., President Medical Staff, Fulton County Medical Center, Mc Connellsburg, PA, p. A596

MARTIN, Sheila, Chief Nursing Officer, Cmh Regional Health System, Wilmington, OH, p. A553

MARTIN, Sherri, M.D., President Medical Staff, Adventhealth Shawnee Mission, Shawnee Mission, KS, p. A276

MARTIN, Stacy, Director Human Resources, Grant Regional Health Center, Lancaster, WI, p. A787

MARTIN, Susan, Chief Financial Officer and Vice President, Finance, Middlesex Hospital, Middletown, CT, p. A123

MARTIN, Tom, Senior Vice President, Strategy and Information Technology Officer, Evergreenhealth, Kirkland, WA, p. A759

MARTIN, Tracie, M.D., Chief Medical Officer, Mercyone Oakland Medical Center, Oakland, NE, p. A436

MARTIN, Val, Director Financial Management Services Center, Veterans Affairs Salt Lake City Health Care System, Salt Lake City, UT, p. A733

MARTIN, W., Chief Operating Officer, Providence Hospital, Columbia, SC, p. A618

MARTIN, Wendy, Chief Executive Officer, Jefferson Hospital, Louisville, GA, p. A175

MARTIN-LINNARD, Tamara, R.N., Chief Clinical Officer, Great Plains Health, North Platte, NE, p. A436

MARTIN-PRATT, Diane, Director Information Systems, Niagara Falls Memorial Medical Center, Niagara Falls, NY, p. A493

MARTINEZ, Albino, Director Budget and Finance, Miners' Colfax Medical Center, Raton, NM, p. A471

MARTINEZ, Darlene, Director Finance, New Mexico Behavioral Health Institute At Las Vegas, Las Vegas, NM, p. A470

MARTINEZ, Eddie, Chief Financial Officer, El Paso Ltac Hospital, El Paso, TX, p. A675

MARTINEZ, Edward, Chief Information Officer, Nicklaus Children's Hospital, Miami, FL, p. A147

MARTINEZ, Eleanor, Chief Nursing Officer, Alhambra Hospital Medical Center, Alhambra, CA, p. A55

MARTINEZ, Francisco, Executive Director, Hospital San Antonio, Mayaguez, PR, p. A808

MARTINEZ, Frank, Senior Vice President Human Resources, East Jefferson General Hospital, Metairie, LA, p. A308

MARTINEZ, Jason, Director Information Technology, West Valley Medical Center, Caldwell, ID, p. A189

MARTINEZ, Jeanine, Director Human Resources, Putnam General Hospital, Eatonton, GA, p. A172

MARTINEZ, Jorge I., Executive Director, Hospital Perea, Mayaguez, PR, p. A808

MARTINEZ, Jose, M.D., Chief Medical Officer, Northwest Medical Center, Margate, FL, p. A145

MARTINEZ, Josue, Coordinator Information Systems, University Hospital, San Juan, PR, p. A811

MARTINEZ, Katherine, Chief Nursing Officer, North Central Surgical Center, Dallas, TX, p. A669

MARTINEZ, Kathryn, Chief Operating Officer and Chief Nursing Officer, Fhn Memorial Hospital, Freeport, IL, p. A205

MARTINEZ, Leanne, Chief Executive Officer and Administrator, Fisher County Hospital District, Rotan, TX, p. A709

MARTINEZ, Lee, Chief Information Officer, Cooley Dickinson Hospital, Northampton, MA, p. A342

MARTINEZ, Louisa, Director of Nursing, Frio Regional Hospital, Pearsall, TX, p. A705

MARTINEZ, Maria, Chief Nursing Officer, La Paz Regional Hospital, Parker, AZ, p. A34

MARTINEZ, Michelle, Chief Executive Officer, U. S. Public Health Service Indian Hospital-Whiteriver, Whiteriver, AZ, p. A41

Controller, Encompass Health Rehabilitation Hospital Of Albuquerque, Albuquerque, NM, p. A467

MARTINEZ, Ozalina, R.N., Director of Nursing, Northeastern Health System Sequoyah, Sallisaw, OK, p. A567

MARTINEZ, Regina, Director Human Resources, La Paz Regional Hospital, Parker, AZ, p. A34

MARTINEZ, Rosette, Acting Chief Executive Officer, Lemuel Shattuck Hospital, Jamaica Plain, MA, p. A340

MARTINEZ, Suzanne, Director Human Resources, Centennial Peaks Hospital, Louisville, CO, p. A116

MARTINEZ, Terri, Chief Financial Officer, Plains Memorial Hospital, Dimmitt, TX, p. A673

MARTINEZ, Tina, Director Human Resources, J. D. Mccarty Center For Children With Developmental Disabilities, Norman, OK, p. A563

MARTINEZ, Virginia, Director Human Resources, Copper Queen Community Hospital, Bisbee, AZ, p. A30

MARTINEZ, Yolanda, Chief Fiscal Services, Edward Hines, Jr. Veterans Affairs Hospital, Hines, IL, p. A207

MARTINEZ, Yvette, Director Human Resources, Sutter Auburn Faith Hospital, Auburn, CA, p. A56

MARTINEZ-TORRES, Daniel, Chief Executive Officer, Hickory Trail Hospital, Desoto, TX, p. A672

MARTING, Bill, Senior Vice President and Chief Financial Officer, The University Of Kansas Hospital, Kansas City, KS, p. A268

MARTINSON, Erling, M.D., Medical Director, Nelson County Health System, Mcville, ND, p. A525

MARTINSON, Tiffany, Director Human Resources, Norton Sound Regional Hospital, Nome, AK, p. A29

MARTOCCIO, Debora, R.N., Chief Operating Officer, Adventhealth Connerton, Land O'Lakes, FL, p. A143

MARTONE, Nancy, Vice President and Chief Human Resources Officer, Hospital For Special Care, New Britain, CT, p. A123

MARTUCCI, Kathleen, Chief Operating Officer, Helen Hayes Hospital, West Haverstraw, NY, p. A502

MARTZ, Dean, Chief Medical Officer, Providence Holy Family Hospital, Spokane, WA, p. A766

Chief Medical Officer, Providence Sacred Heart Medical Center & Children's Hospital, Spokane, WA, p. A766

MARTZ, Michael, Senior Vice President and Chief Information Officer, Mount Nittany Medical Center, State College, PA, p. A608

MARVIN, Ryan, Support Services Director, Rawlins County Health Center, Atwood, KS, p. A262

MARX, Edward, Chief Information Officer, Cleveland Clinic, Cleveland, OH, p. A534

MARX, Kenneth, Chief Financial Officer, Ranken Jordan Pediatric Bridge Hospital, Maryland Heights, MO, p. A411

MARX, Tomasine, Chief Financial Officer and Chief Operating Officer, Ascension Crittenton Hospital Medical Center, Rochester, MI, p. A365

MARX, Troy, Human Resources Director, Upland Hills Health, Dodgeville, WI, p. A782

MARZOLF, Steve, R.N., Chief Nursing Officer, Spectrum Health Pennock, Hastings, MI, p. A357

MASE, Kerin A., President and Chief Executive Officer, Marian Regional Medical Center, Santa Maria, CA, p. A97

MASHAK-EKERN, Jane, Fiscal Officer, Va Medical Center, Tomah, WI, p. A797

MASIELLO, Matthew, M.D., Chief Medical Officer, The Children's Institute Of Pittsburgh, Pittsburgh, PA, p. A603

MASINGALE, Jason, Chief Operating Officer, Arkansas Methodist Medical Center, Paragould, AR, p. A51

MASKELL, Denise, Chief Information Officer, Springfield Hospital Center, Sykesville, MD, p. A333

MASLYN, Jay, Chief Financial Officer, Nicholas H. Noyes Memorial Hospital, Dansville, NY, p. A482

MASON, AJ, Chief Financial Officer, Humboldt County Memorial Hospital, Humboldt, IA, p. A251

MASON, Bill A., Chief Executive Officer, Meadow Wood Behavioral Health System, New Castle, DE, p. A127

MASON, Drew, Chief Executive Officer, Grandview Medical Center, Birmingham, AL, p. A15

MASON, H, M.D., Chief Medical Officer, Baptist Memorial Hospital-Union County, New Albany, MS, p. A398

MASON, Jill, MS, R.N., Chief Nursing Officer, Blessing Hospital, Quincy, IL, p. A218

MASON, John, Chief Information Officer, Hill Country Memorial Hospital, Fredericksburg, TX, p. A679

MASON, Kathy, R.N., MSN, Chief Nursing Officer, Lifecare Hospitals Of Dallas, Dallas, TX, p. A669

MASON, Kay, Chief Financial Officer, Texas Health Heart & Vascular Hospital Arlington, Arlington, TX, p. A654

MASON, Keith, Chief Executive Officer, Bailey Medical Center, Owasso, OK, p. A566

MASON, Phyllis, M.D., Chief Medical Officer, Natchitoches Regional Medical Center, Natchitoches, LA, p. A310

MASON, Ray, Chief Executive Officer, Liberty Dayton Regional Medical Center, Liberty, TX, p. A696

MASON, Rhonda, Vice President of Patient Care Services, Tri-State Memorial Hospital, Clarkston, WA, p. A756

MASON, Sandra, MSN, R.N., Director Nursing Services and Senior Nurse Executive, Robert E. Bush Naval Hospital, Twentynine Palms, CA, p. A102

MASON, Stacie, Vice President and Chief Financial Officer, Integris Grove Hospital, Grove, OK, p. A559

Vice President, Regional Chief Financial Officer, Integris Bass Baptist Health Center, Enid, OK, p. A559

MASON, William, Chief Operating Officer, Brooke Glen Behavioral Hospital, Fort Washington, PA, p. A590

MASON-JONES, Taryn, Chief Nurse Executive, Norristown State Hospital, Norristown, PA, p. A598

MASOOD, Shahid, M.D., Clinical Director, Mildred Mitchell-Bateman Hospital, Huntington, WV, p. A773

MASSA, Rhonda, Director of Nursing, Clarion Psychiatric Center, Clarion, PA, p. A586

MASSAAD, Aziz, M.D., Medical Staff President, Down East Community Hospital, Machias, ME, p. A321

MASSARO, Thomas, M.D., Chief Medical Officer, New Mexico Rehabilitation Center, Roswell, NM, p. A471

MASSELLA, Joan, Administrative Vice President and Chief Nursing Officer, St. Clair Hospital, Pittsburgh, PA, p. A603

MASSENGALE, David, Chief Financial Officer, Methodist Hospital Union County, Morganfield, KY, p. A290

Vice President and Chief Financial Officer, Methodist Hospital, Henderson, KY, p. A285

MASSENGILL, Leigh, Chief Executive Officer, Medical Center Of Trinity, Trinity, FL, p. A161

MASSEY, Gina, Vice President Human Resources, Clarity Child Guidance Center, San Antonio, TX, p. A711

MASSEY, Rocco K., Community Chief Executive Officer, Beckley Arh Hospital, Beckley, WV, p. A770

MASSEY, Steven, President and Chief Executive Officer, Westfields Hospital And Clinic, New Richmond, WI, p. A792

MASSEY, Tami, M.D., Chief of Medical Staff, Edgefield County Healthcare, Edgefield, SC, p. A619

MASSEY, Terry, Chief Fiscal Services, Beckley Veterans Affairs Medical Center, Beckley, WV, p. A770

MASSIELLO, Martin, Executive Vice President and Chief Operating Officer, Eisenhower Health, Rancho Mirage, CA, p. A86

MASSIMILLA, John, FACHE, Vice President and Chief Operating Officer, Wellspan Chambersburg Hospital, Chambersburg, PA, p. A586

MASSMAN, Patty, Director of Nursing, Avera Granite Falls Health Center, Granite Falls, MN, p. A377

MASSOUH, Rafik, M.D., Chief of Staff, Mercy Allen Hospital, Oberlin, OH, p. A547

MAST, Delvin, R.N., Director of Nursing, Weatherford Regional Hospital, Weatherford, OK, p. A572

MAST, Duane, M.D., Medical Director, Hocking Valley Community Hospital, Logan, OH, p. A543

MAST, Joelle, Ph.D., M.D., Chief Medical Officer, Blythedale Children's Hospital, Valhalla, NY, p. A500

MAST, Nathan, Chief Executive Officer, Vibra Hospital Of Mahoning Valley, Boardman, OH, p. A530

MASTALER, Emily, Chief Executive Officer, River Hospital, Alexandria Bay, NY, p. A474

MASTER, Moiz, M.D., Medical Director of Quality, Piedmont Mountainside Hospital, Jasper, GA, p. A174

MASTERS, Emily, Chief Human Relations Officer, Windom Area Health, Windom, MN, p. A388

MASTERS, Ken, Director Information Technology, Chambers Memorial Hospital, Danville, AR, p. A44

MASTERS, Kim, M.D., Medical Director, Saint Simons By-The-Sea Hospital, Saint Simons Island, GA, p. A179

MASTERS, Regina, R.N., MSN, Director of Nursing, Continuing Care Hospital, Lexington, KY, p. A286

MASTERSON, David J., President, Sentara Williamsburg Regional Medical Center, Williamsburg, VA, p. A753

MASTERSON, Paul, Chief Financial Officer, Genesis Healthcare System, Zanesville, OH, p. A554

MASTERSON, Sammie, Director Human Resources, Harney District Hospital, Burns, OR, p. A574

MASTROIANNI, Anthony, Regional Vice President Finance, The William W. Backus Hospital, Norwich, CT, p. A124

MASTROIANNI, Thomas, Director, Human Resources, Vidant North Hospital, Roanoke Rapids, NC, p. A517

MASTROMANNO, Christopher, Chief Executive Officer, Nyc Health + Hospitals / Jacobi, Bronx, NY, p. A477

MATA, Maribel, Director Information Services, Doctors Hospital Of Laredo, Laredo, TX, p. A695

MATA-GUERRERO, Rita, Director of Nursing, Weslaco Regional Rehabilitation Hospital, Weslaco, TX, p. A725

MATAI, Divya, Chief Financial Officer, Northwest Texas Healthcare System, Amarillo, TX, p. A652

MATAMOROS, Mary L., R.N., Administrator, Seaside Behavioral Center - New Orleans, New Orleans, LA, p. A311

MATCHETT, Glenda, Chief Executive Officer, Dallas Regional Medical Center, Mesquite, TX, p. A700

MATEJICKA, Anthony, D.O., M.P.H., Vice President, Chief Medical Officer, Montefiore Nyack Hospital, Nyack, NY, p. A493

MATEJKA, Cheryl, Chief Financial Officer, Mercy Hospital St. Louis, Saint Louis, MO, p. A416

Chief Financial Officer, Mercy Hospital Washington, Washington, MO, p. A420

MATENAER, Thomas, Chief Financial Officer, Banner Gateway Medical Center, Gilbert, AZ, p. A32

MATHAI, George, M.D., Chief of Staff, Three Rivers Hospital, Waverly, TN, p. A650

MATHAI, Matt, M.D., Medical Director, Select Specialty Hospital-Milwaukee, Milwaukee, WI, p. A791

MATHEIS, Tracey, Chief Financial Officer, Moberly Regional Medical Center, Moberly, MO, p. A412

Chief Operating Officer, Moberly Regional Medical Center, Moberly, MO, p. A412

MATHER, Kelly, Chief Executive Officer, Sonoma Valley Hospital, Sonoma, CA, p. A99

MATHER, Martha S., Chief Administrative Officer, Uofl Health - Peace Hospital, Louisville, KY, p. A289

MATHERS, Larry, M.D., Chief of Staff, Tennova Newport Medical Center, Newport, TN, p. A647

MATHES, Lisa, Human Resources Director, Southwest Medical Center, Liberal, KS, p. A269

MATHEW, Finny, President, Integris Bass Baptist Health Center, Enid, OK, p. A559

MATHEWS, Christine, Chief Nursing Officer, First Hospital Wyoming Valley, Kingston, PA, p. A593

Interim President and Chief Executive Officer, Chief Nursing Officer, First Hospital Wyoming Valley, Kingston, PA, p. A593

MATHEWS, Gary, M.D., Medical Doctor, Beaver County Memorial Hospital, Beaver, OK, p. A556

MATHEWS, Nimmy, Acting Director Quality Management, San Carlos Apache Healthcare Corporation, Peridot, AZ, p. A35

MATHEWS, Paul G., CPA, Administrator, Hardtner Medical Center, Olla, LA, p. A312

MATHEWS, Thomas, Chief Financial Officer, Unitypoint Health - Iowa Methodist Medical Center, Des Moines, IA, p. A248

MATHEWSON, Patricia, Chief Nursing Officer, Adventist Health - Tulare, Tulare, CA, p. A102

MATHIAS, Matt, Chief Executive Officer, Stonesprings Hospital Center, Dulles, VA, p. A741

MATHIEU, Angie, System Director Information Technology and Regional Chief Information Officer, The William W. Backus Hospital, Norwich, CT, p. A124

MATHIEU, Lori, MSN, Chief Nursing Officer, Glenwood Regional Medical Center, West Monroe, LA, p. A316

MATHIS, Alison, Chief Nursing Officer, Copiah County Medical Center, Hazlehurst, MS, p. A394

MATHIS, Ashley, Privacy Officer, Columbus Community Hospital, Columbus, TX, p. A664

MATHIS, Jane, Chief Financial Officer, Baylor Scott & White Surgical Hospital Fort Worth, Fort Worth, TX, p. A678

MATHIS, Patricia, Associate Director Patient Care Service, Richard L. Roudebush Veterans Affairs Medical Center, Indianapolis, IN, p. A233

MATHIS, Rebecca, Chief Financial Officer, Amita Health Adventist Medical Center Bolingbrook, Bolingbrook, IL, p. A196

Chief Financial Officer, Amita Health Adventist Medical Center La Grange, La Grange, IL, p. A210

Vice President and Chief Financial Officer, Amita Health Adventist Medical Center - Hinsdale, Hinsdale, IL, p. A208

MATHIS, Robin, Director Human Resources, Methodist Healthcare Olive Branch Hospital, Olive Branch, MS, p. A398

MATHISEN, Arthur, FACHE, President, Memorial Hospital, North Conway, NH, p. A451

MATHUR, Ashish, M.D., Chief of Staff, Siloam Springs Regional Hospital, Siloam Springs, AR, p. A53

MATHUR, Tanmay, Chief Executive Officer, Covington Behavioral Health, Covington, LA, p. A300

MATHURIN, Emile, M.D., JrMedical Director, Encompass Health Rehabilitation Hospital Of Humble, Humble, TX, p. A689

MATHURIN, Venra, Vice President Human Resources, Interfaith Medical Center, Brooklyn, NY, p. A478

MATINCHEV, Borian, M.D., Medical Director, Encompass Health Rehabilitation Hospital, A Partner Of Washington Regional, Fayetteville, AR, p. A45

MATLACK, Victoria, Director and Human Resources Business Partner, Ohiohealth Dublin Methodist Hospital, Dublin, OH, p. A539

Director and Human Resources Business Partner, Ohiohealth Grady Memorial Hospital, Delaware, OH, p. A539

MATNEY, James L., President and Chief Executive Officer, Colquitt Regional Medical Center, Moultrie, GA, p. A177

MATNEY, Patty, Human Resources Consultant, Saint Thomas Hickman Hospital, Centerville, TN, p. A635

MATNEY, Tim, Chief Financial Officer, Logan Regional Medical Center, Logan, WV, p. A774

MATOS, Patricia, Chief Nursing Officer, Stewart & Lynda Resnick Neuropsychiatric Hospital At Ucla, Los Angeles, CA, p. A76

MATSINGER, John, D.O., Chief Medical Officer, Virtua Marlton, Marlton, NJ, p. A458

MATT, Robert, Vice President and Chief Operating Officer, Hancock Regional Hospital, Greenfield, IN, p. A230

MATTERN, Bonnie, Director Human Resources, Chi St. Alexius Health Devils Lake Hospital, Devils Lake, ND, p. A522

MATTERN, Joe, M.D., Chief Medical Officer, Jefferson Healthcare, Port Townsend, WA, p. A762

MATTERN, Karen, Director of Human Resources, Shriners Hospitals For Children-Spokane, Spokane, WA, p. A766

MATTES, Bryan, Associate Administrator, Crossridge Community Hospital, Wynne, AR, p. A54

MATTES, Dennis, Chief Executive Officer, Select Specialty Hospital-Milwaukee, Milwaukee, WI, p. A791

MATTEUCCI, Dolly, Executive Director, Nap. State Hospital, Napa, CA, p. A80

Superintendent, Oregon State Hospital, Salem, OR, p. A581

MATTHEWS, Adora, M.D., Medical Director, Encompass Health Rehabilitation Hospital Of Florence, Florence, SC, p. A619

MATTHEWS, Bryan C., Medical Center Director, Veterans Affairs Gulf Coast Veterans Health Care System, Biloxi, MS, p. A390

MATTHEWS, Carol, Director Human Resources, Saline Memorial Hospital, Benton, AR, p. A42

MATTHEWS, Clinton, President and Chief Executive Officer, Reading Hospital Rehabilitation At Wyomissing, Wyomissing, PA, p. A612

MATTHEWS, Deborah, Chief Nursing Officer, Tanner Medical Center-Carrollton, Carrollton, GA, p. A168

Senior Vice President, Tanner Medical Center-Villa Rica, Villa Rica, GA, p. A182

MATTHEWS, Edward, Chief Financial Officer, San Dimas Community Hospital, San Dimas, CA, p. A93

MATTHEWS, Gwen, R.N., MSN, Chief Executive Officer, Adventist Health Ukiah Valley, Ukiah, CA, p. A102

MATTHEWS, Judith, Nurse Executive, Riverside Tappahannock Hospital, Tappahannock, VA, p. A752

MATTHEWS, Kristopher, Chief Operating Officer, Decatur Health Systems, Oberlin, KS, p. A272

MATTHEWS, Lauren, Chief Financial Officer, Piedmont Newton Hospital, Covington, GA, p. A170

MATTHEWS, Lori, Vice President Information Technology System, Banner Baywood Medical Center, Mesa, AZ, p. A33

MATTHEWS, Melissa, Director Human Resources, Dahl Memorial Healthcare Association, Ekalaka, MT, p. A423

MATTHEWS, Michael, Vice President Human Resources, Holland Hospital, Holland, MI, p. A357

MATTHEWS, Oliver, M.D., Chief Medical Officer, North Alabama Medical Center, Florence, AL, p. A18

MATTHEWS, Ted, Chief Executive Officer, Eastland Memorial Hospital, Eastland, TX, p. A673

MATTHEY, Michael, Facility Chief Information Officer, Louis A. Johnson Veterans Affairs Medical Center, Clarksburg, WV, p. A772

MATTHIAS, Mark, M.D., Vice President of Medical Affairs, St. Cloud Hospital, Saint Cloud, MN, p. A384

MATTHIESSEN, Matthew, Chief Executive Officer, John C. Fremont Healthcare District, Mariposa, CA, p. A77

MATTICE, Gloria, R.N., Director Patient Care, George C. Grap. Community Hospital, Hamburg, IA, p. A251

MATTINGLY, Marty, Administrator, Ascension St. Vincent Warrick, Boonville, IN, p. A224

MATTISON, Denise, Director Finance and Accounting Services, Mayo Clinic Health System In Eau Claire, Eau Claire, WI, p. A783

MATTLY, Sheila, Chief Nursing Officer, Wayne County Hospital, Corydon, IA, p. A246

MATTNER, Matthew, Chief Operating Officer, Lutheran Hospital, Cleveland, OH, p. A534
Chief Operations Officer, Fisher-Titus Medical Center, Norwalk, OH, p. A546

MATTSON, Jodi, Director of Nursing, Cedar Springs Hospital, Colorado Springs, CO, p. A109

MATTSON, Kent D., Chief Executive Officer, Lake Region Healthcare, Fergus Falls, MN, p. A376

MATTSON, Wayne, Management Information Systems Specialist, Rogers Memorial Hospital, Inc., Oconomowoc, WI, p. A793

MATUS, Jose, M.D., Director Medical, Carrus Rehabilitation Hospital, Sherman, TX, p. A715

MATUSZKIEWICZ, Marcin, M.D., Chief of Staff and Medical Director, Jerold Phelp. Community Hospital, Garberville, CA, p. A66

MATZIGKEIT, Linda, Senior Vice President Human Resources, Children's Healthcare Of Atlanta, Atlanta, GA, p. A164

MAUCK, Lynn, R.N., Chief Operating Officer and Chief Nursing Officer, Fishermen's Hospital, Marathon, FL, p. A144

MAURER, Gregory L., Chief Executive Officer, Sheridan Memorial Hospital, Plentywood, MT, p. A426

MAURER, Jackie, Fiscal Officer, Julian F. Keith Alcohol And Drug Abuse Treatment Center, Black Mountain, NC, p. A505

MAURER, Linda, Vice President Patient Care Services, Wilson Memorial Hospital, Sidney, OH, p. A549

MAURER, Marsha, R.N., MS, Chief Nursing Officer Patient Care Services, Beth Israel Deaconess Medical Center, Boston, MA, p. A335

MAURICE, Timothy, Chief Financial Officer, University Of California, Davis Medical Center, Sacramento, CA, p. A90

MAURIN, Michael, Chief Financial Officer, Southern Surgical Hospital, Slidell, LA, p. A315

MAURO, Phyllis, Chief Executive Officer, Amg Specialty Hospital - Las Vegas, Las Vegas, NV, p. A443

MAVROMATIS, Lou, Vice President Information Technology, Medstar Southern Maryland Hospital Center, Clinton, MD, p. A328

MAVROS, George, Chief Operating Officer, Citrus Memorial Health System, Inverness, FL, p. A140

MAXIE, Bryan K., Administrator, Highland Community Hospital, Picayune, MS, p. A398

MAXWELL, Dale, Executive Vice President and Chief Financial Officer, Presbyterian Hospital, Albuquerque, NM, p. A468

MAXWELL, Ronnie, Director Information Systems, Glenwood Regional Medical Center, West Monroe, LA, p. A316

MAY, Brandon, Chief Operating Officer, The Hospitals Of Providence East Campus, El Paso, TX, p. A676
President, Morton Plant North Bay Hospital, New Port Richey, FL, p. A149

MAY, David, Chief of Staff, Richland Hospital, Richland Center, WI, p. A795

MAY, Kevin, Chief Financial Officer, Watauga Medical Center, Boone, NC, p. A505
System Director Finance, Charles A. Cannon Memorial Hospital, Newland, NC, p. A515

MAY, Robin, Director Information Systems, Platte County Memorial Hospital, Wheatland, WY, p. A804

MAY, Ronald, M.D., Vice President Medical Affairs, Carolinaeast Health System, New Bern, NC, p. A515

MAY, Scott, Area Director Technology, Kaiser Permanente Santa Clara Medical Center, Santa Clara, CA, p. A97

MAY, Sonja, Director Human Resources, Morton County Health System, Elkhart, KS, p. A264

MAY, Todd, M.D., Chief Medical Officer, Zuckerberg San Francisco General Hospital And Trauma Center, San Francisco, CA, p. A94

MAY, Troy, Chief Information Officer, Uofl Health - Uofl Hospital, Louisville, KY, p. A289

MAY, William J., Administrator, Hawaii State Hospital, Kaneohe, HI, p. A186

MAYBEN, Casey, Chief Nursing Officer, Ut Health Pittsburg, Pittsburg, TX, p. A706
Interim Chief Executive Officer, Ut Health Pittsburg, Pittsburg, TX, p. A706

MAYCOCK, Adam, Chief Executive Officer, Amita Health Adventist Medical Center - Hinsdale, Hinsdale, IL, p. A208
Chief Executive Officer, Amita Health Adventist Medical Center La Grange, La Grange, IL, p. A210

MAYEAUX, Rachel, Chief Executive Officer, Amg Specialty Hospital-Houma, Houma, LA, p. A303

MAYER, David, Chief of Staff, Wayne County Hospital, Monticello, KY, p. A290

MAYER, Dean, M.D., Chief Medical Officer, Riverton Hospital, Riverton, UT, p. A731

MAYER, Joanne, St. Joseph's Hospital, Tampa, FL, p. A160

MAYER, Peter, Director Information Systems, Bakersfield Heart Hospital, Bakersfield, CA, p. A57

MAYER, William, M.D., Vice President Medical Staff Services, St. Mary's Healthcare, Amsterdam, NY, p. A474

MAYES, Libby, Human Resource Director, Ephraim Mcdowell Regional Medical Center, Danville, KY, p. A282

MAYES, Terri, Vice President and Chief Nursing Officer, Valley Health - Warren Memorial Hospital, Front Royal, VA, p. A742

MAYEWSKI, Raymond, M.D., Chief Medical Officer, Highland Hospital, Rochester, NY, p. A496
M.D., Chief Medical Officer, Strong Memorial Hospital Of The University Of Rochester, Rochester, NY, p. A496

MAYFIELD, Michael, M.D., Chief of Staff, Chicot Memorial Medical Center, Lake Village, AR, p. A48

MAYFIELD, William, M.D., Chief of Staff, Tristar Stonecrest Medical Center, Smyrna, TN, p. A649

MAYHLE, Douglas, M.D., Medical Director, Nicholas H. Noyes Memorial Hospital, Dansville, NY, p. A482

MAYLE, Connie, Vice President Administrative Services, Upmc Horizon, Farrell, PA, p. A590

MAYNARD, Bob, Chief Information Officer, Fairview Regional Medical Center, Fairview, OK, p. A525

MAYO, Hal, Chief Financial Officer, Liberty Dayton Regional Medical Center, Liberty, TX, p. A696

MAYO, Jim, M.D., Clinical Director, Cherry Hospital, Goldsboro, NC, p. A510

MAYO, Michael A., FACHE, President, Baptist Medical Center Jacksonville, Jacksonville, FL, p. A140

MAYO, Randy, Director Information Technology, William Newton Hospital, Winfield, KS, p. A279

MAYO, Robert, M.D., Chief Medical Officer, Rochester General Hospital, Rochester, NY, p. A496
M.D., Executive Vice President, Chief Medical Officer, Rochester Regional Health, Newark-Wayne Community Hospital, Newark, NY, p. A492

MAYORGA, Oliver, M.D., Chief Medical Officer, Lawrence + Memorial Hospital, New London, CT, p. A124
M.D., Chief Medical Officer, Westerly Hospital, Westerly, RI, p. A614

MAYS, Dawn, Chief Nursing Officer, Scott Memorial Health, Scottsburg, IN, p. A240

MAYS, Raymond, M.D., Medical Director, River Crest Hospital, San Angelo, TX, p. A710

MAYS, Sherrie, MSN, R.N., Vice President and Chief Nursing Officer, Baptist Health Corbin, Corbin, KY, p. A282

MAYSENT, Patty, Chief Executive Officer, Uc San Diego Medical Center—Hillcrest, San Diego, CA, p. A92

MAYSILLES, Nancy, R.N., Chief Nursing Officer, Medical Center Of Trinity, Trinity, FL, p. A161

MAYSON, Mark, M.D., Medical Director, Prisma Health Baptist Hospital, Columbia, SC, p. A618

MAZANEC, Lori, Chief Executive Officer, Box Butte General Hospital, Alliance, NE, p. A429

MAZEK, Mariusz, Vice President Information Technology and Chief Information Officer, Roseland Community Hospital, Chicago, IL, p. A200

MAZOUR, Linda, M.D., President, Franklin County Memorial Hospital, Franklin, NE, p. A432

MAZUREK, Michele, Interim Vice President Patient Care Services and Chief Nursing Officer, Mount Sinai Hospital, Chicago, IL, p. A199

MAZZA, Mary, Director Human Resources, Encompass Health Rehabilitation Hospital Of Western Massachusetts, Ludlow, MA, p. A341

MAZZARELLA, Frank, M.D., Chief Medical Officer, Clara Maass Medical Center, Belleville, NJ, p. A452

MAZZARELLI, Anthony J., JD, M.D., Co-President and Chief Executive Officer, Cooper University Health Care, Camden, NJ, p. A453

MAZZO, Joseph, Chief Executive Officer, John Randolp. Medical Center, Hopewell, VA, p. A744

MAZZOLA, Joseph, M.D., Chief Medical Officer, Osceola Regional Medical Center, Kissimmee, FL, p. A142

MAZZONI, Dean, President and Chief Executive Officer, Franciscan Health Michigan City, Michigan City, IN, p. A236

MAZZUCA, Darryl, Director Management Information Systems, Osf Healthcare Little Company Of Mary Medical Center, Evergreen Park, IL, p. A204

MBENGA, Saul, Manager Information Technology, Alliance Healthcare System, Holly Springs, MS, p. A394

MCADAMS, David, Chief Financial Officer, Lindner Center Of Hope, Mason, OH, p. A544

MCADOO, Jackie, Chief Financial Officer, Grady Memorial Hospital, Chickasha, OK, p. A557

MCAFEE, Thomas J., President, North Region, Northwestern Medicine Lake Forest Hospital, Lake Forest, IL, p. A210
Region President, Northwestern Medicine Mchenry, Mchenry, IL, p. A212

MCALISTER, Julene, Administrator, Accord Rehabilition Hospital, Plaquemine, LA, p. A313

MCALISTER, Michael, Chief Executive Officer, Select Specialty Hospital - Dallas Downtown, Dallas, TX, p. A670

MCALISTER, Stephanie, Controller, Tippah County Hospital, Ripley, MS, p. A399

MCALLISTER, Guy, Vice President and Chief Information Officer, Tift Regional Medical Center, Tifton, GA, p. A182

MCALLISTER, Ric, Chief Executive Officer, Creekside Behavioral Health, Kingsport, TN, p. A640

MCALLISTER, Yvonne, Senior Director Human Resources, Southern Maine Health Care - Biddeford Medical Center, Biddeford, ME, p. A319

MCALOON, Richard, Vice President Human Resources, Hartford Hospital, Hartford, CT, p. A122

MCANDREWS, Kevin, Vice President Human Resources, Nexus Specialty Hospital, Shenandoah, TX, p. A715
Vice President, Human Resources, Nexus Specialty Hospital The Woodlands, The Woodlands, TX, p. A720

MCARTHUR, Ronald L., Chief Executive Officer, Summit Healthcare Regional Medical Center, Show Low, AZ, p. A38

MCARTOR, Dana, R.N., Director of Nursing, Perkins County Health Services, Grant, NE, p. A433

MCASKILL, L., M.D., Chief Medical Officer, Englewood Community Hospital, Englewood, FL, p. A137

MCAVOY, Tim, M.D., Medical Director, Rehabilitation Hospital Of Wisconsin, Waukesha, WI, p. A798

MCBEE, John, Chief of Staff, Chi St. Anthony Hospital, Pendleton, OR, p. A578

MCBREARTY, Michael, M.D., Vice President Medical Affairs, Thomas Hospital, Fairhope, AL, p. A18

MCBRIDE, Brandon, Administrator, Logan Regional Hospital, Logan, UT, p. A728
Operations Officer, Logan Regional Hospital, Logan, UT, p. A728

MCBRIDE, Dina, Chief Operating Officer and Director Human Resources, East Adams Rural Healthcare, Ritzville, WA, p. A763

MCBRIDE, Grace, Regional Chief Nursing Officer, Amita Health Mercy Medical Center, Aurora, IL, p. A195

MCBRIDE, Jason, Chief Executive Officer, Pawhuska Hospital, Pawhuska, OK, p. A566

MCBRIDE, Lamar, Chief Executive Officer, Vibra Hospital Of Denver, Thornton, CO, p. A119

MCBROOM, Robert, M.D., Medical Director, Kp. Promise Hospital Of Wichita Falls, Wichita Falls, TX, p. A725

MCBRYDE, Robin, Chief Information Officer, Alexandria Veterans Affairs Health Care System, Pineville, LA, p. A312

MCCAA, Karen, R.N., Vice President Patient Care Services and Chief Nursing Officer, Baptist Medical Center South, Montgomery, AL, p. A22

MCCABE, Mary, Chief Financial Officer, North Colorado Medical Center, Greeley, CO, p. A113

MCCABE, Patrick, Senior Vice President Finance and Chief Financial Officer, Bridgeport Hospital, Bridgeport, CT, p. A121

MCCABE, Patrick G. Jr, FACHE, President and Chief Executive Officer, Levi Hospital, Hot Springs National Park, AR, p. A47

MCCABE, Steve, Chief Executive Officer, Montevista Hospital, Las Vegas, NV, p. A443
Chief Executive Officer, Strategic Behavioral Health - Wilmington, Leland, NC, p. A513

MCCAFFERTY, Michael, Chief Executive Officer, Sheridan Memorial Hospital, Sheridan, WY, p. A804

MCCAFFREY, Anne E., President and Chief Executive Officer, Eastern Niagara Hospital, Lockport, NY, p. A487

MCCAHILL, Connie, R.N., President and Chief Executive Officer, Cameron Memorial Community Hospital, Angola, IN, p. A223

MCCAHILL, Mary, Chief Nursing Officer, Thorek Memorial Hospital, Chicago, IL, p. A201

MCCAIN, Rebecca J., Chief Executive Officer, Electra Memorial Hospital, Electra, TX, p. A676

MCCALL, Brad, Vice President Operations, Baylor Scott & White The Heart Hospital Denton, Denton, TX, p. A671
Vice President Operations, Baylor Scott & White The Heart Hospital Plano, Plano, TX, p. A706

MCCALL, Harlo, Chief Executive Officer, Encompass Health Rehabilitation Hospital Of Texarkana, Texarkana, TX, p. A720

MCCALL, Lee, Chief Executive Officer, Neshoba County General Hospital, Philadelphia, MS, p. A398

MCCALL, Mona, R.N., Director of Nursing, Acadia-St. Landry Hospital, Church Point, LA, p. A299

MCCALL, Pam, Director Human Resources, Heatherhill Care Communities, Chardon, OH, p. A531

MCCALLISTER, Bob, Director Human Resources, Baptist Memorial Hospital-Golden Triangle, Columbus, MS, p. A391

MCCALLISTER, Darla, Chief Financial Officer, Lakeside Women's Hospital, Oklahoma City, OK, p. A564

MCCALLISTER, Dianne, M.D., Chief Medical Officer, Medical Center Of Aurora, Aurora, CO, p. A107

MCCALLISTER, Sean, Chief Executive Officer, Johnson County Healthcare Center, Buffalo, WY, p. A801

MCCAMPBELL, Kellie, Coordinator Human Resources, Kindred Hospital-Chattanooga, Chattanooga, TN, p. A635

MCCAMPBELL, Marcia, M.D., Chief Medical Officer, Shasta Regional Medical Center, Redding, CA, p. A87

MCCANDLESS, David, Vice President Medical Affairs, Upmc Northwest, Seneca, PA, p. A607

MCCANN, Barbara, Director Human Resources, Sunrise Canyon Hospital, Lubbock, TX, p. A698

MCCANN, Kyle, Chief Operating Officer, St. Joseph's Hospital, Savannah, GA, p. A180

MCCANN, Lew, Director Management Information Systems, Osf Holy Family Medical Center, Monmouth, IL, p. A212

MCCARTAN, Mary, Manager Human Resources, Va Long Beach Healthcare System, Long Beach, CA, p. A73

MCCARTER, Alyssa, Chief Financial Officer, W. J. Mangold Memorial Hospital, Lockney, TX, p. A696

MCCARTER, Scott, Chief Information Officer, Karmanos Cancer Center, Detroit, MI, p. A353

MCCARTHY, Brian, Director Information Systems, Salem Medical Center, Salem, NJ, p. A462

MCCARTHY, Cynthia, Chief Nursing Officer, Texas Health Harris Methodist Hospital Stephenville, Stephenville, TX, p. A717

MCCARTHY, Katherine, Director Human Resources, Arbour H. R. I. Hospital, Brookline, MA, p. A337

MCCARTHY, Maureen, M.D., Chief of Staff, Phoenix Veterans Affairs Health Care System, Phoenix, AZ, p. A36

MCCARTHY, Rick, Chief Information Officer, White Plains Hospital Center, White Plains, NY, p. A502

MCCARTHY, Sandra Mac, Chief Nursing Officer, Arnot Ogden Medical Center, Elmira, NY, p. A483

MCCARTHY, Tim, President Puerto Rico Division, First Hospital Panamericano, Cidra, PR, p. A807

MCCARTNEY, Daryl, M.D., President Medical Staff, Emanuel Medical Center, Swainsboro, GA, p. A181

MCCARTY, Daniel, Chief Operating Officer, Orange City Area Health System, Orange City, IA, p. A255

MCCARTY, Jacob M., Chief Executive Officer, Kindred Hospital-San Francisco Bay Area, San Leandro, CA, p. A95

MCCARTY, Kirk, R.N., MSN, Chief Executive Officer, Sky Ridge Medical Center, Lone Tree, CO, p. A116

MCCARTY, Melany, R.N., Chief Clinical Officer, Vibra Hospital Of Amarillo, Amarillo, TX, p. A652

MCCARTY, Tim, Chief Information Officer, Oakbend Medical Center, Richmond, TX, p. A708

MCCARTY, Wendy, Director Human Resources, Hillsboro Community Hospital, Hillsboro, KS, p. A266

MCCARY, Steve C., Administrator, Riverside Doctors' Hospital Williamsburg, Williamsburg, VA, p. A753

MCCASKILL, Rodney, M.D., Interim Chief Medical Officer, Johnston Health, Smithfield, NC, p. A518

MCCASLIN, Anna, Director Finance, Boys Town National Research Hospital, Omaha, NE, p. A436

MCCASLIN, Jami, Director Human Resources, Providence Hood River Memorial Hospital, Hood River, OR, p. A576

MCCAULEY, Bryan, Chief Financial Officer, Covington Behavioral Health, Covington, LA, p. A300

MCCAULEY, Dudley, Controller, Lincoln County Medical Center, Ruidoso, NM, p. A471

MCCAULEY, Jason, Administrator, Jane Phillip. Nowata Health Center, Nowata, OK, p. A563

MCCAULEY, Sue, Director Finance, Mercyone Primghar Medical Center, Primghar, IA, p. A256

MCCAWLEY, Thomas, Vice President, Beloit Health System, Beloit, WI, p. A781

MCCHESNEY, Lisa, R.N., Senior Director Information Systems, Upmc Hamot, Erie, PA, p. A590

MCCLAIN, April, Director, Acute Care, Valley Health - Shenandoah Memorial Hospital, Woodstock, VA, p. A754

MCCLAIN, James, Deputy Director, Clement J. Zablocki Veterans Affairs Medical Center, Milwaukee, WI, p. A791

MCCLAIN, Richard, M.D., Chief Medical Officer, Chickasaw Nation Medical Center, Ada, OK, p. A555

MCCLAIN, Tami, Human Resources Operations Specialist, Leconte Medical Center, Sevierville, TN, p. A649

MCCLANAHAN, Gary, Chief Information Officer, Northeastern Health System Sequoyah, Sallisaw, OK, p. A567

MCCLARIGAN, Linda, R.N., Chief Nursing Officer, Adirondack Health, Saranac Lake, NY, p. A497

MCCLASKEY, Cynthia, Ph.D., Director, Southwestern Virginia Mental Health Institute, Marion, VA, p. A745

MCCLEARY, Heather, Director Human Resources, Coulee Medical Center, Grand Coulee, WA, p. A759

MCCLEESE, Randy, Chief Information Officer, Methodist Hospital Union County, Morganfield, KY, p. A290

Chief Information Officer, Methodist Hospital, Henderson, KY, p. A285

Vice President Information Services and Chief Information Officer, St. Claire Healthcare, Morehead, KY, p. A290

MCCLELAND, Trey, R.N., Director of Nursing, Richardson Medical Center, Rayville, LA, p. A313

MCCLELLAN, Ashley, FACHE, Chief Executive Officer, Research Medical Center, Kansas City, MO, p. A409

MCCLELLAN, Kathryn, Chief Information Officer, Memorial Health, Savannah, GA, p. A180

Senior Vice President and Chief Information Officer, Froedtert West Bend Hospital, West Bend, WI, p. A799

MCCLELLAND, Patricia, Director Human Resources, South Texas Health System, Edinburg, TX, p. A674

MCCLINTICK, Cliff, Chief Information Officer, Lindner Center Of Hope, Mason, OH, p. A544

MCCLOSKEY, Louis, Chief Human Resources, Wilmington Veterans Affairs Medical Center, Wilmington, DE, p. A128

MCCLUNG, Lyle, M.D., Chief of Staff, Carilion Stonewall Jackson Hospital, Lexington, VA, p. A744

MCCLURE, Kenneth, M.D., Chief of Staff, Longview Regional Medical Center, Longview, TX, p. A697

MCCLURG, Cathy, Director Human Resources, William Newton Hospital, Winfield, KS, p. A279

MCCLURG, Chris, Vice President Finance and Chief Financial Officer, St. Claire Healthcare, Morehead, KY, p. A290

MCCLUSKEY, Diane, Chief Human Resources Officer, Twin Cities Community Hospital, Templeton, CA, p. A101

MCCLUSKEY, Scott, Chief Financial Officer, Tyler County Hospital, Woodville, TX, p. A726

MCCLUSKEY, Tabb, M.D., Chief Medical Officer, Hendricks Community Hospital Association, Hendricks, MN, p. A378

MCCOBB, David, Chief Information Officer, Emanate Health Foothill Presbyterian Hospital, Glendora, CA, p. A67

MCCOIC, Kristie, Clinic Operations Officer and Director Human Resources, Gundersen St. Joseph's Hospital And Clinics, Hillsboro, WI, p. A786

MCCOLL, Karen, M.D., Chief Medical Officer, Meadows Regional Medical Center, Vidalia, GA, p. A182

MCCOLLUM, Joann, Chief Nursing Officer, Bolivar Medical Center, Cleveland, MS, p. A391

MCCOLLUM, Kathleen, Senior Vice President, Clinical Integration and Chief Operating Officer, University Of Maryland Baltimore Washington Medical Center, Glen Burnie, MD, p. A330

MCCOLM, Denni, Chief Information Officer, Citizens Memorial Hospital, Bolivar, MO, p. A402

MCCOMB, Canise, Director Human Resources, Graham Hospital Association, Canton, IL, p. A196

MCCONKEY, Teresa, MSN, R.N., Vice President of Nursing and Chief Nursing Officer, Graham Hospital Association, Canton, IL, p. A196

MCCONNACHIE, Angela, Chief Executive Officer and Chief Nursing Officer, Deckerville Community Hospital, Deckerville, MI, p. A352

MCCONNELL, C. William, Ph.D., Chief Executive Officer, Kingman Regional Medical Center, Kingman, AZ, p. A33

MCCONNELL, George, Director, Morris Village Alcohol And Drug Addiction Treatment Center, Columbia, SC, p. A617

MCCONNELL, Linda, R.N., MSN, FACHE, Associate Medical Center Director Patient Care Services, James H. Quillen Veterans Affairs Medical Center, Mountain Home, TN, p. A646

MCCONNELL, Nicole, Senior Vice President, Human Resources, SHDS, Spectrum Health - Butterworth Hospital, Grand Rapids, MI, p. A356

MCCONNELL, Patrick, Chief Financial Officer, West Park Hospital, Cody, WY, p. A802

MCCONNELL, Ron, Chief Operating Officer, Upmc Altoona, Altoona, PA, p. A584

MCCORMACK, J. David., Chief Executive Officer, Vaughan Regional Medical Center, Selma, AL, p. A24

MCCORMACK, Jane, R.N., MSN, Vice President, Chief Nursing Officer and Nursing and Patient Care Services, Unity Hospital, Rochester, NY, p. A496

MCCORMACK-MILLER, Linda, Chief Nursing Officer, Faxton St. Luke's Healthcare, Utica, NY, p. A500

MCCORMICK, Brad, Chief Financial Officer, Natchitoches Regional Medical Center, Natchitoches, LA, p. A310

MCCORMICK, Daniel, M.D., President and Chief Executive Officer, Franciscan Health Crown Point, Crown Point, IN, p. A226

MCCORMICK, David, Chief Financial Officer, Northwest Hospital, Assistant Vice President, Finance, LifeBridge Health, Northwest Hospital, Randallstown, MD, p. A331

MCCORMICK, Dee, Director Personnel and Human Resources, Coon Memorial Hospital, Dalhart, TX, p. A667

MCCORMICK, Jason, Interim Chief Financial Officer, Melissa Memorial Hospital, Holyoke, CO, p. A114

MCCORMICK, Jayne, M.D., Chief Medical Officer CDS, Presbyterian Hospital, Albuquerque, NM, p. A468

MCCORMICK, John, President and Chief Executive Officer, Oak Valley Hospital, Oakdale, CA, p. A82

MCCORMICK, Kevin, M.D., Associate Medical Director, Jones Memorial Hospital, Wellsville, NY, p. A502

MCCORMICK, Martha, Chief Executive Officer, Unity Medical Center, Manchester, TN, p. A643

MCCORMICK, Pam, Director Human Resources, Permian Regional Medical Center, Andrews, TX, p. A653

MCCOY, Adriene, Chief Human Resource Officer, Baptist Health South Florida, Baptist Hospital Of Miami, Miami, FL, p. A146

Corporate Vice President, Baptist Health South Florida, Homestead Hospital, Homestead, FL, p. A140

MCCOY, Andrea, M.D., Chief Medical Officer, Cap. Regional Health System, Cap. May Court House, NJ, p. A453

MCCOY, Janice, MS, R.N., Chief Clinical Officer, Promise Hospital Of Florida At The Villages, Oxford, FL, p. A152

MCCOY, Jessica, Director Human Resources, Cedar Springs Hospital, Colorado Springs, CO, p. A109

MCCOY, Josh, Administrator, Adena Greenfield Medical Center, Greenfield, OH, p. A541

MCCOY, Melissa, Vice President and Chief Financial Officer, West Virginia University Hospitals, Morgantown, WV, p. A775

MCCOY, Michael, M.D., Chief Medical Officer, Great River Medical Center, West Burlington, IA, p. A260

MCCOY, Mike, Chief Executive Officer, Chambers Memorial Hospital, Danville, AR, p. A44

MCCOY, Shawn W., Chief Executive Officer, Deaconess Midtown Hospital, Evansville, IN, p. A227

MCCOY, Stephanie, President and Chief Executive Officer, Jackson General Hospital, Ripley, WV, p. A776

MCCRAW, Nicki, Assistant Vice President Human Resources, Uw Medicine/Harborview Medical Center, Seattle, WA, p. A764

MCCREA, Kim, Chief Human Resources Officer, Ortonville Area Health Services, Ortonville, MN, p. A382

MCCREA, Yvette, Chief Human Resources, Winn Army Community Hospital, Hinesville, GA, p. A174

MCCREADY, David O., President, Brigham And Women's Faulkner Hospital, Boston, MA, p. A335

MCCREARY, Michael, Chief of Services, Mercy Hospital Washington, Washington, MO, p. A420

MCCREARY, William, Vice President and Chief Information Officer, The University Of Toledo Medical Center, Toledo, OH, p. A551

MCCRIMMON, Scott, Manager Information Technology, Northern Arizona Veterans Affairs Health Care System, Prescott, AZ, p. A37

MCCROSKEY, Mark, Vice President Operations, Northeastern Health System, Tahlequah, OK, p. A569

MCCUE, Jennifer, Director Patient Care, Summersville Regional Medical Center, Summersville, WV, p. A777

MCCUE, Raymond, M.D., Vice President, Medical Affairs and Chief Medical Officer, Chesapeake Regional Medical Center, Chesapeake, VA, p. A740

MCCUE, Robert, Vice President Finance, Mid Coast Hospital, Brunswick, ME, p. A319

MCCUE, Steven, Chief Financial Officer, Umass Memorial-Marlborough Hospital, Marlborough, MA, p. A341

MCCULLER, Renee, R.N., MSN, Chief Nursing Officer, Willis-Knighton Medical Center, Shreveport, LA, p. A315

MCCULLEY, Becky, Chief Operations Officer, University Of Texas Southwestern Medical Center, Dallas, TX, p. A671

MCCULLEY, Larry W., President and Chief Executive Officer, Touchette Regional Hospital, Centreville, IL, p. A197

MCCULLOCH, Greg, CPA, Vice President of Finance and Chief Financial Officer, Adventist Health Sonora, Sonora, CA, p. A99

MCCULLOCH, Liz, Chief Information Resource Management Systems, Cheyenne Veterans Affairs Medical Center, Cheyenne, WY, p. A802

MCCULLOUGH, Barbara, Vice President Human Resources, Washington Hospital, Washington, PA, p. A610

MCCULLOUGH, Bobby, Chief Executive Officer, Memorial Satilla Health, Waycross, GA, p. A183

MCCULLOUGH, Erin, Chief Clinical Officer, Kindred Hospital-Philadelphia, Philadelphia, PA, p. A601

MCCULLOUGH, Mary Kelly, Associate Director Patient Care Services, Lexington Veterans Affairs Medical Center, Lexington, KY, p. A286

MCCULLOUGH, Patrick, M.D., Chief Medical Services, Summit Behavioral Healthcare, Cincinnati, OH, p. A533

MCCULLOUGH, Wadra, Chief Nursing Officer, Wellstar Spalding Regional Hospital, Griffin, GA, p. A173

MCCULLY, Michael, Chief Operating Officer, Northport Veterans Affairs Medical Center, Northport, NY, p. A493

MCCUNE, Becky, Director Human Resources, Community Relations and Education, Coffeyville Regional Medical Center, Coffeyville, KS, p. A262

MCCURDY, Brent, Director Management Information, St. Croix Regional Medical Center, St Croix Falls, WI, p. A796

MCCUTCHAN, Matt, Chief Financial Officer, Greater Regional Medical Center, Creston, IA, p. A247

MCCUTCHEON, Edna I., Chief Executive Officer, Norristown State Hospital, Norristown, PA, p. A598

MCDADE, Len, Chief Executive Officer, Ochsner Extended Care Hospital, New Orleans, LA, p. A311

MCDANALD, Matt, M.D., Chief Medical Officer, Baptist Health La Grange, La Grange, KY, p. A285

MCDANEL, Joyce, Vice President Human Resources and Education, Unitypoint Health - Iowa Methodist Medical Center, Des Moines, IA, p. A248

MCDANIEL, Amy, Chief Executive Officer, Iowa Specialty Hospital-Belmond, Belmond, IA, p. A244

MCDANIEL, Donald Chief Financial Officer, Paris Regional Medical Center, Paris, TX, p. A704

MCDANIEL, Emily, Administrator, Oceans Behavioral Hospital Of Lake Charles, Lake Charles, LA, p. A307

MCDANIEL, Kim, Director Human Resources, Encompass Health Rehabilitation Hospital Of Montgomery, Montgomery, AL, p. A22

MCDANIEL, Kristie, Director Information Technology, Ferrell Hospital, Eldorado, IL, p. A203

MCDANIEL, LaDonna, Financial Manager, Prattville Baptist Hospital, Prattville, AL, p. A24

MCDANIEL, Levi, M.D., Chief of Staff, Wabash General Hospital, Mount Carmel, IL, p. A213

MCDANIEL, Randy, Information Systems Director, Jackson Purchase Medical Center, Mayfield, KY, p. A290

MCDANIEL, Suzie, Chief Human Resource Officer, Bay Area Hospital, Coos Bay, OR, p. A574

MCDAVID, Clarence, Vice President Human Resources, Rose Medical Center, Denver, CO, p. A111

MCDERMOTT, James, M.D., Chief of Staff, Sedan City Hospital, Sedan, KS, p. A276

MCDERMOTT, Mary, MSN, MS, R.N., Senior Vice President Patient Care Services and Chief Nursing Officer, Phelp. Memorial Hospital Center, Sleep. Hollow, NY, p. A498

MCDERMOTT, Michael P., M.D., President and Chief Executive Officer, Mary Washington Hospital, Fredericksburg, VA, p. A742

M.D., President and Chief Executive Officer, Stafford Hospital, Stafford, VA, p. A752

MCDEVITT, Robert, M.D., Chief of Staff, Wilson Memorial Hospital, Sidney, OH, p. A549

MCDONAGH, Andrew, M.D., Chief Medical Officer, Aurora West Allis Medical Center, West Allis, WI, p. A799

MCDONALD, Amanda, MSN, Chief Nurse Executive, Kerrville State Hospital, Kerrville, TX, p. A692

MCDONALD, Carl, Senior Director, Human Resources, Cleveland Clinic Florida, Weston, FL, p. A162

MCDONALD, Connie, Chief Financial Officer, Marion Veterans Affairs Medical Center, Marion, IL, p. A211

MCDONALD, Edward, Chief Financial Officer, Adventist Health St. Helena, Vallejo, CA, p. A103

MCDONALD, Elizabeth, Director Human Resources, Wayne Memorial Hospital, Honesdale, PA, p. A592

MCDONALD, Frederick Joseph., Commanding Officer, Naval Hospital Oak Harbor, Oak Harbor, WA, p. A761

MCDONALD, Gary, Associate Administrator Human Resources, Stone County Medical Center, Mountain View, AR, p. A50

MCDONALD, Gregory, Vice President Finance and Chief Financial Officer, Roswell Park Comprehensive Cancer Center, Buffalo, NY, p. A480

MCDONALD, Holly, Controller, Boundary Community Hospital, Bonners Ferry, ID, p. A189

MCDONALD, Jeff, Information Technology Manager, Adventhealth Wauchula, Wauchula, FL, p. A161

MCDONALD, John, M.D., Chief Medical Officer, Medical City North Hills, North Richland Hills, TX, p. A703

Chief Executive Officer, Lee's Summit Medical Center, Lee's Summit, MO, p. A410

Chief Operating Officer, Northwest Texas Healthcare System, Amarillo, TX, p. A652

MCDONALD, Larry, Director Human Resources, Miami Jewish Home And Hospital For Aged, Miami, FL, p. A146

MCDONALD, Mark, M.D., President and Chief Executive Officer, Institute For Orthopaedic Surgery, Lima, OH, p. A543

MCDONALD, Ruth, M.D., Chief Medical Officer, Seattle Children's Hospital, Seattle, WA, p. A764

MCDONALD, Shari, Vice President Patient Care Services, Mercy Hospital, Buffalo, NY, p. A480

MCDONALD, Shelly, Chief Human Resources Officer, Ness County Hospital District No 2, Ness City, KS, p. A272

MCDONALD, Stanton, M.D., Medical Director, Heber Valley Hospital, Heber City, UT, p. A728

MCDONALD, Susan, Vice President, Medical Affairs, Sentara Rmh Medical Center, Harrisonburg, VA, p. A743

MCDONALD, Tedd, M.D., Chief Medical Officer, Banner Churchill Community Hospital, Fallon, NV, p. A442

MCDONALD-PINKETT, Shelly, Chief Medical Officer, Howard University Hospital, Washington, DC, p. A129

MCDONELL, Stephanie, Vice President and Chief Information Officer, United Regional Health Care System, Wichita Falls, TX, p. A725

MCDONNELL, Jennifer, Director, Human Resources, Southern Hills Hospital And Medical Center, Las Vegas, NV, p. A444

MCDONNELL, Michael, M.D., Chief Medical Officer, Mercy Hospital And Medical Center, Chicago, IL, p. A199

MCDONNELL, Nancy, Manager Information Systems, Illinois Valley Community Hospital, Peru, IL, p. A217

MCDONNELL, Stephen, Director Human Resources, Chesapeake Regional Medical Center, Chesapeake, VA, p. A740

MCDOUGAL, Tom R. Jr, FACHE, Chief Executive Officer, Merit Health Biloxi, Biloxi, MS, p. A389

MCDOUGLE, Mark, Executive Vice President and Chief Operating Officer, Maimonides Medical Center, Brooklyn, NY, p. A478

MCDOWELL, Paul, Deputy Chief Financial Officer, Mission Hospital, Asheville, NC, p. A504

Vice President Finance and Chief Financial Officer, King's Daughters Medical Center, Ashland, KY, p. A280

MCDOWELL, Richard, M.D., Medical Director, Kona Community Hospital, Kealakekua, HI, p. A186

Chief Financial Officer, Ridge Behavioral Health System, Lexington, KY, p. A287

MCDOWELL, Wendy, R.N., Director of Nursing, Weisbrod Memorial County Hospital, Eads, CO, p. A112

MCDOWN, Missy, Director Information Systems, Ascension Via Christi Hospital, Pittsburg, KS, p. A274

MCDRURY, Martha, R.N., Chief Operating Officer and Chief Nursing Officer, Holy Family Hospital, Methuen, MA, p. A341

MCEACHERN, John, Controller, Sebastian River Medical Center, Sebastian, FL, p. A157

MCEACHIN, Brenda, Human Resources Director, Jeff Davis Hospital, Hazlehurst, GA, p. A173

MCELDOWNEY, Erin, Manager Human Resources, Haven Behavioral Hospital Of Phoenix, Phoenix, AZ, p. A35

MCELMURRAY, Dodie, FACHE, Chief Executive Officer, University of Mississippi. Medical Center Grenada, Grenada, MS, p. A393

FACHE, Chief Executive Officer, University Of Mississippi. Medical Center Holmes County, Lexington, MS, p. A396

MCELRATH, Matthew, Chief Human Resources Officer, Keck Hospital Of Usc, Los Angeles, CA, p. A74

Chief Human Resources Officer, Usc Norris Comprehensive Cancer Center, Los Angeles, CA, p. A76

MCELROY, Kevin, Chief Human Resources Officer, Mackinac Straits Health System, Inc., Saint Ignace, MI, p. A366

MCENIRY, Allen, Executive Director, Patrick B. Harris Psychiatric Hospital, Anderson, SC, p. A615

MCENTEE, Chris, Network Specialist, Van Buren County Hospital, Keosauqua, IA, p. A252

MCENTEE, Kara, Chief Financial Officer, Van Buren County Hospital, Keosauqua, IA, p. A252

MCENTIRE, Ann, MSN, R.N., Chief Nursing Officer, Citizens Baptist Medical Center, Talladega, AL, p. A24

MCEUEN, Jacqueline, Coordinator Human Resources, Bellville Medical Center, Bellville, TX, p. A659

MCEVILLY, Kerrie, Vice President Finance, Stevens Community Medical Center, Morris, MN, p. A381

MCEWAN, Kevin, MSN, R.N., Chief Nursing Officer, Madison Memorial Hospital, Rexburg, ID, p. A192

MCEWEN, David, Chief Executive Officer, Dmc Huron Valley-Sinai Hospital, Commerce Township. MI, p. A351

MCEWEN, Michelle, President and Chief Executive Officer, Speare Memorial Hospital, Plymouth, NH, p. A451

MCFADDEN, Krista, President, Trumbull Memorial Hospital, Warren, OH, p. A551

MCFADYEN, David M., FACHE, President, Saint Alphonsus Regional Medical Center, Boise, ID, p. A188

MCFALL, Cathy, Human Resources Manager, Kiowa County Memorial Hospital, Greensburg, KS, p. A265

MCFALL, Vicky, Chief Executive Officer, Monroe County Medical Center, Tompkinsville, KY, p. A293

MCFALL-ROBERTS, Ebuni, Director Human Resources, Holly Hill Hospital, Raleigh, NC, p. A516

MCFARLAND, Kenneth D., Chief Executive Officer, Fountain Valley Regional Hospital And Medical Center, Fountain Valley, CA, p. A64

MCFARLAND, Nita, Director of Nursing, Kingman Community Hospital, Kingman, KS, p. A268

MCFARLAND, Pamela, Interim Chief Executive Officer, Memorial Hospital Of Texas County, Guymon, OK, p. A560

MCFARLAND, Rhonda, Director Human Resources, Atrium Health Anson, Wadesboro, NC, p. A519

Director Human Resources, Atrium Health Union, Monroe, NC, p. A514

MCFARLAND, Rodney, M.D., Medical Director, Freeman Neosho Hospital, Neosho, MO, p. A412

MCFARLAND, Tracee, Chief Financial Officer, Claiborne Medical Center, Tazewell, TN, p. A650

MCFARLANE, Michael, Chief Human Resource Officer, St. Louis Psychiatric Rehabilitation Center, Saint Louis, MO, p. A417

Director Human Resource, Hawthorn Children Psychiatric Hospital, Saint Louis, MO, p. A415

Director Human Resources, Metropolitan St. Louis Psychiatric Center, Saint Louis, MO, p. A416

MCFERRAN, Virginia, Chief Information Officer, Ucla Medical Center-Santa Monica, Santa Monica, CA, p. A98

MCGAHAN, Thomas, M.D., Chief Medical Officer, Emory Saint Joseph's Hospital Of Atlanta, Atlanta, GA, p. A164

MCGAHEY, Nikki, Information Officer, Jefferson County Hospital, Waurika, OK, p. A571

MCGARIGLE, Kristine, R.N., Vice President Patient Care, Ascension Good Samaritan Hospital, Merrill, WI, p. A790

MCGARVEY, Missy, Chief Information Officer, Twin Valley Behavioral Healthcare, Columbus, OH, p. A537

MCGEE, Angela, Vice President Nursing Services, Aultman Orrville Hospital, Orrville, OH, p. A547

MCGEE, Genemarie, R.N., MS, Chief Nursing Officer, Sentara Leigh Hospital, Norfolk, VA, p. A748

MCGEE, Jessica, Chief Financial Officer, Amg Specialty Hospital-Lafayette, Lafayette, LA, p. A305

Chief Financial Officer, Sage Specialty Hospital (Ltac), Denham Springs, LA, p. A301

MCGEE, Kevin, Chief Executive Officer, River Point Behavioral Health, Jacksonville, FL, p. A141

Interim Chief Executive Officer, Lincoln Prairie Behavioral Health Center, Springfield, IL, p. A220

MCGEE, Terry, Chief Operations Officer, Central State Hospital, Milledgeville, GA, p. A177

MCGEEHAN, Paul, M.D., Chief Medical Staff, Lecom Corry Memorial Hospital, Corry, PA, p. A587

MCGETTIGAN, Ryan, Chief Information Officer, Coatesville Veterans Affairs Medical Center, Coatesville, PA, p. A587

MCGHEE, Kenneth, Vice President and Chief Financial Officer, Loretto Hospital, Chicago, IL, p. A199

MCGHEE, Michael, M.D., Medical Director, Unity Psychiatric Care-Clarksville, Clarksville, TN, p. A636

MCGIBBON, Monica, Chief Nursing Officer, Terence Cardinal Cooke Health Care Center, New York, NY, p. A492

MCGILL, Brittini, MSN, R.N., Chief Nursing Officer, Norman Regional Health System, Norman, OK, p. A563

MCGILL, Martha, Executive Vice President and Chief Operating Officer, Nicklaus Children's Hospital, Miami, FL, p. A147

MCGILL, Rusty, System Director Information Technology, Indiana University Health Arnett Hospital, Lafayette, IN, p. A234

MCGILL, Suzanne, Director of Nursing, Atmore Community Hospital, Atmore, AL, p. A14

Interim Chief Executive Officer, Atmore Community Hospital, Atmore, AL, p. A14

MCGILL, Timothy W., Chief Executive Officer, Livingston Regional Hospital, Livingston, TN, p. A642

MCGILVRAY, Greg, Chief Financial Officer, Medical Center Enterprise, Enterprise, AL, p. A18

MCGIMSEY, Erika, Controller, Uofl Health - Shelbyville Hospital, Shelbyville, KY, p. A293

MCGINLEY, Mary Ann, Ph.D., Senior Vice President, Patient Services and Chief Nursing Officer, Thomas Jefferson University Hospitals, Philadelphia, PA, p. A602

MCGINNIS, Brian, Director Finance, Aurora Medical Center Of Oshkosh, Oshkosh, WI, p. A793

MCGINNIS, Christina, Director Information Technology, Menorah Medical Center, Overland Park, KS, p. A274

MCGINNIS, Jeff, M.D., President Medical Staff, Saint Josep. Mount Sterling, Mount Sterling, KY, p. A290

MCGIRL, John, Chief Human Resources Officer, Nch Baker Hospital, Naples, FL, p. A148

MCGLADE, Jim, Director Human Resources, United Hospital, Saint Paul, MN, p. A385

Vice President, Human Resources, Mercy Hospital, Coon Rapids, MN, p. A374

MCGLEW, Timothy, Chief Executive Officer, Kern Valley Healthcare District, Lake Isabella, CA, p. A70

MCGLON, Tracy, Director Human Resources, Gulf Coast Regional Medical Center, Panama City, FL, p. A153

MCGLYNN, Mia, Director Management Information Systems, Plantation General Hospital, Plantation, FL, p. A154

MCGOVERN, Charles, Chief of Staff, Margaret Mary Health, Batesville, IN, p. A223

MCGOVERN, Joanne, MSN, R.N., Chief Nursing Officer, Cancer Treatment Centers Of America-Eastern Regional Medical Center, Philadelphia, PA, p. A599

MCGOVERN, Julia, Vice President Human Resources, Chilton Medical Center, Pompton Plains, NJ, p. A462

MCGOVERN, Julie, Vice President Human Resources, Anne Arundel Medical Center, Annapolis, MD, p. A324

MCGOVERN, Kimberly, Manager Human Resources, Hackettstown Medical Center, Hackettstown, NJ, p. A456

MCGOVERN, Pam, Director Technology, Huggins Hospital, Wolfeboro, NH, p. A451

MCGOVERN, Sandra, Chief Nursing Officer, Up Health System-Bell, Ishpeming, MI, p. A358

MCGOWEN, Bernard, M.D., Medical Director, Kindred Hospital Tarrant County-Arlington, Arlington, TX, p. A653

MCGOWIN, Norman, M.D., IIIChief of Staff, Regional Medical Center Of Central Alabama, Greenville, AL, p. A19

MCGRAIL, David, Vice President Finance, Carney Hospital, Boston, MA, p. A335

MCGRAIL, Robert, Chief Executive Officer, Midmichigan Medical Center - West Branch, West Branch, MI, p. A369

MCGRATH, Denise B., Chief Executive Officer, Sea Pines Rehabilitation Hospital, Melbourne, FL, p. A145

MCGRATH, John, Chief Information Officer, Mclaren Port Huron, Port Huron, MI, p. A364

MCGRATH, Kelly, Chief Medical Officer, Clearwater Valley Hospital And Clinics, Orofino, ID, p. A192

MCGRATH, Lynn, M.D., Vice President Medical Affairs, Deborah Heart And Lung Center, Browns Mills, NJ, p. A453

MCGRAW, Belinda, Director Human Resources, Boulder City Hospital, Boulder City, NV, p. A441

MCGRAW, Kathleen, M.D., Chief Medical Officer, Brattleboro Memorial Hospital, Brattleboro, VT, p. A735

MCGRAW, Scott, M.D., Medical Director, Baylor Surgical Hospital At Las Colinas, Irving, TX, p. A690

MCGREEVY, John, FACHE, President, Methodist Southlake Hospital, Southlake, TX, p. A716

MCGREGOR, Catherine, Deputy Director Facility and Administrative Services, Capital District Psychiatric Center, Albany, NY, p. A474

MCGREGOR, Julie, Director Human Resources, Uofl Health - Mary And Elizabeth Hospital, Louisville, KY, p. A289
Vice President and Chief People Officer, Uofl Health - Jewish Hospital, Louisville, KY, p. A288
Vice President, Human Resources and Organization Development, Columbus Regional Hospital, Columbus, IN, p. A225

MCGREGOR, Robert, M.D., Chief Medical Officer, Akron Children's Hospital, Akron, OH, p. A527

MCGREW, David, Chief Financial Officer, San Mateo Medical Center, San Mateo, CA, p. A96

MCGREW, Deborah, Vice President and Chief Operating Officer, University Of Texas Medical Branch, Galveston, TX, p. A680

MCGREW, Diane, Chief Nurse Executive, Montgomery County Memorial Hospital, Red Oak, IA, p. A256

MCGRIFF, Marchelle, Chief Nursing Executive, Sutter Medical Center, Sacramento, Sacramento, CA, p. A90

MCGUE, Lisa, Controller, Encompass Health Rehabilitation Hospital Of Northern Kentucky, Edgewood, KY, p. A282

MCGUFFIN, Patty, Chief Nursing Officer, Allen County Regional Hospital, Iola, KS, p. A267

MCGUIGAN, Kevin, M.D., Medical Director, St. Lawrence Rehabilitation Center, Lawrenceville, NJ, p. A457

MCGUILL, Gail, R.N., MSN, Chief Nursing Officer and Administrative Director of Patient Care Services, Shriners Hospitals For Children-Salt Lake City, Salt Lake City, UT, p. A732

MCGUINNESS, Patrick, Chief Information Management, Keller Army Community Hospital, West Point, NY, p. A502

MCGUIRE, Ann, Regional Vice President Human Resources, Indiana University Health Ball Memorial Hospital, Muncie, IN, p. A237

MCGUIRE, Christie, R.N., Chief Nursing Officer, Salinas Valley Memorial Healthcare System, Salinas, CA, p. A90

MCGUIRE, Cynthia, FACHE, President and Chief Executive Officer, Monadnock Community Hospital, Peterborough, NH, p. A451

MCGUIRE, Patrick, Chief Financial Officer, Michigan Market, Ascension Macomb-Oakland Hospital, Warren, MI, p. A368

MCGUIRE, Shane, Chief Executive Officer, Columbia County Health System, Dayton, WA, p. A757

MCGUIRK, Christina, R.N., Chief Nursing Officer, Health Central Hospital, Ocoee, FL, p. A150

MCGUIRT, Jacob, Chief Executive Officer, Pam Specialty Hospital Of Sarasota, Sarasota, FL, p. A157

MCGURK, Kevin, Controller, Bellin Psychiatric Center, Green Bay, WI, p. A785

MCHARDY, Bryson, M.D., President Medical Staff, Hannibal Regional Hospital, Hannibal, MO, p. A407

MCHUGH, Matthew, Director Information Services, Vaughan Regional Medical Center, Selma, AL, p. A24

MCHUGH, Ryan, M.D., Chief of Staff, The Medical Center Of Southeast Texas, Port Arthur, TX, p. A707

MCHUGH, William, M.D., Medical Director and Chief Medical Officer, Trinitas Regional Medical Center, Elizabeth, NJ, p. A455

MCILROY, Gail, Director Medical Records, Kp. Promise Hospital Of Wichita Falls, Wichita Falls, TX, p. A725

MCILVAIN, Spencer, Director of Human Resources, Peterson Healthcare And Rehabilitation Hospital, Wheeling, WV, p. A778

MCILWAIN, T, M.D., Vice President and Chief Medical Officer, Charleston Area Medical Center, Charleston, WV, p. A771

MCINERNEY, Terry, Director of Nursing, Inpatient, Navos, Seattle, WA, p. A763

MCINTOSH, Craig, Chief Information Officer, Northwest Specialty Hospital, Post Falls, ID, p. A192

MCINTOSH, Eric, Vice President Human Resources, Upmc Jameson, New Castle, PA, p. A598

MCINTOSH, Ernasha, Interim Director of Nursing, Sage Memorial Hospital, Ganado, AZ, p. A31

MCINTOSH, Joe, Director Management Information Systems, Logansport State Hospital, Logansport, IN, p. A235

MCINTOSH, Tyler, Chief Financial Officer, Creek Nation Community Hospital, Okemah, OK, p. A563

MCINTYRE, Cindy, R.N., Administrative Director Clinical Services, Magee General Hospital, Magee, MS, p. A396

MCINTYRE, Daniel J., President, Charlotte Hungerford Hospital, Torrington, CT, p. A125

MCIWAIN, John, Director Human Resources, Wayne Memorial Hospital, Jesup, GA, p. A174

MCKAIN, Rick, Chief Executive Officer, Anderson County Hospital, Garnett, KS, p. A265

MCKALE, Brigitte, MSN, FACHE, Vice President and Chief Nurse Executive, Pali Momi Medical Center, Aiea, HI, p. A184

MCKAY, Amy, Chief Nursing Officer, Mid—America Rehabilitation Hospital, Shawnee Mission, KS, p. A276

MCKAY, Daniel E., Chief Executive Officer, Ephraim Mcdowell Regional Medical Center, Danville, KY, p. A282

MCKAY, Danny H., Administrator, Noxubee General Hospital, Macon, MS, p. A396

MCKAY, Ronda, R.N., Vice President Patient Care Services, Chief Nursing Officer, Community Hospital, Munster, IN, p. A237

MCKEAN, Heather, Director of Patient Care Services, Providence Seward Medical Center, Seward, AK, p. A29

MCKEE, Debra, R.N., Chief Clinical Officer and Chief Nursing Officer, Joint Township District Memorial Hospital, Saint Marys, OH, p. A548

MCKEE, Michele, Vice President and Chief Financial Officer, St. Louis Children's Hospital, Saint Louis, MO, p. A417

MCKEE, Willis, M.D., JrChief Medical Officer, Frankfort Regional Medical Center, Frankfort, KY, p. A283

MCKEEBY, Ben, Senior Vice President and Chief Information Officer, Grady Memorial Hospital, Atlanta, GA, p. A164

MCKEEBY, Jon, Chief Information Officer, National Institutes Of Health Clinical Center, Bethesda, MD, p. A327

MCKEEN, Marcia, Director Human Resources, Twin Valley Behavioral Healthcare, Columbus, OH, p. A537

MCKELDIN, Pat, Human Resource Business Partner, Kaiser Permanente Manteca Medical Center, Manteca, CA, p. A77

MCKENDREE, Rodney, Senior Vice President and Chief Financial Officer, Nemours Children's Hospital, Orlando, FL, p. A151

MCKENNA, Dennis, M.D., Interim Vice President Medical Affairs, Albany Medical Center, Albany, NY, p. A474
M.D., President and Chief Executive Officer, Albany Medical Center, Albany, NY, p. A474

MCKENNA, John F., Chief Executive Officer and Managing Director, Rockford Center, Newark, DE, p. A128

MCKENNA, Kelly, Chief Executive Officer, Huntington Creek Recovery Center, Shickshinny, PA, p. A608

MCKENNA, Quinn, Chief Operating Officer, Stanford Health Care, Palo Alto, CA, p. A84

MCKENNERY, Kay, Chief Executive Officer, Cross Creek Hospital, Austin, TX, p. A655

MCKENNEY, Jennifer, M.D., Chief Medical Officer, Fredonia Regional Hospital, Fredonia, KS, p. A264

MCKENZIE, Jackie, Director Administrative Services, Beacham Memorial Hospital, Magnolia, MS, p. A396

MCKENZIE, Kimberly, R.N., MSN, Chief Nursing Officer and Chief Operations Officer, Harbor-Ucla Medical Center, Torrance, CA, p. A101
R.N., MSN, Interim Chief Executive Officer, Harbor-Ucla Medical Center, Torrance, CA, p. A101

MCKENZIE, Margaret, M.D., President, South Pointe Hospital, Warrensville Heights, OH, p. A552

MCKENZIE, Sandra, Executive Vice President and Chief Operating Officer, Hamilton Medical Center, Dalton, GA, p. A170

MCKENZIE, Troy, Chief information Officer, Faith Community Hospital, Jacksboro, TX, p. A691

MCKEON, John, Vice President Human Resources, Kingsbrook Jewish Medical Center, Brooklyn, NY, p. A478

MCKEON, Sean, Director, Information Technology, Franciscan Children's, Brighton, MA, p. A336

MCKEOWN, Colleen, Senior Vice President and Area Manager, Kaiser Permanente Antioch Medical Center, Antioch, CA, p. A56
Senior Vice President and Area Manager, Kaiser Permanente Walnut Creek Medical Center, Walnut Creek, CA, p. A104

MCKERNAN, James, Chief Operating Officer, Bronson Battle Creek Hospital, Battle Creek, MI, p. A349

MCKERNAN, Kathleen, Director Information Systems, Pioneers Memorial Healthcare District, Brawley, CA, p. A58

MCKEVETT, Timothy M., President and Chief Executive Officer, Beloit Health System, Beloit, WI, p. A781

MCKIBBEN, Leeanna, R.N., MSN, Vice President Patient Services and Chief Nursing Officer, Upmc Mckeesport, Mckeesport, PA, p. A596
R.N., MSN, Vice President Patient Services and Chief Nursing Officer, Upmc Mercy, Pittsburgh, PA, p. A604

MCKIBBEN, Sean, President and Chief Operating Officer, Mount Carmel West, Columbus, OH, p. A536

MCKIDDY, Paul, Director Information Technology, Monroe County Medical Center, Tompkinsville, KY, p. A293

MCKIE, Kathy, Director Human Resources, Montrose Memorial Hospital, Montrose, CO, p. A117

MCKILLIP, Ed, Vice President Finance, Riddle Hospital, Media, PA, p. A597

MCKIMMY, Doyle L., FACHE, Chief Executive Officer, Jewell County Hospital, Mankato, KS, p. A270

MCKINLEY, Alton, Chief Financial Officer, Veterans Affairs North Texas Health Care System, Dallas, TX, p. A671

MCKINLEY, Bryan, Chief Financial Officer, St. Mark's Hospital, Salt Lake City, UT, p. A733

MCKINLEY, Ivy, Director Human Resources, Amita Health Holy Family Medical Center, Des Plaines, IL, p. A202
Regional Human Resources Officer, Community First Medical Center, Chicago, IL, p. A198

MCKINLEY, John, Director, Information Technology, Community Mental Health Center, Lawrenceburg, IN, p. A235

MCKINLEY, Mike, Information Security Officer, West Texas Veterans Affairs Health Care System, Big Spring, TX, p. A660

MCKINLEY, Ronald, Ph.D., Vice President Human Resources and Employee Services, University Of Texas Medical Branch, Galveston, TX, p. A680

MCKINNEY, Brenda, Chief Executive Officer, Reeves County Hospital District, Pecos, TX, p. A705

MCKINNEY, Bruce, Business Officer, Administrative Services, Central Prison Hospital, Raleigh, NC, p. A516

MCKINNEY, Dan, Administrator, Hermann Area District Hospital, Hermann, MO, p. A407

MCKINNEY, Dana, Chief Nursing Officer, Select Specialty Hospital-Madison, Madison, WI, p. A787

MCKINNEY, Daniel, Chief Executive Officer, South Baldwin Regional Medical Center, Foley, AL, p. A18

MCKINNEY, James, Warden, Iowa Medical And Classification Center, Coralville, IA, p. A246

MCKINNEY, Jillyan, Chief Executive Officer, Littleton Adventist Hospital, Littleton, CO, p. A116

MCKINNEY, Rachael, FACHE, Chief Executive Officer, Sutter Davis Hospital, Davis, CA, p. A62

MCKINNEY, Rex, President and Chief Executive Officer, Decatur County Memorial Hospital, Greensburg, IN, p. A230

MCKINNEY, Thomas, Chief Executive Officer, Christus Santa Rosa Hospital - San Marcos, San Marcos, TX, p. A714

MCKINNON, Mark, M.D., Chief of Staff, North Runnels Hospital, Winters, TX, p. A726

MCKINNON, Ron, Chief Information Officer, Ellis Hospital, Schenectady, NY, p. A498

MCKINSTRY, Merissa, Chief Operating Officer, Columbus Dublin Springs, Dublin, OH, p. A539

MCKNIGHT, David, CPA, Chief Executive Officer, Spotsylvania Regional Medical Center, Fredericksburg, VA, p. A742

MCKNIGHT, Stephanie, Hospital Nursing Manager, Sanford Bagley Medical Center, Bagley, MN, p. A372

MCKNIGHT, Tim, M.D., Chief of Staff, Trinity Hospital Twin City, Dennison, OH, p. A539

MCKOY, Lori, Business Partner, Pender Memorial Hospital, Burgaw, NC, p. A505

MCKULA, Tim, Vice President Information Systems and Chief Information Officer, Shirley Ryan Abilitylab, Chicago, IL, p. A200

MCKUNE, Jeff, Chief Health Informatics Officer, Phelp. Health, Rolla, MO, p. A414

MCLAIN, Allen, M.D., Chief of Staff, Grisell Memorial Hospital District One, Ransom, KS, p. A275

MCLAIN, John R., Chief Executive Officer, Starr Regional Medical Center, Athens, TN, p. A634

MCLANE, Kerry, Chief Executive Officer, Select Specialty Hospital-Muskegon, Muskegon, MI, p. A362
Interim Chief Executive Officer, Select Specialty Hospital-Omaha, Omaha, NE, p. A438

MCLARIN, Benita, Chief Operating Officer, Santa Clara Valley Medical Center, San Jose, CA, p. A95

MCLARTY, Walter, Chief Human Resources Officer, Bethesda North Hospital, Cincinnati, OH, p. A532
Chief Human Resources Officer, Good Samaritan Hospital, Cincinnati, OH, p. A532

MCLAUGHLIN, Amy, CPA, Chief Financial Officer, Manning Regional Healthcare Center, Manning, IA, p. A253

MCLAUGHLIN, Cathy, R.N., MSN, Chief Nursing Officer, Medical City Arlington, Arlington, TX, p. A653

MCLAUGHLIN, Dan C., Chief Executive Officer, Menifee Valley Medical Center, Sun City, CA, p. A100
Chief Hospital Executive Officer, Hemet Valley Medical Center, Hemet, CA, p. A68

MCLAUGHLIN, Diana, Chief Financial Officer, Memorial Hospital, North Conway, NH, p. A451

MCLAUGHLIN, Kathryn, Chief Nursing Officer, Hemet Valley Medical Center, Hemet, CA, p. A68

MCLAUGHLIN, Leslie, Director of Business Development, Michiana Behavioral Health Center, Plymouth, IN, p. A239

MCLAUGHLIN, Maribeth, R.N., Vice President Patient Care Services, Upmc Magee-Womens Hospital, Pittsburgh, PA, p. A604

MCLAUGHLIN, Mederic D., Executive Director, Veritas Collaborative, Atlanta, GA, p. A165

MCLAUGHLIN, Pamela, Chief Financial Officer, Encompass Health Rehabilitation Hospital Of Austin, Austin, TX, p. A656

MCLAUGHLIN, Rebecca, Chief Human Resource Officer, Banner Goldfield Medical Center, Apache Junction, AZ, p. A30

MCLAUGHLIN, Richard, M.D., Chief Medical Officer, Pottstown Hospital, Pottstown, PA, p. A605

MCLAUGHLIN, Sherry, Director Human Resources, Forrest City Medical Center, Forrest City, AR, p. A45

MCLAWS, Douglas, D.O., Chief Medical Officer, Manning Regional Healthcare Center, Manning, IA, p. A253

MCLEAN, Chris, Chief Administrative Officer, Methodist Healthcare Memphis Hospitals, Memphis, TN, p. A644

MCLEAN, Cindy, R.N., MSN, Director of Nursing, Central Prison Hospital, Raleigh, NC, p. A538

MCLEAN, Georgia, Director Human Resources, Mount Sinai Medical Center, Miami Beach, FL, p. A148

MCLEAN, John J., M.D., Chief Executive Officer, Prairieville Family Hospital, Prairieville, LA, p. A313

MCLEAN, Robb, M.D., Chief Medical Officer, Unm Sandoval Regional Medical Center, Inc., Rio Rancho, NM, p. A471

MCLENDON, Carla, Director Human Resources, Appling Healthcare System, Baxley, GA, p. A167
Director Information Resource Management Services, Charles George Veterans Affairs Medical Center, Asheville, NC, p. A504

MCLENDON, John, Senior Vice President and Chief Information Officer, Amita Health Adventist Medical Center Bolingbrook, Bolingbrook, IL, p. A196
Vice President and Chief Information Officer, Johns Hopkins All Children's Hospital, Saint Petersburg, FL, p. A156

MCLENDON, Tom, Administrator, Evergreen Medical Center, Evergreen, AL, p. A18

MCLEOD, Les, Director of Nursing Services, Blue Mountain Hospital District, John Day, OR, p. A576

MCLEOD, Margie, Director Information Technology, North Canyon Medical Center, Gooding, ID, p. A190

MCLEOD, Michael, M.D., Chief Medical Officer, Cuero Regional Hospital, Cuero, TX, p. A667

MCLEOD, Sheldon, Chief Executive Officer, Nyc Health + Hospitals / Kings County, Brooklyn, NY, p. A478
Chief Operating Officer, Nyc Health + Hospitals / North Central Bronx, Bronx, NY, p. A477

MCLIN, Robert D., President and Chief Executive Officer, Good Samaritan Hospital, Vincennes, IN, p. A242

MCLOONE, Paul, M.D., Chief Medical Officer, Unitypoint Health - Trinity Bettendorf, Bettendorf, IA, p. A244
M.D., Chief Medical Officer, Unitypoint Health - Trinity Rock Island, Rock Island, IL, p. A218

MCMAHAN, Casey, Chief Executive Officer, Oakwood Springs, Oklahoma City, OK, p. A565

MCMAHAN, Steve, M.D., Chief Medical Officer, Glenwood Regional Medical Center, West Monroe, LA, p. A316

MCMAHON, Alisha, Director Human Resources, Mountrail County Medical Center, Stanley, ND, p. A526

MCMAHON, Andrew, Chief Fiscal Officer, Veterans Affairs Central Western Massachusetts Healthcare System, Leeds, MA, p. A340

MCMAHON, Chris, Chief Operating Officer, The Medical Center Of Southeast Texas, Port Arthur, TX, p. A707

MCMAHON, Elaine, Administrator, Kwajalein Hospital, Kwajalein Atoll, MH, p. A805

MCMAHON, Eugene, Senior Vice President and Chief Medical Officer, Capital Health Medical Center-Hopewell, Pennington, NJ, p. A461
Senior Vice President and Chief Medical Officer, Capital Health Regional Medical Center, Trenton, NJ, p. A464

MCMAHON, Leigh, MS, R.N., Senior Vice President Patient Care Services and Chief Nursing Officer, White Plains Hospital Center, White Plains, NY, p. A502

MCMAHON, Nancy, Vice President Human Resources, Miriam Hospital, Providence, RI, p. A613

MCMANAMAN, Craig, M.D., Chief of Staff, Mclaren Thumb Region, Bad Axe, MI, p. A349

MCMANMON, Kristin, President, Ascension All Saints, Racine, WI, p. A794

MCMANUS, Doug, Chief Medical Officer, Aurora Medical Center Grafton, Grafton, WI, p. A784

MCMANUS, Marybeth, Chief Nursing Officer, Long Island Jewish Medical Center, New Hyde Park, NY, p. A489

MCMANUS, Michael T., President, Memorial Hospital East, Shiloh, IL, p. A220
President, Memorial Hospital, Belleville, IL, p. A195

MCMANUS, Ronald, Senior Vice President Clinical Services and Business Entities, Peconic Bay Medical Center, Riverhead, NY, p. A496

MCMASTER, Dawn, Human Resources Director, Encompass Health Rehabilitation Hospital Of Franklin, Franklin, TN, p. A638

MCMASTER, Sandra, Regional Chief Information Officer, Kauai Veterans Memorial Hospital, Waimea, HI, p. A187
Regional Chief Information Officer, Samuel Mahelona Memorial Hospital, Kapaa, HI, p. A186

MCMATH, Mark, Chief Information Officer, Musc Health Of Medical University Of South Carolina, Charleston, SC, p. A616

MCMENAMIN, Anneliese, Senior Vice President Information Technology and Program Services, Jefferson Stratford Hospital, Stratford, NJ, p. A463

MCMILLAN, Deborah, Director Human Resources, Glenn Medical Center, Willows, CA, p. A105

MCMILLAN, Donn, Chief Information Officer, Peacehealth Sacred Heart Medical Center University District, Eugene, OR, p. A575
Senior Director, IST Client Liaison, Peacehealth Southwest Medical Center, Vancouver, WA, p. A768

MCMILLAN, Douglas A., Administrator and Chief Executive Officer, West Park Hospital, Cody, WY, p. A802

MCMILLAN, Jon, Chief Financial Officer, Banner Lassen Medical Center, Susanville, CA, p. A100

MCMILLAN, Sheila, Chief Financial Officer, Park Nicollet Methodist Hospital, Saint Louis Park, MN, p. A385

MCMILLEN, Eric, FACHE, Chief Executive Officer, Ochsner Medical Center - Baton Rouge, Baton Rouge, LA, p. A297

MCMILLIN, Lori, Administrator, Mercy Hospital Tishomingo, Tishomingo, OK, p. A569

MCMILLION, Kelley, Chief Nursing Officer, Clay County Memorial Hospital, Henrietta, TX, p. A684

MCMINN, Ken, Director Information Technology, Scotland County Hospital, Memphis, MO, p. A412

MCMINN, Melvin, Director Human Resources, Wernersville State Hospital, Wernersville, PA, p. A610

MCMINOWAY, Kelly, R.N., Vice President, Nursing, Baptist Health Floyd, New Albany, IN, p. A237

MCMULLAN, Cheryl, Chief Financial Officer, Baylor Scott & White Medical Center-Waxahachie, Waxahachie, TX, p. A724

MCMULLAN, Heidi, R.N., Chief Nursing Officer, Wellspan Philhaven, Mount Gretna, PA, p. A597

MCMULLAN, Rosemary, Chief Human Resources, Mayo Clinic Hospital In Florida, Jacksonville, FL, p. A141

MCMURRAY, Rob, Chief Financial Officer, Christianacare, Newark, DE, p. A128

MCMURRAY, Sharon, Director, Human Resources, Rock Springs, Georgetown, TX, p. A681

MCMURREN, Mary Anne, R.N., Chief Administrative Officer, Peacehealth Sacred Heart Medical Center University District, Eugene, OR, p. A575

MCMURREY, Jean Ann, R.N., MSN, Chief Nursing Officer, Southern Tennessee Regional Health System-Winchester, Winchester, TN, p. A650

MCNABB, Dana, Human Resources Manager, Field Memorial Community Hospital, Centreville, MS, p. A390

MCNABB, Teresita, FACHE, R.N., Vice President Nursing Services, Terrebonne General Medical Center, Houma, LA, p. A303

MCNAIR, Lisa, CPA, Senior Vice President and Chief Financial Officer, Chi St. Josep. Regional Health Center, Bryan, TX, p. A661

MCNAIR, Rebekah, Director Human Resources, Encompass Health Rehabilitation Hospital Of Chattanooga, Chattanooga, TN, p. A635

MCNAIR, Scott, Chief Financial Officer, Neshoba County General Hospital, Philadelphia, MS, p. A398

MCNALLY, Colleen, M.D., Chief Medical Officer, Sharp Mary Birch Hospital For Women And Newborns, San Diego, CA, p. A92

MCNALLY, Joseph, M.D., Medical Director, Streamwood Behavioral Health Center, Streamwood, IL, p. A221

MCNALLY, Kathy, Chief Nursing Officer, Encompass Health Rehabilitation Hospital At Cincinnati, Cincinnati, OH, p. A532

MCNALLY, Lou-Ann, Executive Director Human Resources and Staff Development, Claxton-Hepburn Medical Center, Ogdensburg, NY, p. A493

MCNAMARA, John, M.D., Senior Vice President, Chief Medical Officer, Torrance Memorial Medical Center, Torrance, CA, p. A101

MCNAMARA, Marilyn, M.D., Chief Medical Officer, Southwest General Health Center, Middleburg Heights, OH, p. A545

MCNAMARA, Mike, Chief Information Officer, Mee Memorial Hospital, King City, CA, p. A69

MCNAMARA, Steve, Chief Financial Officer, Memorialcare, Orange Coast Memorial Medical Center, Fountain Valley, CA, p. A64

MCNAMARA, Thomas, D.O., Vice President Medical Affairs, Wellstar Cobb Hospital, Austell, GA, p. A166

MCNAMARA, Timothy, Senior Vice President Human Resources, Olean General Hospital, Olean, NY, p. A494

MCNAMEE, Hugar, D.O., Chief Medical Officer, Adventhealth Zephyrhills, Zephyrhills, FL, p. A162

MCNATT, James, Chief Financial Officer, Carrollton Regional Medical Center, Carrollton, TX, p. A663

MCNAUGHTON, Kathy, Chief Information Officer, Nemaha County Hospital, Auburn, NE, p. A429

MCNAUGHTON, Richard, Chief Information Management Service, Maine Veterans Affairs Medical Center, Augusta, ME, p. A318

MCNEA, Melvin, Chief Executive Officer, Great Plains Health, North Platte, NE, p. A436

MCNEAR, Michael, M.D., Chief Medical Officer, Jersey Community Hospital, Jerseyville, IL, p. A209

MCNEECE, Steve, Interim Chief Executive Officer, Mineral Community Hospital, Superior, MT, p. A428

MCNEEL, Jacob, D.O., Chief of Staff, Plateau Medical Center, Oak Hill, WV, p. A775

MCNEEL, Wakelin, M.D., Medical Director, Bhc Alhambra Hospital, Rosemead, CA, p. A88

MCNEIL, Ane, Vice President Human Resources, St. Josep. Mercy Oakland, Pontiac, MI, p. A364

MCNEILL, Michael, Chief Financial Management, New Mexico Veterans Affairs Health Care System - Raymond G. Murphy Medical Center, Albuquerque, NM, p. A468

MCNICHOLS, Janiece, Chief Financial Officer, St. Mary-Corwin Medical Center, Pueblo, CO, p. A118

MCNULTY, Bruce, Chief Medical Officer, Swedish Covenant Hospital, Chicago, IL, p. A201

MCNULTY, Stephanie, Chief Operating Officer, St. Petersburg General Hospital, Saint Petersburg, FL, p. A156

MCNULTY, Timothy, Director Human Resources, Spring Harbor Hospital, Westbrook, ME, p. A323

MCNUTT, Elena, Chief Nursing Officer, Desert Springs Hospital Medical Center, Las Vegas, NV, p. A443

MCNUTT, Mike, Assistant Administrator, Covenant Hospital Plainview, Plainview, TX, p. A706

MCNUTT, Pamela, Senior Vice President and Chief Information Officer, Methodist Dallas Medical Center, Dallas, TX, p. A669
Senior Vice President and Chief Information Officer, Methodist Mansfield Medical Center, Mansfield, TX, p. A699
Senior Vice President and Chief Information Officer, Methodist Richardson Medical Center, Richardson, TX, p. A708
Vice President Information Systems, Methodist Charlton Medical Center, Dallas, TX, p. A669

MCPEAK, Sara, Chief Nursing Officer, Carlinville Area Hospital, Carlinville, IL, p. A196

MCPHERSON, Lon, M.D., Senior Vice President Medical Affairs and Chief Quality Officer, Adventhealth Ocala, Ocala, FL, p. A149

MCPHERSON, Valarie, MSN, Chief Nursing Executive, California Hospital Medical Center, Los Angeles, CA, p. A73

MCQUAID, David, FACHE, Chief Operating Officer, Ohio State University Wexner Medical Center, Columbus, OH, p. A536

MCQUAID, David P., FACHE, Chief Operating Officer, Ohio State University Wexner Medical Center, Columbus, OH, p. A536

MCQUAIDE, Ben, M.D., Chief of Staff, Clark Regional Medical Center, Winchester, KY, p. A294

MCQUILLEN, Daniel, M.D., Chief of Medical Staff, Mercyone New Hampton Medical Center, New Hampton, IA, p. A255

MCQUILLEN, Paul, M.D., Chief Medical Officer, Ascension St. John Jane Phillips, Bartlesville, OK, p. A556

MCQUISTAN, Bob, Vice President Finance, York General, York, NE, p. A440

MCQUISTON, Mike, Administrative Director Human Resources, Wise Health System, Decatur, TX, p. A671

MCRAE, Ashley, Chief Clinical Officer, Kindred Hospital North Florida, Green Cove Springs, FL, p. A139

MCRAE, Colin, Chief Executive Officer, Tennova Healthcare-Jefferson Memorial Hospital, Jefferson City, TN, p. A640

MCREYNOLDS, John, Chief Operating Officer, North Valley Hospital, Tonasket, WA, p. A767

MCRIMMON, Dana, Chief Financial Officer, Mesilla Valley Hospital, Las Cruces, NM, p. A470

MCROBERTS, Kevin, FACHE, Senior Vice President of Operations, Lake Regional Health System, Osage Beach, MO, p. A413

MCSWEENEY, Christine, FACHE, President and Chief Executive Officer, Bob Wilson Memorial Grant County Hospital, Ulysses, KS, p. A278

FACHE, President and Chief Executive Officer, St. Catherine Hospital, Garden City, KS, p. A264

MCTAGGART, Jac, Chief Executive Officer, Sanford Hillsboro Medical Center, Hillsboro, ND, p. A524

Chief Executive Officer, Sanford Mayville Medical Center, Mayville, ND, p. A525

MCTERNAN, Josep. L., Chief Executive Officer, Wyoming County Community Hospital, Warsaw, NY, p. A501

MCTIGRIT, Chris, Manager Information Technology, Delta Memorial Hospital, Dumas, AR, p. A44

MCTIGUE, Mary, Vice President Patient Care Services and Chief Nursing Officer, Trinitas Regional Medical Center, Elizabeth, NJ, p. A455

MCTIGUE, Michael, Chief Information Officer, Clara Maass Medical Center, Belleville, NJ, p. A452

Chief Information Officer, Saint Barnabas Medical Center, Livingston, NJ, p. A457

MCVAY, Tara, Chief Nursing Officer, Logansport Memorial Hospital, Logansport, IN, p. A235

MCVEIGH, Kevin, Chief Human Resources Officer, Banner Desert Medical Center, Mesa, AZ, p. A33

MCVEY, Eric, M.D., IIIExecutive Vice President Medical Affairs and Quality, St. Dominic-Jackson Memorial Hospital, Jackson, MS, p. A395

MCVEY, Lynn, Chief Operating Officer, Hudson Regional Hospital, Secaucus, NJ, p. A463

MCVEY, Marian, Chief Nursing Officer, Prisma Health North Greenville, Travelers Rest, SC, p. A625

MCWAY, Jacob, Senior Vice President and Chief Financial Officer, Cox Medical Centers, Springfield, MO, p. A418

MCWHERTER, Joe, Chief Financial Officer, Baptist Memorial Hospital-Desoto, Southaven, MS, p. A400

MCWILLIAMS, Jill, Chief Nursing Officer, Sierra Nevada Memorial Hospital, Grass Valley, CA, p. A67

MEACHAM, Byanka, Director Human Resources, Montgomery County Emergency Service, Norristown, PA, p. A598

MEACHEM, Michelle, Director Human Resources, The University Of Vermont Health Network Elizabethtown Community Hospital, Elizabethtown, NY, p. A483

MEAD, Linda, Director Human Resources, Margaretville Hospital, Margaretville, NY, p. A488

MEAD, Richard, Senior Director Human Resources, Saint Francis Memorial Hospital, San Francisco, CA, p. A94

MEAD, Rick, Human Resources Leader, Kaiser Permanente Oakland Medical Center, Oakland, CA, p. A82

MEADE, Andrew, Chief Executive Officer, Encompass Health Rehabilitation Hospital Of San Antonio, San Antonio, TX, p. A711

Chief Executive Officer, Select Specialty Hospital-Longview, Longview, TX, p. A697

MEADE, Robert C., Chief Executive Officer, Doctors Hospital Of Sarasota, Sarasota, FL, p. A157

MEADE, Teresa, R.N., Chief Nursing Officer, Boone Memorial Hospital, Madison, WV, p. A774

MEADOWS, Barbara, Chief Financial Manager, Captain James A. Lovell Federal Health Care Center, North Chicago, IL, p. A214

MEADOWS, Danny, M.D., Medical Director, Logansport State Hospital, Logansport, IN, p. A235

MEADOWS, Hal, M.D., Chief Medical Officer, Banner Lassen Medical Center, Susanville, CA, p. A100

MEADOWS, Nancy, Chief Financial Officer, Methodist Hospital, San Antonio, TX, p. A712

MEADOWS, Sheila, Chief Human Resources Officer, Mission Hospital, Asheville, NC, p. A504

MEADOWS, Theresa, Chief Information Officer, Cook Children's Medical Center, Fort Worth, TX, p. A678

MEANEY, Chris Ann, Vice President of Patient Care Service and Chief Nursing Officer, Bristol Health, Bristol, CT, p. A121

MEANS, Dennis, M.D., Vice President Medical Affairs, Carilion New River Valley Medical Center, Christiansburg, VA, p. A740

MEANS, Paul, M.D., President Medical Staff, Highlands Hospital, Connellsville, PA, p. A587

MEARNS, Stephanie, Vice President Patient Care Services and Chief Nurse Executive, Seton Medical Center, Daly City, CA, p. A62

MEARS, Terry, Director Information Systems, Duke Regional Hospital, Durham, NC, p. A508

MECHAM, Cindy, Health Information Director, Mountain View Hospital, Payson, UT, p. A730

MECKEL, Marsha, R.N., Vice President Clinical Services and Chief Nursing Executive, Community Hospital Anderson, Anderson, IN, p. A223

MEDAGLIA, Guy A., President and Chief Executive Officer, Saint Anthony Hospital, Chicago, IL, p. A200

MEDCIROS, Ron, Director Applied Information Technology, Worcester Recovery Center And Hospital, Worcester, MA, p. A347

MEDEROS, Ana J., Chief Executive Officer, Palmetto General Hospital, Hialeah, FL, p. A139

MEDINA, Alberto, Information Technology Senior Consultant, Hospital Manati Medical Center, Manati, PR, p. A808

MEDINA, Betsmari, Director Human Resources, Dr. Ramon E. Betances Hospital-Mayaguez Medical Center Branch, Mayaguez, PR, p. A808

MEDINA, Ed, M.D., Medical Director, Phillip. County Hospital, Malta, MT, p. A426

MEDINA, Eleanor, M.D., Chief Medical Officer, Behavioral Center Of Michigan, Warren, MI, p. A369

MEDINA, Luz, Controller, Bayamon Medical Center, Bayamon, PR, p. A806

MEDINA, Marco, Chief Information Officer, Stanton County Hospital, Johnson, KS, p. A267

MEDINA, Obdulia, MSN, Associate Director for Administrative Support, Clinical Management and Ambulatory Care, Ashford Presbyterian Community Hospital, San Juan, PR, p. A809

MEDINA, Shelby, Chief Executive Officer, Windom Area Health, Windom, MN, p. A388

MEDINA CRUZ, Victor L., M.D., Administrator, Hospital Cuidado Agudo Especializado En Pacientes Politraumatizados, San Juan, PR, p. A810

MEDLAND, Jacqueline, MS, Ph.D., President and Chief Nursing Officer, Highlands-Cashiers Hospital, Highlands, NC, p. A512

MEDLEY, Barry, Director Information Systems, Southwell Medical, Adel, GA, p. A163

MEDLEY, Dennis, Chief Executive Officer and Administrator, Physicians' Medical Center, New Albany, IN, p. A237

Chief Executive Officer, Physicians' Medical Center, New Albany, IN, p. A237

MEDLEY, Sonya, Director of Human Resources, Regional Medical Center, Orangeburg, SC, p. A623

MEDLIN, John, Chief Nursing Officer, North Carolina Specialty Hospital, Durham, NC, p. A509

MEDLOCK, Darci, Manager Human Resources, Ascension St. Vincent Dunn, Bedford, IN, p. A224

MEDOVICH, Lisa, Chief Financial Officer, Peterson Health, Kerrville, TX, p. A693

MEEKER, Brian, D.O., President Medical Staff, Virginia Gay Hospital, Vinton, IA, p. A259

MEEKER, Chris, M.D., Chief Medical Officer, Sanford Medical Center Bismarck, Bismarck, ND, p. A521

MEEKER, Christina, Director Human Resources, Strategic Behavioral Health - Raleigh, Garner, NC, p. A510

MEEKINS, Lance, Chief Executive Officer, Nocona General Hospital, Nocona, TX, p. A703

MEEKINS, Michelle, Manager Human Resources, Sentara Virginia Beach General Hospital, Virginia Beach, VA, p. A753

MEEKS, Deborah, Chief Nursing Officer, Harlingen Medical Center, Harlingen, TX, p. A683

MEENK, Susan, Vice President Human Resources, Providence St. Peter Hospital, Olympia, WA, p. A761

MEESE, Larry R. Jr, FACHE, Chief Executive Officer, Lane Regional Medical Center, Zachary, LA, p. A317

MEESIG, Deborah, M.D., Chief of Staff, Chillicothe Veterans Affairs Medical Center, Chillicothe, OH, p. A531

MEGEHEE, Mark, Vice President and Chief Information Officer, Decatur Morgan Hospital, Decatur, AL, p. A17

MEGGS, Christi, Director, Musc Health Marion Medical Center, Mullins, SC, p. A623

MEGLEMRE, Amy, R.N., MSN, Senior Vice President and Chief Nursing Officer, Olathe Medical Center, Olathe, KS, p. A272

MEGLI, Cami, Controller, Morrison Community Hospital, Morrison, IL, p. A213

MEGLIOLA, Donna, Assistant Vice President, Johnson Memorial Hospital, Stafford Springs, CT, p. A125

MEGUIAR, Ramon, M.D., Chief Medical Officer, Memorial Health, Savannah, GA, p. A180

MEHAFFEY, M. Beth, Senior Vice President Human Resources, Baptist Medical Center Jacksonville, Jacksonville, FL, p. A140

MEHINDRU, Vinay, M.D., Medical Director, Rockledge Regional Medical Center, Rockledge, FL, p. A155

M.D., Vice President/Chief Medical Officer, Adventhealth Waterman, Tavares, FL, p. A160

MEHLHAUS, Brian, M.D., Chief of Staff, Boone County Hospital, Boone, IA, p. A244

MEHR, Nicholle, Vice President Operations, Mclaren Oakland, Pontiac, MI, p. A364

MEHTA, Kalpana, Chief Fiscal Services, Jesse Brown Veterans Affairs Medical Center, Chicago, IL, p. A198

MEHTA, Umesh, M.D., Chief Medical Officer, Hackensack Meridian Health Carrier Clinic, Belle Mead, NJ, p. A452

MEIDINGER, Sue, Manager Business Office, Linton Hospital, Linton, ND, p. A524

MEIDL, M. Mikela., Interim President, Osf Healthcare Saint Anthony's Health Center, Alton, IL, p. A194

MEIER, Suzanne, System Director, Compensation and Human Resources Technology, Memorial Hermann Memorial City Medical Center, Houston, TX, p. A687

MEIERS, Dawn, Coordinator Medical Staff and Personnel Services, Southeast Michigan Surgical Hospital, Warren, MI, p. A369

MEIGS, Jeffrey, Chief Financial Officer, Louis A. Weiss Memorial Hospital, Chicago, IL, p. A199

MEIGS, John, M.D., JrChief of Staff, Bibb Medical Center, Centreville, AL, p. A16

MEINDEL, Nympha, R.N., Chief Information Officer, North Shore University Hospital, Manhasset, NY, p. A487

MEINKE, Kenneth, Senior Vice President Administrative Services, Finance and Chief Financial Officer, Spartanburg Medical Center - Church Street Campus, Spartanburg, SC, p. A624

MEINKE, Victor, Chief Financial Officer, Jewish Home Of San Francisco, San Francisco, CA, p. A93

MEINKOTH, Jennifer, Executive Director I.S., Memorial Hospital East, Shiloh, IL, p. A220

Executive Director, IS, Memorial Hospital, Belleville, IL, p. A195

MEISINGER, Alan, Chief Financial Officer, Herington Municipal Hospital, Herington, KS, p. A266

MEISNER, Anne, MSN, President and Chief Executive Officer, Southeastern Regional Medical Center, Newnan, GA, p. A178

MEISTER, Steven, M.D., Vice President, Ambulatory Services, Avera Marshall Regional Medical Center, Marshall, MN, p. A380

MEKHAEL, Hani, M.D., Chief Staff, Havenwyck Hospital, Auburn Hills, MI, p. A349

MELAHN, William, M.D., Vice President Medical Affairs and Chief Medical Officer, St. Claire Healthcare, Morehead, KY, p. A290

MELAHOURES, Holly, D.O., Chief Medical Officer, Mercyone Newton Medical Center, Newton, IA, p. A255

MELAN, Kristen, Director Human Resources Administration, Good Shepherd Specialty Hospital, Bethlehem, PA, p. A584

MELANCON, Eric, Chief of Staff, Ochsner St. Mary, Morgan City, LA, p. A309

MELAND, Jeff, M.D., Vice President, Chief Medical Officer, Northfield Hospital And Clinics, Northfield, MN, p. A382

MELARAGNO, Robert, Vice President Finance, O'Bleness Memorial Hospital, Athens, OH, p. A528

MELBOURNE, John, M.D., Medical Director, Conifer Park, Glenville, NY, p. A484

MELBY, Gina, Chief Executive Officer, Jfk Medical Center, Atlantis, FL, p. A131

MELBY, Larry, Chief Executive Officer, Select Specialty Hospital-Palm Beach, Lake Worth, FL, p. A143

MELBY, Rachel, Vice President, Chief Financial Officer, Crawford County Memorial Hospital, Denison, IA, p. A248

MELCHER, Nancy, Chief Nursing Officer, Wellstar North Fulton Hospital, Roswell, GA, p. A179

MELCHIOR, Eric, Executive Vice President and Chief Financial Officer, Greater Baltimore Medical Center, Baltimore, MD, p. A324

MELCHIORRE, Lisa, R.N., MS, Chief Operating Officer and Chief Nursing Officer, St. Luke's Elmore, Mountain Home, ID, p. A191

MELEAR, Brian, Chief Executive Officer, Raulerson Hospital, Okeechobee, FL, p. A150

MELEAR, David, Chief Executive Officer, Cumberland Hall Hospital, Hopkinsville, KY, p. A285

MELENDEZ, Alma, Controller, Dimmit Regional Hospital, Carrizo Springs, TX, p. A662

MELENDEZ, Jose, M.D., Chief Medical Officer, Uchealth Memorial Hospital, Colorado Springs, CO, p. A109

MELENDEZ, Pedro, Chief Executive Director, Hospital Menonita De Cayey, Cayey, PR, p. A807
Chief Executive Officer, Centro De Salud Conductual Menonita-Cima, Aibonito, PR, p. A806
Chief Executive Officer, Mennonite General Hospital, Aibonito, PR, p. A806
Executive Director, Hospital Menonita De Caguas, Caguas, PR, p. A806

MELINE, Brenda, Manager Human Resources, Patients' Hospital Of Redding, Redding, CA, p. A87

MELL, Kevin, Vice President Operations, Medstar Montgomery Medical Center, Olney, MD, p. A331

MELLETT, David, Chief Financial Officer, Harrison Memorial Hospital, Cynthiana, KY, p. A282

MELLGREN, Gustave, M.D., Chief of Staff, Glacial Ridge Health System, Glenwood, MN, p. A377

MELLO, Brett, Chief Information Officer, Cayuga Medical Center At Ithaca, Ithaca, NY, p. A485

MELLO, Paul, Manager Data Processing, Dsh Metropolitan, Norwalk, CA, p. A81

MELLOWS, George, Facility Director, Hawthorn Center, Northville, MI, p. A363

MELNIKOFF, Jean, Vice President Human Resources, Kaiser Permanente Medical Center, Honolulu, HI, p. A184

MELO, Kathleen, Administrator, The Willough At Naples, Naples, FL, p. A149

MELTON, Anne, Chief Nursing Officer, Sumner Regional Medical Center, Gallatin, TN, p. A638

MELTON, Chad, Chief Executive Officer, Fauquier Hospital, Warrenton VA, p. A753

MELTON, Jessica, Interim President, Sentara Norfolk General Hospital, Norfolk, VA, p. A748

MELTON, Josh, Chief Information Officer, St. Bernards Medical Center, Jonesboro, AR, p. A48

MELTVEDT, Robert, M.D., JrVice President Medical Affairs, Valley Health - Warren Memorial Hospital, Front Royal, VA, p. A742

MELTZER, David, Chief Financial Officer, Texas Health Presbyterian Hospital Denton, Denton, TX, p. A672

MELVILLE, Carol, Director Human Resources, Hca Houston Healthcare West, Houston, TX, p. A686

MELVIN, Susan, D.O., Chief Medical Officer, Long Beach Medical Center, Long Beach, CA, p. A72

MENA, Theodore, Chief Executive Officer, Select Specialty Hospital-Orlando, Orlando, FL, p. A152

MENDELOWITZ, Susan, R.N., FACHE, Executive Vice President and Chief Operating Officer, Bergen New Bridge Medical Center, Paramus, NJ, p. A460

MENDEZ, Alex, Executive Vice President of Operations and Chief Financial Officer, Mount Sinai Medieal Center, Miami Beach, FL, p. A148

MENDEZ, Kim, Ed.D., R.N., Chief Nurse Officer, Nyc Health + Hospitals / Bellevue, New York, NY, p. A491

MENDEZ, Lincoln S., Chief Executive Officer, Boca Raton Regional Hospital, Boca Raton, FL, p. A132

MENDEZ, Nicholas Paul., Chief Executive Officer and Director of Nursing, Pam Specialty Hospital Of Hammond, Hammond, LA, p. A302

MENDIOLA-BALDERAS, Rosie, Director Information Systems, South Texas Health System, Edinburg, TX, p. A674

MENDIZABAL, Oscar, Chief Nursing Officer, Highlands Rehabilitation Hospital, El Paso, TX, p. A675

MENDOZA, Carlos, Controller, Baptist Memorial Rehabilitation Hospital, Germantown, TN, p. A638

MENDOZA, Christopher, Chief Executive Officer, Alliancehealth Ponca City, Ponca City, OK, p. A567

MENDOZA, Dana, Chief Information Officer, Maui Memorial Medical Center, Wailuku, HI, p. A187

MENDOZA, Joseph, M.D., Medical Director, Porterville Developmental Center, Porterville, CA, p. A86
Chief Financial Officer, Hillcrest Hospital Cushing, Cushing, OK, p. A558
Chief Financial Officer, Hillcrest Hospital Henryetta, Henryetta, OK, p. A560
Chief Financial Officer, Hillcrest Medical Center, Tulsa, OK, p. A569

MENDOZA, Yolanda, Director Human Resources, Rehabilitation Hospital Of Southern New Mexico, Las Cruces, NM, p. A470

MENDYKA, Nick, Chief Financial Officer, University Of Virginia Medical Center, Charlottesville, VA, p. A740

MENEFEE, Jason, Chief Financial Officer, Mccamey County Hospital District, Mccamey, TX, p. A700

MENEN, Michael, M.D., Chief Medical Officer, Bon Secours St. Francis Medical Center, Midlothian, VA, p. A746

MENGENHAUSEN, Jeff, Chief Executive Officer, Madelia Community Hospital, Madelia, MN, p. A379

MENGLE, Scott, Vice President Human Resources, Penn State Health St. Joseph, Reading, PA, p. A606

MENKES, Jeffrey, President and Chief Executive Officer, Burke Rehabilitation Hospital, White Plains, NY, p. A502

MENNONNA, Guy, Senior Vice President Human Resources, Bergen New Bridge Medical Center, Paramus, NJ, p. A460

MENON, Rema, M.D., Clinical Director, Parsons State Hospital And Training Center, Parsons, KS, p. A274

MENSCH, Alan, M.D., Senior Vice President Medical Affairs, Plainview Hospital, Plainview, NY, p. A495

MENSEN, Amy, Chief Operating Officer, Regional Medical Center, Manchester, IA, p. A253

MENTGEN, John, FACHE, President and Chief Executive Officer, Regional West Medical Center, Scottsbluff, NE, p. A439

MENTHCOAST, Lynn, Chief Fiscal Service, Tennessee Valley Healthcare System, Nashville, TN, p. A647

MENTINK, Terri, Chief Financial Officer, Mercyone Oakland Medical Center, Oakland, NE, p. A436

MENTZEL, Bridget, Director Human Resources, Mercy Health - West Hospital, Cincinnati, OH, p. A533

MENTZER, Larry, Chief Human Resources Officer, Veterans Affairs Roseburg Healthcare System, Roseburg, OR, p. A581

MENZEL, Colette, Ph.D., Chief Operating Officer and Chief Financial Officer, Antelop. Valley Hospital, Lancaster, CA, p. A71

MENZIE, Sue, R.N., Director Patient Care, Sierra Tucson, Tucson, AZ, p. A40

MERCADO, Felix, Chief Executive Officer, Lawrence General Hospital, Lawrence, MA, p. A340

MERCADO, Gloria, Director of Nursing, Mennonite General Hospital, Aibonito, PR, p. A806

MERCADO, Leda, Chief Operating Officer, Hospital Menonita De Cayey, Cayey, PR, p. A807

MERCER, David, Coordinator Information Systems, Baptist Memorial Hospital-Union City, Union City, TN, p. A650

MERCER, Jonathan, FACHE, Senior Vice President, Chief Operating Officer, Carolinas Healthcare System Blue Ridge, Morganton, NC, p. A515

MERCER, Shawna, Director Human Resources, Kansas Neurological Institute, Topeka, KS, p. A277

MERCER, William, M.D., Director, Peterson Healthcare And Rehabilitation Hospital, Wheeling, WV, p. A778

MERCHANT, Deven, M.D., Chief Medical Executive, Sutter Davis Hospital, Davis, CA, p. A62

MERCIER, Murry, Chief Information Officer, Promedica Toledo Hospital, Toledo, OH, p. A550

MERCKENS, Natalie, Chief Executive Officer, Kindred Hospital-Ontario, Ontario, CA, p. A82

MERCULIEFF, Leatha N., Hospital Administrator, Wrangell Medical Center, Wrangell, AK, p. A29

MERCURI, Ralph, Vice President and Chief Financial Officer, Major Hospital, Shelbyville, IN, p. A240

MERE, Mohammed, Chief Information Officer, Oneida Healthcare, Oneida, NY, p. A494

MEREDITH, Katie, Chief Nursing Officer, Select Specialty Hospital-Lexington, Lexington, KY, p. A287

MEREDITH, Keith, Chief Operating Officer, Salem Regional Medical Center, Salem, OH, p. A548

MEREDITH, Ty, Chief Executive Officer, Peak View Behavioral Health, Colorado Springs, CO, p. A109

MEREK, Gloria, Director of Nursing, Springfield Hospital Center, Sykesville, MD, p. A333

MERGEN, Lynn M., Chief Executive Officer, Medical Center Barbour, Eufaula, AL, p. A18

MERILLO, Myra, Supervisor Health Information Management, Encompass Health Rehabilitation Hospital Of Spring Hill, Brooksville, FL, p. A133

MERINGOLO, Francis, Vice President Human Resources, Umass Memorial-Marlborough Hospital, Marlborough, MA, p. A341

MERIWETHER, Wayne, Chief Executive Officer, Twin Lakes Regional Medical Center, Leitchfield, KY, p. A286

MERKEL, Rebecca, Privacy Officer, Franciscan Health Carmel, Carmel, IN, p. A225

MERKLE, John F., Medical Center Director, Tuscaloosa Veterans Affairs Medical Center, Tuscaloosa, AL, p. A25

MERKLEY, Jason R., Chief Executive Officer, Brookings Health System, Brookings, SD, p. A626

MERKLIN, Paul, Vice President Finance and Chief Financial Officer, Adventhealth Manchester, Manchester, KY, p. A289

MERRIFIELD, Matt, Chief Operating Officer, Aiken Regional Medical Centers, Aiken, SC, p. A615

MERRIGAN, Mary, Manager Public Relations, Sanford Vermillion Medical Center, Vermillion, SD, p. A632

MERRILL, Cheryl, MSN, R.N., Senior Vice President Patient Care Services and Chief Nursing Officer, North Shore Medical Center, Salem, MA, p. A344

MERRILL, Chuck, M.D., Vice President Medical Affairs, Marian Regional Medical Center, Santa Maria, CA, p. A97

MERRILL, Rick W., System President and Chief Executive Officer, Cook Children's Medical Center, Fort Worth, TX, p. A678

MERRILL, Stacie, Chief Nursing Officer, Baylor Scott & White Surgical Hospital Fort Worth, Fort Worth, TX, p. A678

MERRITT, Becky, Director Human Resources, Houston Methodist Clear Lake Hospital, Nassau Bay, TX, p. A702

MERRITT, Belinda, M.D., Medical Director, West Tennessee Rehabilitation Hospital Cane Creek, Martin, TN, p. A643

MERRITT, Bradley, M.D., Medical Director, Christus Trinity Mother Frances Rehabilitation Hospital, A Partner Of Encompass Health, Tyler, TX, p. A721

MERRITT, Janet, Chief Financial Officer, Ascension St. Vincent Williamsport, Williamsport, IN, p. A242

MERRITT, Trevor, Director Human Resources, Star Valley Health, Afton, WY, p. A801

MERRY, Duane, Chief Information Officer, Little Falls Hospital, Little Falls, NY, p. A487

MERRYMAN, Mary, Regional Director Information Management, Christus Health Shreveport-Bossier, Shreveport, LA, p. A314

MERRYWELL, Paul, Chief Information Officer, Sycamore Shoals Hospital, Elizabethton, TN, p. A637

MERSON, John, M.D., Chief of Staff, John Muir Medical Center, Concord, Concord, CA, p. A61

MESA, Gustavo, Chief Information Officer, San Juan City Hospital, San Juan, PR, p. A811

MESIC, John, M.D., Chief Medical Officer, Sutter Auburn Faith Hospital, Auburn, CA, p. A56

MESICK, Marc, Vice President and Chief Financial Officer, Ellis Hospital, Schenectady, NY, p. A498

MESKAN, Paula, R.N., Chief Nursing Officer, River's Edge Hospital And Clinic, Saint Peter, MN, p. A385

MESORAS, Amber, Chief Human Resources Officer, Veterans Affairs Pittsburgh Healthcare System, Pittsburgh, PA, p. A604

MESSA-GILL, Nicole, Manager Human Resources, Northlake Behavioral Health System, Mandeville, LA, p. A308

MESSELT, Mary Jo, Manager Human Resources, Mercy Hospital Watonga, Watonga, OK, p. A571
Senior Human Resources Manager, Mercy Hospital Logan County, Guthrie, OK, p. A559

MESSER, Kelly, Director of Finance, Devereux Hospital And Children's Center Of Florida, Melbourne, FL, p. A145

MESSER, Mark, D.O., Clinical Director, Terrell State Hospital, Terrell, TX, p. A719

MESSERSMITH, Scott, Director Human Resources, Columbus Community Hospital, Columbus, NE, p. A431

MESSINA, Arlene, R.N., MSN, Director of Nursing, Riverside Doctors' Hospital Williamsburg, Williamsburg, VA, p. A753

MESSINA, Daniel J., Ph.D., FACHE, President and Chief Executive Officer, Richmond University Medical Center, Staten Island, NY, p. A498

MESSMAN, Catherine, Chief Financial Officer, Mills-Peninsula Health Services, Burlingame, CA, p. A59

MESTAS, Lisa, Associate Administrator and System Chief Nursing Officer, Usa Health University Hospital, Mobile, AL, p. A22

MESTER, Sulynn, R.N., Chief Nursing Officer, Childress Regional Medical Center, Childress, TX, p. A663

MESZLER, Lori, Chief Financial Officer, Helen Hayes Hospital, West Haverstraw, NY, p. A502

METCALF, Angie, Vice President and Chief Human Resource Officer, Cleveland Clinic Martin North Hospital, Stuart, FL, p. A158

METCALF, Chris, Director of Nursing, Utah State Hospital, Provo, UT, p. A731

METCALF, Kathleen, Chief Information Officer, Uh Samaritan Medical Center, Ashland, OH, p. A528

METCALF, Peter, M.D., President Medical Staff, Genesis Medical Center, Silvis, Silvis, IL, p. A220

METHE, Joan, Chief Information Officer, Mercy Medical Center, Springfield, MA, p. A344

METHVEN, Jeffrey, Vice President Ambulatory Services and Chief Human Resources Officer, Saratoga Hospital, Saratoga Springs, NY, p. A497

METHVIN, Jeff, Manager Information Technology, St. Luke Hospital And Living Center, Marion, KS, p. A270

METIKO, Olushola, M.D., Medical Director, Central Prison Hospital, Raleigh, NC, p. A516

METINKO, Andrew, M.D., Chief Medical Officer, The Hsc Pediatric Center, Washington, DC, p. A130

METIVIER, Roberta, Vice President Human Resources and Administrator, Western Main Nursing Home, Stephens Memorial Hospital, Norway, ME, p. A321

METRO, Michelle, Vice President Nursing, Cloud County Health Center, Concordia, KS, p. A263

METTE, Stephen, M.D., Interim Chief Executive Officer, Uams Medical Center, Little Rock, AR, p. A49

METTEAUER, Kenneth, Chief Financial Officer, Redmond Regional Medical Center, Rome, GA, p. A179

METZ, Amy, Chief Executive Officer, Regency Hospital Of Florence, Florence, SC, p. A619

METZ, Bruce, Ph.D., Senior Vice President and Chief Information Officer, Lahey Hospital & Medical Center, Burlington, Burlington, MA, p. A337

METZ, Carl, Vice President, Ephraim Mcdowell Fort Logan Hospital, Stanford, KY, p. A293

METZGER, Alysha, Director Human Resources, Hill Country Memorial Hospital, Fredericksburg, TX, p. A679

METZGER, Cynthia, Chief Nursing and Operations Officer, Little River Memorial Hospital, Ashdown, AR, p. A42

METZGER, Terry, Chief Financial Officer, Ascension St. Vincent Seton Specialty Hospital, Indianapolis, IN, p. A231
Vice President, Finance, Ascension St. Vincent Indianapolis Hospital, Indianapolis, IN, p. A231

MEUER, Lynn, Interim Chief Nursing Officer, Sibley Memorial Hospital, Washington, DC, p. A130

MEURER, Bryan, Director Information Systems, Mat-Su Regional Medical Center, Palmer, AK, p. A29

MEWHIRTER, Michael, President, Fort Hamilton Hospital, Hamilton, OH, p. A542

MEYER, Anthony, M.D., Medical Director, Aurora Psychiatric Hospital, Wauwatosa, WI, p. A799

MEYER, Barb, Executive Director of Nursing, Gibson Area Hospital And Health Services, Gibson City, IL, p. A206

MEYER, Cameron, CPA, Chief Financial Officer, Excelsior Springs Hospital, Excelsior Springs, MO, p. A406

MEYER, Cheryl, MSN, Director of Nursing, Haven Behavioral Senior Care Of Dayton, Dayton, OH, p. A538
Director Human Resources, Gundersen Palmer Lutheran Hospital And Clinics, West Union, iA, p. A260

MEYER, Daniel, President, Aurora Baycare Medical Center, Green Bay, WI, p. A785

MEYER, Daniel T., President, Aurora Baycare Medical Center, Green Bay, WI, p. A785

MEYER, Gordon, Director Human Resources, Surgeons Choice Medical Center, Southfield, MI, p. A367

MEYER, Gregg S., M.D., Interim President, Newton-Wellesley Hospital, Newton Lower Falls, MA, p. A342

MEYER, Jeffrey K., Interim Chief Executive Officer, Osceola Medical Center, Osceola, WI, p. A793

MEYER, Karen, Vice President Finance and Chief Financial Officer, Rush Memorial Hospital, Rushville, IN, p. A240

MEYER, Kurt, Chief Human Resource Officer, Saint Josep. Health System, Mishawaka, IN, p. A236
Chief Human Resources Officer, Plymouth Medical Center, Plymouth, IN, p. A239

MEYER, Mark, Chief Financial Officer, Grady Memorial Hospital, Atlanta, GA, p. A164

MEYER, Michele, R.N., Vice President of Operations, Mercy Hospital Jefferson, Festus, MO, p. A406

MEYER, Michele C., R.N., Chief Executive Officer, Washington County Memorial Hospital, Potosi, MO, p. A414

MEYER, Morgan, Chief Financial Officer, Howard County Medical Center, Saint Paul, NE, p. A439

MEYER, Nate, Director Finance, Alomere Health, Alexandria, MN, p. A371

MEYER, Robert L., President and Chief Executive Officer, Phoenix Children's Hospital, Phoenix, AZ, p. A36

MEYER, Roger, M.D., Chief of Staff, Friend Community Healthcare System, Friend, NE, p. A432

MEYER, Ryan, Vice President Operations, Mercyone Cedar Falls Medical Center, Cedar Falls, IA, p. A244
Vice President Operations, Mercyone Waterloo Medical Center, Waterloo, IA, p. A259

MEYER, Timothy, M.D., Chief of Staff, Marshfield Medical Center - Neillsville, Neillsville, WI, p. A792

MEYER, Traci, Director Human Resources, Canyon Vista Medical Center, Sierra Vista, AZ, p. A38

MEYER, Wessel, M.D., Chief of Staff, Veterans Affairs Central California Health Care System, Fresno, CA, p. A66

MEYERHOEFER, Todd, M.D., Vice President Medical Affairs, Cleveland Clinic Union Hospital, Dover, OH, p. A539

MEYERS, Audrey, FACHE, President and Chief Executive Officer, Valley Hospital, Ridgewood, NJ, p. A462

MEYERS, Betty, Chief Financial Officer, Crook County Medical Services District, Sundance, WY, p. A804

MEYERS, Larry, Chief Information Officer, Wilson Memorial Hospital, Sidney, OH, p. A549

MEYERS, Mark, M.D., Chief of Staff, Battle Mountain General Hospital, Battle Mountain, NV, p. A441

MEYERS, Russell, FACHE, President and Chief Executive Officer, Midland Memorial Hospital, Midland, TX, p. A701

MEYERS, William, Chief Information Officer, St. Luke's Hospital, Chesterfield, MO, p. A404

MEZA, Eduardo, M.D., Medical Director, Prairie St. John's, Fargo, ND, p. A523

MEZA, Lourdes, Coordinator Human Resources, West Covina Medical Center, West Covina, CA, p. A104

MEZOFF, Adam, M.D., Vice President and Chief Medical Officer, Dayton Children's Hospital, Dayton, OH, p. A538

MHERABI, Nader, Senior Vice President and Vice Dean, Chief Information Officer, Nyu Langone Hospitals, New York, NY, p. A492

MIANO, Christena, Vice President, Human Resources, Medical Center Of Trinity, Trinity, FL, p. A161

MICAN, Deborah, R.N., Chief Nursing Officer, Capital Health Medical Center-Hopewell, Pennington, NJ, p. A461

MICCOLI, Vincent, Executive Director, Kirby Forensic Psychiatric Center, New York, NY, p. A490
Executive Director, Manhattan Psychiatric Center-Ward's Island, New York, NY, p. A490

MICHAEL, Amy, Chief Operating Officer, Sullivan County Memorial Hospital, Milan, MO, p. A412

MICHAEL, Elizabeth, R.N., MS, Vice President Patient Care Services and Chief Nursing Officer, Stillwater Medical Center, Stillwater, OK, p. A568

MICHAEL, Richard, M.D., Vice President Medical Affairs, Christus Health Shreveport-Bossier, Shreveport, LA, p. A314

MICHAELS, Stephen, M.D., Chief Operating Officer and Chief Medical Officer, Medstar St. Mary's Hospital, Leonardtown, MD, p. A331

MICHALSKI, Carrie, President and Chief Executive Officer, Riverview Health, Crookston, MN, p. A374

MICHEL, Diane, Senior Vice President, Chief Nursing Officer, Children's Hospital, New Orleans, LA, p. A310

MICHEL, George, Chief Operating Officer, Larkin Community Hospital-South Miami Campus, South Miami, FL, p. A157

MICHEL, Randall, M.D., Chief of Staff, Lompoc Valley Medical Center, Lompoc, CA, p. A72

MICHEL-OGBORN, Deborah, Chief Information Resource Management, North Florida/South Georgia Veteran's Health System, Gainesville, FL, p. A138

MICHELE, Margorie, Chief Human Resources Officer, Penn Presbyterian Medical Center, Philadelphia, PA, p. A601

MICHELEN, Jeannith, Chief Implementation Officer, Nyc Health + Hospitals / Elmhurst, Elmhurst, NY, p. A483
Senior Associate Executive Director, Nyc Health + Hospitals / Lincoln, Bronx, NY, p. A477
Senior Associate Executive Director, Nyc Health + Hospitals / Queens, Jamaica, NY, p. A486

MICHELL, Pamela R.N., Vice President, Chief Nursing Officer, Adventhealth Ocala, Ocala, FL, p. A149

MICHELSON, Soad, M.D., Senior Medical Director, Clarity Child Guidance Center, San Antonio, TX, p. A711

MICHENER, Scott, M.D., Chief Medical Officer, Comanche County Memorial Hospital, Lawton, OK, p. A561

MICHL, Michelle, Director Human Resources, Mercy Medical Center Mount Shasta, Mount Shasta, CA, p. A80

MICKIEWICZ, Nanette, M.D., President, Dominican Hospital, Santa Cruz, CA, p. A97

MIDDENDORF, Bruce, M.D., Chief Medical Officer, St. Mary's Health Care System, Athens, GA, p. A164

MIDDLEBROOKS, Mark, M.D., Medical Director, Noland Hospital Birmingham, Birmingham, AL, p. A15

MIDDLETON, Jackie, Vice President Human Resources, Methodist Dallas Medical Center, Dallas, TX, p. A669

MIDDLETON, James, MSN, R.N., Chief Nursing Officer, Knox Community Hospital, Mount Vernon, OH, p. A546

MIDDLETON, Robert, MSN, R.N., IIIVice President Ancillary Services, Chief Administrative Officer andChief Construction Executive, Gerald Champion Regional Medical Center, Alamogordo, NM, p. A467

MIDGETT, Jenifer, President and Chief Executive Officer, Temp. St. Luke's Hospital, Tempe, AZ, p. A39

MIDGETT, Steve, R.N., Chief Nursing Officer, Encompass Health Rehabilitation Hospital Of Sugar Land, Sugar Land, TX, p. A717

MIDKIFF, Stephen L., Chief Executive Officer, Lake Norman Regional Medical Center, Mooresville, NC, p. A514

MIDTLIEN, Tonia, Information Systems Support Specialist, Gundersen Boscobel Area Hospital And Clinics, Boscobel, WI, p. A781

MIEDLER, Michael, M.D., Chief Medical Officer, Continuing Care Hospital, Lexington, KY, p. A286

MIELKE, Cary, M.D., Chief of Staff, Shriners Hospitals For Children-Shreveport, Shreveport, LA, p. A314

MIESNER, Gail, Chief Financial Officer, Memorial Hospital, Chester, IL, p. A197

MIGLIETTA, Steve, Chief Financial Officer, Orlando Regional Medical Center, Orlando, FL, p. A151

MIGOYA, Carlos A., President and Chief Executive Officer, Jackson Health System, Miami, FL, p. A146

MIHALJEVIC, Tomislav, M.D., President and Chief Executive Officer, Cleveland Clinic, Cleveland, OH, p. A534

MIKELL, Evarista, Assistant Finance Officer, William S. Middleton Memorial Veterans Hospital, Madison, WI, p. A788

MIKHAIL, Ashraf, M.D., Medical Director, Brynn Marr Hospital, Jacksonville, NC, p. A512

MIKI, Nobuyuki, M.D., Vice President Medical Services and Chief Medical Officer, Kuakini Medical Center, Honolulu, HI, p. A184

MIKITARIAN, George Jr, FACHE, President and Chief Executive Officer, Parrish Medical Center, Titusville, FL, p. A160

MIKITKA, Joseph, Vice President Human Resources, St. Luke's Sacred Heart Campus, Allentown, PA, p. A583

MIKKELSEN, Kallie, Vice President Nursing, Memorial Hospital Of Sweetwater County, Rock Springs, WY, p. A804

MIKKELSON, Tom, M.D., Interim Chief Operating Officer, Touchette Regional Hospital, Centreville, IL, p. A197
M.D., Vice President Medical Affairs, Touchette Regional Hospital, Centreville, IL, p. A197

MIKLAVIC, Kirk, Director Human Resources, Bridgton Hospital, Bridgton, ME, p. A319
Director, Human Resources, Central Maine Medical Center, Lewiston, ME, p. A321

MIKLOS, Maggie, Director Human Resources, Northside Hospital, Saint Petersburg, FL, p. A156

MIKOS, Kathy, Vice President and Chief Nursing Officer, Ingalls Memorial Hospital, Harvey, IL, p. A207

MIKULIC, Jeannie, Director Human Resources, Providence Portland Medical Center, Portland, OR, p. A579

MILAM, Wendy, Chief Nursing Officer, Encompass Health Rehabilitation Hospital Of Ocala, Ocala, FL, p. A150

MILAN, Isabel, R.N., Chief Nursing Officer, Lac+Usc Medical Center, Los Angeles, CA, p. A75

MILAND, Shelly, Chief Financial Officer, Texas Health Specialty Hospital, Fort Worth, TX, p. A679
Group Finance Officer, Texas Health Harris Methodist Hospital Cleburne, Cleburne, TX, p. A663
Group Financial Officer, Texas Health Harris Methodist Hospital Fort Worth, Fort Worth, TX, p. A679

MILANES, Carlos, Chief Executive Officer, Edgefield County Healthcare, Edgefield, SC, p. A619

MILANO, Arthur, Vice President Human Resources, Berkshire Medical Center, Pittsfield, MA, p. A343

MILATOVICH, Natasha, Association Vice President Human Resources, Adventist Health White Memorial, Los Angeles, CA, p. A73

MILAZZO, John, Chief Financial Officer, Merit Health River Region, Vicksburg, MS, p. A401
Chief Financial Officer, Southeast Georgia Health System Camden Campus, Saint Marys, GA, p. A179

MILBURN, Sandra, Director Human Resources, Encompass Health Rehabilitation Hospital Of Memphis, Memphis, TN, p. A644

MILBURN, Sharon, Chief Nursing Officer, Summers County Arh Hospital, Hinton, WV, p. A772

MILES, Ben, President, Parkview Regional Medical Center, Fort Wayne, IN, р. A228

MILES, Dana, Chief Nursing Officer and Chief Clinical Officer, Delta Memorial Hospital, Dumas, AR, p. A44

MILES, John, Chief Financial Officer, Piedmont Newnan Hospital, Newnan, GA, p. A178

MILES, Karen, M.D., Medical Director, Strategic Behavioral Health - Raleigh, Garner, NC, p. A510

MILES, Kerry, Chief Information Officer, Providence St. Peter Hospital, Olympia, WA, p. A761
Site Director, Providence Centralia Hospital, Centralia, WA, p. A756

MILES, Lee Ann, Chief Financial Officer, Harrison County Community Hospital, Bethany, MO, p. A402

MILES, Paul, Chief Operating Officer, Morgan County Arh Hospital, West Liberty, KY, p. A294
Vice President Administration, Whitesburg Arh Hospital, Whitesburg, KY, p. A294

MILES, Scott, Chief Executive Officer, Cedar Creek Hospital Of Michigan, Saint Johns, MI, p. A366
Chief Operating Officer, Forest View Psychiatric Hospital, Grand Rapids, MI, p. A355

MILETO, Dottie, Chief Nursing Officer, Adventhealth Heart Of Florida, Davenport, FL, p. A135

MILEY, Patricia, Director of Finance, Grace Medical Center, Baltimore, MD, p. A324

MILHALTSES, Dean, Chief Operating Officer, Nyc Health + Hospitals / Queens, Jamaica, NY, p. A486

MILIAN, Tony, Chief Financial Officer, Larkin Community Hospital-Palm Springs Campus, Hialeah, FL, p. A139

MILIAZZO, John, Vice President and Chief Financial Officer, Southeast Georgia Health System Brunswick Campus, Brunswick, GA, p. A167

MILICEVIC, Heather, Director Human Resources, Western Reserve Hospital, Cuyahoga Falls, OH, p. A538

MILIUS, Hank A., Chief Executive Officer, Meridian Health Services, Muncie, IN, p. A237

MILLAN, Wilfredo, Chief Operating Officer, Cardiovascular Center Of Puerto Rico And The Caribbean, San Juan, PR, p. A809

MILLARD, Kathleen, Acting Director Nursing, Kalamazoo Psychiatric Hospital, Kalamazoo, MI, p. A359

MILLEN, Peter, Chief Medical Officer MHSATS, Community Behavioral Health Hospital - Rochester, Rochester, MN, p. A384

MILLER, Alicia, Director Human Resources, Aspen Valley Hospital, Aspen, CO, p. A107

MILLER, Andy, Chief Financial Officer, Trident Medical Center, Charleston, SC, p. A616

MILLER, Bob, President, Aurora Lakeland Medical Center, Elkhorn, WI, p. A783
President, Aurora Medical Center Burlington, Burlington, WI, p. A781

MILLER, Brent, Manager Human Resources, Brown County Community Treatment Center, Green Bay, WI, p. A785

MILLER, Brian F., Chief Executive Officer, Dewitt Hospital, Dewitt, AR, p. A44

MILLER, C., M.D., Chief Medical Officer, Our Lady Of The Angels Hospital, Bogalusa, LA, p. A298

MILLER, Carol, R.N., Chief Nursing Officer, Reynolds Memorial Hospital, Glen Dale, WV, p. A772

MILLER, Carrie, Director Human Resources, Promedica Defiance Regional Hospital, Defiance, OH, p. A539

MILLER, Chad, Chief Financial Officer, Merit Health Biloxi, Biloxi, MS, p. A389

MILLER, Chad J., President and Chief Executive Officer, Morrow County Hospital, Mount Gilead, OH, p. A546

MILLER, Chandra, Director of Nursing, John J. Pershing Veterans Affairs Medical Center, Poplar Bluff, MO, p. A413

MILLER, Chris, Chief Financial Officer, Highland Hospital, Charleston, WV, p. A771
Chief Operating Officer, Greeneville Community Hospital West, Greeneville, TN, p. A638

MILLER, Christine, Chief Human Resources Management Services, Maine Veterans Affairs Medical Center, Augusta, ME, p. A318
General Counsel and Vice President Human Resources, Upmc Hanover, Hanover, PA, p. A591

MILLER, Clint, Chief Nursing Officer, Spooner Health, Spooner, WI, p. A796

MILLER, Connie, Vice President Human Resources, Overland Park Regional Medical Center, Overland Park, KS, p. A274

MILLER, Daniel, FACHE, Chief Executive Officer, Methodist Hospital, San Antonio, TX, p. A712
Human Resources Business Partner, University Hospitals Parma Medical Center, Parma, OH, p. A547
Vice President Human Resources, Uh Elyria Medical Center, Elyria, OH, p. A540

MILLER, Debra, Administrator, Crosbyton Clinic Hospital, Crosbyton, TX, p. A666

MILLER, Derek, Senior Vice President and Chief Financial Officer, Southeast Alabama Medical Center, Dothan, AL, p. A18

MILLER, Diane, Administrator, Peterson Healthcare And Rehabilitation Hospital, Wheeling, WV, p. A781

MILLER, Dillon, M.D., Chief Medical Officer, Fannin Regional Hospital, Blue Ridge, GA, p. A167

MILLER, Dionne, Chief Operating Officer, Sutter Roseville Medical Center, Roseville, CA, p. A89

MILLER, Duane, Chief Financial Officer, Chi St. Luke's Health Memorial Livingston, Livingston, TX, p. A696

MILLER, Dyrek, M.D., Chief Medical Staff, Vidant Duplin Hospital, Kenansville, NC, p. A513

MILLER, Elaine, Director of Nursing, Oaklawn Psychiatric Center, Goshen, IN, p. A229

MILLER, Esteban, Chief Medical Officer, Black River Memorial Hospital, Black River Falls, WI, p. A781

MILLER, Gary, Regional Director Information Systems, Plymouth Medical Center, Plymouth, IN, p. A239
Senior Director Information Systems, Saint Josep. Health System, Mishawaka, IN, p. A236

MILLER, Gene, Interim Chief Executive Officer, Jellico Community Hospital, Jellico, TN, p. A640

MILLER, George, President and Chief Executive Officer, Loretto Hospital, Chicago, IL, p. A199

MILLER, Greg, Senior Vice President Operations, Uf Health Jacksonville, Jacksonville, FL, p. A142

MILLER, Hope, Director of Medical Records, Peterson Healthcare And Rehabilitation Hospital, Wheeling, WV, p. A778

MILLER, J, M.D., Chief Medical Officer, Hazard Arh Regional Medical Center, Hazard, KY, p. A284
M.D., Vice President Medical Affairs, Morgan County Arh Hospital, West Liberty, KY, p. A294
M.D., Vice President Medical Affairs, Tug Valley Arh Regional Medical Center, South Williamson, KY, p. A293

MILLER, James, Chief Executive Officer, Rolling Hills Hospital, Franklin, TN, p. A638
Chief Financial Officer, Baptist Medical Center Yazoo, Yazoo City, MS, p. A401

MILLER, Jane, Director Human Resources, Avera Creighton Hospital, Creighton, NE, p. A431
Human Resources Officer, Avera Sacred Heart Hospital, Yankton, SD, p. A633

MILLER, Jason, Chief Financial Officer, The Medical Center Of Southeast Texas, Port Arthur, TX, p. A707

MILLER, Jeff, Chief Operating Officer, Citizens Memorial Hospital, Bolivar, MO, p. A402

MILLER, Jerry, Vice President, Information Services, Memorial Medical Center, Springfield, IL, p. A221

MILLER, Jon, Director Accounting and Information Services, Hancock Regional Hospital, Greenfield, IN, p. A230

MILLER, Joshua, Director Information Systems, Joint Township District Memorial Hospital, Saint Marys, OH, p. A548

MILLER, Joy, Chief Nursing Officer, Cornerstone Hospital Of Little Rock, Little Rock, AR, p. A49

MILLER, Julie, Chief Operating Officer, Williamson Medical Center, Franklin, TN, p. A638

MILLER, Justin, Chief Information Officer and Associate Vice President, The University Of Vermont Health Network - Alice Hyde Medical Center, Malone, NY, p. A487

MILLER, Karen, Chief Financial Officer, San Juan Regional Medical Center, Farmington, NM, p. A469

MILLER, Kay, R.N., MSN, Chief Nursing Officer, Uchealth Greeley, Greeley, CO, p. A114
R.N., MSN, Chief Nursing Officer, Uchealth Memorial Hospital, Colorado Springs, CO, p. A109

MILLER, Keith, Chief Operating Officer, Daviess Community Hospital, Washington, IN, p. A242

MILLER, Ken, Chief Financial Officer, Beaufort Memorial Hospital, Beaufort, SC, p. A615

MILLER, Kevin, President, Chi Health Lakeside, Omaha, NE, p. A436
President, Chi Health Midlands, Papillion, NE, p. A438

MILLER, Kimberly J., FACHE, President, Western Region, Baptist Health - Fort Smith, Fort Smith, AR, p. A46
FACHE, President, Western Region, Baptist Health - Van Buren, Van Buren, AR, p. A54

MILLER, Kris, Senior Human Resources Business Partner, Spectrum Health Reed City Hospital, Reed City, MI, p. A364

MILLER, Krista, R.N., Chief Nursing Officer, Shriners Hospitals For Children-Philadelphia, Philadelphia, PA, p. A602

MILLER, Laurie, Administrative Assistant, Sakakawea Medical Center, Hazen, ND, p. A524

MILLER, Leanne, Director Human Resources, Community Hospital, Mccook, NE, p. A435

MILLER, Lisa, Director Human Resources, Hendry Regional Medical Center, Clewiston, FL, p. A134

MILLER, Maria, Controller, Beaumont Hospital - Grosse Pointe, Grosse Pointe, MI, p. A357

MILLER, Mark, FACHE, Chief Executive Officer, West Hills Hospital And Medical Center, West Hills, CA, p. A104
Chief Financial Officer, Freeman Regional Health Services, Freeman, SD, p. A628

MILLER, Mark A., FACHE, Chief Executive Officer, Harlan County Health System, Alma, NE, p. A429

MILLER, Mary, Vice President Finance and Business Development, Mt. Washington Pediatric Hospital, Baltimore, MD, p. A326

MILLER, Mary Beth, M.D., Chief of Staff, Cheyenne County Hospital, Saint Francis, KS, p. A275

MILLER, Mathew, M.D., Vice President and Chief Medical Officer, St. Josep. Hospital Eureka, Eureka, CA, p. A63

MILLER, Michael, Director Human Resources, Barnes-Jewish St. Peters Hospital, Saint Peters, MO, p. A418
Director Human Resources, Progress West Hospital, O'Fallon, MO, p. A413

MILLER, Michael S., President and Chief Executive Officer, Heritage Valley Kennedy, Mckees Rocks, PA, p. A596

MILLER, Michele, R.N., MSN, Vice President, Acute and Nursing Services, Rutgers University Behavioral Healthcare, Piscataway, NJ, p. A461

MILLER, Michelle, Chief Human Resources, Placentia-Linda Hospital, Placentia, CA, p. A85

MILLER, Mitchell, M.D., Chief Medical Officer, Garfield Memorial Hospital, Panguitch, UT, p. A730

MILLER, Nicole, Director Human Resources, Riverside Shore Memorial Hospital, Onancock, VA, p. A748

MILLER, Patrick, Technology Coordinator, Mountains Community Hospital, Lake Arrowhead, CA, p. A70

MILLER, Paul, Director of Operations, Sanford Chamberlain Medical Center, Chamberlain, SD, p. A627

MILLER, Peter, Chief Financial Officer, North Vista Hospital, North Las Vegas, NV, p. A445

MILLER, Phil., Chief Information Officer, Unity Health White County Medical Center, Searcy, AR, p. A52

MILLER, Redonda G., M.D., President, Johns Hopkins Hospital, Baltimore, MD, p. A324

MILLER, Richard, Ph.D., Vice President Hospital Affairs and Chief Financial Officer, Suny Downstate-University Hospital Of Brooklyn, Brooklyn, NY, p. A479
Administrator Finance, Banner Thunderbird Medical Center, Glendale, AZ, p. A32

MILLER, Rick, Chief Financial Officer, District One Hospital, Faribault, MN, p. A376
Director, Operations and Finance, District One Hospital, Faribault, MN, p. A376
President and Chief Operating Officer, Nationwide Children's Hospital, Columbus, OH, p. A536

MILLER, Rod, Chief Information Technology, Community Hospital, Torrington, WY, p. A804

MILLER, Sandra, MSN, R.N., Interim Vice President, Patient Care Continuum and Chief Nursing Officer, Sarah Bush Lincoln Health Center, Mattoon, IL, p. A211

MILLER, Scott, Vice President and Chief Operating Officer, Adventhealth Hendersonville, Hendersonville, NC, p. A512

MILLER, Shane, Chief Information Officer, Hshs St. Clare Memorial Hospital, Oconto Falls, WI, p. A793
Chief Information Officer, Hshs St. Mary's Hospital Medical Center, Green Bay, WI, p. A785
Chief Information Officer, Hshs St. Nicholas Hospital, Sheboygan, WI, p. A796
Chief Information Officer, Hshs St. Vincent Hospital, Green Bay, WI, p. A785

MILLER, Stacy, Entity Human Resources Officer, Texas Health Presbyterian Hospital Dallas, Dallas, TX, p. A670

MILLER, Steve, Director Information Systems, Baptist Medical Center South, Montgomery, AL, p. A22

MILLER, Susan, Financial Administrator, Faulkton Area Medical Center, Faulkton, SD, p. A628

MILLER, Suzanne, R.N., MSN, Senior Director Patient Care Services and Nursing, St. Luke's Wood River Medical Center, Ketchum, ID, p. A191

MILLER, Tamara, FACHE, Chief Executive Officer and Administrator, Madison Regional Health System, Madison, SD, p. A629

MILLER, Ted, Vice President and Chief Financial Officer, Memorial Hospital And Health Care Center, Jasper, IN, p. A233

MILLER, Thomas, M.D., Medical Director, University Of Utah Health, Salt Lake City, UT, p. A733
Chief Executive Officer, Uofl Health - Uofl Hospital, Louisville, KY, p. A289

MILLER, Timothy, Interim Chief Executive Officer, Palmetto Lowcountry Behavioral Health, Charleston, SC, p. A616

MILLER, Valerie, MSN, R.N., Director of Nursing, Major Hospital, Shelbyville, IN, p. A240

MILLER, Weston, M.D., Chief Medical Officer, Abbeville General Hospital, Abbeville, LA, p. A295

MILLER, William, Coordinator Management Information Systems, Livengrin Foundation, Bensalem, PA, p. A584

MILLER, Zachary T., Interim Chief Executive Officer, Community Hospital, Torrington, WY, p. A804

MILLER-BALFOUR, Pam, Director Human Resources, Socorro General Hospital, Socorro, NM, p. A472

MILLER-COLLETTE, Melody, Director Human Resources, North Okaloosa Medical Center, Crestview, FL, p. A135

MILLICAN, Sharon, Associate Director, Patient Care Services, South Texas Veterans Health Care System, San Antonio, TX, p. A713

MILLIS, David, M.D., Clinical Director, Thomas B. Finan Center, Cumberland, MD, p. A329

MILLS, Amanda, Chief Nursing Officer, Mcleod Health Loris, Loris, SC, p. A622

MILLS, Aundrea, R.N., Chief Nursing Officer, Sovah Health-Danville, Danville, VA, p. A741

MILLS, Chad, Senior Vice President, Chief Information Officer, Children's Mercy Hospital Kansas, Overland Park, KS, p. A273

MILLS, Craig, Vice President Human Resources, Peacehealth Sacred Heart Medical Center University District, Eugene, OR, p. A575

MILLS, Dennis, Chief Human Resources Officer, San Ramon Regional Medical Center, San Ramon, CA, p. A96

MILLS, Gene, Director Information Technology, Scenic Mountain Medical Center, Big Spring, TX, p. A659

MILLS, Jerry, Chief Human Resources Management Services, San Francisco Va Medical Center, San Francisco, CA, p. A94

MILLS, Jim, Regional Director Information Technology, Sutter Medical Center, Sacramento, Sacramento, CA, p. A90

MILLS, John, Chief Operating Officer, Cleveland Clinic Avon Hospital, Avon, OH, p. A528
Senior Vice President Operations, Cleveland Clinic Fairview Hospital, Cleveland, OH, p. A534

MILLS, Kalen, Director Human Resources, Southern Coos Hospital And Health Center, Bandon, OR, p. A573

MILLS, Marianne, R.N., Chairperson, Stanton County Hospital, Johnson, KS, p. A267

MILLS, Scott, M.D., Vice President Medical Staff Administration and Chief Medical Officer, Mid Coast Hospital, Brunswick, ME, p. A319

MILLS, Sean, Chief Financial Officer, Our Lady Of Lourdes Memorial Hospital, Inc., Binghamton, NY, p. A476
  Chief Financial Officer, Samaritan Medical Center, Watertown, NY, p. A502

MILLS, Tylie, R.N., Chief Executive Officer, Pike County Memorial Hospital, Louisiana, MO, p. A411

MILLS, Vicki, Chief Financial Officer, Anderson County Hospital, Garnett, KS, p. A265

MILLS, William, M.D., Senior Vice President Quality and Professional Affairs, Olean General Hospital, Olean, NY, p. A494

MILLS-MATHEWS, Marcy, Director Human Resources, Palms West Hospital, Loxahatchee, FL, p. A144

MILLSAP, Debra, Director of Nursing, River Crest Hospital, San Angelo, TX, p. A710

MILLSAPS, Janet, Chief Human Resources Officer, Harris Regional Hospital, Sylva, NC, p. A519
  Vice President Human Resources, Haywood Regional Medical Center, Clyde, NC, p. A507

MILNE, C, D.O., Medical Director, Pam Specialty Hospital Of Las Vegas, Las Vegas, NV, p. A444

MILNER, Rene, Chief Medical Officer, Osceola Medical Center, Osceola, WI, p. A793

MILONE, Sheri, Chief Executive Officer and Administrator, Lovelace Women's Hospital, Albuquerque, NM, p. A468

MILOVICH, David, Vice President Human Resources, Saint Mary's Regional Medical Center, Reno, NV, p. A446

MILSTEIN, Marc, Vice President Information Resources, University Of Texas Southwestern Medical Center, Dallas, TX, p. A671

MILTON, Kerry, R.N., Chief Nursing Officer, St. Tammany Health System, Covington, LA, p. A300

MILTON, Paul, Executive Vice President and Chief Operating Officer, Ellis Hospital, Schenectady, NY, p. A498

MILTON, Paul A., President and Chief Executive Officer, Ellis Hospital, Schenectady, NY, p. A498

MILTON, S., M.D., Medical Director, Emory Rehabilitation Hospital, Atlanta, GA, p. A164

MILUS, Lori, R.N., MSN, Director of Nursing, Aurora Behavioral Health System West, Glendale, AZ, p. A32

MILVET, Robert W. Jr, Chief Executive Officer, Grant Memorial Hospital, Petersburg, WV, p. A775

MIMS, Staci, Chief Executive Officer, Dorminy Medical Center, Fitzgerald, GA, p. A172
  Chief Nursing Officer, Dorminy Medical Center, Fitzgerald, GA, p. A172

MIMS, Tammy, Chief Executive Officer, Liberty Regional Medical Center, Hinesville, GA, p. A174

MINARD, Keith, Chief Information Officer, Chinese Hospital, San Francisco, CA, p. A93

MINCEY, Wallace, Chief Executive Officer, Clinch Memorial Hospital, Homerville, GA, p. A174

MINEAR, Michael, Senior Vice President and Chief Information Officer, Lehigh Valley Hospital, Allentown, PA, p. A583

MINEAU, Francine, Chief Nursing Officer, Baton Rouge Behavioral Hospital, Baton Rouge, LA, p. A296

MINER, Bill, M.D., Chief of Staff, Huron Regional Medical Center, Huron, SD, p. A629

MINER, Edwina, R.N., Chief Nursing Officer, Ennis Regional Medical Center, Ennis, TX, p. A677

MINER, Greg, Administrator, Dunes Surgical Hospital, Dakota Dunes, SD, p. A627

MINER, John, Chief Financial Officer, Kindred Hospital Central Tampa, Tampa, FL, p. A159

MINGLE, Regina, Senior Vice President and Chief Leadership Officer, Penn Medicine Lancaster General Hospital, Lancaster, PA, p. A594

MINGS, William, M.D., Medical Director, Carl Albert Community Mental Health Center, Mcalester, OK, p. A561

MINIER, Lori, Chief Financial Officer, Benewah Community Hospital, Saint Maries, ID, p. A193

MINIER, Mary, President, Indiana University Health White Memorial Hospital, Monticello, IN, p. A236

MINIOR, Devin, M.D., Chief Medical Officer, Banner Casa Grande Medical Center, Casa Grande, AZ, p. A30

MINISSALE, Joseph, President, Methodist Mckinney Hospital, Mckinney, TX, p. A700

MINKS, Michael, Chief Information Officer VI, Ascension Seton Medical Center Austin, Austin, TX, p. A654
  Chief Information Officer VI, Dell Seton Medical Center At The University Of Texas, Austin, TX, p. A656
  Chief Information Officer, Ascension Seton Edgar B. Davis Hospital, Luling, TX, p. A699

Chief Information Officer, Ascension Seton Northwest, Austin, TX, p. A655
Chief Information Officer, Ascension Seton Shoal Creek, Austin, TX, p. A655

MINNICK, Paul, R.N., MSN, Senior Vice President and Chief Operating Officer, Virtua Voorhees, Voorhees, NJ, p. A465

MINNICK, Peggy, R.N., Chief Executive Officer, Bhc Alhambra Hospital, Rosemead, CA, p. A88

MINNIS, Rosanne, Business Officer, Rochester Psychiatric Center, Rochester, NY, p. A496

MINON, Maria, M.D., Vice President Medical Affairs and Chief Medical Officer, Children's Hospital Of Orange County, Orange, CA, p. A83
  M.D., Vice President Medical Affairs and Chief Medical Officer, Choc Children's At Mission Hospital, Mission Viejo, CA, p. A78

MINOR, Amy, Chief Nursing Officer, Troy Regional Medical Center, Troy, AL, p. A25
  Interim Chief Executive Officer, Troy Regional Medical Center, Troy, AL, p. A25

MINOR, Athena, Chief Nursing Officer, Ohio County Hospital, Hartford, KY, p. A284

MINOR, Beverly, Chief Human Resources, Schleicher County Medical Center, Eldorado, TX, p. A676

MINOR, Blaine, M.D., Chief of Staff, Adventhealth Murray, Chatsworth, GA, p. A168

MINSHEW, Tony, Vice President, Patient Care Services, Conway Medical Center, Conway, SC, p. A618

MINSINGER, Linda, Vice President Hospital Division, Gifford Medical Center, Randolph, VT, p. A736

MINSKY, Bart, Interim Vice President Human Resources, Adventist Health And Rideout, Marysville, CA, p. A77

MINTEER, Laura, Chief Human Resource Officer, Meritus Medical Center, Hagerstown, MD, p. A330

MINTON, Tamra, R.N., MSN, Vice President Patient Care Services and Chief Nursing Officer, Upmc East, Monroeville, PA, p. A597

MINTONYE, Traci, Chief Financial Officer, River Hospital, Alexandria Bay, NY, p. A474

MINTZ, Michael, M.D., Chief Medical Officer, South Texas Surgical Hospital, Corpus Christi, TX, p. A666

MINZEY, Darrick, Vice President Finance, Advocate Condell Medical Center, Libertyville, IL, p. A210

MIRABELLA, Ilene, Director Human Resources, Vibra Hospital Of Southeastern Massachusetts, New Bedford, MA, p. A342

MIRANDA, Ada, M.D., Medical Director, Hospital Metropolitano Dr. Susoni, Arecibo, PR, p. A806

MIRANDA, Casey, Executive Vice President and Chief Operating Officer, Jackson County Memorial Hospital, Altus, OK, p. A555

MIRANDA, Ivette, Chief Executive Officer, Encompass Health Rehabilitation Hospital An Affiliate Of Martin Health, Stuart, FL, p. A158

MIRANDA, Kim, Chief Financial Officer, St. Elizabeth Community Hospital, Red Bluff, CA, p. A87

MIRANDA, Lisa, Vice President Operations, University Medical Center, New Orleans, LA, p. A312

MIRANDA, Michael, Chief of Staff, Mercy Hospital Booneville, Booneville, AR, p. A43

MIRANDA, Vicki, Vice President Human Resources, Dominican Hospital, Santa Cruz, CA, p. A97

MIRANDA, Victor, M.D., Chief of Staff, Mennonite General Hospital, Aibonito, PR, p. A806

MIRANDA JR, SamuelChief Nursing Officer, Good Shepherd Specialty Hospital, Bethlehem, PA, p. A584

MIRE, Troy, Chief Executive Officer and Managing Director, Spring Mountain Treatment Center, Las Vegas, NV, p. A444
  Chief Executive Officer, Spring Mountain Sahara, Las Vegas, NV, p. A444

MIRZA, Irfan, Chief Financial Officer, Plantation General Hospital, Plantation, FL, p. A154

MIRZABEGIAN, Edward, Chief Executive Officer, Antelop. Valley Hospital, Lancaster, CA, p. A71

MISHKIND, Steven, M.D., Chief of Staff, Desoto Memorial Hospital, Arcadia, FL, p. A131

MISKIMEN, Theresa, M.D., Vice President Medical Services, Rutgers University Behavioral Healthcare, Piscataway, NJ, p. A461

MISRA, Sahana, Acting Chief of Staff, Va Portland Healthcare System, Portland, OR, p. A580

MISSERITTI, Colomba, Director Human Resources, Rochester Psychiatric Center, Rochester, NY, p. A496

MISTRETTA, Michael, Vice President and Chief Information Officer, Virginia Hospital Center, Arlington, VA, p. A738

MITCHAM, Debbie, Chief Financial Officer, Northside Hospital, Atlanta, GA, p. A165
  President and Chief Executive Officer, Northside Hospital - Gwinnett, Lawrenceville, GA, p. A175

MITCHELL, Adonna, Director Fiscal Services, North Mississipp. Medical Center-Eupora, Eupora, MS, p. A392

MITCHELL, Andrew J., President and Chief Executive Officer, Peconic Bay Medical Center, Riverhead, NY, p. A496

MITCHELL, Barbara, Director Human Resources, Oasis Behavioral Health - Chandler, Chandler, AZ, p. A31
  Senior Vice President Marketing and Human Resources, Uw Medicine/Valley Medical Center, Renton, WA, p. A763

MITCHELL, Bridgett, Chief Clinical Officer, Advanced Specialty Hospital Of Toledo, Toledo, OH, p. A550

MITCHELL, Camelia, M.D., Medical Director, Texas Rehabilitation Hospital Of Arlington, Arlington, TX, p. A654

MITCHELL, David, Vice President Nursing, Baptist Emergency Hospital, San Antonio, TX, p. A710

MITCHELL, Douglas, Vice President and Chief Nursing Officer, West Virginia University Hospitals, Morgantown, WV, p. A775

MITCHELL, Errol, Chief Financial Officer, Integris Canadian Valley Hospital, Yukon, OK, p. A572

MITCHELL, Heath, Chief Operating Officer, Memorial Hospital, Seminole, TX, p. A714

MITCHELL, Ivan, Chief Operating Officer, Great Plains Health, North Platte, NE, p. A436

MITCHELL, Jenifer, R.N., Director of Nursing Services, Mineral Community Hospital, Superior, MT, p. A428

MITCHELL, Jodie, Facility Financial Director, Monument Health Sturgis Hospital, Sturgis, SD, p. A632

MITCHELL, Joe J., R.N., FACHE, Chief Executive Officer, Acadia General Hospital, Crowley, LA, p. A300

MITCHELL, Karen, Vice President Patient Care Services, Children's Hospital Of The King's Daughters, Norfolk, VA, p. A747

MITCHELL, Kathy, R.N., Chief Nursing Officer, Doctors Hospital Of Sarasota, Sarasota, FL, p. A157
  Chief Nursing Officer, Owensboro Health Muhlenberg Community Hospital, Greenville, KY, p. A284
  Director Human Resources, Marshfield Medical Center - Rice Lake, Rice Lake, WI, p. A795

MITCHELL, Kent, Chief Financial Officer, Hamilton Memorial Hospital District, Mcleansboro, IL, p. A212

MITCHELL, Leah, R.N., Interim Chief Information Officer, Salem Hospital, Salem, OR, p. A581

MITCHELL, Marsha, Director Human Resources, Fleming County Hospital, Flemingsburg, KY, p. A283

MITCHELL, Mary, Chief Resource Management Services, Birmingham Veterans Affairs Medical Center, Birmingham, AL, p. A14

MITCHELL, Morris, Director Human Resources, Poplar Springs Hospital, Petersburg, VA, p. A748

MITCHELL, Naomi, Director Human Resources, Kentucky River Medical Center, Jackson, KY, p. A285

MITCHELL, Perry, M.D., Chief of Staff, Little Colorado Medical Center, Winslow, AZ, p. A41

MITCHELL, Rhonda, Director Human Resources, Stonewall Jackson Memorial Hospital, Weston, WV, p. A777

MITCHELL, Richard, Director Information Technology, Eagleville Hospital, Eagleville, PA, p. A588

MITCHELL, Sarah, Director Finance, Mary S Harper Geriatric Psychiatry Center, Tuscaloosa, AL, p. A25

MITCHELL, Steve, Chief Operating Officer, Memorial Medical Center, Modesto, CA, p. A79

MITCHELL, William, Chief Executive Officer and Administrator, Kindred Hospital Riverside, Perris, CA, p. A85

MITCHELL III, Walton F., Director, Catawba Hospital, Catawba, VA, p. A739

MITCHELL SANCHEZ, Lexi, D.O., Chief of Staff, Clay County Memorial Hospital, Henrietta, TX, p. A684

MITCHUM, Linda, Director of Nursing, William J. Mccord Adolescent Treatment Facility, Orangeburg, SC, p. A623

MITHUN, Robert, M.D., Physician in Chief, Kaiser Permanente San Francisco Medical Center, San Francisco, CA, p. A93

MITRICK, Josep. M., FACHE, President, Baptist Medical Center Beaches, Jacksonville Beach, FL, p. A142

MITRY, Norman F., President and Chief Executive Officer, Heritage Valley Health System, Beaver, PA, p. A584
  President and Chief Executive Officer, Sewickley Valley Hospital, (A Division Of Valley Medical Facilities), Sewickley, PA, p. A608

MITTAL, Vikrant, M.D., Chief Medical Officer, Danville State Hospital, Danville, PA, p. A587

MIXON, Robin, Administrator, North Mississipp. Medical Center-Eupora, Eupora, MS, p. A392

MIYASAWA, Patricia, CPA, Director Fiscal Service, Shriners Hospitals For Children-Honolulu, Honolulu, HI, p. A185

MIZE, David, Director of Information Technology, Marshall Medical Center North, Guntersville, AL, p. A19

MIZE, William, Chief Operating Officer, Trousdale Medical Center, Hartsville, TN, p. A639

MIZELL, Philip. M.D., Medical Director, The Bridgeway, North Little Rock, AR, p. A51

MIZER, Alison, Chief Financial Officer, St. Anthony North Health Campus, Westminster, CO, p. A119

MIZIA, Robert, Director Information Systems and Chief Information Officer, Inspira Medical Center-Woodbury, Woodbury, NJ, p. A466

MLAWSKY, Karen, Senior Vice President and Chief Operations Officer, Tmc Healthcare, Tucson, AZ, p. A41

MMEJE, Ikenna, Chief Operating Officer, Long Beach Medical Center, Long Beach, CA, p. A72

MOAD, Sharon, Human Resources Director Health Information Management, Elkview General Hospital, Hobart, OK, p. A560

MOAK, Jennifer, Business Office Manager, Lawrence County Hospital, Monticello, MS, p. A397

MOATS, Susan, R.N., Chief Nursing Officer, Baylor Scott & White The Heart Hospital Denton, Denton, TX, p. A671
R.N., Vice President Patient Care Services and Chief Nursing Officer, Baylor Scott & White The Heart Hospital Plano, Plano, TX, p. A706

MOCK, Jesse, Chief Executive Officer, University Of Kansas Health System Great Bend Campus, Great Bend, KS, p. A265

MOCK, Presley, M.D., Chief of Staff, Texas Institute For Surgery At Texas Health Presbyterian Dallas, Dallas, TX, p. A670

MOCKUS, Tom, Director Information Services, Mount Desert Island Hospital, Bar Harbor, ME, p. A318

MOE, Jonathan, Chief Operating Officer, Shenandoah Medical Center, Shenandoah, IA, p. A257
President, Chi Health Missouri Valley, Missouri Valley, IA, p. A254

MOEEN, Farida, M.D., Chief Executive Officer, United Memorial Medical Center, Houston, TX, p. A689

MOELLER, Deborah, R.N., MS, Interim Chief Nursing Officer, Baylor Scott & White Medical Center - Sunnyvale, Sunnyvale, TX, p. A718

MOEN, Belinda, R.N., MSN, Interim Director of Nursing, Mountrail County Medical Center, Stanley, ND, p. A526

MOEN, Daniel P., President, St. Francis Medical Center, Trenton, NJ, p. A464

MOEN, Larry, Chief Financial Officer, Coteau Des Prairies Hospital, Sisseton, SD, p. A632

MOFFA, Salvatore, M.D., Vice President, Medical Affairs and Chief Medical Officer, Robert Wood Johnson University Hospital Somerset, Somerville, NJ, p. A463

MOFFAT, Jeanne, Manager Information Technology, Keefe Memorial Hospital, Cheyenne Wells, CO, p. A109

MOFFAT, Jennifer, Staff Accountant, Regional West Garden County, Oshkosh, NE, p. A438

MOFFATT, Dan, Chief Information Officer, Sanford Bemidji Medical Center, Bemidji, MN, p. A372

MOFFET, Chris, Director Information Services, Bob Wilson Memorial Grant County Hospital, Ulysses, KS, p. A278

MOFFITT, Brenda, Chief Nursing Officer, Memorial Health System, Abilene, KS, p. A261

MOGERMAN, Shauna, Chief Executive Officer, Roxbury Treatment Center, Shippensburg, PA, p. A608

MOGG, Cassie, Chief Financial Officer, Covenant Hospital Plainview, Plainview, TX, p. A706

MOHAMED, Antonia, Acting Chief Information Officer, Birmingham Veterans Affairs Medical Center, Birmingham, AL, p. A14

MOHAMMED, Ehtaisham, M.D., Chief Medical Officer, Ridgeview Sibley Medical Center, Arlington, MN, p. A372

MOHAN, Amit, President and Chief Executive Officer, Barlow Respiratory Hospital, Los Angeles, CA, p. A73

MOHAN, Rajesh, M.D., Chief Medical Officer, Monmouth Medical Center, Southern Campus, Lakewood, NJ, p. A457

MOHANDAS, Arjun, M.D., Chief of Staff, Ascension Seton Edgar B. Davis Hospital, Luling, TX, p. A699

MOHLER, Brittany, Director Human Resources, Essentia Health-Deer River, Deer River, MN, p. A375

MOHNK, Richard, Vice President Corporate Services, Bayhealth Medical Center, Dover, DE, p. A127

MOHNKERN, Pearl, Vice President and Director Human Resources, Christus St. Vincent Regional Medical Center, Santa Fe, NM, p. A472

MOHR, Amanda, Chief Nursing Officer, Greater Regional Medical Center, Creston, IA, p. A247

MOHR, Amy, Coordinator Human Resources, Forest Health Medical Center, Ypsilanti, MI, p. A370

MOHR, Angela, R.N., MS, President, Ssm Health St. Anthony Hospital - Shawnee, Shawnee, OK, p. A568

MOHR, Catherine, R.N., MSN, Chief Nursing Officer, Guthrie Robert Packer Hospital, Sayre, PA, p. A606

MOHR, Liz, Assistant Chief Financial Officer, Mercy Health - Fairfield Hospital, Fairfield, OH, p. A540

MOHR, Steven, Senior Vice President and Chief Financial Officer, Huntington Hospital, Pasadena, CA, p. A85

MOISAN, Terrence, M.D., Chief Executive Officer, Palos Health, Palos Heights, IL, p. A216

MOK, Michelle, Chief Financial Officer, Redlands Community Hospital, Redlands, CA, p. A87

MOKDESSI, Margot, Interim Chief Financial Officer, Vermilion Behavioral Health Systems - North Campus, Lafayette, LA, p. A306

MOKRY, Deborah, Chief Nurse Executive, St. Louis Psychiatric Rehabilitation Center, Saint Louis, MO, p. A417

MOL, Stacy, CPA, Director Finance, Spencer Hospital, Spencer, IA, p. A258

MOLACEK, Shane, Chief Information Officer, Valley County Health System, Ord, NE, p. A438

MOLELUS, Elena, Manager Human Resources, Santa Barbara County Psychiatric Health Facility, Santa Barbara, CA, p. A97

MOLINA, Isabel, M.D., Chief Medical Officer, Lamb Healthcare Center, Littlefield, TX, p. A696

MOLINA, Luis F., Chief Executive Officer and Administrator, Community Hospital, Munster, IN, p. A237

MOLINARO, Frank L., Chief Executive Officer, Carondelet St. Joseph's Hospital, Tucson, AZ, p. A40
Chief Executive Officer, Carondelet St. Mary's Hospital, Tucson, AZ, p. A40

MOLITOR, Margie, FACHE, R.N., Chief Executive Officer, Hot Springs County Memorial Hospital, Thermopolis, WY, p. A804

MOLL, Ben, Assistant Chief Financial Officer, Nashoba Valley Medical Center, Ayer, MA, p. A334

MOLL, Eric, Chief Executive Officer, Mason General Hospital And Family Of Clinics, Shelton, WA, p. A765

MOLL, Gudrun, R.N., MSN, Chief Nursing Officer, San Antonio Regional Hospital, Upland, CA, p. A102

MOLL, Jeffrey, M.D., Medical Director, Clarion Psychiatric Center, Clarion, PA, p. A586

MOLL, Michael, M.D., Chief Medical Officer and Chief of Staff, Spanish Peaks Regional Health Center, Walsenburg, CO, p. A119

MOLLER, Dan, M.D., Chief Medical Officer, Willis-Knighton Medical Center, Shreveport, LA, p. A315

MOLLER, Lynn, Chief Financial Officer, Weston County Health Services, Newcastle, WY, p. A803

MOLLOHAN, Joan, Vice President Human Resources, Ochsner Medical Center, New Orleans, LA, p. A311

MOLLOY, Kevin, Senior Vice President and Chief Operating Officer, Mount Sinai Beth Israel, New York, NY, p. A490
Senior Vice President and Chief Operating Officer, Mount Sinai Morningside, New York, NY, p. A490

MOLLOY, Reuben, Chief Information Officer, Governor Juan F. Luis Hospital, Christiansted, VI, p. A812

MOLMEN, David R., Interim Chief Executive Officer, Altru Health System, Grand Forks, ND, p. A523

MOLNAR, Becky, Director of Finance, Cleveland Clinic, Medina Hospital, Medina, OH, p. A545

MOLT, Brianna, Human Resources Director, Genoa Medical Facilities, Genoa, NE, p. A432

MOLYNEUX, Phyllis, Associate Administrator Human Resources and Education, Williamson Medical Center, Franklin, TN, p. A638

MOMEYER, Polly, Manager Human Resources, Lecom Health Millcreek Community Hospital, Erie, PA, p. A590

MOMTAZBAKHSH, Sassan, M.D., Medical Director, Chg Hospital Tucson, Llc, Tucson, AZ, p. A40

MONAGHAN, Aimee, Administrator, Compass Behavioral Center Of Lafayette, Lafayette, LA, p. A305

MONAHAN, Jane, Vice President Ministry, Spiritual Care and Human Resources, Monroe Clinic, Monroe, WI, p. A792

MONASTERIO, Eugene, M.D., Medical Director, Children's Hospital Of Richmond At Vcu-Brook Road Campus, Richmond, VA, p. A750

MONCHER, Daniel, Vice President and Chief Financial Officer, Firelands Regional Health System, Sandusky, OH, p. A549

MONCHER, Daniel J., Interim President and Chief Executive Officer, Firelands Regional Health System, Sandusky, OH, p. A549

MONCRIEF, William, ORH IT Client Executive, Surgeons Choice Medical Center, Southfield, MI, p. A367

MONCZEWSKI, Ted, Vice President Human Resources, St. Vincent Charity Medical Center, Cleveland, OH, p. A535

MONDA, Cam, D.O., Medical Director, Greenwood Regional Rehabilitation Hospital, Greenwood, SC, p. A621

MONETTE, Steven, Chief Financial Officer, Brattleboro Retreat, Brattleboro, VT, p. A735

MONFILS, Michael, M.D., Chief of Medical Staff, Rochelle Community Hospital, Rochelle, IL, p. A218

MONGE, Candice, R.N., Chief Nurse Executive Officer, Marian Regional Medical Center, Santa Maria, CA, p. A97

MONGE, Jacqualyn, Director of Nursing, Ascension Eagle River Hospital, Eagle River, WI, p. A782

Director of Nursing, Howard Young Medical Center, Woodruff, WI, p. A800

MONGELL, Mitchell P., FACHE, Chief Executive Officer, Fort Walton Beach Medical Center, Fort Walton Beach, FL, p. A138

MONGER, Shelton, Director Information Technology, Wayne Healthcare, Greenville, OH, p. A541

MONIACI, Cathy, Administrator, Shriners Hospitals For Children-Houston, Houston, TX, p. A688

MONICAL, Robert, Chief Executive Officer, Lourdes Counseling Center, Richland, WA, p. A763

MONJE, Mary, Chief Financial Officer and Chief Operating Officer, Whittier Hospital Medical Center, Whittier, CA, p. A105
Chief Financial Officer, Ahmc Anaheim Regional Medical Center, Anaheim, CA, p. A55
Chief Operations Officer, Ahmc Anaheim Regional Medical Center, Anaheim, CA, p. A55

MONKRES, Paula, Administrative Assistant and Director Human Resources, Nocona General Hospital, Nocona, TX, p. A703

MONROE, Ame, Director Human Resources, Rolling Plains Memorial Hospital, Sweetwater, TX, p. A718

MONROE, Janet J., R.N., Executive Director, Rockland Psychiatric Center, Orangeburg, NY, p. A494

MONROE, Lori, Director of Nursing, Winnebago Mental Health Institute, Winnebago, WI, p. A800

MONROE, Temple, Director Nursing Operations, Wilson Medical Center, Neodesha, KS, p. A271

MONROIG, Domingo, Executive Director, Castaner General Hospital, Castaner, PR, p. A807

MONROY-MILLER, Cherry, M.D., Acting Medical Director, Greystone Park Psychiatric Hospital, Morris Plains, NJ, p. A458

MONSANTO, Monte, Chief Information Systems, Russell County Hospital, Russell Springs, KY, p. A292

MONSMA, Brian Kent., President, Washington County Hospital, Nashville, IL, p. A214

MONSOUR, Joe, Chief Information Officer, Allegiance Behavioral Health Center Of Plainview, Plainview, TX, p. A706

MONSRUD, Michele, Director Human Resources, Piedmont Walton Hospital, Monroe, GA, p. A177

MONTAGNESE, Robert A., President and Chief Executive Officer, Licking Memorial Hospital, Newark, OH, p. A546

MONTAGUE, Trisha, MSN, R.N., Senior Vice President and Chief Administrator, Arkansas Children's Northwest, Springdale, AR, p. A53

MONTALVO, Eladio, Chief Executive Officer, Fort Duncan Regional Medical Center, Eagle Pass, TX, p. A673

MONTALVO, Jose, M.D., Medical Director, Hospital Del Maestro, San Juan, PR, p. A810

MONTANA, Jennifer, Manager Human Resources, Community Memorial Hospital, Hamilton, NY, p. A485

MONTANA-RHODES, Lou, Vice President of Patient Care Services, Vidant Beaufort Hospital, Washington, NC, p. A519

MONTANO, Maxine, R.N., Chief Nursing Officer, Rolling Plains Memorial Hospital, Sweetwater, TX, p. A718

MONTANO, Mayra, Director Information Systems, Hospital Metropolitano Dr. Susoni, Arecibo, PR, p. A806

MONTANTE, Carl, Director Information Systems and Information Technology, Shriners Hospitals For Children-Portland, Portland, OR, p. A580

MONTANYE, Richard, Director Information Systems, Hunt Regional Medical Center, Greenville, TX, p. A682

MONTANYE-IRELAND, Cherelle, Chief Administrative Officer, Peacehealth St. John Medical Center, Longview, WA, p. A760

MONTENEGRO, Diana, Director Human Resources, Baptist Health South Florida, South Miami Hospital, Miami, FL, p. A146

MONTER, Brian, MSN, R.N., President, University Hospitals Parma Medical Center, Parma, OH, p. A547

MONTESINO-KING, Becky, MS, R.N., MSN, Vice President and Chief Nursing Officer, Baptist Health South Florida, Baptist Hospital Of Miami, Miami, FL, p. A146

MONTGOMERY, James, Chief Nursing Officer, Bear River Valley Hospital, Tremonton, UT, p. A734

MONTGOMERY, Jennifer, FACHE, R.N., President and Chief Executive Officer, Mclaren Port Huron, Port Huron, MI, p. A364
Chief Financial Officer, Washakie Medical Center, Worland, WY, p. A804
President and Chief Executive Officer, St. Luke's Hospital, Maumee, OH, p. A545

MONTGOMERY, Mark, M.D., Chief Medical Officer, Texas Health Harris Methodist Hospital Southwest Fort Worth, Fort Worth, TX, p. A679

MONTGOMERY, Mary Jim, R.N., MSN, FACHE, Chief Operating Officer, Crisp Regional Hospital, Cordele, GA, p. A170

MONTGOMERY, Peggy, Director Medical Records, Arrowhead Behavioral Health Hospital, Maumee, OH, p. A544

MONTGOMERY, Roxie, Director of Nursing, Jane Todd Crawford Hospital, Greensburg, KY, p. A284

MONTGOMERY, Scott, Administrator, Mcleod Health Loris, Loris, SC, p. A622

MONTGOMERY, Sheri, Acting Chief Executive Officer, Good Samaritan Medical Center, West Palm Beach, FL, p. A162

MONTGOMERY, Susan, Chief Nursing Officer, Asante Ashland Community Hospital, Ashland, OR, p. A573

MONTGOMERY, Tina, Chief Financial Officer, Sidney Health Center, Sidney, MT, p. A428

MONTGOMERY-WEST, Megan, Chief Executive Officer, Alvarado Parkway Institute Behavioral Health System, La Mesa, CA, p. A70

MONTMENY, Richard, Vice President Professional Services, On-Site Administrator, St. John's Pleasant Valley Hospital, Camarillo, CA, p. A59

MONTOUR, Vina, Director Information Technology, U. S. Public Health Service Phoenix Indian Medical Center, Phoenix, AZ, p. A37

MONTOYA, Alfred, Director, Manchester Veterans Affairs Medical Center, Manchester, NH, p. A450
Director, Veterans Affairs Connecticut Healthcare System, West Haven, CT, p. A126

MONTOYA, Brooke, Director Human Resources, Lake Granbury Medical Center, Granbury, TX, p. A682

MONTOYA, Lillian, President and Chief Executive Officer, Christus St. Vincent Regional Medical Center, Santa Fe, NM, p. A472

MONTOYA, Lionel, Chief Financial Officer, Steele Memorial Medical Center, Salmon, ID, p. A193

MONZINGO, Ashley, Human Resources, Accounts Payable and Payroll, Top. Surgical Specialty Hospital, Houston, TX, p. A689

MOODY, Christy, R.N., Chief Nursing Officer, Carolina Pines Regional Medical Center, Hartsville, SC, p. A621

MOODY, Crystal, Director Human Resources, Izard County Medical Center, Calico Rock, AR, p. A43

MOODY, David, Vice President Human Resources, Salina Regional Health Center, Salina, KS, p. A275

MOODY, James, Chief Financial Officer, Donalsonville Hospital, Donalsonville, GA, p. A171

MOON, Diane, Chief Financial Officer, Adventist Health And Rideout, Marysville, CA, p. A77

MOON, James, Chief Financial Officer, Pana Community Hospital, Pana, IL, p. A216

MOON, John, Associate Director, Veterans Affairs Eastern Kansas Health Care System, Topeka, KS, p. A277

MOON JR, DavidDirector Information Systems, Lake City Community Hospital, Lake City, SC, p. A622

MOONEY, Claire, R.N., Vice President and Chief Nursing Officer, Jennersville Hospital, West Grove, PA, p. A610

MOONEY, Claire Bradley., R.N., President and Chief Executive Officer, Jennersville Hospital, West Grove, PA, p. A610

MOONEY, Gabriel, Chief Executive Officer, Kittson Memorial Healthcare Center, Hallock, MN, p. A377

MOONEY, Melissa, Director Human Resources, Mercy Rehabilitation Hospital Springfield, Springfield, MO, p. A419

MOONEY, Robert, M.D., Medical Director, Willingway Hospital, Statesboro, GA, p. A181

MOONEY, Susan E., M.D., MS, President and Chief Executive Officer, Alice Peck Day Memorial Hospital, Lebanon, NH, p. A449

MOORE, Amy, Human Resources, Hamilton Hospital, Olney, TX, p. A704

MOORE, Betty, Business Manager, North Mississipp. Medical Center-Iuka, Iuka, MS, p. A394

MOORE, Bill, Chief Human Resources, El Centro Regional Medical Center, El Centro, CA, p. A63

MOORE, Bob, FACHE, Chief Executive Officer, Gateway Regional Medical Center, Granite City, IL, p. A206

MOORE, Brandon, FACHE, Chief Executive Officer, Park Place Surgical Hospital, Lafayette, LA, p. A306

MOORE, Brett, CPA, Assistant Administrator Finance, Sutter Amador Hospital, Jackson, CA, p. A69

MOORE, Brian, President and Chief Executive Officer, Bay Area Hospital, Coos Bay, OR, p. A574

MOORE, Carrie, Director Human Resources, Meadowbrook Rehabilitation Hospital, Gardner, KS, p. A265

MOORE, Cecelia, CPA, Associate Vice Chancellor Finance, Vanderbilt University Medical Center, Nashville, TN, p. A647

MOORE, Christie, Director Human Resources, Encompass Health Rehabilitation Hospital Of The Mid-Cities, Bedford, TX, p. A658

MOORE, Dana, Chief Information Officer, Children's Hospital Colorado, Aurora, CO, p. A107

MOORE, Deborah, Director Human Resources, Walter P. Reuther Psychiatric Hospital, Westland, MI, p. A369

MOORE, Diane, Chief Financial Officer, Memorial Medical Center, Port Lavaca, TX, p. A707

MOORE, Donna, PsyD, Director, Eastern State Hospital, Williamsburg, VA, p. A753

MOORE, Edward H., President and Chief Executive Officer, Harrington Hospital, Southbridge, MA, p. A344

MOORE, Elizabeth, Chief Operating Officer, Silver Hill Hospital, New Canaan, CT, p. A124

MOORE, Emily, Director Human Resources and Information Technology, Haskell Memorial Hospital, Haskell, TX, p. A683

MOORE, Ethel, M.D., Director of Medical Affairs, Fort Belknap Service Unit, Harlem, MT, p. A424

MOORE, Harold, Chief Information Technology Officer, Spartanburg Medical Center - Church Street Campus, Spartanburg, SC, p. A624

MOORE, Jason, Vice President and Chief Operating Officer, Tallahassee Memorial Healthcare, Tallahassee, FL, p. A158

MOORE, Jeffrey, Chief Financial Officer, Fort Walton Beach Medical Center, Fort Walton Beach, FL, p. A138

MOORE, Jody, District Director Human Resources, Kindred Hospital-San Diego, San Diego, CA, p. A91

MOORE, John, FACHE, President, South Lake Hospital, Clermont, FL, p. A134
M.D., Medical Director, Granite County Medical Center, Philipsburg, MT, p. A426
Interim Chief Financial Officer, Huntsville Memorial Hospital, Huntsville, TX, p. A690
Vice President and Chief Financial Officer, Atrium Health Union, Monroe, NC, p. A514

MOORE, Kandi, R.N., Administrator, Specialists Hospital Shreveport, Shreveport, LA, p. A314

MOORE, Karen, FACHE, Senior Vice President Operations and Chief Nursing Officer, Lawrence General Hospital, Lawrence, MA, p. A340
Vice President Information Technology and Chief Information Officer, Southern Regional Medical Center, Riverdale, GA, p. A178

MOORE, Keri, Vice President Human Resources and Support Services, Presbyterian/St. Luke's Medical Center, Denver, CO, p. A111

MOORE, Kermit, R.N., Chief Operating Officer and Chief Nursing Officer, Nemaha County Hospital, Auburn, NE, p. A429

MOORE, Kyna, R.N., Chief Nursing Officer, Pocahontas Memorial Hospital, Buckeye, WV, p. A770
R.N., Director of Nursing, Bath Community Hospital, Hot Springs, VA, p. A744

MOORE, Leigh, Administrative Assistant Human Resources, H. C. Watkins Memorial Hospital, Quitman, MS, p. A399

MOORE, Linda, Manager Human Resources, Seymour Hospital, Seymour, TX, p. A715

MOORE, Margaret, Director Business Office, Sabine County Hospital, Hemphill, TX, p. A683

MOORE, Mary-Katherine, Chief Operating Officer, Prairieville Family Hospital, Prairieville, LA, p. A313

MOORE, Matthew, Director of Financial Reporting, Effingham Hospital, Springfield, GA, p. A180

MOORE, Melinda, Director Human Resources, Multicare Deaconess Hospital, Spokane, WA, p. A765

MOORE, Michael, Director Information Systems, Troy Regional Medical Center, Troy, AL, p. A25

MOORE, Mike, President and Chief Operating Officer, Ascension St. John Jane Phillips, Bartlesville, OK, p. A556

MOORE, Nelda, Director Data Processing, Memorial Hospital And Manor, Bainbridge, GA, p. A166

MOORE, Patricia, Director Human Resources, Valley Behavioral Health System, Barling, AR, p. A42

MOORE, Paul, R.N., Chief Clinical Officer, Mercy Rehabilitation Hospital Springfield, Springfield, MO, p. A419
Chief Information Officer, Connecticut Mental Health Center, New Haven, CT, p. A124

MOORE, Paula, R.N., Chief Clinical Officer, Hugh Chatham Memorial Hospital, Elkin, NC, p. A509

MOORE, Randy, Chief Information Officer, Banner Lassen Medical Center, Susanville, CA, p. A100

MOORE, Rick, Chief Information Officer, Bethesda North Hospital, Cincinnati, OH, p. A532
Chief Information Officer, Good Samaritan Hospital, Cincinnati, OH, p. A532

MOORE, Robin, Chief Human Resources Officer, Concord Hospital, Concord, NH, p. A448

MOORE, Ronald, R.N., MSN, Vice President Professional Practice and Chief Nursing Officer, Charleston Area Medical Center, Charleston, WV, p. A771

MOORE, Samuel, Chief Financial Officer, University Of Kansas Health System St. Francis Campus, Topeka, KS, p. A277

MOORE, Sandee, Chief Operating Officer, Eastern Idaho Regional Medical Center, Idaho Falls, ID, p. A190

MOORE, Saunya, Chief Financial Officer, Parkside Psychiatric Hospital And Clinic, Tulsa, OK, p. A570

MOORE, Shari, Chief Executive Officer, Methodist Rehabilitation Hospital, Dallas, TX, p. A669

MOORE, Steve, Chief Financial Officer, Southern Tennessee Regional Health System-Winchester, Winchester, TN, p. A650

MOORE, Susan, MS, R.N., Chief Nursing Officer, Gothenburg Health, Gothenburg, NE, p. A432

MOORE, Sylvia, Vice President and Chief Operating Officer, Southeast Hospital, Cap. Girardeau, MO, p. A404

MOORE, Tim, Chief Accounting Officer and Vice President Ancillary Services and Finance, Blessing Hospital, Quincy, IL, p. A218
Vice President Finance, Illini Community Hospital, Pittsfield, IL, p. A217

MOORE, Vernon, Senior Vice President Chief Business and Finance, Ut Health North Campus Tyler, Tyler, TX, p. A722

MOORE, VonDa, Administrator, Mercy Hospital Berryville, Berryville, AR, p. A42

MOORE, Warren E., FACHE, President and Chief Executive Officer, Children's Specialized Hospital, New Brunswick, NJ, p. A459

MOORE, Wayne, Interim Administrator, Christus Southeast Texas Jasper Memorial, Jasper, TX, p. A691

MOORE, William, Chief Information Officer, Parrish Medical Center, Titusville, FL, p. A160

MOORE-CONNELLY, Marci, M.D., Vice President Chief Medical Officer, Memorial Hospital Of Carbondale, Carbondale, IL, p. A196

MOORE-HARDY, Cynthia, FACHE, President and Chief Executive Officer, Lake Health, Concord Township. OH, p. A537

MOORE-JONES, Debra, Chief Executive Officer, Parkside Psychiatric Hospital And Clinic, Tulsa, OK, p. A570

MOOREHOUSE, Brett, FACHE, Chief Executive Officer, Ranken Jordan Pediatric Bridge Hospital, Maryland Heights, MO, p. A411

MOORER, Thad, Chief Information Officer, Eastside Psychiatric Hospital, Tallahassee, FL, p. A158

MOORHEAD, David, M.D., Chief Medical Officer, Adventhealth Orlando, Orlando, FL, p. A151

MOORHEAD, Emily, Chief Operating Officer, Dmc - Sinai-Grace Hospital, Detroit, MI, p. A352

MOORMAN, Gary, D.O., Chief Medical Officer, Fisher-Titus Medical Center, Norwalk, OH, p. A546

MOQUIN, Heather, Chief Executive Officer, New Hampshire Hospital, Concord, NH, p. A448

MORA, Debbie, Director, Southwest General Hospital, San Antonio, TX, p. A713

MORACA, Lynn, Director Human Resources, Cleveland Clinic Akron General Lodi Hospital, Lodi, OH, p. A543

MORAHAN, John, Vice President Finance, St. Josep. Hospital, Bethpage, NY, p. A475

MORALES, Armando, Chief Executive Officer, Pam Specialty Hospital Of San Antonio Center, San Antonio, TX, p. A712

MORALES, Autumn, Chief Medical Staff Officer, Clarinda Regional Health Center, Clarinda, IA, p. A246

MORALES, Daniza, Chief Information Officer, Hospital Menonita De Cayey, Cayey, PR, p. A807
Manager Information System, Mennonite General Hospital, Aibonito, PR, p. A806

MORALES, Elsie, Chief Financial Officer, Hospital Universitario Dr. Ramon Ruiz Arnau, Bayamon, PR, p. A806

MORALES, Joel, Chief Financial Officer, Fort Duncan Regional Medical Center, Eagle Pass, TX, p. A673

MORALES, John, Chief Financial Officer, John H. Stroger Jr. Hospital Of Cook County, Chicago, IL, p. A199

MORALES, Kathryn, Director of Finance, Valley Health - Hampshire Memorial Hospital, Romney, WV, p. A776
Director of Finance, Valley Health - War Memorial Hospital, Berkeley Springs, WV, p. A770

MORALES, Kristin, Chief Operating Officer, Harrington Hospital, Southbridge, MA, p. A344

MORALES, Marilyn, Chief Executive Officer, Hospital Buen Samaritano, Aguadilla, PR, p. A805

MORALES, Trish, Director Human Resources, Lakewood Ranch Medical Center, Bradenton, FL, p. A133

MORAN, Alina, President, California Hospital Medical Center, Los Angeles, CA, p. A73

MORAN, Barbara, R.N., Chief Nursing Officer, St. Vincent Charity Medical Center, Cleveland, OH, p. A535

MORAN, Debbie, Executive Director, Carl Albert Community Mental Health Center, Mcalester, OK, p. A561
Executive Director, Jim Taliaferro Community Mental Health, Lawton, OK, p. A561

MORAN, Mary, M.D., Pediatrician in Chief, St. Christopher's Hospital For Children, Philadelphia, PA, p. A602

MORAN, Michael Francis., President and Chief Administrative Officer, Baystate Wing Hospital, Palmer, MA, p. A343

MORAN, Tim, Chief Executive Officer, Chino Valley Medical Center, Chino, CA, p. A60

MORAN, Timothy M., Chief Executive Officer, Glenn Medical Center, Willows, CA, p. A105

MORAN, Vicki, Interim President, Alamance Regional Medical Center, Burlington, NC, p. A506

MORANDEIRA, Ana, Director Marketing, San Juan Capestrano Hospital, San Juan, PR, p. A811

MORASKO, Jerome, Chief Executive Officer, Bucyrus Hospital, Bucyrus, OH, p. A530
President and Chief Executive Officer, Avita Ontario Hospital, Ontario, OH, p. A547
President and Chief Executive Officer, Galion Hospital, Galion, OH, p. A541

MORASKO, Robert A., Chief Executive Officer, Heart Of The Rockies Regional Medical Center, Salida, CO, p. A118

MORAVICK, Donna, R.N., MSN, Executive Director, Southside Hospital, Bay Shore, NY, p. A475

MORDACH, John, Senior Vice President and Chief Financial Officer, Rush University Medical Center, Chicago, IL, p. A200

MORDECAI, Steve, Director Human Resources, Griffin Hospital, Derby, CT, p. A122

MOREFIELD, Terri, Deputy Chief Human Resources Division, Bassett Army Community Hospital, Fort Wainwright, AK, p. A28

MOREH, Swenda, Interim Chief Executive Officer, Bridgepoint Hospital National Harbor, Washington, DC, p. A129
Vice President and Chief Operating Officer, Bridgepoint Hospital National Harbor, Washington, DC, p. A129

MOREHOUSE, Keith, Chief Executive Officer, Perimeter Behavioral Hospital Of Arlington, Arlington, TX, p. A653

MOREIN, Sandy, Chief Nursing Officer, Iberia Medical Center, New Iberia, LA, p. A310

MORELAND, Janet, Hospital Administrator, Lakeside Medical Center, Belle Glade, FL, p. A132

MORELAND, John, M.D., Chief Medical Officer, Marcus Daly Memorial Hospital, Hamilton, MT, p. A424

MORELL, Ixel, Chief Operating Officer, Sierra Vista Hospital, Sacramento, CA, p. A90

MORELLI, Gerald, Director Human Resources, Philadelphia Veterans Affairs Medical Center, Philadelphia, PA, p. A601

MORENO, Debbie, R.N., Patient Care Executive, Adventist Health Lodi Memorial, Lodi, CA, p. A71

MORENO, Jorge, Director Information Technology Operations, Canyon Vista Medical Center, Sierra Vista, AZ, p. A38

MORENO, Robin, Chief Financial Officer, North Texas State Hospital, Wichita Falls Campus, Wichita Falls, TX, p. A725
Financial Officer, North Texas State Hospital, Vernon, TX, p. A723

MORENO, Sandra, Chief Nursing Officer, Orange County Global Medical Center, Inc., Santa Ana, CA, p. A96

MORETTE, Joseph, Executive Vice President, Methodist Rehabilitation Center, Jackson, MS, p. A394

MOREY, Scott, Chief Nursing Officer, Abrazo West Campus, Goodyear, AZ, p. A32

MORGAN, Charlene, Chief Nursing Officer, Henderson County Community Hospital, Lexington, TN, p. A642

MORGAN, David, Vice President and Chief Financial Officer, Bristol Bay Area Health Corporation, Dillingham, AK, p. A28

MORGAN, Dennis, Chief of Staff, Baptist Memorial Hospital-North Mississippi, Oxford, MS, p. A398

MORGAN, Derek, Vice President Human Resources, Kettering Medical Center, Kettering, OH, p. A542
Vice President Human Resources, Sycamore Medical Center, Miamisburg, OH, p. A545

MORGAN, Eric, Chief Executive Officer, Prattville Baptist Hospital, Prattville, AL, p. A24

MORGAN, James, M.D., Chief Medical Officer, Memorial Hospital Of Converse County, Douglas, WY, p. A802

MORGAN, Janelle, Interim Director of Nursing, Howard County Medical Center, Saint Paul, NE, p. A439

MORGAN, Jeff, Director Information Systems, Northeastern Nevada Regional Hospital, Elko, NV, p. A441

MORGAN, Jeffrey, Vice President Finance and Chief Financial Officer, Brooks Memorial Hospital, Dunkirk, NY, p. A482

MORGAN, John, R.N., Chief Executive Officer, Jackson Parish Hospital, Jonesboro, LA, p. A304

MORGAN, Julie, Director of Nursing, St. Helena Parish Hospital, Greensburg, LA, p. A302

MORGAN, Kelly C., President and Chief Executive Officer, Mercy Medical Center, Roseburg, OR, p. A580

MORGAN, Lois, R.N., MSN, Vice President and Chief Nursing Officer, Gibson General Hospital, Princeton, IN, p. A239

MORGAN, Loretta, Director Human Resources, Connally Memorial Medical Center, Floresville, TX, p. A677

MORGAN, Lori J., M.D., President and Chief Executive Officer, Huntington Hospital, Pasadena, CA, p. A85

MORGAN, Mace, Director Information Systems, Minden Medical Center, Minden, LA, p. A309

MORGAN, MacGregor, R.N., Chief Executive Officer, Curahealth Stoughton, Stoughton, MA, p. A345

MORGAN, Marguerite J., Administrator, Florida State Hospital, Chattahoochee, FL, p. A134

MORGAN, Mark E., Medical Center Director, Jack C. Montgomery Veterans Affairs Medical Center, Muskogee, OK, p. A562

MORGAN, Matthew, Associate Administrator, Hillcrest Hospital - South, Tulsa, OK, p. A569

MORGAN, Nyle, Chief Information Officer, Sheridan Memorial Hospital, Sheridan, WY, p. A804

MORGAN, Rose, MS, R.N., Vice President Patient Care Services, Princeton Community Hospital, Princeton, WV, p. A776

MORGAN, Shawn, Finance Officer, Northern Navajo Medical Center, Shiprock, NM, p. A472

MORGAN, Susan, Director of Nursing Services, Prairie Community Hospital, Terry, MT, p. A428

MORGAN, Teresa, Assistant Vice President Human Resources, Shannon Medical Center, San Angelo, TX, p. A710
Chief Financial Officer, Mcgehee Hospital, Mcgehee, AR, p. A50

MORGAN-FINE, Richard, IT Director, Clarinda Regional Health Center, Clarinda, IA, p. A246

MORGESE, Vincent, M.D., Executive Vice President, Chief Operating Officer and Chief Medical Officer, Queen Of The Valley Medical Center, Napa, CA, p. A80

MORIN, Gretchen, Chief Administrative Officer, Bon Secours St. Francis Hospital, Charleston, SC, p. A616

MORIN, Richard, R.N., Interim Chief Executive Officer, Christus Spohn Hospital Alice, Alice, TX, p. A651
R.N., Interim Chief Executive Officer, Christus Spohn Hospital Kleberg, Kingsville, TX, p. A693

MORIN, Robert, Chief Financial Officer and Chief Operating Officer, Sturgis Hospital, Sturgis, MI, p. A367

MORIN, Robert J., Chief Financial Officer and Chief Operating Officer, Sturgis Hospital, Sturgis, MI, p. A367

MORIN-SCRIBNER, Nicole, Director Human Resources, St. Mary's Regional Medical Center, Lewiston, ME, p. A321

MORISCO, Antonietta, M.D., Medical Director, Chairman Anesthesiology, Jamaica Hospital Medical Center, Jamaica, NY, p. A486

MORITZ, Kathy, Chief Nursing Officer, Winneshiek Medical Center, Decorah, IA, p. A248

MORITZ, Mary, Administrator Human Resources, Humboldt County Memorial Hospital, Humboldt, IA, p. A251

MORK, David L. Jr, Chief Executive Officer, Roosevelt Warm Springs Rehabilitation And Specialty Hospitals - Ltac, Warm Springs, GA, p. A182
Jr, Chief Executive Officer, Roosevelt Warm Springs Rehabilitation Hospital - Rehab, Warm Springs, GA, p. A183

MORKRID, Shirley, Chief Nursing Officer, Liberty Medical Center, Chester, MT, p. A422

MORLOCK, Paul, FACHE, Vice President Human Resources and Occupational Health, Children's Hospital Of The King's Daughters, Norfolk, VA, p. A747

MORON, David, M.D., Clinical Director, Rio Grande State Center/South Texas Health Care System, Harlingen, TX, p. A683

MORONY, David, Chief Financial Officer, Casa Colina Hospital And Centers For Healthcare, Pomona, CA, p. A86

MORQUECHO, Adam, Director Information Technology, Huntington Beach Hospital, Huntington Beach, CA, p. A68

MORREALE, Daniel, Chief Information Officer, Hunterdon Healthcare, Flemington, NJ, p. A455
Vice President and Chief Information Officer, Kingsbrook Jewish Medical Center, Brooklyn, NY, p. A478

MORREALE, Gene, President and Chief Executive Officer, Oneida Healthcare, Oneida, NY, p. A494

MORRELL, Dan, Manager Information Systems, Sierra Vista Hospital, Truth Or Consequences, NM, p. A473

MORRELL, Glen, M.D., Chief Medical Officer, Layton Hospital, Layton, UT, p. A728

MORRELL, Jeffrey F., Chief Executive Officer, Intermountain Hospital, Boise, ID, p. A188

MORREY, Michael, Executive Vice President, Mayo Clinic Health System - Franciscan Healthcare In La Crosse, La Crosse, WI, p. A787
Regional Chair-Admin SWWI, Mayo Clinic Health System - Franciscan Healthcare In Sparta, Sparta, WI, p. A796

MORRIONE, Thomas, Medical Director, New England Rehabilitation Hospital Of Portland, Portland, ME, p. A322

MORRIS, Alexander, Corporate Director Human Resources, Fort Washington Medical Center, Oxen Hill, MD, p. A331

MORRIS, Barbara, R.N., Chief Nursing Officer, Pam Rehabilitation Hospital Of Beaumont, Beaumont, TX, p. A658

MORRIS, Christi, Director of Nursing, Bayside Community Hospital, Anahuac, TX, p. A653

MORRIS, Christopher, Director Human Resources, Ascension Southeast Wisconsin Hospital - Elmbrook Campus, Brookfield, WI, p. A781
Senior Director, Human Resources, Ascension Southeast Wisconsin Hospital - St. Joseph's Campus, Milwaukee, WI, p. A790

MORRIS, Clayton, Medical Director, Griffin Memorial Hospital, Norman, OK, p. A563

MORRIS, Debbie, Director Human Resources, Marcus Daly Memorial Hospital, Hamilton, MT, p. A424

MORRIS, Dennis, Area Finance Officer, Kaiser Permanente Oakland Medical Center, Oakland, CA, p. A82

MORRIS, Donald, Vice President Human Resources, Hillcrest Medical Center, Tulsa, OK, p. A569

MORRIS, Douglas, Chief Financial Officer, Eden Springs Health Care Center, Green Springs, OH, p. A541
Chief Financial Officer, Vibra Hospital Of Northwestern Indiana, Crown Point, IN, p. A226
Chief Financial Officer, Vibra Hospital Of Southeastern Michigan, Llc, Lincoln Park, MI, p. A360

MORRIS, Janet, Director Human Resources, Encompass Rehabilitation Hospital Of Lakeview, Elizabethtown, KY, p. A282

MORRIS, Janice, Accountant, Crossridge Community Hospital, Wynne, AR, p. A54

MORRIS, Jarrett, Controller and Chief Information Officer, Atrium Health Lincoln, Lincolnton, NC, p. A514
Controller, Atrium Health Lincoln, Lincolnton, NC, p. A514

MORRIS, Jerry, Administrator, Higgins General Hospital, Bremen, GA, p. A167
Administrator, Tanner Medical Center/East Alabama, Wedowee, AL, p. A25

MORRIS, Jim, Vice President Finance, Baptist Health La Grange, La Grange, KY, p. A285
Vice President Finance, Baptist Health Louisville, Louisville, KY, p. A287

MORRIS, Jonathan, M.D., Senior Vice President and Chief Information Officer, Wellstar Cobb Hospital, Austell, GA, p. A166

MORRIS, Lisa, Vice President Human Resources, Swedish Medical Center, Englewood, CO, p. A112

MORRIS, Marsha, Manager Information Services, Fairview Park Hospital, Dublin, GA, p. A172

MORRIS, Mary, Chief Financial Officer, Purcell Municipal Hospital, Purcell, OK, p. A567

MORRIS, Matthew, Vice President Patient Care Services and Chief Nursing Officer, Atlantic General Hospital, Berlin, MD, p. A327

MORRIS, Nerissa, Senior Vice President and Chief Human Resource Officer, Cincinnati Children's Hospital Medical Center, Cincinnati, OH, p. A532

MORRIS, Philip. Chief Operating Officer, Hca Houston Healthcare West, Houston, TX, p. A686

MORRIS, R. Randall., Administrator, West Carroll Memorial Hospital, Oak Grove, LA, p. A312

MORRIS, Scott, Vice President Information Systems, Eskenazi Health, Indianapolis, IN, p. A231

MORRIS, Tony, Business Manager, Cherokee Mental Health Institute, Cherokee, IA, p. A245

MORRIS, Will, Director Information Technology, Panola Medical Center, Batesville, MS, p. A389

MORRISON, Deane, Chief Information Officer, Concord Hospital, Concord, NH, p. A448

MORRISON, Dereck, Assistant Administrator, Bryan W. Whitfield Memorial Hospital, Demopolis, AL, p. A17

MORRISON, Devin, Director for Administration, Naval Hospital Pensacola, Pensacola, FL, p. A153

MORRISON, Dianne, Director Human Resources, Mizell Memorial Hospital, Opp. AL, p. A23

MORRISON, J., M.D., M.P.H., Chief Medical Officer, Baylor Scott & White Medical Center - Hillcrest, Waco, TX, p. A724

MORRISON, James, Chief Information Officer, Madigan Army Medical Center, Tacoma, WA, p. A767

MORRISON, Kathy, Executive Director Human Resources, St. Catherine Hospital, Garden City, KS, p. A264

MORRISON, Kevin, Chief Financial Officer, Dickenson Community Hospital, Clintwood, VA, p. A740

MORRISON, Maureen, Vice President, Finance, Advocate Trinity Hospital, Chicago, IL, p. A197

MORRISON, Michael, Chief Financial Officer, Tristar Skyline Medical Center, Nashville, TN, p. A647

MORRISON, Michele, R.N., M.P.H., Chief Hospital Executive, Hackensack Meridian Health Southern Ocean Medical Center, Manahawkin, NJ, p. A458

MORRISON, Olivia, Human Resource Manager, Encompass Health Rehabilitation Hospital Of Parkersburg, Parkersburg, WV, p. A775

MORRISON, Sarah, President and Chief Executive Officer, Shepherd Center, Atlanta, GA, p. A165

MORRISSETT, Barbara, Vice President Human Resources, St. Mary's Medical Center, San Francisco, CA, p. A94

MORRISSETTE, Daniel, Chief Financial Officer, Stanford Health Care, Palo Alto, CA, p. A84

MORRISSEY, Moira, Chief Operating Officer and General Counsel, Four Winds Hospital, Katonah, NY, p. A486

MORRISSEY, Una, R.N., MSN, Senior Vice President Operations, Chief Operating Officer and Chief Nursing Officer, New York Community Hospital, Brooklyn, NY, p. A478

MORROW, Charles, M.D., Chief Medical Officer, Spartanburg Medical Center - Church Street Campus, Spartanburg, SC, p. A624

MORROW, Ginger, Entity Human Resources Officer, Texas Health Harris Methodist Hospital Fort Worth, Fort Worth, TX, p. A679

MORROW, Jennifer, Director Human Resources, San Joaquin Valley Rehabilitation Hospital, Fresno, CA, p. A66

MORROW, Laurie, Executive Director Human Resources, Washington Regional Medical Center, Fayetteville, AR, p. A45

MORROW, Pat, Director Human Resources, Walker Baptist Medical Center, Jasper, AL, p. A20

MORROW, Randy, Vice President and Chief Operating Officer, Boone Hospital Center, Columbia, MO, p. A405

MORROW, Sarah, Vice President Human Resources, Capital Region Medical Center, Jefferson City, MO, p. A408

MORROW, Shawn, Chief Executive Officer, Lds Hospital, Salt Lake City, UT, p. A732

MORROW, W., M.D., Executive Vice President and Chief Medical Officer, Children's Medical Center Dallas, Dallas, TX, p. A668

MORSCHAUSER, Roberta, Administrator, Brown County Community Treatment Center, Green Bay, WI, p. A785

MORSE, Brad S., FACHE, Interim Chief Executive Officer, Mccurtain Memorial Hospital, Idabel, OK, p. A560

MORSE, Craig, Chief Financial Officer, Carlsbad Medical Center, Carlsbad, NM, p. A468

MORSE, Douglas E., Chief Executive Officer and Administrator, Hansen Family Hospital, Iowa Falls, IA, p. A252

MORSE, Jason, Director Information Technology, Cumberland Healthcare, Cumberland, WI, p. A782

MORSTAD, Joan, Director Information Systems, Coliseum Medical Centers, Macon, GA, p. A176

MORTENSEN, Lorrie, MSN, R.N., Director, Patient Care, Floyd Valley Healthcare, Le Mars, IA, p. A253

MORTENSEN, Shane, Chief Financial Officer, San Luis Valley Health Conejos County Hospital, La Jara, CO, p. A115
Chief Financial Officer, San Luis Valley Health, Alamosa, CO, p. A107

MORTENSON, June, R.N., Director of Nursing, Power County Hospital District, American Falls, ID, p. A188

MORTINSEN, Roy, M.D., Chief of Staff, Sanford Vermillion Medical Center, Vermillion, SD, p. A632

MORTON, David, M.D., Clinical Director, West Central Georgia Regional Hospital, Columbus, GA, p. A169

MORTON, Leslie, Manager Human Resources, Riverview Regional Medical Center, Gadsden, AL, p. A19

MORTON, Lucas, Regional Chief Financial Officer, Osf Heart Of Mary Medical Center, Urbana, IL, p. A222
Regional Chief Financial Officer, Osf Sacred Heart Medical Center, Danville, IL, p. A202

MORTON, Robert, M.D., Medical Director, Rolling Hills Hospital, Ada, OK, p. A555

MORTON, Stephanie, Chief Information Officer, Providence Alaska Medical Center, Anchorage, AK, p. A27

MORTON, Steve, M.D., Chief Medical Officer, Continuecare Hospital At Baptist Health Corbin, Corbin, KY, p. A282

MORTON ROWE, Laura, Director of Human Resources, Providence Saint John's Health Center, Santa Monica, CA, p. A97

MORTOZA, Angela, Chief Executive Officer, Dallas County Hospital, Perry, IA, p. A256

MOSBY, Charmaine, Area Director Health Information Management, Kp. Promise Hospital Of Baton Rouge, Baton Rouge, LA, p. A297

MOSCA, Philip. M.D., President, Medical Staff, Integris Southwest Medical Center, Oklahoma City, OK, p. A564

MOSCATO, Mary K., FACHE, President, Hebrew Rehabilitation Center, Roslindale, MA, p. A344

MOSCHKAU, Don, Senior Director Human Resources, University Of Minnesota, Minneapolis, MN, p. A381

MOSCOSO, Ricardo, M.D., Medical Director, University Hospital, San Juan, PR, p. A811

MOSEL, Lindy, Director of Nursing, Memorial Community Health, Aurora, NE, p. A429

MOSELY, Chisty, Director Information Management, Saint Simons By-The-Sea Hospital, Saint Simons Island, GA, - p. A179

MOSER, Cindy, Director Human Resources, Allegheny Valley Hospital, Natrona Heights, PA, p. A598

MOSER, Joseph, M.D., Chief Medical Officer, University Of Maryland Charles Regional Medical Center, La Plata, MD, p. A330

MOSER, Kevin, Vice President of Operations, Baptist Health Madisonville, Madisonville, KY, p. A289

MOSER, Nathan, Information Technology Engineer, Audubon County Memorial Hospital And Clinics, Audubon, IA, p. A243

MOSER, Neal, M.D., Medical Director, Encompass Health Rehabilitation Hospital Of Northern Kentucky, Edgewood, KY, p. A282

MOSESIAN, Robert, Controller, Encompass Health Rehabilitation Hospital Of Bakersfield, Bakersfield, CA, p. A57

MOSHER, Guy Manager Information Systems, Geneva General Hospital, Geneva, NY, p. A484
Manager Information Systems, Soldiers And Sailors Memorial Hospital, Penn Yan, NY, p. A495

MOSHIER, John, Director Human Resources, Clara Barton Hospital, Hoisington, KS, p. A266

MOSHIRPUR, Jasmin, M.D., Chief Medical Officer, Nyc Health + Hospitals / Queens, Jamaica, NY, p. A486
M.D., Dean and Medical Director, Nyc Health + Hospitals / Elmhurst, Elmhurst, NY, p. A483

MOSHOFSKY, Bill, M.D., Chief of Staff, Peacehealth Sacred Heart Medical Center University District, Eugene, OR, p. A575

MOSIER, Dawn, Director Human Resources, Encompass Health Rehabilitation Institute Of Tucson, Tucson, AZ, p. A40

MOSIER, John, D.O., Chief of Staff, Herington Municipal Hospital, Herington, KS, p. A266

MOSLEY, J. Christopher., Chief Executive Officer, Cartersville Medical Center, Cartersville, GA, p. A168

MOSLEY, Tonja, Chief Financial Officer, Adventhealth Heart Of Florida, Davenport, FL, p. A135
Chief Financial Officer, Wellington Regional Medical Center, Wellington, FL, p. A161

MOSMEYER, Kathleen, Director Human Resources, Citizens Medical Center, Victoria, TX, p. A723

MOSS, Austin, Vice President Human Resources, Jennie Stuart Medical Center, Hopkinsville, KY, p. A285

MOSS, Barry, Chief Executive Officer, Merit Health Central, Jackson, MS, p. A394

MOSS, Bradley, Administrator, Unity Psychiatric Care-Huntsville, Huntsville, AL, p. A20

MOSS, C, M.D., Chief Medical Officer, Coastal Virginia Rehabilitation, Newport News, VA, p. A746

MOSS, Jennifer, MS, R.N., Chief Clinical Officer, Kirby Medical Center, Monticello, IL, p. A212

MOSS, Keith, Vice President & Chief Medical Informatics Officers, Riverside Medical Center, Kankakee, IL, p. A209

MOSS, Misty, Director Business Administration, Logansport State Hospital, Logansport, IN, p. A235

MOSS, Ray, Vice President and Chief Information Officer, Henry Mayo Newhall Hospital, Valencia, CA, p. A103

MOSS, Shelby, Human Resource Officer, Sheridan County Health Complex, Hoxie, KS, p. A266

MOSS, Stuart, Chief Financial Officer, Kessler Marlton Rehabilitation, Marlton, NJ, p. A458

MOSS, Tyler, Chief Financial Officer, Milford Valley Memorial Hospital, Milford, UT, p. A729

MOST, Kevin, D.O., Chief Medical Officer, Northwestern Medicine Central Dupage Hospital, Winfield, IL, p. A222

MOSTOFI, Ann, MSN, R.N., Vice President Patient Care and Chief Nursing Officer, Eisenhower Health, Rancho Mirage, CA, p. A86

MOTAKEF, Shahin, FACHE, President, Baylor Scott & White Medical Center - Temple, Temple, TX, p. A719

MOTEJZIK, Thomas, Director Information Systems, Carlsbad Medical Center, Carlsbad, NM, p. A468

MOTONAGA, Gregg, M.D., Chief of Staff, Central Peninsula Hospital, Soldotna, AK, p. A29

MOTT, Daman, MSN, Chief Nursing Officer, Doctors Hospital Of Laredo, Laredo, TX, p. A695

MOTT, William, Chief Operating Officer, Ascension Macomb-Oakland Hospital, Warren, MI, p. A368

MOTTE, Michael J., Chief Executive Officer, Lower Bucks Hospital, Bristol, PA, p. A585

MOUGHAN, Jennifer, Chief Human Resources Officer, Virtua Our Lady Of Lourdes Hospital, Camden, NJ, p. A453

MOUISSET, Rena, Director Human Resources and Contract Compliance, St. Martin Hospital, Breaux Bridge, LA, p. A298

MOULTON, Susan, Director Health Information Management, Spring Harbor Hospital, Westbrook, ME, p. A323

MOUNIE, Mike, Director Finance, Sentara Obici Hospital, Suffolk, VA, p. A752

MOUNTAIN, J, Chief Financial Officer, Rivervalley Behavioral Health Hospital, Owensboro, KY, p. A291

MOUSA, Ayman, R.N., Ph.D., Chief Executive Officer, Pacifica Hospital Of The Valley, Sun Valley, CA, p. A100

MOUSA, Cindy, Director Human Resources, Touro Infirmary, New Orleans, LA, p. A311

MOUSTAKAKIS, John, Senior Vice President Information Systems and Chief Information Officer, Westchester Medical Center, Valhalla, NY, p. A501

MOVSESIAN, Gregory, M.D., Acting Chief of Staff, Aleda E. Lutz Veterans Affairs Medical Center, Saginaw, MI, p. A365

MOWAN, Chris, Chief Executive Officer, Medical City Dallas, Dallas, TX, p. A669

MOYA, Linda, Director Human Resources, Mesilla Valley Hospital, Las Cruces, NM, p. A470

MOYANO, Mathias, Chief Human Resource Officer, Delta Community Medical Center, Delta, UT, p. A727
Chief Human Resource Officer, Fillmore Community Hospital, Fillmore, UT, p. A728

MOYER, Dale, Vice President Information Systems, Evangelical Community Hospital, Lewisburg, PA, p. A595

MOYER, Douglas J., President, Sentara Rmh Medical Center, Harrisonburg, VA, p. A743

MOYER, Karen, R.N., Senior Vice President and Chief Nursing Officer, Mount Sinai Medical Center, Miami Beach, FL, p. A148

MRAMOR, Joann, Director Human Resources, Seven Rivers Regional Medical Center, Crystal River, FL, p. A135

MUCARIA, Jaclyn, President, New York-Presbyterian Queens, Flushing, NY, p. A484

MUCK, Erin, Chief Executive Officer, Crawford County Memorial Hospital, Denison, IA, p. A248

MUDEN, Todd, Section Head Information Management, Mayo Clinic Health System - Northland In Barron, Barron, WI, p. A781

MUDRY, Janel, Chief Operating Officer, Washington Health System Greene, Waynesburg, PA, p. A610

MUELLER, Arthur, Director Management Information Systems, Cuero Regional Hospital, Cuero, TX, p. A667

MUELLER, Charles, M.D., Chief of Staff, Texas County Memorial Hospital, Houston, MO, p. A407

MUELLER, Donald, Chief Executive Officer, St. Christopher's Hospital For Children, Philadelphia, PA, p. A602

MUELLER, Eric, Chief Executive Officer and Market Chief Executive Officer, Vibra Hospital Of Amarillo, Amarillo, TX, p. A652

MUELLER, Karen, R.N., Chief Nursing Officer, Mount Desert Island Hospital, Bar Harbor, ME, p. A318

MUELLER, Michael, Chief Financial Officer, Health Central Hospital, Ocoee, FL, p. A150

MUELLER, Paul A., Chief Executive Officer, Hospital Division, Rogers Memorial Hospital, Inc., Oconomowoc, WI, p. A793

MUELLER, Paul S., Regional Vice President, Mayo Clinic Health System - Franciscan Healthcare In La Crosse, La Crosse, WI, p. A787
Regional Vice President, Mayo Clinic Health System - Franciscan Healthcare In Sparta, Sparta, WI, p. A796

MUGGLI, David D., FACHE, Chief Executive Officer, Select Specialty Hospital-Cincinnati, Cincinnati, OH, p. A533
FACHE, Interim Chief Executive Officer, Select Specialty Hospital - Cincinnati North, Cincinnati, OH, p. A533

MUHAMMAD, Mark, Manager Human Resources, Michael E. Debakey Veterans Affairs Medical Center, Houston, TX, p. A687

MUHS, David, Chief Financial Officer, Henry County Health Center, Mount Pleasant, IA, p. A254

MUILENBURG, Jeff, Chief of Staff, Memorial Community Health, Aurora, NE, p. A429

MULDER, Doris, Vice President Nursing, Beloit Health System, Beloit, WI, p. A781

MULDERIG, Marsha, R.N., MSN, Chief Nursing Officer, Crisp Regional Hospital, Cordele, GA, p. A170

MULDOON, Sean, M.D., Chief Medical Officer, Kindred Hospital-New Jersey Morris County, Dover, NJ, p. A454
M.D., Senior Vice President and Chief Medical Officer-Kindred Healthcare, Hospital Division, Kindred Hospital Northland, Kansas City, MO, p. A409

MULIS, Becky, Director of Health Information Management Systems, Four County Counseling Center, Logansport, IN, p. A235

MULKEY, Peter, Chief Executive Officer, Clinch Valley Medical Center, Richlands, VA, p. A749

MULLEN, Michelle, Chief Clinical Officer, Bridgepoint Hospital Capitol Hill, Washington, DC, p. A129

MULLENAX, Paul, Business Manager, Wyoming State Hospital, Evanston, WY, p. A802

MULLENDER, Monica, Director of Nursing, Osborne County Memorial Hospital, Osborne, KS, p. A273

MULLENS, Allen, M.D., Chief Medical Staff, Norton Community Hospital, Norton, VA, p. A748

MULLER, Donna, Vice President Finance, Southern Region, Upmc Hanover, Hanover, PA, p. A591
Vice President Finance, Southern Region, Upmc Memorial, York, PA, p. A612
MULLER, Oz, Director Human Resources, Porter Adventist Hospital, Denver, CO, p. A111
MULLERY CHHR, Barbara, Vice President Administration, Robert Wood Johnson University Hospital Rahway, Rahway, NJ, p. A462
MULLIGAN, Lisa, Commanding Officer, Naval Medical Center, Portsmouth, VA, p. A749
MULLIGAN, Marie, R.N., MSN, Vice President Nursing, Mather Hospital, Port Jefferson, NY, p. A495
MULLINAX, Bradley, Chief Administrative Officer, Saint Thomas Dekalb Hospital, Smithville, TN, p. A649
MULLINGS, Donna, Director of Nursing, Assumption Community Hospital, Napoleonville, LA, p. A309
MULLINS, Bandy, M.D., Chief of Staff, Summersville Regional Medical Center, Summersville, WV, p. A777
MULLINS, Brad, Director Information Technology, Gove County Medical Center, Quinter, KS, p. A275
MULLINS, Bryan, Chief Operating Officer, Johnston Memorial Hospital, Abingdon, VA, p. A738
MULLINS, Cindy, Director Information Technology, Saint Mary's Regional Medical Center, Reno, NV, p. A446
MULLINS, Dustin, Chief Human Resources, Bayne-Jones Army Community Hospital, Fort Polk, LA, p. A301
Chief Resource Management, Bayne-Jones Army Community Hospital, Fort Polk, LA, p. A301
MULLINS, Erin, D.O., Chief Medical Staff, Dickenson Community Hospital, Clintwood, VA, p. A740
MULLINS, Michelle, Chief Information Officer, Oklahoma Heart Hospital, Oklahoma City, OK, p. A565
MULLIS, Jeffrey, Interim Chief Financial Officer, Bayfront Health Port Charlotte, Port Charlotte, FL, p. A154
Interim Chief Financial Officer, Piedmont Walton Hospital, Monroe, GA, p. A177
MULROONEY, JoAnn, R.N., Chief Operating Officer, Trinity Health System, Steubenville, OH, p. A550
MULTACH, Mark, M.D., Chief Medical Officer, Mount Sinai Hospital, Chicago, IL, p. A199
MULTACK, Richard, D.O., Vice President Medical Management, Advocate South Suburban Hospital, Hazel Crest, IL, p. A207
MULVEHILL, Mitchell, Group Financial Officer, Texas Health Harris Methodist Hospital Southlake, Southlake, TX, p. A716
MULVEY, Lee, Human Resource Officer, Texas Health Harris Methodist Hospital Hurst-Euless-Bedford, Bedford, TX, p. A659
MUMFORD, Stephen, Chief Operating Officer, Baton Rouge General Medical Center, Baton Rouge, LA, p. A296
MUMOLIE, Gina, Senior Vice President and Chief Nurse Executive, Inspira Medical Center-Woodbury, Woodbury, NJ, p. A466
Senior Vice President Hospital Administration, Capital Health Regional Medical Center, Trenton, NJ, p. A464
MUMPOWER, Rebecca, Director Marketing, Mesilla Valley Hospital, Las Cruces, NM, p. A470
MUNA, Esther L., FACHE, Chief Executive Officer, Commonwealth Health Center, Saipan, MP, p. A805
MUNCHEL, Bryan, Senior Vice President and Chief Information Officer, Pam Specialty Hospital Of Covington, Covington, LA, p. A300
MUNGOVAN, Sandy, Chief Information Officer, Harbor-Ucla Medical Center, Torrance, CA, p. A101
MUNHOLLAND, Cleta, Administrator, Louisiana Extended Care Hospital Of West Monroe, West Monroe, LA, p. A316
Administrator, Specialty Hospital, Monroe, LA, p. A309
MUNIR, Amjad, M.D., Medical Director, Encompass Health Rehabilitation Hospital Of Chattanooga, Chattanooga, TN, p. A635
MUNLEY, William, Administrator, Shriners Hospitals For Children-Greenville, Greenville, SC, p. A620
MUNOZ, Alejandro, M.D., Chief Medical Officer, Cedar Crest Hospital And Residential Treatment Center, Belton, TX, p. A659
MUNOZ, Anthony, Chief, Civilian Human Resources Branch, Madigan Army Medical Center, Tacoma, WA, p. A767
MUNOZ, Astro, Executive Director, First Hospital Panamericano, Cidra, PR, p. A807
MUNOZ, Thalia H., R.N., MS, Chief Executive Officer, Starr County Memorial Hospital, Rio Grande City, TX, p. A709
MUNSHI, Imtiaz, M.D., Chief of Staff, Richard L. Roudebush Veterans Affairs Medical Center, Indianapolis, IN, p. A233
MUNSON, Bill, Vice President and Chief Financial Officer, Boulder Community Health, Boulder, CO, p. A108
MUNSON, Jennifer, Chief Financial Officer, Three Rivers Hospital, Brewster, WA, p. A756
MUNSON, John, Vice President and Chief Financial Officer, St. Anthony Regional Hospital, Carroll, IA, p. A244

MUNTEFERING, Denise, Vice President Patient Care Services, Avera St. Benedict Health Center, Parkston, SD, p. A630
MUNTZ, Dana M., Chief Executive Officer, Ascension St. Vincent Jennings, North Vernon, IN, p. A238
Chief Executive Officer, Ascension St. Vincent Salem, Salem, IN, p. A240
MUNTZ, Tim, President and Chief Executive Officer, St. Margaret's Hospital, Spring Valley, IL, p. A220
MUNYAN, Lori, Director, Human Resources, Encompass Health Rehabilitation Hospital Of Toms River, Toms River, NJ, p. A464
MURANSKY, Ed, Owner, Surgical Hospital At Southwoods, Youngstown, OH, p. A554
MURCHISON, Sandra, Director Medical Records, Coosa Valley Medical Center, Sylacauga, AL, p. A24
MURDAUGH, Laura, Finance Director, William J. Mccord Adolescent Treatment Facility, Orangeburg, SC, p. A623
MURDOCH, William, M.D., Medical Director, Loma Linda University Behavioral Medicine Center, Redlands, CA, p. A87
MURDOCK, Guy, Vice President Human Resources, Nexus Children's Hospital Houston, Houston, TX, p. A688
MURDOCK, Mark, FACHE, Medical Center Director, Dayton Veterans Affairs Medical Center, Dayton, OH, p. A538
MURDOCK, William, Vice President Finance, Mcdonough District Hospital, Mb, IL, p. A211
MURDOCK-LANGAN, Patricia, M.D., Chief Medical Officer, Chi Health Lakeside, Omaha, NE, p. A436
M.D., Chief Medical Officer, Chi Health Midlands, Papillion, NE, p. A438
MURDY, James, Chief Financial Officer, Wheeling Hospital, Wheeling, WV, p. A778
MURILLO, Jeremias, M.D., Chief Medical Officer, Newark Beth Israel Medical Center, Newark, NJ, p. A459
MURIN, William, Chief Human Resources Officer, Uc San Diego Medical Center—Hillcrest, San Diego, CA, p. A92
MURO, Deborah, Chief Information Officer, El Camino Hospital, Mountain View, CA, p. A80
MURPHREE, Shari, Chief Executive Officer, Willow Crest Hospital, Miami, OK, p. A562
MURPHY, Bobbie, R.N., Chief Nursing Officer, Bristol Regional Medical Center, Bristol, TN, p. A634
MURPHY, Brian, M.D., Chief Executive Officer, Valley View Hospital, Glenwood Springs, CO, p. A113
Senior Director Admissions and Referral Services, Hebrew Rehabilitation Center, Roslindale, MA, p. A344
Vice President Information Systems, Sarah Bush Lincoln Health Center, Mattoon, IL, p. A211
MURPHY, Bruce, M.D., President and Chief Executive Officer, Arkansas Heart Hospital, Little Rock, AR, p. A48
MURPHY, Charles, Associate Vice President Human Resources, Strong Memorial Hospital Of The University Of Rochester, Rochester, NY, p. A496
MURPHY, Christine, MS, Chief Operating Officer, Cypress Grove Behavioral Health, Bastrop. LA, p. A296
MURPHY, Colleen, M.D., Chief of Staff, Clay County Hospital, Flora, IL, p. A205
MURPHY, Elizabeth, R.N., FACHE, Chief Nursing Officer, Mercy Health Saint Mary's, Grand Rapids, MI, p. A356
MURPHY, Evelyn, Chief Nursing Officer, St. Mary's Sacred Heart Hospital, Lavonia, GA, p. A175
MURPHY, J, Chief Financial Officer, North Baldwin Infirmary, Bay Minette, AL, p. A14
MURPHY, Janice G., President and Chief Executive Office, St. Vincent Charity Medical Center, Cleveland, OH, p. A535
MURPHY, John, M.D., Vice President Medical Affairs and Chief Medical Officer, Rhode Island Hospital, Providence, RI, p. A614
MURPHY, Julie, Chief Financial Officer, Saint Luke's North Hospital - Barry Road, Kansas City, MO, p. A409
MURPHY, Kathy, Site Manager, Mescalero Public Health Service Indian Hospital, Mescalero, NM, p. A471
MURPHY, Kelly, Vice President Human Resources, Colorado Canyons Hospital And Medical Center, Fruita, CO, p. A113
MURPHY, Kevin, Chief Financial Officer, Signature Healthcare Brockton Hospital, Brockton, MA, p. A337
Director, Information Technology Services, Bayfront Health St. Petersburg, Saint Petersburg, FL, p. A156
MURPHY, Kyle, Director Information Technology, Mayhill Hospital, Denton, TX, p. A672
MURPHY, Linda, Chief Financial Officer, Osborne County Memorial Hospital, Osborne, KS, p. A273
MURPHY, Lionel, Chief Executive Officer, Bethesda Rehabilitation Hospital, Baton Rouge, LA, p. A296
Chief Executive Officer, Southeast Regional Medical Center, Kentwood, LA, p. A304
MURPHY, Marie, Director Human Resources, Effingham Hospital, Springfield, GA, p. A180
MURPHY, Mark, Interim President and Chief Executive Officer, Rome Memorial Hospital, Rome, NY, p. A497

MURPHY, Mary, MSN, Regional Chief Nursing Officer, Amita Health Adventist Medical Center La Grange, La Grange, IL, p. A210
MSN, Vice President and Chief Nursing Officer, Amita Health Adventist Medical Center - Hinsdale, Hinsdale, IL, p. A208
MURPHY, Matthew, Chief Financial Officer, Compass Memorial Healthcare, Marengo, IA, p. A253
MURPHY, Maureen, M.D., Director of Medical Affairs, Ssm Health St. Clare Hospital-Baraboo, Baraboo, WI, p. A780
MURPHY, Michael, M.D., JD, Chief Medical Officer, Sharp Grossmont Hospital, La Mesa, CA, p. A70
Interim Chief Executive Officer, Mercy Regional Medical Center, Durango, CO, p. A111
MURPHY, Michael D., FACHE, Chief Executive Officer, Abilene Regional Medical Center, Abilene, TX, p. A651
MURPHY, Nancy, Vice President, Human Resources, Franciscan Children's, Brighton, MA, p. A336
MURPHY, Peter J., Senior Vice President and Chief Operating Officer, Franciscan Health Mooresville, Mooresville, IN, p. A237
MURPHY, Richard J., President and Chief Executive Officer, Mount Sinai South Nassau, Oceanside, NY, p. A493
MURPHY, Rita, Director Human Resources, Cobre Valley Regional Medical Center, Globe, AZ, p. A32
MURPHY, Sheryl, Chief Nursing Officer and Director of Clinical Services, Peacehealth Peace Island Medical Center, Friday Harbor, WA, p. A758
MURPHY, Steve, Director Information Systems, Ssm Health St. Mary's Hospital Centralia, Centralia, IL, p. A196
FM-East Region IS, Ssm Health Good Samaritan Hospital, Mount Vernon, IL, p. A213
MURPHY, Steven, Executive Director, Devereux Hospital And Children's Center Of Florida, Melbourne, FL, p. A145
MURPHY, Terry, Director Information Services, Phoenixville Hospital, Phoenixville, PA, p. A602
President and Chief Executive Officer, Bayhealth Medical Center, Dover, DE, p. A127
MURPHY, Theresa, Chief Nursing Officer, Usc Verdugo Hills Hospital, Glendale, CA, p. A67
MURPHY, Timothy, R.N., Chief Nursing Officer, Encompass Health Rehabilitation Hospital Of Desert Canyon, Las Vegas, NV, p. A443
Vice President Human Resources, Mercy Hospital Joplin, Joplin, MO, p. A408
MURPHY, Tom, Chief Executive Officer, Minidoka Memorial Hospital, Rupert, ID, p. A193
MURPHY-FROBISH, Erin, Vice President Human Resources, Morris Hospital & Healthcare Centers, Morris, IL, p. A213
MURPHY-MIJARES, Monique, Chief Information Officer, Valley View Medical Center, Fort Mohave, AZ, p. A31
MURRAY, Alexander, Interim Associate Director, Veterans Affairs Gulf Coast Veterans Health Care System, Biloxi, MS, p. A390
MURRAY, Beverly, Director of Human Resources, Providence Tarzana Medical Center, Tarzana, CA, p. A100
MURRAY, Brian, M.D., Medical Director, Erie County Medical Center, Buffalo, NY, p. A479
Chief Financial Officer, Gunnison Valley Hospital, Gunnison, UT, p. A728
MURRAY, Cindy, R.N., Chief Nursing Officer and Chief Operating Officer, Baylor Scott & White Medical Center-Waxahachie, Waxahachie, TX, p. A724
MURRAY, Denise R., Chief Executive Officer, Anmed Health Rehabilitation Hospital, Anderson, SC, p. A615
MURRAY, Diana, Director Information Systems, Grand River Hospital District, Rifle, CO, p. A118
MURRAY, Kent, M.D., Chief of Staff, Robert J. Dole Veterans Affairs Medical Center, Wichita, KS, p. A279
MURRAY, Kevin, M.D., Director Medical Services, Lake Taylor Transitional Care Hospital, Norfolk, VA, p. A748
Senior Vice President, Mather Hospital, Port Jefferson, NY, p. A495
MURRAY, Marisa, CPA, Director Finance, Hshs St. Francis Hospital, Litchfield, IL, p. A210
MURRAY, Meggan, Assistant Vice President Finance, Terrebonne General Medical Center, Houma, LA, p. A303
MURRAY, Sherri, Chief Financial Officer, Montgomery General Hospital, Montgomery, WV, p. A774
MURRAY, Wesley E., Chief Executive Officer, Texas County Memorial Hospital, Houston, MO, p. A407
MURRELL, Joseph, Chief Executive Officer, Wayne County Hospital, Monticello, KY, p. A290
MURRILL, Michael, President and Chief Executive Officer, Adventhealth Gordon, Calhoun, GA, p. A168
President and Chief Executive Officer, Adventhealth Murray, Chatsworth, GA, p. A168
MURROW, Carol, Vice President Business Development, Cox Medical Center Branson, Branson, MO, p. A403
MURRY, Jim, Chief Information Officer, Stony Brook University Hospital, Stony Brook, NY, p. A499

MURTHY, Anandhi, Chief Medical Officer, Harrison Community Hospital, Cadiz, OH, p. A530

MURTHY, Bangalore, M.D., Director Medical Staff, Jackson Park Hospital And Medical Center, Chicago, IL, p. A198

MURZYN, Derek, Chief Executive Officer, Carolinas Continuecare Hospital At University, Charlotte, NC, p. A507 Market Chief Executive Officer, Carolinas Continuecare Hospital At Pineville, Charlotte, NC, p. A507

MUSACK, Scott, Chief Information Officer, La Downtown Medical Center, Llc, Los Angeles, CA, p. A75

MUSANTE, David, M.D., Medical Director, North Carolina Specialty Hospital, Durham, NC, p. A509

MUSGRAVE, Chelsea, Director of Human Resources, Clay County Hospital, Flora, IL, p. A205

MUSICH, Trisha, R.N., Regional Chief Nursing Officer, Chicago Metro, Amita Health Resurrection Medical Center, Chicago, IL, p. A197

MUSKRAT, Lisa, Chief Executive Officer, Regency Hospital Of Northwest Arkansas - Springdale, Springdale, AR, p. A53

MUSSI, Alexis, Chief Executive Officer, Southern Hills Hospital And Medical Center, Las Vegas, NV, p. A444

MUSSI, Natalie, President and Chief Executive Officer, Los Robles Hospital And Medical Center, Thousand Oaks, CA, p. A101

MUSSO, Lewis, Vice President Human Resources, Trinity Health System, Steubenville, OH, p. A550

MUSTACCHIA, Michele, Chief Human Resources Officer, Banner Gateway Medical Center, Gilbert, AZ, p. A32

MUSTARD, Ruth, R.N., MSN, Associate Director Nursing and Patient Services, Wm. Jennings Bryan Dorn Veterans Affairs Medical Center, Columbia, SC, p. A618

MUSTIAN, J. Perry, President and Chief Executive Officer, John D. Archbold Memorial Hospital, Thomasville, GA, p. A182

MUSUNURU, J.R., M.D., Executive Director, Fond Du Lac County Mental Health Center, Fond Du Lac, WI, p. A784

MUTHU, Karthik, Chief Executive Officer, Encompass Health Rehabilitation Hospital Of Ocala, Ocala, FL, p. A150

MUTTERER, Michael, Senior Vice President and Chief Nursing Officer, Riverside Medical Center, Kankakee, IL, p. A209

MUTZ, Jeffrey, Human Resources Director, Northfield Hospital And Clinics, Northfield, MN, p. A382

MUTZIGER, John, M.D., Chief Medical Officer, Laird Hospital, Union, MS, p. A400

MWANIKI, Mary, Chief Financial Officer, Encompass Health Rehabilitation Hospital Of The Mid-Cities, Bedford, TX, p. A658

MWEBE, David, M.D., Chief of Staff, Osmond General Hospital, Osmond, NE, p. A438

MYATT, Kevin, Senior Vice President Human Resources, Yale-New Haven Hospital, New Haven, CT, p. A124

MYCROFT, Tina, Senior Vice President, Chief Financial Officer, Evergreenhealth, Kirkland, WA, p. A759

MYDLER, Todd, M.D., Vice President and Chief Medical Officer, Good Samaritan Medical Center, Lafayette, CO, p. A115

MYERS, Becky, Human Resources Specialist, Illini Community Hospital, Pittsfield, IL, p. A217

MYERS, Chrissy, R.N., Director of Nursing, Unity Psychiatric Care-Clarksville, Clarksville, TN, p. A636

MYERS, Douglas, Executive Vice President and Chief Financial Officer, Phoenix Children's Hospital, Phoenix, AZ, p. A36

MYERS, Ed, Administrator, Shriners Hospitals For Children-Philadelphia, Philadelphia, PA, p. A602

MYERS, Gabby, Human Resources Director, Advanced Diagnostics Hospital, Houston, TX, p. A684

MYERS, Grace, MSN, Vice President, Nurse Executive, Sentara Princess Anne Hospital, Virginia Beach, VA, p. A753

MYERS, Jeffrey D., President and Chief Executive Officer, Hamilton Medical Center, Dalton, GA, p. A170

MYERS, Jerry, M.D., Chief Executive Officer and Medical Director, Kell West Regional Hospital, Wichita Falls, TX, p. A725

MYERS, Joseph, President and Chief Executive Officer, Penn Highlands Huntingdon, Huntingdon, PA, p. A592

MYERS, Josette M., Chief Executive Officer, Encompass Health Rehabilitation Hospital Of Mechanicsburg, Mechanicsburg, PA, p. A596

MYERS, Julie, Chief Executive Officer, Kindred Hospital-Westminster, Westminster, CA, p. A105

MYERS, Kathy, MS, R.N., Chief Nursing Officer, Tennova Healthcare-Lafollette Medical Center, La Follette, TN, p. A642

MYERS, Kevin, Director Information Systems, Lake Granbury Medical Center, Granbury, TX, p. A682 Director Information Technology, Wilson Medical Center, Neodesha, KS, p. A271

MYERS, Kimberly, Director Human Resources, Guthrie County Hospital, Guthrie Center, IA, p. A250

MYERS, Lisa, Director Human Resources, Heritage Oaks Hospital, Sacramento, CA, p. A89

MYERS, Mary, R.N., MSN, Chief Nursing Officer, Ascension St. Vincent Indianapolis Hospital, Indianapolis, IN, p. A231

MYERS, Michelle, Director Human Resources, Adventhealth Wauchula, Wauchula, FL, p. A161

MYERS, Paul, M.D., Neonatologist and Chief Medical Officer, Children's Hospital Of Wisconsin-Fox Valley, Neenah, WI, p. A792

MYERS, Philip. M.D., Vice President Medical Affairs, Uh Samaritan Medical Center, Ashland, OH, p. A528

MYERS, Randy, Chief Information Officer, Rehoboth Mckinley Christian Health Care Services, Gallup. NM, p. A469

MYERS, Robert, Chief Operating Officer, Goshen Health, Goshen, IN, p. A229

MYERS, Shane, Chief Operating Officer, Iberia Medical Center, New Iberia, LA, p. A310

MYERS, Sheri, Vice President Patient Care Services, Mclaren Central Michigan, Mount Pleasant, MI, p. A362

MYERS, Theresa, Personnel Director, Fallon Medical Complex, Baker, MT, p. A421

MYERS, William, Chief Executive Officer, Montgomery County Emergency Service, Norristown, PA, p. A598

MYHRE, Tracy, R.N., MSN, Chief Nursing Officer, Tomah Health, Tomah, WI, p. A797

MYLAVARAPU, Sarada, M.D., Chief Medical Officer, Woodland Healthcare, Woodland, CA, p. A105

MYSTER, Jennifer, President, Park Nicollet Methodist Hospital, Saint Louis Park, MN, p. A385

# N

NABEL, Elizabeth, M.D., President, Brigham And Women's Hospital, Boston, MA, p. A335

NABULSHI, Sari, M.D., Chief Medical Officer, Medical Center Health System, Odessa, TX, p. A703

NACEY, Marley, Director Finance, Sentara Virginia Beach General Hospital, Virginia Beach, VA, p. A753

NACHTIGAL, Amy, Chief Financial Officer, Saint Luke's Hospital Of Kansas City, Kansas City, MO, p. A409

NACHTRIEB, Han, Vice President Human Resources, Seattle Cancer Care Alliance, Seattle, WA, p. A764

NACION, Glenn, Vice President Human Resources, Trinitas Regional Medical Center, Elizabeth, NJ, p. A455

NADEAU, Barbara, Chief Human Resources Management Service, White River Junction Veterans Affairs Medical Center, White River Junction, VT, p. A737

NADER, Daniel, D.O., Chief of Staff, Southwestern Regional Medical Center, Tulsa, OK, p. A570

NADER, Keoni, Director Human Resources, Louis A. Weiss Memorial Hospital, Chicago, IL, p. A199

NADER, Rick, Chief Financial Officer, Haxtun Hospital District, Haxtun, CO, p. A114

NADKARNI, Manasi, M.D., Vice President Medical Affairs, Unitypoint Health - Trinity Muscatine, Muscatine, IA, p. A254

NADLE, Patricia, R.N., Chief Nursing Officer, St. Josep. Health Services Of Rhode Island, North Providence, RI, p. A613

NADLER, Tammy, Chief Financial Officer, Golden Valley Memorial Healthcare, Clinton, MO, p. A405

NADOLNY, Stephanie, Vice President of Hospital Operations, Spaulding Rehabilitation Hospital Cap. Cod, East Sandwich, MA, p. A338

NAEGLER, Rick, Chief Executive Officer, Lake City Medical Center, Lake City, FL, p. A143

NAFZIGER, Laurie N., President and Chief Executive Officer, Oaklawn Psychiatric Center, Goshen, IN, p. A229

NAFZIGER, Steve, M.D., Vice President Medical Affairs, Parkview Medical Center, Pueblo, CO, p. A118

NAG, Pratip. Vice President, Chief Medical Officer, Katherine Shaw Bethea Hospital, Dixon, IL, p. A202

NAGARAJ, Alaka, M.D., Medical Director, Regency Hospital Of Minneapolis, Golden Valley, MN, p. A377

NAGARAJ, Raghava, M.D., Chief Medical Officer, Wake Forest Baptist Health-Lexington Medical Center, Lexington, NC, p. A514

NAGATOSHI, Holly, R.N., Chief Nursing Officer, San Dimas Community Hospital, San Dimas, CA, p. A93

NAGLER, Richard, M.D., Chief of Staff, Mayo Clinic Health System - Northland In Barron, Barron, WI, p. A781

NAGOWSKI, Michael, Chief Executive Officer, Cap. Fear Valley Medical Center, Fayetteville, NC, p. A510

NAGY, Jeff, Chief Financial Officer, River Bend Hospital, West Lafayette, IN, p. A242

NAGY, Linda, MSN, R.N., Chief Nursing Officer, Brattleboro Retreat, Brattleboro, VT, p. A735

NAGY, Ryan, M.D., President and Chief Medical Officer, Indiana University Health University Hospital, Indianapolis, IN, p. A232

NAHM, Christopher, M.D., Chief Medical Officer, Livingston Regional Hospital, Livingston, TN, p. A642

NAIBERK, Donald T., Administrator and Chief Executive Officer, Butler County Health Care Center, David City, NE, p. A431

NAIDU, Murali, M.D., Chief Executive Officer, Doctors Hospital Of Manteca, Manteca, CA, p. A77

NAIL, Cheryl, R.N., Chief Nursing Officer, City Hospital At White Rock, Dallas, TX, p. A668

NAIR, Chand, M.D., Medical Director, Brooke Glen Behavioral Hospital, Fort Washington, PA, p. A590

NAIR, Vijayachandran, M.D., Chief of Staff, John J. Pershing Veterans Affairs Medical Center, Poplar Bluff, MO, p. A413

NAJIEB, La Donna, Vice President, Human Resources, San Antonio Regional Hospital, Upland, CA, p. A102

NAJIEB, LaDonna, Service Area Director Human Resources, Providence Saint Josep. Medical Center, Burbank, CA, p. A59

NAJJAR, Maher, M.D., Medical Director, Kindred Hospital Chicago-Northlake, Northlake, IL, p. A214

NAKAMOTO, Kenneth, M.D., Vice President Medical Affairs, Pomona Valley Hospital Medical Center, Pomona, CA, p. A86

NAKAMURA, Bridget, Director Information Systems, Adventist Health Simi Valley, Simi Valley, CA, p. A98

NAKASUJI, Jody, Chief Financial Officer, Harbor-Ucla Medical Center, Torrance, CA, p. A101

NALDI, Robert, Chief Financial Officer, Maimonides Medical Center, Brooklyn, NY, p. A478

NALL, Brian, Chief Executive Officer, North Country Hospital And Health Center, Newport, VT, p. A736

NALL, Wes, Chief Financial Officer, Monroe County Hospital, Monroeville, AL, p. A22 Interim Chief Executive Officer, Monroe County Hospital, Monroeville, AL, p. A22

NALLEY, Leanna, Director Human Resources, Texas Health Harris Methodist Hospital Southwest Fort Worth, Fort Worth, TX, p. A679

NANCE, Brett, M.D., Chief Medical Officer, Bear River Valley Hospital, Tremonton, UT, p. A734

NANCE, Christi, R.N., MSN, Chief Nursing Officer, Northwest Specialty Hospital, Post Falls, ID, p. A192

NAPIER, Frank, Interim Chief Financial Officer, Cobre Valley Regional Medical Center, Globe, AZ, p. A32

NAPIERKOWSKI, Daniel, M.D., President, Marymount Hospital, Garfield Heights, OH, p. A541

NAPOLITANO, Mary, Director Human Resources, Specialty Hospital Of Central Jersey, Lakewood, NJ, p. A457

NARAMORE, G, M.D., Chief Medical Officer and in house Legal Counsel, Blount Memorial Hospital, Maryville, TN, p. A643

NARANJO, Maria, Director Human Resources, Memorial Hospital West, Pembroke Pines, FL, p. A153

NARROW, Ann, Director of Nursing, River Hospital, Alexandria Bay, NY, p. A474

NARVAEZ, Andrea, R.N., Chief Nursing Officer, Parker Adventist Hospital, Parker, CO, p. A117

NASEM, Charles D., FACHE, Chief Executive Officer, Select Specialty Hospital-Tulsa Midtown, Tulsa, OK, p. A570

NASER, Bashar, Chief Financial Officer, Gerald Champion Regional Medical Center, Alamogordo, NM, p. A467

NASET-PAYNE, Janet, MS, R.N., Chief Nursing Officer, Van Diest Medical Center, Webster City, IA, p. A260

NASH, Daniel, Chief Information Officer, Emanate Health Inter-Community Hospital, Covina, CA, p. A61

NASH, Ernest, Chief Financial Officer, South Texas Rehabilitation Hospital, Brownsville, TX, p. A661 Chief Financial Officer, Weslaco Regional Rehabilitation Hospital, Weslaco, TX, p. A725

NASH, Gayle, R.N., M.P.H., Chief Nursing Officer, Mountainview Regional Medical Center, Las Cruces, NM, p. A470

NASH, Jacqueline, Controller, Beaumont Hospital, Wayne, Wayne, MI, p. A369

NASH, John D., FACHE, President and Chief Executive Officer, Franciscan Children's, Brighton, MA, p. A336

NASH, Sandra, Chief Fiscal Service, James H. Quillen Veterans Affairs Medical Center, Mountain Home, TN, p. A646

NASH, Tim, M.D., Chief of Staff, Board Vice Chairman, Marshall Medical Center, Lewisburg, TN, p. A642

NASH, Torrey, M.D., Chief of Medical Staff, Weiser Memorial Hospital, Weiser, ID, p. A193

NASHID, Nadia, M.D., Chief of Staff, Windham Hospital, Willimantic, CT, p. A126

NASLUND, Kevin, Manager Information Technology, Cherokee Regional Medical Center, Cherokee, IA, p. A245

NASO, Leanne, Chief Operating Officer, Parker Adventist Hospital, Parker, CO, p. A117

NASRALLAH, Fadi, M.D., Vice President Medical Affairs, Christus Mother Frances Hospital - Tyler, Tyler, TX, p. A721

NASSIEF, Raymond, Senior Vice President, Hospital Operations and Support Services, John Muir Medical Center, Walnut Creek, Walnut Creek, CA, p. A104

NASSTROM, Jeff, D.O., Chief of Staff, Mitchell County Regional Health Center, Osage, IA, p. A255

NAST, Ed, M.D., Chief Medical Officer, Oak Hill Hospital, Brooksville, FL, p. A133

NATAL, Yesenia, Coordinator Human Resources, Hospital Pavia Arecibo, Arecibo, PR, p. A806

NATCHER, Charles, Chief Financial Officer, Kindred Hospital-Los Angeles, Los Angeles, CA, p. A75

NATELSON, Richard, M.D., Chief of Staff, Steele Memorial Medical Center, Salmon, ID, p. A193

NATH, Dilip. Sc.D., Associate Chief Information Officer, Suny Downstate-University Hospital Of Brooklyn, Brooklyn, NY, p. A479

NATH, Pravene, Chief Information Officer, Stanford Health Care, Palo Alto, CA, p. A84

NATHANSON, Andrea, Director Finance, Baystate Franklin Medical Center, Greenfield, MA, p. A339

NATHEM, Joanne, MSN, R.N., Chief Clinical and Nursing Officer, Waverly Health Center, Waverly, IA, p. A259

NATRAJAN, Sunil, M.D., Medical Director, Curahealth Tucson, Tucson, AZ, p. A40

NAU, James, Manager Computer and Applications Support, Delaware Psychiatric Center, New Castle, DE, p. A127

NAUMAN, Michael, Chief Information Officer and Corporate Vice President, Children's Hospital Of Wisconsin-Fox Valley, Neenah, WI, p. A792

Chief Information Officer, Children's Hospital Of Wisconsin, Milwaukee, WI, p. A791

NAVA, Madeline, Chief Executive Officer, Plantation General Hospital, Plantation, FL, p. A154

NAVARRO, Beth, Chief Clinical Officer, Kindred Hospital-Sycamore, Sycamore, IL, p. A221

NAVARRO, Ramomita, Director Human Resources, University Hospital, San Juan, PR, p. A811

NAVARRO, Tess, Chief Financial Officer, Laguna Honda Hospital And Rehabilitation Center, San Francisco, CA, p. A93

NAVAS, Manuel, M.D., Medical Director, Hospital San Pablo Del Este, Fajardo, PR, p. A807

NAWROCKI, Edward, President, St. Luke's Hospital - Anderson Campus, Easton, PA, p. A589

NAZ, Haroon, Chief Executive Officer, Pinnacle Hospital, Crown Point, IN, p. A226

NAZARIAN, Alexander, CPA, Chief Financial Officer, Salem Township Hospital, Salem, IL, p. A219

NAZARIO, Uriel, M.D., Chief of Medical Staff, Kindred Hospital North Florida, Green Cove Springs, FL, p. A139

NAZE, Jesse, Chief Financial Officer, Fall River Hospital, Hot Springs, SD, p. A628

NAZEER, Imran, M.D., Chief of Staff, Woodland Heights Medical Center, Lufkin, TX, p. A698

NAZIR, Tariq, Interim Director Information Technology, Signature Psychiatric Hospital, Kansas City, MO, p. A409

NDOMEA, Feisal, Director Case Management, Kindred Hospital Sugar Land, Sugar Land, TX, p. A717

NDOW, Emmanuel, Chief Information Officer, Marion General Hospital, Marion, IN, p. A236

NEAL, Alisha, Chief Financial Officer, Ochsner Medical Center - North Shore, Slidell, LA, p. A315

NEAL, Bob, Information Technology, Sparrow Ionia Hospital, Ionia, MI, p. A358

NEAL, Kaley, Chief Financial Officer, Shenandoah Medical Center, Shenandoah, IA, p. A257

NEAL, Robert, Manager Information Technology Services, Newman Memorial Hospital, Shattuck, OK, p. A568

NEAL, Roger, Chief Operating Officer, Duncan Regional Hospital, Duncan, OK, p. A558

NEAL, Terrell, R.N., Chief Executive Officer, St. Charles Parish Hospital, Luling, LA, p. A307

NEAL, Thomas, Chief Executive Officer, Berwick Hospital Center, Berwick, PA, p. A584

NEALE, Debra, R.N., Chief Nursing Officer, O'Connor Hospital, Delhi, NY, p. A482

NEALON, Matthew, Vice President, Chief Financial Officer, University Of Cincinnati Medical Center, Cincinnati, OH, p. A533

NEAR, Holly, Chief Administrative Officer, Harsha Behavioral Center, Terre Haute, IN, p. A241

NEAT, Gary, Chief Information Officer, Ephraim Mcdowell Regional Medical Center, Danville, KY, p. A282

Director Information Systems, Ephraim Mcdowell Fort Logan Hospital, Stanford, KY, p. A293

NEBLETT, Meika, M.D., Chief Medical Officer, Community Medical Center, Toms River, NJ, p. A464

NECAS, Kevin, Chief Financial Officer, University Of Missouri Health Care, Columbia, MO, p. A405

NEEB, Verette, R.N., MSN, Chief Nursing Officer, Baylor Scott & White Medical Center-Uptown, Dallas, TX, p. A667

NEECE, Patrick, Chief Information Officer, Jefferson Regional Medical Center, Pine Bluff, AR, p. A52

Chief Information Officer, Lake Regional Health System, Osage Beach, MO, p. A413

NEEDHAM, Kim, Assistant Chief Executive Officer, Vista Health, Waukegan, IL, p. A222

NEEDHAM, Tammy, Chief Nursing Officer, Chatham Hospital, Siler City, NC, p. A518

NEEDLES, Kim, Manager Business Office, Patients' Hospital Of Redding, Redding, CA, p. A87

NEELAGARU, Narasimhulu, M.D., Chief of Staff, Northridge Medical Center, Commerce, GA, p. A169

NEELY, Denise, Vice President and Chief Nursing Officer, Bronson Methodist Hospital, Kalamazoo, MI, p. A359

NEELY, Jill, Chief Financial Officer, Titusville Area Hospital, Titusville, PA, p. A608

NEELY, K. Dale., FACHE, Chief Executive Officer, Encompass Health Rehabilitation Hospital Of Tallahassee, Tallahassee, FL, p. A158

NEELY, Kathy, R.N., Interim Vice President Patient Care Services, Chi St. Vincent Infirmary Medical Center, Little Rock, AR, p. A49

R.N., Interim Vice President Patient Care Services, Chi St. Vincent Morrilton, Morrilton, AR, p. A50

NEELY, Randall, CEO, Simpson General Hospital, Mendenhall, MS, p. A396

NEENAN, Sharon, Interim Chief Nursing Officer, Grant, Ohiohealth Grant Medical Center, Columbus, OH, p. A536

NEERGHEEN, Chabilal, M.D., Medical Director, Western Massachusetts Hospital, Westfield, MA, p. A346

NEESEN, Cindy, Director of Information Technology, Butler County Health Care Center, David City, NE, p. A431

NEET, Bradley D., FACHE, Chief Executive Officer, Southwest Healthcare System, Murrieta, CA, p. A80

NEFF, Kris, Chief Operating Officer, Samaritan Healthcare, Moses Lake, WA, p. A760

NEFF, Mark J., FACHE, President and Chief Executive Officer, St. Claire Healthcare, Morehead, KY, p. A290

NEFF, Richard, M.D., Interim Chief Medical Officer, Flagstaff Medical Center, Flagstaff, AZ, p. A31

NEFF, William, M.D., Chief Medical Officer, Uchealth Medical Center Of The Rockies, Loveland, CO, p. A117

NEGRON, Manuel, Chief Information Technology Service, Veterans Affairs Caribbean Healthcare System, San Juan, PR, p. A811

NEGULESCU, Catalina, M.D., Medical Officer, Baton Rouge Rehabilitation Hospital, Baton Rouge, LA, p. A296

NEIGER, Kelly, Chief Financial Officer, Barton Memorial Hospital, South Lake Tahoe, CA, p. A99

NEIKIRK, Richard, Chief Executive Officer, Cumberland County Hospital, Burkesville, KY, p. A281

NEIL, Eric, Interim Chief Information Officer, Uw Medicine/Northwest Hospital & Medical Center, Seattle, WA, p. A764

NEIL, William, Vice President and Chief Information Officer, Cleveland Clinic Indian River Hospital, Vero Beach, FL, p. A161

NEILSON, Carol, CPA, Controller, Encompass Health Rehabilitation Hospital Of Sugar Land, Sugar Land, TX, p. A717

NEILSON, Erinn, Chief Nursing Officer, Minidoka Memorial Hospital, Rupert, ID, p. A193

NEILSON, Karen, Administrator, Safe Haven Hospital Of Pocatello, Pocatello, ID, p. A192

NEILSON, Richard, Director of Information Services, Timpanogos Regional Hospital, Orem, UT, p. A730

NEIMAN, Carla, Chief Financial Officer, Clark Fork Valley Hospital, Plains, MT, p. A426

NEITZEL, Monte, Chief Executive Officer, Greater Regional Medical Center, Creston, IA, p. A247

NELKIN MCCORMICK, Elizabeth, MSN, R.N., Senior Vice President and Chief Nursing Officer, Memorial Sloan-Kettering Cancer Center, New York, NY, p. A490

NELL, Sergio, Director Information Systems, Watsonville Community Hospital, Watsonville, CA, p. A104

NELLSCH, Verner, M.D., Chief of Staff, Chi St. Luke's Health Memorial Livingston, Livingston, TX, p. A696

NELSON, Allison, Chief Financial Officer, Sanford Canby Medical Center, Canby, MN, p. A374

Chief Financial Officer, Sanford Clear Lake Medical Center, Clear Lake, SD, p. A627

NELSON, Barbara, Ph.D., R.N., Chief Nursing Executive, Sutter Roseville Medical Center, Roseville, CA, p. A89

NELSON, Barry, MSN, Vice President Nursing, Chief Nurse Executive, Carolinas Healthcare System Blue Ridge, Morganton, NC, p. A515

NELSON, Bill, Chief Executive Officer, La Downtown Medical Center, Llc, Los Angeles, CA, p. A75

Chief Executive Officer, Mille Lacs Health System, Onamia, MN, p. A382

NELSON, Carol, Director Human Resources, Montevista Hospital, Las Vegas, NV, p. A443

NELSON, Charles, Chief Executive Officer, Dickinson County Healthcare System, Iron Mountain, MI, p. A358

NELSON, Cory D., Administrator, Sioux Center Health, Sioux Center, IA, p. A258

NELSON, David, FACHE, Chief Financial Officer, Hshs Sacred Heart Hospital, Eau Claire, WI, p. A783

FACHE, Divisional Chief Financial Officer, Hshs St. Joseph's Hospital, Chippewa Falls, WI, p. A781

M.D., Medical Director, Barlow Respiratory Hospital, Los Angeles, CA, p. A73

NELSON, David A., President and Chief Executive Officer, Chi St. Francis Health, Breckenridge, MN, p. A373

NELSON, Dawn, Director Human Resources, Sagewest Health Care, Riverton, WY, p. A803

NELSON, Diane, R.N., Chief Nursing Officer, Kindred Hospital-Albuquerque, Albuquerque, NM, p. A467

NELSON, Elaine, R.N., MSN, Chief Nursing Officer, Texas Health Harris Methodist Hospital Fort Worth, Fort Worth, TX, p. A679

NELSON, Heather, Senior Vice President and Chief Information Officer, University Of Chicago Medical Center, Chicago, IL, p. A201

NELSON, Jack, Vice President Finance and Chief Financial Officer, Heritage Valley Kennedy, Mckees Rocks, PA, p. A596

NELSON, Jackie, Director Human Resources, Hansford Hospital, Spearman, TX, p. A716

NELSON, James, Senior Vice President Finance and Strategic Planning, Fort Healthcare, Fort Atkinson, WI, p. A784

NELSON, Jamie, Vice President and Chief Information Officer, Hospital For Special Surgery, New York, NY, p. A490

NELSON, Jennifer, Senior Human Resource Business Partner, Spectrum Health United Hospital, Greenville, MI, p. A356

NELSON, Jody, Chief Executive Officer, St. Luke's Medical Center, Crosby, ND, p. A522

NELSON, John, Chief of Staff, Merit Health Biloxi, Biloxi, MS, p. A389

NELSON, Joseph, M.D., President Medical Staff, Lewis-Gale Medical Center, Boones Mill, VA, p. A739

NELSON, Julia, Vice President of Human Resources, Northern Regional Hospital, Mount Airy, NC, p. A515

NELSON, Katey, Chief Human Resource Officer, Sanpete Valley Hospital, Mount Pleasant, UT, p. A729

Director Human Resources, Sevier Valley Hospital, Richfield, UT, p. A731

NELSON, Kellie, Director Human Resources, Aurora Medical Center Kenosha, Kenosha, WI, p. A786

NELSON, Kenneth, R.N., IIIChief Nursing Officer, Hshs St. Vincent Hospital, Green Bay, WI, p. A785

NELSON, Kerri, Chief Financial Officer, Spectrum Health Ludington Hospital, Ludington, MI, p. A361

NELSON, Lucy, Director Finance, Vice President, Maniilaq Health Center, Kotzebue, AK, p. A29

NELSON, Lynn, R.N., R.N., Chief Nursing Officer and Chief Operating Officer, St. John's Riverside Hospital, Yonkers, NY, p. A503

NELSON, Marlin, Vice President Fiscal Services, Divine Savior Healthcare, Portage, WI, p. A794

NELSON, Martha, Chief Financial Officer, Antelop. Memorial Hospital, Neligh, NE, p. A435

Chief Financial Officer, Niobrara Valley Hospital, Lynch, NE, p. A435

NELSON, Melissa, Assistant Administrator, Baptist Memorial Hospital For Women, Memphis, TN, p. A644

NELSON, Meredith, Chief Financial Officer, Willamette Valley Medical Center, Mcminnville, OR, p. A577

NELSON, Michael, Chief Financial Officer, Select Specialty Hospital Midtown Atlanta, Atlanta, GA, p. A165

Executive Vice President and Chief Financial Officer, Pomona Valley Hospital Medical Center, Pomona, CA, p. A86

NELSON, Nan, Senior Vice President Finance, Aurora St. Luke's Medical Center, Milwaukee, WI, p. A790

NELSON, Nancy, Director Human Resources, Intermountain Hospital, Boise, ID, p. A188

NELSON, Nick, Director Support Services, Adams Memorial Hospital, Decatur, IN, p. A226

NELSON, Peggy, Chief Executive Officer, Encompass Health Rehabilitation Hospital Of Desert Canyon, Las Vegas, NV, p. A443

NELSON, Raymond, Acting Chief Information Resource Management, Fargo Veterans Affairs Health Care System, Fargo, ND, p. A523

NELSON, Richard, Chief of Human Resources Management Services, Central Arkansas Veterans Healthcare System, Little Rock, AR, p. A49

NELSON, Robin, Chief Financial Officer, Gundersen St. Joseph's Hospital And Clinics, Hillsboro, WI, p. A786
Interim Chief Executive Officer, Gundersen St. Joseph's Hospital And Clinics, Hillsboro, WI, p. A786

NELSON, Selena, Chief Financial Officer, Fallon Medical Complex, Baker, MT, p. A421

NELSON, Siri, Chief Executive Officer, Marshall Medical Center, Placerville, CA, p. A85

NELSON, Stephanie, CPA, Vice President and Chief Financial Officer, Christus Santa Rosa Hospital - San Marcos, San Marcos, TX, p. A714

NELSON, Stewart, Vice President and Chief Financial Officer, Sentara Halifax Regional Hospital, South Boston, VA, p. A751
Vice President and Chief Financial Officer, Sentara Martha Jefferson Hospital, Charlottesville, VA, p. A739
Vice President and Chief Financial Officer, Sentara Rmh Medical Center, Harrisonburg, VA, p. A743

NELSON, Suzanne, R.N., Director of Nursing, Salt Lake Behavioral Health, Salt Lake City, UT, p. A732

NELSON, Tara, Chief Clinic Officer, Hutchinson Health, Hutchinson, MN, p. A378

NELSON, Tricia, Chief Financial Officer, Riverwoods Behavioral Health System, Riverdale, GA, p. A178

NELSON, Trudy, Chief Human Resource Officer, Niobrara Valley Hospital, Lynch, NE, p. A435

NELSON-JONES, Susan, Director Human Resources, Adventist Health Tehachapi Valley, Tehachapi, CA, p. A100

NEMECHEK, Victor, M.D., Chief of Staff and Chief Medical Officer, Sheridan County Health Complex, Hoxie, KS, p. A266

NEMETH, Jim, Senior Vice President of Patient Care Services and Chief Nursing Officer, Memorial Healthcare, Owosso, MI, p. A363

NEMI, Neil, Administrator Facility Information Center, Richard H. Hutchings Psychiatric Center, Syracuse, NY, p. A499

NEONAKIS, Stephanie, Manager Human Resources, Uh Regional Hospitals, Cleveland, OH, p. A535

NERMOE, Bryan, President, Sanford Medical Center Fargo, Fargo, ND, p. A523

NESMITH, Nikki, Chief Nursing Officer, Evans Memorial Hospital, Claxton, GA, p. A168

NESPOLI, John L., President, St. Luke's - Lehighton Campus, Lehighton, PA, p. A595

NESS, David, Vice President Operations, Unitypoint Health - Grinnell Regional Medical Center, Grinnell, IA, p. A250

NESS, Joe, Chief Operating Officer, Ohsu Hospital, Portland, OR, p. A579

NESS, Jon, Chief Executive Officer, Kootenai Health, Coeur D'Alene, ID, p. A190

NESSEL, Mark, Executive Vice President and Chief Operating Officer, Virtua Willingboro Hospital, Willingboro, NJ, p. A466
Senior Vice President and Chief Operating Officer, Virtua Our Lady Of Lourdes Hospital, Camden, NJ, p. A453

NESSELRODT, Derek, Director Information Systems, Grant Memorial Hospital, Petersburg, WV, p. A775

NESTER, Brian A., D.O., President and Chief Executive Officer, Lehigh Valley Hospital, Allentown, PA, p. A583

NESTER, Darlene, Chief Human Resources Officer, Hilton Head Hospital, Hilton Head Island, SC, p. A621
Market Chief Human Resources Officer, Coastal Carolina Hospital, Hardeeville, SC, p. A621

NESTER, Michael, Administrator, H. C. Watkins Memorial Hospital, Quitman, MS, p. A399

NESTER WOLFE, Cheryl R., R.N., President and Chief Executive Officer, Salem Hospital, Salem, OR, p. A581

NESTLER, Nicole, Division Director Human Resources, Chi Mercy Health, Valley City, ND, p. A526

NETTERVILLE, Chad, Administrator and Chief Executive Officer, Field Memorial Community Hospital, Centreville, MS, p. A390

NETTLES, Angela, Vice President, Human Resources and Support Services, Kershawhealth, Camden, SC, p. A615

NETTLES, Robert, Director Human Resources, Mountainview Hospital, Las Vegas, NV, p. A443

NETZER, Craig, M.D., President Medical Staff, Wilcox Medical Center, Lihue, HI, p. A186

NEUBERT, Todd, Chief Executive Officer, Riverton Hospital, Riverton, UT, p. A731

NEUENDORF, Deborah, Vice President Administration, New York-Presbyterian/Hudson Valley Hospital, Cortlandt Manor, NY, p. A482

NEUENDORF, James, M.D., Medical Director, Saint Joseph's Medical Center, Yonkers, NY, p. A502

NEUENDORF, Michael, Chief Executive Officer, Princeton Baptist Medical Center, Birmingham, AL, p. A15
Chief Executive Officer, Walker Baptist Medical Center, Jasper, AL, p. A20

NEUFELD, Ellis, M.D., Chief Medical Officer, St. Jude Children's Research Hospital, Memphis, TN, p. A645

NEUFELDER, Daniel, President, Indiana University Health Arnett Hospital, Lafayette, IN, p. A234

NEUGENT, Kevin, Chief Information Officer, Sparrow Eaton Hospital, Charlotte, MI, p. A351

NEUJAHR, Elias, Chief Executive Officer, Children's Hospital Of Richmond At Vcu-Brook Road Campus, Richmond, VA, p. A750

NEUMAN, Keith, Chief Information Officer, Lutheran Hospital Of Indiana, Fort Wayne, IN, p. A228
Chief Information Officer, Orthopaedic Hospital Of Lutheran Health Network, Fort Wayne, IN, p. A228

NEUMAN, Michael, Vice President Finance, Kennedy Krieger Institute, Baltimore, MD, p. A324

NEUMEISTER, Daniel, Senior Vice President and Chief Operating Officer, Searhc Mt. Edgecumbe Hospital, Sitka, AK, p. A29

NEUNER, Kathy, R.N., Chief Nursing Officer, Clark Memorial Health, Jeffersonville, IN, p. A233

NEUSCHWANGER, Elizabeth, Chief Nursing Officer, Van Wert County Hospital, Van Wert, OH, p. A551

NEUVIRTH, Stephanie, Chief Human Resource and Diversity Officer, City Of Hope's Helford Clinical Research Hospital, Duarte, CA, p. A62

NEVAREZ, Domingo, Chief Executive Officer, Hospital Metropolitan, San Juan, PR, p. A810

NEVILLE, Bette, R.N., MSN, Vice President and Chief Nursing Officer, Northern Light Mercy Hospital, Portland, ME, p. A322

NEVILLE, Lawrence, Chief Medical Officer, Peacehealth Southwest Medical Center, Vancouver, WA, p. A768

NEVILLE, Ryan T., FACHE, President and Chief Executive Officer, Marshfield Medical Center - Neilsville, Neillsville, WI, p. A792

NEVIN, James, M.D., Vice President and Chief Medical Officer, Bromenn Medical Center, Normal, IL, p. A214

NEVIN, Janice E., M.D., M.P.H., Chief Executive Officer, Christianacare, Newark, DE, p. A128

NEVINS, Norm, Manager Human Resources, Kansas Medical Center, Andover, KS, p. A261

NEWBY, Doug, Chief Information Officer, Highlands Medical Center, Scottsboro, AL, p. A24

NEWBY, Jennifer, Operations Director Support Services and Finance, Memorial Community Hospital And Health System, Blair, NE, p. A430

NEWCOMB, James, M.D., Vice President Medical Affairs, Slidell Memorial Hospital, Slidell, LA, p. A315
M.D., Vice President Medical, Ochsner Medical Center - North Shore, Slidell, LA, p. A315

NEWCOMB, Michael, D.O., Senior Vice President and Chief Operating Officer, Legacy Meridian Park Medical Center, Tualatin, OR, p. A582
D.O., Senior Vice President and Chief Operating Officer, Legacy Mount Hood Medical Center, Gresham, OR, p. A575
D.O., Senior Vice President and Chief Operating Officer, Legacy Salmon Creek Medical Center, Vancouver, WA, p. A768

NEWCOMER, Jeremy, Director Information Services, Elmira Psychiatric Center, Elmira, NY, p. A483

NEWCOMER, Peter, M.D., Chief Medical Officer, University Hospital, Madison, WI, p. A788

NEWELL, Dan, Chief Financial Officer, Highlands Medical Center, Scottsboro, AL, p. A24

NEWELL, Janice, Chief Information Officer, Swedish Medical Center-Cherry Hill Campus, Seattle, WA, p. A764
Chief Information Officer, Swedish Medical Center-First Hill, Seattle, WA, p. A764

NEWELL, Richard, Chief Executive Officer, Pottstown Hospital, Pottstown, PA, p. A605

NEWEY, Mark, D.O., Chief of Staff, Mercy Hospital Healdton, Healdton, OK, p. A560

NEWHOUSE, Chuck, M.D., Chief of Staff, Boundary Community Hospital, Bonners Ferry, ID, p. A189

NEWHOUSE, Paul R., President, Union Medical Center, Union, SC, p. A625

NEWLAND, Judy, R.N., Chief Nursing Officer, Incline Village Community Hospital, Incline Village, NV, p. A442
R.N., Chief Operating Officer, Tahoe Forest Hospital District, Truckee, CA, p. A102

NEWMAN, Billy, Department Head, Naval Hospital Lemoore, Lemoore, CA, p. A71

NEWMAN, Carlotta, Human Resources Manager, Northeast Georgia Medical Center Barrow, Winder, GA, p. A183

NEWMAN, Cynthia, Manager Human Resources, Petersburg Medical Center, Petersburg, AK, p. A29

NEWMAN, Dan, Chief Executive Officer, Houston Methodist Clear Lake Hospital, Nassau Bay, TX, p. A702

NEWMAN, Edith, Interim Administrator, John J. Madden Mental Health Center, Hines, IL, p. A208

NEWMAN, Jennifer, Director of Human Resources, Grace Cottage Hospital, Townshend, VT, p. A737

NEWMAN, Jinny, Director Human Resources, Emanuel Medical Center, Swainsboro, GA, p. A181

NEWMAN, John, M.D., Chief Medical Officer, Aurora Medical Center Of Oshkosh, Oshkosh, WI, p. A793

NEWMAN, John B., M.D., President, Aurora Medical Center Of Oshkosh, Oshkosh, WI, p. A793

NEWMAN, JW, Chief Operating Officer, Medical City Fort Worth, Fort Worth, TX, p. A678

NEWMAN, Karen, Ed.D., MSN, R.N., Vice President and Chief Nursing Officer, Baptist Health Louisville, Louisville, KY, p. A287

NEWMAN, Kurt, M.D., President and Chief Executive Officer, Children's National Hospital, Washington, DC, p. A129

NEWMAN, Mark, M.D., Executive Vice President of Health Affairs, University Of Kentucky Albert B. Chandler Hospital, Lexington, KY, p. A287

NEWMAN, Sonya, R.N., Chief Nursing Officer, Blount Memorial Hospital, Maryville, TN, p. A643

NEWMILLER, Vicki, Chief Executive Officer, Great Falls Clinic Hospital, Great Falls, MT, p. A424

NEWMYER, Joyce, President, Adventist Health Portland, Portland, OR, p. A579

NEWQUIST, Dennis, Director Information Systems, Abilene Regional Medical Center, Abilene, TX, p. A651

NEWSOM, Jeremiah, M.D., Medical Director, Ochsner Extended Care Hospital, New Orleans, LA, p. A311

NEWSOM, Terri, Vice President of Finance and Chief Financial Officer, Prisma Health Greenville Memorial Hospital, Greenville, SC, p. A620

NEWSWANGER, Jeff, M.D., Chief Medical Officer, Adventhealth Manchester, Manchester, KY, p. A289

NEWTON, Gail, R.N., MSN, Vice President Patient Care Services, St. Luke's Hospital - Warren Campus, Phillipsburg, NJ, p. A461

NEWTON, Jennifer, R.N., Chief Nursing Officer, Neosho Memorial Regional Medical Center, Chanute, KS, p. A262

NEWTON, Keith, Chief Executive Officer, Northern Louisiana Medical Center, Ruston, LA, p. A313

NEWTON, Steven R., FACHE, President, Baylor University Medical Center, Dallas, TX, p. A668

NEWTON, Susan, Chief Operating Officer, Broward Health North, Deerfield Beach, FL, p. A136

NEWTON, Terri, Chief Nursing Officer, Lakewood Regional Medical Center, Lakewood, CA, p. A71

NEWTON, Wilma, Executive Vice President and Chief Financial Officer, St. Vincent's Birmingham, Birmingham, AL, p. A15

NEYENHOUSE, Rich, Director Information Technology, Thayer County Health Services, Hebron, NE, p. A433

NEZBETH, Jacqueline, Human Resources Officer, Select Specialty Hospital Of Southeast Ohio, Newark, OH, p. A546

NG, Anthony, M.D., Vice President and Chief Medical Officer, The Acadia Hospital, Bangor, ME, p. A318

NG, Hong-Kin, M.D., Chief Medical Officer, Roane General Hospital, Spencer, WV, p. A777

NG, Thomas, Chief Information Officer, Collingsworth General Hospital, Wellington, TX, p. A724

NG, Vincent, Director, Veterans Affairs Boston Healthcare System Brockton Division, Brockton, MA, p. A337
Director, Veterans Affairs Boston Healthcare System, West Roxbury, MA, p. A345

NGIRAISUI, Clarinda, Director, Human Resources, Commonwealth Health Center, Saipan, MP, p. A805

NGUYEN, Abby, R.N., Chief Nursing Officer, Genesis Healthcare System, Zanesville, OH, p. A554

NGUYEN, Bach, Director Information Systems, Northwest Texas Healthcare System, Amarillo, TX, p. A652

NGUYEN, Jinhee, Patient Care Executive, Adventist Health Glendale, Glendale, CA, p. A66

NGUYEN, Nga, Manager Human Resources and Organizational Development, Glendale Memorial Hospital And Health Center, Glendale, CA, p. A67

NIBLOCK, Jenny, Chief Clinical Officer, Citizens Medical Center, Colby, KS, p. A263

NICASTRO, Pamela, Director Human Resources, Brylin Hospitals, Buffalo, NY, p. A479

NICAUD, Kent, President and Chief Executive Officer, Memorial Hospital At Gulfport, Gulfport, MS, p. A393

NICHELSON, Kathleen, Director Human Resources, Horsham Clinic, Ambler, PA, p. A584

NICHOLAS, Angela, Vice President, Medical Affairs, Einstein Medical Center Montgomery, East Norriton, PA, p. A589

NICHOLAS, Chris, Vice President and Administrator, Renown Rehabilitation Hospital, Reno, NV, p. A446
Vice President and Administrator, Renown South Meadows Medical Center, Reno, NV, p. A446

NICHOLAS, David, Chief Executive Officer, St. John Rehabilitation Hospital, Broken Arrow, OK, p. A557

NICHOLS, Amanda, M.D., Chief of Staff, Sistersville General Hospital, Sistersville, WV, p. A776

NICHOLS, Barbara, R.N., President and Chief Executive Officer, Lecom Corry Memorial Hospital, Corry, PA, p. A587

NICHOLS, Bryan, Chief Financial Officer, Baylor Scott & White The Heart Hospital Denton, Denton, TX, p. A671
Chief Financial Officer, Baylor Scott & White The Heart Hospital Plano, Plano, TX, p. A706

NICHOLS, Carl Senior Vice President, Chief Operating Officer, Davis Medical Center, Elkins, WV, p. A772

NICHOLS, Christopher, Chief Executive Officer, Fillmore County Hospital, Geneva, NE, p. A432

NICHOLS, Dia, President and Chief Executive Officer, Amita Health Elk Grove Village, Elk Grove Village, IL, p. A204

NICHOLS, Donna, R.N., Chief Nursing Officer, Goodall-Witcher Hospital, Clifton, TX, p. A664

NICHOLS, Laura, Director Human Resources, Hancock Regional Hospital, Greenfield, IN, p. A230

NICHOLS, Michael, Chief Information Officer, Masonicare Health Center, Wallingford, CT, p. A126

NICHOLS, Nathan, Director of Finance, Sterling Regional Medcenter, Sterling, CO, p. A119

NICHOLS, Randy, Chief Financial Officer, Great River Medical Center, Blytheville, AR, p. A43
Chief Financial Officer, South Mississipp. County Regional Medical Center, Osceola, AR, p. A51

NICHOLS, Robin, Interim Chief Financial Officer, Emory Decatur Hospital, Decatur, GA, p. A171

NICHOLS, Steve, Chief Executive Officer, North Mississipp. Medical Center Gilmore-Amory, Amory, MS, p. A389

NICHOLS, Suzanne, Director Human Resources, Muleshoe Area Medical Center, Muleshoe, TX, p. A702

NICHOLS, Terry, Chief Executive Officer, Pineville Community Health Center, Pineville, KY, p. A292

NICHOLSON, Britain, M.D., Chief Medical Officer, Massachusetts General Hospital, Boston, MA, p. A336

NICHOLSON, Charles, Vice President, Medical Affairs, Sentara Albemarle Medical Center, Elizabeth City, NC, p. A509

NICHOLSON, Chrissy, Vice President of Human Resources, Delta Regional Medical Center, Greenville, MS, p. A392

NICHOLSON, Cindy, Director Human Resources, Shelby Baptist Medical Center, Alabaster, AL, p. A13

NICHOLSON, Debra, Manager Finance, Central Alabama Veterans Health Care System, Montgomery, AL, p. A22

NICHOLSON, H., M.D., M.P.H., Physician in Chief, Phoenix Children's Hospital, Phoenix, AZ, p. A36

NICHOLSON, Jack, Chief Executive Officer, Kindred Hospital-Louisville, Louisville, KY, p. A288

NICHOLSON, Kristin, Coordinator Human Resources, Genesis Medical Center, Dewitt, De Witt, IA, p. A248

NICHOLSON, Molly, MS, R.N., Chief Nurse Executive, Osf Heart Of Mary Medical Center, Urbana, IL, p. A222
MS, R.N., Vice President of Patient Care/Chief Nurse Executive, Osf Sacred Heart Medical Center, Danville, IL, p. A202

NICHOSON, Julia, M.D., Chief Medical Officer, Drew Memorial Health System, Monticello, AR, p. A50

NICKEL, Jarret, Operations Executive, North Central Health Care, Wausau, WI, p. A798

NICKEL, Kathleen, Director Communications, Mercy Medical Center, Roseburg, OR, p. A580

NICKELL, Angela, Executive Director, Sequel Pomegranate Health Systems, Columbus, OH, p. A537

NICKELL, Jerry, Vice President Human Resource and Mission, Saint Alphonsus Medical Center - Baker City, Baker City, OR, p. A573

NICKELS, John, M.D., President Medical Staff, Grace Hospital, Cleveland, OH, p. A534

NICKENS, John R. IV, President and Chief Executive Officer, Children's Hospital, New Orleans, LA, p. A310

NICKENS, Wesley, M.D., Chief of Staff, Collingsworth General Hospital, Wellington, TX, p. A724

NICKRAND, Tami, Director Information Technology, Harbor Beach Community Hospital, Harbor Beach, MI, p. A357

NICKS, Bret, M.D., Chief Medical Officer and Chief of Staff, Wake Forest Baptist Health-Davie Medical Center, Bermuda Run, NC, p. A505

NICOLAS, Fadi, M.D., Chief Medical Officer, Sharp Mesa Vista Hospital, San Diego, CA, p. A92

NICOLAY, Donald, M.D., Chief Medical Officer, Community Hospital, Grand Junction, CO, p. A113

NICOLL, C., M.D., Ph.D., Chief of Staff, San Francisco Va Medical Center, San Francisco, CA, p. A94

NICOLSON, Lynne, M.D., Medical Director, Sunnyview Rehabilitation Hospital, Schenectady, NY, p. A498

NICOSIA, Chris, Chief Financial Officer, Corpus Christi Medical Center, Corpus Christi, TX, p. A666

NIEDEREE, Laurie, M.D., Chief Medical Officer, Alta View Hospital, Sandy, UT, p. A733

NIEDERPRUEM, Mark L., FACHE, Administrator, Shriners Hospitals For Children-Chicago, Chicago, IL, p. A201

NIELSEN, Ben, Chief Operating Officer, Ridgeview Sibley Medical Center, Arlington, MN, p. A372

NIELSEN, Gwen, Manager Human Resources, Indianhead Medical Center, Shell Lake, WI, p. A796

NIELSEN, Helen, Director Human Resources, Lovelace Medical Center, Albuquerque, NM, p. A467
Director Human Resources, Lovelace Unm Rehabilitation Hospital, Albuquerque, NM, p. A467

NIELSEN, Kristine, Manager Human Resources, Memorial Community Hospital And Health System, Blair, NE, p. A430

NIELSEN, Randy, Director Information Technology, Arbor Health, Morton Hospital, Morton, WA, p. A760

NIELSEN, Wayne, Director Human Resources, Ocala Regional Medical Center, Ocala, FL, p. A150

NIELSON, Curtis, Chief Financial Officer, South Lincoln Medical Center, Kemmerer, WY, p. A802

NIELSON, Lars, M.D., Chief Medical Officer, Weeks Medical Center, Lancaster, NH, p. A449

NIELSON, P, M.D., Chief of Staff, Kahuku Medical Center, Kahuku, HI, p. A185

NIELSON, Yvonne, Chief Nursing Officer, Director Quality Management and Regulatory Compliance, Mountain West Medical Center, Tooele, UT, p. A733

NIEMALA, Amanda, Director of Information Services, Bigfork Valley Hospital, Bigfork, MN, p. A372

NIEMANN, Lynne, Director Nurses and Patient Care, Community Memorial Hospital, Sumner, IA, p. A259

NIENHUIS, Jamie, Chief Nursing Officer, Cavalier County Memorial Hospital And Clinics, Langdon, ND, p. A524

NIERMAN, Stephen A., President, Winter Haven Hospital, Winter Haven, FL, p. A162

NIERMANN, Michelle, President and Chief Executive Officer, Unitypoint Health - St. Luke's Hospital, Cedar Rapids, IA, p. A245

NIES, Lynn, Human Resources Officer, Erie Veterans Affairs Medical Center, Erie, PA, p. A589

NIESE, Mel, Chief Fiscal Service, Va Palo Alto Health Care System, Palo Alto, CA, p. A84

NIESEN, Matthew, M.D., Chief of the Medical Staff, Prairie Ridge Health, Inc., Columbus, WI, p. A782

NIESSINK, Henry, Regional Director Information Technology Services, Mercy Medical Center Redding, Redding, CA, p. A87
Senior Manager Information Technology Systems, St. Elizabeth Community Hospital, Red Bluff, CA, p. A87

NIEVES, Deborah, Director Management Information Systems, Hospital San Francisco, San Juan, PR, p. A810

NIEVES, Erick, M.D., Medical Director, Hospital San Carlos Borromeo, Moca, PR, p. A808

NIEVES, James F., Executive Director, San Juan City Hospital, San Juan, PR, p. A811

NIGG, Nicole, Chief Executive Officer, Mercyone Clive Rehabilitation Hospital, Clive, IA, p. A246

NIGH, Andrew, M.D., Chief of Staff, Indiana University Health West Hospital, Avon, IN, p. A223

NIGHMAN, Mike, Facility Coordinator Information Systems, Shelby Baptist Medical Center, Alabaster, AL, p. A13

NIGHTENGALE, Randy, Chief Financial Officer, Bingham Memorial Hospital, Blackfoot, ID, p. A188

NIGHTINGALE, Judi, R.N., Dr.PH, Chief Nursing Officer, Riverside University Health System-Medical Center, Moreno Valley, CA, p. A80

NIGON, Scott, Finance Senior Manager, Essentia Health St. Mary's Hospital Of Superior, Superior, WI, p. A797

NIGRIN, Daniel, M.D., Vice President Information Services and Chief Information Officer, Boston Children's Hospital, Boston, MA, p. A335

NIHALANI, Sunil, M.D., Chief Medical Staff, Adventhealth Lake Wales, Lake Wales, FL, p. A143

NIJOKA, Monica, Chief Nursing Officer, Baton Rouge General Medical Center, Baton Rouge, LA, p. A296

NILES, Heather, Director Human Resources Operations, Mercyhealth Hospital And Medical Center - Harvard, Harvard, IL, p. A207

NILEST, Nicholas, Chief Executive Officer, New Braunfels Regional Rehabilitation Hospital, New Braunfels, TX, p. A703

NIMMO, Ben, M.D., Medical Director, Pinnacle Pointe Hospital, Little Rock, AR, p. A49

NIMMO, Brian, Director, Huntington Veterans Affairs Medical Center, Huntington, WV, p. A773

NIMS, Carrie, Director of Nursing, Post Acute/Warm Springs Specialty Hospital Of San Antonio, San Antonio, TX, p. A713

NINNEMAN, David, Associate Director, Cincinnati Veterans Affairs Medical Center, Cincinnati, OH, p. A532

NIPPER, Nathan, Chief Operating Officer, Piedmont Fayette Hospital, Fayetteville, GA, p. A172

Vice President and Chief Operating Officer, Piedmont Newnan Hospital, Newnan, GA, p. A178

NIPPERT, Kathi, Acting Chief Human Resources Officer, Kansas City Veterans Affairs Medical Center, Kansas City, MO, p. A408

NISH, Paulette, Chief Nursing Officer, Geisinger Jersey Shore Hospital, Jersey Shore, PA, p. A593

NISKANEN, Brian, Chief Medical Officer, Welia Health, Mora, MN, p. A381

NISKANEN, Grant, M.D., Vice President Medical Affairs, Sky Lakes Medical Center, Klamath Falls, OR, p. A576

NISSEN, Beth, Director Human Resources, Troy Regional Medical Center, Troy, AL, p. A25

NIU, Paul, Chief Medical Officer, Corona Regional Medical Center, Corona, CA, p. A61

NIX, Alisha, Director Human Resources, Wilbarger General Hospital, Vernon, TX, p. A723

NIX, Bo, Chief Information Officer, Madison Valley Medical Center, Ennis, MT, p. A423

NIX, Julie, Vice President and Administrator, Baptist Health Rehabilitation Institute, Little Rock, AR, p. A49

NIXDORF, David, Director Support Services, Frances Mahon Deaconess Hospital, Glasgow, MT, p. A424

NIXON, James, Chief Operating Officer, Meadows Regional Medical Center, Vidalia, GA, p. A182

NIXON, Myra, Director Human Resources, Encompass Health Rehabilitation Hospital Of Concord, Concord, NH, p. A448

NIZAMI, Nassar, Chief Information Officer, Thomas Jefferson University Hospitals, Philadelphia, PA, p. A602

NNAJI, Felix, Chief Medical Staff, Bolivar General Hospital, Bolivar, TN, p. A634

NOAK, Amy, Director Human Resources, St. David's Round Rock Medical Center, Round Rock, TX, p. A710

NOAKES, Timothy, Chief Financial Officer, Memorial Hospital Los Banos, Los Banos, CA, p. A76

NOBLE, Angela, Director of Nursing, West Feliciana Hospital, Saint Francisville, LA, p. A313

NOBLE, Dave, Director of Nursing, Livingstone Healthcare, Livingston, MT, p. A426

NOBLE, Lloyd, Chief Executive Officer, Valley Hospital Phoenix, Phoenix, AZ, p. A37

NOBLE, Mallie S., Administrator, Mary Breckinridge Arh Hospital, Hyden, KY, p. A285

NOBLES, Diane, Nurse Executive, East Mississipp. State Hospital, Meridian, MS, p. A397

NOBLES, Sharon, Chief Financial Officer, North Mississipp. Health Services, Inc., Tupelo, MI, p. A368
Interim Chief Financial Officer, Baptist Hospital, Pensacola, FL, p. A153

NOBLES, Trent, Chief Executive Officer, Southside Regional Medical Center, Petersburg, VA, p. A749

NOCKOWITZ, Richard, M.D., Medical Director, Ohio Hospital For Psychiatry, Columbus, OH, p. A536

NOE, Sharon, Chief Executive Officer, Cobalt Rehabilitation Hospital, Surprise, AZ, p. A39

NOEL, Bill, Chief Operating Officer, Grand River Hospital District, Rifle, CO, p. A118

NOEL, Vicki, Vice President Human Resources, Southern Ohio Medical Center, Portsmouth, OH, p. A548

NOEL III, Philip J., Chief Executive Officer, Ottumwa Regional Health Center, Ottumwa, IA, p. A256

NOESS, Bobbi, Director of Nursing, Bowdle Hospital, Bowdle, SD, p. A626

NOFFSINGER, Sandy, Executive Assistant, Risk Manager and Director Marketing, Dundy County Hospital, Benkelman, NE, p. A430

NOGLER, Wendy, Director Human Resources, Lincoln County Health System, Fayetteville, TN, p. A638

NOKELS, Kevin J., FACHE, President and Chief Executive Officer, St. Luke's Hospital, Duluth, MN, p. A375

NOLAN, Brittney, Chief Executive Officer, Glen Oaks Hospital, Greenville, TX, p. A682

NOLAN, Douglas, M.D., Medical Director, Cherokee Nation W.W. Hastings Indian Hospital, Tahlequah, OK, p. A569

NOLAN, Heather, Director Information Services, Northern Louisiana Medical Center, Ruston, LA, p. A313

NOLAN, Jennifer, President and Chief Executive Officer, Chi Flaget Memorial Hospital, Bardstown, KY, p. A280

NOLAN, Matthew, Chief Operating Officer, The University Of Vermont Health Network Elizabethtown Community Hospital, Elizabethtown, NY, p. A483

NOLAN, Patrick, Chief Operating Officer, Inspira Medical Center-Woodbury, Woodbury, NJ, p. A466
Vice President Finance and Chief Financial Officer, Gillette Children's Specialty Healthcare, Saint Paul, MN, p. A385

NOLAN, Roz, Interim Chief Nursing Officer, Community Hospital Of San Bernardino, San Bernardino, CA, p. A91

NOLASCO, Wanda, Chief Nursing Officer, Fairmount Behavioral Health System, Philadelphia, PA, p. A600

NOLD, Pam, Chief Nurse Executive, Northwest Missouri Psychiatric Rehabilitation Center, Saint Joseph, MO, p. A415

NOLE, Penny, Director of Patient Care Services, The Medical Center At Caverna, Horse Cave, KY, p. A285

NOLEN, Benny, President and Chief Executive Officer, Methodist Hospital Union County, Morganfield, KY, p. A290

NOLES, Coy, Chief Financial Officer Consultant, Hamilton Hospital, Olney, TX, p. A704

NOLL, David, Director, Adventist Health St. Helena, Saint Helena, CA, p. A90

NOLL, Gerald, Chief Financial Officer, Rogers Memorial Hospital, Inc., Oconomowoc, WI, p. A793

NOLLEY, Dexter, Chief Human Resources Officer, Duke Regional Hospital, Durham, NC, p. A508

NOLT, Lori, Director Information Technology, Wellspan Philhaven, Mount Gretna, PA, p. A597

NOLTE, Darlene, Chief Human Resource Officer, Saint Francis Hospital Vinita, Vinita, OK, p. A571

NONNEMAN, Lisa, Director Information Technology Services, Mary Lanning Healthcare, Hastings, NE, p. A433

NOONAN, Anna T., President and Chief Operating Officer, The University Of Vermont Health Network Central Vermont Medical Center, Berlin, VT, p. A735

NOONAN, Kathryn, Director Information Management, Lemuel Shattuck Hospital, Jamaica Plain, MA, p. A340

NOONE, Thomas, M.D., Chief Medical Officer, Bayfront Health Port Charlotte, Port Charlotte, FL, p. A154

NOPWASKEY, Cristen, Chief Information Officer, Weirton Medical Center, Weirton, WV, p. A777

NORBURY, Denise, MS, R.N., Regional Chief Executive Officer, Center For Behavioral Medicine, Kansas City, MO, p. A408
MS, R.N., Regional Executive Officer, Northwest Missouri Psychiatric Rehabilitation Center, Saint Joseph, MO, p. A415

NORBY, Michael, Chief Financial Officer, Harris Health System, Houston, TX, p. A685

NORD, Gay, Chief Executive Officer, West Florida Hospital, Pensacola, FL, p. A154

NORD, Stanley, Chief Financial Officer, Hca Houston Healthcare West, Houston, TX, p. A686

NORDAHL, Richard, Senior Director, Sanford Sheldon Medical Center, Sheldon, IA, p. A257

NORDAHL, Richard E., Senior Director, Sanford Sheldon Medical Center, Sheldon, IA, p. A257

NORDBERG, Traci, Chief Human Resources Officer, Vanderbilt University Medical Center, Nashville, TN, p. A647

NORDBY, Betsy, Director of Human Resources, St. Croix Regional Medical Center, St Croix Falls, WI, p. A796

NORDBY, Shawn, Chief Financial Officer, Mary Lanning Healthcare, Hastings, NE, p. A433

NORDELL, Cindy, Chief Nursing Officer, Encompass Health Rehabilitation Hospital Of Colorado Springs, Colorado Springs, CO, p. A109

NORDENG, Rod, Administrator, Floyd County Medical Center, Charles City, IA, p. A245

NORDIN, Danna, Director Human Resources, Anchor Hospital, Atlanta, GA, p. A164

NORDLUND, Sarah, Director of Nursing, Garfield County Health Center, Jordan, MT, p. A425

NORDSTROM, Janice, Director Human Resources, Landmark Hospital Of Joplin, Joplin, MO, p. A408

NORDSTROM, Katie, Director Human Resources, Beartooth Billings Clinic, Red Lodge, MT, p. A427

NORDWICK, Thomas, FACHE, Chief Executive Officer, Uvalde Memorial Hospital, Uvalde, TX, p. A722

NORDYKE, Charles, Chief Executive Officer, Clarinda Regional Health Center, Clarinda, IA, p. A246

NORDYKE, Melissa, Chief Financial Officer, Ascension Seton Smithville, Smithville, TX, p. A716

NOREEN, James, M.D., Chief Medical Officer, Regina Hospital, Hastings, MN, p. A378

NORELDIN, Mohsen, M.D., President Medical Staff, Athol Hospital, Athol, MA, p. A334

NORELL, Brett William., Interim Chief Executive Officer, Holy Family Memorial, Manitowoc, WI, p. A788

NOREM, Ashley, Chief Information Systems, Starke Hospital, Knox, IN, p. A234

NOREN, Tom, M.D., Chief Medical Officer, Up Health System-Marquette, Marquette, MI, p. A361

NORGAARD, Margaret B., Chief Executive Officer, Poplar Community Hospital, Poplar, MT, p. A427
Chief Executive Officer, Trinity Hospital, Wolf Point, MT, p. A428

NORICK, Laurence, M.D., Clinical Director, U. S. Public Health Service Indian Hospital, Parker, AZ, p. A34

NORMAN, Andrea, Chief Executive Officer, Valley Behavioral Health System, Barling, AR, p. A42

NORMAN, Daniel, Regional Service Manager, Unitypoint Health - Allen Hospital, Waterloo, IA, p. A259

NORMAN, Debbie, MSN, R.N., Chief Nursing Officer, Elkview General Hospital, Hobart, OK, p. A560
Director Human Resources, Central Louisiana Surgical Hospital, Alexandria, LA, p. A295

NORMAN, Jimmy, Chief Financial Officer, Mountain Lakes Medical Center, Clayton, GA, p. A168

NORMAN, Laura, Chief Development and Information Officer, Windhaven Psychiatric Hospital, Prescott Valley, AZ, p. A37

NORMAN, Lori, Chief Financial Officer, Encompass Health Rehabilitation Hospital Of Gadsden, Gadsden, AL, p. A19

NORMAN, Michael, Executive Vice President and Chief Operating Officer, Landmark Hospital Of Cap. Girardeau, Cap. Girardeau, MO, p. A403

NORMINGTON-SLAY, Jeremy, FACHE, Chief Executive Officer, Ascension Good Samaritan Hospital, Merrill, WI, p. A790
FACHE, President, North Central Region, Marshfield Medical Center - Weston, Weston, WI, p. A799
FACHE, President, Ascension Our Lady Of Victory Hospital, Stanley, WI, p. A796

NORQUEST, Cathy, Director Human Resources, York General, York, NE, p. A440

NORRICK, Michael, Director of Campus Operations, Prisma Health Laurens County Hospital, Clinton, SC, p. A617

NORRIS, Beth Vice President Patient Care Services, Thibodaux Regional Health System, Thibodaux, LA, p. A316

NORRIS, David, Chief Medical Staff, Sweetwater Hospital, Sweetwater, TN, p. A650

NORRIS, Katrina, Superintendent, Richmond State Hospital, Richmond, IN, p. A239

NORRIS, Lucy, Administrator Interim Chief Nursing Officer, Multicare Good Samaritan Hospital, Puyallup. WA, p. A762

NORTH, Mark, Chief Financial Officer, Rmc Anniston, Anniston, AL, p. A13

NORTH, Ralene, Chief Nurse Executive, Massena Hospital, Inc., Massena, NY, p. A488

NORTHCUTT, Lynn, Chief Information Officer, Musc Health Florence Medical Center, Florence, SC, p. A619

NORTHERN, Gail, Director Human Resources, Blue Mountain Hospital, Blanding, UT, p. A727

NORTHUP, Carol, R.N., Chief Nursing Officer and Chief Operating Officer, J. Arthur Dosher Memorial Hospital, Southport, NC, p. A518

NORTHUP, Jeffrey, D.O., Chief Medical Officer, Knox Community Hospital, Mount Vernon, OH, p. A546

NORTON, Andrew, M.D., Chief Medical Officer, Bryn Mawr Hospital, Bryn Mawr, PA, p. A585
M.D., Chief Medical Officer, Paoli Hospital, Paoli, PA, p. A599

NORTON, Bill, Chief Nursing Officer, Rehoboth Mckinley Christian Health Care Services, Gallup. NM, p. A469

NORTON, Carole, Chief Nursing Officer, Stonewall Jackson Memorial Hospital, Weston, WV, p. A777

NORTON, Julie, Vice President, Operational Finance, Avera Mckennan Hospital And University Health Center, Sioux Falls, SD, p. A631

NORTON, Lizette, Vice President, Human Resources, Loma Linda University Children's Hospital, Loma Linda, CA, p. A71

NORTON, Meg, Executive Vice President and Chief Administrative Officer, Rady Children's Hospital - San Diego, San Diego, CA, p. A91

NORTON, Sidney, Chief Financial Officer, Primary Children's Hospital, Salt Lake City, UT, p. A732

NORTON, Susan, Vice President Human Resources, Augusta University Medical Center, Augusta, GA, p. A165

NORTON-ROSKO, Peggy, R.N., Regional Chief Nursing Officer, Loyola University Medical Center, Maywood, IL, p. A211

NORVILLE, Amy, Vice President Support Services, St. Luke's Hospital, Columbus, NC, p. A508

NORWOOD, William, Vice President, Human Resources, Brattleboro Memorial Hospital, Brattleboro, VT, p. A735

NOSACKA, David, Chief Financial Officer, Hshs St. Elizabeth's Hospital, O'Fallon, IL, p. A215
Southern Illinois Division Chief Financial Officer, Hshs St. Joseph's Hospital, Highland, IL, p. A207

NOSACKA, Mark, Chief Executive Officer, Piedmont Medical Center, Rock Hill, SC, p. A624

NOSBISCH, Don, Director Human Resources, Floyd County Medical Center, Charles City, IA, p. A245

NOSEWORTHY, Ed, Chief Executive Officer, Adventhealth Daytona Beach, Daytona Beach, FL, p. A136

NOSKIN, Gary, Senior Vice President and Chief Medical Officer, Northwestern Memorial Hospital, Northwestern Memorial Hospital, Chicago, IL, p. A200

NOSKO, Jeannine, Vice President Patient Care, Aspirus Wausau Hospital, Inc., Wausau, WI, p. A798

NOSTRANT, Hunter Kyle., Chief Executive Officer, Helen Newberry Joy Hospital, Newberry, MI, p. A363

NOTEMAN, Laurali, Director Human Resources, Kane County Hospital, Kanab, UT, p. A728

NOTTER, Pat, R.N., Chief Nursing Officer and Director Quality, Melissa Memorial Hospital, Holyoke, CO, p. A114

NOTTINGHAM, Cheryl, Chief Financial Officer, Atlantic General Hospital, Berlin, MD, p. A327

NOUNA, Nabil, M.D., Chief of Staff, Ascension Allegan Hospital, Allegan, MI, p. A348

NOVAK, Charles, M.D., Chief Medical Officer, Intermountain Hospital, Boise, ID, p. A188

NOVAK, Christopher, Chief Operating Officer, Amita Health Alexian Brothers Behavioral Health Hospital, Hoffman Estates, IL, p. A208

NOVAK, Georgene, Director Human Resources, Littleton Regional Healthcare, Littleton, NH, p. A450

NOVAK, Jerald, Chief People Officer, University Of Vermont Medical Center, Burlington, VT, p. A735

NOVAK, Kristen, Director, Human Resources, Hudson Hospital And Clinic, Hudson, WI, p. A786
Manager Human Resources, River Falls Area Hospital, River Falls, WI, p. A795

NOVAK, Matthew, President, Mease Countryside Hospital, Safety Harbor, FL, p. A155
President, Mease Dunedin Hospital, Dunedin, FL, p. A137

NOVAK, Michael, Vice President and Chief Operating Officer, Montefiore Nyack Hospital, Nyack, NY, p. A493
Vice President, Operations and Chief Information Officer, Saint Mary's Hospital, Waterbury, CT, p. A126

NOVELLO, Regina, R.N., Chief Operating Officer, Healdsburg District Hospital, Healdsburg, CA, p. A68

NOVICK, Peggy, Vice President, Clinical Support and Outpatient Services, Milford Regional Medical Center, Milford, MA, p. A341

NOVOA LOYOLA, Jose, M.D., Medical Director, Cardiovascular Center Of Puerto Rico And The Caribbean, San Juan, PR, p. A809

NOVOSEL, Stacie, Vice President, Human Resources, South Bay Hospital, Sun City Center, FL, p. A158

NOWACHEK, Debra, Director Human Resources, Unitypoint Health - Grinnell Regional Medical Center, Grinnell, IA, p. A250

NOWICKI, Becky, Director Human Resources, Michiana Behavioral Health Center, Plymouth, IN, p. A239

NOWICKI, Michelle, R.N., MSN, Chief Nurse Executive, Kaiser Permanente Baldwin Park Medical Center, Baldwin Park, CA, p. A57

NOWLIN, Jeffrey, President and Chief Operating Officer, St. John Medical Center, Tulsa, OK, p. A571

NOWLIN, Jeffrey D., President and Chief Operating Officer, St. John Medical Center, Tulsa, OK, p. A571

NOWLING, Tara, Director Human Resources, Monroe County Hospital, Monroeville, AL, p. A22

NOYES, Vikki, Executive Vice President and Chief Operating Officer, Confluence Health/Central Washington Hospital, Wenatchee, WA, p. A768

NUAKO, Kofi, M.D., President Medical Staff, Baptist Memorial Hospital-Union City, Union City, TN, p. A650

NUDD, Brandon M., Chief Executive Officer, Castle Rock Adventist Hospital, Castle Rock, CO, p. A108

NUGENT, Shelly, R.N., Director Nurses and Infection Control, Louisiana Extended Care Hospital Of West Monroe, West Monroe, LA, p. A316

NUGENT, Victoria, Chief Nursing Officer, Dignity Health Arizona General Hospital, Laveen, AZ, p. A33

NUMMI, Lisa, MSN, R.N., Chief Operating Officer, Blake Medical Center, Bradenton, FL, p. A132

NUNEZ, Humberto, M.D., Chief Medical Officer, Mission Regional Medical Center, Mission, TX, p. A701

NUNEZ, Michael, Chief Financial Officer, University Medical Center Of El Paso, El Paso, TX, p. A676

NUNEZ, Milton, Executive Director, Nyc Health + Hospitals / Lincoln, Bronx, NY, p. A477

NUNEZ, Sheila, Director Human Resources, Eastern New Mexico Medical Center, Roswell, NM, p. A471

NUNN, Brian, R.N., Chief Executive Officer, Encompass Health Rehabilitation Hospital Of Florence, Florence, SC, p. A619

NUNN, Chalmers, M.D., Chief Medical Officer and Senior Vice President, Centra Lynchburg General Hospital, Lynchburg, VA, p. A745

NUNN, Vernell, Chief Executive Officer, Summitridge Hospital, Lawrenceville, GA, p. A175

NUNNELLY, Sarah, Executive Vice President and Chief Operating Officer, East Alabama Medical Center, Opelika, AL, p. A23

NURY, Alex, Chief Information Officer, Providence Tarzana Medical Center, Tarzana, CA, p. A100

NUSBAUM, Neil, M.D., Chief of Staff, Veterans Affairs Central Western Massachusetts Healthcare System, Leeds, MA, p. A340

NUSS, Suzanne, Ph.D., R.N., Chief Nursing Officer, Nebraska Medicine - Nebraska Medical Center, Omaha, NE, p. A437

NUSS, Suzanne Langan., Ph.D., R.N., Vice President of Operations and Chief Nursing Officer, Nebraska Medicine - Bellevue, Bellevue, NE, p. A440

NUSSBAUM, Joseph, M.D., Chief of Staff, California Hospital Medical Center, Los Angeles, CA, p. A73

NUSSBAUM, Mark, Vice President Operations, Marymount Hospital, Garfield Heights, OH, p. A541

NUTTER, Robert, President and Chief Executive Officer, Littleton Regional Healthcare, Littleton, NH, p. A450

NUTTING, Ron, M.D., Chief Medical Officer, Reading Hospital, West Reading, PA, p. A610

NWATUOBI, Joyce, Vice President Finance, Aurora Medical Center - Manitowoc County, Two Rivers, WI, p. A797

NWOKIKE, Jerome, M.D., Medical Director, Spring Mountain Treatment Center, Las Vegas, NV, p. A444

NYAMU, Samuel, M.D., Chief Medical Officer, Sanford Aberdeen Medical Center, Aberdeen, SD, p. A626

NYBERG, Amy, President and Chief Operating Officer, Coordinated Health-Bethlehem, Bethlehem, PA, p. A584
President, Lehigh Valley Health Network At Coordinated Health, Allentown, PA, p. A583

NYBERG, Becky, Chief Financial Officer, Bloomington Meadows Hospital, Bloomington, IN, p. A224

NYHUIS, Jenifer, Chief Executive Officer, Vista Del Mar Hospital, Ventura, CA, p. A103

NYIKES, Debra, Director Finance and Chief Financial Officer, Cleveland Clinic Children's Hospital For Rehabilitation, Cleveland, OH, p. A534

NYKAMP, Robert, Vice President and Chief Operating Officer, Pine Rest Christian Mental Health Services, Grand Rapids, MI, p. A356

NYLUND, Barbara, M.D., Chief of Staff, Novato Community Hospital, Novato, CA, p. A81

NYMOEN, Gary, Chief Financial Officer, Hialeah Hospital, Hialeah, FL, p. A139

NYSTROM, Dale, M.D., Chief Medical Officer, Physician, Hawarden Regional Healthcare, Hawarden, IA, p. A251

## O

O CONNOR, Joyce, Chief Operating Officer, Taunton State Hospital, Taunton, MA, p. A345

OAKES, Julie, R.N., Manager Risk and Quality, Ocean Beach Hospital, Ilwaco, WA, p. A759

OAKES FERRUCCI, Susan, MS, Vice President Patient Services and Chief Nursing Officer, Cobleskill Regional Hospital, Cobleskill, NY, p. A481

OAKLEY, Lisa, Chief Financial Officer, Harper County Community Hospital, Buffalo, OK, p. A557

OAKLEY, Sarah, R.N., MSN, Vice President Nursing, North Kansas City Hospital, North Kansas City, MO, p. A413

OAXACA, Norma, Director Human Resources, Peak Behavioral Health Services, Santa Teresa, NM, p. A472

OBANDO, Alisha, Director of Nursing, Chadron Community Hospital And Health Services, Chadron, NE, p. A431

OBERHEU, Todd, Administrator, Lincoln County Medical Center, Ruidoso, NM, p. A471

OBERMIER, Jenny, Senior Vice President, Chief Operating Officer and Chief Nursing Officer, York General, York, NE, p. A440

OBERSTAR, Joel V., M.D., Chief Executive Officer and Chief Medical Officer, Prairiecare - Brooklyn Park, Brooklyn Park, MN, p. A373

OBEY, Bianca, Chief Financial Officer, Alexandria Veterans Affairs Health Care System, Pineville, LA, p. A312

OCASIO, J, Vice President Human Resources, Holy Cross Hospital, Silver Spring, MD, p. A332

OCEGUERA, Louis, M.D., Medical Director, Little Falls Hospital, Little Falls, NY, p. A487

OCHOA, Mark, M.D., Deputy Commander, Clinical Services, Irwin Army Community Hospital, Junction City, KS, p. A267

OCHOA, Monica, Chief Executive Officer, Georgetown Behavioral Health Institute, Georgetown, TX, p. A681

OCHOA, Nikki, Interim Chief Financial Officer, St. Joseph's Medical Center, Stockton, CA, p. A100

ODATO, David, Chief Administrative and Chief Human Resources Officer, Ucsf Medical Center, San Francisco, CA, p. A94

ODEGAARD, Daniel, FACHE, Chief Executive Officer, Caldwell Medical Center, Princeton, KY, p. A292

ODELL, Michelle, Director of Public Affairs, Kaiser Permanente South Sacramento Medical Center, Sacramento, CA, p. A89

ODEN, Greg, Chief Medical Officer, Merit Health Central, Jackson, MS, p. A394

ODEN, Ryan, D.O., Chief of Staff, Arbuckle Memorial Hospital, Sulphur, OK, p. A568

ODEN, Tracie, Vice President, Human Resources, Northwest Hospital, Randallstown, MD, p. A331

ODETOYINBO, Adedapo, M.D., Chief Medical Office, Emory Johns Creek Hospital, Johns Creek, GA, p. A174

ODLE, Susan, Administrator, St. Josep. Memorial Hospital, Murphysboro, IL, p. A213

ODOL, Corey, Director Business Development, Psychiatric Institute Of Washington, Washington, DC, p. A130

ODOM, Jake, Chief Information Officer, Trinity Hospital, Weaverville, CA, p. A104

ODOM, Jennifer, Interim Director Human Resources, Flowers Hospital, Dothan, AL, p. A17

ODOM, Lee Ann, Division President, Beaumont Hospital - Taylor, Taylor, MI, p. A367
Interim President, Beaumont Hospital - Trenton, Trenton, MI, p. A368

ODOM, Robbin, R.N., MSN, Chief Nursing Officer, Christus Ochsner Lake Area Hospital, Lake Charles, LA, p. A306

ODOM, Terry, Chief Executive Officer, Powell Valley Healthcare, Powell, WY, p. A803

ODONELL, John, Director Information Systems, Cherokee Medical Center, Gaffney, SC, p. A620

ODUWOLE, Adedapo, M.D., Medical Director, Lighthouse Behavioral Health Hospital, Conway, SC, p. A618

OEHLKE, Tammy, Director Human Resources, St. Mark's Medical Center, La Grange, TX, p. A694

OEHMKE, Brittni, Administrator, Hanover Hospital, Hanover, KS, p. A265

OETTING, Phyllis, Director Human Resources, Mitchell County Hospital Health Systems, Beloit, KS, p. A262

OETZEL, Gerald, Chief Financial Officer, Temple University Hospital, Philadelphia, PA, p. A602

OFFUTT, Dan, Manager Finance, Knox County Hospital, Knox City, TX, p. A694

OFSTEDAL, Jeff, Manager Information Technology, Glacial Ridge Health System, Glenwood, MN, p. A377

OGASAWARA, Keith, M.D., Associate Medical Director and Professional Chief of Staff, Kaiser Permanente Medical Center, Honolulu, HI, p. A184

OGAWA, Quin, Chief Financial Officer, Sutter Health Kahi Mohala, Ewa Beach, HI, p. A184
Vice President Finance and Chief Financial Officer, Kuakini Medical Center, Honolulu, HI, p. A184

OGDEN, Judy, Director Information Technology, Franklin Medical Center, Winnsboro, LA, p. A317

OGDEN, Lesley, M.D., Chief Executive Officer, Samaritan North Lincoln Hospital, Lincoln City, OR, p. A577
M.D., Chief Executive Officer, Samaritan Pacific Communities Hospital, Newport, OR, p. A578

OGDEN, Michael L., President and Chief Executive Officer, Little Falls Hospital, Little Falls, NY, p. A487

OGG, Tom, Chief Information Officer, Olmsted Medical Center, Rochester, MN, p. A384

OGIER, Katie, Director of Nursing, Rock County Hospital, Bassett, NE, p. A429

OGILVIE, Richard, Chief Information Officer, Southwestern Vermont Medical Center, Bennington, VT, p. A735

OGLESBY, Lorie, Director of Human Resources, Baptist Health Madisonville, Madisonville, KY, p. A289

OGLESBY, Lorri, Chief Nursing Officer, Encompass Health Rehabilitation Hospital Of Texarkana, Texarkana, TX, p. A720

OGROD, Eugene, M.D., Chief Medical Officer, Hca Houston Healthcare Kingwood, Kingwood, TX, p. A693

OH, Christina E., Chief Executive Officer, Abrazo West Campus, Goodyear, AZ, p. A32

OHL, Connie, Acting Chief Human Resources, Veterans Affairs Illiana Health Care System, Danville, IL, p. A202

OHMART, Dean, Vice President Financial Services and Chief Financial Officer, Western Missouri Medical Center, Warrensburg, MO, p. A420

OHRT, James, M.D., Director Medical Staff, Henderson Health Care Services, Henderson, NE, p. A433

OJEDA, Guadalupe, R.N., Chief Nursing Officer, West Covina Medical Center, West Covina, CA, p. A104

OJOMO, Karanita, M.D., Chief of Staff, Lewisgale Hospital Pulaski, Pulaski, VA, p. A749

OKABE, David, Executive Vice President, Chief Financial Officer and Treasurer, Pali Momi Medical Center, Aiea, HI, p. A184
Executive Vice President, Chief Financial Officer and Treasurer, Straub Medical Center, Honolulu, HI, p. A185
Executive Vice President, Chief Financial Officer and Treasurer, Wilcox Medical Center, Lihue, HI, p. A186
Senior Vice President, Chief Financial Officer and Treasurer, Kapiolani Medical Center For Women & Children, Honolulu, HI, p. A184

OKEN, Jeffrey, Vice President of Medical Affairs, Northwestern Medicine Marianjoy Rehabilitation Hospital, Wheaton, IL, p. A222

OKESON, Keith, President and Chief Executive Officer, Lifecare Medical Center, Roseau, MN, p. A384

OKEY, Suzi, Director of Nursing, Southwest Health, Platteville, WI, p. A794

OKONIEWSKI, Susan, M.D., Chief of Staff, Chi St. Gabriel's Health, Little Falls, MN, p. A379

OKSENDAHL, Elaine, Director Human Resources and Risk Management, Schick Shadel Hospital, Seattle, WA, p. A763

OKUHARA, Mary, Chief Human Resource Officer, Lakewood Regional Medical Center, Lakewood, CA, p. A71

OKUNO-JONES, Susan, Vice President Patient Care Services and Chief Nursing Executive, Advocate Good Samaritan Hospital, Downers Grove, IL, p. A203

OLANDER, Scott, Chief Financial Officer, Evergreenhealth Monroe, Monroe, WA, p. A760

OLASON, Roxanne, R.N., FACHE, Vice President and Chief Nursing Officer, Skagit Valley Hospital, Mount Vernon, WA, p. A761

OLDER, Michael, M.D., President Medical Staff, Nashoba Valley Medical Center, Ayer, MA, p. A334

OLDHAM, Jennie, Director Human Resources, Goodall-Witcher Hospital, Clifton, TX, p. A664

OLDHAM, Lawrence, Chief Financial Officer, Arise Austin Medical Center, Austin, TX, p. A654

OLDHAM, Marriner, M.D., Chief Medical Officer, U. S. Air Force Regional Hospital, Elmendorf Afb, AK, p. A28

OLDHAM, Nate, M.D., Chief Medical Officer, Ferrell Hospital, Eldorado, IL, p. A203

OLEJNICZAK, David R., Chief Administrative Officer, Marshfield Medical Center - Minocqua, Minocqua, WI, p. A791

OLEKSYK, Mike, M.D., Vice President and Chief Medical Officer, Baptist Hospital, Pensacola, FL, p. A153

OLESTON, Caryn, FACHE, MSN, R.N., Chief Nursing Officer, Mercyhealth Hospital And Medical Center - Harvard, Harvard, IL, p. A207
FACHE, MSN, R.N., Chief Nursing Officer, Mercyhealth Hospital And Medical Center - Walworth, Lake Geneva, WI, p. A787

OLESZAK, Randy, Director Fiscal Services, Milwaukee County Behavioral Health Division, Milwaukee, WI, p. A791

OLEY, Edwin M., President and Chief Executive Officer, Mercy Regional Medical Center, Lorain, OH, p. A544

OLIGSCHLAEGER, David, Medical Staff President, Hshs Good Shepherd Hospital, Shelbyville, IL, p. A220

OLIND, Shelby, Chief Executive Officer, Encompass Health Reading Rehabilitation Hospital, Reading, PA, p. A606

OLINDE, Chad E., CPA, Administrator and Chief Executive Officer, Pointe Coupee General Hospital, New Roads, LA, p. A312

OLINGER, Richard, Chief Financial Officer, Lecom Health Millcreek Community Hospital, Erie, PA, p. A590

OLINSKI, Janis, R.N., Vice President Clinical Services, Harrison Community Hospital, Cadiz, OH, p. A530

OLIPHANT, Gerald, Executive Vice President and Chief Operating Officer, Good Samaritan Hospital, Cincinnati, OH, p. A532

OLIPHANT, Jenny, Executive Vice President and Chief Operating Officer, Bethesda North Hospital, Cincinnati, OH, p. A532

OLIPHANT, Phillip. Chief Information Officer, U. S. Air Force Regional Hospital, Elmendorf Afb, AK, p. A28

OLIVARES, Andy, Chief Executive Officer, Lakeview Specialty Hospital And Rehab, Waterford, WI, p. A798

OLIVARES, Rafael, Controller, Starr County Memorial Hospital, Rio Grande City, TX, p. A709

OLIVAREZ, Lorenzo, Senior Vice President and Chief Financial Officer, Bsa Hospital, Llc, Amarillo, TX, p. A652

OLIVAS, Ray, Chief Fiscal Service, West Texas Veterans Affairs Health Care System, Big Spring, TX, p. A660

OLIVE, Alan C., Chief Executive Officer, Northern Nevada Medical Center, Sparks, NV, p. A446

OLIVENCIA, Humberto, M.D., Medical Director, Hospital Perea, Mayaguez, PR, p. A808

OLIVER, Carlene, Superintendent, Evansville Psychiatric Children Center, Evansville, IN, p. A227

OLIVER, David, Director Information Systems, King's Daughters Medical Center, Ashland, KY, p. A280

OLIVER, Doug, Chief Financial Officer, Windhaven Psychiatric Hospital, Prescott Valley, AZ, p. A37

OLIVER, Michelle, Chief Nursing Executive, Hshs Good Shepherd Hospital, Shelbyville, IL, p. A220

OLIVER, Rae, Chief Executive Officer, Cypress Creek Hospital, Houston, TX, p. A685

OLIVER, Rick, Information Technology, Hamilton Hospital, Olney, TX, p. A704

OLIVER, Rosalie, Chief Financial Officer, Adventhealth Sebring, Sebring, FL, p. A157
Senior Vice President and Chief Financial Officer, Adventhealth Wauchula, Wauchula, FL, p. A161

OLIVERA, Sue, Vice President, Aultman Hospital, Canton, OH, p. A530

OLIVERAS, Freddy, Chief Information Officer, Martin County Hospital District, Stanton, TX, p. A717

OLIVERAS LAGUNA, Ana, Administrator, Caribbean Medical Center, Fajardo, PR, p. A807

OLIVIER, Edward, Chief Financial Officer, Martha's Vineyard Hospital, Oak Bluffs, MA, p. A343
Chief Financial Officer, Northern Light Ca Dean Hospital, Greenville, ME, p. A320

OLIVIER III, Athan J., R.N., MSN, FACHE, Administrator and Chief Executive Officer, Iberia Rehabilitation Hospital, New Iberia, LA, p. A310

OLLI, Cindy, R.N., Chief Nursing Officer, Schoolcraft Memorial Hospital, Manistique, MI, p. A361

OLLIE, Edwin, Executive Vice President and Chief Financial Officer, New Hanover Regional Medical Center, Wilmington, NC, p. A520

OLLSON, Joanne, Vice President Human Resources, Baystate Noble Hospital, Westfield, MA, p. A346

OLM-SHIPMAN, Bobby, Chief Executive Officer, Saint Luke's East Hospital, Lee's Summit, MO, p. A411
Chief Executive Officer, Saint Luke's South Hospital, Overland Park, KS, p. A274

OLMSTEAD, David, Director, Human Resources, City Hospital At White Rock, Dallas, TX, p. A668

OLMSTEAD, Linda, Director, Human Resources, Uw Medicine/Northwest Hospital & Medical Center, Seattle, WA, p. A764

OLNEY, Garry M., Chief Executive Officer, Providence Little Company Of Mary Medical Center - Torrance, Torrance, CA, p. A101
Chief Executive Officer, Providence Little Company Of Mary Medical Center San Pedro, San Pedro, CA, p. A96

OLS, Timothy A., FACHE, Chief Executive Officer, Baylor Scott & White Medical Center - Llano, Llano, TX, p. A696
FACHE, President, Baylor Scott & White Medical Center - Marble Falls, Marble Falls, TX, p. A699

OLSCAMP, Karen E., President and Chief Executive Officer, University Of Maryland Baltimore Washington Medical Center, Glen Burnie, MD, p. A330

OLSEN, Debbie, Human Resource Partner, Sparrow Ionia Hospital, Ionia, MI, p. A358

OLSEN, Jennifer, M.D., Chief of Staff, North Canyon Medical Center, Gooding, ID, p. A190

OLSEN, Karen, R.N., Chief Nursing Officer, Mission Hospital, Asheville, NC, p. A504

OLSEN, Meredith, Administrator, West Florida Community Care Center, Milton, FL, p. A148

OLSEN, Ryan, Chief Operating Officer, Saddleback Medical Center, Laguna Hills, CA, p. A70

OLSEN, Sabrina, Chief Financial Officer, Duke University Hospital, Durham, NC, p. A508

OLSON, Cheryl, Vice President, Palomar Medical Center Poway, Poway, CA, p. A86

OLSON, Craig, Director Information Technology, Southwestern Regional Medical Center, Tulsa, OK, p. A570

OLSON, Dave, Director of Nursing, Montana State Hospital, Warm Springs, MT, p. A428

OLSON, Diana, Chief Human Resources Officer, Mercy Health - Willard Hospital, Willard, OH, p. A553
Director Human Resources, Mercy Tiffin Hospital, Tiffin, OH, p. A550

OLSON, Eric, Chief Financial Officer, Providence Portland Medical Center, Portland, OR, p. A579

OLSON, Erik, Chief Executive Officer, Renown Regional Medical Center, Reno, NV, p. A446

OLSON, Forrest, M.D., Chief Medical Officer, Enloe Medical Center, Chico, CA, p. A60

OLSON, Gary R., Interim President and Chief Executive Officer, St. Luke's Hospital, Chesterfield, MO, p. A404

OLSON, John, M.D., Medical Director, Marshfield Medical Center - Rice Lake, Rice Lake, WI, p. A795

OLSON, Joni, Chief Executive Officer, Gundersen Tri-County Hospital And Clinics, Whitehall, WI, p. A799

OLSON, Karissa, Chief Executive Officer, Cobalt Rehabilitation Hospital, Fargo, ND, p. A522

OLSON, Kevin, Director Information Systems, Ssm Health St. Anthony Hospital - Oklahoma City, Oklahoma City, OK, p. A566

OLSON, Kristi, Chief Executive Officer, St. Thomas More Hospital, Canon City, CO, p. A108

OLSON, Lacey, M.D., Chief Medical Staff, Sanford Chamberlain Medical Center, Chamberlain, SD, p. A627

OLSON, Lynn, Director Human Resources, Hendricks Community Hospital Association, Hendricks, MN, p. A378

OLSON, Marcia, Business Office Manager, Webster County Community Hospital, Red Cloud, NE, p. A439
Director Finance and Controller, Monument Health Spearfish Hospital, Spearfish, SD, p. A632

OLSON, MariBeth, R.N., Vice President Patient Care Services, Mercy Hospital, Coon Rapids, MN, p. A374

OLSON, Mark, M.D., Chief of Staff, Lincoln Community Hospital And Nursing Home, Hugo, CO, p. A114
Interim Chief Information Officer, Behavioral Health Network, Natchaug Hospital, Mansfield Center, CT, p. A123

OLSON, Michael R., Chief Executive Officer, Citizens Medical Center, Victoria, TX, p. A723

OLSON, Steven, Administrator Patient Care Services, Carthage Area Hospital, Carthage, NY, p. A481

OLSON, Tim, Senior Vice President Finance, Thedacare Regional Medical Center-Appleton, Appleton, WI, p. A779
Senior Vice President Finance, Thedacare Regional Medical Center-Neenah, Neenah, WI, p. A792

OLSON, Tracy, Human Resource Officer, Avera St. Luke's Hospital, Aberdeen, SD, p. A626

OLSZYK, Mark, M.D., Vice President Medical Affairs and Chief Medical Officer, Carroll Hospital Center, Westminster, MD, p. A333

OLTMANN, Michael, M.D., Chief Medical Officer, Baptist Health Medical Center-Stuttgart, Stuttgart, AR, p. A53

OMAN, Michelle, D.O., Chief Medical Officer, Essentia Health Northern Pines Medical Center, Aurora, MN, p. A372
D.O., Chief Medical Officer, Essentia Health-Virginia, Virginia, MN, p. A387

OMILUSIK, Kevin, M.D., Chief Medical Officer, Munson Medical Center, Traverse City, MI, p. A368

OMOLARA, Khar, M.D., Chief Medical Staff, Jefferson County Hospital, Fayette, MS, p. A392

OMRAN, Yasser, M.D., President Medical Staff, Pomerene Hospital, Millersburg, OH, p. A545

OMTA, Stephen, Chief Operating Officer, Peacehealth St. Josep. Medical Center, Bellingham, WA, p. A755

OMURA, David, MS, Director, Wm. Jennings Bryan Dorn Veterans Affairs Medical Center, Columbia, SC, p. A618

ONEAL, Karen, Chief Financial Officer, Burke Medical Center, Waynesboro, GA, p. A183

ONEILL, Steve, Chief Information Officer, Nyc Health + Hospitals / Henry J Carter Specialty Hospital And Medical Center, New York, NY, p. A491

ONG, Richard, Chief Information Officer, Saint Vincent Hospital, Erie, PA, p. A590

ONI, Buki, M.D., Chief Medical Officer, Kenmare Community Hospital, Kenmare, ND, p. A524

ONIFATHER, Jeff, Chief Financial Officer, Cornerstone Of Medical Arts Center Hospital, Fresh Meadows, NY, p. A484

ONO, Craig, M.D., Chief of Staff, Shriners Hospitals For Children-Honolulu, Honolulu, HI, p. A185

ONOFRE, Bonnie, Chief Nursing Officer, South Lake Hospital, Clermont, FL, p. A134

OPBROEK, Steve, Manager Information Technology, Skyline Hospital, White Salmon, WA, p. A769

OPHAUG, Courtney, FACHE, Chief Executive Officer, Banner Estrella Medical Center, Phoenix, AZ, p. A35

OPHEIKENS, Robyn, Assistant Administrator Human Resources, St. Mark's Hospital, Salt Lake City, UT, p. A733

OPP, Andrew, M.D., Medical Chief of Staff, Saunders Medical Center, Wahoo, NE, p. A440

OPPONG, Bernard, D.O., Chief of Staff, Madison Health, London, OH, p. A543

OPRANDI, Allison, M.D., Chief Medical Officer, Aultman Hospital, Canton, OH, p. A530

OPRISKO, Judy, Vice President, Allied Services Rehabilitation Hospital, Scranton, PA, p. A606

OPSETH, Gregory, Chief Nursing Officer, Guthrie County Hospital, Guthrie Center, IA, p. A250

OPSTEDAHL, DeeAnna, R.N., Interim President, Chi St. Alexius Health - Dickinson Medical Center, Dickinson, ND, p. A522
R.N., Vice President Patient Care Services, Chi St. Alexius Health - Dickinson Medical Center, Dickinson, ND, p. A522

OPSUT, Jennifer, Interim Chief Operating Officer, West Valley Medical Center, Caldwell, ID, p. A189

OQUENDO, Tanja, Chief Human Resources Officer, Chi Flaget Memorial Hospital, Bardstown, KY, p. A280

ORAVEC, Jon, Vice President, Human Resources, Howard County General Hospital, Columbia, MD, p. A328

ORAZINE, Jay, Director Information Services, Baptist Health Paducah, Paducah, KY, p. A291

ORCUTT, David, Chief Executive Officer, Lake Granbury Medical Center, Granbury, TX, p. A682

OREGEL, Omar, Controller, Kindred Hospital-Ontario, Ontario, CA, p. A82

ORELLANA, Feliipe, Chief Medical Officer, Barnes-Jewish St. Peters Hospital, Saint Peters, MO, p. A418

OREN, Cole, R.N., Chief Nursing Officer, Select Specialty Hospital-Durham, Durham, NC, p. A509

OREOL, Harry, Acting Chief Executive Officer, Dsh Patton, Patton, CA, p. A85

ORIOL, Albert, Vice President Information Management and Chief Information Officer, Rady Children's Hospital - San Diego, San Diego, CA, p. A91

ORLANDI, Mary, Manager Human Resources, Carney Hospital, Boston, MA, p. A335

ORLANDO, Anthony, Senior Vice President Finance, Englewood Health, Englewood, NJ, p. A455

ORLANDO, Kristin, Chief Executive Officer, Mid-Hudson Forensic Psychiatric Center, New Hampton, NY, p. A489

ORLANDO, Lorraine, Vice President Human Resources, New York-Presbyterian Queens, Flushing, NY, p. A484

ORMAN, Bernard A. Jr, FACHE, Chief Executive Officer, Samaritan Hospital, Macon, MO, p. A411

ORMOND, Evalyn, Chief Executive Officer, Union General Hospital, Farmerville, LA, p. A301

ORMOND, Jack, Chief Financial Officer, Cuba Memorial Hospital, Cuba, NY, p. A482

ORNELAS, Henry, Chief Operating Officer, Lac+Usc Medical Center, Los Angeles, CA, p. A75
Chief Operating Officer, Salinas Valley Memorial Healthcare System, Salinas, CA, p. A90

OROZCO, Jorge, Chief Executive Officer, Lac+Usc Medical Center, Los Angeles, CA, p. A75

ORR, Karen, Administrator and Chief Nursing Officer, Providence Medical Center, Kansas City, KS, p. A267
Chief Nursing Officer, Providence Medical Center, Kansas City, KS, p. A267

ORR, Natassia, Chief Operating Officer, Broward Health Medical Center, Fort Lauderdale, FL, p. A137

ORRICK, Charles H., Administrator, Donalsonville Hospital, Donalsonville, GA, p. A171

ORRILL, Neil, Director of Finance, Optim Medical Center - Screven, Sylvania, GA, p. A181

ORSINI, Alexander, M.D., Medical Director, Baptist Health Extended Care Hospital, Little Rock, AR, p. A48

ORSINI, John, Executive Vice President and Chief Financial Officer, Northwestern Medicine Central Dupage Hospital, Winfield, IL, p. A222
Senior Vice President, Chief Financial Officer, Northwestern Medicine Kishwaukee Hospital, Dekalb, IL, p. A202

ORSINI, Thomas J., President and Chief Executive Officer, Lake Taylor Transitional Care Hospital, Norfolk, VA, p. A748

ORT, Linda, Chief Financial Officer, Piggott Community Hospital, Piggott, AR, p. A52

ORTEGA, Becky, Manager Human Resources, Avista Adventist Hospital, Louisville, CO, p. A116

ORTEGA, Cesar, M.D., Chief of Staff, United Memorial Medical Center, Houston, TX, p. A689

ORTEGA, Charlie, Administrative Director Information Systems, The Hospitals Of Providence Sierra Campus, El Paso, TX, p. A676

ORTEGA, Debbie, Chief Human Resource Officer and Vice President Administrative Services, Huntington Hospital, Pasadena, CA, p. A85

ORTEGA, Elizbeth, Chief Executive Officer, Woman's Hospital Of Texas, Houston, TX, p. A689

ORTEGA, Jose, Chief Operating Officer, Greater El Monte Community Hospital, South El Monte, CA, p. A99

ORTEGA, Riane, Chief Executive Officer, Compass Behavioral Center Of Houma, Houma, LA, p. A303

ORTEGO, Ashley, Director Human Resources and Marketing, Springhill Medical Center, Springhill, LA, p. A315

ORTH, Angela P., Executive Officer, Randolp. Hospital, Asheboro, NC, p. A504

ORTHAUS, Denis, Director Human Resources, Wellspan Philhaven, Mount Gretna, PA, p. A597

ORTIZ, Andrew, Senior Vice President, Human Resources and Organization Development, Cedars-Sinai Medical Center, Los Angeles, CA, p. A73

ORTIZ, Bienvenido, Coordinator Information Systems, Hospital De Damas, Ponce, PR, p. A809

ORTIZ, Edson, Chief Information Officer, Hospital Pavia Yauco, Yauco, PR, p. A811

ORTIZ, Evelyn, Director Human Resources, Hospital Menonita De Cayey, Cayey, PR, p. A807
Director Human Resources, Mennonite General Hospital, Aibonito, PR, p. A806

ORTIZ, Francisco, M.D., Chief of Staff, Jackson County Hospital District, Edna, TX, p. A674

ORTIZ, Jose, Chief Financial Officer, Ryder Memorial Hospital, Humacao, PR, p. A808

ORTIZ, Migdalia, Director Human Resources, Hospital San Carlos Borromeo, Moca, PR, p. A808

ORTIZ, Nancy, Director Human Resource and Marketing, Frio Regional Hospital, Pearsall, TX, p. A705

ORTIZ, Norma, M.D., Medical Director, Bayamon Medical Center, Bayamon, PR, p. A806

ORTIZ BAEZ, Felix, Administrator, I. Gonzalez Martinez Oncologic Hospital, Hato Rey, PR, p. A808

ORTIZ JR, BlasAssistant Superintendent and Public Information Officer, Rio Grande State Center/South Texas Health Care System, Harlingen, TX, p. A683

ORTO, Victoria, R.N., Chief Nursing and Patient Care Services Officer, Duke Regional Hospital, Durham, NC, p. A508

ORTOLANI, Philip. Vice President Operations, Mid Coast Hospital, Brunswick, ME, p. A319

ORTON, Wendy, Chief Nursing Officer, Alleghany Memorial Hospital, Sparta, NC, p. A518

OSANTOSKI, Tina, Director Human Resources, Harbor Beach Community Hospital, Harbor Beach, MI, p. A357

OSARIO, Cesar, Specialist Information Technology, Cedar Crest Hospital And Residential Treatment Center, Belton, TX, p. A659

OSBERG, Art, M.D., Chief Medical Officer, Ocala Regional Medical Center, Ocala, FL, p. A150

OSBORN, Kim, Chief Financial Officer, Sequoia Hospital, Redwood City, CA, p. A88

OSBORN, Tom, D.O., Chief Medical Staff, Holdenville General Hospital, Holdenville, OK, p. A560

OSBORNE, Anna, Chief Human Resources Management Service, West Texas Veterans Affairs Health Care System, Big Spring, TX, p. A660

OSBORNE, Phil, Director Information Technology, Bourbon Community Hospital, Paris, KY, p. A292

OSBORNE, Stacey, Chief Nursing Officer, Geisinger-Lewistown Hospital, Lewistown, PA, p. A595

OSCADAL, Martin, Senior Vice President Human Resources, St. Elizabeth Florence, Florence, KY, p. A283

Senior Vice President Human Resources, St. Elizabeth Fort Thomas, Fort Thomas, KY, p. A283

Vice President Human Resources, St. Elizabeth Edgewood, Edgewood, KY, p. A282

OSE, Peggy, FACHE, MSN, R.N., Chief Nursing Officer, Aspirus Riverview Hospital And Clinics, Inc., Wisconsin Rapids, WI, p. A800

OSEGARD, Jeff, Chief Information Officer, Cass County Health System, Atlantic, IA, p. A243

OSEHOBO, Philip. M.D., Chief Medical Officer, Wellstar Spalding Regional Hospital, Griffin, GA, p. A173

OSER, William, M.D., Chief Medical Officer, Jfk Johnson Rehabilitation Institute At Hackensack Meridian Health, Edison, NJ, p. A454

M.D., Senior Vice President and Chief Medical Officer, Hackensack Meridian Health Jfk Medical Center, Edison, NJ, p. A454

OSHIRO, Shari Ann, Chief Medical Director, Rehabilitation Hospital Of The Pacific, Honolulu, HI, p. A185

OSINSKI, Kathleen, Chief Human Resources Service, John D. Dingell Veterans Affairs Medical Center, Detroit, MI, p. A353

OSLIN, Dave, M.D., Chief of Staff, Philadelphia Veterans Affairs Medical Center, Philadelphia, PA, p. A601

OSSELLO, Susan, Chief Financial Officer, Granite County Medical Center, Philipsburg, MT, p. A426

OSTASZEWSKI, Patricia, MS, Chief Executive Officer, Encompass Health Rehabilitation Hospital Of Toms River, Toms River, NJ, p. A464

OSTBERG, Melissa, Chief Financial Officer, Marias Medical Center, Shelby, MT, p. A427

OSTBLOOM, Jan, Human Resources Consultant, Uofl Health - Peace Hospital, Louisville, KY, p. A289

OSTEEN, Tom, Director Area Technology, Kaiser Permanente Manteca Medical Center, Manteca, CA, p. A77

OSTENSON, Scott, Chief Financial Officer, Jacobson Memorial Hospital Care Center, Elgin, ND, p. A522

OSTER, Kurt, Human Resources Officer, Carl Vinson Veterans Affairs Medical Center, Dublin, GA, p. A171

OSTERBERG, Valerie, Chief Financial Officer, Sanford Vermillion Medical Center, Vermillion, SD, p. A632

OSTERHOUT, David, Assistant Superintendent and Chief Financial Officer, El Paso Psychiatric Center, El Paso, TX, p. A675

OSTERLY, Eric, Chief Financial Officer, Adventhealth Fish Memorial, Orange City, FL, p. A150

OSTLIG, Jane, Chief Medical Officer, Sanford Mayville Medical Center, Mayville, ND, p. A525

OSTRANDER, Maria, R.N., MSN, Chief Nurse Executive, San Antonio State Hospital, San Antonio, TX, p. A713

OSTROW, Peter, M.D., President Medical Staff, Beth Israel Deaconess Hospital-Needham Campus, Needham, MA, p. A342

OSWAL, Arvind, Chief Financial Officer, Arrowhead Regional Medical Center, Colton, CA, p. A60

OSWALD, Jessica, Chief Executive Officer, St. Elias Specialty Hospital, Anchorage, AK, p. A27

OSWALD, Traci, Vice President Human Resources, Bucyrus Hospital, Bucyrus, OH, p. A530

Vice President of Human Resources, Galion Hospital, Galion, OH, p. A541

Vice President, Chief Human Resources, Avita Ontario Hospital, Ontario, OH, p. A547

OTERO, Jorge Torres., Executive Director, Hospital Del Maestro, San Juan, PR, p. A810

OTHOLE, Jean, Chief Executive Officer, U. S. Public Health Service Indian Hospital, Zuni, NM, p. A473

OTOMO, Ellen, Interim Hospital Administrator, Chicago-Read Mental Health Center, Chicago, IL, p. A198

OTOTT, Kelly, R.N., Chief Nursing Officer, Washington County Hospital, Washington, KS, p. A278

OTT, Darin, D.O., Chief of Staff, Kane County Hospital, Kanab, UT, p. A728

OTT, Eugene J. Jr, Chief Executive Officer, Eagleville Hospital, Eagleville, PA, p. A588

OTT, Laurie, Vice President Human Resources and President University Health Care Foundation, University Hospital, Augusta, GA, p. A166

OTT, Mark, M.D., Regional Chief Medical Director, Intermountain Medical Center, Murray, UT, p. A729

OTT, Pamela, Vice President Finance, Aurora Sheboygan Memorial Medical Center, Sheboygan, WI, p. A796

OTTE, Elaine, Chief Operating Officer, Clarinda Regional Health Center, Clarinda, IA, p. A246

OTTEN, Sharon, Vice President Nursing, Advocate South Suburban Hospital, Hazel Crest, IL, p. A207

OTTENBACHER, John, Chief of Staff, Bowdle Hospital, Bowdle, SD, p. A626

OTTENS, Mark, Chief Nursing Officer, Baptist Memorial Hospital-North Mississippi, Oxford, MS, p. A398

OTTLEY, Shawn, R.N., Chief Clinical Officer, Cascade Medical Center, Leavenworth, WA, p. A760

OTTMAR, Kellie, Manager Information Services, East Adams Rural Healthcare, Ritzville, WA, p. A763

OTTO, Sara, Chief Compliance Officer, North Canyon Medical Center, Gooding, ID, p. A190

OTTOLINO, Joseph, Chief Executive Officer, West Suburban Medical Center, Oak Park, IL, p. A215

OUBRE, Chris, Information Technology Director, Garden Park Medical Center, Gulfport, MS, p. A393

OUELETTE, Lisa, Director Human Resources, Beaumont Hospital - Troy, Troy, MI, p. A368

OUELLETTE, Demetra, Chief Operating Officer, Rehabilitation Hospital Of Rhode Island, North Smithfield, RI, p. A613

OUNGST, Laurie, Chief Administrative Officer, Ascension Eagle River Hospital, Eagle River, WI, p. A782

Chief Administrative Officer, Ascension Sacred Heart Hospital, Tomahawk, WI, p. A797

Chief Administrative Officer, Ascension St. Mary's Hospital, Rhinelander, WI, p. A795

Chief Administrative Officer, Howard Young Medical Center, Woodruff, WI, p. A800

Vice President, Operations, Ascension Eagle River Hospital, Eagle River, WI, p. A782

OURS, Matt, Chief Executive Officer and Managing Director, Rivendell Behavioral Health, Bowling Green, KY, p. A281

OUSEY, Tracy, Director Human Resources, Washington County Hospital And Clinics, Washington, IA, p. A259

OUTHIER, Amy, Director Health Information Management, Weatherford Regional Hospital, Weatherford, OK, p. A572

OUTLAW, Debbie, R.N., Director Patient Care Services, Coastal Virginia Rehabilitation, Newport News, VA, p. A746

OVANDO, Benjamin, Chief Operations Officer, Rancho Los Amigos National Rehabilitation Center, Downey, CA, p. A62

OVERBEY, William J., Chief Executive Officer, Kansas Rehabilitation Hospital, Topeka, KS, p. A277

OVERBY, Roger, Executive Director Information Systems, Greene County Medical Center, Jefferson, IA, p. A252

OVERSTREET, Alyson, Chief Financial Officer, Grove Hill Memorial Hospital, Grove Hill, AL, p. A19

OVERSTREET, Amy, Director Human Resources, Trousdale Medical Center, Hartsville, TN, p. A639

OVERTON, Camie, Chief Executive Officer, Curahealth Tucson, Tucson, AZ, p. A40

OVERTON, Deana, Director Human Resources, Mitchell County Hospital, Colorado City, TX, p. A664

OVERTON, Saundra, R.N., Chief Nursing Officer, Royal Oaks Hospital, Windsor, MO, p. A420

OVESON, Mark, M.D., Chief Medical Staff, Central Valley Medical Center, Nephi, UT, p. A729

OWEN, Amber, Regional Vice President, Human Resources, Texas Health Huguley Hospital Fort Worth South, Burleson, TX, p. A662

OWEN, Sabrina, Human Resources Officer, Va Central Iowa Health Care System, Des Moines, IA, p. A249

OWENS, Arthur Douglas., Administrator, Georgetown Behavioral Hospital, Georgetown, OH, p. A541

OWENS, Beverly, Controller, Rehabilitation Hospital, Navicent Health, Macon, GA, p. A176

OWENS, Brian, Chief Operating Officer, Lindner Center Of Hope, Mason, OH, p. A544

OWENS, Craig A., President, Wellstar Douglas Hospital, Douglasville, GA, p. A171

OWENS, Daniel, Chief Executive Officer, Emory University Hospital Midtown, Atlanta, GA, p. A164

OWENS, Kevin, M.D., Chief Medical Officer, Minidoka Memorial Hospital, Rupert, ID, p. A193

OWENS, Mark, M.D., Vice President Medical Affairs, Mercy San Juan Medical Center, Carmichael, CA, p. A59

OWENS, Nancy, Administrator, Christus Dubuis Hospital Of Fort Smith, Fort Smith, AR, p. A46

OWENS, Paul, M.D., Chief Medical Officer, Hackettstown Medical Center, Hackettstown, NJ, p. A456

OWENS, Rick, Administrator, D. W. Mcmillan Memorial Hospital, Brewton, AL, p. A16

OWENS, Royce, Chief Operating Officer, Baylor Scott & White Medical Center - Llano, Llano, TX, p. A696

OWENS, Stephanie, Manager Human Resources, Mcdowell Arh Hospital, Mcdowell, KY, p. A290

OWENS, Thomas, M.D., President, Duke University Hospital, Durham, NC, p. A508

OWENSBY, Terri, R.N., Chief Nursing Executive, Kaiser Permanente South Sacramento Medical Center, Sacramento, CA, p. A89

OWINGS, Karen, MSN, Vice President, Patient Care Services, Medstar Union Memorial Hospital, Baltimore, MD, p. A325

OWREY, Donald R., President, Upmc Williamsport, Williamsport, PA, p. A611

OXFORD, Michelle, Chief Operating Officer, Acting Chief Executive Officer, Bakersfield Heart Hospital, Bakersfield, CA, p. A57

OXFORD, Tammy, Director Human Resources, Bob Wilson Memorial Grant County Hospital, Ulysses, KS, p. A278

OXLEY, Dawn, R.N., Associate Director Patient Care Services and Nurse Executive, Iowa City Va Health Care System, Iowa City, IA, p. A252

OXLEY, James, D.O., Vice President Medical Affairs, Garnet Health Medical Center - Catskills, Middletown, NY, p. A488

OXLEY, Scott, President, The Acadia Hospital, Bangor, ME, p. A318

OXTON, Alice, Director Information Technology, Sentara Obici Hospital, Suffolk, VA, p. A752

OZBORN, Charles, M.D., Chief of Staff, North Mississipp. Medical Center-Eupora, Eupora, MS, p. A392

OZBURN, Thomas H., Chief Executive Officer, Parkridge Medical Center, Chattanooga, TN, p. A636

OZEL, A, M.D., Chief Medical Officer, Northeast Rehabilitation Hospital, Salem, NH, p. A451

OZMENT, Mary, Chief Nursing Officer, Hillcrest Hospital Pryor, Pryor, OK, p. A567

OZMUN, Andrew, Chief Financial Officer, Alta View Hospital, Sandy, UT, p. A733

Chief Financial Officer, Riverton Hospital, Riverton, UT, p. A731

OZUAH, Philip O., M.D., Ph.D., Chief Executive Officer, Montefiore Medical Center, Bronx, NY, p. A477

O'BRIEN, Daniel, Vice President and Chief Financial Officer, Community Hospital, Munster, IN, p. A237

O'BRIEN, David, Chief Operating Officer, St. Mary's Medical Center, West Palm Beach, FL, p. A162

Interim Chief Executive Officer, St. Mary's Medical Center, West Palm Beach, FL, p. A162

O'BRIEN, Elizabeth, Chief Financial Officer, Northern Nevada Adult Mental Health Services, Sparks, NV, p. A446

O'BRIEN, Jane, M.D., Medical Director, Franciscan Children's, Brighton, MA, p. A336

O'BRIEN, Karen, Director Human Resources, Gerald Champion Regional Medical Center, Alamogordo, NM, p. A467

O'BRIEN, Kevin, Chief Executive Officer, Harper County Community Hospital, Buffalo, OK, p. A557

O'BRIEN, Laureen, Chief Information Officer, Providence Newberg Medical Center, Newberg, OR, p. A578

O'BRIEN, Renee, Director Human Resources, Greater Binghamton Health Center, Binghamton, NY, p. A475

O'BRIEN, Tim, Chief Executive Officer, Hackensack Meridian Health Mountainside Medical Center, Montclair, NJ, p. A458

O'BRIEN-PARADIS, Katie, M.D., Chief Medical Officer, Chi Oakes Hospital, Oakes, ND, p. A525

O'BRYANT, G. Mark., President and Chief Executive Officer, Tallahassee Memorial Healthcare, Tallahassee, FL, p. A158

O'CONNELL, Brian, Director Information Services, North Star Behavioral Health System, Anchorage, AK, p. A27

O'CONNELL, Melody, Director Human Resources, St. Bernard Parish Hospital, Chalmette, LA, p. A299

O'CONNELL, Sara, Director Human Resources, Mount Desert Island Hospital, Bar Harbor, ME, p. A318

O'CONNELL, Tim, Chief Financial Officer, Lincoln Hospital, Davenport, WA, p. A757

O'CONNOR, Betty, Chief Nursing Officer, Crouse Health, Syracuse, NY, p. A499

O'CONNOR, Colleen, Director Human Resources, Centerstone Hospital, Bradenton, FL, p. A132

O'CONNOR, David, Executive Vice President and Chief Financial Officer, Caromont Regional Medical Center, Gastonia, NC, p. A510

O'CONNOR, Dennis, M.D., Medical Director, Ira Davenport Memorial Hospital, Bath, NY, p. A475

O'CONNOR, James, Chief Administrative Officer, St. Catherine Of Siena Medical Center, Smithtown, NY, p. A498
President, St. Charles Hospital, Port Jefferson, NY, p. A495

O'CONNOR, Kathy, Vice President Finance and Controller, St. Josep. Mercy Livingston Hospital, Howell, MI, p. A358
Vice President Finance, St. Josep. Mercy Ann Arbor, Ypsilanti, MI, p. A370

O'CONNOR, Kevin, D.O., President, Medical Staff, Spectrum Health United Hospital, Greenville, MI, p. A356

O'CONNOR, Michael, M.D., Chief Medical Officer, Banner Baywood Medical Center, Mesa, AZ, p. A33
Senior Vice President Finance, Wellspan York Hospital, York, PA, p. A612

O'CONNOR, Thomas, President, United Hospital, Saint Paul, MN, p. A385

O'CONNOR, Tim, Area Finance Officer, Kaiser Permanente Santa Clara Medical Center, Santa Clara, CA, p. A97

O'CONNOR, Timothy, Executive Vice President and Chief Financial Officer, Lahey Hospital & Medical Center, Burlington, Burlington, MA, p. A337

O'CONNOR-SNYDER, Judy, R.N., Chief Nursing Officer, Mercy Hospital Lebanon, Lebanon, MO, p. A410

O'DEA, Edward, Executive Vice President and Chief Financial Officer, Lehigh Valley Hospital, Allentown, PA, p. A583

O'DELL, Darrell, Director Information Services, Good Samaritan Hospital, San Jose, CA, p. A94

O'DELL, Edward, D.O., Chief Medical Officer, Nazareth Hospital, Philadelphia, PA, p. A601

O'DELL, Michael, Chief Financial Officer, Sheridan County Health Complex, Hoxie, KS, p. A266

O'DONNELL, Jan, Chief Nursing Officer, South Texas Surgical Hospital, Corpus Christi, TX, p. A666

O'DONNELL, John, Director of Information Technology Services, Spartanburg Medical Center - Mary Black, Spartanburg, SC, p. A624

O'DONNELL, Michael, CPA, Chief Financial Officer, Peconic Bay Medical Center, Riverhead, NY, p. A496

O'DONNELL, Patrick W., President and Chief Executive Officer, Wellspan Chambersburg Hospital, Chambersburg, PA, p. A586

O'DONOGHUE, Brian, M.D., Chief Medical Officer, Breckinridge Memorial Hospital, Hardinsburg, KY, p. A284

O'DONOVAN, Bryan J., President and Chief Executive Officer, St. James Hospital, Hornell, NY, p. A485

O'FLANAGAN, Jayne, Director Human Resources, Incline Village Community Hospital, Incline Village, NV, p. A442

O'GORMAN, Victoria, Administrator, Kaiser Permanente Fremont Medical Center, Fremont, CA, p. A65

O'HAODHA, Levon, Chief of Staff, Hudson Hospital And Clinic, Hudson, WI, p. A786

O'HARA, Denise, Vice President Human Resources, Wilson Medical Center, Wilson, NC, p. A520

O'HARA, Kathleen, Vice President Human Resources, Erie County Medical Center, Buffalo, NY, p. A479

O'HARA, Michael, Senior Executive Director Human Resources, Houston Medical Center, Warner Robins, GA, p. A183
Senior Executive Director, Perry Hospital, Perry, GA, p. A178

O'HAVER, Tim, Market President, St. Elizabeth Hospital, Enumclaw, WA, p. A758
President, St. Clare Hospital, Lakewood, WA, p. A760
President, St. Josep. Medical Center, Tacoma, WA, p. A767

O'HEARN, John, Chief Executive Officer, Select Specialty Hospital-Dallas, Carrollton, TX, p. A663

O'HERN, Mark, President, Upmc East, Monroeville, PA, p. A597
President, Upmc Mckeesport, Mckeesport, PA, p. A596

O'KEEFE, James M., President and Chief Executive Officer, Mile Bluff Medical Center, Mauston, WI, p. A789

O'KEEFE, John, Chief Executive Officer, Select Specialty Hospital-Gulfport, Gulfport, MS, p. A393
Chief Nursing Officer, Day Kimball Hospital, Putnam, CT, p. A124

O'KEEFE, Kathy, Executive Director, Pilgrim Psychiatric Center, Brentwood, NY, p. A476

Interim Executive Director, Sagamore Children's Psychiatric Center, Dix Hills, NY, p. A482

O'KEEFE, Michael N., Chief Executive Officer, Encompass Health Rehabilitation Hospital Of Sioux Falls, Sioux Falls, SD, p. A631

O'KEEFE, Trish, Ph.D., R.N., President, Morristown Medical Center, Morristown, NJ, p. A458

O'LAIRE, Beth, Manager Human Resources, Ascension Calumet Hospital, Chilton, WI, p. A781

O'LEARY, Bill, Chief Executive Officer, Pondera Medical Center, Conrad, MT, p. A422

O'LEARY, Daniel, M.D., Chief Medical Officer, Umass Memorial Healthalliance-Clinton Hospital, Leominster, MA, p. A340

O'LEARY, Kevin, Senior Vice President and Chief Financial Officer, Exeter Hospital, Exeter, NH, p. A449

O'LEARY, Megan, Vice President Human Resources and Rehabilitation Services, Mckenzie-Willamette Medical Center, Springfield, OR, p. A581

O'LEARY, Rand, FACHE, President, Northern Light Eastern Maine Medical Center, Bangor, ME, p. A318

O'LOUGHLIN, James F., Chief Executive Officer, Aiken Regional Medical Centers, Aiken, SC, p. A615

O'MALLEY, Constance, President, Beaumont Hospital - Farmington Hills, Farmington Hills, MI, p. A354

O'MALLEY, John F., FACHE, President, St. Josep. Mercy Livingston Hospital, Howell, MI, p. A358

O'MALLEY, Jon P., Chief Executive Officer, Select Specialty Hospital-Macomb County, Mount Clemens, MI, p. A362

O'MALLEY, Joseph, Interim Chief Financial Officer, John C. Fremont Healthcare District, Mariposa, CA, p. A77

O'MALLEY, Mary Jo, R.N., MS, Vice President Diagnostics and Support Services, Oconomowoc Memorial Hospital, Oconomowoc, WI, p. A792

O'MALLEY, Trevor, Site Manager, Amita Health Saint Josep. Hospital, Elgin, IL, p. A203

O'NEAL, Charlotte, Vice President Human Resources, Research Medical Center, Kansas City, MO, p. A409

O'NEAL, Jessica, Chief Operating Officer, West Florida Hospital, Pensacola, FL, p. A154

O'NEAL, Lewis, R.N., MSN, Chief Nursing Officer, Chi Saint Josep. London, London, KY, p. A287

O'NEAL, Michael, M.D., Chief Medical Officer, Ochsner Lsu Health Shreveport - Monroe Medical Center, Monroe, LA, p. A309
Chief Executive Officer, George C. Grap. Community Hospital, Hamburg, IA, p. A251

O'NEAL, Timothy, Chief Nursing Officer, Poplar Bluff Regional Medical Center, Poplar Bluff, MO, p. A414

O'NEIL, Alan, Chief Executive Officer, Unity Medical Center, Grafton, ND, p. A523

O'NEIL, Jeremy, Administrator, Providence Valdez Medical Center, Valdez, AK, p. A29

O'NEILL, Beth, Chief Nursing Officer, Morgan Memorial Hospital, Madison, GA, p. A176

O'NEILL, Lynn, R.N., Chief Nursing Officer, Medical City Lewisville, Lewisville, TX, p. A696

O'NEILL, Melissa, Vice President Human Resources, Advocate Sherman Hospital, Elgin, IL, p. A203

O'NEILL, Michael, M.D., Chief Medical Officer, Eastside Medical Center, Snellville, GA, p. A180

O'NEILL, Stephan, Vice President Information Services, Hartford Hospital, Hartford, CT, p. A122

O'REAR, Caleb F., Chief Executive Officer, Alta Vista Regional Hospital, Las Vegas, NM, p. A470

O'REILLY, Frank, Director, Dr. J. Corrigan Mental Health Center, Fall River, MA, p. A338

O'REILLY, Terrance, Chief Executive Officer, Dallas Behavioral Healthcare Hospital, Desoto, TX, p. A672

O'ROURKE, Jane, R.N., Chief Nursing Officer, Vice President Operations, St. Peter's Hospital, Albany, NY, p. A474

O'ROURKE, Michael, Regional Human Resource Officer, Amita Health Mercy Medical Center, Aurora, IL, p. A195
Regional Human Resources Lead, Amita Health Saint Josep. Hospital, Elgin, IL, p. A203

O'sHEA, James, Chief Operating Officer, Baton Rouge Behavioral Hospital, Baton Rouge, LA, p. A296

O'sTEEN, Neil, Director Information Technology, Bacon County Hospital And Health System, Alma, GA, p. A163

O'sTEEN, Tony, Chief Financial Officer, Meadows Regional Medical Center, Vidalia, GA, p. A182

O'sULLIVAN, Barbara, M.D., M.P.H., Medical Director, Rockefeller University Hospital, New York, NY, p. A492

O'sULLIVAN, Paul, FACHE, Chief Executive Officer, Memorial Hermann Greater Heights Hospital, Houston, TX, p. A687
FACHE, Chief Executive Officer, Memorial Hermann Memorial City Medical Center, Houston, TX, p. A687

O'TOOL, Nick, Vice President Operational Finance, Chi Health Lakeside, Omaha, NE, p. A436

# P

PAASCH, Michael, Regional Chief Information Officer, Ssm Health St. Mary's Hospital - St. Louis, Saint Louis, MO, p. A417
Regional Vice President and Chief Information Officer, Ssm Cardinal Glennon Children's Hospital, Saint Louis, MO, p. A416
Vice President, Regional Chief Information Officer, Ssm Health St. Clare Hospital - Fenton, Fenton, MO, p. A406

PABLO, Gary, M.D., Chief Medical Officer, Sacred Heart Hospital On The Emerald Coast, Miramar Beach, FL, p. A148
M.D., Chief Medical Officer, Sacred Heart Hospital On The Gulf, Port St Joe, FL, p. A155

PABON, Jose, Director Operations, Wilma N. Vazquez Medical Center, Vega Baja, PR, p. A811

PABON-RAMIREZ, Felix, Chief Information Officer, St. Charles Hospital, Port Jefferson, NY, p. A495

PACCA, Richard, M.D., Chief of Staff, Granville Health System, Oxford, NC, p. A516

PACCAPANICCIA, Dominic, Chief Operating Officer, Indiana Regional Medical Center, Indiana, PA, p. A592

PACE, Dewane, President and Chief Executive Officer, Haxtun Hospital District, Haxtun, CO, p. A114

PACE, Kathleen, MSN, R.N., Chief Nursing Officer, Englewood Community Hospital, Englewood, FL, p. A137

PACE, Kelly, Director Human Resource, Strategic Behavioral Health - Wilmington, Leland, NC, p. A513

PACEK, Thomas, Vice President Information Systems and Chief Information Officer, Inspira Medical Center-Elmer, Elmer, NJ, p. A455
Vice President Information Systems and Chief Information Officer, Inspira Medical Center-Vineland, Vineland, NJ, p. A465

PACEY, Amy, Vice President Human Resources, Good Samaritan Medical Center, Lafayette, CO, p. A115

PACHECO, Robert, Vice President Finance, Women & Infants Hospital Of Rhode Island, Providence, RI, p. A614

PACINI, Jenna, Human Resources Specialist, Belmont Behavioral Hospital, Philadelphia, PA, p. A599

PACK, Natalie, Chief Financial Officer, St. David's North Austin Medical Center, Austin, TX, p. A656

PACK, William, Chief Financial Officer, Memorial Hermann - Texas Medical Center, Houston, TX, p. A687

PACKER, Eric, Chief Executive Officer, Cedar City Hospital, Cedar City, UT, p. A727

PACKER, Lee, Administrator, South Florida State Hospital, Hollywood, FL, p. A140

PACKER, Melanie, Administrative Assistant, Director of Human Resources, Clearsky Rehabilitation Hospital Of Leesville, Leesville, LA, p. A307

PACKER, Steven J., M.D., President and Chief Executive Officer, Community Hospital Of The Monterey Peninsula, Monterey, CA, p. A79

PACURA, Lori, MSN, R.N., President, Holy Cross Hospital, Chicago, IL, p. A198

PACYNA, Andrew, Acting Director, Veterans Affairs Ann Arbor Healthcare System, Ann Arbor, MI, p. A348
Deputy Director, Louis Stokes Cleveland Veterans Affairs Medical Center, Cleveland, OH, p. A534

PADDEN, Ernest, Chief Financial Officer, Bon Secours Maryview Medical Center, Portsmouth, VA, p. A749

PADEN, Tawnya, Director Human Resources, Weatherford Regional Hospital, Weatherford, OK, p. A572

PADGETT, Doug, President and Chief Executive Officer, Totally Kids Rehabilitation Hospital, Loma Linda, CA, p. A72

PADGETT, Martin, Acting Chief Executive Officer, Scott Memorial Health, Scottsburg, IN, p. A240
President and Chief Executive Officer, Clark Memorial Health, Jeffersonville, IN, p. A233

PADGETT, Shirley, Director Human Resources, Southwell Medical, Adel, GA, p. A163

PADILLA, Ami, Director Human Resources, Arroyo Grande Community Hospital, Arroyo Grande, CA, p. A56

PADILLA, Kathy, Chief Nursing Officer, Marcus Daly Memorial Hospital, Hamilton, MT, p. A424

PADULA, Judy, MSN, R.N., Vice President Patient Care Services and Chief Nursing Officer, St. Joseph's University Medical Center, Paterson, NJ, p. A460

PAFFORD, Roger, M.D., Medical Director, Mineral Community Hospital, Superior, MT, p. A428

PAGE, Alison, Chief Executive Officer, Western Wisconsin Health, Baldwin, WI, p. A780

PAGE, Bob, Chief Executive Officer, The University Of Kansas Hospital, Kansas City, KS, p. A268

PAGE, Cynthia, FACHE, Chief Operating Officer, Oss Health, York, PA, p. A612

PAGE, Deborah, Chief Human Resources Officer, Duke University Hospital, Durham, NC, p. A508

PAGE, Heather, MSN, Director of Nursing, Chi St. Josep. Health Burleson Hospital, Caldwell, TX, p. A662

PAGE, Keith Allen., President and Chief Executive Officer, Anderson Hospital, Maryville, IL, p. A211

PAGE, Nancy, MS, R.N., Chief Nursing Officer, Upstate University Hospital, Syracuse, NY, p. A500

PAGE, Pattie, Director Marketing and Public Relations, Eastside Medical Center, Snellville, GA, p. A180

PAGE, Robert Chief Information and Technology Officer, Memphis Veterans Affairs Medical Center, Memphis, TN, p. A644

PAGE, Rodger, President, Mercy Medical Center Mount Shasta, Mount Shasta, CA, p. A80

PAGE, Sue, Director Human Resources, Monroe County Medical Center, Tompkinsville, KY, p. A293

PAGE, Susan M., President and Chief Executive Officer, Pratt Regional Medical Center, Pratt, KS, p. A275

PAGE, William, CPA, Chief Financial Officer, Franklin Medical Center, Winnsboro, LA, p. A317

PAGELER, Robert, Chief Information Officer, Confluence Health/Central Washington Hospital, Wenatchee, WA, p. A768

Chief Information Officer, Confluence Health/Wenatchee Valley Hospital, Wenatchee, WA, p. A768

PAGET, Cindy, Chief Human Resources Officer, Forks Community Hospital, Forks, WA, p. A758

PAGLIUZZA, Greg, Chief Financial Officer, Unitypoint Health - Trinity Bettendorf, Bettendorf, IA, p. A244

PAGNINI, Janie, Administrator Accounting, Atascadero State Hospital, Atascadero, CA, p. A56

PAGUAGA, Ana, Director of Human Resources, Coral Gables Hospital, Coral Gables, FL, p. A135

PAHE, Gary, Manager Human Resources, Sage Memorial Hospital, Ganado, AZ, p. A31

PAHL, Jodi, Chief Nurse Executive, Mercy Health - St. Rita's Medical Center, Lima, OH, p. A543

PAI, Ajith, PharmD, FACHE, President, Texas Health Harris Methodist Hospital Cleburne, Cleburne, TX, p. A663

PAIGE, Peter, Chief Medical Officer, Jackson Health System, Miami, FL, p. A146

PAINE, Chad, Director Client Services, Pottstown Hospital, Pottstown, PA, p. A605

PAINE, Lincoln, M.D., Medical Director, River Oaks Hospital, New Orleans, LA, p. A311

PAINE, Russ, Human Resources Officer, Erlanger Western Carolina Hospital, Murphy, NC, p. A515

PAINTER, Jeff, Manager Information Technology, Summit Pacific Medical Center, Elma, WA, p. A757

PAIRISH, Katherine, Chief Financial Officer, Eastern Plumas Health Care, Portola, CA, p. A86

PALADINO, James, Controller, New England Rehabilitation Hospital Of Portland, Portland, ME, p. A322

PALAGI, Pam, Montana Region Chief Financial Officer, St. Vincent Healthcare, Billings, MT, p. A421

PALAZZOLO, Chris, President and Chief Executive Officer, Ascension Crittenton Hospital Medical Center, Rochester, MI, p. A365

President and Chief Executive Officer, Ascension Genesys Hospital, Grand Blanc, MI, p. A355

PALERMO, Robert, Vice President Finance, Hackensack Meridian Health Ocean Medical Center, Brick Township, NJ, p. A453

PALICKA, Martha, Director Information Systems, Bartlett Regional Hospital, Juneau, AK, p. A28

PALIGO, Terry, Chief Financial Officer, Union County Hospital, Anna, IL, p. A194

PALKOWSKI, Chris, M.D., Physician in Chief, Kaiser Permanente Sacramento Medical Center, Sacramento, CA, p. A89

PALLIN, Angel, Senior Vice President of Operations, Mount Sinai Medical Center, Miami Beach, FL, p. A148

PALMER, Charles, Director Information Technology, Tidalhealth Nanticoke, Seaford, DE, p. A128

PALMER, Debra, MS, R.N., Chief Human Resources Officer and Corporate Compliance Officer, Fairfield Medical Center, Lancaster, OH, p. A542

PALMER, Heather, Chief Nursing Officer, Belton Regional Medical Center, Belton, MO, p. A402

PALMER, Janel, Director Human Resources, Greenwood County Hospital, Eureka, KS, p. A264

PALMER, Katie, Manager Human Resources, Sanford Aberdeen Medical Center, Aberdeen, SD, p. A626

PALMER, Keith, Assistant Administrator, Winkler County Memorial Hospital, Kermit, TX, p. A692

PALMER, Kelly, D.O., Medical Director, State Hospital South, Blackfoot, ID, p. A188

PALMER, Stephanie, Chief Nursing Officer, Encompass Health Valley Of The Sun Rehabilitation Hospital, Glendale, AZ, p. A32

PALMER, Trisha, Director, St. James Healthcare, Butte, MT, p. A422

PALMIER, Michael, Chief Human Resources Management, Overton Brooks Veterans Affairs Medical Center, Shreveport, LA, p. A314

PALMUCCI, Jeffrey, Chief Executive Officer, Vanderbilt Stallworth Rehabilitation Hospital, Nashville, TN, p. A647

PALO, Alan, Chief Financial Officer, Sarah D. Culbertson Memorial Hospital, Rushville, IL, p. A219

PALUMBO, Christopher M., Chief Executive Officer, Nebraska Spine Hospital, Omaha, NE, p. A437

PALUMBO, Michael, D.O., Vice President Medical Affairs and Chief Education, Northern Light Inland Hospital, Waterville, ME, p. A323

M.D., Executive Vice President and Medical Director, White Plains Hospital Center, White Plains, NY, p. A502

PAM, Brower, Chief Financial Officer, Christus Spohn Hospital Corpus Christi Memorial, Corpus Christi, TX, p. A665

PAMPERIEN, Linda, Chief Financial Officer, Texas County Memorial Hospital, Houston, MO, p. A407

PANDO, Terry, R.N., Associate Executive Director and Chief Nursing Officer, Staten Island University Hospital, Staten Island, NY, p. A499

PANDOLPH, Philip E., FACHE, Chief Executive Officer, Meadville Medical Center, Meadville, PA, p. A596

PANDYA, Kamel, Director Information Services, San Antonio Regional Hospital, Upland, CA, p. A102

PANDYA, Sherrie, Administrator, Kane County Hospital, Kanab, UT, p. A728

PANESAR, Mandip. M.D., Medical Director, Wyoming County Community Hospital, Warsaw, NY, p. A501

PANKEY, De'Niro, Director Information Systems, Corona Regional Medical Center, Corona, CA, p. A61

PANKEY, Susan, Chief Nursing Officer, Davis County Hospital And Clinics, Bloomfield, IA, p. A244

PANKOW, Thomas, Chief Information Officer, Jackson Park Hospital And Medical Center, Chicago, IL, p. A198

PANKOWSKI, Charles, Manager Human Resources, Select Specialty Hospital-Columbus, Columbus, OH, p. A537

PANLASIGUI, Bonnie, Chief Operating Officer, St. Mary Medical Center Long Beach, Long Beach, CA, p. A72

PANNAGL, Bryan, Chief Financial Officer, Christus Coushatta Health Care Center, Coushatta, LA, p. A299

Chief Financial Officer, Christus Health Shreveport-Bossier, Shreveport, LA, p. A314

PANNELL, Kenneth, Chief Financial Officer, Chi St. Josep. College Station Hospital, College Station, TX, p. A664

PANNIKODE, Shalima, Senior Vice President Chief Information and Digital Officer, Wellstar Kennestone Hospital, Marietta, GA, p. A176

PANNULLO, Ava, M.D., Vice President Medical Services and Physician in Chief, Hebrew Senior Care, West Hartford, CT, p. A126

PANSA, Leonard, Senior Vice President Human Resources and Administrative Services, Mercy Medical Center, Springfield, MA, p. A344

PANZA, Louis J. Jr, President and Chief Executive Officer, Monongahela Valley Hospital, Monongahela, PA, p. A597

PAOLINELLI, Karen, Chief Executive Officer, Madera Community Hospital, Madera, CA, p. A76

PAOLUCCI, Benjamin, D.O., Chief of Staff, Southeast Michigan Surgical Hospital, Warren, MI, p. A369

PAPA, Alan, President, Uh Ahuja Medical Center, Beachwood, OH, p. A529

PAPA, AnnMarie, R.N., Vice President and Chief Nursing Officer, Einstein Medical Center Montgomery, East Norriton, PA, p. A589

PAPALIA, Fern, Director of Nursing, Essex County Hospital Center, Cedar Grove, NJ, p. A453

PAPALIA, Mark, President, Upmc Kane, Kane, PA, p. A593

PAPE, Becky A., R.N., Chief Executive Officer, Good Samaritan Regional Medical Center, Corvallis, OR, p. A574

PAPE, David, Vice President, Information Technology, Palomar Medical Center Poway, Poway, CA, p. A86

PAPKA, Lauren, Chief Administrative Officer, St. Mary's Sacred Heart Hospital, Lavonia, GA, p. A175

PAPPAN, Clayton, Director Human Resources and Marketing, South Central Kansas Medical Center, Arkansas City, KS, p. A261

PAPPAS, Michael, Chief Fiscal Service Officer, Louis Stokes Cleveland Veterans Affairs Medical Center, Cleveland, OH, p. A534

PAPPAS, Sheryl, Chief Financial Officer, Sanford Webster Medical Center, Webster, SD, p. A633

PAPPAS, Theron, Director Management Information Systems, Holy Family Memorial, Manitowoc, WI, p. A788

PAQUETTE, Julie, M.D., Chief Medical Officer, Providence Seaside Hospital, Seaside, OR, p. A581

PARADIS, Brian, Chief Operating Officer, Adventhealth Orlando, Orlando, FL, p. A151

PARADIS, James, President, Paoli Hospital, Paoli, PA, p. A599

PARADIS, Jeanne, Director Information Services, The Acadia Hospital, Bangor, ME, p. A318

PARAUDA, Martina A., Director, Veterans Affairs New York Harbor Healthcare System, Brooklyn, NY, p. A479

PARAVATE, Chris, Chief Information Officer, Northeast Georgia Medical Center, Gainesville, GA, p. A173

PARAVISINI, Nilda, Director Human Resources, Hospital Manati Medical Center, Manati, PR, p. A808

PARCEL, Jim, Director Information Technology, Maury Regional Hospital, Columbia, TN, p. A636

PARCHMENT, Deborah, Executive Director, Kingsboro Psychiatric Center, Brooklyn, NY, p. A478

PARDA, David S., M.D., President, Allegheny General Hospital, Pittsburgh, PA, p. A602

PARDEE, Wendy Ann., President and Chief Executive Officer, The Children's Institute Of Pittsburgh, Pittsburgh, PA, p. A603

PARDUE, Helen, Interim Chief Nursing Officer, Johnson County Community Hospital, Mountain City, TN, p. A645

PAREEK, Yogesh, M.D., Clinical Director, Brown County Community Treatment Center, Green Bay, WI, p. A785

PARENT, Paula, Chief Nursing Officer and Director of Human Resources, Cary Medical Center, Caribou, ME, p. A320

Chief Nursing Officer, Cary Medical Center, Caribou, ME, p. A320

PARET, Jason, Chief Executive Officer, Catalina Island Medical Center, Avalon, CA, p. A56

PARHAM, Eva, R.N., Chief Nurse Executive, Central State Hospital, Petersburg, VA, p. A748

PARHAM, Michael, R.N., Chief Nursing Officer, Riverside Hospital, Alexandria, LA, p. A296

PARHAM, Tracy, University Of North Carolina Hospitals, Chapel Hill, NC, p. A506

Health Care System Chief Information Officer, Unc Rex Health Care, Raleigh, NC, p. A517

PARIGI, John Interim Chief Financial Officer, Healdsburg District Hospital, Healdsburg, CA, p. A68

PARIS, Claire, M.D., Vice President and Chief Medical Officer, Unc Lenoir Healthcare, Kinston, NC, p. A513

PARIS, David, Chief Executive Officer, Perry County General Hospital, Richton, MS, p. A399

PARIS, Heather, Chief Administrator Officer and Chief Financial Officer, Greene County Medical Center, Jefferson, IA, p. A252

PARIS, Karen, Controller, Crittenden County Hospital, Marion, KY, p. A289

PARIS, Sherri, Chief Operating Officer, Providence Milwaukie Hospital, Milwaukie, OR, p. A578

PARIS, Trevor, M.D., Medical Director, Brooks Rehabilitation Hospital, Jacksonville, FL, p. A141

PARISI, James, Chief Executive Officer, Chi St. Luke's Health-Lakeside Hospital, The Woodlands, TX, p. A720

Chief Executive Officer, Chi St. Luke's Health-The Woodlands Hospital, The Woodlands, TX, p. A720

PARISKY, Yuri, M.D., Chief of Staff, Mammoth Hospital, Mammoth Lakes, CA, p. A77

PARK, Bockhi, Chief Executive Officer, Encino Hospital Medical Center, Encino, CA, p. A63

Chief Executive Officer, Sherman Oaks Hospital, Sherman Oaks, CA, p. A98

PARK, Chong, M.D., President, Canonsburg Hospital, Canonsburg, PA, p. A586

M.D., President, Jefferson Hospital, Jefferson Hills, PA, p. A593

PARK, Denten, Chief Executive Officer, Northwest Health Physicians' Specialty Hospital, Fayetteville, AR, p. A45

PARK, Gary L., President, University Of North Carolina Hospitals, Chapel Hill, NC, p. A506

PARK, Jessica, Director Accounting, Penn Highlands Brookville, Brookville, PA, p. A585

PARK, Jung, Interim Chief Information Officer, Connecticut Children's Medical Center, Hartford, CT, p. A122

PARK, Kelly, R.N., Chief Nursing Officer, Sweeny Community Hospital, Sweeny, TX, p. A718

R.N., Interim Chief Executive Officer, Sweeny Community Hospital, Sweeny, TX, p. A718

PARK, Rustin, Director of Nursing, Seven Hills Hospital, Henderson, NV, p. A442

PARK, Theron, Chief Executive Officer, Chi St. Josep. College Station Hospital, College Station, TX, p. A664

Chief Executive Officer, Chi St. Josep. Health Burleson Hospital, Caldwell, TX, p. A662

Chief Executive Officer, Chi St. Josep. Health Grimes Hospital, Navasota, TX, p. A703

Chief Executive Officer, Chi St. Josep. Health Madison Hospital, Madisonville, TX, p. A699

Chief Executive Officer, Chi St. Josep. Regional Health Center, Bryan, TX, p. A661

PARKE, Carol, Chief Operating Officer, SUN Kentucky, Sun Behavioral Kentucky, Erlanger, KY, p. A283

PARKER, Audrey, Budget Analyst, Twelve Clans Unity Hospital, Winnebago, NE, p. A440

PARKER, Charisse, Director Human Resources, Tennova Healthcare-Shelbyville, Shelbyville, TN, p. A649

PARKER, Cynthia, R.N., Administrator and Director of Nursing, Carson Tahoe Continuing Care Hospital, Carson City, NV, p. A441

PARKER, David, VP Information Technology, Magnolia Regional Health Center, Corinth, MS, p. A391

PARKER, Deanna, Director Human Resources, J. Arthur Dosher Memorial Hospital, Southport, NC, p. A518

PARKER, Donald J., President, Hackensack Meridian Health Carrier Clinic, Belle Mead, NJ, p. A452

PARKER, Janie, Chief Financial Officer, Hardin County General Hospital, Rosiclare, IL, p. A219

PARKER, Jim, FACHE, Chief Executive Officer, Webster County Memorial Hospital, Webster Springs, WV, p. A777

PARKER, Lori, Chief Nursing Officer, Gonzales Healthcare Systems, Gonzales, TX, p. A681

PARKER, Michael, M.D., Chief of Staff, Sharon Hospital, Sharon, CT, p. A125

PARKER, Ralph, Chief Nursing Officer, Olympic Medical Center, Port Angeles, WA, p. A762

PARKER, Richard, M.D., President, Hillcrest Hospital, Hillcrest Hospital, Cleveland, OH, p. A534

PARKER, Robert, Chief Executive Officer, Lake Cumberland Regional Hospital, Somerset, KY, p. A293

PARKER, Sandra, M.D., Chief Medical Officer, Eastpointe Hospital, Daphne, AL, p. A17

PARKER, Theresa, Regional Finance Director, Transylvania Regional Hospital, Brevard, NC, p. A505

PARKER, Thomas, Chief Executive Officer, Mammoth Hospital, Mammoth Lakes, CA, p. A77

President, Upper Valley Medical Center, Troy, OH, p. A551

PARKER, Tina, Director Human Resources, Encompass Health Rehabilitation Hospital Midland Odessa, Midland, TX, p. A701

PARKER, Travis, Director Human Resources, Southwest Health System, Cortez, CO, p. A109

PARKER, Valerie, M.D., Clinical Director, U. S. Public Health Service Indian Hospital, Rosebud, SD, p. A631

PARKHILL, Cherie, Chief Financial Officer, Crosbyton Clinic Hospital, Crosbyton, TX, p. A666

PARKHURST, James E., President and Chief Executive Officer, Newport Bay Hospital, Newport Beach, CA, p. A81

PARKHURST, Jennifer, Chief Financial Officer, City Of Hope's Helford Clinical Research Hospital, Duarte, CA, p. A62

PARKHURST, Phyllis, Vice President Support Services, Newport Bay Hospital, Newport Beach, CA, p. A81

PARKINSON, Justin, M.D., President Medical Staff, Jordan Valley Medical Center West Valley Campus, West Valley City, UT, p. A734

PARKINSON, Michelle, Director Human Resources, Prairie St. John's, Fargo, ND, p. A523

PARKS, Audrey, Chief Information Officer, Salinas Valley Memorial Healthcare System, Salinas, CA, p. A90

PARKS, Cary, Chief Information Resource Management, Hampton Veterans Affairs Medical Center, Hampton, VA, p. A743

PARKS, Dave, Chief Information Officer, Three Rivers Health, Three Rivers, MI, p. A368

PARKS, Jody, Administrator, Ottawa County Health Center, Minneapolis, KS, p. A271

PARKS, Kathi, Director of Nursing, South Lincoln Medical Center, Kemmerer, WY, p. A802

PARKS, Kelvin L., Interim Director, Veterans Health Care System Of The Ozarks, Fayetteville, AR, p. A45

PARKS, Kyle, M.D., Chief of Staff, Evans Memorial Hospital, Claxton, GA, p. A168

PARKS, Michelle, Administrator, Rivervalley Behavioral Health Hospital, Owensboro, KY, p. A291

PARKS, Peggy, R.N., Chief Nursing Officer, Northeast Regional Medical Center, Kirksville, MO, p. A410

PARKS, Sherry, R.N., MS, Chief Nursing Officer, Saint Alphonsus Regional Medical Center, Boise, ID, p. A188

PARKS, Vicki, Chief Financial Officer, Jackson Purchase Medical Center, Mayfield, KY, p. A290

PARMER, David N., FACHE, Chief Executive Officer, Baptist Hospitals Of Southeast Texas, Beaumont, TX, p. A658

PARMER, Michael, Chief Medical Officer, Carepartners Health Services, Asheville, NC, p. A504

PARNEL, George, Chief Financial Officer, Clifton T. Perkins Hospital Center, Jessup. MD, p. A330

PARNELL, Linda, Chief Nursing Officer, Musc Health Marion Medical Center, Mullins, SC, p. A623

PAROBEK, James, President, Texas Health Presbyterian Hospital Dallas, Dallas, TX, p. A670

PAROD, Daniel A., President, Ascension St. Vincent Evansville, Evansville, IN, p. A227

PAROSKI, Margaret, M.D., Executive Vice President and Chief Medical Officer, Kaleida Health, Buffalo, NY, p. A480

PARR, James, Chief Financial Officer, Salem Health West Valley, Dallas, OR, p. A574

Chief Financial Officer, Salem Hospital, Salem, OR, p. A581

PARR, Lynnette, Chief Financial Officer, Down East Community Hospital, Machias, ME, p. A321

PARRA, Joseph, M.D., Chief Medical Officer, North Florida Regional Medical Center, Gainesville, FL, p. A138

PARRA, Kristin, Chief Nursing Officer, Yuma Rehabilitation Hospital, A Partnership Of Encompass Health And Yrmc, Yuma, AZ, p. A41

PARRA, Michelle, Director Human Resources, Kindred Hospital South Bay, Gardena, CA, p. A66

PARRADO, Carlos, M.D., Chief Medical Officer, Roosevelt Warm Springs Rehabilitation And Specialty Hospitals - Ltac, Warm Springs, GA, p. A182

PARRINELLO, Kathleen, Ph.D., Chief Operating Officer, Strong Memorial Hospital Of The University Of Rochester, Rochester, NY, p. A496

PARRISH, Becky, Director Human Resources, Southern Virginia Regional Medical Center, Emporia, VA, p. A741

PARRISH, Carl, Chief Fiscal Service, James E. Van Zandt Veterans Affairs Medical Center, Altoona, PA, p. A584

PARRISH, Denise, Interim Chief Administrative Officer, Ascension Northeast Wisconsin Mercy Hospital, Oshkosh, WI, p. A793

PARRISH, Suann, Chief Financial Officer, Yoakum County Hospital, Denver City, TX, p. A672

PARRISH, Todd, M.D., Chief of Staff, Ut Health Jacksonville, Jacksonville, TX, p. A691

PARRY, Kayla, Manager Human Resources, Ivinson Memorial Hospital, Laramie, WY, p. A803

PARRY, Mary, Vice President Operations and Chief Operating Officer, Oneida Healthcare, Oneida, NY, p. A494

PARRY, Timothy, R.N., Chief Operating Officer, Highland District Hospital, Hillsboro, OH, p. A542

PARSI, Kia, M.D., Chief Medical Officer, Chi St. Josep. Regional Health Center, Bryan, TX, p. A661

M.D., Chief Medical Officer, Chi St. Joseph's Health, Park Rapids, MN, p. A382

PARSLEY, George, Chief Operating Officer, Detar Healthcare System, Victoria, TX, p. A723

PARSON, Charlynne, Nurse Executive, Moccasin Bend Mental Health Institute, Chattanooga, TN, p. A635

PARSONS, Beth, R.N., Administrator, Christus Dubuis Hospital Of Alexandria, Alexandria, LA, p. A295

PARSONS, Brad H., FACHE, Chief Executive Officer, Baptist Memorial Hospital - Memphis, Memphis, TN, p. A643

PARSONS, Brent, Chief Executive Officer, Moberly Regional Medical Center, Moberly, MO, p. A412

PARSONS, John, R.N., Chief Nursing Officer, Trustpoint Rehabilitation Hospital Of Lubbock, Lubbock, TX, p. A698

PARSONS, Terri L., Administrator, Advanced Care Hospital Of White County, Searcy, AR, p. A52

PARTEE, Paris, Associate Administrator and Director Human Resources, John H. Stroger Jr. Hospital Of Cook County, Chicago, IL, p. A199

PARTENZA, John, Vice President and Treasurer, Northern Westchester Hospital, Mount Kisco, NY, p. A488

PARTHEMORE, Warrenette, Director Human Resources, Promedica Memorial Hospital, Fremont, OH, p. A540

PARTIN, James, M.D., Chief Medical Director, Hill Country Memorial Hospital, Fredericksburg, TX, p. A679

PARTON, Gerald L., FACHE, President and Chief Executive Officer, East Jefferson General Hospital, Metairie, LA, p. A308

PARTRIDGE, Susan, Director Human Resources, Nantucket Cottage Hospital, Nantucket, MA, p. A342

PARUCH, Randy, Director, Information Systems, Holland Hospital, Holland, MI, p. A357

PASCASCIO, Dellone, Chief Nursing Officer, Lac-Olive View-Ucla Medical Center, Sylmar, CA, p. A100

PASCO, Teri, Director Human Resources, East Liverpool City Hospital, East Liverpool, OH, p. A539

PASCUAL, Bolivar, M.D., Medical Director, Essex County Hospital Center, Cedar Grove, NJ, p. A453

PASCUZZI, Robert, Chief Financial Officer, Mercy San Juan Medical Center, Carmichael, CA, p. A59

PASQUALE, Mark, Chief Information Officer, Integris Baptist Medical Center, Oklahoma City, OK, p. A564

Chief Information Officer, Integris Southwest Medical Center, Oklahoma City, OK, p. A564

PASS, Christian, Interim Chief Financial Officer, John Muir Medical Center, Concord, Concord, CA, p. A61

Senior Vice President & Chief Financial Officer, John Muir Medical Center, Walnut Creek, Walnut Creek, CA, p. A104

Senior Vice President and Chief Financial Officer, John Muir Behavioral Health Center, Concord, CA, p. A61

PASSAFARO, David, Chief Executive Officer, New England Baptist Hospital, Boston, MA, p. A336

PASSANNANTE, Anthony Jr, M.D., FACC, President and Chief Hospital Executive, Hackensack Meridian Health Palisades Medical Center, North Bergen, NJ, p. A460

PASSARELLI, Theresa, Human Resources Generalist, Warm Springs Medical Center, Warm Springs, GA, p. A183

PASSMANN, Frederic, M.D., Chief of Staff, Stonewall Memorial Hospital, Aspermont, TX, p. A654

PASSMORE, Gary, Chief Information Officer, Endless Mountain Health Systems, Montrose, PA, p. A597

PASTIAN, Andre, R.N., MSN, Chief Nursing Officer, Boulder City Hospital, Boulder City, NV, p. A441

PASTOR, Robert II, R.N., Chief Executive Officer, Rainy Lake Medical Center, International Falls, MN, p. A378

PASTORE, Raymond, M.D., Chief Medical Officer, St. John's Episcopal Hospital, Far Rockaway, NY, p. A483

PASTRANA, Guillermo, Executive Director, Hospital Pavia-Hato Rey, San Juan, PR, p. A810

PASZTOR, Barbara, R.N., Vice President Nursing and Patient Care Services, Bluffton Hospital, Bluffton, OH, p. A529

R.N., Vice President Patient Care Services and Chief Nursing Officer, Blanchard Valley Hospital, Findlay, OH, p. A540

PATCHELL, Lee, Lead Human Resources Business Partner, Presbyterian Hospital, Albuquerque, NM, p. A468

PATE, John, M.D., Chief Medical Officer, Tri-County Hospital, Wadena, MN, p. A387

PATE, Lois, R.N., Chief Nursing Officer, Island Hospital, Anacortes, WA, p. A755

PATE, Warren, Chief Financial Officer, South Bay Hospital, Sun City Center, FL, p. A158

PATEL, Amita, M.D., Medical Director, Haven Behavioral Senior Care Of Dayton, Dayton, OH, p. A538

PATEL, Bimal, President, Hartford Hospital, Hartford, CT, p. A122

PATEL, Binesh, M.D., Chief Medical Officer, Mclaren Flint, Flint, MI, p. A354

PATEL, Deepak, M.D., Medical Director, Cumberland Hall Hospital, Hopkinsville, KY, p. A285

PATEL, Dilip. M.D., Chief of Staff, Greater El Monte Community Hospital, South El Monte, CA, p. A99

PATEL, Fatma, M.D., Vice President Medical Affairs, Niagara Falls Memorial Medical Center, Niagara Falls, NY, p. A493

PATEL, Govind, M.D., Medical Director, Encompass Health Rehabilitation Hospital Of Morgantown, Morgantown, WV, p. A774

PATEL, Hema, Director Medical Records, Riverwoods Behavioral Health System, Riverdale, GA, p. A178

PATEL, Joy, Chief Executive Officer, Lifecare Hospitals Of Dallas, Dallas, TX, p. A669

PATEL, Maheshkumar, M.D., Medical Director, Center For Behavioral Medicine, Kansas City, MO, p. A408

PATEL, Malini, M.D., Medical Director, Elgin Mental Health Center, Elgin, IL, p. A203

PATEL, Malisha, Senior Vice President and Chief Executive Officer, Memorial Hermann Sugar Land Hospital, Sugar Land, TX, p. A717

PATEL, Natu, M.D., Chief of Staff, Phoebe Worth Medical Center, Sylvester, GA, p. A181

PATEL, Nirav, M.D., Chief of Staff, Los Alamitos Medical Center, Los Alamitos, CA, p. A73

PATEL, Paryus, M.D., Chief Medical Officer, Centinela Hospital Medical Center, Inglewood, CA, p. A69

PATEL, Prakash, M.D., Chief of Staff, Kindred Hospital-La Mirada, La Mirada, CA, p. A70

PATEL, Pravin, M.D., Acting President and Chief Executive Officer, Southern Virginia Mental Health Institute, Danville, VA, p. A741

PATEL, Pravinchandra, M.D., Chief Medical Officer, Barnes-Kasson County Hospital, Susquehanna, PA, p. A608

PATEL, Rajesh, M.D., Chief of Staff, Upmc Lock Haven, Lock Haven, PA, p. A595

PATEL, Rakesh, D.O., Medical Director, Encompass Health Rehabilitation Hospital Of Altoona, Altoona, PA, p. A583

PATEL, Shailesh, M.D., Medical Director, Anchor Hospital, Atlanta, GA, p. A164

PATEL, Shalin, M.D., Chief Medical Officer, Memorial Hermann Rehabilitation Hospital - Katy, Katy, TX, p. A692

PATEL, Sharad, M.D., Medical Director, Adventhealth Connerton, Land O'Lakes, FL, p. A143

PATEL, Shatish, M.D., Chief Medical Officer, Atrium Medical Center, Stafford, TX, p. A716

PATEL, Tanay, M.D., Chief of Staff, Golden Plains Community Hospital, Borger, TX, p. A660

PATEL, Viraj, M.D., Chief Medical Officer, Unity Medical & Surgical Hospital, Mishawaka, IN, p. A236

PATER, Tom, Chief Financial Officer, Rml Specialty Hospital, Hinsdale, IL, p. A208

PATHAK, Rajiv, Chief of Staff, Marshall Medical Center, Placerville, CA, p. A85

PATIL, Steve, Chief Financial Officer, W. G. (Bill) Heffner Veterans Affairs Medical Center, Salisbury, NC, p. A518

PATILLO, Laura, Manager Human Resources, Fresno Surgical Hospital, Fresno, CA, p. A65

PATIN, Al, R.N., Senior Vice President and Chief Operating Officer, Lafayette General Medical Center, Lafayette, LA, p. A305

PATINO, Beth, Chief Information Officer, Emory Decatur Hospital, Decatur, GA, p. A171

PATMAS, Michael, M.D., Chief Medical Officer, Gritman Medical Center, Moscow, ID, p. A191

PATRIAS, Thomas, FACHE, Chief Operating Officer, Tulane Health System, New Orleans, LA, p. A311

PATRICK, Calvin Director Information Services, Adventhealth New Smyrna Beach, New Smyrna Beach, FL, p. A149

PATRICK, Chad, Chief Executive Officer, Mission Hospital, Asheville, NC, p. A504

PATRICK, Christian, M.D., Chief Medical Officer, Baptist Memorial Hospital - Memphis, Memphis, TN, p. A643

PATRICK, Devin, Manager Human Resources, Utah State Hospital, Provo, UT, p. A731

PATRICK, Lisa, Chief Operating Officer, Caldwell Memorial Hospital, Columbia, LA, p. A299

PATRICK, Ronald, Chief Financial Officer, Northwest Medical Center, Tucson, AZ, p. A40

PATRICK, Sandra, Chief Financial Officer, Three Rivers Hospital, Waverly, TN, p. A650

PATRICK, Sean, Director Information Systems, Gifford Medical Center, Randolph, VT, p. A736

PATRIZIO, Eugene, Chief Executive Officer, Memorial Medical Center, Modesto, CA, p. A79

PATRONIS, Michael G., Chief Executive Officer, Springhill Medical Center, Springhill, LA, p. A315

PATTEN, William D. Jr, Chief Executive Officer, Holy Cross Hospital, Taos, NM, p. A473

PATTERSON, Barbara, Chief Financial Officer, Provident Hospital Of Cook County, Chicago, IL, p. A200

PATTERSON, Betsy, R.N., FACHE, Chief Nursing Officer, Baylor Scott & White Medical Center - Llano, Llano, TX, p. A696

PATTERSON, Camie, Chief Operating Officer, Manatee Memorial Hospital, Bradenton, FL, p. A133

PATTERSON, Christina, Chief Financial Officer, Saint Thomas River Park Hospital, Mc Minnville, TN, p. A643

PATTERSON, Dave, Chief Information Officer, Memorial Hospital Of Converse County, Douglas, WY, p. A802

PATTERSON, David, Director Human Resources, Parkside Psychiatric Hospital And Clinic, Tulsa, OK, p. A570

PATTERSON, Debbie, Director Health Information Management, Wesley Rehabilitation Hospital, Wichita, KS, p. A279

PATTERSON, Devasha, Director of Human Resources, Northwest Mississipp. Medical Center, Clarksdale, MS, p. A391

PATTERSON, Diane, Senior Vice President, Chief Operating Officer and Chief Nursing Officer, Virginia Mason Memorial, Yakima, WA, p. A769

PATTERSON, Elmore, Administrator, Allen County Regional Hospital, Iola, KS, p. A267

PATTERSON, James, M.D., Chief of Medical Staff, Bates County Memorial Hospital, Butler, MO, p. A403

PATTERSON, Jan, Chief Nursing Officer, Avera St. Luke's Hospital, Aberdeen, SD, p. A626

PATTERSON, Jeff, Chief Executive Officer, Abrazo Arrowhead Campus, Glendale, AZ, p. A32
Chief Executive Officer, Nacogdoches Medical Center, Nacogdoches, TX, p. A702

PATTERSON, Karen, Deputy Director Operations, Elmira Psychiatric Center, Elmira, NY, p. A483

PATTERSON, Larry, Deputy Commander Administration, Bayne-Jones Army Community Hospital, Fort Polk, LA, p. A301

PATTERSON, Lisa, Director Human Resources, Pointe Coupee General Hospital, New Roads, LA, p. A312

PATTERSON, Marcia, MSN, R.N., Chief Nursing Officer, Nor-Lea Hospital District, Lovington, NM, p. A470
Chief Financial Officer, Valley Regional Medical Center, Brownsville, TX, p. A661

PATTERSON, Maria, Manager Health Information Management, Canyon Ridge Hospital, Chino, CA, p. A60

PATTERSON, Melanie, R.N., Vice President Patient Care Services and Chief Nursing Officer, Children's Hospital Of Orange County, Orange, CA, p. A83

PATTERSON, Michael C., Chief Executive Officer, Flint River Community Hospital, Montezuma, GA, p. A177

PATTERSON, Michael N., Chief Executive Officer, Havasu Regional Medical Center, Lake Havasu City, AZ, p. A33

PATTERSON, Mike, Director of Operations, Northside Hospital-Cherokee, Canton, GA, p. A168

PATTERSON, Philip A., President, Ascension Providence, Waco, TX, p. A723

PATTERSON, Renee, Vice President Employment and Training Services, Rogers Memorial Hospital, Inc., Oconomowoc, WI, p. A793

PATTERSON, Robert, Vice President Human Resources and Rehabilitation Services, The University Of Vermont Health Network Central Vermont Medical Center, Berlin, VT, p. A735

PATTERSON, Russ, Director Information Technology, St. Rose Dominican Hospitals - Siena Campus, Henderson, NV, p. A442
Site Manager Information Technology, St. Rose Dominican Hospitals - San Martin Campus, Las Vegas, NV, p. A444

PATTERSON, Sam, Chief Financial Officer, Bay Area Hospital, Coos Bay, OR, p. A574

PATTERSON, Steve, Chief Executive Officer, Select Specialty Hospital-Springfield, Springfield, MO, p. A419

PATTERSON, Stuart, M.D., Chief of Staff, Bartow Regional Medical Center, Bartow, FL, p. A131

PATTERSON, Todd, Chief Executive Officer, Washington County Hospital And Clinics, Washington, IA, p. A259

PATTERSON, Tony, Chief Financial Officer, Ephraim Mcdowell James B. Haggin Memorial Hospital, Harrodsburg, KY, p. A284

PATTI, Rosa, Chief Financial Officer, Cameron Regional Medical Center, Cameron, MO, p. A403

PATTON, Christina, Chief Financial Officer, Colorado Plains Medical Center, Fort Morgan, CO, p. A112

PATTON, Daniel, Director Information Systems, Henrico Doctors' Hospital, Richmond, VA, p. A750

PATTON, David J., President, Upmc St. Margaret, Pittsburgh, PA, p. A604

PATTON, Joy, Director Information Technology, Pamp. Regional Medical Center, Pampa, TX, p. A704

PATTON, Kevin, Chief Executive Officer, Old Vineyard Behavioral Health Services, Winston, NC, p. A520

PATTON, Meghan, Vice President Human Resources, Abington Jefferson Health, Abington, PA, p. A583
Vice President Human Resources, Abington-Lansdale Hospital Jefferson Health, Lansdale, PA, p. A594

PATTON, Sally, R.N., MS, Chief Nursing Officer, New London Hospital, New London, NH, p. A450

PATTON, William Pat., Chief Executive Officer, Hospital District 6 - Patterson Health Center, Anthony, KS, p. A261

PAUL, Allison, R.N., Chief Nursing Officer, Hshs St. John's Hospital, Springfield, IL, p. A220

PAUL, Darrick, Chief People Officer, Musc Health Of Medical University Of South Carolina, Charleston, SC, p. A616

PAUL, Donn, Chief Human Resources, Lackey Memorial Hospital, Forest, MS, p. A392

PAUL, Joseph, Chief Financial Officer, Broward Health Imperial Point, Fort Lauderdale, FL, p. A137

PAUL, Lise, Vice President Reimbursement and Network Planning, Hebrew Rehabilitation Center, Roslindale, MA, p. A344

PAUL, Mary, Chief Information Officer, Ascension Columbia St. Mary's Hospital Milwaukee, Milwaukee, WI, p. A790
Chief Information Officer, Ascension Columbia St. Mary's Hospital Ozaukee, Mequon, WI, p. A790
Vice President and Chief Information Officer, Ascension Columbia St. Mary's Milwaukee Hospital, Milwaukee, WI, p. A790

PAUL, West, M.D., Ph.D., Senior Vice President and Chief Quality and Medical Staff Officer, Wakemed Raleigh Campus, Raleigh, NC, p. A517
M.D., Ph.D., Senior Vice President, Chief Quality and Medical Staff Officer, Wakemed Cary Hospital, Cary, NC, p. A506

PAULEY, Clarence, Senior Vice President and Chief Human Resources Officer, University Of Cincinnati Medical Center, Cincinnati, OH, p. A533

PAULMEYER, Steven, M.D., Senior Executive, Medical Services, Beatrice Community Hospital And Health Center, Beatrice, NE, p. A430

PAULS, Scott, Director Information Technology- HealthNet Connect, Guttenberg Municipal Hospital And Clinics, Guttenberg, IA, p. A250

PAULSEN, Lisa, R.N., Chief Nursing Officer, Audubon County Memorial Hospital And Clinics, Audubon, IA, p. A243

PAULSEN, Susan, Director Human Resources, Northridge Hospital Medical Center, Northridge, CA, p. A81

PAULSON, Adam, Director Finance, Centracare - Melrose, Melrose, MN, p. A380

PAULSON, Erik, Director of Finance, J. D. Mccarty Center For Children With Developmental Disabilities, Norman, OK, p. A563

PAULSON, Gordon, Manager Human Resources, Glacial Ridge Health System, Glenwood, MN, p. A377

PAULUS, Terresa, Chief Nursing Officer, Banner Goldfield Medical Center, Apache Junction, AZ, p. A30
Chief Nursing Officer, Banner Ironwood Medical Center, San Tan Valley, AZ, p. A38

PAUTLER, Steve, Ph.D., Chief Executive Officer, Ste. Genevieve County Memorial Hospital, Ste Genevieve, MO, p. A419

PAVALONIS, Diane, Chief Nurse Executive, Western State Hospital, Staunton, VA, p. A752

PAVIA, Antoine, M.D., Medical Director, Hospital Pavia Arecibo, Arecibo, PR, p. A806

PAVIK, Sarah, Director Human Resources and Guest Services, Inova Loudoun Hospital, Leesburg, VA, p. A744

PAVILANIS, Charlotte, R.N., Vice President of Clinical Services and Chief Nursing Officer, Sturgis Hospital, Sturgis, MI, p. A367

PAVLATOS, Thales, Medical Director, Ohio Valley Surgical Hospital, Springfield, OH, p. A549

PAWAR, Ganesh, M.D., Chief of Staff, Marshfield Medical Center - Ladysmith, Ladysmith, WI, p. A787

PAWLEK, Kenny, Chief Operating Officer, Usc Verdugo Hills Hospital, Glendale, CA, p. A67

PAWLOSKI, Paula, Chief Nursing Officer, Lifecare Behavioral Health Hospital, Pittsburgh, PA, p. A603

PAWLOWICZ, James, Director Human Resources, Shriners Hospitals For Children-Chicago, Chicago, IL, p. A201

PAWLOWSKI, Phil, Chief Financial Officer, Glenbeigh Hospital And Outpatient Centers, Rock Creek, OH, p. A548

PAWOLA, Ken, Chief Operating Officer, Rml Specialty Hospital, Hinsdale, IL, p. A208

PAXSON, Gary, MS, R.N., President and Chief Executive Officer, White River Medical Center, Batesville, AR, p. A42

PAXTON, Douglas V., Director, Veterans Affairs Roseburg Healthcare System, Roseburg, OR, p. A581

PAYNE, Angel, Clinical Director, Director of Nursing, Sonora Behavioral Health Hospital, Tucson, AZ, p. A40

PAYNE, Ellen, Chief Operating Officer, Georgetown Behavioral Health Institute, Georgetown, TX, p. A681

PAYNE, James, Director Information Systems, Southern Tennessee Regional Health System-Winchester, Winchester, TN, p. A650

PAYNE, Jason, Executive Vice President and Chief Operating Officer, Rush Foundation Hospital, Meridian, MS, p. A397

PAYNE, Jill, Executive Vice President and Chief Nursing Officer, Medical Center At Bowling Green, Bowling Green, KY, p. A281

PAYNE, Judy H., Chief Executive Officer, Turning Point Hospital, Moultrie, GA, p. A177

PAYNE, Keela, Director Human Resources, Hamilton General Hospital, Hamilton, TX, p. A682

PAYNE, Kenneth, Chief Financial Officer, Holzer Medical Center, Gallipolis, OH, p. A541

PAYNE, Michael, M.D., Chief of Staff, Dallas County Medical Center, Fordyce, AR, p. A45

PAYNE, Rick, Director Information Systems, Santa Rosa Medical Center, Milton, FL, p. A148

PAYNE, Steven, Chief Financial Officer, Jordan Valley Medical Center West Valley Campus, West Valley City, UT, p. A734

PAYTON, Becky, Vice President Human Resources, Mercy Hospital Oklahoma City, Oklahoma City, OK, p. A564

PAYTON, Robert, Chief Medical Officer, Edward Hospital, Naperville, IL, p. A213

PAZDERNIK, Mary, Chief Financial Officer, Mahnomen Health Center, Mahnomen, MN, p. A379

PEA, Richard, Director Human Resources, Memorial Hospital And Health Care Center, Jasper, IN, p. A233

PEABODY, Kim, Chief Operating Officer, The Brook Hospital - Kmi, Louisville, KY, p. A288

PEACE III, Lother E., President and Chief Executive Officer, Russell Medical, Alexander City, AL, p. A13

PEACH, Larry, Chief Financial Officer, Jefferson County Health Center, Fairfield, IA, p. A250

PEACH, Susan M., R.N., Chief Executive Officer, Sumner Regional Medical Center, Gallatin, TN, p. A638

PEACOCK, Tammy, Ph.D., Facility Director, Northern Virginia Mental Health Institute, Falls Church, VA, p. A741

PEARCE, Barbara, Interim Chief Executive Officer, The Connecticut Hospice, Branford, CT, p. A121

PEARCE, Darren, Executive Director, Rehabilitation Hospital, Navicent Health, Macon, GA, p. A176

PEARCE, Kelly, FACHE, Vice President Operations, Ssm Health Depaul Hospital - St. Louis, Bridgeton, MO, p. A403

PEARCE, Marc B., Chief Executive Officer, Pam Specialty Hospital Of Shreveport South, Shreveport, LA, p. A314

PEARCE, Margaret, R.N., Ph.D., Chief Nursing Officer, University Of Utah Health, Salt Lake City, UT, p. A733

PEARCH, William, Chief Information Officer, Yukon-Kuskokwim Delta Regional Hospital, Bethel, AK, p. A27

PEARCY, Joetta, Director, Human Resources, Glendive Medical Center, Glendive, MT, p. A424

PEARCY, Steve, Director Human Resources, Community Hospital North, Indianapolis, IN, p. A231

PEARLMAN, Helen, Nurse Executive, Minneapolis Veterans Affairs Health Care System, Minneapolis, MN, p. A381

PEARSON, Bruce, Senior Vice President and Chief Operating Officer, Honorhealth Scottsdale Thompson Peak Medical Center, Scottsdale, AZ, p. A38

PEARSON, Christine, Chief Financial Officer, Anmed Health Medical Center, Anderson, SC, p. A615

PEARSON, Dawn, Director Human Resources, Encompass Health Rehabilitation Hospital Of Vineland, Vineland, NJ, p. A465

PEARSON, Jeff, Vice President and Chief Information Officer, Christus Mother Frances Hospital - Tyler, Tyler, TX, p. A721

PEARSON, Kellie, Chief Human Resource Officer, St. Christopher's Hospital For Children, Philadelphia, PA, p. A602

PEARSON, Kim, Nursing Director, Essentia Health St. Mary's Hospital Of Superior, Superior, WI, p. A797

PEARSON, Kim Renee., Administrator, Essentia Health St. Mary's Hospital Of Superior, Superior, WI, p. A797

PEARSON, Madelyn, R.N., Senior Vice President Patient Care Services and Chief Nursing Officer, Brigham And Women's Hospital, Boston, MA, p. A335

PEARSON, Marshall, Director Management Information Systems, St. David's North Austin Medical Center, Austin, TX, p. A656

PEARSON, Matt, Chief Executive Officer, Curahealth Nashville, Nashville, TN, p. A646

PEARSON, Nancy, MSN, R.N., Director, Nursing, Novant Health Thomasville Medical Center, Thomasville, NC, p. A519

PEARSON, Susan, M.D., Chief Medical Officer, Mayo Clinic Health System In Mankato, Mankato, MN, p. A379

PEAVY, Mike, Chief Information Officer, Rush Foundation Hospital, Meridian, MS, p. A397
Chief Information Officer, Specialty Hospital Of Meridian, Meridian, MS, p. A397

PEBURN, Eric, Chief Financial Officer, Halifax Health Medical Center Of Daytona Beach, Daytona Beach, FL, p. A136

PECHOUS, Bryan, M.D., Vice President Medical Affairs, Unitypoint Health - Finley Hospital, Dubuque, IA, p. A249

PECK, Amy, R.N., Chief Nursing Officer, Memorial Regional Health, Craig, CO, p. A110

PECK, Bob, Chief Financial Officer, Wesley Rehabilitation Hospital, Wichita, KS, p. A279

PECK, Darin, M.D., Chief of Staff, Northern Light Ca Dean Hospital, Greenville, ME, p. A320

PECK, Michael, Assistant Administrator, Caribou Memorial Hospital And Living Center, Soda Springs, ID, p. A193

PECK, Robert, M.D., Chief Medical Officer, Mayo Clinic Health System In Eau Claire, Eau Claire, WI, p. A783

PECKHAM, Gregory, Associate Vice President, Operations, Promedica Bixby Hospital, Adrian, MI, p. A348
Associate Vice President, Operations, Promedica Herrick Hospital, Tecumseh, MI, p. A368

PEDANO, Andrea, D.O., Chief Medical Officer, Suburban Community Hospital, East Norriton, PA, p. A589

PEDERSEN, Darren, Coordinator Information Technology, Weisman Children's Rehabilitation Hospital, Marlton, NJ, p. A458

PEDERSEN, Paul, M.D., Vice President and Chief Medical Officer, Osf St. Josep. Medical Center, Bloomington, IL, p. A195

PEDERSON, Bryan, Human Resources Manager, Tri-County Hospital, Wadena, MN, p. A387

PEDERSON, Karn, Manager Health Information Management, Mckenzie County Healthcare System, Watford City, ND, p. A526

PEDERSON, Randall K., Chief Executive Officer, Tioga Medical Center, Tioga, ND, p. A526

PEDLEY, Joe, CPA, Vice President and Chief Financial Officer, Lmh Health, Lawrence, KS, p. A269

PEDLOW, Bernadette, Senior Vice President Business and Chief Operating Officer, Albany Medical Center, Albany, NY, p. A474

PEDRETTI, Jennalee, Vice President Operations, Regional Health Services Of Howard County, Cresco, IA, p. A247

PEDROZA, Fernando, Vice President Information Technology, Uchealth Poudre Valley Hospital, Fort Collins, CO, p. A112

PEEBLES, Wanda, Chief Nursing Officer, Jp. Health Network, Fort Worth, TX, p. A678

PEEK, Chris, Chief Executive Officer, Caromont Regional Medical Center, Gastonia, NC, p. A510

PEELER, Cindy, R.N., Chief Nursing Officer, Adair County Health System, Greenfield, IA, p. A250

PEELGREN, Jim, Chief Information Officer, Adventist Health - Tulare, Tulare, CA, p. A102

PEEPLES, Jonnitra, Chief Human Resource Officer, Vibra Hospital Of Richmond, Richmond, VA, p. A751

PEER, Julianne, President, Penn Highlands Brookville, Brookville, PA, p. A585

PEERY, Lori, Chief Human Resource Management Services, Va Palo Alto Health Care System, Palo Alto, CA, p. A84

PEET, Carole, R.N., MSN, Chief Executive Officer, Virginia Mason Memorial, Yakima, WA, p. A769

PEET, Fred, Chief Information Officer, Yuma Regional Medical Center, Yuma, AZ, p. A41

PEGE, Diane, M.D., Vice President Medical Affairs, Sutter Lakeside Hospital, Lakeport, CA, p. A71

PEGLOW, Robert, Interim Chief Administrative Officer, Saint Thomas Stones River Hospital, Woodbury, TN, p. A650

PEIFFER, Paul, Chief Financial Officer and Vice President, Jackson Hospital And Clinic, Montgomery, AL, p. A22

PEIL, Michael, M.D., Chief Medical Director, Kindred Hospital Peoria, Peoria, IL, p. A216

PEKOFSKE, Robert, Vice President Finance, Advocate Christ Medical Center, Oak Lawn, IL, p. A215

PELEUSES, John, Interim Chief Executive Officer, Sonoma West Medical Center, Sebastopol, CA, p. A98

PELFREY, Joy, R.N., MSN, Vice President and Chief Nursing Officer, Cabell Huntington Hospital, Huntington, WV, p. A772

PELHAM, Wesley, Florida State Hospital, Chattahoochee, FL, p. A134

PELKOWSKI, Margaret, R.N., Vice President Patient Care Services, Calvary Hospital, Bronx, NY, p. A476

PELLEGRIN, Kimberley, Director, Human Resources, Red River Hospital, Llc, Wichita Falls, TX, p. A725

PELLEGRINO, Ron, Chief Operating Officer, West Virginia University Hospitals, Morgantown, WV, p. A775

PELLICONE, John, M.D., Chief Medical Officer, Nyc Health + Hospitals / Metropolitan, New York, NY, p. A491

PELOT, Jeff, Interim Chief Information Officer, Denver Health, Denver, CO, p. A110

PELTIER, Casey, Director Human Resources, Thibodaux Regional Health System, Thibodaux, LA, p. A316

PELTIER, Glenn, Chief Financial Officer, Christus Mother Frances Hospital - Winnsboro, Winnsboro, TX, p. A726

PELTIER, Robert, M.D., Chief Medical Officer, North Oaks Medical Center, Hammond, LA, p. A302
M.D., Senior Vice President, Chief Medical Officer, North Oaks Health System, North Oaks Rehabilitation Hospital, Hammond, LA, p. A302

PELTON, Ed, Chief of Staff, Chadron Community Hospital And Health Services, Chadron, NE, p. A431

PELUSO, Josep. J., Chief Executive Officer, Tyrone Hospital, Tyrone, PA, p. A609

PEMBERTON, Edith, Chief Financial Officer, East Morgan County Hospital, Brush, CO, p. A108

PEMBERTON, Stacy, Chief Nursing Officer, Grand River Hospital District, Rifle, CO, p. A118

PEMELTON, Debbie, Director Human Resources, Weslaco Regional Rehabilitation Hospital, Weslaco, TX, p. A725

PENA, Carolina, Assistant Director Administrator, Larkin Community Hospital-South Miami Campus, South Miami, FL, p. A157

PENA, Jessica, Manager Finance, Christus Spohn Hospital Kleberg, Kingsville, TX, p. A693

PENA, Terry, Chief Operating Officer and Chief Nursing Officer, Mountains Community Hospital, Lake Arrowhead, CA, p. A70

PENCO, Kris, Director Information Systems, Coffeyville Regional Medical Center, Coffeyville, KS, p. A262

PENDER, Carol, Assistant Vice President Human Resources, Walden Behavioral Care, Waltham, MA, p. A345

PENDER, Debra, MS, R.N., Vice President Nursing, Mercy Hospital Ardmore, Ardmore, OK, p. A556

PENDERGRAFT, Tina, Chief Nursing Officer, Satanta District Hospital And Long Term Care, Satanta, KS, p. A276

PENDLEBURY, Sharon, Chief Executive Officer, Clear View Behavioral Health, Johnstown, CO, p. A114

PENDLETON, Brian, Chief Nursing Officer, Riverton Hospital, Riverton, UT, p. A731

PENDLETON, Gretchen, Director Human Resources, Suburban Community Hospital, East Norriton, PA, p. A589

PENDLETON, Timothy, M.D., President Medical Staff, Penn Highlands Brookville, Brookville, PA, p. A585

PENICK, Lisa, R.N., Chief Nursing Officer, Carroll County Memorial Hospital, Carrollton, KY, p. A281

PENLAND, Jennifer, Controller, Kindred Hospital Tarrant County-Arlington, Arlington, TX, p. A653

PENN, Nicholas, Chief Financial Officer, Hopedale Medical Complex, Hopedale, IL, p. A208

PENN, Shelia, Facility Director, Bryce Hospital, Tuscaloosa, AL, p. A25

PENNACCHIO, Suzanne, MSN, R.N., Chief Nursing Officer, Nyc Health + Hospitals / Jacobi, Bronx, NY, p. A477

PENNER, Jerome, Chief Executive Officer, Murray-Calloway County Hospital, Murray, KY, p. A291

PENNEY, Cindy, R.N., Vice President Nursing, Mercyone Iowa City Medical Center, Iowa City, IA, p. A252

PENNEY, Jan, R.N., Vice President and Chief Nursing Officer, Midmichigan Medical Center-Midland, Midland, MI, p. A361

PENNINGTON, Brian Keith., President and Chief Executive Officer, Medical West, Bessemer, AL, p. A14

PENNINGTON, Kim, Chief Executive Officer, Select Specialty Hospital-Lexington, Lexington, KY, p. A287

PENNINGTON, Stephen G., Chief Executive Officer, East Georgia Regional Medical Center, Statesboro, GA, p. A181

PENNINO, Jackie, Director Human Resources, Old Vineyard Behavioral Health Services, Winston, NC, p. A520

PENNISSON, Jay, Chief Financial Officer, West Jefferson Medical Center, Marrero, LA, p. A308

PENNY, Tracy, Interim Chief Executive Officer, Vibra Specialty Hospital At Desoto, Desoto, TX, p. A673

PENUEL, Jennifer, Director Human Resources, Madison Medical Center, Fredericktown, MO, p. A406

PEOPLES, Kathleen, R.N., MS, Vice President of Nursing, Ascension St. Vincent Kokomo, Kokomo, IN, p. A234

PEOPLES, Kyle, Director Technology Management Services, Springfield Hospital, Springfield, VT, p. A736

PEOPLES, Lynn, Interim Chief Nursing Officer, Person Memorial Hospital, Roxboro, NC, p. A517

PEOPLES, Phyllis L., President and Chief Executive Officer, Terrebonne General Medical Center, Houma, LA, p. A303

PEPE, Joseph, M.D., President and Chief Executive Officer, Catholic Medical Center, Manchester, NH, p. A450

PEPPEL, David, Executive Director, Elmira Psychiatric Center, Elmira, NY, p. A483
Executive Director, Greater Binghamton Health Center, Binghamton, NY, p. A475

PEPPER, L., M.D., President, Medical Staff, Monongahela Valley Hospital, Monongahela, PA, p. A597

PEPPLER, Lisa, Financial Manager, Parkview Whitley Hospital, Columbia City, IN, p. A225

PERAL, Sherry, Director Information Systems, Oak Valley Hospital, Oakdale, CA, p. A82

PERALES, Lisa, Chief Nursing Officer, Fairlawn Rehabilitation Hospital, Worcester, MA, p. A346

PERALTA, Pennie, R.N., VP, Nursing & Chief Nursing Officer, Bon Secours St. Francis Hospital, Charleston, SC, p. A616

PERARD, Anie, M.D., President, Medical Staff, Clarion Hospital, Clarion, PA, p. A586

PEREA, Ely, Director and Chief Executive Officer, Covenant Specialty Hospital, Lubbock, TX, p. A697

PEREACE, Vicki, Manager Human Resources, William Bee Ririe Hospital, Ely, NV, p. A441

PEREIRA, Raul, M.D., Medical Director, Ryder Memorial Hospital, Humacao, PR, p. A808

PEREL, Michael, Regional Chief Financial Officer, Kauai Veterans Memorial Hospital, Waimea, HI, p. A187
Regional Chief Financial Officer, Samuel Mahelona Memorial Hospital, Kapaa, HI, p. A186

PEREZ, Berenice, Chief Nursing Officer, Ashford Presbyterian Community Hospital, San Juan, PR, p. A809

PEREZ, Carmen, Director Human Resources, Doctors' Center Hospital San Juan, San Juan, PR, p. A810

PEREZ, David, Vice President and Chief Information Officer, Eisenhower Health, Rancho Mirage, CA, p. A86

PEREZ, Eddie, R.N., Chief Clinical Officer/Chief Nurse Executive, Acuity Specialty Hospital Of Southern New Jersey, Willingboro, NJ, p. A466

PEREZ, Edwin, M.D., Chief of Medical Staff, Marshall County Hospital, Benton, KY, p. A280

PEREZ, Francisco, Manager Management Information Systems, Hospital De La Universidad De Puerto Rico/Dr. Federico Trilla, Carolina, PR, p. A807

PEREZ, Joe, Associate Director, South Texas Veterans Health Care System, San Antonio, TX, p. A713

PEREZ, Lisa, R.N., Director Nursing, Meadowbrook Rehabilitation Hospital, Gardner, KS, p. A265

PEREZ, Mercedes, Vice President Nursing, Larkin Community Hospital-South Miami Campus, South Miami, FL, p. A157

PEREZ, Nina, R.N., MSN, Chief Nursing Officer, North Okaloosa Medical Center, Crestview, FL, p. A135

PEREZ, Tony, M.D., President Medical Staff, Uofl Health - Shelbyville Hospital, Shelbyville, KY, p. A293

PEREZ, III, Miguel, Chief Information Officer, Driscoll Children's Hospital, Corpus Christi, TX, p. A666

PEREZ-GUERRA, Francisco, Chief Executive Officer, Gundersen Moundview Hospital & Clinics, Friendship. WI, p. A784

PEREZ-MIR, Ernesto, Vice President, Chief Nursing Officer, Newyork-Presbyterian Brooklyn Methodist Hospital, Brooklyn, NY, p. A478

PERI, Gil, President and Chief Operating Officer, Connecticut Children's Medical Center, Hartford, CT, p. A122

PERKERSON, Robyn, R.N., Administrator, Pam Specialty Hospital Of Rocky Mount, Rocky Mount, NC, p. A517

PERKES, Neil, Operations Officer, Logan Regional Hospital, Logan, UT, p. A728

PERKET, William, Vice President Human Resources, North Country Hospital And Health Center, Newport, VT, p. A736

PERKINS, Brett, M.D., Chief Medical Staff, Madison County Memorial Hospital, Madison, FL, p. A144

PERKINS, Chris, Director Information Services, Clinch Valley Medical Center, Richlands, VA, p. A749

PERKINS, Dan, Corporate Director Human Resources, Cornerstone Hospitals West Monroe, West Monroe, LA, p. A316
  Vice President of Human Resources, Solara Hospital Harlingen, Harlingen, TX, p. A683

PERKINS, Kathryn, M.D., Chief Medical Officer, Banner Boswell Medical Center, Sun City, AZ, p. A39
  M.D., Chief Medical Officer, Banner Thunderbird Medical Center, Glendale, AZ, p. A32

PERKINS, Lewis, R.N., MSN, JrChief Nursing Officer, Integris Baptist Medical Center, Oklahoma City, OK, p. A564

PERKINS, Mike, Vice President and Administrator, Baptist Health Medical Center - North Little Rock, North Little Rock, AR, p. A51

PERKINS, Richard, Chief Financial Officer, Baylor Scott & White Medical Center - Hillcrest, Waco, TX, p. A724

PERKINS, Shelley K., Commanding Officer, Naval Hospital Camp Pendleton, Camp Pendleton, CA, p. A59

PERKINS, Sherry B., Ph.D., R.N., President, Anne Arundel Medical Center, Annapolis, MD, p. A324

PERKINS, Tom, Chief Information Officer, Shannon Medical Center, San Angelo, TX, p. A710

PERKINS-PEPPERS, Andrea, Chief Information Officer, Forks Community Hospital, Forks, WA, p. A758

PERL, Lawrence, M.D., Chief Medical Officer, Columbia Memorial Hospital, Hudson, NY, p. A485

PERLA, Salvatore, President, Norwood Hospital, Norwood, MA, p. A343

PERLICH, Gwynn, Chief Operating Officer, Ascension St. Vincent Evansville, Evansville, IN, p. A227

PERLSTEIN, David A., M.D., President and Chief Executive Officer, St. Barnabas Hospital, Bronx, NY, p. A477

PERMANN, Darcy, Manager Business Office, Landmann-Jungman Memorial Hospital Avera, Scotland, SD, p. A631

PERNICE, Paul, Vice President Finance, Beebe Healthcare, Lewes, DE, p. A127

PERRAS, Joseph, M.D., Chief Medical Officer, Mt. Ascutney Hospital And Health Center, Windsor, VT, p. A737

PERRAS, Josep. L., M.D., President and Chief Executive Officer, Mt. Ascutney Hospital And Health Center, Windsor, VT, p. A737

PERRIN, Cynthia K., President and Chief Executive Officer, Texas Health Presbyterian Hospital Of Rockwall, Rockwall, TX, p. A709

PERROTTE, Kenneth, Director Operations, Rockland Children's Psychiatric Center, Orangeburg, NY, p. A494

PERROTTI, Paul, CPA, Chief Financial Officer, Wellstar West Georgia Medical Center, Lagrange, GA, p. A175

PERRY, Carol, R.N., Vice President and Chief Nursing Officer, Stormont Vail Health, Topeka, KS, p. A277

PERRY, Cheryl, Chief Financial Officer, Integris Baptist Medical Center, Oklahoma City, OK, p. A564
  Chief Financial Officer, Vibra Hospital Of Southeastern Massachusetts, New Bedford, MA, p. A342
  Executive Director Human Resources, Paris Regional Medical Center, Paris, TX, p. A704

PERRY, Cynthia, M.D., Chief of Staff, Stephens Memorial Hospital, Breckenridge, TX, p. A660

PERRY, Darrin, Chief Information Officer and Senior Vice President, St. Jude Children's Research Hospital, Memphis, TN, p. A645

PERRY, Donald, M.D., Chief Medical Officer, Madison Parish Hospital, Tallulah, LA, p. A316

PERRY, Doug, M.D., Chief of Staff, Baptist Medical Center Leake, Carthage, MS, p. A390

PERRY, Faye, Chief Nursing Officer, Tennova Healthcare-Clarksville, Clarksville, TN, p. A636

PERRY, Jan, R.N., Vice President Patient Care Services, Community Medical Center, Missoula, MT, p. A426

PERRY, Jeff, Director Information Technology, St. John's Pleasant Valley Hospital, Camarillo, CA, p. A59

Director Information Technology, St. John's Regional Medical Center, Oxnard, CA, p. A83

PERRY, Jeffery, President and Chief Executive Officer, Atchison Hospital, Atchison, KS, p. A261

PERRY, Julia, Director Human Resources, Regions Behavioral Hospital, Baton Rouge, LA, p. A297

PERRY, Karen, Chief Information Resource Management Services, James H. Quillen Veterans Affairs Medical Center, Mountain Home, TN, p. A646

PERRY, Kathleen, Senior Vice President and Chief Information Officer, Mercy Medical Center, Baltimore, MD, p. A325

PERRY, Matthew, Director Information Systems, Andalusia Health, Andalusia, AL, p. A13

PERRY, Matthew J., President and Chief Executive Officer, Genesis Healthcare System, Zanesville, OH, p. A554

PERRY, Melanie A., Chief Executive Officer, Washington County Hospital, Plymouth, NC, p. A516

PERRY, Nini, Chief Nursing Officer, Georgetown Behavioral Health Institute, Georgetown, TX, p. A681

PERRY, Rhonda, Chief Financial Officer, Medical Center, Navicent Health, Macon, GA, p. A176

PERRY, Robert, Senior Vice President, Chief Information Officer, Carilion Franklin Memorial Hospital, Rocky Mount, VA, p. A751

PERRY, Sally, Chief Executive Officer, Coastal Harbor Treatment Center, Savannah, GA, p. A180

PERRY, Sharon, Chief Nursing Officer, Emanuel Medical Center, Turlock, CA, p. A102

PERRY, Shaun, Chief Information Officer, Mcgehee Hospital, Mcgehee, AR, p. A50

PERRY, Solette, Regional Director Human Resources, Kauai Veterans Memorial Hospital, Waimea, HI, p. A187

PERRY, Teresa, Chief Financial Officer, Up Health System-Bell, Ishpeming, MI, p. A358

PERRY, Tim, Executive Director of Human Resources, Baptist Health Corbin, Corbin, KY, p. A282

PERRY, V, Chief Financial Officer, Adventist Health Portland, Portland, OR, p. A579

PERRY GRIMES, Amy, Chief Operating Officer, Riverside Hospital, Alexandria, LA, p. A296

PERRYMAN, Mike, Chief Financial Officer, Baptist Memorial Hospital-Union City, Union City, TN, p. A650

PERSILY, Cynthia A., Ph.D., R.N., Chief Executive Officer, Highland Hospital, Charleston, WV, p. A771

PERSING, Tamara Chief Nursing Officer, Evangelical Community Hospital, Lewisburg, PA, p. A595

PERSOHN, Lori, R.N., MSN, Vice President, Patient Services and Chief Nursing Officer, Memorial Hospital And Health Care Center, Jasper, IN, p. A233

PERT, Robert, Vice President Finance and Chief Financial Officer, United Regional Health Care System, Wichita Falls, TX, p. A725

PERUGINO, Antonio, Vice President Finance, Hospitals, Vassar Brothers Medical Center, Poughkeepsie, NY, p. A495

PESCHEL, Colleen, Director Human Resources, Sutter Medical Center, Sacramento, Sacramento, CA, p. A90

PESKIN, Ted, M.D., Acute Care Medical Director, Hilo Medical Center, Hilo, HI, p. A184

PESONEN-JOHNSON, Alice, Chief Nursing Officer, Chi St. Francis Health, Breckenridge, MN, p. A373

PESTLE, Janet, R.N., MSN, Chief Nursing Officer, United Hospital, Saint Paul, MN, p. A385

PETER, David, M.D., Senior Vice President Medical Affairs and Chief Medical Director, Cleveland Clinic Akron General, Akron, OH, p. A527
  M.D., Senior Vice President Medical Affairs and Chief Medical Officer, Cleveland Clinic Akron General Lodi Hospital, Lodi, OH, p. A543

PETER, Douglas, M.D., Chief Medical Officer, Gallup Indian Medical Center, Gallup. NM, p. A469

PETER, Jan, Vice President Fiscal Services and Chief Financial Officer, Good Shepherd Health Care System, Hermiston, OR, p. A576

PETER, John, M.D., Vice President Medical Affairs, Ssm Cardinal Glennon Children's Hospital, Saint Louis, MO, p. A416

PETERMAN, John, Vice President and Administrator, Riverside Shore Memorial Hospital, Onancock, VA, p. A748

PETERMAN, Tammy, R.N., MS, Executive Vice President, Chief Operating Officer and Chief Nursing Officer, The University Of Kansas Hospital, Kansas City, KS, p. A268

PETERMEIER, Jill, Senior Executive Human Resources, Unitypoint Health - Marshalltown, Marshalltown, IA, p. A254

PETERS, Amy, R.N., Chief Nursing Officer, Truman Medical Center-Hospital Hill, Kansas City, MO, p. A410
  R.N., Chief Nursing Officer, Truman Medical Center-Lakewood, Kansas City, MO, p. A410

PETERS, Bruce, Chief Executive Officer, Mercy Hospitals Of Bakersfield, Bakersfield, CA, p. A57

Vice President and Chief Operating Officer, Bakersfield Memorial Hospital, Bakersfield, CA, p. A57

PETERS, Candace, R.N., Director of Nursing, Webster County Community Hospital, Red Cloud, NE, p. A439

PETERS, Connie, R.N., President, Chi Health Schuyler, Schuyler, NE, p. A439

PETERS, Dave, Chief Human Resources Officer, Veterans Affairs Nebraska-Western Iowa Health Care System - Lincoln, Lincoln, NE, p. A435

PETERS, Gerald, Vice President Information Technologies and Chief Information Officer, Lake Health, Concord Township. OH, p. A537

PETERS, Holli, Director Health Information Management, Holton Community Hospital, Holton, KS, p. A266

PETERS, Jan, Vice President Human Resources, Saint Vincent Hospital, Worcester, MA, p. A346

PETERS, John, Interim Chief Financial Officer, Santa Rosa Memorial Hospital, Santa Rosa, CA, p. A98

PETERS, Mary, Chief Information Officer, Womack Army Medical Center, Fort Bragg, NC, p. A510
  Chief Nursing Executive, Unitypoint Health - Finley Hospital, Dubuque, IA, p. A249

PETERS, Patrick, Chief Executive Officer, Guthrie County Hospital, Guthrie Center, IA, p. A250

PETERS, Suzanne, Vice President Human Resources, Munson Medical Center, Traverse City, MI, p. A368

PETERS, Violeta, R.N., Chief Executive Officer and Interim Center Director, Specialty Hospital Of Central Jersey, Lakewood, NJ, p. A457

PETERS, Wayne, Administrator, Southern Virginia Mental Health Institute, Danville, VA, p. A741

PETERSEN, Brenda, Human Resources, Sanford Wheaton Medical Center, Wheaton, MN, p. A388

PETERSEN, Debbie, R.N., Chief Operating Officer and Chief Nursing Officer, Spalding Rehabilitation Hospital, Aurora, CO, p. A107

PETERSEN, Julie, CPA, Chief Executive Officer, Kittitas Valley Healthcare, Ellensburg, WA, p. A757

PETERSEN, Richard W., President and Chief Executive Officer, Maine Medical Center, Portland, ME, p. A322

PETERSEN, Susan, Human Resources, Lincoln Community Hospital And Nursing Home, Hugo, CO, p. A114

PETERSEN, Tina, Chief Nursing Officer, Hillcrest Hospital Cushing, Cushing, OK, p. A558

PETERSON, Alison, Vice President Medical Affairs, United Hospital, Saint Paul, MN, p. A385

PETERSON, Anne, Vice President Human Resources and Support Services, Licking Memorial Hospital, Newark, OH, p. A546

PETERSON, Bill, Director Human Resources, Saint Francis Hospital Muskogee, Muskogee, OK, p. A562

PETERSON, Brett, Director of Information Services, Adventhealth North Pinellas, Tarpon Springs, FL, p. A160

PETERSON, Carrie, Director of Nursing, Henderson Health Care Services, Henderson, NE, p. A433

PETERSON, Chad, Chief Information Officer, Northwood Deaconess Health Center, Northwood, ND, p. A525

PETERSON, Cheryl, Business Office Manager, Surgical Institute of Reading, Wyomissing, PA, p. A612

PETERSON, Dan, Chief Executive Officer, Sutter Santa Rosa Regional Hospital, Santa Rosa, CA, p. A98

PETERSON, David, Senior Vice President, Chief Technology Officer, Erlanger Medical Center, Chattanooga, TN, p. A635

PETERSON, Denise, R.N., FACHE, President and Chief Executive Officer, Hebrew Senior Care, West Hartford, CT, p. A126

PETERSON, Douglas R., President and Chief Executive Officer, Adventhealth Durand, Durand, WI, p. A782

PETERSON, Eric, Director, Ogden Regional Medical Center, Ogden, UT, p. A730

PETERSON, Erica, Chief Executive Officer and Chief Financial Officer, Sanford Chamberlain Medical Center, Chamberlain, SD, p. A627
  Chief Executive Officer, Sanford Chamberlain Medical Center, Chamberlain, SD, p. A627

PETERSON, James, Human Resources Leader, Kaiser Permanente South Sacramento Medical Center, Sacramento, CA, p. A89

PETERSON, Jeff, M.D., Chief of Staff, Essentia Health-Ada, Ada, MN, p. A371

PETERSON, Jeffrey, M.D., Medical Director, Cooperstown Medical Center, Cooperstown, ND, p. A522

PETERSON, Josilyn, Chief Financial Officer, Ballinger Memorial Hospital, Ballinger, TX, p. A657

PETERSON, Judy, R.N., Chief Nursing Officer, Ut Health Carthage, Carthage, TX, p. A663

PETERSON, Julie, Chief Financial Officer, Sutter Delta Medical Center, Antioch, CA, p. A56

PETERSON, Kathy, Director Information Services, Osf Saint Anthony Medical Center, Rockford, IL, p. A219

PETERSON, Katie, R.N., Chief Nursing Officer, Pender Community Hospital, Pender, NE, p. A439

PETERSON, Larry, Chief Financial Officer, Allen County Regional Hospital, Iola, KS, p. A267

PETERSON, Linda, M.D., Vice President Medical Affairs, Mclaren Greater Lansing, Lansing, MI, p. A360

PETERSON, Lynn, R.N., Director Nursing Services, Newport Hospital And Health Services, Newport, WA, p. A761

PETERSON, Mackenzie, M.D., Chief of Staff, Anderson County Hospital, Garnett, KS, p. A265

PETERSON, Michael, FACHE, Chief Operating Officer, Northern Light Sebasticook Valley Hospital, Pittsfield, ME, p. A322

FACHE, President, Androscoggin Valley Hospital, Berlin, NH, p. A448

M.D., Chief of Staff, Pineville Community Health Center, Pineville, KY, p. A292

PETERSON, Robert, CPA, Chief Financial Officer, Hackettstown Medical Center, Hackettstown, NJ, p. A456

Chief Executive Officer, Millinocket Regional Hospital, Millinocket, ME, p. A321

PETERSON, Ron, FACHE, President and Chief Executive Officer, Baxter Regional Medical Center, Mountain Home, AR, p. A50

PETERSON, Scott, Vice President of People and Organizational Development, Tidalhealth Peninsula, Salisbury, MD, p. A332

PETERSON, Scott J., Chief Executive Officer, Encompass Health Rehabilitation Hospital Of Franklin, Franklin, TN, p. A638

PETERSON, Seth, Director Information Services, Coshocton Regional Medical Center, Coshocton, OH, p. A538

PETERSON, Shelley, R.N., Vice President Patient Services and Chief Nursing Officer, St. Mary's Hospital And Medical Center, Grand Junction, CO, p. A113

PETERSON, Steve, M.D., Chief of Staff, Chi Health Plainview, Plainview, NE, p. A439

PETERSON, Steven, Chief Information Officer, Vice President of Operations, Garrett Regional Medical Center, Oakland, MD, p. A331

PETERSON, Susan, Human Resources Director, Arrowhead Regional Medical Center, Colton, CA, p. A60

PETERSON, Tim, M.D., Chief of Staff, Meeker Memorial Hospital, Litchfield, MN, p. A379

PETIK, Jason, Chief Executive Officer, Sidney Regional Medical Center, Sidney, NE, p. A439

PETIT, Ashley, Chief Information Officer, Northside Hospital - Gwinnett, Lawrenceville, GA, p. A175

PETITT, Michael, Director of Finance, Ascension Southeast Wisconsin Hospital - Elmbrook Campus, Brookfield, WI, p. A781

Director of Finance, Ascension Southeast Wisconsin Hospital - St. Joseph's Campus, Milwaukee, WI, p. A790

PETRE, Patrick A., Chief Executive Officer, Garfield Medical Center, Monterey Park, CA, p. A79

PETRICEVIC, Lili, Chief Executive Officer, Sheridan Community Hospital, Sheridan, MI, p. A366

PETRIK, Jennifer, Interim Chief Nursing Officer, Multicare Deaconess Hospital, Spokane, WA, p. A765

PETRILLO, Mary Ann, R.N., MSN, Acting Associate Director Nursing and Patient Clinical Services, Bedford Veterans Affairs Medical Center, Edith Nourse Rogers Memorial Veterans Hospital, Bedford, MA, p. A334

PETRILLO, Nancy, Director Human Resources, Matheny Medical And Educational Center, Peapack, NJ, p. A460

PETRINA, Robert, Chief Financial Officer, Alta Bates Summit Medical Center-Alta Bates Campus, Berkeley, CA, p. A58

PETRINI, Lindsey, Chief Operating Officer, Wellstar North Fulton Hospital, Roswell, GA, p. A179

PETRITZ, Jennifer, Director Human Resources, University Of Washington Medical Center, Seattle, WA, p. A764

PETROWER, Stacey, President, New York-Presbyterian/ Hudson Valley Hospital, Cortlandt Manor, NY, p. A482

PETRY, Fernando, M.D., Vice President and Chief Medical Officer, Cleveland Clinic Martin North Hospital, Stuart, FL, p. A158

PETRY, Gary, M.D., Chief of Staff, St. Vincent General Hospital District, Leadville, CO, p. A115

PETTIGREW, Dennis, Chief Operating Officer, Saint Michael's Medical Center, Newark, NJ, p. A460

PETTIGREW, Rob, Director Information Technology, Wyoming Medical Center, Casper, WY, p. A801

PETTIJOHN, Kim, R.N., MSN, Chief Nursing Officer, The Spine Hospital Of Louisiana At The Neuromedical Center, Baton Rouge, LA, p. A298

PETTIJOHN, Trent, M.D., Chief Medical Officer, Baylor Scott & White The Heart Hospital Denton, Denton, TX, p. A671

M.D., Chief Medical Officer, Baylor Scott & White The Heart Hospital Plano, Plano, TX, p. A706

PETTINATO, Jim, Director Patient Care Services, Wayne Memorial Hospital, Honesdale, PA, p. A592

PETTIT, Amy, R.N., Vice President Nursing Services and Chief Nursing Officer, Schneck Medical Center, Seymour, IN, p. A240

PETTIT, Donny, Chief Financial Officer, Coon Memorial Hospital, Dalhart, TX, p. A667

PETTIT, Harlan, M.D., Chief of Medical Staff, Fishermen's Hospital, Marathon, FL, p. A144

PETTITE, Shirley, Chief Human Resources Officer, Tennessee Valley Healthcare System, Nashville, TN, p. A647

PETTREY, Lisa J., MSN, R.N., Chief Executive Officer, Select Specialty Hospital-Columbus, Columbus, OH, p. A537

PETTUS, Jay, Chief Financial Officer, Oviedo Medical Center, Oviedo, FL, p. A152

PETTY, Jane, Director Human Resources, Southern Tennessee Regional Health System-Pulaski, Pulaski, TN, p. A648

PETTY, Russ, M.D., Chief of Staff, Towner County Medical Center, Cando, ND, p. A521

PETULA, Ronald, Chief Financial Officer, Good Shepherd Rehabilitation Hospital, Allentown, PA, p. A583

Chief Financial Officer, Good Shepherd Specialty Hospital, Bethlehem, PA, p. A584

Vice President Finance, Good Shepherd Penn Partners Specialty Hospital At Rittenhouse, Philadelphia, PA, p. A600

PEVEY, Bradley, Chief Executive Officer, The Neuromedical Center Rehabilitation Hospital, Baton Rouge, LA, p. A297

PFAFF, Joni, Chief Nursing Officer, Grisell Memorial Hospital District One, Ransom, KS, p. A275

PFAFF, Tony, Chief Executive Officer, Deer Lodge Medical Center, Deer Lodge, MT, p. A423

PFALTZGRAFF, George, Chief Medical Officer, Hansen Family Hospital, Iowa Falls, IA, p. A252

PFAU, Ben, Chief Facility and Information Officer, Bay Area Hospital, Coos Bay, OR, p. A574

PFAU, Beth, M.D., Chief Medical Officer, Larue D. Carter Memorial Hospital, Indianapolis, IN, p. A232

PFEFFER, Amy, Chief Financial Officer, Sturdy Memorial Hospital, Attleboro, MA, p. A334

PFEFFER, Daniel, Chief Nurse Executive, Weisman Children's Rehabilitation Hospital, Marlton, NJ, p. A458

PFEFFER, Michael, M.D., Chief Information Officer, Ronald Reagan Ucla Medical Center, Los Angeles, CA, p. A75

M.D., Chief Medical Informatics Officer, UCLA Health, Stewart & Lynda Resnick Neuropsychiatric Hospital At Ucla, Los Angeles, CA, p. A76

PFEIFER, Mark, M.D., Senior Vice President and Chief Medical Officer, Uofl Health - Uofl Hospital, Louisville, KY, p. A289

PFEIFFER, James A., FACHE, President and Chief Executive Officer, Self Regional Healthcare, Greenwood, SC, p. A621

PFEIFFER, Margaret, R.N., MSN, Vice President Patient Care Services, Good Samaritan Hospital, Los Angeles, CA, p. A74

PFISTER, Joann, Director Human Resources, Providence Willamette Falls Medical Center, Oregon City, OR, p. A578

PFISTER, Pam, Chief Executive Officer, Morrison Community Hospital, Morrison, IL, p. A213

PFISTER, Scott, Director Finance, Providence St. Vincent Medical Center, Portland, OR, p. A580

PFLEIGER, Dennis, President, St. Luke's Hospital - Quakertown Campus, Quakertown, PA, p. A605

PFRANK, Kym, Senior Vice President and Chief Operating Officer, Union Hospital, Terre Haute, IN, p. A241

PHAM, Bong, Chief Medical Officer, Kit Carson County Health Service District, Burlington, CO, p. A108

PHAM, K, M.D., Chief of Staff, Winkler County Memorial Hospital, Kermit, TX, p. A692

PHELAN, Cynthia, Vice President Human Resources, Lawrence General Hospital, Lawrence, MA, p. A340

PHELPS, Britton, Chief Executive Officer, Merit Health Madison, Canton, MS, p. A390

PHELPS, Craig, M.D., Chief of Staff, Great Plains Regional Medical Center, Elk City, OK, p. A558

PHELPS, David E., President and Chief Executive Officer, Berkshire Medical Center, Pittsfield, MA, p. A343

PHELPS, Gail, R.N., Chief Nursing Officer, Haxtun Hospital District, Haxtun, CO, p. A114

PHELPS, Joel, President and Chief Executive Officer, Salina Regional Health Center, Salina, KS, p. A275

PHELPS, Kathleen, Director Human Resources, Treasure Valley Hospital, Boise, ID, p. A189

PHELPS, Lisa, Senior Vice President, Human Resources, Phoenix Children's Hospital, Phoenix, AZ, p. A36

PHELPS, Michael, President and Chief Executive Officer, Ridgeview Medical Center, Waconia, MN, p. A387

PHETTEPLACE, Danial, Director Information Technology, Gundersen St. Joseph's Hospital And Clinics, Hillsboro, WI, p. A786

PHILIP, Merry, M.D., Chief Nursing Officer, University Of Texas Medical Branch, Galveston, TX, p. A680

PHILIP, Neena, R.N., Vice President of Patient Care Services and Chief Nursing Officer, Carepoint Health Hoboken University Medical Center, Hoboken, NJ, p. A456

PHILIPS III, Grady W., President, Valley Health - Winchester Medical Center, Winchester, VA, p. A754

PHILLIPS, Alan, Controller, Encompass Health Nittany Valley Rehabilitation Hospital, Pleasant Gap. PA, p. A605

PHILLIPS, Barry, Executive Director Human Resources, Camden General Hospital, Camden, TN, p. A634

PHILLIPS, Bill, Vice President Information Services, University Health System, San Antonio, TX, p. A714

PHILLIPS, Courtney, Chief Executive Officer, South Sunflower County Hospital, Indianola, MS, p. A394

PHILLIPS, David D., Chief Executive Officer and Administrator, Wvu Medicine - Barnesville Hospital, Barnesville, OH, p. A528

PHILLIPS, David L., Chief Operating Officer, St. John Broken Arrow, Broken Arrow, OK, p. A556

President and Chief Operating Officer, St. John Owasso, Owasso, OK, p. A566

PHILLIPS, Donna, President, Bryn Mawr Rehabilitation Hospital, Malvern, PA, p. A596

PHILLIPS, Eddie, M.D., Chief Medical Affairs, Baptist Health Medical Center - North Little Rock, North Little Rock, AR, p. A51

M.D., Chief Medical Officer, Baptist Health Medical Center-Arkadelphia, Arkadelphia, AR, p. A42

PHILLIPS, Frank, M.D., Chief of Staff, Cherokee Medical Center, Gaffney, SC, p. A620

PHILLIPS, Glenn, Director Information Systems, Gadsden Regional Medical Center, Gadsden, AL, p. A19

PHILLIPS, John, Vice President Information Services, Chi St. Josep. Regional Health Center, Bryan, TX, p. A661

PHILLIPS, John E., FACHE, President, Methodist Dallas Medical Center, Dallas, TX, p. A669

PHILLIPS, Jonathan, Chief Operating Officer, Ochsner Lsu Health Shreveport - Monroe Medical Center, Monroe, LA, p. A309

PHILLIPS, Kelly, M.D., M.P.H., Clinical Director and Chief Staff, Spring Grove Hospital Center, Baltimore, MD, p. A326

PHILLIPS, Kimberly, Chief Financial Officer, The Children's Home Of Pittsburgh, Pittsburgh, PA, p. A603

PHILLIPS, Lionel, Vice President Financial Services, Fauquier Hospital, Warrenton, VA, p. A753

PHILLIPS, Mark, Chief Nursing Officer, The Hospitals Of Providence Memorial Campus, El Paso, TX, p. A676

PHILLIPS, Mike, Chief Executive Officer, Wyoming Behavioral Institute, Casper, WY, p. A801

PHILLIPS, Monie Director Clinical Informatics, Jackson Parish Hospital, Jonesboro, LA, p. A304

PHILLIPS, Paul, Chief Financial Officer, Taylor Regional Hospital, Campbellsville, KY, p. A281

PHILLIPS, Robert, M.D., Ph.D., FACC, Executive Vice President and Chief Medical Officer, Houston Methodist Hospital, Houston, TX, p. A686

PHILLIPS, Sarah, Manager Human Resources, Morgan Memorial Hospital, Madison, GA, p. A176

PHILLIPS, Steve, Information Officer, Greene County General Hospital, Linton, IN, p. A235

PHILLIPS, Tammy, Director, Information Systems, Texas Health Presbyterian Hospital Dallas, Dallas, TX, p. A670

PHILLIPS, Traci, Superintendent, Big Spring State Hospital, Big Spring, TX, p. A659

PHINNEY, Cody, Administrator, Northern Nevada Adult Mental Health Services, Sparks, NV, p. A446

PHIPPS, Emily, Director Human Resources, Oklahoma Center For Orthopedic And Multi-Specialty Surgery, Oklahoma City, OK, p. A565

PHIPPS, Jackie, Director Human Resources, Johnston Memorial Hospital, Abingdon, VA, p. A738

PHIPPS ADAMS, Holly, Vice President of Human Resources, Carroll Hospital Center, Westminster, MD, p. A333

PIANALTO, Eric, Chief Executive Officer, Mercy Hospital Rogers, Rogers, AR, p. A52

PIATKOWSKI, Shannon, Director Information Technology, Blake Medical Center, Bradenton, FL, p. A132

PIAZZA, Doreen, Acting Executive Director, South Beach Psychiatric Center, Staten Island, NY, p. A498

PIAZZA, Kenneth P., Medical Center Director, Bath Veterans Affairs Medical Center, Bath, NY, p. A475

PIAZZA, Tony, Director Human Resources, Titus Regional Medical Center, Mount Pleasant, TX, p. A702

PICAZA, Jose, M.D., Chief of Staff, Unicoi County Memorial Hospital, Erwin, TN, p. A638

PICCIONE, Elizabeth, M.D., Chief Medical Officer, Upmc Jameson, New Castle, PA, p. A598

PICCIONE, Jennifer, Chief Nursing and Clinical Services Officer, Madison Health, London, OH, p. A543

PICKARD, Bert, Chief Financial Officer, North Mississipp. Medical Center Gilmore-Amory, Amory, MS, p. A389

PICKARTS, Lisa, Vice President Patient Services, Sauk Prairie Healthcare, Prairie Du Sac, WI, p. A794

PICKEL, Joseph, Director Resource Management, Walter Reed National Military Medical Center, Bethesda, MD, p. A328

PICKENS, Gayle, Chief Executive Officer, Putnam County Memorial Hospital, Unionville, MO, p. A420

PICKENS, Ramona, Chief Operating Officer, East Cooper Medical Center, Mount Pleasant, SC, p. A622
Chief Operating Officer, Piedmont Medical Center, Rock Hill, SC, p. A624

PICKER, Josephine, MSN, R.N., Director of Nursing, Asheville Specialty Hospital, Asheville, NC, p. A504

PICKERING, David, System Director, Applications, Linden Oaks Hospital, Naperville, IL, p. A214

PICKETT, Jerry, Chief Financial Officer, Goodall-Witcher Hospital, Clifton, TX, p. A664

PICKETT, Lisa, M.D., Chief Medical Officer, Duke University Hospital, Durham, NC, p. A508

PICKLER, Nancy, Director of Human Resources, Encompass Health Rehabilitation Hospital Of East Valley, Mesa, AZ, p. A34

PICOU, Timothy, Manager Information Technology, Lower Umpqua Hospital District, Reedsport, OR, p. A580

PIEDRAFITE, JoAnn, R.N., Chief Nursing Officer, Saint Vincent Hospital, Worcester, MA, p. A346

PIEFFER, Paul, Chief Operating Officer, Great River Medical Center, Blytheville, AR, p. A43
Chief Operating Officer, South Mississipp. County Regional Medical Center, Osceola, AR, p. A51

PIEH, Samuel, Chief Operating Officer, Dmc Huron Valley-Sinai Hospital, Commerce Township. MI, p. A351

PIEPER, Blaine, Chief Executive Officer, Ohio County Hospital, Hartford, KY, p. A284

PIEPER, Kevin, Chief Medical Officer, Kadlec Regional Medical Center, Richland, WA, p. A763

PIERCE, Christy, Director of Human Resources, Katherine Shaw Bethea Hospital, Dixon, IL, p. A202

PIERCE, Earl, Chief Financial Officer, Winner Regional Healthcare Center, Winner, SD, p. A633

PIERCE, Felicia, R.N., Chief Nursing Officer, Great River Medical Center, Blytheville, AR, p. A43
R.N., Chief Nursing Officer, South Mississipp. County Regional Medical Center, Osceola, AR, p. A51

PIERCE, James, Administrator, Community Behavioral Health Hospital - Rochester, Rochester, MN, p. A384

PIERCE, Jeff, Chief Human Resource Officer, Marshall Medical Center, Lewisburg, TN, p. A642
Manager Human Resources, Wayne Medical Center, Waynesboro, TN, p. A650

PIERCE, Jennifer, Administrative Director of Finance, Ssm Health St. Anthony Hospital - Shawnee, Shawnee, OK, p. A568

PIERCE, John, Acting President, Monument Health Rapid City Hospital, Rapid City, SD, p. A630

PIERCE, Kenneth, Chief Financial Officer, Brookhaven Hospital, Tulsa, OK, p. A569

PIERCE, Kristine, Director Human Resources, Newport News Behavioral Health Center, Newport News, VA, p. A747

PIERCE, Laura, Director Human Resources, Memorial Medical Center, Las Cruces, NM, p. A470

PIERCE, Margaret H., Executive Director, Kaiser Permanente Baldwin Park Medical Center, Baldwin Park, CA, p. A57

PIERCE, Pamela, Deputy Chief Executive Officer, Windhaven Psychiatric Hospital, Prescott Valley, AZ, p. A37

PIERCE, Pat, Director Information Systems, Lakewood Regional Medical Center, Lakewood, CA, p. A71

PIERCE, Reid, M.D., Chief Medical Officer, Jefferson Regional Medical Center, Pine Bluff, AR, p. A52

PIERCE, Tiffany, Director Human Resources, Wellstone Regional Hospital, Jeffersonville, IN, p. A233

PIERDON, Steven, M.D., Executive Vice President and Chief Medical Officer, Geisinger Wyoming Valley Medical Center, Wilkes Barre, PA, p. A611

PIERESCHI, Giovanni, Vice President Enterprise Information and Chief Information Officer, Hima San Pablo Caguas, Caguas, PR, p. A806
Vice President Management Information Systems, Hospital Hima De Humacao, Humacao, PR, p. A808

PIERLUISI, Guillermo, Vice President of Medical Affairs, Wellstar Paulding Hospital, Hiram, GA, p. A174

PIERRE, Letonia, Coordinator Human Resources, Assumption Community Hospital, Napoleonville, LA, p. A309

PIERSON, Cindy, Interim Chief Nursing Officer, Highlands-Cashiers Hospital, Highlands, NC, p. A512

PIERSON, Jerome, Chief Medical Officer, Mercyone Siouxland Medical Center, Sioux City, IA, p. A258

PIERSON, Kyle, Chief Financial Officer, Roane General Hospital, Spencer, WV, p. A777

PIERSON, Lois, Chief Financial Officer, Uthealth Harris County Psychiatric Center, Houston, TX, p. A689

PIETRYKOWSKI, Susan, Commander, U. S. Air Force Hospital, Hampton, VA, p. A743

PIETSCH, Al, CPA, Senior Vice President and Chief Financial Officer, University Of Maryland Baltimore Washington Medical Center, Glen Burnie, MD, p. A330

PIETSCH, Brandon E., Administrator, Centracare Health-Paynesville, Paynesville, MN, p. A383

PIFKO, Duane, Interim Director Financial Services, Daniel Drake Center For Post Acute Care, Cincinnati, OH, p. A532

PIGG, Russell, Chief Executive Officer, North Alabama Medical Center, Florence, AL, p. A18

PIGOTT, John, M.D., Chief Medical Officer, Tulane Health System, New Orleans, LA, p. A311

PIGOTT, Tom, Chief Operating Officer, Abbeville General Hospital, Abbeville, LA, p. A295

PIKE, David, Interim Chief Financial Officer, Memorial Hospital Of Carbon County, Rawlins, WY, p. A803

PIKE, Irving, M.D., Senior Vice President and Chief Medical Officer, John Muir Medical Center, Walnut Creek, Walnut Creek, CA, p. A104

PIKE, Pauline, Chief Operating Officer, Beverly Hospital, Beverly, MA, p. A334

PIKE, Randi, Director of Nursing, Pioneer Medical Center, Big Timber, MT, p. A421

PIKE, Ronald, M.D., Medical Director, Adcare Hospital Of Worcester, Worcester, MA, p. A346

PIKE, Tim, M.D., Chief Medical Officer, Portsmouth Regional Hospital, Portsmouth, NH, p. A451

PIKER, John, M.D., Medical Director, Villa Feliciana Medical Complex, Jackson, LA, p. A303

PIKULA, Shirley, MSN, Associate Director Patient Center Care, San Francisco Va Medical Center, San Francisco, CA, p. A94

PIL, Pieter, M.D., Chief Medical Staff, Martha's Vineyard Hospital, Oak Bluffs, MA, p. A343

PILANT, Jason B., President and Chief Administrative Officer, Roane Medical Center, Harriman, TN, p. A639

PILCHER, Shane, Administrative Director Information Systems, Siskin Hospital For Physical Rehabilitation, Chattanooga, TN, p. A636

PILE, Larry, Director Human Resources, Deaconess Midtown Hospital, Evansville, IN, p. A227

PILE, Mindi, Chief Operations Officer, Summit Medical Center, Casper, WY, p. A801

PILGRIM, Patti, Chief Financial Officer, Sutter Davis Hospital, Davis, CA, p. A62

PILLOT, Juan, M.D., Medical Director, Hospital Pavia Yauco, Yauco, PR, p. A811

PILNEY, Jeffrey, Chief Medical Officer, Pocahontas Memorial Hospital, Buckeye, WV, p. A770

PILON, Michele, President and Chief Nursing Officer, Transylvania Regional Hospital, Brevard, NC, p. A505

PILOT, Dave, Chief Financial Officer, Essentia Health-St. Joseph's Medical Center, Brainerd, MN, p. A373

PINA, Joseph, M.D., Chief Executive Officer, Inova Mount Vernon Hospital, Alexandria, VA, p. A738

PINA, Julie, Assistant Vice President Patient Care Services and Chief Nursing Officer, Driscoll Children's Hospital, Corpus Christi, TX, p. A666

PINE, Richard M., President and Chief Executive Officer, Livengrin Foundation, Bensalem, PA, p. A584

PINEIRO, Carlos, President, Hospital Hima De Humacao, Humacao, PR, p. A808

PINELLE, Brian, R.N., Chief Nursing Officer, Gulf Coast Regional Medical Center, Panama City, FL, p. A153

PINER, Thomas, Director for Resources Management, Naval Medical Center San Diego, San Diego, CA, p. A91

PINERO, Efrain, Administrator, Hospital Oriente, Humacao, PR, p. A808

PINETTE, Jameson, Chief Executive Officer, Arbour H. R. I. Hospital, Brookline, MA, p. A337

PINKELMAN, Janet, Director Human Resources, Faith Regional Health Services, Norfolk, NE, p. A435

PINKERTON, Jay, M.D., Chief Medical Officer, George Regional Hospital, Lucedale, MS, p. A396
M.D., Chief of Staff, Greene County Hospital, Leakesville, MS, p. A396

PINKOSKY, Frank, Executive Vice President, Guthrie Troy Community Hospital, Troy, PA, p. A609
Senior Vice President, Guthrie Robert Packer Hospital, Sayre, PA, p. A606

PINO, Elena, Chief Operating Officer and Chief Nursing Officer, Premier Specialty Hospital Of El Paso, El Paso, TX, p. A675

PINO, Joseph, M.D., Chief Medical Officer, Regional Medical Center Bayonet Point, Hudson, FL, p. A140

PINON, Richard, Chief Medical Officer, Eastern New Mexico Medical Center, Roswell, NM, p. A471

PINSKY, Karen, M.D., Chief Medical Information Officer, Chester County Hospital, West Chester, PA, p. A610

PINTER, Tabatha, Director of Nursing, George Regional Hospital, Lucedale, MS, p. A396
Director of Nursing, Greene County Hospital, Leakesville, MS, p. A396

PINTO, Frank, Chief Information Officer, The Hospital Of Central Connecticut, New Britain, CT, p. A123

PIO RODA, Claro, Dr.PH, Vice President, Finance and Chief Financial Officer, Howard County General Hospital, Columbia, MD, p. A328

PIPER, Angel, Chief Executive Officer, Ohio Hospital For Psychiatry, Columbus, OH, p. A536

PIPER, Burt, Chief Operating Officer, Ephraim Mcdowell Regional Medical Center, Danville, KY, p. A282

PIPER, Kevin, Director Information Systems, Adventhealth Deland, Deland, FL, p. A136

PIPER, Vicky, Regional Vice President Human Resources, Loyola University Medical Center, Maywood, IL, p. A211

PIPGRASS, Michele, Chief Fiscal Service, Oklahoma City Veterans Affairs Medical Center, Oklahoma City, OK, p. A565

PIPKINS, David, Chief Executive Officer, Kate Dishman Rehabilitation Hospital, Beaumont, TX, p. A658

PIPP, Darren, M.D., Chief Medical Officer, Monroe Clinic, Monroe, WI, p. A792

PIPPIN, Kim, Chief Nursing Officer, Select Specialty Hospital-Augusta, Augusta, GA, p. A166

PIRANI, John, M.D., Chief Medical Officer, Gadsden Regional Medical Center, Gadsden, AL, p. A19

PIRO, Michael, Chief Information Officer, St. John's Episcopal Hospital, Far Rockaway, NY, p. A483

PIRRI, Christine, Vice President Human Resources, Little Falls Hospital, Little Falls, NY, p. A487

PIRTLE, Kathleen, Director Human Resources, Encompass Health Rehabilitation Hospital Of Wichita Falls, Wichita Falls, TX, p. A725

PISANO, Thomas, M.D., Chief Professional Services, Connecticut Valley Hospital, Middletown, CT, p. A123

PISCIOTTA, Michael J., Chief Executive Officer, Southern Surgical Hospital, Slidell, LA, p. A315

PISICOTTA, Robert, Chief Nursing Officer, Baylor Scott & White Continuing Care Hospital-Temple, Temple, TX, p. A718

PISTERS, Peter, M.D., President, University Of Texas M.D. Anderson Cancer Center, Houston, TX, p. A689

PISZCZATOSKI, Thomas, Chief Human Resource Officer, St. Mary's Medical Center, West Palm Beach, FL, p. A162

PITCHER, Ellen, Chief Nursing Officer and Chief Operating Officer, El Paso Children's Hospital, El Paso, TX, p. A674

PITCHER, Kerry, Administrator, Lanai Community Hospital, Lanai City, HI, p. A186
Chief Executive Officer, Kula Hospital, Kula, HI, p. A186

PITMAN, David, Vice President Finance, Medstar Harbor Hospital, Baltimore, MD, p. A325

PITNEY, Aaron, Hospital Commander, General Leonard Wood Army Community Hospital, Fort Leonard Wood, MO, p. A406

PITTMAN, Cyndi, Chief Financial Officer, Baptist Memorial Hospital - Memphis, Memphis, TN, p. A643

PITTMAN, Jennifer, Chief Financial Officer, Shelby Baptist Medical Center, Alabaster, AL, p. A13

PITTMAN, Jeremy, Chief Financial Officer, Castle Rock Adventist Hospital, Castle Rock, CO, p. A108

PITTMAN, Michael, Chief Nursing Officer, Sovah Health-Martinsville, Martinsville, VA, p. A746

PITTMAN, Scott, Chief Operating Officer, Buchanan General Hospital, Grundy, VA, p. A743

PITTS, Celeste, Chief Financial Officer, Upper Connecticut Valley Hospital, Colebrook, NH, p. A448

PITTS, Lynn, Director Human Resources, Calhoun-Liberty Hospital, Blountstown, FL, p. A132

PITTS, Robert, Executive Director, Wilmington Treatment Center, Wilmington, NC, p. A520

PITZER, Jeremy, Chief Executive Officer, River Place Behavioral Health, La Place, LA, p. A305

PIVONKA, Mary, Director Quality Management, Rockland Children's Psychiatric Center, Orangeburg, NY, p. A494

PIZ, Tom, Director Human Resources, Fremont Hospital, Fremont, CA, p. A65

PIZARRO, Hugo, Vice President Human Resources, Terence Cardinal Cooke Health Care Center, New York, NY, p. A492

PIZZI, Chris, Chief Operating Officer and Chief Financial Officer, Providence Medford Medical Center, Medford, OR, p. A578

PIZZINO, Mary, Chief Information Officer, Effingham Hospital, Springfield, GA, p. A180

PLAGGEMEYER, Rikki, Director Acute Care Nursing, Monument Health Sturgis Hospital, Sturgis, SD, p. A632

PLAISANCE, Erika, Chief Nursing Officer, Ochsner Extended Care Hospital, New Orleans, LA, p. A311

PLAISANCE, Stephen, Chief Financial Officer, Meeker Memorial Hospital, Litchfield, MN, p. A379

PLAKUN, Eric M., M.D., Medical Center Director and Chief Executive Officer, Austen Riggs Center, Stockbridge, MA, p. A345

PLAMANN, Joy, R.N., Chief Nursing and Operating Officer, St. Cloud Hospital, Saint Cloud, MN, p. A384

PLAMONDON, Richard, Vice President Finance and Chief Financial Officer, St. Josep. Hospital, Nashua, NH, p. A450

PLANO, Crystal, Controller, Ascension St. Vincent Dunn, Bedford, IN, p. A224

PLANT, Steven, Chief Financial Officer, Cottage Hospital, Woodsville, NH, p. A451

PLANTE, Vanessa, Chief Clinical Officer, Rehabilitation Hospital Of Wisconsin, Waukesha, WI, p. A798

PLASEK, James, M.D., Chief of Staff, Memorial Health Care Systems, Seward, NE, p. A439

PLASKETT, Darice S., R.N., FACHE, Interim Chief Executive Officer, Governor Juan F. Luis Hospital, Christiansted, VI, p. A812

PLASS, Mary Ellen, MS, R.N., Senior Vice President and Chief Nursing Officer, Columbia Memorial Hospital, Hudson, NY, p. A485

PLATE, James, M.D., Chief of Staff, Kimball Health Services, Kimball, NE, p. A434

PLATEL, Raylene, M.D., Chief Medical Officer, Citrus Memorial Health System, Inverness, FL, p. A140

PLATER, Queenie, Vice President, Human Resources National Capital Region Johns Hopkins Medicine, Sibley Memorial Hospital, Washington, DC, p. A130
Vice President, Human Resources National Capital Region Johns Hopkins Medicine, Suburban Hospital, Bethesda, MD, p. A327

PLATT, Dwayne, M.D., Chief Medical Officer, Conemaugh Meyersdale Medical Center, Meyersdale, PA, p. A597

PLATT, James, Chief Executive Officer, Jackson Hospital, Marianna, FL, p. A145

PLATZ, Scott, Director Finance, Uh Regional Hospitals, Cleveland, OH, p. A535

PLAUTH, William, M.D., Vice President Operations and Chief Medical Officer, Mercy Regional Medical Center, Durango, CO, p. A111

PLAVIAK, David, Interim Chief Financial Officer, Novant Health Uva Health System Culpeper Medical Center, Culpeper, VA, p. A740

PLAVIN, Joshua, M.D., Medical Director Medicine Division, Gifford Medical Center, Randolph, VT, p. A736

PLAYER, Tamara, Chief Executive Officer, Windhaven Psychiatric Hospital, Prescott Valley, AZ, p. A37

PLAZA, Marta Rivera., Chief Executive Officer and Managing Director, San Juan Capestrano Hospital, San Juan, PR, p. A811

PLEDGER, Michelle, Coordinator Human Resources, Grady General Hospital, Cairo, GA, p. A167

PLEMEL, Jeff, Director Health Information, Ccm Health, Montevideo, MN, p. A381

PLEMMONS, Debra, Chief Nursing Officer, Middle Park Health-Kremmling, Kremmling, CO, p. A114

PLESKOW, Eric D., President and Chief Executive Officer, Brylin Hospitals, Buffalo, NY, p. A479

PLESS, Katy, Director of Human Resources, Carepartners Health Services, Asheville, NC, p. A504

PLUARD, Dennis, Vice President Finance and Support Services, Sarah Bush Lincoln Health Center, Mattoon, IL, p. A211

PLUMLEE, Steve, Chief Executive Officer, Select Specialty Hospital-North Knoxville, Powell, TN, p. A648

PLUMMER, Dan, Senior Vice President, Operations, Legent Orthopedic + Spine Hospital, San Antonio, TX, p. A712

PLUMMER, Doug, Chief Operating Officer, Sabine Medical Center, Many, LA, p. A308

PLUNKETT, Alicia, Chief Nurse Executive, Parkwood Behavioral Health System, Olive Branch, MS, p. A398

PLYMELL, Shane, Chief Executive Officer, Shannon Medical Center, San Angelo, TX, p. A710

PLYWACZYNSKI, Russell, CPA, Director of Finance, St. Joseph's Hospital Of Buckhannon, Buckhannon, WV, p. A771

POBLETE, Ronald, M.D., President Medical and Dental Staff, St. Mary's General Hospital, Passaic, NJ, p. A460

POCCHIARI, Michael, Director Human Resources, Garden Park Medical Center, Gulfport, MS, p. A393

POCOCK, Donald, Vice-President Medical Affairs, Carteret Health Care, Morehead City, NC, p. A514

PODESTA, Charles, Chief Information Officer, Uci Medical Center, Orange, CA, p. A83

PODGES, Christopher, Vice President and Chief Information Officer, Munson Medical Center, Traverse City, MI, p. A368

PODNOS, Yale, M.D., Chief Medical Officer, West Hills Hospital And Medical Center, West Hills, CA, p. A104

PODZIMEK, Marcia, Chief Human Resources Officer, Wagner Community Memorial Hospital Avera, Wagner, SD, p. A632

POE, Dale, Chief Executive Officer, Encompass Health Rehabilitation Hospital Of Petersburg, Petersburg, VA, p. A748
Vice President and Chief Financial Officer, Hawkins County Memorial Hospital, Rogersville, TN, p. A648
Vice President Finance and Operations, Holston Valley Medical Center, Kingsport, TN, p. A641

POE, Terri, Chief Nursing Officer, University Of Alabama Hospital, Birmingham, AL, p. A16

POEHLER, Kathy, Vice President, Human Resources, University Of Maryland Baltimore Washington Medical Center, Glen Burnie, MD, p. A330

POFAHL, Barnetta, Director Human Resources, Wagoner Community Hospital, Wagoner, OK, p. A571

POFF, Heather, Director Human Resources, Princeton Community Hospital, Princeton, WV, p. A776

POFFENBARGER, John, Director Fiscal Services, Northern Virginia Mental Health Institute, Falls Church, VA, p. A741

POGAS, George, CPA, Senior Vice President and Chief Financial Officer, Witham Health Services, Lebanon, IN, p. A235

POGLIANO, Chris, M.D., Chief Medical Staff, Aspirus Ironwood Hospitals & Clinics, Inc., Ironwood, MI, p. A358

POGUE, Rick, Vice President, Human Resources, Newyork-Presbyterian Brooklyn Methodist Hospital, Brooklyn, NY, p. A478

POHAR, Mark, Executive Director, Margaretville Hospital, Margaretville, NY, p. A488

POHJALA, Eric, Chief Financial Officer, Upmc Wellsboro, Wellsboro, PA, p. A610
Executive Vice President and Chief Financial Officer, Upmc Muncy, Muncy, PA, p. A598
Executive Vice President and Chief Financial Officer, Upmc Williamsport, Williamsport, PA, p. A611

POHL, Ann-Marie, Vice President and Chief Nursing Officer, Lima Memorial Health System, Lima, OH, p. A543

POHL, David, M.D., Chief of Staff, Cornerstone Specialty Hospitals Austin, Austin, TX, p. A655
M.D., Chief of Staff, Hillcrest Hospital - South, Tulsa, OK, p. A569

POHLMAN, John, Vice President Finance and Administration, St. Catherine Of Siena Medical Center, Smithtown, NY, p. A498

POIROT, Diane, Vice President Human Resources, Harris Health System, Houston, TX, p. A685

POISKER, Karen, MSN, Vice President Patient Care Services and Chief Nursing Officer, Tidalhealth Peninsula, Salisbury, MD, p. A332

POISSON, Keith, Executive Vice President and Chief Operating Officer, Greater Baltimore Medical Center, Baltimore, MD, p. A324

POITINGER, Kevin, Chief Executive Officer and Managing Director, Holly Hill Hospital, Raleigh, NC, p. A516

POKORZYNSKI, Debra, Vice President of Nursing, Midmichigan Medical Center - Alpena, Alpena, MI, p. A348

POLAND, David, Interim Chief Human Resource Officer, Ahn Grove City, Grove City, PA, p. A591

POLASHEK, Maurene, Chief Financial Officer, Oro Valley Hospital, Oro Valley, AZ, p. A34

POLEGA, Steve, Chief Nursing Officer, Metro Health - University Of Michigan Health, Wyoming, MI, p. A370

POLHILL, James, M.D., Chief Medical Officer, Jefferson Hospital, Louisville, GA, p. A175

POLIKAITIS, Audrius, Chief Information Officer, University Of Illinois Hospital & Health Sciences System, Chicago, IL, p. A201

POLING, Rodney, M.D., Medical Director, Unity Psychiatric Care-Columbia, Columbia, TN, p. A637

POLING, Susan, Director Human Resources, King's Daughters' Health, Madison, IN, p. A236

POLIS, Nikki, Ph.D., Chief Nurse Executive, Methodist Healthcare Memphis Hospitals, Memphis, TN, p. A644

POLISKNOWSKI, John, Chief Nursing Officer, Northside Hospital, Saint Petersburg, FL, p. A156

POLITE, Elmer, Chief Financial Officer, Coliseum Northside Hospital, Macon, GA, p. A176

POLITIS, Christos, M.D., Chief Medical Officer, Memorial Hospital Of Tampa, Tampa, FL, p. A159

POLITO, Janine, Chief Human Resources Officer, Banner Ironwood Medical Center, San Tan Valley, AZ, p. A38

POLIVKA, Maureen, Chief Nursing Officer, Hill Country Memorial Hospital, Fredericksburg, TX, p. A679

POLIZZI, Arturo, President and Chief Executive Officer, Christ Hospital, Cincinnati, OH, p. A532

POLIZZOTTI, Barbara, Controller, Encompass Health Rehabilitation Hospital Of New England, Woburn, MA, p. A346

POLIZZOTTO, Mike, Chief Medical Officer, Swedishamerican - A Division Of Uw Health, Rockford, IL, p. A219

POLK, Brent, M.D., Chair Department of Pediatrics and Vice President Academic Affairs, Children's Hospital Los Angeles, Los Angeles, CA, p. A74

POLK, Claire, Chief Financial Officer, Lake Norman Regional Medical Center, Mooresville, NC, p. A514

POLK, Monica, M.D., Chief Medical Officer, Salt Lake Behavioral Health, Salt Lake City, UT, p. A732

POLKOW, Craig, Vice President, Finance, Ascension St. Vincent Evansville, Evansville, IN, p. A227

POLLACK, Neil, Senior Administrator, Terence Cardinal Cooke Health Care Center, New York, NY, p. A492

POLLAK, Erich, M.D., Chief of Staff, West Covina Medical Center, West Covina, CA, p. A104

POLLARD, Amy, R.N., President and Chief Executive Officer, Nicholas H. Noyes Memorial Hospital, Dansville, NY, p. A482

POLLARD, Anthony, D.O., Chief Medical Officer, Amg Specialty Hospital - Las Vegas, Las Vegas, NV, p. A443

POLLARD, Timothy, Interim Chief Financial Officer, Ozarks Medical Center, West Plains, MO, p. A420

POLLARD-LEIGHTON, Heather, Director of Administrative Services, Upper Connecticut Valley Hospital, Colebrook, NH, p. A448

POLLART, Leslie, R.N., Chief Nursing Officer, Memorial Regional Hospital, Hollywood, FL, p. A140

POLLMAN, Brian, Chief Medical Officer, Hutchinson Health, Hutchinson, MN, p. A378

POLLOCK, Jeffrey, Chief Information Officer, Wentworth-Douglass Hospital, Dover, NH, p. A448

POLO, James, M.D., Chief Medical Officer, Western State Hospital, Tacoma, WA, p. A767

POLO, Therese, Medical Staff President, Carlinville Area Hospital, Carlinville, IL, p. A196

POLSELLI, Donna, Chief Operating Officer, Franciscan Children's, Brighton, MA, p. A336

POLSTER, Peggy, Manager Personnel and Administrative Assistant, Falls Community Hospital And Clinic, Marlin, TX, p. A699

POLTAWSKY, Jeffrey S., President and Market Leader, Multicare Mary Bridge Children's Hospital And Health Center, Tacoma, WA, p. A767

POLUNAS, David M., Director, Colorado Mental Health Institute At Fort Logan, Denver, CO, p. A110

POLZIN, Greg, Chief Financial Officer, Iowa Specialty Hospital-Belmond, Belmond, IA, p. A244
Chief Financial Officer, Iowa Specialty Hospital-Clarion, Clarion, IA, p. A246

PONCE, Agustin, Supervisor Maintenance, Castaner General Hospital, Castaner, PR, p. A807

PONCE, Joseph, Chief Information Management, Dwight David Eisenhower Army Medical Center, Fort Gordon, GA, p. A173

PONCE, Martha, Director Information Technologies and Telecommunications, Providence Saint John's Health Center, Santa Monica, CA, p. A97

PONCZOCHA, John, Chief Executive Officer, Select Specialty Hospital-Downriver, Wyandotte, MI, p. A370

POND, Dwight, TIS Boise, Saint Alphonsus Regional Medical Center, Boise, ID, p. A188

POND-BELL, Michele, R.N., Nurse Administrator, Cassia Regional Hospital, Burley, ID, p. A189

PONDER, Beverly, Executive Assistant and Human Resources Coordinator, Covington County Hospital, Collins, MS, p. A391

PONDER, David, Information Technology Officer, Claremore Indian Hospital, Claremore, OK, p. A557

PONETA, Jan, Director Information Services, Mercy Hospital Jefferson, Festus, MO, p. A406

PONOZZO, Nancy, MSN, R.N., Chief Nursing Officer, Aspirus Iron River Hospitals & Clinics, Inc., Iron River, MI, p. A358

PONTICELLO, Nat, Vice President Human Resources, Valley Children's Healthcare, Madera, CA, p. A76

PONTIOUS, Becky, Human Resources/Accounting, Loring Hospital, Sac City, IA, p. A257

PONTIOUS, Michael, M.D., Chief of Staff, St. Mary's Regional Medical Center, Enid, OK, p. A559

PONTON, Elyonel, Executive Director, Hospital Episcopal San Lucas Guayama, Guayama, PR, p. A807

POOK, Lots, Chief Information Officer, National Jewish Health, Denver, CO, p. A110

POOL, Ashley, Chief Executive Officer, Lakeland Community Hospital, Haleyville, AL, p. A20

POOLE, Andrew Interim Chief Financial Officer, Oaklawn Hospital, Marshall, MI, p. A361

POOLE-ADAMS, Veronica, R.N., Vice President, Chief Operating Officer and Chief Nursing Executive, Atrium Health Cleveland, Shelby, NC, p. A518

POORE, Caleb, Chief Financial Officer, Callaway District Hospital, Callaway, NE, p. A430

POORE, Justin, D.O., Chief Medical Staff, Cloud County Health Center, Concordia, KS, p. A263

POORE, Luke David., Chief Executive Officer, Kearney County Health Services, Minden, NE, p. A435

POORTEN, Kevin, President, Northwestern Medicine Central Dupage Hospital, Winfield, IL, p. A222

POOS, Joshua, M.D., President Medical Staff, Community Hospital Of Staunton, Staunton, IL, p. A221

POPE, Alan, M.D., Chief Medical Officer, Virtua Our Lady Of Lourdes Hospital, Camden, NJ, p. A453
M.D., Vice President, Medical Affairs, Virtua Willingboro Hospital, Willingboro, NJ, p. A466

POPE, Alice, Chief Financial Officer, Honorhealth Scottsdale Thompson Peak Medical Center, Scottsdale, AZ, p. A38

POPE, Brad, Vice President Human Resources, Chi Memorial, Chattanooga, TN, p. A635

POPE, David, Senior Vice President, Operations, Scotland Health Care System, Laurinburg, NC, p. A513

POPE, Eddie, Chief Information Officer, Lackey Memorial Hospital, Forest, MS, p. A392

POPE, James W., FACHE, President and Chief Executive Officer, Van Wert County Hospital, Van Wert, OH, p. A551

POPE, Jayne E., R.N., FACHE, Chief Executive Officer, Hill Country Memorial Hospital, Fredericksburg, TX, p. A679

POPE, Richard, Vice President Human Resources, Jackson County Memorial Hospital, Altus, OK, p. A555

POPE, Robert, Director I, Ascension St. Vincent Anderson, Anderson, IN, p. A223

POPE, Susan, Director Human Resources, Wills Memorial Hospital, Washington, GA, p. A183

POPHAN, Cameron, Chief Financial Officer, Hca Houston Healthcare Northwest, Houston, TX, p. A685

POPKIN, Steven, Chief Executive Officer, Lompoc Valley Medical Center, Lompoc, CA, p. A72
Chief Executive Officer, Parkview Community Hospital Medical Center, Riverside, CA, p. A88

POPLAWSKI, Christine, Chief Financial Officer, Cherokee Medical Center, Gaffney, SC, p. A620

POPLI, Anand, Medical Director, Porter-Starke Services, Valparaiso, IN, p. A241

POPOWYCZ, Alex, Chief Information Officer, Health First Viera Hospital, Melbourne, FL, p. A145
Senior Vice President and Chief Information Officer, Health First Cap. Canaveral Hospital, Cocoa Beach, FL, p. A134
Senior Vice President and Chief Information Officer, Health First Palm Bay Hospital, Palm Bay, FL, p. A152

POPP, Adam, Chief Financial Officer, Prairie Lakes Healthcare System, Watertown, SD, p. A633
Director Information Systems, Avera St. Benedict Health Center, Parkston, SD, p. A630

POPPEN, Jeffrey, Chief Financial Officer, Sanford Aberdeen Medical Center, Aberdeen, SD, p. A626

POPPERT, Dale, M.D., Chief of Staff, Kaiser Permanente Antioch Medical Center, Antioch, CA, p. A56

POPPY, Bill, Chief Information Officer, Virginia Mason Medical Center, Seattle, WA, p. A765

POPRAWSKI, Teresa, Chief Medical Officer, Hartgrove Hospital, Chicago, IL, p. A198

POQUETTE, Gary R., FACHE, Chief Executive Officer, Mimbres Memorial Hospital, Deming, NM, p. A469

PORADA, John, Chief Financial Officer, Tristar Southern Hills Medical Center, Nashville, TN, p. A647

PORCELLI, Cheri, MSN, R.N., Chief Nursing Officer, Deer's Head Hospital Center, Salisbury, MD, p. A332

PORCO, Albert, Director Management Information Systems, Hackensack Meridian Health Palisades Medical Center, North Bergen, NJ, p. A460

PORSA, Esmaeil, M.D., President and Chief Executive Officer, Harris Health System, Houston, TX, p. A685

PORTCHY, Mindy, Manager Human Resources, Summit Pacific Medical Center, Elma, WA, p. A757

PORTER, Bruce, Chief Financial Officer, Red River Hospital, Llc, Wichita Falls, TX, p. A725

PORTER, Daniel, Senior Vice President and Chief Financial Officer, J. Arthur Dosher Memorial Hospital, Southport, NC, p. A518

PORTER, Glen, Vice President Human Resources, Essentia Health St. Mary's Medical Center, Duluth, MN, p. A375

PORTER, Greg, Chief Financial Officer, Rio Grande Hospital, Del Norte, CO, p. A110

PORTER, Heather, Chief Clinical Officer, Newton Medical Center, Newton, KS, p. A272

PORTER, James, Chief Financial Officer, Brookdale Hospital Medical Center, New York, NY, p. A489
Chief Financial Officer, St. Bernard Hospital And Health Care Center, Chicago, IL, p. A201

PORTER, Jim, Chief Financial Officer, Southern Virginia Regional Medical Center, Emporia, VA, p. A741

PORTER, Jody, R.N., Senior Vice President Patient Care Services and Chief Nursing Officer, Greater Baltimore Medical Center, Baltimore, MD, p. A324

PORTER, Lance, Chief Executive Officer, Banner Payson Medical Center, Payson, AZ, p. A34

PORTER, Laura, Executive Director, Good Shepherd Penn Partners Specialty Hospital At Rittenhouse, Philadelphia, PA, p. A600

PORTER, Lisa, Director Human Resources, Leadership and Education, Veterans Affairs Salt Lake City Health Care System, Salt Lake City, UT, p. A733

PORTER, Sharon, Chief Financial Officer, Pappas Rehabilitation Hospital For Children, Canton, MA, p. A338

PORTER, Stephen D., Chief Executive Officer, Piedmont Fayette Hospital, Fayetteville, GA, p. A172

PORTER, T, Director Human Resources, Bennett County Hospital And Nursing Home, Martin, SD, p. A629

PORTER, Trever, Chief Financial Officer, Layton Hospital, Layton, UT, p. A728
Chief Financial Officer, Mckay-Dee Hospital, Ogden, UT, p. A730

PORTMAN, Angela, Chief Executive Officer, Breckinridge Memorial Hospital, Hardinsburg, KY, p. A284

PORTNER, Barry, M.D., Chief of Staff, Prowers Medical Center, Lamar, CO, p. A115

PORWOLL, Amy, Vice President of Information Systems, St. Cloud Hospital, Saint Cloud, MN, p. A384

POSCH, Tim, Business Manager and Director Personnel, Parsons State Hospital And Training Center, Parsons, KS, p. A274

POSECAI, Scott, Executive Vice President and Chief Financial Officer, Ochsner Medical Center, New Orleans, LA, p. A311

POSEY, Dawn, Chief Operating Officer, Kp. Promise Hospital Of Vicksburg, Vicksburg, MS, p. A400

POSEY, Richard, Director Human Resources, Prisma Health Baptist Easley Hospital, Easley, SC, p. A619

POSS, Rick, Interim Chief Executive Officer, Wheatland Memorial Healthcare, Harlowton, MT, p. A424

POST, Daniel, Chief Executive Officer, Banner - University Medical Center Phoenix, Phoenix, AZ, p. A35

POST, Eleanor, R.N., Chief Nursing Officer, Piedmont Rockdale Hospital, Conyers, GA, p. A170

POST, Gwen, R.N., Chief Nursing Officer, Sanford Worthington Medical Center, Worthington, MN, p. A388

POST, John, M.D., Medical Director, Morrill County Community Hospital, Bridgeport, NE, p. A430

POST, Kimberly, Senior Vice President and Chief Clinical Officer, Honorhealth Scottsdale Thompson Peak Medical Center, Scottsdale, AZ, p. A38
Senior Vice President and Chief Executive Officer, Honorhealth Scottsdale Osborn Medical Center, Scottsdale, AZ, p. A38

POST, Michael A., Chief Executive Officer, Select Specialty Hospital-Erie, Erie, PA, p. A590
Chief Executive Officer, The Pavilion At Williamsburg Place, Williamsburg, VA, p. A753

POSTERNACK, Charles, M.D., Vice President, Boca Raton Regional Hospital, Boca Raton, FL, p. A132

POSTON, Anne, Director of Human Resources/Compliance, Lake City Community Hospital, Lake City, SC, p. A622

POSTULKA, Carol, Administrative Coordinator, Avera Gregory Hospital, Gregory, SD, p. A628

POTEATE, Kathy, Human Resources Manager, Hugh Chatham Memorial Hospital, Elkin, NC, p. A509

POTEETE, Robin, Manager Human Resources, Hawkins County Memorial Hospital, Rogersville, TN, p. A648

POTEMPA, Debra, Vice President, Mercyhealth Hospital And Trauma Center - Janesville, Janesville, WI, p. A786

POTITADKUL, Wendy, Chief Information Officer, Sunrise Canyon Hospital, Lubbock, TX, p. A698

POTTENGER, Jay, Chief Executive Officer, Garfield County Health Center, Jordan, MT, p. A425

POTTER, Carolyn, Chief Human Resources Officer, Mclaren Bay Region, Bay City, MI, p. A349
Vice President Human Resources, Mclaren Bay Special Care, Bay City, MI, p. A349
Vice President Human Resources, Mclaren Central Michigan, Mount Pleasant, MI, p. A362

POTTER, Val, Director Human Resources, Ascension St. Vincent Salem, Salem, IN, p. A240

POTTS, Mary Ann, Director Personnel, Community Hospitals And Wellness Centers, Bryan, OH, p. A530

POUND, Steve, Vice President Human Resources, St. Joseph's Hospital, Savannah, GA, p. A180

POUND, Terry, Chief Financial Officer, Hospital District No 1 Of Rice County, Lyons, KS, p. A270

POUND, Veronica, R.N., Administrator, Socorro General Hospital, Socorro, NM, p. A472
R.N., Interim Administrator and Director of Patient Care, Socorro General Hospital, Socorro, NM, p. A472

POVICH, Mark, D.O., Medical Director, Osf St. Francis Hospital And Medical Group. Escanaba, MI, p. A354

POWE, Lee, Director Management Information Systems, Hugh Chatham Memorial Hospital, Elkin, NC, p. A509

POWEL, Linda, M.D., Medical Director, Odessa Memorial Healthcare Center, Odessa, WA, p. A761

POWELL, Adam, Program Manager, Marion Veterans Affairs Medical Center, Marion, IL, p. A211

POWELL, Amy, Director Human Resources, Johnson Regional Medical Center, Clarksville, AR, p. A43

POWELL, Candy, Administrator, Collingsworth General Hospital, Wellington, TX, p. A724

POWELL, Charles, Chief Financial Officer, Arkansas Surgical Hospital, North Little Rock, AR, p. A51

POWELL, D, Chief Information Officer, Strong Memorial Hospital Of The University Of Rochester, Rochester, NY, p. A496

POWELL, Hannah, Chief Nursing Officer, Mercy Hospital Kingfisher, Kingfisher, OK, p. A560

POWELL, Holly, Interim Chief Executive Officer, Continuecare Hospital At Hendrick Medical Center, Abilene, TX, p. A651

POWELL, Jackie, Director Human Resources, Pemiscot Memorial Health System, Hayti, MO, p. A407

POWELL, James, Associate Administrator, Banner Gateway Medical Center, Gilbert, AZ, p. A32

POWELL, Jimmy, Manager Human Resources, Harry S. Truman Memorial Veterans Hospital, Columbia, MO, p. A405

POWELL, Josh, Facility Controller, Cox Monett Hospital, Monett, MO, p. A412

POWELL, Karen, Vice President, Human Resources, Mary Free Bed Rehabilitation Hospital, Grand Rapids, MI, p. A356

POWELL, Kay, Director Human Resources, Christus Southeast Texas Jasper Memorial, Jasper, TX, p. A691

POWELL, Michelle, Chief Executive Officer, Select Rehabilitation Hospital Of Denton, Denton, TX, p. A672

POWELL, Parker, Chief Executive Officer, Glendive Medical Center, Glendive, MT, p. A424

POWELL, Tammy, FACHE, M.P.H., President, Ssm Health St. Anthony Hospital - Oklahoma City, Oklahoma City, OK, p. A566

POWELL, Traci, Director Human Resources, Encompass Health Rehabilitation Hospital Of Panama City, Panama City, FL, p. A153

POWELL, Virginia, Director Finance, Wilmington Treatment Center, Wilmington, NC, p. A520

POWELL-STAFFORD, Valerie L., Chief Executive Officer, Northside Hospital, Saint Petersburg, FL, p. A156

POWER, Bob, Vice President Information Services, Good Samaritan Regional Medical Center, Corvallis, OR, p. A574

POWER, Robert, Chief Information Officer, Samaritan Pacific Communities Hospital, Newport, OR, p. A578
Vice President Information Services, Samaritan Lebanon Community Hospital, Lebanon, OR, p. A577

POWERS, Anthony, Interim President and Vice President of Patient Services, Baptist Health Corbin, Corbin, KY, p. A282

POWERS, Barbara, R.N., Chief Nursing Officer, Austin Lakes Hospital, Austin, TX, p. A655

POWERS, Brent, M.D., Vice President/Chief Medical Officer, Lexington Medical Center, West Columbia, SC, p. A625

POWERS, Jamekia, Assistant Director Human Resources, Georgia Regional Hospital At Savannah, Savannah, GA, p. A180

POWERS, Judi, Chief Executive Officer, Advanced Care Hospital Of Montana, Billings, MT, p. A421

POWERS, Kelli, Chief Financial Officer, Huntsville Hospital, Huntsville, AL, p. A20
President, Decatur Morgan Hospital, Decatur, AL, p. A17

POWERS, Mary, R.N., MSN, Senior Vice President and Chief Nursing Officer, Manchester Memorial Hospital, Manchester, CT, p. A122
R.N., MSN, Senior Vice President and Chief Nursing Officer, Rockville General Hospital, Vernon, CT, p. A125

POWERS, Ryan, Vice President Finance, Spectrum Health Zeeland Community Hospital, Zeeland, MI, p. A370

POWRIE, Raymond, M.D., Senior Vice President Quality and Clinical Effectiveness, Women & Infants Hospital Of Rhode Island, Providence, RI, p. A614

POYNTER, Carmen, Director Human Resources, Rockcastle Regional Hospital And Respiratory Care Center, Mount Vernon, KY, p. A291

POYTHRESS, Antoine, Chief Financial Officer, Washington County Regional Medical Center, Sandersville, GA, p. A179
Interim Chief Executive Officer, Washington County Regional Medical Center, Sandersville, GA, p. A179

PRABHAKARAN, Madhan, M.D., Chief Medical Officer, Palo Alto County Health System, Emmetsburg, IA, p. A249

PRACHEIL, Michael, Chief Financial Officer, Gothenburg Health, Gothenburg, NE, p. A432

PRACHT, Matthew, Vice President Finance, Scotland Health Care System, Laurinburg, NC, p. A513

PRADA, Janina, Director Information Services, University Medical Center Of El Paso, El Paso, TX, p. A676
Director Information Technology, El Paso Children's Hospital, El Paso, TX, p. A674

PRAFKA, David, Ed.D., Director of Human Resources, Vidant Edgecombe Hospital, Tarboro, NC, p. A519

PRAKASH, Amitabh, M.D., Chief Medical Officer, Ahmc Anaheim Regional Medical Center, Anaheim, CA, p. A55

PRAKASH, Vijay, Information Systems Officer, Essex County Hospital Center, Cedar Grove, NJ, p. A453

PRATER, Jeffrey, Chief Executive Officer, Carson Valley Medical Center, Gardnerville, NV, p. A442

PRATER, Marsha, Ph.D., R.N., Senior Vice President and Chief Nursing Officer, Memorial Medical Center, Springfield, IL, p. A221

PRATER, Robin, Director Human Resources, Rusk Rehabilitation Hospital, Columbia, MO, p. A405

PRATHER, Rachael, Chief Nursing Officer, Ferrell Hospital, Eldorado, IL, p. A203

PRATT, Audra, Chief Human Resource Officer, Ascension St. Vincent Indianapolis Hospital, Indianapolis, IN, p. A231

PRATT, Bailey, Chief Financial Officer, Saint Thomas Rutherford Hospital, Murfreesboro, TN, p. A646

PRATT, Debra, Chief Financial Officer, Washington County Memorial Hospital, Potosi, MO, p. A414

PRATT, Dustin, M.D., Chief of Staff, Childress Regional Medical Center, Childress, TX, p. A663

PRATT, Lisa, Vice President, Human Resources, Mclean Hospital, Belmont, MA, p. A334

PRATT, MaryEllen, FACHE, Chief Executive Officer, St. James Parish Hospital, Lutcher, LA, p. A307

PRATT, Ramona, Chief Nursing Officer, Pih Health Hospital - Whittier, Whittier, CA, p. A105

PRATT, Timothy, M.D., Vice President Medical Affairs and Chief Medical Officer, Ssm Health St. Clare Hospital - Fenton, Fenton, MO, p. A406

PRATT, Troy, Information Technology Site Director, Covenant Medical Center, Lubbock, TX, p. A697

PREAU, William, M.D., Medical Director, Avala, Covington, LA, p. A300

PRECOURT, Justin, Chief Nursing Officer, Umass Memorial Medical Center, Worcester, MA, p. A347

PREIB, Barbara, Director of Nursing, Chicago Behavioral Hospital, Des Plaines, IL, p. A202

PREISINGER, Andrea, Director Human Resources, Menninger Clinic, Houston, TX, p. A687

PREMO, Mark, Senior Director HC Intelligence, Providence Portland Medical Center, Portland, OR, p. A579

PRENTISS, Kristin, Chief Financial Officer, Specialty Hospital Of Central Jersey, Lakewood, NJ, p. A457

PRESCOTT, Tina, Vice President, Hospital Services, Jackson-Madison County General Hospital, Jackson, TN, p. A639

PRESNELL, Elizabeth, Assistant Vice President of Finance, St. Luke's Hospital, Columbus, NC, p. A508

PRESSMAN, Sean, Chief Executive Officer, Lewisgale Hospital Pulaski, Pulaski, VA, p. A749

PRESTEGAARD, Benjamin, Chief Medical Officer, Uh Portage Medical Center, Ravenna, OH, p. A548

PRESTON, Tara, Director Human Resources, Bingham Memorial Hospital, Blackfoot, ID, p. A188
Director Human Resources, Idaho Doctor's Hospital, Blackfoot, ID, p. A188

PRESTON, Traci, Director of Nursing, Cap. Fear Valley - Bladen County Hospital, Elizabethtown, NC, p. A509

PRESTRIDGE, Tim, Interim Chief Financial Officer, Logan Memorial Hospital, Russellville, KY, p. A293

PRETE, Mark, M.D., Vice President Medical Affairs, Charlotte Hungerford Hospital, Torrington, CT, p. A125

PRETTYMAN, Edgar E., PsyD, Chief Executive Officer, Texas Neurorehab Center, Austin, TX, p. A657
PsyD, Chief Executive Officer, Texas Star Recovery, Austin, TX, p. A657

PRETZLAFF, Robert, M.D., Chief Medical Officer, St. Rose Dominican Hospitals - San Martin Campus, Las Vegas, NV, p. A444

PREWITT, Connie, Chief Financial Officer, Billings Clinic, Billings, MT, p. A421

PREWITT, Margaret, Vice President Patient Services and Chief Nursing Officer, St. Catherine Hospital, Garden City, KS, p. A264

PRIBITKIN, Edmund, M.D., Chief Medical Officer, Thomas Jefferson University Hospitals, Philadelphia, PA, p. A602

PRICE, Bernard, Chief Human Resources Officer, Medical Center, Navicent Health, Macon, GA, p. A176

PRICE, Connie, M.D., Chief Medical Officer, Denver Health, Denver, CO, p. A110

PRICE, David, Chief Executive Officer, Honorhealth Deer Valley Medical Center, Phoenix, AZ, p. A36

Chief Executive Officer, Honorhealth Scottsdale Thompson Peak Medical Center, Scottsdale, AZ, p. A38

PRICE, James, Hospital Administrator, State Hospital South, Blackfoot, ID, p. A188

PRICE, John, M.D., Chief of Staff, Fairview Regional Medical Center, Fairview, OK, p. A559
Chief Financial Officer, King's Daughters' Health, Madison, IN, p. A236

PRICE, Kelley, R.N., Chief Nursing Officer, Battle Mountain General Hospital, Battle Mountain, NV, p. A441

PRICE, Kevin, Vice President and Chief Operating Officer, Sparrow Clinton Hospital, Saint Johns, MI, p. A366
Vice President and Chief Operating Officer, Sparrow Ionia Hospital, Ionia, MI, p. A358

PRICE, Kim, Chief Executive Officer, Franklin General Hospital, Hampton, IA, p. A251

PRICE, Larry, Chief Executive Officer, Limestone Medical Center, Groesbeck, TX, p. A682

PRICE, Lea, Administrator, Tulsa Center For Behavioral Health, Tulsa, OK, p. A571

PRICE, Lorraine, Associate Director, Hampton Veterans Affairs Medical Center, Hampton, VA, p. A743

PRICE, Manuel, Director Information Systems, Brookwood Baptist Medical Center, Birmingham, AL, p. A14

PRICE, Meredith, Vice President Fiscal Services and Chief Financial Officer, St. Joseph's Hospital Health Center, Syracuse, NY, p. A499

PRICE, Mindy, R.N., Chief Executive Officer, Rosebud Health Care Center, Forsyth, MT, p. A423

PRICE, Norman M., FACHE, Chief Executive Officer, Southwest Mississipp. Regional Medical Center, Mccomb, MS, p. A396

PRICE, Sam, Executive Vice President Finance/Chief Financial Officer, East Alabama Medical Center, Opelika, AL, p. A23

PRICE, Shari, Director Information Services, Baptist Health Louisville, Louisville, KY, p. A287

PRICE, Terry, Director Information Technology, Great Plains Regional Medical Center, Elk City, OK, p. A558

PRICE, Tonya, Chief Nursing Officer, Wilbarger General Hospital, Vernon, TX, p. A723

PRICE, Walter, Director Information Technology, Newport Hospital And Health Services, Newport, WA, p. A761

PRICE-YONTS, Melody, Chief Executive Officer, Acoma-Canoncito-Laguna Hospital, Acoma, NM, p. A467

PRICKEL, Trisha, Information Systems Director, Margaret Mary Health, Batesville, IN, p. A223

PRIDDY, Ernest Chief Financial Officer, Old Vineyard Behavioral Health Services, Winston, NC, p. A520

PRIDDY, Steven, M.D., VP of Physician Affairs/Chief Medical Officer, Ascension St. Vincent Carmel Hospital, Carmel, IN, p. A225

PRIDEAUX, Heather, Chief Financial Officer, Rawlins County Health Center, Atwood, KS, p. A262

PRIDGEN, Kim, Chief Financial Officer, Northcrest Medical Center, Springfield, TN, p. A650

PRIES, Kathleen, Director Human Resources, Nazareth Hospital, Philadelphia, PA, p. A601

PRIEST, Bill, Chief Administrative Officer, Marshfield Medical Center - Eau Claire Hospital, Eau Claire, WI, p. A783

PRIEST, David, Director Information Systems, Munson Healthcare Charlevoix Hospital, Charlevoix, MI, p. A350

PRIEST, Geoff, M.D., Chief Medical Officer, Unitypoint Health Meriter, Madison, WI, p. A788

PRIEST, Mike, M.D., Chief of Staff, Pawhuska Hospital, Pawhuska, OK, p. A566

PRIETTO, Carlos, President and Chief Executive Officer, Hoag Orthopedic Institute, Irvine, CA, p. A69

PRIHODA, Matt, M.D., Chief of Staff, Washington County Hospital And Clinics, Washington, IA, p. A259

PRILUTSKY, Michael, President and Chief Executive Officer, Jersey City Medical Center, Jersey City, NJ, p. A456

PRIMACK, Matthew Lee., President, Advocate Condell Medical Center, Libertyville, IL, p. A210

PRINCE, Clay, M.D., Chief Medical Officer, Madison Memorial Hospital, Rexburg, ID, p. A192

PRINCE, Kem, Manager of Finance, Parkview Noble Hospital, Kendallville, IN, p. A233

PRINCE, Michele, Chief Operating Officer, Lewis County General Hospital, Lowville, NY, p. A487

PRINCE, Sue, Director Information Systems, Northern Westchester Hospital, Mount Kisco, NY, p. A488

PRINCIPE, Adam, Chief Executive Officer, Select Specialty Hospital-Pensacola, Pensacola, FL, p. A154

PRINCIPE, Hector, M.D., Director, Hospital Universitario Dr. Ramon Ruiz Arnau, Bayamon, PR, p. A806

PRINGLE-MILLER, Letitia, Administrative Director, Prisma Health Tuomey Hospital, Sumter, SC, p. A624

PRINTY, Wayne, Chief Financial Officer and Senior Vice President Finance, Lincolnhealth, Damariscotta, ME, p. A320

PRIORE, Jacqueline, Chief Nursing Officer, Samaritan Hospital - Main Campus, Troy, NY, p. A500

PRISELAC, Thomas M., President and Chief Executive Officer, Cedars-Sinai Medical Center, Los Angeles, CA, p. A73

PRISTER, James R., President and Chief Executive Officer, Rml Specialty Hospital, Hinsdale, IL, p. A208

PRITCHARD, Jason, Chief Financial Officer, Hackensack Meridian Health Pascack Valley Medical Center, Westwood, NJ, p. A465

PRITCHARD, Joann, Chief Financial Officer, Erie Veterans Affairs Medical Center, Erie, PA, p. A589

PRITCHETT, Greg, Chief Financial Officer, Cuero Regional Hospital, Cuero, TX, p. A667

PRIVETT, David, Deputy Director, Western New York Children's Psychiatric Center, West Seneca, NY, p. A502

PROBASCO, Brent, Chief Financial Officer, Cass Regional Medical Center, Harrisonville, MO, p. A407

PROBST, Nancy, R.N., Chief Nursing Officer, Bigfork Valley Hospital, Bigfork, MN, p. A372

PROBUS, Kimberly, Chief Nursing Officer, Opelousas General Health System, Opelousas, LA, p. A312

PROCHASKA, Jodi, Chief Financial Officer, Butler County Health Care Center, David City, NE, p. A431

PROCHILO, John F. Jr, Chief Executive Officer, Northeast Rehabilitation Hospital, Salem, NH, p. A451

PROCHNOW, Bryan, Chief Financial Officer, Matagorda Regional Medical Center, Bay City, TX, p. A657

PROCTOR, Brandy, Director of Nursing, North Star Behavioral Health System, Anchorage, AK, p. A27

PROCTOR, Jason, Chief Operating Officer, Christus Mother Frances Hospital - Tyler, Tyler, TX, p. A721

PROCTOR, Jason J., Chief Executive Officer, Christus Mother Frances Hospital - Tyler, Tyler, TX, p. A721

PROCTOR, Quinn, Director Human Resources, Claremore Indian Hospital, Claremore, OK, p. A557

PROCTOR, Sandra, R.N., MS, Chief Nurse Executive, Memorial Medical Center, Modesto, CA, p. A79

PROCTOR, Scott, Chief Executive Officer, Safe Haven Hospital Of Treasure Valley, Boise, ID, p. A188

PROCTOR, Stephen, Director of Human Resources/Risk, Russellville Hospital, Russellville, AL, p. A24

PROFOTA, Lori, Chief Nursing Officer, Copley Hospital, Morrisville, VT, p. A736

PRONGER, Derk, Chief Operating Officer, Munson Medical Center, Traverse City, MI, p. A368

PRONI, John, CPA, Manager Finance and Operations, Baycare Alliant Hospital, Dunedin, FL, p. A136

PROPP, Elizabeth, Vice President Finance and Chief Financial Officer, Dameron Hospital, Stockton, CA, p. A99

PROSKOCIL, Danielle, Director Human Resources, Valley County Health System, Ord, NE, p. A438

PROSPER, Charles, Chief Executive NW, Peacehealth St. Josep. Medical Center, Bellingham, WA, p. A755

PROSSER, Alita, Chief Financial Officer, Baylor Scott & White Medical Center - Temple, Temple, TX, p. A719

PROSSER, Edna, Chief Nursing Officer, Ozark Health Medical Center, Clinton, AR, p. A43

PROSSER, Joseph, M.D., Chief Medical Officer, Texas Health Harris Methodist Hospital Fort Worth, Fort Worth, TX, p. A679

PROUD, James, Vice President Human Resources and Marketing, Uniontown Hospital, Uniontown, PA, p. A609

PROVENZANO, Jeff, Vice President and Chief Financial Officer, Midmichigan Medical Center-Clare, Clare, MI, p. A351
Vice President and Chief Financial Officer, Midmichigan Medical Center-Gladwin, Gladwin, MI, p. A355
Vice President and Chief Financial Officer, Midmichigan Medical Center-Gratiot, Alma, MI, p. A348

PROVENZANO, Stacey, Chief Operating Officer, Greystone Park Psychiatric Hospital, Morris Plains, NJ, p. A458

PROVINCE, Wing, M.D., Chief Medical Officer, Park City Hospital, Park City, UT, p. A730

PROVOST, Deborah, Chief Nursing Officer, Baystate Franklin Medical Center, Greenfield, MA, p. A339

PRUESS, Mark, M.D., Chief Medical Staff, Sparta Community Hospital, Sparta, IL, p. A220

PRUETT-BAER, Karen, Senior Nurse Executive, Naval Hospital Oak Harbor, Oak Harbor, WA, p. A761

PRUITT, Jeffrey, M.D., Chief of Staff, Mercy Hospital Of Defiance, Defiance, OH, p. A539

PRUKOP, Jeff, Director Professional Services, Jackson County Hospital District, Edna, TX, p. A674

PRUNCHUNAS, Edward, Executive Vice President and Chief Financial Officer, Cedars-Sinai Medical Center, Los Angeles, CA, p. A73

PRUNOSKE, Mark, Chief Financial Officer and Senior Vice President Finance, F. F. Thompson Hospital, Canandaigua, NY, p. A481

PRYBYLO, Mary, Senior Vice President and President, St. Josep. Hospital, Bangor, ME, p. A318

PRYOR, David, President, Athens-Limestone Hospital, Athens, AL, p. A14

PRYOR, Vincent, Senior Vice President and Chief Financial Officer, Silver Cross Hospital, New Lenox, IL, p. A214

PRZESTRZELSKI, David, Associate Director, Patient Care Services and Chief Nursing Executive, Charles George Veterans Affairs Medical Center, Asheville, NC, p. A504

PRZYBYLSKI, David, Controller, Sparrow Specialty Hospital, Lansing, MI, p. A360

PSAILA, Justin, M.D., Vice President Medical Affairs, St. Luke's Hospital - Anderson Campus, Easton, PA, p. A589

PSARRAS, James, M.D., Chief Medical Officer, Windsor-Laurelwood Center For Behavioral Medicine, Willoughby, OH, p. A553

PSCODNA, Susan, Director Human Resources, Mercy Hospital Of Defiance, Defiance, OH, p. A539

PUCHBAUER, Aaron, President, Hshs Good Shepherd Hospital, Shelbyville, IL, p. A220

PUCKETT, Clay, Assistant Administrator and Chief Information Officer, Blount Memorial Hospital, Maryville, TN, p. A643

PUCKETT, Mark, Chief Executive Officer, Rock Springs, Georgetown, TX, p. A681

PUCLIK, Becky, Division Chief People Officer, Hshs St. John's Hospital, Springfield, IL, p. A220

PUENTES, Francisco, Human Resource Officer, San Diego County Psychiatric Hospital, San Diego, CA, p. A92

PUFFENBERGER, James, Vice President and Chief Financial Officer, Mercy Hospital Of Defiance, Defiance, OH, p. A539

PUFFENBERGER, Sheila, Manager Information Technology, Hillsdale Hospital, Hillsdale, MI, p. A357

PUGH, Larry, Vice President and Chief Financial Officer, Beverly Hospital, Montebello, CA, p. A79

PUGH, Marcia, Chief Executive Officer, Greene County Health System, Eutaw, AL, p. A18

PUGH, Melodee, Director Human Resources, Navarro Regional Hospital, Corsicana, TX, p. A666

PUGH, Ryan, Chief Financial Officer, Western Plains Medical Complex, Dodge City, KS, p. A263

PUGSLEY, Tim, Chief Information Officer, Orthonebraska Hospital, Omaha, NE, p. A437

PUKALA, Shirley, R.N., Assistant Administrator Operations, St. Lawrence Rehabilitation Center, Lawrenceville, NJ, p. A457

PULASKI, Jason, Controller, Encompass Health Reading Rehabilitation Hospital, Reading, PA, p. A606

PULEO, Mark, Vice President and Chief Human Resources Officer, Henry Mayo Newhall Hospital, Valencia, CA, p. A103

PULIDO, Michael, Chief Administrative Officer, Mosaic Life Care At St. Josep. - Medical Center, Saint Joseph, MO, p. A415

PULIS, Autumn, Chief Nursing Officer, Select Specialty Hospital-Oklahoma City, Oklahoma City, OK, p. A566

PULLARKAT, Sajit, Chief Executive Officer and Managing Director, Centennial Hills Hospital Medical Center, Las Vegas, NV, p. A443

PULLEN, Connie, R.N., Chief Nursing Officer, Willamette Valley Medical Center, Mcminnville, OR, p. A577

PULLIAM, Elizabeth, Chief Financial Officer, Christus Mother Frances Hospital - Jacksonville, Jacksonville, TX, p. A691

PULLIN, Dennis W., FACHE, President and Chief Executive Officer, Virtua Marlton, Marlton, NJ, p. A458
FACHE, President and Chief Executive Officer, Virtua Memorial, Mount Holly, NJ, p. A458
FACHE, President and Chief Executive Officer, Virtua Voorhees, Voorhees, NJ, p. A465

PULLINS, Ruth, Chief Human Resources Officer, Truman Medical Center-Hospital Hill, Kansas City, MO, p. A410
Chief Human Resources Officer, Truman Medical Center-Lakewood, Kansas City, MO, p. A410

PULLMAN, Debbie, Director Finance, Avera Hand County Memorial Hospital, Miller, SD, p. A629

PULLMAN, Jayson, Chief Executive Officer, Hawarden Regional Healthcare, Hawarden, IA, p. A251

PULVER, Dayna, Director of Nursing, Friend Community Healthcare System, Friend, NE, p. A432

PUMMEL, Keely, Director, Financial Operations, Ohiohealth Dublin Methodist Hospital, Dublin, OH, p. A539

PUMPHREY, Robbin, Chief Nursing Officer, Jackson Hospital, Marianna, FL, p. A145

PUNG, Margaret, R.N., Chief Nursing Officer, Uthealth Harris County Psychiatric Center, Houston, TX, p. A689

PUNJABI, Rishab, Chief Financial Officer, Kindred Hospital-La Mirada, La Mirada, CA, p. A70

PUORTO, Charlene, Chief Nursing Officer, Capital District Psychiatric Center, Albany, NY, p. A474

PURCELL, Deborah, Director of Information Technology, Caldwell Unc Health Care, Lenoir, NC, p. A513

PURCELL, Terrance, Director Information Services, Lea Regional Medical Center, Hobbs, NM, p. A470

PURCELL, Tom, Chief Medical Officer, Uchealth Highlands Ranch Hospital, Highlands Ranch, CO, p. A114

PURDY, Bruce, M.D., Chief of Staff, Muleshoe Area Medical Center, Muleshoe, TX, p. A702

PURINGTON, Denise, Vice President and Chief Information Officer, Elliot Hospital, Manchester, NH, p. A450

PURINTON, Sandy, Chief Nursing Officer, Trego County-Lemke Memorial Hospital, Wakeeney, KS, p. A278

PURKEYPILE, Dallas, Chief Executive Officer, Adventhealth Ottawa, Ottawa, KS, p. A273

PURMONT, Tiffany, Supervisor Medical Records, Monroe County Hospital, Forsyth, GA, p. A172

PUROHIT, Divyesh, M.D., Chief of Staff, Sullivan County Community Hospital, Sullivan, IN, p. A241

PUROHIT, Kumar, Chief Financial Officer, Rockford Center, Newark, DE, p. A128

PUROHIT, Shamb, Chief Financial Officer, Colquitt Regional Medical Center, Moultrie, GA, p. A177

PURRINGTON, Janice, Coordinator Medical Records, Avera Hand County Memorial Hospital, Miller, SD, p. A629

PURSLEY, Roger, Chief Executive Officer, Western Mental Health Institute, Bolivar, TN, p. A634

PURTLE, Mark, M.D., Vice President Medical Affairs, Unitypoint Health - Iowa Methodist Medical Center, Des Moines, IA, p. A248

PURVANCE, Clint, M.D., President and Chief Executive Officer, Barton Memorial Hospital, South Lake Tahoe, CA, p. A99

PURVES, Stephen A., FACHE, President and Chief Executive Officer, Valleywise Health, Phoenix, AZ, p. A37

PURVIS, Kevin, Chief Information Officer, Community Howard Regional Health, Kokomo, IN, p. A234

PURVIS, Michael, Chief Executive Officer, Candler County Hospital, Metter, GA, p. A176

PURVIS, Michael L., Chief Executive Officer, Novato Community Hospital, Novato, CA, p. A81

PUSHARD, Roland, Director of Nursing, Riverview Psychiatric Center, Augusta, ME, p. A318

PUSTINA, Karl, Vice President Finance, Upland Hills Health, Dodgeville, WI, p. A782

PUTHOFF, Timothy, Chief Executive Officer, Brookwood Baptist Medical Center, Birmingham, AL, p. A14

PUTNAM, Mark, M.D., Medical Director, Haven Behavioral Hospital Of Eastern Pennsylvania, Reading, PA, p. A606

PUTNAM, Maureen, Director Human Resources, Oss Health, York, PA, p. A612

PUTNAM, Skip. Chief Executive Officer, Northside Hospital-Forsyth, Cumming, GA, p. A170

PUTNAM, Stewart, Executive Vice President and Chief Operating Officer, Unity Hospital, Rochester, NY, p. A496

PUTNAM, Timothy L., FACHE, President and Chief Executive Officer, Margaret Mary Health, Batesville, IN, p. A223

PUTZ, Kim, R.N., Director, Nursing Hospital, Ridgeview Le Sueur Medical Center, Le Sueur, MN, p. A378

PUVOGEL, LuAnn, R.N., Chief Executive Officer, Salina Surgical Hospital, Salina, KS, p. A276

PUZO, Thomas C., President and Chief Executive Officer, Cornerstone Of Medical Arts Center Hospital, Fresh Meadows, NY, p. A484

PUZZUTO, David, M.D., Vice President Medical Affairs and Chief Medical Officer, Waterbury Hospital, Waterbury, CT, p. A126

PYGON, Bernard, M.D., Chief Medical Officer, University Of Illinois Hospital & Health Sciences System, Chicago, IL, p. A201

PYLE, Diana, Director Human Resources and Executive Assistant to Chief Executive Officer, Cedar County Memorial Hospital, El Dorado Springs, MO, p. A405

PYLE, Julia, R.N., Chief Nursing Officer, Newman Regional Health, Emporia, KS, p. A264

PYLE, Rick, Director Information Systems, Harrisburg Medical Center, Harrisburg, IL, p. A206

PYLE FARRELL, Martha, Vice President Human Resources and General Counsel, Massachusetts Eye And Ear, Boston, MA, p. A336

PYRAH, Scott, Director Information Systems, St. Luke's Rehabilitation Hospital, Boise, ID, p. A189

# Q

QUACKENBUSH, Kirk, M.D., Chief of Staff, Platte Valley Medical Center, Brighton, CO, p. A108

QUAGLIERI, Mike, Chief Financial Officer, North Central Surgical Center, Dallas, TX, p. A669

QUALLS, Brenda, Chief Financial Officer, Navicent Health Baldwin, Milledgeville, GA, p. A177

QUALLS, Hugh, Administrator, Mount Grant General Hospital, Hawthorne, NV, p. A442

QUAMMEN, Becky, Chief Information Officer, Howard University Hospital, Washington, DC, p. A129

QUARANTE, Dino, CPA, Chief Financial Officer, Oasis Behavioral Health - Chandler, Chandler, AZ, p. A31

QUARLES, Christopher, M.D., Director Medical Services, Naval Hospital Jacksonville, Jacksonville, FL, p. A141

QUATE, Becky, Vice President Nursing and Patient Care Services, Iredell Health System, Statesville, NC, p. A519

QUATROCHE, Thomas J. Jr, President and Chief Executive Officer, Erie County Medical Center, Buffalo, NY, p. A479

QUATTROCCHI, Robert, President and Chief Executive Officer, Northside Hospital, Atlanta, GA, p. A165

QUEBEDEAUX, Jay, FACHE, Chief Executive Officer, Mena Regional Health System, Mena, AR, p. A50

QUEBODEAUX, Bryce, Chief Executive Officer, Abrom Kaplan Memorial Hospital, Kaplan, LA, p. A304

QUEEN, Sharon, R.N., Chief Nursing Officer, Piedmont Walton Hospital, Monroe, GA, p. A177

QUENAN, James, M.D., Chief Medical Officer, Amery Hospital And Clinic, Amery, WI, p. A779

QUICHOCHO, Vince, Manager Information Systems, Guam Memorial Hospital Authority, Tamuning, GU, p. A805

QUIGLEY, Stephen J., Chief Executive Officer, Southwood Psychiatric Hospital, Pittsburgh, PA, p. A603

QUILLIN, Gayla, Administrator, Parmer Medical Center, Friona, TX, p. A680

QUIN, Robert, Regional Vice President Finance, and Chief Financial Officer, Unitypoint Health - Peoria, Peoria, IL, p. A217

QUINLAN, Patrick, M.D., Chief Executive Officer, Ochsner Clinic Foundation & International Services, Exec. Director Ochsner Center for Community, Ochsner Medical Center, New Orleans, LA, p. A311

QUINLIVAN, John, Chief Executive Officer, Redmond Regional Medical Center, Rome, GA, p. A179

QUINLIVAN, Kathy, Director Management Information Systems, Avera Sacred Heart Hospital, Yankton, SD, p. A633

QUINN, Clifton, Chief Executive Officer, Select Specialty Hospital-Birmingham, Birmingham, AL, p. A15

QUINN, Donna, Vice President Operations, Driscoll Children's Hospital, Corpus Christi, TX, p. A666

QUINN, Jennifer, Quality and Safety Coordinator, Thedacare Medical Center-Shawano, Shawano, WI, p. A795

QUINN, Judith, Vice President Patient Care Services, Cap. Cod Hospital, Hyannis, MA, p. A340

QUINN, Kevin, Chief Executive Officer, Byrd Regional Hospital, Leesville, LA, p. A307

QUINN, Mary, Administrative Assistant, Casey County Hospital, Liberty, KY, p. A287
Administrative Assistant, Jane Todd Crawford Hospital, Greensburg, KY, p. A284
Executive Vice President, Chief Administrative Officer, St. Jude Children's Research Hospital, Memphis, TN, p. A645

QUINN, Paul, Information Systems Manager, Kern Valley Healthcare District, Lake Isabella, CA, p. A70

QUINN, Tim, M.D., Executive Vice President and Chief of Clinical Operations and President Mercy Care Management, Mercy Medical Center - Cedar Rapids, Cedar Rapids, IA, p. A245

QUINONES, Yolanda, Director Finance, I. Gonzalez Martinez Oncologic Hospital, Hato Rey, PR, p. A808

QUINONEZ, Yolanda, Chief Financial Officer, Hospital De La Universidad De Puerto Rico/Dr. Federico Trilla, Carolina, PR, p. A807

QUINTANA, Erika, Chief Nursing Officer, Windsor-Laurelwood Center For Behavioral Medicine, Willoughby, OH, p. A553

QUINTANA, Francisco, Warden, Federal Medical Center, Lexington, KY, p. A286

QUINTANILLA, Dana, Director Human Resources, Sweeny Community Hospital, Sweeny, TX, p. A718

QUINTO, Mike, Chief Information Officer, Watauga Medical Center, Boone, NC, p. A505

QUINTON, J. Ben., Administrator, William Newton Hospital, Winfield, KS, p. A279

QUINTYNE, Stephen, Chief Executive Officer, The Vines, Ocala, FL, p. A150

QUIRICONI, Stephan, Chief Financial Officer, Bon Secours St. Mary's Hospital, Richmond, VA, p. A749
Vice President Finance, Bon Secours Memorial Regional Medical Center, Mechanicsville, VA, p. A746
Vice President, Finance, Bon Secours St. Francis Medical Center, Midlothian, VA, p. A746

QUIRING, Brenda, R.N., Director of Nursing, Stillwater Medical Perry, Perry, OK, p. A567

QUIRKE, David, Vice President Information Services, Frederick Health, Frederick, MD, p. A329

# R

QUITO, Arturo, M.D., Chief of Staff, Erlanger Bledsoe Hospital, Pikeville, TN, p. A648

QUO, Justin, Chief of Staff, Chi Lakewood Health, Baudette, MN, p. A372

RAAUM, Elizabeth, Manger Business Office, Roosevelt Medical Center, Culbertson, MT, p. A422

RABAGO, Janie, Chief Accountant, San Antonio State Hospital, San Antonio, TX, p. A713

RABE, Robbie, Chief Operatiang Officer, Ascension Seton Bastrop. Bastrop. TX, p. A657
Chief Operating Officer, Ascension Seton Smithville, Smithville, TX, p. A716

RABEL, Jonas, President, Integris Grove Hospital, Grove, OK, p. A559
President, Integris Miami Hospital, Miami, OK, p. A562

RABIDEAU, Ray, M.D., Senior Vice President and Chief Medical Officer, Memorial Hospital, North Conway, NH, p. A451

RABIN, Barry, M.D., Regional Medical Director, Linden Oaks Hospital, Naperville, IL, p. A214

RABINE, Traci, Vice President Clinic Operations, Prairie Lakes Healthcare System, Watertown, SD, p. A633

RABINOWITZ, Jordy, Senior Vice President Human Resources Operations, Westchester Medical Center, Valhalla, NY, p. A501

RABNER, Barry S., President and Chief Executive Officer, Princeton Healthcare System, Penn Medicine Princeton Medical Center, Plainsboro, NJ, p. A461

RABON, Catherine, M.D., Chief Medical Officer, Mcleod Health Clarendon, Manning, SC, p. A622

RABORN, Janelle, Chief Operating Officer, Lovelace Women's Hospital, Albuquerque, NM, p. A468

RACHAL, Paul, M.D., Chief Medical Officer, Pointe Coupee General Hospital, New Roads, LA, p. A312

RACHUIG, Sue, Director Information Services, Tulane Health System, New Orleans, LA, p. A311

RACICOT, Mark, Chief Executive Officer, North Shore Medical Center, Miami, FL, p. A147

RACZEK, James, M.D., Sr. Vice President of Operations and Chief Medical Officer, Northern Light Eastern Maine Medical Center, Bangor, ME, p. A318

RADANDT, Jeremiah, President, Children's Medical Center Plano, Plano, TX, p. A706

RADCLIFF, Joey, Chief Financial Officer, St. Bernards Five Rivers, Pocahontas, AR, p. A52

RADCLIFFE, Eric, M.D., Medical Director, United Hospital Center, Bridgeport, WV, p. A770

RADDEN, April, Vice President of Human Resources, Aventura Hospital And Medical Center, Aventura, FL, p. A131

RADEBAUGH, Barbara, Chief Executive Officer, Perimeter Behavioral Hospital Of West Memphis, West Memphis, AR, p. A54

RADEMACHER, Frank, Director, Information Systems, St. Josep. Mercy Livingston Hospital, Howell, MI, p. A358
Senior Director Information Systems, St. Josep. Mercy Ann Arbor, Ypsilanti, MI, p. A370

RADER, Herbert, M.D., Advisor for Medical Affairs, New York Community Hospital, Brooklyn, NY, p. A478

RADFORD, Angie, R.N., Director of Nursing, Wills Memorial Hospital, Washington, GA, p. A183

RADFORD, Jeffrey, Chief Executive Officer, Select Specialty Hospital-Tri Cities, Bristol, TN, p. A634

RADKE, Erma, Director of Operations, Oakleaf Surgical Hospital, Altoona, WI, p. A779

RADNER, Allen, M.D., Chief Medical Officer, Salinas Valley Memorial Healthcare System, Salinas, CA, p. A90

RADOTICH, Maureen, Director Human Resources, Providence Valdez Medical Center, Valdez, AK, p. A29

RADTKE, Lisa, Chief Administrative Officer, Winneshiek Medical Center, Decorah, IA, p. A248

RADUNSKY, Daniel, M.D., Medical Staff President, Union County General Hospital, Clayton, NM, p. A468

RADZEVICH, Jason, Vice President Finance, Beth Israel Deaconess Hospital Plymouth, Plymouth, MA, p. A343

RAETHEL, Kathryn A., R.N., M.P.H., President and Chief Executive Officer, Adventist Health Castle, Kailua, HI, p. A185

RAETZ, Elizabeth, R.N., MSN, Vice President Nursing and Chief Nursing Officer, Chi Health St Elizabeth, Lincoln, NE, p. A434

RAFALA, Paula, Director, Human Resources, Memorial Medical Center, Modesto, CA, p. A79

RAFFERTY, Joyce, Vice President Finance, The University Of Vermont Health Network-Champlain Valley Physicians Hospital, Plattsburgh, NY, p. A495

RAFFERTY, Patrick W., Chief Executive Officer, Coast Plaza Hospital, Norwalk, CA, p. A81

RAFFOUL, John, Chief Executive Officer, Adventist Health White Memorial, Los Angeles, CA, p. A73

RAFUS, Matthew, Chief Information Officer, White River Junction Veterans Affairs Medical Center, White River Junction, VT, p. A737

RAGAIN, Michael, M.D., Chief Medical Officer and Senior Vice President, University Medical Center, Lubbock, TX, p. A698

RAGAS, Rene J., President and Chief Executive Officer, Northshore Market, Our Lady Of The Angels Hospital, Bogalusa, LA, p. A298

RAGER, Claudia, R.N., Vice President Patient Care Services, Conemaugh Memorial Medical Center, Johnstown, PA, p. A593

RAGGIO, Sharon, President and Chief Executive Officer, West Springs Hospital, Grand Junction, CO, p. A113

RAGLE, Bertha, Director Personnel, Crossridge Community Hospital, Wynne, AR, p. A54

RAGONESE-GREEN, Virginia, Chief Nursing Officer, Encompass Health Rehabilitation Hospital Of Northwest Tucson, Tucson, AZ, p. A40

RAGSDALE, Sarah, Chief Nursing Officer, Smith County Memorial Hospital, Smith Center, KS, p. A276

RAGUKAS, Judith, Interim Chief Nursing Officer, Tyler Memorial Hospital, Tunkhannock, PA, p. A609

RAHDERT, Richard, M.D., Medical Director, River Bend Hospital, West Lafayette, IN, p. A242

RAHMAN, Randy, Chief Information Officer, Miami County Medical Center, Paola, KS, p. A274
Vice President and Chief Information Officer, Olathe Medical Center, Olathe, KS, p. A272

RAHMAN, Syed, M.D., Chief of Staff, Horizon Specialty Hospital, Las Vegas, NV, p. A443

RAHN, Kevin, President Medical Staff, Orthopaedic Hospital Of Lutheran Health Network, Fort Wayne, IN, p. A228

RAINA, Suresh, M.D., Vice President Medical Staff and Chief Medical Officer, Hackensack Meridian Health Palisades Medical Center, North Bergen, NJ, p. A460

RAINBOLT, Mike, Chief Financial Officer, Rivendell Behavioral Health Services Of Arkansas, Benton, AR, p. A42

RAINES, Jill, R.N., Chief of Clinical Quality, Greene County General Hospital, Linton, IN, p. A235

RAINEY, Jackie, Chief Financial Officer, Little River Memorial Hospital, Ashdown, AR, p. A42

RAINEY, Mark, Director Human Resources, Texas Health Presbyterian Hospital Kaufman, Kaufman, TX, p. A692

RAINEY, Michelle, Senior Vice President and Chief Nursing Officer, Pikeville Medical Center, Pikeville, KY, p. A292

RAINS, Celeste, D.O., Chief of Staff, Logan County Hospital, Oakley, KS, p. A272

RAINS, Debbie, Coordinator Health Information Management, Erlanger Bledsoe Hospital, Pikeville, TN, p. A648

RAINS, Della, Chief Nursing Officer, Continuecare Hospital At Baptist Health Corbin, Corbin, KY, p. A282

RAINS, Jeff G., Chief Executive Officer, Baptist Medical Center East, Montgomery, AL, p. A22

RAINS, John, Chief Executive Officer, Atoka County Medical Center, Atoka, OK, p. A556

RAINS, Paul, R.N., MSN, President, St. Joseph's Behavioral Health Center, Stockton, CA, p. A100

RAINS, Ronald, Chief Executive Officer, University Behavioral Health Of Denton, Denton, TX, p. A672

RAINS, Steve, Director Information Services, Mckee Medical Center, Loveland, CO, p. A117

RAISNER, Gary, Chief Operating Officer, Norristown State Hospital, Norristown, PA, p. A598

RAJ, Bharath, M.D., Medical Director, Kingwood Pines Hospital, Kingwood, TX, p. A693

RAJ, Joe, Administrative Director, Finance, Promedica Bixby Hospital, Adrian, MI, p. A348
Administrative Director, Finance, Promedica Herrick Hospital, Tecumseh, MI, p. A368

RAJEWSKI, Frank, Chief Financial Officer, Rooks County Health Center, Plainville, KS, p. A274

RAJPARA, Suresh, M.D., Chief Medical Officer, Jerome Golden Center For Behavioral Health, Inc., West Palm Beach, FL, p. A162

RAJU, Vasudeva, M.D., Chief, Long Term Acute Care Medicine, Nyc Health + Hospitals / Henry J Carter Specialty Hospital And Medical Center, New York, NY, p. A491

RAK, Roger, Director Human Resources, South Shore Hospital, Chicago, IL, p. A201

RAKES, Lori, Chief Operating Officer, Cartersville Medical Center, Cartersville, GA, p. A168

RAKOV, Robert, M.D., Chief Medical Officer, Cogdell Memorial Hospital, Snyder, TX, p. A716

RAMA-BANAAG, Gemma, R.N., MSN, Chief Nursing Officer, Paradise Valley Hospital, National City, CA, p. A81

RAMAGE, Gary, M.D., Chief Medical Officer, Mckenzie County Healthcare System, Watford City, ND, p. A526

RAMAN, Jayashree, Vice President and Chief Information Officer, Reading Hospital, West Reading, PA, p. A610

RAMAZANI, Regina, Chief Financial Officer, Garden Park Medical Center, Gulfport, MS, p. A393
Chief Financial Officer, Tulane Health System, New Orleans, LA, p. A311
Chief Operating Officer, Garden Park Medical Center, Gulfport, MS, p. A393

RAMEY, Rita, Director Information Systems, Buchanan General Hospital, Grundy, VA, p. A743

RAMEY, Robert L., President, Baptist Health Madisonville, Madisonville, KY, p. A289

RAMEY, Steve, Chief Financial Officer, Southampton Memorial Hospital, Franklin, VA, p. A742

RAMIREZ, Ana, Director of Nursing, Mesa Springs, Fort Worth, TX, p. A679

RAMIREZ, Arthur, M.D., Medical Director, El Paso Behavioral Health System, El Paso, TX, p. A674
M.D., Medical Director, Mesilla Valley Hospital, Las Cruces, NM, p. A470

RAMIREZ, Clara, Manager, French Hospital Medical Center, San Luis Obispo, CA, p. A95

RAMIREZ, Corazon, M.D., Chief Executive Officer, Saint Camillus Medical Center, Hurst, TX, p. A690

RAMIREZ, Eleanor, R.N., MS, Interim President and Chief Executive Officer, St. Francis Medical Center, Lynwood, CA, p. A76

RAMIREZ, Harvey, Chief Information Officer, Coleman County Medical Center, Coleman, TX, p. A664

RAMIREZ, Jaime, Chief Executive Officer, Mccamey County Hospital District, Mccamey, TX, p. A700

RAMIREZ, Omar, Chief Executive Officer, Los Angeles Community Hospital At Los Angeles, Los Angeles, CA, p. A75

RAMIREZ, Ruben, M.D., Chief of Staff, Monterey Park Hospital, Monterey Park, CA, p. A79

RAMIREZ, Susan, Chief Nursing Officer, Encompass Health Rehabilitation Hospital Of Las Vegas, Las Vegas, NV, p. A443

RAMIREZ, Venus V., Executive Director, Hospital San Pablo Del Este, Fajardo, PR, p. A807

RAMIREZ, Willie, Manager Labor Relations, Laguna Honda Hospital And Rehabilitation Center, San Francisco, CA, p. A93

RAMLO, Ricki, Chief Operating Officer and Human Resources, Jamestown Regional Medical Center, Jamestown, ND, p. A524

RAMLOCHAN, Tara, Chief Executive Officer, Meade District Hospital, Meade, KS, p. A271

RAMON, Maggie, Chief Financial Officer, Cochran Memorial Hospital, Morton, TX, p. A702

RAMOS, Eduardo, M.D., Medical Director, Encompass Health Rehabilitation Hospital Of San Juan, San Juan, PR, p. A810

RAMOS, Gracie, Chief Human Resources Officer, Ogallala Community Hospital, Ogallala, NE, p. A436

RAMOS, Holly, R.N., Chief Clinical Officer, Kindred Hospital-Ontario, Ontario, CA, p. A82

RAMOS, Jessie, Manager Human Resources, Skyline Hospital, White Salmon, WA, p. A769

RAMOS, Jet, Head Staff Administration, Naval Hospital Camp Pendleton, Camp Pendleton, CA, p. A59

RAMOS, Raymond, FACHE, Chief Operating Officer, Doctors Hospital Of Laredo, Laredo, TX, p. A695

RAMPAT, Ananda, Chief Financial Officer, Northwest Medical Center, Margate, FL, p. A145

RAMPP, Randal, M.D., Chief Medical Officer, Saint Thomas River Park Hospital, Mc Minnville, TN, p. A643

RAMSAMY, Dev, Chief Financial Officer, St. Rose Dominican Hospitals - San Martin Campus, Las Vegas, NV, p. A444

RAMSAY, Carla, Chief Human Resource Officer, Garfield Memorial Hospital, Panguitch, UT, p. A730

RAMSER, Emmett, Chief Administrative Officer, Norton Children's Hospital, Louisville, KY, p. A288

RAMSEY, Antonina, Senior Vice President and Chief Human Resource Officer, Henry Ford Hospital, Detroit, MI, p. A353

RAMSEY, Beryl, FACHE, Interim Chief Executive Officer, Venice Regional Bayfront Health, Venice, FL, p. A161

RAMSEY, David L., President and Chief Executive Officer, Charleston Area Medical Center, Charleston, WV, p. A771

RAMSEY, Kristin, R.N., Senior Vice President and Chief Nursing Executive, Northwestern Memorial Hospital, Northwestern Memorial Hospital, Chicago, IL, p. A200

RAMSEY, Lisa, Chief Financial Officer, Prairie View, Newton, KS, p. A272

RAMSEY, Rance, Chief Executive Officer, Cheyenne County Hospital, Saint Francis, KS, p. A275

RAMSEY, Rhonda, Controller, Encompass Health Deaconess Rehabilitation Hospital, Newburgh, IN, p. A238

RAMSEY, Ross, M.D., Chief of Staff, Scheurer Health, Pigeon, MI, p. A363

RAMSEY, Roy M., Executive Director, Bradford Health Services At Warrior Lodge, Warrior, AL, p. A25

RAMSEY, Thomas, Chief Financial Officer, Hancock Medical Center, Bay Saint Louis, MS, p. A389

RAMTHUN, Jane, Chief Financial Officer, Story County Medical Center, Nevada, IA, p. A254

RANA, Chaula, M.D., Medical Director, Encompass Health Rehabilitation Hospital Of San Antonio, San Antonio, TX, p. A711

RANDALL, Andrea, Chief Executive Officer, Haskell County Community Hospital, Stigler, OK, p. A568

RANDALL, Cherry, Business Officer, Greater Binghamton Health Center, Binghamton, NY, p. A475

RANDALL, Jody, MSN, R.N., Chief Executive Officer/Chief Nursing Officer, Woodlands Specialty Hospital, The Woodlands, TX, p. A721

RANDALL, Kevin, Chief Financial Officer, Crouse Health, Syracuse, NY, p. A499

RANDALL, Rebecca, Chief Nursing Officer, Greenwood County Hospital, Eureka, KS, p. A264

RANDAZZO, Vince, Interim Chief Information Officer, The Hospitals Of Providence Transmountain Campus, El Paso, TX, p. A676

Texas Regional Director Information Systems, Tenet Account, The Hospitals Of Providence Memorial Campus, El Paso, TX, p. A676

RANDLE, Emily, Vice President Operations, Memorialcare, Orange Coast Memorial Medical Center, Fountain Valley, CA, p. A64

RANDOLPH, Arianne, Director Human Resources, Uchealth Pikes Peak Regional Hospital, Woodland Park, CO, p. A120

RANDOLPH, Bonnie, M.D., Chief of Staff, Community Hospital, Torrington, WY, p. A804

RANDOLPH, Joseph, M.D., Chairman Medical Executive Committee, Orthoindy Hospital, Indianapolis, IN, p. A232

RANDOLPH, Karsten, Executive Vice President and Chief Financial Officer, Adventhealth Shawnee Mission, Shawnee Mission, KS, p. A276

RANDOLPH, Linda, Director Personnel Services, Washington County Hospital, Chatom, AL, p. A16

RANDOLPH, Mark, Chief Operating Officer, Ochsner Lsu Health Shreveport - Academic Medical Center, Shreveport, LA, p. A314

RANEY, Hollie, Director of Nursing, Dallas County Medical Center, Fordyce, AR, p. A45

RANEY, Lance C., Commander, Womack Army Medical Center, Fort Bragg, NC, p. A510

RANG, Robert A., R.N., MSN, Chief Executive Officer, Providence Seward Medical Center, Seward, AK, p. A29

RANGE, Bonny, MSN, Chief Nursing Officer, Holy Family Memorial, Manitowoc, WI, p. A788

RANKIN, Charlotte, R.N., Chief Operating Officer, Mercy Hospital Rogers, Rogers, AR, p. A52

RANKIN, Cynthia, Chief Nursing Officer, Lovelace Unm Rehabilitation Hospital, Albuquerque, NM, p. A467

RANKIN, Linda, Chief Nursing Officer, Wickenburg Community Hospital, Wickenburg, AZ, p. A41

RANNEY, Timothy, M.D., Chief Medical Officer, Seton Medical Center, Daly City, CA, p. A62

RANSOM, Natalie, Chief Nursing Officer, Mountainview Hospital, Las Vegas, NV, p. A443

Chief Nursing Officer, North Florida Regional Medical Center, Gainesville, FL, p. A138

RAO, Kalapala, M.D., Medical Director, Encompass Health Rehabilitation Hospital Of Parkersburg, Parkersburg, WV, p. A775

RAPENSKE, Jennifer, Manager Financial Services, Mercyone New Hampton Medical Center, New Hampton, IA, p. A255

RAPP, Catherine, R.N., MS, Vice President Nursing, Oconomowoc Memorial Hospital, Oconomowoc, WI, p. A792

RAPP, David, Chief Information Officer, Wheeling Hospital, Wheeling, WV, p. A778

RAPP, Ronald, Vice President Finance, Upmc Cole, Coudersport, PA, p. A587

RAPPACH, Shannon, Chief Fiscal Services, Dayton Veterans Affairs Medical Center, Dayton, OH, p. A538

RASCHKE, Judy, Director Human Resources, Pipestone County Medical Center Avera, Pipestone, MN, p. A383

RASHID, Harun, Vice President and Chief Information Officer, Akron Children's Hospital, Akron, OH, p. A527

RASHILLA, Matt, Chief Information and Application Officer, Monongahela Valley Hospital, Monongahela, PA, p. A597

RASK, Brenda, Vice President Operations, Chi St Alexius Health Carrington Medical Center, Carrington, ND, p. A522

RASKE, Jamie, Information Technology Lead, Avera St. Mary's Hospital, Pierre, SD, p. A630

RASMUSSEN, Diane, Director Human Resources, Cambridge Medical Center, Cambridge, MN, p. A373

RASMUSSEN, Jeanell, R.N., Vice President Patient Care Services and Chief Nursing Officer, St. Michael Medical Center, Bremerton, WA, p. A756

RASMUSSEN, John, Vice President for Information Technology, Medstar Georgetown University Hospital, Washington, DC, p. A129

RASMUSSEN, Rick, Chief Executive Officer, Northwest Specialty Hospital, Post Falls, ID, p. A192

RASMUSSEN, Ron, M.D., Chief Medical Officer, Palms Of Pasadena Hospital, Saint Petersburg, FL, p. A156

RASMUSSEN, Scott, Director Human Resources, Lincoln Regional Center, Lincoln, NE, p. A434

RASMUSSON, Duane, Vice President Human Resources, St. Cloud Hospital, Saint Cloud, MN, p. A384

RASOOL, Chaudri, D.O., Chief of Staff, Gundersen Palmer Lutheran Hospital And Clinics, West Union, IA, p. A260

RASOR, Linda, R.N., Chief Executive Officer, Plains Memorial Hospital, Dimmitt, TX, p. A673

RASTER, Robert, M.D., Medical Director, Michiana Behavioral Health Center, Plymouth, IN, p. A239

RASTOGI, Amit, M.D., Chief Executive, Jupiter Medical Center, Jupiter, FL, p. A142

RATAJ, Marianne, Chief Nursing Officer, Mercy Hospital Fort Smith, Fort Smith, AR, p. A46

RATCLIFF, David, M.D., Chief Medical Affairs, Washington Regional Medical Center, Fayetteville, AR, p. A45

RATCLIFF, Paul, Director Information Services, Carrollton Regional Medical Center, Carrollton, TX, p. A663

RATH, Megan, Chief Financial Officer, South Central Health, Wishek, ND, p. A526

RATHGABER, Scott W., M.D., Chief Executive Officer, Gundersen Lutheran Medical Center, La Crosse, WI, p. A787

RATLIFF, Ada, Chief Executive Officer, Claiborne County Medical Center, Port Gibson, MS, p. A399

Chief Information Officer, Claiborne County Medical Center, Port Gibson, MS, p. A399

RATLIFF, Bonnie, Chief Information Officer, Columbia Memorial Hospital, Hudson, NY, p. A485

RATLIFF, Kim, Director Health Information Management, Southwestern Virginia Mental Health Institute, Marion, VA, p. A745

RATLIFF, Simon, Chief Operating Officer, Logan Regional Medical Center, Logan, WV, p. A774

Interim Chief Executive Officer, Logan Regional Medical Center, Logan, WV, p. A774

RATLIFF, Steve, Director Information Technology, Guadalup. Regional Medical Center, Seguin, TX, p. A714

RATLIFF, Tammy, Chief Executive Officer, Regency Hospital Of Greenville, Greenville, SC, p. A620

RATNASAMY, Suthanthira M., R.N., FACHE, Chief Executive Officer, Kindred Hospital Central Tampa, Tampa, FL, p. A159

RATTLE, John, Chief Financial Officer, West Springs Hospital, Grand Junction, CO, p. A113

RATTRAY, Cindy, Director Human Resources, Uofl Health - Shelbyville Hospital, Shelbyville, KY, p. A293

RAU, Frederick, M.D., Chief of Staff, Terrebonne General Medical Center, Houma, LA, p. A303

RAU, John, President and Chief Executive Officer, Stevens Community Medical Center, Morris, MN, p. A381

RAU, Robin, Chief Executive Officer, Miller County Hospital, Colquitt, GA, p. A169

RAUB, Jessica, Director Health Information Management, Seven Hills Hospital, Henderson, NV, p. A442

RAUCH, Rhonda, Chief Nursing Officer, Lovelace Regional Hospital - Roswell, Roswell, NM, p. A471

RAUCH, Scott, Vice President Human Resources, Reid Health, Richmond, IN, p. A239

RAUCH, Scott L., M.D., President and Psychiatrist in Chief, Mclean Hospital, Belmont, MA, p. A344

RAUH, Bradley, Vice President, Chief Operating Officer, Southwest General Health Center, Middleburg Heights, OH, p. A545

RAUNER, Mary, R.N., Chief Nursing Officer, Suburban Community Hospital, East Norriton, PA, p. A589

RAUPERS, Deb, MSN, R.N., Chief Nursing Officer, Guthrie Corning Hospital, Corning, NY, p. A481

MSN, R.N., Vice President Patient Services and Chief Nursing Officer, Cayuga Medical Center At Ithaca, Ithaca, NY, p. A485

RAUSCH, Scott, Chief Executive Officer, Methodist Ambulatory Surgery Hospital - Northwest, San Antonio, TX, p. A712

RAUTIO, Wendy, Chief Financial Officer, Helen Newberry Joy Hospital, Newberry, MI, p. A363

Chief Financial Officer, Munising Memorial Hospital, Munising, MI, p. A362

RAVA ESQ, LindaDirector Human Resources, St. John Vianney Hospital, Downingtown, PA, p. A588

RAVELING, Lynn, Chief Financial Officer, Pocahontas Community Hospital, Pocahontas, IA, p. A256

RAWLEY, Jennifer, PharmD, Chief Executive Officer, Select Specialty Hospital-Durham, Durham, NC, p. A509

RAWLINGS, Linda, Director Human Resources and Personnel, Three Rivers Hospital, Waverly, TN, p. A650

RAWLINGS, Michael, Interim Chief Operating Officer, Nyc Health + Hospitals / Bellevue, New York, NY, p. A491

RAWLINGS, Patrick, Chief Human Resource Officer, Saint Francis Hospital, Charleston, WV, p. A771

Human Resources Director, Thomas Memorial Hospital, South Charleston, WV, p. A777

RAWLINGS, Sheri, Chief Information Officer, San Juan Regional Medical Center, Farmington, NM, p. A469

RAWSON, Richard, Chief Executive Officer, Adventist Health And Rideout, Marysville, CA, p. A77

RAY, Beverly, Director Human Resources, West Tennessee Healthcare Dyersburg Hospital, Dyersburg, TN, p. A637

RAY, Brenda, Director Human Resources, Huntsville Memorial Hospital, Huntsville, TX, p. A690

RAY, Denise, Chief Executive Officer, Piedmont Mountainside Hospital, Jasper, GA, p. A174

RAY, Diane, R.N., FACHE, Senior Vice President and Chief Operating Officer; Network Chief Nursing Officer, St. Luke's Hospital, Chesterfield, MO, p. A404

RAY, Donald, Vice President Operations, University Of Maryland Medical Center Midtown Campus, Baltimore, MD, p. A326

RAY, Elaine, Administrator, Choate Mental Health Center, Anna, IL, p. A194

RAY, Jerilyn, Manager Human Resources, St. Elizabeth Hospital, Enumclaw, WA, p. A758

RAY, Joel, MSN, Vice President and Chief Nursing Officer, Unc Rex Health Care, Raleigh, NC, p. A517

RAY, Kirk M., President and Chief Executive Officer, Mclaren Greater Lansing, Lansing, MI, p. A360

RAY, Marge, Director Information Systems, Mercyone Cedar Falls Medical Center, Cedar Falls, IA, p. A244

Director Information Systems, Mercyone Waterloo Medical Center, Waterloo, IA, p. A259

RAY, Rachel, Chief Financial Officer, Unity Medical Center, Grafton, ND, p. A523

RAY, Roger, M.D., Executive Vice President and Chief Medical Officer, Atrium Health's Carolinas Medical Center, Charlotte, NC, p. A506

RAYBOURN, Gina, Director Health Information, Ellett Memorial Hospital, Appleton City, MO, p. A402

RAYLS, Kim, Director Human Resources, Twin Lakes Regional Medical Center, Leitchfield, KY, p. A286

RAYMER, Chris Lee., MSN, Chief Executive Officer, Great River Medical Center, Blytheville, AR, p. A43

MSN, Chief Executive Officer, South Mississipp. County Regional Medical Center, Osceola, AR, p. A51

RAYMOND, Dee, Director Human Resources, Rosebud Health Care Center, Forsyth, MT, p. A423

RAYMOND, Heather, Area Public Relations Director, Kaiser Permanente Fontana Medical Center, Fontana, CA, p. A64

RAYMOND, Jane, Vice President and Chief Operating Officer, Reston Hospital Center, Reston, VA, p. A749

RAYMOND, Katherine, Chief Nursing Officer, St. Rose Dominican Hospitals - San Martin Campus, Las Vegas, NV, p. A444

RAYMOND, Mindy, Vice President Human Resources, Boca Raton Regional Hospital, Boca Raton, FL, p. A132

RAYMOND, Scott, Director Information Systems, Memorialcare, Orange Coast Memorial Medical Center, Fountain Valley, CA, p. A64

RAYNER, Thomas, Senior Vice President and Chief Operating Officer, Kaweah Delta Medical Center, Visalia, CA, p. A104

RAYNES, Scott, President, Baptist Hospital, Pensacola, FL, p. A153

President, Gulf Breeze Hospital, Gulf Breeze, FL, p. A139

RAYNOR, Robert, Human Resources Director, Park Royal Hospital, Fort Myers, FL, p. A138

RAYUDU, Subbu, M.D., Chief of Staff, Alliance Healthcare System, Holly Springs, MS, p. A394

RAZMIC, Tammy, Associate Administrator Finance and Chief Financial Officer, Inova Mount Vernon Hospital, Alexandria, VA, p. A738

RAZO, Virginia, Chief Executive Officer, Curry General Hospital, Gold Beach, OR, p. A575

REA, Jerry A., Ph.D., Superintendent, Parsons State Hospital And Training Center, Parsons, KS, p. A274

READ, Eddie, Interim Chief Financial Officer, Val Verde Regional Medical Center, Del Rio, TX, p. A671

READ, John, Chief Nursing Officer, Allegiance Specialty Hospital Of Greenville, Greenville, MS, p. A392

READ, Paul, R.N., MSN, Vice President and Chief Nursing Officer, Springhill Memorial Hospital, Mobile, AL, p. A22

READ, Richard, Chief Financial Officer, Central Florida Regional Hospital, Sanford, FL, p. A156

READER, G., M.D., Chief Medical Officer, Kansas Medical Center, Andover, KS, p. A261

READING, Jared, M.D., Chief of Staff, Uvalde Memorial Hospital, Uvalde, TX, p. A722

READY, Janet, Chief Operating Officer, St. Joseph's Hospital Health Center, Syracuse, NY, p. A499

REALE, Kelli, Vice President Human Resources, Southeast Georgia Health System Brunswick Campus, Brunswick, GA, p. A167
  Vice President Human Resources, Upmc Mckeesport, Mckeesport, PA, p. A596

REAM, Tom, Regional Chief Information Officer, Sutter Auburn Faith Hospital, Auburn, CA, p. A56

REAMER, Roger J., Chief Executive Officer, Memorial Health Care Systems, Seward, NE, p. A439

REAMES, Jim, Director Human Resources, Bayfront Health St. Petersburg, Saint Petersburg, FL, p. A156

REANDEAU, Michael, Chief Information Officer, Mills-Peninsula Health Services, Burlingame, CA, p. A59

REARDON, Malissa, R.N., Interim Chief Nursing Officer, Allen Parish Community Healthcare, Kinder, LA, p. A305

REASONER, Vanessa, Chief Executive Officer, Grace Medical Center, Lubbock, TX, p. A697

REASY, Stephanie, Administrator and Chief Executive Officer, Avera De Smet Memorial Hospital, De Smet, SD, p. A627
  Administrator and Chief Executive Officer, Avera Weskota Memorial Hospital, Wessington Springs, SD, p. A633

REBERRY, Darinda, MSN, R.N., President and Chief Executive Officer, Western Missouri Medical Center, Warrensburg, MO, p. A420

REBLOCK, Kimberly, M.D., Chief Operating Officer, The Children's Home Of Pittsburgh, Pittsburgh, PA, p. A603

REBOCK, Michael, Chief Medical Officer, Beaumont Hospital - Farmington Hills, Farmington Hills, MI, p. A354

RECA, Thomas Deputy Executive Director and Chief Financial Officer, Staten Island University Hospital, Staten Island, NY, p. A499

RECHNER, Paula, M.D., Chief Medical Officer, War Memorial Hospital, Sault Sainte Marie, MI, p. A366

RECHSTEINER, Hans, M.D., Chief of Staff, Burnett Medical Center, Grantsburg, WI, p. A785

RECKERT, Sandy, Director Communications and Public Affairs, Johns Hopkins Bayview Medical Center, Baltimore, MD, p. A324

RECTOR, Hallie, Chief Nursing Officer, Lds Hospital, Salt Lake City, UT, p. A732

RECTOR, Jeanne, Chief Nursing Officer, Carroll County Memorial Hospital, Carrollton, MO, p. A404

RECUPERO, David, Chief Financial Officer, San Gorgonio Memorial Hospital, Banning, CA, p. A58

REDD, Brook, M.D., Chief of Staff, Sanford Medical Center Thief River Falls, Thief River Falls, MN, p. A386

REDD, Dakota, R.N., Chief Clinical Officer, Kindred Hospital-St. Louis, Saint Louis, MO, p. A416

REDDING, Georgia, Director Human Resources, Forbes Hospital, Monroeville, PA, p. A597

REDDING, Lisa, Manager Human Resources, Morgan County Arh Hospital, West Liberty, KY, p. A294

REDDY, Challa, M.D., President Medical Staff, Mayo Regional Hospital, Dover—Foxcroft, ME, p. A320

REDDY, Sridhar, M.D., Chief Medical Officer, Lake Huron Medical Center, Port Huron, MI, p. A364

REDDY, Vikrum, M.D., Vice President and Chief Medical Officer, Wellstar Kennestone Hospital, Marietta, GA, p. A176

REDHORSE-CHARLEY, Gloria, Director Human Resources, Northern Navajo Medical Center, Shiprock, NM, p. A472

REDING, Janeen, Ed.D., Market Vice President of Human Resources, Chi St. Anthony Hospital, Pendleton, OR, p. A578

REDINGTON, James, M.D., Chief of Staff, Bath Community Hospital, Hot Springs, VA, p. A744

REDLER, Kathleen, Director Patient Care Services, Shriners Hospitals For Children-Shreveport, Shreveport, LA, p. A314

REDMOND, Paula, Controller, Encompass Health Rehabilitation Hospital Of Tustin, Tustin, CA, p. A102

REDRICK, Heather, Chief Nursing Officer, Emory Johns Creek Hospital, Johns Creek, GA, p. A174

REECE, Morris, EVP/COO, Laird Hospital, Union, MS, p. A400

REECER, Jeff, FACHE, Chief Executive Officer, Texas Health Presbyterian Hospital Denton, Denton, TX, p. A672

REED, Alex, Chief Information Officer, Avita Ontario Hospital, Ontario, OH, p. A547
  Chief Information Officer, Bucyrus Hospital, Bucyrus, OH, p. A530
  Chief Information Officer, Galion Hospital, Galion, OH, p. A541

REED, Cindy, Director Community Relations, Austin State Hospital, Austin, TX, p. A655

REED, David, M.D., Chief Medical Officer, Louisiana Extended Care Hospital Of Lafayette, Lafayette, LA, p. A305

REED, Fred, M.D., Chief of Staff, Lincoln Hospital, Davenport, WA, p. A757

REED, Helen, Director Health Information, North Mississipp. Medical Center-Eupora, Eupora, MS, p. A392

REED, Jason, Chief Executive Officer, Beacham Memorial Hospital, Magnolia, MS, p. A396

REED, John, M.D., Medical Director, Baptist Memorial Hospital-Golden Triangle, Columbus, MS, p. A391

REED, Kathleen, Manager Human Resources, Missouri Baptist Sullivan Hospital, Sullivan, MO, p. A419

REED, Kim, Director Human Resources, Dekalb Regional Medical Center, Fort Payne, AL, p. A19

REED, Kirby, Director Information Systems, Franciscan Health Rensselear, Rensselaer, IN, p. A239

REED, Laura, R.N., Chief Nursing Executive, Bethesda Hospital, Saint Paul, MN, p. A385
  R.N., Chief Nursing Executive, St. John's Hospital, Maplewood, MN, p. A380

REED, Leslie, Chief Financial Officer, Wright Memorial Hospital, Trenton, MO, p. A419

REED, Linda, Vice President and Chief Information Officer, St. Joseph's University Medical Center, Paterson, NJ, p. A460
  Vice President Information Systems and Chief Information Officer, Newton Medical Center, Newton, NJ, p. A460

REED, Margaret, R.N., Chief Nursing Officer, Altru Health System, Grand Forks, ND, p. A523

REED, Pamela R., Chief Executive Officer, Kindred Hospital Melbourne, Melbourne, FL, p. A145

REED, Renee, Director Human Resources, Ascension Via Christi Hospital, Manhattan, Manhattan, KS, p. A270
  Director Human Resources, Wamego Health Center, Wamego, KS, p. A278

REED, Tim, Vice President and Chief Financial Officer, Virginia Mason Memorial, Yakima, WA, p. A769

REED, Tina, Director of Human Resources, Encompass Health Rehabilitation Hospital Of Modesto, Modesto, CA, p. A78

REED, Tracy, Vice President Patient Care Services, Chief Nursing Officer, Siskin Hospital For Physical Rehabilitation, Chattanooga, TN, p. A636

REED, Zachary, Chief Operating Officer, Henrico Doctors' Hospital, Richmond, VA, p. A750

REEDER, Carol, R.N., Chief Nursing Officer, St. Josep. Hospital Eureka, Eureka, CA, p. A63

REEDER, Elizabeth, Director Human Resources, Trinity Hospital, Weaverville, CA, p. A104

REEDER, Janet, MSN, R.N., Chief Nurse Executive, Kaiser Westside Medical Center, Hillsboro, OR, p. A576

REEDER, Wendy, R.N., Chief Nursing Officer, Harrison Memorial Hospital, Cynthiana, KY, p. A282

REEDY, Janet, Manager Human Resources, St. Thomas More Hospital, Canon City, CO, p. A108

REEL, Micah, Director of Bio-Med, Potomac Valley Hospital, Keyser, WV, p. A773

REEL, Stephanie, Senior Vice President Information Services, Johns Hopkins Hospital, Baltimore, MD, p. A324

REES, Adam, President, Essentia Health-St. Joseph's Medical Center, Brainerd, MN, p. A373

REES, Jeff, Director Information Systems, Bacharach Institute For Rehabilitation, Pomona, NJ, p. A461

REES, Matthew, Administrator, Jerold Phelp. Community Hospital, Garberville, CA, p. A66

REES, Stephen, M.D., Vice President Medical Affairs, Lafayette General Medical Center, Lafayette, LA, p. A305

REESE, Bert, Chief Information Officer, Sentara Leigh Hospital, Norfolk, VA, p. A748
  Chief Information Officer, Sentara Norfolk General Hospital, Norfolk, VA, p. A748
  Chief Information Officer, Sentara Princess Anne Hospital, Virginia Beach, VA, p. A753

REESE, Jeff, Chief Financial Officer, Rusk Rehabilitation Hospital, Columbia, MO, p. A405

REESE, Jeffrey, Chief Executive Officer, Van Matre Encompass Health Rehabilitation Hospital, Rockford, IL, p. A219

REESE, Maryann, R.N., FACHE, President and Chief Executive Officer, Saint Francis Medical Center, Cap. Girardeau, MO, p. A403

REESE, Mike, Chief Financial Officer, Ou Medical Center, Oklahoma City, OK, p. A565

REESE, Todd, Director Human Performance, Adventist Health Castle, Kailua, HI, p. A185

REETZ, Brenda, FACHE, Chief Executive Officer, Greene County General Hospital, Linton, IN, p. A235

REETZ, Renee, Director Human Resources, Ascension Standish Hospital, Standish, MI, p. A367

REEVE, Jay A., Ph.D., President and Chief Executive Officer, Eastside Psychiatric Hospital, Tallahassee, FL, p. A158

REEVES, Andrew, M.D., Director Medical Affairs, New Ulm Medical Center, New Ulm, MN, p. A382

REEVES, Cory, President and Chief Executive Officer, Adventhealth Hendersonville, Hendersonville, NC, p. A512

REEVES, Danny, Chief Financial Officer, Penrose-St. Francis Health Services, Colorado Springs, CO, p. A109

REEVES, Katy, Vice President Human Resources, Fauquier Hospital, Warrenton, VA, p. A753

REEVES, Matthew, D.O., Chief Medical Officer, Atrium Medical Center, Middletown, OH, p. A545

REEVES, Mike, Chief Information Officer, St. John Owasso, Owasso, OK, p. A566
  Vice President, St. John Medical Center, Tulsa, OK, p. A571

REEVES, Pamela J., M.D., Director, John D. Dingell Veterans Affairs Medical Center, Detroit, MI, p. A353

REEVES, Steve, M.D., Chief Medical Staff, Greater Regional Medical Center, Creston, IA, p. A247

REEVES, Susan, Chief Nursing Executive, Dartmouth-Hitchcock Medical Center, Lebanon, NH, p. A449

REEVES, Timothy, Administrator, Bucktail Medical Center, Renovo, PA, p. A606

REEVES, Valerie, Chief Financial Officer, Integris Miami Hospital, Miami, OK, p. A562

REFFNER, Gina, Chief Financial Officer, Little Colorado Medical Center, Winslow, AZ, p. A41

REFNESS, Kristen, Director, Financial Operations, Linden Oaks Hospital, Naperville, IL, p. A214

REGAN, Timothy, M.D., President and Chief Medical Officer, Lakeland Regional Health Medical Center, Lakeland, FL, p. A143

REGEN, Debbie, R.N., Chief Nursing Officer, Hackensack Meridian Health Mountainside Medical Center, Montclair, NJ, p. A458

REGIER, Donald, M.D., Chief Medical Officer, Sedgwick County Health Center, Julesburg, CO, p. A114

REGIER, Steve, Chief Financial Officer, Kearney Regional Medical Center, Kearney, NE, p. A434

REGISTER, Kellie, Director of Nursing, Clinch Memorial Hospital, Homerville, GA, p. A174

REGULA, John, Chief Information Officer, Allied Services Rehabilitation Hospital, Scranton, PA, p. A606
  Chief Information Officer, John Heinz Institute Of Rehabilitation Medicine, Wilkes-Barre, PA, p. A611

REHBEIN, Beth, Chief Nursing and Quality Officer, Story County Medical Center, Nevada, IA, p. A254

REHM, Janice, Manager Human Resources, Usa Health Children's & Women's Hospital, Mobile, AL, p. A22

REHM, Micah, Chief Nursing Officer, Forrest General Hospital, Hattiesburg, MS, p. A393

REHMER, Patricia, MSN, FACHE, President, Natchaug Hospital, Mansfield Center, CT, p. A123

REHN, Lindsay, Executive Director of Financial Operations, Wellstar Paulding Hospital, Hiram, GA, p. A174

REHN, Ronald G., Chief Executive Officer, Providence Mount Carmel Hospital, Colville, WA, p. A757
  Chief Executive Officer, Providence St. Joseph's Hospital, Chewelah, WA, p. A756

REICH, David, M.D., President and Chief Operating Officer, The Mount Sinai Hospital, New York, NY, p. A492

REICH, David L., M.D., President and Chief Operating Officer, The Mount Sinai Hospital, New York, NY, p. A492

REICH, Joanne, R.N., Chief Nursing Officer, Jersey City Medical Center, Jersey City, NJ, p. A456

REICH, Joel, M.D., Senior Vice President Medical Affairs, Manchester Memorial Hospital, Manchester, CT, p. A122
  M.D., Senior Vice President Medical Affairs, Rockville General Hospital, Vernon, CT, p. A125

REICHARD, Steve, Manager Information Systems, Brigham City Community Hospital, Brigham City, UT, p. A727

REICHENBACH, Geri, Nurse Executive, Curahealth Heritage Valley, Beaver, PA, p. A584

REICHFIELD, Michael L., President, Ohiohealth Doctors Hospital, Columbus, OH, p. A536

REICHLE, Paula, Senior Vice President and Chief Operating Officer, Sparrow Hospital, Lansing, MI, p. A360

REICHMAN, Joseph, M.D., Vice President Medical Affairs and Clinical Effectiveness, Hackensack Meridian Health Riverview Medical Center, Red Bank, NJ, p. A462

REID, Bernadette, Vice President, Information Technology and Chief Information Officer, Torrance Memorial Medical Center, Torrance, CA, p. A101

REID, Bev, Chief Financial Officer, St. Luke Hospital And Living Center, Marion, KS, p. A270

REID, Colleen, Chief Financial Officer, Carson Valley Medical Center, Gardnerville, NV, p. A442

REID, Dereesa, Administrator, Shriners Hospitals For Children-Portland, Portland, OR, p. A580

REID, Jim, Vice President and Chief Information Officer, Covenant Children's Hospital, Lubbock, TX, p. A697

REID, Kelly, Human Resources Director, South Mississipp. State Hospital, Purvis, MS, p. A399

REID, Kenneth G., President and Chief Executive Officer, Carlinville Area Hospital, Carlinville, IL, p. A196

REID, Ofrona, M.D., Chief Medical Officer, Oneida Healthcare, Oneida, NY, p. A494

REID, Patricia, Director of Nursing, Marion General Hospital, Columbia, MS, p. A391

REID, Richard, Vice President Chief Finance Officer, Sparrow Carson Hospital, Carson City, MI, p. A350

REID, Stephanie, R.N., Vice President of Patient Care Services and Chief Nursing Officer, Carroll Hospital Center, Westminster, MD, p. A333

REID TINIO, Gina, M.P.H., MS, Ph.D., Vice President, Chief Nurse Executive, Northwestern Medicine Delnor Hospital, Geneva, IL, p. A206

REIDER, Rochelle, Vice President Patient Care, Avera Queen Of Peace Hospital, Mitchell, SD, p. A629

REIDY, Christopher, Site Financial Officer, Community Medical Center, Toms River, NJ, p. A464

REIDY, Margaret, M.D., Vice President Medical Affairs, Upmc Presbyterian, Pittsburgh, PA, p. A604

REIFSTECK, Jeff, Assistant Vice President Chief Information Officer, White River Medical Center, Batesville, AR, p. A42

REILLY, Brian, Chief Financial Officer, Robert Wood Johnson University Hospital, New Brunswick, NJ, p. A459

REILLY, Janelle, Chief Executive Officer, Chi Memorial, Chattanooga, TN, p. A635

REILLY, Joanne, Administrator, Hudson County Meadowview Psychiatric Hospital, Secaucus, NJ, p. A462

REILLY, John, M.D., Vice President Medical Affairs and Chief Medical Officer, Mercy Medical Center, Rockville Centre, NY, p. A497

REILLY, Robert, Vice President and Chief Financial Officer, Anne Arundel Medical Center, Annapolis, MD, p. A324

REILLY, Tiffany, Director Human Resources, Lifescape, Sioux Falls, SD, p. A631

REIMER, Arlo, M.D., Chief of Staff, Kearny County Hospital, Lakin, KS, p. A268

REIMER, Ronda, Chief Nursing Officer and Assistant Administrator, Franklin General Hospital, Hampton, IA, p. A251

REIN, Bill, Administrator, Wyoming State Hospital, Evanston, WY, p. A802

REIN, Mitchell, M.D., Chief Medical Officer, North Shore Medical Center, Salem, MA, p. A344

REINBOTH, Thomas, Chief Financial Officer, Roxborough Memorial Hospital, Philadelphia, PA, p. A601

REINER, Mark, Chief Medical Office, Executive, St. Anthony's Rehabilitation Hospital, Lauderdale Lakes, FL, p. A144

REINERT, Brenda, Director Human Resources, Tomah Health, Tomah, WI, p. A797

REINERT, Chad, Chief Information Officer, Hamilton General Hospital, Hamilton, TX, p. A682

REINHARD, Diane, R.N., Vice President of Patient Care Services, Craig Hospital, Englewood, CO, p. A112

REINHARD, Russ, Chief Executive, Providence Willamette Falls Medical Center, Oregon City, OR, p. A578

REINHARDT, Tom, Chief Executive Officer, Cascade Medical Center, Cascade, ID, p. A189

REINKE, Bradley, M.D., Vice President Medical Affairs and Chief Medical Officer, Dameron Hospital, Stockton, CA, p. A99

REINKING, Cheryl, R.N., MS, Chief Nursing Officer, El Camino Hospital, Mountain View, CA, p. A80

REINTJES, Stephen Sr, M.D., President and Chief Medical Officer, North Kansas City Hospital, North Kansas City, MO, p. A413

REIS, David, Ph.D., Interim Chief Information Officer, University Of Miami Hospital And Clinics, Miami, FL, p. A147

REISELT, Doug, Vice President and Chief Information Officer, Baptist Memorial Hospital - Memphis, Memphis, TN, p. A643

Vice President and Chief Information Officer, Baptist Memorial Hospital-Collierville, Collierville, TN, p. A636

REISING, Robyn, R.N., Chief Nursing Officer, Hshs St. Mary's Hospital, Decatur, IL, p. A202

REISMAN, Ernestine, Vice President Human Resources, Down East Community Hospital, Machias, ME, p. A321

REISS, Deanna, Hospital Director of Nursing, Devereux Children's Behavioral Health Center, Malvern, PA, p. A596

REITZ, Brent, President, Adventist Healthcare Physical Health And Rehabilitation, Rockville, MD, p. A332

REITZ, Robert, Ph.D., Chief Executive Officer, Fulton State Hospital, Fulton, MO, p. A407

REITZEL, David, Chief Information Officer, Brookdale Hospital Medical Center, New York, NY, p. A489

REKLIS, Chip. Director Information Systems, Scotland Health Care System, Laurinburg, NC, p. A513

REKOWSKI, Christian, Information Technology Director, Jenkins County Medical Center, Millen, GA, p. A177

Information Technology Manager, Optim Medical Center - Screven, Sylvania, GA, p. A181

RELPH, Daren, Chief Executive Officer, Wayne County Hospital, Corydon, IA, p. A246

REMALEY, Anne, Vice President Human Resources, Acmh Hospital, Kittanning, PA, p. A593

REMARK, Megan, President and Chief Executive Officer, Regions Hospital, Saint Paul, MN, p. A385

REMBIS, Michael A., FACHE, Chief Executive Officer, Maui Memorial Medical Center, Wailuku, HI, p. A187

REMBOLD, Abbey, Human Resources Senior Generalist, Valley Health - Hampshire Memorial Hospital, Romney, WV, p. A776

Human Resources Senior Generalist, Valley Health - War Memorial Hospital, Berkeley Springs, WV, p. A770

Manager, Human Resource Business Partnerships, Valley Health - Shenandoah Memorial Hospital, Woodstock, VA, p. A754

REMER, Joseph, Chief Financial Officer, Hartgrove Hospital, Chicago, IL, p. A198

REMIGIO, Odalys, Assistant Vice President, Finance, Baptist Health South Florida, West Kendall Baptist Hospital, Miami, FL, p. A146

REMILLARD, John R., President, The University Of Vermont Health Network Elizabethtown Community Hospital, Elizabethtown, NY, p. A483

REMINGTON, Amanda, Director Human Resources, Wellstar Spalding Regional Hospital, Griffin, GA, p. A173

Director Human Resources, Wellstar Sylvan Grove Hospital, Jackson, GA, p. A174

REMLEY, Richard, Chief Executive Officer, Southcoast Behavioral Health, Dartmouth, MA, p. A338

REMSPECHER, Mark, Director Human Resources, Southeast Missouri Mental Health Center, Farmington, MO, p. A406

RENDA, Nick, Chief Financial Officer, Merit Health Woman's Hospital, Flowood, MS, p. A392

RENDER-LEACH, Cynthia, Director Human Resources, Highland Community Hospital, Picayune, MS, p. A398

RENEAU, John, Medical Director, Encompass Health Rehabilitation Hospital Of Las Vegas, Las Vegas, NV, p. A443

RENEAU, Vickie, Administrator and Chief Nursing Executive, Unitypoint Health-Keokuk, Keokuk, IA, p. A252

RENEY, Michael, Senior Vice President for Finance and Chief Financial Officer, Dana-Farber Cancer Institute, Boston, MA, p. A335

RENFREE, Mark, Chief Financial Officer, La Rabida Children's Hospital, Chicago, IL, p. A199

RENIER, Hugh, M.D., Vice President Medical Affairs, Essentia Health Duluth, Duluth, MN, p. A375

M.D., Vice President Medical Affairs, Essentia Health St. Mary's Medical Center, Duluth, MN, p. A375

RENKIEWICZ, Ginger, Chief Clinical Officer, Chief Nursing Executive, and Chief Quality Officer, Unitypoint Health - Trinity Rock Island, Rock Island, IL, p. A218

RENN, Amy, Interim Administrator, Patient Care and Nursing, Ascension Via Christi Hospital, Pittsburg, KS, p. A274

RENNEKER, James, FACHE, MSN, R.N., Vice President and Chief Nursing Officer, Methodist Hospitals, Gary, IN, p. A229

RENNER, Dianne, Director Human Resources, Logansport State Hospital, Logansport, IN, p. A235

RENNING, Kathryn, Director of Nursing, Cherry County Hospital, Valentine, NE, p. A440

RENO, Kelly, R.N., Chief Nursing Officer, Menorah Medical Center, Overland Park, KS, p. A274

RENO, Mike, Chief Operating Officer, Hill Country Memorial Hospital, Fredericksburg, TX, p. A679

RENO, William, M.D., IIIPresident Medical Staff, Merit Health Wesley, Hattiesburg, MS, p. A393

RENSHAW, Dee, Chief Executive Officer, Hillcrest Hospital Henryetta, Henryetta, OK, p. A560

RENTAS, Margarita, R.N., Nursing Director, Castaner General Hospital, Castaner, PR, p. A807

REOHR, Sara, Regional Controller, West Gables Rehabilitation Hospital, Miami, FL, p. A147

REPAC, Kimberly, Senior Vice President and Chief Financial Officer, Western Maryland Regional Medical Center, Cumberland, MD, p. A329

REPASS, Lois, Quality Assurance Specialist and Coordinator Performance Improvement, Northern Nevada Adult Mental Health Services, Sparks, NV, p. A446

REPETTI III, Gregory George., FACHE, Chief Executive Officer, Multicare Valley Hospital, Spokane Valley, WA, p. A766

FACHE, President, Multicare Deaconess Hospital, Spokane, WA, p. A765

REPKO, Keith D., Director, Veterans Affairs St. Louis Health Care System, Saint Louis, MO, p. A418

REPPY, William, President, Lehigh Valley Hospital - Schuylkill, Pottsville, PA, p. A605

RESCH, Ned, Chief Executive Officer, Platte County Memorial Hospital, Wheatland, WY, p. A804

RESETAR, Gayle, Vice President and Chief Operating Officer, Tidelands Georgetown Memorial Hospital, Georgetown, SC, p. A620

RESLER, Lori, R.N., Chief Nurse, Sullivan County Community Hospital, Sullivan, IN, p. A241

RESSLER, David, Chief Executive Officer, Aspen Valley Hospital, Aspen, CO, p. A107

RESSLER, Dennis, Vice President, Finance and Chief Financial Officer, Hendricks Regional Health, Danville, IN, p. A226

RESTREPO, Nicolas, M.D., Vice President Medical Affairs, Valley Health - Winchester Medical Center, Winchester, VA, p. A754

RESTUCCIA, Michael, Chief Information Officer, Hospital Of The University Of Pennsylvania, Philadelphia, PA, p. A600

RETALIC, Tammy, R.N., MS, Chief Nursing Officer, Hebrew Rehabilitation Center, Roslindale, MA, p. A344

RETHAMEL, Terry, Director of Support Services, Newport News Behavioral Health Center, Newport News, VA, p. A747

RETHORST, Richard, Chief of Medical Staff, Franklin Hospital District, Benton, IL, p. A195

RETTGER, Linda, M.D., President Medical Staff, Upmc Kane, Kane, PA, p. A593

RETTIG, Jeffrey, D.O., Chief of Staff, Limestone Medical Center, Groesbeck, TX, p. A682

RETZNER, Kim, Chief Executive Officer, Brentwood Springs, Newburgh, IN, p. A238

REULAND, Charles, Sc.D., Executive Vice President and Chief Operatng Officer, Johns Hopkins Hospital, Baltimore, MD, p. A324

REUST, Michele, Controller, Memorial Hospital Of Texas County, Guymon, OK, p. A560

REUTTINGER, H., D.O., Chief Medical Officer, Administration, Garden City Hospital, Garden City, MI, p. A355

REVELS, Beverly, Director Human Resources, Sutter Amador Hospital, Jackson, CA, p. A69

REVELS, Tonya, Senior Strategic Business Partner, Mcdowell Hospital, Marion, NC, p. A514

REVERMAN, Larry, Director Information Systems, Clark Memorial Health, Jeffersonville, IN, p. A233

REVIEL, Jackie Costley., R.N., Chief Executive Officer, Allen Parish Community Healthcare, Kinder, LA, p. A305

REWERTS, Karen, System Vice President Finance, Ssm Health St. Josep. - St. Charles, Saint Charles, MO, p. A414

System Vice President of Finance, Ssm Cardinal Glennon Children's Hospital, Saint Louis, MO, p. A416

System Vice President of Finance, Ssm Health St. Mary's Hospital - St. Louis, Saint Louis, MO, p. A417

REXFORD, Linda, Director Human Resources, Weeks Medical Center, Lancaster, NH, p. A449

REYES, Anthony, Information Technology Director, Commonwealth Health Center, Saipan, MP, p. A805

REYES, Glenda, Chief Financial Officer, Northwest Medical Center, Winfield, AL, p. A26

REYES, Marco, Executive Director, Hospital Psiquiatrico Metropolitano, Cabo Rojo, PR, p. A806

REYES, Netonua, MSN, Chief Operating Officer and Chief Nursing Officer, Broward Health Imperial Point, Fort Lauderdale, FL, p. A137

REYES, Raul, M.D., Medical Director, San Juan City Hospital, San Juan, PR, p. A811

REYES, Roxanne, Director of Nursing, Cornerstone Regional Hospital, Edinburg, TX, p. A673

REYKA, Michael, Ph.D., Chief Executive Officer, Western Maryland Hospital Center, Hagerstown, MD, p. A330

REYNA, Krista, Chief Nursing Officer, Mcbride Orthopedic Hospital, Oklahoma City, OK, p. A564

REYNGOUDT, Mark, Chief Financial Officer, Brandywine Hospital, Coatesville, PA, p. A587

REYNOLDS, Angela, Chief Financial Officer, Lewis-Gale Medical Center, Boones Mill, VA, p. A739

REYNOLDS, Denise, Chief Nursing Officer, Memorial Hospital Miramar, Miramar, FL, p. A148

REYNOLDS, Doug, Area Finance Officer, Kaiser Permanente Redwood City Medical Center, Redwood City, CA, p. A87

REYNOLDS, Ian, Chief Medical Officer, Advanced Diagnostics Hospital, Houston, TX, p. A684

REYNOLDS, James, M.D., Medical Director, Northwest Missouri Psychiatric Rehabilitation Center, Saint Joseph, MO, p. A415

REYNOLDS, Jay, M.D., Chief Medical Officer and Chief Clinical Officer, The Aroostook Medical Center, Presque Isle, ME, p. A322

REYNOLDS, Katelyn, Manager Human Resources, Greeley County Health Services, Tribune, KS, p. A278

REYNOLDS, Lauren, Associate Director of Nursing, Baptist Health Medical Center-Stuttgart, Stuttgart, AR, p. A53

REYNOLDS, Lennetta, Administrative Supervisor, Community Behavioral Health Hospital - Annandale, Annandale, MN, p. A371

REYNOLDS, Michael, Chief Financial Officer, Medical Center Barbour, Eufaula, AL, p. A18

REYNOLDS, Mike, Chief Financial Officer, Delta Specialty Hospital, Memphis, TN, p. A644
    Chief Financial Officer, Newberry County Memorial Hospital, Newberry, SC, p. A623

REYNOLDS, Paul, M.D., Medical Director, Coleman County Medical Center, Coleman, TX, p. A664

REYNOLDS, Ray, Chief Executive Officer, Glen Rose Medical Center, Glen Rose, TX, p. A681

REYNOLDS, Robert, Director Information Systems, Mary Rutan Hospital, Bellefontaine, OH, p. A529

REYNOLDS, Ronald J., President, Upmc Lock Haven, Lock Haven, PA, p. A595
    President, Upmc Muncy, Muncy, PA, p. A598

REYNOLDS, Scott, Vice President Finance, Mercy Hospital Springfield, Springfield, MO, p. A419

REYNOLDS, Tammy, Assistant Vice President, Nursing Operations, The University Of Vermont Health Network - Alice Hyde Medical Center, Malone, NY, p. A487

REYNOLDS, Teresa, Chief Operating Officer, Haywood Regional Medical Center, Clyde, NC, p. A507

REYNOLDS, Todd, Chief Information Officer, Memorial Medical Center Of Ashland, Ashland, WI, p. A779

REYNOLDS, Vance V., FACHE, CPA, Chief Executive Officer, Musc Health Florence Medical Center, Florence, SC, p. A619
    FACHE, CPA, Chief Executive Officer, Musc Health Marion Medical Center, Mullins, SC, p. A623

REYNOLDS-GOSSETTE, Youdie, Controller, Wilma N. Vazquez Medical Center, Vega Baja, PR, p. A811

REZAC, Julie A., R.N., Chief Executive Officer, Saunders Medical Center, Wahoo, NE, p. A440

RHEINHEIMER, Rick, Chief Clinical Officer, Kindred Hospital-Chattanooga, Chattanooga, TN, p. A635

RHINE, Kathleen, President and Chief Executive Officer, Mount Nittany Medical Center, State College, PA, p. A608

RHINEHART, Jennie R., Administrator and Chief Executive Officer, Community Hospital, Tallassee, AL, p. A24

RHOADES, Charles E., M.D., Chief Executive Officer, Kansas City Orthopaedic Institute, Leawood, KS, p. A269

RHOADES, Shelly, Chief Financial Officer, Clarion Psychiatric Center, Clarion, PA, p. A586

RHOADS, Jack, M.D., Medical Director, Landmark Hospital Of Joplin, Joplin, MO, p. A408

RHOADS, Pam, Chief Financial Officer, Fairfax Behavioral Health, Kirkland, WA, p. A759

RHODES, David, M.D., Senior Vice President Medical Affairs and Chief Medical Officer, Rapides Regional Medical Center, Alexandria, LA, p. A295

RHODES, Helen, R.N., Associate Director Operations, Veterans Affairs Northern Indiana Health Care System, Fort Wayne, IN, p. A229

RHODES, Tracey, Coordinator Human Resources, Evergreen Medical Center, Evergreen, AL, p. A18

RHOTON, Stephanie, Director, Patient Care Services, Indian Path Community Hospital, Kingsport, TN, p. A641

RHYNE, Craig, M.D., FACS, Chief Medical Officer, Covenant Children's Hospital, Lubbock, TX, p. A697
    M.D., FACS, Chief Medical Officer, Covenant Medical Center, Lubbock, TX, p. A697

RHYNE, Dennis, M.D., Acting Medical Director, Fairbanks, Indianapolis, IN, p. A232

RHYNE, Tim, Personnel Officer, Ventura County Medical Center, Ventura, CA, p. A103

RIAL, Joanne, Chief Financial Officer, Cumberland Hospital For Children And Adolescents, New Kent, VA, p. A746

RIALS, Joe, Director Fiscal Services, North Mississipp. State Hospital, Tupelo, MS, p. A400

RIALS, Loren, Chief Financial Officer, Musc Health Florence Medical Center, Florence, SC, p. A619
    Chief Financial Officer, Musc Health Marion Medical Center, Mullins, SC, p. A623

RIANO, Omaira, Chief Nursing Officer, Encompass Health Rehabilitation Hospital Of Sunrise, Sunrise, FL, p. A158

RIBA, Chris, Director Human Resources, Western Wisconsin Health, Baldwin, WI, p. A780

RICARDO, Jennifer, Director of Human Resources, Westchester General Hospital, Miami, FL, p. A147

RICCI, Lynn, President and Chief Executive Officer, Hospital For Special Care, New Britain, CT, p. A123

RICCIARDI, Patrice, Director Human Resources, Columbus Hospital Ltach, Newark, NJ, p. A459

RICCIO, Dustin, M.D., President Eastern Region, Newark-Wayne Community Hospital, Newark, NY, p. A492
    M.D., President, Clifton Springs Hospital And Clinic, Clifton Springs, NY, p. A481

RICCIO, John, M.D., Chief Medical Officer, Auburn Community Hospital, Auburn, NY, p. A475

RICCIONI, Michel, Chief Financial Officer, Petaluma Valley Hospital, Petaluma, CA, p. A85
    Chief Financial Officer, Queen's North Hawaii Community Hospital, Kamuela, HI, p. A186
    Chief Financial Officer, St. Josep. Hospital Eureka, Eureka, CA, p. A63
    Chief Financial Officer, The Queen's Medical Center, Honolulu, HI, p. A185
    Vice President and Chief Financial Officer, Northern California Region, Queen Of The Valley Medical Center, Napa, CA, p. A80

RICCITELLI, Anthony, Chief Operating Officer, Worcester Recovery Center And Hospital, Worcester, MA, p. A347

RICCITELLI, Vincent, Chief Financial Officer, Salem Medical Center, Salem, NJ, p. A462

RICE, Aimee, Human Resources Manager, Riverview Psychiatric Center, Augusta, ME, p. A318

RICE, Amy, Chief Executive Officer, Helena Regional Medical Center, Helena, AR, p. A46
    Chief Financial Officer, Helena Regional Medical Center, Helena, AR, p. A46

RICE, Bernard, Chief Compliance Officer, Rangely District Hospital, Rangely, CO, p. A118
    Chief Information Officer, Nemours Children's Hospital, Orlando, FL, p. A151

RICE, Carolyn, M.D., Director Medical Services, Naval Hospital Pensacola, Pensacola, FL, p. A153

RICE, Cathy, Director Support Services, Clifton-Fine Hospital, Star Lake, NY, p. A498

RICE, Craig, Director Information Technology, Schneck Medical Center, Seymour, IN, p. A240

RICE, James W., Director, Oscar G. Johnson Veterans Affairs Medical Center, Iron Mountain, MI, p. A358

RICE, Mark, CPA, Chief Financial Officer, Geisinger Jersey Shore Hospital, Jersey Shore, PA, p. A593

RICE, Mark J., Administrator, Ruston Regional Specialty Hospital, Ruston, LA, p. A313
    Chief Executive Officer, Mid-Jefferson Extended Care Hospital Of Beaumont, Beaumont, TX, p. A658

RICE, Peter, M.D., Medical Director, Peacehealth Ketchikan Medical Center, Ketchikan, AK, p. A28

RICE, Tim, President and Chief Executive Officer, Lakewood Health System, Staples, MN, p. A386

RICH, Anna, Chief Financial Officer, Pam Specialty Hospital Of Las Vegas, Las Vegas, NV, p. A444

RICH, Bill, Chief Executive Officer, Tennova Healthcare-Shelbyville, Shelbyville, TN, p. A649

RICH, Deborah, R.N., Chief Nursing Officer, Encompass Health Rehabilitation Hospital Of New England, Woburn, MA, p. A346

RICH, Judy F., MSN, R.N., President and Chief Executive Officer, Tmc Healthcare, Tucson, AZ, p. A41

RICH, Kori, Chief Executive Officer, The Physicians Centre Hospital, Bryan, TX, p. A661

RICH, Philip. M.D., Chief Medical Officer, West Hills Hospital, Reno, NV, p. A446

RICHARD, Andrea, M.D., Chief Medical Officer, Warren State Hospital, Warren, PA, p. A609

RICHARD, Angelique, R.N., Ph.D., Vice President Clinical Nursing, Chief Nursing Officer and Associate Dean for Practice, College of Nursing, Rush University Medical Center, Chicago, IL, p. A200

RICHARD, Brandi, Chief Nursing Officer, Michiana Behavioral Health Center, Plymouth, IN, p. A239

RICHARD, Brent, Administrative Director Information Systems, Southern Ohio Medical Center, Portsmouth, OH, p. A548

RICHARD, Christina, Chief Executive Officer, Kindred Hospital Tarrant County-Arlington, Arlington, TX, p. A653

RICHARD, Thomas, Director Budget and Revenue Cycle, Carris Health - Redwood, Redwood Falls, MN, p. A383

RICHARD, Tim, IT Coordinator, Crawford Memorial Hospital, Robinson, IL, p. A218

RICHARDS, Craig A., Chief Executive Officer, Mildred Mitchell-Bateman Hospital, Huntington, WV, p. A773

RICHARDS, Frank, Chief Information Officer, Geisinger Medical Center, Danville, PA, p. A588
    Chief Information Officer, Geisinger Wyoming Valley Medical Center, Wilkes Barre, PA, p. A611

RICHARDS, Jaena, Chief Financial Officer, Deer Lodge Medical Center, Deer Lodge, MT, p. A423

RICHARDS, Jennifer, Ph.D., R.N., Chief Nursing Officer Acute Services, Renown Regional Medical Center, Reno, NV, p. A446
    Ph.D., R.N., Chief Nursing Officer, Renown Rehabilitation Hospital, Reno, NV, p. A446
    Ph.D., R.N., Chief Nursing Officer, Renown South Meadows Medical Center, Reno, NV, p. A446

RICHARDS, Jon, Chief Financial Officer, Tennova Newport Medical Center, Newport, TN, p. A647

RICHARDS, Jonathan, Chief Financial Officer, David Grant Usaf Medical Center, Travis Afb, CA, p. A101

RICHARDS, Judith, Director of Nursing, Adcare Hospital Of Worcester, Worcester, MA, p. A346

RICHARDS, Kelly, Senior Vice President and Chief Nursing Officer, Mercyone Cedar Falls Medical Center, Cedar Falls, IA, p. A244
    Senior Vice President and Chief Nursing Officer, Mercyone Oelwein Medical Center, Oelwein, IA, p. A255
    Vice President and Chief Nursing Officer, Mercyone Waterloo Medical Center, Waterloo, IA, p. A259

RICHARDS, Mandy, R.N., MSN, System Chief Nursing Officer, Allina Health Vice President of Care, Abbott Northwestern Hospital, Minneapolis, MN, p. A380

RICHARDS, Nate, Director Information Technology, Mitchell County Hospital Health Systems, Beloit, KS, p. A262

RICHARDS, Sheila, Human Resources Director, Dallas Medical Center, Dallas, TX, p. A668

RICHARDS, Stanlee, R.N., MS, Chief Nurse Executive, Nyc Health + Hospitals / Henry J Carter Specialty Hospital And Medical Center, New York, NY, p. A491

RICHARDS, Thom, Director Information Technology, Knoxville Hospital & Clinics, Knoxville, IA, p. A253

RICHARDSON, Crystal, Chief Nursing Officer, Vibra Hospital Of Richmond, Richmond, VA, p. A751

RICHARDSON, David, M.D., Chief of Staff, Delta Specialty Hospital, Memphis, TN, p. A644

RICHARDSON, Denise, R.N., MSN, Senior Vice President and Chief Nursing Officer, St. Barnabas Hospital, Bronx, NY, p. A477

RICHARDSON, Dwayne, Chief Operating Officer, Placentia-Linda Hospital, Placentia, CA, p. A85

RICHARDSON, Greg, Assistant Administrator Human Resources, Piedmont Newton Hospital, Covington, GA, p. A170

RICHARDSON, Irene, Chief Executive Officer, Memorial Hospital Of Sweetwater County, Rock Springs, WY, p. A804

RICHARDSON, James, Chief Medical Officer, Holy Cross Hospital, Chicago, IL, p. A198

RICHARDSON, Judy, M.D., President Medical Staff, Mid-Columbia Medical Center, The Dalles, OR, p. A582

RICHARDSON, Karen, Senior Vice President and Chief Financial Officer, Ascension Providence, Waco, TX, p. A723

RICHARDSON, Keith, President and Chief Executive Officer, East Liverpool City Hospital, East Liverpool, OH, p. A539

RICHARDSON, Kevin, M.D., Chief of Staff, Southwest Mississipp. Regional Medical Center, Mccomb, MS, p. A396

RICHARDSON, Kirk, R.N., Senior Vice President, Chief Operating Officer, and Chief Nursing Officer, Bronson Lakeview Hospital, Paw Paw, MI, p. A363
    R.N., Vice President, Chief Operating Officer and Chief Nursing Officer, Bronson South Haven Hospital, South Haven, MI, p. A367

RICHARDSON, Lonnie, Chief Information Officer, University Medical Center, Las Vegas, NV, p. A444

RICHARDSON, Nathaniel Jr, President and Chief Executive Officer, University Of Maryland Capital Region Health Prince George's Hospital Center, Cheverly, MD, p. A328

RICHARDSON, Pamela, Business Manager, Central Regional Hospital, Butner, NC, p. A506

RICHARDSON, Robert, Information Technology Administrator, Porter Regional Hospital, Valparaiso, IN, p. A241

RICHARDSON, Robert Stephen. Jr, Administrator, Regions Behavioral Hospital, Baton Rouge, LA, p. A297

RICHARDSON, Rodney, Director of Information Technology, Baptist Health Corbin, Corbin, KY, p. A282

RICHARDSON, Sarah, Director Information Systems, Belton Regional Medical Center, Belton, MO, p. A402

RICHARDSON, Stanley, Coordinator Human Resources and Payroll Benefits, Kindred Hospital-San Antonio, San Antonio, TX, p. A711

RICHARDSON, Teresa, Chief Clinical Officer, Kindred Hospital Indianapolis North, Indianapolis, IN, p. A232

RICHARDSON, Terika, M.P.H., President, Advocate Lutheran General Hospital, Park Ridge, IL, p. A216

RICHARDSON, Terrie, Coordinator Human Resources, Select Specialty Hospital-Augusta, Augusta, GA, p. A166

RICHARDSON, Timothy, M.D., Chief of Staff, Maine Veterans Affairs Medical Center, Augusta, ME, p. A318

RICHARDSON, Todd, Chief Information Officer, Aspirus Medford Hospital & Clinics, Inc., Medford, WI, p. A789

RICHASON JR, PaulChief Medical Officer, Conway Medical Center, Conway, SC, p. A618

RICHASON, Amie, Vice President Human Resources, Leesburg Regional Medical Center, Leesburg, FL, p. A144

Vice President Human Resources, The Villages Regional Hospital, The Villages, FL, p. A160

RICHAUD, Benjamin, Interim Chief Executive Officer, Merit Health River Region, Vicksburg, MS, p. A401

RICHBOURG, Gail, Director Human Resources, Mcleod Health Clarendon, Manning, SC, p. A622

RICHBURG, Melanie, Chief Executive Officer, Lynn County Hospital District, Tahoka, TX, p. A718

RICHCREEK, Keith, Manager Technical Services, Lafayette Regional Health Center, Lexington, MO, p. A411

RICHENS, Ken, Chief Information Officer, Central Valley Medical Center, Nephi, UT, p. A729

RICHERT, Ed, M.D., Chief of Staff, Modoc Medical Center, Alturas, CA, p. A55

RICHETTI, Michael, Chief Information Officer, Chilton Medical Center, Pompton Plains, NJ, p. A462

RICHHART, David, Chief Financial Officer, North Valley Hospital, Whitefish, MT, p. A428

RICHMAN, Craig, M.D., Medical Director, Meadows Psychiatric Center, Centre Hall, PA, p. A586

RICHMAN, Jonathan, M.D., Chief of Staff, Chase County Community Hospital, Imperial, NE, p. A433

RICHMAN, Timothy, President and Chief Executive Officer, Ascension Southeast Wisconsin Hospital - Elmbrook Campus, Brookfield, WI, p. A781

RICHMOND, Andy, Director Information Technology, Choctaw Memorial Hospital, Hugo, OK, p. A560

RICHMOND, Brett M., President and Chief Executive Officer, Methodist Fremont Health, Fremont, NE, p. A432

RICHMOND, Christine, Director of Nursing, Community Care Hospital, New Orleans, LA, p. A310

RICHMOND, Craig, Senior Vice President and Chief Financial Officer, Metrohealth Medical Center, Cleveland, OH, p. A535

RICHMOND, Ira, Associate Director Patient Care Services, Veterans Affairs Pittsburgh Healthcare System, Pittsburgh, PA, p. A604

RICHOUX, Jacquelyn, Chief Financial Officer, Lady Of The Sea General Hospital, Cut Off, LA, p. A300

RICHTER, Daniel, M.D., Chief of Staff, Chi Health Missouri Valley, Missouri Valley, IA, p. A254

RICHTER, Thomas V., Chief Executive Officer, Pioneer Memorial Hospital And Health Services, Viborg, SD, p. A632

RICK, Bob, Vice President Information Technology, Usmd Hospital At Arlington, Arlington, TX, p. A654

RICKARD, Sheryl, Chief Executive Officer, Bonner General Health, Sandpoint, ID, p. A193

RICKENS, Chris, R.N., MS, Senior Vice President and Chief Nursing Officer, Upmc Altoona, Altoona, PA, p. A584

RICKS, Edward, Vice President and Chief Information Officer, Beaufort Memorial Hospital, Beaufort, SC, p. A615

RICKS, Loretha, Human Resources Supervisor, Southampton Memorial Hospital, Franklin, VA, p. A742

RICKS, Michael, Chief Operating Officer, Hoag Memorial Hospital Presbyterian, Newport Beach, CA, p. A81

RICO, Carrie, Chief Human Resource Officer, Keefe Memorial Hospital, Cheyenne Wells, CO, p. A109

RICO, Richard, Vice President and Chief Financial Officer, Sky Lakes Medical Center, Klamath Falls, OR, p. A576

RIDDER, Terri, Director Human Resources, St. Francis Memorial Hospital, West Point, NE, p. A440

RIDDLE, Joel, Senior Director Human Resources, Caromont Regional Medical Center, Gastonia, NC, p. A510

RIDDLE, Kent, Chief Executive Officer, Mary Free Bed Rehabilitation Hospital, Grand Rapids, MI, p. A356

RIDDLE, Ross, D.O., Medical Director, Elkview General Hospital, Hobart, OK, p. A560

RIDGE, Lisa Carolyn., Chief Executive Officer, Van Diest Medical Center, Webster City, IA, p. A260

RIDGEWAY, Michael, Chief Executive Officer, Mesquite Rehabilitation Institute, Mesquite, TX, p. A701

Chief Executive Officer, Mesquite Specialty Hospital, Mesquite, TX, p. A701

RIDLEN, Deborah, CPA, Vice President Finance and Chief Financial Officer, Schneck Medical Center, Seymour, IN, p. A240

RIDLEY, John, Executive Vice President & Chief Operating Officer, Decatur Memorial Hospital, Decatur, IL, p. A202

RIDLEY, Pam, Director Information Systems, Henry County Medical Center, Paris, TN, p. A648

RIDLEY, Zena, Director Human Resources, Harbor Oaks Hospital, New Baltimore, MI, p. A362

RIDNER, Sheila, R.N., Director of Nursing, Unity Psychiatric Care-Columbia, Columbia, TN, p. A637

RIEBER, Dan, Chief Financial Officer, Uchealth Memorial Hospital, Colorado Springs, CO, p. A109

RIEBER, Jim, Director Information Systems, Perham Health, Perham, MN, p. A383

RIECHERS, Thomas, M.D., Chief Medical Staff, Mercy Hospital Washington, Washington, MO, p. A420

RIECK, Amy, Human Resources Officer, Greater Regional Medical Center, Creston, IA, p. A247

RIEDEL, Sherry, Chief Financial Management Service, John D. Dingell Veterans Affairs Medical Center, Detroit, MI, p. A353

RIEDLINGER, Floyd, Director Human Resources, West Jefferson Medical Center, Marrero, LA, p. A308

RIEG, Kevin, M.D., President Medical Staff, Ascension Via Christi Rehabilitation Hospital, Wichita, KS, p. A278

RIEGER, Bill, Chief Information Officer, Flagler Hospital, Saint Augustine, FL, p. A155

RIEGER, Tim, Chief Financial Officer, Mercy Health - St. Rita's Medical Center, Lima, OH, p. A543

RIEGERT, Patricia, Director Fiscal Services, Danville State Hospital, Danville, PA, p. A587

RIEKE, Diane, Director Patient Care Services, Patients' Hospital Of Redding, Redding, CA, p. A87

RIEKS, Katie, Chief Nursing Officer, Hansen Family Hospital, Iowa Falls, IA, p. A252

RIER, Kirk, Chief Operating Officer, Iowa Specialty Hospital-Clarion, Clarion, IA, p. A246

RIES, Heather, Chief Nursing Officer, Regional Medical Center, Manchester, IA, p. A253

RIESER, Michael, M.D., Medical Director, Ridge Behavioral Health System, Lexington, KY, p. A287

RIETSEMA, Wouter, M.D., Chief Quality and Information Officer, The University Of Vermont Health Network-Champlain Valley Physicians Hospital, Plattsburgh, NY, p. A495

RIEVES, Cheryl, Chief Nurse Executive Lorain Region, Mercy Allen Hospital, Oberlin, OH, p. A547

RIFFLE, Virginia, Vice President Patient Care Services, Samaritan North Lincoln Hospital, Lincoln City, OR, p. A577

RIGAS, Warren, Executive Vice President and Chief Operating Officer, Floyd Medical Center, Rome, GA, p. A179

RIGDON, Alice, Vice President Finance, Saint Josep. Hospital, Denver, CO, p. A111

RIGDON, Edward, M.D., Chief Medical Officer, Merit Health Rankin, Brandon, MS, p. A390

RIGDON, Pam, Director Nursing, Laird Hospital, Union, MS, p. A400

RIGGIN, Andrew, Chief Executive Officer, Bennett County Hospital And Nursing Home, Martin, SD, p. A629

RIGGLE, Vikki, Director Human Resources, Eastern Louisiana Mental Health System, Jackson, LA, p. A303

RIGGS, Jennifer, R.N., Chief Nurse Officer, Mainegeneral Medical Center, Augusta, ME, p. A318

RIGGS, Richard, M.D., Senior Vice President Medical Affairs and Chief Medical Officer, Cedars-Sinai Medical Center, Los Angeles, CA, p. A73

RIGNEY, Alice, Chief Human Resources Officer, Abbeville Area Medical Center, Abbeville, SC, p. A615

RIGSBEE CARROLL, Cristina, Chief Operating Officer, Granville Health System, Oxford, NC, p. A516

RIGSBY, Diane, Chief Information Officer, Capital Hospice, Arlington, VA, p. A738

RIKER, Yvette, Chief Operating Officer, Reeves County Hospital District, Pecos, TX, p. A705

RILEY, Colleen, M.D., Medical Director, Laguna Honda Hospital And Rehabilitation Center, San Francisco, CA, p. A93

RILEY, Jennifer, Vice President Operations, Memorial Regional Health, Craig, CO, p. A110

RILEY, Jim, Director Information Technology, Wagoner Community Hospital, Wagoner, OK, p. A571

RILEY, Joe B., FACHE, President and Chief Executive Officer, Jackson Hospital And Clinic, Montgomery, AL, p. A22

RILEY, Kenneth, Director Information Systems, Baystate Wing Hospital, Palmer, MA, p. A343

RILEY, Linzie, Interim Human Resource Manager, Lifecare Hospitals Of Dallas, Dallas, TX, p. A669

RILEY, Mike, President and Chief Operating Officer, Novant Health Huntersville Medical Center, Huntersville, NC, p. A512

RILEY, Randy, Fiscal and Administrative Manager, Northwest Missouri Psychiatric Rehabilitation Center, Saint Joseph, MO, p. A415

RILEY, Robert, Interim Chief Financial Officer, East Jefferson General Hospital, Metairie, LA, p. A308

RILEY, Susan, Director Human Resources, Encompass Health Rehabilitation Hospital Of Miami, Cutler Bay, FL, p. A135

RILEY, Wayne J., M.D., M.P.H., President, Suny Downstate-University Hospital Of Brooklyn, Brooklyn, NY, p. A479

RILEY, William, M.D., JrChief of Staff, Memorial Hermann Sugar Land Hospital, Sugar Land, TX, p. A717

RINALDI, Anthony, Executive Vice President, Fairview Hospital, Great Barrington, MA, p. A339

RINALDI, Blythe, Vice President, Mayo Clinic Health System - Northland In Barron, Barron, WI, p. A781

RINDELS, Doris, Vice President Operations, Unitypoint Health - Grinnell Regional Medical Center, Grinnell, IA, p. A250

RINDFLEISCH, Jody, Manager Human Resources, Carris Health - Redwood, Redwood Falls, MN, p. A383

RINDLISBACHER, Diane, Manager Information Systems, Orem Community Hospital, Orem, UT, p. A730

RINEHART, Linda, Director Human Resources, Encompass Health Rehabilitation Hospital Of Treasure Coast, Vero Beach, FL, p. A161

RINEHART, Rick, Vice President, Chief Information Officer, Carle Foundation Hospital, Urbana, IL, p. A221

RINEHART, Tyler, Chief Financial Officer, Center For Behavioral Medicine, Kansas City, MO, p. A408

RINEY, Kirsten, MSN, R.N., Chief Nursing Officer, North Oaks Medical Center, Hammond, LA, p. A302

RING, Brian, Chief Operating Officer, Henry Community Health, New Castle, IN, p. A238

RING, Caroline, Chief Nursing Officer, Spectrum Health Big Rapids Hospital, Big Rapids, MI, p. A349

RINGE, Kathy, Director Human Resources, Sage Rehabilitation Hospital, Baton Rouge, LA, p. A297

RINGER, Dave, M.D., Chief of Staff, St. Mary's Good Samaritan Hospital, Greensboro, GA, p. A173

RINKE, Joseph, Director Human Resources, Streamwood Behavioral Health Center, Streamwood, IL, p. A221

Director of Human Resources, Riveredge Hospital, Forest Park, IL, p. A205

RINKENBERGER, Sean, Chief Financial Officer, St. Andrew's Health Center, Bottineau, ND, p. A521

RINKER, John, Chief Medical Officer, Osf Saint James - John W. Albrecht Medical Center, Pontiac, IL, p. A217

RIOS, Cindy, Chief Financial Officer, Alliancehealth Durant, Durant, OK, p. A558

RIOS, Damaris, Executive Nursing Director, Hospital Metropolitano Dr. Susoni, Arecibo, PR, p. A806

RIOS, Jose, Director Information Services, Adventhealth Murray, Chatsworth, GA, p. A168

RIOS, Margot, R.N., Chief Nursing Officer, Christus Spohn Hospital Alice, Alice, TX, p. A651

RIPPERGER, Ted, Administrative Director Human Resources, Atrium Medical Center, Middletown, OH, p. A545

RIPPEY, Wesley, M.D., Chief Medical Officer, Adventist Health Portland, Portland, OR, p. A579

RIPSCH, Sue, Senior Vice President & Chief Operating Officer, Javon Bea Hospital-Rockton, Rockford, IL, p. A218

RISBY, Emile, M.D., Clinical Director, Georgia Regional Hospital At Atlanta, Decatur, GA, p. A171

RISHA, Holly, Administrative Director Human Resources, College Hospital Cerritos, Cerritos, CA, p. A59

RISINGER, Jeff, Director Human Resources, Uams Medical Center, Little Rock, AR, p. A49

RISK, Carl W. II, President, Elkhart General Hospital, Elkhart, IN, p. A227

RISLOW, Deb, Chief Information Officer, Gundersen Lutheran Medical Center, La Crosse, WI, p. A787

RISOVI, Carol, Human Resources, Chi St Alexius Health Carrington Medical Center, Carrington, ND, p. A522

RISSE, Thomas, Chief Financial Officer and Vice President Business Services, Kaiser Permanente Medical Center, Honolulu, HI, p. A184

RITCHEY, James, Montana Region, Vice President Human Resources, St. Vincent Healthcare, Billings, MT, p. A421

RITCHEY, Jim, Director Human Resources, Sky Ridge Medical Center, Lone Tree, CO, p. A116

RITCHIE, Bruce, Vice President of Finance and Chief Financial Officer, Tidalhealth Peninsula, Salisbury, MD, p. A332

RITCHIE, Eric, M.D., Clinical Director, Chinle Comprehensive Health Care Facility, Chinle, AZ, p. A31

RITCHIE, Jill, Director of Nursing, Ellinwood District Hospital, Ellinwood, KS, p. A264

RITCHIE, Jim, Director Management Information Systems, South Shore Hospital, Chicago, IL, p. A201

RITCHIE, Shannan, Chief Operating Officer, St. Vincent Charity Medical Center, Cleveland, OH, p. A535

RITENOUR, Chad, M.D., Chief Medical Officer, Emory University Hospital, Atlanta, GA, p. A164

RITON, John, Director Information Services, Memorial Hospital Of Tampa, Tampa, FL, p. A159

RITTENOUR, Melanie, Director Human Resources, Paulding County Hospital, Paulding, OH, p. A547

RITTER, Jane, R.N., Vice President, Patient Care and Clinical Services, United Regional Health Care System, Wichita Falls, TX, p. A725

RITTER, Robert, FACHE, Associate Director, Harry S. Truman Memorial Veterans Hospital, Columbia, MO, p. A405

RITTERMEYER, Linda, Chief Nursing Officer, Christus St. Frances Cabrini Hospital, Alexandria, LA, p. A295

RITTMAN, Todd, Director of Nursing, Larue D. Carter Memorial Hospital, Indianapolis, IN, p. A232

RITZ, Andrew, Chief Operatiang Officer, Longmont United Hospital, Longmont, CO, p. A116

RIVAS, Eloy, Director of Information Systems, Venice Regional Bayfront Health, Venice, FL, p. A161

RIVAS, Jose, M.D., Chief of Staff, Community Hospital Of Huntington Park, Huntington Park, CA, p. A68

RIVAS, Ramon, M.D., Medical Director, Hospital San Cristobal, Coto Laurel, PR, p. A807

RIVERA, Angela, Chief Nursing Officer, Beckley Arh Hospital, Beckley, WV, p. A770

RIVERA, Ashley, Chief Executive Officer, West Holt Medical Services, Atkinson, NE, p. A429

RIVERA, Christina, Director Human Resources, Southwest General Hospital, San Antonio, TX, p. A713

RIVERA, Cristina, Chief Executive Officer, Rio Grande Regional Hospital, Mcallen, TX, p. A700

RIVERA, Edgar, Chief Information Officer, Brownfield Regional Medical Center, Brownfield, TX, p. A660

RIVERA, Enrique, Chief Financial Officer, Bella Vista Hospital, Mayaguez, PR, p. A808

RIVERA, Ivonne, Director Finance, Hospital Oriente, Humacao, PR, p. A808

RIVERA, Jamie, Chief Financial Officer, Hospital Pavia Arecibo, Arecibo, PR, p. A806

RIVERA, Joe, Chief Information Technology Officer, Laredo Medical Center, Laredo, TX, p. A695

RIVERA, Jose, Director Human Resources, Hospital Buen Samaritano, Aguadilla, PR, p. A805

RIVERA, Julia, M.D., Chief of Staff, Jackson County Memorial Hospital, Altus, OK, p. A555

RIVERA, Luis, Director Human Resources, San Juan Capestrano Hospital, San Juan, PR, p. A811

RIVERA, Maria, Director Human Resources, Westside Regional Medical Center, Plantation, FL, p. A154

RIVERA, Renee, Executive Director, Rockland Children's Psychiatric Center, Orangeburg, NY, p. A494

RIVERA, Zamarys, R.N., Chief Nursing Officer, Encompass Health Rehabilitation Hospital Of San Juan, San Juan, PR, p. A810

RIVERA MALDONADO, Luis, Executive Director, Bella Vista Hospital, Mayaguez, PR, p. A808

RIVERA-POL, Noriselle, Vice President Finance, Hospital Manati Medical Center, Manati, PR, p. A808

RIVERS, Eric, Chief Information Officer, Mission Community Hospital, Panorama City, CA, p. A84

RIVERS, Jan, Director Human Resources, Ochsner Medical Center - Baton Rouge, Baton Rouge, LA, p. A297

RIVERS, Ken, Chief Operating Officer, Fontana Medical Center, Kaiser Permanente Fontana Medical Center, Fontana, CA, p. A64

RIVERS, Nikki, R.N., Regional Chief Nursing Officer, South Market, Ascension Seton Hays, Kyle, TX, p. A694

RIVES, Patricia, R.N., MSN, Chief Executive Officer, Community Hospital Of Huntington Park, Huntington Park, CA, p. A68

RIVOIRE, John, R.N., MSN, Administrator, Louisiana Extended Care Hospital Of Natchitoches, Natchitoches, LA, p. A309

RIZGALLAH, Ed, Vice President Information Services and Chief Information Officer, Christian Health Care Center, Wyckoff, NJ, p. A466

RIZK, Magdy, M.D., Chief of Staff, Hca Houston Healthcare West, Houston, TX, p. A686

RIZK, Norman, M.D., Chief Medical Officer, Stanford Health Care, Palo Alto, CA, p. A84

RIZK, Rob, Director Information Technology, Good Shepherd Health Care System, Hermiston, OR, p. A576

RIZKALLA, Naseem, M.D., Chief Medical Officer, Aspirus Iron River Hospitals & Clinics, Inc., Iron River, MI, p. A358

RIZZO, Frank, Chief Financial Officer, Central Region, North Shore University Hospital, Manhasset, NY, p. A487

RIZZO, Theresa, Administrator, Franklin County Memorial Hospital, Franklin, NE, p. A432

RIZZUTO, George, CPA, Chief Executive Officer, West Boca Medical Center, Boca Raton, FL, p. A132

ROACH, Bryan, Executive Vice President and Chief Financial Officer, Mount Nittany Medical Center, State College, PA, p. A608

ROACH, Crystal, Chief Financial Officer, Trustpoint Rehabilitation Hospital Of Lubbock, Lubbock, TX, p. A698

ROACH, Dee, M.D., Chief of Staff, Mitchell County Hospital, Colorado City, TX, p. A664

ROACH, Donna, Chief Information Officer, Ascension Via Christi St. Francis, Mulvane, KS, p. A271
Chief Information Officer, Sacred Heart Hospital Pensacola, Pensacola, FL, p. A154

ROACH, Eric, Chief Financial Officer, East Georgia Regional Medical Center, Statesboro, GA, p. A181

ROACH, Geoff, Director Human Resources, Barrett Hospital & Healthcare, Dillon, MT, p. A423

ROACH, Maureen, Senior Chief Financial Officer, Kindred Hospital-St. Louis, Saint Louis, MO, p. A416

ROACH, Renee, System Vice President, Human Resources, Ssm Health St. Clare Hospital - Fenton, Fenton, MO, p. A406
System Vice President, Ssm Health St. Josep. Hospital - Lake Saint Louis, Lake Saint Louis, MO, p. A410

ROACH, Steven P., FACHE, Interim Chief Executive Officer, Umass Memorial Healthalliance-Clinton Hospital, Leominster, MA, p. A340
FACHE, President and Chief Executive Officer, Umass Memorial-Marlborough Hospital, Marlborough, MA, p. A341

ROADER, Charles, Vice President Finance, Edgerton Hospital And Health Services, Edgerton, WI, p. A783

ROAN, Linda, Chief Nursing Officer, East Morgan County Hospital, Brush, CO, p. A108

ROANHORSE, Anslem, Chief Executive Officer, U. S. Public Health Service Indian Hospital, Crownpoint, NM, p. A469

ROARK, Chris, Chief Information Officer, Stillwater Medical Center, Stillwater, OK, p. A568

ROARTY, Maureen, Executive Vice President Human Resources, Nassau University Medical Center, East Meadow, NY, p. A483

ROB, Lee, Director Human Resources, Monroe Regional Hospital, Aberdeen, MS, p. A389

ROBB, Joy, Vice President Human Resources, Prairie View, Newton, KS, p. A272

ROBBINS, Donald, M.D., JrChief Staff, Hills & Dales General Hospital, Cass City, MI, p. A350
Chief Executive Officer, Lawrence County Memorial Hospital, Lawrenceville, IL, p. A210

ROBBINS, Joe, M.D., Vice President Medical Affairs, Sentara Williamsburg Regional Medical Center, Williamsburg, VA, p. A753

ROBBINS, Shannon, Chief Operating Officer, Ohio Hospital For Psychiatry, Columbus, OH, p. A536

ROBEANO, Karen, R.N., Chief Nursing Officer and Vice President Patient Care Services, Firsthealth Moore Regional Hospital, Pinehurst, NC, p. A516

ROBEL, Susan, R.N., Executive Vice President and Chief Nursing Officer, Geisinger Medical Center, Danville, PA, p. A588

ROBERGE, Jeremy, Chief Financial Officer, Huggins Hospital, Wolfeboro, NH, p. A451
Director Reimbursement, Androscoggin Valley Hospital, Berlin, NH, p. A448
President and Chief Executive Officer, Huggins Hospital, Wolfeboro, NH, p. A451

ROBERSON, Ed, Director Information Systems, Hca Houston Healthcare Northwest, Houston, TX, p. A685

ROBERSON, Joe, Chief Executive Officer, Encompass Health Rehabilitation Hospital Of Abilene, Abilene, TX, p. A651

ROBERSON, Lynda, Senior Program Director, Rusk State Hospital, Rusk, TX, p. A710

ROBERSON, Meika, M.D., Chief Medical Officer, Carepoint Health Hoboken University Medical Center, Hoboken, NJ, p. A456

ROBERSON, Scott, Administrator, Alta View Hospital, Sandy, UT, p. A733

ROBERSON, Scotty, Assistant Administrator and Chief Nursing Officer, Usa Health Children's & Women's Hospital, Mobile, AL, p. A22

ROBERT, Jeffery, Chief Operating Officer, Swedish/Issaquah, Issaquah, WA, p. A759

ROBERT, Thomas, Senior Vice President of Finance and Chief Financial Officer, Mercy Medical Center, Springfield, MA, p. A344

ROBERTS, Allyson, CPA, Chief Financial Officer, Nor-Lea Hospital District, Lovington, NM, p. A470

ROBERTS, Andrew, Interim Chief Human Resources Officer, Veterans Affairs Gulf Coast Veterans Health Care System, Biloxi, MS, p. A390

ROBERTS, Barbara, Chief Financial Officer, Robley Rex Veterans Affairs Medical Center, Louisville, KY, p. A288

ROBERTS, Bert, Controller, Miracle Mile Medical Center, Los Angeles, CA, p. A75

ROBERTS, Brad, Network Administrator, Swisher Memorial Healthcare System, Tulia, TX, p. A721

ROBERTS, Cassidi, Chief Nursing Officer, Medical City Mckinney, Mckinney, TX, p. A700

ROBERTS, Cathy, Vice President Mission Integration and Human Resources, Mercy Regional Medical Center, Durango, CO, p. A111

ROBERTS, Celene, Chief Human Resource Officer, Park City Hospital, Park City, UT, p. A730

ROBERTS, Charles, M.D., Executive Vice President and Executive Medical Director, Children's Mercy Hospital Kansas City, Kansas City, MO, p. A408

ROBERTS, Curt L., Market Chief Executive Officer, Cornerstone Specialty Hospitals Austin, Austin, TX, p. A655

ROBERTS, Cyndi, Director Human Resources, Medical City Fort Worth, Fort Worth, TX, p. A678

ROBERTS, David, M.D., Chief Medical Officer, Jackson-Madison County General Hospital, Jackson, TN, p. A639

ROBERTS, David J., M.D., President, North Shore Medical Center, Salem, MA, p. A344

ROBERTS, Deborah, R.N., Chief Nursing Officer, The Core Institute Specialty Hospital, Phoenix, AZ, p. A37

ROBERTS, Debra, Director of Human Resources, Chi St. Luke's Health-Lakeside Hospital, The Woodlands, TX, p. A720

ROBERTS, Jason, Director Information System, Carson Valley Medical Center, Gardnerville, NV, p. A442
Director of Information Services, Barton Memorial Hospital, South Lake Tahoe, CA, p. A99

ROBERTS, Jeff, Director Information Technology, Pinckneyville Community Hospital, Pinckneyville, IL, p. A217

ROBERTS, Kathryn, Director Human Resources, Mercyone Dubuque Medical Center, Dubuque, IA, p. A249

ROBERTS, Kenneth D., President, Mather Hospital, Port Jefferson, NY, p. A495

ROBERTS, Kevin A., FACHE, President and Chief Executive Officer, Adventhealth Central Texas, Killeen, TX, p. A693

ROBERTS, Kim, Chief Strategy Officer, Lucile Packard Children's Hospital Stanford, Palo Alto, CA, p. A84

ROBERTS, Krista, Chief Executive Officer, St. Mary's Regional Medical Center, Enid, OK, p. A559

ROBERTS, Laurel, R.N., MSN, Chief Operating Officer, Rolling Hills Hospital, Franklin, TN, p. A638

ROBERTS, Mark, Chief Operating Officer, Memorial Satilla Health, Waycross, GA, p. A183

ROBERTS, Matthew S., Chief Executive Officer, Raleigh General Hospital, Beckley, WV, p. A770

ROBERTS, Michael, Chief Technology Officer, Highlands Arh Regional Medical Center, Prestonsburg, KY, p. A292

ROBERTS, Nancy, Chief Operating Officer, Providence St. Vincent Medical Center, Portland, OR, p. A580

ROBERTS, Pamela W., Chief Executive Officer, Henderson County Community Hospital, Lexington, TN, p. A642

ROBERTS, Paul L., Director, Cheyenne Veterans Affairs Medical Center, Cheyenne, WY, p. A802

ROBERTS, Paula, Chief Nursing Officer, Cumberland Hospital For Children And Adolescents, New Kent, VA, p. A746

ROBERTS, Rob, Director Information Technology, Benson Hospital, Benson, AZ, p. A30

ROBERTS, Robert, Senior Vice President Financial Services, Baptist Health Medical Center - North Little Rock, North Little Rock, AR, p. A51
Senior Vice President Financial Services, Baptist Health Medical Center-Little Rock, Little Rock, AR, p. A49
Senior Vice President Financial Services, Baptist Health Rehabilitation Institute, Little Rock, AR, p. A49
Vice President and Chief Financial Officer, Baptist Health Medical Center-Arkadelphia, Arkadelphia, AR, p. A42

ROBERTS, Robin, R.N., Chief Nursing Officer, Greeneville Community Hospital West, Greeneville, TN, p. A638

ROBERTS, Ronald, M.D., Chief of Medical Staff, North Sunflower Medical Center, Ruleville, MS, p. A400

ROBERTS, Roslyn, Manager, Northside Hospital-Cherokee, Canton, GA, p. A168

ROBERTS, Shayna, Director Human Resources, Northeastern Health System Sequoyah, Sallisaw, OK, p. A567

ROBERTS, Teresa, Chief Financial Officer, Ringgold County Hospital, Mount Ayr, IA, p. A254

ROBERTSHAW, Hazel, R.N., Ph.D., Chief Nursing Officer, Vice President Patient Services, F. F. Thompson Hospital, Canandaigua, NY, p. A481

ROBERTSON, Carla, Chief Operating Officer and Chief Financial Officer, Saline Memorial Hospital, Benton, AR, p. A42

ROBERTSON, Darcy, Chief Financial Officer, Page Hospital, Page, AZ, p. A34

ROBERTSON, Elizabeth, Area Controller, Encompass Health Rehabilitation Hospital Of Dallas, Dallas, TX, p. A668

ROBERTSON, John L., Administrator, West Central Georgia Regional Hospital, Columbus, GA, p. A169

ROBERTSON, Larry, President, Texas Health Center For Diagnostic & Surgery, Plano, TX, p. A707

ROBERTSON, Laura, R.N., Chief Executive Officer, Banner Desert Medical Center, Mesa, AZ, p. A33

ROBERTSON, Michael, Chief Executive Officer, Piedmont Newnan Hospital, Newnan, GA, p. A178

ROBERTSON, Sara, Director of Human Resources, Mcdonough District Hospital, Mb, IL, p. A211

ROBERTSON, Steve, Executive Vice President and Chief Information Officer, Straub Medical Center, Honolulu, HI, p. A185

Executive Vice President Revenue Cycle Management and Chief Information Officer, Wilcox Medical Center, Lihue, HI, p. A186

Senior Vice President, Pali Momi Medical Center, Aiea, HI, p. A184

Vice President, Kapiolani Medical Center For Women & Children, Honolulu, HI, p. A184

ROBESON, Gail, Vice President Patient Services, Huron Regional Medical Center, Huron, SD, p. A629

ROBICHAUX, Andre', Administrator, Jennings Senior Care Hospital, Jennings, LA, p. A304

ROBICHAUX, Martha, Chief Human Resources Officer, John C. Fremont Healthcare District, Mariposa, CA, p. A77

ROBICHEAUX, Brian, Chief Information Officer, Peterson Health, Kerrville, TX, p. A693

ROBICHEAUX, James Warren., FACHE, Chief Executive Officer, Matagorda Regional Medical Center, Bay City, TX, p. A657

ROBINSON, Aaron, President and Chief Executive Officer, South County Hospital, Wakefield, RI, p. A614

ROBINSON, Adam M., Acting Director, Washington Dc Veterans Affairs Medical Center, Washington, DC, p. A130

Director, Veterans Affairs Maryland Health Care System-Baltimore Division, Baltimore, MD, p. A327

ROBINSON, Anthony, Manager, Human Resources, Mercy Hospital Of Folsom, Folsom, CA, p. A64

ROBINSON, Bradley, Chief Financial Officer, Evans U. S. Army Community Hospital, Fort Carson, CO, p. A112

ROBINSON, Cliff, M.D., Chief of Staff, Central Alabama Veterans Health Care System, Montgomery, AL, p. A22

ROBINSON, Dakota, Interim Chief Financial Officer and Controller, North Caddo Medical Center, Vivian, LA, p. A316

ROBINSON, David, D.O., Medical Director, St. Joseph's Behavioral Health Center, Stockton, CA, p. A100

President and Dental Staff, Community Hospital, Munster, IN, p. A237

ROBINSON, Elena, Chief Human Resources Officer, Hima San Pablo Caguas, Caguas, PR, p. A806

ROBINSON, Girard, M.D., Senior Vice President Medical and Clinical Affairs, Spring Harbor Hospital, Westbrook, ME, p. A323

ROBINSON, Herbert, M.D., Vice President, Chief Medical Information Officer, North Oaks Health System, North Oaks Rehabilitation Hospital, Hammond, LA, p. A302

ROBINSON, Jeanne, Director Human Resources, Inova Fair Oaks Hospital, Fairfax, VA, p. A741

ROBINSON, Jennifer, Administrator, Unity Psychiatric Care-Clarksville, Clarksville, TN, p. A636

Vice President Human Resources, St. Petersburg General Hospital, Saint Petersburg, FL, p. A156

ROBINSON, Mark, FACHE, Chief Executive Officer, St. Mark's Hospital, Salt Lake City, UT, p. A733

Associate Administrator and Chief Financial Officer, Hazel Hawkins Memorial Hospital, Hollister, CA, p. A68

ROBINSON, Mary, Chief Nursing Officer and Vice President Patient Care Services, Texas Health Harris Methodist Hospital Southwest Fort Worth, Fort Worth, TX, p. A679

ROBINSON, Phil, Chief Financial Officer, Saint Agnes Medical Center, Fresno, CA, p. A65

ROBINSON, Phillip D., President, Lankenau Medical Center, Wynnewood, PA, p. A612

ROBINSON, Raymond, Chief Executive Officer, Pembroke Hospital, Pembroke, MA, p. A343

ROBINSON, Ronald, M.D., FACHE, M.P.H., Chief Executive Officer and Chief Medical Officer, Rawlins County Health Center, Atwood, KS, p. A262

ROBINSON, Ronald R., M.D., FACHE, M.P.H., Chief Executive Officer and Chief Medical Officer, Rawlins County Health Center, Atwood, KS, p. A262

M.D., FACHE, M.P.H., Chief Executive Officer, Goodland Regional Medical Center, Goodland, KS, p. A265

ROBINSON, Stephen Jr, FACHE, Chief Executive Officer, Ochsner Medical Center - Kenner, Kenner, LA, p. A304

ROBINSON, Susan, Vice President Human Resources, St. Mary's Medical Center, Huntington, WV, p. A773

ROBINSON, Tim, Chief Executive Officer, Nationwide Children's Hospital, Columbus, OH, p. A536

ROBINSON, Trena, Director, Human Resources, Central Texas Rehabilitation Hospital, Austin, TX, p. A655

ROBINSON, Vance, Chief Information Officer, Iberia Medical Center, New Iberia, LA, p. A310

ROBINSON, William, Director Human Resources, Encompass Health Rehabilitation Hospital Of Erie, Erie, PA, p. A589

Senior Vice President and Chief Financial Officer, Uf Health Rehab Hospital, Gainesville, FL, p. A139

ROBINSON III, James L., PsyD, Hospital Administrator, Kaiser Westside Medical Center, Hillsboro, OR, p. A576

PsyD, Hospital Adminstrator, Kaiser Sunnyside Medical Center, Clackamas, OR, p. A574

ROBISON, Bruce, Vice President and Chief Information Officer, Cox Medical Centers, Springfield, MO, p. A418

ROBISON, John, Chief Executive Officer, Clifton T. Perkins Hospital Center, Jessup. MD, p. A330

ROBISON, Keith, Chief Information Officer, Upmc Chautauqua, Jamestown, NY, p. A486

ROBISON, Neely, Director Human Resources, The Bridgeway, North Little Rock, AR, p. A51

ROBISON, Rob, Director Information Technology, Medical Center Of South Arkansas, El Dorado, AR, p. A44

ROBISON, Ryan, Chief Nursing Officer, Sanpete Valley Hospital, Mount Pleasant, UT, p. A729

ROBISON, Wendell, M.D., Chief of Staff, Sheridan Veterans Affairs Medical Center, Sheridan, WY, p. A804

ROBL, Chris, Human Resources, Ellinwood District Hospital, Ellinwood, KS, p. A264

ROBLES, Burt, Vice President Information Services, Guthrie Robert Packer Hospital, Sayre, PA, p. A606

ROCHA, Israel Jr, Chief Executive Officer, Nyc Health + Hospitals / Elmhurst, Elmhurst, NY, p. A483

Jr, Chief Executive Officer, Nyc Health + Hospitals / Queens, Jamaica, NY, p. A486

ROCHA, Julie, Vice President Human Resources, Mercy Medical Center Merced, Merced, CA, p. A78

ROCHELEAU, John, Vice President Business Support and Information Technology, Bellin Hospital, Green Bay, WI, p. A785

ROCHER, Leslie, Senior Vice President and Chief Medical Officer, Beaumont Hospital - Royal Oak, Royal Oak, MI, p. A365

ROCHESTER, Charmaine, Vice President Finance, Bon Secours-Depaul Medical Center, Norfolk, VA, p. A747

ROCK, Betty, Vice President Nursing and Chief Nursing Officer, Uniontown Hospital, Uniontown, PA, p. A609

ROCK, Brian, Director of Information Systems, Vcu Health Community Memorial Hospital, South Hill, VA, p. A752

ROCK, David, Executive Vice President and Chief Operating Officer, Wyckoff Heights Medical Center, Brooklyn, NY, p. A479

ROCKWELL, Karla, Director of Nursing, Doctors Memorial Hospital, Bonifay, FL, p. A132

ROCKWOOD, John D., President, Medstar National Rehabilitation Hospital, Washington, DC, p. A130

ROCKWOOD, Sylvia, Director Human Resources, Upmc Carlisle, Carlisle, PA, p. A586

RODDEN, Celeste, Chief Information Officer, Hillcrest Hospital Claremore, Claremore, OK, p. A557

RODDY, Thomas, Chief Operating Officer, Saint Thomas Rutherford Hospital, Murfreesboro, TN, p. A646

RODEBUSH, Anthony, Chief Operating Officer, St. Mary's Regional Medical Center, Enid, OK, p. A559

RODEN, George, Vice President Human Resources, Mercy Hospital Aurora, Aurora, MO, p. A402

Vice President Human Resources, Mercy Hospital Cassville, Cassville, MO, p. A404

RODENBAUGH, Cathy, Director Human Resources, Holy Rosary Healthcare, Miles City, MT, p. A426

RODENBERGER, Wendy, Chief Nursing Officer and Vice President, Patient Services, Mary Rutan Hospital, Bellefontaine, OH, p. A529

RODENFELS, Cheryl, System Vice President, IT Operations, Amita Health Saints Mary & Elizabeth Medical Center, Chicago, IL, p. A198

RODER, Darla, Chief Operating Officer, Cavalier County Memorial Hospital And Clinics, Langdon, ND, p. A524

RODERICK, Travis W., Chief Executive Officer, Premier Surgical Institute, Galena, KS, p. A264

RODEWALD, Amanda, Interim Chief Financial Officer, Daviess Community Hospital, Washington, IN, p. A242

RODGE, Mark, Director Information Systems, Eaton Rapids Medical Center, Eaton Rapids, MI, p. A354

RODGERS, April, Vice President, Human Resources, Holy Name Medical Center, Teaneck, NJ, p. A464

RODGERS, Dondie, Interim Chief Nursing Officer, Memorial Hospital Of Texas County, Guymon, OK, p. A560

RODGERS, Jamie, Chief Executive Officer, Choctaw Regional Medical Center, Ackerman, MS, p. A389

RODGERS, Larry, Chief Executive Officer, Kindred Hospital-Albuquerque, Albuquerque, NM, p. A467

RODIS, John F., M.D., President, Saint Francis Hospital And Medical Center, Hartford, CT, p. A122

RODOWICZ, Darlene, Chief Financial Officer, Berkshire Medical Center, Pittsfield, MA, p. A343

RODRIGUES, Pablo, M.D., Medical Director, Vibra Hospital Of Amarillo, Amarillo, TX, p. A652

RODRIGUEZ, Alex, Vice President and Chief Information Officer, St. Elizabeth Edgewood, Edgewood, KY, p. A282

Vice President and Chief Information Officer, St. Elizabeth Florence, Florence, KY, p. A283

Vice President and Chief Information Officer, St. Elizabeth Fort Thomas, Fort Thomas, KY, p. A283

RODRIGUEZ, Asha, Vice President and Facility Executive, Atrium Health Cabarrus, Concord, NC, p. A508

RODRIGUEZ, Betsy, Vice President Human Resources, Barnes-Jewish Hospital, Saint Louis, MO, p. A415

RODRIGUEZ, Candie, Director Human Resources, Hospital San Cristobal, Coto Laurel, PR, p. A807

RODRIGUEZ, Edgardo, Director Management Information Systems, Auxilio Mutuo Hospital, San Juan, PR, p. A809

RODRIGUEZ, Heather, Chief Nursing Officer, Fresno Heart And Surgical Hospital, Fresno, CA, p. A65

RODRIGUEZ, Jaime, Chief Financial Officer, San Juan City Hospital, San Juan, PR, p. A811

RODRIGUEZ, Jose, M.D., Medical Director, Castaner General Hospital, Castaner, PR, p. A807

RODRIGUEZ, Jose Luis., Chief Executive Officer, Hospital Pavia-Santurce, San Juan, PR, p. A810

RODRIGUEZ, Joshua, Chief Executive Officer, Windmoor Healthcare Of Clearwater, Clearwater, FL, p. A134

RODRIGUEZ, Laura, Director Medical Records, Hospital Del Maestro, San Juan, PR, p. A810

RODRIGUEZ, Leticia, Chief Executive Officer, Ward Memorial Hospital, Monahans, TX, p. A702

RODRIGUEZ, Lizzette, Director Finance, Hospital San Francisco, San Juan, PR, p. A810

RODRIGUEZ, Marco, Chief Financial Officer, Valley Baptist Medical Center-Harlingen, Harlingen, TX, p. A683

RODRIGUEZ, Maritza, Chief Financial Officer, Hospital Metropolitan, San Juan, PR, p. A810

RODRIGUEZ, Miguel, Medical Director, Caribbean Medical Center, Fajardo, PR, p. A807

RODRIGUEZ, Onel, Chief Financial Officer, Broward Health Coral Springs, Coral Springs, FL, p. A135

RODRIGUEZ, Oscar, Chief Fiscal Officer, Veterans Affairs Caribbean Healthcare System, San Juan, PR, p. A811

RODRIGUEZ, Patricia M., Senior Vice President and Area Manager, Kaiser Permanente South Sacramento Medical Center, Sacramento, CA, p. A89

RODRIGUEZ, Ramon J., President and Chief Executive Officer, Wyckoff Heights Medical Center, Brooklyn, NY, p. A479

RODRIGUEZ, Rufus, M.D., Medical Director, Mayo Clinic Health System In Fairmont, Fairmont, MN, p. A376

RODRIGUEZ, Sara, Chief Financial Officer, Kindred Hospital Sugar Land, Sugar Land, TX, p. A717

Human Resources, Ascension Seton Smithville, Smithville, TX, p. A716

RODRIGUEZ, Tammy, Vice President Patient Care Services, Adventhealth Central Texas, Killeen, TX, p. A693

RODRIGUEZ, Tomas, Chief Information Technology Officer, First Hospital Panamericano, Cidra, PR, p. A807

RODRIGUEZ, Tony, Director Human Resources, South Texas Rehabilitation Hospital, Brownsville, TX, p. A661

RODRIGUEZ, Vilma, Director Human Resources, Hospital San Pablo Del Este, Fajardo, PR, p. A807

RODRIGUEZ, Wilfredo, M.D., Chief of Staff, Battle Creek Veterans Affairs Medical Center, Battle Creek, MI, p. A349

RODRIGUEZ, Yelitza Sanchez., Executive Director, Metropolitano De La Montana, Utuado, PR, p. A811

RODRIGUEZ COLLAZO, Jose Luis, Executive Director, Hospital Pavia Arecibo, Arecibo, PR, p. A806

RODRIGUEZ SCHMIDT, Myriam, Director Human Resources, Cardiovascular Center Of Puerto Rico And The Caribbean, San Juan, PR, p. A809

RODRIQUEZ, Daisy, Director Human Resources, Fort Duncan Regional Medical Center, Eagle Pass, TX, p. A673

RODRIQUEZ, Monica, Director of Human Resources, Stewart & Lynda Resnick Neuropsychiatric Hospital At Ucla, Los Angeles, CA, p. A76

ROE, Daniel M., Chief Operating Officer, Copper Queen Community Hospital, Bisbee, AZ, p. A30

ROE, Timothy J., M.D., President and Chief Executive Officer, Rehabilitation Hospital Of The Pacific, Honolulu, HI, p. A185

ROEBACK, Jason, Chief Operating Officer, Ahn Grove City, Grove City, PA, p. A591

Chief Operating Officer, Saint Vincent Hospital, Erie, PA, p. A590

ROEBKEN, Curtis, M.D., Chief Medical Staff, Kentfield Hospital, Kentfield, CA, p. A69

ROEBUCK, Amanda, Chief Executive Officer, Genoa Medical Facilities, Genoa, NE, p. A432

ROEDEL, Megan, Chief Operating Officer, Center For Behavioral Medicine, Kansas City, MO, p. A408

ROEDER, Donna, Chief Financial Officer, Jackson County Regional Health Center, Maquoketa, IA, p. A253

ROEDERER, Chris, Senior Vice President Human Resources, Tamp. General Hospital, Tampa, FL, p. A160

ROEHR, Richard, Chief Executive Officer, Amita Health Mercy Medical Center, Aurora, IL, p. A195

Chief Operating Officer, Amita Health Adventist Medical Center Bolingbrook, Bolingbrook, IL, p. A196

Vice President and Chief Operating Officer, Amita Health Adventist Medical Center Glenoaks, Glendale Heights, IL, p. A206

ROEHRLE, Andreas, Director Finance, Sentara Williamsburg Regional Medical Center, Williamsburg, VA, p. A753

ROESER, William, Interim President and Chief Executive Officer, Sparrow Carson Hospital, Carson City, MI, p. A350

President and Chief Executive Officer, Sparrow Ionia Hospital, Ionia, MI, p. A358

ROESLER, Bruce E., FACHE, Chief Executive Officer, Richland Hospital, Richland Center, WI, p. A795

ROETMAN, James D., President and Chief Executive Officer, Pocahontas Community Hospital, Pocahontas, IA, p. A256

ROEVER, Judy, MSN, R.N., Chief Nursing Officer, Scenic Mountain Medical Center, Big Spring, TX, p. A659

ROFFELSEN, Michael S., Chief Executive Officer, Encompass Health Rehabilitation Hospital Of Sunrise, Sunrise, FL, p. A158

ROGALSKI, Robert, President, Sharon Regional Medical Center, Sharon, PA, p. A608

ROGALSKI, Ted, Administrator, Genesis Medical Center-Aledo, Aledo, IL, p. A194

ROGAN, Edie, Manager Human Resources, Eastern State Hospital, Williamsburg, VA, p. A753

ROGAN, James, M.D., Chief Medical Officer, Perry County Memorial Hospital, Tell City, IN, p. A241

ROGERS, Aaron, Chief Executive Officer, Trinity Hospital, Weaverville, CA, p. A104

ROGERS, B. Carter, Chief of Staff, Piedmont Newton Hospital, Covington, GA, p. A170

ROGERS, Bryan R., Group Chief Executive Officer, Placentia-Linda Hospital, Placentia, CA, p. A85

ROGERS, Carrie, Chief Nursing Officer, Southern Tennessee Regional Health System-Lawrenceburg, Lawrenceburg, TN, p. A642

ROGERS, Cathy, Manager Human Resources, Prisma Health Laurens County Hospital, Clinton, SC, p. A617

ROGERS, David, Chief Executive Officer, Ortonville Area Health Services, Ortonville, MN, p. A382

ROGERS, Doris, Vice President Human Resources, Saint Luke's Hospital Of Kansas City, Kansas City, MO, p. A409

ROGERS, Eric, Chief Information Officer, Hebrew Rehabilitation Center, Roslindale, MA, p. A344

ROGERS, Gregory H., President, Midmichigan Medical Center-Midland, Midland, MI, p. A361

ROGERS, James H., FACHE, Chief Executive Officer, Cornerstone Hospital Of Little Rock, Little Rock, AR, p. A49

ROGERS, Jared, M.D., President and Chief Executive Officer, Osf Heart Of Mary Medical Center, Urbana, IL, p. A222

M.D., President and Chief Executive Officer, Osf Sacred Heart Medical Center, Danville, IL, p. A202

ROGERS, Jeremy, Chief Financial Officer, St. Francis Medical Center, Monroe, LA, p. A309

Chief Human Resource Officer, Orem Community Hospital, Orem, UT, p. A730

ROGERS, Jerry, R.N., Director Nurses and Infection Control, Specialty Hospital, Monroe, LA, p. A309

ROGERS, Joseph, Vice President and Chief Operating Officer, Redwood Memorial Hospital, Fortuna, CA, p. A64

ROGERS, Kathy, Vice President Marketing, San Luis Valley Health Conejos County Hospital, La Jara, CO, p. A115

ROGERS, LaDonna, Executive Vice President Human Resources, T. J. Samson Community Hospital, Glasgow, KY, p. A284

ROGERS, Lucy, Chief Information Resource Management Systems, Veterans Affairs North Texas Health Care System, Dallas, TX, p. A671

ROGERS, Mark, Interim Vice President Finance and Chief Financial Officer, Genesis Medical Center - Davenport, Davenport, IA, p. A247

Interim Vice President Finance and Chief Financial Officer, Genesis Medical Center, Silvis, Silvis, IL, p. A220

Vice President, Finance and Chief Financial Officer, Genesis Medical Center-Aledo, Aledo, IL, p. A194

ROGERS, Matt, Chief Financial Officer, Wellspan Philhaven, Mount Gretna, PA, p. A597

ROGERS, Patricia, Director of Nursing, Dahl Memorial Healthcare Association, Ekalaka, MT, p. A423

ROGERS, Randy, FACHE, Chief Executive Officer, Garden Park Medical Center, Gulfport, MS, p. A393

ROGERS, Rich, Vice President Information Services, Prisma Health Greenville Memorial Hospital, Greenville, SC, p. A620

ROGERS, Richard, M.D., Chief Medical Officer, Saint Thomas Rutherford Hospital, Murfreesboro, TN, p. A646

ROGERS, Robert, M.D., Medical Director, Canton-Potsdam Hospital, Potsdam, NY, p. A495

ROGERS, Seth, Chief Executive Officer, Encompass Health Rehabilitation Hospital Of Modesto, Modesto, CA, p. A78

Controller, Encompass Health Rehabilitation Hospital Of Modesto, Modesto, CA, p. A78

ROGERS, Sherry, MS, R.N., Chief Nursing Officer, Redington-Fairview General Hospital, Skowhegan, ME, p. A323

ROGERS, Tammy, Director Human Resources, Mt. San Rafael Hospital, Trinidad, CO, p. A119

ROGERS, Valerie, Director of Nursing, Cherokee Nation W.W. Hastings Indian Hospital, Tahlequah, OK, p. A569

ROGERS, William, Chief Medical Officer, North Mississipp. Medical Center Gilmore-Amory, Amory, MS, p. A389

ROGOLS, Kevin L., FACHE, Administrator, Kalkaska Memorial Health Center, Kalkaska, MI, p. A359

ROGOZ, Brian, Vice President Finance and Treasurer, The Hospital Of Central Connecticut, New Britain, CT, p. A123

ROHAN, Colleen, Director Human Resources, Osf Healthcare Little Company Of Mary Medical Center, Evergreen Park, IL, p. A204

ROHLEDER, Scott, Chief Information Officer, Hays Medical Center, Hays, KS, p. A265

ROHMAN, Ryan, MSN, R.N., Chief Operating Officer, Uchealth Medical Center Of The Rockies, Loveland, CO, p. A117

MSN, R.N., Chief Operating Officer, Uchealth Poudre Valley Hospital, Fort Collins, CO, p. A112

ROHRBACH, Dan D., President, Southwest Health, Platteville, WI, p. A794

ROHRBACK, Allen, Chief Executive Officer, Madison Valley Medical Center, Ennis, MT, p. A423

ROHRBACK, Jenny, Director Human Resource, Ruby Valley Medical Center, Sheridan, MT, p. A428

ROHRER, Harry, Chief Financial Officer, University Of Miami Hospital And Clinics, Miami, FL, p. A147

ROHRER, John J., Director, William S. Middleton Memorial Veterans Hospital, Madison, WI, p. A788

ROHRICH, George A., FACHE, Chief Executive Officer, Lake Chelan Community Hospital And Clinics, Chelan, WA, p. A756

ROIZ, JoAnn, Director Human Resources, Encompass Health Rehabilitation Hospital Of Tustin, Tustin, CA, p. A102

ROJAS, Curtis, Interim Chief Financial Officer, Connally Memorial Medical Center, Floresville, TX, p. A677

ROKER, Christopher, Chief Executive Officer, Nyc Health + Hospitals / Metropolitan, New York, NY, p. A491

ROKOSZ, Gregory, D.O., Senior Vice President Medical and Academic Affairs, Saint Barnabas Medical Center, Livingston, NJ, p. A457

ROLAND, Brian, Chief Executive Officer, Muenster Memorial Hospital, Muenster, TX, p. A702

ROLAND, John, R.N., Chief Operating Officer and Chief Nursing Officer, Bleckley Memorial Hospital, Cochran, GA, p. A169

ROLDAN, Lanyce, Chief Nursing Officer, Penn Medicine Lancaster General Hospital, Lancaster, PA, p. A594

ROLEK, Jim, Chief Human Resources Officer, Vice President, Clara Maass Medical Center, Belleville, NJ, p. A452

ROLEY, Margaret, Chief Nursing Officer, South Baldwin Regional Medical Center, Foley, AL, p. A18

ROLFE, David, Chief Information Officer, Madonna Rehabilitation Hospital, Lincoln, NE, p. A434

ROLFF, Christi, Director Business Development, San Joaquin Valley Rehabilitation Hospital, Fresno, CA, p. A66

ROLING, Robin, FACHE, MS, R.N., Chief Operating Officer, Cheyenne Regional Medical Center, Cheyenne, WY, p. A801

ROLLI, Molli, M.D., Medical Director, Mendota Mental Health Institute, Madison, WI, p. A787

ROLLING, Andy, Director of Finance, Regina Hospital, Hastings, MN, p. A378

ROLLINS, James, Chief Financial Officer, Arbour-Fuller Hospital, Attleboro, MA, p. A334

ROLLINS, Larry, Supervisor Information Technology, Mccamey County Hospital District, Mccamey, TX, p. A700

ROLLINS, Skip. Chief Information Officer, Freeman Health System, Joplin, MO, p. A408

ROMAN, Jody, Chief Human Resource Officer, Hillside Rehabilitation Hospital, Warren, OH, p. A551

ROMAN, Linda, Administrator, Coast Plaza Hospital, Norwalk, CA, p. A81

ROMAN, Marina, M.D., Medical Director, Hospital De La Universidad De Puerto Rico/Dr. Federico Trilla, Carolina, PR, p. A807

ROMANELLO, Marcus, Chief Medical Officer, Fort Hamilton Hospital, Hamilton, OH, p. A542

ROMANIA, Matt, Director of Nursing, Upmc Wellsboro, Wellsboro, PA, p. A610

ROMANICK, Odile, Chief information Officer, Day Kimball Hospital, Putnam, CT, p. A124

ROMANIELLO, Guy, Director Fiscal Services, Belmont Behavioral Hospital, Philadelphia, PA, p. A599

ROMANO, C., M.D., Chief Medical Officer, St. Francis Medical Center, Trenton, NJ, p. A464

ROMANO, Jean, Chief Nursing Officer, Good Shepherd Penn Partners Specialty Hospital At Rittenhouse, Philadelphia, PA, p. A600

ROMANO, Sara, R.N., Vice President, Mountain View Hospital, Gadsden, AL, p. A19

ROMANOWSKI, Ellen, Chief Nursing Officer, Encompass Health Rehabilitation Hospital Of Miami, Cutler Bay, FL, p. A135

ROMANS, Alan, Director Information Technology, Ashland Health Center, Ashland, KS, p. A261

ROMEO, John, Chief Information Officer, Mercy Hospital And Medical Center, Chicago, IL, p. A199

ROMERO, Brenda, Hospital Chief, Presbyterian Espanola Hospital, Espanola, NM, p. A469

ROMERO, Edward, Chief Financial Officer, Rehabilitation Hospital Of Fort Wayne, Fort Wayne, IN, p. A228

ROMERO, Frank, M.D., Chief Medical Officer, Cox Medical Centers, Springfield, MO, p. A418

M.D., Vice President Medical Affairs and Chief Medical Officer, Cox Monett Hospital, Monett, MO, p. A412

ROMERO, Matt, Chief Financial Officer, Oak Hill Hospital, Brooksville, FL, p. A133

ROMIG, Glenn, Chief Financial Officer, Largo Medical Center, Largo, FL, p. A143

ROMINE, Andrew, Chief Executive Officer, Rockledge Regional Medical Center, Rockledge, FL, p. A155

ROMITO, Edmund, Chief Information Officer, Genesis Healthcare System, Zanesville, OH, p. A554

ROMO, Dianna, Director, Human Resources, Emanuel Medical Center, Turlock, CA, p. A102

ROMUALDO, Heather, Chief Information Officer, Intermountain Medical Center, Murray, UT, p. A729

RONAN, Barry P., President and Chief Executive Officer, Western Maryland Regional Medical Center, Cumberland, MD, p. A329

RONAN, John, President, Northern Light Blue Hill Hospital, Blue Hill, ME, p. A319

President, Northern Light Maine Coast Hospital, Ellsworth, ME, p. A320

RONCA, Cyndi, Director Human Resources, Twin Cities Hospital, Niceville, FL, p. A149

RONDE, Christa, Assistant Chief Financial Officer, Palo Verde Hospital, Blythe, CA, p. A58

RONKE, Lisa, Director Finance, St. Michael's Hospital Avera, Tyndall, SD, p. A632

RONNISCH, Kim, Vice President Nursing and Chief Nursing Officer, Ascension Macomb-Oakland Hospital, Warren, MI, p. A368

ROOD, Mandy, Vice President Human Resources, Sparrow Eaton Hospital, Charlotte, MI, p. A351

ROODMAN, Richard D., Chief Executive Officer, Uw Medicine/Valley Medical Center, Renton, WA, p. A763

ROOF, Marie, Executive Vice President Information Systems, Vibra Specialty Hospital Of Portland, Portland, OR, p. A580

ROOKER, Mark, Chief Executive Officer, Hillsboro Community Hospital, Hillsboro, KS, p. A266

ROONERY, Nicole, Chief Nursing Officer, Ivinson Memorial Hospital, Laramie, WY, p. A803

ROONEY, Al, Director Information Systems, St. Vincent Healthcare, Billings, MT, p. A421

ROONEY, David, Administrator Operations, Winneshiek Medical Center, Decorah, IA, p. A248

ROONEY, Thomas, Chief Information Resource Management, Veterans Affairs Hudson Valley Health Care System, Montrose, NY, p. A488

ROOP, Terri, Director Patient Care Services, Dickenson Community Hospital, Clintwood, VA, p. A740

ROOS, Joel A., Commanding Officer, Naval Medical Center San Diego, San Diego, CA, p. A91

ROOSA, Carol, Vice President Information Services and Chief Information Officer, Athol Hospital, Athol, MA, p. A334

ROOSE, Robert, M.D., Chief Medical Officer, Mercy Medical Center, Springfield, MA, p. A344

ROOT, Jim, Vice President Human Resources, Saint Elizabeth's Medical Center, Wabasha, MN, p. A387

ROOT, Rodney, D.O., Vice President Medical Affairs, Bakersfield Memorial Hospital, Bakersfield, CA, p. A57

ROPER, Anne, Chief Executive Officer, Fairlawn Rehabilitation Hospital, Worcester, MA, p. A346

ROPER, Sandra, Chief Human Resources, General Leonard Wood Army Community Hospital, Fort Leonard Wood, MO, p. A406

ROQUE, John, MSN, R.N., Chief Nursing Officer, Medical Center Of Aurora, Aurora, CO, p. A107

MSN, R.N., Chief Nursing Officer, Spalding Rehabilitation Hospital, Aurora, CO, p. A107

ROQUE, Lee Ann, Director of Human Resources, Spartanburg Medical Center - Mary Black, Spartanburg, SC, p. A624

RORRER, Michael, M.D., Chief of Medical Staff, Carilion Tazewell Community Hospital, Tazewell, VA, p. A752

ROSA-TOLEDO, Luis, M.D., Medical Director, Hospital Manati Medical Center, Manati, PR, p. A808

ROSAAEN, Nancy, Chief Executive Officer, Mccone County Health Center, Circle, MT, p. A422

ROSADO, Jose S., Executive Director, Hospital Manati Medical Center, Manati, PR, p. A808

ROSALES, Alvina, R.N., Chief Nursing Officer, Tuba City Regional Health Care Corporation, Tuba City, AZ, p. A39

ROSAS, Efren, M.D., Physician in Chief, Kaiser Permanente San Jose Medical Center, San Jose, CA, p. A94

ROSATI, Rosemarie, Chief Operating Officer, Rutgers University Behavioral Healthcare, Piscataway, NJ, p. A461

ROSBOROUGH, Brian, M.D., Chief Medical Officer, Osf Saint Elizabeth Medical Center, Ottawa, IL, p. A216

ROSCHMANN, Al, M.D., Chief of Staff, Peterson Health, Kerrville, TX, p. A693

ROSE, Cheryl, Human Resources Director, Fulton County Medical Center, Mc Connellsburg, PA, p. A596

ROSE, Hugh, Vice President Fiscal Management, Palos Health, Palos Heights, IL, p. A216

ROSE, Julia, R.N., Director of Nursing, Braxton County Memorial Hospital, Gassaway, WV, p. A772

ROSE, Kim, Chief Information Technology, Crouse Health, Syracuse, NY, p. A499

ROSE, Laura, Chief Financial Officer, Ascension St. Vincent Anderson, Anderson, IN, p. A223

ROSE, Mary, R.N., Chief Clinical Officer, Promedica Coldwater Regional Hospital, Coldwater, MI, p. A351
Chief Nursing Officer, Promedica Coldwater Regional Hospital, Coldwater, MI, p. A351

ROSE, May, Director Human Resources, Memorial Hospital, Chester, IL, p. A197

ROSE, Michael S., President and Chief Executive Officer, Southern New Hampshire Medical Center, Nashua, NH, p. A450

ROSE, Michaell, Chief Operating Officer, St. Joseph's Medical Center, Stockton, CA, p. A100

ROSE, Richard, Associate Director, Manchester Veterans Affairs Medical Center, Manchester, NH, p. A450

ROSE, Robin, R.N., Chief Operating and Clinical Officer, Gibson Area Hospital And Health Services, Gibson City, IL, p. A206
Director of Human Resources, Greene County General Hospital, Linton, IN, p. A235

ROSE, Susan, Chief Executive Officer, Aurora Santa Rosa Hospital, Santa Rosa, CA, p. A98

ROSE, Taylor, Administrator, Big Sky Medical Center, Big Sky, MT, p. A421

ROSELLO, Patricia M., Chief Executive Officer, Baptist Health South Florida, Baptist Hospital Of Miami, Miami, FL, p. A146

ROSEMORE, Michael, M.D., Medical Director, Encompass Health Lakeshore Rehabilitation Hospital, Birmingham, AL, p. A15

ROSEN, Barry, M.D., Vice President Medical Management, Advocate Good Shepherd Hospital, Barrington, IL, p. A195

ROSEN, Jules, M.D., Chief Medical Officer, West Springs Hospital, Grand Junction, CO, p. A113

ROSEN, Michael, M.D., Chief Medical Officer, Havasu Regional Medical Center, Lake Havasu City, AZ, p. A33

ROSEN, Raymond, FACHE, Vice President Operations, Wellspan York Hospital, York, PA, p. A612

ROSENA, Robens, Director Information Systems, Delray Medical Center, Delray Beach, FL, p. A136

ROSENBALM, Jennifer, Manager Business Office, Veterans Affairs Nebraska-Western Iowa Health Care System, Omaha, NE, p. A438

ROSENBAUM, Victor, Chief Operating Officer, Alaska Regional Hospital, Anchorage, AK, p. A27

ROSENBERG, Andrew, M.D., Chief Information Officer, Michigan Medicine, Ann Arbor, MI, p. A348

ROSENBERG, Julie, Administrator, Essentia Health-Graceville, Graceville, MN, p. A377

ROSENBERG, Patricia, R.N., MSN, Chief Nursing Officer, Palm Beach Gardens Medical Center, Palm Beach Gardens, FL, p. A152
R.N., MSN, Chief Nursing Officer, Touro Infirmary, New Orleans, LA, p. A311

ROSENBERG, Steven, Chief Financial Officer, Danbury Hospital, Danbury, CT, p. A121

ROSENBERG, Stuart E., President, Johnson Memorial Hospital, Stafford Springs, CT, p. A125

ROSENBERGER, Robert, Chief Financial Officer, Heritage Valley Health System, Beaver, PA, p. A584

Chief Financial Officer, Sewickley Valley Hospital, (A Division Of Valley Medical Facilities), Sewickley, PA, p. A608

ROSENBLOOM, Mark, M.D., Vice President of Medical Affairs, Health First Holmes Regional Medical Center, Melbourne, FL, p. A145

ROSENBURG, Deborah, Vice President Human Resources, Chesapeake Regional Medical Center, Chesapeake, VA, p. A740

ROSENBURG, Jeffrey, Chief Medical Officer, Sierra Nevada Memorial Hospital, Grass Valley, CA, p. A67

ROSENCRANCE, Daris, Chief Financial Officer, Stonewall Jackson Memorial Hospital, Weston, WV, p. A777

ROSENCRANCE, Gregory, Chief Executive Officer, Cleveland Clinic Indian River Hospital, Vero Beach, FL, p. A161

ROSENDAHL, Lisa, Director Human Resources, St. Cloud Veterans Affairs Health Care System, Saint Cloud, MN, p. A384

ROSENFELD, Merryll, Vice President, Human Resources, Catholic Medical Center, Manchester, NH, p. A450

ROSENFELD, Paul, Acting Chief Executive Officer, Kingsbrook Jewish Medical Center, Brooklyn, NY, p. A478
Chief Operating Officer, Kingsbrook Jewish Medical Center, Brooklyn, NY, p. A478

ROSENSTEIN, Gaynor, Vice President Operations, Bon Secours Community Hospital, Port Jervis, NY, p. A495

ROSENTHAL, Benjamin, Information Systems Director, South Sunflower County Hospital, Indianola, MS, p. A394

ROSENTHAL, Raul, M.D., Interim Chief of Staff, Cleveland Clinic Florida, Weston, FL, p. A162

ROSEQUIST, Helen, Manager Information Systems, Warren General Hospital, Warren, PA, p. A609

ROSETTA, Kathy, Chief Nursing Officer, Laurel Ridge Treatment Center, San Antonio, TX, p. A712

ROSHAN, Payman, Chief Operating Officer, Kaiser Permanente Baldwin Park Medical Center, Baldwin Park, CA, p. A57
Senior Vice President and Area Manager, Kaiser Permanente Panorama City Medical Center, Panorama City, CA, p. A84

ROSHETKO, Chet, Chief Nursing Officer, Eastern State Hospital, Medical Lake, WA, p. A760

ROSILES, Nancy, Director Human Resources, Encompass Health Rehabilitation Hospital Of Arlington, Arlington, TX, p. A653

ROSKE, Jeff, D.O., Chief Medical Staff, Community Memorial Hospital, Sumner, IA, p. A259

ROSKOS, Tom, Chief Executive Officer, Edgewood Surgical Hospital, Transfer, PA, p. A609

ROSLER, Andrea, Vice President Human Resources, Huntsville Hospital, Huntsville, AL, p. A20

ROSS, Adia, Chief Medical Officer, Duke Regional Hospital, Durham, NC, p. A508

ROSS, Chad, Chief Operating Officer, Mary Rutan Hospital, Bellefontaine, OH, p. A529

ROSS, Charles, M.D., Vice President Medical Affairs, Chilton Medical Center, Pompton Plains, NJ, p. A462

ROSS, Christopher, Chief Information Technology Officer, Mayo Clinic Hospital - Rochester, Rochester, MN, p. A384

ROSS, Darrell, Chief Nursing Officer, Dequincy Memorial Hospital, Dequincy, LA, p. A301

ROSS, Denzil, Chief Operating Officer, Lovelace Medical Center, Albuquerque, NM, p. A467
Interim Chief Executive Officer, Lovelace Medical Center, Albuquerque, NM, p. A467

ROSS, Douglas B., M.D., President, Chi St. Vincent Hot Springs, Hot Springs, AR, p. A47

ROSS, Hoyt, Chief Executive Officer, Promise Hospital Of Florida At The Villages, Oxford, FL, p. A152

ROSS, Jacqueline, Chief Human Resources Officer, Mann-Grandstaff Veterans Affairs Medical Center, Spokane, WA, p. A765

ROSS, Jay, Chief Financial Officer, Chi St. Joseph's Health, Park Rapids, MN, p. A382
Vice President of Finance, Chi Lakewood Health, Baudette, MN, p. A372

ROSS, Jeffrey, M.D., Chief Medical Officer, King's Daughters Medical Center, Brookhaven, MS, p. A390
M.D., Medical Director, Amg Specialty Hospital-Albuquerque, Albuquerque, NM, p. A467

ROSS, John, Vice President, Franciscan Health Mooresville, Mooresville, IN, p. A237

ROSS, Johnny, Executive Medical Director, Encompass Health Rehabilitation Hospital Of Austin, Austin, TX, p. A656

ROSS, Kevin, M.D., Chief of Medical Staff, Frances Mahon Deaconess Hospital, Glasgow, MT, p. A424

ROSS, Laurie, Chief Nursing Officer, Southampton Memorial Hospital, Franklin, VA, p. A742

ROSS, Mychelle, R.N., Chief Nursing Officer, Cherokee Medical Center, Gaffney, SC, p. A620

ROSS, Phil, Chief Executive Officer, Surgical Hospital Of Oklahoma, Oklahoma City, OK, p. A566

ROSS, Randall W., FACHE, President and Chief Executive Officer, Mercy Hospital Of Folsom, Folsom, CA, p. A64

ROSS, Robert, Chief Operating Officer, Medstar Washington Hospital Center, Washington, DC, p. A130

ROSS, Shana, Vice President Human Resources, Bayhealth Medical Center, Dover, DE, p. A127

ROSS, Yolanda, Director Human Resources, Millwood Hospital, Arlington, TX, p. A653

ROSS-COLE, Melissa, Director Human Resources, Regency Hospital Of Northwest Arkansas - Springdale, Springdale, AR, p. A53

ROSS-SPANG, Carol, Chief Human Resources Officer, Methodist Healthcare Memphis Hospitals, Memphis, TN, p. A644

ROSSI, Alfred N., M.D., Chief Executive Officer, Hopedale Medical Complex, Hopedale, IL, p. A208

ROSSI, Coleen, Director Quality Services, Encompass Health Rehabilitation Hospital Of Toms River, Toms River, NJ, p. A464

ROSSI, Lawrence, M.D., Clinical Director, Trenton Psychiatric Hospital, Trenton, NJ, p. A464

ROSSI, Mark, Chief Operating Officer and General Counsel, Hopedale Medical Complex, Hopedale, IL, p. A208

ROSSMANN, Barbara W., R.N., President and Chief Executive Officer, Henry Ford Macomb Hospitals, Clinton Township. MI, p. A351

ROSSMANN, Samuel H., Chief Executive Officer, Top. Surgical Specialty Hospital, Houston, TX, p. A689

ROSVOLD, Robert, Director Finance, Virtua Voorhees, Voorhees, NJ, p. A465

ROTENBERRY-BAGGETT, Katie, Administrative Assistant and Human Resources, Yalobusha General Hospital, Water Valley, MS, p. A401

ROTERT, Angela, Chief Clinical Officer, Kindred Hospital-Indianapolis, Indianapolis, IN, p. A232

ROTGER, Lindsey, Chief Nursing Officer, West Tennessee Rehabilitation Hospital Cane Creek, Martin, TN, p. A643

ROTH, Anna M., R.N., MS, M.P.H., Chief Executive Officer, Contra Costa Regional Medical Center, Martinez, CA, p. A77

ROTH, Chad, Director Information Services, Prairie View, Newton, KS, p. A272

ROTH, Dan, M.D., Vice President Medical Affairs, Mercy Health - Anderson Hospital, Cincinnati, OH, p. A532

ROTH, Diane, Chief Financial Officer, Piedmont Rockdale Hospital, Conyers, GA, p. A170

ROTH, Eugene, Vice President Information Services, Mercy Hospital St. Louis, Saint Louis, MO, p. A416

ROTH, Mark, Chief Financial Officer, Mountain Valley Regional Rehabilitation Hospital, Prescott Valley, AZ, p. A37

ROTH, Norman G., President, Greenwich Hospital, Greenwich, CT, p. A122

ROTH, Randy, Chief Medical Officer, Singing River Health System, Pascagoula, MS, p. A398

ROTH-MALLEK, Nancy, Vice President of Finance, Aspirus Riverview Hospital And Clinics, Inc., Wisconsin Rapids, WI, p. A800

ROTHBERG, Kathryn, Director Human Resources, Evergreenhealth Monroe, Monroe, WA, p. A760

ROTHBERGER, Richard, Corporate Executive Vice President and Chief Financial Officer, Scripp. Green Hospital, La Jolla, CA, p. A69

ROTHENBERGER, David, Chief Financial Officer, Summit Healthcare Regional Medical Center, Show Low, AZ, p. A38

ROTHERMICH, Anthony, Administrator, Mercy Hospital Lincoln, Troy, MO, p. A419

ROTHERMICH, Michael, M.D., Chief of Staff, Hermann Area District Hospital, Hermann, MO, p. A407

ROTHFIELD, Kenneth, M.D., Chief Medical Officer, Medical City Dallas, Dallas, TX, p. A669

ROTHMAN, Marc, M.D., Medical Director, Friends Hospital, Philadelphia, PA, p. A600

ROTHSCHILD, Marylee, M.D., Chief of Staff, Robley Rex Veterans Affairs Medical Center, Louisville, KY, p. A288

ROTSTED, Scott T., Chief Executive Officer, California Rehabilitation Institute, Los Angeles, CA, p. A73

ROTTINGHAUS, David, M.D., Director, Butler Health System, Butler, PA, p. A585

ROTY, Christopher, President, Baptist Health Paducah, Paducah, KY, p. A291

ROUGH, Vicki, Chief Nursing Officer, Highlands Hospital, Connellsville, PA, p. A587

ROUILLARD, Smita, M.D., Physician in Chief, Kaiser Permanente Fresno Medical Center, Fresno, CA, p. A65

ROULEAU, Greg, Vice President Nursing, Mercy Medical Center Merced, Merced, CA, p. A78

ROUND, Laurie, MS, R.N., Vice President and Chief Nursing Officer, Bromenn Medical Center, Normal, IL, p. A214

ROUNDS, Jason, FACHE, President, Christus St. Michael Health System, Texarkana, TX, p. A719

---

ROUNDY, Ann, Vice President of Employee and Support Services, Prairie Ridge Health, Inc., Columbus, WI, p. A782

ROUNSLEY, Joan, Director Human Resources, Geisinger Jersey Shore Hospital, Jersey Shore, PA, p. A593

ROUNSLEY, Karen, Controller, Encompass Health Rehabilitation Hospital Of Salisbury, Salisbury, MD, p. A332

ROUSSE, Michael, M.D., Chief Medical Officer, Northeastern Vermont Regional Hospital, Saint Johnsbury, VT, p. A736

ROUSSEAU, Mickie, Director Human Resources, Terrebonne General Medical Center, Houma, LA, p. A303

ROUSSEL, Steve, Chief Financial Officer, Baylor Scott & White Medical Center At - Mckinney, Mckinney, TX, p. A700

Vice President Finance, Baylor Scott & White Medical Center-Irving, Irving, TX, p. A690

ROUTH, Lori, R.N., Nurse Administrator, Mayo Clinic Health System - Albert Lea And Austin, Albert Lea, MN, p. A371

ROUX, Roger, Chief Financial Officer, Rady Children's Hospital - San Diego, San Diego, CA, p. A91

ROUZER, Cindy, Director Human Resources, Spooner Health, Spooner, WI, p. A796

ROVITO, Kevin, Chief Financial Officer, Jackson Hospital, Marianna, FL, p. A145

ROW, Tracy, Manager Business Office, Fredonia Regional Hospital, Fredonia, KS, p. A264

ROW, Tyler, Director Information Technology, Fredonia Regional Hospital, Fredonia, KS, p. A264

ROWAN, Cary, Chief Financial Officer, Astria Sunnyside Hospital, Sunnyside, WA, p. A766

ROWAN, Mark, Interim Chief Information Officer, Rome Memorial Hospital, Rome, NY, p. A497

ROWAN, R, Director Human Resources, Neosho Memorial Regional Medical Center, Chanute, KS, p. A262

ROWE, Chad, Human Resource Director, Aspirus Keweenaw Hospital, Inc., Laurium, MI, p. A360

ROWE, Jeanne, M.D., Chief Medical Officer, Shore Medical Center, Somers Point, NJ, p. A463

ROWE, Melissa S., Chief Executive Officer, Grover C. Dils Medical Center, Caliente, NV, p. A441

ROWE, Paul, Director Information Technology, St. Francis Hospital, Wilmington, DE, p. A128

ROWE, Richard M., PharmD, Chief Executive Officer, Garden Grove Hospital And Medical Center, Garden Grove, CA, p. A66

PharmD, Chief Executive Officer, Huntington Beach Hospital, Huntington Beach, CA, p. A68

ROWE, Scott, Chief Executive Officer, Encompass Health Rehabilitation Hospital Of Chattanooga, Chattanooga, TN, p. A635

ROWE, Wilma, M.D., Senior Vice President Medical Affairs, Mercy Medical Center, Baltimore, MD, p. A325

ROWELL, Becky, R.N., Director, Allendale County Hospital, Fairfax, SC, p. A619

ROWELL, Julie, R.N., Chief Nursing Officer, Thomas Hospital, Fairhope, AL, p. A18

ROWELL, Roberta, President, Uh Regional Hospitals, Cleveland, OH, p. A535

ROWEN, Lisa, R.N., Chief Nursing Officer, University Of Maryland Medical Center Midtown Campus, Baltimore, MD, p. A326

R.N., Senior Vice President and Chief Nursing Officer, University Of Maryland Medical Center, Baltimore, MD, p. A326

ROWLAND, Claire, Director Human Resources, Vermilion Behavioral Health Systems - North Campus, Lafayette, LA, p. A306

ROWLAND, Gerald, M.D., Chief Medical Officer, Cedar City Hospital, Cedar City, UT, p. A727

ROWLAND, Michael, M.D., Vice President Medical Affairs, Franklin Memorial Hospital, Farmington, ME, p. A320

ROWLAND, Nick, Chief Executive Officer, Pushmataha Hospital, Antlers, OK, p. A555

Chief Operating Officer, Pushmataha Hospital, Antlers, OK, p. A555

Interim Chief Executive Officer, Choctaw Memorial Hospital, Hugo, OK, p. A560

ROWLAND, Robert, M.D., Medical Director, Encompass Health Rehabilitation Hospital Of Tallahassee, Tallahassee, FL, p. A158

ROWLAND, Ruby, Strategic Partner, Highlands-Cashiers Hospital, Highlands, NC, p. A512

ROWLAND, Ted, Chief of Medical Staff, Atoka County Medical Center, Atoka, OK, p. A556

ROWLANDS, Dewey, Vice President and Chief Financial Officer, Rome Memorial Hospital, Rome, NY, p. A497

ROWLEY, Charla, Chief Financial Officer, Southwest Mississipp. Regional Medical Center, Mccomb, MS, p. A396

ROWLEY, Mike, Chief Executive Officer, Springbrook Behavioral Health, Travelers Rest, SC, p. A625

ROY, Ashley, Vice President of Nursing Services, Specialty Hospital Of Meridian, Meridian, MS, p. A397

ROY, Jennifer, R.N., Chief Nursing Officer, Carondelet St. Mary's Hospital, Tucson, AZ, p. A40

ROY, Linda, R.N., Chief Nursing Officer, Walter B. Jones Alcohol And Drug Abuse Treatment Center, Greenville, NC, p. A511

ROY, Rock, Professional Services Director, Power County Hospital District, American Falls, ID, p. A188

ROY, Schindelheim, M.D., Chief of Staff, Mee Memorial Hospital, King City, CA, p. A69

ROYAL, Keli, Chief Human Resources Officer, Shenandoah Medical Center, Shenandoah, IA, p. A257

ROYAL, Shawanna, R.N., Director Nursing, Strategic Behavioral Health - Raleigh, Garner, NC, p. A510

ROYAL, Ty, Executive Director of Human Resources and Support Services, Gibson Area Hospital And Health Services, Gibson City, IL, p. A206

ROYE, G., M.D., Senior Vice President of Medical Affairs and Chief Medical Officer, Miriam Hospital, Providence, RI, p. A613

ROYNE, Sharon, Senior Vice President: Human Resources, St. Anne Hospital, Burien, WA, p. A756

ROYSTER, Kirsten, President and Chief Operating Officer, Novant Health Medical Park Hospital, Winston, NC, p. A520

ROZELL, Becky, Vice President, Human Resources, Madison Health, London, OH, p. A543

ROZENBOOM, Steve, Chief Financial Officer, Holy Cross Hospital, Taos, NM, p. A473

ROZENFELD, Jon, President, Ssm Health St. Mary's Hospital, Madison, WI, p. A788

ROZIER, Derek, Chief Financial Officer, Liberty Regional Medical Center, Hinesville, GA, p. A174

ROZNOVSKY, Karen, Director Human Resources, Yoakum Community Hospital, Yoakum, TX, p. A726

RUBANO, Kathleen, MSN, R.N., Chief Nursing Officer, Corpus Christi Medical Center, Corpus Christi, TX, p. A666

RUBE, David, M.D., Clinical Director, New York City Children's Center, Jamaica, NY, p. A486

RUBEN, Wanda, R.N., Chief Nursing Officer, Garden Grove Hospital And Medical Center, Garden Grove, CA, p. A66

RUBENS, Deborah, Director Human Resources, Shriners Hospitals For Children-Northern California, Sacramento, CA, p. A89

RUBERG, Greg, FACHE, President and Chief Executive Officer, Lake View Hospital, Two Harbors, MN, p. A386

RUBERTE, Henry, Administrator, Hospital San Gerardo, San Juan, PR, p. A810

RUBERTI, Charlene, Director Information Technology Development, Ancora Psychiatric Hospital, Hammonton, NJ, p. A456

RUBIN, Nancy, Vice President Human Resources, Motion Picture And Television Fund Hospital And Residential Services, Woodland Hills, CA, p. A105

RUBIN, Randy, Senior Vice President and Chief Financial Officer, Mercyone Des Moines Medical Center, Des Moines, IA, p. A248

RUBIN, Vincent, Chief Financial Officer, Southern California Hospital At Culver City, Culver City, CA, p. A62

RUBINATE, Donna, R.N., Chief Operating Officer, Good Samaritan Medical Center, Brockton, MA, p. A337

RUBINO, Mark, M.D., Chief Medical Officer, Forbes Hospital, Monroeville, PA, p. A597

M.D., President, Forbes Hospital, Monroeville, PA, p. A597

RUBINSTEIN, Mitchell, M.D., Chief Medical Officer, St. Petersburg General Hospital, Saint Petersburg, FL, p. A156

RUBIO, Felipe, M.D., Medical Director, Kindred Hospital-Dayton, Dayton, OH, p. A538

RUBLE, Justin, Director Human Resources, Jefferson Medical Center, Ranson, WV, p. A776

Director, Human Resources, Berkeley Medical Center, Martinsburg, WV, p. A774

RUBY, Blaine, M.D., Chief of Staff, Johnson County Healthcare Center, Buffalo, WY, p. A801

RUCH, Jordan, Vice President and Chief Information Officer, Robert Wood Johnson University Hospital Somerset, Somerville, NJ, p. A463

RUCHTI, Robert D., Chief Executive Officer, Buchanan General Hospital, Grundy, VA, p. A743

RUCKER, Alisa, Vice President Finance and Chief Financial Officer, Washington Hospital, Washington, PA, p. A610

RUCKER, Genifer, President, Christus Spohn Hospital Beeville, Beeville, TX, p. A659

RUCKER, Jodi, MSN, R.N., Vice President Patient Care Services and Chief Nursing Officer, Promedica Memorial Hospital, Fremont, OH, p. A540

RUCKER, Rick, Chief Operating Officer, Highland Hospital, Charleston, WV, p. A771

RUDBERG, Susan, M.D., Chief Medical Officer, Fairview Range Medical Center, Hibbing, MN, p. A378

RUDD, Adam, Chief Executive Officer, Largo Medical Center, Largo, FL, p. A143

RUDD, Barry, Chief Information Officer, Memorial Satilla Health, Waycross, GA, p. A183

RUDD, Jedd, Director of Ancillary Services and Safety, Mad River Community Hospital, Arcata, CA, p. A56

RUDD, Taylor, Chief Operating Officer, St. Josep. Regional Medical Center, Lewiston, ID, p. A191

RUDDEN, Elizabeth, Vice President Human Resources, Connecticut Children's Medical Center, Hartford, CT, p. A122

RUDE, Erik G., Commander, William Beaumont Army Medical Center, El Paso, TX, p. A676

RUDEK, Charles, Chief Information Officer, Upmc Jameson, New Castle, PA, p. A598

Chief Information Officer, Upmc St. Margaret, Pittsburgh, PA, p. A604

RUDITZ, Bettiann, MS, R.N., Chief Nursing Officer, Broward Health North, Deerfield Beach, FL, p. A136

RUDLOFF, Roger, M.D., President Medical Staff, Antelop. Memorial Hospital, Neligh, NE, p. A435

RUDOLPH, Dawn, President, Sacred Heart Hospital Pensacola, Pensacola, FL, p. A154

RUDQUIST, Debra, FACHE, President and Chief Executive Officer, Amery Hospital And Clinic, Amery, WI, p. A779

RUDZIK, Carrie, Chief Administrative Officer, Eastern State Hospital, Lexington, KY, p. A286

RUDZIK, Donna, Director Human Resources, Christus Mother Frances Hospital - Sulphur Springs, Sulphur Springs, TX, p. A718

RUE, Loring, M.D., Senior Vice President, Quality Patient Safety and Clinical Effectiveness, University Of Alabama Hospital, Birmingham, AL, p. A16

RUE, Robert, Chief Financial Officer, Ellenville Regional Hospital, Ellenville, NY, p. A483

RUECKERT, Sebastian, M.D., Chief Medical Officer, Christian Hospital, Saint Louis, MO, p. A415

M.D., Vice President and Chief Medical Officer, Alton Memorial Hospital, Alton, IL, p. A194

RUEDISUELI, Amy, Vice President of Finance, Mckenzie Health System, Sandusky, MI, p. A366

RUELLO, Rocky, Vice President Human Resources, Mercy Hospital St. Louis, Saint Louis, MO, p. A416

RUFF, Robin, Chief Financial Officer, Uchealth Pikes Peak Regional Hospital, Woodland Park, CO, p. A120

RUFF, Victoria, M.D., Medical Director, Select Specialty Hospital-Columbus, Columbus, OH, p. A537

RUFFIN, Janet, R.N., Chief Nursing Officer, Temecula Valley Hospital, Temecula, CA, p. A100

RUFFIN, Marshall, Chief Information Officer, Inova Fair Oaks Hospital, Fairfax, VA, p. A741

RUFFING, Cindy, Director Human Resources, Siloam Springs Regional Hospital, Siloam Springs, AR, p. A53

RUFFOLO, Josep. A., President and Chief Executive Officer, Niagara Falls Memorial Medical Center, Niagara Falls, NY, p. A493

RUGGIERO, Joanne, Interim Chief Nursing Officer, Pennsylvania Hospital, Philadelphia, PA, p. A601

RUGGIERO, Taren, R.N., MSN, Vice President and Chief Nursing Officer, Holy Cross Hospital, Fort Lauderdale, FL, p. A137

RUIZ, Irene, Area Human Resources Director, Kaiser Permanente Fontana Medical Center, Fontana, CA, p. A64

RUIZ, Javier, M.D., Medical Director, Intracare North Hospital, Houston, TX, p. A686

RUIZ, Kathleen, M.D., Associate Director Patient Care Services, Veterans Affairs Caribbean Healthcare System, San Juan, PR, p. A811

RUIZ, Patricia, R.N., Chief Nursing Officer, Nyc Health + Hospitals / Coney Island, Brooklyn, NY, p. A478

RUIZ, Tony, Senior Vice President, Chief Operating Officer, Medical Center Health System, Odessa, TX, p. A703

RULAND, Jyl, Chief Financial Officer, Clearwater Valley Hospital And Clinics, Orofino, ID, p. A192

Chief Financial Officer, St. Mary's Hospital, Cottonwood, ID, p. A190

RULE, Jonathan, Chief Hospital Executive, Integris Health Edmond, Edmond, OK, p. A558

RULLI, Sheila, Director Human Resources, Kidspeace Children's Hospital, Orefield, PA, p. A599

RUMMEL, Jennifer, Director Human Resources, Freestone Medical Center, Fairfield, TX, p. A677

Director Human Resources, Ut Health Athens, Athens, TX, p. A654

RUMPH, Jerald W., Chief Executive Officer, Mercy Rehabilitation Hospital St. Louis, Chesterfield, MO, p. A404

RUNKLE, Thomas, MS, Ph.D., Chief Operating Officer, St. Christopher's Hospital For Children, Philadelphia, PA, p. A602

RUNNELS, Clay, Vice President Chief Medical Officer Washington County, Johnson City Medical Center, Johnson City, TN, p. A640

RUNYAN, Mark, Director Information Services, Salt Lake Regional Medical Center, Salt Lake City, UT, p. A732
Director Information Systems, Jordan Valley Medical Center West Valley Campus, West Valley City, UT, p. A734

RUNYON, Annette, Vice President and Administrator, Medical Center At Franklin, Franklin, KY, p. A283

RUNYON, Mark, Chief Financial Officer, Tamp. General Hospital, Tampa, FL, p. A160

RUPA, Maitra, M.D., Acting Medical Director, Chester Mental Health Center, Chester, IL, p. A197

RUPERT, Duke, Chief Operating Officer, Allegheny General Hospital, Pittsburgh, PA, p. A602

RUPERT, James, Chief Fiscal Services, Battle Creek Veterans Affairs Medical Center, Battle Creek, MI, p. A349

RUPERT, Michael, Chief Financial Officer, Va Long Beach Healthcare System, Long Beach, CA, p. A73

RUPP, Connie, MSN, R.N., Executive Vice President and Chief Nursing Officer, Regional West Medical Center, Scottsbluff, NE, p. A439

RUPP, Robert, Chief Executive Officer, Ennis Regional Medical Center, Ennis, TX, p. A677
Chief Executive Officer, Parkview Regional Hospital, Mexia, TX, p. A701

RUPPERT, Jennifer, Chief Financial Officer, Iowa City Va Health Care System, Iowa City, IA, p. A252

RUPPERT SCHILLER, Kerri, Senior Vice President and Chief Financial Officer, Children's Hospital Of Orange County, Orange, CA, p. A83
Senior Vice President and Chief Financial Officer, Choc Children's At Mission Hospital, Mission Viejo, CA, p. A78

RUSCH, Brett, M.D., Acting Director, White River Junction Veterans Affairs Medical Center, White River Junction, VT, p. A737

RUSH, Andrew G., President, Upmc Somerset, Somerset, PA, p. A608

RUSH, Ann, Chief Financial Officer, Penobscot Valley Hospital, Lincoln, ME, p. A321

RUSH, Cindy, Director Human Resources, Clay County Medical Center, Clay Center, KS, p. A262

RUSH, Jeff, Chief Financial Officer, Rutherford Regional Health System, Rutherfordton, NC, p. A517

RUSH, Matthew, FACHE, President and Chief Executive Officer, Sparrow Eaton Hospital, Charlotte, MI, p. A351

RUSHIN, Denise, Director Human Resources, Poplar Bluff Regional Medical Center, Poplar Bluff, MO, p. A414

RUSHING, R Lynn., Chief Executive Officer, Brook Lane Health Services, Hagerstown, MD, p. A330

RUSHING, Randy, Chief Financial Officer, Massac Memorial Hospital, Metropolis, IL, p. A212

RUSHLOW, David, Vice President Medical Affairs, Mayo Clinic Health System - Franciscan Healthcare In La Crosse, La Crosse, WI, p. A787

RUSK, Scott, M.D., Chief Medical Officer, St. Josep. Hospital Orange, Orange, CA, p. A83

RUSNACZYK, John, Senior Vice President and Chief Financial Officer, St. Vincent Charity Medical Center, Cleveland, OH, p. A535

RUSNAK, Greg, Executive Vice President and Chief Operating Officer, Prisma Health Greenville Memorial Hospital, Greenville, SC, p. A620

RUSS, Nicole, Director Colleague Relations, Alliance Community Hospital, Alliance, OH, p. A527

RUSSELL, Bill, Senior Chief Information Officer, Mission Hospital Mission Viejo, Mission Viejo, CA, p. A78

RUSSELL, Brant, R.N., Chief Operating Officer, Ascension St. John Hospital, Detroit, MI, p. A352

RUSSELL, Dardanella, Chief Human Resources Management Service, Veterans Affairs Hudson Valley Health Care System, Montrose, NY, p. A488

RUSSELL, Donald, AMITA Health Senior Vice President and Chief Human Resources Officer, Amita Health Adventist Medical Center Glenoaks, Glendale Heights, IL, p. A206
Senior Vice President and Chief Human Resources Officer, Amita Health Elk Grove Village, Elk Grove Village, IL, p. A204
Senior Vice President and Chief Human Resources Officer, Amita Health Hoffman Estates, Hoffman Estates, IL, p. A208

RUSSELL, Erin, Controller, Kindred Hospital-San Antonio, San Antonio, TX, p. A711

RUSSELL, Freda, R.N., Chief Executive Officer and Chief Nursing Officer, Three Rivers Hospital, Waverly, TN, p. A650

RUSSELL, Georgette, Vice President of Talent & Organizational Effectiveness, Sparrow Carson Hospital, Carson City, MI, p. A350

RUSSELL, John D., President and Chief Executive Officer, Prairie Ridge Health, Inc., Columbus, WI, p. A782

RUSSELL, Jon, Senior Vice President & Chief Information Officer, John Muir Medical Center, Walnut Creek, Walnut Creek, CA, p. A104

Senior Vice President and Chief Information Officer, John Muir Medical Center, Concord, Concord, CA, p. A61

RUSSELL, Karen, Director of Employee Relations, Osf Saint Elizabeth Medical Center, Ottawa, IL, p. A216

RUSSELL, Kathy, R.N., Chief Nursing Officer, Bluegrass Community Hospital, Versailles, KY, p. A294

RUSSELL, Kendrick, Chief Human Resources Officer, Abrazo Scottsdale Campus, Phoenix, AZ, p. A35

RUSSELL, Kimberly, Chief Nursing Officer, Mercy Hospital Booneville, Booneville, AR, p. A43

RUSSELL, Laurie, Director Human Resources, Lea Regional Medical Center, Hobbs, NM, p. A470

RUSSELL, Linda, Vice President and Chief Nursing Officer, Self Regional Healthcare, Greenwood, SC, p. A621

RUSSELL, Patti, Vice President Nursing, Masonicare Health Center, Wallingford, CT, p. A126

RUSSELL, Ricky, Chief Human Resource Officer, Carondelet St. Mary's Hospital, Tucson, AZ, p. A40

RUSSELL, Robert, Associate Executive Director Operations, Penn Presbyterian Medical Center, Philadelphia, PA, p. A601

RUSSELL, Shelia, Director Human Resources, Jamestown Regional Medical Center, Jamestown, TN, p. A640

RUSSELL, Shelly, Chief Executive Officer, Mitchell County Regional Health Center, Osage, IA, p. A255

RUSSELL, Sherrie, AMITA Health Senior Vice President and Chief Information Officer, Amita Health Adventist Medical Center Glenoaks, Glendale Heights, IL, p. A206
Senior Vice President & Chief Information Officer, Amita Health Elk Grove Village, Elk Grove Village, IL, p. A204
Senior Vice President and Chief Information Officer, Amita Health Hoffman Estates, Hoffman Estates, IL, p. A208
Vice President and Chief Information Officer, Amita Health Alexian Brothers Behavioral Health Hospital, Hoffman Estates, IL, p. A208

RUSSELL, Susan, Chief Financial Officer, Och Regional Medical Center, Starkville, MS, p. A400
Chief Nursing Officer, Singing River Health System, Pascagoula, MS, p. A398

RUSSELL-JENKINS, Shane, M.D., Medical Director, Windhaven Psychiatric Hospital, Prescott Valley, AZ, p. A37

RUSSO, Arthur, M.D., Director Medical Affairs, Harrington Hospital, Southbridge, MA, p. A344

RUSSO, Kimberly, Chief Executive Officer, George Washington University Hospital, Washington, DC, p. A129

RUSSO, Mike, Vice President Information Systems, Chi St. Josep. Health Grimes Hospital, Navasota, TX, p. A703

RUSSO, Paul M., FACHE, Director, Bay Pines Veterans Affairs Healthcare System, Bay Pines, FL, p. A131

RUST, Jeff, Information Technology Systems Site Manager, Chi St. Alexius Health - Williston Medical Center, Williston, ND, p. A526

RUST, Steve, Director, Human Resources, Scripp. Memorial Hospital-Encinitas, Encinitas, CA, p. A63

RUTH, Daniel R., President and Chief Executive Officer, Jewish Home Of San Francisco, San Francisco, CA, p. A93

RUTH, Ed, President, Mercy Allen Hospital, Oberlin, OH, p. A547

RUTH, Joseph, Executive Vice President and Chief Operating Officer, Sparrow Hospital, Lansing, MI, p. A360

RUTHERFORD, Eddie, Director of Pharmacy, Tyler Holmes Memorial Hospital, Winona, MS, p. A401

RUTHERFORD, Jeremiah, Chief Medical Officer, Cornerstone Hospital Of Oklahoma-Muskogee, Muskogee, OK, p. A562

RUTHERFORD, Peter, M.D., Chief Executive Officer, Confluence Health/Central Washington Hospital, Wenatchee, WA, p. A768
M.D., Chief Executive Officer, Confluence Health/ Wenatchee Valley Hospital, Wenatchee, WA, p. A768

RUTHERFORD, Ronald, Chief Information Officer, Beth Israel Deaconess Hospital Plymouth, Plymouth, MA, p. A343

RUTHERFORD, Theresa, R.N., MS, FACHE, President and Chief Executive Officer, Hshs St. Anthony's Memorial Hospital, Effingham, IL, p. A203

RUTHS, Steve, M.D., Chief Medical Officer, Vista Del Mar Hospital, Ventura, CA, p. A103

RUTKOWSKI, Jennifer, R.N., MSN, Vice President Professional Services, Grant Regional Health Center, Lancaster, WI, p. A787

RUTKOWSKI, Jim, Chief Financial Officer, United Hospital Center, Bridgeport, WV, p. A770

RUTLEDGE, Debra, R.N., Vice President Nursing Services, Chi Health Plainview, Plainview, NE, p. A439

RUTLEDGE, Rebel, Director Human Resources, Grady Memorial Hospital, Chickasha, OK, p. A557

RUWOLDT, Steven, Chief Operating Officer, Memorial Medical Center, Las Cruces, NM, p. A470

RUZICK, Laura E., Medical Center Director, Richard L. Roudebush Veterans Affairs Medical Center, Indianapolis, IN, p. A233

RYAN, Chris, Chief Information Officer, Auburn Community Hospital, Auburn, NY, p. A475

RYAN, Christie, Chief Nursing Officer, Encompass Health Rehabilitation Hospital Of Sewickley, Sewickley, PA, p. A607

RYAN, Christina, R.N., Chief Executive Officer and Chief Nursing Officer, The Women's Hospital, Newburgh, IN, p. A238

RYAN, Christina M., R.N., Chief Executive Officer, The Women's Hospital, Newburgh, IN, p. A238

RYAN, Connie, Chief Nursing Officer, Select Specialty Hospital-Tulsa Midtown, Tulsa, OK, p. A570

RYAN, David, Vice President Human Resources, Melrosewakefield Healthcare, Melrose, MA, p. A341

RYAN, Debora, R.N., Vice President Patient Care, St. Francis Regional Medical Center, Shakopee, MN, p. A386

RYAN, Dennis, Senior Vice President and Chief Financial Officer, Children's Hospital Of The King's Daughters, Norfolk, VA, p. A747

RYAN, Emily, Chief Executive Officer, Medical Behavioral Hospital Of Mishawaka, Knox, IN, p. A234

RYAN, Frank, Chief Financial Officer, Manchester Veterans Affairs Medical Center, Manchester, NH, p. A450

RYAN, Jeffrey, Chief Operating Officer, Cancer Treatment Centers Of America-Eastern Regional Medical Center, Philadelphia, PA, p. A599
Senior Vice President, Finance and Business Development, Cancer Treatment Centers Of America-Eastern Regional Medical Center, Philadelphia, PA, p. A599

RYAN, John, M.D., Chief Medical Officer, Surgeons Choice Medical Center, Southfield, MI, p. A367

RYAN, Lisa, Coordinator Human Resources, Hampstead Hospital, Hampstead, NH, p. A449

RYAN, Maria, Ph.D., Chief Executive Officer, Cottage Hospital, Woodsville, NH, p. A451

RYAN, Mike, Director of Information Services, Gunnison Valley Hospital, Gunnison, UT, p. A728

RYAN, Patrice, Vice President Human Resources, Goleta Valley Cottage Hospital, Santa Barbara, CA, p. A96
Vice President Human Resources, Santa Barbara Cottage Hospital, Santa Barbara, CA, p. A97
Vice President Human Resources, Santa Ynez Valley Cottage Hospital, Solvang, CA, p. A99

RYAN, Patricia, Chief Executive Officer, Eden Medical Center, Castro Valley, CA, p. A59

RYAN, Patrick, Chief Human Resources Officer, Helen Hayes Hospital, West Haverstraw, NY, p. A502

RYAN, Patrick G., Chief Executive Officer, Promise Hospital Of Fort Myers, Fort Myers, FL, p. A138

RYAN, Rebecca, Interim Director Human Resources and Employee Health, Adventist Health Ukiah Valley, Ukiah, CA, p. A102

RYAN, Robert, M.D., Chief Medical Officer, Guadalup. Regional Medical Center, Seguin, TX, p. A714

RYAN, Sharon, Regional Controller, Select Specialty Hospital-Macomb County, Mount Clemens, MI, p. A362

RYAN, Tim, Chief Financial Officer, Centennial Peaks Hospital, Louisville, CO, p. A116

RYAN, William, Vice President and Chief Financial Officer, Uf Health Jacksonville, Jacksonville, FL, p. A142

RYBA, Janice L., JD, Chief Executive Officer, St. Mary Medical Center, Hobart, IN, p. A230

RYBA, Thomas L., Chief Executive Officer, Lighthouse Behavioral Health Hospital, Conway, SC, p. A618

RYBA, Tomi S., President and Chief Executive Officer, Regional Medical Center Of San Jose, San Jose, CA, p. A95

RYBICKI, Cathy, Chief Operating Officer, Spectrum Health Reed City Hospital, Reed City, MI, p. A364

RYBOLT, Andrew, Chief Financial Officer, El Paso Children's Hospital, El Paso, TX, p. A674

RYCKMAN, George, D.O., Chief of Staff, Paul Oliver Memorial Hospital, Frankfort, MI, p. A355

RYDER, Doug, President, Holy Cross Germantown Hospital, Germantown, MD, p. A329

RYDER, Jeff, Director Information Systems, Saint Josep. Mount Sterling, Mount Sterling, KY, p. A290

RYDER, Ronald, D.O., President of the Medical Staff, Robert Wood Johnson University Hospital At Hamilton, Hamilton, NJ, p. A456

RYERSE, David, Chief Executive Officer, Stillwater Billings Clinic, Columbus, MT, p. A422

RYKOWSKI, Margaret A., Acting Chief Executive Officer, Laguna Honda Hospital And Rehabilitation Center, San Francisco, CA, p. A93

RYLAND, Jennifer, R.N., Chief Administrative Officer, Jackson Medical Center, Jackson, AL, p. A20

RYLAND, Jennifer M., R.N., Chief Executive Officer, Jackson Medical Center, Jackson, AL, p. A20

RYLAND, Steven, Interim Chief Executive Officer, Hillside Rehabilitation Hospital, Warren, OH, p. A551

RYLE, Barry, Chief Information Officer, Oswego Hospital, Oswego, NY, p. A494

RYMER, Brandy, Coordinator Human Resources, Adventhealth Murray, Chatsworth, GA, p. A168

RYON, Joel, M.D., Chief of Staff, Henry County Health Center, Mount Pleasant, IA, p. A254

RYS, Jan, R.N., Chief Executive Officer, Straith Hospital For Special Surgery, Southfield, MI, p. A367

RYSTROM, Jennifer, R.N., Chief Nursing Officer, West Holt Medical Services, Atkinson, NE, p. A429

RZOMP, Kimberly, Vice President and Chief Financial Officer, Wellspan Chambersburg Hospital, Chambersburg, PA, p. A586

Vice President Finance, Wellspan Waynesboro Hospital, Waynesboro, PA, p. A610

# S

SAAD, Michael, Vice President and Chief Information Officer, University Of Tennessee Medical Center, Knoxville, TN, p. A641

SAADAT, Annette, Human Resources Business Partner, Saint Josep. Mount Sterling, Mount Sterling, KY, p. A290

SAALFELD, Thomas, Senior Vice President and Chief Operating Officer, St. Elizabeth Fort Thomas, Fort Thomas, KY, p. A283

SAARI, Heidi, Director, Human Resources, Upper Connecticut Valley Hospital, Colebrook, NH, p. A448

SAAVEDRA, JayLynn, Chief Information Officer, U. S. Public Health Service Indian Hospital, Parker, AZ, p. A34

SABANDIT, Elizabeth, Director Human Resources, Alhambra Hospital Medical Center, Alhambra, CA, p. A55

SABBAGHIAN, Bahman, M.D., Chief Medical Officer, Acadia General Hospital, Crowley, LA, p. A300

SABELLA, Deborah, R.N., Chief Executive Officer, Landmark Hospital Of Cap. Girardeau, Cap. Girardeau, MO, p. A403

SABHARRWAL, Parajeet, Chief Executive Officer, Minimally Invasive Surgery Hospital, Lenexa, KS, p. A269

SABIA, John, M.D., Vice President Medical Affairs, Northern Dutchess Hospital, Rhinebeck, NY, p. A496

SABOTTA, John, Director Information Systems, St. Margaret's Hospital, Spring Valley, IL, p. A220

SABUS, Matt, Chief Information Officer, St. Francis Memorial Hospital, West Point, NE, p. A440

SACHARSKI, Steve, Chief Financial Officer, Havenwyck Hospital, Auburn Hills, MI, p. A349

SACHDEV, Aruna, M.D., Medical Director, Pappas Rehabilitation Hospital For Children, Canton, MA, p. A338

SACHDEV, Vish, M.D., Chief Medical Officer, Brookwood Baptist Medical Center, Birmingham, AL, p. A14

SACHDEVA, Sandeep. M.D., Vice President Medical Affairs, Swedish/Edmonds, Edmonds, WA, p. A757

SACHS, Henry, M.D., IIIMedical Director, Emma Pendleton Bradley Hospital, East Providence, RI, p. A613

SACHTJEN, Mistie, Chief Executive Officer, Community Memorial Hospital, Burke, SD, p. A626

SACHTLEBEN, Michael, President, Medstar Georgetown University Hospital, Washington, DC, p. A129

SACKETT, John, President SGMC and Executive Vice President and Chief Operating Officer, Adventist Healthcare Shady Grove Medical Center, Rockville, MD, p. A332

SACKETT, Walter, President, Sycamore Medical Center, Miamisburg, OH, p. A545

SACKMANN, Charles, M.D., Chief of Staff, East Adams Rural Healthcare, Ritzville, WA, p. A763

SADA, Judy, Chief Financial Officer, Memorial Hospital Miramar, Miramar, FL, p. A148

SADDORIS, Debbie, Vice President Human Resources, Sarah Bush Lincoln Health Center, Mattoon, IL, p. A211

SADLER, Cindy, Chief Nursing Officer, Iron County Medical Center, Pilot Knob, MO, p. A413

SADLER, Donna, Director Human Resources, Arkansas State Hospital, Little Rock, AR, p. A48

SADLER, Joy, Director Human Resources, Bear River Valley Hospital, Tremonton, UT, p. A734

SADLER BELL, Kelli, R.N., Vice President, Chief Nursing Officer, Novant Health Charlotte Orthopaedic Hospital, Charlotte, NC, p. A507

R.N., Vice President, Chief Nursing Officer, Novant Health Presbyterian Medical Center, Charlotte, NC, p. A507

SADOFF, Jennifer, Chief Executive Officer, Moab Regional Hospital, Moab, UT, p. A729

SADR, Farrokh, M.D., Chief Medical Officer, St. Luke's Sacred Heart Campus, Allentown, PA, p. A583

SADRO, Cheryl, Executive Vice President Chief Business and Finance Officer, University Of Texas Medical Branch, Galveston, TX, p. A680

SAELEE, Sheba, Chief Clinical Office and Chief Operating Officer, Vibra Hospital Of Northern California, Redding, CA, p. A87

SAENZ, Luis, M.D., Medical Director, Hospital Menonita De Cayey, Cayey, PR, p. A807

SAENZ, Melanie, Regional Human Resources Officer, Amita Health Saints Mary & Elizabeth Medical Center, Chicago, IL, p. A198

SAFAEE SEMIROMI, Masood, M.D., Chief Medical Officer, Mckay-Dee Hospital, Ogden, UT, p. A730

SAFDAR, Aamir, M.D., Chief Medical Officer, Riveredge Hospital, Forest Park, IL, p. A205

SAFFA, Steve, Director Human Resources, University Of Kansas Health System St. Francis Campus, Topeka, KS, p. A277

SAFLEY, Thomas, Chief Financial Officer, St. Josep. Regional Medical Center, Lewiston, ID, p. A191

SAGE, Kelly, Chief Nursing Officer, Hshs St. Anthony's Memorial Hospital, Effingham, IL, p. A203

SAGE, Zachary, Interim Director, Amarillo Veterans Affairs Health Care System, Amarillo, TX, p. A652

SAGER, Kelly, R.N., President and Chief Executive Officer, Hshs Holy Family Hospital In Greenville, Greenville, IL, p. A206

SAGGAR, Sonny, M.D., Chief Executive Officer, St. Alexius Hospital - Broadway Campus, Saint Louis, MO, p. A417

SAGGIO, Thomas, Chief Nursing Officer, St. Alexius Hospital - Broadway Campus, Saint Louis, MO, p. A417

SAGMIT, Rodney, Chief Information Management, Va Long Beach Healthcare System, Long Beach, CA, p. A73

SAHA, Sanjay, Chief Operating Officer, Sibley Memorial Hospital, Washington, DC, p. A130

SAHLOLBEI, Hossain, M.D., Chief of Staff, Palo Verde Hospital, Blythe, CA, p. A58

SAHLSTROM, Christopher, M.D., Chief of Staff, Mat-Su Regional Medical Center, Palmer, AK, p. A29

SAHMAUNT, Sarabeth, Supervisory Accountant, Lawton Indian Hospital, Lawton, OK, p. A561

SAIA, Carrie L., Chief Executive Officer, Holton Community Hospital, Holton, KS, p. A266

SAINBERT, Wilmino, Chief Human Resources Management Service, Northport Veterans Affairs Medical Center, Northport, NY, p. A493

SAINTZ, Jeffrey, Vice President Human Resources, Titusville Area Hospital, Titusville, PA, p. A608

SAIYED, Ashfaq, M.D., Medical Director, Irwin County Hospital, Ocilla, GA, p. A178

SAIZ, Claudia, Chief Executive Officer, Advanced Care Hospital Of Southern New Mexico, Las Cruces, NM, p. A470

SAJID, Muhammad, M.D., Medical Director, Lincoln Trail Behavioral Health System, Radcliff, KY, p. A292

SAKOVITS, Steven, Vice President Information Systems and Chief Information Officer, Stamford Hospital, Stamford, CT, p. A125

SALAKI, Jana, Regional Director Human Resources, Wellspan Ephrata Community Hospital, Ephrata, PA, p. A589

SALAMANCA, Mary, Director Human Resources, Encompass Health Rehabilitation Hospital Of Spring Hill, Brooksville, FL, p. A133

SALAMONE, Joanna, Senior Vice President Clinical Services and Chief Nursing Officer, Southern Maine Health Care - Biddeford Medical Center, Biddeford, ME, p. A319

SALANDI, John, Chief Executive Officer, Landmark Hospital Of Savannah, Savannah, GA, p. A180

SALAS, Dawn, Controller, Encompass Health Rehabilitation Hospital An Affiliate Of Martin Health, Stuart, FL, p. A158

SALAS, Victor, M.D., President Medical Staff, Unitypoint Health - Jones Regional Medical Center, Anamosa, IA, p. A243

SALAWAY, Tarek, Chief Operating Officer, Usc Norris Comprehensive Cancer Center, Los Angeles, CA, p. A76

Senior Vice President and Area Manager, Kaiser Permanente San Rafael Medical Center, San Rafael, CA, p. A96

Senior Vice President and Area Manager, Kaiser Permanente Santa Rosa Medical Center, Santa Rosa, CA, p. A98

SALAZAR, Eloisa, Chief Financial Officer, South Texas Veterans Health Care System, San Antonio, TX, p. A713

SALAZAR, Leanne, Chief Operating Officer, Oak Hill Hospital, Brooksville, FL, p. A133

SALAZAR, Linda, Information Technology Leader, Kaiser Permanente Baldwin Park Medical Center, Baldwin Park, CA, p. A57

SALAZAR, Pamela, M.D., Chief of Staff, Walton Rehabilitation Hospital, Augusta, GA, p. A166

SALAZAR, Serafin, M.D., Chief of Staff, Parkview Community Hospital Medical Center, Riverside, CA, p. A88

SALCEDO, Nydimar, Chief Human Resources Officer, Castaner General Hospital, Castaner, PR, p. A807

SALDIVAR, Antoninette, Vice President, Human Resources, Bridgepoint Hospital National Harbor, Washington, DC, p. A129

SALDIVAR, Duke, FACHE, Chief Executive Officer, Warm Springs Rehabilitation Hospital Of Kyle, Kyle, TX, p. A694

SALEEBY, Manhal, M.D., Chief of Staff, Vcu Health Community Memorial Hospital, South Hill, VA, p. A752

SALEEM, David, Director Information Technology, Greystone Park Psychiatric Hospital, Morris Plains, NJ, p. A458

SALEM, Gary, M.D., Vice President Medical Affairs, Mclaren Lapeer Region, Lapeer, MI, p. A360

SALEM, Michael, M.D., President and Chief Executive Officer, National Jewish Health, Denver, CO, p. A110

SALGADO, Joe, M.D., Chief of Staff, Artesia General Hospital, Artesia, NM, p. A468

M.D., Interim Chief Executive Officer, Artesia General Hospital, Artesia, NM, p. A468

SALINAS, Amaro, Assistant Administrator and Human Resource Officer, Starr County Memorial Hospital, Rio Grande City, TX, p. A709

SALINAS, Daniel, M.D., Senior Vice President and Chief Medical Officer, Children's Healthcare Of Atlanta, Atlanta, GA, p. A164

SALINAS, Noe, Vice President Information Technology, Nexus Specialty Hospital The Woodlands, The Woodlands, TX, p. A720

Vice President Information Technology, Nexus Specialty Hospital, Shenandoah, TX, p. A715

SALING, Christopher, Chief Human Resource Officer, Mckay-Dee Hospital, Ogden, UT, p. A730

SALISBURY, Dennis, M.D., Vice President for Medical Affairs, St. James Healthcare, Butte, MT, p. A422

SALISBURY, Renee, Director Human Resources, Osf Saint Luke Medical Center, Kewanee, IL, p. A209

SALISBURY, Tracy, Director Human Resources, Hiram W. Davis Medical Center, Petersburg, VA, p. A748

Regional Manager Human Resources, Central State Hospital, Petersburg, VA, p. A748

SALL, Jordan, Chief of Staff, Spectrum Health Gerber Memorial, Fremont, MI, p. A355

SALLER, William, Chief Financial Officer, Rio Grande Regional Hospital, Mcallen, TX, p. A700

SALLEY, Wanda, Vice President Human Resources, West Florida Hospital, Pensacola, FL, p. A154

SALLIS, Tom, Director Information Systems, Baptist Health - Fort Smith, Fort Smith, AR, p. A46

SALLOUM, Fadi, M.D., Medical Director, Select Specialty Hospital-Pontiac, Pontiac, MI, p. A364

SALMAN, Wael, M.D., Vice President Medical Affairs, Memorial Healthcare, Owosso, MI, p. A363

SALMANULLAH, Muhammad, Chief Medical Director, Encompass Health Rehabilitation Hospital Of Concord, Concord, NH, p. A448

SALOM, Ira, M.D., Clinical Director, Northern Navajo Medical Center, Shiprock, NM, p. A472

SALOME, Jenny, Chief Financial Officer and Assistant Administrator, Northwest Hills Surgical Hospital, Austin, TX, p. A656

SALOMON, Kathryn, Director Human Resources, Kona Community Hospital, Kealakekua, HI, p. A186

SALTER, Cherry, Director of Nursing, Hardtner Medical Center, Olla, LA, p. A312

SALTONSTALL, Christine, Chief Financial Officer, Kindred Hospital-Baldwin Park, Baldwin Park, CA, p. A58

SALTZGABER, Lee, Chief Medical Officer, Gerald Champion Regional Medical Center, Alamogordo, NM, p. A467

SALVADOR, Ed, Chief Financial Officer, St. Jude Medical Center, Fullerton, CA, p. A66

SALVATI, Mario, Director Fiscal Services, Shriners Hospitals For Children-Philadelphia, Philadelphia, PA, p. A602

SALVI, Donna, Chief Nursing Officer, Watsonville Community Hospital, Watsonville, CA, p. A104

SALVINO, Sonia, Vice President Finance, Uh Cleveland Medical Center, Cleveland, OH, p. A535

SALVITTI, Alfred, Chief Financial Officer, Eagleville Hospital, Eagleville, PA, p. A588

SALVO, Stephen, Vice President Human Resources, Anna Jaques Hospital, Newburyport, MA, p. A342

SALWAN, Manav, Medical Director, Kindred Hospital-Sycamore, Sycamore, IL, p. A221

SALY, David, Director, Information Services, Largo Medical Center, Largo, FL, p. A143

SALYER, Steven, Chief Operating Officer, Up Health System-Marquette, Marquette, MI, p. A361

SALZMAN, Shona, Chief Operating Officer, William Newton Hospital, Winfield, KS, p. A279

SAMBASIVAN, Venkataraman, M.D., Chief Medical Officer, Lourdes Medical Center, Pasco, WA, p. A762

SAMILO, Nick, Vice President Fiscal Services and Chief Financial Officer, Atrium Health Stanly, Albemarle, NC, p. A504

SAMMARCO, Michael, M.D., Chief Financial Officer, Erie County Medical Center, Buffalo, NY, p. A479

SAMMONS, Craig, Chief Financial Officer, Sky Ridge Medical Center, Lone Tree, CO, p. A116

SAMMONS, Jacquelyn, R.N., Supervisor, Child And Adolescent Behavioral Health Services, Willmar, MN, p. A388

SAMMS, Caswell, Network Chief Financial Officer, Nyc Health + Hospitals / Lincoln, Bronx, NY, p. A477

SAMORA, Martha, R.N., FACHE, Chief Executive Officer, Encompass Health Rehabilitation Hospital Of Bakersfield, Bakersfield, CA, p. A57

SAMPAGA, Arthur, Chief Nursing Officer, Hilo Medical Center, Hilo, HI, p. A184

SAMPSON, Arthur J., FACHE, President, Miriam Hospital, Providence, RI, p. A613

SAMPSON, Bob, Senior Vice President, Human Resources, Evergreenhealth, Kirkland, WA, p. A759
   Vice President Human Resources, Redwood Memorial Hospital, Fortuna, CA, p. A64

SAMPSON, Jill, Director Human Resources, Lemuel Shattuck Hospital, Jamaica Plain, MA, p. A340

SAMROW, Kevin, Chief Executive Officer, Alliancehealth Durant, Durant, OK, p. A558
   Chief Executive Officer, Alliancehealth Madill, Madill, OK, p. A561

SAMS, Alfred, President and Chief Executive Officer, St. Andrew's Health Center, Bottineau, ND, p. A521

SAMS, James, Chief of Staff, Mckenzie Health System, Sandusky, MI, p. A366

SAMSON, Ley, Director Management Information Systems, Hca Houston Healthcare Clear Lake, League City, TX, p. A695

SAMUDRALA, Siresha, M.D., Medical Director, Mercy Rehabilitation Hospital St. Louis, Chesterfield, MO, p. A404

SAMUEL, Nicole, Chief Financial Officer, Sierra Vista Hospital, Sacramento, CA, p. A90

SAMUELS, Christopher, Chief of Staff, Skyline Hospital, White Salmon, WA, p. A769

SAMUELSON, Kimberly, Director of Information Management, Highland-Clarksburg Hospital, Clarksburg, WV, p. A771

SAMYN, Mike, Vice President, Finance and Chief Financial Officer, St. Mary Mercy Hospital, Livonia, MI, p. A360

SAMZ, Jeff, Chief Operating Officer, Huntsville Hospital, Huntsville, AL, p. A20

SAN FILIPPO, Bruce, M.D., Chief Medical Officer, Memorial Medical Center, Las Cruces, NM, p. A470

SANBORN, Michael, FACHE, MS, President, Baylor Scott & White All Saints Medical Center - Fort Worth, Fort Worth, TX, p. A678

SANBORN, Randall, Director Information Systems, Garden City Hospital, Garden City, MI, p. A355

SANCHEZ, Alberto, Chief Executive Officer, Solara Hospital Harlingen, Harlingen, TX, p. A683

SANCHEZ, Alvaro, M.D., Chief Medical Officer, Ridgeview Medical Center, Waconia, MN, p. A387

SANCHEZ, Antonio, M.D., Executive Director, Northport Veterans Affairs Medical Center, Northport, NY, p. A493

SANCHEZ, Arnaldo, M.D., Chief Operating Officer, Hospital Episcopal San Lucas Guayama, Guayama, PR, p. A807

SANCHEZ, Emalie, Director Human Resources, Baylor Scott & White Medical Center-Uptown, Dallas, TX, p. A667

SANCHEZ, Esperanza, Chief Clinical Officer, Kindred Hospital-La Mirada, La Mirada, CA, p. A70

SANCHEZ, Freddie, Director Information Systems, Fountain Valley Regional Hospital And Medical Center, Fountain Valley, CA, p. A64

SANCHEZ, Holly, Chief Information Officer, Slidell Memorial Hospital, Slidell, LA, p. A315
   Chief Operating Officer, Slidell Memorial Hospital, Slidell, LA, p. A315

SANCHEZ, John, Vice President Human Resources, White Plains Hospital Center, White Plains, NY, p. A502

SANCHEZ, Jose R., President and Chief Executive Officer, Norwegian American Hospital, Chicago, IL, p. A200

SANCHEZ, Nancy, Senior Vice President and Vice Dean Human Resources, Nyu Langone Hospitals, New York, NY, p. A492

SANCHEZ, Rebecca, R.N., M.P.H., Director of Nursing, Texas Center For Infectious Disease, San Antonio, TX, p. A713

SANCHEZ-BICKLEY, Michelle, Chief Human Resources Officer, Renown Regional Medical Center, Reno, NV, p. A446
   Vice President Human Resources, Renown Rehabilitation Hospital, Reno, NV, p. A446

Vice President Human Resources, Renown South Meadows Medical Center, Reno, NV, p. A446

SANCHEZ-RICO, Gloria, Chief Nursing Officer and Vice President, Huntington Hospital, Pasadena, CA, p. A85

SAND, Michelle, R.N., MSN, Vice President and Chief Nursing Officer, Cascade Valley Hospital, Arlington, WA, p. A755

SANDAGER, Brian, Chief Information Officer, Lowell General Hospital, Lowell, MA, p. A341

SANDBERG, Susan, R.N., Chief Executive Officer, Melrosewakefield Healthcare, Melrose, MA, p. A341

SANDBERG, Todd, Chief Executive Officer, Riverwood Healthcare Center, Aitkin, MN, p. A371

SANDBULTE, Nyla, R.N., Director of Nursing, Sanford Luverne Medical Center, Luverne, MN, p. A379

SANDER, Cindy, Coordinator Human Resources, Kindred Hospital-St. Louis, Saint Louis, MO, p. A416

SANDERS, Amy, Chief Human Resources, Captain James A. Lovell Federal Health Care Center, North Chicago, IL, p. A214

SANDERS, Hannah, M.D., Medical Director, Cordova Community Medical Center, Cordova, AK, p. A28

SANDERS, Harv, Chief Financial Officer, Rhea Medical Center, Dayton, TN, p. A637

SANDERS, Jeff, Senior Vice President, Chief Operating Officer, Maine Medical Center, Portland, ME, p. A322

SANDERS, Jeffrey, M.D., Chief of Staff, Carson Tahoe Health, Carson City, NV, p. A441

SANDERS, Kelly, Vice President Human Resources, Good Shepherd Health Care System, Hermiston, OR, p. A576

SANDERS, Kenneth, Administrator and Chief Executive Officer, Dallas County Medical Center, Fordyce, AR, p. A45

SANDERS, Kimberly, Chief Nursing Officer, Baptist Memorial Hospital-Carroll County, Huntingdon, TN, p. A639

SANDERS, Kirk, M.D., Chief of Staff, Lifebrite Community Hospital Of Stokes, Danbury, NC, p. A508

SANDERS, Kris, Chief Financial Officer, Methodist Healthcare Olive Branch Hospital, Olive Branch, MS, p. A398

SANDERS, Kyle, Chief Financial Officer, Nea Baptist Memorial Hospital, Jonesboro, AR, p. A48

SANDERS, Michael, MS, Chief Operating Officer, Kp. Promise Hospital Of Baton Rouge, Baton Rouge, LA, p. A297

SANDERS, Michael B., President, Monroe Clinic, Monroe, WI, p. A792

SANDERS, Patrick, Chief Operating Officer, Hartgrove Hospital, Chicago, IL, p. A198

SANDERS, R. Bradley, D.O., Executive Medical Director, Alvarado Parkway Institute Behavioral Health System, La Mesa, CA, p. A70

SANDERS, Robert, M.D., Chief Medical Officer, Texoma Medical Center, Denison, TX, p. A671

SANDERS, Sheila, Chief Information Officer, Emory University Hospital, Atlanta, GA, p. A164

SANDERS, Steve, Chief Financial Officer, Washington County Hospital And Clinics, Washington, IA, p. A259

SANDERS, Susie, Chief Financial Officer, Cherry Hospital, Goldsboro, NC, p. A510

SANDHU, Harminder, M.D., Chief of Staff, Bridgepoint Hospital Capitol Hill, Washington, DC, p. A129

SANDIFER, Ron, Chief Information Officer, Community Memorial Hospital, Ventura, CA, p. A103

SANDIN, James, M.D., Assistant Administrator Medical Affairs, Hunt Regional Medical Center, Greenville, TX, p. A682

SANDLES, Christopher R., FACHE, Medical Center Director, South Texas Veterans Health Care System, San Antonio, TX, p. A713

SANDLIN, Michael, M.D., Chief of Staff, Muscogee Creek Nation Medical Center, Okmulgee, OK, p. A566

SANDMANN, Patty, Senior Director of Nursing, Burgess Health Center, Onawa, IA, p. A255

SANDS, Dennis, Chief Medical Officer, Osf Healthcare Saint Anthony's Health Center, Alton, IL, p. A194

SANDS, Mark, M.D., Chief Medical Officer, Stony Brook University Hospital, Stony Brook, NY, p. A499

SANDS, Sherry, R.N., Chief Nursing Officer, Southern Tennessee Regional Health System-Pulaski, Pulaski, TN, p. A648

SANDS, Tiffany, Manager Health Information, Arbuckle Memorial Hospital, Sulphur, OK, p. A568

SANDS, Tom, Interim Chief Executive Officer, Carney Hospital, Boston, MA, p. A335

SANDSTROM, C, Vice President and Chief Financial Officer, The Aroostook Medical Center, Presque Isle, ME, p. A322

SANDUJA, Sourabh, Administrator, Altus Baytown Hospital, Baytown, TX, p. A657

SANFORD, Lisa, VP Patient Care/CNO, Holy Rosary Healthcare, Miles City, MT, p. A426

SANFORD, Ricca, Director Human Resources, Regional West Garden County, Oshkosh, NE, p. A438

SANFORD, Sharon, Director Human Resources, Jersey Community Hospital, Jerseyville, IL, p. A209

SANFORD, Stacy, Chief Executive Officer, Oceans Behavioral Hospital Abilene, Abilene, TX, p. A651

SANGER, David, M.D., Chief Medical Officer, University Of Kansas Health System Pawnee Valley Campus, Larned, KS, p. A268

SANGER, Ken, R.N., Chief Nursing Officer and Chief Operations Officer, Lake Huron Medical Center, Port Huron, MI, p. A364

SANGER, Neal, Vice President Information Services, Mayo Clinic Health System - Franciscan Healthcare In La Crosse, La Crosse, WI, p. A787

SANGHA, Harbaksh, M.D., Chief Medical Officer, Lake Regional Health System, Osage Beach, MO, p. A413

SANGHI, Harishankar, M.D., Clinical Director, St. Lawrence Psychiatric Center, Ogdensburg, NY, p. A493

SANKARAN, Jaya, M.D., Chief of Staff, Ascension Standish Hospital, Standish, MI, p. A367

SANKE, Kristina, Chief Financial Officer, Orchard Hospital, Gridley, CA, p. A67

SANKOORIKAL, Joseph, M.D., Chief Medical Staff, Kansas Rehabilitation Hospital, Topeka, KS, p. A277

SANKS, Claude, Chief Medical Staff, Effingham Hospital, Springfield, GA, p. A180

SANNUTO, John, Chief Executive Officer, Wellbridge Healthcare Greater Dallas, Plano, TX, p. A707

SANSOM, Christine, Chief Nursing Officer, Mclaren Port Huron, Port Huron, MI, p. A364

SANSONE, John, Vice President, Human Resources, Monadnock Community Hospital, Peterborough, NH, p. A451

SANTA ANA, Coleen F., President, Sentara Obici Hospital, Suffolk, VA, p. A752

SANTANA, Leticia, Administrator Medical Records, Bayamon Medical Center, Bayamon, PR, p. A806

SANTANGELO, Craig, Director Information Services, Medical City Arlington, Arlington, TX, p. A653

SANTANGELO, Joe, M.D., Vice President of Medical Affairs, Munson Healthcare Cadillac Hospital, Cadillac, MI, p. A350

SANTANGELO, John, Director Information Technology, Cleveland Clinic Florida, Weston, FL, p. A162

SANTARELLI, James, M.D., President Medical Staff, Aurora Medical Center Kenosha, Kenosha, WI, p. A786

SANTIAGO, Alejandro, Director Finance, Doctors' Center Hospital San Juan, San Juan, PR, p. A810

SANTIAGO, Anthony, Chief Executive Officers, Huhukam Memorial Hospital, Sacaton, AZ, p. A37

SANTIAGO, Julio, M.D., Chief of Staff, Genesis Medical Center-Aledo, Aledo, IL, p. A194

SANTIAGO, Manuel, Chief Information Officer, Hospital Metropolitan, San Juan, PR, p. A810

SANTIAGO, Orlando, Human Resources Officer, Hospital Del Maestro, San Juan, PR, p. A810

SANTIAGO, Sugehi, Director, Hospital San Francisco, San Juan, PR, p. A810

SANTIAGO, Ubaldo, M.D., Chairman, Doctors' Center Hospital San Juan, San Juan, PR, p. A810

SANTIESTEBAN, Nancy, Director Patient Care Services, Presbyterian Espanola Hospital, Espanola, NM, p. A469

SANTILLI, Robert J., Chief Executive Officer, Gunnison Valley Hospital, Gunnison, CO, p. A114

SANTINA, Ray, Director Information Systems, Psychiatric Institute Of Washington, Washington, DC, p. A130

SANTISTEVAN, Vivian, Chief Human Resources, Tsehootsooi Medical Center, Fort Defiance, AZ, p. A31

SANTMAN, Kim, Vice President Finance, St. Margaret's Hospital, Spring Valley, IL, p. A220

SANTORA, Judith, Chief Human Resource Officer, Lutheran Hospital, Cleveland, OH, p. A534
   Human Resources Business Partner, Marymount Hospital, Garfield Heights, OH, p. A541

SANTORI, Stephanie H., Chief Executive Officer, Vermilion Behavioral Health Systems - North Campus, Lafayette, LA, p. A306

SANTOS, Alfred, Chief Executive Officer, Encompass Health Rehabilitation Hospital Of Northern Virginia, Aldie, VA, p. A738

SANTOS, Daniel, Director Ancillary Services, Pacifica Hospital Of The Valley, Sun Valley, CA, p. A100

SANTOS, David, President and Chief Executive Officer, Adventist Health Clear Lake, Clearlake, CA, p. A60
   President Chief Executive Officer, Adventist Health Clear Lake, Clearlake, CA, p. A60

SANTOS, Deborah, R.N., Chief Nursing Officer, Encompass Health Rehabilitation Hospital Of Western Massachusetts, Ludlow, MA, p. A341

SANTOS, Gloria, R.N., MS, Chief Nursing Officer, Adventhealth Sebring, Sebring, FL, p. A157

R.N., MS, Vice President and Chief Nursing Officer, Adventhealth Wauchula, Wauchula, FL, p. A161

SANTOS, Ismael, Director Human Resources, Valle Vista Health System, Greenwood, IN, p. A230

SANTOS, Lori, Chief Financial Officer, St. Peter's Hospital, Albany, NY, p. A474

SANTUCCI, James, Chief Operating Officer, Desert Regional Medical Center, Palm Springs, CA, p. A83

SANTULLI, Patricia, Director Human Resources, Elmira Psychiatric Center, Elmira, NY, p. A483

SANVILLE, David, Chief Financial Officer, Mt. Ascutney Hospital And Health Center, Windsor, VT, p. A737

SANWARI, Murtaza, Senior Vice President and Area Manager, Kaiser Permanente Woodland Hills Medical Center, Woodland Hills, CA, p. A105

SANZONE, Frank, Manager Information Technology, Ascension Brighton Center For Recovery, Brighton, MI, p. A350

SAPMAZ, Cagri, Information Technology Director, Bolivar Medical Center, Cleveland, MS, p. A391

SAPORITO, Angie, Administrator, Mercy Hospital Columbus, Columbus, KS, p. A263

SAPORITO, Joann, R.N., Vice President Nursing Services, Oak Valley Hospital, Oakdale, CA, p. A82

SAPP, Tracy, Director Human Resources, Encompass Health Rehabilitation Hospital Of Ocala, Ocala, FL, p. A150

SAPPENFIELD, Debra, R.N., Chief Nursing Officer, Hemphill County Hospital, Canadian, TX, p. A662

SAPPINGTON-CRITTENDEN, Shana, Chief Operating Officer, Westside Regional Medical Center, Plantation, FL, p. A154

SARBACHER, James, Chief Information Officer, State Hospital North, Orofino, ID, p. A192

SARDANA, Sadhana, M.D., Clinical Director, Rockland Children's Psychiatric Center, Orangeburg, NY, p. A494

SARDELLA, Jeff, Director Information Technology, Terrebonne General Medical Center, Houma, LA, p. A303

SARDONE, Frank J., President and Chief Executive Officer, Bronson Battle Creek Hospital, Battle Creek, MI, p. A349
President and Chief Executive Officer, Bronson Methodist Hospital, Kalamazoo, MI, p. A359

SARDUY, Innette, M.P.H., R.N., Associate Director Patient Care Services and Nurse Executive, Louis Stokes Cleveland Veterans Affairs Medical Center, Cleveland, OH, p. A534

SARGENT, Kimberly, Vice President Patient Services, St. Luke's Hospital - Miners Campus, Coaldale, PA, p. A587

SARGENT, Kurt, CPA, Vice President Operational Finance, Chi St. Alexius Health Devils Lake Hospital, Devils Lake, ND, p. A522
CPA, Vice President, Operational Finance, Chi St Alexius Health Carrington Medical Center, Carrington, ND, p. A522

SARGENT, Teresa, Vice President Human Resources, Saint Alphonsus Regional Medical Center, Boise, ID, p. A188

SARIAN, Michael, Interim Chief Executive Officer, La Palma Intercommunity Hospital, La Palma, CA, p. A70

SARMENTO, Joann, Manager Human Resources, Fairchild Medical Center, Yreka, CA, p. A106

SARNECKI, Robert, Interim Chief Information Officer, Children's Of Alabama, Birmingham, AL, p. A15

SAROFIN, Michelle, Superintendent, Albert J. Solnit Psychiatric Center - South Campus, Middletown, CT, p. A123

SARROS, Steven, Vice President and Chief Information Officer, Baptist Hospital, Pensacola, FL, p. A153

SARROUI, B, M.D., Chief of Staff, Advanced Specialty Hospital Of Toledo, Toledo, OH, p. A550

SARTAIN, Jarred, M.D., President Medical Staff, North Mississipp. Medical Center-Hamilton, Hamilton, AL, p. A20

SARTAIN, Lisa, Vice President, Human Resources, Bellevue Hospital, Bellevue, OH, p. A529

SARVEPALLI, Raghu, M.D., Vice President of Medical Affairs, Ascension St. Mary's Of Michigan, Saginaw, MI, p. A365

SARVER, Troy, R.N., Chief Nursing Officer, Texas Orthopedic Hospital, Houston, TX, p. A688

SAS, Mary, Vice President, Valley Health - Hampshire Memorial Hospital, Romney, WV, p. A776

SASSER, Kelley, Director Information Systems, Adventhealth Zephyrhills, Zephyrhills, FL, p. A162

SATHER, Sonia, M.D., President Medical Staff, Spencer Hospital, Spencer, IA, p. A258

SATTAR, Parhez, Senior Director Information Technology, Grande Ronde Hospital, La Grande, OR, p. A576

SATTERWHITE, Glenda, Director of Nursing, Oklahoma Forensic Center, Vinita, OK, p. A571

SAUCERMAN-HOWARD, Kelli, Vice President Patient Care Services, Chi Health Creighton University Medical Center - Bergan Mercy, Omaha, NE, p. A436

SAUDE, Aaron, Chief Executive Officer, Bigfork Valley Hospital, Bigfork, MN, p. A372

SAUDER, Chris, Vice President and Chief Financial Officer, Adventhealth Carrollwood, Tampa, FL, p. A159

SAUER, Bernie, Director Information Technology, San Gabriel Valley Medical Center, San Gabriel, CA, p. A94

SAUER, Mary, R.N., Chief Nursing Officer, Cleveland Clinic Avon Hospital, Avon, OH, p. A528

SAUERBREI, Teresa, Chief Nursing Officer, Compass Memorial Healthcare, Marengo, IA, p. A253

SAUERS, Preston, Chief Financial Officer, Ellsworth County Medical Center, Ellsworth, KS, p. A264

SAUM, Anita, Director Human Resources, Encompass Health Rehabilitation Hospital Of Tinton Falls, Tinton Falls, NJ, p. A464

SAUNDERS, John, M.D., Senior Vice President Medical Affairs and Chief Medical Officer, Greater Baltimore Medical Center, Baltimore, MD, p. A324

SAUNDERS, Jonathan, Chief Financial Officer, Baylor Scott & White Medical Center - Trophy Club, Trophy Club, TX, p. A721

SAUNDERS, M, R.N., MS, Vice President Nursing, Upmc Hanover, Hanover, PA, p. A591

SAUNDERS, Ninfa M., President and Chief Executive Officer, Medical Center, Navicent Health, Macon, GA, p. A176

SAURO, Anthony, Chief Information Officer, Pointe Coupee General Hospital, New Roads, LA, p. A312

SAUS, Heather, Human Resource Generalist, Edwin Shaw Rehab, Copley, OH, p. A537

SAUSEDO, Rhonda, Chief Nursing Officer, Placentia-Linda Hospital, Placentia, CA, p. A85

SAUTER, Michael, M.D., Chief Medical Officer, St. Charles Hospital, Port Jefferson, NY, p. A495

SAVAGE, Elizabeth, Senior Vice President and Chief Human Resource Officer and Vice President Community Health and Wellness, Valley Health - Winchester Medical Center, Winchester, VA, p. A754

SAVAGE, Ginny, Director of Human Resources, Carolina Center For Behavioral Health, Greer, SC, p. A621

SAVAGE, Heather, Director Human Resources, The Rehabilitation Institute Of St. Louis, Saint Louis, MO, p. A417

SAVAGE, Jeanne, M.D., Chief Medical Officer, Willamette Valley Medical Center, Mcminnville, OR, p. A577

SAVAGE, Steve, Chief Executive Officer, Stonecrest Center, Detroit, MI, p. A353

SAVANT, Amy, Administrator and Chief Executive Officer, Beacon Behavioral Hospital, Bunkie, LA, p. A299

SAVITSKY, Marian, R.N., Chief Nursing Officer, Sky Ridge Medical Center, Lone Tree, CO, p. A116

SAVOY, Greg, M.D., Chief Medical Officer, Savoy Medical Center, Mamou, LA, p. A307

SAWA, Kendall, R.N., Chief Operating Officer, Providence Portland Medical Center, Portland, OR, p. A579

SAWALLISH, Trevor, Senior Vice President Clinical Operations and Chief Operating Officer, Children's Hospitals And Clinics Of Minnesota, Minneapolis, MN, p. A380

SAWDEY, Don, M.D., Medical Director, Daniels Memorial Healthcare Center, Scobey, MT, p. A427

SAWICKI, Mitzi, Director of Nursing, Havenwyck Hospital, Auburn Hills, MI, p. A349

SAWYER, Anne, Chief Financial Officer, Wayne County Hospital, Monticello, KY, p. A290

SAWYER, Colleen A., R.N., MSN, Executive Director, Mohawk Valley Psychiatric Center, Utica, NY, p. A500
R.N., MSN, Executive Director, Richard H. Hutchings Psychiatric Center, Syracuse, NY, p. A499

SAWYER, Dorothy, Chief Executive Officer, Inland Northwest Behavioral Health, Spokane, WA, p. A765

SAWYER, Holly, Director and Human Resources Business Partner, Piedmont Fayette Hospital, Fayetteville, GA, p. A172

SAWYER, Josep. T. Jr, President and Chief Operating Officer, Guthrie Robert Packer Hospital, Sayre, PA, p. A606

SAWYER, Regina, Vice President Chief Nursing Officer, Kaweah Delta Medical Center, Visalia, CA, p. A104

SAWYER, Scott, Chief Financial Officer, Community Medical Center, Inc., Falls City, NE, p. A432

SAWYER, Stephen, Chief Financial Officer, Norton Community Hospital, Norton, VA, p. A748

SAWYER, Sydney, R.N., Chief Executive Officer, Lackey Memorial Hospital, Forest, MS, p. A392

SAXON, Kathy, R.N., Interim President, Adventist Healthtillamook, Tillamook, OR, p. A582
R.N., Vice President Patient Care Services, Adventist Healthtillamook, Tillamook, OR, p. A582

SAXTON, Beth, R.N., Chief Executive Officer, Yuma District Hospital, Yuma, CO, p. A120

SAYAH, Assaad, M.D., Chief Executive Officer, Cambridge Health Alliance, Cambridge, MA, p. A337
M.D., Chief Medical Officer, Cambridge Health Alliance, Cambridge, MA, p. A337

SAYLER, Elizabeth, M.D., Chief of Staff, Monument Health Lead-Deadwood Hospital, Deadwood, SD, p. A627

SAYLER, Roger, Finance Officer, Fargo Veterans Affairs Health Care System, Fargo, ND, p. A523

SAYLES, Debbie, R.N., Vice President and Chief Nursing Officer, Texas Scottish Rite Hospital For Children, Dallas, TX, p. A670

SAYRE, Amy, Director Human Resources, Pershing Memorial Hospital, Brookfield, MO, p. A403

SAYRE, Cindy, Ph.D., R.N., Chief Nursing Officer, University Of Washington Medical Center, Seattle, WA, p. A764

SBARDELLA, Steven, M.D., FABC, President Clinical Operations and Chief Medical Officer, Melrosewakefield Healthcare, Melrose, MA, p. A341

SCAFIDDI, Darlene, R.N., MSN, Vice President Nursing and Patient Care Services, Pomona Valley Hospital Medical Center, Pomona, CA, p. A86

SCAGLIONE, Kim, Vice President Human Resources, Baptist Health Louisville, Louisville, KY, p. A287

SCALES, Melisa, Director of Nursing, Parkview Hospital, Wheeler, TX, p. A725

SCALES, Yolanda, R.N., Director of Nursing, Bethesda Rehabilitation Hospital, Baton Rouge, LA, p. A296

SCAMARDO, Luke, M.D., Chief of Staff, Chi St. Josep. Health Grimes Hospital, Navasota, TX, p. A703

SCAMINACI, Peter, President, Mercy Medical Center, Rockville Centre, NY, p. A497
President, St. Josep. Hospital, Bethpage, NY, p. A475

SCANLON, Donald, Chief Corporate Services, Mount Sinai Health System, Mount Sinai Beth Israel, New York, NY, p. A490
Chief Corporate Services, Mount Sinai Health System, Mount Sinai Morningside, New York, NY, p. A490
Chief Corporate Services, Mount Sinai Health System, New York Eye And Ear Infirmary Of Mount Sinai, New York, NY, p. A490
Chief Financial Officer, The Mount Sinai Hospital, New York, NY, p. A492

SCANLON, John, DPM, Chief Medical Officer, Chestnut Hill Hospital, Philadelphia, PA, p. A599

SCANLON, Kerri, MSN, Executive Director, Glen Cove Hospital, Glen Cove, NY, p. A484

SCANNELL, Donna, Vice President Information Technology, Kaiser Permanente Medical Center, Honolulu, HI, p. A184

SCANZERA, Christopher, Vice President and Chief Information Officer, Atlanticare Regional Medical Center, Atlantic City, NJ, p. A452

SCARBORO, Parrish, Chief Executive Officer, San Dimas Community Hospital, San Dimas, CA, p. A93

SCARBROUGH, Keith, Director, Information Systems, Saint Francis Hospital, Memphis, TN, p. A645

SCARLETT, Kamesha, Chief Information Resource Management, Veterans Affairs New Jersey Health Care System, East Orange, NJ, p. A454

SCARTEZINA, Angie, Chief Nursing Officer, Primary Children's Hospital, Salt Lake City, UT, p. A732

SCENNA, Maria, Chief Executive Officer, Cancer Treatment Centers Of America-Eastern Regional Medical Center, Philadelphia, PA, p. A599

SCEPANSKI, Theresa, Vice President People and Organizational Development, University Health System, San Antonio, TX, p. A714

SCHAAB, Ben, Vice President, Chief Financial Officer, Cgh Medical Center, Sterling, IL, p. A221

SCHAACK, Gregory, CPA, Vice President and Chief Financial Officer, Candler Hospital, Savannah, GA, p. A179
CPA, Vice President and Chief Financial Officer, St. Joseph's Hospital, Savannah, GA, p. A180

SCHAAL, Dawn M., Interim Director, Veterans Affairs Hudson Valley Health Care System, Montrose, NY, p. A488

SCHABELMAN, Esti, Chief Medical Officer, Grace Medical Center, Baltimore, MD, p. A324

SCHACKMUTH, Eric, M.D., Chief of Staff, Abilene Regional Medical Center, Abilene, TX, p. A651

SCHAD, Todd, M.D., Medical Director, Sauk Prairie Healthcare, Prairie Du Sac, WI, p. A794

SCHADE, Sue, Interim Chief Information Officer, Uh Cleveland Medical Center, Cleveland, OH, p. A535

SCHADLER, Gene, Superintendent, Evansville State Hospital, Evansville, IN, p. A227

SCHAEF, Toby, Director Information Technology, Memorial Hospital Of Carbon County, Rawlins, WY, p. A803

SCHAEFER, Jamie, Vice President Finance, Avera Sacred Heart Hospital, Yankton, SD, p. A633

SCHAEFER, Kevin, Manager Information Services, River's Edge Hospital And Clinic, Saint Peter, MN, p. A385

SCHAEFER, Matthew, President and Chief Executive Officer, East Tennessee Children's Hospital, Knoxville, TN, p. A641

SCHAEFER, Michael, Executive Vice President and Chief Financial Officer, Methodist Charlton Medical Center, Dallas, TX, p. A669

SCHAEFER, Michelle, Chief Financial Officer, Lillian M. Hudspeth Memorial Hospital, Sonora, TX, p. A716

SCHAEFER, Stephen, Chief Executive Officer, Encompass Health Rehabilitation Hospital Of Colorado Springs, Colorado Springs, CO, p. A109

SCHAEFFER, Andre, M.D., Chief of Staff, Union General Hospital, Blairsville, GA, p. A167

SCHAEFFER, Richard, Vice President Information Systems and Chief Information Officer, St. Clair Hospital, Pittsburgh, PA, p. A603

SCHAFER, Laurie, Chief Nursing Officer, San Juan Health Service District, Monticello, UT, p. A729

SCHAFER, Michael, Chief Executive Officer and Administrator, Spooner Health, Spooner, WI, p. A796

SCHAFER, Mona, Regional Manager Human Resources, Milbank Area Hospital Avera, Milbank, SD, p. A629

SCHAFFER, John, R.N., Director of Nursing, Clifton-Fine Hospital, Star Lake, NY, p. A498

SCHAFFER, Megan, Administrative Assistant, Surgical Institute Of Reading, Wyomissing, PA, p. A612

SCHAFFER, Renee, Coordinator Human Resources, Select Specialty Hospital-Wichita, Wichita, KS, p. A279

SCHAFFNER, Leroy, Interim Chief Executive Officer, Ochiltree General Hospital, Perryton, TX, p. A705

SCHAFFNER, Richard, Executive Vice President and Chief Operating Officer, Beebe Healthcare, Lewes, DE, p. A127

SCHAFSNITZ, Patricia, Director of Nursing Services, Mckenzie Health System, Sandusky, MI, p. A366

SCHALES, Marion, Chief Financial Officer, Highland Hospital, Oakland, CA, p. A82

SCHALL, Dee, R.N., Chief Nursing Officer, Baptist Health Medical Center-Hot Spring County, Malvern, AR, p. A50

SCHALSKI, Paula, Director Human Resources, Pushmataha Hospital, Antlers, OK, p. A555

SCHALTZ, Linda, MSN, R.N., Chief Nursing Officer, Spectrum Health United Hospital, Greenville, MI, p. A356

SCHAMP, Cindy K., FACHE, President, Baylor Scott & White Medical Center-Irving, Irving, TX, p. A690

SCHANDL, Brian, Chief Information Officer, Marshall Browning Hospital, Du Quoin, IL, p. A203

SCHANDORF-LARTEY, Michael, M.D., Chief Medical Officer, Doctors Hospital Of Sarasota, Sarasota, FL, p. A157

SCHAPP, Susan, Vice President Finance and Treasurer, Charlotte Hungerford Hospital, Torrington, CT, p. A125

SCHARBER, Laurel, Administrative Assistant and Coordinator Human Resources, Kindred Hospital-Ontario, Ontario, CA, p. A82

SCHARENBROCK, Chris, M.D., Chief Medical Staff, David Grant Usaf Medical Center, Travis Afb, CA, p. A101

SCHARFF, Tom, Director Information Services, University Hospital And Medical Center, Tamarac, FL, p. A159

SCHARNBERG, Cathi, R.N., M.P.H., Vice President Patient Services, Avera Holy Family Hospital, Estherville, IA, p. A249

SCHARNHORST, Alicia, Human Resources and Administrative Assistant, Garfield County Public Hospital District, Pomeroy, WA, p. A762

SCHARR, Vickie, Chief Financial Officer, Bakersfield Heart Hospital, Bakersfield, CA, p. A57

SCHATTSCHNEIDER, Tami, Chief Nursing Officer, St. Agnes Hospital, Fond Du Lac, WI, p. A784

SCHAUF, Jeffrey, Director Information Systems, Wesley Healthcare Center, Wichita, KS, p. A279

SCHAUF, Kyle, M.D., President Medical Staff, Integris Grove Hospital, Grove, OK, p. A559

SCHAWL, Bud, Chief Executive Officer, Kindred Hospital Las Vegas-Sahara, Henderson, NV, p. A442

SCHECKEL, Jill, Ph.D., Chief Executive Officer, Palo Verde Behavioral Health, Tucson, AZ, p. A40

SCHEERER, Dan, M.D., Chief Medical Officer, Genesis Healthcare System, Zanesville, OH, p. A554

SCHEETZ, Allison, M.D., Medical Director, Rehabilitation Hospital, Navicent Health, Macon, GA, p. A176

SCHEFFLER, Robert, Chief Executive Officer, Haven Behavioral Hospital Of Eastern Pennsylvania, Reading, PA, p. A606

Chief Executive Officer, Haven Behavioral Hospital Of Philadelphia, Philadelphia, PA, p. A600

SCHEFFLER, Tom, Chief Fiscal Officer, Veterans Affairs Maryland Health Care System-Baltimore Division, Baltimore, MD, p. A327

SCHEINBART, Lee, M.D., Vice President Medical Affairs, Health First Community Hospitals, Health First Cap. Canaveral Hospital, Cocoa Beach, FL, p. A134

M.D., Vice President Medical Affairs, Health First Community Hospitals, Health First Palm Bay Hospital, Palm Bay, FL, p. A152

SCHEINBLUM, Richard, Chief Financial Officer, Monadnock Community Hospital, Peterborough, NH, p. A451

SCHELBAR, E, M.D., Medical Director, Select Specialty Hospital-Tulsa Midtown, Tulsa, OK, p. A570

SCHELL, James, M.D., Vice President Medical Affairs, Saint Francis Medical Center, Cap. Girardeau, MO, p. A403

SCHELL, Jonathan, Chief Nursing Officer, Drew Memorial Health System, Monticello, AR, p. A50

SCHEMER, Tonia, Interim Chief Human Resources, St. Josep. Mercy Livingston Hospital, Howell, MI, p. A358

SCHENKER, Amy, Human Resources Director, Shriners Hospitals For Children-Tampa, Tampa, FL, p. A159

SCHEPICI, Denise, M.P.H., Chief Executive Officer and President, Martha's Vineyard Hospital, Oak Bluffs, MA, p. A343

SCHEPMANN, Jane, Vice President and Chief Nursing Officer, Clara Barton Hospital, Hoisington, KS, p. A266

SCHEPPERS, Levi, Chief Executive Officer, Orthonebraska Hospital, Omaha, NE, p. A437

SCHEPPERS, Lisa, Chief Medical Officer, Regional West Medical Center, Scottsbluff, NE, p. A439

SCHER, Kathleen, Ed.D., R.N., Chief Nursing Officer, Jamaica Hospital Medical Center, Jamaica, NY, p. A486

SCHERER, Timothy, M.D., Chief Medical Officer, Southern New Hampshire Medical Center, Nashua, NH, p. A450

SCHERLER, Jay, Vice President Finance and Chief Information Officer, Ascension Providence, Waco, TX, p. A723

SCHERLING, Adam, President, Grundy County Memorial Hospital, Grundy Center, IA, p. A250

SCHERNECK, Michael D., President and Chief Executive Officer, Southeast Georgia Health System Brunswick Campus, Brunswick, GA, p. A167

SCHEVING, Travis, Chief Financial Officer, Holy Rosary Healthcare, Miles City, MT, p. A426

SCHEXNAYDER, Glenn, M.D., Chief of Staff, Prevost Memorial Hospital, Donaldsonville, LA, p. A301

SCHEY, David, Chief Financial Officer, Brook Lane Health Services, Hagerstown, MD, p. A330

SCHICK, Eric, Chief Financial Officer, Saint Francis Hospital South, Tulsa, OK, p. A570

Senior Vice President and Chief Financial Officer, Saint Francis Health System, Saint Francis Hospital, Tulsa, OK, p. A570

Senior Vice President, Chief Administrative Officer and Chief Financial Officer, Laureate Psychiatric Clinic And Hospital, Tulsa, OK, p. A569

SCHIEBER, Steven M., FACHE, Chief Executive Officer, Critical Access Region, Saint Luke's Health System, Hedrick Medical Center, Chillicothe, MO, p. A404

FACHE, Interim Chief Executive Officer, Wright Memorial Hospital, Trenton, MO, p. A419

SCHIEFELBEIN, Shelia, Coordinator Human Resources, Northwest Florida Community Hospital, Chipley, FL, p. A134

SCHIERECK, Stacie, Director Management Services, Mendota Mental Health Institute, Madison, WI, p. A787

SCHIESL, Troy, Director Information Services, Bellin Psychiatric Center, Green Bay, WI, p. A785

SCHIESLER, Hannah, Interim Assistant Director Human Resources, Baptist Hospitals Of Southeast Texas, Beaumont, TX, p. A658

SCHILLER, Ann Mattia, Vice President Human Resources, College Medical Center, Long Beach, CA, p. A72

SCHILLER, Jonathan, Chief Executive Officer, Garnet Health Medical Center - Catskills, Harris, NY, p. A485

SCHIMEROWSKI, Deb, Regional Chief Financial Officer, Amita Health St. Mary's Hospital, Kankakee, IL, p. A209

Regional Finance Officer, Amita Health Saint Josep. Medical Center, Joliet, IL, p. A209

SCHIMMING, Christopher, M.D., Medical Director, Mayo Clinic Health System In Waseca, Waseca, MN, p. A387

SCHIMMING, Michael, Director Financial Services, Shriners Hospitals For Children-Galveston, Galveston, TX, p. A680

Director Fiscal Services, Shriners Hospitals For Children-Houston, Houston, TX, p. A688

SCHINDEL, Lester P., Interim Chief Executive Officer, Waterbury Hospital, Waterbury, CT, p. A126

SCHIPPER, Brad, Chief Operating Officer, Sanford Usd Medical Center, Sioux Falls, SD, p. A631

SCHIPPER, Jody, Director of Nursing, Grundy County Memorial Hospital, Grundy Center, IA, p. A250

SCHLABACH, Michael, M.D., Chief Medical Officer, Baylor Scott & White Medical Center - Brenham, Brenham, TX, p. A660

SCHLADER, Rod G., President and Chief Executive Officer, Mercyone North Iowa Medical Center, Mason City, IA, p. A254

SCHLAGER, Robert, M.D., Chief Medical Officer, Northern Light Sebasticook Valley Hospital, Pittsfield, ME, p. A322

SCHLAGGER, Bradley, M.D., President and Chief Executive Officer, Kennedy Krieger Institute, Baltimore, MD, p. A324

SCHLECHT, Dara, Chief Nursing Officer, St. Francis Memorial Hospital, West Point, NE, p. A440

SCHLECHTER, Sandy, Chief Executive Officer, Bowdle Hospital, Bowdle, SD, p. A626

SCHLEETER, Larry, Chief Human Resources Officer, Memorial Health, Marysville, OH, p. A544

SCHLEGEL, Patricia, Executive Director Finance, Ridgeview Le Sueur Medical Center, Le Sueur, MN, p. A378

SCHLEICHER, Larry, Manager Information Services, Warner Hospital And Health Services, Clinton, IL, p. A201

SCHLEIF, John, Senior Vice President and Chief Operating Officer, Henry Mayo Newhall Hospital, Valencia, CA, p. A103

SCHLENKER, Jim, Chief Operating Officer, Good Shepherd Health Care System, Hermiston, OR, p. A576

SCHLESKE, Brenda, Administrator, Community Behavioral Health Hospital - Fergus Falls, Fergus Falls, MN, p. A376

SCHLESSMAN, Alissa, Administrator, Beaver County Memorial Hospital, Beaver, OK, p. A556

SCHLEY, Kurt, Chief Executive Officer, Chi St. Alexius Health, Bismarck, ND, p. A521

SCHLICHTMAN, Beth, Chief Human Resources Officer, Brodstone Memorial Hospital, Superior, NE, p. A440

SCHLICHTMANN, Phyllis J., R.N., Chief Executive Officer, Kessler Marlton Rehabilitation, Marlton, NJ, p. A458

SCHLIECH, Roxane, Chief Financial Officer, Gundersen Tri-County Hospital And Clinics, Whitehall, WI, p. A799

SCHLUETER, Ann, Chief Operating Officer, Community Hospital-Fairfax, Fairfax, MO, p. A406

SCHLUNTZ, Ana, Director of Human Resources, Harlan County Health System, Alma, NE, p. A429

SCHLUTER, Robin M., Chief Executive Officer, Regional Health Services Of Howard County, Cresco, IA, p. A247

SCHMAEDECKE, Dena, Vice President Human Resources, North Suburban Medical Center, Thornton, CO, p. A119

SCHMALLEN, Dede, Chief Human Resources Officer, Wickenburg Community Hospital, Wickenburg, AZ, p. A41

SCHMEDEMANN, Isabel, Chief Executive Officer and Administrator, Herington Municipal Hospital, Herington, KS, p. A266

SCHMERBECK, Vic, Chief Executive Officer, Baylor Scott & White Emergency Hospital - Grand Prairie, Grand Prairie, TX, p. A682

Chief Executive Officer, Baylor Scott & White Emergency Hospital - Rockwall, Rockwall, TX, p. A709

Chief Executive Officer, Baylor Scott & White Emergency Hospital—Burleson, Burleson, TX, p. A662

Chief Executive Officer, Baylor Scott & White Emergency Hospitals—Aubrey, Aubrey, TX, p. A654

Chief Executive Officer, Baylor Scott & White Emergency Medical Center- Cedar Park, Cedar Park, TX, p. A663

SCHMID, Nancy, R.N., MS, Associate Director Patient Care Services, Coatesville Veterans Affairs Medical Center, Coatesville, PA, p. A587

SCHMIDGALL, Brandon, Chief Executive Officer, Salem Health West Valley, Dallas, OR, p. A574

SCHMIDT, Allen, M.D., President, Medical Staff, Decatur Morgan Hospital, Decatur, AL, p. A17

SCHMIDT, Barbara, Chief Executive Officer, Mesa Springs Fort Worth, TX, p. A679

SCHMIDT, Bobbi, Chief Nursing Officer, Select Specialty Hospital-Cincinnati, Cincinnati, OH, p. A533

SCHMIDT, Brent, Administrator, Sevier Valley Hospital, Richfield, UT, p. A731

SCHMIDT, Constance, FACHE, R.N., Chief Executive Officer, St. Anthony North Health Campus, Westminster, CO, p. A119

SCHMIDT, Gary R., Interim President and Chief Executive Officer, Good Shepherd Rehabilitation Hospital, Allentown, PA, p. A583

SCHMIDT, Janie, Director of Nursing, Greeley County Health Services, Tribune, KS, p. A278

SCHMIDT, Joan, Director Human Resources, Eden Springs Health Care Center, Green Springs, OH, p. A541

SCHMIDT, Mark C., President, Monument Health Custer Hospital, Custer, SD, p. A627

President, Monument Health Lead-Deadwood Hospital, Deadwood, SD, p. A627

SCHMIDT, Milan, Medical Director, North Shore Health, Grand Marais, MN, p. A377

SCHMIDT, Richard O. Jr, President and Chief Executive Officer, Froedtert South - Kenosha Medical Center, Kenosha, WI, p. A786

SCHMIDT, Robert, Director Human Resources, Hocking Valley Community Hospital, Logan, OH, p. A543

SCHMIDT, Rosanne, R.N., Chief Nursing Officer, Chi St. Alexius Health, Bismarck, ND, p. A521

SCHMIDT, Steve, Director Information Systems, Evans Memorial Hospital, Claxton, GA, p. A168

SCHMIDT, Veronica, President and Chief Executive Officer, Jennie M. Melham Memorial Medical Center, Broken Bow, NE, p. A440

SCHMIDT, William, Chief Executive Officer, Thedacare Medical Center-Shawano, Shawano, WI, p. A795
President and Chief Executive Officer, Thedacare Medical Center-New London, New London, WI, p. A792

SCHMIDTBERGER, Sheryl, Chief Financial Officer, Alliancehealth Ponca City, Ponca City, OK, p. A567

SCHMIDTKE, Holly, R.N., Interim President, Aurora West Allis Medical Center, West Allis, WI, p. A799

SCHMIEDT, Jason, Chief Financial Officer, Clinch Valley Medical Center, Richlands, VA, p. A749

SCHMIER, Joseph, Interim Director Human Resources, North Valley Hospital, Whitefish, MT, p. A428

SCHMIESING, Karee, Director of Nursing, Sleep. Eye Medical Center, Sleep. Eye, MN, p. A386

SCHMITS, Peggy, Director, Nursing Operations, New Braunfels Regional Rehabilitation Hospital, New Braunfels, TX, p. A703

SCHMITT, John, Senior Vice President and Chief Financial Officer, Kingsbrook Jewish Medical Center, Brooklyn, NY, p. A478

SCHMITT, Josep. Senior Vice President Finance and Chief Financial Officer, Henry Ford Hospital, Detroit, MI, p. A353
Chief Financial Officer, Va Greater Los Angeles Healthcare System, Los Angeles, CA, p. A76
Chief Information Officer, St. Elizabeth's Medical Center, Brighton, MA, p. A337

SCHMITT, Karl, M.D., Chief of Staff, St. Elizabeth Edgewood, Edgewood, KY, p. A282

SCHMITT, Robert C. II, CPA, FACHE, Chief Executive Officer, Gibson Area Hospital And Health Services, Gibson City, IL, p. A206

SCHMITT, Thomas M., Chief Executive Officer, Kansas Spine & Specialty Hospital, Wichita, KS, p. A279

SCHMITTOU, Stephanie, MSN, R.N., Chief Nursing Officer, Magnolia Regional Medical Center, Magnolia, AR, p. A49

SCHMITZ, Bonnie, Chief Financial Officer, Ripon Medical Center, Ripon, WI, p. A795
Chief Financial Officer, Waupun Memorial Hospital, Waupun, WI, p. A798
Vice President and Chief Financial Officer, St. Agnes Hospital, Fond Du Lac, WI, p. A784

SCHMITZ, Christopher, Associate Vice President, Director Human Resources, Stoughton Hospital Association, Stoughton, WI, p. A797

SCHMITZ, Douglas, Director of Nursing, Long-Term Acute Care Hospital, Mosaic Life Care At St. Joseph, Saint Joseph, MO, p. A415

SCHMITZ, Jessica, Director of Nursing, Roosevelt Medical Center, Culbertson, MT, p. A422

SCHMITZ, Joseph, Chief Financial Officer, St. Cloud Veterans Affairs Health Care System, Saint Cloud, MN, p. A384

SCHMOTZER, Dave, Chief Financial Officer, Bryn Mawr Rehabilitation Hospital, Malvern, PA, p. A596

SCHMOYER, Leah, Human Resources Director, Buffalo Hospital, Buffalo, MN, p. A373

SCHMUS, Angie, Chief Information Technology, Aleda E. Lutz Veterans Affairs Medical Center, Saginaw, MI, p. A365

SCHNABEL, Annette D., FACHE, President and Chief Executive Officer, Parkland Health Center - Farmington Community, Farmington, MO, p. A406
FACHE, President and Chief Executive Officer, Parkland Health Center-Bonne Terre, Bonne Terre, MO, p. A402

SCHNACK, Tim, Chief Financial Officer, Chi Health Immanuel, Omaha, NE, p. A436
Chief Financial Officer, Chi Health Plainview, Plainview, NE, p. A439
Chief Financial Officer, Chi Health Schuyler, Schuyler, NE, p. A439
Vice President Financial Services, Chi Health Creighton University Medical Center - Bergan Mercy, Omaha, NE, p. A436
Vice President Operations Finance, Chi Health St. Mary's, Nebraska City, NE, p. A435

SCHNEDLER, Lisa W., FACHE, President and Chief Executive Officer, Upland Hills Health, Dodgeville, WI, p. A782

SCHNEIDER, Barbara, R.N., Chief Executive Officer, Foothill Regional Medical Center, Tustin, CA, p. A102

SCHNEIDER, Brenda, Chief Financial Officer, Skyline Hospital, White Salmon, WA, p. A769

SCHNEIDER, Brian, Chief Financial Officer, Dupont Hospital, Fort Wayne, IN, p. A228

SCHNEIDER, Carol L., President and Chief Executive Officer, Mercy Hospital And Medical Center, Chicago, IL, p. A199

SCHNEIDER, Frank, FACHE, Chief Executive Officer, Gateway Rehabilitation Hospital, Florence, KY, p. A283

SCHNEIDER, Gina, Director Human Resources, Northwest Specialty Hospital, Post Falls, ID, p. A192

SCHNEIDER, Jennifer, Vice President of Finance, Saint Francis Hospital And Medical Center, Hartford, CT, p. A122

SCHNEIDER, Jessie, Director Human Resources, Community Memorial Healthcare, Marysville, KS, p. A270

SCHNEIDER, John, M.D., Medical Director, Milwaukee County Behavioral Health Division, Milwaukee, WI, p. A791
Human Resources Director, Putnam Community Medical Center, Palatka, FL, p. A152

SCHNEIDER, Kimberly, Director Human Resources, Pottstown Hospital, Pottstown, PA, p. A605

SCHNEIDER, Shanon, Chief Information Officer, Greeley County Health Services, Tribune, KS, p. A278

SCHNEIDER, Stacie, Director Human Resources, Aurora Sheboygan Memorial Medical Center, Sheboygan, WI, p. A796

SCHNEIDER, Stephen, Manager Information Services, Alaska Psychiatric Institute, Anchorage, AK, p. A27

SCHNEIDER, Steven E., M.D., President, Saint Mary's Hospital, Waterbury, CT, p. A126

SCHNEIDER, Thomas, D.O., Chief of Staff, Jack C. Montgomery Veterans Affairs Medical Center, Muskogee, OK, p. A562

SCHNEIDER, Valerie, Director Human Resources, Gove County Medical Center, Quinter, KS, p. A275

SCHNELL, Dawn, Chief Nursing Officer and Interim Senior Director, Sanford Jackson Medical Center, Jackson, MN, p. A378
Chief Nursing Officer, Sanford Jackson Medical Center, Jackson, MN, p. A378

SCHNELLER, Sharon, Chief Nursing Officer, Olmsted Medical Center, Rochester, MN, p. A384

SCHNIEDERS, Michael H., FACHE, President, Chi Health Good Samaritan, Kearney, NE, p. A433

SCHNIER, Martin, D.O., Chief of Staff, West Texas Veterans Affairs Health Care System, Big Spring, TX, p. A660

SCHNITTKER, Kira, Director of Nursing, St. Vincent's Blount, Oneonta, AL, p. A23

SCHNOOR, Jeff, Director Information Systems, Swedish Medical Center, Englewood, CO, p. A112

SCHOCK, Marilyn, President, Uchealth Greeley, Greeley, CO, p. A114

SCHOELLER, Betsy, Director Human Resources and Education, Mary Greeley Medical Center, Ames, IA, p. A243

SCHOEN, Greg, M.D., Regional Medical Director, Fairview Northland Medical Center, Princeton, MN, p. A383
M.D., Vice President Medical Affairs, Fairview Lakes Health Services, Wyoming, MN, p. A388

SCHOENDALER, Hannah, Chief Nursing Officer, Sheridan County Health Complex, Hoxie, KS, p. A266

SCHOENECKER, Perry, M.D., Chief of Staff, Shriners Hospitals For Children-St. Louis, Saint Louis, MO, p. A416

SCHOENER, Timothy, Chief Information Officer, Upmc Muncy, Muncy, PA, p. A598
Senior Vice President and Chief Information Officer, Upmc Wellsboro, Wellsboro, PA, p. A610
Vice President and Chief Information Officer, Upmc Williamsport, Williamsport, PA, p. A611

SCHOENIG, Thomas, Chief Information Officer, Amita Health Adventist Medical Center La Grange, La Grange, IL, p. A210
Chief Information Officer, Jupiter Medical Center, Jupiter, FL, p. A142

SCHOENIG, Tom, Regional Director Information Services, Valley Hospital Medical Center, Las Vegas, NV, p. A445

SCHOETTLE, Steve, M.D., Chief Medical Staff, Ozark Health Medical Center, Clinton, AR, p. A43

SCHOFIELD, Joseph, Chief Operating Officer, Suburban Community Hospital, East Norriton, PA, p. A589

SCHOFIELD, Sherry, Director Human Resources, Sovah Health-Martinsville, Martinsville, VA, p. A746

SCHOLEFIELD, Robert, MS, R.N., Executive Vice President and Chief Operating Officer, Faxton St. Luke's Healthcare, Utica, NY, p. A500

SCHOLL, Shyanne, Interim Human Resources Director, Friend Community Healthcare System, Friend, NE, p. A432

SCHOLZ, Suzanne, Director Medical Records, Horsham Clinic, Ambler, PA, p. A584

SCHOMBURG, Jennifer, Chief Administrative Officer, Oro Valley Hospital, Oro Valley, AZ, p. A34
Chief Executive Officer, Northwest Medical Center, Tucson, AZ, p. A40

SCHONEBERY, Jeremy, Director Information Technology, Heart Of America Medical Center, Rugby, ND, p. A525

SCHONS, Jeri, R.N., Chief Nursing Officer, Sanford Tracy Medical Center, Tracy, MN, p. A386

SCHOOL, Peggy, Director of Nursing, Thedacare Medical Center-New London, New London, WI, p. A792

SCHOOLER, Rick, Vice President and Chief Information Officer, Orlando Regional Medical Center, Orlando, FL, p. A151

SCHOONOVER, Michele, Chief Executive Officer, Virginia Gay Hospital, Vinton, IA, p. A259

SCHOPP, Mary, Senior Vice President Human Resources, Rush University Medical Center, Chicago, IL, p. A200

SCHORER, Emily, Senior Vice President Human Resources, Cap. Cod Hospital, Hyannis, MA, p. A340
Vice President, Human Resources, Falmouth Hospital, Falmouth, MA, p. A339

SCHOTT, Connie, Vice President, Human Resources, Ozarks Medical Center, West Plains, MO, p. A420

SCHOTTEL, Roxanne, Chief Executive Officer, Washington County Hospital, Washington, KS, p. A278

SCHOWENGERDT, Daniel, M.D., Chief of Staff, Comanche County Hospital, Coldwater, KS, p. A263

SCHRADER, Guillermo, M.D., Acting Medical Director, Eastern State Hospital, Williamsburg, VA, p. A753

SCHRAEDER, David, Director Information Systems, Russell Regional Hospital, Russell, KS, p. A275

SCHRAMM, Michael, Chief Executive Officer, Rice Memorial Hospital, Willmar, MN, p. A388

SCHRAMM, Steven, Chief Financial Officer, Mountain View Hospital, Payson, UT, p. A730

SCHRANT, Benjamin, M.D., Chief of Staff, Northeast Regional Medical Center, Kirksville, MO, p. A410

SCHREFFLER, Mary Jane, Director Human Resources, Meadows Psychiatric Center, Centre Hall, PA, p. A586

SCHREIBER, Anne, Manager Human Resources, Fairfax Behavioral Health, Kirkland, WA, p. A759

SCHREIBER, Elizabeth, R.N., Director Patient Care Services, Flambeau Hospital, Park Falls, WI, p. A794

SCHREIER, Garett, R.N., Associate Director, Nursing and Patient Care Services, Ralp. H. Johnson Veterans Affairs Medical Center, Charleston, SC, p. A616

SCHREINER, David L., FACHE, President and Chief Executive Officer, Katherine Shaw Bethea Hospital, Dixon, IL, p. A202

SCHREINER, Jim, Chief Information Officer, Graham Hospital Association, Canton, IL, p. A196

SCHREINER, Kimberly, MSN, R.N., Vice President of Nursing & Chief Nursing Officer, Magruder Memorial Hospital, Port Clinton, OH, p. A548

SCHRIER, Erick, Supervisor Information Technology, Van Diest Medical Center, Webster City, IA, p. A260

SCHROCK, Bonnie, FACHE, Chief Operating Officer, Baptist Health Paducah, Paducah, KY, p. A291

SCHRODER, Loren, Chief Financial Officer, Phelp. Memorial Health Center, Holdrege, NE, p. A433

SCHROEDER, Brian, M.D., Senior Vice President and Chief Medical Officer, Sparrow Hospital, Lansing, MI, p. A360

SCHROEDER, Catherine, Deputy Chief Information Officer, Brigham And Women's Faulkner Hospital, Boston, MA, p. A335

SCHROEDER, Cygnet, D.O., Medical Director, Encompasss Health Rehabilitation Hospital Of Fort Smith, Fort Smith, AR, p. A46

SCHROEDER, Destiny, Information Systems Director, Rawlins County Health Center, Atwood, KS, p. A262

SCHROEDER, Heather, R.N., Vice President Nursing, Aurora Baycare Medical Center, Green Bay, WI, p. A785

SCHROEDER, Joanne, President, Munson Healthcare Charlevoix Hospital, Charlevoix, MI, p. A350

SCHROEDER, Rick, Chief Executive Officer, North Big Horn Hospital District, Lovell, WY, p. A803

SCHROEDER, Russell, Chief Nursing Officer, Bayfront Health Punta Gorda, Punta Gorda, FL, p. A155

SCHROEDL, Greg, M.D., Vice President, Medical and Chief Medical Officer, Uw Medicine/Northwest Hospital & Medical Center, Seattle, WA, p. A764

SCHROEPPEL, Stacie, Director of Human Resources, Baptist Memorial Rehabilitation Hospital, Germantown, TN, p. A638

SCHROYER, Mike K., FACHE, MSN, R.N., President, Baptist Health Floyd, New Albany, IN, p. A237

SCHRUMPF, Jason, President, Missouri Delta Medical Center, Sikeston, MO, p. A418

SCHUBACH, Michael, Chief People Officer, Carroll County Memorial Hospital, Carrollton, MO, p. A404

SCHUCK, Eric, M.D., Chief Medical Officer, Tristar Southern Hills Medical Center, Nashville, TN, p. A647

SCHUCKMAN, Tim, Chief Financial Officer, Jennie M. Melham Memorial Medical Center, Broken Bow, NE, p. A430

SCHUE, Janine, Executive Vice President, Chief Human Resources Officer, Rochester Regional Health, Newark-Wayne Community Hospital, Newark, NY, p. A492
Senior Vice President Human Resources, Rochester General Hospital, Rochester, NY, p. A496

SCHUELER, Joe, Chief Financial Officer, Morrow County Hospital, Mount Gilead, OH, p. A546

SCHUERCH, Timothy, President and Chief Executive Officer, Maniilaq Health Center, Kotzebue, AK, p. A29

SCHUESSLER, Dwight, Chief Information Officer, Iowa City Va Health Care System, Iowa City, IA, p. A252

SCHUESSLER, James P., Chief Executive Officer, Healdsburg District Hospital, Healdsburg, CA, p. A68

SCHULER, Allison, R.N., Chief Nursing Officer, Baptist Medical Center Attala, Kosciusko, MS, p. A395

SCHULER, Kathy, R.N., MS, Chief Operating Officer and Chief Nursing Officer, Winchester Hospital, Winchester, MA, p. A346

SCHULHOF, Alicia, President and Chief Executive Officer, Indiana University Health North Hospital, Carmel, IN, p. A225

SCHULTE, Mark, FACHE, President, Monument Health Sturgis Hospital, Sturgis, SD, p. A632

SCHULTES, Jeremy, Administrator and Chief Executive Officer, Philip Health Services, Philip. SD, p. A630

SCHULTHEIS, Hal, Director Information Systems, Tristar Hendersonville Medical Center, Hendersonville, TN, p. A639

SCHULTZ, Bradley, Chief Financial Officer, Wesley Healthcare Center, Wichita, KS, p. A279

SCHULTZ, David W., FACHE, President, Peninsula Region, St. Anthony Hospital, Gig Harbor, WA, p. A758
FACHE, President, Peninsula Region, St. Michael Medical Center, Bremerton, WA, p. A756

SCHULTZ, Diana, Chief Executive Officer, Rio Vista Behavioral Health, El Paso, TX, p. A675

SCHULTZ, Jacky, MSN, R.N., President, Suburban Hospital, Bethesda, MD, p. A327

SCHULTZ, Jim, Chief Executive Officer, Edgerton Hospital And Health Services, Edgerton, WI, p. A783

SCHULTZ, Kurt, Chief Financial Officer, Cornerstone Hospitals West Monroe, West Monroe, LA, p. A316
Chief Financial Officer, Solara Hospital Harlingen, Harlingen, TX, p. A683
Group Chief Financial Officer, Chg Hospital Tucson, Llc, Tucson, AZ, p. A40

SCHULTZ, Mary, Director Human Resources, Sturgis Hospital, Sturgis, MI, p. A367

SCHULTZ, Merrilee, Chief Finance, Sanford Usd Medical Center, Sioux Falls, SD, p. A631

SCHULTZ, Patrick, Vice President Nursing, Sanford Medical Center Bismarck, Bismarck, ND, p. A521

SCHULTZ, Rachelle H., Ed.D., President and Chief Executive Officer, Winona Health, Winona, MN, p. A388

SCHULTZ, Sharon, Chief Nurse Executive and Vice President, Tri-City Medical Center, Oceanside, CA, p. A82

SCHULTZ, Teresa, R.N., Vice President of Patient Care, Rogers Memorial Hospital, Inc., Oconomowoc, WI, p. A793

SCHULTZ, Vince, M.D., Chief Medical Officer, Munson Healthcare Grayling Hospital, Grayling, MI, p. A356

SCHULZ, Ken, Chief Operating Officer, North Dakota State Hospital, Jamestown, ND, p. A524

SCHULZ, Leah, Director of Nursing, North Dakota State Hospital, Jamestown, ND, p. A524

SCHULZ, Marcie, Director Patient Care, Sakakawea Medical Center, Hazen, ND, p. A524

SCHULZ, Susan, Chief Nursing Officer, Beaumont Hospital - Trenton, Trenton, MI, p. A368

SCHUMACHER, Ann, R.N., MSN, FACHE, President, Chi Health Immanuel, Omaha, NE, p. A436
R.N., MSN, FACHE, President, Chi Health Mercy Council Bluffs, Council Bluffs, IA, p. A247

SCHUMACHER, Debbie, Chief Human Resource Officer, Clearwater Valley Hospital And Clinics, Orofino, ID, p. A192
Chief Human Resource Officer, St. Mary's Hospital, Cottonwood, ID, p. A190

SCHUMACHER, Kevin, Director of Information Systems, Lifecare Medical Center, Roseau, MN, p. A384

SCHUMACHER, Paul, Chief Operating Officer, Mcleod Health Clarendon, Manning, SC, p. A622

SCHUMACHER, Rodney, Interim Chief Executive Officer, San Angelo Community Medical Center, San Angelo, TX, p. A710

SCHUMANN, Vera, Director of Finance and Controller, North Shore Health, Grand Marais, MN, p. A377

SCHUSTER, Carol, R.N., Chief Nursing Officer and Vice President Patient Care Services, Franciscan Health Crown Point, Crown Point, IN, p. A226

SCHUSTER, Christine C., R.N., President and Chief Executive Officer, Emerson Hospital, Concord, MA, p. A338

SCHUSTER, Emmett, Interim Chief Executive Officer, Odessa Memorial Healthcare Center, Odessa, WA, p. A761

SCHUSTER, Janet, Chief Nursing Officer, Lutheran Hospital, Cleveland, OH, p. A534

SCHUSTER, Lexie, Vice President Human Resources, Good Samaritan Hospital, Los Angeles, CA, p. A74

SCHUSTER, Todd, Administrator, Saint Francis Hospital Vinita, Vinita, OK, p. A571
Vice President and Administrator, Saint Francis Hospital South, Tulsa, OK, p. A570

SCHUSTER, Tony, M.D., Vice President of Physician Services, Mease Countryside Hospital, Safety Harbor, FL, p. A155
M.D., Vice President of Physician Services, Mease Dunedin Hospital, Dunedin, FL, p. A137

SCHWAB, Bob, M.D., Chief Medical Officer, Texas Health Presbyterian Hospital Allen, Allen, TX, p. A652

SCHWABENBAUER, Mary Ann, Director Information Technology, Penn Highlands Elk, Saint Marys, PA, p. A606

SCHWAEGEL, Glen, Chief Financial Officer, Progress West Hospital, O'Fallon, MO, p. A413
Vice President and Chief Financial Officer, Barnes-Jewish St. Peters Hospital, Saint Peters, MO, p. A418

SCHWAN, Karin, Chief Nursing Officer, Vice President Patient Care Services, Uh Samaritan Medical Center, Ashland, OH, p. A528

SCHWANER, Charles Chief Financial Officer, Doctors Hospital Of Sarasota, Sarasota, FL, p. A157

SCHWANKE, Daniel, Interim Chief Executive Officer, Rochelle Community Hospital, Rochelle, IL, p. A218

SCHWARM, Tony, FACHE, President, Missouri Baptist Sullivan Hospital, Sullivan, MO, p. A419

SCHWARTZ, Ave, Chief Information Officer, Austen Riggs Center, Stockbridge, MA, p. A345

SCHWARTZ, David, D.O., Vice President, Medical Affairs, Sentara Northern Virginia Medical Center, Woodbridge, VA, p. A754
M.D., Chief Medical Officer, Saint Francis Hospital-Bartlett, Bartlett, TN, p. A634
M.D., Chief Medical Officer, Saint Francis Hospital, Memphis, TN, p. A645

SCHWARTZ, Jack, Director Information Technology, Kittitas Valley Healthcare, Ellensburg, WA, p. A757

SCHWARTZ, Jonathon, M.D., Chief Medical Officer, Spaulding Hospital For Continuing Medical Care Cambridge, Cambridge, MA, p. A338

SCHWARTZ, Kenneth, M.D., Medical Director, Griffin Hospital, Derby, CT, p. A122

SCHWARTZ, Kim, Assistant Administrator Human Resources and Operations, Boone County Hospital, Boone, IA, p. A244

SCHWARTZ, Michael, M.D., Chief of Staff, College Hospital Costa Mesa, Costa Mesa, CA, p. A61

SCHWARTZ, Mitchell, M.D., Chief Medical Officer, Anne Arundel Medical Center, Annapolis, MD, p. A324

SCHWARTZ, Peggy, Vice President Human Resources, Wayne Healthcare, Greenville, OH, p. A541

SCHWARTZ, Peter, Director Information Systems, Hackensack Meridian Health Carrier Clinic, Belle Mead, NJ, p. A452

SCHWARTZ, Roberta, Ph.D., Executive Vice President, Houston Methodist Hospital, Houston, TX, p. A686

SCHWARTZ, Ronald, M.D., Medical Director, Masonicare Health Center, Wallingford, CT, p. A126

SCHWARTZ, Sharon, Director Medical Records, Baylor Scott & White Medical Center - Brenham, Brenham, TX, p. A660

SCHWARTZ, Stephanie L., FACHE, Vice President AHS and President CMC, Chilton Medical Center, Pompton Plains, NJ, p. A462

SCHWARZ, John, Vice President Administration, Lankenau Medical Center, Wynnewood, PA, p. A612

SCHWARZKOPF, Ruth, Chief Nursing Officer, West Boca Medical Center, Boca Raton, FL, p. A132

SCHWEBLER, Michael W., President and Chief Executive Officer, Highpoint Health, Lawrenceburg, IN, p. A235

SCHWEICKHARDT, Mary Jo, Vice President Human Resources, Medstar Georgetown University Hospital, Washington, DC, p. A129

SCHWEIGERT, Nicole, Director Human Resources, Texas Health Presbyterian Hospital Flower Mound, Flower Mound, TX, p. A677

SCHWEIGHART, Karen, R.N., MS, Administrator, Andrew Mcfarland Mental Health Center, Springfield, IL, p. A220

SCHWEIKART, Jay, Chief Financial Officer, Kindred Hospital-Sycamore, Sycamore, IL, p. A221

SCHWEIZER, Kim, Director Human Resources, Excelsior Springs Hospital, Excelsior Springs, MO, p. A406

SCHWENN, Krystal, Chief Financial Officer, Phillip. County Health Systems, Phillipsburg, KS, p. A274

SCHWIEGER, Kay, Chief Human Resources Officer, Clement J. Zablocki Veterans Affairs Medical Center, Milwaukee, WI, p. A791

SCHWIND, David, Chief Financial Officer, Capital Hospice, Arlington, VA, p. A738

SCHWINGLER, Joyce, Chief Financial Officer, Eureka Community Health Services Avera, Eureka, SD, p. A628

SCIARRA, Michael, M.D., Chief Medical Officer, Hudson Regional Hospital, Secaucus, NJ, p. A463

SCIARRO, Jason, Chief Operating Officer, Butler Health System, Butler, PA, p. A585

SCIMECA, Paul, Senior Vice President Operations and Chief Operating Officer, Glens Falls Hospital, Glens Falls, NY, p. A484

SCIONTI, Jeff, Chief Executive Officer, Frisbie Memorial Hospital, Rochester, NH, p. A451

SCIOSCIA, Angela, M.D., Chief Medical Officer, Uc San Diego Medical Center—Hillcrest, San Diego, CA, p. A92

SCLAMA, Tony, M.D., Vice President Medical Affairs, Medstar Franklin Square Medical Center, Baltimore, MD, p. A325

SCOGGIN, Terry, Chief Executive Officer, Titus Regional Medical Center, Mount Pleasant, TX, p. A702
Chief Financial Officer, Titus Regional Medical Center, Mount Pleasant, TX, p. A702

SCOGGINS, James, Director of Nursing, Arkansas State Hospital, Little Rock, AR, p. A48
Interim Chief Executive Officer, Arkansas State Hospital, Little Rock, AR, p. A48

SCOGNA, Stephen, President and Chief Executive Officer, Northwest Community Healthcare, Arlington Heights, IL, p. A194

SCORZELLI, Gerard, Chief Financial Officer, Albany Stratton Veterans Affairs Medical Center, Albany, NY, p. A474

SCOTFORD, Lucrecia, Executive Vice President and Chief Operations Officer, Bristol Bay Area Health Corporation, Dillingham, AK, p. A28

SCOTT, Alan, M.D., Chief of Staff, East Georgia Regional Medical Center, Statesboro, GA, p. A181

SCOTT, Colleen, Vice President Finance, Waterbury Hospital, Waterbury, CT, p. A126

SCOTT, Cullen, Chief Executive Officer, Northwest Hills Surgical Hospital, Austin, TX, p. A656

SCOTT, Damien, Chief Executive Officer, Emanuel Medical Center, Swainsboro, GA, p. A181

SCOTT, Daniel, Director of Information Systems, Good Samaritan Hospital, Vincennes, IN, p. A242

SCOTT, Doug, Vice President Human Resources, Rmc Anniston, Anniston, AL, p. A13

SCOTT, Ernie, Director Human Resources, Natchitoches Regional Medical Center, Natchitoches, LA, p. A310

SCOTT, Gilbert, Regional Hospital Administrator, Georgia Regional Hospital At Atlanta, Decatur, GA, p. A171

SCOTT, Henry, Executive Director, Technical Services, Piedmont Newnan Hospital, Newnan, GA, p. A178

SCOTT, James, M.D., Vice President Medical Affairs, Candler Hospital, Savannah, GA, p. A179
M.D., Vice President Medical Affairs, St. Joseph's Hospital, Savannah, GA, p. A180

SCOTT, Jeffrey, Chief Information Officer, Ascension St. Vincent Kokomo, Kokomo, IN, p. A234

SCOTT, Jennifer, Director of Informatics, Carepartners Health Services, Asheville, NC, p. A504

SCOTT, Jo Ellen, R.N., MS, Senior Vice President of Patient Care Services and Chief Nursing Officer, Indiana University Health Tipton Hospital, Tipton, IN, p. A241

SCOTT, Julie, Chief Nursing Officer, Encompass Health Rehabilitation Hospital Of York, York, PA, p. A612

SCOTT, Karen, Vice President Patient Care, Adventist Health Howard Memorial, Willits, CA, p. A105

SCOTT, Kelley, Interim Chief Nursing Officer, Grant Memorial Hospital, Petersburg, WV, p. A775

SCOTT, Lincoln, Vice President Human Resources, Southeast Hospital, Cap. Girardeau, MO, p. A404

SCOTT, M Daryl, Assistant Vice President, Jefferson Regional Medical Center, Pine Bluff, AR, p. A52

SCOTT, Margie A., M.D., Director, Central Arkansas Veterans Healthcare System, Little Rock, AR, p. A49

SCOTT, Martha, Chief Patient Care Officer, Covington County Hospital, Collins, MS, p. A391

SCOTT, Monica, Chief Financial Officer, Great Plains Regional Medical Center, Elk City, OK, p. A558

SCOTT, Rhonda, Ph.D., R.N., Chief Operating Officer, Grady Memorial Hospital, Atlanta, GA, p. A164

SCOTT, Robert, Vice President and Chief Human Resources Officer, Memorial Medical Center, Springfield, IL, p. A221

SCOTT, Sam, Vice President Financial Services, St. Dominic-Jackson Memorial Hospital, Jackson, MS, p. A395

SCOTT, Sharon, Health Information Director, Allegiance Specialty Hospital Of Greenville, Greenville, MS, p. A392

SCOTT, Steve, Chief Operating Officer, Sheridan Community Hospital, Sheridan, MI, p. A366

SCOTT, Steven M., President, Ssm Health Saint Louis University Hospital, Saint Louis, MO, p. A417

SCOTT, Susan, Chief Nurse Executive, Ventura County Medical Center, Ventura, CA, p. A103

SCOTT, Thomas, CPA, Chief Financial Officer, Saint Clare's Denville Hospital, Denville, NJ, p. A454
Senior Vice President and Chief Operating Officer, Centrastate Healthcare System, Freehold, NJ, p. A455

SCOTT, Tina, Acting Health Director, Choctaw Health Center, Philadelphia, MS, p. A398

SCOTT, Todd, Chief Financial Officer, Vibra Hospital Of Sacramento, Folsom, CA, p. A64

SCOTT, Travis, Service Unit Director, U. S. Public Health Service Indian Hospital, Pine Ridge, SD, p. A630

SCOTT, Veronica, Business Office Manager, Inspire Specialty Hospital, Midwest City, OK, p. A562

SCOTT, William, M.D., Chief of Staff, Dardanelle Regional Medical Center, Dardanelle, AR, p. A44

M.D., Vice President Medical Affairs, Regional Medical Center Of San Jose, San Jose, CA, p. A95

Chief Financial Officer, Kp. Promise Hospital Of Overland Park, Overland Park, KS, p. A274

SCOUFOS, Jennifer, M.D., Chief of Staff, Northeastern Health System Sequoyah, Sallisaw, OK, p. A567

SCOVILL, Terry, Chief Executive Officer, Intracare North Hospital, Houston, TX, p. A686

SCOWN, Kent, Director Operations and Information Services, Jerold Phelp. Community Hospital, Garberville, CA, p. A66

SCREMIN, Karen, Vice President Finance, Lutheran Medical Center, Wheat Ridge, CO, p. A120

SCRIVO JR, JosephDirector Human Resources, Mercy Hospital, Buffalo, NY, p. A480

SCROGGIN, Christy, Director Operations and Human Resources, Conway Regional Rehabilitation Hospital, Conway, AR, p. A44

SCROGGINS, Todd, Chief Financial Officer, Wise Health System, Decatur, TX, p. A671

SCROGGS, Amy, Chief Nursing Officer, Delano Regional Medical Center, Delano, CA, p. A62

SCRUGGS, Sherry, Administrator, Milan General Hospital, Milan, TN, p. A645

SCUDDER, Angela, MSN, R.N., Vice President Patient Care Services, Highpoint Health, Lawrenceburg, IN, p. A235

SCUDERI, Denise, Vice President Patient Care Services, Mayo Regional Hospital, Dover—Foxcroft, ME, p. A320

SCULCO, Dawn, Chief Nursing Officer, Valley View Hospital, Glenwood Springs, CO, p. A113

SCULL, Stephen, Vice President Ethics and Compliance officer, Rapides Regional Medical Center, Alexandria, LA, p. A295

SCULLY, Charles, Chief Information Officer, Honorhealth Scottsdale Thompson Peak Medical Center, Scottsdale, AZ, p. A38

SCULLY, Kem, Chief Executive Officer and Chief Nursing Officer, Purcell Municipal Hospital, Purcell, OK, p. A567

SCULLY, Trish, Director Human Resources, Taunton State Hospital, Taunton, MA, p. A345

Manager Employment Services, Pappas Rehabilitation Hospital For Children, Canton, MA, p. A338

SCZYGELSKI, Sidney, Senior Vice President Finance and Chief Financial Officer, Aspirus Wausau Hospital, Inc., Wausau, WI, p. A798

SEAGER, Jerry, Assistant Vice President and Chief Financial Officer, Inova Fair Oaks Hospital, Fairfax, VA, p. A741

SEAGO, Terri, Chief Financial Officer, Baptist Memorial Hospital-Collierville, Collierville, TN, p. A636

SEAGRAM, Patricia, Vice President Human Resources, Henry Ford Allegiance Health, Jackson, MI, p. A359

SEAGROVES, Matthew, Chief Financial Officer, Bayfront Health Brooksville, Brooksville, FL, p. A133

SEAHORN, Martha, Chief Nursing Officer, Gadsden Regional Medical Center, Gadsden, AL, p. A19

SEAL, John, Director Human Resources, Riverside Medical Center, Franklinton, LA, p. A302

Interim Chief Financial Officer Director Human Resources, Riverside Medical Center, Kankakee, IL, p. A209

SEAL, Ronald T., Chief Executive Officer, Texoma Medical Center, Denison, TX, p. A671

SEALE, Corey, Chief Operating Officer, Kaiser Permanente Moreno Valley Medical Center, Moreno Valley, CA, p. A80

SEALE, Jonathan, Chief Information Officer, Erie Veterans Affairs Medical Center, Erie, PA, p. A589

SEALS, Robert, D.O., Medical Director, Sparrow Carson Hospital, Carson City, MI, p. A350

SEAMON, Robert L., Chief Executive Officer, Copper Queen Community Hospital, Bisbee, AZ, p. A30

SEARLE, Anne, Chief Information Officer, Penn Medicine Princeton Medical Center, Plainsboro, NJ, p. A461

SEARLS, Barbara, Chief Financial Officer, Searhc Mt. Edgecumbe Hospital, Sitka, AK, p. A29

SEARLS, Gary, Chief Financial Officer, Brandon Regional Hospital, Brandon, FL, p. A133

SEARS, Erin, Associate Director of Operations, Providence Veterans Affairs Medical Center, Providence, RI, p. A613

SEARS, Marilyn, Chief Financial Officer, Hshs Good Shepherd Hospital, Shelbyville, IL, p. A220

SEARS, Tina, Director Patient Care Services, Sullivan County Memorial Hospital, Milan, MO, p. A412

SEASE, Peggy, Vice President Human Resources, Dch Regional Medical Center, Tuscaloosa, AL, p. A25

SEAVER, Roger E., President and Chief Executive Officer, Henry Mayo Newhall Hospital, Valencia, CA, p. A103

SEBEK, Brenda, R.N., Administrator, Chi Health St. Mary's, Nebraska City, NE, p. A435

SEBENALER, Ginette, Associate Chief Financial Officer, Aspen Valley Hospital, Aspen, CO, p. A107

SECKINGER, Mark R., President, O'Bleness Memorial Hospital, Athens, OH, p. A528

SECOR, April, R.N., Chief Nursing Officer, Hillcrest Hospital Henryetta, Henryetta, OK, p. A560

SECOR, Diane, Director Human Resources, Lawrence Medical Center, Moulton, AL, p. A22

SECURRO, Matthew, Vice President, Human Resources, Conway Medical Center, Conway, SC, p. A618

SEDA, Jolene, Vice President Chief Experience Officer, Virginia Mason Memorial, Yakima, WA, p. A769

SEEDER, Rachael, Controller, Santiam Hospital, Stayton, OR, p. A582

SEELEY, Hollie, Chief Operating Officer, Rose Medical Center, Denver, CO, p. A111

Interim Chief Executive Officer and Chief Operating Officer, Rose Medical Center, Denver, CO, p. A111

SEELEY, Kevin, Chief Information Officer, Mike O'Callaghan Federal Hospital, Nellis Afb, NV, p. A445

SEELEY, Pam, Chief Nursing Officer, Elmira Psychiatric Center, Elmira, NY, p. A483

SEELEY, Steven, Vice President, Chief Operating Officer, Chief Nursing Officer, Jupiter Medical Center, Jupiter, FL, p. A142

SEELY, Paula, Manager Human Resources, Kossuth Regional Health Center, Algona, IA, p. A243

SEEMS, Steven, Director of Information Technology, Phillip. County Health Systems, Phillipsburg, KS, p. A274

SEESE, Rebecca, Chief Operating Officer, U. S. Air Force Regional Hospital, Elmendorf Afb, AK, p. A28

SEESEE, Alan, Chief Executive Officer, Capital Regional Medical Center, Tallahassee, FL, p. A158

SEEVER, Jennifer, Regional Chief Financial Officer, Sedan City Hospital, Sedan, KS, p. A276

SEGAL, Jonathan, Chief Financial Officer, New York State Psychiatric Institute, New York, NY, p. A491

SEGAL, Rebecca, Chief Executive Officer, Rutherford Regional Health System, Rutherfordton, NC, p. A517

SEGAL, Stanton, M.D., Chief Medical Officer, Jefferson Health Northeast, Philadelphia, PA, p. A600

SEGAL, Tanya, Director, St. Luke's Easton Campus, Easton, PA, p. A589

SEGAWA, Lance, Chief Executive Officer, Kauai Veterans Memorial Hospital, Waimea, HI, p. A186

Chief Executive Officer, Samuel Mahelona Memorial Hospital, Kapaa, HI, p. A186

SEGER, LaDonna, Director Information Services, Saint Luke's North Hospital - Barry Road, Kansas City, MO, p. A409

SEGIN, Robert, Chief Financial Officer, Virtua Memorial, Mount Holly, NJ, p. A458

Executive Vice President & Chief Financial Officer, Virtua Marlton, Marlton, NJ, p. A458

SEGUR, Jennifer, Chief Nursing Officer and Chief Clinical Officer, Adventhealth North Pinellas, Tarpon Springs, FL, p. A160

SEGURA, Mario, Director of Nursing, Starr County Memorial Hospital, Rio Grande City, TX, p. A709

SEHNERT, Laura, M.D., Chief Medical Officer, Uchealth Yamp. Valley Medical Center, Steamboat Springs, CO, p. A118

SEHRT, Lori, Associate Chief Financial Officer Northern Colorado, Banner Fort Collins Medical Center, Fort Collins, CO, p. A112

Chief Financial Officer, Mckee Medical Center, Loveland, CO, p. A117

SEIBERT, Jenee, Chief Finance Officer, Fulton County Health Center, Wauseon, OH, p. A552

SEIBOLD, Spencer, M.D., Chief of Medical Staff, Power County Hospital District, American Falls, ID, p. A188

SEID, Lynette, Area Chief Financial Officer, Kaiser Permanente San Diego Medical Center, San Diego, CA, p. A91

SEIDL, Doris, Vice President Human Resources, Mclaren Port Huron, Port Huron, MI, p. A364

SEIDMAN, Robert, Chief Operating Officer, Health Alliance Hospital - Broadway Campus, Kingston, NY, p. A486

Chief Operating Officer, Health Alliance Hospital - Mary's Avenue Campus, Kingston, NY, p. A487

SEIFER, Jill, Vice President Human Resources, Oaklawn Psychiatric Center, Goshen, IN, p. A229

SEIFERT, Debra, Director Human Resources, Lake Huron Medical Center, Port Huron, MI, p. A364

SEILER, Gregory A., Chief Executive Officer, Methodist Hospital South, Jourdanton, TX, p. A691

SEIM, Lori, R.N., Director Nursing Services, First Care Health Center, Park River, ND, p. A525

SEIP, Jeffrey, M.D., Chief Medical Staff, Hi-Desert Medical Center, Joshua Tree, CA, p. A69

SEIPLE, Donald, President, St. Luke's Monroe, Stroudsburg, PA, p. A608

SEIRER, Jeff, Interim Chief Financial Officer, Ascension Via Christi St. Francis, Mulvane, KS, p. A271

SEITZ, Kimberly, Area Human Resources Leader, Kaiser Permanente Redwood City Medical Center, Redwood City, CA, p. A87

SEITZ, Tawnya, Acting Chief Executive Officer, Lincoln County Hospital, Lincoln, KS, p. A269

Chief Financial Officer, Lincoln County Hospital, Lincoln, KS, p. A269

SELBY, Eric, R.N., Chief Nursing Officer, Chicot Memorial Medical Center, Lake Village, AR, p. A48

SELBY, Victoria Vice President, Ancillary and Support Services, Community Hospital Of San Bernardino, San Bernardino, CA, p. A91

SELF, Chris, Chief Executive Officer, Adventhealth Manchester, Manchester, KY, p. A289

SELFRIDGE, Tara, Manager Human Resources, Purcell Municipal Hospital, Purcell, OK, p. A567

SELHORST, Sonya, R.N., Administrator and Chief Nursing Officer, Mercy Hospital Of Defiance, Defiance, OH, p. A539

SELIG, Doug, MSN, R.N., Vice President of Patient Services, Parkview Huntington Hospital, Huntington, IN, p. A230

SELIGA, Patricia, R.N., Chief Nursing Officer, Moses Taylor Hospital, Scranton, PA, p. A607

SELIGMAN, Morris, M.D., Chief Medical Officer and Chief Medical Information Officer, Sycamore Shoals Hospital, Elizabethton, TN, p. A637

SELL, Paula, Director Human Resources, Allen County Regional Hospital, Iola, KS, p. A267

SELL, Teri, Payroll and Personnel Coordinator, Jennie M. Melham Memorial Medical Center, Broken Bow, NE, p. A430

SELLA, John, Controller, Spectrum Health Gerber Memorial, Fremont, MI, p. A355

SELLE, Ginger, Vice President Patient Care Services, Ssm Health St. Clare Hospital-Baraboo, Baraboo, WI, p. A780

SELLE, Justin, Chief Executive Officer, Hshs St. Nicholas Hospital, Sheboygan, WI, p. A796

SELLERS, Laura, Director Information Systems, Youth Villages Inner Harbour Campus, Douglasville, GA, p. A171

SELLERS, Liz, R.N., MSN, Chief Executive Officer, Pioneers Medical Center, Meeker, CO, p. A117

SELLERS, Mary, Chief Information Officer, Navos, Seattle, WA, p. A763

SELLERS, Robert R., President, Clay County Hospital, Flora, IL, p. A205

SELLHEIM, Kevin, Administrator, Sleep. Eye Medical Center, Sleep. Eye, MN, p. A386

SELLS, Matt, Chief Executive Officer, Shenandoah Medical Center, Shenandoah, IA, p. A257

SELMAN, David, Chief Executive Officer, Select Specialty Hospital-Phoenix Downtown, Phoenix, AZ, p. A36

SELMAN, J Peter., FACHE, Chief Executive Officer, Baptist Medical Center South, Montgomery, AL, p. A22

SELMON, Patricia, Director Public Relations and Chief Human Resources, Jefferson County Hospital, Fayette, MS, p. A392

SELPH, Wendy, Director Human Resources, Dodge County Hospital, Eastman, GA, p. A172

SELSOR, Doug, Director Finance, Select Rehabilitation Hospital Of Denton, Denton, TX, p. A672

SELVAM, A, M.D., Chief of Staff, Northern Arizona Veterans Affairs Health Care System, Prescott, AZ, p. A37

SELVIDGE, Sandra, Chief Fiscal Service, Cincinnati Veterans Affairs Medical Center, Cincinnati, OH, p. A532

SELZ, Timothy, Vice President, Garnet Health Medical Center - Catskills, Middletown, NY, p. A488

SEMELSBERGER, Kimberly, CPA, Chief Financial Officer, Conemaugh Nason Medical Center, Roaring Spring, PA, p. A606

SEMERDJIAN, Nancy, R.N., Chief Nursing Officer, Northshore University Health System, Evanston, IL, p. A204

SEMERE, Jana, Chief Nursing Officer, Leonard J. Chabert Medical Center, Houma, LA, p. A303

Chief Nursing Officer, Ochsner St. Anne General Hospital, Raceland, LA, p. A313

SEMINARO, Anthony, Chief Financial Officer, Mercy Health - St. Elizabeth Youngstown Hospital, Youngstown, OH, p. A554

Chief Financial Youngstown, Mercy Health - St. Elizabeth Boardman Hospital, Boardman, OH, p. A529

SEMRAU, Clint, President Medical Staff, Aspirus Medford Hospital & Clinics, Inc., Medford, WI, p. A789

SENDAYDIEGO, Fe, Director Information Systems, Sonoma Valley Hospital, Sonoma, CA, p. A99

SENDEN, Luke, Chief Financial Officer, Box Butte General Hospital, Alliance, NE, p. A429

SENDROS, Isaac, Chief Executive Officer, Avista Adventist Hospital, Louisville, CO, p. A116
SENGER, Joshua, Chief Financial Officer, Chi St. Francis Health, Breckenridge, MN, p. A373
SENGER, Richard, Chief Financial Officer, Portsmouth Regional Hospital, Portsmouth, NH, p. A451
SENGER, Tricia, Chief Financial Officer, St. Luke's Elmore, Mountain Home, ID, p. A191
SENKER, Margaret, Chief Information Officer, Veterans Affairs Western New York Healthcare System-Buffalo Division, Buffalo, NY, p. A480
SENKER, Thomas J., FACHE, President, Medstar Montgomery Medical Center, Olney, MD, p. A331
SENN, Sheila, PsyD, Chief Clinical and Administrative Officer, Community First Medical Center, Chicago, IL, p. A198
SENNEFF, Robert G., FACHE, President and Chief Executive Officer, Graham Hospital Association, Canton, IL, p. A196
SENNETT, Paul, Chief Financial Officer, Centinela Hospital Medical Center, Inglewood, CA, p. A69
SENNISH, James, Vice President Human Resources, Firelands Regional Health System, Sandusky, OH, p. A549
SENSAT, Marsha, Chief Nursing Officer, St. John's Health, Jackson, WY, p. A802
SEPP, Howard W. Jr, Vice-President and Administrator, Southeast Georgia Health System Camden Campus, Saint Marys, GA, p. A179
SEQUIN, Shannon, MSN, Chief Nursing Officer, Select Specialty Hospital-Saginaw, Saginaw, MI, p. A366
SERENO, Joseph, Chief Financial Officer, Lovelace Women's Hospital, Albuquerque, NM, p. A468
SERFLING, G Aubrey., President and Chief Executive Officer, Eisenhower Health, Rancho Mirage, CA, p. A86
SERGEANT, Lindy, Medical Staff President, Community Hospital Of Bremen, Bremen, IN, p. A225
SERKETICH, Steve, Manager Information Services, Aurora Sheboygan Memorial Medical Center, Sheboygan, WI, p. A796
SERLE, John, FACHE, President and Chief Executive Officer, Lourdes Medical Center, Pasco, WA, p. A762
SERNYAK, Michael, M.D., Director, Connecticut Mental Health Center, New Haven, CT, p. A124
SERRANO, Jeff, Chief Executive Officer, Rainier Springs Hospital, Vancouver, WA, p. A768
SERRANO, Jorge L Matta., Administrator, Auxilio Mutuo Hospital, San Juan, PR, p. A809
SERRANO, Lorenzo, Chief Executive Officer, Winkler County Memorial Hospital, Kermit, TX, p. A692
SERZAN, Megan, Director of Quality, Compliance, Risk & Safety, Asheville Specialty Hospital, Asheville, NC, p. A504
SESSIONS, Jerry, M.D., Chief Medical Staff, Springhill Medical Center, Springhill, LA, p. A315
SESSLER, Connie, Director Human Resources, St. Luke's Hospital, Maumee, OH, p. A545
SESTERHENN, Steven, Vice President, Unitypoint Health - Allen Hospital, Waterloo, IA, p. A259
SETHI, Sanjiv, M.D., Medical Director, Fulton State Hospital, Fulton, MO, p. A407
SETHNEY, Julie, R.N., Vice President Patient Care, Fairview Ridges Hospital, Burnsville, MN, p. A373
SETLIFF, Chad, President and Chief Operating Officer, Novant Health Forsyth Medical Center, Winston, NC, p. A520
SETTLE, Andrea, Director Human Resources, Taylor Regional Hospital, Campbellsville, KY, p. A281
SETTLES, Allicia, Chief Nursing Officer, Ut Health Quitman, Quitman, TX, p. A708
SETTLES, April, Chief Financial Officer, Greene County General Hospital, Linton, IN, p. A235
SETZER, Jeffery, Administrator Information Systems, J. D. Mccarty Center For Children With Developmental Disabilities, Norman, OK, p. A563
SETZER, Randy, Financial Services Manager, Waukesha County Mental Health Center, Waukesha, WI, p. A798
SETZKORN-MEYER, Marsha, Director Public Relations and Marketing, Hillsboro Community Hospital, Hillsboro, KS, p. A266
SEVCO, Mark, Chief Operating Officer, Upmc Pinnacle Harrisburg, Harrisburg, PA, p. A591
President, Upmc Children's Hospital Of Pittsburgh, Pittsburgh, PA, p. A603
SEVILLIAN, Clarence, President and Chief Executive Officer, Mclaren Bay Region, Bay City, MI, p. A349
SEWATSKY, Mary, M.D., Chief Medical Officer, Moses Taylor Hospital, Scranton, PA, p. A607
SEWELL, Lance, Chief Financial Officer, South Lake Hospital, Clermont, FL, p. A134
SEWELL, Leigh, Chief Executive Officer, Bon Secours Memorial Regional Medical Center, Mechanicsville, VA, p. A746
Chief Executive Officer, Bon Secours-Richmond Community Hospital, Richmond, VA, p. A749

SEWICK, Alayne, Vice President Human Resources, Medical City Mckinney, Mckinney, TX, p. A700
SEXTON, Charles, Manager Human Resources, Cumberland Medical Center, Crossville, TN, p. A637
SEXTON, Cindy, Chief Financial Officer, St. David's Round Rock Medical Center, Round Rock, TX, p. A710
SEXTON, Kevin, Director Information Systems, Raleigh General Hospital, Beckley, WV, p. A770
SEXTON, William P., Chief Executive Officer, Crossing Rivers Health Medical Center, Prairie Du Chien, WI, p. A794
SEYBOLD, Henry, Senior Vice President and Chief Financial Officer, North Kansas City Hospital, North Kansas City, MO, p. A413
SEYMOUR, Barbara, Vice President of Nursing, Health First Holmes Regional Medical Center, Melbourne, FL, p. A145
SEYMOUR, Claudette, Director Personnel, Memphis Mental Health Institute, Memphis, TN, p. A644
SEYMOUR, Jose, Chief Information Resource Management, James A. Haley Veterans' Hospital-Tampa, Tampa, FL, p. A159
SEYMOUR, Robert, Chief Financial Officer/Senior Director Finance, Grande Ronde Hospital, La Grande, OR, p. A576
SEYMOUR, Ryan, Chief Executive Officer, Baylor Scott & White Institute For Rehabilitation-Fort Worth, Fort Worth, TX, p. A678
Chief Executive Officer, Baylor Scott & White Institute For Rehabilitation-Frisco, Frisco, TX, p. A680
SEYMOUR, Sally, Chief Operating Officer, Medical Center Of Trinity, Trinity, FL, p. A161
SGARLATA, Lisa, MSN, Chief Patient Care Officer, Cap. Coral Hospital, Cap. Coral, FL, p. A134
MSN, Chief Patient Care Officer, Gulf Coast Medical Center, Fort Myers, FL, p. A138
SHACKELFORD, Gerald, Staff Support Specialist, Texas Center For Infectious Disease, San Antonio, TX, p. A713
SHACKELFORD, J. Larry., CPA, President and Chief Executive Officer, Washington Regional Medical Center, Fayetteville, AR, p. A45
SHACKELFORD, Paul, M.D., Chief Medical Officer, Vidant Medical Center, Greenville, NC, p. A511
SHACKLETON, Carol, M.D., Medical Director, Gothenburg Health, Gothenburg, NE, p. A432
SHADENSACK, Don, Vice President Clinical Services, Osf St. Mary Medical Center, Galesburg, IL, p. A205
SHADOWENS, Karen, CPA, Chief Financial Officer, Van Wert County Hospital, Van Wert, OH, p. A551
SHAFER, Kenny, Chief Operating Officer, Johnson City Medical Center, Johnson City, TN, p. A640
SHAFER, Robert, Vice President Finance, Mercyone Dubuque Medical Center, Dubuque, IA, p. A249
Vice President Finance, Mercyone Dyersville Medical Center, Dyersville, IA, p. A249
SHAFFER, Jeraldene, MSN, Chief Nursing Officer, Roseland Community Hospital, Chicago, IL, p. A200
SHAFICI, Khaled, M.D., President Medical Staff, Cornerstone Hospitals West Monroe, West Monroe, LA, p. A316
SHAFIU, Mohamed, M.D., Chief of Staff, Val Verde Regional Medical Center, Del Rio, TX, p. A671
SHAH, Beena, M.D., Chief of Staff and Chief Medical Officer, Anaheim Global Medical Center, Anaheim, CA, p. A55
SHAH, Jayendra, M.D., Chief Medical Officer, Southern Arizona Veterans Affairs Health Care System, Tucson, AZ, p. A41
SHAH, Paresh, Director Information Systems, Reston Hospital Center, Reston, VA, p. A749
SHAH, Syed, M.D., Chief of Staff, Pioneer Memorial Hospital And Health Services, Viborg, SD, p. A632
SHAH, Vital, M.D., Associate Director and Chief Medical Officer, Central State Hospital, Louisville, KY, p. A288
SHAH, Yogesh, M.D., Chief Medical Officer, Broadlawns Medical Center, Des Moines, IA, p. A248
SHAHAN, Matthew, Chief Executive Officer, West River Regional Medical Center, Hettinger, ND, p. A524
SHAHI, Niloo, Chief Operating Officer, Lac-Olive View-Ucla Medical Center, Sylmar, CA, p. A100
SHAHNAM, Melissa, Director Human Resources, Mon Health Medical Center, Morgantown, WV, p. A774
SHAHRYAR, Syed, M.D., Medical Director, Kp. Promise Hospital Of Phoenix, Mesa, AZ, p. A34
SHAHZADA, Kamran, M.D., Chief Medical Staff, South Central Kansas Medical Center, Arkansas City, KS, p. A261
SHAIFFER, Mandy, Chief Nursing Officer, Mt. San Rafael Hospital, Trinidad, CO, p. A119
SHAKOOR, Arif, Chief of Staff, Raulerson Hospital, Okeechobee, FL, p. A150
SHALLOCK, James, Chief Financial Officer, Memorial Hermann Greater Heights Hospital, Houston, TX, p. A687
SHAMBURG, Steffen, M.D., Chief of Staff, Hiawatha Community Hospital, Hiawatha, KS, p. A266

SHANAHAN, Thomas, CPA, Chief Financial Officer and Senior Vice President, Hackensack Meridian Health Raritan Bay Medical Center, Perth Amboy, NJ, p. A461
CPA, Chief Operating Officer, Hackensack Meridian Health Raritan Bay Medical Center, Perth Amboy, NJ, p. A461
Vice President, Human Resources, Children's Hospital Of Wisconsin-Fox Valley, Neenah, WI, p. A792
Vice President, Human Resources, Children's Hospital Of Wisconsin, Milwaukee, WI, p. A791
SHANKS-CONNORS, Tanya, R.N., MSN, Interim President, Legacy Mount Hood Medical Center, Gresham, OR, p. A575
SHANLEY, Diane, Deputy Service Unit Director, U. S. Public Health Service Indian Hospital-Sells, Sells, AZ, p. A38
SHANLEY, Linda, Vice President, Chief Information Officer, Saint Francis Hospital And Medical Center, Hartford, CT, p. A122
SHANLEY, Thomas, President and Chief Executive Officer, Ann & Robert H. Lurie Children's Hospital Of Chicago, Chicago, IL, p. A198
SHANNON, David A., Interim Chief Executive Officer, Three Rivers Health, Three Rivers, MI, p. A368
President and Chief Executive Officer, Three Rivers Hospital, Waverly, TN, p. A650
SHANNON, Greg, Chief Human Resources Officer, Golden Valley Memorial Healthcare, Clinton, MO, p. A405
SHANNON, Lori, President, Ascension St. Vincent Heart Center, Indianapolis, IN, p. A231
SHANNON, Patrick, Chief Operating Officer, Baptist Hospitals Of Southeast Texas, Beaumont, TX, p. A658
SHANNON, Richard, M.D., Chief of Staff, Montrose Memorial Hospital, Montrose, CO, p. A117
SHANNON, Scott, Director Finance, Socorro General Hospital, Socorro, NM, p. A472
SHAPE, Amy, Information Technology, North Dakota State Hospital, Jamestown, ND, p. A524
SHAPIRO, David, M.D., Vice President Medical Affairs and Chief Medical Officer, Ascension Columbia St. Mary's Hospital Milwaukee, Milwaukee, WI, p. A790
M.D., Vice President Medical Affairs and Chief Medical Officer, Ascension Columbia St. Mary's Hospital Ozaukee, Mequon, WI, p. A790
M.D., Vice President Medical Affairs and Chief Medical Officer, Ascension Columbia St. Mary's Milwaukee Hospital, Milwaukee, WI, p. A790
SHAPIRO, Louis A., President and Chief Executive Officer, Hospital For Special Surgery, New York, NY, p. A490
SHAPIRO, Marc, M.D., Chief Medical Officer, Adventist Health Clear Lake, Clearlake, CA, p. A60
SHAPIRO, Steven, M.D., Chief Medical Officer, Bon Secours St. Francis Hospital, Charleston, SC, p. A616
M.D., Chief Medical Officer, Roper St. Francis Mount Pleasant Hospital, Mount Pleasant, SC, p. A622
M.D., Vice President Medical Affairs, Roper Hospital, Charleston, SC, p. A616
SHAPIRO, Wendy, Chief Executive Officer, Clarion Psychiatric Center, Clarion, PA, p. A586
SHARANGPANI, Rojesh, M.D., Chief of Staff, Capital Medical Center, Olympia, WA, p. A761
SHARKEY, Linda, R.N., MSN, Vice President Patient Care Services and Chief Nurse Executive, Fauquier Hospital, Warrenton, VA, p. A753
SHARLOW, Joseph, M.D., Chief of Staff, Ste. Genevieve County Memorial Hospital, Ste Genevieve, MO, p. A419
SHARMA, Adhi, M.D., Senior Vice President, Medical Affairs and Chief Medical Officer, Mount Sinai South Nassau, Oceanside, NY, p. A493
SHARMA, Aika, M.D., President Medical Staff, Alameda Hospital, Alameda, CA, p. A55
SHARMA, Chandra, M.D., Chief of Staff, Welch Community Hospital, Welch, WV, p. A777
SHARMA, Roger, Executive Vice President/Chief Financial Officer, Emanate Health Inter-Community Hospital, Covina, CA, p. A61
SHARMA, Sanjay, Chief Executive Officer, Galesburg Cottage Hospital, Galesburg, IL, p. A205
SHARMA, Satish, M.D., Chief of Staff, Providence Veterans Affairs Medical Center, Providence, RI, p. A613
SHARON, Joesph, Associate Director, Wilkes-Barre Veterans Affairs Medical Center, Wilkes-Barre, PA, p. A611
SHARON, Sandy, Senior Vice President and Area Manager, Kaiser Permanente Sacramento Medical Center, Sacramento, CA, p. A89
SHARP, Alan, Chief Financial Officer, Saint Thomas Dekalb Hospital, Smithville, TN, p. A649
Chief Financial Officer, Saint Thomas Stones River Hospital, Woodbury, TN, p. A650
SHARP, ArvaDell, Director of Nursing, Pembina County Memorial Hospital And Wedgewood Manor, Cavalier, ND, p. A522

SHARP, Cheryl, Chief Financial Office, Miami County Medical Center, Paola, KS, p. A274

SHARP, Cindy, M.D., Chief Medical Officer, Madison Valley Medical Center, Ennis, MT, p. A423

SHARP, Gary, Director Information Technology, Southern Hills Hospital And Medical Center, Las Vegas, NV, p. A444

SHARP, Gina, FACHE, President and Chief Executive Officer, Linden Oaks Hospital, Naperville, IL, p. A214

SHARP, Greg, M.D., Senior Vice President and Chief Medical Officer, Arkansas Children's Hospital, Little Rock, AR, p. A48

SHARP, John, Chief Financial Officer, Seton Medical Center Harker Heights, Harker Heights, TX, p. A683

SHARP, Julie, Supervisor Human Resources, Chase County Community Hospital, Imperial, NE, p. A433

SHARP, Mike, Interim Director, Wellstar Atlanta Medical Center, Atlanta, GA, p. A165

SHARP, Patrick, President and Chief Executive Officer, Fairview Range Medical Center, Hibbing, MN, p. A378

SHARP, Ray, Chief Information Officer, Katherine Shaw Bethea Hospital, Dixon, IL, p. A202

SHARP, Rebecca, Chief Financial Officer, Wagoner Community Hospital, Wagoner, OK, p. A571

SHARP, Richard, M.D., Medical Director, Christus St. Michael Rehabilitation Hospital, Texarkana, TX, p. A719

SHARP, Robin, M.D., Chief of Staff, Northern Louisiana Medical Center, Ruston, LA, p. A313

SHARP, Tanya, President and Chief Executive Officer, Boone County Health Center, Albion, NE, p. A429

SHARP, Tony, Supervisor Information System, Sweetwater Hospital, Sweetwater, TN, p. A650

SHARPE, Deborah, R.N., Director of Nursing, West Springs Hospital, Grand Junction, CO, p. A113

SHARPTON, Debra, Director of Nursing, Devereux Advanced Behavioral Health Georgia, Kennesaw, GA, p. A174

SHARUM, Melinda, Director Human Resources, Mercy Hospital Ardmore, Ardmore, OK, p. A556
Director Human Resources, Mercy Hospital Healdton, Healdton, OK, p. A560

SHATRAW, Thomas, Director Human Resources, Samaritan Medical Center, Watertown, NY, p. A502

SHAUGHNESSY, John, Regional Chief Financial Officer, Christus Ochsner St. Patrick, Lake Charles, LA, p. A306

SHAUGHNESSY, Mary, Vice President Finance, Spaulding Hospital For Continuing Medical Care Cambridge, Cambridge, MA, p. A338
Vice President Finance, Spaulding Rehabilitation Hospital Cap. Cod, East Sandwich, MA, p. A338

SHAULL, Heather, Chief Financial Officer, Adair County Health System, Greenfield, IA, p. A250

SHAULL, Ty, President and Chief Executive Officer, Wyandot Memorial Hospital, Upper Sandusky, OH, p. A551

SHAUNESSY, Celia, Vice President Human Resources, Ascension St. Michael's Hospital, Stevens Point, WI, p. A796

SHAVER, Chris, Vice President Human Resources, Covenant Children's Hospital, Lubbock, TX, p. A697
Vice President Human Resources, Covenant Medical Center, Lubbock, TX, p. A697
Vice President Human Resources, Covenant Specialty Hospital, Lubbock, TX, p. A697

SHAVER, Jennifer, Director of Nursing, Gouverneur Hospital, Gouverneur, NY, p. A485

SHAVER, John, Chief Financial Officer, Baystate Noble Hospital, Westfield, MA, p. A346

SHAVER, Robert, M.D., Vice President Medical Affairs, Wellspan Good Samaritan Hospital, Lebanon, PA, p. A595

SHAW, David, Director Information Technology, Forrest City Medical Center, Forrest City, AR, p. A45

SHAW, David B., Chief Executive Officer and Administrator, Nor-Lea Hospital District, Lovington, NM, p. A470

SHAW, Douglas A., Chief Executive Officer, Mad River Community Hospital, Arcata, CA, p. A56

SHAW, Gary, President and Chief Executive Officer, Nantucket Cottage Hospital, Nantucket, MA, p. A342

SHAW, Greg, Vice President, Finance, Aspirus Medford Hospital & Clinics, Inc., Medford, WI, p. A789

SHAW, Howard, M.D., Chief Medical Officer, Medical City Denton, Denton, TX, p. A672

SHAW, Jan, Director Personnel, River Bend Hospital, West Lafayette, IN, p. A242

SHAW, Jean, Chief Financial Officer, Valley Regional Hospital, Claremont, NH, p. A448

SHAW, John, M.D., Medical Director, Southern Indiana Rehabilitation Hospital, New Albany, IN, p. A238

SHAW, Kendra, Chief Information Officer, Western Wisconsin Health, Baldwin, WI, p. A780

SHAW, Kimberly, President and Chief Executive Officer, St. Rose Dominican Hospitals - San Martin Campus, Las Vegas, NV, p. A444

Vice President Patient Care and Chief Nursing Executive, Mercy Medical Center Redding, Redding, CA, p. A87

SHAW, Mandy, M.D., Chief of Staff, Sidney Regional Medical Center, Sidney, NE, p. A439

SHAW, Violet, R.N., Director of Nursing, Grafton City Hospital, Grafton, WV, p. A772

SHAWGO, Darla, Director Human Resources, Sparta Community Hospital, Sparta, IL, p. A220

SHAWN, D.J., Director Human Resources, Alliancehealth Madill, Madill, OK, p. A561

SHEA, Drew, Chief Financial Officer, City Hospital At White Rock, Dallas, TX, p. A668

SHEA, Natalie, Chief Nursing Officer, Mercyone Elkader Medical Center, Elkader, IA, p. A249

SHEAR, Larry, Administrative Assistant, Norwood Health Center, Marshfield, WI, p. A789

SHEARER, Christopher, M.D., Chief Medical Officer, Honorhealth John C. Lincoln Medical Center, Phoenix, AZ, p. A36

SHEARER, Laura, R.N., MSN, Senior Vice President and Chief Nursing Officer, Phoebe Putney Memorial Hospital, Albany, GA, p. A163

SHEARER, Ron, M.D., Regional Medical Director, Peacehealth Peace Harbor Medical Center, Florence, OR, p. A575

SHEARS, Ann Marie, Vice President Patient Care Services, Robert Wood Johnson University Hospital Rahway, Rahway, NJ, p. A462

SHEEHAN, Karen, Vice President and Chief Information Officer, Swedish Covenant Hospital, Chicago, IL, p. A201

SHEEHAN, Terrence, M.D., Medical Director, Adventist Healthcare Physical Health And Rehabilitation, Rockville, MD, p. A332

SHEEHY, Earl Nielsen., FACHE, Chief Executive Officer, Ray County Memorial Hospital, Richmond, MO, p. A414

SHEERIN, Rick, Vice President Fiscal Officer, Polk Medical Center, Cedartown, GA, p. A168
Vice President Fiscal Services, Floyd Medical Center, Rome, GA, p. A179

SHEETS, Cindy, Vice President Information Systems and Chief Information Officer, Ohiohealth Medcentral Mansfield Hospital, Mansfield, OH, p. A544

SHEFFIELD, Aubrey, Administrative Assistant Human Resources and Public Relations, Grove Hill Memorial Hospital, Grove Hill, AL, p. A19

SHEFFIELD, Loretta, Chief Executive Officer, Select Specialty Hospital-Miami, Miami, FL, p. A147

SHEFFIELD, Nichol, Chief Executive Officer, Pacific Grove Hospital, Riverside, CA, p. A88

SHEFIELD, Jennifer, M.D., Chief of Staff, West River Regional Medical Center, Hettinger, ND, p. A524

SHEFTE, David H., Chief Executive Officer, Encompass Health Rehabilitation Hospital Of Littleton, Littleton, CO, p. A115

SHEGOLEV, Igor, Vice President Human Resources, Carondelet St. Joseph's Hospital, Tucson, AZ, p. A40

SHEHAN, Mary, R.N., MSN, Chief Executive Officer, Louis A. Weiss Memorial Hospital, Chicago, IL, p. A199

SHEHATA, Nady, M.D., Vice President Medical Affairs, Sisters Of Charity Hospital Of Buffalo, Buffalo, NY, p. A480

SHEHI, G, M.D., Medical Director, Mountain View Hospital, Gadsden, AL, p. A19

SHEHI, Jay, Chief Executive Officer, Alliance Health Center, Meridian, MS, p. A397

SHEIKH, Azad, Chief Medical Officer, Adventist Health And Rideout, Marysville, CA, p. A77

SHEINBEIN, David, Chief Medical Officer, Banner - University Medical Center South, Tucson, AZ, p. A39

SHELAK, Matt, Chief Executive Officer, Roxborough Memorial Hospital, Philadelphia, PA, p. A601
Chief Executive Officer, Suburban Community Hospital, East Norriton, PA, p. A589

SHELBURNE, John, M.D., Chief of Staff, Durham Veterans Affairs Medical Center, Durham, NC, p. A509

SHELBY, Dennis R., Chief Executive Officer, Wilson Medical Center, Neodesha, KS, p. A271

SHELBY, Joyce, Manager Human Resources, Hardin County General Hospital, Rosiclare, IL, p. A219

SHELDON, Lyle Ernest., FACHE, President and Chief Executive Officer, University Of Maryland Harford Memorial Hospital, Havre De Grace, MD, p. A330
FACHE, President and Chief Executive Officer, University Of Maryland Upper Chesapeake Medical Center, Bel Air, MD, p. A327

SHELDON, Monica, Chief Executive Officer, Northern Cochise Community Hospital, Willcox, AZ, p. A41

SHELFORD, Dave, Assistant Superintendent, Richmond State Hospital, Richmond, IN, p. A239

SHELL, John, M.D., Chief Medical Officer, Coffey County Hospital, Burlington, KS, p. A262

SHELL, Steve, Chief Executive Officer, Reno Behavioral Healthcare Hospital, Reno, NV, p. A445

SHELLENBERGER, David, President, St. John Vianney Hospital, Downingtown, PA, p. A588

SHELLS, Tammy, Chief Nursing Officer, Belmont Pines Hospital, Youngstown, OH, p. A553

SHELSTAD, Erik, M.D., Chief of Staff, Johnson Memorial Health Services, Dawson, MN, p. A375

SHELT, Elizabeth, Civilian Personnel Officer, Dwight David Eisenhower Army Medical Center, Fort Gordon, GA, p. A173

SHELTON, Amy, Chief Nursing Officer, St. Vincent's East, Birmingham, AL, p. A15

SHELTON, Angela, Chief Financial Officer, Jack Hughston Memorial Hospital, Phenix City, AL, p. A23

SHELTON, Carol, Director Human Resources, Lovelace Women's Hospital, Albuquerque, NM, p. A468

SHELTON, Darlene, Coordinator Team Resources, Baycare Alliant Hospital, Dunedin, FL, p. A136

SHELTON, Jared, President, Texas Health Presbyterian Hospital Allen, Allen, TX, p. A652

SHELTON, Jeffrey Dewayne., Chief Executive Officer, Chadron Community Hospital And Health Services, Chadron, NE, p. A431

SHELTON, Kathy, Director Human Resources, Ut Health Pittsburg, Pittsburg, TX, p. A706

SHELTON, Richard, M.D., Chief Medical Officer, Baptist Health Richmond, Richmond, KY, p. A292

SHELTON, Tom, Coordinator of Nursing Services, Porterville Developmental Center, Porterville, CA, p. A86

SHENDELL-FALIK, Nancy, R.N., President, Baystate Medical Center, Springfield, MA, p. A344
R.N., Senior Vice President, Chief Operating Officer and Chief Nursing Officer, Baystate Medical Center, Springfield, MA, p. A344

SHENEFIELD, Jason, Senior Vice President and Chief Operating Officer, Phelp. Health, Rolla, MO, p. A414

SHENGLE, Lori, Director Information Technology, Morrill County Community Hospital, Bridgeport, NE, p. A430

SHENNAR, Arek, Chief Information Officer, Kingman Regional Medical Center, Kingman, AZ, p. A33

SHEPARD, Bridget, Vice President Human Resources, Wabash General Hospital, Mount Carmel, IL, p. A213

SHEPARD, Karen, Senior Vice President and Chief Financial Officer, St. Charles Prineville, Prineville, OR, p. A580

SHEPARD, Megan, Director Clinical Services, Odessa Memorial Healthcare Center, Odessa, WA, p. A761

SHEPARD, Melissa, Chief Financial Officer, Heart Of America Medical Center, Rugby, ND, p. A525

SHEPARD, Sheila, Controller, Encompass Health Rehabilitation Hospital Of Humble, Humble, TX, p. A689

SHEPARDSON, Dean, Chief Financial Officer, Banner Estrella Medical Center, Phoenix, AZ, p. A35

SHEPARDSON, Heather, Vice President Human Resources, Carilion Roanoke Memorial Hospital, Roanoke, VA, p. A751

SHEPHARD, Bryan, Chief Financial Officer, Tristar Summit Medical Center, Hermitage, TN, p. A639

SHEPHARD, Russ, Senior Systems Analyst, West Tennessee Healthcare Dyersburg Hospital, Dyersburg, TN, p. A637

SHEPHERD, Ethan, Director Human Resources, Abilene Regional Medical Center, Abilene, TX, p. A651

SHEPHERD, Jamie, Chief Operating Officer, Shepherd Center, Atlanta, GA, p. A165

SHEPHERD, Linda, R.N., Chief Nursing Officer, Johnston Memorial Hospital, Abingdon, VA, p. A738

SHEPHERD, Mary, Chief Operating Officer, Northside Hospital - Gwinnett, Lawrenceville, GA, p. A175

SHEPLER, Mary, R.N., Seniro Vice President, Chief Nursing Officer, Evergreenhealth, Kirkland, WA, p. A759

SHEPPARD, Ballard, Ph.D., Chief Executive Officer, Rivendell Behavioral Health Services Of Arkansas, Benton, AR, p. A42

SHEPPARD, Sandy, Vice President Patient Services, Wake Forest Baptist Health - Wilkes Medical Center, North Wilkesboro, NC, p. A516

SHEPPARD, Sharon, Manager Human Resources, Sycamore Shoals Hospital, Elizabethton, TN, p. A637

SHEPPARD, Varinya, R.N., Chief Nursing Officer, St. Elizabeth Medical Center, Utica, NY, p. A500

SHERBONDY, Beverly, Assistant Vice President, Human Resources, Temple University Hospital - Jeanes Campus, Philadelphia, PA, p. A602

SHERBONDY, Lori, Director Human Resources, Battle Mountain General Hospital, Battle Mountain, NV, p. A441

SHERER, Janet, Chief of Patient Care Services, Springfield Hospital, Springfield, VT, p. A736

SHERER, Susan, Chief Information Resource Management, Dayton Veterans Affairs Medical Center, Dayton, OH, p. A538

SHERIDAN, Cheryl, R.N., Senior Vice President Patient Care Services, Rochester General Hospital, Rochester, NY, p. A496

SHERIDAN, Elizabeth, Chief Operating Officer and Chief Nursing Executive, Inspira Medical Center-Elmer, Elmer, NJ, p. A455
Chief Operating Officer and Chief Nursing Executive, Inspira Medical Center-Vineland, Vineland, NJ, p. A465
SHERIDAN, Kolbe, Chief Executive Officer, Barstow Community Hospital, Barstow, CA, p. A58
SHERMAN, Angelina, R.N., MSN, Chief Nursing Officer, The Rehabilitation Institute Of St. Louis, Saint Louis, MO, p. A417
SHERMAN, Frederick, M.D., Chief Medical Officer, The Children's Home Of Pittsburgh, Pittsburgh, PA, p. A603
SHERMAN, Sheila, Vice President Patient Care Services, Vail Health, Vail, CO, p. A119
SHERMAN, Stephanie, Chief Human Resources Officer, West Boca Medical Center, Boca Raton, FL, p. A132
SHERON, William E., Chief Executive Officer, Wooster Community Hospital, Wooster, OH, p. A553
SHERRILL, Angela, Chief Information Officer, Laird Hospital, Union, MS, p. A400
SHERRILL, Diane, R.N., Director of Nursing, Medical Arts Hospital, Lamesa, TX, p. A694
SHERROD, Michael, Chief Executive Officer, Tristar Greenview Regional Hospital, Bowling Green, KY, p. A281
SHERRON, Tammy, Vice President Finance, Carolinaeast Health System, New Bern, NC, p. A515
SHERRY, Bernie, Ministry Market Executive for Ascension Wisconsin, Midwest Orthopedic Specialty Hospital, Franklin, WI, p. A784
SHERRY, Mark, Regional Director Human Resource Strategic Services, Austin/Round Rock Region, Baylor Scott & White Medical Center - Round Rock, Round Rock, TX, p. A709
SHERWIN, Charles H., President, Midmichigan Medical Center - Alpena, Alpena, MI, p. A348
SHERWOOD, Jennifer, Division, Human Resource Business Partner, Banner - University Medical Center South, Tucson, AZ, p. A39
SHERWOOD, Matthew, Chief Financial Officer, Unity Medical & Surgical Hospital, Mishawaka, IN, p. A236
SHETTLESWORTH, Amanda, Director Human Resources, Bloomington Meadows Hospital, Bloomington, IN, p. A224
SHETTY, Atul, Chief of Staff, Weirton Medical Center, Weirton, WV, p. A777
SHEW, Angel, Director Area Technology, Kaiser Permanente South San Francisco, South San Francisco, CA, p. A99
SHEWBRIDGE, Richard K., President, Cleveland Clinic, Medina Hospital, Medina, OH, p. A545
SHEYKA, Patricia, Chief Nursing Officer, Gila Regional Medical Center, Silver City, NM, p. A472
SHICKOLOVICH, William, Chief Information Officer, Tufts Medical Center, Boston, MA, p. A336
SHIELDS, Charlie, Chief Executive Officer, Truman Medical Center-Lakewood, Kansas City, MO, p. A410
President and Chief Executive Officer, Truman Medical Center-Hospital Hill, Kansas City, MO, p. A410
SHIELDS, Stuart, Director, G. Werber Bryan Psychiatric Hospital, Columbia, SC, p. A617
SHIELDS, Todd, Vice President and Administrator, St. Charles Prineville, Prineville, OR, p. A580
SHIFF, Mary, Chief Financial Officer, Kindred Chicago-Central Hospital, Chicago, IL, p. A199
SHIFFERMILLER, William, M.D., Vice President Medical Affairs, Nebraska Methodist Hospital, Omaha, NE, p. A437
SHIHADY, Sharon, Director Human Resources, West Tennessee Rehabilitation Hospital Cane Creek, Martin, TN, p. A643
SHIKIAR, Mindy, MSN, Chief Operating Officer, Boca Raton Regional Hospital, Boca Raton, FL, p. A132
SHILKAITIS, Mary, Vice President Patient Care and Chief Nursing Officer, Rush-Copley Medical Center, Aurora, IL, p. A195
SHILLING, Stacy, Controller, Chi St. Vincent Sherwood Rehabilitation Hospital, Sherwood, AR, p. A53
SHIM, Eunmee, R.N., MSN, Vice President Operations, Adventist Healthcare Shady Grove Medical Center, Rockville, MD, p. A332
SHIMAMOTO, Kevin, Vice President and Chief Informational Officer, Valley Children's Healthcare, Madera, CA, p. A76
SHINAGAWA, Nathan, Chief Operating Officer, Banner Del E. Webb Medical Center, Sun City West, AZ, p. A39
SHINER, Cindy, Manager Human Resources, Lebanon Veterans Affairs Medical Center, Lebanon, PA, p. A594
SHINGLETON, Kathy, Ed.D., Vice President, Human Resources, Virginia Mason Medical Center, Seattle, WA, p. A765
SHINICK, Mary, Vice President Human Resources, Montefiore Nyack Hospital, Nyack, NY, p. A493
SHIPLEY, Carolyn, R.N., Chief Nursing Officer, Roane Medical Center, Harriman, TN, p. A639

SHIPLEY, Janice, M.D., Chief Medical Officer, Cibola General Hospital, Grants, NM, p. A469
SHIPLEY, Kurt, Chief Financial Officer, Jordan Valley Medical Center, West Jordan, UT, p. A734
SHIPP, Geraldine, Director of Risk Management, Sampson Regional Medical Center, Clinton, NC, p. A507
SHIRAH, Anita, Director Human Resources, Usa Health University Hospital, Mobile, AL, p. A22
SHIRLEY, Christian, Director Human Resources, Geisinger Encompass Health Rehabilitation Hospital, Danville, PA, p. A587
SHIRLEY, Douglas, Senior Executive Vice President and Chief Financial Officer, Cooper University Health Care, Camden, NJ, p. A453
SHIRLEY, Steve, Chief Information Officer, Parkview Medical Center, Pueblo, CO, p. A118
SHIVELY, Lori, Vice President of Finance, Munson Healthcare Grayling Hospital, Grayling, MI, p. A356
SHIVERY, Toni, Vice President Human Resources, University Of Maryland Harford Memorial Hospital, Havre De Grace, MD, p. A330
Vice President Human Resources, University Of Maryland Upper Chesapeake Medical Center, Bel Air, MD, p. A327
SHMERLING, James E., President and Chief Executive Officer, Connecticut Children's Medical Center, Hartford, CT, p. A122
SHOBE, Susan, Director Administration and Support Services, Alton Mental Health Center, Alton, IL, p. A194
SHOCK, Ernest, Chief Nursing Officer, Abbeville Area Medical Center, Abbeville, SC, p. A615
SHOCKEY, Kathryn, Director Human Resources, Monument Health Lead-Deadwood Hospital, Deadwood, SD, p. A627
SHOCKNEY, Brian T., FACHE, President, Indiana University Health Bloomington Hospital, Bloomington, IN, p. A224
SHOEMAKER, Matt, D.O., Vice President and Chief Medical Officer, Southeast Hospital, Cap. Girardeau, MO, p. A404
SHOENER, Carl, Chief Information Officer, Lehigh Valley Hospital - Hazleton, Hazleton, PA, p. A592
SHOFNER, Connie, Chief Nursing Officer, Carlsbad Medical Center, Carlsbad, NM, p. A468
SHOLTIS, Bridget, Chief Financial Officer, Mclaren Port Huron, Port Huron, MI, p. A364
SHOMAKER, Susan, Director Information Management Systems, J. Arthur Dosher Memorial Hospital, Southport, NC, p. A518
SHOOK, Susan, Interim Chief Executive Officer, Adventhealth Murray, Chatsworth, GA, p. A168
SHOOK, Teressia, Chief Financial Officer, Clinch Memorial Hospital, Homerville, GA, p. A174
SHOPTAW, Michele, Director of Nursing, Chambers Memorial Hospital, Danville, AR, p. A44
SHORES, Larry, M.D., Executive Medical Director, Cedar Springs Hospital, Colorado Springs, CO, p. A109
SHORT, M, Vice President Information Services, Samaritan Medical Center, Watertown, NY, p. A502
SHORT, Penny, R.N., President, Tidalhealth Nanticoke, Seaford, DE, p. A128
SHORT, Peter, M.D., Senior Vice President Medical Affairs, Beverly Hospital, Beverly, MA, p. A334
SHORT, Ted, Chief Financial Officer, Fairview Park Hospital, Dublin, GA, p. A172
SHORT, W, M.D., Chief Medical Officer, Memorial Health System, Abilene, KS, p. A261
SHORTER, Beryl, Chief Operating Officer, Director Performance Improvement, Kingwood Pines Hospital, Kingwood, TX, p. A693
SHOUKAIR, Sami, M.D., Chief Medical Officer, La Palma Intercommunity Hospital, La Palma, CA, p. A70
SHOULDERS, Valerie, R.N., Chief Nursing Officer, Encompass Health Rehabilitation Hospital Of Franklin, Franklin, TN, p. A638
SHOUP, Barbara, R.N., Chief Nursing Officer, Ascension Brighton Center For Recovery, Brighton, MI, p. A350
SHOUP, Emily, Director Nursing Services, Roundup Memorial Healthcare, Roundup. MT, p. A427
SHOUSE, Shellie, Chief Financial Officer, Bluegrass Community Hospital, Versailles, KY, p. A294
SHOWALTER, Amy, R.N., Chief Operating Officer, Sheltering Arms Hospital South, Midlothian, VA, p. A746
R.N., Chief Operating Officer, Sheltering Arms Rehabilitation Hospital, Mechanicsville, VA, p. A746
SHOWALTER, Will, Senior Vice President and Chief information Officer, Wake Forest Baptist Health-Lexington Medical Center, Lexington, NC, p. A514
SHOWALTER, William, Senior Vice President and Chief Information Officer, Information Technology Services, Wake Forest Baptist Health-Davie Medical Center, Bermuda Run, NC, p. A505
SHOWS, Carla, Human Resource and Payroll Clerk, George Regional Hospital, Lucedale, MS, p. A396

Payroll Clerk, Greene County Hospital, Leakesville, MS, p. A396
SHRAKE, Kevin L., Chief Executive Officer, Kindred Hospital-St. Louis, Saint Louis, MO, p. A416
SHREEVE, Susan, Chief Financial Officer, Research Medical Center, Kansas City, MO, p. A409
SHRESTHA, Sanjeeb, M.D., Chief Medical Staff, Medical City Weatherford, Weatherford, TX, p. A724
SHREVE, Susan, Executive Director Information Technology, Boone Memorial Hospital, Madison, WV, p. A774
SHRIDE, Chris, President, Amita Health St. Mary's Hospital, Kankakee, IL, p. A209
SHRINER, Anne, M.D., Senior Vice President, Chief Medical Officer, Nash Unc Health Care, Rocky Mount, NC, p. A517
SHRIVASTAVA, Rakesh, M.D., Chief Medical Officer, Cornerstone Hospital Of Oklahoma-Shawnee, Shawnee, OK, p. A568
SHRIVER, Debra, R.N., MSN, Chief Nurse Executive, Unitypoint Health - Trinity Regional Medical Center, Fort Dodge, IA, p. A250
SHRIVER, Kren, M.D., Clinical Director, Capital District Psychiatric Center, Albany, NY, p. A474
SHROADES, David, Vice President Technology Services, Alliance Community Hospital, Alliance, OH, p. A527
SHROCK, Lynda, Vice President Human Resources, Logansport Memorial Hospital, Logansport, IN, p. A235
SHROFF, Divya, Chief Medical Officer, Tristar Ashland City Medical Center, Ashland City, TN, p. A634
SHROFF, Rajendra, M.D., Administrative Medical Director, Ssm Health St. Mary's Hospital Centralia, Centralia, IL, p. A196
SHUART, Jeffery, M.D., Chief of Staff, Blackwell Regional Hospital, Blackwell, OK, p. A556
SHUFFIELD, Shawn, Interim Chief Information Officer, St. Josep. Medical Center, Tacoma, WA, p. A767
SHUFFLEBARGER, Tom, Chief Operating Officer, Children's Of Alabama, Birmingham, AL, p. A15
SHUFORD, Little, Health Information Manager, Kindred Hospital-Greensboro, Greensboro, NC, p. A511
SHUGARMAN, Mark D., Administrator, Shriners Hospitals For Children - Cincinnati, Cincinnati, OH, p. A533
SHUGART, Susan, Chief Operating Officer, Carolina Pines Regional Medical Center, Hartsville, SC, p. A621
SHUGART, Susan C., Chief Executive Officer, Kershawhealth, Camden, SC, p. A615
SHUGHART, Deborah, Chief Financial Officer, Fulton County Medical Center, Mc Connellsburg, PA, p. A596
SHUGRUE, Dianne, President and Chief Executive Officer, Glens Falls Hospital, Glens Falls, NY, p. A484
SHULER, Conrad, M.D., Chief Medical Officer, Prisma Health Oconee Memorial Hospital, Seneca, SC, p. A624
SHULL, Jennifer, R.N., Chief Nursing Officer, Adventhealth Fish Memorial, Orange City, FL, p. A150
SHULMAN, Michael, Pysician-in-Chief, Kaiser Permanente Santa Rosa Medical Center, Santa Rosa, CA, p. A98
SHULTS, Randi L., Chief Executive Officer, North Carolina Specialty Hospital, Durham, NC, p. A509
SHUMAKER, Bradley, Chief Medical Officer, Orange Park Medical Center, Orange Park, FL, p. A150
SHUMAN, Betty, Director Human Resources, Wesley Rehabilitation Hospital, Wichita, KS, p. A279
SHUMAN, Daniel, D.O., Chief Medical Officer, Ashland Health Center, Ashland, KS, p. A261
SHUMATE, Kim, Human Resources Officer, Ohio State University Wexner Medical Center, Columbus, OH, p. A536
SHUMWAY, Barbara, Director Human Resources, North Big Horn Hospital District, Lovell, WY, p. A803
SHUPERT, Charlene, Director Staff Services, Carrus Rehabilitation Hospital, Sherman, TX, p. A715
Director Staff Services, Carrus Specialty Hospital, Sherman, TX, p. A715
SHUPP, Susan, Chief Human Resources Officer, Nemaha County Hospital, Auburn, NE, p. A429
SHURTZ, Marc, Interim Chief Executive Officer and Chief Financial Officer, Orleans Community Health, Medina, NY, p. A488
SHUSHTARI, J., M.D., Chief Medical Officer, Hospital For Special Care, New Britain, CT, p. A123
SHUTE, Keith, M.D., Senior Vice President Medical Affairs and Clinical Services, Androscoggin Valley Hospital, Berlin, NH, p. A448
SHYSHKA, Susan, Associate Director, Va Greater Los Angeles Healthcare System, Los Angeles, CA, p. A76
SIAL, Ajay, Chief Financial Officer, UC Irvine Health, Uci Medical Center, Orange, CA, p. A83
SIBBITT, Stephen, M.D., Chief Medical Officer, Baylor Scott & White Medical Center - Temple, Temple, TX, p. A719
SIBLEY, Beth, Director of Nursing, Sage Rehabilitation Hospital, Baton Rouge, LA, p. A297

SIBLEY, Jeri, Director Revenue Cycle, Riverside Tappahannock Hospital, Tappahannock, VA, p. A752

SICA, Vincent A., President and Chief Executive Officer, Desoto Memorial Hospital, Arcadia, FL, p. A131

SICHTS, Pam, Director Human Resources, Sycamore Springs, Lafayette, IN, p. A234

SICILIA, Bruce, M.D., Medical Director, Encompass Health Rehabilitation Hospital Of York, York, PA, p. A612

SICKLES, Alan, M.D., Chief Executive Officer, Saint Michael's Medical Center, Newark, NJ, p. A460

SICKLES, Doyle, M.D., Chief of Medical Staff, Stonewall Jackson Memorial Hospital, Weston, WV, p. A777

SIDDIQI, Ather, M.D., Medical Director, Nexus Specialty Hospital The Woodlands, The Woodlands, TX, p. A720
M.D., Medical Director, Nexus Specialty Hospital, Shenandoah, TX, p. A715

SIDDIQI, Syed, M.D., President Medical Staff, Raleigh General Hospital, Beckley, WV, p. A770

SIDDIQUI, Joseph, Vice President Human Resources, The Aroostook Medical Center, Presque Isle, ME, p. A322

SIDER, Tod, M.D., Chief of Staff, Parkview Wabash Hospital, Wabash, IN, p. A242

SIDES, Tim, Chief Financial Officer, Valle Vista Health System, Greenwood, IN, p. A230

SIDLO, Brad, Chief Executive Officer, Carrus Rehabilitation Hospital, Sherman, TX, p. A715
Chief Executive Officer, Carrus Specialty Hospital, Sherman, TX, p. A715

SIDMAN, Robert, M.D., Regional Vice President, Medical Affairs, The William W. Backus Hospital, Norwich, CT, p. A124

SIDONE, LeighAnn, MSN, R.N., Chief Nursing Officer, Suburban Hospital, Bethesda, MD, p. A327

SIDWELL, Sherry, Chief Operating Officer, Vice President Integrated Support Services, Community Hospital Anderson, Anderson, IN, p. A223

SIEBENALER, Christopher, Regional Senior Vice President and Chief Executive Officer, Houston Methodist Sugar Land Hospital, Sugar Land, TX, p. A717

SIEBERT, Matt, Assistant Administrator Ancillary Services, Hermann Area District Hospital, Hermann, MO, p. A407

SIEG, Greg, Support Services Executive, Healthsource Saginaw, Inc., Saginaw, MI, p. A365

SIEGEL, Fredric, M.D., Chief of Staff, Desert View Hospital, Pahrump, NV, p. A445

SIEGEL, Lesley, M.D., Medical Director, Albert J. Solnit Psychiatric Center - South Campus, Middletown, CT, p. A123

SIEGEL, Tiffany, Chief Nursing Officer, Fulton County Health Center, Wauseon, OH, p. A552

SIEGELMAN, Gary, M.D., MSC, Senior Vice President and Chief Medical Officer, Bayhealth Medical Center, Dover, DE, p. A127

SIEGFRIED, Carole, MSN, R.N., Campus Nurse Executive, Prisma Health Richland Hospital, Columbia, SC, p. A618

SIEGLE, Lora, M.D., Chief Medical Officer, Morris County Hospital, Council Grove, KS, p. A263

SIEGLEN, Linda, M.D., Chief Medical Officer, Mission Hospital Mission Viejo, Mission Viejo, CA, p. A78

SIEGMAN, Ira, M.D., Chief Medical Officer, Northside Hospital, Saint Petersburg, FL, p. A156

SIEGRIST, Steve, Director of Human Resources, Mesa View Regional Hospital, Mesquite, NV, p. A445

SIEK, Terry, MSN, R.N., Chief Nursing Officer, Hays Medical Center, Hays, KS, p. A265

SIEMERS, Tom, Chief Executive Officer, Wilbarger General Hospital, Vernon, TX, p. A723

SIERZENSKI, Paul, M.D., Chief Medical Officer Acute Services, Renown Regional Medical Center, Reno, NV, p. A446
M.D., Chief Medical Officer Acute Services, Renown Rehabilitation Hospital, Reno, NV, p. A446
M.D., Chief Medical Officer Acute Services, Renown South Meadows Medical Center, Reno, NV, p. A446

SIEVERT, Deana, MSN, R.N., Chief Nursing Officer, Promedica Toledo Hospital, Toledo, OH, p. A550

SIEWERT, Charles, Director Human Resources, Buffalo Psychiatric Center, Buffalo, NY, p. A479
Director Human Resources, Western New York Children's Psychiatric Center, West Seneca, NY, p. A502

SIFERS, Carl, Director Information Technology and System Services, Centerpoint Medical Center, Independence, MO, p. A407

SIFFRING, Connie K., Chief Executive Officer, Select Specialty Hospital - Lincoln, Lincoln, NE, p. A435

SIGEL, Heather, Director of Clinical Services, Valley Health - War Memorial Hospital, Berkeley Springs, WV, p. A770

SIGNOR, Kristin, Director Finance, Sunnyview Rehabilitation Hospital, Schenectady, NY, p. A501

SIGREST, Marion, M.D., Chief of Staff, Baptist Medical Center Yazoo, Yazoo City, MS, p. A401

SIJ, Mark, D.O., Chief Executive Officer, Texas Health Presbyterian Hospital Kaufman, Kaufman, TX, p. A692

SIKAND, Mehar, Manager Human Resources, Shriners Hospitals For Children-Shreveport, Shreveport, LA, p. A314

SILARD, Kathleen A., R.N., MS, FACHE, President and Chief Executive Officer, Stamford Hospital, Stamford, CT, p. A125

SILAS, Maria, Manager Human Resources, Suny Downstate-University Hospital Of Brooklyn, Brooklyn, NY, p. A479

SILBER, Steven, M.D., Senior Vice President Medical Affairs, Newyork-Presbyterian Brooklyn Methodist Hospital, Brooklyn, NY, p. A478

SILBERMAN, Sam, Chief Financial Officer, San Antonio Behavioral Healthcare Hospital, San Antonio, TX, p. A713

SILLS, Doug, Chief Executive Officer, Santa Rosa Medical Center, Milton, FL, p. A148

SILLS, John, Chief Information Officer, Health Central Hospital, Ocoee, FL, p. A150

SILLYMAN, Bryce, Chief Operating Officer, Pottstown Hospital, Pottstown, PA, p. A605

SILSBEE, Dave, Chief Information Officer, Cary Medical Center, Caribou, ME, p. A320

SILVA, Francisco, Financial Director, Hospital Metropolitano Dr. Susoni, Arecibo, PR, p. A806

SILVA, Shawn, Chief Executive Officer, Heritage Oaks Hospital, Sacramento, CA, p. A89

SILVA-STEELE, Jamie A., FACHE, R.N., President and Chief Executive Officer, Unm Sandoval Regional Medical Center, Inc., Rio Rancho, NM, p. A471

SILVEIRA, Mike, Director Human Resources Business Partners, Kaiser Permanente Fresno Medical Center, Fresno, CA, p. A65

SILVER, Michael, M.D., Chief Information Officer, Rush Oak Park Hospital, Oak Park, IL, p. A215
M.D., Vice President Medical Affairs, Rush Oak Park Hospital, Oak Park, IL, p. A215

SILVER, Timothy, M.D., Medical Director, SAH-S, Sheltering Arms Hospital South, Midlothian, VA, p. A746

SILVERIA, Rich, Executive Vice President and Chief Financial Officer, University Of Chicago Medical Center, Chicago, IL, p. A201

SILVERMAN, Daniel, M.D., Chief Medical Officer, Acute Care Troy, Samaritan Hospital - Main Campus, Troy, NY, p. A500
M.D., Vice President and Chief Medical Officer, Sinai Hospital Of Baltimore, Baltimore, MD, p. A326

SILVERMAN, Michael, Chief Operating Officer, St. Catherine Of Siena Medical Center, Smithtown, NY, p. A498

SILVERSTEIN, Joel, M.D., Chief Medical Officer, Copley Hospital, Morrisville, VT, p. A736

SILVERSTEIN, Kenneth, M.D., Chief Clinical Officer, Christianacare, Newark, DE, p. A128

SILVERTHORNE, Samuel, Chief Information Officer, U. S. Air Force Medical Center Keesler, Keesler Afb, MS, p. A395

SILVESTRI, Scott, Chief Financial Officer, Hospital Financial Operations, Guthrie Robert Packer Hospital, Sayre, PA, p. A606

SILVEUS, Patrick, M.D., Medical Director, Kosciusko Community Hospital, Warsaw, IN, p. A242

SILVEY, Christie, Director People Services, Hshs St. Joseph's Hospital, Highland, IL, p. A207

SILVIA, Charles, M.D., Chief Medical Officer and Vice President Medical Affairs, Tidalhealth Peninsula, Salisbury, MD, p. A332

SIMCHUK, Cathy, Chief Operating Officer, Providence Holy Family Hospital, Spokane, WA, p. A766

SIMIA, Greg, Chief Financial Officer, Hshs St. Clare Memorial Hospital, Oconto Falls, WI, p. A793
Chief Financial Officer, Hshs St. Mary's Hospital Medical Center, Green Bay, WI, p. A785
Chief Financial Officer, Hshs St. Nicholas Hospital, Sheboygan, WI, p. A796
Chief Financial Officer, Hshs St. Vincent Hospital, Green Bay, WI, p. A785

SIMKINS, Palma, Chief Human Resources Management Services, Battle Creek Veterans Affairs Medical Center, Battle Creek, MI, p. A349

SIMMERMON, Eric, Chief Nursing Officer, Lea Regional Medical Center, Hobbs, NM, p. A470

SIMMONS, Angela L., Chief Executive Officer, Encompass Health Rehabilitation Hospital Of Humble, Humble, TX, p. A689

SIMMONS, Barbara, R.N., Chief Executive Officer, Westside Regional Medical Center, Plantation, FL, p. A154

SIMMONS, Brad, Chief Operating Officer, Saint Luke's Hospital Of Kansas City, Kansas City, MO, p. A409
Chief Operating Officer, University Of California, Davis Medical Center, Sacramento, CA, p. A90
Interim Chief Executive Officer, University Of California, Davis Medical Center, Sacramento, CA, p. A90

SIMMONS, Daniel, Senior Vice President and Treasurer, Monongahela Valley Hospital, Monongahela, PA, p. A597

SIMMONS, Dorlynn, Chief Executive Officer, Mescalero Public Health Service Indian Hospital, Mescalero, NM, p. A471

SIMMONS, Dwayne, Interim Chief Information Officer, Montefiore St. Luke's Cornwall, Newburgh, NY, p. A492

SIMMONS, Jodi, Chief Nursing Officer, Hillcrest Medical Center, Tulsa, OK, p. A569

SIMMONS, Kermit C., Administrator, Louisiana Extended Care Hospital Of Lafayette, Lafayette, LA, p. A305

SIMMONS, Rickie, Controller, Kindred Hospital North Florida, Green Cove Springs, FL, p. A139

SIMMONS, Shelley, Chief Nursing Officer, Jackson County Memorial Hospital, Altus, OK, p. A555

SIMMONS, Taquisa, Interim Director, Hampton Veterans Affairs Medical Center, Hampton, VA, p. A743

SIMMS, Miquel, R.N., Chief Nursing Officer, Queen's North Hawaii Community Hospital, Kamuela, HI, p. A186

SIMODEJKA, John E., Chief Executive Officer, Select Specialty Hospital-Camp Hill, Camp Hill, PA, p. A586

SIMON, Anha, Director Human Resources, Riceland Medical Center, Winnie, TX, p. A726

SIMON, Ashley, Chief Financial Officer, Kansas Surgery And Recovery Center, Wichita, KS, p. A279

SIMON, Brenda, Chief Executive Officer, Northern Colorado Rehabilitation Hospital, Johnstown, CO, p. A114

SIMON, Daniel I., M.D., President, Uh Cleveland Medical Center, Cleveland, OH, p. A535

SIMON, Joan, R.N., FACHE, Chief Nursing Officer, Kootenai Health, Coeur D'Alene, ID, p. A190

SIMON, Kareen, Vice President of Operations, Wheeling Hospital, Wheeling, WV, p. A778

SIMON, Kenneth, M.D., Chief of Staff, Veterans Affairs Gulf Coast Veterans Health Care System, Biloxi, MS, p. A390

SIMON, Laura, R.N., MSN, Director Quality Operations and Nursing, Baton Rouge Rehabilitation Hospital, Baton Rouge, LA, p. A296
R.N., MSN, Director, Quality Operations and Nursing, Baton Rouge Rehabilitation Hospital, Baton Rouge, LA, p. A296

SIMON, Mark, System Chief Information Officer, Benefis Health System, Great Falls, MT, p. A424

SIMON, Patricia, Chief Nursing Officer, Encompass Health Rehabilitation Hospital Of Charleston, Charleston, SC, p. A616

SIMON, Richard, M.D., Chief of Staff, Uconn, John Dempsey Hospital, Farmington, CT, p. A122

SIMON, Stuart, M.D., Medical Director, North Central Surgical Center, Dallas, TX, p. A669

SIMON, Teresa, Director Information Systems, Nacogdoches Medical Center, Nacogdoches, TX, p. A702

SIMON, Thresa, M.D., Medical Director, Poplar Springs Hospital, Petersburg, VA, p. A748

SIMONEAU, Lisa J., FACHE, Director, Sioux Falls Veterans Affairs Health Care System, Sioux Falls, SD, p. A632

SIMONEAUX, Katherine, Administrator, Oceans Behavioral Hospital Of Opelousas, Opelousas, LA, p. A312

SIMONIN, Steven J., President and Chief Executive Officer, Iowa Specialty Hospital-Clarion, Clarion, IA, p. A246

SIMONS, Christa, Chief Operating Officer, Greene County Medical Center, Jefferson, IA, p. A252

SIMONS, Janice, FACHE, Chief Executive Officer, Medina Regional Hospital, Hondo, TX, p. A684

SIMONSON, Paul, Vice President, Trinity Health, Minot, ND, p. A525

SIMPSON, Brenda, R.N., Chief Nursing Officer, Largo Medical Center, Largo, FL, p. A143
Chief Nursing Officer, Northeast Georgia Medical Center, Gainesville, GA, p. A173

SIMPSON, Chris, Chief Executive Officer, Cornerstone Hospitals West Monroe, West Monroe, LA, p. A316

SIMPSON, Greg, Chief Nursing Officer, St. Josep. Medical Center, Kansas City, MO, p. A409

SIMPSON, Julie, Vice President Human Resources, University Of Tennessee Medical Center, Knoxville, TN, p. A641

SIMPSON, Keith, Chief Operating Officer, Jennings American Legion Hospital, Jennings, LA, p. A304

SIMPSON, Laura, Director Human Resources, Sabine County Hospital, Hemphill, TX, p. A683

SIMPSON, Mark, Chief Executive Officer, Welch Community Hospital, Welch, WV, p. A777

SIMPSON, Merridth, Director Human Resources, Methodist Charlton Medical Center, Dallas, TX, p. A669

SIMPSON, Mikael, Chief Executive Officer, Pam Rehabilitation Hospital Of Humble, Humble, TX, p. A690

SIMPSON, Rae, R.N., Chief Nursing Officer, Western State Hospital, Tacoma, WA, p. A767

SIMPSON, Reagan, Chief Executive Officer, St. Luke's Rehabilitation Hospital, Chesterfield, MO, p. A404

SIMPSON, Robert, Vice President Operations, Methodist Richardson Medical Center, Richardson, TX, p. A708

SIMPSON, Ryan, President and Chief Executive Officer, Medical Center Of Aurora, Aurora, CO, p. A107
President and Chief Executive Officer, Spalding Rehabilitation Hospital, Aurora, CO, p. A107

SIMPSON, Shawndra, Interim Chief Executive Officer, Sutter Surgical Hospital - North Valley, Yuba City, CA, p. A106

SIMPSON, Sheila, Vice President Human Resources, Palmetto Lowcountry Behavioral Health, Charleston, SC, p. A616

SIMPSON, Steve, Chief Executive Officer, Northeastern Nevada Regional Hospital, Elko, NV, p. A441

SIMPSON-TUGGLE, Deloris, Vice President Human Resources and Organizational Development and Chief Human Resources Officer, Greater Baltimore Medical Center, Baltimore, MD, p. A324

SIMS, Anthony, M.D., Chief of Staff, Dekalb Regional Medical Center, Fort Payne, AL, p. A19

SIMS, Blake, Chief Executive Officer, Northern Colorado Long Term Acute Hospital, Johnstown, CO, p. A114

SIMS, Charles, M.D., Chief of Staff, Chi St. Luke's Health-The Woodlands Hospital, The Woodlands, TX, p. A720

SIMS, Jason, M.D., Chief Medical Officer, Cleveland Area Hospital, Cleveland, OK, p. A557
Facility Information Security Officer, Medical City North Hills, North Richland Hills, TX, p. A703

SIMS, Jeffrey, Chief Executive Officer, Heartland Behavioral Healthcare, Massillon, OH, p. A544

SIMS, Joni, Chief Nursing Officer, Owensboro Health Regional Hospital, Owensboro, KY, p. A291

SIMS, Jyric, FACHE, Chief Executive Officer, Medical City Fort Worth, Fort Worth, TX, p. A678

SIMS, Mark E., Chief Executive Officer, Grand Strand Medical Center, Myrtle Beach, SC, p. A623

SIMS, Paula, Chief Nursing Officer, Trusted Medical Centers-Mansfield, Mansfield, TX, p. A699

SIMZYK, Monica, Regional Chief Human Resources Officer, Amita Health St. Mary's Hospital, Kankakee, IL, p. A209
Regional Human Resource Officer, Amita Health Saint Josep. Medical Center, Joliet, IL, p. A209

SINCICH, Robert, Vice President Human Resources, Trumbull Memorial Hospital, Warren, OH, p. A551

SINCLAIR, Bradley, Chief Financial Officer, Touro Infirmary, New Orleans, LA, p. A311

SINCLAIR, Kathy, Vice President Human Resources, Spartanburg Medical Center - Church Street Campus, Spartanburg, SC, p. A624

SINCLAIR, Kyle E., Chief Executive Officer, Kindred Hospital San Antonio Central, San Antonio, TX, p. A711

SINCLAIR, Laura, Director Human Resources, Kansas City Orthopaedic Institute, Leawood, KS, p. A269

SINCLAIR, Noreen, Human Resources Administrator, Connecticut Veterans Home And Hospital, Rocky Hill, CT, p. A125

SINCLAIR-CHUNG, Opal, R.N., MS, Chief Nursing Officer, Deputy Executive Director, Nyc Health + Hospitals / Kings County, Brooklyn, NY, p. A478

SINCOCK, Gregory, Information Technology Leader, Kaiser Permanente West Los Angeles Medical Center, Los Angeles, CA, p. A74

SINDLINGER, Julie, Director of Human Resources, Weston County Health Services, Newcastle, WY, p. A803

SINEK, James J., FACHE, President, Boone Hospital Center, Columbia, MO, p. A405

SINGER, Gary, Interim Chief Financial Officer, Galesburg Cottage Hospital, Galesburg, IL, p. A205

SINGER, John Chief Operating Officer, Munson Healthcare Charlevoix Hospital, Charlevoix, MI, p. A350

SINGH, Amandeep. Chief Medical Officer, Monroe Hospital, Bloomington, IN, p. A224

SINGH, Amarjit, M.D., President and Chief Executive Officer, Brunswick Psych Center, Amityville, NY, p. A474

SINGH, Gagandeep. M.D., Chief Medical Officer Behavioral Health, Banner Behavioral Health Hospital - Scottsdale, Scottsdale, AZ, p. A38

SINGH, Himanshu, M.D., Associate Director, Veterans Affairs Ann Arbor Healthcare System, Ann Arbor, MI, p. A348

SINGH, Leighton, M.D., Chief of Staff, Prairie Lakes Healthcare System, Watertown, SD, p. A633

SINGH, Manish, M.D., Chief Executive Officer, Doctor's Hospital At Renaissance, Edinburg, TX, p. A674

SINGH, Matab, Chief of Staff, Good Samaritan Hospital, Bakersfield, CA, p. A57

SINGH, Sabi, Chief Operating Officer, University Of Iowa Hospitals And Clinics, Iowa City, IA, p. A252

SINGH, Vijayant, M.D., Chief Hospital Executive, Carepoint Health Bayonne Medical Center, Bayonne, NJ, p. A452

SINGLES, James, Chief Financial Officer, Marlette Regional Hospital, Marlette, MI, p. A361

SINGLETARY-TWYMAN, Michelle, Chief Nursing Officer, Rockford Center, Newark, DE, p. A128

SINGLETON, Al, M.D., Chief Psychiatry and Chief Medical Staff, Colorado Mental Health Institute At Pueblo, Pueblo, CO, p. A117

SINGLETON, Roy, Director Computer Information Systems, Palmdale Regional Medical Center, Palmdale, CA, p. A84

SINHA, Sunil, M.D., FACHE, Chief Medical Officer, Bon Secours Memorial Regional Medical Center, Mechanicsville, VA, p. A746

SINIARD, Sandra, Vice President of Patient Care Services, Chi Memorial Hospital - Georgia, Fort Oglethorpe, GA, p. A173

SINICKAS, Robert, Director Information Services, Northwestern Medicine Marianjoy Rehabilitation Hospital, Wheaton, IL, p. A222

SINICROPE JR, FrankVice President Financial Services, Princeton Community Hospital, Princeton, WV, p. A776

SINISI, Albert, Director Information Systems, Pontiac General Hospital, Pontiac, MI, p. A364

SINK, Kristi M., President, Uh Elyria Medical Center, Elyria, OH, p. A540

SINNOTT, James, M.D., Chief Medical Staff, Coquille Valley Hospital, Coquille, OR, p. A574

SINNOTT, Lisa, Director Human Resources, Acuity Specialty Hospital Of Southern New Jersey, Willingboro, NJ, p. A466

SINOPOLI, Angelo, M.D., Vice President Clinical Integration and Chief Medical Officer, Prisma Health Greenville Memorial Hospital, Greenville, SC, p. A620

SINOTTE, Brian, President, Ingalls Memorial Hospital, Harvey, IL, p. A207

SINYARD, Robert, M.D., Chief Medical Officer, Piedmont Athens Regional Medical Center, Athens, GA, p. A163
M.D., Chief Medical Officer, Piedmont Walton Medical Center, Monroe, GA, p. A177

SIOSON, Stephanie, Director Human Resources, Garden Grove Hospital And Medical Center, Garden Grove, CA, p. A66
Director Human Resources, Huntington Beach Hospital, Huntington Beach, CA, p. A68
Director Human Resources, La Palma Intercommunity Hospital, La Palma, CA, p. A70
Director Human Resources, West Anaheim Medical Center, Anaheim, CA, p. A55

SIOUFI, Habib, M.D., Chief Medical Officer, Umass Memorial-Marlborough Hospital, Marlborough, MA, p. A341

SIPEK, John, Supervisor Client Services, Aurora Medical Center In Washington County, Hartford, WI, p. A786

SIRIANNI, Peter, M.D., President Medical Staff, Christus Mother Frances Hospital - Jacksonville, Jacksonville, TX, p. A691

SIRIVAR, Wendy, Chief Nurse Officer, San Ramon Regional Medical Center, San Ramon, CA, p. A96

SIRK, Donald, Director Information Systems, Medstar St. Mary's Hospital, Leonardtown, MD, p. A331

SIROIS, Peter, President and Chief Executive Officer, Northern Maine Medical Center, Fort Kent, ME, p. A320

SIROTTA, Ted, Chief Financial Officer, Vail Health, Vail, CO, p. A119
Senior Vice President and Chief Financial Officer, Henry Mayo Newhall Hospital, Valencia, CA, p. A103

SISILLO, Sabato, M.D., Chief Medical Officer, Providence Medical Center, Kansas City, KS, p. A267
M.D., Chief Medical Officer, Saint John Hospital, Leavenworth, KS, p. A269

SISK, Glenn C., President, Coosa Valley Medical Center, Sylacauga, AL, p. A24

SISK, Jack, Chief Financial Officer, Punxsutawney Area Hospital, Punxsutawney, PA, p. A605

SISK, Lori, R.N., Chief Executive Officer, Sanford Canby Medical Center, Canby, MN, p. A374
R.N., Chief Executive Officer, Sanford Clear Lake Medical Center, Clear Lake, SD, p. A627

SISK, Susan, Chief Financial Officer, Chi St. Alexius Health, Bismarck, ND, p. A521

SISLER, Debbie, Director, Human Resource, Vidant Roanoke-Chowan Healthcare, Ahoskie, NC, p. A504

SISON, Joseph, M.D., Medical Director, Heritage Oaks Hospital, Sacramento, CA, p. A89

SISON-MARTINEZ, MBA, Romida, R.N., Vice President Nursing, Ssm Health St. Mary's Hospital - Audrain, Mexico, MO, p. A412

SISSON, William G., FACHE, President, Baptist Health Lexington, Lexington, KY, p. A286

SISTO, Steven, Senior Vice President and Chief Operating Officer, Methodist Hospital Of Southern California, Arcadia, CA, p. A56

SISTRUNK, Heather, R.N., Chief Executive Officer, Merit Health Rankin, Brandon, MS, p. A390
R.N., Chief Executive Officer, Merit Health Woman's Hospital, Flowood, MS, p. A392

SITLINGER, James, Chief Human Resources Management, Charles George Veterans Affairs Medical Center, Asheville, NC, p. A504

SITTIG, Kevin, M.D., Senior Associate Dean and Chief Medical Officer, Ochsner Lsu Health Shreveport - Academic Medical Center, Shreveport, LA, p. A314

SIU, Max, Chief Information Officer, Hackensack Meridian Health Mountainside Medical Center, Montclair, NJ, p. A458

SIVAK, Steven, M.D., Chief Medical Officer, Einstein Physicians Philadelphia, Einstein Medical Center Philadelphia, Philadelphia, PA, p. A600

SIVEK, Carla, Director, Coatesville Veterans Affairs Medical Center, Coatesville, PA, p. A587

SIVLEY, Susanna, Chief Personnel Officer, Highlands Medical Center, Scottsboro, AL, p. A24

SIX, Deborah, Coordinator Data Processing, Wayne Memorial Hospital, Jesup. GA, p. A174

SIX, Stephanie, Chief Executive Officer, Northeastern Health System Sequoyah, Sallisaw, OK, p. A567

SIZELOVE, Lyn, Director of Nursing, Beaver County Memorial Hospital, Beaver, OK, p. A556

SJOBERG, Rochelle, Chief Human Resources Officer, Ely-Bloomenson Community Hospital, Ely, MN, p. A376

SKABELUND, Hoyt, Chief Executive Officer, Banner Fort Collins Medical Center, Fort Collins, CO, p. A112
Chief Executive Officer, Mckee Medical Center, Loveland, CO, p. A117
Chief Executive Officer, North Colorado Medical Center, Greeley, CO, p. A113

SKAGGS, Lynda, Chief Nursing Officer, Fleming County Hospital, Flemingsburg, KY, p. A283

SKALA, Pat, Chief Information Officer, Laguna Honda Hospital And Rehabilitation Center, San Francisco, CA, p. A93

SKALSKI, Eileen, Chief Nursing Officer, Encompass Health Rehabilitation Hospital Of Hamarville, Pittsburgh, PA, p. A603

SKARKA, Kathy, MSN, R.N., Executive Vice President Patient Care Services, Nassau University Medical Center, East Meadow, NY, p. A483

SKARULIS, Patricia, Senior Vice President and Chief Information Systems Officer, Memorial Sloan-Kettering Cancer Center, New York, NY, p. A490

SKARZYNSKI, Joseph, M.D., Medical Director, Nyc Health + Hospitals / North Central Bronx, Bronx, NY, p. A477

SKEANS, John, Chief Financial Officer, Northwest Community Healthcare, Arlington Heights, IL, p. A194

SKEEN, Steven, R.N., Chief Nursing Officer, Mizell Memorial Hospital, Opp. AL, p. A23

SKELDON, Timothy, Chief Financial Officer, Thomas Memorial Hospital, South Charleston, WV, p. A777
Senior Vice President and Chief Financial Officer, Parrish Medical Center, Titusville, FL, p. A160

SKELTON, Jenny, System Integration Manager, The Women's Hospital, Newburgh, IN, p. A238

SKELTON, Katie, MSN, R.N., Vice President Nursing and Chief Nursing Officer, St. Josep. Hospital Orange, Orange, CA, p. A83

SKEVINGTON, John, Chief Executive Officer, Parkland Medical Center, Derry, NH, p. A448

SKIBBA, Joshua, Chief Medical Officer, Ohio County Hospital, Hartford, KY, p. A284

SKIDMORE, Jocelyn, Director Finance, Mosaic Medical Center - Maryville, Maryville, MO, p. A411

SKIDMORE, Kim, Chief Executive Officer, Izard County Medical Center, Calico Rock, AR, p. A43

SKIEM, Paul, Senior Vice President Human Resources, Amita Health Saint Francis Hospital Evanston, Evanston, IL, p. A204

SKIFF, Jessica, Director Human Resources, Lewis County General Hospital, Lowville, NY, p. A487

SKILLINGS, Lois N., R.N., MSN, FACHE, President and Chief Executive Officer, Mid Coast Hospital, Brunswick, ME, p. A319

SKILLINGS, Michelle, Chief Nursing Officer, Franklin Foundation Hospital, Franklin, LA, p. A301

SKINNER, Christopher, Chief of Staff, Spectrum Health Big Rapids Hospital, Big Rapids, MI, p. A349

SKINNER, Eileen F., FACHE, Administrator, Shriners Hospitals For Children-Boston, Boston, MA, p. A336

SKINNER, Gary, Director Information Technology, Rehabilitation Hospital Of Indiana, Indianapolis, IN, p. A233

SKINNER, Gwendolyn, Operational Vice President, Devereux Advanced Behavioral Health Georgia, Kennesaw, GA, p. A174

SKINNER, Kellcie, Controller, Newman Memorial Hospital, Shattuck, OK, p. A568

SKINNER, Kristina, Director Quality, Sanpete Valley Hospital, Mount Pleasant, UT, p. A729

SKINNER, Marjorie, Director Finance, Pershing General Hospital, Lovelock, NV, p. A445

SKINNER, Richard, Chief Information Technology Officer, University Of Virginia Medical Center, Charlottesville, VA, p. A740

SKIPPER, Kymberli, Manager Human Resources, Prattville Baptist Hospital, Prattville, AL, p. A24

SKIPPER, Michelle, Director Human Resources, Kaiser Permanente Riverside Medical Center, Riverside, CA, p. A88

SKJOLDEN, Jessica, M.D., Chief of Staff, St. Andrew's Health Center, Bottineau, ND, p. A521

SKLAMBERG, Todd, President, Sunrise Hospital And Medical Center, Las Vegas, NV, p. A444

SKLAR, Joel, M.D., Chief Medical Officer, Marinhealth Medical Center, Greenbrae, CA, p. A67

SKOWRON, Paul, Chief Executive Officer, Warner Hospital And Health Services, Clinton, IL, p. A201

SKRINDE, Tracie, Senior Human Resources Partner, Peacehealth United General Medical Center, Sedro, WA, p. A765

SKRIPPS, Michele M., R.N., Chief Executive Officer, Encompass Health Rehabilitation Hospital Of Charleston, Charleston, SC, p. A616

SKULA, Erika, President and Chief Executive Officer, Adventhealth Carrollwood, Tampa, FL, p. A159

SKULA, Joe, Director Human Resources, Adventhealth Manchester, Manchester, KY, p. A289

SKVARENINA, Michael, Assistant Vice President Information Systems, Holy Name Medical Center, Teaneck, NJ, p. A464

SLABA, Bryan, Chief Executive Officer, Wagner Community Memorial Hospital Avera, Wagner, SD, p. A632

SLABIK, Shauna, Chief Financial Officer, Sanford Mayville Medical Center, Mayville, ND, p. A525

SLACK, Lina, Human Resources Leader, Kaiser Permanente San Jose Medical Center, San Jose, CA, p. A94

SLACK, Randy, Chief Financial Officer, Nacogdoches Medical Center, Nacogdoches, TX, p. A702

SLAGLE, Julie, R.N., MSN, Vice President Patient Care Services, Sidney Regional Medical Center, Sidney, NE, p. A439

SLATE, Sonny, Chief Operating Officer, Georgia Regional Hospital At Atlanta, Decatur, GA, p. A171

SLATER, Bill, Chief Financial Officer, Hegg Health Center Avera, Rock Valley, IA, p. A257

SLATER, Craig, M.D., Chief Medical Officer, Atrium Health Union, Monroe, NC, p. A514

SLATER-NESUOLD, Stephanie, Director of Nursing, Landmark Hospital Of Joplin, Joplin, MO, p. A408

SLATON, Brenda, Superintendent, Rusk State Hospital, Rusk, TX, p. A710

SLATTERY, Greg, Vice President Information, Community Hospitals And Wellness Centers, Bryan, OH, p. A530

SLATTERY, Robert, Vice President of Operations, Bridgton Hospital, Bridgton, ME, p. A319

SLATTERY, Susan, Director Human Resources, Unitypoint Health - St. Luke's Hospital, Cedar Rapids, IA, p. A245

SLATTMAN, Robin, Chief Nursing Officer, Memorial Health, Marysville, OH, p. A544

SLAVIN, Kevin J., FACHE, President and Chief Executive Officer, St. Joseph's University Medical Center, Paterson, NJ, p. A460

SLAVIN, Peter L., M.D., President, Massachusetts General Hospital, Boston, MA, p. A336

SLAWITSKY, Bruce, Vice President Human Resources, Hospital For Special Surgery, New York, NY, p. A490

SLAYMAN, Aubree, Director Patient Services, Miami County Medical Center, Paola, KS, p. A274

SLAYTON, Val, M.D., Vice President Medical Affairs, Uofl Health - Mary And Elizabeth Hospital, Louisville, KY, p. A289

SLEDGE, Cynthia, M.D., Medical Director, Bryce Hospital, Tuscaloosa, AL, p. A25

SLEDGE, Tasha, Director Human Resources, Texas Health Harris Methodist Hospital Southlake, Southlake, TX, p. A716

SLEDGE, Thomas, Chief Executive Officer, North Texas Medical Center, Gainesville, TX, p. A680

SLEDGE, Tom, Chief Operating Officer, Northwest Medical Center - Springdale, Springdale, AR, p. A53

SLEE, Kim, Chief Operating Officer, Fulton County Medical Center, Mc Connellsburg, PA, p. A596

SLEEPER, Justin, Vice President Clinical Operations, Behavioral Health Network, Natchaug Hospital, Mansfield Center, CT, p. A123

SLEIME, Melanie, Director Human Resources, Memorial Hospital, North Conway, NH, p. A451

SLEITER, Michelle, Chief Executive Officer, Humboldt County Memorial Hospital, Humboldt, IA, p. A251

SLENSZAK, David, Director, Information Services, Williamsburg Regional Hospital, Kingstree, SC, p. A622

SLESSOR, Steve Robert., Chief Executive Officer, Buchanan County Health Center, Independence, IA, p. A251

SLETTE, Katie, Director Human Resources, New Ulm Medical Center, New Ulm, MN, p. A382

SLICK, Lois, Director of Human Resources, Lifecare Medical Center, Roseau, MN, p. A384

SLIDER, Carol, Chief Nursing Officer, Titus Regional Medical Center, Mount Pleasant, TX, p. A702

SLIGER, Susan, Director Human Resources, War Memorial Hospital, Sault Sainte Marie, MI, p. A366

SLITER, Elizabeth, M.D., Chairman Medical Staff, Decatur Health Systems, Oberlin, KS, p. A272

SLIVA, Paul, Chief Information Officer, Boone County Hospital, Boone, IA, p. A244

SLIWA, James, M.D., Chief Medical Officer, Shirley Ryan Abilitylab, Chicago, IL, p. A200

SLIWINSKI, Jeff, Chief Financial Officer, Hca Houston Healthcare Clear Lake, League City, TX, p. A695

SLIWINSKI, Ron, Chief of Hospital Division, University Hospital, Madison, WI, p. A788

SLOAN, Brian, Chief Operating Officer, Duke Raleigh Hospital, Raleigh, NC, p. A516

SLOAN, D Christopher, Chief Operating Officer, Capital Medical Center, Olympia, WA, p. A761

SLOAN, Patrick, Chief Financial Officer, Memorial Satilla Health, Waycross, GA, p. A183

SLOAN, Prudence, Coordinator Human Resources, Select Specialty Hospital-Pittsburgh/Upmc, Pittsburgh, PA, p. A603

SLOAN, Ronald A., FACHE, President, The Outer Banks Hospital, Nags Head, NC, p. A515

SLOAN, Steve, Chief Financial Officer, Lake Cumberland Regional Hospital, Somerset, KY, p. A293

SLOCUM, Brandon, Senior Vice President and Chief Financial Officer, Medical West, Bessemer, AL, p. A14

SLOCUM, Gregg Y., Chief Executive Officer, Valley Forge Medical Center And Hospital, Norristown, PA, p. A598

SLONIKER, Amanda, Director of Nursing, Heartland Behavioral Health Services, Nevada, MO, p. A412

SLONIM, Sheryl, Executive Vice President and Chief Nursing Officer, Holy Name Medical Center, Teaneck, NJ, p. A464

SLONINA, Marrianne, Director Human Resources, Georgetown Community Hospital, Georgetown, KY, p. A284

SLOPER, Carol, Manager Information Technology, Cheyenne County Hospital, Saint Francis, KS, p. A275

SLUCK, Jeana, R.N., Executive Director Nursing Clinical Inpatient Departments, Allied Services Rehabilitation Hospital, Scranton, PA, p. A606

SLUSHER, Carlene, Director Finance, Seneca Healthcare District, Chester, CA, p. A60

SLUSHER, Michael, FACHE, Community Chief Executive Officer, Middlesboro Arh Hospital, Middlesboro, KY, p. A290

SLUSHER, W. James (Jamie), M.D., Chief of Staff, Jackson Parish Hospital, Jonesboro, LA, p. A304

SLUTSKER, Vladimir, Medical Director, Encompass Health Rehabilitation Hospital Of Gadsden, Gadsden, AL, p. A19

SLYTER, Mark, FACHE, President and Chief Operating Officer, Chandler Regional Medical Center, Chandler, AZ, p. A30
FACHE, President and Chief Operating Officer, Mercy Gilbert Medical Center, Gilbert, AZ, p. A32

SLYTER, Mark F., FACHE, President and Chief Operating Officer, Chandler Regional Medical Center, Chandler, AZ, p. A30
FACHE, President and Chief Operating Officer, Mercy Gilbert Medical Center, Gilbert, AZ, p. A32

SMAJSTRLA, Julie, Director Nursing, Seymour Hospital, Seymour, TX, p. A715

SMALE, Cindy, Director, Human Resources, Iredell Health System, Statesville, NC, p. A519

SMALL, Becky, Chief Human Resources Officer, Kindred Hospital-Aurora, Aurora, CO, p. A107
Chief Nursing Officer, North Texas Medical Center, Gainesville, TX, p. A680

SMALL, Donna, R.N., Chief Nursing Officer, St. Mary's Medical Center, West Palm Beach, FL, p. A162

SMALL, Jonathan, Chief Operations Information and Technology, John D. Dingell Veterans Affairs Medical Center, Detroit, MI, p. A353

SMALL, Terry, Assistant Chief Executive Officer, William R. Sharpe, Jr. Hospital, Weston, WV, p. A777

SMALLEY, Ben, Administrator, Cassia Regional Hospital, Burley, ID, p. A189

SMALLWOOD, Ravae, IS Coordinator, Chi Health Missouri Valley, Missouri Valley, IA, p. A254

SMANIK, Robert, Vice President of Operatoins, Bristol Health, Bristol, CT, p. A121

SMARR, Susan, M.D., Physician-in-Chief, Kaiser Permanente Santa Clara Medical Center, Santa Clara, CA, p. A97

SMART, Dan, Chief Information Management Officer, Permian Regional Medical Center, Andrews, TX, p. A653

SMART, Melissa, Communication ad Public Relations Specialist, Texas Health Presbyterian Hospital Denton, Denton, TX, p. A672

SMART, Paul, CPA, Chief Financial Officer, Franklin County Medical Center, Preston, ID, p. A192

SMART, Robert M., Chief Executive Officer, Encompass Health Rehabilitation Hospital Of The Mid-Cities, Bedford, TX, p. A658

SMART, Stephanie, Chief Nursing Officer, United Hospital Center, Bridgeport, WV, p. A770

SMENDIK, Douglas, M.D., Hospital Medical Director, Spectrum Health Pennock, Hastings, MI, p. A357

SMIDT, Jessica, R.N., Director of Nursing, Pipestone County Medical Center Avera, Pipestone, MN, p. A383

SMIGA, Lance, Chief Financial Officer, Jackson County Hospital District, Edna, TX, p. A674

SMILEY, Christy, Leader Human Resources, Ssm Health St. Mary's Hospital - Audrain, Mexico, MO, p. A412

SMITH, Agnes, MSN, R.N., Chief Nursing Officer, Twin County Regional Healthcare, Galax, VA, p. A743

SMITH, Alan, Chief Financial Officer, Huntington Beach Hospital, Huntington Beach, CA, p. A68
Chief Financial Officer, La Palma Intercommunity Hospital, La Palma, CA, p. A70

SMITH, Alyshia, R.N., Interim Director, Phoenix Veterans Affairs Health Care System, Phoenix, AZ, p. A36

SMITH, Andrew, Chief Financial Officer, Blake Medical Center, Bradenton, FL, p. A132

SMITH, Angie, Chief Nursing Officer, St. Bernards Medical Center, Jonesboro, AR, p. A48

SMITH, Ann, Senior Vice President, Inpatient Services and Interim Chief Administrative Officer, University Of Cincinnati Medical Center, Cincinnati, OH, p. A533

SMITH, Anton C., Administrator, Shriners Hospitals For Children-Honolulu, Honolulu, HI, p. A185

SMITH, Barbara, Senior Vice President & Chief Operating Officer, Robert Wood Johnson University Hospital At Hamilton, Hamilton, NJ, p. A456

SMITH, Bennie, Chief Information Officer, Lady Of The Sea General Hospital, Cut Off, LA, p. A300
Director Human Resources and Risk Management, Lady Of The Sea General Hospital, Cut Off, LA, p. A300

SMITH, Bernie, Chief Financial Officer, Guthrie Troy Community Hospital, Troy, PA, p. A609

SMITH, Bethany, Controller, West Tennessee Rehabilitation Hospital Cane Creek, Martin, TN, p. A643
Director of Finance, Chi Oakes Hospital, Oakes, ND, p. A525
Vice President Finance, Chi Mercy Health, Valley City, ND, p. A526

SMITH, Betsy, Chief Nursing Officer, Effingham Hospital, Springfield, GA, p. A180

SMITH, Beverly, Chief Nursing Officer, Southside Regional Medical Center, Petersburg, VA, p. A749

SMITH, Blythe, Administrative Assistant, Faulkton Area Medical Center, Faulkton, SD, p. A628

SMITH, Bobby, Vice President Physician Services and Quality, Illinois Valley Community Hospital, Peru, IL, p. A217

SMITH, Bradley, President and Chief Executive Officer, Rush Memorial Hospital, Rushville, IN, p. A240

SMITH, Brenda, Director Financial Services, Alliance Health Center, Meridian, MS, p. A397

SMITH, Brent, Chief Executive Officer, Comanche County Memorial Hospital, Lawton, OK, p. A561

SMITH, Brian, Chief Financial Officer, Beth Israel Deaconess Hospital-Needham Campus, Needham, MA, p. A342
Director of Operations, Wamego Health Center, Wamego, KS, p. A278
Vice President Human Resources, Lexington Medical Center, West Columbia, SC, p. A625

SMITH, C, M.D., Chief Medical Officer, Jay Hospital, Jay, FL, p. A142

SMITH, Candice, MSN, Chief Nursing Officer, Hereford Regional Medical Center, Hereford, TX, p. A684

SMITH, Carl, Chief Information Officer, King's Daughters Medical Center, Brookhaven, MS, p. A390

SMITH, Carol, R.N., Director Operations and Nursing, Novant Health Medical Park Hospital, Winston, NC, p. A520
Vice President Patient Care and Chief Nursing Officer, Tift Regional Medical Center, Tifton, GA, p. A182

SMITH, Carole, Senior Human Resource Business Partner, Banner Del E. Webb Medical Center, Sun City West, AZ, p. A39

SMITH, Charles, Chief Executive Officer, Encompass Health Rehabilitation Hospital Of Utah, Sandy, UT, p. A733

SMITH, Cheryl, Manager Human Resources, New Braunfels Regional Rehabilitation Hospital, New Braunfels, TX, p. A703

SMITH, Chris, Chief Information Officer, Falls Community Hospital And Clinic, Marlin, TX, p. A699

SMITH, Connie, FACHE, MSN, R.N., Chief Executive Officer, Medical Center At Bowling Green, Bowling Green, KY, p. A281

SMITH, Dan, Director Human Resources, Austin Lakes Hospital, Austin, TX, p. A655
Director Human Resources, Memorial Hospital, Carthage, IL, p. A196
SMITH, Danelle, Chief Executive Officer, Twelve Clans Unity Hospital, Winnebago, NE, p. A440
SMITH, Daniel, Chief Financial Officer, Palo Pinto General Hospital, Mineral Wells, TX, p. A701
Chief Financial Officer, Samaritan Pacific Communities Hospital, Newport, OR, p. A578
Chief Financial Officer, Top. Surgical Specialty Hospital, Houston, TX, p. A689
Vice President Finance, Good Samaritan Regional Medical Center, Corvallis, OR, p. A574
Vice President Finance, Samaritan Albany General Hospital, Albany, OR, p. A573
Vice President Finance, Samaritan Lebanon Community Hospital, Lebanon, OR, p. A577
SMITH, Darrin, Chief Operating Officer, Parkview Medical Center, Pueblo, CO, p. A118
SMITH, Darwin, Vice President Human Resources, Cleveland Clinic Union Hospital, Dover, OH, p. A539
SMITH, David, Chief Executive Officer, Baylor Scott & White Institute For Rehabilitation - Dallas, Dallas, TX, p. A667
President and Chief Executive Officer, Grant Regional Health Center, Lancaster, WI, p. A787
SMITH, Debra, Chief Nursing Officer, Encompass Health Rehabilitation Hospital Of Kingsport, Kingsport, TN, p. A640
SMITH, Denise, Director Health Information, Encompass Health Rehabilitation Hospital Of Chattanooga, Chattanooga, TN, p. A635
SMITH, Diana, Chief Financial Officer, Kp. Promise Hospital Of Dallas, Dallas, TX, p. A668
SMITH, Dianne, Director Personnel and Human Resources, Potomac Valley Hospital, Keyser, WV, p. A773
SMITH, Dick, Director Human Resources, West Park Hospital, Cody, WY, p. A802
SMITH, Dirkland T., Chief Executive Officer, Faulkton Area Medical Center, Faulkton, SD, p. A628
SMITH, Donna, R.N., Vice President Chief Operating Officer and Chief Nursing Officer, Clifton Springs Hospital And Clinic, Clifton Springs, NY, p. A481
Chief Nursing Officer, Barstow Community Hospital, Barstow, CA, p. A58
SMITH, Donnie, Chief Human Resources Officer, Laird Hospital, Union, MS, p. A400
Director Human Resources, Rush Foundation Hospital, Meridian, MS, p. A397
SMITH, Doug, Chief Financial Officer, Stephens Memorial Hospital, Breckenridge, TX, p. A660
Interim Chief Executive Officer and Chief Financial Officer, Stephens Memorial Hospital, Breckenridge, TX, p. A660
SMITH, Edward H., President and Chief Executive Officer, St. Anthony Regional Hospital, Carroll, IA, p. A244
SMITH, Eli, Chief Operating Officer, West Jefferson Medical Center, Marrero, LA, p. A308
SMITH, Eric, Chief Financial Officer, Bayfront Health St. Petersburg, Saint Petersburg, FL, p. A156
SMITH, Ericka, Chief Operating Officer, Monterey Park Hospital, Monterey Park, CA, p. A79
SMITH, Erin, Chief Operating Officer, East Georgia Regional Medical Center, Statesboro, GA, p. A181
SMITH, Eugene, Chief Information Officer, Maniilaq Health Center, Kotzebue, AK, p. A29
SMITH, G. Todd., Chief Executive Officer, Mercy Medical Center Redding, Redding, CA, p. A87
SMITH, Gary, Chief Operating Officer, Aurelia Osborn Fox Memorial Hospital, Oneonta, NY, p. A494
SMITH, Gene, Chief Executive Officer, North Alabama Specialty Hospital, Athens, AL, p. A14
SMITH, Geoffrey, Chief Financial Officer, Lebanon Veterans Affairs Medical Center, Lebanon, PA, p. A594
SMITH, Gia, Chief Executive Officer, Central Valley Specialty Hospital, Modesto, CA, p. A78
SMITH, Greg, Chief Medical Officer, Lake Region Healthcare, Fergus Falls, MN, p. A376
SMITH, Gregory, M.D., Chief Executive Officer, Fort Belknap Service Unit, Harlem, MT, p. A424
Senior Vice President and Chief Information Officer, Ascension Southeast Wisconsin Hospital - Franklin Campus, Franklin, WI, p. A784
Senior Vice President and Chief Information Officer, Ascension Southeast Wisconsin Hospital - St. Francis Campus, Milwaukee, WI, p. A790
Senior Vice President and Chief Information Officer, Midwest Orthopedic Specialty Hospital, Franklin, WI, p. A784
SMITH, Gretchen, Vice President of Operations, Risk and Compliance, and Chief Operating Officer, Rush Memorial Hospital, Rushville, IN, p. A240

SMITH, Heather, Chief Executive Officer, Conemaugh Meyersdale Medical Center, Meyersdale, PA, p. A597
Chief Operating Officer, Welch Community Hospital, Welch, WV, p. A777
SMITH, Holt, Chief Financial Officer, Musc Health Lancaster Medical Center, Lancaster, SC, p. A622
SMITH, Jack, Acting Chief Information Resources Management Service, Veterans Affairs Sierra Nevada Health Care System, Reno, NV, p. A446
SMITH, Jackie, R.N., Chief Nursing Officer, Holdenville General Hospital, Holdenville, OK, p. A560
SMITH, James E., Superintendent, North Texas State Hospital, Wichita Falls Campus, Wichita Falls, TX, p. A725
Superintendent, North Texas State Hospital, Vernon, TX, p. A723
SMITH, Jameson, President, Saint Josep. Hospital, Denver, CO, p. A111
SMITH, Jamie, Supervisor Health Information Management Systems, Encompass Health Rehabilitation Hospital Of Sewickley, Sewickley, PA, p. A607
SMITH, Janet, Chief Financial Officer, Troy Regional Medical Center, Troy, AL, p. A25
Chief Financial Officer, Wiregrass Medical Center, Geneva, AL, p. A19
SMITH, Jared M., Chief Executive Officer, Broward Health Coral Springs, Coral Springs, FL, p. A135
SMITH, Jason, Chief Medical Officer, Marshfield Medical Center - Beaver Dam, Beaver Dam, WI, p. A781
Chief Operating Officer, Piedmont Athens Regional Medical Center, Athens, GA, p. A163
SMITH, Jay, Director Information Systems, Brownwood Regional Medical Center, Brownwood, TX, p. A661
SMITH, Jeanna, Administrative Assistant and Human Resources Officer, Polk Medical Center, Cedartown, GA, p. A168
SMITH, Jeffrey, Executive Vice President Hospital Operations and Chief Operating Officer, Cedars-Sinai Medical Center, Los Angeles, CA, p. A73
Senior Vice President and Chief Medical Officer, Aurora St. Luke's Medical Center, Milwaukee, WI, p. A790
SMITH, Jesse, Director of Nursing, Keefe Memorial Hospital, Cheyenne Wells, CO, p. A109
SMITH, Jim, Director Information Systems, Washington County Memorial Hospital, Potosi, MO, p. A414
SMITH, Jo Beth, Chief Operating Officer, Medical Arts Hospital, Lamesa, TX, p. A694
Vice President Human Resources, Decatur County Hospital, Leon, IA, p. A253
SMITH, JoAnn, R.N., Chief Nursing Officer, and Vice President Patient Care Services, Unc Rockingham Health Care, Eden, NC, p. A509
SMITH, Joanne C., M.D., President and Chief Executive Officer, Shirley Ryan Abilitylab, Chicago, IL, p. A200
SMITH, Jodi, Administrative Assistant Human Resources, Eureka Springs Hospital, Eureka Springs, AR, p. A45
SMITH, Jon, Chief Financial Officer, Lost Rivers Medical Center, Arco, ID, p. A188
SMITH, Jonathan, Assistant Administrator and Chief Financial Officer, Blount Memorial Hospital, Maryville, TN, p. A643
SMITH, Joseph S., Chief Executive Officer, Boone County Hospital, Boone, IA, p. A244
SMITH, Julia, Chief Financial Officer, Kindred Hospital-Chattanooga, Chattanooga, TN, p. A635
Chief Financial Officer, Vibra Hospital Of Charleston, Mt. Pleasant, SC, p. A622
SMITH, Julie, R.N., MSN, Director of Nursing, Jersey Community Hospital, Jerseyville, IL, p. A209
Director Human Resources, Encompass Health Lakeshore Rehabilitation Hospital, Birmingham, AL, p. A15
Senior Human Resources Strategic Partner, Providence Milwaukie Hospital, Milwaukie, OR, p. A578
SMITH, Karen, Director Information Services, Chilton Medical Center, Pompton Plains, NJ, p. A462
SMITH, Karla, Director Human Resources, St. Peter's Hospital, Helena, MT, p. A425
SMITH, Karyl, Director Human Resources, Harbor-Ucla Medical Center, Torrance, CA, p. A101
SMITH, Kathy, MSN, R.N., Nurse Executive, Summit Behavioral Healthcare, Cincinnati, OH, p. A533
SMITH, Kelli, M.D., Chief of Staff, Magee General Hospital, Magee, MS, p. A396
SMITH, Kenneth, Chief Medical Officer, John C. Fremont Healthcare District, Mariposa, CA, p. A77
SMITH, Kevin, D.O., Chief of Staff, Munson Healthcare Otsego Memorial Hospital, Gaylord, MI, p. A355
M.D., Interim Chief Medical Officer, Loyola University Medical Center, Maywood, IL, p. A211
Area Finance Officer, Kaiser Permanente South Sacramento Medical Center, Sacramento, CA, p. A89

SMITH, Kris, Controller, Chi St. Josep. Health Rehabilitation Hospital, An Affiliate Of Encompass Health, Bryan, TX, p. A661
SMITH, Kyle, Director Information Systems, Iredell Health System, Statesville, NC, p. A519
SMITH, Lana, Human Resources Director, Ashe Memorial Hospital, Jefferson, NC, p. A513
SMITH, Larry, Senior Vice President and Chief Financial Officer, Uw Medicine/Valley Medical Center, Renton, WA, p. A763
SMITH, Laura, Chief Executive Officer, Ellett Memorial Hospital, Appleton City, MO, p. A402
SMITH, LaVonne, Director Health Information Technology, Tomah Health, Tomah, WI, p. A797
SMITH, Leanne, Chief Financial Officer, Windsor-Laurelwood Center For Behavioral Medicine, Willoughby, OH, p. A553
SMITH, Leora, Information System and Health Information Management Team Leader, Phelp. Memorial Health Center, Holdrege, NE, p. A433
SMITH, Linda, Director Human Resources, Clay County Hospital, Ashland, AL, p. A14
Vice President Human Resources, Central Florida Regional Hospital, Sanford, FL, p. A156
SMITH, Lori, Chief Financial Officer, North Big Horn Hospital District, Lovell, WY, p. A803
Vice President Human Resources, St. Bernards Medical Center, Jonesboro, AR, p. A48
SMITH, Lorie, Director Human Resources, Conemaugh Nason Medical Center, Roaring Spring, PA, p. A606
SMITH, Lorraine, Chief Executive Officer, Monroe County Hospital, Forsyth, GA, p. A172
SMITH, Lory Beth, Manager Human Resource, South Texas Surgical Hospital, Corpus Christi, TX, p. A666
SMITH, M. Scott, President, St. Anthony's Hospital, Saint Petersburg, FL, p. A156
SMITH, Marisa, Director, Hca Houston Healthcare Tomball, Tomball, TX, p. A721
SMITH, Mark, M.D., Chief Medical Officer, Methodist Richardson Medical Center, Richardson, TX, p. A708
Director Human Resources, Providence Holy Family Hospital, Spokane, WA, p. A766
Director Human Resources, Providence Sacred Heart Medical Center & Children's Hospital, Spokane, WA, p. A766
Director Nursing Operations, Northern Colorado Rehabilitation Hospital, Johnstown, CO, p. A114
SMITH, Mark T., JD, CPA, President and Chief Operating Officer, Multicare Auburn Medical Center, Auburn, WA, p. A755
JD, CPA, President and Chief Operating Officer, Multicare Covington Medical Center, Covington, WA, p. A757
SMITH, Marsh, Manager Health Information, University Behavioral Health Of Denton, Denton, TX, p. A672
SMITH, Martha, R.N., Chief Nursing Officer, New Orleans East Hospital, New Orleans, LA, p. A310
Chief Executive Officer, Kapiolani Medical Center For Women & Children, Honolulu, HI, p. A184
Executive Vice President, Pali Momi Medical Center, Aiea, HI, p. A184
SMITH, Mary Clare., Director, Western State Hospital, Staunton, VA, p. A752
SMITH, Matt, Interim Chief Executive Officer, Bourbon Community Hospital, Paris, KY, p. A292
SMITH, Matthew, M.D., Vice President Medical Affairs and Chief Medical Officer, Carrollton Regional Medical Center, Carrollton, TX, p. A663
SMITH, Megan, M.D., Chief Medical Staff, Community Memorial Hospital, Burke, SD, p. A626
SMITH, Melinda, Chief Information Systems, H. C. Watkins Memorial Hospital, Quitman, MS, p. A399
SMITH, Melissa, Controller, Select Specialty Hospital-Jackson, Jackson, MS, p. A395
Interim Vice President Human Resources, North Memorial Health Hospital, Robbinsdale, MN, p. A383
SMITH, Michael, Director of Nursing, Cypress Creek Hospital, Houston, TX, p. A685
SMITH, Michelle, R.N., MSN, FACHE, Vice President Nursing Chief Nursing Officer Chief Experience Officer, Prisma Health Greenville Memorial Hospital, Greenville, SC, p. A620
Coordinator Human Resources, Baton Rouge Rehabilitation Hospital, Baton Rouge, LA, p. A296
SMITH, Mickey, Chief Executive Officer, Oak Hill Hospital, Brooksville, FL, p. A133
SMITH, Mike, Chief Information Officer, Cap. Coral Hospital, Cap. Coral, FL, p. A134
Chief Information Officer, Gulf Coast Medical Center, Fort Myers, FL, p. A138
Chief Information Officer, Lee Memorial Hospital, Fort Myers, FL, p. A138

SMITH, Missy, Coordinator Human Resources, Scotland County Hospital, Memphis, MO, p. A412

SMITH, Mona, Chief Nursing Officer, Santa Cruz Valley Regional Hospital, Green Valley, AZ, p. A33

SMITH, Moneca, Chief Nursing Officer, The University Of Toledo Medical Center, Toledo, OH, p. A551

SMITH, Nadine, Director Human Resources, Reeves County Hospital District, Pecos, TX, p. A705

SMITH, Neil, D.O., President, Cleveland Clinic Fairview Hospital, Cleveland, OH, p. A534

SMITH, Nekisha, Chief Operating Officer, Riverland Medical Center, Ferriday, LA, p. A301

SMITH, Nelson, Chief Executive Officer, Poplar Springs Hospital, Petersburg, VA, p. A748

SMITH, Nicholas T., Chief Executive Officer, Larkin Community Hospital-Palm Springs Campus, Hialeah, FL, p. A139

SMITH, Nicole, Director Human Resources, Hi-Desert Medical Center, Joshua Tree, CA, p. A69

SMITH, Norine, Chief Executive Officer, Red Lake Indian Health Service Hospital, Red Lake, MN, p. A383

SMITH, Oliver, President and Chief Executive Officer, Paris Community Hospital, Paris, IL, p. A216

SMITH, Paige Leann., President, Selby General Hospital, Marietta, OH, p. A544

SMITH, Pam, Chief Nursing Officer, Encompass Health Rehabilitation Hospital Of Richardson, Richardson, TX, p. A708

SMITH, Pamela, Commander, U. S. Air Force Regional Hospital, Eglin Afb, FL, p. A137

SMITH, Patricia, Chief Nursing Officer, Prisma Health Oconee Memorial Hospital, Seneca, SC, p. A624

SMITH, Patrick, M.D., Chief Medical Officer, Abrazo Arrowhead Campus, Glendale, AZ, p. A32

Director Information Technology, Clay County Hospital, Ashland, AL, p. A14

SMITH, Patsy, Director Human Resources, Hereford Regional Medical Center, Hereford, TX, p. A684

SMITH, Peg, Vice President and Chief Nursing Officer, Chandler Regional Medical Center, Chandler, AZ, p. A30

SMITH, Phyllis, Associate Director, Birmingham Veterans Affairs Medical Center, Birmingham, AL, p. A14

Vice President Human Resources, Northeastern Health System, Tahlequah, OK, p. A569

SMITH, Randall, Executive Vice President, Jackson Park Hospital And Medical Center, Chicago, IL, p. A198

SMITH, Randy, Senior Vice President and Chief Nursing Officer, South Georgia Medical Center, Valdosta, GA, p. A182

SMITH, Rebecca, Chief Operating Officer and Chief Nursing Officer, Caldwell Unc Health Care, Lenoir, NC, p. A513

SMITH, Rhonda, Applications Support Manager, Uh Portage Medical Center, Ravenna, OH, p. A548

Chief Nursing Officer, Benewah Community Hospital, Saint Maries, ID, p. A193

Director Human Resources, Shriners Hospitals For Children-Portland, Portland, OR, p. A580

SMITH, Rich, Vice President Human Resources, Kaiser Sunnyside Medical Center, Clackamas, OR, p. A574

Vice President Human Resources, Kaiser Westside Medical Center, Hillsboro, OR, p. A576

SMITH, Richard, Chief Financial Officer, Jfk Johnson Rehabilitation Institute At Hackensack Meridian Health, Edison, NJ, p. A454

Chief of Staff, Carroll County Memorial Hospital, Carrollton, MO, p. A404

Senior Vice President and Chief Financial Officer, Hackensack Meridian Health Jfk Medical Center, Edison, NJ, p. A454

Senior Vice President Finance, Hackensack Meridian Health Shore Rehabilitation Institute, Brick, NJ, p. A452

SMITH, Rick, Chief Financial Officer, Mason General Hospital And Family Of Clinics, Shelton, WA, p. A765

Chief Operating Officer, Health Central Hospital, Ocoee, FL, p. A150

Director Information Services, Cibola General Hospital, Grants, NM, p. A469

Director Information Systems, Jamestown Regional Medical Center, Jamestown, TN, p. A640

Senior Vice President Human Resources and Chief Administrative Officer, Vail Health, Vail, CO, p. A119

SMITH, Robert, M.D., Chief Medical Officer, Kettering Medical Center, Kettering, OH, p. A542

M.D., Chief Medical Officer, Sycamore Medical Center, Miamisburg, OH, p. A545

SMITH, Robert M., M.D., Director, Va San Diego Healthcare System, San Diego, CA, p. A93

SMITH, Robin, Chief Nursing Officer, Indiana University Health White Memorial Hospital, Monticello, IN, p. A236

SMITH, Rodney, Vice President and Administrator, Herrin Hospital, Herrin, IL, p. A207

SMITH, Ruth, Division Human Resources Business Partner, Banner Lassen Medical Center, Susanville, CA, p. A100

SMITH, Ryan, Senior Vice President Information Technology, Banner - University Medical Center South, Tucson, AZ, p. A39

SMITH, Ryan K., Chief Executive Officer, South Peninsula Hospital, Homer, AK, p. A28

SMITH, Scott, M.D., Chief Executive Officer and Chief Medical Officer, Adams Memorial Hospital, Decatur, IN, p. A226

M.D., Chief Medical Officer, Adams Memorial Hospital, Decatur, IN, p. A226

SMITH, Sherry, Manager Human Resources, Dallas County Hospital, Perry, IA, p. A256

SMITH, Shirley, Chief Financial Officer, Andalusia Health, Andalusia, AL, p. A13

SMITH, Sid, Director Information Resources, Larned State Hospital, Larned, KS, p. A268

SMITH, Skip. Vice President Finance, Iredell Health System, Statesville, NC, p. A519

SMITH, Stacey, R.N., Director of Nursing, Jefferson Hospital, Louisville, GA, p. A175

SMITH, Stephen, President and Chief Operating Officer, Novant Health Uva Health System Haymarket Medical Center, Haymarket, VA, p. A744

President and Chief Operating Officer, Novant Health Uva Health System Prince William Medical Center, Manassas, VA, p. A745

SMITH, Steve, M.D., Chief of Staff, Providence Kodiak Island Medical Center, Kodiak, AK, p. A28

Chief Financial Officer, Kansas Heart Hospital, Wichita, KS, p. A278

President and Chief Financial Officer, Chi St. Gabriel's Health, Little Falls, MN, p. A379

SMITH, Steven, Chief Information Officer, Northshore University Health System, Evanston, IL, p. A204

SMITH, Steven L., Chief Executive Officer, Huntsville Memorial Hospital, Huntsville, TX, p. A690

SMITH, Suzanne, R.N., MSN, Chief Nursing Officer, San Juan Regional Medical Center, Farmington, NM, p. A469

SMITH, Tammy, Director, Allendale County Hospital, Fairfax, SC, p. A619

SMITH, Taylor, Chief Financial Officer, Eureka Springs Hospital, Eureka Springs, AR, p. A45

SMITH, Teresa, Chief Financial Officer, Memorial Hospital, Carthage, IL, p. A196

SMITH, Terrance, M.D., Chairman Medical Staff, Sanford Clear Lake Medical Center, Clear Lake, SD, p. A627

SMITH, Terri, Chief Operating Officer, Sacred Heart Hospital Pensacola, Pensacola, FL, p. A154

SMITH, Thomas, M.D., Vice President Medical Affairs, Hutchinson Regional Medical Center, Hutchinson, KS, p. A266

SMITH, Tiffani, Chief Human Resources Officer, Stonesprings Hospital Center, Dulles, VA, p. A741

SMITH, Tim, Senior Vice President and Chief Executive Officer, Sharp Memorial Hospital, San Diego, CA, p. A92

SMITH, Todd A., Chief Executive Officer, Aurora Charter Oak Hospital, Covina, CA, p. A61

SMITH, Toni, Chief Nursing Officer, Kern Medical, Bakersfield, CA, p. A57

SMITH, Tonya, Chief Financial Officer, Usmd Hospital At Arlington, Arlington, TX, p. A654

SMITH, Tracy, Director Human Resources, Mercy St. Francis Hospital, Mountain View, MO, p. A412

SMITH, Trevor, Chief Management Information Services, Gunnison Valley Hospital, Gunnison, CO, p. A114

SMITH, Tripp. Chief Executive Officer, Encompass Health Rehabilitation Hospital Of Largo, Largo, FL, p. A143

SMITH, Trisha, Chief Financial Officer, Mimbres Memorial Hospital, Deming, NM, p. A469

SMITH, Tyson, M.D., Chief Medical Officer, Haywood Regional Medical Center, Clyde, NC, p. A507

SMITH, Vanessa, Chief Human Resources Officer, Community Medical Center, Toms River, NJ, p. A464

SMITH, Vincent, Chief Information Officer, Nyc Health + Hospitals / Queens, Jamaica, NY, p. A486

SMITH, W., M.D., Chief Medical Officer, Och Regional Medical Center, Starkville, MS, p. A400

SMITH, Wade, Chief Operating Officer, Drew Memorial Health System, Monticello, AR, p. A50

SMITH, Wendell, Chief Operating Officer, St. James Behavioral Health Hospital, Gonzales, LA, p. A302

SMITH, William, M.D., Chief Medical Officer, Cullman Regional Medical Center, Cullman, AL, p. A17

SMITH-ZUBA, Lorraina, R.N., MSN, Chief Nursing Officer, Porter Medical Center, Middlebury, VT, p. A736

SMITHBURG, Donald R., Interim Chief Executive Officer, Rehoboth Mckinley Christian Health Care Services, Gallup. NM, p. A469

SMITHERS, John, Network Specialist, River Hospital, Alexandria Bay, NY, p. A474

SMITHHART, Paula, Director Human Resources, Coryell Health, Gatesville, TX, p. A681

SMITHSON, Tracey, MSN, R.N., Chief Nursing Officer, Eastside Medical Center, Snellville, GA, p. A180

SMITTLE, Tammy, R.N., Chief Executive Officer, Arise Austin Medical Center, Austin, TX, p. A654

R.N., Chief Executive Officer, The Hospital At Westlake Medical Center, Austin, TX, p. A657

SMOKER, Bret, M.D., Clinical Director, Phs Santa Fe Indian Hospital, Santa Fe, NM, p. A472

SMOKOVITZ, Ryan, Chief Executive Officer, Encompass Health Rehabilitation Hospital At Cincinnati, Cincinnati, OH, p. A532

SMOLIK, Trisha, R.N., MSN, Chief Nursing Officer, Select Specialty Hospital - Lincoln, Lincoln, NE, p. A435

SMORRA, Colleen, Assistant Administrator, Hackensack Meridian Health Pascack Valley Medical Center, Westwood, NJ, p. A465

SMOTHERS, Kevin, M.D., Vice President Chief Medical Officer, Adventist Healthcare Shady Grove Medical Center, Rockville, MD, p. A332

SMOTHERS, Mark, M.D., Chief Medical Officer, University Of Mississipp. Medical Center Holmes County, Lexington, MS, p. A396

SMOTHERS, Stephen, Director Information Systems, Medical Center Enterprise, Enterprise, AL, p. A18

SMYTH, Thomas, President and Chief Executive Officer, University Of Maryland St. Josep. Medical Center, Towson, MD, p. A333

SNAPP, Jeremy, Director Information Systems, Lindsborg Community Hospital, Lindsborg, KS, p. A270

SNAPP, William Executive Vice President Finance and Chief Financial Officer, Ephraim Mcdowell Regional Medical Center, Danville, KY, p. A282

Vice President and Chief Financial Officer, Ephraim Mcdowell Fort Logan Hospital, Stanford, KY, p. A293

SNAVELY, Gretchen, Director Human Resources, Holton Community Hospital, Holton, KS, p. A266

SNEDEGAR, Michael, Chief Financial Officer, Bourbon Community Hospital, Paris, KY, p. A292

SNEED, Farron, Chief Operating Officer, Hillcrest Medical Center, Tulsa, OK, p. A569

SNEFF, Mark, Vice President Human Resources, Good Shepherd Penn Partners Specialty Hospital At Rittenhouse, Philadelphia, PA, p. A600

SNELGROVE, Steven C., President, Howard County General Hospital, Columbia, MD, p. A328

SNELL, Dan, Chief Medical Officer, Portneuf Medical Center, Pocatello, ID, p. A192

SNELL, Peggy, Chief Finance Officer, Cherry County Hospital, Valentine, NE, p. A440

SNENK, Don, Chief Financial Officer, Mercy Catholic Medical Center - Mercy Fitzgerald Campus, Darby, PA, p. A588

SNIDER, Charles, Vice President Human Resources, Oak Hill Hospital, Brooksville, FL, p. A133

SNIDER, Cheryl, Director Human Resources, St. Vincent General Hospital District, Leadville, CO, p. A115

SNIDER, Glenn, M.D., Chief of Staff, Louis A. Johnson Veterans Affairs Medical Center, Clarksburg, WV, p. A772

SNIDER, Glenn R., M.D., Interim Director, Louis A. Johnson Veterans Affairs Medical Center, Clarksburg, WV, p. A772

SNIDER, Tim, Senior Vice President for Finance, Upper Valley Medical Center, Troy, OH, p. A551

SNIDER, Timothy, Manager Information Systems, Fannin Regional Hospital, Blue Ridge, GA, p. A167

SNIPES, Rob, Administrator, Optim Medical Center - Tattnall, Reidsville, GA, p. A178

SNODGRASS, Elizabeth, Chief Executive Officer, Livingston Hospital And Healthcare Services, Salem, KY, p. A293

SNOOK, Joel, Chief Financial Officer, Westchester General Hospital, Miami, FL, p. A147

SNOW, Dorothy, M.D., Chief of Staff, Veterans Affairs Maryland Health Care System-Baltimore Division, Baltimore, MD, p. A327

SNOW, Jason, Director People Services, Hshs St. Elizabeth's Hospital, O'Fallon, IL, p. A215

SNOW, John, Chief Executive Officer, Granville Health System, Oxford, NC, p. A516

SNOW, Josh, Chief Executive Officer, Davis Regional Medical Center, Statesville, NC, p. A519

SNOW, Meldon L., Chief Executive Officer, Logan County Hospital, Oakley, KS, p. A272

SNOW, Ryan, Director Human Resources, Habersham Medical Center, Demorest, GA, p. A171

Administrator, Chatuge Regional Hospital And Nursing Home, Hiawassee, GA, p. A173

SNOWDON, Susan, Director Information Technology, Four Winds Hospital, Saratoga Springs, NY, p. A497

SNYDER, Alice, Vice President, Chief Nursing Officer, Osf St. Mary Medical Center, Galesburg, IL, p. A205

SNYDER, Bobby, Chief Executive Officer, Inspire Specialty Hospital, Midwest City, OK, p. A562

SNYDER, David, M.D., Chief of Staff, Emory Long-Term Acute Care, Decatur, GA, p. A171

SNYDER, Donald, M.D., Chief Medical Officer, Rush Memorial Hospital, Rushville, IN, p. A240

SNYDER, John, Executive Vice President and System Chief Operating Officer, Carle Foundation Hospital, Urbana, IL, p. A221

SNYDER, Kristi, Vice President Human Resources, Charleston Area Medical Center, Charleston, WV, p. A771

SNYDER, Kristine, Chief Operating Officer, Fulton County Health Center, Wauseon, OH, p. A552

SNYDER, Kyle C., Chief Administrative Officer, Geisinger Holy Spirit, Camp Hill, PA, p. A585

SNYDER, Leah, Director Health Information Services, Loring Hospital, Sac City, IA, p. A257

SNYDER, Mary, Chief Operations Officer, Montrose Memorial Hospital, Montrose, CO, p. A117

SNYDER, Matthew, R.N., Director of Nursing, Johnson County Hospital, Tecumseh, NE, p. A440

SNYDER, Norman, M.D., Medical Director, Vantage Point Of Northwest Arkansas, Fayetteville, AR, p. A45

SNYDER, Phyllis, Chief Nursing Officer, Corona Regional Medical Center, Corona, CA, p. A61

SNYDER, R, Chief Operating Officer, Torrance State Hospital, Torrance, PA, p. A608

SNYDER, Renae, Chief Financial Officer, Sakakawea Medical Center, Hazen, ND, p. A524

SNYDER, Ron, Chief Operating Officer, Ohiohealth Hardin Memorial Hospital, Kenton, OH, p. A542

SNYDER, Sheree, Manager Human Resources, Hillcrest Hospital Henryetta, Henryetta, OK, p. A560

SNYDER, Steve, Chief Financial Officer, Ohio Hospital For Psychiatry, Columbus, OH, p. A536

SNYDER, Tom, Interim Chief Executive Officer, Community Memorial Hospital, Redfield, SD, p. A630

SNYDER, Tony, Chief Executive Officer, Aultman Hospital, Canton, OH, p. A530

SNYDER, Vicky, Chief Operating Officer, Cleveland Clinic, Medina Hospital, Medina, OH, p. A545

SOARES, Brian, Chief Executive Officer, Select Specialty Hospital-Miami Lakes, Miami Lakes, FL, p. A148

SOARES, Jair C., M.D., Executive Director, Uthealth Harris County Psychiatric Center, Houston, TX, p. A689

SODERLING, Marcia, R.N., Hospital Nurse Executive, Legacy Mount Hood Medical Center, Gresham, OR, p. A575

SOEKEN, Charles, Director Information Technology, Providence Medical Center, Kansas City, KS, p. A267
Director Information Technology, Saint John Hospital, Leavenworth, KS, p. A269

SOGARD, Matt, Chief Executive Officer, Overland Park Regional Medical Center, Overland Park, KS, p. A274

SOGLIN, David, Chief Medical Officer, La Rabida Children's Hospital, Chicago, IL, p. A199

SOHN, Steven, M.D., President Medical Staff, Dallas County Hospital, Perry, IA, p. A256

SOILEAU, D. Kirk., FACHE, Chief Executive Officer, Natchitoches Regional Medical Center, Natchitoches, LA, p. A310

SOIMAN, Erika, CPA, Chief Financial Officer, Nyc Health + Hospitals / Woodhull, Brooklyn, NY, p. A479

SOJKA, Matthew, M.D., Vice President Medical Affairs, Mercyone Cedar Falls Medical Center, Cedar Falls, IA, p. A244
M.D., Vice President, Medical Affairs, Mercyone Waterloo Medical Center, Waterloo, IA, p. A259

SOKOLA, Thomas P., Chief Administrative Officer, Geisinger Medical Center, Danville, PA, p. A588

SOLAIMAN, Shereen, Vice President Human Resources, Ohiohealth Riverside Methodist Hospital, Columbus, OH, p. A537

SOLA', Ivan', President Medical Staff, Upmc Carlisle, Carlisle, PA, p. A586

SOLBERG, Bradley V., FACHE, President, Osf Saint James - John W. Albrecht Medical Center, Pontiac, IL, p. A217

SOLBERG, Don, M.D., Chief Medical Officer, Kittitas Valley Healthcare, Ellensburg, WA, p. A757

SOLCHER, Barry, M.D., Chief of Staff, The Physicians Centre Hospital, Bryan, TX, p. A661

SOLDO, Stephen, M.D., Chief Medical Officer, Saint Agnes Medical Center, Fresno, CA, p. A65

SOLE, Kelly, Chief Operating Officer, Appalachian Behavioral Healthcare, Athens, OH, p. A528

SOLEM, Terry, Vice President of Human Resources, Northwest Community Healthcare, Arlington Heights, IL, p. A194

SOLER, Eddie, Chief Financial Officer, Adventhealth Orlando, Orlando, FL, p. A151

SOLES, Jason, Manager Information Systems, St. James Hospital, Hornell, NY, p. A485

SOLHEIM, John H., Chief Executive Officer, Trios Health, Kennewick, WA, p. A759

SOLIE, Carol, M.D., Vice President, Quality and Medical Safety, Wyoming Medical Center, Casper, WY, p. A801

SOLIMAN, Russell, Director Information Services, Amita Health St. Mary's Hospital, Kankakee, IL, p. A209

SOLIN, Andrea, Chief Financial Officer, Lovelace Unm Rehabilitation Hospital, Albuquerque, NM, p. A467
Chief Financial Officer, Lovelace Westside Hospital, Albuquerque, NM, p. A467

SOLINSKI, Ruth, Senior Director Human Resources, Up Health System-Marquette, Marquette, MI, p. A361

SOLIS, Gloria, R.N., MSN, Chief Nursing Officer, Saint Luke's East Hospital, Lee's Summit, MO, p. A411

SOLIVAN, Jose, Chief Financial Officer, Hospital Menonita De Cayey, Cayey, PR, p. A807
Chief Financial Officer, Mennonite General Hospital, Aibonito, PR, p. A806

SOLIZ, Mindy, Director Human Resource Strategy, Christus Spohn Hospital Kleberg, Kingsville, TX, p. A693
Director Human Resources, Christus Spohn Hospital Alice, Alice, TX, p. A651

SOLLIS, Jeff, Chief Executive Officer, Eastern Idaho Regional Medical Center, Idaho Falls, ID, p. A190

SOLOMON, John, M.D., Director, South Carolina Department Of Corrections Hospital, Columbia, SC, p. A618

SOLOMON, Oliver, M.D., Chief Medical Officer, Glendora Community Hospital, Glendora, CA, p. A67

SOLOMON-OWENS, Felicia, Director Human Resources, Fayette Medical Center, Fayette, AL, p. A18

SOLORIO, Roberta, Vice President, Chief Human Resource Officer, Midland Memorial Hospital, Midland, TX, p. A701

SOLORZANO, Rosa, Interim Director Human Resources, Astria Toppenish Hospital, Toppenish, WA, p. A768

SOLOW, Jodie, Director of Human Resources, Chatham Hospital, Siler City, NC, p. A518

SOLTIS, Les, Director - Human Resources, St. Francis Hospital, Federal Way, WA, p. A758

SOLVERSON, Paul, Senior Vice President and Chief Information Officer, Cap. Cod Hospital, Hyannis, MA, p. A340
Senior Vice President and Chief Information Officer, Falmouth Hospital, Falmouth, MA, p. A339

SOMERS, Tyrel, M.D., Chief Medical Officer, Russell Regional Hospital, Russell, KS, p. A275

SOMERVILLE, Jacqueline, R.N., Ph.D., Senior Vice President and Chief Nursing Officer, Southcoast Hospitals Group. Fall River, MA, p. A339

SOMMERS, Belinda, Chief Information Officer, Lake Charles Memorial Hospital, Lake Charles, LA, p. A307

SOMMERS, Dorene, Associate Director Patient Care Services, Erie Veterans Affairs Medical Center, Erie, PA, p. A589

SONA, Kent, Vice President, Chief Information Officer, Methodist Fremont Health, Fremont, NE, p. A432

SONATORE, Carol, D.O., Medical Director, Encompass Health Rehabilitation Hospital Of Toms River, Toms River, NJ, p. A464

SONDAG, Timothy, Senior Nursing Officer, Hopedale Medical Complex, Hopedale, IL, p. A208

SONDERMAN, Betty, Manager Human Resources, Ridgeview Institute, Smyrna, GA, p. A180

SONDERMAN, Thomas, M.D., Vice President and Chief Medical Officer, Columbus Regional Hospital, Columbus, IN, p. A225

SONEL, Ali, M.D., Chief of Staff, Veterans Affairs Pittsburgh Healthcare System, Pittsburgh, PA, p. A604

SONENREICH, Steven D., President and Chief Executive Officer, Mount Sinai Medical Center, Miami Beach, FL, p. A148

SONES, Danielle, Administrator, Beacon Behavioral Hospital - Northshore, Lacombe, LA, p. A305

SONG, Daniel, Chief Financial Officer, Monterey Park Hospital, Monterey Park, CA, p. A79

SONGER, Lucille, Chief Nursing Officer, Athol Hospital, Athol, MA, p. A334

SONGER, Pat, Chief Operations Officer, Cascade Medical Center, Leavenworth, WA, p. A760

SONGY, David, President and Chief Executive Officer, Saint Luke Institute, Silver Spring, MD, p. A332

SONI, Anita, M.D., Chief Medical Officer, Nyc Health + Hospitals / Lincoln, Bronx, NY, p. A477

SONNENBERG, Martha, M.D., Chief of Staff, Southern California Hospital At Culver City, Culver City, CA, p. A62

SONNENBERG, William, M.D., President Medical Staff, Titusville Area Hospital, Titusville, PA, p. A608

SONNENSCHEIN, Silvia, M.D., Chief of Staff, Kohala Hospital, Kohala, HI, p. A186

SONTZ, Jennifer, Director Human Resources, Evansville Psychiatric Children Center, Evansville, IN, p. A227

Director Human Resources, Evansville State Hospital, Evansville, IN, p. A227

SOODJINDA, Michael, Chief Financial Officer, Morton County Health System, Elkhart, KS, p. A264

SOOHOO, Richard, Chief Financial Officer, Sutter Medical Center, Sacramento, Sacramento, CA, p. A90

SOPER, Brent, Chief Financial Officer, Adventist Health Bakersfield, Bakersfield, CA, p. A57

SOPIARZ, Ed, Chief Financial Officer, University Behavioral Health Of Denton, Denton, TX, p. A672

SOPKO, Joseph, M.D., Chief Medical Officer, St. Vincent Charity Medical Center, Cleveland, OH, p. A535

SOPT, Michael, M.D., Chief of Staff, Brooks County Hospital, Quitman, GA, p. A178

SORBELLO, Bud, Director Management Information Systems, New York-Presbyterian/Hudson Valley Hospital, Cortlandt Manor, NY, p. A482

SORENSEN, Bonny, Chief Financial Officer, Wadley Regional Medical Center At Hope, Hope, AR, p. A47
Chief Financial Officer, Wadley Regional Medical Center, Texarkana, TX, p. A720

SORENSEN, Damon, Chief Financial Officer, Mclaren Bay Region, Bay City, MI, p. A349

SORENSEN, Vanessa, Chief Nursing Officer, Summit Medical Center, Casper, WY, p. A801

SORENSON, Chris, Chief Health Information Officer, Sheltering Arms Hospital South, Midlothian, VA, p. A746
Chief Information Officer, Sheltering Arms Rehabilitation Hospital, Mechanicsville, VA, p. A746

SORENSON, Dennis, Supervisor Information Technology, Bronson South Haven Hospital, South Haven, MI, p. A367

SORENSON, Eric, Chief Financial Officer, Veterans Affairs Loma Linda Healthcare System, Loma Linda, CA, p. A72

SORENSON, Sheri, Manager Business Office, Highland Ridge Hospital, Midvale, UT, p. A728

SORENSON, Tawnya, Director of Nursing, Kittson Memorial Healthcare Center, Hallock, MN, p. A377

SORRELL, Dierdra, R.N., MSN, Chief Executive Officer, Clifton-Fine Hospital, Star Lake, NY, p. A498

SORRELL, Rachel, Chief Financial Officer, Tsehootsooi Medical Center, Fort Defiance, AZ, p. A31

SORRELL, Ralph. Chief Financial Officer, Adena Greenfield Medical Center, Greenfield, OH, p. A541

SORRELLS, Dwane, Chief Information Officer, Choctaw Nation Health Care Center, Talihina, OK, p. A569

SOSA, Phillip. Chief Financial Officer, El Paso Behavioral Health System, El Paso, TX, p. A674

SOSA-GUERRERO, Sandra, Chief Executive Officer, Larkin Community Hospital-South Miami Campus, South Miami, FL, p. A157

SOSEBEE, Tonya, MSN, R.N., Chief Operating and Nursing Officer, Texas Health Harris Methodist Hospital Azle, Azle, TX, p. A657

SOSNOW, Peter, Medical Director, O'Connor Hospital, Delhi, NY, p. A482

SOSNOWSKI, Karen, Director, Human Resources, Saint Clare's Denville Hospital, Denville, NJ, p. A454

SOTERAKIS, Jack, M.D., Executive Vice President Medical Affairs, St. Francis Hospital, The Heart Center, Roslyn, NY, p. A497

SOTO, Ciria, Director Human Resources, Sonora Behavioral Health Hospital, Tucson, AZ, p. A40

SOTO, Juan, Director Information Systems, Hospital San Carlos Borromeo, Moca, PR, p. A808

SOTOIZAGUIRRE, Felix, Chief Financial Officer, Wellstar North Fulton Hospital, Roswell, GA, p. A179

SOTOS, Steven, M.D., President Medical Staff, Lifecare Behavioral Health Hospital, Pittsburgh, PA, p. A603

SOUDERS, Stuart, Chief, Human Resources, William S. Middleton Memorial Veterans Hospital, Madison, WI, p. A788

SOUKUP, Paul, Chief Financial Officer, St. Luke Community Healthcare, Ronan, MT, p. A427

SOULAR, Dan, M.D., Vice President, Medical Affairs, Grand Itasca Clinic And Hospital, Grand Rapids, MN, p. A377

SOULE, Joyce, R.N., MSN, Chief Nursing Officer, Medical City Dallas, Dallas, TX, p. A669

SOUR, Kay, Director of Nursing, Christus Coushatta Health Care Center, Coushatta, LA, p. A299

SOURBEER, Jay C., Commanding Officer, Robert E. Bush Naval Hospital, Twentynine Palms, CA, p. A102

SOUTHER, Geoffrey, Chief Operating Officer, New Hampshire Hospital, Concord, NH, p. A448

SOUTHERLAND, David, Vice President of Operations, Petaluma Valley Hospital, Petaluma, CA, p. A85

SOUTHERN, Joel, R.N., MSN, Chief Executive Officer, Northwest Mississipp. Medical Center, Clarksdale, MS, p. A391

SOUTHWICK, Mitch, Chief Operating Officer, Mclaren Bay Region, Bay City, MI, p. A349

SOUTHWICK, William, R.N., MS, Chief Executive Officer, Banner Behavioral Health Hospital - Scottsdale, Scottsdale, AZ, p. A38

SOUTHWORTH, Scott, M.D., Medical Director, South Davis Community Hospital, Bountiful, UT, p. A727

SOUZA, Beatrix, Chief Executive Officer, Buffalo Psychiatric Center, Buffalo, NY, p. A479

SOUZA, Darlene, Vice President, St. Josep. Health Services Of Rhode Island, North Providence, RI, p. A613

SOUZA, Greg, Vice President Human Resources, Lucile Packard Children's Hospital Stanford, Palo Alto, CA, p. A84

SOUZA, Jim, Chief Medical Officer, St. Luke's Regional Medical Center, Boise, ID, p. A189

SOUZA, Liz, Coordinator Nursing Services, Atascadero State Hospital, Atascadero, CA, p. A56

SOUZA, Michael, Chief Executive Officer, Landmark Medical Center, Woonsocket, RI, p. A614
    Chief Executive Officer, Rehabilitation Hospital Of Rhode Island, North Smithfield, RI, p. A613

SOVETSKHY, Ed, Director Information Services, Portsmouth Regional Hospital, Portsmouth, NH, p. A451

SOWDERS, Dale, President and Chief Executive Officer, Holland Hospital, Holland, MI, p. A357

SOWELL, Ronald, FACHE, Chief Financial Officer, Medical Center At Scottsville, Scottsville, KY, p. A293
    FACHE, Executive Vice President and Chief Financial Officer, The Medical Center At Caverna, Horse Cave, KY, p. A285
    FACHE, Executive Vice President, Chief Financial Officer, The Medical Center Albany, Albany, KY, p. A280
    FACHE, Executive Vice President, Commonwealth Regional Specialty Hospital, Bowling Green, KY, p. A280
    FACHE, Executive Vice President, Medical Center At Bowling Green, Bowling Green, KY, p. A281
    FACHE, Executive Vice President, Medical Center At Franklin, Franklin, KY, p. A283

SOWELL, Vincent, Chief Nursing Officer, Otto Kaiser Memorial Hospital, Kenedy, TX, p. A692

SOWERS, Chuck, Vice President Finance and Chief Financial Officer, Mercy Gilbert Medical Center, Gilbert, AZ, p. A32

SOWIZRAL, Shirley, Chief Executive Officer, Wernersville State Hospital, Wernersville, PA, p. A610

SPACK, Paula, R.N., MSN, Vice President Nursing, Punxsutawney Area Hospital, Punxsutawney, PA, p. A605

SPACKMAN, Jared, Chief Financial Officer, Davis Hospital And Medical Center, Layton, UT, p. A728
    Chief Operating Officer, Davis Hospital And Medical Center, Layton, UT, p. A728

SPACONE, Celia, M.D., Director Operations, Buffalo Psychiatric Center, Buffalo, NY, p. A479

SPADONI, Robert, Vice President of Hospital Operations, Rush Oak Park Hospital, Oak Park, IL, p. A215

SPAGNA, Lauren, Marketing Director, West Boca Medical Center, Boca Raton, FL, p. A132

SPAHLINGER, David, M.D., President, Michigan Medicine, Ann Arbor, MI, p. A348

SPAHR, Kristen, Director of Marketing, Desoto Memorial Hospital, Arcadia, FL, p. A131

SPAIN, Jeanine, R.N., MS, Vice President, Chief Operating Officer and Chief Nursing Officer, Unitypoint Health - Peoria, Peoria, IL, p. A217
    R.N., MS, Vice President, Chief Operating Officer and Chief Nursing Officer, Unitypoint Health - Proctor, Peoria, IL, p. A217
    R.N., MS, Vice President, Chief Operating Officer and Chief Nursing Officer, Unitypoint Health-Pekin Hospital, Pekin, IL, p. A216

SPAIN, Steve, Chief Operating Officer, Larned State Hospital, Larned, KS, p. A268

SPAIN, Tom, Director Operations Finance, Chi St. Alexius Health-Turtle Lake Hospital, Turtle Lake, ND, p. A526

SPANBAUER, Lisa, Financial Program Supervisor, Winnebago Mental Health Institute, Winnebago, WI, p. A800

SPANGHER, Guido, M.D., Clinical Director, Big Spring State Hospital, Big Spring, TX, p. A659

SPANGLER, Mark, M.D., Chief Medical Officer, Gibson Area Hospital And Health Services, Gibson City, IL, p. A206

SPANGLER, Michael, Health Information Management Services Supervisor, Encompass Health Rehabilitation Hospital Of Tallahassee, Tallahassee, FL, p. A158

SPANGLER, Wendell, M.D., Chief of Staff, Paulding County Hospital, Paulding, OH, p. A547

SPANN, Debbie, Director Human Resources, Morehouse General Hospital, Bastrop. LA, p. A296

SPANN, Lori, Director Human Resources, Iberia Medical Center, New Iberia, LA, p. A310

SPANO, Jason, Director of Information Technology, Prowers Medical Center, Lamar, CO, p. A115

SPARE, John, Accountant, Parsons State Hospital And Training Center, Parsons, KS, p. A274

SPARGER, Kathy, R.N., MSN, Chief Nursing Officer, Baptist Health South Florida, South Miami Hospital, Miami, FL, p. A146

SPARKMAN, Dena C., Community Chief Executive Officer, Whitesburg Arh Hospital, Whitesburg, KY, p. A294

SPARKMAN, Jill, Director Human Resources, Odessa Regional Medical Center, Odessa, TX, p. A704

SPARKS, Dennis, Vice President Human Resources, Saint Michael's Medical Center, Newark, NJ, p. A460
    Vice President of Human Resources, Saint Francis Hospital And Medical Center, Hartford, CT, p. A122

SPARKS, Gary R., Administrator, Crossridge Community Hospital, Wynne, AR, p. A54

SPARKS, Holly, Chief Clinical Officer, South Sunflower County Hospital, Indianola, MS, p. A394

SPARKS, Jason, Director, Human Resources, Encompass Health Rehabilitation Hospital At Cincinnati, Cincinnati, OH, p. A532

SPARKS, Lisa, R.N., Chief Nursing Officer and Vice President Patient Care Services, Indiana University Health West Hospital, Avon, IN, p. A223

SPARKS, Victor, M.D., Chief of Staff, Marshall Medical Center North, Guntersville, AL, p. A19

SPARKS, Wendy, Chief Operating Officer, North Colorado Medical Center, Greeley, CO, p. A113

SPARLING, Nicki, Manager Human Resources, Major Hospital, Shelbyville, IN, p. A240

SPARROW, Francis, M.D., Medical Director, Wellspan Philhaven, Mount Gretna, PA, p. A597

SPARROW, Robert, M.D., Vice President, Chief Medical Officer, Osf Saint Francis Medical Center, Peoria, IL, p. A217

SPARTA, Mark, President, Hackensack Meridian Health Hackensack University Medical Center, Hackensack, NJ, p. A455

SPARTZ, Dale, Chief Human Resources Officer, University Of Utah Health, Salt Lake City, UT, p. A733

SPATH, Deborah, R.N., MSN, Associate Director Patient and Nurses Services, Albany Stratton Veterans Affairs Medical Center, Albany, NY, p. A474

SPEARE, Mark, Senior Associate Director Patient Relations and Human Resources, Ucla Medical Center-Santa Monica, Santa Monica, CA, p. A98

SPEARS, David, D.O., Chief of Staff, Selby General Hospital, Marietta, OH, p. A544

SPEARS, Gina, Chief Financial Officer, Thomas B. Finan Center, Cumberland, MD, p. A329

SPEARS, Kevin, Chief Executive Officer, Stone County Medical Center, Mountain View, AR, p. A50

SPEARS, LaLana, Supervisor Accounting, Claremore Indian Hospital, Claremore, OK, p. A557

SPEARS, Michael, Human Resource Leader, Ssm Health St. Anthony Hospital - Shawnee, Shawnee, OK, p. A568

SPEAS, Ryan, Chief Financial Officer, Mackinac Straits Health System, Inc., Saint Ignace, MI, p. A366
    Director Finance, Livingston Healthcare, Livingston, MT, p. A426

SPEASE, Dorothy, Manager Business Office, Douglas County Memorial Hospital, Armour, SD, p. A626

SPECK, Michelle, Vice President Human Resources, Upmc Altoona, Altoona, PA, p. A584
    Vice President Human Resources, Upmc Bedford, Everett, PA, p. A590

SPECKMAN, Kelly Ann, Chief Financial Officer, Kearny County Hospital, Lakin, KS, p. A268

SPEEK, Timothy Director of Nursing, Glenn Medical Center, Willows, CA, p. A105

SPEELMAN, Steven, Director Information Systems, Novant Health Uva Health System Culpeper Medical Center, Culpeper, VA, p. A740

SPEER, Kevin, President and Chief Executive Officer, Hendricks Regional Health, Danville, IN, p. A226

SPEER-SMITH, Carol, R.N., Chief Nursing Officer, Oroville Hospital, Oroville, CA, p. A83

SPEIGHT, Becky, Chief Financial Officer and Administrator, Crescent Medical Center Lancaster, Lancaster, TX, p. A695

SPEIGHT, Marianne, Vice President Information System and Chief Information Officer, Cincinnati Children's Hospital Medical Center, Cincinnati, OH, p. A532

SPELL, Kenneth R., Chief Executive Officer, Baptist Health South Florida, Homestead Hospital, Homestead, FL, p. A140

SPELL, Nicole, Director Human Resources, Vidant Bertie Hospital, Windsor, NC, p. A520
    Director Human Resources, Vidant Chowan Hospital, Edenton, NC, p. A509

SPELLBERG, Brad, M.D., Chief Medical Officer, Lac+Usc Medical Center, Los Angeles, CA, p. A75

SPELLMAN, Warren K., Chief Executive Officer, Grady Memorial Hospital, Chickasha, OK, p. A557

SPELLMEIER, Rhonda, R.N., Director of Nursing, Sabetha Community Hospital, Sabetha, KS, p. A275

SPELLS-WILSON, Debbie, R.N., Chief Operating Officer and Chief Nursing Officer, Conemaugh Miners Medical Center, Hastings, PA, p. A592

SPENCE, Andre, Chief Medical Staff, Sanford Bagley Medical Center, Bagley, MN, p. A372

SPENCE, Ben, Chief Financial Officer, Cap. Coral Hospital, Cap. Coral, FL, p. A134
    Chief Financial Officer, Gulf Coast Medical Center, Fort Myers, FL, p. A138
    Chief Financial Officer, Lee Memorial Hospital, Fort Myers, FL, p. A138

SPENCE, Karie, Director Human Resources, Miller County Hospital, Colquitt, GA, p. A169

SPENCE, Karla, Director of Nursing, St. Andrew's Health Center, Bottineau, ND, p. A521

SPENCE, Monte, Chief Operating Officer, Rehabilitation Hospital Of Indiana, Indianapolis, IN, p. A233

SPENCE, Sheldon, Director of Revenue Cycle, IT, Memorial Hospital Of Texas County, Guymon, OK, p. A560

SPENCE, Steven, M.D., Chief Medical Officer, Jackson Hospital, Marianna, FL, p. A145

SPENCE, Terri, Chief Information Officer, Bon Secours Maryview Medical Center, Portsmouth, VA, p. A749
    Chief Information Officer, Bon Secours St. Mary's Hospital, Richmond, VA, p. A749
    Vice President and Regional Chief Information Officer, Bon Secours St. Francis Medical Center, Midlothian, VA, p. A746
    Vice President Information Services, Bon Secours Mary Immaculate Hospital, Newport News, VA, p. A746

SPENCER, Jim, Director Information System, Mcleod Health Cheraw, Cheraw, SC, p. A617

SPENCER, Marie, Chief Nursing Officer and Senior Administrator, Burke Rehabilitation Hospital, White Plains, NY, p. A502

SPENCER, Mike, Chief Information Officer, Henry Community Health, New Castle, IN, p. A238

SPENCER, Misti, Director Inpatient Services, Selby General Hospital, Marietta, OH, p. A544

SPENCER, Rachelle, Chief Executive Officer, Encompass Health Rehabilitation Hospital Of Albuquerque, Albuquerque, NM, p. A467

SPENCER, Sarah, M.D., Chief of Staff, South Peninsula Hospital, Homer, AK, p. A28

SPENCER, Scott, Chief Financial Officer, South Shore Hospital, Chicago, IL, p. A201

SPENCER, Susan, Chief Financial Officer, Samaritan Hospital, Macon, MO, p. A411

SPENCER, Todd, M.D., Chief Medical Staff, Adventist Health Reedley, Reedley, CA, p. A88

SPERDUTI, Karen, Chief Operating Officer, Saint Camillus Medical Center, Hurst, TX, p. A690

SPERLING, Deanna, R.N., President and Chief Executive Officer, Rwjbarnabas Health Behavioral Health Center, Toms River, NJ, p. A464

SPERLING, Louis, Vice President Human Resources, Rhode Island Hospital, Providence, RI, p. A614

SPERLING, Walter, M.D., Medical Director, Ellenville Regional Hospital, Ellenville, NY, p. A483

SPERRAZZA, John, Chief Operating Officer, Sisters Of Charity Hospital Of Buffalo, Buffalo, NY, p. A480

SPERRING, Jeff, M.D., Chief Executive Officer, Seattle Children's Hospital, Seattle, WA, p. A764

SPHON, John, Chief Executive Officer, Excela Frick Hospital, Mount Pleasant, PA, p. A598
    Chief Executive Officer, Excela Health Westmoreland Hospital, Greensburg, PA, p. A591
    Chief Executive Officer, Excela Latrobe Area Hospital, Latrobe, PA, p. A594

SPICER, Joan, R.N., Chief Nursing Officer, San Mateo Medical Center, San Mateo, CA, p. A96

SPICER, Michael J., President and Chief Executive Officer, Saint Joseph's Medical Center, Yonkers, NY, p. A502

SPICER, Randy, Information Technology Supervisor, Central State Hospital, Louisville, KY, p. A288

SPICER, Sam, M.D., Vice President Medical Affairs, New Hanover Regional Medical Center, Wilmington, NC, p. A520

SPIDLE, Tara, Chief Financial Officer, Decatur County Hospital, Leon, IA, p. A253

SPIERS, Deborah, Administrator, Oceans Behavioral Hospital Of Greater New Orleans, Kenner, LA, p. A74

SPIGEL, Michael, Executive Vice President & Chief Operating Officer, Brooks Rehabilitation Hospital, Jacksonville, FL, p. A141

SPIGNER, Jason, Vice President Human Resources, Advocate Good Shepherd Hospital, Barrington, IL, p. A195

SPIKE, Jennifer, Director Human Resources, St. James Hospital, Hornell, NY, p. A485

SPILLERS, David S., Chief Executive Officer, Huntsville Hospital, Huntsville, AL, p. A20

SPILSBURY, Lauren, R.N., MSN, Vice President for Patient Care Services, Redlands Community Hospital, Redlands, CA, p. A87

SPINA, Lori, Vice President Human Resources, Good Samaritan Hospital Medical Center, West Islip. NY, p. A502

SPINALE, Joseph, D.O., Chief Medical Officer, St. Joseph's Hospital Health Center, Syracuse, NY, p. A499

SPIRITOS, Michael, Chief Medical Officer, Duke Raleigh Hospital, Raleigh, NC, p. A516

SPISSO, Johnese, Chief Executive Officer, Ronald Reagan Ucla Medical Center, Los Angeles, CA, p. A75

SPITSER, Christy, Vice President Finance and Business Development, Chi Saint Josep. London, London, KY, p. A287

Vice President Finance, Chi Saint Josep. Berea, Berea, KY, p. A280

SPIVEY, Amy, Chief Medical Officer, Mccullough-Hyde Memorial Hospital/Trihealth, Oxford, OH, p. A547

SPIVEY, Courtney, Chief Nursing Officer, Hardin County General Hospital, Rosiclare, IL, p. A219

SPIVEY, David A., President and Chief Executive Officer, St. Mary Mercy Hospital, Livonia, MI, p. A360

SPLITT, Richie, FACHE, President and Chief Executive Officer, Norman Regional Health System, Norman, OK, p. A563

SPOELMA, Susan, MSN, R.N., Chief Nursing Officer, Healdsburg District Hospital, Healdsburg, CA, p. A68

SPONAUGLE, Dale, M.D., Medical Staff President, Orleans Community Health, Medina, NY, p. A488

SPONSLER, Betsy, Chief Financial Officer, Valley Hospital Medical Center, Las Vegas, NV, p. A445

SPOON, Barry, M.D., Chief of Staff, Mercy St. Francis Hospital, Mountain View, MO, p. A412

SPOONER, Allan M., President and Chief Executive Officer, Franciscan Health Olympia Fields, Olympia Fields, IL, p. A215

SPOONER, Jennifer, Controller, Encompass Health Rehabilitation Hospital Of Tallahassee, Tallahassee, FL, p. A158

SPOOR, David, R.N., Vice President, Patient Care Services and Chief Nursing Officer, Sturdy Memorial Hospital, Attleboro, MA, p. A334

SPORE, Larry, Chief Financial Officer, Lawrence County Memorial Hospital, Lawrenceville, IL, p. A210

SPRADLIN, John, Information Systems Director, Franklin Foundation Hospital, Franklin, LA, p. A301

SPRAGUE, F., M.D., Chief Medical Officer, Mercy Health Hackley Campus, Muskegon, MI, p. A362

SPRAKER, Larissa, Vice President Business Development and Chief Strategy Officer, Mercy Gilbert Medical Center, Gilbert, AZ, p. A32

SPRANGER, Lance, Chief Information Officer, St. John's Health, Jackson, WY, p. A802

SPRATT, Kelly, President, Buffalo Hospital, Buffalo, MN, p. A373

President, Cambridge Medical Center, Cambridge, MN, p. A373

SPRAY, William R., Chief Executive Officer, Southern Tennessee Regional Health System-Winchester, Winchester, TN, p. A650

SPREER-ALBERT, Frances, Chief Financial Officer and Executive Vice President, Albany Medical Center, Albany, NY, p. A474

SPRIGGS, Larry, CPA, Controller, Encompass Health Rehabilitation Hospital Of San Antonio, San Antonio, TX, p. A711

SPRINGATE, Brian, Chief Executive Officer, Fleming County Hospital, Flemingsburg, KY, p. A283

SPRINGER, Amy, Medical Director, Webster County Community Hospital, Red Cloud, NE, p. A439

SPRINGER, Dan, Chief Executive Officer, Lea Regional Medical Center, Hobbs, NM, p. A470

Interim Chief Executive Officer, Carlsbad Medical Center, Carlsbad, NM, p. A468

SPRINGER, Madge, Director Human Resources, Adventhealth Waterman, Tavares, FL, p. A160

SPRINGER, Rebecca, MSN, R.N., Chief Nursing Officer, Hendry Regional Medical Center, Clewiston, FL, p. A134

SPRINGER, Theresa, Chief Financial Officer, Osf Holy Family Medical Center, Monmouth, IL, p. A212

SPRINGMANN, Tressa, Vice President and Chief Information Officer, Levindale Hebrew Hospital And Nursing, Baltimore, MD, p. A325

Vice President and Chief Information Officer, Northwest Hospital, Randallstown, MD, p. A331

SPRINKEL, George, Chief Financial Officer, Tennova Healthcare-Clarksville, Clarksville, TN, p. A636

SPRINKLE, Patricia, Vice President, Human Resources, Bluffton Regional Medical Center, Bluffton, IN, p. A224

SPROTT, Kendell R., M.D., JD, President and Chief Executive Officer, Matheny Medical And Educational Center, Peapack, NJ, p. A460

SPROUT, Merry, R.N., Chief Nursing Officer, Antelop. Memorial Hospital, Neligh, NE, p. A435

SPROWL, Chris, M.D., Vice President, Peacehealth St. Josep. Medical Center, Bellingham, WA, p. A755

SPRYS, Michael, D.O., Chief of Staff, Medical Arts Hospital, Lamesa, TX, p. A694

SPUHLER, Richard, Chief Executive Officer, Brigham City Community Hospital, Brigham City, UT, p. A727

SPURLOCK, James, D.O., Chief of Staff, Saint Thomas Stones River Hospital, Woodbury, TN, p. A650

SPURLOCK, Steve, Director Information Systems, Buena Vista Regional Medical Center, Storm Lake, IA, p. A258

SPYKERMAN, Connie, Chief Nursing Officer, Pelham Medical Center, Greer, SC, p. A621

SPYROW, Florence (Flo)., Chief Administrative Officer, Flagstaff Medical Center, Flagstaff, AZ, p. A31

SQUIRES, Danny, Assistant Vice President and Chief Financial Officer Network Hospital, Wake Forest Baptist Health-Lexington Medical Center, Lexington, NC, p. A514

Chief Financial Officer, Wake Forest Baptist Health-Davie Medical Center, Bermuda Run, NC, p. A505

SQUIRES, Elizabeth, R.N., Chief Nursing Officer, Encompass Health Rehabilitation Hospital Of Tallahassee, Tallahassee, FL, p. A158

SQUIRES, Paula, Senior Vice President, Chief Human Resources Officer and Chief Human Resources Officer, Baystate Medical Center, Springfield, MA, p. A344

SQUIRES, Teresa, R.N., Chief Nursing Officer, Lake District Hospital, Lakeview, OR, p. A577

SQUIRRELL, Sarah, Commissioner of Vermont Department of Mental Health, Vermont Psychiatric Care Hospital, Berlin, VT, p. A735

SRAON, Karandeep. Interim Director, Aleda E. Lutz Veterans Affairs Medical Center, Saginaw, MI, p. A365

SREBINSKI, Ron, Chief Financial Officer, Mclaren Caro Region, Caro, MI, p. A350

SRIBNICK, Wayne, M.D., Senior Vice President and Chief Medical Officer, Providence Hospital, Columbia, SC, p. A618

SRIPADA, Subra, Exec. Vice President, Chief Transformation Officer and Chief Information Officer, Beaumont Hospital - Taylor, Taylor, MI, p. A367

Executive Vice President, Chief Transformation Officer and Chief Information Officer, Beaumont Hospital - Dearborn, Dearborn, MI, p. A352

Executive Vice President, Chief Transformation Officer and Chief Information Officer, Beaumont Hospital, Wayne, Wayne, MI, p. A369

Executive Vice President, Chief Transportation Officer and Chief Information Officer, Beaumont Hospital - Farmington Hills, Farmington Hills, MI, p. A354

Executive Vice President, Chief Transportation Officer and Chief Information Officer, Beaumont Hospital - Grosse Pointe, Grosse Pointe, MI, p. A357

Executive Vice President, Chief Transportation Officer and Chief Information Officer, Beaumont Hospital - Royal Oak, Royal Oak, MI, p. A365

Executive Vice President, Chief Transportation Officer and Chief Information Officer, Beaumont Hospital - Troy, Troy, MI, p. A368

SRIVASTAVA, Mohit, M.D., Chief of Staff, Bunkie General Hospital, Bunkie, LA, p. A299

ST CLAIR, Jeffery M., President and Chief Executive Officer, Springhill Memorial Hospital, Mobile, AL, p. A22

ST. AUBYN, Lisa, Chief Executive Officer, Signature Psychiatric Hospital, Kansas City, MO, p. A409

ST. LOUIS, Charles, Director of Patient Care Services, Sutter Health Kahi Mohala, Ewa Beach, HI, p. A184

ST. PETER, Colette, Senior Manager Human Resources, Mercy Hospital Carthage, Carthage, MO, p. A404

ST. PIERRE, Fran, R.N., Chief Nursing Officer, Northshore Rehabilitation Hospital, Lacombe, LA, p. A305

STACEY, Brian, Chief Financial Officer, Nyc Health + Hospitals / Queens, Jamaica, NY, p. A486

STACEY, Susan, Chief Nursing Officer, Providence Sacred Heart Medical Center & Children's Hospital, Spokane, WA, p. A766

STACIE, Beverly, Director Human Resources, Clifton T. Perkins Hospital Center, Jessup. MD, p. A330

STACKHOUSE, Jenni, Chief Financial Officer, River Point Behavioral Health, Jacksonville, FL, p. A141

STACKHOUSE, Rebecca J., Medical Center Director, Salem Veterans Affairs Medical Center, Salem, VA, p. A751

STACKHOUSE, Sharon, Assistant Administrator and Director Risk Management, Peachford Behavioral Health System, Atlanta, GA, p. A165

STACY, Doug, Director Information Technology, Up Health System-Marquette, Marquette, MI, p. A361

STADHEIM, Barbara, Chief Nursing Officer, West River Regional Medical Center, Hettinger, ND, p. A524

STADHEIM, Nathan, Chief Financial Officer, West River Regional Medical Center, Hettinger, ND, p. A524

STADLER, James, M.D., Associate Administrator Medical Services, Guam Memorial Hospital Authority, Tamuning, GU, p. A805

STADLER, Thomas, M.D., Vice President Medical Affairs and Chief Medical Officer, Madonna Rehabilitation Hospital, Lincoln, NE, p. A434

STAFFORD, Tom, Chief Information Officer, Halifax Health Medical Center Of Daytona Beach, Daytona Beach, FL, p. A136

STAFFORD, Walt, Director Information Technology, Chatuge Regional Hospital And Nursing Home, Hiawassee, GA, p. A173

STAGG, Kevin, Executive Vice President Finance and Chief Financial Officer, Christian Health Care Center, Wyckoff, NJ, p. A466

STAGGS, Nathan, Chief Executive Officer, Anson General Hospital, Anson, TX, p. A653

STAHL, Anthony, FACHE, Ph.D., Chief Executive Officer, Adventist Healthcare White Oak Medical Center, Silver Spring, MD, p. A332

STAHL, Kathy, Chief Nursing Officer, Wheeling Hospital, Wheeling, WV, p. A778

STAHL, Pam, Regional Chief Human Resources Officer, Providence Holy Cross Medical Center, Mission Hills, CA, p. A78

STAHL, Steven, Director Human Resources, Columbia County Health System, Dayton, WA, p. A757

STAHL, William, Chief Operating Officer, Rooks County Health Center, Plainville, KS, p. A274

STAHLKUPPE, Robert, M.D., Chief of Staff, Chatuge Regional Hospital And Nursing Home, Hiawassee, GA, p. A173

STAHULAK, Brian, R.N., Chief Nursing Officer, Ann & Robert H. Lurie Children's Hospital Of Chicago, Chicago, IL, p. A198

STAIGER, Tom, Medical Director, University Of Washington Medical Center, Seattle, WA, p. A764

STAIGL, Christine, Chief Nursing Officer, Tristar Skyline Medical Center, Nashville, TN, p. A647

STALCUP, Connie, Manager Information Systems, Erlanger Western Carolina Hospital, Murphy, NC, p. A515

STALCUP, Linda, Chief Executive Officer, Stevens County Hospital, Hugoton, KS, p. A266

STALKER, Neil, M.D., Chief of Staff, Dukes Memorial Hospital, Peru, IN, p. A239

STALL, Kristi, Chief Human Resources Officer, Mahnomen Health Center, Mahnomen, MN, p. A379

STALLINGS, Jay, Chief Executive Officer, Washakie Medical Center, Worland, WY, p. A804

STALLINGS, Terry, M.D., Chief Medical Officer, West Florida Hospital, Pensacola, FL, p. A154

STALLINGS-SICARD, Lori, R.N., Chief Nursing Officer, Dmc Huron Valley-Sinai Hospital, Commerce Township. MI, p. A351

STALLONE, Martin, M.D., President and Chief Executive Officer, Cayuga Medical Center At Ithaca, Ithaca, NY, p. A485

STALLWORTH, David, M.D., Chief of Staff, Monroe County Hospital, Monroeville, AL, p. A22

STALLWORTH, Monica, M.D., Chief of Staff, Western Maryland Hospital Center, Hagerstown, MD, p. A330

STALLWORTH, Teresa, M.D., Clinical Director, San Antonio State Hospital, San Antonio, TX, p. A713

STALNAKER, Avah, Chief Executive Officer, Stonewall Jackson Memorial Hospital, Weston, WV, p. A777

STAMAS, Peter, M.D., Vice President Medical Affairs, Marshfield Medical Center, Marshfield, WI, p. A789

STAMOPOULOS, Marion, Vice President Human Resources, Deborah Heart And Lung Center, Browns Mills, NJ, p. A453

STAMOS, George, M.D., Chief Medical Officer, Overland Park Regional Medical Center, Overland Park, KS, p. A274

STAMPER, Wendy, Controller, Cameron Memorial Community Hospital, Angola, IN, p. A223

STAMPOHAR, Jeffry, Vice President of Hospital, Chi Lakewood Health, Baudette, MN, p. A372

STANBRO, Dave, Director Human Resources, Arnot Ogden Medical Center, Elmira, NY, p. A483

Director Human Resources, Ira Davenport Memorial Hospital, Bath, NY, p. A475

STANDARD, Heather, Chief Nursing Officer, Northeast Georgia Medical Center Barrow, Winder, GA, p. A183

STANDER, Paul, M.D., Chief Medical Officer, Banner - University Medical Center Phoenix, Phoenix, AZ, p. A35

STANDIFORD, Steven, M.D., Chief of Staff, Cancer Treatment Centers Of America-Eastern Regional Medical Center, Philadelphia, PA, p. A599

STANDLEE, Cynthia, R.N., Chief Nursing Officer, Mercy Hospital Ada, Ada, OK, p. A555

STANFORD, Brion, Director Human Resources, New Orleans East Hospital, New Orleans, LA, p. A310

STANFORD, Tracy, Director Human Resources, Baylor Scott & White All Saints Medical Center - Fort Worth, Fort Worth, TX, p. A678

STANGE, Della, Director Human Resources, Southwest Healthcare System, Murrieta, CA, p. A80

STANGE-KOLO, Tracey, Vice President Human Resources, Upmc Somerset, Somerset, PA, p. A608
Vice President Human Resources, Upmc St. Margaret, Pittsburgh, PA, p. A604
Vice President, Human Resources, Upmc Mercy, Pittsburgh, PA, p. A604

STANGL, Abbey, Chief Financial Officer, Cass County Health System, Atlantic, IA, p. A243

STANIC, Steve, Vice President and Chief Information Officer, Mississipp. Baptist Medical Center, Jackson, MS, p. A395
Vice President and Chief Information Officer, Select Specialty Hospital - Belhaven, Jackson, MS, p. A395

STANKO, Shelley, M.D., Chief Medical Officer, Chi Saint Josep. London, London, KY, p. A287

STANLEY, Cassandra, Director Personnel, Eastern Shore Hospital Center, Cambridge, MD, p. A328

STANLEY, Donna, R.N., Chief Nursing Officer, Ut Health Henderson, Henderson, TX, p. A683

STANLEY, Jeff, Chief Executive Officer, Cavalier County Memorial Hospital And Clinics, Langdon, ND, p. A524

STANLEY, Jennifer, M.D., Chief Medical Officer, Ascension St. Vincent Jennings, North Vernon, IN, p. A238

STANLEY, Mark, Director Fiscal Services, Middle Tennessee Mental Health Institute, Nashville, TN, p. A646

STANSBERY, Shawn, M.D., Chief of Staff, Wood County Hospital, Bowling Green, OH, p. A530

STANSBURY, Bill, Chief Financial Officer, Jackson Parish Hospital, Jonesboro, LA, p. A304

STANSBURY, Kevin M., Chief Executive Officer, Lincoln Community Hospital And Nursing Home, Hugo, CO, p. A114

STANSKI, Vickie, Financial Manager, Parkview Lagrange Hospital, Lagrange, IN, p. A235

STANTON, Lowell, Chief Financial Officer, Our Lady Of The Lake Regional Medical Center, Baton Rouge, LA, p. A297

STANTON, Melanie, R.N., Chief Nursing Officer, Sycamore Shoals Hospital, Elizabethton, TN, p. A637
R.N., Chief Nursing Officer, Unicoi County Memorial Hospital, Erwin, TN, p. A638

STANTON, Melanie Steagall., Chief Executive Officer, Franklin Woods Community Hospital, Johnson City, TN, p. A640

STANTON, Mike, D.O., Medical Director, Baylor Scott & White Medical Center - Trophy Club, Trophy Club, TX, p. A721

STANUSH, Chris, Director Information Management, San Antonio State Hospital, San Antonio, TX, p. A713

STANZIONE, Dominick, President and Chief Executive Officer, Brookdale Hospital Medical Center, New York, NY, p. A489

STAPELFELDT, Stephanie, Director, Human Resources, South Lake Hospital, Clermont, FL, p. A134

STAPLES, Janet, Vice President Human Resources, South Central Regional Medical Center, Laurel, MS, p. A395

STAPLES-EVANS, Helen, Chief Nursing Officer, LLUCH, Loma Linda University Children's Hospital, Loma Linda, CA, p. A71

STAPLETON, Carla, Director Human Resources, Paul B. Hall Regional Medical Center, Paintsville, KY, p. A292

STAPLETON, Kathleen, Chief Financial Officer, Prisma Health Baptist Easley Hospital, Easley, SC, p. A619

STAPLETON, Michael, President and Chief Executive Officer, F. F. Thompson Hospital, Canandaigua, NY, p. A481

STAPLETON, Robert, Director Administration, Richard H. Hutchings Psychiatric Center, Syracuse, NY, p. A499

STARA, Jeanne, R.N., MSN, Chief Nursing Officer, Alliancehealth Ponca City, Ponca City, OK, p. A567

STARCK, Rebecca, M.D., President, Cleveland Clinic Avon Hospital, Avon, OH, p. A528

STAREN, Edgar, M.D., Interim Chief Executive Officer, Abrazo Central Campus, Phoenix, AZ, p. A35
M.D., Interim Chief Executive Officer, Abrazo Scottsdale Campus, Phoenix, AZ, p. A35

STARK, David, Chief Financial Officer, Lancaster Rehabilitation Hospital, Lancaster, PA, p. A594

STARK, David A., FACHE, President and Chief Executive Officer, Unitypoint Health - Iowa Methodist Medical Center, Des Moines, IA, p. A248

STARK, Donna, Director Human Resources, Baylor Scott & White Medical Center - Grapevine, Grapevine, TX, p. A682

STARK, Patricia Ann, R.N., CNO, Adventhealth Deland, Deland, FL, p. A136

STARK, Sharon, R.N., Manager Clinical Information Systems, Methodist Mckinney Hospital, Mckinney, TX, p. A700

STARK, Steve Lee., Chief Executive Officer, Orchard Hospital, Gridley, CA, p. A67

STARKEBAUM, Gordon, M.D., Chief of Staff, Veterans Affairs Puget Sound Health Care System, Seattle, WA, p. A764

STARKES, Henry, M.D., Medical Director, Orchard Hospital, Gridley, CA, p. A67

STARKEY, Michele, Director Human Resources, North Shore Health, Grand Marais, MN, p. A377

STARLING, James, M.D., Chief Medical Officer, Sovah Health-Danville, Danville, VA, p. A741

STARLING, Susan, President and Chief Executive Officer, Mercy Health - Marcum And Wallace, Irvine, KY, p. A285

STARLING, Terri, Director of Human Resources, Lakeside Behavioral Health System, Memphis, TN, p. A644

STARNES, Gregory D., Chief Executive Officer, Fayette County Hospital, Vandalia, IL, p. A222

STARR, Erin, Chief Nursing Officer, Jefferson Community Health And Life, Fairbury, NE, p. A431

STARR, Kay, Manager Human Resources, Vernon Memorial Healthcare, Elk Mound, WI, p. A783

STASI, Joseph, Chief Financial Officer, Saint Luke's East Hospital, Lee's Summit, MO, p. A411

STASKIN, David, Director Human Resources, Encompass Health Rehabilitation Hospital Of Mechanicsburg, Mechanicsburg, PA, p. A596

STASNEY, Amy, R.N., Chief Executive Officer, Cornerstone Hospital Of Houston At Clearlake, Webster, TX, p. A724

STATEN, Gary L., Chief Executive Officer, Trace Regional Hospital, Houston, MS, p. A394

STATES, Chuck, Director Information Systems, Punxsutawney Area Hospital, Punxsutawney, PA, p. A605

STATON, Donna, Chief Information Officer, Fauquier Hospital, Warrenton, VA, p. A753

STATON, John, Senior Vice President Operations, Olathe Medical Center, Olathe, KS, p. A272

STATON, Paul, Chief Financial Officer, Ronald Reagan Ucla Medical Center, Los Angeles, CA, p. A75
Chief Financial Officer, Ucla Medical Center-Santa Monica, Santa Monica, CA, p. A98

STATZ, Chris, Chief Financial Officer, Lincoln Prairie Behavioral Health Center, Springfield, IL, p. A220

STATZ, Linda, System Director, Employee Experience, Ssm Health St. Mary's Hospital, Madison, WI, p. A788

STAUB, David, M.D., Chief of Staff, Coteau Des Prairies Hospital, Sisseton, SD, p. A632

STAUB, Julie, Chief Human Resources Officer, Jackson Health System, Miami, FL, p. A146

STAUFFER, Karla, Vice President People Resources, Billings Clinic, Billings, MT, p. A421

STAUFFER, Keith, Regional Chief Information Officer, Chi St Alexius Health Carrington Medical Center, Carrington, ND, p. A522

STAUSS, Laura, Director of Human Resources, Huggins Hospital, Wolfeboro, NH, p. A451

STEAD, William, Associate Vice Chancellor Health Affairs, Director Informatics Center and Chief Strategy and Information Officer, Vanderbilt University Medical Center, Nashville, TN, p. A647

STEADHAM, Mark B., President and Chief Executive Officer, Morris Hospital & Healthcare Centers, Morris, IL, p. A213

STEAGALL, Susan, Vice President Information Services, Vcu Medical Center, Richmond, VA, p. A751

STEARNS, Charles, Area Information Officer, Kaiser Westside Medical Center, Hillsboro, OR, p. A576

STEARNS, Zebediah, M.D., Chief of Staff, Mercy Regional Medical Center, Ville Platte, LA, p. A316

STECKEL, Cindy, Ph.D., R.N., Vice President Chief Nurse and Operations Executive, Scripp. Memorial Hospital-La Jolla, La Jolla, CA, p. A70

STECKELBERG, James, M.D., Chief Medical Staff, Syracuse Area Health, Syracuse, NE, p. A440

STECKER, Tim, Chief Financial Officer, Kindred Hospital-Denver, Denver, CO, p. A110

STEED, Robert, Director Information Systems, Capital Regional Medical Center, Tallahassee, FL, p. A158

STEEL, Diana, Vice President Human Resources, West Hills Hospital And Medical Center, West Hills, CA, p. A104

STEELE, Anthony, M.D., Chief Medical Officer, Witham Health Services, Lebanon, IN, p. A235

STEELE, Chrys, Director Information Systems, Musc Health Lancaster Medical Center, Lancaster, SC, p. A622

STEELE, David, Vice President Chief Information Officer, Leesburg Regional Medical Center, Leesburg, FL, p. A144

STEELE, Mark, M.D., Chief Medical Officer, Truman Medical Center-Hospital Hill, Kansas City, MO, p. A410
M.D., Chief Medical Officer, Truman Medical Center-Lakewood, Kansas City, MO, p. A410

STEELE, Michael, M.D., Chief of Staff, Perry County Memorial Hospital, Perryville, MO, p. A413

STEELE, Sherri, Chief Nursing Officer, Providence Medford Medical Center, Medford, OR, p. A578
Chief Nursing Officer, Santiam Hospital, Stayton, OR, p. A582

STEELE, Terry, Vice President Finance and Chief Financial Officer, Holland Hospital, Holland, MI, p. A357

STEELMAN, Jeffrey, Director Information Systems, Lewisgale Hospital Alleghany, Low Moor, VA, p. A745

STEELY, Karen, Chief Operating Officer, Adventhealth Gordon, Calhoun, GA, p. A168
Chief Operating Officer, Adventhealth Murray, Chatsworth, GA, p. A168

STEEN, Jon, Director Human Resources, Davis Medical Center, Elkins, WV, p. A772

STEFANEK, Allen, Chief Executive Officer, West Anaheim Medical Center, Anaheim, CA, p. A55

STEFFEN, Daniel, Vice President, Operations, Mercy Hospital, Coon Rapids, MN, p. A374

STEFFEN, Elizabeth, Director Information Technology, Seneca Healthcare District, Chester, CA, p. A60

STEFFEN, Lorri, Director of Nursing, Osage Beach Center For Cognitive Disorders, Osage Beach, MO, p. A413

STEFFENS, Aaron, Chief Operating Officer, Mercy Hospital Oklahoma City, Oklahoma City, OK, p. A564

STEFFIN, Renee, Chief Nursing Officer, Cuyuna Regional Medical Center, Crosby, MN, p. A374

STEFL, William, Director Information Systems, Mercy Health Hackley Campus, Muskegon, MI, p. A362

STEGALL, Christopher, Regional Chief Financial Officer and Chief Operating Officer, Kp. Promise Hospital Of Vicksburg, Vicksburg, MS, p. A400

STEGER, Elizabeth, FACHE, R.N., Chief Nursing Officer, Ascension Seton Medical Center Austin, Austin, TX, p. A654

STEGGE, Sherri, Director Human Resources, Kaiser Permanente Vallejo Medical Center, Vallejo, CA, p. A103

STEHLY, Sarah, Vice President Human Resources, Advocate Condell Medical Center, Libertyville, IL, p. A210

STEHMER, Marie, Senior Director of Human Resources, Peacehealth Sacred Heart Medical Center At Riverbend, Springfield, OR, p. A581

STEICHEN, Barry, Executive Vice President and Chief Operating Officer, Saint Francis Health System, Saint Francis Hospital, Tulsa, OK, p. A570
Executive Vice President and Chief Operating Officer, Saint Francis Hospital South, Tulsa, OK, p. A570

STEICHEN, Elizabeth, Human Resources, Lewis And Clark Specialty Hospital, Yankton, SD, p. A633

STEICHEN, Terry, Business Officer, Lewis And Clark Specialty Hospital, Yankton, SD, p. A633

STEIGMAN, Don, Chief Operating Officer, Jackson Health System, Miami, FL, p. A146

STEIGMEYER, Robert P., President and Chief Executive Officer, Concord Hospital, Concord, NH, p. A448

STEIN, Brad, Chief Financial Officer, Medical City Plano, Plano, TX, p. A707

STEIN, Cathy, Chief Inpatient Services, Sagamore Children's Psychiatric Center, Dix Hills, NY, p. A482

STEIN, Eric H., FACHE, President, Cobleskill Regional Hospital, Cobleskill, NY, p. A481

STEIN, Keith, M.D., Chief Medical Officer, Baptist Medical Center Beaches, Jacksonville Beach, FL, p. A142
M.D., Senior Vice President Medical Affairs and Chief Medical Officer, Baptist Medical Center Jacksonville, Jacksonville, FL, p. A140

STEIN, Patrick, M.D., Clinical Director, Western New York Children's Psychiatric Center, West Seneca, NY, p. A502

STEIN, Paul, Chief Operating Officer, Mainegeneral Medical Center, Augusta, ME, p. A318

STEIN, Robert, M.D., Vice President Medical Management, Advocate Christ Medical Center, Oak Lawn, IL, p. A215
Chief Executive Officer, Kindred Hospital Houston Medical Center, Houston, TX, p. A686

STEIN, Sandra, Chief Human Resources Management, Veterans Affairs Central California Health Care System, Fresno, CA, p. A66

STEIN, Sheldon J., President and Chief Executive Officer, Mt. Washington Pediatric Hospital, Baltimore, MD, p. A326

STEINBERG, James, M.D., Chief Medical Officer, Emory University Hospital Midtown, Atlanta, GA, p. A164

STEINBLOCK, Matthew, Director Information Systems, Syracuse Area Health, Syracuse, NE, p. A440

STEINER, Scott, FACHE, Chief Executive Officer, Dmc - Detroit Receiving Hospital, Detroit, MI, p. A352
FACHE, Chief Executive Officer, Dmc Harper University Hospital, Detroit, MI, p. A353
FACHE, Chief Executive Officer, Phoebe Putney Memorial Hospital, Albany, GA, p. A163

STEINES, Brian, Chief Financial Officer, Northeast Georgia Medical Center, Gainesville, GA, p. A173

STEINES, Jeanne, D.O., Medical Director, Connecticut Mental Health Center, New Haven, CT, p. A124

STEINGALL, Patricia, MS, R.N., R.N., MS, Vice President, Patient Care Services, Hunterdon Healthcare, Flemington, NJ, p. A455

STEINHART, Curt, M.D., Chief Medical Officer, Ou Medical Center, Oklahoma City, OK, p. A565

STEINKE, Paul, D.O., President and Chief Executive Officer, Cgh Medical Center, Sterling, IL, p. A221
Chief Financial Officer, St. Bernardine Medical Center, San Bernardino, CA, p. A91

STEINMANN, Robin, Chief Human Resources Officer, Anderson Hospital, Maryville, IL, p. A211

STEINSICK, Bill, M.D., Chief Medical Staff, Asante Ashland Community Hospital, Ashland, OR, p. A573

STELL, G, M.D., Medical Director, Minden Medical Center, Minden, LA, p. A309

STELLER, Wayne, Vice President Chief Nursing Officer, The Acadia Hospital, Bangor, ME, p. A318

STELLING, Jonathan, M.D., Vice President Medical Affairs, Chi Health St. Mary's, Nebraska City, NE, p. A435

STELTENPOHL, Robert, Vice President, Southern Indiana Rehabilitation Hospital, New Albany, IN, p. A238

STELTER, Carolyn, M.D., Chief of Staff, Ridgeview Le Sueur Medical Center, Le Sueur, MN, p. A378

STELZER, Jason, Director Human Resources, Ssm Health St. Clare Hospital-Baraboo, Baraboo, WI, p. A780

STENCEL, Lindsay, Chief Administrative Officer, Baptist Memorial Hospital-Collierville, Collierville, TN, p. A636

STENDEL-FREELS, Robin, Coordinator Human Resources, Amg Specialty Hospital-Albuquerque, Albuquerque, NM, p. A467

STENERSON, David, Vice President and Chief Financial Officer, Osf Saint Anthony Medical Center, Rockford, IL, p. A219

STENGER, George, D.O., Chief of Staff, Okeene Municipal Hospital, Okeene, OK, p. A563

STENGER, John, Acting Associate Director, Charlie Norwood Veterans Affairs Medical Center, Augusta, GA, p. A166

STENGER, Michael J, Chief Executive Officer, Western Arizona Regional Medical Center, Bullhead City, AZ, p. A30

STENGER, Sandra, Acting Chief Human Resources, Cincinnati Veterans Affairs Medical Center, Cincinnati, OH, p. A532

STENNETT, Kevin, M.D., Chief of Staff, W. J. Mangold Memorial Hospital, Lockney, TX, p. A696

STENSON, James, Chief Information Officer, Syracuse Veterans Affairs Medical Center, Syracuse, NY, p. A500

STENSRUD, Kirk A., Chief Executive Officer, Glacial Ridge Health System, Glenwood, MN, p. A377

STENSTROM, Ella, Vice President and Chief Financial Officer, Adventhealth Hendersonville, Hendersonville, NC, p. A512

STEPANSKY, David, Chief Medical Officer, Phoenixville Hospital, Phoenixville, PA, p. A602

STEPHAN, Reid, Chief Information Officer, St. Luke's Regional Medical Center, Boise, ID, p. A189

STEPHENS, Brian, President and Chief Executive Officer, Door County Medical Center, Sturgeon Bay, WI, p. A797

STEPHENS, Carrie, Director Information Technology, Saunders Memorial Medical Center, Wahoo, NE, p. A440

STEPHENS, Debra, Director Personnel, Riverland Medical Center, Ferriday, LA, p. A301

STEPHENS, Eddy, Vice President Information Technology, Mobile Infirmary Medical Center, Mobile, AL, p. A22

STEPHENS, Ellen, Vice President Information Services, Mercy Hospital Oklahoma City, Oklahoma City, OK, p. A564

STEPHENS, Heather, Director of Information Health Technology, Ssm Health St. Clare Hospital-Baraboo, Baraboo, WI, p. A780

STEPHENS, Jeremy, Vice President and Chief Human Resources Officer, St. Josep. Mercy Chelsea, Chelsea, MI, p. A351

STEPHENS, Kathy, Vice President of Patient Care, Decatur County Memorial Hospital, Greensburg, IN, p. A230

STEPHENS, Larry, Chief Financial Officer, Collingsworth General Hospital, Wellington, TX, p. A724
Chief Financial Officer, Kimble Hospital, Junction, TX, p. A691
Chief Financial Officer, Sabine County Hospital, Hemphill, TX, p. A683
Chief Financial Officer, Schleicher County Medical Center, Eldorado, TX, p. A676

STEPHENS, Linda, R.N., Chief Nursing Officer, Memorial Hermann Northeast, Humble, TX, p. A690

STEPHENS, Maria, Director Human Resources, Education and Occupational Health and Wellness, Vcu Health Community Memorial Hospital, South Hill, VA, p. A752

STEPHENS, Mike, Chief Financial Officer, Nch Baker Hospital, Naples, FL, p. A148

STEPHENS, Norman F., Chief Executive Officer, Vista Health, Waukegan, IL, p. A222

STEPHENS, Royce, Director Finance, Intermountain Medical Center, Murray, UT, p. A729

STEPHENS, Ruth M., MSN, R.N., Chief Executive Officer, Pawnee County Memorial Hospital And Rural Health Clinic, Pawnee City, NE, p. A438

STEPHENS, Terry A., Chief Executive Officer, River Park Hospital, Huntington, WV, p. A773

STEPHENSON, Darlene, Chief Executive Officer, Bon Secours Mary Immaculate Hospital, Newport News, VA, p. A746
Vice President Operations, Bon Secours Mary Immaculate Hospital, Newport News, VA, p. A746

STEPHENSON, Michelle, R.N., Executive Vice President & Chief Operations Officer, Ann & Robert H. Lurie Children's Hospital Of Chicago, Chicago, IL, p. A198

STEPHENSON, Ron, Chief Operating Officer, Long Island Community Hospital, Patchogue, NY, p. A494

STEPNEY, Precious, Executive Director, Bronx Psychiatric Center, Bronx, NY, p. A476

STEPP, Dana, Human Resources Officer, Mercy Health - Marcum And Wallace, Irvine, KY, p. A285

STERBACH, Maureen, Vice President Human Resources, St. Joseph's Hospital And Medical Center, Phoenix, AZ, p. A36

STERN, Barry, President and Chief Executive Officer, New York Community Hospital, Brooklyn, NY, p. A478

STERNBERG, Paul, M.D., Professor and Chairman, Vanderbilt University Medical Center, Nashville, TN, p. A647

STERUD, Brian, Chief Information Officer, Faith Regional Health Services, Norfolk, NE, p. A435

STETTHEIMER, Timothy, Vice President and Chief Information Officer, St. Vincent's Birmingham, Birmingham, AL, p. A15

STEVEN, Eva, Chief Financial Officer, Roosevelt General Hospital, Portales, NM, p. A471

STEVENS, Ann Marie., R.N., Chief Executive Officer, Tyler Memorial Hospital, Tunkhannock, PA, p. A609

STEVENS, Ben, Chief Financial Officer, Buchanan County Health Center, Independence, IA, p. A251

STEVENS, Bryan, Chief Financial Officer, Field Memorial Community Hospital, Centreville, MS, p. A390
Interim Chief Financial Officer, Copiah County Medical Center, Hazlehurst, MS, p. A394

STEVENS, Chris, Chief Information Officer, Billings Clinic, Billings, MT, p. A421

STEVENS, Emily, Chief Nursing Officer, Mat-Su Regional Medical Center, Palmer, AK, p. A29
Chief Nursing Officer, Western Arizona Regional Medical Center, Bullhead City, AZ, p. A30

STEVENS, Jeffrey, Executive Vice President and Chief Human Resource Officer, Thomas Jefferson University Hospitals, Philadelphia, PA, p. A602

STEVENS, Kelly, Manager Human Resources, St. Josep. Memorial Hospital, Murphysboro, IL, p. A213

STEVENS, Lori, MSN, R.N., Interim Chief Nursing Officer, Verde Valley Medical Center, Cottonwood, AZ, p. A31

STEVENS, Mark, M.D., Chief Medical Staff, Marion General Hospital, Columbia, MS, p. A391
Director Human Resources, St. Luke's Jerome, Jerome, ID, p. A190
Senior Director Human Resources, St. Luke's Magic Valley Medical Center, Twin Falls, ID, p. A193

STEVENS, Rick, President, Christian Hospital, Saint Louis, MO, p. A415

STEVENS, Rodney, East Central Region Director of Nursing Practice, Indiana University Health Blackford Hospital, Hartford City, IN, p. A230

STEVENS, Scot, Chief Executive Officer, Northern Utah Rehabilitation Hospital, South Ogden, UT, p. A733

STEVENS, Shelbourn, President and Chief Operating Officer, Novant Health Brunswick Medical Center, Bolivia, NC, p. A505

STEVENS, Susan, Human Resources Strategic Business Partner, Transylvania Regional Hospital, Brevard, NC, p. A505
Information Technology Specialist, Fallon Medical Complex, Baker, MT, p. A421

STEVENS, Tammy, Chief Executive Officer, Madison County Memorial Hospital, Madison, FL, p. A144

STEVENSON, Angelia, Manager Finance, Tuscaloosa Veterans Affairs Medical Center, Tuscaloosa, AL, p. A25

STEVENSON, Brett, Controller, Kindred Hospital Northland, Kansas City, MO, p. A409

STEVENSON, John, M.D., Senior Vice President and Chief Medical Officer, South Shore Hospital, South Weymouth, MA, p. A344

STEVENSON, Linda, Chief Information Officer, Fisher-Titus Medical Center, Norwalk, OH, p. A546

STEVERSON, Denise, Director Human Resources, Dorminy Medical Center, Fitzgerald, GA, p. A172

STEVES, Sonja, Senior Vice President Human Resources and Marketing, Legacy Emanuel Medical Center, Portland, OR, p. A579

Senior Vice President Human Resources, Legacy Mount Hood Medical Center, Gresham, OR, p. A575
Senior Vice President Human Resources, Legacy Salmon Creek Medical Center, Vancouver, WA, p. A768
Vice President Human Resources and Marketing, Legacy Meridian Park Medical Center, Tualatin, OR, p. A582
Vice President Marketing, Legacy Good Samaritan Medical Center, Portland, OR, p. A579

STEWARD, Rachel, Director Human Resources, Hillcrest Hospital - South, Tulsa, OK, p. A569

STEWARD, Todd E., FACHE, Chief Executive Officer, St. David's Medical Center, Austin, TX, p. A656
FACHE, Chief Executive Officer, St. David's South Austin Medical Center, Austin, TX, p. A656

STEWART, Anne, Vice President and Chief Nursing Officer, Beaumont Hospital - Royal Oak, Royal Oak, MI, p. A365

STEWART, Brandi, R.N., Vice President and Chief Nursing Officer, Integris Grove Hospital, Grove, OK, p. A559

STEWART, Candy, Vice President People and Culture, Chief Human Resouces Officer, Texas Health Presbyterian Hospital Of Rockwall, Rockwall, TX, p. A709

STEWART, Caroline, Chief Nursing Officer, Citrus Memorial Health System, Inverness, FL, p. A140
Chief Nursing Officer, Fort Walton Beach Medical Center, Fort Walton Beach, FL, p. A138

STEWART, Christine R., FACHE, Chief Executive Officer, Russellville Hospital, Russellville, AL, p. A24

STEWART, Clint, Chief Financial Officer, Blue Ridge Regional Hospital, Spruce Pine, NC, p. A518
Regional Director of Finance East, Mcdowell Hospital, Marion, NC, p. A514

STEWART, Daniel, M.D., Vice President Medical Affairs, Bronson Battle Creek Hospital, Battle Creek, MI, p. A349

STEWART, David, Senior Vice President and Chief Financial Officer, Mercy Medical Center, Canton, OH, p. A531

STEWART, Douglas, PsyD, President, Unity Hospital, Rochester, NY, p. A496

STEWART, Greg, Chief Executive Officer, Wellstone Regional Hospital, Jeffersonville, IN, p. A233

STEWART, Hedda, Director Human Resources, Neshoba County General Hospital, Philadelphia, MS, p. A398

STEWART, James, Chief Medical Officer, North Kansas City Hospital, North Kansas City, MO, p. A413

STEWART, Jane, Director Information Services, Jfk Medical Center, Atlantis, FL, p. A131

STEWART, Jessi, Director Human Resources, Rockford Center, Newark, DE, p. A128

STEWART, John, Director Finance, Burke Rehabilitation Hospital, White Plains, NY, p. A502

STEWART, Kelly, Director of Human Resources, Community Mental Health Center, Lawrenceburg, IN, p. A235

STEWART, Kendall, M.D., Chief Medical Officer, Southern Ohio Medical Center, Portsmouth, OH, p. A548

STEWART, Marc, M.D., Vice President and Medical Director, Seattle Cancer Care Alliance, Seattle, WA, p. A764

STEWART, Marty, Chief Information Officer, Anmed Health Medical Center, Anderson, SC, p. A615

STEWART, Michael K., Chief Executive Officer, Saline Memorial Hospital, Benton, AR, p. A42

STEWART, Pamela, Director of Nursing, Washington County Regional Medical Center, Sandersville, GA, p. A179

STEWART, Patty, Chief Executive Officer, Gonzales Healthcare Systems, Gonzales, TX, p. A681
Chief Financial Officer, Gonzales Healthcare Systems, Gonzales, TX, p. A681

STEWART, Paul, M.D., Medical Director, Kindred Hospital Las Vegas-Sahara, Henderson, NV, p. A442

STEWART, Paul R., President and Chief Executive Officer, Sky Lakes Medical Center, Klamath Falls, OR, p. A576

STEWART, Ronnelle, Chief Human Resources Officer, Brookwood Baptist Medical Center, Birmingham, AL, p. A14

STEWART, Roxane, Chief Financial Officer, Magnolia Regional Medical Center, Magnolia, AR, p. A49

STEWART, Russell, D.O., Medical Director, Braxton County Memorial Hospital, Gassaway, WV, p. A772

STEWART, Scott, M.D., Vice President Medical Management, Good Samaritan Medical Center, Brockton, MA, p. A337
Manager Information Services, Rochelle Community Hospital, Rochelle, IL, p. A218

STEWART, Stephen, M.D., Vice President Medical Affairs, Ssm Health St. Mary's Hospital - Jefferson City, Jefferson City, MO, p. A408

STEWART, Stephen C., Chief Executive Officer, Holdenville General Hospital, Holdenville, OK, p. A560

STEWART, Tim, Chief Information Officer, Abbeville Area Medical Center, Abbeville, SC, p. A615

STEWART JR, LarryChief Medical Officer and Vice President, Medical Affairs, Perry Hospital, Perry, GA, p. A178

STIBAL, Melinda, R.N., MSN, Interim President, Legacy Meridian Park Medical Center, Tualatin, OR, p. A582

STIEKES, Robert, Chief Operating Officer, Wilkes-Barre General Hospital, Wilkes-Barre, PA, p. A611

STIFF, Patrick, Coordinator Information Technology, Madison County Memorial Hospital, Madison, FL, p. A144

STIFFARM, Garland, Chief Executive Officer, Blackfeet Community Hospital, Saint Mary, MT, p. A427

STIFFARM, Kevin J., Chief Executive Officer, Indian Health Service Hospital, Rapid City, SD, p. A630

STIKELEATHER, Janie, Director Marketing and Community Relations, Davis Regional Medical Center, Statesville, NC, p. A519

STILES, Geoffrey, M.D., Chief Medical Officer, Sharp Memorial Hospital, San Diego, CA, p. A92

STILGENBAUER, Mike, Director Finance, Marymount Hospital, Garfield Heights, OH, p. A541

STILLER, Brian G., Director Medical Center, Veterans Affairs Western New York Healthcare System-Buffalo Division, Buffalo, NY, p. A480

STILSON, Dwain, Chief Financial Officer, Mosaic Life Care At St. Josep. - Medical Center, Saint Joseph, MO, p. A415

STILTNER, Wanda, Director Human Resources, Buchanan General Hospital, Grundy, VA, p. A743

STIMPSON, Dan, Chief Financial Officer, Banner Del E. Webb Medical Center, Sun City West, AZ, p. A39

STIMPSON, Jared, Chief Financial Officer, Central Carolina Hospital, Sanford, NC, p. A518
Vice Presdient and Chief Financial Officer, Gibson General Hospital, Princeton, IN, p. A239

STIMSON, Judi, Chief Financial Officer, Desert Regional Medical Center, Palm Springs, CA, p. A83
Chief Financial Officer, Palm Beach Gardens Medical Center, Palm Beach Gardens, FL, p. A152

STIMSON, Michael, Chief Nursing Officer, Adventhealth Waterman, Tavares, FL, p. A160

STINGLEY, Susan, Chief Nursing Officer, Kearny County Hospital, Lakin, KS, p. A268

STINNETT, Thomas, M.D., Chief Medical Officer, Conway Behavioral Health Hospital, Conway, AR, p. A43

STINSON, Katy, Director Information Services, Alliancehealth Durant, Durant, OK, p. A558

STINSON, Martha, Director of Information Technology, Palms West Hospital, Loxahatchee, FL, p. A144

STINSON, Michael, Human Resources Coordinator, Select Specialty Hospital-Durham, Durham, NC, p. A509

STIPE, Christopher R., FACHE, Chief Executive Officer, Manhattan Surgical, Manhattan, KS, p. A270

STITH, Melanie, Vice President Human Resources, Roper Hospital, Charleston, SC, p. A616
Vice President Human Resources, Roper St. Francis Mount Pleasant Hospital, Mount Pleasant, SC, p. A622

STITT, Bobby, R.N., Administrator, Mercy Hospital Logan County, Guthrie, OK, p. A559
R.N., Administrator, Mercy Hospital Watonga, Watonga, OK, p. A571

STITT, Patrick, Director of Information Systems, Fishermen's Hospital, Marathon, FL, p. A144

STOBER, Karick, Chief Financial Officer, Pam Specialty Hospital Of Covington, Covington, LA, p. A300

STOCK, Constance, M.D., Chief Medical Officer, Monument Health Sturgis Hospital, Sturgis, SD, p. A632

STOCK, Greg K., FACHE, Chief Executive Officer, Thibodaux Regional Health System, Thibodaux, LA, p. A316

STOCK, Lesa, R.N., Chief Clinical Officer, Citizens Memorial Hospital, Bolivar, MO, p. A402

STOCK, Neil, Director Technology and Facilities, Mercy Regional Medical Center, Durango, CO, p. A111

STOCKARD, Herbert, M.D., Chief Medical Officer, Mercy St. Anne Hospital, Toledo, OH, p. A550

STOCKER, Trena, Chief Nursing Executive, Mercy Health - Marcum And Wallace, Irvine, KY, p. A285

STOCKS, Gregory, M.D., Chief of Staff, Texas Orthopedic Hospital, Houston, TX, p. A688

STOCKTON, David, Chief Operating Officer, Redmond Regional Medical Center, Rome, GA, p. A179

STOCKTON, Linda, Chief Executive Officer, Seven Rivers Regional Medical Center, Crystal River, FL, p. A135

STOCKTON, Rick, Chief Executive Officer, Promise Hospital Of Louisiana - Shreveport Campus, Shreveport, LA, p. A314

STODDARD, Mark R., Chief Executive Officer, Central Valley Medical Center, Nephi, UT, p. A729

STOFFERSON, Laura, Chief Nursing Officer, Shenandoah Medical Center, Shenandoah, IA, p. A257

STOGSDILL, Don, Chief Medical Officer, Ascension St. Vincent Heart Center, Indianapolis, IN, p. A231

STOJAKOVICH, Edward, Chief Financial Officer, Dominion Hospital, Falls Church, VA, p. A741

Chief Financial Officer, Reston Hospital Center, Reston, VA, p. A749

STOKER, Rick, Director Management Information Systems, Tristar Horizon Medical Center, Dickson, TN, p. A637

STOKER, Vicki, Chief Nursing Officer, University Behavioral Health Of Denton, Denton, TX, p. A672

STOKES, Eric, Vice President of Operations, Decatur County Memorial Hospital, Greensburg, IN, p. A230

STOKES, Gary L., Interim Chief Executive Officer, Nacogdoches Memorial Hospital, Nacogdoches, TX, p. A702

STOKES, Laura, Director Human Resources, Roosevelt Warm Springs Rehabilitation And Specialty Hospitals - Ltac, Warm Springs, GA, p. A182
Director Human Resources, Roosevelt Warm Springs Rehabilitation Hospital - Rehab, Warm Springs, GA, p. A183
Human Resources Director, Upson Regional Medical Center, Thomaston, GA, p. A181

STOKES, Letha, Chief Executive Officer, Medical Arts Hospital, Lamesa, TX, p. A694

STOKES, Priscilla, MS, R.N., Vice President Patient Care and Hospital Operations, Unitypoint Health - St. Lukes's Sioux City, Sioux City, IA, p. A258

STOKES, Richard, CPA, JrChief Financial Officer, Gila Regional Medical Center, Silver City, NM, p. A472

STOKES, Richard W. Jr, CPA, Interim Chief Executive Officer, Gila Regional Medical Center, Silver City, NM, p. A472

STOKES, Tina, Manager Human Resources, Regency Hospital Of Florence, Florence, SC, p. A619

STOKOE, Shelby, Chief Financial Officer, Providence Holy Family Hospital, Spokane, WA, p. A766
Senior Director Finance, Providence Sacred Heart Medical Center & Children's Hospital, Spokane, WA, p. A766

STOLDT, Garrick, Vice President and Chief Financial Officer, Saint Peter's University Hospital, New Brunswick, NJ, p. A459

STOLLAR, Joseph, Chief Information Officer, Johnson County Hospital, Tecumseh, NE, p. A440

STOLLER, Theo, Chief Executive Officer, Jacobson Memorial Hospital Care Center, Elgin, ND, p. A522

STOLTMAN, Erin, Administrator, Essentia Health-Ada, Ada, MN, p. A371

STOLTZ, Kim, Controller, Rehabilitation Hospital Of Wisconsin, Waukesha, WI, p. A798

STOLTZ, Kyla, Vice President Human Resources, Centerpoint Medical Center, Independence, MO, p. A407

STOLYAR, Edward, D.O., Divisional Chief Informational Officer, New York Community Hospital, Brooklyn, NY, p. A478

STOMBERG, LeAnn, Chief Financial Officer, Minneapolis Veterans Affairs Health Care System, Minneapolis, MN, p. A381

STONE, Dan, Senior Community Chief Executive Officer, Hazard Arh Regional Medical Center, Hazard, KY, p. A284

STONE, Darlene, Chief Experience Officer, Stormont Vail Health, Topeka, KS, p. A277
Vice President Human Resources, Baptist Hospital, Pensacola, FL, p. A153

STONE, Duncan, D.D.S., Chief Medical Staff, Mississipp. State Hospital, Whitfield, MS, p. A401

STONE, Jeanette, Vice President Operations, Baptist Health South Florida, South Miami Hospital, Miami, FL, p. A146

STONE, Jill, Manager Human Resources, Lynn County Hospital District, Tahoka, TX, p. A718

STONE, Joanna, Chief Nursing Officer, Livingston Hospital And Healthcare Services, Salem, KY, p. A293

STONE, Levi, R.N., Chief Nursing Officer and Chief Operating Officer, Odessa Regional Medical Center, Odessa, TX, p. A704

STONE, Loren, Chief Executive Officer, Endless Mountain Health Systems, Montrose, PA, p. A597

STONE, Patricia, R.N., MSN, Senior Vice President Operations and Chief Nursing Officer, Adventist Health White Memorial, Los Angeles, CA, p. A73

STONE, Richard, Manager, Technical Services, Uhs Chenango Memorial Hospital, Norwich, NY, p. A493

STONE, Robert, President and Chief Executive Officer, City Of Hope's Helford Clinical Research Hospital, Duarte, CA, p. A62

STONE, Ronald, Regional Chief Human Resource Officer, Long Island Jewish Medical Center, New Hyde Park, NY, p. A489

STONE, Sam, Operations Administrator, Essentia Health-Virginia, Virginia, MN, p. A387

STONE, Susan, R.N., Ph.D., Senior Vice President and Chief Executive Officer, Sharp Coronado Hospital And Healthcare Center, Coronado, CA, p. A61
Director Human Resources, Claiborne Medical Center, Tazewell, TN, p. A650

STONE, Terry, Chief Financial Officer and Chief Information Officer, Willap. Harbor Hospital, South Bend, WA, p. A765

STONE, Thomas J., FACHE, Chief Executive Officer, Doctor's Memorial Hospital, Perry, FL, p. A154

STONEBURNER, Marianna, R.N., Chief Nursing Officer, Upmc Jameson, New Castle, PA, p. A598

STONER, Jamey, Chief Financial Officer, Frye Regional Medical Center, Hickory, NC, p. A512

STONER, Steve, Chief Information Officer, Richard L. Roudebush Veterans Affairs Medical Center, Indianapolis, IN, p. A233

STONESTREET, Jana, R.N., Ph.D., Chief Nursing Officer, Tulane Health System, New Orleans, LA, p. A311

STOPPER, Jim, CPA, Chief Financial Officer, Evangelical Community Hospital, Lewisburg, PA, p. A595

STOPPLER, Maria, Chief Executive Officer, Granite County Medical Center, Philipsburg, MT, p. A426

STOREY, Kam, Director Human Resources, Sebastian River Medical Center, Sebastian, FL, p. A157

STOREY, Kevin L., President, Baptist Health Medical Center-Stuttgart, Stuttgart, AR, p. A53
Vice President and Administrator, Baptist Health Medical Center-Heber Springs, Heber Springs, AR, p. A46

STORFJELL, Judith, Ph.D., R.N., Senior Vice President and Chief Nursing Officer, Loma Linda University Medical Center, Loma Linda, CA, p. A72

STORK, Elizabeth, Chief Human Resources Officer, Barton Memorial Hospital, South Lake Tahoe, CA, p. A99

STORM, Dave, Director Business Support, Hshs St. Anthony's Memorial Hospital, Effingham, IL, p. A203

STORR, Katie, Director of Human Resources, Mississipp. State Hospital, Whitfield, MS, p. A401

STORRS, Elaine, Chief Nursing Officer, Springfield Regional Medical Center, Springfield, OH, p. A549

STORTO, David E., President, Spaulding Rehabilitation Hospital, Charlestown, MA, p. A338

STOTLER, Sherry, R.N., MSN, Chief Nursing Officer, Valleywise Health, Phoenix, AZ, p. A37

STOTTLEMYRE, Georgan, Chief Human Relations Officer, Northern Inyo Hospital, Bishop. CA, p. A58

STOTTS, Vicki, Coordinator Human Resources, Flint River Community Hospital, Montezuma, GA, p. A177

STOUGH, Joe, Interim President, Mobile Infirmary Medical Center, Mobile, AL, p. A22

STOUT, Amanda, Chief Nursing Officer, Minneola District Hospital, Minneola, KS, p. A271

STOUT, Bess, Director Human Resources, Tennova Healthcare-Lafollette Medical Center, La Follette, TN, p. A642

STOUT, Cindy, R.N., Chief Executive Officer, El Paso Children's Hospital, El Paso, TX, p. A674

STOUT, Deana, Vice President Financial Services, Medstar Good Samaritan Hospital, Baltimore, MD, p. A325
Vice President, Finance, Medstar Union Memorial Hospital, Baltimore, MD, p. A325

STOUT, Kimberly, Chief Nursing Officer and Chief Operating Officer, Mcalester Regional Health Center, Mcalester, OK, p. A562

STOUT, Louis, Chief Nursing Officer and Deputy Commander Health Readiness, Madigan Army Medical Center, Tacoma, WA, p. A767

STOUT, Patsy, Director Personnel, Richland Parish Hospital-Delhi, Delhi, LA, p. A300

STOUT-TORRES, Sherri, R.N., Chief Nursing Executive, Sutter Maternity And Surgery Center Of Santa Cruz, Santa Cruz, CA, p. A97

STOVALL, Henry, Regional President, Sacred Heart Hospital On The Emerald Coast, Miramar Beach, FL, p. A148
Regional President, Sacred Heart Hospital On The Gulf, Port St Joe, FL, p. A155

STOVALL, Richard, Senior Vice President Fiscal Services and Chief Financial Officer, Southern Regional Medical Center, Riverdale, GA, p. A178

STOVALL, Shella D., R.N., Interim Director, Veterans Affairs Salt Lake City Health Care System, Salt Lake City, UT, p. A733

STOVER, Benny, Vice President Finance, Mercy Hospital Rogers, Rogers, AR, p. A52

STOVER, George M., Chief Executive Officer, Hospital District No 1 Of Rice County, Lyons, KS, p. A270

STOVER, Nick, Director Information Systems, Plateau Medical Center, Oak Hill, WV, p. A775

STOVER, Patricia, Administrator Nursing, Doylestown Hospital, Doylestown, PA, p. A588

STOVER, Raymond, President and Chief Executive Officer, Midmichigan Medical Center-Clare, Clare, MI, p. A351
President and Chief Executive Officer, Midmichigan Medical Center-Gladwin, Gladwin, MI, p. A355

STOVER, Theresa, Chief Human Resource Officer, Edgefield County Healthcare, Edgefield, SC, p. A619

STOWE, Mary, Senior Vice President and Chief Nursing Officer, Children's Medical Center Dallas, Dallas, TX, p. A668
Senior Vice President and Chief Nursing Officer, Children's Medical Center Plano, Plano, TX, p. A706

STOWELL, Dana, Chief Information Officer, Mccurtain Memorial Hospital, Idabel, OK, p. A560

STOWMAN, Amber, Controller, Chi Lisbon Health, Lisbon, ND, p. A525

STOY, Gale, Manager Information Systems, Mid Coast Hospital, Brunswick, ME, p. A319

STOYANOFF, Pamela, Executive Vice President and Chief Operating Officer, Methodist Dallas Medical Center, Dallas, TX, p. A669
President and Chief Operating Officer, Methodist Charlton Medical Center, Dallas, TX, p. A669

STRABEL, Elizabeth, M.D., Chief Medical Staff, Divine Savior Healthcare, Portage, WI, p. A794

STRACHAN, Ronald, Chief Information Officer, Mclaren Bay Region, Bay City, MI, p. A349
Chief Information Officer, Mclaren Flint, Flint, MI, p. A354

STRACK, Kirk, Assistant Chief Financial Officer, Uofl Health - Uofl Hospital, Louisville, KY, p. A289

STRADER, Lynn, Chief Financial Officer, Chippenham Hospital, Richmond, VA, p. A750

STRADER, Yvonne, Chief Nursing Officer, Providence St. Mary Medical Center, Walla Walla, WA, p. A768

STRADTMAN, Jackie, Director Human Resources, Chi St. Josep. Health Burleson Hospital, Caldwell, TX, p. A662

STRAHAN, Greg, President and Chief Executive Officer, Owensboro Health Regional Hospital, Owensboro, KY, p. A291

STRAIN, Donna, Director Human Resources, Ray County Memorial Hospital, Richmond, MO, p. A414

STRAMOWSKI, Mallary, Chief Human Resources Officer, Select Specialty Hospital-Madison, Madison, WI, p. A787

STRAND, Eric, Director Information Services, North Florida Regional Medical Center, Gainesville, FL, p. A138

STRANGE, Julia, Chief Executive Officer, Benson Hospital, Benson, AZ, p. A30

STRASSER, Michael, Vice President and Chief Financial Officer, Mercy Medical Center Merced, Merced, CA, p. A78

STRASSNER III, Lawrence, Ph.D., FACHE, R.N., MS, Senior Vice President Operations and Chief Nursing Officer, Medstar Franklin Square Medical Center, Baltimore, MD, p. A325

STRATON, Sam, Chief Nursing Officer, Saint Thomas West Hospital, Nashville, TN, p. A646

STRATTON, Emilee, Chief Financial Officer, Childress Regional Medical Center, Childress, TX, p. A663

STRATTON, James, Regional Vice President Finance, Ssm Health St. Mary's Hospital - Audrain, Mexico, MO, p. A412
Vice President Finance, Ssm Health St. Mary's Hospital - Jefferson City, Jefferson City, MO, p. A408

STRATTON, Joseph, FACHE, Chief Executive Officer, River's Edge Hospital And Clinic, Saint Peter, MN, p. A385

STRATTON, Mary, Director Human Resources, River Park Hospital, Huntington, WV, p. A773

STRAUGHAN, Janet, Manager Human Resources, Highlands Rehabilitation Hospital, El Paso, TX, p. A675

STRAUGHAN, John, Director Information Technology, Wallowa Memorial Hospital, Enterprise, OR, p. A574

STRAUMAN, Karen, R.N., Chief Nurse Executive, Kaiser Permanente Fresno Medical Center, Fresno, CA, p. A65

STRAUMANIS, John, M.D., Vice President Medical Affairs and Chief Medical Officer, University Of Maryland Rehabilitation & Orthopaedic Institute, Baltimore, MD, p. A327

STRAUSS, Alan, Chief Financial Officer, Carondelet Holy Cross Hospital, Nogales, AZ, p. A34
Chief Financial Officer, Carondelet St. Joseph's Hospital, Tucson, AZ, p. A40

STRAUSS, Thomas J., Interim President and Chief Executive Officer, Mercy Medical Center, Canton, OH, p. A531

STRAWN, Keith, Vice President Human Resources, New Hanover Regional Medical Center, Wilmington, NC, p. A520

STRAWSER, Debbie, Director Human Resources, Lindner Center Of Hope, Mason, OH, p. A544

STRAYHORN, Shelly, R.N., Chief Nursing Officer, Wadley Regional Medical Center At Hope, Hope, AR, p. A47
R.N., Chief Nursing Officer, Wadley Regional Medical Center, Texarkana, TX, p. A720

STRBICH, Steve, D.O., Chief of Staff, Spectrum Health Ludington Hospital, Ludington, MI, p. A361

STREATER, Vivian, Chief Nursing Officer and Co-Acting Chief Executive Officer, Broughton Hospital, Morganton, NC, p. A515
Co-Acting Chief Executive Officer, Broughton Hospital, Morganton, NC, p. A515

STRECKER, Kevin, President, Ascension Via Christi St. Francis, Mulvane, KS, p. A271

STRECKER, Robert, M.D., Chief of Staff, Colorado River Medical Center, Needles, CA, p. A81

STREDNEY, Thomas, Chief Human Resources Management Service, Aleda E. Lutz Veterans Affairs Medical Center, Saginaw, MI, p. A365

STREET, Rex, Senior Vice President and Chief Financial Officer, Alamance Regional Medical Center, Burlington, NC, p. A506

STREET, Scott, Chief Executive Officer, Medical Center Of South Arkansas, El Dorado, AR, p. A44

STREETER, Matthew, Chief Financial Officer, Southwest Health, Platteville, WI, p. A794

STREETER, Maxine, Administrator, Reception And Medical Center, Lake Butler, FL, p. A143

STREETER, Robert, M.D., Vice President Medical Affairs, Mercy Medical Center Merced, Merced, CA, p. A78

STREICH, Rebecca, Manager Human Resources and Education Manager, Hutchinson Health, Hutchinson, MN, p. A378

STREIT, Loren, Director Human Resources, Geary Community Hospital, Junction City, KS, p. A267

STREJC, Irene, M.P.H., R.N., Vice President, Nursing, Methodist Richardson Medical Center, Richardson, TX, p. A708

STRICKER, Sean, Chief Executive Officer, Regency Hospital Of Minneapolis, Golden Valley, MN, p. A377

STRICKER, Steven, M.D., Physician in Chief, Kaiser Permanente Vallejo Medical Center, Vallejo, CA, p. A103

STRICKLAND, Christopher, Chief Executive Officer, Haskell Memorial Hospital, Haskell, TX, p. A683

STRICKLAND, David, Area Information Officer, Kaiser Permanente Los Angeles Medical Center, Los Angeles, CA, p. A74

STRICKLAND, Lee, Regional Director Information Technology, Adventhealth Hendersonville, Hendersonville, NC, p. A512

STRICKLAND, Morris, Chief Financial Officer, Helen Keller Hospital, Sheffield, AL, p. A24

STRICKLER, David, Chief Financial Officer, Nexus Specialty Hospital The Woodlands, The Woodlands, TX, p. A720
Chief Financial Officer, Nexus Specialty Hospital, Shenandoah, TX, p. A715

STRICKLER, Jeffery C., R.N., President and Chief Executive Officer, Chatham Hospital, Siler City, NC, p. A518

STRICKLER, Stephen, Director of Nursing, Sistersville General Hospital, Sistersville, WV, p. A776

STRICKLING, Keith, Chief Accountant, Jay Hospital, Jay, FL, p. A142
Chief Financial Officer, Atmore Community Hospital, Atmore, AL, p. A14

STRIEBICH, Shannon, Chief Executive Officer, St. Josep. Mercy Oakland, Pontiac, MI, p. A364

STRIKE, Helen J., R.N., President, Regina Hospital, Hastings, MN, p. A378
R.N., President, River Falls Area Hospital, River Falls, WI, p. A795

STRING, Sherrie, Senior Vice President Human Resources, Hackensack Meridian Health Bayshore Community Hospital, Holmdel, NJ, p. A456
Senior Vice President Human Resources, Hackensack Meridian Health Ocean Medical Center, Brick Township. NJ, p. A453
Senior Vice President Human Resources, Hackensack Meridian Health Riverview Medical Center, Red Bank, NJ, p. A462

STRINGFELLOW, Grace, M.D., Chief of Staff, Veterans Affairs Nebraska-Western Iowa Health Care System, Omaha, NE, p. A438

STRINGOS, Gust, M.D., Medical Staff Director, Redington-Fairview General Hospital, Skowhegan, ME, p. A323

STRIPLIN, Elizabeth, Chief Financial Officer, Rehabilitation Hospital Of Southern New Mexico, Las Cruces, NM, p. A470

STRITTMATTER, Julie, Director Human Resources, Baylor University Medical Center, Dallas, TX, p. A668

STROBEL, Deb, R.N., Chief Nursing Officer, Russell Regional Hospital, Russell, KS, p. A275

STROBEL, Jane, Vice President and Chief Financial Officer, Mercy Regional Medical Center, Durango, CO, p. A111

STROBEL, Rand, Regional Chief Information Officer, Information Technology Services, St. Michael Medical Center, Bremerton, WA, p. A756
Regional Chief Information Officer, St. Francis Hospital, Federal Way, WA, p. A758

STRODE, Marc, Chief Executive Officer, Methodist Stone Oak Hospital, San Antonio, TX, p. A712

STROH, Rhonda, Chief Human Resources Officer, Community Memorial Hospital, Redfield, SD, p. A630

STROHECKER, Sharon, R.N., MSN, Vice President Clinical Operations and Chief Nursing Officer, Penn State Health St. Joseph, Reading, PA, p. A606

STROHLA, Patti, R.N., Chief Nursing Officer, Franklin Regional Hospital, Franklin, NH, p. A449

STROM, Lisa, Director Information Systems, North Big Horn Hospital District, Lovell, WY, p. A803

STROMBERG, Audrey, Administrator, Roosevelt Medical Center, Culbertson, MT, p. A422

STROMSTAD, Darlene, FACHE, President and Chief Executive Officer, Faxton St. Luke's Healthcare, Utica, NY, p. A500
FACHE, President and Chief Executive Officer, St. Elizabeth Medical Center, Utica, NY, p. A500

STRONESKI, Donna, Vice President, Human Resources, Middlesex Hospital, Middletown, CT, p. A123

STRONG, David, Chief Financial Officer/Vice President Finance, Cox Medical Center Branson, Branson, MO, p. A403

STRONG, Melissa, Chief Nursing Officer, Mason General Hospital And Family Of Clinics, Shelton, WA, p. A765

STRONG, Tanya, Manager Information Technology, Harney District Hospital, Burns, OR, p. A574

STROSS, Daniel, Chief Information Officer, Ascension Genesys Hospital, Grand Blanc, MI, p. A355
Chief Information Officer, Ascension St. Josep. Hospital, Tawas City, MI, p. A367
Chief Information Officer, Ascension St. Mary's Of Michigan, Saginaw, MI, p. A365

STROTHER, James, Site Director Information Technology Systems, Mercyone Des Moines Medical Center, Des Moines, IA, p. A248

STROTHKAMP, Brad, Chief Information Systems, Lakeland Behavioral Health System, Springfield, MO, p. A418

STROUCKEN, Christian, Chief Operating Officer, Carney Hospital, Boston, MA, p. A335

STROUD, Justin, Chief Financial Officer, Merit Health Central, Jackson, MS, p. A394

STROUP, Jeff, Chief Operating Officer, Oklahoma State University Medical Center, Tulsa, OK, p. A570

STROUSE, Thomas, M.D., Medical Director and Professor of Clinical Psych, Stewart & Lynda Resnick Neuropsychiatric Hospital At Ucla, Los Angeles, CA, p. A76

STRUB, Lisa, Chief Operating Officer, Centennial Peaks Hospital, Louisville, CO, p. A116

STRUYK, Douglas A., CPA, President and Chief Executive Officer, Christian Health Care Center, Wyckoff, NJ, p. A466

STRZELECKI, Sarah, Ed.D., R.N., Chief Nursing Officer, Phoenixville Hospital, Phoenixville, PA, p. A602

STRZEMPKO, Stanley, M.D., Vice President Medical Affairs and Chief Medical Officer, Baystate Noble Hospital, Westfield, MA, p. A346

STUART, Danna, M.D., Chief Medical Officer, Newman Memorial Hospital, Shattuck, OK, p. A568

STUART, Philip J., Administrator and Chief Executive Officer, Tomah Health, Tomah, WI, p. A797

STUART, Robin, Chief Executive Officer, Morrill County Community Hospital, Bridgeport, NE, p. A430

STUBBLEFIELD, Greg, President, Baptist Health Extended Care Hospital, Little Rock, AR, p. A48

STUBBS, Don, Vice President Human Resources, Candler Hospital, Savannah, GA, p. A179

STUBBS, Kay, Chief Nursing Officer, Northwest Medical Center, Tucson, AZ, p. A40

STUBITSCH, Brian, M.D., Chief Medical Officer, Edgerton Hospital And Health Services, Edgerton, WI, p. A783

STUCKY, Nancy, Director Human Resources and Public Relations, Kingman Community Hospital, Kingman, KS, p. A268

STUCZYNSKI, Joseph, Administrator and Chief Executive Officer, Memorial Hospital Pembroke, Pembroke Pines, FL, p. A153

STUDEBAKER, Shelly, Human Resources Assistant, Clinch Memorial Hospital, Homerville, GA, p. A174

STUDER, Tim, President Medical Staff, Perham Health, Perham, MN, p. A383

STUDLEY, Jason A., FACHE, President, Sentara Halifax Regional Hospital, South Boston, VA, p. A751

STUENKEL, Kurt, FACHE, President and Chief Executive Officer, Floyd Medical Center, Rome, GA, p. A179

STUEVE, Jo, Executive Vice President and Co-Chief Operating Officer, Children's Mercy Hospital Kansas City, Kansas City, MO, p. A408

STUHLMILLER, Michael, Chief Financial Officer, Mann-Grandstaff Veterans Affairs Medical Center, Spokane, WA, p. A765

STULTS, Cynthia, Executive Assistant and Human Resources Director, Rangely District Hospital, Rangely, CO, p. A118

STULTS, Kim, Director, Information Systems, Bellevue Hospital, Bellevue, OH, p. A529

STUMBO, Kathy, President, Arh Our Lady Of The Way, Martin, KY, p. A289

STUMME, Sarah, Director Human Resources, Owatonna Hospital, Owatonna, MN, p. A382

STUMP, Lisa, Interim Chief Information Officer, Yale-New Haven Hospital, New Haven, CT, p. A124

STUMP, Tammie, R.N., Chief Executive Officer, Union County General Hospital, Clayton, NM, p. A468

STUMP, Veronica, Director of Nursing, Carilion Giles Community Hospital, Pearisburg, VA, p. A748

STUMPO, Barbara, R.N., Vice President Patient Care Services, Griffin Hospital, Derby, CT, p. A122

STUNKARD, Jill, R.N., MSN, Associate Chief Nurse Executive and Interim Chief Nursing Officer, Einstein Medical Center Philadelphia, Philadelphia, PA, p. A600

STURGEON, Jim, Area Director Human Resources, Kindred Hospital Las Vegas-Sahara, Henderson, NV, p. A442

STURGILL, Lori, Vice President Business Partnership. Mercy Hospital Springfield, Springfield, MO, p. A419

STURGIS, Gayle, Chief Nursing Officer, Risk Management, Great Plains Regional Medical Center, Elk City, OK, p. A558

STURGIS, Jonathan, Chief Financial Officer, Houston Methodist Baytown Hospital, Baytown, TX, p. A657

STURGIS, Paul, Chief Human Resource Officer, Sparrow Specialty Hospital, Lansing, MI, p. A360
    Director Human Resources, Dmc - Rehabilitation Institute Of Michigan, Detroit, MI, p. A352
    Vice President and Chief Human Resources Officer, Sparrow Hospital, Lansing, MI, p. A360

STURLER, Kelly, Chief Nursing Officer, Mckee Medical Center, Loveland, CO, p. A117

STURM, Heidi, Executive Director of Nursing, The Healthcenter, Kalispell, MT, p. A425

STURM, Kathy, R.N., Vice President, Chief Nursing Officer, Davis Medical Center, Elkins, WV, p. A772

STURMAN, Jeffrey, Senior Vice President and Chief Information Officer, Memorial Regional Hospital, Hollywood, FL, p. A140

STURSA, Robin, Chief Information Officer, St. Vincent Charity Medical Center, Cleveland, OH, p. A535
    Vice President, Chief Information Officer, Mercy Medical Center, Canton, OH, p. A531

STUWE, Shannon, Director of Nursing, Faulkton Area Medical Center, Faulkton, SD, p. A628

STYER, Brent, Chief Information Officer, Summers County Arh Hospital, Hinton, WV, p. A772
    Director Information Technology, Whitesburg Arh Hospital, Whitesburg, KY, p. A294

STYRON, Stacie, Chief Nursing Officer, Lamb Healthcare Center, Littlefield, TX, p. A696

SUAREZ, Irma, Deputy Executive Director, Nyc Health + Hospitals / Woodhull, Brooklyn, NY, p. A479

SUAREZ, Lauren, Chief Executive Officer, Encompass Health Rehabilitation Hospital Of Austin, Austin, TX, p. A656

SUAREZ, Orlando, Director Information Technology, Larkin Community Hospital-South Miami Campus, South Miami, FL, p. A157

SUBIA, Corina, Director Human Resources, Ward Memorial Hospital, Monahans, TX, p. A702

SUBLETTE, Elizabeth, Director Finance, Providence Willamette Falls Medical Center, Oregon City, OR, p. A578

SUBRAMANIAN, Aarti, Vice President and Chief Financial Officer, Psychiatric Institute Of Washington, Washington, DC, p. A130

SUCATO, Daniel, M.D., MS, Chief of Staff, Texas Scottish Rite Hospital For Children, Dallas, TX, p. A670

SUCHER, Therese, Senior Vice President Operations, Southern Regional Medical Center, Riverdale, GA, p. A178

SUDAK, Mariellena, R.N., MSN, Vice President and Chief Nursing Officer, Palomar Medical Center Escondido, Escondido, CA, p. A63

SUDBURY, Russ, M.D., President Medical Staff, Ascension Sacred Heart Hospital, Tomahawk, WI, p. A797

SUDDUTH, Anthony G., CPA, Chief Executive Officer, Southwest Health System, Cortez, CO, p. A109

SUDICKY, Mary, Chief Financial Officer, St. Mary Medical Center, Hobart, IN, p. A230

SUDOLCAN, Joseph, M.D., Medical Director, Reagan Memorial Hospital, Big Lake, TX, p. A659

SUGAR, Bev, Associate Administrator and Director Human Resources, Inova Mount Vernon Hospital, Alexandria, VA, p. A738

SUGDEN, Elizabeth, M.D., Chief Medical Officer, St. Luke's Jerome, Jerome, ID, p. A190

SUGG, Amy, Director Human Resources, Scott Regional Hospital, Morton, MS, p. A397

SUGGS, Heather, Manager Human Resources, Jay Hospital, Jay, FL, p. A142

SUHR, Nancy, Manager Human Resources, Pender Community Hospital, Pender, NE, p. A439

SUITTER, Marie, Chief Financial Officer, The Acadia Hospital, Bangor, ME, p. A318

SUKENIK, Richard, CPA, Vice President Finance and Chief Financial Officer, Chan Soon-Shiong Medical Center, Windber, PA, p. A611

SUKIN, Debra F., Ph.D., Regional Senior Vice President and Chief Executive Officer, Houston Methodist The Woodlands Hospital, The Woodlands, TX, p. A720

SUKSI, Eugene, Chief Executive Officer, Southern Coos Hospital And Health Center, Bandon, OR, p. A573

SULIT, Teresa, Director of Human Resources, Seven Hills Hospital, Henderson, NV, p. A442

SULLIVAN, Christopher, M.D., Chief Medical Officer, Centerpoint Medical Center, Independence, MO, p. A407

SULLIVAN, Daniel, D.O., Chief Medical Officer, Vice President Medical Administration, Elmhurst Hospital, Elmhurst, IL, p. A204

SULLIVAN, David, Director Human Resources, Ohiohealth Doctors Hospital, Columbus, OH, p. A536

SULLIVAN, Denis, Chief Human Resources Management, Veterans Affairs Black Hills Health Care System, Fort Meade, SD, p. A628

SULLIVAN, Denise, Chief Executive Officer, Sycamore Springs, Lafayette, IN, p. A234

SULLIVAN, Donald, M.D., Medical Director, Encompass Health Rehabilitation Hospital Of North Memphis, Memphis, TN, p. A644

SULLIVAN, Gregory, Manager Human Resources, Girard Medical Center, Girard, KS, p. A265

SULLIVAN, James, M.D., Chief Medical Officer, Butler Hospital, Providence, RI, p. A613

SULLIVAN, John, M.D., Chief Medical Officer, St. Clair Hospital, Pittsburgh, PA, p. A603
    M.D., Chief of Staff, Ennis Regional Medical Center, Ennis, TX, p. A677

SULLIVAN, Katherine, Director, Human Resources, Moab Regional Hospital, Moab, UT, p. A729

SULLIVAN, Kathleen, M.D., Chief of Staff, Saddleback Medical Center, Laguna Hills, CA, p. A70

SULLIVAN, Lowery, M.D., Chief Medical Officer, Northwestern Medical Center, Saint Albans, VT, p. A736

SULLIVAN, Martha, Chief Information Officer, Harrison Memorial Hospital, Cynthiana, KY, p. A282

SULLIVAN, Mary, R.N., MSN, Chief Nursing Officer, Overlook Medical Center, Summit, NJ, p. A463

SULLIVAN, Michael, M.D., Chief Medical Officer, Northern Maine Medical Center, Fort Kent, ME, p. A320
    M.D., Medical Director Emergency Services, Peacehealth Peace Island Medical Center, Friday Harbor, WA, p. A758

SULLIVAN, Patrick, Chief Operating Officer, St. John's Episcopal Hospital, Far Rockaway, NY, p. A483

SULLIVAN, Peter, Chief Executive Officer, Riverside Medical Center, Franklinton, LA, p. A302

SULLIVAN, Shannon, President and Chief Operating Officer, Women & Infants Hospital Of Rhode Island, Providence, RI, p. A614

SULLIVAN, Staci, R.N., Chief Nursing Officer, Lane Regional Medical Center, Zachary, LA, p. A317

SULLIVAN, Theresa, Chief Executive Officer, Samaritan Healthcare, Moses Lake, WA, p. A760

SULLIVAN, Thomas, Vice President Fiscal Services, Harrington Hospital, Southbridge, MA, p. A344

SULLIVAN, William, Mount Auburn Hospital, Cambridge, MA, p. A338

SULLIVAN SMITH, Mary, R.N., MS, Senior Vice President, Chief Operating Officer and Chief Nursing Officer, New England Baptist Hospital, Boston, MA, p. A336

SULLIVANT, Laura, Area Chief Information Officer, Kaiser Permanente San Diego Medical Center, San Diego, CA, p. A91

SULSER, Jamey, Director Human Resources, South Davis Community Hospital, Bountiful, UT, p. A727

SULU, Dorothy, Budget Analyst, Hop. Health Care Center, Keams Canyon, AZ, p. A33

SULZEN, Jessica, Director Human Resources, Belton Regional Medical Center, Belton, MO, p. A402

SUMMERLIN, Craig, Chief Human Resources Officer, Singing River Health System, Pascagoula, MS, p. A398

SUMMERLIN, Valerie, R.N., MS, Chief Nursing Officer, Adventist Healthcare Physical Health And Rehabilitation, Rockville, MD, p. A332

SUMMERS, Barbara, Ph.D., R.N., Vice President Nursing Practice and Chief Nursing Officer, University Of Texas M.D. Anderson Cancer Center, Houston, TX, p. A689

SUMMERS, Curtis, Chief Executive Officer, Summit Medical Center, Edmond, OK, p. A558

SUMMERS, Debra, Chief Nursing Officer, Calhoun-Liberty Hospital, Blountstown, FL, p. A132

SUMMERS, Greg, Regional Director, Field Technical Services, Santa Rosa Memorial Hospital, Santa Rosa, CA, p. A98

SUMMERS, Jeff, M.D., Medical Director, Select Specialty Hospital-North Knoxville, Powell, TN, p. A648

SUMMERS, Kelly, Chief Information Officer, Valleywise Health, Phoenix, AZ, p. A37

SUMMERS, Paul, Interim Chief Financial Officer, Uhs Delaware Valley Hospital, Walton, NY, p. A501
    President and Chief Executive Officer, Uhs Delaware Valley Hospital, Walton, NY, p. A501

SUMMERS-MAIN, Theresa, R.N., President, Genesis Medical Center, Silvis, Silvis, IL, p. A220

SUMMERSON, Tonya, Chief Clinical Officer, Dallas County Hospital, Perry, IA, p. A256

SUMMERVILLE, Wendell, Chief Financial Officer, Bryce Hospital, Tuscaloosa, AL, p. A25

SUMMITT, Dave, Chief Information Security Officer, H. Lee Moffitt Cancer Center And Research Institute, Tampa, FL, p. A159

SUMNER, Donna, Director, Human Resources and Organizational Development, St. Josep. Medical Center, Kansas City, MO, p. A409

SUMNER, Jack, Assistant Administrator Finance, Providence Newberg Medical Center, Newberg, OR, p. A578

SUMNER, John, Chief Executive Officer, Trigg County Hospital, Cadiz, KY, p. A281

SUMPTER, Nikki, Senior Vice President Human Resources, Jp. Health Network, Fort Worth, TX, p. A678

SUMRA, K, M.D., Chief of Staff, Pembina County Memorial Hospital And Wedgewood Manor, Cavalier, ND, p. A522

SUMRALL, Mary, Chief Nursing Officer, Baptist Memorial Hospital-Golden Triangle, Columbus, MS, p. A391

SUMTER, Rob, Executive Vice President and Chief Operating Officer, Regional One Health, Memphis, TN, p. A645
    Executive Vice President and Chief Operation Officer, Regional One Health, Memphis, TN, p. A645

SUN RHODES, Neil, M.D., Chief Medical Officer, Blackfeet Community Hospital, Saint Mary, MT, p. A427

SUND, Lynn A., Interim Administrator, Oklahoma State University Medical Center, Tulsa, OK, p. A570

SUNDARAMOORTHY, Abirammy, M.D., Chief Medical Officer, Uh Conneaut Medical Center, Conneaut, OH, p. A537

SUNDBERG, Karl, Chief Executive Officer, South Lincoln Medical Center, Kemmerer, WY, p. A802

SUNDBERG, Nita, Director Human Resources, Three Rivers Behavioral Health, West Columbia, SC, p. A625

SUNDBLOM, Karin, MSN, R.N., Chief Nursing Officer, Saint Luke's Cushing Hospital, Leavenworth, KS, p. A269

SUNDERLIN, Tammy, Director of Nursing, Auburn Community Hospital, Auburn, NY, p. A475

SUNDHOLM, Jeffrey, Chief Information Officer, Myrtue Medical Center, Harlan, IA, p. A251

SUNDRUD, Diane, Director Human Resources, Essentia Health-Fosston, Fosston, MN, p. A376
    Human Resource Service Partner, Essentia Health St. Mary's - Detroit Lakes, Detroit Lakes, MN, p. A375

SUNGA, Marcos, M.D., Chief of Staff, Hardin County General Hospital, Rosiclare, IL, p. A219

SUNQUIST, Joanne, Chief Information Officer East Region, St. Joseph's Hospital, Saint Paul, MN, p. A385
    Chief Information Officer, Woodwinds Health Campus, Woodbury, MN, p. A388

SUNTAY, Renato, Chief Financial Officer, Meadville Medical Center, Meadville, PA, p. A596

SUNTHA, Mohan, M.D., President and Chief Executive Officer, University Of Maryland Medical Center Midtown Campus, Baltimore, MD, p. A326
    M.D., President and Chief Executive Officer, University Of Maryland Medical Center, Baltimore, MD, p. A326

SUNTRAPAK, Todd A., President and Chief Executive Officer, Valley Children's Healthcare, Madera, CA, p. A76

SUPPLEE, Linda, Chief Executive Officer, Select Specialty Hospital Of Southeast Ohio, Newark, OH, p. A546

SURBER, Randy, Chief Executive Officer, Adventhealth Sebring, Sebring, FL, p. A157

SURBER, Shannon, Chief Operating Officer, Peacehealth Sacred Heart Medical Center At Riverbend, Springfield, OR, p. A581

SURCOUF, Shelli, Chief Financial Officer, Georgetown Behavioral Health Institute, Georgetown, TX, p. A681

SURESH, Srinivasan, M.D., Chief Medical Information Officer, Upmc Children's Hospital Of Pittsburgh, Pittsburgh, PA, p. A603

SURGUY, Jean, Vice President, Chief Nursing Officer, Mile Bluff Medical Center, Mauston, WI, p. A789

SURKALA, Karen, President, Westfield Memorial Hospital, Westfield, NY, p. A502

SURL, Deepak, Chief Information Officer, Eastern New Mexico Medical Center, Roswell, NM, p. A471

SURO, Marta, Chief Operating Officer, Mennonite General Hospital, Aibonito, PR, p. A806

SUROWITZ, Dale, Chief Executive, Providence Tarzana Medical Center, Tarzana, CA, p. A100

SURRATT, Shawn, M.D., Chief of Staff, Memorial Hospital And Manor, Bainbridge, GA, p. A166

SURROCK, Lester, Chief Financial Officer, Mission Regional Medical Center, Mission, TX, p. A701

SUSICK, Nancy, MSN, President, Beaumont Hospital - Royal Oak, Royal Oak, MI, p. A365

SUSIE-LATTNER, Debra, M.D., Vice President Medical Management, Advocate Condell Medical Center, Libertyville, IL, p. A210

SUSSMAN, Andrew, M.D., Chief Operating Officer, Umass Memorial Medical Center, Worcester, MA, p. A347

SUSSMAN, Howard, M.D., Chief Medical Officer, St. Josep. Hospital, Bethpage, NY, p. A475

SUSTERICH, Tim, Chief Financial Officer and Chief Operating Officer, Memorial Healthcare, Owosso, MI, p. A363

SUTARIA, Saumya, M.D., Chief Operating Officer, Hca Houston Healthcare Tomball, Tomball, TX, p. A721

SUTER, Brian, Chief Financial Officer, Mayo Clinic Health System In Fairmont, Fairmont, MN, p. A376

SUTER, Lorenzo, Chief Executive Officer, Dupont Hospital, Fort Wayne, IN, p. A228

SUTER, Mia, Chief Administration Officer, Owensboro Health Regional Hospital, Owensboro, KY, p. A291

SUTHERLAND, Shea, Chief Financial Officer, Merit Health Madison, Canton, MS, p. A390

SUTIKA, John, President, Penn Highlands Dubois, Dubois, PA, p. A588

SUTTON, Andrew, Chief Human Resources Officer, Coatesville Veterans Affairs Medical Center, Coatesville, PA, p. A587

Chief, Human Resources Management Service, James A. Haley Veterans' Hospital-Tampa, Tampa, FL, p. A159

SUTTON, Angie, Chief Financial Officer, Genoa Medical Facilities, Genoa, NE, p. A432

SUTTON, Elaine, Chief Information Officer, Pershing Memorial Hospital, Brookfield, MO, p. A403

SUTTON, Fred, M.D., Chief Medical Officer, Harris Health System, Houston, TX, p. A685

SUTTON, Gilbert Jr, Regional Hospital Administrator/ Chief Executive Officer, Central State Hospital, Milledgeville, GA, p. A177

SUTTON, Janet, D.O., Medical Director, Mclaren Bay Special Care, Bay City, MI, p. A349

SUTTON, Jeffrey, Chief Information Officer, Lexington Veterans Affairs Medical Center, Lexington, KY, p. A286

SUTTON, Jesse, Senior Vice President and Chief Financial Officer, Texas Health Huguley Hospital Fort Worth South, Burleson, TX, p. A662

SUTTON, Julie, Director Performance Improvement, State Hospital South, Blackfoot, ID, p. A188

SUTTON, Michael, Chief Financial Officer, Chi Memorial, Chattanooga, TN, p. A635

SUTTON, Michele Kidd., FACHE, President and Chief Executive Officer, North Oaks Medical Center, Hammond, LA, p. A302

SUTTON, Rhonda, Director Human Resources, Richland Hospital, Richland Center, WI, p. A795

SUTTON, Richard O., FACHE, Chief Executive Officer, Southeast Alabama Medical Center, Dothan, AL, p. A18

SUTTON, Thomas, Associate Director, North Florida/South Georgia Veteran's Health System, Gainesville, FL, p. A138

SUVACAROV, Maria, Chief Clinical Officer, Kindred Hospital Chicago-Northlake, Northlake, IL, p. A214

SUVER, James A., FACHE, Chief Executive Officer, Ridgecrest Regional Hospital, Ridgecrest, CA, p. A88

SUZUKI, Daniel, M.D., Medical Director, Las Encinas Hospital, Pasadena, CA, p. A85

SVARC, Mackenzie, Finance Director, Friend Community Healthcare System, Friend, NE, p. A432

SVEC, David, M.D., Chief Medical Officer, Stanford Health Care - Valleycare, Pleasanton, CA, p. A85

SVENDSEN, Mark, M.D., Medical Director, Mayo Clinic Health System - Red Cedar In Menomonie, Menomonie, WI, p. A789

SWAGERTY, Jill, Director Human Resources, Union County General Hospital, Clayton, NM, p. A468

SWAIN, Art, Vice President Support Services, Joint Township District Memorial Hospital, Saint Marys, OH, p. A548

SWANDAL, Dianne, R.N., MSN, Vice President Patient Care, St. Josep. Hospital, Bangor, ME, p. A318

SWANGER, Cae, Chief Information Officer, Riverside Community Hospital, Riverside, CA, p. A88

SWANGER, Carol, Chief Nursing Officer, Kansas Rehabilitation Hospital, Topeka, KS, p. A277

SWANK, Georgia, Chief Nursing Officer, Ridge Behavioral Health System, Lexington, KY, p. A287

SWANSBORO, Pam, R.N., Chief Nursing Officer, Conemaugh Meyersdale Medical Center, Meyersdale, PA, p. A597

SWANSON, Nicole, Vice President of Nursing, Aurora Medical Center - Bay Area, Marinette, WI, p. A788

SWARTOUT, Paula, Human Resources Manager, Dickinson County Healthcare System, Iron Mountain, MI, p. A358

SWARTWOOD, Peggy, Assistant Vice President, Finance and Controller, Uhs Chenango Memorial Hospital, Norwich, NY, p. A493

SWARTWOOD, Philip. Director Information Systems, Ahn Grove City, Grove City, PA, p. A591

SWARTZ, Edward, Chief Financial Officer, Spring Grove Hospital Center, Baltimore, MD, p. A326

SWARTZ, Michael J., FACHE, Interim Director, Veterans Affairs Western New York Healthcare System-Batavia Division, Batavia, NY, p. A475

SWAYNE, Angela, M.D., Chief Medical Officer, Piedmont Fayette Hospital, Fayetteville, GA, p. A172

SWEARINGEN, Angela, Vice President Finance, St. Mary's Medical Center, Huntington, WV, p. A773

SWEAT, Holli, Associate Administrator and Chief Nursing Officer, Memorial Satilla Health, Waycross, GA, p. A183

SWEAT, Kendra, Director Human Resources, Power County Hospital District, American Falls, ID, p. A188

SWEENEY, Brian, President and Chief Operating Officer, Jefferson Stratford Hospital, Stratford, NJ, p. A463

SWEENEY, Janey, Chief Nursing Officer, Suncoast Behavioral Health Center, Bradenton, FL, p. A133

SWEENEY, Michael, Chief Informatics Officer, Temple University Hospital - Jeanes Campus, Philadelphia, PA, p. A602

Chief Information Officer, Fox Chase Cancer Center-American Oncologic Hospital, Philadelphia, PA, p. A600

SWEENEY, Shaun, R.N., Vice President Patient Care Services, Hackensack Meridian Health Carrier Clinic, Belle Mead, NJ, p. A452

SWEET, Jeremiah, Chief Financial Officer, Oneida Healthcare, Oneida, NY, p. A494

SWEET, Mary, Administrator, Kiowa County Memorial Hospital, Greensburg, KS, p. A265

SWEET, Renae, Chief Financial Officer, Surprise Valley Health Care District, Cedarville, CA, p. A59

SWEET, Terrance, Director Information Technology, Winnebago Mental Health Institute, Winnebago, WI, p. A800

SWEETAPPLE, Carolyn, Ph.D., R.N., CPA, Executive Director, South Oaks Hospital, Amityville, NY, p. A474

SWEHA, Amir, M.D., Vice President Medical Administration, Methodist Hospital Of Sacramento, Sacramento, CA, p. A89

SWEITZER, Gregory, Chief Medical Officer, Wright Patterson Medical Center, Wright, OH, p. A553

SWENSON, Daniel J., FACHE, Administrator, Centracare - Long Prairie, Long Prairie, MN, p. A379

SWENSON, Jennifer, President and Chief Executive Officer, Adventist Health Simi Valley, Simi Valley, CA, p. A98

SWENSON, Nina, Director Business Services, Newport Bay Hospital, Newport Beach, CA, p. A81

SWENSON, Paula, R.N., Vice President and Chief Nursing Officer, St. Catherine Hospital, East Chicago, IN, p. A227

SWENSON, Warren, Chief Financial Officer, United Medical Rehabilitation Hospital, Hammond, LA, p. A302

SWICK, Michael D., President and Chief Executive Officer, Lima Memorial Health System, Lima, OH, p. A543

SWIDERSKI, Tom, Chief Financial Officer, Orthopaedic Hospital Of Wisconsin, Glendale, WI, p. A784

SWIERS, Debbie, Director of Nursing, Haven Behavioral Hospital Of Phoenix, Phoenix, AZ, p. A35

SWIFT, Brian, Senior Administrator Plant Operations, Burke Rehabilitation Hospital, White Plains, NY, p. A502

SWIFT, Nick, Chief Financial Officer, Maury Regional Hospital, Columbia, TN, p. A636

SWIGER, Jared, Director Information Systems, Ashtabula County Medical Center, Ashtabula, OH, p. A528

SWINDELL, Terry, Chief Financial Officer, Camden General Hospital, Camden, TN, p. A634

SWINDLE, Patrick, Chief Executive Officer, Seton Medical Center Harker Heights, Harker Heights, TX, p. A683

SWINDLER, Diana, Chief Financial Officer, Tri Valley Health System, Cambridge, NE, p. A430

SWINGLE, Dale, Vice President Information Services, Guthrie Troy Community Hospital, Troy, PA, p. A609

SWINKO JR, PaulCorporate Vice President and Chief Financial Officer, Bassett Medical Center, Cooperstown, NY, p. A481

SWINT, Ken, Adminstrative Director Finance, Promedica Memorial Hospital, Fremont, OH, p. A540

Director Finance, Promedica Defiance Regional Hospital, Defiance, OH, p. A539

Vice President Finance and Chief Financial Officer, Promedica Fostoria Community Hospital, Fostoria, OH, p. A540

SWINT, Patricia, Director Information Management Systems, Promedica Defiance Regional Hospital, Defiance, OH, p. A539

Director Information Technology, St. Luke's Hospital, Maumee, OH, p. A545

SWISHER, Kay, Chief Nursing Officer, Prisma Health Laurens County Hospital, Clinton, SC, p. A617

SWISSHELM, Patricia, Acting Chief Fiscal Service, Lexington Veterans Affairs Medical Center, Lexington, KY, p. A286

SWOFFORD, William, M.D., Chief of Staff, Miller County Hospital, Colquitt, GA, p. A169

SY, Annette, Chief Nursing Officer, Keck Hospital Of Usc, Los Angeles, CA, p. A74

Chief Nursing Officer, Usc Norris Comprehensive Cancer Center, Los Angeles, CA, p. A76

SYED, Imran, Manager Technology Information Services, Spectrum Health Zeeland Community Hospital, Zeeland, MI, p. A370

SYED, Mamoon, Vice President Human Resources, Children's Hospital Of Orange County, Orange, CA, p. A83

Vice President Human Resources, Rady Children's Hospital - San Diego, San Diego, CA, p. A91

SYKES, Angel, Director Human Resources, Memorial Hospital And Manor, Bainbridge, GA, p. A166

SYKES, Christina, Director Human Resources, Labette Health, Parsons, KS, p. A274

SYKES, Lisa, Director Information Services, Atrium Health Union, Monroe, NC, p. A514

IS/Communications Director, Atrium Health Anson, Wadesboro, NC, p. A519

Manager, Information Services, Atrium Health Cabarrus, Concord, NC, p. A508

SYKES, Rebecca, Chief Information Officer, Mercy Health - Fairfield Hospital, Fairfield, OH, p. A540

Chief Information Officer, Mercy St. Anne Hospital, Toledo, OH, p. A550

Senior Vice President Resource Management, Chief Information Officer, Mercy Health - St. Charles Hospital, Oregon, OH, p. A547

SYLVIA-HUTCHINSON, Doreen, Vice President Operations and Chief Nurse Executive, Fairview Hospital, Great Barrington, MA, p. A339

SYNDER, Jennifer, Chief Executive Officer, Hill Crest Behavioral Health Services, Birmingham, AL, p. A15

SYNDERGAARD, Christy, Vice President Nursing, Cherokee Regional Medical Center, Cherokee, IA, p. A245

SYNNESTVEDT, Eric, Director Information Technology, Southside Regional Medical Center, Petersburg, VA, p. A749

SYPIEN, Troy, Director Information Technology and Systems, Medical City Dallas, Dallas, TX, p. A669

Director Information Technology and Systems, Tristar Skyline Medical Center, Nashville, TN, p. A647

SZABO, Sandor, M.D., Ph.D., M.P.H., Chief of Staff, Va Long Beach Healthcare System, Long Beach, CA, p. A73

SZAPOR, Ann, Vice President and Chief Nursing Officer, Memorial Hermann Greater Heights Hospital, Houston, TX, p. A687

SZCZEPANSKI, Bernadette, Senior Vice President, Human Resources, Northwestern Medicine Mchenry, Mchenry, IL, p. A212

SZCZUROWSKI, Richard, Director Human Resources, Norristown State Hospital, Norristown, PA, p. A598

SZEKELY, Lauraine, R.N., Senior Vice President, Patient Care, Northern Westchester Hospital, Mount Kisco, NY, p. A488

SZEWCZYK, Edwin, Chief Financial Officer, Wetzel County Hospital, New Martinsville, WV, p. A775

SZKLANY, Chelsea, Hospital Administrator, Southern Nevada Adult Mental Health Services, Las Vegas, NV, p. A444

SZOSTEK, Joshua, Chief Financial Officer, Curahealth Jacksonville, Jacksonville, FL, p. A141

SZUMEL, Richard C., M.D., Chief Executive Officer, Union Hospital, Elkton, MD, p. A329

SZURA, Kathleen, R.N., Chief Nursing Officer, Encompass Health Rehabilitation Hospital Of Bakersfield, Bakersfield, CA, p. A57

SZYMANIAK, Michael, Deputy Commander for Nursing, Bayne-Jones Army Community Hospital, Fort Polk, LA, p. A301

SZYSKA, Julie, Chief Executive Officer and Managing Director, Havenwyck Hospital, Auburn Hills, MI, p. A349

# T

TAAFFE, Janette, Vice President, Human Resource, St. Luke's Hospital, Chesterfield, MO, p. A404

TABAK, Jeremy, M.D., President Medical Staff, Baptist Health South Florida, South Miami Hospital, Miami, FL, p. A146

TABIBI, Wasae, M.D., President Medical Staff, Plaza Specialty Hospital, Houston, TX, p. A688

TABOR, J., Executive Vice President, Chief Financial Officer, Erlanger Medical Center, Chattanooga, TN, p. A635

TABOR, Jeffrey, Director Human Resources, Jackson General Hospital, Ripley, WV, p. A776

TABOR, Tammie, Chief Executive Officer, Vibra Rehabilitation Hospital Of Amarillo, Amarillo, TX, p. A652

TABORA, Knaya, Chief Operating Officer and Chief Nursing Officer, Colorado River Medical Center, Needles, CA, p. A81

TABUENCA, Arnold, M.D., Medical Director, Riverside University Health System-Medical Center, Moreno Valley, CA, p. A80

TACHIBANA, Charleen, R.N., Senior Vice President and Chief Nursing Officer, Virginia Mason Medical Center, Seattle, WA, p. A765

TACKETT, Andrea, Chief of Staff, French Hospital Medical Center, San Luis Obispo, CA, p. A95

TACKETT, Sharon, R.N., Chief Nursing Officer, Monroe Surgical Hospital, Monroe, LA, p. A309

TACKITT, Sue, Chief Nursing Officer, Connally Memorial Medical Center, Floresville, TX, p. A677

TADURAN, Virgilio, M.D., Chief Medical Officer, Satanta District Hospital And Long Term Care, Satanta, KS, p. A276

TADYCH, Michael C., FACHE, Director, Veterans Affairs Puget Sound Health Care System, Seattle, WA, p. A764

TAFFE, Patrick, Vice President Information Services, North Memorial Health Hospital, Robbinsdale, MN, p. A383

TAFFER, Hayley, Chief Nursing Officer, Martin General Hospital, Williamston, NC, p. A520

TAFOYA, Debbie, Vice President and Chief Information Officer, Huntington Hospital, Pasadena, CA, p. A85

TAFOYA, Tabatha, Director Human Resources, Newman Regional Health, Emporia, KS, p. A264

TAFT, Kenneth, Executive Vice President and Chief Operating Officer, Bronson Methodist Hospital, Kalamazoo, MI, p. A359

TAGGART, Travis, Director Information Technology, Rivervalley Behavioral Health Hospital, Owensboro, KY, p. A291

TAGGE, Gordon, M.D., President Medical Staff, Three Rivers Hospital, Brewster, WA, p. A756

TAHAN, Pamela S., Chief Executive Officer, Wellington Regional Medical Center, Wellington, FL, p. A161

TAHBO, Robin, Financial Management Officer, U. S. Public Health Service Indian Hospital, Parker, AZ, p. A34

TAHIR, Fahad, Chief Executive Officer, Saint Thomas West Hospital, Nashville, TN, p. A646

TAILLEFER, Marguerite, M.D., Acting President Medical Staff, Sarah D. Culbertson Memorial Hospital, Rushville, IL, p. A219

TAKACS, Susan, Market Chief Operating Officer, Physicians Regional - Pine Ridge, Naples, FL, p. A149

TAKES, Kay, R.N., President, Mercyone Dubuque Medical Center, Dubuque, IA, p. A249

R.N., President, Mercyone Dyersville Medical Center, Dyersville, IA, p. A249

TAKEUCHI, Susi, Chief Human Resources and Organization Development Officer, Ronald Reagan Ucla Medical Center, Los Angeles, CA, p. A75

TALBERT, Adrienne, Interim Administrator, Prisma Health North Greenville, Travelers Rest, SC, p. A625

TALBERT, Bradley S., FACHE, President and Chief Executive Officer, Memorial Hospital Jacksonville, Jacksonville, FL, p. A141

TALBOT, Jack, Director, Human Resources, West Chester Hospital, West Chester, OH, p. A552

TALBOT, Lisa, Director Human Resources, St. David's South Austin Medical Center, Austin, TX, p. A656

TALBOT, Tom, Chief Executive Officer, Community Mental Health Center, Lawrenceburg, IN, p. A235

TALBOTT, Ellen, MSN, R.N., Vice President Patient Care Services, Mclaren Bay Region, Bay City, MI, p. A349

TALBOTT, Sarah, Chief Nursing Officer, Sanford Chamberlain Medical Center, Chamberlain, SD, p. A627

TALLEY, Cyndi, Director Information Systems, Tristar Greenview Regional Hospital, Bowling Green, KY, p. A281

TALLEY, Linda, MS, R.N., Vice President and Chief Nursing Officer, Children's National Hospital, Washington, DC, p. A129

TALLEY, Rockey, M.D., Chief Medical Officer, Alliancehealth Midwest, Midwest City, OK, p. A562

TALLEY, Stephanie, Chief Human Resource Officer, The Hospitals Of Providence Sierra Campus, El Paso, TX, p. A676

Chief Human Resource Officer, The Hospitals Of Providence Transmountain Campus, El Paso, TX, p. A676

Director Human Resources, Baylor Scott & White Medical Center - Centennial, Frisco, TX, p. A680

Market Chief Human Resource Officer, The Hospitals Of Providence Memorial Campus, El Paso, TX, p. A676

TALLEY, Tracey, Chief Financial and Information Officer, Kalispell Regional Healthcare, Kalispell, MT, p. A425

TALLON, Joe, Vice President Finance, Salina Regional Health Center, Salina, KS, p. A275

TALLON, Richard, Chief Financial Officer, Jefferson County Hospital, Waurika, OK, p. A571

TALTY, Stephen, M.D., Medical Director, Van Matre Encompass Health Rehabilitation Hospital, Rockford, IL, p. A219

TAM, David A., M.D., FACHE, President, Beebe Healthcare, Lewes, DE, p. A127

TAMANAHA, Nona, Vice President Human Resources, The Queen's Medical Center, Honolulu, HI, p. A185

TAMAYO, Loree, Chief Executive Officer, Coon Memorial Hospital, Dalhart, TX, p. A667

TAMBON, Natalie, Director of Human Resources, Jenkins County Medical Center, Millen, GA, p. A177

Director of Human Resources, Optim Medical Center - Screven, Sylvania, GA, p. A181

TAMBURELLO, Leonardo, Chief Financial Officer, New York Community Hospital, Brooklyn, NY, p. A478

TAMMARO, Vincent, Chief Financial Officer, Yale-New Haven Hospital, New Haven, CT, p. A124

TAMMINEN, John, M.D., President Medical Staff, Carilion Giles Community Hospital, Pearisburg, VA, p. A748

TAN, Bradford, M.D., Chief Medical Officer, Midwestern Regional Medical Center, Zion, IL, p. A222

TANCREDO, Beth, Director Operations, South Florida Baptist Hospital, Plant City, FL, p. A154

TANDE, Brett, Chief Financial Officer, Santa Ynez Valley Cottage Hospital, Solvang, CA, p. A99

TANDON, Satwant, M.D., Director of Clinical Services, Oklahoma Forensic Center, Vinita, OK, p. A571

TANDY, Gary, Chief Financial Officer, Pershing Memorial Hospital, Brookfield, MO, p. A403

TANDY, William, Chief Information Officer, Upmc Hanover, Hanover, PA, p. A591

TANEBAUM, Cynthia, Director Information Services, Medstar Harbor Hospital, Baltimore, MD, p. A325

TANEJA, K. Singh, Chief Operating Officer, Saint Elizabeths Hospital, Washington, DC, p. A130

TANG, Francis, Chief Information Officer, Rancho Los Amigos National Rehabilitation Center, Downey, CA, p. A62

TANG, Shirley, R.N., Chief Nursing Officer, Monterey Park Hospital, Monterey Park, CA, p. A79

TANGEMAN, Todd, Chief Operating Officer and Chief Human Resource Officer, Newton Medical Center, Newton, KS, p. A272

Chief Operating Officer, Newton Medical Center, Newton, KS, p. A272

TANGO, Jonathan, Vice President, Operations, Monmouth Medical Center, Southern Campus, Lakewood, NJ, p. A457

TANGUAY, Denis, Chief Information Officer, Central Maine Medical Center, Lewiston, ME, p. A321

TANJUAKIO, Robert, Chief Information Resources Management, Edward Hines, Jr. Veterans Affairs Hospital, Hines, IL, p. A207

TANKEL, Nancy, R.N., Chief Nurse Executive, Kaiser Permanente Woodland Hills Medical Center, Woodland Hills, CA, p. A105

TANNENBAUM, Scott, M.D., Medical Director, Encompass Health Rehabilitation Hospital Of Sunrise, Sunrise, FL, p. A158

TANNER, Ashley, Director of Nursing, Wiregrass Medical Center, Geneva, AL, p. A19

TANNER, Doug, Chief Executive Officer, Grove Hill Memorial Hospital, Grove Hill, AL, p. A19

TANNER, James, M.D., Chief Medical Officer, Northwest Medical Center - Springdale, Springdale, AR, p. A53

TANNOS, Paul, Chief Financial Officer, The Physicians Centre Hospital, Bryan, TX, p. A661

TANTHOREY, Geoff, Director, Information Systems, Granville Health System, Oxford, NC, p. A516

TANZELLA, Richard, Chief Executive Officer, Piedmont Rockdale Hospital, Conyers, GA, p. A170

TAPLETT, Dean, Controller, Quincy Valley Medical Center, Quincy, WA, p. A762

TAPLIN, Tyrrell, Chief Executive Officer, Encompass Health Rehabilitation Hospital Of Arlington, Arlington, TX, p. A653

TAPP, Gina, Director Human Resources, Samaritan North Lincoln Hospital, Lincoln City, OR, p. A577

Director Human Resources, Samaritan Pacific Communities Hospital, Newport, OR, p. A578

TAPPER, Shane, Director Management Information Systems, Fort Madison Community Hospital, Fort Madison, IA, p. A250

TARAR, Ahmad, M.D., Medical Director, Heartland Behavioral Health Services, Nevada, MO, p. A412

TARASOVICH, James, Chief Financial Officer, Mayo Clinic Health System In Saint James, Saint James, MN, p. A384

TARBAY, Amy, Director Nursing Services, Naval Hospital Pensacola, Pensacola, FL, p. A153

TARBET, Joyce, M.D., Chief Medical Officer, Murray County Medical Center, Slayton, MN, p. A386

TARDIF, Kathleen, Director of Human Resources, Central Regional Hospital, Butner, NC, p. A506

TARNOFF, Michael, M.D., Interim Chief Executive Officer, Tufts Medical Center, Boston, MA, p. A336

TAROLA, Robert, Chief Financial Officer, Osf Healthcare Little Company Of Mary Medical Center, Evergreen Park, IL, p. A204

TARRANT, Jeffrey S., FACHE, Chief Executive Officer, Upson Regional Medical Center, Thomaston, GA, p. A181

TARRANT, Maureen, President and Chief Executive Officer, Presbyterian/St. Luke's Medical Center, Denver, CO, p. A111

TARULLI, Pamela, Senior Vice President Human Resources, Good Samaritan Regional Medical Center, Suffern, NY, p. A499

TARVER, Dennis, Director Information Technology, Elkview General Hospital, Hobart, OK, p. A560

TARVER, Jeanette, Director of Finance, Sonoma Valley Hospital, Sonoma, CA, p. A99

TARVER, Rebecca, Chief Nursing Officer, Bates County Memorial Hospital, Butler, MO, p. A403

TASSIN, Bruce J., President, Chi Saint Josep. Health, Lexington, KY, p. A286

TATE, Charlene, M.D., Chief Medical Staff and Clinical Services, Eleanor Slater Hospital, Cranston, RI, p. A613

TATE, Charles, Director Information Technology, Lallie Kemp Medical Center, Independence, LA, p. A303

TATE, James, M.D., Chief of Staff, Patients' Hospital Of Redding, Redding, CA, p. A87

TATE, Jean, Vice President Human Resources, Riverview Health, Crookston, MN, p. A374

TATE, Joel W., FACHE, Chief Executive Officer, Clay County Hospital, Ashland, AL, p. A14

TATE, Mary Lou, Chief Financial Officer, Morris Hospital & Healthcare Centers, Morris, IL, p. A213

TATE CURTI, Joseph, Chief Operating Officer, Elliot Hospital, Manchester, NH, p. A450

TATRO, Chad, Supervisor Information Systems, Northeast Regional Medical Center, Kirksville, MO, p. A410

TATRO ESQ, MaryChief Nursing Officer, Millinocket Regional Hospital, Millinocket, ME, p. A321

TAUL, Kelly, Business Manager, Meadowbrook Rehabilitation Hospital, Gardner, KS, p. A265

TAUNTON, David, M.D., Chief of Staff, Texas Health Harris Methodist Hospital Southlake, Southlake, TX, p. A716

TAUPIN, Michel, M.D., Chief Medical Officer, Abington-Lansdale Hospital Jefferson Health, Lansdale, PA, p. A594

TAUTZ, Linda, Chief Executive Officer, Dignity Health Rehabilitation Hospital, Henderson, NV, p. A442

TAVARES-SILVA, Naomi, Center Director, Pocasset Mental Health Center, Pocasset, MA, p. A343

TAVARY, James, Chief Executive Officer, Wickenburg Community Hospital, Wickenburg, AZ, p. A41

TAWNEY, Michael, D.O., Vice President Medical Affairs, Mclaren Port Huron, Port Huron, MI, p. A364

TAYLOR, Adam, Manager Information Technology, Northern Inyo Hospital, Bishop. CA, p. A58

TAYLOR, Adrienne, Director of Health Information Management, Northwest Mississipp. Medical Center, Clarksdale, MS, p. A391

TAYLOR, Al, Vice President and Administrator, Memorial Hospital Of Carbondale, Carbondale, IL, p. A196

TAYLOR, Alice, R.N., MSN, Chief Executive Officer, Broward Health North, Deerfield Beach, FL, p. A136

TAYLOR, Amy, Chief Financial Officer, Oklahoma Center For Orthopedic And Multi-Specialty Surgery, Oklahoma City, OK, p. A565

TAYLOR, Anthony, Manager Information Technology, Cherokee Indian Hospital, Cherokee, NC, p. A507

TAYLOR, Beth, Vice President, Human Resources, Newton-Wellesley Hospital, Newton Lower Falls, MA, p. A342

TAYLOR, Brenda, Director Information Systems, Texas Health Harris Methodist Hospital Cleburne, Cleburne, TX, p. A663

TAYLOR, Brett, Director Hospital Information Systems, Van Wert County Hospital, Van Wert, OH, p. A551

TAYLOR, Carol M., R.N., Regional Director Clinical Operations, Kaiser Permanente Capitol Hill Campus, Seattle, WA, p. A763

TAYLOR, Cecilia, Chief Financial Officer, Midwestern Regional Medical Center, Zion, IL, p. A222

TAYLOR, Cherie, Chief Executive Officer, Northern Rockies Medical Center, Cut Bank, MT, p. A423

TAYLOR, Cheryl, R.N., Director of Nursing, Henry Ford Kingswood Hospital, Ferndale, MI, p. A354

TAYLOR, Christina, Director Human Resources, The Brook Hospital - Kmi, Louisville, KY, p. A288

TAYLOR, Dana, Chief Operating Officer, Fairfield Memorial Hospital, Fairfield, IL, p. A205

TAYLOR, Deborah, Chief Information Officer, Chatham Hospital, Siler City, NC, p. A518

TAYLOR, Debra, Chief Nursing Officer, Paris Regional Medical Center, Paris, TX, p. A704

TAYLOR, Dwayne, Chief Executive Officer, Sycamore Shoals Hospital, Elizabethton, TN, p. A637

TAYLOR, Dylan, Chief Administrative Officer, Aspirus Ontonagon Hospital, Inc., Ontonagon, MI, p. A363

TAYLOR, Ernest, M.D., Vice President Medical Affairs, St. Mary's Medical Center, Huntington, WV, p. A773

TAYLOR, Eulon, Clinical Director, North Texas State Hospital, Wichita Falls Campus, Wichita Falls, TX, p. A725

TAYLOR, Faye, R.N., Director of Nursing, Stephens County Hospital, Toccoa, GA, p. A182

TAYLOR, Gregory, M.D., Vice President and Chief Operating Officer, High Point Medical Center, High Point, NC, p. A512

TAYLOR, Heather, Human Resources Manager, Tippah County Hospital, Ripley, MS, p. A399

TAYLOR, Heidi, President, Morton Hospital And Medical Center, Taunton, MA, p. A345

TAYLOR, Janey, Chief Information and Technology, Overton Brooks Veterans Affairs Medical Center, Shreveport, LA, p. A314

TAYLOR, Jay, M.D., Chief of Medical Staff, Pondera Medical Center, Conrad, MT, p. A422

TAYLOR, Jeff, Vice President Finance, St. Luke's Regional Medical Center, Boise, ID, p. A189

TAYLOR, Jeremy, Director Information Services, Saint Francis Hospital, Charleston, WV, p. A771

TAYLOR, Jim, Chief Business Office, North Florida/South Georgia Veteran's Health System, Gainesville, FL, p. A138

TAYLOR, Joel, Chief Executive Officer, Coastal Carolina Hospital, Hardeeville, SC, p. A621
Chief Information Officer, Carepoint Health Bayonne Medical Center, Bayonne, NJ, p. A452
Chief Information Officer, Carepoint Health Hoboken University Medical Center, Hoboken, NJ, p. A456

TAYLOR, Judd, Chief Financial Officer, Eastern Idaho Regional Medical Center, Idaho Falls, ID, p. A190
Chief Financial Officer, Ogden Regional Medical Center, Ogden, UT, p. A730

TAYLOR, Julia, Area Director Human Resources, Vibra Hospital of Charleston, Mt. Pleasant, SC, p. A622

TAYLOR, Julie, FACHE, Chief Executive Officer, Alaska Regional Hospital, Anchorage, AK, p. A27
Chief Executive Officer, West Tennessee Healthcare Rehabilitation Hospital Jackson, Jackson, TN, p. A640

TAYLOR, Kendra, MSN, R.N., President and Chief Executive Officer, Salem Township Hospital, Salem, IL, p. A219

TAYLOR, Konnie, Chief Financial Officer, Carl Albert Community Mental Health Center, Mcalester, OK, p. A561

TAYLOR, Kristie, Chief Financial Officer, Southern Tennessee Regional Health System-Lawrenceburg, Lawrenceburg, TN, p. A642

TAYLOR, Lora, Director Human Resources and Compliance Officer, Unitypoint Health-Keokuk, Keokuk, IA, p. A252

TAYLOR, Marc, IS Director, Mountain West Medical Center, Tooele, UT, p. A733

TAYLOR, Marcia, Chief Executive Officer, Select Specialty Hospital-Memphis, Memphis, TN, p. A645

TAYLOR, Melissa, R.N., MSN, Chief Nursing Officer, Lexington Medical Center, West Columbia, SC, p. A625

TAYLOR, Meredith, Controller, South Sunflower County Hospital, Indianola, MS, p. A394

TAYLOR, Merle, Vice President Operations, Upmc St. Margaret, Pittsburgh, PA, p. A604

TAYLOR, Michael, M.D., Chief Medical Officer, Cleveland Clinic Avon Hospital, Avon, OH, p. A528
Chief Information Officer, Bon Secours St. Francis Hospital, Charleston, SC, p. A616
Senior Vice President Human Resources, Sentara Leigh Hospital, Norfolk, VA, p. A748
Vice President Financial Services and Chief Financial Officer, St. Rose Hospital, Hayward, CA, p. A68
Vice President Human Resources, Sentara Princess Anne Hospital, Virginia Beach, VA, p. A753

TAYLOR, Mimi, Corporate Vice President Information Technology, Baptist Health South Florida, Baptist Hospital Of Miami, Miami, FL, p. A146
Corporate Vice President Information Technology, Baptist Health South Florida, Homestead Hospital, Homestead, FL, p. A140
Vice President Information Technology, Baptist Health South Florida, Mariners Hospital, Tavernier, FL, p. A160
Vice President Information Technology, Baptist Health South Florida, South Miami Hospital, Miami, FL, p. A146

TAYLOR, Nick, Chief Executive Officer, Baylor Scott & White Medical Center-Uptown, Dallas, TX, p. A667

TAYLOR, Paul, Administrator, Ozarks Community Hospital, Gravette, AR, p. A46

TAYLOR, Ralph, Chief Nursing Officer, Sebastian River Medical Center, Sebastian, FL, p. A157

TAYLOR, Renae, Chief Nursing Officer, Southeastern Health, Lumberton, NC, p. A514

TAYLOR, Richard, Chief Financial Officer, Western Mental Health Institute, Bolivar, TN, p. A634

TAYLOR, Robbie, Director Human Resources, North Sunflower Medical Center, Ruleville, MS, p. A400

TAYLOR, Robert, Director Information Services, St. Christopher's Hospital For Children, Philadelphia, PA, p. A602

TAYLOR, Ross, M.D., Clinical Director, Austin State Hospital, Austin, TX, p. A655

TAYLOR, Sarah, Chief Human Resources, National Jewish Health, Denver, CO, p. A110

TAYLOR, Scotty, Information Technology Director, East Mississipp. State Hospital, Meridian, MS, p. A397

TAYLOR, Sharon, Human Resources Director, Allegiance Specialty Hospital Of Greenville, Greenville, MS, p. A392

TAYLOR, Sheri, Director Human Resources, Union General Hospital, Farmerville, LA, p. A301

TAYLOR, Stacy, Chief Financial Officer, Nemaha County Hospital, Auburn, NE, p. A429

TAYLOR, Steve, Chief Information Officer, Anderson Regional Health System South, Meridian, MS, p. A397

TAYLOR, Steven, Regional Chief Executive Officer, Blackwell Regional Hospital, Blackwell, OK, p. A556
Regional Chief Executive Officer, Stillwater Medical Perry, Perry, OK, p. A567

TAYLOR, Steven L., Chief Executive Officer, Harrison County Hospital, Corydon, IN, p. A226

TAYLOR, Sue, Vice President Nursing, Vidant Duplin Hospital, Kenansville, NC, p. A513

TAYLOR, Susan L., JD, Chief Executive Officer, College Hospital Costa Mesa, Costa Mesa, CA, p. A61

TAYLOR, Todd, Chief Executive Officer, Stafford County Hospital, Stafford, KS, p. A277

TAYLOR, Tyler, Chief Executive Officer, Wayne Medical Center, Waynesboro, TN, p. A650

TAYLOR, Tyrone, Chief Financial Officer, Veterans Affairs New Jersey Health Care System, East Orange, NJ, p. A454

TAYLOR, Venus, Director Human Resources, Bhc Alhambra Hospital, Rosemead, CA, p. A88

TAYLOR, Wes, Chief Executive Officer, Ashley Regional Medical Center, Vernal, UT, p. A734

TEAFF, Sarah, Chief Operating Officer, St. Luke Community Healthcare, Ronan, MT, p. A427

TEAGUE, Dean, FACHE, Chief Executive Officer, Calverthealth Medical Center, Prince Frederick, MD, p. A331

TEAGUE, Lara, R.N., Chief Nursing Officer, Lillian M. Hudspeth Memorial Hospital, Sonora, TX, p. A716

TEAHL, Bradley, Director Human Resources, Encompass Health Rehabilitation Hospital Of York, York, PA, p. A612

TEAL, Amy, Chief Executive Officer, Lancaster Rehabilitation Hospital, Lancaster, PA, p. A594

TEAL, Barbara, R.N., Associate Director Patient Care Services and Nurse Executive, Sioux Falls Veterans Affairs Health Care System, Sioux Falls, SD, p. A632

TEAL, Cydney, M.D., Vice President Medical Affairs, Union Hospital, Elkton, MD, p. A329

TEATER, Phyllis, Chief Information Officer, Ohio State University Wexner Medical Center, Columbus, OH, p. A536

TEATSORTH, Neil, Vice President Human Resources, Norwegian American Hospital, Chicago, IL, p. A200

TEBBE, James, M.D., Vice President Medical Affairs, Ochsner Medical Center - Kenner, Kenner, LA, p. A304

TEDDER, Cookie, Human Resources Manager, Texas Health Center For Diagnostic & Surgery, Plano, TX, p. A707

TEDESCO, Art, Interim Chief Financial Officer, Gaylord Specialty Healthcare, Wallingford, CT, p. A126

TEEL, David, Financial Officer, Terrell State Hospital, Terrell, TX, p. A719

TEETER, Stephen, Business Manager, Hawaii State Hospital, Kaneohe, HI, p. A186

TEFFETELLER, Scott L., SVP, Regional Operating Officer, Chicago Metro & President and CEO, AMITA Health Resurrection Medica, Amita Health Resurrection Medical Center, Chicago, IL, p. A197

TEICHMEIER, Laura, Director Human Resources, Memorial Community Health, Aurora, NE, p. A429

TEIGEN, Seth R., Chief Executive Officer, Mission Hospital Mission Viejo, Mission Viejo, CA, p. A78
President, Ascension Southeast Wisconsin Hospital - Franklin Campus, Franklin, WI, p. A784
President, Ascension Southeast Wisconsin Hospital - St. Francis Campus, Milwaukee, WI, p. A790

TEITELBAUM, Karen, Chief Executive Officer, Schwab Rehabilitation Hospital, Chicago, IL, p. A200

TEJADA, Vanessa, Director Human Resources, Encompass Health Rehabilitation Hospital Of San Antonio, San Antonio, TX, p. A711

TEJEDA, Nicholas R., FACHE, Market Chief Executive Officer, The Hospitals Of Providence Memorial Campus, El Paso, TX, p. A676

TELHIARD, Nicole, MSN, Chief Nursing Officer, Our Lady Of The Lake Regional Medical Center, Baton Rouge, LA, p. A297

TELITZ, Rita, Chief Administrative Officer, Marshfield Medical Center - Ladysmith, Ladysmith, WI, p. A787

TELL, Marjorie, Vice President Information Technology, Aspirus Riverview Hospital And Clinics, Inc., Wisconsin Rapids, WI, p. A800

TELLES, Ron, Chief Financial Officer, Whidbeyhealth, Coupeville, WA, p. A757
Interim Chief Executive Officer, Whidbeyhealth, Coupeville, WA, p. A757

TELLOR, Tammy, Acting Director Human Resources, Choate Mental Health Center, Anna, IL, p. A194

TELTHORSTER, M.ED, Marcia, Vice President Human Resources, Penn Medicine Princeton Medical Center, Plainsboro, NJ, p. A461

TEMPLE, Amber, Director Human Resources, Morrison Community Hospital, Morrison, IL, p. A213

TEMPLE, Regina, President and Chief Executive Officer, Regional Medical Center Bayonet Point, Hudson, FL, p. A140

TEMPLE, Richard, Chief Information Officer, Deborah Heart And Lung Center, Browns Mills, NJ, p. A453

TEMPLE, Timothy, Executive Director Information Technology, Ozarks Medical Center, West Plains, MO, p. A420

TEMPLETON, Gary, M.D., Medical Director, Regency Hospital Of Northwest Arkansas - Springdale, Springdale, AR, p. A53

TEMPLETON, Sheryl, Chief Financial Officer, Scotland County Hospital, Memphis, MO, p. A412

TEMPLETON, William, M.D., IIIMedical Director, Clark Memorial Health, Jeffersonville, IN, p. A233

TEMPLIN, Nancy, Vice President Finance and Chief Financial Officer, Johns Hopkins All Children's Hospital, Saint Petersburg, FL, p. A156

TENEWITZ, Edward, M.D., Chief of Staff, Healthmark Regional Medical Center, Defuniak Springs, FL, p. A136

TENHENGEL-DEVILLE, Michelle, Chief Executive Officer, Regency Hospital Of South Atlanta, East Point, GA, p. A172

TENHOUSE, Steven D., FACHE, Chief Executive Officer, Kirby Medical Center, Monticello, IL, p. A212

TENNEY, Ralph, Chief Information Officer, Ascension Crittenton Hospital Medical Center, Rochester, MI, p. A365
Chief Information Officer, Ascension Macomb-Oakland Hospital, Warren, MI, p. A368
Chief Information Officer, Ascension St. John Hospital, Detroit, MI, p. A352

TENNISON, Gary, M.D., Chief of Staff, Crawford Memorial Hospital, Robinson, IL, p. A218

TENNYSON, Ruby, Director Administration, Naval Hospital Jacksonville, Jacksonville, FL, p. A141

TENREIRO, Edgardo J., FACHE, Chief Executive Officer, Baton Rouge General Medical Center, Baton Rouge, LA, p. A296
FACHE, President and Chief Executive Officer, The General, Baton Rouge, LA, p. A297

TEPEDINO, Miguel, M.D., Chief Medicine, Lake City Medical Center, Lake City, FL, p. A143

TEPPER, Gil, M.D., Chief Executive Officer, Miracle Mile Medical Center, Los Angeles, CA, p. A75
M.D., Chief of Staff, Miracle Mile Medical Center, Los Angeles, CA, p. A75

TER HORST, Thomas, Vice President Human Resources, Aurora St. Luke's Medical Center, Milwaukee, WI, p. A790

TERAULT, Chelsey, Manager Human Resources, Pembina County Memorial Hospital And Wedgewood Manor, Cavalier, ND, p. A522

TERBUSH, Jennifer, Vice President, Patient Services, Hills & Dales General Hospital, Cass City, MI, p. A350

TERI, Anthony, Director Information Technology, Hackensack Meridian Health Pascack Valley Medical Center, Westwood, NJ, p. A465

TERPSTRA, John, M.D., Chief Medical Officer, Mercer Health, Coldwater, OH, p. A535

TERPSTRA, Kelli, R.N., Senior Director, Our Children's House, Dallas, TX, p. A670

TERRELL, Jay, Manager Management Information Systems, Riverview Regional Medical Center, Gadsden, AL, p. A19

TERRESON, Gregg, Chief Financial Officer, Cascade Behavioral Hospital, Tukwila, WA, p. A768

TERRINONI, Gary G., President and Chief Executive Officer, Brooklyn Hospital Center, Brooklyn, NY, p. A477

TERRY, Darrell K. Sr, M.P.H., FACHE, President and Chief Executive Officer, Newark Beth Israel Medical Center, Newark, NJ, p. A459

TERRY, Randi, Site Director Management Information Systems, Munson Healthcare Cadillac Hospital, Cadillac, MI, p. A350

TERRY, Richard, Vice President & Chief Information Officer, Sparrow Carson Hospital, Carson City, MI, p. A350

TERRY, Robert, Interim Chief Executive Officer, Ut Health Quitman, Quitman, TX, p. A708

TERRY, Teresa, Director Human Resource, Payroll, Fisher County Hospital District, Rotan, TX, p. A709

TERRY-WILLIAMS, Teresa, R.N., Chief Nursing Officer, Pennsylvania Psychiatric Institute, Harrisburg, PA, p. A591

TERTEL, Jenifer, Director Human Resources, Medical City Dallas, Dallas, TX, p. A669

TERWILLIGER, George, Chief Medical Officer, Grace Cottage Hospital, Townshend, VT, p. A737

TERWILLIGER, James, Executive Vice President and Chief Operating Officer, Dana-Farber Cancer Institute, Boston, MA, p. A335

TERWILLIGER, Michael, Chief Financial Officer, Friends Hospital, Philadelphia, PA, p. A600

TESKE, Mark, Chief Financial Officer, Hill Crest Behavioral Health Services, Birmingham, AL, p. A15

TESSARZIK, Connie, Business Manager, Albert J. Solnit Psychiatric Center - South Campus, Middletown, CT, p. A123

TESTA, Nick, M.D., Chief Medical Officer, Providence Saint Josep. Medical Center, Burbank, CA, p. A59

TESTER, Shawn, Chief Executive Officer, Northeastern Vermont Regional Hospital, Saint Johnsbury, VT, p. A736

TEUBNER, Sandra, Chief Financial Officer, St. Aloisius Medical Center, Harvey, ND, p. A524

TEUFEL, George, Vice President Finance, Advocate Good Shepherd Hospital, Barrington, IL, p. A195

TEUSCHER, Jill, Chief Nursing Officer, Heber Valley Hospital, Heber City, UT, p. A728

TEVES, Alicia, Coordinator Human Resources, Molokai General Hospital, Kaunakakai, HI, p. A186

TEW, Brian, Chief Executive Officer, Garnet Health Medical Center - Catskills, Middletown, NY, p. A488

TEWARI, Arun, M.D., Chief Medical Officer, Henry Community Health, New Castle, IN, p. A238

THACKER, Adam, Chief Operating Officer, Good Samaritan Hospital, Vincennes, IN, p. A242

THACKER, Roland, Chief Financial Officer, Piedmont Columbus Regional Northside, Columbus, GA, p. A169

THAKOR, Pratapji, M.D., Chief of Staff, South Mississipp. County Regional Medical Center, Osceola, AR, p. A51

THAKUR, Abhash, M.D., Chief of Staff, Greenwood Leflore Hospital, Greenwood, MS, p. A392

THALER, Klaus, FACS, M.D., Chief Medical Officer, Houston Methodist Baytown Hospital, Baytown, TX, p. A657

THAMA, Todd, Chief Operating Officer, Fairfax Behavioral Health, Kirkland, WA, p. A759

THAMES, Stephen, Chief Financial Officer, Allen Parish Community Healthcare, Kinder, LA, p. A305

THARP, Beth S., R.N., President and Chief Executive Officer, Community Hospital Anderson, Anderson, IN, p. A223

THARP, Stephen, Medical Director, Indiana University Health Frankfort, Frankfort, IN, p. A229

Regional Chief Medical Officer, Ascension St. Vincent Clay Hospital, Brazil, IN, p. A224

THAUNG, Htin, M.D., Chief Medical Officer, Ward Memorial Hospital, Monahans, TX, p. A702

THAYER, Charles, M.D., Chief Medical Officer, Morton Hospital And Medical Center, Taunton, MA, p. A345

THAYER, Gilbert, M.D., Chief Medical Staff, Hardin Medical Center, Savannah, TN, p. A649

THAYER, Kendra, MSN, R.N., Chief Nursing Officer, Vice President Clinical Services, Garrett Regional Medical Center, Oakland, MD, p. A331

THEILER, Teresa, Chief Administrative Officer, Ascension St. Michael's Hospital, Stevens Point, WI, p. A796

THEIRING, James, Chief Executive Officer, Mission Community Hospital, Panorama City, CA, p. A84

THEISEN, Janet, Chief Information Officer, Sanford Tracy Medical Center, Tracy, MN, p. A386

Chief Information Officer, Sanford Westbrook Medical Center, Westbrook, MN, p. A387

THELEN, Deann, Vice President and Administrator, Jackson-Madison County General Hospital, Jackson, TN, p. A639

THELEN, Raymond, Vice President and Chief Financial Officer, Masonicare Health Center, Wallingford, CT, p. A126

THEOBALD, Terry, Chief Information Officer, Ventura County Medical Center, Ventura, CA, p. A103

THEODOROU, Andreas, Chief Medical Officer, Banner - University Medical Center Tucson, Tucson, AZ, p. A39

THEOHARES, Nick, Executive Director, Operations, Ascension St. Vincent Anderson, Anderson, IN, p. A223

THERADY, Agnes, MSN, FACHE, Vice President and Chief Nursing Officer, Franciscan Health Carmel, Carmel, IN, p. A225

MSN, FACHE, Vice President and Chief Nursing Officer, Franciscan Health Indianapolis, Indianapolis, IN, p. A232

MSN, FACHE, Vice President and Chief Nursing Officer, Franciscan Health Mooresville, Mooresville, IN, p. A237

THERIAC, Gary, Director Information Technology, Lawrence County Memorial Hospital, Lawrenceville, IL, p. A210

THERMITUS, Manoucheka, Chief Operating Officer, Saint Francis Hospital, Memphis, TN, p. A645

THERRIEN, Charles D., President, Northern Light Mercy Hospital, Portland, ME, p. A322

THERRIEN, Tinna, R.N., Chief Information Officer and Senior Director Ancillary Services, Gothenburg Health, Gothenburg, NE, p. A432

THETFORD, Carol, Chief Nursing Officer, Baptist Memorial Hospital For Women, Memphis, TN, p. A644

THEUS, Will, M.D., Chief of Staff, Adventhealth Gordon, Calhoun, GA, p. A168

THIBERT, Kimberly, R.N., MSN, Vice President Patient Care Services and Chief Nursing Officer, Samaritan Medical Center, Watertown, NY, p. A502

THIBODEAU, Helene, R.N., MSN, Vice President Patient Care Services, Northeast Rehabilitation Hospital, Salem, NH, p. A451

THIBODEAU, Jan, Director Human Resources, Encompass Health Rehabilitation Hospital Of Princeton, Princeton, WV, p. A776

THIBODEAUX, Anita, Chief Nursing Officer, Beauregard Health System, De Ridder, LA, p. A300

THIBODEAUX, Annette, Director Human Resources, Savoy Medical Center, Mamou, LA, p. A307

THIBODEAUX, Douglas, M.D., Chief Medical Officer, Oakbend Medical Center, Richmond, TX, p. A708

THIEL, David, M.D., Medical Director, Mayo Clinic Hospital In Florida, Jacksonville, FL, p. A141

THIEL, Stefanie, Senior Human Resources Business Partner, Saint Alphonsus Medical Center - Nampa, Nampa, ID, p. A192

Senior Human Resources Business Partner, Saint Alphonsus Medical Center - Ontario, Ontario, OR, p. A578

THIELEMIER, Kevin, Director Human Resources, Arkansas Methodist Medical Center, Paragould, AR, p. A51

THIELEN, Kent, M.D., Vice President Operations, Mayo Clinic Hospital In Florida, Jacksonville, FL, p. A141

THIELEN, Kurt, Associate Director, Minneapolis Veterans Affairs Health Care System, Minneapolis, MN, p. A381

THIELS, Dustin, Chief Executive Officer, Options Behavioral Health System, Indianapolis, IN, p. A232

THIEME, Ron, Ph.D., Chief Knowledge and Information Officer, Community Hospital North, Indianapolis, IN, p. A231

THIES, Dana, Director of Nursing, Meadows Psychiatric Center, Centre Hall, PA, p. A586

THILGES, Michael, Chief Financial Officer, Clarke County Hospital, Osceola, IA, p. A256

THILL, Jennifer, Chief of Staff, Mid-Valley Hospital, Omak, WA, p. A761

THIRUMALAREDDY, Joseph, M.D., Chief of Staff, South Central Health, Wishek, ND, p. A526

THOELE, Theresa, Director Human Resources, Coffey County Hospital, Burlington, KS, p. A262

THOENDEL, Victor, M.D., Chief Medical Officer, Butler County Health Care Center, David City, NE, p. A431

THOENY, Ben, Director Human Resources, Frances Mahon Deaconess Hospital, Glasgow, MT, p. A424

THOMAN, Dawn, Vice President Human Resources, Cloud County Health Center, Concordia, KS, p. A263

THOMAN, Michele, Chief Nursing Officer, Nch Baker Hospital, Naples, FL, p. A148

Chief Operating Officer, Palmetto General Hospital, Hialeah, FL, p. A139

THOMAS, Abbie, Chief Financial Officer, Nemaha Valley Community Hospital, Seneca, KS, p. A276

THOMAS, Andrea, Chief Operating Officer, St. Cloud Regional Medical Center, Saint Cloud, FL, p. A156

THOMAS, Andrew, M.D., Chief Medical Officer, Ohio State University Wexner Medical Center, Columbus, OH, p. A536

THOMAS, Anthony, Chief Executive Officer, Rooks County Health Center, Plainville, KS, p. A274

THOMAS, Brian E., Administrator, Alton Mental Health Center, Alton, IL, p. A194

THOMAS, Brian N., President and Chief Executive Officer, Jefferson Regional Medical Center, Pine Bluff, AR, p. A52

THOMAS, Brook, Chief Financial Officer, West Boca Medical Center, Boca Raton, FL, p. A132

THOMAS, Calvin Chief Operating Officer, St. Lucie Medical Center, Port St Lucie, FL, p. A155

THOMAS, Chris, FACHE, President and Chief Executive Officer, Community Hospital, Grand Junction, CO, p. A113

THOMAS, Christina, Chief Executive Officer, Caribou Memorial Hospital And Living Center, Soda Springs, ID, p. A193

THOMAS, Clay, Chief Operating Officer, Covenant Children's Hospital, Lubbock, TX, p. A697

THOMAS, Cristina, Chief Information Systems, Pella Regional Health Center, Pella, IA, p. A256

THOMAS, Curt, Administrator, Ness County Hospital District No 2, Ness City, KS, p. A272

THOMAS, David, President Medical Staff, Riddle Hospital, Media, PA, p. A597

THOMAS, Deana, Vice President Finance and Chief Financial Officer, North Arkansas Regional Medical Center, Harrison, AR, p. A46

THOMAS, Debora, Chief Financial Officer, Adventhealth Daytona Beach, Daytona Beach, FL, p. A136

THOMAS, Debra, Vice President of Patient Care Services and Chief Nursing Officer, Penn Highlands Brookville, Brookville, PA, p. A585

THOMAS, Denise, Chief Financial Officer, Spring View Hospital, Lebanon, KY, p. A286

THOMAS, Dennis, Chief Executive Officer, Hardeman County Memorial Hospital, Quanah, TX, p. A708

THOMAS, Frank D., Chief Executive Officer, Citizens Baptist Medical Center, Talladega, AL, p. A24

THOMAS, Gene, Vice President, Information Systems, Chief Information Officer, Memorial Hospital At Gulfport, Gulfport, MS, p. A393

THOMAS, George, M.D., Chief of Staff, Palo Pinto General Hospital, Mineral Wells, TX, p. A701

THOMAS, Gina, Chief Nursing Officer and Director of Patient Care Services, Carle Richland Memorial Hospital, Olney, IL, p. A215

THOMAS, Jayne, Chief Nursing Officer, Integris Deaconess, Oklahoma City, OK, p. A564

Chief Nursing Officer, Southwestern Medical Center, Lawton, OK, p. A561

THOMAS, Jeff, Chief Financial Officer, Heartland Regional Medical Center, Marion, IL, p. A211

THOMAS, Jennifer, Chief Operating Officer and Director of Public Relations, Lake Butler Hospital, Lake Butler, FL, p. A142

THOMAS, Jill, Director of Nursing, Western State Hospital, Hopkinsville, KY, p. A285

THOMAS, John, Chief Operating Officer, San Mateo Medical Center, San Mateo, CA, p. A96

THOMAS, Keith, M.D., Chief of Staff, Blue Mountain Hospital District, John Day, OR, p. A576

THOMAS, Kirk E., Chief Administrative Officer, Geisinger-Lewistown Hospital, Lewistown, PA, p. A595

THOMAS, Maggie, Vice President Human Resources and Practice Management, South County Hospital, Wakefield, RI, p. A614

THOMAS, Michael, Associate Administrator, Wayne County Hospital, Corydon, IA, p. A246

Chief Executive Officer, Encompass Health Rehabilitation Hospital Of Altamonte Springs, Altamonte Springs, FL, p. A131

President and Chief Administrative Officer, John Muir Medical Center, Concord, Concord, CA, p. A61

THOMAS, Missy, Chief Nursing Officer, Medical Center Barbour, Eufaula, AL, p. A18

THOMAS, Nicky, Director Human Resources, Baptist Memorial Hospital-Union City, Union City, TN, p. A650

THOMAS, Patricia, Chief Nursing Officer, Sentara Halifax Regional Hospital, South Boston, VA, p. A751

THOMAS, Paula, Vice President Patient Services, Upmc Bedford, Everett, PA, p. A590

THOMAS, Robert, M.D., Chief of Staff, Middlesboro Arh Hospital, Middlesboro, KY, p. A290

THOMAS, Ron, M.D., Chief Medical Officer, Adventhealth Palm Coast, Palm Coast, FL, p. A152

THOMAS, Russell, M.D., Chief of Staff, Rice Medical Center, Eagle Lake, TX, p. A673

THOMAS, Ruth, Chief Operating Officer, Mercy Catholic Medical Center - Mercy Fitzgerald Campus, Darby, PA, p. A588

THOMAS, Sarah, Director of Human Resources, Encompass Health Rehabilitation Hospital Of Littleton, Littleton, CO, p. A115

THOMAS, Scott, Administrative Director Human Resources and Communications, Granville Health System, Oxford, NC, p. A516

THOMAS, Shamieka, Administrator, Oceans Behavioral Hospital Of Pasadena, Pasadena, TX, p. A705

THOMAS, Shawn, Director Human Resources, Banner Payson Medical Center, Payson, AZ, p. A34

THOMAS, Spencer, Chief Executive Officer, Central Carolina Hospital, Sanford, NC, p. A518

THOMAS, Sue, Manager Human Resources, Beckley Arh Hospital, Beckley, WV, p. A770

THOMAS, Sylvia, Chief Nursing Officer, Jack Hughston Memorial Hospital, Phenix City, AL, p. A23

THOMAS, Tenny, M.D., Chief Medical Officer, Beth Israel Deaconess Hospital Plymouth, Plymouth, MA, p. A343

THOMAS, Twilla, Chief Nursing Officer, Pamp. Regional Medical Center, Pampa, TX, p. A704

THOMAS, William, M.D., JrMedical Director Clinical and Internal Affairs, Molokai General Hospital, Kaunakakai, HI, p. A186

THOMAS, Wilson A., Chief Executive Officer, Southern Virginia Regional Medical Center, Emporia, VA, p. A741

THOMAS JR, PhillipDirector Human Resources, Jackson Parish Hospital, Jonesboro, LA, p. A304

THOMAS-BOYD, Sharon, Chief Operating Officer, Oaklawn Hospital, Marshall, MI, p. A361

THOMAS-FOLDS, Lana, System Director Human Resources, Jack Hughston Memorial Hospital, Phenix City, AL, p. A23

THOMAS-WILLIAMS, Jovita, Senior Vice President of Human Resources, Massachusetts General Hospital, Boston, MA, p. A336

THOMASON, Corey, Controller, Encompass Health Rehabilitation Hospital, A Partner Of Washington Regional, Fayetteville, AR, p. A45

THOMMAN, Connie, Director of Nursing, Covenant Hospital-Levelland, Levelland, TX, p. A695

THOMPSON, Alan, M.D., President Medical Staff, Warm Springs Medical Center, Warm Springs, GA, p. A183

THOMPSON, Amy, M.D., Chief Executive Officer, Covenant Children's Hospital, Lubbock, TX, p. A697

THOMPSON, Angela, Director of Human Resources, Merit Health Biloxi, Biloxi, MS, p. A389

THOMPSON, Becki, President, Chi Oakes Hospital, Oakes, ND, p. A525

THOMPSON, Belinda, Coordinator Human Resources, Encompass Health Rehabilitation Hospital Of Salisbury, Salisbury, MD, p. A332

THOMPSON, Bobby, Director Information Technology, Stephens Memorial Hospital, Breckenridge, TX, p. A660

THOMPSON, Brian, R.N., Chief Nursing Officer, West Calcasieu Cameron Hospital, Sulphur, LA, p. A315

THOMPSON, Chad, Chief Financial Officer, Lallie Kemp Medical Center, Independence, LA, p. A303

THOMPSON, Charles, M.D., Chief Medical Officer, Nacogdoches Medical Center, Nacogdoches, TX, p. A702

THOMPSON, Charlotte, Chief Financial Officer, Reeves Memorial Medical Center, Bernice, LA, p. A298

THOMPSON, Cheryl, Chief Nursing Officer, Garden Park Medical Center, Gulfport, MS, p. A393

Facility Director Human Resources, Connecticut Valley Hospital, Middletown, CT, p. A123

THOMPSON, Christopher, Human Resources Manager, Middlesboro Arh Hospital, Middlesboro, KY, p. A290

THOMPSON, Cindy, Chief Financial Officer, Northwest Surgical Hospital, Oklahoma City, OK, p. A565

THOMPSON, Craig, Chief Executive Officer, Golden Valley Memorial Healthcare, Clinton, MO, p. A405

THOMPSON, Craig B., M.D., President and Chief Executive Officer, Memorial Sloan-Kettering Cancer Center, New York, NY, p. A490

THOMPSON, Cynthia, Chief Financial Officer, Houlton Regional Hospital, Houlton, ME, p. A321

THOMPSON, Dale, Chief Financial Officer, Mclaren Greater Lansing, Lansing, MI, p. A360

THOMPSON, David, M.D., Chief of Staff, Richardson Medical Center, Rayville, LA, p. A313

THOMPSON, David M., Chief Executive Officer, Sutter Tracy Community Hospital, Tracy, CA, p. A101

THOMPSON, Debbie, Chief Financial Officer, Sweetwater Hospital, Sweetwater, TN, p. A650

THOMPSON, Greg, Chief Medical Officer, Gundersen Lutheran Medical Center, La Crosse, WI, p. A787

Corporate Director, Human Resources, Orlando Regional Medical Center, Orlando, FL, p. A151

THOMPSON, Ivan, Vice President, Chief Human Resource Officer, University Of Texas Southwestern Medical Center, Dallas, TX, p. A671

THOMPSON, James H., Ph.D., FACHE, Owner and Chief Executive Officer, Healthmark Regional Medical Center, Defuniak Springs, FL, p. A136

THOMPSON, John, M.D., Chief of Staff, Eastern Louisiana Mental Health System, Jackson, LA, p. A303

THOMPSON, Julie, Chief Adminstrative Officer and Chief Nursing Officer, Bluffton Regional Medical Center, Bluffton, IN, p. A224

Chief Operating Officer and Chief Nursing Officer, Bluffton Regional Medical Center, Bluffton, IN, p. A224

Manager Personnel and Payroll, Mayers Memorial Hospital District, Fall River Mills, CA, p. A64

THOMPSON, Lennis Vice President and Chief Financial Officer, Hardin Memorial Health, Elizabethtown, KY, p. A282

THOMPSON, Les, Chief Human Resources Officer, Promedica Toledo Hospital, Toledo, OH, p. A550

THOMPSON, Linda, Chief Operating Officer, Fairfax Community Hospital, Fairfax, OK, p. A559

Senior Vice President, Human Resources and Service Excellence, New England Baptist Hospital, Boston, MA, p. A336

THOMPSON, Lisa, MSN, R.N., Director of Nursing, Hiawatha Community Hospital, Hiawatha, KS, p. A266

THOMPSON, Lori, Manager Human Resources, Orthonebraska Hospital, Omaha, NE, p. A437

THOMPSON, Mark, Market Chief Financial Officer Northern Region and Chief Financial Officer, Mercy Health - St. Charles Hospital, Oregon, OH, p. A547

System Chief Financial Officer, Thedacare Regional Medical Center-Neenah, Neenah, WI, p. A792

Vice President Financial Services, Monument Health Rapid City Hospital, Rapid City, SD, p. A630

THOMPSON, Nate, Chief Executive Officer, Story County Medical Center, Nevada, IA, p. A254

THOMPSON, Ormand P., President, Thomas Hospital, Fairhope, AL, p. A18

THOMPSON, Pamela, Chief Operations Officer, Huhukam Memorial Hospital, Sacaton, AZ, p. A37

THOMPSON, Patti, Chief Operating Officer, San Luis Valley Health, Alamosa, CO, p. A107

THOMPSON, Patty, Area Compliance Officer, Kaiser Permanente Fresno Medical Center, Fresno, CA, p. A65

THOMPSON, Randell, Chief Nursing Officer, Plateau Medical Center, Oak Hill, WV, p. A775

THOMPSON, Randy, Chief Executive Officer, Encompass Health Rehabilitation Hospital Of Montgomery, Montgomery, AL, p. A22

THOMPSON, Reanna, R.N., Chief Operating Officer and Chief Nursing Officer, Pih Health Hospital - Whittier, Whittier, CA, p. A105

THOMPSON, Ronnie, Chief Financial Officer, Belton Regional Medical Center, Belton, MO, p. A402

THOMPSON, Sarah, Director Health Information Management, Hardtner Medical Center, Olla, LA, p. A312

THOMPSON, Scott, Chief Executive Officer, Russell County Hospital, Russell Springs, KY, p. A292

THOMPSON, Selva, R.N., Chief Nurse Executive, Gallup Indian Medical Center, Gallup. NM, p. A469

THOMPSON, Sheila, Director Human Resources, Hamilton Memorial Hospital District, Mcleansboro, IL, p. A212

THOMPSON, Stacey, Superintendent, Austin State Hospital, Austin, TX, p. A655

THOMPSON, Stuart, Vice President Human Resources, Memorial Hospital Jacksonville, Jacksonville, FL, p. A141

THOMPSON, Tim, Senior Vice President and Chief Informatics Officer, St. Anthony's Hospital, Saint Petersburg, FL, p. A156

Senior Vice President and Chief Information Officer, St. Joseph's Hospital, Tampa, FL, p. A160

Senior Vice President, Chief Information Officer, South Florida Baptist Hospital, Plant City, FL, p. A154

Senior Vice President, Informant Services and Chief Information Officer, Mease Countryside Hospital, Safety Harbor, FL, p. A155

Senior Vice President, Information Services and Chief Information Officer, Mease Dunedin Hospital, Dunedin, FL, p. A137

THOMPSON, Timothy, Senior Vice President and Chief Information Officer, Morton Plant Hospital, Clearwater, FL, p. A134

Senior Vice President and Chief Information Officer, Morton Plant North Bay Hospital, New Port Richey, FL, p. A149

THOMPSON, Tina, Coordinator Human Resources, Firsthealth Montgomery Memorial Hospital, Troy, NC, p. A519

THOMPSON, Vera, Director Human Resources, Kingsboro Psychiatric Center, Brooklyn, NY, p. A478

THOMPSON, Vicki, MSN, Community Chief Nursing Officer, Middlesboro Arh Hospital, Middlesboro, KY, p. A290

THOMPSON, Wayne, Interim Chief Executive Officer and Chief Financial Officer, Northlake Behavioral Health System, Mandeville, LA, p. A308

THOMPSON, Wayne D., Interim Chief Executive Officer, Panola Medical Center, Batesville, MS, p. A389

THOMPSON, Wesley, M.D., President Medical Staff, Fairfield Memorial Hospital, Fairfield, IL, p. A205

THOMPSON, William, Chief Financial Officer, Mississipp. Baptist Medical Center, Jackson, MS, p. A395

THOMPSON-COOK, Timothy, Chief Operating Officer, Contra Costa Regional Medical Center, Martinez, CA, p. A77

THOMS, Hunter, Chief Executive Officer, Fairfax Community Hospital, Fairfax, OK, p. A559

THOMSEN, Sue, Chief Financial Officer, New Braunfels Regional Rehabilitation Hospital, New Braunfels, TX, p. A703

THOMSEN, Vicki, Director Human Resources, Aurora Behavioral Health System East, Tempe, AZ, p. A39

Director Human Resources, Aurora Behavioral Health System West, Glendale, AZ, p. A32

THOMSON, Doug, M.D., Chief Medical Officer, Commonwealth Regional Specialty Hospital, Bowling Green, KY, p. A280

THOMSON, Nicole, Chief Financial Officer, St. Louise Regional Hospital, Gilroy, CA, p. A66

THOMSON, Steven, M.D., Medical Director, Heartland Behavioral Healthcare, Massillon, OH, p. A544

THORDARSON, Heidar, Chief Financial Officer, Adventist Health Castle, Kailua, HI, p. A185

THORE, Joe, Chief Operating Officer, Ashe Memorial Hospital, Jefferson, NC, p. A513

THORELL, Nicole, R.N., MSN, Chief Nursing Officer, Lexington Regional Health Center, Lexington, NE, p. A434

THORESON, Shane, M.D., Chief Medical Officer, Community Memorial Healthcare, Marysville, KS, p. A270

THORN, Eugene Vice President Finance and Chief Financial Officer, Cleveland Clinic Union Hospital, Dover, OH, p. A539

THORN, Margaret, Interim Director of Nursing, Red Bay Hospital, Red Bay, AL, p. A24

THORN, Mark, FACHE, Executive Director, Finance, Mercy Hospital Lincoln, Troy, MO, p. A419

THORNBRUGH, Mitchell, Acting Chief Information Officer, Cherokee Nation W.W. Hastings Indian Hospital, Tahlequah, OK, p. A569

Administrative Officer, Cherokee Nation W.W. Hastings Indian Hospital, Tahlequah, OK, p. A569

THORNBURY, Neil, Chief Executive Officer, T. J. Samson Community Hospital, Glasgow, KY, p. A284

Chief Executive Officer, T.J. Health Columbia, Columbia, KY, p. A281

THORNE, Dana, Administrator Human Resources, Valley Hospital Medical Center, Las Vegas, NV, p. A445

THORNELL, Louise, Ph.D., R.N., Chief Nursing Officer, Christus St. Michael Health System, Texarkana, TX, p. A719

THORNELL, Timothy, FACHE, President and Chief Executive Officer, Cheyenne Regional Medical Center, Cheyenne, WY, p. A801

THORNSBERRY, Michael, M.D., Chief Medical Officer, Texas Health Specialty Hospital, Fort Worth, TX, p. A679

THORNTON, Amie D., Chief Hospital Executive, Hackensack Meridian Health Jfk Medical Center, Edison, NJ, p. A454

THORNTON, Carol, Director Human Resources, Cherry Hospital, Goldsboro, NC, p. A510

THORNTON, Cayetano, Chief Information Officer, Walter Reed National Military Medical Center, Bethesda, MD, p. A328

THORNTON, Daryl, Chief Operating Officer, Kansas Medical Center, Andover, KS, p. A261

THORNTON, Jan, Chief Nursing Officer, Bay Medical Sacred Heart, Panama City, FL, p. A152

THORNTON, Jillisa, Director of Nursing, Coastal Harbor Treatment Center, Savannah, GA, p. A180

THORNTON, Laird, Director Information Systems, Alta Vista Regional Hospital, Las Vegas, NM, p. A470

THORNTON, Thomas, M.D., Vice President of Medical Affairs, Midmichigan Medical Center - Alpena, Alpena, MI, p. A348

THORPE, Judith, R.N., MSN, Vice President and Chief Nursing Officer, Umass Memorial Healthalliance-Clinton Hospital, Leominster, MA, p. A340

THORPE, Linda, Chief Executive Officer, East Morgan County Hospital, Brush, CO, p. A108

THORPE, Wendy, Area Director Information Systems, St. Josep. Hospital Eureka, Eureka, CA, p. A63

THORSEN, Erik, President and Chief Executive Officer, Columbia Memorial Hospital, Astoria, OR, p. A573

THORWALD, Robert, Chief Information Officer, Washington Hospital Healthcare System, Fremont, CA, p. A65

THOTAKURA, Raj, M.D., Medical Director, Old Vineyard Behavioral Health Services, Winston, NC, p. A520

THRASHER, Amanda, Director Nursing, Ellsworth County Medical Center, Ellsworth, KS, p. A264

THRASHER, Kimberly, Controller, Encompass Health Lakeshore Rehabilitation Hospital, Birmingham, AL, p. A15

THRASHER, Sherri, Executive Human Resources Partner, Spectrum Health Pennock, Hastings, MI, p. A357

THREEWITS, Sheree, Director Human Resources, Manatee Memorial Hospital, Bradenton, FL, p. A133

THRIFT, William, Chief Nursing Officer, Brandon Regional Hospital, Brandon, FL, p. A133

THULI, Karen, Information Systems Coordinator, Upland Hills Health, Dodgeville, WI, p. A782

THUN, Todd, Director Human Resources, Montana State Hospital, Warm Springs, MT, p. A428

THUN, Tracey, Director Business and Support Services, Montana State Hospital, Warm Springs, MT, p. A428

THUNELL, Adam, Chief Operating Officer and Vice President Operations, Community Memorial Hospital, Ventura, CA, p. A103

THURBER, Joe, Director Information Technology, Central Regional Hospital, Butner, NC, p. A506

THURMER, DeAnn, President and Chief Nursing Officer, Ripon Medical Center, Ripon, WI, p. A795
President and Chief Nursing Officer, Waupun Memorial Hospital, Waupun, WI, p. A798

THURSTON, Thomas, M.D., Medical Director, J. D. Mccarty Center For Children With Developmental Disabilities, Norman, OK, p. A563

THYGESON, Cindy, M.D., Director Medical Affairs, Sutter Center For Psychiatry, Sacramento, CA, p. A90

THYNE, Shannon, Chief Medical Officer, Lac-Olive View-Ucla Medical Center, Sylmar, CA, p. A100

TIBBITS, Dick, Vice President and Chief Operating Officer, Adventhealth Tampa, Tampa, FL, p. A159

TIBBITS, Richard, Vice President and Chief Operating Officer, Loma Linda University Medical Center-Murrieta, Murrieta, CA, p. A80

TICE, Evan, Director Information Technology and Systems, Sky Ridge Medical Center, Lone Tree, CO, p. A116

TICE, Heidi, Chief Financial Officer, Cheyenne County Hospital, Saint Francis, KS, p. A275

TICE, Kirk C., President and Chief Executive Officer, Robert Wood Johnson University Hospital Rahway, Rahway, NJ, p. A462

TICE, Linda, Director Information Systems, Sagewest Health Care, Riverton, WY, p. A803

TICHENOR, John, Chief Financial Officer, Ohio County Hospital, Hartford, KY, p. A284

TICHENOR, Rick, Chief Executive Officer, Accel Rehabilitation Hospital Of Plano, Plano, TX, p. A706

TIDWELL, Jan, Chief Nursing Officer, Cartersville Medical Center, Cartersville, GA, p. A168

TIDWELL, Tim, Human Resources Director, Wiregrass Medical Center, Geneva, AL, p. A19

TIDWELL, Wesley, Chief Operating Officer, Memorial Hermann Greater Heights Hospital, Houston, TX, p. A687

TIEDE, Brad, Director Information Systems, Memorial Community Health, Aurora, NE, p. A429

TIEDT, Douglas, M.D., Chief of Staff, Musc Health Lancaster Medical Center, Lancaster, SC, p. A622

TIEDT, Jerry, Director Information Systems, Waverly Health Center, Waverly, IA, p. A259

TIEFENTHALER, Brenda, R.N., MSN, Vice President Patient Care and Informatics, Spencer Hospital, Spencer, IA, p. A258

TIEMENS, Linda, Chief Executive Officer, Vibra Hospital Of Richmond, Richmond, VA, p. A751

TIERNEY, Gregory, M.D., President, BMG AND BHS Chief Medical Officer, Benefis Health System, Great Falls, MT, p. A424

TIERNEY, Mark, Chief Financial Officer, Manatee Memorial Hospital, Bradenton, FL, p. A133

TIESI, Jeffrey, Executive Vice President and Chief Operating Officer, Excela Frick Hospital, Mount Pleasant, PA, p. A598
Executive Vice President and Chief Operating Officer, Excela Health Westmoreland Hospital, Greensburg, PA, p. A591
Executive Vice President and Chief Operating Officer, Excela Latrobe Area Hospital, Latrobe, PA, p. A594

TIETJEN, Patricia, M.D., Vice President, Medical Affairs, Danbury Hospital, Danbury, CT, p. A121

TIFF, Nikki, Human Resources Analyst, Avera Flandreau Hospital, Flandreau, SD, p. A628
Regional Manager Human Resources, Avera Dells Area Hospital, Dell Rapids, SD, p. A627

TIGGELAAR, Tom, Vice President Finance, Mayo Clinic Health System - Franciscan Healthcare In La Crosse, La Crosse, WI, p. A787

TILGHMAN, Bradley, Controller, Encompass Health Rehabilitation Hospital Of Panama City, Panama City, FL, p. A153

TILLER, Debra, Director Personnel and Administrative Secretary, Healthmark Regional Medical Center, Defuniak Springs, FL, p. A136

TILLER, Jaconna Joni, Chief Nursing Officer, Alliancehealth Midwest, Midwest City, OK, p. A562

TILLETT, Grant, Chief Information Officer, Prairie Lakes Healthcare System, Watertown, SD, p. A633

TILLMAN, Jill, Assistant Chief Executive Officer, Brandywine Hospital, Coatesville, PA, p. A587

TILLMAN, Kanner, Chief Financial Officer, Encino Hospital Medical Center, Encino, CA, p. A63

TILLMAN, Michael C., President and Chief Executive Officer, United Hospital Center, Bridgeport, WV, p. A770

TILLMAN, Pamela, Administrator, Lifebrite Community Hospital Of Stokes, Danbury, NC, p. A508

TILLMAN, Pamela P., Administrator, Lifebrite Community Hospital Of Stokes, Danbury, NC, p. A508

TILLMAN, Randy, M.D., Chief Medical Staff, Riverbridge Specialty Hospital, Vidalia, LA, p. A316

TILLMAN-TAYLOR, Susan, Manager Human Resources, Hackensack Meridian Health Southern Ocean Medical Center, Manahawkin, NJ, p. A458

TILSON, Natalie, Controller, Encompass Health Rehabilitation Hospital Of Kingsport, Kingsport, TN, p. A640

TIMANUS, Anthony, Chief Executive Officer, Avera Gregory Hospital, Gregory, SD, p. A628

TIMBERS, Christopher, Chief Information Officer, Sibley Memorial Hospital, Washington, DC, p. A130
Vice President and Chief Information Officer, Northbay Medical Center, Fairfield, CA, p. A63

TIMBERS, William, M.D., Interim Chief Medical Officer, Northern Inyo Hospital, Bishop, CA, p. A58

TIMM, Doreen, MSN, Senior Director and Chief Nursing Officer, Javon Bea Hospital-Rockton, Rockford, IL, p. A218

TIMM, Karen, R.N., MSN, Vice President Patient Services, St. Anthony Regional Hospital, Carroll, IA, p. A244

TIMM, Mark, Executive Director Human Resources, Yavapai Regional Medical Center, Prescott, AZ, p. A37

TIMM, Matt, M.D., Medical Director, Pender Community Hospital, Pender, NE, p. A439

TIMMER, Kari, Chief Financial Officer, Sioux Center Health, Sioux Center, IA, p. A258

TIMMERMAN, Jo, Manager Accounting, Norwood Health Center, Marshfield, WI, p. A789

TIMMONS, Laurene, Chief Financial Officer, Upmc East, Monroeville, PA, p. A597
Chief Financial Officer, Upmc Mckeesport, Mckeesport, PA, p. A596

TIMPE, James, Chief Executive Officer, Hshs St. Francis Hospital, Litchfield, IL, p. A210

TIMPE, Ron, Chief Financial Officer, Floyd County Medical Center, Charles City, IA, p. A245

TINCH, Roberta, Chief Operations Officer, Spotsylvania Regional Medical Center, Fredericksburg, VA, p. A742

TINCHER, Pat, Director Finance, Aspirus Langlade Hospital, Antigo, WI, p. A779

TINDLE, Jeff A., Chief Executive Officer, Carroll County Memorial Hospital, Carrollton, MO, p. A404

TINDLE, Tim, Chief Information Officer, Harris Health System, Houston, TX, p. A685

TINGEY, Ryan, Chief Operating Officer, Henderson Hospital, Henderson, NV, p. A442

TINGSTAD, Jonathan, Vice President and Chief Financial Officer, Seattle Cancer Care Alliance, Seattle, WA, p. A764

TINKEL, Chad, President and Chief Executive Officer, Community Hospitals And Wellness Centers-Montpelier, Montpelier, OH, p. A546
President and Chief Executive Officer, Community Hospitals And Wellness Centers, Bryan, OH, p. A530

TINNERELLO, Jeremy, MSN, R.N., President, Glenwood Regional Medical Center, West Monroe, LA, p. A316

TINNERELLO, Jeremy M., MSN, R.N., President, Glenwood Regional Medical Center, West Monroe, LA, p. A316

TINNEY, Sean, FACHE, Chief Operating Officer, Medical West, Bessemer, AL, p. A14

TINSA, Udom, M.D., Medical Director, Ashley Medical Center, Ashley, ND, p. A521

TINSLEY, Cassie, Director, Human Resources, Powell Valley Healthcare, Powell, WY, p. A803

TINSLEY, Nancy M., R.N., FACHE, President, Advocate Good Samaritan Hospital, Downers Grove, IL, p. A203

TIPPIN, Philip M., Chief Medical Officer, Chambers Memorial Hospital, Danville, AR, p. A44

TIPPIN, Russell, Chief Executive Officer, Medical Center Health System, Odessa, TX, p. A703

TIPPS, Linda, Director Human Resources, Southern Tennessee Regional Health System-Winchester, Winchester, TN, p. A650

TIPTON, Maggie, Chief Information Officer, Unicoi County Memorial Hospital, Erwin, TN, p. A638

TIPTON, Melissa, Human Resource Director, Hshs St. Mary's Hospital, Decatur, IL, p. A202

TIPTON, Peggy, Chief Operating Officer and Chief Nursing Officer, Oklahoma Heart Hospital, Oklahoma City, OK, p. A565

TIPTON, Regina, Hospital Administrator, Rehabilitation Hospital, Navicent Health, Macon, GA, p. A176

TIRA, Cheryl, Director Information Systems, Columbus Community Hospital, Columbus, NE, p. A431

TIRADO, Norma, Vice President, Human Resources and Health Information Technology, Lakeland Hospital, Watervliet, Watervliet, MI, p. A369

TISDALE, Willis, Director Human Resources, Shriners Hospitals For Children-Greenville, Greenville, SC, p. A620

TISDALL, Renae, Chief Financial Officer, Mobridge Regional Hospital, Mobridge, SD, p. A629

TISONE, Tom, Chief Executive Officer, Rusk Rehabilitation Hospital, Columbia, MO, p. A405

TISSIER, Becky, Chief Fiscal Service, Veterans Affairs Illiana Health Care System, Danville, IL, p. A202

TITO, David, M.D., President Medical Staff, Riverside Community Hospital, Riverside, CA, p. A88

TITSWORTH, Sue, Director Human Resources, Coleman County Medical Center, Coleman, TX, p. A664

TITTLE, JoDee, Chief Executive Officer, Plumas District Hospital, Quincy, CA, p. A86

TITUS, Monica B., R.N., Chief Executive Officer, Encompass Health Rehabilitation Hospital Of Vineland, Vineland, NJ, p. A465

TOALSON, Jason, Chief Executive Officer, Cottonwood Springs Hospital, Olathe, KS, p. A272

TOBEY, Shelley, R.N., MS, Chief Operating Officer and Chief Nursing Officer, Texas Health Presbyterian Hospital Flower Mound, Flower Mound, TX, p. A677

TOBIN, Hugh, Chief Financial Officer, Davis Regional Medical Center, Statesville, NC, p. A519

TOBIN, Ryan, President and Chief Executive Officer, Swedish Medical Center, Englewood, CO, p. A112

TOBIN-PAYNE, Cindy, Director, Magee Rehabilitation Hospital, Philadelphia, PA, p. A601

TOBITT, Allyssa, Chief Operating Officer, Doctors Hospital Of Sarasota, Sarasota, FL, p. A157

TOBLER, Randy, M.D., Chief Executive Officer, Scotland County Hospital, Memphis, MO, p. A412
M.D., Chief Medical Officer, Scotland County Hospital, Memphis, MO, p. A412

TOCCO-BRADLEY, Rosalie, Ph.D., M.D., Chief Medical Officer, St. Josep. Mercy Ann Arbor, Ypsilanti, MI, p. A370
Ph.D., M.D., Chief Medical Officer, St. Josep. Mercy Livingston Hospital, Howell, MI, p. A358

TODD, David, M.D., President Medical Staff, Pam Specialty Hospital Of Lufkin, Lufkin, TX, p. A698

TODD, Kimberly, Chief Nursing Officer, Alliancehealth Clinton, Clinton, OK, p. A557

TODD, Mark, Senior Systems Administrator, Hamilton Memorial Hospital District, Mcleansboro, IL, p. A212

TODD, Nate, Chief Financial Officer, Central Arkansas Veterans Healthcare System, Little Rock, AR, p. A49

TODD, Robbie, Director Information Technology, Horn Memorial Hospital, Ida Grove, IA, p. A251

TODD, Steve J., Chief Executive Officer, St. Luke Community Healthcare, Ronan, MT, p. A427

TODOROW, Thomas, Chief Financial Officer and Executive Vice President, Children's Hospital Of Philadelphia, Philadelphia, PA, p. A599

TOEDT, Michael, M.D., Director Clinical Services, Cherokee Indian Hospital, Cherokee, NC, p. A507

TOFANI, Barbara, R.N., MSN, Senior Vice President and Chief Nursing Officer, Cincinnati Children's Hospital Medical Center, Cincinnati, OH, p. A532

TOFT, Kari, Vice President, Chief Information Officer, Regions Hospital, Saint Paul, MN, p. A385

TOJINO, Allan, Director, Information Systems, Paradise Valley Hospital, National City, CA, p. A81

TOKAR, Andrew, Chief Financial Officer, Overlake Medical Center, Bellevue, WA, p. A755

TOL, Daryl, President and Chief Executive Officer, Adventhealth Orlando, Orlando, FL, p. A151

TOLBERT, James, Director Information Systems, Saint Francis Hospital Muskogee, Muskogee, OK, p. A562

TOLEDO, Iris, Chief Nursing Officer, Hospital Pavia Arecibo, Arecibo, PR, p. A806

TOLLEFSON, Sue, Coordinator Payroll Personnel, Avera Granite Falls Health Center, Granite Falls, MN, p. A377

TOLLEY, Cherie, Chief Executive Officer, Willingway Hospital, Statesboro, GA, p. A181

TOLSON, Rick, Chief Administrative Officer and Chief Human Resources Officer, Christ Hospital, Cincinnati, OH, p. A532
Divisional Chief People Officer, Hshs St. Joseph's Hospital, Chippewa Falls, WI, p. A781

TOMAS, George, Director Information Services, Griffin Hospital, Derby, CT, p. A122

TOMASESKI, Gina, Chief Executive Officer, Icare Rehabilitation Hospital, Flower Mound, TX, p. A677

TOMASO, Nancy, Vice President, Patient Care Services, Milford Regional Medical Center, Milford, MA, p. A341

TOME, Michael, M.D., Medical Director, Kaiser Permanente Los Angeles Medical Center, Los Angeles, CA, p. A74

TOMLIN, Jeffrey, M.D., Chief Executive Officer, Evergreenhealth, Kirkland, WA, p. A759

TOMLIN, Kerry, Associate Administrator, Clay County Hospital, Ashland, AL, p. A14

TOMLIN, Teresa, R.N., Chief Nursing Officer, Hospital District 6 - Patterson Health Center, Anthony, KS, p. A261

TOMLINSON, Charles, M.D., Chief Medical Officer, Atrium Health Cleveland, Shelby, NC, p. A518

TOMLINSON, David, Executive Vice President Chief Financial Officer and Chief Information Officer, Northwestern Medicine Mchenry, Mchenry, IL, p. A212

TOMLINSON, Sallie, Manager Human Resources, Arbuckle Memorial Hospital, Sulphur, OK, p. A568

TOMORY, Gerald, M.D., Regional Medical Director, Kauai Veterans Memorial Hospital, Waimea, HI, p. A187
M.D., Regional Medical Director, Samuel Mahelona Memorial Hospital, Kapaa, HI, p. A186

TOMPKINS, Charles, M.D., Chief of Staff, Crenshaw Community Hospital, Luverne, AL, p. A21

TOMPKINS, Kim, Director Information Services, Detar Healthcare System, Victoria, TX, p. A723

TOMPKINS, Tommy, Vice President, Finance and Chief Financial Officer, Yukon-Kuskokwim Delta Regional Hospital, Bethel, AK, p. A27

TONER, Tina, Chief Nursing Officer, Jefferson Healthcare, Port Townsend, WA, p. A762

TONEY, Patty, R.N., MSN, Chief Nurse Executive, Christus Santa Rosa Health System, San Antonio, TX, p. A711

TONG, Cheryl, Corporate Chief Financial Officer, Community Hospital Of Huntington Park, Huntington Park, CA, p. A68

TONGATE, Scott, Chief Financial Officer, Macon Community Hospital, Lafayette, TN, p. A642

TONJES, Ken, Chief Financial Officer, Peacehealth Ketchikan Medical Center, Ketchikan, AK, p. A28

TONN, Deb, Vice President Patient Care, Campbell County Health, Gillette, WY, p. A802

TONNU, Lannie, Senior Vice President and Chief Financial Officer, Children's Hospital Los Angeles, Los Angeles, CA, p. A74

TOOKE, Ryan, Chief Executive Officer, Dahl Memorial Healthcare Association, Ekalaka, MT, p. A423

TOOLE, LaDon, Chief Executive Officer, Dodge County Hospital, Eastman, GA, p. A172

TOOLE, Patricia, Chief Hospital Executive, Hackensack Meridian Health Carrier Clinic, Belle Mead, NJ, p. A452

TOON, William, Chief Information Officer, Baptist Hospitals Of Southeast Texas, Beaumont, TX, p. A658

TOPOLEWSKI, Ted, Chief Executive Officer, Madison Parish Hospital, Tallulah, LA, p. A316

TOPPEN, Jacki, Director of Nursing, Prairie St. John's, Fargo, ND, p. A523

TORBETT, Russell, Director Human Resources, Creek Nation Community Hospital, Okemah, OK, p. A563

TORCHIA, Jude, Chief Executive Officer, Orthocolorado Hospital, Lakewood, CO, p. A115

TORCHIA, Lisa, MSN, R.N., Vice President and Chief Nursing Officer, Geisinger Holy Spirit, Camp Hill, PA, p. A585

TORGE, Andrew, Director Human Resources, Shasta Regional Medical Center, Redding, CA, p. A87

TORMANEN, John, Director Mission and Human Resources, Chi St. Joseph's Health, Park Rapids, MN, p. A382

TORO PALACIOS, Belinda L., Executive Director, Doctors Center, Manati, PR, p. A808

TORONTOW, R., M.D., Chief Medical Staff, Cedar County Memorial Hospital, El Dorado Springs, MO, p. A405

TORREGROSSA, Tonia, Chief Nursing Officer, Horizon Medical Center, Llc, Denton, TX, p. A672

TORRES, Anthony, M.D., Chief Medical Officer, Yavapai Regional Medical Center, Prescott, AZ, p. A37
Manager Information Technology, Blue Mountain Hospital, Blanding, UT, p. A727

TORRES, Jose M., Executive Director, St. Luke's Episcopal Hospital, Ponce, PR, p. A809

TORRES, Maribel, Chief Nursing Officer, Hialeah Hospital, Hialeah, FL, p. A139

TORRES, Mayra, CPA, Chief Financial Officer, Ashford Presbyterian Community Hospital, San Juan, PR, p. A809

TORRES, Paul, M.D., Medical Staff President, Excelsior Springs Hospital, Excelsior Springs, MO, p. A406

TORRES, Tammy, R.N., MSN, Chief Executive Officer, Salem Medical Center, Salem, NJ, p. A462

TORRES, Victor, Information Technology Specialist Administrator, El Paso Behavioral Health System, El Paso, TX, p. A674

TORRES AYALA, Eugenio, Director Information Systems, Cardiovascular Center Of Puerto Rico And The Caribbean, San Juan, PR, p. A809

TORSCH, Peter, Chief Financial Officer, St. Charles Parish Hospital, Luling, LA, p. A307

TORTELLA, Anthony, Chief Financial Officer, Fairmount Behavioral Health System, Philadelphia, PA, p. A600

TOSTEBERG, Chris, Superintendent, Cherokee Mental Health Institute, Cherokee, IA, p. A245

TOSTENSON, Brad, Chief Information Officer, Essentia Health-Graceville, Graceville, MN, p. A377

TOSTI, Debra, Chief Executive Officer, Tewksbury Hospital, Tewksbury, MA, p. A345

TOTAH, Sam, Chief Operating Officer, Kaiser Permanente San Diego Medical Center, San Diego, CA, p. A91

TOUCHSTONE, Pat, Chief Nursing Officer, Crane Memorial Hospital, Crane, TX, p. A666

TOUPS, Sharon, Senior Vice President and Chief Operating Officer, St. Tammany Health System, Covington, LA, p. A300

TOURE', Joahd, M.D., Chief Medical Officer, Adirondack Health, Saranac Lake, NY, p. A497

TOURIGNY, Barry, Human Resources Director, Johnson City Medical Center, Johnson City, TN, p. A640
Vice President Human Resources and Organizational Development, Cabell Huntington Hospital, Huntington, WV, p. A772

TOUSIGNANT, Grace, R.N., MSN, Chief Nursing Officer, Aspirus Ironwood Hospitals & Clinics, Inc., Ironwood, MI, p. A358
R.N., MSN, Chief Nursing Officer, Aspirus Keweenaw Hospital, Inc., Laurium, MI, p. A360

TOUSSI, Anita, M.D., Chief Medical Officer, Paris Community Hospital, Paris, IL, p. A216

TOUVELLE, Cynthia, R.N., Senior Director Care Management and Chief Nursing Officer, Wvu Medicine - Barnesville Hospital, Barnesville, OH, p. A528

TOWERY, O, M.D., Chief of Staff, John Muir Behavioral Health Center, Concord, CA, p. A61

TOWLE, Sonya, Director Human Resources, Essentia Health Moose Lake, Moose Lake, MN, p. A381

TOWN, Alex, Chief Financial Officer, Samaritan Healthcare, Moses Lake, WA, p. A760
Vice President Finance, Tri-State Memorial Hospital, Clarkston, WA, p. A756

TOWNDROW, Geraldine, R.N., Senior Vice President Nursing, Lutheran Medical Center, Wheat Ridge, CO, p. A120

TOWNE, Jana, Nurse Executive, U. S. Public Health Service Indian Hospital-Whiteriver, Whiteriver, AZ, p. A41

TOWNER, Chad, Chief Executive Officer, Saint Josep. Health System, Mishawaka, IN, p. A236

TOWNES, Tim, Director Information Systems, Grandview Medical Center, Birmingham, AL, p. A15

TOWNLEY, Nancy, R.N., Senior Vice President Operations, United Regional Health Care System, Wichita Falls, TX, p. A725

TOWNSEND, Alan, Interim Chief Financial Officer, Jp. Health Network, Fort Worth, TX, p. A678

TOWNSEND, Cathy, Chief Nursing Officer, Banner - University Medical Center South, Tucson, AZ, p. A39

TOWNSEND, Dona, Chief Nursing Officer, Navarro Regional Hospital, Corsicana, TX, p. A666

TOWNSEND, Gary, Chief Information Officer, Hurley Medical Center, Flint, MI, p. A354

TOWNSEND, Lori, Chief Nursing Officer, Methodist Hospital, San Antonio, TX, p. A712

TOWNSEND, Michael, Chief Information Officer, James Cancer Hospital And Solove Research Institute, Columbus, OH, p. A536

TOWNSEND, Mike, Interim Director Health Information Systems, Grady Memorial Hospital, Chickasha, OK, p. A557

TOWNSEND, Sammuel, LAN Administrator, University Of Mississipp. Medical Center Holmes County, Lexington, MS, p. A396

TOWNSEND, Tanya, Senior Vice President, Chief Information Officer (part of LCMC), Children's Hospital, New Orleans, LA, p. A310

TOY, Linda, Director Information Systems, Havasu Regional Medical Center, Lake Havasu City, AZ, p. A33

TOY, Stanley Jr, M.D., Chief Executive Officer, Greater El Monte Community Hospital, South El Monte, CA, p. A99

TRABAL, Milton, Chief Financial Officer, Clarinda Regional Health Center, Clarinda, IA, p. A246

TRACEY, Karen, Chief Human Resources, Select Specialty Hospital-Greensboro, Greensboro, NC, p. A511

TRACY, Allen, Senior Vice President and Chief Financial Officer, Uh St. John Medical Center, Westlake, OH, p. A553

TRACY, Karen, R.N., Chief Operating Officer, Rochelle Community Hospital, Rochelle, IL, p. A218

TRACY, Larry A. Jr, FACHE, President, Memorial Hospital Of South Bend, South Bend, IN, p. A240

TRACY, Pat, Administrator, Ridgeview Behavioral Hospital, Middle Point, OH, p. A545

TRACY, Timothy J., Senior Director, Sanford Vermillion Medical Center, Vermillion, SD, p. A632

TRACY JR, ThomasChief Medical Officer, Penn State Milton S. Hershey Medical Center, Hershey, PA, p. A592

TRACZ, Robert, CPA, Senior Vice President and Chief Financial Officer, Lake Health, Concord Township. OH, p. A537

TRAHAN, Belinda, Chief Nursing Officer, Louisiana Extended Care Hospital Of Lafayette, Lafayette, LA, p. A305

TRAHAN, Jennifer, Assistant Vice President Human Resources, Our Lady Of Lourdes Regional Medical Center, Lafayette, LA, p. A306

TRAHAN, Leslie T., Chief Executive Officer, South Cameron Memorial Hospital, Cameron, LA, p. A299

TRAIL, Alan, Director Information Systems, Owensboro Health Muhlenberg Community Hospital, Greenville, KY, p. A284

TRAINER, Michael, Chief Financial Officer, Akron Children's Hospital, Akron, OH, p. A527

TRAINOR, Karyn, Director Human Resources, Providence St. Patrick Hospital, Missoula, MT, p. A426

TRAINOR, Paul, Senior Vice President Finance and Chief Financial Officer, Southern New Hampshire Medical Center, Nashua, NH, p. A450

TRAISTER, Lynne, Controller, Encompass Health Rehabilitation Hospital Of Tinton Falls, Tinton Falls, NJ, p. A464

TRAMMELL, Patrick, Chief Executive Officer, Dekalb Regional Medical Center, Fort Payne, AL, p. A19

TRAMP, Francis G., President, Burgess Health Center, Onawa, IA, p. A255

TRAN, Ann, Chief Financial Officer, Pike County Memorial Hospital, Louisiana, MO, p. A411

TRAN, Khiem, M.D., Acting Chief of Staff, Veterans Affairs Illiana Health Care System, Danville, IL, p. A202

TRAN, Lac, Senior Vice President Information Services, Rush University Medical Center, Chicago, IL, p. A200

TRAN, Richard, Director Information Technology, Galesburg Cottage Hospital, Galesburg, IL, p. A205

TRAN, Thanh, FACHE, Chief Executive Officer, North Central Surgical Center, Dallas, TX, p. A669

TRANCHINA, Scott, R.N., MSN, Administrator, Cobalt Rehabilitation Hospital Of New Orleans, New Orleans, LA, p. A310

TRANSIER, Rhonda, Financial Officer, Rusk State Hospital, Rusk, TX, p. A710

TRANTALIS, Carolyn, R.N., MSN, Chief Operating Officer, East Region, Windham Hospital, Willimantic, CT, p. A126
R.N., MSN, Regional Vice President, Clinical Services and Operations, The William W. Backus Hospital, Norwich, CT, p. A124

TRANTHAM, Susan, Director Human Resources, Encompass Health Rehabilitation Hospital Of Florence, Florence, SC, p. A619

TRAPNELL, Kerry A., Chief Executive Officer, Elbert Memorial Hospital, Elberton, GA, p. A172

TRAPP, John, Vice President Medical Affairs, Bryan Medical Center, Lincoln, NE, p. A434

TRAVIS, Calee, R.N., Chief Nursing Officer, Baylor Scott & White Medical Center - Centennial, Frisco, TX, p. A680

TRAVIS, David, Chief Financial Officer, Freestone Medical Center, Fairfield, TX, p. A677
Chief Financial Officer, Ut Health Athens, Athens, TX, p. A654

TRAVIS, Dee Dee, Vice President Community Relations, Calais Regional Hospital, Calais, ME, p. A319

TRAVIS, Sara, Chief Nursing Officer and Assistant Administrator, Palo Alto County Health System, Emmetsburg, IA, p. A249

TRAWICK, Thomas S., M.D., Chief Executive Officer, Christus Health Shreveport-Bossier, Shreveport, LA, p. A314

TRAYLOR, Desiree, Chief Information Officer, Chickasaw Nation Medical Center, Ada, OK, p. A555

TRAYLOR, Jerri, Director Human Resources, The Women's Hospital, Newburgh, IN, p. A238

TRAYNOR, Karen, Chief Financial Officer, Richland Hospital, Richland Center, WI, p. A795

TREACY, Nancy, Director Finance, Cambridge Medical Center, Cambridge, MN, p. A373

TREACY-SHIFF, Mary, Vice President Finance, Advocate Good Samaritan Hospital, Downers Grove, IL, p. A203

TREADWAY, Michael, Controller, Christus Trinity Mother Frances Rehabilitation Hospital, A Partner Of Encompass Health, Tyler, TX, p. A721

TREADWELL, Karen, Director Human Resources, Lake Martin Community Hospital, Dadeville, AL, p. A17

TREASE, Kevin, Chief Information Officer, Antelop. Memorial Hospital, Neligh, NE, p. A435

TREASURE, Angela, Chief Nursing Officer, Portneuf Medical Center, Pocatello, ID, p. A192

TREASURE, Jeffrey, Chief Financial Officer, Northern Arizona Healthcare, Flagstaff Medical Center, Flagstaff, AZ, p. A31

Chief Financial Officer, Northern Arizona Healthcare, Verde Valley Medical Center, Cottonwood, AZ, p. A31

TREECE, Amy, M.D., Medical Director, Prisma Health North Greenville, Travelers Rest, SC, p. A625

TREGLOWN, Brad, Director Information Systems, Redmond Regional Medical Center, Rome, GA, p. A179

TREHAN, Rajeev, M.D., M.P.H., Chief of Staff, Veterans Affairs Eastern Kansas Health System, Topeka, KS, p. A277

TREITLER, Scot, Chief Operating Officer, Cypress Pointe Surgical Hospital, Hammond, LA, p. A302

TREMAINE, Lisa, Manager Human Resources, Carson Valley Medical Center, Gardnerville, NV, p. A442

TREMBLE, Nakia, Chief Executive Officer, Kindred Hospital Indianapolis North, Indianapolis, IN, p. A232

TREMONTI, Carl, Chief Financial Officer, Mease Countryside Hospital, Safety Harbor, FL, p. A155

Chief Financial Officer, Mease Dunedin Hospital, Dunedin, FL, p. A137

Chief Financial Officer, Morton Plant Hospital, Clearwater, FL, p. A134

Chief Financial Officer, Morton Plant Hospital North Bay Hospital, New Port Richey, FL, p. A149

Chief Financial Officer, South Florida Baptist Hospital, Plant City, FL, p. A154

Chief Financial Officer, St. Anthony's Hospital, Saint Petersburg, FL, p. A156

TREMONTI, Yvette, Chief Financial Officer, H. Lee Moffitt Cancer Center And Research Institute, Tampa, FL, p. A159

TRENDE, Gary, FACHE, Associate Director, Tuscaloosa Veterans Affairs Medical Center, Tuscaloosa, AL, p. A25

TRENSCHEL, Robert, D.O., FACHE, M.P.H., President and Chief Executive Officer, Yuma Regional Medical Center, Yuma, AZ, p. A41

TRENT, Cindy, Manager Personnel, Fall River Hospital, Hot Springs, SD, p. A628

TRESSLER, Carrie, Vice President of Nursing and Chief Nursing Officer, Rush Memorial Hospital, Rushville, IN, p. A240

TRETINA, Mike, Senior Vice President and Chief Financial Officer, Bayhealth Medical Center, Dover, DE, p. A127

TRETTER, Stan, M.D., Chief Medical Officer, Memorial Hospital And Health Care Center, Jasper, IN, p. A233

TREVATHAN, Dave, Director Information Systems, Rose Medical Center, Denver, CO, p. A111

TREVINO, Jorge, Chief Executive Officer, Baptist Medical Center, San Antonio, TX, p. A711

TREVINO, Malissa, Director Human Resources, Pecos County Memorial Hospital, Fort Stockton, TX, p. A677

TREVINO, Paul, President and Chief Executive Officer, Christus Southeast Texas Hospital - St. Elizabeth, Beaumont, TX, p. A658

TREVISANI, Michael, M.D., Senior Vice President and Chief Medical Officer, Faxton St. Luke's Healthcare, Utica, NY, p. A500

TRIANA, Rudy, M.D., Chief of Staff, Jackson Purchase Medical Center, Mayfield, KY, p. A290

TRICKEY, Donna, R.N., Chief Nursing Officer, Fairview Park Hospital, Dublin, GA, p. A172

TRICOU, John, M.D., Chief of Staff, Iroquois Memorial Hospital And Resident Home, Watseka, IL, p. A222

TRIGG, Terry, Director Human Resources, Merit Health Wesley, Hattiesburg, MS, p. A393

TRIMBLE, Deborah, R.N., Chief Executive Officer, Paul B. Hall Regional Medical Center, Paintsville, KY, p. A292

TRIMBLE, Donald, CPA, Chief Financial Officer, Vibra Specialty Hospital At Desoto, Desoto, TX, p. A673

TRIMBLE, Lisa, Controller, Encompass Health Rehabilitation Hospital Of Middletown, Middletown, DE, p. A127

TRIMBLE, Melody, Chief Executive Officer, St. Francis Hospital, Columbus, GA, p. A169

TRIMM, Robert, Administrator, North Mississipp. Medical Center-Hamilton, Hamilton, AL, p. A20

TRIMMER, Mary, Interim Chief Operating Officer, Mount Carmel West, Columbus, OH, p. A536

TRIMMER, Matthew, Director Information Services, Holy Cross Hospital, Silver Spring, MD, p. A332

TRINH, Khiet, M.D., Chief Medical Officer, Bon Secours St. Mary's Hospital, Richmond, VA, p. A749

TRIPLETT, Daniel, Acting Chief Operating Officer, Springfield Hospital Center, Sykesville, MD, p. A333

TRIPLETT, John, D.O., President Medical Staff, Arh Our Lady Of The Way, Martin, KY, p. A289

TRIPLETT, Ruby, Chief Nursing Officer, Bailey Medical Center, Owasso, OK, p. A566

TRIPP, Gina, Director Information Systems, Tirr Memorial Hermann, Houston, TX, p. A688

TRIPP, Kelly, Executive Director, Sojourn At Seneca Senior Behavioral Health, Tiffin, OH, p. A550

TRIPPEL, Donald, Chief Financial Officer, Hugh Chatham Memorial Hospital, Elkin, NC, p. A509

TRIVEDI, Harsh, M.D., President and Chief Executive Officer, Sheppard Pratt Health System, Baltimore, MD, p. A326

TRIVETTE, Chastity, Chief Executive Officer, Johnson County Community Hospital, Mountain City, TN, p. A645

TRIVETTE, Theresa, R.N., Chief Nursing Officer, Adventhealth Tampa, Tampa, FL, p. A159

TROCINO, Mark, Chief Information Officer, Emory Hillandale Hospital, Lithonia, GA, p. A175

TROGMAN, Richard, FACHE, Chief Operating Officer, Kaiser Permanente Woodland Hills Medical Center, Woodland Hills, CA, p. A105

TROLLOPE, Grant, Chief Financial Officer, Northeastern Nevada Regional Hospital, Elko, NV, p. A441

TROMBATORE, Beverly, R.N., Director Managed Information Systems, Matagorda Regional Medical Center, Bay City, TX, p. A657

TROMBLEE, Julie, R.N., Chief Nursing Officer, The University Of Vermont Health Network Elizabethtown Community Hospital, Elizabethtown, NY, p. A483

TROMPETER, Dawn, President, Osf Saint Paul Medical Center, Mendota, IL, p. A212

TRONCONE, Michael, Chief Human Resources Officer, Calvary Hospital, Bronx, NY, p. A476

TROSIN, Jill, R.N., MSN, Vice President Patient Care Services, Chief Nursing Officer, St. Luke's Hospital, Maumee, OH, p. A545

TROTTER, Shaunda, R.N., Chief Nursing Officer, Anmed Health Medical Center, Anderson, SC, p. A615

TROTTER, Wally, Director Human Resources, Mountain View Hospital, Payson, UT, p. A730

TROTTIER, Timothy R., Chief Executive Officer, St. Josep. Regional Medical Center, Lewiston, ID, p. A191

TROUBLEFIELD, David, Director, Human Resources, Hemphill County Hospital, Canadian, TX, p. A662

TROUP, Bill, M.D., Chief of Staff, Stanton County Hospital, Johnson, KS, p. A267

TROUP, Matthew, FACHE, President and Chief Executive Officer, Conway Regional Medical Center, Conway, AR, p. A44

TROUT, Eugene, Chief Financial Officer, Weirton Medical Center, Weirton, WV, p. A777

TROUTMAN, Gary, CPA, Chief Financial Officer, Baptist Hospitals Of Southeast Texas, Beaumont, TX, p. A658

TROWBRIDGE, William, President and Chief Executive Officer, Regional Mental Health Center, Merrillville, IN, p. A236

TROWHILL, Jan, Director Health Information Management Systems, West Tennessee Rehabilitation Hospital Cane Creek, Martin, TN, p. A643

TROXELL, Larry, Chief Executive Officer, Comanche County Medical Center, Comanche, TX, p. A665

TROY, Patrick, R.N., MSN, Associate Director Patient Care Services, Veterans Affairs New Jersey Health Care System, East Orange, NJ, p. A454

TROY, Peggy N., President and Chief Executive Officer, Children's Hospital Of Wisconsin-Fox Valley, Neenah, WI, p. A792

President and Chief Executive Officer, Children's Hospital Of Wisconsin, Milwaukee, WI, p. A791

TROYER, David, Chief Information Officer, Veterans Affairs Northern Indiana Health Care System, Fort Wayne, IN, p. A229

TROYER, Devin, M.D., Medical Director, Encompass Health Rehabilitation Hospital Of Columbia, Columbia, SC, p. A617

TROYO-SAUVIAC, Glynda, Chief Executive Officer, Vibra Hospital Of Central Dakotas, Mandan, ND, p. A525

TRUAX, Christopher, FACHE, Chief Administrative Officer, Lake Health Beachwood Medical Center, Beachwood, OH, p. A529

TRUE, Terry, M.D., Chief of Staff, Shoals Hospital, Muscle Shoals, AL, p. A22

TRUELOVE, Lynn, Chief Executive Officer, Stone County Hospital, Wiggins, MS, p. A401

TRUESDALE, Fred A. Jr, Administrator, North Mississipp. Medical Center-Iuka, Iuka, MS, p. A394

TRUESDALE JR, FredAdministrator, North Mississipp. Medical Center-Iuka, Iuka, MS, p. A394

TRUESDELL, Shannon, Chief Operating Officer, Marshall Medical Center, Placerville, CA, p. A85

TRUITT, Louise, Human Resource Director, Coliseum Northside Hospital, Macon, GA, p. A176

Vice President Human Resources, Capital Regional Medical Center, Tallahassee, FL, p. A158

TRUJILLO, Cynthia, Director Human Resources, New Mexico Rehabilitation Center, Roswell, NM, p. A471

TRUJILLO, Jesse, Chief Information Officer, St. Mark's Hospital, Salt Lake City, UT, p. A733

TRUMAN, Julia, Chief Operating Officer, Multicare Tacoma General Hospital, Tacoma, WA, p. A767

Vice President Human Resources, Fort Walton Beach Medical Center, Fort Walton Beach, FL, p. A138

TRUMAN, Lisa, Chief Nursing Officer, Sea Pines Rehabilitation Hospital, Melbourne, FL, p. A145

TRUMAN, Mark, Vice President of Operations, Baptist Health Floyd, New Albany, IN, p. A237

TRYON, Ellen, R.N., Chief Nursing Officer, Adventist Health Portland, Portland, OR, p. A579

TSAI, James C., M.D., President, New York Eye And Ear Infirmary Of Mount Sinai, New York, NY, p. A490

TSALATE, Cynthia, Human Resource Specialist, U. S. Public Health Service Indian Hospital, Zuni, NM, p. A473

TSAMBIRAS, Petros, M.D., Chief of Staff, Adventhealth Dade City, Dade City, FL, p. A135

TSAO, Sean, Director Information Technology, Blue Mountain Hospital District, John Day, OR, p. A576

TSE, Graham, M.D., Chief Medical Officer, Miller Children's & Women's Hospital Long Beach, Long Beach, CA, p. A72

TSENG, Allen, Chief Operations Officer, Memorial Hermann Memorial City Medical Center, Houston, TX, p. A687

TSUNEISHI, Lani, Nursing Services Manager, Hawaii State Hospital, Kaneohe, HI, p. A186

TUBBS, John, M.D., Chief of Staff, Rock County Hospital, Bassett, NE, p. A429

M.D., Chief of Staff, West Holt Medical Services, Atkinson, NE, p. A429

TUBBS, Mary Beth, Chief Nursing Officer, Astria Sunnyside Hospital, Sunnyside, WA, p. A766

TUBERVILLE, Abby, Human Resource Manager, Fillmore County Hospital, Geneva, NE, p. A432

TUCK, Greg, Area Information Officer, Kaiser Permanente San Jose Medical Center, San Jose, CA, p. A94

TUCKER, Albert, Chief Financial Officer, Miami Veterans Affairs Healthcare System, Miami, FL, p. A147

TUCKER, Amy, M.D., Chief Medical Officer, Upstate University Hospital, Syracuse, NY, p. A500

TUCKER, Andy, Chief Financial Officer, South Mississipp. State Hospital, Purvis, MS, p. A399

TUCKER, Bruce, Director, Canandaigua Veterans Affairs Medical Center, Canandaigua, NY, p. A480

TUCKER, Cathy, Director Human Resources, Iraan General Hospital, Iraan, TX, p. A690

TUCKER, Denis, Chief Information Officer, Wilkes-Barre General Hospital, Wilkes-Barre, PA, p. A611

TUCKER, Ian, M.D., Vice President Medical Affairs, Johnson Memorial Hospital, Stafford Springs, CT, p. A125

TUCKER, John, Chief Executive Officer, Mt. San Rafael Hospital, Trinidad, CO, p. A119

Chief Nursing Executive, Center For Behavioral Medicine, Kansas City, MO, p. A408

TUCKER, Joseph, Senior Vice President and Chief Financial Officer, Fort Washington Medical Center, Oxen Hill, MD, p. A331

TUCKER, Josep. B., Interim President and Chief Executive Officer, Fort Washington Medical Center, Oxen Hill, MD, p. A331

TUCKER, Mona, Vice President Human Resources, Bsa Hospital, Llc, Amarillo, TX, p. A652

TUCKER, Rebecca, Chief Financial Officer, Memorial Hermann Northeast, Humble, TX, p. A690

President, Texas Health Harris Methodist Hospital Southwest Fort Worth, Fort Worth, TX, p. A679

TUCKER, Ron, Business Office Manager, Kiowa County Memorial Hospital, Greensburg, KS, p. A265

TUCKER, Sarah, Chief Nursing Officer, Bradley County Medical Center, Warren, AR, p. A54

TUCKER, Theresa, Human Resources Officer, Sioux Center Health, Sioux Center, IA, p. A258

TUDELA, John, M.D., Director of Medical Affairs, Commonwealth Health Center, Saipan, MP, p. A805

TUDOR, Brandon, Chief Executive Officer, Encompass Health Rehabilitation Hospital Of Plano, Plano, TX, p. A707

TUDOR, Nathan, Chief Executive Officer, El Camp. Memorial Hospital, El Campo, TX, p. A674

Chief Executive Officer, Palacios Community Medical Center, Palacios, TX, p. A704

TULLIER, Debbie, Chief Executive Officer, Perimeter Behavioral Hospital Of New Orleans, Kenner, LA, p. A304

TULLIS, Bea, Chief Financial Officer and Budget Officer, Broughton Hospital, Morganton, NC, p. A515

TULLMAN, Stephen M., President and Chief Executive Officer, Phoenixville Hospital, Phoenixville, PA, p. A602

TUMA, Bonnie, Human Resources Team Lead, National Institutes Of Health Clinical Center, Bethesda, MD, p. A327

TUMA, Roman, Chief Medical Officer, St. Luke's Easton Campus, Easton, PA, p. A589

TUMLIN, Richard, Chief Administrative Officer, Saint Thomas Highlands Hospital, Sparta, TN, p. A649

TUMMURU, Ramireddy, M.D., Chief Medical Officer, Porter Regional Hospital, Valparaiso, IN, p. A241

TUNGATE, Rex A., Chief Executive Officer, Casey County Hospital, Liberty, KY, p. A287

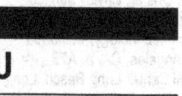

Chief Executive Officer, Jane Todd Crawford Hospital, Greensburg, KY, p. A284

TUNNELL, Richard, Chief Information Officer, University Hospital, Newark, NJ, p. A460

TUPPER, David, Chief Executive Officer, Solara Hospital Mcallen, Mcallen, TX, p. A700

TUPPER, Malinda, Vice President and Chief Financial Officer, Kaweah Delta Medical Center, Visalia, CA, p. A104

TUPPONCE, David, M.D., President, Central Maine Medical Center, Lewiston, ME, p. A321

TURBAK, Shelly, R.N., Chief Nursing Officer, Prairie Lakes Healthcare System, Watertown, SD, p. A633

TUREK, Beth, Site Manager Information Systems, Advocate South Suburban Hospital, Hazel Crest, IL, p. A207

TUREK, Derrill, R.N., Chief Nursing Officer, Blue Mountain Hospital, Blanding, UT, p. A727

TURK, Edward, Vice President Finance, Scripp. Mercy Hospital, San Diego, CA, p. A92

TURK, Jan, Chief Executive Officer, Cornerstone Hospitals Southwest Louisiana, Lake Charles, LA, p. A306

TURKAL-BARRETT, Kari, Flight Commander Resource Management Officer, Mike O'Callaghan Federal Hospital, Nellis Afb, NV, p. A445

TURKEL, Brooks M., President, Upmc Lititz, Lititz, PA, p. A595

TURLEY, Mary Ann, D.O., Medical Director, Honorhealth Deer Valley Medical Center, Phoenix, AZ, p. A36

TURLEY, Matt, Interim Director Information Systems, Greenbrier Valley Medical Center, Ronceverte, WV, p. A776

TURMAN, Anna, Division Vice President, Chief Information Officer, Chi Health Creighton University Medical Center - Bergan Mercy, Omaha, NE, p. A436

TURMAN, Tracy, Administrator, Uva Transitional Care Hospital, Charlottesville, VA, p. A740

TURNBULL, James, Chief Information Officer, University Of Utah Health, Salt Lake City, UT, p. A733

TURNBULL, Rosie, Director Human Resources, St. Lawrence Psychiatric Center, Ogdensburg, NY, p. A493

TURNER, Barbara, Director of Nursing, Austen Riggs Center, Stockbridge, MA, p. A345

TURNER, Bill, Vice President Human Resources, Valir Rehabilitation Hospital, Oklahoma City, OK, p. A566

TURNER, Brenda, Chief Human Resources Officer, Palomar Medical Center Escondido, Escondido, CA, p. A63
Chief Human Resources Officer, Palomar Medical Center Poway, Poway, CA, p. A86

TURNER, Chad, Chief Financial Officer, Star Valley Health, Afton, WY, p. A801

TURNER, Cindy, Chief Executive Officer, Bacon County Hospital And Health System, Alma, GA, p. A163

TURNER, Cindy R., Chief Executive Officer, Bacon County Hospital And Health System, Alma, GA, p. A163

TURNER, Dale, Chief Operating Officer, Reedsburg Area Medical Center, Reedsburg, WI, p. A795

TURNER, Davin, D.O., President and Chief Medical Officer, Mosaic Life Care At St. Josep. - Medical Center, Saint Joseph, MO, p. A415

TURNER, Deanna, Executive Director, Eden Springs Health Care Center, Green Springs, OH, p. A541

TURNER, Jeff, FACHE, Chief Executive Officer, Moore County Hospital District, Dumas, TX, p. A673

TURNER, Karen, Chief Nursing Officer, Seneca Healthcare District, Chester, CA, p. A60

TURNER, Karissa, President and Chief Executive Officer, Wabash General Hospital, Mount Carmel, IL, p. A213
Vice President Operations, Wabash General Hospital, Mount Carmel, IL, p. A213

TURNER, Kevin, M.D., Medical Director, Pathways Of Tennessee, Jackson, TN, p. A639

TURNER, Mark, Manager Information Technology, Ojai Valley Community Hospital, Ojai, CA, p. A82

TURNER, Mark S., Chief Executive Officer, Capital Medical Center, Olympia, WA, p. A761

TURNER, Marquita, Chief Operating Officer and Chief Nursing Officer, Atrium Medical Center, Middletown, OH, p. A545

TURNER, Maurita, Team Leader Health Information Systems Services, Chi St. Josep. Health Madison Hospital, Madisonville, TX, p. A699

TURNER, Melissa, Senior Vice President Human Resources, Bridgeport Hospital, Bridgeport, CT, p. A121

TURNER, Michael, Chief Information Officer, Plaza Specialty Hospital, Houston, TX, p. A688
Director Human Resources, Moberly Regional Medical Center, Moberly, MO, p. A412

TURNER, Nancy, Director Communications, Sutter Roseville Medical Center, Roseville, CA, p. A89

TURNER, Peggy, Assistant Vice President and Director of Nursing, Unity Health White County Medical Center, Searcy, AR, p. A52

TURNER, Ralph, Chief Operating Officer, Cleveland Clinic Indian River Hospital, Vero Beach, FL, p. A161

TURNER, Randy, Chief Human Resource Management Services, Boise Veterans Affairs Medical Center, Boise, ID, p. A188

TURNER, Robert A., Chief Executive Officer, Ad Hospital East, Houston, TX, p. A684

TURNER, Sara, Director Human Resources, Alvarado Hospital Medical Center, San Diego, CA, p. A91

TURNER, Saundra, Director Human Resources, Mercy Hospital Jefferson, Festus, MO, p. A406

TURNER, Sherrilyn, Director Human Resources, Southeast Colorado Hospital District, Springfield, CO, p. A118

TURNER, Spencer, FACHE, President, Texas Health Presbyterian Hospital Flower Mound, Flower Mound, TX, p. A677

TURNER, Steve, Director Information Technology, Salem Township Hospital, Salem, IL, p. A219

TURNER, Teri, Chief Nursing Officer, Haskell Memorial Hospital, Haskell, TX, p. A683

TURNER, Tiffany, MSN, R.N., Vice President of Nursing and Chief Nursing Officer, Paris Community Hospital, Paris, IL, p. A216

TURNER, Will, President, Baylor Scott & White Medical Center-Waxahachie, Waxahachie, TX, p. A724

TURNEY, Amanda, Director Human Resources, Cochran Memorial Hospital, Morton, TX, p. A702

TURNEY, David, Chief Information Officer, Cochran Memorial Hospital, Morton, TX, p. A702

TURNEY, Larry, Administrator, Cochran Memorial Hospital, Morton, TX, p. A702

TURNQUIST, Carrie, Director Human Resources, Buena Vista Regional Medical Center, Storm Lake, IA, p. A258

TURO, Albert, Vice President Human Resources, St. Mary's Healthcare, Amsterdam, NY, p. A474

TURPEN, Brad, FACHE, Chief Executive Officer, Valor Health, Emmett, ID, p. A190

TURPIN, Debra, R.N., MSN, Vice President Patient Care Services and Chief Nursing Officer, Alton Memorial Hospital, Alton, IL, p. A194

TURPIN, James, Chief of Staff, Ephraim Mcdowell Fort Logan Hospital, Stanford, KY, p. A293
Human Resources, Breckinridge Memorial Hospital, Hardinsburg, KY, p. A284

TURQUEZA, Sandra, Human Resources Business Partner, Chi Saint Josep. Berea, Berea, KY, p. A287
Senior Human Resources Business Partner, Chi Saint Josep. London, London, KY, p. A287

TURSKY, Martin, President and Chief Executive Officer, Mclaren Central Michigan, Mount Pleasant, MI, p. A362

TURSO, Janet, Controller, Encompass Health Rehabilitation Hospital Of Toms River, Toms River, NJ, p. A464

TURTON, Jonathan, FACHE, President, Southwest General Hospital, San Antonio, TX, p. A713

TUSCANY, Joanne, Director Human Resources, Ascension St. John Hospital, Detroit, MI, p. A352
Senior Director Human Resources, Ascension Macomb-Oakland Hospital, Warren, MI, p. A368

TUSTEN, Jay, Chief Executive Officer, Stanton County Hospital, Johnson, KS, p. A267

TUSTIN, Bill, Chief Operating Officer, Piedmont Columbus Regional Midtown, Columbus, GA, p. A169

TUTT, Michael, M.D., Chief Medical Officer, Tsehootsooi Medical Center, Fort Defiance, AZ, p. A31

TUTTLE, Casey, Director Information Technology, Sistersville General Hospital, Sistersville, WV, p. A776

TUTTLE, Kathryn, R.N., Director of Nursing, Memorial Medical Center Of Ashland, Ashland, WI, p. A779

TVEIT, Charles B., Chief Executive Officer, Lake District Hospital, Lakeview, OR, p. A577

TWARDY, Cindi, Manager Human Resources, Meeker Memorial Hospital, Litchfield, MN, p. A379

TWEED, Frances, R.N., Executive Director and Administrator, New Mexico Behavioral Health Institute At Las Vegas, Las Vegas, NM, p. A470

TWEHOUS, Debra, Medical Director, Fairlawn Rehabilitation Hospital, Worcester, MA, p. A346

TWIDDWELL, Lisa, Administrator, Madison Medical Center, Fredericktown, MO, p. A406

TWIGG, Nicole, Director Human Resources, Brook Lane Health Services, Hagerstown, MD, p. A330

TYE, Angie, Director Human Resources, Waverly Health Center, Waverly, IA, p. A259

TYLER, Holley, R.N., Chief Nursing Officer, Woman's Hospital Of Texas, Houston, TX, p. A689

TYLER, James E., Chief Executive Officer, Smyth County Community Hospital, Marion, VA, p. A745

TYLER, Kevin, M.D., President Medical Staff, Penn Highlands Clearfield, Clearfield, PA, p. A586

TYLER, Kimberly, Director of Nursing, St. Mary's Good Samaritan Hospital, Greensboro, GA, p. A173

TYLER, Philene, Chief Finance Officer, Chinle Comprehensive Health Care Facility, Chinle, AZ, p. A31

TYLER, Richard, Corporate Director Human Resources, Conway Regional Medical Center, Conway, AR, p. A44

TYLER, Rick, M.D., Vice President Medical Affairs, Christus Southeast Texas Hospital - St. Elizabeth, Beaumont, TX, p. A658

TYLER, Rob, Chief Financial Officer, West Oaks Hospital, Houston, TX, p. A689

TYLER, Tanya, Vice President Human Resources, Chi St. Luke's Health Memorial Lufkin, Lufkin, TX, p. A698

TYO, Joanne, Chief Financial Officer, Carolinas Continuecare Hospital At Pineville, Charlotte, NC, p. A507

TYRA, Diana, Director Health Information, Kentucky River Medical Center, Jackson, KY, p. A285

TYRELL, Wade, Chief Executive Officer and Chief Nursing Officer, Sterling Regional Medcenter, Sterling, CO, p. A119

TYRRELL, Wade Chief Executive Officer and Chief Nursing Officer, Sterling Regional Medcenter, Sterling, CO, p. A119

TYSON, Rhoda, Chief Information Officer, Central Alabama Veterans Health Care System, Montgomery, AL, p. A22

# U

UBER, Charlotte M., Chief Executive Officer, Warren State Hospital, Warren, PA, p. A609

UDALL, Ben, M.D., Chief of Staff, Kimble Hospital, Junction, TX, p. A691

UDANI, Neil, M.D., Chief Medical Officer, Saint Clare's Denville Hospital, Denville, NJ, p. A454

UDOVICH, Christopher, M.D., Chief of Staff, Silver Cross Hospital, New Lenox, IL, p. A214

UFFER, Mark H., Chief Executive Officer, Corona Regional Medical Center, Corona, CA, p. A61

UGHOUWA, Ejiro, M.D., Chief of Staff, Allen Parish Community Healthcare, Kinder, LA, p. A305

UGWUEKE, Michael Sr, President and Chief Executive Officer, Methodist Healthcare Memphis Hospitals, Memphis, TN, p. A644

UHARRIET, Bart, Director Information Services, Mississipp. State Hospital, Whitfield, MS, p. A401

UHL, Michael, President, Atrium Medical Center, Middletown, OH, p. A545

UHLIR, Tricia, Chief Executive Officer, Fall River Hospital, Hot Springs, SD, p. A628

ULERY, Brian, Chief Operating Officer, Thomas Memorial Hospital, South Charleston, WV, p. A777
Senior Vice President and Chief Operating Officer, Saint Francis Hospital, Charleston, WV, p. A771

ULETT, John, Vice President and Chief Information Officer, Centrastate Healthcare System, Freehold, NJ, p. A455

ULFERTS, Wendy, Vice President and Chief Nursing Officer, Maple Grove Hospital, Maple Grove, MN, p. A380

ULI, James, Chief Financial Officer, Loma Linda University Medical Center-Murrieta, Murrieta, CA, p. A80
Chief Financial Officer, Providence Saint John's Health Center, Santa Monica, CA, p. A97

ULIBARRI, Laura, M.D., Chief of Staff, Catalina Island Medical Center, Avalon, CA, p. A56

ULLRICH, John, M.D., Chief of Staff, Ivinson Memorial Hospital, Laramie, WY, p. A803

ULMER, Becky, R.N., Director of Nursing, Jasper General Hospital, Bay Springs, MS, p. A389

ULMER, Carlton, Chief Executive Officer, Medical City Plano, Plano, TX, p. A707

ULMER, Carol, Chief Executive Officer, Select Specialty Hospital-Sioux Falls, Sioux Falls, SD, p. A631

ULREICH, Shawn, MSN, R.N., Vice President Clinical Operations and Chief Nursing Executive, Spectrum Health - Butterworth Hospital, Grand Rapids, MI, p. A356

ULRICH, Alan, Chief Financial Officer, Guam Memorial Hospital Authority, Tamuning, GU, p. A805

ULRICH, James P. Jr, Chief Executive Officer, York General, York, NE, p. A440

ULRICH, Kari, R.N., Chief Nursing Officer, Director Operating Room, Surgical Specialty Center Of Baton Rouge, Baton Rouge, LA, p. A297

ULSETH, Randy, Chief Executive Officer, Welia Health, Mora, MN, p. A381

ULVELING, Kyle, M.D., Chief of Staff, St. Anthony Regional Hospital, Carroll, IA, p. A244

UMBERGER, Lori, Chief Nursing Officer, Boys Town National Research Hospital, Omaha, NE, p. A436

UMHAU, John, M.D., Clinical Director, U. S. Public Health Service Indian Hospital-Whiteriver, Whiteriver, AZ, p. A41

UNDERDAHL, Steve, President and Chief Executive Officer, Northfield Hospital And Clinics, Northfield, MN, p. A382

UNDERHILL, Robert, Director of Business Services, Central State Hospital, Louisville, KY, p. A288

UNDERWOOD, Ashley, Administrator, Adventhealth Rollins Brook, Lampasas, TX, p. A694

UNDERWOOD, Debbie, Manager Human Resources, Plains Memorial Hospital, Dimmitt, TX, p. A673

UNDERWOOD, Jerri, R.N., Chief Nursing Officer, Parkridge Medical Center, Chattanooga, TN, p. A636

UNDERWOOD, Kelsey, Director of Nursing, Gundersen Tri-County Hospital And Clinics, Whitehall, WI, p. A799

UNDERWOOD, Ken, Chief Executive Officer, Hazel Hawkins Memorial Hospital, Hollister, CA, p. A68

UNDERWOOD, Phillip. Chief Executive Officer, Kindred Hospital-Dayton, Dayton, OH, p. A538

UNDERWOOD, Vickie, Director Human Resources, Wyandot Memorial Hospital, Upper Sandusky, OH, p. A551

UNDERWOOD, Virgil, Chief Executive Officer, Boone Memorial Hospital, Madison, WV, p. A774

UNDLIN, Cassie, Chief Operating Officer, Navos, Seattle, WA, p. A763

UNELL, Deonna, Chief Executive Officer, Baylor Surgical Hospital At Las Colinas, Irving, TX, p. A690

UNG, David, Director, Information Technology, California Hospital Medical Center, Los Angeles, CA, p. A73
Site Director, St. Mary Medical Center Long Beach, Long Beach, CA, p. A72

UNGER, Henry, M.D., Senior Vice President and Chief Medical Officer, Holy Redeemer Hospital, Meadowbrook, PA, p. A596

UNGER, Kevin L., Ph.D., FACHE, President and Chief Executive Officer, Uchealth Medical Center Of The Rockies, Loveland, CO, p. A117
Ph.D., FACHE, President and Chief Executive Officer, Uchealth Poudre Valley Hospital, Fort Collins, CO, p. A112

UNHEE, Kim, President, Mount Carmel St. Ann's, Westerville, OH, p. A553

UNITAN, Carol, M.D., Chief Medical Officer, Kaiser Westside Medical Center, Hillsboro, OR, p. A576

UNRUH, Greg, Chief Executive Officer, Citizens Medical Center, Colby, KS, p. A263

UNZEN, John, Chief Financial Officer, Mille Lacs Health System, Onamia, MN, p. A382

UPCHURCH, Jim, M.D., Chief Medical Officer, Crow/Northern Cheyenne Hospital, Crow Agency, MT, p. A422

UPCRAFT, Jeffrey, Director Information Services, Southwest Healthcare System, Murrieta, CA, p. A80

UPFIELD, Jaclyn, Chief Operating Officer, G. Werber Bryan Psychiatric Hospital, Columbia, SC, p. A617

UPHOFF, Kimberly, Vice President Operations, Sarah Bush Lincoln Health Center, Mattoon, IL, p. A211

UPSHAW, Joy, Chief Nursing Officer, Oklahoma State University Medical Center, Tulsa, OK, p. A570

UPTON, Daniel, Vice President and Chief Financial Officer, Doylestown Hospital, Doylestown, PA, p. A588

UPTON, Matthew, Chief Medical Information Officer, Thomas Memorial Hospital, South Charleston, WV, p. A777
Chief Medical Officer and Chief Medical Information Officer, Saint Francis Hospital, Charleston, WV, p. A771

URAIZEE, Rizwan, Chief Financial Officer, Kedren Community Mental Health Center, Los Angeles, CA, p. A75

URBAN, Frank, Chief Financial Officer, Southwood Psychiatric Hospital, Pittsburgh, PA, p. A603

URBAN, Melanie D., Administrator, University Of Kansas Health System Pawnee Valley Campus, Larned, KS, p. A268

URBANCSIK, Don, Director Finance, Euclid Hospital, Euclid, OH, p. A540
Director Finance, Lutheran Hospital, Cleveland, OH, p. A534

URBISTONDO, Lisa, Chief Financial Officer, Medical Center Of Peach County, Navicent Health, Bryon, GA, p. A167

URDANETA, Alfonso, M.D., President Medical Staff, Washington County Hospital, Nashville, IL, p. A214

URISH, Abigail, M.D., Chief of Staff, Rangely District Hospital, Rangely, CO, p. A118

URLAUB, Charles J., President and Chief Executive Offricer, Mount St. Mary's Hospital And Health Center, Lewiston, NY, p. A487

URQUHART, Mary, R.N., Vice President Patient Care, Brattleboro Memorial Hospital, Brattleboro, VT, p. A735
Vice President Patient Care Services and Director of Quality, New England Sinai Hospital And Rehabilitation Center, Stoughton, MA, p. A345

URQUHART, Mary Beth., Interim President, Vice President Patient Care Services and Chief Nursing Officer, New England Sinai Hospital And Rehabilitation Center, Stoughton, MA, p. A345

URQUHART, Teresa C., Chief Executive Officer, Palm Beach Gardens Medical Center, Palm Beach Gardens, FL, p. A152

URQUIA, Arianna, Chief Financial Officer, Nicklaus Children's Hospital, Miami, FL, p. A147

URSCHEL, Dorothy, Chief Operating Officer, Columbia Memorial Hospital, Hudson, NY, p. A485

USELMAN, Krista, Chief Executive Officer, Encompass Health Rehabilitation Hospital The Vintage, Houston, TX, p. A685

USELMAN, Melissa, Chief Financial Officer, Gundersen Boscobel Area Hospital And Clinics, Boscobel, WI, p. A781

UTECHT, Tom, M.D., Chief Medical Officer, Community Regional Medical Center, Fresno, CA, p. A65
M.D., Corporate Chief Quality Officer, Fresno Heart And Surgical Hospital, Fresno, CA, p. A65
M.D., Senior Vice President and Chief Quality Officer, Community Behavioral Health Center, Fresno, CA, p. A65

UTLEY, Donna, Vice President Human Resources, Mercy San Juan Medical Center, Carmichael, CA, p. A59

UTLEY, Renee, Chief Financial Officer, Hamilton Center, Terre Haute, IN, p. A241

UTTENDORFSKY, Rob, Director Information Management, Lewis County General Hospital, Lowville, NY, p. A487

UTTERBACK, Julie, Chief Financial Officer, Roane Medical Center, Harriman, TN, p. A639

UYEMURA, Monte, M.D., Chief of Staff, Wray Community District Hospital, Wray, CO, p. A120

UZABEL, Samuel, M.D., Chief Medical Officer, Bonner General Health, Sandpoint, ID, p. A193

# V

VAAGENES, Carl P., Chief Executive Officer, Alomere Health, Alexandria, MN, p. A371

VAALER, Mark, M.D., Chief Medical Officer, South Florida Baptist Hospital, Plant City, FL, p. A154

VACCARO, Stacey, Chief Operating Officer, The Children's Institute Of Pittsburgh, Pittsburgh, PA, p. A603

VACHON, Scott, Director Information Technology, Littleton Regional Healthcare, Littleton, NH, p. A450

VADYAK, Karen, Chief Nursing Officer, St. Luke's Easton Campus, Easton, PA, p. A589

VAEZAZIZI, Reza, M.D., Chief of Staff, Southwest Healthcare System, Murrieta, CA, p. A80

VAGUE, Jeff, Regional Manager Information Systems, Mercy Hospitals Of Bakersfield, Bakersfield, CA, p. A57

VAHLBERG, Susan, Director Employee and Community Relations, Valor Health, Emmett, ID, p. A190

VAIL, B, Director Information Systems, Morehouse General Hospital, Bastrop. LA, p. A296

VAIL, Bryan, Chief Information Officer, Clement J. Zablocki Veterans Affairs Medical Center, Milwaukee, WI, p. A791

VAIL, Lisa, R.N., Chief Nursing Officer and Vice President Patient Care Services, Bryan Medical Center, Lincoln, NE, p. A434

VAIL, Ronald, M.D., Chief of Staff, Lower Umpqua Hospital District, Reedsport, OR, p. A580

VAILLANCOURT, Alex, Chief Information Officer, Christ Hospital, Cincinnati, OH, p. A532

VAILLANCOURT, Stacy, Vice President Marketing, Communications, Advocacy and Human Resources, Saint Agnes Medical Center, Fresno, CA, p. A65

VALDENEGRO, Maria, Chief Financial Officer, Meadow Wood Behavioral Health System, New Castle, DE, p. A127

VALDERAZ, Leonard, Administrator, Sunrise Canyon Hospital, Lubbock, TX, p. A698

VALDESPINO, Gustavo A., President and Chief Executive Officer, Valley Presbyterian Hospital, Van Nuys, CA, p. A103

VALENCA, Robert, Director, Human Resources, Colleton Medical Center, Walterboro, SC, p. A625

VALENCERINA, Madeline, Chief Operating Officer, Kedren Community Mental Health Center, Los Angeles, CA, p. A75

VALENTE, Anthony, M.D., Vice President Medical Affairs, Lehigh Valley Hospital - Hazleton, Hazleton, PA, p. A592

VALENTE, T., M.D., Medical Director, Lifestream Behavioral Center, Leesburg, FL, p. A144

VALENTIN, Carlos, Chief Financial Officer, St. Luke's Episcopal Hospital, Ponce, PR, p. A809

VALENTIN, Leonardo, Chief Executive Officer, Professional Hospital Guaynabo, Guaynabo, PR, p. A807

VALENTINE, Lisa R., Chief Executive Officer, Orange Park Medical Center, Orange Park, FL, p. A150

VALENTINE, Mark, President, Baylor Scott & White The Heart Hospital Denton, Denton, TX, p. A671

President, Baylor Scott & White The Heart Hospital Plano, Plano, TX, p. A706

VALENTINI, Rudolph, M.D., Chief Medical Officer, Dmc - Children's Hospital Of Michigan, Detroit, MI, p. A352

VALENTO, Jessica, Director Information Systems, Fairview Range Medical Center, Hibbing, MN, p. A378

VALLE, Bernardo, Vice President Human Resources, Usmd Hospital At Arlington, Arlington, TX, p. A654

VALLE, David, Chief Information Officer, Hospital Pavia Arecibo, Arecibo, PR, p. A806

VALLE, Karla, Area Chief Financial Officer, Kaiser Permanente Panorama City Medical Center, Panorama City, CA, p. A84

VALLELY, Ian, Information Technology Site Leader, Sequoia Hospital, Redwood City, CA, p. A88

VALLIDO, Gabe, Chief Information Officer, Naval Hospital Camp Pendleton, Camp Pendleton, CA, p. A59

VALLIERE, George, Chief Executive Officer, Claremore Indian Hospital, Claremore, OK, p. A557

VAN BREE, Margaret M., Dr.PH, President, Rhode Island Hospital, Providence, RI, p. A614

VAN BRUNT, Lisa, Chief Nursing Officer, Washakie Medical Center, Worland, WY, p. A804

VAN BUSKIRK, George, M.D., Chief of Staff, Bay Pines Veterans Affairs Healthcare System, Bay Pines, FL, p. A131

VAN BUSKIRK, Kryder Medical Staff President at EMRMC, Ephraim Mcdowell Regional Medical Center, Danville, KY, p. A282

VAN CAMP, Keith, Vice President Information Services, St. Dominic-Jackson Memorial Hospital, Jackson, MS, p. A395

VAN CLEAVE, Chad, Chief Financial Officer, Columbus Community Hospital, Columbus, NE, p. A431

VAN DECAR, Tama, M.D., Chief Medical Officer, Fort Walton Beach Medical Center, Fort Walton Beach, FL, p. A138

VAN DEELEN, Nicholas, Chief Medical Officer and Vice President, Medical Affairs, St. Luke's Hospital, Duluth, MN, p. A375

VAN DRIEL, Allen, Chief Executive Officer, Smith County Memorial Hospital, Smith Center, KS, p. A276

VAN DUREN, Michael, M.D., Chief Medical Officer, Bay Area Hospital, Coos Bay, OR, p. A574

VAN DYK, Holly, M.D., Interim Chief Medical Officer, Tuba City Regional Health Care Corporation, Tuba City, AZ, p. A39

VAN EECKHOUT, Barbara, M.D., Chief of Staff, Los Alamos Medical Center, Los Alamos, NM, p. A470

VAN EPERN, Keri, Manager Human Resources, Aspirus Ironwood Hospitals & Clinics, Inc., Ironwood, MI, p. A358

VAN ESSENDELFT, Seth, Vice President and Chief Financial Officer, Lawrence + Memorial Hospital, New London, CT, p. A124
Vice President and Chief Financial Officer, Westerly Hospital, Westerly, RI, p. A614

VAN ETTEN, Mark, M.D., Chief of Staff, Spooner Health, Spooner, WI, p. A796

VAN GENDEREN, Nathan, Executive Vice President and Chief Financial Officer, Mercy Medical Center - Cedar Rapids, Cedar Rapids, IA, p. A245

VAN HOET, Jim, Chief Financial Officer, Coffey County Hospital, Burlington, KS, p. A262

VAN HOUDEN, Charles, M.D., Chief Medical Officer, Neosho Memorial Regional Medical Center, Chanute, KS, p. A262

VAN KAMPEN, Cindy, Chief Nursing Officer, North Ottawa Community Hospital, Grand Haven, MI, p. A355

VAN MATRE, Jennifer, Chief Financial Officer, Trinity Hospital, Weaverville, CA, p. A104

VAN MEETEREN, Robert, President and Chief Executive Officer, Reedsburg Area Medical Center, Reedsburg, WI, p. A795

VAN METER, Rex, Chief Hospital Executive, Integris Baptist Medical Center, Oklahoma City, OK, p. A564
President, Integris Deaconess, Oklahoma City, OK, p. A564

VAN NATTA, Timothy, M.D., Chief Medical Officer, Harbor-Ucla Medical Center, Torrance, CA, p. A101

VAN RYBROEK, Greg, Chief Executive Officer, Mendota Mental Health Institute, Madison, WI, p. A787

VAN SCOYK, Mitch, Manager Information Systems, Delta County Memorial Hospital, Delta, CO, p. A110

VAN VICKLE, Robin, Chief Financial Officer, Bristow Medical Center, Bristow, OK, p. A556

VAN VRANKEN, Arthur, M.D., Chief Medical Officer, Essentia Health-Graceville, Graceville, MN, p. A377

VAN WAGONER, Scott, M.D., Chief Medical Officer, American Fork Hospital, American Fork, UT, p. A727

VAN WHY, Susan, Director Human Resources, St. Luke's Hospital - Miners Campus, Coaldale, PA, p. A587

VAN WINKLE, James, M.D., Chief of Staff, Unity Medical Center, Manchester, TN, p. A643

VAN WINKLE, Melanie, Chief Financial Officer, Mammoth Hospital, Mammoth Lakes, CA, p. A77

VAN ZANTEN, Lorinda, MSN, Chief Executive, Providence Newberg Medical Center, Newberg, OR, p. A578

VANATOR, John, CPA, Chief Executive Officer, Indiana University Health Jay Hospital, Portland, IN, p. A239
CPA, Chief Financial Officer, Indiana University Health Ball Memorial Hospital, Muncie, IN, p. A237
CPA, Chief Financial Officer, Indiana University Health Blackford Hospital, Hartford City, IN, p. A230

VANBOEKEL, Tony, Director Information Systems, Shasta Regional Medical Center, Redding, CA, p. A87

VANCE, Derek, FACHE, President, Chi Health Nebraska Heart, Lincoln, NE, p. A434
FACHE, President, Chi Health St Elizabeth, Lincoln, NE, p. A434

VANCE, Ellen, Chief Human Resources Officer, Sheltering Arms Hospital South, Midlothian, VA, p. A746

VANCE, Mark, M.D., Chief Medical Officer, Quincy Valley Medical Center, Quincy, WA, p. A762

VANCE, Ruth, Director Information Systems, Quincy Valley Medical Center, Quincy, WA, p. A762

VANCE, Stacie, Chief Nursing Officer and Vice President Operations, Orthoindy Hospital, Indianapolis, IN, p. A232
Chief Nursing Officer and, Orthoindy Hospital, Indianapolis, IN, p. A232

VANCE, Steven, Information Technology Director, Lake District Hospital, Lakeview, OR, p. A577

VANDENBARK, Heather, Human Resources Specialist, State Hospital North, Orofino, ID, p. A192

VANDENBERG, Andra, Director Human Resources, Butler County Health Care Center, David City, NE, p. A431

VANDENBOSCH, Dan, Chief Information Officer, Madison County Health Care System, Winterset, IA, p. A260

VANDERHOOFT, J, M.D., President Medical Staff, St. Mark's Hospital, Salt Lake City, UT, p. A733

VANDERMARK, Jay, Chief Financial Officer, Veterans Affairs Northern Indiana Health Care System, Fort Wayne, IN, p. A229

VANDERMEER, Nick, Director Information Systems, Banner Payson Medical Center, Payson, AZ, p. A34

VANDERPOL, Antoinette, Chief of Staff, Avera St. Benedict Health Center, Parkston, SD, p. A630

VANDERPOOL, Lee, Vice President, Dominican Hospital, Santa Cruz, CA, p. A97

VANDERSCHAAFF, Trixie, Chief Nursing Officer, St. Anthony Summit Medical Center, Frisco, CO, p. A113

VANDERSLICE, Douglas, Senior Vice President and Chief Financial Officer, Boston Children's Hospital, Boston, MA, p. A335

VANDERSTOUW, Karl, Vice President and Chief Information Officer, Unc Lenoir Healthcare, Kinston, NC, p. A513

VANDERVEER, Mark, Chief Financial Officer, Gunnison Valley Hospital, Gunnison, CO, p. A114

VANDERVLIET, William, M.D., Vice President Medical Affairs, Holland Hospital, Holland, MI, p. A357

VANDERWEGE, Larry, Administrator, Lindsborg Community Hospital, Lindsborg, KS, p. A270

VANDEWEGE, Dana, Director Human Resources, Capital Medical Center, Olympia, WA, p. A761
Director Human Resources, Providence Centralia Hospital, Centralia, WA, p. A756

VANDONKELAAR, Rodney, Chief Financial Officer, Carolina Pines Regional Medical Center, Hartsville, SC, p. A621
Chief Financial Officer, Saint Thomas Highlands Hospital, Sparta, TN, p. A649

VANDORT, Patti, MSN, R.N., Vice President Nursing/Chief Nursing Officer, Holland Hospital, Holland, MI, p. A357

VANDRUFF, John, M.D., Chief of Staff, Banner Payson Medical Center, Payson, AZ, p. A34

VANDYKE, Yvonne, R.N., MSN, Chief Nursing Officer, Texas Market, Ascension Seton Northwest, Austin, TX, p. A655

VANEK, James, Chief Executive Officer, Columbus Community Hospital, Columbus, TX, p. A664

VANES, Wendell, Chief Financial Officer, Saint Mary's Regional Medical Center, Russellville, AR, p. A52

VANHAREN, James, M.D., Medical Director, Forest View Psychiatric Hospital, Grand Rapids, MI, p. A355

VANHOUWELING, Mason, Chief Executive Officer, University Medical Center, Las Vegas, NV, p. A444

VANHOY, Michael, Director of Quality, Uva Encompass Health Rehabilitation Hospital, Charlottesville, VA, p. A740

VANHYNING, Jill, Director of Human Resources, Fairfield Memorial Hospital, Fairfield, IL, p. A205

VANKEKERIX, Emily, Director Human Resources, Osceola Regional Health Center, Sibley, IA, p. A257

VANNATTER, Mistie, Chief Nursing Officer, Advanced Care Hospital Of White County, Searcy, AR, p. A52

VANNETT, Vince, Director Human Resources, Jellico Community Hospital, Jellico, TN, p. A640

VANO, Ann, Vice President Human Resources, Ascension Of Providence Hospital, Southfield Campus, Southfield, MI, p. A367

Vice President, Human Resources, Ascension Crittenton Hospital Medical Center, Rochester, MI, p. A365

VANOSDOL, Thomas J., Chief Executive Officer, St. Vincent's Medical Center Riverside, Jacksonville, FL, p. A141
Chief Executive Officer, St. Vincent's Medical Center Southside, Jacksonville, FL, p. A141

VANSANT, Scott, M.D., Chief Medical Officer, Central State Hospital, Milledgeville, GA, p. A177

VANSTRIEN, Amy, Director Talent Operations, Midwestern Regional Medical Center, Zion, IL, p. A222

VANTONGEREN, Teri, Director Information Services, Spectrum Health Pennock, Hastings, MI, p. A357

VANWALLAGHEN, Brenda, Interim Chief Nursing Officer, Dmc - Children's Hospital Of Michigan, Detroit, MI, p. A352

VANWICHEN, Ward C., Chief Executive Officer, Marias Medical Center, Shelby, MT, p. A427

VANWYHE, Brenda, Senior Vice President Finance and Chief Financial Officer, Rush-Copley Medical Center, Aurora, IL, p. A195

VARELA, Alberto M., M.D., President, Inspira Ponce, Ponce, PR, p. A809

VARELA, Nancy, Director Human Resources, Dsh Patton, Patton, CA, p. A85

VARGA, Patrick, Chief Operating Officer, Mercy Medical Center Redding, Redding, CA, p. A87

VARGAS, Idelfonso, Executive Director, Dr. Ramon E. Betances Hospital-Mayaguez Medical Center Branch, Mayaguez, PR, p. A808

VARGAS, Jose, M.D., Medical Director, West Gables Rehabilitation Hospital, Miami, FL, p. A147

VARGAS, Margie, Chief Human Resources Officer, Memorial Regional Hospital, Hollywood, FL, p. A140

VARGAS, Marisol, Director Finance, Hospital Del Maestro, San Juan, PR, p. A810

VARGAS, Nancy, Chief Human Resources, St. Joseph's Behavioral Health Center, Stockton, CA, p. A100
Director Human Resources, Mark Twain Medical Center, San Andreas, CA, p. A90
Vice President Human Resources, St. Joseph's Medical Center, Stockton, CA, p. A100

VARGAS-MAHAR, Monica, FACHE, Chief Executive Officer, The Hospitals Of Providence East Campus, El Paso, TX, p. A676

VARGHESE, Bindu, R.N., Chief Executive Officer, Encompass Health Rehabilitation Hospital Of Sugar Land, Sugar Land, TX, p. A717

VARGHESE, Roy, M.D., Chief of Staff, Mary Breckinridge Arh Hospital, Hyden, KY, p. A285

VARGHESE, Shibu, Vice President Human Resources, University Of Texas M.D. Anderson Cancer Center, Houston, TX, p. A689

VARIALE, Vincenzo, Chief Executive Officer, North Vista Hospital, North Las Vegas, NV, p. A445

VARIAN, Grant, M.D., Medical Director, Mary Rutan Hospital, Bellefontaine, OH, p. A529

VARK, Lawrence, M.D., Chief Medical Officer, Creek Nation Community Hospital, Okemah, OK, p. A563

VARLEY, Kevin, Chief Financial Officer, Curahealth Pittsburgh, Oakdale, PA, p. A598

VARNADO, Anjanette, M.D., Chief Medical Officer, St. Helena Parish Hospital, Greensburg, LA, p. A302

VARNADO, Darryl, Executive Vice President and Chief People Officer, Children's National Hospital, Washington, DC, p. A129

VARNADO, Donna, Vice President Finance, Cypress Pointe Surgical Hospital, Hammond, LA, p. A302

VARNADO, Kim, R.N., Chief Nursing Officer, Highland Community Hospital, Picayune, MS, p. A398

VARNADOE, Milo, Director Information Systems, Warm Springs Medical Center, Warm Springs, GA, p. A183

VARNADOE, Tiffany G., Chief Executive Officer and Chief Financial Officer, Burke Medical Center, Waynesboro, GA, p. A183

VARNAM, Jessica, Chief of Staff, Grant Regional Health Center, Lancaster, WI, p. A787

VARNER, Terry, Administrator, Yalobusha General Hospital, Water Valley, MS, p. A401

VARNEY, Tim, R.N., Chief Nursing Officer, Select Specialty Hospital-Ann Arbor, Ypsilanti, MI, p. A370

VARTANIAN, Sarkis, Chief Nursing Officer, Whittier Hospital Medical Center, Whittier, CA, p. A105

VARTELAS, Helene M., MSN, Chief Executive Officer, Connecticut Valley Hospital, Middletown, CT, p. A123

VASCONCELLOS, Jacques, Director, Operations, Winter Haven Hospital, Winter Haven, FL, p. A162

VASEK, Barbara, Director Information Technology, Yoakum Community Hospital, Yoakum, TX, p. A726

VASHISHTA, Ashok, M.D., Vice President Medical Affairs, Mclaren Central Michigan, Mount Pleasant, MI, p. A362

VASIL, Kathleen, Vice President Finance, St. Charles Hospital, Port Jefferson, NY, p. A495

VASILE, Ann, M.D., Medical Director, Encompass Health Rehabilitation Hospital Of Tustin, Tustin, CA, p. A102

VASQUEZ, Alberto, Administrator, Garfield Memorial Hospital, Panguitch, UT, p. A730

VASQUEZ, Barbara, Chief Nursing Officer, Kingwood Pines Hospital, Kingwood, TX, p. A693

VASQUEZ, Carlos, Vice President and Chief Operating Officer, Franciscan Health Rensselear, Rensselaer, IN, p. A239

VASQUEZ, Christann, Executive Vice President and Chief Operating Officer, University Health System, San Antonio, TX, p. A714
Regional Hospital President, Ascension Seton Medical Center Austin, Austin, TX, p. A654
Regional Hospital President, Ascension Seton Shoal Creek, Austin, TX, p. A655
Regional Hospital President, Dell Seton Medical Center At The University Of Texas, Austin, TX, p. A656

VASQUEZ, George, Chief Technology Officer, Clovis Community Medical Center, Clovis, CA, p. A60
Corporate Chief Information Officer, Fresno Heart And Surgical Hospital, Fresno, CA, p. A65
Vice President Information Services, Community Behavioral Health Center, Fresno, CA, p. A65

VASQUEZ, Jill, Manager Human Resources, Spectrum Health Ludington Hospital, Ludington, MI, p. A361
Senior Business Partner, Spectrum Health Gerber Memorial, Fremont, MI, p. A355

VASQUEZ, Nelson, Vice President Finance, Jackson Park Hospital And Medical Center, Chicago, IL, p. A198

VASQUEZ, Stacy J., Chief Executive Officer, Birmingham Veterans Affairs Medical Center, Birmingham, AL, p. A14
Director, Beckley Veterans Affairs Medical Center, Beckley, WV, p. A770

VASS, Paula, Vice President Clinical Operations, Walden Behavioral Care, Waltham, MA, p. A345

VASTOLA, David, Medical Director, Searhc Mt. Edgecumbe Hospital, Sitka, AK, p. A29

VASUNAGA, Amy, Chief Nurse Executive, Leahi Hospital, Honolulu, HI, p. A184

VATH, Richard, M.D., Vice President Medical Affairs, Our Lady Of The Lake Regional Medical Center, Baton Rouge, LA, p. A297

VAUGHAN, Alan, Director Information Technology, Share Medical Center, Alva, OK, p. A555

VAUGHAN, Amanda, Chief Financial Officer, Bob Wilson Memorial Grant County Hospital, Ulysses, KS, p. A278
Chief Financial Officer, St. Catherine Hospital, Garden City, KS, p. A264

VAUGHAN, Brandon, Chief Financial Officer and Vice President Finance, Jamestown Regional Medical Center, Jamestown, ND, p. A524

VAUGHAN, Dee, Director Information Technology, Hermann Area District Hospital, Hermann, MO, p. A407

VAUGHAN, Peggy, M.D., Senior Vice President Medical Affairs, University Of Maryland Harford Memorial Hospital, Havre De Grace, MD, p. A330
M.D., Senior Vice President Medical Affairs, University Of Maryland Upper Chesapeake Medical Center, Bel Air, MD, p. A327

VAUGHAN, Rob, Chief Financial Officer, Carilion New River Valley Medical Center, Christiansburg, VA, p. A740

VAUGHN, Barbara, R.N., Chief Nursing Officer, Carrollton Regional Medical Center, Carrollton, TX, p. A663

VAUGHN, Debbie, Chief Nursing Officer, The Medical Center Of Southeast Texas, Port Arthur, TX, p. A707

VAUGHN, Joseph, Director, W. G. (Bill) Heffner Veterans Affairs Medical Center, Salisbury, NC, p. A518

VAUGHN, Kerry, Chief Information Officer, St. Mary's Health Care System, Athens, GA, p. A164

VAUGHN, Michael, Director of Nursing, Southeast Rehabilitation Hospital, Lake Village, AR, p. A48

VAUGHN, Sandy, Director Information Services, Baylor Scott & White All Saints Medical Center - Fort Worth, Fort Worth, TX, p. A678
Director Information Systems, Baylor Scott & White Medical Center - Grapevine, Grapevine, TX, p. A682

VAUGHN, Ted, Director Human Resources, Unitypoint Health - Trinity Regional Medical Center, Fort Dodge, IA, p. A250

VAUGHN, Vickie, Chief Nursing Officer, Tennova Healthcare-Shelbyville, Shelbyville, TN, p. A649

VAUGHN ESQ, SharmaChief Nursing Officer, Rangely District Hospital, Rangely, CO, p. A118

VAVARUTSOS, Tony, Director Information Systems, Thorek Memorial Hospital, Chicago, IL, p. A201

VAZQUEZ, Brunilda, Medical Director, Hospital De Psiquiatria, San Juan, PR, p. A810

VAZQUEZ, Emilio, M.D., Chief Medical Officer, Parkview Dekalb Hospital, Auburn, IN, p. A223

VAZQUEZ, Francisco, Director, Michael E. Debakey Veterans Affairs Medical Center, Houston, TX, p. A687

VAZQUEZ, Joe, Chief Financial Officer, Methodist Hospital South, Jourdanton, TX, p. A691

VEACH, Jamie, Chief Operating Officer, Clay County Hospital, Flora, IL, p. A205

VEAL, Bonita, Chief Nursing Officer, Anaheim Global Medical Center, Anaheim, CA, p. A55

VEDRAL-BARON, Jennifer, Health System Director, Tennessee Valley Healthcare System, Nashville, TN, p. A647

VEERAMACHANENI, Harish, M.D., Chief of Staff, Wayne Medical Center, Waynesboro, TN, p. A650

VEESER, Tom, Chief Nursing Officer, Ascension St. Michael's Hospital, Stevens Point, WI, p. A796

VEGA, James, Director Information Systems, Palm Beach Gardens Medical Center, Palm Beach Gardens, FL, p. A152

VEGA, Jane, Executive Director, Industrial Hospital, San Juan, PR, p. A811

VEGA, Maria, Director Human Resources, Auxilio Mutuo Hospital, San Juan, PR, p. A809

VEGA, Mary, R.N., MSN, Vice President Nursing, St. Margaret's Hospital, Spring Valley, IL, p. A214

VEGA, Oscar, M.D., Chief Medical Officer, Las Palmas Medical Center, El Paso, TX, p. A675

VEGA, Zoraida, MSN, R.N., Chief Nursing Officer, St. Luke's Episcopal Hospital, Ponce, PR, p. A809

VEILLETTE, Michael, Senior Vice President and Chief Financial Officer, Manchester Memorial Hospital, Manchester, CT, p. A122

Senior Vice President and Chief Financial Officer, Rockville General Hospital, Vernon, CT, p. A125

VEILLEUX, Jeffrey, Executive Vice President and Chief Financial Officer, Swedish Medical Center-First Hill, Seattle, WA, p. A764

Senior Vice President and Chief Financial Officer, Swedish Medical Center-Cherry Hill Campus, Seattle, WA, p. A764

VEILLON, Paul, CPA, Chief Financial Officer, Christus Dubuis Hospital Of Fort Smith, Fort Smith, AR, p. A46

CPA, Chief Financial Officer, Christus Dubuis Hospital Of Hot Springs, Hot Springs National Park, AR, p. A47

VEIT, Amanda, R.N., Chief Nursing Officer, Presbyterian/St. Luke's Medical Center, Denver, CO, p. A111

VELA, Javier, Director Information Technology, Baylor Scott & White Medical Center-Uptown, Dallas, TX, p. A667

VELA, Manuel, President and Chief Executive Officer, Valley Baptist Medical Center-Harlingen, Harlingen, TX, p. A683

VELARDI, Antonio, M.D., Chief Quality Officer, Health Central Hospital, Ocoee, FL, p. A150

VELASCO, Paul, IT Manager, Kit Carson County Health Service District, Burlington, CO, p. A108

VELASQUEZ, Alfred, Area Information Officer, Kaiser Permanente Moreno Valley Medical Center, Moreno Valley, CA, p. A80

Area Information Officer, Kaiser Permanente Riverside Medical Center, Riverside, CA, p. A88

VELASQUEZ, Lin, Vice President Human Resources, St. Louise Regional Hospital, Gilroy, CA, p. A66

VELEZ, Luz, Director-Administration of Nursing Services, Hospital San Carlos Borromeo, Moca, PR, p. A808

VELEZ, Pablo, R.N., Ph.D., Chief Executive Officer, Sharp Chula Vista Medical Center, Chula Vista, CA, p. A60

VELEZ, Raul, Information Technology Director, North Alabama Medical Center, Florence, AL, p. A18

VENABLE, Jennifer, Chief Financial Officer, Washington County Hospital, Nashville, IL, p. A214

VENABLE, Mark, Director Human Resources, Shriners Hospitals For Children-St. Louis, Saint Louis, MO, p. A416

Interim Administrator, Shriners Hospitals For Children-St. Louis, Saint Louis, MO, p. A416

VENABLE, Robert, M.D., Chief Medical Staff, Washington County Hospital, Plymouth, NC, p. A516

VENDETTI, Marilouise, M.D., Chief Medical Officer, Atlanticare Regional Medical Center, Atlantic City, NJ, p. A452

VENEZIANO, Terri, Interim Chief Nursing Officer, Columbus Regional Healthcare System, Whiteville, NC, p. A519

VENGCO, Joel, MS, Vice President, Chief Information Officer, Baystate Medical Center, Springfield, MA, p. A344

VENHUIZEN, Pamela, Chief Human Resources Officer, Cooperstown Medical Center, Cooperstown, ND, p. A522

VENOIT, Jon-Paul, Chief Operating Officer, Masonicare Health Center, Wallingford, CT, p. A126

President and Chief Executive Officer, Masonicare Health Center, Wallingford, CT, p. A126

VENTURA, Rosemary, M.D., Chief Nursing Informatics Officer, New York-Presbyterian Hospital, New York, NY, p. A491

VENTURA, Sylvia, R.N., MS, Chief Nursing Officer, Olympia Medical Center, Los Angeles, CA, p. A75

VENTURELLA, James, Vice President Information Technology, West Virginia University Hospitals, Morgantown, WV, p. A775

VENUTO, Frank, Chief Human Capital Officer, Nebraska Medicine - Nebraska Medical Center, Omaha, NE, p. A437

VERA, Danny, PharmD, Regional Vice President and Chief Operating Officer, Cascade Valley Hospital, Arlington, WA, p. A755

VERA, Luis, M.D., Medical Director, Kensington Hospital, Philadelphia, PA, p. A601

VERAGIWALA, Jignesh, Chief of Staff, Mercy Hospital Logan County, Guthrie, OK, p. A559

VERCHER, Gretchen, Chief Nursing Officer, Encompass Health Rehabilitation Hospital Of Montgomery, Montgomery, AL, p. A22

VERDEJA, Juan-Carlos, M.D., President of Medical Staff, Baptist Health South Florida, West Kendall Baptist Hospital, Miami, FL, p. A146

VERFURTH, Larry, D.O., Executive Vice President and Chief Medical Officer, Christus Good Shepherd Medical Center-Marshall, Marshall, TX, p. A700

VERGA, Josep. P., FACHE, Chief Executive Officer, Guam Memorial Hospital Authority, Tamuning, GU, p. A805

VERGARA, Aimee, Chief Executive Officer, Hospital For Extended Recovery, Norfolk, VA, p. A748

VERGONIO, Merlinda, Chief Information Management and Technology, U. S. Air Force Hospital, Hampton, VA, p. A743

VERGOS, Katherine, FACHE, President, St. Agnes Hospital, Fond Du Lac, WI, p. A784

VERINDER, David, President and Chief Executive Officer, Sarasota Memorial Health Care System, Sarasota, FL, p. A157

VERMA, Virendar, M.D., Medical Director, Encompass Health Rehabilitation Hospital Of Jonesboro, Jonesboro, AR, p. A47

VERMILLION, Kerry, Senior Vice President Finance and Chief Financial Officer, Gulf Breeze Hospital, Gulf Breeze, FL, p. A139

VERMULEN, Peter, Director Information Technology, Schick Shadel Hospital, Seattle, WA, p. A763

VERRETTE, Paul, M.D., Chief Medical Officer, St. Bernard Parish Hospital, Chalmette, LA, p. A299

VERRETTE, Paula, M.D., Senior Vice President Quality and Physician Services and Chief Medical Officer, Huntington Hospital, Pasadena, CA, p. A85

VERRILL, Alan, M.D., President Medical Staff, Bridgton Hospital, Bridgton, ME, p. A319

VERSALOVIC, Jim, M.D., Ph.D., Interim Physican-in-Chief, Texas Children's Hospital, Houston, TX, p. A688

VERVALIN, Paul, Interim Chief Executive Officer, Guthrie Corning Hospital, Corning, NY, p. A481

VETTER, Norman, Chief Executive Officer, Division of Substance Abuse and Mental Health, Delaware Psychiatric Center, New Castle, DE, p. A127

VETTER, Rich, M.D., Associate Chief, Essentia Health St. Mary's - Detroit Lakes, Detroit Lakes, MN, p. A375

VIALL, John, M.D., Vice President Medical Affairs, Holzer Medical Center, Gallipolis, OH, p. A541

VIATOR, Dionne, CPA, FACHE, President and Chief Executive Officer, Iberia Medical Center, New Iberia, LA, p. A310

VIBETO, Brett, M.D., Chief of Staff, Chi St. Alexius Health - Williston Medical Center, Williston, ND, p. A526

VIBHAKAR, Neel, M.D., Senior Vice President and Chief Medical Officer, University Of Maryland Baltimore Washington Medical Center, Glen Burnie, MD, p. A330

VICE, Jeff, Chief Operating Officer, Starke Hospital, Knox, IN, p. A234

VICENTE, Oscar, Chief Financial Officer, Palmetto General Hospital, Hialeah, FL, p. A139

VICENTI, Darren, M.D., Clinical Director, Hop. Health Care Center, Keams Canyon, AZ, p. A33

VICKERS, Cynthia, R.N., Assistant Administrator for Nursing Services, Memorial Hospital And Manor, Bainbridge, GA, p. A166

VICKERS, Dave, Chief Financial Officer, Los Alamitos Medical Center, Los Alamitos, CA, p. A73

VICKERS, Don, Chief Executive Officer, Cleveland Emergency Hospital, Cleveland, TX, p. A664

Chief Executive Officer, St. Michael's Elite Hospital, Sugar Land, TX, p. A718

VICKERS, Kathy, Director Human Resources, Vantage Point Of Northwest Arkansas, Fayetteville, AR, p. A45

VICKERY, Ian, Director Information Technology, D. W. Mcmillan Memorial Hospital, Brewton, AL, p. A16

VICKERY, Tim, Chief Information Officer, St. Mary's Sacred Heart Hospital, Lavonia, GA, p. A175

VICKROY, Joseph, M.D., Medical Director, Encompass Health Rehabilitation Hospital Of Utah, Sandy, UT, p. A733

VICKS, Ray, Senior Vice President, Finance and Chief Financial Officer, The Hsc Pediatric Center, Washington, DC, p. A130

VICTORIA, Mario, M.D., Vice President, Medical Affairs, Samaritan Medical Center, Watertown, NY, p. A502

VIEIRA, Jeanette, Chief Executive, Providence Hood River Memorial Hospital, Hood River, OR, p. A576

VIEIRA, Terri, President, Northern Light Inland Hospital, Waterville, ME, p. A323

President, Northern Light Sebasticook Valley Hospital, Pittsfield, ME, p. A322

VIELKIND, James, Chief Financial Officer, Cobleskill Regional Hospital, Cobleskill, NY, p. A481

Chief Financial Officer, Little Falls Hospital, Little Falls, NY, p. A487

VIENNEAU, Marie E., FACHE, President and Chief Executive Officer, Mayo Regional Hospital, Dover—Foxcroft, ME, p. A320

FACHE, President, Northern Light Ca Dean Hospital, Greenville, ME, p. A320

VIERLING, Taryn, Chief Nursing Officer, Select Specialty Hospital Of Southeast Ohio, Newark, OH, p. A546

VIG, Vibha, Chief of Staff, Merit Health Madison, Canton, MS, p. A390

VIGIL, Kevin, Director Information Systems, Los Alamos Medical Center, Los Alamos, NM, p. A470

VIGILANTE, Sarah, Manager Human Resources, Mammoth Hospital, Mammoth Lakes, CA, p. A77

VIGNA, Greg, M.D., Medical Director, Encompass Health Rehabilitation Hospital Of Modesto, Modesto, CA, p. A78

VIGNERI, Joseph, M.D., Chief Medical Officer, Summit Medical Center, Casper, WY, p. A801

VILANOVA, Lynda, Director Patient Care Services, Shriners Hospitals For Children-Spokane, Spokane, WA, p. A766

VILAR, Ramon J., Administrator, Wilma N. Vazquez Medical Center, Vega Baja, PR, p. A811

VILHAUER, Beverly, Chief Executive Officer, South Central Health, Wishek, ND, p. A526

VILLA, Alex, Chief Executive Officer, Tennova Healthcare-Clarksville, Clarksville, TN, p. A636

VILLA, Jo Ellen, R.N., Chief Executive Officer, Community Hospital Of Anaconda, Anaconda, MT, p. A421

VILLA, Maria, Interim Chief Nursing Officer, Kendall Regional Medical Center, Miami, FL, p. A146

VILLAFRANCO, Brenda, Administrator, Memorial Hermann First Colony Hospital, Sugar Land, TX, p. A717

VILLAFUERTE, Herbert, Chief Operating Officer and Chief Nursing Officer, Garfield Medical Center, Monterey Park, CA, p. A79

Chief Operating Officer/Chief Nursing Officer, Garfield Medical Center, Monterey Park, CA, p. A79

VILLANI, Travis A., FACHE, Chief Executive Officer and Administrator, Physicians' Hospital In Anadarko, Anadarko, OK, p. A555

VILLANO, Jeremi, M.D., Chief of Staff, Crook County Medical Services District, Sundance, WY, p. A804

VILLARREAL, Xavier, FACHE, Chief Executive Officer, Hillcrest Medical Center, Tulsa, OK, p. A569

VILLARRUZ, Alex, Chief Executive Officer, Healthbridge Children's Hospital, Orange, CA, p. A83

VILLEGAS, Lorraine, Manager Human Resources, Paradise Valley Hospital, National City, CA, p. A81

VILLEGAS, William, Vice President Finance, Fort Hamilton Hospital, Hamilton, OH, p. A542

VILLIGRAN, Anthony, Chief Financial Officer, Medical City Mckinney, Mckinney, TX, p. A700

VILUMS, Karlis, Chief Financial Officer, Broadlawns Medical Center, Des Moines, IA, p. A248

VINAS, Elmo, Director Human Resources, Franklin Foundation Hospital, Franklin, LA, p. A301

VINCENT, Cynthia, Vice President Finance and Operations, St. Francis Regional Medical Center, Shakopee, MN, p. A386

VINCENT, David, Director Information Systems, Canonsburg Hospital, Canonsburg, PA, p. A586

VINCENT, Joan, MSN, MS, R.N., Vice President Patient Care Services and Chief Nurse Executive, Adventist Healthcare Shady Grove Medical Center, Rockville, MD, p. A332

VINCENT, Larry, Chief Financial Officer, Delta County Memorial Hospital, Delta, CO, p. A110

VINCENT, Laurence, Chief Nursing Officer, University Hospital & Clinics, Lafayette, LA, p. A306

VINCENT, Mitchell, Vice President Organizational Support, Fairview Range Medical Center, Hibbing, MN, p. A378

VINCENT, Paula, MSN, President and Chief Operating Officer, Novant Health Presbyterian Medical Center, Charlotte, NC, p. A507

VINCENT, Scott, Chief Executive Officer, John C. Stennis Memorial Hospital, De Kalb, MS, p. A391

Chief Human Resource Officer, Specialty Hospital Of Meridian, Meridian, MS, p. A397

VINCENZ, Felix, Chief Operating Officer, St. Louis Psychiatric Rehabilitation Center, Saint Louis, MO, p. A417

VINCIFORA, Teresa, Chief Operating Officer, Benson Hospital, Benson, AZ, p. A30

VINCIGUERRA, Tracy, Chief Executive Officer, Encompass Health Rehabilitation Hospital Of Morgantown, Morgantown, WV, p. A774

VINCK, Jaime W., MC, Chief Executive Officer, Sierra Tucson, Tucson, AZ, p. A40

VINSANT, George, M.D., Chief Medical Officer, Tennova Healthcare-Lafollette Medical Center, La Follette, TN, p. A642

VIOLETTE, Brenda, M.D., Director Medical Staff, Firelands Regional Health System, Sandusky, OH, p. A549

VIRGEN, Tomas, R.N., MSN, Chief Operating Officer, El Centro Regional Medical Center, El Centro, CA, p. A63

VISCONI, Deborah D., President and Chief Executive Officer, Bergen New Bridge Medical Center, Paramus, NJ, p. A460

VISH, Nancy, Ph.D., FACHE, R.N., President, Baylor Scott & White Heart & Vascular Hospital-Dallas, Dallas, TX, p. A667

VISSA, Sriram, M.D., Vice President Medical Affairs, Ssm Health Depaul Hospital - St. Louis, Bridgeton, MO, p. A403

VISSER, Jessica, R.N., Vice President Patient Care Services and Chief Nursing Officer, Mount St. Mary's Hospital And Health Center, Lewiston, NY, p. A487

VISSER-LYNCH, Amy, Chief Nursing Officer, Mt. Ascutney Hospital And Health Center, Windsor, VT, p. A737

VISSERS, Robert, M.D., President and Chief Executive Officer, Boulder Community Health, Boulder, CO, p. A108

VITAL, Dale, Chief Nursing Officer, Memorialcare, Orange Coast Memorial Medical Center, Fountain Valley, CA, p. A64

VITALE-NOLEN, Roberta, Administrator, Patient Care Services, New Hampshire Hospital, Concord, NH, p. A448

VITALI, Joe, Director Information Technology, Parkside Psychiatric Hospital And Clinic, Tulsa, OK, p. A570

VITALI, Vincent, Chief Information Officer, Rml Specialty Hospital, Hinsdale, IL, p. A208

VITIELLO, Jon, Senior Vice President, Finance Operations and Analytics, Mercy Hospital Oklahoma City, Oklahoma City, OK, p. A564

VITOLAS, Victor, Acting Chief Information Technology Services, Central Texas Veterans Health Care System, Temple, TX, p. A719

VIVIANO, Paul S., President and Chief Executive Officer, Children's Hospital Los Angeles, Los Angeles, CA, p. A74

VIVIT, Romeo, Chief Surgeon, U. S. Public Health Service Indian Hospital, Rosebud, SD, p. A631

VIVODA, Michael, Senior Vice President Human Resources, Northwestern Medicine Valley West Hospital, Sandwich, IL, p. A219

Senior Vice President, Administration, Northwestern Memorial Hospital, Chicago, IL, p. A200

Senior Vice President, Human Resources, Northwestern Medicine Kishwaukee Hospital, Dekalb, IL, p. A202

VIZCARRA, Edred, M.D., Chief of Staff, St. Luke Community Healthcare, Ronan, MT, p. A427

VLAHAVAS, Beth, R.N., MSN, Vice President Patient Care Services and Chief Nursing Officer, Mercy Medical Center, Rockville Centre, NY, p. A497

VLARS, Scott, Chief Information Technology Services, Wilmington Veterans Affairs Medical Center, Wilmington, DE, p. A128

VLOSICH, Kristopher Wade., Director, Oklahoma City Veterans Affairs Medical Center, Oklahoma City, OK, p. A565

VOCCA, Lori, Vice President Human Resources, Providence Regional Medical Center Everett, Everett, WA, p. A758

VOECKS, Barbara, Chief Information Officer, Ortonville Area Health Services, Ortonville, MN, p. A382

VOELKEL, Jonathon, Chief Executive Officer, Reagan Memorial Hospital, Big Lake, TX, p. A659

VOELKER, Justin, Chief Financial Officer, Multicare Valley Hospital, Spokane Valley, WA, p. A766

VOELKER, Thomas, M.D., Chief Medical Officer, Aspirus Riverview Hospital And Clinics, Inc., Wisconsin Rapids, WI, p. A800

VOGEL, Clay, Administrator and Chief Executive Officer, Coleman County Medical Center, Coleman, TX, p. A664

VOGELSANG, Mark, Director Information Services, Providence Holy Family Hospital, Spokane, WA, p. A766

VOGENTIZ, William, M.D., Medical Director, Anmed Health Rehabilitation Hospital, Anderson, SC, p. A615

VOGT, Dennis, Director Information Technology, Madison Health, London, OH, p. A543

VOGT, Sam, Manager Human Resources, Hebrew Senior Care, West Hartford, CT, p. A126

VOHS, Lester, Manager Information Systems, Cass Regional Medical Center, Harrisonville, MO, p. A407

VOIGHT, John, Chief Nursing Officer, Oviedo Medical Center, Oviedo, FL, p. A152

VOIGT, Jordan, President, Genesis Medical Center - Davenport, Davenport, IA, p. A247

VOISARD, Victor, Director Human Resources, San Gabriel Valley Medical Center, San Gabriel, CA, p. A94

VOISELLE, Dana, Director Human Resources and Community Relations, Baptist Medical Center Beaches, Jacksonville Beach, FL, p. A142

VOKOUN, Cory, Chief Nursing Officer, Nevada Regional Medical Center, Nevada, MO, p. A413

VOLINSKI, Douglas, Vice President and Chief Financial Officer, Duncan Regional Hospital, Duncan, OK, p. A558

VOLK, Charles, M.D., Regional Chief Medical Officer, Christus Spohn Hospital Corpus Christi Memorial, Corpus Christi, TX, p. A665

VOLKERDING, Elizabeth, Director Workforce Excellence, San Juan Regional Medical Center, Farmington, NM, p. A469

VOLLER, Kristi, Director of Nursing, Mobridge Regional Hospital, Mobridge, SD, p. A629

VOLLMER, Kris, Director Patient Care Services, Avera Tyler Hospital, Tyler, MN, p. A387

VOLOCH, Bill, President and Chief Executive Officer, Wesley Healthcare Center, Wichita, KS, p. A279

VOLOVIC, Mark, Chief Information Officer, Indiana Regional Medical Center, Indiana, PA, p. A592

VOLPE, Buddy, Director Human Resources, Peterson Health, Kerrville, TX, p. A693

VOLPE, Michele M., Chief Executive Officer, Penn Presbyterian Medical Center, Philadelphia, PA, p. A601

VON ARX, Michelle, Chief Executive Officer, Penn State Hershey Rehabilitation Hospital, Hummelstown, PA, p. A592

VON BEHREN, Rachel, Director Financial Services, Unitypoint Health - Jones Regional Medical Center, Anamosa, IA, p. A243

VON NIEDA, Tij, Chief Executive Officer, Encompass Health Rehabilitation Hospital Of Las Vegas, Las Vegas, NV, p. A443

VONACHEN, April, Chief Financial Officer and Vice President Financial Services, Cumberland Medical Center, Crossville, TN, p. A637

VONFELDT, Krystal, M.D., Chief of Staff, Duncan Regional Hospital, Duncan, OK, p. A558

VONK, Brandon, Administrator, Bear River Valley Hospital, Tremonton, UT, p. A734

VOOYS, Nathan, Chief Executive Officer, Terre Haute Regional Hospital, Terre Haute, IN, p. A241

VOS, Helen, R.N., Interim Chief Nursing Officer, Peacehealth Southwest Medical Center, Vancouver, WA, p. A768

VOSHELL, Shane, Director Human Resources, Adventist Health Portland, Portland, OR, p. A579

VOSKUIL, Scott, M.D., Chief Medical Officer, Aurora Medical Center - Manitowoc County, Two Rivers, WI, p. A797

VOSS, Daryle, FACHE, President and Chief Executive Officer, Mercy Hospital Ardmore, Ardmore, OK, p. A556

VOSS, Kinsi, R.N., Chief Nursing Officer, Throckmorton County Memorial Hospital, Throckmorton, TX, p. A721

VOSS, Peter, M.D., Chief Medical Officer, Indiana University Health Ball Memorial Hospital, Muncie, IN, p. A237

VOSS, Robert, Chief Financial Officer, Laredo Specialty Hospital, Laredo, TX, p. A695

VOSS, Wayne M., Chief Executive Officer, Houston Methodist West Hospital, Houston, TX, p. A686

VOSSLER, Jeffrey, Chief Financial Officer, Joint Township District Memorial Hospital, Saint Marys, OH, p. A548

VRANA, Daniel, Area Controller, Encompass Health Rehabilitation Hospital Of Sewickley, Sewickley, PA, p. A607

Controller, Encompass Health Rehabilitation Hospital Of Hamarville, Pittsburgh, PA, p. A603

VRBA, Frank, Chief Information Officer, Annie Jeffrey Memorial County Health Center, Osceola, NE, p. A438

VRBAS, Laken, R.N., Director of Nursing, Dundy County Hospital, Benkelman, NE, p. A430

VROBEL, Matthew, Vice President, Medical Operations, Cleveland Clinic, Medina Hospital, Medina, OH, p. A545

VRONKO, Jeremy, Manager Information Services, Spectrum Health Gerber Memorial, Fremont, MI, p. A355

Manager, Information Services, Spectrum Health Ludington Hospital, Ludington, MI, p. A361

VUCETIC, Raymond, Chief Executive Officer, Summit Medical Center, Casper, WY, p. A801

VUCHAK, Jerry, Senior Vice President, Chief Information Officer, Children's Hospital And Medical Center, Omaha, NE, p. A437

VUKICH, David, M.D., Senior Vice President, Chief Medical Officer and Chief Quality Officer, Uf Health Jacksonville, Jacksonville, FL, p. A142

VUKSTA, Jeanne, Chief Financial Officer, Bacharach Institute For Rehabilitation, Pomona, NJ, p. A461

VUTRANO, Frank, Chief Financial Officer, Wyckoff Heights Medical Center, Brooklyn, NY, p. A479

VYZOUREK, Treg, Chief Executive Officer, Brodstone Memorial Hospital, Superior, NE, p. A440

# W

WAALA, Shelly, Vice President Patient Care Services and Chief Nursing Officer, Froedtert West Bend Hospital, West Bend, WI, p. A799

WABLE, Chad W., Chief Executive Officer, City Hospital At White Rock, Dallas, TX, p. A668

WACHOWIAK, Darrell, Associate Vice President Operations, Promedica Bay Park Hospital, Oregon, OH, p. A547

WACK, Mark, Chief Financial Officer, Memorial Hospital At Gulfport, Gulfport, MS, p. A393

WACKERFUSS, Toni, Chief Executive Officer, Encompass Health Rehabilitation Hospital Of Memphis, Memphis, TN, p. A644

WADDELL, Kathy, Administrator, Wayne General Hospital, Waynesboro, MS, p. A401

WADDELL, Lesa, Director Human Resources, Compass Memorial Healthcare, Marengo, IA, p. A253

WADE, Bruce, Vice President Human Resources, Indiana University Health Bedford Hospital, Bedford, IN, p. A224

WADE, Cynthia, R.N., Executive Vice President and Chief Operating Officer, Lincolnhealth, Damariscotta, ME, p. A320

WADE, Donna, Senior Director Human Resources, Comanche County Memorial Hospital, Lawton, OK, p. A561

WADE, Glenn, Director Information Systems, Saint Thomas Highlands Hospital, Sparta, TN, p. A649

WADE, Hong, Chief Financial Officer, Sweeny Community Hospital, Sweeny, TX, p. A718

WADE, Hope, Chief Operating Officer, Christus St. Vincent Regional Medical Center, Santa Fe, NM, p. A472

WADE, Jacqueline, Ph.D., Director, Desert Willow Treatment Center, Las Vegas, NV, p. A443

WADE, Jon, Chief Executive Officer, Presbyterian Santa Fe Medical Center, Santa Fe, NM, p. A472

WADE, Susan, Vice President, Hendrick Health System, Abilene, TX, p. A651

WADEWITZ, Martin, Chief Operations Officer/ Vice President, Operations, Angel Medical Center, Franklin, NC, p. A510

WADLE, Don, Interim Director Human Resources, Portneuf Medical Center, Pocatello, ID, p. A192

Vice President Clinical and Support Services, Portneuf Medical Center, Pocatello, ID, p. A192

WADSWORTH, Barbara, MSN, R.N., FACHE, Chief Nursing Officer, Bryn Mawr Hospital, Bryn Mawr, PA, p. A585

WAFFORD, Marty, Under Secretary of Support and Programs, Chickasaw Nation Medical Center, Ada, OK, p. A555

WAFLE, Sue, Director, Human Resources, Mile Bluff Medical Center, Mauston, WI, p. A789

WAGERS, Rick, Senior Executive Vice President and Chief Financial Officer, Regional One Health, Memphis, TN, p. A645

WAGGENER, Yvonne, Chief Financial Officer, Mountains Community Hospital, Lake Arrowhead, CA, p. A70

WAGGONER, Jeff, M.D., Chief of Staff, Weisbrod Memorial County Hospital, Eads, CO, p. A112

WAGGONER, Michelle, Chief Executive Officer, Community Memorial Hospital, Hicksville, OH, p. A542

WAGLEY, Ronnie, Market Chief Executive Officer, Select Specialty Hospital-Gainesville, Gainesville, FL, p. A139

WAGNER, Dale, Chief Financial Officer, Kindred Hospital-Westminster, Westminster, CA, p. A105

WAGNER, Danny, Chief Human Resource Officer, Allegiance Behavioral Health Center Of Plainview, Plainview, TX, p. A706

WAGNER, David, Chief Information Management Service, Veterans Affairs Gulf Coast Veterans Health Care System, Biloxi, MS, p. A390

WAGNER, David S., Chief Executive Officer, Hca Houston Healthcare Pearland, Pearland, TX, p. A705

WAGNER, Elaina, Director Human Resources, Astria Sunnyside Hospital, Sunnyside, WA, p. A766

WAGNER, Fred, Chief Financial Officer, Osf St. Francis Hospital And Medical Group. Escanaba, MI, p. A354

WAGNER, Gwendolyn, R.N., MSN, Chief Nursing Officer, Mission Community Hospital, Panorama City, CA, p. A84

WAGNER, Janet, R.N., Chief Executive Officer, Mills-Peninsula Health Services, Burlingame, CA, p. A59

WAGNER, Jefferey, Director, Information Technology, Lake Huron Medical Center, Port Huron, MI, p. A364

WAGNER, Jesse, M.D., Chief Medical Officer and Vice President, Quality and Patient Safety, Middlesex Hospital, Middletown, CT, p. A123

WAGNER, John, President and Chief Executive Officer, Hshs St. Joseph's Hospital, Chippewa Falls, WI, p. A781

WAGNER, Kelley, Director Employee Relations, Osf St. Josep. Medical Center, Bloomington, IL, p. A195

WAGNER, Linda, Chief Financial Officer, Sanford Worthington Medical Center, Worthington, MN, p. A388

WAGNER, Lynne, R.N., Chief Nursing Officer, Rose Medical Center, Denver, CO, p. A111

WAGNER, Randall, Chief Operating Officer, Mercy Health Saint Mary's, Grand Rapids, MI, p. A356

WAGNER, Renee, M.D., Chief Medical Officer, Fairfield Medical Center, Lancaster, OH, p. A542

WAGNER, Russell, Executive Vice President and Chief Financial Officer, Holy Redeemer Hospital, Meadowbrook, PA, p. A596

WAGNER, Sarah, Human Resources Officer, Memorial Hospital Of Texas County, Guymon, OK, p. A560

WAGNER, Sherrie, Manager Human Resources, The Core Institute Specialty Hospital, Phoenix, AZ, p. A37

WAGNER, Suzie, Director Human Resources, Encompass Health Rehabilitation Hospital Of Alexandria, Alexandria, LA, p. A295

WAGNER, Terry, R.N., Chief Operating Officer, Pocahontas Memorial Hospital, Buckeye, WV, p. A770

WAGNER, Timothy, M.D., Chief Medical Staff, Yoakum Community Hospital, Yoakum, TX, p. A726

WAGNER, Tom, Interim Vice President Finance, Avera St. Mary's Hospital, Pierre, SD, p. A630

WAGNER, Vanessa, Chief Financial Officer, Lawrence Memorial Hospital, Walnut Ridge, AR, p. A54

WAGNON, LaNell, Director Medical Records, Comanche County Hospital, Coldwater, KS, p. A263

WAGONER, Craig, Chief Executive Officer, Community Behavioral Health Center, Fresno, CA, p. A65
Chief Executive Officer, Community Regional Medical Center, Fresno, CA, p. A65

WAGONER, Dean, Director Human Resources, Good Samaritan Hospital, Vincennes, IN, p. A242

WAGONER, Renee R.N., Director of Nursing, Gove County Medical Center, Quinter, KS, p. A275

WAHAB, Amir, M.D., Medical Staff President, Abraham Lincoln Memorial Hospital, Lincoln, IL, p. A210

WAHL, Josephine, R.N., MS, FACHE, VP, Patient Care Services & CNO, Henry Ford Wyandotte Hospital, Wyandotte, MI, p. A370

WAHL, Tony, Chief Executive Officer, Baylor Scott & White Texas Spine & Joint Hospital-Tyler, Tyler, TX, p. A721

WAHLERS, Brenda, M.D., Chief of Staff, Upmc Cole, Coudersport, PA, p. A587

WAHLUND, Keith, Vice President Human Resources, Essentia Health Fargo, Fargo, ND, p. A522

WAIBEL, David, M.D., Medical Director, Clarks Summit State Hospital, Clarks Summit, PA, p. A586

WAIDE, Mary Beth, JD, MS, R.N., Chief Executive Officer, Deer's Head Hospital Center, Salisbury, MD, p. A332

WAIN, Matthew, Chief Executive Officer, Emory University Hospital, Atlanta, GA, p. A164

WAIND, Mark, Chief Information Officer, Altru Health System, Grand Forks, ND, p. A523

WAIT, Wendy, Chief Financial Officer, Montgomery County Emergency Service, Norristown, PA, p. A598

WAITE, Douglas, M.D., Chief Medical Officer, Saint Vincent Hospital, Worcester, MA, p. A346
Senior Vice President and Chief Financial Officer, Ascension Seton Highland Lakes, Burnet, TX, p. A662
Senior Vice President and Chief Financial Officer, Ascension Seton Williamson, Round Rock, TX, p. A709

WAITES, Alan, Chief Financial Officer, Gove County Medical Center, Quinter, KS, p. A275

WAJDA, David, Chief Financial Officer, Nazareth Hospital, Philadelphia, PA, p. A601

WAKEFIELD, Brett, Director Human Resources, Thorek Memorial Hospital, Chicago, IL, p. A201
Vice President Human Resources, Gottlieb Memorial Hospital, Melrose Park, IL, p. A212

WAKEFIELD, Jeffrey, CPA, Vice President and Chief Financial Officer, Unc Lenoir Healthcare, Kinston, NC, p. A513

WAKEFIELD, Mamie, Chief Financial Officer, Miriam Hospital, Providence, RI, p. A613
Senior Vice President and Chief Financial Officer, Rhode Island Hospital, Providence, RI, p. A614
Vice President Finance and Chief Financial Officer, Emma Pendleton Bradley Hospital, East Providence, RI, p. A613

WAKEM, Jennifer, Chief Financial Officer, University Medical Center, Las Vegas, NV, p. A444

WAKIM, Tina, Vice President Information, Northside Hospital, Atlanta, GA, p. A165

WAKO, Elizabeth, Chief Operating Officer, Swedish Medical Center-First Hill, Seattle, WA, p. A764

WAKULCHIK, Grace, R.N., MSN, President and Chief Executive Officer, Akron Children's Hospital, Akron, OH, p. A527

WALAS, Steven, Chief Executive Officer, Encompass Health Rehabilitation Hospital Of Salisbury, Salisbury, MD, p. A332

WALCEK, Peter, Vice President Finance, Wentworth-Douglass Hospital, Dover, NH, p. A448

WALCH, Tina, M.D., Medical Director, South Oaks Hospital, Amityville, NY, p. A474

WALCZAK, Laura, President, Ssm Health St. Clare Hospital-Baraboo, Baraboo, WI, p. A780

WALCZYK-JOERS, Barbara, President and Chief Executive Officer, Gillette Children's Specialty Healthcare, Saint Paul, MN, p. A385

WALD, Barry, Chief Financial Officer, Wake Forest Baptist Health - Wilkes Medical Center, North Wilkesboro, NC, p. A516

WALDBART, Andy, Department Manager, Heart Of The Rockies Regional Medical Center, Salida, CO, p. A118

WALDBILLIG, Karla, Director Human Resources, Unitypoint Health - Finley Hospital, Dubuque, IA, p. A249

WALDBILLIG, Kurt, Chief Executive Officer, Meeker Memorial Hospital, Litchfield, MN, p. A379

WALDEN, Anita, Vice President and Chief Nursing Officer, Decatur Morgan Hospital, Decatur, AL, p. A17

WALDERA, John, Director Information Technology, Gundersen Tri-County Hospital And Clinics, Whitehall, WI, p. A799

WALDO, Bruce, Chief Executive Officer, Aurora Behavioral Health System East, Tempe, AZ, p. A39
Chief Executive Officer, Aurora Behavioral Health System West, Glendale, AZ, p. A32

WALDO, Gail, Director Information Technology, Piedmont Rockdale Hospital, Conyers, GA, p. A170

WALDRON, Michele, Senior Vice President and Chief Financial Officer, Valley Children's Healthcare, Madera, CA, p. A76

WALDRON, Ray, Director Information Technology, Gordon Memorial Health Services, Gordon, NE, p. A432

WALDRON, Sheila, Finance Manager, Providence Milwaukie Hospital, Milwaukie, OR, p. A578

WALDROP, Catherine M., Administrator, Southeast Rehabilitation Hospital, Lake Village, AR, p. A48
Administrator, Sterlington Rehabilitation Hospital, Bastrop. LA, p. A296

WALDROP, Cathy, Director, Hospital Nursing Services, North Mississipp. Medical Center-Pontotoc, Pontotoc, MS, p. A399

WALI, Jyotika, M.D., Chief of Staff, Kindred Hospital-Brea, Brea, CA, p. A58

WALIGURA, R, D.O., Vice President Medical Affairs, Chief Medical Officer, Upmc Mckeesport, Mckeesport, PA, p. A596

WALK, Rex D., Chief Executive Officer, Phillip. County Health Systems, Phillipsburg, KS, p. A274

WALKENHORST, Debbie, Network Vice President, Ssm Cardinal Glennon Children's Hospital, Saint Louis, MO, p. A416
System Vice President Talent Management, Ssm Health St. Josep. - St. Charles, Saint Charles, MO, p. A414

WALKER, Alene, Director Human Resources, Quincy Valley Medical Center, Quincy, WA, p. A762

WALKER, Alexander, Executive Vice President Operations and Strategic Development, Catholic Medical Center, Manchester, NH, p. A450

WALKER, Amy, MSN, Chief Nursing Officer, Delta Regional Medical Center, Greenville, MS, p. A392

WALKER, Angela, Manager Human Resources, Aspire Hospital, Conroe, TX, p. A665

WALKER, Annette, Associate Director, John D. Dingell Veterans Affairs Medical Center, Detroit, MI, p. A353

WALKER, Beth, Director, Information Technology, Emanuel Medical Center, Turlock, CA, p. A102

WALKER, C, M.D., Chief of Staff, Donalsonville Hospital, Donalsonville, GA, p. A171

WALKER, Candace, Chief Financial Officer, East Central Regional Hospital, Augusta, GA, p. A166

WALKER, Carol, Chief Financial Officer, Oklahoma Heart Hospital, Oklahoma City, OK, p. A565

WALKER, Carrie, Executive Director Human Resources, Jones Memorial Hospital, Wellsville, NY, p. A502

WALKER, Cass, Vice President Administrative & Support Services, Franklin Regional Hospital, Franklin, NH, p. A449
Vice President Administrative & Support Services, Lakes Region General Hospital, Laconia, NH, p. A449

WALKER, Charles, Director Human Resource, Lawrence Memorial Hospital, Walnut Ridge, AR, p. A54
Director Information Technology, Kimball Health Services, Kimball, NE, p. A434

WALKER, Christopher, Chief Nursing Officer and Operating Officer, Sharp Coronado Hospital And Healthcare Center, Coronado, CA, p. A61

WALKER, Codie, Chief Financial Officer, Salem Veterans Affairs Medical Center, Salem, VA, p. A751

WALKER, Dan, Chief Nursing Officer, Lincoln Community Hospital And Nursing Home, Hugo, CO, p. A114

WALKER, David, Interim Chief Executive Officer, George E. Weems Memorial Hospital, Apalachicola, FL, p. A131

WALKER, David M., M.D., Medical Center Director, G.V. (Sonny) Montgomery Veterans Affairs Medical Center, Jackson, MS, p. A394

WALKER, Dawn, D.O., Chief of Staff, Northern Cochise Community Hospital, Willcox, AZ, p. A41

WALKER, Derrick, M.D., Chief Medical Officer, Brigham City Community Hospital, Brigham City, UT, p. A727

WALKER, Donna, Chief Nurse Executive, Weeks Medical Center, Lancaster, NH, p. A449

WALKER, Durwin, M.D., Chief Medical Officer, Sage Specialty Hospital (Ltac), Denham Springs, LA, p. A301

WALKER, Gerri H., President and Chief Executive Officer, North Philadelphia Health System, Philadelphia, PA, p. A601

WALKER, Gregory J., Chief Executive Officer, Wentworth-Douglass Hospital, Dover, NH, p. A448

WALKER, Imani, M.D., Medical Director, Gateways Hospital And Mental Health Center, Los Angeles, CA, p. A74

WALKER, Jan, Director Human Resources, Centra Lynchburg General Hospital, Lynchburg, VA, p. A745
Director Human Resources, Glenwood Regional Medical Center, West Monroe, LA, p. A316

WALKER, Janice, R.N., Senior Executive Vice President and System Chief Nursing Officer, Baylor Scott & White All Saints Medical Center - Fort Worth, Fort Worth, TX, p. A678

WALKER, Jeff, Chief Operating Officer, City Of Hope's Helford Clinical Research Hospital, Duarte, CA, p. A62

WALKER, Jeremy, Vice President and Chief Financial Officer, Hendrick Health System, Abilene, TX, p. A651

WALKER, John, Chief Operating Officer, Medical City Denton, Denton, TX, p. A672

WALKER, Jon, M.D., Chief Medical Officer, Wise Health System, Decatur, TX, p. A671

WALKER, Kimberly, Director of Human Resources, Northcrest Medical Center, Springfield, TN, p. A650

WALKER, Kristie, M.P.H., Director of Human Resources, Wythe County Community Hospital, Wytheville, VA, p. A754

WALKER, LeRoy, Vice President Human Resources, Emory Decatur Hospital, Decatur, GA, p. A171

WALKER, Linda, Chief Executive Officer, Val Verde Regional Medical Center, Del Rio, TX, p. A671

WALKER, Lynette, R.N., Ph.D., Vice President Human Resources, Baptist Health Lexington, Lexington, KY, p. A286

WALKER, Mary, Manager Information Technology, Encompass Health Rehabilitation Hospital Of Wichita Falls, Wichita Falls, TX, p. A725

WALKER, Matthew, Chief Executive Officer and Administrator, William Bee Ririe Hospital, Ely, NV, p. A441

WALKER, Melissa, CPA, Chief Financial Officer, North Texas Medical Center, Gainesville, TX, p. A680

WALKER, Pandora, Director, Human Resources, Beaumont Hospital - Grosse Pointe, Grosse Pointe, MI, p. A357

WALKER, Randy, Chief Nursing Officer, Hillcrest Hospital Claremore, Claremore, OK, p. A557
Director Nursing Services, State Hospital South, Blackfoot, ID, p. A188
Vice President, Methodist Dallas Medical Center, Dallas, TX, p. A669

WALKER, Robert, M.D., Medical Director, Encompass Health Rehabilitation Hospital Of Princeton, Princeton, WV, p. A776

WALKER, Robert L., FACHE, President and Chief Executive Officer, Texas Scottish Rite Hospital For Children, Dallas, TX, p. A670

WALKER, Robin, Chief Nursing Officer, Field Memorial Community Hospital, Centreville, MS, p. A390

WALKER, Samuel, Director of IT, Pocahontas Memorial Hospital, Buckeye, WV, p. A770

WALKER, Scott, Chief Financial Officer, Southeastern Regional Medical Center, Newnan, GA, p. A178
Chief Human Resource Officer, American Fork Hospital, American Fork, UT, p. A727

WALKER, Taylor, Chief Financial Officer, Marshall Medical Center North, Guntersville, AL, p. A19
Chief Financial Officer, Marshall Medical Center South, Boaz, AL, p. A16

WALKER, Tim, Manager Information Services, Peacehealth Ketchikan Medical Center, Ketchikan, AK, p. A28

WALKER, Todd, President, Prisma Health Baptist Easley Hospital, Easley, SC, p. A619

WALKER, Troy, Director Finance, Ssm Health St. Clare Hospital-Baraboo, Baraboo, WI, p. A780

WALKER, Tyree, Chief Human Resources Officer, Vidant Medical Center, Greenville, NC, p. A511

WALKER, Virginia, Vice President Nursing Services and Chief Nursing Officer, Kuakini Medical Center, Honolulu, HI, p. A184

WALL, Daniel J., President and Chief Executive Officer, Emma Pendleton Bradley Hospital, East Providence, RI, p. A613

WALL, Debbie, Chief Nursing Officer, Cherry Hospital, Goldsboro, NC, p. A510

WALL, Doug, M.D., Vice President Medical Affairs, Novant Health Uva Health System Prince William Medical Center, Manassas, VA, p. A745

M.D., Vice President of Medical Affairs, Novant Health Uva Health System Haymarket Medical Center, Haymarket, VA, p. A744

WALL, Heather, Chief Nursing Officer, Peacehealth Sacred Heart Medical Center At Riverbend, Springfield, OR, p. A581

WALL, Kathryn, Executive Vice President Human Resources and Organizational Development, Stafford Hospital, Stafford, VA, p. A752

Executive Vice President, Human Resources and Organizational Development, Mary Washington Hospital, Fredericksburg, VA, p. A742

WALLACE, Brad, Director Information Services, Grays Harbor Community Hospital, Aberdeen, WA, p. A755

WALLACE, Carolyn, Director Human Resources, Connecticut Mental Health Center, New Haven, CT, p. A124

WALLACE, Chauncey, Director of Hospital Operations, The Woods At Parkside, Gahanna, OH, p. A540

WALLACE, Cyndi, R.N., MSN, Chief Nursing Officer, Cedar City Hospital, Cedar City, UT, p. A727

WALLACE, Cynthia, M.D., Medical Director, Vibra Specialty Hospital Of Portland, Portland, OR, p. A580

WALLACE, David, Chief Executive Officer, Mat-Su Regional Medical Center, Palmer, AK, p. A29

WALLACE, Dianne, County Information Manager, Douglas County Community Mental Health Center, Omaha, NE, p. A437

WALLACE, Donna, Chief Operating Officer and Chief Financial Officer, Christus Mother Frances Hospital - Sulphur Springs, Sulphur Springs, TX, p. A718

WALLACE, Glenn, Chief Executive Officer, Medical City Alliance, Fort Worth, TX, p. A678

WALLACE, Kristina, R.N., Chief Executive Officer, Ou Medical Center, Oklahoma City, OK, p. A565

WALLACE, Mark, Chief Financial Officer, Cumberland Hall Hospital, Hopkinsville, KY, p. A285

Director Human Resources, Adventist Health Lodi Memorial, Lodi, CA, p. A71

WALLACE, Mark A., FACHE, President and Chief Executive Officer, Texas Children's Hospital, Houston, TX, p. A688

WALLACE, Melanie, Manager Human Resources, Sutter Tracy Community Hospital, Tracy, CA, p. A101

WALLACE, Michael S., President and Chief Executive Officer, Fort Healthcare, Fort Atkinson, WI, p. A784

WALLACE, Nancy, Division Senior Vice President, Chief Human Resource Officer, Chi Health Lakeside, Omaha, NE, p. A436

Division Senior Vice President, Chief Human Resource Officer, Chi Health Midlands, Papillion, NE, p. A438

Senior Vice President Human Resources, Chi Health Mercy Council Bluffs, Council Bluffs, IA, p. A247

Senior Vice President, Chief Human Resources Officer, Chi Health St Elizabeth, Lincoln, NE, p. A434

Vice President Human Resources, CHI Health, Chi Health Saint Francis, Grand Island, NE, p. A433

Vice President Human Resources, Chi Health Immanuel, Omaha, NE, p. A436

Vice President Human Resources, Chi Health Schuyler, Schuyler, NE, p. A439

WALLACE, Penny, Chief Financial Officer, Guadalup. Regional Medical Center, Seguin, TX, p. A714

WALLACE, Tabatha, Director Human Resources, Adventhealth Dade City, Dade City, FL, p. A135

WALLACE-MOORE, Patrice, Chief Executive Officer and Executive Director, Arms Acres, Carmel, NY, p. A481

WALLACH, Perry, M.D., Chief Medical Officer, Ut Health East Texas Rehabilitation Hospital, Tyler, TX, p. A722

WALLEN, Carla, Manager Human Resources, Cass Regional Medical Center, Harrisonville, MO, p. A407

WALLENTINE, Jeffrey, Chief of Staff, Mountain View Hospital, Payson, UT, p. A730

WALLER, Ernie, Director Information Technology, Ed Fraser Memorial Hospital, Macclenny, FL, p. A144

WALLER, Kenneth, Fiscal Administrator, Deer's Head Hospital Center, Salisbury, MD, p. A332

WALLER, Matthew, Chief Executive Officer, Liberty Medical Center, Chester, MT, p. A422

WALLER, Raymond, Director and Administrator, Ascension Brighton Center For Recovery, Brighton, MI, p. A350

WALLER, Raymond A., Director and Administrator, Ascension Brighton Center For Recovery, Brighton, MI, p. A350

WALLINE, Linda, R.N., Ph.D., MSN, Vice President Nursing, Columbus Community Hospital, Columbus, NE, p. A431

WALLING, Vernon, M.D., Chief Medical Officer, Sun Behavioral Houston, Houston, TX, p. A688

M.D., Executive Medical Director, West Oaks Hospital, Houston, TX, p. A689

WALLINGA, Joel, Chief Financial Officer, Veterans Affairs Ann Arbor Healthcare System, Ann Arbor, MI, p. A348

WALLINGA, Melvin, M.D., Medical Director, St. Michael's Hospital Avera, Tyndall, SD, p. A632

WALLIS, Christian, Vice President Operations, Advocate Condell Medical Center, Libertyville, IL, p. A210

WALLIS, Eric, R.N., President, Henry Ford West Bloomfield Hospital, West Bloomfield, MI, p. A369

WALLIS, Pam, MSN, Vice President Nursing Services, Magnolia Regional Health Center, Corinth, MS, p. A391

WALLMAN, Gerald H., Administrator, West Covina Medical Center, West Covina, CA, p. A104

WALLS, Craig, M.D., Ph.D., Chief Medical Officer, Natividad Medical Center, Salinas, CA, p. A90

WALLS, Martha, R.N., MSN, Chief Nursing Officer, Crestwood Medical Center, Huntsville, AL, p. A20

WALLS, Randy, Manager Information Services, Fairbanks, Indianapolis, IN, p. A232

WALLS, Ron, M.D., Executive Vice President and Chief Operating Officer, Brigham And Women's Hospital, Boston, MA, p. A335

WALLSCHLAEGER, Erich, Chief Financial Officer, Cedar Park Regional Medical Center, Cedar Park, TX, p. A663

WALRATH, Andrea, Chief Operating Officer, Forest Health Medical Center, Ypsilanti, MI, p. A370

WALRAVEN, Jeff, Chief Executive Officer, Lindsay Municipal Hospital, Lindsay, OK, p. A561

WALSER, Bill, Coordinator Technology, Cameron Regional Medical Center, Cameron, MO, p. A403

WALSH, Brad, M.D., Chief of Staff, Ashley County Medical Center, Crossett, AR, p. A44

WALSH, Catherine, Interim Nursing Executive, Mercy Regional Medical Center, Lorain, OH, p. A544

WALSH, Debbie, MSN, Chief Operating Officer, Maui Memorial Medical Center, Wailuku, HI, p. A187

WALSH, Gerard W., Chief Executive Officer, St. John's Episcopal Hospital, Far Rockaway, NY, p. A483

WALSH, John, FACHE, Chief Administrative Officer, Uofl Health - Jewish Hospital, Louisville, KY, p. A288

Chief Fiscal Services, Veterans Affairs Hudson Valley Health Care System, Montrose, NY, p. A488

WALSH, Kate, M.P.H., President and Chief Executive Officer, Boston Medical Center, Boston, MA, p. A335

WALSH, Katherine, MS, R.N., Dr.PH, Vice President and Chief Nursing Officer, Houston Methodist Hospital, Houston, TX, p. A686

WALSH, Kim, Chief Nursing Officer, Signature Healthcare Brockton Hospital, Brockton, MA, p. A337

WALSH, Len, Executive Vice President and Chief Operating Officer, St. Barnabas Hospital, Bronx, NY, p. A477

WALSH, Linda, R.N., MSN, Vice President Chief Nursing Executive, Hackensack Meridian Health Bayshore Community Hospital, Holmdel, NJ, p. A456

WALSH, Marcia, M.P.H., Chief Operating Officer, Community Healthcare System, Onaga, KS, p. A273

WALSH, Marilyn, Vice President Human Resources, Kent County Memorial Hospital, Warwick, RI, p. A614

WALSH, Mary, R.N., MSN, Vice President Patient Care Services and Chief Nursing Officer, Mount Sinai Beth Israel, New York, NY, p. A490

R.N., MSN, Vice President Patient Care Services and Chief Nursing Officer, Mount Sinai Morningside, New York, NY, p. A490

WALSH, Michael, Senior Vice President Finance and Chief Financial Officer, Abington Jefferson Health, Abington, PA, p. A583

Senior Vice President Finance and Chief Financial Officer, Abington-Lansdale Hospital Jefferson Health, Lansdale, PA, p. A594

WALSH, Michele, Chief Nursing Officer, St. Mary's Healthcare, Amsterdam, NY, p. A474

WALSTON, John, Chief Information Officer, Southern Arizona Veterans Affairs Health Care System, Tucson, AZ, p. A41

WALTER, Gayle, Director of Nursing, Thomas B. Finan Center, Cumberland, MD, p. A329

WALTER, Melissa, Director Human Resources, Clarinda Regional Health Center, Clarinda, IA, p. A246

WALTER, Stephen, Senior Vice President and Chief Financial Officer, Community Behavioral Health Center, Fresno, CA, p. A65

Senior Vice President and Chief Financial Officer, Community Regional Medical Center, Fresno, CA, p. A65

WALTERS, Cindy, Chief Executive Officer, Acadia-St. Landry Hospital, Church Point, LA, p. A299

WALTERS, Jane, Director of Nursing, Mendota Mental Health Institute, Madison, WI, p. A787

WALTERS, Kevin, Chief Financial Officer, St. Rose Dominican Hospitals - Rose De Lima Campus, Henderson, NV, p. A442

WALTERS, Leah, R.N., Director of Nursing, Mountain Valley Regional Rehabilitation Hospital, Prescott Valley, AZ, p. A37

WALTERS, Leslie, MSN, Chief Nursing Officer, Clarion Hospital, Clarion, PA, p. A586

WALTERS, Todd, Director of UHC Information Technology Services, Ochsner Lsu Health Shreveport - Monroe Medical Center, Monroe, LA, p. A309

WALTHALL, Wayne, Vice President and Chief Financial Officer, St. John Medical Center, Tulsa, OK, p. A571

WALTHER, Diane, Controller, Henry County Hospital, Napoleon, OH, p. A546

WALTON, Amy, M.D., Chief Medical Officer, Ascension Seton Shoal Creek, Austin, TX, p. A655

WALTON, Dawn, Chief Financial Officer, Children's Of Alabama, Birmingham, AL, p. A15

WALTON, Gary, M.D., Chief Medical Officer, Hill Hospital Of Sumter County, York, AL, p. A26

WALTON, Georgian, Director Human Resources, Elbert Memorial Hospital, Elberton, GA, p. A172

WALTZ, Dan, Vice President and Chief Information Officer, Midmichigan Medical Center-Gladwin, Gladwin, MI, p. A355

WALZ, Rachel, Director Patient Care, Centracare Health-Paynesville, Paynesville, MN, p. A383

WALZ-ALLEN, Miranda, Chief Executive Officer, Seiling Regional Medical Center, Seiling, OK, p. A568

WAMPLER, Andrew, Chief Financial Officer, Franklin Woods Community Hospital, Johnson City, TN, p. A640

Chief Financial Officer, Margaret R. Pardee Memorial Hospital, Hendersonville, NC, p. A512

Vice President, Operational Excellence, Indian Path Community Hospital, Kingsport, TN, p. A641

WAMSLEY, Marie, Chief Financial Officer, Memorial Hospital Of Lafayette County, Darlington, WI, p. A782

WANG, Ted, Chief Financial Officer, Ucsf Benioff Children's Hospital Oakland, Oakland, CA, p. A82

WANG, William, M.D., Chief Operating Officer, Nyc Health + Hospitals / Metropolitan, New York, NY, p. A491

WANG, MD, Shu-Ming, Vice President Medical Affairs, Chi Health Saint Francis, Grand Island, NE, p. A433

WANGSMO, Gary, Chief Financial Officer, Mee Memorial Hospital, King City, CA, p. A69

WANGSNESS, Erik, Chief Executive Officer, Adventhealth Wesley Chapel, Wesley Chapel, FL, p. A161

WANLY, Bahaa, Interim Chief Operating Officer, Salem Hospital, Salem, OR, p. A581

WANNER, David, Chief Information Officer, Trinity Health, Minot, ND, p. A525

Director Information Technology, Kenmare Community Hospital, Kenmare, ND, p. A524

WAPPELHORST, Andrea, Chief Nursing Officer, Top. Surgical Specialty Hospital, Houston, TX, p. A689

WAR, Melissa, Chief Executive Officer, Orthopedic Specialty Hospital Of Nevada, Las Vegas, NV, p. A443

WARD, Brook, President and Chief Executive Officer, Washington Hospital, Washington, PA, p. A610

WARD, Celia, Controller and Chief Financial Officer, Doctors Memorial Hospital, Bonifay, FL, p. A132

WARD, Charlotte, Entity Financial Officer, Texas Health Harris Methodist Hospital Southwest Fort Worth, Fort Worth, TX, p. A679

WARD, Chris, Chief Nursing Officer, Comanche County Memorial Hospital, Lawton, OK, p. A561

Director Management Information Systems, Dorminy Medical Center, Fitzgerald, GA, p. A172

WARD, David, Chief Financial Officer and Chief Acquisition Officer, Cabell Huntington Hospital, Huntington, WV, p. A772

WARD, Dillon, Management Information Systems Specialist, Tennova Healthcare-Lafollette Medical Center, La Follette, TN, p. A642

WARD, Elizabeth, Chief Financial Officer, Tidelands Georgetown Memorial Hospital, Georgetown, SC, p. A620

Chief Financial Officer, Tidelands Waccamaw Community Hospital, Murrells Inlet, SC, p. A623

WARD, Jeffery, Director Human Resources, Cedar Park Regional Medical Center, Cedar Park, TX, p. A663

WARD, Julie, MSN, R.N., Chief Nursing Officer, St. Joseph's Hospital And Medical Center, Phoenix, AZ, p. A36

MSN, R.N., Vice President Patient Care Services, Hutchinson Regional Medical Center, Hutchinson, KS, p. A266

Vice President Finance, Northeastern Health System, Tahlequah, OK, p. A569

WARD, Kevin, Chief Operating Officer, Jewish Home Of San Francisco, San Francisco, CA, p. A93

Vice President and Chief Financial Officer, New York-Presbyterian Queens, Flushing, NY, p. A484

WARD, Kimberly, Chief Nurse Officer, St. Luke's Rehabilitation Institute, Spokane, WA, p. A766

WARD, Lesli, Vice President Human Resources, Uf Health Jacksonville, Jacksonville, FL, p. A142

WARD, Lisa, Director Information Systems, Columbus Regional Healthcare System, Whiteville, NC, p. A519

WARD, Lorna, MSN, R.N., Chief Nursing Officer, Novant Health Brunswick Medical Center, Bolivia, NC, p. A505

WARD, Louis, Chief Operating Officer, Mayers Memorial Hospital District, Fall River Mills, CA, p. A64

WARD, Louis James., Interim Chief Executive Officer, Mayers Memorial Hospital District, Fall River Mills, CA, p. A64

WARD, Mark, M.D., Chief of Staff, Roundup Memorial Healthcare, Roundup. MT, p. A427

WARD, Michael, Chief Executive Officer, Encompass Health Rehabilitation Hospital Of Henderson, Henderson, NV, p. A442

Director Information Services, Anderson Hospital, Maryville, IL, p. A211

WARD, Mike, Chief Information Officer, Morristown-Hamblen Healthcare System, Morristown, TN, p. A645

Covenant Health, Senior Vice President and Chief Information Officer, Methodist Medical Center Of Oak Ridge, Oak Ridge, TN, p. A648

Senior Vice President Chief Information Officer, Roane Medical Center, Harriman, TN, p. A639

WARD, Rhonda, R.N., MSN, Chief Nursing Officer, Littleton Adventist Hospital, Littleton, CO, p. A116

WARD, Rory, Chief Financial Officer, Pushmataha Hospital, Antlers, OK, p. A555

WARD, Silva, Director Human Resources, Center For Behavioral Medicine, Kansas City, MO, p. A408

WARD, Stormy, Chief Nurse Executive, Big Spring State Hospital, Big Spring, TX, p. A659

WARD, Virginia, Human Resources Officer, Robert E. Bush Naval Hospital, Twentynine Palms, CA, p. A102

WARDA, Paul, Chief Financial Officer, Medstar Georgetown University Hospital, Washington, DC, p. A129

WARDEN, Michael, Senior Vice President Information Technology, Banner - University Medical Center Phoenix, Phoenix, AZ, p. A35

WARDLE, Andrea, Chief Nursing Officer, Fillmore Community Hospital, Fillmore, UT, p. A728

WARDROP, Daniel, M.D., Medical Director, Heart Of The Rockies Regional Medical Center, Salida, CO, p. A118

WARE, Bobbie, R.N., FACHE, Vice President Patient Care and Chief Nursing Officer, Mississipp. Baptist Medical Center, Jackson, MS, p. A395

WARE, Bobbie K., R.N., FACHE, Chief Executive Officer, Mississipp. Baptist Medical Center, Jackson, MS, p. A395

WARE, Dana, M.D., Chief of Staff, Seneca Healthcare District, Chester, CA, p. A60

WARE, Jeff, Information Technology Support Technician, Stillwater Medical Perry, Perry, OK, p. A567

WARE, John, Director of Human Resources, Venice Regional Bayfront Health, Venice, FL, p. A161

WARE, Judy, Chief Financial Officer, Monroe County Hospital, Forsyth, GA, p. A172

Chief Financial Officer, Putnam General Hospital, Eatonton, GA, p. A172

Director Human Resources, Johnson Memorial Hospital, Franklin, IN, p. A229

WARE, Kathy, Director of Nursing, Daniels Memorial Healthcare Center, Scobey, MT, p. A427

WARE, Raynard, Vice President of Opeartions, Palms Of Pasadena Hospital, Saint Petersburg, FL, p. A156

WARE, Risa, Commander, Irwin Army Community Hospital, Junction City, KS, p. A267

WARFIELD, William, Chief Human Resources Management, Veterans Affairs Boston Healthcare System, West Roxbury, MA, p. A345

WARING, Lance, Director Human Resources, Texas Health Harris Methodist Hospital Azle, Azle, TX, p. A657

WARLICK, Mark, Chief Information Officer, Elkhart General Hospital, Elkhart, IN, p. A227

Chief Information Officer, Memorial Hospital Of South Bend, South Bend, IN, p. A240

WARLITNER, Todd, Vice President Business Operations, The Outer Banks Hospital, Nags Head, NC, p. A515

WARM, Ira, Senior Vice President Human Resources, Brooklyn Hospital Center, Brooklyn, NY, p. A477

WARMAN, Debbie, Vice President Human Resources, Metrohealth Medical Center, Cleveland, OH, p. A535

WARMBOLD, Steve, Director Information Management Service Line, Veterans Affairs St. Louis Health Care System, Saint Louis, MO, p. A418

WARMERDAM, David, Chief Financial Officer, Brynn Marr Hospital, Jacksonville, NC, p. A512

WARNER, Christopher, Commander, Madigan Army Medical Center, Tacoma, WA, p. A767

WARNER, Grady, Director of Information Technology, Burgess Health Center, Onawa, IA, p. A255

WARNER, John, M.D., Chief Executive Officer, Interim Chief Medical Officer, University of Texas Southwestern Medical Center, Dallas, TX, p. A671

M.D., Chief Executive Officer, University Of Texas Southwestern Medical Center, Dallas, TX, p. A671

WARNER, Petra, Chief of Staff, Shriners Hospitals For Children - Cincinnati, Cincinnati, OH, p. A533

WARNER, Tracy, Chief Executive Officer, Greene County Medical Center, Jefferson, IA, p. A252

WARNER LYNN, Lynne, R.N., Administrator, Ephraim Mcdowell James B. Haggin Memorial Hospital, Harrodsburg, KY, p. A284

WARNER-PACHECO, Paula, Chief Human Resources, Rio Grande Hospital, Del Norte, CO, p. A110

WARNING, Kendra, Chief Financial Officer, Davis County Hospital And Clinics, Bloomfield, IA, p. A244

WARNOCK, Dawn, Director Medical Records, Taylor Regional Hospital, Hawkinsville, GA, p. A173

WARREN, Brent, President Medical Staff, Iredell Health System, Statesville, NC, p. A519

WARREN, Charlene, R.N., Chief Nursing Officer, Greenbrier Valley Medical Center, Ronceverte, WV, p. A776

WARREN, Danny, Chief Financial Officer, Venice Regional Bayfront Health, Venice, FL, p. A161

WARREN, Denise, R.N., Executive Vice President and Chief Operating Officer, Wakemed Cary Hospital, Cary, NC, p. A506

R.N., Executive Vice President and Chief Operating Officer, Wakemed Raleigh Campus, Raleigh, NC, p. A517

WARREN, Gidgett, Director of Nursing, T.J. Health Columbia, Columbia, KY, p. A281

WARREN, Jana, Human Resources Business Partner, Piedmont Henry Hospital, Stockbridge, GA, p. A181

WARREN, Karen, Fiscal Officer, Porterville Developmental Center, Porterville, CA, p. A86

WARREN, Linda, Director Human Resources, Cogdell Memorial Hospital, Snyder, TX, p. A716

WARREN, Sarah, Coordinator Human Resources, Hickory Trail Hospital, Desoto, TX, p. A672

WARREN, Seth, President and Chief Executive Officer, Riverview Health, Noblesville, IN, p. A238

WARREN, Shanna, Director Human Resources, Medical City Plano, Plano, TX, p. A707

WARREN, Terri, Chief Financial Officer, Adventhealth Waterman, Tavares, FL, p. A160

WARREN, Wm. Michael. Jr, President and Chief Executive Officer, Children's Of Alabama, Birmingham, AL, p. A15

WARRENER, Gerald, M.D., Chief Medical Officer, Parkview Noble Hospital, Kendallville, IN, p. A233

WARRIN, Richard, Chief Operating Officer, Musc Health Lancaster Medical Center, Lancaster, SC, p. A622

WARRINER, Ken, Market Chief Financial Officer, Physicians Regional - Pine Ridge, Naples, FL, p. A149

WARSING, Tracy, M.D., Site Leader Chief of Staff, Mayo Clinic Health System - Franciscan Healthcare In Sparta, Sparta, WI, p. A796

WARTELLE, Scott, Chief Financial Officer, Sierra Vista Regional Medical Center, San Luis Obispo, CA, p. A96

Chief Financial Officer, Twin Cities Community Hospital, Templeton, CA, p. A101

WARWICK, Taylor, Vice President Operations, Saint Luke's South Hospital, Overland Park, KS, p. A274

WAS, Gregory J., CPA, Chief Executive Officer, White Mountain Regional Medical Center, Springerville, AZ, p. A39

WASEK, Arthur, Director Human Resources, Panola Medical Center, Batesville, MS, p. A389

WASHBURN, Geoff, Vice President Human Resources, Los Robles Hospital And Medical Center, Thousand Oaks, CA, p. A101

WASHBURN, Geoffrey, Vice President, Regional Medical Center Bayonet Point, Hudson, FL, p. A140

WASHBURN, Tonya, M.D., Medical Director, Valir Rehabilitation Hospital, Oklahoma City, OK, p. A566

WASHECKA, James, Chief Financial Officer, Hillcrest Hospital - South, Tulsa, OK, p. A569

WASHINGTON, Carolyn, Director of Human Resources, United Memorial Medical Center, Houston, TX, p. A689

WASHINGTON, Glen A., Chief Executive Officer, Pleasant Valley Hospital, Point Pleasant, WV, p. A776

WASHINGTON, Stephanie, Director Community Relations and Human Resources, Baptist Medical Center Yazoo, Yazoo City, MS, p. A401

Human Resources Director, Baptist Medical Center Attala, Kosciusko, MS, p. A395

WASHINGTON, Tarra, Chief Executive Officer, Kindred Hospital-New Jersey Morris County, Dover, NJ, p. A454

WASHINGTON, Vindell, M.D., Vice President Performance Excellence and Technology, Our Lady Of The Lake Regional Medical Center, Baton Rouge, LA, p. A297

WASILICK, Tamara, Director Operations, Kidspeace Children's Hospital, Orefield, PA, p. A599

WATERS, Bill, M.D., Chief Medical Officer, Higgins General Hospital, Bremen, GA, p. A167

WATERS, Danny, Director, Information Services, Palms Of Pasadena Hospital, Saint Petersburg, FL, p. A156

WATERS, Eric, Vice President Operations, Pen Bay Medical Center, Rockport, ME, p. A322

WATERS, Gina, Director Human Resources, Evans Memorial Hospital, Claxton, GA, p. A168

WATERS, Jerod, Chief Nursing Officer, Chickasaw Nation Medical Center, Ada, OK, p. A555

WATERS, Karen, Chief Nursing Officer, Ascension St. Vincent Warrick, Boonville, IN, p. A224

WATERS, Laura, Vice President Human Resources, Garrett Regional Medical Center, Oakland, MD, p. A331

WATERS, Nancy, Interim Chief Information Officer, High Point Medical Center, High Point, NC, p. A512

WATERS, Tony, Chief Information Officer, Emanuel Medical Center, Swainsboro, GA, p. A181

WATERS, William, M.D., Chief Medical Officer, Tanner Medical Center-Carrollton, Carrollton, GA, p. A168

M.D., Executive Vice President, Tanner Medical Center-Villa Rica, Villa Rica, GA, p. A182

WATHEN, Cheryl, Interim Chief Financial Officer, Deaconess Midtown Hospital, Evansville, IN, p. A227

WATHEN, Susan, Vice President Human Resources, Hannibal Regional Hospital, Hannibal, MO, p. A407

WATKINS, Anne Marie, R.N., Chief Nurse Executive, Kaiser Permanente San Diego Medical Center, San Diego, CA, p. A91

WATKINS, James, M.D., President Medical Staff, Providence Willamette Falls Medical Center, Oregon City, OR, p. A578

WATKINS, Michael, Chief Operating Officer, North Oaks Medical Center, Hammond, LA, p. A302

WATKINS, Michelle, Human Resources Manager, Greenwood Regional Rehabilitation Hospital, Greenwood, SC, p. A621

WATKINS, Pamela, Chief Financial Officer, Atlanta Veterans Affairs Medical Center, Decatur, GA, p. A170

WATKINS, Paul, JD, President, Northridge Hospital Medical Center, Northridge, CA, p. A81

WATKINS, Rolanda, Chief Human Resources Management Service, Dayton Veterans Affairs Medical Center, Dayton, OH, p. A538

WATKINS, Steve, Chief Executive Officer, Lifescape, Sioux Falls, SD, p. A631

WATRIDGE, Donna, R.N., Chief Nursing Officer, Hackettstown Medical Center, Hackettstown, NJ, p. A456

R.N., Director of Operations, Hackettstown Medical Center, Hackettstown, NJ, p. A456

WATSON, B, M.D., Chief Medical Staff, North Mississipp. Medical Center-West Point, West Point, MS, p. A401

WATSON, Barbara, Chief Nursing Officer, Osceola Regional Medical Center, Kissimmee, FL, p. A142

WATSON, Betty, Chief Financial Officer, Syringa Hospital And Clinics, Grangeville, ID, p. A190

WATSON, Chad, Market Controller, Kindred Hospital Indianapolis North, Indianapolis, IN, p. A232

WATSON, Cheryl, Chief Information Officer, Howard County Medical Center, Saint Paul, NE, p. A439

WATSON, Dalph, Director of Human Resources, Beaumont Hospital - Farmington Hills, Farmington Hills, MI, p. A354

WATSON, Deagan, Chief Executive Officer, Lakeview Behavioral Health, Norcross, GA, p. A178

WATSON, Dean, M.D., Chief Medical Officer, Tallahassee Memorial Healthcare, Tallahassee, FL, p. A158

WATSON, Deborah, R.N., Chief Nursing Officer, Providence Mount Carmel Hospital, Colville, WA, p. A757

R.N., Chief Nursing Officer, Providence St. Joseph's Hospital, Chewelah, WA, p. A756

Senior Vice President and Chief Operating Officer, Bayhealth Medical Center, Dover, DE, p. A127

WATSON, Deidre, Director Human Resources, Belmont Pines Hospital, Youngstown, OH, p. A553

WATSON, Dolores, Director Health Information Management, Arms Acres, Carmel, NY, p. A481

WATSON, H. Alan., FACHE, Chief Executive Officer, Maury Regional Hospital, Columbia, TN, p. A636

WATSON, Heath, Controller, Encompass Health Rehabilitation Hospital Of Dothan, Dothan, AL, p. A17

Controller, Encompass Health Rehabilitation Hospital Of Montgomery, Montgomery, AL, p. A22

WATSON, Kathy, R.N., Administrator and Chief Nursing Officer, Saint Thomas Hospital For Spinal Surgery, Nashville, TN, p. A646

WATSON, Lisa, Chief Executive Officer, Chi St. Vincent Sherwood Rehabilitation Hospital, Sherwood, AR, p. A53

WATSON, Luke, M.D., Chief of Staff, College Medical Center, Long Beach, CA, p. A72

WATSON, Lynn, Interim Chief Nursing Officer, Amita Health Saint Josep. Medical Center, Joliet, IL, p. A209

WATSON, Margie Chief Nursing Officer, Sabine County Hospital, Hemphill, TX, p. A683

WATSON, Michael, M.D., Chief of Staff, Memorial Hospital, Seminole, TX, p. A714

WATSON, Nathan, M.D., JrChief of Staff, Carrus Specialty Hospital, Sherman, TX, p. A715

WATSON, Rob, M.D., Chief Medical Officer, Baylor Scott & White Medical Center - Round Rock, Round Rock, TX, p. A709

WATSON, Scott, Administrator, Mercy Hospital Carthage, Carthage, MO, p. A404

WATSON, Shane, Chief Executive Officer, Red Bud Regional Hospital, Red Bud, IL, p. A218

WATSON, Susan, MSN, R.N., Vice President, Bronson Battle Creek Hospital, Battle Creek, MI, p. A349

WATSON, Teresa C., Vice President, Facility Executive, Atrium Health Lincoln, Lincolnton, NC, p. A514

WATSON, Thelma, M.D., Medical Director, Schneider Regional Medical Center, Saint Thomas, VI, p. A812

WATSON, Thomas, M.D., Chief of Staff, Mayers Memorial Hospital District, Fall River Mills, CA, p. A64

WATSON, Trey, Network Administrator, Sumner County Hospital District 1, Caldwell, KS, p. A262

WATSON, Vicki, Manager Human Resources, Select Specialty Hospital-Jackson, Jackson, MS, p. A395

WATT, Andrew, M.D., Vice President, Information Technology & Services, Chief Information Officer, Chief Medical Information Officer, Southern New Hampshire Medical Center, Nashua, NH, p. A450

WATT, Ella, Chief Financial Officer, University Of New Mexico Hospitals, Albuquerque, NM, p. A468

WATTENBARGER, J., M.D., Chief of Staff, Shriners Hospitals For Children-Greenville, Greenville, SC, p. A620

WATTENBARGER, Mike, Chief Information Officer, Lifecare Behavioral Health Hospital, Pittsburgh, PA, p. A603

WATTOO, Dost, M.D., Chief of Staff, Valley Hospital Medical Center, Las Vegas, NV, p. A445

WATTS, Blake, Chief Operating Officer, Piedmont Rockdale Hospital, Conyers, GA, p. A170

WATTS, Chris, President, Barnes-Jewish St. Peters Hospital, Saint Peters, MO, p. A418
President, Progress West Hospital, O'Fallon, MO, p. A413

WATTS, Dawn, Chief Executive Officer, Encompasss Health Rehabilitation Hospital Of Fort Smith, Fort Smith, AR, p. A46

WATTS, Lynda, Vice President, Chief Nursing Officer, Fort Sanders Regional Medical Center, Knoxville, TN, p. A641

WATTS, Trice, Chief Financial Officer and Chief Executive Officer, Greeley County Health Services, Tribune, KS, p. A278
Chief Financial Officer, Greeley County Health Services, Tribune, KS, p. A278

WAY, Dee, Director Human Resources, Jerold Phelp. Community Hospital, Garberville, CA, p. A66

WAY, M. Todd., President, Central Region, Hackensack Meridian Health Riverview Medical Center, Red Bank, NJ, p. A462

WAYNE, Ann, Chief Executive Officer, Sun Behavioral Delaware, Georgetown, DE, p. A127

WAYNE, Denise, Chief Executive Officer, Pioneer Specialty Hospital, Pontiac, MI, p. A364

WAYNE, Jason, Network Administrator, Suburban Community Hospital, East Norriton, PA, p. A589

WAZWAZ, Al, Chief Executive Officer, Kindred Chicago-Central Hospital, Chicago, IL, p. A199

WEATHERFORD, Cynthia, R.N., Administrator and Director of Nursing, Mercy St. Francis Hospital, Mountain View, MO, p. A412

WEATHERFORD, Dennis, Chief Executive Officer, Putnam County Hospital, Greencastle, IN, p. A229

WEATHERLY, Daniel, Chief Operating Officer, Cap. Fear Valley Medical Center, Fayetteville, NC, p. A510

WEATHERSBY, Mae, R.N., Chief Clinical Officer, Vibra Specialty Hospital At Desoto, Desoto, TX, p. A673

WEATHERWAX, Lisa, R.N., Chief Nursing Officer, Iowa Specialty Hospital-Belmond, Belmond, IA, p. A244

WEATHERWAX, Marlene, Vice President and Chief Financial Officer, Columbus Regional Hospital, Columbus, IN, p. A225

WEAVER, Angie, Director Human Resources, North Mississipp. Medical Center Gilmore-Amory, Amory, MS, p. A389

WEAVER, Daryl W., Chief Executive Officer, Baptist Medical Center Leake, Carthage, MS, p. A390

WEAVER, Douglas K., FACHE, Chief Executive Officer, Hillcrest Hospital Pryor, Pryor, OK, p. A567

WEAVER, Greg, Chief Operating Officer, Bates County Memorial Hospital, Butler, MO, p. A403
Interim Chief Executive Officer, Bates County Memorial Hospital, Butler, MO, p. A403

WEAVER, Harry, M.D., Chief of Staff, Covenant Hospital-Levelland, Levelland, TX, p. A695

WEAVER, Jason, Director Finance, Centracare - Monticello, Monticello, MN, p. A381
Director Information Systems, Southern Tennessee Regional Health System-Lawrenceburg, Lawrenceburg, TN, p. A642

WEAVER, Joe, Chief Executive Officer, Rmc-Stringfellow Memorial Hospital, Anniston, AL, p. A13

WEAVER, Kimberli, Chief Nursing Officer, Regional Medical Center Of Central Alabama, Greenville, AL, p. A19

WEAVER, Rudolph, Vice President Human Resources, Southwestern Vermont Medical Center, Bennington, VT, p. A735

WEAVER, Sabrina, Director of Human Resources, Marshall Medical Center North, Guntersville, AL, p. A19

WEAVER, William, Chief Executive Officer, Brentwood Hospital, Shreveport, LA, p. A314

WEBB, Chuck, Interim Chief Executive Officer, River Oaks Hospital, New Orleans, LA, p. A311

WEBB, Darrallyn, R.N., Chief Nursing Officer, Conway Regional Rehabilitation Hospital, Conway, AR, p. A44

WEBB, David, Chief Financial Officer, Baptist Memorial Hospital-Golden Triangle, Columbus, MS, p. A391

WEBB, Dee, Vice President Human Resources, St. Bernardine Medical Center, San Bernardino, CA, p. A91

WEBB, Donald, Chief Executive Officer, Williamson Medical Center, Franklin, TN, p. A638

WEBB, Jeffrey, CPA, Chief Financial Officer, Franciscan Health Rensselaer, Rensselaer, IN, p. A239

WEBB, Joseph, Chief Executive Officer, Nashville General Hospital, Nashville, TN, p. A646

WEBB, Kimberly, Chief Financial Officer, Kootenai Health, Coeur D'Alene, ID, p. A190

WEBB, Kristen, Chief Nursing Officer, Duncan Regional Hospital, Duncan, OK, p. A558

WEBB, Linda, R.N., Chief Nursing Executive, Pulaski Memorial Hospital, Winamac, IN, p. A242

WEBB, Lisa, Vice President for Operational Finance, Chi Health Good Samaritan, Kearney, NE, p. A433
Vice President Operational Finance, Chi Health Saint Francis, Grand Island, NE, p. A433

WEBB, Melanie, Vice President Human Resources, Hca Houston Healthcare Medical Center, Houston, TX, p. A685
Vice President Human Resources, Hca Houston Healthcare Northwest, Houston, TX, p. A685

WEBB, Paula, Chief Financial Officer and Compliance Officer, Lake Butler Hospital, Lake Butler, FL, p. A142

WEBB, Renick, M.D., Chief Medical Director, Central Louisiana Surgical Hospital, Alexandria, LA, p. A295

WEBB, Rhonda, M.D., Chief Executive Officer, Pagosa Springs Medical Center, Pagosa Springs, CO, p. A117

WEBB, Steven B., FACHE, President and Chief Executive Officer, Unity Health White County Medical Center, Searcy, AR, p. A52

WEBB, William, Assistant Superintendent, Eastern Shore Hospital Center, Cambridge, MD, p. A328

WEBBER, Cathy, Director of Health Information Management, Franklin County Memorial Hospital, Franklin, NE, p. A432

WEBBER, Denise, President and Chief Executive Officer, Stillwater Medical Center, Stillwater, OK, p. A568

WEBBER, Joyce, Chief Financial Officer, Spalding Rehabilitation Hospital, Aurora, CO, p. A107

WEBER, Barbara, Chief Operating Officer, Unitypoint Health - Trinity Rock Island, Rock Island, IL, p. A218

WEBER, Carmen, Administrator, Eureka Community Health Services Avera, Eureka, SD, p. A628

WEBER, Deborah, Chief Human Resource Officer, Northeast Georgia Medical Center, Gainesville, GA, p. A173

WEBER, Dee, Vice President Human Resources, Southwest General Health Center, Middleburg Heights, OH, p. A545

WEBER, Frank, Chief Executive Officer, Select Specialty Hospital-Charleston, Charleston, WV, p. A771

WEBER, Gordon, Chief Operating Officer, Clarks Summit State Hospital, Clarks Summit, PA, p. A586

WEBER, Lauren, Administrator, Oceans Behavioral Hospital Longview, Longview, TX, p. A697

WEBER, Mark, M.D., President Medical Staff, Midmichigan Medical Center - West Branch, West Branch, MI, p. A369

WEBER, Rebecca, Senior Vice President and Chief Information Officer, Hackensack Meridian Health Bayshore Community Hospital, Holmdel, NJ, p. A456
Senior Vice President and Chief Information Officer, Hackensack Meridian Health Jersey Shore University Medical Center, Neptune, NJ, p. A459
Senior Vice President and Chief Information Officer, Hackensack Meridian Health Ocean Medical Center, Brick Township. NJ, p. A453
Senior Vice President and Chief Information Officer, Hackensack Meridian Health Southern Ocean Medical Center, Manahawkin, NJ, p. A458

Senior Vice President Information Technology, Hackensack Meridian Health Riverview Medical Center, Red Bank, NJ, p. A462

WEBER, Stephen, M.D., Senior Vice President Clinical Effectiveness and Chief Medical Officer, University Of Chicago Medical Center, Chicago, IL, p. A201

WEBER, Trish, R.N., FACHE, Vice President Operations and Chief Nursing Officer, Franciscan Health Michigan City, Michigan City, IN, p. A236

WEBER, Wilson, Chief Operating Officer, Continuecare Hospital At Baptist Health Corbin, Corbin, KY, p. A282

WEBSTER, Cindy, Vice President Financial Services, Licking Memorial Hospital, Newark, OH, p. A546

WEBSTER, David, Commanding Officer, Naval Hospital Pensacola, Pensacola, FL, p. A153

WEBSTER, Gwen, M.D., President Medical Staff, Texas Health Presbyterian Hospital Plano, Plano, TX, p. A707

WEBSTER, Janice, Director Human Resources, West Oaks Hospital, Houston, TX, p. A689

WEBSTER, Kathleen, R.N., MSN, Vice President Patient Services, New York-Presbyterian/Hudson Valley Hospital, Cortlandt Manor, NY, p. A482

WEBSTER, Mark, Vice President Finance, New York-Presbyterian/Hudson Valley Hospital, Cortlandt Manor, NY, p. A482

WEBSTER, Nancy, Administrator and Chief Operating Officer, St. Luke's Rehabilitation Institute, Spokane, WA, p. A766

WEBSTER, Richard, R.N., President and Chief Executive Officer, Thomas Jefferson University Hospital, Magee Rehabilitation Hospital, Philadelphia, PA, p. A601
R.N., President, Thomas Jefferson University Hospitals, Philadelphia, PA, p. A602

WECKENBORG, Janet, Vice President Operations, Capital Region Medical Center, Jefferson City, MO, p. A408

WECKESSER, Kim, Director Human Resources, Munson Healthcare Manistee Hospital, Manistee, MI, p. A361

WEDDLE, Chari, Chief Human Resource Management Service, Richard L. Roudebush Veterans Affairs Medical Center, Indianapolis, IN, p. A233

WEDGEWORTH, Joyce, Financial Clerk, Hill Hospital Of Sumter County, York, AL, p. A26

WEDGWORTH, Megan, Chief Executive Officer, Vantage Point Of Northwest Arkansas, Fayetteville, AR, p. A45

WEE, Donald, Chief Executive Officer, Tri-State Memorial Hospital, Clarkston, WA, p. A756

WEED, Warren, Director Associate Relations, Merit Health Woman's Hospital, Flowood, MS, p. A392
Director Human Resources, Merit Health River Oaks, Flowood, MS, p. A392

WEEDEN, Gerard, Chief Medical Officer, Vibra Hospital Of Richmond, Richmond, VA, p. A751

WEEKS, Doug, FACHE, Executive Vice President and Chief Operations Officer, Baptist Health Medical Center - North Little Rock, North Little Rock, AR, p. A51

WEEKS, Ed, Manager Information Services, Paris Community Hospital, Paris, IL, p. A216

WEELDREYER, Jim, Manager Information Technology, Pershing General Hospital, Lovelock, NV, p. A445

WEEMS, Reva, Director Human Resources, Gateway Regional Medical Center, Granite City, IL, p. A206

WEEMS, Taylor, Vice President, Chief Information Officer, Midland Memorial Hospital, Midland, TX, p. A701

WEG, Jennifer, MS, R.N., Executive Director, Sanford Worthington Medical Center, Worthington, MN, p. A388

WEGHORST, George, M.D., Chief Medical Officer, Providence Newberg Medical Center, Newberg, OR, p. A578

WEGLARZ, Ron, Chief Executive Officer and Managing Director, Streamwood Behavioral Health Center, Streamwood, IL, p. A221

WEGLEITNER, Theodore, Chief Executive Officer and President, Lakeview Hospital, Stillwater, MN, p. A386

WEHBEH, Wehbeh, M.D., Chief Medical Officer, Nyc Health + Hospitals / Coney Island, Brooklyn, NY, p. A478

WEHLING, Ed, Chief Medical Staff, Decatur County Hospital, Leon, IA, p. A253

WEHLING, Robert, Interim Chief Financial Officer, Saint Alphonsus Medical Center - Baker City, Baker City, OR, p. A573

WEHNER, Jill, Vice President Financial Services, Harbor Beach Community Hospital, Harbor Beach, MI, p. A357

WEHRMEISTER, Erica, Chief Operating Officer, Ascension St. Vincent Indianapolis Hospital, Indianapolis, IN, p. A231
President Central Region, Ascension St. Vincent Indianapolis Hospital, Indianapolis, IN, p. A231
President Central Region, Ascension St. Vincent Seton Specialty Hospital, Indianapolis, IN, p. A231

WEIDER, Will, Chief Information Officer, Ascension Calumet Hospital, Chilton, WI, p. A781
Chief Information Officer, Ascension Northeast Wisconsin Mercy Hospital, Oshkosh, WI, p. A793

Chief Information Officer, Ascension Northeast Wisconsin St. Elizabeth Hospital, Appleton, WI, p. A779

Chief Information Officer, Ascension St. Michael's Hospital, Stevens Point, WI, p. A796

Chief Information Officer, Marshfield Medical Center, Marshfield, WI, p. A789

WEIDNER, Deborah, Medical Director, Natchaug Hospital, Mansfield Center, CT, p. A123

WEIDNER, Peter, Director Information Technology, St. John's Riverside Hospital, Yonkers, NY, p. A503

WEIGEL, Cherry, Director Health Information Management, Rc Hospital And Clinics, Olivia, MN, p. A382

WEILAND, David, M.D., Chief Medical Officer, Largo Medical Center, Largo, FL, p. A143

WEIMER, Linn, Chief Information Officer, Adena Medical Center, Chillicothe, OH, p. A531

WEINER, Gary, Chief Information Officer, St. Catherine Hospital, East Chicago, IN, p. A227

Vice President Information Technology and Chief Information Officer, St. Mary Medical Center, Hobart, IN, p. A230

Vice President Information Technology, Chief Information Officer, Community Hospital, Munster, IN, p. A237

WEINER, Jared, Chief Financial Officer, Upmc Magee-Womens Hospital, Pittsburgh, PA, p. A604

Chief Financial Officer, Upmc Mercy, Pittsburgh, PA, p. A604

Chief Financial Officer, Upmc Presbyterian, Pittsburgh, PA, p. A604

WEINER, Jerome, M.D., Senior Vice President Medical Affairs, Good Samaritan Hospital Medical Center, West Islip, NY, p. A502

WEINER, Richard, M.D., Chief Executive Officer and Chief Medical Officer, Winchester Hospital, Winchester, MA, p. A346

WEINER, Richard I., M.D., Chief Executive Officer and Chief Medical Officer, Winchester Hospital, Winchester, MA, p. A346

WEINGART, Steve, Chief Financial Officer, Los Alamos Medical Center, Los Alamos, NM, p. A470

WEINGARTNER, Ronald, Vice President Administration, St. Charles Hospital, Port Jefferson, NY, p. A495

WEINKRANTZ, Alan, Chief Financial Officer, Finance, Rutgers University Behavioral Healthcare, Piscataway, NJ, p. A461

WEINMANN, Shannon, Director Human Resources, Community Medical Center, Inc., Falls City, NE, p. A432

WEINREIS, Brian, Vice President Operations and Finance, Abbott Northwestern Hospital, Minneapolis, MN, p. A380

WEINSTEIN, Barry, Chief Financial Officer, Four Winds Hospital, Katonah, NY, p. A486

WEINSTEIN, Brian, M.D., Chief of Staff, Westside Regional Medical Center, Plantation, FL, p. A154

WEINSTEIN, Freddie, M.D., Chief Medical Officer, Dominican Hospital, Santa Cruz, CA, p. A97

WEINTRAUB, Breton, Director, Fargo Veterans Affairs Health Care System, Fargo, ND, p. A523

WEIR, Elizabeth, MSN, R.N., Site Administrator and Vice President of Nursing, Ira Davenport Memorial Hospital, Bath, NY, p. A475

WEIR, Tim W., FACHE, Chief Executive Officer, Olmsted Medical Center, Rochester, MN, p. A384

WEIS, Brian, M.D., Chief Medical Officer, Northwest Texas Healthcare System, Amarillo, TX, p. A652

WEIS, Charles, Chief Financial Officer, Mount Sinai Hospital, Chicago, IL, p. A199

Chief Financial Officer, Schwab Rehabilitation Hospital, Chicago, IL, p. A200

Executive Vice President and Chief Financial Officer, Holy Cross Hospital, Chicago, IL, p. A198

WEIS, Harry, Chief Executive Officer, Tahoe Forest Hospital District, Truckee, CA, p. A102

WEIS, Maurine, Vice President Patient Care Services and Chief Nursing Officer, Promedica Monroe Regional Hospital, Monroe, MI, p. A362

WEIS, Robert, Director Information Systems, Bingham Memorial Hospital, Blackfoot, ID, p. A188

Director Information Technology, Idaho Doctor's Hospital, Blackfoot, ID, p. A188

WEISENFREUND, Jochanan, M.D., Senior Vice President Academic and Medical Affairs, Interfaith Medical Center, Brooklyn, NY, p. A478

WEISER, Marcus, D.O., Chief of Staff, Community Healthcare System, Onaga, KS, p. A273

WEISFIELD, Phyllis, Chief Executive Officer and Managing Director, Horsham Clinic, Ambler, PA, p. A584

WEISHAPL, Natasha, Manager Business Office and Human Resources, Decatur Health Systems, Oberlin, KS, p. A272

WEISKITTEL, Scott, Chief Operating Officer, Trident Medical Center, Charleston, SC, p. A616

WEISS, Anthony, M.D., Chief Medical Officer, Beth Israel Deaconess Medical Center, Boston, MA, p. A335

WEISS, David, M.D., Vice President, Medical Operations, Peninsula Region, St. Michael Medical Center, Bremerton, WA, p. A756

WEISS, Patrice, Executive Vice President, Administration, Carilion Franklin Memorial Hospital, Rocky Mount, VA, p. A751

WEISS, Phyllis, Director Human Resources, Alameda Hospital, Alameda, CA, p. A55

WEISS, Terri, Chief Financial Officer, Encompass Health Rehabilitation Hospital Vision Park, Shenandoah, TX, p. A715

WEISSENBERGER, Ralf, Director Information Systems, Adventist Health White Memorial, Los Angeles, CA, p. A73

WEISSER, Lisa, Supervisor Finance, Wagner Community Memorial Hospital Avera, Wagner, SD, p. A632

WEISSLER, Jonathan, M.D., Chief Medical Officer, Lifecare Hospitals Of Dallas, Dallas, TX, p. A669

WEISTREICH, Tracy, Ph.D., R.N., Associate Director Patient Care Services/Nurse Executive, Veterans Affairs Roseburg Healthcare System, Roseburg, OR, p. A581

WEISUL, Jonathan, M.D., Vice President Medical Affairs and Chief Medical Officer, Christus Coushatta Health Care Center, Coushatta, LA, p. A299

WEITZEL, Cassie, Director, Human Resources, Nicholas H. Noyes Memorial Hospital, Dansville, NY, p. A482

WELANDER, Jennifer, CPA, Senior Vice President Finance and Chief Financial Officer, St. Charles Bend, Bend, OR, p. A573

CPA, Senior Vice President Finance and Chief Financial Officer, St. Charles Redmond, Redmond, OR, p. A580

WELANDER, Michelle, FACHE, R.N., Chief Nursing Officer, Och Regional Medical Center, Starkville, MS, p. A400

WELCH, Abbey, Director Human Resources, Harmon Memorial Hospital, Hollis, OK, p. A560

WELCH, Andrew, Director, New Mexico Veterans Affairs Health Care System - Raymond G. Murphy Medical Center, Albuquerque, NM, p. A468

Interim Director, Veterans Affairs Loma Linda Healthcare System, Loma Linda, CA, p. A72

WELCH, Bryant, Chief Human Resources, Washington Hospital Healthcare System, Fremont, CA, p. A65

WELCH, David, M.D., Medical Director, Clifton-Fine Hospital, Star Lake, NY, p. A498

Chief Executive Officer, Simpson General Hospital, Mendenhall, MS, p. A396

Director Information Technology, Simpson General Hospital, Mendenhall, MS, p. A396

WELCH, Denise, Chief Financial Officer, Arbuckle Memorial Hospital, Sulphur, OK, p. A568

WELCH, Donald, Chief Operating Officer, Adventhealth Zephyrhills, Zephyrhills, FL, p. A162

WELCH, Douglas, Chief Executive Officer, Doctors Hospital, Augusta, GA, p. A166

WELCH, Gary, Assistant to the Chief Executive Officer and Administrative Director Support Systems, Bon Secours Memorial Regional Medical Center, Mechanicsville, VA, p. A746

WELCH, Nicole, Chief Human Resources Officer, Fairbanks Memorial Hospital, Fairbanks, AK, p. A28

WELCH, Rosemary, R.N., Vice President and Chief Nursing Officer, Medstar National Rehabilitation Hospital, Washington, DC, p. A130

WELCH, Sherri, R.N., Chief Nursing Officer, Chi St. Josep. College Station Hospital, College Station, TX, p. A664

WELCH, Thomas, M.D., Chief Medical Officer, Mercy St. Vincent Medical Center, Toledo, OH, p. A550

WELCH, Tony, Senior Vice President and Chief Human Resources Officer, Phoebe Putney Memorial Hospital, Albany, GA, p. A163

Vice President Human Resources, Southeast Alabama Medical Center, Dothan, AL, p. A18

WELDAY, Doug, Chief Financial Officer, Northshore University Health System, Evanston, IL, p. A204

WELDING, Theodore L., Chief Executive Officer, Kindred Hospital South Florida-Fort Lauderdale, Fort Lauderdale, FL, p. A137

WELDON, James, Chief Information Officer, North Mississipp. Health Services, Inc., Tupelo, MI, p. A368

WELDY, Alan, Vice President Human Resources, Compliance and Legal Services, Goshen Health, Goshen, IN, p. A229

WELKIE, Katy MBA, R.N., Chief Executive Officer, Primary Children's Hospital, Salt Lake City, UT, p. A732

WELLBROCK, Jenna, Chief Nursing Officer, Gateway Rehabilitation Hospital, Florence, KY, p. A283

WELLING, Lynn, M.D., Chief Medical Officer, Sharp Chula Vista Medical Center, Chula Vista, CA, p. A60

WELLING, Michele, M.D., Chief of Staff, Bluegrass Community Hospital, Versailles, KY, p. A294

WELLINGTON, Kara, Chief Clinical Officer, Loring Hospital, Sac City, IA, p. A257

WELLMAN, Amanda, MSN, R.N., Chief Nursing Officer, Select Specialty Hospital-Omaha, Omaha, NE, p. A438

WELLMAN, James, Senior Director Information Services, Comanche County Memorial Hospital, Lawton, OK, p. A561

WELLMAN, Sonia I., Chief Executive Officer, Memorial Hospital Of Tampa, Tampa, FL, p. A159

WELLMANN, Jane, Chief Financial Officer, Baylor Scott & White Medical Center - Brenham, Brenham, TX, p. A660

WELLS, A, Chief Financial Officer, Cornerstone Hospital Of Houston At Clearlake, Webster, TX, p. A724

WELLS, Carol, R.N., MSN, Chief Nursing Officer, Central Louisiana Surgical Hospital, Alexandria, LA, p. A295

WELLS, Craig, Chief Information Officer, George C. Grap. Community Hospital, Hamburg, IA, p. A251

WELLS, Crystal, Administrator, Grady General Hospital, Cairo, GA, p. A167

WELLS, Dale, Chief Financial and Operating Officer, Alliance Community Hospital, Alliance, OH, p. A527

WELLS, Daren, Chief Executive Officer, Cache Valley Hospital, North Logan, UT, p. A729

WELLS, James, R.N., Chief Nursing Officer, Kingman Regional Medical Center, Kingman, AZ, p. A33

WELLS, Jason, Chief Human Resources Management Service, Fargo Veterans Affairs Health Care System, Fargo, ND, p. A523

President and Chief Executive Officer, Adventist Health Howard Memorial, Willits, CA, p. A105

WELLS, Jimmy, Chief Nursing and Administrative Officer, Westside Surgical Hospital, Houston, TX, p. A689

WELLS, Jonathan, Supervisor Information Technology, Kansas Surgery And Recovery Center, Wichita, KS, p. A279

WELLS, Mallory, CPA, Chief Financial Officer, Richardson Medical Center, Rayville, LA, p. A313

WELLS, Pamela, R.N., MSN, Chief Nursing Officer, Sharp Memorial Hospital, San Diego, CA, p. A92

WELLS, Robert, M.D., Chief Medical Officer, Providence Portland Medical Center, Portland, OR, p. A579

WELLS, Roxie Cannon., M.D., President, Hoke Hospital, Raeford, NC, p. A516

WELLS, Scott, MSN, R.N., Vice President Patient Care Services, Caromont Regional Medical Center, Gastonia, NC, p. A510

WELLS, Valerie, Manager Human Resources, Encompass Health Rehabilitation Hospital The Woodlands, Conroe, TX, p. A665

WELSER, Jeremy, Director Information Systems, Bonner General Health, Sandpoint, ID, p. A193

WELSH, J. Luckey. Jr, Chief Executive Officer, Cherry Hospital, Goldsboro, NC, p. A510

WELSH, Jamie, Interim Chief Human Resources Officer, Santa Rosa Memorial Hospital, Santa Rosa, CA, p. A98

WELSH, Joyce, R.N., MS, Vice President of Clinical Services and Chief Nursing Officer, Emerson Hospital, Concord, MA, p. A338

WELSH, Kathy, Director of Human Resources, The Healthcenter, Kalispell, MT, p. A425

WELTON, Brian, Chief Executive Officer and Administrator, Baptist Memorial Hospital - Crittenden, Inc., West Memphis, AR, p. A54

WELTON, Jill, President and Chief Executive Officer, Glendale Memorial Hospital And Health Center, Glendale, CA, p. A67

WELTON, Mark, M.D., Chief Medical Officer, Bethesda Hospital, Saint Paul, MN, p. A385

M.D., Chief Medical Officer, St. John's Hospital, Maplewood, MN, p. A380

WEMPE, John, M.D., Chief of Staff, Sioux Falls Veterans Affairs Health Care System, Sioux Falls, SD, p. A632

WENDELL, David, Manager, Information Systems, St. Mary's Medical Center, Huntington, WV, p. A773

WENDELL, Sean, CPA, Chief Executive Officer, Beacon Behavioral Hospital - New Orleans, New Orleans, LA, p. A310

WENDT, Alvin, Acting Chief Executive Officer, Dignity Health East Valley Rehabilitation Hospital, Chandler, AZ, p. A31

WENGER, Cheryl, Manager Health Information and Quality Assurance, Hiawatha Community Hospital, Hiawatha, KS, p. A266

WENGER, Jill, Chief Human Resources Officer, Atchison Hospital, Atchison, KS, p. A261

WENGER-KELLER, David, M.D., Chief of Staff, Fort Madison Community Hospital, Fort Madison, IA, p. A250

WENTWORTH, Cynthia, Chief Human Resource Officer, East Morgan County Hospital, Brush, CO, p. A108

WENTZ, Jim, Chief Financial Officer, Chi Flaget Memorial Hospital, Bardstown, KY, p. A280

WENTZ, Robert J., President and Chief Executive Officer, Oroville Hospital, Oroville, CA, p. A83

WENTZEL, Chris, M.D., Interim Medical Director, Guthrie Corning Hospital, Corning, NY, p. A481

WENZEL, Matthew, President and Chief Executive Officer, Great River Medical Center, West Burlington, IA, p. A260

WERFT, Ronald C., President and Chief Executive Officer, Goleta Valley Cottage Hospital, Santa Barbara, CA, p. A96
President and Chief Executive Officer, Santa Barbara Cottage Hospital, Santa Barbara, CA, p. A97
President and Chief Executive Officer, Santa Ynez Valley Cottage Hospital, Solvang, CA, p. A99

WERKIN, Dave, Vice President Finance and Chief Financial Officer, Trinity Health System, Steubenville, OH, p. A550

WERNER, John W., Chief Executive Officer, Brown County Hospital, Ainsworth, NE, p. A429

WERNER, Katie, Chief Financial Officer, Pembina County Memorial Hospital And Wedgewood Manor, Cavalier, ND, p. A522

WERNER, Kurt, M.D., Chief of Staff, Veterans Affairs Montana Health Care System, Fort Harrison, MT, p. A423

WERNER, Ted, Chief Executive Officer, Pam Rehabilitation Hospital Of Dover, Dover, DE, p. A127

WERNER, Tiffany, Senior Human Resource Business Partner, Banner Baywood Medical Center, Mesa, AZ, p. A33
Senior Human Resource Business Partner, Banner Heart Hospital, Mesa, AZ, p. A34

WERNKE, Chris, Chief Operating Officer, Dominican Hospital, Santa Cruz, CA, p. A97

WERTH-SWEENEY, Stacey, Facility Operating Officer, Lincoln Regional Center, Lincoln, NE, p. A434

WERTHMAN, Ronald, Senior Vice President Finance, Chief Financial Officer and Treasurer, Johns Hopkins Hospital, Baltimore, MD, p. A324

WERTZ, Jackie, Director Human Resources, George C. Grap. Community Hospital, Hamburg, IA, p. A251

WESCOATT, Sampson, Manager Information Technology, Molokai General Hospital, Kaunakakai, HI, p. A186

WESCOTT, Lisle, President, Ssm Health St. Josep. - St. Charles, Saint Charles, MO, p. A414
President, Ssm Health St. Josep. Hospital - Lake Saint Louis, Lake Saint Louis, MO, p. A410

WESENER DIECK, Jill, Human Resources Operations Manager, Gundersen Tri-County Hospital And Clinics, Whitehall, WI, p. A799

WESLEY, Deb, MSN, Chief Nursing Officer, Children's Of Alabama, Birmingham, AL, p. A15

WESLEY, Jim, Senior Vice President and Chief Information Officer, John Muir Behavioral Health Center, Concord, CA, p. A61

WESLEY, Mary Lou, R.N., Senior Vice President and Chief Nursing Officer, Sparrow Hospital, Lansing, MI, p. A360

WESOLOWSKI, Paul, Chief Operating Officer, Vcu Medical Center, Richmond, VA, p. A751

WESP, Clyde, M.D., Chief Medical Officer, Valley Presbyterian Hospital, Van Nuys, CA, p. A103

WESSELS, Jana, Associate Vice President Human Resources, University Of Iowa Hospitals And Clinics, Iowa City, IA, p. A252

WEST, Andrea, MS, Vice President of Human Resources, Columbus Regional Healthcare System, Whiteville, NC, p. A519

WEST, Brenda, R.N., MSN, Chief Nursing Officer, Evergreenhealth Monroe, Monroe, WA, p. A760
Vice President, Information Services and Interim Chief Information Officer, Einstein Medical Center Philadelphia, Philadelphia, PA, p. A600

WEST, Bridgette, Director Patient Access Services, Cobleskill Regional Hospital, Cobleskill, NY, p. A481

WEST, Charles, M.D., Chief Medical Officer, Randolp. Hospital, Asheboro, NC, p. A504

WEST, Christopher, Chief Executive Officer, Cascade Behavioral Hospital, Tukwila, WA, p. A768

WEST, Darren, M.D., Interim Chief Medical Officer, Banner Ironwood Medical Center, San Tan Valley, AZ, p. A38

WEST, David, Chief Operating Officer, Swedish Medical Center-Cherry Hill Campus, Seattle, WA, p. A764

WEST, David R., Chief Operating Officer, Swedish Medical Center-Cherry Hill Campus, Seattle, WA, p. A764
Vice President, Operations, Swedish/Edmonds, Edmonds, WA, p. A757

WEST, James R., President and Chief Executive Officer, Pih Health Hospital - Downey, Downey, CA, p. A62
President and Chief Executive Officer, Pih Health Hospital - Whittier, Whittier, CA, p. A105

WEST, Jennifer, R.N., Chief Nursing Officer, South Texas Spine And Surgical Hospital, San Antonio, TX, p. A713

WEST, Judith, Senior Vice President Human Resources and Chief Human Resources Officer, Maine Medical Center, Portland, ME, p. A322

WEST, Melissa, Chief Financial Officer, Cedar Crest Hospital And Residential Treatment Center, Belton, TX, p. A659

WEST, Michael, M.D., Chief of Staff, Mccurtain Memorial Hospital, Idabel, OK, p. A560
Manager Systems Account, New England Sinai Hospital And Rehabilitation Center, Stoughton, MA, p. A345

WEST, Steve, M.D., Chief Medical Officer, Capital Regional Medical Center, Tallahassee, FL, p. A158

WEST, Tamara, R.N., MSN, Vice President Patient Care, Nicholas H. Noyes Memorial Hospital, Dansville, NY, p. A482

WESTENFELDER, Grant, M.D., Chief Medical Officer, Midwest Medical Center, Galena, IL, p. A205

WESTER, K Scott., FACHE, President and Chief Executive Officer, Our Lady Of The Lake Regional Medical Center, Baton Rouge, LA, p. A297

WESTERCHIL, Beth, R.N., Chief Nurse Executive, De Soto Regional Health System, Mansfield, LA, p. A308

WESTERFIELD, Jerry, M.D., Chief of Medical Staff, Russell County Hospital, Russell Springs, KY, p. A292

WESTERHEIDE, Karen, Chief Financial Officer, Veterans Affairs St. Louis Health Care System, Saint Louis, MO, p. A418

WESTERMAN, Mandy, Chief Executive Officer, West Oaks Hospital, Houston, TX, p. A689

WESTFALL, Gay, Senior Vice President Human Resources, Kaiser Permanente Sacramento Medical Center, Sacramento, CA, p. A89

WESTFALL, Roger, Director, Western State Hospital, Hopkinsville, KY, p. A285

WESTIN, Robert, M.D., Chief Medical Officer, Cuyuna Regional Medical Center, Crosby, MN, p. A374

WESTMAN, Ken, Chief Executive Officer, Barrett Hospital & Healthcare, Dillon, MT, p. A423

WESTMORELAND, Penny, Chief Financial Officer, Lakeland Community Hospital, Haleyville, AL, p. A20
Chief Financial Officer, Red Bay Hospital, Red Bay, AL, p. A24
Chief Financial Officer, Russellville Hospital, Russellville, AL, p. A24

WESTON, Betty, Chief Human Resources Officer, U. S. Public Health Service Phoenix Indian Medical Center, Phoenix, AZ, p. A37

WESTON, Lori, Administrator, Park City Hospital, Park City, UT, p. A730

WESTON, Nicholas (Ty), Interim Chief Executive Officer, Mangum Regional Medical Center, Mangum, OK, p. A561

WESTON, Susan, CPA, Chief Financial Officer, Mountrail County Medical Center, Stanley, ND, p. A526

WESTON, Terry, M.D., Vice President Physician Services, Ohiohealth Medcentral Mansfield Hospital, Mansfield, OH, p. A544

WESTON-HALL, Patricia, Chief Executive Officer, Glenbeigh Hospital And Outpatient Centers, Rock Creek, OH, p. A548

WESTOVER, Teresa, Director Human Resources, North Texas Medical Center, Gainesville, TX, p. A680

WESTPHAL, Chris, Chief Information Technology Officer, Southeast Colorado Hospital District, Springfield, CO, p. A118

WESTPHAL, James, M.D., AMHD Medical Director, Hawaii State Hospital, Kaneohe, HI, p. A186

WESTPHAL, Laura, R.N., Vice President Patient Care Services, Adventist Health Castle, Kailua, HI, p. A185

WESTPHAL, Susan, Assistant Administrator, Patient Care Services, Fairchild Medical Center, Yreka, CA, p. A106

WESTRUM, Jennifer, Administrator, Community Behavioral Health Hospital - Alexandria, Alexandria, MN, p. A371

WESTRY, Tanza, Chief Financial Officer, Hunter Holmes Mcguire Veterans Affairs Medical Center-Richmond, Richmond, VA, p. A750

WESTWOOD, Denise, Chief Nursing Officer, Weirton Medical Center, Weirton, WV, p. A777

WETHAL, Robert, R.N., Vice President Patient Care Services and Chief Nursing Officer, Mercyone Dubuque Medical Center, Dubuque, IA, p. A249

WETMORE, Melanie, MSN, R.N., Chief Nursing Officer, Regional Medical Center Bayonet Point, Hudson, FL, p. A140

WETTLAUFER, Debbie, Chief Financial Officer, French Hospital Medical Center, San Luis Obispo, CA, p. A95

WETTON, Darlene, R.N., Chief Executive Officer, Temecula Valley Hospital, Temecula, CA, p. A100

WETZ, Staci, Chief Financial Officer, Shannon Medical Center, San Angelo, TX, p. A710

WETZEL, James, M.D., Senior Vice President, Chief Medical Officer, Olathe Medical Center, Olathe, KS, p. A272

WETZEL, Lou, M.D., Chief of Staff, The University Of Kansas Hospital, Kansas City, KS, p. A268

WEYMOUTH, Deborah K., FACHE, Chief Executive Officer, Manchester Memorial Hospital, Manchester, CT, p. A122

FACHE, Chief Executive Officer, Rockville General Hospital, Vernon, CT, p. A125

WEYMOUTH, Linda, Chief Financial Officer, Suncoast Behavioral Health Center, Bradenton, FL, p. A133

WHALEN, David, Chief Executive Officer, Twin Cities Hospital, Niceville, FL, p. A149

WHALEN, Megan, Vice President, Human Resources, Palms Of Pasadena Hospital, Saint Petersburg, FL, p. A156

WHALEN, Patti, Manager Human Resources, Wichita County Health Center, Leoti, KS, p. A269

WHALEN, Thomas, M.D., Chief Medical Officer, Lehigh Valley Hospital, Allentown, PA, p. A583
Vice President Finance, Good Samaritan Medical Center, Brockton, MA, p. A337

WHALEY, Alan, Chief Operating Officer, Usa Health Children's & Women's Hospital, Mobile, AL, p. A22

WHALEY, Joseph, Chief, Human Resources Management Service, Fayetteville Veterans Affairs Medical Center, Fayetteville, NC, p. A510

WHALEY, Mary, Director of Acute Care, Johnson County Healthcare Center, Buffalo, WY, p. A801

WHARTON, Joe, M.D., Chief of Staff, Bradley County Medical Center, Warren, AR, p. A54

WHEAT, Ken, Senior Vice President and Chief Financial Officer, Eisenhower Health, Rancho Mirage, CA, p. A86

WHEAT, Terry, R.N., M.P.H., Director of Patient Care Services, Shriners Hospitals For Children-Chicago, Chicago, IL, p. A201

WHEATLEY, Bernard, FACHE, Chief Executive Officer, Schneider Regional Medical Center, Saint Thomas, VI, p. A812

WHEATLEY, Cathleen, R.N., President and System Chief Nurse Executive and Senior Vice President of Clinical Operations, Wake Forest Baptist Medical Center, Winston, NC, p. A520

WHEATLEY, Jane, Chief Executive Officer, Taylor Regional Hospital, Campbellsville, KY, p. A281

WHEATLEY, Richard, Chief Information Officer, Cap. Regional Health System, Cap. May Court House, NJ, p. A453

WHEATLEY, Samuel, Chief Medical Officer, Columbus Regional Healthcare System, Whiteville, NC, p. A519

WHEATLEY, Sonya, Human Resources Manager, Central State Hospital, Louisville, KY, p. A288

WHEATLEY, Stephen J., Director of Operations, Franciscan Health Carmel, Carmel, IN, p. A225

WHEATON, David, Director Human Resources, Northern Light Blue Hill Hospital, Blue Hill, ME, p. A319

WHEATON, Tammy, Interim Chief Nursing Officer, Union County Hospital, Anna, IL, p. A194

WHEELAN, Kevin, M.D., Medical Director, Baylor Scott & White Heart & Vascular Hospital-Dallas, Dallas, TX, p. A667

WHEELER, Brent, Vice President of Operations, Mclaren Flint, Flint, MI, p. A354

WHEELER, Cambria, Communications and Marketing, Adventist Health Clear Lake, Clearlake, CA, p. A60

WHEELER, Dane, Chief Financial Officer, Adams Memorial Hospital, Decatur, IN, p. A226

WHEELER, Dawne, Chief Executive Officer, Select Specialty Hospital-Akron, Akron, OH, p. A527

WHEELER, Frankie, Director, Human Resources, Saint Elizabeths Hospital, Washington, DC, p. A130

WHEELER, James, Vice President Human Relations and Community Development, Androscoggin Valley Hospital, Berlin, NH, p. A448

WHEELER, Lynette, MSN, Chief Operating Officer, Truman Medical Center-Lakewood, Kansas City, MO, p. A410

WHEELER, Newman, Chief Executive Officer, Yoakum County Hospital, Denver City, TX, p. A672

WHEELER, Penny, M.D., President and Chief Medical Officer, Abbott Northwestern Hospital, Minneapolis, MN, p. A380

WHEELER, Philip. Director Finance, Mercy Health - Clermont Hospital, Batavia, OH, p. A528

WHEELER, Rebecca, Director Finance, Kaiser Permanente Baldwin Park Medical Center, Baldwin Park, CA, p. A57

WHEELER, Robert, Controller, Encompass Health Rehabilitation Hospital Of Florence, Florence, SC, p. A619
Vice President Human Resources, South Shore Hospital, South Weymouth, MA, p. A344

WHEELER, William, M.D., Chief of Staff, Benewah Community Hospital, Saint Maries, ID, p. A193

WHEELER, Zachariah, Senior Vice President Human Resources, John D. Archbold Memorial Hospital, Thomasville, GA, p. A182

WHEELER-MOORE, Juanita, Director Financial Services, Four Winds Hospital, Saratoga Springs, NY, p. A497

WHEELES, Locke, Information Technology Manager, Field Memorial Community Hospital, Centreville, MS, p. A390

WHEELUS, Matthew, Chief Operating Officer, Spring Valley Hospital Medical Center, Las Vegas, NV, p. A444

Vice President, Chief Operating Officer, St. Michael Medical Center, Bremerton, WA, p. A756

WHELAN, Laurie, Senior Vice President Finance and Chief Financial Officer, Hospital For Special Care, New Britain, CT, p. A123

WHELAN, Thomas, Chief Executive Officer, Cibola General Hospital, Grants, NM, p. A469

WHERRY, Robin, Risk Manager and Director Quality Assurance and Health Information Management, Encompass Health Rehabilitation Hospital Of Morgantown, Morgantown, WV, p. A774

WHICHARD, Nick, Chief Information Officer, St. Luke's Hospital, Columbus, NC, p. A508

WHIDDON, William, Chief Financial Officer, Woodland Heights Medical Center, Lufkin, TX, p. A698

WHILDEN, Sean, Chief Financial Officer, Houston Medical Center, Warner Robins, GA, p. A183

Chief Financial Officer, Perry Hospital, Perry, GA, p. A178

WHILEY, Karen, Chief Nursing Officer and Vice President Operations, Fairview Lakes Health Services, Wyoming, MN, p. A388

Vice President Patient Care Services, Fairview Northland Medical Center, Princeton, MN, p. A383

WHILLOCK, Mary, R.N., MS, Associate Nursing Officer and Chief Operating Officer, Adventhealth Carrollwood, Tampa, FL, p. A159

WHIPKEY, Jared, Chief Financial Officer, Santa Rosa Medical Center, Milton, FL, p. A148

WHIPPLE, C, Director of Nursing, Upmc Muncy, Muncy, PA, p. A598

WHIPPLE, Jennifer, Director Nursing, Lane County Hospital, Dighton, KS, p. A263

WHIPPLE, Michael, Chief Financial Officer, Mercy St. Anne Hospital, Toledo, OH, p. A550

WHITAKER, Catherine, MSN, R.N., Vice President and Chief Nursing Officer, University Of Maryland Baltimore Washington Medical Center, Glen Burnie, MD, p. A330

WHITAKER, Charles, Director Information Technology, Madison Parish Hospital, Tallulah, LA, p. A316

WHITAKER, Chasity, Administrative Assistant, Madison Parish Hospital, Tallulah, LA, p. A316

WHITAKER, Cynthia, Chief Nursing Officer, Henry County Medical Center, Paris, TN, p. A648

WHITAKER, Doris, Vice President and Manager, Mercy Hospital Booneville, Booneville, AR, p. A43

WHITAKER, Jimmy, Director Information Systems, Central Carolina Hospital, Sanford, NC, p. A518

WHITAKER, Robert, President and Chief Executive Officer, Southwest Medical Center, Liberal, KS, p. A269

WHITAKER, Stacy, M.D., Medical Staff President, Grande Ronde Hospital, La Grande, OR, p. A576

WHITAKER, Stephanie, Chief Nursing Officer, Baptist Health - Fort Smith, Fort Smith, AR, p. A46

WHITE, Alexander, Vice President Medical Affairs, Carney Hospital, Boston, MA, p. A335

WHITE, Andrea, Chief Executive Officer, Kindred Hospital-Chattanooga, Chattanooga, TN, p. A635

WHITE, Beverly, MS, Facility Director, Mary S Harper Geriatric Psychiatry Center, Tuscaloosa, AL, p. A25

WHITE, Brian, Director Strategic Operations, Vidant Chowan Hospital, Edenton, NC, p. A509

Director Strategic Planning, Vidant Bertie Hospital, Windsor, NC, p. A520

WHITE, Bruce, Administrator, Covenant Hospital-Levelland, Levelland, TX, p. A695

WHITE, Bruce D., Chief Executive Officer, Knox Community Hospital, Mount Vernon, OH, p. A546

WHITE, Catherine, Chief Financial Officer, Harney District Hospital, Burns, OR, p. A574

WHITE, Christina, Financial Manager, Avoyelles Hospital, Marksville, LA, p. A308

WHITE, Cindy, CPA, Vice President of Operations, Integris Canadian Valley Hospital, Yukon, OK, p. A572

WHITE, Darrell, R.N., Administrator and Chief Nursing Officer, Tristar Ashland City Medical Center, Ashland City, TN, p. A634

WHITE, Darryl, M.D., Chief of Staff, Freestone Medical Center, Fairfield, TX, p. A677

WHITE, Deborah, Human Resource Coordinator, Faith Community Hospital, Jacksboro, TX, p. A691

WHITE, Denise, MSN, Chief Nurse Executive and Vice President Facility Executive, Atrium Health Union, Monroe, NC, p. A514

MSN, Chief Nurse Executive, Atrium Health Anson, Wadesboro, NC, p. A519

MSN, Vice President, Facility Executive, Atrium Health Union, Monroe, NC, p. A514

Administrator, Beacon Behavioral Hospital, Lutcher, LA, p. A307

WHITE, Diane, Chief Clinical Officer and Chief Nursing Officer, Bridgepoint Hospital National Harbor, Washington, DC, p. A129

WHITE, Gary, M.D., Chief Medical Staff, Uintah Basin Medical Center, Roosevelt, UT, p. A731

WHITE, Harold, Vice Chancellor, Ochsner Lsu Health Shreveport - Academic Medical Center, Shreveport, LA, p. A314

WHITE, J, Director Information Systems, Merit Health River Region, Vicksburg, MS, p. A401

WHITE, Jason, M.D., Chief Medical Officer, Mclaren Bay Region, Bay City, MI, p. A349

WHITE, Jean, Vice President Finance, Avera Heart Hospital Of South Dakota, Sioux Falls, SD, p. A631

WHITE, Jennifer, Interim Chief Executive Officer, Eleanor Slater Hospital, Cranston, RI, p. A613

WHITE, Jim, Chief Information Officer, Lompoc Valley Medical Center, Lompoc, CA, p. A72

WHITE, Joanne, Chief Information Officer, Wood County Hospital, Bowling Green, OH, p. A530

WHITE, Joe, Chief Operating Officer, Tristar Southern Hills Medical Center, Nashville, TN, p. A647

WHITE, Joel, Chief Operating Officer, Select Specialty Hospital-Omaha, Omaha, NE, p. A438

WHITE, John, Chief Financial Officer, Wythe County Community Hospital, Wytheville, VA, p. A754

WHITE, Joseph, FACHE, President and Chief Executive Officer, Lowell General Hospital, Lowell, MA, p. A341

WHITE, Josh, Chief Medical Officer, Deckerville Community Hospital, Deckerville, MI, p. A352

WHITE, Karen, Chief Nursing Officer, Central Montana Medical Center, Lewistown, MT, p. A425

Interim Vice President of Human Resources, Navos, Seattle, WA, p. A763

WHITE, Kelli, Director, Human Resources, Centerpointe Hospital, Saint Charles, MO, p. A414

WHITE, Kelly, Vice President of Patient Care and Chief Nursing Officer, North Memorial Health Hospital, Robbinsdale, MN, p. A383

WHITE, Kendall, Chief Information Officer, Mount Auburn Hospital, Cambridge, MA, p. A338

WHITE, Kevin A., Administrator, Medicine Lodge Memorial Hospital, Medicine Lodge, KS, p. A271

WHITE, Kishah, Director Human Resources, Bon Secours St. Mary's Hospital, Richmond, VA, p. A749

WHITE, Knicole, Vice-President, Human Resources, Kendall Regional Medical Center, Miami, FL, p. A146

WHITE, Linda E., Chief Executive Officer, Methodist Hospital, Henderson, KY, p. A285

WHITE, Lindy P., Vice President and Chief Executive Officer, Holston Valley Medical Center, Kingsport, TN, p. A641

Vice President, Chief Executive Officer of Kingsport Market Operations, Indian Path Community Hospital, Kingsport, TN, p. A641

WHITE, Mary-Louise, M.D., Chief Operating Officer, Dr. Solomon Carter Fuller Mental Health Center, Boston, MA, p. A335

WHITE, Mike, Chief Financial Officer, Hansen Family Hospital, Iowa Falls, IA, p. A252

WHITE, Nathan, Chief Information Officer, Charles A. Cannon Memorial Hospital, Newland, NC, p. A515

WHITE, Pamela, R.N., MSN, Chief Nursing Officer, Mayo Clinic Health System In Eau Claire, Eau Claire, WI, p. A783

Chief Nursing Officer, North Mississipp. Medical Center-West Point, West Point, MS, p. A401

WHITE, Patricia, Vice President Human Resources, Seton Medical Center, Daly City, CA, p. A62

WHITE, Patty, R.N., Director Patient Care Services, Lecom Corry Memorial Hospital, Corry, PA, p. A587

WHITE, Randy, Chief Nursing Officer, Baptist Memorial Hospital-Union County, New Albany, MS, p. A398

WHITE, Sabrina, Coordinator Human Resources, Select Specialty Hospital-Charleston, Charleston, WV, p. A771

WHITE, Sam, Chief Nursing Officer, Gateway Regional Medical Center, Granite City, IL, p. A206

WHITE, Shawna, Chief Information Officer, Magee Rehabilitation Hospital, Philadelphia, PA, p. A601

WHITE, Shelia, Director Human Resources, Bon Secours-Richmond Community Hospital, Richmond, VA, p. A749

WHITE, Shirley, Director Human Resources, Ashley County Medical Center, Crossett, AR, p. A44

WHITE, Tania, Director Human Resources, Loretto Hospital, Chicago, IL, p. A199

WHITE, Trina, President and Chief Executive Officer, Sutter Maternity And Surgery Center Of Santa Cruz, Santa Cruz, CA, p. A97

WHITE, Vicki, R.N., MS, Chief Nurse Executive, Mills-Peninsula Health Services, Burlingame, CA, p. A59

Chief Nursing Officer, Santa Rosa Memorial Hospital, Santa Rosa, CA, p. A98

WHITE, Vivian, Chief Executive Officer, Encompass Health Rehabilitation Hospital Of Richmond, Richmond, VA, p. A750

WHITE, Wesley, Chief Financial Officer, Teton Valley Health Care, Driggs, ID, p. A190

WHITE HOUSE, Judy, FACHE, Vice President Human Resources, St. Mary's Hospital And Medical Center, Grand Junction, CO, p. A113

WHITE-JACOBS, Mary Beth, FACHE, R.N., Chief Executive Officer, Black River Memorial Hospital, Black River Falls, WI, p. A781

WHITE-TREVINO, Karen, Chief Nursing Officer, West Florida Hospital, Pensacola, FL, p. A154

WHITED, Brian, M.D., President and Chief Executive Officer, Mayo Clinic Health System In Lake City, Lake City, MN, p. A378

M.D., President and Chief Executive Officer, Mayo Clinic Health System In Red Wing, Red Wing, MN, p. A383

M.D., Vice Chair Mayo Clinic Health System, Mayo Clinic Health System In Cannon Falls, Cannon Falls, MN, p. A374

M.D., Vice Chair, Mayo Health System, Mayo Clinic Health System - Albert Lea And Austin, Albert Lea, MN, p. A371

WHITED, Steve, Chief Executive Officer, Minnie Hamilton Healthcare Center, Grantsville, WV, p. A772

WHITEHEAD, Alva, M.D., Vice President Medical Services, Mcleod Regional Medical Center, Florence, SC, p. A619

WHITEHEAD, Noemi, Administrative Director Human Resources, Sutter Delta Medical Center, Antioch, CA, p. A56

WHITEHOUSE, Alan, Chief Information Officer, Wellstar West Georgia Medical Center, Lagrange, GA, p. A175

WHITEHURST, Rob, Chief, Office of Information and Technology, Veterans Affairs Ann Arbor Healthcare System, Ann Arbor, MI, p. A348

WHITELEY, Earl S., FACHE, Chief Executive Officer, Jenkins County Medical Center, Millen, GA, p. A177

WHITESIDE, Anne, Vice President Nursing, Valley Health - Winchester Medical Center, Winchester, VA, p. A754

WHITESIDE, John, Chief Executive Officer, Los Alamos Medical Center, Los Alamos, NM, p. A470

WHITESIDE, Patrick, Manager Information Services, Spectrum Health Big Rapids Hospital, Big Rapids, MI, p. A349

WHITFIELD, Bruce, CPA, Chief Executive Officer and Chief Financial Officer, Cabinet Peaks Medical Center, Libby, MT, p. A425

WHITFIELD, Jay, Chief Financial Officer, Baylor University Medical Center, Dallas, TX, p. A668

WHITING, Barbara, Director Health Information Management, Kp. Promise Hospital Of Vicksburg, Vicksburg, MS, p. A400

WHITIS, Matt, Chief Medical Officer, Mahaska Health Partnership, Oskaloosa, IA, p. A256

WHITLATCH, Kristie, President, King's Daughters Medical Center, Ashland, KY, p. A280

WHITLEY, Carolynn, Chief Nursing Officer, Chi St. Vincent Sherwood Rehabilitation Hospital, Sherwood, AR, p. A53

WHITLEY, Darla, Manager Health Information Technology, Syringa Hospital And Clinics, Grangeville, ID, p. A190

WHITLEY, Kay L., President and Chief Executive Officer, Spanish Peaks Regional Health Center, Walsenburg, CO, p. A119

WHITLEY, Myra, Vice President, Human Resources, Columbus Specialty Hospital, Columbus, GA, p. A169

WHITLEY, Pam, R.N., Chief Nursing Officer and Chief Operating Officer, Medical City Green Oaks Hospital, Dallas, TX, p. A669

R.N., Chief Operating Officer and Chief Nursing Officer, Medical City Green Oaks Hospital, Dallas, TX, p. A669

WHITLOCK, John, Chief Financial Officer, Central Maine Medical Center, Lewiston, ME, p. A321

WHITMER, David, FACHE, Director, Carl Vinson Veterans Affairs Medical Center, Dublin, GA, p. A171

WHITMORE, Ray, Chief Financial Officer, Mccurtain Memorial Hospital, Idabel, OK, p. A560

WHITMORE, Stewart, Chief Financial Officer, North Florida Regional Medical Center, Gainesville, FL, p. A138

Chief Financial Officer, Putnam Community Medical Center, Palatka, FL, p. A152

WHITMORE ESQ, DawnDirector of Nursing, Aurora Behavioral Health System East, Tempe, AZ, p. A39

WHITNEY, Donald, Director Human Resources, Kindred Hospital-Albuquerque, Albuquerque, NM, p. A467

WHITNUM, Rhonda, Director Health Improvement Management, Prague Community Hospital, Prague, OK, p. A567

WHITSON, Charles, CPA, Senior Vice President Finance, Lake Charles Memorial Hospital, Lake Charles, LA, p. A307

WHITT, Alicia, R.N., Chief Nursing Officer, Stephens Memorial Hospital, Breckenridge, TX, p. A660

WHITT, Horace, Chief Executive Officer and Chief Operating Officer, Refugio County Memorial Hospital, Refugio, TX, p. A708

WHITT, Stevan, M.D., Chief Medical Officer, University Of Missouri Health Care, Columbia, MO, p. A405

WHITTAKER, Kelly, Vice President Nursing, Mclaren Caro Region, Caro, MI, p. A350

WHITTAKER, Shawn, Chief Nursing Officer, Miller County Hospital, Colquitt, GA, p. A169

WHITTAKER, Sheena, M.D., Chief Medical Officer, Northern Light Maine Coast Hospital, Ellsworth, ME, p. A320

WHITTEMORE, Marjorie, Director Human Resources, Rio Grande Regional Hospital, Mcallen, TX, p. A700

WHITTEMORE, Scott, Chief Financial Officer and Chief of Ancillary Services, Springfield Hospital, Springfield, VT, p. A736

Chief Financial Officer, University Of Mississipp. Medical Center Grenada, Grenada, MS, p. A393

Chief Financial Officer, University Of Mississipp. Medical Center Holmes County, Lexington, MS, p. A396

WHITTEN, Jacquelyn, MSN, R.N., Chief Nursing Executive, Vice President of Nursing, Advocate Trinity Hospital, Chicago, IL, p. A197

WHITTINGTON, Bruce, Vice President Human Resources, University Of Kansas Health System Pawnee Valley Campus, Larned, KS, p. A268

WHITTINGTON, Dorothy, Chief Financial Officer, Ochsner Lsu Health Shreveport - Monroe Medical Center, Monroe, LA, p. A309

WHITTINGTON, Hilary, Chief Financial Officer, Jefferson Healthcare, Port Townsend, WA, p. A762

WHITTINGTON, Laurie, Chief Operating Officer, Memorial Health, Marysville, OH, p. A544

WHITTINGTON, Michael, R.N., Chief Executive Officer and Administrator, Hood Memorial Hospital, Amite, LA, p. A296

WHITTINGTON, Shane, Chief Financial Officer, Caldwell Medical Center, Princeton, KY, p. A292

WHITTINGTON-GEPPERT, Kelley, Director Human Resources, Munson Healthcare Cadillac Hospital, Cadillac, MI, p. A350

WHITTON, Beth, Director Human Resources, Ocean Beach Hospital, Ilwaco, WA, p. A759

WHOLLEY, Diane, Director Fiscal Services, Bridgewater State Hospital, Bridgewater, MA, p. A336

WHORLEY, Chris, Chief Information Officer, Nashville General Hospital, Nashville, TN, p. A646

WHYBROW, Peter, M.D., Chief Executive Officer, Stewart & Lynda Resnick Neuropsychiatric Hospital At Ucla, Los Angeles, CA, p. A76

WHYTE, Brett, M.D., Chief of Medical Staff, Winona Health, Winona, MN, p. A388

WIATREK, Joseph, Director Information Technology, Otto Kaiser Memorial Hospital, Kenedy, TX, p. A692

WIBBENMEYER, Christopher, Director Human Resources, Perry County Memorial Hospital, Perryville, MO, p. A413

WIBBENS, Cheryl, M.D., Vice President Medical Staff Affairs, Memorial Hospital Of South Bend, South Bend, IN, p. A240

WIBBLESMAN, Christopher, M.D., Chief of Staff, Colorado Canyons Hospital And Medical Center, Fruita, CO, p. A113

WIBORG, Shelley, MS, R.N., Chief Nursing Officer, Osf Saint Luke Medical Center, Kewanee, IL, p. A209

MS, R.N., Director of Nursing, Osf Holy Family Medical Center, Monmouth, IL, p. A212

WICKE, Julius Vice President Finance and Hospital Financial Officer, Baylor Scott & White Heart & Vascular Hospital-Dallas, Dallas, TX, p. A667

WICKE, Regina, Chief Financial Officer, Columbus Community Hospital, Columbus, TX, p. A664

WICKENS, Amy, Executive Director Human Resources, Decatur County Memorial Hospital, Greensburg, IN, p. A230

WICKER, Kenneth R., FACHE, Chief Executive Officer, Bayfront Health Brooksville, Brooksville, FL, p. A133

FACHE, Chief Executive Officer, St. Petersburg General Hospital, Saint Petersburg, FL, p. A156

WICKIZER, Boyd, M.D., JrChief Medical Officer, Southside Regional Medical Center, Petersburg, VA, p. A749

WICKLANDER, Jeff, President, North Memorial Health Hospital, Robbinsdale, MN, p. A383

WICKLINE, Melissa, Director Marketing, Greenbrier Valley Medical Center, Ronceverte, WV, p. A776

WICKLUND, Grant, SCL Health Regional President, Western Colorado and President, Lutheran Medical Center, Lutheran Medical Center, Wheat Ridge, CO, p. A120

WIDAWSKY, Daniel, Chief Financial Officer, Nyu Langone Hospitals, New York, NY, p. A492

WIDDER, John, Director, Los Ninos Hospital, Phoenix, AZ, p. A36

WIDEMAN, Jeff, Director Information Systems, North Mississipp. Medical Center Gilmore-Amory, Amory, MS, p. A389

WIDGER, Judy, M.D., Chief of Staff, Healdsburg District Hospital, Healdsburg, CA, p. A68

WIDICK, Brent, Superintendent, Kansas Neurological Institute, Topeka, KS, p. A277

WIDNER, Eric W., FACHE, Division President, Beaumont Hospital, Wayne, Wayne, MI, p. A369

WIDRA, Linda, FACHE, Ph.D., R.N., Chief Operating Officer, Lakewood Ranch Medical Center, Bradenton, FL, p. A133

WIEBE, Trevor, Business Office Manager, Information Technology, Mercy Hospital Inc., Moundridge, KS, p. A271

WIECZOREK, Pawel, Director Information Technology, Brylin Hospitals, Buffalo, NY, p. A479

WIEMAN, Jason S., Director, Fort Belvoir Community Hospital, Fort Belvoir, VA, p. A742

WIENS, Ron, Chief Financial Officer, Shodair Children's Hospital, Helena, MT, p. A425

WIENTJES, Keri, Director Human Resources, Mobridge Regional Hospital, Mobridge, SD, p. A629

WIERZBICKI, Barb, Manager Human Resources, Select Specialty Hospital-Downriver, Wyandotte, MI, p. A370

WIESMAN, David, Interim Chief Financial Officer, Fayette County Hospital, Vandalia, IL, p. A222

WIESMANN, Marie, Vice President of Nursing and Chief Nursing Officer, Fort Healthcare, Fort Atkinson, WI, p. A784

WIESNER, Jerry, Administrator and Chief Executive Officer, Southwest Healthcare Services, Bowman, ND, p. A521

WIEWORA, Ron, M.D., Chief Medical Officer, Lakeside Medical Center, Belle Glade, FL, p. A132

WIGGINS, Carla, Director Human Resources, Livingston Hospital And Healthcare Services, Salem, KY, p. A293

WIGGINS, John, Chief Financial Officer, Evans Memorial Hospital, Claxton, GA, p. A168

WIGGINS, Marjorie, Senior Vice President, Chief Nursing Officer, Maine Medical Center, Portland, ME, p. A322

WIGHTMAN, Lori, R.N., FACHE, Chief Executive Officer, Bothwell Regional Health Center, Sedalia, MO, p. A418

WIGMAN, Cathryn, Director Human Resources, Encompass Health Rehabilitation Hospital Of Braintree, Braintree, MA, p. A336

WIIK, Jennifer, Chief Nursing Officer, Ortonville Area Health Services, Ortonville, MN, p. A382

WIJAYA, Joanne, MSN, R.N., Chief Operating Officer and Risk Manager, Hampton Behavioral Health Center, Westampton, NJ, p. A465

WILBUR, Bruce, M.D., Chief Medical Officer, Good Samaritan Hospital, San Jose, CA, p. A94

WILBUR, Thomas W., Chief Executive Officer and Superintendent, Newport Hospital And Health Services, Newport, WA, p. A761

WILBURN, Sue, Vice President Human Resources and Organizational Development, East Tennessee Children's Hospital, Knoxville, TN, p. A641

WILCHER, Greta, Senior Vice President and Chief Financial Officer, Mercy Hospital Fort Smith, Fort Smith, AR, p. A46

Senior Vice President and Chief Financial Officer, Mercy Hospital Waldron, Waldron, AR, p. A54

WILCOX, Bill, Chief Information Technology Officer, Bristol Bay Area Health Corporation, Dillingham, AK, p. A28

WILCOX, Byron, Chief Financial Management Officer, Standing Rock Service Unit, Fort Yates Hospital, Indian Health Service, Dhhs, Fort Yates, ND, p. A523

WILCOX, David, Chief Financial Officer, Regional Medical Center Of Central Alabama, Greenville, AL, p. A19

WILCOX, Jack, Chief Financial Officer, Ennis Regional Medical Center, Ennis, TX, p. A677

Chief Financial Officer, Parkview Regional Hospital, Mexia, TX, p. A701

WILCOX, Jim, Chief Executive Officer, Legent Hospital Of El Paso, El Paso, TX, p. A675

WILCOX, Kyle, Vice President Finance, Unitypoint Health - Grinnell Regional Medical Center, Grinnell, IA, p. A250

WILCOX, Robert, Chief Financial Officer, Munson Healthcare Charlevoix Hospital, Charlevoix, MI, p. A350

WILCOXON, Phillip. Chief Executive Officer, Perimeter Behavioral Hospital Of Dallas, Garland, TX, p. A681

WILCZEK, Joseph, Chief Executive Officer, St. Elizabeth Hospital, Enumclaw, WA, p. A758

WILCZEK, Vincent, Controller, Pratt Regional Medical Center, Pratt, KS, p. A275

WILDA, Joshua, Chief Information Officer, Metro Health - University Of Michigan Health, Wyoming, MI, p. A370

WILDE, Gary, President and Chief Executive Officer, Community Memorial Hospital, Ventura, CA, p. A103

WILDER, Janet, Director Human Resources, Barbourville Arh Hospital, Barbourville, KY, p. A280

WILDER, Stephen, Director Human Resources, Parkwest Medical Center, Knoxville, TN, p. A641

WILDER, Susan, Director Financial Services, Roosevelt Warm Springs Rehabilitation And Specialty Hospitals - Ltac, Warm Springs, GA, p. A182

Director Financial Services, Roosevelt Warm Springs Rehabilitation Hospital - Rehab, Warm Springs, GA, p. A183

WILDHAGEN, Quentin, Systems Administrator, Izard County Medical Center, Calico Rock, AR, p. A43

WILEY, Chuck, Manager Information Systems, Harrison County Hospital, Corydon, IN, p. A226

WILEY, Donald J., President and Chief Executive Officer, St. Joseph's Medical Center, Stockton, CA, p. A100

WILEY, George, Chief Financial Officer, Desert Springs Hospital Medical Center, Las Vegas, NV, p. A443

WILEY, Mark, Manager Information Systems Development, Upmc Bedford, Everett, PA, p. A590

WILEY, Ronette, R.N., Executive Vice President and Chief Operating Officer, Bassett Medical Center, Cooperstown, NY, p. A481

WILFONG, Mario, Chief Financial Officer, Upmc Children's Hospital Of Pittsburgh, Pittsburgh, PA, p. A603

WILHELM, Connie, Chief Financial Officer, Swisher Memorial Healthcare System, Tulia, TX, p. A721

WILHELM, Margo, Chief Financial Officer, Austin Oaks Hospital, Austin, TX, p. A655

WILHELM, Paul, M.D., Chief of Staff, Kiowa District Healthcare, Kiowa, KS, p. A268

WILHITE, James, Director Systems Information, North Mississipp. State Hospital, Tupelo, MS, p. A400

WILHITE, Jerald, Administrator Human Resources, Heartland Behavioral Healthcare, Massillon, OH, p. A544

WILHOITE, David, CPA, Senior Vice President Finance and Chief Financial Officer, Trousdale Medical Center, Hartsville, TN, p. A639

WILKE, Kris, Manager Health Information, Avera Granite Falls Health Center, Granite Falls, MN, p. A377

WILKEN, Thomas, Senior Vice President and Chief Human Resources Officer, Christus Mother Frances Hospital - Tyler, Tyler, TX, p. A721

Vice President Human Resources, Ascension Seton Williamson, Round Rock, TX, p. A709

WILKENS, Gregory, M.D., Chief of Staff, Jellico Community Hospital, Jellico, TN, p. A640

WILKER, Johnathan, Vice President Finance and Chief Financial Officer, Faith Regional Health Services, Norfolk, NE, p. A435

WILKERSON, Jacquelyn, R.N., Chief Nursing Officer, Conway Regional Medical Center, Conway, AR, p. A44

WILKERSON-UDDYBACK, Patricia, M.D., Chief Medical Officer, Dmc - Detroit Receiving Hospital, Detroit, MI, p. A352

M.D., Chief Medical Officer, Dmc Harper University Hospital, Detroit, MI, p. A353

WILKES, Chris, MS, Executive Director, Human Resources, Blount Memorial Hospital, Maryville, TN, p. A643

WILKES, Margaret, Chief Fiscal Officer, Charles George Veterans Affairs Medical Center, Asheville, NC, p. A504

WILKIE, Chance, Information Technology Specialist, Indian Health Service - Quentin N. Burdick Memorial Health Care Facility, Belcourt, ND, p. A521

WILKIE, Paula, Chief Financial Officer, Presentation Medical Center, Rolla, ND, p. A525

WILKINS, Joseph, Chief Executive Officer, Wythe County Community Hospital, Wytheville, VA, p. A754

WILKINSON, Kyle, Chief Financial Officer, Morgan Memorial Hospital, Madison, GA, p. A176

WILKINSON, Thomas, R.N., Chief Nursing Officer, John C. Fremont Healthcare District, Mariposa, CA, p. A77

WILKS, Angela, Finance Director, Missouri Baptist Sullivan Hospital, Sullivan, MO, p. A419

WILL, DeDe, Director Finance, Douglas County Community Mental Health Center, Omaha, NE, p. A437

WILL, Jeoff, Chief Operating Office, Acute Care Services, Bethesda Hospital, Saint Paul, MN, p. A385

Chief Operating Officer, Acute Care Services, Bethesda Hospital, Saint Paul, MN, p. A385

Chief Operating Officer, Acute Care Services, Fairview Ridges Hospital, Burnsville, MN, p. A373

Chief Operating Officer, Acute Care Services, Fairview Southdale Hospital, Edina, MN, p. A376

WILL, Nicole, Human Resources Officer, Herington Municipal Hospital, Herington, KS, p. A266

WILLAMS, Mike, Chief Information Officer, Fhn Memorial Hospital, Freeport, IL, p. A205

WILLARD, Cheri, MSN, R.N., Chief Nursing Officer, Evanston Regional Hospital, Evanston, WY, p. A802

MSN, R.N., Interim Chief Executive Officer, Evanston Regional Hospital, Evanston, WY, p. A802

WILLARD, Craig, Director Information Technology and Systems, Frankfort Regional Medical Center, Frankfort, KY, p. A283

WILLE, Matt, President and Chief Executive Officer, Munson Medical Center, Traverse City, MI, p. A368

WILLEMSEN, Jane, President and Chief Administrative Officer, John Muir Medical Center, Concord, Concord, CA, p. A61
President and Chief Administrative Officer, John Muir Medical Center, Walnut Creek, Walnut Creek, CA, p. A104

WILLERT, Todd, Chief Executive Officer, Community Healthcare System, Onaga, KS, p. A273

WILLET, Terry, Chief Financial Officer, Allen Parish Community Healthcare, Kinder, LA, p. A305

WILLETT, Richard, Chief Executive Officer, Redington-Fairview General Hospital, Skowhegan, ME, p. A323

WILLETT, Simon, Director Administrative Operations, South Texas Veterans Health Care System, San Antonio, TX, p. A713

WILLETT, Vita M., Executive Director, Kaiser Permanente Riverside Medical Center, Riverside, CA, p. A88
Senior Vice President, Area Manager, Kaiser Permanente Moreno Valley Medical Center, Moreno Valley, CA, p. A80

WILLEY, Randy, Business Manager, Lincoln Regional Center, Lincoln, NE, p. A434

WILLHITE, Jean, Director Human Resources, Sutter Solano Medical Center, Vallejo, CA, p. A103

WILLIAMS, Adrian, Chief Executive Officer, Serenity Springs Specialty Hospital, Ruston, LA, p. A313

WILLIAMS, Alec, Chief Information Officer, Southwest General Health Center, Middleburg Heights, OH, p. A545

WILLIAMS, Angela, Chief Executive Officer, Clearsky Rehabilitation Hospital Of Rosepine, Leesville, LA, p. A307

WILLIAMS, Antoinette, Chief Nursing Officer, John H. Stroger Jr. Hospital Of Cook County, Chicago, IL, p. A199

WILLIAMS, Arthur, M.D., Medical Director, Encompass Health Rehabilitation Hospital Of Braintree, Braintree, MA, p. A336

WILLIAMS, Bernett, Interim Chief Human Resource Officer, Akron Children's Hospital, Akron, OH, p. A527

WILLIAMS, Beth, R.N., Chief Nursing Officer, Conway Behavioral Health Hospital, Conway, AR, p. A43

WILLIAMS, Beverly, R.N., Chief Nursing Officer, Washington County Memorial Hospital, Potosi, MO, p. A414

WILLIAMS, Bob, President and Chief Executive Officer, Bsa Hospital, Llc, Amarillo, TX, p. A652

WILLIAMS, Brian, Web Services and Information Technology Manager, St. Joseph's Hospital Of Buckhannon, Buckhannon, WV, p. A771

WILLIAMS, Brian A., Chief Executive Officer, Labette Health, Parsons, KS, p. A274

WILLIAMS, Brit, M.D., President Medical Staff, Warner Hospital And Health Services, Clinton, IL, p. A201

WILLIAMS, Bryan, R.N., Vice President Patient Care Services, Chi St. Vincent Hot Springs, Hot Springs, AR, p. A47

WILLIAMS, CarolAnn, Chief Financial Officer, Massachusetts Eye And Ear, Boston, MA, p. A336

WILLIAMS, Cecile, Assistant Administrator, Shamrock General Hospital, Shamrock, TX, p. A715

WILLIAMS, Charles E., President and Chief Executive Officer, Regional Medical Center, Orangeburg, SC, p. A623

WILLIAMS, Chris, FACHE, Vice President Operations, Perry Memorial Hospital, Princeton, IL, p. A218

WILLIAMS, Christine, Chief Financial Officer, University Medical Center, New Orleans, LA, p. A312

WILLIAMS, Christopher, M.D., Chief of Staff, Pioneers Medical Center, Meeker, CO, p. A117

WILLIAMS, Craig T., President, St. Elizabeth's Medical Center, Brighton, MA, p. A337

WILLIAMS, Damita, Ed.D., R.N., MSN, Chief Nursing Officer, Medical City Fort Worth, Fort Worth, TX, p. A678
Ed.D., R.N., MSN, Chief Nursing Officer, Medical City Plano, Plano, TX, p. A707

WILLIAMS, Dan, Vice President Finance and Support, Liberty Hospital, Liberty, MO, p. A411

WILLIAMS, Dana, Chief Financial Officer, Baptist Memorial Hospital-North Mississippi, Oxford, MS, p. A398

WILLIAMS, Dana D., Chief Executive Officer, Jennings American Legion Hospital, Jennings, LA, p. A304

WILLIAMS, Danielle H., Administrator, Caldwell Memorial Hospital, Columbia, LA, p. A299

WILLIAMS, Darek, Director Human Resources, Elgin Mental Health Center, Elgin, IL, p. A203

WILLIAMS, Darlene, R.N., Administrator, Chi St. Luke's Health Memorial San Augustine, San Augustine, TX, p. A714

WILLIAMS, David, M.D., Chief Medical Officer, Ascension St. Vincent Kokomo, Kokomo, IN, p. A234
Director Information Technology, Franklin Hospital District, Benton, IL, p. A195

WILLIAMS, Dionne, Director Human Resources, Vaughan Regional Medical Center, Selma, AL, p. A24

WILLIAMS, Don, Chief Executive Officer, Iroquois Memorial Hospital And Resident Home, Watseka, IL, p. A222

WILLIAMS, Douglas, Senior Vice President, Administrator, Saint Francis Hospital, Tulsa, OK, p. A570

WILLIAMS, Frank, Executive Vice President/ Medical Director, Kedren Community Mental Health Center, Los Angeles, CA, p. A75

WILLIAMS, Greg, Chief Financial Officer, Pih Health Hospital - Downey, Downey, CA, p. A62
Chief Financial Officer, Pih Health Hospital - Whittier, Whittier, CA, p. A105

WILLIAMS, Holly, Human Resources Director, Russell Medical, Alexander City, AL, p. A13

WILLIAMS, Jackie, Director Human Resources, Merit Health Madison, Canton, MS, p. A390

WILLIAMS, James, M.D., Chief of Staff, Thedacare Medical Center-Waupaca, Waupaca, WI, p. A798
Chief Executive Officer, Pearl River County Hospital, Poplarville, MS, p. A399
Vice President and Chief Nursing Officer, Mclaren Flint, Flint, MI, p. A354

WILLIAMS, James R., Chief Executive Officer, Minden Medical Center, Minden, LA, p. A309

WILLIAMS, Jason, Director Information Systems, Olympia Medical Center, Los Angeles, CA, p. A75

WILLIAMS, Jennifer, Director, Human Resources, Western Maryland Regional Medical Center, Cumberland, MD, p. A329
Vice President of Finance/Chief Financial Officer, Wayne Healthcare, Greenville, OH, p. A541

WILLIAMS, Jeremy, Chief Financial Officer, Banner Boswell Medical Center, Sun City, AZ, p. A39

WILLIAMS, Joan, Administrative Assistant/Human Resources, Lamb Healthcare Center, Littlefield, TX, p. A696

WILLIAMS, John, Administrator and Chief Executive Officer, Nell J. Redfield Memorial Hospital, Malad City, ID, p. A191
Chief Financial Officer, Upson Regional Medical Center, Thomaston, GA, p. A181
Chief Information Officer, Bay Pines Veterans Affairs Healthcare System, Bay Pines, FL, p. A131

WILLIAMS, Johnny, Interim Chief Financial Officer and Director Financial Services, Rapides Regional Medical Center, Alexandria, LA, p. A295

WILLIAMS, Joyce, Consultant Human Resources and Organizational Development, Memorial Hermann Rehabilitation Hospital - Katy, Katy, TX, p. A692

WILLIAMS, Julie, Chief Financial Officer, Muenster Memorial Hospital, Muenster, TX, p. A702

WILLIAMS, Kathy, Chief Nursing Officer, Eastern New Mexico Medical Center, Roswell, NM, p. A471

WILLIAMS, Kenneth, M.D., Medical Director, United Medical Healthwest New Orleans, Llc, Gretna, LA, p. A302
Chief Information Officer, Fayetteville Veterans Affairs Medical Center, Fayetteville, NC, p. A510

WILLIAMS, Kim, R.N., MS, Chief Executive Officer, Providence Regional Medical Center Everett, Everett, WA, p. A758

WILLIAMS, Kristy, Manager Finance, John J. Pershing Veterans Affairs Medical Center, Poplar Bluff, MO, p. A413

WILLIAMS, L, M.D., Vice President and Chief Medical Director, High Point Medical Center, High Point, NC, p. A512

WILLIAMS, Laci, Director Human Resources, Kearny County Hospital, Lakin, KS, p. A268

WILLIAMS, Lana, Chief Nursing Officer, Arkansas Methodist Medical Center, Paragould, AR, p. A51

WILLIAMS, Linda, Director of Nursing, Villa Feliciana Medical Complex, Jackson, LA, p. A303

WILLIAMS, Lorie, R.N., Vice President Nursing, Samaritan Pacific Communities Hospital, Newport, OR, p. A578

WILLIAMS, Lynn, Vice President Human Resources, Commonwealth Regional Specialty Hospital, Bowling Green, KY, p. A280
Vice President Human Resources, Medical Center At Bowling Green, Bowling Green, KY, p. A281
Vice President Human Resources, Medical Center At Scottsville, Scottsville, KY, p. A293
Vice President, Human Resources, The Medical Center Albany, Albany, KY, p. A280
Vice President, Human Resources, The Medical Center At Caverna, Horse Cave, KY, p. A285

WILLIAMS, Margaret, Chief Financial Officer, Baptist Memorial Hospital For Women, Memphis, TN, p. A644

WILLIAMS, Margo, R.N., Chief Nursing Officer, Anderson County Hospital, Garnett, KS, p. A265

WILLIAMS, Mary, Director Human Resources, Orleans Community Health, Medina, NY, p. A488

WILLIAMS, Matthew, R.N., Chief Executive Officer, Olympia Medical Center, Los Angeles, CA, p. A75
R.N., Chief Financial Officer, Olympia Medical Center, Los Angeles, CA, p. A75

WILLIAMS, Michael, FACHE, Vice President Human Resources, Community Howard Regional Health, Kokomo, IN, p. A234
Chief Financial Officer, Limestone Medical Center, Groesbeck, TX, p. A682

Chief Information Officer, Lmh Health, Lawrence, KS, p. A269

WILLIAMS, Michelle, Administrator, Sedan City Hospital, Sedan, KS, p. A276

WILLIAMS, Mickey, Manager Information Technology, Moccasin Bend Mental Health Institute, Chattanooga, TN, p. A635

WILLIAMS, Nancy M., R.N., Administrator, Brooks County Hospital, Quitman, GA, p. A178

WILLIAMS, Nichelle, Director, Hiram W. Davis Medical Center, Petersburg, VA, p. A748

WILLIAMS, Nicole, Chief Operating Officer, Columbia Memorial Hospital, Astoria, OR, p. A573
Director of Human Resources Operations, Dmc Huron Valley-Sinai Hospital, Commerce Township. MI, p. A351

WILLIAMS, Pamela, Director Human Resources, Unity Health White County Medical Center, Searcy, AR, p. A52
Regional Vice President, Ridgeview Le Sueur Medical Center, Le Sueur, MN, p. A378

WILLIAMS, Perry E. Sr, Administrator and Chief Executive Officer, Alliance Healthcare System, Holly Springs, MS, p. A394

WILLIAMS, Qiana, Director, Human Resource Business Partner, Grant, Ohiohealth Grant Medical Center, Columbus, OH, p. A536

WILLIAMS, R D, Chief Executive Officer, Hendry Regional Medical Center, Clewiston, FL, p. A134

WILLIAMS, Rachael, Chief Nursing Officer, Merit Health Biloxi, Biloxi, MS, p. A389

WILLIAMS, Randy, Director Management Information Systems, Maria Parham Medical Center, Henderson, NC, p. A511

WILLIAMS, Reginald, M.D., Medical Staff President, Curry General Hospital, Gold Beach, OR, p. A575

WILLIAMS, Richard, Chief Operating Officer, Southwest Mississipp. Regional Medical Center, Mccomb, MS, p. A396

WILLIAMS, Robert, M.D., Chief Medical Staff, Wills Memorial Hospital, Washington, GA, p. A183
Chief Executive Officer, Encompass Health Rehabilitation Hospital Of Princeton, Princeton, WV, p. A776

WILLIAMS, Roberta, Director of Nursing, U. S. Public Health Service Indian Hospital, Cass Lake, MN, p. A374

WILLIAMS, Roby D., Administrator, Hardin County General Hospital, Rosiclare, IL, p. A219

WILLIAMS, Rodney, M.D., JD, MS, Vice President Medical Affairs, Good Samaritan Regional Medical Center, Suffern, NY, p. A499

WILLIAMS, Sabrina, Interim Vice President Human Resources, Brigham And Women's Hospital, Boston, MA, p. A335

WILLIAMS, Sandra, Chief Financial Officer, Cap. Fear Valley Medical Center, Fayetteville, NC, p. A510

WILLIAMS, Scott, Chief Executive Officer, Centerpointe Hospital, Saint Charles, MO, p. A414
Chief Executive Officer, Rehabilitation Hospital Of Northwest Ohio, Toledo, OH, p. A550
Chief Operating Officer, Cookeville Regional Medical Center, Cookeville, TN, p. A637

WILLIAMS, Sean J., President and Chief Executive Officer, Mercyone Iowa City Medical Center, Iowa City, IA, p. A252

WILLIAMS, Shane, Director Information Systems, Davis Hospital And Medical Center, Layton, UT, p. A728

WILLIAMS, Sheri, Chief Operating Officer, Guadalup. Regional Medical Center, Seguin, TX, p. A714

WILLIAMS, Stephanie, R.N., Chief Nursing Officer, Washington Hospital Healthcare System, Fremont, CA, p. A65
Market Director Human Resources, Lake Norman Regional Medical Center, Mooresville, NC, p. A514

WILLIAMS, Stephen Tyler., Chief Executive Officer, Habersham Medical Center, Demorest, GA, p. A171

WILLIAMS, Sue Ann, Chief Executive Officer, Southeast Health Center Of Stoddard County, Dexter, MO, p. A405

WILLIAMS, Susan, M.D., Chief Medical Officer, Conemaugh Memorial Medical Center, Johnstown, PA, p. A593
M.D., Chief Medical Officer, Conemaugh Miners Medical Center, Hastings, PA, p. A592

WILLIAMS, Teresa, R.N., Regional Administrator, Mercy Hospital Booneville, Booneville, AR, p. A43
R.N., Regional Administrator, Mercy Hospital Ozark, Ozark, AR, p. A51
R.N., Regional Administrator, Mercy Hospital Paris, Paris, AR, p. A51
R.N., Regional Administrator, Mercy Hospital Waldron, Waldron, AR, p. A54

WILLIAMS, Thaddeus, Controller, Encompass Health Rehabilitation Hospital Of North Memphis, Memphis, TN, p. A644

WILLIAMS, Theresa, MSN, Chief Nursing Officer, Slidell Memorial Hospital, Slidell, LA, p. A315

WILLIAMS, Todd, Chief Financial Officer, Siloam Springs Regional Hospital, Siloam Springs, AR, p. A53

WILLIAMS, Tom, Chief Executive Officer, Johnston Health, Smithfield, NC, p. A518
Vice President Human Resources, Lake Regional Health System, Osage Beach, MO, p. A413

WILLIAMS, Tricia, Chief Executive Officer, Fremont Hospital, Fremont, CA, p. A65

WILLIAMS, Wade, Chief Information Officer, Unc Rockingham Health Care, Eden, NC, p. A509

WILLIAMS, Wendell, M.D., JrMedical Director, Curahealth Jacksonville, Jacksonville, FL, p. A141

WILLIAMS JR, JohnChief Financial Officer, Veterans Affairs Gulf Coast Veterans Health Care System, Biloxi, MS, p. A390

WILLIAMSON, Alan, M.D., Chief Medical Officer, Eisenhower Health, Rancho Mirage, CA, p. A86

WILLIAMSON, Barry, President Medical Staff, Southeastern Health, Lumberton, NC, p. A514

WILLIAMSON, John, Human Resources Site Manager, Baptist Health South Florida, Mariners Hospital, Tavernier, FL, p. A160

WILLIAMSON, Judy, R.N., Administrator, Layton Hospital, Layton, UT, p. A728

WILLIAMSON, Sharon, Chief Information Technology, Robert J. Dole Veterans Affairs Medical Center, Wichita, KS, p. A279

WILLIE, David, Chief Financial Officer, Yuma Regional Medical Center, Yuma, AZ, p. A41

WILLIFORD, Sandy, Chief Health Information Management and Revenue Administration, Charlie Norwood Veterans Affairs Medical Center, Augusta, GA, p. A166

WILLIS, Bill, Director Information Technology, River Point Behavioral Health, Jacksonville, FL, p. A141

WILLIS, Danielle, CPA, Interim Chief Financial Officer, Manager Finance, New Orleans East Hospital, New Orleans, LA, p. A310

WILLIS, Darrell, M.D., Chief of Staff, Dr. Dan C. Trigg Memorial Hospital, Tucumcari, NM, p. A473

WILLIS, Debby, Chief Executive Officer, Crestwyn Behavioral Health, Memphis, TN, p. A644

WILLIS, Jayne, Vice President, System Chief Nurse Executive, Orlando Regional Medical Center, Orlando, FL, p. A151

WILLIS, Jonathon, Director Information Services, Tennova Healthcare-Shelbyville, Shelbyville, TN, p. A649

WILLIS, Joy, Acting Chief Fiscal Service, G.V. (Sonny) Montgomery Veterans Affairs Medical Center, Jackson, MS, p. A394

WILLIS, Kathy, M.D., Medical Director, Lallie Kemp Medical Center, Independence, LA, p. A303

WILLIS, Raymond, IT Manager, Choctaw Health Center, Philadelphia, MS, p. A398

WILLIS, Sandra, Director of Human Resources, Citizens Baptist Medical Center, Talladega, AL, p. A24

WILLIS, Toni, M.D., Medical Director, Encompass Health Rehabilitation Hospital Of The Mid-Cities, Bedford, TX, p. A658

WILLIS, Wendy, Vice President Human Resources, Children's Hospital, New Orleans, LA, p. A310

WILLMANN, Adam, President and Chief Executive Officer, Goodall-Witcher Hospital, Clifton, TX, p. A664

WILLMON, Brian, M.D., Medical Director, Plains Regional Medical Center, Clovis, NM, p. A469

WILLMORE, Lois, Supervisor Health Information Management, Cedar County Memorial Hospital, El Dorado Springs, MO, p. A405

WILLOUGHBY, Kirsten, Director of Nursing, Big Horn County Memorial Hospital, Hardin, MT, p. A424

WILLS, Andrea, R.N., Chief Nursing Executive, Munising Memorial Hospital, Munising, MI, p. A362

WILLS, Andy, M.D., Medical Director, Colquitt Regional Medical Center, Moultrie, GA, p. A177

WILLS, Kim, Chief Operating Officer, Southwell Medical, Adel, GA, p. A163

WILLS, Laura S., Administrator, Noland Hospital Birmingham, Birmingham, AL, p. A15
Administrator, Noland Hospital Shelby, Alabaster, AL, p. A13

WILLS, Michele, Registered Health Information Administrator, Caro Community Hospital, Caro, MI, p. A350

WILLS, Robert, M.D., Chief Medical Officer, Arise Austin Medical Center, Austin, TX, p. A654

WILLS, Shannon, Director Human Resources, Delray Medical Center, Delray Beach, FL, p. A136

WILLS, Tom, R.N., Chief Operating Officer, Merit Health Central, Jackson, MS, p. A394

WILLSHER, Jay, Chief Operating Officer, Unitypoint Health - Trinity Bettendorf, Bettendorf, IA, p. A244

WILLSIE, Brett, Vice President Human Resources, Sentara Northern Virginia Medical Center, Woodbridge, VA, p. A754

WILMOT, Joan, Chief Finance Officer, White River Junction Veterans Affairs Medical Center, White River Junction, VT, p. A737

WILMOTH, Donna, Vice President Patient Care Services and Chief Nursing Officer, Sentara Williamsburg Regional Medical Center, Williamsburg, VA, p. A753

WILMS, Mike, Director Information Systems, Regional Medical Center Bayonet Point, Hudson, FL, p. A140

WILSON, Alice, FACHE, Vice President Administration, St. Luke's Hospital - Warren Campus, Phillipsburg, NJ, p. A461

WILSON, Amy, M.D., Medical Director, Baylor Scott & White Institute For Rehabilitation - Dallas, Dallas, TX, p. A667

WILSON, Andrew, Chief Executive Officer, Cornerstone Regional Hospital, Edinburg, TX, p. A673

WILSON, Bill, Chief Financial Officer, North Carolina Specialty Hospital, Durham, NC, p. A509

WILSON, Bobbie, Director Human Resources, Crete Area Medical Center, Crete, NE, p. A431

WILSON, Carolyn, R.N., Chief Operating Officer, Beaumont Hospital - Farmington Hills, Farmington Hills, MI, p. A354
R.N., Chief Operating Officer, Beaumont Hospital - Grosse Pointe, Grosse Pointe, MI, p. A357
R.N., Chief Operating Officer, Beaumont Hospital - Taylor, Taylor, MI, p. A367
R.N., Chief Operating Officer, Beaumont Hospital - Troy, Troy, MI, p. A368
R.N., Chief Operating Officer, Beaumont Hospital, Wayne, Wayne, MI, p. A369
R.N., Executive Vice President, Chief Operating Officer, Beaumont Hospital - Trenton, Trenton, MI, p. A368
Chief Operating Officer, Beaumont Hospital - Dearborn, Dearborn, MI, p. A352

WILSON, Charlene, Vice President Human Resources, St. Francis Hospital, Wilmington, DE, p. A128

WILSON, Chase, Chief Financial Officer, Sycamore Shoals Hospital, Elizabethton, TN, p. A637

WILSON, Christopher, M.D., Inpatient Medical Director, South Texas Rehabilitation Hospital, Brownsville, TX, p. A661

WILSON, Christy, Chief Financial Officer, Merit Health Rankin, Brandon, MS, p. A390

WILSON, Clifford, Chief Operating Officer, Southern Tennessee Regional Health System-Winchester, Winchester, TN, p. A650

WILSON, Colleen, Chief Nursing Officer, Southern Inyo Healthcare District, Lone Pine, CA, p. A72

WILSON, Craig, Chief Medical Officer, Ascension St. Vincent Fishers, Fishers, IN, p. A228

WILSON, Cynthia, Director, NDI Advanced Treatment Center, Nursing and BHRA Unit Services, Neurodiagnostic Institute And Advanced Treatment Center, Indianapolis, IN, p. A232

WILSON, David, M.D., Chief of Staff, St. Vincent's Blount, Oneonta, AL, p. A23

WILSON, David C., President, North Mississipp. Health Services, Inc., Tupelo, MI, p. A368

WILSON, Deb, Director Human Resources, Kalispell Regional Healthcare, Kalispell, MT, p. A425

WILSON, Deborah J., Chief Executive Officer, Lawrence General Hospital, Lawrence, MA, p. A340

WILSON, Debra, MSN, Vice President and Chief Nursing Officer, Saint Luke's Hospital Of Kansas City, Kansas City, MO, p. A409

WILSON, Eleanor, R.N., MSN, Vice President and Chief Operating Officer, Doylestown Hospital, Doylestown, PA, p. A588

WILSON, Elizabeth, Coordinator Human Resources, Select Specialty Hospital - Cincinnati North, Cincinnati, OH, p. A533

WILSON, Erin, Human Resource Director, Bear Valley Community Hospital, Big Bear Lake, CA, p. A58

WILSON, Fiore, Director Information Systems, Castleview Hospital, Price, UT, p. A731

WILSON, Hamlin, Senior Vice President Human Resources, Holston Valley Medical Center, Kingsport, TN, p. A641

WILSON, Jason, Administrator and Chief Executive Officer, American Fork Hospital, American Fork, UT, p. A727

WILSON, Jodi, President and Chief Operating Officer, Diley Ridge Medical Center, Canal Winchester, OH, p. A530

WILSON, John, Chief Operating Officer, Murray-Calloway County Hospital, Murray, KY, p. A291
Vice President, Human Resources, Murray-Calloway County Hospital, Murray, KY, p. A291

WILSON, John W., Chief Executive Officer, Friend Community Healthcare System, Friend, NE, p. A432

WILSON, Kathey, Acting Chief Executive Officer, U. S. Public Health Service Indian Hospital, Rosebud, SD, p. A631

WILSON, Kenna, Vice President Chief Nursing Officer, Integris Bass Baptist Health Center, Enid, OK, p. A559

WILSON, Kim, Human Resources Coordinator, Cordova Community Medical Center, Cordova, AK, p. A28

WILSON, Kimberly, Director Human Resources, University Of Kentucky Albert B. Chandler Hospital, Lexington, KY, p. A287

WILSON, Lawrence, M.D., Vice President, Chief Medical Officer, Midland Memorial Hospital, Midland, TX, p. A701

WILSON, Lerae, Vice President Patient Services and Chief Nursing Officer, St. Claire Healthcare, Morehead, KY, p. A290

WILSON, Loretta, Administrator, Hill Hospital Of Sumter County, York, AL, p. A26

WILSON, Mallory, Administrative Assistant and Human Resources Coordinator, Select Specialty Hospital-North Knoxville, Powell, TN, p. A648

WILSON, Margaret G., R.N., MSN, Acting Director, Lebanon Veterans Affairs Medical Center, Lebanon, PA, p. A594

WILSON, Morgan, Director Health Information Management, Millwood Hospital, Arlington, TX, p. A653

WILSON, Nadine, Manager, Human Resources, Jerome Golden Center For Behavioral Health, Inc., West Palm Beach, FL, p. A162

WILSON, Nancy, Chief Financial Officer, Parkview Community Hospital Medical Center, Riverside, CA, p. A88

WILSON, Nathan, R.N., Vice President and Chief Nursing Officer, Baptist Health La Grange, La Grange, KY, p. A285

WILSON, Nicole, Manager Human Resources, Bliant Specialty Hospital, New Orleans, LA, p. A310

WILSON, Patricia, Senior Vice President Human Resources, Englewood Health, Englewood, NJ, p. A455

WILSON, Regina, R.N., Director of Nursing, Share Medical Center, Alva, OK, p. A555

WILSON, Robert, D.O., Director Medical Services, Eagleville Hospital, Eagleville, PA, p. A588
Vice President and Chief Information Officer, Crozer-Chester Medical Center, Upland, PA, p. A609
Vice President and Chief Information Officer, Delaware County Memorial Hospital, Drexel Hill, PA, p. A588

WILSON, Roy, M.D., Medical Director, St. Louis Psychiatric Rehabilitation Center, Saint Louis, MO, p. A417

WILSON, Sara, Director Human Resources, Cheyenne County Hospital, Saint Francis, KS, p. A275

WILSON, Shelley, R.N., Chief Nursing Officer, Henry Community Health, New Castle, IN, p. A238

WILSON, Sherry, R.N., Chief Nursing Officer, Mayers Memorial Hospital District, Fall River Mills, CA, p. A64

WILSON, Sondra Dianne., R.N., MSN, Chief Executive Officer, Tyler County Hospital, Woodville, TX, p. A726

WILSON, Stephan, Chief Financial Officer, Lifescape, Sioux Falls, SD, p. A631
Chief Financial Officer, Montrose Memorial Hospital, Montrose, CO, p. A117

WILSON, Tammie, R.N., MSN, Chief Nursing Officer, Fayette County Memorial Hospital, Washington Court House, OH, p. A552

WILSON, Terrance E., President and Chief Executive Officer, Franciscan Health Lafayette East, Lafayette, IN, p. A234

WILSON, William, M.D., Chief Medical Officer, Uci Medical Center, Orange, CA, p. A83

WILSON-NEIL, Carla, FACHE, Chief Operating Officer, Spectrum Health Pennock, Hastings, MI, p. A357

WILSON-STUBBS, Yolande, President, Amita Health Holy Family Medical Center, Des Plaines, IL, p. A202

WILTERMOOD, Michael C., President and Chief Executive Officer, Enloe Medical Center, Chico, CA, p. A60

WILTROUT, Kristy, R.N., Chief Operating Officer, Vernon Memorial Healthcare, Elk Mound, WI, p. A783

WILTROUT, Terry, President, Washington Health System Greene, Waynesburg, PA, p. A610

WILVER JR, DonaldVice President Human Resources, Upmc Williamsport, Williamsport, PA, p. A611

WIMMER, Keri, R.N., Patient Care Director, Centracare - Melrose, Melrose, MN, p. A380

WINBERY, Ben, Chief Financial Officer, Vantage Point Of Northwest Arkansas, Fayetteville, AR, p. A45

WINCHESTER, Matthew, Chief Executive Officer, Highland Springs Hospital, Highland Hills, OH, p. A542

WINDAS, Allison, Director of Patient Care Services-Nurse Executive, Shriners Hospitals For Children-Greenville, Greenville, SC, p. A620

WINDHAM, Joel, Vice President Human Resources, Anderson Regional Health System South, Meridian, MS, p. A397
Vice President Human Resources, Anderson Regional Health System, Meridian, MS, p. A397

WINDHAM, William, Chief Executive Officer, Lewisgale Hospital Alleghany, Low Moor, VA, p. A745

WINDLAND, J, M.D., Chief of Staff, Southern Tennessee Regional Health System-Pulaski, Pulaski, TN, p. A648

WINDOLOVICH, Winona, Associate Chief Information Officer, Zuckerberg San Francisco General Hospital And Trauma Center, San Francisco, CA, p. A94

WINDROW, Matthew, M.D., Chief of Staff, Medina Regional Hospital, Hondo, TX, p. A684

WINDSOR, Bonnie, Senior Vice President Human Resources, Johns Hopkins Hospital, Baltimore, MD, p. A324

WINEGARNER, Rodney, Chief Financial Officer, Mercy Hospitals Of Bakersfield, Bakersfield, CA, p. A57

WINEKAUF, Glen, Chief Executive Officer, Horn Memorial Hospital, Ida Grove, IA, p. A251

WINFREE, Kersey, M.D., Chief Medical Officer, Ssm Health St. Anthony Hospital - Oklahoma City, Oklahoma City, OK, p. A566

WING, Lilly, Chief Nursing Officer, Three Rivers Behavioral Health, West Columbia, SC, p. A625

WING, Yakesun, Business Strategy and Finance Leader, Kaiser Permanente Walnut Creek Medical Center, Walnut Creek, CA, p. A104

WINGET, Mary, Director Human Resources, Minden Medical Center, Minden, LA, p. A309

WINGFIELD, Gena, Senior Vice President and Chief Financial Officer, Arkansas Children's Hospital, Little Rock, AR, p. A48

WINGO, Michelle, Director Human Resources, Piedmont Geriatric Hospital, Burkeville, VA, p. A739

WINIGER, Cecilia, Community Outreach and Communication Manager, Adventist Health Howard Memorial, Willits, CA, p. A105

WINK, Jeri, Director Human Resources, Grandview Medical Center, Birmingham, AL, p. A15

WINKELMAN, Dan, President and Chief Executive Officer, Yukon-Kuskokwim Delta Regional Hospital, Bethel, AK, p. A27

WINKLER, Gordon W., Administrator and Chief Executive Officer, Ringgold County Hospital, Mount Ayr, IA, p. A254

WINN, Ann, M.D., R.N., FACHE, Chief Nursing Officer, Methodist Stone Oak Hospital, San Antonio, TX, p. A712

WINN, Cameron, Director Information Services, Ashley Regional Medical Center, Vernal, UT, p. A734

WINN, Eleyce, Chief Executive Officer, Regency Hospital Of Northwest Indiana, East Chicago, IN, p. A226

WINN, Holly, FACHE, Chief Operating Officer, Black River Memorial Hospital, Black River Falls, WI, p. A781

WINNER, Douglas, Chief Financial Officer, Acute Care Operations, Ascension Of Providence Hospital, Southfield Campus, Southfield, MI, p. A367

WINNETT, Steve, Chief Executive Officer, Advanced Diagnostics Hospital, Houston, TX, p. A684

WINNING, Jane, Chief Nursing Officer, Madera Community Hospital, Madera, CA, p. A76

WINSTON, Bob, M.D., Medical Director, Vermilion Behavioral Health Systems - North Campus, Lafayette, LA, p. A306

WINSTON, Patricia, FACHE, MS, R.N., Vice President, Chief Administrative Officer and Chief Operating Officer, Suny Downstate-University Hospital Of Brooklyn, Brooklyn, NY, p. A479

WINT, Jesse, Director of Nursing, Hardin Medical Center, Savannah, TN, p. A649

WINTER, Jennifer, Chief Medical Information Officer, Fort Healthcare, Fort Atkinson, WI, p. A784

WINTER, Jon, D.O., Chief of Staff, Camden General Hospital, Camden, TN, p. A634

WINTER, Melissa, R.N., MSN, Chief Operating Officer and Chief Nursing Officer, Baylor Scott & White Medical Center At - Mckinney, Mckinney, TX, p. A700

WINTER-CLARK, Jan, Chief Executive Officer, Bristow Medical Center, Bristow, OK, p. A556

WINTERS, Heidi, Business Partner Human Resources, Chi Health Missouri Valley, Missouri Valley, IA, p. A254

WINTERS, Mary, Interim Chief Nursing Officer, St. James Healthcare, Butte, MT, p. A422

WINTERS, Shane, Chief Information Officer, Jersey Community Hospital, Jerseyville, IL, p. A209

WIRJO, Jonathan, M.D., Medical Director, Seven Hills Hospital, Henderson, NV, p. A442

WIRTHGEN, Doug, Chief Information Officer, Va Palo Alto Health Care System, Palo Alto, CA, p. A84

Facility Chief Information Officer, Veterans Affairs Loma Linda Healthcare System, Loma Linda, CA, p. A72

WIRTZ, David, Senior LAN Administrator, Evansville State Hospital, Evansville, IN, p. A227

Supervisor Information Technology, Evansville Psychiatric Children Center, Evansville, IN, p. A227

WIRZMAN, Jillian, Cheif Nursing Officer, Fort Lauderdale Behavioral Health Center, Oakland Park, FL, p. A149

WISBY, Kendra, R.N., Chief Nursing Officer, Oakdale Community Hospital, Oakdale, LA, p. A312

WISE, Claude, Chief Executive Officer, Valley Hospital Medical Center, Las Vegas, NV, p. A445

WISE, Dan, Manager Information Technology, Sarah D. Culbertson Memorial Hospital, Rushville, IL, p. A219

WISE, Elizabeth, R.N., MS, Chief Nursing Officer and Vice President, Patient Care Services, Saint Peter's University Hospital, New Brunswick, NJ, p. A459

President and Chief Executive Officer, Lehigh Valley Hospital - Pocono, East Stroudsburg, PA, p. A589

WISE, Jennifer, Chief Nursing Officer, Ochsner St. Mary, Morgan City, LA, p. A309

WISE, Jerry R., Chief Executive Officer, Northridge Medical Center, Commerce, GA, p. A169

WISE, Josh, Director Information Technology, Lawrence Memorial Hospital, Walnut Ridge, AR, p. A54

WISE, Kim, Director Human Resources, Bronson South Haven Hospital, South Haven, MI, p. A367

WISE, Teresa, R.N., Chief Nursing Officer, Mena Regional Health System, Mena, AR, p. A50

WISE, Timothy, Director, Information Technology, Wellstone Regional Hospital, Jeffersonville, IN, p. A233

WISEMAN, Josh, Chief Financial Officer, Va Portland Healthcare System, Portland, OR, p. A580

WISEMANN, Jacob, Chief Financial Officer, Parkland Medical Center, Derry, NH, p. A448

WISEMORE, Donna, R.N., Vice President and Chief Nursing Officer, Parkview Dekalb Hospital, Auburn, IN, p. A223

WISER, Justin, Chief Financial Officer, Bear River Valley Hospital, Tremonton, UT, p. A734

Chief Financial Officer, Cassia Regional Hospital, Burley, ID, p. A189

Chief Financial Officer, Logan Regional Hospital, Logan, UT, p. A728

WISLER, Tam, Director Human Resources, Columbus Dublin Springs, Dublin, OH, p. A539

WISMANN, Andrea, M.D., Chief of Staff, Southeast Colorado Hospital District, Springfield, CO, p. A118

WISMER, Doug, Chief Financial Officer, Thayer County Health Services, Hebron, NE, p. A433

WISNER, Donna, Chief Financial Officer, Warner Hospital And Health Services, Clinton, IL, p. A201

WISNIESKI, Thomas, FACHE, Director, North Florida/South Georgia Veteran's Health System, Gainesville, FL, p. A138

WISNIEWSKI, Cass, Interim Chief Financial Officer, Hurley Medical Center, Flint, MI, p. A354

WISNOSKI, Joseph, Chief Financial Officer, Mather Hospital, Port Jefferson, NY, p. A495

WISSMAN, Sheryl, M.D., Chief Medical Officer, Ascension Crittenton Hospital Medical Center, Rochester, MI, p. A365

WISWELL, Ashleigh, Chief Operations Officer, Moore County Hospital District, Dumas, TX, p. A673

WITENSKE, James, Chief Information Officer, Jefferson Hospital, Jefferson Hills, PA, p. A593

WITHAM, Val, Director Health Information, Avera Flandreau Hospital, Flandreau, SD, p. A628

Director of Health Information, Avera Dells Area Hospital, Dell Rapids, SD, p. A627

WITHERELL, Jodi, Vice President Patient Care and Quality, Brooks Memorial Hospital, Dunkirk, NY, p. A482

WITHERSPOON, Lynn, Vice President and Chief Information Officer, Ochsner Medical Center, New Orleans, LA, p. A311

WITKOP, Kimberly, M.D., Chief Medical Officer, Snoqualmie Valley Hospital District, Snoqualmie, WA, p. A765

M.D., Interim Chief Executive Officer, Snoqualmie Valley Hospital District, Snoqualmie, WA, p. A765

WITKOWICZ, Victor, Senior Vice President and Chief Financial Officer, Madonna Rehabilitation Hospital, Lincoln, NE, p. A434

WITMER, Bruce, M.D., Medical Director, Fresno Surgical Hospital, Fresno, CA, p. A65

WITT, Cheryl, Human Resources Director, Kaiser Permanente Moreno Valley Medical Center, Moreno Valley, CA, p. A80

WITT, David, Chief Financial Officer, Meadows Psychiatric Center, Centre Hall, PA, p. A586

Vice President Finances, Houston Methodist Clear Lake Hospital, Nassau Bay, TX, p. A702

WITT, Jana, Chief Executive Officer, Cedar County Memorial Hospital, El Dorado Springs, MO, p. A405

WITT, Laura, Administrator Human Resources, Banner Thunderbird Medical Center, Glendale, AZ, p. A32

WITT, Lori, Site Finance Director, Mercy Health - Marcum And Wallace, Irvine, KY, p. A285

WITT, Sarah, Director Human Resources, Richmond State Hospital, Richmond, IN, p. A239

WITT, Stephen, President and Chief Executive Officer, College Hospital Cerritos, Cerritos, CA, p. A59

WITT, Ty, M.D., Chief Medical Officer, Lake Chelan Community Hospital And Clinics, Chelan, WA, p. A756

WITTE, Kari, Director Patient Care, Windom Area Health, Windom, MN, p. A388

WITTE, Russell, Director Information Technology, Citizens Medical Center, Victoria, TX, p. A723

WITTENSTEIN, Robin D., Ed.D., Chief Executive Officer, Denver Health, Denver, CO, p. A110

WITTHAUS, Patricia, Director Information Services, Valley Regional Hospital, Claremont, NH, p. A448

WITTMAN, Thomas, Chief Information Officer, Uofl Health - Jewish Hospital, Louisville, KY, p. A288

WITTWER, Julie, Chief Financial Officer, South Texas Surgical Hospital, Corpus Christi, TX, p. A666

WLEKLINSKI, Maria, Chief Nursing Officer, Siloam Springs Regional Hospital, Siloam Springs, AR, p. A53

WODARZ, Christopher, Chief, Resource Management Division, Tripler Army Medical Center, Honolulu, HI, p. A185

WODICKA, Mary Jo, Vice President Human Resources, Ascension All Saints, Racine, WI, p. A794

WOELKERS, Joe, Executive Vice President and Chief Staff, Ut Health North Campus Tyler, Tyler, TX, p. A722

WOELTJEN, Bill, Chief Financial Officer, Sarasota Memorial Health Care System, Sarasota, FL, p. A157

WOEN, Linda, Director Human Resources, Yuma Rehabilitation Hospital, A Partnership Of Encompass Health And Yrmc, Yuma, AZ, p. A41

WOHLFARDT, Diana, Director Human Resources, Nashville General Hospital, Nashville, TN, p. A646

WOHLFORD, Steve, Chief Operating Officer, Johnson Memorial Hospital, Franklin, IN, p. A229

WOHLMAN, John, Manager Information Systems, Shoshone Medical Center, Kellogg, ID, p. A191

WOITALEWICZ, Rebecca, Chief Financial Officer, Children's Hospitals And Clinics Of Minnesota, Minneapolis, MN, p. A380

WOJNO, Kathy, R.N., MSN, Administrator, Memorial Hospital Of Gardena, Gardena, CA, p. A66

WOJTALEWICZ, Jeanette, Chief Financial Officer, Chi Health Mercy Council Bluffs, Council Bluffs, IA, p. A247

WOLAK, Robert, Chief Information Resource Management Service, G.V. (Sonny) Montgomery Veterans Affairs Medical Center, Jackson, MS, p. A394

WOLBERS, Chad, President and Chief Executive Officer, Unitypoint Health - Finley Hospital, Dubuque, IA, p. A249

WOLCOTT, Daniel, President and Chief Executive Officer, Adventist Health Lodi Memorial, Lodi, CA, p. A71

WOLD, Lynn, President and Chief Executive Officer, Unitypoint Health - St. Lukes's Sioux City, Sioux City, IA, p. A258

WOLESKE, Chris, President and Chief Executive Officer, Bellin Hospital, Green Bay, WI, p. A785

WOLF, Brenda J., President and Chief Executive Officer, La Rabida Children's Hospital, Chicago, IL, p. A199

WOLF, Chris, Director Information Technology, Clay County Medical Center, Clay Center, KS, p. A262

WOLF, Gregory, Director Information Systems, Shriners Hospitals For Children-Honolulu, Honolulu, HI, p. A185

WOLF, Heather, Manager Human Resources, Employee Health, Information Technology, Support Services, Mercyone Newton Medical Center, Newton, IA, p. A255

Manager Human Resources, Employee Health, InformationTechnology, Support Servicess, Mercyone Newton Medical Center, Newton, IA, p. A255

WOLF, Jack, Vice President Information Systems, Montefiore Medical Center, Bronx, NY, p. A477

WOLF, Manuela, FACHE, R.N., President and Chief Executive Officer, Memorial Community Hospital And Health System, Blair, NE, p. A430

WOLF, Marc, Assistant Vice President Human Resources, St. Barnabas Hospital, Bronx, NY, p. A477

WOLF, Randall, Vice President Finance, Perry County Memorial Hospital, Perryville, MO, p. A413

WOLF, Robin, Chief Nursing Officer, Pam Specialty Hospital Of Las Vegas, Las Vegas, NV, p. A444

WOLF, Stephanne, Chief Nursing Officer, Morris County Hospital, Council Grove, KS, p. A263

WOLF, Steven, D.O., Chief of Staff, Shriners Hospitals For Children-Galveston, Galveston, TX, p. A680

WOLF, Tricia, Director Information Technology, Oss Health, York, PA, p. A612

WOLFE, Anita, Chief Nurse Executive, Multicare Tacoma General Hospital, Tacoma, WA, p. A767

WOLFE, Brian, Chief of Staff, Allen County Regional Hospital, Iola, KS, p. A267

WOLFE, Cathy, Vice President Patient Care and Chief Nursing Officer, Parkview Wabash Hospital, Wabash, IN, p. A242

WOLFE, Darryl, Chief Executive Officer, Olympic Medical Center, Port Angeles, WA, p. A762

Chief Operating Officer, Olympic Medical Center, Port Angeles, WA, p. A762

WOLFE, John, Chief Financial Officer, Saint Elizabeth's Medical Center, Wabasha, MN, p. A387

WOLFE, Lisa, President, Chi Health Mercy Corning, Corning, IA, p. A246

WOLFE, Lois, Director Human Resources, Geisinger-Community Medical Center, Scranton, PA, p. A607

WOLFE, Phillip. Vice President of Professional Operations, Good Samaritan Hospital, Los Angeles, CA, p. A74

WOLFE, Scott, Chief Financial Officer, Piedmont Fayette Hospital, Fayetteville, GA, p. A172

WOLFE, Scott R., CPA, President, St. Luke's Hospital - Warren Campus, Phillipsburg, NJ, p. A461

WOLFE, Sean, Vice President Finance and Chief Financial Officer, Community Hospital, Mccook, NE, p. A435

WOLFE, Stephen A., President and Chief Executive Officer, Indiana Regional Medical Center, Indiana, PA, p. A592

WOLFE, Teresa, Manager Human Resources, Kansas Heart Hospital, Wichita, KS, p. A278

WOLFENBARGER, Carol C., FACHE, MSN, President, Mcdowell Hospital, Marion, NC, p. A514

WOLFF, David, Director Information Technology, Newberry County Memorial Hospital, Newberry, SC, p. A623

WOLFF, Holly, Chief Executive Officer, Roundup Memorial Healthcare, Roundup. MT, p. A427

WOLFF, Kristine, Vice President and Chief Nursing Officer, Upmc Somerset, Somerset, PA, p. A608

WOLFF, Patrice, Director Information Services, Westfields Hospital And Clinic, New Richmond, WI, p. A792
Director Management Information Systems, Amery Hospital And Clinic, Amery, WI, p. A779

WOLFGANG, Tony, Chief Financial Officer, Coatesville Veterans Affairs Medical Center, Coatesville, PA, p. A587

WOLK, Helene, Senior Vice President Operations and Chief Operating Officer, Englewood Health, Englewood, NJ, p. A455

WOLKART, Kristin, R.N., President and Chief Executive Officer, St. Francis Medical Center, Monroe, LA, p. A309

WOLOSZYN, Daniel B., Chief Executive Officer, Rehabilitation Hospital Of Indiana, Indianapolis, IN, p. A233

WOLTEMATH, Kelli, D.O., Chief Medical Staff, George C. Grap. Community Hospital, Hamburg, IA, p. A251

WOLTERMAN, Robert K., Chief Executive Officer, Ochsner Medical Center, New Orleans, LA, p. A311

WOLTHER, Eunice, Public Information Officer, Colorado Mental Health Institute At Pueblo, Pueblo, CO, p. A117

WOLTHOFF, Matt, Chief Executive Officer, Harlingen Medical Center, Harlingen, TX, p. A683

WOLTHUIZEN, Dianne, Director Human Resources, Sanford Sheldon Medical Center, Sheldon, IA, p. A257

WOLZ, John, M.D., Chief Medical Staff, Yuma District Hospital, Yuma, CO, p. A120

WOMACK, Heather, Chief Executive Officer, Houston Physicians Hospital, Webster, TX, p. A724

WOMACK, James, Administrator, Mitchell County Hospital, Camilla, GA, p. A168

WONG, Anne Marie, M.D., Chief Medical Officer, Grays Harbor Community Hospital, Aberdeen, WA, p. A755

WONG, Art, Chief Financial Officer, Heritage Oaks Hospital, Sacramento, CA, p. A89

WONG, Bryan, M.D., Medical Director, Ventura County Medical Center, Ventura, CA, p. A103

WONG, Davies, M.D., Medical Director, Kindred Hospital-San Diego, San Diego, CA, p. A91

WONG, Dionne, Vice President and Chief Human Resources Officer, Broward Health Medical Center, Fort Lauderdale, FL, p. A137

WONG, Karen, Chief Human Resources Officer, Mee Memorial Hospital, King City, CA, p. A69

WONG, Philip. PsyD, Chief Executive Officer, Gateways Hospital And Mental Health Center, Los Angeles, CA, p. A74
PsyD, Chief Operating Officer, Gateways Hospital And Mental Health Center, Los Angeles, CA, p. A74

WONG, Wesley, M.D., Acting Vice President Medical and Academic Affairs, Community Hospital North, Indianapolis, IN, p. A231

WONNACOTT, Matthew, M.D., Chief Medical Officer, Barton Memorial Hospital, South Lake Tahoe, CA, p. A99

WONSER, Matt, Director, Information Services, Providence Regional Medical Center Everett, Everett, WA, p. A758

WOOD, Aaron C., Chief Executive Officer and Administrator, Sanpete Valley Hospital, Mount Pleasant, UT, p. A729

WOOD, Bud, Chief Human Resources Officer, Saint Thomas West Hospital, Nashville, TN, p. A646

WOOD, Cathy, Vice President, Human Resources, Memorial Hospital At Gulfport, Gulfport, MS, p. A393

WOOD, Clyde, Chief Executive Officer, Tennova North Knoxville Medical Center, Powell, TN, p. A648

WOOD, David P., FACHE, Director, Boise Veterans Affairs Medical Center, Boise, ID, p. A188

WOOD, Drew, Director Information Technology, Eureka Springs Hospital, Eureka Springs, AR, p. A45

WOOD, Gregory C., President and Chief Executive Officer, Scotland Health Care System, Laurinburg, NC, p. A513

WOOD, Jim, Chief Administrative Officer, Confluence Health/ Central Washington Hospital, Wenatchee, WA, p. A768
Chief Human Resources Officer, Confluence Health/ Wenatchee Valley Hospital, Wenatchee, WA, p. A768

WOOD, Joann, M.D., Chief Medical Officer, Baptist Memorial Hospital-Desoto, Southaven, MS, p. A400

WOOD, John, Chief Executive Officer, Central Texas Rehabilitation Hospital, Austin, TX, p. A655

WOOD, Joseph, Vice President and Chief Information Officer, Long Island Community Hospital, Patchogue, NY, p. A494

WOOD, Joyce, Vice President Organizational Improvement and Chief Nursing Officer, Riverview Health, Noblesville, IN, p. A238

WOOD, Lawrence, M.D., Chief Medical Officer, Littleton Adventist Hospital, Littleton, CO, p. A116

WOOD, Richard, Chief Financial Officer, Seton Medical Center, Daly City, CA, p. A62

WOOD, Sandy, MSN, R.N., Vice President Patient Services and Chief Nursing Officer, O'Bleness Memorial Hospital, Athens, OH, p. A528

WOOD, Thomas, M.D., Chief Medical Officer, Page Hospital, Page, AZ, p. A34

WOOD, Tina, Chief Operating Officer, Dmc Harper University Hospital, Detroit, MI, p. A353
Chief Operations Officer, Dmc - Detroit Receiving Hospital, Detroit, MI, p. A352

WOOD, Troy, Chief Executive Officer, Lakeview Hospital, Bountiful, UT, p. A727

WOOD, Wendy, Chief Executive Officer, Sana Behavioral Hospital, Las Vegas, NV, p. A444

WOOD, William, M.D., Vice President Medical Affairs, St. Josep. Hospital, Bangor, ME, p. A318

WOOD JR, PhillipChief Information Officer, Cap. Fear Valley Medical Center, Fayetteville, NC, p. A510

WOODALL, Lois, Director Human Resources, Lighthouse Behavioral Health Hospital, Conway, SC, p. A618

WOODARD, Andy, President and Chief Executive Officer, Forrest General Hospital, Hattiesburg, MS, p. A393

WOODARD, James, Chief Nursing Officer, St. Thomas More Hospital, Canon City, CO, p. A108

WOODARD, Victor, Manager Information Technology, Dodge County Hospital, Eastman, GA, p. A172

WOODHOUSE, Janice, Director of Nursing, Missouri River Medical Center, Fort Benton, MT, p. A423

WOODIN, Josep. L., Chief Executive Officer, Copley Hospital, Morrisville, VT, p. A736

WOODRICH, John T., President and Chief Executive Officer, Executive Vice President Bryan Health, Bryan Medical Center, Lincoln, NE, p. A434

WOODROW, Victoria, Chief Executive Officer, Hamilton Memorial Hospital District, Mcleansboro, IL, p. A212

WOODRUFF, Kathy, R.N., MSN, Chief Nursing Officer, Marshall Medical Center North, Guntersville, AL, p. A19

WOODRUFF, Stephen, M.D., Chief Medical Officer, Nea Baptist Memorial Hospital, Jonesboro, AR, p. A48

WOODS, Bob, Chief Information Officer, Stanford Health Care - Valleycare, Pleasanton, CA, p. A85

WOODS, Brian, Human Resources Director, Andalusia Health, Andalusia, AL, p. A13

WOODS, Cheryl, Chief Nursing Officer, Ochsner Medical Center - North Shore, Slidell, LA, p. A315

WOODS, Dan, Chief Executive Officer, El Camino Hospital, Mountain View, CA, p. A80

WOODS, Dillon, Director Human Resources, Passavant Area Hospital, Jacksonville, IL, p. A209

WOODS, Eugene A., FACHE, President and Chief Executive Officer, Atrium Health's Carolinas Medical Center, Charlotte, NC, p. A506

WOODS, Fred, Chief Financial Officer, The Bridgeway, North Little Rock, AR, p. A51

WOODS, Gina, Chief Nursing Officer, Southeastern Ohio Regional Medical Center, Cambridge, OH, p. A530

WOODS, Jennifer, R.N., MSN, Chief Nursing Officer, Mclaren Northern Michigan, Petoskey, MI, p. A363

WOODS, Josh, Director Information Systems, Camden Clark Medical Center, Parkersburg, WV, p. A775

WOODS, Julia, MSN, Vice President and Chief Nursing Officer, Saint Luke's South Hospital, Overland Park, KS, p. A274

WOODS, Marc, Assistant Chief Nurse Executive, Eastern State Hospital, Lexington, KY, p. A286

WOODS, Matthew, Vice President Finance, Winchester Hospital, Winchester, MA, p. A346

WOODS, Rashawn, Vice President Human Resources, Barlow Respiratory Hospital, Los Angeles, CA, p. A73

WOODS, Rebecca, Chief Information Officer, Porter Medical Center, Middlebury, VT, p. A736

WOODS, Regetta, Chief Nursing Officer and Chief Clinical Officer, Riverbridge Specialty Hospital, Vidalia, LA, p. A316

WOODS, Suzanne, Chief Executive Officer, Medical Center Enterprise, Enterprise, AL, p. A18
Senior Vice President of Nursing, Memorial Hospital Jacksonville, Jacksonville, FL, p. A141

WOODS, Theresa, MSN, R.N., FACHE, Chief Nursing Officer, Jennings American Legion Hospital, Jennings, LA, p. A304

WOODS, Trina, Administrator, Noland Hospital Anniston, Anniston, AL, p. A13

WOODS, Willard, M.D., Chief Medical Officer, Platte County Memorial Hospital, Wheatland, WY, p. A804

WOODSON, Leslie, Chief Nursing Officer, Mesa View Regional Hospital, Mesquite, NV, p. A445

WOODSON, Stephen, D.O., Chief of Staff, Haskell County Community Hospital, Stigler, OK, p. A568

WOODWARD, Ashley, Director Financial Services, Valley County Health System, Ord, NE, p. A438

WOODWARD, Martin, Director Acute Care Services, Larry B. Zieverink, Sr. Alcoholism Treatment Center, Raleigh, NC, p. A516

WOODWARD, Martin D., Director Acute Care Services, Larry B. Zieverink, Sr. Alcoholism Treatment Center, Raleigh, NC, p. A516

WOODWARD, Russell, M.D., Chief Medical Officer, Methodist Hospital, San Antonio, TX, p. A712

WOODWORTH, Connie, Vice President Finance, Beverly Hospital, Beverly, MA, p. A334

WOODYARD, Nancy, Chief Financial Officer, Neosho Memorial Regional Medical Center, Chanute, KS, p. A262

WOOLDRIDGE, Joseph, Chief Financial Officer, Brownwood Regional Medical Center, Brownwood, TX, p. A661

WOOLLEY, Diane, Vice President Human Resources, Waterbury Hospital, Waterbury, CT, p. A126

WOOLLEY, Jacqueline, Vice President Human Resources, Southern New Hampshire Medical Center, Nashua, NH, p. A450
Vice President Human Resources, St. Josep. Hospital, Nashua, NH, p. A450

WOOLLEY, Russell, Chief Operating Officer, St. Anne Hospital, Burien, WA, p. A756

WOOLLEY, Sheila, R.N., M.P.H., Vice President, Patient Care Services, Wentworth-Douglass Hospital, Dover, NH, p. A448

WOOLSTENHULME, Daren, Chief Financial Officer, Salt Lake Behavioral Health, Salt Lake City, UT, p. A732

WOOTEN, Scott, Senior Vice President and Chief Financial Officer, Baptist Medical Center Beaches, Jacksonville Beach, FL, p. A142
Senior Vice President and Chief Financial Officer, Baptist Medical Center Jacksonville, Jacksonville, FL, p. A140

WOOTEN, Terrence, Vice President of Operations, Support Services, Mission Hospital Mission Viejo, Mission Viejo, CA, p. A78

WOOTTON, Aaron, Vice President, Health Information Systems and Chief Information Officer, Henry Ford Allegiance Health, Jackson, MI, p. A359

WORATSCHEK, Alan, System Director of Information Services, Desert Springs Hospital Medical Center, Las Vegas, NV, p. A443

WORD, Jenni, R.N., Chief Nursing Officer, Wallowa Memorial Hospital, Enterprise, OR, p. A574

WORDEN, Beth, Director Nursing Services, Mcpherson Hospital, Mcpherson, KS, p. A270

WORDEN, Connie, Chief Human Resources Officer, Fountain Valley Regional Hospital And Medical Center, Fountain Valley, CA, p. A64

WORDEN, Jerry, Chief Financial Officer, Dickinson County Healthcare System, Iron Mountain, MI, p. A358

WORDEN, Kieth, Director Human Resources, Mildred Mitchell-Bateman Hospital, Huntington, WV, p. A773

WORKMAN, Donovan, Director Human Capital Management, Appalachian Behavioral Healthcare, Athens, OH, p. A528

WORKMAN, Jessika, Chief Nursing Officer, Wesley Rehabilitation Hospital, Wichita, KS, p. A279

WORKMAN, Madison, Chief Operating Officer, Coral Gables Hospital, Coral Gables, FL, p. A135

WORLEY, Amanda, Chief Human Resources Officer, Sheltering Arms Rehabilitation Hospital, Mechanicsville, VA, p. A746

WORLEY, Stella, Director of Finance, Keefe Memorial Hospital, Cheyenne Wells, CO, p. A109
Interim Chief Executive Officer, Keefe Memorial Hospital, Cheyenne Wells, CO, p. A109

WORMAN, Scott, Chief of Staff, Tri-City Medical Center, Oceanside, CA, p. A82

WORRELL, James, Chief Financial Officer, Pioneers Medical Center, Meeker, CO, p. A117

WORSLEY, Thomas, Chief Executive Officer, Monument Health Spearfish Hospital, Spearfish, SD, p. A632

WORSOWICZ, Gregory, M.D., Medical Director, Rusk Rehabilitation Hospital, Columbia, MO, p. A405

WORTHAM, Christopher, Chief Executive Officer, South Plains Rehabilitation Hospital, Lubbock, TX, p. A698

WORTHAM, Turner, Chief Financial Officer, Grand Strand Medical Center, Myrtle Beach, SC, p. A623

WORTHLEY, Ronnette, Manager Human Resource, Nemaha Valley Community Hospital, Seneca, KS, p. A276

WORTHY, David, M.D., Vice President and Chief Medical Officer, Baptist Health Corbin, Corbin, KY, p. A282

WRAALSTAD, Kimber L., FACHE, Administrator, North Shore Health, Grand Marais, MN, p. A377

WRAGGE, Jean, Chief Nursing Officer, Limestone Medical Center, Groesbeck, TX, p. A682

WRATCHFORD, R. Austin, Chief Operating Officer, Parkview Regional Hospital, Mexia, TX, p. A701

WRAY, Christine R., President, Medstar Southern Maryland Hospital Center, Clinton, MD, p. A328
President, Medstar St. Mary's Hospital, Leonardtown, MD, p. A331

WRAY, Dean, Vice President Finance, Southern Ohio Medical Center, Portsmouth, OH, p. A548

WRAY, Kelli, Assistant Chief Nursing Officer, Southern Hills Hospital And Medical Center, Las Vegas, NV, p. A444

WRAY, Thomas, Director Information, Geisinger-Bloomsburg Hospital, Bloomsburg, PA, p. A585

WREN, Jason, President and Chief Executive Officer, Wise Health System, Decatur, TX, p. A671

WREN, Kyle, Chief Executive Officer, Rangely District Hospital, Rangely, CO, p. A118

WREN, Mark, M.D., Medical Director, Encompass Health Rehabilitation Hospital Of Texarkana, Texarkana, TX, p. A720

WREN, Timothy, Chief Financial Officer, Abbeville Area Medical Center, Abbeville, SC, p. A615

WRIGHT, Albert L. Jr, President and Chief Executive Officer, West Virginia University Hospitals, Morgantown, WV, p. A775

WRIGHT, Ann, R.N., MSN, Assistant Central Delivery System CNO, Presbyterian Hospital, Albuquerque, NM, p. A468

WRIGHT, April, Human Resources Officer, Collingsworth General Hospital, Wellington, TX, p. A724

WRIGHT, Birch, Chief Operating Officer and Administrator, Washington Regional Medical Center, Fayetteville, AR, p. A45

WRIGHT, Brady, Information Technology Network Administrator, Washington County Hospital, Chatom, AL, p. A16

WRIGHT, Calvin, Chief Information Officer, Hutchinson Regional Medical Center, Hutchinson, KS, p. A266

WRIGHT, Carlene, Chief Financial Officer, Vibra Hospital Of Amarillo, Amarillo, TX, p. A652

WRIGHT, Carol, Chief Nursing Officer, Alliancehealth Madill, Madill, OK, p. A561

WRIGHT, Charles, Chief Financial Officer, Ashe Memorial Hospital, Jefferson, NC, p. A513

WRIGHT, Coleby, Chief Executive Officer, Park Royal Hospital, Fort Myers, FL, p. A138

WRIGHT, Connie, Vice President Human Resources, Texas Scottish Rite Hospital For Children, Dallas, TX, p. A670

WRIGHT, Creighton, M.D., Vice President Medical Administration, Mercy Health - West Hospital, Cincinnati, OH, p. A533

WRIGHT, Daniel, Director Information Technology, Saint Alphonsus Medical Center - Nampa, Nampa, ID, p. A192

WRIGHT, Dawn, Vice President Human Resources, Upmc Muncy, Muncy, PA, p. A598
Vice President Human Resources, Upmc Wellsboro, Wellsboro, PA, p. A610

WRIGHT, Debra J., R.N., Chief Executive Officer, Howard Memorial Hospital, Nashville, AR, p. A51

WRIGHT, Dustin, Chief Executive Officer, Floyd Valley Healthcare, Le Mars, IA, p. A253

WRIGHT, Fran, Director of Nursing, Broadwater Health Center, Townsend, MT, p. A428

WRIGHT, Jeffery, Chief Financial Officer, Dmc - Sinai-Grace Hospital, Detroit, MI, p. A352

WRIGHT, Jennifer, Vice President Human Resources, Christus St. Michael Rehabilitation Hospital, Texarkana, TX, p. A719
Vice President Operations, Christus St. Michael Health System, Texarkana, TX, p. A719

WRIGHT, Joe, Chief Executive Officer, North Runnels Hospital, Winters, TX, p. A726
Chief Financial Officer, Mitchell County Hospital, Colorado City, TX, p. A664

WRIGHT, Jordan, Chief Executive Officer, St. Elizabeth Community Hospital, Red Bluff, CA, p. A87

WRIGHT, Julie, Director Human Resources, Ridgeview Psychiatric Hospital And Center, Oak Ridge, TN, p. A648

WRIGHT, Kenneth, Chief Financial Officer, Webster County Memorial Hospital, Webster Springs, WV, p. A777

WRIGHT, Krista, Director Human Resources, Indiana University Health Frankfort, Frankfort, IN, p. A229

WRIGHT, Kyle, Management Information System Director, Doctor's Memorial Hospital, Perry, FL, p. A154

WRIGHT, Linda, Chief Financial Officer, Encompass Health Rehabilitation Hospital Of Alexandria, Alexandria, LA, p. A295
Director Information, Ottawa County Health Center, Minneapolis, KS, p. A271

WRIGHT, Mark, Chief Financial Officer, Aultman Specialty Hospital, Canton, OH, p. A531

Chief Financial Officer, Aurelia Osborn Fox Memorial Hospital, Oneonta, NY, p. A494
Vice President, Aultman Hospital, Canton, OH, p. A530

WRIGHT, Mary, Senior Vice President, Patient Services, Torrance Memorial Medical Center, Torrance, CA, p. A101
Vice President Nursing Services and Chief Nursing Officer, Guthrie Cortland Regional Medical Center, Cortland, NY, p. A482

WRIGHT, Nancy, M.D., Chief Medical Staff, Alta Vista Regional Hospital, Las Vegas, NM, p. A470

WRIGHT, Peter J., FACHE, President, Bridgton Hospital, Bridgton, ME, p. A319
FACHE, President, Rumford Hospital, Rumford, ME, p. A323

WRIGHT, Phillip L., FACHE, Chief Executive Officer, Select Specialty Hospital Hampton Roads, Newport News, VA, p. A747

WRIGHT, Philoron, FACHE, Chief Operating Officer, Adventhealth Ocala, Ocala, FL, p. A149

WRIGHT, Robert N., Chief Executive Officer, Newman Regional Health, Emporia, KS, p. A264

WRIGHT, Rory, M.D., President Medical Staff, Orthopaedic Hospital Of Wisconsin, Glendale, WI, p. A784

WRIGHT, Sandrea, Chief Executive Officer, Ashland Health Center, Ashland, KS, p. A261

WRIGHT, Sharon, R.N., Vice President and Chief Nursing Officer, Hardin Memorial Health, Elizabethtown, KY, p. A282

WRIGHT, Stephanie, Director Human Resources Management, Va San Diego Healthcare System, San Diego, CA, p. A93

WRIGHT, Stuart, CPA, Chief Financial Officer, Upstate University Hospital, Syracuse, NY, p. A500

WRIGHT, Tom, Director Human Resources, Kindred Hospital Riverside, Perris, CA, p. A85

WRIGHT, Toni, Director Human Resources, Bridgepoint Hospital Capitol Hill, Washington, DC, p. A129

WRIGHT, Trevor, Chief Operating Officer, Loma Linda University Children's Hospital, Loma Linda, CA, p. A71
Chief Operating Officer, Loma Linda University Medical Center, Loma Linda, CA, p. A72

WRIGHT-WHITAKER, Ruth, Director Information Services, Chi Memorial Hospital - Georgia, Fort Oglethorpe, GA, p. A173

WRINN, Denise, Vice President Finance and Chief Financial Officer, Guthrie Cortland Regional Medical Center, Cortland, NY, p. A482

WROBLEWSKI, Edmund, M.D., Vice President Medical Affairs and Chief Medical Officer, Goleta Valley Cottage Hospital, Santa Barbara, CA, p. A96
M.D., Vice President Medical Affairs and Chief Medical Officer, Santa Barbara Cottage Hospital, Santa Barbara, CA, p. A97
M.D., Vice President Medical Affairs and Chief Medical Officer, Santa Ynez Valley Cottage Hospital, Solvang, CA, p. A99

WROGG, Frank, Director Information Technology, Mayo Clinic Health System - Red Cedar In Menomonie, Menomonie, WI, p. A789

WU, Kenneth, M.D., Medical Director, Kessler Marlton Rehabilitation, Marlton, NJ, p. A458

WUCHTER, Greg, R.N., MSN, Chief Executive Officer, Select Specialty Hospital-Savannah, Savannah, GA, p. A180

WUENSCHEL, Diedra, D.O., President Medical Staff, Coryell Health, Gatesville, TX, p. A681

WUNDERWALD, Wendie, R.N., Vice President Patient Care Services, Samaritan Lebanon Community Hospital, Lebanon, OR, p. A577

WURGLER, Brad, Chief Financial Officer, Perham Health, Perham, MN, p. A383

WURSTER, Rosemary, M.P.H., R.N., Chief Nursing Officer, Reading Hospital, West Reading, PA, p. A610

WURTZEL, Leann, Director Human Resources, Mayo Clinic Health System - Red Cedar In Menomonie, Menomonie, WI, p. A789

WYATT, Christopher B., President, Cox Barton County Memorial Hospital, Lamar, MO, p. A410

WYATT, Christy, R.N., Interim Chief Nursing Officer, Jackson Parish Hospital, Jonesboro, LA, p. A304

WYATT, Jana, Chief Executive Officer, Mizell Memorial Hospital, Opp. AL, p. A23

WYDICK, Sue, Director Human Resources, Ohio County Hospital, Hartford, KY, p. A284

WYDRA, Lana, Vice President Human Resources, Nathan Littauer Hospital And Nursing Home, Gloversville, NY, p. A485

WYER, Jolena, R.N., Chief Nursing Officer, Oklahoma Center For Orthopedic And Multi-Specialty Surgery, Oklahoma City, OK, p. A565

WYERS, Michael, Chief Financial Officer, Medical Center Of Trinity, Trinity, FL, p. A161

WYLER, Allyson, Vice President, Operations, Advocate Lutheran General Hospital, Park Ridge, IL, p. A216

WYLIE, Eugene, Chief Human Resources Officer, Veterans Affairs Loma Linda Healthcare System, Loma Linda, CA, p. A72

WYLIE, Patrick, Director Information Systems, Petaluma Valley Hospital, Petaluma, CA, p. A85

WYMAN, David, President and Chief Executive Officer, Gracie Square Hospital, New York, NY, p. A489

WYMER, Melanie, Director Human Resources, Highland District Hospital, Hillsboro, OH, p. A542

WYNN, Katherine, Director Human Resource, Oklahoma Heart Hospital, Oklahoma City, OK, p. A565

WYNN, Leanna, Affiliate Vice President and Chief Nursing Officer, Passavant Area Hospital, Jacksonville, IL, p. A209

WYNN, Paige, Administrator, Irwin County Hospital, Ocilla, GA, p. A178
Chief Financial Officer, Dorminy Medical Center, Fitzgerald, GA, p. A172

WYNNE, David, President Medical Staff, Grandview Medical Center, Birmingham, AL, p. A15

WYNNE, Scott, Chief Information Officer Director, Bleckley Memorial Hospital, Cochran, GA, p. A169

WYSE, Debbie, Controller, Quillen Rehabilitation Hospital, Johnson City, TN, p. A640

WYSOCKI, Greg, Chief Financial Officer, Austin Lakes Hospital, Austin, TX, p. A655

WYSONG-HARDER, Alyson, Chief Executive Officer, Heartland Behavioral Health Services, Nevada, MO, p. A412

# Y

YABUT, Eduardo, M.D., Medical Director, North Dakota State Hospital, Jamestown, ND, p. A524

YAEGER, Eric, M.D., Chief Medical Officer, Kindred Hospital-Aurora, Aurora, CO, p. A107
M.D., Medical Director, Kindred Hospital-Denver, Denver, CO, p. A110

YAEGER, Kristy, Vice President, Patient Care Services and Chief Nursing Officer, Hudson Hospital And Clinic, Hudson, WI, p. A786

YAHNER, Michael, Chief Financial Officer, Torrance State Hospital, Torrance, PA, p. A608

YAKE, Laurie, Vice President Finance, Aurora Medical Center Kenosha, Kenosha, WI, p. A786

YAKLIN, Shelleye, President and Chief Executive Officer, North Ottawa Community Hospital, Grand Haven, MI, p. A355

YAKOVENKO, Gene, Director of Finance, Amita Health Holy Family Medical Center, Des Plaines, IL, p. A202

YAKULIS, Paul, MS, R.N., Senior Vice President Human Resources, Lankenau Medical Center, Wynnewood, PA, p. A612

YALLOWITZ, Joseph, M.D., Vice President and Chief Medical Officer, Valley Hospital, Ridgewood, NJ, p. A462

YAMADA, Jeff, Vice President, Virginia Mason Memorial, Yakima, WA, p. A769

YANEZ, Maria, Chief Financial Officer, Baptist Health South Florida, Doctors Hospital, Coral Gables, FL, p. A135

YANGA, Ismael, M.D., Chief Medical Officer, Ascension Brighton Center For Recovery, Brighton, MI, p. A350

YANIK, Sahin, M.D., Vice President Medical Administration, St. John's Regional Medical Center, Oxnard, CA, p. A83
M.D., Vice President Medical Associate, St. John's Pleasant Valley Hospital, Camarillo, CA, p. A59

YANKTON, Nikki, Director Human Resources, Oakleaf Surgical Hospital, Altoona, WI, p. A779

YANNI, Anthony, M.D., Vice President Medical Affairs, Regional Hospital Of Scranton, Scranton, PA, p. A607

YAP, Elvy, Director of Finance, Rush Oak Park Hospital, Oak Park, IL, p. A215

YAP, Eric, Chief Executive Officer, Ohiohealth Rehabilitation Hospital, Columbus, OH, p. A536

YAP, Winston, M.D., Chief Medical Officer, Carroll County Memorial Hospital, Carrollton, KY, p. A281

YARBOROUGH, Dianne, Director of Information Technology, Baylor Scott & White Medical Center - Centennial, Frisco, TX, p. A680

YARBROUGH, Ruth, Vice President, Javon Bea Hospital-Rockton, Rockford, IL, p. A218

YARLING, John, M.D., Medical Director, Four County Counseling Center, Logansport, IN, p. A235

YARMEL, Jeffrey, Chief Operating Officer, St. Mary Medical Center, Langhorne, PA, p. A594

YARN, Jayce, Director Information Technology, Marias Medical Center, Shelby, MT, p. A427

YAROCH, Julie, President, Promedica Bixby Hospital, Adrian, MI, p. A348

President, Promedica Herrick Hospital, Tecumseh, MI, p. A368

YARTYM, Jennifer, President, Guthrie Cortland Regional Medical Center, Cortland, NY, p. A482

YATES, Ann, R.N., MSN, Chief Nursing Officer, Ascension St. Vincent Mercy, Elwood, IN, p. A227

YATES, Ann C., R.N., MSN, Administrator and Chief Nursing Officer, Ascension St. Vincent Mercy, Elwood, IN, p. A227

YATES, Brent, Chief Executive Officer, Mercy Rehabilitation Hospital Springfield, Springfield, MO, p. A419

YATES, Jackie, R.N., Nurse Executive, Mississipp. State Hospital, Whitfield, MS, p. A401

YATES, Jeremy, Chief Executive Officer, Encompass Health Rehabilitation Hospital Of Northern Kentucky, Edgewood, KY, p. A282

YATES, Katie, Chief Financial Officer, South Sunflower County Hospital, Indianola, MS, p. A394

YATES, Ralph, D.O., Chief Medical Officer, Salem Health West Valley, Dallas, OR, p. A574

D.O., Chief Medical Officer, Salem Hospital, Salem, OR, p. A581

YATES, Randy, M.D., Chief Medical Officer, Straub Medical Center, Honolulu, HI, p. A185

YATES, Vinson, President, Ohiohealth Medcentral Mansfield Hospital, Mansfield, OH, p. A544

President, Ohiohealth Medcentral Shelby Hospital, Shelby, OH, p. A549

YATSATTIE, Clyde, Administrative Officer, U. S. Public Health Service Indian Hospital, Zuni, NM, p. A473

YAWORSKY, Jason, Senior Vice President Information Systems and Chief Information Officer, Olean General Hospital, Olean, NY, p. A494

YAZAWA, Albert, M.D., Regional Medical Director, Leahi Hospital, Honolulu, HI, p. A184

YBARRA, Farra, R.N., Chief Nursing Officer, Coal County General Hospital, Coalgate, OK, p. A558

YEAGER, Angela, Director Information Technology, Palacios Community Medical Center, Palacios, TX, p. A704

YEAGER, Dianne, Chief Executive Officer, Crane Memorial Hospital, Crane, TX, p. A666

YEAGER, Kerry, Director Information Technology, Berwick Hospital Center, Berwick, PA, p. A584

YEAGER, Kevin, Vice President Fiscal Services, Holzer Medical Center - Jackson, Jackson, OH, p. A542

YEARY, John M., FACHE, Chief Executive Officer, Freestone Medical Center, Fairfield, TX, p. A677

YEATES, Alan, Vice President Fiscal Services, Wyandot Memorial Hospital, Upper Sandusky, OH, p. A551

YEATES, Diane, FACHE, Chief Operating Officer, Terrebonne General Medical Center, Houma, LA, p. A303

YEATS, Melania, M.D., Chief Medical Officer, San Juan Regional Medical Center, Farmington, NM, p. A469

YEE, Martin, M.D., Medical Director, Encompass Health Rehabilitation Hospital Of East Valley, Mesa, AZ, p. A34

YEH, Ada, Chief Executive Officer, Chapman Global Medical Center, Orange, CA, p. A82

Chief Executive Officer, South Coast Global Medical Center, Santa Ana, CA, p. A96

Chief Operating Officer and Chief Nursing Officer, Chapman Global Medical Center, Orange, CA, p. A82

YEHL, Warren, Chief Executive Officer, Eastern New Mexico Medical Center, Roswell, NM, p. A471

YEHLEN, Lorraine, R.N., Vice President Patient Care Services, Dch Regional Medical Center, Tuscaloosa, AL, p. A25

YEITRAKIS, Dawn, Vice President, Nursing, Medstar St. Mary's Hospital, Leonardtown, MD, p. A331

YELKEN, Kari, R.N., Director of Nursing, Franklin County Memorial Hospital, Franklin, NE, p. A432

YELVINGTON, Fleury, Administrator, Shriners Hospitals For Children-Tampa, Tampa, FL, p. A159

YERRELL-GARRETT, Lori, Interim Chief Nursing Executive, Saint Elizabeths Hospital, Washington, DC, p. A130

YETMAN, Robert, M.D., Medical Director, Nexus Children's Hospital Houston, Houston, TX, p. A688

YETTER, Tad, M.D., President Medical Staff, Mason District Hospital, Havana, IL, p. A207

YEUNG, Christopher, M.D., Chief of Staff, The Core Institute Specialty Hospital, Phoenix, AZ, p. A37

YHLEN, David, Chief Operating Officer, Inspira Medical Center-Elmer, Elmer, NJ, p. A455

YI, Brenda, Director Medical Resource Management and Chief Financial Officer, U. S. Air Force Medical Center Keesler, Keesler Afb, MS, p. A395

YIM, Janet, Director Information Services, St. Mary Mercy Hospital, Livonia, MI, p. A360

YIN, Khin, Medical Director, Rehabilitation Hospital Of Rhode Island, North Smithfield, RI, p. A613

YINGLING, Barbara, R.N., Senior Vice President Patient Care Services and Chief Nursing Officer, Mercy Medical Center, Canton, OH, p. A531

YITTA, Prasad, M.D., Medical Director, River Hospital, Alexandria Bay, NY, p. A474

YOCHELSON, Michael, M.D., Vice President and Medical Director, Medstar National Rehabilitation Hospital, Washington, DC, p. A130

YOCHUM, Richard E., FACHE, President and Chief Executive Officer, Pomona Valley Hospital Medical Center, Pomona, CA, p. A86

YODER, Lamont M., R.N., MSN, FACHE, Chief Executive Officer, Banner Baywood Medical Center, Mesa, AZ, p. A33

R.N., MSN, FACHE, Chief Executive Officer, Banner Gateway Medical Center, Gilbert, AZ, p. A32

R.N., MSN, FACHE, Chief Executive Officer, Banner Heart Hospital, Mesa, AZ, p. A34

YODER, Leslie, Executive Director, Finance, Community Hospital South, Indianapolis, IN, p. A231

YODER, Zachary, Chief Nursing Officer, Hshs St. Joseph's Hospital, Breese, IL, p. A196

YOE, Adam, Chief Executive Officer, Encompass Health Rehabilitation Hospital Of North Memphis, Memphis, TN, p. A644

YOO, George, M.D., Chief Medical Officer, Karmanos Cancer Center, Detroit, MI, p. A353

YOO, Jamie, Chief Executive Officer, Anaheim Global Medical Center, Anaheim, CA, p. A55

YOON, Chris, M.D., Medical Director, Encompass Health Rehabilitation Hospital Of Bakersfield, Bakersfield, CA, p. A57

YORK, Christopher, FACHE, President, Baylor Scott & White Medical Center - Grapevine, Grapevine, TX, p. A682

YORK, Don, Vice President and Chief Human Resource Officer, Sky Lakes Medical Center, Klamath Falls, OR, p. A576

YORK, Linda, Director Human Resource, Memorial Hospital Of Converse County, Douglas, WY, p. A802

YORK, Russell, Vice President and Chief Financial Officer, Select Specialty Hospital - Belhaven, Jackson, MS, p. A395

YOSHII, Brian, Vice President Information Technology and Chief Information Officer, The Queen's Medical Center, Honolulu, HI, p. A185

YOSHIOKA, Lori, Director of Human Resources, Rehabilitation Hospital Of The Pacific, Honolulu, HI, p. A185

YOUNADAM, Sandro, M.D., Chief Medical Officer, Ottumwa Regional Health Center, Ottumwa, IA, p. A256

YOUNG, Aaron, Chief Information Officer, Summit Healthcare Regional Medical Center, Show Low, AZ, p. A38

YOUNG, Abby, Chief Nursing Officer, Iowa Specialty Hospital-Clarion, Clarion, IA, p. A246

YOUNG, Angela, Human Resources Officer, Chillicothe Veterans Affairs Medical Center, Chillicothe, OH, p. A531

YOUNG, Anita, Chief Operating Officer, Adventhealth Waterman, Tavares, FL, p. A160

YOUNG, Anthony, Chief Executive Officer, Ochsner St. Mary, Morgan City, LA, p. A309

Chief Executive Officer, Post Acute Medical Specialty Hospital Of Tulsa, Tulsa, OK, p. A570

Information Services Specialist, Chester Mental Health Center, Chester, IL, p. A197

YOUNG, Barry, Director Human Resources, Western Mental Health Institute, Bolivar, TN, p. A634

YOUNG, Bev, Director Human Resources, Frankfort Regional Medical Center, Frankfort, KY, p. A283

YOUNG, Bryce, Chief Operating Officer, Hays Medical Center, Hays, KS, p. A265

Chief Operating Officer, University Of Kansas Health System Pawnee Valley Campus, Larned, KS, p. A268

YOUNG, C. Ray, M.D., Chief Medical Officer, Bourbon Community Hospital, Paris, KY, p. A292

YOUNG, Christine, MSN, R.N., Vice President of Patient Services and Chief Nursing Officer, Akron Children's Hospital, Akron, OH, p. A527

YOUNG, David, Senior Vice President Planning and Technology, Trousdale Medical Center, Hartsville, TN, p. A639

YOUNG, Debra, R.N., MSN, Vice President, Patient Services and Chief Nursing Officer, Up Health System-Portage, Hancock, MI, p. A357

YOUNG, Duke, Chief Executive Officer, Kimble Hospital, Junction, TX, p. A691

YOUNG, Eric, M.D., Chief of Staff, Veterans Affairs Ann Arbor Healthcare System, Ann Arbor, MI, p. A348

Chief Financial Officer, Selby General Hospital, Marietta, OH, p. A544

Director Information Technology and Systems, South Bay Hospital, Sun City Center, FL, p. A158

Vice President Finance and Chief Financial Officer, Marietta Memorial Hospital, Marietta, OH, p. A544

YOUNG, Gladys, M.D., Chief of Staff, Liberty Medical Center, Chester, MT, p. A422

YOUNG, James, M.D., Chief of Staff, Mcgehee Hospital, Mcgehee, AR, p. A50

YOUNG, Jeffrey, Chief Human Resource Officer, South Texas Veterans Health Care System, San Antonio, TX, p. A713

Chief Information Officer, Children's Hospitals And Clinics Of Minnesota, Minneapolis, MN, p. A380

YOUNG, John E., Interim Chief Executive Officer, Columbus Regional Healthcare System, Whiteville, NC, p. A519

YOUNG, Joyce, Ph.D., R.N., Vice President, Patient Services and Chief Nursing Officer, St. Josep. Mercy Ann Arbor, Ypsilanti, MI, p. A370

Ph.D., R.N., Vice President, Patient Services and Chief Nursing Officer, St. Josep. Mercy Livingston Hospital, Howell, MI, p. A358

YOUNG, Lisa, CPA, Chief Financial Officer, Continuecare Hospital At Baptist Health Corbin, Corbin, KY, p. A282

CPA, Chief Financial Officer, Continuecare Hospital At Hendrick Medical Center, Abilene, TX, p. A651

YOUNG, Martha, Director Human Resources, Cumberland County Hospital, Burkesville, KY, p. A281

YOUNG, Mary, Director Human Resources, Colorado Mental Health Institute At Pueblo, Pueblo, CO, p. A117

YOUNG, Mary C., Chief Executive Officer, Moccasin Bend Mental Health Institute, Chattanooga, TN, p. A635

YOUNG, Mary Lou, Chief Nursing Officer, Continuecare Hospital At Baptist Health Paducah, Paducah, KY, p. A291

YOUNG, Michael, Chief Financial Officer, Mad River Community Hospital, Arcata, CA, p. A56

YOUNG, Michael A., FACHE, President and Chief Executive Officer, Temple University Hospital, Philadelphia, PA, p. A602

YOUNG, Pam, Director Human Resources, Davis County Hospital And Clinics, Bloomfield, IA, p. A244

YOUNG, Patty, R.N., Chief Nursing Officer, Ashland Health Center, Ashland, KS, p. A261

YOUNG, Rhonda, Human Resource Director, Encompass Health Rehabilitation Hospital Of Gadsden, Gadsden, AL, p. A19

YOUNG, Richard T., FACHE, Director, Walter P. Reuther Psychiatric Hospital, Westland, MI, p. A369

YOUNG, Roberta, Vice President Nursing, Sanford Medical Center Fargo, Fargo, ND, p. A523

YOUNG, Sabrina, Administrative Support Director, South Mississipp. State Hospital, Purvis, MS, p. A399

Director, South Mississipp. State Hospital, Purvis, MS, p. A399

YOUNG, Shalen, Chief Financial Officer, Arizona Orthopedic Surgical Hospital, Chandler, AZ, p. A30

YOUNG, Sheila, Vice President Human Resources, Mobile Infirmary Medical Center, Mobile, AL, p. A22

YOUNG, Stephanie, Associate Director, Aleda E. Lutz Veterans Affairs Medical Center, Saginaw, MI, p. A365

YOUNG, Terry, Chief Information Officer, Plains Memorial Hospital, Dimmitt, TX, p. A673

YOUNG, Theresa, Senior Vice President Human Resources, Nemours Children's Hospital, Orlando, FL, p. A151

YOUNG, Tiffany, Chief Financial Officer, Acadia-St. Landry Hospital, Church Point, LA, p. A299

YOUNG, William, Chief Information Officer, Berkshire Medical Center, Pittsfield, MA, p. A343

YOUNG, William A. Jr, President and Chief Executive Officer, Southwest General Health Center, Middleburg Heights, OH, p. A545

YOUNGBLOOD, Carrie, Director of Human Resources, Kittitas Valley Healthcare, Ellensburg, WA, p. A757

YOUNGBLOOD, Elizabeth, President and Chief Executive Officer, Baylor St. Luke's Medical Center Mcnair Campus, Houston, TX, p. A684

President and Chief Executive Officer, Baylor St. Luke's Medical Center, Houston, TX, p. A684

YOUNGBLOOD, Erin, Chief Human Resources Officer, Behavioral Center Of Michigan, Warren, MI, p. A369

YOUNGMAN, Darrell, D.O., Chief Medical Officer, Ascension Via Christi St. Francis, Mulvane, KS, p. A271

YOURTEE, Edward, M.D., Chief Medical Officer, Parkland Medical Center, Derry, NH, p. A448

YOURZEK, Tari, Chief Nursing Officer, Boundary Community Hospital, Bonners Ferry, ID, p. A189

YOUSAITIS, Zoe, Director Human Resources, Eagleville Hospital, Eagleville, PA, p. A588

YOUSO, Michael, Chief Executive Officer, Essentia Health Moose Lake, Moose Lake, MN, p. A381

YOUSSEF, Moudy, M.D., Chief Medical Officer, Fairchild Medical Center, Yreka, CA, p. A106

YU, Henry, Vice President Finance and Chief Financial Officer, California Pacific Medical Center-St. Luke's Campus, San Francisco, CA, p. A93

Vice President Finance and Chief Financial Officer, California Pacific Medical Center, San Francisco, CA, p. A93

YUHAS, Joel P., FACHE, Chief Executive Officer, Uchealth Grandview Hospital, Colorado Springs, CO, p. A109
  FACHE, President and Chief Executive Officer, Uchealth Memorial Hospital, Colorado Springs, CO, p. A109
YUHAS, John, D.O., Medical Director, Eden Springs Health Care Center, Green Springs, OH, p. A541
YULICH, Michael, Director Information Technology, St. Francis Medical Center, Trenton, NJ, p. A464
YUNGMANN, Michael, President and Chief Executive Officer, Lourdes Hospital, Paducah, KY, p. A291
YUNUSOV, Ed, Chief Information Officer, Creedmoor Psychiatric Center, Jamaica, NY, p. A486
  Coordinator Facility Information Center, New York City Children's Center, Jamaica, NY, p. A486
YUST, Randall, Chief Financial Officer NCR, Indiana University Health Tipton Hospital, Tipton, IN, p. A241
  Chief Operating Officer and Chief Financial Officer, Indiana University Health North Hospital, Carmel, IN, p. A225

# Z

ZABAWSKI, Denise, Vice President Information Services and Chief Information Officer, Nationwide Children's Hospital, Columbus, OH, p. A536
ZABIELSKI, Gerald, M.D., Chief Medical Staff, Wright Memorial Hospital, Trenton, MO, p. A419
ZABROWSKI, John, Senior Vice President and Chief Financial Officer, Virginia Hospital Center, Arlington, VA, p. A738
ZACHARIASEN, Keith, Chief Financial Officer, Wamego Health Center, Wamego, KS, p. A278
ZACHARY, Kevin, Chief Executive Officer, Colorado Plains Medical Center, Fort Morgan, CO, p. A112
ZACHRY, Jan, R.N., Vice President Administrator and Chief Operations Executive, Scripp. Memorial Hospital-Encinitas, Encinitas, CA, p. A63
ZACIEWSKI, Gary, Chief Executive Officer, Regency Hospital Of Toledo, Sylvania, OH, p. A550
ZAFEREO, Carolyn, Chief Accounting Officer, Citizens Medical Center, Victoria, TX, p. A723
ZAFONTE, Ross, D.O., Chief, Physical Medicine and Rehabilitation and Vice President Medical Affairs, Research and Education, Spaulding Rehabilitation Hospital, Charlestown, MA, p. A338
ZAGERMAN, Robert, Chief Financial Officer, Brooke Glen Behavioral Hospital, Fort Washington, PA, p. A590
ZAHN, Chip. Chief Operating Officer, Medical City Las Colinas, Irving, TX, p. A690
ZAID, Ahmad, Chief Executive Officer, Atrium Medical Center, Stafford, TX, p. A716
ZAJEC, Doris, Director Human Resources, South Pointe Hospital, Warrensville Heights, OH, p. A552
ZAJIC, Holly, Chief Operating Officer, Ivinson Memorial Hospital, Laramie, WY, p. A803
ZAJICEK, Tammy, Director of Nursing, Jackson County Hospital District, Edna, TX, p. A674
ZAKAI, Aminadav, M.D., Medical Director, Arbour-Fuller Hospital, Attleboro, MA, p. A334
ZALDIVAR, Rogelio, M.D., Medical Director, Westchester General Hospital, Miami, FL, p. A147
ZALESKI, Theodore, M.D., Vice President Clinical Effectiveness, Hackensack Meridian Health Southern Ocean Medical Center, Manahawkin, NJ, p. A458
ZALUD, Nicolette, Customer Site Manager, Mclaren Central Michigan, Mount Pleasant, MI, p. A362
ZALUSKI, Heather, M.D., President Medical Staff, Shodair Children's Hospital, Helena, MT, p. A425
ZAMBITO, Paolo, R.N., Chief Operating Officer, East Jefferson General Hospital, Metairie, LA, p. A308
ZAMBRELLO, Sally, Chief Information Officer, Carondelet St. Joseph's Hospital, Tucson, AZ, p. A40
ZAMORA DE AGUERO, Hilde, Human Resources Site Director, Baptist Health South Florida, West Kendall Baptist Hospital, Miami, FL, p. A146
ZAMPINI, Maria, Chief Operating Officer, University Medical Center Of El Paso, El Paso, TX, p. A676
ZANE, Kristi, Chief Human Resources Officer, Crawford Memorial Hospital, Robinson, IL, p. A218
ZANGER, Albert, Vice President, Chief Financial Officer, University Of Maryland Charles Regional Medical Center, La Plata, MD, p. A330
ZANI, Carl, Chief Technology Director, Memorial Health, Marysville, OH, p. A544
ZANIS, Tina, Director Information Systems, Lehigh Valley Hospital - Schuylkill, Pottsville, PA, p. A605

ZANNI, David M., Administrator, Adena Pike Medical Center, Waverly, OH, p. A552
ZANT, Dan, M.D., Chief of Staff, Morgan Memorial Hospital, Madison, GA, p. A176
ZARAK, Tamie, Director Human Resources, Marshfield Medical Center - Neillsville, Neillsville, WI, p. A792
ZAREMA, Claudette, M.D., Medical Officer, Alaska Psychiatric Institute, Anchorage, AK, p. A27
ZAUNER, Janiece, Chief Nursing Officer, Providence Seaside Hospital, Seaside, OR, p. A581
  Chief Operating Officer, Providence Seaside Hospital, Seaside, OR, p. A581
ZAUNER, Mike, Chief Executive Officer, Sierra Vista Hospital, Sacramento, CA, p. A90
ZAVALA, Jocelyn, Senior Information Technology Coordinator, Riveredge Hospital, Forest Park, IL, p. A205
ZAVATCHEN, Nancy, Director Information Technology, Cullman Regional Medical Center, Cullman, AL, p. A17
ZAVODNICK, Jacquelyn, M.D., Medical Director, Devereux Children's Behavioral Health Center, Malvern, PA, p. A596
ZAWACKI, Brenda, Chief Operating Manager, Providence Kodiak Island Medical Center, Kodiak, AK, p. A28
ZAWOJSKI, Paula, Regional Director, Human Resources, Amita Health Resurrection Medical Center, Chicago, IL, p. A197
ZDEBLICK, Mick, Chief Executive Officer, Asante Rogue Regional Medical Center, Medford, OR, p. A577
ZDRODOWSKI, Michael, Vice President of Operations and Ambulatory Services, Munson Healthcare Cadillac Hospital, Cadillac, MI, p. A350
ZECHMAN, David M., FACHE, President and Chief Executive Officer, Mclaren Northern Michigan, Petoskey, MI, p. A363
ZEDNICEK, Allison, Chief Executive Officer, Desert Parkway Behavioral Healthcare Hospital, Las Vegas, NV, p. A443
ZEHM, Laura, Vice President and Chief Financial Officer, Community Hospital Of The Monterey Peninsula, Monterey, CA, p. A79
ZEHNER, Douglas, Chief Financial Officer, Newark Beth Israel Medical Center, Newark, NJ, p. A459
ZEIGLER, Michele, Vice President and Chief Information Officer, Wellspan Chambersburg Hospital, Chambersburg, PA, p. A586
  Vice President Information Services, Wellspan Waynesboro Hospital, Waynesboro, PA, p. A610
ZEISEL, Henry, Chief Financial Officer, Northern Region, Amita Health Elk Grove Village, Elk Grove Village, IL, p. A204
  Chief Financial Officer, Northern Region, Amita Health Hoffman Estates, Hoffman Estates, IL, p. A208
ZEITLER, Irvin, D.O., Vice President Medical Affairs, Shannon Medical Center, San Angelo, TX, p. A710
ZEITLER, Jenny, Network Administrator, North Okaloosa Medical Center, Crestview, FL, p. A135
ZELENKA, Anthony, President and Chief Executive Officer, Jefferson Medical Center, Ranson, WV, p. A776
  President and Chief Operating Officer, Berkeley Medical Center, Martinsburg, WV, p. A774
ZELIN, Mira, D.O., Medical Director, Encompass Health Rehabilitation Hospital Of Spring Hill, Brooksville, FL, p. A133
ZELL, John, Chief Financial Officer, Osf St. Josep. Medical Center, Bloomington, IL, p. A195
ZELLER, Brad, Vice President Operations, Hayward Area Memorial Hospital And Water's Edge, Hayward, WI, p. A786
ZELLER, Paul, Vice President Human Resources, Medstar Southern Maryland Hospital Center, Clinton, MD, p. A328
ZELLER, Sonya, R.N., Vice President, Chief Operating Officer and Chief Nursing Officer, Indiana University Health Paoli Hospital, Paoli, IN, p. A238
ZEMAN, Brian, Chief Human Resources, Salem Veterans Affairs Medical Center, Salem, VA, p. A751
ZEMAN, Mark, Chief Information Officer, Upstate University Hospital, Syracuse, NY, p. A500
ZENGER, Andrew, Chief Operating Officer, Medical City Mckinney, Mckinney, TX, p. A700
ZENGOTITA, Jamie, M.D., Chief Medical Staff, Mercy Hospital Cassville, Cassville, MO, p. A404
ZENN, Michael B., Chief Executive Officer, University Of Illinois Hospital & Health Sciences System, Chicago, IL, p. A201
ZENNA, Rita, R.N., Vice President Patient Care Services, Deborah Heart And Lung Center, Browns Mills, NJ, p. A453
ZENONE, Michael, Chief Financial Officer, Emerald Coast Behavioral Hospital, Panama City, FL, p. A152
ZEPHIER, Michelle, Human Resource Specialist, U. S. Public Health Service Indian Hospital, Rosebud, SD, p. A631
ZEPS, Joseph, Vice President Finance, Tomah Health, Tomah, WI, p. A797
ZEPS, Julie, Vice President Human Resources, Aspirus Medford Hospital & Clinics, Inc., Medford, WI, p. A789
ZERINGUE, Rhonda, R.N., Chief Nursing Officer, St. James Parish Hospital, Lutcher, LA, p. A307

ZERRER, Lana, M.D., Chief of Staff, Harry S. Truman Memorial Veterans Hospital, Columbia, MO, p. A405
ZEVENBERGEN, Glenn, Chief Executive Officer, Hegg Health Center Avera, Rock Valley, IA, p. A257
ZEWE, Jeff S., R.N., Chief Executive Officer, Olean General Hospital, Olean, NY, p. A494
ZEYNELOGLU, Nejat, Vice President and Chief Quality Medical Officer, Long Island Community Hospital, Patchogue, NY, p. A494
ZHANG, George, Administrator, Ascension St. Vincent Dunn, Bedford, IN, p. A224
ZHANG, Jian Q., Chief Executive Officer, Chinese Hospital, San Francisco, CA, p. A93
ZHIRKIN, Georgii, Chief Financial Officer, Community Mental Health Center, Lawrenceburg, IN, p. A235
ZIA, Hasan, Vice President of Medical Affairs and Chief Medical Officer, Sibley Memorial Hospital, Washington, DC, p. A130
ZIA, Hasan A., Interim President and Chief Executive Officer, Sibley Memorial Hospital, Washington, DC, p. A130
ZIEGELE, Paul, Chief Financial Officer, Chinese Hospital, San Francisco, CA, p. A93
ZIEGLER, John, FACHE, Vice President Human Resources, Memorial Hospital East, Shiloh, IL, p. A220
  FACHE, Vice President Human Resources, Memorial Hospital, Belleville, IL, p. A195
ZIELAZINSKI, Mark, Chief Information and Technology Integration Officer, Marinhealth Medical Center, Greenbrae, CA, p. A67
ZIELINSKI, Sharon, Chief Information Resource Officer, Veterans Affairs Maryland Health Care System-Baltimore Division, Baltimore, MD, p. A327
  Manager Health Information, Encompass Health Rehabilitation Hospital Of Erie, Erie, PA, p. A589
ZIEMAN, Michael A., FACHE, Administrator, Gulfport Behavioral Health System, Gulfport, MS, p. A393
ZIEMIANSKI, Karen, R.N., MS, Senior Vice President Nursing, Erie County Medical Center, Buffalo, NY, p. A479
ZIENIEWICZ, Stephen P., FACHE, President and Chief Executive Officer, Saint Barnabas Medical Center, Livingston, NJ, p. A457
ZIEROLD, Bob, Senior Vice President, Chief Human Resources Officer, Christian Health Care Center, Wyckoff, NJ, p. A466
ZIGLOR, Danyale, Vice President, Wellstar Cobb Hospital, Austell, GA, p. A166
  Vice President, Wellstar Douglas Hospital, Douglasville, GA, p. A171
ZILE, Ron, M.D., Chief of Staff, Highland District Hospital, Hillsboro, OH, p. A542
ZILKOW, Jon, Chief Financial Officer, Southwest Healthcare System, Murrieta, CA, p. A80
ZILLER, Andrew, M.D., Chief Medical Officer, Rose Medical Center, Denver, CO, p. A111
ZILLMAN, Sally, Interim Vice President, Patient Care Services, Marshfield Medical Center - Weston, Weston, WI, p. A799
ZIMA, Cheryl, Vice President Human Resources Ministry Health Care, Marshfield Medical Center, Marshfield, WI, p. A789
ZIMMEL, Robert, Senior Vice President Human Resources, St. Luke's University Hospital - Bethlehem Campus, Bethlehem, PA, p. A585
ZIMMER, Jan, R.N., MSN, R.N., MS, Chief Nursing Officer, West Tennessee Healthcare Dyersburg Hospital, Dyersburg, TN, p. A637
ZIMMERLI, Bert, Executive Vice President and Chief Financial Officer, Sevier Valley Hospital, Richfield, UT, p. A731
ZIMMERLY, Kara, Manager Human Resources, Promedica Bay Park Hospital, Oregon, OH, p. A547
ZIMMERMAN, Aimee, R.N., Chief Operations Officer, Logan County Hospital, Oakley, KS, p. A272
ZIMMERMAN, Anne, Senior Director Patient Care Services and Chief Nursing Officer, Mercy Tiffin Hospital, Tiffin, OH, p. A550
ZIMMERMAN, David, M.D., Chief of Staff, Swain Community Hospital, Bryson City, NC, p. A505
ZIMMERMAN, Don, Director Human Resources, Morris County Hospital, Council Grove, KS, p. A263
ZIMMERMAN, Keith, Chief Executive Officer, Medical City Arlington, Arlington, TX, p. A653
ZIMMERMAN, Michael, Human Resource Officer, Osf Heart Of Mary Medical Center, Urbana, IL, p. A222
  Human Resource Officer, Osf Sacred Heart Medical Center, Danville, IL, p. A202
ZIMMERMAN, Shelley, Chief Executive Officer, Windsor-Laurelwood Center For Behavioral Medicine, Willoughby, OH, p. A553
ZIMMERMANN, Deb, R.N., Chief Nursing Officer and Vice President Patient Care Services, Vcu Medical Center, Richmond, VA, p. A751
ZIMMERMANN, Wayne, Chief Operating Officer, Nyc Health + Hospitals / Elmhurst, Elmhurst, NY, p. A483

ZINAMAN, Michael, M.D., Acting Chief Medical Officer, Nyc Health + Hospitals / Jacobi, Bronx, NY, p. A477

ZINK, Jayne, Director of Nursing, Ohio Hospital For Psychiatry, Columbus, OH, p. A536

ZINK, Summer, Chief Financial Officer, Ellinwood District Hospital, Ellinwood, KS, p. A264

ZINKER, Dena, MSN, R.N., Vice President Patient Services, Colquitt Regional Medical Center, Moultrie, GA, p. A177

ZINKULA, Lisa, Chief Financial Officer, Grundy County Memorial Hospital, Grundy Center, IA, p. A250

ZINN, David, M.D., Vice President Medical Affairs, Rmc Anniston, Anniston, AL, p. A13

ZINN, Troy, Chief Executive Officer, Cameron Hospital, Cameron, TX, p. A662

ZINNER, Barbara, Chief Nursing Officer, Marymount Hospital, Garfield Heights, OH, p. A541

ZINNI, Melissa, Chief Financial Officer, Hampton Behavioral Health Center, Westampton, NJ, p. A465

ZINSMEISTER, Mary Sue, Chief Nursing Officer, Rockledge Regional Medical Center, Rockledge, FL, p. A155

ZIOBRO, Ronald, Chief Operating Officer, St. Luke's Easton Campus, Easton, PA, p. A589

ZIOLKOWSKI, David, Chief Executive Officer, Person Memorial Hospital, Roxboro, NC, p. A517

ZIRBSER, Glenn, Senior Vice President Finance and Chief Financial Officer, Jefferson Stratford Hospital, Stratford, NJ, p. A463

ZIRGER, Marion, Chief Financial Officer, Minneola District Hospital, Minneola, KS, p. A271

ZIRKELBACH, Mark, Chief Information Officer, Loma Linda University Children's Hospital, Loma Linda, CA, p. A71
Chief Information Officer, Loma Linda University Medical Center, Loma Linda, CA, p. A72

ZIRKELBACK, Mark, Chief Information Officer, Loma Linda University Behavioral Medicine Center, Redlands, CA, p. A87

ZIRKLE, Isaiah, Chief Operating Officer, West Hills Hospital And Medical Center, West Hills, CA, p. A104

ZIRKLE, William, Manager Information Systems, Sentara Halifax Regional Hospital, South Boston, VA, p. A751

ZISKIN, Robert, Chief Information Officer, Northport Veterans Affairs Medical Center, Northport, NY, p. A493

ZOCH, Jeremy, Chief Executive, St. Josep. Hospital Orange, Orange, CA, p. A83
Executive Vice President and Chief Operating Officer, St. Josep. Hospital Orange, Orange, CA, p. A83

ZOESCH, Jim, Information Technology Director, Prosser Memorial Health, Prosser, WA, p. A762

ZOGELMAN, Sharon, Director Human Resources, St. Luke Hospital And Living Center, Marion, KS, p. A270

ZOLKIWSKY, Walter, M.D., Chief Medical Officer, Reston Hospital Center, Reston, VA, p. A749
M.D., Chief Medical Officer, Stonesprings Hospital Center, Dulles, VA, p. A741

ZOMCHECK, Daniel, Interim Director, Captain James A. Lovell Federal Health Care Center, North Chicago, IL, p. A214

ZOMCHEK, Daniel, Ph.D., Chief Executive Officer and Medical Center Director, Clement J. Zablocki Veterans Affairs Medical Center, Milwaukee, WI, p. A791

ZOOK, Danette, Chief Financial Officer, Mercyone North Iowa Medical Center, Mason City, IA, p. A254

ZOOK, Lori, Chief Financial Officer, River's Edge Hospital And Clinic, Saint Peter, MN, p. A385

ZORZA, Elizabeth, Assistant Administrator, Osf St. Francis Hospital And Medical Group. Escanaba, MI, p. A354

ZOUCHA, Larry, Chief Information Officer, Boone County Health Center, Albion, NE, p. A429

ZUANICH, Elizabeth, Chief Financial Officer, Providence Little Company Of Mary Medical Center - Torrance, Torrance, CA, p. A101
Chief Financial Officer, Providence Little Company Of Mary Medical Center San Pedro, San Pedro, CA, p. A96

ZUBER, Steven, Vice President, Methodist Jennie Edmundson Hospital, Council Bluffs, IA, p. A247

ZUEL, Sally, Vice President Human Resources, Union Hospital, Terre Haute, IN, p. A241

ZUHD, Dajani, M.D., President Medical Staff, Punxsutawney Area Hospital, Punxsutawney, PA, p. A605

ZUKOWSKI, Andrew, Chief Financial Officer, Unc Rex Health Care, Raleigh, NC, p. A517

ZULIANI, Michael E., Chief Executive Officer, Encompass Health Rehabilitation Hospital Of Huntington, Huntington, WV, p. A773

ZULTANKY, Lynne, Director Corporate Communications and Media Relations, Bon Secours-Depaul Medical Center, Norfolk, VA, p. A747

ZUMALT, Ryan, Chief Executive Officer, Vibra Hospital Of Boise, Boise, ID, p. A189

ZUMPANO, Anthony, Chief Financial Officer, Penn Presbyterian Medical Center, Philadelphia, PA, p. A601

ZUMSTEIN, James, M.D., Chief of Medicine, Jack Hughston Memorial Hospital, Phenix City, AL, p. A23

ZUTZ-WICZEK, Sandy, Chief Operating Officer, Welia Health, Mora, MN, p. A381

ZVANUT, Michelle, Vice President Human Resources, Boone Hospital Center, Columbia, MO, p. A405

ZWALLY, Paula, Director Quality Improvement Services and Compliance, Southwest Connecticut Mental Health System, Bridgeport, CT, p. A121

ZWANZIGER, Marcia, Vice President Finance, Huron Regional Medical Center, Huron, SD, p. A629

ZWEIFEL, Mary A., MS, President and Chief Executive Officer, Sheltering Arms Hospital South, Midlothian, VA, p. A746
MS, President and Chief Executive Officer, Sheltering Arms Rehabilitation Hospital, Mechanicsville, VA, p. A746

ZWENG, Thomas, Executive Vice President and Chief Medical Officer, Novant Health Brunswick Medical Center, Bolivia, NC, p. A505
Executive Vice President and Chief Medical Officer, Novant Health Charlotte Orthopaedic Hospital, Charlotte, NC, p. A507
Executive Vice President and Chief Medical Officer, Novant Health Forsyth Medical Center, Winston, NC, p. A520
Executive Vice President and Chief Medical Officer, Novant Health Huntersville Medical Center, Huntersville, NC, p. A512
Executive Vice President and Chief Medical Officer, Novant Health Matthews Medical Center, Matthews, NC, p. A514
Executive Vice President and Chief Medical Officer, Novant Health Medical Park Hospital, Winston, NC, p. A520
Executive Vice President and Chief Medical Officer, Novant Health Presbyterian Medical Center, Charlotte, NC, p. A507
Executive Vice President and Chief Medical Officer, Novant Health Rowan Medical Center, Salisbury, NC, p. A518
Executive Vice President and Chief Medical Officer, Novant Health Thomasville Medical Center, Thomasville, NC, p. A519

ZWICKER, Mike, Chief Executive Officer, St. Aloisius Medical Center, Harvey, ND, p. A524

ZWIEFEL, Laura, Chief Executive Officer, Hancock County Health System, Britt, IA, p. A244

ZWIEG, Faye, R.N., Vice President and Chief Nursing Officer, Aurora St. Luke's Medical Center, Milwaukee, WI, p. A790

ZWINGER, Glenn, Manager Information Systems Services, Veterans Affairs Puget Sound Health Care System, Seattle, WA, p. A764

ZYCH, Anita, Director of Nursing, Arrowhead Behavioral Health Hospital, Maumee, OH, p. A544

ZYLA, Jeffrey, Chief Financial Officer, Abrazo Scottsdale Campus, Phoenix, AZ, p. A35

# AHA Membership Categories

*The American Hospital Association is primarily an organization of hospitals and related institutions. Its object, according to its bylaws, is "to promote high–quality health care and health services for all the people through leadership in the development of public policy, leadership in the representation and advocacy of hospital and health care organization interests, and leadership in the provision of services to assist hospitals and health care organizations in meeting the health care needs of their communities."*

## Institutional Members

**Hospitals or health services organizations or systems which provide a continuum of integrated, community health resources and which include at least one licensed hospital that is owned, leased, managed or religiously sponsored**

Institutional members include hospitals, health care systems, integrated delivery systems, and physician hospital organizations (PHOs) and health maintenance organizations (HMOs) wholly or partially owned by or owning a member hospital or system. An Institutional member hospital, health care system or integrated delivery system may, at its discretion and upon approval of a membership application by the Association chief executive officer, extend membership to the health care provider organizations, other than a hospital that it owns, leases, or fully controls.

### Freestanding Health Care Provider Organizations

These are health provider organizations, other than registered hospitals, that provide patient care services, including, but not limited to, ambulatory, preventive, rehabilitative, specialty, post–acute and continuing care, as well as physician groups, health insurance services, and staff and group model health maintenance organizations without a hospital component. Freestanding Health Care Provider Organizations members are not owned or controlled by an Institutional member hospital, health care system or integrated delivery system member. They may, however, be part of an organization eligible for, but not holding, Institutional membership.

### Other Organizations

This category includes organizations interested in the objectives of the American Hospital Association, but not eligible for Institutional or Freestanding Health Care Provider Organization Membership. Organizations eligible for Other membership shall include, but not be limited to, associations, societies, foundations, corporations, educational and academic institutions, companies, government agencies, international health providers, and organizations having an interest in and a desire to support the objectives of the Association.

### Provisional Members

Hospitals that are in the planning or construction stage and that, on completion, will be eligible for institutional membership. Provisional membership may also be granted to applicant institutions that cannot, at present, meet the requirements of Institutional or Freestanding Health Care Provider Organization membership.

### Government Institution Group Members

Groups of government hospitals operated by the same unit of government may obtain institutional membership under a group plan. Membership dues are based on a special schedule set forth in the bylaws of the AHA.

## Other Institutional Members

### Hospitals

*U.S. hospitals and hospitals in areas associated with the U.S. that are Institutional members of the American Hospital Association are included in the list of hospitals in section A. Canadian Institutional members of the American Hospital Association are listed below.*

### Canada

**ALBERTA**

Lamont: LAMONT HEALTH CARE CENTRE, P O Bag 10, Zip T0B 2R0; tel. 780/895–2211; Harold James, Executive Director

**MANITOBA**

Winnipeg: RIVERVIEW HEALTH CENTRE, 1 Morley Avenue East, Zip R3L 2P4; tel. 204/452–3411; Norman R. Kasian, President and Chief Executive Officer

**ONTARIO**

**Renfrew:** RENFREW VICTORIA HOSPITAL, 499 Raglan Street North, Zip K7V 1P6, tel. 613/432–4851; Randy V. Penney, President and Chief Executive Officer

**Thornhill:** SHOULDICE HOSPITAL, 7750 Bayview Avenue, Zip L3T 4A3; tel. 905/889–1125; John Hughes, Chief Administrative Officer

# Associated University Programs in Health Administration

## IOWA

**Iowa City:** DEPARTMENT OF HEALTH MANAGEMENT AND POLICY, UNIVERSITY OF IOWA, 105 River Street, N232A CPHB, Zip 52246; tel. 319/384–3830; Keith Mueller, Professor and Head

## MARYLAND

**Bethesda:** NAVY MEDICINE PROFESSIONAL DEVELOPMENT CENTER, Naval Medicine, Education and Training Command, 8901 Wisconsin Avenue, Building 1, Zip 20889-5611; tel. 301/295–1251; Commander DuWayne Griepentrog, Director Administration

## MISSOURI

**Columbia:** UNIVERSITY OF MISSOURI, HEALTH MANAGEMENT AND INFORMATICS, CE707 Clinical Support and Education Building, DC 00600, One Hospital Drive, Zip 65212; tel. 573/882–6179; Eduardo Simoes; Chair

## TEXAS

**San Antonio:** ARMY-BAYLOR UNIVERSITY PROGRAM IN HEALTH CARE ADMINISTRATION, 3151 Scott Road, Bldg 2841, Zip 78234–6135; tel. 210/221–6443; Lieutenant Colonel M Nicholas Coppola, Program Director

**Sheppard AFB:** U.S. AIR FORCE SCHOOL OF HEALTH CARE SCIENCES, Building 1900, MST/114, Academic Library, Zip 76311; tel. 817/851–2511

## PUERTO RICO

**San Juan:** SCHOOL OF PUBLIC HEALTH, P O Box 5067, Zip 00936; tel. 809/767–9626; Orlando Nieves, Dean

# Hospital Schools of Nursing

## PENNSYLVANIA

**New Castle:** JAMESON HOSPITAL School of Nursing

# Nonhospital Preacute and Postacute Care Facilities

### CALIFORNIA

**Winterhaven:** U. S. PUBLIC HEALTH SERVICE INDIAN HOSPITAL, P O Box 1368, Zip 85366–1368; tel. 760/572–0217; Geniel Harrison, Clinic Director

### DELAWARE

**Newark:** HEALTH CARE CENTER AT CHRISTIANA, 200 Hygeia Drive, Zip 19714; tel. 302/623–0100; Douglas P. Azar, Senior Vice President, Medical Group

### FLORIDA

**Jacksonville:** NEMOURS CHILDREN'S CLINIC, 807 Children's Way, Zip 32207; tel. 904/390–3600; William A. Cover, Administrator

### GEORGIA

**Calhoun:** ALLIANT HEALTH PLANS, INC., 401 South Wall Street, Ste 201, Zip 30701; tel. 706/629–8848; Judy Pair, Chief Executive Officer

GEORGIA HEALTH PLUS, 401 South Wall Street, Ste 201, Zip 30701; tel. 706/629–1833;

**Rome:** CENTREX, 420 East Second Avenue, Zip 30161; tel. 706/235–1006; Dee B. Russell, Chief Executive Officer

COMMUNITY HOSPICECARE, P O Box 233, Zip 30162–0233; tel. 706/232–0807; Kurt Stuenkel, President and Chief Executive Officer

FLOYD HOME HEALTH AGENCY, P O Box 6248, Zip 30162–6248; tel. 706/802–4600; Kurt Stuenkel, President and Chief Executive Officer

FLOYD MEDICAL OUTPATIENT SURGERY, P O Box 233, Zip 30162–0233; tel. 706/802–2070; Kurt Stuenkel, President and Chief Executive Officer

FLOYD REHABILITATION CENTER, P O Box 233, Zip 30162–0233; tel. 706/802–2091; Kurt Stuenkel, President and Chief Executive Officer

### HAWAII

**Honolulu:** MALUHIA HOSPITAL, 1027 Hala Drive, Zip 96817; tel. 808/832–5874; Derek Akiyoshi, Chief Executive Officer

### ILLINOIS

**Oak Forest:** OAK FOREST HEALTH CENTER OF COOK COUNTY, 15900 South Cicero Avenue, Zip 60452–4006; tel. 708/687–7200;

### MAINE

**Damariscotta:** COVE'S EDGE, 26 Schooner Street, Zip 4543; tel. 207/563–4645; Judy McGuire, Administrator

MILES MEDICAL GROUP, INC., 35 Miles Street, Zip 4543; tel. 207/563–1234; Stacey Miller-Friant, Vice President, Physician Services

**Kennebunk:** SOUTHERN MAINE HEALTH AND HOME SERVICES, P O Box 739, Zip 4043; tel. 207/985–4767; Elaine Brady, Executive Director

### MARYLAND

**Baltimore:** ST. AGNES HEALTH SERVICES, 900 Caton Avenue, Zip 21229; tel. 410/368–2945; Peter Clay, Senior Vice President Managed Care

ST. AGNES HOME CARE AND HOSPICE, 3421 Benson Avenue, Suite G100, Zip 21227; tel. 410/368–2825; Robin Dowell, Director

**Ellicott City:** ST. AGNES NURSING AND REHABILITATION CENTER, 3000 North Ridge Road, Zip 21043; tel. 410/461–7577; Barbara A. Gustke, Administrator Extended Care Facility

### MASSACHUSETTS

**Boston:** JOSLIN DIABETES CENTER, One Joslin Place, Zip 2215; tel. 617/732–2400; John L. Brooks, President and Chief Executive Officer

**Springfield:** BAY STATE VISITING NURSE ASSOCIATION AND HOSPICE, 50 Maple Street, Zip 1105; tel. 413/781–5070; Ruth Odgren, President

### MICHIGAN

**Big Rapids:** MECOSTA HEALTH SERVICES, 650 Linden Street, Zip 49307; tel. 231/796–3200; Gail Bullard, Director

**Sault Sainte Marie:** SAULT SAINTE MARIE TRIBAL HEALTH AND HUMAN SERVICES CENTER, 2864 Ashmun Street, Zip 49783; tel. 906/495–5651; Russell Vizina, Division Director Health

### MISSOURI

**Independence:** SURGI-CARE CENTER OF INDEPENDENCE, 2311 Redwood Avenue, Zip 64057; tel. 816/373–7995;

### NEBRASKA

**North Platte:** GREAT PLAINS PHO, INC., P O Box 1167, Zip 69103; tel. 308/535–7496; Todd Hlavaty, Chairman

### NEW JERSEY

**Jersey City:** ST. FRANCIS HOSPITAL, 25 McWilliams Place, Zip 07302–1698; tel. 201/418–1000;

**Millburn:** ATLANTIC HOME CARE AND HOSPICE, 33 Bleeker Street, Zip 7041; tel. 973/379–8400; Susan Quinn, Administrator

**Morristown:** ALLIANCE IMAGING CENTER, 65 Maple Street, Zip 7960; tel. 973/267–5700; Barbara Picorale, Administrator

**Succasunna:** DIALYSIS CENTER OF NORTHWEST NEW JERSEY, 170 Righter Road, Zip 7876; tel. 973/584–1117; Carol Cahill, Administrator

### NEW MEXICO

**Albuquerque:** ALBUQUERQUE IHS HEALTH CENTER, 801 Vassar Drive NE, Zip 87106–2799; tel. 505/248–4000; Maria Rickert, Chief Executive Officer

### NEW YORK

**Tuckahoe:** HOME NURSING ASSOCIATION OF WESTCHESTER, 69 Main Street, Zip 10707; tel. 919/961–2818; Mary Wehrberger, Director

### NORTH CAROLINA

**Jefferson:** AMH SEGRAVES CARE CENTER, 200 Hospital Avenue, Zip 28640; tel. 336/246–7101;

**Wilson:** WILMED NURSING CARE CENTER, 1705 Tarboro Street SW, Zip 27893–3428; tel. 252/399–8998; Randy Smithey, Administrator

### OHIO

**Cleveland:** METROHEALTH CENTER FOR SKILLED NURSING CARE, 4229 Pearl Road, Zip 44109; tel. 216/957–3675; Yvette Bozman, Administrator

### OKLAHOMA

**Clinton:** U. S. PUBLIC HEALTH SERVICE INDIAN HOS-PITAL, Route 1, Box 3060, Zip 73601–9303; tel. 580/323–2884;

**Eufaula:** EUFALA INDIAN HEALTH CENTER, 800 Forest Avenue, Zip 74432; tel. 918/689–2547; Shelly Crow, Health System Administrator

**Okmulgee:** OKMULGEE INDIAN HEALTH SYSTEM, 1313 East 20th, Zip 74447; tel. 918/758–1926; Kara Lee, Administrator

**Sapulpa:** SAPULPA INDIAN HEALTH CENTER, 1125 East Clevelend, Zip 74066; tel. 918/224–9310; Sid Daniels, Acting Administrator

### PENNSYLVANIA

**Warminster:** ABINGTON MEMORIAL HEALTH CENTER - WARMINSTER CAMPUS, 225 Newtown Road, Zip 18974–5221; tel. 215/441–6600; Kathleen Farrell, Executive Director

### TEXAS

**Dallas:** SURGICARE OF TRAVIS CENTER, INC., 13355 Noel Road, Suite 650, Zip 75240–6694; tel. 713/520–1782;

**Houston:** GRAMERCY OUTPATIENT SURGERY CENTER. LTD., 2727 Gramercy, Zip 77025; tel. 713/660–6900; Hamel Patel, Administrator

**Houston:** WEST HOUSTON SURGICARE, 970 Campbell Road, Zip 77024; tel. 713/461–3547;

**Webster:** BAY AREA SURGICARE CENTER, 502 Medical Center Boulevard, Zip 77598; tel. 281/332–2433; Carol Simons, Administrator

### WISCONSIN

**Green Bay:** UNITY HOSPICE, P O Box 28345, Zip 54324–8345; tel. 920/494–0225; Donald Seibel, Executive Director

# Provisional Hospitals

*This listing includes organizations that, as of September 16, 2015, were in the planning or construction stage and that, on completion, will be eligible for Institutional membership. Some hospitals are granted provisional membership for reasons related to other Association requirements. Hospitals classified as provisional members for reasons other than being under construction are indicated by a bullet (●).*

## TEXAS

Houston: BAYLOR ST. LUKE'S MEDICAL CENTER MCNAIR CAMPUS, One Baylor Plaza, BCM 100, Zip 77030–3411; tel. 713/798–4951; Paul Klotman, M.D., President

Marble Falls: WAYNE & EILEEN HURD REGIONAL MEDICAL CENTER – SCOTT & WHITE, 800 West Highway 71, Zip 78654; tel. 830/598–1204; Eric N. Looper, Chief Executive Officer

## GUAM

Dededo: GUAM REGIONAL MEDICAL CITY, P.O. Box 3830, Zip 96932; tel. 671/649–4764; Gloria Long, Chief Operating Officer

# Associate Members

## Ambulatory Centers and Home Care Agencies

### UNITED STATES

#### NEW YORK

MIDTOWN SURGERY CENTER, 305 East 47th Street, Zip 10017–2303; tel. 212/751–2100; Julia Ferguson, Director, Operations

#### PENNSYLVANIA

WILLS EYE HOSPITAL, 840 Walnut Street, Philadelphia, Zip 19107–5109; tel. 215/928–3000; Joseph P. Bilson, Executive Director

## Blue Cross Plans

### UNITED STATES

#### ARIZONA

BLUE CROSS AND BLUE SHIELD OF ARIZONA, Box 13466, Phoenix, Zip 85002–3466; tel. 602/864–4541; Vishu Jhaveri; Senior Vice President and Chief Medical Officer

*The members listed in* **bold** *are Associate Advantage members*

# Other Members

## UNITED STATES

### Architecture

DEVENNEY GROUP ARCHITECTS, 201 West Indian School Road, Phoenix, Arizona Zip 85013–3203; tel: 602/943–8950, Julie Barkenbush, Chief Executive Officer; devenneygroup.com

MATTHEI AND COLIN ASSOCIATES, 332 South Michigan Avenue, Suite 614, Chicago, Illinois Zip 60604; tel: 312/939–4002, Randall Bacidore, Principal; mca-architecture.com/

MESSER CONSTRUCTION COMPANY, 643 West Court Street, Cincinnati, Ohio Zip 45203–1511; tel: 513/242–1541, Peter Bergman, Vice President; messer.com

### Bank

HEALTHCARE ASSOCIATES CREDIT UNION, 1151 East Warrenville Road, Naperville, Illinois Zip 60563; tel: 630/276–5771, Jennifer Kleinhenz, Senior Vice President Strategic Initiatives; hacu.org

TD BANK, 2130 Centre Park West Drive, 2nd Floor, West Palm Beach, Florida Zip 33409–6411; tel: 561/352–2086, Colleen Mullaney, Senior Vice President; tdbank.com

### Communication Systems Org

AVAILITY, LLC, 750 Old Hickory Boulevard, Building 2 Suite 270, Brentwood, Tennessee Zip 37027–4528; tel: 615/760–3361, Ashleigh Eisinger, Events and Social Media Specialist; availity.com

### Construction Firm

POETTKER CONSTRUCTION COMPANY, 308 South Germantown Road, Breese, Illinois Zip 62230; tel: 618/526–7213, Curtis C. Rommerskirchen, Brand Ambassador for Healthcare Facility Services; poettkerconstruction.com

### Consulting Firm

AON RISK SOLUTIONS, 5600 West 83rd Street, 8200 Tower, Minneapolis, Minnesota Zip 55402–3721; tel: 952/807–0768, James Craig Nelson, Senior Vice President; stratford360.com

ARAMARK, 10510 Twin Lakes Boulevard, Charlotte, North Carolina Zip 28269–7658; tel: 704/948–4774, Tom Elmore, Director, Industry Relations; aramark.com

AVIVA HEALTHCARE SOLUTIONS, 98 Golden Eye Lane, Port Monmouth, New Jersey Zip 07758–1647; tel: 800/530–5728, Thomas Bojko, President and Managing Partner; avivahealthsolutions.com

CARE TECH SOLUTIONS, 901 Wilshire Drive, Suite 100, Troy, Michigan Zip 48084; tel: 248/823–0950, Jody Meehan, Vice President, Marketing, Communications, and Government Affairs; caretech.com/

CARERISE|CARERISE INDEX, PO Box 880, Mandeville, Louisiana Zip 70470–0880; tel: 985/727–4740, Tim G Goux, Founder; carerise.com

CLEARWATER COMPLIANCE LLC, 106 Windward Point, Hendersonville, Tennessee Zip 37075–5108; tel: 615/800–7988, Kathy S. Ebbert, Chief Operating Officer; clearwatercompliance.com

CREATE PPO, 317 6th Avenue, Suite 1440, Des Moines, Iowa Zip 50309–4131; tel: 515/657–4888, Clayton R. Copple, President and Chief Executive Officer; createppo.com

DRAFFIN TUCKER, 5 Concourse Parkway, Suite 1250, Atlanta, Georgia Zip 30328–5350; tel: 404/220–8484, Sarah Dekutowski, Partner; https://draffin-tucker.com/

EASTER HEALTHCARE CONSULTING, 518 Neilwood Drive, Nashville, Tennessee Zip 37205–3026; tel: 615/424–3642, James G Easter (Jim), Principal and Chief Executive Officer; easterhealthcare.com

ERNST & YOUNG, 150 Fourth Avenue North, Suite 1400, Nashville, Tennessee Zip 37219–2409; tel: 615/252–8254, Chris Barber, US Health Brand, Marketing and Communications Leader; ey.com

GOLDMAN, SACHS AND COMPANY, 200 West Street, New York, New York Zip 10282–2198; tel: 212/902–1000, Cynthia Rivera, Public Sector and Infrastructure Banking

HEALTHCARE CHAPLAINCY NETWORK, INC., 65 Broadway, 12th Floor, New York, New York Zip 10010; tel: 212/644–1111, Eric J. Hall, President and Chief Executive Officer; healthcarechaplaincy.org

HEALTHCARESOURCE, 100 Sylvan Road, Suite 100, Woburn, Massachusetts Zip 01801–1851; tel: 800/691–3737, Sean Parlin, Strategic Alliances Manager; healthcaresource.com

HEALTHEQUITY, INC., 15 West Scenic Pointe Drive, Suite 100, Draper, Utah Zip 84020–6120; tel: 801/727–1000, Stephen Neeleman, Founder and Vice Chairman; healthequity.com

INTERNATIONAL CITIES MANAGEMENT ASSOCIATION-RETIREMENT CORPORATION, 777 North Capitol Street NE, Washington, District of Columbia Zip 20002–4239; tel: 866/265–5126, Kevin F. Orr, Senior Director; icmarc.org

KAUFMAN HALL, 5202 Old Orchard Road, Suite N700, Skokie, Illinois Zip 60077; tel: 847/441–8780, Jason H Sussman, Partner; kaufmanhall.com

LATHAM AND WATKINS, LLP, 633 West 5th Street, Ste 4000, Los Angeles, California Zip 90071; tel: 213/485–1234, Daniel K Settelmayer, Partner; lw.com

MCDONALD HOPKINS, LLC, 600 Superior Avenue East, Suite 2100, Cleveland, Ohio Zip 44114–2690; tel: 216/348–5400, Richard S Cooper, Member; mcdonaldhopkins.com

MCKESSON CORPORATION, 1 Post Street, 33rd Floor, San Francisco, California Zip 94104–5203; tel: 404/338–2985, Anastasia Agapoff, Assistant Manager, Library Operations; mckesson.com/

MILESTONE HEALTHCARE, LLC, 275 West Campbell Road, Suite 300, Richardson, Texas Zip 75080–3560; tel: 800/926–2388, George Thompson, General Manager; milestonehealth.com

NATIONAL CENTER FOR HEALTH STATISTICS, 3311 Toledo Road, Hyattsville, Maryland Zip 20782–2064; tel: 800/232–4636, Monica Deckers, Lead Admin Officer; cdc.gov

NATIONAL MEDICAL FUNDING SERVICES, INC., 1101 Wootton Parkway, 10th Floor, Rockville, Maryland Zip 20852–1059; tel: 301/433–7515, Sandy Waterman, Chief Executive Officer; medx.health

NAVEX GLOBAL, 6000 Meadows Road, Suite 200, Lake Oswego, Oregon Zip 97035–3172; tel: 503/924–1640, Stephen J. Molen, Vice President Strategic Solutions; navexglobal.com

NEWRISTICS, 8777 East Via de Ventura #188, Scottsdale, Arizona Zip 85258; tel: 480/947–8078, Cheryl Palay, Senior Vice President; hsmgroup.com

PROTIVITI, INC., 13727 Noel Road, Suite 800, Dallas, Texas Zip 75240–1336; tel: 214/395–1662, Richard Williams, Managing Director and Global Healthcare Industry Practice; protiviti.com

RYCAN, P O Box 306, Marshall, Minnesota Zip 56258–0306; tel: 800/201–3324, Marg Louwagie, Administrative Assistant; rycan.com

STRATA DECISION TECHNOLOGY; tel: 312/726–1227, Dan Michelson, Chief Executive Officer; stratadecision.com

STROUDWATER ASSOCIATES, 50 Sewall Street, Suite 102, Portland, Maine Zip 04102–2646; tel: 207/221–8255, Marc Voyvodich, Chief Executive Officer; stroudwater.com/

SULLIVAN COTTER & ASSOCIATES, INC, 7733 Forsyth Boulevard, Suite 1100, Clayton, Missouri Zip 63105; tel: 312/564–5883, Sean C. Butler, Director of Client Experience; sullivancotter.com

SYMPLR, 315 Capitol Street, Suite 100, Houston, Texas Zip 77002–2826; tel: 281/863–9500, Rick Pleczko, Chief Executive Officer; vcsdatabase.com

TEAMHEALTH, 265 Brookview Centre Way, Suite 400, Knoxville, Tennessee Zip 37919; tel: 865/293–5486, Leif Murphy, Chief Executive Officer; teamhealth.com

THE CHARTIS GROUP, 220 West Kinzie Street, 5th Floor, Chicago, Illinois Zip 60654–4912; tel: 312/932–3068, Celine White, Manager of Financial Operations; chartis.com

THE QUAMMEN GROUP, INC., 151 Southhall Lane, Suite 168, Maitland, Florida Zip 32751–7486; tel: 407/539–2015, Alexandra Robertson, Director of Marketing; quammengroup.com

VERRAS HEALTHCARE INTERNATIONAL; tel: 888/791–5556, Robert T. Langston, Partner; verras.com/

VIIAD SYSTEMS LLC, 1170 Wheeler Way, Suite 200, Langhorne, Pennsylvania Zip 19047–3243; tel: 866/498–4423, Tricia Bradley, Director, Sales and Marketing Support; viiad.com

WESTERN HEALTHCARE ALLIANCE, 715 Horizon Drive, Suite 401, Grand Junction, Colorado Zip 81506–8731; tel: 970/683–5223, Carolyn Bruce, Chief Executive Officer; wha1.org

XANITOS, INC., 3809 West Chester Pike, Suite 210, Newtown Square, Pennsylvania Zip 19073–2304; tel: 484/654–2300, Graeme A Crothall, Chairman and Chief Executive Officer; xanitos.com

### Educational Services

NATIONAL RURAL HEALTH RESOURCE CENTER, 525 South Lake Avenue, Suite 320, Duluth, Minnesota Zip 55802; tel: 218/727–9390, Sally Buck, Chief Executive Officer; ruralcenter.org

PUBLISHING CONCEPTS INC.; tel: 800/561–4686, Gregg Jones, Education and Careers Director; pcipublishing.com

### Hospice

HOSPICE OF THE VALLEY, 1510 East Flower Street, Phoenix, Arizona Zip 85014–5698; tel: 602/530–6900, Rachel Behrendt, Senior Vice President, Operations; hov.org

### Information Systems

CERNER CORPORATION, 2800 Rockcreek Parkway, Kansas City, Missouri Zip 64117; tel: 816/221–1024, Laurel Vine, Program Manager, Industry Events; cerner.com

EVOLENT, 540 West Madison Street, Suite 1500, Chicago, Illinois Zip 60661; tel: 312/273–6623, Kevin Weinstein, Chief Marketing Officer; valencehealth.com

FLEMING AOD, Inc., 816 Thayer Avenue, Floor 3rd, Silver Spring, Maryland Zip 20910–4508; tel: 202/872–1033, Mary Dalrymple, Managing Director; aod.cx

IMPRIVATA, INC., 10 Maguire Road Building 4, Lexington, Massachusetts Zip 02421–3110; tel: 781/674–2700, Ed Gaudel, Chief Marketing Officer; imprivata.com

KPMG LLP, 200 East Randolph Street, Suite 5500, Chicago, Illinois Zip 60601–6607; tel: 312/665–2073, Edward J Giniat, National Line of Business Leader, Healthcare and Pharmaceuticals Practice; https://home.kpmg.com/us/en/home.html?cid=M–00002211&gclid=CKfszoeUrtACFZSFaQod82wE4g

MEDHOST, 6100 West Plano Parkway, Suite 3100, Plano, Texas Zip 75093–8342; tel: 888/218–4678, Leslie LaFon, Departmental Segment Manager; medhost.com

# Associate Members / Other

REAL TIME MEDICAL SYSTEMS, LLC, 901 Elkridge Landing Road, Linthicum Heights, Maryland Zip 21090–2920; tel: 203/249–0404, Joan Neuscheler, Chief Executive Officer; realtimemed.com

## Insurance Broker

BOSTON MUTUAL LIFE INSURANCE COMPANY, 120 Royall Street, Canton, Massachusetts Zip 2021; tel: 781/828–7000, Peter Tillson, Vice President; bostonmutual.com

CONSTELLATION, 7701 France Avenue South, Suite 500, Minneapolis, Minnesota Zip 55435–3201; tel: 952/838–6700, Holly Freeman, Manager; mmicgroup.com

Ironshore, 300 South Wacker Drive, Chicago, Illinois Zip 60606–6680; tel: 312/496–7535, Daniel R Nash, Senior Vice President Field Operations and Business Development; ironshore.com

LTC SOLUTIONS, 14715 North East 95th Street, Suite 200, Redmond, Washington Zip 98052; tel: 877/286–2852, Christine McCullugh, President; ltc-solutions.com

THE ALLEN J. FLOOD COMPANIES, INC., 2 Madison Avenue, Larchmont, New York Zip 10538; tel: 914/834–9326, Allen J Flood, President; ajfusa.com

## Managed Care/Utilization

CENTENE CORPORATION, 111 East Capitol Street, Suite 500, Jackson, Mississippi Zip 39201; tel: 601/519–6119, K. Michael Bailey, Corporate Vice President; centene.com

## Manufacturer/Supplier

3M, 3M CENTER, Building 275–4E–01, Saint Paul, Minnesota Zip 55144–1000; tel: 612/733–8183, Donald R Brewer, Director Medical–Surgical Markets; 3m.com

GE HEALTHCARE, 9900 West Innovation Drive, RP–2177, Wauwatosa, Wisconsin Zip 53226–4856; tel: 262/290–8769, Kimberly Rutherford, Business Partner and Director, Advertising & Promotion US–Canada Region; www3.gehealthcare.com

HILL–ROM, 1069 State Route 46 East, Batesville, Indiana Zip 47006–9167; tel: 812/934–7958, Thomas J Jeffers, Director Government Relations; hill–rom.com

## Metro Hospital Assn

HOSPITAL ASSOCIATION OF SOUTHERN CALIFORNIA, 515 South Figueroa Street, Suite 1300, Los Angeles, California Zip 90071–3300; tel: 213/538–0700, George W Greene, President and Chief Executive Officer; hasc.org

## Other Health Related

CENTER FOR MEDICAL INTEROPERABILITY, 618 Church Street Suite 220, Nashville, Tennessee Zip 37219–2453; tel: 202/617–6009, Kerry McDermott, Vice President for Public Policy and Communications; medicalinteroperability.org

## Other

A3–ASHLEY ADVERTISING AGENCY, 2825 Soni Drive, Trooper, Pennsylvania Zip 19403–1275; tel: 610/631–5500, Frank Gussoni, President; ashleyadvertising.com

ACADEMIC PARTNERSHIP LLC, 600 North Pearl Street, Suite 900, Dallas, Texas Zip 75201; tel: 682/305–3063, Nimisha Savani, Vertical Chief Healthcare; aphealthcareedge.com

AMC HEALTH, INC., 39 Broadway, Suite 540, New York, New York Zip 10006; tel: 877/776–1746, Joanna Haskin, Vice President Partner Development; amchealth.com

AMERICAN ASSOCIATION FOR WOUND CARE MANAGEMENT, 4109 Glenrose Street, Kensington, Maryland Zip 20895–3718; tel: 301/933–2200, Jule Crider, Executive Director; aawcm.org

AMERICAN ASSOCIATION OF NURSE ANESTHETISTS, 222 South Prospect Avenue, Park Ridge, Illinois Zip 60068–4001; tel: 847/655–1100, Randall Moore, Chief Executive Officer; aana.com

AMERICAN BOARD OF MEDICAL SPECIALTIES, 353 North Clark Street, Suite 1400, Chicago, Illinois Zip 60654–3454; tel: 312/436–2626, Richard D Hawkins, President and Chief Executive Officer; abms.org

AMERICAN COLLEGE OF HEALTHCARE EXECUTIVES, 300 South Riverside Plaza, Suite 1900, Chicago, Illinois Zip 60606–6613; tel: 312/424–2800, Deborah Bowen, President and Chief Executive Officer; ache.org

AMERICAN HEALTH INFORMATION MANAGEMENT ASSOCIATION, 233 North Michigan Avenue, Suite 2150, Chicago, Illinois Zip 60601–5806; tel: 312/233–1100, David A Sweet, Director Library Services; ahima.org

AMERICAN SOCIETY OF ANESTHESIOLOGISTS, 1061 American Lane, Schaumburg, Illinois Zip 60173; tel: 847/268–9160, Paul Pomerantz, Chief Executive Officer; asahq.org

AMN HEALTHCARE, INC., 12400 High Bluff Drive, Suite 100, San Diego, California Zip 92130–3581; tel: 866/871–8519, Steve Wehn, Senior Vice President of Corporate Development; amnhealthcare.com

APOGEE PHYSICIANS, 15059 North Scottsdale Road, Suite 600, Scottsdale, Arizona Zip 85254–2685; tel: 602/778–3600, Michael Gregory, Chairman; apogeephysicians.com

ARENA, 502 South Sharp Street, Suite 2300, Baltimore, Maryland Zip 21201–2445; tel: 888/444–0693, Michael Finn, Vice President, Marketing; arena.io

ARIS RADIOLOGY, 5655 Hudson Drive, Suite 210, Hudson, Ohio Zip 44236; tel: 330/655–3800, Stacey Christofferson, Sales and Marketing; arisradiology.com

ASSOCIATION OF PERIOPERATIVE REGISTERED NURSES, 2170 South Parker Road, Suite 400, Denver, Colorado Zip 80231; tel: 303/755–6304, Linda Kay Groah, Executive Director and Chief Executive Officer; aorn.org

AVATAR SOLUTIONS, 25 East Washington Street, Suite 600, Chicago, Illinois Zip 60602; tel: 312/236–7170, Jeffrey Brady, Chief Executive Officer; hrsolutionsinc.com

BACTES, 8344 Clairemont Mesa Boulevard, Suite 201, San Diego, California Zip 92111–1327; tel: 858/244–1811, Rae Danell, Marketing Coordinator; bactes.com

BLUE CROSS AND BLUE SHIELD ASSOCIATION, 225 North Michigan Avenue, Chicago, Illinois Zip 60601–7680; tel: 312/297–6000, Scott P Serota, President and Chief Executive Officer; bcbs.com

BOARDVANTAGE, 4300 Bohannon Drive, Suite 110, Menlo Park, California Zip 94025; tel: 650/330–2444, Virginia Portillo, Conference and Events Coordinator; boardvantage.com

CANON SOLUTIONS AMERICA, INC., 300 Commerce Square Boulevard, Burlington, New Jersey Zip 08016–1270; tel: 847/706–3411, Paul T Murphy, Director Strategic Contract Support; solutions.canon.com

CAPROCK EMERGENCY HOSPITAL, 1630 Briarcrest Drive, Suite 100, Bryan, Texas Zip 77802–2709; tel: 979/314–2323, Lon Young, Chief Medical Officer; caprocker.com

CARECENTRIX, 20 Church Street, Floor 12th, Hartford, Connecticut Zip 06103–1246; tel: 800/808–1902, Sherl Brand, Senior Vice President Strategic Solutions; carecentrix.com

CERTIPHI SCREENING, INC., 1105 Industrial Highway, Southampton, Pennsylvania Zip 18966; tel: 888/260–1370, Tony D'Orazio, CEO; certiphi.com

CHANGE HEALTHCARE, 3535 Piedmont Road, Suite 800, Atlanta, Georgia Zip 30305–1543; tel: 404/279–5029, Kim R. Williams, Chief Financial Officer; changehealthcare.com

CISCO SYSTEMS, 165 Needletree Lane, Glastonbury, Connecticut Zip 6033; tel: 860/657–8127, Michael Haymaker, Director Healthcare Industry Marketing; cisco.com

COMPREHENSIVE PHARMACY SERVICES, 6409 North Quail Hollow Road, Memphis, Tennessee Zip 38120–1414; tel: 901/748–0470, Walker Upshaw, Chief Development Officer; cpspharm.com

CROSS COUNTRY HEALTHCARE, 5201 Congress Avenue, Boca Raton, Florida Zip 33487–3629; tel: 800/347–2264, Robert Murphy, President Workforce Solutions; crosscountryhealthcare.com

CYRACOM, 5780 North Swan Road, Tucson, Arizona Zip 85718–4527; tel: 800/713–4950, Jeremy Woan, President and Chief Executive Officer; cyracom.com

DISH, PO Box 5096524, Englewood, Colorado Zip 80112–5905; tel: 720/514–6019, Steven Wilson, Manager; dish.com

FIRST AMERICAN EQUIPMENT FINANCE, 255 Woodcliff Drive, Fairport, New York Zip 14450–4219; tel: 585/643–3266, Lori Dennis, Senior Vice President; faef.com

GALLAGHER BENEFIT SERVICES, 6525 Morrison Boulevard, Suite 200, Charlotte, North Carolina Zip 28211–3532; tel: 877/332–2265, James Craig Nelson, Senior Vice President; bfbgallagher.com

GOZIO HEALTH, 75 5th Street NW, Suite 2220, Atlanta, Georgia Zip 30308–1019; tel: 772/444–6946, Barbara Kragor, Vice President Sales and Customer Experience; goziohealth.com

HEALTHCARE REVENUE SOLUTIONS, 4851 Keller Springs Road, Suite 228, Addison, Texas Zip 75001; tel: 972/546–6491, Andre Kus, Chief Executive Officer; healthcarerevenuesolutions.org

HEALTHGRID, 4203 Vineland Road, Suite K6, Orlando, Florida Zip 32811; tel: 855/624–2844, Raj Toleti, Founder and Chief Executive Officer; healthgrid.com

HEALTHWAYS, INC, 701 Cool Springs Boulevard, Franklin, Tennessee Zip 37067–2697; tel: 800/327–3822, Karen Meyer, Principal; healthways.com

HMS, 355 Quartermaster Court, Jeffersonville, Indiana Zip 47130–3670; tel: 812/704–5747, Rich Flaherty, Vice President Sales and Marketing; hms.com

HOOPER, LUNDY & BOOKMAN, INC., 1875 Century Park East, Suite 1600, Los Angeles, California Zip 90067; tel: 310/551–8111, Lloyd Bookman, Partner; health–law.com

HOSPITALRECRUITING.COM, 899 South College Mall Road, Suite 395, Bloomington, Indiana Zip 47401–6301; tel: 800/244–7236, Michael Jones, Managing Partner; hospitalrecruiting.com

HYLAND SOFTWARE, INC., 28500 Clemens Road, Westlake, Ohio Zip 44145; tel: 440/788–5814, Michael Kortan, Director Health Care Solutions; onbase.com

IMALOGIX, 1150 First Avenue, Suite 450, King Of Prussia, Pennsylvania Zip 19406–1363; tel: 855/681–9100, David Steigerwalt, Product Manager; imalogix.com

INNOVATIVE CAPITAL LLC, 1489 Baltimore Pike, Building 400, Springfield, Pennsylvania Zip 19064–3958; tel: 610/543–2490, Alan P Richman, President and Chief Executive Officer; innovativecapital.com

INTALERE; tel: 877/711–5700, Laurie McGrath, Vice President Marketing; amerinet-gpo.com

INTELLICENTRICS, INC., 1420 Lakeside Parkway, Suite 110, Flower Mound, Texas Zip 75028; tel: 972/316–6209, Nimisha Savani, Chief Marketing Officer; intellicentrics.com

INTERACTIVE HEALTH SOLUTIONS, 3800 North Wilke Road, Suite 155, Arlington Heights, Illinois Zip 60004–1278; tel: 847/754–2698, Joseph O'Brien, President; interactivesolutions.com

IP SERVICES, 2896 Crescent Avenue, Suite 201, Eugene, Oregon Zip 97408–7422; tel: 541/343–5974, Mark Allers, Vice President Business Development; ipservices.com

JEWISH GUILD HEALTHCARE, 15 West 65th Street, New York, New York Zip 10023; tel: 212/769–6200, Alan R Morse, President and Chief Executive Officer; jgb.org

LANGUAGE LINE SOLUTIONS, One Lower Ragsdale Drive, Building 2, Monterey, California Zip 93940; tel: 800/752–6096, Suzanne duMont-Perez, Government Relations and Channel Manager; languageline.com

MEDICAL INFORMATION TECHNOLOGY, INC.; tel: 781/821–3000, Lynn Robblee, Supervisor of Event Coordination and Memberships; meditech.com

MEDISOLV, INC., 10440 Little Patuxent Parkway, Suite 1000, Columbia, Maryland Zip 21044–3630; tel: 443/539–0505, Erin Heilman, Marketing Specialist; medisolv.com

MEDNAX SERVICES INC., 1301 Concord Terrace, Sunrise, Florida Zip 33323–2843; tel: 954/384–0175, Roger J Medel, President; mednax.com

MODERN HEALTHCARE, 150 North Michigan Avenue, 17th Floor, Chicago, Illinois Zip 60601–3806; tel: 312/649–5491, Fawn Lopez, Publisher; modernhealthcare.com

MUCH SHELIST, 191 North Wacker Drive, Chicago, Illinois Zip 60606–1615; tel: 312/521–2000, Ned Milenkovich, Partner; muchshelist.com

NATIONAL COUNCIL OF STATE BOARDS OF NURSING, 111 East Wacker Drive, 29th Floor, Chicago, Illinois Zip 60601–4277; tel: 312/525–3600, David Charles Benton, Chief Executive Officer; ncsbn.org

OB HOSPITALIST GROUP, tel: 800/967–2289, Guy Kohn, Director, Marketing; obhg.com

PLANON CORPORATION, 45 Braintree Hill Office Park, Suite 400, Braintree, Massachusetts Zip 02184–8730; tel: 781/356–0999, Ellen Schwier, Marketing Manager; planonsoftware.com

*The members listed in **bold** are Associate Advantage members*

PROASSURANCE, 100 Brookwood Place, Birmingham, Alabama Zip 35209–6811; tel: 205/877–4400, W Stancil Starnes, Chairman, Chief Executive Officer; proassurance.com

PROMED HEALTHCARE FINANCING, 1001 Woodward Avenue, Suite 1700, Detroit, Michigan Zip 48226–1904; tel: 631/707–4347, Dan De Chiaro, Director of Operations; promedhcf.com

QUARLES AND BRADY LLP, 300 North LaSalle Street, Suite 4000, Chicago, Illinois Zip 60654–3422; tel: 312/715–2751, Susan Stewart, Director, Client Relations; quarles.com

RRS, 416 Longshore Drive, Ann Arbor, Michigan Zip 48103; tel: 800/517–9634, Nicole Chardoul, Partner and Vice President; recycle.com

SAN–I–PAK, INC., PO Box 1183, Tracy, California Zip 95378; tel: 209/836–2310, Kristy Coleman, Project Manager; sanipak.com

SIMPLEX GRINNELL, 50 Technology Drive, Westminster, Massachusetts Zip 1441; tel: 978/731–8486, Suzanne Rahall, Marketing Manager, Healthcare Communications; simplexgrinnell.com

SUBWAY, 325 Bic Drive, Milford, Connecticut Zip 6461; tel: 800/888–4848, Joanne Kilgore, Global Account Manager; subway.com

TANDEM HOSPITAL PARTNERS, 1415 Louisiana Street, Houston, Texas Zip 77002–7360; tel: 713/999–0837, Debora Simmons, Chief Quality Officer and Chief Nursing Officer; tandemhospitalpartners.com

THE AMERICAN COLLEGE OF OBSTETRICIANS AND GYNECOLOGISTS, 409 12th Street, SW, Washington, District of Columbia Zip 20024–2188; tel: 202/638–5577, Hal Lawrence, Executive Vice President; acog.org

THE CPI GROUP, 7400 East Orchard Road, Suite 270, Englewood, Colorado Zip 80111; tel: 303/504–9999, John Van Gulik, Business Development Manager; thecpigroup.net

THE WALKER COMPANY, 31090 SW Boones Bend Road, Wilsonville, Oregon Zip 97070–6412; tel: 503/694–8539, Larry W Walker, Principal; walkercompany.com

TRACE SECURITY, 6300 Corporate Boulevard, Baton Rouge, Louisiana Zip 70809–1097; tel: 877/275–3009, Marissa Adams, Marketing Coordinator; tracesecurity.com

TRANSAMERICA RETIREMENT SOLUTIONS, 4 Manhattanville Road, Purchase, New York Zip 10577; tel: 914/697–8952, Peter Kunkel, President and Chief Executive Officer; https://www.trsretire.com

TRAPOLLO, 13900 Lincoln Park Drive, 5th Floor, Herndon, Virginia Zip 20171; tel: 866/807–5047, Lisa Majdi, Marketing Director; trapollo.com

UBS, 315 Deaderick Street, Nashville, Tennessee Zip 37238–3000; tel: 615/393–7549, Whit Mayo, Managing Director; ubs.com

UNIFORM DATA SYSTEM FOR MEDICAL REHABILITATION, 270 Northpointe Parkway, Suite 300, Amherst, New York Zip 14228; tel: 716/817–7800, Troy Hillman, Manager, Analytical Services Group; udsmr.org

USDTL, 1700 South Mount Prospect Road, Des Plaines, Illinois Zip 60018–1804; tel: 847/375–0770, Catharine Steccato, Vice President Business Development; usdtl.com

VANGUARD MODULAR BUILDING SYSTEMS, LLC, 3 Great Valley Parkway, Suite 170, Malvern, Pennsylvania Zip 19355–1417; tel: 610/240–8686, Mark Meyers, Vice President, Marketing Services; vanguardmodular.com

VERISYS CORPORATION, 1001 North Fairfax Avenue, Suite 640, Alexandria, Virginia Zip 22314–1798; tel: 703/535–1471, John Benson, Chief Operating Officer; verisys.com/

VESTAGEN TECHNICAL TEXTILES, INC., tel: 407/781–2395, Brian Crawford, Chief Business Officer; vestagen.com

VIGILANZ CORPORATION, 5775 Wayzata Boulevard, Suite 970, Minneapolis, Minnesota Zip 55416–2669; tel: 855/525–9078, David Goldsteen, Chairman and Chief Executive Officer; vigilanzcorp.com

VITAS HEALTHCARE, 201 South Biscayne Boulevard, Suite 400, Miami, Florida Zip 33131; tel: 305/374–4143, Drew Landmeier, Chief Marketing Officer; vitas.com

VIZIENT, 799 9th Street Northwest, Suite 210, Washington, District of Columbia Zip 20001–5325; tel: 202/354–2600, Shoshana Krilow, Vice President Public Policy and Government Relations; https://www.vizientinc.com/

WELLTOWER, INC., 4500 Dorr Street, Toledo, Ohio Zip 43615–4040; tel: 419/247–2800, Rachel Watson, Assistant Vice President; welltower.com

WITT/KIEFFER, 2015 Spring Rd, Ste 510, Oak Brook, Illinois Zip 60523; tel: 630/990–1370, James Gauss, Chairman of Board Services; wittkieffer.com/

YOURCARE UNIVERSE, INC, 6550 Carothers Parkway, Suite 100, Franklin, Tennessee Zip 37067; tel: 844/641–6800, Lauren Douglass, Brand Manager; yourcareuniverse.com

### Recruitment Services

DOCCAFE.COM, tel: 574/453–3131, Briana Wick, Digital Marketing Director; doccafe.com

### Regional Health Care Assn

TEXAS ORGANIZATION OF RURAL & COMMUNITY HOSPITALS, P O Box 203878, Austin, Texas Zip 78720–3878; tel: 512/873–0045, John Henderson, Chief Executive Officer; torchnet.org

# CANADA

### Provincial Hospital Assn

ONTARIO HOSPITAL ASSOCIATION, 200 Front Street West, Suite 2800, Toronto, Ontario Zip M5V 3L1; tel: 416/205–1300, Hazim Hassan, Vice President, Business Planning and Strategy; oha.com

# BAHAMAS

### Other

PRINCESS MARGARET HOSPITAL, P O Box N–8200, Nassau, tel: 242/322–2861, Mary Elizabeth Lightbourne–Walker, Hospital Administrator; phabahamas.org

# BAHRAIN

### Other

INTERNATIONAL HOSPITAL OF BAHRAIN, P O Box 1084, Manama, tel: 11/759–8222, F. S. Zeerah, President; ihb.net/

# BRAZIL

### Other

HOSPITAL SAMARITANO, RUA CONSELHEIRO BROTERO, 1486, Sao Paulo, Zip 01232–010; tel: 551/821–5300, Luiz Alberto Oliveira De Luca, Corporate Superintendent; samaritano.com.br

# COLOMBIA

### Other

ASOCIACION COLOMBIANA DE HOSPITALES Y CLINICAS, Carrera 4, No 73–15, Bogota, Juan Carlos Giraldo Valencia, Director General; achc.org.co

# DOMINICAN REPUBLIC

### Other

UNITED TELEMEDICINE NETWORK–HOSPITAL CHARLES DE GAULLE, Av Charles de Gaulle #43, Santo Domingo, Zip 11509; tel: 829/345–9335, Horacio Stagno, Commercial Director; hospitalunited.com

# GEORGIA

### Other

BOKHUA MEMORIAL CARDIOVASCULAR CENTER, Chachava 1 Street, Tbilisi, Zip 159, Giorgi Kipiani, Director

INNOVA MEDICAL CENTER, 7A Sandra Euli Street, Tbilisi, Zip 105, Giorgi Kipiani, Director; innovamedical.ge

MARITIME HOSPITAL JSC, Melikishrin 102B, Batumi, Zip 60100, Tamari Kachlishvili, Medical Director; mh.com.ge

MEDI CLUB GEORGIA, 22A, Tashkenti Street, Tbilisi, Zip 160; tel: 995/225–1991, Nugzar Abramishvili, General Director; mediclubgeorgia.ge

TBILISI CENTRAL HOSPITAL, Chachava Street 1, Tbilisi, Zip 159, Ivane Martiashuili, Co–founder; tch.ge

ZHORDANIA CLINIC, Chachava N1, Tbilisi, Zip 159, Tamar Kobiashvili, Director

# JORDAN

### Other

SPECIALTY HOSPITAL, P O Box 930186, Amman, Zip 11193, Fawzi Al–Hammouri, General Manager; specialty–hospital.com

# LEBANON

### Other

SAINT GEORGE HOSPITAL UNIVERSITY MEDICAL CENTER, P O Box 166378, Beirut, Zip 1100–2807; tel: 961/158–5700, Dimitri Haddad, Director; stgeorgehospital.org

# MEXICO

### Other

SHRINERS HOSPITAL FOR CHILDREN, Av Del Iman 257, Col Pedregal de Santa Ursula, Delegacion Coyoacan, Mexico City, Zip 4600; tel: 525/424–7850, Mariano Gonzalez Lugo, Administrator; shrinershospitalsforchildren.org/locations/mexicocity

# MYANMAR

### Other

ASIA ROYAL GENERAL HOSPITAL, 14 Baho Street, Sanchaung Township, Yangon, Zip 11162; tel: 951/153–8055, Myat Thu, Managing Director; asiaroyalmedical.com

# NIGERIA

### Consulting Firm

PETALICE MEDICAL CENTRE, 5/7 Marickson Hospital Way, Uyo, Akwa Ibom State, Zip 520241, Cletus Bassey, Archbishop

# PANAMA

### Other

CLINICA HOSPITAL SAN FERNANDO, S. A., Dept PTY 1663, P O Box 25207, Miami, Florida Zip 33102–5207; tel: 507/305–6399, Jose Manuel Teran Sitton, Medical Director; hospitalsanfernando.com

## PERU

### Other

BRITISH AMERICAN HOSPITAL, Avenue Alfredo Salazar 3 Era, Lima 27, tel: 511/712–3000, Gonzalo Garrido–Lecca, Director; angloamericana.com.pe

## PHILIPPINES

### Other

ST. LUKE'S MEDICAL CENTER, 279 East Rodriguez Sr Boulevard, Quezon City, tel: 632/723–0101, Edgardo R Cortez, President and Chief Executive Officer; stluke.com.ph/home

## SAUDI ARABIA

### Other

ABDUL RAHMAN AL MISHARI GENERAL HOSPITAL, OLAYA, P.O. Box 56929, Riyadh, Zip 11564; tel: 11/465–7700, Abdul Rahman Al Mishari, President; drabdulrahmanalmishari.com.sa/

MUHAMMAD SALEH BASHARAHIL HOSPITAL, P O Box 10505, Madinah Road, Omora Gadida, Makkah, tel: 9/520–4444, Turki M Basharahil, General Manager; msbasharahil.com/

NABIL AL KADI CONSULTANT ENGINEERS, Dammam, Damman, Taufik Ridani, Chief Executive Officer

## SPAIN

### Information Systems

SIGESA, S.A., CALLE GUATEMALA, 14, 4b, Madrid, Zip 28016; tel: 349/345–4018, Francisco Alvarez, Chief Financial Officer; sigesa.com

## TURKEY

### Other

ARTE CERRAHI HASTENESI, 1920 Cad. No:61 Cayyolu, Ankara, Zip 6810; tel: 903/236–1001, Oguz Engiz, Chief Executive Officer; artesaglik.com

## UNITED ARAB EMIRATES

### Other

AMERICAN HOSPITAL–DUBAI, Oud Metha Road, P.O. Box 5566, Dubai, tel: 11/336–7777, Saeed M Almulla, Chairman; https://www.ahdubai.com/en/

## UNITED KINGDOM

### Other

FINANSCO HEALTHCARE, 11A Blacka Moor Road, Sheffield, tel: 448/225–3844, Rukhsar Khan, Chief Executive Officer; finansco.com

# B

## Health Care Systems, Networks and Alliances

**B2** Introduction

3 Statistics for Multihospital Health Care Systems and their Hospitals

4 Health Care Systems and their Hospitals

151 Headquarters of Health Care Systems, Geographically

160 Networks and their Hospitals

176 Alliances

Section B

This section includes listings for networks, health care systems and alliances.

## Health Care Systems

To reflect the diversity that exists among health care organizations, this publication uses the term health care system to identify both multihospital and diversified single hospital systems.

### Multihospital Systems

A multihospital health care system is two or more hospitals owned, leased, sponsored, or contract managed by a central organization.

### Single Hospital Systems

Single, freestanding member hospitals may be categorized as health care systems by bringing into membership three or more, and at least 25 percent, of their owned or leased non–hospital preacute and postacute health care organizations. (For purposes of definition, health care delivery is the availability of professional healthcare staff during all hours of the organization's operations). Organizations provide, or provide and finance, diagnostic, therapeutic, and/or consultative patient or client services that normally precede or follow acute, inpatient, hospitalization; or that serve to prevent or substitute for such hospitalization. These services are provided in either a freestanding facility not eligible for licensure as a hospital under state statue or through one that is a subsidiary of a hospital.

The first part of this section is an alphabetical list of health care systems which are listed under the system by state. Data for this section were compiled from the 2018 *Annual Survey* and the membership information base as published in section A of the *AHA Guide*.

One of the following codes appears after the name of each system listed to indicate the type of organizational control reported by that system:

**CC** Catholic (Roman) church–related system, not–for–profit

**CO** Other church–related system, not–for–profit

**NP** Other not–for–profit system, including nonfederal, governmental systems

**IO** Investor–owned, for profit system

**FG** Federal Government

One of the following codes appears after the name of each hospital to indicate how that hospital is related to the system:

**O** Owned

**L** Leased

**S** Sponsored

**CM** Contract–managed

## Health System Classification System

An identification system for Health Systems was developed jointly by the American Hospital Association's Health Research and Education Trust and Health Forum, and the University of California-Berkeley.[1] A health system is assigned to one of five categories based on how much they differentiate and centralized their hospital services, physician arrangements, and provider-based insurance products. Differentiation refers to the number of different products or services that the organization offers. Centralization refers to whether decision-making and service delivery emanate from the system level more so than individual hospitals.

## Categories:

*Centralized Health System:* A delivery system in which the system centrally organizes individual hospital service delivery, physician arrangements, and insurance product development. The number of different products/services that are offered across the system is moderate.

*Centralized Physician/Insurance Health System:* A delivery system with highly centralized physician arrangements and insurance product development. Within this group, hospital services are relatively decentralized with individual hospitals having discretion over the array of services they offer. The number of different products/services that are offered across the system is moderate.

*Moderately Centralized Health System:* A delivery system that is distinguished by the presence of both centralized and decentralized activity for hospital services, physician arrangements, and insurance product development. For example, a system within this group may have centralized care of expensive, high technology services, such as open heart surgery, but allows individual hospitals to provide an array of other health services based on local needs. The number of different products/services that are offered across the system is moderate.

*Decentralized Health System:* A delivery system with a high degree of decentralized of hospital services, physician arrangements, and insurance product development. Within this group, systems may lack an overarching structure for coordination. Service and product differentiation is high, which may explain why centralization is hard to achieve. In this group, the system may simply service a role in sharing information and providing administrative support to highly developed local delivery systems centered around hospitals.

*Independent Hospital System:* A delivery system with limited differentiation in hospital services, physician arrangements, and insurance product development. These systems are largely horizontal affiliations of autonomous hospitals.

*No Assignment:* For some systems sufficient data from the Annual Survey were not available to determine a cluster assignment.

The second part of this section lists health care systems indexed geographically by state and city. Every effort has been made to be as inclusive and accurate as possible. However, as in all efforts of this type, there may be omissions. For further information, write to the Section for Health Care Systems, American Hospital Association, 155 N. Wacker Drive, Chicago, IL 60606.

## Networks

The *AHA Guide* shows listings of networks. A network is defined as a group of hospitals, physicians, other providers, insurers and/or community agencies that work together to coordinate and deliver a broad spectrum of services to their community. Organizations listed represent the lead or hub of the network activity. Networks are listed by state, then alphabetically by name including participating partners.

The network identification process has purposely been designed to capture networks of varying organization type. Sources include but are not limited to the following: *AHA Annual Survey*, national, state and metropolitan associations, national news and periodical searches, and the networks and their health care providers themselves. Therefore, networks are included regardless of whether a hospital or healthcare system is the network lead. When an individual hospital does appear in the listing, it is indicative of the role the hospital plays as the network lead. In addition, the network listing is not mutually exclusive of the hospital, health care system or alliance listings within this publication.

Networks are very fluid in their composition as goals evolve and partners change. Therefore, some of the networks included in this listing may have dissolved, reformed, or simply been renamed as this section was being produced for publication.

The network identification process is an ongoing and responsive initiative. As more information is collected and validated, it will be made available in other venues, in addition to the *AHA Guide*. For more information concerning the network identification process, please contact The American Hospital Association Resource Center at 312/422–2050.

## Alliances

An alliance is a formal organization, usually owned by shareholders/members, that works on behalf of its individual members in the provision of services and products and in the promotion of activities and ventures. The organization functions under a set of bylaws or other written rules to which each member agrees to abide.

Alliances are listed alphabetically by name. Its members are listed alphabetically by state, city, and then by member name.

[1]Bazzoli, CJ; Shortell, SM; Dubbs, N; Chan, C; and Kralovec, P; "A Taxonomy of Health networks and Systems: Bringing Order Out of Chaos" *Health Services Research*, February; 1999

# Statistics for Health Care Systems and their Hospitals

The following tables describing health care systems refers to information in section B of the 2020 *AHA Guide*.

Table 1 shows the number of health care systems by type of control. Table 2 provides a breakdown of the number of systems that own, lease, sponsor or contract manage hospitals within each control category. Table 3 gives the number of hospitals and beds in each control category as well as total hospitals and beds. Finally, Table 4 shows the percentage of hospitals and beds in each control category.

For more information on health care systems, please write to the Section for Health Care Systems, 155 N. Wacker Drive, Chicago, Illinois 60606 or call 312/422–3000.

Section B

## Table 1. Multihospital Health Care Systems, by Type of Organizaton Control

| Type of Control | Code | Number of Systems |
|---|---|---|
| Catholic (Roman) church–related | CC | 25 |
| Other church–related | CO | 7 |
| Subtotal, church–related | | 32 |
| Other not–for–profit | NP | 312 |
| Subtotal, not–for–profit | | 344 |
| Investor Owned | IO | 78 |
| Federal Government | FG | 7 |
| Total | | 429 |

## Table 2. Multihospital Health Care Systems, by Type of Ownership and Control

| Type of Ownership | Catholic Church–Related (CC) | Other Church–Related (CO) | Total Church–Related (CC + CO) | Other Not–for–Profit (NP) | Total Not–for–Profit (CC, CO, + NP) | Investor–Owned (IO) | Federal Govern–ment (FG) | All Systems |
|---|---|---|---|---|---|---|---|---|
| Systems that only own, lease or sponsor | 17 | 7 | 22 | 188 | 210 | 15 | 6 | 231 |
| Systems that only contract–manage | 0 | 0 | 0 | 12 | 12 | 6 | 0 | 18 |
| Systems that manage, own, lease, or sponsor | 8 | 2 | 10 | 112 | 122 | 57 | 1 | 180 |
| Total | 25 | 7 | 32 | 312 | 344 | 78 | 7 | 429 |

## Table 3. Hospitals and Beds in Multihospital Health Care Systems, by Type of Ownership and Control

| Type of Ownership | Catholic Church–Related (CC) H | B | Other Church–Related (CO) H | B | Total Church–Related (CC + CO) H | B | Other Not–for–Profit (NP) H | B | Total Not–for–Profit (CC, CO, + NP) H | B | Investor–Owned (IO) H | B | Federal Govern–ment (FG) H | B | All Systems H | B |
|---|---|---|---|---|---|---|---|---|---|---|---|---|---|---|---|---|
| Owned, leased or sponsored | 569 | 101,024 | 79 | 19,092 | 648 | 120,116 | 1,687 | 360,051 | 2,335 | 480,167 | 1,347 | 167,292 | 202 | 38,443 | 3,884 | 685,902 |
| Contract–managed | 45 | 2,434 | 3 | 485 | 48 | 2,919 | 131 | 9,706 | 179 | 12,625 | 87 | 4,283 | 0 | 0 | 266 | 16,908 |
| Total | 614 | 103,458 | 82 | 19,577 | 696 | 12,035 | 3,374 | 369,757 | 4,070 | 492,792 | 1,434 | 171,575 | 202 | 38,443 | 5,706 | 702,810 |

**H** = *hospitals;* **B** = *beds.*

## Table 4. Hospitals and Beds in Multihospital Health Care Systems, by Type of Ownership and Control as a Percentage of All Systems

| Type of Ownership | Catholic Church–Related (CC) H | B | Other Church–Related (CO) H | B | Total Church–Related (CC + CO) H | B | Other Not–for–Profit (NP) H | B | Total Not–for–Profit (CC, CO, + NP) H | B | Investor–Owned (IO) H | B | Federal Govern–ment (FG) H | B | All Systems H | B |
|---|---|---|---|---|---|---|---|---|---|---|---|---|---|---|---|---|
| Owned, leased or sponsored | 14.7 | 14.7 | 2.0 | 2.8 | 16.7 | 17.5 | 43.4 | 52.5 | 60.1 | 70.0 | 34.7 | 24.4 | 5.2 | 5.6 | 100 | 100 |
| Contract managed | 16.9 | 14.4 | 1.1 | 2.9 | 18.1 | 17.3 | 49.3 | 52.5 | 67.3 | 74.7 | 32.7 | 24.4 | 0 | 5.6 | 100.1 | 99.8 |
| Total | 10.8 | 14.7 | 1.4 | 2.8 | 12.2 | 17.5 | 59.4 | 52.1 | 71.3 | 70.1 | 25.1 | 24.4 | 3.5 | 5.6 | 99.9 | 100 |

**H** = *hospitals;* **B** = *beds.*

*Please note that figures may not always equal the provided subtotal or total percentages due to rounding.

# Health Care Systems and their Hospitals

**0091: ACADIA HEALTHCARE COMPANY, INC.** (IO)
6100 Tower Circle, Suite 1000, Franklin, TN Zip 37067–1509;
tel. 615/861–6000; Debra Osteen, Chief Executive Officer
**(Decentralized Health System)**

**ARIZONA**: OASIS BEHAVIORAL HEALTH – CHANDLER (O, 146 beds) 2190 North Grace Boulevard, Chandler, AZ, Zip 85225–3416; tel. 480/917–9301; James Gallagher, Chief Executive Officer

SONORA BEHAVIORAL HEALTH HOSPITAL (O, 106 beds) 6050 North Corona Road, #3, Tucson, AZ, Zip 85704–1096; tel. 520/469–8700; Edeli Kinsala, Chief Executive Officer

**ARKANSAS**: CONWAY BEHAVIORAL HEALTH HOSPITAL (O, 80 beds) 2255 Sturgis Road, Conway, AR, Zip 72034–8029; tel. 501/858–3048; Anthony Guild, Chief Executive Officer
**Web address**: www.conwaybh.com

RIVERVIEW BEHAVIORAL HEALTH (O, 62 beds) 701 Arkansas Boulevard, Texarkana, AR, Zip 71854–2105; tel. 870/772–5028; Allison De Bruycker, Chief Executive Officer

VALLEY BEHAVIORAL HEALTH SYSTEM (O, 114 beds) 10301 Mayo Drive, Barling, AR, Zip 72923–1660; tel. 479/494–5700; Andrea Norman, Chief Executive Officer
**Web address**: www.valleybehavioral.com

VANTAGE POINT OF NORTHWEST ARKANSAS (O, 114 beds) 4253 North Crossover Road, Fayetteville, AR, Zip 72703–4596; tel. 479/521–5731; Megan Wedgworth, Chief Executive Officer
**Web address**: www.vantagepointnwa.com

**CALIFORNIA**: PACIFIC GROVE HOSPITAL (O, 68 beds) 5900 Brockton Avenue, Riverside, CA, Zip 92506–1862; tel. 951/275–8400; Nichol Sheffield, Chief Executive Officer
**Web address**: www.pacificgrovehospital.com

SAN JOSE BEHAVIORAL HEALTH (O, 80 beds) 455 Silicon Valley Boulevard, San Jose, CA, Zip 95138–1858; tel. 888/210–2484; Rob Marsh, Chief Executive Officer

**DELAWARE**: MEADOW WOOD BEHAVIORAL HEALTH SYSTEM (O, 53 beds) 575 South Dupont Highway, New Castle, DE, Zip 19720–4606; tel. 302/328–3330; Bill A. Mason, Chief Executive Officer
**Web address**: www.meadowwoodhospital.com

**FLORIDA**: NORTH TAMPA BEHAVIORAL HEALTH (O, 78 beds) 29910 State Road 56, Wesley Chapel, FL, Zip 33543–8800; tel. 813/922–3300; Clint Hauger, Chief Executive Officer
**Web address**: www.northtampabehavioralhealth.com

PARK ROYAL HOSPITAL (O, 114 beds) 9241 Park Royal Drive, Fort Myers, FL, Zip 33908–9204; tel. 239/985–2700; Coleby Wright, Chief Executive Officer

**GEORGIA**: GREENLEAF BEHAVIORAL HEALTH HOSPITAL (O, 103 beds) 2209 Pineview Drive, Valdosta, GA, Zip 31602–7316; tel. 229/247–4357; Bryan D. Adams, Chief Executive Officer
**Web address**: www.greenleafcounseling.net

LAKEVIEW BEHAVIORAL HEALTH (O, 70 beds) 1 Technology Parkway South, Norcross, GA, Zip 30092–2928; tel. 678/713–2600; Deagan Watson, Chief Executive Officer

RIVERWOODS BEHAVIORAL HEALTH SYSTEM (O, 75 beds) 233 Medical Center Drive, Riverdale, GA, Zip 30274–2640; tel. 770/991–8500; Patricia Hamilton, Chief Executive Officer
**Web address**: www.riverwoodsbehavioral.com

**INDIANA**: OPTIONS BEHAVIORAL HEALTH SYSTEM (O, 84 beds) 5602 Caito Drive, Indianapolis, IN, Zip 46226–1346; tel. 317/544–4340; Dustin Thiels, Chief Executive Officer
**Web address**: www.optionsbehavioralhealthsystem.com/

**LOUISIANA**: COVINGTON BEHAVIORAL HEALTH (O, 60 beds) 201 Greenbrier Boulevard, Covington, LA, Zip 70433–7236; tel. 985/893–2970; Tanmay Mathur, Chief Executive Officer

LONGLEAF HOSPITAL (O, 129 beds) 44 Versailles Boulevard, Alexandria, LA, Zip 71303–3960; tel. 318/445–5111; Claire Hick, Chief Executive Officer
**Web address**: www.longleafhospital.com/

RIVER PLACE BEHAVIORAL HEALTH (O, 82 beds) 500 Rue De Sante, La Place, LA, Zip 70068–5418; tel. 985/303–2327; Jeremy Pitzer, Chief Executive Officer
**Web address**: www.riverplacebh.com

VERMILION BEHAVIORAL HEALTH SYSTEMS – NORTH CAMPUS (O, 78 beds) 2520 North University Avenue, Lafayette, LA, Zip 70507–5306; tel. 337/234–5614; Stephanie H. Santori, Chief Executive Officer

**MASSACHUSETTS**: SOUTHCOAST BEHAVIORAL HEALTH (O, 120 beds) 581 Faunce Corner Road, Dartmouth, MA, Zip 02747–1242; tel. 888/210–2475; Richard Remley, Chief Executive Officer
**Web address**: www.southcoastbehavioral.com

**MICHIGAN**: HARBOR OAKS HOSPITAL (O, 99 beds) 35031 23 Mile Road, New Baltimore, MI, Zip 48047–3649; tel. 586/725–5777; Briana Jacob, Chief Executive Officer
**Web address**: www.harboroaks.com

STONECREST CENTER (O, 162 beds) 15000 Gratiot Avenue, Detroit, MI, Zip 48205–1973; tel. 313/245–0600; Steve Savage, Chief Executive Officer

**MISSOURI**: LAKELAND BEHAVIORAL HEALTH SYSTEM (O, 206 beds) 440 South Market Street, Springfield, MO, Zip 65806–2026; tel. 417/865–5581; Nathan Duncan, Chief Executive Officer
**Web address**: www.lakeland–hospital.com

**NEVADA**: SEVEN HILLS HOSPITAL (O, 134 beds) 3021 West Horizon Ridge Parkway, Henderson, NV, Zip 89052–3990; tel. 702/646–5000; Naomi Jones, Chief Executive Officer

**OHIO**: OHIO HOSPITAL FOR PSYCHIATRY (O, 130 beds) 880 Greenlawn Avenue, Columbus, OH, Zip 43223–2616; tel. 614/449–9664; Angel Piper, Chief Executive Officer
**Web address**: www.ohiohospitalforpsychiatry.com/

**OKLAHOMA**: ROLLING HILLS HOSPITAL (O, 108 beds) 1000 Rolling Hills Lane, Ada, OK, Zip 74820–9415; tel. 580/436–3600; Dennis Gober, Interim Chief Executive Officer

**PENNSYLVANIA**: BELMONT BEHAVIORAL HOSPITAL (O, 180 beds) 4200 Monument Road, Philadelphia, PA, Zip 19131–1625; tel. 215/877–2000; Laura Longstreet, Chief Executive Officer
**Web address**: www.einstein.edu/locations/belmont–behavioral–health/

SOUTHWOOD PSYCHIATRIC HOSPITAL (O, 156 beds) 2575 Boyce Plaza Road, Pittsburgh, PA, Zip 15241–3925; tel. 412/257–2290; Stephen J. Quigley, Chief Executive Officer
**Web address**: www.southwoodhospital.com

**PUERTO RICO**: SAN JUAN CAPESTRANO HOSPITAL (O, 158 beds) Rural Route 2, Box 11, San Juan, PR, Zip 926; tel. 787/625–2900; Marta Rivera. Plaza, Chief Executive Officer and Managing Director

**SOUTH CAROLINA**: REBOUND BEHAVIORAL HEALTH (O, 42 beds) 134 East Rebound Road, Lancaster, SC, Zip 29720–7712; tel. 855/999–9501; Cameron Bolish, Chief Executive Officer
**Web address**: www.reboundbehavioralhealth.com

**TENNESSEE**: CRESTWYN BEHAVIORAL HEALTH (O, 80 beds) 9485 Crestwyn Hills Cove, Memphis, TN, Zip 38125–8515; tel. 901/248–1500; Debby Willis, Chief Executive Officer
**Web address**: www.crestwynbh.com

DELTA SPECIALTY HOSPITAL (O, 167 beds) 3000 Getwell Road, Memphis, TN, Zip 38118–2299; tel. 901/369–8100; Andre Cromwell, Chief Executive Officer
**Web address**: www.deltaspecialtyhospital.com

TRUSTPOINT HOSPITAL (O, 155 beds) 1009 North Thompson Lane, Murfreesboro, TN, Zip 37129–4351; tel. 615/867–1111; Beth Goodner, Chief Executive Officer

For explanation of codes following names, see page B2.
★ Indicates Type III membership in the American Hospital Association.

**TEXAS**: CROSS CREEK HOSPITAL (O, 90 beds) 8402 Cross Park Drive, Austin, TX, Zip 78754; tel. 512/215–3900; Kay McKennery, Chief Executive Officer
**Web address**: www.cornerstonehealthcaregroup.com

RED RIVER HOSPITAL, LLC (O, 96 beds) 1505 Eighth Street, Wichita Falls, TX, Zip 76301–3106; tel. 940/322–3171; Jon Lasell, Chief Executive Officer
**Web address**: www.redriverhospital.com

RIO VISTA BEHAVIORAL HEALTH (O, 80 beds) 1390 Northwestern Drive, El Paso, TX, Zip 79912–8003; tel. 915/209–4513; Diana Schultz, Chief Executive Officer

**UTAH**: HIGHLAND RIDGE HOSPITAL (O, 83 beds) 7309 South 180 West, Midvale, UT, Zip 84047–3769; tel. 801/569–2153; Jim Hess, Chief Executive Officer
**Web address**: www.highlandridgehospital.com

**WASHINGTON**: CASCADE BEHAVIORAL HOSPITAL (O, 63 beds) 12844 Military Road South, Tukwila, WA, Zip 98168–3045; tel. 206/244–0180; Christopher West, Chief Executive Officer
**Web address**: www.cascadebh.com

| | | |
|---|---|---|
| Owned, leased, sponsored: | 38 hospitals | 4005 beds |
| Contract–managed: | 0 hospitals | 0 beds |
| Totals: | 38 hospitals | 4005 beds |

---

**★0640: ACUITYHEALTHCARE, LP** (IO)

10735 David Taylor Dr. Suite 200, Charlotte, NC Zip 28262–0052; tel. 704/887–7280; Edwin H. Cooper Jr, President and Chief Executive Officer
**(Independent Hospital System)**

**NEW JERSEY**: ACUITY SPECIALTY HOSPITAL OF NEW JERSEY (O, 30 beds) 1925 Pacific Avenue, 7th Floor, 5 Wellness, Atlantic City, NJ, Zip 08401–6713; tel. 609/441–2122; Kathleen Kerstetter, MSN, R.N., Chief Executive Officer

ACUITY SPECIALTY HOSPITAL OF SOUTHERN NEW JERSEY (O, 53 beds) 218 A Sunset Road, Willingboro, NJ, Zip 08046–1110, 220 Sunset Road, 08046–1110, tel. 609/835–3650; Garrett Arneson, FACHE, R.N., Chief Executive Officer
**Web address**: www.willingboro.acuityhealthcare.net

**OHIO**: ACUITY SPECIALTY HOSPITALS OHIO VALLEY (O, 52 beds) 380 Summit Avenue, 3rd Floor, Steubenville, OH, Zip 43952–2667; tel. 740/283–7600; Dusty A. Bowers, Chief Executive Officer
**Web address**: www.acuityhealthcare.net

| | | |
|---|---|---|
| Owned, leased, sponsored: | 3 hospitals | 135 beds |
| Contract–managed: | 0 hospitals | 0 beds |
| Totals: | 3 hospitals | 135 beds |

---

**0895: ADENA HEALTH SYSTEM** (NP)

272 Hospital Road, Chillicothe, OH Zip 45601–9031, Mailing Address: P.O. 802846, Kansas City, MO, 64180–2846, tel. 740/779–7500; Jeff Graham, President and Chief Executive Officer
**(Independent Hospital System)**

**OHIO**: ADENA GREENFIELD MEDICAL CENTER (O, 25 beds) 550 Mirabeau Street, Greenfield, OH, Zip 45123–1617; tel. 937/981–9400; Josh McCoy, Administrator
**Web address**: www.adena.org

ADENA MEDICAL CENTER (O, 226 beds) 272 Hospital Road, Chillicothe, OH, Zip 45601–9031; tel. 740/779–7500; Jeff Graham, President and Chief Executive Officer

ADENA PIKE MEDICAL CENTER (O, 25 beds) 100 Dawn Lane, Waverly, OH, Zip 45690–9138; tel. 740/947–2186; David M. Zanni, Administrator
**Web address**: www.adena.org

| | | |
|---|---|---|
| Owned, leased, sponsored: | 3 hospitals | 276 beds |
| Contract–managed: | 0 hospitals | 0 beds |
| Totals: | 3 hospitals | 276 beds |

---

**★4165: ADVENTHEALTH** (CO)

900 Hope Way, Altamonte Springs, FL Zip 32714–1502; tel. 407/357–1000; Terry Shaw, President and Chief Executive Officer
**(Decentralized Health System)**

**COLORADO**: AVISTA ADVENTIST HOSPITAL (O, 114 beds) 100 Health Park Drive, Louisville, CO, Zip 80027–9583; tel. 303/673–1000; Isaac Sendros, Chief Executive Officer

CASTLE ROCK ADVENTIST HOSPITAL (O, 53 beds) 2350 Meadows Boulevard, Castle Rock, CO, Zip 80109–8405; tel. 720/455–5000; Brandon M. Nudd, Chief Executive Officer
**Web address**: www.castlerockhospital.org

LITTLETON ADVENTIST HOSPITAL (O, 159 beds) 7700 South Broadway Street, Littleton, CO, Zip 80122–2628; tel. 303/730–8900; Jillyan McKinney, Chief Executive Officer

PARKER ADVENTIST HOSPITAL (O, 152 beds) 9395 Crown Crest Boulevard, Parker, CO, Zip 80138–8573; tel. 303/269–4000; Michael Goebel, Chief Executive Officer
**Web address**: www.parkerhospital.org

PORTER ADVENTIST HOSPITAL (O, 228 beds) 2525 South Downing Street, Denver, CO, Zip 80210–5876; tel. 303/778–1955; Todd Folkenberg, Chief Executive Officer
**Web address**: www.porterhospital.org/poh/home/

**FLORIDA**: ADVENTHEALTH CARROLLWOOD (O, 95 beds) 7171 North Dale Mabry Highway, Tampa, FL, Zip 33614–2665; tel. 813/932–2222; Erika Skula, President and Chief Executive Officer
**Web address**: https://www.floridahospital.com/carrollwood

ADVENTHEALTH CONNERTON (O, 77 beds) 9441 Health Center Drive, Land O'Lakes, FL, Zip 34637–5837; tel. 813/903–3701; Denyse Bales–Chubb, President and Chief Executive Officer

ADVENTHEALTH DADE CITY (O, 120 beds) 13100 Fort King Road, Dade City, FL, Zip 33525–5294; tel. 352/521–1100; Amanda Maggard, Chief Executive Officer
**Web address**: www.floridahospital.com/dade–city

ADVENTHEALTH DAYTONA BEACH (O, 362 beds) 301 Memorial Medical Parkway, Daytona Beach, FL, Zip 32117–5167; tel. 386/676–6000; Ed Noseworthy, Chief Executive Officer
**Web address**: www.floridahospitalmemorial.org

ADVENTHEALTH DELAND (O, 164 beds) 701 West Plymouth Avenue, DeLand, FL, Zip 32720–3236; tel. 386/943–4522; Lorenzo Brown, Chief Executive Officer

ADVENTHEALTH FISH MEMORIAL (O, 197 beds) 1055 Saxon Boulevard, Orange City, FL, Zip 32763–8468; tel. 386/917–5000; Robert Deininger, Chief Executive Officer
**Web address**: www.fhfishmemorial.org

ADVENTHEALTH HEART OF FLORIDA (O, 193 beds) 40100 Highway 27, Davenport, FL, Zip 33837–5906; tel. 863/422–4971; Brian Adams, Chief Executive Officer
**Web address**: www.heartofflorida.com

ADVENTHEALTH LAKE WALES (O, 150 beds) 410 South 11th Street, Lake Wales, FL, Zip 33853–4256; tel. 863/676–1433; Brian Adams, Chief Executive Officer
**Web address**: www.lakewalesmedicalcenter.com

ADVENTHEALTH NEW SMYRNA BEACH (O, 109 beds) 401 Palmetto Street, New Smyrna Beach, FL, Zip 32168–7399; tel. 386/424–5000; Dennis Hernandez, Chief Executive Officer
**Web address**: https://www.floridahospital.com/new–smyrna

ADVENTHEALTH NORTH PINELLAS (O, 187 beds) 1395 South Pinellas Avenue, Tarpon Springs, FL, Zip 34689–3790; tel. 727/942–5000; Jason Dunkel, President and Chief Executive Officer
**Web address**: www.fhnorthpinellas.com/

ADVENTHEALTH OCALA (O, 357 beds) 1500 SW 1st Avenue, Ocala, FL, Zip 34471–6504, Mailing Address: P.O. Box 6000, 34478–6000, tel. 352/351–7200; Joe Johnson, FACHE, Chief Executive Officer

ADVENTHEALTH ORLANDO (O, 3890 beds) 601 East Rollins Street, Orlando, FL, Zip 32803–1248; tel. 407/303–6611; Daryl Tol, President and Chief Executive Officer
**Web address**: www.floridahospital.com/orlando

ADVENTHEALTH PALM COAST (O, 99 beds) 60 Memorial Medical Parkway, Palm Coast, FL, Zip 32164–5980; tel. 386/586–2000; Ronald Jimenez, M.D., Chief Executive Officer

ADVENTHEALTH SEBRING (O, 180 beds) 4200 Sun'n Lake Boulevard, Sebring, FL, Zip 33872–1986, Mailing Address: P.O. Box 9400, 33871–9400, tel. 863/314–4466; Randy Surber, Chief Executive Officer
**Web address**: www.floridahospital.com/heartland/our–location

---

For explanation of codes following names, see page B2.
★ Indicates Type III membership in the American Hospital Association.

ADVENTHEALTH TAMPA (O, 536 beds) 3100 East Fletcher Avenue, Tampa, FL, Zip 33613–4688; tel. 813/971–6000; Denyse Bales–Chubb, Chief Executive Officer
**Web address**: www.floridahospital.com/tampa

ADVENTHEALTH WATERMAN (O, 300 beds) 1000 Waterman Way, Tavares, FL, Zip 32778–5266; tel. 352/253–3333; Abel Biri, Chief Executive Officer

ADVENTHEALTH WAUCHULA (O, 25 beds) 533 West Carlton Street, Wauchula, FL, Zip 33873–3407; tel. 863/773–3101; Denise Grimsley, R.N., Vice President and Administrator
**Web address**: www.fh.floridahospital.com/heartland/home.aspx

ADVENTHEALTH WESLEY CHAPEL (O, 145 beds) 2600 Bruce B Downs Bouelvard, Wesley Chapel, FL, Zip 33544–9207; tel. 813/929–5000; Erik Wangsness, Chief Executive Officer

ADVENTHEALTH ZEPHYRHILLS (O, 149 beds) 7050 Gall Boulevard, Zephyrhills, FL, Zip 33541–1399; tel. 813/788–0411; Amanda Maggard, President and Chief Executive Officer
**Web address**: www.fhzeph.org

**GEORGIA**: ADVENTHEALTH GORDON (O, 83 beds) 1035 Red Bud Road, Calhoun, GA, Zip 30701–2082, Mailing Address: P.O. Box 12938, 30703–7013, tel. 706/629–2895; Michael Murrill, President and Chief Executive Officer

ADVENTHEALTH MURRAY (O, 12 beds) 707 Old Dalton Ellijay Road, Chatsworth, GA, Zip 30705–2060, Mailing Address: P.O. Box 1406, 30705–1406, tel. 706/695–4564; Michael Murrill, President and Chief Executive Officer
**Web address**: www.murraymedical.org/

**ILLINOIS**: AMITA HEALTH ADVENTIST MEDICAL CENTER – HINSDALE (O, 261 beds) 120 North Oak Street, Hinsdale, IL, Zip 60521–3890; tel. 630/856–6001; Adam Maycock, Chief Executive Officer
**Web address**: www.AMITAhealth.org

AMITA HEALTH ADVENTIST MEDICAL CENTER BOLINGBROOK (O, 134 beds) 500 Remington Boulevard, Bolingbrook, IL, Zip 60440–4906; tel. 630/312–5000; Bruce C. Christian, Chief Executive Officer

AMITA HEALTH ADVENTIST MEDICAL CENTER GLENOAKS (O, 143 beds) 701 Winthrop Avenue, Glendale Heights, IL, Zip 60139–1403; tel. 630/545–8000; Bruce C. Christian, President and Chief Executive Officer
**Web address**: www.AMITAHealth.org

AMITA HEALTH ADVENTIST MEDICAL CENTER LA GRANGE (O, 200 beds) 5101 South Willow Spring Road, La Grange, IL, Zip 60525–2600; tel. 708/245–9000; Adam Maycock, Chief Executive Officer
**Web address**: www.keepingyouwell.com

**KANSAS**: ADVENTHEALTH OTTAWA (O, 38 beds) 1301 South Main Street, Ottawa, KS, Zip 66067–3598; tel. 785/229–8200; Dallas Purkeypile, Chief Executive Officer

ADVENTHEALTH SHAWNEE MISSION (O, 397 beds) 9100 West 74th Street, Shawnee Mission, KS, Zip 66204–4004, Box 2923, 66201–1323, tel. 913/676–2000; Michael Knecht, President
**Web address**: www.shawneemission.org

**KENTUCKY**: ADVENTHEALTH MANCHESTER (O, 49 beds) 210 Marie Langdon Drive, Manchester, KY, Zip 40962–6388; tel. 606/598–5104; Chris Self, Chief Executive Officer
**Web address**: www.manchestermemorial.org

**NORTH CAROLINA**: ADVENTHEALTH HENDERSONVILLE (O, 86 beds) 100 Hospital Drive, Hendersonville, NC, Zip 28792–5272; tel. 828/684–8501; Cory Reeves, President and Chief Executive Officer

**TEXAS**: ADVENTHEALTH CENTRAL TEXAS (O, 177 beds) 2201 South Clear Creek Road, Killeen, TX, Zip 76549–4110; tel. 254/526–7523; Kevin A. Roberts, FACHE, President and Chief Executive Officer
**Web address**: www.mplex.org

ADVENTHEALTH ROLLINS BROOK (O, 35 beds) 608 North Key Avenue, Lampasas, TX, Zip 76550–1106, Mailing Address: P.O. Box 589, 76550–0032, tel. 512/556–3682; Ashley Underwood, Administrator
**Web address**: www.mplex.org

TEXAS HEALTH HUGULEY HOSPITAL FORT WORTH SOUTH (C, 193 beds) 11801 South Freeway, Burleson, TX, Zip 76028–7021, Mailing Address: P.O. Box 6337, Fort Worth, 76115–0337, tel. 817/293–9110; Penny Johnson, Chief Executive Officer

**WISCONSIN**: ADVENTHEALTH DURAND (O, 25 beds) 1220 Third Avenue West, Durand, WI, Zip 54736–1600, Mailing Address: P.O. Box 224, 54736–0224, tel. 715/672–4211; Douglas R. Peterson, President and Chief Executive Officer
**Web address**: www.chippewavalleyhospital.com/

| | | |
|---|---|---|
| Owned, leased, sponsored: | 37 hospitals | 9681 beds |
| Contract–managed: | 1 hospitals | 193 beds |
| Totals: | 38 hospitals | 9874 beds |

★**0235: ADVENTIST HEALTH** (CO)
One Adventist Health Way, Roseville, CA Zip 95661–3266, Mailing Address: P.O. Box 619002, 95661–9002, tel. 916/406–0000; Scott Reiner, Chief Executive Officer
**(Decentralized Health System)**

**CALIFORNIA**: ADVENTIST HEALTH – TULARE (L, 103 beds) 869 North Cherry Street, Tulare, CA, Zip 93274–2287; tel. 559/688–0821; Randy Dodd, President
**Web address**: www.tulareregional.org

ADVENTIST HEALTH BAKERSFIELD (O, 254 beds) 2615 Chester Avenue, Bakersfield, CA, Zip 93301–2014, Mailing Address: P.O. Box 2615, 93303–2615, tel. 661/395–3000; Sharlet Briggs, Ph.D., Market Chief Executive Officer and President

ADVENTIST HEALTH CLEAR LAKE (O, 25 beds) 15630 18th Avenue, Clearlake, CA, Zip 95422–9336, Mailing Address: P.O. Box 6710, 95422, tel. 707/994–6486; David Santos, President and Chief Executive Officer
**Web address**: www.adventisthealth.org

ADVENTIST HEALTH GLENDALE (O, 502 beds) 1509 Wilson Terrace, Glendale, CA, Zip 90048; tel. 818/409–8000; Alice H. Issai, President
**Web address**: https://www.adventisthealth.org/glendale/

ADVENTIST HEALTH HANFORD (O, 199 beds) 115 Mall Drive, Hanford, CA, Zip 93230–3513; tel. 559/582–9000; Wayne Ferch, President and Chief Executive Officer

ADVENTIST HEALTH HOWARD MEMORIAL (L, 25 beds) One Marcela Drive, Willits, CA, Zip 95490–4298; tel. 707/459–6801; Jason Wells, President and Chief Executive Officer
**Web address**: www.howardhospital.com

ADVENTIST HEALTH LODI MEMORIAL (O, 194 beds) 975 South Fairmont Avenue, Lodi, CA, Zip 95240–5118, Mailing Address: P.O. Box 3004, 95241–1908, tel. 209/334–3411; Daniel Wolcott, President and Chief Executive Officer

ADVENTIST HEALTH REEDLEY (L, 49 beds) 372 West Cypress Avenue, Reedley, CA, Zip 93654–2199; tel. 559/638–8155; Wayne Ferch, President and Chief Executive Officer
**Web address**: https://www.adventisthealth.org/reedley/

ADVENTIST HEALTH SIMI VALLEY (O, 144 beds) 2975 North Sycamore Drive, Simi Valley, CA, Zip 93065–1277; tel. 805/955–6000; Jennifer Swenson, President and Chief Executive Officer
**Web address**: www.simivalleyhospital.com

ADVENTIST HEALTH SONORA (O, 152 beds) 1000 Greenley Road, Sonora, CA, Zip 95370–4819; tel. 209/536–5000; Michelle Fuentes, President
**Web address**: www.sonoramedicalcenter.org/

ADVENTIST HEALTH ST. HELENA (O, 81 beds) 10 Woodland Road, Saint Helena, CA, Zip 94574–9554; tel. 707/963–3611; Steven Herber, M.D., FACS, President and Chief Executive Officer

ADVENTIST HEALTH ST. HELENA (O, 61 beds) 525 Oregon Street, Vallejo, CA, Zip 94590–3201; tel. 707/648–2200; Steven Herber, M.D., FACS, President and Chief Executive Officer
**Web address**: www.sthelenahospitals.org/location/center-for-behavioral-health

ADVENTIST HEALTH TEHACHAPI VALLEY (C, 24 beds) 115 West 'E' Street, Tehachapi, CA, Zip 93561–1607, Mailing Address: P.O. Box 1900, 93581–1900, tel. 661/823–3000; David Eastman, Interim Chief Executive Officer

ADVENTIST HEALTH UKIAH VALLEY (O, 50 beds) 275 Hospital Drive, Ukiah, CA, Zip 95482–4531; tel. 707/462–3111; Gwen Matthews, R.N., MSN, Chief Executive Officer
**Web address**: www.adventisthealth.org

ADVENTIST HEALTH WHITE MEMORIAL (O, 353 beds) 1720 Cesar Chavez Avenue, Los Angeles, CA, Zip 90033–2414; tel. 323/268–5000; John Raffoul, Chief Executive Officer

For explanation of codes following names, see page B2.
★ Indicates Type III membership in the American Hospital Association.

ADVENTIST HEALTH AND RIDEOUT (O, 219 beds) 726 Fourth Street, Marysville, CA, Zip 95901–5600; tel. 530/749–4300; Richard Rawson, Chief Executive Officer
**Web address**: www.frhg.org

CENTRAL VALLEY GENERAL HOSPITAL (O, 49 beds) 1025 North Douty Street, Hanford, CA, Zip 93230–3722, Mailing Address: P.O. Box 480, 93232–2113, tel. 559/583–2100; Wayne Ferch, President and Chief Executive Officer
**Web address**: www.hanfordhealth.com

MENDOCINO COAST DISTRICT HOSPITAL (L, 25 beds) 700 River Drive, Fort Bragg, CA, Zip 95437–5495; tel. 707/961–1234; Wayne Allen, Interim Chief Executive Officer

**HAWAII**: ADVENTIST HEALTH CASTLE (O, 150 beds) 640 Ulukahiki Street, Kailua, HI, Zip 96734–4454; tel. 808/263–5500; Kathryn A. Raethel, R.N., M.P.H., President and Chief Executive Officer
**Web address**: www.castlemed.org

**OREGON**: ADVENTIST HEALTH PORTLAND (O, 170 beds) 10123 SE Market Street, Portland, OR, Zip 97216–2599; tel. 503/257–2500; Joyce Newmyer, President

ADVENTIST HEALTHTILLAMOOK (L, 25 beds) 1000 Third Street, Tillamook, OR, Zip 97141–3430; tel. 503/842–4444; Kathy Saxon, R.N., Interim President
**Web address**: https://www.adventisthealth.org/tillamook/

| Owned, leased, sponsored: | 20 hospitals | 2830 beds |
| Contract–managed: | 1 hospitals | 24 beds |
| Totals: | 21 hospitals | 2854 beds |

## 0214: ADVENTIST HEALTHCARE (NP)

820 West Diamond Avenue, Suite 600, Gaithersburg, MD Zip 20878–1419; tel. 301/315–3185; Terry Forde, President and Chief Executive Officer
**(Independent Hospital System)**

**DISTRICT OF COLUMBIA**: HOWARD UNIVERSITY HOSPITAL (C, 217 beds) 2041 Georgia Avenue NW, Washington, DC, Zip 20060–0002; tel. 202/865–6100; Anita L.A. Jenkins, FABC, Chief Executive Officer

**MARYLAND**: ADVENTIST HEALTHCARE WHITE OAK MEDICAL CENTER (O, 222 beds) 11890 Healing Way, Silver Spring, MD, Zip 20904; tel. 240/637–4000; Anthony Stahl, FACHE, Ph.D., Chief Executive Officer
**Web address**: https://www.adventisthealthcare.com

ADVENTIST HEALTHCARE PHYSICAL HEALTH AND REHABILITATION (O, 97 beds) 9909 Medical Center Drive, Rockville, MD, Zip 20850–6361; tel. 240/864–6000; Brent Reitz, President

ADVENTIST HEALTHCARE SHADY GROVE MEDICAL CENTER (O, 460 beds) 9901 Medical Center Drive, Rockville, MD, Zip 20850–3395; tel. 240/826–6000; John Sackett , President SGMC and Executive Vice President and Chief Operating Officer
**Web address**: www.adventisthealthcare.com

| Owned, leased, sponsored: | 3 hospitals | 779 beds |
| Contract–managed: | 1 hospitals | 217 beds |
| Totals: | 4 hospitals | 996 beds |

## ★1032: ADVOCATE AURORA HEALTH (NP)

3075 Highland Parkway, Suite 600, Downers Grove, IL Zip 60515–5563; tel. 630/929–8700; Jim Skogsbergh, President and Chief Executive Officer
**(Decentralized Health System)**

**ILLINOIS**: ADVOCATE CHRIST MEDICAL CENTER (O, 796 beds) 4440 West 95th Street, Oak Lawn, IL, Zip 60453–2699; tel. 708/684–8000; Richard Heim, President
**Web address**: www.advocatehealth.com/christ

ADVOCATE CONDELL MEDICAL CENTER (O, 283 beds) 801 South Milwaukee Avenue, Libertyville, IL, Zip 60048–3199; tel. 847/362–2900; Matthew Lee. Primack, President

ADVOCATE GOOD SAMARITAN HOSPITAL (O, 293 beds) 3815 Highland Avenue, Downers Grove, IL, Zip 60515–1590; tel. 630/275–5900; Nancy M. Tinsley, R.N., FACHE, President
**Web address**: www.advocatehealth.com/gsam

ADVOCATE GOOD SHEPHERD HOSPITAL (O, 176 beds) 450 West Highway 22, Barrington, IL, Zip 60010–1919; tel. 847/381–0123; Karen A. Lambert, President

ADVOCATE ILLINOIS MASONIC MEDICAL CENTER (O, 319 beds) 836 West Wellington Avenue, Chicago, IL, Zip 60657–5147; tel. 773/975–1600; Susan Nordstrom. Lopez, President
**Web address**: www.advocatehealth.com/masonic

ADVOCATE LUTHERAN GENERAL HOSPITAL (O, 651 beds) 1775 Dempster Street, Park Ridge, IL, Zip 60068–1174; tel. 847/723–2210; Terika Richardson, M.P.H., President
**Web address**: www.advocatehealth.com/luth/

ADVOCATE SHERMAN HOSPITAL (O, 271 beds) 1425 North Randall Road , Elgin, IL, Zip 60123–2300; tel. 847/742–9800; Sheri De Shazo, R.N., President
**Web address**: www.advocatehealth.com/sherman

ADVOCATE SOUTH SUBURBAN HOSPITAL (O, 222 beds) 17800 South Kedzie Avenue, Hazel Crest, IL, Zip 60429–0989; tel. 708/799–8000; Rashard Johnson, President
**Web address**: www.advocatehealth.com/ssub/

ADVOCATE TRINITY HOSPITAL (O, 142 beds) 2320 East 93rd Street, Chicago, IL, Zip 60617–3909; tel. 773/967–2000; Rashard Johnson, President

**WISCONSIN**: AURORA BAYCARE MEDICAL CENTER (O, 167 beds) 2845 Greenbrier Road, Green Bay, WI, Zip 54311–6519, Mailing Address: P.O. Box 8900, 54308–8900, tel. 920/288–8000; Daniel T. Meyer, President
**Web address**: www.aurorabaycare.com

AURORA LAKELAND MEDICAL CENTER (O, 64 beds) W3985 County Road NN, Elkhorn, WI, Zip 53121–4389; tel. 262/741–2000; Bob Miller, President
**Web address**: www.aurorahealthcare.org

AURORA MEDICAL CENTER – BAY AREA (O, 59 beds) 3003 University Drive, Marinette, WI, Zip 54143–4110; tel. 715/735–4200; Edward A. Harding, FACHE, President
**Web address**: www.bamc.org

AURORA MEDICAL CENTER – MANITOWOC COUNTY (O, 62 beds) 5000 Memorial Drive, Two Rivers, WI, Zip 54241–3900; tel. 920/794–5000; Cathie A. Kocourek, President
**Web address**: www.aurorahealthcare.org

AURORA MEDICAL CENTER BURLINGTON (O, 38 beds) 252 McHenry Street, Burlington, WI, Zip 53105–1828; tel. 262/767–6000; Bob Miller, President

AURORA MEDICAL CENTER GRAFTON (O, 132 beds) 975 Port Washington Road, Grafton, WI, Zip 53024–9201; tel. 262/329–1000; David Graebner, President
**Web address**: www.aurorahealthcare.org

AURORA MEDICAL CENTER KENOSHA (O, 83 beds) 10400 75th Street, Kenosha, WI, Zip 53142–7884; tel. 262/948–5600; Lisa Just, President

AURORA MEDICAL CENTER SUMMIT (O, 91 beds) 36500 Aurora Drive, Summit, WI, Zip 53066–4899; tel. 262/434–1000; Jessica Bauer, President
**Web address**: www.aurorahealthcare.org

AURORA MEDICAL CENTER IN WASHINGTON COUNTY (O, 35 beds) 1032 East Sumner Street, Hartford, WI, Zip 53027–1698; tel. 262/673–2300; Jessica Bauer, President
**Web address**: www.aurorahealthcare.org

AURORA MEDICAL CENTER OF OSHKOSH (O, 72 beds) 855 North Westhaven Drive, Oshkosh, WI, Zip 54904–7668; tel. 920/456–6000; John B. Newman, M.D., President

AURORA PSYCHIATRIC HOSPITAL (O, 91 beds) 1220 Dewey Avenue, Wauwatosa, WI, Zip 53213–2598; tel. 414/454–6600; Peter Carlson, President, Behavioral Health Services
**Web address**: www.aurorahealthcare.org

AURORA SHEBOYGAN MEMORIAL MEDICAL CENTER (O, 127 beds) 2629 North Seventh Street, Sheboygan, WI, Zip 53083–4998; tel. 920/451–5000; David Graebner, President

AURORA SINAI MEDICAL CENTER (O, 202 beds) 945 North 12th Street, Milwaukee, WI, Zip 53233–1337, Mailing Address: P.O. Box 342, 53201–0342, tel. 414/219–2000; Carrie Killoran, President
**Web address**: www.aurorahealthcare.org

AURORA ST. LUKE'S MEDICAL CENTER (O, 711 beds) 2900 West Oklahoma Avenue, Milwaukee, WI, Zip 53215–4330, Mailing Address: P.O. Box 2901, 53201–2901, tel. 414/649–6000; Marie Golanowski, R.N., MS, President

For explanation of codes following names, see page B2.
★ Indicates Type III membership in the American Hospital Association.

AURORA WEST ALLIS MEDICAL CENTER (O, 219 beds) 8901 West Lincoln Avenue, West Allis, WI, Zip 53227–2409, Mailing Address: P.O. Box 27901, 53227–0901, tel. 414/328–6000; Holly Schmidtke, R.N., Interim President
**Web address**: www.aurorahealthcare.org

| Owned, leased, sponsored: | 24 hospitals | 5306 beds |
|---|---|---|
| Contract–managed: | 0 hospitals | 0 beds |
| Totals: | 24 hospitals | 5306 beds |

---

### 0312: AHMC & HEALTHCARE, INC. (IO)
55 South Raymond Avenue, Suite 105, Alhambra, CA Zip 91801–7101; tel. 626/457–7400; Jonathan Wu, M.D., President and Chairman
**(Independent Hospital System)**

CALIFORNIA:  AHMC ANAHEIM REGIONAL MEDICAL CENTER (O, 223 beds) 1111 West La Palma Avenue, Anaheim, CA, Zip 92801–2881; tel. 714/774–1450; Richard Castro, Chief Executive Officer

ALHAMBRA HOSPITAL MEDICAL CENTER (O, 144 beds) 100 South Raymond Avenue, Alhambra, CA, Zip 91801–3199, Mailing Address: P.O. Box 510, 91802–2510, tel. 626/570–1606; Iris Lai, Chief Executive Officer
**Web address**: www.alhambrahospital.com

GARFIELD MEDICAL CENTER (O, 195 beds) 525 North Garfield Avenue, Monterey Park, CA, Zip 91754–1205; tel. 626/573–2222; Patrick A. Petre, Chief Executive Officer
**Web address**: www.garfieldmedicalcenter.com

GREATER EL MONTE COMMUNITY HOSPITAL (O, 117 beds) 1701 Santa Anita Avenue, South El Monte, CA, Zip 91733–3411; tel. 626/579–7777; Stanley Toy Jr, M.D., Chief Executive Officer
**Web address**: www.greaterelmonte.com

MONTEREY PARK HOSPITAL (O, 101 beds) 900 South Atlantic Boulevard, Monterey Park, CA, Zip 91754–4780; tel. 626/570–9000; Philip A. Cohen, Chief Executive Officer

PARKVIEW COMMUNITY HOSPITAL MEDICAL CENTER (O, 193 beds) 3865 Jackson Street, Riverside, CA, Zip 92503–3998; tel. 951/688–2211; Steven Popkin, Chief Executive Officer
**Web address**: www.pchmc.org

SAN GABRIEL VALLEY MEDICAL CENTER (O, 273 beds) 438 West Las Tunas Drive, San Gabriel, CA, Zip 91776–1216, Mailing Address: P.O. Box 1507, 91778–1507, tel. 626/289–5454; Jonathon F. Aquino, Chief Executive Officer
**Web address**: www.sgvmc.org

WHITTIER HOSPITAL MEDICAL CENTER (O, 100 beds) 9080 Colima Road, Whittier, CA, Zip 90605–1600; tel. 562/945–3561; Richard Castro, Chief Executive Officer
**Web address**: www.whittierhospital.com

| Owned, leased, sponsored: | 8 hospitals | 1346 beds |
|---|---|---|
| Contract–managed: | 0 hospitals | 0 beds |
| Totals: | 8 hospitals | 1346 beds |

---

### 0225: ALAMEDA HEALTH SYSTEM (NP)
15400 Foothill Boulevard, San Leandro, CA Zip 94578–1009; tel. 510/677–7920; Delvecchio Finley, Chief Executive Officer
**(Moderately Centralized Health System)**

CALIFORNIA:  ALAMEDA HOSPITAL (O, 215 beds) 2070 Clinton Avenue, Alameda, CA, Zip 94501–4397; tel. 510/522–3700; Delvecchio Finley, Chief Executive Officer
**Web address**: www.alamedahealthsystem.org

HIGHLAND HOSPITAL (O, 372 beds) 1411 East 31st Street, Oakland, CA, Zip 94602–1018; tel. 510/437–4800; Delvecchio Finley, Chief Executive Officer
**Web address**: www.alamedahealthsystem.org

SAN LEANDRO HOSPITAL (O, 48 beds) 13855 East 14th Street, San Leandro, CA, Zip 94578–2600; tel. 510/357–6500; James E T. Jackson, M.P.H., Chief Administrative Officer
**Web address**: www.sanleandrohospital.org

| Owned, leased, sponsored: | 3 hospitals | 635 beds |
|---|---|---|
| Contract–managed: | 0 hospitals | 0 beds |
| Totals: | 3 hospitals | 635 beds |

---

### 1020: ALECTO HEALTHCARE (IO)
16310 Bake Parkway, Suite 200, Irvine, CA Zip 92618–4684; tel. 949/783–3988; Lex Reddy, Chief Executive Officer
**(Independent Hospital System)**

CALIFORNIA:  OLYMPIA MEDICAL CENTER (O, 204 beds) 5900 West Olympic Boulevard, Los Angeles, CA, Zip 90036–4671; tel. 310/657–5900; Matthew Williams, R.N., Chief Executive Officer

ST. ROSE HOSPITAL (C, 150 beds) 27200 Calaroga Avenue, Hayward, CA, Zip 94545–4383; tel. 510/264–4000; Aman Dhuper, President and Chief Executive Officer
**Web address**: www.srhca.org

TEXAS:  WILSON N. JONES REGIONAL MEDICAL CENTER (O, 109 beds) 500 North Highland Avenue, Sherman, TX, Zip 75092–7354; tel. 903/870–4611; Cory Countryman, Chief Executive Officer

| Owned, leased, sponsored: | 2 hospitals | 313 beds |
|---|---|---|
| Contract–managed: | 1 hospitals | 150 beds |
| Totals: | 3 hospitals | 463 beds |

---

### ★0199: ALLEGHENY HEALTH NETWORK (NP)
120 5th Avenue, FAPHM–294E, Pittsburgh, PA Zip 15222–3000; tel. 412/359–3131; Cynthia Hundorfean, President and Chief Executive Officer
**(Independent Hospital System)**

NEW YORK:  WESTFIELD MEMORIAL HOSPITAL (O, 4 beds) 189 East Main Street, Westfield, NY, Zip 14787–1195; tel. 716/326–4921; Karen Surkala, President
**Web address**: https://www.ahn.org/locations/westfield–memorial–hospital

PENNSYLVANIA:  AHN GROVE CITY (O, 35 beds) 631 North Broad Street Extension, Grove City, PA, Zip 16127–4603; tel. 724/450–7000; Allan Klapper, M.D., Chief Executive Officer
**Web address**: www.gcmcpa.org

ALLEGHENY GENERAL HOSPITAL (O, 401 beds) 320 East North Avenue, Pittsburgh, PA, Zip 15212–4756; tel. 412/359–3131; David S. Parda, M.D., President

ALLEGHENY VALLEY HOSPITAL (O, 83 beds) 1301 Carlisle Street, Natrona Heights, PA, Zip 15065–1152; tel. 724/224–5100; Vicenta Gaspar-Yoo, M.D., President and Chief Executive Officer
**Web address**: www.wpahs.org

CANONSBURG HOSPITAL (O, 42 beds) 100 Medical Boulevard, Canonsburg, PA, Zip 15317–9762; tel. 724/745–6100; Chong Park, M.D., President

FORBES HOSPITAL (O, 315 beds) 2570 Haymaker Road, Monroeville, PA, Zip 15146–3513; tel. 412/858–2000; Mark Rubino, M.D., President
**Web address**: www.ahn.org

JEFFERSON HOSPITAL (O, 303 beds) 565 Coal Valley Road, Jefferson Hills, PA, Zip 15025–3703, Box 18119, Pittsburgh, 15236–0119, tel. 412/469–5000; Chong Park, M.D., President

SAINT VINCENT HOSPITAL (O, 280 beds) 232 West 25th Street, Erie, PA, Zip 16544–0002; tel. 814/452–5000; Christopher Clark, D.O., President and Chief Executive Officer
**Web address**: www.svhs.org

WEST PENN HOSPITAL (O, 270 beds) 4800 Friendship Avenue, Pittsburgh, PA, Zip 15224–1722; tel. 412/578–5000; Ronald J. Andro, R.N., MS, President and Chief Executive Officer
**Web address**: www.wpahs.org

| Owned, leased, sponsored: | 9 hospitals | 1733 beds |
|---|---|---|
| Contract–managed: | 0 hospitals | 0 beds |
| Totals: | 9 hospitals | 1733 beds |

---

### 0413: ALLEGIANCE HEALTH MANAGEMENT (IO)
504 Texas Street, Suite 200, Shreveport, LA Zip 71101–3526; tel. 318/226–8202; Rock Bordelon, President and Chief Executive Officer
**(Independent Hospital System)**

---

For explanation of codes following names, see page B2.
★ Indicates Type III membership in the American Hospital Association.

**ARKANSAS:** EUREKA SPRINGS HOSPITAL (O, 15 beds) 24 Norris Street, Eureka Springs, AR, Zip 72632–3541; tel. 479/253–7400; Kathy Hall, Interim Chief Executive Officer
**Web address:** www.eurekaspringshospital.com

**LOUISIANA:** BIENVILLE MEDICAL CENTER (O, 21 beds) 1175 Pine Street, Suite 200, Arcadia, LA, Zip 71001–3122; tel. 318/263–4700; Kirk Lemoine, Chief Executive Officer
**Web address:** www.bienvillemedicalcenter.net/

BYRD REGIONAL HOSPITAL (O, 60 beds) 1020 West Fertitta Boulevard, Leesville, LA, Zip 71446–4645; tel. 337/239–9041; Kevin Quinn, Chief Executive Officer
**Web address:** www.byrdregional.com/

MERCY REGIONAL MEDICAL CENTER (O, 109 beds) 800 East Main Street, Ville Platte, LA, Zip 70586–4618; tel. 337/363–5684; Kristopher Aguillard, Chief Executive Officer
**Web address:** www.mercyregionalmedicalcenter.com

MINDEN MEDICAL CENTER (O, 161 beds) 1 Medical Plaza Place, Minden, LA, Zip 71055–3330, Mailing Address: P.O. Box 5003, 71058–5003, tel. 318/377–2321; James R. Williams, Chief Executive Officer
**Web address:** www.mindenmedicalcenter.com

NORTHERN LOUISIANA MEDICAL CENTER (O, 91 beds) 401 East Vaughn Avenue, Ruston, LA, Zip 71270–5950; tel. 318/254–2100; Keith Newton, Chief Executive Officer
**Web address:** www.northernlouisianamedicalcenter.com

SABINE MEDICAL CENTER (O, 24 beds) 240 Highland Drive, Many, LA, Zip 71449–3718; tel. 318/256–5691; Dale Anderson, Chief Executive Officer

**MISSISSIPPI:** ALLEGIANCE SPECIALTY HOSPITAL OF GREENVILLE (O, 39 beds) 300 South Washington Avenue, 3rd Floor, Greenville, MS, Zip 38701–4719; tel. 662/332–7344; Vearnail Herzog, Chief Executive Officer
**Web address:** www.ahmgt.com

**TEXAS:** ALLEGIANCE BEHAVIORAL HEALTH CENTER OF PLAINVIEW (O, 20 beds) 2601 Dimmit Road, Suite 400, Suite 400, Plainview, TX, Zip 79072–1833; tel. 806/296–9191; William E. Ernst, Chief Executive Officer

| Owned, leased, sponsored: | 9 hospitals | 540 beds |
| Contract–managed: | 0 hospitals | 0 beds |
| Totals: | 9 hospitals | 540 beds |

**0317: ALLIANT MANAGEMENT SERVICES** (IO)
2650 Eastpoint Parkway, Suite 300, Louisville, KY Zip 40223–5164; tel. 502/992–3525; Jim L. Coleman Jr, President and Chief Executive Officer
**(Moderately Centralized Health System)**

**FLORIDA:** CALHOUN–LIBERTY HOSPITAL (C, 25 beds) 20370 NE Burns Avenue, Blountstown, FL, Zip 32424–1045, Mailing Address: P.O. Box 419, 32424–0419, tel. 850/674–5411; Janet Kinney, Chief Executive Officer
**Web address:** www.calhounlibertyhospital.com

NORTHWEST FLORIDA COMMUNITY HOSPITAL (C, 59 beds) 1360 Brickyard Road, Chipley, FL, Zip 32428–6303, Mailing Address: P.O. Box 889, 32428–0889, tel. 850/638–1610; Michael A. Kozar, Chief Executive Officer
**Web address:** www.nfch.org

**ILLINOIS:** FAYETTE COUNTY HOSPITAL (O, 110 beds) 650 West Taylor Street, Vandalia, IL, Zip 62471–1296; tel. 618/283–1231; Gregory D. Starnes, Chief Executive Officer
**Web address:** www.fayettecountyhospital.org

GIBSON AREA HOSPITAL AND HEALTH SERVICES (C, 67 beds) 1120 North Melvin Street, Gibson City, IL, Zip 60936–1477, Mailing Address: P.O. Box 429, 60936–0429, tel. 217/784–4251; Robert C. Schmitt II, CPA, FACHE, Chief Executive Officer

PARIS COMMUNITY HOSPITAL (C, 25 beds) 721 East Court Street, Paris, IL, Zip 61944–2460; tel. 217/465–4141; Oliver Smith, President and Chief Executive Officer
**Web address:** www.pariscommunityhospital.com

WABASH GENERAL HOSPITAL (C, 25 beds) 1418 College Drive, Mount Carmel, IL, Zip 62863–2638; tel. 618/262–8621; Karissa Turner, President and Chief Executive Officer

**INDIANA:** PERRY COUNTY MEMORIAL HOSPITAL (C, 25 beds) 8885 State Road 237, Tell City, IN, Zip 47586–2750; tel. 812/547–7011; Brian J. Herwig, President and Chief Executive Officer
**Web address:** www.pchospital.org

**KENTUCKY:** BRECKINRIDGE MEMORIAL HOSPITAL (C, 43 beds) 1011 Old Highway 60, Hardinsburg, KY, Zip 40143–2597; tel. 270/756–7000; Angela Portman, Chief Executive Officer
**Web address:** www.breckinridgehealth.org/

CARROLL COUNTY MEMORIAL HOSPITAL (C, 25 beds) 309 11th Street, Carrollton, KY, Zip 41008–1400; tel. 502/732–4321; Harry Hays, Chief Executive Officer

TWIN LAKES REGIONAL MEDICAL CENTER (C, 75 beds) 910 Wallace Avenue, Leitchfield, KY, Zip 42754–2414; tel. 270/259–9400; Wayne Meriwether, Chief Executive Officer
**Web address:** www.tlrmc.com

| Owned, leased, sponsored: | 1 hospitals | 110 beds |
| Contract–managed: | 9 hospitals | 369 beds |
| Totals: | 10 hospitals | 479 beds |

**★0041: ALLINA HEALTH** (NP)
2925 Chicago Avenue, Minneapolis, MN Zip 55407–1321, Mailing Address: P.O. Box 43, 55440–0043, tel. 612/262–5000; Penny Ann. Wheeler, M.D., Chief Executive Officer
**(Moderately Centralized Health System)**

**MINNESOTA:** ABBOTT NORTHWESTERN HOSPITAL (O, 697 beds) 800 East 28th Street, Minneapolis, MN, Zip 55407–3799; tel. 612/863–4000; Ann Madden Rice, President
**Web address:** www.abbottnorthwestern.com

BUFFALO HOSPITAL (O, 39 beds) 303 Catlin Street, Buffalo, MN, Zip 55313–1947; tel. 763/682–1212; Kelly Spratt, President

CAMBRIDGE MEDICAL CENTER (O, 57 beds) 701 South Dellwood Street, Cambridge, MN, Zip 55008–1920; tel. 763/689–7700; Kelly Spratt, President
**Web address:** www.allina.com/ahs/cambridge.nsf

DISTRICT ONE HOSPITAL (O, 34 beds) 200 State Avenue, Faribault, MN, Zip 55021–6345; tel. 507/334–6451; David L. Albrecht, President
**Web address:** www.allinahealth.org/District–One–Hospital/

MERCY HOSPITAL (O, 471 beds) 4050 Coon Rapids Boulevard, Coon Rapids, MN, Zip 55433–2586; tel. 763/236–6000; Sara J. Criger, President

NEW ULM MEDICAL CENTER (O, 44 beds) 1324 Fifth Street North, New Ulm, MN, Zip 56073–1553; tel. 507/217–5000; Toby Freier, President
**Web address:** www.newulmmedicalcenter.com

OWATONNA HOSPITAL (O, 42 beds) 2250 NW 26th Street, Owatonna, MN, Zip 55060–5503; tel. 507/451–3850; David L. Albrecht, President
**Web address:** www.owatonnahospital.com

REGINA HOSPITAL (O, 49 beds) 1175 Nininger Road, Hastings, MN, Zip 55033–1098; tel. 651/480–4100; Helen J. Strike, R.N., President

ST. FRANCIS REGIONAL MEDICAL CENTER (O, 89 beds) 1455 St Francis Avenue, Shakopee, MN, Zip 55379–3380; tel. 952/428–3000; Amy L. Jerdee, R.N., President
**Web address:** www.stfrancis–shakopee.com

UNITED HOSPITAL (O, 380 beds) 333 North Smith Avenue, Saint Paul, MN, Zip 55102–2389; tel. 651/241–8000; Thomas O'Connor, President

**WISCONSIN:** RIVER FALLS AREA HOSPITAL (O, 18 beds) 1629 East Division Street, River Falls, WI, Zip 54022–1571; tel. 715/425–6155; Helen J. Strike, R.N., President
**Web address:** www.allina.com

| Owned, leased, sponsored: | 11 hospitals | 1920 beds |
| Contract–managed: | 0 hospitals | 0 beds |
| Totals: | 11 hospitals | 1920 beds |

**0877: ALTAPOINTE HEALTH SYSTEMS** (IO)
5750–A Southland Drive, Mobile, AL Zip 36693–3316; tel. 251/473–4423; J. Tuerk. Schlesinger, Chief Executive Officer

For explanation of codes following names, see page B2.
★ Indicates Type III membership in the American Hospital Association.

**ALABAMA:** BAYPOINTE BEHAVIORAL HEALTH (O, 60 beds) 5800 Southland Drive, Mobile, AL, Zip 36693–3313; tel. 251/661–0153; Jarett Crum, Hospital Director
**Web address:** www.altapointe.org

EASTPOINTE HOSPITAL (O, 50 beds) 7400 Roper Lane, Daphne, AL, Zip 36526–5274; tel. 251/378–6500; Philip L. Cusa, Hospital Director
**Web address:** www.altapointe.org/eastpointe.php

| | | |
|---|---|---|
| Owned, leased, sponsored: | 2 hospitals | 110 beds |
| Contract–managed: | 0 hospitals | 0 beds |
| Totals: | 2 hospitals | 110 beds |

**2295: AMERICAN PROVINCE OF LITTLE COMPANY OF MARY SISTERS** (CO)
9350 South California Avenue, Evergreen Park, IL Zip 60805–2595; tel. 708/229–5095; Sister, Carol Pacini, Region Leader
**(Moderately Centralized Health System)**

**INDIANA:** MEMORIAL HOSPITAL AND HEALTH CARE CENTER (O, 137 beds) 800 West Ninth Street, Jasper, IN, Zip 47546–2516; tel. 812/996–2345; E Kyle. Bennett, President and Chief Executive Officer
**Web address:** www.mhhcc.org

| | | |
|---|---|---|
| Owned, leased, sponsored: | 1 hospitals | 137 beds |
| Contract–managed: | 0 hospitals | 0 beds |
| Totals: | 1 hospitals | 137 beds |

**0644: AMG INTEGRATED HEALTHCARE MANAGEMENT** (IO)
101 La Rue France, Suite 500, Lafayette, LA Zip 70508–3144; tel. 337/269–9828; Timothy W. Howard, Chief Executive Officer
**(Independent Hospital System)**

**KANSAS:** AMG SPECIALTY HOSPITAL–WICHITA (O, 26 beds) 8080 East Pawnee Street, Wichita, KS, Zip 67207–5475; tel. 316/682–0004; Robert A. Loepp Jr, FACHE, Chief Executive Officer
**Web address:** www.amgwichita.com/

**LOUISIANA:** AMG PHYSICAL REHABILITATION HOSPITAL (O, 24 beds) 5025 Keystone Boulevard, Suite 200, Covington, LA, Zip 70433; tel. 985/888–0301; John Derrick. Landreneau, R.N., Chief Executive Officer

AMG SPECIALTY HOSPITAL–HOUMA (O, 40 beds) 629 Dunn Street, Houma, LA, Zip 70360–4707; tel. 985/274–0001; Rachel Mayeaux, Chief Executive Officer
**Web address:** www.amghouma.com/

AMG SPECIALTY HOSPITAL–LAFAYETTE (O, 18 beds) 4811 Ambassador Caffery Parkway, 4th Floor, Lafayette, LA, Zip 70508–7265; tel. 337/839–9880; April Ebeling, Chief Executive Officer

AMG SPECIALTY HOSPITAL–ZACHARY (O, 16 beds) 4601 McHugh Road, Building B, Zachary, LA, Zip 70791–5348; tel. 225/683–1600; Meagan Falgout, Chief Executive Officer
**Web address:** www.amgzachary.com/

LAFAYETTE PHYSICAL REHABILITATION HOSPITAL (O, 32 beds) 307 Polly Lane, Lafayette, LA, Zip 70508–4960; tel. 337/314–1111; Bruce J. Bartels, Chief Executive Officer

THE NEUROMEDICAL CENTER REHABILITATION HOSPITAL (O, 23 beds) 10101 Park Rowe Avenue, Suite 500, Baton Rouge, LA, Zip 70810–1685; tel. 225/906–2999; Bradley Pevey, Chief Executive Officer
**Web address:** www.theneuromedicalcenter.com

**NEVADA:** AMG SPECIALTY HOSPITAL – LAS VEGAS (O, 24 beds) 4015 Mcleod Drive, Las Vegas, NV, Zip 89121–4305; tel. 702/433–2200; Phyllis Mauro, Chief Executive Officer
**Web address:** www.amgihm.com/locations/#map_top

**NEW MEXICO:** AMG SPECIALTY HOSPITAL–ALBUQUERQUE (O, 24 beds) 5400 Gibson Boulevard SE, 3rd Floor, Albuquerque, NM, Zip 87108–4729, 5400 Gibson Boulevad SE, 3rd Floor, 87108–4729, tel. 505/842–5550; Kendra Camp, R.N., Chief Executive Officer

**OKLAHOMA:** OKC–AMG SPECIALTY HOSPITAL (O, 30 beds) 4300 West Memorial Road, 2nd Floor, Oklahoma City, OK, Zip 73120–8304; tel. 405/936–5822; Erick Heflin, R.N., Chief Executive Officer
**Web address:** www.https://amgmercy.com/

| | | |
|---|---|---|
| Owned, leased, sponsored: | 10 hospitals | 257 beds |
| Contract–managed: | 0 hospitals | 0 beds |
| Totals: | 10 hospitals | 257 beds |

**★0389: ANMED HEALTH** (NP)
800 North Fant Street, Anderson, SC Zip 29621–5793; tel. 864/512–1000; William A. Kenley, Chief Executive Officer
**(Independent Hospital System)**

**SOUTH CAROLINA:** ANMED HEALTH CANNON (O, 24 beds) 123 W G Acker Drive, Pickens, SC, Zip 29671–2739, Mailing Address: P.O. Box 188, 29671–0188, tel. 864/878–4791; Brandon Clary, President and Chief Executive Officer
**Web address:** www.cannonhospital.org

ANMED HEALTH MEDICAL CENTER (O, 358 beds) 800 North Fant Street, Anderson, SC, Zip 29621–5793; tel. 864/512–1000; William A. Kenley, Chief Executive Officer

| | | |
|---|---|---|
| Owned, leased, sponsored: | 2 hospitals | 382 beds |
| Contract–managed: | 0 hospitals | 0 beds |
| Totals: | 2 hospitals | 382 beds |

**★0866: APPALACHIAN REGIONAL HEALTHCARE SYSTEM** (NP)
336 Deerfield Road, Boone, NC Zip 28607–5008, Mailing Address: P.O. Box 2600, 28607–2600, tel. 828/262–4100; Charles Mantooth, President and Chief Executive Officer
**(Independent Hospital System)**

**NORTH CAROLINA:** BLOWING ROCK REHABILITATION & DAVANT EXTENDED CARE CENTER (C, 72 beds) 418 Chestnut Street, Blowing Rock, NC, Zip 28605–0148, Mailing Address: P.O. Box 148, 28605–0148, tel. 828/295–3136; Elizabeth Hayes, R.N., Interim Administrator

CHARLES A. CANNON MEMORIAL HOSPITAL (C, 35 beds) 434 Hospital Drive, Newland, NC, Zip 28646, Mailing Address: P.O. Box 767, Linville, 28646–0767, tel. 828/737–7000; Carmen Lacey, MSN, R.N., President
**Web address:** www.https://apprhs.org/locations/cannon–memorial–hospital

WATAUGA MEDICAL CENTER (C, 99 beds) 336 Deerfield Road, Boone, NC, Zip 28607–5008, Mailing Address: P.O. Box 2600, 28607–2600, tel. 828/262–4100; Charles Mantooth, President and Chief Executive Officer
**Web address:** www.https://apprhs.org/contact-us

| | | |
|---|---|---|
| Owned, leased, sponsored: | 0 hospitals | 0 beds |
| Contract–managed: | 3 hospitals | 206 beds |
| Totals: | 3 hospitals | 206 beds |

**0145: APPALACHIAN REGIONAL HEALTHCARE, INC.** (NP)
2260 Executive Drive, Lexington, KY Zip 40505–4810, Mailing Address: P.O. Box 8086, 40533–8086, tel. 859/226–2440; Joseph Grossman, President and Chief Executive Officer
**(Moderately Centralized Health System)**

**KENTUCKY:** ARH OUR LADY OF THE WAY (O, 25 beds) 11203 Main Street, Martin, KY, Zip 41649; tel. 606/285–6400; Kathy Stumbo, President
**Web address:** www.saintjosephmartin.org

HARLAN ARH HOSPITAL (O, 103 beds) 81 Ball Park Road, Harlan, KY, Zip 40831–1792; tel. 606/573–8100; Donald R. Fields, Community Chief Executive Officer

HAZARD ARH REGIONAL MEDICAL CENTER (O, 358 beds) 100 Medical Center Drive, Hazard, KY, Zip 41701–9421; tel. 606/439–6600; Dan Stone, Senior Community Chief Executive Officer
**Web address:** www.arh.org

HIGHLANDS ARH REGIONAL MEDICAL CENTER (O, 139 beds) 5000 Kentucky Route 321, Prestonsburg, KY, Zip 41653–1273, Mailing Address: P.O. Box 668, 41653–0668, tel. 606/886–8511; Timothy A. Hatfield, Community Chief Executive Officer
**Web address:** www.arh.org

For explanation of codes following names, see page B2.
★ Indicates Type III membership in the American Hospital Association.

MARY BRECKINRIDGE ARH HOSPITAL (O, 25 beds) 130 Kate Ireland Drive, Hyden, KY, Zip 41749–9071, Mailing Address: P.O. Box 447–A, 41749–0717, tel. 606/672–2901; Mallie S. Noble, Administrator

MCDOWELL ARH HOSPITAL (O, 25 beds) Route 122, McDowell, KY, Zip 41647, Mailing Address: P.O. Box 247, 41647–0247, tel. 606/377–3400; Russell Barker, Community Chief Executive Officer
**Web address:** www.arh.org

MIDDLESBORO ARH HOSPITAL (O, 46 beds) 3600 West Cumberland Avenue, Middlesboro, KY, Zip 40965–2614, Mailing Address: P.O. Box 340, 40965–0340, tel. 606/242–1100; Michael Slusher, FACHE, Community Chief Executive Officer
**Web address:** www.arh.org/middlesboro

MORGAN COUNTY ARH HOSPITAL (L, 25 beds) 476 Liberty Road, West Liberty, KY, Zip 41472–2049, P O Box 579, 41472–0579, tel. 606/743–3186; Stephen M. Gavalchik, FACHE, Community Chief Executive Officer
**Web address:** www.arh.org

TUG VALLEY ARH REGIONAL MEDICAL CENTER (O, 123 beds) 260 Hospital Drive, South Williamson, KY, Zip 41503–4072; tel. 606/237–1710; Timothy A. Hatfield, Community Chief Executive Officer

WHITESBURG ARH HOSPITAL (O, 90 beds) 240 Hospital Road, Whitesburg, KY, Zip 41858–7627; tel. 606/633–3500; Dena C. Sparkman, Community Chief Executive Officer
**Web address:** www.arh.org/whitesburg

**WEST VIRGINIA:** BECKLEY ARH HOSPITAL (O, 167 beds) 306 Stanaford Road, Beckley, WV, Zip 25801–3142; tel. 304/255–3000; Rocco K. Massey, Community Chief Executive Officer

SUMMERS COUNTY ARH HOSPITAL (L, 25 beds) 115 Summers Hospital Road, Hinton, WV, Zip 25951–5172, Mailing Address: P.O. Box 940, 25951–0940, tel. 304/466–1000; Wesley Dangerfield, Community Chief Executive Officer
**Web address:** www.arh.org

| | | |
|---|---|---|
| Owned, leased, sponsored: | 12 hospitals | 1151 beds |
| Contract–managed: | 0 hospitals | 0 beds |
| Totals: | 12 hospitals | 1151 beds |

---

**★0104: ARCHBOLD MEDICAL CENTER** (NP)
910 South Broad Street, Thomasville, GA Zip 31792–6113; tel. 229/228–2739; J. Perry Mustian, President and Chief Executive Officer
**(Moderately Centralized Health System)**

**GEORGIA:** BROOKS COUNTY HOSPITAL (L, 25 beds) 903 North Court Street, Quitman, GA, Zip 31643–1315, Mailing Address: P.O. Box 5000, 31643–5000, tel. 229/263–4171; Nancy M. Williams, R.N., Administrator
**Web address:** www.archbold.org

GRADY GENERAL HOSPITAL (L, 39 beds) 1155 Fifth Street SE, Cairo, GA, Zip 39828–3142, Mailing Address: P.O. Box 360, 39828–0360, tel. 229/377–1150; Crystal Wells, Administrator

JOHN D. ARCHBOLD MEMORIAL HOSPITAL (O, 305 beds) 915 Gordon Avenue, Thomasville, GA, Zip 31792–6614, Mailing Address: P.O. Box 1018, 31799–1018, tel. 229/228–2000; J. Perry Mustian, President and Chief Executive Officer
**Web address:** www.archbold.org

MITCHELL COUNTY HOSPITAL (L, 181 beds) 90 East Stephens Street, Camilla, GA, Zip 31730–1836, Mailing Address: P.O. Box 639, 31730–0639, tel. 229/336–5284; James Womack, Administrator

| | | |
|---|---|---|
| Owned, leased, sponsored: | 4 hospitals | 550 beds |
| Contract–managed: | 0 hospitals | 0 beds |
| Totals: | 4 hospitals | 550 beds |

---

**★0069: ARDENT HEALTH SERVICES** (IO)
1 Burton Hills Boulevard, Suite 250, Nashville, TN Zip 37215–6195; tel. 615/296–3000; Marty J. Bonick, FACHE, President and Chief Executive Officer
**(Decentralized Health System)**

**IDAHO:** PORTNEUF MEDICAL CENTER (O, 175 beds) 777 Hospital Way, Pocatello, ID, Zip 83201–5175; tel. 208/239–1000; Jordan Herget, Chief Executive Officer
**Web address:** www.portmed.org

**KANSAS:** UNIVERSITY OF KANSAS HEALTH SYSTEM ST. FRANCIS CAMPUS (O, 264 beds) 1700 SW 7th Street, Topeka, KS, Zip 66606–1690; tel. 785/295–8000; Steven Anderson, Chief Executive Officer

**NEW JERSEY:** HACKENSACK MERIDIAN HEALTH MOUNTAINSIDE MEDICAL CENTER (O, 202 beds) 1 Bay Avenue, Montclair, NJ, Zip 07042–4898; tel. 973/429–6000; Tim O'Brien, Chief Executive Officer
**Web address:** www.mountainsidenow.com

HACKENSACK MERIDIAN HEALTH PASCACK VALLEY MEDICAL CENTER (O, 128 beds) 250 Old Hook Road, Westwood, NJ, Zip 07675–3123; tel. 201/383–1035; Emily L. Holliman, Chief Executive Officer
**Web address:** www.hackensackumcpv.com/

**NEW MEXICO:** LOVELACE MEDICAL CENTER (O, 247 beds) 601 Martin Luther King Avenue NE, Albuquerque, NM, Zip 87102–3619; tel. 505/727–8000; Denzil Ross, Interim Chief Executive Officer

LOVELACE REGIONAL HOSPITAL – ROSWELL (O, 26 beds) 117 East 19th Street, Roswell, NM, Zip 88201–5151; tel. 575/627–7000; Buddy Daniels, Chief Executive Officer
**Web address:** www.lovelace.com

LOVELACE UNM REHABILITATION HOSPITAL (O, 52 beds) 505 Elm Street NE, Albuquerque, NM, Zip 87102–2500; tel. 505/727–4700; Derrick Jones, Chief Executive Officer
**Web address:** www.lovelace.com

LOVELACE WESTSIDE HOSPITAL (O, 80 beds) 10501 Golf Course Road NW, Albuquerque, NM, Zip 87114–5000; tel. 505/727–8000; Amy Blasing, Chief Executive Officer

LOVELACE WOMEN'S HOSPITAL (O, 78 beds) 4701 Montgomery Boulevard NE, Albuquerque, NM, Zip 87109–1251; tel. 505/727–7800; Sheri Milone, Chief Executive Officer and Administrator
**Web address:** www.lovelace.com/albuquerque–hospital/lovelace–womens–hospital#.UDZ17KDhf48

**OKLAHOMA:** BAILEY MEDICAL CENTER (O, 37 beds) 10502 North 110th East Avenue, Owasso, OK, Zip 74055–6655; tel. 918/376–8000; Keith Mason, Chief Executive Officer

HILLCREST HOSPITAL – SOUTH (O, 168 beds) 8801 South 101st East Avenue, Tulsa, OK, Zip 74133–5716; tel. 918/294–4000; Bennett Geister, Chief Executive Officer
**Web address:** www.southcresthospital.com

HILLCREST HOSPITAL CLAREMORE (O, 49 beds) 1202 North Muskogee Place, Claremore, OK, Zip 74017–3036; tel. 918/341–2556; David Chaussard, Chief Executive Officer
**Web address:** www.hillcrestclaremore.com

HILLCREST HOSPITAL CUSHING (O, 54 beds) 1027 East Cherry Street, Cushing, OK, Zip 74023–4101; tel. 918/225–2915; David Long, Interim Chief Executive Officer
**Web address:** www.hillcrestcushing.com/

HILLCREST HOSPITAL HENRYETTA (O, 39 beds) 2401 West Main Street, Henryetta, OK, Zip 74437–3893, Mailing Address: P.O. Box 1269, 74437–1269, tel. 918/650–1100; Dee Renshaw, Chief Executive Officer
**Web address:** www.hillcresthenryetta.com/

HILLCREST HOSPITAL PRYOR (O, 22 beds) 111 North Bailey Street, Pryor, OK, Zip 74361–4201; tel. 918/825–1600; Douglas K. Weaver, FACHE, Chief Executive Officer
**Web address:** www.hillcrestpryor.com/

HILLCREST MEDICAL CENTER (O, 510 beds) 1120 South Utica Avenue, Tulsa, OK, Zip 74104–4090; tel. 918/579–1000; Xavier Villarreal, FACHE, Chief Executive Officer
**Web address:** www.hillcrestmedicalcenter.com

TULSA SPINE AND SPECIALTY HOSPITAL (O, 38 beds) 6901 South Olympia Avenue, Tulsa, OK, Zip 74132–1843; tel. 918/388–5701; Trent Gastineau, Chief Executive Officer

**TEXAS:** BSA HOSPITAL, LLC (O, 355 beds) 1600 Wallace Boulevard, Amarillo, TX, Zip 79106–1799; tel. 806/212–2000; Bob Williams, President and Chief Executive Officer
**Web address:** www.bsahs.org

PHYSICIANS SURGICAL HOSPITAL – QUAIL CREEK (O, 40 beds) 6819 Plum Creek, Amarillo, TX, Zip 79124–1602; tel. 806/354–6100; Todd Greene, Chief Executive Officer
**Web address:** www.physurg.com

---

For explanation of codes following names, see page B2.
★ Indicates Type III membership in the American Hospital Association.

Section B

SETON MEDICAL CENTER HARKER HEIGHTS (O, 83 beds) 850 West Central Texas Expressway, Harker Heights, TX, Zip 76548–1890; tel. 254/690–0900; Patrick Swindle, Chief Executive Officer
**Web address:** www.setonharkerheights.net

UT HEALTH ATHENS (O, 90 beds) 2000 South Palestine Street, Athens, TX, Zip 75751–5610; tel. 903/676–1000; Scott Campbell, Chief Executive Officer

UT HEALTH CARTHAGE (O, 23 beds) 409 Cottage Road, Carthage, TX, Zip 75633–1466; tel. 903/693–3841; Mark Leitner, FACHE, Chief Executive Officer
**Web address:** www.https://uthealthcarthage.com/

UT HEALTH EAST TEXAS REHABILITATION HOSPITAL (O, 36 beds) 701 Olympic Plaza Circle, Tyler, TX, Zip 75701–1950, Mailing Address: P.O. Box 7530, 75711–7530, tel. 903/596–3000; Laurie Lehnhof–Watts, Administrator and Chief Nursing Officer

UT HEALTH HENDERSON (O, 41 beds) 300 Wilson Street, Henderson, TX, Zip 75652–5956; tel. 903/657–7541; Mark Leitner, FACHE, Administrator
**Web address:** www.https://uthealthhenderson.com/

UT HEALTH JACKSONVILLE (O, 38 beds) 501 South Ragsdale Street, Jacksonville, TX, Zip 75766–2413; tel. 903/541–5000; DeLeigh Haley, Chief Executive Officer
**Web address:** www.https://uthealthjacksonville.com/

UT HEALTH PITTSBURG (O, 25 beds) 2701 Highway 271 North, Pittsburg, TX, Zip 75686–1032; tel. 903/946–5000; Casey Mayben, Interim Chief Executive Officer
**Web address:** www.https://uthealthpittsburg.com/

UT HEALTH QUITMAN (O, 25 beds) 117 Winnsboro Street, Quitman, TX, Zip 75783–2144, Mailing Address: P.O. Box 1000, 75783–1000, tel. 903/763–6300; Robert Terry, Interim Chief Executive Officer
**Web address:** www.https://uthealthquitman.com/

UT HEALTH SPECIALTY HOSPITAL (O, 30 beds) 1000 South Beckham, 5th Floor, Tyler, TX, Zip 75701–1908, Mailing Address: P.O. Box 7018, 75711–7018, tel. 903/596–3600; Jimmy Clark, Administrator

UT HEALTH TYLER (O, 399 beds) 1000 South Beckham Street, Tyler, TX, Zip 75701–1908, Box 6400, 75711–6400, tel. 903/597–0351; Vicki R. Briggs, Chief Executive Officer
**Web address:** www.https://uthealthtylerhospital.com/

| Owned, leased, sponsored: | 29 hospitals | 3354 beds |
|---|---|---|
| Contract–managed: | 0 hospitals | 0 beds |
| Totals: | 29 hospitals | 3354 beds |

---

**0809: ARNOT HEALTH** (NP)
600 Roe Avenue, Elmira, NY Zip 14905–1629; tel. 607/737–4100; Jonathan I. Lawrence, President and Chief Executive Officer
**(Independent Hospital System)**

**NEW YORK:** ARNOT OGDEN MEDICAL CENTER (O, 266 beds) 600 Roe Avenue, Elmira, NY, Zip 14905–1629; tel. 607/737–4100; Jonathan I. Lawrence, President and Chief Executive Officer

IRA DAVENPORT MEMORIAL HOSPITAL (O, 135 beds) 7571 State Route 54, Bath, NY, Zip 14810–9590; tel. 607/776–8500; Elizabeth Weir, MSN, R.N., Site Administrator and Vice President of Nursing
**Web address:** www.arnothealth.org

| Owned, leased, sponsored: | 2 hospitals | 401 beds |
|---|---|---|
| Contract–managed: | 0 hospitals | 0 beds |
| Totals: | 2 hospitals | 401 beds |

---

★**0094: ASANTE HEALTH SYSTEM** (NP)
2650 Siskiyou Boulevard, Suite 200, Medford, OR Zip 97504–8170; tel. 541/789–4100; Scott A. Kelly, President and Chief Executive Officer
**(Centralized Health System)**

**OREGON:** ASANTE ASHLAND COMMUNITY HOSPITAL (O, 38 beds) 280 Maple Street, Ashland, OR, Zip 97520–1593; tel. 541/201–4000; Sheila Clough, Chief Executive Officer
**Web address:** www.ashlandhospital.org

ASANTE ROGUE REGIONAL MEDICAL CENTER (O, 343 beds) 2825 East Barnett Road, Medford, OR, Zip 97504–8332; tel. 541/789–7000; Mick Zdeblick, Chief Executive Officer
**Web address:** www.asante.org

ASANTE THREE RIVERS MEDICAL CENTER (O, 122 beds) 500 SW Ramsey Avenue, Grants Pass, OR, Zip 97527–5554; tel. 541/472–7000; Win Howard, Chief Executive Officer

| Owned, leased, sponsored: | 3 hospitals | 503 beds |
|---|---|---|
| Contract–managed: | 0 hospitals | 0 beds |
| Totals: | 3 hospitals | 503 beds |

---

★**0198: ASCENSION HEALTHCARE** (CO)
101 South Hanley Road, Suite 450, Saint Louis, MO Zip 63105–3406; tel. 314/733–8000; Joseph R. Impicciche, JD, President and Chief Executive Officer
**(Decentralized Health System)**

**ALABAMA:** PROVIDENCE HOSPITAL (S, 305 beds) 6801 Airport Boulevard, Mobile, AL, Zip 36608–3785, Mailing Address: P.O. Box 850429, 36685–0429, tel. 251/633–1000; Todd S. Kennedy, President and Chief Executive Officer
**Web address:** www.providencehospital.org

ST. VINCENT'S BIRMINGHAM (S, 409 beds) 810 St Vincent's Drive, Birmingham, AL, Zip 35205–1695, Mailing Address: P.O. Box 12407, 35202–2407, tel. 205/939–7000; Andrew Gnann, President

ST. VINCENT'S BLOUNT (S, 25 beds) 150 Gilbreath, Oneonta, AL, Zip 35121–2827, Mailing Address: P.O. Box 1000, 35121–0013, tel. 205/274–3000; Suzannah Campbell, President
**Web address:** www.stvhs.com

ST. VINCENT'S CHILTON HOSPITAL (L, 36 beds) 2030 Lay Dam Road, Clanton, AL, Zip 35045; tel. 205/258–4400; Andrew Gnann, President

ST. VINCENT'S EAST (S, 362 beds) 50 Medical Park East Drive, Birmingham, AL, Zip 35235–9987; tel. 205/838–3000; Suzannah Campbell, President
**Web address:** www.stvhs.com

ST. VINCENT'S ST. CLAIR (S, 40 beds) 7063 Veterans Parkway, Pell City, AL, Zip 35125–1499; tel. 205/814–2105; Suzannah Campbell, President
**Web address:** www.stvhs.com

**FLORIDA:** BAY MEDICAL SACRED HEART (O, 74 beds) 615 North Bonita Avenue, Panama City, FL, Zip 32401–3600, Mailing Address: P.O. Box 59515, 32412–0515, tel. 850/769–1511; Heath Evans, President

SACRED HEART HOSPITAL PENSACOLA (S, 465 beds) 5151 North Ninth Avenue, Pensacola, FL, Zip 32504–8795, Mailing Address: P.O. Box 2700, 32513–2700, tel. 850/416–7000; Dawn Rudolph, President
**Web address:** www.https://healthcare.ascension.org/Locations/Florida/FLPEN/Pensacola–Sacred–Heart–Hospital–Pensacola

SACRED HEART HOSPITAL ON THE EMERALD COAST (S, 76 beds) 7800 Highway 98 West, Miramar Beach, FL, Zip 32550; tel. 850/278–3000; Henry Stovall, Regional President

SACRED HEART HOSPITAL ON THE GULF (S, 12 beds) 3801 East Highway 98, Port St Joe, FL, Zip 32456–5318; tel. 850/229–5600; Henry Stovall, Regional President
**Web address:** www.sacred–heart.org/gulf/

ST. VINCENT'S MEDICAL CENTER CLAY COUNTY (O, 106 beds) 1670 St. Vincent's Way, Middleburg, FL, Zip 32068–8427, 1670 St. Vincents Way, 32068–8447, tel. 904/602–1000; James Machado, President
**Web address:** www.jaxhealth.com/

ST. VINCENT'S MEDICAL CENTER RIVERSIDE (S, 479 beds) 1 Shircliff Way, Jacksonville, FL, Zip 32204–4748, Mailing Address: P.O. Box 2982, 32203–2982, tel. 904/308–7300; Thomas J. VanOsdol, Chief Executive Officer

ST. VINCENT'S MEDICAL CENTER SOUTHSIDE (S, 260 beds) 4201 Belfort Road, Jacksonville, FL, Zip 32216–1431; tel. 904/296–3700; Thomas J. VanOsdol, Chief Executive Officer
**Web address:** www.jaxhealth.com

**ILLINOIS:** AMITA HEALTH ALEXIAN BROTHERS BEHAVIORAL HEALTH HOSPITAL (O, 141 beds) 1650 Moon Lake Boulevard, Hoffman Estates, IL, Zip 60169–1010; tel. 847/882–1600; Clayton Ciha, President and Chief Executive Officer
**Web address:** www.abbhh.org

For explanation of codes following names, see page B2.
★ Indicates Type III membership in the American Hospital Association.

Section B

AMITA HEALTH ELK GROVE VILLAGE (O, 376 beds) 800 Biesterfield Road, Elk Grove Village, IL, Zip 60007–3397; tel. 847/437–5500; Dia Nichols, President and Chief Executive Officer
**Web address**: www.AMITAHealth.org

AMITA HEALTH HOFFMAN ESTATES (O, 298 beds) 1555 Barrington Road, Hoffman Estates, IL, Zip 60169–1019; tel. 847/843–2000; Polly J. Davenport, FACHE, R.N., President and Chief Executive Officer
**Web address**: www.AMITAHealth.org

AMITA HEALTH HOLY FAMILY MEDICAL CENTER (O, 178 beds) 100 North River Road, Des Plaines, IL, Zip 60016–1255; tel. 847/297–1800; Yolande Wilson–Stubbs, President

AMITA HEALTH MERCY MEDICAL CENTER (O, 292 beds) 1325 North Highland Avenue, Aurora, IL, Zip 60506–1449; tel. 630/859–2222; Richard Roehr, Chief Executive Officer
**Web address**: www.presencehealth.org/mercy/

AMITA HEALTH RESURRECTION MEDICAL CENTER (O, 337 beds) 7435 West Talcott Avenue, Chicago, IL, Zip 60631–3746; tel. 773/774–8000; Scott L. Teffeteller, SVP, Regional Operating Officer, Chicago Metro & President and CEO, AMITA Health Resurrection Medical Center Chicago
**Web address**: www.presencehealth.org

AMITA HEALTH SAINT FRANCIS HOSPITAL EVANSTON (O, 215 beds) 355 Ridge Avenue, Evanston, IL, Zip 60202–3399; tel. 847/316–4000; Kenneth Jones, President
**Web address**: www.reshealth.org

AMITA HEALTH SAINT JOSEPH HOSPITAL (O, 361 beds) 2900 North Lake Shore Drive, Chicago, IL, Zip 60657–6274; tel. 773/665–3000; James D. Baird, President

AMITA HEALTH SAINT JOSEPH HOSPITAL (O, 184 beds) 77 North Airlite Street, Elgin, IL, Zip 60123–4912; tel. 847/695–3200; Polly J. Davenport, FACHE, R.N., President and Chief Executive Officer
**Web address**: www.provena.org

AMITA HEALTH SAINT JOSEPH MEDICAL CENTER (O, 485 beds) 333 North Madison Street, Joliet, IL, Zip 60435–8200; tel. 815/725–7133; Herbert Buchanan, President
**Web address**: www.presencehealth.org/stjoes

AMITA HEALTH SAINTS MARY & ELIZABETH MEDICAL CENTER (O, 495 beds) 2233 West Division Street, Chicago, IL, Zip 60622–3086; tel. 312/770–2000; Robert Dahl, President and Chief Executive Officer

AMITA HEALTH ST. MARY'S HOSPITAL (O, 182 beds) 500 West Court Street, Kankakee, IL, Zip 60901–3661; tel. 815/937–2400; Chris Shride, President
**Web address**: www.presencehealth.org/presence–st–marys–hospital–kankakee

OUR LADY OF THE RESURRECTION–LONG TERM CARE (O, 50 beds) 5645 West Addison Street, Chicago, IL, Zip 60634

RESURRECTION NURSING PAVILION (O, 295 beds) 1001 North Greenwood, Park Ridge, IL, Zip 60068, Patricia Tiernan, Administrator

**INDIANA**: ASCENSION ST. VINCENT ANDERSON (S, 152 beds) 2015 Jackson Street, Anderson, IN, Zip 46016–4339; tel. 765/649–2511; Nick Theohares, Executive Director, Operations
**Web address**: www.stvincent.org/anderson

ASCENSION ST. VINCENT CARMEL HOSPITAL (S, 121 beds) 13500 North Meridian Street, Carmel, IN, Zip 46032–1456; tel. 317/582–7000; Julie Manas, Regional President
**Web address**: https://www.stvincent.org

ASCENSION ST. VINCENT CLAY HOSPITAL (S, 25 beds) 1206 East National Avenue, Brazil, IN, Zip 47834–2797, 1206 East National Ave , 47834–0489, tel. 812/442–2500; Jerry Laue, Administrator

ASCENSION ST. VINCENT DUNN (S, 35 beds) 1600 23rd Street, Bedford, IN, Zip 47421–4704; tel. 812/275–3331; George Zhang, Administrator
**Web address**: www.stvincent.org/St–Vincent–Dunn/Default.aspx

ASCENSION ST. VINCENT EVANSVILLE (S, 432 beds) 3700 Washington Avenue, Evansville, IN, Zip 47714–0541; tel. 812/485–4000; Daniel A. Parod, President

ASCENSION ST. VINCENT FISHERS (S, 46 beds) 13861 Olio Road, Fishers, IN, Zip 46037–3487; tel. 317/415–9000; Julie Manas, Regional President
**Web address**: www.stvincent.org

ASCENSION ST. VINCENT HEART CENTER (S, 80 beds) 10580 North Meridian Street, Indianapolis, IN, Zip 46290–1028; tel. 317/583–5000; Lori Shannon, President

ASCENSION ST. VINCENT INDIANAPOLIS HOSPITAL (S, 840 beds) 2001 West 86th Street, Indianapolis, IN, Zip 46260–1991, Mailing Address: P.O. Box 40970, 46240–0970, tel. 317/338–2345; Erica Wehrmeister, President Central Region
**Web address**: www.stvincent.org

ASCENSION ST. VINCENT JENNINGS (S, 17 beds) 301 Henry Street, North Vernon, IN, Zip 47265–1097; tel. 812/352–4200; Dana M. Muntz, Chief Executive Officer
**Web address**: www.stvincent.org

ASCENSION ST. VINCENT KOKOMO (S, 117 beds) 1907 West Sycamore Street, Kokomo, IN, Zip 46901–4197; tel. 765/452–5611; Margaret M. Johnson, President, St. Vincent Northwest Region

ASCENSION ST. VINCENT MERCY (S, 15 beds) 1331 South 'A' Street, Elwood, IN, Zip 46036–1942; tel. 765/552–4600; Ann C. Yates, R.N., MSN, Administrator and Chief Nursing Officer
**Web address**: www.stvincent.org

ASCENSION ST. VINCENT RANDOLPH (S, 20 beds) 473 Greenville Avenue, Winchester, IN, Zip 47394–9436; tel. 765/584–0004; Carla Fouse, Administrator and Chief Nursing Officer
**Web address**: www.stvincent.org

ASCENSION ST. VINCENT SALEM (S, 25 beds) 911 North Shelby Street, Salem, IN, Zip 47167–1694; tel. 812/883–5881; Dana M. Muntz, Chief Executive Officer

ASCENSION ST. VINCENT SETON SPECIALTY HOSPITAL (S, 74 beds) 8050 Township Line Road, Indianapolis, IN, Zip 46260–2478; tel. 317/415–8500; Erica Wehrmeister, President Central Region
**Web address**: www.stvincent.org/

ASCENSION ST. VINCENT WARRICK (S, 35 beds) 1116 Millis Avenue, Boonville, IN, Zip 47601–2204; tel. 812/897–4800; Marty Mattingly, Administrator
**Web address**: www.https://healthcare.ascension.org

ASCENSION ST. VINCENT WILLIAMSPORT (S, 16 beds) 412 North Monroe Street, Williamsport, IN, Zip 47993–1049; tel. 765/762–4000; Trina Marlatt, R.N., MSN, Administrator
**Web address**: www.stvincent.org

DAVIESS COMMUNITY HOSPITAL (C, 72 beds) 1314 East Walnut Street, Washington, IN, Zip 47501–2860, Mailing Address: P.O. Box 760, 47501–0760, tel. 812/254–2760; Tracy Conroy, Chief Executive Officer

**KANSAS**: ASCENSION VIA CHRISTI HOSPITAL ON ST. TERESA (O, 48 beds) 14800 West St. Teresa, Wichita, KS, Zip 67235–9602; tel. 316/796–7000; Laurie Labarca, President
**Web address**: www.via–christi.org/st–teresa

ASCENSION VIA CHRISTI HOSPITAL, MANHATTAN (O, 88 beds) 1823 College Avenue, Manhattan, KS, Zip 66502–3346; tel. 785/776–3322; Robert C. Copple, FACHE, Senior Administrator

ASCENSION VIA CHRISTI HOSPITAL (O, 91 beds) 1 Mt. Carmel Way, Pittsburg, KS, Zip 66762–7587; tel. 620/231–6100; Randall R. Cason, FACHE, Senior Administrator
**Web address**: www.viachristi.org/pittsburg

ASCENSION VIA CHRISTI REHABILITATION HOSPITAL (O, 21 beds) 1151 North Rock Road, Wichita, KS, Zip 67206–1262; tel. 316/634–3400; Laurie Labarca, President
**Web address**: www.via–christi.org

ASCENSION VIA CHRISTI ST. FRANCIS (O, 653 beds) 211 N College Ave, Mulvane, KS, Zip 67110, 929 North St Francis Street, Wichita, 67214–3882, tel. 316/268–5000; Kevin Strecker, President
**Web address**: www.via–christi.org

**MARYLAND**: SAINT AGNES HEALTHCARE (S, 367 beds) 900 Caton Avenue, Baltimore, MD, Zip 21229–5201; tel. 667/234–6000; Edward Lovern, President and Chief Executive Officer

**MICHIGAN**: ASCENSION ALLEGAN HOSPITAL (O, 25 beds) 555 Linn Street, Allegan, MI, Zip 49010–1524; tel. 269/673–8424; Peter U. Bergmann, President
**Web address**: www.aghosp.org

ASCENSION BORGESS HOSPITAL (S, 308 beds) 1521 Gull Road, Kalamazoo, MI, Zip 49048–1640; tel. 269/226–7000; Peter U. Bergmann, President and Chief Executive Officer

ASCENSION BORGESS–LEE HOSPITAL (S, 25 beds) 420 West High Street, Dowagiac, MI, Zip 49047–1943; tel. 269/782–8681; Peter U. Bergmann, President
**Web address**: www.borgess.com

For explanation of codes following names, see page B2.
★ Indicates Type III membership in the American Hospital Association.

ASCENSION BRIGHTON CENTER FOR RECOVERY (S, 99 beds) 12851 Grand River Road, Brighton, MI, Zip 48116–8506; tel. 810/227–1211; Raymond A. Waller, Director and Administrator

ASCENSION CRITTENTON HOSPITAL MEDICAL CENTER (O, 226 beds) 1101 West University Drive, Rochester, MI, Zip 48307–1831; tel. 248/652–5000; Chris Palazzolo, President and Chief Executive Officer
**Web address:** www.crittenton.com

ASCENSION GENESYS HOSPITAL (S, 428 beds) One Genesys Parkway, Grand Blanc, MI, Zip 48439–8066; tel. 810/606–5000; Chris Palazzolo, President and Chief Executive Officer

ASCENSION MACOMB–OAKLAND HOSPITAL (S, 523 beds) 11800 East 12 Mile Road, Warren, MI, Zip 48093–3472; tel. 586/573–5000; Gary Druskovich, M.D., President
**Web address:** www.stjohnprovidence.org/macomb–oakland/

ASCENSION RIVER DISTRICT HOSPITAL (S, 24 beds) 4100 River Road, East China, MI, Zip 48054–2909; tel. 810/329–7111; Kevin Grady, M.D., President
**Web address:** www.stjohnprovidence.org/RiverDistrict/

ASCENSION ST. JOHN HOSPITAL (S, 592 beds) 22101 Moross Road, Detroit, MI, Zip 48236–2148; tel. 313/343–4000; Kevin Grady, M.D., President

ASCENSION ST. JOSEPH HOSPITAL (S, 47 beds) 200 Hemlock Street, Tawas City, MI, Zip 48763–9237, Mailing Address: P.O. Box 659, 48764–0659, tel. 989/362–3411; Stephanie J. Duggan, M.D., President
**Web address:** www.sjhsys.org

ASCENSION ST. MARY'S OF MICHIGAN (S, 179 beds) 800 South Washington Avenue, Saginaw, MI, Zip 48601–2594; tel. 989/907–8000; Stephanie J. Duggan, M.D., President

ASCENSION STANDISH HOSPITAL (S, 54 beds) 805 West Cedar Street, Standish, MI, Zip 48658–9526; tel. 989/846–4521; Stephanie J. Duggan, M.D., President
**Web address:** www.stmarysofmichigan.org/standish

ASCENSION OF PROVIDENCE HOSPITAL, SOUTHFIELD CAMPUS (S, 628 beds) 16001 West Nine Mile Road, Southfield, MI, Zip 48075; tel. 248/849–3400; Joseph R. Hurshe, President

**MINNESOTA:** SAINT ELIZABETH'S MEDICAL CENTER (O, 153 beds) 1200 Grant Boulevard West, Wabasha, MN, Zip 55981–1042; tel. 651/565–4531; Thomas Crowley, President and Chief Executive Officer
**Web address:** www.stelizabethswabasha.org

**NEW YORK:** OUR LADY OF LOURDES MEMORIAL HOSPITAL, INC. (S, 154 beds) 169 Riverside Drive, Binghamton, NY, Zip 13905–4246; tel. 607/798–5111; Kathryn Connerton, President and Chief Executive Officer

ST. MARY'S HEALTHCARE (S, 290 beds) 427 Guy Park Avenue, Amsterdam, NY, Zip 12010–1054; tel. 518/842–1900; Scott Bruce, President
**Web address:** www.smha.org

**OKLAHOMA:** ASCENSION ST. JOHN JANE PHILLIPS (O, 106 beds) 3500 East Frank Phillips Boulevard, Bartlesville, OK, Zip 74006–2411; tel. 918/333–7200; Mike Moore, President and Chief Operating Officer

JANE PHILLIPS NOWATA HEALTH CENTER (O, 15 beds) 237 South Locust Street, Nowata, OK, Zip 74048–3660; tel. 918/273–3102; Jason McCauley, Administrator
**Web address:** www.jpmc.org

ST. JOHN BROKEN ARROW (O, 44 beds) 1000 West Boise Circle, Broken Arrow, OK, Zip 74012–4900; tel. 918/994–8100; David L. Phillips, Chief Operating Officer

ST. JOHN MEDICAL CENTER (O, 523 beds) 1923 South Utica Avenue, Tulsa, OK, Zip 74104–6502; tel. 918/744–2345; Jeffrey D. Nowlin, President and Chief Operating Officer
**Web address:** www.sjmc.org

ST. JOHN OWASSO (O, 36 beds) 12451 East 100th Street North, Owasso, OK, Zip 74055–4600; tel. 918/274–5000; David L. Phillips, President and Chief Operating Officer

ST. JOHN SAPULPA (O, 25 beds) 1004 East Bryan Avenue, Sapulpa, OK, Zip 74066–4513, Mailing Address: P.O. Box 1368, 74067–1368, tel. 918/224–4280; Michael Christian, Chief Operating Officer
**Web address:** www.stjohnhealthsystem.com/sapulpa

**TENNESSEE:** SAINT THOMAS DEKALB HOSPITAL (O, 56 beds) 520 West Main Street, Smithville, TN, Zip 37166–1138, Mailing Address: P.O. Box 640, 37166–0640, tel. 615/215–5000; Bradley Mullinax, Chief Administrative Officer
**Web address:** www.dekalbcommunityhospital.com

SAINT THOMAS HICKMAN HOSPITAL (S, 25 beds) 135 East Swan Street, Centerville, TN, Zip 37033–1417; tel. 931/729–4271; Kevin Campbell, Chief Executive Officer

SAINT THOMAS HIGHLANDS HOSPITAL (O, 60 beds) 401 Sewell Road, Sparta, TN, Zip 38583–1299; tel. 931/738–9211; Richard Tumlin, Chief Administrative Officer
**Web address:** www.whitecountyhospital.com

SAINT THOMAS HOSPITAL FOR SPINAL SURGERY (S, 23 beds) 2011 Murphy Avenue, Suite 400, Nashville, TN, Zip 37203–2065; tel. 615/341–7500; Kathy Watson, R.N., Administrator and Chief Nursing Officer

SAINT THOMAS RIVER PARK HOSPITAL (O, 85 beds) 1559 Sparta Street, Mc Minnville, TN, Zip 37110–1316; tel. 931/815–4000; Dale Humphrey, Chief Executive Officer
**Web address:** www.riverparkhospital.com

SAINT THOMAS RUTHERFORD HOSPITAL (S, 286 beds) 1700 Medical Center Parkway, Murfreesboro, TN, Zip 37129–2245; tel. 615/396–4100; Gordon B. Ferguson, President and Chief Executive Officer
**Web address:** www.mtmc.org

SAINT THOMAS STONES RIVER HOSPITAL (O, 60 beds) 324 Doolittle Road, Woodbury, TN, Zip 37190–1139; tel. 615/563–4001; Robert Peglow, Interim Chief Administrative Officer
**Web address:** www.stonesriverhospital.com

SAINT THOMAS WEST HOSPITAL (S, 395 beds) 4220 Harding Road, Nashville, TN, Zip 37205–2095, Mailing Address: P.O. Box 380, 37202–0380, tel. 615/222–2111; Fahad Tahir, Chief Executive Officer

**TEXAS:** ASCENSION PROVIDENCE (S, 284 beds) 6901 Medical Parkway, Waco, TX, Zip 76712–7998, Mailing Address: P.O. Box 2589, 76702–2589, tel. 254/751–4000; Philip A. Patterson, President
**Web address:** www.providence.net

ASCENSION SETON BASTROP (O, 7 beds) 630 TX–71 West, Bastrop, TX, Zip 78602–4234; tel. 737/881–7400; Andy Davis, Chief Executive Officer

ASCENSION SETON EDGAR B. DAVIS HOSPITAL (S, 25 beds) 130 Hays Street, Luling, TX, Zip 78648–3207; tel. 830/875–7000; Scott O. Fuller, President and Chief Executive Officer
**Web address:** www.seton.net/locations/edgar_davis/

ASCENSION SETON HAYS (O, 150 beds) 6001 Kyle Parkway, Kyle, TX, Zip 78640–6112; tel. 512/504–5000; Katherine Henderson, Regional Hospital President

ASCENSION SETON HIGHLAND LAKES (S, 19 beds) 3201 South Water Street, Burnet, TX, Zip 78611–4510, Mailing Address: P.O. Box 1219, 78611–7219, tel. 512/715–3000; Scott O. Fuller, President and Chief Executive Officer
**Web address:** www.seton.net

ASCENSION SETON MEDICAL CENTER AUSTIN (S, 382 beds) 1201 West 38th Street, Austin, TX, Zip 78705–1006; tel. 512/324–1000; Christann Vasquez, Regional Hospital President

ASCENSION SETON NORTHWEST (S, 117 beds) 11113 Research Boulevard, Austin, TX, Zip 78759–5236; tel. 512/324–6000; Katherine Henderson, Regional Hospital President
**Web address:** www.seton.net

ASCENSION SETON SHOAL CREEK (S, 70 beds) 3501 Mills Avenue, Austin, TX, Zip 78731–6391; tel. 512/324–2000; Christann Vasquez, Regional Hospital President

ASCENSION SETON SMITHVILLE (O, 5 beds) 1201 Hill Road, Smithville, TX, Zip 78957; tel. 512/237–3214; Andy Davis, Chief Executive Officer
**Web address:** www.https://healthcare.ascension.org/Locations/Texas/TXAUS/Smithville–Ascension–Seton–Smithville

ASCENSION SETON SOUTHWEST (S, 11 beds) 7900 F M 1826, Building 1, Austin, TX, Zip 78737–1407; tel. 512/324–9000; Katherine Henderson, Regional Hospital President

ASCENSION SETON WILLIAMSON (S, 140 beds) 201 Seton Parkway, Round Rock, TX, Zip 78665–8000; tel. 512/324–4000; Katherine Henderson, Regional Hospital President
**Web address:** www.seton.net/williamson

DELL CHILDREN'S MEDICAL CENTER OF CENTRAL TEXAS (S, 240 beds) 4900 Mueller Boulevard, Austin, TX, Zip 78723–3079; tel. 512/324–0000; Debra M. Brown, Vice President Patient Care and Chief Operating Officer

DELL SETON MEDICAL CENTER AT THE UNIVERSITY OF TEXAS (O, 211 beds) 1500 Red River Street, Austin, TX, Zip 78701; tel. 512/324–7000; Christann Vasquez, Regional Hospital President
**Web address:** www.seton.net/locations/dell–seton/

For explanation of codes following names, see page B2.
★ Indicates Type III membership in the American Hospital Association.

**WISCONSIN**: ASCENSION ALL SAINTS (O, 278 beds) 3801 Spring Street, Racine, WI, Zip 53405–1690; tel. 262/687–4011; Kristin McManmon, President
**Web address**: www.allsaintshealth.com

ASCENSION CALUMET HOSPITAL (O, 25 beds) 614 Memorial Drive, Chilton, WI, Zip 53014–1597; tel. 920/849–2386; Jenny Derks, Chief Administrative Officer

ASCENSION COLUMBIA ST. MARY'S HOSPITAL MILWAUKEE (S, 277 beds) 2301 North Lake Drive, Milwaukee, WI, Zip 53211–4508; tel. 414/291–1000; Travis Andersen, Chief Executive Officer
**Web address**: www.columbia–stmarys.org

ASCENSION COLUMBIA ST. MARY'S HOSPITAL OZAUKEE (S, 124 beds) 13111 North Port Washington Road, Mequon, WI, Zip 53097–2416; tel. 262/243–7300; Kelly Elkins, President and Chief Executive Officer
**Web address**: www.columbia–stmarys.org

ASCENSION COLUMBIA ST. MARY'S MILWAUKEE HOSPITAL (S, 15 beds) 2323 North Lake Drive, Milwaukee, WI, Zip 53211–4508, 2301 North Lake Drive, 53211–4508, tel. 414/585–1000; Kelly Elkins, President and Chief Executive Officer

ASCENSION EAGLE RIVER HOSPITAL (O, 14 beds) 201 Hospital Road, Eagle River, WI, Zip 54521–8835; tel. 715/479–7411; Laurie Oungst, Chief Administrative Officer
**Web address**: www.ministryhealth.org

ASCENSION GOOD SAMARITAN HOSPITAL (O, 3 beds) 601 South Center Avenue, Merrill, WI, Zip 54452–3404; tel. 715/536–5511; Jeremy Normington–Slay, FACHE, Chief Executive Officer
**Web address**: www.ministryhealth.org

ASCENSION NORTHEAST WISCONSIN MERCY HOSPITAL (O, 132 beds) 500 South Oakwood Road, Oshkosh, WI, Zip 54904–7944; tel. 920/223–2000; Denise Parrish, Interim Chief Administrative Officer
**Web address**: www.affinityhealth.org

ASCENSION NORTHEAST WISCONSIN ST. ELIZABETH HOSPITAL (O, 190 beds) 1506 South Oneida Street, Appleton, WI, Zip 54915–1305; tel. 920/738–2000; Monica Hilt, President and Regional Vice President

ASCENSION OUR LADY OF VICTORY HOSPITAL (O, 2 beds) 1120 Pine Street, Stanley, WI, Zip 54768–1297; tel. 715/644–5571; Jeremy Normington–Slay, FACHE, President
**Web address**: www.ministryhealth.org

ASCENSION SACRED HEART HOSPITAL (O, 8 beds) 401 West Mohawk Drive, Tomahawk, WI, Zip 54487–2274; tel. 715/453–7700; Laurie Oungst, Chief Administrative Officer
**Web address**: www.ministryhealth.org

ASCENSION SOUTHEAST WISCONSIN HOSPITAL – ELMBROOK CAMPUS (O, 60 beds) 19333 West North Avenue, Brookfield, WI, Zip 53045–4198; tel. 262/785–2000; Timothy Richman, President and Chief Executive Officer

ASCENSION SOUTHEAST WISCONSIN HOSPITAL – FRANKLIN CAMPUS (O, 46 beds) 10101 South 27th Street, Franklin, WI, Zip 53132–7209; tel. 414/325–4700; Seth R. Teigen, President
**Web address**: www.mywheaton.org/

ASCENSION SOUTHEAST WISCONSIN HOSPITAL – ST. FRANCIS CAMPUS (O, 120 beds) 3237 South 16th Street, Milwaukee, WI, Zip 53215; tel. 414/647–5000; Seth R. Teigen, President
**Web address**: www.mywheaton.org/stfrancis

ASCENSION SOUTHEAST WISCONSIN HOSPITAL – ST. JOSEPH'S CAMPUS (O, 170 beds) 5000 West Chambers Street, Milwaukee, WI, Zip 53210–1650; tel. 414/447–2000; Kevin Kluesner, Chief Administrative Officer

ASCENSION ST. MARY'S HOSPITAL (O, 64 beds) 2251 North Shore Drive, Rhinelander, WI, Zip 54501–6710; tel. 715/361–2000; Laurie Oungst, Chief Administrative Officer
**Web address**: www.ministryhealth.org

ASCENSION ST. MICHAEL'S HOSPITAL (O, 27 beds) 900 Illinois Avenue, Stevens Point, WI, Zip 54481–3196; tel. 715/346–5000; Teresa Theiler, Chief Administrative Officer
**Web address**: www.ministryhealth.org/SMH/home.nws

HOWARD YOUNG MEDICAL CENTER (O, 50 beds) 240 Maple Street, Woodruff, WI, Zip 54568–9190, Mailing Address: P.O. Box 470, 54568–0470, tel. 715/356–8000; Laurie Oungst, Chief Administrative Officer
**Web address**: www.ministryhealth.org

MIDWEST ORTHOPEDIC SPECIALTY HOSPITAL (O, 16 beds) 10101 South 27th Street, 2nd Floor, Franklin, WI, Zip 53132–7209; tel. 414/817–5800; Bernie Sherry, Ministry Market Executive for Ascension Wisconsin

| | | |
|---|---|---|
| **Owned, leased, sponsored:** | 111 hospitals | 18632 beds |
| **Contract–managed:** | 1 hospitals | 72 beds |
| **Totals:** | 112 hospitals | 18704 beds |

---

**★0519: ASPIRUS, INC.** (NP)
2200 Westwood Drive, Wausau, WI Zip 54401–7806; tel. 715/847–2118; Matthew Heywood, Chief Executive Officer
**(Moderately Centralized Health System)**

**MICHIGAN**: ASPIRUS IRON RIVER HOSPITALS & CLINICS, INC. (O, 12 beds) 1400 West Ice Lake Road, Iron River, MI, Zip 49935–9526; tel. 906/265–6121; Connie L. Koutouzos, R.N., MSN, Chief Executive Officer
**Web address**: www.aspirus.org

ASPIRUS IRONWOOD HOSPITALS & CLINICS, INC. (O, 25 beds) N10561 Grand View Lane, Ironwood, MI, Zip 49938–9622; tel. 906/932–2525; Paula L. Chermside, Chief Executive Officer
**Web address**: www.aspirus.org

ASPIRUS KEWEENAW HOSPITAL, INC. (O, 25 beds) 205 Osceola Street, Laurium, MI, Zip 49913–2134; tel. 906/337–6500; Christine K. Harff, UP Regional President
**Web address**: www.aspirus.org

ASPIRUS ONTONAGON HOSPITAL, INC. (O, 56 beds) 601 South Seventh Street, Ontonagon, MI, Zip 49953–1459; tel. 906/884–8000; Dylan Taylor, Chief Executive Officer
**Web address**: www.aspirus.org

**WISCONSIN**: ASPIRUS LANGLADE HOSPITAL (O, 24 beds) 112 East Fifth Avenue, Antigo, WI, Zip 54409–2796; tel. 715/623–2331; Andrew J. Barth, Executive Director
**Web address**: www.aspirus.org

ASPIRUS MEDFORD HOSPITAL & CLINICS, INC. (O, 124 beds) 135 South Gibson Street, Medford, WI, Zip 54451; tel. 715/748–8100; Dale Hustedt, President
**Web address**: www.aspirus.org

ASPIRUS RIVERVIEW HOSPITAL AND CLINICS, INC. (O, 91 beds) 410 Dewey Street, Wisconsin Rapids, WI, Zip 54494–4715, Mailing Address: P.O. Box 8080, 54495–8080, tel. 715/423–6060; Todd Burch, Chief Executive Officer
**Web address**: www.aspirus.org

ASPIRUS WAUSAU HOSPITAL, INC. (O, 307 beds) 333 Pine Ridge Boulevard, Wausau, WI, Zip 54401–4187; tel. 715/847–2121; Darrell Lentz, President

| | | |
|---|---|---|
| **Owned, leased, sponsored:** | 8 hospitals | 664 beds |
| **Contract–managed:** | 0 hospitals | 0 beds |
| **Totals:** | 8 hospitals | 664 beds |

---

**1031: ASTRIA HEALTH** (NP)
1806 Yakima Valley Highway, Sunnyside, WA Zip 98944–2263; tel. 509/837–1330; John Gallagher, President and Chief Executive Officer
**(Independent Hospital System)**

**WASHINGTON**: ASTRIA SUNNYSIDE HOSPITAL (O, 25 beds) 1016 Tacoma Avenue, Sunnyside, WA, Zip 98944–2263, Mailing Address: P.O. Box 719, 98944–0719, tel. 509/837–1500; Brian P. Gibbons Jr, Chief Executive Officer
**Web address**: www.astria.health/

ASTRIA TOPPENISH HOSPITAL (O, 48 beds) 502 West Fourth Avenue, Toppenish, WA, Zip 98948–1616, Mailing Address: P.O. Box 672, 98948–0672, tel. 509/865–3105; Michael J. Arno, President
**Web address**: www.astria.health/

| | | |
|---|---|---|
| **Owned, leased, sponsored:** | 2 hospitals | 73 beds |
| **Contract–managed:** | 0 hospitals | 0 beds |
| **Totals:** | 2 hospitals | 73 beds |

For explanation of codes following names, see page B2.
★ Indicates Type III membership in the American Hospital Association.

**★0865: ATLANTIC HEALTH SYSTEM** (NP)

475 South Street, Morristown, NJ Zip 07960–6459, Mailing Address: P.O. Box 1905, 07962–1905, tel. 973/660–3270; Brian A. Gragnolati, FACHE, President and Chief Executive Officer **(Decentralized Health System)**

**NEW JERSEY:** CHILTON MEDICAL CENTER (O, 133 beds) 97 West Parkway, Pompton Plains, NJ, Zip 07444–1696; tel. 973/831–5000; Stephanie L. Schwartz, FACHE, Vice President AHS and President CMC

HACKETTSTOWN MEDICAL CENTER (O, 61 beds) 651 Willow Grove Street, Hackettstown, NJ, Zip 07840–1799; tel. 908/852–5100; Robert H. Adams, President, Western Region
**Web address:** www.atlantichealth.org

MORRISTOWN MEDICAL CENTER (O, 737 beds) 100 Madison Avenue, Morristown, NJ, Zip 07960–6136; tel. 973/971–5000; Trish O'Keefe, Ph.D., R.N., President
**Web address:** www.atlantichealth.org/Morristown/

NEWTON MEDICAL CENTER (O, 148 beds) 175 High Street, Newton, NJ, Zip 07860–1004; tel. 973/383–2121; Robert H. Adams, President, Western Region
**Web address:** www.atlantichealth.org/newton/

OVERLOOK MEDICAL CENTER (O, 384 beds) 99 Beauvoir Avenue, Summit, NJ, Zip 07901–3533; tel. 908/522–2000; Alan R. Lieber, President, Overlook Medical Center, Vice President, Atlantic Health System
**Web address:** www.atlantichealth.org/Overlook

| | | |
|---|---|---|
| Owned, leased, sponsored: | 5 hospitals | 1463 beds |
| Contract–managed: | 0 hospitals | 0 beds |
| Totals: | 5 hospitals | 1463 beds |

**★0705: ATRIUM HEALTH** (NP)

1000 Blythe Boulevard, Charlotte, NC Zip 28203–5871, Mailing Address: P.O. 32861, 28232–2861, tel. 704/355–2000; Eugene A. Woods, FACHE, President and Chief Executive Officer **(Centralized Health System)**

**NORTH CAROLINA:** ATRIUM HEALTH ANSON (O, 15 beds) 2301 US Highway 74 W, Wadesboro, NC, Zip 28170–7554, 2301 U.S Highway 74 West, 28170, tel. 704/994–4500; Dave Anderson, FACHE, Vice President and Administrator
**Web address:** www.carolinashealthcare.org/anson

ATRIUM HEALTH CABARRUS (O, 455 beds) 920 Church Street North, Concord, NC, Zip 28025–2983; tel. 704/403–3000; Asha Rodriguez, Vice President and Facility Executive

ATRIUM HEALTH CLEVELAND (L, 230 beds) 201 East Grover Street, Shelby, NC, Zip 28150–3917; tel. 980/487–3000; Brian Gwyn, West Market President– Atrium Health
**Web address:** www.clevelandregional.org

ATRIUM HEALTH LINCOLN (O, 101 beds) 433 McAlister Road, Lincolnton, NC, Zip 28092–4147, Mailing Address: P.O. 677, 28093–0677, tel. 980/212–2000; Teresa C. Watson, Vice President, Facility Executive

ATRIUM HEALTH PINEVILLE (O, 250 beds) 10628 Park Road, Charlotte, NC, Zip 28210–8407; tel. 704/667–1000; Alicia Campbell, Vice President, Facility Executive
**Web address:** www.carolinashealthcare.org/pineville

ATRIUM HEALTH STANLY (C, 109 beds) 301 Yadkin Street, Albemarle, NC, Zip 28001–3441, Mailing Address: P.O. Box 1489, 28002–1489, tel. 704/984–4000; Brian Freeman, President

ATRIUM HEALTH UNION (L, 219 beds) 600 Hospital Drive, Monroe, NC, Zip 28112–6000, Mailing Address: P.O. Box 5003, 28111–5003, tel. 980/993–3100; Denise White, MSN, Vice President, Facility Executive
**Web address:** www.carolinashealthcare.org/union

ATRIUM HEALTH UNIVERSITY CITY (O, 100 beds) 8800 North Tryon Street, Charlotte, NC, Zip 28262–3300, Mailing Address: P.O. Box 560727, 28256–0727, tel. 704/863–6000; William H. Leonard, President

ATRIUM HEALTH'S CAROLINAS MEDICAL CENTER (O, 1287 beds) 1000 Blythe Boulevard, Charlotte, NC, Zip 28203–5871, Mailing Address: P.O. Box 32861, 28232–2861, tel. 704/355–2000; Eugene A. Woods, FACHE, President and Chief Executive Officer
**Web address:** www.carolinashealthcare.org/cmc

ATRIUM HEALTH'S CAROLINAS REHABILITATION (O, 150 beds) 1100 Blythe Boulevard, Charlotte, NC, Zip 28203–5864; tel. 704/355–4300; Robert G. Larrison Jr, President
**Web address:** www.carolinashealthcare.org/rehabilitation

CAROLINAS HEALTHCARE SYSTEM BLUE RIDGE (C, 156 beds) 2201 South Sterling Street, Morganton, NC, Zip 28655–4058; tel. 828/580–5000; Kathy C. Bailey, President and Chief Executive Officer
**Web address:** www.blueridgehealth.org

COLUMBUS REGIONAL HEALTHCARE SYSTEM (C, 85 beds) 500 Jefferson Street, Whiteville, NC, Zip 28472–3634; tel. 910/642–8011; John E. Young, Interim Chief Executive Officer
**Web address:** www.crhealthcare.org/

SCOTLAND HEALTH CARE SYSTEM (C, 104 beds) 500 Lauchwood Drive, Laurinburg, NC, Zip 28352–5599; tel. 910/291–7000; Gregory C. Wood, President and Chief Executive Officer

ST. LUKE'S HOSPITAL (C, 35 beds) 101 Hospital Drive, Columbus, NC, Zip 28722–6418; tel. 828/894–3311; Michelle Fortune, R.N., Chief Executive Officer
**Web address:** www.saintlukeshospital.com

| | | |
|---|---|---|
| Owned, leased, sponsored: | 9 hospitals | 2807 beds |
| Contract–managed: | 5 hospitals | 489 beds |
| Totals: | 14 hospitals | 3296 beds |

**0859: AULTMAN HEALTH FOUNDATION** (NP)

2600 Sixth Street SW, Canton, OH Zip 44710–1702; tel. 330/363–6192; Edward J. Roth III, President and Chief Executive Officer **(Moderately Centralized Health System)**

**OHIO:** ALLIANCE COMMUNITY HOSPITAL (O, 202 beds) 200 East State Street, Alliance, OH, Zip 44601–4936; tel. 330/596–6000; Ryan Jones, Chief Executive Officer

AULTMAN HOSPITAL (O, 532 beds) 2600 Sixth Street SW, Canton, OH, Zip 44710–1702; tel. 330/452–9911; Tony Snyder, Chief Executive Officer
**Web address:** www.aultman.com

AULTMAN ORRVILLE HOSPITAL (O, 25 beds) 832 South Main Street, Orrville, OH, Zip 44667–2208; tel. 330/682–3010; Jennifer Kessel, Chief Executive Officer
**Web address:** www.aultmanorrville.org

AULTMAN SPECIALTY HOSPITAL (O, 16 beds) 2600 Sixth Street, SW, Canton, OH, Zip 44710–1702; tel. 330/363–4000; Ryan Kuharich, Chief Executive Officer

| | | |
|---|---|---|
| Owned, leased, sponsored: | 4 hospitals | 775 beds |
| Contract–managed: | 0 hospitals | 0 beds |
| Totals: | 4 hospitals | 775 beds |

**0869: AVANTI HOSPITALS** (IO)

222 North Sepulveda Boulevard, Suite 950, El Segundo, CA Zip 90245–5614; tel. 310/356–0550; Michael A. Rembis, FACHE, Corporate Chief Executive Officer **(Independent Hospital System)**

**CALIFORNIA:** COAST PLAZA HOSPITAL (O, 123 beds) 13100 Studebaker Road, Norwalk, CA, Zip 90650–2500; tel. 562/868–3751; Patrick W. Rafferty, Chief Executive Officer
**Web address:** www.avantihospitals.com/coast–plaza–hospital

COMMUNITY HOSPITAL OF HUNTINGTON PARK (O, 81 beds) 2623 East Slauson Avenue, Huntington Park, CA, Zip 90255–2926; tel. 323/583–1931; Patricia Rives, R.N., MSN, Chief Executive Officer

EAST LOS ANGELES DOCTORS HOSPITAL (O, 127 beds) 4060 Whittier Boulevard, Los Angeles, CA, Zip 90023–2526; tel. 323/268–5514; Gerald B. Clute, Chief Executive Officer
**Web address:** www.avantihospitals.com

MEMORIAL HOSPITAL OF GARDENA (O, 172 beds) 1145 West Redondo Beach Boulevard, Gardena, CA, Zip 90247–3528; tel. 310/532–4200; Kathy Wojno, R.N., MSN, Administrator

| | | |
|---|---|---|
| Owned, leased, sponsored: | 4 hospitals | 503 beds |
| Contract–managed: | 0 hospitals | 0 beds |
| Totals: | 4 hospitals | 503 beds |

For explanation of codes following names, see page B2.
★ Indicates Type III membership in the American Hospital Association.

**★5255: AVERA HEALTH** (CO)

3900 West Avera Drive, Suite 300, Sioux Falls, SD Zip 57108–5721; tel. 605/322–4700; Bob Sutton, President and Chief Executive Officer
**(Decentralized Health System)**

**IOWA:** AVERA HOLY FAMILY HOSPITAL (O, 25 beds) 826 North Eighth Street, Estherville, IA, Zip 51334–1598; tel. 712/362–2631; Deborah L. Herzberg, R.N., MS, FACHE, Administrator
**Web address:** www.avera–holyfamily.org

AVERA MERRILL PIONEER HOSPITAL (L, 11 beds) 1100 South 10th Avenue, Rock Rapids, IA, Zip 51246–2020; tel. 712/472–5400; Craig Hohn, Chief Executive Officer
**Web address:** https://www.avera.org

FLOYD VALLEY HEALTHCARE (C, 25 beds) 714 Lincoln Street NE, Le Mars, IA, Zip 51031–3314; tel. 712/546–7871; Dustin Wright, Chief Executive Officer

HEGG HEALTH CENTER AVERA (C, 85 beds) 1202 21st Avenue, Rock Valley, IA, Zip 51247–1497; tel. 712/476–8000; Glenn Zevenbergen, Chief Executive Officer
**Web address:** www.hegghc.org

LAKES REGIONAL HEALTHCARE (C, 30 beds) 2301 Highway 71 South, Spirit Lake, IA, Zip 51360–0159; tel. 712/336–1230; Jason Harrington, FACHE, President and Chief Executive Officer
**Web address:** www.lakeshealth.org

OSCEOLA REGIONAL HEALTH CENTER (C, 25 beds) 600 9th Avenue North, Sibley, IA, Zip 51249–1012, Mailing Address: P.O. Box 258, 51249–0258, tel. 712/754–2574; Ben Davis, Chief Executive Officer

SIOUX CENTER HEALTH (C, 88 beds) 1101 9th Street SE, Sioux Center, IA, Zip 51250; tel. 712/722–8107; Cory D. Nelson, Administrator
**Web address:** www.siouxcenterhealth.org

**MINNESOTA:** AVERA GRANITE FALLS HEALTH CENTER (L, 82 beds) 345 Tenth Avenue, Granite Falls, MN, Zip 56241–1499; tel. 320/564–3111; Thomas Kooiman, Chief Executive Officer

AVERA MARSHALL REGIONAL MEDICAL CENTER (O, 111 beds) 300 South Bruce Street, Marshall, MN, Zip 56258–3900; tel. 507/532–9661; Mary B. Maertens, FACHE, President and Chief Executive Officer
**Web address:** www.avera.org

AVERA TYLER HOSPITAL (C, 40 beds) 240 Willow Street, Tyler, MN, Zip 56178–1166; tel. 507/247–5521; Allen Anderson, Administrator
**Web address:** www.avera.org

PIPESTONE COUNTY MEDICAL CENTER AVERA (C, 18 beds) 916 4th Avenue SW, Pipestone, MN, Zip 56164–1890; tel. 507/825–5811; Bradley D. Burris, Chief Executive Officer

**NEBRASKA:** AVERA CREIGHTON HOSPITAL (O, 70 beds) 1503 Main Street, Creighton, NE, Zip 68729–3007, Mailing Address: P.O. Box 186, 68729–0186, tel. 402/358–5700; Todd Consbruck, Chief Executive Officer
**Web address:** www.avera.org/creighton/

AVERA ST. ANTHONY'S HOSPITAL (O, 25 beds) 300 North Second Street, O'Neill, NE, Zip 68763–1514, Mailing Address: P.O. Box 270, Oneill, 68763–0270, tel. 402/336–2611; Todd Consbruck, President and Chief Executive Officer
**Web address:** www.avera.org/st–anthonys

**SOUTH DAKOTA:** AVERA DE SMET MEMORIAL HOSPITAL (L, 6 beds) 306 Prairie Avenue SW, De Smet, SD, Zip 57231–2285, Mailing Address: P.O. Box 160, 57231–0160, tel. 605/854–6100; Stephanie Reasy, Administrator and Chief Executive Officer

AVERA DELLS AREA HOSPITAL (L, 23 beds) 909 North Iowa Avenue, Dell Rapids, SD, Zip 57022–1231; tel. 605/428–5431; Scott James. Hargens, Administrator and Chief Executive Officer
**Web address:** https://www.avera.org/locations/profile/avera–dells–area–hospital/

AVERA FLANDREAU HOSPITAL (L, 18 beds) 214 North Prairie Street, Flandreau, SD, Zip 57028–1243; tel. 605/997–2433; Scott James. Hargens, Administrator and Chief Executive Officer
**Web address:** www.avera.org/flandreau–medical/

AVERA GETTYSBURG HOSPITAL (O, 59 beds) 606 East Garfield Avenue, Gettysburg, SD, Zip 57442–1398; tel. 605/765–2488; Kristi Livermont, Administrator
**Web address:** www.avera.org/st–marys–pierre/gettysburg–hospital/

AVERA GREGORY HOSPITAL (O, 65 beds) 400 Park Avenue, Gregory, SD, Zip 57533–1302, Mailing Address: P.O. Box 408, 57533–0408, tel. 605/835–8394; Anthony Timanus, Chief Executive Officer
**Web address:** www.gregoryhealthcare.org

AVERA HAND COUNTY MEMORIAL HOSPITAL (L, 9 beds) 300 West Fifth Street, Miller, SD, Zip 57362–1238; tel. 605/853–2421; Bryan Breitling, Administrator
**Web address:** www.avera.org

AVERA HEART HOSPITAL OF SOUTH DAKOTA (O, 53 beds) 4500 West 69th Street, Sioux Falls, SD, Zip 57108–8148; tel. 605/977–7000; Michael Gibbs, President

AVERA MCKENNAN HOSPITAL AND UNIVERSITY HEALTH CENTER (O, 500 beds) 1325 South Cliff Avenue, Sioux Falls, SD, Zip 57105–1007, Mailing Address: P.O. Box 5045, 57117–5045, tel. 605/322–8000; David Flicek, President and Chief Executive Officer
**Web address:** www.averamckennan.org

AVERA QUEEN OF PEACE HOSPITAL (O, 159 beds) 525 North Foster, Mitchell, SD, Zip 57301–2999; tel. 605/995–2000; Douglas R. Ekeren, FACHE, Interim Regional President and Chief Executive Officer

AVERA SACRED HEART HOSPITAL (O, 286 beds) 501 Summit Avenue, Yankton, SD, Zip 57078–3855; tel. 605/668–8000; Douglas R. Ekeren, FACHE, Regional President and Chief Executive Officer, Administration
**Web address:** www.averasacredheart.com

AVERA ST. BENEDICT HEALTH CENTER (O, 99 beds) 401 West Glynn Drive, Parkston, SD, Zip 57366–9605; tel. 605/928–3311; Rita Blasius, President and Chief Executive Officer

AVERA ST. LUKE'S HOSPITAL (O, 212 beds) 305 South State Street, Aberdeen, SD, Zip 57401–4527; tel. 605/622–5000; Todd Forkel, President and Chief Executive Officer
**Web address:** www.avera.org/st–lukes–hospital/

AVERA ST. MARY'S HOSPITAL (O, 110 beds) 801 East Sioux Avenue, Pierre, SD, Zip 57501–3323; tel. 605/224–3100; Mikel Holland, M.D., President and Chief Medical Officer
**Web address:** www.avera.org/st–marys–pierre/

AVERA WESKOTA MEMORIAL HOSPITAL (L, 23 beds) 604 First Street NE, Wessington Springs, SD, Zip 57382–2166; tel. 605/539–1201; Stephanie Reasy, Administrator and Chief Executive Officer
**Web address:** www.averaweskota.org

EUREKA COMMUNITY HEALTH SERVICES AVERA (C, 4 beds) 410 Ninth Street, Eureka, SD, Zip 57437–2182, Mailing Address: P.O. Box 517, 57437–0517, tel. 605/284–2661; Carmen Weber, Administrator

LANDMANN–JUNGMAN MEMORIAL HOSPITAL AVERA (C, 10 beds) 600 Billars Street, Scotland, SD, Zip 57059–2026; tel. 605/583–2226; Melissa Gale, Chief Executive Officer
**Web address:** www.ljmh.org

MARSHALL COUNTY HEALTHCARE CENTER AVERA (C, 18 beds) 413 Ninth Street, Britton, SD, Zip 57430–2274; tel. 605/448–2253; Nick Fosness, Chief Executive Officer
**Web address:** www.avera.org

MILBANK AREA HOSPITAL AVERA (L, 25 beds) 301 Flynn Drive, Milbank, SD, Zip 57252–1508; tel. 605/432–4538; Natalie Gauer, Administrator

PLATTE HEALTH CENTER AVERA (C, 59 beds) 601 East Seventh, Platte, SD, Zip 57369–2123, Mailing Address: P.O. Box 200, 57369–0200, tel. 605/337–3364; Mark Burket, Chief Executive Officer
**Web address:** www.phcavera.org

ST. MICHAEL'S HOSPITAL AVERA (C, 25 beds) 410 West 16th Avenue, Tyndall, SD, Zip 57066–2318; tel. 605/589–2100; Carol Deurmier, Chief Executive Officer
**Web address:** www.stmichaels–bhfp.org

WAGNER COMMUNITY MEMORIAL HOSPITAL AVERA (C, 20 beds) 513 Third Street SW, Wagner, SD, Zip 57380–9675, Mailing Address: P.O. Box 280, 57380–0280, tel. 605/384–3611; Bryan Slaba, Chief Executive Officer
**Web address:** www.avera.org/wagnerhospital

| Owned, leased, sponsored: | 21 hospitals | 1971 beds |
|---|---|---|
| Contract–managed: | 13 hospitals | 447 beds |
| **Totals:** | 34 hospitals | 2418 beds |

**★0633: AVITA HEALTH SYSTEM** (NP)

269 Portland Way South, Galion, OH Zip 44833–2399; tel. 419/468–4841; Jerome Morasko, President and Chief Executive Officer
**(Independent Hospital System)**

For explanation of codes following names, see page B2.
★ Indicates Type III membership in the American Hospital Association.

Section B

**OHIO:** AVITA ONTARIO HOSPITAL (O, 26 beds) 715 Richland Mall, Ontario, OH, Zip 44906–3802; tel. 567/307–7666; Jerome Morasko, President and Chief Executive Officer
**Web address:** www.avitahealth.org

BUCYRUS HOSPITAL (O, 25 beds) 629 North Sandusky Avenue, Bucyrus, OH, Zip 44820–1821; tel. 419/562–4677; Jerome Morasko, Chief Executive Officer

GALION HOSPITAL (O, 35 beds) 269 Portland Way South, Galion, OH, Zip 44833–2399; tel. 419/468–4841; Jerome Morasko, President and Chief Executive Officer
**Web address:** www.avitahs.org

| | | |
|---|---|---|
| Owned, leased, sponsored: | 3 hospitals | 86 beds |
| Contract–managed: | 0 hospitals | 0 beds |
| Totals: | 3 hospitals | 86 beds |

---

**1033: BALLAD HEALTH** (NP)

303 Med Tech Parkway, Johnson City, TN Zip 37604–2391; tel. 423/230–8200; Alan M. Levine, President and Chief Executive Officer

**(Centralized Health System)**

**TENNESSEE:** BRISTOL REGIONAL MEDICAL CENTER (O, 296 beds) 1 Medical Park Boulevard, Bristol, TN, Zip 37620–7430; tel. 423/844–1121; Chad Couch, M.D., Interim Chief Executive Officer
**Web address:** www.balladhealth.org

FRANKLIN WOODS COMMUNITY HOSPITAL (O, 102 beds) 300 MedTech Parkway, Johnson City, TN, Zip 37604–2277; tel. 423/302–1000; Melanie Steagall. Stanton, Chief Executive Officer
**Web address:** www.msha.com

GREENEVILLE COMMUNITY HOSPITAL WEST (O, 15 beds) 401 Takoma Avenue, Greeneville, TN, Zip 37743–4647; tel. 423/639–3151; Tammy Albright, Chief Executive Officer

HANCOCK COUNTY HOSPITAL (O, 10 beds) 1519 Main Street, Sneedville, TN, Zip 37869–3657; tel. 423/733–5000; Rebecca Beck, President
**Web address:** www.wellmont.org/Hospitals/Hancock–County–Hospital.aspx

HAWKINS COUNTY MEMORIAL HOSPITAL (O, 16 beds) 851 Locust Street, Rogersville, TN, Zip 37857–2407, Mailing Address: P.O. Box 130, 37857–0130, tel. 423/921–7000; Regina Day, Chief Executive Officer
**Web address:** www.wellmont.org

HOLSTON VALLEY MEDICAL CENTER (O, 336 beds) 130 West Ravine Street, Kingsport, TN, Zip 37660–3837, Mailing Address: P.O. Box 238, 37662–0238, tel. 423/224–4000; Lindy P. White, Vice President and Chief Executive Officer

INDIAN PATH COMMUNITY HOSPITAL (O, 117 beds) 2000 Brookside Drive, Kingsport, TN, Zip 37660–4627; tel. 423/857–7000; Lindy P. White, Vice President, Chief Executive Officer of Kingsport Market Operations
**Web address:** www.balladhealth.org

JOHNSON CITY MEDICAL CENTER (O, 585 beds) 400 North State of Franklin Road, Johnson City, TN, Zip 37604–6094; tel. 423/431–6111; Stan Hickson, FACHE, Chief Executive Officer
**Web address:** www.msha.com

JOHNSON COUNTY COMMUNITY HOSPITAL (O, 2 beds) 1901 South Shady Street, Mountain City, TN, Zip 37683–2271; tel. 423/727–1100; Chastity Trivette, Chief Executive Officer

SYCAMORE SHOALS HOSPITAL (O, 74 beds) 1501 West Elk Avenue, Elizabethton, TN, Zip 37643–2874; tel. 423/542–1300; Dwayne Taylor, Chief Executive Officer
**Web address:** www.msha.com

UNICOI COUNTY MEMORIAL HOSPITAL (O, 50 beds) 2030 Temple Hill Road, Erwin, TN, Zip 37650, Mailing Address: P.O. Box 802, 37650–0802, tel. 423/743–3141; Eric Carroll, Chief Executive Officer
**Web address:** www.msha.com

**VIRGINIA:** DICKENSON COMMUNITY HOSPITAL (O, 11 beds) 312 Hospital Drive, Clintwood, VA, Zip 24228, Mailing Address: P.O. Box 1440, 24228–1440, tel. 276/926–0300; Mark T. Leonard, Chief Executive Officer

JOHNSTON MEMORIAL HOSPITAL (O, 116 beds) 16000 Johnston Memorial Drive, Abingdon, VA, Zip 24211–7659; tel. 276/258–1000; John Jeter, Chief Executive Officer
**Web address:** www.jmh.org

LONESOME PINE HOSPITAL (O, 16 beds) 1990 Holton Avenue East, Big Stone Gap, VA, Zip 24219–3350; tel. 276/523–3111; Mark T. Leonard, Interim Chief Executive Officer
**Web address:** www.wellmont.org

MOUNTAIN VIEW REGIONAL MEDICAL CENTER (O, 70 beds) 310 Third Street NE, Norton, VA, Zip 24273–1137; tel. 276/679–9100; Mark T. Leonard, Interim Chief Executive Officer
**Web address:** www.wellmont.org

NORTON COMMUNITY HOSPITAL (O, 66 beds) 100 15th Street NW, Norton, VA, Zip 24273–1616; tel. 276/679–9600; Mark T. Leonard, Chief Executive Officer

RUSSELL COUNTY MEDICAL CENTER (O, 78 beds) 58 Carroll Street, Lebanon, VA, Zip 24266, Mailing Address: P.O. Box 3600, 24266–0200, tel. 276/883–8000; Stephen K. Givens, Assistant Vice President and Administrator
**Web address:** www.mountainstateshealth.com/rcmc

SMYTH COUNTY COMMUNITY HOSPITAL (O, 153 beds) 245 Medical Park Drive, Marion, VA, Zip 24354, Mailing Address: P.O. Box 880, 24354–0880, tel. 276/378–1000; James E. Tyler, Chief Executive Officer
**Web address:** www.msha.com/scch

| | | |
|---|---|---|
| Owned, leased, sponsored: | 18 hospitals | 2113 beds |
| Contract–managed: | 0 hospitals | 0 beds |
| Totals: | 18 hospitals | 2113 beds |

---

**★0194: BANNER HEALTH** (NP)

2901 North Central Avenue Suite 160, Phoenix, AZ Zip 85012–2702, 2901 North Central Avenue, Suite 160, 85012–2700, tel. 602/747–4000; Peter S. Fine, FACHE, President and Chief Executive Officer

**(Centralized Health System)**

**ARIZONA:** BANNER – UNIVERSITY MEDICAL CENTER PHOENIX (O, 745 beds) 1111 East McDowell Road, Phoenix, AZ, Zip 85006–2666, Mailing Address: P.O. Box 2989, 85062–2989, tel. 602/239–2000; Daniel Post, Chief Executive Officer
**Web address:** www.bannerhealth.com/Locations/Arizona/Banner+Good+Samaritan+Medical+Center

BANNER – UNIVERSITY MEDICAL CENTER SOUTH (O, 245 beds) 2800 East Ajo Way, Tucson, AZ, Zip 85713–6289; tel. 520/874–2000; Sarah Frost, Chief Executive Officer
**Web address:** www.bannerhealth.com

BANNER – UNIVERSITY MEDICAL CENTER TUCSON (O, 583 beds) 1501 North Campbell Avenue, Tucson, AZ, Zip 85719; tel. 520/694–0111; Sarah Frost, Chief Executive Officer
**Web address:** https://www.bannerhealth.com/locations/tucson/banner–university–medical–center–tucson

BANNER BAYWOOD MEDICAL CENTER (O, 359 beds) 6644 East Baywood Avenue, Mesa, AZ, Zip 85206–1797; tel. 480/321–2000; Lamont M. Yoder, R.N., MSN, FACHE, Chief Executive Officer

BANNER BEHAVIORAL HEALTH HOSPITAL – SCOTTSDALE (O, 128 beds) 7575 East Earll Drive, Scottsdale, AZ, Zip 85251–6915; tel. 480/941–7500; William Southwick, R.N., MS, Chief Executive Officer
**Web address:** https://www.bannerhealth.com/locations/scottsdale/banner–behavioral–health–hospital

BANNER BOSWELL MEDICAL CENTER (O, 436 beds) 10401 West Thunderbird Boulevard, Sun City, AZ, Zip 85351–3004; tel. 623/832–4000; Sharon Lind, MSN, FACHE, Chief Executive Officer
**Web address:** www.bannerhealth.com/locations/sun–city/banner–boswell–medical–center

BANNER CASA GRANDE MEDICAL CENTER (O, 123 beds) 1800 East Florence Boulevard, Casa Grande, AZ, Zip 85122–5399; tel. 520/381–6300; Brian Kellar, Chief Executive Officer

BANNER DEL E. WEBB MEDICAL CENTER (O, 433 beds) 14502 West Meeker Boulevard, Sun City West, AZ, Zip 85375–5299; tel. 623/524–4000; Sharon Lind, MSN, FACHE, Chief Executive Officer
**Web address:** www.bannerhealth.com/Locations/Arizona/Banner+Del+Webb+Medical+Center/

---

For explanation of codes following names, see page B2.
★ Indicates Type III membership in the American Hospital Association.

BANNER DESERT MEDICAL CENTER (O, 595 beds) 1400 South Dobson Road, Mesa, AZ, Zip 85202–4707; tel. 480/412–3000; Laura Robertson, R.N., Chief Executive Officer

BANNER ESTRELLA MEDICAL CENTER (O, 317 beds) 9201 West Thomas Road, Phoenix, AZ, Zip 85037–3332; tel. 623/327–4000; Courtney Ophaug, FACHE, Chief Executive Officer
**Web address**: www.bannerhealth.com/Locations/Arizona/Banner+Estrella+Medical+Center/

BANNER GATEWAY MEDICAL CENTER (O, 177 beds) 1900 North Higley Road, Gilbert, AZ, Zip 85234–1604; tel. 480/543–2000; Lamont M. Yoder, R.N., MSN, FACHE, Chief Executive Officer
**Web address**: www.bannerhealth.com/Locations/Arizona/Banner+Gateway+Medical+Center/

BANNER GOLDFIELD MEDICAL CENTER (O, 20 beds) 2050 West Southern Avenue, Apache Junction, AZ, Zip 85120–7305; tel. 480/733–3300; Robert Gardner, Chief Executive Officer
**Web address**: www.bannerhealth.com/Locations/Arizona/Banner+Goldfield+Medical+Center/_Welcome+to+to+Banner+Goldfield.htm

BANNER HEART HOSPITAL (O, 111 beds) 6750 East Baywood Avenue, Mesa, AZ, Zip 85206–1749; tel. 480/854–5000; Lamont M. Yoder, R.N., MSN, FACHE, Chief Executive Officer

BANNER IRONWOOD MEDICAL CENTER (O, 53 beds) 37000 North Gantzel Road, San Tan Valley, AZ, Zip 85140–7303; tel. 480/394–4000; Robert Gardner, Chief Executive Officer
**Web address**: www.bannerhealth.com/Locations/Arizona/Banner+Ironwood/

BANNER PAYSON MEDICAL CENTER (O, 25 beds) 807 South Ponderosa Street, Payson, AZ, Zip 85541–5599; tel. 928/474–3222; Lance Porter, Chief Executive Officer
**Web address**: www.paysonhospital.com

BANNER THUNDERBIRD MEDICAL CENTER (O, 555 beds) 5555 West Thunderbird Road, Glendale, AZ, Zip 85306–4696; tel. 602/865–5555; Debbie Flores, Chief Executive Officer

PAGE HOSPITAL (C, 25 beds) 501 North Navajo Drive; Page, AZ, Zip 86040, Mailing Address: P.O. Box 1447, 86040–1447, tel. 928/645–2424; Susan Eubanks, Chief Executive Officer
**Web address**: www.bannerhealth.com/Locations/Arizona/Page+Hospital

**CALIFORNIA**: BANNER LASSEN MEDICAL CENTER (O, 25 beds) 1800 Spring Ridge Drive, Susanville, CA, Zip 96130–6100; tel. 530/252–2000; Sandy Dugger, Chief Executive Officer
**Web address**: https://www.bannerhealth.com/locations/susanville/banner–lassen–medical–center

**COLORADO**: BANNER FORT COLLINS MEDICAL CENTER (O, 23 beds) 4700 Lady Moon Drive, Fort Collins, CO, Zip 80528–4426; tel. 970/821–4000; Hoyt Skabelund, Chief Executive Officer

EAST MORGAN COUNTY HOSPITAL (L, 22 beds) 2400 West Edison Street, Brush, CO, Zip 80723–1640; tel. 970/842–6200; Linda Thorpe, Chief Executive Officer
**Web address**: www.emchbrush.com

MCKEE MEDICAL CENTER (O, 73 beds) 2000 Boise Avenue, Loveland, CO, Zip 80538–4281; tel. 970/669–4640; Hoyt Skabelund, Chief Executive Officer
**Web address**: www.mckeeloveland.com

NORTH COLORADO MEDICAL CENTER (O, 369 beds) 1801 16th Street, Greeley, CO, Zip 80631–5154; tel. 970/352–4121; Hoyt Skabelund, Chief Executive Officer

STERLING REGIONAL MEDCENTER (O, 25 beds) 615 Fairhurst Street, Sterling, CO, Zip 80751–4523; tel. 970/522–0122; Wade Tyrell, Chief Executive Officer and Chief Nursing Officer
**Web address**: https://www.bannerhealth.com/locations/sterling/sterling–regional–medcenter

**NEBRASKA**: OGALLALA COMMUNITY HOSPITAL (L, 18 beds) 2601 North Spruce Street, Ogallala, NE, Zip 69153–2465; tel. 308/284–4011; Timothy Gullingsrud, Chief Executive Officer
**Web address**: https://www.bannerhealth.com/locations/ogallala/ogallala–community–hospital

**NEVADA**: BANNER CHURCHILL COMMUNITY HOSPITAL (O, 25 beds) 801 East Williams Avenue, Fallon, NV, Zip 89406–3052; tel. 775/423–3151; Robert H. Carnahan II, R.N., Chief Executive Officer

**WYOMING**: COMMUNITY HOSPITAL (O, 20 beds) 2000 Campbell Drive, Torrington, WY, Zip 82240–1597; tel. 307/532–4181; Zachary T. Miller, Interim Chief Executive Officer
**Web address**: www.bannerhealth.com/Locations/Wyoming/Community+Hospital/

PLATTE COUNTY MEMORIAL HOSPITAL (L, 25 beds) 201 14th Street, Wheatland, WY, Zip 82201–3201, Mailing Address: P.O. Box 848, 82201–0848, tel. 307/322–3636; Ned Resch, Chief Executive Officer
**Web address**: https://www.bannerhealth.com/locations/wheatland/platte–county–memorial–hospital

WASHAKIE MEDICAL CENTER (L, 18 beds) 400 South 15th Street, Worland, WY, Zip 82401–3531, Mailing Address: P.O. Box 700, 82401–0700, tel. 307/347–3221; Jay Stallings, Chief Executive Officer
**Web address**: https://www.bannerhealth.com/locations/worland/washakie–medical–center

| | | |
|---|---|---|
| Owned, leased, sponsored: | 27 hospitals | 5548 beds |
| Contract-managed: | 1 hospitals | 25 beds |
| **Totals:** | 28 hospitals | 5573 beds |

---

**★0005: BAPTIST HEALTH** (NP)
841 Prudential Drive, Suite 1601, Jacksonville, FL Zip 32207–8202; tel. 904/202–2000; Brett McClung, President and Chief Executive Officer
**(Moderately Centralized Health System)**

**FLORIDA**: BAPTIST MEDICAL CENTER BEACHES (O, 135 beds) 1350 13th Avenue South, Jacksonville Beach, FL, Zip 32250–3205; tel. 904/627–2900; Joseph M. Mitrick, FACHE, President

BAPTIST MEDICAL CENTER JACKSONVILLE (O, 955 beds) 800 Prudential Drive, Jacksonville, FL, Zip 32207–8202; tel. 904/202–2000; Michael A. Mayo, FACHE, President
**Web address**: www.e–baptisthealth.com

BAPTIST MEDICAL CENTER NASSAU (O, 52 beds) 1250 South 18th Street, Fernandina Beach, FL, Zip 32034–3098; tel. 904/321–3500; Edward T. Hubel, FACHE, President

| | | |
|---|---|---|
| Owned, leased, sponsored: | 3 hospitals | 1142 beds |
| Contract-managed: | 0 hospitals | 0 beds |
| **Totals:** | 3 hospitals | 1142 beds |

---

**★0355: BAPTIST HEALTH** (NP)
9601 Baptist Health Drive, Little Rock, AR Zip 72205–6321; tel. 501/202–2000; Troy R. Wells, Chief Executive Officer
**(Centralized Physician/Insurance Health System)**

**ARKANSAS**: BAPTIST HEALTH – FORT SMITH (O, 281 beds) 1001 Towson Avenue, Fort Smith, AR, Zip 72901–4921, Mailing Address: P.O. Box 2406, 72917–7006, tel. 479/441–4000; Kimberly J. Miller, FACHE, President, Western Region

BAPTIST HEALTH – VAN BUREN (O, 17 beds) East Main and South 20th Streets, Van Buren, AR, Zip 72956–5715, Mailing Address: P.O. Box 409, 72957–0409, tel. 479/474–3401; Kimberly J. Miller, FACHE, President, Western Region
**Web address**: https://www.sparkshealth.com/

BAPTIST HEALTH EXTENDED CARE HOSPITAL (O, 36 beds) 9601 Baptist Health Drive, Little Rock, AR, Zip 72205–7202; tel. 501/202–1070; Greg Stubblefield, President

BAPTIST HEALTH MEDICAL CENTER – CONWAY (O, 111 beds) 1555 Exchange Avenue, Conway, AR, Zip 72032–7824; tel. 501/585–2000; Tim Bowen, Vice President and Administrator
**Web address**: www.baptist–health.com/location/baptist–health–medical–center–conway–conway

BAPTIST HEALTH MEDICAL CENTER – NORTH LITTLE ROCK (O, 177 beds) 3333 Springhill Drive, North Little Rock, AR, Zip 72117–2922; tel. 501/202–3000; Mike Perkins, Vice President and Administrator

For explanation of codes following names, see page B2.
★ Indicates Type III membership in the American Hospital Association.

BAPTIST HEALTH MEDICAL CENTER–ARKADELPHIA (L, 25 beds) 3050 Twin Rivers Drive, Arkadelphia, AR, Zip 71923–4299; tel. 870/245–2622; Tony Hardage, PharmD, Assistant Vice President and Administrator
**Web address:** www.baptist–health.com/locations/accesspoint. aspx?accessPointID=187

BAPTIST HEALTH MEDICAL CENTER–HEBER SPRINGS (O, 25 beds) 1800 Bypass Road, Heber Springs, AR, Zip 72543–9135; tel. 501/887–3000; Kevin L. Storey, Vice President and Administrator
**Web address:** www.baptist–health.com/maps–directions/bhmc–heber–springs

BAPTIST HEALTH MEDICAL CENTER–HOT SPRING COUNTY (L, 72 beds) 1001 Schneider Drive, Malvern, AR, Zip 72104–4811; tel. 501/332–1000; Tony Hardage, PharmD, Interim Chief Executive Officer
**Web address:** https://www.baptist–health.com/location/baptist–health–medical–center–hot–spring–county–hot–spring–county

BAPTIST HEALTH MEDICAL CENTER–LITTLE ROCK (O, 657 beds) 9601 Baptist Health Drive, Little Rock, AR, Zip 72205–7299; tel. 501/202–2000; Greg Crain, FACHE, Senior Vice President and Administrator

BAPTIST HEALTH MEDICAL CENTER–STUTTGART (L, 41 beds) 1703 North Buerkle Road, Stuttgart, AR, Zip 72160–1905, Mailing Address: P.O. Box 1905, 72160–1905, tel. 870/673–3511; Kevin L. Storey, President
**Web address:** https://www.baptist–health.com/location/baptist–health–medical–center–stuttgart–stuttgart

BAPTIST HEALTH REHABILITATION INSTITUTE (O, 120 beds) 9501 Baptist Health Drive, Little Rock, AR, Zip 72205–6225; tel. 501/202–7000; Julie Nix, Vice President and Administrator

| | | |
|---|---|---|
| Owned, leased, sponsored: | 11 hospitals | 1562 beds |
| Contract–managed: | 0 hospitals | 0 beds |
| Totals: | 11 hospitals | 1562 beds |

## 0315: BAPTIST HEALTH (CO)

2701 Eastpoint Parkway, Louisville, KY Zip 40223; tel. 502/896–5000; Gerard Colman, Ph.D., Chief Executive Officer
**(Centralized Physician/Insurance Health System)**

**INDIANA:** BAPTIST HEALTH FLOYD (O, 236 beds) 1850 State Street, New Albany, IN, Zip 47150–4997; tel. 812/949–5500; Mike K. Schroyer, FACHE, MSN, R.N., President
**Web address:** www.baptisthealth.com/floyd

**KENTUCKY:** BAPTIST HEALTH CORBIN (O, 273 beds) 1 Trillium Way, Corbin, KY, Zip 40701–8420; tel. 606/528–1212; Anthony Powers, Interim President and Vice President of Patient Services
**Web address:** www.baptisthealth.com/corbin

BAPTIST HEALTH LA GRANGE (O, 65 beds) 1025 New Moody Lane, La Grange, KY, Zip 40031–9154; tel. 502/222–5388; Clint Kaho, President
**Web address:** www.baptisthealthlagrange.com

BAPTIST HEALTH LEXINGTON (O, 434 beds) 1740 Nicholasville Road, Lexington, KY, Zip 40503–1499; tel. 859/260–6100; William G. Sisson, FACHE, President
**Web address:** www.baptisthealthlexington.com

BAPTIST HEALTH LOUISVILLE (O, 500 beds) 4000 Kresge Way, Louisville, KY, Zip 40207–4676; tel. 502/897–8100; Larry W. Gray, President

BAPTIST HEALTH MADISONVILLE (O, 175 beds) 900 Hospital Drive, Madisonville, KY, Zip 42431–1694; tel. 270/825–5100; Robert L. Ramey, President
**Web address:** www.baptisthealthmadisonville.com

BAPTIST HEALTH PADUCAH (O, 188 beds) 2501 Kentucky Avenue, Paducah, KY, Zip 42003–3200; tel. 270/575–2100; Christopher Roty, President
**Web address:** www.baptisthealthpaducah.com

BAPTIST HEALTH RICHMOND (O, 60 beds) 801 Eastern Bypass, Richmond, KY, Zip 40475–2405, Mailing Address: P.O. Box 1600, 40476–2603, tel. 859/623–3131; Greg Donavan. Gerard, President
**Web address:** www.baptisthealthrichmond.com

HARDIN MEMORIAL HEALTH (C, 268 beds) 913 North Dixie Avenue, Elizabethtown, KY, Zip 42701–2503; tel. 270/737–1212; Dennis B. Johnson, President and Chief Executive Officer

| | | |
|---|---|---|
| Owned, leased, sponsored: | 8 hospitals | 1931 beds |
| Contract–managed: | 1 hospitals | 268 beds |
| Totals: | 9 hospitals | 2199 beds |

## 0150: BAPTIST HEALTH (NP)

301 Brown Springs Road, Montgomery, AL Zip 36117–7005; tel. 334/273–4400; W Russell. Tyner, President and Chief Executive Officer
**(Independent Hospital System)**

**ALABAMA:** BAPTIST MEDICAL CENTER EAST (O, 150 beds) 400 Taylor Road, Montgomery, AL, Zip 36117–3512, Mailing Address: P.O. Box 241267, 36124–1267, tel. 334/747–8330; Jeff G. Rains, Chief Executive Officer
**Web address:** www.baptistfirst.org

BAPTIST MEDICAL CENTER SOUTH (O, 371 beds) 2105 East South Boulevard, Montgomery, AL, Zip 36116–2409, Box 11010, 36111–0010, tel. 334/288–2100; J Peter. Selman, FACHE, Chief Executive Officer

PRATTVILLE BAPTIST HOSPITAL (O, 55 beds) 124 South Memorial Drive, Prattville, AL, Zip 36067–3619, Mailing Address: P.O. Box 681630, 36068–1638, tel. 334/365–0651; Eric Morgan, Chief Executive Officer
**Web address:** www.baptistfirst.org/facilities/prattville–baptist–hospital/default.aspx

| | | |
|---|---|---|
| Owned, leased, sponsored: | 3 hospitals | 576 beds |
| Contract–managed: | 0 hospitals | 0 beds |
| Totals: | 3 hospitals | 576 beds |

## ★0185: BAPTIST HEALTH CARE CORPORATION (NP)

1717 North 'E' Street, Suite 402, Pensacola, FL Zip 32501–6377, Mailing Address: P.O. Box 17500, 32522–7500, tel. 850/434–4011; Mark T. Faulkner, President
**(Centralized Physician/Insurance Health System)**

**FLORIDA:** BAPTIST HOSPITAL (O, 340 beds) 1000 West Moreno Street, Pensacola, FL, Zip 32501–2316, Mailing Address: P.O. Box 17500, 32522–7500, tel. 850/434–4011; Scott Raynes, President
**Web address:** www.ebaptisthealthcare.org

GULF BREEZE HOSPITAL (O, 65 beds) 1110 Gulf Breeze Parkway, Gulf Breeze, FL, Zip 32561–4884; tel. 850/934–2000; Scott Raynes, President

JAY HOSPITAL (L, 21 beds) 14114 Alabama Street, Jay, FL, Zip 32565–1219; tel. 850/675–8000; Michael T. Hutchins, Administrator
**Web address:** www.bhcpns.org/jayhospital/

| | | |
|---|---|---|
| Owned, leased, sponsored: | 3 hospitals | 426 beds |
| Contract–managed: | 0 hospitals | 0 beds |
| Totals: | 3 hospitals | 426 beds |

## ★0122: BAPTIST HEALTH SOUTH FLORIDA (NP)

6855 Red Road, Suite 600, Coral Gables, FL Zip 33143–3632; tel. 786/662–7111; Brian E. Keeley, President and Chief Executive Officer
**(Centralized Health System)**

**FLORIDA:** BAPTIST HEALTH SOUTH FLORIDA, BAPTIST HOSPITAL OF MIAMI (O, 720 beds) 8900 North Kendall Drive, Miami, FL, Zip 33176–2197; tel. 786/596–1960; Patricia M. Rosello, Chief Executive Officer

BAPTIST HEALTH SOUTH FLORIDA, DOCTORS HOSPITAL (O, 126 beds) 5000 University Drive, Coral Gables, FL, Zip 33146–2094; tel. 786/308–3000; Javier Hernandez–Lichtl, Chief Executive Officer
**Web address:** www.baptisthealth.net

BAPTIST HEALTH SOUTH FLORIDA, HOMESTEAD HOSPITAL (O, 147 beds) 975 Baptist Way, Homestead, FL, Zip 33033–7600; tel. 786/243–8000; Kenneth R. Spell, Chief Executive Officer
**Web address:** www.baptisthealth.net

For explanation of codes following names, see page B2.
★ Indicates Type III membership in the American Hospital Association.

BAPTIST HEALTH SOUTH FLORIDA, MARINERS HOSPITAL (O, 25 beds) 91500 Overseas Highway, Tavernier, FL, Zip 33070–2547; tel. 305/434–3000; Rick Freeburg, Chief Executive Officer
**Web address:** www.baptisthealth.net/en/facilities/mariners–hospital/Pages/default.aspx

BAPTIST HEALTH SOUTH FLORIDA, SOUTH MIAMI HOSPITAL (O, 336 beds) 6200 SW 73rd Street, Miami, FL, Zip 33143–4679; tel. 786/662–4000; William M. Duquette, Chief Executive Officer
**Web address:** www.baptisthealth.net

BAPTIST HEALTH SOUTH FLORIDA, WEST KENDALL BAPTIST HOSPITAL (O, 133 beds) 9555 SW 162nd Avenue, Miami, FL, Zip 33196–6408; tel. 786/467–2000; Lourdes Boue, Chief Executive Officer

BETHESDA HOSPITAL EAST (O, 481 beds) 2815 South Seacrest Boulevard, Boynton Beach, FL, Zip 33435–7995; tel. 561/737–7733; Nelson Lazo, Chief Executive Officer
**Web address:** www.bethesdaweb.com

FISHERMEN'S HOSPITAL (O, 4 beds) 3301 Overseas Highway, Marathon, FL, Zip 33050–2329; tel. 305/743–5533; Rick Freeburg, Chief Executive Officer
**Web address:** www.fishermenshospital.org

| | | |
|---|---|---|
| **Owned, leased, sponsored:** | 8 hospitals | 1972 beds |
| **Contract–managed:** | 0 hospitals | 0 beds |
| **Totals:** | 8 hospitals | 1972 beds |

---

★**1625: BAPTIST MEMORIAL HEALTH CARE CORPORATION** (NP) 350 North Humphreys Boulevard, Memphis, TN Zip 38120–2177; tel. 901/227–5117; Jason Little, President and Chief Executive Officer
**(Moderately Centralized Health System)**

**ARKANSAS:** BAPTIST MEMORIAL HOSPITAL – CRITTENDEN, INC. (O, 11 beds) 2100 North 7th Street, West Memphis, AR, Zip 72301–2017; tel. 870/394–7800; Brian Welton, Chief Executive Officer and Administrator

NEA BAPTIST MEMORIAL HOSPITAL (O, 228 beds) 4800 East Johnson Avenue, Jonesboro, AR, Zip 72401–8413; tel. 870/936–1000; Samuel Lynd, Administrator and Chief Executive Officer
**Web address:** https://www.baptistonline.org/locations/nea

**MISSISSIPPI:** BAPTIST MEDICAL CENTER ATTALA (O, 25 beds) 220 Highway 12 West, Kosciusko, MS, Zip 39090–3208, Mailing Address: P.O. Box 887, 39090–0887, tel. 662/289–4311; Robert Coleman, Chief Executive Officer
**Web address:** www.mbhs.org/locations/baptist–medical–center–attala/

BAPTIST MEDICAL CENTER LEAKE (O, 25 beds) 1100 Highway 16 E, Carthage, MS, Zip 39051–3809, Mailing Address: P.O. Box 909, 39051–0909, tel. 601/267–1100; Daryl W. Weaver, Chief Executive Officer

BAPTIST MEDICAL CENTER YAZOO (O, 25 beds) 823 Grand Avenue, Yazoo City, MS, Zip 39194–3233; tel. 662/746–2261; Robert Coleman, Chief Executive Officer
**Web address:** www.mbhs.org/locations/baptist–medical–center–yazoo/

BAPTIST MEMORIAL HOSPITAL – CALHOUN (L, 145 beds) 140 Burke–Calhoun City Road, Calhoun City, MS, Zip 38916–9690; tel. 662/628–6611; Collin Cheek, Administrator

BAPTIST MEMORIAL HOSPITAL–BOONEVILLE (L, 63 beds) 100 Hospital Street, Booneville, MS, Zip 38829–3359; tel. 662/720–5000; James Grantham, Administrator and Chief Executive Officer
**Web address:** www.bmhcc.org/booneville

BAPTIST MEMORIAL HOSPITAL–DESOTO (O, 229 beds) 7601 Southcrest Parkway, Southaven, MS, Zip 38671–4742; tel. 662/772–4000; Brian Hogan, Chief Executive Officer
**Web address:** www.baptistonline.org/desoto/

BAPTIST MEMORIAL HOSPITAL–GOLDEN TRIANGLE (O, 236 beds) 2520 Fifth Street North, Columbus, MS, Zip 39705–2095, Mailing Address: P.O. Box 1307, 39703–1307, tel. 662/244–1000; Paul Cade, Administrator and Chief Executive Officer

BAPTIST MEMORIAL HOSPITAL–NORTH MISSISSIPPI (O, 184 beds) 2301 South Lamar Boulevard, Oxford, MS, Zip 38655–5373, Mailing Address: P.O. Box 946, 38655–6002, tel. 662/232–8100; William C. Henning, Administrator and Chief Executive Officer
**Web address:** www.baptistonline.org/north–mississippi/

BAPTIST MEMORIAL HOSPITAL–UNION COUNTY (L, 101 beds) 200 Highway 30 West, New Albany, MS, Zip 38652–3112; tel. 662/538–7631; James Grantham, Administrator and Chief Executive Officer

MISSISSIPPI BAPTIST MEDICAL CENTER (O, 638 beds) 1225 North State Street, Jackson, MS, Zip 39202–2064; tel. 601/968–1000; Bobbie K. Ware, R.N., FACHE, Chief Executive Officer
**Web address:** www.mbhs.org

**TENNESSEE:** BAPTIST MEMORIAL HOSPITAL – MEMPHIS (O, 584 beds) 6019 Walnut Grove Road, Memphis, TN, Zip 38120–2173; tel. 901/226–5000; Brad H. Parsons, FACHE, Chief Executive Officer

BAPTIST MEMORIAL HOSPITAL FOR WOMEN (O, 140 beds) 6225 Humphreys Boulevard, Memphis, TN, Zip 38120–2373; tel. 901/227–9000; Kevin R. Hammeran, Chief Executive Officer and Administrator
**Web address:** www.baptistonline.org/womens/

BAPTIST MEMORIAL HOSPITAL–CARROLL COUNTY (O, 35 beds) 631 R.B. Wilson Drive, Huntingdon, TN, Zip 38344–1727; tel. 731/986–4461; Susan M. Breeden, Administrator and Chief Executive Officer
**Web address:** www.baptistonline.org/huntingdon/

BAPTIST MEMORIAL HOSPITAL–COLLIERVILLE (O, 51 beds) 1500 West Poplar Avenue, Collierville, TN, Zip 38017–0601; tel. 901/861–9400; Lindsay Stencel, Chief Administrative Officer

BAPTIST MEMORIAL HOSPITAL–TIPTON (O, 50 beds) 1995 Highway 51 South, Covington, TN, Zip 38019–3635; tel. 901/476–2621; Parker Harris, Chief Executive Officer and Administrator
**Web address:** www.baptistonline.org/tipton/

BAPTIST MEMORIAL HOSPITAL–UNION CITY (O, 63 beds) 1201 Bishop Street, Union City, TN, Zip 38261–5403, Mailing Address: P.O. Box 310, 38281–0310, tel. 731/885–2410; Barry Bondurant, Administrator and Chief Executive Officer
**Web address:** www.baptistonline.org/union–city/

BAPTIST MEMORIAL REHABILITATION HOSPITAL (O, 49 beds) 1240 South Germantown Road, Germantown, TN, Zip 38138–2226; tel. 901/275–3300; Christopher L. Bariola, Chief Executive Officer

BAPTIST MEMORIAL RESTORATIVE CARE HOSPITAL (O, 30 beds) 6019 Walnut Grove Road, Memphis, TN, Zip 38120–2113; tel. 901/226–4200; William Fox, Chief Executive Officer
**Web address:** www.baptistonline.org/restorative–care/

| | | |
|---|---|---|
| **Owned, leased, sponsored:** | 20 hospitals | 2912 beds |
| **Contract–managed:** | 0 hospitals | 0 beds |
| **Totals:** | 20 hospitals | 2912 beds |

---

★**0528: BASSETT HEALTHCARE NETWORK** (NP) 1 Atwell Road, Cooperstown, NY Zip 13326–1301; tel. 607/547–3456; William F. Streck, M.D., President and Chief Executive Officer
**(Independent Hospital System)**

**NEW YORK:** AURELIA OSBORN FOX MEMORIAL HOSPITAL (O, 184 beds) 1 Norton Avenue, Oneonta, NY, Zip 13820–2629; tel. 607/432–2000; Jeff Joyner, President
**Web address:** www.bassett.org/ao–fox–hospital/

BASSETT MEDICAL CENTER (O, 152 beds) One Atwell Road, Cooperstown, NY, Zip 13326–1394; tel. 607/547–3456; William W. LeCates, M.D., President

COBLESKILL REGIONAL HOSPITAL (O, 40 beds) 178 Grandview Drive, Cobleskill, NY, Zip 12043–5144; tel. 518/254–3456; Eric H. Stein, FACHE, President
**Web address:** www.bassett.org

LITTLE FALLS HOSPITAL (O, 25 beds) 140 Burwell Street, Little Falls, NY, Zip 13365–1725; tel. 315/823–1000; Michael L. Ogden, President and Chief Executive Officer
**Web address:** www.bassett.org

O'CONNOR HOSPITAL (O, 16 beds) 460 Andes Road, State Route 28, Delhi, NY, Zip 13753–7407; tel. 607/746–0300; Scott Bonderoff, President

| | | |
|---|---|---|
| **Owned, leased, sponsored:** | 5 hospitals | 417 beds |
| **Contract–managed:** | 0 hospitals | 0 beds |
| **Totals:** | 5 hospitals | 417 beds |

For explanation of codes following names, see page B2.
★ Indicates Type III membership in the American Hospital Association.

**★0918: BAYLOR SCOTT & WHITE HEALTH** (NP)
4005 Crutcher Street, Suite 310, Dallas, TX Zip 75246–1779;
tel. 214/820–0111; James H. Hinton, Chief Executive Officer
**(Centralized Physician/Insurance Health System)**

**TEXAS**: BAYLOR SCOTT & WHITE ALL SAINTS MEDICAL CENTER – FORT
WORTH (O, 377 beds) 1400 Eighth Avenue, Fort Worth, TX, 76104–
4192; tel. 817/926–2544; Michael Sanborn, FACHE, MS, President
**Web address**: www.baylorhealth.com/PhysiciansLocations/AllSaints/
Pages/Default.aspx

BAYLOR SCOTT & WHITE CONTINUING CARE HOSPITAL–TEMPLE (O, 48 beds)
546 North Kegley Road, Temple, TX, Zip 76502–4069; tel. 254/215–0900;
Michael Davis, Administrator

BAYLOR SCOTT & WHITE HOSPITAL MEDICAL CENTER – COLLEGE STATION
(O, 119 beds) 700 Scott & White Drive, College Station, TX, Zip 77845;
tel. 979/207–0100; Jason Jennings, FACHE, President
**Web address**: www.sw.org/location/college–station–hospital

BAYLOR SCOTT & WHITE MEDICAL CENTER – AUSTIN (O, 25 beds) 5251
West US Highway 290, Austin, TX, Zip 78735; tel. 512/654–2100; Jay Fox,
Chief Executive Officer
**Web address**: https://www.bswhealth.com/locations/austin–medical–center/
pages/default.aspx

BAYLOR SCOTT & WHITE MEDICAL CENTER – BRENHAM (O, 44 beds) 700
Medical Parkway, Brenham, TX, Zip 77833–5498; tel. 979/337–5000; Jason
Jennings, FACHE, President

BAYLOR SCOTT & WHITE MEDICAL CENTER – BUDA (O, 15 beds) 5330
Overpass Drive, Buda, TX, Zip 78610–2300; tel. 737/999–6200; Jay Fox,
President
**Web address**: https://www.bswhealth.com/locations/buda/Pages/default.aspx

BAYLOR SCOTT & WHITE MEDICAL CENTER – CENTENNIAL (O, 106 beds)
12505 Lebanon Road, Frisco, TX, Zip 75035–8298; tel. 972/963–3333;
Ryan Gebhart, President

BAYLOR SCOTT & WHITE MEDICAL CENTER – GRAPEVINE (O, 270 beds) 1650
West College Street, Grapevine, TX, Zip 76051–3565; tel. 817/481–1588;
Christopher York, FACHE, President
**Web address**: https://www.baylorhealth.com/PhysiciansLocations/
Grapevine/Pages/Default.aspx

BAYLOR SCOTT & WHITE MEDICAL CENTER – HILLCREST (C, 226 beds) 100
Hillcrest Medical Boulevard, Waco, TX, Zip 76712–8897; tel. 254/202–2000;
Rebecca Kay. Hardie, Interim President
**Web address**: www.sw.org/hillcrest–medical–center

BAYLOR SCOTT & WHITE MEDICAL CENTER – LAKE POINTE (O, 176 beds)
6800 Scenic Drive, Rowlett, TX, Zip 75088–4552, Mailing Address: P.O.
Box 1550, 75030–1550, tel. 972/412–2273; Donas Cole, FACHE, President

BAYLOR SCOTT & WHITE MEDICAL CENTER – LLANO (O, 10 beds) 200 West
Ollie Street, Llano, TX, Zip 78643–2628; tel. 325/247–5040; Timothy A. Ols,
FACHE, Chief Executive Officer
**Web address**: www.bwshealth.com

BAYLOR SCOTT & WHITE MEDICAL CENTER – MARBLE FALLS (O, 46 beds)
800 West Highway 71, Marble Falls, TX, Zip 78654; tel. 830/201–8000;
Timothy A. Ols, FACHE, President

BAYLOR SCOTT & WHITE MEDICAL CENTER – PFLUGERVILLE (O, 12
beds) 2600 East Pflugerville Parkway, Pflugerville, TX, Zip 78660–5998;
tel. 512/654–6100; Jay Fox, Chief Executive Officer
**Web address**: https://www.bswhealth.com/locations/pflugerville–mc

BAYLOR SCOTT & WHITE MEDICAL CENTER – PLANO (O, 124 beds) 4700
Alliance Boulevard, Plano, TX, Zip 75093–5323; tel. 469/814–2000; Jerri
Garison, R.N., President

BAYLOR SCOTT & WHITE MEDICAL CENTER – ROUND ROCK (O, 173 beds)
300 University Boulevard, Round Rock, TX, Zip 78665–1032; tel. 512/509–
0100; John M. Lambert, President
**Web address**: www.sw.org

BAYLOR SCOTT & WHITE MEDICAL CENTER – TAYLOR (O, 25 beds) 305
Mallard Lane, Taylor, TX, Zip 76574–1208; tel. 512/352–7611; Jay Fox, Chief
Executive Officer
**Web address**: https://www.bswhealth.com/locations/taylor/pages/default.
aspx?utm_source=BSWHealth.com–Taylor&utm_medium=offline&utm_
campaign=BSWHealth.com&utm_term=BSWHealth.com–Taylor&utm_
content=redirect

BAYLOR SCOTT & WHITE MEDICAL CENTER – TEMPLE (O, 644 beds) 2401
South 31st Street, Temple, TX, Zip 76508–0002; tel. 254/724–2111; Shahin
Motakef, FACHE, President
**Web address**: https://www.bswhealth.com/locations/temple/Pages/default.aspx

BAYLOR SCOTT & WHITE MEDICAL CENTER AT – MCKINNEY (O, 143 beds)
5252 West University Drive, McKinney, TX, Zip 75071–7822; tel. 469/764–
1000; Erin Blair, Interim Chief Executive Officer

BAYLOR SCOTT & WHITE MEDICAL CENTER–IRVING (L, 233 beds) 1901 North
MacArthur Boulevard, Irving, TX, Zip 75061–2220; tel. 972/579–8100; Cindy
K. Schamp, FACHE, President
**Web address**: www.bswhealth.com

BAYLOR SCOTT & WHITE MEDICAL CENTER–WAXAHACHIE (O, 129 beds)
2400 North I–35E, Waxahachie, TX, Zip 75165; tel. 469/843–4000; Will
Turner, President

BAYLOR SCOTT & WHITE SURGICAL HOSPITAL–SHERMAN (O, 12 beds) 3601
North Calais Street, Sherman, TX, Zip 75090–1785; tel. 903/870–0999;
Marc Devorsetz, Chief Executive Officer
**Web address**: www.heritageparksurgicalhospital.com

BAYLOR UNIVERSITY MEDICAL CENTER (O, 857 beds) 3500 Gaston Avenue,
Dallas, TX, Zip 75246–2088; tel. 214/820–0111; Steven R. Newton, FACHE,
President
**Web address**: www.baylorhealth.com/PhysiciansLocations/Dallas/Pages/
Default.aspx

| | | |
|---|---|---|
| Owned, leased, sponsored: | 21 hospitals | 3588 beds |
| Contract–managed: | 1 hospitals | 226 beds |
| Totals: | 22 hospitals | 3814 beds |

**★1095: BAYSTATE HEALTH, INC.** (NP)
280 Chestnut Street, Springfield, MA Zip 01199–0001;
tel. 413/794–0000; Mark A. Keroack, M.D., M.P.H., President and
Chief Executive Officer
**(Centralized Physician/Insurance Health System)**

**MASSACHUSETTS**: BAYSTATE FRANKLIN MEDICAL CENTER (O, 89 beds) 164
High Street, Greenfield, MA, Zip 01301–2613; tel. 413/773–0211; Ronald
Bryant, President
**Web address**: www.baystatehealth.org

BAYSTATE MEDICAL CENTER (O, 734 beds) 759 Chestnut Street, Springfield, MA,
Zip 01199–0001; tel. 413/794–0000; Nancy Shendell–Falik, R.N., President
**Web address**: www.baystatehealth.org/bmc

BAYSTATE NOBLE HOSPITAL (O, 85 beds) 115 West Silver Street, Westfield,
MA, Zip 01085–3628; tel. 413/568–2811; Ronald Bryant, President
**Web address**: www.baystatehealth.org/locations/noble–hospital

BAYSTATE WING HOSPITAL (O, 74 beds) 40 Wright Street, Palmer, MA,
Zip 01069–1138; tel. 413/283–7651; Michael Francis. Moran, President and
Chief Administrative Officer

| | | |
|---|---|---|
| Owned, leased, sponsored: | 4 hospitals | 982 beds |
| Contract–managed: | 0 hospitals | 0 beds |
| Totals: | 4 hospitals | 982 beds |

**★0940: BEACON HEALTH SYSTEM** (NP)
615 North Michigan Street, South Bend, IN Zip 46601–1033;
tel. 574/647–1000; Kreg Gruber, Chief Executive Officer
**(Centralized Physician/Insurance Health System)**

**INDIANA**: COMMUNITY HOSPITAL OF BREMEN (O, 21 beds) 1020 High Road,
Bremen, IN, Zip 46506–1093, Mailing Address: P.O. Box 8, 46506–0008,
tel. 574/546–2211; David Bailey, FACHE, Chief Executive Officer
**Web address**: www.bremenhospital.com

ELKHART GENERAL HOSPITAL (O, 247 beds) 600 East Boulevard, Elkhart,
IN, Zip 46514–2499, Mailing Address: P.O. Box 1329, 46515–1329,
tel. 574/294–2621; Carl W. Risk II, President
**Web address**: www.egh.org

MEMORIAL HOSPITAL OF SOUTH BEND (O, 430 beds) 615 North Michigan
Street, South Bend, IN, Zip 46601–1033; tel. 574/647–1000; Larry A. Tracy
Jr, FACHE, President
**Web address**: www.beaconhealthsystem.org

For explanation of codes following names, see page B2.
★ Indicates Type III membership in the American Hospital Association.

**LOUISIANA**: BEACON BEHAVIORAL HOSPITAL (O, 17 beds) 323 Evergreen Street, Bunkie, LA, Zip 71322–1307; tel. 318/346–3143; Amy Savant, Administrator and Chief Executive Officer

| | | |
|---|---|---|
| Owned, leased, sponsored: | 4 hospitals | 715 beds |
| Contract–managed: | 0 hospitals | 0 beds |
| Totals: | 4 hospitals | 715 beds |

---

**★0953: BEAUMONT HEALTH** (NP)

26901 Beaumont Boulevard, Southfield, MI Zip 48033–3849; tel. 248/898–5000; John T. Fox, President and Chief Executive Officer

**(Centralized Health System)**

**MICHIGAN**: BEAUMONT HOSPITAL – DEARBORN (O, 632 beds) 18101 Oakwood Boulevard, Dearborn, MI, Zip 48124–4089, Mailing Address: P.O. Box 2500, 48123–2500, tel. 313/593–7000; David Claeys, FACHE, Chief Executive Officer
**Web address**: www.beaumont.org

BEAUMONT HOSPITAL – FARMINGTON HILLS (O, 307 beds) 28050 Grand River Avenue, Farmington Hills, MI, Zip 48336–5933; tel. 248/471–8000; Constance O'Malley, President
**Web address**: www.beaumont.org

BEAUMONT HOSPITAL – GROSSE POINTE (O, 280 beds) 468 Cadieux Road, Grosse Pointe, MI, Zip 48230–1507; tel. 313/473–1000; James Lynch, M.D., Interim Chief Executive Officer
**Web address**: www.beaumont.org

BEAUMONT HOSPITAL – ROYAL OAK (O, 1109 beds) 3601 West Thirteen Mile Road, Royal Oak, MI, Zip 48073–6712; tel. 248/898–5000; Nancy Susick, MSN, President
**Web address**: www.beaumont.org

BEAUMONT HOSPITAL – TAYLOR (O, 180 beds) 10000 Telegraph Road, Taylor, MI, Zip 48180–3330; tel. 313/295–5000; Lee Ann Odom, Division President
**Web address**: www.beaumont.org

BEAUMONT HOSPITAL – TRENTON (O, 193 beds) 5450 Fort Street, Trenton, MI, Zip 48183–4625; tel. 734/671–3800; Lee Ann Odom, Interim President
**Web address**: www.beaumont.org

BEAUMONT HOSPITAL – TROY (O, 520 beds) 44201 Dequindre Road, Troy, MI, Zip 48085–1117; tel. 248/964–5000; James Lynch, M.D., Interim President
**Web address**: www.beaumont.org

BEAUMONT HOSPITAL, WAYNE (O, 185 beds) 33155 Annapolis Street, Wayne, MI, Zip 48184–2405; tel. 734/467–4000; Eric W. Widner, FACHE, Division President

| | | |
|---|---|---|
| Owned, leased, sponsored: | 8 hospitals | 3406 beds |
| Contract–managed: | 0 hospitals | 0 beds |
| Totals: | 8 hospitals | 3406 beds |

---

**0538: BENEFIS HEALTH SYSTEM** (NP)

1101 26th Street South, Great Falls, MT Zip 59405–5161; tel. 406/455–5000; John H. Goodnow, Chief Executive Officer
**(Moderately Centralized Health System)**

**MONTANA**: BENEFIS HEALTH SYSTEM (O, 502 beds) 1101 26th Street South, Great Falls, MT, Zip 59405–5104; tel. 406/455–5000; John H. Goodnow, Chief Executive Officer

BENEFIS TETON MEDICAL CENTER (O, 25 beds) 915 4th Street North West, Choteau, MT, Zip 59422–9123; tel. 406/466–5763; Louie King, Chief Executive Officer
**Web address**: www.tetonmedicalcenter.net

MISSOURI RIVER MEDICAL CENTER (C, 25 beds) 1501 St Charles Street, Fort Benton, MT, Zip 59442–0249, Mailing Address: P.O. Box 249, 59442–0249, tel. 406/622–3331; Louie King, President, Harry Bold Nursing Home Administrator
**Web address**: www.mrmcfb.org

| | | |
|---|---|---|
| Owned, leased, sponsored: | 2 hospitals | 527 beds |
| Contract–managed: | 1 hospitals | 25 beds |
| Totals: | 3 hospitals | 552 beds |

---

**★2435: BERKSHIRE HEALTH SYSTEMS, INC.** (NP)

725 North Street, Pittsfield, MA Zip 01201–4124; tel. 413/447–2750; David E. Phelps, President and Chief Executive Officer
**(Moderately Centralized Health System)**

**MASSACHUSETTS**: BERKSHIRE MEDICAL CENTER (O, 271 beds) 725 North ST, Pittsfield, MA, Zip 01201–4124, 725 North Street, 01201–4124, tel. 413/447–2000; David E. Phelps, President and Chief Executive Officer

FAIRVIEW HOSPITAL (O, 25 beds) 29 Lewis Avenue, Great Barrington, MA, Zip 01230–1713; tel. 413/528–0790; Eugene A. Dellea, President
**Web address**: www.bhs1.org/body_fh.cfm?id=39

| | | |
|---|---|---|
| Owned, leased, sponsored: | 2 hospitals | 296 beds |
| Contract–managed: | 0 hospitals | 0 beds |
| Totals: | 2 hospitals | 296 beds |

---

**★0949: BETH ISRAEL LAHEY HEALTH** (NP)

109 Brookline Avenue, Boston, MA Zip 02215–3903; tel. 617/667–7000; Kevin Tabb, M.D., President and Chief Executive Officer

**MASSACHUSETTS**: ANNA JAQUES HOSPITAL (O, 123 beds) 25 Highland Avenue, Newburyport, MA, Zip 01950–3894; tel. 978/463–1000; Mark L. Goldstein, President and Chief Executive Officer

BETH ISRAEL DEACONESS HOSPITAL PLYMOUTH (O, 170 beds) 275 Sandwich Street, Plymouth, MA, Zip 02360–2196; tel. 508/746–2000; Kevin B. Coughlin, President and Chief Executive Officer
**Web address**: www.bidplymouth.org

BETH ISRAEL DEACONESS HOSPITAL–MILTON (O, 100 beds) 199 Reedsdale Road, Milton, MA, Zip 02186–3926; tel. 617/696–4600; Richard W. Fernandez, President and Chief Executive Officer

BETH ISRAEL DEACONESS HOSPITAL–NEEDHAM CAMPUS (O, 52 beds) 148 Chestnut Street, Needham, MA, Zip 2492; tel. 781/453–3000; John M. Fogarty, President and Chief Executive Officer
**Web address**: www.bidneedham.org/

BETH ISRAEL DEACONESS MEDICAL CENTER (O, 719 beds) 330 Brookline Avenue, Boston, MA, Zip 02215–5491; tel. 617/667–7000; Peter J. Healy, President and Chief Executive Officer

BEVERLY HOSPITAL (O, 320 beds) 85 Herrick Street, Beverly, MA, Zip 01915–1777; tel. 978/922–3000; Philip M. Cormier, Chief Executive Officer
**Web address**: www.beverlyhospital.org

LAHEY HOSPITAL & MEDICAL CENTER, BURLINGTON (O, 345 beds) 41 Mall Road, Burlington, MA, Zip 01805–0001, 31 Mall Road, 01805–0001, tel. 781/744–5100; David L. Longworth, M.D., Chief Executive Officer
**Web address**: www.lahey.org

MOUNT AUBURN HOSPITAL (O, 205 beds) 330 Mount Auburn Street, Cambridge, MA, Zip 02138–5597; tel. 617/492–3500; Jeanette G. Clough, President and Chief Executive Officer
**Web address**: www.mountauburnhospital.org

NEW ENGLAND BAPTIST HOSPITAL (O, 113 beds) 125 Parker Hill Avenue, Boston, MA, Zip 02120–2847; tel. 617/754–5800; David Passafaro, Chief Executive Officer

WINCHESTER HOSPITAL (O, 189 beds) 41 Highland Avenue, Winchester, MA, Zip 01890–1496; tel. 781/729–9000; Richard I. Weiner, M.D., Chief Executive Officer and Chief Medical Officer
**Web address**: www.winchesterhospital.org

| | | |
|---|---|---|
| Owned, leased, sponsored: | 10 hospitals | 2336 beds |
| Contract–managed: | 0 hospitals | 0 beds |
| Totals: | 10 hospitals | 2336 beds |

---

**★0051: BJC HEALTHCARE** (NP)

4901 Forest Park Avenue, Suite 1200, Saint Louis, MO Zip 63108–1402; tel. 314/286–2000; Richard J. Liekweg, President and Chief Executive Officer
**(Centralized Health System)**

---

For explanation of codes following names, see page B2.
★ Indicates Type III membership in the American Hospital Association.

Section B

**ILLINOIS**: ALTON MEMORIAL HOSPITAL (O, 224 beds) One Memorial Drive, Alton, IL, Zip 62002–6722; tel. 618/463–7311; David A. Braasch, President
**Web address**: www.altonmemorialhospital.org

MEMORIAL HOSPITAL EAST (O, 51 beds) 1404 Cross Street, Shiloh, IL, Zip 62269–2988; tel. 618/607–1000; Michael T. McManus, President
**Web address**: www.memhospeast.com

MEMORIAL HOSPITAL (O, 217 beds) 4500 Memorial Drive, Belleville, IL, Zip 62226–5399; tel. 618/233–7750; Michael T. McManus, President

**MISSOURI**: BARNES–JEWISH HOSPITAL (O, 1395 beds) 1 Barnes–Jewish Hospital Plaza, Saint Louis, MO, Zip 63110–1003; tel. 314/747–3000; John Lynch, M.D., President
**Web address**: www.barnesjewish.org

BARNES–JEWISH ST. PETERS HOSPITAL (O, 102 beds) 10 Hospital Drive, Saint Peters, MO, Zip 63376–1659; tel. 636/916–9000; Chris Watts, President
**Web address**: www.bjsph.org/

BARNES–JEWISH WEST COUNTY HOSPITAL (O, 68 beds) 12634 Olive Boulevard, Saint Louis, MO, Zip 63141–6337; tel. 314/996–8000; Ann Abad, President

BOONE HOSPITAL CENTER (L, 280 beds) 1600 East Broadway, Columbia, MO, Zip 65201–5844; tel. 573/815–8000; James J. Sinek, FACHE, President
**Web address**: www.boone.org

CHRISTIAN HOSPITAL (O, 233 beds) 11133 Dunn Road, Saint Louis, MO, Zip 63136–6119; tel. 314/653–5000; Rick Stevens, President
**Web address**: www.christianhospital.org

MISSOURI BAPTIST MEDICAL CENTER (O, 449 beds) 3015 North Ballas Road, Saint Louis, MO, Zip 63131–2329; tel. 314/996–5000; John Antes, President
**Web address**: www.missouribaptist.org

MISSOURI BAPTIST SULLIVAN HOSPITAL (O, 35 beds) 751 Sappington Bridge Road, Sullivan, MO, Zip 63080–2354; tel. 573/468–4186; Tony Schwarm, FACHE, President
**Web address**: www.missouribaptistsullivan.org

PARKLAND HEALTH CENTER – FARMINGTON COMMUNITY (O, 102 beds) 1101 West Liberty Street, Farmington, MO, Zip 63640–1921; tel. 573/756–6451; Annette D. Schnabel, FACHE, President and Chief Executive Officer

PARKLAND HEALTH CENTER–BONNE TERRE (O, 3 beds) 7245 Raider Road, Bonne Terre, MO, Zip 63628; tel. 573/358–1400; Annette D. Schnabel, FACHE, President and Chief Executive Officer
**Web address**: www.parklandhealthcenter.org

PROGRESS WEST HOSPITAL (O, 74 beds) Two Progress Point Parkway, O'Fallon, MO, Zip 63368–2208; tel. 636/344–1000; Chris Watts, President
**Web address**: www.progresswest.org

ST. LOUIS CHILDREN'S HOSPITAL (O, 344 beds) One Children's Place, Saint Louis, MO, Zip 63110–1002; tel. 314/454–6000; Trisha Lollo, President
**Web address**: www.stlouischildrens.org

| | | |
|---|---|---|
| Owned, leased, sponsored: | 14 hospitals | 3577 beds |
| Contract–managed: | 0 hospitals | 0 beds |
| Totals: | 14 hospitals | 3577 beds |

---

### ★0852: BLANCHARD VALLEY HEALTH SYSTEM (NP)

1900 South Main Street, Findlay, OH Zip 45840–1214; tel. 419/423–4500; Scott C. Malaney, FACHE, President and Chief Executive Officer
**(Centralized Physician/Insurance Health System)**

**OHIO**: BLANCHARD VALLEY HOSPITAL (O, 159 beds) 1900 South Main Street, Findlay, OH, Zip 45840–1214; tel. 419/423–4500; Scott C. Malaney, FACHE, President and Chief Executive Officer
**Web address**: www.bvhealthsystem.org

BLUFFTON HOSPITAL (O, 25 beds) 139 Garau Street, Bluffton, OH, Zip 45817–1027; tel. 419/358–9010; Christine Keller, Chief Administrative Officer
**Web address**: www.bvhealthsystem.org/

| | | |
|---|---|---|
| Owned, leased, sponsored: | 2 hospitals | 184 beds |
| Contract–managed: | 0 hospitals | 0 beds |
| Totals: | 2 hospitals | 184 beds |

---

### 5085: BON SECOURS MERCY HEALTH (CO)

1505 Marriottsville Road, Marriottsville, MD Zip 21104–1399; tel. 410/442–5511; John M. Starcher, Chief Executive Officer
**(Moderately Centralized Health System)**

**SOUTH CAROLINA**: BON SECOURS ST. FRANCIS HEALTH SYSTEM (O, 352 beds) One St Francis Drive, Greenville, SC, Zip 29601–3207; tel. 864/255–1000; Matthew T. Caldwell, President
**Web address**: www.stfrancishealth.org

**VIRGINIA**: BON SECOURS MARY IMMACULATE HOSPITAL (O, 238 beds) 2 Bernardine Drive, Newport News, VA, Zip 23602–4499; tel. 757/886–6000; Darlene Stephenson, Chief Executive Officer

BON SECOURS MARYVIEW MEDICAL CENTER (O, 466 beds) 3636 High Street, Portsmouth, VA, Zip 23707–3270; tel. 757/398–2200; Paul Gaden, Chief Executive Officer
**Web address**: www.bonsecourshamptonroads.com

BON SECOURS MEMORIAL REGIONAL MEDICAL CENTER (O, 225 beds) 8260 Atlee Road, Mechanicsville, VA, Zip 23116–1844; tel. 804/764–6000; Leigh Sewell, Chief Executive Officer
**Web address**: www.bonsecours.com

BON SECOURS ST. FRANCIS MEDICAL CENTER (O, 130 beds) 13710 St Francis Boulevard, Midlothian, VA, Zip 23114–3267; tel. 804/594–7300; Chris Accashian, Chief Executive Officer

BON SECOURS ST. MARY'S HOSPITAL (O, 391 beds) 5801 Bremo Road, Richmond, VA, Zip 23226–1907; tel. 804/285–2011; Francine Barr, R.N., MS, Chief Executive Officer
**Web address**: www.bonsecours.com

BON SECOURS–DEPAUL MEDICAL CENTER (O, 204 beds) 150 Kingsley Lane, Norfolk, VA, Zip 23505–4650; tel. 757/889–5000; Paul Gaden, Chief Executive Officer

BON SECOURS–RICHMOND COMMUNITY HOSPITAL (O, 85 beds) 1500 North 28th Street, Richmond, VA, Zip 23223–5396, Mailing Address: P.O. Box 27184, 23261–7184, tel. 804/225–1700; Leigh Sewell, Chief Executive Officer
**Web address**: www.bonsecours.com

RAPPAHANNOCK GENERAL HOSPITAL (O, 35 beds) 101 Harris Drive, Kilmarnock, VA, Zip 22482–3880, Mailing Address: P.O. Box 1449, 22482–1449, tel. 804/435–8000; Chris Accashian, Chief Executive Officer

SOUTHAMPTON MEMORIAL HOSPITAL (O, 72 beds) 100 Fairview Drive, Franklin, VA, Zip 23851–1238, Mailing Address: P.O. Box 817, 23851–0817, tel. 757/569–6100; Kimberly W. Marks, Chief Executive Officer
**Web address**: www.smhfranklin.com

SOUTHERN VIRGINIA REGIONAL MEDICAL CENTER (O, 80 beds) 727 North Main Street, Emporia, VA, Zip 23847–1274; tel. 434/348–4400; Wilson A. Thomas, Chief Executive Officer

SOUTHSIDE REGIONAL MEDICAL CENTER (O, 294 beds) 200 Medical Park Boulevard, Petersburg, VA, Zip 23805–9274; tel. 804/765–5000; Trent Nobles, Chief Executive Officer
**Web address**: www.srmconline.com

| | | |
|---|---|---|
| Owned, leased, sponsored: | 12 hospitals | 2572 beds |
| Contract–managed: | 0 hospitals | 0 beds |
| Totals: | 12 hospitals | 2572 beds |

---

### 2455: BRADFORD HEALTH SERVICES (IO)

2101 Magnolia Avenue South, Suite 518, Birmingham, AL Zip 35205–2853; tel. 205/251–7753; Jerry W. Crowder, President and Chief Executive Officer

---

For explanation of codes following names, see page B2.
★ Indicates Type III membership in the American Hospital Association.

**ALABAMA**: BRADFORD HEALTH SERVICES AT HUNTSVILLE (O, 84 beds) 1600 Browns Ferry Road, Madison, AL, Zip 35758–9601, Mailing Address: P.O. Box 1488, 35758–0176, tel. 256/461–7272; Bob Hinds, Executive Director
**Web address**: www.bradfordhealth.com

BRADFORD HEALTH SERVICES AT WARRIOR LODGE (O, 100 beds) 1189 Allbritt Road, Warrior, AL, Zip 35180, Mailing Address: P.O. Box 129, 35180–0129, tel. 205/647–1945; Roy M. Ramsey, Executive Director

| | | |
|---|---|---|
| Owned, leased, sponsored: | 2 hospitals | 184 beds |
| Contract–managed: | 0 hospitals | 0 beds |
| Totals: | 2 hospitals | 184 beds |

---

## 0352: BRIDGEPOINT HEALTHCARE (IO)

155 Fleet Street, Portsmouth, NH Zip 03801–4050; tel. 603/570–4888; Marc C. Ferrell, President and Chief Executive Officer
**(Independent Hospital System)**

**DISTRICT OF COLUMBIA**: BRIDGEPOINT HOSPITAL CAPITOL HILL (O, 177 beds) 223 7th Street, NE, Washington, DC, Zip 20002–7045; tel. 202/546–5700; James Linhares, Chief Executive Officer
**Web address**: www.bridgepointhealthcare.com/

BRIDGEPOINT HOSPITAL NATIONAL HARBOR (O, 82 beds) 4601 Martin Luther King Jr Avenue, SW, Washington, DC, Zip 20032–1131; tel. 202/574–5700; Swenda Moreh, Interim Chief Executive Officer
**Web address**: www.bridgepointhealthcare.com/

| | | |
|---|---|---|
| Owned, leased, sponsored: | 2 hospitals | 259 beds |
| Contract–managed: | 0 hospitals | 0 beds |
| Totals: | 2 hospitals | 259 beds |

---

## ★0595: BRONSON HEALTHCARE GROUP (NP)

301 John Street, Kalamazoo, MI Zip 49007–5295; tel. 269/341–6000; Bill Manns, Chief Executive Officer
**(Centralized Health System)**

**MICHIGAN**: BRONSON BATTLE CREEK HOSPITAL (O, 198 beds) 300 North Avenue, Battle Creek, MI, Zip 49017–3307; tel. 269/245–8000; Frank J. Sardone, President and Chief Executive Officer
**Web address**: www.bronsonhealth.com

BRONSON LAKEVIEW HOSPITAL (O, 35 beds) 408 Hazen Street, Paw Paw, MI, Zip 49079–1019, Mailing Address: P.O. Box 209, 49079–0209, tel. 269/657–3141; Kirk Richardson, R.N., Senior Vice President, Chief Operating Officer, and Chief Nursing Officer
**Web address**: www.bronsonhealth.com/lakeview

BRONSON METHODIST HOSPITAL (O, 415 beds) 601 John Street, Kalamazoo, MI, Zip 49007–5346; tel. 269/341–6000; Frank J. Sardone, President and Chief Executive Officer

BRONSON SOUTH HAVEN HOSPITAL (O, 49 beds) 955 South Bailey Avenue, South Haven, MI, Zip 49090–6743; tel. 269/637–5271; Kirk Richardson, R.N., Vice President, Chief Operating Officer and Chief Nursing Officer
**Web address**: www.sh–hs.org

| | | |
|---|---|---|
| Owned, leased, sponsored: | 4 hospitals | 697 beds |
| Contract–managed: | 0 hospitals | 0 beds |
| Totals: | 4 hospitals | 697 beds |

---

## ★3115: BROWARD HEALTH (NP)

1800 NW 49th Street, Fort Lauderdale, FL Zip 33309–3092; tel. 954/355–4400; Gino Santorio, President and Chief Executive Officer

**FLORIDA**: BROWARD HEALTH CORAL SPRINGS (O, 220 beds) 3000 Coral Hills Drive, Coral Springs, FL, Zip 33065–4108; tel. 954/344–3000; Jared M. Smith, Chief Executive Officer
**Web address**: www.browardhealth.org

BROWARD HEALTH IMPERIAL POINT (O, 193 beds) 6401 North Federal Highway, Fort Lauderdale, FL, Zip 33308–1495; tel. 954/776–8500; Randy Gross, Chief Executive Officer
**Web address**: www.browardhealth.org

BROWARD HEALTH MEDICAL CENTER (O, 614 beds) 1600 South Andrews Avenue, Fort Lauderdale, FL, Zip 33316–2510; tel. 954/355–4400; Heather Havericak, Chief Executive Officer

BROWARD HEALTH NORTH (O, 331 beds) 201 East Sample Road, Deerfield Beach, FL, Zip 33064–3502; tel. 954/941–8300; Alice Taylor, R.N., MSN, Chief Executive Officer
**Web address**: www.browardhealth.org

| | | |
|---|---|---|
| Owned, leased, sponsored: | 4 hospitals | 1358 beds |
| Contract–managed: | 0 hospitals | 0 beds |
| Totals: | 4 hospitals | 1358 beds |

---

## ★0400: BRYAN HEALTH (NP)

1600 South 48th Street, Lincoln, NE Zip 68506–1283, 1600 S 48th ST, 68506–1283, tel. 402/481–1111; Russell R. Gronewold, President and Chief Executive Officer
**(Moderately Centralized Health System)**

**IOWA**: CLARINDA REGIONAL HEALTH CENTER (C, 25 beds) 220 Essie Davison Drive, Clarinda, IA, Zip 51632–2915, Mailing Address: P.O. Box 217, 51632–0217, tel. 712/542–2176; Charles Nordyke, Chief Executive Officer
**Web address**: www.clarindahealth.com

**NEBRASKA**: BRYAN MEDICAL CENTER (O, 546 beds) 1600 South 48th Street, Lincoln, NE, Zip 68506–1299; tel. 402/481–1111; John T. Woodrich, President and Chief Executive Officer, Executive Vice President Bryan Health
**Web address**: www.bryanhealth.com

CRETE AREA MEDICAL CENTER (O, 24 beds) 2910 Betten Drive, Crete, NE, Zip 68333–3084, Mailing Address: P.O. Box 220, 68333–0220, tel. 402/826–2102; Stephanie Boldt, President and Chief Executive Officer
**Web address**: www.creteareamedicalcenter.com

MERRICK MEDICAL CENTER (O, 65 beds) 1715 26th Street, Central City, NE, Zip 68826–9620; tel. 308/946–3015; Patrick Avila, President and Chief Executive Officer

SAUNDERS MEDICAL CENTER (C, 16 beds) 1760 County Road J, Wahoo, NE, Zip 68066–4152; tel. 402/443–4191; Julie A. Rezac, R.N., Chief Executive Officer
**Web address**: www.saundersmedicalcenter.com

| | | |
|---|---|---|
| Owned, leased, sponsored: | 3 hospitals | 635 beds |
| Contract–managed: | 2 hospitals | 41 beds |
| Totals: | 5 hospitals | 676 beds |

---

## ★9655: BUREAU OF MEDICINE AND SURGERY, DEPARTMENT OF THE NAVY (FG)

7700 Arlington Boulevard, Suite 5126, Falls Church, VA Zip 22042; tel. 202/762–3701; Rear Admiral, Bruce Gillingham, MC, USN, Surgeon General of the Navy and Chief, Bureau of Medicine and Surgery
**(Independent Hospital System)**

**CALIFORNIA**: NAVAL HOSPITAL CAMP PENDLETON (O, 72 beds) 200 Mercy Circle, Camp Pendleton, CA, Zip 92055–5191, Mailing Address: P.O. Box 555191, 92055–5191, tel. 760/725–1304; Captain, Shelley K. Perkins, Commanding Officer
**Web address**: https://www.med.navy.mil/sites/cpen/newSite/Pages/default.aspx

NAVAL HOSPITAL LEMOORE (O, 16 beds) 937 Franklin Avenue, Lemoore, CA, Zip 93246–0001; tel. 559/998–4481; Captain, Kristen Attenbury, Commanding Officer

For explanation of codes following names, see page B2.
★ Indicates Type III membership in the American Hospital Association.

Section B

NAVAL MEDICAL CENTER SAN DIEGO (O, 285 beds) 34800 Bob Wilson Drive, San Diego, CA, Zip 92134–5000; tel. 619/532–6400; Captain, Joel A. Roos, Commanding Officer
**Web address:** www.med.navy.mil/sites/nmcsd/Pages/default.aspx

ROBERT E. BUSH NAVAL HOSPITAL (O, 29 beds) 1145 Sturgis Road, Twentynine Palms, CA, Zip 92278, Box 788250, MCAGCC, 92278–8250, tel. 760/830–2190; Captain, Jay C. Sourbeer, Commanding Officer
**Web address:** www.med.navy.mil/sites/nhtp/Pages/default.aspx

**FLORIDA:** NAVAL HOSPITAL JACKSONVILLE (O, 64 beds) 2080 Child Street, Jacksonville, FL, Zip 32214–5000; tel. 904/542–7300; Captain, Matthew Case, MSC, USN, Commanding Officer
**Web address:** www.med.navy.mil/SITES/NAVALHOSPITALJAX/Pages/default.aspx

NAVAL HOSPITAL PENSACOLA (O, 28 beds) 6000 West Highway 98, Pensacola, FL, Zip 32512–0003; tel. 850/505–6601; Captain, David Webster, Commanding Officer
**Web address:** https://www.med.navy.mil/sites/pcola

**GUAM:** U. S. NAVAL HOSPITAL GUAM (O, 55 beds) Building #50 Farenholt Avenue, Agana, GU, Zip 96910, PSC 490, Box 208, FPO, 96540, tel. 671/344–9340; Captain, Daniel Cornwell, Command Officer

**MARYLAND:** WALTER REED NATIONAL MILITARY MEDICAL CENTER (O, 251 beds) 8901 Wisconsin Avenue, Bethesda, MD, Zip 20889–5600; tel. 301/295–4611; Captain, Mark A. Kobelja, MC, USN, Director
**Web address:** www.wrnmmc.capmed.mil/SitePages/home.aspx

**NORTH CAROLINA:** NAVAL HOSPITAL CAMP LEJEUNE (O, 117 beds) 100 Brewster Boulevard, Camp Lejeune, NC, Zip 28547–2538, Mailing Address: P.O. Box 10100, 28547–0100, tel. 910/450–4300; Captain, Rick Freedman, Commanding Officer
**Web address:** www.med.navy.mil/sites/nhcl/Pages/default.aspx

**SOUTH CAROLINA:** NAVAL HOSPITAL BEAUFORT (O, 20 beds) 1 Pinckney Boulevard, Beaufort, SC, Zip 29902–6122; tel. 843/228–5301; Lieutenant Commander, Willie Brown, Director Administration
**Web address:** www.med.navy.mil/sites/nhbeaufort/Pages/Welcome_Page.aspx

**VIRGINIA:** NAVAL MEDICAL CENTER (O, 274 beds) 620 John Paul Jones Circle, Portsmouth, VA, Zip 23708–2197; tel. 757/953–1980; Captain, Lisa Mulligan, Commanding Officer

**WASHINGTON:** NAVAL HOSPITAL BREMERTON (O, 23 beds) One Boone Road, Bremerton, WA, Zip 98312–1898; tel. 360/475–4000; Captain, Shannon J. Johnson, Commanding Officer
**Web address:** https://www.med.navy.mil/sites/nhbrem/Pages/Default.aspx

NAVAL HOSPITAL OAK HARBOR (O, 29 beds) 3475 North Saratoga Street, Oak Harbor, WA, Zip 98278–8800; tel. 360/257–9500; Commander, Frederick Joseph. McDonald, Commanding Officer
**Web address:** www.med.navy.mil/sites/nhoh/Pages/default.aspx

| | | |
|---|---|---|
| Owned, leased, sponsored: | 13 hospitals | 1263 beds |
| Contract–managed: | 0 hospitals | 0 beds |
| Totals: | 13 hospitals | 1263 beds |

---

**0113: CANCER TREATMENT CENTERS OF AMERICA** (IO)
1336 Basswood Road, Schaumburg, IL Zip 60173–4544; tel. 847/342–7400; Pat A. Basu, M.D., President and Chief Executive Officer

**ARIZONA:** WESTERN REGIONAL MEDICAL CENTER (O, 11 beds) 14200 West Celebrate Life way, Goodyear, AZ, Zip 85338–3005; tel. 623/207–3000; Robert Gould, President and Chief Executive Officer
**Web address:** www.cancercenter.com/western–hospital.cfm

**GEORGIA:** SOUTHEASTERN REGIONAL MEDICAL CENTER (O, 50 beds) 600 Celebrate Life Parkway, Newnan, GA, Zip 30265–8000; tel. 770/400–6000; Anne Meisner, MSN, President and Chief Executive Officer
**Web address:** www.cancercenter.com/southeastern–hospital.cfm

**ILLINOIS:** MIDWESTERN REGIONAL MEDICAL CENTER (O, 72 beds) 2520 Elisha Avenue, Zion, IL, Zip 60099–2587; tel. 847/872–4561; Scott Jones, President and Chief Executive Officer
**Web address:** www.cancercenter.com

**OKLAHOMA:** SOUTHWESTERN REGIONAL MEDICAL CENTER (O, 40 beds) 10109 East 79th Street, Tulsa, OK, Zip 74133–4564; tel. 918/286–5000; Jay Foley, President and Chief Executive Officer

**PENNSYLVANIA:** CANCER TREATMENT CENTERS OF AMERICA–EASTERN REGIONAL MEDICAL CENTER (O, 56 beds) 1331 East Wyoming Avenue, Philadelphia, PA, Zip 19124–3808; tel. 215/537–7400; Maria Scenna, Chief Executive Officer
**Web address:** www.cancercenter.com

| | | |
|---|---|---|
| Owned, leased, sponsored: | 5 hospitals | 229 beds |
| Contract–managed: | 0 hospitals | 0 beds |
| Totals: | 5 hospitals | 229 beds |

---

**★0124: CAPE COD HEALTHCARE, INC.** (NP)
27 Park Street, Hyannis, MA Zip 02601–5230; tel. 508/862–5121; Michael K. Lauf, President and Chief Executive Officer
**(Centralized Health System)**

**MASSACHUSETTS:** CAPE COD HOSPITAL (O, 259 beds) 27 Park Street, Hyannis, MA, Zip 02601–5230; tel. 508/771–1800; Michael K. Lauf, President and Chief Executive Officer

FALMOUTH HOSPITAL (O, 95 beds) 100 Ter Heun Drive, Falmouth, MA, Zip 02540–2599; tel. 508/548–5300; Lori Jewett, R.N., Chief Executive Officer
**Web address:** www.capecodhealth.org

| | | |
|---|---|---|
| Owned, leased, sponsored: | 2 hospitals | 354 beds |
| Contract–managed: | 0 hospitals | 0 beds |
| Totals: | 2 hospitals | 354 beds |

---

**0835: CAPE FEAR VALLEY HEALTH SYSTEM** (NP)
1638 Owen Drive, Fayetteville, NC Zip 28304–3424, Mailing Address: P.O. Box 2000, 28302–2000, tel. 910/615–4000; Michael Nagowski, President and Chief Executive Officer
**(Independent Hospital System)**

**NORTH CAROLINA:** CAPE FEAR VALLEY – BLADEN COUNTY HOSPITAL (O, 25 beds) 501 South Poplar Street, Elizabethtown, NC, Zip 28337–9375, Mailing Address: P.O. Box 398, 28337–0398, tel. 910/862–5100; Stephen Fife, Interim Chief Executive Officer
**Web address:** www.bchn.org

CAPE FEAR VALLEY MEDICAL CENTER (O, 620 beds) 1638 Owen Drive, Fayetteville, NC, Zip 28304–3431, Mailing Address: P.O. Box 2000, 28302–2000, tel. 910/615–4000; Michael Nagowski, Chief Executive Officer

HARNETT HEALTH SYSTEM (C, 105 beds) 800 Tilghman Drive, Dunn, NC, Zip 28334–5599, Mailing Address: P.O. Box 1706, 28335–1706, tel. 910/892–1000; Kevin Jackson, Interim Chief Executive Officer
**Web address:** www.myharnetthealth.org/

HIGHSMITH–RAINEY SPECIALTY HOSPITAL (O, 66 beds) 150 Robeson Street, Fayetteville, NC, Zip 28301–5570; tel. 910/615–1000; Kevin Jackson, On Site Administrator
**Web address:** www.capefearvalley.com

HOKE HOSPITAL (O, 41 beds) 210 Medical Pavilion Drive, Raeford, NC, Zip 28376–9111; tel. 910/904–8000; Roxie Cannon. Wells, M.D., President

| | | |
|---|---|---|
| Owned, leased, sponsored: | 4 hospitals | 752 beds |
| Contract–managed: | 1 hospitals | 105 beds |
| Totals: | 5 hospitals | 857 beds |

---

For explanation of codes following names, see page B2.
★ Indicates Type III membership in the American Hospital Association.

Section B

★**0297: CAPITAL HEALTH** (NP)
750 Brunswick Avenue, Trenton, NJ Zip 08638–4143;
tel. 609/394–6000; Al Maghazeh, Ph.D., FACHE, President and
Chief Executive Officer
**(Independent Hospital System)**

**NEW JERSEY:** CAPITAL HEALTH MEDICAL CENTER–HOPEWELL (O, 171 beds)
1 Capital Way, Pennington, NJ, Zip 08534–2520; tel. 609/303–4000; Al
Maghazeh, Ph.D., FACHE, President and Chief Executive Officer
**Web address:** www.capitalhealth.org

CAPITAL HEALTH REGIONAL MEDICAL CENTER (O, 168 beds) 750 Brunswick
Avenue, Trenton, NJ, Zip 08638–4143; tel. 609/394–6000; Al Maghazeh,
Ph.D., FACHE, President and Chief Executive Officer
**Web address:** www.capitalhealth.org

| | | |
|---|---|---|
| Owned, leased, sponsored: | 2 hospitals | 339 beds |
| Contract–managed: | 0 hospitals | 0 beds |
| Totals: | 2 hospitals | 339 beds |

★**0099: CARE NEW ENGLAND HEALTH SYSTEM** (NP)
45 Willard Avenue, Providence, RI Zip 02905–3218;
tel. 401/453–7900; James E. Fanale, M.D., President, Chief
Executive Officer and Chief Clinical Officer
**(Moderately Centralized Health System)**

**RHODE ISLAND:** BUTLER HOSPITAL (O, 143 beds) 345 Blackstone Boulevard,
Providence, RI, Zip 02906–4829; tel. 401/455–6200; Mary Marran, MS,
President and Chief Operating Officer
**Web address:** www.butler.org

KENT COUNTY MEMORIAL HOSPITAL (O, 306 beds) 455 Tollgate Road,
Warwick, RI, Zip 02886–2770; tel. 401/737–7000; Robert Haffey, R.N.,
President and Chief Operating Officer
**Web address:** www.kentri.org

WOMEN & INFANTS HOSPITAL OF RHODE ISLAND (O, 247 beds) 101 Dudley
Street, Providence, RI, Zip 02905–2499; tel. 401/274–1100; Shannon
Sullivan, President and Chief Operating Officer

| | | |
|---|---|---|
| Owned, leased, sponsored: | 3 hospitals | 696 beds |
| Contract–managed: | 0 hospitals | 0 beds |
| Totals: | 3 hospitals | 696 beds |

**0931: CAREPOINT HEALTH** (IO)
10 Exchange Place, 15th Floor, Jersey City, NJ Zip 07302–3918;
tel. 201/821–8900; Achintya Moulick, M.D., Chief Executive
Officer

**NEW JERSEY:** CAREPOINT HEALTH BAYONNE MEDICAL CENTER (O, 178
beds) 29th Street & Avenue E, Bayonne, NJ, Zip 07002–4699, 29 East
29 Street, 07002–4699, tel. 201/858–5000; Vijayant Singh, M.D., Chief
Hospital Executive

CAREPOINT HEALTH CHRIST HOSPITAL (O, 376 beds) 176 Palisade Avenue,
Jersey City, NJ, Zip 07306–1196, 176 Palisades Avenue, 07306–1196,
tel. 201/795–8200; Marie Theresa Duffy, Chief Hospital Executive
**Web address:** www.carepointhealth.org

CAREPOINT HEALTH HOBOKEN UNIVERSITY MEDICAL CENTER (O, 228 beds)
308 Willow Avenue, Hoboken, NJ, Zip 07030–3889; tel. 201/418–1000; Ann
P. Logan, R.N., Ph.D., Chief Hospital Executive

| | | |
|---|---|---|
| Owned, leased, sponsored: | 3 hospitals | 782 beds |
| Contract–managed: | 0 hospitals | 0 beds |
| Totals: | 3 hospitals | 782 beds |

★**0070: CARILION CLINIC** (NP)
1906 Belleview Avenue SE, Roanoke, VA Zip 24014–1838, Mailing Address: P.O. Box 13727, 24036–3727, tel. 540/981–7000;
Nancy Howell. Agee, President and Chief Executive Officer
**(Moderately Centralized Health System)**

**VIRGINIA:** CARILION FRANKLIN MEMORIAL HOSPITAL (O, 17 beds) 180 Floyd
Avenue, Rocky Mount, VA, Zip 24151–1389; tel. 540/483–5277; Carl T.
Cline, Vice President, Carilion Clinic and Hospital Administrator
**Web address:** www.carilionclinic.org/CFMH

CARILION GILES COMMUNITY HOSPITAL (O, 12 beds) 159 Hartley Way,
Pearisburg, VA, Zip 24134–2471; tel. 540/921–6000; William Flattery, Vice
President and Administrator Western Division

CARILION NEW RIVER VALLEY MEDICAL CENTER (O, 95 beds) 2900 Lamb
Circle, Christiansburg, VA, Zip 24073–6344, Mailing Address: P.O. Box 5,
Radford, 24143–0005, tel. 540/731–2000; William Flattery, Vice President
and Administrator Western Division
**Web address:** www.carilionclinic.org/Carilion/cnrv

CARILION ROANOKE MEMORIAL HOSPITAL (O, 641 beds) 1906 Belleview
Avenue Southeast, Roanoke, VA, Zip 24014–1838, Mailing Address: P.O.
Box 13367, 24033–3367, tel. 540/981–7000; Steven C. Arner, President
**Web address:** www.carilionclinic.org

CARILION STONEWALL JACKSON HOSPITAL (O, 14 beds) 1 Health Circle,
Lexington, VA, Zip 24450–2492; tel. 540/458–3300; Greg T. Madsen, Chief
Executive Officer

CARILION TAZEWELL COMMUNITY HOSPITAL (O, 5 beds) 388 Ben Bolt
Avenue, Tazewell, VA, Zip 24651–9700; tel. 276/988–8700; Alicia Bales,
Senior Director, Chief Executive Officer and Chief Nursing Officer
**Web address:** www.carilionclinic.org

| | | |
|---|---|---|
| Owned, leased, sponsored: | 6 hospitals | 784 beds |
| Contract–managed: | 0 hospitals | 0 beds |
| Totals: | 6 hospitals | 784 beds |

★**2575: CARLE HEALTH** (NP)
611 West Park Street, Urbana, IL Zip 61801–2595;
tel. 217/383–3311; James C. Leonard, M.D., President and Chief
Executive Officer
**(Moderately Centralized Health System)**

**ILLINOIS:** BROMENN MEDICAL CENTER (O, 203 beds) 1304 Franklin
Avenue, Normal, IL, Zip 61761–3558, Mailing Address: P.O. Box 2850,
Bloomington, 61702–2850, tel. 309/454–1400; Colleen Kannaday, FACHE,
President
**Web address:** www.advocatehealth.com/bromenn

CARLE FOUNDATION HOSPITAL (O, 456 beds) 611 West Park Street, Urbana,
IL, Zip 61801–2529; tel. 217/383–3311; James C. Leonard, M.D., President
and Chief Executive Officer
**Web address:** www.carle.org

CARLE HOOPESTON REGIONAL HEALTH CENTER (O, 13 beds) 701 East
Orange Street, Hoopeston, IL, Zip 60942–1801; tel. 217/283–5531; Harry
Brockus, Chief Executive Officer

CARLE RICHLAND MEMORIAL HOSPITAL (O, 65 beds) 800 East Locust
Street, Olney, IL, Zip 62450–2553; tel. 618/395–2131; Harry Brockus, Chief
Executive Officer
**Web address:** www.carlermh.com

EUREKA HOSPITAL (O, 11 beds) 101 South Major Street, Eureka, IL,
Zip 61530–1246; tel. 309/467–2371; Colleen Kannaday, FACHE, President

| | | |
|---|---|---|
| Owned, leased, sponsored: | 5 hospitals | 748 beds |
| Contract–managed: | 0 hospitals | 0 beds |
| Totals: | 5 hospitals | 748 beds |

**0656: CARRUS HOSPITALS** (IO)
1810 West US Highway 82, Sherman, TX Zip 75092–7069;
tel. 903/870–2600; Jon Michael. Rains, President and Chief
Operating Officer
**(Independent Hospital System)**

**TEXAS:** CARRUS REHABILITATION HOSPITAL (O, 24 beds) 1810 West US
Highway 82, Suite 100, Sherman, TX, Zip 75092–7069; tel. 903/870–
2600; Brad Sidlo, Chief Executive Officer
**Web address:** www.carrushospital.com

For explanation of codes following names, see page B2.
★ Indicates Type III membership in the American Hospital Association.

Health Care Systems, Networks and Alliances **B27**

CARRUS SPECIALTY HOSPITAL (O, 33 beds) 1810 West US Highway 82, Sherman, TX, Zip 75092–7069; tel. 903/870–2600; Brad Sidlo, Chief Executive Officer

| | | |
|---|---|---|
| Owned, leased, sponsored: | 2 hospitals | 57 beds |
| Contract–managed: | 0 hospitals | 0 beds |
| Totals: | 2 hospitals | 57 beds |

## 0903: CATHOLIC HEALTH SERVICES (CO)

4790 North State Road 7, Lauderdale Lakes, FL Zip 33319–5860; tel. 954/484–1515; Joseph M. Catania, President and Chief Executive Officer

**FLORIDA:** ST. ANTHONY'S REHABILITATION HOSPITAL (S, 26 beds) 3485 NW 30th Street, Lauderdale Lakes, FL, Zip 33311–1890; tel. 954/739–6233; Joseph M. Catania, Chief Executive Officer

ST. CATHERINE'S REHABILITATION HOSPITAL (S, 60 beds) 1050 NE 125th Street, North Miami, FL, Zip 33161–5881; tel. 305/357–1735; Jaime Gonzalez, Administrator
**Web address:** www.catholichealthservices.org

| | | |
|---|---|---|
| Owned, leased, sponsored: | 2 hospitals | 86 beds |
| Contract–managed: | 0 hospitals | 0 beds |
| Totals: | 2 hospitals | 86 beds |

## 0233: CATHOLIC HEALTH SERVICES OF LONG ISLAND (CO)

992 North Village Avenue, 1st Floor, Rockville Centre, NY Zip 11570–1002; tel. 516/705–3700; Alan D. Guerci, M.D., President and Chief Executive Officer
**(Centralized Health System)**

**NEW YORK:** GOOD SAMARITAN HOSPITAL MEDICAL CENTER (O, 471 beds) 1000 Montauk Highway, West Islip, NY, Zip 11795–4927; tel. 631/376–3000; Ruth E Hennessey, President
**Web address:** www.good–samaritan–hospital.org

MERCY MEDICAL CENTER (O, 196 beds) 1000 North Village Avenue, Rockville Centre, NY, Zip 11570–1000; tel. 516/705–2525; Peter Scaminaci, President

ST. CATHERINE OF SIENA MEDICAL CENTER (O, 521 beds) 50 Route 25–A, Smithtown, NY, Zip 11787–1348; tel. 631/862–3000; James O'Connor, Chief Administrative Officer
**Web address:** www.stcatherines.chsli.org/

ST. CHARLES HOSPITAL (O, 243 beds) 200 Belle Terre Road, Port Jefferson, NY, Zip 11777–1928; tel. 631/474–6000; James O'Connor, President

ST. FRANCIS HOSPITAL, THE HEART CENTER (O, 320 beds) 100 Port Washington Boulevard, Roslyn, NY, Zip 11576–1353; tel. 516/562–6000; Charles Lucore, M.D., President
**Web address:** www.stfrancisheartcenter.com/index.html

ST. JOSEPH HOSPITAL (S, 128 beds) 4295 Hempstead Turnpike, Bethpage, NY, Zip 11714–5769; tel. 516/579–6000; Peter Scaminaci, President

| | | |
|---|---|---|
| Owned, leased, sponsored: | 6 hospitals | 1879 beds |
| Contract–managed: | 0 hospitals | 0 beds |
| Totals: | 6 hospitals | 1879 beds |

## ★0234: CATHOLIC HEALTH SYSTEM (CO)

144 Genesee Street, Buffalo, NY Zip 14203–1560; tel. 716/862–2410; Mark A. Sullivan, FACHE, President and Chief Executive Officer
**(Independent Hospital System)**

**NEW YORK:** FATHER BAKER MANOR (O, 160 beds) 6400 Powers Road, Orchard Park, NY, Zip 14127; tel. 716/667–0001; Christine Kluckhohn, President, Continuing Care

KENMORE MERCY HOSPITAL (O, 325 beds) 2950 Elmwood Avenue, Kenmore, NY, Zip 14217–1390; tel. 716/447–6100; Walter Ludwig, President
**Web address:** www.chsbuffalo.org

MCAULEY RESIDENCE (O, 160 beds) 1503 Military Road, Kenmore, NY, Zip 14217; tel. 716/447–6600; Christine Kluckhohn, President, Continuing Care

MERCY HOSPITAL (O, 436 beds) 565 Abbott Road, Buffalo, NY, Zip 14220–2095; tel. 716/826–7000; Eddie Bratko, President
**Web address:** www.chsbuffalo.org

MERCY NURSING FACILITY (O, 74 beds) 565 Abbott Road, Buffalo, NY, Zip 14220; tel. 716/828–2301; Christine Kluckhohn, President, Continuing Care

MOUNT ST. MARY'S HOSPITAL AND HEALTH CENTER (O, 164 beds) 5300 Military Road, Lewiston, NY, Zip 14092–1903; tel. 716/297–4800; Charles J. Urlaub, President and Chief Executive Officer
**Web address:** www.msmh.org

NAZARETH HOME (O, 125 beds) 291 West North Street, Buffalo, NY, Zip 14201; tel. 716/881–2323; Christine Kluckhohn, President, Continuing Care

SISTERS OF CHARITY HOSPITAL OF BUFFALO (O, 388 beds) 2157 Main Street, Buffalo, NY, Zip 14214–2692; tel. 716/862–1000; Martin W. Boryszak, President
**Web address:** www.chsbuffalo.org

ST. CATHERINE LABOURE (O, 80 beds) 2157 Main Street, Buffalo, NY, Zip 14214; tel. 716/862–1451; Christine Kluckhohn, President, Continuing Care

ST. ELIZABETH'S HOME (O, 117 beds) 5539 Broadway, Lancaster, NY, Zip 14086; tel. 716/683–5150; Christine Kluckhohn, President, Continuing Care

ST. FRANCIS OF BUFFALO (O, 120 beds) 34 Benwood Avenue, Buffalo, NY, Zip 14214; tel. 716/862–2500; Christine Kluckhohn, President, Continuing Care

ST. FRANCIS OF WILLIAMSVILLE (O, 142 beds) 147 Reist Street, Williamsville, NY, Zip 14221; tel. 716/633–5400; Christine Kluckhohn, President, Continuing Care

ST. JOSEPH MANOR (O, 22 beds) 2211 West State Street, Olean, NY, Zip 14760; tel. 716/372–7810; Christine Kluckhohn, President, Continuing Care

| | | |
|---|---|---|
| Owned, leased, sponsored: | 13 hospitals | 2313 beds |
| Contract–managed: | 0 hospitals | 0 beds |
| Totals: | 13 hospitals | 2313 beds |

## ★0991: CAYUGA HEALTH SYSTEM (NP)

101 Dates Drive, Ithaca, NY Zip 14850–1342; tel. 607/274–4011; Martin Stallone, M.D., President and Chief Executive Officer
**(Independent Hospital System)**

**NEW YORK:** CAYUGA MEDICAL CENTER AT ITHACA (O, 193 beds) 101 Dates Drive, Ithaca, NY, Zip 14850–1342; tel. 607/274–4011; Martin Stallone, M.D., President and Chief Executive Officer

SCHUYLER HOSPITAL (O, 145 beds) 220 Steuben Street, Montour Falls, NY, Zip 14865–9709; tel. 607/535–7121; Rebecca Gould, President and Chief Financial Officer
**Web address:** www.schuylerhospital.org

| | | |
|---|---|---|
| Owned, leased, sponsored: | 2 hospitals | 338 beds |
| Contract–managed: | 0 hospitals | 0 beds |
| Totals: | 2 hospitals | 338 beds |

## ★0984: CEDARS–SINAI HEALTH SYSTEM (NP)

8700 Beverly Boulevard, West Hollywood, CA Zip 90048–1865, Box 48750, Los Angeles, 90048–0750, tel. 310/423–5000; Thomas M. Priselac, President and Chief Executive Officer
**(Moderately Centralized Health System)**

**CALIFORNIA:** CEDARS–SINAI MEDICAL CENTER (O, 886 beds) 8700 Beverly Boulevard, Los Angeles, CA, Zip 90048–1865; tel. 310/423–5000; Thomas M. Priselac, President and Chief Executive Officer

MARINA DEL REY HOSPITAL (O, 145 beds) 4650 Lincoln Boulevard, Marina Del Rey, CA, Zip 90292–6306; tel. 310/823–8911; Paulette Heitmeyer, Administrator and Chief Operating Officer
**Web address:** www.marinahospital.com

For explanation of codes following names, see page B2.
★ Indicates Type III membership in the American Hospital Association.

TORRANCE MEMORIAL MEDICAL CENTER (O, 436 beds) 3330 Lomita Boulevard, Torrance, CA, Zip 90505–5073; tel. 310/325–9110; Craig Leach, President and Chief Executive Officer
**Web address:** www.torrancememorial.org

| | | |
|---|---|---|
| Owned, leased, sponsored: | 3 hospitals | 1467 beds |
| Contract–managed: | 0 hospitals | 0 beds |
| Totals: | 3 hospitals | 1467 beds |

★**2265: CENTRA HEALTH, INC.** (NP)
1901 Tate Springs Road, Lynchburg, VA Zip 24501–1109; tel. 434/200–3000; Andrew Mueller, M.D., President and Chief Executive Officer
**(Moderately Centralized Health System)**

**VIRGINIA:** CENTRA BEDFORD MEMORIAL HOSPITAL (O, 145 beds) 1613 Oakwood Street, Bedford, VA, Zip 24523–1213; tel. 540/586–2441; Patti Jurkus, Vice President and Chief Executive Officer
**Web address:** www.bmhva.com

CENTRA LYNCHBURG GENERAL HOSPITAL (O, 1037 beds) 1901 Tate Springs Road, Lynchburg, VA, Zip 24501–1109; tel. 434/200–4700; Michael Elliott, Acting Chief Executive Officer

CENTRA SOUTHSIDE COMMUNITY HOSPITAL (O, 86 beds) 800 Oak Street, Farmville, VA, Zip 23901–1199; tel. 434/392–8811; Thomas Angelo, Chief Executive Officer
**Web address:** www.sch.centrahealth.com/

| | | |
|---|---|---|
| Owned, leased, sponsored: | 3 hospitals | 1268 beds |
| Contract–managed: | 0 hospitals | 0 beds |
| Totals: | 3 hospitals | 1268 beds |

★**0184: CENTRACARE HEALTH** (NP)
1406 Sixth Avenue North, Saint Cloud, MN Zip 56303–1900; tel. 320/251–2700; Kenneth D. Holmen, M.D., President and Chief Executive Officer
**(Moderately Centralized Health System)**

**MINNESOTA:** CARRIS HEALTH – REDWOOD (O, 25 beds) 100 Fallwood Road, Redwood Falls, MN, Zip 56283–1828; tel. 507/637–4500; Carnie Allex, Administrator
**Web address:** www.redwoodareahospital.org

CENTRACARE – LONG PRAIRIE (O, 20 beds) 20 Ninth Street SE, Long Prairie, MN, Zip 56347–1404; tel. 320/732–2141; Daniel J. Swenson, FACHE, Administrator

CENTRACARE – MELROSE (O, 93 beds) 525 Main Street West, Melrose, MN, Zip 56352–1043; tel. 320/256–4231; Gerry Gilbertson, FACHE, Administrator
**Web address:** www.centracare.com

CENTRACARE – MONTICELLO (O, 122 beds) 1013 Hart Boulevard, Suite 1, Monticello, MN, Zip 55362–8230; tel. 763/295–2945; John Hering, M.D., Administrator
**Web address:** www.centracare.com

CENTRACARE HEALTH–PAYNESVILLE (O, 66 beds) 200 West 1st Street, Paynesville, MN, Zip 56362–1496; tel. 320/243–3767; Brandon E. Pietsch, Administrator
**Web address:** www.centracare.com

CENTRACARE HEALTH–SAUK CENTRE (O, 85 beds) 425 North Elm Street, Sauk Centre, MN, Zip 56378–1010; tel. 320/352–2221; Delano Christianson, Administrator
**Web address:** www.centracare.com/hospitals/sauk_centre/index.html

RICE MEMORIAL HOSPITAL (L, 164 beds) 301 Becker Avenue SW, Willmar, MN, Zip 56201–3395; tel. 320/235–4543; Michael Schramm, Chief Executive Officer
**Web address:** www.ricehospital.com

ST. CLOUD HOSPITAL (O, 477 beds) 1406 Sixth Avenue North, Saint Cloud, MN, Zip 56303–1901; tel. 320/251–2700; Craig J. Broman, FACHE, President

| | | |
|---|---|---|
| Owned, leased, sponsored: | 8 hospitals | 1052 beds |
| Contract–managed: | 0 hospitals | 0 beds |
| Totals: | 8 hospitals | 1052 beds |

★**1007: CENTRAL MAINE HEALTHCARE** (NP)
300 Main Street, Lewiston, ME Zip 04240–7027; tel. 207/795–0111; Jeffrey L. Brickman, FACHE, Chief Executive Officer
**(Independent Hospital System)**

**MAINE:** BRIDGTON HOSPITAL (O, 22 beds) 10 Hospital Drive, Bridgton, ME, Zip 04009–1148; tel. 207/647–6000; Peter J. Wright, FACHE, President
**Web address:** www.bridgtonhospital.org

CENTRAL MAINE MEDICAL CENTER (O, 190 beds) 300 Main Street, Lewiston, ME, Zip 04240–7027; tel. 207/795–0111; David Tupponce, M.D., President
**Web address:** www.cmmc.org

RUMFORD HOSPITAL (O, 25 beds) 420 Franklin Street, Rumford, ME, Zip 04276–2145; tel. 207/369–1000; Peter J. Wright, FACHE, President
**Web address:** www.rumfordhospital.org

| | | |
|---|---|---|
| Owned, leased, sponsored: | 3 hospitals | 237 beds |
| Contract–managed: | 0 hospitals | 0 beds |
| Totals: | 3 hospitals | 237 beds |

**1039: CHILDREN'S HEALTH** (NP)
1935 Medical District Drive, Dallas, TX Zip 75235–7701; tel. 214/456–7000; Christopher J. Durovich, President and Chief Executive Officer
**(Centralized Health System)**

**TEXAS:** CHILDREN'S MEDICAL CENTER DALLAS (O, 386 beds) 1935 Medical District Drive, Pavilion, 3rd Floor, Dallas, TX, Zip 75235–7701; tel. 214/456–7000; David T. Berry, President
**Web address:** www.childrens.com

CHILDREN'S MEDICAL CENTER PLANO (O, 72 beds) 7601 Preston Road, Plano, TX, Zip 75024–3214; tel. 469/303–7000; Jeremiah Radandt, President
**Web address:** https://www.childrens.com/location–landing/locations–and–directions/childrens–health–plano

OUR CHILDREN'S HOUSE (O, 39 beds) 1340 Empire Central Drive, Dallas, TX, Zip 75247–4022; tel. 214/867–6700; David T. Berry, President, System Clinical Operations

| | | |
|---|---|---|
| Owned, leased, sponsored: | 3 hospitals | 497 beds |
| Contract–managed: | 0 hospitals | 0 beds |
| Totals: | 3 hospitals | 497 beds |

**0407: CHILDREN'S HOSPITAL AND HEALTH SYSTEM** (NP)
9000 West Wisconsin Avenue, Milwaukee, WI Zip 53226–4810, P O Box 1997, 53201–1997, tel. 414/226–2000; Peggy N. Troy, President and Chief Executive Officer
**(Independent Hospital System)**

**WISCONSIN:** CHILDREN'S HOSPITAL OF WISCONSIN–FOX VALLEY (O, 16 beds) 130 Second Street, Neenah, WI, Zip 54956–2883; tel. 920/969–7900; Peggy N. Troy, President and Chief Executive Officer
**Web address:** www.chw.org

CHILDREN'S HOSPITAL OF WISCONSIN (O, 185 beds) 9000 West Wisconsin Avenue, Milwaukee, WI, Zip 53226–4810, Mailing Address: P.O. Box 1997, 53201–1997, tel. 414/266–2000; Peggy N. Troy, President and Chief Executive Officer
**Web address:** www.chw.org

| | | |
|---|---|---|
| Owned, leased, sponsored: | 2 hospitals | 201 beds |
| Contract–managed: | 0 hospitals | 0 beds |
| Totals: | 2 hospitals | 201 beds |

For explanation of codes following names, see page B2.
★ Indicates Type III membership in the American Hospital Association.

Section B

★**0131: CHRISTIANACARE** (NP)
501 West 14th Street, Wilmington, DE Zip 19801–1013, Mailing Address: P.O. Box 1668, 19899–1668, tel. 302/733–1000; Janice E. Nevin, M.D., M.P.H., Chief Executive Officer
**(Independent Hospital System)**

**DELAWARE**: CHRISTIANACARE (O, 1074 beds) 4755 Ogletown–Stanton Road, Newark, DE, Zip 19718–0002, Mailing Address: P.O. Box 6001, 19718, tel. 302/733–1000; Janice E. Nevin, M.D., M.P.H., Chief Executive Officer
**Web address**: www.christianacare.org

| | | |
|---|---|---|
| Owned, leased, sponsored: | 1 hospitals | 1074 beds |
| Contract–managed: | 0 hospitals | 0 beds |
| Totals: | 1 hospitals | 1074 beds |

★**0192: CHRISTUS HEALTH** (CO)
919 Hidden Ridge Drive, Irving, TX Zip 75038; tel. 469/282–2000; Ernie W. Sadau, Chief Executive Officer
**(Moderately Centralized Health System)**

**LOUISIANA**: CHRISTUS COUSHATTA HEALTH CARE CENTER (O, 25 beds) 1635 Marvel Street, Coushatta, LA, Zip 71019–9022, Mailing Address: P.O. Box 589, 71019–0589, tel. 318/932–2000; Brandon Hillman, R.N., Administrator
**Web address**: www.christuscoushatta.org

CHRISTUS HEALTH SHREVEPORT–BOSSIER (O, 188 beds) 1453 East Bert Kouns Industrial Loop, Shreveport, LA, Zip 71105–6800; tel. 318/681–5000; Thomas S. Trawick, M.D., Chief Executive Officer

CHRISTUS OCHSNER LAKE AREA HOSPITAL (O, 88 beds) 4200 Nelson Road, Lake Charles, LA, Zip 70605–4118; tel. 337/474–6370; Kevin Holland, Chief Executive Officer, CHRISTUS Southwestern Louisiana
**Web address**: www.Lakeareamc.com

CHRISTUS OCHSNER ST. PATRICK (O, 160 beds) 524 Dr Michael Debakey Drive, Lake Charles, LA, Zip 70601–5799, Mailing Address: P.O. Box 3401, 70602–3401, tel. 337/436–2511; Kevin Holland, Chief Executive Officer, CHRISTUS Southwestern Louisiana

CHRISTUS ST. FRANCES CABRINI HOSPITAL (O, 293 beds) 3330 Masonic Drive, Alexandria, LA, Zip 71301–3899; tel. 318/487–1122; Chris Karam, FACHE, President and Chief Executive Officer, Senior Vice President Group Operations
**Web address**: www.cabrini.org/

NATCHITOCHES REGIONAL MEDICAL CENTER (C, 91 beds) 501 Keyser Avenue, Natchitoches, LA, Zip 71457–6036, Mailing Address: P.O. Box 2009, 71457–2009, tel. 318/214–4200; D. Kirk. Soileau, FACHE, Chief Executive Officer
**Web address**: www.nrmchospital.org

SAVOY MEDICAL CENTER (C, 60 beds) 801 Poinciana Avenue, Mamou, LA, Zip 70554–2298; tel. 337/468–5261; Eugene H. Burge Jr, Chief Executive Officer

**NEW MEXICO**: CHRISTUS ST. VINCENT REGIONAL MEDICAL CENTER (O, 219 beds) 455 Saint Michaels Drive, Santa Fe, NM, Zip 87505–7601, Mailing Address: P.O. Box 2107, 87505, tel. 505/983–3361; Lillian Montoya, President and Chief Executive Officer
**Web address**: www.stvin.org

**TEXAS**: CHRISTUS GOOD SHEPHERD MEDICAL CENTER–MARSHALL (O, 368 beds) 811 South Washington Avenue, Marshall, TX, Zip 75670–5336, Mailing Address: P.O. Box 1599, 75671–1599, tel. 903/927–6000; Todd Hancock, President and Chief Executive Officer

CHRISTUS MOTHER FRANCES HOSPITAL – JACKSONVILLE (O, 23 beds) 2026 South Jackson, Jacksonville, TX, Zip 75766–5822; tel. 903/541–4500; Barry D. Lofquist, Chief Executive Officer
**Web address**: www.tmfhs.org/jacksonville

CHRISTUS MOTHER FRANCES HOSPITAL – SULPHUR SPRINGS (O, 62 beds) 115 Airport Road, Sulphur Springs, TX, Zip 75482–2105; tel. 903/885–7671; Paul Harvey, President and Chief Executive Officer
**Web address**: www.tmfhc.org/maps–and–locations/locations–profile/?id=72&searchId=8bcb329f–a152–e611–b37f–2c768a4e1b84&sort=11&page=1&pageSize=10

CHRISTUS MOTHER FRANCES HOSPITAL – TYLER (O, 463 beds) 800 East Dawson Street, Tyler, TX, Zip 75701–2036; tel. 903/593–8441; Jason J. Proctor, Chief Executive Officer
**Web address**: www.tmfhc.org

CHRISTUS MOTHER FRANCES HOSPITAL – WINNSBORO (O, 23 beds) 719 West Coke Road, Winnsboro, TX, Zip 75494–3011; tel. 903/342–5227; Paul Harvey, Chief Executive Officer
**Web address**: www.tmfhs.org

CHRISTUS SANTA ROSA HEALTH SYSTEM (O, 397 beds) 333 North Santa Rosa Street, San Antonio, TX, Zip 78207–3108, 100 NE Loop 410 Suite 800, 78216–4749, tel. 210/704–2000; Dean Alexander, President and Chief Executive Officer

CHRISTUS SANTA ROSA HOSPITAL – SAN MARCOS (O, 111 beds) 1301 Wonder World Drive, San Marcos, TX, Zip 78666–7544; tel. 512/353–8979; Thomas McKinney, Chief Executive Officer
**Web address**: https://www.christushealth.org/santa–rosa/san–marcos

CHRISTUS SOUTHEAST TEXAS HOSPITAL – ST. ELIZABETH (O, 367 beds) 2830 Calder Avenue, Beaumont, TX, Zip 77702–1809, Mailing Address: P.O. Box 5405, 77726–5405, tel. 409/892–7171; Paul Trevino, President and Chief Executive Officer

CHRISTUS SOUTHEAST TEXAS JASPER MEMORIAL (O, 38 beds) 1275 Marvin Hancock Drive, Jasper, TX, Zip 75951–4995; tel. 409/384–5461; Wayne Moore, Interim Administrator
**Web address**: www.christusjasper.org

CHRISTUS SPOHN HOSPITAL ALICE (O, 54 beds) 2500 East Main Street, Alice, TX, Zip 78332–4169; tel. 361/661–8000; Richard Morin, R.N., Interim Chief Executive Officer

CHRISTUS SPOHN HOSPITAL BEEVILLE (O, 49 beds) 1500 East Houston Street, Beeville, TX, Zip 78102–5312; tel. 361/354–2000; Genifer Rucker, President
**Web address**: www.christusspohn.org

CHRISTUS SPOHN HOSPITAL CORPUS CHRISTI MEMORIAL (O, 488 beds) 2606 Hospital Boulevard, Corpus Christi, TX, Zip 78405–1804, Mailing Address: P.O. Box 5280, 78405, tel. 361/902–4000; Osbert Blow, M.D., Ph.D., FACS, President and Chief Medical Officer

CHRISTUS SPOHN HOSPITAL KLEBERG (O, 50 beds) 1311 General Cavazos Boulevard, Kingsville, TX, Zip 78363–7130; tel. 361/595–1661; Richard Morin, R.N., Interim Chief Executive Officer
**Web address**: www.christusspohn.org

CHRISTUS ST. MICHAEL HEALTH SYSTEM (O, 354 beds) 2600 St Michael Drive, Texarkana, TX, Zip 75503–5220; tel. 903/614–1000; Jason Rounds, FACHE, President

CHRISTUS ST. MICHAEL REHABILITATION HOSPITAL (O, 50 beds) 2400 St Michael Drive, Texarkana, TX, Zip 75503–2374; tel. 903/614–4000; Patrick Flannery, Administrator
**Web address**: www.christusstmichael.org/rehab

CHILDREN'S HOSPITAL OF SAN ANTONIO (O, 220 beds) 333 North Santa Rosa Street, San Antonio, TX, Zip 78207; tel. 210/704–2011; Cris Daskevich, Chief Executive Officer
**Web address**: www.chofsa.org/

KATE DISHMAN REHABILITATION HOSPITAL (O, 27 beds) 2830 Calder Street, 6th Floor, Beaumont, TX, Zip 77702–1809; tel. 409/899–8380; David Pipkins, Chief Executive Officer
**Web address**: www.christushospital.org

| | | |
|---|---|---|
| Owned, leased, sponsored: | 23 hospitals | 4117 beds |
| Contract–managed: | 2 hospitals | 151 beds |
| Totals: | 25 hospitals | 4268 beds |

★**0212: CLEVELAND CLINIC HEALTH SYSTEM** (NP)
9500 Euclid, Cleveland, OH Zip 44195–5108; tel. 216/444–2200; Tomislav Mihaljevic, M.D., Chief Executive Officer and President
**(Centralized Health System)**

**FLORIDA**: CLEVELAND CLINIC FLORIDA (O, 206 beds) 2950 Cleveland Clinic Boulevard, Weston, FL, Zip 33331–3602; tel. 954/659–5000; Wael Barsoum, M.D., President
**Web address**: www.clevelandclinic.org/florida

For explanation of codes following names, see page B2.
★ Indicates Type III membership in the American Hospital Association.

CLEVELAND CLINIC INDIAN RIVER HOSPITAL (O, 220 beds) 1000 36th Street, Vero Beach, FL, Zip 32960–6592; tel. 772/567–4311; Gregory Rosencrance, Chief Executive Officer
**Web address**: https://www.indianrivermedicalcenter.com/

CLEVELAND CLINIC MARTIN NORTH HOSPITAL (O, 507 beds) 200 SE Hospital Avenue, Stuart, FL, Zip 34994–2346, Mailing Address: P.O. Box 9010, 34995–9010, tel. 772/287–5200; Robert L. Lord, JD, President and Chief Executive Officer

**OHIO**: CLEVELAND CLINIC AKRON GENERAL LODI HOSPITAL (O, 20 beds) 225 Elyria Street, Lodi, OH, Zip 44254–1096; tel. 330/948–1222; Dana Kocsis, Vice President, Nursing and Operations
**Web address**: www.lodihospital.org

CLEVELAND CLINIC AKRON GENERAL (O, 482 beds) 1 Akron General Avenue, Akron, OH, Zip 44307–2433; tel. 330/344–6000; Brian J. Harte, M.D., President

CLEVELAND CLINIC AVON HOSPITAL (O, 126 beds) 33300 Cleveland Clinic Boulevard, Avon, OH, Zip 44011; tel. 440/695–5000; Rebecca Starck, M.D., President
**Web address**: www.my.clevelandclinic.org

CLEVELAND CLINIC CHILDREN'S HOSPITAL FOR REHABILITATION (O, 25 beds) 2801 Martin Luther King Jr Drive, Cleveland, OH, Zip 44104–3865; tel. 216/448–6400; Michelle Marks, D.O., Medical Director
**Web address**: www.my.clevelandclinic.org/childrens–hospital/default.aspx

CLEVELAND CLINIC FAIRVIEW HOSPITAL (O, 460 beds) 18101 Lorain Avenue, Cleveland, OH, Zip 44111–5656; tel. 216/476–7000; Neil Smith, D.O., President
**Web address**: www.fairviewhospital.org

CLEVELAND CLINIC UNION HOSPITAL (O, 136 beds) 659 Boulevard, Dover, OH, Zip 44622–2077; tel. 330/343–3311; Bruce James, President and Chief Executive Officer
**Web address**: www.unionhospital.org

CLEVELAND CLINIC, MEDINA HOSPITAL (O, 148 beds) 1000 East Washington Street, Medina, OH, Zip 44256–2170; tel. 330/725–1000; Richard K. Shewbridge, President
**Web address**: www.medinahospital.org

CLEVELAND CLINIC (O, 1294 beds) 9500 Euclid Avenue, Cleveland, OH, Zip 44195–5108; tel. 216/444–2200; Tomislav Mihaljevic, M.D., President and Chief Executive Officer

EDWIN SHAW REHAB (O, 35 beds) 4389 Medina Road, Copley, OH, Zip 44321–1388; tel. 234/815–5100; Geoffrey Hall, Chief Executive Officer
**Web address**: www.edwinshaw.com

EUCLID HOSPITAL (O, 166 beds) 18901 Lake Shore Boulevard, Euclid, OH, Zip 44119–1090; tel. 216/531–9000; Teresa Dews, M.D., President
**Web address**: www.euclidhospital.org

HILLCREST HOSPITAL (O, 440 beds) 6780 Mayfield Road, Cleveland, OH, Zip 44124–2203; tel. 440/312–4500; Richard Parker, M.D., President, Hillcrest Hospital
**Web address**: www.hillcresthospital.org

LUTHERAN HOSPITAL (O, 194 beds) 1730 West 25th Street, Cleveland, OH, Zip 44113–3170; tel. 216/696–4300; Donald A. Malone Jr, M.D., President

MARYMOUNT HOSPITAL (O, 269 beds) 12300 McCracken Road, Garfield Heights, OH, Zip 44125–2975; tel. 216/581–0500; Daniel Napierkowski, M.D., President
**Web address**: www.marymount.org

SOUTH POINTE HOSPITAL (O, 163 beds) 20000 Harvard Road, Warrensville Heights, OH, Zip 44122–6805; tel. 216/491–6000; Margaret McKenzie, M.D., President

| | | |
|---|---|---|
| Owned, leased, sponsored: | 17 hospitals | 4891 beds |
| Contract–managed: | 0 hospitals | 0 beds |
| Totals: | 17 hospitals | 4891 beds |

---

**0076: COLLEGE HEALTH ENTERPRISES** (IO)
11627 Telegraph Road, Suite 200, Santa Fe Springs, CA Zip 90670–6814; tel. 562/923–9449; Barry J. Weiss, Chairman of the Board

**CALIFORNIA**: COLLEGE HOSPITAL CERRITOS (O, 187 beds) 10802 College Place, Cerritos, CA, Zip 90703–1579; tel. 562/924–9581; Stephen Witt, President and Chief Executive Officer
**Web address**: www.collegehospitals.com

COLLEGE HOSPITAL COSTA MESA (O, 122 beds) 301 Victoria Street, Costa Mesa, CA, Zip 92627–7131; tel. 949/642–2734; Susan L. Taylor, JD, Chief Executive Officer
**Web address**: www.collegehospitals.com/cosHome

| | | |
|---|---|---|
| Owned, leased, sponsored: | 2 hospitals | 309 beds |
| Contract–managed: | 0 hospitals | 0 beds |
| Totals: | 2 hospitals | 309 beds |

---

**0161: COLUMBUS REGIONAL HEALTHCARE SYSTEM** (NP)
707 Center Street, Suite 400, Columbus, GA Zip 31901–1575; tel. 706/660–6100; M. Scott. Hill, Chief Executive Officer
**(Independent Hospital System)**

**GEORGIA**: AZALEA TRACE (O, 110 beds) 910 Talbotton Road, Columbus, GA, Zip 31901; tel. 706/323–9513; Todd West, Administrator

HAMILTON HOUSE NURSING CENTER/ADULT LIVING CENTER (O, 128 beds) 1911 Hamilton Road, Columbus, GA, Zip 31901; tel. 706/571–1850; John Sims, Administrator

MARION MEMORIAL NURSING HOME (O, 70 beds) Highway 41, Buena Vista, GA, Zip 31803, Mailing Address: P.O. Box 197, 31803, tel. 229/649–7100; Barbara Mitchell, Administrator

| | | |
|---|---|---|
| Owned, leased, sponsored: | 3 hospitals | 308 beds |
| Contract–managed: | 0 hospitals | 0 beds |
| Totals: | 3 hospitals | 308 beds |

---

★**0948: COMMONSPIRIT HEALTH** (CO)
444 West Lake Street Suite 2500, Chicago, IL Zip 60606–0097; tel. 312/741–7000; Lloyd H. Dean, Chief Executive Officer

**ARIZONA**: CHANDLER REGIONAL MEDICAL CENTER (O, 338 beds) 1955 West Frye Road, Chandler, AZ, Zip 85224–6282; tel. 480/728–3000; Mark F. Slyter, FACHE, President and Chief Operating Officer
**Web address**: www.chandlerregional.com

DIGNITY HEALTH ARIZONA GENERAL HOSPITAL (O, 16 beds) 7171 South 51st Avenue, Laveen, AZ, Zip 85339–2923; tel. 623/584–5100; Jane E. Hanson, R.N., Chief Executive Officer
**Web address**: www.dignityhealth.org/arizonageneral/

MERCY GILBERT MEDICAL CENTER (S, 197 beds) 3555 South Val Vista Road, Gilbert, AZ, Zip 85297–7323; tel. 480/728–8000; Mark F. Slyter, FACHE, President and Chief Operating Officer

ST. JOSEPH'S HOSPITAL AND MEDICAL CENTER (S, 609 beds) 350 West Thomas Road, Phoenix, AZ, Zip 85013–4496, Mailing Address: P.O. Box 2071, 85001–2071, tel. 602/406–3000; Gabrielle Finley–Hazle, President and Chief Executive Officer
**Web address**: www.stjosephs–phx.org

**ARKANSAS**: CHI ST. VINCENT HOT SPRINGS (O, 241 beds) 300 Werner Street, Hot Springs, AR, Zip 71913–6406; tel. 501/622–1000; Douglas B. Ross, M.D., President

CHI ST. VINCENT INFIRMARY MEDICAL CENTER (S, 307 beds) Two St Vincent Circle, Little Rock, AR, Zip 72205–5499; tel. 501/552–3000; Chad S. Aduddell, Market Chief Executive Officer
**Web address**: www.chistvincent.com/

CHI ST. VINCENT MEDICAL CENTER–NORTH (S, 68 beds) 2215 Wildwood Avenue, Sherwood, AR, Zip 72120–5089; tel. 501/552–7100; Shawn Barnett, President and Chief Executive Officer

CHI ST. VINCENT MORRILTON (S, 25 beds) 4 Hospital Drive, Morrilton, AR, Zip 72110–4510; tel. 501/977–2300; Leslie Arnold, Chief Executive Officer and Administrator
**Web address**: www.chistvincent.com/Hospitals/st–vincent–morrilton

**CALIFORNIA**: BAKERSFIELD MEMORIAL HOSPITAL (O, 401 beds) 420 34th Street, Bakersfield, CA, Zip 93301–2237; tel. 661/327–1792; Ken Keller, President and Chief Executive Officer
**Web address**: www.bakersfieldmemorial.org

CALIFORNIA HOSPITAL MEDICAL CENTER (O, 318 beds) 1401 South Grand Avenue, Los Angeles, CA, Zip 90015–3010; tel. 213/748–2411; Alina Moran, President
**Web address**: www.chmcla.org

---

For explanation of codes following names, see page B2.
★ Indicates Type III membership in the American Hospital Association.

Section B

COMMUNITY HOSPITAL OF SAN BERNARDINO (O, 379 beds) 1805 Medical Center Drive, San Bernardino, CA, Zip 92411–1214; tel. 909/887–6333; June Collison, President
**Web address:** www.dignityhealth.org/san–bernardino

DOMINICAN HOSPITAL (S, 223 beds) 1555 Soquel Drive, Santa Cruz, CA, Zip 95065–1794; tel. 831/462–7700; Nanette Mickiewicz, M.D., President

FRENCH HOSPITAL MEDICAL CENTER (O, 72 beds) 1911 Johnson Avenue, San Luis Obispo, CA, Zip 93401–4197; tel. 805/543–5353; Alan Iftiniuk, Chief Executive Officer
**Web address:** www.frenchmedicalcenter.org

GLENDALE MEMORIAL HOSPITAL AND HEALTH CENTER (O, 334 beds) 1420 South Central Avenue, Glendale, CA, Zip 91204–2594; tel. 818/502–1900; Jill Welton, President and Chief Executive Officer

MARIAN REGIONAL MEDICAL CENTER (S, 286 beds) 1400 East Church Street, Santa Maria, CA, Zip 93454–5906; tel. 805/739–3000; Kerin A. Mase, President and Chief Executive Officer
**Web address:** www.marianmedicalcenter.org

MARK TWAIN MEDICAL CENTER (O, 25 beds) 768 Mountain Ranch Road, San Andreas, CA, Zip 95249–9998; tel. 209/754–3521; Doug Archer, President and Chief Executive Officer

MERCY GENERAL HOSPITAL (S, 277 beds) 4001 'J' Street, Sacramento, CA, Zip 95819–3600; tel. 916/453–4545; Edmundo Castaneda, President
**Web address:** www.mercygeneral.org

MERCY HOSPITAL OF FOLSOM (S, 106 beds) 1650 Creekside Drive, Folsom, CA, Zip 95630–3400; tel. 916/983–7400; Randall W. Ross, FACHE, President and Chief Executive Officer

MERCY HOSPITALS OF BAKERSFIELD (S, 204 beds) 2215 Truxtun Avenue, Bakersfield, CA, Zip 93301–3698, Mailing Address: P.O. Box 119, 93302–0119, tel. 661/632–5000; Bruce Peters, Chief Executive Officer
**Web address:** www.mercybakersfield.org

MERCY MEDICAL CENTER MERCED (S, 186 beds) 333 Mercy Avenue, Merced, CA, Zip 95340–8319; tel. 209/564–5000; Charles Kassis, President
**Web address:** www.mercymercedcares.org

MERCY MEDICAL CENTER MOUNT SHASTA (S, 33 beds) 914 Pine Street, Mount Shasta, CA, Zip 96067–2143; tel. 530/926–6111; Rodger Page, President
**Web address:** www.mercymtshasta.org

MERCY MEDICAL CENTER REDDING (S, 260 beds) 2175 Rosaline Avenue, Redding, CA, Zip 96001–2549, Mailing Address: P.O. Box 496009, 96049–6009, tel. 530/225–6000; G. Todd. Smith, Chief Executive Officer
**Web address:** www.mercy.org

MERCY SAN JUAN MEDICAL CENTER (S, 370 beds) 6501 Coyle Avenue, Carmichael, CA, Zip 95608–0306; tel. 916/537–5000; Michael Korpiel, FACHE, Chief Executive Officer

METHODIST HOSPITAL OF SACRAMENTO (O, 329 beds) 7500 Hospital Drive, Sacramento, CA, Zip 95823–5477; tel. 916/423–3000; Phyllis Baltz, Chief Executive Officer
**Web address:** www.methodistsacramento.org

NORTHRIDGE HOSPITAL MEDICAL CENTER (O, 394 beds) 18300 Roscoe Boulevard, Northridge, CA, Zip 91328–4167; tel. 818/885–8500; Paul Watkins, JD, President

SAINT FRANCIS MEMORIAL HOSPITAL (O, 239 beds) 900 Hyde Street, San Francisco, CA, Zip 94109–4899, Mailing Address: P.O. Box 7726, 94120–7726, tel. 415/353–6000; David Klein, M.D., President
**Web address:** www.saintfrancismemorial.org

SEQUOIA HOSPITAL (O, 114 beds) 170 Alameda De Las Pulgas, Redwood City, CA, Zip 94062–2799; tel. 650/369–5811; Bill Graham, President

SIERRA NEVADA MEMORIAL HOSPITAL (O, 104 beds) 155 Glasson Way, Grass Valley, CA, Zip 95945–5723, Mailing Address: P.O. Box 1029, 95945–1029, tel. 530/274–6000; Brian Evans Esq, M.D., President and Chief Executive Officer
**Web address:** www.snmh.org

ST. BERNARDINE MEDICAL CENTER (S, 342 beds) 2101 North Waterman Avenue, San Bernardino, CA, Zip 92404–4855; tel. 909/883–8711; Douglas V. Kleam, President
**Web address:** www.stbernardinemedicalcenter.com

ST. ELIZABETH COMMUNITY HOSPITAL (S, 65 beds) 2550 Sister Mary Columba Drive, Red Bluff, CA, Zip 96080–4397; tel. 530/529–8000; Jordan Wright, Chief Executive Officer

ST. JOHN'S PLEASANT VALLEY HOSPITAL (S, 127 beds) 2309 Antonio Avenue, Camarillo, CA, Zip 93010–1414; tel. 805/389–5800; Darren W. Lee, President and Chief Executive Officer
**Web address:** www.dignityhealth.org/pleasantvalley

ST. JOHN'S REGIONAL MEDICAL CENTER (S, 139 beds) 1600 North Rose Avenue, Oxnard, CA, Zip 93030–3723; tel. 805/988–2500; Darren W. Lee, President and Chief Executive Officer
**Web address:** www.stjohnshealth.org

ST. JOSEPH'S BEHAVIORAL HEALTH CENTER (S, 35 beds) 2510 North California Street, Stockton, CA, Zip 95204–5568; tel. 209/461–2000; Paul Rains, R.N., MSN, President
**Web address:** www.stjosephscanhelp.org

ST. JOSEPH'S MEDICAL CENTER (S, 273 beds) 1800 North California Street, Stockton, CA, Zip 95204–6019, Mailing Address: P.O. Box 213008, 95213–9008, tel. 209/943–2000; Donald J. Wiley, President and Chief Executive Officer
**Web address:** www.stjosephsCARES.org

ST. MARY MEDICAL CENTER LONG BEACH (S, 307 beds) 1050 Linden Avenue, Long Beach, CA, Zip 90813–3321, Mailing Address: P.O. Box 887, 90801–0887, tel. 562/491–9000; Carolyn P. Caldwell, FACHE, President and Chief Executive Officer

ST. MARY'S MEDICAL CENTER (S, 232 beds) 450 Stanyan Street, San Francisco, CA, Zip 94117–1079; tel. 415/668–1000; David Klein, M.D., President and Chief Executive Officer
**Web address:** www.stmarysmedicalcenter.com

WOODLAND HEALTHCARE (O, 105 beds) 1325 Cottonwood Street, Woodland, CA, Zip 95695–5199; tel. 530/662–3961; Edmundo Castaneda, President and Chief Executive Officer
**Web address:** www.woodlandhealthcare.org

**COLORADO:** LONGMONT UNITED HOSPITAL (S, 131 beds) 1950 Mountain View Avenue, Longmont, CO, Zip 80501–3162; tel. 303/651–5111; Christina Johnson, M.D., Chief Executive Officer

MERCY REGIONAL MEDICAL CENTER (S, 82 beds) 1010 Three Springs Boulevard, Durango, CO, Zip 81301–8296; tel. 970/247–4311; Michael Murphy, Interim Chief Executive Officer
**Web address:** www.mercydurango.org

ORTHOCOLORADO HOSPITAL (O, 48 beds) 11650 West 2nd Place, Lakewood, CO, Zip 80228–1527; tel. 720/321–5000; Jude Torchia, Chief Executive Officer
**Web address:** www.orthocolorado.org

PENROSE–ST. FRANCIS HEALTH SERVICES (S, 444 beds) 2222 North Nevada Avenue, Colorado Springs, CO, Zip 80907–6799; tel. 719/776–5000; Brian Erling, M.D., Chief Executive Officer

ST. ANTHONY HOSPITAL (S, 237 beds) 11600 West Second Place, Lakewood, CO, Zip 80228–1527; tel. 720/321–0000; Kevin Jenkins, Chief Executive Officer
**Web address:** www.stanthonyhosp.org

ST. ANTHONY NORTH HEALTH CAMPUS (S, 100 beds) 14300 Orchard Parkway, Westminster, CO, Zip 80023–9206; tel. 720/627–0000; Constance Schmidt, FACHE, R.N., Chief Executive Officer
**Web address:** https://www.centura.org/locations/st-anthony-north-health-campus?utm_source=yext&utm_medium=organic_google&utm_term=ST_ANTHONY_NORTH_HEALTH_CAMPUS&utm_content=facilities_landing_page

ST. ANTHONY SUMMIT MEDICAL CENTER (S, 34 beds) 340 Peak One Drive, Frisco, CO, Zip 80443, Mailing Address: P.O. Box 738, 80443–0738, tel. 970/668–3300; Lee Boyles, Chief Executive Officer

ST. MARY–CORWIN MEDICAL CENTER (S, 42 beds) 1008 Minnequa Avenue, Pueblo, CO, Zip 81004–3798; tel. 719/557–4000; Michael Cafasso, Chief Executive Officer
**Web address:** www.stmarycorwin.org

ST. THOMAS MORE HOSPITAL (S, 25 beds) 1338 Phay Avenue, Canon City, CO, Zip 81212–2302; tel. 719/285–2000; Kristi Olson, Chief Executive Officer

**GEORGIA:** CHI MEMORIAL HOSPITAL – GEORGIA (O, 35 beds) 100 Gross Crescent Circle, Fort Oglethorpe, GA, Zip 30742–3669; tel. 706/858–2000; Angie Hullander, Administrator and Special Operations
**Web address:** www.memorial.org/chi–memorial–hospital–georgia

**IOWA:** CHI HEALTH MERCY CORNING (S, 22 beds) 603 Rosary Drive, Corning, IA, Zip 50841–1683; tel. 641/322–3121; Lisa Wolfe, President
**Web address:** www.alegent.com

For explanation of codes following names, see page B2.
★ Indicates Type III membership in the American Hospital Association.

CHI HEALTH MERCY COUNCIL BLUFFS (S, 146 beds) 800 Mercy Drive, Council Bluffs, IA, Zip 51503–3128; tel. 712/328–5000; Ann Schumacher, R.N., MSN, FACHE, President
**Web address**: www.chihealth.com/chi–health–mercy–council–bluffs

CHI HEALTH MISSOURI VALLEY (S, 12 beds) 631 North Eighth Street, Missouri Valley, IA, Zip 51555–1102; tel. 712/642–2784; Jonathan Moe, President
**Web address**: www.chihealth.com/chi–health–missouri–valley

KNOXVILLE HOSPITAL & CLINICS (C, 25 beds) 1002 South Lincoln Street, Knoxville, IA, Zip 50138–3155; tel. 641/842–2151; Kevin Kincaid, Chief Executive Officer

MADISON COUNTY HEALTH CARE SYSTEM (C, 12 beds) 300 West Hutchings Street, Winterset, IA, Zip 50273–2109; tel. 515/462–2373; Marcia Hendricks, FACHE, R.N., Chief Executive Officer
**Web address**: www.madisonhealth.com

MERCYONE CENTERVILLE MEDICAL CENTER (S, 42 beds) 1 St Joseph's Drive, Centerville, IA, Zip 52544–8055; tel. 641/437–4111; Matthew Johnson, President

MERCYONE DES MOINES MEDICAL CENTER (S, 696 beds) 1111 6th Avenue, Des Moines, IA, Zip 50314–2611; tel. 515/247–3121; Karl Keeler, President
**Web address**: www.mercydesmoines.org

MERCYONE NEWTON MEDICAL CENTER (O, 34 beds) 204 North Fourth Avenue East, Newton, IA, Zip 50208–3100; tel. 641/792–1273; Laurie A. Conner, FACHE, President
**Web address**: www.skiffmed.com

**KANSAS**: BOB WILSON MEMORIAL GRANT COUNTY HOSPITAL (O, 26 beds) 415 North Main Street, Ulysses, KS, Zip 67880–2133; tel. 620/356–1266; Christine McSweeney, FACHE, President and Chief Executive Officer

ST. CATHERINE HOSPITAL (S, 100 beds) 401 East Spruce Street, Garden City, KS, Zip 67846–5679; tel. 620/272–2561; Christine McSweeney, FACHE, President and Chief Executive Officer
**Web address**: www.StCatherineHosp.org

**KENTUCKY**: CHI FLAGET MEMORIAL HOSPITAL (S, 42 beds) 4305 New Shepherdsville Road, Bardstown, KY, Zip 40004–9019; tel. 502/350–5000; Jennifer Nolan, President and Chief Executive Officer

CHI SAINT JOSEPH BEREA (S, 25 beds) 305 Estill Street, Berea, KY, Zip 40403–1909; tel. 859/986–3151; Terrence G. Deis, CPA, FACHE, President
**Web address**: www.kentuckyonehealth.org/berea

CHI SAINT JOSEPH EAST (S, 150 beds) 150 North Eagle Creek Drive, Lexington, KY, Zip 40509–1805; tel. 859/967–5000; Jason M. Adams, President
**Web address**: www.sjhlex.org

CHI SAINT JOSEPH HEALTH (S, 307 beds) One St Joseph Drive, Lexington, KY, Zip 40504–3754; tel. 859/313–1000; Bruce J. Tassin, President
**Web address**: www.chisaintjosephhealth.org/saint–joseph–hospital–lexington

CHI SAINT JOSEPH LONDON (S, 116 beds) 1001 Saint Joseph Lane, London, KY, Zip 40741–8345; tel. 606/330–6000; Terrence G. Deis, CPA, FACHE, President
**Web address**: www.saintjosephhealthsystem.org

CONTINUING CARE HOSPITAL (S, 23 beds) 1 Saint Joseph Drive, Lexington, KY, Zip 40504–3742; tel. 859/967–5744; Robert C. Desotelle, President and Chief Executive Officer

SAINT JOSEPH MOUNT STERLING (S, 42 beds) 225 Falcon Drive, Mount Sterling, KY, Zip 40353–1158, Mailing Address: P.O. Box 7, 40353–0007, tel. 859/497–5000; Terrence G. Deis, CPA, FACHE, President
**Web address**: www.sjhlex.org

TAYLOR REGIONAL HOSPITAL (C, 90 beds) 1700 Old Lebanon Road, Campbellsville, KY, Zip 42718–9600; tel. 270/465–3561; Jane Wheatley, Chief Executive Officer

**MINNESOTA**: CHI LAKEWOOD HEALTH (S, 55 beds) 600 Main Avenue South, Baudette, MN, Zip 56623–2855; tel. 218/634–2120; Jeffry Stampohar, Vice President of Hospital
**Web address**: www.lakewoodhealthcenter.org

CHI ST. FRANCIS HEALTH (S, 105 beds) 2400 St Francis Drive, Breckenridge, MN, Zip 56520–1025; tel. 218/643–3000; David A. Nelson, President and Chief Executive Officer
**Web address**: www.sfcare.org

CHI ST. GABRIEL'S HEALTH (S, 25 beds) 815 Second Street SE, Little Falls, MN, Zip 56345–3596; tel. 320/632–5441; Steve Smith, President and Chief Financial Officer
**Web address**: www.stgabriels.com

CHI ST. JOSEPH'S HEALTH (S, 25 beds) 600 Pleasant Avenue, Park Rapids, MN, Zip 56470–1431; tel. 218/732–3311; Benjamin Koppelman, President
**Web address**: www.sjahs.org

**NEBRASKA**: CHI HEALTH CREIGHTON UNIVERSITY MEDICAL CENTER – BERGAN MERCY (S, 385 beds) 7500 Mercy Road, Omaha, NE, Zip 68124–2319; tel. 402/398–6060; Jayleen Casano, Ph.D., FACHE, President
**Web address**: www.chihealth.com/chi–health–bergan–mercy

CHI HEALTH GOOD SAMARITAN (S, 218 beds) 10 East 31st Street, Kearney, NE, Zip 68847–2926, Mailing Address: P.O. Box 1990, 68848–1990, tel. 308/865–7100; Michael H. Schnieders, FACHE, President

CHI HEALTH IMMANUEL (S, 269 beds) 6901 North 72nd Street, Omaha, NE, Zip 68122–1799; tel. 402/572–2121; Ann Schumacher, R.N., MSN, FACHE, President
**Web address**: www.alegent.com/immanuel

CHI HEALTH LAKESIDE (S, 137 beds) 6901 N 72nd St, Omaha, NE, Zip 68122, 16901 Lakeside Hills Court, 68130–2318, tel. 402/717–8000; Kevin Miller, President

CHI HEALTH MIDLANDS (S, 28 beds) 11111 South 84th Street, Papillion, NE, Zip 68046–4122; tel. 402/593–3000; Kevin Miller, President
**Web address**: www.CHIhealth.com

CHI HEALTH NEBRASKA HEART (S, 54 beds) 7500 South 91st Street, Lincoln, NE, Zip 68526–9437; tel. 402/327–2700; Derek Vance, FACHE, President

CHI HEALTH PLAINVIEW (S, 15 beds) 704 North Third Street, Plainview, NE, Zip 68769–2047, Mailing Address: P.O. Box 489, 68769–0489, tel. 402/582–4245; Gregory Beckmann, Regional President
**Web address**: www.alegentcreighton.com/plainview–hospital

CHI HEALTH SAINT FRANCIS (S, 165 beds) 2620 West Faidley Avenue, Grand Island, NE, Zip 68803–4297, Mailing Address: P.O. Box 9804, 68802–9804, tel. 308/384–4600; Edward J. Hannon, FACHE, President

CHI HEALTH SCHUYLER (S, 25 beds) 104 West 17th Street, Schuyler, NE, Zip 68661–1304; tel. 402/352–2441; Connie Peters, R.N., President
**Web address**: www.alegent.org

CHI HEALTH ST ELIZABETH (S, 235 beds) 555 South 70th Street, Lincoln, NE, Zip 68510–2494; tel. 402/219–8000; Derek Vance, FACHE, President

CHI HEALTH ST. MARY'S (S, 18 beds) 1301 Grundman Boulevard, Nebraska City, NE, Zip 68410; tel. 402/873–3321; Daniel DeFreece, M.D., Interim President
**Web address**: www.chihealthstmarys.com

**NEVADA**: ST. ROSE DOMINICAN HOSPITALS – ROSE DE LIMA CAMPUS (S, 10 beds) 102 East Lake Mead Parkway, Henderson, NV, Zip 89015–5524; tel. 702/616–5000; Tom Burns, Chief Operating Officer and Chief Nurse Executive

ST. ROSE DOMINICAN HOSPITALS – SAN MARTIN CAMPUS (O, 147 beds) 8280 West Warm Springs Road, Las Vegas, NV, Zip 89113–3612; tel. 702/492–8000; Kimberly Shaw, President and Chief Executive Officer
**Web address**: www.strosehospitals.org

ST. ROSE DOMINICAN HOSPITALS – SIENA CAMPUS (S, 326 beds) 3001 St Rose Parkway, Henderson, NV, Zip 89052; tel. 702/616–5000; Lawrence Barnard, President and Chief Executive Officer

**NORTH DAKOTA**: CHI LISBON HEALTH (S, 25 beds) 905 Main Street, Lisbon, ND, Zip 58054–4334, Mailing Address: P.O. Box 353, 58054–0353, tel. 701/683–6400; Keith E. Heuser, Administrator
**Web address**: www.lisbonhospital.com

CHI MERCY HEALTH (S, 19 beds) 570 Chautauqua Boulevard, Valley City, ND, Zip 58072–3199; tel. 701/845–6400; Keith E. Heuser, President
**Web address**: www.mercyhospitalvalleycity.org

CHI OAKES HOSPITAL (S, 20 beds) 1200 North Seventh Street, Oakes, ND, Zip 58474–2502; tel. 701/742–3291; Becki Thompson, President

CHI ST ALEXIUS HEALTH CARRINGTON MEDICAL CENTER (S, 25 beds) 800 North Fourth Street, Carrington, ND, Zip 58421–1217, Mailing Address: P.O. Box 461, 58421–0461, tel. 701/652–3141; Mariann Doeling, R.N., President
**Web address**: www.carringtonhealthcenter.org

CHI ST. ALEXIUS HEALTH – DICKINSON MEDICAL CENTER (S, 25 beds) 2500 Fairway Street, Dickinson, ND, Zip 58601–4399; tel. 701/456–4000; DeeAnna Opstedahl, R.N., Interim President
**Web address**: www.stjoeshospital.org

For explanation of codes following names, see page B2.
★ Indicates Type III membership in the American Hospital Association.

Section B

CHI ST. ALEXIUS HEALTH – WILLISTON MEDICAL CENTER (S, 25 beds) 1301 15th Avenue West, Williston, ND, Zip 58801–3896; tel. 701/774–7400; Dan Bjerknes, President
**Web address:** www.mercy-williston.org

CHI ST. ALEXIUS HEALTH DEVILS LAKE HOSPITAL (S, 25 beds) 1031 Seventh Street NE, Devils Lake, ND, Zip 58301–2798; tel. 701/662–2131; Andrew Lankowicz, FACHE, President

CHI ST. ALEXIUS HEALTH–GARRISON MEMORIAL HOSPITAL (O, 50 beds) 407 Third Avenue SE, Garrison, ND, Zip 58540–7235; tel. 701/463–2275; Tod Graeber, Administrator
**Web address:** www.garrisonmh.com

CHI ST. ALEXIUS HEALTH–TURTLE LAKE HOSPITAL (O, 25 beds) 220 Fifth Avenue, Turtle Lake, ND, Zip 58575–4005, Mailing Address: P.O. Box 280, 58575–0280, tel. 701/448–2331; Tod Graeber, Administrator
**Web address:** www.wrtc.com/cullum/hospital

CHI ST. ALEXIUS HEALTH (O, 237 beds) 900 East Broadway, Bismarck, ND, Zip 58501–4586, Mailing Address: P.O. Box 5510, 58506–5510, tel. 701/530–7000; Kurt Schley, Chief Executive Officer

**OHIO:** GOOD SAMARITAN HOSPITAL (S, 355 beds) 375 Dixmyth Avenue, Cincinnati, OH, Zip 45220–2489; tel. 513/862–1400; Jamie Easterling, Executive Director, Operations
**Web address:** www.trihealth.com

PROVIDENCE CARE CENTER (O, 138 beds) 2025 Hayes Avenue, Sandusky, OH, Zip 44870, Rick G. Ryan, Administrator and Chief Executive Officer

TRINITY HEALTH SYSTEM (O, 277 beds) 380 Summit Avenue, Steubenville, OH, Zip 43952–2699; tel. 740/283–7000; Matthew Grimshaw, Market Chief Executive Officer
**Web address:** www.trinityhealth.com

TRINITY HOSPITAL TWIN CITY (O, 12 beds) 819 North First Street, Dennison, OH, Zip 44621–1098; tel. 740/922–2800; Teresa Gagliardi, R.N., Vice President of Hospital Operations and Site Administrator
**Web address:** www.trinitytwincity.org

**OREGON:** CHI ST. ANTHONY HOSPITAL (S, 25 beds) 2801 St Anthony Way, Pendleton, OR, Zip 97801–3800; tel. 541/276–5121; Harold S. Geller, Chief Executive Officer

MERCY MEDICAL CENTER (S, 140 beds) 2700 Stewart Parkway, Roseburg, OR, Zip 97471–1281; tel. 541/673–0611; Kelly C. Morgan, President and Chief Executive Officer
**Web address:** www.mercyrose.org

**TENNESSEE:** CHI MEMORIAL (S, 423 beds) 2525 De Sales Avenue, Chattanooga, TN, Zip 37404–1161; tel. 423/495–2525; Janelle Reilly, Chief Executive Officer
**Web address:** www.memorial.org

**TEXAS:** BAYLOR ST. LUKE'S MEDICAL CENTER MCNAIR CAMPUS (O, 256 beds) One Baylor Plaza, BCM 100, Houston, TX, Zip 77030–3411; tel. 713/798–4951; Elizabeth Youngblood, President and Chief Executive Officer

BAYLOR ST. LUKE'S MEDICAL CENTER (O, 634 beds) 6720 Bertner Avenue, Houston, TX, Zip 77030–2697, Mailing Address: P.O. Box 20269, 77225–0269, tel. 832/355–1000; Elizabeth Youngblood, President and Chief Executive Officer
**Web address:** www.stlukestexas.com

CHI ST. JOSEPH COLLEGE STATION HOSPITAL (O, 144 beds) 1604 Rock Prairie Road, College Station, TX, Zip 77845–8345; tel. 979/764–5100; Theron Park, Chief Executive Officer

CHI ST. JOSEPH HEALTH BURLESON HOSPITAL (O, 12 beds) 1101 Woodson Drive, Caldwell, TX, Zip 77836–1052, Mailing Address: P.O. Box 360, 77836–0360, tel. 979/567–3245; Theron Park, Chief Executive Officer
**Web address:** www.chistjoseph.org/

CHI ST. JOSEPH HEALTH GRIMES HOSPITAL (O, 18 beds) 210 South Judson Street, Navasota, TX, Zip 77868–3704; tel. 936/825–6585; Theron Park, Chief Executive Officer
**Web address:** www.st-joseph.org

CHI ST. JOSEPH HEALTH MADISON HOSPITAL (O, 25 beds) 100 West Cross Street, Madisonville, TX, Zip 77864–2432, Box 698, 77864–0698, tel. 936/348–2631; Theron Park, Chief Executive Officer

CHI ST. JOSEPH REGIONAL HEALTH CENTER (O, 222 beds) 2801 Franciscan Drive, Bryan, TX, Zip 77802–2599; tel. 979/776–3777; Theron Park, Chief Executive Officer
**Web address:** www.st-joseph.org

CHI ST. LUKE'S HEALTH – PATIENTS MEDICAL CENTER (O, 61 beds) 4600 East Sam Houston Parkway South, Pasadena, TX, Zip 77505–3948; tel. 713/948–7000; Steven Foster, Chief Executive Officer

CHI ST. LUKE'S HEALTH BRAZOSPORT (O, 103 beds) 100 Medical Drive, Lake Jackson, TX, Zip 77566–5674; tel. 979/297–4411; Al Guevara Jr, FACHE, President
**Web address:** www.chistlukesbrazosport.org

CHI ST. LUKE'S HEALTH MEMORIAL LIVINGSTON (O, 66 beds) 1717 Highway 59 Loop North, Livingston, TX, Zip 77351–5710, Mailing Address: P.O. Box 1257, 77351–0022, tel. 936/329–8700; Kristi Froese, R.N., Vice President Clinical Operations
**Web address:** https://www.chistlukeshealthmemorial.org/centers/livingston

CHI ST. LUKE'S HEALTH MEMORIAL LUFKIN (O, 194 beds) 1201 West Frank Avenue, Lufkin, TX, Zip 75904–3357, Mailing Address: P.O. Box 1447, 75902–1447, tel. 936/634–8111; Monte J. Bostwick, Market Chief Executive Officer
**Web address:** www.memorialhealth.us/centers/lufkin

CHI ST. LUKE'S HEALTH MEMORIAL SAN AUGUSTINE (O, 9 beds) 511 East Hospital Street, San Augustine, TX, Zip 75972–2121, Mailing Address: P.O. Box 658, 75972–0658, tel. 936/275–3446; Darlene Williams, R.N., Administrator
**Web address:** www.memorialhealth.org

CHI ST. LUKE'S HEALTH–LAKESIDE HOSPITAL (O, 30 beds) 17400 St. Luke's Way, The Woodlands, TX, Zip 77384–8036; tel. 936/266–9000; James Parisi, Chief Executive Officer

CHI ST. LUKE'S HEALTH–THE WOODLANDS HOSPITAL (O, 204 beds) 17200 St. Luke's Way, The Woodlands, TX, Zip 77384–8007; tel. 936/266–2000; James Parisi, Chief Executive Officer
**Web address:** www.stlukeswoodlands.com

CHI ST. LUKE'S HOSPITAL – THE VINTAGE HOSPITAL (O, 78 beds) 20171 Chasewood Park Drive, Houston, TX, Zip 77070–1437; tel. 832/534–5000; Mario J. Garner, Ed.D., FACHE, Chief Executive Officer
**Web address:** https://www.chistlukeshealth.org/locations/vintage–hospital

ST. LUKE'S SUGAR LAND HOSPITAL (O, 96 beds) 1317 Lake Pointe Parkway, Sugar Land, TX, Zip 77478–3997; tel. 281/637–7000; Steven Foster, President and Interim Chief Executive Officer

**WASHINGTON:** ST. ANNE HOSPITAL (O, 115 beds) 16251 Sylvester Road SW, Burien, WA, Zip 98166–3052; tel. 206/244–9970; Russell Woolley, Chief Operating Officer
**Web address:** https://www.chifranciscan.org/highline–medical–center.html

ST. ANTHONY HOSPITAL (O, 112 beds) 11567 Canterwood Boulevard NW, Gig Harbor, WA, Zip 98332–5812; tel. 253/530–2000; David W. Schultz, FACHE, President, Peninsula Region
**Web address:** www.chifranciscan.org/

ST. CLARE HOSPITAL (S, 104 beds) 11315 Bridgeport Way SW, Lakewood, WA, Zip 98499–3004; tel. 253/985–1711; Tim O'Haver, President
**Web address:** www.fhshealth.org

ST. ELIZABETH HOSPITAL (S, 25 beds) 1455 Battersby Avenue, Enumclaw, WA, Zip 98022–3634, Mailing Address: P.O. Box 218, 98022–0218, tel. 360/802–8800; Tim O'Haver, Market President

ST. FRANCIS HOSPITAL (S, 124 beds) 34515 Ninth Avenue South, Federal Way, WA, Zip 98003–6799; tel. 253/944–8100; Dino Johnson, R.N., Chief Operating Officer
**Web address:** www.fhshealth.org

ST. JOSEPH MEDICAL CENTER (S, 366 beds) 1717 South 'J' Street, Tacoma, WA, Zip 98405–3004, Mailing Address: P.O. Box 2197, 98401–2197, tel. 253/426–4101; Tim O'Haver, President

ST. MICHAEL MEDICAL CENTER (O, 232 beds) 2520 Cherry Avenue, Bremerton, WA, Zip 98310–4229; tel. 360/744–3911; David W. Schultz, FACHE, President, Peninsula Region
**Web address:** www.chifranciscan.org/harrison

| | | |
|---|---|---|
| **Owned, leased, sponsored:** | 120 hospitals | 18278 beds |
| **Contract-managed:** | 3 hospitals | 127 beds |
| **Totals:** | 123 hospitals | 18405 beds |

For explanation of codes following names, see page B2.
★ Indicates Type III membership in the American Hospital Association.

**★0401: COMMUNITY HEALTH NETWORK** (NP)
7330 Shadeland Station, Indianapolis, IN Zip 46256–3957; tel. 317/355–1411; Bryan A. Mills, President and Chief Executive Officer
**(Independent Hospital System)**

**INDIANA:** COMMUNITY HOSPITAL ANDERSON (O, 140 beds) 1515 North Madison Avenue, Anderson, IN, Zip 46011–3453; tel. 765/298–4242; Beth S. Tharp, R.N., President and Chief Executive Officer

COMMUNITY HOSPITAL EAST (O, 181 beds) 1500 North Ritter Avenue, Indianapolis, IN, Zip 46219–3095; tel. 317/355–1411; David Kiley, M.D., Senior Vice President, President Indianapolis Region
**Web address:** www.ecommunity.com/east/

COMMUNITY HOSPITAL NORTH (O, 353 beds) 7150 Clearvista Drive, Indianapolis, IN, Zip 46256–1695, 7250 Clearvista Drive, Suite 200, 46256–1695, tel. 317/355–2469; David Kiley, M.D., Indianapolis Region President

COMMUNITY HOSPITAL SOUTH (O, 171 beds) 1402 East County Line Road South, Indianapolis, IN, Zip 46227–0963; tel. 317/887–7000; David Kiley, M.D., Indianapolis Region President
**Web address:** www.ecommunity.com

COMMUNITY HOWARD REGIONAL HEALTH (O, 196 beds) 3500 South Lafountain Street, Kokomo, IN, Zip 46902–3803, Mailing Address: P.O. Box 9011, 46904–9011, tel. 765/453–0702; Joseph Hooper, President and Chief Executive Officer
**Web address:** www.howardregional.org

| | | |
|---|---|---|
| Owned, leased, sponsored: | 5 hospitals | 1041 beds |
| Contract–managed: | 0 hospitals | 0 beds |
| Totals: | 5 hospitals | 1041 beds |

**★0080: COMMUNITY HEALTH SYSTEMS, INC.** (IO)
4000 Meridian Boulevard, Franklin, TN Zip 37067–6325, Mailing Address: P.O. Box 689020, 37068–9020, tel. 615/465–7000; Wayne T. Smith, Chairman, President and Chief Executive Officer
**(Decentralized Health System)**

**ALABAMA:** CRESTWOOD MEDICAL CENTER (O, 180 beds) One Hospital Drive, Huntsville, AL, Zip 35801–3403; tel. 256/429–4000; Pamela Hudson, M.D., Chief Executive Officer
**Web address:** www.crestwoodmedcenter.com

FLOWERS HOSPITAL (O, 147 beds) 4370 West Main Street, Dothan, AL, Zip 36305–4000, Mailing Address: P.O. Box 6907, 36302–6907, tel. 334/793–5000; Jeffrey M. Brannon, Chief Executive Officer

GADSDEN REGIONAL MEDICAL CENTER (O, 279 beds) 1007 Goodyear Avenue, Gadsden, AL, Zip 35903–1195; tel. 256/494–4000; Corey Ewing, Chief Executive Officer
**Web address:** www.gadsdenregional.com

GRANDVIEW MEDICAL CENTER (O, 379 beds) 3690 Grandview Parkway, Birmingham, AL, Zip 35243–3326; tel. 205/971–1000; Drew Mason, Chief Executive Officer

MEDICAL CENTER ENTERPRISE (O, 99 beds) 400 North Edwards Street, Enterprise, AL, Zip 36330–2510; tel. 334/347–0584; Suzanne Woods, Chief Executive Officer
**Web address:** www.mcehospital.com

SOUTH BALDWIN REGIONAL MEDICAL CENTER (L, 112 beds) 1613 North McKenzie Street, Foley, AL, Zip 36535–2299; tel. 251/949–3400; Daniel McKinney, Chief Executive Officer
**Web address:** www.southbaldwinrmc.com

**ALASKA:** MAT–SU REGIONAL MEDICAL CENTER (O, 74 beds) 2500 South Woodworth Loop, Palmer, AK, Zip 99645–8984, Mailing Address: P.O. Box 1687, 99645–1687, tel. 907/861–6000; David Wallace, Chief Executive Officer

**ARIZONA:** NORTHWEST MEDICAL CENTER (O, 270 beds) 6200 North La Cholla Boulevard, Tucson, AZ, Zip 85741–3599; tel. 520/742–9000; Jennifer Schomburg, Chief Executive Officer
**Web address:** www.northwestmedicalcenter.com

ORO VALLEY HOSPITAL (O, 146 beds) 1551 East Tangerine Road, Oro Valley, AZ, Zip 85755–6213; tel. 520/901–3500; Jennifer Schomburg, Chief Administrative Officer

WESTERN ARIZONA REGIONAL MEDICAL CENTER (O, 106 beds) 2735 Silver Creek Road, Bullhead City, AZ, Zip 86442–8303; tel. 928/763–2273; Michael J Stenger, Chief Executive Officer
**Web address:** www.warmc.com

**ARKANSAS:** MEDICAL CENTER OF SOUTH ARKANSAS (L, 121 beds) 700 West Grove Street, El Dorado, AR, Zip 71730–4416; tel. 870/863–2000; Scott Street, Chief Executive Officer

NORTHWEST HEALTH PHYSICIANS' SPECIALTY HOSPITAL (O, 20 beds) 3873 North Parkview Drive, Fayetteville, AR, Zip 72703–6286; tel. 479/571–7070; Denten Park, Chief Executive Officer
**Web address:** www.pshfay.com

NORTHWEST MEDICAL CENTER – SPRINGDALE (O, 366 beds) 609 West Maple Avenue, Springdale, AR, Zip 72764–5394, Mailing Address: P.O. Box 47, 72765–0047, tel. 479/751–5711; Hans Driessnack, Chief Executive Officer

SILOAM SPRINGS REGIONAL HOSPITAL (O, 44 beds) 603 North Progress Avenue, Siloam Springs, AR, Zip 72761–4352; tel. 479/215–3000; Adam Bracks, Chief Executive Officer
**Web address:** www.ssrh.net

**FLORIDA:** BAYFRONT HEALTH BROOKSVILLE (L, 120 beds) 17240 Cortez Boulevard, Brooksville, FL, Zip 34601–8921, Mailing Address: P.O. Box 37, 34605–0037, tel. 352/796–5111; Kenneth R. Wicker, FACHE, Chief Executive Officer
**Web address:** www.brooksvilleregionalhospital.org

BAYFRONT HEALTH PORT CHARLOTTE (O, 254 beds) 2500 Harbor Boulevard, Port Charlotte, FL, Zip 33952–5000; tel. 941/766–4122; Eric Kaplan, Interim Chief Executive Officer and Chief Operating Officer
**Web address:** www.bayfrontcharlotte.com

BAYFRONT HEALTH PUNTA GORDA (O, 190 beds) 809 East Marion Avenue, Punta Gorda, FL, Zip 33950–3819, Mailing Address: P.O. Box 51–1328, 33951–1328, tel. 941/639–3131; Eric Kaplan, Interim Chief Executive Officer

BAYFRONT HEALTH ST. PETERSBURG (O, 480 beds) 701 Sixth Street South, Saint Petersburg, FL, Zip 33701–4891; tel. 727/823–1234; Sharon Hayes, Chief Executive Officer
**Web address:** www.bayfrontstpete.com

LOWER KEYS MEDICAL CENTER (L, 90 beds) 5900 College Road, Key West, FL, Zip 33040–4396, Mailing Address: P.O. Box 9107, 33041–9107, tel. 305/294–5531; David Clay, Chief Executive Officer

NORTH OKALOOSA MEDICAL CENTER (O, 110 beds) 151 Redstone Avenue SE, Crestview, FL, Zip 32539–6026; tel. 850/689–8100; Ronnie Daves, Chief Executive Officer
**Web address:** www.northokaloosa.com

PHYSICIANS REGIONAL – PINE RIDGE (O, 70 beds) 6101 Pine Ridge Road, Naples, FL, Zip 34119–3900; tel. 239/348–4000; Scott Lowe, Market Chief Executive Officer

SANTA ROSA MEDICAL CENTER (L, 68 beds) 6002 Berryhill Road, Milton, FL, Zip 32570–5062; tel. 850/626–7762; Doug Sills, Chief Executive Officer
**Web address:** www.santarosamedicalcenter.org

SEVEN RIVERS REGIONAL MEDICAL CENTER (O, 128 beds) 6201 North Suncoast Boulevard, Crystal River, FL, Zip 34428–6712; tel. 352/795–6560; Linda Stockton, Chief Executive Officer

VENICE REGIONAL BAYFRONT HEALTH (O, 221 beds) 540 The Rialto, Venice, FL, Zip 34285–2900; tel. 941/485–7711; Beryl Ramsey, FACHE, Interim Chief Executive Officer
**Web address:** www.veniceregional.com

**GEORGIA:** EAST GEORGIA REGIONAL MEDICAL CENTER (O, 149 beds) 1499 Fair Road, Statesboro, GA, Zip 30458–1683, Mailing Address: P.O. Box 1048, 30459–1048, tel. 912/486–1000; Stephen G. Pennington, Chief Executive Officer

**INDIANA:** BLUFFTON REGIONAL MEDICAL CENTER (O, 54 beds) 303 South Main Street, Bluffton, IN, Zip 46714–2503; tel. 260/824–3210; Julie Thompson, Chief Adminstrative Officer and Chief Nursing Officer
**Web address:** www.blufftonregional.com

DUKES MEMORIAL HOSPITAL (O, 25 beds) 275 West 12th Street, Peru, IN, Zip 46970–1638; tel. 765/472–8000; Debra Close, Chief Executive Officer
**Web address:** www.dukesmemorialhosp.com

DUPONT HOSPITAL (O, 131 beds) 2520 East Dupont Road, Fort Wayne, IN, Zip 46825–1675; tel. 260/416–3000; Lorenzo Suter, Chief Executive Officer

For explanation of codes following names, see page B2.
★ Indicates Type III membership in the American Hospital Association.

Section B

KOSCIUSKO COMMUNITY HOSPITAL (O, 72 beds) 2101 East Dubois Drive, Warsaw, IN, Zip 46580–3288; tel. 574/267–3200; Jae Dale, Chief Executive Officer
**Web address:** www.kch.com

LA PORTE HOSPITAL (O, 91 beds) 1007 Lincolnway, La Porte, IN, Zip 46350–3201, Mailing Address: P.O. Box 250, 46352–0250, tel. 219/326–1234; Ashley Dickinson, Chief Executive Officer

LUTHERAN HOSPITAL OF INDIANA (O, 407 beds) 7950 West Jefferson Boulevard, Fort Wayne, IN, Zip 46804–4140; tel. 260/435–7001; Brady Dubois, Chief Executive Officer
**Web address:** www.lutheranhospital.com

ORTHOPAEDIC HOSPITAL OF LUTHERAN HEALTH NETWORK (O, 43 beds) 7952 West Jefferson Boulevard, Fort Wayne, IN, Zip 46804–4140; tel. 260/435–2999; Lorie Ailor, Chief Executive Officer, Chief Administrative Officer, Network Vice President Orthopedics and Sports Medicine

PORTER REGIONAL HOSPITAL (O, 276 beds) 85 East U. S. Highway 6, Valparaiso, IN, Zip 46383–8947; tel. 219/983–8300; Sean T. Dardeau, FACHE, Chief Executive Officer
**Web address:** www.porterhealth.com

REHABILITATION HOSPITAL OF FORT WAYNE (O, 36 beds) 7970 West Jefferson Boulevard, Fort Wayne, IN, Zip 46804–4140; tel. 260/435–6100; Ryan Cassedy, Chief Administrative Officer

ST. JOSEPH HOSPITAL (O, 162 beds) 700 Broadway, Fort Wayne, IN, Zip 46802–1493; tel. 260/425–3000; Lisa Dolan, Interim Chief Executive Officer
**Web address:** www.stjoehospital.com

STARKE HOSPITAL (O, 15 beds) 102 East Culver Road, Knox, IN, Zip 46534–2216, Mailing Address: P.O. Box 339, 46534–0339, tel. 574/772–6231; Ashley Dickinson, Chief Executive Officer
**Web address:** https://www.starkehealth.com

**MISSISSIPPI:** MERIT HEALTH BILOXI (L, 101 beds) 150 Reynoir Street, Biloxi, MS, Zip 39530–4199, Mailing Address: P.O. Box 128, 39533–0128, tel. 228/432–1571; Tom R. McDougal Jr, FACHE, Chief Executive Officer
**Web address:** www.merithealthbiloxi.com

MERIT HEALTH CENTRAL (L, 230 beds) 1850 Chadwick Drive, Jackson, MS, Zip 39204–3479, Mailing Address: P.O. Box 59001, 39284–9001, tel. 601/376–1000; Barry Moss, Chief Executive Officer
**Web address:** www.merithealthcentral.com/

MERIT HEALTH MADISON (L, 43 beds) 161 River Oaks Drive, Canton, MS, Zip 39046–5375, Mailing Address: P.O. 1607, 39046–5375, tel. 601/855–4000; Britton Phelps, Chief Executive Officer

MERIT HEALTH NATCHEZ (O, 136 beds) 54 Seargent 'S' Prentiss Drive, Natchez, MS, Zip 39120–4726; tel. 601/443–2100; Lance Boyd, Chief Executive Officer
**Web address:** www.natchezregional.com

MERIT HEALTH RANKIN (L, 134 beds) 350 Crossgates Boulevard, Brandon, MS, Zip 39042–2698; tel. 601/825–2811; Heather Sistrunk, R.N., Chief Executive Officer

MERIT HEALTH RIVER OAKS (O, 118 beds) 1030 River Oaks Drive, Flowood, MS, Zip 39232–9553, Mailing Address: P.O. Box 5100, Jackson, 39296–5100, tel. 601/932–1030; L Dwayne. Blaylock, Chief Executive Officer
**Web address:** https://www.merithealthriveroaks.com/

MERIT HEALTH RIVER REGION (O, 361 beds) 2100 Highway 61 North, Vicksburg, MS, Zip 39183–8211, Mailing Address: P.O. Box 590, 39181–0590, tel. 601/883–5000; Benjamin Richaud, Interim Chief Executive Officer

MERIT HEALTH WESLEY (O, 211 beds) 5001 Hardy Street, Hattiesburg, MS, Zip 39402–1308, Mailing Address: P.O. Box 16509, 39404–6509, tel. 601/268–8000; Matthew Banks, Chief Executive Officer
**Web address:** www.wesley.com

MERIT HEALTH WOMAN'S HOSPITAL (O, 60 beds) 1026 North Flowood Drive, Flowood, MS, Zip 39232–9532, 1026 North Flowood Drive, 39232, tel. 601/932–1000; Heather Sistrunk, R.N., Chief Executive Officer

**MISSOURI:** MOBERLY REGIONAL MEDICAL CENTER (O, 99 beds) 1515 Union Avenue, Moberly, MO, Zip 65270–9449; tel. 660/263–8400; Brent Parsons, Chief Executive Officer
**Web address:** https://www.moberlyregionalmedicalcenter.com

NORTHEAST REGIONAL MEDICAL CENTER (L, 50 beds) 315 South Osteopathy Street, Kirksville, MO, Zip 63501–6401, Mailing Address: P.O. Box C8502, 63501–8599, tel. 660/785–1000; Ranee C. Brayton, FACHE, MSN, R.N., Chief Executive Officer

POPLAR BLUFF REGIONAL MEDICAL CENTER (O, 255 beds) 3100 Oak Grove Road, Poplar Bluff, MO, Zip 63901, Mailing Address: P.O. Box 88, 63902–0088, tel. 573/776–2000; Bryan S. Bateman, Chief Executive Officer
**Web address:** www.poplarbluffregional.com

**NEW MEXICO:** CARLSBAD MEDICAL CENTER (O, 66 beds) 2430 West Pierce Street, Carlsbad, NM, Zip 88220–3597; tel. 575/887–4100; Dan Springer, Interim Chief Executive Officer

EASTERN NEW MEXICO MEDICAL CENTER (O, 149 beds) 405 West Country Club Road, Roswell, NM, Zip 88201–5209; tel. 575/622–8170; Warren Yehl, Chief Executive Officer
**Web address:** www.enmmc.com

LEA REGIONAL MEDICAL CENTER (O, 84 beds) 5419 North Lovington Highway, Hobbs, NM, Zip 88240–9125, Mailing Address: P.O. Box 3000, 88241–9501, tel. 575/492–5000; Dan Springer, Chief Executive Officer
**Web address:** www.learegionalmedical.com

MOUNTAINVIEW REGIONAL MEDICAL CENTER (O, 142 beds) 4311 East Lohman Avenue, Las Cruces, NM, Zip 88011–8255; tel. 575/556–7600; Derrick Cuenca, Chief Executive Officer

**NORTH CAROLINA:** DAVIS REGIONAL MEDICAL CENTER (O, 130 beds) 218 Old Mocksville Road, Statesville, NC, Zip 28625–1930, Mailing Address: P.O. Box 1823, 28687–1823, tel. 704/873–0281; Josh Snow, Chief Executive Officer
**Web address:** www.davisregional.com

LAKE NORMAN REGIONAL MEDICAL CENTER (O, 123 beds) 171 Fairview Road, Mooresville, NC, Zip 28117–9500, Mailing Address: P.O. Box 3250, 28117–3250, tel. 704/660–4000; Stephen L. Midkiff, Chief Executive Officer

**OKLAHOMA:** ALLIANCEHEALTH CLINTON (O, 49 beds) 100 North 30th Street, Clinton, OK, Zip 73601–3117; tel. 580/323–2363; Landon E. Hise, Chief Executive Officer
**Web address:** www.alliancehealthclinton.com

ALLIANCEHEALTH DURANT (O, 140 beds) 1800 University Boulevard, Durant, OK, Zip 74701–3006, Mailing Address: P.O. Box 1207, 74702–1207, tel. 580/924–3080; Kevin Samrow, Chief Executive Officer
**Web address:** www.alliancehealthdurant.com/

ALLIANCEHEALTH MADILL (O, 23 beds) 901 South Fifth Avenue, Madill, OK, Zip 73446–3640, Mailing Address: P.O. Box 827, 73446–0827, tel. 580/795–3384; Kevin Samrow, Chief Executive Officer
**Web address:** www.myalliancehealth.com

ALLIANCEHEALTH MIDWEST (L, 255 beds) 2825 Parklawn Drive, Midwest City, OK, Zip 73110–4258; tel. 405/610–4411; Clay Franklin, Chief Executive Officer
**Web address:** www.myalliancehealth.com

ALLIANCEHEALTH PONCA CITY (O, 74 beds) 1900 North 14th Street, Ponca City, OK, Zip 74601–2099; tel. 580/765–3321; Christopher Mendoza, Chief Executive Officer
**Web address:** www.AllianceHealthPoncaCity.com

ALLIANCEHEALTH SEMINOLE (O, 32 beds) 2401 Wrangler Boulevard, Seminole, OK, Zip 74868–1917; tel. 405/303–4000; Damon Brown, Interim Chief Executive Officer
**Web address:** www.alliancehealthseminole.com/

ALLIANCEHEALTH WOODWARD (L, 40 beds) 900 17th Street, Woodward, OK, Zip 73801–2448; tel. 580/256–5511; Landon E. Hise, Interim Chief Executive Officer
**Web address:** www.woodwardhospital.com

**PENNSYLVANIA:** BERWICK HOSPITAL CENTER (O, 101 beds) 701 East 16th Street, Berwick, PA, Zip 18603–2397; tel. 570/759–5000; Thomas Neal, Chief Executive Officer
**Web address:** www.commonwealthhealth.net

FIRST HOSPITAL WYOMING VALLEY (O, 149 beds) 562 Wyoming Avenue, Kingston, PA, Zip 18704–3721; tel. 570/552–3900; Christine Mathews, Interim President and Chief Executive Officer, Chief Nursing Officer

MOSES TAYLOR HOSPITAL (O, 213 beds) 700 Quincy Avenue, Scranton, PA, Zip 18510–1724; tel. 570/770–5000; Michael L. Brown, President and Chief Executive Officer
**Web address:** https://www.commonwealthhealth.net/

REGIONAL HOSPITAL OF SCRANTON (O, 186 beds) 746 Jefferson Avenue, Scranton, PA, Zip 18510–1624; tel. 570/348–7100; Michael L. Brown, Chief Executive Officer

For explanation of codes following names, see page B2.
★ Indicates Type III membership in the American Hospital Association.

Section B

TYLER MEMORIAL HOSPITAL (O, 44 beds) 5950 State Route 6, Tunkhannock, PA, Zip 18657–7905; tel. 570/836–2161; Ann Marie. Stevens, R.N., Chief Executive Officer
**Web address:** www.tylermemorialhospital.net

WILKES–BARRE GENERAL HOSPITAL (O, 374 beds) 575 North River Street, Wilkes–Barre, PA, Zip 18764–0001; tel. 570/829–8111; Cornelio R. Catena, President and Chief Executive Officer

**TENNESSEE:** TENNOVA HEALTHCARE – CLEVELAND (O, 183 beds) 2305 Chambliss Avenue NW, Cleveland, TN, Zip 37311–3847, P O Box 3060, 37320–3060, tel. 423/559–6000; J. T. Barnhart, Chief Executive Officer
**Web address:** www.skyridgemedicalcenter.net

TENNOVA HEALTHCARE–CLARKSVILLE (O, 172 beds) 651 Dunlop Lane, Clarksville, TN, Zip 37040–5015, Mailing Address: P.O. Box 31629, 37040–0028, tel. 931/502–1000; Alex Villa, Chief Executive Officer
**Web address:** www.tennova.com/

TENNOVA HEALTHCARE–HARTON (O, 135 beds) 1801 North Jackson Street, Tullahoma, TN, Zip 37388–8259; tel. 931/393–3000; Richard Ellis, Chief Executive Officer
**Web address:** www.hartonmedicalcenter.com

TENNOVA HEALTHCARE–JEFFERSON MEMORIAL HOSPITAL (L, 58 beds) 110 Hospital Drive, Jefferson City, TN, Zip 37760–5281; tel. 865/471–2500; Colin McRae, Chief Executive Officer

TENNOVA HEALTHCARE–LAFOLLETTE MEDICAL CENTER (O, 164 beds) 923 East Central Avenue, La Follette, TN, Zip 37766–2768, Mailing Address: P.O. Box 1301, 37766–1301, tel. 423/907–1200; Mark Cain, Chief Executive Officer
**Web address:** www.tennova.com

TENNOVA HEALTHCARE–SHELBYVILLE (O, 49 beds) 2835 Highway 231 North, Shelbyville, TN, Zip 37160–7327; tel. 931/685–5433; Bill Rich, Chief Executive Officer
**Web address:** www.Tennova.com

TENNOVA NEWPORT MEDICAL CENTER (O, 47 beds) 435 Second Street, Newport, TN, Zip 37821–3799; tel. 423/625–2200; Matthew Littlejohn, Chief Executive Officer

TENNOVA NORTH KNOXVILLE MEDICAL CENTER (O, 220 beds) 7565 Dannaher Way, Powell, TN, Zip 37849–4029; tel. 865/859–8000; Clyde Wood, Chief Executive Officer
**Web address:** https://www.tennovanorthknoxville.com/

**TEXAS:** ABILENE REGIONAL MEDICAL CENTER (O, 205 beds) 6250 US Highway 83/84, Abilene, TX, Zip 79606–5299; tel. 325/428–1000; Michael D. Murphy, FACHE, Chief Executive Officer

BROWNWOOD REGIONAL MEDICAL CENTER (O, 148 beds) 1501 Burnet Road, Brownwood, TX, Zip 76801–8520, Mailing Address: P.O. Box 760, 76804–0760, tel. 325/646–8541; Jace Jones, Interim Chief Executive Officer
**Web address:** www.brmc–cares.com

CEDAR PARK REGIONAL MEDICAL CENTER (O, 108 beds) 1401 Medical Parkway, Cedar Park, TX, Zip 78613–7763; tel. 512/528–7000; Carl (Bo) Beaudry, Chief Executive Officer

DETAR HEALTHCARE SYSTEM (O, 235 beds) 506 East San Antonio Street, Victoria, TX, Zip 77901–6060, Mailing Address: P.O. Box 2089, 77902–2089, tel. 361/575–7441; Bernard Leger, Chief Executive Officer
**Web address:** www.detar.com

HILL REGIONAL HOSPITAL (O, 25 beds) 101 Circle Drive, Hillsboro, TX, Zip 76645–2670; tel. 254/580–8500; Michael J. Ellis, FACHE, Chief Executive Officer

LAKE GRANBURY MEDICAL CENTER (L, 73 beds) 1310 Paluxy Road, Granbury, TX, Zip 76048–5655; tel. 817/573–2273; David Orcutt, Chief Executive Officer
**Web address:** www.lakegranburymedicalcenter.com

LAREDO MEDICAL CENTER (O, 326 beds) 1700 East Saunders Avenue, Laredo, TX, Zip 78041–5474, Mailing Address: P.O. Box 2068, 78044–2068, tel. 956/796–5000; Enrique Gallegos, Chief Executive Officer

LONGVIEW REGIONAL MEDICAL CENTER (O, 168 beds) 2901 North Fourth Street, Longview, TX, Zip 75605–5191, Mailing Address: P.O. Box 14000, 75607–4000, tel. 903/758–1818; Douglas R. Luckett, Interim Chief Executive Officer
**Web address:** www.longviewregional.com

NAVARRO REGIONAL HOSPITAL (O, 49 beds) 3201 West State Highway 22, Corsicana, TX, Zip 75110–2469; tel. 903/654–6800; Curt M. Junkins, Chief Executive Officer

SAN ANGELO COMMUNITY MEDICAL CENTER (O, 131 beds) 3501 Knickerbocker Road, San Angelo, TX, Zip 76904–7698; tel. 325/949–9511; Rodney Schumacher, Interim Chief Executive Officer
**Web address:** www.sacmc.com

WOODLAND HEIGHTS MEDICAL CENTER (O, 124 beds) 505 South John Redditt Drive, Lufkin, TX, Zip 75904–3157, Mailing Address: P.O. Box 150610, 75904, tel. 936/634–8311; Andrew Emery, Chief Executive Officer

**WEST VIRGINIA:** GREENBRIER VALLEY MEDICAL CENTER (O, 113 beds) 202 Maplewood Avenue, Ronceverte, WV, Zip 24970–1334, Mailing Address: P.O. Box 497, 24970–0497, tel. 304/647–4411; Jim Hobson, Chief Executive Officer
**Web address:** www.gvmc.com

PLATEAU MEDICAL CENTER (O, 25 beds) 430 Main Street, Oak Hill, WV, Zip 25901–3455; tel. 304/469–8600; Christopher L. Howe, R.N., Chief Executive Officer

| | | |
|---|---|---|
| Owned, leased, sponsored: | 88 hospitals | 12465 beds |
| Contract–managed: | 0 hospitals | 0 beds |
| **Totals:** | **88 hospitals** | **12465 beds** |

**0249: COMMUNITY HEALTHCARE SYSTEM** (NP)
901 MacArthur Boulevard, Hammond, IN Zip 46321–2959; tel. 219/836–1600; Donald P. Fesko, President and Chief Executive Officer
**(Independent Hospital System)**

**INDIANA:** COMMUNITY HOSPITAL (O, 510 beds) 901 Macarthur Boulevard, Munster, IN, Zip 46321–2959; tel. 219/836–1600; Luis F. Molina, Chief Executive Officer and Administrator
**Web address:** www.comhs.org

ST. CATHERINE HOSPITAL (O, 220 beds) 4321 Fir Street, East Chicago, IN, Zip 46312–3097; tel. 219/392–1700; Leo Correa, Chief Executive Officer and Administrator

ST. MARY MEDICAL CENTER (O, 200 beds) 1500 South Lake Park Avenue, Hobart, IN, Zip 46342–6699; tel. 219/942–0551; Janice L. Ryba, JD, Chief Executive Officer
**Web address:** www.comhs.org

| | | |
|---|---|---|
| Owned, leased, sponsored: | 3 hospitals | 930 beds |
| Contract–managed: | 0 hospitals | 0 beds |
| **Totals:** | **3 hospitals** | **930 beds** |

**★0384: COMMUNITY HOSPITAL CORPORATION** (NP)
7800 North Dallas Parkway, Suite 200, Plano, TX Zip 75024–6116; tel. 972/943–6400; Jim R. Kendrick, President and Chief Executive Officer
**(Moderately Centralized Health System)**

**ARKANSAS:** ARKANSAS CONTINUED CARE HOSPITAL (C, 44 beds) 3024 Red Wolf Boulevard, Jonesboro, AR, Zip 72401–7415; tel. 870/819–4040; Vincent Gore, Chief Executive Officer

**KENTUCKY:** CONTINUECARE HOSPITAL AT BAPTIST HEALTH CORBIN (O, 32 beds) 1 Trillium Way, Lower Level, Corbin, KY, Zip 40701–8727; tel. 606/523–5150; Tuan Le, Chief Executive Officer
**Web address:** www.continuecare.com

CONTINUECARE HOSPITAL AT BAPTIST HEALTH PADUCAH (O, 37 beds) 2501 Kentucky Avenue, 5th Floor, Paducah, KY, Zip 42003–3813; tel. 270/575–2598; Lee Gentry, FACHE, Chief Executive Officer
**Web address:** www.continuecare.org/paducah//

CONTINUECARE HOSPITAL AT MADISONVILLE (O, 35 beds) 900 Hospital Drive, 4th Floor, Madisonville, KY, Zip 42431–1644; tel. 270/825–5450; Kenneth F. Graves III, Chief Executive Officer

**LOUISIANA:** MOREHOUSE GENERAL HOSPITAL (C, 49 beds) 323 West Walnut Avenue, Bastrop, LA, Zip 71220–4521, Mailing Address: P.O. Box 1060, 71221–1060, tel. 318/283–3600; Derrick A. Frazier, FACHE, Chief Executive Officer
**Web address:** www.mghospital.com

For explanation of codes following names, see page B2.
★ Indicates Type III membership in the American Hospital Association.

**NEW MEXICO:** UNION COUNTY GENERAL HOSPITAL (C, 25 beds) 300 Wilson Street, Clayton, NM, Zip 88415–3304, Mailing Address: P.O. Box 489, 88415–0489, tel. 575/374–2585; Tammie Stump, R.N., Chief Executive Officer
**Web address:** www.ucgh.net/

**NORTH CAROLINA:** CAROLINAS CONTINUECARE HOSPITAL AT PINEVILLE (O, 40 beds) 10648 Park Road, Charlotte, NC, Zip 28210; tel. 704/667–8050; Derek Murzyn, Market Chief Executive Officer
**Web address:** www.continuecare.org/pineville/

CAROLINAS CONTINUECARE HOSPITAL AT UNIVERSITY (O, 35 beds) 8800 North Tryon Street, Charlotte, NC, Zip 28262–3300; tel. 704/863–8300; Derek Murzyn, Chief Executive Officer
**Web address:** www.continuecare.org/charlotte//

**SOUTH CAROLINA:** CONTINUECARE HOSPITAL AT PALMETTO HEALTH BAPTIST (O, 35 beds) Taylor at Marion Street, Columbia, SC, Zip 29220, Mailing Address: P.O. 11069, 29211–1069, tel. 803/296–3757; Wayne B. Boutwell, Chief Executive Officer
**Web address:** www.continuecare.org/palmetto//

**TENNESSEE:** JELLICO COMMUNITY HOSPITAL (O, 47 beds) 188 Hospital Lane, Jellico, TN, Zip 37762–4400; tel. 423/784–7252; Gene Miller, Interim Chief Executive Officer
**Web address:** www.jellicomc.com/

**TEXAS:** BAPTIST HOSPITALS OF SOUTHEAST TEXAS (O, 307 beds) 3080 College Street, Beaumont, TX, Zip 77701–4689, Mailing Address: P.O. Box 1591, 77704–1591, tel. 409/212–5000; David N. Parmer, FACHE, Chief Executive Officer

CONTINUECARE HOSPITAL AT HENDRICK MEDICAL CENTER (O, 23 beds) 1900 Pine Street, 7th Floor, Jones Building, Abilene, TX, Zip 79601–2432; tel. 325/670–6251; Holly Powell, Interim Chief Executive Officer
**Web address:** www.continuecare.org/hendrick/

CONTINUECARE HOSPITAL AT MEDICAL CENTER (ODESSA) (O, 25 beds) 500 West Fourth Street, 4th Floor, Odessa, TX, Zip 79761–5001; tel. 432/640–4380; Laci Harris, Chief Executive Officer
**Web address:** www.continuecare.org/odessa//

FREESTONE MEDICAL CENTER (C, 28 beds) 125 Newman Street, Fairfield, TX, Zip 75840–1499; tel. 903/389–2121; John M. Yeary, FACHE, Chief Executive Officer
**Web address:** www.freestonemc.com/

ST. MARK'S MEDICAL CENTER (O, 38 beds) One St Mark's Place, La Grange, TX, Zip 78945; tel. 979/242–2200; Barry Harding, Interim Chief Executive Officer
**Web address:** www.smmctx.org

TYLER CONTINUECARE HOSPITAL (O, 51 beds) 800 East Dawson, 4th Floor, Tyler, TX, Zip 75701–2036; tel. 903/531–4080; Stephanie Hyde, R.N., MSN, Chief Executive Officer

YOAKUM COMMUNITY HOSPITAL (O, 23 beds) 1200 Carl Ramert Drive, Yoakum, TX, Zip 77995–4868; tel. 361/293–2321; Karen Barber, R.N., Chief Executive Officer
**Web address:** www.yoakumhospital.org

| | | |
|---|---|---|
| Owned, leased, sponsored: | 13 hospitals | 728 beds |
| Contract–managed: | 4 hospitals | 146 beds |
| Totals: | 17 hospitals | 874 beds |

**1085: COMMUNITY MEDICAL CENTERS** (NP)
Fresno and Maddy Drive, Fresno, CA Zip 93721, Mailing Address: P.O. Box 1232, 93715–1232, tel. 559/459–6000; Tim A. Joslin, President and Chief Executive Officer
**(Independent Hospital System)**

**CALIFORNIA:** CLOVIS COMMUNITY MEDICAL CENTER (O, 109 beds) 2755 Herndon Avenue, Clovis, CA, Zip 93611–6801; tel. 559/324–4000; Craig Castro, Chief Executive Officer
**Web address:** www.communitymedical.org

COMMUNITY BEHAVIORAL HEALTH CENTER (O, 61 beds) 7171 North Cedar Avenue, Fresno, CA, Zip 93720–3311; tel. 559/449–8000; Craig Wagoner, Chief Executive Officer

COMMUNITY REGIONAL MEDICAL CENTER (O, 852 beds) 2823 Fresno Street, Fresno, CA, Zip 93721–1324, Mailing Address: P.O. Box 1232, 93715–1232, tel. 559/459–6000; Craig Wagoner, Chief Executive Officer
**Web address:** www.communitymedical.org

FRESNO HEART AND SURGICAL HOSPITAL (O, 60 beds) 15 East Audubon Drive, Fresno, CA, Zip 93720–1542; tel. 559/433–8000; Ben Armfield, Associate Administrator

| | | |
|---|---|---|
| Owned, leased, sponsored: | 4 hospitals | 1082 beds |
| Contract–managed: | 0 hospitals | 0 beds |
| Totals: | 4 hospitals | 1082 beds |

**0990: COMMUNITY MEMORIAL HEALTH SYSTEM** (NP)
147 North Brent Street, Ventura, CA Zip 93003–2809; tel. 805/652–5011; Gary Wilde, President and Chief Executive Officer
**(Independent Hospital System)**

**CALIFORNIA:** COMMUNITY MEMORIAL HOSPITAL (O, 284 beds) 147 North Brent Street, Ventura, CA, Zip 93003–2809; tel. 805/652–5011; Gary Wilde, President and Chief Executive Officer
**Web address:** www.cmhshealth.org

OJAI VALLEY COMMUNITY HOSPITAL (O, 96 beds) 1306 Maricopa Highway, Ojai, CA, Zip 93023–3163; tel. 805/646–1401; Haady Lashkari, Chief Administrative Officer
**Web address:** www.cmhshealth.org/locations/ojai–valley–community–hospital/

| | | |
|---|---|---|
| Owned, leased, sponsored: | 2 hospitals | 380 beds |
| Contract–managed: | 0 hospitals | 0 beds |
| Totals: | 2 hospitals | 380 beds |

**0909: COMPASS HEALTH** (NP)
713 North Avenue L, Crowley, LA Zip 70526–3832; tel. 337/788–3330; Mark J. Cullen, Chairman

**LOUISIANA:** COMPASS BEHAVIORAL CENTER OF ALEXANDRIA (O, 36 beds) 6410 Masonic Drve, Alexandria, LA, Zip 71301–2319; tel. 318/442–3163; Micah J. Hicks, R.N., Chief Executive Officer, CENLA Regional

COMPASS BEHAVIORAL CENTER OF HOUMA (O, 20 beds) 4701 West Park Avenue, Houma, LA, Zip 70364–4426; tel. 985/876–1715; Riane Ortega, Chief Executive Officer
**Web address:** www.compasshealthcare.com/site83.php

COMPASS BEHAVIORAL CENTER OF LAFAYETTE (O, 24 beds) 312 Youngsville Highway, Lafayette, LA, Zip 70508; tel. 337/534–4655; Aimee Monaghan, Administrator
**Web address:** www.compasshealthcare.com

COMPASS BEHAVIORAL CENTER OF MARKSVILLE (O, 16 beds) 137 Dr. Childress Drive, Marksville, LA, Zip 71351; tel. 318/256–3332; Jaime Lucas, Administrator
**Web address:** https://www.compasshealthcare.com/locations/

| | | |
|---|---|---|
| Owned, leased, sponsored: | 4 hospitals | 96 beds |
| Contract–managed: | 0 hospitals | 0 beds |
| Totals: | 4 hospitals | 96 beds |

**0999: CONCORD HEALTHCARE GROUP** (IO)
111 Clifton AVenue, Lakewood, NJ Zip 8701; tel. 214/396–3462; Joe Neuman, Chief Executive Officer
**(Independent Hospital System)**

**OKLAHOMA:** INSPIRE SPECIALTY HOSPITAL (O, 31 beds) 8210 National Avenue, Midwest City, OK, Zip 73110–8518; tel. 405/739–0800; Bobby Snyder, Chief Executive Officer

For explanation of codes following names, see page B2.
★ Indicates Type III membership in the American Hospital Association.

**TEXAS:** PREMIER SPECIALTY HOSPITAL OF EL PASO (O, 32 beds) 2311 North Oregon Street, 5th Floor, El Paso, TX, Zip 79902–3216; tel. 915/545–1823; Jose Huerta, Chief Executive Officer
**Web address:** www.specialtyhospitalmesahills.com/

| | | |
|---|---|---|
| Owned, leased, sponsored: | 2 hospitals | 63 beds |
| Contract–managed: | 0 hospitals | 0 beds |
| Totals: | 2 hospitals | 63 beds |

**0950: CONE HEALTH** (NP)
1200 North Elm Street, Greensboro, NC Zip 27401–1004; tel. 336/832–7000; Terry Akin, President and Chief Executive Officer
**(Independent Hospital System)**

**NORTH CAROLINA:** ALAMANCE REGIONAL MEDICAL CENTER (O, 329 beds) 1240 Huffman Mill Road, Burlington, NC, Zip 27215–8700, Mailing Address: P.O. Box 202, 27216–0202, tel. 336/538–7000; Vicki Moran, Interim President
**Web address:** www.armc.com

MOSES H. CONE MEMORIAL HOSPITAL (O, 910 beds) 1200 North Elm Street, Greensboro, NC, Zip 27401–1020; tel. 336/832–7000; Preston W. Hammock, President

| | | |
|---|---|---|
| Owned, leased, sponsored: | 2 hospitals | 1239 beds |
| Contract–managed: | 0 hospitals | 0 beds |
| Totals: | 2 hospitals | 1239 beds |

**0014: CONNECTICUT DEPARTMENT OF MENTAL HEALTH AND ADDICTION SERVICES** (NP)
410 Capitol Avenue, Hartford, CT Zip 06106–1367, Mailing Address: P.O. Box 341431, 06134–1431, tel. 860/418–7000; Miriam Delphin–Rittmon, Ph.D., Commissioner
**(Independent Hospital System)**

**CONNECTICUT:** CONNECTICUT MENTAL HEALTH CENTER (O, 32 beds) 34 Park Street, New Haven, CT, Zip 06519–1109, Mailing Address: P.O. Box 1842, 06508–1842, tel. 203/974–7144; Michael Sernyak, M.D., Director
**Web address:** www.ct.gov/dmhas/cwp/view.asp?a=2906&q=334596

CONNECTICUT VALLEY HOSPITAL (O, 361 beds) 1000 Silver Street, Middletown, CT, Zip 06457–3947; tel. 860/262–5000; Helene M. Vartelas, MSN, Chief Executive Officer

SOUTHWEST CONNECTICUT MENTAL HEALTH SYSTEM (O, 62 beds) 1635 Central Avenue, Bridgeport, CT, Zip 06610–2717; tel. 203/551–7400; Alicia Feller, Chief Executive Officer
**Web address:** www.ct.gov/dmhas/cwp/view.asp?a=2946&q=378936

| | | |
|---|---|---|
| Owned, leased, sponsored: | 3 hospitals | 455 beds |
| Contract–managed: | 0 hospitals | 0 beds |
| Totals: | 3 hospitals | 455 beds |

**★0016: COOK COUNTY HEALTH AND HOSPITALS SYSTEM** (NP)
1900 West Polk Street, Suite 220, Chicago, IL Zip 60612–3723; tel. 312/864–6820; Debra D. Carey, Interim Chief Executive Officer
**(Independent Hospital System)**

**ILLINOIS:** JOHN H. STROGER JR. HOSPITAL OF COOK COUNTY (O, 446 beds) 1969 West Ogden Avenue, Chicago, IL, Zip 60612–3714; tel. 312/864–6000; Debra D. Carey, Interim Chief Executive Officer
**Web address:** www.cookcountyhealth.net

PROVIDENT HOSPITAL OF COOK COUNTY (O, 25 beds) 500 East 51st Street, Chicago, IL, Zip 60615–2494; tel. 312/572–2000; Debra D. Carey, Interim Chief Executive Officer
**Web address:** www.ccbhs.org/pages/ProvidentHospitalofCookCounty.htm

| | | |
|---|---|---|
| Owned, leased, sponsored: | 2 hospitals | 471 beds |
| Contract–managed: | 0 hospitals | 0 beds |
| Totals: | 2 hospitals | 471 beds |

**0905: CORNERSTONE HEALTHCARE GROUP** (IO)
2200 Ross Avenue, Suite 5400, Dallas, TX Zip 75201–7984; tel. 469/621–6700; Steve Jakubcanin, President and Chief Executive Officer
**(Independent Hospital System)**

**ARIZONA:** CHG HOSPITAL TUCSON, LLC (O, 32 beds) 7220 East Rosewood Drive, Tucson, AZ, Zip 85710–1350; tel. 520/546–4595; Debora Bornmann, Chief Executive Officer

**ARKANSAS:** CORNERSTONE HOSPITAL OF LITTLE ROCK (O, 30 beds) 2 Saint Vincent Circle, 6th Floor, Little Rock, AR, Zip 72205–5423; tel. 501/265–0600; James H. Rogers, FACHE, Chief Executive Officer
**Web address:** www.chghospitals.com/littlerock/

**LOUISIANA:** CORNERSTONE HOSPITALS BOSSIER CITY (O, 54 beds) 4900 Medical Drive, Bossier City, LA, Zip 71112–4521; tel. 318/747–9500; Sheri Burnette, R.N., Chief Executive Officer
**Web address:** www.chghospitals.com/

CORNERSTONE HOSPITALS SOUTHWEST LOUISIANA (O, 30 beds) 524 Doctor Michael Debakey Drive, Lake Charles, LA, Zip 70601–5725; tel. 337/310–6000; Jan Turk, Chief Executive Officer

CORNERSTONE HOSPITALS WEST MONROE (O, 40 beds) 6198 Cypress Street, West Monroe, LA, Zip 71291–9010; tel. 318/396–5600; Chris Simpson, Chief Executive Officer
**Web address:** www.chghospitals.com/chwm.html

**OKLAHOMA:** CORNERSTONE HOSPITAL OF OKLAHOMA–MUSKOGEE (O, 41 beds) 351 South 40th Street, Muskogee, OK, Zip 74401–4916; tel. 918/682–6161; Craig Koele, Chief Executive Officer
**Web address:** www.chghospitals.com/muskogee/

CORNERSTONE HOSPITAL OF OKLAHOMA–SHAWNEE (O, 34 beds) 1900 Gordon Cooper Drive, 2nd Floor, Shawnee, OK, Zip 74801–8603, Mailing Address: P.O. Box 1245, 74802–1245, tel. 405/395–5800; Kristopher Karns, Chief Executive Officer

**TEXAS:** CHG CORNERSTONE HOSPITAL CONROE (O, 41 beds) 1500 Grand Lake Drive, Conroe, TX, Zip 77304–2891; tel. 936/523–1800; Suzanne Kretschmer, Chief Executive Officer
**Web address:** www.chghospitals.com/conroe/

CORNERSTONE HOSPITAL OF HOUSTON AT CLEARLAKE (O, 148 beds) 709 Medical Center Boulevard, Webster, TX, Zip 77598; tel. 281/332–3322; Amy Stasney, R.N., Chief Executive Officer

CORNERSTONE HOSPITAL–MEDICAL CENTER OF HOUSTON (O, 35 beds) 2001 Hermann Drive, Houston, TX, Zip 77004; tel. 832/649–6200; Guido J. Cubellis, Chief Executive Officer
**Web address:** www.chghospitals.com

CORNERSTONE SPECIALTY HOSPITALS AUSTIN (O, 86 beds) 4207 Burnet Road, Austin, TX, Zip 78756–3396; tel. 512/706–1900; Curt L. Roberts, Market Chief Executive Officer

SOLARA HOSPITAL HARLINGEN (O, 70 beds) 508 Victoria Lane, Harlingen, TX, Zip 78550–3225; tel. 956/425–9600; Alberto Sanchez, Chief Executive Officer
**Web address:** www.chghospitals.com/harlingen/

SOLARA HOSPITAL MCALLEN (O, 78 beds) 301 West Expressway 83, 8th Floor, McAllen, TX, Zip 78503–3045; tel. 956/632–4880; David Tupper, Chief Executive Officer

**WEST VIRGINIA:** CORNERSTONE HOSPITAL OF HUNTINGTON (O, 28 beds) 2900 First Avenue, Two East, Huntington, WV, Zip 25702–1241; tel. 304/399–2600; Cynthia Isaacs, Chief Executive Officer
**Web address:** www.chghospitals.com

| | | |
|---|---|---|
| Owned, leased, sponsored: | 14 hospitals | 747 beds |
| Contract–managed: | 0 hospitals | 0 beds |
| Totals: | 14 hospitals | 747 beds |

**★0103: COTTAGE HEALTH** (NP)
400 West Pueblo Street, Santa Barbara, CA Zip 93105–4353, P O Box 689, 93102–0689, tel. 805/569–7290; Ronald C. Werft, President and Chief Executive Officer
**(Independent Hospital System)**

For explanation of codes following names, see page B2.
★ Indicates Type III membership in the American Hospital Association.

**CALIFORNIA:** GOLETA VALLEY COTTAGE HOSPITAL (O, 28 beds) 351 South Patterson Avenue, Santa Barbara, CA, Zip 93111–2496, Box 6306, 93160–6306, tel. 805/967–3411; Ronald C. Werft, President and Chief Executive Officer
**Web address:** www.sbch.org

SANTA BARBARA COTTAGE HOSPITAL (O, 392 beds) 400 West Pueblo Street, Santa Barbara, CA, Zip 93105–4390, Mailing Address: P.O. Box 689, 93102–0689, tel. 805/682–7111; Ronald C. Werft, President and Chief Executive Officer

SANTA YNEZ VALLEY COTTAGE HOSPITAL (O, 11 beds) 2050 Viborg Road, Solvang, CA, Zip 93463–2295; tel. 805/688–6431; Ronald C. Werft, President and Chief Executive Officer
**Web address:** www.cottagehealthsystem.org

| | | |
|---|---|---|
| Owned, leased, sponsored: | 3 hospitals | 431 beds |
| Contract–managed: | 0 hospitals | 0 beds |
| Totals: | 3 hospitals | 431 beds |

**★5885: COVENANT HEALTH** (CO)

100 Ames Pond Drive, Suite 102, Tewksbury, MA Zip 01876–1240; tel. 978/654–6363; Stephen J. Grubbs, President and Chief Executive Officer
**(Independent Hospital System)**

**MAINE:** ST. JOSEPH HOSPITAL (O, 84 beds) 360 Broadway, Bangor, ME, Zip 04401–3979, Mailing Address: P.O. Box 403, 04402–0403, tel. 207/262–1000; Mary Prybylo, Senior Vice President and President

ST. MARY'S REGIONAL MEDICAL CENTER (O, 350 beds) 93 Campus Avenue, Lewiston, ME, Zip 04240–6030, Mailing Address: P.O. Box 291, 04243–0291, tel. 207/777–8100; Steven C. Jorgensen, President
**Web address:** www.stmarysmaine.com

**NEW HAMPSHIRE:** ST. JOSEPH HOSPITAL (O, 135 beds) 172 Kinsley Street, Nashua, NH, Zip 03060–3648; tel. 603/882–3000; John A. Jurczyk, FACHE, Senior Vice President and President
**Web address:** www.stjosephhospital.com

| | | |
|---|---|---|
| Owned, leased, sponsored: | 3 hospitals | 569 beds |
| Contract–managed: | 0 hospitals | 0 beds |
| Totals: | 3 hospitals | 569 beds |

**0123: COVENANT HEALTH** (NP)

100 Fort Sanders West Boulevard, Knoxville, TN Zip 37922–3353; tel. 865/531–5555; James VanderSteeg, President and Chief Executive Officer
**(Centralized Health System)**

**TENNESSEE:** CLAIBORNE MEDICAL CENTER (L, 105 beds) 1850 Old Knoxville Road, Tazewell, TN, Zip 37879–3625; tel. 423/626–4211; Patricia P. Ketterman, R.N., President and Chief Administrative Officer
**Web address:** www.claibornehospital.org

CUMBERLAND MEDICAL CENTER (O, 85 beds) 421 South Main Street, Crossville, TN, Zip 38555–5031; tel. 931/484–9511; David V. Bunch, President and Chief Administrative Officer

FORT LOUDOUN MEDICAL CENTER (L, 30 beds) 550 Fort Loudoun Medical Center Drive, Lenoir City, TN, Zip 37772–5673; tel. 865/271–6000; Jeffrey Feike, President and Chief Administrative Officer
**Web address:** www.covenanthealth.com

FORT SANDERS REGIONAL MEDICAL CENTER (O, 389 beds) 1901 West Clinch Avenue , Knoxville, TN, Zip 37916–2307; tel. 865/541–1111; Keith Altshuler, President and Chief Administrative Officer

LECONTE MEDICAL CENTER (O, 128 beds) 742 Middle Creek Road, Sevierville, TN, Zip 37862–5019, Mailing Address: P.O. Box 8005, 37864–8005, tel. 865/446–7000; Gaye Jolly, FACHE, President and Chief Administrative Officer
**Web address:** www.lecontemedicalcenter.com

METHODIST MEDICAL CENTER OF OAK RIDGE (O, 210 beds) 990 Oak Ridge Turnpike, Oak Ridge, TN, Zip 37830–6976, Mailing Address: P.O. Box 2529, 37831–2529, tel. 865/835–1000; Jeremy Biggs, President and Chief Administrative Officer

MORRISTOWN–HAMBLEN HEALTHCARE SYSTEM (O, 115 beds) 908 West Fourth North Street, Morristown, TN, Zip 37814–3894, Mailing Address: P.O. Box 1178, 37816–1178, tel. 423/492–9000; Gordon Lintz, President and Chief Administrative Officer
**Web address:** www.morristownhamblen.com

PARKWEST MEDICAL CENTER (O, 417 beds) 9352 Park West Boulevard, Knoxville, TN, Zip 37923–4325, Mailing Address: P.O. Box 22993, 37933–0993, tel. 865/373–1000; Neil Heatherly, Chief Executive Officer

ROANE MEDICAL CENTER (O, 52 beds) 8045 Roane Medical Center Dr, Harriman, TN, Zip 37748–8333; tel. 865/316–1000; Jason B. Pilant, President and Chief Administrative Officer
**Web address:** www.roanemedical.com

| | | |
|---|---|---|
| Owned, leased, sponsored: | 9 hospitals | 1531 beds |
| Contract–managed: | 0 hospitals | 0 beds |
| Totals: | 9 hospitals | 1531 beds |

**★0036: COVENANT HEALTH SYSTEM** (NP)

3615 19th Street, Lubbock, TX Zip 79410–1203; tel. 806/725–0447; Richard H. Parks, FACHE, President and Chief Executive Officer

| | | |
|---|---|---|
| Owned, leased, sponsored: | 0 hospitals | 0 beds |
| Contract–managed: | 0 hospitals | 0 beds |
| Totals: | 0 hospitals | 0 beds |

**0179: COXHEALTH** (NP)

1423 North Jefferson Avenue, Springfield, MO Zip 65802–1988; tel. 417/269–3108; Steven D. Edwards, President and Chief Executive Officer
**(Centralized Physician/Insurance Health System)**

**MISSOURI:** COX BARTON COUNTY MEMORIAL HOSPITAL (O, 25 beds) 29 NW First Lane, Lamar, MO, Zip 64759–8105; tel. 417/681–5100; Christopher B. Wyatt, President
**Web address:** www.bcmh.net

COX MEDICAL CENTER BRANSON (O, 126 beds) 525 Branson Landing Boulevard, Branson, MO, Zip 65616–2052, Mailing Address: P.O. Box 650, 65615–0650, tel. 417/335–7000; William K. Mahoney, FACHE, President and Senior Vice President, Community Hospital Group

COX MEDICAL CENTERS (O, 673 beds) 1423 North Jefferson Street, Springfield, MO, Zip 65802–1988; tel. 417/269–3000; Steven D. Edwards, President and Chief Executive Officer
**Web address:** www.coxhealth.com

COX MONETT HOSPITAL (O, 25 beds) 801 North Lincoln Avenue, Monett, MO, Zip 65708–1641; tel. 417/235–3144; Darren Bass, President

| | | |
|---|---|---|
| Owned, leased, sponsored: | 4 hospitals | 849 beds |
| Contract–managed: | 0 hospitals | 0 beds |
| Totals: | 4 hospitals | 849 beds |

**0930: CRC HEALTH GROUP, INC.** (IO)

20400 Stevens Creek Boulevard, Suite 600, Cupertino, CA Zip 95014–2217; tel. 866/540–5240; Jerome E. Rhodes, Chief Executive Officer
**(Independent Hospital System)**

**ARIZONA:** SIERRA TUCSON (O, 139 beds) 39580 South Lago Del Oro Parkway, Tucson, AZ, Zip 85739–1091; tel. 520/624–4000; Jaime W. Vinck, MC, Chief Executive Officer
**Web address:** www.sierratucson.com

For explanation of codes following names, see page B2.
★ Indicates Type III membership in the American Hospital Association.

**NORTH CAROLINA**: WILMINGTON TREATMENT CENTER (O, 44 beds) 2520 Troy Drive, Wilmington, NC, Zip 28401–7643; tel. 910/762–2727; Robert Pitts, Executive Director
**Web address**: www.wilmtreatment.com

| | | |
|---|---|---|
| Owned, leased, sponsored: | 2 hospitals | 183 beds |
| Contract–managed: | 0 hospitals | 0 beds |
| Totals: | 2 hospitals | 183 beds |

**O960: CURAE HEALTH** (NP)

121 Leinart Street, Clinton, TN Zip 37716–3632, Mailing Address: P.O. Box 358, 37717–0358, tel. 865/269–4074; Steve Clapp, President and Chief Executive Officer
**(Moderately Centralized Health System)**

**ALABAMA**: NORTHWEST MEDICAL CENTER (O, 56 beds) 1530 U S Highway 43, Winfield, AL, Zip 35594–5056; tel. 205/487–7000; Robert Henger, Chief Executive Officer
**Web address**: www.https://northwestmedcenter.net/

RUSSELLVILLE HOSPITAL (O, 92 beds) 15155 Highway 43, Russellville, AL, Zip 35653–1975, Mailing Address: P.O. Box 1089, 35653–1089, tel. 256/332–1611; Christine R. Stewart, FACHE, Chief Executive Officer

**MISSISSIPPI**: NORTHWEST MISSISSIPPI MEDICAL CENTER (O, 181 beds) 1970 Hospital Drive, Clarksdale, MS, Zip 38614–7202, Mailing Address: P.O. Box 1218, 38614–1218, tel. 662/627–3211; Joel Southern, R.N., MSN, Chief Executive Officer
**Web address**: www.northwestmsmedicalcenter.org

| | | |
|---|---|---|
| Owned, leased, sponsored: | 3 hospitals | 329 beds |
| Contract–managed: | 0 hospitals | 0 beds |
| Totals: | 3 hospitals | 329 beds |

**1013: CURAHEALTH HOSPITALS** (IO)

650 Beebalm Lane, Suite 220, Garland, TX Zip 75040–2955; tel. 972/414–2872; Ken McGee, President and Chief Operating Officer
**(Independent Hospital System)**

**ARIZONA**: CURAHEALTH PHOENIX (O, 58 beds) 40 East Indianola Avenue, Phoenix, AZ, Zip 85012–2059; tel. 602/280–7000; Karen Cawley, Chief Executive Officer
**Web address**: www.curahealth.com

CURAHEALTH TUCSON (O, 51 beds) 355 North Wilmot Road, Tucson, AZ, Zip 85711–2601; tel. 520/584–4500; Camie Overton, Chief Executive Officer

**FLORIDA**: CURAHEALTH JACKSONVILLE (O, 62 beds) 4901 Richard Street, Jacksonville, FL, Zip 32207–7328; tel. 904/425–0500; Jerry Deller, Chief Executive Officer
**Web address**: www.specialtyhospitaljax.com

**LOUISIANA**: CURAHEALTH NEW ORLEANS (O, 80 beds) 3801 Bienville Street, 1st Floor, New Orleans, LA, Zip 70119–5251; tel. 504/930–3500; Kristy Caleyo, MSN, R.N., Chief Executive Officer

**MASSACHUSETTS**: CURAHEALTH STOUGHTON (O, 111 beds) 909 Sumner Street, 1st Floor, Stoughton, MA, Zip 02072–3396; tel. 781/297–8200; MacGregor Morgan, R.N., Chief Executive Officer
**Web address**: www.curahealth.com

**OKLAHOMA**: CURAHEALTH HOSPITAL OKLAHOMA CITY (O, 93 beds) 1407 North Robinson Avenue, Oklahoma City, OK, Zip 73103–4823; tel. 405/232–8000; Brenda Hood, Chief Executive Officer

**PENNSYLVANIA**: CURAHEALTH HERITAGE VALLEY (O, 35 beds) 1000 Dutch Ridge Road, Beaver, PA, Zip 15009–9727; tel. 724/773–8480; Carol Falo, R.N., Chief Executive Officer
**Web address**: www.curahealth.com

CURAHEALTH PITTSBURGH (O, 31 beds) 7777 Steubenville Pike, Oakdale, PA, Zip 15071–3409; tel. 412/494–5500; Carol Falo, R.N., Chief Executive Officer

**TENNESSEE**: CURAHEALTH NASHVILLE (O, 60 beds) 1412 County Hospital Road, Nashville, TN, Zip 37218–3007; tel. 615/687–2600; Matt Pearson, Chief Executive Officer
**Web address**: www.curahealth.com

**TEXAS**: COBALT REHABILITATION HOSPITAL EL PASO (O, 42 beds) 1600 East Cliff Drive, El Paso, TX, Zip 79902–5130; tel. 915/975–8630; Jack Boggess, Chief Executive Officer

COBALT REHABILITATION HOUSTON HEIGHTS (O, 35 beds) 1917 Ashland Street, 4th Floor, Houston, TX, Zip 77008–3907; tel. 713/814–9114; Jeff Crawford, Chief Executive Officer
**Web address**: www.curahealth.com/locations/rehabilitation–houston–heights/

| | | |
|---|---|---|
| Owned, leased, sponsored: | 11 hospitals | 658 beds |
| Contract–managed: | 0 hospitals | 0 beds |
| Totals: | 11 hospitals | 658 beds |

**★0864: DAVIS HEALTH SYSTEM** (NP)

Reed Street and Gorman Avenue, Elkins, WV Zip 26241, Mailing Address: P.O. Box 1697, 26241–1697, tel. 304/636–3300; Vance Jackson, FACHE, President and Chief Executive Officer
**(Independent Hospital System)**

**WEST VIRGINIA**: BROADDUS HOSPITAL (O, 72 beds) 1 Healthcare Drive, Philippi, WV, Zip 26416–9405, Mailing Address: P.O. Box 930, 26416–0930, tel. 304/457–1760; Dana L. Gould, Chief Executive Officer
**Web address**: www.davishealthsystem.org/

DAVIS MEDICAL CENTER (O, 80 beds) Gorman Avenue and Reed Street, Elkins, WV, Zip 26241, Mailing Address: P.O. Box 1484, 26241–1484, tel. 304/636–3300; Vance Jackson, FACHE, Chief Executive Officer

WEBSTER COUNTY MEMORIAL HOSPITAL (C, 15 beds) 324 Miller Mountain Drive, Webster Springs, WV, Zip 26288–1087, Mailing Address: P.O. Box 312, 26288–0312, tel. 304/847–5682; Jim Parker, FACHE, Chief Executive Officer
**Web address**: www.wcmhwv.org

| | | |
|---|---|---|
| Owned, leased, sponsored: | 2 hospitals | 152 beds |
| Contract–managed: | 1 hospitals | 15 beds |
| Totals: | 3 hospitals | 167 beds |

**1825: DCH HEALTH SYSTEM** (NP)

809 University Boulevard East, Tuscaloosa, AL Zip 35401–2029; tel. 205/759–7111; Bryan N. Kindred, FACHE, President and Chief Executive Officer
**(Independent Hospital System)**

**ALABAMA**: DCH REGIONAL MEDICAL CENTER (O, 687 beds) 809 University Boulevard East, Tuscaloosa, AL, Zip 35401–2029; tel. 205/759–7111; Paul Betz, FACHE, Administrator
**Web address**: www.dchsystem.com

FAYETTE MEDICAL CENTER (L, 167 beds) 1653 Temple Avenue North, Fayette, AL, Zip 35555–1314, P O Drawer 710, 35555–0710, tel. 205/932–5966; Donald J. Jones, FACHE, Administrator

| | | |
|---|---|---|
| Owned, leased, sponsored: | 2 hospitals | 854 beds |
| Contract–managed: | 0 hospitals | 0 beds |
| Totals: | 2 hospitals | 854 beds |

**★0313: DEACONESS HEALTH SYSTEM** (NP)

600 Mary Street, Evansville, IN Zip 47710–1658; tel. 812/450–5000; Shawn W. McCoy, Chief Executive Officer
**(Moderately Centralized Health System)**

**INDIANA**: DEACONESS MIDTOWN HOSPITAL (O, 555 beds) 600 Mary Street, Evansville, IN, Zip 47710–1658; tel. 812/450–5000; Shawn W. McCoy, Chief Executive Officer
**Web address**: www.deaconess.com

GIBSON GENERAL HOSPITAL (C, 70 beds) 1808 Sherman Drive, Princeton, IN, Zip 47670–9931; tel. 812/385–3401; Claudia A. Eisenmann, President and Chief Executive Officer
**Web address**: www.gibsongeneral.com

For explanation of codes following names, see page B2.
★ Indicates Type III membership in the American Hospital Association.

THE WOMEN'S HOSPITAL (O, 74 beds) 4199 Gateway Boulevard, Newburgh, IN, Zip 47630–8940; tel. 812/842–4200; Christina M. Ryan, R.N., Chief Executive Officer

| | | |
|---|---|---|
| Owned, leased, sponsored: | 2 hospitals | 629 beds |
| Contract-managed: | 1 hospitals | 70 beds |
| Totals: | 3 hospitals | 699 beds |

**0330: DEKALB REGIONAL HEALTH SYSTEM** (NP)
2701 North Decatur Road, Decatur, GA Zip 30033–5918; tel. 404/501–1000; Robert E. Wilson Esq, Chief Executive Officer

| | | |
|---|---|---|
| Owned, leased, sponsored: | 0 hospitals | 0 beds |
| Contract-managed: | 0 hospitals | 0 beds |
| Totals: | 0 hospitals | 0 beds |

**★0957: DEPARTMENT OF DEFENSE, HEALTH AFFAIRS** (FG)
1200 Defense Pentagon, Pentagon 3E1070, Washington, DC Zip 20301; tel. 703/697–2111; Honorable, Thomas McCaffery, Assistant Secretary of Defense for Health Affairs

| | | |
|---|---|---|
| Owned, leased, sponsored: | 0 hospitals | 0 beds |
| Contract-managed: | 0 hospitals | 0 beds |
| Totals: | 0 hospitals | 0 beds |

**★9495: DEPARTMENT OF THE AIR FORCE** (FG)
1780 Air Force Pentagon, Room 4E114, Washington, DC Zip 20330–1420; tel. 703/692–6800; Lieutenant General, Dorothy A. Hogg, Surgeon General
**(Independent Hospital System)**

**ALASKA:** U. S. AIR FORCE REGIONAL HOSPITAL (O, 64 beds) 5955 Zeamer Avenue, Elmendorf AFB, AK, Zip 99506–3702; tel. 907/580–3006; Major, Mark Lamey, Commander
**Web address:** www.elmendorf.af.mil/

**CALIFORNIA:** DAVID GRANT USAF MEDICAL CENTER (O, 116 beds) 101 Bodin Circle, Travis AFB, CA, Zip 94535–1809; tel. 707/423–7300; Lieutenant, Michael Higgins, Commander

**FLORIDA:** U. S. AIR FORCE REGIONAL HOSPITAL (O, 57 beds) 307 Boatner Road, Suite 114, Eglin AFB, FL, Zip 32542–1282; tel. 850/883–8221; Colonel, Pamela Smith, Commander
**Web address:** www.eglin.af.mil

**MISSISSIPPI:** U. S. AIR FORCE MEDICAL CENTER KEESLER (O, 56 beds) 301 Fisher Street, Room 1A132, Keesler AFB, MS, Zip 39534–2519; tel. 228/376–2550; Colonel, Thomas Harrell, M.D., Commander
**Web address:** www.keesler.af.mil

**NEVADA:** MIKE O'CALLAGHAN FEDERAL HOSPITAL (O, 46 beds) 4700 Las Vegas Boulevard North, Suite 2419, Nellis AFB, NV, Zip 89191–6600; tel. 702/653–2000; Colonel, Christian Benjamin, USAF, MC, Commander

**OHIO:** WRIGHT PATTERSON MEDICAL CENTER (O, 62 beds) 4881 Sugar Maple Drive, Wright–Patterson AFB, OH, Zip 45433–5529; tel. 937/257–0837; Colonel, Freddie Jenkins, Administrator
**Web address:** www.wpafb.af.mil/units/wpmc/

**VIRGINIA:** U. S. AIR FORCE HOSPITAL (O, 60 beds) 77 Nealy Avenue, Hampton, VA, Zip 23665–2040; tel. 757/764–6969; Colonel, Susan Pietrykowski, Commander

| | | |
|---|---|---|
| Owned, leased, sponsored: | 7 hospitals | 461 beds |
| Contract-managed: | 0 hospitals | 0 beds |
| Totals: | 7 hospitals | 461 beds |

**★9395: DEPARTMENT OF THE ARMY, OFFICE OF THE SURGEON GENERAL** (FG)
5109 Leesburg Pike, Falls Church, VA Zip 22041–3215; tel. 703/681–3000; Lieutenant General, R. Scott. Dingle, The Surgeon General of the U.S. Army
**(Moderately Centralized Health System)**

**ALASKA:** BASSETT ARMY COMMUNITY HOSPITAL (O, 21 beds) 1060 Gaffney Road, Box 7400, Fort Wainwright, AK, Zip 99703–5001, 1060 Gaffney Road, Box 7440, 99703–5001, tel. 907/361–4000; Colonel, Constance Jenkins, Commander
**Web address:** www.alaska.amedd.army.mil

**CALIFORNIA:** WEED ARMY COMMUNITY HOSPITAL (O, 27 beds) Inner Loop Road and 4th Street, Building 166, Fort Irwin, CA, Zip 92310–5065, Mailing Address: P.O. Box 105109, 92310–5109, tel. 760/380–3108; Colonel, Larry O. France, Commander

**COLORADO:** EVANS U. S. ARMY COMMUNITY HOSPITAL (O, 68 beds) 1650 Cochrane Circle, Building 7500, Fort Carson, CO, Zip 80913–4613; tel. 719/526–7200; Colonel, Patrick M. Garman, Commander
**Web address:** www.https://evans.amedd.army.mil/

**GEORGIA:** DWIGHT DAVID EISENHOWER ARMY MEDICAL CENTER (O, 107 beds) 300 West Hospital Road, Fort Gordon, GA, Zip 30905–5741; tel. 706/787–5811; Colonel, John P. Lamoureux, Commander
**Web address:** www.ddeamc.amedd.army.mil

MARTIN ARMY COMMUNITY HOSPITAL (O, 57 beds) 7950 Martin Loop, Fort Benning, GA, Zip 31905–5648, 7950 Martin Loop, B9200, Room 010, 31905–5648, tel. 706/544–2516; Colonel, Marie Dominguez, Commander
**Web address:** www.martin.amedd.army.mil

WINN ARMY COMMUNITY HOSPITAL (O, 37 beds) 1061 Harmon Avenue, Hinesville, GA, Zip 31314–5641, 1061 Harmon Avenue, Suite 2311B, 31314–5641, tel. 912/435–6965; Colonel, Kirk W. Eggleston, Commanding Officer

**HAWAII:** TRIPLER ARMY MEDICAL CENTER (O, 143 beds) 1 Jarrett White Road, Honolulu, HI, Zip 96859–5001; tel. 808/433–6661; Colonel, Martin Doperak, Commander
**Web address:** www.tamc.amedd.army.mil

**KANSAS:** IRWIN ARMY COMMUNITY HOSPITAL (O, 44 beds) 600 Caisson Hill Road, Junction City, KS, Zip 66442–7037; tel. 785/239–7000; Colonel, Risa Ware, Commander
**Web address:** www.iach.amedd.army.mil

**KENTUCKY:** COLONEL FLORENCE A. BLANCHFIELD ARMY COMMUNITY HOSPITAL (O, 66 beds) 650 Joel Drive, Fort Campbell, KY, Zip 42223–5318; tel. 270/798–8040; Colonel, Patrick T. Birchfield, Commanding Officer

**LOUISIANA:** BAYNE–JONES ARMY COMMUNITY HOSPITAL (O, 13 beds) 1585 3rd Street, Building 283, Fort Polk, LA, Zip 71459–5102; tel. 337/531–3928; Colonel, Jody L. Dugai, Commanding Officer
**Web address:** www.https://bjach.polk.amedd.army.mil/

**MARSHALL ISLANDS:** KWAJALEIN HOSPITAL (O, 14 beds) U S Army Kwajalein Atoll, Ocean Road, Kwajalein Atoll, MH, Zip 96555, Ocean Road, Mailing Address: P.O. Box 1607, APO AP, 96555–5000, tel. 805/355–2225; Elaine McMahon, Administrator

**MISSOURI:** GENERAL LEONARD WOOD ARMY COMMUNITY HOSPITAL (O, 46 beds) 4430 Missouri Avenue, Fort Leonard Wood, MO, Zip 65473–8952, Mailing Address: P.O. 4430, 65473–8952, tel. 573/596–0414; Colonel, Aaron Pitney, Hospital Commander
**Web address:** www.glwach.amedd.army.mil/

**NEW YORK:** KELLER ARMY COMMUNITY HOSPITAL (O, 12 beds) 900 Washington Road, West Point, NY, Zip 10996–1197, U S Military Academy, Building 900, 10996–1197, tel. 845/938–5169; Colonel, Amy L. Jackson, Commander

**NORTH CAROLINA:** WOMACK ARMY MEDICAL CENTER (O, 156 beds) 2817 Reilly Road, Fort Bragg, NC, Zip 28310–7302; tel. 910/907–6000; Colonel, Lance C. Raney, Commander
**Web address:** www.wamc.amedd.army.mil/

**SOUTH CAROLINA:** MONCRIEF ARMY COMMUNITY HOSPITAL (O, 60 beds) 4500 Stuart Street, Fort Jackson, SC, Zip 29207–5700; tel. 803/751–2160; Colonel, Traci Crawford, R.N., Commander
**Web address:** www.moncrief.amedd.army.mil

**TEXAS:** BROOKE ARMY MEDICAL CENTER (O, 483 beds) 3551 Roger Brooke Drive, Fort Sam Houston, TX, Zip 78234–4501; tel. 210/916–4141; Brigadier General, Jeffrey Johnson, Commander

For explanation of codes following names, see page B2.
★ Indicates Type III membership in the American Hospital Association.

CARL R. DARNALL ARMY MEDICAL CENTER (O, 109 beds) 36065 Santa Fe Avenue, Fort Hood, TX, Zip 76544–5060; tel. 254/288–8000; Colonel, Richard Malish, M.D., Commander
**Web address:** https://www.crdamc.amedd.army.mil/Default.aspx

WILLIAM BEAUMONT ARMY MEDICAL CENTER (O, 209 beds) 5005 North Piedras Street, El Paso, TX, Zip 79920–5001; tel. 915/742–2121; Colonel, Erik G. Rude, Commander

**VIRGINIA:** FORT BELVOIR COMMUNITY HOSPITAL (O, 46 beds) 9300 Dewitt Loop, Fort Belvoir, VA, Zip 22060–5285; tel. 571/231–3224; Colonel, Jason S. Wieman, Director
**Web address:** www.fbch.capmed.mil/SitePages/Home.aspx

**WASHINGTON:** MADIGAN ARMY MEDICAL CENTER (O, 203 beds) 9040 Jackson Avenue, Tacoma, WA, Zip 98431–1100; tel. 253/968–1110; Colonel, Christopher Warner, Commander
**Web address:** www.mamc.health.mil/

| | | |
|---|---|---|
| Owned, leased, sponsored: | 20 hospitals | 1921 beds |
| Contract–managed: | 0 hospitals | 0 beds |
| **Totals:** | 20 hospitals | 1921 beds |

★**9295: DEPARTMENT OF VETERANS AFFAIRS** (FG)
810 Vermont Avenue NW, Washington, DC Zip 20420–0001; tel. 202/273–5781; Honorable, Robert Wilkie, Secretary
**(Decentralized Health System)**

**ALABAMA:** BIRMINGHAM VETERANS AFFAIRS MEDICAL CENTER (O, 139 beds) 700 South 19th Street, Birmingham, AL, Zip 35233–1927; tel. 205/933–8101; Stacy J. Vasquez, Chief Executive Officer

CENTRAL ALABAMA VETERANS HEALTH CARE SYSTEM (O, 313 beds) 215 Perry Hill Road, Montgomery, AL, Zip 36109–3798; tel. 334/272–4670; Linda  Lake . Boyle, R.N., MSN, Director
**Web address:** www.centralalabama.va.gov/

TUSCALOOSA VETERANS AFFAIRS MEDICAL CENTER (O, 305 beds) 3701 Loop Road East, Tuscaloosa, AL, Zip 35404–5015; tel. 205/554–2000; John F. Merkle, Medical Center Director
**Web address:** www.tuscaloosa.va.gov

**ARIZONA:** NORTHERN ARIZONA VETERANS AFFAIRS HEALTH CARE SYSTEM (O, 147 beds) 500 Highway 89 North, Prescott, AZ, Zip 86313–5000; tel. 928/445–4860; Jean J. Gurga, Medical Center Director

PHOENIX VETERANS AFFAIRS HEALTH CARE SYSTEM (O, 197 beds) 650 East Indian School Road, Phoenix, AZ, Zip 85012–1892; tel. 602/277–5551; Alyshia Smith, R.N., Interim Director
**Web address:** www.phoenix.va.gov/

SOUTHERN ARIZONA VETERANS AFFAIRS HEALTH CARE SYSTEM (O, 328 beds) 3601 Sout 6th Avenue, Tucson, AZ, Zip 85723–0002, 3601 South 6th Avenue, 85723–0002, tel. 520/792–1450; Jennifer S. Gutowski, FACHE, Director
**Web address:** www.tucson.va.gov

**ARKANSAS:** CENTRAL ARKANSAS VETERANS HEALTHCARE SYSTEM (O, 551 beds) 4300 West Seventh Street, Little Rock, AR, Zip 72205–5446; tel. 501/257–1000; Margie A. Scott, M.D., Director

VETERANS HEALTH CARE SYSTEM OF THE OZARKS (O, 52 beds) 1100 North College Avenue, Fayetteville, AR, Zip 72703–1944; tel. 479/443–4301; Kelvin L. Parks, Interim Director
**Web address:** www.fayettevillear.va.gov

**CALIFORNIA:** SAN FRANCISCO VA MEDICAL CENTER (O, 232 beds) 4150 Clement Street, San Francisco, CA, Zip 94121–1545; tel. 415/221–4810; Bonnie S. Graham, Director
**Web address:** www.sanfrancisco.va.gov/

VA GREATER LOS ANGELES HEALTHCARE SYSTEM (O, 708 beds) 11301 Wilshire Boulevard, Los Angeles, CA, Zip 90073–1003; tel. 310/478–3711; Steven E. Braverman, M.D., Director

VA LONG BEACH HEALTHCARE SYSTEM (O, 335 beds) 5901 East 7th Street, Long Beach, CA, Zip 90822–5201; tel. 562/826–8000; Walt Dannenberg, Director
**Web address:** www.longbeach.va.gov/

VA PALO ALTO HEALTH CARE SYSTEM (O, 768 beds) 3801 Miranda Avenue, Palo Alto, CA, Zip 94304–1207; tel. 650/493–5000; Thomas J. Fitzgerald III, Director

VA SAN DIEGO HEALTHCARE SYSTEM (O, 256 beds) 3350 LaJolla Village Drive, San Diego, CA, Zip 92161–0002; tel. 858/552–8585; Robert M. Smith, M.D., Director
**Web address:** www.sandiego.va.gov

VETERANS AFFAIRS CENTRAL CALIFORNIA HEALTH CARE SYSTEM (O, 117 beds) 2615 East Clinton Avenue, Fresno, CA, Zip 93703–2223; tel. 559/225–6100; Stephen R. Bauman, Medical Center Director

VETERANS AFFAIRS LOMA LINDA HEALTHCARE SYSTEM (O, 268 beds) 11201 Benton Street, Loma Linda, CA, Zip 92357–1000; tel. 909/825–7084; Andrew Welch, Interim Director
**Web address:** www.lomalinda.va.gov

**COLORADO:** GRAND JUNCTION VETERANS HEALTH CARE SYSTEM (O, 23 beds) 2121 North Avenue, Grand Junction, CO, Zip 81501–6428; tel. 970/242–0731; Patrick Hull, Acting DirectorSOUTHERN COLORADO HEALTHCARE SYSTEM (O, 299 beds)Las AnimasCO81054–0390719456–1260StuartCCollyer5139873Director

VETERANS AFFAIRS EASTERN COLORADO HEALTH CARE SYSTEM (O, 271 beds) 1055 Clermont Street, Denver, CO, Zip 80220–3877; tel. 303/399–8020; Michael T. Kilmer, Director
**Web address:** www.denver.va.gov/

**CONNECTICUT:** VETERANS AFFAIRS CONNECTICUT HEALTHCARE SYSTEM (O, 177 beds) 950 Campbell Avenue, West Haven, CT, Zip 06516–2770; tel. 203/932–5711; Alfred Montoya, Director

**DELAWARE:** WILMINGTON VETERANS AFFAIRS MEDICAL CENTER (O, 60 beds) 1601 Kirkwood Highway, Wilmington, DE, Zip 19805–4989; tel. 302/994–2511; Robert W. Callahan Jr, Interim Director
**Web address:** www.va.gov/wilmington

**DISTRICT OF COLUMBIA:** WASHINGTON DC VETERANS AFFAIRS MEDICAL CENTER (O, 291 beds) 50 Irving Street NW, Washington, DC, Zip 20422–0002; tel. 202/745–8000; Adam M. Robinson, Acting Director
**Web address:** www.washingtondc.va.gov/

**FLORIDA:** BAY PINES VETERANS AFFAIRS HEALTHCARE SYSTEM (O, 396 beds) 10000 Bay Pines Boulevard, Bay Pines, FL, Zip 33744–8200, Mailing Address: P.O. Box 5005, 33744–5005, tel. 727/398–6661; Paul M. Russo, FACHE, Director
**Web address:** www.baypines.va.gov/

JAMES A. HALEY VETERANS' HOSPITAL–TAMPA (O, 499 beds) 13000 Bruce B Downs Boulevard, Tampa, FL, Zip 33612–4745; tel. 813/972–2000; Joe Battle, Director
**Web address:** www.tampa.va.gov/

MIAMI VETERANS AFFAIRS HEALTHCARE SYSTEM (O, 284 beds) 1201 NW 16th Street, Miami, FL, Zip 33125–1624; tel. 305/575–7000; Kalautie JangDhari, Director

NORTH FLORIDA/SOUTH GEORGIA VETERAN'S HEALTH SYSTEM (O, 324 beds) 1601 SW Archer Road, Gainesville, FL, Zip 32608–1135; tel. 352/376–1611; Thomas Wisnieski, FACHE, Director
**Web address:** www.northflorida.va.gov

WEST PALM BEACH VETERANS AFFAIRS MEDICAL CENTER (O, 300 beds) 7305 North Military Trail, West Palm Beach, FL, Zip 33410–6400; tel. 561/422–8262; Donna Katen-Bahensky, Director

**GEORGIA:** ATLANTA VETERANS AFFAIRS MEDICAL CENTER (O, 273 beds) 1670 Clairmont Road, Decatur, GA, Zip 30033–4004; tel. 404/321–6111; Ann R. Brown, M.D., Director
**Web address:** www.atlanta.va.gov/

CARL VINSON VETERANS AFFAIRS MEDICAL CENTER (O, 178 beds) 1826 Veterans Boulevard, Dublin, GA, Zip 31021–3620; tel. 478/272–1210; David Whitmer, FACHE, Director
**Web address:** www.dublin.va.gov/

CHARLIE NORWOOD VETERANS AFFAIRS MEDICAL CENTER (O, 338 beds) 1 Freedom Way, Augusta, GA, Zip 30904–6285; tel. 706/733–0188; Robin E. Jackson, Ph.D., Interim Acting Director

**IDAHO:** BOISE VETERANS AFFAIRS MEDICAL CENTER (O, 92 beds) 500 West Fort Street, Boise, ID, Zip 83702–4598; tel. 208/422–1000; David P. Wood, FACHE, Director
**Web address:** www.boise.va.gov/

For explanation of codes following names, see page B2.
★ Indicates Type III membership in the American Hospital Association.

Section B

**ILLINOIS:** CAPTAIN JAMES A. LOVELL FEDERAL HEALTH CARE CENTER (O, 281 beds) 3001 Green Bay Road, North Chicago, IL, Zip 60064–3049; tel. 847/688–1900; Daniel Zomcheck, Interim Director
**Web address:** www.lovell.fhcc.va.gov

EDWARD HINES, JR. VETERANS AFFAIRS HOSPITAL (O, 485 beds) 5000 South Fifth Avenue, Hines, IL, Zip 60141–3030, Mailing Address: P.O. Box 5000, 60141–5000, tel. 708/202–8387; Steven E. Braverman, M.D., Director
**Web address:** www.hines.va.gov/

JESSE BROWN VETERANS AFFAIRS MEDICAL CENTER (O, 207 beds) 820 South Damen, Chicago, IL, Zip 60612–3776; tel. 312/569–8387; Rick Ament, Medical Center Director

MARION VETERANS AFFAIRS MEDICAL CENTER (O, 116 beds) 2401 West Main Street, Marion, IL, Zip 62959–1188; tel. 618/997–5311; Jo-Ann M. Ginsberg, R.N., MSN, Director
**Web address:** www.marion.va.gov

VETERANS AFFAIRS ILLIANA HEALTH CARE SYSTEM (O, 221 beds) 1900 East Main Street, Danville, IL, Zip 61832–5198; tel. 217/554–3000; Diana Carranza, Interim Director

**INDIANA:** RICHARD L. ROUDEBUSH VETERANS AFFAIRS MEDICAL CENTER (O, 197 beds) 1481 West Tenth Street, Indianapolis, IN, Zip 46202–2884; tel. 317/554–0000; Laura E. Ruzick, Medical Center Director
**Web address:** www.indianapolis.va.gov

VETERANS AFFAIRS NORTHERN INDIANA HEALTH CARE SYSTEM (O, 217 beds) 2121 Lake Avenue, Fort Wayne, IN, Zip 46805–5100; tel. 260/426–5431; Michael Hershmann, Medical Center Director

**IOWA:** IOWA CITY VA HEALTH CARE SYSTEM (O, 77 beds) 601 Highway 6 West, Iowa City, IA, Zip 52246–2208; tel. 319/338–0581; Judith Johnson-Mekota, Director
**Web address:** www.iowacity.va.gov/

VA CENTRAL IOWA HEALTH CARE SYSTEM (O, 223 beds) 3600 30th Street, Des Moines, IA, Zip 50310–5753; tel. 515/699–5999; Gail L. Graham, Director

**KANSAS:** ROBERT J. DOLE VETERANS AFFAIRS MEDICAL CENTER (O, 41 beds) 5500 East Kellogg, Wichita, KS, Zip 67218–1607; tel. 316/685–2221; Candace Ifabiyi, Medical Center Director
**Web address:** www.wichita.va.gov

VETERANS AFFAIRS EASTERN KANSAS HEALTH CARE SYSTEM (O, 130 beds) 2200 South West Gage Boulevard, Topeka, KS, Zip 66622–0002; tel. 785/350–3111; Anthony Rudy. Klopfer, FACHE, Director
**Web address:** www.topeka.va.gov/

**KENTUCKY:** LEXINGTON VETERANS AFFAIRS MEDICAL CENTER (O, 168 beds) 1101 Veterans Drive, Lexington, KY, Zip 40502–2235; tel. 859/281–4901; James Belmont, Interim Director

ROBLEY REX VETERANS AFFAIRS MEDICAL CENTER (O, 116 beds) 800 Zorn Avenue, Louisville, KY, Zip 40206–1499; tel. 502/287–4000; Marylee Rothschild, M.D., Chief of Staff
**Web address:** www.louisville.va.gov

**LOUISIANA:** ALEXANDRIA VETERANS AFFAIRS HEALTH CARE SYSTEM (O, 144 beds) 2495 Shreveport Highway, 71 N, Pineville, LA, Zip 71360–4044, Mailing Address: P.O. Box 69004, Alexandria, 71306–9004, tel. 318/473–0010; Peter C. Dancy Jr, FACHE, Director

OVERTON BROOKS VETERANS AFFAIRS MEDICAL CENTER (O, 100 beds) 510 East Stoner Avenue, Shreveport, LA, Zip 71101–4295; tel. 318/221–8411; Richard Crockett, Director
**Web address:** www.shreveport.va.gov/

**MAINE:** MAINE VETERANS AFFAIRS MEDICAL CENTER (O, 167 beds) 1 VA Center, Augusta, ME, Zip 04330–6719; tel. 207/623–8411; Tracye B. Davis, Medical Center Director
**Web address:** www.maine.va.gov/

**MARYLAND:** VETERANS AFFAIRS MARYLAND HEALTH CARE SYSTEM–BALTIMORE DIVISION (O, 727 beds) 10 North Greene Street, Baltimore, MD, Zip 21201–1524; tel. 410/605–7001; Adam M. Robinson, Director
**Web address:** www.maryland.va.gov/

**MASSACHUSETTS:** BEDFORD VETERANS AFFAIRS MEDICAL CENTER, EDITH NOURSE ROGERS MEMORIAL VETERANS HOSPITAL (O, 300 beds) 200 Springs Road, Bedford, MA, Zip 01730–1198; tel. 781/687–2000; Joan Clifford, R.N., FACHE, Medical Center Director and Chief Executive Officer

VETERANS AFFAIRS BOSTON HEALTHCARE SYSTEM BROCKTON DIVISION (O, 375 beds) 940 Belmont Street, Brockton, MA, Zip 02301–5596; tel. 508/583–4500; Vincent Ng, Director
**Web address:** www.boston.va.gov/

VETERANS AFFAIRS BOSTON HEALTHCARE SYSTEM (O, 361 beds) 1400 VFW Parkway, West Roxbury, MA, Zip 02132–4927; tel. 617/323–7700; Vincent Ng, Director

VETERANS AFFAIRS CENTRAL WESTERN MASSACHUSETTS HEALTHCARE SYSTEM (O, 117 beds) 421 North Main Street, Leeds, MA, Zip 01053–9764; tel. 413/582–3000; John P. Collins, FACHE, Medical Center Director
**Web address:** www.centralwesternmass.va.gov/

**MICHIGAN:** ALEDA E. LUTZ VETERANS AFFAIRS MEDICAL CENTER (O, 89 beds) 1500 Weiss Street, Saginaw, MI, Zip 48602–5298; tel. 989/497–2500; Karandeep Sraon, Interim Director
**Web address:** www.saginaw.va.gov/

BATTLE CREEK VETERANS AFFAIRS MEDICAL CENTER (O, 242 beds) 5500 Armstrong Road, Battle Creek, MI, Zip 49037–7314; tel. 269/966–5600; James Doelling, Executive Director

JOHN D. DINGELL VETERANS AFFAIRS MEDICAL CENTER (O, 209 beds) 4646 John 'R' Street, Detroit, MI, Zip 48201–1932; tel. 313/576–1000; Pamela J. Reeves, M.D., Director
**Web address:** www.detroit.va.gov/

OSCAR G. JOHNSON VETERANS AFFAIRS MEDICAL CENTER (O, 17 beds) 325 East 'H' Street, Iron Mountain, MI, Zip 49801–4792; tel. 906/774–3300; James W. Rice, Director
**Web address:** www.ironmountain.va.gov/

VETERANS AFFAIRS ANN ARBOR HEALTHCARE SYSTEM (O, 102 beds) 2215 Fuller Road, Ann Arbor, MI, Zip 48105–2399; tel. 734/769–7100; Andrew Pacyna, Acting Director

**MINNESOTA:** MINNEAPOLIS VETERANS AFFAIRS HEALTH CARE SYSTEM (O, 309 beds) One Veterans Drive, Minneapolis, MN, Zip 55417–2399; tel. 612/725–2000; Patrick J. Kelly, FACHE, Director
**Web address:** www.minneapolis.va.gov

ST. CLOUD VETERANS AFFAIRS HEALTH CARE SYSTEM (O, 388 beds) 4801 Veterans Drive, Saint Cloud, MN, Zip 56303–2099; tel. 320/252–1670; Stephen Black, MS, Health Care System Director
**Web address:** www.stcloud.va.gov

**MISSISSIPPI:** G.V. (SONNY) MONTGOMERY VETERANS AFFAIRS MEDICAL CENTER (O, 323 beds) 1500 East Woodrow Wilson Drive, Jackson, MS, Zip 39216–5199; tel. 601/362–4471; David M. Walker, M.D., Medical Center Director

VETERANS AFFAIRS GULF COAST VETERANS HEALTH CARE SYSTEM (O, 392 beds) 400 Veterans Avenue, Biloxi, MS, Zip 39531–2410; tel. 228/523–5000; Bryan C. Matthews, Medical Center Director
**Web address:** www.biloxi.va.gov/

**MISSOURI:** HARRY S. TRUMAN MEMORIAL VETERANS HOSPITAL (O, 126 beds) 800 Hospital Drive, Columbia, MO, Zip 65201–5275; tel. 573/814–6000; Patricia Hall, MSN, Ph.D., R.N., Medical Center Director
**Web address:** www.columbiamo.va.gov

JOHN J. PERSHING VETERANS AFFAIRS MEDICAL CENTER (O, 35 beds) 1500 North Westwood Boulevard, Poplar Bluff, MO, Zip 63901–3318; tel. 573/686–4151; Paul Hopkins, Interim Medical Director
**Web address:** www.poplarbluff.va.gov

KANSAS CITY VETERANS AFFAIRS MEDICAL CENTER (O, 157 beds) 4801 East Linwood Boulevard, Kansas City, MO, Zip 64128–2226; tel. 816/861–4700; David Isaacks, Medical Center Director

VETERANS AFFAIRS ST. LOUIS HEALTH CARE SYSTEM (O, 356 beds) 915 North Grand Boulevard, Saint Louis, MO, Zip 63106–1621; tel. 314/652–4100; Keith D. Repko, Director
**Web address:** www.stlouis.va.gov/

**MONTANA:** VETERANS AFFAIRS MONTANA HEALTH CARE SYSTEM (O, 94 beds) 3687 Veterans Drive, Fort Harrison, MT, Zip 59636–9703, Mailing Address: P.O. Box 1500, 59636–1500, tel. 406/442–6410; Judy A. Hayman, Ph.D., Director

**NEBRASKA:** VETERANS AFFAIRS NEBRASKA–WESTERN IOWA HEALTH CARE SYSTEM – LINCOLN (O, 132 beds) 600 South 70th Street, Lincoln, NE, Zip 68510–2493; tel. 402/489–3802; Don Burman, Director
**Web address:** www.nebraska.va.gov/

For explanation of codes following names, see page B2.
★ Indicates Type III membership in the American Hospital Association.

© 2021 AHA Guide

VETERANS AFFAIRS NEBRASKA–WESTERN IOWA HEALTH CARE SYSTEM (O, 137 beds) 4101 Woolworth Avenue, Omaha, NE, Zip 68105–1873; tel. 402/346–8800; Don Burman, Director
**Web address:** www.nebraska.va.gov/

**NEVADA:** VETERANS AFFAIRS SIERRA NEVADA HEALTH CARE SYSTEM (O, 124 beds) 975 Kirman Avenue, Reno, NV, Zip 89502–0993; tel. 775/786–7200; Lisa M. Howard, Director

VETERANS AFFAIRS SOUTHERN NEVADA HEALTHCARE SYSTEM (O, 90 beds) 6900 North Pecos Road, North Las Vegas, NV, Zip 89086–4400; tel. 702/791–9000; William J. Caron, Chief Executive Officer
**Web address:** www.lasvegas.va.gov/

**NEW HAMPSHIRE:** MANCHESTER VETERANS AFFAIRS MEDICAL CENTER (O, 41 beds) 718 Smyth Road, Manchester, NH, Zip 03104–4098; tel. 603/624–4366; Alfred Montoya, Director

**NEW JERSEY:** VETERANS AFFAIRS NEW JERSEY HEALTH CARE SYSTEM (O, 429 beds) 385 Tremont Avenue, East Orange, NJ, Zip 07018–1095; tel. 973/676–1000; John Griffith, R.N., Associate Director
**Web address:** www.newjersey.va.gov/

**NEW MEXICO:** NEW MEXICO VETERANS AFFAIRS HEALTH CARE SYSTEM – RAYMOND G. MURPHY MEDICAL CENTER (O, 203 beds) 1501 San Pedro SE, Albuquerque, NM, Zip 87108–5153; tel. 505/265–1711; Andrew Welch, Director

**NEW YORK:** ALBANY STRATTON VETERANS AFFAIRS MEDICAL CENTER (O, 121 beds) 113 Holland Avenue, Albany, NY, Zip 12208–3473; tel. 518/626–5000; Darlene DeLancey, Interim Director
**Web address:** www.albany.va.gov/

BATH VETERANS AFFAIRS MEDICAL CENTER (O, 274 beds) 76 Veterans Avenue, Bath, NY, Zip 14810–0842; tel. 607/664–4000; Kenneth P. Piazza, Medical Center Director
**Web address:** www.bath.va.gov

CANANDAIGUA VETERANS AFFAIRS MEDICAL CENTER (O, 196 beds) 400 Fort Hill Avenue, Canandaigua, NY, Zip 14424–1159; tel. 585/394–2000; Bruce Tucker, Director
**Web address:** www.canandaigua.va.gov/

JAMES J. PETERS VETERANS AFFAIRS MEDICAL CENTER (O, 378 beds) 130 West Kingsbridge Road, Bronx, NY, Zip 10468–3904; tel. 718/584–9000; Margaret B. Caplan, Director
**Web address:** www.bronx.va.gov/

NORTHPORT VETERANS AFFAIRS MEDICAL CENTER (O, 254 beds) 79 Middleville Road, Northport, NY, Zip 11768–2200; tel. 631/261–4400; Antonio Sanchez, M.D., Executive Director
**Web address:** www.northport.va.gov/index.asp

SYRACUSE VETERANS AFFAIRS MEDICAL CENTER (O, 160 beds) 800 Irving Avenue, Syracuse, NY, Zip 13210–2716; tel. 315/425–4400; Christopher M. Frani, Interim Director
**Web address:** www.syracuse.va.gov/

VETERANS AFFAIRS HUDSON VALLEY HEALTH CARE SYSTEM (O, 270 beds) 2094 Albany Post Road, Montrose, NY, Zip 10548–1454, Mailing Address: P.O. Box 100, 10548–0100, tel. 914/737–4400; Dawn M. Schaal, Interim Director

VETERANS AFFAIRS NEW YORK HARBOR HEALTHCARE SYSTEM (O, 522 beds) 800 Poly Place, Brooklyn, NY, Zip 11209–7104; tel. 718/630–3500; Martina A. Parauda, Director
**Web address:** www.nyharbor.va.gov

VETERANS AFFAIRS WESTERN NEW YORK HEALTHCARE SYSTEM–BATAVIA DIVISION (O, 128 beds) 222 Richmond Avenue, Batavia, NY, Zip 14020–1288; tel. 585/297–1000; Michael J. Swartz, FACHE, Interim Director
**Web address:** www.buffalo.va.gov/batavia.asp

VETERANS AFFAIRS WESTERN NEW YORK HEALTHCARE SYSTEM–BUFFALO DIVISION (O, 113 beds) 3495 Bailey Avenue, Buffalo, NY, Zip 14215–1129; tel. 716/834–9200; Brian G. Stiller, Director Medical Center
**Web address:** www.buffalo.va.gov/index.asp

**NORTH CAROLINA:** CHARLES GEORGE VETERANS AFFAIRS MEDICAL CENTER (O, 190 beds) 1100 Tunnel Road, Asheville, NC, Zip 28805–2087; tel. 828/298–7911; Cynthia Breyfogle, FACHE, Director
**Web address:** www.asheville.va.gov/

DURHAM VETERANS AFFAIRS MEDICAL CENTER (O, 251 beds) 508 Fulton Street, Durham, NC, Zip 27705–3897; tel. 919/286–0411; Paul Crews, Director

FAYETTEVILLE VETERANS AFFAIRS MEDICAL CENTER (O, 58 beds) 2300 Ramsey Street, Fayetteville, NC, Zip 28301–3899; tel. 910/488–2120; Webster Carl. Bazemore, M.D., Interim Medical Director
**Web address:** www.fayettevillenc.va.gov

W. G. (BILL) HEFFNER VETERANS AFFAIRS MEDICAL CENTER (O, 171 beds) 1601 Brenner Avenue, Salisbury, NC, Zip 28144–2559; tel. 704/638–9000; Joseph Vaughn, Director
**Web address:** www.salisbury.va.gov

**NORTH DAKOTA:** FARGO VETERANS AFFAIRS HEALTH CARE SYSTEM (O, 72 beds) 2101 Elm Street North, Fargo, ND, Zip 58102; tel. 701/232–3241; Breton Weintraub, Director
**Web address:** www.fargo.va.gov/.

**OHIO:** CHILLICOTHE VETERANS AFFAIRS MEDICAL CENTER (O, 295 beds) 17273 State Route 104, Chillicothe, OH, Zip 45601–9718; tel. 740/773–1141; Kathy Berger, R.N., Medical Center Director

CINCINNATI VETERANS AFFAIRS MEDICAL CENTER (O, 268 beds) 3200 Vine Street, Cincinnati, OH, Zip 45220–2288; tel. 513/475–6300; Jane Johnson, Interim Medical Director and Chief Nursing Officer
**Web address:** www.cincinnati.va.gov/

DAYTON VETERANS AFFAIRS MEDICAL CENTER (O, 486 beds) 4100 West Third Street, Dayton, OH, Zip 45428–9000; tel. 937/268–6511; Mark Murdock, FACHE, Medical Center Director
**Web address:** www.dayton.va.gov/

LOUIS STOKES CLEVELAND VETERANS AFFAIRS MEDICAL CENTER (O, 578 beds) 10701 East Boulevard, Cleveland, OH, Zip 44106–1702; tel. 216/791–3800; Jill Dietrich, JD, FACHE, Executive Director

**OKLAHOMA:** JACK C. MONTGOMERY VETERANS AFFAIRS MEDICAL CENTER (O, 89 beds) 1011 Honor Heights Drive, Muskogee, OK, Zip 74401–1318; tel. 918/577–3000; Mark E. Morgan, Medical Center Director
**Web address:** www.muskogee.va.gov

OKLAHOMA CITY VETERANS AFFAIRS MEDICAL CENTER (O, 192 beds) 921 NE 13th Street, Oklahoma City, OK, Zip 73104–5028; tel. 405/456–1000; Kristopher Wade. Vlosich, Director
**Web address:** www.oklahoma.va.gov

**OREGON:** SOUTHERN OREGON–WHITE CITY VETERANS AFFAIRS REHABILITATION CENTER AND CLINICS (O, 1075 beds) 8495 Crater Lake Highway, White City, OR, Zip 97503; tel. 503/826–2111; Frank A. Drake, Director

VA PORTLAND HEALTHCARE SYSTEM (O, 176 beds) 3710 SW U S Veterans Hospital Road, Portland, OR, Zip 97239–2964, 3710 SW US Veterans Hospital Road, 97207–1034, tel. 503/220–8262; Michael W. Fisher, Director
**Web address:** www.portland.va.gov/

VETERANS AFFAIRS ROSEBURG HEALTHCARE SYSTEM (O, 88 beds) 913 NW Garden Valley Boulevard, Roseburg, OR, Zip 97471–6513; tel. 541/440–1000; Douglas V. Paxton, Director
**Web address:** www.roseburg.va.gov/

**PENNSYLVANIA:** COATESVILLE VETERANS AFFAIRS MEDICAL CENTER (O, 118 beds) 1400 Black Horse Hill Road, Coatesville, PA, Zip 19320–2040; tel. 610/384–7711; Carla Sivek, Director

ERIE VETERANS AFFAIRS MEDICAL CENTER (O, 52 beds) 135 East 38th Street, Erie, PA, Zip 16504–1559; tel. 814/860–2576; John Gennaro, FACHE, Director
**Web address:** www.erie.va.gov/

JAMES E. VAN ZANDT VETERANS AFFAIRS MEDICAL CENTER (O, 68 beds) 2907 Pleasant Valley Boulevard, Altoona, PA, Zip 16602–4305; tel. 877/626–2500; Sigrid Andrew, Director

LEBANON VETERANS AFFAIRS MEDICAL CENTER (O, 213 beds) 1700 South Lincoln Avenue, Lebanon, PA, Zip 17042–7529; tel. 717/272–6621; Margaret G. Wilson, R.N., MSN, Acting Director
**Web address:** www.lebanon.va.gov

PHILADELPHIA VETERANS AFFAIRS MEDICAL CENTER (O, 317 beds) 3900 Woodland Avenue, Philadelphia, PA, Zip 19104–4594; tel. 215/823–5800; Admiral, Karen Ann. Flaherty–Oxler, MSN, R.N., Director
**Web address:** www.philadelphia.va.gov/

VETERANS AFFAIRS PITTSBURGH HEALTHCARE SYSTEM (O, 549 beds) University Drive C, Pittsburgh, PA, Zip 15240; tel. 866/482–7488; Donald E. Koenig, Director

For explanation of codes following names, see page B2.
★ Indicates Type III membership in the American Hospital Association.

WILKES–BARRE VETERANS AFFAIRS MEDICAL CENTER (O, 146 beds) 1111 East End Boulevard, Wilkes-Barre, PA, Zip 18711–0030; tel. 570/824-3521; Russell E. Lloyd, Director
**Web address:** www.va.gov/vamcwb

**PUERTO RICO:** VETERANS AFFAIRS CARIBBEAN HEALTHCARE SYSTEM (O, 422 beds) 10 Casia Street, San Juan, PR, Zip 00921–3201; tel. 787/641-7582; Carlos R. Escobar, FACHE, Director

**RHODE ISLAND:** PROVIDENCE VETERANS AFFAIRS MEDICAL CENTER (O, 73 beds) 830 Chalkstone Avenue, Providence, RI, Zip 02908–4799; tel. 401/273-7100; Lawrence B. Connell, Director
**Web address:** www.providence.va.gov/

**SOUTH CAROLINA:** RALPH H. JOHNSON VETERANS AFFAIRS MEDICAL CENTER (O, 98 beds) 109 Bee Street, Charleston, SC, Zip 29401–5799; tel. 843/577-5011; Scott R. Isaacks, FACHE, Director and Chief Executive Officer
**Web address:** www.charleston.va.gov/

WM. JENNINGS BRYAN DORN VETERANS AFFAIRS MEDICAL CENTER (O, 216 beds) 6439 Garners Ferry Road, Columbia, SC, Zip 29209–1639; tel. 803/776-4000; David Omura, MS, Director
**Web address:** www.columbiasc.va.gov/

**SOUTH DAKOTA:** SIOUX FALLS VETERANS AFFAIRS HEALTH CARE SYSTEM (O, 92 beds) 2501 West 22nd Street, Sioux Falls, SD, Zip 57105–1305, Mailing Address: P.O. Box 5046, 57117–5046, tel. 605/336-3230; Lisa J. Simoneau, FACHE, Director
**Web address:** www.siouxfalls.va.gov

VETERANS AFFAIRS BLACK HILLS HEALTH CARE SYSTEM (O, 247 beds) 113 Comanche Road, Fort Meade, SD, Zip 57741–1099; tel. 605/347-2511; Sandra Horsman, Director

**TENNESSEE:** JAMES H. QUILLEN VETERANS AFFAIRS MEDICAL CENTER (O, 98 beds) Corner of Lamont & Veterans Way, Mountain Home, TN, Zip 37684, Mailing Address: P.O. Box 4000, 37684–4000, tel. 423/926-1171; Dean B. Borsos, Medical Center Director
**Web address:** www.mountainhome.va.gov/

MEMPHIS VETERANS AFFAIRS MEDICAL CENTER (O, 251 beds) 1030 Jefferson Avenue, Memphis, TN, Zip 38104–2193; tel. 901/523-8990; David K. Dunning, Medical Center Director and Chief Executive Officer

TENNESSEE VALLEY HEALTHCARE SYSTEM (O, 437 beds) 1310 24th Avenue South, Nashville, TN, Zip 37212–2637; tel. 615/327-4751; Jennifer Vedral-Baron, Health System Director
**Web address:** www.tennesseevalley.va.gov

**TEXAS:** AMARILLO VETERANS AFFAIRS HEALTH CARE SYSTEM (O, 55 beds) 6010 West Amarillo Boulevard, Amarillo, TX, Zip 79106–1992; tel. 806/355-9703; Zachary Sage, Interim Director

CENTRAL TEXAS VETERANS HEALTH CARE SYSTEM (O, 1532 beds) 1901 Veterans Memorial Drive, Temple, TX, Zip 76504–7493; tel. 254/778-4811; Colonel, Michael L. Kiefer, FACHE, Director
**Web address:** www.centraltexas.va.gov/

MICHAEL E. DEBAKEY VETERANS AFFAIRS MEDICAL CENTER (O, 479 beds) 2002 Holcombe Boulevard, Houston, TX, Zip 77030–4298; tel. 713/791-1414; Francisco Vazquez, Director
**Web address:** www.houston.va.gov

SOUTH TEXAS VETERANS HEALTH CARE SYSTEM (O, 268 beds) 7400 Merton Minter Boulevard, San Antonio, TX, Zip 78229–4404; tel. 210/617-5300; Christopher R. Sandles, FACHE, Medical Center Director

VETERANS AFFAIRS NORTH TEXAS HEALTH CARE SYSTEM (O, 853 beds) 4500 South Lancaster Road, Dallas, TX, Zip 75216–7167; tel. 214/742-8387; Stephen R. Holt, M.D., Director
**Web address:** www.northtexas.va.gov/

WEST TEXAS VETERANS AFFAIRS HEALTH CARE SYSTEM (O, 149 beds) 300 Veterans Boulevard, Big Spring, TX, Zip 79720–5500, Big Springs, tel. 432/263-7361; Kalautie JangDhari, Director
**Web address:** www.bigspring.va.gov/about/

**UTAH:** VETERANS AFFAIRS SALT LAKE CITY HEALTH CARE SYSTEM (O, 123 beds) 500 Foothill Drive, Salt Lake City, UT, Zip 84148–0002; tel. 801/582-1565; Shella D. Stovall, R.N., Interim Director
**Web address:** www.saltlakecity.va.gov/

**VERMONT:** WHITE RIVER JUNCTION VETERANS AFFAIRS MEDICAL CENTER (O, 74 beds) 215 North Main Street, White River Junction, VT, Zip 05009–0001; tel. 802/295-9363; Brett Rusch, M.D., Acting Director

**VIRGINIA:** HAMPTON VETERANS AFFAIRS MEDICAL CENTER (O, 451 beds) 100 Emancipation Drive, Hampton, VA, Zip 23667–0001; tel. 757/722-9961; Taquisa Simmons, Interim Director
**Web address:** www.hampton.va.gov/

HUNTER HOLMES MCGUIRE VETERANS AFFAIRS MEDICAL CENTER-RICHMOND (O, 381 beds) 1201 Broad Rock Boulevard, Richmond, VA, Zip 23249–0002; tel. 804/675-5000; J. Ronald. Johnson, Director
**Web address:** www.richmond.va.gov/

SALEM VETERANS AFFAIRS MEDICAL CENTER (O, 191 beds) 1970 Roanoke Boulevard, Salem, VA, Zip 24153–6478; tel. 540/982-2463; Rebecca J. Stackhouse, Medical Center Director
**Web address:** www.salem.va.gov

**WASHINGTON:** MANN–GRANDSTAFF VETERANS AFFAIRS MEDICAL CENTER (O, 68 beds) 4815 North Assembly Street, Spokane, WA, Zip 99205–6197; tel. 509/434-7000; Robert Fischer, M.D., Medical Center Director
**Web address:** www.spokane.va.gov/

VETERANS AFFAIRS PUGET SOUND HEALTH CARE SYSTEM (O, 416 beds) 1660 South Columbian Way, Seattle, WA, Zip 98108–1597; tel. 206/762-1010; Michael C. Tadych, FACHE, Director

**WEST VIRGINIA:** BECKLEY VETERANS AFFAIRS MEDICAL CENTER (O, 173 beds) 200 Veterans Avenue, Beckley, WV, Zip 25801–6499; tel. 304/255-2121; Stacy J. Vasquez, Director
**Web address:** www.beckley.va.gov/

HUNTINGTON VETERANS AFFAIRS MEDICAL CENTER (O, 80 beds) 1540 Spring Valley Drive, Huntington, WV, Zip 25704–9300; tel. 304/429-6741; Brian Nimmo, Director
**Web address:** www.huntington.va.gov/

LOUIS A. JOHNSON VETERANS AFFAIRS MEDICAL CENTER (O, 71 beds) 1 Medical Center Drive, Clarksburg, WV, Zip 26301–4199; tel. 304/623-3461; Glenn R. Snider, M.D., Interim Director

MARTINSBURG VETERANS AFFAIRS MEDICAL CENTER (O, 487 beds) 510 Butler Avenue, Martinsburg, WV, Zip 25405–9990; tel. 304/263-0811; Kenneth W. Allensworth, Interim Medical Center Director
**Web address:** www.martinsburg.va.gov/

**WISCONSIN:** CLEMENT J. ZABLOCKI VETERANS AFFAIRS MEDICAL CENTER (O, 637 beds) 5000 West National Avenue, Milwaukee, WI, Zip 53295–0001; tel. 414/384-2000; Daniel Zomchek, Ph.D., Chief Executive Officer and Medical Center Director
**Web address:** www.milwaukee.va.gov/

VA MEDICAL CENTER (O, 71 beds) 500 East Veterans Street, Tomah, WI, Zip 54660–3105; tel. 608/372-3971; Victoria Brahm, R.N., MSN, Medical Center Director

WILLIAM S. MIDDLETON MEMORIAL VETERANS HOSPITAL (O, 87 beds) 2500 Overlook Terrace, Madison, WI, Zip 53705–2286; tel. 608/256-1901; John J. Rohrer, Director
**Web address:** www.madison.va.gov

**WYOMING:** CHEYENNE VETERANS AFFAIRS MEDICAL CENTER (O, 32 beds) 2360 East Pershing Boulevard, Cheyenne, WY, Zip 82001–5392; tel. 307/778-7550; Paul L. Roberts, Director

SHERIDAN VETERANS AFFAIRS MEDICAL CENTER (O, 145 beds) 1898 Fort Road, Sheridan, WY, Zip 82801–8320; tel. 307/672-3473; Pamela Crowell, Director
**Web address:** www.sheridan.va.gov/

| | | |
|---|---|---|
| **Owned, leased, sponsored:** | 134 hospitals | 33911 beds |
| **Contract–managed:** | 0 hospitals | 0 beds |
| **Totals:** | 134 hospitals | 33911 beds |

**0845: DEVEREUX** (NP)
444 Devereux Drive, Villanova, PA Zip 19085–1932, Mailing Address: P.O. Box 638, 19085–0638, tel. 610/520-3000; Robert Q. Kreider, President and Chief Executive Officer
**(Independent Hospital System)**

For explanation of codes following names, see page B2.
★ Indicates Type III membership in the American Hospital Association.

**FLORIDA**: DEVEREUX HOSPITAL AND CHILDREN'S CENTER OF FLORIDA (O, 100 beds) 8000 Devereux Drive, Melbourne, FL, Zip 32940–7907; tel. 321/242–9100; Steven Murphy, Executive Director
**Web address**: www.devereux.org

**GEORGIA**: DEVEREUX ADVANCED BEHAVIORAL HEALTH GEORGIA (O, 110 beds) 1291 Stanley Road NW, Kennesaw, GA, Zip 30152–4359; tel. 770/427–0147; Gwendolyn Skinner, Operational Vice President

**PENNSYLVANIA**: DEVEREUX CHILDREN'S BEHAVIORAL HEALTH CENTER (O, 49 beds) 655 Sugartown Road, Malvern, PA, Zip 19355–3303, 655 Sugartown Rd, 19355–3303, tel. 800/345–1292; Patricia Hillis-Clark, Executive Director
**Web address**: www.devereux.org

**TEXAS**: DEVEREUX TEXAS TREATMENT NETWORK (O, 31 beds) 1150 Devereux Drive, League City, TX, Zip 77573–2043; tel. 281/335–1000; Pamela E. Helm, Executive Director

| | | |
|---|---|---|
| Owned, leased, sponsored: | 4 hospitals | 290 beds |
| Contract–managed: | 0 hospitals | 0 beds |
| Totals: | 4 hospitals | 290 beds |

---

**0010: DIVISION OF MENTAL HEALTH AND ADDICTION SERVICES, DEPARTMENT OF HUMAN SERVICES, STATE OF NEW JERSEY** (NP)
222 South Warren Street, Trenton, NJ Zip 08608–2306, Mailing Address: P.O. Box 360, 08625–0360, tel. 609/438–4351; Valerie Mielke, Assistant Commissioner
**(Independent Hospital System)**

**NEW JERSEY**: ANCORA PSYCHIATRIC HOSPITAL (O, 465 beds) 301 Spring Garden Road, Hammonton, NJ, Zip 08037–9699; tel. 609/561–1700; Joseph Canale, Acting Chief Executive Officer
**Web address**: https://www.state.nj.us/humanservices/dmhas/resources/services/treatment/aph.html

ARTHUR BRISBANE CHILDREN TREATMENT CENTER (O, 92 beds) County Road 524, Farmingdale, NJ, Zip 7727, Mailing Address: P.O. Box 625, 7727, Vincent Giampeitro, Chief Executive Officer

GREYSTONE PARK PSYCHIATRIC HOSPITAL (O, 468 beds) 59 Koch Avenue, Morris Plains, NJ, Zip 07950–4400; tel. 973/538–1800; Tomika Carter, Chief Executive Officer
**Web address**: https://www.state.nj.us/humanservices/dmhas/resources/services/treatment/gpph.html

TRENTON PSYCHIATRIC HOSPITAL (O, 431 beds) Route 29 and Sullivan Way, Trenton, NJ, Zip 08628–3425, Mailing Address: P.O. Box 7500, West Trenton, 08628–0500, tel. 609/633–1500; Robyn Caporoso, Chief Executive Officer
**Web address**: www.state.nj.us/humanservices/dmhs/oshm/tph/

| | | |
|---|---|---|
| Owned, leased, sponsored: | 4 hospitals | 1456 beds |
| Contract–managed: | 0 hospitals | 0 beds |
| Totals: | 4 hospitals | 1456 beds |

---

**0536: DIVISION OF MENTAL HEALTH, DEPARTMENT OF HUMAN SERVICES** (NP)
319 East Madison Street, S–3B, Springfield, IL Zip 62701–1035; tel. 217/785–6023; Lorrie Rickman. Jones, Ph.D., Director
**(Independent Hospital System)**

**ILLINOIS**: ALTON MENTAL HEALTH CENTER (O, 125 beds) 4500 College Avenue, Alton, IL, Zip 62002–5099; tel. 618/474–3800; Brian E. Thomas, Administrator

ANDREW MCFARLAND MENTAL HEALTH CENTER (O, 142 beds) 901 East Southwind Road, Springfield, IL, Zip 62703–5125; tel. 217/786–6994; Karen Schweighart, R.N., MS, Administrator

CHESTER MENTAL HEALTH CENTER (O, 245 beds) Chester Road, Chester, IL, Zip 62233–0031, Box 31, 62233–0031, tel. 618/826–4571; Leah Hammel, Acting Administrator

CHICAGO–READ MENTAL HEALTH CENTER (O, 200 beds) 4200 North Oak Park Avenue, Chicago, IL, Zip 60634–1457; tel. 773/794–4000; Ellen Otomo, Interim Hospital Administrator

CHOATE MENTAL HEALTH CENTER (O, 79 beds) 1000 North Main Street, Anna, IL, Zip 62906–1699; tel. 618/833–5161; Elaine Ray, Administrator

ELGIN MENTAL HEALTH CENTER (O, 383 beds) 750 South State Street, Elgin, IL, Zip 60123–7692; tel. 847/742–1040; Meredith Kiss, Administrator
**Web address**: www.dhs.state.il.us

JOHN J. MADDEN MENTAL HEALTH CENTER (O, 125 beds) 1200 South First Avenue, Hines, IL, Zip 60141–0800; tel. 708/338–7202; Edith Newman, Interim Administrator

| | | |
|---|---|---|
| Owned, leased, sponsored: | 7 hospitals | 1299 beds |
| Contract–managed: | 0 hospitals | 0 beds |
| Totals: | 7 hospitals | 1299 beds |

---

**★1027: DRH HEALTH** (NP)
1407 North Whisenant Drive, Duncan, OK Zip 73533–1650; tel. 580/252–5300; Jay R. Johnson, FACHE, President and Chief Executive Officer
**(Independent Hospital System)**

**OKLAHOMA**: DUNCAN REGIONAL HOSPITAL (O, 117 beds) 1407 North Whisenant Drive, Duncan, OK, Zip 73533–1650, Mailing Address: P.O. Box 2000, 73534–2000, tel. 580/252–5300; Jay R. Johnson, FACHE, President and Chief Executive Officer

JEFFERSON COUNTY HOSPITAL (L, 8 beds) Highway 70 and 81, Waurika, OK, Zip 73573–3075, Mailing Address: P.O. Box 90, 73573–0090, tel. 580/228–2344; Richard Gillespie, President
**Web address**: www.jeffersoncountyhospital.net

| | | |
|---|---|---|
| Owned, leased, sponsored: | 2 hospitals | 125 beds |
| Contract–managed: | 0 hospitals | 0 beds |
| Totals: | 2 hospitals | 125 beds |

---

**★0861: DUKE LIFEPOINT HEALTHCARE** (IO)
330 Seven Springs Way, Brentwood, TN Zip 37027–5098; tel. 615/920–7000; Jeffrey G. Seraphine, FACHE, President
**(Moderately Centralized Health System)**

**MICHIGAN**: UP HEALTH SYSTEM–MARQUETTE (O, 211 beds) 580 West College Avenue, Marquette, MI, Zip 49855–2736; tel. 906/228–9440; Garfield Atchison, Chief Executive Officer
**Web address**: www.mgh.org

**NORTH CAROLINA**: CENTRAL CAROLINA HOSPITAL (O, 137 beds) 1135 Carthage Street, Sanford, NC, Zip 27330–4162; tel. 919/774–2100; Spencer Thomas, Chief Executive Officer

FRYE REGIONAL MEDICAL CENTER (O, 271 beds) 420 North Center Street, Hickory, NC, Zip 28601–5049, 1950 11th Street Crt. NW, 28601, tel. 828/315–5000; Rod Harkleroad, R.N., Chief Executive Officer
**Web address**: www.fryemedctr.com

HARRIS REGIONAL HOSPITAL (O, 86 beds) 68 Hospital Road, Sylva, NC, Zip 28779–2722; tel. 828/586–7000; Steve Heatherly, Chief Executive Officer
**Web address**: www.westcare.org

HAYWOOD REGIONAL MEDICAL CENTER (O, 146 beds) 262 Leroy George Drive, Clyde, NC, Zip 28721–7430; tel. 828/456–7311; Chris Fensterle, Interim Chief Executive Officer
**Web address**: www.haymed.org

MARIA PARHAM MEDICAL CENTER (O, 115 beds) 566 Ruin Creek Road, Henderson, NC, Zip 27536–2927; tel. 252/438–4143; Bert Beard, Chief Executive Officer

PERSON MEMORIAL HOSPITAL (O, 77 beds) 615 Ridge Road, Roxboro, NC, Zip 27573–4629; tel. 336/599–2121; David Ziolkowski, Chief Executive Officer
**Web address**: www.personhospital.com

For explanation of codes following names, see page B2.
★ Indicates Type III membership in the American Hospital Association.

Section B

RUTHERFORD REGIONAL HEALTH SYSTEM (O, 112 beds) 288 South Ridgecrest Avenue, Rutherfordton, NC, Zip 28139–2838; tel. 828/286–5000; Rebecca Segal, Chief Executive Officer
**Web address**: www.rutherfordhosp.org

SWAIN COMMUNITY HOSPITAL (O, 25 beds) 45 Plateau Street, Bryson City, NC, Zip 28713–4200; tel. 828/488–2155; Steve Heatherly, Chief Executive Officer

WILSON MEDICAL CENTER (O, 244 beds) 1705 Tarboro Street, SW, Wilson, NC, Zip 27893–3428; tel. 252/399–8040; Mark C. Holyoak, FACHE, Chief Executive Officer
**Web address**: www.wilmed.org

**PENNSYLVANIA**: CONEMAUGH MEMORIAL MEDICAL CENTER (O, 509 beds) 1086 Franklin Street, Johnstown, PA, Zip 15905–4398; tel. 814/534–9000; William E. Caldwell Jr, FACHE, Chief Executive Officer

CONEMAUGH MEYERSDALE MEDICAL CENTER (O, 20 beds) 200 Hospital Drive, Meyersdale, PA, Zip 15552–1249; tel. 814/634–5911; Heather Smith, Chief Executive Officer
**Web address**: www.conemaugh.org

CONEMAUGH MINERS MEDICAL CENTER (O, 25 beds) 290 Haida Avenue, Hastings, PA, Zip 16646–5610, Mailing Address: P.O. Box 689, 16646–0689, tel. 814/247–3100; Timothy Harclerode, Chief Executive Officer
**Web address**: www.conemaugh.org

**VIRGINIA**: TWIN COUNTY REGIONAL HEALTHCARE (O, 66 beds) 200 Hospital Drive, Galax, VA, Zip 24333–2227; tel. 276/236–8181; Dale Alward, Chief Executive Officer
**Web address**: www.tcrh.org

| | | |
|---|---|---|
| **Owned, leased, sponsored:** | 14 hospitals | 2044 beds |
| **Contract–managed:** | 0 hospitals | 0 beds |
| **Totals:** | 14 hospitals | 2044 beds |

---

**★0190: DUKE UNIVERSITY HEALTH SYSTEM** (NP)
201 Trent Drive, Durham, NC Zip 27710–3037, Mailing Address: P.O. Box 3701, 27710–3701, tel. 919/684–2255; A. Eugene. Washington, M.D., President and Chief Executive Officer
**(Centralized Health System)**

**NORTH CAROLINA**: DUKE RALEIGH HOSPITAL (O, 181 beds) 3400 Wake Forest Road, Raleigh, NC, Zip 27609–7373; tel. 919/954–3000; Leigh Bleecker, Interim President

DUKE REGIONAL HOSPITAL (L, 227 beds) 3643 North Roxboro Street, Durham, NC, Zip 27704–2763; tel. 919/470–4000; Kathleen B. Galbraith, FACHE, President
**Web address**: www.dukehealth.org

DUKE UNIVERSITY HOSPITAL (O, 974 beds) 2301 Erwin Road, DUMC Box # 3814, Durham, NC, Zip 27705–4699, Mailing Address: P.O. Box 3814, 27710–3708, tel. 919/684–8111; Thomas Owens, M.D., President

| | | |
|---|---|---|
| **Owned, leased, sponsored:** | 3 hospitals | 1382 beds |
| **Contract–managed:** | 0 hospitals | 0 beds |
| **Totals:** | 3 hospitals | 1382 beds |

---

**★0926: EDWARD–ELMHURST HEALTHCARE** (NP)
801 South Washington Street, Naperville, IL Zip 60540–7430; tel. 630/527–3000; Mary Lou Mastro, FACHE, MS, R.N., System Chief Executive Officer
**(Independent Hospital System)**

**ILLINOIS**: EDWARD HOSPITAL (O, 358 beds) 801 South Washington Street, Naperville, IL, Zip 60540–7499; tel. 630/527–3000; Joseph Dant, President and Chief Executive Officer
**Web address**: www.eehealth.org

ELMHURST HOSPITAL (O, 266 beds) 155 East Brush Hill Road, Elmhurst, IL, Zip 60126–5658; tel. 331/221–1000; Pamela L. Dunley, MS, R.N., Chief Executive Officer

LINDEN OAKS HOSPITAL (O, 108 beds) 852 South West Street, Naperville, IL, Zip 60540–6400; tel. 630/305–5500; Gina Sharp, FACHE, President and Chief Executive Officer
**Web address**: https://www.eehealth.org/services/behavioral–health

| | | |
|---|---|---|
| **Owned, leased, sponsored:** | 3 hospitals | 732 beds |
| **Contract–managed:** | 0 hospitals | 0 beds |
| **Totals:** | 3 hospitals | 732 beds |

---

**1685: EINSTEIN HEALTHCARE NETWORK** (NP)
5501 Old York Road, Philadelphia, PA Zip 19141–3098; tel. 215/456–7890; Barry R. Freedman, President and Chief Executive Officer

**PENNSYLVANIA**: EINSTEIN MEDICAL CENTER MONTGOMERY (O, 171 beds) 559 West Germantown Pike, East Norriton, PA, Zip 19403–4250; tel. 484/622–1000; Beth Duffy, Chief Operating Officer

EINSTEIN MEDICAL CENTER PHILADELPHIA (O, 504 beds) 5501 Old York Road, Philadelphia, PA, Zip 19141–3098; tel. 215/456–7890; Dixie James, President and Chief Operating Officer
**Web address**: www.einstein.edu

| | | |
|---|---|---|
| **Owned, leased, sponsored:** | 2 hospitals | 675 beds |
| **Contract–managed:** | 0 hospitals | 0 beds |
| **Totals:** | 2 hospitals | 675 beds |

---

**★0101: EMANATE HEALTH** (NP)
210 West San Bernardino Road, Covina, CA Zip 91723–1515; tel. 626/331–7331; Robert H. Curry, President and Chief Executive Officer

**CALIFORNIA**: EMANATE HEALTH FOOTHILL PRESBYTERIAN HOSPITAL (O, 67 beds) 250 South Grand Avenue, Glendora, CA, Zip 91741–4218; tel. 626/963–8411; Robert H. Curry, President and Chief Executive Officer
**Web address**: www.cvhp.org/Our_Facilities/Foothill_Presbyterian.aspx

EMANATE HEALTH INTER–COMMUNITY HOSPITAL (O, 320 beds) 210 West San Bernadino Road, Covina, CA, Zip 91723–1515, Mailing Address: P.O. Box 6108, 91722–5108, tel. 626/331–7331; Robert H. Curry, President and Chief Executive Officer

| | | |
|---|---|---|
| **Owned, leased, sponsored:** | 2 hospitals | 387 beds |
| **Contract–managed:** | 0 hospitals | 0 beds |
| **Totals:** | 2 hospitals | 387 beds |

---

**0879: EMERUS** (IO)
10077 Grogan's Mill, Suite 100, The Woodlands, TX Zip 77380–1022; tel. 281/292–2450; Craig Goguen, Chief Executive Officer

**OKLAHOMA**: INTEGRIS COMMUNITY HOSPITAL AT COUNCIL CROSSING (C, 64 beds) 9417 North Council Road, Oklahoma City, OK, Zip 73134–2521; tel. 405/500–3280; Shannon Crinole, Chief Executive Officer

**TEXAS**: BAPTIST EMERGENCY HOSPITAL (O, 33 beds) 16088 San Pedro, San Antonio, TX, Zip 78232–2249; tel. 210/402–4092; Shannon Crinion, Chief Executive Officer
**Web address**: www.baptistemergencyhospital.com

BAYLOR SCOTT & WHITE EMERGENCY HOSPITAL – GRAND PRAIRIE (O, 24 beds) 3095 Kingswood Boulevard, Grand Prairie, TX, Zip 75052–4512; tel. 972/854–0009; Vic Schmerbeck, Chief Executive Officer
**Web address**: https://www.bsweh.org/locations/grand–prairie/?utm_source=google&utm_medium=organic&utm_campaign=gmb

BAYLOR SCOTT & WHITE EMERGENCY HOSPITAL – ROCKWALL (O, 8 beds) 1975 Alpha Drive Suite 100, Rockwall, TX, Zip 75087–4951; tel. 214/294–6200; Vic Schmerbeck, Chief Executive Officer
**Web address**: www.bayloremc.com/rockwall

BAYLOR SCOTT & WHITE EMERGENCY HOSPITAL Ã¢â–âⵠBURLESON (O, 24 beds) 12500 South Freeway Suite 100, Burleson, TX, Zip 76028–7128; tel. 214/294–6250; Vic Schmerbeck, Chief Executive Officer
**Web address**: www.bayloremc.com/burleson

BAYLOR SCOTT & WHITE EMERGENCY HOSPITALSÃ¢â¬âAUBREY (O, 40 beds) 26791 Highway 380, Aubrey, TX, Zip 76227; tel. 972/347–2525; Vic Schmerbeck, Chief Executive Officer

MEMORIAL HERMANN FIRST COLONY HOSPITAL (O, 15 beds) 16000 Southwest Freeway, Suite 100, Sugar Land, TX, Zip 77479–2674; tel. 281/277–0911; Brenda Villafranco, Administrator
**Web address:** www.emerus.com

| | | |
|---|---|---|
| **Owned, leased, sponsored:** | 6 hospitals | 144 beds |
| **Contract–managed:** | 1 hospitals | 64 beds |
| **Totals:** | 7 hospitals | 208 beds |

★**0256: EMORY HEALTHCARE** (NP)
1440 Clifton Road NE, Suite 400, Atlanta, GA Zip 30322–1102; tel. 404/778–5000; Dane C. Peterson, President and Chief Operating Officer
**(Centralized Health System)**

**GEORGIA:** EMORY DECATUR HOSPITAL (O, 472 beds) 2701 North Decatur Road, Decatur, GA, Zip 30033–5995; tel. 404/501–1000; Jim Forstner, Chief Executive Officer
**Web address:** www.dekalbmedical.org

EMORY HILLANDALE HOSPITAL (O, 70 beds) 2801 DeKalb Medical Parkway, Lithonia, GA, Zip 30058–4996; tel. 404/501–8000; Jim Forstner, Chief Executive Officer

EMORY JOHNS CREEK HOSPITAL (O, 118 beds) 6325 Hospital Parkway, Johns Creek, GA, Zip 30097–5775; tel. 678/474–7000; Marilyn Margolis, MSN, Chief Executive Officer
**Web address:** www.emoryjohnscreek.com

EMORY LONG–TERM ACUTE CARE (O, 50 beds) 450 North Candler Street, Decatur, GA, Zip 30030–2671; tel. 404/501–6700; Jim Forstner, Chief Executive Officer
**Web address:** www.dekalbmedicalcenter.org

EMORY REHABILITATION HOSPITAL (O, 46 beds) 1441 Clifton Road NE, Atlanta, GA, Zip 30322–1004; tel. 404/712–5512; Michael Eric. Garrard, FACHE, Chief Executive Officer
**Web address:** www.emoryhealthcare.org/rehabilitation

EMORY SAINT JOSEPH'S HOSPITAL OF ATLANTA (O, 352 beds) 5665 Peachtree Dunwoody Road NE, Atlanta, GA, Zip 30342–1701; tel. 678/843–7001; Heather Dexter, Chief Executive Officer

EMORY UNIVERSITY HOSPITAL MIDTOWN (O, 532 beds) 550 Peachtree Street NE, Atlanta, GA, Zip 30308–2247; tel. 404/686–4411; Daniel Owens, Chief Executive Officer
**Web address:** www.emoryhealthcare.org

EMORY UNIVERSITY HOSPITAL (O, 645 beds) 1364 Clifton Road NE, Atlanta, GA, Zip 30322; tel. 404/712–2000; Matthew Wain, Chief Executive Officer
**Web address:** www.emoryhealthcare.org

| | | |
|---|---|---|
| **Owned, leased, sponsored:** | 8 hospitals | 2285 beds |
| **Contract–managed:** | 0 hospitals | 0 beds |
| **Totals:** | 8 hospitals | 2285 beds |

★**0023: ENCOMPASS HEALTH CORPORATION** (IO)
9001 Liberty Parkway, Birmingham, AL Zip 35242–7509; tel. 205/967–7116; Mark J. Tarr, President and Chief Executive Officer
**(Independent Hospital System)**

**ALABAMA:** ENCOMPASS HEALTH LAKESHORE REHABILITATION HOSPITAL (O, 100 beds) 3800 Ridgeway Drive, Birmingham, AL, Zip 35209–5599; tel. 205/868–2000; Michael Bartell, Chief Executive Officer
**Web address:** www.encompasshealth.com/lakeshorerehab

ENCOMPASS HEALTH REHABILITATION HOSPITAL OF DOTHAN (O, 51 beds) 1736 East Main Street, Dothan, AL, Zip 36301–3040, Mailing Address: P.O. Box 6708, 36302–6708, tel. 334/712–6333; Margaret A. Futch, Chief Executive Officer

ENCOMPASS HEALTH REHABILITATION HOSPITAL OF GADSDEN (O, 44 beds) 801 Goodyear Avenue, Gadsden, AL, Zip 35903–1133; tel. 256/439–5000; Kayla Feazell, Chief Executive Officer
**Web address:** www.encompasshealth.com/gadsdenrehab

ENCOMPASS HEALTH REHABILITATION HOSPITAL OF MONTGOMERY (O, 70 beds) 4465 Narrow Lane Road, Montgomery, AL, Zip 36116–2900; tel. 334/284–7700; Randy Thompson, Chief Executive Officer
**Web address:** www.encompasshealth.com/montgomeryrehab

ENCOMPASS HEALTH REHABILITATION HOSPITAL OF SHELBY COUNTY (O, 34 beds) 900 Oak Mountain Commons Lane, Pelham, AL, Zip 35124; tel. 205/216–7600; Nathan Ford, Chief Executive Officer
**Web address:** www.encompasshealth.com/shelbycountyrehab

ENCOMPASS REHABILITATION HOSPITAL OF NORTH ALABAMA (O, 70 beds) 107 Governors Drive SW, Huntsville, AL, Zip 35801–4326; tel. 256/535–2300; Douglas H. Beverly, Chief Executive Officer

REGIONAL REHABILITATION HOSPITAL (O, 58 beds) 3715 Highway 280/431 North, Phenix City, AL, Zip 36867; tel. 334/732–2200; Lora Davis, FACHE, Chief Executive Officer
**Web address:** www.regionalrehabhospital.com

**ARIZONA:** ENCOMPASS HEALTH REHABILITATION HOSPITAL OF EAST VALLEY (O, 60 beds) 5652 East Baseline Road, Mesa, AZ, Zip 85206–4713; tel. 480/567–0350; Elizabeth Gibson, Chief Executive Officer

ENCOMPASS HEALTH REHABILITATION HOSPITAL OF NORTHWEST TUCSON (O, 60 beds) 1921 West Hospital Drive, Tucson, AZ, Zip 85704–7806; tel. 520/742–2800; Jeffrey Christensen, Chief Executive Officer
**Web address:** https://www.encompasshealth.com/northwesttucsonrehab

ENCOMPASS HEALTH REHABILITATION HOSPITAL OF SCOTTSDALE (O, 60 beds) 9630 East Shea Boulevard, Scottsdale, AZ, Zip 85260–6267; tel. 480/551–5400; Kenneth Bell, Chief Executive Officer

ENCOMPASS HEALTH REHABILITATION INSTITUTE OF TUCSON (O, 80 beds) 2650 North Wyatt Drive, Tucson, AZ, Zip 85712–6108; tel. 520/325–1300; Jeffrey Christensen, Chief Executive Officer
**Web address:** https://www.encompasshealth.com/rehabinstituteoftucson

ENCOMPASS HEALTH VALLEY OF THE SUN REHABILITATION HOSPITAL (O, 75 beds) 13460 North 67th Avenue, Glendale, AZ, Zip 85304–1042; tel. 623/878–8800; Beth Bacher, Chief Executive Officer

YUMA REHABILITATION HOSPITAL, A PARTNERSHIP OF ENCOMPASS HEALTH AND YRMC (O, 41 beds) 901 West 24th Street, Yuma, AZ, Zip 85364–6384; tel. 928/726–5000; Ian Hodge, Chief Executive Officer
**Web address:** https://www.encompasshealth.com/yumarehab

**ARKANSAS:** CHI ST. VINCENT HOT SPRINGS REHABILITATION HOSPITAL (O, 40 beds) 1636 Higdon Ferry Road, Hot Springs, AR, Zip 71913–6912; tel. 501/651–2000; Janette Daniels, Chief Executive Officer

CHI ST. VINCENT SHERWOOD REHABILITATION HOSPITAL (O, 80 beds) 2201 Wildwood Avenue, Sherwood, AR, Zip 72120–5074; tel. 501/834–1800; Lisa Watson, Chief Executive Officer
**Web address:** www.stvincentrehabhospital.com/

ENCOMPASS HEALTH REHABILITATION HOSPITAL OF JONESBORO (O, 67 beds) 1201 Fleming Avenue, Jonesboro, AR, Zip 72401–4311, Mailing Address: P.O. Box 1680, 72403–1680, tel. 870/932–0440; Donna Harris, Chief Executive Officer

ENCOMPASS HEALTH REHABILITATION HOSPITAL, A PARTNER OF WASHINGTON REGIONAL (O, 80 beds) 153 East Monte Painter Drive, Fayetteville, AR, Zip 72703–4002; tel. 479/444–2200; Kevin J. Clement, Chief Executive Officer
**Web address:** https://www.encompasshealth.com/fayettevillerehab

ENCOMPASS HEALTH REHABILITATION HOSPITAL OF FORT SMITH (O, 60 beds) 1401 South 'J' Street, Fort Smith, AR, Zip 72901–5155; tel. 479/785–3300; Dawn Watts, Chief Executive Officer
**Web address:** www.healthsouthfortsmith.com

**CALIFORNIA:** ENCOMPASS HEALTH REHABILITATION HOSPITAL OF BAKERSFIELD (O, 70 beds) 5001 Commerce Drive, Bakersfield, CA, Zip 93309–0689; tel. 661/323–5500; Martha Samora, R.N., FACHE, Chief Executive Officer
**Web address:** www.healthsouthbakersfield.com

ENCOMPASS HEALTH REHABILITATION HOSPITAL OF MODESTO (O, 35 beds) 1303 Mable Avenue, Modesto, CA, Zip 95355; tel. 209/857–3400; Seth Rogers, Chief Executive Officer
**Web address:** www.healthsouthmodesto.com/

ENCOMPASS HEALTH REHABILITATION HOSPITAL OF TUSTIN (O, 48 beds) 14851 Yorba Street, Tustin, CA, Zip 92780–2925; tel. 714/832–9200; Diana Hanyak, Chief Executive Officer

For explanation of codes following names, see page B2.
★ Indicates Type III membership in the American Hospital Association.

**COLORADO**: ENCOMPASS HEALTH REHABILITATION HOSPITAL OF COLORADO SPRINGS (O, 60 beds) 325 Parkside Drive, Colorado Springs, CO, Zip 80910–3134; tel. 719/630–8000; Stephen Schaefer, Chief Executive Officer
**Web address**: www.healthsouthcoloradosprings.com

ENCOMPASS HEALTH REHABILITATION HOSPITAL OF LITTLETON (O, 28 beds) 1001 West Mineral Avenue, Littleton, CO, Zip 80120–4507; tel. 303/334–1100; David H. Shefte, Chief Executive Officer
**Web address**: www.healthsouthdenver.com

**DELAWARE**: ENCOMPASS HEALTH REHABILITATION HOSPITAL OF MIDDLETOWN (O, 37 beds) 250 East Hampden Road, Middletown, DE, Zip 19709–5303; tel. 302/464–3400; Mathew Gooch, Chief Executive Officer
**Web address**: www.encompasshealth.com/middletownrehab

**FLORIDA**: ENCOMPASS HEALTH REHABILITATION HOSPITAL AN AFFILIATE OF MARTIN HEALTH (O, 54 beds) 5850 SE Community Drive, Stuart, FL, Zip 34997–6420; tel. 772/324–3500; Ivette Miranda, Chief Executive Officer
**Web address**: www.healthsouthmartin.com

ENCOMPASS HEALTH REHABILITATION HOSPITAL OF ALTAMONTE SPRINGS (O, 60 beds) 831 South State Road 434, Altamonte Springs, FL, Zip 32714–3502; tel. 407/587–8600; Michael Thomas, Chief Executive Officer

ENCOMPASS HEALTH REHABILITATION HOSPITAL OF LARGO (O, 70 beds) 901 North Clearwater–Largo Road, Largo, FL, Zip 33770–4126; tel. 727/586–2999; Tripp Smith, Chief Executive Officer
**Web address**: www.healthsouthlargo.com

ENCOMPASS HEALTH REHABILITATION HOSPITAL OF MIAMI (O, 60 beds) 20601 Old Cutler Road, Cutler Bay, FL, Zip 33189–2400; tel. 305/251–3800; Luis R. Allende Ruiz, Chief Executive Officer
**Web address**: www.healthsouthmiami.com

ENCOMPASS HEALTH REHABILITATION HOSPITAL OF OCALA (O, 60 beds) 2275 SW 22nd Lane, Ocala, FL, Zip 34471–7710; tel. 352/282–4000; Karthik Muthu, Chief Executive Officer
**Web address**: www.healthsouthocala.com

ENCOMPASS HEALTH REHABILITATION HOSPITAL OF PANAMA CITY (O, 75 beds) 1847 Florida Avenue, Panama City, FL, Zip 32405–4640; tel. 850/914–8600; Tony N. Bennett, Chief Executive Officer

ENCOMPASS HEALTH REHABILITATION HOSPITAL OF SARASOTA (O, 96 beds) 6400 Edgelake Drive, Sarasota, FL, Zip 34240–8813; tel. 941/921–8600; Marcus Braz, Chief Executive Officer
**Web address**: www.healthsouthsarasota.com

ENCOMPASS HEALTH REHABILITATION HOSPITAL OF SPRING HILL (O, 80 beds) 12440 Cortez Boulevard, Brooksville, FL, Zip 34613–2628; tel. 352/592–4250; Jeffrey Alexander, Chief Executive Officer

ENCOMPASS HEALTH REHABILITATION HOSPITAL OF SUNRISE (O, 126 beds) 4399 North Nob Hill Road, Sunrise, FL, Zip 33351–5899; tel. 954/749–0300; Michael S. Roffelsen, Chief Executive Officer
**Web address**: www.healthsouthsunrise.com

ENCOMPASS HEALTH REHABILITATION HOSPITAL OF TALLAHASSEE (O, 76 beds) 1675 Riggins Road, Tallahassee, FL, Zip 32308–5315; tel. 850/656–4800; K. Dale. Neely, FACHE, Chief Executive Officer
**Web address**: www.healthsouthtallahassee.com

ENCOMPASS HEALTH REHABILITATION HOSPITAL OF TREASURE COAST (O, 80 beds) 1600 37th Street, Vero Beach, FL, Zip 32960–4863; tel. 772/778–2100; Michael Kissner, Chief Executive Officer
**Web address**: www.healthsouthtreasurecoast.com

SEA PINES REHABILITATION HOSPITAL (O, 90 beds) 101 East Florida Avenue, Melbourne, FL, Zip 32901–8301; tel. 321/984–4600; Denise B. McGrath, Chief Executive Officer

**GEORGIA**: ENCOMPASS HEALTH REHABILITATION HOSPITAL OF NEWNAN (O, 50 beds) 2101 East Newnan Crossing Boulevard, Newnan, GA, Zip 30265–2406; tel. 678/552–6200; Shawn Bright, Chief Executive Officer
**Web address**: www.https://encompasshealth.com/locations/newnanrehab/

ENCOMPASS HEALTH REHABILITATION HOSPITAL OF SAVANNAH (O, 50 beds) 6510 Seawright DR, Savannah, GA, Zip 31406–2752; tel. 800/622–7269; Kathy Kleinsteuber, Chief Executive Officer

WALTON REHABILITATION HOSPITAL (O, 58 beds) 1355 Independence Drive, Augusta, GA, Zip 30901–1037; tel. 706/724–7746; Eric Crossan, Chief Executive Officer
**Web address**: www.healthsouthwalton.com/

**IDAHO**: SAINT ALPHONSUS REGIONAL REHABILITATION HOSPITAL Ã¢â¬âⅩⅩAN AFFILIATE OF ENCOMPASS HEALTH (O, 40 beds) 711 North Curtis Road, Boise, ID, Zip 83706–1445; tel. 208/605–3000; Renee Hinson, Chief Executive Officer

**ILLINOIS**: VAN MATRE ENCOMPASS HEALTH REHABILITATION HOSPITAL (O, 61 beds) 950 South Mulford Road, Rockford, IL, Zip 61108–4274; tel. 815/381–8500; Jeffrey Reese, Chief Executive Officer
**Web address**: www.healthsouth.com

**INDIANA**: ENCOMPASS HEALTH DEACONESS REHABILITATION HOSPITAL (O, 98 beds) 9355 Warrick Trail, Newburgh, IN, Zip 47630–0015; tel. 812/476–9983; Blake Bunner, Chief Executive Officer

**KANSAS**: KANSAS REHABILITATION HOSPITAL (O, 57 beds) 1504 SW Eighth Avenue, Topeka, KS, Zip 66606–1632; tel. 785/235–6600; William J. Overbey, Chief Executive Officer
**Web address**: www.kansasrehabhospital.com

MID–AMERICA REHABILITATION HOSPITAL (O, 98 beds) 5701 West 110th Street, Shawnee Mission, KS, Zip 66211–2503, Overland Park, tel. 913/491–2400; Tiffany Kiehl, Chief Executive Officer

WESLEY REHABILITATION HOSPITAL (O, 65 beds) 8338 West 13th Street North, Wichita, KS, Zip 67212–2984; tel. 316/729–9999; Thomas Laughlin, Chief Executive Officer
**Web address**: www.wesleyrehabhospital.com

**KENTUCKY**: CARDINAL HILL REHABILITATION HOSPITAL (O, 232 beds) 2050 Versailles Road, Lexington, KY, Zip 40504–1405; tel. 859/254–5701; Tara Diebling, Chief Executive Officer

ENCOMPASS HEALTH REHABILITATION HOSPITAL OF NORTHERN KENTUCKY (O, 40 beds) 201 Medical Village Drive, Edgewood, KY, Zip 41017–3407; tel. 859/341–2044; Jeremy Yates, Chief Executive Officer
**Web address**: www.healthsouthkentucky.com

ENCOMPASS REHABILITATION HOSPITAL OF LAKEVIEW (O, 40 beds) 134 Heartland Drive, Elizabethtown, KY, Zip 42701–2778; tel. 270/769–3100; Lori Jarboe, Chief Executive Officer

**LOUISIANA**: ENCOMPASS HEALTH REHABILITATION HOSPITAL OF ALEXANDRIA (O, 47 beds) 104 North Third Street, Alexandria, LA, Zip 71301–8581; tel. 318/449–1370; David Goodson, Chief Executive Officer
**Web address**: www.healthsouthalexandria.com

**MAINE**: NEW ENGLAND REHABILITATION HOSPITAL OF PORTLAND (O, 90 beds) 335 Brighton Avenue, Portland, ME, Zip 04102–2363; tel. 207/775–4000; Jeanine Chesley, Chief Executive Officer
**Web address**: www.nerhp.org

**MARYLAND**: ENCOMPASS HEALTH REHABILITATION HOSPITAL OF SALISBURY (O, 54 beds) 220 Tilghman Road, Salisbury, MD, Zip 21804–1921; tel. 410/546–4600; Steven Walas, Chief Executive Officer
**Web address**: www.healthsouthchesapeake.com

**MASSACHUSETTS**: ENCOMPASS HEALTH REHABILITATION HOSPITAL OF BRAINTREE (O, 187 beds) 250 Pond Street, Braintree, MA, Zip 02184–5351; tel. 781/348–2500; Randy Doherty, CPA, Chief Executive Officer

ENCOMPASS HEALTH REHABILITATION HOSPITAL OF NEW ENGLAND (O, 210 beds) Two Rehabilitation Way, Woburn, MA, Zip 01801–6098; tel. 781/935–5050; David Coggins, MS, Chief Executive Officer
**Web address**: www.newenglandrehab.com

ENCOMPASS HEALTH REHABILITATION HOSPITAL OF WESTERN MASSACHUSETTS (O, 53 beds) 222 State Street, Ludlow, MA, Zip 01056–3437; tel. 413/308–3300; John R. Hunt, Chief Executive Officer

FAIRLAWN REHABILITATION HOSPITAL (O, 110 beds) 189 May Street, Worcester, MA, Zip 01602–4339; tel. 508/791–6351; Anne Roper, Chief Executive Officer
**Web address**: www.fairlawnrehab.org

**MISSISSIPPI**: ENCOMPASS HEALTH REHABILITATION HOSPITAL OF GULFPORT (O, 33 beds) 4500 13th Street, Suite 900, Gulfport, MS, Zip 39501–2515; tel. 228/822–6965; Amber Hester, Chief Executive Officer
**Web address**: www.healthsouthgulfport.com

**MISSOURI**: RUSK REHABILITATION HOSPITAL (O, 60 beds) 315 Business Loop 70 West, Columbia, MO, Zip 65203–3248; tel. 573/817–2703; Tom Tisone, Chief Executive Officer
**Web address**: https://www.encompasshealth.com/locations/ruskrehab

For explanation of codes following names, see page B2.
★ Indicates Type III membership in the American Hospital Association.

THE REHABILITATION INSTITUTE OF ST. LOUIS (O, 131 beds) 4455 Duncan Avenue, Saint Louis, MO, Zip 63110–1111; tel. 314/658–3800; Mark Dwyer, FACHE, Chief Executive Officer
**Web address:** www.rehabinstitutestl

**NEVADA:** ENCOMPASS HEALTH REHABILITATION HOSPITAL OF DESERT CANYON (O, 50 beds) 9175 West Oquendo Road, Las Vegas, NV, Zip 89148–1234; tel. 702/252–7342; Peggy Nelson, Chief Executive Officer

ENCOMPASS HEALTH REHABILITATION HOSPITAL OF HENDERSON (O, 90 beds) 10301 Jeffreys Street, Henderson, NV, Zip 89052–3922; tel. 702/939–9400; Michael Ward, Chief Executive Officer
**Web address:** www.hendersonrehabhospital.com

ENCOMPASS HEALTH REHABILITATION HOSPITAL OF LAS VEGAS (O, 79 beds) 1250 South Valley View Boulevard, Las Vegas, NV, Zip 89102–1861; tel. 702/877–8898; Tij Von Nieda, Chief Executive Officer

**NEW HAMPSHIRE:** ENCOMPASS HEALTH REHABILITATION HOSPITAL OF CONCORD (O, 50 beds) 254 Pleasant Street, Concord, NH, Zip 03301–2508; tel. 603/226–9800; Diana Lachapelle, CPA, Chief Executive Officer
**Web address:** www.healthsouthrehabconcordnh.com

**NEW JERSEY:** ENCOMPASS HEALTH REHABILITATION HOSPITAL OF TINTON FALLS (O, 60 beds) 2 Centre Plaza, Tinton Falls, NJ, Zip 07724–9744; tel. 732/460–5320; Beth Lynch, MS, Chief Executive Officer
**Web address:** www.rehabnjtintonfalls.com/

ENCOMPASS HEALTH REHABILITATION HOSPITAL OF TOMS RIVER (O, 92 beds) 14 Hospital Drive, Toms River, NJ, Zip 08755–6470; tel. 732/244–3100; Patricia Ostaszewski, MS, Chief Executive Officer
**Web address:** www.rehabnjtomsriver.com/

ENCOMPASS HEALTH REHABILITATION HOSPITAL OF VINELAND (O, 41 beds) 1237 West Sherman Avenue, Vineland, NJ, Zip 08360–6920; tel. 856/696–7100; Monica B. Titus, R.N., Chief Executive Officer

**NEW MEXICO:** ENCOMPASS HEALTH REHABILITATION HOSPITAL OF ALBUQUERQUE (O, 87 beds) 7000 Jefferson Street NE, Albuquerque, NM, Zip 87109–4313; tel. 505/344–9478; Rachelle Spencer, Chief Executive Officer
**Web address:** www.encompasshealth.com/albuquerquerehab

**OHIO:** ENCOMPASS HEALTH REHABILITATION HOSPITAL AT CINCINNATI (O, 100 beds) 151 West Galbraith Road, Cincinnati, OH, Zip 45216–1015; tel. 513/418–5600; Ryan Smokovitz, Chief Executive Officer
**Web address:** www.healthsouthatdrake.com

HEALTHSOUTH REHABILITATION HOSPITAL OF DAYTON (O, 50 beds) One Elizabeth Place, Dayton, OH, Zip 45417–3445; tel. 937/424–8200; Lynne Blinco, Chief Executive Officer

MOUNT CARMEL REHABILITATION HOSPITAL (O, 60 beds) 597 Executive Campus Drive, Westerville, OH, Zip 43082–8870; tel. 614/392–3400; Angela Bridges, R.N., Chief Executive Officer
**Web address:** www.encompasshealth.com

**OKLAHOMA:** ST. JOHN REHABILITATION HOSPITAL (O, 40 beds) 1200 West Albany Drive, Broken Arrow, OK, Zip 74012–8146; tel. 918/744–2338; David Nicholas, Chief Executive Officer

**PENNSYLVANIA:** ENCOMPASS HEALTH NITTANY VALLEY REHABILITATION HOSPITAL (O, 73 beds) 550 West College Avenue, Pleasant Gap, PA, Zip 16823–7401; tel. 814/359–3421; Amy Lynn. Adams, Chief Executive Officer
**Web address:** www.nittanyvalleyrehab.com

ENCOMPASS HEALTH READING REHABILITATION HOSPITAL (O, 60 beds) 1623 Morgantown Road, Reading, PA, Zip 19607–9455; tel. 610/796–6000; Shelby Olind, Chief Executive Officer
**Web address:** https://www.encompasshealth.com/readingrehab

ENCOMPASS HEALTH REHABILITATION HOSPITAL OF ALTOONA (O, 80 beds) 2005 Valley View Boulevard, Altoona, PA, Zip 16602–4598; tel. 814/944–3535; Scott Filler, Chief Executive Officer
**Web address:** www.healthsouthaltoona.com

ENCOMPASS HEALTH REHABILITATION HOSPITAL OF ERIE (O, 100 beds) 143 East Second Street, Erie, PA, Zip 16507–1501; tel. 814/878–1200; Janet Hein, Chief Executive Officer

ENCOMPASS HEALTH REHABILITATION HOSPITAL OF HAMARVILLE (O, 50 beds) 320 Guys Run Road, Pittsburgh, PA, Zip 15238–0460, Mailing Address: P.O. Box 11460, 15238–0460, tel. 412/828–1300; Michelle P. Cunningham, Chief Executive Officer
**Web address:** www.healthsouthharmarville.com

ENCOMPASS HEALTH REHABILITATION HOSPITAL OF MECHANICSBURG (O, 75 beds) 175 Lancaster Boulevard, Mechanicsburg, PA, Zip 17055–3562; tel. 717/691–3700; Josette M. Myers, Chief Executive Officer
**Web address:** www.healthsouthpa.com

ENCOMPASS HEALTH REHABILITATION HOSPITAL OF SEWICKLEY (O, 55 beds) 303 Camp Meeting Road, Sewickley, PA, Zip 15143–8322; tel. 412/741–9500; Leah Laffey, R.N., Chief Executive Officer

ENCOMPASS HEALTH REHABILITATION HOSPITAL OF YORK (O, 90 beds) 1850 Normandie Drive, York, PA, Zip 17408–1534; tel. 717/767–6941; Michelle Fitzgerald, R.N., Chief Executive Officer
**Web address:** https://www.encompasshealth.com/yorkrehab

GEISINGER ENCOMPASS HEALTH REHABILITATION HOSPITAL (O, 42 beds) 64 Rehab Lane, Danville, PA, Zip 17821–8498; tel. 570/271–6733; Lorie Dillon, Chief Executive Officer

**PUERTO RICO:** ENCOMPASS HEALTH REHABILITATION HOSPITAL OF MANATI (O, 40 beds) Carretera 2, Kilometro 47 7, Manati, PR, Zip 674; tel. 787/621–3800; Enid Y. Gonzalez, Chief Executive Officer
**Web address:** www.healthsouth.com

ENCOMPASS HEALTH REHABILITATION HOSPITAL OF SAN JUAN (O, 32 beds) University Hospital, 3rd Floor, San Juan, PR, Zip 923, Mailing Address: P.O. Box 70344, 923, tel. 787/274–5100; Daniel Del Castillo, Chief Executive Officer

**SOUTH CAROLINA:** ANMED HEALTH REHABILITATION HOSPITAL (O, 60 beds) 1 Spring Back Way, Anderson, SC, Zip 29621–2676; tel. 864/716–2600; Denise R. Murray, Chief Executive Officer
**Web address:** www.anmedrehab.com

ENCOMPASS HEALTH REHABILITATION HOSPITAL OF CHARLESTON (O, 49 beds) 9181 Medcom Street, Charleston, SC, Zip 29406–9168; tel. 843/820–7777; Michele M. Skripps, R.N., Chief Executive Officer
**Web address:** www.healthsouthcharleston.com

ENCOMPASS HEALTH REHABILITATION HOSPITAL OF COLUMBIA (O, 96 beds) 2935 Colonial Drive, Columbia, SC, Zip 29203–6811; tel. 803/254–7777; Chris Daughtry, Chief Executive Officer

ENCOMPASS HEALTH REHABILITATION HOSPITAL OF FLORENCE (O, 88 beds) 900 East Cheves Street, Florence, SC, Zip 29506–2704; tel. 843/679–9000; Brian Nunn, R.N., Chief Executive Officer
**Web address:** www.healthsouthflorence.com

ENCOMPASS HEALTH REHABILITATION HOSPITAL OF ROCK HILL (O, 50 beds) 1795 Dr. Frank Gaston Boulevard, Rock Hill, SC, Zip 29732–1190; tel. 803/326–3500; Deanna Martin, Chief Executive Officer
**Web address:** www.healthsouthrockhill.com

**TENNESSEE:** ENCOMPASS HEALTH REHABILITATION HOSPITAL OF CHATTANOOGA (O, 50 beds) 2412 McCallie Avenue, Chattanooga, TN, Zip 37404–3398; tel. 423/698–0221; Scott Rowe, Chief Executive Officer
**Web address:** www.healthsouthchattanooga.com

ENCOMPASS HEALTH REHABILITATION HOSPITAL OF FRANKLIN (O, 40 beds) 1000 Physicians Way, Franklin, TN, Zip 37067–1471; tel. 615/721–4000; Scott J. Peterson, Chief Executive Officer

ENCOMPASS HEALTH REHABILITATION HOSPITAL OF KINGSPORT (O, 50 beds) 113 Cassel Drive, Kingsport, TN, Zip 37660–3775; tel. 423/246–7240; Troy Clark, Chief Executive Officer
**Web address:** www.healthsouthkingsport.com

ENCOMPASS HEALTH REHABILITATION HOSPITAL OF MEMPHIS (O, 72 beds) 1282 Union Avenue, Memphis, TN, Zip 38104–3414; tel. 901/722–2000; Toni Wackerfuss, Chief Executive Officer
**Web address:** www.healthsouthmemphis.com

ENCOMPASS HEALTH REHABILITATION HOSPITAL OF NORTH MEMPHIS (O, 50 beds) 4100 Austin Peay Highway, Memphis, TN, Zip 38128–2502; tel. 901/213–5400; Adam Yoe, Chief Executive Officer
**Web address:** www.healthsouthnorthmemphis.com

QUILLEN REHABILITATION HOSPITAL (O, 31 beds) 2511 Wesley Street, Johnson City, TN, Zip 37601–1723; tel. 423/952–1700; Brian Luff, Chief Executive Officer

VANDERBILT STALLWORTH REHABILITATION HOSPITAL (O, 80 beds) 2201 Childrens Way, Nashville, TN, Zip 37212–3165; tel. 615/320–7600; Jeffrey Palmucci, Chief Executive Officer
**Web address:** www.vanderbiltstallworthrehab.com

For explanation of codes following names, see page B2.
★ Indicates Type III membership in the American Hospital Association.

Section B

WEST TENNESSEE HEALTHCARE REHABILITATION HOSPITAL JACKSON (O, 48 beds) 616 West Forest Avenue, Jackson, TN, Zip 38301–3902; tel. 731/574–3000; Julie Taylor, Chief Executive Officer
**Web address:** www.https://encompasshealth.com/locations/jacksonrehab/

WEST TENNESSEE REHABILITATION HOSPITAL CANE CREEK (O, 40 beds) 180 Mount Pelia Road, Martin, TN, Zip 38237–3812; tel. 731/587–4231; Rick Johnson, Chief Executive Officer

**TEXAS:** CHI ST. JOSEPH HEALTH REHABILITATION HOSPITAL, AN AFFILIATE OF ENCOMPASS HEALTH (O, 49 beds) 1600 Joseph Drive, Suite 2000, Bryan, TX, Zip 77802–1502; tel. 979/213–4300; Amy Gray, Chief Executive Officer
**Web address:** www.encompasshealth.com/locations/stjrehab

CHRISTUS TRINITY MOTHER FRANCES REHABILITATION HOSPITAL, A PARTNER OF ENCOMPASS HEALTH (O, 94 beds) 3131 Troup Highway, Tyler, TX, Zip 75701–8352; tel. 903/510–7000; Sharla Anderson, Chief Executive Officer

ENCOMPASS HEALTH REHABILITATION HOSPITAL MIDLAND ODESSA (O, 80 beds) 1800 Heritage Boulevard, Midland, TX, Zip 79707–9750; tel. 432/520–1600; Jason Dan. Hudson, R.N., Chief Executive Officer
**Web address:** www.healthsouthmidland.com

ENCOMPASS HEALTH REHABILITATION HOSPITAL THE VINTAGE (O, 60 beds) 20180 Chasewood Park Drive, Houston, TX, Zip 77070–1436; tel. 281/205–5100; Krista Uselman, Chief Executive Officer
**Web address:** www.reliantnwhouston.com

ENCOMPASS HEALTH REHABILITATION HOSPITAL THE WOODLANDS (O, 84 beds) 18550 'IH' 45 South, Conroe, TX, Zip 77384; tel. 281/364–2000; Jennifer Brewer, Chief Executive Officer

ENCOMPASS HEALTH REHABILITATION HOSPITAL VISION PARK (O, 60 beds) 117 Vision Park Boulevard, Shenandoah, TX, Zip 77384–3001; tel. 936/444–1700; Jennifer Brewer, Chief Executive Officer
**Web address:** www.healthsouthvisionpark.com/

ENCOMPASS HEALTH REHABILITATION HOSPITAL OF ABILENE (O, 60 beds) 6401 Directors Parkway, Abilene, TX, Zip 79606–5869; tel. 325/691–1600; Joe Roberson, Chief Executive Officer

ENCOMPASS HEALTH REHABILITATION HOSPITAL OF ARLINGTON (O, 85 beds) 3200 Matlock Road, Arlington, TX, Zip 76015–2911; tel. 817/468–4000; Tyrrell Taplin, Chief Executive Officer
**Web address:** www.healthsoutharlington.com

ENCOMPASS HEALTH REHABILITATION HOSPITAL OF AUSTIN (O, 60 beds) 330 West Ben White Boulevard, Austin, TX, Zip 78704; tel. 512/730–4800; Lauren Suarez, Chief Executive Officer
**Web address:** www.healthsouthaustin.com

ENCOMPASS HEALTH REHABILITATION HOSPITAL OF CITY VIEW (O, 62 beds) 6701 Oakmont Boulevard, Fort Worth, TX, Zip 76132–2957; tel. 817/370–4700; Janell Briscoe, Chief Executive Officer

ENCOMPASS HEALTH REHABILITATION HOSPITAL OF CYPRESS (O, 60 beds) 13031 Wortham Center Drive, Houston, TX, Zip 77065–5662; tel. 832/280–2500; Sheila A. Bollier, Chief Executive Officer
**Web address:** www.healthsouthcypress.com

ENCOMPASS HEALTH REHABILITATION HOSPITAL OF DALLAS (O, 40 beds) 7930 Northaven Road, Dallas, TX, Zip 75230–3331; tel. 214/706–8200; Daniel MacNicol, Chief Executive Officer

ENCOMPASS HEALTH REHABILITATION HOSPITAL OF HUMBLE (O, 60 beds) 19002 McKay Drive, Humble, TX, Zip 77338–5701; tel. 281/446–6148; Angela L. Simmons, Chief Executive Officer
**Web address:** www.healthsouthhumble.com

ENCOMPASS HEALTH REHABILITATION HOSPITAL OF KATY (O, 40 beds) 23331 Grand Reserve Drive, Katy, TX, Zip 77494; tel. 281/505–3500; Nicholas Hardin, FACHE, Chief Executive Officer

ENCOMPASS HEALTH REHABILITATION HOSPITAL OF PEARLAND (O, 40 beds) 2121 Business Center Drive, Pearland, TX, Zip 77584–2153; tel. 346/907–3000; Michael Cabiro, Chief Executive Officer
**Web address:** https://www.encompasshealth.com/locations/pearlandrehab

ENCOMPASS HEALTH REHABILITATION HOSPITAL OF PLANO (O, 83 beds) 2800 West 15th Street, Plano, TX, Zip 75075–7526; tel. 972/612–9000; Brandon Tudor, Chief Executive Officer

ENCOMPASS HEALTH REHABILITATION HOSPITAL OF RICHARDSON (O, 50 beds) 3351 Waterview Parkway, Richardson, TX, Zip 75080–1449; tel. 972/398–5700; LaDessa Forrest, Administrator
**Web address:** www.relianthcp.com

ENCOMPASS HEALTH REHABILITATION HOSPITAL OF ROUND ROCK (O, 75 beds) 1400 Hesters Crossing Road, Round Rock, TX, Zip 78681–8025; tel. 512/244–4400; David Jones, Chief Executive Officer
**Web address:** https://www.encompasshealth.com/roundrockrehab

ENCOMPASS HEALTH REHABILITATION HOSPITAL OF SAN ANTONIO (O, 96 beds) 9119 Cinnamon Hill, San Antonio, TX, Zip 78240–5401; tel. 210/691–0737; Andrew Meade, Chief Executive Officer
**Web address:** www.hsrioca.com

ENCOMPASS HEALTH REHABILITATION HOSPITAL OF SUGAR LAND (O, 50 beds) 1325 Highway 6, Sugar Land, TX, Zip 77478–4906; tel. 281/276–7574; Bindu Varghese, R.N., Chief Executive Officer

ENCOMPASS HEALTH REHABILITATION HOSPITAL OF TEXARKANA (O, 60 beds) 515 West 12th Street, Texarkana, TX, Zip 75501–4416; tel. 903/735–5000; Harlo McCall, Chief Executive Officer
**Web address:** www.healthsouthtexarkana.com

ENCOMPASS HEALTH REHABILITATION HOSPITAL OF WICHITA FALLS (O, 63 beds) 3901 Armory Road, Wichita Falls, TX, Zip 76302–2204; tel. 940/720–5700; Boyd Davis III, Chief Executive Officer
**Web address:** www.healthsouthwichitafalls.com

ENCOMPASS HEALTH REHABILITATION HOSPITAL OF THE MID-CITIES (O, 60 beds) 2304 State Highway 121, Bedford, TX, Zip 76021–5985; tel. 817/684–2000; Robert M. Smart, Chief Executive Officer
**Web address:** www.relianthcp.com

SOUTH PLAINS REHABILITATION HOSPITAL (C, 40 beds) 5406 Colgate Street, Lubbock, TX, Zip 79416; tel. 806/507–3500; Christopher Wortham, Chief Executive Officer
**Web address:** https://www.encompasshealth.com/locations/southplainsrehab

**UTAH:** ENCOMPASS HEALTH REHABILITATION HOSPITAL OF UTAH (O, 45 beds) 8074 South 1300 East, Sandy, UT, Zip 84094–0743; tel. 801/561–3400; Charles Smith, Chief Executive Officer
**Web address:** https://www.encompasshealth.com/utahrehab

**VIRGINIA:** ENCOMPASS HEALTH REHABILITATION HOSPITAL OF FREDERICKSBURG (O, 40 beds) 300 Park Hill Drive, Fredericksburg, VA, Zip 22401–3387; tel. 540/368–7300; David Cashwell, Chief Executive Officer

ENCOMPASS HEALTH REHABILITATION HOSPITAL OF NORTHERN VIRGINIA (O, 60 beds) 24430 Millstream Drive, Aldie, VA, Zip 20105–3098; tel. 703/957–2000; Alfred Santos, Chief Executive Officer
**Web address:** www.healthsouthnorthernvirginia.com

ENCOMPASS HEALTH REHABILITATION HOSPITAL OF PETERSBURG (O, 53 beds) 95 Medical Park Boulevard, Petersburg, VA, Zip 23805–9233; tel. 804/504–8100; Dale Poe, Chief Executive Officer

ENCOMPASS HEALTH REHABILITATION HOSPITAL OF RICHMOND (O, 28 beds) 5700 Fitzhugh Avenue, Richmond, VA, Zip 23226–1800; tel. 804/288–5700; Vivian White, Chief Executive Officer
**Web address:** https://www.encompasshealth.com

REHABILITATION HOSPITAL OF BRISTOL (O, 25 beds) 103 North Street, Bristol, VA, Zip 24201–3201; tel. 276/642–7900; Troy Clark, Chief Executive Officer
**Web address:** www.rehabilitationhospitalswvirginia.com

UVA ENCOMPASS HEALTH REHABILITATION HOSPITAL (O, 50 beds) 515 Ray C Hunt Drive, Charlottesville, VA, Zip 22903–2981; tel. 434/244–2000; Louis Collier, Chief Executive Officer

**WEST VIRGINIA:** ENCOMPASS HEALTH REHABILITATION HOSPITAL OF HUNTINGTON (O, 60 beds) 6900 West Country Club Drive, Huntington, WV, Zip 25705–2000; tel. 304/733–1060; Michael E. Zuliani, Chief Executive Officer
**Web address:** https://www.encompasshealth.com/huntingtonrehab

ENCOMPASS HEALTH REHABILITATION HOSPITAL OF MORGANTOWN (O, 96 beds) 1160 Van Voorhis Road, Morgantown, WV, Zip 26505–3437; tel. 304/598–1100; Tracy Vinciguerra, Chief Executive Officer
**Web address:** www.healthsouthmountainview.com

ENCOMPASS HEALTH REHABILITATION HOSPITAL OF PARKERSBURG (O, 40 beds) 3 Western Hills Drive, Parkersburg, WV, Zip 26105–8122; tel. 304/420–1300; Alvin R. Lawson, JD, Chief Executive Officer

For explanation of codes following names, see page B2.
★ Indicates Type III membership in the American Hospital Association.

ENCOMPASS HEALTH REHABILITATION HOSPITAL OF PRINCETON (O, 45 beds) 120 Twelfth Street, Princeton, WV, Zip 24740–2352; tel. 304/487–8000; Robert Williams, Chief Executive Officer
**Web address:** www.healthsouthsouthernhills.com

| Owned, leased, sponsored: | 129 hospitals | 8512 beds |
|---|---|---|
| Contract–managed: | 1 hospitals | 40 beds |
| **Totals:** | 130 hospitals | 8552 beds |

## 0959: EPHRAIM MCDOWELL HEALTH (NP)

217 South Third Street, Danville, KY Zip 40422–1823; tel. 859/239–1000; Daniel E. McKay, Chief Executive Officer
**(Independent Hospital System)**

**KENTUCKY:** EPHRAIM MCDOWELL FORT LOGAN HOSPITAL (O, 25 beds) 110 Metker Trail, Stanford, KY, Zip 40484–1020; tel. 606/365–4600; Ina Louise . Glass, MSN, Administrator
**Web address:** www.fortloganhospital.org

EPHRAIM MCDOWELL JAMES B. HAGGIN MEMORIAL HOSPITAL (O, 25 beds) 464 Linden Avenue, Harrodsburg, KY, Zip 40330–1862; tel. 859/734–5441; Lynne Warner Lynn, R.N., Administrator

EPHRAIM MCDOWELL REGIONAL MEDICAL CENTER (O, 159 beds) 217 South Third Street, Danville, KY, Zip 40422–1823; tel. 859/239–1000; Daniel E. McKay, Chief Executive Officer
**Web address:** www.emrmc.org

| Owned, leased, sponsored: | 3 hospitals | 209 beds |
|---|---|---|
| Contract–managed: | 0 hospitals | 0 beds |
| **Totals:** | 3 hospitals | 209 beds |

## 0525: ERLANGER HEALTH SYSTEM (NP)

975 East Third Street, Chattanooga, TN Zip 37403–2147; tel. 423/778–7000; William L. Jackson Jr, M.D., President and Chief Executive Officer
**(Centralized Physician/Insurance Health System)**

**NORTH CAROLINA:** ERLANGER WESTERN CAROLINA HOSPITAL (O, 25 beds) 3990 U S Highway 64 East Alt, Murphy, NC, Zip 28906–7917; tel. 828/837–8161; Mark E. Kimball, Chief Executive Officer
**Web address:** https://www.erlanger.org

**TENNESSEE:** ERLANGER BLEDSOE HOSPITAL (C, 25 beds) 71 Wheeler Avenue, Pikeville, TN, Zip 37367, Mailing Address: P.O. Box 699, 37367–0699, tel. 423/447–2112; Stephanie Boynton, Administrator
**Web address:** www.erlanger.org

ERLANGER MEDICAL CENTER (O, 690 beds) 975 East Third Street, Chattanooga, TN, Zip 37403–2147; tel. 423/778–7000; William L. Jackson Jr, M.D., President and Chief Executive Officer

| Owned, leased, sponsored: | 2 hospitals | 715 beds |
|---|---|---|
| Contract–managed: | 1 hospitals | 25 beds |
| **Totals:** | 3 hospitals | 740 beds |

## 0382: ERNEST HEALTH, INC. (IO)

7770 Jefferson Street NE, Suite 320, Albuquerque, NM Zip 87109–4386; tel. 505/856–5300; Darby Brockette, Chief Executive Officer
**(Independent Hospital System)**

**ARIZONA:** MOUNTAIN VALLEY REGIONAL REHABILITATION HOSPITAL (O, 16 beds) 3700 North Windsong Drive, Prescott Valley, AZ, Zip 86314–1253; tel. 928/759–8800; Judy Baum, Chief Executive Officer
**Web address:** www.mvrrh.ernesthealth.com

REHABILITATION HOSPITAL OF NORTHERN ARIZONA (O, 40 beds) 1851 North Gemini Drive, Flagstaff, AZ, Zip 86001–1607; tel. 928/774–7070; Chris LaFontsee, Chief Executive Officer
**Web address:** www.ernesthealth.com/gallery–item/rehabilitation–hospital–of–northern–arizona/

**COLORADO:** NORTHERN COLORADO LONG TERM ACUTE HOSPITAL (O, 40 beds) 4401 Union Street, Johnstown, CO, Zip 80534; tel. 970/619–3663; Blake Sims, Chief Executive Officer

NORTHERN COLORADO REHABILITATION HOSPITAL (O, 40 beds) 4401 Union Street, Johnstown, CO, Zip 80534–2800; tel. 970/619–3400; Brenda Simon, Chief Executive Officer
**Web address:** www.ncrh.ernesthealth.com

**IDAHO:** NORTHERN IDAHO ADVANCED CARE HOSPITAL (O, 40 beds) 600 North Cecil Road, Post Falls, ID, Zip 83854–6200; tel. 208/262–2800; Una Alderman, Chief Executive Officer

REHABILITATION HOSPITAL OF THE NORTHWEST (O, 25 beds) 3372 East Jenalan Avenue, Post Falls, ID, Zip 83854–7787; tel. 208/262–8700; Darby Brockette, Chief Executive Officer
**Web address:** www.ernesthealth.com

**INDIANA:** LAFAYETTE REGIONAL REHABILITATION HOSPITAL (O, 40 beds) 950 Park East Boulevard, Lafayette, IN, Zip 47905–0792; tel. 765/447–4040; Herschel Carey, Chief Executive Officer
**Web address:** www.lrrh.ernesthealth.com

**MONTANA:** ADVANCED CARE HOSPITAL OF MONTANA (O, 40 beds) 3528 Gabel Road, Billings, MT, Zip 59102–7307; tel. 406/373–8000; Judi Powers, Chief Executive Officer

**NEW MEXICO:** ADVANCED CARE HOSPITAL OF SOUTHERN NEW MEXICO (O, 40 beds) 4451 East Lohman Avenue, Las Cruces, NM, Zip 88011–8267; tel. 575/521–6600; Claudia Saiz, Chief Executive Officer
**Web address:** www.achsnm.ernesthealth.com

REHABILITATION HOSPITAL OF SOUTHERN NEW MEXICO (O, 40 beds) 4441 East Lohman Avenue, Las Cruces, NM, Zip 88011–8267; tel. 575/521–6400; Sabrina Martin, Chief Executive Officer

**OHIO:** REHABILITATION HOSPITAL OF NORTHWEST OHIO (O, 40 beds) 1455 West Medical Loop, Toledo, OH, Zip 43614; tel. 419/214–6600; Scott Williams, Chief Executive Officer

**SOUTH CAROLINA:** GREENWOOD REGIONAL REHABILITATION HOSPITAL (O, 54 beds) 1530 Parkway, Greenwood, SC, Zip 29646–4027; tel. 864/330–1800; Kristin Manske, Chief Executive Officer
**Web address:** www.grrh.ernesthealth.com

**TEXAS:** LAREDO REHABILITATION HOSPITAL (O, 20 beds) 2005a East Bustamante Street, Laredo, TX, Zip 78041; tel. 956/764–8555; Hanna Huang, Administrator and Chief Operating Officer

LAREDO SPECIALTY HOSPITAL (O, 40 beds) 2005 Bustamante Street, Laredo, TX, Zip 78041–5470; tel. 956/753–5353; Hanna Huang, Administrator and Chief Operating Officer
**Web address:** www.lsh.ernesthealth.com

MESQUITE REHABILITATION INSTITUTE (O, 30 beds) 1023 North Belt Line Road, Mesquite, TX, Zip 75149–1788; tel. 972/216–2400; Michael Ridgeway, Chief Executive Officer
**Web address:** www.mesquiterehab.ernesthealth.com/

MESQUITE SPECIALTY HOSPITAL (O, 40 beds) 1024 North Galloway Avenue, Mesquite, TX, Zip 75149–2434; tel. 972/216–2300; Michael Ridgeway, Chief Executive Officer

NEW BRAUNFELS REGIONAL REHABILITATION HOSPITAL (O, 40 beds) 2041 Sundance Parkway, New Braunfels, TX, Zip 78130–2779; tel. 830/625–6700; Nicholas Nilest, Chief Executive Officer
**Web address:** www.nbrrh.ernesthealth.com

SOUTH TEXAS REHABILITATION HOSPITAL (O, 40 beds) 425 East Alton Gloor Boulevard, Brownsville, TX, Zip 78526–3361; tel. 956/554–6000; Leo Garza, Chief Executive Officer

TRUSTPOINT REHABILITATION HOSPITAL OF LUBBOCK (O, 72 beds) 4302A Princeton Street, Lubbock, TX, Zip 79415–1304; tel. 806/749–2222; Craig Bragg, Chief Executive Officer
**Web address:** www.trustpointhospital.com/

**UTAH:** NORTHERN UTAH REHABILITATION HOSPITAL (O, 20 beds) 5825 Harrison Boulevard, South Ogden, UT, Zip 84403–4316; tel. 801/475–5254; Scot Stevens, Chief Executive Officer
**Web address:** www.ernesthealth.com/gallery–item/northern–utah–rehabilitation–hospital/

UTAH VALLEY SPECIALTY HOSPITAL (O, 40 beds) 306 River Bend Lane, Provo, UT, Zip 84604–5625; tel. 801/226–8880; Brynn Beck, Chief Executive Officer

For explanation of codes following names, see page B2.
★ Indicates Type III membership in the American Hospital Association.

**WYOMING**: ELKHORN VALLEY REHABILITATION HOSPITAL (O, 41 beds) 5715 East 2nd Street, Casper, WY, Zip 82609–4322; tel. 307/265–0005; Connie Longwell, Chief Executive Officer
**Web address**: www.evrh.ernesthealth.com/

| | | |
|---|---|---|
| Owned, leased, sponsored: | 22 hospitals | 838 beds |
| Contract–managed: | 0 hospitals | 0 beds |
| Totals: | 22 hospitals | 838 beds |

---

**★0396: ESSENTIA HEALTH** (NP)
502 East Second Street, Duluth, MN Zip 55805–1913; tel. 218/786–8376; David C. Herman, M.D., Chief Executive Officer
**(Moderately Centralized Health System)**

**IDAHO**: CLEARWATER VALLEY HOSPITAL AND CLINICS (O, 23 beds) 301 Cedar, Orofino, ID, Zip 83544–9029; tel. 208/476–4555; Lenne Bonner, President
**Web address**: www.smh–cvhc.org

ST. MARY'S HOSPITAL (O, 28 beds) 701 Lewiston Street , Cottonwood, ID, Zip 83522–9750, Mailing Address: P.O. Box 137, 83522–0137, tel. 208/962–3251; Lenne Bonner, President

**MINNESOTA**: ESSENTIA HEALTH DULUTH (O, 154 beds) 502 East Second Street, Duluth, MN, Zip 55805–1982; tel. 218/727–8762; Bradley Beard, Chief Operating Officer
**Web address**: www.smdcmedicalcenter.org

ESSENTIA HEALTH MOOSE LAKE (O, 25 beds) 4572 County Road 61, Moose Lake, MN, Zip 55767–9405; tel. 218/485–4481; Michael Youso, Chief Executive Officer
**Web address**: www.mercymooselake.org

ESSENTIA HEALTH NORTHERN PINES MEDICAL CENTER (O, 58 beds) 5211 Highway 110, Aurora, MN, Zip 55705–1599; tel. 218/229–2211; Laura Ackman, Chief Operating Officer and Administrator

ESSENTIA HEALTH SANDSTONE (O, 9 beds) 705 Lundorff Drive, Sandstone, MN, Zip 55072–5009; tel. 320/245–2212; Michael D. Hedrix, Administrator and President
**Web address**: www.pinemedicalcenter.org

ESSENTIA HEALTH ST. MARY'S – DETROIT LAKES (O, 132 beds) 1027 Washington Avenue, Detroit Lakes, MN, Zip 56501–3409; tel. 218/847–5611; Ryan Hill, Interim Administrator

ESSENTIA HEALTH ST. MARY'S MEDICAL CENTER (O, 307 beds) 407 East Third Street, Duluth, MN, Zip 55805–1984; tel. 218/786–4000; James Garvey, Senior Vice President Hospital Practice, Essentia Health East
**Web address**: www.essentiahealth.org/StMarysMedicalCenter/FindaClinic/Essentia–HealthSt–Marys–Medical–Center–46.aspx

ESSENTIA HEALTH–ADA (O, 14 beds) 201 9th Street West, Ada, MN, Zip 56510–1279; tel. 218/784–5000; Erin Stoltman, Administrator

ESSENTIA HEALTH–DEER RIVER (O, 52 beds) 115 10th Avenue NE , Deer River, MN, Zip 56636–8795; tel. 218/246–2900; Marsha Green, Administrator and Chief Operating Officer
**Web address**: www.essentiahealth.org

ESSENTIA HEALTH–FOSSTON (O, 74 beds) 900 Hilligoss Boulevard SE, Fosston, MN, Zip 56542–1599; tel. 218/435–1133; Kevin Gish, Administrator and Vice President
**Web address**: www.essentiahealth.org

ESSENTIA HEALTH–GRACEVILLE (O, 55 beds) 115 West Second Street, Graceville, MN, Zip 56240–4845, Mailing Address: P.O. Box 157, 56240–0157, tel. 320/748–7223; Julie Rosenberg, Administrator
**Web address**: www.essentiahealth.org/HolyTrinityHospital/FindaClinic/Essentia–HealthHoly–Trinity–Hospital–96.aspx

ESSENTIA HEALTH–ST. JOSEPH'S MEDICAL CENTER (O, 127 beds) 523 North Third Street, Brainerd, MN, Zip 56401–3098; tel. 218/829–2861; Adam Rees, President

ESSENTIA HEALTH–VIRGINIA (L, 144 beds) 901 Ninth Street North, Virginia, MN, Zip 55792–2398; tel. 218/741–3340; Sam Stone, Operations Administrator
**Web address**: www.essentiahealth.org

**NORTH DAKOTA**: ESSENTIA HEALTH FARGO (O, 137 beds) 3000 32nd Avenue South, Fargo, ND, Zip 58103–6132; tel. 701/364–8000; Al Hurley, West Region Chief Operating Officer
**Web address**: www.essentiahealth.com

**WISCONSIN**: ESSENTIA HEALTH ST. MARY'S HOSPITAL OF SUPERIOR (O, 25 beds) 3500 Tower Avenue, Superior, WI, Zip 54880–5395; tel. 715/817–7000; Kim Renee. Pearson, Administrator

| | | |
|---|---|---|
| Owned, leased, sponsored: | 16 hospitals | 1364 beds |
| Contract–managed: | 0 hospitals | 0 beds |
| Totals: | 16 hospitals | 1364 beds |

---

**0951: EVEREST REHABILITATION HOSPITALS, LLC** (IO)
5100 Belt Line Road, Suite 310, Dallas, TX Zip 75254–7559; tel. 469/713–1145; Jay Quintana, Chief Executive Officer and Co–Founder

**TEXAS**: EVEREST REHABILITATION HOSPITAL LONGVIEW (O, 36 beds) 701 East Loop 281, Longview, TX, Zip 75605–5006; tel. 430/240–4600; Jay Lindsey, Chief Executive Officer
**Web address**: www.everestrehab.com

EVEREST REHABILITATION HOSPITAL TEMPLE (O, 36 beds) 23621 SE H.K. Dodgen Loop, Temple, TX, Zip 76504; tel. 254/410–0555; Michael Hutka, Chief Executive Officer

| | | |
|---|---|---|
| Owned, leased, sponsored: | 2 hospitals | 72 beds |
| Contract–managed: | 0 hospitals | 0 beds |
| Totals: | 2 hospitals | 72 beds |

---

**2395: EXCELA HEALTH** (NP)
532 West Pittsburgh Street, Greensburg, PA Zip 15601, 134 Industrial Park Road, 15601–7328, tel. 724/832–5050; John Sphon, Chief Executive Officer
**(Independent Hospital System)**

**PENNSYLVANIA**: EXCELA FRICK HOSPITAL (O, 33 beds) 508 South Church Street, Mount Pleasant, PA, Zip 15666–1790; tel. 724/547–1500; John Sphon, Chief Executive Officer

EXCELA HEALTH WESTMORELAND HOSPITAL (O, 270 beds) 532 West Pittsburgh Street, Greensburg, PA, Zip 15601–2282; tel. 724/832–4000; John Sphon, Chief Executive Officer
**Web address**: www.excelahealth.org

EXCELA LATROBE AREA HOSPITAL (O, 114 beds) One Mellon Way, Latrobe, PA, Zip 15650–1096; tel. 724/537–1000; John Sphon, Chief Executive Officer
**Web address**: www.excelahealth.org

| | | |
|---|---|---|
| Owned, leased, sponsored: | 3 hospitals | 417 beds |
| Contract–managed: | 0 hospitals | 0 beds |
| Totals: | 3 hospitals | 417 beds |

---

**0814: FAITH REGIONAL HEALTH SERVICES** (NP)
2700 West Norfolk Avenue, Norfolk, NE Zip 68701–4438, Mailing Address: P.O. Box 869, 68702–0869, tel. 402/371–4880; Kelly Driscoll, R.N., FACHE, President and Chief Executive Officer
**(Independent Hospital System)**

**NEBRASKA**: FAITH REGIONAL HEALTH SERVICES (O, 147 beds) 2700 West Norfolk Avenue, Norfolk, NE, Zip 68701–4438, Mailing Address: P.O. Box 869, 68702–0869, tel. 402/371–4880; Kelly Driscoll, R.N., FACHE, President and Chief Executive Officer
**Web address**: www.frhs.org

For explanation of codes following names, see page B2.
★ Indicates Type III membership in the American Hospital Association.

GENOA MEDICAL FACILITIES (C, 58 beds) 706 Ewing Avenue, Genoa, NE, Zip 68640–3035, Mailing Address: P.O. Box 310, 68640–0310, tel. 402/993–2283; Amanda Roebuck, Chief Executive Officer
**Web address**: www.genoamedical.org/

NIOBRARA VALLEY HOSPITAL (C, 20 beds) 401 South Fifth Street, Lynch, NE, Zip 68746–0118, Mailing Address: P.O. Box 118, 68746–0118, tel. 402/569–2451; Kelly Kalkowski, Chief Executive Officer

WEST HOLT MEDICAL SERVICES (C, 17 beds) 406 West Neely Street, Atkinson, NE, Zip 68713–4801; tel. 402/925–2811; Ashley Rivera, Chief Executive Officer
**Web address**: www.westholtmed.org

| | | |
|---|---|---|
| Owned, leased, sponsored: | 1 hospitals | 147 beds |
| Contract–managed: | 3 hospitals | 95 beds |
| Totals: | 4 hospitals | 242 beds |

## 0397: FINGER LAKES HEALTH (NP)

196 North Street, Geneva, NY Zip 14456–1651; tel. 315/787–4000; Jose Acevedo, M.D., President and Chief Executive Officer
**(Independent Hospital System)**

**NEW YORK**: GENEVA GENERAL HOSPITAL (O, 132 beds) 196 North Street, Geneva, NY, Zip 14456–1694; tel. 315/787–4000; Jose Acevedo, M.D., President and Chief Executive Officer
**Web address**: www.flhealth.org

SOLDIERS AND SAILORS MEMORIAL HOSPITAL (O, 186 beds) 418 North Main Street, Penn Yan, NY, Zip 14527–1085; tel. 315/531–2000; Jose Acevedo, M.D., President and Chief Executive Officer
**Web address**: www.flhealth.org

| | | |
|---|---|---|
| Owned, leased, sponsored: | 2 hospitals | 318 beds |
| Contract–managed: | 0 hospitals | 0 beds |
| Totals: | 2 hospitals | 318 beds |

## 1010: FIRST PHYSICIANS CAPITAL GROUP, INC. (IO)

14201 Wireless Way, Suite B–100, Oklahoma City, OK Zip 73134–2521; tel. 405/246–0218; Sean Kirrane, Chief Executive Officer

**OKLAHOMA**: CARNEGIE TRI–COUNTY MUNICIPAL HOSPITAL (C, 17 beds) 102 North Broadway, Carnegie, OK, Zip 73015, Mailing Address: P.O. Box 97, 73015–0097, tel. 580/654–1050; Thomas Henton, Chief Executive Officer

PHYSICIANS' HOSPITAL IN ANADARKO (C, 25 beds) 1002 Central Boulevard East, Anadarko, OK, Zip 73005–4496; tel. 405/247–2551; Travis A. Villani, FACHE, Chief Executive Officer and Administrator
**Web address**: www.anadarkohospital.com

| | | |
|---|---|---|
| Owned, leased, sponsored: | 0 hospitals | 0 beds |
| Contract–managed: | 2 hospitals | 42 beds |
| Totals: | 2 hospitals | 42 beds |

## ★0243: FIRSTHEALTH OF THE CAROLINAS (NP)

155 Memorial Drive, Pinehurst, NC Zip 28374–8710, Mailing Address: P.O. Box 3000, 28374–3000, tel. 910/715–1000; Mickey W. Foster, Chief Executive Officer
**(Centralized Physician/Insurance Health System)**

**NORTH CAROLINA**: FIRSTHEALTH MONTGOMERY MEMORIAL HOSPITAL (O, 5 beds) 520 Allen Street, Troy, NC, Zip 27371–2802; tel. 910/571–5000; Rebecca W. Carter, MSN, R.N., FACHE, President
**Web address**: www.firsthealth.org

FIRSTHEALTH MOORE REGIONAL HOSPITAL (O, 376 beds) 155 Memorial Drive, Pinehurst, NC, Zip 28374–8710, Mailing Address: P.O. Box 3000, 28374–3000, tel. 910/715–1000; Mickey W. Foster, Chief Executive Officer

| | | |
|---|---|---|
| Owned, leased, sponsored: | 2 hospitals | 381 beds |
| Contract–managed: | 0 hospitals | 0 beds |
| Totals: | 2 hospitals | 381 beds |

## 1016: FLOYD HEALTHCARE MANAGEMENT (NP)

304 Turner McCall Boulevard, Rome, GA Zip 30165–5621, Mailing Address: P.O. Box 233, 30162–0233, tel. 706/509–5000; Kurt Stuenkel, FACHE, President and Chief Executive Officer
**(Moderately Centralized Health System)**

**ALABAMA**: FLOYD CHEROKEE MEDICAL CENTER (O, 45 beds) 400 Northwood Drive, Centre, AL, Zip 35960–1023; tel. 256/927–5531; David T. Early, FACHE, Chief Executive Officer
**Web address**: www.cherokeemedicalcenter.com

**GEORGIA**: FLOYD MEDICAL CENTER (O, 327 beds) 304 Turner McCall Boulevard, Rome, GA, Zip 30165–5621, Mailing Address: P.O. Box 233, 30162–0233, tel. 706/509–5000; Kurt Stuenkel, FACHE, President and Chief Executive Officer

POLK MEDICAL CENTER (O, 25 beds) 2360 Rockmart Highway, Cedartown, GA, Zip 30125–6029; tel. 770/748–2500; Tifani Kinard, Administrator and Chief Nursing Officer
**Web address**: www.polkhospital.org

| | | |
|---|---|---|
| Owned, leased, sponsored: | 3 hospitals | 397 beds |
| Contract–managed: | 0 hospitals | 0 beds |
| Totals: | 3 hospitals | 397 beds |

## 5345: FRANCISCAN HEALTH (CO)

1515 Dragoon Trail, Mishawaka, IN Zip 46544–4710, Mailing Address: P.O. Box 1290, 46546–1290, tel. 574/256–3935; Kevin D. Leahy, President and Chief Executive Officer
**(Independent Hospital System)**

**ILLINOIS**: FRANCISCAN HEALTH OLYMPIA FIELDS (O, 329 beds) 20201 South Crawford Avenue, Olympia Fields, IL, Zip 60461–1010; tel. 708/747–4000; Allan M. Spooner, President and Chief Executive Officer

**INDIANA**: FRANCISCAN HEALTH CARMEL (O, 6 beds) 12188B North Meridian Street, Carmel, IN, Zip 46032–4840; tel. 317/705–4500; Stephen J. Wheatley, Director of Operations
**Web address**: www.franciscanalliance.org/hospitals/carmel/Pages/default.aspx

FRANCISCAN HEALTH CRAWFORDSVILLE (O, 40 beds) 1710 Lafayette Road, Crawfordsville, IN, Zip 47933–1099; tel. 765/362–2800; Terrence Klein, Ph.D., Vice President and Chief Operating Officer

FRANCISCAN HEALTH CROWN POINT (O, 254 beds) 1201 South Main Street, Crown Point, IN, Zip 46307–8483; tel. 219/738–2100; Daniel McCormick, M.D., President and Chief Executive Officer
**Web address**: www.franciscanalliance.org

FRANCISCAN HEALTH DYER (O, 341 beds) 24 Joliet Street, Dyer, IN, Zip 46311–1799; tel. 219/865–2141; Patrick J. Maloney, Chief Executive Officer

FRANCISCAN HEALTH HAMMOND (O, 406 beds) 5454 Hohman Avenue, Hammond, IN, Zip 46320–1999; tel. 219/932–2300; Patrick J. Maloney, Chief Executive Officer
**Web address**: https://www.franciscanhealth.org/healthcare–facilities/franciscan–health–hammond–18

FRANCISCAN HEALTH INDIANAPOLIS (O, 485 beds) 8111 South Emerson Avenue, Indianapolis, IN, Zip 46237–8601; tel. 317/528–5000; James Callaghan III, M.D., President and Chief Executive Officer
**Web address**: www.stfrancishospitals.org

FRANCISCAN HEALTH LAFAYETTE EAST (O, 187 beds) 1701 South Creasy Lane, Lafayette, IN, Zip 47905–4972; tel. 765/502–4000; Terrance E. Wilson, President and Chief Executive Officer
**Web address**: www.ste.org

FRANCISCAN HEALTH MICHIGAN CITY (O, 171 beds) 301 West Homer Street, Michigan City, IN, Zip 46360–4358; tel. 219/879–8511; Dean Mazzoni, President and Chief Executive Officer

FRANCISCAN HEALTH MOORESVILLE (O, 115 beds) 1201 Hadley Road, Mooresville, IN, Zip 46158–1789; tel. 317/831–1160; Peter J. Murphy, Senior Vice President and Chief Operating Officer
**Web address**: www.franciscanalliance.org/hospitals/mooresville/Pages/default.aspx

For explanation of codes following names, see page B2.
★ Indicates Type III membership in the American Hospital Association.

FRANCISCAN HEALTH RENSSELEAR (O, 46 beds) 1104 East Grace Street, Rensselaer, IN, Zip 47978–3296; tel. 219/866–5141; Carlos Vasquez, Vice President and Chief Operating Officer
**Web address:** www.franciscanhealth.org

FRANCISCAN HEALTHCARE MUNSTER (O, 32 beds) 701 Superior Avenue, Munster, IN, Zip 46321–4037; tel. 219/924–1300; Patrick J. Maloney, Chief Executive Officer

| | | |
|---|---|---|
| **Owned, leased, sponsored:** | 12 hospitals | 2412 beds |
| **Contract–managed:** | 0 hospitals | 0 beds |
| **Totals:** | 12 hospitals | 2412 beds |

---

### ★1475: FRANCISCAN MISSIONARIES OF OUR LADY HEALTH SYSTEM, INC. (CO)

4200 Essen Lane, Baton Rouge, LA Zip 70809–2158; tel. 225/923–2701; Richard Vath, M.D., President and Chief Executive Officer

**(Moderately Centralized Health System)**

**LOUISIANA:** ASSUMPTION COMMUNITY HOSPITAL (O, 6 beds) 135 Highway 402, Napoleonville, LA, Zip 70390–2217; tel. 985/369–3600; Christina P. Hockaday, FACHE, Chief Executive Officer

OUR LADY OF LOURDES REGIONAL MEDICAL CENTER (O, 296 beds) 4801 Ambassador Caffery Parkway, Lafayette, LA, Zip 70508–6917; tel. 337/470–2000; W. Bryan. Lee, FACHE, Chief Executive Officer
**Web address:** www.lourdesrmc.com

OUR LADY OF THE ANGELS HOSPITAL (O, 57 beds) 433 Plaza Street, Bogalusa, LA, Zip 70427–3793; tel. 985/730–6700; Rene J. Ragas, President and Chief Executive Officer, Northshore Market

OUR LADY OF THE LAKE REGIONAL MEDICAL CENTER (O, 1122 beds) 5000 Hennessy Boulevard, Baton Rouge, LA, Zip 70808–4375; tel. 225/765–6565; K Scott. Wester, FACHE, President and Chief Executive Officer
**Web address:** www.ololrmc.com

ST. FRANCIS MEDICAL CENTER (O, 384 beds) 309 Jackson Street, Monroe, LA, Zip 71201–7407, Mailing Address: P.O. Box 1901, 71210–1901, tel. 318/966–4000; Kristin Wolkart, R.N., President and Chief Executive Officer
**Web address:** www.stfran.com

| | | |
|---|---|---|
| **Owned, leased, sponsored:** | 5 hospitals | 1865 beds |
| **Contract–managed:** | 0 hospitals | 0 beds |
| **Totals:** | 5 hospitals | 1865 beds |

---

### ★1455: FRANCISCAN SISTERS OF CHRISTIAN CHARITY SPONSORED MINISTRIES, INC. (CO)

1415 South Rapids Road, Manitowoc, WI Zip 54220–9302; tel. 920/684–7071; Scott McConnaha, FACHE, President and Chief Executive Officer

**(Moderately Centralized Health System)**

**NEBRASKA:** ST. FRANCIS MEMORIAL HOSPITAL (O, 88 beds) 430 North Monitor Street, West Point, NE, Zip 68788–1555; tel. 402/372–2404; David J. Ameen, Interim President and Chief Executive Officer
**Web address:** www.fcswp.org

**OHIO:** GENESIS HEALTHCARE SYSTEM (O, 321 beds) 2951 Maple Avenue, Zanesville, OH, Zip 43701–1406; tel. 740/454–5000; Matthew J. Perry, President and Chief Executive Officer

**WISCONSIN:** HOLY FAMILY MEMORIAL (O, 67 beds) 2300 Western Avenue, Manitowoc, WI, Zip 54220–3712, Mailing Address: P.O. Box 1450, 54221–1450, tel. 920/320–2011; Brett William. Norell, Interim Chief Executive Officer
**Web address:** www.hfmhealth.org

| | | |
|---|---|---|
| **Owned, leased, sponsored:** | 3 hospitals | 476 beds |
| **Contract–managed:** | 0 hospitals | 0 beds |
| **Totals:** | 3 hospitals | 476 beds |

---

### ★0271: FREEMAN HEALTH SYSTEM (NP)

1102 West 32nd Street, Joplin, MO Zip 64804–3503; tel. 417/347–1111; Paula F. Baker, President and Chief Executive Officer

**(Moderately Centralized Health System)**

**MISSOURI:** FREEMAN HEALTH SYSTEM (O, 380 beds) 1102 West 32nd Street, Joplin, MO, Zip 64804–3503; tel. 417/347–1111; Paula F. Baker, President and Chief Executive Officer
**Web address:** www.freemanhealth.com

FREEMAN NEOSHO HOSPITAL (O, 25 beds) 113 West Hickory Street, Neosho, MO, Zip 64850–1705; tel. 417/455–4352; Renee Denton, Chief Operating Officer
**Web address:** www.freemanhealth.com

NEVADA REGIONAL MEDICAL CENTER (C, 71 beds) 800 South Ash Street, Nevada, MO, Zip 64772–3223; tel. 417/667–3355; Steve Branstetter, Chief Executive Officer
**Web address:** www.nrmchealth.com

| | | |
|---|---|---|
| **Owned, leased, sponsored:** | 2 hospitals | 405 beds |
| **Contract–managed:** | 1 hospitals | 71 beds |
| **Totals:** | 3 hospitals | 476 beds |

---

### 0924: FROEDTERT HEALTH (NP)

9200 West Wisconsin Avenue, Milwaukee, WI Zip 53226–3596, Mailing Address: P.O. Box 26099, 53226–0099, tel. 414/805–3000; Catherine A. Jacobson, President and Chief Executive Officer

**WISCONSIN:** FROEDTERT MENOMONEE FALLS HOSPITAL (O, 202 beds) W180 N8085 Town Hall Road, Menomonee Falls, WI, Zip 53051–3518, Mailing Address: P.O. Box 408, 53052–0408, tel. 262/251–1000; Teresa M. Lux, President and Chief Operating Officer
**Web address:** https://www.froedtert.com

FROEDTERT WEST BEND HOSPITAL (O, 70 beds) 3200 Pleasant Valley Road, West Bend, WI, Zip 53095–9274; tel. 262/836–5533; Allen Ericson, President
**Web address:** www.froedtert.com

FROEDTERT AND THE MEDICAL COLLEGE OF WISCONSIN FROEDTERT HOSPITAL (O, 607 beds) 9200 West Wisconsin Avenue, Milwaukee, WI, Zip 53226–3596, Mailing Address: P.O. Box 26099, 53226–0099, tel. 414/805–3000; Catherine Buck, MSN, R.N., President

| | | |
|---|---|---|
| **Owned, leased, sponsored:** | 3 hospitals | 879 beds |
| **Contract–managed:** | 0 hospitals | 0 beds |
| **Totals:** | 3 hospitals | 879 beds |

---

### 0182: FUNDAMENTAL LONG TERM CARE HOLDINGS, LLC (IO)

930 Ridgebrook Road, Sparks Glencoe, MD Zip 21152–9390; tel. 410/773–1000; W Bradley. Bennett, President and Chief Executive Officer

**(Independent Hospital System)**

**NEVADA:** HARMON MEDICAL AND REHABILITATION HOSPITAL (O, 118 beds) 2170 East Harmon Avenue, Las Vegas, NV, Zip 89119–7840; tel. 702/794–0100; Bonnie Essex. Hillegass, Chief Executive Officer

HORIZON SPECIALTY HOSPITAL (O, 49 beds) 640 Desert Lane, Las Vegas, NV, Zip 89106–4207; tel. 702/382–3155; Darrin Cook, Chief Executive Officer and Administrator
**Web address:** www.horizonspecialtyhosp.com/

SOUTHERN NEVADA MEDICAL AND REHABILITATION CENTER (O, 100 beds) 2945 Casa Vegas, Las Vegas, NV, Zip 89169–2248; tel. 702/735–7179; Maureen Davis, Administrator

| | | |
|---|---|---|
| **Owned, leased, sponsored:** | 3 hospitals | 267 beds |
| **Contract–managed:** | 0 hospitals | 0 beds |
| **Totals:** | 3 hospitals | 267 beds |

---

For explanation of codes following names, see page B2.
★ Indicates Type III membership in the American Hospital Association.

**★0144: GARNET HEALTH** (NP)

707 East Main Street, Middletown, NY Zip 10940–2650; tel. 845/333–1000; Scott Batulis, President and Chief Executive Officer

**(Centralized Health System)**

**NEW YORK:** GARNET HEALTH MEDICAL CENTER – CATSKILLS (O, 340 beds) 707 East Main Street, Middletown, NY, Zip 10940–2650; tel. 845/333–1000; Brian Tew, Chief Executive Officer
**Web address:** www.ormc.org

GARNET HEALTH MEDICAL CENTER – CATSKILLS (O, 125 beds) 68 Harris Bushville Road, Harris, NY, Zip 12742–5030, Mailing Address: P.O. Box 800, 12742–0800, tel. 845/794–3300; Jonathan Schiller, Chief Executive Officer
**Web address:** www.crmcny.org

GARNETT HEALTH MEDICAL CENTER – CATSKILLS (O, 15 beds) 8881 Route 97, Callicoon, NY, Zip 12723; tel. 845/887–5530; Rolland Bojo, R.N., Administrator

| | | |
|---|---|---|
| Owned, leased, sponsored: | 3 hospitals | 480 beds |
| Contract–managed: | 0 hospitals | 0 beds |
| Totals: | 3 hospitals | 480 beds |

**★5570: GEISINGER** (NP)

100 North Academy Avenue, Danville, PA Zip 17822–9800; tel. 570/271–6211; Jaewon Ryu, M.D., President and Chief Executive Officer

**(Centralized Physician/Insurance Health System)**

**NEW JERSEY:** ATLANTICARE REGIONAL MEDICAL CENTER (O, 540 beds) 1925 Pacific Avenue, Atlantic City, NJ, Zip 08401–6713; tel. 609/441–8994; Lori S. Herndon, R.N., President and Chief Executive Officer

**PENNSYLVANIA:** GEISINGER HOLY SPIRIT (O, 311 beds) 503 North 21st Street, Camp Hill, PA, Zip 17011–2204; tel. 717/763–2100; Kyle C. Snyder, Chief Administrative Officer
**Web address:** www.hsh.org

GEISINGER JERSEY SHORE HOSPITAL (O, 25 beds) 1020 Thompson Street, Jersey Shore, PA, Zip 17740–1794; tel. 570/398–0100; Tammy Anderer, Acting President
**Web address:** www.jsh.org

GEISINGER MEDICAL CENTER (O, 527 beds) 100 North Academy Avenue, Danville, PA, Zip 17822–2201; tel. 570/271–6211; Thomas P. Sokola, Chief Administrative Officer

GEISINGER WYOMING VALLEY MEDICAL CENTER (O, 277 beds) 1000 East Mountain Boulevard, Wilkes Barre, PA, Zip 18711–0027; tel. 570/808–7300; Ronald R. Beer, FACHE, Chief Administrative Officer
**Web address:** www.geisinger.org

GEISINGER–BLOOMSBURG HOSPITAL (O, 76 beds) 549 Fair Street, Bloomsburg, PA, Zip 17815–1419; tel. 570/387–2100; Lissa Bryan–Smith, Chief Administrative Officer

GEISINGER–COMMUNITY MEDICAL CENTER (O, 213 beds) 1800 Mulberry Street, Scranton, PA, Zip 18510–2369; tel. 570/703–8000; Ronald R. Beer, FACHE, Chief Administrative Officer
**Web address:** www.geisinger.org/for–patients/locations–directions/gcmc/

GEISINGER–LEWISTOWN HOSPITAL (O, 123 beds) 400 Highland Avenue, Lewistown, PA, Zip 17044–1198; tel. 717/248–5411; Kirk E. Thomas, Chief Administrative Officer

| | | |
|---|---|---|
| Owned, leased, sponsored: | 8 hospitals | 2092 beds |
| Contract–managed: | 0 hospitals | 0 beds |
| Totals: | 8 hospitals | 2092 beds |

**★0311: GENESIS HEALTH SYSTEM** (NP)

1227 East Rusholme Street, Davenport, IA Zip 52803–2498; tel. 563/421–1000; Douglas P. Cropper, President and Chief Executive Officer

**(Centralized Physician/Insurance Health System)**

**ILLINOIS:** GENESIS MEDICAL CENTER, SILVIS (O, 127 beds) 801 Illini Drive, Silvis, IL, Zip 61282–1893; tel. 309/281–4000; Theresa Summers–Main, R.N., President
**Web address:** www.genesishealth.com

GENESIS MEDICAL CENTER–ALEDO (O, 22 beds) 409 NW Ninth Avenue, Aledo, IL, Zip 61231–1296; tel. 309/582–9100; Ted Rogalski, Administrator

**IOWA:** GENESIS MEDICAL CENTER – DAVENPORT (O, 368 beds) 1227 East Rusholme Street, Davenport, IA, Zip 52803–2498; tel. 563/421–1000; Jordan Voigt, President
**Web address:** www.genesishealth.com

GENESIS MEDICAL CENTER, DEWITT (O, 88 beds) 1118 11th Street, De Witt, IA, Zip 52742–1296; tel. 563/659–4200; Curt Coleman, FACHE, Critical Access Hospitals President
**Web address:** www.genesishealth.com

JACKSON COUNTY REGIONAL HEALTH CENTER (C, 12 beds) 700 West Grove Street, Maquoketa, IA, Zip 52060–2163; tel. 563/652–2474; Curt Coleman, FACHE, President
**Web address:** www.jcrhc.org

| | | |
|---|---|---|
| Owned, leased, sponsored: | 4 hospitals | 605 beds |
| Contract–managed: | 1 hospitals | 12 beds |
| Totals: | 5 hospitals | 617 beds |

**0993: GENERAL HEALTH SYSTEM** (NP)

8585 Picardy Avenue, Baton Rouge, LA Zip 70809–3748; tel. 225/763–4000; Edgardo J. Tenreiro, FACHE, Chief Executive Officer

**LOUISIANA:** BATON ROUGE GENERAL MEDICAL CENTER (O, 362 beds) 8585 Picardy Avenue, Baton Rouge, LA, Zip 70809–3679; tel. 225/763–4000; Edgardo J. Tenreiro, FACHE, Chief Executive Officer

THE GENERAL (O, 231 beds) 3600 Florida Street, Suite 2020, Baton Rouge, LA, Zip 70806–3842; tel. 225/381–6393; Edgardo J. Tenreiro, FACHE, President and Chief Executive Officer

| | | |
|---|---|---|
| Owned, leased, sponsored: | 2 hospitals | 593 beds |
| Contract–managed: | 0 hospitals | 0 beds |
| Totals: | 2 hospitals | 593 beds |

**0283: GILLIARD HEALTH SERVICES** (IO)

3091 Carter Hill Road, Montgomery, AL Zip 36111–1801; tel. 334/265–5009; William G. McKenzie, President, Chief Executive Officer and Chairman

**ALABAMA:** EVERGREEN MEDICAL CENTER (O, 44 beds) 101 Crestview Avenue, Evergreen, AL, Zip 36401–3333, Mailing Address: P.O. Box 706, 36401–0706, tel. 251/578–2480; Tom McLendon, Administrator
**Web address:** www.evergreenmedical.org

JACKSON MEDICAL CENTER (O, 26 beds) 220 Hospital Drive, Jackson, AL, Zip 36545–2459, Mailing Address: P.O. Box 428, 36545–0428, tel. 251/246–9021; Jennifer M. Ryland, R.N., Chief Executive Officer
**Web address:** www.jacksonmedicalcenter.org

| | | |
|---|---|---|
| Owned, leased, sponsored: | 2 hospitals | 70 beds |
| Contract–managed: | 0 hospitals | 0 beds |
| Totals: | 2 hospitals | 70 beds |

**0648: GOOD SHEPHERD REHABILITATION NETWORK** (IO)

850 South Fifth Street, Allentown, PA Zip 18103–3308; tel. 610/776–3100; Gary R. Schmidt, Interim President and Chief Executive Officer

**(Independent Hospital System)**

**PENNSYLVANIA:** GOOD SHEPHERD REHABILITATION HOSPITAL (O, 106 beds) 850 South 5th Street, Allentown, PA, Zip 18103–3308; tel. 610/776–3299; Gary R. Schmidt, Interim President and Chief Executive Officer
**Web address:** www.goodshepherdrehab.org

For explanation of codes following names, see page B2.
★ Indicates Type III membership in the American Hospital Association.

Section B

GOOD SHEPHERD SPECIALTY HOSPITAL (O, 32 beds) 2545 Schoenersville Road, 4th Floor, Bethlehem, PA, Zip 18017–7300; tel. 484/884–5051; Jessica Florkowski, Administrator

| Owned, leased, sponsored: | 2 hospitals | 138 beds |
|---|---|---|
| Contract–managed: | 0 hospitals | 0 beds |
| Totals: | 2 hospitals | 138 beds |

---

**★1535: GREAT PLAINS HEALTH ALLIANCE, INC.** (NP)
250 North Rock Road, Suite 160, Wichita, KS Zip 67206–2241; tel. 316/685–1523; Dave Dellasega, President and Chief Executive Officer
**(Decentralized Health System)**

**KANSAS:** ASHLAND HEALTH CENTER (C, 25 beds) 709 Oak Street, Ashland, KS, Zip 67831–0188, Mailing Address: P.O. Box 188, 67831–0188, tel. 620/635–2241; Sandrea Wright, Chief Executive Officer
**Web address:** www.ashlandhc.org

CHEYENNE COUNTY HOSPITAL (L, 16 beds) 210 West First Street, Saint Francis, KS, Zip 67756–3540, Mailing Address: P.O. Box 547, 67756–0547, tel. 785/332–2104; Rance Ramsey, Chief Executive Officer

COMANCHE COUNTY HOSPITAL (C, 12 beds) 202 South Frisco Street, Coldwater, KS, Zip 67029–9101, HC 65, Box 8A, 67029–9500, tel. 620/582–2144; Lisa Brooks, Administrator
**Web address:** www.gpha.com

ELLINWOOD DISTRICT HOSPITAL (L, 25 beds) 605 North Main Street, Ellinwood, KS, Zip 67526–1440; tel. 620/564–2548; Kile Magner, Administrator
**Web address:** www.ellinwooddistricthospital.org

FREDONIA REGIONAL HOSPITAL (C, 25 beds) 1527 Madison Street, Fredonia, KS, Zip 66736–1751, Mailing Address: P.O. Box 579, 66736–0579, tel. 620/378–2121; Johnathan Durrett, Chief Executive Officer
**Web address:** www.fredoniaregionalhospital.org

GRISELL MEMORIAL HOSPITAL DISTRICT ONE (C, 42 beds) 210 South Vermont Avenue, Ransom, KS, Zip 67572–9525; tel. 785/731–2231; Rayna Bittel, Co–Chief Executive Officer and Chief Financial Officer

KIOWA COUNTY MEMORIAL HOSPITAL (L, 15 beds) 721 West Kansas Avenue, Greensburg, KS, Zip 67054–1633; tel. 620/723–3341; Mary Sweet, Administrator
**Web address:** www.kcmh.net

LANE COUNTY HOSPITAL (C, 25 beds) 235 West Vine, Dighton, KS, Zip 67839–0969, Mailing Address: P.O. Box 969, 67839–0969, tel. 620/397–5321; Marcia Gabel, Chief Financial Officer and Co–Chief Executive Officer

MEDICINE LODGE MEMORIAL HOSPITAL (C, 25 beds) 710 North Walnut Street, Medicine Lodge, KS, Zip 67104–1019; tel. 620/886–3771; Kevin A. White, Administrator
**Web address:** www.mlmh.net/

MINNEOLA DISTRICT HOSPITAL (C, 50 beds) 212 Main Street, Minneola, KS, Zip 67865–8511, Mailing Address: P.O. Box 127, 67865–0127, tel. 620/885–4264; Deborah Bruner, Chief Executive Officer and Administrator
**Web address:** www.minneolahealthcare.com

OSBORNE COUNTY MEMORIAL HOSPITAL (C, 25 beds) 424 West New Hampshire Street, Osborne, KS, Zip 67473–2314, Mailing Address: P.O. Box 70, 67473–0070, tel. 785/346–2121; Marianna Harris, Administrator
**Web address:** www.ocmh.org

OTTAWA COUNTY HEALTH CENTER (L, 30 beds) 215 East Eighth, Minneapolis, KS, Zip 67467–1902, Mailing Address: P.O. Box 290, 67467–0290, tel. 785/392–2122; Jody Parks, Administrator

REPUBLIC COUNTY HOSPITAL (L, 25 beds) 2420 'G' Street, Belleville, KS, Zip 66935–2400; tel. 785/527–2254; Rita K. Buurman, Interim Chief Executive Officer
**Web address:** www.rphospital.org

SABETHA COMMUNITY HOSPITAL (L, 25 beds) 14th and Oregon Streets, Sabetha, KS, Zip 66534–0229, Mailing Address: P.O. Box 229, 66534–0229, tel. 785/284–2121; Lora Key, Chief Executive Officer

SATANTA DISTRICT HOSPITAL AND LONG TERM CARE (C, 57 beds) 401 South Cheyenne Street, Satanta, KS, Zip 67870–0159, Mailing Address: P.O. Box 159, 67870–0159, tel. 620/649–2761; Jeremy Clingenpeel, Administrator
**Web address:** www.satantahospital.org

SMITH COUNTY MEMORIAL HOSPITAL (L, 16 beds) 921 East Highway 36, Smith Center, KS, Zip 66967; tel. 785/282–6845; Allen Van Driel, Chief Executive Officer
**Web address:** www.scmhks.org

TREGO COUNTY–LEMKE MEMORIAL HOSPITAL (C, 62 beds) 320 North 13th Street, Wakeeney, KS, Zip 67672–2099; tel. 785/743–2182; David Augustine, Chief Executive Officer
**Web address:** www.tclmh.org

WICHITA COUNTY HEALTH CENTER (C, 42 beds) 211 East Earl Street, Leoti, KS, Zip 67861–9620; tel. 620/375–2233; Teresa Clark, Chief Executive Officer and Administrator

**NEBRASKA:** HARLAN COUNTY HEALTH SYSTEM (C, 19 beds) 717 North Brown Street, Alma, NE, Zip 68920–2132, Mailing Address: P.O. Box 836, 68920–0836, tel. 308/928–2151; Mark A. Miller, FACHE, Chief Executive Officer
**Web address:** www.harlancountyhealth.com

| Owned, leased, sponsored: | 7 hospitals | 152 beds |
|---|---|---|
| Contract–managed: | 12 hospitals | 409 beds |
| Totals: | 19 hospitals | 561 beds |

---

**★0675: GUTHRIE CLINIC** (NP)
One Guthrie Square, Sayre, PA Zip 18840–1625; tel. 570/888–5858; Joseph A. Scopelliti, M.D., President and Chief Executive Officer
**(Moderately Centralized Health System)**

**NEW YORK:** GUTHRIE CORNING HOSPITAL (O, 65 beds) One Guthrie Drive, Corning, NY, Zip 14830–3696; tel. 607/937–7200; Paul VerValin, Interim Chief Executive Officer
**Web address:** www.corninghospital.com

**PENNSYLVANIA:** GUTHRIE ROBERT PACKER HOSPITAL (O, 267 beds) 1 Guthrie Square, Sayre, PA, Zip 18840–1698; tel. 570/888–6666; Joseph T. Sawyer Jr, President and Chief Operating Officer
**Web address:** https://www.guthrie.org/location/robert–packer–hospital

GUTHRIE TOWANDA MEMORIAL HOSPITAL (O, 195 beds) 91 Hospital Drive, Towanda, PA, Zip 18848–9702; tel. 570/265–2191; Felissa Koernig, President and Chief Operating Officer
**Web address:** https://www.guthrie.org/location/guthrie–towanda–memorial–hospital

GUTHRIE TROY COMMUNITY HOSPITAL (O, 25 beds) 275 Guthrie Drive, Troy, PA, Zip 16947; tel. 570/297–2121; Lori Barnett, R.N., MSN, President and Chief Operating Officer

| Owned, leased, sponsored: | 4 hospitals | 552 beds |
|---|---|---|
| Contract–managed: | 0 hospitals | 0 beds |
| Totals: | 4 hospitals | 552 beds |

---

**★1003: HACKENSACK MERIDIAN HEALTH** (NP)
343 Thornall Street, 8th Floor, Edison, NJ Zip 08837–2206, 343 Thornall Street, 08837–2206, tel. 844/464–9355; Robert C. Garrett, FACHE, Chief Executive Officer
**(Centralized Health System)**

**NEW JERSEY:** HACKENSACK MERIDIAN HEALTH BAYSHORE COMMUNITY HOSPITAL (O, 160 beds) 727 North Beers Street, Holmdel, NJ, Zip 07733–1598; tel. 732/739–5900; Frank Citara, Chief Hospital Executive

HACKENSACK MERIDIAN HEALTH CARRIER CLINIC (O, 330 beds) 252 County Route 601, Belle Mead, NJ, Zip 08502–0147, Mailing Address: P.O. Box 147, 08502–0147, tel. 908/281–1000; Donald J. Parker, President
**Web address:** www.carrierclinic.org

---

For explanation of codes following names, see page B2.
★ Indicates Type III membership in the American Hospital Association.

HACKENSACK MERIDIAN HEALTH HACKENSACK UNIVERSITY MEDICAL CENTER (O, 748 beds) 30 Prospect Avenue, Hackensack, NJ, Zip 07601–1914; tel. 201/996–2000; Mark Sparta, President
**Web address**: www.hackensackumc.org

HACKENSACK MERIDIAN HEALTH JFK MEDICAL CENTER (O, 360 beds) 65 James Street, Edison, NJ, Zip 8818; tel. 732/321–7000; Amie D. Thornton, Chief Hospital Executive

HACKENSACK MERIDIAN HEALTH JERSEY SHORE UNIVERSITY MEDICAL CENTER (O, 588 beds) 1945 Route 33, Neptune, NJ, Zip 07754–0397; tel. 732/775–5500; Vito Buccellato, Chief Hospital Executive
**Web address**: www.meridianhealth.com

HACKENSACK MERIDIAN HEALTH OCEAN MEDICAL CENTER (O, 308 beds) 425 Jack Martin Boulevard, Brick Township, NJ, Zip 08724–7732; tel. 732/840–2200; Jason Kreitner, FACHE, Chief Hospital Executive
**Web address**: www.meridianhealth.com

HACKENSACK MERIDIAN HEALTH PALISADES MEDICAL CENTER (O, 152 beds) 7600 River Road, North Bergen, NJ, Zip 07047–6217; tel. 201/854–5000; Anthony Passannante Jr, M.D., FACC, President and Chief Hospital Executive

HACKENSACK MERIDIAN HEALTH RARITAN BAY MEDICAL CENTER (O, 282 beds) 530 New Brunswick Avenue, Perth Amboy, NJ, Zip 08861–3654; tel. 732/442–3700; Thomas Shanahan, CPA, Chief Operating Officer
**Web address**: www.rbmc.org

HACKENSACK MERIDIAN HEALTH RIVERVIEW MEDICAL CENTER (O, 300 beds) 1 Riverview Plaza, Red Bank, NJ, Zip 07701–1864; tel. 732/741–2700; M. Todd. Way, President, Central Region
**Web address**: www.riverviewmedicalcenter.com

HACKENSACK MERIDIAN HEALTH SHORE REHABILITATION INSTITUTE (O, 40 beds) 425 Jack Martin Boulevard, Brick, NJ, Zip 08724–7732; tel. 732/836–4500; Kerri Fitzgerald, Executive Director

HACKENSACK MERIDIAN HEALTH SOUTHERN OCEAN MEDICAL CENTER (O, 156 beds) 1140 Route 72 West, Manahawkin, NJ, Zip 08050–2499; tel. 609/597–6011; Michele Morrison, R.N., M.P.H., Chief Hospital Executive
**Web address**: www.soch.com

JFK JOHNSON REHABILITATION INSTITUTE AT HACKENSACK MERIDIAN HEALTH (O, 94 beds) 65 James Street, Edison, NJ, Zip 8818; tel. 732/321–7050; Anthony Cuzzola, Vice President Operations
**Web address**: www.njrehab.org

| | | |
|---|---|---|
| **Owned, leased, sponsored:** | 12 hospitals | 3518 beds |
| **Contract–managed:** | 0 hospitals | 0 beds |
| **Totals:** | 12 hospitals | 3518 beds |

---

★**0541: HARTFORD HEALTHCARE** (NP)
One State Street, 19th Floor, Hartford, CT Zip 6103; tel. 860/263–4100; Jeffrey A. Flaks, President and Chief Executive Officer
**(Centralized Health System)**

**CONNECTICUT**: CHARLOTTE HUNGERFORD HOSPITAL (O, 72 beds) 540 Litchfield Street, Torrington, CT, Zip 06790–6679, Mailing Address: P.O. Box 988, 06790–0988, tel. 860/496–6666; Daniel J. McIntyre, President

HARTFORD HOSPITAL (O, 982 beds) 80 Seymour Street, Hartford, CT, Zip 06102–8000, Mailing Address: P.O. Box 5037, 06102–5037, tel. 860/545–5000; Bimal Patel, President
**Web address**: www.harthosp.org

MIDSTATE MEDICAL CENTER (O, 97 beds) 435 Lewis Avenue, Meriden, CT, Zip 06451–2101; tel. 203/694–8200; Gary C. Havican, President

NATCHAUG HOSPITAL (O, 57 beds) 189 Storrs Road, Mansfield Center, CT, Zip 06250–1683; tel. 860/456–1311; Patricia Rehmer, MSN, FACHE, President
**Web address**: www.natchaug.org

ST. VINCENT'S MEDICAL CENTER (O, 337 beds) 2800 Main Street, Bridgeport, CT, Zip 06606–4292; tel. 203/576–6000; Vincent DiBattista, Senior Vice President, Fairfield Region President

THE HOSPITAL OF CENTRAL CONNECTICUT (O, 188 beds) 100 Grand Street, New Britain, CT, Zip 06052–2017, Mailing Address: P.O. Box 100, 06052–2017, tel. 860/224–5011; Gary C. Havican, President
**Web address**: www.thocc.org

---

THE WILLIAM W. BACKUS HOSPITAL (O, 183 beds) 326 Washington Street, Norwich, CT, Zip 06360–2740; tel. 860/889–8331; Donna Handley, President
**Web address**: www.backushospital.org

WINDHAM HOSPITAL (O, 42 beds) 112 Mansfield Avenue, Willimantic, CT, Zip 06226–2040; tel. 860/456–9116; Donna Handley, President
**Web address**: www.windhamhospital.org

| | | |
|---|---|---|
| **Owned, leased, sponsored:** | 8 hospitals | 1958 beds |
| **Contract–managed:** | 0 hospitals | 0 beds |
| **Totals:** | 8 hospitals | 1958 beds |

---

**0637: HAVEN BEHAVIORAL HEALTHCARE** (IO)
3102 West End Avenue, Suite 1000, Nashville, TN Zip 37203–1324; tel. 615/393–8800; Kelly Gill, Chief Executive Officer

**ARIZONA**: HAVEN BEHAVIORAL HOSPITAL OF PHOENIX (O, 45 beds) 1201 South 7th Avenue, Suite 200, Phoenix, AZ, Zip 85007–4076; tel. 623/236–2000; Amy Gerberry, Chief Executive Officer

**OHIO**: HAVEN BEHAVIORAL SENIOR CARE OF DAYTON (O, 32 beds) One Elizabeth Place, 4th Floor Southwest Tower, Dayton, OH, Zip 45417–3445; tel. 937/234–0100; Keith Kuhn, Chief Executive Officer
**Web address**: www.havenbehavioraldayton.com/

**PENNSYLVANIA**: HAVEN BEHAVIORAL HOSPITAL OF EASTERN PENNSYLVANIA (O, 48 beds) 145 North 6th Street, 3rd Floor, Reading, PA, Zip 19601–3096; tel. 610/406–4340; Robert Scheffler, Chief Executive Officer

HAVEN BEHAVIORAL HOSPITAL OF PHILADELPHIA (O, 36 beds) 3300 Henry Avenue, Four Falls Building, Suite 100, Philadelphia, PA, Zip 19129–1141; tel. 215/475–3400; Robert Scheffler, Chief Executive Officer
**Web address**: www.https://philadelphia.havenbehavioral.com

| | | |
|---|---|---|
| **Owned, leased, sponsored:** | 4 hospitals | 161 beds |
| **Contract–managed:** | 0 hospitals | 0 beds |
| **Totals:** | 4 hospitals | 161 beds |

---

★**3555: HAWAII HEALTH SYSTEMS CORPORATION** (NP)
3675 Kilauea Avenue, Honolulu, HI Zip 96816–2333; tel. 808/733–4151; Linda Rosen, M.D., Chief Executive Officer
**(Independent Hospital System)**

**HAWAII**: HALE HO'OLA HAMAKUA (O, 77 beds) 45–547 Plumeria Street, Honokaa, HI, Zip 96727–6902; tel. 808/932–4100; Denise Mackey, Administrator
**Web address**: www.halehoolahamakua.org

HILO MEDICAL CENTER (O, 199 beds) 1190 Waianuenue Avenue, Hilo, HI, Zip 96720–2089; tel. 808/932–3000; Dan Brinkman, R.N., Chief Executive Officer

KA'U HOSPITAL (O, 21 beds) 1 Kamani Street, Pahala, HI, Zip 96777, Mailing Address: P.O. Box 40, 96777–0040, tel. 808/932–4200; Merilyn Harris, Administrator
**Web address**: www.hhsc.org

KAUAI VETERANS MEMORIAL HOSPITAL (O, 45 beds) 4643 Waimea Canyon Road, Waimea, HI, Zip 96796, Mailing Address: P.O. Box 337, 96796–0337, tel. 808/338–9431; Lance Segawa, Chief Executive Officer
**Web address**: www.kvmh.hhsc.org

KOHALA HOSPITAL (O, 28 beds) 54–383 Hospital Road, Kohala, HI, Zip 96755, Mailing Address: P.O. Box 10, Kapaau, 96755–0010, tel. 808/889–6211; Jay E. Kreuzer, FACHE, Chief Executive Officer

KONA COMMUNITY HOSPITAL (O, 94 beds) 79–1019 Haukapila Street, Kealakekua, HI, Zip 96750–7920; tel. 808/322–9311; Jay E. Kreuzer, FACHE, Chief Executive Officer
**Web address**: www.kch.hhsc.org

LEAHI HOSPITAL (O, 126 beds) 3675 Kilauea Avenue, Honolulu, HI, Zip 96816–2398; tel. 808/733–8000; Derek Akiyoshi, Chief Executive Officer
**Web address**: www.hhsc.org

MALUHIA HOSPITAL (O, 146 beds) 1027 Hala Drive, Honolulu, HI, Zip 96817; tel. 808/832–5874; Derek Akiyoshi, Chief Executive Officer

---

For explanation of codes following names, see page B2.
★ Indicates Type III membership in the American Hospital Association.

SAMUEL MAHELONA MEMORIAL HOSPITAL (O, 80 beds) 4800 Kawaihau Road, Kapaa, HI, Zip 96746–1971; tel. 808/822–4961; Lance Segawa, Chief Executive Officer
**Web address:** www.smmh.hhsc.org

| | | |
|---|---|---|
| Owned, leased, sponsored: | 9 hospitals | 816 beds |
| Contract–managed: | 0 hospitals | 0 beds |
| Totals: | 9 hospitals | 816 beds |

## 0266: HAWAII PACIFIC HEALTH (NP)

55 Merchant Street, Honolulu, HI Zip 96813–4306; tel. 808/949–9355; Raymond P. Vara Jr, President and Chief Executive Officer
**(Centralized Health System)**

**HAWAII:** KAPIOLANI MEDICAL CENTER FOR WOMEN & CHILDREN (O, 185 beds) 1319 Punahou Street, Honolulu, HI, Zip 96826–1001; tel. 808/983–6000; Martha Smith, Chief Executive Officer

PALI MOMI MEDICAL CENTER (O, 118 beds) 98–1079 Moanalua Road, Aiea, HI, Zip 96701–4713; tel. 808/486–6000; Martha Smith, Executive Vice President
**Web address:** www.palimomi.org

STRAUB MEDICAL CENTER (O, 113 beds) 888 South King Street, Honolulu, HI, Zip 96813–3097; tel. 808/522–4000; Art Gladstone, R.N., Chief Executive Officer
**Web address:** www.straubhealth.org

WILCOX MEDICAL CENTER (O, 65 beds) 3–3420 Kuhio Highway, Lihue, HI, Zip 96766–1099; tel. 808/245–1100; Jen Chahanovich, President and Chief Executive Officer

| | | |
|---|---|---|
| Owned, leased, sponsored: | 4 hospitals | 481 beds |
| Contract–managed: | 0 hospitals | 0 beds |
| Totals: | 4 hospitals | 481 beds |

## ★0048: HCA HEALTHCARE (IO)

One Park Plaza, Nashville, TN Zip 37203–1548; tel. 615/344–5248; Samuel Hazen, President and Chief Executive Officer
**(Decentralized Health System)**

**ALASKA:** ALASKA REGIONAL HOSPITAL (O, 250 beds) 2801 Debarr Road, Anchorage, AK, Zip 99508–2997; tel. 907/264–1754; Julie Taylor, FACHE, Chief Executive Officer
**Web address:** www.alaskaregional.com

**CALIFORNIA:** GOOD SAMARITAN HOSPITAL (O, 474 beds) 2425 Samaritan Drive, San Jose, CA, Zip 95124–3997, Mailing Address: P.O. Box 240002, 95154–2402, tel. 408/559–2011; Joseph DeSchryver, Chief Executive Officer

LOS ROBLES HOSPITAL AND MEDICAL CENTER (O, 382 beds) 215 West Janss Road, Thousand Oaks, CA, Zip 91360–1899; tel. 805/370–4421; Natalie Mussi, President and Chief Executive Officer
**Web address:** www.losrobleshospital.com

REGIONAL MEDICAL CENTER OF SAN JOSE (O, 264 beds) 225 North Jackson Avenue, San Jose, CA, Zip 95116–1603; tel. 408/259–5000; Tomi S. Ryba, President and Chief Executive Officer

RIVERSIDE COMMUNITY HOSPITAL (O, 478 beds) 4445 Magnolia Avenue, Riverside, CA, Zip 92501–4199; tel. 951/788–3000; Jacqueline DeSouza-Van Blaricum, President and Chief Executive Officer
**Web address:** www.riversidecommunityhospital.com

WEST HILLS HOSPITAL AND MEDICAL CENTER (O, 260 beds) 7300 Medical Center Drive, West Hills, CA, Zip 91307–1900; tel. 818/676–4000; Mark Miller, FACHE, Chief Executive Officer

**COLORADO:** MEDICAL CENTER OF AURORA (O, 360 beds) 1501 South Potomac Street, Aurora, CO, Zip 80012–5411; tel. 303/695–2600; Ryan Simpson, President and Chief Executive Officer
**Web address:** www.auroramed.com

NORTH SUBURBAN MEDICAL CENTER (O, 157 beds) 9191 Grant Street, Thornton, CO, Zip 80229–4341; tel. 303/451–7800; Daphne G. David, President and Chief Executive Officer
**Web address:** www.northsuburban.com

PRESBYTERIAN/ST. LUKE'S MEDICAL CENTER (O, 359 beds) 1719 East 19th Avenue, Denver, CO, Zip 80218–1281; tel. 720/754–6000; Maureen Tarrant, President and Chief Executive Officer

ROSE MEDICAL CENTER (O, 248 beds) 4567 East Ninth Avenue, Denver, CO, Zip 80220–3941; tel. 303/320–2121; Hollie Seeley, Interim Chief Executive Officer and Chief Operating Officer
**Web address:** www.rosebabies.com

SKY RIDGE MEDICAL CENTER (O, 272 beds) 10101 Ridge Gate Parkway, Lone Tree, CO, Zip 80124–5522; tel. 720/225–1000; Kirk McCarty, R.N., MSN, Chief Executive Officer

SPALDING REHABILITATION HOSPITAL (O, 100 beds) 900 Potomac Steet, Aurora, CO, Zip 80011–6716; tel. 303/367–1166; Ryan Simpson, President and Chief Executive Officer
**Web address:** www.spaldingrehab.com

SWEDISH MEDICAL CENTER (O, 408 beds) 501 East Hampden Avenue, Englewood, CO, Zip 80113–2702; tel. 303/788–5000; Ryan Tobin, President and Chief Executive Officer
**Web address:** www.swedishhospital.com

**FLORIDA:** AVENTURA HOSPITAL AND MEDICAL CENTER (O, 407 beds) 20900 Biscayne Boulevard, Aventura, FL, Zip 33180–1407; tel. 305/682–7000; David LeMonte, Chief Executive Officer
**Web address:** www.aventurahospital.com

BLAKE MEDICAL CENTER (O, 383 beds) 2020 59th Street West, Bradenton, FL, Zip 34209–4669; tel. 941/792–6611; Randy Currin, Chief Executive Officer

BRANDON REGIONAL HOSPITAL (O, 422 beds) 119 Oakfield Drive, Brandon, FL, Zip 33511–5779; tel. 813/681–5551; Bland Eng, Chief Executive Officer
**Web address:** www.brandonhospital.com

CAPITAL REGIONAL MEDICAL CENTER (O, 270 beds) 2626 Capital Medical Boulevard, Tallahassee, FL, Zip 32308–4499; tel. 850/325–5000; Alan Seesee, Chief Executive Officer
**Web address:** www.capitalregionalmedicalcenter.com

CENTRAL FLORIDA REGIONAL HOSPITAL (O, 221 beds) 1401 West Seminole Boulevard, Sanford, FL, Zip 32771–6764; tel. 407/321–4500; Trey Abshier, Chief Executive Officer

CITRUS MEMORIAL HEALTH SYSTEM (O, 204 beds) 502 West Highland Boulevard, Inverness, FL, Zip 34452–4754; tel. 352/726–1551; Ginger Carroll, Chief Executive Officer
**Web address:** www.citrusmh.com

DOCTORS HOSPITAL OF SARASOTA (O, 155 beds) 5731 Bee Ridge Road, Sarasota, FL, Zip 34233–5056; tel. 941/342–1100; Robert C. Meade, Chief Executive Officer
**Web address:** www.doctorsofsarasota.com

ENGLEWOOD COMMUNITY HOSPITAL (O, 100 beds) 700 Medical Boulevard, Englewood, FL, Zip 34223–3978; tel. 941/475–6571; Michael Ehrat, Chief Executive Officer
**Web address:** www.englewoodcommunityhospital.com

FAWCETT MEMORIAL HOSPITAL (O, 237 beds) 21298 Olean Boulevard, Port Charlotte, FL, Zip 33952–6765; tel. 941/629–1181; Michael Ehrat, Interim Chief Executive Officer

FORT WALTON BEACH MEDICAL CENTER (O, 267 beds) 1000 Mar–Walt Drive, Fort Walton Beach, FL, Zip 32547–6795; tel. 850/862–1111; Mitchell P. Mongell, FACHE, Chief Executive Officer
**Web address:** www.fwbmc.com

GULF COAST REGIONAL MEDICAL CENTER (O, 223 beds) 449 West 23rd Street, Panama City, FL, Zip 32405–4593, Mailing Address: P.O. Box 15309, 32406–5309, tel. 850/769–8341; Brad Griffin, Chief Executive Officer
**Web address:** www.egulfcoastmedical.com

HIGHLANDS REGIONAL MEDICAL CENTER (O, 126 beds) 3600 South Highlands Avenue, Sebring, FL, Zip 33870–5495, Drawer 2066, 33871–2066, tel. 863/385–6101; Jason Kimbrell, Chief Executive Officer
**Web address:** www.highlandsregional.com

JFK MEDICAL CENTER (O, 803 beds) 5301 South Congress Avenue, Atlantis, FL, Zip 33462–1197; tel. 561/965–7300; Gina Melby, Chief Executive Officer

KENDALL REGIONAL MEDICAL CENTER (O, 417 beds) 11750 Bird Road, Miami, FL, Zip 33175–3530; tel. 305/223–3000; Brandon Haushalter, Chief Executive Officer
**Web address:** www.kendallmed.com

For explanation of codes following names, see page B2.
★ Indicates Type III membership in the American Hospital Association.

LAKE CITY MEDICAL CENTER (O, 91 beds) 340 NW Commerce Drive, Lake City, FL, Zip 32055–4709; tel. 386/719–9000; Rick Naegler, Chief Executive Officer

LARGO MEDICAL CENTER (O, 455 beds) 201 14th Street SW, Largo, FL, Zip 33770–3133; tel. 727/588–5200; Adam Rudd, Chief Executive Officer
**Web address**: www.largomedical.com

LAWNWOOD REGIONAL MEDICAL CENTER & HEART INSTITUTE (O, 392 beds) 1700 South 23rd Street, Fort Pierce, FL, Zip 34950–4803; tel. 772/461–4000; Eric Goldman, Chief Executive Officer

MEDICAL CENTER OF TRINITY (O, 340 beds) 9330 State Road 54, Trinity, FL, Zip 34655–1808; tel. 727/834–4900; Leigh Massengill, Chief Executive Officer
**Web address**: www.medicalcentertrinity.com

MEMORIAL HOSPITAL JACKSONVILLE (O, 454 beds) 3625 University Boulevard South, Jacksonville, FL, Zip 32216–4207; tel. 904/702–6111; Bradley S. Talbert, FACHE, President and Chief Executive Officer

MEMORIAL HOSPITAL OF TAMPA (O, 384 beds) 2901 Swann Avenue, Tampa, FL, Zip 33609–4057; tel. 813/873–6400; Sonia I. Wellman, Chief Executive Officer
**Web address**: www.memorialhospitaltampa.com

NORTH FLORIDA REGIONAL MEDICAL CENTER (O, 432 beds) 6500 Newberry Road, Gainesville, FL, Zip 32605–4392, Mailing Address: P.O. Box 147006, 32614–7006, tel. 352/333–4000; Eric Lawson, Chief Executive Officer

NORTHSIDE HOSPITAL (O, 288 beds) 6000 49th Street North, Saint Petersburg, FL, Zip 33709–2145; tel. 727/521–4411; Valerie L. Powell–Stafford, Chief Executive Officer
**Web address**: www.northsidehospital.com

NORTHWEST MEDICAL CENTER (O, 283 beds) 2801 North State Road 7, Margate, FL, Zip 33063–5727; tel. 954/974–0400; Erica Gulrich, Chief Executive Officer

OAK HILL HOSPITAL (O, 280 beds) 11375 Cortez Boulevard, Brooksville, FL, Zip 34613–5409; tel. 352/596–6632; Mickey Smith, Chief Executive Officer
**Web address**: www.oakhillhospital.com

OCALA REGIONAL MEDICAL CENTER (O, 430 beds) 1431 SW First Avenue, Ocala, FL, Zip 34471–6500, Mailing Address: P.O. Box 2200, 34478–2200, tel. 352/401–1000; Chad Christianson, Chief Executive Officer

ORANGE PARK MEDICAL CENTER (O, 314 beds) 2001 Kingsley Avenue, Orange Park, FL, Zip 32073–5156; tel. 904/639–8500; Lisa R. Valentine, Chief Executive Officer
**Web address**: www.opmedical.com

OSCEOLA REGIONAL MEDICAL CENTER (O, 404 beds) 700 West Oak Street, Kissimmee, FL, Zip 34741–4996; tel. 407/846–2266; Davide M. Carbone, FACHE, Chief Executive Officer

OVIEDO MEDICAL CENTER (O, 64 beds) 8300 Red Bug Lake Road, Oviedo, FL, Zip 32765–6801; tel. 407/890–2273; Kenneth C. Donahey, Chief Executive Officer
**Web address**: www.oviedomedicalcenter.com

PALMS WEST HOSPITAL (O, 204 beds) 13001 Southern Boulevard, Loxahatchee, FL, Zip 33470–9203; tel. 561/798–3300; Joshua DeTillio, Chief Executive Officer
**Web address**: www.palmswesthospital.com

PALMS OF PASADENA HOSPITAL (O, 307 beds) 1501 Pasadena Avenue South, Saint Petersburg, FL, Zip 33707–3798; tel. 727/381–1000; Michael Irvin, Chief Executive Officer
**Web address**: www.palmspasadena.com

PLANTATION GENERAL HOSPITAL (O, 752 beds) 401 NW 42nd Avenue, Plantation, FL, Zip 33317–2882; tel. 954/587–5010; Madeline Nava, Chief Executive Officer

POINCIANA MEDICAL CENTER (O, 76 beds) 325 Cypress Parkway, Kissimmee, FL, Zip 34758; tel. 407/530–2000; Christopher Cosby, Chief Executive Officer
**Web address**: www.poincianamedicalcenter.com

PUTNAM COMMUNITY MEDICAL CENTER (O, 99 beds) 611 Zeagler Drive, Palatka, FL, Zip 32177–3810; tel. 386/328–5711; Mark J. Dooley, Chief Executive Officer
**Web address**: www.pcmcfl.com

RAULERSON HOSPITAL (O, 100 beds) 1796 Highway 441 North, Okeechobee, FL, Zip 34972–1918, Mailing Address: P.O. Box 1307, 34973–1307, tel. 863/763–2151; Brian Melear, Chief Executive Officer

REGIONAL MEDICAL CENTER BAYONET POINT (O, 290 beds) 14000 Fivay Road, Hudson, FL, Zip 34667–7199; tel. 727/869–5400; Regina Temple, President and Chief Executive Officer
**Web address**: www.rmchealth.com

SOUTH BAY HOSPITAL (O, 138 beds) 4016 Sun City Center Blvd, Sun City Center, FL, Zip 33573–5298; tel. 813/634–3301; Daniel Bender, Chief Executive Officer
**Web address**: www.southbayhospital.com/

ST. LUCIE MEDICAL CENTER (O, 229 beds) 1800 SE Tiffany Avenue, Port St Lucie, FL, Zip 34952–7521; tel. 772/335–4000; Jay Finnegan, Chief Executive Officer

ST. PETERSBURG GENERAL HOSPITAL (O, 215 beds) 6500 38th Avenue North, Saint Petersburg, FL, Zip 33710–1629; tel. 727/384–1414; Kenneth R. Wicker, FACHE, Chief Executive Officer
**Web address**: www.stpetegeneral.com

TWIN CITIES HOSPITAL (O, 65 beds) 2190 Highway 85 North, Niceville, FL, Zip 32578–1045; tel. 850/678–4131; David Whalen, Chief Executive Officer

UNIVERSITY HOSPITAL AND MEDICAL CENTER (O, 317 beds) 7201 North University Drive, Tamarac, FL, Zip 33321–2996; tel. 954/721–2200; Ben Harris, Chief Executive Officer
**Web address**: www.uhmchealth.com

WEST FLORIDA HOSPITAL (O, 515 beds) 8383 North Davis Highway, Pensacola, FL, Zip 32514–6088; tel. 850/494–4000; Gay Nord, Chief Executive Officer
**Web address**: www.westfloridahospital.com

WESTSIDE REGIONAL MEDICAL CENTER (O, 250 beds) 8201 West Broward Boulevard, Plantation, FL, Zip 33324–2701; tel. 954/473–6600; Barbara Simmons, R.N., Chief Executive Officer

**GEORGIA**: CARTERSVILLE MEDICAL CENTER (O, 119 beds) 960 Joe Frank Harris Parkway, Cartersville, GA, Zip 30120–2129; tel. 770/382–1530; J. Christopher. Mosley, Chief Executive Officer
**Web address**: www.cartersvillemedical.com

COLISEUM MEDICAL CENTERS (O, 310 beds) 350 Hospital Drive, Macon, GA, Zip 31217–3871; tel. 478/765–7000; Stephen J. Daugherty, Chief Executive Officer
**Web address**: www.coliseumhealthsystem.com

COLISEUM NORTHSIDE HOSPITAL (O, 103 beds) 400 Charter Boulevard, Macon, GA, Zip 31210–4853, Mailing Address: P.O. Box 4627, 31208–4627, tel. 478/757–8200; Greg Caples, Chief Executive Officer
**Web address**: www.coliseumhealthsystem.com

DOCTORS HOSPITAL (O, 288 beds) 3651 Wheeler Road, Augusta, GA, Zip 30909–6426; tel. 706/651–3232; Douglas Welch, Chief Executive Officer

EASTSIDE MEDICAL CENTER (O, 310 beds) 1700 Medical Way, Snellville, GA, Zip 30078–2195; tel. 770/979–0200; Trent Lind, Chief Executive Officer
**Web address**: www.eastsidemedical.com

FAIRVIEW PARK HOSPITAL (O, 190 beds) 200 Industrial Boulevard, Dublin, GA, Zip 31021–2997, Mailing Address: P.O. Box 1408, 31040–1408, tel. 478/275–2000; Donald R. Avery, FACHE, President and Chief Executive Officer

MEMORIAL HEALTH (O, 622 beds) 4700 Waters Avenue, Savannah, GA, Zip 31404–6283, Mailing Address: P.O. Box 23089, 31403–3089, tel. 912/350–8000; Shayne George, Chief Executive Officer
**Web address**: www.memorialhealth.com

MEMORIAL SATILLA HEALTH (O, 231 beds) 1900 Tebeau Street, Waycross, GA, Zip 31501–6357, Mailing Address: P.O. Box 139, 31502–0139, tel. 912/283–3030; Bobby McCullough, Chief Executive Officer
**Web address**: www.memorialsatillahealth.com/

REDMOND REGIONAL MEDICAL CENTER (O, 230 beds) 501 Redmond Road, Rome, GA, Zip 30165–1415, Mailing Address: P.O. Box 107001, 30164–7001, tel. 706/291–0291; John Quinlivan, Chief Executive Officer

**IDAHO**: EASTERN IDAHO REGIONAL MEDICAL CENTER (O, 318 beds) 3100 Channing Way, Idaho Falls, ID, Zip 83404–7533, Mailing Address: P.O. Box 2077, 83403–2077, tel. 208/529–6111; Jeff Sollis, Chief Executive Officer
**Web address**: www.eirmc.com

WEST VALLEY MEDICAL CENTER (O, 150 beds) 1717 Arlington, Caldwell, ID, Zip 83605–4802; tel. 208/459–4641; Elizabeth Hunsicker, Chief Executive Officer

For explanation of codes following names, see page B2.
★ Indicates Type III membership in the American Hospital Association.

**INDIANA:** TERRE HAUTE REGIONAL HOSPITAL (O, 278 beds) 3901 South Seventh Street, Terre Haute, IN, Zip 47802–5709; tel. 812/232–0021; Nathan Vooys, Chief Executive Officer
**Web address:** www.regionalhospital.com

**KANSAS:** MENORAH MEDICAL CENTER (O, 158 beds) 5721 West 119th Street, Overland Park, KS, Zip 66209–3722; tel. 913/498–6000; Phil Buttell, Chief Executive Officer
**Web address:** www.menorahmedicalcenter.com

OVERLAND PARK REGIONAL MEDICAL CENTER (O, 283 beds) 10500 Quivira Road, Overland Park, KS, Zip 66215–2306, Mailing Address: P.O. Box 15959, 66215–5959, tel. 913/541–5000; Matt Sogard, Chief Executive Officer

WESLEY HEALTHCARE CENTER (O, 859 beds) 550 North Hillside, Wichita, KS, Zip 67214–4976; tel. 316/962–2000; Bill Voloch, President and Chief Executive Officer
**Web address:** www.wesleymc.com

**KENTUCKY:** FRANKFORT REGIONAL MEDICAL CENTER (O, 173 beds) 299 King's Daughters Drive, Frankfort, KY, Zip 40601–4186; tel. 502/875–5240; Reed Hammond, Chief Executive Officer
**Web address:** www.frankfortregional.com

TRISTAR GREENVIEW REGIONAL HOSPITAL (O, 211 beds) 1801 Ashley Circle, Bowling Green, KY, Zip 42104–3362; tel. 270/793–1000; Michael Sherrod, Chief Executive Officer

**LOUISIANA:** RAPIDES REGIONAL MEDICAL CENTER (O, 357 beds) 211 4th ST, Alexandria, LA, Zip 71301–8421, 211 Fourth Street, 71301–8421, tel. 318/769–3000; Jason E. Cobb, FACHE, Chief Executive Officer
**Web address:** www.rapidesregional.com

TULANE HEALTH SYSTEM (O, 543 beds) 1415 Tulane Avenue, New Orleans, LA, Zip 70112–2600; tel. 504/988–5263; Robert Lynch, M.D., Chief Executive Officer
**Web address:** www.tuhc.com

**MISSISSIPPI:** GARDEN PARK MEDICAL CENTER (O, 68 beds) 15200 Community Road, Gulfport, MS, Zip 39503–3085, Mailing Address: P.O. Box 1240, 39502–1240, tel. 228/575–7000; Randy Rogers, FACHE, Chief Executive Officer
**Web address:** www.gpmedical.com

**MISSOURI:** BELTON REGIONAL MEDICAL CENTER (O, 48 beds) 17065 South 71 Highway, Belton, MO, Zip 64012–4631; tel. 816/348–1200; Todd Krass, Chief Executive Officer
**Web address:** www.beltonregionalmedicalcenter.com

CENTERPOINT MEDICAL CENTER (O, 285 beds) 19600 East 39th Street, Independence, MO, Zip 64057–2301; tel. 816/698–7000; Bret Kolman, CPA, FACHE, Chief Executive Officer
**Web address:** www.centerpointmedical.com

LAFAYETTE REGIONAL HEALTH CENTER (O, 25 beds) 1500 State Street, Lexington, MO, Zip 64067–1107; tel. 660/259–2203; Darrel Box, Chief Executive Officer
**Web address:** www.lafayetteregionalhealthcenter.com

LEE'S SUMMIT MEDICAL CENTER (O, 80 beds) 2100 SE Blue Parkway, Lee's Summit, MO, Zip 64063–1007; tel. 816/282–5000; John McDonald, Chief Executive Officer
**Web address:** www.leessummitmedicalcenter.com

RESEARCH MEDICAL CENTER (O, 489 beds) 2316 East Meyer Boulevard, Kansas City, MO, Zip 64132–1136; tel. 816/276–4000; Ashley McClellan, FACHE, Chief Executive Officer

**NEVADA:** MOUNTAINVIEW HOSPITAL (O, 407 beds) 3100 North Tenaya Way, Las Vegas, NV, Zip 89128–0436; tel. 702/255–5000; Jeremy Bradshaw, Chief Executive Officer
**Web address:** www.mountainview–hospital.com

SOUTHERN HILLS HOSPITAL AND MEDICAL CENTER (O, 252 beds) 9300 West Sunset Road, Las Vegas, NV, Zip 89148–4844; tel. 702/880–2100; Alexis Mussi, Chief Executive Officer
**Web address:** www.southernhillshospital.com

SUNRISE HOSPITAL AND MEDICAL CENTER (O, 762 beds) 3186 South Maryland Parkway, Las Vegas, NV, Zip 89109–2306, Mailing Address: P.O. Box 98530, 89193, tel. 702/731–8000; Todd Sklamberg, President
**Web address:** www.sunrisehospital.com

**NEW HAMPSHIRE:** FRISBIE MEMORIAL HOSPITAL (O, 96 beds) 11 Whitehall Road, Rochester, NH, Zip 03867–3297; tel. 603/332–5211; Jeff Scionti, Chief Executive Officer

PARKLAND MEDICAL CENTER (O, 86 beds) One Parkland Drive, Derry, NH, Zip 03038–2750; tel. 603/432–1500; John Skevington, Chief Executive Officer
**Web address:** www.parklandmedicalcenter.com

PORTSMOUTH REGIONAL HOSPITAL (O, 220 beds) 333 Borthwick Avenue, Portsmouth, NH, Zip 03801–7128; tel. 603/436–5110; Dean Carucci, Chief Executive Officer

**NORTH CAROLINA:** ANGEL MEDICAL CENTER (O, 59 beds) 120 Riverview Street, Franklin, NC, Zip 28734–2612, Mailing Address: P.O. Box 1209, 28744–0569, tel. 828/524–8411; Karen S. Gorby, R.N., MSN, FACHE, Chief Executive Officer and Chief Nursing Officer
**Web address:** www.angelmed.org

ASHEVILLE SPECIALTY HOSPITAL (O, 34 beds) 428 Biltmore Avenue, 4th Floor, Asheville, NC, Zip 28801–4502; tel. 828/213–5400; Julie A. Dikos, President and Chief Executive Officer

BLUE RIDGE REGIONAL HOSPITAL (O, 46 beds) 125 Hospital Drive, Spruce Pine, NC, Zip 28777–3035; tel. 828/765–4201; Tonia Hale, R.N., Chief Executive Officer and Chief Nursing Officer
**Web address:** www.spchospital.org

CAREPARTNERS HEALTH SERVICES (O, 80 beds) 68 Sweeten Creek Road, Asheville, NC, Zip 28803–2318, Mailing Address: P.O. Box 15025, 28813–0025, tel. 828/277–4800; Tracy Buchanan, Chief Executive Officer and President

HIGHLANDS–CASHIERS HOSPITAL (O, 104 beds) 190 Hospital Drive, Highlands, NC, Zip 28741–7600, P O Drawer 190, 28741–0190, tel. 828/526–1200; Jacqueline Medland, MS, Ph.D., President and Chief Nursing Officer
**Web address:** www.hchospital.org

MCDOWELL HOSPITAL (O, 65 beds) 430 Rankin Drive, Marion, NC, Zip 28752–6568, Mailing Address: P.O. Box 730, 28752–0730, tel. 828/659–5000; Carol C. Wolfenbarger, FACHE, MSN, President
**Web address:** www.mission–health.org

MISSION HOSPITAL (O, 815 beds) 509 Biltmore Avenue, Asheville, NC, Zip 28801–4690; tel. 828/213–1111; Chad Patrick, Chief Executive Officer

TRANSYLVANIA REGIONAL HOSPITAL (O, 102 beds) 260 Hospital Drive, Brevard, NC, Zip 28712–3378; tel. 828/884–9111; Michele Pilon, President and Chief Nursing Officer
**Web address:** www.trhospital.org

**SOUTH CAROLINA:** COLLETON MEDICAL CENTER (O, 135 beds) 501 Robertson Boulevard, Walterboro, SC, Zip 29488–5714; tel. 843/782–2000; Jimmy O. Hiott III, Chief Executive Officer
**Web address:** www.colletonmedical.com

GRAND STRAND MEDICAL CENTER (O, 371 beds) 809 82nd Parkway, Myrtle Beach, SC, Zip 29572–4607; tel. 843/692–1000; Mark E. Sims, Chief Executive Officer

TRIDENT MEDICAL CENTER (O, 451 beds) 9330 Medical Plaza Drive, Charleston, SC, Zip 29406–9195; tel. 843/797–7000; Todd Gallati, FACHE, President and Chief Executive Officer
**Web address:** www.tridenthealthsystem.com

**TENNESSEE:** PARKRIDGE MEDICAL CENTER (O, 645 beds) 2333 McCallie Avenue, Chattanooga, TN, Zip 37404–3258; tel. 423/698–6061; Thomas H. Ozburn, Chief Executive Officer
**Web address:** www.parkridgemedicalcenter.com

PINEWOOD SPRINGS (O, 60 beds) 1001 North James M Campbell Boulevard, Columbia, TN, Zip 38401; tel. 931/777–6000; Troy Chisolm, Chief Executive Officer
**Web address:** www.pinewoodsprings.com/

TRISTAR ASHLAND CITY MEDICAL CENTER (O, 12 beds) 313 North Main Street, Ashland City, TN, Zip 37015–1347; tel. 615/792–3030; Darrell White, R.N., Administrator and Chief Nursing Officer

TRISTAR CENTENNIAL MEDICAL CENTER (O, 733 beds) 2300 Patterson Street, Nashville, TN, Zip 37203–1528; tel. 615/342–1000; Scott A. Cihak, President and Chief Executive Officer
**Web address:** www.tristarcentennial.com

For explanation of codes following names, see page B2.
★ Indicates Type III membership in the American Hospital Association.

TRISTAR HENDERSONVILLE MEDICAL CENTER (O, 159 beds) 355 New Shackle Island Road, Hendersonville, TN, Zip 37075–2479; tel. 615/338–1000; Regina Bartlett, Chief Executive Officer
**Web address:** www.hendersonvillemedicalcenter.com

TRISTAR HORIZON MEDICAL CENTER (O, 157 beds) 111 Highway 70 East, Dickson, TN, Zip 37055–2080; tel. 615/446–0446; Jason E. Boyd, Chief Executive Officer

TRISTAR SKYLINE MEDICAL CENTER (O, 407 beds) 3441 Dickerson Pike, Nashville, TN, Zip 37207–2539; tel. 615/769–2000; Dustin Greene, Chief Executive Officer
**Web address:** www.tristarskyline.com

TRISTAR SOUTHERN HILLS MEDICAL CENTER (O, 126 beds) 391 Wallace Road, Nashville, TN, Zip 37211–4859, 3441 Dickerson Pike, 37207, tel. 615/781–4000; Joanna J. Conley, FACHE, Chief Executive Officer
**Web address:** www.tristarsouthernhills.com

TRISTAR STONECREST MEDICAL CENTER (O, 119 beds) 200 StoneCrest Boulevard, Smyrna, TN, Zip 37167–6810; tel. 615/768–2000; Louis Caputo, Chief Executive Officer

TRISTAR SUMMIT MEDICAL CENTER (O, 218 beds) 5655 Frist Boulevard, Hermitage, TN, Zip 37076–2053; tel. 615/316–3000; Brian Marger, Chief Executive Officer
**Web address:** www.summitmedctr.com

**TEXAS:** CORPUS CHRISTI MEDICAL CENTER (O, 426 beds) 3315 South Alameda Street, Corpus Christi, TX, Zip 78411–1883, Mailing Address: P.O. Box 8991, 78468–8991, tel. 361/761–1400; Eric Evans, Chief Executive Officer

HCA HOUSTON HEALTHCARE CLEAR LAKE (O, 591 beds) 620 Power St., League City, TX, Zip 77598–4220, 500 West Medical Center Boulevard, Webster, 77598–4220, tel. 281/332–2511; Todd Caliva, FACHE, Chief Executive Officer
**Web address:** www.clearlakermc.com

HCA HOUSTON HEALTHCARE CONROE (O, 310 beds) 504 Medical Boulevard, Conroe, TX, Zip 77304, Mailing Address: P.O. Box 1538, 77305–1538, tel. 936/539–1111; Matt Davis, FACHE, Chief Executive Officer

HCA HOUSTON HEALTHCARE KINGWOOD (O, 563 beds) 22999 U S Highway 59 North, Kingwood, TX, Zip 77339; tel. 281/348–8000; John Corbeil, Chief Executive Officer
**Web address:** www.kingwoodmedical.com

HCA HOUSTON HEALTHCARE MEDICAL CENTER (O, 147 beds) 1313 Hermann Drive, Houston, TX, Zip 77004–7092; tel. 713/527–5000; Peyton Elliott, Chief Executive Officer
**Web address:** www.https://hcahoustonhealthcare.com/locations/medical–center/

HCA HOUSTON HEALTHCARE NORTHWEST (O, 254 beds) 710 Cypress Creek Parkway, Houston, TX, Zip 77090–3402; tel. 281/440–1000; Scott Davis, Chief Executive Officer

HCA HOUSTON HEALTHCARE PEARLAND (O, 53 beds) 11100 Shadow Creek Parkway, Pearland, TX, Zip 77584–7285; tel. 713/770–7000; David S. Wagner, Chief Executive Officer
**Web address:** www.pearlandmc.com

HCA HOUSTON HEALTHCARE SOUTHEAST (O, 269 beds) 4000 Spencer Highway, Pasadena, TX, Zip 77504–1202; tel. 713/359–2000; Jeanna Bamburg, FACHE, Chief Executive Officer
**Web address:** www.bayshoremedical.com

HCA HOUSTON HEALTHCARE TOMBALL (O, 261 beds) 605 Holderrieth Street, Tomball, TX, Zip 77375–6445; tel. 281/401–7500; Robert Marmerstein, Chief Executive Officer
**Web address:** www.tomballregionalmedicalcenter.com

HCA HOUSTON HEALTHCARE WEST (O, 264 beds) 12141 Richmond Avenue, Houston, TX, Zip 77082–2499; tel. 281/558–3444; Megan Marietta, Chief Executive Officer

LAS PALMAS MEDICAL CENTER (O, 576 beds) 1801 North Oregon Street, El Paso, TX, Zip 79902–3591; tel. 915/521–1200; Don Karl, Interim Chief Executive Officer
**Web address:** www.laspalmashealth.com

MEDICAL CITY ALLIANCE (O, 75 beds) 3101 North Tarrant Parkway, Fort Worth, TX, Zip 76177; tel. 817/639–1000; Glenn Wallace, Chief Executive Officer

MEDICAL CITY ARLINGTON (O, 351 beds) 3301 Matlock Road, Arlington, TX, Zip 76015–2908; tel. 817/465–3241; Keith Zimmerman, Chief Executive Officer
**Web address:** www.medicalcenterarlington.com

MEDICAL CITY DALLAS (O, 876 beds) 7777 Forest Lane, Dallas, TX, Zip 75230–2598; tel. 972/566–7000; Chris Mowan, Chief Executive Officer
**Web address:** www.medicalcityhospital.com

MEDICAL CITY DENTON (O, 185 beds) 3535 South 1–35 East, Denton, TX, Zip 76210; tel. 940/384–3535; Steven Edgar, FACHE, President and Chief Executive Officer
**Web address:** www.dentonregional.com

MEDICAL CITY FORT WORTH (O, 218 beds) 900 Eighth Avenue, Fort Worth, TX, Zip 76104–3902; tel. 817/336–2100; Jyric Sims, FACHE, Chief Executive Officer
**Web address:** www.medicalcityfortworth.com/about/

MEDICAL CITY GREEN OAKS HOSPITAL (O, 124 beds) 7808 Clodus Fields Drive, Dallas, TX, Zip 75251–2206; tel. 972/991–9504; Thomas M. Collins, President, Chairman and Chief Executive Officer

MEDICAL CITY LAS COLINAS (O, 72 beds) 6800 North MacArthur Boulevard, Irving, TX, Zip 75039–2422; tel. 972/969–2000; Daniela Decell, Chief Executive Officer
**Web address:** www.lascolinasmedical.com

MEDICAL CITY LEWISVILLE (O, 156 beds) 500 West Main, Lewisville, TX, Zip 75057–3699; tel. 972/420–1000; LaSharndra Barbarin, Chief Executive Officer
**Web address:** www.lewisvillemedical.com

MEDICAL CITY MCKINNEY (O, 222 beds) 4500 Medical Center Drive, McKinney, TX, Zip 75069–1650; tel. 972/547–8000; Ernest C. Lynch III, FACHE, President and Chief Executive Officer

MEDICAL CITY NORTH HILLS (O, 138 beds) 4401 Booth Calloway Road, North Richland Hills, TX, Zip 76180–7399; tel. 817/255–1000; Mark S. Deno, Chief Executive Officer
**Web address:** www.northhillshospital.com

MEDICAL CITY PLANO (O, 611 beds) 3901 West 15th Street, Plano, TX, Zip 75075–7738; tel. 972/596–6800; Carlton Ulmer, Chief Executive Officer
**Web address:** www.medicalcenterplano.com

MEDICAL CITY WEATHERFORD (O, 82 beds) 713 East Anderson Street, Weatherford, TX, Zip 76086–5705; tel. 682/582–1000; Sean Kamber, Chief Executive Officer
**Web address:** www.weatherfordregional.com

METHODIST AMBULATORY SURGERY HOSPITAL – NORTHWEST (O, 21 beds) 9150 Huebner Road, Suite 100, San Antonio, TX, Zip 78240–1545; tel. 210/575–5000; Scott Rausch, Chief Executive Officer

METHODIST HOSPITAL SOUTH (O, 42 beds) 1905 Highway 97 East, Jourdanton, TX, Zip 78026–1504; tel. 830/769–3515; Gregory A. Seiler, Chief Executive Officer
**Web address:** www.https://sahealth.com/locations/methodisthospitalsouth/

METHODIST HOSPITAL (O, 1667 beds) 7700 Floyd Curl Drive, San Antonio, TX, Zip 78229–3993; tel. 210/575–4000; Daniel Miller, FACHE, Chief Executive Officer
**Web address:** www.sahealth.com

METHODIST STONE OAK HOSPITAL (O, 242 beds) 1139 E Sonterra Boulevard, San Antonio, TX, Zip 78258–4347, 1139 East Sonterra Boulevard, 78258–4347, tel. 210/638–2100; Marc Strode, Chief Executive Officer

PLAZA SPECIALTY HOSPITAL (O, 46 beds) 1300 Binz Street, Houston, TX, Zip 77004–7016; tel. 713/285–1000; Peyton Elliott, Chief Executive Officer
**Web address:** www.plazaspecialtyhospital.com

RIO GRANDE REGIONAL HOSPITAL (O, 304 beds) 101 East Ridge Road, McAllen, TX, Zip 78503–1299; tel. 956/632–6000; Cristina Rivera, Chief Executive Officer
**Web address:** www.riohealth.com

ST. DAVID'S MEDICAL CENTER (O, 607 beds) 919 East 32nd Street, Austin, TX, Zip 78705–2709, Mailing Address: P.O. Box 4039, 78765–4039, tel. 512/476–7111; Todd E. Steward, FACHE, Chief Executive Officer

ST. DAVID'S NORTH AUSTIN MEDICAL CENTER (O, 398 beds) 12221 North MoPac Expressway, Austin, TX, Zip 78758–2496; tel. 512/901–1000; Thomas W. Jackson, Chief Executive Officer
**Web address:** www.northaustin.com

For explanation of codes following names, see page B2.
★ Indicates Type III membership in the American Hospital Association.

ST. DAVID'S ROUND ROCK MEDICAL CENTER (O, 169 beds) 2400 Round Rock Avenue, Round Rock, TX, Zip 78681–4097; tel. 512/341–1000; Jeremy Barclay, Chief Executive Officer
**Web address**: www.stdavids.com

ST. DAVID'S SOUTH AUSTIN MEDICAL CENTER (O, 325 beds) 901 West Ben White Boulevard, Austin, TX, Zip 78704–6903; tel. 512/447–2211; Todd E. Steward, FACHE, Chief Executive Officer

TEXAS ORTHOPEDIC HOSPITAL (O, 49 beds) 7401 South Main Street, Houston, TX, Zip 77030–4509; tel. 713/799–8600; Eric Becker, Chief Executive Officer
**Web address**: www.texasorthopedic.com

VALLEY REGIONAL MEDICAL CENTER (O, 214 beds) 100A Alton Gloor Boulevard, Brownsville, TX, Zip 78526–3354; tel. 956/350–7101; Art Garza, FACHE, Chief Executive Officer
**Web address**: www.valleyregionalmedicalcenter.com

WOMAN'S HOSPITAL OF TEXAS (O, 367 beds) 7600 Fannin Street, Houston, TX, Zip 77054–1906; tel. 713/790–1234; Elizbeth Ortega, Chief Executive Officer
**Web address**: www.womanshospital.com

**UTAH**: BRIGHAM CITY COMMUNITY HOSPITAL (O, 40 beds) 950 South Medical Drive, Brigham City, UT, Zip 84302–4724; tel. 435/734–9471; Richard Spuhler, Chief Executive Officer
**Web address**: www.brighamcityhospital.com

CACHE VALLEY HOSPITAL (O, 28 beds) 2380 North 400 East, North Logan, UT, Zip 84341–6000; tel. 435/713–9700; Daren Wells, Chief Executive Officer

LAKEVIEW HOSPITAL (O, 119 beds) 630 East Medical Drive, Bountiful, UT, Zip 84010–4908; tel. 801/299–2200; Troy Wood, Chief Executive Officer
**Web address**: www.lakeviewhospital.com

LONE PEAK HOSPITAL (O, 32 beds) 1925 South State Street, Draper, UT, Zip 84020; tel. 801/545–8000; Brian Lines, Chief Executive Officer
**Web address**: www.lonepeakhospital.com

MOUNTAIN VIEW HOSPITAL (O, 124 beds) 1000 East 100 North, Payson, UT, Zip 84651–1600; tel. 801/465–7000; Kevin Johnson, Chief Executive Officer

OGDEN REGIONAL MEDICAL CENTER (O, 232 beds) 5475 South 500 East, Ogden, UT, Zip 84405–6905; tel. 801/479–2111; Mark B. Adams, Chief Executive Officer
**Web address**: www.ogdenregional.com

ST. MARK'S HOSPITAL (O, 298 beds) 1200 East 3900 South, Salt Lake City, UT, Zip 84124–1390; tel. 801/268–7111; Mark Robinson, FACHE, Chief Executive Officer
**Web address**: www.stmarkshospital.com

TIMPANOGOS REGIONAL HOSPITAL (O, 106 beds) 750 West 800 North, Orem, UT, Zip 84057–3660; tel. 801/714–6000; Kimball S. Anderson, FACHE, Chief Executive Officer

**VIRGINIA**: CHIPPENHAM HOSPITAL (O, 702 beds) 7101 Jahnke Road, Richmond, VA, Zip 23225–4044; tel. 804/483–0000; William Lunn, M.D., Chief Executive Officer
**Web address**: www.cjwmedical.com

DOMINION HOSPITAL (O, 116 beds) 2960 Sleepy Hollow Road, Falls Church, VA, Zip 22044–2030; tel. 703/536–2000; Lee Higginbotham, Chief Executive Officer
**Web address**: www.dominionhospital.com

HENRICO DOCTORS' HOSPITAL (O, 767 beds) 1602 Skipwith Road, Richmond, VA, Zip 23229–5205; tel. 804/289–4500; Ryan Jensen, Chief Executive Officer

JOHN RANDOLPH MEDICAL CENTER (O, 147 beds) 411 West Randolph Road, Hopewell, VA, Zip 23860–2938; tel. 804/541–1600; Joseph Mazzo, Chief Executive Officer
**Web address**: www.johnrandolphmed.com

LEWIS–GALE MEDICAL CENTER (O, 506 beds) 8633 Grassy Hill Rd, Boones Mill, VA, Zip 24065, 1900 Electric Road, Salem, 24153–7494, tel. 540/776–4000; Lance Jones, Chief Executive Officer

LEWISGALE HOSPITAL ALLEGHANY (O, 205 beds) One ARH Lane, Low Moor, VA, Zip 24457, Mailing Address: P.O. Box 7, 24457–0007, tel. 540/862–6011; William Windham, Chief Executive Officer
• **Web address**: www.alleghanyregional.com

LEWISGALE HOSPITAL MONTGOMERY (O, 146 beds) 3700 South Main Street, Blacksburg, VA, Zip 24060–7081, Mailing Address: P.O. Box 90004, 24062–9004, tel. 540/951–1111; Alan J. Fabian, Chief Executive Officer

LEWISGALE HOSPITAL PULASKI (O, 147 beds) 2400 Lee Highway, Pulaski, VA, Zip 24301–2326, Mailing Address: P.O. Box 759, 24301–0759, tel. 540/994–8100; Sean Pressman, Chief Executive Officer
**Web address**: www.lewisgale.com/

RESTON HOSPITAL CENTER (O, 247 beds) 1850 Town Center Parkway, Reston, VA, Zip 20190–3219; tel. 703/689–9000; John A. Deardorff, President and Chief Executive, Northern Virginia Market

SPOTSYLVANIA REGIONAL MEDICAL CENTER (O, 137 beds) 4600 Spotsylvania Parkway, Fredericksburg, VA, Zip 22408–7762; tel. 540/498–4000; David McKnight, CPA, Chief Executive Officer
**Web address**: www.spotsrmc.com

STONESPRINGS HOSPITAL CENTER (O, 124 beds) 24440 Stone Spring Boulevard, Dulles, VA, Zip 20166–2247; tel. 571/349–4000; Matt Mathias, Chief Executive Officer
**Web address**: www.stonespringshospital.com

| | | |
|---|---|---|
| Owned, leased, sponsored: | 162 hospitals | 45362 beds |
| Contract–managed: | 0 hospitals | 0 beds |
| **Totals:** | 162 hospitals | 45362 beds |

---

**0328: HEALTH FIRST, INC.** (NP)
6450 US Highway 1, Rockledge, FL Zip 32955–5747; tel. 321/434–7000; Steven P. Johnson, Ph.D., President and Chief Executive Officer
**(Centralized Health System)**

**FLORIDA**: HEALTH FIRST CAPE CANAVERAL HOSPITAL (O, 144 beds) 701 West Cocoa Beach Causeway, Cocoa Beach, FL, Zip 32931–5595, Mailing Address: P.O. Box 320069, 32932–0069, tel. 321/799–7111; Brett A. Esrock, FACHE, President
**Web address**: www.health–first.org

HEALTH FIRST HOLMES REGIONAL MEDICAL CENTER (O, 514 beds) 1350 South Hickory Street, Melbourne, FL, Zip 32901–3224; tel. 321/434–7000; Brett A. Esrock, FACHE, Chief Executive Officer
**Web address**: www.health–first.org

HEALTH FIRST PALM BAY HOSPITAL (O, 120 beds) 1425 Malabar Road NE, Palm Bay, FL, Zip 32907–2506; tel. 321/434–8000; Brett A. Esrock, FACHE, President

HEALTH FIRST VIERA HOSPITAL (O, 84 beds) 8745 North Wickham Road, Melbourne, FL, Zip 32940–5997; tel. 321/434–9164; Brett A. Esrock, FACHE, President
**Web address**: www.vierahospital.org

| | | |
|---|---|---|
| Owned, leased, sponsored: | 4 hospitals | 862 beds |
| Contract–managed: | 0 hospitals | 0 beds |
| **Totals:** | 4 hospitals | 862 beds |

---

**0307: HEALTH QUEST SYSTEMS, INC.** (NP)
1351 Route 55 Ste 200, LaGrangeville, NY Zip 12540–5108, 1351 Route 55, 12540–5108, tel. 845/475–9500; Robert Friedberg, President and Chief Executive Officer
**(Independent Hospital System)**

**CONNECTICUT**: SHARON HOSPITAL (O, 60 beds) 50 Hospital Hill Road, Sharon, CT, Zip 06069–2096, Mailing Address: P.O. Box 789, 06069–0789, tel. 860/364–4000; Mark Hirko, M.D., President
**Web address**: www.sharonhospital.com

**NEW YORK**: NORTHERN DUTCHESS HOSPITAL (O, 84 beds) 6511 Springbrook Avenue, Rhinebeck, NY, Zip 12572–3709, Mailing Address: P.O. Box 5002, 12572–5002, tel. 845/876–3001; Denise George, R.N., President
**Web address**: www.health–quest.org/home_nd.cfm?id=9

PUTNAM HOSPITAL CENTER (O, 140 beds) 670 Stoneleigh Avenue, Carmel, NY, Zip 10512–3997; tel. 845/279–5711; Mark Hirko, M.D., President

For explanation of codes following names, see page B2.
★ Indicates Type III membership in the American Hospital Association.

VASSAR BROTHERS MEDICAL CENTER (O, 365 beds) 45 Reade Place, Poughkeepsie, NY, Zip 12601–3947; tel. 845/454–8500; Peter Kelly, President
**Web address:** www.https://patients.healthquest.org/locations/vassar–brothers–medical–center/

| | | |
|---|---|---|
| Owned, leased, sponsored: | 4 hospitals | 649 beds |
| Contract–managed: | 0 hospitals | 0 beds |
| Totals: | 4 hospitals | 649 beds |

## 0342: HEALTHPARTNERS (NP)

8170 33rd Avenue South, Bloomington, MN Zip 55425–4516; tel. 952/883–6000; Andrea Walsh, President and Chief Executive Officer
**(Moderately Centralized Health System)**

**MINNESOTA:** GLENCOE REGIONAL HEALTH (C, 133 beds) 1805 Hennepin Avenue North, Glencoe, MN, Zip 55336–1416; tel. 320/864–3121; Patricia Henderson, R.N., Interim Chief Executive Officer
**Web address:** www.grhsonline.org

HUTCHINSON HEALTH (O, 49 beds) 1095 Highway 15 South, Hutchinson, MN, Zip 55350–3182; tel. 320/234–5000; Jim Lyons, President
**Web address:** www.hutchhealth.com

LAKEVIEW HOSPITAL (O, 67 beds) 927 Churchill Street West, Stillwater, MN, Zip 55082–6605; tel. 651/439–5330; Theodore Wegleitner, Chief Executive Officer and President
**Web address:** www.lakeview.org

PARK NICOLLET METHODIST HOSPITAL (O, 346 beds) 6500 Excelsior Boulevard, Saint Louis Park, MN, Zip 55426–4702; tel. 952/993–5000; Jennifer Myster, President

REGIONS HOSPITAL (O, 463 beds) 640 Jackson Street, Saint Paul, MN, Zip 55101–2595; tel. 651/254–3456; Megan Remark, President and Chief Executive Officer
**Web address:** www.regionshospital.com

**WISCONSIN:** AMERY HOSPITAL AND CLINIC (O, 17 beds) 265 Griffin Street East, Amery, WI, Zip 54001–1439; tel. 715/268–8000; Debra Rudquist, FACHE, President and Chief Executive Officer

HUDSON HOSPITAL AND CLINIC (O, 24 beds) 405 Stageline Road, Hudson, WI, Zip 54016–7848; tel. 715/531–6000; Thomas Borowski, FACHE, President
**Web address:** www.hudsonhospital.org

WESTFIELDS HOSPITAL AND CLINIC (O, 25 beds) 535 Hospital Road, New Richmond, WI, Zip 54017–1449; tel. 715/243–2600; Steven Massey, President and Chief Executive Officer
**Web address:** www.westfieldshospital.com

| | | |
|---|---|---|
| Owned, leased, sponsored: | 7 hospitals | 991 beds |
| Contract–managed: | 1 hospitals | 133 beds |
| Totals: | 8 hospitals | 1124 beds |

## ★0585: HEALTHTECH MANAGEMENT SERVICES (IO)

5110 Maryland Way Suite 200, Brentwood, TN Zip 37027–2307; tel. 615/309–6053; Derek Morkel, Chief Executive Officer
**(Moderately Centralized Health System)**

**ARIZONA:** COBRE VALLEY REGIONAL MEDICAL CENTER (C, 25 beds) 5880 South Hospital Drive, Globe, AZ, Zip 85501–9454; tel. 928/425–3261; Neal Jensen, Chief Executive Officer
**Web address:** www.cvrmc.org

**GEORGIA:** UPSON REGIONAL MEDICAL CENTER (C, 93 beds) 801 West Gordon Street, Thomaston, GA, Zip 30286–3426, Mailing Address: P.O. Box 1059, 30286–0027, tel. 706/647–8111; Jeffrey S. Tarrant, FACHE, Chief Executive Officer
**Web address:** www.urmc.org

**ILLINOIS:** CARLINVILLE AREA HOSPITAL (C, 25 beds) 20733 North Broad Street, Carlinville, IL, Zip 62626–1499; tel. 217/854–3141; Kenneth G. Reid, President and Chief Executive Officer
**Web address:** www.cahcare.com

HAMMOND–HENRY HOSPITAL (C, 61 beds) 600 North College Avenue, Geneseo, IL, Zip 61254–1099; tel. 309/944–6431; Mark Kuhn, Chief Executive Officer
**Web address:** www.hammondhenry.com

HILLSBORO AREA HOSPITAL (C, 25 beds) 1200 East Tremont Street, Hillsboro, IL, Zip 62049–1900; tel. 217/532–6111; Rex H. Brown, President and Chief Executive Officer
**Web address:** www.hillsborohealth.org

**LOUISIANA:** IBERIA MEDICAL CENTER (C, 137 beds) 2315 East Main Street, New Iberia, LA, Zip 70560–4031, Mailing Address: P.O. Box 13338, 70562–3338, tel. 337/364–0441; Dionne Viator, CPA, FACHE, President and Chief Executive Officer

**MONTANA:** BARRETT HOSPITAL & HEALTHCARE (C, 18 beds) 600 Mt Highway 91 South, Dillon, MT, Zip 59725–7379; tel. 406/683–3000; Ken Westman, Chief Executive Officer
**Web address:** www.barretthospital.org

**OREGON:** BLUE MOUNTAIN HOSPITAL DISTRICT (C, 56 beds) 170 Ford Road, John Day, OR, Zip 97845–2009; tel. 541/575–1311; Derek Daly, Chief Executive Officer
**Web address:** www.bluemountainhospital.org

**WISCONSIN:** GRANT REGIONAL HEALTH CENTER (C, 7 beds) 507 South Monroe Street, Lancaster, WI, Zip 53813–2054; tel. 608/723–2143; David Smith, President and Chief Executive Officer
**Web address:** www.grantregional.com

SPOONER HEALTH (C, 20 beds) 1280 Chandler Drive, Spooner, WI, Zip 54801–1299; tel. 715/635–2111; Michael Schafer, Chief Executive Officer and Administrator
**Web address:** www.spoonerhealth.com

TOMAH HEALTH (C, 25 beds) 321 Butts Avenue, Tomah, WI, Zip 54660–1412; tel. 608/372–2181; Philip J. Stuart, Administrator and Chief Executive Officer
**Web address:** www.tomahhospital.org

**WYOMING:** HOT SPRINGS COUNTY MEMORIAL HOSPITAL (C, 25 beds) 150 East Arapahoe Street, Thermopolis, WY, Zip 82443–2498; tel. 307/864–3121; Margie Molitor, FACHE, R.N., Chief Executive Officer

| | | |
|---|---|---|
| Owned, leased, sponsored: | 0 hospitals | 0 beds |
| Contract–managed: | 12 hospitals | 517 beds |
| Totals: | 12 hospitals | 517 beds |

## ★9505: HENRY FORD HEALTH SYSTEM (NP)

One Ford Place, Detroit, MI Zip 48202–3450; tel. 313/876–8708; Wright L. Lassiter III, President and Chief Executive Officer
**(Centralized Health System)**

**MICHIGAN:** HENRY FORD ALLEGIANCE HEALTH (O, 404 beds) 205 North East Avenue, Jackson, MI, Zip 49201–1753; tel. 517/205–4800; Paula R. Autry, FACHE, President and Chief Executive Officer
**Web address:** www.allegiancehealth.org

HENRY FORD ALLEGIANCE SPECIALTY HOSPITAL (O, 44 beds) 110 North Elm Avenue, Jackson, MI, Zip 49202–3595; tel. 517/205–4463; J Mark. Fall, Chief Executive Officer
**Web address:** https://www.henryford.com/locations/allegiance–specialty–hospital

HENRY FORD HOSPITAL (O, 747 beds) 2799 West Grand Boulevard, Detroit, MI, Zip 48202–2608; tel. 313/916–2600; Veronica Hall, R.N., Interim President and Chief Executive Officer

HENRY FORD KINGSWOOD HOSPITAL (O, 101 beds) 10300 West Eight Mile Road, Ferndale, MI, Zip 48220–2100; tel. 248/398–3200; Cathrine Frank, M.D., Chairperson
**Web address:** www.henryford.com

HENRY FORD MACOMB HOSPITALS (O, 415 beds) 15855 19 Mile Road, Clinton Township, MI, Zip 48038–6324; tel. 586/263–2300; Barbara W. Rossmann, R.N., President and Chief Executive Officer
**Web address:** www.henryfordmacomb.com

For explanation of codes following names, see page B2.
★ Indicates Type III membership in the American Hospital Association.

HENRY FORD WEST BLOOMFIELD HOSPITAL (O, 212 beds) 6777 West Maple Road, West Bloomfield, MI, Zip 48322–3013; tel. 248/325–1000; Eric Wallis, R.N., President

HENRY FORD WYANDOTTE HOSPITAL (O, 378 beds) 2333 Biddle Avenue, Wyandotte, MI, Zip 48192–4668; tel. 734/246–6000; Peter Karadjoff, Interim President
**Web address:** www.henryfordhealth.org

| Owned, leased, sponsored: | 7 hospitals | 2301 beds |
|---|---|---|
| Contract–managed: | 0 hospitals | 0 beds |
| Totals: | 7 hospitals | 2301 beds |

## 0309: HERITAGE VALLEY HEALTH SYSTEM (NP)

1000 Dutch Ridge Road, Beaver, PA Zip 15009–9727; tel. 724/773–2024; Norman F. Mitry, President and Chief Executive Officer
**(Independent Hospital System)**

**PENNSYLVANIA:** HERITAGE VALLEY HEALTH SYSTEM (O, 271 beds) 1000 Dutch Ridge Road, Beaver, PA, Zip 15009–9727; tel. 724/728–7000; Norman F. Mitry, President and Chief Executive Officer
**Web address:** www.heritagevalley.org

HERITAGE VALLEY KENNEDY (O, 124 beds) 25 Heckel Road, McKees Rocks, PA, Zip 15136–1694; tel. 412/777–6161; Michael S. Miller, President and Chief Executive Officer
**Web address:** www.ohiovalleyhospital.org

SEWICKLEY VALLEY HOSPITAL, (A DIVISION OF VALLEY MEDICAL FACILITIES) (O, 179 beds) 720 Blackburn Road, Sewickley, PA, Zip 15143–1459; tel. 412/741–6600; Norman F. Mitry, President and Chief Executive Officer
**Web address:** www.heritagevalley.org

| Owned, leased, sponsored: | 3 hospitals | 574 beds |
|---|---|---|
| Contract–managed: | 0 hospitals | 0 beds |
| Totals: | 3 hospitals | 574 beds |

## 1024: HEYWOOD HEALTHCARE (NP)

242 Green Street, Gardner, MA Zip 01440–1336; tel. 978/632–3420; Winfield S. Brown, FACHE, Chief Executive Officer
**(Independent Hospital System)**

**MASSACHUSETTS:** ATHOL HOSPITAL (O, 21 beds) 2033 Main Street, Athol, MA, Zip 01331–3598; tel. 978/249–3511; Winfield S. Brown, FACHE, President and Chief Executive Officer

HEYWOOD HOSPITAL (O, 119 beds) 242 Green Street, Gardner, MA, Zip 01440–1373; tel. 978/632–3420; Winfield S. Brown, FACHE, President and Chief Executive Officer
**Web address:** www.heywood.org

| Owned, leased, sponsored: | 2 hospitals | 140 beds |
|---|---|---|
| Contract–managed: | 0 hospitals | 0 beds |
| Totals: | 2 hospitals | 140 beds |

## 1014: HOLZER HEALTH SYSTEM (NP)

500 Burlington Road, Jackson, OH Zip 45640–9360; tel. 855/446–5937; Michael R. Canady, M.D., Chief Executive Officer
**(Independent Hospital System)**

**OHIO:** HOLZER MEDICAL CENTER – JACKSON (O, 24 beds) 500 Burlington Road, Jackson, OH, Zip 45640–9360; tel. 740/288–4625; Michael R. Canady, M.D., Chief Executive Officer
**Web address:** www.holzer.org

HOLZER MEDICAL CENTER (O, 195 beds) 100 Jackson Pike, Gallipolis, OH, Zip 45631–1563; tel. 740/446–5000; Michael R. Canady, M.D., Interim Chief Executive Officer
**Web address:** www.holzer.org

| Owned, leased, sponsored: | 2 hospitals | 219 beds |
|---|---|---|
| Contract–managed: | 0 hospitals | 0 beds |
| Totals: | 2 hospitals | 219 beds |

## ★0963: HONORHEALTH (NP)

8125 North Hayden Road, Scottsdale, AZ Zip 85258–2463; tel. 480/882–4000; Todd LaPorte, Chief Executive Officer
**(Independent Hospital System)**

**ARIZONA:** HONORHEALTH DEER VALLEY MEDICAL CENTER (O, 204 beds) 19829 North 27th Avenue, Phoenix, AZ, Zip 85027–4002; tel. 623/879–6100; David Price, Chief Executive Officer
**Web address:** www.jcl.com

HONORHEALTH JOHN C. LINCOLN MEDICAL CENTER (O, 262 beds) 250 East Dunlap Avenue, Phoenix, AZ, Zip 85020–2825; tel. 602/943–2381; Gary E. Baker, Chief Executive Officer

HONORHEALTH SCOTTSDALE OSBORN MEDICAL CENTER (O, 347 beds) 7400 East Osborn Road, Scottsdale, AZ, Zip 85251–6403; tel. 480/882–4000; Kimberly Post, Senior Vice President and Chief Executive Officer
**Web address:** www.shc.org

HONORHEALTH SCOTTSDALE SHEA MEDICAL CENTER (O, 409 beds) 9003 East Shea Boulevard, Scottsdale, AZ, Zip 85260–6771; tel. 480/323–3000; Gary E. Baker, Senior Vice President and Chief Executive Officer
**Web address:** www.shc.org

HONORHEALTH SCOTTSDALE THOMPSON PEAK MEDICAL CENTER (O, 92 beds) 7400 East Thompson Peak Parkway, Scottsdale, AZ, Zip 85255–4109; tel. 480/324–7000; David Price, Chief Executive Officer

| Owned, leased, sponsored: | 5 hospitals | 1314 beds |
|---|---|---|
| Contract–managed: | 0 hospitals | 0 beds |
| Totals: | 5 hospitals | 1314 beds |

## ★0642: HOUSTON HEALTHCARE SYSTEM (NP)

1601 Watson Boulevard, Warner Robins, GA Zip 31093–3431, Mailing Address: P.O. Box 2886, 31099–2886, tel. 478/922–4281; Charles G. Briscoe, FACHE, President and Chief Executive Officer
**(Independent Hospital System)**

**GEORGIA:** HOUSTON MEDICAL CENTER (O, 237 beds) 1601 Watson Boulevard, Warner Robins, GA, Zip 31093–3431, Mailing Address: P.O. Box 2886, 31099–2886, tel. 478/922–4281; Charles G. Briscoe, FACHE, Interim President and Chief Executive Officer

PERRY HOSPITAL (O, 39 beds) 1120 Morningside Drive, Perry, GA, Zip 31069–2906; tel. 478/987–3600; David Campbell, Administrator
**Web address:** www.hhc.org

| Owned, leased, sponsored: | 2 hospitals | 276 beds |
|---|---|---|
| Contract–managed: | 0 hospitals | 0 beds |
| Totals: | 2 hospitals | 276 beds |

## ★7235: HOUSTON METHODIST (CO)

6565 Fannin Street, D–200, Houston, TX Zip 77030–2707; tel. 713/441–2221; Marc L. Boom, M.D., Chief Executive Officer
**(Centralized Health System)**

**TEXAS:** HOUSTON METHODIST BAYTOWN HOSPITAL (O, 224 beds) 4401 Garth Road, Administration Department, Baytown, TX, Zip 77521–2122; tel. 281/420–8600; David P. Bernard, FACHE, Chief Executive Officer
**Web address:** www.houstonmethodist.org

HOUSTON METHODIST CLEAR LAKE HOSPITAL (O, 138 beds) 18300 St John Drive, Nassau Bay, TX, Zip 77058–6302; tel. 281/333–5503; Dan Newman, Chief Executive Officer
**Web address:** www.houstonmethodist.org/st-john-clear-lake

For explanation of codes following names, see page B2.
★ Indicates Type III membership in the American Hospital Association.

HOUSTON METHODIST CONTINUING CARE HOSPITAL (O, 58 beds) 701 Fry Road, Katy, TX, Zip 77450–2255; tel. 281/599–5700; Gary L. Kempf, R.N., Administrator

HOUSTON METHODIST HOSPITAL (O, 954 beds) 6565 Fannin Street, D200, Houston, TX, Zip 77030–2707; tel. 713/790–3311; Roberta Schwartz, Ph.D., Executive Vice President
**Web address:** www.methodisthealth.com

HOUSTON METHODIST SUGAR LAND HOSPITAL (O, 318 beds) 16655 SW Freeway, Sugar Land, TX, Zip 77479–2329; tel. 281/274–7000; Christopher Siebenaler, Regional Senior Vice President and Chief Executive Officer

HOUSTON METHODIST THE WOODLANDS HOSPITAL (O, 187 beds) 17201 Interstate 45 South, The Woodlands, TX, Zip 77385; tel. 713/790–3333; Debra F. Sukin, Ph.D., Regional Senior Vice President and Chief Executive Officer
**Web address:** www.houstonmethodist.org/locations/the-woodlands/

HOUSTON METHODIST WEST HOSPITAL (O, 216 beds) 18500 Katy Freeway, Houston, TX, Zip 77094–1110; tel. 832/522–1000; Wayne M. Voss, Chief Executive Officer

HOUSTON METHODIST WILLOWBROOK HOSPITAL (O, 312 beds) 18220 State Highway 249, Houston, TX, Zip 77070–4347; tel. 281/477–1000; Keith Barber, CPA, Chief Executive Officer
**Web address:** www.houstonmethodist.org/locations/willowbrook/

| | | |
|---|---|---|
| Owned, leased, sponsored: | 8 hospitals | 2407 beds |
| Contract–managed: | 0 hospitals | 0 beds |
| Totals: | 8 hospitals | 2407 beds |

---

**★5355: HSHS HOSPITAL SISTERS HEALTH SYSTEM** (CO)
4936 LaVerna Road, Springfield, IL Zip 62707–9797, Mailing Address: P.O. Box 19456, 62794–9456, tel. 217/523–4747; Mary Starmann–Harrison, FACHE, R.N., President and Chief Executive Officer
**(Decentralized Health System)**

ILLINOIS: HSHS GOOD SHEPHERD HOSPITAL (O, 30 beds) 200 South Cedar Street, Shelbyville, IL, Zip 62565–1838; tel. 217/774–3961; Aaron Puchbauer, President
**Web address:** www.mysmh.org

HSHS HOLY FAMILY HOSPITAL IN GREENVILLE (O, 42 beds) 200 Healthcare Drive, Greenville, IL, Zip 62246–1154; tel. 618/664–1230; Kelly Sager, R.N., President and Chief Executive Officer

HSHS ST. ANTHONY'S MEMORIAL HOSPITAL (O, 123 beds) 503 North Maple Street, Effingham, IL, Zip 62401–2099; tel. 217/342–2121; Theresa Rutherford, R.N., MS, FACHE, President and Chief Executive Officer
**Web address:** www.stanthonyshospital.org

HSHS ST. ELIZABETH'S HOSPITAL (O, 144 beds) One St. Elizabeth's Boulevard, O'Fallon, IL, Zip 62269; tel. 618/234–2120; Patricia Fischer, FACHE, R.N., President and Chief Executive Officer

HSHS ST. FRANCIS HOSPITAL (O, 25 beds) 1215 Franciscan Drive, Litchfield, IL, Zip 62056–1799, Mailing Address: P.O. Box 1215, 62056–0999, tel. 217/324–2191; James Timpe, Chief Executive Officer
**Web address:** www.stfrancis-litchfield.org

HSHS ST. JOHN'S HOSPITAL (O, 422 beds) 800 East Carpenter Street, Springfield, IL, Zip 62769–0002; tel. 217/544–6464; Evert J. Kuiper, President and Chief Executive Officer
**Web address:** www.st-johns.org

HSHS ST. JOSEPH'S HOSPITAL (O, 124 beds) 9515 Holy Cross Lane, Breese, IL, Zip 62230–3618, Mailing Address: P.O. 99, 62230–0099, tel. 618/526–4511; Chris Klay, President and Chief Executive Officer

HSHS ST. JOSEPH'S HOSPITAL (O, 25 beds) 12866 Troxler Avenue, Highland, IL, Zip 62249–1698; tel. 618/651–2600; John A. Ludwig, President and Chief Operating Officer
**Web address:** www.stjosephshighland.com

HSHS ST. MARY'S HOSPITAL (O, 230 beds) 1800 East Lake Shore Drive, Decatur, IL, Zip 62521–3883; tel. 217/464–2966; Michael Hicks, President and Chief Executive Officer

WISCONSIN: HSHS SACRED HEART HOSPITAL (O, 205 beds) 900 West Clairemont Avenue, Eau Claire, WI, Zip 54701–6122; tel. 715/717–4121; Sandy Anderson, Interim President
**Web address:** www.sacredhearteauclaire.org

HSHS ST. CLARE MEMORIAL HOSPITAL (O, 20 beds) 855 South Main Street, Oconto Falls, WI, Zip 54154–1296; tel. 920/846–3444; Christopher Brabant, President and Chief Executive Officer
**Web address:** www.stclarememorial.org

HSHS ST. JOSEPH'S HOSPITAL (O, 102 beds) 2661 County Highway I, Chippewa Falls, WI, Zip 54729–5407; tel. 715/723–1811; John Wagner, President and Chief Executive Officer

HSHS ST. MARY'S HOSPITAL MEDICAL CENTER (O, 83 beds) 1726 Shawano Avenue, Green Bay, WI, Zip 54303–3282; tel. 920/498–4200; Brian Charlier, President and Chief Executive Officer
**Web address:** www.stmgb.org

HSHS ST. NICHOLAS HOSPITAL (O, 46 beds) 3100 Superior Avenue, Sheboygan, WI, Zip 53081–1948; tel. 920/459–8300; Justin Selle, Chief Executive Officer
**Web address:** www.stnicholashospital.org

HSHS ST. VINCENT HOSPITAL (O, 255 beds) 835 South Van Buren Street, Green Bay, WI, Zip 54301–3526, Mailing Address: P.O. Box 13508, 54307–3508, tel. 920/433–0111; Brian Charlier, President and Chief Executive Officer

| | | |
|---|---|---|
| Owned, leased, sponsored: | 15 hospitals | 1817 beds |
| Contract–managed: | 0 hospitals | 0 beds |
| Totals: | 15 hospitals | 1817 beds |

---

**0907: HUNT REGIONAL HEALTHCARE** (NP)
4215 Joe Ramsey Boulevard, Greenville, TX Zip 75401–7852, Mailing Address: P.O. Box 1059, 75403–1059, tel. 903/408–5000; Richard Carter, Chief Executive Officer
**(Independent Hospital System)**

TEXAS: HUNT REGIONAL MEDICAL CENTER (O, 167 beds) 4215 Joe Ramsey Boulevard East, Greenville, TX, Zip 75401–7899, Mailing Address: P.O. Box 1059, 75403–1059, tel. 903/408–5000; Richard Carter, District Chief Executive Officer
**Web address:** www.huntregional.org

| | | |
|---|---|---|
| Owned, leased, sponsored: | 1 hospitals | 167 beds |
| Contract–managed: | 0 hospitals | 0 beds |
| Totals: | 1 hospitals | 167 beds |

---

**0117: HUNTSVILLE HOSPITAL HEALTH SYSTEM** (NP)
101 Sivley Road SW, Huntsville, AL Zip 35801–4421; tel. 265/256–1000; David S. Spillers, Chief Executive Officer
**(Independent Hospital System)**

ALABAMA: ATHENS–LIMESTONE HOSPITAL (C, 71 beds) 700 West Market Street, Athens, AL, Zip 35611–2457, Mailing Address: P.O. Box 999, 35612–0999, tel. 256/233–9292; David Pryor, President
**Web address:** www.athenslimestonehospital.com

DECATUR MORGAN HOSPITAL (O, 110 beds) 1201 Seventh Street SE, Decatur, AL, Zip 35601–3303, Mailing Address: P.O. Box 2239, 35609–2239, tel. 256/341–2000; Kelli Powers, President

HELEN KELLER HOSPITAL (C, 143 beds) 1300 South Montgomery Avenue, Sheffield, AL, Zip 35660–6334, Mailing Address: P.O. Box 610, 35660–0610, tel. 256/386–4196; Kyle Buchanan, President
**Web address:** www.helenkeller.com

HUNTSVILLE HOSPITAL (O, 949 beds) 101 Sivley Road SW, Huntsville, AL, Zip 35801–4470; tel. 256/265–1000; David S. Spillers, Chief Executive Officer

LAWRENCE MEDICAL CENTER (C, 43 beds) 202 Hospital Street, Moulton, AL, Zip 35650–1218, Mailing Address: P.O. Box 39, 35650–0039, tel. 256/974–2200; Dean A. Griffin, Chief Executive Officer
**Web address:** www.lawrencemedicalcenter.com

Section B

RED BAY HOSPITAL (C, 22 beds) 211 Hospital Road, Red Bay, AL, Zip 35582–3858, Mailing Address: P.O. Box 490, 35582–0490, tel. 256/356–9532; Sherry Jolley, Director of Operations and Nursing
**Web address:** www.redbayhospital.com

| | | |
|---|---|---|
| Owned, leased, sponsored: | 2 hospitals | 1059 beds |
| Contract–managed: | 4 hospitals | 279 beds |
| Totals: | 6 hospitals | 1338 beds |

---

★**0231: INDIANA UNIVERSITY HEALTH** (NP)
340 West 10th Street, Suite 6100, Indianapolis, IN Zip 46202–3082, Mailing Address: P.O. Box 1367, 46206–1367, tel. 317/962–2000; Dennis M. Murphy, President and Chief Executive Officer
**(Moderately Centralized Health System)**

**INDIANA:** INDIANA UNIVERSITY HEALTH ARNETT HOSPITAL (O, 192 beds) 5165 McCarty Lane, Lafayette, IN, Zip 47905–8764, Mailing Address: P.O. Box 5545, 47903–5545, tel. 765/448–8000; Daniel Neufelder, President

INDIANA UNIVERSITY HEALTH BALL MEMORIAL HOSPITAL (O, 332 beds) 2401 West University Avenue, Muncie, IN, Zip 47303–3499; tel. 765/747–3111; Jeffrey C. Bird, M.D., President
**Web address:** www.iuhealth.org

INDIANA UNIVERSITY HEALTH BEDFORD HOSPITAL (O, 25 beds) 2900 West 16th Street, Bedford, IN, Zip 47421–3583; tel. 812/275–1200; Bradford W. Dykes, President
**Web address:** www.iuhealth.org

INDIANA UNIVERSITY HEALTH BLACKFORD HOSPITAL (O, 15 beds) 410 Pilgrim Boulevard, Hartford City, IN, Zip 47348–1897; tel. 765/348–0300; David W. Hyatt, FACHE, President – Blackford Hospital and Rural Strategy Indiana University Health

INDIANA UNIVERSITY HEALTH BLOOMINGTON HOSPITAL (O, 290 beds) 601 West Second Street, Bloomington, IN, Zip 47403–2317, Mailing Address: P.O. Box 1149, 47402–1149, tel. 812/336–6821; Brian T. Shockney, FACHE, President
**Web address:** www.iuhealth.org

INDIANA UNIVERSITY HEALTH FRANKFORT (C, 25 beds) 1300 South Jackson Street, Frankfort, IN, Zip 46041–3313; tel. 765/656–3000; Kelly Braverman, President
**Web address:** www.stvincent.org

INDIANA UNIVERSITY HEALTH JAY HOSPITAL (C, 37 beds) 500 West Votaw Street, Portland, IN, Zip 47371–1322; tel. 260/726–7131; John Vanator, CPA, Chief Executive Officer
**Web address:** www.iuhealth.org

INDIANA UNIVERSITY HEALTH NORTH HOSPITAL (O, 161 beds) 11700 North Meridian Avenue, Carmel, IN, Zip 46032–4656; tel. 317/688–2000; Alicia Schulhof, President and Chief Executive Officer

INDIANA UNIVERSITY HEALTH PAOLI HOSPITAL (O, 24 beds) 642 West Hospital Road, Paoli, IN, Zip 47454–9672, Mailing Address: P.O. Box 499, 47454–0499, tel. 812/723–2811; Larry Bailey, President
**Web address:** www.iuhealth.org/paoli

INDIANA UNIVERSITY HEALTH TIPTON HOSPITAL (O, 25 beds) 1000 South Main Street, Tipton, IN, Zip 46072–9799; tel. 765/675–8500; Michael Harlowe, President and Chief Executive Officer
**Web address:** www.iuhealth.org

INDIANA UNIVERSITY HEALTH UNIVERSITY HOSPITAL (O, 1296 beds) 550 University Boulevard, Indianapolis, IN, Zip 46202–5149, Mailing Address: P.O. Box 1367, 46206–1367, tel. 317/944–5000; Ryan Nagy, M.D., President and Chief Medical Officer

INDIANA UNIVERSITY HEALTH WEST HOSPITAL (O, 123 beds) 1111 North Ronald Reagan Parkway, Avon, IN, Zip 46123–7085; tel. 317/217–3000; Paul J. Ivkovich, President
**Web address:** www.iuhealth.org

INDIANA UNIVERSITY HEALTH WHITE MEMORIAL HOSPITAL (O, 25 beds) 720 South Sixth Street, Monticello, IN, Zip 47960–8182; tel. 574/583–7111; Mary Minier, President
**Web address:** www.iuhealth.org/white–memorial

REHABILITATION HOSPITAL OF INDIANA (O, 83 beds) 4141 Shore Drive, Indianapolis, IN, Zip 46254–2607; tel. 317/329–2000; Daniel B. Woloszyn, Chief Executive Officer

| | | |
|---|---|---|
| Owned, leased, sponsored: | 12 hospitals | 2591 beds |
| Contract–managed: | 2 hospitals | 62 beds |
| Totals: | 14 hospitals | 2653 beds |

---

**2025: INFIRMARY HEALTH SYSTEM** (NP)
5 Mobile Infirmary Circle, Mobile, AL Zip 36607–3513; tel. 251/435–5500; D Mark. Nix, President and Chief Executive Officer
**(Independent Hospital System)**

**ALABAMA:** ATMORE COMMUNITY HOSPITAL (O, 33 beds) 401 Medical Park Drive, Atmore, AL, Zip 36502–3091; tel. 251/368–2500; Suzanne McGill, Interim Chief Executive Officer

INFIRMARY LONG TERM ACUTE CARE HOSPITAL (L, 38 beds) 5 Mobile Infirmary Circle, Mobile, AL, Zip 36607–3513, Mailing Address: P.O. Box 2226, 36652–2226, tel. 251/660–5239; Susanne Marmande, Administrator
**Web address:** www.theinfirmary.com/

MOBILE INFIRMARY MEDICAL CENTER (O, 554 beds) 5 Mobile Infirmary Drive North, Mobile, AL, Zip 36607–3513, Mailing Address: P.O. Box 2144, 36652–2144, tel. 251/435–2400; Joe Stough, Interim President

NORTH BALDWIN INFIRMARY (L, 50 beds) 1815 Hand Avenue, Bay Minette, AL, Zip 36507–4110, Mailing Address: P.O. Box 1409, 36507–1409, tel. 251/937–5521; Benjamin K. Hansert, Administrator
**Web address:** www.mobileinfirmary.org

THOMAS HOSPITAL (L, 136 beds) 750 Morphy Avenue, Fairhope, AL, Zip 36532–1812, Mailing Address: P.O. Box 929, 36533–0929, tel. 251/928–2375; Ormand P. Thompson, President
**Web address:** www.thomashospital.org

| | | |
|---|---|---|
| Owned, leased, sponsored: | 5 hospitals | 811 beds |
| Contract–managed: | 0 hospitals | 0 beds |
| Totals: | 5 hospitals | 811 beds |

---

★**1305: INOVA HEALTH SYSTEM** (NP)
8110 Gatehouse Road, Suite 200 East, Falls Church, VA Zip 22042–1252; tel. 703/289–2069; J Stephen. Jones, M.D., Chief Executive Officer
**(Centralized Health System)**

**VIRGINIA:** INOVA ALEXANDRIA HOSPITAL (O, 302 beds) 4320 Seminary Road, Alexandria, VA, Zip 22304–1535; tel. 703/504–3167; Rina Bansal, M.D., President

INOVA FAIR OAKS HOSPITAL (O, 201 beds) 3600 Joseph Siewick Drive, Fairfax, VA, Zip 22033–1798; tel. 703/391–3600; Donald Brideau, M.D., Chief Executive Officer
**Web address:** www.inova.org

INOVA FAIRFAX HOSPITAL (O, 1056 beds) 3300 Gallows Road, Falls Church, VA, Zip 22042–3300; tel. 703/776–4001; Susan T. Carroll, FACHE, Acting President
**Web address:** www.inova.org

INOVA LOUDOUN HOSPITAL (O, 288 beds) 44045 Riverside Parkway, Leesburg, VA, Zip 20176–5101, Mailing Address: P.O. Box 6000, 20177–0600, tel. 703/858–6000; Deborah Addo, Chief Executive Officer

INOVA MOUNT VERNON HOSPITAL (O, 237 beds) 2501 Parker's Lane, Alexandria, VA, Zip 22306–3209; tel. 703/664–7000; Joseph Pina, M.D., Chief Executive Officer
**Web address:** www.inova.org

| | | |
|---|---|---|
| Owned, leased, sponsored: | 5 hospitals | 2084 beds |
| Contract–managed: | 0 hospitals | 0 beds |
| Totals: | 5 hospitals | 2084 beds |

---

For explanation of codes following names, see page B2.
★ Indicates Type III membership in the American Hospital Association.

## ★0151: INSPIRA HEALTH NETWORK (NP)

165 Bridgeton Pike, Mullica Hill, NJ Zip 8062; tel. 856/641–8000; Amy B. Mansue, President and Chief Executive Officer
**(Independent Hospital System)**

**NEW JERSEY:** INSPIRA MEDICAL CENTER–ELMER (O, 97 beds) 501 West Front Street, Elmer, NJ, Zip 08318–2101; tel. 856/363–1000; Amy B. Mansue, President and Chief Executive Officer

INSPIRA MEDICAL CENTER–VINELAND (O, 345 beds) 1505 West Sherman Avenue, Vineland, NJ, Zip 08360–6912; tel. 856/641–8000; Amy B. Mansue, President and Chief Executive Officer
**Web address:** www.inspirahealthnetwork.org/?id=5280&sid=1

INSPIRA MEDICAL CENTER–WOODBURY (O, 311 beds) 509 North Broad Street, Woodbury, NJ, Zip 08096–1697; tel. 856/845–0100; Amy B. Mansue, President and Chief Executive Officer
**Web address:** www.inspirahealthnetwork.org/?id=5282&sid=1

| | | |
|---|---|---|
| Owned, leased, sponsored: | 3 hospitals | 753 beds |
| Contract–managed: | 0 hospitals | 0 beds |
| Totals: | 3 hospitals | 753 beds |

## ★0305: INTEGRIS HEALTH (NP)

3366 NW Expressway, Suite 800, Oklahoma City, OK Zip 73112–9756; tel. 405/949–6066; Timothy T. Pehrson, President and Chief Executive Officer
**(Moderately Centralized Health System)**

**OKLAHOMA:** INTEGRIS BAPTIST MEDICAL CENTER (O, 955 beds) 3300 NW Expressway, Oklahoma City, OK, Zip 73112–4418; tel. 405/949–3011; Rex Van Meter, Chief Hospital Executive

INTEGRIS CANADIAN VALLEY HOSPITAL (O, 75 beds) 1201 Health Center Parkway, Yukon, OK, Zip 73099–6381; tel. 405/717–6800; Teresa Gray, President
**Web address:** www.integris–health.com

INTEGRIS DEACONESS (O, 141 beds) 5501 North Portland Avenue, Oklahoma City, OK, Zip 73112–2099; tel. 405/604–6000; Rex Van Meter, President
**Web address:** www.https://integrisok.com/locations/hospital/integris–deaconess

INTEGRIS GROVE HOSPITAL (O, 58 beds) 1001 East 18th Street, Grove, OK, Zip 74344–2907; tel. 918/786–2243; Jonas Rabel, President

INTEGRIS HEALTH EDMOND (O, 40 beds) 4801 Integris Parkway, Edmond, OK, Zip 73034–8864; tel. 405/657–3000; Jonathan Rule, Chief Hospital Executive
**Web address:** www.integrisok.com/edmond

INTEGRIS MIAMI HOSPITAL (O, 39 beds) 200 Second Avenue SW, Miami, OK, Zip 74354–6830; tel. 918/542–6611; Jonas Rabel, President
**Web address:** www.integrisok.com/miami–hospital

INTEGRIS SOUTHWEST MEDICAL CENTER (O, 273 beds) 4401 South Western, Oklahoma City, OK, Zip 73109–3413; tel. 405/636–7000; John Adams, Chief Hospital Executive
**Web address:** www.integrisok.com

INTEGRIS BASS BAPTIST HEALTH CENTER (O, 132 beds) 600 South Monroe Street, Enid, OK, Zip 73701–7211, Mailing Address: P.O. Box 3168, 73702–3168, tel. 580/233–2300; Finny Mathew, President

LAKESIDE WOMEN'S HOSPITAL (O, 23 beds) 11200 North Portland Avenue, Oklahoma City, OK, Zip 73120–5045; tel. 405/936–1500; Kelley Brewer, R.N., MSN, President
**Web address:** www.lakeside–wh.net

| | | |
|---|---|---|
| Owned, leased, sponsored: | 9 hospitals | 1736 beds |
| Contract–managed: | 0 hospitals | 0 beds |
| Totals: | 9 hospitals | 1736 beds |

## ★1815: INTERMOUNTAIN HEALTHCARE, INC. (NP)

36 South State Street, 22nd Floor, Salt Lake City, UT Zip 84111–1453; tel. 801/442–2000; A. Marc. Harrison, M.D., President and Chief Executive Officer
**(Centralized Health System)**

**IDAHO:** CASSIA REGIONAL HOSPITAL (O, 25 beds) 1501 Hiland Avenue, Burley, ID, Zip 83318–2688; tel. 208/678–4444; Ben Smalley, Administrator
**Web address:** www.cassiaregional.org

**UTAH:** ALTA VIEW HOSPITAL (O, 59 beds) 9660 South 1300 East, Sandy, UT, Zip 84094–3793; tel. 801/501–2600; Scott Roberson, Administrator
**Web address:** www.intermountainhealthcare.org

AMERICAN FORK HOSPITAL (O, 78 beds) 170 North 1100 East, American Fork, UT, Zip 84003–2096; tel. 801/855–3300; Jason Wilson, Administrator and Chief Executive Officer

BEAR RIVER VALLEY HOSPITAL (O, 16 beds) 905 North 1000 West, Tremonton, UT, Zip 84337–2497; tel. 435/207–4500; Brandon Vonk, Administrator
**Web address:** www.https://intermountainhealthcare.org/locations/bear–river–valley–hospital/

CEDAR CITY HOSPITAL (O, 48 beds) 1303 North Main Street, Cedar City, UT, Zip 84721–9746; tel. 435/868–5000; Eric Packer, Chief Executive Officer

DELTA COMMUNITY MEDICAL CENTER (O, 18 beds) 126 South White Sage Avenue, Delta, UT, Zip 84624–8937; tel. 435/864–5591; Kurt Forsyth, Administrator
**Web address:** www.https://intermountainhealthcare.org/locations/delta–community–hospital/

DIXIE REGIONAL MEDICAL CENTER (O, 284 beds) 1380 East Medical Center Drive, Saint George, UT, Zip 84790–2123; tel. 435/251–1000; Mitchell Cloward, Administrator
**Web address:** www.intermountainhealthcare.org

FILLMORE COMMUNITY HOSPITAL (O, 7 beds) 674 South Highway 99, Fillmore, UT, Zip 84631–5013; tel. 435/743–5591; Kurt Forsyth, Administrator

GARFIELD MEMORIAL HOSPITAL (C, 15 beds) 200 North 400 East, Panguitch, UT, Zip 84759, Mailing Address: P.O. Box 389, 84759–0389, tel. 435/676–8811; Alberto Vasquez, Administrator
**Web address:** www.ihc.com/hospitals/garfield

HEBER VALLEY HOSPITAL (O, 19 beds) 1485 South Highway 40, Heber City, UT, Zip 84032–3522; tel. 435/654–2500; Si William. Hutt, Administrator

INTERMOUNTAIN MEDICAL CENTER (O, 502 beds) 5121 South Cottonwood Street, Murray, UT, Zip 84107–5701; tel. 801/507–7000; Blair M. Kent, Administrator
**Web address:** www.https://intermountainhealthcare.org/locations/intermountain–medical–center/

LDS HOSPITAL (O, 256 beds) Eighth Avenue and 'C' Street, Salt Lake City, UT, Zip 84143–0001; tel. 801/408–1100; Shawn Morrow, Chief Executive Officer
**Web address:** www.https://intermountainhealthcare.org/locations/lds–hospital/

LAYTON HOSPITAL (O, 33 beds) 201 West Layton Parkway, Layton, UT, Zip 84041–3692; tel. 801/543–6000; Judy Williamson, R.N., Administrator
**Web address:** www.https://intermountainhealthcare.org/locations/layton–hospital/medical–services/

LOGAN REGIONAL HOSPITAL (O, 133 beds) 1400 North 500 East, Logan, UT, Zip 84341–2455; tel. 435/716–1000; Brandon McBride, Administrator

MCKAY–DEE HOSPITAL (O, 299 beds) 4401 Harrison Boulevard, Ogden, UT, Zip 84403–3195; tel. 801/387–2800; Michael A. Clark, Administrator
**Web address:** www.mckay–dee.org

OREM COMMUNITY HOSPITAL (O, 23 beds) 331 North 400 West, Orem, UT, Zip 84057–1999; tel. 801/224–4080; Lenny Lyons, Administrator
**Web address:** www.intermountainhealthcare.org

PARK CITY HOSPITAL (O, 37 beds) 900 Round Valley Drive, Park City, UT, Zip 84060–7552; tel. 435/658–7000; Lori Weston, Administrator

PRIMARY CHILDREN'S HOSPITAL (O, 292 beds) 100 North Mario Capecchi Drive, Intermountain Primary Children's Hospital, Environmental Services, Salt Lake City, UT, Zip 84113–1100; tel. 801/662–1000; Katy Welkie MBA, R.N., Chief Executive Officer
**Web address:** www.intermountainhealthcare.org

RIVERTON HOSPITAL (O, 88 beds) 3741 West 12600 South, Riverton, UT, Zip 84065–7215; tel. 801/285–4000; Todd Neubert, Chief Executive Officer

SANPETE VALLEY HOSPITAL (O, 13 beds) 1100 South Medical Drive, Mount Pleasant, UT, Zip 84647–2222; tel. 435/462–2441; Aaron C. Wood, Chief Executive Officer and Administrator
**Web address:** www.intermountainhealthcare.com

Section B

For explanation of codes following names, see page B2.
★ Indicates Type III membership in the American Hospital Association.

SEVIER VALLEY HOSPITAL (O, 29 beds) 1000 North Main Street, Richfield, UT, Zip 84701–1857; tel. 435/893–4100; Brent Schmidt, Administrator
**Web address:** www.sevierhospital.org

THE ORTHOPEDIC SPECIALTY HOSPITAL (O, 40 beds) 5848 South 300 East, Murray, UT, Zip 84107–6121; tel. 801/314–4100; Adam Chandio, Administrator

UTAH VALLEY HOSPITAL (O, 385 beds) 1034 North 500 West, Provo, UT, Zip 84604–3337; tel. 801/357–7850; Kyle A. Hansen, Chief Executive Officer
**Web address:** www.https://intermountainhealthcare.org/locations/utah–valley–hospital/

| | | |
|---|---|---|
| Owned, leased, sponsored: | 22 hospitals | 2684 beds |
| Contract–managed: | 1 hospitals | 15 beds |
| Totals: | 23 hospitals | 2699 beds |

---

**★0902: IOWA SPECIALTY HOSPITALS** (NP)
1316 South Main Street, Clarion, IA Zip 50525–2019; tel. 515/532–2811; Steven J. Simonin, Chief Executive Officer
**(Independent Hospital System)**

**IOWA:** IOWA SPECIALTY HOSPITAL–BELMOND (C, 22 beds) 403 1st Street SE, Belmond, IA, Zip 50421–1201; tel. 641/444–3223; Amy McDaniel, Chief Executive Officer
**Web address:** www.iowaspecialtyhospital.com

IOWA SPECIALTY HOSPITAL–CLARION (C, 25 beds) 1316 South Main Street, Clarion, IA, Zip 50525–2019; tel. 515/532–2811; Steven J. Simonin, President and Chief Executive Officer
**Web address:** www.iowaspecialtyhospital.com

| | | |
|---|---|---|
| Owned, leased, sponsored: | 0 hospitals | 0 beds |
| Contract–managed: | 2 hospitals | 47 beds |
| Totals: | 2 hospitals | 47 beds |

---

**★7775: JEFFERSON HEALTH** (NP)
925 Chestnut Street, Suite 110, Philadelphia, PA Zip 19107–4216; tel. 610/225–6200; Stephen K. Klasko, M.D., Chief Executive Officer
**(Moderately Centralized Health System)**

**NEW JERSEY:** JEFFERSON STRATFORD HOSPITAL (O, 716 beds) 18 East Laurel Road, Stratford, NJ, Zip 08084–1327; tel. 856/346–6000; Brian Sweeney, President and Chief Operating Officer

**PENNSYLVANIA:** ABINGTON JEFFERSON HEALTH (O, 623 beds) 1200 Old York Road, Abington, PA, Zip 19001–3720; tel. 215/481–2000; Alison Ferren, Interim President and Chief Operating Officer
**Web address:** www.abingtonhealth.org

ABINGTON–LANSDALE HOSPITAL JEFFERSON HEALTH (O, 127 beds) 100 Medical Campus Drive, Lansdale, PA, Zip 19446–1200; tel. 215/368–2100; Alison Ferren, President
**Web address:** www.abingtonhealth.org/find–a–location/abington–lansdale–hospital/#.V5dyVVL9yk4

JEFFERSON HEALTH NORTHEAST (O, 450 beds) 10800 Knights Road, Mansion House, Philadelphia, PA, Zip 19114–4200; tel. 215/612–4000; Richard Galup, President

THOMAS JEFFERSON UNIVERSITY HOSPITALS (O, 883 beds) 111 South 11th Street, Philadelphia, PA, Zip 19107–5084; tel. 215/955–6000; Richard Webster, R.N., President
**Web address:** www.jefferson.edu

| | | |
|---|---|---|
| Owned, leased, sponsored: | 5 hospitals | 2799 beds |
| Contract–managed: | 0 hospitals | 0 beds |
| Totals: | 5 hospitals | 2799 beds |

---

**★0324: JOHN MUIR HEALTH** (NP)
1400 Treat Boulevard, Walnut Creek, CA Zip 94597–2142; tel. 925/941–2100; Calvin K. Knight, President and Chief Executive Officer
**(Independent Hospital System)**

**CALIFORNIA:** JOHN MUIR BEHAVIORAL HEALTH CENTER (O, 73 beds) 2740 Grant Street, Concord, CA, Zip 94520–2265; tel. 925/674–4100; Cindy Bolter, Chief Nursing and Operations Officer
**Web address:** www.johnmuirhealth.com

JOHN MUIR MEDICAL CENTER, CONCORD (O, 215 beds) 2540 East Street, Concord, CA, Zip 94520–1906; tel. 925/682–8200; Jane Willemsen, President and Chief Administrative Officer
**Web address:** www.johnmuirhealth.com

JOHN MUIR MEDICAL CENTER, WALNUT CREEK (O, 420 beds) 1601 Ygnacio Valley Road, Walnut Creek, CA, Zip 94598–3194; tel. 925/939–3000; Jane Willemsen, President and Chief Administrative Officer
**Web address:** https://www.johnmuirhealth.com/

| | | |
|---|---|---|
| Owned, leased, sponsored: | 3 hospitals | 708 beds |
| Contract–managed: | 0 hospitals | 0 beds |
| Totals: | 3 hospitals | 708 beds |

---

**★1015: JOHNS HOPKINS HEALTH SYSTEM** (NP)
733 North Broadway, BRB 104, Baltimore, MD Zip 21205–1832; tel. 410/955–5000; Kevin W. Sowers, MSN, R.N., President
**(Centralized Physician/Insurance Health System)**

**DISTRICT OF COLUMBIA:** SIBLEY MEMORIAL HOSPITAL (O, 273 beds) 5255 Loughboro Road NW, Washington, DC, Zip 20016–2633; tel. 202/537–4000; Hasan A. Zia, Interim President and Chief Executive Officer

**FLORIDA:** JOHNS HOPKINS ALL CHILDREN'S HOSPITAL (O, 259 beds) 501 6th Avenue South, Saint Petersburg, FL, Zip 33701–4634; tel. 727/898–7451; Thomas D. Kmetz, Interim Chief Executive Officer
**Web address:** www.allkids.org

**MARYLAND:** HOWARD COUNTY GENERAL HOSPITAL (O, 259 beds) 5755 Cedar Lane, Columbia, MD, Zip 21044–2999; tel. 410/740–7890; Steven C. Snelgrove, President

JOHNS HOPKINS BAYVIEW MEDICAL CENTER (O, 411 beds) 4940 Eastern Avenue, Baltimore, MD, Zip 21224–2780; tel. 410/550–0100; Richard G. Bennett, M.D., President
**Web address:** www.hopkinsbayview.org

JOHNS HOPKINS HOSPITAL (O, 1008 beds) 600 North Wolfe Street, Admin 104, Baltimore, MD, Zip 21287–1629; tel. 410/955–5000; Redonda G. Miller, M.D., President
**Web address:** www.hopkinsmedicine.org

SUBURBAN HOSPITAL (O, 208 beds) 8600 Old Georgetown Road, Bethesda, MD, Zip 20814–1497; tel. 301/896–3100; Jacky Schultz, MSN, R.N., President
**Web address:** www.suburbanhospital.org

| | | |
|---|---|---|
| Owned, leased, sponsored: | 6 hospitals | 2418 beds |
| Contract–managed: | 0 hospitals | 0 beds |
| Totals: | 6 hospitals | 2418 beds |

---

**★2105: KAISER FOUNDATION HOSPITALS** (NP)
One Kaiser Plaza, 27th Floor – Office #2743, Oakland, CA Zip 94612–3600; tel. 510/271–5910; Gregory A. Adams, Chief Executive Officer and Chairman
**(Decentralized Health System)**

**CALIFORNIA:** KAISER PERMANENTE ANTIOCH MEDICAL CENTER (O, 150 beds) 4501 Sand Creek Road, Antioch, CA, Zip 94531–8687; tel. 925/813–6500; Colleen McKeown, Senior Vice President and Area Manager

KAISER PERMANENTE BALDWIN PARK MEDICAL CENTER (O, 257 beds) 1011 Baldwin Park Boulevard, Baldwin Park, CA, Zip 91706–5806; tel. 626/851–1011; Margaret H. Pierce, Executive Director
**Web address:** www.kp.org

KAISER PERMANENTE DOWNEY MEDICAL CENTER (O, 352 beds) 9333 Imperial Highway, Downey, CA, Zip 90242–2812; tel. 562/657–9000; James Branchick, R.N., MS, Senior Vice President and Area Manager
**Web address:** www.kaiserpermanente.org

---

For explanation of codes following names, see page B2.
★ Indicates Type III membership in the American Hospital Association.

KAISER PERMANENTE FONTANA MEDICAL CENTER (O, 490 beds) 9961 Sierra Avenue, Fontana, CA, Zip 92335–6794; tel. 909/427–5000; Greg Christian, Senior Vice President, Area Manager – San Bernardino County Area
**Web address**: www.kaiserpermanente.org

KAISER PERMANENTE FREMONT MEDICAL CENTER (O, 100 beds) 39400 Paseo Padre Parkway, Fremont, CA, Zip 94538–2310; tel. 510/248–3000; Victoria O'Gorman, Administrator

KAISER PERMANENTE FRESNO MEDICAL CENTER (O, 169 beds) 7300 North Fresno Street, Fresno, CA, Zip 93720–2942; tel. 559/448–4500; Debbie Hemker, Senior Vice President and Area Manager
**Web address**: www.kaiserpermanente.org

KAISER PERMANENTE LOS ANGELES MEDICAL CENTER (O, 528 beds) 4867 Sunset Boulevard, Los Angeles, CA, Zip 90027–5961; tel. 323/783–4011; William N. Grice, Executive Director

KAISER PERMANENTE MANTECA MEDICAL CENTER (O, 213 beds) 1777 West Yosemite Avenue, Manteca, CA, Zip 95337–5187; tel. 209/825–3700; Corwin N. Harper, Senior Vice President and Area Manager
**Web address**: www.kaiserpermanente.org

KAISER PERMANENTE MORENO VALLEY MEDICAL CENTER (O, 94 beds) 27300 Iris Avenue, Moreno Valley, CA, Zip 92555–4800; tel. 951/243–0811; Vita M. Willett, Senior Vice President, Area Manager

KAISER PERMANENTE OAKLAND MEDICAL CENTER (O, 365 beds) 3600 Broadway, Oakland, CA, Zip 94611–5693; tel. 510/752–1000; Jeffrey A. Collins, M.D., Senior Vice President and Area Manager
**Web address**: www.kaiserpermanente.org

KAISER PERMANENTE ORANGE COUNTY ANAHEIM MEDICAL CENTER (O, 478 beds) 3440 East La Palma Avenue, Anaheim, CA, Zip 92806–2020; tel. 714/644–2000; Mark E. Costa, Executive Director
**Web address**: www.kp.org

KAISER PERMANENTE PANORAMA CITY MEDICAL CENTER (O, 218 beds) 13652 Cantara Street, Panorama City, CA, Zip 91402–5497; tel. 818/375–2000; Payman Roshan, Senior Vice President and Area Manager
**Web address**: www.kaiserpermanente.org

KAISER PERMANENTE REDWOOD CITY MEDICAL CENTER (O, 153 beds) 1100 Veterans Boulevard, Redwood City, CA, Zip 94063–2087; tel. 650/299–2000; Michelle Gaskill–Hames, R.N., Senior Vice President & Area Manager

KAISER PERMANENTE RIVERSIDE MEDICAL CENTER (O, 226 beds) 10800 Magnolia Avenue, Riverside, CA, Zip 92505–3000; tel. 951/353–2000; Vita M. Willett, Executive Director
**Web address**: www.kaiserpermanente.org

KAISER PERMANENTE ROSEVILLE MEDICAL CENTER (O, 340 beds) 1600 Eureka Road, Roseville, CA, Zip 95661–3027; tel. 916/784–4000; Gregory A. Adams, Chief Executive Officer and Chairman

KAISER PERMANENTE SACRAMENTO MEDICAL CENTER (O, 200 beds) 2025 Morse Avenue, Sacramento, CA, Zip 95825–2100; tel. 916/973–5000; Sandy Sharon, Senior Vice President and Area Manager
**Web address**: www.kp.org

KAISER PERMANENTE SAN DIEGO MEDICAL CENTER (O, 563 beds) 4647 Zion Avenue, San Diego, CA, Zip 92120–2507; tel. 619/528–5000; Jane Finley, Senior Vice President & Area Manager

KAISER PERMANENTE SAN FRANCISCO MEDICAL CENTER (O, 239 beds) 2425 Geary Boulevard, San Francisco, CA, Zip 94115–3358; tel. 415/833–2000; Ronald Groepper, Senior Vice President and Area Manager
**Web address**: www.kaiserpermanente.org

KAISER PERMANENTE SAN JOSE MEDICAL CENTER (O, 247 beds) 250 Hospital Parkway, San Jose, CA, Zip 95119–1199; tel. 408/972–7000; Irene Chavez, Senior Vice President and Area Manager
**Web address**: www.kaiserpermanente.org

KAISER PERMANENTE SAN LEANDRO MEDICAL CENTER (O, 206 beds) 2500 Merced Street, San Leandro, CA, Zip 94577–4201; tel. 510/454–1000; Thomas S. Hanenburg, Senior Vice President and Area Manager

KAISER PERMANENTE SAN RAFAEL MEDICAL CENTER (O, 116 beds) 99 Montecillo Road, San Rafael, CA, Zip 94903–3397; tel. 415/444–2000; Tarek Salaway, Senior Vice President and Area Manager
**Web address**: www.kaiserpermanente.org

KAISER PERMANENTE SANTA CLARA MEDICAL CENTER (O, 327 beds) 700 Lawrence Expressway, Santa Clara, CA, Zip 95051–5173; tel. 408/851–1000; Christopher L. Boyd, Senior Vice President and Area Manager
**Web address**: www.kaiserpermanente.org

KAISER PERMANENTE SANTA ROSA MEDICAL CENTER (O, 173 beds) 401 Bicentennial Way, Santa Rosa, CA, Zip 95403–2192; tel. 707/393–4000; Tarek Salaway, Senior Vice President and Area Manager

KAISER PERMANENTE SOUTH BAY MEDICAL CENTER (O, 257 beds) 25825 Vermont Avenue, Harbor City, CA, Zip 90710–3599; tel. 310/325–5111; Margie Harrier, MSN, R.N., Senior Vice President and Area Manager
**Web address**: www.kaiserpermanente.org

KAISER PERMANENTE SOUTH SACRAMENTO MEDICAL CENTER (O, 241 beds) 6600 Bruceville Road, Sacramento, CA, Zip 95823–4691; tel. 916/688–2430; Patricia M. Rodriguez, Senior Vice President and Area Manager
**Web address**: www.kp.org

KAISER PERMANENTE SOUTH SAN FRANCISCO (O, 120 beds) 1200 El Camino Real, South San Francisco, CA, Zip 94080–3208; tel. 650/742–2000; Ronald Groepper, Senior Vice President and Area Manager
**Web address**: www.kaiserpermanente.org

KAISER PERMANENTE VACAVILLE MEDICAL CENTER (O, 140 beds) 1 Quality Drive, Vacaville, CA, Zip 95688–9494; tel. 707/624–4000; Norair Jemjemian, Senior Vice President and Area Manager

KAISER PERMANENTE VALLEJO MEDICAL CENTER (O, 248 beds) 975 Sereno Drive, Vallejo, CA, Zip 94589–2441; tel. 707/651–1000; Corwin N. Harper, Senior Vice President and Area Manager
**Web address**: www.kaiserpermanente.org

KAISER PERMANENTE WALNUT CREEK MEDICAL CENTER (O, 233 beds) 1425 South Main Street, Walnut Creek, CA, Zip 94596–5300; tel. 925/295–4000; Colleen McKeown, Senior Vice President and Area Manager

KAISER PERMANENTE WEST LOS ANGELES MEDICAL CENTER (O, 265 beds) 6041 Cadillac Avenue, Los Angeles, CA, Zip 90034–1700; tel. 323/857–2201; Georgina R. Garcia, R.N., Executive Director
**Web address**: www.kaiserpermanente.org

KAISER PERMANENTE WOODLAND HILLS MEDICAL CENTER (O, 185 beds) 5601 DeSoto Avenue, Woodland Hills, CA, Zip 91367–6798; tel. 818/719–2000; Murtaza Sanwari, Senior Vice President and Area Manager
**Web address**: www.kaiserpermanente.org

**HAWAII:** KAISER PERMANENTE MEDICAL CENTER (O, 295 beds) 3288 ★ Moanalua Road, Honolulu, HI, Zip 96819–1469; tel. 808/432–0000; Sam E. Balukoff, Hospital Administrator
**Web address**: www.kaiserpermanente.org

KULA HOSPITAL (C, 6 beds) 100 Keokea Place, Kula, HI, Zip 96790–7450; tel. 808/878–1221; Kerry Pitcher, Chief Executive Officer

LANAI COMMUNITY HOSPITAL (C, 24 beds) 628 Seventh Street, Lanai City, HI, Zip 96763–0650, Mailing Address: P.O. Box 630650, 96763–0650, tel. 808/565–8450; Kerry Pitcher, Administrator
**Web address**: https://www.mauihealthsystem.org/lanai–hospital/

MAUI MEMORIAL MEDICAL CENTER (C, 214 beds) 221 Mahalani Street, Wailuku, HI, Zip 96793–2581; tel. 808/244–9056; Michael A. Rembis, FACHE, Chief Executive Officer
**Web address**: https://www.mauihealthsystem.org/maui–memorial/

**OREGON:** KAISER SUNNYSIDE MEDICAL CENTER (O, 301 beds) 10180 SE Sunnyside Road, Clackamas, OR, Zip 97015–8970; tel. 503/652–2880; James L. Robinson III, PsyD, Hospital Adminstrator

KAISER WESTSIDE MEDICAL CENTER (O, 122 beds) 2875 NE Stucki Avenue, Hillsboro, OR, Zip 97124–5806; tel. 971/310–1000; James L. Robinson III, PsyD, Hospital Administrator
**Web address**: www.kp.org

| | | |
|---|---|---|
| **Owned, leased, sponsored:** | 34 hospitals | 8611 beds |
| **Contract–managed:** | 3 hospitals | 244 beds |
| **Totals:** | 37 hospitals | 8855 beds |

---

**0954: KECK MEDICINE OF USC** (NP)
1510 San Pablo Street, Suite 600, Los Angeles, CA Zip 90033–5405; tel. 323/442–8500; Rod Hanners, Interim Chief Executive Officer
**(Independent Hospital System)**

**CALIFORNIA:** KECK HOSPITAL OF USC (O, 401 beds) 1500 San Pablo Street, Los Angeles, CA, Zip 90033–5313; tel. 323/442–8500; Rodney B. Hanners, Chief Executive Officer
**Web address**: https://www.keckmedicine.org/

For explanation of codes following names, see page B2.
★ Indicates Type III membership in the American Hospital Association.

USC NORRIS COMPREHENSIVE CANCER CENTER (O, 60 beds) 1441 Eastlake Avenue, Los Angeles, CA, Zip 90089–0112; tel. 323/865–3000; Rodney B. Hanners, Chief Executive Officer
**Web address:** www.uscnorriscancerhospital.org

USC VERDUGO HILLS HOSPITAL (O, 154 beds) 1812 Verdugo Boulevard, Glendale, CA, Zip 91208–1409; tel. 818/790–7100; Keith Hobbs, Chief Executive Officer

| | | |
|---|---|---|
| Owned, leased, sponsored: | 3 hospitals | 615 beds |
| Contract-managed: | 0 hospitals | 0 beds |
| Totals: | 3 hospitals | 615 beds |

★**0258: KETTERING HEALTH NETWORK** (NP)
3965 Southern Boulevard, Dayton, OH Zip 45429–1229; tel. 855/536–7543; Fred M. Manchur, Chief Executive Officer
**(Independent Hospital System)**

**OHIO:** FORT HAMILTON HOSPITAL (O, 200 beds) 630 Eaton Avenue, Hamilton, OH, Zip 45013–2770; tel. 513/867–2000; Michael Mewhirter, President
**Web address:** www.khnetwork.org/forthamilton

GRANDVIEW MEDICAL CENTER (O, 301 beds) 405 West Grand Avenue, Dayton, OH, Zip 45405–4796; tel. 937/723–3200; Rebecca Lewis, President

GREENE MEMORIAL HOSPITAL (O, 49 beds) 1141 North Monroe Drive, Xenia, OH, Zip 45385–1600; tel. 937/352–2000; Rick A. Dodds, President
**Web address:** www.ketteringhealth.org/greene

KETTERING HEALTH NETWORK TROY HOSPITAL (O, 28 beds) 600 W Main Street, Troy, OH, Zip 45373–3384; tel. 937/980–7000; Eric E. Lunde, President

KETTERING MEDICAL CENTER (O, 426 beds) 3535 Southern Boulevard, Kettering, OH, Zip 45429–1221; tel. 937/298–4331; Terry M. Burns, President
**Web address:** www.ketteringhealth.org/kettering

SOIN MEDICAL CENTER (O, 133 beds) 3535 Pentagon Boulevard, Beavercreek, OH, Zip 45431–1705; tel. 937/702–4000; Rick A. Dodds, President

SYCAMORE MEDICAL CENTER (O, 168 beds) 4000 Miamisburg–Centerville Road, Miamisburg, OH, Zip 45342–7615; tel. 937/866–0551; Walter Sackett, President
**Web address:** www.khnetwork.org/sycamore

| | | |
|---|---|---|
| Owned, leased, sponsored: | 7 hospitals | 1305 beds |
| Contract-managed: | 0 hospitals | 0 beds |
| Totals: | 7 hospitals | 1305 beds |

★**0026: KINDRED HEALTHCARE** (IO)
680 South Fourth Street, Louisville, KY Zip 40202–2412; tel. 502/596–7300; Pete Kalmey, President, Hospital Division
**(Independent Hospital System)**

**ARIZONA:** DIGNITY HEALTH EAST VALLEY REHABILITATION HOSPITAL (O, 50 beds) 1515 West Chandler Boulevard, Chandler, AZ, Zip 85224–6141; tel. 602/594–5400; Alvin Wendt, Acting Chief Executive Officer
**Web address:** www.dignityhealthevrehab.com

**CALIFORNIA:** KINDRED HOSPITAL PARAMOUNT (O, 148 beds) 16453 South Colorado Avenue, Paramount, CA, Zip 90723–5011; tel. 562/531–3110; Mark Apodaca, Chief Executive Officer
**Web address:** www.promiseeastla.com

KINDRED HOSPITAL RANCHO (O, 55 beds) 10841 White Oak Avenue, Rancho Cucamonga, CA, Zip 91730–3811; tel. 909/581–6400; Lerenda Johnson, Interim Chief Executive Officer

KINDRED HOSPITAL RIVERSIDE (O, 40 beds) 2224 Medical Center Drive, Perris, CA, Zip 92571–2638; tel. 951/436–3535; William Mitchell, Chief Executive Officer and Administrator
**Web address:** www.khriverside.com

KINDRED HOSPITAL SOUTH BAY (O, 84 beds) 1246 West 155th Street, Gardena, CA, Zip 90247–4062; tel. 310/323–5330; Michael D. Kerr, Chief Executive Officer
**Web address:** www.khsouthbay.com/

KINDRED HOSPITAL–BALDWIN PARK (C, 91 beds) 14148 Francisquito Avenue, Baldwin Park, CA, Zip 91706–6120; tel. 626/388–2700; Larry Foster, R.N., MSN, Chief Executive Officer

KINDRED HOSPITAL–BREA (O, 48 beds) 875 North Brea Boulevard, Brea, CA, Zip 92821–2699; tel. 714/529–6842; Kevin Chavez, Chief Executive Officer
**Web address:** www.kindredhospitalbrea.com/

KINDRED HOSPITAL–LA MIRADA (O, 118 beds) 14900 East Imperial Highway, La Mirada, CA, Zip 90638–2172; tel. 562/944–1900; David Kowalski, Chief Executive Officer
**Web address:** www.kindredlamirada.com/

KINDRED HOSPITAL–LOS ANGELES (O, 81 beds) 5525 West Slauson Avenue, Los Angeles, CA, Zip 90056–1067; tel. 310/642–0325; Fiona Basa–Reyes, Chief Executive Officer

KINDRED HOSPITAL–ONTARIO (O, 81 beds) 550 North Monterey Avenue, Ontario, CA, Zip 91764–3399; tel. 909/391–0333; Natalie Merckens, Chief Executive Officer
**Web address:** www.khontario.com/

KINDRED HOSPITAL–SAN DIEGO (O, 60 beds) 1940 El Cajon Boulevard, San Diego, CA, Zip 92104–1096; tel. 619/543–4500; Kerry Ashment, Chief Executive Officer

KINDRED HOSPITAL–SAN FRANCISCO BAY AREA (O, 99 beds) 2800 Benedict Drive, San Leandro, CA, Zip 94577–6840; tel. 510/357–8300; Jacob M. McCarty, Chief Executive Officer
**Web address:** www.kindredhospitalsfba.com

KINDRED HOSPITAL–WESTMINSTER (O, 109 beds) 200 Hospital Circle, Westminster, CA, Zip 92683–3910; tel. 714/893–4541; Julie Myers, Chief Executive Officer
**Web address:** www.khwestminster.com/

**COLORADO:** KINDRED HOSPITAL–AURORA (O, 37 beds) 700 Potomac Street 2nd Floor, Aurora, CO, Zip 80011–6844; tel. 720/857–8333; Marc Lemon, Chief Executive Officer

KINDRED HOSPITAL–DENVER (O, 68 beds) 1920 High Street, Denver, CO, Zip 80218–1213; tel. 303/320–5871; Janelle Kircher, R.N., MSN, Chief Executive Officer
**Web address:** www.kh–denver.com

**FLORIDA:** KINDRED HOSPITAL BAY AREA–TAMPA (O, 73 beds) 4555 South Manhattan Avenue, Tampa, FL, Zip 33611–2397; tel. 813/839–6341; Cindy Jackson, Chief Executive Officer
**Web address:** www.khtampa.com/

KINDRED HOSPITAL CENTRAL TAMPA (O, 109 beds) 4801 North Howard Avenue, Tampa, FL, Zip 33603–1411; tel. 813/874–7575; Suthanthira M. Ratnasamy, R.N., FACHE, Chief Executive Officer

KINDRED HOSPITAL MELBOURNE (O, 60 beds) 765 West Nasa Boulevard, Melbourne, FL, Zip 32901–1815; tel. 321/733–5725; Pamela R. Reed, Chief Executive Officer
**Web address:** www.khmelbourne.com

KINDRED HOSPITAL NORTH FLORIDA (O, 80 beds) 801 Oak Street, Green Cove Springs, FL, Zip 32043–4317; tel. 904/284–9230; Susan Drago, R.N., Chief Executive Officer

KINDRED HOSPITAL OCALA (O, 31 beds) 1500 SW 1st Avenue, Ocala, FL, Zip 34471–6504; tel. 352/369–0513; Merlene Bhoorasingh, Administrator
**Web address:** www.kindredocala.com/

KINDRED HOSPITAL SOUTH FLORIDA–FORT LAUDERDALE (O, 123 beds) 1516 East Las Olas Boulevard, Fort Lauderdale, FL, Zip 33301–2399; tel. 954/764–8900; Theodore L. Welding, Chief Executive Officer
**Web address:** www.khfortlauderdale.com/

KINDRED HOSPITAL THE PALM BEACHES (O, 70 beds) 5555 West Blue Heron Boulevard, Riviera Beach, FL, Zip 33418–7813; tel. 561/840–0754; Elayne Lopreato, Chief Executive Officer

**ILLINOIS:** KINDRED CHICAGO–CENTRAL HOSPITAL (O, 187 beds) 4058 West Melrose Street, Chicago, IL, Zip 60641–4797; tel. 773/736–7000; Al Wazwaz, Chief Executive Officer
**Web address:** www.khchicagocentral.com

KINDRED HOSPITAL CHICAGO–NORTHLAKE (O, 94 beds) 365 East North Avenue, Northlake, IL, Zip 60164–2628; tel. 708/345–8100; Brinsley Lewis, FACHE, Chief Executive Officer
**Web address:** www.kindrednorthlake.com/

For explanation of codes following names, see page B2.
★ Indicates Type III membership in the American Hospital Association.

KINDRED HOSPITAL PEORIA (O, 50 beds) 500 West Romeo B Garrett Avenue, Peoria, IL, Zip 61605–2301; tel. 309/680–1500; Christopher Curry, Chief Executive Officer

KINDRED HOSPITAL–SYCAMORE (O, 69 beds) 225 Edward Street, Sycamore, IL, Zip 60178–2137; tel. 815/895–2144; Beverly Foster, Chief Executive Officer
**Web address**: www.kindredhospitalsyc.com/

**INDIANA**: KINDRED HOSPITAL INDIANAPOLIS NORTH (O, 45 beds) 8060 Knue Road, Indianapolis, IN, Zip 46250–1976; tel. 317/813–8900; Nakia Tremble, Chief Executive Officer

KINDRED HOSPITAL NORTHWEST INDIANA (O, 70 beds) 5454 Hohman Avenue, 5th Floor, Hammond, IN, Zip 46320–1931; tel. 219/937–9900; Sohail Azeem, Chief Executive Officer
**Web address**: www.khnwindiana.com

KINDRED HOSPITAL–INDIANAPOLIS (O, 59 beds) 1700 West 10th Street, Indianapolis, IN, Zip 46222–3802; tel. 317/636–4400; Brad Klawitter, Chief Executive Officer

**KENTUCKY**: KINDRED HOSPITAL–LOUISVILLE (O, 117 beds) 1313 Saint Anthony Place, Louisville, KY, Zip 40204–1740; tel. 502/587–7001; Jack Nicholson, Chief Executive Officer
**Web address**: www.kindredlouisville.com

**MISSOURI**: KINDRED HOSPITAL NORTHLAND (O, 35 beds) 500 Northwest 68th Street, Kansas City, MO, Zip 64118–2455; tel. 816/420–6300; Laura Inge, MSN, R.N., Chief Executive Officer
**Web address**: www.khnorthland.com

KINDRED HOSPITAL–ST. LOUIS (O, 98 beds) 4930 Lindell Boulevard, Saint Louis, MO, Zip 63108–1510; tel. 314/361–8700; Kevin L. Shrake, Chief Executive Officer
**Web address**: www.kindredstlouis.com/

MERCY REHABILITATION HOSPITAL ST. LOUIS (O, 90 beds) 14561 North Outer Forty Road, Chesterfield, MO, Zip 63017; tel. 314/881–4000; Jerald W. Rumph, Chief Executive Officer

**MONTANA**: THE REHABILITATION HOSPITAL OF MONTANA (O, 34 beds) 3572 Hesper Road, Billings, MT, Zip 59102–6891; tel. 406/413–6200; Julie Hauk, Chief Executive Officer
**Web address**: https://www.rehabhospitalofmontana.com/

**NEVADA**: KINDRED HOSPITAL LAS VEGAS–SAHARA (O, 238 beds) 102 East Mead Parkway, 3rd Floor, Henderson, NV, Zip 89015; tel. 702/871–1418; Bud Schawl, Chief Executive Officer
**Web address**: www.kindredhospitallvs.com/

**NEW JERSEY**: KINDRED HOSPITAL–NEW JERSEY MORRIS COUNTY (O, 117 beds) 400 West Blackwell Street, Dover, NJ, Zip 07801–2525; tel. 973/537–3818; Tarra Washington, Chief Executive Officer

**NEW MEXICO**: KINDRED HOSPITAL–ALBUQUERQUE (O, 61 beds) 700 High Street NE, Albuquerque, NM, Zip 87102–2565; tel. 505/242–4444; Larry Rodgers, Chief Executive Officer
**Web address**: www.kindredalbuquerque.com/

**NORTH CAROLINA**: KINDRED HOSPITAL–GREENSBORO (O, 101 beds) 2401 Southside Boulevard, Greensboro, NC, Zip 27406–3311; tel. 336/271–2800; Mary-Lyn Baldauf, Chief Executive Officer
**Web address**: www.khgreensboro.com

**OHIO**: KINDRED HOSPITAL LIMA (O, 26 beds) 730 West Market Street, 6th Floor, Lima, OH, Zip 45801–4602; tel. 419/224–1888; Susan Krinke, Chief Executive Officer
**Web address**: www.khlima.com

KINDRED HOSPITAL–DAYTON (O, 67 beds) 707 South Edwin C Moses Boulevard, Dayton, OH, Zip 45417–3462; tel. 937/222–5963; Phillip Underwood, Chief Executive Officer

UH AVON REHABILITATION HOSPITAL (O, 50 beds) 37900 Chester Road, Avon, OH, Zip 44011–1044; tel. 440/695–7100; Andrew Goldfrach, Chief Executive Officer
**Web address**: www.uhhospitals.org/uh-avon-rehabilitation-hospital

UH REHABILITATION HOSPITAL (O, 50 beds) 23333 Harvard Road, Beachwood, OH, Zip 44122–6232; tel. 216/593–2200; Mirza Baig, M.D., Medical Director
**Web address**: www.uhhospitals.org

**PENNSYLVANIA**: KINDRED HOSPITAL–PHILADELPHIA (O, 82 beds) 6129 Palmetto Street, Philadelphia, PA, Zip 19111–5729; tel. 215/722–8555; Michele S. Basile, Chief Executive Officer

**TENNESSEE**: KINDRED HOSPITAL–CHATTANOOGA (O, 39 beds) 709 Walnut Street, Chattanooga, TN, Zip 37402–1916; tel. 423/266–7721; Andrea White, Chief Executive Officer
**Web address**: www.kindredchattanooga.com/

**TEXAS**: KINDRED HOSPITAL CLEAR LAKE (O, 110 beds) 350 Blossom Street, Webster, TX, Zip 77598; tel. 281/316–7800; Angel Gradney, Chief Executive Officer

KINDRED HOSPITAL DALLAS CENTRAL (O, 60 beds) 8050 Meadow Road, Dallas, TX, Zip 75231–3406; tel. 469/232–6500; Kyron J. Kooken, MS, Chief Executive Officer
**Web address**: www.khdallascentral.com/

KINDRED HOSPITAL EL PASO (O, 52 beds) 1740 Curie Drive, El Paso, TX, Zip 79902–2901; tel. 915/351–9044; America Jones, R.N., Chief Executive Officer

KINDRED HOSPITAL HOUSTON MEDICAL CENTER (O, 105 beds) 6441 Main Street, Houston, TX, Zip 77030–1596; tel. 713/790–0500; Robert Stein, Chief Executive Officer
**Web address**: www.khhouston.com/

KINDRED HOSPITAL SAN ANTONIO CENTRAL (O, 44 beds) 111 Dallas Street, 4th Floor, San Antonio, TX, Zip 78205–1201; tel. 210/297–7185; Kyle E. Sinclair, Chief Executive Officer
**Web address**: www.kindredsanantoniocentral.com/

KINDRED HOSPITAL SUGAR LAND (O, 105 beds) 1550 First Colony Boulevard, Sugar Land, TX, Zip 77479–4000; tel. 281/275–6000; John D. Cross, Chief Executive Officer

KINDRED HOSPITAL TARRANT COUNTY–ARLINGTON (O, 147 beds) 1000 North Cooper Street, Arlington, TX, Zip 76011–5540; tel. 817/548–3400; Christina Richard, Chief Executive Officer
**Web address**: www.kindredhospitalarl.com/

KINDRED HOSPITAL–HOUSTON NORTHWEST (O, 84 beds) 11297 Fallbrook Drive, Houston, TX, Zip 77065–4292; tel. 281/897–8114; Tracy Kohler, Chief Executive Officer

KINDRED HOSPITAL–MANSFIELD (O, 55 beds) 1802 Highway 157 North, Mansfield, TX, Zip 76063–3923; tel. 817/473–6101; Tyler Cummings, Administrator and Chief Executive Officer
**Web address**: www.kindredmansfield.com

KINDRED HOSPITAL–SAN ANTONIO (O, 59 beds) 3636 Medical Drive, San Antonio, TX, Zip 78229–2183; tel. 210/616–0616; Abiola Anyebe, Interim Chief Executive Officer

**WASHINGTON**: KINDRED HOSPITAL SEATTLE–FIRST HILL (O, 10 beds) 1334 Terry Avenue, Seattle, WA, Zip 98101–2747; tel. 206/682–2661; Minta Albietz, Resource Chief Executive Officer
**Web address**: www.khseattlefirsthill.com

**WISCONSIN**: REHABILITATION HOSPITAL OF WISCONSIN (O, 40 beds) 1625 Coldwater Creek Drive, Waukesha, WI, Zip 53188–8028; tel. 262/521–8800; Brad Anderson, Chief Executive Officer
**Web address**: www.rehabhospitalwi.com

| | | |
|---|---|---|
| Owned, leased, sponsored: | 55 hospitals | 4274 beds |
| Contract–managed: | 1 hospitals | 91 beds |
| **Totals:** | **56 hospitals** | **4365 beds** |

**0333: KPC HEALTHCARE, INC.** (IO)
1301 North Tustin Avenue, Santa Ana, CA Zip 92705–8619; tel. 714/953–3652; Peter R. Baronoff, Chief Executive Officer and Managing Director
**(Independent Hospital System)**

**ARIZONA**: KPC PROMISE HOSPITAL OF PHOENIX (O, 40 beds) 433 East 6th Street, Mesa, AZ, Zip 85203–7104; tel. 480/427–3000; Wayne Kinsey, Chief Executive Officer

**CALIFORNIA**: ANAHEIM GLOBAL MEDICAL CENTER (O, 188 beds) 1025 South Anaheim Boulevard, Anaheim, CA, Zip 92805–5806; tel. 714/533–6220; Jamie Yoo, Chief Executive Officer
**Web address**: www.anaheim–gmc.com

For explanation of codes following names, see page B2.
★ Indicates Type III membership in the American Hospital Association.

CHAPMAN GLOBAL MEDICAL CENTER (O, 100 beds) 2601 East Chapman Avenue, Orange, CA, Zip 92869–3296; tel. 714/633–0011; Ada Yeh, Chief Executive Officer
**Web address**: www.Chapmanglobalmedicalcenter.com

ORANGE COUNTY GLOBAL MEDICAL CENTER, INC. (O, 282 beds) 1001 North Tustin Avenue, Santa Ana, CA, Zip 92705–3577; tel. 714/953–3500; Ann Abe, Interim Chief Executive Officer
**Web address**: www.orangecounty–gmc.com

SOUTH COAST GLOBAL MEDICAL CENTER (O, 178 beds) 2701 South Bristol Street, Santa Ana, CA, Zip 92704–6278; tel. 714/754–5454; Ada Yeh, Chief Executive Officer

**KANSAS**:  KPC PROMISE HOSPITAL OF OVERLAND PARK (O, 104 beds) 6509 West 103rd Street, Overland Park, KS, Zip 66212–1728; tel. 913/649–3701; Robert Beck, Chief Executive Officer
**Web address**: www.overlandpark.kpcph.com

**LOUISIANA**:  KPC PROMISE HOSPITAL OF BATON ROUGE (O, 39 beds) 5130 Mancuso Lane, Baton Rouge, LA, Zip 70809–3583; tel. 225/490–9600; Kiley P. Cedotal, FACHE, Chief Executive Officer

**MISSISSIPPI**:  KPC PROMISE HOSPITAL OF VICKSBURG (L, 27 beds) 1111 North Frontage Road, 2nd Floor, Vicksburg, MS, Zip 39180–5102; tel. 601/619–3526; Kiley P. Cedotal, FACHE, Chief Executive Officer
**Web address**: www.vicksburg.kpcph.com/

**TEXAS**:  KPC PROMISE HOSPITAL OF DALLAS (O, 66 beds) 7955 Harry Hines Boulevard, Dallas, TX, Zip 75235–3305; tel. 214/637–0000; Kiley P. Cedotal, FACHE, Chief Executive Officer

KPC PROMISE HOSPITAL OF WICHITA FALLS (O, 31 beds) 1103 Grace Street, Wichita Falls, TX, Zip 76301–4414; tel. 940/720–6633; Rachel Bailey, Chief Executive Officer
**Web address**: www.wichitafalls.kpcph.com/

**UTAH**:  KPC PROMISE HOSPITAL OF SALT LAKE (O, 41 beds) 8 Avenue, C Street, Salt Lake City, UT, Zip 84143; tel. 801/408–7110; Wayne Kinsey, Chief Executive Officer
**Web address**: www.saltlake.kpcph.com/

| | | |
|---|---|---|
| Owned, leased, sponsored: | 11 hospitals | 1096 beds |
| Contract–managed: | 0 hospitals | 0 beds |
| Totals: | 11 hospitals | 1096 beds |

---

**0911: LAFAYETTE GENERAL HEALTH** (NP)
920 West Pinhook Road, Lafayette, LA Zip 70503–2455; tel. 337/289–7991; David L. Callecod, President and Chief Executive Officer
**(Independent Hospital System)**

**LOUISIANA**:  ABROM KAPLAN MEMORIAL HOSPITAL (C, 35 beds) 1310 West Seventh Street, Kaplan, LA, Zip 70548–2910; tel. 337/643–8300; Bryce Quebodeaux, Chief Executive Officer

ACADIA GENERAL HOSPITAL (C, 140 beds) 1305 Crowley Rayne Highway, Crowley, LA, Zip 70526–8202; tel. 337/783–3222; Joe J. Mitchell, R.N., FACHE, Chief Executive Officer
**Web address**: www.acadiageneral.com

LAFAYETTE GENERAL MEDICAL CENTER (O, 440 beds) 1214 Coolidge Boulevard, Lafayette, LA, Zip 70503–2696, Mailing Address: P.O. Box 52009 OCS, 70505–2009, tel. 337/289–7991; Patrick W. Gandy Jr, CPA, Executive Vice President and Chief Executive Officer
**Web address**: www.lafayettegeneral.com

ST. MARTIN HOSPITAL (C, 25 beds) 210 Champagne Boulevard, Breaux Bridge, LA, Zip 70517–3700, Mailing Address: P.O. Box 357, 70517–0357, tel. 337/332–2178; Glenn Dailey, Chief Executive Officer

UNIVERSITY HOSPITAL & CLINICS (L, 52 beds) 2390 West Congress Street, Lafayette, LA, Zip 70506–4298; tel. 337/261–6000; Katherine D. Hebert, MS, Chief Executive Officer
**Web address**: www.lafayettegeneral.com

| | | |
|---|---|---|
| Owned, leased, sponsored: | 2 hospitals | 492 beds |
| Contract–managed: | 3 hospitals | 200 beds |
| Totals: | 5 hospitals | 692 beds |

---

**0393: LANDMARK HOSPITALS** (IO)
3255 Independence Street, Cape Girardeau, MO Zip 63701–4914; tel. 573/335–1091; William K. Kapp III, M.D., President and Chief Executive Officer
**(Independent Hospital System)**

**FLORIDA**:  LANDMARK HOSPITAL OF SOUTHWEST FLORIDA (O, 50 beds) 1285 Creekside Boulevard East, Naples, FL, Zip 34108; tel. 239/529–1800; Susan P. Bailey, R.N., Chief Executive Officer
**Web address**: https://www.landmarkhospitals.com/critical–care–hospital–system/critical–care–hospital–southwest–florida/

**GEORGIA**:  LANDMARK HOSPITAL OF ATHENS (O, 42 beds) 775 Sunset Drive, Athens, GA, Zip 30606–2211; tel. 706/425–1500; Vivian Goff, R.N., Chief Executive Officer

LANDMARK HOSPITAL OF SAVANNAH (O, 50 beds) 800 East 68th Street, Savannah, GA, Zip 31405–4710; tel. 912/298–1000; John Salandi, Chief Executive Officer
**Web address**: www.landmarkhospitals.com/savannah

**MISSOURI**:  LANDMARK HOSPITAL OF CAPE GIRARDEAU (O, 30 beds) 3255 Independence Street, Cape Girardeau, MO, Zip 63701–4914; tel. 573/335–1091; Deborah Sabella, R.N., Chief Executive Officer
**Web address**: www.landmarkhospitals.com

LANDMARK HOSPITAL OF COLUMBIA (O, 23 beds) 604 Old 63 North, Columbia, MO, Zip 65201–6308; tel. 573/499–6600; Nickie Hunt, Chief Executive Officer
**Web address**: www.landmarkhospitals.com

LANDMARK HOSPITAL OF JOPLIN (O, 28 beds) 2040 West 32nd Street, Joplin, MO, Zip 64804–3512; tel. 417/627–1300; Suzann Gomillion, Interim Chief Executive Officer

| | | |
|---|---|---|
| Owned, leased, sponsored: | 6 hospitals | 223 beds |
| Contract–managed: | 0 hospitals | 0 beds |
| Totals: | 6 hospitals | 223 beds |

---

**0932: LCMC HEALTH** (NP)
200 Henry Clay Avenue, New Orleans, LA Zip 70118–5720; tel. 504/899–9511; Greg Feirn, CPA, President and Chief Executive Officer
**(Moderately Centralized Health System)**

**LOUISIANA**:  CHILDREN'S HOSPITAL (O, 170 beds) 200 Henry Clay Avenue, New Orleans, LA, Zip 70118–5720; tel. 504/899–9511; John R. Nickens IV, President and Chief Executive Officer
**Web address**: www.chnola.org

NEW ORLEANS EAST HOSPITAL (C, 34 beds) 5620 Read Boulevard, New Orleans, LA, Zip 70127–3106, 5620 Read Blvd, 70127–3106, tel. 504/592–6600; Takeisha C. Davis, M.D., M.P.H., President and Chief Executive Officer
**Web address**: www.noehospital.org

TOURO INFIRMARY (O, 280 beds) 1401 Foucher Street, New Orleans, LA, Zip 70115–3593; tel. 504/897–7011; Manuel Linares, President and Chief Executive Officer

UNIVERSITY MEDICAL CENTER (O, 366 beds) 2000 Canal Street, New Orleans, LA, Zip 70112–3018; tel. 504/702–3000; Danny Hardman, FACHE, R.N., Chief Executive Officer
**Web address**: www.umcno.org

WEST JEFFERSON MEDICAL CENTER (C, 252 beds) 1101 Medical Center Boulevard, Marrero, LA, Zip 70072–3191; tel. 504/347–5511; Rob Calhoun, President and Chief Executive Offricer
**Web address**: www.wjmc.org

| | | |
|---|---|---|
| Owned, leased, sponsored: | 3 hospitals | 816 beds |
| Contract–managed: | 2 hospitals | 286 beds |
| Totals: | 5 hospitals | 1102 beds |

---

★**0369: LEE HEALTH** (NP)
2776 Cleveland Avenue, Fort Myers, FL Zip 33901–5864, Mailing Address: P.O. Box 2218, 33902–2218, tel. 239/343–2000; Lawrence Antonucci, M.D., President and Chief Executive Officer
**(Moderately Centralized Health System)**

For explanation of codes following names, see page B2.
★ Indicates Type III membership in the American Hospital Association.

Section B

**FLORIDA**: CAPE CORAL HOSPITAL (O, 291 beds) 636 Del Prado Boulevard, Cape Coral, FL, Zip 33990–2695; tel. 239/424–2000; Lawrence Antonucci, M.D., President and Chief Executive Officer

GULF COAST MEDICAL CENTER (O, 431 beds) 13681 Doctor's Way, Fort Myers, FL, Zip 33912–4300; tel. 239/343–1000; Lawrence Antonucci, M.D., President and Chief Executive Officer
**Web address**: www.leememorial.org

LEE MEMORIAL HOSPITAL (O, 874 beds) 2776 Cleveland Avenue, Fort Myers, FL, Zip 33901–5855, Mailing Address: P.O. Box 2218, 33902–2218, tel. 239/343–2000; Lawrence Antonucci, M.D., President and Chief Executive Officer

| | | |
|---|---|---|
| Owned, leased, sponsored: | 3 hospitals | 1596 beds |
| Contract–managed: | 0 hospitals | 0 beds |
| Totals: | 3 hospitals | 1596 beds |

**★2755: LEGACY HEALTH** (NP)
1919 NW Lovejoy Street, Portland, OR Zip 97209–1503; tel. 503/415–5600; Kathryn G. Correia, President and Chief Executive Officer
**(Centralized Health System)**

**OREGON**: LEGACY EMANUEL MEDICAL CENTER (O, 536 beds) 2801 North Gantenbein Avenue, Portland, OR, Zip 97227–1674; tel. 503/413–2200; Trent Green, President
**Web address**: www.legacyhealth.org

LEGACY GOOD SAMARITAN MEDICAL CENTER (O, 218 beds) 1015 NW 22nd Avenue, Portland, OR, Zip 97210–3099; tel. 503/413–7711; Jonathan Avery, President
**Web address**: www.legacyhealth.org

LEGACY MERIDIAN PARK MEDICAL CENTER (O, 149 beds) 19300 SW 65th Avenue, Tualatin, OR, Zip 97062–9741; tel. 503/692–1212; Melinda Stibal, R.N., MSN, Interim President
**Web address**: www.legacyhealth.org

LEGACY MOUNT HOOD MEDICAL CENTER (O, 98 beds) 24800 SE Stark, Gresham, OR, Zip 97030–3378; tel. 503/667–1122; Tanya Shanks–Connors, R.N., MSN, Interim President

LEGACY SILVERTON MEDICAL CENTER (O, 47 beds) 139 Breyonna Way, Silverton, OR, Zip 97381, 342 Fairview Street, 97381–1993, tel. 503/873–1500; Sarah Brewer, President
**Web address**: www.legacyhealth.org/locations/hospitals/legacy–silverton–medical–center.aspx

**WASHINGTON**: LEGACY SALMON CREEK MEDICAL CENTER (O, 208 beds) 2211 NE 139th Street, Vancouver, WA, Zip 98686–2742; tel. 360/487–1000; Jon Hersen, President

| | | |
|---|---|---|
| Owned, leased, sponsored: | 6 hospitals | 1256 beds |
| Contract–managed: | 0 hospitals | 0 beds |
| Totals: | 6 hospitals | 1256 beds |

**★0370: LEHIGH VALLEY HEALTH NETWORK** (NP)
1200 South Cedar Crest Boulevard, Allentown, PA Zip 18103–6202, Mailing Address: P.O. Box 689, 18105–1556, tel. 610/402–8000; Brian A. Nester, D.O., President and Chief Executive Officer
**(Moderately Centralized Health System)**

**PENNSYLVANIA**: LEHIGH VALLEY HOSPITAL – HAZLETON (O, 120 beds) 700 East Broad Street, Hazleton, PA, Zip 18201–6897; tel. 570/501–4000; John R. Fletcher, President
**Web address**: www.lvhn.org/hazleton/

LEHIGH VALLEY HOSPITAL – POCONO (O, 239 beds) 206 East Brown Street, East Stroudsburg, PA, Zip 18301–3006; tel. 570/421–4000; Elizabeth Wise, President and Chief Executive Officer

LEHIGH VALLEY HOSPITAL – SCHUYLKILL (O, 186 beds) 420 South Jackson Street, Pottsville, PA, Zip 17901–3625; tel. 570/621–5000; William Reppy, President
**Web address**: www.schuylkillhealth.com

LEHIGH VALLEY HOSPITAL (O, 1044 beds) 1200 South Cedar Crest Boulevard, Allentown, PA, Zip 18103–6248, Mailing Address: P.O. Box 689, 18105–1556, tel. 610/402–8000; Brian A. Nester, D.O., President and Chief Executive Officer

| | | |
|---|---|---|
| Owned, leased, sponsored: | 4 hospitals | 1589 beds |
| Contract–managed: | 0 hospitals | 0 beds |
| Totals: | 4 hospitals | 1589 beds |

**0632: LHC GROUP** (IO)
420 West Pinhook Road, Lafayette, LA Zip 70503–2131; tel. 337/233–1307; Keith G. Myers, Chairman and Chief Executive Officer
**(Independent Hospital System)**

**ARKANSAS**: CHRISTUS DUBUIS HOSPITAL OF FORT SMITH (O, 25 beds) 7301 Rogers Avenue, 4th Floor, Fort Smith, AR, Zip 72903–4100; tel. 479/314–4900; Nancy Owens, Administrator
**Web address**: www.christusdubuis.org/fortsmith

CHRISTUS DUBUIS HOSPITAL OF HOT SPRINGS (O, 27 beds) 300 Werner Street, 3rd Floor East, Hot Springs National Park, AR, Zip 71913–6406; tel. 501/609–4300; Kathy DeVore, R.N., Administrator

**LOUISIANA**: CHRISTUS DUBUIS HOSPITAL OF ALEXANDRIA (O, 25 beds) 3330 Masonic Drive, 4th Floor, Alexandria, LA, Zip 71301–3841; tel. 318/448–4938; Beth Parsons, R.N., Administrator
**Web address**: www.christusdubuis.org/CHRISTUSDubuisHospitalofAlexandriaLA

LOUISIANA EXTENDED CARE HOSPITAL OF LAFAYETTE (O, 42 beds) 2810 Ambassador Caffery Parkway, 6th Floor, Lafayette, LA, Zip 70506–5906; tel. 337/289–8180; Kermit C. Simmons, Administrator
**Web address**: www.lhcgroup.com

LOUISIANA EXTENDED CARE HOSPITAL OF NATCHITOCHES (O, 21 beds) 501 Keyser Avenue, Natchitoches, LA, Zip 71457–6018; tel. 318/354–2044; John Rivoire, R.N., MSN, Administrator
**Web address**: www.https://lhcgroup.com/locations/louisiana–extended–care–hospital–of–natchitoches/

LOUISIANA EXTENDED CARE HOSPITAL OF WEST MONROE (O, 18 beds) 503 McMillan Road, 3rd Floor, West Monroe, LA, Zip 71291–5327; tel. 318/329–4378; Cleta Munholland, Administrator

OCHSNER EXTENDED CARE HOSPITAL (O, 32 beds) 2614 Jefferson Highway, 2nd Floor, New Orleans, LA, Zip 70121–3828; tel. 504/314–4242; Len McDade, Chief Executive Officer
**Web address**: www.lhcgroup.com/

SPECIALTY HOSPITAL (O, 32 beds) 309 Jackson Street, 7th Floor, Monroe, LA, Zip 71201–7407, Mailing Address: P.O. Box 1532, 71210–1532, tel. 318/966–7045; Cleta Munholland, Administrator

ST. LANDRY EXTENDED CARE HOSPITAL (O, 41 beds) 539 East Prudhomme Street, 6th Floor, Opelousas, LA, Zip 70570–6499; tel. 337/948–2251; Biff David, R.N., Administrator
**Web address**: www.lhcgroup.com

**TEXAS**: CHRISTUS DUBUIS HOSPITAL OF BEAUMONT (O, 33 beds) 2830 Calder Avenue, 4th Floor, Beaumont, TX, Zip 77702–1809; tel. 409/899–7680; Jason Baker, Administrator
**Web address**: www.christusdubuis.org/BeaumontandPortArthurSystem–CHRISTUSDubuisHospitalofBeaumont

| | | |
|---|---|---|
| Owned, leased, sponsored: | 10 hospitals | 296 beds |
| Contract–managed: | 0 hospitals | 0 beds |
| Totals: | 10 hospitals | 296 beds |

**0158: LIFEBRIDGE HEALTH** (NP)
2401 West Belvedere Avenue, Baltimore, MD Zip 21215–5216; tel. 410/601–5134; Neil M. Meltzer, President and Chief Executive Officer
**(Moderately Centralized Health System)**

**MARYLAND**: CARROLL HOSPITAL CENTER (O, 113 beds) 200 Memorial Avenue, Westminster, MD, Zip 21157–5799; tel. 410/848–3000; Garrett W. Hoover, FACHE, President and Chief Operating Officer, Senior Vice President LifeBridge Health
**Web address**: www.carrollhospitalcenter.org

For explanation of codes following names, see page B2.
★ Indicates Type III membership in the American Hospital Association.

GRACE MEDICAL CENTER (O, 68 beds) 2000 West Baltimore Street, Baltimore, MD, Zip 21223–1558; tel. 410/362–3000; Daniel Blum, President

LEVINDALE HEBREW HOSPITAL AND NURSING (O, 490 beds) 2434 West Belvedere Avenue, Baltimore, MD, Zip 21215–5267; tel. 410/601–2400; Deborah Graves, R.N., President and Chief Operating Officer
**Web address:** www.sinai–balt.com

NORTHWEST HOSPITAL (O, 178 beds) 5401 Old Court Road, Randallstown, MD, Zip 21133–5185; tel. 410/521–2200; Craig Carmichael, President and Chief Operating Officer, Senior Vice President, LifeBridge Health
**Web address:** www.lifebridgehealth.org

SINAI HOSPITAL OF BALTIMORE (O, 289 beds) 2401 West Belvedere Avenue, Baltimore, MD, Zip 21215–5271; tel. 410/601–9000; Daniel Blum, President and Chief Operating Officer, Senior Vice President LifeBridge Health

| | | |
|---|---|---|
| Owned, leased, sponsored: | 5 hospitals | 1138 beds |
| Contract–managed: | 0 hospitals | 0 beds |
| Totals: | 5 hospitals | 1138 beds |

---

**0947: LIFEBRITE HOSPITAL GROUP, LLC** (IO)
3970 Five Forks Trickum Road SW Suite A, Lilburn, GA Zip 30047–2339; tel. 678/505–9657; Christian Al. Fletcher, Chief Executive Officer

**GEORGIA:** LIFEBRITE COMMUNITY HOSPITAL OF EARLY (O, 152 beds) 11740 Columbia Street, Blakely, GA, Zip 39823–2574; tel. 229/723–4241; Ginger Cushing, Chief Executive Officer
**Web address:** www.pchearly.com

**NORTH CAROLINA:** LIFEBRITE COMMUNITY HOSPITAL OF STOKES (O, 65 beds) 1570 NC 8 & 89 Highway North, Danbury, NC, Zip 27016, Mailing Address: P.O. Box 10, 27016–0010, tel. 336/593–2831; Pamela P. Tillman, Administrator

| | | |
|---|---|---|
| Owned, leased, sponsored: | 2 hospitals | 217 beds |
| Contract–managed: | 0 hospitals | 0 beds |
| Totals: | 2 hospitals | 217 beds |

---

**★0191: LIFECARE MANAGEMENT SERVICES** (IO)
5340 Legacy Drive, Suite 150, Plano, TX Zip 75024–3131; tel. 469/241–2100; James E. Murray, Chief Executive Officer
**(Independent Hospital System)**

**PENNSYLVANIA:** LIFECARE BEHAVIORAL HEALTH HOSPITAL (O, 49 beds) 225 Penn Avenue, Pittsburgh, PA, Zip 15221–2148; tel. 469/247–2000; Steven Jarrell, Chief Executive Officer
**Web address:** www.lifecare–hospitals.com

**TEXAS:** LIFECARE HOSPITALS OF DALLAS (O, 113 beds) 1950 Record Crossing Road, Dallas, TX, Zip 75235–6223; tel. 214/640–9600; Joy Patel, Chief Executive Officer

| | | |
|---|---|---|
| Owned, leased, sponsored: | 2 hospitals | 162 beds |
| Contract–managed: | 0 hospitals | 0 beds |
| Totals: | 2 hospitals | 162 beds |

---

**★0180: LIFEPOINT HEALTH** (IO)
330 Seven Springs Way, Brentwood, TN Zip 37027–4536; tel. 615/920–7000; David M. Dill, President and Chief Executive Officer
**(Decentralized Health System)**

**ALABAMA:** ANDALUSIA HEALTH (O, 78 beds) 849 South Three Notch Street, Andalusia, AL, Zip 36420–5325, Mailing Address: P.O. Box 760, 36420–1214, tel. 334/222–8466; Clint Kendall, R.N., Chief Executive Officer
**Web address:** www.andalusiahealth.com

NORTH ALABAMA MEDICAL CENTER (O, 321 beds) 1701 Veterans Drive, Florence, AL, Zip 35630–6033; tel. 256/629–1000; Russell Pigg, Chief Executive Officer
**Web address:** www.https://namccares.com/

SHOALS HOSPITAL (O, 137 beds) 201 Avalon Avenue, Muscle Shoals, AL, Zip 35661–2805, Mailing Address: P.O. Box 3359, 35662–3359, tel. 256/386–1600; Kidada Hawkins, Chief Executive Officer
**Web address:** www.shoalshospital.com

VAUGHAN REGIONAL MEDICAL CENTER (O, 149 beds) 1015 Medical Center Parkway, Selma, AL, Zip 36701–6352; tel. 334/418–4100; J. David. McCormack, Chief Executive Officer

**ARIZONA:** CANYON VISTA MEDICAL CENTER (O, 100 beds) 5700 East Highway 90, Sierra Vista, AZ, Zip 85635–9110; tel. 520/263–2000; Bob Gomes, FACHE, President and Chief Executive Officer
**Web address:** www.canyonvistamedicalcenter.com/

HAVASU REGIONAL MEDICAL CENTER (O, 162 beds) 101 Civic Center Lane, Lake Havasu City, AZ, Zip 86403–5683; tel. 928/855–8185; Michael N. Patterson, Chief Executive Officer

VALLEY VIEW MEDICAL CENTER (O, 84 beds) 5330 South Highway 95, Fort Mohave, AZ, Zip 86426–9225; tel. 928/788–2273; Feliciano Jiron, Chief Executive Officer
**Web address:** www.valleyviewmedicalcenter.net

**ARKANSAS:** NATIONAL PARK MEDICAL CENTER (O, 181 beds) 1910 Malvern Avenue, Hot Springs, AR, Zip 71901–7799; tel. 501/321–1000; Joann Ettien, R.N., MS, Interim Chief Executive Officer

SAINT MARY'S REGIONAL MEDICAL CENTER (O, 136 beds) 1808 West Main Street, Russellville, AR, Zip 72801–2724; tel. 479/968–2841; Bob Honeycutt, Chief Executive Officer
**Web address:** www.saintmarysregional.com

SALINE MEMORIAL HOSPITAL (O, 133 beds) 1 Medical Park Drive, Benton, AR, Zip 72015–3354; tel. 501/776–6000; Michael K. Stewart, Chief Executive Officer

**COLORADO:** COLORADO PLAINS MEDICAL CENTER (L, 50 beds) 1000 Lincoln Street, Fort Morgan, CO, Zip 80701–3298; tel. 970/867–3391; Kevin Zachary, Chief Executive Officer
**Web address:** www.coloradoplainsmedicalcenter.com

**GEORGIA:** ST. FRANCIS HOSPITAL (O, 302 beds) 2122 Manchester Expressway, Columbus, GA, Zip 31904–6878, Mailing Address: P.O. Box 7000, 31908–7000, tel. 706/596–4000; Melody Trimble, Chief Executive Officer
**Web address:** www.mystfrancis.com

**IDAHO:** ST. JOSEPH REGIONAL MEDICAL CENTER (O, 123 beds) 415 Sixth Street, Lewiston, ID, Zip 83501–2431; tel. 208/743–2511; Timothy R. Trottier, Chief Executive Officer

**INDIANA:** CLARK MEMORIAL HEALTH (O, 185 beds) 1220 Missouri Avenue, Jeffersonville, IN, Zip 47130–3743, Mailing Address: P.O. Box 69, 47131–0600, tel. 812/282–6631; Martin Padgett, President and Chief Executive Officer
**Web address:** www.clarkmemorial.org

SCOTT MEMORIAL HEALTH (O, 25 beds) 1415 North Gardner Street, Scottsburg, IN, Zip 47170, Box 430, 47170–0430, tel. 812/752–3456; Martin Padgett, Acting Chief Executive Officer
**Web address:** www.scottmemorial.com

**IOWA:** OTTUMWA REGIONAL HEALTH CENTER (O, 86 beds) 1001 Pennsylvania Avenue, Ottumwa, IA, Zip 52501–2186; tel. 641/684–2300; Philip J. Noel III, Chief Executive Officer
**Web address:** www.ottumwaregionalhealth.com

**KANSAS:** WESTERN PLAINS MEDICAL COMPLEX (O, 45 beds) 3001 Avenue 'A', Dodge City, KS, Zip 67801–6508, Mailing Address: P.O. Box 1478, 67801–1478, tel. 620/225–8400; Jerry Dooley, Interim Chief Executive Officer
**Web address:** www.westernplainsmc.com

**KENTUCKY:** BLUEGRASS COMMUNITY HOSPITAL (O, 16 beds) 360 Amsden Avenue, Versailles, KY, Zip 40383–1286; tel. 859/873–3111; Tommy Haggard, Chief Executive Officer

BOURBON COMMUNITY HOSPITAL (O, 58 beds) 9 Linville Drive, Paris, KY, Zip 40361–2196; tel. 859/987–3600; Matt Smith, Interim Chief Executive Officer
**Web address:** www.bourbonhospital.com

---

For explanation of codes following names, see page B2.
★ Indicates Type III membership in the American Hospital Association.

CLARK REGIONAL MEDICAL CENTER (O, 79 beds) 175 Hospital Drive, Winchester, KY, Zip 40391–9591; tel. 859/745–3500; Aphreikah DuHaney–West, Chief Executive Officer
**Web address:** www.clarkregional.org

FLEMING COUNTY HOSPITAL (O, 52 beds) 55 Foundation Drive, Flemingsburg, KY, Zip 41041–9815, Mailing Address: P.O. Box 388, 41041–0388, tel. 606/849–5000; Brian Springate, Chief Executive Officer

GEORGETOWN COMMUNITY HOSPITAL (O, 58 beds) 1140 Lexington Road, Georgetown, KY, Zip 40324–9362; tel. 502/868–1100; William Haugh, Administrator
**Web address:** www.georgetowncommunityhospital.com

JACKSON PURCHASE MEDICAL CENTER (O, 227 beds) 1099 Medical Center Circle, Mayfield, KY, Zip 42066–1159; tel. 270/251–4100; David Anderson, Chief Executive Officer
**Web address:** www.jacksonpurchase.com

LAKE CUMBERLAND REGIONAL HOSPITAL (O, 295 beds) 305 Langdon Street, Somerset, KY, Zip 42503–2750, Mailing Address: P.O. Box 620, 42502–0620, tel. 606/679–7441; Robert Parker, Chief Executive Officer
**Web address:** www.lakecumberlandhospital.com

LOGAN MEMORIAL HOSPITAL (O, 30 beds) 1625 South Nashville Road, Russellville, KY, Zip 42276–8834, Mailing Address: P.O. Box 10, 42276–0010, tel. 270/726–4011; James Bills, Chief Executive Officer

MEADOWVIEW REGIONAL MEDICAL CENTER (O, 100 beds) 989 Medical Park Drive, Maysville, KY, Zip 41056–8750; tel. 606/759–5311; Joseph G. Koch, Chief Executive Officer
**Web address:** www.meadowviewregional.com

SPRING VIEW HOSPITAL (O, 60 beds) 320 Loretto Road, Lebanon, KY, Zip 40033–1300; tel. 270/692–3161; Reba Celsor, Chief Executive Officer

**MICHIGAN:** UP HEALTH SYSTEM–BELL (O, 25 beds) 901 Lakeshore Drive, Ishpeming, MI, Zip 49849–1367; tel. 906/486–4431; Mitchell D. Leckelt, Chief Executive Officer
**Web address:** www.bellhospital.org

UP HEALTH SYSTEM–PORTAGE (O, 96 beds) 500 Campus Drive, Hancock, MI, Zip 49930–1569; tel. 906/483–1000; Edward E. Freysinger, Chief Executive Officer

**MISSISSIPPI:** BOLIVAR MEDICAL CENTER (L, 129 beds) 901 East Sunflower Road, Cleveland, MS, Zip 38732–2833, Mailing Address: P.O. Box 1380, 38732–1380, tel. 662/846–0061; Robert L. Marshall Jr, FACHE, Chief Executive Officer
**Web address:** www.bolivarmedical.com

**MONTANA:** COMMUNITY MEDICAL CENTER (O, 135 beds) 2827 Fort Missoula Road, Missoula, MT, Zip 59804–7408; tel. 406/728–4100; Dean French, M.D., Chief Executive Officer

**NEVADA:** NORTHEASTERN NEVADA REGIONAL HOSPITAL (O, 75 beds) 2001 Errecart Boulevard, Elko, NV, Zip 89801–8333; tel. 775/738–5151; Steve Simpson, Chief Executive Officer
**Web address:** www.nnrhospital.com

**NEW MEXICO:** LOS ALAMOS MEDICAL CENTER (O, 24 beds) 3917 West Road, Los Alamos, NM, Zip 87544–2293; tel. 505/661–9500; John Whiteside, Chief Executive Officer

MEMORIAL MEDICAL CENTER (L, 173 beds) 2450 South Telshor Boulevard, Las Cruces, NM, Zip 88011–5076; tel. 575/522–8641; John Harris, Chief Executive Officer
**Web address:** www.mmclc.org

**OHIO:** CMH REGIONAL HEALTH SYSTEM (O, 119 beds) 610 West Main Street, Wilmington, OH, Zip 45177–2125; tel. 937/382–6611; Lance Beus, Chief Executive Officer
**Web address:** www.cmhregional.com

**OKLAHOMA:** SOUTHWESTERN MEDICAL CENTER (O, 178 beds) 5602 SW Lee Boulevard, Lawton, OK, Zip 73505–9635; tel. 580/531–4700; Elizabeth Jones, Chief Executive Officer

**OREGON:** WILLAMETTE VALLEY MEDICAL CENTER (O, 60 beds) 2700 SE Stratus Avenue, McMinnville, OR, Zip 97128–6255; tel. 503/472–6131; Lorinda Bergen, Chief Executive Officer
**Web address:** www.willamettevalleymedical.com/

**PENNSYLVANIA:** CONEMAUGH NASON MEDICAL CENTER (O, 45 beds) 105 Nason Drive, Roaring Spring, PA, Zip 16673–1202; tel. 814/224–2141; Timothy Harclerode, Chief Executive Officer

**SOUTH CAROLINA:** CAROLINA PINES REGIONAL MEDICAL CENTER (O, 105 beds) 1304 West Bobo Newsom Highway, Hartsville, SC, Zip 29550–4710; tel. 843/339–2100; William Little, Chief Executive Officer
**Web address:** www.cprmc.com

KERSHAWHEALTH (O, 76 beds) 1315 Roberts Street, Camden, SC, Zip 29020–3737, Mailing Address: P.O. Box 7003, 29021–7003, tel. 803/432–4311; Susan C. Shugart, Chief Executive Officer

PROVIDENCE HOSPITAL (O, 216 beds) 2435 Forest Drive, Columbia, SC, Zip 29204–2098; tel. 803/865–4500; Terry Gunn, FACHE, Chief Executive Officer
**Web address:** www.sistersofcharityhealth.org/health–care/providence–hospitals/

**TENNESSEE:** LIVINGSTON REGIONAL HOSPITAL (O, 82 beds) 315 Oak Street, Livingston, TN, Zip 38570–1728, Mailing Address: P.O. Box 550, 38570–0550, tel. 931/823–5611; Timothy W. McGill, Chief Executive Officer
**Web address:** www.MyLivingstonHospital.com

RIVERVIEW REGIONAL MEDICAL CENTER (O, 35 beds) 158 Hospital Drive, Carthage, TN, Zip 37030–1096; tel. 615/735–1560; Michael Herman, Chief Executive Officer

SOUTHERN TENNESSEE REGIONAL HEALTH SYSTEM–LAWRENCEBURG (O, 80 beds) 1607 South Locust Avenue, Lawrenceburg, TN, Zip 38464–4011, Mailing Address: P.O. Box 847, 38464–0847, tel. 931/762–6571; Adam Martin, Chief Executive Officer
**Web address:** www.crocketthospital.com

SOUTHERN TENNESSEE REGIONAL HEALTH SYSTEM–PULASKI (O, 38 beds) 1265 East College Street, Pulaski, TN, Zip 38478–4541; tel. 931/363–7531; James H. Edmondson, Chief Executive Officer
**Web address:** www.southerntnpulaski.com/

SOUTHERN TENNESSEE REGIONAL HEALTH SYSTEM–WINCHESTER (O, 190 beds) 185 Hospital Road, Winchester, TN, Zip 37398–2404; tel. 931/967–8200; William R. Spray, Chief Executive Officer
**Web address:** www.southerntennessee.com

STARR REGIONAL MEDICAL CENTER (O, 63 beds) 1114 West Madison Avenue, Athens, TN, Zip 37303–4150, Mailing Address: P.O. Box 250, 37371–0250, tel. 423/745–1411; John R. McLain, Chief Executive Officer

SUMNER REGIONAL MEDICAL CENTER (O, 110 beds) 555 Hartsville Pike, Gallatin, TN, Zip 37066–2400, Mailing Address: P.O. Box 1558, 37066–1558, tel. 615/452–4210; Susan M. Peach, R.N., Chief Executive Officer
**Web address:** www.mysumnermedical.com

TROUSDALE MEDICAL CENTER (O, 25 beds) 500 Church Street, Hartsville, TN, Zip 37074–1744; tel. 615/374–2221; Michael Herman, Chief Executive Officer
**Web address:** www.mytrousdalemedical.com

**TEXAS:** ENNIS REGIONAL MEDICAL CENTER (L, 58 beds) 2201 West Lampasas Street, Ennis, TX, Zip 75119–5644; tel. 972/875–0900; Robert Rupp, Chief Executive Officer

PALESTINE REGIONAL MEDICAL CENTER–EAST (O, 120 beds) 2900 South Loop 256, Palestine, TX, Zip 75801–6958; tel. 903/731–1000; Roy Finch, Chief Executive Officer
**Web address:** www.palestineregional.com

PARIS REGIONAL MEDICAL CENTER (O, 171 beds) 865 Deshong Drive, Paris, TX, Zip 75460–9313, Mailing Address: P.O. Box 9070, 75461–9070, tel. 903/785–4521; Steve Hyde, Chief Executive Officer

PARKVIEW REGIONAL HOSPITAL (L, 58 beds) 600 South Bonham, Mexia, TX, Zip 76667–3603; tel. 254/562–5332; Robert Rupp, Chief Executive Officer
**Web address:** www.parkviewregional.com

**UTAH:** ASHLEY REGIONAL MEDICAL CENTER (O, 39 beds) 150 West 100 North, Vernal, UT, Zip 84078–2036; tel. 435/789–3342; Wes Taylor, Chief Executive Officer
**Web address:** www.ashleyregional.com

CASTLEVIEW HOSPITAL (O, 49 beds) 300 North Hospital Drive, Price, UT, Zip 84501–4200; tel. 435/637–4800; Greg Cook, Chief Executive Officer

For explanation of codes following names, see page B2.
★ Indicates Type III membership in the American Hospital Association.

**VIRGINIA:** CLINCH VALLEY MEDICAL CENTER (O, 95 beds) 6801 Governor G C Peery Highway, Richlands, VA, Zip 24641–2194; tel. 276/596–6000; Peter Mulkey, Chief Executive Officer
**Web address:** www.clinchvalleymedicalcenter.com

FAUQUIER HOSPITAL (O, 86 beds) 500 Hospital Drive, Warrenton, VA, Zip 20186–3099; tel. 540/316–5000; Chad Melton, Chief Executive Officer
**Web address:** www.fauquierhealth.org/

SOVAH HEALTH–DANVILLE (O, 250 beds) 142 South Main Street, Danville, VA, Zip 24541–2922; tel. 434/799–2100; Alan Larson, Chief Executive Officer

SOVAH HEALTH–MARTINSVILLE (O, 150 beds) 320 Hospital Drive, Martinsville, VA, Zip 24112–1981, Mailing Address: P.O. Box 4788, 24115–4788, tel. 276/666–7200; Alan Larson, Market President
**Web address:** www.martinsvillehospital.com

WYTHE COUNTY COMMUNITY HOSPITAL (L, 70 beds) 600 West Ridge Road, Wytheville, VA, Zip 24382–1099; tel. 276/228–0200; Joseph Wilkins, Chief Executive Officer
**Web address:** www.wcchcares.com

**WASHINGTON:** CAPITAL MEDICAL CENTER (O, 52 beds) 3900 Capital Mall Drive SW, Olympia, WA, Zip 98502–5026; tel. 360/754–5858; Mark S. Turner, Chief Executive Officer
**Web address:** www.capitalmedical.com

LOURDES COUNSELING CENTER (O, 20 beds) 1175 Carondelet Drive, Richland, WA, Zip 99354–3300; tel. 509/943–9104; Robert Monical, Chief Executive Officer
**Web address:** www.lourdeshealth.net

LOURDES MEDICAL CENTER (O, 53 beds) 520 North Fourth Avenue, Pasco, WA, Zip 99301–5257; tel. 509/547–7704; John Serle, FACHE, President and Chief Executive Officer

TRIOS HEALTH (O, 109 beds) 900 South Auburn Street, Kennewick, WA, Zip 99336–5621, Mailing Address: P.O. Box 6128, 99336–0128, tel. 509/586–6111; John H. Solheim, Chief Executive Officer
**Web address:** www.trioshealth.org

**WEST VIRGINIA:** LOGAN REGIONAL MEDICAL CENTER (O, 129 beds) 20 Hospital Drive, Logan, WV, Zip 25601–3452; tel. 304/831–1101; Simon Ratliff, Interim Chief Executive Officer

RALEIGH GENERAL HOSPITAL (O, 229 beds) 1710 Harper Road, Beckley, WV, Zip 25801–3397; tel. 304/256–4100; Matthew S. Roberts, Chief Executive Officer
**Web address:** www.raleighgeneral.com

**WISCONSIN:** WATERTOWN REGIONAL MEDICAL CENTER (O, 64 beds) 125 Hospital Drive, Watertown, WI, Zip 53098–3303; tel. 920/261–4210; Richard Keddington, Chief Executive Officer
**Web address:** www.watertownregional.com/Main/Home.aspx

**WYOMING:** SAGEWEST HEALTH CARE (O, 93 beds) 2100 West Sunset Drive, Riverton, WY, Zip 82501–2274; tel. 307/856–4161; John Ferrelli, Chief Executive Officer

| Owned, leased, sponsored: | 68 hospitals | 7246 beds |
|---|---|---|
| Contract–managed: | 0 hospitals | 0 beds |
| Totals: | 68 hospitals | 7246 beds |

---

**0060: LIFESPAN CORPORATION** (NP)
167 Point Street, Providence, RI Zip 02903–4771; tel. 401/444–3500; Timothy J. Babineau, M.D., President and Chief Executive Officer
**(Centralized Health System)**

**RHODE ISLAND:** EMMA PENDLETON BRADLEY HOSPITAL (O, 70 beds) 1011 Veterans Memorial Parkway, East Providence, RI, Zip 02915–5099; tel. 401/432–1000; Daniel J. Wall, President and Chief Executive Officer

MIRIAM HOSPITAL (O, 247 beds) 164 Summit Avenue, Providence, RI, Zip 02906–2853; tel. 401/793–2500; Arthur J. Sampson, FACHE, President
**Web address:** www.lifespan.org

NEWPORT HOSPITAL (O, 104 beds) 11 Friendship Street, Newport, RI, Zip 02840–2299; tel. 401/846–6400; Crista F. Durand, President

RHODE ISLAND HOSPITAL (O, 682 beds) 593 Eddy Street, Providence, RI, Zip 02903–4900; tel. 401/444–4000; Margaret M. Van Bree, Dr.PH, President
**Web address:** www.rhodeislandhospital.org/

| Owned, leased, sponsored: | 4 hospitals | 1103 beds |
|---|---|---|
| Contract–managed: | 0 hospitals | 0 beds |
| Totals: | 4 hospitals | 1103 beds |

---

**2175: LOMA LINDA UNIVERSITY ADVENTIST HEALTH SCIENCES CENTER** (NP)
11175 Campus Street, Loma Linda, CA Zip 92350–1700; tel. 909/558–7572; Richard H. Hart, President and Chief Executive Officer
**(Centralized Health System)**

**CALIFORNIA:** LOMA LINDA UNIVERSITY BEHAVIORAL MEDICINE CENTER (O, 89 beds) 1710 Barton Road, Redlands, CA, Zip 92373–5304; tel. 909/558–9200; Edward Field, Administrator
**Web address:** www.llu.edu

LOMA LINDA UNIVERSITY CHILDREN'S HOSPITAL (O, 343 beds) 11234 Anderson Street, Loma Linda, CA, Zip 92354–2804; tel. 909/558–8000; Kerry Heinrich, JD, Chief Executive Officer
**Web address:** www.llu.edu/lluch

LOMA LINDA UNIVERSITY MEDICAL CENTER–MURRIETA (O, 111 beds) 28062 Baxter Road , Murrieta, CA, Zip 92563–1401; tel. 951/290–4000; Peter Baker, Senior Vice President and Administrator
**Web address:** www.llumcmurrieta.org

LOMA LINDA UNIVERSITY MEDICAL CENTER (O, 533 beds) 11234 Anderson Street, Loma Linda, CA, Zip 92354–2804, Mailing Address: P.O. Box 2000, 92354–0200, tel. 909/558–4000; Kerry Heinrich, JD, Chief Executive Officer

| Owned, leased, sponsored: | 4 hospitals | 1076 beds |
|---|---|---|
| Contract–managed: | 0 hospitals | 0 beds |
| Totals: | 4 hospitals | 1076 beds |

---

**5755: LOS ANGELES COUNTY–DEPARTMENT OF HEALTH SERVICES** (NP)
313 North Figueroa Street, Room 912, Los Angeles, CA Zip 90012–2691; tel. 213/240–8101; Mitchell H. Katz, M.D., Director
**(Moderately Centralized Health System)**

**CALIFORNIA:** HARBOR–UCLA MEDICAL CENTER (O, 373 beds) 1000 West Carson Street, Torrance, CA, Zip 90502–2059; tel. 310/222–2345; Kimberly McKenzie, R.N., MSN, Interim Chief Executive Officer
**Web address:** www.harbor–ucla.org

LAC+USC MEDICAL CENTER (O, 538 beds) 2051 Marengo Street, Los Angeles, CA, Zip 90033–1352; tel. 323/409–1000; Jorge Orozco, Chief Executive Officer

LAC–OLIVE VIEW–UCLA MEDICAL CENTER (O, 202 beds) 14445 Olive View Drive, Sylmar, CA, Zip 91342–1438; tel. 818/364–1555; Judith Maass, Chief Executive Officer
**Web address:** www.dhs.lacounty.gov/wps/portal/dhs/oliveview

RANCHO LOS AMIGOS NATIONAL REHABILITATION CENTER (O, 207 beds) 7601 East Imperial Highway, Downey, CA, Zip 90242–3496; tel. 562/401–7111; Aries Limbaga, R.N., Chief Executive Officer

| Owned, leased, sponsored: | 4 hospitals | 1320 beds |
|---|---|---|
| Contract–managed: | 0 hospitals | 0 beds |
| Totals: | 4 hospitals | 1320 beds |

---

**0047: LOUISIANA STATE HOSPITALS** (NP)
628 North 4th Street, Baton Rouge, LA Zip 70802–5342, Mailing Address: P.O. Box 629, 70821–0628, tel. 225/342–9500; Shelby Price, Chief Executive Officer
**(Independent Hospital System)**

**LOUISIANA:** CENTRAL LOUISIANA STATE HOSPITAL (O, 120 beds) 242 West Shamrock Avenue, Pineville, LA, Zip 71360–6439, Mailing Address: P.O. Box 5031, 71361–5031, tel. 318/484–6200; Sandra Duck, R.N., MSN, Mental Hospital Administrator 2

EASTERN LOUISIANA MENTAL HEALTH SYSTEM (O, 473 beds) 4502 Highway 10, Jackson, LA, Zip 70748, Mailing Address: P.O. Box 498, 70748–0498, tel. 225/634–0100; Hampton P. S. Lea, Chief Executive Officer
**Web address:** www.new.dhh.louisiana.gov/index.cfm/directory/detail/219

| Owned, leased, sponsored: | 2 hospitals | 593 beds |
|---|---|---|
| Contract–managed: | 0 hospitals | 0 beds |
| Totals: | 2 hospitals | 593 beds |

★**0320: LRGHEALTHCARE** (NP)
80 Highland Street, Laconia, NH Zip 03246–3298; tel. 603/524–3211; Kevin Donovan, FACHE, President and Chief Executive Officer
**(Independent Hospital System)**

**NEW HAMPSHIRE:** FRANKLIN REGIONAL HOSPITAL (O, 31 beds) 15 Aiken Avenue, Franklin, NH, Zip 03235–1299; tel. 603/934–2060; Kevin Donovan, FACHE, President and Chief Executive Officer

LAKES REGION GENERAL HOSPITAL (O, 82 beds) 80 Highland Street, Laconia, NH, Zip 03246–3298; tel. 603/524–3211; Kevin Donovan, FACHE, President and Chief Executive Officer
**Web address:** www.lrgh.org

| Owned, leased, sponsored: | 2 hospitals | 113 beds |
|---|---|---|
| Contract–managed: | 0 hospitals | 0 beds |
| Totals: | 2 hospitals | 113 beds |

★**1325: M HEALTH FAIRVIEW** (NP)
2450 Riverside Avenue, Minneapolis, MN Zip 55454–1400; tel. 612/672–6141; James Hereford, President and Chief Executive Officer
**(Centralized Health System)**

**MINNESOTA:** BETHESDA HOSPITAL (O, 114 beds) 559 Capitol Boulevard, Saint Paul, MN, Zip 55103–2101; tel. 651/232–2000; Jeoff Will, Chief Operating Office, Acute Care Services
**Web address:** www.healtheast.org

FAIRVIEW LAKES HEALTH SERVICES (O, 38 beds) 5200 Fairview Boulevard, Wyoming, MN, Zip 55092–8013; tel. 651/982–7000; Lia Christiansen, Chief Operating Officer, Acute Care Hospitals

FAIRVIEW NORTHLAND MEDICAL CENTER (O, 23 beds) 911 Northland Drive, Princeton, MN, Zip 55371–2173; tel. 763/389–1313; Lia Christiansen, Chief Operating Officer, Acute Care Hospitals
**Web address:** www.northland.fairview.org

FAIRVIEW RANGE MEDICAL CENTER (O, 72 beds) 750 East 34th Street, Hibbing, MN, Zip 55746–4600; tel. 218/262–4881; Patrick Sharp, President and Chief Executive Officer

FAIRVIEW RIDGES HOSPITAL (O, 162 beds) 201 East Nicollet Boulevard, Burnsville, MN, Zip 55337–5799; tel. 952/892–2000; Jeoff Will, Chief Operating Officer, Acute Care Services
**Web address:** www.fairview.org

FAIRVIEW SOUTHDALE HOSPITAL (O, 316 beds) 6401 France Avenue South, Edina, MN, Zip 55435–2199; tel. 952/924–5000; Jeoff Will, Chief Operating Officer, Acute Care Services
**Web address:** www.fairview.org

GRAND ITASCA CLINIC AND HOSPITAL (O, 31 beds) 1601 Golf Course Road, Grand Rapids, MN, Zip 55744–8648; tel. 218/326–5000; Jean MacDonell, President and Chief Executive Officer

ST. JOHN'S HOSPITAL (O, 192 beds) 1575 Beam Avenue, Maplewood, MN, Zip 55109–1126; tel. 651/232–7000; Lia Christiansen, Chief Operating Officer, Acute Care Hospitals
**Web address:** www.stjohnshospital–mn.org

ST. JOSEPH'S HOSPITAL (O, 239 beds) 45 West 10th Street, Saint Paul, MN, Zip 55102–1053; tel. 651/232–3000; Lia Christiansen, Chief Operating Officer, Acute Care Hospitals
**Web address:** www.healtheast.org

UNIVERSITY OF MINNESOTA (O, 861 beds) 2450 Riverside Avenue, Minneapolis, MN, Zip 55454–1400, 2520 University Ave SE Ste 201, 55414, tel. 612/624–8618; John Doherty, Co–President, M Health

WOODWINDS HEALTH CAMPUS (O, 86 beds) 1925 Woodwinds Drive, Woodbury, MN, Zip 55125–4445; tel. 651/232–0228; Lia Christiansen, Chief Operating Officer, Acute Care Hospitals
**Web address:** www.woodwinds.org

| Owned, leased, sponsored: | 11 hospitals | 2134 beds |
|---|---|---|
| Contract–managed: | 0 hospitals | 0 beds |
| Totals: | 11 hospitals | 2134 beds |

**0614: MAINEHEALTH** (NP)
110 Free Street, Portland, ME Zip 04101–3537; tel. 207/661–7001; William L. Caron Jr, President
**(Moderately Centralized Health System)**

**MAINE:** LINCOLNHEALTH (O, 91 beds) 35 Miles Street, Damariscotta, ME, Zip 04543–4047; tel. 207/563–1234; James W. Donovan, President

MAINE MEDICAL CENTER (O, 758 beds) 22 Bramhall Street, Portland, ME, Zip 04102–3175; tel. 207/662–0111; Richard W. Petersen, President and Chief Executive Officer
**Web address:** www.mmc.org

PEN BAY MEDICAL CENTER (O, 151 beds) 6 Glen Cove Drive, Rockport, ME, Zip 04856–4240; tel. 207/921–8000; Mark Fourre, President
**Web address:** www.penbayhealthcare.org

SPRING HARBOR HOSPITAL (O, 100 beds) 123 Andover Road, Westbrook, ME, Zip 04092–3850; tel. 207/761–2200; Mary Jane Krebs, FACHE, President
**Web address:** www.springharbor.org

STEPHENS MEMORIAL HOSPITAL (O, 25 beds) 181 Main Street, Norway, ME, Zip 04268–5664; tel. 207/743–5933; Timothy A. Churchill, President

WALDO COUNTY GENERAL HOSPITAL (O, 25 beds) 118 Northport Avenue, Belfast, ME, Zip 04915–6072, Mailing Address: P.O. Box 287, 04915–0287, tel. 207/338–2500; Mark Fourre, President
**Web address:** www.wcgh.org

**NEW HAMPSHIRE:** MEMORIAL HOSPITAL (O, 70 beds) 3073 White Mountain Highway, North Conway, NH, Zip 03860–7101; tel. 603/356–5461; Arthur Mathisen, FACHE, President
**Web address:** www.memorialhospitalnh.org

| Owned, leased, sponsored: | 7 hospitals | 1220 beds |
|---|---|---|
| Contract–managed: | 0 hospitals | 0 beds |
| Totals: | 7 hospitals | 1220 beds |

**1975: MARSHALL HEALTH SYSTEM** (NP)
227 Britany Road, Guntersville, AL Zip 35976–5766; tel. 256/894–6615; Cheryl M. Hays, FACHE, President
**(Independent Hospital System)**

**ALABAMA:** MARSHALL MEDICAL CENTER NORTH (O, 76 beds) 8000 Alabama Highway 69, Guntersville, AL, Zip 35976; tel. 256/753–8000; Cheryl M. Hays, FACHE, Chief Executive Officer
**Web address:** www.mmcenters.com

MARSHALL MEDICAL CENTER SOUTH (O, 107 beds) U S Highway 431 North, Boaz, AL, Zip 35957–0999, Mailing Address: P.O. Box 758, 35957–0758, tel. 256/593–8310; Cheryl M. Hays, FACHE, Chief Executive Officer
**Web address:** www.mmcenters.com//index.php/facilities/marshall_south

| Owned, leased, sponsored: | 2 hospitals | 183 beds |
|---|---|---|
| Contract–managed: | 0 hospitals | 0 beds |
| Totals: | 2 hospitals | 183 beds |

★**1022: MARSHFIELD CLINIC HEALTH SYSTEM** (NP)
1000 North Oak Avenue, Marshfield, WI Zip 54449–5703; tel. 800/782–8581; Susan Turney, M.D., MS, Chief Executive Officer
**(Moderately Centralized Health System)**

For explanation of codes following names, see page B2.
★ Indicates Type III membership in the American Hospital Association.

**WISCONSIN:** FLAMBEAU HOSPITAL (O, 25 beds) 98 Sherry Avenue, Park Falls, WI, Zip 54552–1467, Mailing Address: P.O. Box 310, 54552–0310, tel. 715/762–2484; James R. Braun, Chief Administrative Officer and Chief Financial Officer
**Web address:** www.flambeauhospital.org

MARSHFIELD MEDICAL CENTER – BEAVER DAM (O, 163 beds) 707 South University Avenue, Beaver Dam, WI, Zip 53916–3089; tel. 920/887–7181; Angelia Foster, Chief Administrative Officer

MARSHFIELD MEDICAL CENTER – EAU CLAIRE HOSPITAL (O, 44 beds) 2310 Craig Road, Eau Claire, WI, Zip 54701–6128; tel. 715/858–8100; Bill Priest, Chief Administrative Officer
**Web address:** https://www.marshfieldclinic.org

MARSHFIELD MEDICAL CENTER – LADYSMITH (O, 25 beds) 900 College Avenue West, Ladysmith, WI, Zip 54848–2116; tel. 715/532–5561; Jeff Euclide, R.N., Chief Administrative Officer

MARSHFIELD MEDICAL CENTER – MINOCQUA (O, 19 beds) 9576 State Highway 70, Minocqua, WI, Zip 54548; tel. 715/358–1710; David R. Olejniczak, Chief Administrative Officer
**Web address:** www.marshfieldclinic.org

MARSHFIELD MEDICAL CENTER – NEILSVILLE (O, 16 beds) 216 Sunset Place, Neillsville, WI, Zip 54456–1799; tel. 715/743–3101; Ryan T. Neville, FACHE, President and Chief Executive Officer
**Web address:** www.memorialmedcenter.org

MARSHFIELD MEDICAL CENTER – RICE LAKE (O, 40 beds) 1700 West Stout Street, Rice Lake, WI, Zip 54868–5000; tel. 715/234–1515; Bradley D. Groseth, Chief Administrative Officer
**Web address:** www.lakeviewmedical.com

MARSHFIELD MEDICAL CENTER – WESTON (O, 49 beds) 3400 Ministry Parkway, Weston, WI, Zip 54476–5220; tel. 715/393–3000; Jeremy Normington–Slay, FACHE, President, North Central Region

MARSHFIELD MEDICAL CENTER (O, 200 beds) 611 St Joseph Avenue, Marshfield, WI, Zip 54449–1898; tel. 715/387–1713; Pat Board, Chief Administrative Officer
**Web address:** www.stjosephs–marshfield.org

| | | |
|---|---|---|
| Owned, leased, sponsored: | 9 hospitals | 581 beds |
| Contract–managed: | 0 hospitals | 0 beds |
| Totals: | 9 hospitals | 581 beds |

---

★**0523: MARY WASHINGTON HEALTHCARE** (NP)
1001 Sam Perry Boulevard, Suite 1005, Fredericksburg, VA Zip 22401–4453; tel. 540/741–3100; Michael P. McDermott, M.D., President and Chief Executive Officer
**(Centralized Health System)**

**VIRGINIA:** MARY WASHINGTON HOSPITAL (O, 451 beds) 1001 Sam Perry Boulevard, Fredericksburg, VA, Zip 22401–3354; tel. 540/741–1100; Michael P. McDermott, M.D., President and Chief Executive Officer

STAFFORD HOSPITAL (O, 82 beds) 101 Hospital Center Boulevard, Stafford, VA, Zip 22554–6200; tel. 540/741–9000; Michael P. McDermott, M.D., President and Chief Executive Officer
**Web address:** www.mwhc.com

| | | |
|---|---|---|
| Owned, leased, sponsored: | 2 hospitals | 533 beds |
| Contract–managed: | 0 hospitals | 0 beds |
| Totals: | 2 hospitals | 533 beds |

---

★**1785: MASS GENERAL BRIGHAM** (NP)
800 Boylston Street, Suite 1150, Boston, MA Zip 02199–8123; tel. 617/278–1004; Anne Klibanski, M.D., President and Chief Executive Officer
**(Decentralized Health System)**

**MASSACHUSETTS:** BRIGHAM AND WOMEN'S FAULKNER HOSPITAL (O, 171 beds) 1153 Centre Street, Boston, MA, Zip 02130–3446; tel. 617/983–7000; David O. McCready, President

BRIGHAM AND WOMEN'S HOSPITAL (O, 822 beds) 75 Francis Street, Boston, MA, Zip 02115–6110; tel. 617/732–5500; Elizabeth Nabel, M.D., President
**Web address:** www.brighamandwomens.org

COOLEY DICKINSON HOSPITAL (O, 141 beds) 30 Locust Street, Northampton, MA, Zip 01060–2093, Mailing Address: P.O. Box 5001, 01061–5001, tel. 413/582–2000; Joanne Marqusee, President and Chief Executive Officer
**Web address:** www.cooleydickinson.org

MARTHA'S VINEYARD HOSPITAL (O, 86 beds) One Hospital Road, Oak Bluffs, MA, Zip 2557, Mailing Address: P.O. Box 1477, 02557–1477, tel. 508/693–0410; Denise Schepici, M.P.H., Chief Executive Officer and President
**Web address:** www.mvhospital.com/

MASSACHUSETTS EYE AND EAR (O, 41 beds) 243 Charles Street, Boston, MA, Zip 02114–3002; tel. 617/523–7900; John R. Fernandez, President and Chief Executive Officer

MASSACHUSETTS GENERAL HOSPITAL (O, 1035 beds) 55 Fruit Street, Boston, MA, Zip 02114–2696; tel. 617/726–2000; Peter L. Slavin, M.D., President
**Web address:** www.massgeneral.org

MCLEAN HOSPITAL (O, 217 beds) 115 Mill Street, Belmont, MA, Zip 02478–1064; tel. 617/855–2000; Scott L. Rauch, M.D., President and Psychiatrist in Chief
**Web address:** www.mcleanhospital.org

NANTUCKET COTTAGE HOSPITAL (O, 14 beds) 57 Prospect Street, Nantucket, MA, Zip 02554–2799; tel. 508/825–8100; Gary Shaw, President and Chief Executive Officer

NEWTON–WELLESLEY HOSPITAL (O, 201 beds) 2014 Washington Street, Newton Lower Falls, MA, Zip 02462–1699; tel. 617/243–6000; Gregg S. Meyer, M.D., Interim President
**Web address:** www.nwh.org

NORTH SHORE MEDICAL CENTER (O, 362 beds) 81 Highland Avenue, Salem, MA, Zip 01970–2714; tel. 978/741–1200; David J. Roberts, M.D., President

SPAULDING HOSPITAL FOR CONTINUING MEDICAL CARE CAMBRIDGE (O, 118 beds) 1575 Cambridge Street, Cambridge, MA, Zip 02138–4308; tel. 617/876–4344; Maureen Banks, President
**Web address:** www.spauldingnetwork.org

SPAULDING REHABILITATION HOSPITAL CAPE COD (O, 60 beds) 311 Service Road, East Sandwich, MA, Zip 02537–1370; tel. 508/833–4000; Maureen Banks, President

SPAULDING REHABILITATION HOSPITAL (O, 132 beds) 300 First Avenue, Charlestown, MA, Zip 02129–3109; tel. 617/952–5000; David E. Storto, President
**Web address:** www.spauldingrehab.org

**NEW HAMPSHIRE:** WENTWORTH–DOUGLASS HOSPITAL (O, 142 beds) 789 Central Avenue, Dover, NH, Zip 3820; tel. 603/742–5252; Gregory J. Walker, Chief Executive Officer

| | | |
|---|---|---|
| Owned, leased, sponsored: | 14 hospitals | 3542 beds |
| Contract–managed: | 0 hospitals | 0 beds |
| Totals: | 14 hospitals | 3542 beds |

---

**0013: MASSACHUSETTS DEPARTMENT OF MENTAL HEALTH** (NP)
25 Staniford Street, Boston, MA Zip 02114–2575; tel. 617/626–8123; Joan Mikula, Interim Commissioner

**MASSACHUSETTS:** DR. J. CORRIGAN MENTAL HEALTH CENTER (O, 16 beds) 49 Hillside Street, Fall River, MA, Zip 02720–5266; tel. 508/235–7200; Frank O'Reilly, Director

TAUNTON STATE HOSPITAL (O, 45 beds) 60 Hodges Avenue Extension, Taunton, MA, Zip 02780–3034, Mailing Address: P.O. 4007, 02780–0997, tel. 508/977–3000; Joyce O Connor, Chief Operating Officer

WORCESTER RECOVERY CENTER AND HOSPITAL (O, 126 beds) 309 Belmont Street, Worcester, MA, Zip 01604–1695; tel. 508/368–3300; Anthony Riccitelli, Chief Operating Officer

| | | |
|---|---|---|
| Owned, leased, sponsored: | 3 hospitals | 187 beds |
| Contract–managed: | 0 hospitals | 0 beds |
| Totals: | 3 hospitals | 187 beds |

---

**0280: MASSACHUSETTS DEPARTMENT OF PUBLIC HEALTH** (NP)
250 Washington Street, Boston, MA Zip 02108–4619; tel. 617/624–6000; Betsy L. Schwechheimer, Bureau Director
**(Independent Hospital System)**

---

For explanation of codes following names, see page B2.
★ Indicates Type III membership in the American Hospital Association.

© 2021 AHA Guide

**MASSACHUSETTS:** LEMUEL SHATTUCK HOSPITAL (O, 260 beds) 170 Morton Street, Jamaica Plain, MA, Zip 02130–3735; tel. 617/522–8110; Rosette Martinez, Acting Chief Executive Officer

PAPPAS REHABILITATION HOSPITAL FOR CHILDREN (O, 80 beds) 3 Randolph Street, Canton, MA, Zip 02021–2351; tel. 781/828–2440; Brian V. Devin, Chief Executive Officer
**Web address:** www.mhsf.us/

TEWKSBURY HOSPITAL (O, 381 beds) 365 East Street, Tewksbury, MA, Zip 01876–1998; tel. 978/851–7321; Debra Tosti, Chief Executive Officer
**Web address:** www.mass.gov

WESTERN MASSACHUSETTS HOSPITAL (O, 80 beds) 91 East Mountain Road, Westfield, MA, Zip 01085–1801; tel. 413/562–4131; Valenda M. Liptak, Chief Executive Officer
**Web address:** www.mass.gov/eohhs/gov/departments/dph/programs/western–massachusetts–hospital.html

| | | |
|---|---|---|
| Owned, leased, sponsored: | 4 hospitals | 801 beds |
| Contract–managed: | 0 hospitals | 0 beds |
| Totals: | 4 hospitals | 801 beds |

---

**★0882: MAURY REGIONAL HEALTH SYSTEM** (NP)
1224 Trotwood Avenue, Columbia, TN Zip 38401–4802; tel. 931/381–1111; H. Alan. Watson, FACHE, Chief Executive Officer
**(Independent Hospital System)**

**TENNESSEE:** MARSHALL MEDICAL CENTER (O, 12 beds) 1080 North Ellington Parkway, Lewisburg, TN, Zip 37091–2227, Mailing Address: P.O. Box 1609, 37091–1609, tel. 931/359–6241; Phyllis Brown, Chief Executive Officer
**Web address:** www.mauryregional.com

MAURY REGIONAL HOSPITAL (O, 208 beds) 1224 Trotwood Avenue, Columbia, TN, Zip 38401–4802; tel. 931/381–1111; H. Alan. Watson, FACHE, Chief Executive Officer

WAYNE MEDICAL CENTER (L, 25 beds) 103 J V Mangubat Drive, Waynesboro, TN, Zip 38485–2440, Mailing Address: P.O. Box 580, 38485–0580, tel. 931/722–5411; Tyler Taylor, Chief Executive Officer
**Web address:** www.mauryregional.com

| | | |
|---|---|---|
| Owned, leased, sponsored: | 3 hospitals | 245 beds |
| Contract–managed: | 0 hospitals | 0 beds |
| Totals: | 3 hospitals | 245 beds |

---

**★1875: MAYO CLINIC** (NP)
200 First Street SW, Rochester, MN Zip 55905–0002; tel. 507/284–2511; Gianrico Farrugia, M.D., President
**(Decentralized Health System)**

**ARIZONA:** MAYO CLINIC HOSPITAL (O, 280 beds) 5777 East Mayo Boulevard, Phoenix, AZ, Zip 85054–4502; tel. 480/342–2000; Richard Gray, M.D., Vice President Operations
**Web address:** www.mayoclinic.org/arizona/

**FLORIDA:** MAYO CLINIC HOSPITAL IN FLORIDA (O, 304 beds) 4500 San Pablo Road South, Jacksonville, FL, Zip 32224–1865; tel. 904/953–2000; Kent Thielen, M.D., Vice President Operations
**Web address:** www.mayoclinic.org/jacksonville/

**IOWA:** FLOYD COUNTY MEDICAL CENTER (C, 25 beds) 800 Eleventh Street, Charles City, IA, Zip 50616–3499; tel. 641/228–6830; Rod Nordeng, Administrator
**Web address:** www.fcmc.us.com/

WINNESHIEK MEDICAL CENTER (C, 25 beds) 901 Montgomery Street, Decorah, IA, Zip 52101–2325; tel. 563/382–2911; Lisa Radtke, Chief Administrative Officer
**Web address:** www.winmedical.org

**MINNESOTA:** MAYO CLINIC HEALTH SYSTEM – ALBERT LEA AND AUSTIN (O, 81 beds) 404 West Fountain Street, Albert Lea, MN, Zip 56007–2473; tel. 507/373–2384; Brian Whited, M.D., Vice Chair, Mayo Health System

MAYO CLINIC HEALTH SYSTEM IN CANNON FALLS (O, 15 beds) 32021 County Road 24 Boulevard, Cannon Falls, MN, Zip 55009–1898; tel. 507/263–4221; Brian Whited, M.D., Vice Chair Mayo Clinic Health System
**Web address:** www.mayoclinichealthsystem.org/locations/cannon–falls

MAYO CLINIC HEALTH SYSTEM IN FAIRMONT (O, 23 beds) 800 Medical Center Drive, Fairmont, MN, Zip 56031–4575; tel. 507/238–8100; James Hebl, M.D., Regional Vice President
**Web address:** www.fairmontmedicalcenter.org

MAYO CLINIC HEALTH SYSTEM IN LAKE CITY (O, 102 beds) 500 West Grant Street, Lake City, MN, Zip 55041–1143; tel. 651/345–3321; Brian Whited, M.D., President and Chief Executive Officer
**Web address:** www.lakecitymedicalcenter.org

MAYO CLINIC HEALTH SYSTEM IN MANKATO (O, 170 beds) 1025 Marsh Street, Mankato, MN, Zip 56001–4752; tel. 507/625–4031; James Hebl, M.D., Regional Vice President
**Web address:** www.mayoclinichealthsystem.org

MAYO CLINIC HEALTH SYSTEM IN NEW PRAGUE (O, 19 beds) 301 Second Street NE, New Prague, MN, Zip 56071–1799; tel. 952/758–4431; James Hebl, M.D., Regional Vice President
**Web address:** www.mayoclinichealthsystem.org/locations/new–prague

MAYO CLINIC HEALTH SYSTEM IN RED WING (O, 28 beds) 701 Hewitt Boulevard, Red Wing, MN, Zip 55066–2848, Mailing Address: P.O. Box 95, 55066–0095, tel. 651/267–5000; Brian Whited, M.D., President and Chief Executive Officer
**Web address:** www.mayoclinichealthsystem.org/locations/red–wing

MAYO CLINIC HEALTH SYSTEM IN SAINT JAMES (O, 9 beds) 1101 Moulton and Parsons Drive, Saint James, MN, Zip 56081–5550; tel. 507/375–3261; James Hebl, M.D., Regional Vice President
**Web address:** www.mayoclinichealthsystem.org/locations/st–james

MAYO CLINIC HEALTH SYSTEM IN WASECA (O, 12 beds) 501 North State Street, Waseca, MN, Zip 56093–2811; tel. 507/835–1210; James Hebl, M.D., Regional Vice President
**Web address:** www.mayoclinichealthsystem.org

MAYO CLINIC HOSPITAL – ROCHESTER (O, 1287 beds) 1216 Second Street SW, Rochester, MN, Zip 55902–1906; tel. 507/255–5123; Kenneth F. Ackerman, FACHE, Hospital Administrator

**WISCONSIN:** MAYO CLINIC HEALTH SYSTEM – CHIPPEWA VALLEY IN BLOOMER (O, 18 beds) 1501 Thompson Street, Bloomer, WI, Zip 54724–1299; tel. 715/568–2000; Richard Helmers, M.D., Regional Vice President
**Web address:** www.bloomermedicalcenter.org

MAYO CLINIC HEALTH SYSTEM – FRANCISCAN HEALTHCARE IN LA CROSSE (O, 100 beds) 700 West Avenue South, La Crosse, WI, Zip 54601–4783; tel. 608/785–0940; Paul S. Mueller, Regional Vice President
**Web address:** www.franciscanskemp.org

MAYO CLINIC HEALTH SYSTEM – FRANCISCAN HEALTHCARE IN SPARTA (O, 15 beds) 310 West Main Street, Sparta, WI, Zip 54656–2171; tel. 608/269–2132; Paul S. Mueller, Regional Vice President
**Web address:** www.mayoclinichealthsystem.org

MAYO CLINIC HEALTH SYSTEM – NORTHLAND IN BARRON (O, 23 beds) 1222 East Woodland Avenue, Barron, WI, Zip 54812–1798; tel. 715/537–3186; Richard Helmers, M.D., Regional Vice President

MAYO CLINIC HEALTH SYSTEM – OAKRIDGE IN OSSEO (O, 14 beds) 13025 Eighth Street, Osseo, WI, Zip 54758–7634, Mailing Address: P.O. Box 70, 54758–0070, tel. 715/597–3121; Richard Helmers, M.D., Regional Vice President
**Web address:** www.mayoclinichealthsystem.org/locations/osseo

MAYO CLINIC HEALTH SYSTEM – RED CEDAR IN MENOMONIE (O, 19 beds) 2321 Stout Road, Menomonie, WI, Zip 54751–2397; tel. 715/235–5531; Richard Helmers, M.D., Regional Vice President

MAYO CLINIC HEALTH SYSTEM IN EAU CLAIRE (O, 201 beds) 1221 Whipple Street, Eau Claire, WI, Zip 54703–5270, Mailing Address: P.O. Box 4105, 54702, tel. 715/838–3311; Richard Helmers, M.D., Regional Vice President
**Web address:** www.mhs.mayo.edu

| | | |
|---|---|---|
| Owned, leased, sponsored: | 19 hospitals | 2720 beds |
| Contract–managed: | 2 hospitals | 50 beds |
| Totals: | 21 hospitals | 2770 beds |

For explanation of codes following names, see page B2.
★ Indicates Type III membership in the American Hospital Association.

## 0252: MCLAREN HEALTH CARE CORPORATION (NP)

3373 Regency Park Drive, Grand Blanc, MI Zip 48439, One McLaren Parkway, 48439, tel. 810/342–1100; Philip A. Incarnati, President and Chief Executive Officer

**(Centralized Physician/Insurance Health System)**

**MICHIGAN**: MARWOOD MANOR NURSING HOME (O, 106 beds) 1300 Beard Street, Port Huron, MI, Zip 48060; tel. 818/982–2594; Brian Oberly, Administrator

MCLAREN BAY REGION (O, 338 beds) 1900 Columbus Avenue, Bay City, MI, Zip 48708–6831; tel. 989/894–3000; Clarence Sevillian, President and Chief Executive Officer
**Web address**: www.mclaren.org/bayregion

MCLAREN BAY SPECIAL CARE (O, 26 beds) 3250 East Midland Road, Suite 1, Bay City, MI, Zip 48706–2835; tel. 989/667–6851; Monica Baranski, MS, R.N., President

MCLAREN CARO REGION (O, 25 beds) 401 North Hooper Street, Caro, MI, Zip 48723–1476, Mailing Address: P.O. Box 435, 48723–0435, tel. 989/673–3141; Marc Augsburger, R.N., President and Chief Executive Officer
**Web address**: www.cch–mi.org

MCLAREN CENTRAL MICHIGAN (O, 78 beds) 1221 South Drive, Mount Pleasant, MI, Zip 48858–3257; tel. 989/772–6700; Martin Tursky, President and Chief Executive Officer
**Web address**: www.cmch.org

MCLAREN FLINT (O, 378 beds) 401 South Ballenger Highway, Flint, MI, Zip 48532–3685; tel. 810/342–2000; Chad M. Grant, President and Chief Executive Officer

MCLAREN GREATER LANSING (O, 321 beds) 401 West Greenlawn Avenue, Lansing, MI, Zip 48910–2819; tel. 517/975–6000; Kirk M. Ray, President and Chief Executive Officer
**Web address**: www.mclaren.org

MCLAREN LAPEER REGION (O, 131 beds) 1375 North Main Street, Lapeer, MI, Zip 48446–1350; tel. 810/667–5500; Chris Candela, President and Chief Executive Officer
**Web address**: www.lapeerregional.org

MCLAREN MACOMB (O, 288 beds) 1000 Harrington Boulevard, Mount Clemens, MI, Zip 48043–2992; tel. 586/493–8000; Thomas M. Brisse, President and Chief Executive Officer
**Web address**: www.mclaren.org/macomb/macomb.aspx

MCLAREN NORTHERN MICHIGAN (O, 188 beds) 416 Connable Avenue, Petoskey, MI, Zip 49770–2297; tel. 231/487–4000; David M. Zechman, FACHE, President and Chief Executive Officer
**Web address**: www.northernhealth.org

MCLAREN OAKLAND (O, 277 beds) 50 North Perry Street, Pontiac, MI, Zip 48342–2253; tel. 248/338–5000; Margaret Dimond, Ph.D., President and Chief Executive Officer
**Web address**: www.mclaren.org/oakland

MCLAREN PORT HURON (O, 186 beds) 1221 Pine Grove Avenue, Port Huron, MI, Zip 48060–3511; tel. 810/987–5000; Jennifer Montgomery, FACHE, R.N., President and Chief Executive Officer
**Web address**: www.porthuronhospital.org

MCLAREN THUMB REGION (O, 46 beds) 1100 South Van Dyke Road, Bad Axe, MI, Zip 48413–9615; tel. 989/269–9521; Michael Eric. Johnston, President and Chief Executive Officer

| | | |
|---|---|---|
| Owned, leased, sponsored: | 13 hospitals | 2388 beds |
| Contract–managed: | 0 hospitals | 0 beds |
| Totals: | 13 hospitals | 2388 beds |

## 0874: MCLEOD HEALTH (NP)

555 East Cheves Street, Florence, SC Zip 29506–2617, Mailing Address: P.O. Box 100551, 29502–0551, tel. 843/777–2000; Robert L. Colones, President and Chief Executive Officer

**(Centralized Health System)**

**SOUTH CAROLINA**: MCLEOD HEALTH CHERAW (O, 32 beds) 711 Chesterfield Highway, Cheraw, SC, Zip 29520–7002; tel. 843/537–7881; Virginia Hardee, Interim Administrator
**Web address**: www.chesterfieldgeneral.com

MCLEOD HEALTH CLARENDON (C, 36 beds) 10 Hospital Street, Manning, SC, Zip 29102–3153, Mailing Address: P.O. Box 550, 29102–0550, tel. 803/433–3000; Rachel Gainey, Administrator

MCLEOD HEALTH DARLINGTON (O, 40 beds) 701 Cashua Ferry Road, Darlington, SC, Zip 29532–8488, Mailing Address: P.O. Box 1859, 29540, tel. 843/395–1100; Virginia Hardee, Administrator
**Web address**: www.mcleodhealth.org

MCLEOD HEALTH DILLON (O, 34 beds) 301 East Jackson Street, Dillon, SC, Zip 29536–2509, Mailing Address: P.O. Box 1327, 29536–1327, tel. 843/774–4111; Joan Ervin, Administrator
**Web address**: www.mcleodhealth.org

MCLEOD HEALTH LORIS (O, 132 beds) 3655 Mitchell Street, Loris, SC, Zip 29569–2827; tel. 843/716–7000; Scott Montgomery, Administrator
**Web address**: www.mcleodhealth.org

MCLEOD REGIONAL MEDICAL CENTER (O, 464 beds) 555 East Cheves Street, Florence, SC, Zip 29506–2617, Mailing Address: P.O. Box 100551, 29502–0551, tel. 843/777–2000; Robert L. Colones, President and Chief Executive Officer

| | | |
|---|---|---|
| Owned, leased, sponsored: | 5 hospitals | 702 beds |
| Contract–managed: | 1 hospitals | 36 beds |
| Totals: | 6 hospitals | 738 beds |

## ★1001: MEADVILLE MEDICAL CENTER (NP)

751 Liberty Street, Meadville, PA Zip 16335–2559; tel. 814/333–5000; Philip E. Pandolph, FACHE, Chief Executive Officer

**(Independent Hospital System)**

**PENNSYLVANIA**: MEADVILLE MEDICAL CENTER (O, 234 beds) 751 Liberty Street, Meadville, PA, Zip 16335–2559; tel. 814/333–5000; Philip E. Pandolph, FACHE, Chief Executive Officer
**Web address**: www.mmchs.org

TITUSVILLE AREA HOSPITAL (O, 25 beds) 406 West Oak Street, Titusville, PA, Zip 16354–1404; tel. 814/827–1851; Lee M. Clinton, FACHE, President and Chief Executive Officer
**Web address**: www.titusvillehospital.org

| | | |
|---|---|---|
| Owned, leased, sponsored: | 2 hospitals | 259 beds |
| Contract–managed: | 0 hospitals | 0 beds |
| Totals: | 2 hospitals | 259 beds |

## 0520: MED CENTER HEALTH (NP)

800 Park Street, Bowling Green, KY Zip 42101–2356; tel. 270/745–1500; Connie Smith, FACHE, MSN, R.N., President and Chief Executive Officer

**(Centralized Physician/Insurance Health System)**

**KENTUCKY**: COMMONWEALTH REGIONAL SPECIALTY HOSPITAL (O, 28 beds) 250 Park Drive, 6th Floor, Bowling Green, KY, Zip 42101–1760, Mailing Address: P.O. Box 90010, 42102–9010, tel. 270/796–6200; Christa Atkins, Administrator
**Web address**: www.commonwealthregionalspecialtyhospital.org

MEDICAL CENTER AT BOWLING GREEN (O, 337 beds) 250 Park Street, Bowling Green, KY, Zip 42101–1795, Mailing Address: P.O. Box 90010, 42102–9010, tel. 270/745–1000; Connie Smith, FACHE, MSN, R.N., Chief Executive Officer

MEDICAL CENTER AT FRANKLIN (O, 25 beds) 1100 Brookhaven Road, Franklin, KY, Zip 42134–2746; tel. 270/598–4800; Annette Runyon, Vice President and Administrator
**Web address**: www.themedicalcenterfranklin.org

MEDICAL CENTER AT SCOTTSVILLE (O, 135 beds) 456 Burnley Road, Scottsville, KY, Zip 42164–6355; tel. 270/622–2800; Eric Hagan, R.N., Executive Vice President and Administrator
**Web address**: www.themedicalcenterscottsville.org/

For explanation of codes following names, see page B2.
★ Indicates Type III membership in the American Hospital Association.

THE MEDICAL CENTER ALBANY (C, 42 beds) 723 Burkesville Road, Albany, KY, Zip 42602–1654; tel. 606/387–8000; Laura Belcher, Administrator
**Web address:** www.chc.net/services/hospitals/the_medical_center_at_albany.aspx

THE MEDICAL CENTER AT CAVERNA (O, 25 beds) 1501 South Dixie Street, Horse Cave, KY, Zip 42749–1477; tel. 270/786–2191; Alan B. Alexander, FACHE, Vice President and Administrator
**Web address:** www.TheMedicalCenterCaverna.org

| | | |
|---|---|---|
| Owned, leased, sponsored: | 5 hospitals | 550 beds |
| Contract–managed: | 1 hospitals | 42 beds |
| Totals: | 6 hospitals | 592 beds |

---

**★0971: MEDISYS HEALTH NETWORK** (NP)
8900 Van Wyck Expressway, Jamaica, NY Zip 11418–2832; tel. 718/206–6000; Bruce J. Flanz, President and Chief Executive Officer
**(Moderately Centralized Health System)**

**NEW YORK:** FLUSHING HOSPITAL MEDICAL CENTER (C, 299 beds) 4500 Parsons Boulevard, Flushing, NY, Zip 11355–2205; tel. 718/670–5000; Bruce J. Flanz, President and Chief Executive Officer

JAMAICA HOSPITAL MEDICAL CENTER (C, 632 beds) 8900 Van Wyck Expressway, Jamaica, NY, Zip 11418–2832; tel. 718/206–6000; Bruce J. Flanz, President and Chief Executive Officer
**Web address:** www.Jamaicahospital.org

| | | |
|---|---|---|
| Owned, leased, sponsored: | 0 hospitals | 0 beds |
| Contract–managed: | 2 hospitals | 931 beds |
| Totals: | 2 hospitals | 931 beds |

---

**★0154: MEDSTAR HEALTH** (NP)
10980 Grantchester Way, Columbia, MD Zip 21044–2665; tel. 410/772–6500; Kenneth A. Samet, President and Chief Executive Officer
**(Centralized Health System)**

**DISTRICT OF COLUMBIA:** MEDSTAR GEORGETOWN UNIVERSITY HOSPITAL (O, 408 beds) 3800 Reservoir Road NW, Washington, DC, Zip 20007–2197; tel. 202/444–2000; Michael Sachtleben, President

MEDSTAR NATIONAL REHABILITATION HOSPITAL (O, 137 beds) 102 Irving Street NW, Washington, DC, Zip 20010–2949; tel. 202/877–1000; John D. Rockwood, President
**Web address:** www.medstarnrh.org

MEDSTAR WASHINGTON HOSPITAL CENTER (O, 758 beds) 110 Irving Street NW, Washington, DC, Zip 20010–3017; tel. 202/877–7000; Gregory J. Argyros, M.D., Senior Vice President and President

**MARYLAND:** MEDSTAR FRANKLIN SQUARE MEDICAL CENTER (O, 369 beds) 9000 Franklin Square Drive, Baltimore, MD, Zip 21237–3901; tel. 443/777–7000; Stuart M. Levine, M.D., President
**Web address:** www.medstarfranklin.org

MEDSTAR GOOD SAMARITAN HOSPITAL (O, 199 beds) 5601 Loch Raven Boulevard, Baltimore, MD, Zip 21239–2995; tel. 443/444–8000; Bradley Chambers, President and Senior Vice President, MedStar Health
**Web address:** www.goodsam–md.org

MEDSTAR HARBOR HOSPITAL (O, 128 beds) 3001 South Hanover Street, Baltimore, MD, Zip 21225–1290; tel. 410/350–3200; Jill Donaldson, President
**Web address:** www.harborhospital.org

MEDSTAR MONTGOMERY MEDICAL CENTER (O, 98 beds) 18101 Prince Philip Drive, Olney, MD, Zip 20832–1512; tel. 301/774–8882; Thomas J. Senker, FACHE, President
**Web address:** www.medstarmontgomery.org

MEDSTAR SOUTHERN MARYLAND HOSPITAL CENTER (O, 135 beds) 7503 Surratts Road, Clinton, MD, Zip 20735–3358; tel. 301/868–8000; Christine R. Wray, President

MEDSTAR ST. MARY'S HOSPITAL (O, 96 beds) 25500 Point Lookout Road, Leonardtown, MD, Zip 20650–2015, Mailing Address: P.O. 527, 20650–0527, tel. 301/475–6001; Christine R. Wray, President
**Web address:** www.medstarstmarys.org

MEDSTAR UNION MEMORIAL HOSPITAL (O, 214 beds) 201 East University Parkway, Baltimore, MD, Zip 21218–2895; tel. 410/554–2000; Bradley Chambers, President

| | | |
|---|---|---|
| Owned, leased, sponsored: | 10 hospitals | 2542 beds |
| Contract–managed: | 0 hospitals | 0 beds |
| Totals: | 10 hospitals | 2542 beds |

---

**0998: MEMORIAL HEALTH SYSTEM** (NP)
401 Matthew Street, Marietta, OH Zip 45750–1635; tel. 740/374–1400; J Scott. Cantley, President and Chief Executive Officer
**(Independent Hospital System)**

**OHIO:** MARIETTA MEMORIAL HOSPITAL (O, 218 beds) 401 Matthew Street, Marietta, OH, Zip 45750–1699; tel. 740/374–1400; J Scott. Cantley, President and Chief Executive Officer
**Web address:** www.mhsystem.org

SELBY GENERAL HOSPITAL (O, 35 beds) 1106 Colegate Drive, Marietta, OH, Zip 45750–1323; tel. 740/568–2000; Paige Leann. Smith, President
**Web address:** www.selbygeneral.org

| | | |
|---|---|---|
| Owned, leased, sponsored: | 2 hospitals | 253 beds |
| Contract–managed: | 0 hospitals | 0 beds |
| Totals: | 2 hospitals | 253 beds |

---

**★0086: MEMORIAL HEALTH SYSTEM** (NP)
701 North First Street, Springfield, IL Zip 62781–0001; tel. 217/788–3000; Edgar J. Curtis, FACHE, President and Chief Executive Officer
**(Centralized Health System)**

**ILLINOIS:** ABRAHAM LINCOLN MEMORIAL HOSPITAL (O, 25 beds) 200 Stahlhut Drive, Lincoln, IL, Zip 62656–5066; tel. 217/732–2161; Dolan Dalpoas, President and Chief Executive Officer
**Web address:** www.almh.org

DECATUR MEMORIAL HOSPITAL (O, 304 beds) 2300 North Edward Street, Decatur, IL, Zip 62526–4192; tel. 217/876–8121; Drew Early, President and Chief Executive Officer

MEMORIAL MEDICAL CENTER (O, 456 beds) 701 North First Street, Springfield, IL, Zip 62781–0001; tel. 217/788–3000; Charles D. Callahan, Ph.D., President and Chief Executive Officer
**Web address:** www.memorialmedical.com

PASSAVANT AREA HOSPITAL (O, 103 beds) 1600 West Walnut Street, Jacksonville, IL, Zip 62650–1136; tel. 217/245–9541; Scott Boston, R.N., MS, President and Chief Executive Officer

TAYLORVILLE MEMORIAL HOSPITAL (O, 25 beds) 201 East Pleasant Street, Taylorville, IL, Zip 62568–1597; tel. 217/824–3331; Kimberly L. Bourne, President and Chief Executive Officer
**Web address:** www.taylorvillememorial.org

| | | |
|---|---|---|
| Owned, leased, sponsored: | 5 hospitals | 913 beds |
| Contract–managed: | 0 hospitals | 0 beds |
| Totals: | 5 hospitals | 913 beds |

---

**★0083: MEMORIAL HEALTHCARE SYSTEM** (NP)
3501 Johnson Street, Hollywood, FL Zip 33021–5421; tel. 954/987–2000; Aurelio Fernandez, Chief Executive Officer
**(Centralized Health System)**

**FLORIDA:** MEMORIAL HOSPITAL MIRAMAR (O, 178 beds) 1901 SW 172nd Avenue, Miramar, FL, Zip 33029–5592; tel. 954/538–5000; Grisel Fernandez–Bravo, R.N., Administrator and Chief Executive Officer

MEMORIAL HOSPITAL PEMBROKE (L, 190 beds) 7800 Sheridan Street, Pembroke Pines, FL, Zip 33024–2536; tel. 954/883–8482; Joseph Stuczynski, Administrator and Chief Executive Officer
**Web address:** www.memorialpembroke.com/

MEMORIAL HOSPITAL WEST (O, 485 beds) 703 North Flamingo Road, Pembroke Pines, FL, Zip 33028–1014; tel. 954/436–5000; Leah A. Carpenter, Administrator and Chief Executive Officer

For explanation of codes following names, see page B2.
★ Indicates Type III membership in the American Hospital Association.

**Section B**

MEMORIAL REGIONAL HOSPITAL (O, 1013 beds) 3501 Johnson Street, Hollywood, FL, Zip 33021–5421; tel. 954/987–2000; Judy Frum, Interim Chief Executive Officer
**Web address:** www.mhs.net

| Owned, leased, sponsored: | 4 hospitals | 1866 beds |
| Contract–managed: | 0 hospitals | 0 beds |
| Totals: | 4 hospitals | 1866 beds |

---

**★2645: MEMORIAL HERMANN HEALTH SYSTEM** (NP)
929 Gessner, Suite 2700, Houston, TX Zip 77024–2593; tel. 713/338–5555; David L. Callender, M.D., President and Chief Executive Officer
**(Centralized Health System)**

**TEXAS:** MEMORIAL HERMANN – TEXAS MEDICAL CENTER (O, 1068 beds) 6411 Fannin Street, Houston, TX, Zip 77030–1501; tel. 713/704–4000; Gregory Haralson, FACHE, Senior Vice President and Chief Executive Officer

MEMORIAL HERMANN GREATER HEIGHTS HOSPITAL (O, 1521 beds) 1635 North Loop West, Houston, TX, Zip 77008–1532; tel. 713/867–3380; Paul O'Sullivan, FACHE, Chief Executive Officer
**Web address:** www.memorialhermann.org

MEMORIAL HERMANN KATY HOSPITAL (O, 199 beds) 23900 Katy Freeway, Katy, TX, Zip 77494–1323; tel. 281/644–7000; Jerry Ashworth, Senior Vice President and Chief Executive Officer
**Web address:** www.memorialhermann.org/locations/katy/

MEMORIAL HERMANN MEMORIAL CITY MEDICAL CENTER (L, 421 beds) 1760 Barker Cypress Rd, Apt 1412, Houston, TX, Zip 77084, 921 Gessner Road, 77024–2501, tel. 713/242–3000; Paul O'Sullivan, FACHE, Chief Executive Officer

MEMORIAL HERMANN NORTHEAST (O, 242 beds) 18951 North Memorial Drive, Humble, TX, Zip 77338–4297; tel. 281/540–7700; Justin Kendrick, Senior Vice President and Chief Executive Officer
**Web address:** www.memorialhermann.org/locations/northeast/

MEMORIAL HERMANN REHABILITATION HOSPITAL – KATY (O, 35 beds) 21720 Kingsland Boulevard, 2nd Floor, Katy, TX, Zip 77450–2550; tel. 800/447–3422; Rhonda Abbott, Interim Chief Executive Officer

MEMORIAL HERMANN SUGAR LAND HOSPITAL (O, 149 beds) 17500 West Grand Parkway South, Sugar Land, TX, Zip 77479–2562; tel. 281/725–5000; Malisha Patel, Senior Vice President and Chief Executive Officer
**Web address:** www.memorialhermann.org

TIRR MEMORIAL HERMANN (O, 134 beds) 1333 Moursund Street, Houston, TX, Zip 77030–3405; tel. 713/799–5000; Rhonda Abbott, Interim Chief Executive Officer

| Owned, leased, sponsored: | 8 hospitals | 3769 beds |
| Contract–managed: | 0 hospitals | 0 beds |
| Totals: | 8 hospitals | 3769 beds |

---

**0084: MEMORIALCARE** (NP)
17360 Brookhurst Street, Fountain Valley, CA Zip 92708–3720, Mailing Address: P.O. Box 1428, Long Beach, 90801–1428, tel. 714/377–2900; Barry S. Arbuckle, Ph.D., President and Chief Executive Officer
**(Centralized Health System)**

**CALIFORNIA:** LONG BEACH MEDICAL CENTER (O, 458 beds) 2801 Atlantic Avenue, Long Beach, CA, Zip 90806–1701, Mailing Address: P.O. Box 1428, 90801–1428, tel. 562/933–2000; John Bishop, Chief Executive Officer

MEMORIALCARE, ORANGE COAST MEMORIAL MEDICAL CENTER (O, 218 beds) 9920 Talbert Avenue, Fountain Valley, CA, Zip 92708–5115; tel. 714/378–7000; Marcia Manker, Chief Executive Officer
**Web address:** www.memorialcare.org

MILLER CHILDREN'S & WOMEN'S HOSPITAL LONG BEACH (O, 371 beds) 2801 Atlantic Avenue, Long Beach, CA, Zip 90806–1701; tel. 562/933–5437; John Bishop, Chief Executive Officer

SADDLEBACK MEDICAL CENTER (O, 250 beds) 24451 Health Center Drive, Laguna Hills, CA, Zip 92653–3689; tel. 949/837–4500; Marcia Manker, Chief Executive Officer
**Web address:** www.memorialcare.org

| Owned, leased, sponsored: | 4 hospitals | 1297 beds |
| Contract–managed: | 0 hospitals | 0 beds |
| Totals: | 4 hospitals | 1297 beds |

---

**★5185: MERCY** (CO)
14528 South Outer 40, Suite 100, Chesterfield, MO Zip 63017–5743; tel. 314/579–6100; Lynn Britton, President and Chief Executive Officer
**(Decentralized Health System)**

**ARKANSAS:** MERCY HOSPITAL BERRYVILLE (O, 25 beds) 214 Carter Street, Berryville, AR, Zip 72616–4303; tel. 870/423–3355; VonDa Moore, Administrator

MERCY HOSPITAL BOONEVILLE (O, 25 beds) 880 West Main Street, Booneville, AR, Zip 72927–3443; tel. 479/675–2800; Teresa Williams, R.N., Regional Administrator
**Web address:** https://www.mercy.net/practice/mercy–hospital–booneville/our–locations/

MERCY HOSPITAL FORT SMITH (O, 356 beds) 7301 Rogers Avenue, Fort Smith, AR, Zip 72903–4189, Mailing Address: P.O. Box 17000, 72917–7000, tel. 479/314–6000; Ryan T. Gehrig, FACHE, President
**Web address:** www.mercy.net/fortsmithar

MERCY HOSPITAL OZARK (O, 25 beds) 801 West River Street, Ozark, AR, Zip 72949–3023; tel. 479/667–4138; Teresa Williams, R.N., Regional Administrator
**Web address:** https://www.mercy.net/practice/mercy–hospital–ozark/

MERCY HOSPITAL PARIS (O, 16 beds) 500 East Academy, Paris, AR, Zip 72855–4040; tel. 479/963–6101; Teresa Williams, R.N., Regional Administrator

MERCY HOSPITAL ROGERS (O, 194 beds) 2710 Rife Medical Lane, Rogers, AR, Zip 72758–1452; tel. 479/338–8000; Eric Pianalto, Chief Executive Officer
**Web address:** https://www.mercy.net/practice/mercy–hospital–northwest–arkansas/

MERCY HOSPITAL WALDRON (O, 24 beds) 1341 West 6th Street, Waldron, AR, Zip 72958–7642; tel. 479/637–4135; Teresa Williams, R.N., Regional Administrator
**Web address:** https://www.mercy.net/practice/mercy–hospital–waldron/

**KANSAS:** MERCY HOSPITAL COLUMBUS (O, 18 beds) 220 North Pennsylvania Avenue, Columbus, KS, Zip 66725–1110; tel. 620/429–2545; Angie Saporito, Administrator
**Web address:** www.mercy.net/newsroom–mercy–maude–norton–hospital–quick–facts

**MISSOURI:** MERCY HOSPITAL AURORA (L, 25 beds) 500 Porter Street, Aurora, MO, Zip 65605–2365; tel. 417/678–2122; Nicki Gamet, R.N., Administrator

MERCY HOSPITAL CARTHAGE (L, 25 beds) 3125 Dr Russell Smith Way, Carthage, MO, Zip 64836–7402; tel. 417/358–8121; Scott Watson, Administrator
**Web address:** www.mercy.net

MERCY HOSPITAL CASSVILLE (L, 18 beds) 94 Main Street, Cassville, MO, Zip 65625–1610; tel. 417/847–6000; Nicki Gamet, R.N., Administrator
**Web address:** www.mercy.net/northwestar/practice/mercy–hospital–cassville

MERCY HOSPITAL JEFFERSON (O, 203 beds) 1400 US Highway 61 South, Festus, MO, Zip 63028–4100, Mailing Address: P.O. Box 350, Crystal City, 63019–0350, tel. 636/933–1000; Eric Ammons, President

MERCY HOSPITAL JOPLIN (O, 237 beds) 100 Mercy Way, Joplin, MO, Zip 64804–1626; tel. 417/781–2727; Jeremy Drinkwitz, President and Chief Executive Officer
**Web address:** www.mercy.net/joplinmo

MERCY HOSPITAL LEBANON (O, 58 beds) 100 Hospital Drive, Lebanon, MO, Zip 65536–9210; tel. 417/533–6100; Nicki Gamet, R.N., Administrator
**Web address:** www.mercy.net/practice/mercy–hospital–lebanon

For explanation of codes following names, see page B2.
★ Indicates Type III membership in the American Hospital Association.

MERCY HOSPITAL LINCOLN (L, 9 beds) 1000 East Cherry Street, Troy, MO, Zip 63379–1513; tel. 636/528–8551; Anthony Rothermich, Administrator
**Web address**: www.mercy.net

MERCY HOSPITAL SOUTH (O, 538 beds) 10010 Kennerly Road, Saint Louis, MO, Zip 63128–2106; tel. 314/525–1000; Sean Hogan, FACHE, President

MERCY HOSPITAL SPRINGFIELD (O, 665 beds) 1235 East Cherokee Street, Springfield, MO, Zip 65804–2263; tel. 417/820–2000; Brent Hubbard, FACHE, President and Chief Operating Officer
**Web address**: www.mercy.net/springfieldmo

MERCY HOSPITAL ST. LOUIS (O, 783 beds) 615 South New Ballas Road, Saint Louis, MO, Zip 63141–8277; tel. 314/251–6000; Stephen Mackin, President

MERCY HOSPITAL WASHINGTON (O, 71 beds) 901 East Fifth Street, Washington, MO, Zip 63090–3127; tel. 636/239–8000; Eric J. Eoloff, President
**Web address**: www.mercy.net

MERCY ST. FRANCIS HOSPITAL (O, 20 beds) 100 West Highway 60, Mountain View, MO, Zip 65548–7125; tel. 417/934–7000; Cynthia Weatherford, R.N., Administrator and Director of Nursing

**OKLAHOMA:** MERCY HEALTH LOVE COUNTY (C, 25 beds) 300 Wanda Street, Marietta, OK, Zip 73448–1200; tel. 580/276–3347; Richard Barker, Administrator and Chief Executive Officer
**Web address**: www.mercyhealthlovecounty.com

MERCY HOSPITAL ADA (L, 156 beds) 430 North Monte Vista, Ada, OK, Zip 74820–4610; tel. 580/332–2323; Terence Farrell, President

MERCY HOSPITAL ARDMORE (O, 190 beds) 1011 14th Avenue NW, Ardmore, OK, Zip 73401–1828; tel. 580/223–5400; Daryle Voss, FACHE, President and Chief Executive Officer
**Web address**: www.mercyok.net

MERCY HOSPITAL HEALDTON (L, 22 beds) 3462 Hospital Road, Healdton, OK, Zip 73438–6124, Mailing Address: P.O. Box 928, 73438–0928, tel. 580/229–0701; Nichole Barrett, R.N., Interim Administrator
**Web address**: www.mercyok.com

MERCY HOSPITAL KINGFISHER (L, 25 beds) 1000 Hospital Cirle, Kingfisher, OK, Zip 73750–5002, Mailing Address: P.O. Box 59, 73750–0059, tel. 405/375–3141; Brian Denton, Administrator
**Web address**: https://www.mercy.net/practice/mercy–hospital–kingfisher/

MERCY HOSPITAL LOGAN COUNTY (O, 25 beds) 200 South Academy Road, Guthrie, OK, Zip 73044–8727, Mailing Address: P.O. Box 1017, 73044–1017, tel. 405/282–6700; Bobby Stitt, R.N., Administrator

MERCY HOSPITAL OKLAHOMA CITY (O, 349 beds) 4300 West Memorial Road, Oklahoma City, OK, Zip 73120–8362; tel. 405/755–1515; Jim Gebhart Jr, FACHE, President
**Web address**: www.mercyok.net

MERCY HOSPITAL TISHOMINGO (L, 12 beds) 1000 South Byrd Street, Tishomingo, OK, Zip 73460–3299; tel. 580/371–2327; Lori McMillin, Administrator
**Web address**: www.mercy.net/

MERCY HOSPITAL WATONGA (L, 25 beds) 500 North Clarence Nash Boulevard, Watonga, OK, Zip 73772–2845, Mailing Address: P.O. Box 370, 73772–0370, tel. 580/623–7211; Bobby Stitt, R.N., Administrator
**Web address**: www.mercy.net/watongaok/practice/mercy–hospital–watonga

| | | |
|---|---|---|
| Owned, leased, sponsored: | 28 hospitals | 4139 beds |
| Contract–managed: | 1 hospitals | 25 beds |
| Totals: | 29 hospitals | 4164 beds |

**5155: MERCY HEALTH** (CO)
1701 Mercy Health Place, Cincinnati, OH Zip 45237; tel. 513/639–2800; John M. Starcher, President and Chief Executive Officer
**(Moderately Centralized Health System)**

**KENTUCKY:** LOURDES HOSPITAL (O, 281 beds) 1530 Lone Oak Road, Paducah, KY, Zip 42003–7900, Mailing Address: P.O. Box 7100, 42002–7100, tel. 270/444–2444; Michael Yungmann, President and Chief Executive Officer
**Web address**: www.lourdes–pad.org

MERCY HEALTH – MARCUM AND WALLACE (O, 25 beds) 60 Mercy Court, Irvine, KY, Zip 40336–1331; tel. 606/723–2115; Susan Starling, President and Chief Executive Officer

**OHIO:** INSTITUTE FOR ORTHOPAEDIC SURGERY (O, 3 beds) 801 Medical Drive, Suite B, Lima, OH, Zip 45804–4030; tel. 419/224–7586; Mark McDonald, M.D., President and Chief Executive Officer
**Web address**: www.ioshospital.com

MERCY ALLEN HOSPITAL (O, 25 beds) 200 West Lorain Street, Oberlin, OH, Zip 44074–1077; tel. 440/775–1211; Ed Ruth, President
**Web address**: www.mercyonline.org/mercy_allen_hospital.aspx

MERCY HEALTH – ST. CHARLES HOSPITAL (O, 279 beds) 2600 Navarre Avenue, Oregon, OH, Zip 43616–3297; tel. 419/696–7200; Craig Albers, President and Chief Operating Officer
**Web address**: www.mercyweb.org

MERCY HEALTH – ANDERSON HOSPITAL (O, 281 beds) 7500 State Road, Cincinnati, OH, Zip 45255–2492; tel. 513/624–4500; Ken James, President and Chief Executive Officer of East Market

MERCY HEALTH – CLERMONT HOSPITAL (O, 178 beds) 3000 Hospital Drive, Batavia, OH, Zip 45103–1921; tel. 513/732–8200; Shane Knisley, President
**Web address**: https://www.mercy.com

MERCY HEALTH – FAIRFIELD HOSPITAL (O, 145 beds) 3000 Mack Road, Fairfield, OH, Zip 45014–5335; tel. 513/870–7000; Justin Krueger, FACHE, President
**Web address**: https://www.mercy.com

MERCY HEALTH – ST. ELIZABETH BOARDMAN HOSPITAL (O, 217 beds) 8401 Market Street, Boardman, OH, Zip 44512–6777; tel. 330/729–2929; Eugenia Aubel, President, St. Elizabeth Boardman Hospital

MERCY HEALTH – ST. ELIZABETH YOUNGSTOWN HOSPITAL (O, 396 beds) 1044 Belmont Avenue, Youngstown, OH, Zip 44504–1096, Mailing Address: P.O. Box 1790, 44501–1790, tel. 330/746–7211; Donald E. Kline, President and Chief Executive Officer
**Web address**: www.mercy.com

MERCY HEALTH – ST. JOSEPH WARREN HOSPITAL (O, 136 beds) 667 Eastland Avenue SE, Warren, OH, Zip 44484–4531, 627 Eastland Avenue , 44484–4531, tel. 330/841–4000; Kathy Cook, FACHE, MSN, President

MERCY HEALTH – ST. RITA'S MEDICAL CENTER (O, 271 beds) 730 West Market Street, Lima, OH, Zip 45801–4602; tel. 419/227–3361; Dale Gisi, President
**Web address**: www.stritas.org

MERCY HEALTH – WEST HOSPITAL (O, 250 beds) 3300 Mercy Health Boulevard, Cincinnati, OH, Zip 45211–1103; tel. 513/215–5000; Michael Kramer, Chief Executive Officer

MERCY HEALTH – WILLARD HOSPITAL (O, 20 beds) 1100 Neal Zick Road, Willard, OH, Zip 44890–9287; tel. 419/964–5000; B Lynn. Detterman, President and Chief Executive Officer
**Web address**: www.mercyweb.org

MERCY HOSPITAL OF DEFIANCE (O, 23 beds) 1404 East Second Street, Defiance, OH, Zip 43512–2440; tel. 419/782–8444; B Lynn. Detterman, President and Chief Executive Officer

MERCY MEMORIAL HOSPITAL (O, 25 beds) 904 Scioto Street, Urbana, OH, Zip 43078–2200; tel. 937/653–5231; Matthew T. Caldwell, President and Chief Executive Officer
**Web address**: www.health–partners.org

MERCY REGIONAL MEDICAL CENTER (O, 259 beds) 3700 Kolbe Road, Lorain, OH, Zip 44053–1697; tel. 440/960–4000; Edwin M. Oley, President and Chief Executive Officer

MERCY ST. ANNE HOSPITAL (O, 96 beds) 3404 West Sylvania Avenue, Toledo, OH, Zip 43623–4467; tel. 419/407–2663; Bradley J. Bertke, President and Chief Operating Officer
**Web address**: www.mercyweb.org

MERCY ST. VINCENT MEDICAL CENTER (O, 350 beds) 2213 Cherry Street, Toledo, OH, Zip 43608–2691; tel. 419/251–3232; Jeffrey Dempsey, President
**Web address**: www.mercyweb.org

MERCY TIFFIN HOSPITAL (O, 45 beds) 45 St Lawrence Drive, Tiffin, OH, Zip 44883–8310; tel. 419/455–7000; B Lynn. Detterman, President and Chief Executive Officer

SPRINGFIELD REGIONAL MEDICAL CENTER (O, 259 beds) 100 Medical Center Drive, Springfield, OH, Zip 45504–2687; tel. 937/523–1000; Adam Groshans, President
**Web address**: www.community–mercy.org

For explanation of codes following names, see page B2.
★ Indicates Type III membership in the American Hospital Association.

THE JEWISH HOSPITAL – MERCY HEALTH (O, 209 beds) 4777 East Galbraith Road, Cincinnati, OH, Zip 45236–2725; tel. 513/686–3000; Patricia Davis–Hagens, R.N., Central Market Leader and President
**Web address:** www.jewishhospitalcincinnati.com/

| | | |
|---|---|---|
| Owned, leased, sponsored: | 22 hospitals | 3773 beds |
| Contract–managed: | 0 hospitals | 0 beds |
| Totals: | 22 hospitals | 3773 beds |

## 0649: MERCY HEALTH SYSTEM (NP)

1000 Mineral Point Avenue, Janesville, WI Zip 53548–2940, Mailing Address: P.O. Box 5003, 53547–5003, tel. 608/756–6000; Javon R. Bea, President and Chief Executive Officer
**(Centralized Physician/Insurance Health System)**

**ILLINOIS:** JAVON BEA HOSPITAL–ROCKTON (O, 282 beds) 2400 North Rockton Avenue, Rockford, IL, Zip 61103–3655; tel. 815/971–5000; Javon R. Bea, President and Chief Executive Officer
**Web address:** www.rhsnet.org

MERCYHEALTH HOSPITAL AND MEDICAL CENTER – HARVARD (O, 58 beds) 901 Grant Street, Harvard, IL, Zip 60033–1898, Mailing Address: P.O. Box 850, 60033–0850, tel. 815/943–5431; Javon R. Bea, Chief Executive Officer

**WISCONSIN:** MERCYHEALTH HOSPITAL AND MEDICAL CENTER – WALWORTH (O, 17 beds) N2950 State Road 67, Lake Geneva, WI, Zip 53147–2655; tel. 262/245–0535; Javon R. Bea, President and Chief Executive Officer
**Web address:** www.mercyhealthsystem.org

MERCYHEALTH HOSPITAL AND TRAUMA CENTER – JANESVILLE (O, 135 beds) 1000 Mineral Point Avenue, Janesville, WI, Zip 53548–2982, Mailing Address: P.O. Box 5003, 53547–5003, tel. 608/756–6000; Javon R. Bea, President and Chief Executive Officer

| | | |
|---|---|---|
| Owned, leased, sponsored: | 4 hospitals | 492 beds |
| Contract–managed: | 0 hospitals | 0 beds |
| Totals: | 4 hospitals | 492 beds |

## 0944: MERCYONE (NP)

1449 NW 128th Stret, Clive, IA Zip 50325–7400; tel. 515/358–9200; Robert P. Ritz, Chief Executive Officer

**IOWA:** ADAIR COUNTY HEALTH SYSTEM (C, 17 beds) 609 SE Kent Street, Greenfield, IA, Zip 50849–9454; tel. 641/743–2123; Marcia Hendricks, FACHE, R.N., Chief Executive Officer
**Web address:** www.adaircountyhealthsystem.org

DALLAS COUNTY HOSPITAL (C, 15 beds) 610 10th Street, Perry, IA, Zip 50220–2221; tel. 515/465–3547; Angela Mortoza, Chief Executive Officer
**Web address:** www.dallascohospital.org

DAVIS COUNTY HOSPITAL AND CLINICS (C, 13 beds) 509 North Madison Street, Bloomfield, IA, Zip 52537–1271; tel. 641/664–2145; Veronica Fuhs, Chief Executive Officer

DECATUR COUNTY HOSPITAL (C, 11 beds) 1405 NW Church Street, Leon, IA, Zip 50144–1299; tel. 641/446–4871; Mike Johnston, Chief Executive Officer
**Web address:** www.decaturcountyhospital.org

GUTTENBERG MUNICIPAL HOSPITAL AND CLINICS (C, 20 beds) 200 Main Street, Guttenberg, IA, Zip 52052–9108, Mailing Address: P.O. Box 550, 52052–0550, tel. 563/252–1121; Tim Ahlers, Chief Executive Officer

MANNING REGIONAL HEALTHCARE CENTER (C, 27 beds) 1550 6th Street, Manning, IA, Zip 51455–1093; tel. 712/655–2072; Linn Block, R.N., Chief Executive Officer
**Web address:** www.mrhcia.com

MERCYONE IOWA CITY MEDICAL CENTER (C, 223 beds) 500 East Market Street, Iowa City, IA, Zip 52245–2689; tel. 319/339–0300; Sean J. Williams, President and Chief Executive Officer

MONROE COUNTY HOSPITAL AND CLINICS (C, 25 beds) 6580 165th Street, Albia, IA, Zip 52531–8793; tel. 641/932–2134; Veronica Fuhs, Chief Executive Officer
**Web address:** www.mchalbia.com

RINGGOLD COUNTY HOSPITAL (C, 16 beds) 504 North Cleveland Street, Mount Ayr, IA, Zip 50854–2201; tel. 641/464–3226; Gordon W. Winkler, Administrator and Chief Executive Officer
**Web address:** www.rchmtayr.org

VAN DIEST MEDICAL CENTER (C, 25 beds) 2350 Hospital Drive, Webster City, IA, Zip 50595–6600, Mailing Address: P.O. Box 430, 50595–0430, tel. 515/832–9400; Lisa Carolyn. Ridge, Chief Executive Officer
**Web address:** www.vandiestmc.org

WAYNE COUNTY HOSPITAL (C, 25 beds) 417 South East Street, Corydon, IA, Zip 50060–1860, Mailing Address: P.O. Box 305, 50060–0305, tel. 641/872–2260; Daren Relph, Chief Executive Officer

| | | |
|---|---|---|
| Owned, leased, sponsored: | 0 hospitals | 0 beds |
| Contract–managed: | 11 hospitals | 417 beds |
| Totals: | 11 hospitals | 417 beds |

## ★2735: METHODIST HEALTH SYSTEM (NP)

1441 North Beckley Avenue, Dallas, TX Zip 75203–1201, Mailing Address: P.O. Box 655999, 75265–5999, tel. 214/947–8181; James C. Scoggin Jr, Chief Executive Officer
**(Centralized Physician/Insurance Health System)**

**TEXAS:** METHODIST CHARLTON MEDICAL CENTER (O, 273 beds) 3500 West Wheatland Road, Dallas, TX, Zip 75237–3460, Mailing Address: P.O. Box 225357, 75222–5357, tel. 214/947–7777; Fran Laukaitis, FACHE, R.N., President
**Web address:** www.methodisthealthsystem.org/charlton

METHODIST DALLAS MEDICAL CENTER (O, 387 beds) 1441 North Beckley Avenue, Dallas, TX, Zip 75203–1201, Mailing Address: P.O. Box 655999, 75265–5999, tel. 214/947–8181; John E. Phillips, FACHE, President

METHODIST MANSFIELD MEDICAL CENTER (O, 254 beds) 2700 East Broad Street, Mansfield, TX, Zip 76063–5899; tel. 682/622–2000; Juan Fresquez, President
**Web address:** www.methodisthealthsystem.org/mansfield

METHODIST RICHARDSON MEDICAL CENTER (O, 259 beds) 2831 East President George Bush Highway, Richardson, TX, Zip 75082–3561; tel. 469/204–1000; E. Kenneth. Hutchenrider Jr, FACHE, President
**Web address:** www.methodisthealthsystem.org/richardson

METHODIST SOUTHLAKE HOSPITAL (O, 12 beds) 421 East State Highway 114, Southlake, TX, Zip 76092; tel. 817/865–4400; John McGreevy, FACHE, President

| | | |
|---|---|---|
| Owned, leased, sponsored: | 5 hospitals | 1185 beds |
| Contract–managed: | 0 hospitals | 0 beds |
| Totals: | 5 hospitals | 1185 beds |

## ★9345: METHODIST LE BONHEUR HEALTHCARE (CO)

1211 Union Avenue, Suite 700, Memphis, TN Zip 38104–6600; tel. 901/516–0791; Michael Ugwueke Sr, President and Chief Executive Officer
**(Centralized Physician/Insurance Health System)**

**MISSISSIPPI:** METHODIST HEALTHCARE OLIVE BRANCH HOSPITAL (O, 53 beds) 4250 Bethel Road, Olive Branch, MS, Zip 38654–8737; tel. 662/932–9000; David G. Baytos, President
**Web address:** www.methodisthealth.org/olivebranch

**TENNESSEE:** METHODIST HEALTHCARE MEMPHIS HOSPITALS (O, 1362 beds) 1265 Union Avenue, Memphis, TN, Zip 38104–3415; tel. 901/516–7000; Michael Ugwueke Sr, President and Chief Executive Officer

| | | |
|---|---|---|
| Owned, leased, sponsored: | 2 hospitals | 1415 beds |
| Contract–managed: | 0 hospitals | 0 beds |
| Totals: | 2 hospitals | 1415 beds |

## ★0001: MIDMICHIGAN HEALTH (NP)

4000 Wellness Drive, Midland, MI Zip 48670–0001; tel. 989/839–3000; Diane Postler–Slattery, Ph.D., President and Chief Executive Officer
**(Centralized Physician/Insurance Health System)**

For explanation of codes following names, see page B2.
★ Indicates Type III membership in the American Hospital Association.

**Section B**

**MICHIGAN**: MIDMICHIGAN MEDICAL CENTER – ALPENA (O, 125 beds) 1501 West Chisholm Street, Alpena, MI, Zip 49707–1401; tel. 989/356–7000; Charles H. Sherwin, President
**Web address**: www.midmichigan.org

MIDMICHIGAN MEDICAL CENTER – WEST BRANCH (O, 88 beds) 2463 South M–30, West Branch, MI, Zip 48661–1199; tel. 989/345–3660; Robert McGrail, Chief Executive Officer
**Web address**: www.wbrmc.com

MIDMICHIGAN MEDICAL CENTER–CLARE (O, 49 beds) 703 North McEwan Street, Clare, MI, Zip 48617–1440; tel. 989/802–5000; Raymond Stover, President and Chief Executive Officer

MIDMICHIGAN MEDICAL CENTER–GLADWIN (O, 25 beds) 515 Quarter Street, Gladwin, MI, Zip 48624–1959; tel. 989/426–9286; Raymond Stover, President and Chief Executive Officer
**Web address**: www.midmichigan.org

MIDMICHIGAN MEDICAL CENTER–GRATIOT (O, 97 beds) 300 East Warwick Drive, Alma, MI, Zip 48801–1014; tel. 989/463–1101; Marita Hattem–Schiffman, President

MIDMICHIGAN MEDICAL CENTER–MIDLAND (O, 270 beds) 4000 Wellness Drive, Midland, MI, Zip 48670–2000; tel. 989/839–3000; Gregory H. Rogers, President
**Web address**: www.midmichigan.org

| | | |
|---|---|---|
| Owned, leased, sponsored: | 6 hospitals | 654 beds |
| Contract–managed: | 0 hospitals | 0 beds |
| Totals: | 6 hospitals | 654 beds |

**0368: MINNESOTA DEPARTMENT OF HUMAN SERVICES** (NP)
540 Cedar Street, Saint Paul, MN Zip 55101–2208, Mailing Address: P.O. Box 64998, 55164–0998, tel. 651/431–3212; Anne Barry, Deputy Commissioner
**(Independent Hospital System)**

**MINNESOTA**: ANOKA METRO REGIONAL TREATMENT CENTER (O, 200 beds) 3301 Seventh Avenue, Anoka, MN, Zip 55303–4516, 3301 Seventh Avenue North, 55303–4516, tel. 651/431–5000; Rochelle M. Fischer, Hospital Administrator
**Web address**: www.health.state.mn.us

COMMUNITY BEHAVIORAL HEALTH HOSPITAL – ALEXANDRIA (O, 16 beds) 1610 8th Avenue East, Alexandria, MN, Zip 56308–2472; tel. 320/335–6201; Jennifer Westrum, Administrator

COMMUNITY BEHAVIORAL HEALTH HOSPITAL – ANNANDALE (O, 16 beds) 400 Annandale Boulevard, Annandale, MN, Zip 55302–3141; tel. 651/259–3850; James P. Kelly, FACHE, Administrator
**Web address**: www.health.state.mn.us

COMMUNITY BEHAVIORAL HEALTH HOSPITAL – BAXTER (O, 16 beds) 14241 Grand Oaks Drive, Baxter, MN, Zip 56425–8749; tel. 218/316–3101; Ryan D. Cerney, Administrator
**Web address**: www.business.explorebrainerdlakes.com/list/member/community–behavioral–health–hospital–baxter–8647

COMMUNITY BEHAVIORAL HEALTH HOSPITAL – BEMIDJI (O, 16 beds) 800 Bemidji Avenue North, Bemidji, MN, Zip 56601–3054; tel. 218/308–2400; Larry A. Laudon, Administrator

COMMUNITY BEHAVIORAL HEALTH HOSPITAL – FERGUS FALLS (O, 16 beds) 1801 West Alcott Avenue, Fergus Falls, MN, Zip 56537–2661, Mailing Address: P.O. Box 478, 56538–0478, tel. 218/332–5001; Brenda Schleske, Administrator

COMMUNITY BEHAVIORAL HEALTH HOSPITAL – ROCHESTER (O, 8 beds) 251 Wood Lake Drive SE, Rochester, MN, Zip 55904–5530; tel. 507/206–2561; James Pierce, Administrator
**Web address**: www.health.state.mn.us

| | | |
|---|---|---|
| Owned, leased, sponsored: | 7 hospitals | 288 beds |
| Contract–managed: | 0 hospitals | 0 beds |
| Totals: | 7 hospitals | 288 beds |

★**2475: MISSISSIPPI COUNTY HOSPITAL SYSTEM** (NP)
1520 North Division Street, Blytheville, AR Zip 72315–1448, Mailing Address: P.O. Box 108, 72316–0108, tel. 870/838–7300; Chris Lee. Raymer, MSN, Chief Executive Officer

| | | |
|---|---|---|
| Owned, leased, sponsored: | 0 hospitals | 0 beds |
| Contract–managed: | 0 hospitals | 0 beds |
| Totals: | 0 hospitals | 0 beds |

**0017: MISSISSIPPI STATE DEPARTMENT OF MENTAL HEALTH** (NP)
1101 Robert E Lee Building, 239 North Lamar Street, Jackson, MS Zip 39201–1101; tel. 601/359–1288; Diana S. Mikula, Executive Director
**(Independent Hospital System)**

**MISSISSIPPI**: EAST MISSISSIPPI STATE HOSPITAL (O, 267 beds) 1818 College Drive, Meridian, MS, Zip 39307, Box 4128, West Station, 39304–4128, tel. 601/482–6186; Charles Carlisle, Director
**Web address**: www.emsh.state.ms.us

MISSISSIPPI STATE HOSPITAL (O, 349 beds) 3550 Highway 468 West, Whitfield, MS, Zip 39193–5529, Mailing Address: P.O. Box 157–A, 39193–0157, tel. 601/351–8000; James G. Chastain, FACHE, Director

NORTH MISSISSIPPI STATE HOSPITAL (O, 50 beds) 1937 Briar Ridge Road, Tupelo, MS, Zip 38804–5963; tel. 662/690–4200; Paul A. Callens, Ph.D., Director
**Web address**: www.nmsh.state.ms.us

SOUTH MISSISSIPPI STATE HOSPITAL (O, 50 beds) 823 Highway 589, Purvis, MS, Zip 39475–4194; tel. 601/794–0100; Sabrina Young, Director
**Web address**: www.smsh.ms.gov/

| | | |
|---|---|---|
| Owned, leased, sponsored: | 4 hospitals | 716 beds |
| Contract–managed: | 0 hospitals | 0 beds |
| Totals: | 4 hospitals | 716 beds |

★**0970: MON HEALTH SYSTEM** (NP)
1200 J. D. Anderson Drive, Morgantown, WV Zip 26505–3494; tel. 304/598–1200; David Goldberg, President and Chief Executive Officer
**(Independent Hospital System)**

**WEST VIRGINIA**: MON HEALTH MEDICAL CENTER (O, 185 beds) 1200 J D Anderson Drive, Morgantown, WV, Zip 26505–3486; tel. 304/598–1200; David Goldberg, President and Chief Executive Officer
**Web address**: www.mongeneral.com

PRESTON MEMORIAL HOSPITAL (O, 25 beds) 150 Memorial Drive, Kingwood, WV, Zip 26537–1495; tel. 304/329–1400; Melissa Lockwood, Chief Executive Officer

STONEWALL JACKSON MEMORIAL HOSPITAL (O, 70 beds) 230 Hospital Plaza, Weston, WV, Zip 26452–8558; tel. 304/269–8000; Avah Stalnaker, Chief Executive Officer
**Web address**: www.stonewallhospital.com

| | | |
|---|---|---|
| Owned, leased, sponsored: | 3 hospitals | 280 beds |
| Contract–managed: | 0 hospitals | 0 beds |
| Totals: | 3 hospitals | 280 beds |

**0343: MONTEFIORE HEALTH SYSTEM** (NP)
111 East 210th Street, Bronx, NY Zip 10467–2490; tel. 718/920–4321; Philip O. Ozuah, M.D., Ph.D., Chief Executive Officer
**(Centralized Physician/Insurance Health System)**

**NEW YORK**: BURKE REHABILITATION HOSPITAL (O, 150 beds) 785 Mamaroneck Avenue, White Plains, NY, Zip 10605–2523; tel. 914/597–2500; Jeffrey Menkes, President and Chief Executive Officer

For explanation of codes following names, see page B2.
★ Indicates Type III membership in the American Hospital Association.

MONTEFIORE MEDICAL CENTER (O, 1545 beds) 111 East 210th Street, Bronx, NY, Zip 10467–2401; tel. 718/920–4321; Philip O. Ozuah, M.D., Ph.D., Chief Executive Officer
**Web address**: www.montefiore.org

MONTEFIORE MOUNT VERNON (O, 60 beds) 12 North Seventh Avenue, Mount Vernon, NY, Zip 10550–2098; tel. 914/664–8000; Jaccel Kouns, R.N., MS, Vice President and Executive Director

MONTEFIORE NEW ROCHELLE (O, 237 beds) 16 Guion Place, New Rochelle, NY, Zip 10801–5502; tel. 914/365–5000; Anthony Alfano, Vice President Executive Director
**Web address**: www.montefiorehealthsystem.org

MONTEFIORE NYACK HOSPITAL (O, 245 beds) 160 North Midland Avenue, Nyack, NY, Zip 10960–1998; tel. 845/348–2000; Mark Geller, M.D., President and Chief Executive Officer
**Web address**: https://www.montefiorenyack.org/

MONTEFIORE ST. LUKE'S CORNWALL (O, 128 beds) 70 Dubois Street, Newburgh, NY, Zip 12550–4851; tel. 845/561–4400; Joan Cusack–McGuirk, President and Chief Executive Officer

WHITE PLAINS HOSPITAL CENTER (O, 292 beds) 41 East Post Road, White Plains, NY, Zip 10601–4699; tel. 914/681–0600; Susan Fox, President and Chief Executive Officer
**Web address**: www.wphospital.org

| Owned, leased, sponsored: | 7 hospitals | 2657 beds |
|---|---|---|
| Contract–managed: | 0 hospitals | 0 beds |
| Totals: | 7 hospitals | 2657 beds |

---

★**8495: MONUMENT HEALTH** (NP)
353 Fairmont Boulevard, Rapid City, SD Zip 57701–7375, Mailing Address: P.O. Box 6000, 57709–6000, tel. 605/719–1000; Paulette Davidson, FACHE, President and Chief Executive Officer
**(Moderately Centralized Health System)**

**SOUTH DAKOTA**: MONUMENT HEALTH CUSTER HOSPITAL (O, 87 beds) 1039 Montgomery Street, Custer, SD, Zip 57730–1397; tel. 605/673–2229; Mark C. Schmidt, President
**Web address**: www.regionalhealth.com

MONUMENT HEALTH LEAD–DEADWOOD HOSPITAL (O, 8 beds) 61 Charles Street, Deadwood, SD, Zip 57732–1303; tel. 605/717–6000; Mark C. Schmidt, President
**Web address**: www.regionalhealth.com

MONUMENT HEALTH RAPID CITY HOSPITAL (O, 375 beds) 353 Fairmont Boulevard, Rapid City, SD, Zip 57701–7393, Mailing Address: P.O. Box 6000, 57709–6000, tel. 605/755–1000; John Pierce, Acting President

MONUMENT HEALTH SPEARFISH HOSPITAL (O, 35 beds) 1440 North Main Street, Spearfish, SD, Zip 57783–1504; tel. 605/644–4000; Thomas Worsley, Chief Executive Officer
**Web address**: www.regionalhealth.com/Our–Locations/Regional–Hospitals/Spearfish–Regional–Hospital.aspx

MONUMENT HEALTH STURGIS HOSPITAL (O, 109 beds) 2140 Junction Avenue, Sturgis, SD, Zip 57785–2452; tel. 605/720–2400; Mark Schulte, FACHE, President
**Web address**: www.https://directory.monument.health/facility/sd/sturgis/2140–junction–avenue–6671505

PHILIP HEALTH SERVICES (C, 48 beds) 503 West Pine Street, Philip, SD, Zip 57567–3300, Mailing Address: P.O. Box 790, 57567–0790, tel. 605/859–2511; Jeremy Schultes, Administrator and Chief Executive Officer

**WYOMING**: WESTON COUNTY HEALTH SERVICES (C, 70 beds) 1124 Washington Boulevard, Newcastle, WY, Zip 82701–2972; tel. 307/746–4491; Maureen K. Cadwell, Chief Executive Officer
**Web address**: www.wchs–wy.org

| Owned, leased, sponsored: | 5 hospitals | 614 beds |
|---|---|---|
| Contract–managed: | 2 hospitals | 118 beds |
| Totals: | 7 hospitals | 732 beds |

---

**1335: MORTON PLANT MEASE HEALTH CARE** (NP)
2985 Drew Street, Clearwater, FL Zip 33759, Mailing Address: P.O. Box 210, 33757–0210, tel. 727/462–7000; Glenn D. Waters, FACHE, President

**FLORIDA**: MORTON PLANT HOSPITAL (O, 650 beds) 300 Pinellas Street, Clearwater, FL, Zip 33756–3804, Mailing Address: P.O. Box 210, 33757–0210, tel. 727/462–7000; Lou Galdieri, R.N., President

MORTON PLANT NORTH BAY HOSPITAL (O, 217 beds) 6600 Madison Street, New Port Richey, FL, Zip 34652–1900; tel. 727/842–8468; Brandon May, President
**Web address**: www.mpmhealth.com

MORTON PLANT REHABILITATION CENTER (O, 126 beds) 400 Corbett Street, Belleair, FL, Zip 34640; tel. 813/462–7600; Linda A. Kirk, Administrator

| Owned, leased, sponsored: | 3 hospitals | 993 beds |
|---|---|---|
| Contract–managed: | 0 hospitals | 0 beds |
| Totals: | 3 hospitals | 993 beds |

---

★**0946: MOSAIC LIFE CARE** (NP)
5325 Faraon Street, Saint Joseph, MO Zip 64506–3488; tel. 816/271–6000; Samuel Mark. Laney, M.D., Chief Executive Officer

**MISSOURI**: LONG–TERM ACUTE CARE HOSPITAL, MOSAIC LIFE CARE AT ST. JOSEPH (O, 41 beds) 5325 Faraon Street, Saint Joseph, MO, Zip 64506–3488; tel. 816/271–6000; Dana Anderson, R.N., Administrator
**Web address**: https://www.mymosaiclifecare.org/General/Long–Term–Acute–Care–Hospital/

MOSAIC LIFE CARE AT ST. JOSEPH – MEDICAL CENTER (O, 352 beds) 5325 Faraon Street, Saint Joseph, MO, Zip 64506–3488; tel. 816/271–6000; Samuel Mark. Laney, M.D., Chief Executive Officer

MOSAIC MEDICAL CENTER – ALBANY (O, 25 beds) 705 North College Street, Albany, MO, Zip 64402–1433; tel. 660/726–3941; Jon D. Doolittle, Regional President
**Web address**: www.northwestmedicalcenter.org

MOSAIC MEDICAL CENTER – MARYVILLE (O, 50 beds) 2016 South Main Street, Maryville, MO, Zip 64468–2655; tel. 660/562–2600; Nate Blackford, President

| Owned, leased, sponsored: | 4 hospitals | 468 beds |
|---|---|---|
| Contract–managed: | 0 hospitals | 0 beds |
| Totals: | 4 hospitals | 468 beds |

---

★**0917: MOUNT SINAI HEALTH SYSTEM** (NP)
One Gustave L. Levy Place, New York, NY Zip 10029; tel. 212/659–8888; Kenneth L. Davis, M.D., President and Chief Executive Officer
**(Centralized Health System)**

**NEW YORK**: MOUNT SINAI BETH ISRAEL (O, 510 beds) First Avenue and 16th Street, New York, NY, Zip 10003–3803; tel. 212/420–2000; Jeremy Boal, M.D., President
**Web address**: www.bethisraelny.org

MOUNT SINAI MORNINGSIDE (O, 749 beds) 1111 Amsterdam Avenue, New York, NY, Zip 10025–1716; tel. 212/523–4000; Arthur A. Gianelli, M.P.H., President
**Web address**: https://www.mountsinai.org/locations/morningside

NEW YORK EYE AND EAR INFIRMARY OF MOUNT SINAI (O, 17 beds) 310 East 14th Street, New York, NY, Zip 10003–4201; tel. 212/979–4000; James C. Tsai, M.D., President

THE MOUNT SINAI HOSPITAL (O, 1198 beds) One Gustave L Levy Place, Mailing Address: P.O. Box 1068, New York, NY, Zip 10029–0310; tel. 212/241–6500; David L. Reich, M.D., President and Chief Operating Officer
**Web address**: www.mountsinai.org

| Owned, leased, sponsored: | 4 hospitals | 2474 beds |
|---|---|---|
| Contract–managed: | 0 hospitals | 0 beds |
| Totals: | 4 hospitals | 2474 beds |

---

**0952: MOUNTAIN HEALTH NETWORK** (IO)
517 9th Street, Huntington, WV Zip 25701–2020; tel. 304/781–4466; Michael Mullins, President and Chief Executive Officer

For explanation of codes following names, see page B2.
★ Indicates Type III membership in the American Hospital Association.

**WEST VIRGINIA**: CABELL HUNTINGTON HOSPITAL (O, 319 beds) 1340 Hal Greer Boulevard, Huntington, WV, Zip 25701–0195; tel. 304/526–2000; Kevin N. Fowler, President and Chief Executive Officer
**Web address**: www.cabellhuntington.org

PLEASANT VALLEY HOSPITAL (O, 149 beds) 2520 Valley Drive, Point Pleasant, WV, Zip 25550–2031; tel. 304/675–4340; Glen A. Washington, Chief Executive Officer
**Web address**: www.pvalley.org

ST. MARY'S MEDICAL CENTER (O, 393 beds) 2900 First Avenue, Huntington, WV, Zip 25702–1272; tel. 304/526–1234; Todd Campbell, Chief Executive Officer

| | | |
|---|---|---|
| Owned, leased, sponsored: | 3 hospitals | 861 beds |
| Contract–managed: | 0 hospitals | 0 beds |
| Totals: | 3 hospitals | 861 beds |

**6555: MULTICARE HEALTH SYSTEM** (NP)
315 Martin Luther King Jr Way, Tacoma, WA Zip 98405–4234, Mailing Address: P.O. Box 5299, 98415–0299, tel. 253/403–1000; William G. Robertson, President and Chief Executive Officer
**(Centralized Physician/Insurance Health System)**

**WASHINGTON**: MULTICARE AUBURN MEDICAL CENTER (O, 153 beds) 202 North Division, Plaza One, Auburn, WA, Zip 98001–4908; tel. 253/833–7711; Mark T. Smith, JD, CPA, President and Chief Operating Officer

MULTICARE DEACONESS HOSPITAL (O, 352 beds) 800 West Fifth Avenue, Spokane, WA, Zip 99204–2803, Mailing Address: P.O. Box 248, 99210–0248, tel. 509/458–5800; Gregory George, FACHE, President
**Web address**: https://www.multicare.org/deaconess–hospital/

MULTICARE GOOD SAMARITAN HOSPITAL (O, 350 beds) 401 15th Avenue SE, Puyallup, WA, Zip 98372–3770, Mailing Address: P.O. Box 1247, 98371–0192, tel. 253/697–4000; James Beatty, President and Chief Operating Officer

MULTICARE MARY BRIDGE CHILDREN'S HOSPITAL AND HEALTH CENTER (O, 75 beds) 317 Martin Luther King Jr Way, Tacoma, WA, Zip 98405–4234, Mailing Address: P.O. Box 5299, 98415–0299, tel. 253/403–1400; Jeffrey S. Poltawsky, President and Market Leader
**Web address**: www.multicare.org/marybridge

MULTICARE TACOMA GENERAL HOSPITAL (O, 458 beds) 315 Martin Luther King Jr Way, Tacoma, WA, Zip 98405–4234, Mailing Address: P.O. Box 5299, 98415–0299, tel. 253/403–1000; Laureen Driscoll, President

MULTICARE VALLEY HOSPITAL (O, 123 beds) 12606 East Mission Avenue, Spokane Valley, WA, Zip 99216–1090; tel. 509/924–6650; Gregory George, Repetti III, FACHE, Chief Executive Officer
**Web address**: www.valleyhospital.org

MULTICARE COVINGTON MEDICAL CENTER (O, 58 beds) 17700 SE 272nd Street, Covington, WA, Zip 98042–4951; tel. 253/372–6500; Mark T. Smith, JD, CPA, President and Chief Operating Officer

| | | |
|---|---|---|
| Owned, leased, sponsored: | 7 hospitals | 1569 beds |
| Contract–managed: | 0 hospitals | 0 beds |
| Totals: | 7 hospitals | 1569 beds |

**★1465: MUNSON HEALTHCARE** (NP)
1105 Sixth Street, Traverse City, MI Zip 49684–2386; tel. 231/935–6703; Edwin Ness, President and Chief Executive Officer
**(Centralized Health System)**

**MICHIGAN**: KALKASKA MEMORIAL HEALTH CENTER (C, 112 beds) 419 South Coral Street, Kalkaska, MI, Zip 49646–2503; tel. 231/258–7500; Kevin L. Rogols, FACHE, Administrator

MUNSON HEALTHCARE CADILLAC HOSPITAL (O, 49 beds) 400 Hobart Street, Cadillac, MI, Zip 49601–2389; tel. 231/876–7200; Peter Marinoff Jr, President
**Web address**: www.mercyhealthcadillac.com/welcome–cadillac

MUNSON HEALTHCARE CHARLEVOIX HOSPITAL (O, 25 beds) 14700 Lake Shore Drive, Charlevoix, MI, Zip 49720–1999; tel. 231/547–4024; Joanne Schroeder, President
**Web address**: www.cah.org

MUNSON HEALTHCARE GRAYLING HOSPITAL (O, 110 beds) 1100 East Michigan Avenue, Grayling, MI, Zip 49738–1312; tel. 989/348–5461; Kirsten Korth–White, President
**Web address**: https://www.munsonhealthcare.org

MUNSON HEALTHCARE MANISTEE HOSPITAL (O, 45 beds) 1465 East Parkdale Avenue, Manistee, MI, Zip 49660–9709; tel. 231/398–1000; James Barker, Chief Executive Officer
**Web address**: www.westshoremedcenter.org

MUNSON HEALTHCARE OTSEGO MEMORIAL HOSPITAL (O, 80 beds) 825 North Center Avenue, Gaylord, MI, Zip 49735–1592; tel. 989/731–2100; Thomas R. Lemon, Chief Executive Officer

MUNSON MEDICAL CENTER (O, 442 beds) 1105 Sixth Street, Traverse City, MI, Zip 49684–2386; tel. 231/935–5000; Matt Wille, President and Chief Executive Officer
**Web address**: www.munsonhealthcare.org

PAUL OLIVER MEMORIAL HOSPITAL (O, 43 beds) 224 Park Avenue, Frankfort, MI, Zip 49635–9658; tel. 231/352–2200; James Barker, President and Chief Executive Officer
**Web address**: www.munsonhealthcare.org

| | | |
|---|---|---|
| Owned, leased, sponsored: | 7 hospitals | 794 beds |
| Contract–managed: | 1 hospitals | 112 beds |
| Totals: | 8 hospitals | 906 beds |

**★0976: MUSC HEALTH** (NP)
171 Ashley Ave, Charleston, SC Zip 29425–8908; tel. 843/792–2300; Patrick J. Cawley, Chief Executive Officer

**SOUTH CAROLINA**: MUSC HEALTH CHESTER MEDICAL CENTER (O, 12 beds) 1 Medical Park Drive, Chester, SC, Zip 29706–9769; tel. 803/581–3151; J. Scott Broome, Chief Executive Officer
**Web address**: www.muschealth.org/locations/chester–medical–center

MUSC HEALTH FLORENCE MEDICAL CENTER (O, 384 beds) 805 Pamplico Highway, Florence, SC, Zip 29505–6050, Mailing Address: P.O. Box 100550, 29502–0550, tel. 843/674–5000; Vance V. Reynolds, FACHE, CPA, Chief Executive Officer

MUSC HEALTH LANCASTER MEDICAL CENTER (O, 111 beds) 800 West Meeting Street, Lancaster, SC, Zip 29720–2298; tel. 803/286–1214; J. Scott Broome, Chief Executive Officer
**Web address**: www.springsmemorial.com

MUSC HEALTH MARION MEDICAL CENTER (O, 138 beds) 2829 East Highway 76, Mullins, SC, Zip 29574–6035, P O Drawer 1150, Marion, 29571–1150, tel. 843/431–2000; Vance V. Reynolds, FACHE, CPA, Chief Executive Officer

MUSC HEALTH OF MEDICAL UNIVERSITY OF SOUTH CAROLINA (O, 779 beds) 169 Ashley Avenue, Charleston, SC, Zip 29425–8905; tel. 843/792–2300; Patrick J. Cawley, Chief Executive Officer, MUSC Health and Vice President for Health Affairs, University
**Web address**: www.muschealth.com

| | | |
|---|---|---|
| Owned, leased, sponsored: | 5 hospitals | 1424 beds |
| Contract–managed: | 0 hospitals | 0 beds |
| Totals: | 5 hospitals | 1424 beds |

**0261: NATIONAL SURGICAL HEALTHCARE** (IO)
250 South Wacker Drive, Suite 500, Chicago, IL Zip 60606–5897; tel. 312/627–8400; David Crane, Chief Executive Officer
**(Independent Hospital System)**

**ARIZONA**: ARIZONA SPINE AND JOINT HOSPITAL (O, 23 beds) 4620 East Baseline Road, Mesa, AZ, Zip 85206–4624; tel. 480/832–4770; Todd Greene, Chief Executive Officer

**GEORGIA**: JENKINS COUNTY MEDICAL CENTER (O, 25 beds) 931 East Winthrope Avenue, Millen, GA, Zip 30442–1839; tel. 478/982–4221; Earl S. Whiteley, FACHE, Chief Executive Officer
**Web address**: www.https://jenkinsmedicalcenter.com/

For explanation of codes following names, see page B2.
★ Indicates Type III membership in the American Hospital Association.

**Section B**

OPTIM MEDICAL CENTER – SCREVEN (O, 25 beds) 215 Mims Road, Sylvania, GA, Zip 30467–2097; tel. 912/564–7426; Suzanne Doscher, FACHE, Chief Executive Officer
**Web address:** www.optimhealth.com

OPTIM MEDICAL CENTER – TATTNALL (O, 25 beds) 247 South Main Street, Reidsville, GA, Zip 30453–4605; tel. 912/557–1000; Rob Snipes, Administrator

**IDAHO:** NORTHWEST SPECIALTY HOSPITAL (O, 32 beds) 1593 East Polston Avenue, Post Falls, ID, Zip 83854–5326; tel. 208/262–2300; Rick Rasmussen, Chief Executive Officer
**Web address:** www.northwestspecialtyhospital.com

**MICHIGAN:** SOUTHEAST MICHIGAN SURGICAL HOSPITAL (O, 13 beds) 21230 Dequindre, Warren, MI, Zip 48091–2287; tel. 586/427–1000; Barry Cullen, Chief Executive Officer
**Web address:** www.nshinc.com

**NORTH CAROLINA:** NORTH CAROLINA SPECIALTY HOSPITAL (O, 18 beds) 3916 Ben Franklin Boulevard, Durham, NC, Zip 27704–2383, Mailing Address: P.O. 15819, 27704–2383, tel. 919/956–9300; Randi L. Shults, Chief Executive Officer

**TEXAS:** SOUTH TEXAS SPINE AND SURGICAL HOSPITAL (O, 30 beds) 18600 Hardy Oak Boulevard, San Antonio, TX, Zip 78258–4206; tel. 210/507–4090; Angie Kauffman, Chief Executive Officer
**Web address:** www.southtexassurgical.com

SOUTH TEXAS SURGICAL HOSPITAL (O, 20 beds) 6130 Parkway Drive, Corpus Christi, TX, Zip 78414–2455; tel. 361/993–2000; David G. Covert, Chief Executive Officer
**Web address:** www.southtexassurgicalhospital.com

**WISCONSIN:** OAKLEAF SURGICAL HOSPITAL (O, 13 beds) 1000 OakLeaf Way, Altoona, WI, Zip 54701–3016; tel. 715/831–8130; Anne Hargrave-Thomas, Chief Executive Officer
**Web address:** www.oakleafmedical.com

| Owned, leased, sponsored: | 10 hospitals | 224 beds |
|---|---|---|
| Contract–managed: | 0 hospitals | 0 beds |
| **Totals:** | 10 hospitals | 224 beds |

---

**0923: NAVICENT HEALTH** (NP)
777 Hemlock Street, MSC 105, Macon, GA Zip 31201–2155, 777 Hemlock Street, 31201–2155, tel. 478/633–1000; Ninfa M. Saunders, President and Chief Executive Officer
**(Moderately Centralized Health System)**

**GEORGIA:** MEDICAL CENTER OF PEACH COUNTY, NAVICENT HEALTH (O, 25 beds) 1960 Highway 247 Connector, Bryon, GA, Zip 31008; tel. 478/654–2000; Laura Gentry, Administrator

MEDICAL CENTER, NAVICENT HEALTH (O, 586 beds) 777 Hemlock Street, Macon, GA, Zip 31201–2155; tel. 478/633–1000; Ninfa M. Saunders, President and Chief Executive Officer
**Web address:** https://www.navicenthealth.org/

NAVICENT HEALTH BALDWIN (O, 90 beds) 821 North Cobb Street, Milledgeville, GA, Zip 31061–2351, Mailing Address: P.O. Box 690, 31059–0690, tel. 478/454–3505; Todd Dixon, R.N., Chief Executive Officer
**Web address:** www.navicenthealth.org/nhb/home

REHABILITATION HOSPITAL, NAVICENT HEALTH (O, 58 beds) 3351 Northside Drive, Macon, GA, Zip 31210–2587; tel. 478/201–6500; Regina Tipton, Hospital Administrator

| Owned, leased, sponsored: | 4 hospitals | 759 beds |
|---|---|---|
| Contract–managed: | 0 hospitals | 0 beds |
| **Totals:** | 4 hospitals | 759 beds |

---

★**9265: NEBRASKA METHODIST HEALTH SYSTEM, INC.** (CO)
8511 West Dodge Road, Omaha, NE Zip 68114–3403; tel. 402/354–5411; Stephen L. Goeser, FACHE, President and Chief Executive Officer
**(Centralized Physician/Insurance Health System)**

**IOWA:** METHODIST JENNIE EDMUNDSON HOSPITAL (O, 120 beds) 933 East Pierce Street, Council Bluffs, IA, Zip 51503–4652, Mailing Address: P.O. Box 2C, 51502–3002, tel. 712/396–6000; Steven P. Baumert, President and Chief Executive Officer

**NEBRASKA:** METHODIST FREMONT HEALTH (L, 181 beds) 450 East 23rd Street, Fremont, NE, Zip 68025–2387; tel. 402/721–1610; Brett M. Richmond, President and Chief Executive Officer
**Web address:** www.fremonthealth.com

NEBRASKA METHODIST HOSPITAL (O, 390 beds) 8303 Dodge Street, Omaha, NE, Zip 68114–4199; tel. 402/354–4000; Josie Abboud, R.N., FACHE, President and Chief Executive Officer
**Web address:** www.bestcare.org

| Owned, leased, sponsored: | 3 hospitals | 691 beds |
|---|---|---|
| Contract–managed: | 0 hospitals | 0 beds |
| **Totals:** | 3 hospitals | 691 beds |

---

**0892: NEMOURS** (NP)
10140 Centurion Parkway North, Jacksonville, FL Zip 32256–0532; tel. 904/697–4100; R. Lawrence. Moss, M.D., President and Chief Executive Officer
**(Independent Hospital System)**

**DELAWARE:** ALFRED I. DUPONT HOSPITAL FOR CHILDREN (O, 208 beds) 1600 Rockland Road, Wilmington, DE, Zip 19803–3616, Box 269, 19899–0269, tel. 302/651–4000; Jay S. Greenspan, M.D., Chief Executive Officer

**FLORIDA:** NEMOURS CHILDREN'S HOSPITAL (O, 108 beds) 13535 Nemours Parkway, Orlando, FL, Zip 32827–7402; tel. 407/567–4000; Randall W. Hartley, Interim President
**Web address:** www.nemours.org

| Owned, leased, sponsored: | 2 hospitals | 316 beds |
|---|---|---|
| Contract–managed: | 0 hospitals | 0 beds |
| **Totals:** | 2 hospitals | 316 beds |

---

**0620: NEUROPSYCHIATRIC HOSPITALS** (IO)
1625 East Jefferson Boulevard, Mishawaka, IN Zip 46545–7103; tel. 574/255–1400; Cameron R. Gilbert, Ph.D., President and Chief Executive Officer

**INDIANA:** DOCTORS NEUROPSYCHIATRIC HOSPITAL AND RESEARCH INSTITUTE (O, 37 beds) 417 South Whitlock Street, Bremen, IN, Zip 46506–1626; tel. 574/546–0330; Christy Gilbert, Interim Chief Executive Officer

MEDICAL BEHAVIORAL HOSPITAL OF MISHAWAKA (O, 30 beds) 5985 E 200 S , Knox, IN, Zip 46534, 1625 East Jefferson Boulevard, Mishawaka, 46545–7103, tel. 574/255–1400; Emily Ryan, Chief Executive Officer
**Web address:** www.physicianshospitalsystem.net/

NEUROPSYCHIATRIC HOSPITAL OF INDIANAPOLIS (O, 50 beds) 6720 Parkdale Place, Indianapolis, IN, Zip 46254–4668; tel. 317/744–9200; Tracy Davis, Chief Executive Officer
**Web address:** https://www.neuropsychiatrichospitals.net

NEUROBEHAVIORAL HOSPITAL OF NW INDIANA (O, 70 beds) 9330 Broadway, Crown Point, IN, Zip 46307–9830; tel. 219/648–2400; Bob Kedelis, Chief Executive Officer

| Owned, leased, sponsored: | 4 hospitals | 187 beds |
|---|---|---|
| Contract–managed: | 0 hospitals | 0 beds |
| **Totals:** | 4 hospitals | 187 beds |

---

★**0213: NEW HANOVER REGIONAL MEDICAL CENTER** (NP)
2131 South 17th Street, Wilmington, NC Zip 28401–7407; tel. 910/343–7040; John H. Gizdic, President and Chief Executive Officer
**(Moderately Centralized Health System)**

---

For explanation of codes following names, see page B2.
★ Indicates Type III membership in the American Hospital Association.

**NORTH CAROLINA:** NEW HANOVER REGIONAL MEDICAL CENTER (O, 720 beds) 2131 South 17th Street, Wilmington, NC, Zip 28401–7483, Mailing Address: P.O. Box 9000, 28402–9000, tel. 910/343–7000; Andre Boyd Sr, Executive Vice President, Hospital Division
**Web address:** www.nhrmc.org

PENDER MEMORIAL HOSPITAL (C, 64 beds) 507 East Freemont Street, Burgaw, NC, Zip 28425–5131; tel. 910/259–5451; Ruth Glaser, President
**Web address:** www.pendermemorial.org

| Owned, leased, sponsored: | 1 hospitals | 720 beds |
|---|---|---|
| Contract–managed: | 1 hospitals | 64 beds |
| **Totals:** | 2 hospitals | 784 beds |

---

**0009: NEW YORK STATE OFFICE OF MENTAL HEALTH** (NP)
44 Holland Avenue, Albany, NY Zip 12208–3411; tel. 518/474–7056; Ann Sullivan, M.D., Commissioner
**(Independent Hospital System)**

**NEW YORK:** BRONX PSYCHIATRIC CENTER (O, 156 beds) 1500 Waters Place, Bronx, NY, Zip 10461–2796; tel. 718/931–0600; Precious Stepney, Executive Director
**Web address:** www.omh.ny.gov

BUFFALO PSYCHIATRIC CENTER (O, 240 beds) 400 Forest Avenue, Buffalo, NY, Zip 14213–1298; tel. 716/885–2261; Beatrix Souza, Chief Executive Officer

CAPITAL DISTRICT PSYCHIATRIC CENTER (O, 200 beds) 75 New Scotland Avenue, Albany, NY, Zip 12208–3474; tel. 518/549–6000; William Dickson, Executive Director
**Web address:** www.omh.ny.gov/omhweb/facilities/cdpc/facility.htm

CENTRAL NEW YORK PSYCHIATRIC CENTER (O, 226 beds) 9005 Old River Road, Marcy, NY, Zip 13403–3000, Mailing Address: P.O. Box 300, 13403–0300, tel. 315/765–3600; Maureen Bosco, Executive Director
**Web address:** www.omh.ny.gov

CREEDMOOR PSYCHIATRIC CENTER (O, 322 beds) 79–25 Winchester Boulevard, Jamaica, NY, Zip 11427–2128; tel. 718/264–3600; Ann Marie. Barbarotta, Executive Director
**Web address:** www.omh.ny.gov

ELMIRA PSYCHIATRIC CENTER (O, 61 beds) 100 Washington Street, Elmira, NY, Zip 14901–2898; tel. 607/737–4739; David Peppel, Executive Director

GREATER BINGHAMTON HEALTH CENTER (O, 86 beds) 425 Robinson Street, Binghamton, NY, Zip 13904–1735; tel. 607/724–1391; David Peppel, Executive Director
**Web address:** www.omh.ny.gov/omhweb/facilities/bipc/facility.htm

KINGSBORO PSYCHIATRIC CENTER (O, 290 beds) 681 Clarkson Avenue, Brooklyn, NY, Zip 11203–2125; tel. 718/221–7395; Deborah Parchment, Executive Director
**Web address:** www.omh.ny.gov/omhweb/facilities/kbpc/facility/htm

KIRBY FORENSIC PSYCHIATRIC CENTER (O, 193 beds) 600 East 125th Street, New York, NY, Zip 10035–6000; tel. 646/672–5800; Vincent Miccoli, Executive Director
**Web address:** https://www.omh.ny.gov/omhweb/facilities/krpc/

MANHATTAN PSYCHIATRIC CENTER–WARD'S ISLAND (O, 745 beds) 600 East 125th Street, New York, NY, Zip 10035–6000; tel. 646/672–6767; Vincent Miccoli, Executive Director
**Web address:** www.omh.ny.gov

MID–HUDSON FORENSIC PSYCHIATRIC CENTER (O, 285 beds) Route 17M, New Hampton, NY, Zip 10958, Mailing Address: P.O. Box 158, 10958–0158, tel. 845/374–8700; Kristin Orlando, Chief Executive Officer

MOHAWK VALLEY PSYCHIATRIC CENTER (O, 614 beds) 1400 Noyes Street, Utica, NY, Zip 13502–3854; tel. 315/738–3800; Colleen A. Sawyer, R.N., MSN, Executive Director
**Web address:** www.omh.ny.gov/omhweb/facilities/mvpc/facility.htm

NEW YORK CITY CHILDREN'S CENTER (O, 102 beds) 74–03 Commonwealth Boulevard, Jamaica, NY, Zip 11426–1890; tel. 718/264–4506; Kanika Jefferies, Executive Director

NEW YORK STATE PSYCHIATRIC INSTITUTE (O, 58 beds) 1051 Riverside Drive, New York, NY, Zip 10032–1007; tel. 646/774–5000; Jeffrey A. Lieberman, M.D., Executive Director
**Web address:** www.nyspi.org

PILGRIM PSYCHIATRIC CENTER (O, 569 beds) 998 Crooked Hill Road, Brentwood, NY, Zip 11717–1019; tel. 631/761–3500; Kathy O'Keefe, Executive Director

RICHARD H. HUTCHINGS PSYCHIATRIC CENTER (O, 131 beds) 620 Madison Street, Syracuse, NY, Zip 13210–2319; tel. 315/426–3632; Colleen A. Sawyer, R.N., MSN, Executive Director
**Web address:** www.omh.ny.gov

ROCHESTER PSYCHIATRIC CENTER (O, 180 beds) 1111 Elmwood Avenue, Rochester, NY, Zip 14620–3005; tel. 585/241–1200; Philip Griffin, Director of Operations

ROCKLAND CHILDREN'S PSYCHIATRIC CENTER (O, 54 beds) 599 Convent Road, Orangeburg, NY, Zip 10962–1162; tel. 845/359–7400; Renee Rivera, Executive Director
**Web address:** www.omh.ny.gov/

ROCKLAND PSYCHIATRIC CENTER (O, 525 beds) 140 Old Orangeburg Road, Orangeburg, NY, Zip 10962–1157; tel. 845/359–1000; Janet J. Monroe, R.N., Executive Director
**Web address:** www.omh.ny.gov/

SAGAMORE CHILDREN'S PSYCHIATRIC CENTER (O, 54 beds) 197 Half Hollow Road, Dix Hills, NY, Zip 11746–5861; tel. 631/370–1700; Kathy O'Keefe, Interim Executive Director

SOUTH BEACH PSYCHIATRIC CENTER (O, 340 beds) 777 Seaview Avenue, Staten Island, NY, Zip 10305–3409; tel. 718/667–2300; Doreen Piazza, Acting Executive Director
**Web address:** www.omh.ny.gov/omhweb/facilities/sbpc/facility.htm

ST. LAWRENCE PSYCHIATRIC CENTER (O, 146 beds) 1 Chimney Point Drive, Ogdensburg, NY, Zip 13669–2291; tel. 315/541–2001; Timothy Farrell, Executive Director

WESTERN NEW YORK CHILDREN'S PSYCHIATRIC CENTER (O, 46 beds) 1010 East and West Road, West Seneca, NY, Zip 14224–3602; tel. 716/677–7000; Kathe Hayes, Executive Director
**Web address:** www.omh.ny.gov

| Owned, leased, sponsored: | 23 hospitals | 5623 beds |
|---|---|---|
| Contract–managed: | 0 hospitals | 0 beds |
| **Totals:** | 23 hospitals | 5623 beds |

---

**★0142: NEWYORK–PRESBYTERIAN** (NP)
525 East 68th Street, Box 182, New York, NY Zip 10065; tel. 212/746–3745; Steven J. Corwin, M.D., President and Chief Executive Officer
**(Centralized Health System)**

**NEW YORK:** NEW YORK–PRESBYTERIAN HOSPITAL (O, 2592 beds) 525 East 68th Street, New York, NY, Zip 10065–4870; tel. 212/746–5454; Steven J. Corwin, M.D., President and Chief Executive Officer
**Web address:** www.nyp.org

NEW YORK–PRESBYTERIAN QUEENS (O, 510 beds) 56–45 Main Street, Flushing, NY, Zip 11355–5045; tel. 718/670–1231; Jaclyn Mucaria, President
**Web address:** www.nyhq.org

NEW YORK–PRESBYTERIAN/HUDSON VALLEY HOSPITAL (O, 116 beds) 1980 Crompond Road, Cortlandt Manor, NY, Zip 10567–4182; tel. 914/737–9000; Stacey Petrower, President
**Web address:** www.hvhc.org

NEWYORK–PRESBYTERIAN BROOKLYN METHODIST HOSPITAL (O, 591 beds) 506 Sixth Street, Brooklyn, NY, Zip 11215–3609; tel. 718/780–3000; Robert Guimento, President

| Owned, leased, sponsored: | 4 hospitals | 3809 beds |
|---|---|---|
| Contract–managed: | 0 hospitals | 0 beds |
| **Totals:** | 4 hospitals | 3809 beds |

---

**0353: NEXUS HEALTH SYSTEMS** (IO)
One Riverway, Suite 600, Houston, TX Zip 77056–1993; tel. 713/355–6111; John W. Cassidy, M.D., President, Chief Executive Officer and Chief Medical Officer
**(Independent Hospital System)**

For explanation of codes following names, see page B2.
★ Indicates Type III membership in the American Hospital Association.

**CALIFORNIA**: HEALTHBRIDGE CHILDREN'S HOSPITAL (O, 27 beds) 393 South Tustin Street, Orange, CA, Zip 92866–2501; tel. 714/289–2400; Alex Villarruz, Chief Executive Officer
**Web address**: www.HealthBridgeOrange.com

**TEXAS**: NEXUS CHILDREN'S HOSPITAL HOUSTON (O, 40 beds) 2929 Woodland Park Drive, Houston, TX, Zip 77082–2687; tel. 281/293–7774; Mary Harbeson, R.N., Chief Executive Officer

NEXUS SPECIALTY HOSPITAL (O, 76 beds) 123 Vision Park Boulevard, Shenandoah, TX, Zip 77384–3001; tel. 281/364–0317; Eric Cantrell, Chief Executive Officer
**Web address**: www.nexusspecialty.com

| | | |
|---|---|---|
| Owned, leased, sponsored: | 3 hospitals | 143 beds |
| Contract–managed: | 0 hospitals | 0 beds |
| Totals: | 3 hospitals | 143 beds |

## 0349: NOLAND HEALTH SERVICES, INC. (NP)

600 Corporate Parkway, Suite 100, Birmingham, AL Zip 35242–5451; tel. 205/783–8484; Gary M. Glasscock, President and Chief Executive Officer

**ALABAMA**: NOLAND HOSPITAL ANNISTON (O, 38 beds) 400 East 10th Street, 4th Fl, Anniston, AL, Zip 36207–4716; tel. 256/741–6141; Trina Woods, Administrator
**Web address**: www.nolandhealth.com

NOLAND HOSPITAL BIRMINGHAM (O, 45 beds) 50 Medical Park East Drive, 8th Floor, Birmingham, AL, Zip 35235; tel. 205/808–5100; Laura S. Wills, Administrator

NOLAND HOSPITAL DOTHAN (O, 38 beds) 1108 Ross Clark Circle, 4th Floor, Dothan, AL, Zip 36301–3022; tel. 334/699–4300; Kaye Burk, Administrator
**Web address**: www.nolandhealth.com

NOLAND HOSPITAL MONTGOMERY (O, 65 beds) 1725 Pine Street, 5 North, Montgomery, AL, Zip 36106–1109; tel. 334/240–0532; William Elsesser, Administrator

NOLAND HOSPITAL SHELBY (O, 52 beds) 1000 First Street North, 3rd Floor, Alabaster, AL, Zip 35007–8703; tel. 205/620–8641; Laura S. Wills, Administrator
**Web address**: www.nolandhospitals.com

NOLAND HOSPITAL TUSCALOOSA (O, 32 beds) 809 University Blvd E, 4th Fl, Tuscaloosa, AL, Zip 35401–2029; tel. 205/759–7241; Jack Gibson, Administrator

| | | |
|---|---|---|
| Owned, leased, sponsored: | 6 hospitals | 270 beds |
| Contract–managed: | 0 hospitals | 0 beds |
| Totals: | 6 hospitals | 270 beds |

## 1030: NORTH COUNTRY HEALTHCARE (NP)

600 Saint Johnsbury Road, Littleton, NH Zip 03561–3442; tel. 603/444–9000; Thomas Mee, R.N., Chief Executive Officer
**(Moderately Centralized Health System)**

| | | |
|---|---|---|
| Owned, leased, sponsored: | 0 hospitals | 0 beds |
| Contract–managed: | 0 hospitals | 0 beds |
| Totals: | 0 hospitals | 0 beds |

## 0887: NORTH MEMORIAL HEALTH CARE (NP)

3300 Oakdale Avenue North, Robbinsdale, MN Zip 55422–2926; tel. 763/520–5200; J. Kevin. Croston, M.D., Chief Executive Officer
**(Centralized Physician/Insurance Health System)**

**MINNESOTA**: MAPLE GROVE HOSPITAL (C, 108 beds) 9875 Hospital Drive, Maple Grove, MN, Zip 55369–4648; tel. 763/581–1000; Andrew S. Cochrane, Chief Executive Officer
**Web address**: www.maplegrovehospital.org

NORTH MEMORIAL HEALTH HOSPITAL (O, 358 beds) 3300 Oakdale Avenue North, Robbinsdale, MN, Zip 55422–2926; tel. 763/520–5200; Jeff Wicklander, President
**Web address**: www.northmemorial.com

| | | |
|---|---|---|
| Owned, leased, sponsored: | 1 hospitals | 358 beds |
| Contract–managed: | 1 hospitals | 108 beds |
| Totals: | 2 hospitals | 466 beds |

## ★0032: NORTH MISSISSIPPI HEALTH SERVICES, INC. (NP)

830 South Gloster Street, Tupelo, MS Zip 38801–4996; tel. 662/377–3136; M. Shane. Spees, President and Chief Executive Officer
**(Centralized Physician/Insurance Health System)**

**ALABAMA**: NORTH MISSISSIPPI MEDICAL CENTER–HAMILTON (O, 15 beds) 1256 Military Street South, Hamilton, AL, Zip 35570–5003; tel. 205/921–6200; Robert Trimm, Administrator
**Web address**: www.nmhs.net

**MICHIGAN**: NORTH MISSISSIPPI HEALTH SERVICES, INC. (O, 741 beds) 830 South Gloster Street, Tupelo, MI, Zip 38801–4934; tel. 662/377–3136; David C. Wilson, President
**Web address**: www.nmhs.net

**MISSISSIPPI**: NORTH MISSISSIPPI MEDICAL CENTER GILMORE–AMORY (O, 95 beds) 1105 Earl Frye Boulevard, Amory, MS, Zip 38821–5500, Mailing Address: P.O. Box 459, 38821–0459, tel. 662/256–7111; Steve Nichols, Chief Executive Officer

NORTH MISSISSIPPI MEDICAL CENTER–EUPORA (O, 74 beds) 70 Medical Plaza, Eupora, MS, Zip 39744–4018; tel. 662/258–6221; Robin Mixon, Administrator
**Web address**: www.nmhs.net/eupora

NORTH MISSISSIPPI MEDICAL CENTER–IUKA (O, 48 beds) 1777 Curtis Drive, Iuka, MS, Zip 38852–1001, Mailing Address: P.O. Box 860, 38852–0860, tel. 662/423–6051; Fred A. Truesdale Jr, Administrator

NORTH MISSISSIPPI MEDICAL CENTER–PONTOTOC (L, 69 beds) 176 South Main Street, Pontotoc, MS, Zip 38863–3311, Mailing Address: P.O. Box 790, 38863–0790, tel. 662/488–7640; Leslia Carter, Administrator
**Web address**: www.nmhs.net

NORTH MISSISSIPPI MEDICAL CENTER–WEST POINT (O, 49 beds) 835 Medical Center Drive, West Point, MS, Zip 39773–9320; tel. 662/495–2300; Barry L. Keel, Administrator
**Web address**: www.nmhs.net/westpoint

| | | |
|---|---|---|
| Owned, leased, sponsored: | 7 hospitals | 1091 beds |
| Contract–managed: | 0 hospitals | 0 beds |
| Totals: | 7 hospitals | 1091 beds |

## 0867: NORTH OAKS HEALTH SYSTEM (NP)

15790 Paul Vega MD Drive, Hammond, LA Zip 70403–1436, Mailing Address: P.O. Box 2668, 70404–2668, tel. 985/345–2700; Michele Kidd. Sutton, FACHE, President and Chief Executive Officer
**(Independent Hospital System)**

**LOUISIANA**: NORTH OAKS MEDICAL CENTER (O, 248 beds) 15790 Paul Vega, MD, Drive, Hammond, LA, Zip 70403–1436, Mailing Address: P.O. Box 2668, 70404–2668, tel. 985/345–2700; Michele Kidd. Sutton, FACHE, President and Chief Executive Officer

NORTH OAKS REHABILITATION HOSPITAL (O, 27 beds) 1900 South Morrison Boulevard, Hammond, LA, Zip 70403–5742; tel. 985/542–7777; Mac Barrient, Administrator
**Web address**: www.northoaks.org

| | | |
|---|---|---|
| Owned, leased, sponsored: | 2 hospitals | 275 beds |
| Contract–managed: | 0 hospitals | 0 beds |
| Totals: | 2 hospitals | 275 beds |

For explanation of codes following names, see page B2.
★ Indicates Type III membership in the American Hospital Association.

**1018: NORTHEAST GEORGIA HEALTH SYSTEM** (NP)

743 Spring Street NE, Gainesville, GA Zip 30501–3715; tel. 770/219–9000; Carol H. Burrell, President and Chief Executive Officer

**(Centralized Physician/Insurance Health System)**

**GEORGIA:** NORTHEAST GEORGIA MEDICAL CENTER BARROW (O, 30 beds) 316 North Broad Street, Winder, GA, Zip 30680–2150, Mailing Address: P.O. Box 688, 30680–0688, tel. 770/867–3400; Chad Hatfield, Chief Executive Officer
**Web address:** www.barrowregional.com

NORTHEAST GEORGIA MEDICAL CENTER BRASELTON (O, 100 beds) 1400 River Place, Braselton, GA, Zip 30517–5600; tel. 770/219–9000; Carol H. Burrell, Chief Executive Officer

NORTHEAST GEORGIA MEDICAL CENTER LUMPKIN (O, 49 beds) 227 Mountain Drive, Dahlonega, GA, Zip 30533–1606; tel. 770/219–9000; Carol H. Burrell, Chief Executive Officer
**Web address:** https://www.nghs.com/locations/lumpkin/

NORTHEAST GEORGIA MEDICAL CENTER (O, 887 beds) 743 Spring Street NE, Gainesville, GA, Zip 30501–3899; tel. 770/219–3553; Carol H. Burrell, Chief Executive Officer

| Owned, leased, sponsored: | 4 hospitals | 1066 beds |
|---|---|---|
| Contract–managed: | 0 hospitals | 0 beds |
| Totals: | 4 hospitals | 1066 beds |

**0281: NORTHERN ARIZONA HEALTHCARE** (NP)

1200 North Beaver Street, Flagstaff, AZ Zip 86001–3118; tel. 928/779–3366; Florence (Flo). Spyrow, President and Chief Executive Officer

**(Moderately Centralized Health System)**

**ARIZONA:** FLAGSTAFF MEDICAL CENTER (O, 264 beds) 1200 North Beaver Street, Flagstaff, AZ, Zip 86001–3118; tel. 928/779–3366; Florence (Flo). Spyrow, Chief Administrative Officer
**Web address:** www.nahealth.com

VERDE VALLEY MEDICAL CENTER (O, 87 beds) 269 South Candy Lane, Cottonwood, AZ, Zip 86326–4170; tel. 928/639–6000; Barbara Firminger, Chief Administrative Officer
**Web address:** www.https://nahealth.com/

| Owned, leased, sponsored: | 2 hospitals | 351 beds |
|---|---|---|
| Contract–managed: | 0 hospitals | 0 beds |
| Totals: | 2 hospitals | 351 beds |

★**0555: NORTHERN LIGHT HEALTH** (NP)

43 Whiting Hill Road, Brewer, ME Zip 04412–1005; tel. 207/973–7045; Timothy Dentry, President and Chief Executive Officer
**(Moderately Centralized Health System)**

**MAINE:** MAYO REGIONAL HOSPITAL (O, 25 beds) 897 West Main Street, Dover–Foxcroft, ME, Zip 04426–1099; tel. 207/564–8401; Marie E. Vienneau, FACHE, President and Chief Executive Officer

NORTHERN LIGHT BLUE HILL HOSPITAL (O, 23 beds) 57 Water Street, Blue Hill, ME, Zip 04614–5231, Mailing Address: P.O. Box 1029, 04614–1029, tel. 207/374–3400; John Ronan, President
**Web address:** www.bhmh.org

NORTHERN LIGHT CA DEAN HOSPITAL (O, 25 beds) 364 Pritham Avenue, Greenville, ME, Zip 04441–1395, Mailing Address: P.O. Box 1129, 04441–1129, tel. 207/695–5200; Marie E. Vienneau, FACHE, President
**Web address:** www.cadean.org

NORTHERN LIGHT EASTERN MAINE MEDICAL CENTER (O, 392 beds) 489 State Street, Bangor, ME, Zip 04401–6674, Mailing Address: P.O. Box 404, 04402–0404, tel. 207/973–7000; Rand O'Leary, FACHE, President

NORTHERN LIGHT INLAND HOSPITAL (O, 29 beds) 200 Kennedy Memorial Drive, Waterville, ME, Zip 04901–4595; tel. 207/861–3000; Terri Vieira, President
**Web address:** www.inlandhospital.org

NORTHERN LIGHT MAINE COAST HOSPITAL (O, 52 beds) 50 Union Street, Ellsworth, ME, Zip 04605–1599; tel. 207/664–5311; John Ronan, President

NORTHERN LIGHT MERCY HOSPITAL (O, 104 beds) 144 State Street, Portland, ME, Zip 04101–3795; tel. 207/879–3000; Charles D. Therrien, President
**Web address:** www.https://northernlighthealth.org/Mercy–Hospital

NORTHERN LIGHT SEBASTICOOK VALLEY HOSPITAL (O, 25 beds) 447 North Main Street, Pittsfield, ME, Zip 04967–3707; tel. 207/487–4000; Terri Vieira, President
**Web address:** www.sebasticookvalleyhealth.org

THE ACADIA HOSPITAL (O, 68 beds) 268 Stillwater Avenue, Bangor, ME, Zip 04401–3945, Mailing Address: P.O. Box 422, 04402–0422, tel. 207/973–6100; Scott Oxley, President

THE AROOSTOOK MEDICAL CENTER (O, 114 beds) 140 Academy Street, Presque Isle, ME, Zip 04769–3171, Mailing Address: P.O. Box 151, 04769–0151, tel. 207/768–4000; Gregory LaFrancois, President
**Web address:** www.tamc.org

| Owned, leased, sponsored: | 10 hospitals | 857 beds |
|---|---|---|
| Contract–managed: | 0 hospitals | 0 beds |
| Totals: | 10 hospitals | 857 beds |

**0470: NORTHSHORE UNIVERSITY HEALTHSYSTEM** (NP)

1301 Central Street, Evanston, IL Zip 60201–1613; tel. 847/570–2000; J. P. Gallagher, President and Chief Executive Officer

**ILLINOIS:** NORTHSHORE UNIVERSITY HEALTH SYSTEM (O, 663 beds) 2650 Ridge Avenue, Evanston, IL, Zip 60201–1613; tel. 847/570–2000; J. P. Gallagher, President and Chief Executive Officer
**Web address:** www.northshore.org

SWEDISH COVENANT HOSPITAL (O, 267 beds) 5145 North California Avenue, Chicago, IL, Zip 60625–3661; tel. 773/878–8200; Anthony Guaccio, President and Chief Executive Officer
**Web address:** www.schosp.org

| Owned, leased, sponsored: | 2 hospitals | 930 beds |
|---|---|---|
| Contract–managed: | 0 hospitals | 0 beds |
| Totals: | 2 hospitals | 930 beds |

★**0410: NORTHSIDE HEALTHCARE SYSTEM** (NP)

1000 Johnson Ferry Road NE, Atlanta, GA Zip 30342–1611; tel. 404/851–8000; Robert Quattrocchi, President and Chief Executive Officer

**GEORGIA:** NORTHSIDE HOSPITAL – GWINNETT (L, 556 beds) 1000 Medical Center Boulevard, Lawrenceville, GA, Zip 30046–7694, Mailing Address: P.O. Box 348, 30046–0348, tel. 678/312–1000; Debbie Mitcham, President and Chief Executive Officer

NORTHSIDE HOSPITAL–CHEROKEE (O, 130 beds) 450 Northside Cherokee Boulevard, Canton, GA, Zip 30115–8015, Mailing Address: P.O. Box 906, 30169–0906, tel. 770/720–5100; William M. Hayes, Chief Executive Officer
**Web address:** www.northside.com

NORTHSIDE HOSPITAL–FORSYTH (O, 319 beds) 1200 Northside Forsyth Drive, Cumming, GA, Zip 30041–7659; tel. 770/844–3200; Skip Putnam, Chief Executive Officer
**Web address:** www.northside.com

NORTHSIDE HOSPITAL (O, 506 beds) 1000 Johnson Ferry Road NE, Atlanta, GA, Zip 30342–1611; tel. 404/851–8000; Robert Quattrocchi, President and Chief Executive Officer

| Owned, leased, sponsored: | 4 hospitals | 1511 beds |
|---|---|---|
| Contract–managed: | 0 hospitals | 0 beds |
| Totals: | 4 hospitals | 1511 beds |

★**0062: NORTHWELL HEALTH** (NP)

2000 Marcus Avenue, New Hyde Park, NY Zip 11042; tel. 516/321–6666; Michael J. Dowling, President and Chief Executive Officer

**(Centralized Health System)**

For explanation of codes following names, see page B2.
★ Indicates Type III membership in the American Hospital Association.

Section B

**NEW YORK:** GLEN COVE HOSPITAL (O, 119 beds) 101 St Andrews Lane, Glen Cove, NY, Zip 11542–2254; tel. 516/674–7300; Kerri Scanlon, MSN, Executive Director

HUNTINGTON HOSPITAL (O, 280 beds) 270 Park Avenue, Huntington, NY, Zip 11743–2799; tel. 631/351–2000; Nick Fitterman, M.D., Executive Director **Web address:** www.https://huntington.northwell.edu

LENOX HILL HOSPITAL (O, 414 beds) 100 East 77th Street, New York, NY, Zip 10075–1850; tel. 212/434–2000; Jill Kalman, M.D., Executive Director **Web address:** www.lenoxhillhospital.org

LONG ISLAND JEWISH MEDICAL CENTER (O, 1522 beds) 270–05 76th Avenue, New Hyde Park, NY, Zip 11040–1496; tel. 718/470–7000; Michael Goldberg, Executive Director

MATHER HOSPITAL (O, 248 beds) 75 North Country Road, Port Jefferson, NY, Zip 11777–2190; tel. 631/473–1320; Kenneth D. Roberts, President **Web address:** www.matherhospital.com

NORTH SHORE UNIVERSITY HOSPITAL (O, 831 beds) 300 Community Drive, Manhasset, NY, Zip 11030–3816; tel. 516/562–0100; Alessandro Bellucci, M.D., Executive Director

NORTHERN WESTCHESTER HOSPITAL (O, 195 beds) 400 East Main Street, Mount Kisco, NY, Zip 10549–3477, 400 East Main Street, G–02, 10549–3477, tel. 914/666–1200; Derek Anderson, Executive Director **Web address:** www.nwhc.net

PECONIC BAY MEDICAL CENTER (O, 170 beds) 1300 Roanoke Avenue, Riverhead, NY, Zip 11901–2031; tel. 631/548–6000; Andrew J. Mitchell, President and Chief Executive Officer **Web address:** www.pbmchealth.org

PHELPS MEMORIAL HOSPITAL CENTER (O, 153 beds) 701 North Broadway, Sleepy Hollow, NY, Zip 10591–1020; tel. 914/366–3000; Eileen Egan Esq, Executive Director

PLAINVIEW HOSPITAL (O, 156 beds) 888 Old Country Road, Plainview, NY, Zip 11803–4978; tel. 516/719–3000; Michael Fener, Executive Director **Web address:** https://www.planview.com/

SOUTH OAKS HOSPITAL (O, 202 beds) 400 Sunrise Highway, Amityville, NY, Zip 11701–2508; tel. 631/264–4000; Carolyn Sweetapple, Ph.D., R.N., CPA, Executive Director

SOUTHSIDE HOSPITAL (O, 305 beds) 301 East Main Street, Bay Shore, NY, Zip 11706–8458; tel. 631/968–3000; Donna Moravick, R.N., MSN, Executive Director **Web address:** https://www.northwell.edu/find–care/locations/southside–hospital

STATEN ISLAND UNIVERSITY HOSPITAL (O, 627 beds) 475 Seaview Avenue, Staten Island, NY, Zip 10305–3436; tel. 718/226–9000; Brahim Ardolic, M.D., Chief Executive Officer **Web address:** www.siuh.edu

| | | |
|---|---|---|
| Owned, leased, sponsored: | 13 hospitals | 5222 beds |
| Contract–managed: | 0 hospitals | 0 beds |
| Totals: | 13 hospitals | 5222 beds |

---

**★0024: NORTHWESTERN MEMORIAL HEALTHCARE** (NP)
251 East Huron Street, Chicago, IL Zip 60611–2908; tel. 312/926–2000; Dean M. Harrison, President and Chief Executive Officer **(Centralized Health System)**

**ILLINOIS:** NORTHWESTERN MEDICINE CENTRAL DUPAGE HOSPITAL (O, 419 beds) 25 North Winfield Road, Winfield, IL, Zip 60190; tel. 630/933–1600; Kevin Poorten, President **Web address:** www.nm.org

NORTHWESTERN MEDICINE DELNOR HOSPITAL (O, 159 beds) 300 Randall Road, Geneva, IL, Zip 60134–4200; tel. 630/208–3000; Maureen A. Bryant, FACHE, President **Web address:** www.nm.org

NORTHWESTERN MEDICINE KISHWAUKEE HOSPITAL (O, 98 beds) 1 Kish Hospital Drive, DeKalb, IL, Zip 60115–9602, Mailing Address: P.O. Box 707, 60115–0707, tel. 815/756–1521; Jay Anderson, President

NORTHWESTERN MEDICINE LAKE FOREST HOSPITAL (O, 120 beds) 1000 North Westmoreland Road, Lake Forest, IL, Zip 60045–1696, 1000 N Westmoreland Road, 60045–1658, tel. 847/234–5600; Thomas J. McAfee, President, North Region **Web address:** www.nm.org

NORTHWESTERN MEDICINE MARIANJOY REHABILITATION HOSPITAL (O, 127 beds) 26 West 171 Roosevelt Road, Wheaton, IL, Zip 60187–0795, Mailing Address: P.O. Box 795, 60187–0795, tel. 630/909–8000; Julie L. Creamer, President **Web address:** www.marianjoy.org

NORTHWESTERN MEDICINE MCHENRY (O, 350 beds) 4201 Medical Center Drive, McHenry, IL, Zip 60050–8409; tel. 815/344–5000; Thomas J. McAfee, Region President

NORTHWESTERN MEDICINE VALLEY WEST HOSPITAL (O, 25 beds) 1302 North Main Street, Sandwich, IL, Zip 60548–2587; tel. 815/786–8484; Jay Anderson, President **Web address:** www.nm.org

NORTHWESTERN MEMORIAL HOSPITAL (O, 894 beds) 251 East Huron Street, Chicago, IL, Zip 60611–2908; tel. 312/926–2000; Julie L. Creamer, President, Northwestern Memorial Hospital and Senior Vice President Northwestern Memorial HealthCare

| | | |
|---|---|---|
| Owned, leased, sponsored: | 8 hospitals | 2192 beds |
| Contract–managed: | 0 hospitals | 0 beds |
| Totals: | 8 hospitals | 2192 beds |

---

**★2285: NORTON HEALTHCARE** (NP)
4967 US Highway 42, Suite 100, Louisville, KY Zip 40222–6363, Mailing Address: P.O. Box 35070, 40232–5070, tel. 502/629–8000; Russell Cox, President and Chief Executive Officer **(Centralized Health System)**

**KENTUCKY:** NORTON CHILDREN'S HOSPITAL (O, 279 beds) 231 East Chestnut Street, Louisville, KY, Zip 40202–1821; tel. 502/629–6000; Emmett Ramser, Chief Administrative Officer **Web address:** www.kosairchildrens.com/

NORTON HOSPITAL (O, 1263 beds) 200 East Chestnut Street, Louisville, KY, Zip 40202–1800, Mailing Address: P.O. Box 35070, 40232–5070, tel. 502/629–8000; Matthew Ayers, Chief Administrative Officer

| | | |
|---|---|---|
| Owned, leased, sponsored: | 2 hospitals | 1542 beds |
| Contract–managed: | 0 hospitals | 0 beds |
| Totals: | 2 hospitals | 1542 beds |

---

**★0139: NOVANT HEALTH** (NP)
2085 Frontis Plaza Boulevard, Winston Salem, NC Zip 27103–5614; tel. 336/718–5600; Carl S. Armato, President and Chief Executive Officer **(Independent Hospital System)**

**NORTH CAROLINA:** ASHE MEMORIAL HOSPITAL (C, 25 beds) 200 Hospital Avenue, Jefferson, NC, Zip 28640–9244; tel. 336/846–7101; Laura Lambeth, Chief Executive Officer **Web address:** www.ashememorial.org

NOVANT HEALTH BRUNSWICK MEDICAL CENTER (O, 54 beds) 240 Hospital Drive NE, Bolivia, NC, Zip 28422–8346; tel. 910/721–1000; Shelbourn Stevens, President and Chief Operating Officer **Web address:** https://www.novanthealth.org

NOVANT HEALTH CHARLOTTE ORTHOPAEDIC HOSPITAL (O, 15 beds) 1901 Randolph Road, Charlotte, NC, Zip 28207–1195; tel. 704/316–2000; Jamie Feinour, Interim President

NOVANT HEALTH FORSYTH MEDICAL CENTER (O, 740 beds) 3333 Silas Creek Parkway, Winston–Salem, NC, Zip 27103–3090; tel. 336/718–5000; Chad Setliff, President and Chief Operating Officer **Web address:** https://www.novanthealth.org

NOVANT HEALTH HUNTERSVILLE MEDICAL CENTER (O, 91 beds) 10030 Gilead Road, Huntersville, NC, Zip 28078–7545, Mailing Address: P.O. Box 3508, 28070–3508, tel. 704/316–4000; Mike Riley, President and Chief Operating Officer

NOVANT HEALTH MATTHEWS MEDICAL CENTER (O, 117 beds) 1500 Matthews Township Parkway, Matthews, NC, Zip 28105–4656; tel. 704/384–6500; Jason Bernd, President and Chief Operating Officer **Web address:** https://www.novanthealth.org

For explanation of codes following names, see page B2.
★ Indicates Type III membership in the American Hospital Association.

**B94** Health Care Systems, Networks and Alliances © 2021 AHA Guide

NOVANT HEALTH MEDICAL PARK HOSPITAL (O, 21 beds) 1950 South Hawthorne Road, Winston–Salem, NC, Zip 27103–3993; tel. 336/718–0600; Kirsten Royster, President and Chief Operating Officer
**Web address**: www.novanthealth.org

NOVANT HEALTH MINT HILL MEDICAL CENTER (O, 36 beds) 8201 Healthcare Loop, Charlotte, NC, Zip 28215–7072; tel. 980/302–1000; Joy Greear, President

NOVANT HEALTH PRESBYTERIAN MEDICAL CENTER (O, 440 beds) 200 Hawthorne Lane, Charlotte, NC, Zip 28204–2528, Mailing Address: P.O. Box 33549, 28233–3549, tel. 704/384–4000; Paula Vincent, MSN, President and Chief Operating Officer
**Web address**: www.novanthealth.org

NOVANT HEALTH ROWAN MEDICAL CENTER (O, 149 beds) 612 Mocksville Avenue, Salisbury, NC, Zip 28144–2799; tel. 704/210–5000; Dari Caldwell, R.N., Ph.D., FACHE, President and Chief Operating Officer
**Web address**: https://www.novanthealth.org/rowan–medical–center.aspx

NOVANT HEALTH THOMASVILLE MEDICAL CENTER (O, 87 beds) 207 Old Lexington Road, Thomasville, NC, Zip 27360–3428, Mailing Address: P.O. Box 789, 27361–0789, tel. 336/472–2000; Jon D. Applebaum, President and Chief Operating Officer
**Web address**: www.thomasvillemedicalcenter.org

**VIRGINIA**: NOVANT HEALTH UVA HEALTH SYSTEM CULPEPER MEDICAL CENTER (O, 68 beds) 501 Sunset Lane, Culpeper, VA, Zip 22701–3917, Mailing Address: P.O. Box 592, 22701–0500, tel. 540/829–4100; Jeff Hetmanski, President and Chief Operating Officer

NOVANT HEALTH UVA HEALTH SYSTEM HAYMARKET MEDICAL CENTER (O, 18 beds) 15225 Heathcote Boulevard, Haymarket, VA, Zip 20155–4023, 14535 John Marshall Hwy, Gainesville, 20155–4023, tel. 571/284–1000; Stephen Smith, President and Chief Operating Officer
**Web address**: www.novanthealth.org

NOVANT HEALTH UVA HEALTH SYSTEM PRINCE WILLIAM MEDICAL CENTER (O, 87 beds) 8700 Sudley Road, Manassas, VA, Zip 20110–4418, Mailing Address: P.O. Box 2610, 20108–0867, tel. 703/369–8000; Stephen Smith, President and Chief Operating Officer
**Web address**: www.pwhs.org

| | | |
|---|---|---|
| Owned, leased, sponsored: | 13 hospitals | 1923 beds |
| Contract–managed: | 1 hospitals | 25 beds |
| Totals: | 14 hospitals | 1948 beds |

---

**★0811: NUVANCE HEALTH** (NP)

24 Hospital Avenue, Danbury, CT Zip 06810–6099; tel. 203/739–7066; John M. Murphy, M.D., President and Chief Executive Officer
**(Centralized Physician/Insurance Health System)**

**CONNECTICUT**: DANBURY HOSPITAL (O, 286 beds) 24 Hospital Avenue, Danbury, CT, Zip 06810–6099; tel. 203/739–7000; Sharon Adams, President

NORWALK HOSPITAL (O, 161 beds) 34 Maple Street, Norwalk, CT, Zip 06850–3894; tel. 203/852–2000; Peter Cordeau, President
**Web address**: www.norwalkhospital.org

| | | |
|---|---|---|
| Owned, leased, sponsored: | 2 hospitals | 447 beds |
| Contract–managed: | 0 hospitals | 0 beds |
| Totals: | 2 hospitals | 447 beds |

---

**★3075: NYC HEALTH + HOSPITALS** (NP)

125 Worth Street, Room 514, New York, NY Zip 10013–4006; tel. 212/788–3321; Mitchell H. Katz, M.D., Chief Executive Officer
**(Decentralized Health System)**

**NEW YORK**: NYC HEALTH + HOSPITALS / BELLEVUE (O, 682 beds) 462 First Avenue, New York, NY, Zip 10016–9198; tel. 212/562–4141; William Hicks, Chief Executive Officer
**Web address**: www.nyc.gov/bellevue

NYC HEALTH + HOSPITALS / CONEY ISLAND (O, 371 beds) 2601 Ocean Parkway, Brooklyn, NY, Zip 11235–7795; tel. 718/616–3000; Svetlana Lipyanskaya, Chief Executive Officer

NYC HEALTH + HOSPITALS / ELMHURST (O, 508 beds) 79–01 Broadway, Elmhurst, NY, Zip 11373–1329; tel. 718/334–4000; Israel Rocha Jr, Chief Executive Officer
**Web address**: www.nyc.gov/html/hhc/ehc/html/home/home.shtml

NYC HEALTH + HOSPITALS / GOUVERNEUR (O, 196 beds) 227 Madison Street, New York, NY, Zip 10002; tel. 212/238–7000; Martha Adams Sullivan, Chief Executive Officer

NYC HEALTH + HOSPITALS / HARLEM (O, 245 beds) 506 Lenox Avenue, New York, NY, Zip 10037–1802; tel. 212/939–1000; Ebone' Carrington, Chief Executive Officer and Chief Operating Officer
**Web address**: www.nyc.gov/html/hhc/harlem

NYC HEALTH + HOSPITALS / HENRY J CARTER SPECIALTY HOSPITAL AND MEDICAL CENTER (O, 365 beds) 1752 Park Avenue, New York, NY, Zip 10035; tel. 646/686–0000; Floyd R. Long, Executive Director

NYC HEALTH + HOSPITALS / JACOBI (O, 388 beds) 1400 Pelham Parkway South, Bronx, NY, Zip 10461–1197; tel. 718/918–5000; Christopher Mastromanno, Chief Executive Officer
**Web address**: www.nyc.gov/html/hhc/jacobi/home.html

NYC HEALTH + HOSPITALS / KINGS COUNTY (O, 544 beds) 451 Clarkson Avenue, Brooklyn, NY, Zip 11203–2054; tel. 718/245–3131; Sheldon Mcleod, Chief Executive Officer

NYC HEALTH + HOSPITALS / LINCOLN (O, 362 beds) 234 East 149th Street, Bronx, NY, Zip 10451–5504, 234 East 149th Street, Room 923, 10451–5504, tel. 718/579–5700; Milton Nunez, Executive Director
**Web address**: www.nyc.gov/html/hhc/lincoln/

NYC HEALTH + HOSPITALS / METROPOLITAN (O, 281 beds) 1901 First Avenue, New York, NY, Zip 10029–7404; tel. 212/423–6262; Christopher Roker, Chief Executive Officer
**Web address**: www.nyc.gov/html/hhc/mhc/html/home/home.shtml

NYC HEALTH + HOSPITALS / NORTH CENTRAL BRONX (O, 142 beds) 3424 Kossuth Avenue, Bronx, NY, Zip 10467–2489; tel. 718/519–3500; Cristina Contreras, Executive Director

NYC HEALTH + HOSPITALS / QUEENS (O, 253 beds) 82–68 164th Street, Jamaica, NY, Zip 11432–1104; tel. 718/883–3000; Israel Rocha Jr, Chief Executive Officer
**Web address**: www.nyc.gov/html/hhc/qhc/html/home/home.shtml

NYC HEALTH + HOSPITALS / SEA VIEW (O, 304 beds) 460 Brielle Avenue, Staten Island, NY, Zip 10314; tel. 212/390–8181; Jane M. Lyons, Executive Director

NYC HEALTH + HOSPITALS / WOODHULL (O, 274 beds) 760 Broadway, Brooklyn, NY, Zip 11206–5383; tel. 718/963–8000; Gregory Calliste, Ph.D., FACHE, Chief Executive Officer
**Web address**: https://www.nychealthandhospitals.org/Woodhull/

| | | |
|---|---|---|
| Owned, leased, sponsored: | 14 hospitals | 4915 beds |
| Contract–managed: | 0 hospitals | 0 beds |
| Totals: | 14 hospitals | 4915 beds |

---

**0616: OCEANS HEALTHCARE** (IO)

5360 Legacy Drive, Suite 101, Plano, TX Zip 75024–3130; tel. 972/464–0022; Stuart Archer, Chief Executive Officer
**(Independent Hospital System)**

**LOUISIANA**: OCEANS BEHAVIORAL HOSPITAL OF ALEXANDRIA (O, 24 beds) 2621 North Bolton Avenue, Alexandria, LA, Zip 71303–4506; tel. 318/448–8473; Lee Edge, Administrator

OCEANS BEHAVIORAL HOSPITAL OF BATON ROUGE (O, 20 beds) 11135 Florida Boulevard, Baton Rouge, LA, Zip 70815–2013; tel. 225/356–7030; Valerie Dalton, R.N., Administrator
**Web address**: www.obhbr.info/

OCEANS BEHAVIORAL HOSPITAL OF BROUSSARD (O, 38 beds) 418 Albertson Parkway, Broussard, LA, Zip 70518–4971; tel. 337/237–6444; Amy Dysart–Credeur, Administrator

For explanation of codes following names, see page B2.
★ Indicates Type III membership in the American Hospital Association.

OCEANS BEHAVIORAL HOSPITAL OF DERIDDER (O, 20 beds) 1420 Blankenship Drive, Deridder, LA, Zip 70634–4604; tel. 337/460–9472; Stuart Archer, Chief Executive Officer, Oceans Healthcare
**Web address:** www.obhd.info/

OCEANS BEHAVIORAL HOSPITAL OF GREATER NEW ORLEANS (O, 30 beds) 716 Village Road, Kenner, LA, Zip 70065–2751; tel. 504/464–8895; Deborah Spiers, Administrator
**Web address:** www.obhgno.info/

OCEANS BEHAVIORAL HOSPITAL OF LAKE CHARLES (O, 40 beds) 4250 5th Avenue, Lake Charles, LA, Zip 70607–3900; tel. 337/474–7581; Emily McDaniel, Administrator

OCEANS BEHAVIORAL HOSPITAL OF OPELOUSAS (O, 20 beds) 1310 Heather Drive, Opelousas, LA, Zip 70570–7714; tel. 337/948–8820; Katherine Simoneaux, Administrator
**Web address:** www.obho.info/

**NEW JERSEY:** NORTHBROOK BEHAVIORAL HEALTH HOSPITAL (O, 153 beds) 425 Woodbury Turnersville Road, Blackwood, NJ, Zip 08012–2960; tel. 856/374–6500; Avi Feigenbaum, Chief Executive Officer
**Web address:** www.northbrookbhh.com

**TEXAS:** OCEANS BEHAVIORAL HEALTH CENTER PERMIAN BASIN (O, 62 beds) 3300 South FM 1788, Midland, TX, Zip 79706–2601; tel. 432/561–5915; Emileh Flitton, Administrator

OCEANS BEHAVIORAL HOSPITAL ABILENE (O, 90 beds) 4225 Woods Place, Abilene, TX, Zip 79602–7991; tel. 325/691–0030; Stacy Sanford, Chief Executive Officer
**Web address:** www.oceansabilene.com

OCEANS BEHAVIORAL HOSPITAL KATY (O, 48 beds) 455 Park Grove Lane, Katy, TX, Zip 77450–1572; tel. 281/492–8888; Stuart Archer, Chief Executive Officer
**Web address:** www.memorialhermann.org/locations/katy–rehab/

OCEANS BEHAVIORAL HOSPITAL LONGVIEW (O, 24 beds) 615 Clinic Drive, Longview, TX, Zip 75605–5172; tel. 903/212–3105; Lauren Weber, Administrator

OCEANS BEHAVIORAL HOSPITAL LUFKIN (O, 24 beds) 302 Gobblers Knob Road, Lufkin, TX, Zip 75904–5419; tel. 936/632–2276; Laci Laird, Chief Executive Officer
**Web address:** www.oceanslufkin.com/

OCEANS BEHAVIORAL HOSPITAL OF PASADENA (O, 22 beds) 4001 Preston Drive, Pasadena, TX, Zip 77505–2069; tel. 832/619–8836; Shamieka Thomas, Administrator
**Web address:** www.https://oceanshealthcare.com/pasadena

| | | |
|---|---|---|
| **Owned, leased, sponsored:** | 14 hospitals | 615 beds |
| **Contract–managed:** | 0 hospitals | 0 beds |
| **Totals:** | 14 hospitals | 615 beds |

**★0359: OCHSNER HEALTH** (NP)
1514 Jefferson Highway, New Orleans, LA Zip 70121–2429; tel. 800/874–8984; Warner L. Thomas, FACHE, President and Chief Executive Officer
**(Centralized Health System)**

**LOUISIANA:** LEONARD J. CHABERT MEDICAL CENTER (C, 80 beds) 1978 Industrial Boulevard, Houma, LA, Zip 70363–7094; tel. 985/873–2200; Timothy J. Allen, FACHE, Chief Executive Officer

OCHSNER MEDICAL CENTER – BATON ROUGE (O, 162 beds) 17000 Medical Center Drive, Baton Rouge, LA, Zip 70816–3224; tel. 225/752–2470; Eric McMillen, FACHE, Chief Executive Officer
**Web address:** https://www.ochsner.org/locations/ochsner–medical–center–baton–rouge

OCHSNER MEDICAL CENTER – KENNER (O, 110 beds) 180 West Esplanade Avenue, Kenner, LA, Zip 70065–6001; tel. 504/468–8600; Stephen Robinson Jr, FACHE, Chief Executive Officer
**Web address:** https://www.ochsner.org/locations/ochsner–medical–center–kenner/

OCHSNER MEDICAL CENTER – NORTH SHORE (L, 145 beds) 100 Medical Center Drive, Slidell, LA, Zip 70461–5520; tel. 985/649–7070; Sandy Badinger, Chief Executive Officer
**Web address:** https://www.ochsner.org/locations/ochsner–medical–center–north–shore/

OCHSNER MEDICAL CENTER (O, 962 beds) 1514 Jefferson Highway, New Orleans, LA, Zip 70121–2429; tel. 504/842–3000; Robert K. Wolterman, Chief Executive Officer

OCHSNER ST. ANNE GENERAL HOSPITAL (O, 35 beds) 4608 Highway 1, Raceland, LA, Zip 70394–2623; tel. 985/537–6841; Timothy J. Allen, FACHE, Chief Executive Officer
**Web address:** www.ochsner.org/locations/ochsner–st–anne

OCHSNER ST. MARY (C, 164 beds) 1125 Marguerite Street, Morgan City, LA, Zip 70380–1855, Mailing Address: P.O. Box 2308, 70381–2308, tel. 985/384–2200; Anthony Young, Chief Executive Officer

SLIDELL MEMORIAL HOSPITAL (C, 175 beds) 1001 Gause Boulevard, Slidell, LA, Zip 70458–2987; tel. 985/280–2200; Sandy Badinger, Chief Executive Officer
**Web address:** www.slidellmemorial.org

ST. BERNARD PARISH HOSPITAL (C, 40 beds) 8000 West Judge Perez Drive, Chalmette, LA, Zip 70043–1668; tel. 504/826–9500; Kimberly Keene, R.N., Chief Executive Officer

ST. CHARLES PARISH HOSPITAL (C, 59 beds) 1057 Paul Maillard Road, Luling, LA, Zip 70070–4349, Mailing Address: P.O. Box 87, 70070–0087, tel. 985/785–6242; Terrell Neal, R.N., Chief Executive Officer
**Web address:** https://www.ochsner.org/locations/st–charles–parish–hospital/

**MISSISSIPPI:** HANCOCK MEDICAL CENTER (C, 102 beds) 149 Drinkwater Boulevard, Bay Saint Louis, MS, Zip 39520–1658, Bay St Louis, tel. 228/467–8600; Alan Hodges, Chief Executive Officer
**Web address:** www.ochsner.org/locations/hancock–medical–center

| | | |
|---|---|---|
| **Owned, leased, sponsored:** | 5 hospitals | 1414 beds |
| **Contract–managed:** | 6 hospitals | 620 beds |
| **Totals:** | 11 hospitals | 2034 beds |

**0978: OGLETHORPE RECOVERY AND BEHAVIORAL HOSPITALS** (IO)
201 North Franklin Street, Tampa, FL Zip 33602–5182; tel. 813/978–1933; John Picciano, Chief Executive Officer

**FLORIDA:** PORT ST. LUCIE HOSPITAL (O, 75 beds) 2550 SE Walton Road, Port St Lucie, FL, Zip 34952–7168; tel. 772/335–0400; Patrick Kiley, Administrator

SPRINGBROOK HOSPITAL (O, 66 beds) 7007 Grove Road, Brooksville, FL, Zip 34609–8610; tel. 352/596–4306; Mercy Estevez, Chief Executive Officer
**Web address:** www.springbrookhospital.org/

THE BLACKBERRY CENTER (O, 64 beds) 91 Beehive Circle, Saint Cloud, FL, Zip 34769–1432, St. Cloud, tel. 321/805–5090; Rick Bennett, Director
**Web address:** www.blackberrycenter.com

**LOUISIANA:** BATON ROUGE BEHAVIORAL HOSPITAL (O, 15 beds) 4040 North Boulevard, Baton Rouge, LA, Zip 70806–3829; tel. 225/300–8470; Clay Aguillard, R.N., Administrator

**NEVADA:** VANCE JOHNSON RECOVERY CENTER (O, 44 beds) 2651 Westwood Drive, Las Vegas, NV, Zip 89109–1117; tel. 888/828–2623; Dan Mager, Administrator
**Web address:** https://www.oglethorpeinc.com/vance–johnson–recovery–center/

**OHIO:** GEORGETOWN BEHAVIORAL HOSPITAL (O, 46 beds) 425 Home Street, Georgetown, OH, Zip 45121–1407; tel. 937/483–4933; Arthur Douglas. Owens, Administrator
**Web address:** https://www.gbhoh.com

RIDGEVIEW BEHAVIORAL HOSPITAL (O, 40 beds) 17872 Lincoln Highway, Middle Point, OH, Zip 45863–9700; tel. 419/968–2950; Pat Tracy, Administrator

| | | |
|---|---|---|
| **Owned, leased, sponsored:** | 7 hospitals | 350 beds |
| **Contract–managed:** | 0 hospitals | 0 beds |
| **Totals:** | 7 hospitals | 350 beds |

For explanation of codes following names, see page B2.
★ Indicates Type III membership in the American Hospital Association.

## 0537: OHIO DEPARTMENT OF MENTAL HEALTH (NP)

30 East Broad Street, 8th Floor, Columbus, OH Zip 43215–3430; tel. 614/466–2297; Tracy Plouck, Director

**(Independent Hospital System)**

**OHIO:** APPALACHIAN BEHAVIORAL HEALTHCARE (O, 224 beds) 100 Hospital Drive, Athens, OH, Zip 45701–2301; tel. 740/594–5000; Jane E. Krason, R.N., Chief Executive Officer
**Web address:** www.mh.state.oh.us

HEARTLAND BEHAVIORAL HEALTHCARE (O, 152 beds) 3000 Erie Stree South, Massillon, OH, Zip 44646–7993, 3000 Erie Street South, 44646–7976, tel. 330/833–3135; Jeffrey Sims, Chief Executive Officer
**Web address:** www.mh.state.oh.us/ibhs/bhos/hoh.html

NORTHCOAST BEHAVIORAL HEALTHCARE (O, 258 beds) 1756 Sagamore Road, Northfield, OH, Zip 44067–1086; tel. 330/467–7131; Douglas W. Kern, Chief Executive Officer

NORTHWEST OHIO PSYCHIATRIC HOSPITAL (O, 112 beds) 930 Detroit Avenue, Toledo, OH, Zip 43614–2701; tel. 419/381–1881; Brett M. Johnson, Chief Executive Officer
**Web address:** www.mh.state.oh.us/

SUMMIT BEHAVIORAL HEALTHCARE (O, 291 beds) 1101 Summit Road, Cincinnati, OH, Zip 45237–2652; tel. 513/948–3600; Elizabeth Banks, Chief Executive Officer
**Web address:** www.mh.state.oh.us/

TWIN VALLEY BEHAVIORAL HEALTHCARE (O, 178 beds) 2200 West Broad Street, Columbus, OH, Zip 43223–1297; tel. 614/752–0333; Veronica Lofton, Acting Chief Executive Officer
**Web address:** www.mh.state.oh.us/ibhs/bhos/tvbh.html

| Owned, leased, sponsored: | 6 hospitals | 1215 beds |
| Contract–managed: | 0 hospitals | 0 beds |
| Totals: | 6 hospitals | 1215 beds |

## ★0251: OHIO STATE UNIVERSITY HEALTH SYSTEM (NP)

370 West Ninth Avenue, Columbus, OH Zip 43210–1238; tel. 614/685–9015; David P. McQuaid, FACHE, Chief Executive Officer

**(Centralized Physician/Insurance Health System)**

**OHIO:** JAMES CANCER HOSPITAL AND SOLOVE RESEARCH INSTITUTE (O, 344 beds) 460 West Tenth Avenue, Columbus, OH, Zip 43210–1240; tel. 614/293–3300; William Farrar, M.D., Interim Chief Executive Officer
**Web address:** www.https://cancer.osu.edu/

OHIO STATE UNIVERSITY WEXNER MEDICAL CENTER (O, 1124 beds) 410 West 10th Avenue, Columbus, OH, Zip 43210–1240; tel. 614/293–8000; David P. McQuaid, FACHE, Chief Operating Officer
**Web address:** www.medicalcenter.osu.edu

| Owned, leased, sponsored: | 2 hospitals | 1468 beds |
| Contract–managed: | 0 hospitals | 0 beds |
| Totals: | 2 hospitals | 1468 beds |

## ★0162: OHIOHEALTH (NP)

3430 Ohio Health Parkway, Columbus, OH Zip 43202–1575; tel. 614/544–4455; Stephen Markovich, M.D., President and Chief Executive Officer

**(Moderately Centralized Health System)**

**OHIO:** MORROW COUNTY HOSPITAL (C, 22 beds) 651 West Marion Road, Mount Gilead, OH, Zip 43338–1027; tel. 419/946–5015; Chad J. Miller, President and Chief Executive Officer
**Web address:** www.morrowcountyhospital.com

O'BLENESS MEMORIAL HOSPITAL (O, 69 beds) 55 Hospital Drive, Athens, OH, Zip 45701–2302; tel. 740/593–5551; Mark R. Seckinger, President

OHIOHEALTH BERGER HOSPITAL (L, 56 beds) 600 North Pickaway Street, Circleville, OH, Zip 43113–1447; tel. 740/474–2126; Tim A. Colburn, President and Chief Executive Officer
**Web address:** www.bergerhealth.com

OHIOHEALTH DOCTORS HOSPITAL (O, 206 beds) 5100 West Broad Street, Columbus, OH, Zip 43228–1607; tel. 614/544–1000; Michael L. Reichfield, President
**Web address:** www.ohiohealth.com

OHIOHEALTH DUBLIN METHODIST HOSPITAL (O, 120 beds) 7500 Hospital Drive, Dublin, OH, Zip 43016–8518; tel. 614/544–8000; Steve Bunyard, President

OHIOHEALTH GRADY MEMORIAL HOSPITAL (O, 61 beds) 561 West Central Avenue, Delaware, OH, Zip 43015–1410; tel. 740/615–1000; Steve Bunyard, President
**Web address:** www.ohiohealth.com

OHIOHEALTH GRANT MEDICAL CENTER (O, 471 beds) 111 South Grant Avenue, Columbus, OH, Zip 43215–1898; tel. 614/566–9000; Michael Lawson, President and Chief Operating Officer

OHIOHEALTH HARDIN MEMORIAL HOSPITAL (O, 25 beds) 921 East Franklin Street, Kenton, OH, Zip 43326–2099; tel. 419/673–0761; Ron Snyder, Chief Operating Officer
**Web address:** www.hardinmemorial.org

OHIOHEALTH MARION GENERAL HOSPITAL (O, 229 beds) 1000 McKinley Park Drive, Marion, OH, Zip 43302–6397; tel. 740/383–8400; Curtis Gingrich, M.D., Chief Operating Officer
**Web address:** www.ohiohealth.com/mariongeneral

OHIOHEALTH MEDCENTRAL MANSFIELD HOSPITAL (O, 249 beds) 335 Glessner Avenue, Mansfield, OH, Zip 44903–2265; tel. 419/526–8000; Vinson Yates, President

OHIOHEALTH MEDCENTRAL SHELBY HOSPITAL (O, 25 beds) 199 West Main Street, Shelby, OH, Zip 44875–1490; tel. 419/342–5015; Vinson Yates, President
**Web address:** www.medcentral.org/body.cfm?id=153

OHIOHEALTH RIVERSIDE METHODIST HOSPITAL (O, 754 beds) 3535 Olentangy River Road, Columbus, OH, Zip 43214–3998; tel. 614/566–5000; Brian Jepson, President

| Owned, leased, sponsored: | 11 hospitals | 2265 beds |
| Contract–managed: | 1 hospitals | 22 beds |
| Totals: | 12 hospitals | 2287 beds |

## 0018: OKLAHOMA DEPARTMENT OF MENTAL HEALTH AND SUBSTANCE ABUSE SERVICES (NP)

1200 NE 13th Street, Oklahoma City, OK Zip 73117–1022, Mailing Address: P.O. Box 53277, 73152–3277, tel. 405/522–3908; Terri White, Commissioner

**(Independent Hospital System)**

**OKLAHOMA:** GRIFFIN MEMORIAL HOSPITAL (O, 120 beds) 900 East Main Street, Norman, OK, Zip 73071–5305, Mailing Address: P.O. Box 151, 73070–0151, tel. 405/573–6600; Henry Hartsell, Ph.D., Executive Director

NORTHWEST CENTER FOR BEHAVIORAL HEALTH (O, 24 beds) 193461 East County Road, #304, Fort Supply, OK, Zip 73841, 1222 10th Street, Suite 211, Woodward, 73801–3156, tel. 580/766–2311; Cathy Billings, Interim Executive Director
**Web address:** www.ncbhok.org/

OKLAHOMA FORENSIC CENTER (O, 200 beds) 24800 South 4420 Road, Vinita, OK, Zip 74301–5544, Mailing Address: P.O. Box 69, 74301–0069, tel. 918/256–7841; Kevan Finley, Chief Executive Officer
**Web address:** www.odmhsas.org

| Owned, leased, sponsored: | 3 hospitals | 344 beds |
| Contract–managed: | 0 hospitals | 0 beds |
| Totals: | 3 hospitals | 344 beds |

## 3355: ORLANDO HEALTH (NP)

1414 Kuhl Avenue, Orlando, FL Zip 32806–2093; tel. 321/843–7000; David W. Strong, President and Chief Executive Officer

**(Moderately Centralized Health System)**

---

For explanation of codes following names, see page B2.
★ Indicates Type III membership in the American Hospital Association.

Section B

**FLORIDA:** HEALTH CENTRAL HOSPITAL (O, 439 beds) 10000 West Colonial Drive, Ocoee, FL, Zip 34761–3499; tel. 407/296–1000; Mark A. Marsh, President
**Web address:** www.orlandohealth.com/facilities/health–central–hospital

ORLANDO REGIONAL MEDICAL CENTER (O, 1342 beds) 52 West Underwood Street, Orlando, FL, Zip 32806; tel. 407/841–5111; Mark A. Jones, President

SOUTH LAKE HOSPITAL (O, 170 beds) 1900 Don Wickham Drive, Clermont, FL, Zip 34711–1979; tel. 352/394–4071; John Moore, FACHE, President
**Web address:** www.southlakehospital.com

ST. CLOUD REGIONAL MEDICAL CENTER (O, 84 beds) 2906 17th Street, Saint Cloud, FL, Zip 34769–6099; tel. 407/892–2135; Brent Burish, Chief Executive Officer
**Web address:** www.stcloudregional.com

| Owned, leased, sponsored: | 4 hospitals | 2035 beds |
|---|---|---|
| Contract–managed: | 0 hospitals | 0 beds |
| Totals: | 4 hospitals | 2035 beds |

---

**★5335: OSF HEALTHCARE** (CO)
800 NE Glen Oak Avenue, Peoria, IL Zip 61603–3200; tel. 309/655–2850; Robert Sehring, Chief Executive Officer
**(Moderately Centralized Health System)**

**ILLINOIS:** OSF HEALTHCARE SAINT ANTHONY'S HEALTH CENTER (O, 49 beds) 1 Saint Anthony's Way, Alton, IL, Zip 62002–4579, Mailing Address: P.O. 340, 62002–0340, tel. 618/465–2571; Sister, M. Mikela. Meidl, Interim President

OSF HEALTHCARE LITTLE COMPANY OF MARY MEDICAL CENTER (O, 251 beds) 2800 West 95th Street, Evergreen Park, IL, Zip 60805–2795; tel. 708/422–6200; Kathleen Kinsella, President
**Web address:** https://www.osfhealthcare.org/little–company–of–mary/

OSF HEART OF MARY MEDICAL CENTER (O, 181 beds) 1400 West Park Street, Urbana, IL, Zip 61801–2396, Mailing Address: P.O. Box 6259, Peoria, 61601, tel. 217/337–2000; Jared Rogers, M.D., President and Chief Executive Officer

OSF HOLY FAMILY MEDICAL CENTER (O, 23 beds) 1000 West Harlem Avenue, Monmouth, IL, Zip 61462–1007; tel. 309/734–3141; Jackie Kernan, President
**Web address:** www.osfholyfamily.org

OSF SACRED HEART MEDICAL CENTER (O, 115 beds) 812 North Logan, Danville, IL, Zip 61832–3788; tel. 217/443–5000; Jared Rogers, M.D., President and Chief Executive Officer

OSF SAINT ANTHONY MEDICAL CENTER (O, 235 beds) 5666 East State Street, Rockford, IL, Zip 61108–2425; tel. 815/226–2000; Paula A. Carynski, MS, R.N., President
**Web address:** www.osfhealth.com

OSF SAINT ELIZABETH MEDICAL CENTER (O, 87 beds) 1100 East Norris Drive, Ottawa, IL, Zip 61350–1687; tel. 815/433–3100; Kenneth Beutke, President

OSF SAINT FRANCIS MEDICAL CENTER (O, 629 beds) 530 NE Glen Oak Avenue, Peoria, IL, Zip 61637–0001; tel. 309/655–2000; Robert G. Anderson Jr, President
**Web address:** www.osfsaintfrancis.org

OSF SAINT JAMES – JOHN W. ALBRECHT MEDICAL CENTER (O, 42 beds) 2500 West Reynolds, Pontiac, IL, Zip 61764–9774; tel. 815/842–2828; Bradley V. Solberg, FACHE, President
**Web address:** www.osfsaintjames.org

OSF SAINT LUKE MEDICAL CENTER (O, 25 beds) 1051 West South Street, Kewanee, IL, Zip 61443–8354, Mailing Address: P.O. Box 747, 61443–0747, tel. 309/852–7500; Jacqueline D. Kernan, President

OSF SAINT PAUL MEDICAL CENTER (O, 25 beds) 1401 East 12th Street, Mendota, IL, Zip 61342–9216; tel. 815/539–7461; Dawn Trompeter, President
**Web address:** https://www.osfhealthcare.org/saint–paul

OSF ST. JOSEPH MEDICAL CENTER (O, 149 beds) 2200 East Washington Street, Bloomington, IL, Zip 61701–4323; tel. 309/662–3311; Lynn Fulton, President

OSF ST. MARY MEDICAL CENTER (O, 73 beds) 3333 North Seminary Street, Galesburg, IL, Zip 61401–1299; tel. 309/344–3161; Lisa DeKezel, President
**Web address:** www.osfstmary.org

SAINT CLARE HOME (O, 0 beds) 5533 North Galena Road, Peoria Heights, IL, Zip 61614–4499; tel. 309/682–5428; Candy Conover, Administrator

ST. ANTHONY'S CONTINUING CARE CENTER (O, 179 beds) 767 30th Street, Rock Island, IL, Zip 61201, Sister, Mary Anthony. Mazzaferri, Administrator

**MICHIGAN:** OSF ST. FRANCIS HOSPITAL AND MEDICAL GROUP (O, 25 beds) 3401 Ludington Street, Escanaba, MI, Zip 49829–1377; tel. 906/786–3311; David Lord, President
**Web address:** www.osfstfrancis.org

| Owned, leased, sponsored: | 16 hospitals | 2088 beds |
|---|---|---|
| Contract–managed: | 0 hospitals | 0 beds |
| Totals: | 16 hospitals | 2088 beds |

---

**0982: OWENSBORO HEALTH** (NP)
1201 Pleasant Valley Road, Owensboro, KY Zip 42303–9811; tel. 270/417–2000; Greg Strahan, Interim Chief Executive Officer
**(Moderately Centralized Health System)**

**KENTUCKY:** OWENSBORO HEALTH MUHLENBERG COMMUNITY HOSPITAL (O, 105 beds) 440 Hopkinsville Street, Greenville, KY, Zip 42345–1124, Mailing Address: P.O. Box 387, 42345–0378, tel. 270/338–8000; Ed Heath, FACHE, Chief Executive Officer
**Web address:** www.owensborohealth.org/

OWENSBORO HEALTH REGIONAL HOSPITAL (O, 360 beds) 1201 Pleasant Valley Road, Owensboro, KY, Zip 42303; tel. 270/417–2000; Greg Strahan, President and Chief Executive Officer

| Owned, leased, sponsored: | 2 hospitals | 465 beds |
|---|---|---|
| Contract–managed: | 0 hospitals | 0 beds |
| Totals: | 2 hospitals | 465 beds |

---

**★7555: PALOMAR HEALTH** (NP)
456 East Grand Avenue, Escondido, CA Zip 92025–3319; tel. 760/740–6393; Diane Hansen, Chief Executive Officer
**(Independent Hospital System)**

**CALIFORNIA:** PALOMAR MEDICAL CENTER ESCONDIDO (O, 344 beds) 2185 West Citracado Parkway, Escondido, CA, Zip 92029–4159; tel. 760/739–3000; Mariellena Sudak, R.N., MSN, Vice President and Chief Nursing Officer
**Web address:** www.palomarhealth.org

PALOMAR MEDICAL CENTER POWAY (O, 201 beds) 15615 Pomerado Road, Poway, CA, Zip 92064–2460; tel. 858/613–4000; Cheryl Olson, Vice President
**Web address:** www.pph.org

| Owned, leased, sponsored: | 2 hospitals | 545 beds |
|---|---|---|
| Contract–managed: | 0 hospitals | 0 beds |
| Totals: | 2 hospitals | 545 beds |

---

**★0159: PARKVIEW HEALTH** (NP)
10501 Corporate Drive, Fort Wayne, IN Zip 46845–1700; tel. 260/373–7001; Michael J. Packnett, President and Chief Executive Officer
**(Centralized Physician/Insurance Health System)**

**INDIANA:** PARKVIEW ORTHO HOSPITAL (O, 37 beds) 11130 Parkview Circle Drive, Fort Wayne, IN, Zip 46845–1735; tel. 260/672–5000; Julie Fleck, Chief Operating Officer
**Web address:** www.parkview.com

PARKVIEW DEKALB HOSPITAL (O, 57 beds) 1316 East Seventh Street, Auburn, IN, Zip 46706–2515, Mailing Address: P.O. Box 542, 46706–0542, tel. 260/925–4600; Natasha Eicher, President and Chief Executive Officer
**Web address:** www.dekalbhealth.com

For explanation of codes following names, see page B2.
★ Indicates Type III membership in the American Hospital Association.

PARKVIEW HUNTINGTON HOSPITAL (O, 36 beds) 2001 Stults Road, Huntington, IN, Zip 46750–1291; tel. 260/355–3000; Juli Johnson, MSN, R.N., President
**Web address:** www.parkview.com

PARKVIEW LAGRANGE HOSPITAL (O, 25 beds) 207 North Townline Road, LaGrange, IN, Zip 46761–1325; tel. 260/463–9000; Jordi K. Disler, President
**Web address:** www.parkview.com

PARKVIEW NOBLE HOSPITAL (O, 31 beds) 401 Sawyer Road, Kendallville, IN, Zip 46755–2568; tel. 260/347–8700; Gary W. Adkins, President

PARKVIEW REGIONAL MEDICAL CENTER (O, 738 beds) 11109 Parkview Plaza Drive, Fort Wayne, IN, Zip 46845–1701; tel. 260/266–1000; Ben Miles, President
**Web address:** www.parkview.com

PARKVIEW WABASH HOSPITAL (O, 18 beds) 10 John Kissinger Drive, Wabash, IN, Zip 46992–1648; tel. 260/563–3131; Marilyn J. Custer-Mitchell, President

PARKVIEW WHITLEY HOSPITAL (O, 30 beds) 1260 East State Road 205, Columbia City, IN, Zip 46725–9492; tel. 260/248–9000; Scott F. Gabriel, President
**Web address:** www.parkview.com

| Owned, leased, sponsored: | 8 hospitals | 972 beds |
|---|---|---|
| Contract–managed: | 0 hospitals | 0 beds |
| Totals: | 8 hospitals | 972 beds |

★**5415: PEACEHEALTH** (CO)
1115 SE 164th Avenue, Vancouver, WA Zip 98683; tel. 360/729–1000; Elizabeth Dunne, President and Chief Executive Officer
**(Moderately Centralized Health System)**

**ALASKA:** PEACEHEALTH KETCHIKAN MEDICAL CENTER (L, 50 beds) 3100 Tongass Avenue, Ketchikan, AK, Zip 99901–5746; tel. 907/225–5171; Joe Mark, Interim Chief Administrator
**Web address:** www.peacehealth.org

**OREGON:** PEACEHEALTH COTTAGE GROVE COMMUNITY MEDICAL CENTER (O, 14 beds) 1515 Village Drive, Cottage Grove, OR, Zip 97424–9700; tel. 541/942–0511; Tim Herrmann, R.N., Administrator

PEACEHEALTH PEACE HARBOR MEDICAL CENTER (O, 21 beds) 400 Ninth Street, Florence, OR, Zip 97439–7398; tel. 541/997–8412; Jason F. Hawkins, Chief Administrative Officer
**Web address:** www.peacehealth.org

PEACEHEALTH SACRED HEART MEDICAL CENTER UNIVERSITY DISTRICT (O, 93 beds) 1255 Hilyard Street, Eugene, OR, Zip 97401–3700, Mailing Address: P.O. Box 10905, 97440–2905, tel. 541/686–7300; Mary Anne McMurren, R.N., Chief Administrative Officer

PEACEHEALTH SACRED HEART MEDICAL CENTER AT RIVERBEND (O, 379 beds) 3333 Riverbend Drive, Springfield, OR, Zip 97477–8800; tel. 541/222–7300; Mary E. Kingston, FACHE, R.N., Chief Executive
**Web address:** www.peacehealth.org

**WASHINGTON:** PEACEHEALTH PEACE ISLAND MEDICAL CENTER (O, 10 beds) 1117 Spring Street, Friday Harbor, WA, Zip 98250–9782; tel. 360/378–2141; Jack Estrada, Chief Administrative Officer

PEACEHEALTH SOUTHWEST MEDICAL CENTER (O, 436 beds) 400 NE Mother Joseph Place, Vancouver, WA, Zip 98664–3200, Mailing Address: P.O. Box 1600, 98668–1600, tel. 360/256–2000; Sean Gregory, Chief Executive
**Web address:** www.peacehealth.org

PEACEHEALTH ST. JOHN MEDICAL CENTER (O, 180 beds) 1615 Delaware Street, Longview, WA, Zip 98632–2367, Mailing Address: P.O. Box 3002, 98632–0302, tel. 360/414–2000; Cherelle Montanye–Ireland, Chief Administrative Officer

PEACEHEALTH ST. JOSEPH MEDICAL CENTER (O, 255 beds) 2901 Squalicum Parkway, Bellingham, WA, Zip 98225–1851; tel. 360/734–5400; Charles Prosper, Chief Executive NW
**Web address:** www.peacehealth.org

PEACEHEALTH UNITED GENERAL MEDICAL CENTER (C, 25 beds) 2000 Hospital Drive, Sedro–Woolley, WA, Zip 98284–4327; tel. 360/856–6021; Christopher Johnston, Chief Administrative Officer
**Web address:** www.peacehealth.org/united–general

| Owned, leased, sponsored: | 9 hospitals | 1438 beds |
|---|---|---|
| Contract–managed: | 1 hospitals | 25 beds |
| Totals: | 10 hospitals | 1463 beds |

**0989: PENN STATE HERSHEY HEALTH SYSTEM** (NP)
500 University Drive, Hershey, PA Zip 17033–2360; tel. 717/531–8521; Stephen M. Massini, Chief Executive Officer
**(Independent Hospital System)**

**PENNSYLVANIA:** PENN STATE HEALTH ST. JOSEPH (O, 180 beds) 2500 Bernville Road, Reading, PA, Zip 19605–9453, Mailing Address: P.O. Box 316, 19603–0316, tel. 610/378–2000; Joseph Frank, Interim President

PENN STATE MILTON S. HERSHEY MEDICAL CENTER (O, 531 beds) 500 University Drive, Hershey, PA, Zip 17033–2360, Mailing Address: P.O. Box 850, 17033–0850, tel. 717/531–8521; Deborah Berini, President
**Web address:** www.pennstatehershey.org/

| Owned, leased, sponsored: | 2 hospitals | 711 beds |
|---|---|---|
| Contract–managed: | 0 hospitals | 0 beds |
| Totals: | 2 hospitals | 711 beds |

**0973: PERIMETER HEALTHCARE** (IO)
2520 Northwinds Parkway Suite 550, Alpharetta, GA Zip 30009–2236; tel. 470/554–7902; James R. Laughlin, President and Chief Executive Officer

**ARKANSAS:** PERIMETER BEHAVIORAL HOSPITAL OF WEST MEMPHIS (O, 24 beds) 600 North Seventh Street, West Memphis, AR, Zip 72301–3235; tel. 870/394–7100; Barbara Radebaugh, Chief Executive Officer
**Web address:** https://www.perimeterhealthcare.com

**LOUISIANA:** PERIMETER BEHAVIORAL HOSPITAL OF NEW ORLEANS (O, 36 beds) 3639 Loyola Drive, Kenner, LA, Zip 70065; tel. 504/305–2700; Debbie Tullier, Chief Executive Officer
**Web address:** https://www.lakepineshospital.com/

**MISSOURI:** PERIMETER BEHAVIORAL HOSPITAL OF SPRINGFIELD (O, 32 beds) 2828 North National Avenue, Springfield, MO, Zip 65803–4306; tel. 417/799–7474; Lynn Lemke, Chief Executive Officer
**Web address:** www.perimeterhealthcare.com

**TEXAS:** PERIMETER BEHAVIORAL HOSPITAL OF ARLINGTON (O, 116 beds) 7000 US Highway 287 South, Arlington, TX, Zip 76001; tel. 817/662–6342; Keith Morehouse, Chief Executive Officer

PERIMETER BEHAVIORAL HOSPITAL OF DALLAS (O, 100 beds) 2696 West Walnut Street, Garland, TX, Zip 75042–6441; tel. 972/370–5517; Phillip Wilcoxon, Chief Executive Officer
**Web address:** https://www.perimeterhealthcare.com/facilities/perimeter–behavioral–hospital–of–dallas/

| Owned, leased, sponsored: | 5 hospitals | 308 beds |
|---|---|---|
| Contract–managed: | 0 hospitals | 0 beds |
| Totals: | 5 hospitals | 308 beds |

★**0314: PHOEBE PUTNEY HEALTH SYSTEM** (NP)
417 Third Avenue, Albany, GA Zip 31701–1943; tel. 229/312–1000; Scott Steiner, FACHE, Chief Executive Officer
**(Independent Hospital System)**

**GEORGIA:** PHOEBE PUTNEY MEMORIAL HOSPITAL (O, 442 beds) 417 West Third Avenue, Albany, GA, Zip 31701–1943, Mailing Address: P.O. Box 3770, 31706–3770, tel. 229/312–4100; Scott Steiner, FACHE, Chief Executive Officer
**Web address:** www.phoebeputney.com

---

For explanation of codes following names, see page B2.
★ Indicates Type III membership in the American Hospital Association.

PHOEBE SUMTER MEDICAL CENTER (O, 54 beds) 126 Highway, 280 West, Americus, GA, Zip 31719, 126 Highway 280 West, 31719, tel. 229/924–6011; Brandi Lunneborg, Chief Executive Officer

PHOEBE WORTH MEDICAL CENTER (O, 18 beds) 807 South Isabella Street, Sylvester, GA, Zip 31791–7554, Mailing Address: P.O. Box 545, 31791–0545, tel. 229/776–6961; Kim Gilman, Chief Executive Officer
**Web address:** www.phoebeputney.com

SOUTHWEST GEORGIA REGIONAL MEDICAL CENTER (O, 25 beds) 361 Randolph Street, Cuthbert, GA, Zip 39840–6127; tel. 229/732–2181; Kim Gilman, Chief Executive Officer and Chief Nursing Officer

| | | |
|---|---|---|
| Owned, leased, sponsored: | 4 hospitals | 539 beds |
| Contract–managed: | 0 hospitals | 0 beds |
| Totals: | 4 hospitals | 539 beds |

## 0043: PHYSICIANS FOR HEALTHY HOSPITALS (IO)

1117 East Devonshire Avenue, Hemet, CA Zip 92543–3083; tel. 951/652–2811; Joel M. Bergenfeld, Chief Executive Officer

**CALIFORNIA:** HEMET VALLEY MEDICAL CENTER (O, 238 beds) 1117 East Devonshire Avenue, Hemet, CA, Zip 92543–3083; tel. 951/652–2811; Dan C. McLaughlin, Chief Hospital Executive Officer

MENIFEE VALLEY MEDICAL CENTER (O, 84 beds) 28400 McCall Boulevard, Sun City, CA, Zip 92585–9537; tel. 951/679–8888; Dan C. McLaughlin, Chief Executive Officer
**Web address:** www.menifeevalleymedicalcenter.com/

| | | |
|---|---|---|
| Owned, leased, sponsored: | 2 hospitals | 322 beds |
| Contract–managed: | 0 hospitals | 0 beds |
| Totals: | 2 hospitals | 322 beds |

## 0310: PIEDMONT HEALTHCARE (NP)

1800 Howell Mill Road NW, Suite 850, Roswell, GA Zip 30076, Atlanta, tel. 404/425–1314; Kevin Brown, President and Chief Executive Officer
**(Moderately Centralized Health System)**

**GEORGIA:** PIEDMONT ATHENS REGIONAL MEDICAL CENTER (O, 345 beds) 1199 Prince Avenue, Athens, GA, Zip 30606–2797; tel. 706/475–7000; Michael Burnett, Chief Executive Officer
**Web address:** https://www.piedmont.org/locations/piedmont–athens

PIEDMONT COLUMBUS REGIONAL MIDTOWN (O, 510 beds) 710 Center Street, Columbus, GA, Zip 31901–1527, Mailing Address: P.O. Box 951, 31902–0951, tel. 706/571–1000; M. Scott. Hill, President and Chief Executive Officer
**Web address:** www.columbusregional.com

PIEDMONT COLUMBUS REGIONAL NORTHSIDE (O, 100 beds) 100 Frist Court, Columbus, GA, Zip 31909–3578, Mailing Address: P.O. Box 7188, 31908–7188, tel. 706/494–2100; M. Scott. Hill, President and Chief Executive Officer

PIEDMONT FAYETTE HOSPITAL (O, 210 beds) 1255 Highway 54 West, Fayetteville, GA, Zip 30214–4526; tel. 770/719–7000; Stephen D. Porter, Chief Executive Officer
**Web address:** www.piedmont.org

PIEDMONT HENRY HOSPITAL (L, 258 beds) 1133 Eagle's Landing Parkway, Stockbridge, GA, Zip 30281–5099; tel. 678/604–1000; Lily Henson, M.D., Chief Executive Officer
**Web address:** www.piedmont.org

PIEDMONT HOSPITAL (O, 512 beds) 1968 Peachtree Road NW, Atlanta, GA, Zip 30309–1281; tel. 404/605–5000; Patrick M. Battey, FACS, M.D., Chief Executive Officer

PIEDMONT MOUNTAINSIDE HOSPITAL (O, 52 beds) 1266 Highway 515 South, Jasper, GA, Zip 30143–4872; tel. 706/692–2441; Denise Ray, Chief Executive Officer
**Web address:** https://www.piedmont.org

PIEDMONT NEWNAN HOSPITAL (O, 146 beds) 745 Poplar Road, Newnan, GA, Zip 30265–1618; tel. 770/400–1000; Michael Robertson, Chief Executive Officer

PIEDMONT NEWTON HOSPITAL (O, 103 beds) 5126 Hospital Drive, Covington, GA, Zip 30014–2567; tel. 770/786–7053; David Kent, Chief Executive Officer
**Web address:** www.newtonmedical.com

PIEDMONT ROCKDALE HOSPITAL (O, 158 beds) 1412 Milstead Avenue NE, Conyers, GA, Zip 30012–3877; tel. 770/918–3000; Richard Tanzella, Chief Executive Officer
**Web address:** www.rockdalemedicalcenter.org

PIEDMONT WALTON HOSPITAL (O, 52 beds) 2151 West Spring Street, Monroe, GA, Zip 30655–3115, Mailing Address: P.O. 1346, 30655–1346, tel. 770/267–8461; Larry W. Ebert Jr, Chief Executive Officer

| | | |
|---|---|---|
| Owned, leased, sponsored: | 11 hospitals | 2446 beds |
| Contract–managed: | 0 hospitals | 0 beds |
| Totals: | 11 hospitals | 2446 beds |

## ★0958: PIH HEALTH (NP)

12401 Washington Boulevard, Whittier, CA Zip 90602–1006; tel. 562/698–0811; James R. West, President and Chief Executive Officer
**(Moderately Centralized Health System)**

**CALIFORNIA:** GOOD SAMARITAN HOSPITAL (O, 402 beds) 1225 Wilshire Boulevard, Los Angeles, CA, Zip 90017–2395; tel. 213/977–2121; Andrew B. Leeka, President and Chief Executive Officer
**Web address:** www.goodsam.org

PIH HEALTH HOSPITAL – DOWNEY (O, 156 beds) 11500 Brookshire Avenue, Downey, CA, Zip 90241–4917; tel. 562/904–5000; James R. West, President and Chief Executive Officer

PIH HEALTH HOSPITAL – WHITTIER (O, 255 beds) 12401 Washington Boulevard, Whittier, CA, Zip 90602–1099; tel. 562/698–0811; James R. West, President and Chief Executive Officer
**Web address:** www.PIHHealth.org

| | | |
|---|---|---|
| Owned, leased, sponsored: | 3 hospitals | 813 beds |
| Contract–managed: | 0 hospitals | 0 beds |
| Totals: | 3 hospitals | 813 beds |

## ★0617: POST ACUTE MEDICAL, LLC (IO)

1828 Good Hope Road, Suite 102, Enola, PA Zip 17025–1233; tel. 717/731–9660; Anthony F. Misitano, President and Chief Executive Officer
**(Independent Hospital System)**

**COLORADO:** PAM SPECIALTY HOSPITAL OF DENVER (O, 63 beds) 1690 Meade Street, Denver, CO, Zip 80204–1552, 1690 North Meade Street, 80204–1552, tel. 303/264–6900; Cindy Chaney, Chief Executive Officer
**Web address:** www.https://postacutemedical.com/facilities/find–facility/specialty–hospitals/PAM–Specialty–Hospital–of–Denver

**FLORIDA:** PAM SPECIALTY HOSPITAL OF SARASOTA (O, 40 beds) 6150 Edgelake Drive, Sarasota, FL, Zip 34240–8803; tel. 941/342–3000; Jacob McGuirt, Chief Executive Officer
**Web address:** www.lifecare–hospitals.com/hospital.php?id=23

**KANSAS:** REHABILITATION HOSPITAL OF OVERLAND PARK (O, 45 beds) 5100 Indian Creek Parkway, Overland Park, KS, Zip 66207–4115; tel. 913/544–1957; John Hughes, Chief Executive Officer

**LOUISIANA:** PAM SPECIALTY HOSPITAL OF COVINGTON (O, 42 beds) 20050 Crestwood Boulevard, Covington, LA, Zip 70433–5207; tel. 985/875–7525; Brian Davis, Chief Executive Officer
**Web address:** www.postacutemedical.com

PAM SPECIALTY HOSPITAL OF HAMMOND (O, 40 beds) 42074 Veterans Avenue, Hammond, LA, Zip 70403–1408; tel. 985/902–8148; Nicholas Paul. Mendez, Chief Executive Officer and Director of Nursing

PAM SPECIALTY HOSPITAL OF SHREVEPORT SOUTH (O, 54 beds) 8001 Youree Drive, Shreveport, LA, Zip 71115–2302; tel. 318/212–2200; Marc B. Pearce, Chief Executive Officer
**Web address:** www.postacutemedical.com

For explanation of codes following names, see page B2.
★ Indicates Type III membership in the American Hospital Association.

**MISSOURI:** ST. LUKE'S REHABILITATION HOSPITAL (O, 35 beds) 14709 Olive Boulevard, Chesterfield, MO, Zip 63017–2221; tel. 314/317–5700; Reagan Simpson, Chief Executive Officer
**Web address:** www.https://postacutemedical.com/facilities/find–facility/ rehabilitation–hospitals/St–Lukes–Rehabilitation–Hospital

**NEVADA:** PAM REHABILITATION HOSPITAL OF CENTENNIAL HILLS (O, 44 beds) 6166 North Durango Drive, Las Vegas, NV, Zip 89149; tel. 725/223–4100; Samantha Billig, Chief Executive Officer

PAM SPECIALTY HOSPITAL OF LAS VEGAS (O, 70 beds) 2500 North Tenaya, Las Vegas, NV, Zip 89128–0482; tel. 702/562–2021; Ryan Keele, Chief Executive Officer
**Web address:** www.https://postacutemedical.com/

PAM SPECIALTY HOSPITAL OF SPARKS (O, 21 beds) 2375 East Prater Way, Sparks, NV, Zip 89434–9641; tel. 775/355–5600; Gary Brooks, Chief Executive Officer

**NORTH CAROLINA:** PAM SPECIALTY HOSPITAL OF ROCKY MOUNT (O, 43 beds) 1051 Noell Lane, Rocky Mount, NC, Zip 27804–1761; tel. 252/451–2300; Robyn Perkerson, R.N., Administrator
**Web address:** www.lifecare–hospitals.com

**OHIO:** PAM SPECIALTY HOSPITAL OF DAYTON (O, 44 beds) 4000 Miamisburg–Centerville Road, Miamisburg, OH, Zip 45342–7615; tel. 937/384–8300; Karla Cody, Chief Executive Officer
**Web address:** www.https://postacutemedical.com

**OKLAHOMA:** PAM REHABILITATION HOSPITAL OF TULSA (O, 41 beds) 10020 East 91st Street, Tulsa, OK, Zip 74133; tel. 918/893–2400; Thomas Biby, Chief Executive Officer

POST ACUTE MEDICAL SPECIALTY HOSPITAL OF TULSA (O, 60 beds) 3219 South 79th East Avenue, Tulsa, OK, Zip 74145–1343; tel. 918/663–8183; Anthony Young, Chief Executive Officer
**Web address:** www.postacutetulsa.com

**PENNSYLVANIA:** PAM SPECIALTY HOSPITAL OF WILKES–BARRE (O, 36 beds) 575 North River Street, 7th Floor, Wilkes Barre, PA, Zip 18702–2634; tel. 570/208–3310; David Long, Chief Executive Officer
**Web address:** www.warmsprings.org/our–facilities/hospitals/post–acute–medical–specialty–hospital–wilkes–barre/

**TEXAS:** PAM REHABILITATION HOSPITAL OF ALLEN (O, 40 beds) 1001 Raintree Circle, Allen, TX, Zip 75013–4912; tel. 972/908–2015; Jennifer Beuerlein, Chief Executive Officer

PAM REHABILITATION HOSPITAL OF BEAUMONT (O, 61 beds) 3340 Plaza 10 Boulevard, Beaumont, TX, Zip 77707–2551; tel. 409/835–0835; Todd Lorenz, Administrator
**Web address:** www.postacutemedical.com/our–facilities/outpatient–rehabilitation/rehabilitation–hospital–beaumont/

PAM REHABILITATION HOSPITAL OF CLEAR LAKE (O, 90 beds) 110 East Medical Center Boulevard, Webster, TX, Zip 77598–4301; tel. 832/224–9500; Claudia Hauser, Chief Executive Officer
**Web address:** www.https://postacutemedical.com

PAM REHABILITATION HOSPITAL OF CORPUS CHRISTI (O, 40 beds) 345 South Water Street, Corpus Christi, TX, Zip 78401–2819; tel. 361/500–0600; Hector Bernal, Chief Executive Officer
**Web address:** www.postacutemedical.com

PAM REHABILITATION HOSPITAL OF HUMBLE (O, 46 beds) 18839 McKay Drive, Humble, TX, Zip 77338–5721; tel. 281/446–3655; Mikael Simpson, Chief Executive Officer

PAM REHABILITATION HOSPITAL OF ROUND ROCK (O, 40 beds) 351 Seton Parkway, Round Rock, TX, Zip 78665–8001; tel. 737/708–9800; Troy Lee, Chief Executive Officer
**Web address:** www.postacutemedical.com

PAM REHABILITATION HOSPITAL OF VICTORIA (O, 26 beds) 101 James Coleman Drive, Victoria, TX, Zip 77904–3147; tel. 361/220–7900; Tommy Beyer, Director of Operations

PAM SPECIALTY HOSPITAL OF LUFKIN (O, 26 beds) 1201 West Frank Avenue, D5, Lufkin, TX, Zip 75904–3357, Mailing Address: P.O. Box 1447, 75902–1447, tel. 936/639–7530
**Web address:** www.postacutemedical.com/facilities/find–facility/specialty–hospitals/PAM–Specialty–Hospital–Lufkin

PAM SPECIALTY HOSPITAL OF LULING (O, 34 beds) 200 Memorial Drive, Luling, TX, Zip 78648–3213; tel. 830/875–8400; Jana Kuykendall, Chief Executive Officer
**Web address:** www.warmsprings.org

PAM SPECIALTY HOSPITAL OF NEW BRAUNFELS (O, 40 beds) 1445 Hanz Drive, New Braunfels, TX, Zip 78130–2567; tel. 830/627–7600; Angela Jaco, Chief Executive Officer

PAM SPECIALTY HOSPITAL OF SAN ANTONIO CENTER (O, 62 beds) 8902 Floyd Curl Drive, San Antonio, TX, Zip 78240–1681; tel. 210/690–7000; Armando Morales, Chief Executive Officer
**Web address:** www.lifecare–hospitals.com

PAM SPECIALTY HOSPITAL OF VICTORIA NORTH (O, 26 beds) 102 Medical Drive, Victoria, TX, Zip 77904–3101; tel. 361/576–6200; Christina Adrean, Chief Executive Officer

PAM SPECIALTY HOSPITAL OF VICTORIA SOUTH (O, 23 beds) 506 East San Antonio Street, 3rd Floor, Victoria, TX, Zip 77901–6060; tel. 361/575–1445; Christina Adrean, Chief Executive Officer
**Web address:** www.warmsprings.org/our–facilities/hospitals/post–acute–medical–specialty–hospital–victoria/

POST ACUTE MEDICAL SPECIALTY HOSPITAL OF CORPUS CHRISTI – NORTH (O, 41 beds) 600 Elizabeth Street, 3rd Floor, Corpus Christi, TX, Zip 78404–2235; tel. 361/881–3223; Hector Bernal, Chief Executive Officer
**Web address:** www.postacutemedical.com/our–facilities/hospitals/post–acute–medical–specialty–hospital–corpus–christi/

POST ACUTE MEDICAL SPECIALTY HOSPITAL OF TEXARKANA – NORTH (O, 30 beds) 2400 St Michael Drive, 2nd Floor, Texarkana, TX, Zip 75503–2372; tel. 903/614–7600; Greg Lessard, Chief Executive Officer

POST ACUTE/WARM SPRINGS SPECIALTY HOSPITAL OF SAN ANTONIO (O, 26 beds) 5418 N Loop 1604 W, San Antonio, TX, Zip 78247; tel. 210/921–3550; Kristen Lowe, Chief Executive Officer
**Web address:** www.postacutemedical.com

WARM SPRINGS REHABILITATION HOSPITAL OF KYLE (O, 40 beds) 5980 Kyle Parkway, Kyle, TX, Zip 78640–2400; tel. 512/262–0821; Duke Saldivar, FACHE, Chief Executive Officer
**Web address:** www.warmsprings.org/our–facilities/outpatient–rehabilitation/warm–springs–rehabilitation–center–kyle/

WARM SPRINGS REHABILITATION HOSPITAL OF SAN ANTONIO (O, 139 beds) 5101 Medical Drive, San Antonio, TX, Zip 78229–4801; tel. 210/616–0100; Peter Drew, Chief Executive Officer
**Web address:** www.postacutemedical.com/our–facilities/hospitals/warm–springs–rehabilitation–hospital–san–antonio/

| | | |
|---|---|---|
| **Owned, leased, sponsored:** | 33 hospitals | 1508 beds |
| **Contract–managed:** | 0 hospitals | 0 beds |
| **Totals:** | 33 hospitals | 1508 beds |

**0240: PREFERRED MANAGEMENT CORPORATION** (IO)
120 West MacArthur, Suite 121, Shawnee, OK Zip 74804–2005; tel. 405/878–0202; Donald Freeman, President and Chief Executive Officer
**(Independent Hospital System)**

**OKLAHOMA:** ARBUCKLE MEMORIAL HOSPITAL (C, 15 beds) 2011 West Broadway Street, Sulphur, OK, Zip 73086–4221, Mailing Address: P.O. Box 1109, 73086–8109, tel. 580/622–2161; Jeremy A. Jones, Chief Executive Officer

**TEXAS:** COLEMAN COUNTY MEDICAL CENTER (L, 25 beds) 310 South Pecos Street, Coleman, TX, Zip 76834–4159; tel. 325/625–2135; Clay Vogel, Administrator and Chief Executive Officer
**Web address:** www.colemantexas.org/hospital.html

COLLINGSWORTH GENERAL HOSPITAL (L, 13 beds) 1013 15th Street, Wellington, TX, Zip 79095–3703, Mailing Address: P.O. Box 1112, 79095–1112, tel. 806/447–2521; Candy Powell, Administrator
**Web address:** www.collingsworthgeneral.net

CULBERSON HOSPITAL (L, 14 beds) Eisenhower–Farm Market Road 2185, Van Horn, TX, Zip 79855, Mailing Address: P.O. Box 609, 79855–0609, tel. 432/283–2760; Rick Gray, Chief Executive Officer

KIMBLE HOSPITAL (L, 15 beds) 349 Reid Road, Junction, TX, Zip 76849–3049; tel. 325/446–3321; Duke Young, Chief Executive Officer
**Web address:** www.kimblehospital.org/

For explanation of codes following names, see page B2.
★ Indicates Type III membership in the American Hospital Association.

MULESHOE AREA MEDICAL CENTER (L, 25 beds) 708 South First Street, Muleshoe, TX, Zip 79347–3627; tel. 806/272–4524; Dennis Fleenor, R.N., Administrator
**Web address**: www.mahdtx.org

PARMER MEDICAL CENTER (C, 15 beds) 1307 Cleveland Street, Friona, TX, Zip 79035–1121; tel. 806/250–2754; Gayla Quillin, Administrator

SABINE COUNTY HOSPITAL (L, 25 beds) 2301 Worth Street, Hemphill, TX, Zip 75948–7216, Mailing Address: P.O. Box 750, 75948–0750, tel. 409/787–3300; Jerry Howell, Administrator
**Web address**: www.sabinecountyhospital.com/

SCHLEICHER COUNTY MEDICAL CENTER (L, 14 beds) 102 North US Highway 277, Eldorado, TX, Zip 76936–4010; tel. 325/853–2507; Paul Burke, Administrator

| Owned, leased, sponsored: | 7 hospitals | 131 beds |
| Contract–managed: | 2 hospitals | 30 beds |
| Totals: | 9 hospitals | 161 beds |

---

**★0977: PREMIER HEALTH** (NP)

110 North Main Street Suite 390, Dayton, OH Zip 45402–3720; tel. 937/499–9401; Mary H. Boosalis, President and Chief Executive Officer

**(Centralized Physician/Insurance Health System)**

**OHIO**: ATRIUM MEDICAL CENTER (O, 129 beds) One Medical Center Drive, Middletown, OH, Zip 45005–1066; tel. 513/424–2111; Michael Uhl, President
**Web address**: www.PremierHealth.com

MIAMI VALLEY HOSPITAL (O, 754 beds) One Wyoming Street, Dayton, OH, Zip 45409–2793; tel. 937/208–8000; Michael J. Maiberger, President

UPPER VALLEY MEDICAL CENTER (O, 85 beds) 3130 North County Road 25A, Troy, OH, Zip 45373–1309; tel. 937/440–4000; Thomas Parker, President
**Web address**: www.uvmc.com

| Owned, leased, sponsored: | 3 hospitals | 968 beds |
| Contract–managed: | 0 hospitals | 0 beds |
| Totals: | 3 hospitals | 968 beds |

---

**★3505: PRESBYTERIAN HEALTHCARE SERVICES** (NP)

9521 San Mateo Blvd. NE, Albuquerque, NM Zip 87113, Mailing Address: P.O. Box 26666, 87125–6666, tel. 505/841–1234; Dale Maxwell, Chief Executive Officer

**(Centralized Physician/Insurance Health System)**

**NEW MEXICO**: DR. DAN C. TRIGG MEMORIAL HOSPITAL (L, 4 beds) 301 East Miel De Luna Avenue, Tucumcari, NM, Zip 88401–3810, Mailing Address: P.O. Box 608, 88401–0608, tel. 575/461–7000; Vickie Gutierrez, Chief Executive

LINCOLN COUNTY MEDICAL CENTER (L, 25 beds) 211 Sudderth Drive, Ruidoso, NM, Zip 88345–6043, Mailing Address: P.O. Box 8000, 88355–8000, tel. 575/257–8200; Todd Oberheu, Administrator
**Web address**: www.phs.org

PLAINS REGIONAL MEDICAL CENTER (O, 81 beds) 2100 North Doctor Martin Luther King Boulevard, Clovis, NM, Zip 88101–9412, Mailing Address: P.O. Box 1688, 88102–1688, tel. 575/769–2141; Jorge Cruz, Interim Chief Executive Officer

PRESBYTERIAN ESPANOLA HOSPITAL (O, 46 beds) 1010 Spruce Street, Espanola, NM, Zip 87532–2746; tel. 505/753–7111; Brenda Romero, Hospital Chief
**Web address**: www.phs.org

PRESBYTERIAN HOSPITAL (O, 643 beds) 1100 Central Avenue SE, Albuquerque, NM, Zip 87106–4934, Mailing Address: P.O. Box 26666, 87125–6666, tel. 505/841–1234; Devon Hyde, Vice President, Chief Administrative Officer

PRESBYTERIAN SANTA FE MEDICAL CENTER (O, 24 beds) 4801 Beckner Road, Santa Fe, NM, Zip 87507; tel. 505/772–1234; Jon Wade, Chief Executive Officer
**Web address**: www.https://santa–fe–medical–center.phs.org/Pages/default.aspx

SOCORRO GENERAL HOSPITAL (O, 24 beds) 1202 Highway 60 West, Socorro, NM, Zip 87801–3914, Mailing Address: P.O. Box 1009, 87801–1009, tel. 575/835–1140; Veronica Pound, R.N., Administrator

| Owned, leased, sponsored: | 7 hospitals | 847 beds |
| Contract–managed: | 0 hospitals | 0 beds |
| Totals: | 7 hospitals | 847 beds |

---

**0357: PRIME HEALTHCARE** (IO)

3300 East Guasti Road, Ontario, CA Zip 91761–8655; tel. 909/235–4400; Prem Reddy, M.D., Chairman, President and Chief Executive Officer

**(Moderately Centralized Health System)**

**ALABAMA**: RIVERVIEW REGIONAL MEDICAL CENTER (O, 280 beds) 600 South Third Street, Gadsden, AL, Zip 35901–5399; tel. 256/543–5200; John Langlois, Chief Executive Officer
**Web address**: www.riverviewregional.com

**CALIFORNIA**: ALVARADO HOSPITAL MEDICAL CENTER (O, 137 beds) 6655 Alvarado Road, San Diego, CA, Zip 92120–5208; tel. 619/287–3270; Robin Gomez, R.N., MSN, Administrator

CENTINELA HOSPITAL MEDICAL CENTER (O, 369 beds) 555 East Hardy Street, Inglewood, CA, Zip 90301–4011, Mailing Address: P.O. Box 720, 90312–6720, tel. 310/673–4660; Linda Bradley, Chief Executive Officer
**Web address**: www.centinelamed.com

CHINO VALLEY MEDICAL CENTER (O, 112 beds) 5451 Walnut Avenue, Chino, CA, Zip 91710–2672; tel. 909/464–8600; Tim Moran, Chief Executive Officer

DESERT VALLEY HOSPITAL (O, 110 beds) 16850 Bear Valley Road, Victorville, CA, Zip 92395–5795; tel. 760/241–8000; Fred Hunter, R.N., Chief Executive Officer
**Web address**: www.dvmc.com

ENCINO HOSPITAL MEDICAL CENTER (O, 78 beds) 16237 Ventura Boulevard, Encino, CA, Zip 91436–2272; tel. 818/995–5000; Bockhi Park, Chief Executive Officer
**Web address**: www.encinomed.com

GARDEN GROVE HOSPITAL AND MEDICAL CENTER (O, 167 beds) 12601 Garden Grove Boulevard, Garden Grove, CA, Zip 92843–1959; tel. 714/537–5160; Richard M. Rowe, PharmD, Chief Executive Officer
**Web address**: www.gardengrovehospital.com

GLENDORA COMMUNITY HOSPITAL (O, 128 beds) 150 West Route 66, Glendora, CA, Zip 91740–6207; tel. 626/852–5000; Sofia Abrina, R.N., Chief Executive Officer
**Web address**: www.evhmc.com

HUNTINGTON BEACH HOSPITAL (O, 102 beds) 17772 Beach Boulevard, Huntington Beach, CA, Zip 92647–6896; tel. 714/843–5000; Richard M. Rowe, PharmD, Chief Executive Officer
**Web address**: www.hbhospital.com

LA PALMA INTERCOMMUNITY HOSPITAL (O, 140 beds) 7901 Walker Street, La Palma, CA, Zip 90623–1764; tel. 714/670–7400; Michael Sarian, Interim Chief Executive Officer
**Web address**: www.lapalmaintercommunityhospital.com

MONTCLAIR HOSPITAL MEDICAL CENTER (O, 102 beds) 5000 San Bernardino Street, Montclair, CA, Zip 91763–2326; tel. 909/625–5411; Sofia Abrina, R.N., Administrator
**Web address**: www.montclair–hospital.com

PARADISE VALLEY HOSPITAL (O, 256 beds) 2400 East Fourth Street, National City, CA, Zip 91950–2099; tel. 619/470–4321; Neerav Jadeja, Chief Executive Officer
**Web address**: www.paradisevalleyhospital.org

SAN DIMAS COMMUNITY HOSPITAL (O, 101 beds) 1350 West Covina Boulevard, San Dimas, CA, Zip 91773–3219; tel. 909/599–6811; Parrish Scarboro, Chief Executive Officer
**Web address**: www.sandimashospital.com/

SHASTA REGIONAL MEDICAL CENTER (O, 100 beds) 1100 Butte Street, Redding, CA, Zip 96001–0853, Mailing Address: P.O. Box 496072, 96049–6072, tel. 530/244–5400; Casey Fatch, Chief Executive Officer

SHERMAN OAKS HOSPITAL (O, 90 beds) 4929 Van Nuys Boulevard, Sherman Oaks, CA, Zip 91403–1777; tel. 818/981–7111; Bockhi Park, Chief Executive Officer
**Web address**: www.shermanoakshospital.com

---

For explanation of codes following names, see page B2.
★ Indicates Type III membership in the American Hospital Association.

ST. FRANCIS MEDICAL CENTER (O, 323 beds) 3630 East Imperial Highway, Lynwood, CA, Zip 90262–2636; tel. 310/900–8900; Eleanor Ramirez, R.N., MS, Interim President and Chief Executive Officer

WEST ANAHEIM MEDICAL CENTER (O, 219 beds) 3033 West Orange Avenue, Anaheim, CA, Zip 92804–3183; tel. 714/827–3000; Allen Stefanek, Chief Executive Officer
**Web address**: www.westanaheimmedctr.com

**FLORIDA**: LEHIGH REGIONAL MEDICAL CENTER (O, 88 beds) 1500 Lee Boulevard, Lehigh Acres, FL, Zip 33936–4835; tel. 239/369–2101; Gary C. Bell, LFACHE, Chief Executive Officer
**Web address**: www.lehighregional.com

**GEORGIA**: SOUTHERN REGIONAL MEDICAL CENTER (O, 331 beds) 11 Upper Riverdale Road SW, Riverdale, GA, Zip 30274–2615; tel. 770/991–8000; Charlotte W. Dupre, Chief Executive Officer

**INDIANA**: MONROE HOSPITAL (O, 32 beds) 4011 South Monroe Medical Park Boulevard, Bloomington, IN, Zip 47403–8000; tel. 812/825–1111; Nancy Bakewell, Administrator
**Web address**: www.monroehospital.com

**KANSAS**: PROVIDENCE MEDICAL CENTER (O, 221 beds) 8929 Parallel Parkway, Kansas City, KS, Zip 66112–1689; tel. 913/596–4000; Karen Orr, Administrator and Chief Nursing Officer

SAINT JOHN HOSPITAL (O, 58 beds) 3500 South Fourth Street, Leavenworth, KS, Zip 66048–5043; tel. 913/680–6000; Paula Ellis, Administrator
**Web address**: www.providence–health.org/sjh

**MICHIGAN**: GARDEN CITY HOSPITAL (O, 162 beds) 6245 Inkster Road, Garden City, MI, Zip 48135–4001; tel. 734/421–3300; Saju George, Chief Executive Officer
**Web address**: www.gch.org

LAKE HURON MEDICAL CENTER (O, 75 beds) 2601 Electric Avenue, Port Huron, MI, Zip 48060–6518; tel. 810/985–1500; Jose Kottoor, Chief Executive Officer
**Web address**: https://www.mylakehuron.com

**MISSOURI**: ST. JOSEPH MEDICAL CENTER (O, 179 beds) 1000 Carondelet Drive, Kansas City, MO, Zip 64114–4673; tel. 816/942–4400; Jodi Fincher, R.N., Administrator
**Web address**: www.stjosephkc.com/

ST. MARY'S MEDICAL CENTER (O, 83 beds) 201 Northwest R D Mize Road, Blue Springs, MO, Zip 64014–2518; tel. 816/228–5900; Drew Grossman, Chief Executive Officer

**NEVADA**: NORTH VISTA HOSPITAL (O, 177 beds) 1409 East Lake Mead Boulevard, North Las Vegas, NV, Zip 89030–7197; tel. 702/649–7711; Vincenzo Variale, Chief Executive Officer
**Web address**: www.northvistahospital.com

SAINT MARY'S REGIONAL MEDICAL CENTER (O, 305 beds) 235 West Sixth Street, Reno, NV, Zip 89503–4548; tel. 775/770–3000; Tiffany Coury, Chief Executive Officer

**NEW JERSEY**: SAINT CLARE'S DENVILLE HOSPITAL (O, 412 beds) 25 Pocono Road, Denville, NJ, Zip 07834–2954; tel. 973/625–6000; Brian Finestein, Chief Executive Officer
**Web address**: www.saintclares.org

SAINT MICHAEL'S MEDICAL CENTER (O, 147 beds) 111 Central Avenue, Newark, NJ, Zip 07102–1909; tel. 973/877–5000; Alan Sickles, M.D., Chief Executive Officer
**Web address**: https://www.smmcnj.com/

ST. MARY'S GENERAL HOSPITAL (O, 287 beds) 350 Boulevard, Passaic, NJ, Zip 07055–2840; tel. 973/365–4300; Edward Condit, President and Chief Executive Officer
**Web address**: www.smh–passaic.org

**OHIO**: COSHOCTON REGIONAL MEDICAL CENTER (O, 44 beds) 1460 Orange Street, Coshocton, OH, Zip 43812–2229, Mailing Address: P.O. Box 1330, 43812–6330, tel. 740/622–6411; Stephanie Conn, Administrator and Chief Nursing Officer
**Web address**: https://www.coshoctonhospital.org

EAST LIVERPOOL CITY HOSPITAL (O, 120 beds) 425 West Fifth Street, East Liverpool, OH, Zip 43920–2498; tel. 330/385–7200; Keith Richardson, President and Chief Executive Officer
**Web address**: www.elch.org

**PENNSYLVANIA**: LOWER BUCKS HOSPITAL (O, 100 beds) 501 Bath Road, Bristol, PA, Zip 19007–3190; tel. 215/785–9200; Michael J. Motte, Chief Executive Officer

ROXBOROUGH MEMORIAL HOSPITAL (O, 131 beds) 5800 Ridge Avenue, Philadelphia, PA, Zip 19128–1737; tel. 215/483–9900; Matt Shelak, Chief Executive Officer
**Web address**: www.roxboroughmemorial.com

SUBURBAN COMMUNITY HOSPITAL (O, 126 beds) 2701 Dekalb Pike, East Norriton, PA, Zip 19401–1820; tel. 610/278–2000; Matt Shelak, Chief Executive Officer

**RHODE ISLAND**: LANDMARK MEDICAL CENTER (O, 140 beds) 115 Cass Avenue, Woonsocket, RI, Zip 02895–4731; tel. 401/769–4100; Michael Souza, Chief Executive Officer
**Web address**: www.landmarkmedcenter.com

REHABILITATION HOSPITAL OF RHODE ISLAND (O, 70 beds) 116 Eddie Dowling Highway, North Smithfield, RI, Zip 02896–7327; tel. 401/766–0800; Michael Souza, Chief Executive Officer

**TEXAS**: DALLAS MEDICAL CENTER (O, 71 beds) Seven Medical Parkway, Dallas, TX, Zip 75234–7823, Mailing Address: P.O. Box 819094, 75381–9094, tel. 972/247–1000; Ruben Garza, Chief Executive Officer
**Web address**: www.dallasmedcenter.com

DALLAS REGIONAL MEDICAL CENTER (O, 127 beds) 1011 North Galloway Avenue, Mesquite, TX, Zip 75149–2433; tel. 214/320–7000; Glenda Matchett, Chief Executive Officer

HARLINGEN MEDICAL CENTER (O, 88 beds) 5501 South Expressway 77, Harlingen, TX, Zip 78550–3213; tel. 956/365–1000; Matt Wolthoff, Chief Executive Officer
**Web address**: www.harlingenmedicalcenter.com

KNAPP MEDICAL CENTER (O, 186 beds) 1401 East Eighth Street, Weslaco, TX, Zip 78596–6640, Mailing Address: P.O. Box 1110, 78599–1110, tel. 956/968–8567; Rene Lopez, Chief Executive Officer
**Web address**: www.knappmed.org

MISSION REGIONAL MEDICAL CENTER (O, 228 beds) 900 South Bryan Road, Mission, TX, Zip 78572–6613; tel. 956/323–9103; Kane A. Dawson, Chief Executive Officer

PAMPA REGIONAL MEDICAL CENTER (O, 91 beds) One Medical Plaza, Pampa, TX, Zip 79065; tel. 806/665–3721; Edwin Leon, Chief Executive Officer
**Web address**: www.prmctx.com

| | | |
|---|---|---|
| **Owned, leased, sponsored:** | 44 hospitals | 6893 beds |
| **Contract-managed:** | 0 hospitals | 0 beds |
| **Totals:** | 44 hospitals | 6893 beds |

**4155: PRISMA HEALTH – MIDLANDS** (NP)
1301 Taylor Street, Suite 9–A, Columbia, SC Zip 29201–2942, Mailing Address: P.O. Box 2266, 29202–2266, tel. 803/296–2100; Mark O'Halla, President and Chief Executive Officer, Prisma Health

**(Centralized Health System)**

**SOUTH CAROLINA**: PRISMA HEALTH BAPTIST HOSPITAL (O, 344 beds) Taylor at Marion Street, Columbia, SC, Zip 29220–0001; tel. 803/296–5010; Michael N. Bundy, Chief Operating Officer

PRISMA HEALTH BAPTIST PARKRIDGE HOSPITAL (O, 76 beds) 400 Palmetto Health Parkway, Columbia, SC, Zip 29212–1760, Mailing Address: P.O. Box 2266, 29202–2266, tel. 803/907–7000; Michael N. Bundy, Chief Operating Officer
**Web address**: www.palmettohealth.org

PRISMA HEALTH RICHLAND HOSPITAL (O, 699 beds) Five Richland Medical Park Drive, Columbia, SC, Zip 29203–6897; tel. 803/434–7000; Robert Cofield, Dr.PH, Chief Executive Officer

PRISMA HEALTH TUOMEY HOSPITAL (O, 230 beds) 129 North Washington Street, Sumter, SC, Zip 29150–4983; tel. 803/774–9000; Michelle Logan-Owens, Ph.D., R.N., Chief Operating Officer
**Web address**: www.tuomey.com

| | | |
|---|---|---|
| **Owned, leased, sponsored:** | 4 hospitals | 1349 beds |
| **Contract-managed:** | 0 hospitals | 0 beds |
| **Totals:** | 4 hospitals | 1349 beds |

For explanation of codes following names, see page B2.
★ Indicates Type III membership in the American Hospital Association.

Section B

**1555: PRISMA HEALTH – UPSTATE** (NP)
701 Grove Road, Greenville, SC Zip 29605–5611; tel. 864/455–7000; Mark O'Halla, Chief Executive Officer
**(Centralized Health System)**

| | | |
|---|---|---|
| Owned, leased, sponsored: | 0 hospitals | 0 beds |
| Contract–managed: | 0 hospitals | 0 beds |
| Totals: | 0 hospitals | 0 beds |

★**0153: PROHEALTH CARE, INC.** (NP)
N17 W24100 Riverwood Drive, Suite 130, Waukesha, WI Zip 53188; tel. 262/928–2242; Susan A. Edwards, President and Chief Executive Officer
**(Centralized Health System)**

**WISCONSIN**: OCONOMOWOC MEMORIAL HOSPITAL (O, 58 beds) 791 Summit Avenue, Oconomowoc, WI, Zip 53066–3896; tel. 262/569–9400; Susan A. Edwards, President and Chief Executive Officer
**Web address**: www.prohealthcare.org/locations/locations–v2–detail/?id=1123

WAUKESHA MEMORIAL HOSPITAL (O, 262 beds) 725 American Avenue, Waukesha, WI, Zip 53188–5099; tel. 262/928–1000; Susan A. Edwards, President and Chief Executive Officer
**Web address**: www.prohealthcare.org/locations/locations–v2–detail/?id=1119

| | | |
|---|---|---|
| Owned, leased, sponsored: | 2 hospitals | 320 beds |
| Contract–managed: | 0 hospitals | 0 beds |
| Totals: | 2 hospitals | 320 beds |

★**0197: PROMEDICA HEALTH SYSTEM** (NP)
100 Madison Avenue, Toledo, OH Zip 43604–1516; tel. 567/585–9601; Randall D. Oostra, FACHE, President and Chief Executive Officer
**(Centralized Physician/Insurance Health System)**

**MICHIGAN**: PROMEDICA BIXBY HOSPITAL (O, 66 beds) 818 Riverside Avenue, Adrian, MI, Zip 49221–1446; tel. 517/265–0900; Julie Yaroch, President
**Web address**: www.promedica.org

PROMEDICA COLDWATER REGIONAL HOSPITAL (O, 62 beds) 274 East Chicago Street, Coldwater, MI, Zip 49036–2041; tel. 517/279–5400; Randy DeGroot, President and Chief Executive Officer
**Web address**: www.chcbc.com

PROMEDICA HERRICK HOSPITAL (O, 10 beds) 500 East Pottawatamie Street, Tecumseh, MI, Zip 49286–2018; tel. 517/424–3000; Julie Yaroch, President
**Web address**: www.promedica.org

PROMEDICA MONROE REGIONAL HOSPITAL (O, 100 beds) 718 North Macomb Street, Monroe, MI, Zip 48162–7815; tel. 734/240–8400; Darrin Arquette, President

**OHIO**: PROMEDICA BAY PARK HOSPITAL (O, 44 beds) 2801 Bay Park Drive, Oregon, OH, Zip 43616–4920; tel. 419/690–7900; Neeraj Kanwal, M.D., Interim President, Metro Region
**Web address**: www.promedica.org

PROMEDICA DEFIANCE REGIONAL HOSPITAL (O, 35 beds) 1200 Ralston Avenue, Defiance, OH, Zip 43512–1396; tel. 419/783–6955; Doug Bush, President
**Web address**: www.promedica.org

PROMEDICA FOSTORIA COMMUNITY HOSPITAL (O, 25 beds) 501 Van Buren Street, Fostoria, OH, Zip 44830–1534, Mailing Address: P.O. Box 907, 44830–0907, tel. 419/435–7734; Pamela M. Jensen, FACHE, President
**Web address**: www.promedica.org

PROMEDICA MEMORIAL HOSPITAL (O, 76 beds) 715 South Taft Avenue, Fremont, OH, Zip 43420–3237; tel. 419/332–7321; Pamela M. Jensen, FACHE, President, Regional Acute Care
**Web address**: https://www.promedica.org

PROMEDICA TOLEDO HOSPITAL (O, 815 beds) 2142 North Cove Boulevard, Toledo, OH, Zip 43606–3896; tel. 419/291–4000; Dawn M. Buskey, President
**Web address**: www.promedica.org

| | | |
|---|---|---|
| Owned, leased, sponsored: | 9 hospitals | 1233 beds |
| Contract–managed: | 0 hospitals | 0 beds |
| Totals: | 9 hospitals | 1233 beds |

**1012: PROSPECT MEDICAL HOLDINGS** (IO)
10780 California Route 2 #400, Los Angeles, CA Zip 90025; tel. 714/796–5900; Mitchell Lew, M.D., President
**(Independent Hospital System)**

**CALIFORNIA**: FOOTHILL REGIONAL MEDICAL CENTER (O, 127 beds) 14662 Newport Avenue, Tustin, CA, Zip 92780–6064; tel. 714/838–9600; Barbara Schneider, R.N., Chief Executive Officer
**Web address**: www.hfcis.cdph.ca.gov/longtermcare/Facility.aspx?fac=060000013

LOS ANGELES COMMUNITY HOSPITAL AT LOS ANGELES (O, 212 beds) 4081 East Olympic Boulevard, Los Angeles, CA, Zip 90023–3330; tel. 323/267–0477; Omar Ramirez, Chief Executive Officer

SOUTHERN CALIFORNIA HOSPITAL AT CULVER CITY (O, 239 beds) 3828 Delmas Terrace, Culver City, CA, Zip 90232–6806; tel. 310/836–7000; Michael R. Klepin, Chief Executive Officer
**Web address**: www.sch–culvercity.com

SOUTHERN CALIFORNIA HOSPITAL AT HOLLYWOOD (O, 45 beds) 6245 De Longpre Avenue, Los Angeles, CA, Zip 90028–9001; tel. 323/462–2271; Bruce P. Grimshaw, FACHE, Chief Executive Officer

**CONNECTICUT**: MANCHESTER MEMORIAL HOSPITAL (O, 156 beds) 71 Haynes Street, Manchester, CT, Zip 06040–4188; tel. 860/646–1222; Deborah K. Weymouth, FACHE, Chief Executive Officer
**Web address**: www.echn.org

ROCKVILLE GENERAL HOSPITAL (O, 47 beds) 31 Union Street, Vernon, CT, Zip 06066–3160; tel. 860/872–0501; Deborah K. Weymouth, FACHE, Chief Executive Officer
**Web address**: www.echn.org

WATERBURY HOSPITAL (O, 176 beds) 64 Robbins Street, Waterbury, CT, Zip 06708–2600; tel. 203/573–6000; Lester P. Schindel, Interim Chief Executive Officer
**Web address**: www.waterburyhospital.org

**NEW JERSEY**: EAST ORANGE GENERAL HOSPITAL (O, 143 beds) 300 Central Avenue, East Orange, NJ, Zip 07018–2897; tel. 973/672–8400; Paige Dworak, FACHE, Chief Executive Officer
**Web address**: www.evh.org

**PENNSYLVANIA**: CROZER–CHESTER MEDICAL CENTER (O, 384 beds) One Medical Center Boulevard, Upland, PA, Zip 19013–3995; tel. 610/447–2000; Michael Curran, President
**Web address**: www.crozer.org

DELAWARE COUNTY MEMORIAL HOSPITAL (O, 168 beds) 501 North Lansdowne Avenue, Drexel Hill, PA, Zip 19026–1114; tel. 610/284–8100; Patrick Kerrwood, President
**Web address**: www.crozer.org

**RHODE ISLAND**: ROGER WILLIAMS MEDICAL CENTER (O, 86 beds) 825 Chalkstone Avenue, Providence, RI, Zip 02908–4735; tel. 401/456–2000; Jeffrey H. Liebman, Chief Executive Officer

ST. JOSEPH HEALTH SERVICES OF RHODE ISLAND (O, 125 beds) 200 High Service Avenue, North Providence, RI, Zip 02904–5199; tel. 401/456–3000; John J. Holiver, Chief Executive Officer
**Web address**: www.saintjosephri.com

| | | |
|---|---|---|
| Owned, leased, sponsored: | 12 hospitals | 1908 beds |
| Contract–managed: | 0 hospitals | 0 beds |
| Totals: | 12 hospitals | 1908 beds |

★**1006: PROVIDENCE ST. JOSEPH HEALTH** (CO)
1801 Lind Avenue Southwest, 9016, Renton, WA Zip 98057–9016; tel. 425/525–3698; Rodney F. Hochman, M.D., President and Chief Executive Officer
**(Decentralized Health System)**

For explanation of codes following names, see page B2.
★ Indicates Type III membership in the American Hospital Association.

**ALASKA**: PROVIDENCE ALASKA MEDICAL CENTER (O, 401 beds) 3200 Providence Drive, Anchorage, AK, Zip 99508–4615, Mailing Address: P.O. Box 196604, 99519–6604, tel. 907/562–2211; Ella M. Goss, MSN, R.N., Chief Executive Officer
**Web address**: www.alaska.providence.org/locations/p/pamc

PROVIDENCE KODIAK ISLAND MEDICAL CENTER (L, 25 beds) 1915 East Rezanof Drive, Kodiak, AK, Zip 99615–6602; tel. 907/486–3281; Regina L. Bishop, Administrator
**Web address**: www.providence.org

PROVIDENCE SEWARD MEDICAL CENTER (C, 46 beds) 417 First Avenue, Seward, AK, Zip 99664, Mailing Address: P.O. Box 365, 99664–0365, tel. 907/224–5205; Robert A. Rang, R.N., MSN, Chief Executive Officer
**Web address**: www.providence.org

PROVIDENCE VALDEZ MEDICAL CENTER (C, 11 beds) 911 Meals Avenue, Valdez, AK, Zip 99686–0550, Mailing Address: P.O. Box 550, 99686–0550, tel. 907/835–2249; Jeremy O'Neil, Administrator
**Web address**: www.providence.org/alaska

**CALIFORNIA**: HOAG MEMORIAL HOSPITAL PRESBYTERIAN (O, 588 beds) One Hoag Drive, Newport Beach, CA, Zip 92663–4120, Mailing Address: P.O. Box 6100, 92658–6100, tel. 949/764–4624; Robert Braithwaite, President and Chief Executive Officer

MISSION HOSPITAL MISSION VIEJO (O, 290 beds) 27700 Medical Center Road, Mission Viejo, CA, Zip 92691–6474; tel. 949/364–1400; Seth R. Teigen, Chief Executive Officer
**Web address**: www.mission4health.com

PROVIDENCE HOLY CROSS MEDICAL CENTER (O, 377 beds) 15031 Rinaldi Street, Mission Hills, CA, Zip 91345–1207; tel. 818/365–8051; Bernard Klein, M.D., Chief Executive
**Web address**: www.https://california.providence.org/holy–cross/Pages/default.aspx

PROVIDENCE LITTLE COMPANY OF MARY MEDICAL CENTER – TORRANCE (O, 386 beds) 4101 Torrance Boulevard, Torrance, CA, Zip 90503–4664; tel. 310/540–7676; Garry M. Olney, Chief Executive Officer
**Web address**: www.providence.org

PROVIDENCE LITTLE COMPANY OF MARY MEDICAL CENTER SAN PEDRO (O, 318 beds) 1300 West Seventh Street, San Pedro, CA, Zip 90732–3505; tel. 310/832–3311; Garry M. Olney, Chief Executive Officer

PROVIDENCE SAINT JOHN'S HEALTH CENTER (O, 234 beds) 2121 Santa Monica Boulevard, Santa Monica, CA, Zip 90404–2091; tel. 310/829–5511; Marcel C. Loh, FACHE, Chief Executive Officer
**Web address**: www.providence.org/saintjohns

PROVIDENCE SAINT JOSEPH MEDICAL CENTER (O, 385 beds) 501 South Buena Vista Street, Burbank, CA, Zip 91505–4866; tel. 818/843–5111; Kelly Linden, Chief Executive Officer

PROVIDENCE TARZANA MEDICAL CENTER (O, 229 beds) 18321 Clark Street, Tarzana, CA, Zip 91356–3521; tel. 818/881–0800; Dale Surowitz, Chief Executive
**Web address**: www.providence.org/tarzana.com

QUEEN OF THE VALLEY MEDICAL CENTER (O, 208 beds) 1000 Trancas Street, Napa, CA, Zip 94558–2906, Mailing Address: P.O. Box 2340, 94558–0688, tel. 707/252–4411; Larry Coomes, Chief Executive Officer

REDWOOD MEMORIAL HOSPITAL (O, 25 beds) 3300 Renner Drive, Fortuna, CA, Zip 95540–3198; tel. 707/725–3361; Roberta Luskin–Hawk, M.D., Chief Executive
**Web address**: www.redwoodmemorial.org/

SANTA ROSA MEMORIAL HOSPITAL (O, 283 beds) 1165 Montgomery Drive, Santa Rosa, CA, Zip 95405–4897, Mailing Address: P.O. Box 522, 95402–0522, tel. 707/546–3210; Tyler Hedden, Interim Chief Executive Officer

ST. JOSEPH HOSPITAL EUREKA (O, 153 beds) 2700 Dolbeer Street, Eureka, CA, Zip 95501–4799; tel. 707/445–8121; Roberta Luskin–Hawk, M.D., Chief Executive
**Web address**: www.stjosepheureka.org

ST. JOSEPH HOSPITAL ORANGE (O, 379 beds) 1100 West Stewart Drive, Orange, CA, Zip 92868–3849, Mailing Address: P.O. Box 5600, 92863–5600, tel. 714/633–9111; Jeremy Zoch, Chief Executive
**Web address**: www.sjo.org

ST. JUDE MEDICAL CENTER (O, 320 beds) 101 East Valencia Mesa Drive, Fullerton, CA, Zip 92835–3875; tel. 714/992–3000; Brian Helleland, Chief Executive Officer

ST. MARY MEDICAL CENTER (O, 213 beds) 18300 Highway 18, Apple Valley, CA, Zip 92307–2206, Mailing Address: P.O. Box 7025, 92307–0725, tel. 760/242–2311; Randall Castillo, Chief Executive Officer
**Web address**: www.stmaryappplevalley.com/

**MONTANA**: GRANITE COUNTY MEDICAL CENTER (C, 25 beds) 310 Sansome Street, Philipsburg, MT, Zip 59858–0729, Mailing Address: P.O. Box 729, 59858–0729, tel. 406/859–3271; Maria Stoppler, Chief Executive Officer

PROVIDENCE ST. JOSEPH MEDICAL CENTER (O, 22 beds) 6 Thirteenth Avenue East, Polson, MT, Zip 59860–5315, Mailing Address: P.O. Box 1010, 59860–1010, tel. 406/883–5377; Devin Huntley, Chief Operating Officer
**Web address**: www.saintjoes.org

PROVIDENCE ST. PATRICK HOSPITAL (O, 200 beds) 500 West Broadway, Missoula, MT, Zip 59802–4096, Mailing Address: P.O. Box 4587, 59806–4587, tel. 406/543–7271; Joyce Dombrouski, R.N., Chief Executive Officer

**OREGON**: PROVIDENCE HOOD RIVER MEMORIAL HOSPITAL (O, 25 beds) 810 12th Street, Hood River, OR, Zip 97031–1587, Mailing Address: P.O. Box 149, 97031–0055, tel. 541/386–3911; Jeanette Vieira, Chief Executive
**Web address**: www.providence.org/hoodriver

PROVIDENCE MEDFORD MEDICAL CENTER (O, 138 beds) 1111 Crater Lake Avenue, Medford, OR, Zip 97504–6241; tel. 541/732–5000; Tom Lorish, M.D., Interim Chief Executive
**Web address**: www.providence.org

PROVIDENCE MILWAUKIE HOSPITAL (O, 60 beds) 10150 SE 32nd Avenue, Milwaukie, OR, Zip 97222–6516; tel. 503/513–8300; Sherri Kulink, Chief Executive Officer
**Web address**: www.providence.org

PROVIDENCE NEWBERG MEDICAL CENTER (O, 40 beds) 1001 Providence Drive, Newberg, OR, Zip 97132–7485; tel. 503/537–1555; Lorinda Van Zanten, MSN, Chief Executive
**Web address**: www.phsor.org

PROVIDENCE PORTLAND MEDICAL CENTER (O, 407 beds) 4805 NE Glisan Street, Portland, OR, Zip 97213–2933; tel. 503/215–5526; Krista Farnham, Chief Executive
**Web address**: www.providence.org

PROVIDENCE SEASIDE HOSPITAL (O, 25 beds) 725 South Wahanna Road, Seaside, OR, Zip 97138–7735; tel. 503/717–7000; Don Lemmon, Chief Executive Officer
**Web address**: www.providence.org

PROVIDENCE ST. VINCENT MEDICAL CENTER (O, 528 beds) 9205 SW Barnes Road, Portland, OR, Zip 97225–6661; tel. 503/216–1234; Janice Burger, Chief Executive

PROVIDENCE WILLAMETTE FALLS MEDICAL CENTER (O, 111 beds) 1500 Division Street, Oregon City, OR, Zip 97045–1597; tel. 503/656–1631; Russ Reinhard, Chief Executive
**Web address**: www.providence.org/pwfmc

**TEXAS**: COVENANT CHILDREN'S HOSPITAL (O, 204 beds) 4015 22nd Place, Lubbock, TX, Zip 79410; tel. 806/725–1011; Amy Thompson, M.D., Chief Executive Officer

COVENANT HOSPITAL PLAINVIEW (O, 68 beds) 2601 Dimmitt Road, Plainview, TX, Zip 79072–1833; tel. 806/296–5531; Alan N. King, FACHE, Chief Executive Officer
**Web address**: www.covenantplainview.org

COVENANT HOSPITAL–LEVELLAND (L, 26 beds) 1900 College Avenue, Levelland, TX, Zip 79336–6508; tel. 806/894–4963; Bruce White, Administrator

COVENANT MEDICAL CENTER (O, 380 beds) 3615 19th Street, Lubbock, TX, Zip 79410–1203, Mailing Address: P.O. Box 1201, 79408–1201, tel. 806/725–0000; Walt Cathey, Chief Executive Officer
**Web address**: www.covenanthealth.org

COVENANT SPECIALTY HOSPITAL (O, 56 beds) 3815 20th Street, Lubbock, TX, Zip 79410–1235; tel. 806/725–9200; Ely Perea, Director and Chief Executive Officer

GRACE MEDICAL CENTER (O, 43 beds) 2412 50th Street, Lubbock, TX, Zip 79412–2494; tel. 806/788–4100; Vanessa Reasoner, Chief Executive Officer
**Web address**: www.gracehealthsystem.com

For explanation of codes following names, see page B2.
★ Indicates Type III membership in the American Hospital Association.

**WASHINGTON**: KADLEC REGIONAL MEDICAL CENTER (O, 260 beds) 888 Swift Boulevard, Richland, WA, Zip 99352–3514; tel. 509/946–4611; Reza Kaleel, Chief Executive
**Web address**: https://www.kadlec.org

PROVIDENCE CENTRALIA HOSPITAL (O, 91 beds) 914 S Scheuber RD, Centralia, WA, Zip 98531–9027, 914 South Scheuber Road, 98531–9027, tel. 360/736–2803; Darin Goss, FACHE, Site Administrator

PROVIDENCE HOLY FAMILY HOSPITAL (O, 191 beds) 5633 North Lidgerwood Street, Spokane, WA, Zip 99208–1224; tel. 509/482–0111; Peggy M. Currie, R.N., Chief Operating Officer
**Web address**: www.providence.org

PROVIDENCE MOUNT CARMEL HOSPITAL (O, 25 beds) 982 East Columbia Avenue, Colville, WA, Zip 99114–3352; tel. 509/685–5100; Ronald G. Rehn, Chief Executive Officer

PROVIDENCE REGIONAL MEDICAL CENTER EVERETT (O, 571 beds) 1321 Colby Avenue, Everett, WA, Zip 98201–1665, Mailing Address: P.O. Box 1147, 98206–1147, tel. 425/261–2000; Kim Williams, R.N., MS, Chief Executive Officer
**Web address**: www.providence.org

PROVIDENCE SACRED HEART MEDICAL CENTER & CHILDREN'S HOSPITAL (O, 656 beds) 101 West Eighth Avenue, Spokane, WA, Zip 99204–2364, Mailing Address: P.O. Box 2555, 99220–2555, tel. 509/474–3131; Peggy M. Currie, R.N., Chief Operating Officer
**Web address**: www.shmc.org

PROVIDENCE ST. JOSEPH'S HOSPITAL (O, 55 beds) 500 East Webster Street, Chewelah, WA, Zip 99109–9523; tel. 509/935–8211; Ronald G. Rehn, Executive Officer

PROVIDENCE ST. MARY MEDICAL CENTER (O, 92 beds) 401 W Poplar Street, Walla Walla, WA, Zip 99362–2846, Mailing Address: P.O. Box 1477, 99362–0312, tel. 509/897–3320; Susan Blackburn, Chief Administrative Officer
**Web address**: www.washington.providence.org/hospitals/st-mary/

PROVIDENCE ST. PETER HOSPITAL (O, 349 beds) 413 Lilly Road NE, Olympia, WA, Zip 98506–5166; tel. 360/491–9480; Darin Goss, FACHE, Chief Executive Officer

ST. LUKE'S REHABILITATION INSTITUTE (O, 72 beds) 711 South Cowley Street, Spokane, WA, Zip 99202–1388; tel. 509/473–6000; Nancy Webster, Administrator and Chief Operating Officer
**Web address**: www.st-lukes.org

SWEDISH MEDICAL CENTER–CHERRY HILL CAMPUS (O, 208 beds) 500 17th Avenue, Seattle, WA, Zip 98122–5711; tel. 206/320–2000; David R. West, Chief Operating Officer

SWEDISH MEDICAL CENTER–FIRST HILL (O, 689 beds) 747 Broadway, Seattle, WA, Zip 98122–4307; tel. 206/386–6000; Elizabeth Wako, Chief Operating Officer
**Web address**: www.swedish.org

SWEDISH/EDMONDS (O, 185 beds) 21601 76th Avenue West, Edmonds, WA, Zip 98026–7506; tel. 425/640–4000; David R. West, Vice President, Operations
**Web address**: www.swedish.org

SWEDISH/ISSAQUAH (O, 153 beds) 751 NE Blakely Drive, Issaquah, WA, Zip 98029–6201; tel. 425/313–4000; R. Guy. Hudson, Chief Executive Officer
**Web address**: www.swedish.org/issaquah

WHITMAN HOSPITAL AND MEDICAL CENTER (C, 21 beds) 1200 West Fairview Street, Colfax, WA, Zip 99111–9579; tel. 509/397–3435; Hank Hanigan, FACHE, Chief Executive Officer

| | | |
|---|---|---|
| Owned, leased, sponsored: | 47 hospitals | 10744 beds |
| Contract–managed: | 4 hospitals | 103 beds |
| Totals: | 51 hospitals | 10847 beds |

**★0011: PUERTO RICO DEPARTMENT OF HEALTH** (NP)
Building 'A' – Medical Center, San Juan, PR Zip 936, Call Box 70184, 936, tel. 787/765–2929; Rafael Rodriguez. Mercado, Secretary of Health
**(Independent Hospital System)**

**PUERTO RICO**: CARDIOVASCULAR CENTER OF PUERTO RICO AND THE CARIBBEAN (O, 164 beds) Americo Miranda Centro Medico, San Juan, PR, Zip 936, Mailing Address: P.O. Box 366528, 00936–6528, tel. 787/754–8500; Carlos Cabrera, Executive Director

HOSPITAL UNIVERSITARIO DR. RAMON RUIZ ARNAU (O, 101 beds) Avenue Laurel #100, Santa Juanita, Bayamon, PR, Zip 956; tel. 787/787–5151; Prudencio A. Laureano, Chief Executive Officer
**Web address**: www.salud.gov.pr/Dept-de-Salud/Pages/Nuestros-Hospitales.aspx

UNIVERSITY HOSPITAL (O, 220 beds) Nineyas 869 Rio Piedras, San Juan, PR, Zip 922, Mailing Address: P.O. Box 2116, 922, tel. 787/754–0101; Jorge Matta. Gonzalez, Executive Director

UNIVERSITY PEDIATRIC HOSPITAL (O, 145 beds) Barrio Monacenno, Carretera 22, Rio Piedras, PR, Zip 935, Mailing Address: P.O. Box 191079, San Juan, 00910–1070, tel. 787/777–3535; Gloria Hernandez, Executive Director
**Web address**: www.md.rcm.upr.edu/pediatrics/university_pediatric_hospital.php

| | | |
|---|---|---|
| Owned, leased, sponsored: | 4 hospitals | 630 beds |
| Contract–managed: | 0 hospitals | 0 beds |
| Totals: | 4 hospitals | 630 beds |

**★0002: QHR HEALTH** (IO)
1573 Mallory Lane, Suite 200, Brentwood, TN Zip 37027, 1573 Mallory Lane, Suite 200, 37027, tel. 800/233–1470; Dwayne Gunter, President and Chief Executive Officer
**(Decentralized Health System)**

**CALIFORNIA**: BEAR VALLEY COMMUNITY HOSPITAL (C, 30 beds) 41870 Garstin Drive, Big Bear Lake, CA, Zip 92315, Mailing Address: P.O. Box 1649, 92315–1649, tel. 909/866–6501; John P. Friel, Chief Executive Officer

**COLORADO**: ARKANSAS VALLEY REGIONAL MEDICAL CENTER (C, 106 beds) 1100 Carson Avenue, La Junta, CO, Zip 81050–2799; tel. 719/383–6000; Lynn Crowell, Chief Executive Officer
**Web address**: www.avrmc.org

COMMUNITY HOSPITAL (C, 44 beds) 2351 G Road, Grand Junction, CO, Zip 81505; tel. 970/242–0920; Chris Thomas, FACHE, President and Chief Executive Officer
**Web address**: www.yourcommunityhospital.com

MONTROSE MEMORIAL HOSPITAL (C, 62 beds) 800 South Third Street, Montrose, CO, Zip 81401–4212; tel. 970/249–2211; James R. Kiser II, Chief Executive Officer

PIONEERS MEDICAL CENTER (C, 40 beds) 100 Pioneers Medical Center Drive, Meeker, CO, Zip 81641–3181; tel. 970/878–5047; Liz Sellers, R.N., MSN, Chief Executive Officer
**Web address**: www.pioneershospital.org

PROWERS MEDICAL CENTER (C, 25 beds) 401 Kendall Drive, Lamar, CO, Zip 81052–3993; tel. 719/336–4343; Karen L. Bryant, Chief Executive Officer

SOUTHEAST COLORADO HOSPITAL DISTRICT (C, 79 beds) 373 East Tenth Avenue, Springfield, CO, Zip 81073–1699; tel. 719/523–4501; David Engel, Chief Executive Officer and Administrator
**Web address**: www.sechosp.org

SPANISH PEAKS REGIONAL HEALTH CENTER (C, 140 beds) 23500 U S Highway 160, Walsenburg, CO, Zip 81089–9524; tel. 719/738–5100; Kay L. Whitley, President and Chief Executive Officer
**Web address**: www.sprhc.org

**FLORIDA**: HENDRY REGIONAL MEDICAL CENTER (C, 25 beds) 524 West Sagamore Avenue, Clewiston, FL, Zip 33440–3514; tel. 863/902–3000; R D Williams, Chief Executive Officer
**Web address**: www.hendryregional.org

JACKSON HOSPITAL (C, 68 beds) 4250 Hospital Drive, Marianna, FL, Zip 32446–1917, Mailing Address: P.O. Box 1608, 32447–5608, tel. 850/526–2200; James Platt, Chief Executive Officer
**Web address**: www.jacksonhosp.com

**IDAHO**: GRITMAN MEDICAL CENTER (C, 25 beds) 700 South Main Street, Moscow, ID, Zip 83843–3056; tel. 208/882–4511; Kara Besst, President and Chief Executive Officer

STEELE MEMORIAL MEDICAL CENTER (C, 18 beds) 203 South Daisy Street, Salmon, ID, Zip 83467–4709; tel. 208/756–5600; Jeanine Gentry, Chief Executive Officer
**Web address**: www.steelemh.org

For explanation of codes following names, see page B2.
★ Indicates Type III membership in the American Hospital Association.

**ILLINOIS:** CRAWFORD MEMORIAL HOSPITAL (C, 25 beds) 1000 North Allen Street, Robinson, IL, Zip 62454–1167; tel. 618/544–3131; Douglas Florkowski, Chief Executive Officer
**Web address:** www.crawfordmh.net

**INDIANA:** SULLIVAN COUNTY COMMUNITY HOSPITAL (C, 25 beds) 2200 North Section Street, Sullivan, IN, Zip 47882–7523, Mailing Address: P.O. Box 10, 47882–0010, tel. 812/268–4311; Michelle Franklin, Chief Executive Officer

**IOWA:** BOONE COUNTY HOSPITAL (C, 25 beds) 1015 Union Street, Boone, IA, Zip 50036–4821; tel. 515/432–3140; Joseph S. Smith, Chief Executive Officer
**Web address:** www.boonehospital.com

**KANSAS:** GREELEY COUNTY HEALTH SERVICES (C, 50 beds) 506 Third Street, Tribune, KS, Zip 67879–9684, Mailing Address: P.O. Box 338, 67879–0338, tel. 620/376–4221; Trice Watts, Chief Financial Officer and Chief Executive Officer

NEOSHO MEMORIAL REGIONAL MEDICAL CENTER (C, 25 beds) 629 South Plummer, Chanute, KS, Zip 66720–1928, Mailing Address: P.O. Box 426, 66720–0426, tel. 620/431–4000; Dennis Franks, FACHE, Chief Executive Officer
**Web address:** www.nmrmc.com

WILSON MEDICAL CENTER (C, 15 beds) 2600 Ottawa Road, Neodesha, KS, Zip 66757–1897, Mailing Address: P.O. Box 360, 66757–0360, tel. 620/325–2611; Dennis R. Shelby, Chief Executive Officer

**KENTUCKY:** CALDWELL MEDICAL CENTER (C, 25 beds) 100 Medical Center Drive, Princeton, KY, Zip 42445–2430, Mailing Address: P.O. Box 410, 42445–0410, tel. 270/365–0300; Daniel Odegaard, FACHE, Chief Executive Officer
**Web address:** www.caldwellhosp.org

OHIO COUNTY HOSPITAL (C, 30 beds) 1211 Main Street, Hartford, KY, Zip 42347–1619; tel. 270/298–7411; Blaine Pieper, Chief Executive Officer

**LOUISIANA:** LANE REGIONAL MEDICAL CENTER (C, 179 beds) 6300 Main Street, Zachary, LA, Zip 70791–4037; tel. 225/658–4000; Larry R. Meese Jr, FACHE, Chief Executive Officer
**Web address:** www.lanermc.org

THIBODAUX REGIONAL HEALTH SYSTEM (C, 154 beds) 602 North Acadia Road, Thibodaux, LA, Zip 70301–4847, Mailing Address: P.O. Box 1118, 70302–1118, tel. 985/447–5500; Greg K. Stock, FACHE, Chief Executive Officer

**MAINE:** CARY MEDICAL CENTER (C, 49 beds) 163 Van Buren Road, Suite 1, Caribou, ME, Zip 04736–3567; tel. 207/498–3111; Kris A. Doody, R.N., Chief Executive Officer
**Web address:** www.carymedicalcenter.org

**MICHIGAN:** THREE RIVERS HEALTH (C, 60 beds) 701 South Health Parkway, Three Rivers, MI, Zip 49093–8352; tel. 269/278–1145; David A. Shannon, Interim Chief Executive Officer
**Web address:** www.threerivershealth.org

**MINNESOTA:** RIVER'S EDGE HOSPITAL AND CLINIC (C, 17 beds) 1900 North Sunrise Drive, Saint Peter, MN, Zip 56082–5376; tel. 507/931–2200; Joseph Stratton, FACHE, Chief Executive Officer
**Web address:** www.rehc.org

**MISSISSIPPI:** KING'S DAUGHTERS MEDICAL CENTER (C, 79 beds) 427 Highway 51 North, Brookhaven, MS, Zip 39601–2350, Mailing Address: P.O. Box 948, 39602–0948, tel. 601/833–6011; Alvin Hoover, FACHE, Chief Executive Officer

MAGNOLIA REGIONAL HEALTH CENTER (C, 200 beds) 611 Alcorn Drive, Corinth, MS, Zip 38834–9321; tel. 662/293–1000; James M. Hobson, Chief Executive Officer
**Web address:** www.mrhc.org

**MONTANA:** CABINET PEAKS MEDICAL CENTER (C, 25 beds) 209 Health Park Drive, Libby, MT, Zip 59923–2130; tel. 406/283–7000; Bruce Whitfield, CPA, Chief Executive Officer and Chief Financial Officer

KALISPELL REGIONAL HEALTHCARE (C, 178 beds) 310 Sunnyview Lane, Kalispell, MT, Zip 59901–3129; tel. 406/752–5111; Craig Lambrecht, M.D., President and Chief Executive Officer
**Web address:** www.krmc.org

NORTH VALLEY HOSPITAL (C, 25 beds) 1600 Hospital Way, Whitefish, MT, Zip 59937–7849; tel. 406/863–3500; Kevin Abel, Chief Executive Officer
**Web address:** www.nvhosp.org

NORTHERN ROCKIES MEDICAL CENTER (C, 29 beds) 802 Second Street SE, Cut Bank, MT, Zip 59427–3329; tel. 406/873–2251; Cherie Taylor, Chief Executive Officer

THE HEALTHCENTER (C, 27 beds) 320 Sunnyview Lane, Kalispell, MT, Zip 59901–3129; tel. 406/751–7550; Tate J. Kreitinger, Chief Executive Officer
**Web address:** www.krmc.org

**NEBRASKA:** PHELPS MEMORIAL HEALTH CENTER (C, 25 beds) 1215 Tibbals Street, Holdrege, NE, Zip 68949–1255; tel. 308/995–2211; Mark Harrel, Chief Executive Officer
**Web address:** www.phelpsmemorial.com

**NEW HAMPSHIRE:** ANDROSCOGGIN VALLEY HOSPITAL (C, 25 beds) 59 Page Hill Road, Berlin, NH, Zip 03570–3531; tel. 603/752–2200; Michael Peterson, FACHE, President

LITTLETON REGIONAL HEALTHCARE (C, 25 beds) 600 Saint Johnsbury Road, Littleton, NH, Zip 03561–3442; tel. 603/444–9000; Robert Nutter, President and Chief Executive Officer
**Web address:** www.littletonhospital.org

UPPER CONNECTICUT VALLEY HOSPITAL (C, 12 beds) 181 Corliss Lane, Colebrook, NH, Zip 03576–3207; tel. 603/237–4971; Scott Colby, President and Chief Executive Officer

WEEKS MEDICAL CENTER (C, 25 beds) 173 Middle Street, Lancaster, NH, Zip 03584–3508; tel. 603/788–4911; Michael Lee, President
**Web address:** www.weeksmedical.org

**NEW MEXICO:** CIBOLA GENERAL HOSPITAL (C, 25 beds) 1016 East Roosevelt Avenue, Grants, NM, Zip 87020–2118; tel. 505/287–4446; Thomas Whelan, Chief Executive Officer
**Web address:** www.cibolahospital.com

HOLY CROSS HOSPITAL (C, 25 beds) 1397 Weimer Road, Taos, NM, Zip 87571–6253; tel. 575/758–8883; William D. Patten Jr, Chief Executive Officer
**Web address:** www.taoshospital.org

SIERRA VISTA HOSPITAL (C, 15 beds) 800 East Ninth Avenue, Truth or Consequences, NM, Zip 87901–1961; tel. 575/894–2111; David Faulkner, Interim Chief Executive Officer

**NEW YORK:** ADIRONDACK HEALTH (C, 120 beds) 2233 State Route 86, Saranac Lake, NY, Zip 12983–5644, Mailing Address: P.O. Box 471, 12983–0471, tel. 518/891–4141; Sylvia Getman, President and Chief Executive Officer
**Web address:** www.adirondackhealth.org

**OHIO:** KNOX COMMUNITY HOSPITAL (C, 71 beds) 1330 Coshocton Road, Mount Vernon, OH, Zip 43050–1495; tel. 740/393–9000; Bruce D. White, Chief Executive Officer
**Web address:** www.kch.org

**SOUTH CAROLINA:** ABBEVILLE AREA MEDICAL CENTER (C, 25 beds) 420 Thomson Circle, Abbeville, SC, Zip 29620–5656, Mailing Address: P.O. Box 887, 29620–0887, tel. 864/366–5011; Cindy Buck, Interim Chief Executive Officer

NEWBERRY COUNTY MEMORIAL HOSPITAL (C, 54 beds) 2669 Kinard Street, Newberry, SC, Zip 29108–2911, Mailing Address: P.O. Box 497, 29108–0497, tel. 803/276–7570; Bruce A. Baldwin, Chief Executive Officer
**Web address:** www.newberryhospital.org

**SOUTH DAKOTA:** HURON REGIONAL MEDICAL CENTER (C, 30 beds) 172 Fourth Street SE, Huron, SD, Zip 57350–2590; tel. 605/353–6200; Erick J. Larson, President and Chief Executive Officer
**Web address:** www.huronregional.org

**TENNESSEE:** MACON COMMUNITY HOSPITAL (C, 25 beds) 204 Medical Drive, Lafayette, TN, Zip 37083–1799, Mailing Address: P.O. Box 378, 37083–0378, tel. 615/666–2147; Thomas J. Kidd, CPA, Chief Executive Officer

RHEA MEDICAL CENTER (C, 25 beds) 9400 Rhea County Highway, Dayton, TN, Zip 37321–7922; tel. 423/775–1121; David Bixler, Chief Executive Officer
**Web address:** www.rheamedical.org

For explanation of codes following names, see page B2.
★ Indicates Type III membership in the American Hospital Association.

Section B

**TEXAS**: GONZALES HEALTHCARE SYSTEMS (C, 33 beds) 1110 Sarah Dewitt Drive, Gonzales, TX, Zip 78629–3311, Mailing Address: P.O. Box 587, 78629–0587, tel. 830/672–7581; Patty Stewart, Chief Executive Officer

MATAGORDA REGIONAL MEDICAL CENTER (C, 58 beds) 104 7th Street, Bay City, TX, Zip 77414–4853; tel. 979/245–6383; James Warren. Robicheaux, FACHE, Chief Executive Officer
**Web address**: www.matagordaregional.org

WILBARGER GENERAL HOSPITAL (C, 27 beds) 920 Hillcrest Drive, Vernon, TX, Zip 76384–3196; tel. 940/552–9351; Tom Siemers, Chief Executive Officer
**Web address**: www.wghospital.com

**VERMONT**: NORTHWESTERN MEDICAL CENTER (C, 47 beds) 133 Fairfield Street, Saint Albans, VT, Zip 05478–1726; tel. 802/524–5911; Gerald J. Barbini, Interim Chief Executive Officer

**WYOMING**: MEMORIAL HOSPITAL OF CARBON COUNTY (C, 25 beds) 2221 West Elm Street, Rawlins, WY, Zip 82301–5108, Mailing Address: P.O. Box 460, 82301–0460, tel. 307/324–2221; Kenneth Harman, Chief Executive Officer
**Web address**: www.imhcc.com

WEST PARK HOSPITAL (C, 112 beds) 707 Sheridan Avenue, Cody, WY, Zip 82414–3409; tel. 307/527–7501; Douglas A. McMillan, Administrator and Chief Executive Officer

| | | |
|---|---|---|
| Owned, leased, sponsored: | 0 hospitals | 0 beds |
| Contract–managed: | 53 hospitals | 2733 beds |
| Totals: | 53 hospitals | 2733 beds |

---

**★0040: QUEEN'S HEALTH SYSTEMS** (NP)

1301 Punchbowl Street, Honolulu, HI Zip 96813–2402; tel. 808/535–5448; Jill Hoggard Green, Ph.D., R.N., President and Chief Executive Officer
**(Moderately Centralized Health System)**

**HAWAII**: MOLOKAI GENERAL HOSPITAL (O, 15 beds) 280 Home Olu Place, Kaunakakai, HI, Zip 96748–0408, Mailing Address: P.O. Box 408, 96748–0408, tel. 808/553–5331; Janice Kalanihuia, President
**Web address**: www.queens.org

QUEEN'S NORTH HAWAII COMMUNITY HOSPITAL (O, 35 beds) 67–1125 Mamalahoa Highway, Kamuela, HI, Zip 96743–8496; tel. 808/885–4444; Cynthia Kamikawa, R.N., MSN, President

THE QUEEN'S MEDICAL CENTER (O, 637 beds) 1301 Punchbowl Street, Honolulu, HI, Zip 96813–2499; tel. 808/691–5100; Jill Hoggard Green, Ph.D., R.N., President and Chief Executive Officer
**Web address**: www.queensmedicalcenter.org

| | | |
|---|---|---|
| Owned, leased, sponsored: | 3 hospitals | 687 beds |
| Contract–managed: | 0 hospitals | 0 beds |
| Totals: | 3 hospitals | 687 beds |

---

**0981: QUORUM HEALTH** (IO)

1573 Mallory Lane, Suite 100, Brentwood, TN Zip 37027; tel. 615/221–1400; Daniel S. Slipkovich, Interim Chief Executive Officer
**(Moderately Centralized Health System)**

**ALABAMA**: DEKALB REGIONAL MEDICAL CENTER (O, 115 beds) 200 Medical Center Drive, Fort Payne, AL, Zip 35968–3458, Mailing Address: P.O. Box 680778, 35968–1608, tel. 256/845–3150; Patrick Trammell, Chief Executive Officer
**Web address**: www.dekalbregional.com

**ARKANSAS**: FORREST CITY MEDICAL CENTER (L, 55 beds) 1601 Newcastle Road, Forrest City, AR, Zip 72335–2218; tel. 870/261–0000; John Ballard, Ph.D., FACHE, Chief Executive Officer

HELENA REGIONAL MEDICAL CENTER (L, 45 beds) 1801 Martin Luther King Drive, Helena, AR, Zip 72342, Mailing Address: P.O. Box 788, 72342–0788, tel. 870/338–5800; Amy Rice, Chief Executive Officer
**Web address**: www.helenarmc.com

**CALIFORNIA**: BARSTOW COMMUNITY HOSPITAL (L, 30 beds) 820 East Mountain View Street, Barstow, CA, Zip 92311–3004; tel. 760/256–1761; Kolbe Sheridan, Chief Executive Officer
**Web address**: www.barstowhospital.com

**GEORGIA**: FANNIN REGIONAL HOSPITAL (O, 50 beds) 2855 Old Highway 5, Blue Ridge, GA, Zip 30513–6248; tel. 706/632–3711; Jason L. Jones, R.N., Chief Executive Officer
**Web address**: www.fanninregionalhospital.com

**ILLINOIS**: CROSSROADS COMMUNITY HOSPITAL (O, 28 beds) 8 Doctors Park Road, Mount Vernon, IL, Zip 62864–6224; tel. 618/244–5500; Amanda J. Basso, Chief Executive Officer
**Web address**: www.crossroadshospital.com

GATEWAY REGIONAL MEDICAL CENTER (O, 127 beds) 2100 Madison Avenue, Granite City, IL, Zip 62040–4799; tel. 618/798–3000; Bob Moore, FACHE, Chief Executive Officer

HEARTLAND REGIONAL MEDICAL CENTER (O, 92 beds) 3333 West DeYoung, Marion, IL, Zip 62959–5884; tel. 618/998–7000; M Edward. Cunningham, Chief Executive Officer
**Web address**: www.heartlandregional.com

RED BUD REGIONAL HOSPITAL (O, 140 beds) 325 Spring Street, Red Bud, IL, Zip 62278–1105; tel. 618/282–3831; Shane Watson, Chief Executive Officer
**Web address**: www.redbudregional.com

UNION COUNTY HOSPITAL (L, 47 beds) 517 North Main Street, Anna, IL, Zip 62906–1696; tel. 618/833–4511; James R. Farris, FACHE, Chief Executive Officer

VISTA HEALTH (O, 190 beds) 1324 North Sheridan Road, Waukegan, IL, Zip 60085–2161; tel. 847/360–3000; Norman F. Stephens, Chief Executive Officer
**Web address**: www.vistahealth.com

**KENTUCKY**: KENTUCKY RIVER MEDICAL CENTER (L, 54 beds) 540 Jett Drive, Jackson, KY, Zip 41339–9622; tel. 606/666–6000; Derek W. Cimala, Chief Executive Officer
**Web address**: www.kentuckyrivermc.com

PAUL B. HALL REGIONAL MEDICAL CENTER (O, 72 beds) 625 James S. Trimble Boulevard, Paintsville, KY, Zip 41240–0000; tel. 606/789–3511; Deborah Trimble, R.N., Chief Executive Officer
**Web address**: www.pbhrmc.com

THREE RIVERS MEDICAL CENTER (O, 90 beds) 2485 Highway 644, Louisa, KY, Zip 41230–9242, Mailing Address: P.O. Box 769, 41230–0769, tel. 606/638–9451; Greg Kiser, Chief Executive Officer

**NEVADA**: MESA VIEW REGIONAL HOSPITAL (O, 25 beds) 1299 Bertha Howe Avenue, Mesquite, NV, Zip 89027–7500; tel. 702/346–8040; Ned Hill, Chief Executive Officer
**Web address**: www.mesaviewhospital.com

**NEW MEXICO**: ALTA VISTA REGIONAL HOSPITAL (O, 54 beds) 104 Legion Drive, Las Vegas, NM, Zip 87701–4804; tel. 505/426–3500; Caleb F. O'Rear, Chief Executive Officer

MIMBRES MEMORIAL HOSPITAL (O, 25 beds) 900 West Ash Street, Deming, NM, Zip 88030–4098, Mailing Address: P.O. Box 710, 88031–0710, tel. 575/546–5800; Gary R. Poquette, FACHE, Chief Executive Officer
**Web address**: www.mimbresmemorial.com

**NORTH CAROLINA**: MARTIN GENERAL HOSPITAL (L, 49 beds) 310 South McCaskey Road, Williamston, NC, Zip 27892–2150, Mailing Address: P.O. Box 1128, 27892–1128, tel. 252/809–6300; John Jacobson, Interim Chief Executive Officer
**Web address**: www.martingeneral.com

**OREGON**: MCKENZIE–WILLAMETTE MEDICAL CENTER (O, 112 beds) 1460 'G' Street, Springfield, OR, Zip 97477–4197; tel. 541/726–4400; David Elgarico, Chief Executive Officer
**Web address**: www.mckweb.com

**TEXAS**: BIG BEND REGIONAL MEDICAL CENTER (O, 25 beds) 2600 North State Highway 118, Alpine, TX, Zip 79830–2002; tel. 432/837–3447; Rick Flores, Interim Chief Executive Officer

**UTAH**: MOUNTAIN WEST MEDICAL CENTER (O, 44 beds) 2055 North Main Street, Tooele, UT, Zip 84074–9819; tel. 435/843–3600; Philip Eaton, Chief Executive Officer
**Web address**: www.mountainwestmc.com

---

For explanation of codes following names, see page B2.
★ Indicates Type III membership in the American Hospital Association.

**WYOMING**: EVANSTON REGIONAL HOSPITAL (O, 42 beds) 190 Arrowhead Drive, Evanston, WY, Zip 82930–9266; tel. 307/789–3636; Cheri Willard, MSN, R.N., Interim Chief Executive Officer

| | | |
|---|---|---|
| Owned, leased, sponsored: | 22 hospitals | 1511 beds |
| Contract–managed: | 0 hospitals | 0 beds |
| Totals: | 22 hospitals | 1511 beds |

---

## 1019: REGIONAL MEDICAL CENTER (NP)

400 East 10th Street, Anniston, AL Zip 36207–4716; tel. 256/235–5121; Louis A. Bass, President and Chief Executive Officer

**(Independent Hospital System)**

**ALABAMA**: RMC ANNISTON (O, 276 beds) 400 East Tenth Street, Anniston, AL, Zip 36207–4716, Mailing Address: P.O. Box 2208, 36202–2208, tel. 256/235–5121; Louis A. Bass, Chief Executive Officer
**Web address**: www.rmccares.org

RMC–STRINGFELLOW MEMORIAL HOSPITAL (O, 88 beds) 301 East 18th Street, Anniston, AL, Zip 36207–3952; tel. 256/235–8900; Joe Weaver, Chief Executive Officer
**Web address**: www.stringfellowmemorial.com

| | | |
|---|---|---|
| Owned, leased, sponsored: | 2 hospitals | 364 beds |
| Contract–managed: | 0 hospitals | 0 beds |
| Totals: | 2 hospitals | 364 beds |

---

## ★2625: RENOWN HEALTH (NP)

50 West Liberty Street, Suite 1100, Reno, NV Zip 89501–1951; tel. 775/982–5529; Anthony D. Slonim, M.D., Dr.PH, President and Chief Executive Officer

**(Centralized Health System)**

**NEVADA**: CARSON VALLEY MEDICAL CENTER (O, 23 beds) 1107 Hwy 395, Gardnerville, NV, Zip 89410, 1107 Highway 395, 89410, tel. 775/782–1500; Jeffrey Prater, Chief Executive Officer
**Web address**: www.cvmchospital.org

RENOWN REGIONAL MEDICAL CENTER (O, 667 beds) 1155 Mill Street, Reno, NV, Zip 89502–1576; tel. 775/982–4100; Erik Olson, Chief Executive Officer
**Web address**: www.renown.org

RENOWN REHABILITATION HOSPITAL (O, 62 beds) 1495 Mill Street, Reno, NV, Zip 89502–1479; tel. 775/982–3500; Chris Nicholas, Vice President and Administrator

RENOWN SOUTH MEADOWS MEDICAL CENTER (O, 76 beds) 10101 Double 'R' Boulevard, Reno, NV, Zip 89521–5931; tel. 775/982–7000; Chris Nicholas, Vice President and Administrator
**Web address**: www.renown.org

| | | |
|---|---|---|
| Owned, leased, sponsored: | 4 hospitals | 828 beds |
| Contract–managed: | 0 hospitals | 0 beds |
| Totals: | 4 hospitals | 828 beds |

---

## ★0964: RIDGEVIEW MEDICAL CENTER (IO)

500 South Maple Street, Waconia, MN Zip 55387–1752; tel. 952/442–2191; Michael Phelps, President and Chief Executive Officer

**(Independent Hospital System)**

**MINNESOTA**: RIDGEVIEW LE SUEUR MEDICAL CENTER (O, 49 beds) 621 South Fourth Street, Le Sueur, MN, Zip 56058–2298; tel. 507/665–3375; Pamela Williams, Regional Vice President
**Web address**: www.mvhc.org

RIDGEVIEW MEDICAL CENTER (O, 104 beds) 500 South Maple Street, Waconia, MN, Zip 55387–1791; tel. 952/442–2191; Michael Phelps, President and Chief Executive Officer
**Web address**: www.ridgeviewmedical.org

RIDGEVIEW SIBLEY MEDICAL CENTER (L, 6 beds) 601 West Chandler Street, Arlington, MN, Zip 55307–2127; tel. 507/964–2271; Ben Nielsen, Chief Operating Officer

| | | |
|---|---|---|
| Owned, leased, sponsored: | 3 hospitals | 159 beds |
| Contract–managed: | 0 hospitals | 0 beds |
| Totals: | 3 hospitals | 159 beds |

---

## 4810: RIVERSIDE HEALTH SYSTEM (NP)

701 Town Center Drive, Suite 1000, Newport News, VA Zip 23606–4286; tel. 757/534–7000; William B. Downey, President and Chief Executive Officer

**(Centralized Health System)**

**VIRGINIA**: RIVERSIDE DOCTORS' HOSPITAL WILLIAMSBURG (O, 14 beds) 1500 Commonwealth Avenue, Williamsburg, VA, Zip 23185–5229; tel. 757/585–2200; Steve C. McCary, Administrator

RIVERSIDE REGIONAL MEDICAL CENTER (O, 307 beds) 500 J Clyde Morris Boulevard, Newport News, VA, Zip 23601–1929; tel. 757/594–2000; Michael J. Doucette, Senior Vice President and Administrator
**Web address**: https://www.riversideonline.com/rrmc/index.cfm

RIVERSIDE SHORE MEMORIAL HOSPITAL (O, 24 beds) 20480 Market Street, Onancock, VA, Zip 23417–4309, Mailing Address: P.O. Box 430, 23417, tel. 757/302–2100; John Peterman, Vice President and Administrator

RIVERSIDE TAPPAHANNOCK HOSPITAL (O, 18 beds) 618 Hospital Road, Tappahannock, VA, Zip 22560–5000; tel. 804/443–3311; Elizabeth J. Martin, Hospital President
**Web address**: https://www.riversideonline.com

RIVERSIDE WALTER REED HOSPITAL (O, 27 beds) 7519 Hospital Drive, Gloucester, VA, Zip 23061–4178, Mailing Address: P.O. Box 1130, 23061–1130, tel. 804/693–8800; Esther Muscari. Desimini, Interim Administrator

| | | |
|---|---|---|
| Owned, leased, sponsored: | 5 hospitals | 390 beds |
| Contract–managed: | 0 hospitals | 0 beds |
| Totals: | 5 hospitals | 390 beds |

---

## ★0046: ROCHESTER REGIONAL HEALTH (NP)

1425 Portland Avenue, 5th Floor, Rochester, NY Zip 14621–3001; tel. 585/922–4000; Eric Bieber, M.D., President and Chief Executive Officer

**(Centralized Health System)**

**NEW YORK**: CLIFTON SPRINGS HOSPITAL AND CLINIC (O, 179 beds) 2 Coulter Road, Clifton Springs, NY, Zip 14432–1189; tel. 315/462–9561; Dustin Riccio, M.D., President

NEWARK–WAYNE COMMUNITY HOSPITAL (O, 289 beds) 1200 Driving Park Avenue, Newark, NY, Zip 14513–1057, Mailing Address: P.O. Box 111, 14513–0111, tel. 315/332–2022; Dustin Riccio, M.D., President Eastern Region
**Web address**: www.rochesterregional.org

ROCHESTER GENERAL HOSPITAL (O, 528 beds) 1425 Portland Avenue, Rochester, NY, Zip 14621–3099; tel. 585/922–4000; Kevin John. Casey, President
**Web address**: https://www.rochesterregional.org/

UNITED MEMORIAL MEDICAL CENTER (O, 133 beds) 127 North Street, Batavia, NY, Zip 14020–1631; tel. 585/343–6030; Daniel P. Ireland, FACHE, President

UNITY HOSPITAL (O, 451 beds) 1555 Long Pond Road, Rochester, NY, Zip 14626–4182; tel. 585/723–7000; Douglas Stewart, PsyD, President
**Web address**: www.unityhealth.org

| | | |
|---|---|---|
| Owned, leased, sponsored: | 5 hospitals | 1580 beds |
| Contract–managed: | 0 hospitals | 0 beds |
| Totals: | 5 hospitals | 1580 beds |

---

## 1044: ROPER ST. FRANCIS HEALTHCARE (NP)

125 Doughty Street, Suite 760, Charleston, SC Zip 29403–5785; tel. 843/402–2273; Brian M. White, Chief Executive Officer

---

For explanation of codes following names, see page B2.
★ Indicates Type III membership in the American Hospital Association.

Section B

**SOUTH CAROLINA**: BON SECOURS ST. FRANCIS HOSPITAL (O, 157 beds) 2095 Henry Tecklenburg Drive, Charleston, SC, Zip 29414–5733; tel. 843/402–1000; Gretchen Morin, Chief Administrative Officer
**Web address**: www.rsfh.com/

ROPER HOSPITAL (O, 290 beds) 316 Calhoun Street, Charleston, SC, Zip 29401–1125; tel. 843/724–2000; Matthew Desmond, Chief Administrative Officer

ROPER ST. FRANCIS HOSPITAL–BERKELEY (O, 50 beds) 100 Callen Boulevard, Summerville, SC, Zip 29486–2807; tel. 854/529–3100; Patrick Bosse, Chief Administrative Officer
**Web address**: https://www.rsfh.com/berkeley–hospital/

ROPER ST. FRANCIS MOUNT PLEASANT HOSPITAL (O, 73 beds) 3500 Highway 17 North, Mount Pleasant, SC, Zip 29466–9123, 3500 North Highway 17, 29466–9123, tel. 843/606–7000; Tavia Buck, Chief Administrative Officer

| | | |
|---|---|---|
| Owned, leased, sponsored: | 4 hospitals | 570 beds |
| Contract–managed: | 0 hospitals | 0 beds |
| Totals: | 4 hospitals | 570 beds |

---

**0348: RURAL COMMUNITY HOSPITALS OF AMERICA** (IO)
1100 Main Street, Suite 2350, Kansas City, MO Zip 64105–5186; tel. 816/474–7800; Paul L. Nusbaum, President and Co–Owner
**(Independent Hospital System)**

**KANSAS**: HILLSBORO COMMUNITY HOSPITAL (O, 15 beds) 701 South Main Street, Hillsboro, KS, Zip 67063–1553; tel. 620/947–3114; Mark Rooker, Chief Executive Officer
**Web address**: www.hchks.com

**NORTH CAROLINA**: WASHINGTON COUNTY HOSPITAL (O, 25 beds) 958 U S Highway 64 East, Plymouth, NC, Zip 27962–9591, Mailing Address: P.O. 707, 27962–9591, tel. 252/793–4135; Melanie A. Perry, Chief Executive Officer

**OKLAHOMA**: DRUMRIGHT REGIONAL HOSPITAL (O, 15 beds) 610 West Bypass , Drumright, OK, Zip 74030–5957; tel. 918/382–2300; Rebecca Benham, Interim Chief Executive Officer
**Web address**: www.drumrighthospital.com/

FAIRFAX COMMUNITY HOSPITAL (O, 15 beds) 40 Hospital Road, Fairfax, OK, Zip 74637–5084; tel. 918/642–3291; Hunter Thoms, Chief Executive Officer

HASKELL COUNTY COMMUNITY HOSPITAL (O, 20 beds) 401 Northwest 'H' Street, Stigler, OK, Zip 74462–1625; tel. 918/967–4682; Andrea Randall, Chief Executive Officer
**Web address**: www.haskellhospital.com

PRAGUE COMMUNITY HOSPITAL (O, 25 beds) 1322 Klabzuba Avenue, Prague, OK, Zip 74864–9005, Mailing Address: P.O. Box S, 74864–1090, tel. 405/567–4922; Jamal Bandeh, Interim Chief Executive Officer

| | | |
|---|---|---|
| Owned, leased, sponsored: | 6 hospitals | 115 beds |
| Contract–managed: | 0 hospitals | 0 beds |
| Totals: | 6 hospitals | 115 beds |

---

**★0109: RURAL HEALTH GROUP** (IO)
48 West 1500 North, Nephi, UT Zip 84648–8900; tel. 435/623–4924; Mark R. Stoddard, President and Chairman
**(Independent Hospital System)**

**UTAH**: CENTRAL VALLEY MEDICAL CENTER (L, 25 beds) 48 West 1500 North, Nephi, UT, Zip 84648–8900; tel. 435/623–3000; Mark R. Stoddard, Chief Executive Officer
**Web address**: www.cvmed.net

| | | |
|---|---|---|
| Owned, leased, sponsored: | 1 hospitals | 25 beds |
| Contract–managed: | 0 hospitals | 0 beds |
| Totals: | 1 hospitals | 25 beds |

---

**0220: RUSH HEALTH SYSTEMS** (NP)
1314 19th Avenue, Meridian, MS Zip 39301–4116; tel. 601/483–0011; Larkin Kennedy, President and Chief Executive Officer
**(Independent Hospital System)**

**ALABAMA**: CHOCTAW GENERAL HOSPITAL (O, 25 beds) 401 Vanity Fair Avenue, Butler, AL, Zip 36904–3032; tel. 205/459–9100; J W. Cowan, Administrator
**Web address**: www.choctawgeneral.com/cgh/

**MISSISSIPPI**: H. C. WATKINS MEMORIAL HOSPITAL (O, 25 beds) 605 South Archusa Avenue, Quitman, MS, Zip 39355–2331; tel. 601/776–6925; Michael Nester, Administrator
**Web address**: www.watkinsmemorialhospital.com/hcwmh/

JOHN C. STENNIS MEMORIAL HOSPITAL (O, 25 beds) 14365 Highway 16 West, De Kalb, MS, Zip 39328–7974; tel. 769/486–1000; Scott Vincent, Chief Executive Officer
**Web address**: www.johncstennismemorialhospital.com/jcsmh/

LAIRD HOSPITAL (O, 25 beds) 25117 Highway 15, Union, MS, Zip 39365–9099; tel. 601/774–8214; Thomas G. Bartlett III, Administrator

RUSH FOUNDATION HOSPITAL (O, 182 beds) 1314 19th Avenue, Meridian, MS, Zip 39301–4195; tel. 601/483–0011; Larkin Kennedy, Chief Executive Officer
**Web address**: www.rushhealthsystems.org/rfh/

SCOTT REGIONAL HOSPITAL (O, 25 beds) 317 Highway 13 South, Morton, MS, Zip 39117–3353, Mailing Address: P.O. Box 259, 39117–0259, tel. 601/732–6301; Heather Davis, Administrator

SPECIALTY HOSPITAL OF MERIDIAN (O, 49 beds) 1314 19th Avenue, Meridian, MS, Zip 39301–4116; tel. 601/703–4211; Kawanda Johnson, Vice President
**Web address**: www.specialtyhospitalofmeridian.com/shm/

| | | |
|---|---|---|
| Owned, leased, sponsored: | 7 hospitals | 356 beds |
| Contract–managed: | 0 hospitals | 0 beds |
| Totals: | 7 hospitals | 356 beds |

---

**★3855: RUSH UNIVERSITY MEDICAL CENTER** (NP)
1653 West Congress Parkway, Chicago, IL Zip 60612–3864; tel. 312/942–5000; Ranga Krishnan, M.D., Chief Executive Officer
**(Moderately Centralized Health System)**

**ILLINOIS**: RUSH OAK PARK HOSPITAL (O, 108 beds) 520 South Maple Avenue, Oak Park, IL, Zip 60304–1097; tel. 708/383–9300; Bruce M. Elegant, FACHE, President and Chief Executive Officer
**Web address**: www.roph.org

RUSH UNIVERSITY MEDICAL CENTER (O, 684 beds) 1653 West Congress Parkway, Chicago, IL, Zip 60612–3833; tel. 312/942–5000; Omar Lateef, D.O., Chief Executive Officer

RUSH–COPLEY MEDICAL CENTER (O, 210 beds) 2000 Ogden Avenue, Aurora, IL, Zip 60504–7222; tel. 630/978–6200; Barry C. Finn, President and Chief Executive Officer
**Web address**: www.rushcopley.com

| | | |
|---|---|---|
| Owned, leased, sponsored: | 3 hospitals | 1002 beds |
| Contract–managed: | 0 hospitals | 0 beds |
| Totals: | 3 hospitals | 1002 beds |

---

**★0994: RWJBARNABAS HEALTH** (NP)
95 Old Short Hills Road, West Orange, NJ Zip 07052–1008; tel. 973/322–4000; Barry Ostrowsky, President and Chief Executive Officer
**(Decentralized Health System)**

**NEW JERSEY**: CHILDREN'S SPECIALIZED HOSPITAL (O, 140 beds) 200 Somerset Street, New Brunswick, NJ, Zip 08901–1942; tel. 732/258–7000; Warren E. Moore, FACHE, President and Chief Executive Officer
**Web address**: www.childrens–specialized.org

CLARA MAASS MEDICAL CENTER (O, 352 beds) One Clara Maass Drive, Belleville, NJ, Zip 07109–3557; tel. 973/450–2000; Mary Ellen Clyne, Ph.D., President and Chief Executive Officer

COMMUNITY MEDICAL CENTER (O, 306 beds) 99 Route 37 West, Toms River, NJ, Zip 08755–6423; tel. 732/557–8000; Patrick Ahearn, Chief Executive Officer
**Web address**: https://www.rwjbh.org/community–medical–center/

For explanation of codes following names, see page B2.
★ Indicates Type III membership in the American Hospital Association.

JERSEY CITY MEDICAL CENTER (O, 332 beds) 355 Grand Street, Jersey City, NJ, Zip 07302–4321; tel. 201/915–2000; Michael Prilutsky, President and Chief Executive Officer

MONMOUTH MEDICAL CENTER, LONG BRANCH CAMPUS (O, 276 beds) 300 Second Avenue, Long Branch, NJ, Zip 07740–6303; tel. 732/222–5200; Eric Carney, Chief Executive Officer
**Web address:** www.barnabashealth.org/hospitals/monmouth_medical/index.html

MONMOUTH MEDICAL CENTER, SOUTHERN CAMPUS (O, 124 beds) 600 River Avenue, Lakewood, NJ, Zip 08701–5237; tel. 732/363–1900; Eric Carney, Chief Executive Officer

NEWARK BETH ISRAEL MEDICAL CENTER (O, 376 beds) 201 Lyons Avenue at Osborne Terrace, Newark, NJ, Zip 07112–2027; tel. 973/926–7000; Darrell K. Terry Sr, M.P.H., FACHE, President and Chief Executive Officer
**Web address:** www.barnabashealth.org/hospitals/newark_beth_israel/index.html

RWJBARNABAS HEALTH BEHAVIORAL HEALTH CENTER (O, 40 beds) 1691 Highway 9, Toms River, NJ, Zip 8754; tel. 732/914–1688; Deanna Sperling, R.N., President and Chief Executive Officer

ROBERT WOOD JOHNSON UNIVERSITY HOSPITAL RAHWAY (O, 93 beds) 865 Stone Street, Rahway, NJ, Zip 07065–2797; tel. 732/381–4200; Kirk C. Tice, President and Chief Executive Officer
**Web address:** www.rwjuhr.com

ROBERT WOOD JOHNSON UNIVERSITY HOSPITAL SOMERSET (O, 297 beds) 110 Rehill Avenue, Somerville, NJ, Zip 08876–2598; tel. 908/685–2200; Anthony V. Cava, MS, FACHE, President and Chief Executive Officer
**Web address:** www.rwjbh.org

ROBERT WOOD JOHNSON UNIVERSITY HOSPITAL AT HAMILTON (O, 164 beds) One Hamilton Health Place, Hamilton, NJ, Zip 08690–3599; tel. 609/586–7900; Richard Freeman, President and Chief Executive Officer
**Web address:** www.rwjhamilton.org

ROBERT WOOD JOHNSON UNIVERSITY HOSPITAL (O, 619 beds) 1 Robert Wood Johnson Place, New Brunswick, NJ, Zip 08901–1928; tel. 732/828–3000; John J. Gantner, President and Chief Executive Officer

SAINT BARNABAS MEDICAL CENTER (O, 561 beds) 94 Old Short Hills Rd, Livingston, NJ, Zip 07039–5672; tel. 973/322–5000; Stephen P. Zieniewicz, FACHE, President and Chief Executive Officer
**Web address:** www.barnabashealth.org/hospitals/saint_barnabas/index.html

| | | |
|---|---|---|
| Owned, leased, sponsored: | 13 hospitals | 3680 beds |
| Contract–managed: | 0 hospitals | 0 beds |
| Totals: | 13 hospitals | 3680 beds |

## 0912: SAFE HAVEN HEALTH CARE (IO)
2520 South 5th Avenue, Pocatello, ID Zip 83204–1923; tel. 800/261–2443; Scott Burpee, President

**IDAHO:** SAFE HAVEN HOSPITAL OF POCATELLO (O, 87 beds) 2520 South 5th Avenue, Pocatello, ID, Zip 83204–1923; tel. 208/232–2570; Karen Neilson, Administrator
**Web address:** www.safehavenhealthcare.org/safehaven_hospital/index.html

SAFE HAVEN HOSPITAL OF TREASURE VALLEY (O, 22 beds) 8050 Northview Street, Boise, ID, Zip 83704–7126; tel. 208/327–0504; Scott Proctor, Chief Executive Officer
**Web address:** www.boisepsychhospital.com

| | | |
|---|---|---|
| Owned, leased, sponsored: | 2 hospitals | 109 beds |
| Contract–managed: | 0 hospitals | 0 beds |
| Totals: | 2 hospitals | 109 beds |

## ★0254: SAINT FRANCIS HEALTH SYSTEM (CO)
6161 South Yale Avenue, Tulsa, OK Zip 74136–1902; tel. 918/494–8454; Jake Henry Jr, President and Chief Executive Officer
**(Centralized Health System)**

**OKLAHOMA:** LAUREATE PSYCHIATRIC CLINIC AND HOSPITAL (O, 106 beds) 6655 South Yale Avenue, Tulsa, OK, Zip 74136–3329; tel. 918/481–4000; Brandon Keppner, Administrator

OKLAHOMA STATE UNIVERSITY MEDICAL CENTER (C, 191 beds) 744 West Ninth Street, Tulsa, OK, Zip 74127–9020; tel. 918/599–1000; Lynn A. Sund, Interim Administrator
**Web address:** www.osumc.net

SAINT FRANCIS HOSPITAL MUSKOGEE (O, 185 beds) 300 Rockefeller Drive, Muskogee, OK, Zip 74401–5081; tel. 918/682–5501; Michele A. Keeling, Vice President and Administrator

SAINT FRANCIS HOSPITAL SOUTH (O, 102 beds) 10501 East 91st Street, Tulsa, OK, Zip 74133–5790; tel. 918/307–6010; Todd Schuster, Vice President and Administrator
**Web address:** www.saintfrancis.com/south/

SAINT FRANCIS HOSPITAL VINITA (O, 70 beds) 735 North Foreman Street, Vinita, OK, Zip 74301–1418; tel. 918/256–7551; Todd Schuster, Administrator
**Web address:** https://www.saintfrancis.com/vinita/Pages/default.aspx

SAINT FRANCIS HOSPITAL (O, 880 beds) 6161 South Yale Avenue, Tulsa, OK, Zip 74136–1902; tel. 918/494–2200; Douglas Williams, Senior Vice President, Administrator

| | | |
|---|---|---|
| Owned, leased, sponsored: | 5 hospitals | 1343 beds |
| Contract–managed: | 1 hospitals | 191 beds |
| Totals: | 6 hospitals | 1534 beds |

## ★0120: SAINT LUKE'S HEALTH SYSTEM (NP)
901 East 104th Street, Mailstop 900N, Kansas City, MO Zip 64131–4517, 901 East 104th Street, 64131–4517, tel. 816/932–2000; Melinda Estes, M.D., President and Chief Executive Officer
**(Centralized Health System)**

**KANSAS:** ANDERSON COUNTY HOSPITAL (L, 42 beds) 421 South Maple, Garnett, KS, Zip 66032–1334, Mailing Address: P.O. Box 309, 66032–0309, tel. 785/448–3131; Rick McKain, Chief Executive Officer
**Web address:** www.saint–lukes.org

SAINT LUKE'S CUSHING HOSPITAL (O, 8 beds) 711 Marshall Street, Leavenworth, KS, Zip 66048–3235; tel. 913/684–1100; Adele Ducharme, MSN, R.N., Chief Executive Officer

SAINT LUKE'S SOUTH HOSPITAL (O, 174 beds) 12300 Metcalf Avenue, Overland Park, KS, Zip 66213–1324; tel. 913/317–7000; Bobby Olm–Shipman, Chief Executive Officer
**Web address:** www.saintlukeshealthsystem.org/south

**MISSOURI:** HEDRICK MEDICAL CENTER (L, 25 beds) 2799 North Washington Street, Chillicothe, MO, Zip 64601–2902; tel. 660/646–1480; Steven M. Schieber, FACHE, Chief Executive Officer, Critical Access Region, Saint Luke's Health System

SAINT LUKE'S EAST HOSPITAL (O, 203 beds) 100 NE Saint Luke's Boulevard, Lee's Summit, MO, Zip 64086–6000; tel. 816/347–5000; Bobby Olm–Shipman, Chief Executive Officer
**Web address:** www.saintlukeskc.org

SAINT LUKE'S HOSPITAL OF KANSAS CITY (O, 482 beds) 4401 Wornall Road, Kansas City, MO, Zip 64111–3220; tel. 816/932–3800; Jani L. Johnson, R.N., MSN, Chief Executive Officer
**Web address:** www.saint–lukes.org

SAINT LUKE'S NORTH HOSPITAL – BARRY ROAD (O, 139 beds) 5830 NW Barry Road, Kansas City, MO, Zip 64154–2778; tel. 816/891–6000; Adele Ducharme, MSN, R.N., Chief Executive Officer

WRIGHT MEMORIAL HOSPITAL (L, 15 beds) 191 Iowa Boulevard, Trenton, MO, Zip 64683–8343; tel. 660/358–5700; Steven M. Schieber, FACHE, Interim Chief Executive Officer
**Web address:** www.saintlukeshealthsystem.org

| | | |
|---|---|---|
| Owned, leased, sponsored: | 8 hospitals | 1088 beds |
| Contract–managed: | 0 hospitals | 0 beds |
| Totals: | 8 hospitals | 1088 beds |

## 0403: SALEM HEALTH (NP)
890 Oak Street Bldg B POB 14001, Salem, OR Zip 97309–5014; tel. 503/561–5200; Cheryl R. Nester Wolfe, R.N., President and Chief Executive Officer
**(Independent Hospital System)**

For explanation of codes following names, see page B2.
★ Indicates Type III membership in the American Hospital Association.

Section B

**OREGON:** SALEM HEALTH WEST VALLEY (O, 6 beds) 525 SE Washington Street, Dallas, OR, Zip 97338–2834, Mailing Address: P.O. Box 378, 97338–0378, tel. 503/623–8301; Brandon Schmidgall, Chief Executive Officer

SALEM HOSPITAL (O, 475 beds) 890 Oak Street SE, Salem, OR, Zip 97301–3959, Mailing Address: P.O. Box 14001, 97309–5014, tel. 503/561–5200; Cheryl R. Nester Wolfe, R.N., President and Chief Executive Officer
**Web address:** www.salemhealth.org

| | | |
|---|---|---|
| Owned, leased, sponsored: | 2 hospitals | 481 beds |
| Contract–managed: | 0 hospitals | 0 beds |
| Totals: | 2 hospitals | 481 beds |

**1002: SALINA REGIONAL HEALTH CENTER** (NP)
400 South Santa Fe Avenue, Salina, KS Zip 67401–4198, Mailing Address: P.O. 5080, 67402–5080, tel. 785/452–7000; Joel Phelps, President and Chief Executive Officer
**(Moderately Centralized Health System)**

**KANSAS:** CLOUD COUNTY HEALTH CENTER (C, 25 beds) 1100 Highland Drive, Concordia, KS, Zip 66901–3923; tel. 785/243–1234; David Garnas, Administrator
**Web address:** www.cchc.com

LINDSBORG COMMUNITY HOSPITAL (C, 12 beds) 605 West Lincoln Street, Lindsborg, KS, Zip 67456–2328; tel. 785/227–3308; Larry VanDerWege, Administrator

SALINA REGIONAL HEALTH CENTER (O, 207 beds) 400 South Santa Fe Avenue, Salina, KS, Zip 67401–4198, Mailing Address: P.O. Box 5080, 67402–5080, tel. 785/452–7000; Joel Phelps, President and Chief Executive Officer
**Web address:** www.srhc.com

| | | |
|---|---|---|
| Owned, leased, sponsored: | 1 hospitals | 207 beds |
| Contract–managed: | 2 hospitals | 37 beds |
| Totals: | 3 hospitals | 244 beds |

**★0186: SAMARITAN HEALTH SERVICES** (NP)
3600 NW Samaritan Drive, Corvallis, OR Zip 97330–3737, Mailing Address: P.O. Box 1068, 97339–1068, tel. 541/768–5001; Doug Boysen, President and Chief Executive Officer
**(Centralized Physician/Insurance Health System)**

**OREGON:** GOOD SAMARITAN REGIONAL MEDICAL CENTER (O, 185 beds) 3600 NW Samaritan Drive, Corvallis, OR, Zip 97330–3737, Mailing Address: P.O. Box 1068, 97339–1068, tel. 541/768–5111; Becky A. Pape, R.N., Chief Executive Officer

SAMARITAN ALBANY GENERAL HOSPITAL (O, 70 beds) 1046 Sixth Avenue, SW, Albany, OR, Zip 97321–1999; tel. 541/812–4000; Dan Keteri, R.N., Chief Executive Officer
**Web address:** www.samhealth.org

SAMARITAN LEBANON COMMUNITY HOSPITAL (O, 25 beds) 525 North Santiam Highway, Lebanon, OR, Zip 97355–4363, Mailing Address: P.O. Box 739, 97355–0739, tel. 541/258–2101; Marty Cahill, Chief Executive Officer
**Web address:** www.samhealth.org

SAMARITAN NORTH LINCOLN HOSPITAL (C, 25 beds) 3043 NE 28th Street, Lincoln City, OR, Zip 97367–4518, Mailing Address: P.O. Box 767, 97367–0767, tel. 541/994–3661; Lesley Ogden, M.D., Chief Executive Officer
**Web address:** www.samhealth.org

SAMARITAN PACIFIC COMMUNITIES HOSPITAL (C, 25 beds) 930 SW Abbey Street, Newport, OR, Zip 97365–4820, Mailing Address: P.O. Box 945, 97365–0072, tel. 541/265–2244; Lesley Ogden, M.D., Chief Executive Officer
**Web address:** www.samhealth.org

| | | |
|---|---|---|
| Owned, leased, sponsored: | 3 hospitals | 280 beds |
| Contract–managed: | 2 hospitals | 50 beds |
| Totals: | 5 hospitals | 330 beds |

**★0914: SAN LUIS VALLEY HEALTH** (NP)
106 Blanca Avenue, Alamosa, CO Zip 81101–2340; tel. 719/589–2511; Konnie Martin, Chief Executive Officer
**(Independent Hospital System)**

**COLORADO:** SAN LUIS VALLEY HEALTH CONEJOS COUNTY HOSPITAL (O, 17 beds) 19021 U S Highway 285, La Jara, CO, Zip 81140–0639, Mailing Address: P.O. Box 639, 81140–0639, tel. 719/274–5121; Kelly Gallegos, Administrator
**Web address:** www.sanluisvalleyhealth.org/locations/conejos–county–hospital

SAN LUIS VALLEY HEALTH (O, 49 beds) 106 Blanca Avenue, Alamosa, CO, Zip 81101–2393; tel. 719/589–2511; Konnie Martin, Chief Executive Officer

| | | |
|---|---|---|
| Owned, leased, sponsored: | 2 hospitals | 66 beds |
| Contract–managed: | 0 hospitals | 0 beds |
| Totals: | 2 hospitals | 66 beds |

**★0530: SANFORD HEALTH** (NP)
2301 East 60th Street North, Sioux Falls, SD Zip 57104–0569, Mailing Address: P.O. 5039, 57117–5039, tel. 605/333–1000; Kelby K. Krabbenhoft, President and Chief Executive Officer
**(Decentralized Health System)**

**IOWA:** ORANGE CITY AREA HEALTH SYSTEM (C, 114 beds) 1000 Lincoln Circle SE, Orange City, IA, Zip 51041–1862; tel. 712/737–4984; Martin W. Guthmiller, Chief Executive Officer
**Web address:** www.ochealthsystem.org

SANFORD SHELDON MEDICAL CENTER (O, 93 beds) 118 North Seventh Avenue, Sheldon, IA, Zip 51201–1235, Mailing Address: P.O. Box 250, 51201–0250, tel. 712/324–5041; Richard E. Nordahl, Senior Director
**Web address:** www.sanfordsheldon.org

**MINNESOTA:** ARNOLD MEMORIAL HEALTH CARE CENTER (L, 50 beds) 601 Louisiana Avenue, Adrian, MN, Zip 56110–0279, Mailing Address: P.O. Box 279, 56110–0279, tel. 507/483–2668; Michele Roban, Administrator

MAHNOMEN HEALTH CENTER (C, 50 beds) 414 West Jefferson Avenue, Mahnomen, MN, Zip 56557–4912, Mailing Address: P.O. Box 396, 56557–0396, tel. 218/935–2511; Dale K. Kruger, Chief Executive Officer
**Web address:** www.mahnomenhealthcenter.com

MURRAY COUNTY MEDICAL CENTER (C, 18 beds) 2042 Juniper Avenue, Slayton, MN, Zip 56172–1017; tel. 507/836–6111; Michael Ladevich, FACHE, Interim Chief Executive Officer
**Web address:** www.murraycountymed.org

ORTONVILLE AREA HEALTH SERVICES (C, 90 beds) 450 Eastvold Avenue, Ortonville, MN, Zip 56278–1133; tel. 320/839–2502; David Rogers, Chief Executive Officer

PERHAM HEALTH (C, 121 beds) 1000 Coney Street West, Perham, MN, Zip 56573–1108; tel. 218/347–4500; Chuck Hofius, Chief Executive Officer
**Web address:** www.perhamhealth.org

SANFORD BAGLEY MEDICAL CENTER (O, 8 beds) 203 Fourth Street NW, Bagley, MN, Zip 56621–8307; tel. 218/694–6501; Robert Belanger, Administrator Director

SANFORD BEMIDJI MEDICAL CENTER (O, 196 beds) 1300 Anne Street NW, Bemidji, MN, Zip 56601–5103; tel. 218/751–5430; Susan Jarvis, President
**Web address:** www.sanfordhealth.org/bemidji

SANFORD CANBY MEDICAL CENTER (L, 78 beds) 112 St Olaf Avenue South, Canby, MN, Zip 56220–1433; tel. 507/223–7277; Lori Sisk, R.N., Chief Executive Officer
**Web address:** www.sanfordcanby.org

SANFORD JACKSON MEDICAL CENTER (O, 16 beds) 1430 North Highway, Jackson, MN, Zip 56143–1093; tel. 507/847–2420; Dawn Schnell, Chief Nursing Officer and Interim Senior Director
**Web address:** www.sanfordjackson.org

SANFORD LUVERNE MEDICAL CENTER (O, 25 beds) 1600 North Kniss Avenue, Luverne, MN, Zip 56156–1067; tel. 507/283–2321; Tammy Loosbrock, Senior Director
**Web address:** www.sanfordluverne.org

For explanation of codes following names, see page B2.
★ Indicates Type III membership in the American Hospital Association.

SANFORD MEDICAL CENTER THIEF RIVER FALLS (O, 25 beds) 3001 Sanford Parkway, Thief River Falls, MN, Zip 56701–2700; tel. 218/681–4747; Brian J. Carlson, FACHE, Executive Director
**Web address:** www.sanfordhealth.org

SANFORD THIEF RIVER FALLS BEHAVIORAL HEALTH CENTER (O, 16 beds) 120 LaBree Avenue South, Thief River Falls, MN, Zip 56701–2819, 3001 Sanford Parkway, 56701–2819, tel. 218/683–4349; Brian J. Carlson, FACHE, Chief Executive Officer

SANFORD TRACY MEDICAL CENTER (O, 25 beds) 251 Fifth Street East, Tracy, MN, Zip 56175–1536; tel. 507/629–8400; Stacy Barstad, Chief Executive Officer
**Web address:** www.sanfordtracy.org

SANFORD WESTBROOK MEDICAL CENTER (L, 8 beds) 920 Bell Avenue, Westbrook, MN, Zip 56183–9669, Mailing Address: P.O. Box 188, 56183–0188, tel. 507/274–6121; Stacy Barstad, Chief Executive Officer
**Web address:** www.sanfordwestbrook.org

SANFORD WHEATON MEDICAL CENTER (O, 15 beds) 401 12th Street North, Wheaton, MN, Zip 56296–1099; tel. 320/563–8226; Chelsie Falk, Senior Director
**Web address:** www.sanfordhealth.org

SANFORD WORTHINGTON MEDICAL CENTER (O, 48 beds) 1018 Sixth Avenue, Worthington, MN, Zip 56187–2202, Mailing Address: P.O. Box 997, 56187–0997, tel. 507/372–2941; Jennifer . Weg, MS, R.N., Executive Director
**Web address:** www.sanfordhealth.org

WINDOM AREA HEALTH (C, 18 beds) 2150 Hospital Drive, Windom, MN, Zip 56101–0339, Mailing Address: P.O. Box 339, 56101–0339, tel. 507/831–2400; Shelby Medina, Chief Executive Officer

**NORTH DAKOTA:** NORTHWOOD DEACONESS HEALTH CENTER (O, 57 beds) 4 North Park Street, Northwood, ND, Zip 58267–4102, Mailing Address: P.O. Box 190, 58267–0190, tel. 701/587–6060; Pete Antonson, Chief Executive Officer
**Web address:** www.ndhc.net

SANFORD HILLSBORO MEDICAL CENTER (C, 46 beds) 12 Third Street SE, Hillsboro, ND, Zip 58045–4840, Mailing Address: P.O. Box 609, 58045–0609, tel. 701/636–3200; Jac McTaggart, Chief Executive Officer

SANFORD MAYVILLE MEDICAL CENTER (O, 10 beds) 42 Sixth Avenue SE, Mayville, ND, Zip 58257–1598; tel. 701/786–3800; Jac McTaggart, Chief Executive Officer
**Web address:** www.unionhospital.com

SANFORD MEDICAL CENTER BISMARCK (O, 227 beds) 300 North Seventh Street, Bismarck, ND, Zip 58501–4439, Mailing Address: P.O. Box 5525, 58506–5525, tel. 701/323–6000; Michael LeBeau, President

SANFORD MEDICAL CENTER FARGO (O, 546 beds) 801 Broadway North, Fargo, ND, Zip 58122–3641; tel. 701/234–2000; Bryan Nermoe, President
**Web address:** www.sanfordhealth.org

**SOUTH DAKOTA:** COMMUNITY MEMORIAL HOSPITAL (C, 16 beds) 809 Jackson Street, Burke, SD, Zip 57523–2065, Mailing Address: P.O. Box 319, 57523–0319, tel. 605/775–2621; Mistie Sachtjen, Chief Executive Officer
**Web address:** www.sanfordhealth.org

COTEAU DES PRAIRIES HOSPITAL (C, 25 beds) 205 Orchard Drive, Sisseton, SD, Zip 57262–2398; tel. 605/698–7647; Craig A. Kantos, Chief Executive Officer
**Web address:** www.cdphospital.com

PIONEER MEMORIAL HOSPITAL AND HEALTH SERVICES (C, 64 beds) 315 North Washington Street, Viborg, SD, Zip 57070–2002, Mailing Address: P.O. Box 368, 57070–0368, tel. 605/326–5161; Thomas V. Richter, Chief Executive Officer
**Web address:** www.pioneermemorial.org

SANFORD ABERDEEN MEDICAL CENTER (O, 54 beds) 2905 3rd Avenue SE, Aberdeen, SD, Zip 57401–5420; tel. 605/626–4200; Ashley M. Erickson, Chief Executive Officer
**Web address:** www.sanfordaberdeen.org/

SANFORD CANTON–INWOOD MEDICAL CENTER (O, 27 beds) 440 North Hiawatha Drive, Canton, SD, Zip 57013–5800; tel. 605/764–1400; Scott C. Larson, Chief Executive Officer

SANFORD CHAMBERLAIN MEDICAL CENTER (O, 68 beds) 300 South Byron Boulevard, Chamberlain, SD, Zip 57325–9741; tel. 605/234–5511; Erica Peterson, Chief Executive Officer
**Web address:** www.sanfordchamberlain.org

SANFORD CLEAR LAKE MEDICAL CENTER (L, 15 beds) 701 Third Avenue South, Clear Lake, SD, Zip 57226–2016; tel. 605/874–2141; Lori Sisk, R.N., Chief Executive Officer
**Web address:** www.sanforddeuelcounty.org

SANFORD USD MEDICAL CENTER (O, 500 beds) 1305 West 18th Street, Sioux Falls, SD, Zip 57105–0496, Mailing Address: P.O. Box 5039, 57117–5039, tel. 605/333–1000; Paul A. Hanson, FACHE, President

SANFORD VERMILLION MEDICAL CENTER (L, 120 beds) 20 South Plum Street, Vermillion, SD, Zip 57069–3346; tel. 605/677–3500; Timothy J. Tracy, Senior Director
**Web address:** www.sanfordvermillion.org

SANFORD WEBSTER MEDICAL CENTER (L, 20 beds) 1401 West 1st Street, Webster, SD, Zip 57274–1054, Mailing Address: P.O. Box 489, 57274–0489, tel. 605/345–3336; Isaac Gerdes, Chief Executive Officer
**Web address:** www.sanfordhealth.org

WINNER REGIONAL HEALTHCARE CENTER (C, 104 beds) 745 East Eighth Street, Winner, SD, Zip 57580–2631; tel. 605/842–7100; Kevin Coffey, Chief Executive Officer

| | | |
|---|---|---|
| Owned, leased, sponsored: | 24 hospitals | 2247 beds |
| Contract–managed: | 11 hospitals | 666 beds |
| **Totals:** | 35 hospitals | 2913 beds |

---

**★5095: SCL HEALTH** (CO)

500 Eldorado Boulevard, Suite 4300, Broomfield, CO Zip 80021; tel. 303/813–5180; Lydia Jumonville, President and Chief Executive Officer

**(Moderately Centralized Health System)**

**COLORADO:** GOOD SAMARITAN MEDICAL CENTER (S, 175 beds) 200 Exempla Circle, Lafayette, CO, Zip 80026–3370; tel. 303/689–4000; Jennifer Alderfer, President

LUTHERAN MEDICAL CENTER (S, 368 beds) 8300 West 38th Avenue, Wheat Ridge, CO, Zip 80033–6005; tel. 303/425–4500; Grant Wicklund, SCL Health Regional President, Western Colorado and President, Lutheran Medical Center
**Web address:** https://www.sclhealth.org/locations/lutheran–medical–center/

PLATTE VALLEY MEDICAL CENTER (C, 97 beds) 1600 Prairie Center Parkway, Brighton, CO, Zip 80601–4006; tel. 303/498–1600; John R. Hicks, President and Chief Executive Officer
**Web address:** www.pvmc.org

SAINT JOSEPH HOSPITAL (O, 379 beds) 1375 East 19th Avenue, Denver, CO, Zip 80218–1126; tel. 303/837–7111; Jameson Smith, President
**Web address:** www.saintjosephdenver.org

ST. MARY'S HOSPITAL AND MEDICAL CENTER (O, 309 beds) 2635 North 7th Street, Grand Junction, CO, Zip 81501–8209, Mailing Address: P.O. Box 1628, 81502–1628, tel. 970/298–2273; Bryan L. Johnson, President
**Web address:** www.stmarygj.com

**MONTANA:** HOLY ROSARY HEALTHCARE (O, 89 beds) 2600 Wilson Street, Miles City, MT, Zip 59301–5094; tel. 406/233–2600; Karen Costello, President

ST. JAMES HEALTHCARE (O, 73 beds) 400 South Clark Street, Butte, MT, Zip 59701–2328; tel. 406/723–2500; Jay Doyle, President and Chief Executive Officer
**Web address:** www.stjameshealthcare.org

ST. VINCENT HEALTHCARE (O, 263 beds) 1233 North 30th Street, Billings, MT, Zip 59101–0165, Mailing Address: P.O. Box 35200, 59107–5200, tel. 406/237–7000; Steve Loveless, Montana Region President

| | | |
|---|---|---|
| Owned, leased, sponsored: | 7 hospitals | 1656 beds |
| Contract–managed: | 1 hospitals | 97 beds |
| **Totals:** | 8 hospitals | 1753 beds |

For explanation of codes following names, see page B2.
★ Indicates Type III membership in the American Hospital Association.

**★1505: SCRIPPS HEALTH** (NP)
4275 Campus Point Court CP112, San Diego, CA Zip 92121–1513, 4275 Campus Point Court, 92121–1513, tel. 858/678–7200; Chris D. Van Gorder, FACHE, President and Chief Executive Officer
**(Centralized Health System)**

**CALIFORNIA:** SCRIPPS GREEN HOSPITAL (O, 150 beds) 10666 North Torrey Pines Road, La Jolla, CA, Zip 92037–1093; tel. 858/455–9100; Carl J. Etter, Chief Executive Officer
**Web address:** www.scrippshealth.org

SCRIPPS MEMORIAL HOSPITAL–ENCINITAS (O, 171 beds) 354 Santa Fe Drive, Encinitas, CA, Zip 92024–5182, Mailing Address: P.O. Box 230817, 92023–0817, tel. 760/633–6501; Carl J. Etter, Chief Executive and Senior Vice President

SCRIPPS MEMORIAL HOSPITAL–LA JOLLA (O, 365 beds) 9888 Genesee Avenue, La Jolla, CA, Zip 92037–1200, Mailing Address: P.O. Box 28, 92038–0028, tel. 858/626–4123; Carl J. Etter, Chief Executive Officer
**Web address:** www.scripps.org/locations/hospitals__scripps–memorial–hospital–la–jolla

SCRIPPS MERCY HOSPITAL (O, 392 beds) 4077 Fifth Avenue, San Diego, CA, Zip 92103–2105; tel. 619/294–8111; Thomas A. Gammiere, Chief Executive, Senior Vice President
**Web address:** www.scrippshealth.org

| | | |
|---|---|---|
| Owned, leased, sponsored: | 4 hospitals | 1078 beds |
| Contract–managed: | 0 hospitals | 0 beds |
| Totals: | 4 hospitals | 1078 beds |

**★0181: SELECT MEDICAL CORPORATION** (IO)
4714 Gettysburg Road, Mechanicsburg, PA Zip 17055–4325; tel. 717/972–1100; David S. Chernow, President and Chief Executive Officer
**(Independent Hospital System)**

**ALABAMA:** SELECT SPECIALTY HOSPITAL–BIRMINGHAM (O, 38 beds) 2010 Brookwood Medical Center Drive, 3rd Floor, Birmingham, AL, Zip 35209–6804; tel. 205/599–4600; Clifton Quinn, Chief Executive Officer
**Web address:** www.birmingham.selectspecialtyhospitals.com

**ARIZONA:** HONORHEALTH REHABILITATION HOSPITAL (O, 50 beds) 8850 East Pima Center Parkway, Scottsdale, AZ, Zip 85258–4619; tel. 480/800–3900; Scott R. Keen, Chief Executive Officer

SELECT SPECIALTY HOSPITAL–PHOENIX DOWNTOWN (O, 32 beds) 1012 East Wiletta Street, 4th Floor, Phoenix, AZ, Zip 85006; tel. 602/839–6550; David Selman, Chief Executive Officer
**Web address:** www.selectmedicalcorp.com

SELECT SPECIALTY HOSPITAL–PHOENIX (O, 48 beds) 350 West Thomas Road, 3rd Floor Main, Phoenix, AZ, Zip 85013–4409; tel. 602/406–6810; Karen Cawley, Chief Executive Officer

**ARKANSAS:** REGENCY HOSPITAL OF NORTHWEST ARKANSAS – SPRINGDALE (O, 25 beds) 609 West Maple Avenue, 6th Fl, Springdale, AR, Zip 72764; tel. 479/757–2600; Lisa Muskrat, Chief Executive Officer
**Web address:** www.regencyhospital.com

SELECT SPECIALTY HOSPITAL–FORT SMITH (O, 34 beds) 1001 Towson Avenue, 6 Central, Fort Smith, AR, Zip 72901–4921; tel. 479/441–3960; Shannon Grams, Chief Executive Officer

**CALIFORNIA:** CALIFORNIA REHABILITATION INSTITUTE (O, 138 beds) 2070 Century Park East, Los Angeles, CA, Zip 90067–1907; tel. 424/363–1000; Scott T. Rotsted, Chief Executive Officer
**Web address:** www.californiarehabinstitute.com/

SELECT SPECIALTY HOSPITAL – SAN DIEGO (C, 80 beds) 555 Washington Street, San Diego, CA, Zip 92103–2294; tel. 619/260–8300; Yameeka Jones, Chief Executive Officer

**DELAWARE:** SELECT SPECIALTY HOSPITAL–WILMINGTON (O, 35 beds) 701 North Clayton Street, 5th Floor, Wilmington, DE, Zip 19805–3948; tel. 302/421–4545; Donna Gares, R.N., FACHE, MSN, Chief Executive Officer
**Web address:** www.wilmington.selectspecialtyhospitals.com

**FLORIDA:** PROMISE HOSPITAL OF FLORIDA AT THE VILLAGES (O, 40 beds) 5050 County Road 472, Oxford, FL, Zip 34484; tel. 352/689–6400; Hoyt Ross, Chief Executive Officer
**Web address:** www.promise–villages.com

PROMISE HOSPITAL OF FORT MYERS (O, 60 beds) 3050 Champion Ring Road, Fort Myers, FL, Zip 33905–5599; tel. 239/313–2900; Patrick G. Ryan, Chief Executive Officer
**Web address:** www.https://fortmyers.selectspecialtyhospitals.com/

SELECT SPECIALTY HOSPITAL DAYTONA BEACH (O, 34 beds) 301 Memorial Medical Parkway, 11th Floor, Daytona Beach, FL, Zip 32117–5167; tel. 386/231–3436; Adrianne Lutes, Chief Executive Officer

SELECT SPECIALTY HOSPITAL–GAINESVILLE (O, 44 beds) 1600 SW Archer Road, 5th Floor, Gainesville, FL, Zip 32610; tel. 352/337–3240; Ronnie Wagley, Market Chief Executive Officer
**Web address:** www.gainesville.selectspecialtyhospitals.com/

SELECT SPECIALTY HOSPITAL–MIAMI LAKES (O, 60 beds) 14001 NW 82nd Avenue, Miami Lakes, FL, Zip 33016–1561; tel. 786/609–9200; Brian Soares, Chief Executive Officer
**Web address:** www.promise–miami.com

SELECT SPECIALTY HOSPITAL–MIAMI (O, 47 beds) 955 NW 3rd Street, Miami, FL, Zip 33128–1274; tel. 305/416–5700; Loretta Sheffield, Chief Executive Officer

SELECT SPECIALTY HOSPITAL–ORLANDO (O, 75 beds) 2250 Bedford Road, Orlando, FL, Zip 32803–1443; tel. 407/303–7869; Theodore Mena, Chief Executive Officer
**Web address:** www.selectspecialtyhospitals.com/company/locations/orlando.aspx

SELECT SPECIALTY HOSPITAL–PALM BEACH (O, 60 beds) 3060 Melaleuca Lane, Lake Worth, FL, Zip 33461–5174; tel. 561/357–7200; Larry Melby, Chief Executive Officer
**Web address:** www.selectspecialtyhospitals.com/company/locations/palmbeach.aspx

SELECT SPECIALTY HOSPITAL–PANAMA CITY (O, 30 beds) 615 North Bonita Avenue, 3rd Floor, Panama City, FL, Zip 32401–3623; tel. 850/767–3180; Randal S. Hamilton, Chief Executive Officer

SELECT SPECIALTY HOSPITAL–PENSACOLA (O, 75 beds) 7000 Cobble Creek Drive, Pensacola, FL, Zip 32504–8638; tel. 850/473–4800; Adam Principe, Chief Executive Officer
**Web address:** www.https://pensacola.selectspecialtyhospitals.com/

SELECT SPECIALTY HOSPITAL–TALLAHASSEE (O, 29 beds) 1554 Surgeons Drive, Tallahassee, FL, Zip 32308–4631; tel. 850/219–6950; Jay Faherty, Chief Executive Officer

UF HEALTH REHAB HOSPITAL (O, 60 beds) 2708 Southwest Archer Road, Gainesville, FL, Zip 32608–1316; tel. 352/265–5499; Marina T. Cecchini, Administrator
**Web address:** www.https://ufhealth.org/uf–health–shands–rehab–hospital

WEST GABLES REHABILITATION HOSPITAL (O, 60 beds) 2525 SW 75th Avenue, Miami, FL, Zip 33155–2800; tel. 305/262–6800; Walter Concepcion, Chief Executive Officer

**GEORGIA:** REGENCY HOSPITAL OF CENTRAL GEORGIA (O, 60 beds) 535 Coliseum Drive, Macon, GA, Zip 31217–0104; tel. 478/803–7300; Wayne B. Boutwell, Chief Executive Officer
**Web address:** www.regencyhospital.com

REGENCY HOSPITAL OF SOUTH ATLANTA (O, 40 beds) 1170 Cleveland Avenue, 4th Floor, East Point, GA, Zip 30344–3615; tel. 404/466–6250; Michelle Tenhengel–deVille, Chief Executive Officer

SELECT SPECIALTY HOSPITAL MIDTOWN ATLANTA (O, 72 beds) 705 Juniper Street NE, Atlanta, GA, Zip 30308–1307; tel. 404/873–2871; Adriene Kinnaird, Chief Executive Officer
**Web address:** www.selectspecialtyhospitals.com/

SELECT SPECIALTY HOSPITAL–AUGUSTA (O, 80 beds) 1537 Walton Way, Augusta, GA, Zip 30904–3764; tel. 706/731–1200; E Rick. Lowe, FACHE, Chief Executive Officer

SELECT SPECIALTY HOSPITAL–SAVANNAH (O, 40 beds) 5353 Reynolds Street, 4 South, Savannah, GA, Zip 31405–6015; tel. 912/819–7982; Greg Wuchter, R.N., MSN, Chief Executive Officer
**Web address:** www.savannah.selectspecialtyhospitals.com

For explanation of codes following names, see page B2.
★ Indicates Type III membership in the American Hospital Association.

**B114** Health Care Systems, Networks and Alliances       © 2021 AHA Guide

**INDIANA**: REGENCY HOSPITAL OF NORTHWEST INDIANA (O, 61 beds) 4321 Fir Street, 4th Floor, East Chicago, IN, Zip 46312–3049; tel. 219/392–7799; Eleyce Winn, Chief Executive Officer
**Web address**: www.regencyhospital.com/company/locations/indiana–northwest–indiana.aspx

SELECT SPECIALTY HOSPITAL–EVANSVILLE (O, 51 beds) 400 SE 4th Street, Evansville, IN, Zip 47713–1206; tel. 812/421–2500; Kristy C. Bruner, Chief Executive Officer
**Web address**: www.selectspecialtyhospitals.com/company/locations/evansville.aspx

**IOWA**: SELECT SPECIALTY HOSPITAL–DES MOINES (O, 30 beds) 1111 6th Avenue, 4th Floor Main, Des Moines, IA, Zip 50314–2610; tel. 515/247–4400; Brent Hanson, Chief Executive Officer
**Web address**: www.selectspecialtyhospitals.com

SELECT SPECIALTY HOSPITAL–QUAD CITIES (O, 50 beds) 1111 West Kimberly Road, Davenport, IA, Zip 52806–5711; tel. 563/468–2000; Codie Dillie, Chief Executive Officer

**KANSAS**: SELECT SPECIALTY HOSPITAL–KANSAS CITY (O, 40 beds) 1731 North 90th Street, Kansas City, KS, Zip 66112–1515; tel. 913/732–5900; Bridgette Hunter, Chief Executive Officer
**Web address**: www.selectspecialtyhospitals.com

SELECT SPECIALTY HOSPITAL–WICHITA (O, 48 beds) 929 North St Francis Street, Wichita, KS, Zip 67214–3821; tel. 316/261–8303; Christopher Keith, Chief Executive Officer
**Web address**: www.selectspecialtyhospitals.com/company/locations/wichita.aspx

**KENTUCKY**: SELECT SPECIALTY HOSPITAL–LEXINGTON (O, 41 beds) 310 South Limestone Street, 3rd Floor, Lexington, KY, Zip 40508–3008; tel. 859/226–7096; Kim Pennington, Chief Executive Officer

SELECT SPECIALTY HOSPITAL–NORTHERN KENTUCKY (O, 33 beds) 85 North Grand Avenue, Fort Thomas, KY, Zip 41075–1793; tel. 859/572–3880; Mavis Bechtle, MSN, R.N., FACHE, Chief Executive Officer
**Web address**: www.selectspecialtyhospitals.com

**LOUISIANA**: NORTHSHORE REHABILITATION HOSPITAL (O, 30 beds) 64030 State Highway 434, Lacombe, LA, Zip 70445; tel. 985/218–4660; Laurel DuPont, Chief Executive Officer

OCHSNER REHABILITATON HOSPITAL WEST CAMPUS (O, 42 beds) 2614 Jefferson Highway, Jefferson, LA, Zip 70121–3828; tel. 504/291–5100; Neil Fedders, Interim Chief Executive Officer
**Web address**: https://www.ochsner.org/services/rehabilitation

**MICHIGAN**: SELECT SPECIALTY HOSPITAL – SPECTRUM HEALTH (O, 36 beds) 1840 Wealthy Street, Southeast, Grand Rapids, MI, Zip 49506–2921; tel. 616/774–3800; Jim Aldrich, Chief Executive Officer
**Web address**: www.https://grandrapids.selectspecialtyhospitals.com

SELECT SPECIALTY HOSPITAL–ANN ARBOR (O, 36 beds) 5301 East Huron River Drive, 7th Floor, Ypsilanti, MI, Zip 48197–1051; tel. 734/712–6751; Bryan Cutliff, Chief Executive Officer

SELECT SPECIALTY HOSPITAL–BATTLE CREEK (O, 25 beds) 300 North Avenue, Battle Creek, MI, Zip 49017–3307; tel. 269/245–4675; Robert Mach, Chief Executive Officer
**Web address**: www.battlecreek.selectspecialtyhospitals.com/

SELECT SPECIALTY HOSPITAL–DOWNRIVER (O, 35 beds) 2333 Biddle Avenue, 8th Floor, Wyandotte, MI, Zip 48192–4668; tel. 734/246–5500; John Ponczocha, Chief Executive Officer

SELECT SPECIALTY HOSPITAL–FLINT (O, 26 beds) 401 South Ballenger Highway, 5th Floor Central, Flint, MI, Zip 48532–3638; tel. 810/342–4545; Christina DeBlouw, Chief Executive Officer
**Web address**: www.selectspecialtyhospitals.com/company/locations/flint.aspx

SELECT SPECIALTY HOSPITAL–GROSSE POINTE (O, 30 beds) 468 Cadieux Road, 3 North East, Grosse Pointe, MI, Zip 48230–1507, 22101 Moross Road, 6th Floor, Detroit, 48236, tel. 313/473–6131; Zaahra Butt, Chief Executive Officer
**Web address**: www.grossepointe.selectspecialtyhospitals.com/

SELECT SPECIALTY HOSPITAL–MACOMB COUNTY (O, 36 beds) 215 North Avenue, Mount Clemens, MI, Zip 48043–1700; tel. 586/307–9000; Jon P. O'Malley, Chief Executive Officer

SELECT SPECIALTY HOSPITAL–MUSKEGON (O, 31 beds) 1700 Clinton Street, 3 South, Muskegon, MI, Zip 49442–5502; tel. 231/728–5811; Kerry McLane, Chief Executive Officer
**Web address**: www.greatlakesspecialtyhospital.com

SELECT SPECIALTY HOSPITAL–PONTIAC (O, 30 beds) 44405 Woodward Avenue, 8th Floor, Pontiac, MI, Zip 48341–5023; tel. 248/452–5252; Peggy Kingston, Chief Executive Officer

SELECT SPECIALTY HOSPITAL–SAGINAW (O, 32 beds) 1447 North Harrison Street, 8th Floor, Saginaw, MI, Zip 48602–4785; tel. 989/583–4235; Matthew J. Campbell Esq, Chief Executive Officer
**Web address**: www.selectspecialtyhospitals.com/company/locations/saginaw.aspx

**MINNESOTA**: REGENCY HOSPITAL OF MINNEAPOLIS (O, 92 beds) 1300 Hidden Lakes Parkway, Golden Valley, MN, Zip 55422–4286; tel. 763/588–2750; Sean Stricker, Chief Executive Officer
**Web address**: www.regencyhospital.com

**MISSISSIPPI**: REGENCY HOSPITAL OF MERIDIAN (O, 40 beds) 1102 Constitution Avenue, 2nd Floor, Meridian, MS, Zip 39301–4001; tel. 601/484–7900; William Heath, Chief Executive Officer

SELECT SPECIALTY HOSPITAL – BELHAVEN (O, 25 beds) 1225 North State Street, Jackson, MS, Zip 39202–2097, Mailing Address: P.O. Box 23695, 39225–3695, tel. 601/968–1000; Robert Shannon. Canard, Chief Executive Officer
**Web address**: www.https://belhaven.selectspecialtyhospitals.com/

SELECT SPECIALTY HOSPITAL–GULFPORT (O, 61 beds) 1520 Broad Avenue, Suite 300, Gulfport, MS, Zip 39501–3601; tel. 228/575–7500; John O'Keefe, Chief Executive Officer
**Web address**: www.selectspecialtyhospitals.com/company/locations/gulfcoast.aspx

SELECT SPECIALTY HOSPITAL–JACKSON (O, 53 beds) 5903 Ridgewood Road, Suite 100, Jackson, MS, Zip 39211–3700; tel. 601/899–3800; Chandler Ewing, Chief Executive Officer

**MISSOURI**: SSM SELECT REHABILITATION HOSPITAL (O, 125 beds) 1027 Bellevue Avenue, 3rd Floor, Richmond Heights, MO, Zip 63117–1851, 1027 Bellevue Avenue, 63117-1851, tel. 314/768–5300; Brenda Hughes, Chief Operating Officer
**Web address**: www.ssm–select.com

SELECT SPECIALTY HOSPITAL–SPRINGFIELD (O, 44 beds) 1630 East Primrose Street, Springfield, MO, Zip 65804–7929; tel. 417/885–4700; Steve Patterson, Chief Executive Officer

SELECT SPECIALTY HOSPITAL–ST. LOUIS (O, 33 beds) 300 First Capitol Drive, Unit 1, Saint Charles, MO, Zip 63301–2844; tel. 636/947–5010; Bruce Eady, Chief Executive Officer
**Web address**: www.selectspecialtyhospitals.com/company/locations/stlouis.aspx

**NEBRASKA**: SELECT SPECIALTY HOSPITAL – LINCOLN (O, 24 beds) 2300 South 16th Street, 7th Floor, Lincoln, NE, Zip 68502–3704; tel. 402/483–8444; Connie K. Siffring, Chief Executive Officer
**Web address**: www.selectmedical.com

SELECT SPECIALTY HOSPITAL–OMAHA (O, 52 beds) 1870 South 75th Street, Omaha, NE, Zip 68124–1700; tel. 402/361–5700; Kerry McLane, Interim Chief Executive Officer

**NEW JERSEY**: KESSLER INSTITUTE FOR REHABILITATION (O, 336 beds) 1199 Pleasant Valley Way, West Orange, NJ, Zip 07052–1424; tel. 973/731–3600; Bonnie A. Evans, Chief Executive Officer
**Web address**: www.kessler–rehab.com

KESSLER MARLTON REHABILITATION (O, 61 beds) 92 Brick Road, Marlton, NJ, Zip 08053–2177; tel. 856/988–8778; Phyllis J. Schlichtmann, R.N., Chief Executive Officer

SELECT SPECIALTY HOSPITAL–NORTHEAST NEW JERSEY (O, 62 beds) 96 Parkway, Rochelle Park, NJ, Zip 07662–4200; tel. 201/221–2352; David Key, Division President
**Web address**: www.northeastnewjersey.selectspecialtyhospitals.com/about/

**NORTH CAROLINA**: SELECT SPECIALTY HOSPITAL–DURHAM (O, 30 beds) 3643 North Roxboro Road, 6th Floor, Durham, NC, Zip 27704–2702; tel. 919/470–9159; Jennifer Rawley, PharmD, Chief Executive Officer
**Web address**: www.selectspecialtyhospitals.com/company/locations/durham.aspx

For explanation of codes following names, see page B2.
★ Indicates Type III membership in the American Hospital Association.

Section B

SELECT SPECIALTY HOSPITAL–GREENSBORO  (O, 30 beds) 1200 North Elm Street, 5th Floor, Greensboro, NC, Zip 27401–1004; tel. 336/832–8571; Deana Knight, Chief Executive Officer
**Web address:** www.selectspecialtyhospitals.com/company/locations/greensboro.aspx

**OHIO:**  CLEVELAND CLINIC REHABILITATION HOSPITAL (O, 180 beds) 33355 Health Campus Boulevard, Avon, OH, Zip 44011; tel. 440/937–9099; Sam Bayoumy, Chief Executive Officer
**Web address:** www.my.clevelandclinic.org

OHIOHEALTH REHABILITATION HOSPITAL (O, 74 beds) 1087 Dennison Avenue, 4th Floor, Columbus, OH, Zip 43201–3201; tel. 614/484–9600; Eric Yap, Chief Executive Officer

REGENCY HOSPITAL CLEVELAND EAST (O, 87 beds) 4200 Interchange Corporate Center Road, Warrensville Heights, OH, Zip 44128–5631; tel. 216/910–3800; Lisa Deering, Chief Executive Officer
**Web address:** www.regencyhospital.com/

REGENCY HOSPITAL OF COLUMBUS (O, 66 beds) 1430 South High Street, Columbus, OH, Zip 43207–1045; tel. 614/456–0300; Kindra Marks, Chief Executive Officer
**Web address:** www.regencyhospital.com/

REGENCY HOSPITAL OF TOLEDO (O, 45 beds) 5220 Alexis Road, Sylvania, OH, Zip 43560–2504; tel. 419/318–5700; Gary Zaciewski, Chief Executive Officer

SELECT SPECIALTY HOSPITAL – BOARDMAN (O, 24 beds) 8401 Market Street, 7 South, Boardman, OH, Zip 44512–6725; tel. 330/729–1750; Jodi Costello, Chief Executive Officer
**Web address:** www.selectspecialtyhospitals.com/

SELECT SPECIALTY HOSPITAL – CINCINNATI NORTH (O, 41 beds) 10500 Montgomery Road, Cincinnati, OH, Zip 45242–4402; tel. 513/865–5300; David D. Muggli, FACHE, Interim Chief Executive Officer

SELECT SPECIALTY HOSPITAL – CLEVELAND GATEWAY (O, 143 beds) 2351 East 22nd Street, 7th Floor, Cleveland, OH, Zip 44115–3111; tel. 216/363–2671; Julie Idoine–Fries, Chief Executive Officer
**Web address:** www.selectspecialtyhospitals.com/

SELECT SPECIALTY HOSPITAL OF SOUTHEAST OHIO (O, 35 beds) 2000 Tamarack Road, Newark, OH, Zip 43055; tel. 740/588–7888; Linda Supplee, Chief Executive Officer
**Web address:** www.selectspecialtyhospitals.com/company/locations/zanesville.aspx

SELECT SPECIALTY HOSPITAL–AKRON (O, 60 beds) 200 East Market Street, Akron, OH, Zip 44308–2015; tel. 330/761–7500; Dawne Wheeler, Chief Executive Officer
**Web address:** www.selectspecialtyhospitals.com/company/locations/akron.aspx

SELECT SPECIALTY HOSPITAL–CANTON (O, 30 beds) 1320 Mercy Drive NW, 6th Floor, Canton, OH, Zip 44708–2614; tel. 330/489–8189; Sherri Becker, Chief Executive Officer
**Web address:** www.selectspecialtyhospitals.com/company/locations/canton.aspx

SELECT SPECIALTY HOSPITAL–CINCINNATI (O, 30 beds) 375 Dixmyth Avenue, 15th Floor, Cincinnati, OH, Zip 45220–2475; tel. 513/862–4444; David D. Muggli, FACHE, Chief Executive Officer

SELECT SPECIALTY HOSPITAL–COLUMBUS (O, 162 beds) 1087 Dennison Avenue, Columbus, OH, Zip 43201–3201; tel. 614/458–9000; Lisa J. Pettrey, MSN, R.N., Chief Executive Officer
**Web address:** www.selectspecialtyhospitals.com/company/locations/columbus.aspx

SELECT SPECIALTY HOSPITAL–YOUNGSTOWN (O, 56 beds) 1044 Belmont Avenue, Youngstown, OH, Zip 44504–1006; tel. 330/480–2349; Jodi Costello, Chief Executive Officer
**Web address:** www.selectspecialtyhospitals.com/company/locations/youngstown.aspx

TRIHEALTH REHABILITATION HOSPITAL (O, 60 beds) 2155 Dana Avenue, Cincinnati, OH, Zip 45207; tel. 513/601–0600; Daphne Glenn, Chief Executive Officer
**Web address:** www.trihealthrehab.com

**OKLAHOMA:**  SELECT SPECIALTY HOSPITAL–OKLAHOMA CITY (O, 72 beds) 3524 NW 56th Street, Oklahoma City, OK, Zip 73112–4518; tel. 405/606–6700; Kelly Duke, Chief Executive Officer

SELECT SPECIALTY HOSPITAL–TULSA MIDTOWN (O, 52 beds) 1125 South Trenton Avenue, 3rd Floor, Tulsa, OK, Zip 74120–5418; tel. 918/579–7300; Charles D. Nasem, FACHE, Chief Executive Officer
**Web address:** www.tulsa.selectspecialtyhospitals.com/

**PENNSYLVANIA:**  HELEN M. SIMPSON REHABILITATION HOSPITAL (C, 50 beds) 4300 Londonderry Road, Harrisburg, PA, Zip 17109–5317; tel. 717/920–4300; Mark Freeburn, Chief Executive Officer
**Web address:** www.simpson–rehab.com/

PENN STATE HERSHEY REHABILITATION HOSPITAL (O, 98 beds) 1135 Old West Chocolate Avenue, Hummelstown, PA, Zip 17036; tel. 717/832–2600; Michelle Von Arx, Chief Executive Officer

SELECT SPECIALTY HOSPITAL–CAMP HILL (O, 92 beds) 503 North 21st Street, 5th Floor, Camp Hill, PA, Zip 17011–2204; tel. 717/972–4575; John E. Simodejka, Chief Executive Officer
**Web address:** www.camphill.selectspecialtyhospitals.com/

SELECT SPECIALTY HOSPITAL–DANVILLE (O, 30 beds) 100 North Academy Avenue, 3rd Floor, Danville, PA, Zip 17822–3050; tel. 570/214–9653; Brian Mann, Chief Executive Officer

SELECT SPECIALTY HOSPITAL–ERIE (O, 50 beds) 252 West 11th Street, Erie, PA, Zip 16501–1702; tel. 814/874–5300; Michael A. Post, Chief Executive Officer
**Web address:** www.erie.selectspecialtyhospitals.com/

SELECT SPECIALTY HOSPITAL–JOHNSTOWN (O, 39 beds) 320 Main Street, 3rd Floor, Johnstown, PA, Zip 15901–1601; tel. 814/534–7300; Kelly Blake, Chief Executive Officer
**Web address:** www.selectspecialtyhospitals.com/company/locations/johnstown.aspx

SELECT SPECIALTY HOSPITAL–LAUREL HIGHLANDS (O, 40 beds) One Mellon Way, 3rd Floor, Latrobe, PA, Zip 15650–1197; tel. 724/539–3870; Stacy Carson, Chief Executive Officer

SELECT SPECIALTY HOSPITAL–MCKEESPORT (O, 30 beds) 1500 Fifth Avenue, 6th Floor, McKeesport, PA, Zip 15132–2422; tel. 412/664–2900; Laurie Kozorosky, Chief Executive Officer
**Web address:** www.mckeesport.selectspecialtyhospitals.com/

SELECT SPECIALTY HOSPITAL–PITTSBURGH/UPMC (O, 32 beds) 200 Lothrop Street, E824, Pittsburgh, PA, Zip 15213–2536; tel. 412/586–9800; Darrell Jones, Interim Chief Executive Officer

**SOUTH CAROLINA:**  REGENCY HOSPITAL OF FLORENCE (O, 40 beds) 121 East Cedar Street, 4th Floor, Florence, SC, Zip 29506–2576; tel. 843/661–3471; Amy Metz, Chief Executive Officer
**Web address:** www.regencyhospital.com

REGENCY HOSPITAL OF GREENVILLE (O, 32 beds) One St Francis Drive, 4th Floor, Greenville, SC, Zip 29601–3955; tel. 864/255–1438; Tammy Ratliff, Chief Executive Officer
**Web address:** www.regencyhospital.com

**SOUTH DAKOTA:**  SELECT SPECIALTY HOSPITAL–SIOUX FALLS (O, 24 beds) 1305 West 18th Street, Sioux Falls, SD, Zip 57105–0401; tel. 605/312–9500; Carol Ulmer, Chief Executive Officer
**Web address:** www.selectspecialtyhospitals.com/company/locations/siouxfalls.aspx

**TENNESSEE:**  SELECT SPECIALTY HOSPITAL–MEMPHIS (O, 39 beds) 5959 Park Avenue, 12th Floor, Memphis, TN, Zip 38119–5200; tel. 901/765–1245; Marcia Taylor, Chief Executive Officer

SELECT SPECIALTY HOSPITAL–NASHVILLE (O, 70 beds) 2000 Hayes Street, Nashville, TN, Zip 37203–2318; tel. 615/284–4599; Jennifer Causey, Chief Executive Officer
**Web address:** www.selectspecialtyhospitals.com/company/locations/nashville.aspx

SELECT SPECIALTY HOSPITAL–NORTH KNOXVILLE (O, 33 beds) 7557B Dannaher Drive, Suite 145, Powell, TN, Zip 37849–3568; tel. 865/512–2450; Steve Plumlee, Chief Executive Officer
**Web address:** www.northknoxville.selectspecialtyhospitals.com/

SELECT SPECIALTY HOSPITAL–TRI CITIES (O, 33 beds) One Medical Park Boulevard, 5th Floor, Bristol, TN, Zip 37620–8964; tel. 423/844–5900; Jeffrey Radford, Chief Executive Officer
**Web address:** www.tricities.selectspecialtyhospitals.com/

**TEXAS:**  BAYLOR SCOTT & WHITE INSTITUTE FOR REHABILITATION – LAKEWAY (O, 36 beds) 2000 Medical Drive, Lakeway, TX, Zip 78734–4200; tel. 512/263–4500; Deborah Hopps, R.N., FACHE, Chief Executive Officer

For explanation of codes following names, see page B2.
★ Indicates Type III membership in the American Hospital Association.

BAYLOR SCOTT & WHITE INSTITUTE FOR REHABILITATION–FORT WORTH (C, 42 beds) 6601 Harris Parkway, Fort Worth, TX, Zip 76132–6108; tel. 817/433–9600; Ryan Seymour, Chief Executive Officer
**Web address**: www.baylorhealth.com/PhysiciansLocations/BIR/Pages/Default.aspx

BAYLOR SCOTT & WHITE INSTITUTE FOR REHABILITATION–FRISCO (O, 44 beds) 2990 Legacy Drive, Frisco, TX, Zip 75034–6066; tel. 469/888–5100; Ryan Seymour, Chief Executive Officer

SELECT REHABILITATION HOSPITAL OF DENTON (O, 44 beds) 2620 Scripture Street, Denton, TX, Zip 76201–4315; tel. 940/297–6500; Michelle Powell, Chief Executive Officer
**Web address**: www.selectrehab–denton.com/

SELECT SPECIALTY HOSPITAL – DALLAS DOWNTOWN (O, 26 beds) 3500 Gaston Avenue, Floors 3&4 Jonsson, Dallas, TX, Zip 75246–2017; tel. 469/801–4500; Michael McAlister, Chief Executive Officer
**Web address**: www.dallasdowntown.selectspecialtyhospitals.com/

SELECT SPECIALTY HOSPITAL–DALLAS (O, 60 beds) 2329 West Parker Road, Carrollton, TX, Zip 75010–4713; tel. 469/892–1400; John O'Hearn, Chief Executive Officer

SELECT SPECIALTY HOSPITAL–LONGVIEW (O, 32 beds) 700 East Marshall Avenue, 1st Floor, Longview, TX, Zip 75601–5580; tel. 903/315–1100; Andrew Meade, Chief Executive Officer
**Web address**: www.longview.selectspecialtyhospitals.com/

**VIRGINIA**: COASTAL VIRGINIA REHABILITATION (C, 35 beds) 245 Chesapeake Avenue, Newport News, VA, Zip 23607–6038; tel. 757/928–8000; Daniel Ballin, Administrator
**Web address**: www.riversideonline.com/rri/index.cfm

SELECT SPECIALTY HOSPITAL HAMPTON ROADS (O, 50 beds) 245 Chesapeake Avenue, Newport News, VA, Zip 23607–6038; tel. 757/534–5000; Phillip L. Wright, FACHE, Chief Executive Officer

**WEST VIRGINIA**: SELECT SPECIALTY HOSPITAL–CHARLESTON (O, 32 beds) 333 Laidley Street, 3rd Floor East, Charleston, WV, Zip 25301–1614; tel. 304/720–7234; Frank Weber, Chief Executive Officer
**Web address**: www.selectspecialtyhospitals.com/company/locations/charleston.aspx

**WISCONSIN**: SELECT SPECIALTY HOSPITAL–MADISON (O, 58 beds) 801 Braxton Place, Madison, WI, Zip 53715–1415; tel. 608/260–2700; Catherine Heimbecher, Chief Executive Officer
**Web address**: www.madison.selectspecialtyhospitals.com

SELECT SPECIALTY HOSPITAL–MILWAUKEE (O, 34 beds) 8901 West Lincoln Avenue, 2nd Floor, Milwaukee, WI, Zip 53227–2409, West Allis, tel. 414/328–7700; Dennis Mattes, Chief Executive Officer

| | | |
|---|---|---|
| **Owned, leased, sponsored:** | 103 hospitals | 5492 beds |
| **Contract–managed:** | 4 hospitals | 207 beds |
| **Totals:** | 107 hospitals | 5699 beds |

---

★**2565: SENTARA HEALTHCARE** (NP)
6015 Poplar Hall Drive, Norfolk, VA Zip 23502–3819; tel. 757/455–7000; Howard P. Kern, Chief Executive Officer
**(Centralized Physician/Insurance Health System)**

**NORTH CAROLINA**: SENTARA ALBEMARLE MEDICAL CENTER (L, 109 beds) 1144 North Road Street, Elizabeth City, NC, Zip 27909–3473, Mailing Address: P.O. Box 1587, 27906–1587, tel. 252/335–0531; Phillip E. Jackson, President
**Web address**: www.albemarlehealth.org

**VIRGINIA**: SENTARA CAREPLEX HOSPITAL (O, 169 beds) 3000 Coliseum Drive, Hampton, VA, Zip 23666–5963; tel. 757/736–1000; Kirkpatrick Conley, President

SENTARA HALIFAX REGIONAL HOSPITAL (O, 441 beds) 2204 Wilborn Avenue, South Boston, VA, Zip 24592–1638; tel. 434/517–3100; Jason A. Studley, FACHE, President
**Web address**: www.hrhs.org

SENTARA LEIGH HOSPITAL (O, 247 beds) 830 Kempsville Road, Norfolk, VA, Zip 23502–3920; tel. 757/261–6000; Joanne Inman, President

SENTARA MARTHA JEFFERSON HOSPITAL (O, 144 beds) 500 Martha Jefferson Drive, Charlottesville, VA, Zip 22911–4668; tel. 434/654–7000; Jonathan S. Davis, FACHE, President
**Web address**: www.marthajefferson.org

SENTARA NORFOLK GENERAL HOSPITAL (O, 500 beds) 600 Gresham Drive, Norfolk, VA, Zip 23507–1904; tel. 757/388–3000; Jessica Melton, Interim President
**Web address**: www.sentara.com

SENTARA NORTHERN VIRGINIA MEDICAL CENTER (O, 183 beds) 2300 Opitz Boulevard, Woodbridge, VA, Zip 22191–3399; tel. 703/523–1000; Katherine Johnson, Ph.D., President
**Web address**: www.sentara.com/northernvirginia

SENTARA OBICI HOSPITAL (O, 175 beds) 2800 Godwin Boulevard, Suffolk, VA, Zip 23434–8038; tel. 757/934–4000; Coleen F. Santa Ana, President

SENTARA PRINCESS ANNE HOSPITAL (O, 153 beds) 2025 Glenn Mitchell Drive, Virginia Beach, VA, Zip 23456–0178; tel. 757/507–1000; Paul Gaden, Chief Executive Officer
**Web address**: www.sentara.com

SENTARA RMH MEDICAL CENTER (O, 244 beds) 2010 Health Campus Drive, Harrisonburg, VA, Zip 22801–3293; tel. 540/689–1000; Douglas J. Moyer, President

SENTARA VIRGINIA BEACH GENERAL HOSPITAL (O, 204 beds) 1060 First Colonial Road, Virginia Beach, VA, Zip 23454–3002; tel. 757/395–8000; Elwood Bernard. Boone III, FACHE, President
**Web address**: www.sentara.com

SENTARA WILLIAMSBURG REGIONAL MEDICAL CENTER (O, 145 beds) 100 Sentara Circle, Williamsburg, VA, Zip 23188–5713; tel. 757/984–6000; David J. Masterson, President
**Web address**: www.sentara.com

| | | |
|---|---|---|
| **Owned, leased, sponsored:** | 12 hospitals | 2714 beds |
| **Contract–managed:** | 0 hospitals | 0 beds |
| **Totals:** | 12 hospitals | 2714 beds |

---

★**2065: SHARP HEALTHCARE** (NP)
8695 Spectrum Center Boulevard, San Diego, CA Zip 92123–1489; tel. 858/499–4000; Christopher Howard, President and Chief Executive Officer
**(Centralized Health System)**

**CALIFORNIA**: SHARP CHULA VISTA MEDICAL CENTER (O, 343 beds) 751 Medical Center Court, Chula Vista, CA, Zip 91911–6699; tel. 619/502–5800; Pablo Velez, R.N., Ph.D., Chief Executive Officer

SHARP CORONADO HOSPITAL AND HEALTHCARE CENTER (L, 181 beds) 250 Prospect Place, Coronado, CA, Zip 92118–1999; tel. 619/522–3600; Susan Stone, R.N., Ph.D., Senior Vice President and Chief Executive Officer
**Web address**: www.sharp.com

SHARP GROSSMONT HOSPITAL (L, 524 beds) 5555 Grossmont Center Drive, La Mesa, CA, Zip 91942–3019, Mailing Address: P.O. 158, 91944–0158, tel. 619/740–6000; Scott Evans, PharmD, FACHE, Senior Vice President and Chief Executive Officer
**Web address**: www.sharp.com

SHARP MARY BIRCH HOSPITAL FOR WOMEN AND NEWBORNS (O, 206 beds) 3003 Health Center Drive, San Diego, CA, Zip 92123–2700; tel. 858/939–3400; Trisha Khaleghi, Senior Vice President and Chief Executive Officer

SHARP MEMORIAL HOSPITAL (O, 459 beds) 7901 Frost Street, San Diego, CA, Zip 92123–2701; tel. 858/939–3400; Tim Smith, Senior Vice President and Chief Executive Officer
**Web address**: www.sharp.com

SHARP MESA VISTA HOSPITAL (O, 174 beds) 7850 Vista Hill Avenue, San Diego, CA, Zip 92123–2717; tel. 858/278–4110; Trisha Khaleghi, Senior Vice President and Chief Executive Officer
**Web address**: www.sharp.com

| | | |
|---|---|---|
| **Owned, leased, sponsored:** | 6 hospitals | 1887 beds |
| **Contract–managed:** | 0 hospitals | 0 beds |
| **Totals:** | 6 hospitals | 1887 beds |

For explanation of codes following names, see page B2.
★ Indicates Type III membership in the American Hospital Association.

## 4125: SHRINERS HOSPITALS FOR CHILDREN (NP)

2900 North Rocky Point Drive, Tampa, FL Zip 33607–1435, Mailing Address: P.O. Box 31356, 33631–3356, tel. 813/281–0300; John P. McCabe, Executive Vice President

**(Independent Hospital System)**

**CALIFORNIA**: SHRINERS HOSPITALS FOR CHILDREN–NORTHERN CALIFORNIA (O, 60 beds) 2425 Stockton Boulevard, Sacramento, CA, Zip 95817–2215; tel. 916/453–2000; Margaret Bryan, Administrator

**FLORIDA**: SHRINERS HOSPITALS FOR CHILDREN–TAMPA (O, 60 beds) 12502 USF Pine Drive, Tampa, FL, Zip 33612–9499; tel. 813/972–2250; Fleury Yelvington, Administrator
**Web address**: www.shrinershospitalsforchildren.org/Hospitals/Locations/ Tampa.aspx

**HAWAII**: SHRINERS HOSPITALS FOR CHILDREN–HONOLULU (O, 16 beds) 1310 Punahou Street, Honolulu, HI, Zip 96826–1099; tel. 808/941–4466; Anton C. Smith, Administrator

**ILLINOIS**: SHRINERS HOSPITALS FOR CHILDREN–CHICAGO (O, 36 beds) 2211 North Oak Park Avenue, Chicago, IL, Zip 60707–3392; tel. 773/622–5400; Mark L. Niederpruem, FACHE, Administrator
**Web address**: www.shrinershospitalsforchildren.org/Hospitals/Locations/ Chicago.aspx

**LOUISIANA**: SHRINERS HOSPITALS FOR CHILDREN–SHREVEPORT (O, 45 beds) 3100 Samford Avenue, Shreveport, LA, Zip 71103–4289; tel. 318/222–5704; Garry Kim. Green, FACHE, Administrator

**MASSACHUSETTS**: SHRINERS HOSPITALS FOR CHILDREN–BOSTON (O, 18 beds) 51 Blossom Street, Boston, MA, Zip 02114–2601; tel. 617/722–3000; Eileen F. Skinner, FACHE, Administrator
**Web address**: www.shrinershospitalsforchildren.org/Hospitals/Locations/ Boston

SHRINERS HOSPITALS FOR CHILDREN–SPRINGFIELD (O, 20 beds) 516 Carew Street, Springfield, MA, Zip 01104–2396; tel. 413/787–2000; H Lee. Kirk Jr, FACHE, Administrator
**Web address**: www.shrinershospitalsforchildren.org/Hospitals/Locations/ Springfield.aspx

**MISSOURI**: SHRINERS HOSPITALS FOR CHILDREN–ST. LOUIS (O, 12 beds) 4400 Clayton Avenue, Saint Louis, MO, Zip 63110–1624; tel. 314/432–3600; Mark Venable, Interim Administrator
**Web address**: https://www.shrinershospitalsforchildren.org

**OHIO**: SHRINERS HOSPITALS FOR CHILDREN – CINCINNATI (O, 30 beds) 3229 Burnet Avenue, Cincinnati, OH, Zip 45229–3095; tel. 513/872–6000; Mark D. Shugarman, Administrator

**OREGON**: SHRINERS HOSPITALS FOR CHILDREN–PORTLAND (O, 12 beds) 3101 SW Sam Jackson Park Road, Portland, OR, Zip 97239–3009; tel. 503/241–5090; Dereesa Reid, Administrator
**Web address**: www.shrinershospitalsforchildren.org/portland

**PENNSYLVANIA**: SHRINERS HOSPITALS FOR CHILDREN–PHILADELPHIA (O, 39 beds) 3551 North Broad Street, Philadelphia, PA, Zip 19140–4160; tel. 215/430–4000; Ed Myers, Administrator

**SOUTH CAROLINA**: SHRINERS HOSPITALS FOR CHILDREN–GREENVILLE (O, 15 beds) 950 West Faris Road, Greenville, SC, Zip 29605–4277; tel. 864/271–3444; William Munley, Administrator
**Web address**: www.greenvilleshrinershospital.org

**TEXAS**: SHRINERS HOSPITALS FOR CHILDREN–GALVESTON (O, 15 beds) 815 Market Street, Galveston, TX, Zip 77550–2725; tel. 409/770–6600; Mary Jaco, Administrator

SHRINERS HOSPITALS FOR CHILDREN–HOUSTON (O, 40 beds) 6977 Main Street, Houston, TX, Zip 77030–3701; tel. 713/797–1616; Cathy Moniaci, Administrator
**Web address**: www.shrinershospitalsforchildren.org/Locations/ houston

**UTAH**: SHRINERS HOSPITALS FOR CHILDREN–SALT LAKE CITY (O, 12 beds) 1275 East Fairfax Road, Salt Lake City, UT, Zip 84103–4399; tel. 801/536–3500; Kevin Martin, M.P.H., R.N., FACHE, Administrator
**Web address**: www.shrinershospitalsforchildren.org/Hospitals/Locations/ SaltLakeCity.aspx

**WASHINGTON**: SHRINERS HOSPITALS FOR CHILDREN–SPOKANE (O, 30 beds) 911 West Fifth Avenue, Spokane, WA, Zip 99204–2901, Mailing Address: P.O. Box 2472, 99210–2472, tel. 509/455–7844; Peter G. Brewer, Administrator
**Web address**: www.shrinershospitalsforchildren.org/Hospitals/Locations/ Spokane.aspx

| | | |
|---|---|---|
| Owned, leased, sponsored: | 16 hospitals | 460 beds |
| Contract–managed: | 0 hospitals | 0 beds |
| **Totals:** | **16 hospitals** | **460 beds** |

## 0360: SIGNATURE HEALTHCARE SERVICES (IO)

4238 Green River Road, Corona, CA Zip 92880–1669; tel. 951/549–8032; Soon K. Kim, M.D., President and Chief Executive Officer

**(Independent Hospital System)**

**ARIZONA**: AURORA BEHAVIORAL HEALTH SYSTEM EAST (O, 70 beds) 6350 South Maple Street, Tempe, AZ, Zip 85283–2857; tel. 480/345–5400; Bruce Waldo, Chief Executive Officer

AURORA BEHAVIORAL HEALTH SYSTEM WEST (O, 100 beds) 6015 West Peoria Avenue, Glendale, AZ, Zip 85302–1213; tel. 623/344–4400; Bruce Waldo, Chief Executive Officer
**Web address**: www.aurorabehavioral.com

**CALIFORNIA**: AURORA BEHAVIORAL HEALTHCARE SAN DIEGO (O, 80 beds) 11878 Avenue of Industry, San Diego, CA, Zip 92128–3490; tel. 858/487–3200; Alain Azcona, Chief Executive Officer
**Web address**: www.sandiego.aurorabehavioral.com/

AURORA CHARTER OAK HOSPITAL (O, 146 beds) 1161 East Covina Boulevard, Covina, CA, Zip 91724–1599; tel. 626/966–1632; Todd A. Smith, Chief Executive Officer
**Web address**: www.charteroakhospital.com

AURORA SANTA ROSA HOSPITAL (O, 95 beds) 1287 Fulton Road, Santa Rosa, CA, Zip 95401–4923; tel. 707/800–7700; Susan Rose, Chief Executive Officer
**Web address**: www.aurorasantarosa.com

BAKERSFIELD BEHAVIORAL HEALTHCARE HOSPITAL (O, 60 beds) 5201 White Lane, Bakersfield, CA, Zip 93309; tel. 877/755–4907; Jeff Chinn, Interim Chief Executive Officer

LAS ENCINAS HOSPITAL (O, 118 beds) 2900 East Del Mar Boulevard, Pasadena, CA, Zip 91107–4399; tel. 626/795–9901; Trevor Asmus, Chief Executive Officer
**Web address**: www.lasencinashospital.com

VISTA DEL MAR HOSPITAL (O, 87 beds) 801 Seneca Street, Ventura, CA, Zip 93001–1411; tel. 805/653–6434; Jenifer Nyhuis, Chief Executive Officer
**Web address**: www.vistadelmarhospital.com

**MASSACHUSETTS**: WESTBOROUGH BEHAVIORAL HEALTHCARE HOSPITAL (O, 120 beds) 300 Friberg Parkway, Westborough, MA, Zip 01581–3900; tel. 508/329–6112; Erika Heckman, Chief Executive Officer

**NEVADA**: DESERT PARKWAY BEHAVIORAL HEALTHCARE HOSPITAL (O, 152 beds) 3247 South Maryland Parkway, Las Vegas, NV, Zip 89109–2412; tel. 702/776–3500; Allison Zednicek, Chief Executive Officer
**Web address**: https://www.desertparkway.com/

RENO BEHAVIORAL HEALTHCARE HOSPITAL (O, 124 beds) 6940 Sierra Center Parkway, Reno, NV, Zip 89511; tel. 877/787–8518; Steve Shell, Chief Executive Officer
**Web address**: www.renobehavioral.com

**TEXAS**: DALLAS BEHAVIORAL HEALTHCARE HOSPITAL (O, 116 beds) 800 Kirnwood Drive, Desoto, TX, Zip 75115–2000; tel. 855/982–0897; Terrance O'Reilly, Chief Executive Officer

GEORGETOWN BEHAVIORAL HEALTH INSTITUTE (O, 118 beds) 3101 South Austin Avenue, Georgetown, TX, Zip 78626–7541; tel. 512/819–1100; Monica Ochoa, Chief Executive Officer
**Web address**: www.georgetownbehavioral.com

HOUSTON BEHAVIORAL HEALTHCARE HOSPITAL (O, 25 beds) 2801 Gessner Road, Houston, TX, Zip 77080–2503; tel. 832/834–7710; Roy Hollis, Chief Executive Officer
**Web address**: www.houstonbehavioralhealth.com/

For explanation of codes following names, see page B2.
★ Indicates Type III membership in the American Hospital Association.

SAN ANTONIO BEHAVIORAL HEALTHCARE HOSPITAL (O, 198 beds) 8550 Huebner Road, San Antonio, TX, Zip 78240–1803; tel. 210/541–5300; Aleen Davis. Arabit, Chief Executive Officer

| Owned, leased, sponsored: | 15 hospitals | 1609 beds |
| Contract–managed: | 0 hospitals | 0 beds |
| Totals: | 15 hospitals | 1609 beds |

★0284: SINAI HEALTH SYSTEM (NP)

1500 South Fairfield Avenue, Chicago, IL Zip 60608–1782; tel. 773/542–2000; Karen Teitelbaum, President and Chief Executive Officer

**(Centralized Health System)**

ILLINOIS: HOLY CROSS HOSPITAL (O, 155 beds) 2701 West 68th Street, Chicago, IL, Zip 60629–1882; tel. 773/884–9000; Lori Pacura, MSN, R.N., President

MOUNT SINAI HOSPITAL (O, 284 beds) 1500 South Fairfield Avenue, Chicago, IL, Zip 60608–1729; tel. 773/542–2000; Loren Chandler, President
**Web address:** www.sinai.org

SCHWAB REHABILITATION HOSPITAL (O, 52 beds) 1401 South California Avenue, Chicago, IL, Zip 60608–1858; tel. 773/522–2010; Karen Teitelbaum, Chief Executive Officer
**Web address:** www.schwabrehab.org

| Owned, leased, sponsored: | 3 hospitals | 491 beds |
| Contract–managed: | 0 hospitals | 0 beds |
| Totals: | 3 hospitals | 491 beds |

5125: SISTERS OF CHARITY HEALTH SYSTEM (CO)

2475 East 22nd Street, Cleveland, OH Zip 44115–3221; tel. 216/363–2797; Thomas J. Strauss, Chief Executive Officer

**(Moderately Centralized Health System)**

OHIO: MERCY MEDICAL CENTER (O, 338 beds) 1320 Mercy Drive NW, Canton, OH, Zip 44708–2641; tel. 330/489–1000; Thomas J. Strauss, Interim President and Chief Executive Officer
**Web address:** www.cantonmercy.org

ST. VINCENT CHARITY MEDICAL CENTER (O, 208 beds) 2351 East 22nd Street, Cleveland, OH, Zip 44115–3111; tel. 216/861–6200; Janice G. Murphy, President and Chief Executive Office

| Owned, leased, sponsored: | 2 hospitals | 546 beds |
| Contract–managed: | 0 hospitals | 0 beds |
| Totals: | 2 hospitals | 546 beds |

5805: SISTERS OF MARY OF THE PRESENTATION HEALTH SYSTEM (CO)

1202 Page Drive SW, Fargo, ND Zip 58103–2340, Mailing Address: P.O. Box 10007, 58106–0007, tel. 701/237–9290; Aaron K. Alton, President and Chief Executive Officer

**(Moderately Centralized Health System)**

ILLINOIS: ST. MARGARET'S HOSPITAL (O, 44 beds) 600 East First Street, Spring Valley, IL, Zip 61362–1512; tel. 815/664–5311; Tim Muntz, President and Chief Executive Officer
**Web address:** www.aboutsmh.org

NORTH DAKOTA: PRESENTATION MEDICAL CENTER (O, 25 beds) 213 Second Avenue NE, Rolla, ND, Zip 58367–7153, Mailing Address: P.O. Box 759, 58367–0759, tel. 701/477–3161; Chris Albertson, Chief Executive Officer and President
**Web address:** www.pmc-rolla.com

ST. ALOISIUS MEDICAL CENTER (O, 110 beds) 325 East Brewster Street, Harvey, ND, Zip 58341–1653; tel. 701/324–4651; Mike Zwicker, Chief Executive Officer

ST. ANDREW'S HEALTH CENTER (O, 25 beds) 316 Ohmer Street, Bottineau, ND, Zip 58318–1045; tel. 701/228–9300; Alfred Sams, President and Chief Executive Officer
**Web address:** www.standrewshealth.com

| Owned, leased, sponsored: | 4 hospitals | 204 beds |
| Contract–managed: | 0 hospitals | 0 beds |
| Totals: | 4 hospitals | 204 beds |

0997: SKAGIT REGIONAL HEALTH (NP)

1415 E Kincaid Street, Mount Vernon, WA Zip 98274–4126; tel. 360/424–4111; Brian K. Ivie, President and Chief Executive Officer

**(Independent Hospital System)**

WASHINGTON: CASCADE VALLEY HOSPITAL (L, 48 beds) 330 South Stillaguamish Avenue, Arlington, WA, Zip 98223–1642; tel. 360/435–2133; Brian K. Ivie, President and Chief Executive Officer

SKAGIT VALLEY HOSPITAL (O, 173 beds) 300 Hospital Parkway, Mount Vernon, WA, Zip 98273, Mailing Address: P.O. Box 1376, 98273–1376, tel. 360/424–4111; Brian K. Ivie, President and Chief Executive Officer
**Web address:** www.skagitregionalhealth.org

| Owned, leased, sponsored: | 2 hospitals | 221 beds |
| Contract–managed: | 0 hospitals | 0 beds |
| Totals: | 2 hospitals | 221 beds |

1042: SOLUTIONHEALTH (NP)

One Elliot Way, Manchester, NH Zip 03103–3502; tel. 603/663–2990; Sherry Hausmann, President and Chief Executive Officer

NEW HAMPSHIRE: ELLIOT HOSPITAL (O, 268 beds) One Elliot Way, Manchester, NH, Zip 03103–3502; tel. 603/669–5300; Greg Baxter, M.D., President

SOUTHERN NEW HAMPSHIRE MEDICAL CENTER (O, 163 beds) 8 Prospect Street, Nashua, NH, Zip 03060–3925, Mailing Address: P.O. Box 2014, 03061–2014, tel. 603/577–2000; Michael S. Rose, President and Chief Executive Officer
**Web address:** www.snhhs.org

| Owned, leased, sponsored: | 2 hospitals | 431 beds |
| Contract–managed: | 0 hospitals | 0 beds |
| Totals: | 2 hospitals | 431 beds |

★1034: SOUTH GEORGIA MEDICAL CENTER (NP)

2501 North Patterson Street, Valdosta, GA Zip 31602–1735, Mailing Address: P.O. Box 1727, 31603–1727, tel. 229/333–1000; Ronald Dean, Chief Executive Officer

**(Independent Hospital System)**

GEORGIA: SOUTH GEORGIA MEDICAL CENTER BERRIEN CAMPUS (O, 39 beds) 1221 East McPherson Avenue, Nashville, GA, Zip 31639–2326; tel. 229/433–8600; Richard Huth, Administrator
**Web address:** www.sgmc.org/

SOUTH GEORGIA MEDICAL CENTER LANIER CAMPUS (O, 25 beds) 116 West Thigpen Avenue, Lakeland, GA, Zip 31635–1011; tel. 229/482–3110; Geoff Hardy, Administrator

SOUTH GEORGIA MEDICAL CENTER (O, 302 beds) 2501 North Patterson Street, Valdosta, GA, Zip 31602–1735, Mailing Address: P.O. Box 1727, 31603–1727, tel. 229/333–1000; Ronald Dean, Chief Executive Officer
**Web address:** www.sgmc.org

| Owned, leased, sponsored: | 3 hospitals | 366 beds |
| Contract–managed: | 0 hospitals | 0 beds |
| Totals: | 3 hospitals | 366 beds |

★0253: SOUTHEAST GEORGIA HEALTH SYSTEM (NP)

2415 Parkwood Drive, Brunswick, GA Zip 31520–4722, Mailing Address: P.O. Box 1518, 31521–1518, tel. 912/466–7000; Michael D. Scherneck, President and Chief Executive Officer

*For explanation of codes following names, see page B2.*
*★ Indicates Type III membership in the American Hospital Association.*

**GEORGIA**: SOUTHEAST GEORGIA HEALTH SYSTEM BRUNSWICK CAMPUS (O, 532 beds) 2415 Parkwood Drive, Brunswick, GA, Zip 31520–4722, P O Box 1518, 31521–1518, tel. 912/466–7000; Michael D. Scherneck, President and Chief Executive Officer
**Web address**: www.sghs.org

SOUTHEAST GEORGIA HEALTH SYSTEM CAMDEN CAMPUS (O, 40 beds) 2000 Dan Proctor Drive, Saint Marys, GA, Zip 31558–3810; tel. 912/576–6200; Howard W. Sepp Jr, Vice–President and Administrator
**Web address**: www.sghs.org

| | | |
|---|---|---|
| Owned, leased, sponsored: | 2 hospitals | 572 beds |
| Contract–managed: | 0 hospitals | 0 beds |
| Totals: | 2 hospitals | 572 beds |

## 0628: SOUTHEASTHEALTH (NP)

1701 Lacey Street, Cape Girardeau, MO Zip 63701–5230; tel. 573/334–4822; Kenneth Bateman, CPA, Chief Executive Officer
**(Moderately Centralized Health System)**

**MISSOURI**: SOUTHEAST HEALTH CENTER OF STODDARD COUNTY (L, 36 beds) 1200 North One Mile Road, Dexter, MO, Zip 63841–1000; tel. 573/624–5566; Sue Ann Williams, Chief Executive Officer
**Web address**: www.sehealth.org

SOUTHEAST HOSPITAL (O, 170 beds) 1701 Lacey Street, Cape Girardeau, MO, Zip 63701–5230; tel. 573/334–4822; Kenneth Bateman, CPA, President and Chief Executive Officer

| | | |
|---|---|---|
| Owned, leased, sponsored: | 2 hospitals | 206 beds |
| Contract–managed: | 0 hospitals | 0 beds |
| Totals: | 2 hospitals | 206 beds |

## 4175: SOUTHERN ILLINOIS HEALTHCARE (NP)

1239 East Main Street, Carbondale, IL Zip 62901–3114, Mailing Address: P.O. Box 3988, 62902–3988, tel. 618/457–5200; Rex P. Budde, President and Chief Executive Officer
**(Independent Hospital System)**

**ILLINOIS**: HERRIN HOSPITAL (O, 114 beds) 201 South 14th Street, Herrin, IL, Zip 62948–3631; tel. 618/942–2171; Rodney Smith, Vice President and Administrator

MEMORIAL HOSPITAL OF CARBONDALE (O, 167 beds) 405 West Jackson Street, Carbondale, IL, Zip 62901–1467, Mailing Address: P.O. Box 10000, 62902–9000, tel. 618/549–0721; Al Taylor, Vice President and Administrator
**Web address**: www.sih.net

ST. JOSEPH MEMORIAL HOSPITAL (O, 25 beds) 2 South Hospital Drive, Murphysboro, IL, Zip 62966–3333; tel. 618/684–3156; Susan Odle, Administrator
**Web address**: www.sih.net

| | | |
|---|---|---|
| Owned, leased, sponsored: | 3 hospitals | 306 beds |
| Contract–managed: | 0 hospitals | 0 beds |
| Totals: | 3 hospitals | 306 beds |

## 0652: SOUTHWEST HEALTH SYSTEMS (NP)

215 Marion Avenue, Mccomb, MS Zip 39648–2705, Mailing Address: P.O. Box 1307, 39649–1307, tel. 601/249–5500; Charla Rowley, Chief Executive Officer
**(Independent Hospital System)**

**MISSISSIPPI**: LAWRENCE COUNTY HOSPITAL (O, 25 beds) Highway 84 East, Monticello, MS, Zip 39654–0788, Mailing Address: P.O. Box 788, 39654–0788, tel. 601/587–4051; Phillip W. Langston, Administrator
**Web address**: www.smrmc.com

SOUTHWEST MISSISSIPPI REGIONAL MEDICAL CENTER (O, 143 beds) 215 Marion Avenue, McComb, MS, Zip 39648–2705, Mailing Address: P.O. Box 1307, 39649–1307, tel. 601/249–5500; Norman M. Price, FACHE, Chief Executive Officer

| | | |
|---|---|---|
| Owned, leased, sponsored: | 2 hospitals | 168 beds |
| Contract–managed: | 0 hospitals | 0 beds |
| Totals: | 2 hospitals | 168 beds |

## 0164: SOUTHWEST HEALTHCARE SYSTEM (IO)

7025 N Scottsdale Road Suite 9347, Scottsdale, AZ Zip 85253–3675, 7025 North Scottsdale Road, Suite 9347, 85251–3331, tel. 480/518–5444; Paul R. Tuft, President
**(Independent Hospital System)**

**CALIFORNIA**: PACIFICA HOSPITAL OF THE VALLEY (O, 231 beds) 9449 San Fernando Road, Sun Valley, CA, Zip 91352–1489; tel. 818/767–3310; Ayman Mousa, R.N., Ph.D., Chief Executive Officer
**Web address**: www.pacificahospital.com

| | | |
|---|---|---|
| Owned, leased, sponsored: | 1 hospitals | 231 beds |
| Contract–managed: | 0 hospitals | 0 beds |
| Totals: | 1 hospitals | 231 beds |

## ★1245: SPARROW HEALTH SYSTEM (NP)

1215 East Michigan Avenue, Lansing, MI Zip 48912–1811; tel. 517/364–1000; James F. Dover, FACHE, President and Chief Executive Officer
**(Centralized Health System)**

**MICHIGAN**: SPARROW CARSON HOSPITAL (O, 48 beds) 406 East Elm Street, Carson City, MI, Zip 48811–9693, Mailing Address: P.O. Box 879, 48811–0879, tel. 989/584–3131; William Roeser, Interim President and Chief Executive Officer
**Web address**: www.carsoncityhospital.com

SPARROW CLINTON HOSPITAL (O, 25 beds) 805 South Oakland Street, Saint Johns, MI, Zip 48879–2253; tel. 989/227–3400; Beth Ann Daugherty, M.P.H., R.N., President
**Web address**: www.sparrowclinton.org

SPARROW EATON HOSPITAL (O, 25 beds) 321 East Harris Street, Charlotte, MI, Zip 48813–1629; tel. 517/543–1050; Matthew Rush, FACHE, President and Chief Executive Officer

SPARROW HOSPITAL (O, 632 beds) 1215 East Michigan Avenue, Lansing, MI, Zip 48912–1811; tel. 517/364–1000; Mark Brett, Chief Executive Officer
**Web address**: www.sparrow.org

SPARROW IONIA HOSPITAL (O, 22 beds) 3565 South State Road, Ionia, MI, Zip 48846–1870; tel. 616/523–1400; William Roeser, President and Chief Executive Officer

SPARROW SPECIALTY HOSPITAL (O, 30 beds) 8 West Sparrow Hospital Tower, 1215 East Michigan Avenue, Lansing, MI, Zip 48912; tel. 517/364–4840; Lou Little, President and Chief Executive Officer
**Web address**: www.sparrowspecialty.org

| | | |
|---|---|---|
| Owned, leased, sponsored: | 6 hospitals | 782 beds |
| Contract–managed: | 0 hospitals | 0 beds |
| Totals: | 6 hospitals | 782 beds |

## ★4195: SPARTANBURG REGIONAL HEALTHCARE SYSTEM (NP)

101 East Wood Street, Spartanburg, SC Zip 29303–3040; tel. 864/560–6000; Bruce Holstien, President and Chief Executive Officer
**(Centralized Health System)**

**SOUTH CAROLINA**: CHEROKEE MEDICAL CENTER (O, 44 beds) 1530 North Limestone Street, Gaffney, SC, Zip 29340–4738; tel. 864/487–4271; Cody Butts, President

PELHAM MEDICAL CENTER (O, 48 beds) 250 Westmoreland Road, Greer, SC, Zip 29651–9013; tel. 864/530–6000; Anthony Kouskolekas, FACHE, President
**Web address**: www.pelhammedicalcenter.com

For explanation of codes following names, see page B2.
★ Indicates Type III membership in the American Hospital Association.

SPARTANBURG HOSPITAL FOR RESTORATIVE CARE (O, 116 beds) 389 Serpentine Drive, Spartanburg, SC, Zip 29303–3026; tel. 864/560–3280; Jill Jolley Greene, MSN, R.N., President

SPARTANBURG MEDICAL CENTER – CHURCH STREET CAMPUS (O, 531 beds) 101 East Wood Street, Spartanburg, SC, Zip 29303–3040; tel. 864/560–6000; J Philip. Feisal, President and Chief Executive Officer
**Web address:** www.spartanburgregional.com

SPARTANBURG MEDICAL CENTER – MARY BLACK (O, 160 beds) 1700 Skylyn Drive, Spartanburg, SC, Zip 29307–1061, Mailing Address: P.O. Box 3217, 29304–3217, tel. 864/573–3000; Parkes Coggins, Vice President Hospital Integration

UNION MEDICAL CENTER (O, 50 beds) 322 West South Street, Union, SC, Zip 29379–2857, Mailing Address: P.O. Box 789, 29379–0789, tel. 864/301–2000; Paul R. Newhouse, President
**Web address:** https://www.spartanburgregional.com/locations/union-medical-center/

| | | |
|---|---|---|
| Owned, leased, sponsored: | 6 hospitals | 949 beds |
| Contract–managed: | 0 hospitals | 0 beds |
| Totals: | 6 hospitals | 949 beds |

**★0177: SPECTRUM HEALTH** (NP)

221 Michigan Street NE, Suite 501, Grand Rapids, MI Zip 49503–2543; tel. 616/391–1774; Christina Freese Decker, FACHE, President and Chief Executive Officer

**(Centralized Physician/Insurance Health System)**

**MICHIGAN:** LAKELAND HOSPITAL, WATERVLIET (O, 44 beds) 400 Medical Park Drive, Watervliet, MI, Zip 49098–9225; tel. 269/463–3111; Ray Cruse, Chief Executive Officer

SPECTRUM HEALTH – BUTTERWORTH HOSPITAL (O, 1381 beds) 100 Michigan Street NE, Grand Rapids, MI, Zip 49503–2560; tel. 616/391–1774; Daryl Elmouchi, M.D., President, Spectrum Health West Michigan
**Web address:** www.spectrumhealth.org

SPECTRUM HEALTH BIG RAPIDS HOSPITAL (O, 48 beds) 605 Oak Street, Big Rapids, MI, Zip 49307–2099; tel. 231/796–8691; Andrea M. Leslie, MSN, R.N., President
**Web address:** www.spectrumhealth.org

SPECTRUM HEALTH GERBER MEMORIAL (O, 25 beds) 212 South Sullivan Avenue, Fremont, MI, Zip 49412–1548; tel. 231/924–3300; Randall Kelley, FACHE, President
**Web address:** www.spectrumhealth.org

SPECTRUM HEALTH LAKELAND (O, 300 beds) 1234 Napier Avenue, Saint Joseph, MI, Zip 49085–2158; tel. 269/983–8300; Loren Hamel, M.D., President and Chief Executive Officer

SPECTRUM HEALTH LUDINGTON HOSPITAL (O, 30 beds) One Atkinson Drive, Ludington, MI, Zip 49431–1906, Mailing Address: P.O. 2408, Grand Rapids, 49501–2408, tel. 231/843–2591; Randall Kelley, FACHE, President
**Web address:** www.mmcwm.com

SPECTRUM HEALTH PENNOCK (O, 25 beds) 1009 West Green Street, Hastings, MI, Zip 49058–1710; tel. 269/945–3451; Angela Ditmar, R.N., President

SPECTRUM HEALTH REED CITY HOSPITAL (O, 75 beds) 300 North Patterson Road, Reed City, MI, Zip 49677–8041, Mailing Address: P.O. Box 75, 49677–0075, tel. 231/832–3271; Andrea M. Leslie, MSN, R.N., President
**Web address:** www.spectrumhealth.org/reedcity

SPECTRUM HEALTH UNITED HOSPITAL (O, 131 beds) 615 South Bower Street, Greenville, MI, Zip 48838–2614; tel. 616/754–4691; Andrea M. Leslie, MSN, R.N., President

SPECTRUM HEALTH ZEELAND COMMUNITY HOSPITAL (O, 55 beds) 8333 Felch Street, Zeeland, MI, Zip 49464–2608; tel. 616/772–4644; Ron Lewis, President
**Web address:** www.spectrumhealth.org/zeeland

| | | |
|---|---|---|
| Owned, leased, sponsored: | 10 hospitals | 2114 beds |
| Contract–managed: | 0 hospitals | 0 beds |
| Totals: | 10 hospitals | 2114 beds |

**1037: SPRINGSTONE** (IO)

101 South Fifth Street, Suite 3850, Louisville, KY Zip 40202–3127; tel. 855/595–2292; Phil Spencer, Chief Executive Officer

**COLORADO:** DENVER SPRINGS (O, 96 beds) 8835 American Way, Englewood, CO, Zip 80112–7056; tel. 720/643–4300; Mark Littrell, Chief Executive Officer

**INDIANA:** BRENTWOOD SPRINGS (O, 48 beds) 4488 Roslin Road, Newburgh, IN, Zip 47630; tel. 812/858–7200; Kim Retzner, Chief Executive Officer
**Web address:** www.https://brentwoodsprings.com

SYCAMORE SPRINGS (O, 48 beds) 833 Park East Boulevard, Lafayette, IN, Zip 47905–0785; tel. 765/743–4400; Denise Sullivan, Chief Executive Officer

**KANSAS:** COTTONWOOD SPRINGS HOSPITAL (O, 72 beds) 13351 South Arapaho Drive, Olathe, KS, Zip 66062–1520; tel. 913/353–3000; Jason Toalson, Chief Executive Officer
**Web address:** www.cottonwoodsprings.com

**NORTH CAROLINA:** TRIANGLE SPRINGS HOSPITAL (O, 77 beds) 10901 World Trade Boulevard, Raleigh, NC, Zip 27617–4203; tel. 919/372–4408; Amanda Johanson, Chief Executive Officer
**Web address:** https://www.trianglesprings.com

**OHIO:** BECKETT SPRINGS (O, 96 beds) 8614 Shepherd Farm Drive, West Chester, OH, Zip 45069; tel. 513/942–9500; Neicole Knott, Chief Executive Officer
**Web address:** www.springstone.com/hospitals.stmhl

COLUMBUS DUBLIN SPRINGS (O, 144 beds) 7625 Hospital Drive, Dublin, OH, Zip 43016–9649; tel. 614/717–1800; Garry W. Hoyes, Chief Executive Officer

HIGHLAND SPRINGS HOSPITAL (O, 72 beds) 4199 Mill Pond Drive, Highland Hills, OH, Zip 44122–5731; tel. 602/314–7800; Matthew Winchester, Chief Executive Officer
**Web address:** https://www.highlandspringshealth.com

**OKLAHOMA:** OAKWOOD SPRINGS (O, 72 beds) 13101 Memorial Springs Court, Oklahoma City, OK, Zip 73114–2226; tel. 405/438–3000; Casey McMahan, Chief Executive Officer

**TEXAS:** CARROLLTON SPRINGS (O, 78 beds) 2225 Parker Road, Carrollton, TX, Zip 75010–4711; tel. 972/242–4114; Samantha Castle, Chief Executive Officer
**Web address:** www.carrolltonsprings.com

MESA SPRINGS (O, 72 beds) 5560 Mesa Springs Drive, Fort Worth, TX, Zip 76123; tel. 817/292–4600; Barbara Schmidt, Chief Executive Officer
**Web address:** www.springstone.com/hospitals.stmhl

ROCK SPRINGS (O, 72 beds) 700 Southeast Inner Loop, Georgetown, TX, Zip 78626; tel. 512/819–9400; Mark Puckett, Chief Executive Officer
**Web address:** www.rockspringshealth.com/

WESTPARK SPRINGS (O, 72 beds) 6902 South Peek Road, Richmond, TX, Zip 77407; tel. 832/532–8107; Dustin Davis, Market Chief Executive Officer
**Web address:** www.westparksprings.com/why–westpark–springs/

WOODLAND SPRINGS HOSPITAL (O, 96 beds) 15680 Old Conroe Road, Conroe, TX, Zip 77384; tel. 936/270–7520; Dustin Davis, Chief Executive Officer
**Web address:** https://www.woodlandspringshealth.com/

**WASHINGTON:** RAINIER SPRINGS HOSPITAL (O, 72 beds) 2805 Northeast 129th Street, Vancouver, WA, Zip 98686–3324; tel. 360/356–1890; Jeff Serrano, Chief Executive Officer
**Web address:** https://www.rainiersprings.com

| | | |
|---|---|---|
| Owned, leased, sponsored: | 15 hospitals | 1187 beds |
| Contract–managed: | 0 hospitals | 0 beds |
| Totals: | 15 hospitals | 1187 beds |

**★5455: SSM HEALTH** (CO)

10101 Woodfield Lane, Saint Louis, MO Zip 63132–2937; tel. 314/994–7800; Laura Kaiser, President and Chief Executive Officer

**(Decentralized Health System)**

**ILLINOIS:** CLAY COUNTY HOSPITAL (C, 22 beds) 911 Stacy Burk Drive, Flora, IL, Zip 62839–3241, Mailing Address: P.O. Box 280, 62839–0280, tel. 618/662–2131; Robert R. Sellers, President
**Web address:** www.claycountyhospital.org

For explanation of codes following names, see page B2.
★ Indicates Type III membership in the American Hospital Association.

Section B

SSM HEALTH GOOD SAMARITAN HOSPITAL (O, 134 beds) 1 Good Samaritan Way, Mount Vernon, IL, Zip 62864–2402; tel. 618/242–4600; Jeremy Bradford, President
**Web address:** www.smgsi.com

SSM HEALTH ST. MARY'S HOSPITAL CENTRALIA (O, 124 beds) 400 North Pleasant Avenue, Centralia, IL, Zip 62801–3056; tel. 618/436–8000; Damon R. Harbison, President

WASHINGTON COUNTY HOSPITAL (C, 42 beds) 705 South Grand Avenue, Nashville, IL, Zip 62263–1534; tel. 618/327–8236; Brian Kent. Monsma, President
**Web address:** www.washingtoncountyhospital.org

**MISSOURI:** SSM CARDINAL GLENNON CHILDREN'S HOSPITAL (O, 176 beds) 1465 South Grand Boulevard, Saint Louis, MO, Zip 63104–1095; tel. 314/577–5600; Steven Burghart, President
**Web address:** www.cardinalglennon.com

SSM HEALTH DEPAUL HOSPITAL – ST. LOUIS (O, 523 beds) 12303 De Paul Drive, Bridgeton, MO, Zip 63044–2512; tel. 314/344–6000; Ellis Hawkins, FACHE, President
**Web address:** www.ssmdepaul.com

SSM HEALTH SAINT LOUIS UNIVERSITY HOSPITAL (O, 356 beds) 1201 South Grand Avenue, Saint Louis, MO, Zip 63104–1016, Mailing Address: P.O. Box 15250, 63110–0250, tel. 314/577–8000; Steven M. Scott, President
**Web address:** https://www.ssmhealth.com

SSM HEALTH ST. CLARE HOSPITAL – FENTON (O, 184 beds) 1015 Bowles Avenue, Fenton, MO, Zip 63026–2394; tel. 636/496–2000; Tina Garrison, President

SSM HEALTH ST. JOSEPH – ST. CHARLES (O, 341 beds) 300 First Capitol Drive, Saint Charles, MO, Zip 63301–2844; tel. 636/947–5000; Lisle Wescott, President
**Web address:** www.ssmhealth.com

SSM HEALTH ST. JOSEPH HOSPITAL – LAKE SAINT LOUIS (O, 212 beds) 100 Medical Plaza, Lake Saint Louis, MO, Zip 63367–1366; tel. 636/625–5200; Lisle Wescott, President

SSM HEALTH ST. MARY'S HOSPITAL – AUDRAIN (O, 49 beds) 620 East Monroe Street, Mexico, MO, Zip 65265–2919; tel. 573/582–5000; Michael A. Baumgartner, President
**Web address:** https://www.ssmhealth.com

SSM HEALTH ST. MARY'S HOSPITAL – JEFFERSON CITY (O, 92 beds) 2505 Mission Drive, Jefferson City, MO, Zip 65109; tel. 573/681–3000; Michael A. Baumgartner, President

SSM HEALTH ST. MARY'S HOSPITAL – ST. LOUIS (O, 394 beds) 6420 Clayton Road, Saint Louis, MO, Zip 63117–1811; tel. 314/768–8000; Travis Capers, FACHE, President
**Web address:** www.stmarys–stlouis.com

**OKLAHOMA:** SSM HEALTH ST. ANTHONY HOSPITAL – OKLAHOMA CITY (O, 615 beds) 1000 North Lee Street, Oklahoma City, OK, Zip 73102–1080, Mailing Address: P.O. Box 205, 73101–0205, tel. 405/272–7000; Tammy Powell, FACHE, M.P.H., President

SSM HEALTH ST. ANTHONY HOSPITAL – SHAWNEE (O, 70 beds) 1102 West MacArthur Street, Shawnee, OK, Zip 74804–1744; tel. 405/273–2270; Angela Mohr, R.N., MS, President
**Web address:** www.stanthonyshawnee.com

WEATHERFORD REGIONAL HOSPITAL (C, 22 beds) 3701 East Main Street, Weatherford, OK, Zip 73096–3309; tel. 580/772–5551; Debbie Howe, Chief Executive Officer
**Web address:** www.weatherfordhospital.com

**WISCONSIN:** MONROE CLINIC (O, 58 beds) 515 22nd Avenue, Monroe, WI, Zip 53566–1598; tel. 608/324–2000; Michael B. Sanders, President
**Web address:** www.monroeclinic.org

RIPON MEDICAL CENTER (O, 16 beds) 845 Parkside Street, Ripon, WI, Zip 54971–8505, Mailing Address: P.O. Box 390, 54971–0390, tel. 920/748–3101; DeAnn Thurmer, President and Chief Nursing Officer
**Web address:** www.agnesian.com

SSM HEALTH ST. CLARE HOSPITAL–BARABOO (O, 54 beds) 707 14th Street, Baraboo, WI, Zip 53913–1597; tel. 608/356–1400; Laura Walczak, President

SSM HEALTH ST. MARY'S HOSPITAL JANESVILLE (O, 50 beds) 3400 East Racine Street, Janesville, WI, Zip 53546–2344, 3400 East Racine Steeet, 53546–2344, tel. 608/373–8000; Benjamin Layman, President
**Web address:** www.stmarysjanesville.com

SSM HEALTH ST. MARY'S HOSPITAL (O, 362 beds) 700 South Park Street, Madison, WI, Zip 53715–1830; tel. 608/251–6100; Jon Rozenfeld, President
**Web address:** www.stmarysmadison.com

ST. AGNES HOSPITAL (O, 146 beds) 430 East Division Street, Fond Du Lac, WI, Zip 54935–4560, Mailing Address: P.O. Box 385, 54936–0385, tel. 920/929–2300; Katherine Vergos, FACHE, President

WAUPUN MEMORIAL HOSPITAL (O, 25 beds) 620 West Brown Street, Waupun, WI, Zip 53963–1799; tel. 920/324–5581; DeAnn Thurmer, President and Chief Nursing Officer
**Web address:** www.agnesian.com

| | | |
|---|---|---|
| Owned, leased, sponsored: | 20 hospitals | 3981 beds |
| Contract–managed: | 3 hospitals | 86 beds |
| **Totals:** | 23 hospitals | 4067 beds |

---

**★0250: ST. CHARLES HEALTH SYSTEM, INC.** (NP)
2500 NE Neff Road, Bend, OR Zip 97701–6015; tel. 541/382–4321; Joseph Sluka, President and Chief Executive Officer
**(Centralized Physician/Insurance Health System)**

**OREGON:** ST. CHARLES BEND (O, 305 beds) 2500 NE Neff Road, Bend, OR, Zip 97701–6015; tel. 541/382–4321; Aaron Adams, President

ST. CHARLES MADRAS (O, 25 beds) 470 NE 'A' Street, Madras, OR, Zip 97741–1844; tel. 541/475–3882; David Golda, Vice President Hospital and Administrator
**Web address:** www.stcharleshealthcare.org/Our-Locations/Madras

ST. CHARLES PRINEVILLE (O, 16 beds) 384 SE Combs Flat Road, Prineville, OR, Zip 97754–1206; tel. 541/447–6254; Todd Shields, Vice President and Administrator
**Web address:** www.stcharleshealthcare.org

ST. CHARLES REDMOND (O, 36 beds) 1253 NW Canal Boulevard, Redmond, OR, Zip 97756–1395; tel. 541/548–8131; Aaron Adams, President
**Web address:** www.stcharleshealthcare.org

| | | |
|---|---|---|
| Owned, leased, sponsored: | 4 hospitals | 382 beds |
| Contract–managed: | 0 hospitals | 0 beds |
| **Totals:** | 4 hospitals | 382 beds |

---

**0618: ST. ELIZABETH HEALTHCARE** (CO)
1 Medical Village Drive, Edgewood, KY Zip 41017–3403; tel. 859/301–2000; Garren Colvin, Chief Executive Officer
**(Centralized Physician/Insurance Health System)**

**KENTUCKY:** ST. ELIZABETH EDGEWOOD (O, 490 beds) 1 Medical Village Drive, Edgewood, KY, Zip 41017–3403; tel. 859/301–2000; Garren Colvin, Chief Executive Officer
**Web address:** www.stelizabeth.com

ST. ELIZABETH FLORENCE (O, 147 beds) 4900 Houston Road, Florence, KY, Zip 41042–4824; tel. 859/212–5200; Garren Colvin, Chief Executive Officer
**Web address:** www.stelizabeth.com

ST. ELIZABETH FORT THOMAS (O, 137 beds) 85 North Grand Avenue, Fort Thomas, KY, Zip 41075–1796; tel. 859/572–3100; Garren Colvin, Chief Executive Officer
**Web address:** www.stelizabeth.com

ST. ELIZABETH GRANT (O, 24 beds) 238 Barnes Road, Williamstown, KY, Zip 41097–9482; tel. 859/824–8240; Garren Colvin, Chief Executive Officer
**Web address:** www.stelizabeth.com

| | | |
|---|---|---|
| Owned, leased, sponsored: | 4 hospitals | 798 beds |
| Contract–managed: | 0 hospitals | 0 beds |
| **Totals:** | 4 hospitals | 798 beds |

---

**0928: ST. LAWRENCE HEALTH SYSTEM** (NP)
50 Leroy Street, Potsdam, NY Zip 13676–1799; tel. 315/265–3300; David B. Acker, FACHE, President and Chief Executive Officer
**(Independent Hospital System)**

For explanation of codes following names, see page B2.
★ Indicates Type III membership in the American Hospital Association.

© 2021 AHA Guide

**NEW YORK**: CANTON–POTSDAM HOSPITAL (O, 87 beds) 50 Leroy Street, Potsdam, NY, Zip 13676–1799; tel. 315/265–3300; David B. Acker, FACHE, President and Chief Executive Officer

GOUVERNEUR HOSPITAL (O, 25 beds) 77 West Barney Street, Gouverneur, NY, Zip 13642–1040; tel. 315/287–1000; Eric R. Burch, Chief Executive Officer
**Web address:** www.gvnrhospital.org

MASSENA HOSPITAL, INC. (O, 50 beds) One Hospital Drive, Massena, NY, Zip 13662–1097; tel. 315/764–1711; David Bender, Chief Executive Officer
**Web address:** www.massenahospital.org

| | | |
|---|---|---|
| Owned, leased, sponsored: | 3 hospitals | 162 beds |
| Contract–managed: | 0 hospitals | 0 beds |
| Totals: | 3 hospitals | 162 beds |

★**0972: ST. LUKE'S** (NP)

915 East First Street, Duluth, MN Zip 55805–2107; tel. 218/249–5555; Kevin J. Nokels, FACHE, President and Chief Executive Officer

**MINNESOTA**: LAKE VIEW HOSPITAL (O, 25 beds) 325 11th Avenue, Two Harbors, MN, Zip 55616–1360; tel. 218/834–7300; Greg Ruberg, FACHE, President and Chief Executive Officer
**Web address:** www.lvmhospital.com

ST. LUKE'S HOSPITAL (O, 267 beds) 915 East First Street, Duluth, MN, Zip 55805–2193; tel. 218/249–5555; Kevin J. Nokels, FACHE, President and Chief Executive Officer

| | | |
|---|---|---|
| Owned, leased, sponsored: | 2 hospitals | 292 beds |
| Contract–managed: | 0 hospitals | 0 beds |
| Totals: | 2 hospitals | 292 beds |

★**0356: ST. LUKE'S HEALTH SYSTEM** (NP)

190 East Bannock Street, Boise, ID Zip 83712–6241; tel. 208/381–4200; Chris Roth, President and Chief Executive Officer
**(Moderately Centralized Health System)**

**IDAHO**: ST. LUKE'S ELMORE (L, 49 beds) 895 North Sixth East Street, Mountain Home, ID, Zip 83647–2207, Mailing Address: P.O. Box 1270, 83647–1270, tel. 208/587–8401; Lisa Melchiorre, R.N., MS, Chief Operating Officer and Chief Nursing Officer
**Web address:** www.stlukesonline.org/elmore/

ST. LUKE'S JEROME (O, 18 beds) 709 North Lincoln Street, Jerome, ID, Zip 83338–1851, 709 North Lincoln Avenue, 83338–1851, tel. 208/814–9500; Jill Howell, Chief Operating Officer and Chief Nursing Officer

ST. LUKE'S MAGIC VALLEY MEDICAL CENTER (O, 213 beds) 801 Pole Line Road West, Twin Falls, ID, Zip 83301–5810, Mailing Address: P.O. Box 409, 83303–0409, tel. 208/814–1000; Michael A. Fenello, Vice President Population Health
**Web address:** www.stlukesonline.org

ST. LUKE'S MCCALL (L, 15 beds) 1000 State Street, McCall, ID, Zip 83638–3704; tel. 208/634–2221; Amber Green, R.N., Chief Operating Officer and Chief Nursing Officer

ST. LUKE'S NAMPA (O, 81 beds) 9850 West St.Luke's Drive, Nampa, ID, Zip 83687; tel. 208/505–2000; Joan Agee, Chief Operating Officer and Chief Nursing Officer
**Web address:** https://www.stlukesonline.org/communities–and–locations/facilities/hospitals–and–medical–centers/st–lukes–nampa–medical–center

ST. LUKE'S REGIONAL MEDICAL CENTER (O, 604 beds) 190 East Bannock Street, Boise, ID, Zip 83712–6241; tel. 208/381–2222; John Allen, Interim Chief Executive Officer, Vice President, Population Health

ST. LUKE'S REHABILITATION HOSPITAL (O, 30 beds) 600 North Robbins Road, Boise, ID, Zip 83702–4565, Mailing Address: P.O. Box 1100, 83701–1100, tel. 208/489–4444; Nolan Hoffer, Senior Director
**Web address:** www.idahoelksrehab.org

ST. LUKE'S WOOD RIVER MEDICAL CENTER (O, 25 beds) 100 Hospital Drive, Ketchum, ID, Zip 83340, Mailing Address: P.O. Box 100, 83340–0100, tel. 208/727–8800; Carmen Jacobsen, Chief Operating Officer and Chief Nursing Officer

WEISER MEMORIAL HOSPITAL (C, 18 beds) 645 East Fifth Street, Weiser, ID, Zip 83672–2202; tel. 208/549–0370; Steven D. Hale, FACHE, Chief Executive Officer
**Web address:** www.weisermemorialhospital.org

| | | |
|---|---|---|
| Owned, leased, sponsored: | 8 hospitals | 1035 beds |
| Contract–managed: | 1 hospitals | 18 beds |
| Totals: | 9 hospitals | 1053 beds |

**0862: ST. LUKE'S UNIVERSITY HEALTH NETWORK** (NP)

801 Ostrum Street, Bethlehem, PA Zip 18015–1000; tel. 610/954–4000; Richard A. Anderson, President and Chief Executive Officer
**(Moderately Centralized Health System)**

**NEW JERSEY**: ST. LUKE'S HOSPITAL – WARREN CAMPUS (O, 92 beds) 185 Roseberry Street, Phillipsburg, NJ, Zip 08865–1690; tel. 908/847–6700; Scott R. Wolfe, CPA, President

**PENNSYLVANIA**: ST. LUKE'S – LEHIGHTON CAMPUS (O, 242 beds) 211 North 12th Street, Lehighton, PA, Zip 18235–1138; tel. 610/377–1300; John L. Nespoli, President
**Web address:** www.blmtn.org

ST. LUKE'S EASTON CAMPUS (O, 196 beds) 250 South 21st Street, Easton, PA, Zip 18042–3892; tel. 610/250–4000; Linda J. Grass, President

ST. LUKE'S HOSPITAL – ANDERSON CAMPUS (O, 108 beds) 1872 Riverside Circle, Easton, PA, Zip 18045–5669; tel. 484/503–3000; Edward Nawrocki, President
**Web address:** www.mystlukesonline.org

ST. LUKE'S HOSPITAL – MINERS CAMPUS (O, 97 beds) 360 West Ruddle Street, Coaldale, PA, Zip 18218–1027; tel. 570/645–2131; Wendy Lazo, President

ST. LUKE'S HOSPITAL – QUAKERTOWN CAMPUS (O, 62 beds) 1021 Park Avenue, Quakertown, PA, Zip 18951–1573; tel. 215/538–4500; Dennis Pfleiger, President
**Web address:** https://www.slhn.org/quakertown

ST. LUKE'S SACRED HEART CAMPUS (O, 197 beds) 421 West Chew Street, Allentown, PA, Zip 18102–3490; tel. 610/776–4500; Frank Ford, President

ST. LUKE'S UNIVERSITY HOSPITAL – BETHLEHEM CAMPUS (O, 550 beds) 801 Ostrum Street, Bethlehem, PA, Zip 18015–1065; tel. 484/526–4000; Carol Kuplen, R.N., MSN, President
**Web address:** www.slhn–lehighvalley.org

| | | |
|---|---|---|
| Owned, leased, sponsored: | 8 hospitals | 1544 beds |
| Contract–managed: | 0 hospitals | 0 beds |
| Totals: | 8 hospitals | 1544 beds |

★**0156: STANFORD HEALTH CARE** (NP)

300 Pasteur Drive, Palo Alto, CA Zip 94304–2299; tel. 650/723–4000; David Entwistle, President and Chief Executive Officer
**(Centralized Physician/Insurance Health System)**

**CALIFORNIA**: STANFORD HEALTH CARE – VALLEYCARE (O, 193 beds) 5555 West Las Positas Boulevard, Pleasanton, CA, Zip 94588–4000; tel. 925/847–3000; Tracey Lewis–Taylor, Chief Operating Officer
**Web address:** www.valleycare.com

STANFORD HEALTH CARE (O, 477 beds) 300 Pasteur Drive, Suite H3200, Palo Alto, CA, Zip 94304–2203; tel. 650/723–4000; David Entwistle, President and Chief Executive Officer
**Web address:** www.stanfordhealthcare.org

| | | |
|---|---|---|
| Owned, leased, sponsored: | 2 hospitals | 670 beds |
| Contract–managed: | 0 hospitals | 0 beds |
| Totals: | 2 hospitals | 670 beds |

**0141: STEWARD HEALTH CARE SYSTEM, LLC** (IO)

1900 North Pearl Street, Suite 2400, Dallas, TX Zip 75201; tel. 617/419–4700; Ralph de la Torre, M.D., Chairman and Chief Executive Officer
**(Moderately Centralized Health System)**

For explanation of codes following names, see page B2.
★ Indicates Type III membership in the American Hospital Association.

Section B

**ARIZONA:** MOUNTAIN VISTA MEDICAL CENTER (O, 178 beds) 1301 South Crismon Road, Mesa, AZ, Zip 85209–3767; tel. 480/358–6100; William J. Comer, President

ST. LUKE'S BEHAVIORAL HEALTH CENTER (O, 85 beds) 1800 East Van Buren, Phoenix, AZ, Zip 85006–3742; tel. 602/251–8546; Gregory L. Jahn, R.N., Chief Executive Officer
**Web address:** https://www.stlukesbehavioralhealth.org/

TEMPE ST. LUKE'S HOSPITAL (O, 110 beds) 1500 South Mill Avenue, Tempe, AZ, Zip 85281–6699; tel. 480/784–5510; Jenifer Midgett, President and Chief Executive Officer
**Web address:** www.tempestlukeshospital.com

**ARKANSAS:** WADLEY REGIONAL MEDICAL CENTER AT HOPE (O, 79 beds) 2001 South Main Street, Hope, AR, Zip 71801–8194; tel. 870/722–3800; Thomas D. Gilbert, FACHE, Chief Executive Officer

**COLORADO:** UCHEALTH PIKES PEAK REGIONAL HOSPITAL (O, 15 beds) 16420 West Highway 24, Woodland Park, CO, Zip 80863; tel. 719/687–9999; Ron Fitch, Chief Executive Officer
**Web address:** https://www.uchealth.org/locations/uchealth–pikes–peak–regional–hospital/

**FLORIDA:** MELBOURNE REGIONAL MEDICAL CENTER (O, 119 beds) 250 North Wickham Road, Melbourne, FL, Zip 32935–8625; tel. 321/752–1200; Ron Gicca, Chief Executive Officer
**Web address:** www.wuesthoff.com/locations/wuesthoff–medical–center–melbourne

ROCKLEDGE REGIONAL MEDICAL CENTER (O, 215 beds) 110 Longwood Avenue, Rockledge, FL, Zip 32955–2887, Mailing Address: P.O. Box 565002, Mail Stop 1, 32956–5002, tel. 321/636–2211; Andrew Romine, Chief Executive Officer
**Web address:** www.wuesthoff.org

SEBASTIAN RIVER MEDICAL CENTER (O, 154 beds) 13695 North U S Hwy 1, Sebastian, FL, Zip 32958–3230, Box 780838, 32978–0838, tel. 772/589–3186; Ronald L. Bierman, President
**Web address:** https://www.sebastianrivermedical.org/

**LOUISIANA:** GLENWOOD REGIONAL MEDICAL CENTER (O, 278 beds) 503 McMillan Road, West Monroe, LA, Zip 71291–5327; tel. 318/329–4200; Jeremy M. Tinnerello, MSN, R.N., President

**MASSACHUSETTS:** CARNEY HOSPITAL (O, 81 beds) 2100 Dorchester Avenue, Boston, MA, Zip 02124–5615; tel. 617/296–4000; Tom Sands, Interim Chief Executive Officer
**Web address:** www.carneyhospital.org

GOOD SAMARITAN MEDICAL CENTER (O, 190 beds) 235 North Pearl Street, Brockton, MA, Zip 02301–1794; tel. 508/427–3000; Harrison Bane, President

HOLY FAMILY HOSPITAL (O, 329 beds) 70 East Street, Methuen, MA, Zip 01844–4597; tel. 978/687–0151; Craig A. Jesiolowski, FACHE, President
**Web address:** www.stewardhealth.org/Holy–Family–Hospital

MORTON HOSPITAL AND MEDICAL CENTER (O, 153 beds) 88 Washington Street, Taunton, MA, Zip 02780–2465; tel. 508/828–7000; Heidi Taylor, President
**Web address:** www.mortonhospital.org

NASHOBA VALLEY MEDICAL CENTER (O, 48 beds) 200 Groton Road, Ayer, MA, Zip 01432–3300; tel. 978/784–9000; Korry Dow, President

NEW ENGLAND SINAI HOSPITAL AND REHABILITATION CENTER (O, 212 beds) 150 York Street, Stoughton, MA, Zip 02072–1881; tel. 781/344–0600; Mary Beth. Urquhart, Interim President, Vice President Patient Care Services and Chief Nursing Officer
**Web address:** www.newenglandsinai.org

NORWOOD HOSPITAL (O, 188 beds) 800 Washington Street, Norwood, MA, Zip 02062–3487; tel. 781/769–4000; Salvatore Perla, President

SAINT ANNE'S HOSPITAL (O, 160 beds) 795 Middle Street, Fall River, MA, Zip 02721–1798; tel. 508/674–5741; Michael Bushell, President
**Web address:** www.saintanneshospital.org

ST. ELIZABETH'S MEDICAL CENTER (O, 338 beds) 736 Cambridge Street, Brighton, MA, Zip 02135–2997; tel. 617/789–3000; Craig T. Williams, President

**OHIO:** HILLSIDE REHABILITATION HOSPITAL (O, 65 beds) 8747 Squires Lane NE, Warren, OH, Zip 44484–1649; tel. 330/841–3700; Steven Ryland, Interim Chief Executive Officer
**Web address:** www.https://valleycareofohio.steward.org

TRUMBULL MEMORIAL HOSPITAL (O, 292 beds) 1350 East Market Street, Warren, OH, Zip 44483–6628; tel. 330/841–9011; Krista McFadden, President
**Web address:** www.https://trumbullmemorial.org/?_ga=2.209137234.1564767671.1497292183–315051339.1497292183

**PENNSYLVANIA:** SHARON REGIONAL MEDICAL CENTER (O, 218 beds) 740 East State Street, Sharon, PA, Zip 16146–3395; tel. 724/983–3911; Robert Rogalski, President

**TEXAS:** MEDICAL CENTER OF SOUTHEAST TEXAS (O, 17 beds) 6025 Metropolitan Drive, Beaumont, TX, Zip 77706–2407; tel. 409/617–7700; Becky Ames, Chief Executive Officer
**Web address:** www.medicalcentersetexas.com/

ODESSA REGIONAL MEDICAL CENTER (O, 213 beds) 520 East Sixth Street, Odessa, TX, Zip 79761–4565, Mailing Address: P.O. Box 4859, 79760–4859, tel. 432/582–8000; Stacey L. Brown, Chief Executive Officer
**Web address:** https://www.odessaregionalmedicalcenter.org/

SCENIC MOUNTAIN MEDICAL CENTER (O, 82 beds) 1601 West 11th Place, Big Spring, TX, Zip 79720–4198; tel. 432/263–1211; Stacey L. Brown, President

SOUTHWEST GENERAL HOSPITAL (O, 253 beds) 7400 Barlite Boulevard, San Antonio, TX, Zip 78224–1399; tel. 210/921–2000; Jonathan Turton, FACHE, President
**Web address:** https://www.southwestgeneralhospital.org/

ST. JOSEPH MEDICAL CENTER (O, 463 beds) 1401 St Joseph Parkway, Houston, TX, Zip 77002–8301; tel. 713/757–1000; Kimberly S. Bassett, R.N., President

THE MEDICAL CENTER OF SOUTHEAST TEXAS (O, 136 beds) 2555 Jimmy Johnson Boulevard, Port Arthur, TX, Zip 77640–2007; tel. 409/724–7389; Phillip Craig. Desmond, Chief Executive Officer
**Web address:** https://www.medicalcentersetexas.org/

WADLEY REGIONAL MEDICAL CENTER (O, 178 beds) 1000 Pine Street, Texarkana, TX, Zip 75501–5170; tel. 903/798–8000; Thomas D. Gilbert, FACHE, Chief Executive Officer
**Web address:** www.wadleyhealth.com

**UTAH:** DAVIS HOSPITAL AND MEDICAL CENTER (O, 221 beds) 1600 West Antelope Drive, Layton, UT, Zip 84041–1142; tel. 801/807–1000; Michael Jensen, Chief Executive Officer
**Web address:** www.davishospital.com

JORDAN VALLEY MEDICAL CENTER WEST VALLEY CAMPUS (O, 101 beds) 3460 South Pioneer Parkway, West Valley City, UT, Zip 84120–2049; tel. 801/561–8888; Nathanael Budge, Administrator

JORDAN VALLEY MEDICAL CENTER (O, 183 beds) 3580 West 9000 South, West Jordan, UT, Zip 84088–8812; tel. 801/561–8888; Jon Butterfield, Administrator and Chief Executive Officer
**Web address:** www.jordanvalleymc.com

SALT LAKE REGIONAL MEDICAL CENTER (O, 132 beds) 1050 East South Temple, Salt Lake City, UT, Zip 84102–1507; tel. 801/350–4111; Dale Johns, FACHE, Chief Executive Officer

| | | |
|---|---|---|
| **Owned, leased, sponsored:** | 32 hospitals | 5486 beds |
| **Contract–managed:** | 0 hospitals | 0 beds |
| **Totals:** | 32 hospitals | 5486 beds |

**0858: STRATEGIC BEHAVIORAL HEALTH, LLC** (IO)
8295 Tournament Drive, Suite 201, Memphis, TN Zip 38125–8913; tel. 901/969–3100; Jim Shaheen, President

**COLORADO:** CLEAR VIEW BEHAVIORAL HEALTH (O, 92 beds) 4770 Larimer Parkway, Johnstown, CO, Zip 80534; tel. 970/461–5061; Sharon Pendlebury, Chief Executive Officer

PEAK VIEW BEHAVIORAL HEALTH (O, 112 beds) 7353 Sisters Grove, Colorado Springs, CO, Zip 80923–2615; tel. 719/444–8484; Ty Meredith, Chief Executive Officer
**Web address:** www.strategicbh.com/peakview.html

For explanation of codes following names, see page B2.
★ Indicates Type III membership in the American Hospital Association.

**NEVADA**: MONTEVISTA HOSPITAL (O, 202 beds) 5900 West Rochelle Avenue, Las Vegas, NV, Zip 89103–3327; tel. 702/364–1111; Steve McCabe, Chief Executive Officer
**Web address**: www.montevistahospital.com

**NEW MEXICO**: PEAK BEHAVIORAL HEALTH SERVICES (O, 120 beds) 5065 McNutt Road, Santa Teresa, NM, Zip 88008–9442; tel. 575/589–3000; Sandra Emanuel, Chief Executive Officer

**NORTH CAROLINA**: STRATEGIC BEHAVIORAL HEALTH – RALEIGH (O, 50 beds) 3200 Waterfield Drive, Garner, NC, Zip 27529–7727; tel. 919/800–4400; Matt Doyle, Chief Executive Officer
**Web address**: www.sbcraleigh.com/

STRATEGIC BEHAVIORAL HEALTH – WILMINGTON (O, 112 beds) 2050 Mercantile Drive, Leland, NC, Zip 28451–4053; tel. 910/371–2500; Steve McCabe, Chief Executive Officer
**Web address**: www.sbcwilmington.com/

**TEXAS**: ROCK PRAIRIE BEHAVIORAL HEALTH (O, 72 beds) 3550 Normand Drive, College Station, TX, Zip 77845–6399; tel. 979/703–8848; Jennifer Kelly, Chief Executive Officer

**WISCONSIN**: WILLOW CREEK BEHAVIORAL HEALTH (O, 72 beds) 1351 Ontario Road, Green Bay, WI, Zip 54311–8302; tel. 920/328–1220; Teena Ahuja, Interim Chief Executive Officer and Regional Vice President of Operations
**Web address**: www.willowcreekbh.com

| | | |
|---|---|---|
| Owned, leased, sponsored: | 8 hospitals | 832 beds |
| Contract–managed: | 0 hospitals | 0 beds |
| Totals: | 8 hospitals | 832 beds |

---

★**0399: SUMMA HEALTH** (NP)
1077 Gorge Boulevard, Akron, OH Zip 44310; tel. 330/375–3000; T. Clifford Deveny, M.D., President and Chief Executive Officer
**(Centralized Physician/Insurance Health System)**

**OHIO**: SUMMA HEALTH SYSTEM (O, 721 beds) 525 East Market Street, Akron, OH, Zip 44304–1619; tel. 330/375–3000; David Custodio, M.D., President Summa Akron City and St. Thomas Campuses
**Web address**: www.summahealth.org

SUMMA REHAB HOSPITAL (O, 60 beds) 29 North Adams Street, Akron, OH, Zip 44304–1641; tel. 330/572–7300; Michelle Dudek, President and Chief Executive Officer
**Web address**: www.summarehabhospital.com/

| | | |
|---|---|---|
| Owned, leased, sponsored: | 2 hospitals | 781 beds |
| Contract–managed: | 0 hospitals | 0 beds |
| Totals: | 2 hospitals | 781 beds |

---

★**8795: SUTTER HEALTH** (NP)
2200 River Plaza Drive, Sacramento, CA Zip 95833–4134; tel. 916/887–0000; Sarah Krevans, President and Chief Executive Officer
**(Centralized Health System)**

**CALIFORNIA**: ALTA BATES SUMMIT MEDICAL CENTER – SUMMIT CAMPUS (O, 427 beds) 350 Hawthorne Avenue, Oakland, CA, Zip 94609–3100; tel. 510/655–4000; David D. Clark, FACHE, Chief Executive Officer
**Web address**: www.altabatessummit.com

ALTA BATES SUMMIT MEDICAL CENTER–ALTA BATES CAMPUS (O, 416 beds) 2450 Ashby Avenue, Berkeley, CA, Zip 94705–2067; tel. 510/204–4444; David D. Clark, FACHE, Chief Executive Officer
**Web address**: www.altabatessummit.com

CALIFORNIA PACIFIC MEDICAL CENTER–DAVIES CAMPUS (O, 154 beds) Castro and Duboce Streets, San Francisco, CA, Zip 94114; tel. 415/600–6000; Mary Lanier, Vice President, Post Acute Services and Site Administrator
**Web address**: www.cpmc.org

CALIFORNIA PACIFIC MEDICAL CENTER–ST. LUKE'S CAMPUS (O, 165 beds) 3555 Cesar Chavez Street, San Francisco, CA, Zip 94110–4403; tel. 415/600–6000; Warren S. Browner, M.D., M.P.H., Chief Executive Officer
**Web address**: www.stlukes–sf.org

CALIFORNIA PACIFIC MEDICAL CENTER (O, 640 beds) 2333 Buchanan Street, San Francisco, CA, Zip 94115–1925, Mailing Address: P.O. Box 7999, 94120–7999, tel. 415/600–6000; Warren S. Browner, M.D., M.P.H., Chief Executive Officer

EDEN MEDICAL CENTER (O, 130 beds) 20103 Lake Chabot Road, Castro Valley, CA, Zip 94546–5305; tel. 510/537–1234; Patricia Ryan, Chief Executive Officer
**Web address**: www.edenmedcenter.org

MEMORIAL HOSPITAL LOS BANOS (O, 44 beds) 520 West 'I' Street, Los Banos, CA, Zip 93635–3498; tel. 209/826–0591; Doug Archer, Administrator
**Web address**: www.memoriallosbanos.org/

MEMORIAL MEDICAL CENTER (O, 220 beds) 1700 Coffee Road, Modesto, CA, Zip 95355–2869, Mailing Address: P.O. Box 942, 95353–0942, tel. 209/526–4500; Eugene Patrizio, Chief Executive Officer
**Web address**: www.memorialmedicalcenter.org

MENLO PARK SURGICAL HOSPITAL (O, 16 beds) 570 Willow Road, Menlo Park, CA, Zip 94025–2617; tel. 650/324–8500; Jeanette Engle–Ramirez, Chief Executive Officer

MILLS–PENINSULA HEALTH SERVICES (O, 266 beds) 1501 Trousdale Drive, Burlingame, CA, Zip 94010–3282; tel. 650/696–5400; Janet Wagner, R.N., Chief Executive Officer
**Web address**: www.mills–peninsula.org

NOVATO COMMUNITY HOSPITAL (O, 40 beds) 180 Rowland Way, Novato, CA, Zip 94945–5009, Mailing Address: P.O. Box 1108, 94948–1108, tel. 415/209–1300; Michael L. Purvis, Chief Executive Officer
**Web address**: www.novatocommunity.sutterhealth.org

STANISLAUS SURGICAL HOSPITAL (O, 23 beds) 1421 Oakdale Road, Modesto, CA, Zip 95355–3356; tel. 209/572–2700; Douglas V. Johnson, Chief Executive Officer

SUTTER AMADOR HOSPITAL (O, 52 beds) 200 Mission Boulevard, Jackson, CA, Zip 95642–2564; tel. 209/223–7500; Thomas C. Dickson, Chief Executive Officer
**Web address**: www.sutteramador.org

SUTTER AUBURN FAITH HOSPITAL (O, 72 beds) 11815 Education Street, Auburn, CA, Zip 95602–2410; tel. 530/888–4500; Mitchell J. Hanna, Chief Executive Officer

SUTTER CENTER FOR PSYCHIATRY (O, 71 beds) 7700 Folsom Boulevard, Sacramento, CA, Zip 95826–2608; tel. 916/386–3000; John W. Boyd, PsyD, Chief Executive Officer
**Web address**: www.sutterpsychiatry.org

SUTTER COAST HOSPITAL (O, 49 beds) 800 East Washington Boulevard, Crescent City, CA, Zip 95531–8359; tel. 707/464–8511; Mitchell J. Hanna, Chief Executive Officer

SUTTER DAVIS HOSPITAL (O, 48 beds) 2000 Sutter Place, Davis, CA, Zip 95616–6201, Mailing Address: P.O. Box 1617, 95617–1617, tel. 530/756–6440; Rachael McKinney, FACHE, Chief Executive Officer
**Web address**: www.sutterhealth.org

SUTTER DELTA MEDICAL CENTER (O, 132 beds) 3901 Lone Tree Way, Antioch, CA, Zip 94509–6253; tel. 925/779–7200; Sherie C. Hickman, Chief Executive Officer

SUTTER LAKESIDE HOSPITAL (O, 25 beds) 5176 Hill Road East, Lakeport, CA, Zip 95453–6300; tel. 707/262–5000; Scott Knight, Chief Administrative Officer
**Web address**: www.sutterlakeside.org

SUTTER MATERNITY AND SURGERY CENTER OF SANTA CRUZ (O, 30 beds) 2900 Chanticleer Avenue, Santa Cruz, CA, Zip 95065–1816; tel. 831/477–2200; Trina White, President and Chief Executive Officer

SUTTER MEDICAL CENTER, SACRAMENTO (O, 523 beds) 2801 'L' Street, Sacramento, CA, Zip 95816–5680; tel. 916/454–3333; David Cheney, Chief Executive Officer
**Web address**: www.sutterhealth.org

SUTTER OAKS NURSING CENTER (O, 100 beds) 2600 L Street, Sacramento, CA, Zip 95816–5612; tel. 916/552–2200; John W. Boyd, PsyD, Chief Administrative Officer

---

For explanation of codes following names, see page B2.
★ Indicates Type III membership in the American Hospital Association.

SUTTER ROSEVILLE MEDICAL CENTER (O, 328 beds) One Medical Plaza Drive, Roseville, CA, Zip 95661–3037; tel. 916/781–1000; Brian Alexander, Chief Executive Officer
**Web address:** www.sutterroseville.org

SUTTER SANTA ROSA REGIONAL HOSPITAL (O, 84 beds) 30 Mark West Springs Road, Santa Rosa, CA, Zip 95403; tel. 707/576–4000; Dan Peterson, Chief Executive Officer
**Web address:** www.sutterhealth.org

SUTTER SOLANO MEDICAL CENTER (O, 108 beds) 300 Hospital Drive, Vallejo, CA, Zip 94589–2574, Mailing Address: P.O. Box 3189, 94590–0669, tel. 707/554–4444; Abhishek Dosi, Chief Executive Officer
**Web address:** www.suttersolano.org

SUTTER SURGICAL HOSPITAL – NORTH VALLEY (O, 14 beds) 455 Plumas Boulevard, Yuba City, CA, Zip 95991–5074; tel. 530/749–5700; Shawndra Simpson, Interim Chief Executive Officer

SUTTER TRACY COMMUNITY HOSPITAL (O, 33 beds) 1420 North Tracy Boulevard, Tracy, CA, Zip 95376–3497; tel. 209/835–1500; David M. Thompson, Chief Executive Officer
**Web address:** www.suttertracy.org

**HAWAII:** SUTTER HEALTH KAHI MOHALA (O, 76 beds) 91–2301 Old Fort Weaver Road, Ewa Beach, HI, Zip 96706–3602; tel. 808/671–8511; Claudia Crist, Chief Executive Officer
**Web address:** www.kahimohala.org

| | | |
|---|---|---|
| Owned, leased, sponsored: | 28 hospitals | 4286 beds |
| Contract–managed: | 0 hospitals | 0 beds |
| Totals: | 28 hospitals | 4286 beds |

---

**★0871: SWEDISH HEALTH SERVICES** (NP)
747 Broadway, Seattle, WA Zip 98122–4379; tel. 206/386–6000; R. Guy. Hudson, Chief Executive Officer
**(Independent Hospital System)**

**WASHINGTON:** SWEDISH MEDICAL CENTER–CHERRY HILL CAMPUS (O, 208 beds) 500 17th Avenue, Seattle, WA, Zip 98122–5711; tel. 206/320–2000; David R. West, Chief Operating Officer
**Web address:** www.swedish.org

SWEDISH MEDICAL CENTER–FIRST HILL (O, 689 beds) 747 Broadway, Seattle, WA, Zip 98122–4307; tel. 206/386–6000; Elizabeth Wako, Chief Operating Officer

SWEDISH/EDMONDS (O, 185 beds) 21601 76th Avenue West, Edmonds, WA, Zip 98026–7506; tel. 425/640–4000; David R. West, Vice President, Operations
**Web address:** www.swedish.org

SWEDISH/ISSAQUAH (O, 153 beds) 751 NE Blakely Drive, Issaquah, WA, Zip 98029–6201; tel. 425/313–4000; R. Guy. Hudson, Chief Executive Officer
**Web address:** www.swedish.org/issaquah

| | | |
|---|---|---|
| Owned, leased, sponsored: | 4 hospitals | 1235 beds |
| Contract–managed: | 0 hospitals | 0 beds |
| Totals: | 4 hospitals | 1235 beds |

---

**★0379: TAHOE FOREST HEALTH SYSTEM** (NP)
10121 Pine Avenue, Truckee, CA Zip 96161–4835; tel. 530/587–6011; Harry Weis, Chief Executive Officer

**CALIFORNIA:** TAHOE FOREST HOSPITAL DISTRICT (O, 62 beds) 10121 Pine Avenue, Truckee, CA, Zip 96161–4856, Mailing Address: P.O. Box 759, 96160–0759, tel. 530/587–6011; Harry Weis, Chief Executive Officer
**Web address:** www.tfhd.com

**NEVADA:** INCLINE VILLAGE COMMUNITY HOSPITAL (O, 6 beds) 880 Alder Avenue, Incline Village, NV, Zip 89451–8335; tel. 775/833–4100; Judy Newland, R.N., Chief Nursing Officer

| | | |
|---|---|---|
| Owned, leased, sponsored: | 2 hospitals | 68 beds |
| Contract–managed: | 0 hospitals | 0 beds |
| Totals: | 2 hospitals | 68 beds |

---

**★0341: TANNER HEALTH SYSTEM** (NP)
705 Dixie Street, Carrollton, GA Zip 30117–3818; tel. 770/836–9580; Loy M. Howard, President and Chief Executive Officer

**ALABAMA:** TANNER MEDICAL CENTER/EAST ALABAMA (O, 26 beds) 1032 South Main Street, Wedowee, AL, Zip 36278–7428; tel. 256/357–2111; Jerry Morris, Administrator
**Web address:** www.tanner.org/eastalabama

**GEORGIA:** HIGGINS GENERAL HOSPITAL (O, 23 beds) 200 Allen Memorial Drive, Bremen, GA, Zip 30110–2012; tel. 770/824–2000; Jerry Morris, Administrator

TANNER MEDICAL CENTER–CARROLLTON (O, 142 beds) 705 Dixie Street, Carrollton, GA, Zip 30117–3818; tel. 770/836–9666; Loy M. Howard, Chief Operating Officer
**Web address:** www.tanner.org

TANNER MEDICAL CENTER–VILLA RICA (O, 118 beds) 601 Dallas Highway, Villa Rica, GA, Zip 30180–1202; tel. 770/456–3000; Eric Dalton, Administrator
**Web address:** www.tanner.org

| | | |
|---|---|---|
| Owned, leased, sponsored: | 4 hospitals | 309 beds |
| Contract–managed: | 0 hospitals | 0 beds |
| Totals: | 4 hospitals | 309 beds |

---

**★0169: TEMPLE UNIVERSITY HEALTH SYSTEM** (NP)
3509 North Broad Street, 9th Floor, Philadelphia, PA Zip 19140–4105; tel. 215/707–0900; Michael A. Young, FACHE, Chief Executive Officer
**(Centralized Health System)**

**PENNSYLVANIA:** FOX CHASE CANCER CENTER–AMERICAN ONCOLOGIC HOSPITAL (O, 72 beds) 333 Cottman Avenue, Philadelphia, PA, Zip 19111–2434; tel. 215/728–6900; Richard Fisher, M.D., President and Chief Executive Officer
**Web address:** www.fccc.org

TEMPLE UNIVERSITY HOSPITAL – JEANES CAMPUS (O, 146 beds) 7600 Central Avenue, Philadelphia, PA, Zip 19111–2499; tel. 215/728–2000; Marc P. Hurowitz, D.O., Chief Executive Officer
**Web address:** www.jeanes.com

TEMPLE UNIVERSITY HOSPITAL (O, 732 beds) 3401 North Broad Street, Philadelphia, PA, Zip 19140–5103; tel. 215/707–2000; Michael A. Young, FACHE, President and Chief Executive Officer
**Web address:** www.tuh.templehealth.org/content/default.htm

| | | |
|---|---|---|
| Owned, leased, sponsored: | 3 hospitals | 950 beds |
| Contract–managed: | 0 hospitals | 0 beds |
| Totals: | 3 hospitals | 950 beds |

---

**★0919: TENET HEALTHCARE CORPORATION** (IO)
1445 Ross Avenue, Suite 1400, Dallas, TX Zip 75202–2703, Mailing Address: P.O. Box 1390369, 75313–9036, tel. 469/893–2200; Saumya Sutaria, M.D., President and Chief Operating Officer
**(Decentralized Health System)**

**ALABAMA:** BROOKWOOD BAPTIST MEDICAL CENTER (O, 607 beds) 2010 Brookwood Medical Center Drive, Birmingham, AL, Zip 35209–6875; tel. 205/877–1000; Timothy Puthoff, Chief Executive Officer
**Web address:** https://www.brookwoodbaptisthealth.com/

CITIZENS BAPTIST MEDICAL CENTER (O, 72 beds) 604 Stone Avenue, Talladega, AL, Zip 35160–2217, Mailing Address: P.O. Box 978, 35161–0978, tel. 256/362–8111; Frank D. Thomas, Chief Executive Officer
**Web address:** www.brookwoodbaptisthealth.org

PRINCETON BAPTIST MEDICAL CENTER (O, 315 beds) 701 Princeton Avenue SW, Birmingham, AL, Zip 35211–1303; tel. 205/783–3000; Michael Neuendorf, Chief Executive Officer

---

For explanation of codes following names, see page B2.
★ Indicates Type III membership in the American Hospital Association.

SHELBY BAPTIST MEDICAL CENTER (O, 231 beds) 1000 First Street North, Alabaster, AL, Zip 35007–8703; tel. 205/620–8100; Daniel Listi, Chief Executive Officer
**Web address:** www.brookwoodbaptisthealth.com

WALKER BAPTIST MEDICAL CENTER (O, 158 beds) 3400 Highway 78 East, Jasper, AL, Zip 35501–8907, Mailing Address: P.O. Box 3547, 35502–3547, tel. 205/387–4000; Michael Neuendorf, Chief Executive Officer
**Web address:** www.bhsala.com

**ARIZONA:** ABRAZO ARROWHEAD CAMPUS (O, 217 beds) 18701 North 67th Avenue, Glendale, AZ, Zip 85308–7100; tel. 623/561–1000; Jeff Patterson, Chief Executive Officer

ABRAZO CENTRAL CAMPUS (O, 180 beds) 2000 West Bethany Home Road, Phoenix, AZ, Zip 85015–2443; tel. 602/249–0212; Edgar Staren, M.D., Interim Chief Executive Officer
**Web address:** www.abrazohealth.com

ABRAZO SCOTTSDALE CAMPUS (O, 116 beds) 3929 East Bell Road, Phoenix, AZ, Zip 85032–2196; tel. 602/923–5000; Edgar Staren, M.D., Interim Chief Executive Officer
**Web address:** www.abrazoscottsdale.com

ABRAZO WEST CAMPUS (O, 106 beds) 13677 West McDowell Road, Goodyear, AZ, Zip 85395–2635; tel. 623/882–1500; Christina E. Oh, Chief Executive Officer

CARONDELET HOLY CROSS HOSPITAL (O, 25 beds) 1171 West Target Range Road, Nogales, AZ, Zip 85621–2415; tel. 520/285–3000; Debbie Knapheide, MSN, Site Administrator, Chief Nursing Officer and Chief Operating Officer
**Web address:** www.carondelet.org

CARONDELET ST. JOSEPH'S HOSPITAL (O, 486 beds) 350 North Wilmot Road, Tucson, AZ, Zip 85711–2678; tel. 520/873–3000; Frank L. Molinaro, Chief Executive Officer
**Web address:** www.carondelet.org

CARONDELET ST. MARY'S HOSPITAL (O, 300 beds) 1601 West St Mary's Road, Tucson, AZ, Zip 85745–2682; tel. 520/872–3000; Frank L. Molinaro, Chief Executive Officer
**Web address:** www.carondelet.org

**CALIFORNIA:** DESERT REGIONAL MEDICAL CENTER (L, 382 beds) 1150 North Indian Canyon Drive, Palm Springs, CA, Zip 92262–4872; tel. 760/323–6511; Michele Finney, Chief Executive Officer
**Web address:** www.desertregional.com

DOCTORS HOSPITAL OF MANTECA (O, 56 beds) 1205 East North Street, Manteca, CA, Zip 95336–4900; tel. 209/823–3111; Murali Naidu, M.D., Chief Executive Officer

DOCTORS MEDICAL CENTER OF MODESTO (O, 461 beds) 1441 Florida Avenue, Modesto, CA, Zip 95350–4418, Mailing Address: P.O. Box 4138, 95352–4138, tel. 209/578–1211; Warren J. Kirk, Chief Executive Officer
**Web address:** www.dmc-modesto.com

EMANUEL MEDICAL CENTER (O, 209 beds) 825 Delbon Avenue, Turlock, CA, Zip 95382–2016; tel. 209/667–4200; Lani Dickinson, Chief Executive Officer
**Web address:** www.emanuelmedicalcenter.org

FOUNTAIN VALLEY REGIONAL HOSPITAL AND MEDICAL CENTER (O, 380 beds) 17100 Euclid Street, Fountain Valley, CA, Zip 92708–4043; tel. 714/966–7200; Kenneth D. McFarland, Chief Executive Officer

HI–DESERT MEDICAL CENTER (L, 179 beds) 6601 White Feather Road, Joshua Tree, CA, Zip 92284; tel. 760/366–3711; Karen Faulis, Chief Executive Officer
**Web address:** www.hdmc.org

JFK MEMORIAL HOSPITAL (O, 145 beds) 47111 Monroe Street, Indio, CA, Zip 92201–6799; tel. 760/347–6191; Gary Honts, Chief Executive Officer

LAKEWOOD REGIONAL MEDICAL CENTER (O, 111 beds) 3700 East South Street, Lakewood, CA, Zip 90712–1498, Mailing Address: P.O. Box 6070, 90712, tel. 562/531–2550; John A. Grah, FACHE, Chief Executive Officer
**Web address:** www.lakewoodregional.com

LOS ALAMITOS MEDICAL CENTER (O, 120 beds) 3751 Katella Avenue, Los Alamitos, CA, Zip 90720–3164; tel. 562/598–1311; Kent G. Clayton, Chief Executive Officer
**Web address:** www.losalamitosmedctr.com

PLACENTIA–LINDA HOSPITAL (O, 74 beds) 1301 North Rose Drive, Placentia, CA, Zip 92870–3899; tel. 714/993–2000; Bryan R. Rogers, Group Chief Executive Officer
**Web address:** www.placentialinda.com

SAN RAMON REGIONAL MEDICAL CENTER (O, 123 beds) 6001 Norris Canyon Road, San Ramon, CA, Zip 94583–5400; tel. 925/275–9200; Ann Lucena, Chief Executive Officer

SIERRA VISTA REGIONAL MEDICAL CENTER (O, 74 beds) 1010 Murray Avenue, San Luis Obispo, CA, Zip 93405–1806, Mailing Address: P.O. Box 1367, 93405, tel. 805/546–7600; Mark P. Lisa, FACHE, Chief Executive Officer
**Web address:** www.sierravistaregional.com

TWIN CITIES COMMUNITY HOSPITAL (O, 49 beds) 1100 Las Tablas Road, Templeton, CA, Zip 93465–9796; tel. 805/434–3500; Mark P. Lisa, FACHE, Chief Executive Officer
**Web address:** www.twincitieshospital.com

**FLORIDA:** CORAL GABLES HOSPITAL (O, 256 beds) 3100 Douglas Road, Coral Gables, FL, Zip 33134–6914; tel. 305/445–8461; Cristina Jimenez, Chief Executive Officer
**Web address:** www.coralgableshospital.com

DELRAY MEDICAL CENTER (O, 536 beds) 5352 Linton Boulevard, Delray Beach, FL, Zip 33484–6580; tel. 561/498–4440; Margaret Gill, Chief Executive Officer

GOOD SAMARITAN MEDICAL CENTER (O, 225 beds) 1309 North Flagler Drive, West Palm Beach, FL, Zip 33401–3499; tel. 561/655–5511; Sheri Montgomery, Acting Chief Executive Officer
**Web address:** www.goodsamaritanmc.com

HIALEAH HOSPITAL (O, 191 beds) 651 East 25th Street, Hialeah, FL, Zip 33013–3878; tel. 305/693–6100; Michael J. Bell, Chief Executive Officer

NORTH SHORE MEDICAL CENTER (O, 816 beds) 1100 NW 95th Street, Miami, FL, Zip 33150–2098; tel. 305/835–6000; Mark Racicot, Chief Executive Officer
**Web address:** www.northshoremedical.com

PALM BEACH GARDENS MEDICAL CENTER (L, 202 beds) 3360 Burns Road, Palm Beach Gardens, FL, Zip 33410–4323; tel. 561/622–1411; Teresa C. Urquhart, Chief Executive Officer
**Web address:** www.pbgmc.com

PALMETTO GENERAL HOSPITAL (O, 360 beds) 2001 West 68th Street, Hialeah, FL, Zip 33016–1898; tel. 305/823–5000; Ana J. Mederos, Chief Executive Officer
**Web address:** www.palmettogeneral.com

ST. MARY'S MEDICAL CENTER (O, 460 beds) 901 45th Street, West Palm Beach, FL, Zip 33407–2495; tel. 561/844–6300; David O'Brien, Interim Chief Executive Officer

WEST BOCA MEDICAL CENTER (O, 195 beds) 21644 State Road 7, Boca Raton, FL, Zip 33428–1899; tel. 561/488–8000; George Rizzuto, CPA, Chief Executive Officer
**Web address:** www.westbocamedctr.com

**MASSACHUSETTS:** METROWEST MEDICAL CENTER (O, 160 beds) 115 Lincoln Street, Framingham, MA, Zip 01702–6342; tel. 508/383–1000; Andrew D. Harding, R.N., Chief Executive Officer

SAINT VINCENT HOSPITAL (O, 283 beds) 123 Summer Street, Worcester, MA, Zip 01608–1216; tel. 508/363–5000; Carolyn Jackson, Chief Executive Officer
**Web address:** www.stvincenthospital.com

**MICHIGAN:** DMC – CHILDREN'S HOSPITAL OF MICHIGAN (O, 227 beds) 3901 Beaubien Street, Detroit, MI, Zip 48201–2119; tel. 313/745–5852; Jill Bembas, Executive Assistant
**Web address:** www.chmkids.org

DMC – DETROIT RECEIVING HOSPITAL (O, 219 beds) 4201 Saint Antoine Street, Detroit, MI, Zip 48201–2153; tel. 313/745–3000; Scott Steiner, FACHE, Chief Executive Officer
**Web address:** www.dmc.org

DMC – REHABILITATION INSTITUTE OF MICHIGAN (O, 69 beds) 261 Mack Avenue, Detroit, MI, Zip 48201–2495; tel. 313/745–1203; Patty Jobbitt, Chief Executive Officer
**Web address:** www.rimrehab.org

DMC – SINAI–GRACE HOSPITAL (O, 267 beds) 6071 West Outer Drive, Detroit, MI, Zip 48235–2679; tel. 313/966–3300; Daniel Jackson, President

DMC HARPER UNIVERSITY HOSPITAL (O, 394 beds) 3990 John 'R' Street, Detroit, MI, Zip 48201–2018; tel. 313/745–8040; Scott Steiner, FACHE, Chief Executive Officer
**Web address:** www.harperhospital.org

For explanation of codes following names, see page B2.
★ Indicates Type III membership in the American Hospital Association.

DMC HURON VALLEY–SINAI HOSPITAL (O, 156 beds) 1 William Carls Drive, Commerce Township, MI, Zip 48382–2201; tel. 248/937–3300; David McEwen, Chief Executive Officer
**Web address**: www.hvsh.org

**SOUTH CAROLINA**: COASTAL CAROLINA HOSPITAL (O, 35 beds) 1000 Medical Center Drive, Hardeeville, SC, Zip 29927–3446; tel. 843/784–8000; Joel Taylor, Chief Executive Officer

EAST COOPER MEDICAL CENTER (O, 140 beds) 2000 Hospital Drive, Mount Pleasant, SC, Zip 29464–3764; tel. 843/881–0100; Patrick Downes, Chief Executive Officer
**Web address**: www.eastcoopermedctr.com

HILTON HEAD HOSPITAL (O, 93 beds) 25 Hospital Center Boulevard, Hilton Head Island, SC, Zip 29926–2738; tel. 843/681–6122; Jeremy L. Clark, Market Chief Executive Officer

PIEDMONT MEDICAL CENTER (O, 279 beds) 222 Herlong Avenue, Rock Hill, SC, Zip 29732; tel. 803/329–1234; Mark Nosacka, Chief Executive Officer
**Web address**: www.piedmontmedicalcenter.com

**TENNESSEE**: SAINT FRANCIS HOSPITAL–BARTLETT (O, 156 beds) 2986 Kate Bond Road, Bartlett, TN, Zip 38133–4003; tel. 901/820–7000; Christopher Locke, Chief Executive Officer
**Web address**: www.saintfrancisbartlett.com

SAINT FRANCIS HOSPITAL (O, 415 beds) 5959 Park Avenue, Memphis, TN, Zip 38119–5198; tel. 901/765–1000; Sally A. Hurt–Deitch, FACHE, R.N., MSN, Chief Executive Officer
**Web address**: www.saintfrancishosp.com

**TEXAS**: BAPTIST MEDICAL CENTER (O, 1570 beds) 111 Dallas Street, San Antonio, TX, Zip 78205–1230; tel. 210/297–7000; Jorge Trevino, Chief Executive Officer

NACOGDOCHES MEDICAL CENTER (O, 117 beds) 4920 NE Stallings Drive, Nacogdoches, TX, Zip 75965–1200; tel. 936/569–9481; Jeff Patterson, Chief Executive Officer
**Web address**: www.nacmedicalcenter.com

RESOLUTE HEALTH (O, 70 beds) 555 Creekside Crossing, New Braunfels, TX, Zip 78130–2594; tel. 830/500–6000; Mark L. Bernard, Chief Executive Officer

THE HOSPITALS OF PROVIDENCE EAST CAMPUS (O, 182 beds) 3280 Joe Battle Boulevard, El Paso, TX, Zip 79938–2622; tel. 915/832–2000; Monica Vargas–Mahar, FACHE, Chief Executive Officer
**Web address**: www.sphn.com

THE HOSPITALS OF PROVIDENCE MEMORIAL CAMPUS (O, 332 beds) 2001 North Oregon Street, El Paso, TX, Zip 79902–3368; tel. 915/577–6625; Nicholas R. Tejeda, FACHE, Market Chief Executive Officer
**Web address**: www.thehospitalsofprovidence.com

THE HOSPITALS OF PROVIDENCE SIERRA CAMPUS (O, 180 beds) 1625 Medical Center Drive, El Paso, TX, Zip 79902–5005; tel. 915/747–4000; Rob J. Anderson, Chief Executive Officer

THE HOSPITALS OF PROVIDENCE TRANSMOUNTAIN CAMPUS (O, 106 beds) 2000 Transmountain Road, El Paso, TX, Zip 79911; tel. 915/877–8300; Tasha Hopper, Chief Executive Officer
**Web address**: https://www.thehospitalsofprovidence.com/our–locations/transmountain

VALLEY BAPTIST MEDICAL CENTER–BROWNSVILLE (O, 225 beds) 1040 West Jefferson Street, Brownsville, TX, Zip 78520–6338, Mailing Address: P.O. Box 3590, 78523–3590, tel. 956/698–5400; Leslie Bingham, Senior Vice President and Chief Executive Officer

VALLEY BAPTIST MEDICAL CENTER–HARLINGEN (O, 432 beds) 2101 Pease Street, Harlingen, TX, Zip 78550–8307, P O Drawer 2588, 78551–2588, tel. 956/389–1100; Manuel Vela, President and Chief Executive Officer
**Web address**: www.valleybaptist.net/harlingen/index.htm

| | | |
|---|---|---|
| Owned, leased, sponsored: | 57 hospitals | 14524 beds |
| Contract–managed: | 0 hospitals | 0 beds |
| Totals: | 57 hospitals | 14524 beds |

---

**0876: TENNESSEE HEALTH MANAGEMENT** (IO)
52 West Eighth Street, Parsons, TN Zip 38363–4656, Mailing Address: P.O. 10, 38363–0010, tel. 731/847–6343; Dennis Berry, Chief Executive Officer

**ALABAMA**: UNITY PSYCHIATRIC CARE–HUNTSVILLE (O, 20 beds) 5315 Millennium Drive NW, Huntsville, AL, Zip 35806–2458; tel. 256/964–6700; Bradley Moss, Administrator
**Web address**: www.thmgt.com/locations/behavioral–healthcare–center–at–huntsville

**TENNESSEE**: UNITY PSYCHIATRIC CARE–CLARKSVILLE (O, 26 beds) 930 Professional Park Drive, Clarksville, TN, Zip 37040–5136; tel. 931/538–6420; Jennifer Robinson, Administrator

UNITY PSYCHIATRIC CARE–COLUMBIA (O, 16 beds) 1400 Rosewood Drive, Columbia, TN, Zip 38401–4878; tel. 931/388–6573; Paula Chennault, Administrator
**Web address**: www.unitypsych.com

UNITY PSYCHIATRIC CARE–MARTIN (O, 16 beds) 458 Hannings Lane, Martin, TN, Zip 38237–3308; tel. 731/588–2830; Carrie Brawley, Administrator
**Web address**: www.unitypsych.com

| | | |
|---|---|---|
| Owned, leased, sponsored: | 4 hospitals | 78 beds |
| Contract–managed: | 0 hospitals | 0 beds |
| Totals: | 4 hospitals | 78 beds |

---

**0020: TEXAS DEPARTMENT OF STATE HEALTH SERVICES** (NP)
1100 West 49th Street, Austin, TX Zip 78756–3199; tel. 512/458–7111; Stacey Thompson, Superintendent
**(Independent Hospital System)**

**TEXAS**: AUSTIN STATE HOSPITAL (O, 263 beds) 4110 Guadalupe Street, Austin, TX, Zip 78751–4296; tel. 512/452–0381; Stacey Thompson, Superintendent
**Web address**: www.dshs.state.tx.us/mhhospitals/austinsh/default.shtm

BIG SPRING STATE HOSPITAL (O, 144 beds) 1901 North Highway 87, Big Spring, TX, Zip 79720–0283; tel. 432/267–8216; Traci Phillips, Superintendent
**Web address**: www.dshs.state.tx.us/mhhospitals/BigSpringSH/default.shtm

EL PASO PSYCHIATRIC CENTER (O, 74 beds) 4615 Alameda Avenue, El Paso, TX, Zip 79905–2702; tel. 915/532–2202; Zulema Carrillo, Superintendent

KERRVILLE STATE HOSPITAL (O, 218 beds) 721 Thompson Drive, Kerrville, TX, Zip 78028–5154; tel. 830/896–2211; Leigh Ann Fitzpatrick, Superintendent
**Web address**: www.dshs.state.tx.us/mhhospitals/KerrvilleSH/default.shtm

NORTH TEXAS STATE HOSPITAL (O, 562 beds) 4730 College Drive, Vernon, TX, Zip 76384–4009, Mailing Address: P.O. Box 2231, 76385–2231, tel. 940/552–9901; James E. Smith, Superintendent

RIO GRANDE STATE CENTER/SOUTH TEXAS HEALTH CARE SYSTEM (O, 55 beds) 1401 South Rangerville Road, Harlingen, TX, Zip 78552–7638; tel. 956/364–8000; Sonia Hernandez–Keeble, Superintendent
**Web address**: www.dshs.state.tx.us/mhhospitals/RioGrandeSC/default.shtm

RUSK STATE HOSPITAL (O, 277 beds) 805 North Dickinson, Rusk, TX, Zip 75785–2333, Mailing Address: P.O. Box 318, 75785–0318, tel. 903/683–3421; Brenda Slaton, Superintendent
**Web address**: www.dshs.state.tx.us/mhhospitals/RuskSH/default.shtm

SAN ANTONIO STATE HOSPITAL (O, 264 beds) 6711 South New Braunfels, Suite 100, San Antonio, TX, Zip 78223–3006; tel. 210/531–7711; Robert C. Arizpe, Superintendent
**Web address**: www.dshs.state.tx.us/mhhospitals/SanAntonioSH/default.shtm

TERRELL STATE HOSPITAL (O, 288 beds) 1200 East Brin Street, Terrell, TX, Zip 75160–2938, Mailing Address: P.O. Box 70, 75160–9000, tel. 972/524–6452; Dorothy Floyd, Ph.D., Superintendent
**Web address**: www.dshs.state.tx.us/mhhospitals/terrellsh

TEXAS CENTER FOR INFECTIOUS DISEASE (O, 50 beds) 2303 SE Military Drive, San Antonio, TX, Zip 78223–3597; tel. 210/534–8857; James N. Elkins, FACHE, Director

| | | |
|---|---|---|
| Owned, leased, sponsored: | 10 hospitals | 2195 beds |
| Contract–managed: | 0 hospitals | 0 beds |
| Totals: | 10 hospitals | 2195 beds |

---

**★0129: TEXAS HEALTH RESOURCES** (NP)
612 East Lamar Boulevard, Suite 900, Arlington, TX Zip 76011–4130; tel. 682/236–7900; Barclay E. Berdan, FACHE, Chief Executive Officer
**(Centralized Physician/Insurance Health System)**

---

For explanation of codes following names, see page B2.
★ Indicates Type III membership in the American Hospital Association.

**TEXAS:** TEXAS HEALTH ARLINGTON MEMORIAL HOSPITAL (O, 234 beds) 800 West Randol Mill Road, Arlington, TX, Zip 76012–2503; tel. 817/548–6100; Blake Kretz, FACHE, President
**Web address:** www.arlingtonmemorial.org

TEXAS HEALTH FRISCO (O, 63 beds) 12400 Dallas Parkway, Frisco, TX, Zip 75033–4224; tel. 469/495–2000; Brett D. Lee, President
**Web address:** https://www.texashealth.org/locations/texas–health–frisco

TEXAS HEALTH HARRIS METHODIST HOSPITAL ALLIANCE (O, 101 beds) 10864 Texas Health Trail, Fort Worth, TX, Zip 76244–4897; tel. 682/212–2000; Clint Abernathy, President

TEXAS HEALTH HARRIS METHODIST HOSPITAL AZLE (O, 31 beds) 108 Denver Trail, Azle, TX, Zip 76020–3614; tel. 817/444–8600; Tonya Sosebee, MSN, R.N., Chief Operating and Nursing Officer
**Web address:** www.texashealth.org/Azle

TEXAS HEALTH HARRIS METHODIST HOSPITAL CLEBURNE (O, 92 beds) 201 Walls Drive, Cleburne, TX, Zip 76033–4007; tel. 817/641–2551; Ajith Pai, PharmD, FACHE, President
**Web address:** www.texashealth.org

TEXAS HEALTH HARRIS METHODIST HOSPITAL FORT WORTH (O, 647 beds) 1301 Pennsylvania Avenue, Fort Worth, TX, Zip 76104–2122; tel. 817/250–2000; Joseph DeLeon, President
**Web address:** www.texashealth.org

TEXAS HEALTH HARRIS METHODIST HOSPITAL HURST–EULESS–BEDFORD (O, 285 beds) 1600 Hospital Parkway, Bedford, TX, Zip 76022–6913; tel. 817/685–4000; Fraser Hay, President

TEXAS HEALTH HARRIS METHODIST HOSPITAL SOUTHWEST FORT WORTH (O, 231 beds) 6100 Harris Parkway, Fort Worth, TX, Zip 76132–4199; tel. 817/433–5000; Rebecca Tucker, President
**Web address:** www.texashealth.org

TEXAS HEALTH HARRIS METHODIST HOSPITAL STEPHENVILLE (O, 41 beds) 411 North Belknap Street, Stephenville, TX, Zip 76401–3415; tel. 254/965–1500; Christopher Leu, President
**Web address:** www.texashealth.org/landing.cfm?id=108

TEXAS HEALTH PRESBYTERIAN HOSPITAL ALLEN (O, 52 beds) 1105 Central Expressway North, Suite 140, Allen, TX, Zip 75013–6103; tel. 972/747–1000; Jared Shelton, President

TEXAS HEALTH PRESBYTERIAN HOSPITAL DALLAS (O, 632 beds) 8200 Walnut Hill Lane, Dallas, TX, Zip 75231–4426; tel. 214/345–6789; James Parobek, President
**Web address:** www.texashealth.org

TEXAS HEALTH PRESBYTERIAN HOSPITAL DENTON (O, 236 beds) 3000 North I–35, Denton, TX, Zip 76201–5119; tel. 940/898–7000; Jeff Reecer, FACHE, Chief Executive Officer
**Web address:** www.dentonhospital.com

TEXAS HEALTH PRESBYTERIAN HOSPITAL KAUFMAN (O, 47 beds) 850 Ed Hall Drive, Kaufman, TX, Zip 75142–1861, Mailing Address: P.O. Box 1108, 75142–5401, tel. 972/932–7200; Mark Sij, D.O., Chief Executive Officer
**Web address:** www.texashealth.org/Kaufman

TEXAS HEALTH PRESBYTERIAN HOSPITAL PLANO (O, 309 beds) 6200 West Parker Road, Plano, TX, Zip 75093–8185; tel. 972/981–8000; Joshua Floren, President

TEXAS HEALTH SPECIALTY HOSPITAL (O, 10 beds) 1301 Pennsylvania Avenue, 4th Floor, Fort Worth, TX, Zip 76104–2190; tel. 817/250–5500; Barclay E. Berdan, FACHE, Chief Executive Officer
**Web address:** https://www.texashealth.org/texas–health–specialty–hospital/

| | | |
|---|---|---|
| Owned, leased, sponsored: | 15 hospitals | 3011 beds |
| Contract–managed: | 0 hospitals | 0 beds |
| Totals: | 15 hospitals | 3011 beds |

**1038: THE CARPENTER HEALTH NETWORK** (IO)
10615 Jefferson Highway, Baton Rouge, LA Zip 70809–7230; tel. 225/769–4180; Pat Mitchell, Chief Executive Officer

**LOUISIANA:** SAGE REHABILITATION HOSPITAL (O, 45 beds) 8000 Summa Avenue, Baton Rouge, LA, Zip 70809–3423, Mailing Address: P.O. Box 82681, 70884–2681, tel. 225/819–0703; Karen Crayton, Administrator

SAGE SPECIALTY HOSPITAL (LTAC) (O, 117 beds) 8375 Florida Boulevard, Denham Springs, LA, Zip 70726–7806; tel. 225/665–2664; Sharon Faulkner, R.N., Administrator
**Web address:** https://www.thecarpenterhealthnetwork.com/locations/sage–specialty–hospital/

| | | |
|---|---|---|
| Owned, leased, sponsored: | 2 hospitals | 162 beds |
| Contract–managed: | 0 hospitals | 0 beds |
| Totals: | 2 hospitals | 162 beds |

★**1040: THE UNIVERSITY OF KANSAS HEALTH SYSTEM** (NP)
4000 Cambridge Street, Kansas City, KS Zip 66160–0001; tel. 913/588–1227; Bob Page, President and Chief Executive Officer
**(Moderately Centralized Health System)**

**KANSAS:** HAYS MEDICAL CENTER (O, 127 beds) 2220 Canterbury Drive, Hays, KS, Zip 67601–2370, Mailing Address: P.O. Box 8100, 67601–8100, tel. 785/623–5000; Edward Herrman, R.N., FACHE, President and Chief Executive Officer
**Web address:** www.haysmed.com

THE UNIVERSITY OF KANSAS HOSPITAL (O, 916 beds) 4000 Cambridge Street, MS 3011, Kansas City, KS, Zip 66160–8501; tel. 913/588–5000; Bob Page, Chief Executive Officer

UNIVERSITY OF KANSAS HEALTH SYSTEM GREAT BEND CAMPUS (O, 33 beds) 514 Cleveland Street, Great Bend, KS, Zip 67530–3562; tel. 620/792–8833; Jesse Mock, Chief Executive Officer
**Web address:** www.gbregional.com

UNIVERSITY OF KANSAS HEALTH SYSTEM PAWNEE VALLEY CAMPUS (O, 22 beds) 923 Carroll Avenue, Larned, KS, Zip 67550–2429; tel. 620/285–3161; Melanie D. Urban, Administrator

| | | |
|---|---|---|
| Owned, leased, sponsored: | 4 hospitals | 1098 beds |
| Contract–managed: | 0 hospitals | 0 beds |
| Totals: | 4 hospitals | 1098 beds |

**2445: THEDACARE, INC.** (NP)
122 East College Avenue, Appleton, WI Zip 54911–5794, Mailing Address: P.O. Box 8025, 54912–8025, tel. 920/830–5889; Imran A. Andrabi, M.D., President and Chief Executive Officer
**(Moderately Centralized Health System)**

**WISCONSIN:** THEDA CARE MEDICAL CENTER – WILD ROSE (O, 25 beds) 601 Grove Avenue, Wild Rose, WI, Zip 54984–6903, Mailing Address: P.O. Box 243, 54984–0243, tel. 920/622–3257; Tammy Bending, Vice President
**Web address:** https://www.thedacare.org

THEDACARE MEDICAL CENTER–BERLIN (O, 25 beds) 225 Memorial Drive, Berlin, WI, Zip 54923–1295; tel. 920/361–1313; Tammy Bending, Vice President, Critical Access Hospital

THEDACARE MEDICAL CENTER–NEW LONDON (O, 25 beds) 1405 Mill Street, New London, WI, Zip 54961–0307, Mailing Address: P.O. Box 307, 54961–0307, tel. 920/531–2000; William Schmidt, President and Chief Executive Officer
**Web address:** www.thedacare.org

THEDACARE MEDICAL CENTER–SHAWANO (O, 22 beds) 100 County Road B, Shawano, WI, Zip 54166–2127; tel. 715/526–2111; William Schmidt, Chief Executive Officer
**Web address:** www.shawanomed.org

THEDACARE MEDICAL CENTER–WAUPACA (O, 25 beds) 800 Riverside Drive, Waupaca, WI, Zip 54981–1999; tel. 715/258–1000; David Corso, Vice President Critical Access Hospitals
**Web address:** www.riversidemedical.org

THEDACARE REGIONAL MEDICAL CENTER–APPLETON (O, 147 beds) 1818 North Meade Street, Appleton, WI, Zip 54911–3496; tel. 920/731–4101; Thomas J. Arquilla, Chief Strategy Officer

For explanation of codes following names, see page B2.
★ Indicates Type III membership in the American Hospital Association.

Section B

THEDACARE REGIONAL MEDICAL CENTER–NEENAH (O, 164 beds) 130 Second Street, Neenah, WI, Zip 54956–2883, Mailing Address: P.O. Box 2021, 54957–2021, tel. 920/729–3100; Mark Thompson, System Chief Financial Officer **Web address:** www.thedacare.org

| | | |
|---|---|---|
| Owned, leased, sponsored: | 7 hospitals | 433 beds |
| Contract–managed: | 0 hospitals | 0 beds |
| Totals: | 7 hospitals | 433 beds |

★**0643: THOMAS HEALTH SYSTEM, INC.** (NP)

4605 MacCorkle Avenue SW, South Charleston, WV Zip 25309–1311; tel. 304/766–3600; Daniel Lauffer, FACHE, President and Chief Executive Officer

**(Independent Hospital System)**

**WEST VIRGINIA:** SAINT FRANCIS HOSPITAL (O, 65 beds) 333 Laidley Street, Charleston, WV, Zip 25301–1628, Mailing Address: P.O. Box 471, 25322–0471, tel. 304/347–6500; Daniel Lauffer, FACHE, President and Chief Executive Officer

THOMAS MEMORIAL HOSPITAL (O, 214 beds) 4605 MacCorkle Avenue SW, South Charleston, WV, Zip 25309–1398; tel. 304/766–3600; Daniel Lauffer, FACHE, President and Chief Executive Officer **Web address:** www.thomashealth.org

| | | |
|---|---|---|
| Owned, leased, sponsored: | 2 hospitals | 279 beds |
| Contract–managed: | 0 hospitals | 0 beds |
| Totals: | 2 hospitals | 279 beds |

**0992: TIDALHEALTH** (IO)

100 East Carroll Street, Salisbury, MD Zip 21801–5422; tel. 410/546–6400; Steven E. Leonard, President and Chief Executive Officer

**DELAWARE:** TIDALHEALTH NANTICOKE (O, 99 beds) 801 Middleford Road, Seaford, DE, Zip 19973–3636; tel. 302/629–6611; Penny Short, R.N., President **Web address:** www.nanticoke.org

**MARYLAND:** TIDALHEALTH PENINSULA (O, 298 beds) 100 East Carroll Street, Salisbury, MD, Zip 21801–5422; tel. 410/546–6400; Steven E. Leonard, President and Chief Executive Officer **Web address:** www.peninsula.org

| | | |
|---|---|---|
| Owned, leased, sponsored: | 2 hospitals | 397 beds |
| Contract–managed: | 0 hospitals | 0 beds |
| Totals: | 2 hospitals | 397 beds |

★**0812: TIDELANDS HEALTH** (NP)

606 Black River Road, Georgetown, SC Zip 29440–3304, Mailing Address: P.O. Box 421718, 29442–4203, tel. 843/527–7000; Bruce P. Bailey, President and Chief Executive Officer

**SOUTH CAROLINA:** TIDELANDS GEORGETOWN MEMORIAL HOSPITAL (O, 136 beds) 606 Black River Road, Georgetown, SC, Zip 29440–3368, Drawer 421718, 29442–4203, tel. 843/527–7000; Bruce P. Bailey, Chief Executive Officer **Web address:** www.tidelandshealth.org

TIDELANDS WACCAMAW COMMUNITY HOSPITAL (O, 126 beds) 4070 Highway 17 Bypass, Murrells Inlet, SC, Zip 29576–5033, P O Drawer 3350, 29576–2673, tel. 843/652–1000; Bruce P. Bailey, Chief Executive Officer

| | | |
|---|---|---|
| Owned, leased, sponsored: | 2 hospitals | 262 beds |
| Contract–managed: | 0 hospitals | 0 beds |
| Totals: | 2 hospitals | 262 beds |

★**0910: TIFT REGIONAL HEALTH SYSTEM** (NP)

901 East 18th Street, Tifton, GA Zip 31794–3648; tel. 229/353–6100; Christopher Dorman, President and Chief Executive Officer

**(Independent Hospital System)**

**GEORGIA:** SOUTHWELL MEDICAL (O, 155 beds) 260 MJ Taylor Road, Adel, GA, Zip 31620–3485; tel. 229/896–8000; Christopher Dorman, Chief Executive Officer **Web address:** www.cookmedicalcenter.com

TIFT REGIONAL MEDICAL CENTER (O, 181 beds) 901 East 18th Street, Tifton, GA, Zip 31794–3648, Drawer 747, 31793–0747, tel. 229/382–7120; Christopher Dorman, President and Chief Executive Officer **Web address:** www.tiftregional.com

| | | |
|---|---|---|
| Owned, leased, sponsored: | 2 hospitals | 336 beds |
| Contract–managed: | 0 hospitals | 0 beds |
| Totals: | 2 hospitals | 336 beds |

★**1029: TOWER HEALTH** (NP)

Sixth Avenue and Spruce Street, West Reading, PA Zip 19611; tel. 610/988–8000; Clinton Matthews, President and Chief Executive Officer

**(Moderately Centralized Health System)**

**PENNSYLVANIA:** BRANDYWINE HOSPITAL (O, 169 beds) 201 Reeceville Road, Coatesville, PA, Zip 19320–1536; tel. 610/383–8000; Vik Acharya, M.P.H., Chief Executive Officer **Web address:** www.https://brandywine.towerhealth.org/

CHESTNUT HILL HOSPITAL (O, 212 beds) 8835 Germantown Avenue, Philadelphia, PA, Zip 19118–2718; tel. 215/248–8200; John D. . Cacciamani, M.D., Chief Executive Officer **Web address:** www.chhealthsystem.com

JENNERSVILLE HOSPITAL (O, 63 beds) 1015 West Baltimore Pike, West Grove, PA, Zip 19390–9459; tel. 610/869–1000; Claire Bradley. Mooney, R.N., President and Chief Executive Officer **Web address:** www.jennersville.com

PHOENIXVILLE HOSPITAL (O, 137 beds) 140 Nutt Road, Phoenixville, PA, Zip 19460–3900, Mailing Address: P.O. Box 3001, 19460–0916, tel. 610/983–1000; Stephen M. Tullman, President and Chief Executive Officer

POTTSTOWN HOSPITAL (O, 232 beds) 1600 East High Street, Pottstown, PA, Zip 19464–5093; tel. 610/327–7000; Richard Newell, Chief Executive Officer **Web address:** www.https://pottstown.towerhealth.org/

READING HOSPITAL (O, 732 beds) Sixth Avenue and Spruce Street, West Reading, PA, Zip 19611–1428, Mailing Address: P.O. Box 16052, 19612–6052, tel. 610/988–8000; William Jennings, President and Chief Executive Officer **Web address:** www.readinghospital.org

ST. CHRISTOPHER'S HOSPITAL FOR CHILDREN (O, 121 beds) 3601 A Street, Philadelphia, PA, Zip 19134–1043, 160 E. Erie Avenue, 19134–1011, tel. 215/427–5000; Donald Mueller, Chief Executive Officer

| | | |
|---|---|---|
| Owned, leased, sponsored: | 7 hospitals | 1666 beds |
| Contract–managed: | 0 hospitals | 0 beds |
| Totals: | 7 hospitals | 1666 beds |

★**0906: TRINITY HEALTH** (CO)

20555 Victor Parkway, Livonia, MI Zip 48152–7031; tel. 734/343–1000; Michael A. Slubowski, FACHE, President and Chief Executive Officer

**(Decentralized Health System)**

**CALIFORNIA:** SAINT AGNES MEDICAL CENTER (O, 436 beds) 1303 East Herndon Avenue, Fresno, CA, Zip 93720–3397; tel. 559/450–3000; Nancy Hollingsworth, R.N., MSN, President and Chief Executive Officer **Web address:** www.samc.com

**CONNECTICUT:** JOHNSON MEMORIAL HOSPITAL (O, 78 beds) 201 Chestnut Hill Road, Stafford Springs, CT, Zip 06076–4005; tel. 860/684–4251; Stuart E. Rosenberg, President

MOUNT SINAI REHABILITATION HOSPITAL (O, 32 beds) 490 Blue Hills Avenue, Hartford, CT, Zip 06112–1513; tel. 860/714–3500; Robert J. Krug, M.D., Chief Executive Officer **Web address:** www.stfranciscare.org

For explanation of codes following names, see page B2.
★ Indicates Type III membership in the American Hospital Association.

© 2021 AHA Guide

SAINT FRANCIS HOSPITAL AND MEDICAL CENTER (O, 412 beds) 114 Woodland Street, Hartford, CT, Zip 06105–1208; tel. 860/714–4000; John F. Rodis, M.D., President

SAINT MARY'S HOSPITAL (O, 187 beds) 56 Franklin Street, Waterbury, CT, Zip 06706–1281; tel. 203/709–6000; Steven E. Schneider, M.D., President
**Web address:** www.stmh.org

**DELAWARE:** ST. FRANCIS HOSPITAL (O, 154 beds) 701 North Clayton Street, Wilmington, DE, Zip 19805, Mailing Address: P.O. Box 2500, 19805–0500, tel. 302/421–4100; Brandon Harvath, President and Chief Operating Officer
**Web address:** www.stfrancishealthcare.org

**FLORIDA:** BARTOW REGIONAL MEDICAL CENTER (O, 72 beds) 2200 Osprey Boulevard, Bartow, FL, Zip 33830–3308; tel. 863/533–8111; Karen Kerr, R.N., President
**Web address:** www.bartowregional.com

BAYCARE ALLIANT HOSPITAL (S, 34 beds) 601 Main Street, MS#402, Dunedin, FL, Zip 34698–5848; tel. 727/736–9991; Jacqueline Arocho, Administrator
**Web address:** www.baycare.org

HOLY CROSS HOSPITAL (O, 365 beds) 4725 North Federal Highway, Fort Lauderdale, FL, Zip 33308–4668, Mailing Address: P.O. Box 23460, 33307–3460, tel. 954/771–8000; Mark Doyle, President and Chief Executive Officer
**Web address:** www.holy–cross.com

MEASE COUNTRYSIDE HOSPITAL (C, 311 beds) 3231 McMullen Booth Road, Safety Harbor, FL, Zip 34695–6607; tel. 727/725–6111; Matthew Novak, President

MEASE DUNEDIN HOSPITAL (C, 120 beds) 601 Main Street, Dunedin, FL, Zip 34698–5891; tel. 727/733–1111; Matthew Novak, President
**Web address:** www.mpmhealth.com

SOUTH FLORIDA BAPTIST HOSPITAL (S, 141 beds) 301 North Alexander Street, Plant City, FL, Zip 33563–4303; tel. 813/757–1200; Karen Kerr, R.N., President
**Web address:** www.https://baycare.org/sfbh

ST. ANTHONY'S HOSPITAL (S, 358 beds) 1200 Seventh Avenue North, Saint Petersburg, FL, Zip 33705–1388, Mailing Address: P.O. Box 12588, 33733–2588, tel. 727/825–1100; M. Scott Smith, President
**Web address:** www.stanthonys.com/

ST. JOSEPH'S HOSPITAL (S, 1062 beds) 3001 West Martin Luther King Jr. Boulevard, Tampa, FL, Zip 33607–6387, Mailing Address: P.O. Box 4227, 33677–4227, tel. 813/870–4000; Kimberly Guy, President

WINTER HAVEN HOSPITAL (S, 361 beds) 200 Avenue F NE, Winter Haven, FL, Zip 33881–4193; tel. 863/293–1121; Stephen A. Nierman, President
**Web address:** www.winterhavenhospital.org

**GEORGIA:** ST. MARY'S GOOD SAMARITAN HOSPITAL (O, 25 beds) 5401 Lake Oconee Parkway, Greensboro, GA, Zip 30642–4232; tel. 706/453–7331; Tanya M. Adcock, President

ST. MARY'S HEALTH CARE SYSTEM (O, 173 beds) 1230 Baxter Street, Athens, GA, Zip 30606–3791; tel. 706/389–3000; D. Montez. Carter, Chief Executive Officer
**Web address:** www.stmarysathens.com

ST. MARY'S SACRED HEART HOSPITAL (O, 41 beds) 367 Clear Creek Parkway, Lavonia, GA, Zip 30553–4173; tel. 706/356–7800; Jeff English, President
**Web address:** www.stmaryssacredheart.org/

**IDAHO:** SAINT ALPHONSUS MEDICAL CENTER – NAMPA (O, 106 beds) 4300 East Flamingo Avenue, Nampa, ID, Zip 83686–6008; tel. 208/205–1000; Travis Leach, President

SAINT ALPHONSUS REGIONAL MEDICAL CENTER (O, 392 beds) 1055 N Curtis Rd , Boise, ID, Zip 83706–1309, 1055 North Curtis Road, 83706–1309, tel. 208/367–2121; David M. McFadyen, FACHE, President
**Web address:** www.saintalphonsus.org

**ILLINOIS:** GOTTLIEB MEMORIAL HOSPITAL (O, 166 beds) 701 West North Avenue, Melrose Park, IL, Zip 60160–1612; tel. 708/681–3200; Mary Elizabeth. Cleary, President
**Web address:** www.gottliebhospital.org

LOYOLA UNIVERSITY MEDICAL CENTER (O, 524 beds) 2160 South First Avenue, Maywood, IL, Zip 60153–3328; tel. 708/216–9000; Tad A. Gomez, President

MACNEAL HOSPITAL (O, 358 beds) 3249 South Oak Park Avenue, Berwyn, IL, Zip 60402–0715; tel. 708/783–9100; Mary Elizabeth. Cleary, President
**Web address:** www.macneal.com

MERCY HOSPITAL AND MEDICAL CENTER (O, 354 beds) 2525 South Michigan Avenue, Chicago, IL, Zip 60616–2333; tel. 312/567–2000; Carol L. Schneider, President and Chief Executive Officer
**Web address:** www.mercy–chicago.org

**INDIANA:** PLYMOUTH MEDICAL CENTER (O, 48 beds) 1915 Lake Avenue, Plymouth, IN, Zip 46563–9366, Mailing Address: P.O. Box 670, 46563–0670, tel. 574/948–4000; Christopher J. Karam, President

SAINT JOSEPH HEALTH SYSTEM (O, 300 beds) 5215 Holy Cross Parkway, Mishawaka, IN, Zip 46545–1469; tel. 574/335–5000; Chad Towner, Chief Executive Officer
**Web address:** www.sjmed.com

**IOWA:** FRANKLIN GENERAL HOSPITAL (C, 77 beds) 1720 Central Avenue East, Suite A, Hampton, IA, Zip 50441–1867; tel. 641/456–5000; Kim Price, Chief Executive Officer
**Web address:** www.franklingeneral.com

HANCOCK COUNTY HEALTH SYSTEM (C, 25 beds) 532 First Street NW, Britt, IA, Zip 50423–1227; tel. 641/843–5000; Laura Zwiefel, Chief Executive Officer

HANSEN FAMILY HOSPITAL (C, 21 beds) 920 South Oak, Iowa Falls, IA, Zip 50126–9506; tel. 641/648–4631; Douglas E. Morse, Chief Executive Officer and Administrator
**Web address:** www.hansenfamilyhospital.com

HAWARDEN REGIONAL HEALTHCARE (C, 20 beds) 1111 11th Street, Hawarden, IA, Zip 51023–1999; tel. 712/551–3100; Jayson Pullman, Chief Executive Officer

KOSSUTH REGIONAL HEALTH CENTER (C, 23 beds) 1515 South Phillips Street, Algona, IA, Zip 50511–3649; tel. 515/295–2451; Darlene M. Elbert, R.N., MS, Chief Executive Officer and Chief Nursing Officer
**Web address:** www.krhc.org

MERCYONE CEDAR FALLS MEDICAL CENTER (C, 50 beds) 515 College Street, Cedar Falls, IA, Zip 50613–2500; tel. 319/268–3000; MaryJo Kavalier, Administrator
**Web address:** www.MercyOne.org

MERCYONE CLINTON MEDICAL CENTER (O, 193 beds) 1410 North Fourth Street, Clinton, IA, Zip 52732–2940; tel. 563/244–5555; Amy Berentes, R.N., MSN, Executive Vice President and Chief Operating Officer
**Web address:** www.mercyclinton.com

MERCYONE DUBUQUE MEDICAL CENTER (O, 234 beds) 250 Mercy Drive, Dubuque, IA, Zip 52001–7360; tel. 563/589–8000; Kay Takes, R.N., President
**Web address:** www.mercydubuque.com

MERCYONE DYERSVILLE MEDICAL CENTER (O, 20 beds) 1111 Third Street SW, Dyersville, IA, Zip 52040–1725; tel. 563/875–7101; Kay Takes, R.N., President
**Web address:** www.mercydubuque.com/mercy–dyersville

MERCYONE ELKADER MEDICAL CENTER (C, 15 beds) 901 Davidson Street NW, Elkader, IA, Zip 52043–9015; tel. 563/245–7000; Brooke Kensinger, Chief Executive Officer
**Web address:** www.centralcommunityhospital.com

MERCYONE NEW HAMPTON MEDICAL CENTER (O, 11 beds) 308 North Maple Avenue, New Hampton, IA, Zip 50659–1142; tel. 641/394–4121; Aaron Flugum, Chief Executive Officer
**Web address:** www.mercynewhampton.com

MERCYONE NORTH IOWA MEDICAL CENTER (O, 228 beds) 1000 Fourth Street SW, Mason City, IA, Zip 50401–2800; tel. 641/428–7000; Rod G. Schlader, President and Chief Executive Officer

MERCYONE OELWEIN MEDICAL CENTER (C, 56 beds) 201 Eighth Avenue SE, Oelwein, IA, Zip 50662–2447; tel. 319/283–6000; Jill Groth, Site Administrator
**Web address:** www.wheatoniowa.org

MERCYONE PRIMGHAR MEDICAL CENTER (O, 11 beds) 255 North Welch Avenue, Primghar, IA, Zip 51245–7765, Mailing Address: P.O. Box 528, 51245–0528, tel. 712/957–2300; Misty Dulin, CAH, Director
**Web address:** www.baumharmon.org

MERCYONE SIOUXLAND MEDICAL CENTER (O, 199 beds) 801 Fifth Street, Sioux City, IA, Zip 51101–1326, Mailing Address: P.O. Box 3168, 51102–3168, tel. 712/279–2010; Beth Hughes, President
**Web address:** www.mercysiouxcity.com

For explanation of codes following names, see page B2.
★ Indicates Type III membership in the American Hospital Association.

Section B

MERCYONE WATERLOO MEDICAL CENTER (C, 240 beds) 3421 West Ninth Street, Waterloo, IA, Zip 50702–5401; tel. 319/272–8000; Jack Dusenbery, President and Chief Executive Officer
**Web address:** www.MercyOne.org

MITCHELL COUNTY REGIONAL HEALTH CENTER (C, 25 beds) 616 North Eighth Street, Osage, IA, Zip 50461–1498; tel. 641/732–6000; Shelly Russell, Chief Executive Officer

PALO ALTO COUNTY HEALTH SYSTEM (C, 47 beds) 3201 First Street, Emmetsburg, IA, Zip 50536–2516; tel. 712/852–5500; Brett Antczak, Chief Executive Officer
**Web address:** www.pachs.com

REGIONAL HEALTH SERVICES OF HOWARD COUNTY (C, 19 beds) 235 Eighth Avenue West, Cresco, IA, Zip 52136–1098; tel. 563/547–2101; Robin M. Schluter, Chief Executive Officer

**MARYLAND:** HOLY CROSS GERMANTOWN HOSPITAL (O, 72 beds) 19801 Observation Drive, Germantown, MD, Zip 20876–4070; tel. 301/557–6000; Doug Ryder, President
**Web address:** www.holycrosshealth.org/germantown

HOLY CROSS HOSPITAL (O, 367 beds) 1500 Forest Glen Road, Silver Spring, MD, Zip 20910–1487; tel. 301/754–7000; Louis Damiano, M.D., President
**Web address:** www.holycrosshealth.org

**MASSACHUSETTS:** FARREN CARE CENTER (O, 72 beds) 340 Montague City Road, Turners Falls, MA, Zip 01376–9983; tel. 413/774–3111; James Clifford, Administrator

MERCY MEDICAL CENTER (O, 329 beds) 271 Carew Street, Springfield, MA, Zip 01104–2398, Mailing Address: P.O. Box 9012, 01102–9012, tel. 413/748–9000; Deborah Bitsoli, CPA, President
**Web address:** www.mercycares.com

**MICHIGAN:** MERCY HEALTH HACKLEY CAMPUS (O, 366 beds) 1700 Clinton Street, Muskegon, MI, Zip 49442–5502, Mailing Address: P.O. Box 3302, 49443–3302, tel. 231/726–3511; Gary Allore, President
**Web address:** www.mercyhealthmuskegon.com

MERCY HEALTH SAINT MARY'S (O, 283 beds) 200 Jefferson Avenue Southeast, Grand Rapids, MI, Zip 49503–4598, 200 Jefferson Avenue SE, 49503–4598, tel. 616/685–5000; David Baumgartner, M.D., Interim President

MERCY HEALTH, LAKESHORE CAMPUS (O, 24 beds) 72 South State Street, Shelby, MI, Zip 49455–1299; tel. 231/861–2156; John T. Foss, Vice President, Operations
**Web address:** www.mercyhealthmuskegon.com

ST. JOSEPH MERCY ANN ARBOR (O, 509 beds) 5301 Mcauley Drive, Ypsilanti, MI, Zip 48197–1051, Mailing Address: P.O. Box 995, Ann Arbor, 48106–0995, tel. 734/712–3456; Alonzo T. Lewis, Senior Vice President, Operations

ST. JOSEPH MERCY CHELSEA (O, 96 beds) 775 South Main Street, Chelsea, MI, Zip 48118–1383; tel. 734/593–6000; Nancy Kay. Graebner, President and Chief Executive Officer
**Web address:** www.cch.org

ST. JOSEPH MERCY LIVINGSTON HOSPITAL (O, 38 beds) 620 Byron Road, Howell, MI, Zip 48843–1093; tel. 517/545–6000; John F. O'Malley, FACHE, President
**Web address:** www.stjoeslivingston.org/livingston

ST. JOSEPH MERCY OAKLAND (O, 396 beds) 44405 Woodward Avenue, Pontiac, MI, Zip 48341–5023; tel. 248/858–3000; Shannon Striebich, Chief Executive Officer
**Web address:** www.stjoesoakland.com

ST. MARY MERCY HOSPITAL (O, 304 beds) 36475 Five Mile Road, Livonia, MI, Zip 48154–1988; tel. 734/655–4800; David A. Spivey, President and Chief Executive Officer

**NEBRASKA:** MERCYONE OAKLAND MEDICAL CENTER (O, 18 beds) 601 East Second Street, Oakland, NE, Zip 68045–1499; tel. 402/685–5601; Rita Going, Director of Critical Access Hospitals
**Web address:** www.oaklandhospital.org

PENDER COMMUNITY HOSPITAL (C, 61 beds) 100 Hospital Drive , Pender, NE, Zip 68047–0100, Mailing Address: P.O. Box 100, 68047–0100, tel. 402/385–3083; Melissa Kelly, Chief Executive Officer and Chief Financial Officer
**Web address:** www.pendercommunityhospital.com

**NEW JERSEY:** ST. FRANCIS MEDICAL CENTER (O, 142 beds) 601 Hamilton Avenue, Trenton, NJ, Zip 08629–1986; tel. 609/599–5000; Daniel P. Moen, President

**NEW YORK:** BURDETT BIRTH CENTER (O, 15 beds) 2215 Burdett Avenue, Suite 200, Troy, NY, Zip 12180–2466; tel. 518/271–3393; JoAnn Lionarons, Director
**Web address:** www.burdettbirthcenter.org/

SAMARITAN HOSPITAL – MAIN CAMPUS (O, 265 beds) 2215 Burdett Avenue, Troy, NY, Zip 12180–2475; tel. 518/271–3300; Michael S. Finegan, President, Acute Care
**Web address:** www.sphp.com/sam

ST. JOSEPH'S HOSPITAL HEALTH CENTER (O, 451 beds) 301 Prospect Avenue, Syracuse, NY, Zip 13203–1807; tel. 315/448–5111; Leslie Paul. Luke, President and Chief Executive Officer

ST. PETER'S HOSPITAL (O, 442 beds) 315 South Manning Boulevard, Albany, NY, Zip 12208–1789; tel. 518/525–1550; Michael S. Finegan, President, Acute Care
**Web address:** https://www.sphp.com/location/st-peters-hospital

SUNNYVIEW REHABILITATION HOSPITAL (O, 115 beds) 1270 Belmont Avenue, Schenectady, NY, Zip 12308–2104; tel. 518/382–4500; Edward Eisenman, Chief Executive Officer
**Web address:** www.sunnyview.org

**NORTH CAROLINA:** ST. JOSEPH OF THE PINES HOSPITAL (O, 204 beds) 590 Central Drive, Southern Pines, NC, Zip 28387; tel. 910/246–1000; Ken Cormier, President and Chief Executive Officer

**OHIO:** MOUNT CARMEL NEW ALBANY SURGICAL HOSPITAL (O, 60 beds) 7333 Smith's Mill Road, New Albany, OH, Zip 43054–9291; tel. 614/775–6600; Diane Doucette, R.N., President
**Web address:** www.mountcarmelhealth.com

MOUNT CARMEL ST. ANN'S (O, 281 beds) 500 South Cleveland Avenue, Westerville, OH, Zip 43081–8998; tel. 614/898–4000; Kim Unhee, President
**Web address:** www.mountcarmelhealth.com

MOUNT CARMEL WEST (O, 488 beds) 793 West State Street, Columbus, OH, Zip 43222–1551; tel. 614/234–5000; Sean McKibben, President and Chief Operating Officer

**OREGON:** SAINT ALPHONSUS MEDICAL CENTER – BAKER CITY (S, 25 beds) 3325 Pocahontas Road, Baker City, OR, Zip 97814–1464; tel. 541/523–6461; Priscilla Lynn, President and Chief Executive Officer
**Web address:** https://www.saintalphonsus.org/bakercity

SAINT ALPHONSUS MEDICAL CENTER – ONTARIO (S, 35 beds) 351 SW Ninth Street, Ontario, OR, Zip 97914–2693; tel. 541/881–7000; Kenneth Hart, President
**Web address:** www.saintalphonsus.org/ontario

**PENNSYLVANIA:** MERCY CATHOLIC MEDICAL CENTER – MERCY FITZGERALD CAMPUS (O, 340 beds) 1500 Lansdowne Avenue, Suite 100, Darby, PA, Zip 19023–1200; tel. 610/237–4000; Christopher Cullom, President

NAZARETH HOSPITAL (O, 162 beds) 2601 Holme Avenue, Philadelphia, PA, Zip 19152–2096; tel. 215/335–6000; Michael Magro, D.O., President
**Web address:** www.nazarethhospital.org

ST. MARY MEDICAL CENTER (O, 353 beds) 1201 Langhorne–Newtown Road, Langhorne, PA, Zip 19047–1201; tel. 215/710–2000; Lawrence Brilliant, M.D., Vice President and Chief Medical Officer

| | | |
|---|---|---|
| **Owned, leased, sponsored:** | 59 hospitals | 13327 beds |
| **Contract–managed:** | 15 hospitals | 1110 beds |
| **Totals:** | 74 hospitals | 14437 beds |

**★9255: TRUMAN MEDICAL CENTERS** (NP)
2301 Holmes Street, Kansas City, MO Zip 64108–2677; tel. 816/404–1000; Charlie Shields, Chief Executive Officer
**(Independent Hospital System)**

**MISSOURI:** TRUMAN MEDICAL CENTER–HOSPITAL HILL (O, 249 beds) 2301 Holmes Street, Kansas City, MO, Zip 64108–2640; tel. 816/404–1000; Charlie Shields, President and Chief Executive Officer

For explanation of codes following names, see page B2.
★ Indicates Type III membership in the American Hospital Association.

TRUMAN MEDICAL CENTER–LAKEWOOD (O, 298 beds) 7900 Lee's Summit Road, Kansas City, MO, Zip 64139–1236; tel. 816/404–7000; Charlie Shields, Chief Executive Officer
**Web address:** www.trumed.org

| Owned, leased, sponsored: | 2 hospitals | 547 beds |
|---|---|---|
| Contract–managed: | 0 hospitals | 0 beds |
| **Totals:** | **2 hospitals** | **547 beds** |

## 9195: U. S. INDIAN HEALTH SERVICE (FG)

801 Thompson Avenue, Rockville, MD Zip 20852–1627; tel. 301/443–1083; Rear Admiral, Michael Weahkee, Assistant Surgeon General, USPHS Director, Indian Health Service
**(Independent Hospital System)**

**ARIZONA:** CHINLE COMPREHENSIVE HEALTH CARE FACILITY (O, 60 beds) Highway 191, Hospital Road, Chinle, AZ, Zip 86503, Highway 191 Hospital Drive, 86503–8000, tel. 928/674–7001; Darlene Chee, Acting Chief Executive Officer

HOPI HEALTH CARE CENTER (O, 15 beds) Highway 264 Mile Marker 388, Keams Canyon, AZ, Zip 86042, Mailing Address: P.O. Box 4000, Polacca, 86042–4000, tel. 928/737–6000; Mose Herne, Chief Executive Officer
**Web address:** www.ihs.gov/index.asp

SAN CARLOS APACHE HEALTHCARE CORPORATION (O, 12 beds) 103 Medicine Way Road, Peridot, AZ, Zip 85542; tel. 928/475–1400; Victoria D. Began, R.N., MS, President and Chief Executive Officer
**Web address:** www.ihs.gov

U. S. PUBLIC HEALTH SERVICE INDIAN HOSPITAL–SELLS (O, 12 beds) Highway 86 & Topawa Road, Sells, AZ, Zip 85634, Mailing Address: P.O. Box 548, 85634–0548, tel. 520/383–7251; Troy Klarkowski, Administrator and Chief Executive Officer

U. S. PUBLIC HEALTH SERVICE INDIAN HOSPITAL–WHITERIVER (O, 35 beds) 200 West Hospital Drive, Whiteriver, AZ, Zip 85941–0860, State Route 73, Box 860, 85941–0860, tel. 928/338–4911; Michelle Martinez, Chief Executive Officer
**Web address:** www.ihs.gov

U. S. PUBLIC HEALTH SERVICE INDIAN HOSPITAL (O, 20 beds) 12033 Agency Road, Parker, AZ, Zip 85344–7718; tel. 928/669–2137; Elizabeth Helsel, Chief Executive Officer

U. S. PUBLIC HEALTH SERVICE PHOENIX INDIAN MEDICAL CENTER (O, 127 beds) 4212 North 16th Street, Phoenix, AZ, Zip 85016–5389; tel. 602/263–1200; Deanna Dick, Chief Executive Officer
**Web address:** www.ihs.gov

**MARYLAND:** NATIONAL INSTITUTES OF HEALTH CLINICAL CENTER (O, 121 beds) 9000 Rockville Pike, Building 10, Room 6–2551, Bethesda, MD, Zip 20892–1504; tel. 301/496–4000; James K. Gilman, M.D., Chief Executive Officer
**Web address:** www.clinicalcenter.nih.gov

**MINNESOTA:** RED LAKE INDIAN HEALTH SERVICE HOSPITAL (O, 19 beds) 24760 Hospital Drive, Red Lake, MN, Zip 56671, Mailing Address: P.O. Box 497, 56671–0497, tel. 218/679–3912; Norine Smith, Chief Executive Officer
**Web address:** www.rlnnredlakehospital.com/

U. S. PUBLIC HEALTH SERVICE INDIAN HOSPITAL (O, 9 beds) 425 7th Street North West, Cass Lake, MN, Zip 56633; tel. 218/335–3200; Louis P. Erdrich, Acting Chief Executive Officer

**MONTANA:** BLACKFEET COMMUNITY HOSPITAL (O, 25 beds) 760 New Hospital Circle, Saint Mary, MT, Zip 59417–0760, Mailing Address: P.O. Box 760, Browning, 59417–0760, tel. 406/338–6100; Garland Stiffarm, Chief Executive Officer
**Web address:** www.ihs.gov

CROW/NORTHERN CHEYENNE HOSPITAL (O, 24 beds) 10110 South 7650 East, Crow Agency, MT, Zip 59022–0009, Mailing Address: P.O. Box 9, 59022–0009, tel. 406/638–2626; Darren Crowe, Chief Executive Officer
**Web address:** https://www.ihs.gov/billings/healthcarefacilities/crow/

FORT BELKNAP SERVICE UNIT (O, 6 beds) 669 Agency Main Street, Harlem, MT, Zip 59526–9455; tel. 406/353–3100; Gregory Smith, M.D., Chief Executive Officer
**Web address:** www.ihs.gov

**NEW MEXICO:** ACOMA–CANONCITO–LAGUNA HOSPITAL (O, 6 beds) 80B Veterans Boulevard, Acoma, NM, Zip 87034, Mailing Address: P.O. Box 130, San Fidel, 87049–0130, tel. 505/552–5300; Melody Price–Yonts, Chief Executive Officer
**Web address:** www.ihs.gov/albuquerque/index.cfm?module=dsp_abq_acoma_canoncito_laguna

GALLUP INDIAN MEDICAL CENTER (O, 57 beds) 516 East Nizhoni Boulevard, Gallup, NM, Zip 87301–5748, Mailing Address: P.O. Box 1337, 87301, tel. 505/722–1000; Sayeeda Hyder, Acting Chief Executive Officer

MESCALERO PUBLIC HEALTH SERVICE INDIAN HOSPITAL (O, 13 beds) 318 Abalone Loop, Mescalero, NM, Zip 88340, Box 210, 88340–0210, tel. 505/464–3801; Dorlynn Simmons, Chief Executive Officer
**Web address:** www.ihs.gov

NORTHERN NAVAJO MEDICAL CENTER (O, 68 beds) Highway 491 North, Shiprock, NM, Zip 87420–0160, Mailing Address: P.O. Box 160, 87420–0160, tel. 505/368–6001; Fannessa Comer, Chief Executive Officer
**Web address:** www.ihs.gov/

PHS SANTA FE INDIAN HOSPITAL (O, 4 beds) 1700 Cerrillos Road, Santa Fe, NM, Zip 87505–3554; tel. 505/988–9821; Leslie Dye, Chief Executive Officer

U. S. PUBLIC HEALTH SERVICE INDIAN HOSPITAL (O, 12 beds) Route 9 and State Road 371, Crownpoint, NM, Zip 87313, Mailing Address: P.O. Box 358, 87313–0358, tel. 505/786–5291; Anslem Roanhorse, Chief Executive Officer
**Web address:** www.ihs.gov

U. S. PUBLIC HEALTH SERVICE INDIAN HOSPITAL (O, 32 beds) Route 301 North B Street, Zuni, NM, Zip 87327, Mailing Address: P.O. Box 467, 87327–0467, tel. 505/782–4431; Jean Othole, Chief Executive Officer
**Web address:** www.ihs.gov

**NORTH DAKOTA:** INDIAN HEALTH SERVICE – QUENTIN N. BURDICK MEMORIAL HEALTH CARE FACILITY (O, 29 beds) 1300 Hospital Loop, Belcourt, ND, Zip 58316, Mailing Address: P.O. Box 160, 58316–0160, tel. 701/477–6111; Shelly Harris, Chief Executive Officer
**Web address:** www.ihs.gov

STANDING ROCK SERVICE UNIT, FORT YATES HOSPITAL, INDIAN HEALTH SERVICE, DHHS (O, 14 beds) 10 North River Road, Fort Yates, ND, Zip 58538, Mailing Address: P.O. Box 'J', 58538, tel. 701/854–3831; Jana Gipp, Chief Executive Officer
**Web address:** www.ihs.gov

**OKLAHOMA:** CLAREMORE INDIAN HOSPITAL (O, 44 beds) 101 South Moore Avenue, Claremore, OK, Zip 74017–5091; tel. 918/342–6200; George Valliere, Chief Executive Officer

LAWTON INDIAN HOSPITAL (O, 26 beds) 1515 Lawrie Tatum Road, Lawton, OK, Zip 73507–3099; tel. 580/353–0350; Lenora Littledeer, R.N., Chief Executive Officer and Chief Nursing Officer
**Web address:** www.ihs.gov

**SOUTH DAKOTA:** INDIAN HEALTH SERVICE HOSPITAL (O, 9 beds) 3200 Canyon Lake Drive, Rapid City, SD, Zip 57702–8197; tel. 605/355–2280; Kevin J. Stiffarm, Chief Executive Officer
**Web address:** www.ihs.gov

U. S. PUBLIC HEALTH SERVICE INDIAN HOSPITAL (O, 8 beds) 317 Main Street, Eagle Butte, SD, Zip 57625–1012, Mailing Address: P.O. Box 1012, 57625–1012, tel. 605/964–7724; Charles Fisher, Chief Executive Officer

U. S. PUBLIC HEALTH SERVICE INDIAN HOSPITAL (O, 45 beds) East Highway 18, Pine Ridge, SD, Zip 57770, Mailing Address: P.O. Box 1201, 57770–1201, tel. 605/867–5131; Travis Scott, Service Unit Director
**Web address:** www.ihs.gov

U. S. PUBLIC HEALTH SERVICE INDIAN HOSPITAL (O, 35 beds) Highway 18, Soldier Creek Road, Rosebud, SD, Zip 57570; tel. 605/747–2231; Kathey Wilson, Acting Chief Executive Officer
**Web address:** www.ihs.gov

| Owned, leased, sponsored: | 28 hospitals | 887 beds |
|---|---|---|
| Contract–managed: | 0 hospitals | 0 beds |
| **Totals:** | **28 hospitals** | **887 beds** |

## ★9105: UAB HEALTH SYSTEM (NP)

500 22nd Street South, Suite 408, Birmingham, AL Zip 35233–3110; tel. 205/975–5362; Reid F. Jones, Chief Executive Officer
**(Centralized Physician/Insurance Health System)**

For explanation of codes following names, see page B2.
★ Indicates Type III membership in the American Hospital Association.

Section B

**ALABAMA**: BRYAN W. WHITFIELD MEMORIAL HOSPITAL (C, 47 beds) 105 U S Highway 80 East, Demopolis, AL, Zip 36732–3616, Mailing Address: P.O. Box 890, 36732–0890, tel. 334/289–4000; Douglas L. Brewer, Chief Executive Officer
**Web address:** www.bwwmh.com

MEDICAL WEST (O, 231 beds) 995 Ninth Avenue SW, Bessemer, AL, Zip 35022–4527; tel. 205/481–7000; Brian Keith. Pennington, President and Chief Executive Officer

UNIVERSITY OF ALABAMA HOSPITAL (O, 1188 beds) 619 19th Street South, Birmingham, AL, Zip 35249–1900; tel. 205/934–4011; Reid F. Jones, Chief Executive Officer
**Web address:** www.uabmedicine.org

| | | |
|---|---|---|
| Owned, leased, sponsored: | 2 hospitals | 1419 beds |
| Contract–managed: | 1 hospitals | 47 beds |
| Totals: | 3 hospitals | 1466 beds |

## ◇0082: UC HEALTH (NP)
3200 Burnet Avenue, Cincinnati, OH Zip 45229–3019; tel. 513/585–6000; Richard P. Lofgren, M.D., M.P.H., President and Chief Executive Officer
**(Moderately Centralized Health System)**

**OHIO**: DANIEL DRAKE CENTER FOR POST ACUTE CARE (O, 202 beds) 151 West Galbraith Road, Cincinnati, OH, Zip 45216–1015; tel. 513/418–2500; Lafe Bauer, Vice President, Post Acute Care Services and Chief Administrative Officer
**Web address:** www.uchealth.com/danieldrakecenter/

UNIVERSITY OF CINCINNATI MEDICAL CENTER (O, 577 beds) 234 Goodman Street, Cincinnati, OH, Zip 45219–2316; tel. 513/584–1000; Ann Smith, Senior Vice President, Inpatient Services and Interim Chief Administrative Officer

WEST CHESTER HOSPITAL (O, 174 beds) 7700 University Drive, West Chester, OH, Zip 45069–2505; tel. 513/298–3000; Tom G. Daskalakis, Chief Administrative Officer
**Web address:** www.uchealth.com/westchesterhospital

| | | |
|---|---|---|
| Owned, leased, sponsored: | 3 hospitals | 953 beds |
| Contract–managed: | 0 hospitals | 0 beds |
| Totals: | 3 hospitals | 953 beds |

## ★0381: UCHEALTH (NP)
2315 East Harmony Road, Suite 200, Fort Collins, CO Zip 80528–8620; tel. 970/495–7000; Elizabeth B. Concordia, President and Chief Executive Officer
**(Moderately Centralized Health System)**

**COLORADO**: UCHEALTH BROOMFIELD HOSPITAL (O, 40 beds) 11820 Destination Drive, Broomfield, CO, Zip 80021; tel. 303/460–6000; Lonnie Cramer, President
**Web address:** www.uchealth.org/pages/OHAM/OrgUnitDetails.aspx?

UCHEALTH GRANDVIEW HOSPITAL (O, 22 beds) 5623 Pulpit Peak View, Colorado Springs, CO, Zip 80918; tel. 719/272–3600; Joel P. Yuhas, FACHE, Chief Executive Officer
**Web address:** https://www.uchealth.org/Pages/OHAM/OrgUnitDetails.aspx?OrganizationalUnitId=514

UCHEALTH GREELEY (O, 25 beds) 6767 29th Street, Greeley, CO, Zip 80634–5474; tel. 970/652–2000; Marilyn Schock, President
**Web address:** https://www.uchealth.org/locations/uchealth–greeley–medical–clinic/

UCHEALTH HIGHLANDS RANCH HOSPITAL (O, 72 beds) 1500 Park Central Drive, Highlands Ranch, CO, Zip 80129–6688; tel. 720/848–0000; Diane M. Cookson, President
**Web address:** https://www.uchealth.org/locations/uchealth–highlands–ranch–hospital/

UCHEALTH LONGS PEAK HOSPITAL (O, 51 beds) 1750 East Ken Pratt Boulevard, Longmont, CO, Zip 80504–5311; tel. 970/237–7850; Lonnie Cramer, President

UCHEALTH MEDICAL CENTER OF THE ROCKIES (O, 220 beds) 2500 Rocky Mountain Avenue, Loveland, CO, Zip 80538–9004; tel. 970/624–2500; Kevin L. Unger, Ph.D., FACHE, President and Chief Executive Officer
**Web address:** www.medctrrockies.org

UCHEALTH MEMORIAL HOSPITAL (L, 459 beds) 1400 East Boulder Street, Colorado Springs, CO, Zip 80909–5599; tel. 719/365–5000; Joel P. Yuhas, FACHE, President and Chief Executive Officer
**Web address:** www.uchealth.org/southerncolorado

UCHEALTH POUDRE VALLEY HOSPITAL (O, 305 beds) 1024 South Lemay Avenue, Fort Collins, CO, Zip 80524–3998, 2315 East Harmony Road, Suite 200, 80528, tel. 970/495–7000; Kevin L. Unger, Ph.D., FACHE, President and Chief Executive Officer

UCHEALTH YAMPA VALLEY MEDICAL CENTER (O, 39 beds) 1024 Central Park Drive, Steamboat Springs, CO, Zip 80487–8813; tel. 970/879–1322; Soniya Fidler, MS, President
**Web address:** https://www.uchealth.org/locations/uchealth–yampa–valley–medical–center/

UNIVERSITY OF COLORADO HOSPITAL (O, 829 beds) 12401 East 17th Avenue, MS F417, Aurora, CO, Zip 80045–2545; tel. 720/848–0000; Christopher A. Gessner, President and Chief Executive Officer

| | | |
|---|---|---|
| Owned, leased, sponsored: | 10 hospitals | 2062 beds |
| Contract–managed: | 0 hospitals | 0 beds |
| Totals: | 10 hospitals | 2062 beds |

## ★0111: UF HEALTH SHANDS (NP)
1600 SW Archer Road, Gainesville, FL Zip 32610–0326; tel. 352/733–1500; Edward Jimenez, Chief Executive Officer
**(Moderately Centralized Health System)**

**FLORIDA**: LEESBURG REGIONAL MEDICAL CENTER (O, 329 beds) 600 East Dixie Avenue, Leesburg, FL, Zip 34748–5999; tel. 352/323–5762; Donald G. Henderson, FACHE, President and Chief Executive Officer
**Web address:** www.centralfloridahealth.org

THE VILLAGES REGIONAL HOSPITAL (O, 307 beds) 1451 El Camino Real, The Villages, FL, Zip 32159–0041; tel. 352/751–8000; Donald G. Henderson, FACHE, President and Chief Executive Officer
**Web address:** www.cfhalliance.org

UF HEALTH JACKSONVILLE (O, 644 beds) 655 West Eighth Street, Jacksonville, FL, Zip 32209–6595; tel. 904/244–0411; Leon L. Haley Jr, M.D., Chief Executive Officer

UF HEALTH SHANDS HOSPITAL (O, 1015 beds) 1600 SW Archer Road, Gainesville, FL, Zip 32610–3003, Mailing Address: P.O. 100326, 32610–0326, tel. 352/265–0111; Edward Jimenez, Chief Executive Officer
**Web address:** www.https://ufhealth.org/

| | | |
|---|---|---|
| Owned, leased, sponsored: | 4 hospitals | 2295 beds |
| Contract–managed: | 0 hospitals | 0 beds |
| Totals: | 4 hospitals | 2295 beds |

## ★0224: UMASS MEMORIAL HEALTH CARE, INC. (NP)
1 Biotech Park, Worcester, MA Zip 01605–2982; tel. 508/334–0100; Eric Dickson, M.D., President and Chief Executive Officer
**(Centralized Physician/Insurance Health System)**

**MASSACHUSETTS**: UMASS MEMORIAL HEALTHALLIANCE–CLINTON HOSPITAL (O, 152 beds) 60 Hospital Road, Leominster, MA, Zip 01453–2205; tel. 978/466–2000; Steven P. Roach, FACHE, Interim Chief Executive Officer

UMASS MEMORIAL MEDICAL CENTER (O, 671 beds) 119 Belmont Street, Worcester, MA, Zip 01605–2982; tel. 508/334–1000; Michael Gustafson, M.D., President
**Web address:** www.umassmemorial.org

UMASS MEMORIAL–MARLBOROUGH HOSPITAL (O, 67 beds) 157 Union ST, Marlborough, MA, Zip 01752–1297; tel. 508/481–5000; Steven P. Roach, FACHE, President and Chief Executive Officer
**Web address:** www.marlboroughhospital.org

| | | |
|---|---|---|
| Owned, leased, sponsored: | 3 hospitals | 890 beds |
| Contract–managed: | 0 hospitals | 0 beds |
| Totals: | 3 hospitals | 890 beds |

For explanation of codes following names, see page B2.
★ Indicates Type III membership in the American Hospital Association.

## ★0901: UNC HEALTH CARE (NP)

101 Manning Drive, Chapel Hill, NC Zip 27514–4220; tel. 919/966–4131; Wesley Burks, M.D., Chief Executive Officer **(Moderately Centralized Health System)**

**NORTH CAROLINA:** CALDWELL UNC HEALTH CARE (O, 82 beds) 321 Mulberry Street SW, Lenoir, NC, Zip 28645–5720, Mailing Address: P.O. Box 1890, 28645–1890, tel. 828/757–5100; Laura J. Easton, President and Chief Executive Officer

CHATHAM HOSPITAL (O, 25 beds) 475 Progress Boulevard, Siler City, NC, Zip 27344–6787, Mailing Address: P.O. Box 649, 27344–0649, tel. 919/799–4000; Jeffery C. Strickler, R.N., President and Chief Executive Officer
**Web address:** www.chathamhospital.org

JOHNSTON HEALTH (C, 153 beds) 509 North Bright Leaf Blvd, Smithfield, NC, Zip 27577–4407, Mailing Address: P.O. Box 1376, 27577–1376, tel. 919/934–8171; Tom Williams, Chief Executive Officer
**Web address:** www.johnstonhealth.org

MARGARET R. PARDEE MEMORIAL HOSPITAL (C, 158 beds) 800 North Justice Street, Hendersonville, NC, Zip 28791–3410; tel. 828/696–1000; James M. Kirby II, President and Chief Executive Officer

NASH UNC HEALTH CARE (C, 249 beds) 2460 Curtis Ellis Drive, Rocky Mount, NC, Zip 27804–2237; tel. 252/962–8000; L. Lee. Isley, FACHE, Ph.D., President and Chief Executive Officer
**Web address:** www.nhcs.org

ONSLOW MEMORIAL HOSPITAL (C, 149 beds) 317 Western Boulevard, Jacksonville, NC, Zip 28546–6379, Mailing Address: P.O. Box 1358, 28541–1358, tel. 910/577–2345; Penney Burlingame Deal, FACHE, R.N., Chief Executive Officer

UNC LENOIR HEALTHCARE (C, 176 beds) 100 Airport Road, Kinston, NC, Zip 28501–1634, Mailing Address: P.O. Box 1678, 28503–1678, tel. 252/522–7000; Robert A. Enders Jr, President and Chief Executive Officer
**Web address:** www.lenoirmemorial.org

UNC REX HEALTH CARE (O, 666 beds) 4420 Lake Boone Trail, Raleigh, NC, Zip 27607–6599; tel. 919/784–3100; Ernest L. Bovio Jr, President
**Web address:** www.rexhealth.com

UNC ROCKINGHAM HEALTH CARE (O, 188 beds) 117 East King's Highway, Eden, NC, Zip 27288–5201; tel. 336/623–9711; Steven E. Eblin, Interim President and Chief Executive Officer

UNIVERSITY OF NORTH CAROLINA HOSPITALS (O, 951 beds) 101 Manning Drive, Chapel Hill, NC, Zip 27514–4220; tel. 984/974–1000; Gary L. Park, President
**Web address:** www.unchealthcare.org

WAYNE UNC HEALTH CARE (C, 274 beds) 2700 Wayne Memorial Drive, Goldsboro, NC, Zip 27534–9494, Mailing Address: P.O. Box 8001, 27533–8001, tel. 919/736–1110; Janie Jaberg, FACHE, President and Chief Executive Officer
**Web address:** www.waynehealth.org

| | | |
|---|---|---|
| **Owned, leased, sponsored:** | 5 hospitals | 1912 beds |
| **Contract–managed:** | 6 hospitals | 1159 beds |
| **Totals:** | 11 hospitals | 3071 beds |

## 0922: UNION GENERAL HOSPITAL, INC. (NP)

35 Hospital Road, Blairsville, GA Zip 30512–3139; tel. 706/745–2111; Mike Gowder, Chief Executive Officer

**GEORGIA:** CHATUGE REGIONAL HOSPITAL AND NURSING HOME (O, 150 beds) 110 Main Street, Hiawassee, GA, Zip 30546–3408, Mailing Address: P.O. Box 509, 30546–0509, tel. 706/896–2222; Ryan Snow, Administrator
**Web address:** www.chatugeregionalhospital.org

UNION GENERAL HOSPITAL (O, 195 beds) 35 Hospital Road, Blairsville, GA, Zip 30512–3139; tel. 706/745–2111; Kevin Bierschenk, Chief Executive Officer
**Web address:** www.uniongeneralhospital.com

| | | |
|---|---|---|
| **Owned, leased, sponsored:** | 2 hospitals | 345 beds |
| **Contract–managed:** | 0 hospitals | 0 beds |
| **Totals:** | 2 hospitals | 345 beds |

## 0288: UNITED HEALTH SERVICES (NP)

10–42 Mitchell Avenue, Binghamton, NY Zip 13903–1617; tel. 607/762–2200; John M. Carrigg, President and Chief Executive Officer
**(Independent Hospital System)**

**NEW YORK:** UHS CHENANGO MEMORIAL HOSPITAL (O, 138 beds) 179 North Broad Street, Norwich, NY, Zip 13815–1097; tel. 607/337–4111; Drake M. Lamen, M.D., President and Chief Executive Officer

UHS DELAWARE VALLEY HOSPITAL (O, 25 beds) 1 Titus Place, Walton, NY, Zip 13856–1498; tel. 607/865–2100; Paul Summers, President and Chief Executive Officer
**Web address:** www.uhs.net/locations/

UNITED HEALTH SERVICES HOSPITALS–BINGHAMTON (O, 464 beds) 10–42 Mitchell Avenue, Binghamton, NY, Zip 13903–1678; tel. 607/763–6000; John M. Carrigg, President and Chief Executive Officer

| | | |
|---|---|---|
| **Owned, leased, sponsored:** | 3 hospitals | 627 beds |
| **Contract–managed:** | 0 hospitals | 0 beds |
| **Totals:** | 3 hospitals | 627 beds |

## 9605: UNITED MEDICAL CORPORATION (IO)

603 Main Street, Windermere, FL Zip 34786–3548, Mailing Address: P.O. Box 1100, 34786–1100, tel. 407/876–2200; Donald R. Dizney, Chairman and Chief Executive Officer

**PUERTO RICO:** HOSPITAL PAVIA–HATO REY (O, 180 beds) 435 Ponce De Leon Avenue, San Juan, PR, Zip 00917–3428, Mailing Address: P.O. 190828, 00917–3428, tel. 787/641–2323; Guillermo Pastrana, Executive Director

HOSPITAL PAVIA–SANTURCE (O, 197 beds) 1462 Asia Street, San Juan, PR, Zip 00909–2143, Box 11137, Santurce Station, 00910–1137, tel. 787/727–6060; Jose Luis. Rodriguez, Chief Executive Officer
**Web address:** www.paviahealth.com

HOSPITAL PEREA (O, 103 beds) 15 Basora Street, Mayaguez, PR, Zip 681, Mailing Address: P.O. Box 170, 681, tel. 787/834–0101; Jorge I. Martinez, Executive Director

HOSPITAL SAN FRANCISCO (O, 133 beds) 371 Avenida De Diego, San Juan, PR, Zip 00923–1711, Mailing Address: P.O. Box 29025, 00929–0025, tel. 787/767–5100; Marcos Aguila, Chief Executive Officer
**Web address:** www.metropavia.com/SanFrancisco.cfm

SAN JORGE CHILDREN'S HOSPITAL (O, 167 beds) 258 San Jorge Street, Santurce, Santurce, PR, Zip 00912–3310, Mailing Address: P.O. 6308, San Juan, 00912–3310, tel. 787/727–1000; Domingo Cruz, Senior Vice President Operations
**Web address:** www.sanjorgechildrenshospital.com

| | | |
|---|---|---|
| **Owned, leased, sponsored:** | 5 hospitals | 780 beds |
| **Contract–managed:** | 0 hospitals | 0 beds |
| **Totals:** | 5 hospitals | 780 beds |

## 0937: UNITED MEDICAL REHABILITATION HOSPITALS (IO)

3201 Wall Boulevard, Suite B, Gretna, LA Zip 70056–7755; tel. 504/433–5551; John E.H. Mills, President and Chief Executive Officer

**LOUISIANA:** UNITED MEDICAL HEALTHWEST NEW ORLEANS, LLC (O, 21 beds) 3201 Wall Boulevard, Suite B, Gretna, LA, Zip 70056–7755; tel. 504/433–5551; Kian Marigny, Administrator

UNITED MEDICAL REHABILITATION HOSPITAL (O, 20 beds) 15717 Belle Drive, Hammond, LA, Zip 70403–1439; tel. 985/340–5998; Cyrillia Bonds, R.N., Administrator
**Web address:** www.umrhospital.com

| | | |
|---|---|---|
| **Owned, leased, sponsored:** | 2 hospitals | 41 beds |
| **Contract–managed:** | 0 hospitals | 0 beds |
| **Totals:** | 2 hospitals | 41 beds |

Section B

For explanation of codes following names, see page B2.
★ Indicates Type III membership in the American Hospital Association.

★**0968: UNITED STATES COAST GUARD** (FG)
2703 Martin Luther King Jr. Avenue Southeast, Washington, DC Zip 20593–7907; tel. 202/372–4500; Rear Admiral, Dana Thomas, M.D., Director, Health, Safety & Work–Life Chief Medical Officer

| | | |
|---|---|---|
| Owned, leased, sponsored: | 0 hospitals | 0 beds |
| Contract–managed: | 0 hospitals | 0 beds |
| Totals: | 0 hospitals | 0 beds |

**0322: UNITED SURGICAL PARTNERS INTERNATIONAL** (IO)
15305 Dallas Parkway, Suite 1600, Addison, TX Zip 75001–6491; tel. 972/713–3500; Brett Brodnax, Chief Executive Officer
**(Independent Hospital System)**

**ARIZONA:** ARIZONA ORTHOPEDIC SURGICAL HOSPITAL (O, 24 beds) 2905 West Warner Road, Suite 1, Chandler, AZ, Zip 85224–1674; tel. 480/603–9000; Patricia K. Alice, Chief Executive Officer
**Web address:** www.azosh.com

**OKLAHOMA:** OKLAHOMA CENTER FOR ORTHOPEDIC AND MULTI–SPECIALTY SURGERY (O, 9 beds) 8100 South Walker, Suite C, Oklahoma City, OK, Zip 73139–9402, Mailing Address: P.O. Box 890609, 73189–0609, tel. 405/602–6500; Daniel J. Coats, Chief Executive Officer

**TEXAS:** BAYLOR SCOTT & WHITE MEDICAL CENTER – SUNNYVALE (O, 70 beds) 231 South Collins Road, Sunnyvale, TX, Zip 75182–4624; tel. 972/892–3000; Jon Duckert, FACHE, Chief Executive Officer
**Web address:** www.BaylorScottandWhite.com/Sunnyvale

BAYLOR SCOTT & WHITE MEDICAL CENTER–UPTOWN (O, 24 beds) 2727 East Lemmon Avenue, Dallas, TX, Zip 75204–2895; tel. 214/443–3000; Nick Taylor, Chief Executive Officer
**Web address:** www.bmcuptown.com

BAYLOR SCOTT & WHITE MEDICAL CENTERâ€“FRISCO (O, 68 beds) 5601 Warren Parkway, Frisco, TX, Zip 75034–4069; tel. 214/407–5000; Trevor Castaneda, Chief Executive Officer

BAYLOR SURGICAL HOSPITAL AT LAS COLINAS (O, 12 beds) 400 West Lyndon B Johnson Freeway, Plaza 1, Suite 250, Irving, TX, Zip 75063–3718; tel. 972/868–4000; Deonna Unell, Chief Executive Officer
**Web address:** www.baylorhealth.com/About/Community/Assessments/West/ICSH/Pages/Default.aspx

TOPS SURGICAL SPECIALTY HOSPITAL (O, 15 beds) 17080 Red Oak Drive, Houston, TX, Zip 77090–2602; tel. 281/539–2900; Samuel H. Rossmann, Chief Executive Officer

| | | |
|---|---|---|
| Owned, leased, sponsored: | 7 hospitals | 222 beds |
| Contract–managed: | 0 hospitals | 0 beds |
| Totals: | 7 hospitals | 222 beds |

★**0061: UNITYPOINT HEALTH** (NP)
1776 West Lakes Parkway, Suite 400, West Des Moines, IA Zip 50266–8393; tel. 515/241–6161; Susan K. Thompson, R.N., Interim Chief Executive Officer
**(Decentralized Health System)**

**ILLINOIS:** MEMORIAL HOSPITAL (O, 18 beds) 1454 North County Road 2050, Carthage, IL, Zip 62321–3551, Mailing Address: P.O. Box 160, 62321–0160, tel. 217/357–8500; Ada Bair, Chief Executive Officer
**Web address:** www.mhtlc.org

UNITYPOINT HEALTH – PEORIA (O, 275 beds) 221 NE Glen Oak Avenue, Peoria, IL, Zip 61636–4310; tel. 309/672–5522; Keith Knepp, M.D., President and Chief Executive Officer
**Web address:** www.unitypoint.org/peoria

UNITYPOINT HEALTH – PROCTOR (O, 135 beds) 5409 North Knoxville Avenue, Peoria, IL, Zip 61614–5069; tel. 309/691–1000; Keith Knepp, M.D., President and Chief Executive Officer
**Web address:** www.proctor.org

UNITYPOINT HEALTH – TRINITY ROCK ISLAND (O, 325 beds) 2701 17th Street, Rock Island, IL, Zip 61201–5393; tel. 309/779–5000; Robert J. Erickson, President and Chief Executive Officer

UNITYPOINT HEALTH–PEKIN HOSPITAL (O, 86 beds) 600 South 13th Street, Pekin, IL, Zip 61554–4936; tel. 309/347–1151; Keith Knepp, M.D., President and Chief Executive Officer
**Web address:** www.pekinhospital.org

**IOWA:** BUCHANAN COUNTY HEALTH CENTER (O, 58 beds) 1600 First Street East, Independence, IA, Zip 50644–3155; tel. 319/332–0999; Steve Robert. Slessor, Chief Executive Officer
**Web address:** www.bchealth.info

BUENA VISTA REGIONAL MEDICAL CENTER (C, 35 beds) 1525 West Fifth Street, Storm Lake, IA, Zip 50588–3027, Mailing Address: P.O. Box 309, 50588–0309, tel. 712/732–4030; Steven Colerick, Chief Executive Officer
**Web address:** www.bvrmc.org

CHEROKEE REGIONAL MEDICAL CENTER (O, 25 beds) 300 Sioux Valley Drive, Cherokee, IA, Zip 51012–1205; tel. 712/225–5101; Gary W. Jordan, FACHE, Chief Executive Officer

CLARKE COUNTY HOSPITAL (C, 25 beds) 800 South Fillmore Street, Osceola, IA, Zip 50213–1619; tel. 641/342–2184; Brian G. Evans, FACHE, Chief Executive Officer
**Web address:** www.clarkehosp.org

COMMUNITY MEMORIAL HOSPITAL (C, 16 beds) 909 West First Street, Sumner, IA, Zip 50674–1203, Mailing Address: P.O. Box 148, 50674–0148, tel. 563/578–3275; Dawn Everding, President and Chief Financial Officer
**Web address:** www.cmhsumner.org

COMPASS MEMORIAL HEALTHCARE (O, 25 beds) 300 West May Street, Marengo, IA, Zip 52301–1261; tel. 319/642–5543; Barry Goettsch, FACHE, Chief Executive Officer

GREATER REGIONAL MEDICAL CENTER (C, 25 beds) 1700 West Townline Street Suite 3, Creston, IA, Zip 50801–1099; tel. 641/782–7091; Monte Neitzel, Chief Executive Officer
**Web address:** www.greaterregional.org

GREENE COUNTY MEDICAL CENTER (C, 85 beds) 1000 West Lincolnway, Jefferson, IA, Zip 50129–1645; tel. 515/386–2114; Tracy Warner, Chief Executive Officer
**Web address:** www.gcmchealth.com

GRUNDY COUNTY MEMORIAL HOSPITAL (C, 25 beds) 201 East 'J' Avenue, Grundy Center, IA, Zip 50638–2096; tel. 319/824–5421; Adam Scherling, President

GUTHRIE COUNTY HOSPITAL (C, 17 beds) 710 North 12th Street, Guthrie Center, IA, Zip 50115–1544; tel. 641/332–2201; Patrick Peters, Chief Executive Officer
**Web address:** www.guthriecountyhospital.org

HUMBOLDT COUNTY MEMORIAL HOSPITAL (C, 49 beds) 1000 North 15th Street, Humboldt, IA, Zip 50548–1008; tel. 515/332–4200; Michelle Sleiter, Chief Executive Officer
**Web address:** www.humboldthospital.org

LORING HOSPITAL (C, 25 beds) 211 Highland Avenue, Sac City, IA, Zip 50583–2424; tel. 712/662–7105; Stacy Johnson, Chief Executive Officer
**Web address:** www.loringhospital.org

LUCAS COUNTY HEALTH CENTER (C, 21 beds) 1200 North Seventh Street, Chariton, IA, Zip 50049–1258; tel. 641/774–3000; Jay Christensen, FACHE, Interim Chief Executive Officer

POCAHONTAS COMMUNITY HOSPITAL (C, 20 beds) 606 NW Seventh Street, Pocahontas, IA, Zip 50574–1099; tel. 712/335–3501; James D. Roetman, President and Chief Executive Officer
**Web address:** www.pocahontashospital.org

STEWART MEMORIAL COMMUNITY HOSPITAL (C, 25 beds) 1301 West Main, Lake City, IA, Zip 51449–1585; tel. 712/464–3171; Cynthia L. Carstens, R.N., Chief Executive Officer

STORY COUNTY MEDICAL CENTER (C, 82 beds) 640 South 19th Street, Nevada, IA, Zip 50201–2902; tel. 515/382–2111; Nate Thompson, Chief Executive Officer
**Web address:** www.storymedical.org

UNITYPOINT HEALTH – ALLEN HOSPITAL (O, 204 beds) 1825 Logan Avenue, Waterloo, IA, Zip 50703–1916; tel. 319/235–3941; Pamela K. Delagardelle, President and Chief Executive Officer
**Web address:** www.unitypoint.org/waterloo

For explanation of codes following names, see page B2.
★ Indicates Type III membership in the American Hospital Association.

UNITYPOINT HEALTH – FINLEY HOSPITAL (O, 112 beds) 350 North Grandview Avenue, Dubuque, IA, Zip 52001–6393; tel. 563/582–1881; Chad Wolbers, President and Chief Executive Officer

UNITYPOINT HEALTH – GRINNELL REGIONAL MEDICAL CENTER (O, 49 beds) 210 Fourth Avenue, Grinnell, IA, Zip 50112–1898; tel. 641/236–7511; Jennifer Havens, Chief Executive Officer
**Web address:** www.grmc.us

UNITYPOINT HEALTH – IOWA METHODIST MEDICAL CENTER (O, 758 beds) 1200 Pleasant Street, Des Moines, IA, Zip 50309–1406; tel. 515/241–6212; David A. Stark, FACHE, President and Chief Executive Officer

UNITYPOINT HEALTH – JONES REGIONAL MEDICAL CENTER (O, 22 beds) 1795 Highway 64 East, Anamosa, IA, Zip 52205–2112; tel. 319/462–6131; Eric Briesemeister, Chief Executive Officer
**Web address:** www.jonesregional.org

UNITYPOINT HEALTH – MARSHALLTOWN (O, 27 beds) 3 South Fourth Avenue, Marshalltown, IA, Zip 50158–2998; tel. 641/754–5151; Jennifer Friedly, President
**Web address:** www.https://marshalltown.unitypoint.org

UNITYPOINT HEALTH – ST. LUKE'S HOSPITAL (O, 349 beds) 1026 'A' Avenue NE, Cedar Rapids, IA, Zip 52402–3026, Mailing Address: P.O. Box 3026, 52406–3026, tel. 319/369–7211; Michelle Niermann, President and Chief Executive Officer

UNITYPOINT HEALTH – ST. LUKES'S SIOUX CITY (O, 165 beds) 2720 Stone Park Boulevard, Sioux City, IA, Zip 51104–3734; tel. 712/279–3500; Lynn Wold, President and Chief Executive Officer
**Web address:** www.stlukes.org

UNITYPOINT HEALTH – TRINITY BETTENDORF (O, 95 beds) 4500 Utica Ridge Road, Bettendorf, IA, Zip 52722–1626; tel. 563/742–5000; Robert J. Erickson, President and Chief Executive Officer

UNITYPOINT HEALTH – TRINITY MUSCATINE (O, 45 beds) 1518 Mulberry Avenue, Muscatine, IA, Zip 52761–3499; tel. 563/264–9100; Robert J. Erickson, President and Chief Executive Officer
**Web address:** www.unitypoint.org/quadcities/trinity–muscatine.aspx

UNITYPOINT HEALTH – TRINITY REGIONAL MEDICAL CENTER (O, 49 beds) 802 Kenyon Road, Fort Dodge, IA, Zip 50501–5795; tel. 515/573–3101; Leah Glasgo, Chief Executive Officer

UNITYPOINT HEALTH–KEOKUK (O, 42 beds) 1600 Morgan Street, Keokuk, IA, Zip 52632–3456; tel. 319/524–7150; Vickie Reneau, Administrator and Chief Nursing Executive
**Web address:** www.keokukhealthsystems.org

**WISCONSIN:** MEMORIAL HOSPITAL OF LAFAYETTE COUNTY (O, 25 beds) 800 Clay Street, Darlington, WI, Zip 53530–1228, Mailing Address: P.O. Box 70, 53530–0070, tel. 608/776–4466; Kathleen Kuepers, Chief Executive Officer

UNITYPOINT HEALTH MERITER (O, 214 beds) 202 South Park Street, Madison, WI, Zip 53715–1507; tel. 608/417–6000; Sue Erickson, President and Chief Executive Officer
**Web address:** www.meriter.com

| Owned, leased, sponsored: | 22 hospitals | 2814 beds |
| Contract–managed: | 13 hospitals | 450 beds |
| **Totals:** | 35 hospitals | 3264 beds |

## 9555: UNIVERSAL HEALTH SERVICES, INC. (IO)

367 South Gulph Road, King of Prussia, PA Zip 19406–3121, Mailing Address: P.O. Box 61558, 19406–0958, tel. 610/768–3300; Alan B. Miller, Chairman and Chief Executive Officer
**(Decentralized Health System)**

**ALABAMA:** HILL CREST BEHAVIORAL HEALTH SERVICES (O, 80 beds) 6869 Fifth Avenue South, Birmingham, AL, Zip 35212–1866; tel. 205/833–9000; Jennifer Synder, Chief Executive Officer
**Web address:** www.hillcrestbhs.com

LAUREL OAKS BEHAVIORAL HEALTH CENTER (O, 38 beds) 700 East Cottonwood Road, Dothan, AL, Zip 36301–3644; tel. 334/794–7373; Derek Johnson, Chief Executive Officer

**ALASKA:** NORTH STAR BEHAVIORAL HEALTH SYSTEM (O, 200 beds) 2530 DeBarr Circle, Anchorage, AK, Zip 99508–2948; tel. 907/258–7575; Alan Barnes, Interim Chief Executive Officer
**Web address:** www.northstarbehavioral.com

**ARIZONA:** PALO VERDE BEHAVIORAL HEALTH (O, 48 beds) 2695 North Craycroft Road, Tucson, AZ, Zip 85712–2244; tel. 520/322–2888; Jill Scheckel, Ph.D., Chief Executive Officer

VALLEY HOSPITAL PHOENIX (O, 122 beds) 3550 East Pinchot Avenue, Phoenix, AZ, Zip 85018–7434; tel. 602/957–4000; Lloyd Noble, Chief Executive Officer
**Web address:** www.valleyhospital–phoenix.com

**ARKANSAS:** PINNACLE POINTE HOSPITAL (O, 127 beds) 11501 Financial Center Parkway, Little Rock, AR, Zip 72211–3715; tel. 501/223–3322; Shane Frazier, Chief Executive Officer

RIVENDELL BEHAVIORAL HEALTH SERVICES OF ARKANSAS (O, 80 beds) 100 Rivendell Drive, Benton, AR, Zip 72019–9100; tel. 501/316–1255; Ballard Sheppard, Ph.D., Chief Executive Officer
**Web address:** www.rivendellofarkansas.com

SPRINGWOODS BEHAVIORAL HEALTH HOSPITAL (O, 80 beds) 1955 West Truckers Drive, Fayetteville, AR, Zip 72704–5637; tel. 479/973–6000; Jordon Babcock, Chief Executive Officer
**Web address:** www.springwoodsbehavioral.com

THE BRIDGEWAY (L, 124 beds) 21 Bridgeway Road, North Little Rock, AR, Zip 72113–9516; tel. 501/771–1500; Sherrie James, R.N., Chief Executive Officer
**Web address:** www.thebridgeway.com

**CALIFORNIA:** BHC ALHAMBRA HOSPITAL (O, 97 beds) 4619 North Rosemead Boulevard, Rosemead, CA, Zip 91770–1478, Mailing Address: P.O. Box 369, 91770–0369, tel. 626/286–1191; Peggy Minnick, R.N., Chief Executive Officer
**Web address:** www.bhcalhambra.com

CANYON RIDGE HOSPITAL (O, 107 beds) 5353 'G' Street, Chino, CA, Zip 91710–5250; tel. 909/590–3700; Stephanie Bernier, Chief Executive Officer

CORONA REGIONAL MEDICAL CENTER (O, 238 beds) 800 South Main Street, Corona, CA, Zip 92882–3400; tel. 951/737–4343; Mark H. Uffer, Chief Executive Officer
**Web address:** www.coronaregional.com

DEL AMO HOSPITAL (O, 70 beds) 23700 Camino Del Sol, Torrance, CA, Zip 90505–5000; tel. 310/530–1151; Steven Hytry, PsyD, Chief Executive Officer
**Web address:** www.delamohospital.com

FREMONT HOSPITAL (O, 148 beds) 39001 Sundale Drive, Fremont, CA, Zip 94538–2005; tel. 510/796–1100; Tricia Williams, Chief Executive Officer

HERITAGE OAKS HOSPITAL (O, 120 beds) 4250 Auburn Boulevard, Sacramento, CA, Zip 95841–4164; tel. 916/489–3336; Shawn Silva, Chief Executive Officer
**Web address:** www.heritageoakshospital.com

PALMDALE REGIONAL MEDICAL CENTER (O, 184 beds) 38600 Medical Center Drive, Palmdale, CA, Zip 93551–4483; tel. 661/382–5000; Richard Allen, Chief Executive Officer

SIERRA VISTA HOSPITAL (O, 171 beds) 8001 Bruceville Road, Sacramento, CA, Zip 95823–2329; tel. 916/288–0300; Mike Zauner, Chief Executive Officer
**Web address:** www.sierravistahospital.com

SOUTHWEST HEALTHCARE SYSTEM (O, 231 beds) 25500 Medical Center Drive, Murrieta, CA, Zip 92562–5965; tel. 951/696–6000; Bradley D. Neet, FACHE, Chief Executive Officer

TEMECULA VALLEY HOSPITAL (O, 140 beds) 31700 Temecula Parkway, Temecula, CA, Zip 92592–5896; tel. 951/331–2216; Darlene Wetton, R.N., Chief Executive Officer
**Web address:** www.temeculavalleyhospital.com

**COLORADO:** CEDAR SPRINGS HOSPITAL (O, 110 beds) 2135 Southgate Road, Colorado Springs, CO, Zip 80906–2693; tel. 719/633–4114; David Franklin, Chief Executive Officer

CENTENNIAL PEAKS HOSPITAL (O, 104 beds) 2255 South 88th Street, Louisville, CO, Zip 80027–9716; tel. 303/673–9990; Sean Forster, Interim Chief Executive Officer
**Web address:** www.centennialpeaks.com

HIGHLANDS BEHAVIORAL HEALTH SYSTEM (O, 86 beds) 8565 South Poplar Way, Littleton, CO, Zip 80130–3602; tel. 720/348–2800; Elicia Bunch, Chief Executive Officer

**Section B**

For explanation of codes following names, see page B2.
★ Indicates Type III membership in the American Hospital Association.

**DELAWARE**: DOVER BEHAVIORAL HEALTH SYSTEM (O, 80 beds) 725 Horsepond Road, Dover, DE, Zip 19901–7232; tel. 302/741–0140; Jean-Charles Constant, Administrator
**Web address**: www.doverbehavioral.com

ROCKFORD CENTER (O, 138 beds) 100 Rockford Drive, Newark, DE, Zip 19713–2121; tel. 302/996–5480; John F. McKenna, Chief Executive Officer and Managing Director
**Web address**: www.rockfordcenter.com

**DISTRICT OF COLUMBIA**: GEORGE WASHINGTON UNIVERSITY HOSPITAL (O, 395 beds) 900 23rd Street NW, Washington, DC, Zip 20037–2342; tel. 202/715–4000; Kimberly Russo, Chief Executive Officer
**Web address**: www.gwhospital.com

**FLORIDA**: CENTRAL FLORIDA BEHAVIORAL HOSPITAL (O, 126 beds) 6601 Central Florida Parkway, Orlando, FL, Zip 32821–8064; tel. 407/370–0111; Vickie Lewis, Chief Executive Officer
**Web address**: www.centralfloridabehavioral.com

EMERALD COAST BEHAVIORAL HOSPITAL (O, 86 beds) 1940 Harrison Avenue, Panama City, FL, Zip 32405–4542; tel. 850/763–0017; Tim Bedford, Chief Executive Officer
**Web address**: www.emeraldcoastbehavioral.com

FORT LAUDERDALE BEHAVIORAL HEALTH CENTER (L, 100 beds) 5757 North Dixie Highway, Oakland Park, FL, Zip 33301–2393; tel. 954/734–2000; Manuel R. Llano, Chief Executive Officer

LAKEWOOD RANCH MEDICAL CENTER (O, 120 beds) 8330 Lakewood Ranch Boulevard, Bradenton, FL, Zip 34202–5174; tel. 941/782–2100; Andrew Guz, Chief Executive Officer
**Web address**: www.lakewoodranchmedicalcenter.com

MANATEE MEMORIAL HOSPITAL (O, 319 beds) 206 Second Street East, Bradenton, FL, Zip 34208–1000; tel. 941/746–5111; Kevin DiLallo, Chief Executive Officer

RIVER POINT BEHAVIORAL HEALTH (O, 92 beds) 6300 Beach Boulevard, Jacksonville, FL, Zip 32216–2782; tel. 904/724–9202; Kevin McGee, Chief Executive Officer
**Web address**: www.riverpointbehavioral.com

SUNCOAST BEHAVIORAL HEALTH CENTER (O, 60 beds) 4480 51st Street West, Bradenton, FL, Zip 34210–2855; tel. 941/251–5000; Brandy Hamilton, Chief Executive Officer

THE VINES (O, 98 beds) 3130 SW 27th Avenue, Ocala, FL, Zip 34471–4306; tel. 352/671–3130; Stephen Quintyne, Chief Executive Officer
**Web address**: www.thevineshospital.com

WEKIVA SPRINGS (O, 60 beds) 3947 Salisbury Road, Jacksonville, FL, Zip 32216–6115; tel. 904/296–3533; Sheila Carr, Chief Executive Officer
**Web address**: www.wekivacenter.com

WELLINGTON REGIONAL MEDICAL CENTER (L, 235 beds) 10101 Forest Hill Boulevard, Wellington, FL, Zip 33414–6199; tel. 561/798–8500; Pamela S. Tahan, Chief Executive Officer
**Web address**: www.wellingtonregional.com

WINDMOOR HEALTHCARE OF CLEARWATER (O, 100 beds) 11300 U S 19 North, Clearwater, FL, Zip 33764; tel. 727/541–2646; Joshua Rodriguez, Chief Executive Officer

**GEORGIA**: ANCHOR HOSPITAL (O, 124 beds) 5454 Yorktowne Drive, Atlanta, GA, Zip 30349–5317; tel. 770/991–6044; Luis Betances, Chief Executive Officer
**Web address**: www.anchorhospital.com

COASTAL HARBOR TREATMENT CENTER (O, 191 beds) 1150 Cornell Avenue, Savannah, GA, Zip 31406–2702; tel. 912/354–3911; Sally Perry, Chief Executive Officer
**Web address**: www.coastalharbor.com

PEACHFORD BEHAVIORAL HEALTH SYSTEM (O, 246 beds) 2151 Peachford Road, Atlanta, GA, Zip 30338–6599; tel. 770/455–3200; Matthew Crouch, Chief Executive Officer and Managing Director

SAINT SIMONS BY-THE-SEA HOSPITAL (O, 101 beds) 2927 Demere Road, Saint Simons Island, GA, Zip 31522–1620; tel. 912/638–1999; Chris Little, Chief Executive Officer
**Web address**: www.ssbythesea.com

TURNING POINT HOSPITAL (O, 69 beds) 3015 Veterans Parkway South, Moultrie, GA, Zip 31788–6705, Mailing Address: P.O. Box 1177, 31776–1177, tel. 229/985–4815; Judy H. Payne, Chief Executive Officer

**IDAHO**: INTERMOUNTAIN HOSPITAL (O, 140 beds) 303 North Allumbaugh Street, Boise, ID, Zip 83704–9208; tel. 208/377–8400; Jeffrey F. Morrell, Chief Executive Officer
**Web address**: www.intermountainhospital.com

**ILLINOIS**: GARFIELD PARK HOSPITAL (O, 88 beds) 520 North Ridgeway Avenue, Chicago, IL, Zip 60624–1232; tel. 773/265–3700; Steven Airhart, Chief Executive Officer
**Web address**: www.garfieldparkhospital.com

HARTGROVE HOSPITAL (O, 160 beds) 5730 West Roosevelt Road, Chicago, IL, Zip 60644–1580; tel. 773/413–1700; Steven Airhart, Chief Executive Officer
**Web address**: www.hartgrovehospital.com

LINCOLN PRAIRIE BEHAVIORAL HEALTH CENTER (O, 97 beds) 5230 South Sixth Street, Springfield, IL, Zip 62703–5128; tel. 217/585–1180; Kevin McGee, Interim Chief Executive Officer

RIVEREDGE HOSPITAL (O, 210 beds) 8311 West Roosevelt Road, Forest Park, IL, Zip 60130–2500; tel. 708/771–7000; Carey Carlock, Chief Executive Officer
**Web address**: www.riveredgehospital.com

STREAMWOOD BEHAVIORAL HEALTH CENTER (O, 178 beds) 1400 East Irving Park Road, Streamwood, IL, Zip 60107–3203; tel. 630/837–9000; Ron Weglarz, Chief Executive Officer and Managing Director

THE PAVILION (O, 106 beds) 809 West Church Street, Champaign, IL, Zip 61820–3399; tel. 217/373–1700; Joseph King, Acting Chief Executive Officer
**Web address**: www.pavilionhospital.com

**INDIANA**: BLOOMINGTON MEADOWS HOSPITAL (O, 71 beds) 3600 North Prow Road, Bloomington, IN, Zip 47404–1616; tel. 812/331–8000; Christopher Dowers, Chief Executive Officer

MICHIANA BEHAVIORAL HEALTH CENTER (O, 75 beds) 1800 North Oak Drive, Plymouth, IN, Zip 46563–3492; tel. 574/936–3784; Zach Glassburn, Chief Executive Officer
**Web address**: www.https://michianabehavioralhealth.com

VALLE VISTA HEALTH SYSTEM (O, 132 beds) 898 East Main Street, Greenwood, IN, Zip 46143–1400; tel. 317/887–1348; Sergio Chapman Cianci, Chief Executive Officer
**Web address**: www.vallevistahospital.com

WELLSTONE REGIONAL HOSPITAL (O, 100 beds) 2700 Vissing Park Road, Jeffersonville, IN, Zip 47130–5989; tel. 812/284–8000; Greg Stewart, Chief Executive Officer

**KENTUCKY**: CUMBERLAND HALL HOSPITAL (O, 97 beds) 270 Walton Way, Hopkinsville, KY, Zip 42240–6808; tel. 270/886–1919; David Melear, Chief Executive Officer
**Web address**: www.cumberlandhallhospital.com

LINCOLN TRAIL BEHAVIORAL HEALTH SYSTEM (O, 140 beds) 3909 South Wilson Road, Radcliff, KY, Zip 40160–8944, Mailing Address: P.O. Box 369, 40159–0369, tel. 270/351–9444; Leslie Flechler, Chief Executive Officer
**Web address**: www.lincolnbehavioral.com

RIDGE BEHAVIORAL HEALTH SYSTEM (O, 110 beds) 3050 Rio Dosa Drive, Lexington, KY, Zip 40509–1540; tel. 859/269–2325; Nina W. Eisner, Chief Executive Officer and Managing Director

RIVENDELL BEHAVIORAL HEALTH (O, 125 beds) 1035 Porter Pike, Bowling Green, KY, Zip 42103–9581; tel. 270/843–1199; Matt Ours, Chief Executive Officer and Managing Director
**Web address**: www.rivendellbehavioral.com

THE BROOK HOSPITAL – KMI (O, 110 beds) 8521 Old LaGrange Road, Louisville, KY, Zip 40242–3800; tel. 502/426–6380; Paul Andrews, Chief Executive Officer
**Web address**: www.thebrookhospitals.com

THE BROOK AT DUPONT (O, 88 beds) 1405 Browns Lane, Louisville, KY, Zip 40207–4608; tel. 502/896–0495; Paul Andrews, Chief Executive Officer

**LOUISIANA**: BRENTWOOD HOSPITAL (O, 238 beds) 1006 Highland Avenue, Shreveport, LA, Zip 71101–4103; tel. 318/678–7500; William Weaver, Chief Executive Officer
**Web address**: www.brentwoodbehavioral.com

RIVER OAKS HOSPITAL (O, 126 beds) 1525 River Oaks Road West, New Orleans, LA, Zip 70123–2162; tel. 504/734–1740; Chuck Webb, Interim Chief Executive Officer
**Web address**: www.riveroakshospital.com

For explanation of codes following names, see page B2.
★ Indicates Type III membership in the American Hospital Association.

Section B

**MASSACHUSETTS**: ARBOUR H. R. I. HOSPITAL (O, 76 beds) 227 Babcock Street, Brookline, MA, Zip 02446–6799; tel. 617/731–3200; Jameson Pinette, Chief Executive Officer
**Web address**: www.HRIHospital.com

ARBOUR HOSPITAL (O, 118 beds) 49 Robinwood Avenue, Boston, MA, Zip 02130–2156; tel. 617/522–4400; Eric Kennedy, Chief Executive Officer

ARBOUR–FULLER HOSPITAL (O, 46 beds) 200 May Street, Attleboro, MA, Zip 02703–5520; tel. 508/761–8500; Rachel Legend, Chief Executive Officer
**Web address**: www.arbourhealth.com

PEMBROKE HOSPITAL (O, 115 beds) 199 Oak Street, Pembroke, MA, Zip 02359–1953; tel. 781/829–7000; Raymond Robinson, Chief Executive Officer

**MICHIGAN**: CEDAR CREEK HOSPITAL OF MICHIGAN (O, 54 beds) 101 W Townsend Road, Saint Johns, MI, Zip 48879–9200; tel. 833/837–0923; Scott Miles, Chief Executive Officer
**Web address**: www.cedarcreekhospital.com

FOREST VIEW PSYCHIATRIC HOSPITAL (O, 108 beds) 1055 Medical Park Drive SE, Grand Rapids, MI, Zip 49546–3607; tel. 616/942–9610; Jill A. Krause, Chief Executive Officer
**Web address**: www.forestviewhospital.com

HAVENWYCK HOSPITAL (O, 243 beds) 1525 University Drive, Auburn Hills, MI, Zip 48326–2673; tel. 248/373–9200; Julie Szyska, Chief Executive Officer and Managing Director

**MISSISSIPPI**: ALLIANCE HEALTH CENTER (O, 154 beds) 5000 Highway 39 North, Meridian, MS, Zip 39301–1021; tel. 601/483–6211; Jay Shehi, Chief Executive Officer
**Web address**: www.alliancehealthcenter.com

BRENTWOOD BEHAVIORAL HEALTHCARE OF MISSISSIPPI (O, 105 beds) 3531 East Lakeland Drive, Jackson, MS, Zip 39232–8839; tel. 601/936–2024; Michael J. Carney, Chief Executive Officer

GULFPORT BEHAVIORAL HEALTH SYSTEM (O, 89 beds) 11150 Highway 49 North, Gulfport, MS, Zip 39503–4110; tel. 228/831–1700; Michael A. Zieman, FACHE, Administrator
**Web address**: www.gulfportmemorial.com

PARKWOOD BEHAVIORAL HEALTH SYSTEM (O, 148 beds) 8135 Goodman Road, Olive Branch, MS, Zip 38654–2103; tel. 662/895–4900; Vincent Brummett, Chief Executive Officer
**Web address**: www.parkwoodbhs.com

**MISSOURI**: HEARTLAND BEHAVIORAL HEALTH SERVICES (O, 69 beds) 1500 West Ashland Street, Nevada, MO, Zip 64772–1710; tel. 417/667–2666; Alyson Wysong–Harder, Chief Executive Officer
**Web address**: www.heartlandbehavioral.com

**NEVADA**: CENTENNIAL HILLS HOSPITAL MEDICAL CENTER (O, 165 beds) 6900 North Durango Drive, Las Vegas, NV, Zip 89149–4409; tel. 702/835–9700; Sajit Pullarkat, Chief Executive Officer and Managing Director

DESERT SPRINGS HOSPITAL MEDICAL CENTER (O, 293 beds) 2075 East Flamingo Road, Las Vegas, NV, Zip 89119–5121; tel. 702/733–8800; Christopher Loftus, Chief Executive Officer
**Web address**: www.desertspringshospital.com

DESERT VIEW HOSPITAL (O, 25 beds) 360 South Lola Lane, Pahrump, NV, Zip 89048–0884; tel. 775/751–7500; Susan Davila, Chief Executive Officer

HENDERSON HOSPITAL (O, 145 beds) 1050 West Galleria Drive, Henderson, NV, Zip 89011; tel. 702/963–7000; Samuel Kaufman, Chief Executive Officer
**Web address**: www.hendersonhospital.com/

NORTHERN NEVADA MEDICAL CENTER (O, 108 beds) 2375 East Prater Way, Sparks, NV, Zip 89434–9641; tel. 775/331–7000; Alan C. Olive, Chief Executive Officer

SPRING MOUNTAIN SAHARA (O, 30 beds) 5460 West Sahara, Las Vegas, NV, Zip 89146–3307; tel. 702/216–8900; Troy Mire, Chief Executive Officer
**Web address**: www.springmountainsahara.com

SPRING MOUNTAIN TREATMENT CENTER (L, 110 beds) 7000 West Spring Mountain Road, Las Vegas, NV, Zip 89117–3816; tel. 702/873–2400; Troy Mire, Chief Executive Officer and Managing Director

SPRING VALLEY HOSPITAL MEDICAL CENTER (O, 169 beds) 5400 South Rainbow Boulevard, Las Vegas, NV, Zip 89118–1859; tel. 702/853–3000; Leonard Freehof, Chief Executive Officer and Managing Director
**Web address**: www.springvalleyhospital.com

SUMMERLIN HOSPITAL MEDICAL CENTER (O, 148 beds) 657 Town Center Drive, Las Vegas, NV, Zip 89144–6367; tel. 702/233–7000; Robert S. Freymuller, Chief Executive Officer

VALLEY HOSPITAL MEDICAL CENTER (O, 365 beds) 620 Shadow Lane, Las Vegas, NV, Zip 89106–4119; tel. 702/388–4000; Claude Wise, Chief Executive Officer
**Web address**: www.valleyhospital.net

WEST HILLS HOSPITAL (O, 190 beds) 1240 East Ninth Street, Reno, NV, Zip 89512–2964; tel. 775/323–0478; Char Buehrle, Interim Chief Executive Officer
**Web address**: www.westhillshospital.net

**NEW JERSEY**: HAMPTON BEHAVIORAL HEALTH CENTER (O, 120 beds) 650 Rancocas Road, Westampton, NJ, Zip 08060–5613; tel. 609/267–7000; Craig Hilton, Chief Executive Officer and Managing Director

SUMMIT OAKS HOSPITAL (O, 122 beds) 19 Prospect Street, Summit, NJ, Zip 07901–2530; tel. 908/522–7000; Ross Friedman, Chief Executive Officer
**Web address**: www.summitoakshospital.com/

**NEW MEXICO**: MESILLA VALLEY HOSPITAL (O, 105 beds) 3751 Del Rey Boulevard, Las Cruces, NM, Zip 88012–8526; tel. 575/382–3500; Anna Laliotis, Chief Executive Officer

**NORTH CAROLINA**: BRYNN MARR HOSPITAL (O, 99 beds) 192 Village Drive, Jacksonville, NC, Zip 28546–7299; tel. 910/577–1400; Allison Davenport, Chief Executive Officer
**Web address**: www.brynnmarr.org

HOLLY HILL HOSPITAL (O, 285 beds) 3019 Falstaff Road, Raleigh, NC, Zip 27610–1812; tel. 919/250–7000; Kevin Poitinger, Chief Executive Officer and Managing Director
**Web address**: www.hollyhillhospital.com

OLD VINEYARD BEHAVIORAL HEALTH SERVICES (O, 148 beds) 3637 Old Vineyard Road, Winston–Salem, NC, Zip 27104–4842; tel. 336/794–3550; Kevin Patton, Chief Executive Officer
**Web address**: www.oldvineyardbhs.com

**NORTH DAKOTA**: PRAIRIE ST. JOHN'S (O, 94 beds) 510 4th Street South, Fargo, ND, Zip 58103–1914; tel. 701/476–7200; Jeff Herman, Chief Executive Officer
**Web address**: www.prairie–stjohns.com

**OHIO**: ARROWHEAD BEHAVIORAL HEALTH HOSPITAL (O, 48 beds) 1725 Timber Line Road, Maumee, OH, Zip 43537–4015; tel. 419/891–9333; Theresa Contreras, Chief Executive Officer

BELMONT PINES HOSPITAL (O, 96 beds) 615 Churchill–Hubbard Road, Youngstown, OH, Zip 44505–1379; tel. 330/759–2700; Lisa Cocca, Chief Executive Officer
**Web address**: www.belmontpines.com

WINDSOR–LAURELWOOD CENTER FOR BEHAVIORAL MEDICINE (O, 159 beds) 35900 Euclid Avenue, Willoughby, OH, Zip 44094–4648; tel. 440/953–3000; Shelley Zimmerman, Chief Executive Officer
**Web address**: www.windsorlaurelwood.com

**OKLAHOMA**: CEDAR RIDGE HOSPITAL (O, 172 beds) 6501 NE 50th Street, Oklahoma City, OK, Zip 73141–9118; tel. 405/605–6111; Heather Joseph, Chief Executive Officer

ST. MARY'S REGIONAL MEDICAL CENTER (O, 124 beds) 305 South Fifth Street, Enid, OK, Zip 73701–5899, Mailing Address: P.O. Box 232, 73702–0232, tel. 580/233–6100; Krista Roberts, Chief Executive Officer
**Web address**: www.stmarysregional.com

**OREGON**: CEDAR HILLS HOSPITAL (O, 78 beds) 10300 SW Eastridge Street, Portland, OR, Zip 97225–5004; tel. 503/944–5000; Elizabeth Hutter, Chief Executive Officer
**Web address**: www.cedarhillshospital.com

**PENNSYLVANIA**: BROOKE GLEN BEHAVIORAL HOSPITAL (O, 146 beds) 7170 Lafayette Avenue, Fort Washington, PA, Zip 19034–2301; tel. 215/641–5300; Neil Callahan, Chief Executive Officer

CLARION PSYCHIATRIC CENTER (O, 96 beds) 2 Hospital Drive, Clarion, PA, Zip 16214–8502; tel. 814/226–9545; Wendy Shapiro, Chief Executive Officer
**Web address**: www.clarioncenter.com

FAIRMOUNT BEHAVIORAL HEALTH SYSTEM (O, 235 beds) 561 Fairthorne Avenue, Philadelphia, PA, Zip 19128–2499; tel. 215/487–4000; Mark L. Howard, Chief Executive Officer
**Web address**: www.fairmountbhs.com

For explanation of codes following names, see page B2.
★ Indicates Type III membership in the American Hospital Association.

FOUNDATIONS BEHAVIORAL HEALTH (O, 58 beds) 833 East Butler Avenue, Doylestown, PA, Zip 18901-2280; tel. 215/345-0444; Gina Fusco, M.D., Chief Executive Officer
**Web address**: www.fbh.com

FRIENDS HOSPITAL (O, 192 beds) 4641 Roosevelt Boulevard, Philadelphia, PA, Zip 19124-2343; tel. 215/831-4600; Elizabeth Conlin, PsyD, Chief Executive Officer

HORSHAM CLINIC (O, 206 beds) 722 East Butler Pike, Ambler, PA, Zip 19002-2310; tel. 215/643-7800; Phyllis Weisfield, Chief Executive Officer and Managing Director
**Web address**: www.horshamclinic.com

MEADOWS PSYCHIATRIC CENTER (O, 119 beds) 132 The Meadows Drive, Centre Hall, PA, Zip 16828-9231; tel. 814/364-2161; David Grabowski, Chief Executive Officer
**Web address**: www.themeadows.net

ROXBURY TREATMENT CENTER (O, 94 beds) 601 Roxbury Road, Shippensburg, PA, Zip 17257-9302; tel. 800/648-4673; Shauna Mogerman, Chief Executive Officer

**PUERTO RICO**: FIRST HOSPITAL PANAMERICANO (O, 153 beds) State Road 787 KM 1 5, Cidra, PR, Zip 739, Mailing Address: P.O. Box 1400, 739, tel. 787/739-5555; Astro Munoz, Executive Director
**Web address**: www.hospitalpanamericano.com

**SOUTH CAROLINA**: AIKEN REGIONAL MEDICAL CENTERS (O, 299 beds) 302 University Parkway, Aiken, SC, Zip 29801-6302; tel. 803/641-5000; James F. O'Loughlin, Chief Executive Officer
**Web address**: www.aikenregional.com

CAROLINA CENTER FOR BEHAVIORAL HEALTH (O, 130 beds) 2700 East Phillips Road, Greer, SC, Zip 29650-4816; tel. 864/235-2335; Jerry Chapman, Chief Executive Officer
**Web address**: www.thecarolinacenter.com

LIGHTHOUSE BEHAVIORAL HEALTH HOSPITAL (O, 105 beds) 152 Waccamaw Medical Park Drive, Conway, SC, Zip 29526-8901; tel. 843/347-8871; Thomas L. Ryba, Chief Executive Officer

PALMETTO LOWCOUNTRY BEHAVIORAL HEALTH (O, 100 beds) 2777 Speissegger Drive, Charleston, SC, Zip 29405-8229; tel. 843/747-5830; Timothy Miller, Interim Chief Executive Officer
**Web address**: www.palmettobehavioralhealth.com

THREE RIVERS BEHAVIORAL HEALTH (O, 122 beds) 2900 Sunset Boulevard, West Columbia, SC, Zip 29169-3422; tel. 803/796-9911; Shannon Marcus, Chief Executive Officer
**Web address**: www.threeriversbehavioral.org

**TENNESSEE**: LAKESIDE BEHAVIORAL HEALTH SYSTEM (O, 345 beds) 2911 Brunswick Road, Memphis, TN, Zip 38133-4199; tel. 901/377-4700; Joy Golden, Chief Executive Officer
**Web address**: www.lakesidebhs.com

ROLLING HILLS HOSPITAL (O, 130 beds) 2014 Quail Hollow Circle, Franklin, TN, Zip 37067-5967; tel. 615/628-5700; James Miller, Chief Executive Officer

**TEXAS**: AUSTIN LAKES HOSPITAL (O, 58 beds) 1025 East 32nd Street, Austin, TX, Zip 78705-2714; tel. 512/544-5253; Robert J. Lerma, MS, Chief Executive Officer
**Web address**: www.austinlakeshospital.com

AUSTIN OAKS HOSPITAL (O, 80 beds) 1407 West Stassney Lane, Austin, TX, Zip 78745-2947; tel. 512/440-4800; Steve Kelly, Chief Executive Officer
**Web address**: www.austinoakshospital.com

BEHAVIORAL HOSPITAL OF BELLAIRE (O, 122 beds) 5314 Dashwood Drive, Houston, TX, Zip 77081-4603; tel. 713/600-9500; Eric Amoh, Chief Executive Officer

CORNERSTONE REGIONAL HOSPITAL (L, 14 beds) 2302 Cornerstone Boulevard, Edinburg, TX, Zip 78539-8471; tel. 956/618-4444; Andrew Wilson, Chief Executive Officer
**Web address**: www.cornerstoneregional.com

CYPRESS CREEK HOSPITAL (O, 128 beds) 17750 Cali Drive, Houston, TX, Zip 77090-2700; tel. 281/586-7600; Rae Oliver, Chief Executive Officer
**Web address**: www.cypresscreekhospital.com

DOCTORS HOSPITAL OF LAREDO (O, 183 beds) 10700 McPherson Road, Laredo, TX, Zip 78045-6268; tel. 956/523-2000; Emma Krabill, Chief Executive Officer
**Web address**: www.doctorshosplaredo.com

EL PASO BEHAVIORAL HEALTH SYSTEM (O, 166 beds) 1900 Denver Avenue, El Paso, TX, Zip 79902-3008; tel. 915/544-4000; Phuong Cardoza, Chief Executive Officer

FORT DUNCAN REGIONAL MEDICAL CENTER (O, 101 beds) 3333 North Foster Maldonado Boulevard, Eagle Pass, TX, Zip 78852-5893; tel. 830/773-5321; Eladio Montalvo, Chief Executive Officer
**Web address**: www.fortduncanmedicalcenter.com

GARLAND BEHAVIORAL HOSPITAL (O, 72 beds) 2300 Marie Curie Boulevard, 5th Floor, Garland, TX, Zip 75402; tel. 972/487-5309; Kimberly Lynn. Bunnell, Chief Executive Officer

GLEN OAKS HOSPITAL (O, 54 beds) 301 Division Street, Greenville, TX, Zip 75401-4101; tel. 903/454-6000; Brittney Nolan, Chief Executive Officer
**Web address**: www.glenoakshospital.com

HICKORY TRAIL HOSPITAL (O, 86 beds) 2000 Old Hickory Trail, Desoto, TX, Zip 75115-2242; tel. 972/298-7323; Daniel Martinez-Torres, Chief Executive Officer
**Web address**: www.hickorytrail.com

KINGWOOD PINES HOSPITAL (O, 52 beds) 2001 Ladbrook Drive, Kingwood, TX, Zip 77339-3004; tel. 281/404-1001; Kristin Harris, Chief Executive Officer

LAUREL RIDGE TREATMENT CENTER (O, 208 beds) 17720 Corporate Woods Drive, San Antonio, TX, Zip 78259-3500; tel. 210/491-9400; Jacob Cuellar, M.D., Chief Executive Officer
**Web address**: www.laurelridgetc.com

MAYHILL HOSPITAL (O, 59 beds) 2809 South Mayhill Road, Denton, TX, Zip 76208-5910; tel. 940/239-3000; Loren Fouch, Chief Executive Officer

MILLWOOD HOSPITAL (O, 134 beds) 1011 North Cooper Street, Arlington, TX, Zip 76011-5517; tel. 817/261-3121; Brian Gill, Chief Executive Officer
**Web address**: www.millwoodhospital.com

NORTHWEST TEXAS HEALTHCARE SYSTEM (O, 431 beds) 1501 South Coulter Avenue, Amarillo, TX, Zip 79106-1770, Mailing Address: P.O. Box 1110, 79105-1110, tel. 806/354-1000; Ryan Chandler, Chief Executive Officer

RIVER CREST HOSPITAL (O, 80 beds) 1636 Hunters Glen Road, San Angelo, TX, Zip 76901-5016; tel. 325/949-5722; Angela Harris, Chief Executive Officer
**Web address**: www.rivercresthospital.com

SOUTH TEXAS HEALTH SYSTEM (O, 820 beds) 1400 West Trenton Road, Edinburg, TX, Zip 78539-9105, 1102 West Trenton Road, 78539-9105, tel. 956/388-6000; Lance Ames, Chief Executive Officer

TEXAS NEUROREHAB CENTER (O, 47 beds) 1106 West Dittmar Road, Building 9, Austin, TX, Zip 78745-6328, Mailing Address: P.O. Box 150459, 78715-0459, tel. 512/444-4835; Edgar E. Prettyman, PsyD, Chief Executive Officer
**Web address**: www.texasneurorehab.com

TEXOMA MEDICAL CENTER (O, 414 beds) 5016 South US Highway 75 , Denison, TX, Zip 75020-4584, Mailing Address: P.O. Box 890, 75021-0890, tel. 903/416-4000; Ronald T. Seal, Chief Executive Officer
**Web address**: www.texomamedicalcenter.net

UNIVERSITY BEHAVIORAL HEALTH OF DENTON (O, 104 beds) 2026 West University Drive, Denton, TX, Zip 76201-0644; tel. 940/320-8100; Ronald Rains, Chief Executive Officer

WEST OAKS HOSPITAL (O, 160 beds) 6500 Hornwood Drive, Houston, TX, Zip 77074-5095; tel. 713/995-0909; Mandy Westerman, Chief Executive Officer
**Web address**: www.westoakshospital.com

**UTAH**: PROVO CANYON BEHAVIORAL HOSPITAL (O, 80 beds) 1350 East 750 North, Orem, UT, Zip 84097-4345; tel. 801/852-2273; Jeremy Cottle, Ph.D., Chief Executive Officer
**Web address**: www.pcbh.com

SALT LAKE BEHAVIORAL HEALTH (O, 118 beds) 3802 South 700 East, Salt Lake City, UT, Zip 84106-1182; tel. 801/264-6000; Kreg Gillman, Chief Executive Officer
**Web address**: www.saltlakebehavioralhealth.com

**VIRGINIA**: CUMBERLAND HOSPITAL FOR CHILDREN AND ADOLESCENTS (O, 118 beds) 9407 Cumberland Road, New Kent, VA, Zip 23124-2029; tel. 804/966-2242; Patrice Gay. Brooks, Chief Executive Officer

POPLAR SPRINGS HOSPITAL (O, 180 beds) 350 Poplar Drive, Petersburg, VA, Zip 23805-9367; tel. 804/733-6874; Nelson Smith, Chief Executive Officer
**Web address**: www.poplarsprings.com

For explanation of codes following names, see page B2.
★ Indicates Type III membership in the American Hospital Association.

VIRGINIA BEACH PSYCHIATRIC CENTER (O, 100 beds) 1100 First Colonial Road, Virginia Beach, VA, Zip 23454–2403; tel. 757/496–6000; Kurt Hooks, Chief Executive Officer

**WASHINGTON:** FAIRFAX BEHAVIORAL HEALTH (O, 221 beds) 10200 NE 132nd Street, Kirkland, WA, Zip 98034–2899; tel. 425/821–2000; Ron Escarda, Interim Chief Executive Officer
**Web address**: www.fairfaxhospital.com

**WEST VIRGINIA:** RIVER PARK HOSPITAL (O, 175 beds) 1230 Sixth Avenue, Huntington, WV, Zip 25701–2312, Mailing Address: P.O. Box 1875, 25719–1875, tel. 304/526–9111; Terry A. Stephens, Chief Executive Officer

**WYOMING:** WYOMING BEHAVIORAL INSTITUTE (O, 114 beds) 2521 East 15th Street, Casper, WY, Zip 82609–4126; tel. 307/237–7444; Mike Phillips, Chief Executive Officer
**Web address**: www.wbihelp.com

| | | |
|---|---|---|
| Owned, leased, sponsored: | 142 hospitals | 19768 beds |
| Contract–managed: | 0 hospitals | 0 beds |
| Totals: | 142 hospitals | 19768 beds |

---

**★0896: UNIVERSITY HEALTH CARE SYSTEM** (NP)
1350 Walton Way, Augusta, GA Zip 30901–2629; tel. 706/722–9011; James R. Davis, President and Chief Executive Officer
**(Independent Hospital System)**

**GEORGIA:** UNIVERSITY HOSPITAL MCDUFFIE (O, 22 beds) 2460 Washington Road, NE, Thomson, GA, Zip 30824; tel. 706/595–1411; Bob Kepshire, R.N., MS, Administrator and Chief Nursing Officer

UNIVERSITY HOSPITAL (O, 568 beds) 1350 Walton Way, Augusta, GA, Zip 30901–2629; tel. 706/722–9011; James R. Davis, Chief Executive Officer
**Web address**: www.universityhealth.org

| | | |
|---|---|---|
| Owned, leased, sponsored: | 2 hospitals | 590 beds |
| Contract–managed: | 0 hospitals | 0 beds |
| Totals: | 2 hospitals | 590 beds |

---

**0961: UNIVERSITY HEALTH SYSTEM** (NP)
1501 Kings Highway, Shreveport, LA Zip 71103–4228; tel. 318/675–5000; Daniel J. Snyder, Chief Executive Officer
**(Moderately Centralized Health System)**

**LOUISIANA:** OCHSNER LSU HEALTH SHREVEPORT – ACADEMIC MEDICAL CENTER (O, 386 beds) 1501 Kings Highway, Shreveport, LA, Zip 71103–4228, Mailing Address: P.O. Box 33932, 71130–3932, tel. 318/675–5000; Charles D. Daigle, Chief Executive Officer

OCHSNER LSU HEALTH SHREVEPORT – MONROE MEDICAL CENTER (O, 123 beds) 4864 Jackson Street, Monroe, LA, Zip 71202–6497, Mailing Address: P.O. Box 1881, 71210–8005, tel. 318/330–7000; Charles D. Daigle, Chief Executive Officer
**Web address**: www.uhsystem.com

| | | |
|---|---|---|
| Owned, leased, sponsored: | 2 hospitals | 509 beds |
| Contract–managed: | 0 hospitals | 0 beds |
| Totals: | 2 hospitals | 509 beds |

---

**★0112: UNIVERSITY HOSPITALS** (NP)
11100 Euclid Avenue, Cleveland, OH Zip 44106–5000; tel. 216/844–1000; Thomas F. Zenty III, Chief Executive Officer
**(Centralized Health System)**

**OHIO:** RAINBOW BABIES AND CHILDREN'S HOSPITAL (O, 190 beds) 2101 Adelbert Road, Cleveland, OH, Zip 44106–2624; tel. 216/844–3911; Patricia DePompei, President

UH AHUJA MEDICAL CENTER (O, 144 beds) 3999 Richmond Road, Beachwood, OH, Zip 44122–6046; tel. 216/593–5500; Alan Papa, President
**Web address**: https://www.uhhospitals.org

UH CLEVELAND MEDICAL CENTER (O, 916 beds) 11100 Euclid Avenue, Cleveland, OH, Zip 44106–1716; tel. 216/844–1000; Daniel I. Simon, M.D., President
**Web address**: www.UHhospitals.org

UH CONNEAUT MEDICAL CENTER (O, 25 beds) 158 West Main Road, Conneaut, OH, Zip 44030–2039; tel. 440/593–1131; M Steven. Jones, President
**Web address**: www.uhhospitals.org

UH ELYRIA MEDICAL CENTER (O, 202 beds) 630 East River Street, Elyria, OH, Zip 44035–5902; tel. 440/329–7500; Kristi M. Sink, President
**Web address**: www.uhhospitals.org/elyria

UH GEAUGA MEDICAL CENTER (O, 143 beds) 13207 Ravenna Road, Chardon, OH, Zip 44024–7032; tel. 440/269–6000; Donald DeCarlo, M.D., President

UH GENEVA MEDICAL CENTER (O, 25 beds) 870 West Main Street, Geneva, OH, Zip 44041–1295; tel. 440/466–1141; M Steven. Jones, President
**Web address**: www.uhhs.com

UH PORTAGE MEDICAL CENTER (O, 130 beds) 6847 North Chestnut Street, Ravenna, OH, Zip 44266–3929, Mailing Address: P.O. Box 1204, 44266–1204, tel. 330/297–0811; William Benoit, President
**Web address**: www.uhportage.org

UH REGIONAL HOSPITALS (O, 101 beds) 27100 Chardon Road, Cleveland, OH, Zip 44143–1116; tel. 440/585–6500; Roberta Rowell, President

UH SAMARITAN MEDICAL CENTER (O, 39 beds) 1025 Center Street, Ashland, OH, Zip 44805–4011; tel. 419/289–0491; Todd Harford, President
**Web address**: www.samaritanhospital.org

UH ST. JOHN MEDICAL CENTER (O, 179 beds) 29000 Center Ridge Road, Westlake, OH, Zip 44145–5293; tel. 440/835–8000; Robert G. David, President
**Web address**: https://www.uhhospitals.org

UNIVERSITY HOSPITALS PARMA MEDICAL CENTER (O, 261 beds) 7007 Powers Boulevard, Parma, OH, Zip 44129–5495; tel. 440/743–3000; Brian Monter, MSN, R.N., President

| | | |
|---|---|---|
| Owned, leased, sponsored: | 12 hospitals | 2355 beds |
| Contract–managed: | 0 hospitals | 0 beds |
| Totals: | 12 hospitals | 2355 beds |

---

**★0915: UNIVERSITY HOSPITALS AND HEALTH SYSTEM** (NP)
2500 North State Street, Jackson, MS Zip 39216–4500; tel. 601/984–1000; Kevin S. Cook, Chief Executive Officer
**(Decentralized Health System)**

**MISSISSIPPI:** UNIVERSITY OF MISSISSIPPI MEDICAL CENTER GRENADA (C, 58 beds) 960 Avent Drive, Grenada, MS, Zip 38901–5230; tel. 662/227–7000; Dodie McElmurray, FACHE, Chief Executive Officer
**Web address**: www.glmc.net/

UNIVERSITY OF MISSISSIPPI MEDICAL CENTER HOLMES COUNTY (O, 25 beds) 239 Bowling Green Road, Lexington, MS, Zip 39095–5167; tel. 601/496–5200; Dodie McElmurray, FACHE, Chief Executive Officer
**Web address**: www.ummchealth.com/holmes/

UNIVERSITY OF MISSISSIPPI MEDICAL CENTER (O, 697 beds) 2500 North State Street, Jackson, MS, Zip 39216–4505; tel. 601/984–1000; Britt Crewse, Chief Executive Officer

| | | |
|---|---|---|
| Owned, leased, sponsored: | 2 hospitals | 722 beds |
| Contract–managed: | 1 hospitals | 58 beds |
| Totals: | 3 hospitals | 780 beds |

---

**★6405: UNIVERSITY OF CALIFORNIA SYSTEMWIDE ADMINISTRATION** (NP)
1111 Franklin Street, 11th Floor, Oakland, CA Zip 94607–5200; tel. 510/987–9071; John D. Stobo, M.D., Executive Vice President and Chief Executive Officer
**(Decentralized Health System)**

**CALIFORNIA:** RONALD REAGAN UCLA MEDICAL CENTER (O, 445 beds) 757 Westwood Plaza, Los Angeles, CA, Zip 90095–8358; tel. 310/825–9111; Johnese Spisso, Chief Executive Officer
**Web address**: www.uclahealth.org

STEWART & LYNDA RESNICK NEUROPSYCHIATRIC HOSPITAL AT UCLA (O, 74 beds) 150 UCLA Medical Plaza, Los Angeles, CA, Zip 90095–8353; tel. 310/825–9989; Peter Whybrow, M.D., Chief Executive Officer

For explanation of codes following names, see page B2.
★ Indicates Type III membership in the American Hospital Association.

Section B

UC SAN DIEGO MEDICAL CENTER Ã¢â¬â⧠HILLCREST (O, 776 beds) 200 West Arbor Drive, San Diego, CA, Zip 92103–9000; tel. 619/543–6222; Patty Maysent, Chief Executive Officer
**Web address:** www.https://health.ucsd.edu

UCI MEDICAL CENTER (O, 402 beds) 101 The City Drive South, Orange, CA, Zip 92868–3298; tel. 714/456–6011; Chad T. Lefteris, Chief Executive Officer

UCLA MEDICAL CENTER–SANTA MONICA (O, 281 beds) 1250 16th Street, Santa Monica, CA, Zip 90404–1249; tel. 310/319–4000; Richard Azar, Chief Operating Officer
**Web address:** www.healthcare.ucla.edu

UCSF MEDICAL CENTER (O, 820 beds) 500 Parnassus Avenue, San Francisco, CA, Zip 94143–0296, 500 Parnassus Avenue, Box 0296, 94143–0296, tel. 415/476–1000; Mark R. Laret, Chief Executive Officer

UNIVERSITY OF CALIFORNIA, DAVIS MEDICAL CENTER (O, 617 beds) 2315 Stockton Boulevard, Sacramento, CA, Zip 95817–2282; tel. 916/734–2011; Brad Simmons, Interim Chief Executive Officer
**Web address:** www.ucdmc.ucdavis.edu

| Owned, leased, sponsored: | 7 hospitals | 3415 beds |
|---|---|---|
| Contract–managed: | 0 hospitals | 0 beds |
| Totals: | 7 hospitals | 3415 beds |

---

★**0058: UNIVERSITY OF CHICAGO MEDICINE** (NP)
5841 South Maryland Avenue, Chicago, IL Zip 60637–1447; tel. 773/702–6240; Kenneth Polonsky, M.D., President
**(Centralized Health System)**

**ILLINOIS:** INGALLS MEMORIAL HOSPITAL (O, 199 beds) One Ingalls Drive, Harvey, IL, Zip 60426–3591; tel. 708/333–2300; Brian Sinotte, President

UNIVERSITY OF CHICAGO MEDICAL CENTER (O, 698 beds) 5841 South Maryland Avenue, Chicago, IL, Zip 60637–1443; tel. 773/702–1000; Thomas E. Jackiewicz, President
**Web address:** www.uchospitals.edu

| Owned, leased, sponsored: | 2 hospitals | 897 beds |
|---|---|---|
| Contract–managed: | 0 hospitals | 0 beds |
| Totals: | 2 hospitals | 897 beds |

---

★**0216: UNIVERSITY OF MARYLAND MEDICAL SYSTEM** (NP)
250 West Pratt Street, 24th Floor, Baltimore, MD Zip 21201–1595; tel. 410/328–8667; Mohan Suntha, M.D., President and Chief Executive Officer
**(Moderately Centralized Health System)**

**MARYLAND:** MT. WASHINGTON PEDIATRIC HOSPITAL (O, 61 beds) 1708 West Rogers Avenue, Baltimore, MD, Zip 21209–4545; tel. 410/578–8600; Sheldon J. Stein, President and Chief Executive Officer

UNIVERSITY OF MARYLAND BALTIMORE WASHINGTON MEDICAL CENTER (O, 272 beds) 301 Hospital Drive, Glen Burnie, MD, Zip 21061–5899; tel. 410/787–4000; Karen E. Olscamp, President and Chief Executive Officer
**Web address:** www.mybwmc.org

UNIVERSITY OF MARYLAND CAPITAL REGION HEALTH PRINCE GEORGE'S HOSPITAL CENTER (O, 245 beds) 3001 Hospital Drive, Cheverly, MD, Zip 20785–1189; tel. 301/618–2000; Nathaniel Richardson Jr, President and Chief Executive Officer
**Web address:** www.princegeorgeshospital.org

UNIVERSITY OF MARYLAND CHARLES REGIONAL MEDICAL CENTER (O, 108 beds) 5 Garrett Avenue, La Plata, MD, Zip 20646–5960, Mailing Address: P.O. Box 1070, 20646–1070, tel. 301/609–4000; Noel A. Cervino, President and Chief Executive Officer
**Web address:** www.charlesregional.org

UNIVERSITY OF MARYLAND HARFORD MEMORIAL HOSPITAL (O, 82 beds) 501 South Union Avenue, Havre De Grace, MD, Zip 21078–3493; tel. 443/843–5000; Lyle Ernest. Sheldon, FACHE, President and Chief Executive Officer

UNIVERSITY OF MARYLAND MEDICAL CENTER MIDTOWN CAMPUS (O, 189 beds) 827 Linden Avenue, Baltimore, MD, Zip 21201–4606; tel. 410/225–8000; Mohan Suntha, M.D., President and Chief Executive Officer
**Web address:** www.ummidtown.org/

UNIVERSITY OF MARYLAND MEDICAL CENTER (O, 693 beds) 22 South Greene Street, Baltimore, MD, Zip 21201–1595; tel. 410/328–9199; Mohan Suntha, M.D., President and Chief Executive Officer
**Web address:** www.umm.edu

UNIVERSITY OF MARYLAND REHABILITATION & ORTHOPAEDIC INSTITUTE (O, 141 beds) 2200 Kernan Drive, Baltimore, MD, Zip 21207–6697; tel. 410/448–2500; Cynthia Kelleher, M.P.H., President and Chief Executive Officer

UNIVERSITY OF MARYLAND SHORE MEDICAL CENTER AT CHESTERTOWN (O, 124 beds) 100 Brown Street, Chestertown, MD, Zip 21620–1499; tel. 410/778–3300; Kenneth D. Kozel, FACHE, President and Chief Executive Officer
**Web address:** www.umms.org/hospitals/shore–health–system.htm

UNIVERSITY OF MARYLAND SHORE MEDICAL CENTER AT DORCHESTER (O, 47 beds) 300 Byrn Street, Cambridge, MD, Zip 21613–1908; tel. 410/228–5511; Kenneth D. Kozel, FACHE, President and Chief Executive Officer

UNIVERSITY OF MARYLAND SHORE MEDICAL CENTER AT EASTON (O, 132 beds) 219 South Washington Street, Easton, MD, Zip 21601–2996; tel. 410/822–1000; Kenneth D. Kozel, FACHE, President and Chief Executive Officer
**Web address:** www.shorehealth.org

UNIVERSITY OF MARYLAND ST. JOSEPH MEDICAL CENTER (O, 287 beds) 7601 Osler Drive, Towson, MD, Zip 21204–7582; tel. 410/337–1000; Thomas Smyth, President and Chief Executive Officer

UNIVERSITY OF MARYLAND UPPER CHESAPEAKE MEDICAL CENTER (O, 149 beds) 500 Upper Chesapeake Drive, Bel Air, MD, Zip 21014–4324; tel. 443/643–1000; Lyle Ernest. Sheldon, FACHE, President and Chief Executive Officer
**Web address:** www.uchs.org

| Owned, leased, sponsored: | 13 hospitals | 2530 beds |
|---|---|---|
| Contract–managed: | 0 hospitals | 0 beds |
| Totals: | 13 hospitals | 2530 beds |

---

★**0227: UNIVERSITY OF MISSOURI HEALTH CARE** (NP)
One Hospital Drive, DC 031, Columbia, MO Zip 65212–0001; tel. 573/882–4141; Jonathan W. Curtright, Chief Executive Officer and Chief Operating Officer
**(Moderately Centralized Health System)**

**MISSOURI:** CAPITAL REGION MEDICAL CENTER (O, 114 beds) 1125 Madison Street, Jefferson City, MO, Zip 65101–5200, Mailing Address: P.O. Box 1128, 65102–1128, tel. 573/632–5000; Gaspare Calvaruso, President
**Web address:** www.crmc.org

UNIVERSITY OF MISSOURI HEALTH CARE (O, 603 beds) One Hospital Drive, Columbia, MO, Zip 65212–0001; tel. 573/882–4141; Jonathan W. Curtright, Chief Executive Officer
**Web address:** www.muhealth.org

| Owned, leased, sponsored: | 2 hospitals | 717 beds |
|---|---|---|
| Contract–managed: | 0 hospitals | 0 beds |
| Totals: | 2 hospitals | 717 beds |

---

**0021: UNIVERSITY OF NEW MEXICO HOSPITALS** (NP)
915 Camino De Salud, Albuquerque, NM Zip 87131–0001; tel. 505/272–5849; Michael Chicarelli, R.N., Interim Chief Executive Officer
**(Moderately Centralized Health System)**

**NEW MEXICO:** UNM SANDOVAL REGIONAL MEDICAL CENTER, INC. (O, 60 beds) 3001 Broadmoor Boulevard NE, Rio Rancho, NM, Zip 87131; tel. 505/994–7000; Jamie A. Silva-Steele, FACHE, R.N., President and Chief Executive Officer
**Web address:** www.hsc.unm.edu/health/locations/sandoval–regional–medical–center.html

UNIVERSITY OF NEW MEXICO HOSPITALS (O, 537 beds) 2211 Lomas Boulevard NE, Albuquerque, NM, Zip 87106–2745; tel. 505/272–2111; Kathleen R. Becker, M.P.H., JD, Chief Executive Officer

| Owned, leased, sponsored: | 2 hospitals | 597 beds |
|---|---|---|
| Contract–managed: | 0 hospitals | 0 beds |
| Totals: | 2 hospitals | 597 beds |

---

For explanation of codes following names, see page B2.
★ Indicates Type III membership in the American Hospital Association.

★**0168: UNIVERSITY OF PENNSYLVANIA HEALTH SYSTEM** (NP)
3400 Civic Center Bouelvard, Suite A–5, Philadelphia, PA
Zip 19104–5127; tel. 215/662–2203; Kevin B. Mahoney, Chief
Executive Officer
**(Moderately Centralized Health System)**

**NEW JERSEY**: PENN MEDICINE PRINCETON MEDICAL CENTER (O, 355 beds)
One Plainsboro Road, Plainsboro, NJ, Zip 08536–1913; tel. 609/853–
7100; Barry S. Rabner, President and Chief Executive Officer, Princeton
Healthcare System

**PENNSYLVANIA**: CHESTER COUNTY HOSPITAL (O, 224 beds) 701 East
Marshall Street, West Chester, PA, Zip 19380–4412; tel. 610/431–5000;
Michael J. Duncan, President and Chief Executive Officer
**Web address**: www.chestercountyhospital.org

HOSPITAL OF THE UNIVERSITY OF PENNSYLVANIA (O, 807 beds) 3400 Spruce
Street, Philadelphia, PA, Zip 19104–4206; tel. 215/662–4000; Regina
Cunningham, Ph.D., R.N., Chief Executive Officer

PENN MEDICINE LANCASTER GENERAL HOSPITAL (O, 603 beds) 555 North
Duke Street, Lancaster, PA, Zip 17602–2250; tel. 717/544–5511; Jan L.
Bergen, President and Chief Executive Officer
**Web address**: www.lancastergeneralhealth.org

PENN PRESBYTERIAN MEDICAL CENTER (O, 375 beds) 51 North 39th Street,
Philadelphia, PA, Zip 19104–2699; tel. 215/662–8000; Michele M. Volpe,
Chief Executive Officer
**Web address**: www.pennmedicine.org/pmc/

PENNSYLVANIA HOSPITAL (O, 440 beds) 800 Spruce Street, Philadelphia, PA,
Zip 19107–6192; tel. 215/829–3000; Theresa M. . Larivee, Chief Executive
Officer

| | | |
|---|---|---|
| Owned, leased, sponsored: | 6 hospitals | 2804 beds |
| Contract–managed: | 0 hospitals | 0 beds |
| Totals: | 6 hospitals | 2804 beds |

★**0223: UNIVERSITY OF ROCHESTER MEDICAL CENTER** (NP)
601 Elmwood Ave Box 623, Rochester, NY Zip 14642–0002,
601 Elmwood Avenue, 14642–0002, tel. 585/275–2100; Mark
B. Taubman, M.D., Chief Executive Officer
**(Moderately Centralized Health System)**

**NEW YORK**: F. F. THOMPSON HOSPITAL (O, 291 beds) 350 Parrish Street,
Canandaigua, NY, Zip 14424–1731; tel. 585/396–6000; Michael Stapleton,
President and Chief Executive Officer

HIGHLAND HOSPITAL (O, 261 beds) 1000 South Avenue, Rochester, NY,
Zip 14620–2733; tel. 585/473–2200; Steven I. Goldstein, President and
Chief Executive Officer
**Web address**: https://www.urmc.rochester.edu/highland

JONES MEMORIAL HOSPITAL (O, 33 beds) 191 North Main Street, Wellsville,
NY, Zip 14895–1150, Mailing Address: P.O. Box 72, 14895–0072,
tel. 585/593–1100; Eva Benedict, R.N., President and Chief Executive
Officer
**Web address**: www.jmhny.org

NICHOLAS H. NOYES MEMORIAL HOSPITAL (O, 40 beds) 111 Clara Barton
Street, Dansville, NY, Zip 14437–9503; tel. 585/335–6001; Amy Pollard,
R.N., President and Chief Executive Officer

ST. JAMES HOSPITAL (O, 127 beds) 7329 Seneca Road North, Hornell, NY,
Zip 14843; tel. 607/247–2200; Bryan J. O'Donovan, President and Chief
Executive Officer
**Web address**: www.stjamesmercy.org

STRONG MEMORIAL HOSPITAL OF THE UNIVERSITY OF ROCHESTER (O, 878
beds) 601 Elmwood Avenue, Rochester, NY, Zip 14642–0002, 601 Elmwood
Avenue, Box 612, 14642–0002, tel. 585/275–2100; Steven I. Goldstein,
President and Chief Executive Officer
**Web address**: www.urmc.rochester.edu

| | | |
|---|---|---|
| Owned, leased, sponsored: | 6 hospitals | 1630 beds |
| Contract–managed: | 0 hospitals | 0 beds |
| Totals: | 6 hospitals | 1630 beds |

★**0033: UNIVERSITY OF TEXAS SYSTEM** (NP)
601 Colorado Street, Suite 205, Austin, TX Zip 78701–2904;
tel. 512/499–4224; John M. Zerwas, M.D., Executive Vice
Chancellor
**(Moderately Centralized Health System)**

**TEXAS**: UT HEALTH NORTH CAMPUS TYLER (O, 114 beds) 11937 Highway
271, Tyler, TX, Zip 75708–3154; tel. 903/877–7777; Cody Boyd, Chief
Executive Officer

UTHEALTH HARRIS COUNTY PSYCHIATRIC CENTER (C, 217 beds) 2800 South
MacGregor Way, Houston, TX, Zip 77021–1000; tel. 713/741–7870; Jair C.
Soares, M.D., Executive Director
**Web address**: www.https://hcpc.uth.edu/

UNIVERSITY OF TEXAS M.D. ANDERSON CANCER CENTER (O, 670 beds)
1515 Holcombe Boulevard, Unit 1491, Houston, TX, Zip 77030–4000;
tel. 713/792–2121; Peter Pisters, M.D., President

UNIVERSITY OF TEXAS MEDICAL BRANCH (O, 541 beds) 301 University
Boulevard, Galveston, TX, Zip 77555–0128; tel. 409/772–1011; Timothy J.
Harlin, M.D., Chief Executive Officer and Executive Vice President
**Web address**: www.utmb.edu

| | | |
|---|---|---|
| Owned, leased, sponsored: | 3 hospitals | 1325 beds |
| Contract–managed: | 1 hospitals | 217 beds |
| Totals: | 4 hospitals | 1542 beds |

**0983: UOFL HEALTH** (IO)
530 South Jackson Street, Louisville, KY Zip 40202–1675;
tel. 502/562–3000; Thomas Miller, Chief Executive
Officer

**KENTUCKY**: UOFL HEALTH – JEWISH HOSPITAL (O, 426 beds) 200 Abraham
Flexner Way, Louisville, KY, Zip 40202–1886; tel. 502/587–4011; John
Walsh, FACHE, Chief Administrative Officer
**Web address**: https://www.kindredhealthcare.com/locations/transitional–
care–hospitals/kindred–hospital–louisville–at–jewish–hospital

UOFL HEALTH – MARY AND ELIZABETH HOSPITAL (O, 170 beds) 1850
Bluegrass Avenue, Louisville, KY, Zip 40215–1199; tel. 502/361–6000;
Melisa Adkins, Chief Executive Officer
**Web address**: www.jhsmh.org

UOFL HEALTH – PEACE HOSPITAL (O, 220 beds) 2020 Newburg Road,
Louisville, KY, Zip 40205–1879; tel. 502/479–4500; Martha S. Mather, Chief
Administrative Officer

UOFL HEALTH – SHELBYVILLE HOSPITAL (O, 30 beds) 727 Hospital Drive,
Shelbyville, KY, Zip 40065–1699; tel. 502/647–4000; Aaron Garofola, Chief
Executive Officer
**Web address**: www.kentuckyonehealth.org/jewish–hospital–shelbyville

| | | |
|---|---|---|
| Owned, leased, sponsored: | 4 hospitals | 846 beds |
| Contract–managed: | 0 hospitals | 0 beds |
| Totals: | 4 hospitals | 846 beds |

★**0137: UPMC** (NP)
600 Grant Street, US Steel Tower, Suite 6262, Pittsburgh, PA
Zip 15219–2702; tel. 412/647–8762; Jeffrey A. Romoff, President and Chief Executive Officer
**(Decentralized Health System)**

**NEW YORK**: UPMC CHAUTAUQUA (O, 111 beds) 207 Foote Avenue,
Jamestown, NY, Zip 14701–7077, Mailing Address: P.O. Box 840,
14702–0840, tel. 716/487–0141; Brian Durniok, President

**PENNSYLVANIA**: UPMC ALTOONA (O, 346 beds) 620 Howard Avenue,
Altoona, PA, Zip 16601–4804; tel. 814/889–2011; Jan E. Fisher, President
**Web address**: www.altoonaregional.org

UPMC BEDFORD (O, 24 beds) 10455 Lincoln Highway, Everett, PA,
Zip 15537–7046; tel. 814/623–6161; Jan E. Fisher, President
**Web address**: www.upmcbedfordmemorial.com

For explanation of codes following names, see page B2.
★ Indicates Type III membership in the American Hospital Association.

UPMC CARLISLE (O, 153 beds) 361 Alexander Spring Road, Carlisle, PA, Zip 17015–6940; tel. 717/249–1212; Lou Baverso, President

UPMC CHILDREN'S HOSPITAL OF PITTSBURGH (O, 303 beds) One Children's Hospital Drive, 4401 Penn Avenue, Pittsburgh, PA, Zip 15224–1334; tel. 412/692–5325; Mark Sevco, President
Web address: www.chp.edu

UPMC EAST (O, 155 beds) 2775 Mosside Boulevard, Monroeville, PA, Zip 15146–2760; tel. 412/357–3000; Mark O'Hern, President

UPMC HAMOT (O, 345 beds) 201 State Street, Erie, PA, Zip 16550–0002; tel. 814/877–6000; David Gibbons, President
Web address: www.upmc.com/locations/hospitals/hamot

UPMC HANOVER (O, 93 beds) 300 Highland Avenue, Hanover, PA, Zip 17331–2297; tel. 717/316–3711; Michael W. Gaskins, President
Web address: www.hanoverhospital.org

UPMC HORIZON (O, 66 beds) 2200 Memorial Drive, Farrell, PA, Zip 16121–1357; tel. 724/588–2100; Robert Charles. Jackson Jr, President

UPMC JAMESON (O, 90 beds) 1211 Wilmington Avenue, New Castle, PA, Zip 16105–2516; tel. 724/658–9001; Robert Charles. Jackson Jr, President
Web address: www.upmcjameson.com

UPMC KANE (O, 31 beds) 4372 Route 6, Kane, PA, Zip 16735–3060; tel. 814/837–8585; Mark Papalia, President

UPMC LITITZ (O, 90 beds) 1500 Highlands Drive, Lititz, PA, Zip 17543–7694; tel. 717/625–5000; Brooks M. Turkel, President
Web address: www.heartoflancaster.com

UPMC LOCK HAVEN (O, 105 beds) 24 Cree Drive, Lock Haven, PA, Zip 17745–2699; tel. 570/893–5000; Ronald J. Reynolds, President

UPMC MAGEE–WOMENS HOSPITAL (O, 321 beds) 300 Halket Street, Pittsburgh, PA, Zip 15213–3108; tel. 412/641–1000; Richard Beigi, M.D., President
Web address: www.magee.edu

UPMC MCKEESPORT (O, 184 beds) 1500 Fifth Avenue, McKeesport, PA, Zip 15132–2422; tel. 412/664–2000; Mark O'Hern, President

UPMC MEMORIAL (O, 100 beds) 1701 Innovation Drive, York, PA, Zip 17408–8815, Mailing Address: P.O. Box 15118, 17405–7118, tel. 717/843–8623; Michael W. Gaskins, President
Web address: www.mhyork.org

UPMC MERCY (O, 383 beds) 1400 Locust Street, Pittsburgh, PA, Zip 15219–5166; tel. 412/232–8111; Michael A. Grace, President

UPMC MUNCY (O, 158 beds) 215 East Water Street, Muncy, PA, Zip 17756–8700; tel. 570/546–8282; Ronald J. Reynolds, President
Web address: www.susquehannahealth.org

UPMC NORTHWEST (O, 128 beds) 100 Fairfield Drive, Seneca, PA, Zip 16346–2130; tel. 814/676–7600; Brian Durniok, President

UPMC PASSAVANT (O, 306 beds) 9100 Babcock Boulevard, Pittsburgh, PA, Zip 15237–5815; tel. 412/748–6700; Susan E. Hoolahan, R.N., MSN, President
Web address: https://www.upmc.com/locations/hospitals/passavant

UPMC PINNACLE HARRISBURG (O, 665 beds) 111 South Front Street, Harrisburg, PA, Zip 17101–2010, Mailing Address: P.O. Box 8700, 17105–8700, tel. 717/231–8900; Philip Guarneschelli, President and Chief Executive Officer

UPMC PRESBYTERIAN (O, 1409 beds) 200 Lothrop Street, Pittsburgh, PA, Zip 15213–2536; tel. 412/647–2345; John Innocenti Sr, President
Web address: https://www.upmc.com/locations/hospitals/presbyterian/

UPMC SOMERSET (O, 98 beds) 225 South Center Avenue, Somerset, PA, Zip 15501–2088; tel. 814/443–5000; Andrew G. Rush, President
Web address: www.somersethospital.com

UPMC ST. MARGARET (O, 175 beds) 815 Freeport Road, Pittsburgh, PA, Zip 15215–3301; tel. 412/784–4000; David J. Patton, President

UPMC WELLSBORO (O, 20 beds) 32 Central Avenue, Wellsboro, PA, Zip 16901–1899; tel. 570/723–7764; Janie Marie. Hilfiger, Chief Administrative Officer
Web address: www.susquehannahealth.org

UPMC WILLIAMSPORT (O, 250 beds) 700 High Street, Williamsport, PA, Zip 17701–3100; tel. 570/321–1000; Donald R. Owrey, President
Web address: www.susquehannahealth.org

| Owned, leased, sponsored: | 26 hospitals | 6109 beds |
|---|---|---|
| Contract–managed: | 0 hospitals | 0 beds |
| Totals: | 26 hospitals | 6109 beds |

---

**★0066: UPMC SUSQUEHANNA** (NP)
700 High Street , Williamsport, PA Zip 17701–3100; tel. 570/321–1000; Steven P. Johnson, FACHE, President and Chief Executive Officer
**(Moderately Centralized Health System)**

| Owned, leased, sponsored: | 0 hospitals | 0 beds |
|---|---|---|
| Contract–managed: | 0 hospitals | 0 beds |
| Totals: | 0 hospitals | 0 beds |

---

**0816: UPPER ALLEGHENY HEALTH SYSTEM** (NP)
515 Main Street, Olean, NY Zip 14760–3676; tel. 716/375–6190; Jeff S. Zewe, R.N., Chief Executive Officer
**(Independent Hospital System)**

**NEW YORK**: OLEAN GENERAL HOSPITAL (O, 388 beds) 515 Main Street, Olean, NY, Zip 14760–1513; tel. 716/373–2600; Jeff S. Zewe, R.N., Chief Executive Officer

| Owned, leased, sponsored: | 1 hospitals | 388 beds |
|---|---|---|
| Contract–managed: | 0 hospitals | 0 beds |
| Totals: | 1 hospitals | 388 beds |

---

**★0057: USA HEALTH** (NP)
2451 University Hospital Drive, Mobile, AL Zip 36617–2300; tel. 251/471–7000; Owen Bailey, FACHE, Chief Executive Officer and Senior Associate Vice President for Medical Affairs
**(Independent Hospital System)**

**ALABAMA**: USA HEALTH CHILDREN'S & WOMEN'S HOSPITAL (O, 172 beds) 1700 Center Street, Mobile, AL, Zip 36604–3301; tel. 251/415–1000; Chris Jett, Administrator

USA HEALTH UNIVERSITY HOSPITAL (O, 203 beds) 2451 University Hospital Drive, Mobile, AL, Zip 36617–2293; tel. 251/471–7000; Sam Dean, Administrator
Web address: www.usahealthsystem.com/usamc

| Owned, leased, sponsored: | 2 hospitals | 375 beds |
|---|---|---|
| Contract–managed: | 0 hospitals | 0 beds |
| Totals: | 2 hospitals | 375 beds |

---

**0868: USMD HEALTH SYSTEM** (IO)
6333 North State Highway 161 Suite 200, Irving, TX Zip 75038–2229; tel. 214/493–4000; Richard C. Johnston, M.D., Chief Executive Officer and Chief Physician Officer
**(Independent Hospital System)**

**TEXAS**: USMD HOSPITAL AT ARLINGTON (O, 34 beds) 801 West Interstate 20, Arlington, TX, Zip 76017–5851; tel. 817/472–3400; Marcia Crim, R.N., MSN, Chief Executive Officer
Web address: www.usmdarlington.com

| Owned, leased, sponsored: | 1 hospitals | 34 beds |
|---|---|---|
| Contract–managed: | 0 hospitals | 0 beds |
| Totals: | 1 hospitals | 34 beds |

---

**★0860: UVA HEALTH SYSTEM** (NP)
1215 Lee Street, Charlottesville, VA Zip 22908–0816; tel. 434/924–0211; Craig Kent, Chief Executive Officer
**(Centralized Health System)**

---

For explanation of codes following names, see page B2.
★ Indicates Type III membership in the American Hospital Association.

**VIRGINIA:** UVA TRANSITIONAL CARE HOSPITAL (O, 30 beds) 2965 Ivy Rd (250 West), Charlottesville, VA, Zip 22903–9330; tel. 434/924–8245; Tracy Turman, Administrator
**Web address:** www.uvahealth.com/services/transitional–care–hospital

UNIVERSITY OF VIRGINIA MEDICAL CENTER (O, 612 beds) 1215 Lee Street, Charlottesville, VA, Zip 22908–0001, Mailing Address: P.O. Box 800809, 22908–0809, tel. 434/924–0211; Craig Kent, Interim Chief Executive Officer

| | | |
|---|---|---|
| Owned, leased, sponsored: | 2 hospitals | 642 beds |
| Contract–managed: | 0 hospitals | 0 beds |
| Totals: | 2 hospitals | 642 beds |

---

### 1009: UW HEALTH SYSTEM (IO)
600 Highland Avenue, Madison, WI Zip 53792–0001; tel. 608/263–6400; Alan Kaplan, M.D., Chief Executive Officer
**(Moderately Centralized Health System)**

**WISCONSIN:** UW HEALTH REHABILITATION HOSPITAL (O, 43 beds) 5115 North Biltmore Lane, Madison, WI, Zip 53718–2161; tel. 608/592–8100; Mary Kay. Diderrich, R.N., Chief Executive Officer
**Web address:** www.uwhealth.org

UNIVERSITY HOSPITAL (O, 624 beds) 600 Highland Avenue, Madison, WI, Zip 53792–0002; tel. 608/263–6400; Alan Kaplan, M.D., Chief Executive Officer
**Web address:** www.uwhealth.org

| | | |
|---|---|---|
| Owned, leased, sponsored: | 2 hospitals | 667 beds |
| Contract–managed: | 0 hospitals | 0 beds |
| Totals: | 2 hospitals | 667 beds |

---

### ★6415: UW MEDICINE (NP)
1959 NE Pacific Street, Seattle, WA Zip 98195–0001, Mailing Address: P.O. Box 356350, 98195–6350, tel. 206/543–7718; Paul G. Ramsey, M.D., Chief Executive Officer
**(Independent Hospital System)**

**WASHINGTON:** UW MEDICINE/HARBORVIEW MEDICAL CENTER (C, 413 beds) 325 Ninth Avenue, Seattle, WA, Zip 98104–2499, Mailing Address: P.O. Box 359717, 98195–9717, tel. 206/744–3000; Paul Hayes, R.N., Executive Director

UW MEDICINE/NORTHWEST HOSPITAL & MEDICAL CENTER (O, 203 beds) 1550 North 115th Street, Seattle, WA, Zip 98133–8401; tel. 206/364–0500; Cynthia Hecker, R.N., Executive Director
**Web address:** www.uwmedicine.org/Patient–Care/Locations/nwh/Pages/default.aspx

UW MEDICINE/VALLEY MEDICAL CENTER (C, 311 beds) 400 South 43rd Street, Renton, WA, Zip 98055–5714, Mailing Address: P.O. Box 50010, 98058–5010, tel. 425/228–3450; Richard D. Roodman, Chief Executive Officer

UNIVERSITY OF WASHINGTON MEDICAL CENTER (O, 476 beds) 1959 NE Pacific Street, Seattle, WA, Zip 98195–6151; tel. 206/598–3300; Cynthia Hecker, R.N., Executive Director
**Web address:** www.uwmedicine.org/uw–medical–center

| | | |
|---|---|---|
| Owned, leased, sponsored: | 2 hospitals | 679 beds |
| Contract–managed: | 2 hospitals | 724 beds |
| Totals: | 4 hospitals | 1403 beds |

---

### ★0128: VALLEY HEALTH SYSTEM (NP)
220 Campus Boulevard, Suite 420, Winchester, VA Zip 22601–2889, Mailing Address: P.O. Box 3340, 22604–2540, tel. 540/536–8024; Mark S. Nantz, FACHE, President and Chief Executive Officer
**(Moderately Centralized Health System)**

**VIRGINIA:** VALLEY HEALTH – PAGE MEMORIAL HOSPITAL (O, 25 beds) 200 Memorial Drive, Luray, VA, Zip 22835–1005; tel. 540/743–4561; N. Travis. Clark, President
**Web address:** www.valleyhealthlink.com/page

VALLEY HEALTH – SHENANDOAH MEMORIAL HOSPITAL (O, 25 beds) 759 South Main Street, Woodstock, VA, Zip 22664–1127; tel. 540/459–1100; N. Travis. Clark, President
**Web address:** www.valleyhealthlink.com/shenandoah

VALLEY HEALTH – WARREN MEMORIAL HOSPITAL (O, 180 beds) 1000 North Shenandoah Avenue, Front Royal, VA, Zip 22630–3598; tel. 540/636–0300; Floyd Heater, President

VALLEY HEALTH – WINCHESTER MEDICAL CENTER (O, 541 beds) 1840 Amherst Street, Winchester, VA, Zip 22601–2808, Mailing Address: P.O. Box 3340, 22604–2540, tel. 540/536–8000; Grady W. Philips III, President
**Web address:** www.valleyhealthlink.com/WMC

**WEST VIRGINIA:** VALLEY HEALTH – HAMPSHIRE MEMORIAL HOSPITAL (O, 44 beds) 363 Sunrise Boulevard, Romney, WV, Zip 26757–4607; tel. 304/822–4561; Thomas S. Kluge, President
**Web address:** www.valleyhealthlink.com/hampshire

VALLEY HEALTH – WAR MEMORIAL HOSPITAL (O, 41 beds) One Healthy Way, Berkeley Springs, WV, Zip 25411–7463; tel. 304/258–1234; Thomas S. Kluge, President

| | | |
|---|---|---|
| Owned, leased, sponsored: | 6 hospitals | 856 beds |
| Contract–managed: | 0 hospitals | 0 beds |
| Totals: | 6 hospitals | 856 beds |

---

### ★0387: VANDERBILT HEALTH (NP)
1211 22nd Avenue South, Nashville, TN Zip 37232; tel. 615/322–5000; Charles Wright. Pinson, M.D., Deputy Chief Executive Officer and Chief Health System Officer
**(Moderately Centralized Health System)**

**TENNESSEE:** VANDERBILT UNIVERSITY MEDICAL CENTER (O, 1058 beds) 1211 Medical Center Drive, Nashville, TN, Zip 37232–2102; tel. 615/322–5000; Jeffrey R. Balsar, President and Chief Executive Officer Vanderbilt Medical Center and Dean, Vanderbilt University School of Medicine
**Web address:** www.mc.vanderbilt.edu

VANDERBILT WILSON COUNTY HOSPITAL (O, 137 beds) 1411 Baddour Parkway, Lebanon, TN, Zip 37087–2513; tel. 615/444–8262; Jay Hinesley, FACHE, Chief Executive Officer

| | | |
|---|---|---|
| Owned, leased, sponsored: | 2 hospitals | 1195 beds |
| Contract–managed: | 0 hospitals | 0 beds |
| Totals: | 2 hospitals | 1195 beds |

---

### ★0939: VCU HEALTH SYSTEM (NP)
1200 East Marshall Street, Richmond, VA Zip 23298, Mailing Address: P.O. Box 980510, 23298–0510, tel. 804/828–9000; Peter Buckley, M.D., Interim Chief Executive Officer, VCU Health System
**(Moderately Centralized Health System)**

**VIRGINIA:** CHILDREN'S HOSPITAL OF RICHMOND AT VCU–BROOK ROAD CAMPUS (O, 36 beds) 2924 Brook Road, Richmond, VA, Zip 23220–1298; tel. 804/321–7474; Elias Neujahr, Chief Executive Officer
**Web address:** www.chrichmond.org

VCU HEALTH COMMUNITY MEMORIAL HOSPITAL (O, 210 beds) 125 Buena Vista Circle, South Hill, VA, Zip 23970–1431, Mailing Address: P.O. Box 90, 23970–0090, tel. 434/447–3151; W Scott. Burnette, Chief Executive Officer
**Web address:** www.cmh–sh.org

VCU MEDICAL CENTER (O, 812 beds) 1250 East Marshall Street, Richmond, VA, Zip 23298–5051, Mailing Address: P.O. Box 980510, 23298–0510, tel. 804/828–9000; Ron Clark, M.D., Interim Chief Executive Officer

| | | |
|---|---|---|
| Owned, leased, sponsored: | 3 hospitals | 1058 beds |
| Contract–managed: | 0 hospitals | 0 beds |
| Totals: | 3 hospitals | 1058 beds |

---

### 1041: VERITAS COLLABORATIVE (IO)
4024 Stirrup Creek Drive, Durham, NC Zip 27703–9464; tel. 855/875–5812; Stacie McEntyre, Chief Executive Officer

---

For explanation of codes following names, see page B2.
★ Indicates Type III membership in the American Hospital Association.

Section B

**NORTH CAROLINA:** VERITAS COLLABORATIVE (L, 40 beds) 4024 Stirrup Creek Drive, Durham, NC, Zip 27703–9464; tel. 919/908–9730; Sara Hofmeier, Executive Director
**Web address:** www.https://veritascollaborative.com

VERITAS COLLABORATIVE (L, 25 beds) 615 Douglas Street, Suite 500, Durham, NC, Zip 27705–6616; tel. 919/908–9730; Becca Eckstein, Executive Director
**Web address:** www.https://veritascollaborative.com

| | | |
|---|---|---|
| Owned, leased, sponsored: | 2 hospitals | 65 beds |
| Contract–managed: | 0 hospitals | 0 beds |
| Totals: | 2 hospitals | 65 beds |

**1075: VERITY HEALTH SYSTEM** (NP)
2200 West Third Street, Suite 200, Los Angeles, CA Zip 90057–1935, 203 Redwood Shores Parkway, Suite 800, Redwood City, 94065, tel. 650/551–6650; Richard Adcock, President and Chief Executive Officer
**(Independent Hospital System)**

**CALIFORNIA:** SETON MEDICAL CENTER COASTSIDE (O, 116 beds) 600 Marine Boulevard, Moss Beach, CA, Zip 94038–9641; tel. 650/563–7100

SETON MEDICAL CENTER (O, 446 beds) 1900 Sullivan Avenue, Daly City, CA, Zip 94015–2229; tel. 650/992–4000; Mark Fratzke, R.N., President and Chief Executive Officer
**Web address:** www.setonmedicalcenter.org

| | | |
|---|---|---|
| Owned, leased, sponsored: | 2 hospitals | 562 beds |
| Contract–managed: | 0 hospitals | 0 beds |
| Totals: | 2 hospitals | 562 beds |

★**0299: VIBRA HEALTHCARE** (IO)
4600 Lena Drive, Mechanicsburg, PA Zip 17055–4904; tel. 717/591–5700; Brad Hollinger, Chairman and Chief Executive Officer
**(Independent Hospital System)**

**CALIFORNIA:** BALLARD REHABILITATION HOSPITAL (O, 60 beds) 1760 West 16th Street, San Bernardino, CA, Zip 92411–1160; tel. 909/473–1200; Mary Miles. Hunt, Chief Executive Officer
**Web address:** www.ballardrehab.com

KENTFIELD HOSPITAL (O, 60 beds) 1125 Sir Francis Drake Boulevard, Kentfield, CA, Zip 94904–1455; tel. 415/456–9680; Varun Chauhan, Chief Executive Officer
**Web address:** www.kentfieldrehab.com

SAN JOAQUIN VALLEY REHABILITATION HOSPITAL (O, 62 beds) 7173 North Sharon Avenue, Fresno, CA, Zip 93720–3329; tel. 559/436–3600; Mary Jo Jacobson, Chief Executive Officer

VIBRA HOSPITAL OF NORTHERN CALIFORNIA (O, 88 beds) 2801 Eureka Way, Redding, CA, Zip 96001–0222; tel. 530/246–9000; Emily DeFillipo, Chief Executive Officer
**Web address:** www.norcalrehab.com

VIBRA HOSPITAL OF SACRAMENTO (O, 58 beds) 330 Montrose Drive, Folsom, CA, Zip 95630–2720; tel. 916/351–9151; Kimberly C. Long, R.N., MSN, Chief Executive Officer

**COLORADO:** VIBRA HOSPITAL OF DENVER (O, 71 beds) 8451 Pearl Street, Thornton, CO, Zip 80229–4804; tel. 303/288–3000; Lamar McBride, Chief Executive Officer
**Web address:** www.vhdenver.com

**IDAHO:** VIBRA HOSPITAL OF BOISE (O, 60 beds) 6651 West Franklin Road, Boise, ID, Zip 83709–0914; tel. 877/801–2244; Ryan Zumalt, Chief Executive Officer

**INDIANA:** SOUTHERN INDIANA REHABILITATION HOSPITAL (O, 60 beds) 3104 Blackiston Boulevard, New Albany, IN, Zip 47150–9579; tel. 812/941–8300; William Boso, Executive Director, Administrator
**Web address:** www.sirh.org

VIBRA HOSPITAL OF NORTHWESTERN INDIANA (O, 40 beds) 9509 Georgia Street, Crown Point, IN, Zip 46307–6518; tel. 219/472–2200; Craig L. Johnson, FACHE, Chief Executive Officer
**Web address:** www.vhnwindiana.com/

**KENTUCKY:** GATEWAY REHABILITATION HOSPITAL (C, 40 beds) 5940 Merchant Street, Florence, KY, Zip 41042–1158; tel. 859/426–2400; Frank Schneider, FACHE, Chief Executive Officer
**Web address:** www.gatewayflorence.com/

SOUTHERN KENTUCKY REHABILITATION HOSPITAL (O, 60 beds) 1300 Campbell Lane, Bowling Green, KY, Zip 42104–4162; tel. 270/594–5980; Stuart Locke, Chief Executive Officer

**MASSACHUSETTS:** VIBRA HOSPITAL OF SOUTHEASTERN MASSACHUSETTS (O, 90 beds) 4499 Acushnet Avenue, New Bedford, MA, Zip 02745–4707; tel. 508/995–6900; Edward B. Leary, Chief Executive Officer
**Web address:** www.newbedfordrehab.com

VIBRA HOSPITAL OF WESTERN MASSACHUSETTS (O, 174 beds) 1400 State Street, Springfield, MA, Zip 01109–2550; tel. 413/726–6700; Edward B. Leary, Interim Chief Executive Officer
**Web address:** www.vhwmass.com

**MICHIGAN:** VIBRA HOSPITAL OF SOUTHEASTERN MICHIGAN, LLC (O, 220 beds) 26400 West Outer Drive, Lincoln Park, MI, Zip 48146–2088; tel. 313/386–2000; Reginald Lee, Chief Executive Officer
**Web address:** www.vhsemichigan.com/

**NORTH DAKOTA:** VIBRA HOSPITAL OF CENTRAL DAKOTAS (O, 41 beds) 1000 18th Street NW, Mandan, ND, Zip 58554–1612; tel. 701/667–2000; Glynda Troyo–Sauviac, Chief Executive Officer
**Web address:** www.vhcentraldakotas.com

VIBRA HOSPITAL OF FARGO (O, 31 beds) 1720 University Drive South, Fargo, ND, Zip 58103–4940; tel. 701/241–9099; Custer Huseby, Chief Executive Officer

**OHIO:** VIBRA HOSPITAL OF MAHONING VALLEY (O, 42 beds) 8049 South Avenue, Boardman, OH, Zip 44512–6154; tel. 330/726–5000; Nathan Mast, Chief Executive Officer
**Web address:** www.vhmvalley.com

**OREGON:** VIBRA SPECIALTY HOSPITAL OF PORTLAND (O, 68 beds) 10300 NE Hancock Street, Portland, OR, Zip 97220–3831; tel. 503/257–5500; Victor Jackson, Chief Executive Officer

**SOUTH CAROLINA:** VIBRA HOSPITAL OF CHARLESTON (O, 59 beds) 1200 Hospital Drive, Mt. Pleasant, SC, Zip 29464; tel. 843/375–4000; Donald Becker, Chief Executive Officer
**Web address:** www.vhcharleston.com

**TEXAS:** HIGHLANDS REHABILITATION HOSPITAL (O, 41 beds) 1395 George Dieter Drive, El Paso, TX, Zip 79936–7410; tel. 915/298–7222; Steven Alwine, Chief Executive Officer

VIBRA HOSPITAL OF AMARILLO (O, 37 beds) 7501 Wallace Boulevard, Amarillo, TX, Zip 79124–2150; tel. 806/467–7000; Eric Mueller, Executive Officer and Market Chief Executive Officer
**Web address:** www.vhamarillo.com

VIBRA REHABILITATION HOSPITAL OF AMARILLO (O, 44 beds) 7200 West 9th Avenue, Amarillo, TX, Zip 79106–1703; tel. 806/468–2900; Tammie Tabor, Chief Executive Officer
**Web address:** www.vrhamarillo.com

VIBRA SPECIALTY HOSPITAL AT DESOTO (O, 60 beds) 2700 Walker Way, Desoto, TX, Zip 75115–2088; tel. 972/298–1100; Tracy Penny, Interim Chief Executive Officer
**Web address:** www.vshdesoto.com

**VIRGINIA:** VIBRA HOSPITAL OF RICHMOND (O, 60 beds) 2220 Edward Holland Drive, Richmond, VA, Zip 23230–2519; tel. 804/678–7000; Linda Tiemens, Chief Executive Officer
**Web address:** www.vhrichmond.com

| | | |
|---|---|---|
| Owned, leased, sponsored: | 23 hospitals | 1586 beds |
| Contract–managed: | 1 hospitals | 40 beds |
| Totals: | 24 hospitals | 1626 beds |

★**0217: VIDANT HEALTH** (NP)
2100 Stantonsburg Road, Greenville, NC Zip 27834–2818, Mailing Address: P.O. Box 6028, 27835–6028, tel. 252/847–4100; Michael Waldrum, M.D., Chief Executive Officer
**(Moderately Centralized Health System)**

For explanation of codes following names, see page B2.
★ Indicates Type III membership in the American Hospital Association.

**B146** Health Care Systems, Networks and Alliances

© 2021 AHA Guide

**NORTH CAROLINA**: THE OUTER BANKS HOSPITAL (O, 21 beds) 4800 South Croatan Highway, Nags Head, NC, Zip 27959–9704; tel. 252/449–4500; Ronald A. Sloan, FACHE, President
**Web address**: www.theouterbankshospital.com

VIDANT BEAUFORT HOSPITAL (L, 84 beds) 628 East 12th Street, Washington, NC, Zip 27889–3409; tel. 252/975–4100; Debra T. Hernandez, R.N., FACHE, President
**Web address**: www.vidanthealth.com

VIDANT BERTIE HOSPITAL (L, 6 beds) 1403 South King Street, Mailing Address: P.O. Box 40, Windsor, NC, Zip 27983–9666, Mailing Address: P.O. Box 40, 27983–0040, tel. 252/794–6600; Brian Harvill, President
**Web address**: www.vidanthealth.com

VIDANT CHOWAN HOSPITAL (L, 19 beds) 211 Virginia Road, Edenton, NC, Zip 27932–9668, Mailing Address: P.O. Box 629, 27932–0629, tel. 252/482–8451; Brian Harvill, President

VIDANT DUPLIN HOSPITAL (L, 47 beds) 401 North Main Street, Kenansville, NC, Zip 28349–8801, Mailing Address: P.O. Box 278, 28349–0278, tel. 910/296–0941; Jeffery Dial, Interim President
**Web address**: www.vidanthealth.com

VIDANT EDGECOMBE HOSPITAL (O, 58 beds) 111 Hospital Drive, Tarboro, NC, Zip 27886–2011; tel. 252/641–7700; Patrick Heins, President
**Web address**: https://www.vidanthealth.com/edgecombe/default.aspx

VIDANT MEDICAL CENTER (O, 974 beds) 2100 Stantonsburg Road, Greenville, NC, Zip 27834–2818, Mailing Address: P.O. Box 6028, 27835–6028, tel. 252/847–4100; William Brian. Floyd, President

VIDANT NORTH HOSPITAL (O, 142 beds) 250 Smith Church Road, Roanoke Rapids, NC, Zip 27870–4914, Mailing Address: P.O. Box 1089, 27870–1089, tel. 252/535–8011; William Mahone, President
**Web address**: www.https://halifaxregional.org

VIDANT ROANOKE–CHOWAN HOSPITAL (L, 110 beds) 500 South Academy Street, Ahoskie, NC, Zip 27910–3261, Mailing Address: P.O. Box 1385, 27910–1385, tel. 252/209–3000; Judy Bruno, President

| | | |
|---|---|---|
| Owned, leased, sponsored: | 9 hospitals | 1461 beds |
| Contract–managed: | 0 hospitals | 0 beds |
| Totals: | 9 hospitals | 1461 beds |

---

**0012: VIRGINIA DEPARTMENT OF MENTAL HEALTH** (NP)
1220 Bank Street, Richmond, VA Zip 23219–3645, Mailing Address: P.O. Box 1797, 23218–1797, tel. 804/786–3921; James S. Reinhard, M.D., Commissioner
**(Independent Hospital System)**

**VIRGINIA**: CATAWBA HOSPITAL (O, 110 beds) 5525 Catawba Hospital Drive, Catawba, VA, Zip 24070–2115, Mailing Address: P.O. Box 200, 24070–0200, tel. 540/375–4200; Walton F. Mitchell III, Director
**Web address**: www.catawba.dbhds.virginia.gov

CENTRAL STATE HOSPITAL (O, 277 beds) 26317 West Washington Street, Petersburg, VA, Zip 23803–2727, Mailing Address: P.O. Box 4030, 23803–0030, tel. 804/524–7000; Brandi Justice, Interim Director
**Web address**: www.csh.dbhds.virginia.gov

CENTRAL VIRGINIA TRAINING CENTER (O, 1112 beds) 210 East Colony Road, Madison Heights, VA, Zip 24572–2005, Mailing Address: P.O. Box 1098, Lynchburg, 24505–1098, tel. 434/947–6326; David Cole, Assistant Director of Administration, Chief Financial Officer, Department of Behavioral Health and Developmental Service

COMMONWEALTH CENTER FOR CHILDREN AND ADOLESCENTS (O, 60 beds) 1355 Richmond Road, Staunton, VA, Zip 24401–9146, Box 4000, 24402–4000, tel. 540/332–2100; Jaime Bamford, M.D., Director
**Web address**: www.ccca.dbhds.virginia.gov

EASTERN STATE HOSPITAL (O, 300 beds) 4601 Ironbound Road, Williamsburg, VA, Zip 23188–2652; tel. 757/253–5161; Donna Moore, PsyD, Director
**Web address**: www.esh.dmhmrsas.virginia.gov/

HIRAM W. DAVIS MEDICAL CENTER (O, 10 beds) 26317 West Washington Street, Petersburg, VA, Zip 23803–2727, Mailing Address: P.O. Box 4030, 23803–0030, tel. 804/524–7420; Nichelle Williams, Director

NORTHERN VIRGINIA MENTAL HEALTH INSTITUTE (O, 134 beds) 3302 Gallows Road, Falls Church, VA, Zip 22042–3398; tel. 703/207–7100; Tammy Peacock, Ph.D., Facility Director
**Web address**: www.nvmhi.dbhds.virginia.gov

PIEDMONT GERIATRIC HOSPITAL (O, 135 beds) 5001 East Patrick Henry Hwy, Burkeville, VA, Zip 23922–3460, Mailing Address: P.O. Box 427, 23922–0427, tel. 434/767–4401; Emma L. Lowry, M.D., Acting Facility Director, Chief Executive Officer

SOUTHERN VIRGINIA MENTAL HEALTH INSTITUTE (O, 72 beds) 382 Taylor Drive, Danville, VA, Zip 24541–4023; tel. 434/799–6220; William Cook, Director
**Web address**: www.svmhi.dbhds.virginia.gov

SOUTHWESTERN VIRGINIA MENTAL HEALTH INSTITUTE (O, 166 beds) 340 Bagley Circle, Marion, VA, Zip 24354–3390; tel. 276/783–1200; Cynthia McClaskey, Ph.D., Director
**Web address**: www.swvmhi.dmhmrsas.virginia.gov/

WESTERN STATE HOSPITAL (O, 246 beds) 103 Valley Center Drive, Staunton, VA, Zip 24401–9146, Mailing Address: P.O. Box 2500, 24402–2500, tel. 540/332–8000; Mary Clare. Smith, Director
**Web address**: www.dbhds.virginia.gov

| | | |
|---|---|---|
| Owned, leased, sponsored: | 11 hospitals | 2622 beds |
| Contract–managed: | 0 hospitals | 0 beds |
| Totals: | 11 hospitals | 2622 beds |

---

**0986: VIRGINIA MASON HEALTH SYSTEM** (NP)
1100 Ninth Avenue, Seattle, WA Zip 98101–2756, Mailing Address: P.O. Box 900, 98111–0900, tel. 206/223–6600; Gary Kaplan, M.D., FACHE, Chief Executive Officer
**(Moderately Centralized Health System)**

**WASHINGTON**: VIRGINIA MASON MEDICAL CENTER (O, 255 beds) 1100 Ninth Avenue, Seattle, WA, Zip 98101–2756, Mailing Address: P.O. Box 900, 98111–0900, tel. 206/223–6600; Suzanne Anderson, President

VIRGINIA MASON MEMORIAL (O, 226 beds) 2811 Tieton Drive, Yakima, WA, Zip 98902–3761; tel. 509/575–8000; Carole Peet, R.N., MSN, Chief Executive Officer
**Web address**: www.yakimamemorial.org

| | | |
|---|---|---|
| Owned, leased, sponsored: | 2 hospitals | 481 beds |
| Contract–managed: | 0 hospitals | 0 beds |
| Totals: | 2 hospitals | 481 beds |

---

**★6725: VIRTUA HEALTH** (NP)
303 Lippincott Drive, 4th Floor, Marlton, NJ Zip 08053–4160; tel. 856/355–0010; Dennis W. Pullin, FACHE, President and Chief Executive Officer
**(Centralized Health System)**

**NEW JERSEY**: VIRTUA MARLTON (O, 185 beds) 90 Brick Road, Marlton, NJ, Zip 08053–2177; tel. 856/355–6000; Dennis W. Pullin, FACHE, President and Chief Executive Officer
**Web address**: www.virtua.org

VIRTUA MEMORIAL (O, 334 beds) 175 Madison Avenue, Mount Holly, NJ, Zip 08060–2099; tel. 609/267–0700; Dennis W. Pullin, FACHE, President and Chief Executive Officer
**Web address**: www.virtua.org

VIRTUA OUR LADY OF LOURDES HOSPITAL (O, 340 beds) 1600 Haddon Avenue, Camden, NJ, Zip 08103–3117; tel. 856/757–3500; Mark Nessel, Senior Vice President and Chief Operating Officer

VIRTUA VOORHEES (O, 402 beds) 100 Bowman Drive, Voorhees, NJ, Zip 08043–9612; tel. 856/325–3000; Dennis W. Pullin, FACHE, President and Chief Executive Officer
**Web address**: www.virtua.org

---

For explanation of codes following names, see page B2.
★ Indicates Type III membership in the American Hospital Association.

VIRTUA WILLINGBORO HOSPITAL (O, 169 beds) 218–A Sunset Road, Willingboro, NJ, Zip 08046–1162; tel. 609/835–2900; Mark Nessel, Executive Vice President and Chief Operating Officer

| | | |
|---|---|---|
| Owned, leased, sponsored: | 5 hospitals | 1430 beds |
| Contract–managed: | 0 hospitals | 0 beds |
| Totals: | 5 hospitals | 1430 beds |

---

### ★0221: WAKE FOREST BAPTIST HEALTH (NP)
Medical Center Boulevard, Winston–Salem, NC Zip 27157; tel. 336/716–2011; Julie Ann . Freischlag, M.D., Chief Executive Officer
**(Centralized Health System)**

**NORTH CAROLINA**: HIGH POINT MEDICAL CENTER (O, 317 beds) 601 North Elm Street, High Point, NC, Zip 27262–4398, Mailing Address: P.O. Box HP–5, 27261–1899, tel. 336/878–6000; James Hoekstra, M.D., President

WAKE FOREST BAPTIST HEALTH – WILKES MEDICAL CENTER (L, 80 beds) 1370 West 'D' Street, North Wilkesboro, NC, Zip 28659–3506, Mailing Address: P.O. Box 609, 28659–0609, tel. 336/651–8100; Chad J. Brown, M.P.H., FACHE, President
**Web address**: www.wilkesregional.com/

WAKE FOREST BAPTIST HEALTH–DAVIE MEDICAL CENTER (O, 25 beds) 329 NC Highway 801 North, Bermuda Run, NC, Zip 27006; tel. 336/998–1300; Chad J. Brown, M.P.H., FACHE, President

WAKE FOREST BAPTIST HEALTH–LEXINGTON MEDICAL CENTER (O, 77 beds) 250 Hospital Drive, Lexington, NC, Zip 27292–6728, Mailing Address: P.O. Box 1817, 27293–1817, tel. 336/248–5161; William B. James, FACHE, President
**Web address**: www.lexington.wakehealth.edu

WAKE FOREST BAPTIST MEDICAL CENTER (O, 800 beds) Medical Center Boulevard, Winston–Salem, NC, Zip 27157–0001; tel. 336/716–2011; Cathleen Wheatley, R.N., President and System Chief Nurse Executive and Senior Vice President of Clinical Operations
**Web address**: www.wakehealth.edu

| | | |
|---|---|---|
| Owned, leased, sponsored: | 5 hospitals | 1299 beds |
| Contract–managed: | 0 hospitals | 0 beds |
| Totals: | 5 hospitals | 1299 beds |

---

### ★6705: WAKEMED HEALTH & HOSPITALS (NP)
3000 New Bern Avenue, Raleigh, NC Zip 27610–1231; tel. 919/350–8000; Donald R. Gintzig, President and Chief Executive Officer
**(Moderately Centralized Health System)**

**NORTH CAROLINA**: WAKEMED CARY HOSPITAL (O, 178 beds) 1900 Kildaire Farm Road, Cary, NC, Zip 27518–6616; tel. 919/350–8000; Donald R. Gintzig, President and Chief Executive Officer
**Web address**: www.wakemed.org

WAKEMED RALEIGH CAMPUS (O, 695 beds) 3000 New Bern Avenue, Raleigh, NC, Zip 27610–1295; tel. 919/350–8000; Donald R. Gintzig, President and Chief Executive Officer

| | | |
|---|---|---|
| Owned, leased, sponsored: | 2 hospitals | 873 beds |
| Contract–managed: | 0 hospitals | 0 beds |
| Totals: | 2 hospitals | 873 beds |

---

### ★0979: WASHINGTON HEALTH SYSTEM (NP)
155 Wilson Avenue, Washington, PA Zip 15301–3336; tel. 724/225–7000; Brook Ward, President and Chief Executive Officer
**(Independent Hospital System)**

**PENNSYLVANIA**: WASHINGTON HEALTH SYSTEM GREENE (O, 23 beds) 350 Bonar Avenue, Waynesburg, PA, Zip 15370–1608; tel. 724/627–3101; Terry Wiltrout, President
**Web address**: www.southwestregionalmedical.com/

WASHINGTON HOSPITAL (O, 181 beds) 155 Wilson Avenue, Washington, PA, Zip 15301–3398; tel. 724/225–7000; Brook Ward, President and Chief Executive Officer

| | | |
|---|---|---|
| Owned, leased, sponsored: | 2 hospitals | 204 beds |
| Contract–managed: | 0 hospitals | 0 beds |
| Totals: | 2 hospitals | 204 beds |

---

### ★0068: WELLSPAN HEALTH (NP)
45 Monument Road, Suite 200, York, PA Zip 17403–5071; tel. 717/851–2121; Roxanna L. Gapstur, Ph.D., R.N., President and Chief Executive Officer
**(Centralized Physician/Insurance Health System)**

**PENNSYLVANIA**: WELLSPAN CHAMBERSBURG HOSPITAL (O, 285 beds) 112 North Seventh Street, Chambersburg, PA, Zip 17201–1720; tel. 717/267–3000; Patrick W. O'Donnell, President and Chief Executive Officer
**Web address**: www.summithealth.org

WELLSPAN EPHRATA COMMUNITY HOSPITAL (O, 141 beds) 169 Martin Avenue, Ephrata, PA, Zip 17522–1724, Mailing Address: P.O. Box 1002, 17522–1002, tel. 717/733–0311
**Web address**: www.wellspan.org

WELLSPAN GETTYSBURG HOSPITAL (O, 76 beds) 147 Gettys Street, Gettysburg, PA, Zip 17325–2534; tel. 717/334–2121; Jane E. Hyde, President
**Web address**: www.wellspan.org

WELLSPAN GOOD SAMARITAN HOSPITAL (O, 159 beds) 252 South 4th Street, Fourth and Walnut Streets, Lebanon, PA, Zip 17042–1281, Mailing Address: P.O. Box 1281, 17042–1281, tel. 717/270–7500; Thomas R. Harlow, FACHE, President

WELLSPAN PHILHAVEN (O, 118 beds) 283 South Butler Road, Mount Gretna, PA, Zip 17064–6085, Mailing Address: P.O. Box 550, 17064–0550, tel. 717/273–8871; Philip D. Hess, President
**Web address**: www.philhaven.org

WELLSPAN SURGERY AND REHABILLITATION HOSPITAL (O, 72 beds) 55 Monument Road, York, PA, Zip 17403–5023; tel. 717/812–6100; Victoria Diamond, R.N., MS, President

WELLSPAN YORK HOSPITAL (O, 573 beds) 1001 South George Street, York, PA, Zip 17403–3645; tel. 717/851–2345; Victoria Diamond, R.N., MS, President
**Web address**: www.wellspan.org

WELLSPAN WAYNESBORO HOSPITAL (O, 57 beds) 501 East Main Street, Waynesboro, PA, Zip 17268–2394; tel. 717/765–4000; Melissa Dubrow, Vice President and Chief Operating Officer

| | | |
|---|---|---|
| Owned, leased, sponsored: | 8 hospitals | 1481 beds |
| Contract–managed: | 0 hospitals | 0 beds |
| Totals: | 8 hospitals | 1481 beds |

---

### ★0995: WELLSTAR HEALTH SYSTEM (NP)
793 Sawyer Road, Marietta, GA Zip 30062; tel. 770/792–5012; Candice Saunders, President and Chief Executive Officer
**(Centralized Health System)**

**GEORGIA**: WELLSTAR COBB HOSPITAL (O, 372 beds) 3950 Austell Road, Austell, GA, Zip 30106–1121; tel. 470/732–4000; Callie Andrews, President
**Web address**: www.wellstar.org

WELLSTAR DOUGLAS HOSPITAL (O, 108 beds) 8954 Hospital Drive, Douglasville, GA, Zip 30134–2282; tel. 770/949–1500; Craig A. Owens, President
**Web address**: www.wellstar.org

WELLSTAR KENNESTONE HOSPITAL (O, 657 beds) 677 Church Street, Marietta, GA, Zip 30060–1148; tel. 770/793–5000; Mary Chatman, Ph.D., R.N., Senior Vice President and President
**Web address**: www.wellstar.org

WELLSTAR PAULDING HOSPITAL (O, 294 beds) 2518 Jimmy Lee Smith Parkway, Hiram, GA, Zip 30141; tel. 470/644–7000; John Kueven, Senior Vice President and President

---

For explanation of codes following names, see page B2.
★ Indicates Type III membership in the American Hospital Association.

WELLSTAR WINDY HILL HOSPITAL (O, 19 beds) 2540 Windy Hill Road, Marietta, GA, Zip 30067–8632; tel. 770/644–1000; Mary Chatman, Ph.D., R.N., Chief Executive Officer
**Web address:** www.wellstar.org

WELLSTAR ATLANTA MEDICAL CENTER (O, 506 beds) 303 Parkway Drive NE, Atlanta, GA, Zip 30312–1212; tel. 404/265–4000; Stuart D. Downs, R.N., Interim President

WELLSTAR NORTH FULTON HOSPITAL (O, 173 beds) 3000 Hospital Boulevard, Roswell, GA, Zip 30076–3899; tel. 770/751–2500; Jon–Paul Croom, President
**Web address:** www.nfultonhospital.com

WELLSTAR SPALDING REGIONAL HOSPITAL (O, 160 beds) 601 South Eighth Street, Griffin, GA, Zip 30224–4294, P O Drawer 'V', 30224–1168, tel. 770/228–2721; Tamara Ison, Senior Vice President and President

WELLSTAR SYLVAN GROVE HOSPITAL (O, 24 beds) 1050 McDonough Road, Jackson, GA, Zip 30233–1599; tel. 770/775–7861; Tamara Ison, Senior Vice President and President
**Web address:** www.sylvangrovehospital.com

WELLSTAR WEST GEORGIA MEDICAL CENTER (O, 390 beds) 1514 Vernon Road, Lagrange, GA, Zip 30240–4131; tel. 706/882–1411; Coleman Foss, Chief Executive Officer
**Web address:** www.wghealth.org/

| | | |
|---|---|---|
| Owned, leased, sponsored: | 10 hospitals | 2703 beds |
| Contract–managed: | 0 hospitals | 0 beds |
| Totals: | 10 hospitals | 2703 beds |

---

**★0004: WEST TENNESSEE HEALTHCARE** (NP)
620 Skyline Drive, Jackson, TN Zip 38301–3923; tel. 731/541–5000; James E. Ross, President and Chief Executive Officer
**(Centralized Physician/Insurance Health System)**

TENNESSEE: BOLIVAR GENERAL HOSPITAL (O, 12 beds) 650 Nuckolls Road, Bolivar, TN, Zip 38008–1532, Mailing Address: P.O. 509, 38008–0509, tel. 731/658–3100; Ruby Kirby, Chief Executive Officer
**Web address:** www.wth.net

CAMDEN GENERAL HOSPITAL (O, 8 beds) 175 Hospital Drive, Camden, TN, Zip 38320–1617; tel. 731/593–6300; Scott Barber, Administrator
**Web address:** www.wth.net

JACKSON–MADISON COUNTY GENERAL HOSPITAL (O, 632 beds) 620 Skyline Drive, Jackson, TN, Zip 38301–3923; tel. 731/541–5000; Deann Thelen, Vice President and Administrator
**Web address:** www.wth.org

MILAN GENERAL HOSPITAL (O, 28 beds) 4039 Highland Street, Milan, TN, Zip 38358–3483; tel. 731/686–1591; Sherry Scruggs, Administrator

PATHWAYS OF TENNESSEE (O, 25 beds) 238 Summar Drive, Jackson, TN, Zip 38301–3906; tel. 731/541–8200; Pam Henson, Executive Director
**Web address:** www.wth.net/pathways

WEST TENNESSEE HEALTHCARE DYERSBURG HOSPITAL (O, 115 beds) 400 East Tickle Street, Dyersburg, TN, Zip 38024–3120; tel. 731/285–2410; Scott Barber, Interim Chief Executive Officer

WEST TENNESSEE HEALTHCARE VOLUNTEER HOSPITAL (O, 38 beds) 161 Mount Pelia Road, Martin, TN, Zip 38237–3811; tel. 731/587–4261; Donna Barfield, Interim Chief Executive Officer
**Web address:** www.wth.org/locations/west–tennessee–healthcare–volunteer–hospital

| | | |
|---|---|---|
| Owned, leased, sponsored: | 7 hospitals | 858 beds |
| Contract–managed: | 0 hospitals | 0 beds |
| Totals: | 7 hospitals | 858 beds |

---

**★0119: WEST VIRGINIA UNIVERSITY HEALTH SYSTEM** (NP)
One Medical Center, Box 8136, Morgantown, WV Zip 26506–8136; tel. 304/285–7150; Albert L. Wright Jr, President and Chief Executive Officer
**(Moderately Centralized Health System)**

OHIO: WVU MEDICINE – BARNESVILLE HOSPITAL (C, 25 beds) 639 West Main Street, Barnesville, OH, Zip 43713–1039, Mailing Address: P.O. Box 309, 43713–0309, tel. 740/425–3941; David D. Phillips, Chief Executive Officer and Administrator

WEST VIRGINIA: BERKELEY MEDICAL CENTER (O, 195 beds) 2500 Hospital Drive, Martinsburg, WV, Zip 25401–3402; tel. 304/264–1000; Anthony Zelenka, President and Chief Operating Officer
**Web address:** www.cityhospital.org

CAMDEN CLARK MEDICAL CENTER (O, 284 beds) 800 Garfield Avenue, Parkersburg, WV, Zip 26101–5378, Mailing Address: P.O. Box 718, 26102–0718, tel. 304/424–2111; Steve Altmiller, President and Chief Executive Officer
**Web address:** www.camdenclark.org

JEFFERSON MEDICAL CENTER (O, 25 beds) 300 South Preston Street, Ranson, WV, Zip 25438–1631; tel. 304/728–1600; Anthony Zelenka, President and Chief Executive Officer
**Web address:** www.wvuniversityhealthcare.com/locations/Jefferson–Medical–Center.aspx

POTOMAC VALLEY HOSPITAL (O, 25 beds) 100 Pin Oak Lane, Keyser, WV, Zip 26726–5908; tel. 304/597–3500; Mark G. Boucot, FACHE, President and Chief Executive Officer

REYNOLDS MEMORIAL HOSPITAL (O, 50 beds) 800 Wheeling Avenue, Glen Dale, WV, Zip 26038–1697; tel. 304/845–3211; David F. Hess, M.D., Chief Executive Officer
**Web address:** www.reynoldsmemorial.com

ST. JOSEPH'S HOSPITAL OF BUCKHANNON (O, 51 beds) 1 Amalia Drive, Buckhannon, WV, Zip 26201–2276; tel. 304/473–2000; Skip Gjolberg, FACHE, Administrator

UNITED HOSPITAL CENTER (O, 264 beds) 327 Medical Park Drive, Bridgeport, WV, Zip 26330–9006; tel. 681/342–1000; Michael C. Tillman, President and Chief Executive Officer
**Web address:** www.thenewuhc.com

WEST VIRGINIA UNIVERSITY HOSPITALS (O, 657 beds) 1 Medical Center Drive, Morgantown, WV, Zip 26506–4749; tel. 304/598–4000; Albert L. Wright Jr, President and Chief Executive Officer

WETZEL COUNTY HOSPITAL (L, 58 beds) 3 East Benjamin Drive, New Martinsville, WV, Zip 26155–2758; tel. 304/455–8000; David F. Hess, M.D., Chief Executive Officer
**Web address:** www.wetzelcountyhospital.com

WHEELING HOSPITAL (C, 223 beds) 1 Medical Park, Wheeling, WV, Zip 26003–6379; tel. 304/243–3000; Douglass Harrison, Chief Executive Officer
**Web address:** www.wheelinghospital.org

| | | |
|---|---|---|
| Owned, leased, sponsored: | 9 hospitals | 1609 beds |
| Contract–managed: | 2 hospitals | 248 beds |
| Totals: | 11 hospitals | 1857 beds |

---

**★0468: WHITE RIVER HEALTH SYSTEM** (NP)
1710 Harrison Street, Batesville, AR Zip 72501–7303; tel. 870/262–1200; Gary Paxson, MS, R.N., Chief Executive Officer
**(Independent Hospital System)**

ARKANSAS: STONE COUNTY MEDICAL CENTER (O, 25 beds) 2106 East Main Street, Mountain View, AR, Zip 72560–6439, Mailing Address: P.O. Box 510, 72560–0510, tel. 870/269–4361; Kevin Spears, Chief Executive Officer
**Web address:** www.whiteriverhealthsystem.com/doctors/facilities/stone–county–medical–center

WHITE RIVER MEDICAL CENTER (O, 210 beds) 1710 Harrison Street, Batesville, AR, Zip 72501–7303, Mailing Address: P.O. Box 2197, 72503–2197, tel. 870/262–1200; Gary Paxson, MS, R.N., President and Chief Executive Officer

| | | |
|---|---|---|
| Owned, leased, sponsored: | 2 hospitals | 235 beds |
| Contract–managed: | 0 hospitals | 0 beds |
| Totals: | 2 hospitals | 235 beds |

---

For explanation of codes following names, see page B2.
★ Indicates Type III membership in the American Hospital Association.

Section B

**0646: WHITTIER HEALTH NETWORK** (IO)
25 Railroad Square, Haverhill, MA Zip 01832–5721;
tel. 978/556–5858; Alfred J. Arcidi, M.D., President
**(Independent Hospital System)**

**MASSACHUSETTS:** WHITTIER PAVILION (O, 65 beds) 76 Summer Street,
Haverhill, MA, Zip 01830–5814; tel. 978/373–8222; Alfred J. Arcidi, M.D.,
Chief Executive Officer
**Web address:** www.whittierhealth.com

WHITTIER REHABILITATION HOSPITAL (O, 60 beds) 150 Flanders Road,
Westborough, MA, Zip 01581–1017; tel. 508/871–2000; Alfred J. Arcidi,
M.D., Senior Vice President

WHITTIER REHABILITATION HOSPITAL (O, 60 beds) 145 Ward Hill Avenue,
Bradford, MA, Zip 01835–6928; tel. 978/372–8000; Alfred J. Arcidi, M.D.,
Senior Vice President
**Web address:** www.whittierhealth.com

| Owned, leased, sponsored: | 3 hospitals | 185 beds |
| Contract–managed: | 0 hospitals | 0 beds |
| Totals: | 3 hospitals | 185 beds |

**1945: WILLIS–KNIGHTON HEALTH SYSTEM** (NP)
2600 Greenwood Road, Shreveport, LA Zip 71103–3908;
tel. 318/212–4000; James K. Elrod, LFACHE, President and Chief
Executive Officer
**(Moderately Centralized Health System)**

**LOUISIANA:** DE SOTO REGIONAL HEALTH SYSTEM (C, 10 beds) 207 Jefferson
Street, Mansfield, LA, Zip 71052–2603, Mailing Address: P.O. Box 1636,
71052–1636, tel. 318/872–4610; Todd Eppler, FACHE, Chief Executive
Officer

SPRINGHILL MEDICAL CENTER (C, 34 beds) 2001 Doctors Drive, Springhill,
LA, Zip 71075–4526, Mailing Address: P.O. Box 920, 71075–0920,
tel. 318/539–1000; Michael G. Patronis, Chief Executive Officer
**Web address:** www.smccare.com

WILLIS–KNIGHTON MEDICAL CENTER (O, 758 beds) 2600 Greenwood
Road, Shreveport, LA, Zip 71103–3908, Mailing Address: P.O. Box 32600,
71130–2600, tel. 318/212–4000; James K. Elrod, LFACHE, Chief Executive
Officer

| Owned, leased, sponsored: | 1 hospitals | 758 beds |
| Contract–managed: | 2 hospitals | 44 beds |
| Totals: | 3 hospitals | 802 beds |

**1004: WMCHEALTH** (NP)
100 Woods Road, Valhalla, NY Zip 10595–1530; tel. 914/493–
7000; Michael D. Israel, President and Chief Executive Officer
**(Moderately Centralized Health System)**

**NEW YORK:** BON SECOURS COMMUNITY HOSPITAL (O, 143 beds) 160
East Main Street, Port Jervis, NY, Zip 12771–2245, Mailing Address: P.O.
Box 1014, 12771–0268, tel. 845/858–7000; Mary Leahy, M.D., Chief
Executive Officer

GOOD SAMARITAN REGIONAL MEDICAL CENTER (O, 308 beds) 255 Lafayette
Avenue, Suffern, NY, Zip 10901–4869; tel. 845/368–5000; Mary Leahy,
M.D., Chief Executive Officer
**Web address:** www.goodsamhosp.org

HEALTH ALLIANCE HOSPITAL – BROADWAY CAMPUS (O, 150 beds) 396
Broadway, Kingston, NY, Zip 12401–4692; tel. 845/331–3131; Michael
Doyle, M.D., Executive Director and Chief Medical Officer

HEALTH ALLIANCE HOSPITAL – MARY'S AVENUE CAMPUS (O, 105 beds) 105
Marys Avenue, Kingston, NY, Zip 12401–5894; tel. 845/338–2500; Michael
Doyle, M.D., Executive Director and Chief Medical Officer
**Web address:** www.hahv.org

MARGARETVILLE HOSPITAL (O, 15 beds) 42084 State Highway 28,
Margaretville, NY, Zip 12455–2820; tel. 845/586–2631; Mark Pohar,
Executive Director
**Web address:** www.margaretvillehospital.org

ST. ANTHONY COMMUNITY HOSPITAL (O, 60 beds) 15 Maple Avenue,
Warwick, NY, Zip 10990–1028; tel. 845/986–2276; Mary Leahy, M.D., Chief
Executive Officer
**Web address:** www.stanthonycommunityhosp.org

WESTCHESTER MEDICAL CENTER (O, 872 beds) 100 Woods Road, Valhalla,
NY, Zip 10595–1530; tel. 914/493–7000; Michael D. Israel, President and
Chief Executive Officer

| Owned, leased, sponsored: | 7 hospitals | 1653 beds |
| Contract–managed: | 0 hospitals | 0 beds |
| Totals: | 7 hospitals | 1653 beds |

**★0157: YALE NEW HAVEN HEALTH** (NP)
789 Howard Avenue, New Haven, CT Zip 06519–1304;
tel. 203/688–2608; Marna P. Borgstrom, President and Chief
Executive Officer
**(Centralized Physician/Insurance Health System)**

**CONNECTICUT:** BRIDGEPORT HOSPITAL (O, 423 beds) 267 Grant Street,
Bridgeport, CT, Zip 06610–2805, Mailing Address: P.O. Box 5000,
06610–0120, tel. 203/384–3000; Anne Diamond, President

GREENWICH HOSPITAL (O, 184 beds) 5 Perryridge Road, Greenwich, CT,
Zip 06830–4697; tel. 203/863–3000; Norman G. Roth, President
**Web address:** www.greenhosp.org

LAWRENCE + MEMORIAL HOSPITAL (O, 251 beds) 365 Montauk Avenue, New
London, CT, Zip 06320–4769; tel. 860/442–0711; Patrick Green, FACHE,
President and Chief Executive Officer
**Web address:** www.lmhospital.org

YALE–NEW HAVEN HOSPITAL (O, 1455 beds) 20 York Street, New Haven, CT,
Zip 06510–3202; tel. 203/688–4242; Marna P. Borgstrom, Chief Executive
Officer

**RHODE ISLAND:** WESTERLY HOSPITAL (O, 93 beds) 25 Wells Street, Westerly,
RI, Zip 02891–2934; tel. 401/596–6000; Patrick Green, FACHE, President
and Chief Executive Officer
**Web address:** www.westerlyhospital.org

| Owned, leased, sponsored: | 5 hospitals | 2406 beds |
| Contract–managed: | 0 hospitals | 0 beds |
| Totals: | 5 hospitals | 2406 beds |

---

For explanation of codes following names, see page B2.
★ Indicates Type III membership in the American Hospital Association.

## Geographically

### United States

#### ALABAMA

**Anniston:** REGIONAL MEDICAL CENTER 400 East 10th Street, Zip 36207–4716; tel. 256/235–5121; Louis A. Bass, President and Chief Executive Officer, p. B107

#### ARIZONA

**Flagstaff:** NORTHERN ARIZONA HEALTHCARE 1200 North Beaver Street, Zip 86001–3118; tel. 928/779–3366; Florence (Flo) Spyrow, President and Chief Executive Officer, p. B92

**Phoenix:** ★ BANNER HEALTH 2901 North Central Avenue Suite 160, Zip 85012–2702, 2901 North Central Avenue, Suite 160, 85012–2700, tel. 602/747–4000; Peter S. Fine, President and Chief Executive Officer, p. B18

**Scottsdale:** ★ HONORHEALTH 8125 North Hayden Road, Zip 85258–2463; tel. 480/882–4000; Todd LaPorte, Chief Executive Officer, p. B65

SOUTHWEST HEALTHCARE SYSTEM 7025 N Scottsdale Road Suite 9347, Zip 85253–3675, 7025 North Scottsdale Road, Suite 9347, 85251–3331, tel. 480/518–5444; Paul R. Tuft, President, p. B119

#### ARKANSAS

**Batesville:** ★ WHITE RIVER HEALTH SYSTEM 1710 Harrison Street, Zip 72501–7303; tel. 870/262–1200; Gary Paxson, Chief Executive Officer, p. B148

**Birmingham:** BRADFORD HEALTH SERVICES 2101 Magnolia Avenue South, Suite 518, Zip 35205–2853; tel. 205/251–7753; Jerry W. Crowder, President and Chief Executive Officer, p. B24

★ ENCOMPASS HEALTH CORPORATION 9001 Liberty Parkway, Zip 35242–7509; tel. 205/967–7116; Mark J. Tarr, President and Chief Executive Officer, p. B48

NOLAND HEALTH SERVICES, INC. 600 Corporate Parkway, Suite 100, Zip 35242–5451; tel. 205/783–8484; Gary M. Glasscock, President and Chief Executive Officer, p. B90

★ UAB HEALTH SYSTEM 500 22nd Street South, Suite 408, Zip 35233–3110; tel. 205/975–5362; Reid F. Jones, Chief Executive Officer, p. B132

**Blytheville:** ★ MISSISSIPPI COUNTY HOSPITAL SYSTEM 1520 North Division Street, Zip 72315–1448, Mailing Address: P.O. 108, 72316–0108, tel. 870/838–7300; Chris Lee. Raymer, Chief Executive Officer, p. B86

**Guntersville:** MARSHALL HEALTH SYSTEM 227 Britany Road, Zip 35976–5766; tel. 256/894–6615; Cheryl M. Hays, President, p. B78

**Huntsville:** HUNTSVILLE HOSPITAL HEALTH SYSTEM 101 Sivley Road SW, Zip 35801–4421; tel. 265/256–1000; David S. Spillers, Chief Executive Officer, p. B66

**Little Rock:** ★ BAPTIST HEALTH 9601 Baptist Health Drive, Zip 72205–6321; tel. 501/202–2000; Troy R. Wells, Chief Executive Officer, p. B19

**Mobile:** ALTAPOINTE HEALTH SYSTEMS 5750–A Southland Drive, Zip 36693–3316; tel. 251/473–4423; J. Tuerk. Schlesinger, Chief Executive Officer, p. B9

INFIRMARY HEALTH SYSTEM 5 Mobile Infirmary Circle, Zip 36607–3513; tel. 251/435–5500; D Mark. Nix, President and Chief Executive Officer, p. B67

★ USA HEALTH 2451 University Hospital Drive, Zip 36617–2300; tel. 251/471–7000; Owen Bailey, Chief Executive Officer and Senior Associate Vice President for Medical Affairs, p. B143

**Montgomery:** BAPTIST HEALTH 301 Brown Springs Road, Zip 36117–7005; tel. 334/273–4400; W Russell. Tyner, President and Chief Executive Officer, p. B20

GILLIARD HEALTH SERVICES 3091 Carter Hill Road, Zip 36111–1801; tel. 334/265–5009; William G. McKenzie, President, Chief Executive Officer and Chairman, p. B57

**Tuscaloosa:** DCH HEALTH SYSTEM 809 University Boulevard East, Zip 35401–2029; tel. 205/759–7111; Bryan N. Kindred, President and Chief Executive Officer, p. B41

#### CALIFORNIA

**Alhambra:** AHMC & HEALTHCARE, INC. 55 South Raymond Avenue, Suite 105, Zip 91801–7101; tel. 626/457–7400; Jonathan Wu, President and Chairman, p. B8

**Corona:** SIGNATURE HEALTHCARE SERVICES 4238 Green River Road, Zip 92880–1669; tel. 951/549–8032; Soon K. Kim, President and Chief Executive Officer, p. B117

**Covina:** ★ EMANATE HEALTH 210 West San Bernardino Road, Zip 91723–1515; tel. 626/331–7331; Robert H. Curry, President and Chief Executive Officer, p. B47

**Cupertino:** CRC HEALTH GROUP, INC. 20400 Stevens Creek Boulevard, Suite 600, Zip 95014–2217; tel. 866/540–5240; Jerome E. Rhodes, Chief Executive Officer, p. B40

**El Segundo:** AVANTI HOSPITALS 222 North Sepulveda Boulevard, Suite 950, Zip 90245–5614; tel. 310/356–0550; Michael A. Rembis, Corporate Chief Executive Officer, p. B16

**Escondido:** ★ PALOMAR HEALTH 456 East Grand Avenue, Zip 92025–3319; tel. 760/740–6393; Diane Hansen, Chief Executive Officer, p. B97

**Fountain Valley:** MEMORIALCARE 17360 Brookhurst Street, Zip 92708–3720, Mailing Address: P.O. 1428, Long Beach, 90801–1428, tel. 714/377–2900; Barry S. Arbuckle, President and Chief Executive Officer, p. B83

**Fresno:** COMMUNITY MEDICAL CENTERS Fresno and Maddy Drive, Zip 93721, Mailing Address: P.O. 1232, 93715–1232, tel. 559/459–6000; Tim A. Joslin, President and Chief Executive Officer, p. B37

**Hemet:** PHYSICIANS FOR HEALTHY HOSPITALS 1117 East Devonshire Avenue, Zip 92543–3083; tel. 951/652–2811; Joel M. Bergenfeld, Chief Executive Officer, p. B98

**Irvine:** ALECTO HEALTHCARE 16310 Bake Parkway, Suite 200, Zip 92618–4684; tel. 949/783–3988; Lex Reddy, Chief Executive Officer, p. B8

**Loma Linda:** LOMA LINDA UNIVERSITY ADVENTIST HEALTH SCIENCES CENTER 11175 Campus Street, Zip 92350–1700; tel. 909/558–7572; Richard H. Hart, President and Chief Executive Officer, p. B77

**Los Angeles:** KECK MEDICINE OF USC 1510 San Pablo Street, Suite 600, Zip 90033–5405; tel. 323/442–8500; Rod Hanners, Interim Chief Executive Officer, p. B70

LOS ANGELES COUNTY–DEPARTMENT OF HEALTH SERVICES 313 North Figueroa Street, Room 912, Zip 90012–2691; tel. 213/240–8101; Mitchell H. Katz, Director, p. B77

PROSPECT MEDICAL HOLDINGS 10780 California Route 2 #400, Zip 90025; tel. 714/796–5900; Mitchell Lew, President, p. B103

VERITY HEALTH SYSTEM 2200 West Third Street, Suite 200, Zip 90057–1935, 203 Redwood Shores Parkway, Suite 800, Redwood City, 94065, tel. 650/551–6650; Richard Adcock, President and Chief Executive Officer, p. B144

**Oakland:** ★ KAISER FOUNDATION HOSPITALS One Kaiser Plaza, 27th Floor – Office #2743, Zip 94612–3600; tel. 510/271–5910; Gregory A. Adams, Chief Executive Officer and Chairman, p. B69

★ UNIVERSITY OF CALIFORNIA SYSTEMWIDE ADMINISTRATION 1111 Franklin Street, 11th Floor, Zip 94607–5200; tel. 510/987–9071; John D. Stobo, Executive Vice President and Chief Executive Officer, p. B140

**Ontario:** PRIME HEALTHCARE 3300 East Guasti Road, Zip 91761–8655; tel. 909/235–4400; Prem Reddy, Chairman, President and Chief Executive Officer, p. B101

**Palo Alto:** ★ STANFORD HEALTH CARE 300 Pasteur Drive, Zip 94304–2299; tel. 650/723–4000; David Entwistle, President and Chief Executive Officer, p. B122

**Roseville:** ★ ADVENTIST HEALTH One Adventist Health Way, Zip 95661–3266, Mailing Address: P.O. 619002, 95661–9002, tel. 916/406–0000; Scott Reiner, Chief Executive Officer, p. B6

**Sacramento:** ★ SUTTER HEALTH 2200 River Plaza Drive, Zip 95833–4134; tel. 916/887–0000; Sarah Krevans, President and Chief Executive Officer, p. B123

**San Diego:** ★ SCRIPPS HEALTH 4275 Campus Point Court CP112, Zip 92121–1513, 4275 Campus Point Court, 92121–1513, tel. 858/678–7200; Chris D. Van Gorder, President and Chief Executive Officer, p. B112

★ SHARP HEALTHCARE 8695 Spectrum Center Boulevard, Zip 92123–1489; tel. 858/499–4000; Christopher Howard, President and Chief Executive Officer, p. B116

**San Leandro:** ALAMEDA HEALTH SYSTEM 15400 Foothill Boulevard, Zip 94578–1009; tel. 510/677–7920; Delvecchio Finley, Chief Executive Officer, p. B8

**Santa Ana:** KPC HEALTHCARE, INC. 1301 North Tustin Avenue, Zip 92705–8619; tel. 714/953–3652; Peter R. Baronoff, Chief Executive Officer and Managing Director, p. B72

**Santa Barbara:** ★ COTTAGE HEALTH 400 West Pueblo Street, Zip 93105–4353, Mailing Address: P.O. 689, 93102–0689, tel. 805/569–7290; Ronald C. Werft, President and Chief Executive Officer, p. B39

**Santa Fe Springs:** COLLEGE HEALTH ENTERPRISES 11627 Telegraph Road, Suite 200, Zip 90670–6814; tel. 562/923–9449; Barry J. Weiss, Chairman of the Board, p. B30

**Truckee:** ★ TAHOE FOREST HEALTH SYSTEM 10121 Pine Avenue, Zip 96161–4835; tel. 530/587–6011; Harry Weis, Chief Executive Officer, p. B124

**Ventura:** COMMUNITY MEMORIAL HEALTH SYSTEM 147 North Brent Street, Zip 93003–2809; tel. 805/652–5011; Gary Wilde, President and Chief Executive Officer, p. B37

**Walnut Creek:** ★ JOHN MUIR HEALTH 1400 Treat Boulevard, Zip 94597–2142; tel. 925/941–2100; Calvin K. Knight, President and Chief Executive Officer, p. B69

**West Hollywood:** ★ CEDARS–SINAI HEALTH SYSTEM 8700 Beverly Boulevard, Zip 90048–1865, Box 48750, Los Angeles, 90048–0750, tel. 310/423–5000; Thomas M. Priselac, President and Chief Executive Officer, p. B28

**Whittier:** ★ PIH HEALTH 12401 Washington Boulevard, Zip 90602–1006; tel. 562/698–0811; James R. West, President and Chief Executive Officer, p. B99

## COLORADO

**Alamosa:** ★ SAN LUIS VALLEY HEALTH 106 Blanca Avenue, Zip 81101–2340; tel. 719/589–2511; Konnie Martin, Chief Executive Officer, p. B111

**Broomfield:** ★ SCL HEALTH 500 Eldorado Boulevard, Suite 4300, Zip 80021; tel. 303/813–5180; Lydia Jumonville, President and Chief Executive Officer, p. B112

**Fort Collins:** ★ UCHEALTH 2315 East Harmony Road, Suite 200, Zip 80528–8620; tel. 970/495–7000; Elizabeth B. Concordia, President and Chief Executive Officer, p. B132

## CONNECTICUT

**Danbury:** ★ NUVANCE HEALTH 24 Hospital Avenue, Zip 06810–6099; tel. 203/739–7066; John M. Murphy, President and Chief Executive Officer, p. B94

**Hartford:** CONNECTICUT DEPARTMENT OF MENTAL HEALTH AND ADDICTION SERVICES 410 Capitol Avenue, Zip 06106–1367, Mailing Address: P.O. 341431, 06134–1431, tel. 860/418–7000; Miriam Delphin–Rittmon, Commissioner, p. B38

★ HARTFORD HEALTHCARE One State Street, 19th Floor, Zip 6103; tel. 860/263–4100; Jeffrey A. Flaks, President and Chief Executive Officer, p. B58

**New Haven:** ★ YALE NEW HAVEN HEALTH 789 Howard Avenue, Zip 06519–1304; tel. 203/688–2608; Marna P. Borgstrom, President and Chief Executive Officer, p. B148

## DELAWARE

**Wilmington:** ★ CHRISTIANACARE 501 West 14th Street, Zip 19801–1013, Mailing Address: P.O. 1668, 19899–1668, tel. 302/733–1000; Janice E. Nevin, Chief Executive Officer, p. B29

## DISTRICT OF COLUMBIA

**Washington:** ★ DEPARTMENT OF DEFENSE, HEALTH AFFAIRS 1200 Defense Pentagon, Pentagon 3E1070, Zip 20301; tel. 703/697–2111, Honorable, Thomas McCaffery, Assistant Secretary of Defense for Health Affairs, p. B41

★ DEPARTMENT OF THE AIR FORCE 1780 Air Force Pentagon, Room 4E114, Zip 20330–1420; tel. 703/692–6800, Lieutenant General, Dorothy A. Hogg, Surgeon General, p. B41

★ DEPARTMENT OF VETERANS AFFAIRS 810 Vermont Avenue NW, Zip 20420–0001; tel. 202/273–5781, Honorable, Robert Wilkie, Secretary, p. B42

★ UNITED STATES COAST GUARD 2703 Martin Luther King Jr. Avenue Southeast, Zip 20593–7907; tel. 202/372–4500, Rear Admiral, Dana Thomas, Director, Health, Safety & Work–Life Chief Medical Officer, p. B134

## FLORIDA

**Altamonte Springs:** ★ ADVENTHEALTH 900 Hope Way, Zip 32714–1502; tel. 407/357–1000; Terry Shaw, President and Chief Executive Officer, p. B5

**Clearwater:** MORTON PLANT MEASE HEALTH CARE 2985 Drew Street, Zip 33759, Mailing Address: P.O. 210, 33757–0210, tel. 727/462–7000; Glenn D. Waters, President, p. B87

**Coral Gables:** ★ BAPTIST HEALTH SOUTH FLORIDA 6855 Red Road, Suite 600, Zip 33143–3632; tel. 786/662–7111; Brian E. Keeley, President and Chief Executive Officer, p. B20

**Fort Lauderdale:** ★ BROWARD HEALTH 1800 NW 49th Street, Zip 33309–3092; tel. 954/355–4400; Gino Santorio, President and Chief Executive Officer, p. B25

**Fort Myers:** ★ LEE HEALTH 2776 Cleveland Avenue, Zip 33901–5864, Mailing Address: P.O. 2218, 33902–2218, tel. 239/343–2000; Lawrence Antonucci, President and Chief Executive Officer, p. B73

**Gainesville:** ★ UF HEALTH SHANDS 1600 SW Archer Road, Zip 32610–0326; tel. 352/733–1500; Edward Jimenez, Chief Executive Officer, p. B133

**Hollywood:** ★ MEMORIAL HEALTHCARE SYSTEM 3501 Johnson Street, Zip 33021–5421; tel. 954/987–2000; Aurelio Fernandez, Chief Executive Officer, p. B82

**Jacksonville:** ★ BAPTIST HEALTH 841 Prudential Drive, Suite 1601, Zip 32207–8202; tel. 904/202–2000; Brett McClung, President and Chief Executive Officer, p. B19

NEMOURS 10140 Centurion Parkway North, Zip 32256–0532; tel. 904/697–4100; R. Lawrence. Moss, President and Chief Executive Officer, p. B89

**Lauderdale Lakes:** CATHOLIC HEALTH SERVICES 4790 North State Road 7, Zip 33319–5860; tel. 954/484–1515; Joseph M. Catania, President and Chief Executive Officer, p. B27

**Orlando:** ORLANDO HEALTH 1414 Kuhl Avenue, Zip 32806–2093; tel. 321/843–7000; David W. Strong, President and Chief Executive Officer, p. B96

**Pensacola:** ★ BAPTIST HEALTH CARE CORPORATION 1717 North 'E' Street, Suite 402, Zip 32501–6377, Mailing Address: P.O. 17500, 32522–7500, tel. 850/434–4011; Mark T. Faulkner, President, p. B20

**Rockledge:** HEALTH FIRST, INC. 6450 US Highway 1, Zip 32955–5747; tel. 321/434–7000; Steven P. Johnson, President and Chief Executive Officer, p. B63

**Tampa:** OGLETHORPE RECOVERY AND BEHAVIORAL HOSPITALS 201 North Franklin Street, Zip 33602–5182; tel. 813/978–1933; John Picciano, Chief Executive Officer, p. B95

SHRINERS HOSPITALS FOR CHILDREN 2900 North Rocky Point Drive, Zip 33607–1435, Mailing Address: P.O. 31356, 33631–3356, tel. 813/281–0300; John P. McCabe, Executive Vice President, p. B116

**Windermere:** UNITED MEDICAL CORPORATION 603 Main Street, Zip 34786–3548, Mailing Address: P.O. 1100, 34786–1100, tel. 407/876–2200; Donald R. Dizney, Chairman and Chief Executive Officer, p. B134

## GEORGIA

**Albany:** ★ PHOEBE PUTNEY HEALTH SYSTEM 417 Third Avenue, Zip 31701–1943; tel. 229/312–1000; Scott Steiner, Chief Executive Officer, p. B98

**Alpharetta:** PERIMETER HEALTHCARE 2520 Northwinds Parkway Suite 550, Zip 30009–2236; tel. 470/554–7902; James R. Laughlin, President and Chief Executive Officer, p. B98

**Atlanta:** ★ EMORY HEALTHCARE 1440 Clifton Road NE, Suite 400, Zip 30322–1102; tel. 404/778–5000; Dane C. Peterson, President and Chief Operating Officer, p. B48

★ NORTHSIDE HEALTHCARE SYSTEM 1000 Johnson Ferry Road NE, Zip 30342–1611; tel. 404/851–8000; Robert Quattrocchi, President and Chief Executive Officer, p. B92

**Augusta:** ★ UNIVERSITY HEALTH CARE SYSTEM 1350 Walton Way, Zip 30901–2629; tel. 706/722–9011; James R. Davis, President and Chief Executive Officer, p. B139

**Blairsville:** UNION GENERAL HOSPITAL, INC. 35 Hospital Road, Zip 30512–3139; tel. 706/745–2111; Mike Gowder, Chief Executive Officer, p. B133

**Brunswick:** ★ SOUTHEAST GEORGIA HEALTH SYSTEM 2415 Parkwood Drive, Zip 31520–4722, Mailing Address: P.O. 1518, 31521–1518, tel. 912/466–7000; Michael D. Scherneck, President and Chief Executive Officer, p. B118

**Carrollton:** ★ TANNER HEALTH SYSTEM 705 Dixie Street, Zip 30117–3818; tel. 770/836–9580; Loy M. Howard, President and Chief Executive Officer, p. B124

**Columbus:** COLUMBUS REGIONAL HEALTHCARE SYSTEM 707 Center Street, Suite 400, Zip 31901–1575; tel. 706/660–6100; M. Scott. Hill, Chief Executive Officer, p. B31

**Decatur:** DEKALB REGIONAL HEALTH SYSTEM 2701 North Decatur Road, Zip 30033–5918; tel. 404/501–1000; Robert E. Wilson Esq, Chief Executive Officer, p. B41

**Gainesville:** NORTHEAST GEORGIA HEALTH SYSTEM 743 Spring Street NE, Zip 30501–3715; tel. 770/219–9000; Carol H. Burrell, President and Chief Executive Officer, p. B91

**Lilburn:** LIFEBRITE HOSPITAL GROUP, LLC 3970 Five Forks Trickum Road SW Suite A, Zip 30047–2339; tel. 678/505–9657; Christian Al. Fletcher, Chief Executive Officer, p. B75

**Macon:** NAVICENT HEALTH 777 Hemlock Street, MSC 105, Zip 31201–2155, 777 Hemlock Street, 31201–2155, tel. 478/633–1000; Ninfa M. Saunders, President and Chief Executive Officer, p. B89

**Marietta:** ★ WELLSTAR HEALTH SYSTEM 793 Sawyer Road, Zip 30062; tel. 770/792–5012; Candice Saunders, President and Chief Executive Officer, p. B147

**Rome:** FLOYD HEALTHCARE MANAGEMENT 304 Turner McCall Boulevard, Zip 30165–5621, Mailing Address: P.O. 233, 30162–0233, tel. 706/509–5000; Kurt Stuenkel, President and Chief Executive Officer, p. B54

**Roswell:** PIEDMONT HEALTHCARE 1800 Howell Mill Road NW, Suite 850, Zip 30076, Atlanta, tel. 404/425–1314; Kevin Brown, President and Chief Executive Officer, p. B98

**Thomasville:** ★ ARCHBOLD MEDICAL CENTER 910 South Broad Street, Zip 31792–6113; tel. 229/228–2739; J. Perry Mustian, President and Chief Executive Officer, p. B11

**Tifton:** ★ TIFT REGIONAL HEALTH SYSTEM 901 East 18th Street, Zip 31794–3648; tel. 229/353–6100; Christopher Dorman, President and Chief Executive Officer, p. B128

**Valdosta:** ★ SOUTH GEORGIA MEDICAL CENTER 2501 North Patterson Street, Zip 31602–1735, Mailing Address: P.O. 1727, 31603–1727, tel. 229/333–1000; Ronald Dean, Chief Executive Officer, p. B118

**Warner Robins:** ★ HOUSTON HEALTHCARE SYSTEM 1601 Watson Boulevard, Zip 31093–3431, Mailing Address: P.O. 2886, 31099–2886, tel. 478/922–4281; Charles G. Briscoe, President and Chief Executive Officer, p. B65

## HAWAII

**Honolulu:** ★ HAWAII HEALTH SYSTEMS CORPORATION 3675 Kilauea Avenue, Zip 96816–2333; tel. 808/733–4151; Linda Rosen, Chief Executive Officer, p. B59

HAWAII PACIFIC HEALTH 55 Merchant Street, Zip 96813–4306; tel. 808/949–9355; Raymond P. Vara Jr, President and Chief Executive Officer, p. B59

★ QUEEN'S HEALTH SYSTEMS 1301 Punchbowl Street, Zip 96813–2402; tel. 808/535–5448; Jill Hoggard Green, President and Chief Executive Officer, p. B106

## IDAHO

**Boise:** ★ ST. LUKE'S HEALTH SYSTEM 190 East Bannock Street, Zip 83712–6241; tel. 208/381–4200; Chris Roth, President and Chief Executive Officer, p. B121

**Pocatello:** SAFE HAVEN HEALTH CARE 2520 South 5th Avenue, Zip 83204–1923; tel. 800/261–2443; Scott Burpee, President, p. B109

## ILLINOIS

**Carbondale:** SOUTHERN ILLINOIS HEALTHCARE 1239 East Main Street, Zip 62901–3114, Mailing Address: P.O. 3988, 62902–3988, tel. 618/457–5200; Rex P. Budde, President and Chief Executive Officer, p. B118

**Chicago:** ★ COMMONSPIRIT HEALTH 444 West Lake Street Suite 2500, Zip 60606–0097; tel. 312/741–7000; Lloyd H. Dean, Chief Executive Officer, p. B31

★ COOK COUNTY HEALTH AND HOSPITALS SYSTEM 1900 West Polk Street, Suite 220, Zip 60612–3723; tel. 312/864–6820; Debra D. Carey, Interim Chief Executive Officer, p. B38

NATIONAL SURGICAL HEALTHCARE 250 South Wacker Drive, Suite 500, Zip 60606–5897; tel. 312/627–8400; David Crane, Chief Executive Officer, p. B88

★ NORTHWESTERN MEMORIAL HEALTHCARE 251 East Huron Street, Zip 60611–2908; tel. 312/926–2000; Dean M. Harrison, President and Chief Executive Officer, p. B91

★ RUSH UNIVERSITY MEDICAL CENTER 1653 West Congress Parkway, Zip 60612–3864; tel. 312/942–5000; Ranga Krishnan, Chief Executive Officer, p. B109

★ SINAI HEALTH SYSTEM 1500 South Fairfield Avenue, Zip 60608–1782; tel. 773/542–2000; Karen Teitelbaum, President and Chief Executive Officer, p. B117

★ UNIVERSITY OF CHICAGO MEDICINE 5841 South Maryland Avenue, Zip 60637–1447; tel. 773/702–6240; Kenneth Polonsky, President, p. B140

**Downers Grove:** ★ ADVOCATE AURORA HEALTH 3075 Highland Parkway, Suite 600, Zip 60515–5563; tel. 630/929–8700; Jim Skogsbergh, President and Chief Executive Officer, p. B7

**Evanston:** NORTHSHORE UNIVERSITY HEALTHSYSTEM 1301 Central Street, Zip 60201–1613; tel. 847/570–2000; J. P. Gallagher, President and Chief Executive Officer, p. B92

**Evergreen Park:** AMERICAN PROVINCE OF LITTLE COMPANY OF MARY SISTERS 9350 South California Avenue, Zip 60805–2595; tel. 708/229–5095, Sister, Carol Pacini, Region Leader, p. B10

**Naperville:** ★ EDWARD–ELMHURST HEALTHCARE 801 South Washington Street, Zip 60540–7430; tel. 630/527–3000; Mary Lou Mastro, System Chief Executive Officer, p. B47

**Peoria:** ★ OSF HEALTHCARE  800 NE Glen Oak Avenue, Zip 61603–3200; tel. 309/655–2850; Robert Sehring, Chief Executive Officer, p. B96

**Schaumburg:** CANCER TREATMENT CENTERS OF AMERICA 1336 Basswood Road, Zip 60173–4544; tel. 847/342–7400; Pat A. Basu, President and Chief Executive Officer, p. B26

**Springfield:** DIVISION OF MENTAL HEALTH, DEPARTMENT OF HUMAN SERVICES 319 East Madison Street, S–3B, Zip 62701–1035; tel. 217/785–6023; Lorrie Rickman. Jones, Director, p. B46

★ HSHS HOSPITAL SISTERS HEALTH SYSTEM 4936 LaVerna Road, Zip 62707–9797, Mailing Address: P.O. 19456, 62794–9456, tel. 217/523–4747; Mary Starmann–Harrison, President and Chief Executive Officer, p. B66

★ MEMORIAL HEALTH SYSTEM 701 North First Street, Zip 62781–0001; tel. 217/788–3000; Edgar J. Curtis, President and Chief Executive Officer, p. B82

**Urbana:** ★ CARLE HEALTH 611 West Park Street, Zip 61801–2595; tel. 217/383–3311; James C. Leonard, President and Chief Executive Officer, p. B27

## INDIANA

**Evansville:** ★ DEACONESS HEALTH SYSTEM 600 Mary Street, Zip 47710–1658; tel. 812/450–5000; Shawn W. McCoy, Chief Executive Officer, p. B41

**Fort Wayne:** ★ PARKVIEW HEALTH 10501 Corporate Drive, Zip 46845–1700; tel. 260/373–7001; Michael J. Packnett, President and Chief Executive Officer, p. B97

**Hammond:** COMMUNITY HEALTHCARE SYSTEM 901 MacArthur Boulevard, Zip 46321–2959; tel. 219/836–1600; Donald P. Fesko, President and Chief Executive Officer, p. B37

**Indianapolis:** ★ COMMUNITY HEALTH NETWORK 7330 Shadeland Station, Zip 46256–3957; tel. 317/355–1411; Bryan A. Mills, President and Chief Executive Officer, p. B34

★ INDIANA UNIVERSITY HEALTH 340 West 10th Street, Suite 6100, Zip 46202–3082, Mailing Address: P.O. 1367, 46206–1367, tel. 317/962–2000; Dennis M. Murphy, President and Chief Executive Officer, p. B67

**Mishawaka:** FRANCISCAN HEALTH 1515 Dragoon Trail, Zip 46544–4710, Mailing Address: P.O. 1290, 46546–1290, tel. 574/256–3935; Kevin D. Leahy, President and Chief Executive Officer, p. B54

NEUROPSYCHIATRIC HOSPITALS 1625 East Jefferson Boulevard, Zip 46545–7103; tel. 574/255–1400; Cameron R. Gilbert, President and Chief Executive Officer, p. B89

**South Bend:** ★ BEACON HEALTH SYSTEM 615 North Michigan Street, Zip 46601–1033; tel. 574/647–1000; Kreg Gruber, Chief Executive Officer, p. B22

## IOWA

**Clarion:** ★ IOWA SPECIALTY HOSPITALS 1316 South Main Street, Zip 50525–2019; tel. 515/532–2811; Steven J. Simonin, Chief Executive Officer, p. B69

**Clive:** MERCYONE 1449 NW 128th Stret, Zip 50325–7400; tel. 515/358–9200; Robert P. Ritz, Chief Executive Officer, p. B85

**Davenport:** ★ GENESIS HEALTH SYSTEM 1227 East Rusholme Street, Zip 52803–2498; tel. 563/421–1000; Douglas P. Cropper, President and Chief Executive Officer, p. B56

**West Des Moines:** ★ UNITYPOINT HEALTH 1776 West Lakes Parkway, Suite 400, Zip 50266–8393; tel. 515/241–6161; Susan K. Thompson, Interim Chief Executive Officer, p. B134

## KANSAS

**Kansas City:** ★ THE UNIVERSITY OF KANSAS HEALTH SYSTEM 4000 Cambridge Street, Zip 66160–0001; tel. 913/588–1227; Bob Page, President and Chief Executive Officer, p. B128

**Salina:** SALINA REGIONAL HEALTH CENTER 400 South Santa Fe Avenue, Zip 67401–4198, PO Box 5080, 67402–5080, tel. 785/452–7000; Joel Phelps, President and Chief Executive Officer, p. B110

**Wichita:** ★ GREAT PLAINS HEALTH ALLIANCE, INC. 250 North Rock Road, Suite 160, Zip 67206–2241; tel. 316/685–1523; Dave Dellasega, President and Chief Executive Officer, p. B57

Health Care Systems Index

## KENTUCKY

**Bowling Green:** MED CENTER HEALTH 800 Park Street, Zip 42101–2356; tel. 270/745–1500; Connie Smith, President and Chief Executive Officer, p. B81

**Danville:** EPHRAIM MCDOWELL HEALTH 217 South Third Street, Zip 40422–1823; tel. 859/239–1000; Daniel E. McKay, Chief Executive Officer, p. B52

**Edgewood:** ST. ELIZABETH HEALTHCARE 1 Medical Village Drive, Zip 41017–3403; tel. 859/301–2000; Garren Colvin, Chief Executive Officer, p. B121

**Lexington:** APPALACHIAN REGIONAL HEALTHCARE, INC. 2260 Executive Drive, Zip 40505–4810, Mailing Address: P.O. 8086, 40533–8086, tel. 859/226–2440; Joseph Grossman, President and Chief Executive Officer, p. B10

**Louisville:** ALLIANT MANAGEMENT SERVICES 2650 Eastpoint Parkway, Suite 300, Zip 40223–5164; tel. 502/992–3525; Jim L. Coleman Jr, President and Chief Executive Officer, p. B9

BAPTIST HEALTH 2701 Eastpoint Parkway, Zip 40223; tel. 502/896–5000; Gerard Colman, Chief Executive Officer, p. B20

★ KINDRED HEALTHCARE 680 South Fourth Street, Zip 40202–2412; tel. 502/596–7300; Pete Kalmey, President, Hospital Division, p. B93

★ NORTON HEALTHCARE 4967 US Highway 42, Suite 100, Zip 40222–6363, Mailing Address: P.O. 35070, 40232–5070, tel. 502/629–8000; Russell Cox, President and Chief Executive Officer, p. B93

SPRINGSTONE 101 South Fifth Street, Suite 3850, Zip 40202–3127; tel. 855/595–2292; Phil Spencer, Chief Executive Officer, p. B119

UOFL HEALTH 530 South Jackson Street, Zip 40202–1675; tel. 502/562–3000; Thomas Miller, Chief Executive Officer, p. B142

**Owensboro:** OWENSBORO HEALTH 1201 Pleasant Valley Road, Zip 42303–9811; tel. 270/417–2000; Greg Strahan, Interim Chief Executive Officer, p. B97

## LOUISIANA

**Baton Rouge:** ★ FRANCISCAN MISSIONARIES OF OUR LADY HEALTH SYSTEM, INC. 4200 Essen Lane, Zip 70809–2158; tel. 225/923–2701; Richard Vath, President and Chief Executive Officer, p. B55

GENERAL HEALTH SYSTEM 8585 Picardy Avenue, Zip 70809–3748; tel. 225/763–4000; Edgardo J. Tenreiro, Chief Executive Officer, p. B56

LOUISIANA STATE HOSPITALS 628 North 4th Street, Zip 70802–5342, Mailing Address: P.O. 629, 70821–0628, tel. 225/342–9500; Shelby Price, Chief Executive Officer , p. B77

THE CARPENTER HEALTH NETWORK 10615 Jefferson Highway, Zip 70809–7230; tel. 225/769–4180; Pat Mitchell, Chief Executive Officer, p. B127

**Crowley:** COMPASS HEALTH 713 North Avenue L, Zip 70526–3832; tel. 337/788–3330; Mark J. Cullen, Chairman, p. B38

**Gretna:** UNITED MEDICAL REHABILITATION HOSPITALS 3201 Wall Boulevard, Suite B, Zip 70056–7755; tel. 504/433–5551; John E.H. Mills, President and Chief Executive Officer, p. B134

**Hammond:** NORTH OAKS HEALTH SYSTEM 15790 Paul Vega MD Drive, Zip 70403–1436, Mailing Address: P.O. 2668, 70404–2668, tel. 985/345–2700; Michele Kidd. Sutton, President and Chief Executive Officer, p. B91

**Lafayette:** AMG INTEGRATED HEALTHCARE MANAGEMENT 101 La Rue France, Suite 500, Zip 70508–3144; tel. 337/269–9828; Timothy W. Howard, Chief Executive Officer, p. B10

LAFAYETTE GENERAL HEALTH 920 West Pinhook Road, Zip 70503–2455; tel. 337/289–7991; David L. Callecod, President and Chief Executive Officer, p. B73

LHC GROUP 420 West Pinhook Road, Zip 70503–2131; tel. 337/233–1307; Keith G. Myers, Chairman and Chief Executive Officer, p. B74

**New Orleans:** LCMC HEALTH 200 Henry Clay Avenue, Zip 70118–5720; tel. 504/899–9511; Greg Feirn, President and Chief Executive Officer, p. B73

★ OCHSNER HEALTH 1514 Jefferson Highway, Zip 70121–2429; tel. 800/874–8984; Warner L. Thomas, President and Chief Executive Officer, p. B95

**Shreveport:** ALLEGIANCE HEALTH MANAGEMENT 504 Texas Street, Suite 200, Zip 71101–3526; tel. 318/226–8202; Rock Bordelon, President and Chief Executive Officer, p. B8

UNIVERSITY HEALTH SYSTEM 1501 Kings Highway, Zip 71103–4228; tel. 318/675–5000; Daniel J. Snyder, Chief Executive Officer, p. B139

WILLIS–KNIGHTON HEALTH SYSTEM 2600 Greenwood Road, Zip 71103–3908; tel. 318/212–4000; James K. Elrod, President and Chief Executive Officer, p. B148

## MAINE

**Brewer:** ★ NORTHERN LIGHT HEALTH 43 Whiting Hill Road, Zip 04412–1005; tel. 207/973–7045; Timothy Dentry, President and Chief Executive Officer, p. B92

**Lewiston:** ★ CENTRAL MAINE HEALTHCARE 300 Main Street, Zip 04240–7027; tel. 207/795–0111; Jeffrey L. Brickman, Chief Executive Officer, p. B29

**Portland:** MAINEHEALTH 110 Free Street, Zip 04101–3537; tel. 207/661–7001; William L. Caron Jr, President, p. B78

## MARYLAND

**Baltimore:** ★ JOHNS HOPKINS HEALTH SYSTEM 733 North Broadway, BRB 104, Zip 21205–1832; tel. 410/955–5000; Kevin W. Sowers, President, p. B69

LIFEBRIDGE HEALTH 2401 West Belvedere Avenue, Zip 21215–5216; tel. 410/601–5134; Neil M. Meltzer, President and Chief Executive Officer, p. B74

★ UNIVERSITY OF MARYLAND MEDICAL SYSTEM 250 West Pratt Street, 24th Floor, Zip 21201–1595; tel. 410/328–8667; Mohan Suntha, President and Chief Executive Officer, p. B140

**Columbia:** ★ MEDSTAR HEALTH 10980 Grantchester Way, Zip 21044–2665; tel. 410/772–6500; Kenneth A. Samet, President and Chief Executive Officer, p. B82

**Gaithersburg:** ADVENTIST HEALTHCARE 820 West Diamond Avenue, Suite 600, Zip 20878–1419; tel. 301/315–3185; Terry Forde, President and Chief Executive Officer, p. B7

**Marriottsville:** BON SECOURS MERCY HEALTH 1505 Marriottsville Road, Zip 21104–1399; tel. 410/442–5511; John M. Starcher, Chief Executive Officer, p. B24

**Rockville:** U. S. INDIAN HEALTH SERVICE 801 Thompson Avenue, Zip 20852–1627; tel. 301/443–1083, Rear Admiral, Michael Weahkee, Assistant Surgeon General, USPHS Director, Indian Health Service, p. B131

**Salisbury:** TIDALHEALTH 100 East Carroll Street, Zip 21801–5422; tel. 410/546–6400; Steven E. Leonard, President and Chief Executive Officer, p. B128

**Sparks Glencoe:** FUNDAMENTAL LONG TERM CARE HOLDINGS, LLC 930 Ridgebrook Road, Zip 21152–9390; tel. 410/773–1000; W Bradley. Bennett, President and Chief Executive Officer, p. B56

## MASSACHUSETTS

**Boston:** ★ BETH ISRAEL LAHEY HEALTH 109 Brookline Avenue, Zip 02215–3903; tel. 617/667–7000; Kevin Tabb, President and Chief Executive Officer, p. B23

★ MASS GENERAL BRIGHAM 800 Boylston Street, Suite 1150, Zip 02199–8123; tel. 617/278–1004; Anne Klibanski, President and Chief Executive Officer, p. B79

MASSACHUSETTS DEPARTMENT OF MENTAL HEALTH 25 Staniford Street, Zip 02114–2575; tel. 617/626–8123; Joan Mikula, Interim Commissioner, p. B79

MASSACHUSETTS DEPARTMENT OF PUBLIC HEALTH 250 Washington Street, Zip 02108–4619; tel. 617/624–6000; Betsy L. Schwechheimer, Bureau Director, p. B79

**Gardner:** HEYWOOD HEALTHCARE 242 Green Street, Zip 01440–1336; tel. 978/632–3420; Winfield S. Brown, Chief Executive Officer, p. B65

**Haverhill:** WHITTIER HEALTH NETWORK 25 Railroad Square, Zip 01832–5721; tel. 978/556–5858; Alfred J. Arcidi, President, p. B148

**Hyannis:** ★ CAPE COD HEALTHCARE, INC. 27 Park Street, Zip 02601–5230; tel. 508/862–5121; Michael K. Lauf, President and Chief Executive Officer, p. B26

**Pittsfield:** ★ BERKSHIRE HEALTH SYSTEMS, INC. 725 North Street, Zip 01201–4124; tel. 413/447–2750; David E. Phelps, President and Chief Executive Officer, p. B23

**Springfield:** ★ BAYSTATE HEALTH, INC. 280 Chestnut Street, Zip 01199–0001; tel. 413/794–0000; Mark A. Keroack, President and Chief Executive Officer, p. B22

**Tewksbury:** ★ COVENANT HEALTH 100 Ames Pond Drive, Suite 102, Zip 01876–1240; tel. 978/654–6363; Stephen J. Grubbs, President and Chief Executive Officer, p. B39

**Worcester:** ★ UMASS MEMORIAL HEALTH CARE, INC. 1 Biotech Park, Zip 01605–2982; tel. 508/334–0100; Eric Dickson, President and Chief Executive Officer, p. B133

## MICHIGAN

**Detroit:** ★ HENRY FORD HEALTH SYSTEM One Ford Place, Zip 48202–3450; tel. 313/876–8708; Wright L. Lassiter III, President and Chief Executive Officer, p. B64

**Grand Blanc:** MCLAREN HEALTH CARE CORPORATION 3373 Regency Park Drive, Zip 48439, One McLaren Parkway, 48439, tel. 810/342–1100; Philip A. Incarnati, President and Chief Executive Officer, p. B80

**Grand Rapids:** ★ SPECTRUM HEALTH 221 Michigan Street NE, Suite 501, Zip 49503–2543; tel. 616/391–1774; Christina Freese Decker, President and Chief Executive Officer, p. B119

**Kalamazoo:** ★ BRONSON HEALTHCARE GROUP 301 John Street, Zip 49007–5295; tel. 269/341–6000; Bill Manns, Chief Executive Officer, p. B24

**Lansing:** ★ SPARROW HEALTH SYSTEM 1215 East Michigan Avenue, Zip 48912–1811; tel. 517/364–1000; James F. Dover, President and Chief Executive Officer, p. B119

**Livonia:** ★ TRINITY HEALTH 20555 Victor Parkway, Zip 48152–7031; tel. 734/343–1000; Michael A. Slubowski, President and Chief Executive Officer, p. B129

**Midland:** ★ MIDMICHIGAN HEALTH 4000 Wellness Drive, Zip 48670–0001; tel. 989/839–3000; Diane Postler–Slattery, President and Chief Executive Officer, p. B85

**Southfield:** ★ BEAUMONT HEALTH 26901 Beaumont Boulevard, Zip 48033–3849; tel. 248/898–5000; John T. Fox, President and Chief Executive Officer, p. B22

**Traverse City:** ★ MUNSON HEALTHCARE 1105 Sixth Street, Zip 49684–2386; tel. 231/935–6703; Edwin Ness, President and Chief Executive Officer, p. B88

**MINNESOTA**

**Bloomington:** HEALTHPARTNERS 8170 33rd Avenue South, Zip 55425–4516; tel. 952/883–6000; Andrea Walsh, President and Chief Executive Officer, p. B64

**Duluth:** ★ ESSENTIA HEALTH 502 East Second Street, Zip 55805–1913; tel. 218/786–8376; David C. Herman, Chief Executive Officer, p. B53

★ ST. LUKE'S 915 East First Street, Zip 55805–2107; tel. 218/249–5555; Kevin J. Nokels, President and Chief Executive Officer, p. B121

**Minneapolis:** ★ ALLINA HEALTH 2925 Chicago Avenue, Zip 55407–1321, Mailing Address: P.O. 43, 55440–0043, tel. 612/262–5000; Penny Ann. Wheeler, Chief Executive Officer, p. B9

★ M HEALTH FAIRVIEW 2450 Riverside Avenue, Zip 55454–1400; tel. 612/672–6141; James Hereford, President and Chief Executive Officer, p. B9

**Robbinsdale:** NORTH MEMORIAL HEALTH CARE 3300 Oakdale Avenue North, Zip 55422–2926; tel. 763/520–5200; J. Kevin Croston, Chief Executive Officer, p. B91

**Rochester:** ★ MAYO CLINIC 200 First Street SW, Zip 55905–0002; tel. 507/284–2511; Gianrico Farrugia, President, p. B80

**Saint Cloud:** ★ CENTRACARE HEALTH 1406 Sixth Avenue North, Zip 56303–1900; tel. 320/251–2700; Kenneth D. Holmen, President and Chief Executive Officer, p. B28

**Saint Paul:** MINNESOTA DEPARTMENT OF HUMAN SERVICES 540 Cedar Street, Zip 55101–2208, Mailing Address: P.O. 64998, 55164–0998, tel. 651/431–3212; Anne Barry, Deputy Commissioner, p. B86

**Waconia:** ★ RIDGEVIEW MEDICAL CENTER 500 South Maple Street, Zip 55387–1752; tel. 952/442–2191; Michael Phelps, President and Chief Executive Officer, p. B108

**MISSISSIPPI**

**Jackson:** MISSISSIPPI STATE DEPARTMENT OF MENTAL HEALTH 1101 Robert E Lee Building, 239 North Lamar Street, Zip 39201–1101; tel. 601/359–1288; Diana S. Mikula, Executive Director, p. B86

★ UNIVERSITY HOSPITALS AND HEALTH SYSTEM 2500 North State Street, Zip 39216–4500; tel. 601/984–1000; Kevin S. Cook, Chief Executive Officer, p. B140

**Mccomb:** SOUTHWEST HEALTH SYSTEMS 215 Marion Avenue, Zip 39648–2705, Mailing Address: P.O. 1307, 39649–1307, tel. 601/249–5500; Charla Rowley, Chief Executive Officer, p. B118

**Meridian:** RUSH HEALTH SYSTEMS 1314 19th Avenue, Zip 39301–4116; tel. 601/483–0011; Larkin Kennedy, President and Chief Executive Officer, p. B109

**Tupelo:** ★ NORTH MISSISSIPPI HEALTH SERVICES, INC. 830 South Gloster Street, Zip 38801–4996; tel. 662/377–3136; M. Shane. Spees, President and Chief Executive Officer, p. B91

**MISSOURI**

**Cape Girardeau:** LANDMARK HOSPITALS 3255 Independence Street, Zip 63701–4914; tel. 573/335–1091; William K. Kapp III, President and Chief Executive Officer, p. B73

SOUTHEASTHEALTH 1701 Lacey Street, Zip 63701–5230; tel. 573/334–4822; Kenneth Bateman, Chief Executive Officer, p. B118

**Chesterfield:** ★ MERCY 14528 South Outer 40, Suite 100, Zip 63017–5743; tel. 314/579–6100; Lynn Britton, President and Chief Executive Officer, p. B83

**Columbia:** ★ UNIVERSITY OF MISSOURI HEALTH CARE One Hospital Drive, DC 031, Zip 65212–0001; tel. 573/882–4141; Jonathan W. Curtright, Chief Executive Officer and Chief Operating Officer, p. B141

**Joplin:** ★ FREEMAN HEALTH SYSTEM 1102 West 32nd Street, Zip 64804–3503; tel. 417/347–1111; Paula F. Baker, President and Chief Executive Officer, p. B55

**Kansas City:** RURAL COMMUNITY HOSPITALS OF AMERICA 1100 Main Street, Suite 2350, Zip 64105–5186; tel. 816/474–7800; Paul L. Nusbaum, President and Co–Owner, p. B108

★ SAINT LUKE'S HEALTH SYSTEM 901 East 104th Street, Mailstop 900N, Zip 64131–4517, 901 East 104th Street, 64131–4517, tel. 816/932–2000; Melinda Estes, President and Chief Executive Officer, p. B110

★ TRUMAN MEDICAL CENTERS 2301 Holmes Street, Zip 64108–2677; tel. 816/404–1000; Charlie Shields, Chief Executive Officer, p. B131

**Saint Joseph:** ★ MOSAIC LIFE CARE 5325 Faraon Street, Zip 64506–3488; tel. 816/271–6000; Samuel Mark. Laney, Chief Executive Officer, p. B87

**Saint Louis:** ★ ASCENSION HEALTHCARE 101 South Hanley Road, Suite 450, Zip 63105–3406; tel. 314/733–8000; Joseph R. Impicciche, President and Chief Executive Officer, p. B12

★ BJC HEALTHCARE 4901 Forest Park Avenue, Suite 1200, Zip 63108–1402; tel. 314/286–2000; Richard J. Liekweg, President and Chief Executive Officer, p. B23

★ SSM HEALTH 10101 Woodfield Lane, Zip 63132–2937; tel. 314/994–7800; Laura Kaiser, President and Chief Executive Officer, p. B120

**Springfield:** COXHEALTH 1423 North Jefferson Avenue, Zip 65802–1988; tel. 417/269–3108; Steven D. Edwards, President and Chief Executive Officer, p. B40

**MONTANA**

**Great Falls:** BENEFIS HEALTH SYSTEM 1101 26th Street South, Zip 59405–5161; tel. 406/455–5000; John H. Goodnow, Chief Executive Officer, p. B23

**NEVADA**

**Reno:** ★ RENOWN HEALTH 50 West Liberty Street, Suite 1100, Zip 89501–1951; tel. 775/982–5529; Anthony D. Slonim, President and Chief Executive Officer, p. B107

**NEBRASKA**

**Lincoln:** ★ BRYAN HEALTH 1600 South 48th Street, Zip 68506–1283, 1600 S 48th ST, 68506–1283, tel. 402/481–1111; Russell R. Gronewold, President and Chief Executive Officer, p. B25

**Norfolk:** FAITH REGIONAL HEALTH SERVICES 2700 West Norfolk Avenue, Zip 68701–4438, Mailing Address: P.O. 869, 68702–0869, tel. 402/371–4880; Kelly Driscoll, President and Chief Executive Officer, p. B54

**Omaha:** ★ NEBRASKA METHODIST HEALTH SYSTEM, INC. 8511 West Dodge Road, Zip 68114–3403; tel. 402/354–5411; Stephen L. Goeser, President and Chief Executive Officer, p. B89

**New Hampshire**

**Laconia:** ★ LRGHEALTHCARE 80 Highland Street, Zip 03246–3298; tel. 603/524–3211; Kevin Donovan, President and Chief Executive Officer, p. B77

**Littleton:** NORTH COUNTRY HEALTHCARE 600 Saint Johnsbury Road, Zip 03561–3442; tel. 603/444–9000; Thomas Mee, Chief Executive Officer, p. B91

**Manchester:** SOLUTIONHEALTH One Elliot Way, Zip 03103–3502; tel. 603/663–2990; Sherry Hausmann, President and Chief Executive Officer, p. B118

**Portsmouth:** BRIDGEPOINT HEALTHCARE 155 Fleet Street, Zip 03801–4050; tel. 603/570–4888; Marc C. Ferrell, President and Chief Executive Officer, p. B24

**NEW JERSEY**

**Edison:** ★ HACKENSACK MERIDIAN HEALTH 343 Thornall Street, 8th Floor, Zip 08837–2206, 343 Thornall Street, 08837–2206, tel. 844/464–9355; Robert C. Garrett, Chief Executive Officer, p. B58

**Jersey City:** CAREPOINT HEALTH 10 Exchange Place, 15th Floor, Zip 07302–3918; tel. 201/821–8900; Achintya Moulick, Chief Executive Officer, p. B26

**Lakewood:** CONCORD HEALTHCARE GROUP 111 Clifton AVenue, Zip 8701; tel. 214/396–3462; Joe Neuman, Chief Executive Officer, p. B38

**Marlton:** ★ VIRTUA HEALTH 303 Lippincott Drive, 4th Floor, Zip 08053–4160; tel. 856/355–0010; Dennis W. Pullin, President and Chief Executive Officer, p. B146

**Morristown:** ★ ATLANTIC HEALTH SYSTEM 475 South Street, Zip 07960–6459, Mailing Address: P.O. 1905, 07962–1905, tel. 973/660–3270; Brian A. Gragnolati, President and Chief Executive Officer, p. B16

**Mullica Hill:** ★ INSPIRA HEALTH NETWORK 165 Bridgeton Pike, Zip 8062; tel. 856/641–8000; Amy B. Mansue, President and Chief Executive Officer, p. B68

**Trenton:** ★ CAPITAL HEALTH 750 Brunswick Avenue, Zip 08638–4143; tel. 609/394–6000; Al Maghazehe, President and Chief Executive Officer, p. B26

DIVISION OF MENTAL HEALTH AND ADDICTION SERVICES, DEPARTMENT OF HUMAN SERVICES, STATE OF NEW JERSEY 222 South Warren Street, Zip 08608–2306, P.O. Box 360, 08625–0360, tel. 609/438–4351; Valerie Mielke, Assistant Commissioner, p. B46

**West Orange:** ★ RWJBARNABAS HEALTH 95 Old Short Hills Road, Zip 07052–1008; tel. 973/322–4000; Barry Ostrowsky, President and Chief Executive Officer, p. B109

**NEW MEXICO**

**Albuquerque:** ERNEST HEALTH, INC. 7770 Jefferson Street NE, Suite 320, Zip 87109–4386; tel. 505/856–5300; Darby Brockette, Chief Executive Officer, p. B52

★ PRESBYTERIAN HEALTHCARE SERVICES 9521 San Mateo Blvd. NE, Zip 87113, Mailing Address: P.O. 26666, 87125–6666, tel. 505/841–1234; Dale Maxwell, Chief Executive Officer, p. B101

UNIVERSITY OF NEW MEXICO HOSPITALS 915 Camino De Salud, Zip 87131–0001; tel. 505/272–5849; Michael Chicarelli, Interim Chief Executive Officer, p. B141

**NEW YORK**

**Albany:** NEW YORK STATE OFFICE OF MENTAL HEALTH 44 Holland Avenue, Zip 12208–3411; tel. 518/474–7056; Ann Sullivan, Commissioner, p. B89

**Binghamton:** UNITED HEALTH SERVICES 10–42 Mitchell Avenue, Zip 13903–1617; tel. 607/762–2200; John M. Carrigg, President and Chief Executive Officer, p. B134

**Bronx:** MONTEFIORE HEALTH SYSTEM 111 East 210th Street, Zip 10467–2490; tel. 718/920–4321; Philip O. Ozuah, Chief Executive Officer, p. B86

**Buffalo:** ★ CATHOLIC HEALTH SYSTEM 144 Genesee Street, Zip 14203–1560; tel. 716/862–2410; Mark A. Sullivan, President and Chief Executive Officer, p. B28

**Cooperstown:** ★ BASSETT HEALTHCARE NETWORK 1 Atwell Road, Zip 13326–1301; tel. 607/547–3456; William F. Streck, President and Chief Executive Officer, p. B21

**Elmira:** ARNOT HEALTH 600 Roe Avenue, Zip 14905–1629; tel. 607/737–4100; Jonathan I. Lawrence, President and Chief Executive Officer, p. B12

**Geneva:** FINGER LAKES HEALTH 196 North Street, Zip 14456–1651; tel. 315/787–4000; Jose Acevedo, President and Chief Executive Officer, p. B54

**Ithaca:** ★ CAYUGA HEALTH SYSTEM 101 Dates Drive, Zip 14850–1342; tel. 607/274–4011; Martin Stallone, President and Chief Executive Officer, p. B28

**Jamaica:** ★ MEDISYS HEALTH NETWORK 8900 Van Wyck Expressway, Zip 11418–2832; tel. 718/206–6000; Bruce J. Flanz, President and Chief Executive Officer, p. B81

**LaGrangeville:** HEALTH QUEST SYSTEMS, INC. 1351 Route 55 Ste 200, Zip 12540–5108, 1351 Route 55, 12540–5108, tel. 845/475–9500; Robert Friedberg, President and Chief Executive Officer, p. B64

**Middletown:** ★ GARNET HEALTH 707 East Main Street, Zip 10940–2650; tel. 845/333–1000; Scott Batulis, President and Chief Executive Officer, p. B56

**New Hyde Park:** ★ NORTHWELL HEALTH 2000 Marcus Avenue, Zip 11042; tel. 516/321–6666; Michael J. Dowling, President and Chief Executive Officer, p. B92

**New York:** ★ MOUNT SINAI HEALTH SYSTEM One Gustave L. Levy Place, Zip 10029; tel. 212/659–8888; Kenneth L. Davis, President and Chief Executive Officer, p. B87

★ NEWYORK–PRESBYTERIAN 525 East 68th Street, Box 182, Zip 10065; tel. 212/746–3745; Steven J. Corwin, President and Chief Executive Officer, p. B90

★ NYC HEALTH + HOSPITALS 125 Worth Street, Room 514, Zip 10013–4006; tel. 212/788–3321; Mitchell H. Katz, President and Chief Executive Officer, p. B94

**Olean:** UPPER ALLEGHENY HEALTH SYSTEM 515 Main Street, Zip 14760–3676; tel. 716/375–6190; Jeff S. Zewe, Chief Executive Officer, p. B143

**Potsdam:** ST. LAWRENCE HEALTH SYSTEM 50 Leroy Street, Zip 13676–1799; tel. 315/265–3300; David B. Acker, President and Chief Executive Officer, p. B121

**Rochester:** ★ ROCHESTER REGIONAL HEALTH 1425 Portland Avenue, 5th Floor, Zip 14621–3001; tel. 585/922–4000; Eric Bieber, President and Chief Executive Officer, p. B108

★ UNIVERSITY OF ROCHESTER MEDICAL CENTER 601 Elmwood Ave Box 623, Zip 14642–0002, 601 Elmwood Avenue, 14642–0002, tel. 585/275–2100; Mark B. Taubman, Chief Executive Officer, p. B141

**Rockville Centre:** CATHOLIC HEALTH SERVICES OF LONG ISLAND 992 North Village Avenue, 1st Floor, Zip 11570–1002; tel. 516/705–3700; Alan D. Guerci, President and Chief Executive Officer, p. B27

**Valhalla:** WMCHEALTH 100 Woods Road, Zip 10595–1530; tel. 914/493–7000; Michael D. Israel, President and Chief Executive Officer, p. B148

**NORTH CAROLINA**

**Boone:** ★ APPALACHIAN REGIONAL HEALTHCARE SYSTEM 336 Deerfield Road, Zip 28607–5008, Mailing Address: P.O. 2600, 28607–2600, tel. 828/262–4100; Charles Mantooth, President and Chief Executive Officer, p. B10

**Chapel Hill:** ★ UNC HEALTH CARE 101 Manning Drive, Zip 27514–4220; tel. 919/966–4131; Wesley Burks, Chief Executive Officer, p. B133

**Charlotte:** ★ ACUITYHEALTHCARE, LP 10735 David Taylor Dr. Suite 200, Zip 28262–0052; tel. 704/887–7280; Edwin H. Cooper Jr, President and Chief Executive Officer, p. B5

★ ATRIUM HEALTH 1000 Blythe Boulevard, Zip 28203–5871, PO Box 32861, 28232–2861, tel. 704/355–2000; Eugene A. Woods, President and Chief Executive Officer, p. B16

**Durham:** ★ DUKE UNIVERSITY HEALTH SYSTEM 201 Trent Drive, Zip 27710–3037, Mailing Address: P.O. 3701, 27710–3701, tel. 919/684–2255; A. Eugene. Washington, President and Chief Executive Officer, p. B47

VERITAS COLLABORATIVE 4024 Stirrup Creek Drive, Zip 27703–9464; tel. 855/875–5812; Stacie McEntyre, Chief Executive Officer, p. B144

**Fayetteville:** CAPE FEAR VALLEY HEALTH SYSTEM 1638 Owen Drive, Zip 28304–3424, Mailing Address: P.O. 2000, 28302–2000, tel. 910/615–4000; Michael Nagowski, President and Chief Executive Officer, p. B26

**Greensboro:** CONE HEALTH 1200 North Elm Street, Zip 27401–1004; tel. 336/832–7000; Terry Akin, President and Chief Executive Officer, p. B38

**Greenville:** ★ VIDANT HEALTH 2100 Stantonsburg Road, Zip 27834–2818, Mailing Address: P.O. 6028, 27835–6028, tel. 252/847–4100; Michael Waldrum, Chief Executive Officer, p. B145

**Pinehurst:** ★ FIRSTHEALTH OF THE CAROLINAS 155 Memorial Drive, Zip 28374–8710, Mailing Address: P.O. 3000, 28374–3000, tel. 910/715–1000; Mickey W. Foster, Chief Executive Officer, p. B54

**Raleigh:** ★ WAKEMED HEALTH & HOSPITALS 3000 New Bern Avenue, Zip 27610–1231; tel. 919/350–8000; Donald R. Gintzig, President and Chief Executive Officer, p. B146

**Wilmington:** ★ NEW HANOVER REGIONAL MEDICAL CENTER 2131 South 17th Street, Zip 28401–7407; tel. 910/343–7040; John H. Gizdic, President and Chief Executive Officer, p. B89

**Winston Salem:** ★ NOVANT HEALTH 2085 Frontis Plaza Boulevard, Zip 27103–5614; tel. 336/718–5600; Carl S. Armato, President and Chief Executive Officer, p. B93

**Winston–Salem:** ★ WAKE FOREST BAPTIST HEALTH Medical Center Boulevard, Zip 27157; tel. 336/716–2011; Julie Ann . Freischlag, Chief Executive Officer, p. B146

**NORTH DAKOTA**

**Fargo:** SISTERS OF MARY OF THE PRESENTATION HEALTH SYSTEM 1202 Page Drive SW, Zip 58103–2340, Mailing Address: P.O. 10007, 58106–0007, tel. 701/237–9290; Aaron K. Alton, President and Chief Executive Officer, p. B117

**OHIO**

**Akron:** ★ SUMMA HEALTH 1077 Gorge Boulevard, Zip 44310; tel. 330/375–3000; T. Clifford Deveny, President and Chief Executive Officer, p. B123

**Canton:** AULTMAN HEALTH FOUNDATION 2600 Sixth Street SW, Zip 44710–1702; tel. 330/363–6192; Edward J. Roth III, President and Chief Executive Officer, p. B16

**Chillicothe:** ADENA HEALTH SYSTEM 272 Hospital Road, Zip 45601–9031, PO Box 802846, Kansas City, MO, 64180–2846, tel. 740/779–7500; Jeff Graham, President and Chief Executive Officer, p. B5

**Cincinnati:** MERCY HEALTH 1701 Mercy Health Place, Zip 45237; tel. 513/639–2800; John M. Starcher, President and Chief Executive Officer, p. B84

UC HEALTH 3200 Burnet Avenue, Zip 45229–3019; tel. 513/585–6000; Richard P. Lofgren, President and Chief Executive Officer, p. B132

**Cleveland:** ★ CLEVELAND CLINIC HEALTH SYSTEM 9500 Euclid, Zip 44195–5108; tel. 216/444–2200; Tomislav Mihaljevic, Chief Executive Officer and President, p. B30

SISTERS OF CHARITY HEALTH SYSTEM 2475 East 22nd Street, Zip 44115–3221; tel. 216/363–2797; Thomas J. Strauss, Chief Executive Officer, p. B117

★ UNIVERSITY HOSPITALS 11100 Euclid Avenue, Zip 44106–5000; tel. 216/844–1000; Thomas F. Zenty III, Chief Executive Officer, p. B139

**Columbus:** OHIO DEPARTMENT OF MENTAL HEALTH 30 East Broad Street, 8th Floor, Zip 43215–3430; tel. 614/466–2297; Tracy Plouck, Director, p. B95

★ OHIO STATE UNIVERSITY HEALTH SYSTEM 370 West Ninth Avenue, Zip 43210–1238; tel. 614/685–9015; David P. McQuaid, Chief Executive Officer, p. B96

★ OHIOHEALTH 3430 Ohio Health Parkway, Zip 43202–1575; tel. 614/544–4455; Stephen Markovich, President and Chief Executive Officer, p. B96

**Dayton:** ★ KETTERING HEALTH NETWORK 3965 Southern Boulevard, Zip 45429–1229; tel. 855/536–7543; Fred M. Manchur, Chief Executive Officer, p. B71

★ PREMIER HEALTH 110 North Main Street Suite 390, Zip 45402–3720; tel. 937/499–9401; Mary H. Boosalis, President and Chief Executive Officer, p. B100

**Findlay:** ★ BLANCHARD VALLEY HEALTH SYSTEM 1900 South Main Street, Zip 45840–1214; tel. 419/423–4500; Scott C. Malaney, President and Chief Executive Officer, p. B24

**Galion:** ★ AVITA HEALTH SYSTEM 269 Portland Way South, Zip 44833–2399; tel. 419/468–4841; Jerome Morasko, President and Chief Executive Officer, p. B17

**Jackson:** HOLZER HEALTH SYSTEM 500 Burlington Road, Zip 45640–9360; tel. 855/446–5937; Michael R. Canady, Chief Executive Officer, p. B65

**Marietta:** MEMORIAL HEALTH SYSTEM 401 Matthew Street, Zip 45750–1635; tel. 740/374–1400; J Scott. Cantley, President and Chief Executive Officer, p. B82

**Toledo:** ★ PROMEDICA HEALTH SYSTEM 100 Madison Avenue, Zip 43604–1516; tel. 567/585–9601; Randall D. Oostra, President and Chief Executive Officer, p. B102

## OKLAHOMA

**Duncan:** ★ DRH HEALTH 1407 North Whisenant Drive, Zip 73533–1650; tel. 580/252–5300; Jay R. Johnson, President and Chief Executive Officer, p. B46

**Oklahoma City:** FIRST PHYSICIANS CAPITAL GROUP, INC. 14201 Wireless Way, Suite B–100, Zip 73134–2521; tel. 405/246–0218; Sean Kirrane, Chief Executive Officer, p. B54

★ INTEGRIS HEALTH 3366 NW Expressway, Suite 800, Zip 73112–9756; tel. 405/949–6066; Timothy T. Pehrson, President and Chief Executive Officer, p. B68

OKLAHOMA DEPARTMENT OF MENTAL HEALTH AND SUBSTANCE ABUSE SERVICES 1200 NE 13th Street, Zip 73117–1022, Mailing Address: P.O. 53277, 73152–3277, tel. 405/522–3908; Terri White, Commissioner, p. B96

**Shawnee:** PREFERRED MANAGEMENT CORPORATION 120 West MacArthur, Suite 121, Zip 74804–2005; tel. 405/878–0202; Donald Freeman, President and Chief Executive Officer, p. B100

**Tulsa:** ★ SAINT FRANCIS HEALTH SYSTEM 6161 South Yale Avenue, Zip 74136–1902; tel. 918/494–8454; Jake Henry Jr, President and Chief Executive Officer, p. B110

## OREGON

**Bend:** ★ ST. CHARLES HEALTH SYSTEM, INC. 2500 NE Neff Road, Zip 97701–6015; tel. 541/382–4321; Joseph Sluka, President and Chief Executive Officer, p. B121

**Corvallis:** ★ SAMARITAN HEALTH SERVICES 3600 NW Samaritan Drive, Zip 97330–3737, Mailing Address: P.O. 1068, 97339–1068, tel. 541/768–5001; Doug Boysen, President and Chief Executive Officer, p. B110

**Medford:** ★ ASANTE HEALTH SYSTEM 2650 Siskiyou Boulevard, Suite 200, Zip 97504–8170; tel. 541/789–4100; Scott A. Kelly, President and Chief Executive Officer, p. B12

**Portland:** ★ LEGACY HEALTH 1919 NW Lovejoy Street, Zip 97209–1503; tel. 503/415–5600; Kathryn G. Correia, President and Chief Executive Officer, p. B74

**Salem:** SALEM HEALTH 890 Oak Street Bldg B POB 14001, Zip 97309–5014; tel. 503/561–5200; Cheryl R. Nester Wolfe, President and Chief Executive Officer, p. B110

## PENNSYLVANIA

**Allentown:** GOOD SHEPHERD REHABILITATION NETWORK 850 South Fifth Street, Zip 18103–3308; tel. 610/776–3100; Gary R. Schmidt, Interim President and Chief Executive Officer, p. B57

★ LEHIGH VALLEY HEALTH NETWORK 1200 South Cedar Crest Boulevard, Zip 18103–6202, Mailing Address: P.O. 689, 18105–1556, tel. 610/402–8000; Brian A. Nester, President and Chief Executive Officer, p. B74

**Beaver:** HERITAGE VALLEY HEALTH SYSTEM 1000 Dutch Ridge Road, Zip 15009–9727; tel. 724/773–2024; Norman F. Mitry, President and Chief Executive Officer, p. B65

**Bethlehem:** ST. LUKE'S UNIVERSITY HEALTH NETWORK 801 Ostrum Street, Zip 18015–1000; tel. 610/954–4000; Richard A. Anderson, President and Chief Executive Officer, p. B122

**Danville:** ★ GEISINGER 100 North Academy Avenue, Zip 17822–9800; tel. 570/271–6211; Jaewon Ryu, President and Chief Executive Officer, p. B56

**Enola:** ★ POST ACUTE MEDICAL, LLC 1828 Good Hope Road, Suite 102, Zip 17025–1233; tel. 717/731–9660; Anthony F. Misitano, President and Chief Executive Officer, p. B99

**Greensburg:** EXCELA HEALTH 532 West Pittsburgh Street, Zip 15601, 134 Industrial Park Road, 15601–7328, tel. 724/832–5050; John Sphon, Chief Executive Officer, p. B53

**Hershey:** PENN STATE HERSHEY HEALTH SYSTEM 500 University Drive, Zip 17033–2360; tel. 717/531–8521; Stephen M. Massini, Chief Executive Officer, p. B98

**King of Prussia:** UNIVERSAL HEALTH SERVICES, INC. 367 South Gulph Road, Zip 19406–3121, Mailing Address: P.O. 61558, 19406–0958, tel. 610/768–3300; Alan B. Miller, Chairman and Chief Executive Officer, p. B135

**Meadville:** ★ MEADVILLE MEDICAL CENTER 751 Liberty Street, Zip 16335–2559; tel. 814/333–5000; Philip E. Pandolph, Chief Executive Officer, p. B81

**Mechanicsburg:** ★ SELECT MEDICAL CORPORATION 4714 Gettysburg Road, Zip 17055–4325; tel. 717/972–1100; David S. Chernow, President and Chief Executive Officer, p. B112

★ VIBRA HEALTHCARE 4600 Lena Drive, Zip 17055–4904; tel. 717/591–5700; Brad Hollinger, Chairman and Chief Executive Officer, p. B144

**Philadelphia:** EINSTEIN HEALTHCARE NETWORK 5501 Old York Road, Zip 19141–3098; tel. 215/456–7890; Barry R. Freedman, President and Chief Executive Officer, p. B47

★ JEFFERSON HEALTH 925 Chestnut Street, Suite 110, Zip 19107–4216; tel. 610/225–6200; Stephen K. Klasko, Chief Executive Officer, p. B69

★ TEMPLE UNIVERSITY HEALTH SYSTEM 3509 North Broad Street, 9th Floor, Zip 19140–4105; tel. 215/707–0900; Michael A. Young, Chief Executive Officer, p. B125

★ UNIVERSITY OF PENNSYLVANIA HEALTH SYSTEM 3400 Civic Center Bouelvard, Suite A–5, Zip 19104–5127; tel. 215/662–2203; Kevin B. Mahoney, Chief Executive Officer, p. B141

**Pittsburgh:** ★ ALLEGHENY HEALTH NETWORK 120 5th Avenue, FAPHM–294E, Zip 15222–3000; tel. 412/359–3131; Cynthia Hundorfean, President and Chief Executive Officer, p. B8

★ UPMC 600 Grant Street, US Steel Tower, Suite 6262, Zip 15219–2702; tel. 412/647–8762; Jeffrey A. Romoff, President and Chief Executive Officer, p. B142

**Sayre:** ★ GUTHRIE CLINIC One Guthrie Square, Zip 18840–1625; tel. 570/888–5858; Joseph A. Scopelliti, President and Chief Executive Officer, p. B57

**Villanova:** DEVEREUX 444 Devereux Drive, Zip 19085–1932, Mailing Address: P.O. 638, 19085–0638, tel. 610/520–3000; Robert Q. Kreider, President and Chief Executive Officer, p. B46

**Washington:** ★ WASHINGTON HEALTH SYSTEM 155 Wilson Avenue, Zip 15301–3336; tel. 724/225–7000; Brook Ward, President and Chief Executive Officer, p. B146

**West Reading:** ★ TOWER HEALTH Sixth Avenue and Spruce Street, Zip 19611; tel. 610/988–8000; Clinton Matthews, President and Chief Executive Officer, p. B129

**Williamsport:** ★ UPMC SUSQUEHANNA 700 High Street , Zip 17701–3100; tel. 570/321–1000; Steven P. Johnson, President and Chief Executive Officer, p. B143

**York:** ★ WELLSPAN HEALTH 45 Monument Road, Suite 200, Zip 17403–5071; tel. 717/851–2121; Roxanna L. Gapstur, President and Chief Executive Officer, p. B146

## PUERTO RICO

**San Juan:** ★ PUERTO RICO DEPARTMENT OF HEALTH Building 'A' – Medical Center, Zip 936, Call Box 70184, 936, tel. 787/765–2929; Rafael Rodriguez. Mercado, Secretary of Health, p. B105

## RHODE ISLAND

**Providence:** ★ CARE NEW ENGLAND HEALTH SYSTEM 45 Willard Avenue, Zip 02905–3218; tel. 401/453–7900; James E. Fanale, President, Chief Executive Officer and Chief Clinical Officer, p. B26

LIFESPAN CORPORATION 167 Point Street, Zip 02903–4771; tel. 401/444–3500; Timothy J. Babineau, President and Chief Executive Officer, p. B77

## SOUTH CAROLINA

**Anderson:** ★ ANMED HEALTH 800 North Fant Street, Zip 29621–5793; tel. 864/512–1000; William A. Kenley, Chief Executive Officer, p. B10

**Charleston:** ★ MUSC HEALTH 171 Ashley Ave, Zip 29425–8908; tel. 843/792–2300; Patrick J. Cawley, Chief Executive Officer, p. B88

ROPER ST. FRANCIS HEALTHCARE 125 Doughty Street, Suite 760, Zip 29403–5785; tel. 843/402–2273; Brian M. White, Chief Executive Officer, p. B108

**Columbia:** PRISMA HEALTH – MIDLANDS 1301 Taylor Street, Suite 9–A, Zip 29201–2942, Mailing Address: P.O. 2266, 29202–2266, tel. 803/296–2100; Mark O'Halla, President and Chief Executive Officer, Prisma Health , p. B102

**Florence:** MCLEOD HEALTH 555 East Cheves Street, Zip 29506–2617, Mailing Address: P.O. 100551, 29502–0551, tel. 843/777–2000; Robert L. Colones, President and Chief Executive Officer, p. B81

**Georgetown:** ★ TIDELANDS HEALTH 606 Black River Road, Zip 29440–3304, Mailing Address: P.O. 421718, 29442–4203, tel. 843/527–7000; Bruce P. Bailey, President and Chief Executive Officer, p. B128

**Greenville:** PRISMA HEALTH – UPSTATE 701 Grove Road, Zip 29605–5611; tel. 864/455–7000; Mark O'Halla, Chief Executive Officer, p. B102

**Spartanburg:** ★ SPARTANBURG REGIONAL HEALTHCARE SYSTEM 101 East Wood Street, Zip 29303–3040; tel. 864/560–6000; Bruce Holstien, President and Chief Executive Officer, p. B119

## SOUTH DAKOTA

**Rapid City:** ★ MONUMENT HEALTH 353 Fairmont Boulevard, Zip 57701–7375, Mailing Address: P.O. 6000, 57709–6000, tel. 605/719–1000; Paulette Davidson, President and Chief Executive Officer , p. B87

**Sioux Falls:** ★ AVERA HEALTH 3900 West Avera Drive, Suite 300, Zip 57108–5721; tel. 605/322–4700; Bob Sutton, President and Chief Executive Officer, p. B17

★ SANFORD HEALTH 2301 East 60th Street North, Zip 57104–0569, PO Box 5039, 57117–5039, tel. 605/333–1000; Kelby K. Krabbenhoft, President and Chief Executive Officer, p. B111

## TENNESSEE

**Brentwood:** ★ DUKE LIFEPOINT HEALTHCARE 330 Seven Springs Way, Zip 37027–5098; tel. 615/920–7000; Jeffrey G. Seraphine, President, p. B47

★ HEALTHTECH MANAGEMENT SERVICES 5110 Maryland Way Suite 200, Zip 37027–2307; tel. 615/309–6053; Derek Morkel, Chief Executive Officer, p. B64

★ LIFEPOINT HEALTH 330 Seven Springs Way, Zip 37027–4536; tel. 615/920–7000; David M. Dill, President and Chief Executive Officer, p. B75

★ QHR HEALTH 1573 Mallory Lane,  Suite 200, Zip 37027, 1573 Mallory Lane, Suite 200, 37027, tel. 800/233–1470; Dwayne Gunter, President and Chief Executive Officer, p. B105

QUORUM HEALTH 1573 Mallory Lane, Suite 100, Zip 37027; tel. 615/221–1400; Daniel S. Slipkovich, Interim Chief Executive Officer, p. B107

**Chattanooga:** ERLANGER HEALTH SYSTEM 975 East Third Street, Zip 37403–2147; tel. 423/778–7000; William L. Jackson Jr, President and Chief Executive Officer, p. B52

**Clinton:** CURAE HEALTH 121 Leinart Street, Zip 37716–3632, Mailing Address: P.O. 358, 37717–0358, tel. 865/269–4074; Steve Clapp, President and Chief Executive Officer, p. B40

**Columbia:** ★ MAURY REGIONAL HEALTH SYSTEM 1224 Trotwood Avenue, Zip 38401–4802; tel. 931/381–1111; H. Alan. Watson, Chief Executive Officer, p. B80

**Franklin:** ACADIA HEALTHCARE COMPANY, INC. 6100 Tower Circle, Suite 1000, Zip 37067–1509; tel. 615/861–6000; Debra Osteen, Chief Executive Officer, p. B4

★ COMMUNITY HEALTH SYSTEMS, INC. 4000 Meridian Boulevard, Zip 37067–6325, Mailing Address: P.O. 689020, 37068–9020, tel. 615/465–7000; Wayne T. Smith, Chairman, President and Chief Executive Officer, p. B34

**Jackson:** ★ WEST TENNESSEE HEALTHCARE 620 Skyline Drive, Zip 38301–3923; tel. 731/541–5000; James E. Ross, President and Chief Executive Officer, p. B147

**Johnson City:** BALLAD HEALTH 303 Med Tech Parkway, Zip 37604–2391; tel. 423/230–8200; Alan M. Levine, President and Chief Executive Officer, p. B18

**Knoxville:** COVENANT HEALTH 100 Fort Sanders West Boulevard, Zip 37922–3353; tel. 865/531–5555; James VanderSteeg, President and Chief Executive Officer, p. B39

**Memphis:** ★ BAPTIST MEMORIAL HEALTH CARE CORPORATION 350 North Humphreys Boulevard, Zip 38120–2177; tel. 901/227–5117; Jason Little, President and Chief Executive Officer, p. B21

★ METHODIST LE BONHEUR HEALTHCARE 1211 Union Avenue, Suite 700, Zip 38104–6600; tel. 901/516–0791; Michael Ugwueke Sr, President and Chief Executive Officer, p. B85

STRATEGIC BEHAVIORAL HEALTH, LLC 8295 Tournament Drive, Suite 201, Zip 38125–8913; tel. 901/969–3100; Jim Shaheen, President, p. B123

**Nashville:** ★ ARDENT HEALTH SERVICES 1 Burton Hills Boulevard, Suite 250, Zip 37215–6195; tel. 615/296–3000; Marty J. Bonick, President and Chief Executive Officer, p. B11

HAVEN BEHAVIORAL HEALTHCARE 3102 West End Avenue, Suite 1000, Zip 37203–1324; tel. 615/393–8800; Kelly Gill, Chief Executive Officer, p. B58

★ HCA HEALTHCARE One Park Plaza, Zip 37203–1548; tel. 615/344–5248; Samuel Hazen, President and Chief Executive Officer, p. B59

★ VANDERBILT HEALTH 1211 22nd Avenue South, Zip 37232; tel. 615/322–5000; Charles Wright. Pinson, Deputy Chief Executive Officer and Chief Health System Officer, p. B144

**Parsons:** TENNESSEE HEALTH MANAGEMENT 52 West Eighth Street, Zip 38363–4656, PO Box 10, 38363–0010, tel. 731/847–6343; Dennis Berry, Chief Executive Officer, p. B126

## TEXAS

**Addison:** UNITED SURGICAL PARTNERS INTERNATIONAL 15305 Dallas Parkway, Suite 1600, Zip 75001–6491; tel. 972/713–3500; Brett Brodnax, Chief Executive Officer, p. B134

**Arlington:** ★ TEXAS HEALTH RESOURCES 612 East Lamar Boulevard, Suite 900, Zip 76011–4130; tel. 682/236–7900; Barclay E. Berdan, Chief Executive Officer, p. B127

**Austin:** TEXAS DEPARTMENT OF STATE HEALTH SERVICES 1100 West 49th Street, Zip 78756–3199; tel. 512/458–7111; Stacey Thompson, Superintendent, p. B127

★ UNIVERSITY OF TEXAS SYSTEM 601 Colorado Street, Suite 205, Zip 78701–2904; tel. 512/499–4224; John M. Zerwas, Executive Vice Chancellor, p. B142

**Dallas:** ★ BAYLOR SCOTT & WHITE HEALTH 4005 Crutcher Street, Suite 310, Zip 75246–1779; tel. 214/820–0111; James H. Hinton, Chief Executive Officer, p. B22

CHILDREN'S HEALTH 1935 Medical District Drive, Zip 75235–7701; tel. 214/456–7000; Christopher J. Durovich, President and Chief Executive Officer, p. B29

CORNERSTONE HEALTHCARE GROUP 2200 Ross Avenue, Suite 5400, Zip 75201–7984; tel. 469/621–6700; Steve Jakubcanin, President and Chief Executive Officer, p. B38

EVEREST REHABILITATION HOSPITALS, LLC 5100 Belt Line Road, Suite 310, Zip 75254–7559; tel. 469/713–1145; Jay Quintana, Chief Executive Officer and Co–Founder, p. B53

★ METHODIST HEALTH SYSTEM 1441 North Beckley Avenue, Zip 75203–1201, Mailing Address: P.O. 655999, 75265–5999, tel. 214/947–8181; James C. Scoggin Jr, Chief Executive Officer, p. B85

STEWARD HEALTH CARE SYSTEM, LLC 1900 North Pearl Street, Suite 2400, Zip 75201; tel. 617/419–4700; Ralph de la Torre, Chairman and Chief Executive Officer, p. B122

★ TENET HEALTHCARE CORPORATION 1445 Ross Avenue, Suite 1400, Zip 75202–2703, Mailing Address: P.O. 1390369, 75313–9036, tel. 469/893–2200; Saumya Sutaria, President and Chief Operating Officer, p. B125

**Garland:** CURAHEALTH HOSPITALS 650 Beebalm Lane, Suite 220, Zip 75040–2955; tel. 972/414–2872; Ken McGee, President and Chief Operating Officer, p. B40

**Greenville:** HUNT REGIONAL HEALTHCARE 4215 Joe Ramsey Boulevard, Zip 75401–7852, Mailing Address: P.O. 1059, 75403–1059, tel. 903/408–5000; Richard Carter, Chief Executive Officer, p. B66

**Houston:** ★ HOUSTON METHODIST 6565 Fannin Street, D–200, Zip 77030–2707; tel. 713/441–2221; Marc L. Boom, Chief Executive Officer, p. B66

★ MEMORIAL HERMANN HEALTH SYSTEM 929 Gessner, Suite 2700, Zip 77024–2593; tel. 713/338–5555; David L. Callender, President and Chief Executive Officer, p. B82

NEXUS HEALTH SYSTEMS One Riverway, Suite 600, Zip 77056–1993; tel. 713/355–6111; John W. Cassidy, President, Chief Executive Officer and Chief Medical Officer, p. B90

**Irving:** ★ CHRISTUS HEALTH 919 Hidden Ridge Drive, Zip 75038; tel. 469/282–2000; Ernie W. Sadau, Chief Executive Officer, p. B29

USMD HEALTH SYSTEM 6333 North State Highway 161 Suite 200, Zip 75038–2229; tel. 214/493–4000; Richard C. Johnston, Chief Executive Officer and Chief Physician Officer, p. B143

**Lubbock:** ★ COVENANT HEALTH SYSTEM 3615 19th Street, Zip 79410–1203; tel. 806/725–0447; Richard H. Parks, President and Chief Executive Officer, p. B40

**Plano:** ★ COMMUNITY HOSPITAL CORPORATION 7800 North Dallas Parkway, Suite 200, Zip 75024–6116; tel. 972/943–6400; Jim R. Kendrick, President and Chief Executive Officer, p. B37

★ LIFECARE MANAGEMENT SERVICES 5340 Legacy Drive, Suite 150, Zip 75024–3131; tel. 469/241–2100; James E. Murray, Chief Executive Officer, p. B75

OCEANS HEALTHCARE 5360 Legacy Drive, Suite 101, Zip 75024–3130; tel. 972/464–0022; Stuart Archer, Chief Executive Officer, p. B94

**Sherman:** CARRUS HOSPITALS 1810 West US Highway 82, Zip 75092–7069; tel. 903/870–2600; Jon Michael. Rains, President and Chief Operating Officer, p. B27

**The Woodlands:** EMERUS 10077 Grogan's Mill, Suite 100, Zip 77380–1022; tel. 281/292–2450; Craig Goguen, Chief Executive Officer, p. B48

## UTAH

**Nephi:** ★ RURAL HEALTH GROUP 48 West 1500 North, Zip 84648–8900; tel. 435/623–4924; Mark R. Stoddard, President and Chairman, p. B108

**Salt Lake City:** ★ INTERMOUNTAIN HEALTHCARE, INC. 36 South State Street, 22nd Floor, Zip 84111–1453; tel. 801/442–2000; A. Marc. Harrison, President and Chief Executive Officer, p. B68

## VIRGINIA

**Charlottesville:** ★ UVA HEALTH SYSTEM 1215 Lee Street, Zip 22908–0816; tel. 434/924–0211; Craig Kent, Chief Executive Officer, p. B143

**Falls Church:** ★ BUREAU OF MEDICINE AND SURGERY, DEPARTMENT OF THE NAVY 7700 Arlington Boulevard, Suite 5126, Zip 22042; tel. 202/762–3701; Rear Admiral, Bruce Gillingham, Surgeon General of the Navy and Chief, Bureau of Medicine and Surgery, p. B25

★ DEPARTMENT OF THE ARMY, OFFICE OF THE SURGEON GENERAL 5109 Leesburg Pike, Zip 22041–3215; tel. 703/681–3000, Lieutenant General, R. Scott. Dingle, The Surgeon General of the U.S. Army, p. B41

★ INOVA HEALTH SYSTEM 8110 Gatehouse Road, Suite 200 East, Zip 22042–1252; tel. 703/289–2069; J Stephen. Jones, Chief Executive Officer, p. B67

**Fredericksburg:** ★ MARY WASHINGTON HEALTHCARE 1001 Sam Perry Boulevard, Suite 1005, Zip 22401–4453; tel. 540/741–3100; Michael P. McDermott, President and Chief Executive Officer, p. B79

**Lynchburg:** ★ CENTRA HEALTH, INC. 1901 Tate Springs Road, Zip 24501–1109; tel. 434/200–3000; Andrew Mueller, President and Chief Executive Officer, p. B28

**Newport News:** RIVERSIDE HEALTH SYSTEM 701 Town Center Drive, Suite 1000, Zip 23606–4286; tel. 757/534–7000; William B. Downey, President and Chief Executive Officer, p. B108

**Norfolk:** ★ SENTARA HEALTHCARE 6015 Poplar Hall Drive, Zip 23502–3819; tel. 757/455–7000; Howard P. Kern, Chief Executive Officer, p. B115

**Richmond:** ★ VCU HEALTH SYSTEM 1200 East Marshall Street, Zip 23298, Mailing Address: P.O. 980510, 23298–0510, tel. 804/828–9000; Peter Buckley, Interim Chief Executive Officer, VCU Health System, p. B144

VIRGINIA DEPARTMENT OF MENTAL HEALTH 1220 Bank Street, Zip 23219–3645, Mailing Address: P.O. 1797, 23218–1797, tel. 804/786–3921; James S. Reinhard, Commissioner, p. B145

**Roanoke:** ★ CARILION CLINIC 1906 Belleview Avenue SE, Zip 24014–1838, Mailing Address: P.O. 13727, 24036–3727, tel. 540/981–7000; Nancy Howell. Agee, President and Chief Executive Officer, p. B27

**Winchester:** ★ VALLEY HEALTH SYSTEM 220 Campus Boulevard, Suite 420, Zip 22601–2889, Mailing Address: P.O. 3340, 22604–2540, tel. 540/536–8024; Mark S. Nantz, President and Chief Executive Officer, p. B143

## WEST VIRGINIA

**Elkins:** ★ DAVIS HEALTH SYSTEM Reed Street and Gorman Avenue, Zip 26241, Mailing Address: P.O. 1697, 26241–1697, tel. 304/636–3300; Vance Jackson, President and Chief Executive Officer, p. B40

**Huntington:** MOUNTAIN HEALTH NETWORK 517 9th Street, Zip 25701–2020; tel. 304/781–4466; Michael Mullins, President and Chief Executive Officer, p. B87

**Morgantown:** ★ MON HEALTH SYSTEM 1200 J. D. Anderson Drive, Zip 26505–3494; tel. 304/598–1200; David Goldberg, President and Chief Executive Officer, p. B86

★ WEST VIRGINIA UNIVERSITY HEALTH SYSTEM One Medical Center, Box 8136, Zip 26506–8136; tel. 304/285–7150; Albert L. Wright Jr, President and Chief Executive Officer, p. B147

**South Charleston:** ★ THOMAS HEALTH SYSTEM, INC. 4605 MacCorkle Avenue SW, Zip 25309–1311; tel. 304/766–3600; Daniel Lauffer, President and Chief Executive Officer, p. B128

## WISCONSIN

**Appleton:** THEDACARE, INC. 122 East College Avenue, Zip 54911–5794, Mailing Address: P.O. 8025, 54912–8025, tel. 920/830–5889; Imran A. Andrabi, President and Chief Executive Officer, p. B128

**Janesville:** MERCY HEALTH SYSTEM 1000 Mineral Point Avenue, Zip 53548–2940, Mailing Address: P.O. 5003, 53547–5003, tel. 608/756–6000; Javon R. Bea, President and Chief Executive Officer, p. B84

**Madison:** UW HEALTH SYSTEM 600 Highland Avenue, Zip 53792–0001; tel. 608/263–6400; Alan Kaplan, Chief Executive Officer, p. B143

**Manitowoc:** ★ FRANCISCAN SISTERS OF CHRISTIAN CHARITY SPONSORED MINISTRIES, INC. 1415 South Rapids Road, Zip 54220–9302; tel. 920/684–7071; Scott McConnaha, FACHE, President and Chief Executive Officer, p. B55

**Marshfield:** ★ MARSHFIELD CLINIC HEALTH SYSTEM 1000 North Oak Avenue, Zip 54449–5703; tel. 800/782–8581; Susan Turney, Chief Executive Officer, p. B78

**Milwaukee:** CHILDREN'S HOSPITAL AND HEALTH SYSTEM 9000 West Wisconsin Avenue, Zip 53226–4810, Mailing Address: P.O. 1997, 53201–1997, tel. 414/226–2000; Peggy N. Troy, President and Chief Executive Officer, p. B29

FROEDTERT HEALTH 9200 West Wisconsin Avenue, Zip 53226–3596, Mailing Address: P.O. 26099, 53226–0099, tel. 414/805–3000; Catherine A. Jacobson, President and Chief Executive Officer, p. B55

**Waukesha:** ★ PROHEALTH CARE, INC. N17 W24100 Riverwood Drive, Suite 130, Zip 53188; tel. 262/928–2242; Susan A. Edwards, President and Chief Executive Officer, p. B102

**Wausau:** ★ ASPIRUS, INC. 2200 Westwood Drive, Zip 54401–7806; tel. 715/847–2118; Matthew Heywood, Chief Executive Officer, p. B15

## WASHINGTON

**Mount Vernon:** SKAGIT REGIONAL HEALTH 1415 E Kincaid Street, Zip 98274–4126; tel. 360/424–4111; Brian K. Ivie, President and Chief Executive Officer, p. B118

**Renton:** ★ PROVIDENCE ST. JOSEPH HEALTH 1801 Lind Avenue Southwest, 9016, Zip 98057–9016; tel. 425/525–3698; Rodney F. Hochman, President and Chief Executive Officer, p. B103

**Seattle:** ★ SWEDISH HEALTH SERVICES 747 Broadway, Zip 98122–4379; tel. 206/386–6000; R. Guy. Hudson, Chief Executive Officer, p. B124

★ UW MEDICINE 1959 NE Pacific Street, Zip 98195–0001, Mailing Address: P.O. 356350, 98195–6350, tel. 206/543–7718; Paul G. Ramsey, Chief Executive Officer, p. B143

VIRGINIA MASON HEALTH SYSTEM 1100 Ninth Avenue, Zip 98101–2756, P.O. Box 900, 98111–0900, tel. 206/223–6600; Gary Kaplan, Chief Executive Officer, p. B146

**Sunnyside:** ASTRIA HEALTH 1806 Yakima Valley Highway, Zip 98944–2263; tel. 509/837–1330; John Gallagher, President and Chief Executive Officer, p. B15

**Tacoma:** MULTICARE HEALTH SYSTEM 315 Martin Luther King Jr Way, Zip 98405–4234, Mailing Address: P.O. 5299, 98415–0299, tel. 253/403–1000; William G. Robertson, President and Chief Executive Officer, p. B87

**Vancouver:** ★ PEACEHEALTH 1115 SE 164th Avenue, Zip 98683; tel. 360/729–1000; Elizabeth Dunne, President and Chief Executive Officer, p. B97

# Networks and their Hospitals

## ARIZONA

**HONORHEALTH**
**8125 North Hayden Road, Scottsdale, AZ Zip 85258–2463; tel. 480/882–4000; Todd LaPorte, Chief Executive Officer**

HONORHEALTH DEER VALLEY MEDICAL CENTER, 19829 North 27th Avenue, Phoenix, AZ, Zip 85027–4002; tel. 623/879–6100; David Price, Chief Executive Officer

HONORHEALTH JOHN C. LINCOLN MEDICAL CENTER, 250 East Dunlap Avenue, Phoenix, AZ, Zip 85020–2825; tel. 602/943–2381; Gary E. Baker, Chief Executive Officer

HONORHEALTH REHABILITATION HOSPITAL, 8850 East Pima Center Parkway, Scottsdale, AZ, Zip 85258–4619; tel. 480/800–3900; Scott R. Keen, Chief Executive Officer

HONORHEALTH SCOTTSDALE OSBORN MEDICAL CENTER, 7400 East Osborn Road, Scottsdale, AZ, Zip 85251–6403; tel. 480/882–4000; Kimberly Post, Senior Vice President and Chief Executive Officer

HONORHEALTH SCOTTSDALE SHEA MEDICAL CENTER, 9003 East Shea Boulevard, Scottsdale, AZ, Zip 85260–6771; tel. 480/323–3000; Gary E. Baker, Senior Vice President and Chief Executive Officer

HONORHEALTH SCOTTSDALE THOMPSON PEAK MEDICAL CENTER, 7400 East Thompson Peak Parkway, Scottsdale, AZ, Zip 85255–4109; tel. 480/324–7000; David Price, Chief Executive Officer

**NORTHERN ARIZONA HEALTHCARE**
**1200 North Beaver Street, Flagstaff, AZ Zip 86001–3118; tel. 928/779–3366; Robert P. Thames, President and Chief Executive Officer**

FLAGSTAFF MEDICAL CENTER, 1200 North Beaver Street, Flagstaff, AZ, Zip 86001–3118; tel. 928/779–3366; Florence (Flo) Spyrow, Chief Administrative Officer

VERDE VALLEY MEDICAL CENTER, 269 South Candy Lane, Cottonwood, AZ, Zip 86326–4170; tel. 928/639–6000; Barbara Firminger, Chief Administrative Officer

## CALIFORNIA

**ADVENTIST HEALTH NORTHERN CALIFORNIA NETWORK**
**463 Aviation Boulevard, Santa Rosa, CA Zip 95403–1079; tel. 707/571–2893; Jeff Eller, FACHE, President and Chief Executive Officer**

ADVENTIST HEALTH CLEAR LAKE, 15630 18th Avenue, Clearlake, CA, Zip 95422–9336, Mailing Address: P.O. Box 6710, 95422, tel. 707/994–6486; David Santos, President and Chief Executive Officer

ADVENTIST HEALTH HOWARD MEMORIAL, One Marcela Drive, Willits, CA, Zip 95490–4298; tel. 707/459–6801; Jason Wells, President and Chief Executive Officer

ADVENTIST HEALTH ST. HELENA, 10 Woodland Road, Saint Helena, CA, Zip 94574–9554; tel. 707/963–3611; Steven Herber, M.D., FACS, President and Chief Executive Officer

ADVENTIST HEALTH ST. HELENA, 525 Oregon Street, Vallejo, CA, Zip 94590–3201; tel. 707/648–2200; Steven Herber, M.D., FACS, President and Chief Executive Officer

ADVENTIST HEALTH UKIAH VALLEY, 275 Hospital Drive, Ukiah, CA, Zip 95482–4531; tel. 707/462–3111; Gwen Matthews, R.N., MSN, Chief Executive Officer

**PROVIDENCE HEALTH AND SERVICES – SOUTHERN CALIFORNIA**
**Regional Administration, 20555 Earl Street, Torrance, CA Zip 90503–3006; tel. 310/793–8087; Erik G. Wexler, Chief Executive Officer**

PROVIDENCE HOLY CROSS MEDICAL CENTER, 15031 Rinaldi Street, Mission Hills, CA, Zip 91345–1207; tel. 818/365–8051; Bernard Klein, M.D., Chief Executive

PROVIDENCE LITTLE COMPANY OF MARY MEDICAL CENTER – TORRANCE, 4101 Torrance Boulevard, Torrance, CA, Zip 90503–4664; tel. 310/540–7676; Garry M. Olney, Chief Executive Officer

PROVIDENCE LITTLE COMPANY OF MARY MEDICAL CENTER SAN PEDRO, 1300 West Seventh Street, San Pedro, CA, Zip 90732–3505; tel. 310/832–3311; Garry M. Olney, Chief Executive Officer

PROVIDENCE SAINT JOHN'S HEALTH CENTER, 2121 Santa Monica Boulevard, Santa Monica, CA, Zip 90404–2091; tel. 310/829–5511; Marcel C. Loh, FACHE, Chief Executive Officer

PROVIDENCE SAINT JOSEPH MEDICAL CENTER, 501 South Buena Vista Street, Burbank, CA, Zip 91505–4866; tel. 818/843–5111; Kelly Linden, Chief Executive Officer

PROVIDENCE TARZANA MEDICAL CENTER, 18321 Clark Street, Tarzana, CA, Zip 91356–3521; tel. 818/881–0800; Dale Surowitz, Chief Executive

**ST. JOSEPH HOAG HEALTH**
**3345 Michelson Drive, Suite 100, Irvine, CA Zip 92612–0693; tel. 949/381–4019; Richard Afable, M.D., M.P.H., President and Chief Executive Officer**

HOAG MEMORIAL HOSPITAL PRESBYTERIAN, One Hoag Drive, Newport Beach, CA, Zip 92663–4120, Mailing Address: P.O. Box 6100, 92658–6100, tel. 949/764–4624; Robert Braithwaite, President and Chief Executive Officer

MISSION HOSPITAL MISSION VIEJO, 27700 Medical Center Road, Mission Viejo, CA, Zip 92691–6474; tel. 949/364–1400; Seth R. Teigen, Chief Executive Officer

ST. JOSEPH HOSPITAL ORANGE, 1100 West Stewart Drive, Orange, CA, Zip 92868–3849, Mailing Address: P.O. Box 5600, 92863–5600, tel. 714/633–9111; Jeremy Zoch, Chief Executive

ST. MARY MEDICAL CENTER, 18300 Highway 18, Apple Valley, CA, Zip 92307–2206, Mailing Address: P.O. Box 7025, 92307–0725, tel. 760/242–2311; Randall Castillo, Chief Executive Officer

## COLORADO

**CENTURA HEALTH**
**188 Inverness Drive West, Suite 500, Englewood, CO Zip 80112–5204; tel. 303/290–6500; Peter D. Banko, FACHE, President and Chief Executive Officer**

AVISTA ADVENTIST HOSPITAL, 100 Health Park Drive, Louisville, CO, Zip 80027–9583; tel. 303/673–1000; Isaac Sendros, Chief Executive Officer

CASTLE ROCK ADVENTIST HOSPITAL, 2350 Meadows Boulevard, Castle Rock, CO, Zip 80109–8405; tel. 720/455–5000; Brandon M. Nudd, Chief Executive Officer

LITTLETON ADVENTIST HOSPITAL, 7700 South Broadway Street, Littleton, CO, Zip 80122–2628; tel. 303/730–8900; Jillyan McKinney, Chief Executive Officer

PARKER ADVENTIST HOSPITAL, 9395 Crown Crest Boulevard, Parker, CO, Zip 80138–8573; tel. 303/269–4000; Michael Goebel, Chief Executive Officer

PENROSE–ST. FRANCIS HEALTH SERVICES, 2222 North Nevada Avenue, Colorado Springs, CO, Zip 80907–6799; tel. 719/776–5000; Brian Erling, M.D., Chief Executive Officer

PORTER ADVENTIST HOSPITAL, 2525 South Downing Street, Denver, CO, Zip 80210–5876; tel. 303/778–1955; Todd Folkenberg, Chief Executive Officer

RAWLINS COUNTY HEALTH CENTER, 707 Grant Street, Atwood, KS, Zip 67730–1526, Mailing Address: P.O. Box 47, 67730–0047, tel. 785/626–3211; Ronald R. Robinson, M.D., FACHE, M.P.H., Chief Executive Officer and Chief Medical Officer

ST. ANTHONY HOSPITAL, 11600 West Second Place, Lakewood, CO, Zip 80228–1527; tel. 720/321–0000; Kevin Jenkins, Chief Executive Officer

ST. ANTHONY NORTH HEALTH CAMPUS, 14300 Orchard Parkway, Westminster, CO, Zip 80023–9206; tel. 720/627–0000; Constance Schmidt, FACHE, R.N., Chief Executive Officer

ST. ANTHONY SUMMIT MEDICAL CENTER, 340 Peak One Drive, Frisco, CO, Zip 80443, Mailing Address: P.O. Box 738, 80443–0738, tel. 970/668–3300; Lee Boyles, Chief Executive Officer

ST. MARY–CORWIN MEDICAL CENTER, 1008 Minnequa Avenue, Pueblo, CO, Zip 81004–3798; tel. 719/557–4000; Michael Cafasso, Chief Executive Officer

ST. THOMAS MORE HOSPITAL, 1338 Phay Avenue, Canon City, CO, Zip 81212–2302; tel. 719/285–2000; Kristi Olson, Chief Executive Officer

ST. VINCENT GENERAL HOSPITAL DISTRICT, 822 West 4th Street, Leadville, CO, Zip 80461–3897; tel. 719/486–0230; Gary Campbell, Chief Executive Officer

**COMMUNITY HEALTH PROVIDERS ORGANIZATION**
**2021 North 12th Street, Grand Junction, CO Zip 81501–2980; tel. 970/256–6200; Chris Thomas, FACHE, President and Chief Executive Officer**

COMMUNITY HOSPITAL, 2351 G Road, Grand Junction, CO, Zip 81505; tel. 970/242–0920; Chris Thomas, FACHE, President and Chief Executive Officer

**HCA HEALTHONE, LLC**
**4900 South Monaco Street, Suite 380, Denver, CO Zip 80237–3487; tel. 303/788–2500; Sylvia Young, FACHE, President**

MEDICAL CENTER OF AURORA, 1501 South Potomac Street, Aurora, CO, Zip 80012–5411; tel. 303/695–2600; Ryan Simpson, President and Chief Executive Officer

NORTH SUBURBAN MEDICAL CENTER, 9191 Grant Street, Thornton, CO, Zip 80229–4341; tel. 303/451–7800; Daphne G. David, President and Chief Executive Officer

PRESBYTERIAN/ST. LUKE'S MEDICAL CENTER, 1719 East 19th Avenue, Denver, CO, Zip 80218–1281; tel. 720/754–6000; Maureen Tarrant, President and Chief Executive Officer

ROSE MEDICAL CENTER, 4567 East Ninth Avenue, Denver, CO, Zip 80220–3941; tel. 303/320–2121; Hollie Seeley, Interim Chief Executive Officer and Chief Operating Officer

SKY RIDGE MEDICAL CENTER, 10101 Ridge Gate Parkway, Lone Tree, CO, Zip 80124–5522; tel. 720/225–1000; Kirk McCarty, R.N., MSN, Chief Executive Officer

SPALDING REHABILITATION HOSPITAL, 900 Potomac Steet, Aurora, CO, Zip 80011–6716; tel. 303/367–1166; Ryan Simpson, President and Chief Executive Officer

SWEDISH MEDICAL CENTER, 501 East Hampden Avenue, Englewood, CO, Zip 80113–2702; tel. 303/788–5000; Ryan Tobin, President and Chief Executive Officer

## CONNECTICUT

**EASTERN CONNECTICUT HEALTH NETWORK**
**71 Haynes Street, Manchester, CT Zip 06040–4131; tel. 860/533–3400; Michael F. Collins, Interim President and Chief Executive Officer**

MANCHESTER MEMORIAL HOSPITAL, 71 Haynes Street, Manchester, CT, Zip 06040–4188; tel. 860/646–1222; Deborah K. Weymouth, FACHE, Chief Executive Officer

ROCKVILLE GENERAL HOSPITAL, 31 Union Street, Vernon, CT, Zip 06066–3160; tel. 860/872–0501; Deborah K. Weymouth, FACHE, Chief Executive Officer

## FLORIDA

**BAYCARE HEALTH SYSTEM**
**2985 Drew Street, Clearwater, FL Zip 33759–3012; tel. 877/692–2922; Tommy Inzina, President and Chief Executive Officer**

BARTOW REGIONAL MEDICAL CENTER, 2200 Osprey Boulevard, Bartow, FL, Zip 33830–3308; tel. 863/533–8111; Karen Kerr, R.N., President

BAYCARE ALLIANT HOSPITAL, 601 Main Street, MS#402, Dunedin, FL, Zip 34698–5848; tel. 727/736–9991; Jacqueline Arocho, Administrator

MEASE COUNTRYSIDE HOSPITAL, 3231 McMullen Booth Road, Safety Harbor, FL, Zip 34695–6607; tel. 727/725–6111; Matthew Novak, President

MEASE DUNEDIN HOSPITAL, 601 Main Street, Dunedin, FL, Zip 34698–5891; tel. 727/733–1111; Matthew Novak, President

MORTON PLANT HOSPITAL, 300 Pinellas Street, Clearwater, FL, Zip 33756–3804, Mailing Address: P.O. Box 210, 33757–0210, tel. 727/462–7000; Lou Galdieri, R.N., President

MORTON PLANT NORTH BAY HOSPITAL, 6600 Madison Street, New Port Richey, FL, Zip 34652–1900; tel. 727/842–8468; Brandon May, President

SOUTH FLORIDA BAPTIST HOSPITAL, 301 North Alexander Street, Plant City, FL, Zip 33563–4303; tel. 813/757–1200; Karen Kerr, R.N., President

ST. ANTHONY'S HOSPITAL, 1200 Seventh Avenue North, Saint Petersburg, FL, Zip 33705–1388, Mailing Address: P.O. Box 12588, 33733–2588, tel. 727/825–1100; M. Scott Smith, President

ST. JOSEPH'S HOSPITAL, 3001 West Martin Luther King Jr. Boulevard, Tampa, FL, Zip 33607–6387, Mailing Address: P.O. Box 4227, 33677–4227, tel. 813/870–4000; Kimberly Guy, President

WINTER HAVEN HOSPITAL, 200 Avenue F NE, Winter Haven, FL, Zip 33881–4193; tel. 863/293–1121; Stephen A. Nierman, President

## GEORGIA

**ST. JOSEPH'S/CANDLER HEALTH SYSTEM, INC.**
**5353 Reynolds Street, Savannah, GA Zip 31405–6015; tel. 912/819–6000; Paul P. Hinchey, President and Chief Executive Officer**

APPLING HEALTHCARE SYSTEM, 163 East Tollison Street, Baxley, GA, Zip 31513–0120; tel. 912/367–9841; Randy Crawford, Chief Executive Officer

CANDLER HOSPITAL, 5353 Reynolds Street, Savannah, GA, Zip 31405–6015; tel. 912/819–6000; Paul P. Hinchey, President and Chief Executive Officer

EFFINGHAM HOSPITAL, 459 Highway 119 South, Springfield, GA, Zip 31329–3021, Mailing Address: P.O. Box 386, 31329–0386, tel. 912/754–6451; Francine Baker–Witt, R.N., Chief Executive Officer

EMORY UNIVERSITY HOSPITAL, 1364 Clifton Road NE, Atlanta, GA, Zip 30322; tel. 404/712–2000; Matthew Wain, Chief Executive Officer

LIBERTY REGIONAL MEDICAL CENTER, 462 Elma G Miles Parkway, Hinesville, GA, Zip 31313–4000, Mailing Address: P.O. Box 919, 31310–0919, tel. 912/369–9400; Tammy Mims, Chief Executive Officer

MEADOWS REGIONAL MEDICAL CENTER, One Meadows Parkway, Vidalia, GA, Zip 30474–8759, Mailing Address: P.O. Box 1048, 30475–1048, tel. 912/535–5555; Alan Kent, Chief Executive Officer

ST. JOSEPH'S HOSPITAL, 11705 Mercy Boulevard, Savannah, GA, Zip 31419–1791; tel. 912/819–4100; Paul P. Hinchey, President and Chief Executive Officer

## IDAHO

**THE HOSPITAL COOPERATIVE**
**500 South 11th Avenue Suite 503, Pocatello, ID Zip 83201–4881; tel. 208/239–1951; Jon Smith, Executive Director**

BEAR LAKE MEMORIAL HOSPITAL, 164 South Fifth Street, Montpelier, ID, Zip 83254–1597; tel. 208/847–1630; Michael Blauer, Chief Executive Officer

BINGHAM MEMORIAL HOSPITAL, 98 Poplar Street, Blackfoot, ID, Zip 83221–1799; tel. 208/785–4100; Jake Erickson, Chief Executive Officer

CARIBOU MEMORIAL HOSPITAL AND LIVING CENTER, 300 South Third West, Soda Springs, ID, Zip 83276–1598; tel. 208/547–3341; Christina Thomas, Chief Executive Officer

EASTERN IDAHO REGIONAL MEDICAL CENTER, 3100 Channing Way, Idaho Falls, ID, Zip 83404–7533, Mailing Address: P.O. Box 2077, 83403–2077, tel. 208/529–6111; Jeff Sollis, Chief Executive Officer

FRANKLIN COUNTY MEDICAL CENTER, 44 North First East Street, Preston, ID, Zip 83263–1399; tel. 208/852–0137; Darin Dransfield, Chief Executive Officer

LOST RIVERS MEDICAL CENTER, 551 Highland Drive, Arco, ID, Zip 83213–9771, Mailing Address: P.O. Box 145, 83213–0145, tel. 208/527–8206; Brad Huerta, Chief Executive Officer and Administrator

MADISON MEMORIAL HOSPITAL, 450 East Main Street, Rexburg, ID, Zip 83440–2048, Mailing Address: P.O. Box 310, 83440–0310, tel. 208/359–6900; Rachel Ann. Gonzales, Chief Executive Officer

MINIDOKA MEMORIAL HOSPITAL, 1224 Eighth Street, Rupert, ID, Zip 83350–1599; tel. 208/436–0481; Tom Murphy, Chief Executive Officer

NELL J. REDFIELD MEMORIAL HOSPITAL, 150 North 200 West, Malad City, ID, Zip 83252–1239, Box 126, 83252–0126, tel. 208/766–2231; John Williams, Administrator and Chief Executive Officer

PORTNEUF MEDICAL CENTER, 777 Hospital Way, Pocatello, ID, Zip 83201–5175; tel. 208/239–1000; Jordan Herget, Chief Executive Officer

POWER COUNTY HOSPITAL DISTRICT, 510 Roosevelt Street, American Falls, ID, Zip 83211–1362, Mailing Address: P.O. Box 420, 83211–0420, tel. 208/226–3200; Dallas Clinger, Administrator

STAR VALLEY HEALTH, 901 Adams Street, Afton, WY, Zip 83110–9621, Mailing Address: P.O. Box 579, 83110–0579, tel. 307/885–5800; Bren Lowe, Chief Executive Officer

STEELE MEMORIAL MEDICAL CENTER, 203 South Daisy Street, Salmon, ID, Zip 83467–4709; tel. 208/756–5600; Jeanine Gentry, Chief Executive Officer

TETON VALLEY HEALTH CARE, 120 E Howard Avenue, Driggs, ID, Zip 83422–5112, 120 East Howard Avenue, 83422–5112, tel. 208/354–2383; Keith Gnagey, Chief Executive Officer

## ILLINOIS

**AMITA HEALTH**
**2601 Navistar Drive, Lisle, IL Zip 60532–3661; tel. 224/273–4121; Keith Parrott, FACHE, President and Chief Executive Officer**

AMITA HEALTH ADVENTIST MEDICAL CENTER – HINSDALE, 120 North Oak Street, Hinsdale, IL, Zip 60521–3890; tel. 630/856–6001; Adam Maycock, Chief Executive Officer

AMITA HEALTH ADVENTIST MEDICAL CENTER BOLINGBROOK , 500 Remington Boulevard, Bolingbrook, IL, Zip 60440–4906; tel. 630/312–5000; Bruce C. Christian, Chief Executive Officer

AMITA HEALTH ADVENTIST MEDICAL CENTER GLENOAKS, 701 Winthrop Avenue, Glendale Heights, IL, Zip 60139–1403; tel. 630/545–8000; Bruce C. Christian, President and Chief Executive Officer

AMITA HEALTH ADVENTIST MEDICAL CENTER LA GRANGE, 5101 South Willow Spring Road, La Grange, IL, Zip 60525–2600; tel. 708/245–9000; Adam Maycock, Chief Executive Officer

AMITA HEALTH ALEXIAN BROTHERS BEHAVIORAL HEALTH HOSPITAL, 1650 Moon Lake Boulevard, Hoffman Estates, IL, Zip 60169–1010; tel. 847/882–1600; Clayton Ciha, President and Chief Executive Officer

**MERCY HEALTH CORPORATION**
**2400 North Rockton Avenue, Rockford, IL Zip 61103–3655; tel. 608/756–6000; Javon R. Bea, President and Chief Executive Officer**

JAVON BEA HOSPITAL–ROCKTON, 2400 North Rockton Avenue, Rockford, IL, Zip 61103–3655; tel. 815/971–5000; Javon R. Bea, President and Chief Executive Officer

MERCYHEALTH HOSPITAL AND MEDICAL CENTER – HARVARD, 901 Grant Street, Harvard, IL, Zip 60033–1898, Mailing Address: P.O. Box 850, 60033–0850, tel. 815/943–5431; Javon R. Bea, Chief Executive Officer

MERCYHEALTH HOSPITAL AND MEDICAL CENTER – WALWORTH, N2950 State Road 67, Lake Geneva, WI, Zip 53147–2655; tel. 262/245–0535; Javon R. Bea, President and Chief Executive Officer

MERCYHEALTH HOSPITAL AND TRAUMA CENTER – JANESVILLE, 1000 Mineral Point Avenue, Janesville, WI, Zip 53548–2982, Mailing Address: P.O. Box 5003, 53547–5003, tel. 608/756–6000; Javon R. Bea, President and Chief Executive Officer

Section B

## INDIANA

### LUTHERAN HEALTH NETWORK
**7950 West Jefferson Boulevard, Fort Wayne, IN Zip 46804–4140; tel. 260/435–7001; Michael Poore, Regional Vice President**

BLUFFTON REGIONAL MEDICAL CENTER, 303 South Main Street, Bluffton, IN, Zip 46714–2503; tel. 260/824–3210; Julie Thompson, Chief Adminstrative Officer and Chief Nursing Officer

DUKES MEMORIAL HOSPITAL, 275 West 12th Street, Peru, IN, Zip 46970–1638; tel. 765/472–8000; Debra Close, Chief Executive Officer

DUPONT HOSPITAL, 2520 East Dupont Road, Fort Wayne, IN, Zip 46825–1675; tel. 260/416–3000; Lorenzo Suter, Chief Executive Officer

KOSCIUSKO COMMUNITY HOSPITAL, 2101 East Dubois Drive, Warsaw, IN, Zip 46580–3288; tel. 574/267–3200; Jae Dale, Chief Executive Officer

LUTHERAN HOSPITAL OF INDIANA, 7950 West Jefferson Boulevard, Fort Wayne, IN, Zip 46804–4140; tel. 260/435–7001; Brady Dubois, Chief Executive Officer

ORTHOPAEDIC HOSPITAL OF LUTHERAN HEALTH NETWORK, 7952 West Jefferson Boulevard, Fort Wayne, IN, Zip 46804–4140; tel. 260/435–2999; Lorie Ailor, Chief Executive Officer, Chief Administrative Officer, Network Vice President Orthopedics and Sports Medicine

REHABILITATION HOSPITAL OF FORT WAYNE, 7970 West Jefferson Boulevard, Fort Wayne, IN, Zip 46804–4140; tel. 260/435–6100; Ryan Cassedy, Chief Administrative Officer

ST. JOSEPH HOSPITAL, 700 Broadway, Fort Wayne, IN, Zip 46802–1493; tel. 260/425–3000; Lisa Dolan, Interim Chief Executive Officer

### ST. VINCENT HEALTH
**10330 North Meridian Street, Indianapolis, IN Zip 46290; tel. 317/338–2273; Jonathan Nalli, Senior Vice President, Ascension Health and Indiana Ministry Market Executive**

ASCENSION ST. VINCENT ANDERSON , 2015 Jackson Street, Anderson, IN, Zip 46016–4339; tel. 765/649–2511; Nick Theohares, Executive Director, Operations

ASCENSION ST. VINCENT CARMEL HOSPITAL, 13500 North Meridian Street, Carmel, IN, Zip 46032–1456; tel. 317/582–7000; Julie Manas, Regional President

ASCENSION ST. VINCENT CLAY HOSPITAL, 1206 East National Avenue, Brazil, IN, Zip 47834–2797, 1206 East National Ave , 47834–0489, tel. 812/442–2500; Jerry Laue, Administrator

ASCENSION ST. VINCENT DUNN , 1600 23rd Street, Bedford, IN, Zip 47421–4704; tel. 812/275–3331; George Zhang, Administrator

ASCENSION ST. VINCENT EVANSVILLE, 3700 Washington Avenue, Evansville, IN, Zip 47714–0541; tel. 812/485–4000; Daniel A. Parod, President

ASCENSION ST. VINCENT FISHERS , 13861 Olio Road, Fishers, IN, Zip 46037–3487; tel. 317/415–9000; Julie Manas, Regional President

ASCENSION ST. VINCENT HEART CENTER, 10580 North Meridian Street, Indianapolis, IN, Zip 46290–1028; tel. 317/583–5000; Lori Shannon, President

ASCENSION ST. VINCENT INDIANAPOLIS HOSPITAL, 2001 West 86th Street, Indianapolis, IN, Zip 46260–1991, Mailing Address: P.O. Box 40970, 46240–0970, tel. 317/338–2345; Erica Wehrmeister, President Central Region

ASCENSION ST. VINCENT JENNINGS , 301 Henry Street, North Vernon, IN, Zip 47265–1097; tel. 812/352–4200; Dana M. Muntz, Chief Executive Officer

ASCENSION ST. VINCENT MERCY , 1331 South 'A' Street, Elwood, IN, Zip 46036–1942; tel. 765/552–4600; Ann C. Yates, R.N., MSN, Administrator and Chief Nursing Officer

ASCENSION ST. VINCENT RANDOLPH , 473 Greenville Avenue, Winchester, IN, Zip 47394–9436; tel. 765/584–0004; Carla Fouse, Administrator and Chief Nursing Officer

ASCENSION ST. VINCENT SALEM , 911 North Shelby Street, Salem, IN, Zip 47167–1694; tel. 812/883–5881; Dana M. Muntz, Chief Executive Officer

ASCENSION ST. VINCENT SETON SPECIALTY HOSPITAL, 8050 Township Line Road, Indianapolis, IN, Zip 46260–2478; tel. 317/415–8500; Erica Wehrmeister, President Central Region

ASCENSION ST. VINCENT WARRICK , 1116 Millis Avenue, Boonville, IN, Zip 47601–2204; tel. 812/897–4800; Marty Mattingly, Administrator

ASCENSION ST. VINCENT WILLIAMSPORT , 412 North Monroe Street, Williamsport, IN, Zip 47993–1049; tel. 765/762–4000; Trina Marlatt, R.N., MSN, Administrator

### SUBURBAN HEALTH ORGANIZATION
**2780 Waterfront Parkway East Drive, Suite 300, Indianapolis, IN Zip 46214; tel. 317/692–5222; Dave Lippincott, President**

GOSHEN HEALTH, 200 High Park Avenue, Goshen, IN, Zip 46526–4899, Mailing Address: P.O. Box 139, 46527–0139, tel. 574/533–2141; Randal Christophel, President and Chief Executive Officer

HANCOCK REGIONAL HOSPITAL, 801 North State Street, Greenfield, IN, Zip 46140–1270, Mailing Address: P.O. Box 827, 46140–0827, tel. 317/462–5544; Steven V. Long, FACHE, President and Chief Executive Officer

HENDRICKS REGIONAL HEALTH, 1000 East Main Street, Danville, IN, Zip 46122–1948, Mailing Address: P.O. Box 409, 46122–0409, tel. 317/745–4451; Kevin Speer, President and Chief Executive Officer

HENRY COMMUNITY HEALTH, 1000 North 16th Street, New Castle, IN, Zip 47362–4319, Mailing Address: P.O. Box 490, 47362–0490, tel. 765/521–0890; Paul Janssen, President and Chief Executive Officer

JOHNSON MEMORIAL HOSPITAL, 1125 West Jefferson Street, Franklin, IN, Zip 46131–2140, Mailing Address: P.O. Box 549, 46131–0549, tel. 317/736–3300; Larry Heydon, President and Chief Executive Officer

MAJOR HOSPITAL, 150 West Washington Street, Shelbyville, IN, Zip 46176–1236, 2451 Intelliplex Drive, 46176, tel. 317/392–3211; John M. Horner, President and Chief Executive Officer

MARGARET MARY HEALTH, 321 Mitchell Avenue, Batesville, IN, Zip 47006–8909, Mailing Address: P.O. Box 226, 47006–0226, tel. 812/934–6624; Timothy L. Putnam, FACHE, President and Chief Executive Officer

RIVERVIEW HEALTH, 395 Westfield Road, Noblesville, IN, Zip 46060–1425, Mailing Address: P.O. Box 220, 46061–0220, tel. 317/773–0760; Seth Warren, President and Chief Executive Officer

RUSH MEMORIAL HOSPITAL, 1300 North Main Street, Rushville, IN, Zip 46173–1198; tel. 765/932–4111; Bradley Smith, President and Chief Executive Officer

WITHAM HEALTH SERVICES, 2605 North Lebanon Street, Lebanon, IN, Zip 46052–1476, Mailing Address: P.O. Box 1200, 46052–3005, tel. 765/485–8000; Raymond V. Ingham, Ph.D., President and Chief Executive Officer

## IOWA

### GENESIS HEALTH SYSTEM
**1227 East Rusholme Street, Davenport, IA Zip 52803–2459; tel. 563/421–1000; Douglas P. Cropper, President and Chief Executive Officer**

GENESIS MEDICAL CENTER – DAVENPORT, 1227 East Rusholme Street, Davenport, IA, Zip 52803–2498; tel. 563/421–1000; Jordan Voigt, President

GENESIS MEDICAL CENTER, DEWITT, 1118 11th Street, De Witt, IA, Zip 52742–1296; tel. 563/659–4200; Curt Coleman, FACHE, Critical Access Hospitals President

GENESIS MEDICAL CENTER, SILVIS, 801 Illini Drive, Silvis, IL, Zip 61282–1893; tel. 309/281–4000; Theresa Summers–Main, R.N., President

GENESIS MEDICAL CENTER–ALEDO, 409 NW Ninth Avenue, Aledo, IL, Zip 61231–1296; tel. 309/582–9100; Ted Rogalski, Administrator

### MERCYONE
**1449 NW 128th Street, Building 5, Suite 200, Clive, IA Zip 50325; tel. 515/358–9200; Robert P. Ritz, Chief Executive Officer**

ADAIR COUNTY HEALTH SYSTEM, 609 SE Kent Street, Greenfield, IA, Zip 50849–9454; tel. 641/743–2123; Marcia Hendricks, FACHE, R.N., Chief Executive Officer

BOONE COUNTY HOSPITAL, 1015 Union Street, Boone, IA, Zip 50036–4821; tel. 515/432–3140; Joseph S. Smith, Chief Executive Officer

MERCYONE PRIMGHAR MEDICAL CENTER, 255 North Welch Avenue, Primghar, IA, Zip 51245–7765, Mailing Address: P.O. Box 528, 51245–0528, tel. 712/957–2300; Misty Dulin, CAH, Director

## KANSAS

### HEALTH INNOVATIONS NETWORK OF KANSAS
**1500 SW 10th Avenue, Topeka, KS Zip 66604–1301; tel. 785/354–6137; Kristi Gosser, Network Operations Director**

ASCENSION VIA CHRISTI HOSPITAL, MANHATTAN, 1823 College Avenue, Manhattan, KS, Zip 66502–3346; tel. 785/776–3322; Robert C. Copple, FACHE, Senior Administrator

ATCHISON HOSPITAL, 800 Raven Hill Drive, Atchison, KS, Zip 66002–9204; tel. 913/367–2131; Jeffery Perry, President and Chief Executive Officer

CLAY COUNTY MEDICAL CENTER, 617 Liberty Street, Clay Center, KS, Zip 67432–1564, Mailing Address: P.O. Box 512, 67432–0512, tel. 785/632–2144; Austin M. Gillard, Chief Executive Officer

COFFEY COUNTY HOSPITAL, 801 North 4th Street, Burlington, KS, Zip 66839–2602; tel. 620/364–2121; Leonard Hernandez, Chief Executive Officer

COMMUNITY HEALTHCARE SYSTEM, 120 West Eighth Street, Onaga, KS, Zip 66521–9574; tel. 785/889–4272; Todd Willert, Chief Executive Officer

F. W. HUSTON MEDICAL CENTER, 408 Delaware Street, Winchester, KS, Zip 66097–4003; tel. 913/774–4340; LaMont Cook, Administrator

GEARY COMMUNITY HOSPITAL, 1102 St Mary's Road, Junction City, KS, Zip 66441–4196, Mailing Address: P.O. Box 490, 66441–0490, tel. 785/238–4131; Frank Corcoran, R.N., Chief Executive Officer

HERINGTON MUNICIPAL HOSPITAL, 100 East Helen Street, Herington, KS, Zip 67449–1606; tel. 785/258–2207; Isabel Schmedemann, Chief Executive Officer and Administrator

HIAWATHA COMMUNITY HOSPITAL, 300 Utah Street, Hiawatha, KS, Zip 66434–2314; tel. 785/742–2131; John Broberg, Chief Executive Officer

IRWIN ARMY COMMUNITY HOSPITAL, 600 Caisson Hill Road, Junction City, KS, Zip 66442–7037; tel. 785/239–7000; Colonel, Risa Ware, Commander

KANSAS REHABILITATION HOSPITAL, 1504 SW Eighth Avenue, Topeka, KS, Zip 66606–1632; tel. 785/235–6600; William J. Overbey, Chief Executive Officer

MORRIS COUNTY HOSPITAL, 600 North Washington Street, Council Grove, KS, Zip 66846–1422; tel. 620/767–6811; Kevin Leeper, Chief Executive Officer

NEMAHA VALLEY COMMUNITY HOSPITAL, 1600 Community Drive, Seneca, KS, Zip 66538–9739; tel. 785/336–6181; Kiley Floyd, Chief Executive Officer

NEWMAN REGIONAL HEALTH, 1201 West 12th Avenue, Emporia, KS, Zip 66801–2597; tel. 620/343–6800; Robert N. Wright, Chief Executive Officer

SABETHA COMMUNITY HOSPITAL, 14th and Oregon Streets, Sabetha, KS, Zip 66534–0229, Mailing Address: P.O. Box 229, 66534–0229, tel. 785/284–2121; Lora Key, Chief Executive Officer

STORMONT VAIL HEALTH, 1500 SW Tenth Avenue, Topeka, KS, Zip 66604–1353; tel. 785/354–6000; Rob Kenagy, M.D., President and Chief Executive Officer

WAMEGO HEALTH CENTER, 711 Genn Drive, Wamego, KS, Zip 66547–1179; tel. 785/456–2295; Steve Land, Senior Administrator

WASHINGTON COUNTY HOSPITAL, 304 East Third Street, Washington, KS, Zip 66968–2033; tel. 785/325–2211; Roxanne Schottel, Chief Executive Officer

**MED-OP, INC.**
**220 Canterbury Drive, Hays, KS Zip 67601; tel. 785/623–2301; Shae Veach, Executive Director**

CITIZENS MEDICAL CENTER, 100 East College Drive, Colby, KS, Zip 67701–3799; tel. 785/462–7511; Greg Unruh, Chief Executive Officer

CLARA BARTON HOSPITAL, 250 West Ninth Street, Hoisington, KS, Zip 67544–1706; tel. 620/653–2114; James Blackwell, President and Chief Executive Officer

GOODLAND REGIONAL MEDICAL CENTER, 220 West Second Street, Goodland, KS, Zip 67735–1602; tel. 785/890–3625; Ronald R. Robinson, M.D., FACHE, M.P.H., Chief Executive Officer

GOVE COUNTY MEDICAL CENTER, 520 West Fifth Street, Quinter, KS, Zip 67752–0129, Mailing Address: P.O. Box 129, 67752–0129, tel. 785/754–3341; David Caudill, Chief Executive Officer

GRAHAM COUNTY HOSPITAL, 304 West Prout Street, Hill City, KS, Zip 67642–1435; tel. 785/421–2121; Melissa Atkins, CPA, Chief Executive Officer

HAYS MEDICAL CENTER, 2220 Canterbury Drive, Hays, KS, Zip 67601–2370, Mailing Address: P.O. Box 8100, 67601–8100, tel. 785/623–5000; Edward Herrman, R.N., FACHE, President and Chief Executive Officer

LOGAN COUNTY HOSPITAL, 211 Cherry Street, Oakley, KS, Zip 67748–1201; tel. 785/672–3211; Meldon L. Snow, Chief Executive Officer

NESS COUNTY HOSPITAL DISTRICT NO 2, 312 Custer Street, Ness City, KS, Zip 67560–1654; tel. 785/798–2291; Curt Thomas, Administrator

NORTON COUNTY HOSPITAL, 102 East Holme, Norton, KS, Zip 67654–1406, Mailing Address: P.O. Box 250, 67654–0250, tel. 785/877–3351; Gina Frack, Chief Executive Officer

ROOKS COUNTY HEALTH CENTER, 1210 North Washington Street, Plainville, KS, Zip 67663–1632, Mailing Address: P.O. Box 389, 67663–0389, tel. 785/434–4553; Anthony Thomas, Chief Executive Officer

RUSH COUNTY MEMORIAL HOSPITAL, 801 Locust Street, La Crosse, KS, Zip 67548–9673, Mailing Address: P.O. Box 520, 67548–0520, tel. 785/222–2545; Michael Cooper, Chief Executive Officer

RUSSELL REGIONAL HOSPITAL, 200 South Main Street, Russell, KS, Zip 67665–2920; tel. 785/483–3131; Sharon Collins, Chief Executive Officer

SCOTT COUNTY HOSPITAL, 201 East Albert Avenue, Scott City, KS, Zip 67871–1203; tel. 620/872–5811; David Mark. Burnett, President and Chief Executive Officer

SHERIDAN COUNTY HEALTH COMPLEX, 826 18th Street, Hoxie, KS, Zip 67740–0167, Mailing Address: P.O. Box 167, 67740–0167, tel. 785/675–3281; Niceta Farber, Chief Executive Officer

UNIVERSITY OF KANSAS HEALTH SYSTEM PAWNEE VALLEY CAMPUS, 923 Carroll Avenue, Larned, KS, Zip 67550–2429; tel. 620/285–3161; Melanie D. Urban, Administrator

**PIONEER HEALTH NETWORK, INC.**
**310 East Walnut Street, Suite 210, Garden City, KS Zip 67846–5565; tel. 620/276–6100; Mary Adam, Executive Director**

BOB WILSON MEMORIAL GRANT COUNTY HOSPITAL, 415 North Main Street, Ulysses, KS, Zip 67880–2133; tel. 620/356–1266; Christine McSweeney, FACHE, President and Chief Executive Officer

CITIZENS MEDICAL CENTER, 100 East College Drive, Colby, KS, Zip 67701–3799; tel. 785/462–7511; Greg Unruh, Chief Executive Officer

EDWARDS COUNTY MEDICAL CENTER, 620 West Eighth Street, Kinsley, KS, Zip 67547–2329, Mailing Address: P.O. Box 99, 67547–0099, tel. 620/659–3621; Jimmie W. Hansel, Ph.D., Chief Executive Officer

GREELEY COUNTY HEALTH SERVICES, 506 Third Street, Tribune, KS, Zip 67879–9684, Mailing Address: P.O. Box 338, 67879–0338, tel. 620/376–4221; Trice Watts, Chief Financial Officer and Chief Executive Officer

HAMILTON COUNTY HOSPITAL, 700 North Huser Street, Syracuse, KS, Zip 67878–0948, Mailing Address: P.O. Box 948, 67878–0948, tel. 620/384–7461; Brandon Bullard, Chief Executive Officer

HODGEMAN COUNTY HEALTH CENTER, 809 Bramley Street, Jetmore, KS, Zip 67854–9320, Mailing Address: P.O. Box 310, 67854–0310, tel. 620/357–8361; Phil Ginder, Chief Executive Officer

KEARNY COUNTY HOSPITAL, 500 Thorpe Street, Lakin, KS, Zip 67860–9625; tel. 620/355–7111; David Hofmeister, Chief Executive Officer

LANE COUNTY HOSPITAL, 235 West Vine, Dighton, KS, Zip 67839–0969, Mailing Address: P.O. Box 969, 67839–0969, tel. 620/397–5321; Marcia Gabel, Chief Financial Officer and Co–Chief Executive Officer

LOGAN COUNTY HOSPITAL, 211 Cherry Street, Oakley, KS, Zip 67748–1201; tel. 785/672–3211; Meldon L. Snow, Chief Executive Officer

MEADE DISTRICT HOSPITAL, 510 East Carthage Street, Meade, KS, Zip 67864–6401, Mailing Address: P.O. Box 820, 67864–0820, tel. 620/873–2141; Tara Ramlochan, Chief Executive Officer

MINNEOLA DISTRICT HOSPITAL, 212 Main Street, Minneola, KS, Zip 67865–8511, Mailing Address: P.O. Box 127, 67865–0127, tel. 620/885–4264; Deborah Bruner, Chief Executive Officer and Administrator

MORTON COUNTY HEALTH SYSTEM, 445 Hilltop Street, Elkhart, KS, Zip 67950–0937, Mailing Address: P.O. Box 937, 67950–0937, tel. 620/697–2141; Patrick Custer, Interim Chief Executive Officer

SATANTA DISTRICT HOSPITAL AND LONG TERM CARE, 401 South Cheyenne Street, Satanta, KS, Zip 67870–0159, Mailing Address: P.O. Box 159, 67870–0159, tel. 620/649–2761; Jeremy Clingenpeel, Administrator

SCOTT COUNTY HOSPITAL, 201 East Albert Avenue, Scott City, KS, Zip 67871–1203; tel. 620/872–5811; David Mark. Burnett, President and Chief Executive Officer

SOUTHWEST MEDICAL CENTER, 315 West 15th Street, Liberal, KS, Zip 67901–2455, Box 1340, 67905–1340, tel. 620/624–1651; Robert Whitaker, President and Chief Executive Officer

ST. CATHERINE HOSPITAL, 401 East Spruce Street, Garden City, KS, Zip 67846–5679; tel. 620/272–2561; Christine McSweeney, FACHE, President and Chief Executive Officer

STANTON COUNTY HOSPITAL, 404 North Chestnut Street, Johnson, KS, Zip 67855–5001, Mailing Address: P.O. Box 779, 67855–0779, tel. 620/492–6250; Jay Tusten, Chief Executive Officer

STEVENS COUNTY HOSPITAL, 1006 South Jackson Street, Hugoton, KS, Zip 67951–2858, Mailing Address: P.O. Box 10, 67951–0010, tel. 620/544–8511; Linda Stalcup, Chief Executive Officer

WICHITA COUNTY HEALTH CENTER, 211 East Earl Street, Leoti, KS, Zip 67861–9620; tel. 620/375–2233; Teresa Clark, Chief Executive Officer and Administrator

**SUNFLOWER HEALTH NETWORK**
**400 South Santa Fe Avenue, Salina, KS Zip 67401–4144; tel. 785/452–6102; Heather Fuller, Executive Director**

CLAY COUNTY MEDICAL CENTER, 617 Liberty Street, Clay Center, KS, Zip 67432–1564, Mailing Address: P.O. Box 512, 67432–0512, tel. 785/632–2144; Austin M. Gillard, Chief Executive Officer

CLOUD COUNTY HEALTH CENTER, 1100 Highland Drive, Concordia, KS, Zip 66901–3923; tel. 785/243–1234; David Garnas, Administrator

ELLSWORTH COUNTY MEDICAL CENTER, 1604 Aylward Street, Ellsworth, KS, Zip 67439–0087, Mailing Address: P.O. Box 87, 67439–0087, tel. 785/472–3111; Andrew P. Bair, Chief Executive Officer

HERINGTON MUNICIPAL HOSPITAL, 100 East Helen Street, Herington, KS, Zip 67449–1606; tel. 785/258–2207; Isabel Schmedemann, Chief Executive Officer and Administrator

HILLSBORO COMMUNITY HOSPITAL, 701 South Main Street, Hillsboro, KS, Zip 67063–1553; tel. 620/947–3114; Mark Rooker, Chief Executive Officer

HOSPITAL DISTRICT NO 1 OF RICE COUNTY, 619 South Clark Street, Lyons, KS, Zip 67554–3003, Mailing Address: P.O. Box 828, 67554–0828, tel. 620/257–5173; George M. Stover, Chief Executive Officer

JEWELL COUNTY HOSPITAL, 100 Crestvue Avenue, Mankato, KS, Zip 66956–2407, Mailing Address: P.O. Box 327, 66956–0327, tel. 785/378–3137; Doyle L. McKimmy, FACHE, Chief Executive Officer

LINCOLN COUNTY HOSPITAL, 624 North Second Street, Lincoln, KS, Zip 67455–1738, Mailing Address: P.O. Box 406, 67455–0406, tel. 785/524–4403; Tawnya Seitz, Acting Chief Executive Officer

LINDSBORG COMMUNITY HOSPITAL, 605 West Lincoln Street, Lindsborg, KS, Zip 67456–2328; tel. 785/227–3308; Larry VanDerWege, Administrator

MEMORIAL HEALTH SYSTEM, 511 NE Tenth Street, Abilene, KS, Zip 67410–2153; tel. 785/263–2100; Harold Courtois, Chief Executive Officer

MITCHELL COUNTY HOSPITAL HEALTH SYSTEMS, 400 West 8th Street, Beloit, KS, Zip 67420–1605, Mailing Address: P.O. Box 399, 67420–0399, tel. 785/738–2266; Jeremy Armstrong, FACHE, Chief Executive Officer

OSBORNE COUNTY MEMORIAL HOSPITAL, 424 West New Hampshire Street, Osborne, KS, Zip 67473–2314, Mailing Address: P.O. Box 70, 67473–0070, tel. 785/346–2121; Marianna Harris, Administrator

OTTAWA COUNTY HEALTH CENTER, 215 East Eighth, Minneapolis, KS, Zip 67467–1902, Mailing Address: P.O. Box 290, 67467–0290, tel. 785/392–2122; Jody Parks, Administrator

REPUBLIC COUNTY HOSPITAL, 2420 'G' Street, Belleville, KS, Zip 66935–2400; tel. 785/527–2254; Rita K. Buurman, Interim Chief Executive Officer

SALINA REGIONAL HEALTH CENTER, 400 South Santa Fe Avenue, Salina, KS, Zip 67401–4198, Mailing Address: P.O. Box 5080, 67402–5080, tel. 785/452–7000; Joel Phelps, President and Chief Executive Officer

Section B

SMITH COUNTY MEMORIAL HOSPITAL, 921 East Highway 36, Smith Center, KS, Zip 66967; tel. 785/282-6845; Allen Van Driel, Chief Executive Officer

## KENTUCKY

### COMMONWEALTH HEALTH CORPORATION
**800 Park Street, Bowling Green, KY Zip 42101-2356; tel. 270/745-1500; Connie Smith, FACHE, MSN, R.N., Chief Executive Officer**

COMMONWEALTH REGIONAL SPECIALTY HOSPITAL, 250 Park Drive, 6th Floor, Bowling Green, KY, Zip 42101-1760, Mailing Address: P.O. Box 90010, 42102-9010, tel. 270/796-6200; Christa Atkins, Administrator

MEDICAL CENTER AT BOWLING GREEN, 250 Park Street, Bowling Green, KY, Zip 42101-1795, Mailing Address: P.O. Box 90010, 42102-9010, tel. 270/745-1000; Connie Smith, FACHE, MSN, R.N., Chief Executive Officer

MEDICAL CENTER AT FRANKLIN, 1100 Brookhaven Road, Franklin, KY, Zip 42134-2746; tel. 270/598-4800; Annette Runyon, Vice President and Administrator

MEDICAL CENTER AT SCOTTSVILLE, 456 Burnley Road, Scottsville, KY, Zip 42164-6355; tel. 270/622-2800; Eric Hagan, R.N., Executive Vice President and Administrator

### COMMUNITY CARE NETWORK
**110 A Second Street, Henderson, KY Zip 42420; tel. 619/278-2273; Roberta Alexander, Director**

ASCENSION ST. VINCENT EVANSVILLE, 3700 Washington Avenue, Evansville, IN, Zip 47714-0541; tel. 812/485-4000; Daniel A. Parod, President

BAPTIST HEALTH MADISONVILLE, 900 Hospital Drive, Madisonville, KY, Zip 42431-1694; tel. 270/825-5100; Robert L. Ramey, President

BAPTIST HEALTH PADUCAH, 2501 Kentucky Avenue, Paducah, KY, Zip 42003-3200; tel. 270/575-2100; Christopher Roty, President

CALDWELL MEDICAL CENTER, 100 Medical Center Drive, Princeton, KY, Zip 42445-2430, Mailing Address: P.O. Box 410, 42445-0410, tel. 270/365-0300; Daniel Odegaard, FACHE, Chief Executive Officer

CRITTENDEN COUNTY HOSPITAL, 520 West Gum Street, Marion, KY, Zip 42064-1516, Mailing Address: P.O. Box 386, 42064-0386, tel. 270/965-5281; Jonathan Gleason, Chief Executive Officer

ENCOMPASS HEALTH DEACONESS REHABILITATION HOSPITAL, 9355 Warrick Trail, Newburgh, IN, Zip 47630-0015; tel. 812/476-9983; Blake Bunner, Chief Executive Officer

JENNIE STUART MEDICAL CENTER, 320 West 18th Street, Hopkinsville, KY, Zip 42240-1965, Mailing Address: P.O. Box 2400, 42241-2400, tel. 270/887-0100; Eric A. Lee, President and Chief Executive Officer

LINCOLN TRAIL BEHAVIORAL HEALTH SYSTEM, 3909 South Wilson Road, Radcliff, KY, Zip 40160-8944, Mailing Address: P.O. Box 369, 40159-0369, tel. 270/351-9444; Leslie Flechler, Chief Executive Officer

LIVINGSTON HOSPITAL AND HEALTHCARE SERVICES, 131 Hospital Drive, Salem, KY, Zip 42078-8043; tel. 270/988-2299; Elizabeth Snodgrass, Chief Executive Officer

MEDICAL CENTER AT FRANKLIN, 1100 Brookhaven Road, Franklin, KY, Zip 42134-2746; tel. 270/598-4800; Annette Runyon, Vice President and Administrator

METHODIST HOSPITAL UNION COUNTY, 4604 Highway 60 West, Morganfield, KY, Zip 42437-9570; tel. 270/389-5000; Benny Nolen, President and Chief Executive Officer

METHODIST HOSPITAL, 1305 North Elm Street, Henderson, KY, Zip 42420-2775, Mailing Address: P.O. Box 48, 42419-0048, tel. 270/827-7700; Linda E. White, Chief Executive Officer

MURRAY-CALLOWAY COUNTY HOSPITAL, 803 Poplar Street, Murray, KY, Zip 42071-2432; tel. 270/762-1100; Colonel, Jerome Penner, Chief Executive Officer

NORTON CHILDREN'S HOSPITAL, 231 East Chestnut Street, Louisville, KY, Zip 40202-1821; tel. 502/629-6000; Emmett Ramser, Chief Administrative Officer

NORTON HOSPITAL, 200 East Chestnut Street, Louisville, KY, Zip 40202-1800, Mailing Address: P.O. Box 35070, 40232-5070, tel. 502/629-8000; Matthew Ayers, Chief Administrative Officer

OHIO COUNTY HOSPITAL, 1211 Main Street, Hartford, KY, Zip 42347-1619; tel. 270/298-7411; Blaine Pieper, Chief Executive Officer

OWENSBORO HEALTH MUHLENBERG COMMUNITY HOSPITAL, 440 Hopkinsville Street, Greenville, KY, Zip 42345-1124, Mailing Address: P.O. Box 387, 42345-0378, tel. 270/338-8000; Ed Heath, FACHE, Chief Executive Officer

RIVERVALLEY BEHAVIORAL HEALTH HOSPITAL, 1000 Industrial Drive, Owensboro, KY, Zip 42301-8715; tel. 270/689-6500; Wanda Figuerora Peralta, President and Chief Executive Officer

SAINT THOMAS WEST HOSPITAL, 4220 Harding Road, Nashville, TN, Zip 37205-2095, Mailing Address: P.O. Box 380, 37202-0380, tel. 615/222-2111; Fahad Tahir, Chief Executive Officer

TRIGG COUNTY HOSPITAL, 254 Main Street, Cadiz, KY, Zip 42211-9153, Mailing Address: P.O. Box 312, 42211-0312, tel. 270/522-3215; John Sumner, Chief Executive Officer

UOFL HEALTH – MARY AND ELIZABETH HOSPITAL , 1850 Bluegrass Avenue, Louisville, KY, Zip 40215-1199; tel. 502/361-6000; Melisa Adkins, Chief Executive Officer

### KENTUCKYONE
**200 Abraham Flexner Way, Louisville, KY Zip 40202-2877; tel. 502/587-4011; Charles W. Neumann, Interim President and Chief Executive Officer**

CHI FLAGET MEMORIAL HOSPITAL, 4305 New Shepherdsville Road, Bardstown, KY, Zip 40004-9019; tel. 502/350-5000; Jennifer Nolan, President and Chief Executive Officer

CHI SAINT JOSEPH BEREA, 305 Estill Street, Berea, KY, Zip 40403-1909; tel. 859/986-3151; Terrence G. Deis, CPA, FACHE, President

CHI SAINT JOSEPH EAST, 150 North Eagle Creek Drive, Lexington, KY, Zip 40509-1805; tel. 859/967-5000; Jason M. Adams, President

CHI SAINT JOSEPH HEALTH, One St Joseph Drive, Lexington, KY, Zip 40504-3754; tel. 859/313-1000; Bruce J. Tassin, President

CHI SAINT JOSEPH LONDON, 1001 Saint Joseph Lane, London, KY, Zip 40741-8345; tel. 606/330-6000; Terrence G. Deis, CPA, FACHE, President

CONTINUING CARE HOSPITAL, 1 Saint Joseph Drive, Lexington, KY, Zip 40504-3742; tel. 859/967-5744; Robert C. Desotelle, President and Chief Executive Officer

SAINT JOSEPH MOUNT STERLING, 225 Falcon Drive, Mount Sterling, KY, Zip 40353-1158, Mailing Address: P.O. Box 7, 40353-0007, tel. 859/497-5000; Terrence G. Deis, CPA, FACHE, President

UOFL HEALTH – JEWISH HOSPITAL , 200 Abraham Flexner Way, Louisville, KY, Zip 40202-1886; tel. 502/587-4011; John Walsh, FACHE, Chief Administrative Officer

UOFL HEALTH – MARY AND ELIZABETH HOSPITAL , 1850 Bluegrass Avenue, Louisville, KY, Zip 40215-1199; tel. 502/361-6000; Melisa Adkins, Chief Executive Officer

UOFL HEALTH – PEACE HOSPITAL, 2020 Newburg Road, Louisville, KY, Zip 40205-1879; tel. 502/479-4500; Martha S. Mather, Chief Administrative Officer

### ST. ELIZABETH HEALTHCARE
**1 Medical Village Drive, Edgewood, KY Zip 41017-3403; tel. 859/301-2000; Garren Colvin, Chief Executive Officer**

ST. ELIZABETH EDGEWOOD, 1 Medical Village Drive, Edgewood, KY, Zip 41017-3403; tel. 859/301-2000; Garren Colvin, Chief Executive Officer

ST. ELIZABETH FLORENCE, 4900 Houston Road, Florence, KY, Zip 41042-4824; tel. 859/212-5200; Garren Colvin, Chief Executive Officer

ST. ELIZABETH FORT THOMAS, 85 North Grand Avenue, Fort Thomas, KY, Zip 41075-1796; tel. 859/572-3100; Garren Colvin, Chief Executive Officer

ST. ELIZABETH GRANT , 238 Barnes Road, Williamstown, KY, Zip 41097-9482; tel. 859/824-8240; Garren Colvin, Chief Executive Officer

## MASSACHUSETTS

### LAHEY HEALTH
**41 Mall Road, Burlington, MA Zip 01805-0001; tel. 781/744-7100; Howard R. Grant, M.D., President and Chief Executive Officer**

BEVERLY HOSPITAL, 85 Herrick Street, Beverly, MA, Zip 01915-1777; tel. 978/922-3000; Philip M. Cormier, Chief Executive Officer

LAHEY HOSPITAL & MEDICAL CENTER, BURLINGTON, 41 Mall Road, Burlington, MA, Zip 01805-0001, 31 Mall Road, 01805-0001, tel. 781/744-5100; David L. Longworth, M.D., Chief Executive Officer

WINCHESTER HOSPITAL, 41 Highland Avenue, Winchester, MA, Zip 01890-1496; tel. 781/729-9000; Richard I. Weiner, M.D., Chief Executive Officer and Chief Medical Officer

### WELLFORCE
**800 District Avenue, Suite 520, Burlington, MA Zip 01803-5057; tel. 978/942-2220; Michael J. Dandorph, President and Chief Executive Officer**

LOWELL GENERAL HOSPITAL, 295 Varnum Avenue, Lowell, MA, Zip 01854-2134; tel. 978/937-6000; Joseph White, FACHE, President and Chief Executive Officer

MELROSEWAKEFIELD HEALTHCARE, 585 Lebanon Street, Melrose, MA, Zip 02176-3225; tel. 781/979-3000; Susan Sandberg, R.N., Chief Executive Officer

TUFTS MEDICAL CENTER, 800 Washington Street, Boston, MA, Zip 02111-1552; tel. 617/636-5000; Michael Tarnoff, M.D., Interim Chief Executive Officer

## MICHIGAN

### ASCENSION GENESYS HOSPITAL
**1 Genesys Parkway, Grand Blanc, MI Zip 48439-8065; tel. 810/606-5000; Elizabeth Aderholdt, Chief Executive Officer**

ASCENSION MACOMB-OAKLAND HOSPITAL, 11800 East 12 Mile Road, Warren, MI, Zip 48093-3472; tel. 586/573-5000; Gary Druskovich, M.D., President

ASCENSION ST. JOSEPH HOSPITAL, 200 Hemlock Street, Tawas City, MI, Zip 48763-9237, Mailing Address: P.O. Box 659, 48764-0659, tel. 989/362-3411; Stephanie J. Duggan, M.D., President

ASCENSION ST. MARY'S OF MICHIGAN, 800 South Washington Avenue, Saginaw, MI, Zip 48601–2594; tel. 989/907–8000; Stephanie J. Duggan, M.D., President

**LAKELAND REGIONAL HEALTH SYSTEM**
**1234 Napier Avenue, Saint Joseph, MI Zip 49085–2112; tel. 269/983–8300; Loren Hamel, M.D., President and Chief Executive Officer**

LAKELAND HOSPITAL, WATERVLIET, 400 Medical Park Drive, Watervliet, MI, Zip 49098–9225; tel. 269/463–3111; Ray Cruse, Chief Executive Officer

SPECTRUM HEALTH LAKELAND , 1234 Napier Avenue, Saint Joseph, MI, Zip 49085–2158; tel. 269/983–8300; Loren Hamel, M.D., President and Chief Executive Officer

**ST. JOHN PROVIDENCE HEALTH SYSTEM**
**28000 Dequindre Drive, Warren, MI Zip 48092; tel. 866/501–3627; Jean Meyer, President and Chief Executive Officer**

ASCENSION BRIGHTON CENTER FOR RECOVERY, 12851 Grand River Road, Brighton, MI, Zip 48116–8506; tel. 810/227–1211; Raymond A. Waller, Director and Administrator

ASCENSION MACOMB–OAKLAND HOSPITAL, 11800 East 12 Mile Road, Warren, MI, Zip 48093–3472; tel. 586/573–5000; Gary Druskovich, M.D., President

ASCENSION RIVER DISTRICT HOSPITAL, 4100 River Road, East China, MI, Zip 48054–2909; tel. 810/329–7111; Kevin Grady, M.D., President

ASCENSION ST. JOHN HOSPITAL, 22101 Moross Road, Detroit, MI, Zip 48236–2148; tel. 313/343–4000; Kevin Grady, M.D., President

ASCENSION OF PROVIDENCE HOSPITAL, SOUTHFIELD CAMPUS, 16001 West Nine Mile Road, Southfield, MI, Zip 48075; tel. 248/849–3400; Joseph R. Hurshe, President

**UPPER PENINSULA HEALTH CARE NETWORK (UPHCN)**
**228 West Washington Street, Marquette, MI Zip 49855–4330; tel. 906/225–3146; Dennis Smith, Chief Executive Officer**

ASPIRUS IRON RIVER HOSPITALS & CLINICS, INC., 1400 West Ice Lake Road, Iron River, MI, Zip 49935–9526; tel. 906/265–6121; Connie L. Koutouzos, R.N., MSN, Chief Executive Officer

ASPIRUS IRONWOOD HOSPITALS & CLINICS, INC., N10561 Grand View Lane, Ironwood, MI, Zip 49938–9622; tel. 906/932–2525; Paula L. Chermside, Chief Executive Officer

ASPIRUS KEWEENAW HOSPITAL, INC., 205 Osceola Street, Laurium, MI, Zip 49913–2134; tel. 906/337–6500; Christine K. Harff, UP Regional President

ASPIRUS ONTONAGON HOSPITAL, INC., 601 South Seventh Street, Ontonagon, MI, Zip 49953–1459; tel. 906/884–8000; Dylan Taylor, Chief Administrative Officer

BARAGA COUNTY MEMORIAL HOSPITAL, 18341 U.S. Highway 41, L'Anse, MI, Zip 49946–8024; tel. 906/524–3300; Margie Hale, R.N., MSN, Chief Executive Officer

DICKINSON COUNTY HEALTHCARE SYSTEM, 1721 South Stephenson Avenue, Iron Mountain, MI, Zip 49801–3637; tel. 906/774–1313; Charles Nelson, Chief Executive Officer

HELEN NEWBERRY JOY HOSPITAL, Helen Newberry Joy Hospital Annex, 502 West Harrie Street, Newberry, MI, Zip 49868–1209; tel. 906/293–9200; Hunter Kyle. Nostrant, Chief Executive Officer

MACKINAC STRAITS HEALTH SYSTEM, INC., 1140 North State Street, Saint Ignace, MI, Zip 49781–1048; tel. 906/643–8585; Karen Cheeseman, Chief Executive Officer

MUNISING MEMORIAL HOSPITAL, 1500 Sand Point Road, Munising, MI, Zip 49862–1406; tel. 906/387–4110; Melissa Hall, Chief Executive Officer

SCHOOLCRAFT MEMORIAL HOSPITAL, 7870W US Highway 2, Manistique, MI, Zip 49854–8992; tel. 906/341–3200; Robert Crumb, MS, Chief Executive Officer

UP HEALTH SYSTEM–BELL , 901 Lakeshore Drive, Ishpeming, MI, Zip 49849–1367; tel. 906/486–4431; Mitchell D. Leckelt, Chief Executive Officer

UP HEALTH SYSTEM–PORTAGE, 500 Campus Drive, Hancock, MI, Zip 49930–1569; tel. 906/483–1000; Edward E. Freysinger, Chief Executive Officer

WAR MEMORIAL HOSPITAL, 500 Osborn Boulevard, Sault Sainte Marie, MI, Zip 49783–1884; tel. 906/635–4460; David B. Jahn, President and Chief Executive Officer

## MINNESOTA

**NORTHWEST METRO ALLIANCE**
**c/0 Mercy Hospital, 4050 Coon Rapids Boulevard, Coon Rapids, MN Zip 55433–2586; tel. 763/236–6000; Sara J. Criger, President**

MERCY HOSPITAL, 4050 Coon Rapids Boulevard, Coon Rapids, MN, Zip 55433–2586; tel. 763/236–6000; Sara J. Criger, President

## MISSOURI

**HEALTH NETWORK OF MISSOURI**
**One Hospital Drive, Room C1213, DC 079.00, Columbia, MO Zip 65212; tel. 573/815–8000; Marty McCormick, Chief Executive Officer**

BOTHWELL REGIONAL HEALTH CENTER, 601 East 14th Street, Sedalia, MO, Zip 65301–5972, Mailing Address: P.O. Box 1706, 65302–1706, tel. 660/826–8833; Lori Wightman, R.N., FACHE, Chief Executive Officer

CAPITAL REGION MEDICAL CENTER, 1125 Madison Street, Jefferson City, MO, Zip 65101–5200, Mailing Address: P.O. Box 1128, 65102–1128, tel. 573/632–5000; Gaspare Calvaruso, President

HANNIBAL REGIONAL HOSPITAL, 6000 Hospital Drive, Hannibal, MO, Zip 63401–6887, Mailing Address: P.O. Box 551, 63401–0551, tel. 573/248–1300; C Todd. Ahrens, President and Chief Executive Officer

LAKE REGIONAL HEALTH SYSTEM, 54 Hospital Drive, Osage Beach, MO, Zip 65065–3050; tel. 573/348–8000; Dane W. Henry, FACHE, Chief Executive Officer

SAINT FRANCIS MEDICAL CENTER, 211 St Francis Drive, Cape Girardeau, MO, Zip 63703–5049; tel. 573/331–3000; Maryann Reese, R.N., FACHE, President and Chief Executive Officer

UNIVERSITY OF MISSOURI HEALTH CARE, One Hospital Drive, Columbia, MO, Zip 65212–0001; tel. 573/882–4141; Jonathan W. Curtright, Chief Executive Officer

**MERCY HEALTH EAST**
**615 South New Ballas Road, Saint Louis, MO Zip 63141–8221; tel. 314/364–3000; Donn Sorensen, Regional President, West Communities**

MERCY HOSPITAL JEFFERSON, 1400 US Highway 61 South, Festus, MO, Zip 63028–4100, Mailing Address: P.O. Box 350, Crystal City, 63019–0350, tel. 636/933–1000; Eric Ammons, President

MERCY HOSPITAL ST. LOUIS , 615 South New Ballas Road, Saint Louis, MO, Zip 63141–8277; tel. 314/251–6000; Stephen Mackin, President

MERCY HOSPITAL WASHINGTON, 901 East Fifth Street, Washington, MO, Zip 63090–3127; tel. 636/239–8000; Eric J. Eoloff, President

**MOSAIC LIFE CARE X**
**5325 Faraon Street, Saint Joseph, MO Zip 64506–3488; tel. 816/271–6000**

LONG–TERM ACUTE CARE HOSPITAL, MOSAIC LIFE CARE AT ST. JOSEPH, 5325 Faraon Street, Saint Joseph, MO, Zip 64506–3488; tel. 816/271–6000; Dana Anderson, R.N., Administrator

MOSAIC LIFE CARE AT ST. JOSEPH – MEDICAL CENTER, 5325 Faraon Street, Saint Joseph, MO, Zip 64506–3488; tel. 816/271–6000; Samuel Mark. Laney, M.D., Chief Executive Officer

MOSAIC MEDICAL CENTER – ALBANY, 705 North College Street, Albany, MO, Zip 64402–1433; tel. 660/726–3941; Jon D. Doolittle, Regional President

## MONTANA

**MONTANA HEALTH NETWORK**
**519 Pleasant Street, Miles City, MT Zip 59301–3030; tel. 406/234–1420; Janet Bastian, Chief Executive Officer**

BILLINGS CLINIC, 2800 10th Avenue North, Billings, MT, Zip 59101–0703, Mailing Address: P.O. Box 37000, 59107–7000, tel. 406/657–4000; Scott J. Ellner, D.O., M.P.H., FACS, Chief Executive Officer

CENTRAL MONTANA MEDICAL CENTER, 408 Wendell Avenue, Lewistown, MT, Zip 59457–2261; tel. 406/535–7711; Laura Bennett, Chief Executive Officer

DAHL MEMORIAL HEALTHCARE ASSOCIATION, 215 Sandy Street, Ekalaka, MT, Zip 59324, Mailing Address: P.O. Box 46, 59324–0046, tel. 406/775–8730; Ryan Tooke, Chief Executive Officer

DANIELS MEMORIAL HEALTHCARE CENTER, 105 Fifth Avenue East, Scobey, MT, Zip 59263, Mailing Address: P.O. Box 400, 59263–0400, tel. 406/487–2296; Eric Connell, Chief Executive Officer

FALLON MEDICAL COMPLEX, 202 South 4th Street West, Baker, MT, Zip 59313–9156, Mailing Address: P.O. Box 820, 59313–0820, tel. 406/778–3331; David Espeland, Chief Executive Officer

FRANCES MAHON DEACONESS HOSPITAL, 621 Third Street South, Glasgow, MT, Zip 59230–2699; tel. 406/228–3500; Randall G. Holom, Chief Executive Officer

GLENDIVE MEDICAL CENTER, 202 Prospect Drive, Glendive, MT, Zip 59330–1999; tel. 406/345–3306; Parker Powell, Chief Executive Officer

HOLY ROSARY HEALTHCARE, 2600 Wilson Street, Miles City, MT, Zip 59301–5094; tel. 406/233–2600; Karen Costello, President

MCCONE COUNTY HEALTH CENTER, 605 Sullivan Avenue, Circle, MT, Zip 59215, Mailing Address: P.O. Box 48, 59215–0048, tel. 406/485–3381; Nancy Rosaaen, Chief Executive Officer

PHILLIPS COUNTY HOSPITAL, 311 South 8th Avenue East, Malta, MT, Zip 59538–0640, Mailing Address: P.O. Box 640, 59538–0640, tel. 406/654–1100; Scott A. Duke, Interim Chief Executive Officer

ROOSEVELT MEDICAL CENTER, 818 Second Avenue East, Culbertson, MT, Zip 59218, Mailing Address: P.O. Box 419, 59218–0419, tel. 406/787–6401; Audrey Stromberg, Administrator

Section B

SHERIDAN MEMORIAL HOSPITAL, 440 West Laurel Avenue, Plentywood, MT, Zip 59254–1596; tel. 406/765–3700; Gregory L. Maurer, Chief Executive Officer

SIDNEY HEALTH CENTER, 216 14th Avenue SW, Sidney, MT, Zip 59270–3586; tel. 406/488–2100; Jennifer Doty, Chief Executive Officer

STILLWATER BILLINGS CLINIC, 44 West Fourth Avenue North, Columbus, MT, Zip 59019–0959, Mailing Address: P.O. Box 959, 59019–0959, tel. 406/322–5316; David Ryerse, Chief Executive Officer

WHEATLAND MEMORIAL HEALTHCARE, 530 Third Street North West, Harlowton, MT, Zip 59036, Mailing Address: P.O. Box 287, 59036–0287, tel. 406/632–4351; Rick Poss, Interim Chief Executive Officer

## NEBRASKA

### CHI HEALTH
**12809 West Dodge Road, Omaha, NE Zip 68154–2155; tel. 402/343–4300; Cliff Robertson, M.D., President and Chief Executive Officer**

CHI HEALTH CREIGHTON UNIVERSITY MEDICAL CENTER – BERGAN MERCY, 7500 Mercy Road, Omaha, NE, Zip 68124–2319; tel. 402/398–6060; Jayleen Casano, Ph.D., FACHE, President

CHI HEALTH GOOD SAMARITAN , 10 East 31st Street, Kearney, NE, Zip 68847–2926, Mailing Address: P.O. Box 1990, 68848–1990, tel. 308/865–7100; Michael H. Schnieders, FACHE, President

CHI HEALTH IMMANUEL, 6901 North 72nd Street, Omaha, NE, Zip 68122–1799; tel. 402/572–2121; Ann Schumacher, R.N., MSN, FACHE, President

CHI HEALTH LAKESIDE , 6901 N 72nd St, Omaha, NE, Zip 68122, 16901 Lakeside Hills Court, 68130–2318, tel. 402/717–8000; Kevin Miller, President

CHI HEALTH MERCY CORNING, 603 Rosary Drive, Corning, IA, Zip 50841–1683; tel. 641/322–3121; Lisa Wolfe, President

CHI HEALTH MERCY COUNCIL BLUFFS, 800 Mercy Drive, Council Bluffs, IA, Zip 51503–3128; tel. 712/328–5000; Ann Schumacher, R.N., MSN, FACHE, President

CHI HEALTH MIDLANDS , 11111 South 84th Street, Papillion, NE, Zip 68046–4122; tel. 402/593–3000; Kevin Miller, President

CHI HEALTH MISSOURI VALLEY, 631 North Eighth Street, Missouri Valley, IA, Zip 51555–1102; tel. 712/642–2784; Jonathan Moe, President

CHI HEALTH NEBRASKA HEART , 7500 South 91st Street, Lincoln, NE, Zip 68526–9437; tel. 402/327–2700; Derek Vance, FACHE, President

CHI HEALTH PLAINVIEW , 704 North Third Street, Plainview, NE, Zip 68769–2047, Mailing Address: P.O. Box 489, 68769–0489, tel. 402/582–4245; Gregory Beckmann, Regional President

CHI HEALTH SAINT FRANCIS, 2620 West Faidley Avenue, Grand Island, NE, Zip 68803–4297, Mailing Address: P.O. Box 9804, 68802–9804, tel. 308/384–4600; Edward J. Hannon, FACHE, President

CHI HEALTH SCHUYLER, 104 West 17th Street, Schuyler, NE, Zip 68661–1304; tel. 402/352–2441; Connie Peters, R.N., President

CHI HEALTH ST ELIZABETH , 555 South 70th Street, Lincoln, NE, Zip 68510–2494; tel. 402/219–8000; Derek Vance, FACHE, President

CHI HEALTH ST. MARY'S , 1301 Grundman Boulevard, Nebraska City, NE, Zip 68410; tel. 402/873–3321; Daniel DeFreece, M.D., Interim President

### NEBRASKA MEDICINE
**987400 Nebraska Medical Center, Omaha, NE Zip 68198–7400; tel. 877/763–0000; James Linder, M.D., Chief Executive Officer**

NEBRASKA MEDICINE – BELLEVUE, 2500 Bellevue Medical Center Drive, Bellevue, NE, Zip 68123–1591; tel. 402/763–3000; Suzanne Langan. Nuss, Ph.D., R.N., Vice President of Operations and Chief Nursing Officer

NEBRASKA MEDICINE – NEBRASKA MEDICAL CENTER, 987400 Nebraska Medical Center, Omaha, NE, Zip 68198–7400; tel. 402/552–2000; James Linder, M.D., Chief Executive Officer

### NORTHEAST HEALTH SERVICES
**704 North Third Street, c/o CHI Plainview, Plainview, NE Zip 68769–2047; tel. 402/358–5700; Gregory Beckmann, Chief Executive Officer**

AVERA CREIGHTON HOSPITAL, 1503 Main Street, Creighton, NE, Zip 68729–3007, Mailing Address: P.O. Box 186, 68729–0186, tel. 402/358–5700; Todd Consbruck, Chief Executive Officer

CHI HEALTH PLAINVIEW , 704 North Third Street, Plainview, NE, Zip 68769–2047, Mailing Address: P.O. Box 489, 68769–0489, tel. 402/582–4245; Gregory Beckmann, Regional President

OSMOND GENERAL HOSPITAL, 402 North Maple Street, Osmond, NE, Zip 68765–5726, Mailing Address: P.O. Box 429, 68765–0429, tel. 402/748–3393; Lon Knievel, Chief Executive Officer

## NEW HAMPSHIRE

### CARING COMMUNITY NETWORK OF THE TWIN RIVERS
**c/o First Health, 841 Central Street, Franklin, NH Zip 03235–2026; tel. 603/934–0177; Rick Silverberg, Managing Director**

FRANKLIN REGIONAL HOSPITAL, 15 Aiken Avenue, Franklin, NH, Zip 03235–1299; tel. 603/934–2060; Kevin Donovan, FACHE, President and Chief Executive Officer

## NEW JERSEY

### QUALCARE, INC.
**242 Old New Brunswick Road, Piscataway, NJ Zip 08854–3754; tel. 732/562–2800; Jerry Eisenberg, Network Contact**

CAPITAL HEALTH MEDICAL CENTER–HOPEWELL, 1 Capital Way, Pennington, NJ, Zip 08534–2520; tel. 609/303–4000; Al Maghazehe, Ph.D., FACHE, President and Chief Executive Officer

CAREPOINT HEALTH CHRIST HOSPITAL, 176 Palisade Avenue, Jersey City, NJ, Zip 07306–1196, 176 Palisades Avenue, 07306–1196, tel. 201/795–8200; Marie Theresa Duffy, Chief Hospital Executive

CHILTON MEDICAL CENTER, 97 West Parkway, Pompton Plains, NJ, Zip 07444–1696; tel. 973/831–5000; Stephanie L. Schwartz, FACHE, Vice President AHS and President CMC

CLARA MAASS MEDICAL CENTER, One Clara Maass Drive, Belleville, NJ, Zip 07109–3557; tel. 973/450–2000; Mary Ellen Clyne, Ph.D., President and Chief Executive Officer

DEBORAH HEART AND LUNG CENTER, 200 Trenton Road, Browns Mills, NJ, Zip 08015–1705; tel. 609/893–6611; Joseph Chirichella, President and Chief Executive Officer

ENGLEWOOD HEALTH, 350 Engle Street, Englewood, NJ, Zip 07631–1898; tel. 201/894–3000; Warren Geller, President and Chief Executive Officer

HACKENSACK MERIDIAN HEALTH HACKENSACK UNIVERSITY MEDICAL CENTER, 30 Prospect Avenue, Hackensack, NJ, Zip 07601–1914; tel. 201/996–2000; Mark Sparta, President

HACKENSACK MERIDIAN HEALTH JFK MEDICAL CENTER, 65 James Street, Edison, NJ, Zip 8818; tel. 732/321–7000; Amie D. Thornton, Chief Hospital Executive

HACKENSACK MERIDIAN HEALTH OCEAN MEDICAL CENTER, 425 Jack Martin Boulevard, Brick Township, NJ, Zip 08724–7732; tel. 732/840–2200; Jason Kreitner, FACHE, Chief Hospital Executive

HACKENSACK MERIDIAN HEALTH RARITAN BAY MEDICAL CENTER, 530 New Brunswick Avenue, Perth Amboy, NJ, Zip 08861–3654; tel. 732/442–3700; Thomas Shanahan, CPA, Chief Operating Officer

HACKENSACK MERIDIAN HEALTH RIVERVIEW MEDICAL CENTER, 1 Riverview Plaza, Red Bank, NJ, Zip 07701–1864; tel. 732/741–2700; M. Todd. Way, President, Central Region

HACKETTSTOWN MEDICAL CENTER, 651 Willow Grove Street, Hackettstown, NJ, Zip 07840–1799; tel. 908/852–5100; Robert H. Adams, President, Western Region

INSPIRA MEDICAL CENTER–VINELAND, 1505 West Sherman Avenue, Vineland, NJ, Zip 08360–6912; tel. 856/641–8000; Amy B. Mansue, President and Chief Executive Officer

PENN MEDICINE PRINCETON MEDICAL CENTER, One Plainsboro Road, Plainsboro, NJ, Zip 08536–1913; tel. 609/853–7100; Barry S. Rabner, President and Chief Executive Officer, Princeton Healthcare System

PIEDMONT MOUNTAINSIDE HOSPITAL, 1266 Highway 515 South, Jasper, GA, Zip 30143–4872; tel. 706/692–2441; Denise Ray, Chief Executive Officer

ROBERT WOOD JOHNSON UNIVERSITY HOSPITAL, 1 Robert Wood Johnson Place, New Brunswick, NJ, Zip 08901–1928; tel. 732/828–3000; John J. Gantner, President and Chief Executive Officer

SAINT MICHAEL'S MEDICAL CENTER, 111 Central Avenue, Newark, NJ, Zip 07102–1909; tel. 973/877–5000; Alan Sickles, M.D., Chief Executive Officer

SALEM MEDICAL CENTER, 310 Woodstown Road, Salem, NJ, Zip 08079–2080; tel. 856/935–1000; Tammy Torres, R.N., MSN, Chief Executive Officer

ST. MARY'S GENERAL HOSPITAL, 350 Boulevard, Passaic, NJ, Zip 07055–2840; tel. 973/365–4300; Edward Condit, President and Chief Executive Officer

UNIVERSITY HOSPITAL, 150 Bergen Street, Newark, NJ, Zip 07103–2496; tel. 973/972–4300; Shereef Elnahal, M.D., President and Chief Executive Officer

VIRTUA MARLTON, 90 Brick Road, Marlton, NJ, Zip 08053–2177; tel. 856/355–6000; Dennis W. Pullin, FACHE, President and Chief Executive Officer

## NEW MEXICO

### NEW MEXICO RURAL HOSPITAL NETWORK
**7471 Pan American Freeway NE, Albuquerque, NM Zip 87109; tel. 505/346–0216; Stephen Stoddard, FACHE, Executive Director**

ARTESIA GENERAL HOSPITAL, 702 North 13th Street, Artesia, NM, Zip 88210–1199; tel. 575/748–3333; Joe Salgado, M.D., Interim Chief Executive Officer

CIBOLA GENERAL HOSPITAL, 1016 East Roosevelt Avenue, Grants, NM, Zip 87020–2118; tel. 505/287–4446; Thomas Whelan, Chief Executive Officer

GUADALUPE COUNTY HOSPITAL, 117 Camino de Vida, Santa Rosa, NM, Zip 88435–2267; tel. 575/472–3417; Christina Campos, Administrator

HOLY CROSS HOSPITAL, 1397 Weimer Road, Taos, NM, Zip 87571–6253; tel. 575/758–8883; William D. Patten, Jr., Chief Executive Officer

MINERS' COLFAX MEDICAL CENTER, 200 Hospital Drive, Raton, NM, Zip 87740–2099; tel. 575/445–7700; Bo Beames, Interim Chief Executive Officer

NOR–LEA HOSPITAL DISTRICT, 1600 North Main Avenue, Lovington, NM, Zip 88260–2871; tel. 575/396–6611; David B. Shaw, Chief Executive Officer and Administrator

REHOBOTH MCKINLEY CHRISTIAN HEALTH CARE SERVICES, 1901 Red Rock Drive, Gallup, NM, Zip 87301–5683; tel. 505/863–7000; Donald R. Smithburg, Interim Chief Executive Officer

ROOSEVELT GENERAL HOSPITAL, 42121 U S Highway 70, Portales, NM, Zip 88130, Mailing Address: P.O. Box 868, 88130–0868, tel. 575/359–1800; Kaye Green, FACHE, Chief Executive Officer

SIERRA VISTA HOSPITAL, 800 East Ninth Avenue, Truth or Consequences, NM, Zip 87901–1961; tel. 575/894–2111; David Faulkner, Interim Chief Executive Officer

UNION COUNTY GENERAL HOSPITAL, 300 Wilson Street, Clayton, NM, Zip 88415–3304, Mailing Address: P.O. Box 489, 88415–0489, tel. 575/374–2585; Tammie Stump, R.N., Chief Executive Officer

## NEW YORK

### ARDENT SOLUTIONS, INC.
**85 North Main Street, Suite 4, Wellsville, NY Zip 14895–1254; tel. 585/593–5223; Carrie Whitwood, Executive Director**

JONES MEMORIAL HOSPITAL, 191 North Main Street, Wellsville, NY, Zip 14895–1150, Mailing Address: P.O. Box 72, 14895–0072, tel. 585/593–1100; Eva Benedict, R.N., President and Chief Executive Officer

### ARNOT HEALTH
**600 Roe Avenue, Elmira, NY Zip 14905–1629; tel. 607/737–4100; Robert K. Lambert, M.D., FACHE, President and Chief Executive Officer**

ARNOT OGDEN MEDICAL CENTER, 600 Roe Avenue, Elmira, NY, Zip 14905–1629; tel. 607/737–4100; Jonathan I. Lawrence, President and Chief Executive Officer

IRA DAVENPORT MEMORIAL HOSPITAL, 7571 State Route 54, Bath, NY, Zip 14810–9590; tel. 607/776–8500; Elizabeth Weir, MSN, R.N., Site Administrator and Vice President of Nursing

### BASSETT HEALTHCARE NETWORK
**1 Atwell Road, Cooperstown, NY Zip 13326–1301; tel. 607/547–3456; William F. Streck, M.D., President and Chief Executive Officer**

AURELIA OSBORN FOX MEMORIAL HOSPITAL, 1 Norton Avenue, Oneonta, NY, Zip 13820–2629; tel. 607/432–2000; Jeff Joyner, President

BASSETT MEDICAL CENTER, One Atwell Road, Cooperstown, NY, Zip 13326–1394; tel. 607/547–3456; William W. LeCates, M.D., President

COBLESKILL REGIONAL HOSPITAL, 178 Grandview Drive, Cobleskill, NY, Zip 12043–5144; tel. 518/254–3456; Eric H. Stein, FACHE, President

LITTLE FALLS HOSPITAL, 140 Burwell Street, Little Falls, NY, Zip 13365–1725; tel. 315/823–1000; Michael L. Ogden, President and Chief Executive Officer

O'CONNOR HOSPITAL, 460 Andes Road, State Route 28, Delhi, NY, Zip 13753–7407; tel. 607/746–0300; Scott Bonderoff, President

### GREAT LAKES HEALTH SYSTEM OF WESTERN NEW YORK
**726 Exchange Street, Suite 522, Buffalo, NY Zip 14210–1485; tel. 716/859–8820; Jody Lomeo, Interim Chief Executive Officer**

ERIE COUNTY MEDICAL CENTER, 462 Grider Street, Buffalo, NY, Zip 14215–3098; tel. 716/898–3000; Thomas J. Quatroche, Jr., President and Chief Executive Officer

KALEIDA HEALTH, 100 High Street, Buffalo, NY, Zip 14203–1154; tel. 716/859–5600; Jody Lomeo, Chief Executive Officer

### LAKE ERIE REGIONAL HEALTH SYSTEM OF NEW YORK
**529 Central Avenue, Dunkirk, NY Zip 14048–2514; tel. 716/366–1111; J. Gary Rhodes, FACHE, Interim Chief Executive Officer**

BROOKS MEMORIAL HOSPITAL, 529 Central Avenue, Dunkirk, NY, Zip 14048–2599; tel. 716/366–1111; Mary E. LaRowe, FACHE, President and Chief Executive Officer

### MOHAWK VALLEY HEALTH SYSTEM (MVHS)
**1656 Champlin Avenue, Utica, NY Zip 13502–4830; tel. 315/624–6002; Darlene Stromstad, FACHE, President and Chief Executive Officer**

FAXTON ST. LUKE'S HEALTHCARE, 1656 Champlin Avenue, Utica, NY, Zip 13502–4830, Mailing Address: P.O. Box 479, 13503–0479, tel. 315/624–6000; Darlene Stromstad, FACHE, President and Chief Executive Officer

ST. ELIZABETH MEDICAL CENTER, 2209 Genesee Street, Utica, NY, Zip 13501–5999; tel. 315/798–8100; Darlene Stromstad, FACHE, President and Chief Executive Officer

### MOUNT SINAI NYU HEALTH NETWORK
**One Gustave L. Levy Place, New York, NY Zip 10029; tel. 212/659–8888; Arthur A. Klein, M.D., President**

ENGLEWOOD HEALTH, 350 Engle Street, Englewood, NJ, Zip 07631–1898; tel. 201/894–3000; Warren Geller, President and Chief Executive Officer

HUDSON REGIONAL HOSPITAL, 55 Meadowlands Parkway, Secaucus, NJ, Zip 07094–2977; tel. 201/392–3100; Nizar Kifaieh, M.D., President and Chief Executive Officer

JAMES J. PETERS VETERANS AFFAIRS MEDICAL CENTER, 130 West Kingsbridge Road, Bronx, NY, Zip 10468–3904; tel. 718/584–9000; Margaret B. Caplan, Director

JERSEY CITY MEDICAL CENTER, 355 Grand Street, Jersey City, NJ, Zip 07302–4321; tel. 201/915–2000; Michael Prilutsky, President and Chief Executive Officer

MONTEFIORE ST. LUKE'S CORNWALL, 70 Dubois Street, Newburgh, NY, Zip 12550–4851; tel. 845/561–4400; Joan Cusack–McGuirk, President and Chief Executive Officer

MORRISTOWN MEDICAL CENTER, 100 Madison Avenue, Morristown, NJ, Zip 07960–6136; tel. 973/971–5000; Trish O'Keefe, Ph.D., R.N., President

NYC HEALTH + HOSPITALS / ELMHURST, 79–01 Broadway, Elmhurst, NY, Zip 11373–1329; tel. 718/334–4000; Israel Rocha, Jr., Chief Executive Officer

NYC HEALTH + HOSPITALS / QUEENS , 82–68 164th Street, Jamaica, NY, Zip 11432–1104; tel. 718/883–3000; Israel Rocha, Jr., Chief Executive Officer

OVERLOOK MEDICAL CENTER, 99 Beauvoir Avenue, Summit, NJ, Zip 07901–3533; tel. 908/522–2000; Alan R. Lieber, President, Overlook Medical Center, Vice President, Atlantic Health System

PHELPS MEMORIAL HOSPITAL CENTER, 701 North Broadway, Sleepy Hollow, NY, Zip 10591–1020; tel. 914/366–3000; Eileen Egan, Esq., Executive Director

ST. JOHN'S RIVERSIDE HOSPITAL, 967 North Broadway, Yonkers, NY, Zip 10701–1399; tel. 914/964–4444; Ronald J. Corti, President and Chief Executive Officer

ST. JOSEPH'S UNIVERSITY MEDICAL CENTER, 703 Main Street, Paterson, NJ, Zip 07503–2691; tel. 973/754–2000; Kevin J. Slavin, FACHE, President and Chief Executive Officer

THE MOUNT SINAI HOSPITAL, One Gustave L Levy Place, Mailing Address: P.O. Box 1068, New York, NY, Zip 10029–0310; tel. 212/241–6500; David L. Reich, M.D., President and Chief Operating Officer

VASSAR BROTHERS MEDICAL CENTER, 45 Reade Place, Poughkeepsie, NY, Zip 12601–3947; tel. 845/454–8500; Peter Kelly, President

### NEW YORK PRESBYTERIAN REGIONAL HOSPITAL NETWORK
**525 East 68th Street, Box 182, New York, NY Zip 10065–4870; tel. 212/746–3745; Steven J. Corwin, M.D., President and Chief Executive Officer**

GRACIE SQUARE HOSPITAL, 420 East 76th Street, New York, NY, Zip 10021–3396; tel. 212/988–4400; David Wyman, President and Chief Executive Officer

NEW YORK COMMUNITY HOSPITAL, 2525 Kings Highway, Brooklyn, NY, Zip 11229–1705; tel. 718/692–5300; Barry Stern, President and Chief Executive Officer

NEWYORK–PRESBYTERIAN BROOKLYN METHODIST HOSPITAL, 506 Sixth Street, Brooklyn, NY, Zip 11215–3609; tel. 718/780–3000; Robert Guimento, President

### RURAL HEALTH NETWORK OF OSWEGO COUNTY
**10 George Street, Oswego, NY Zip 13126; tel. 315/592–0827; Brian Coleman, Coordinator**

OSWEGO HOSPITAL, 110 West Sixth Street, Oswego, NY, Zip 13126–2507; tel. 315/349–5511; Michael Harlovic, R.N., President and Chief Executive Officer

### STELLARIS HEALTH
**135 Bedford Rd, Armonk, NY Zip 10504–1945; tel. 914/273–5454; Sharon A. Lucian, President and Chief Executive Officer**

NORTHERN WESTCHESTER HOSPITAL, 400 East Main Street, Mount Kisco, NY, Zip 10549–3477, 400 East Main Street, G–02, 10549–3477, tel. 914/666–1200; Derek Anderson, Executive Director

PHELPS MEMORIAL HOSPITAL CENTER, 701 North Broadway, Sleepy Hollow, NY, Zip 10591–1020; tel. 914/366–3000; Eileen Egan, Esq., Executive Director

WHITE PLAINS HOSPITAL CENTER, 41 East Post Road, White Plains, NY, Zip 10601–4699; tel. 914/681–0600; Susan Fox, President and Chief Executive Officer

## NORTH CAROLINA

### COASTAL CAROLINAS HEALTH ALLIANCE
**5305–M Wrightsville Avenue, Wilmington, NC Zip 28403; tel. 910/332–8012; Yvonne Hughes, Chief Executive Officer**

CAPE FEAR VALLEY – BLADEN COUNTY HOSPITAL, 501 South Poplar Street, Elizabethtown, NC, Zip 28337–9375, Mailing Address: P.O. Box 398, 28337–0398, tel. 910/862–5100; Stephen Fife, Interim Chief Executive Officer

COLUMBUS REGIONAL HEALTHCARE SYSTEM, 500 Jefferson Street, Whiteville, NC, Zip 28472–3634; tel. 910/642–8011; John E. Young, Interim Chief Executive Officer

Section B

J. ARTHUR DOSHER MEMORIAL HOSPITAL, 924 North Howe Street, Southport, NC, Zip 28461–3099; tel. 910/457–3800; Brad L. Hilaman, M.D., JD, Chief Executive Officer

MCLEOD HEALTH LORIS, 3655 Mitchell Street, Loris, SC, Zip 29569–2827; tel. 843/716–7000; Scott Montgomery, Administrator

MCLEOD REGIONAL MEDICAL CENTER, 555 East Cheves Street, Florence, SC, Zip 29506–2617, Mailing Address: P.O. Box 100551, 29502–0551, tel. 843/777–2000; Robert L. Colones, President and Chief Executive Officer

NEW HANOVER REGIONAL MEDICAL CENTER, 2131 South 17th Street, Wilmington, NC, Zip 28401–7483, Mailing Address: P.O. Box 9000, 28402–9000, tel. 910/343–7000; Andre Boyd, Sr., Executive Vice President, Hospital Division

PENDER MEMORIAL HOSPITAL, 507 East Freemont Street, Burgaw, NC, Zip 28425–5131; tel. 910/259–5451; Ruth Glaser, President

SAMPSON REGIONAL MEDICAL CENTER, 607 Beaman Street, Clinton, NC, Zip 28328–2697, Mailing Address: P.O. Box 260, 28329–0260, tel. 910/592–8511; Shawn Howerton, M.D., Chief Executive Officer and President, Medical Staff

SCOTLAND HEALTH CARE SYSTEM, 500 Lauchwood Drive, Laurinburg, NC, Zip 28352–5599; tel. 910/291–7000; Gregory C. Wood, President and Chief Executive Officer

SOUTHEASTERN HEALTH, 300 West 27th Street, Lumberton, NC, Zip 28358–3075, Mailing Address: P.O. Box 1408, 28359–1408, tel. 910/671–5000; Joann Anderson, President and Chief Executive Officer

VIDANT DUPLIN HOSPITAL, 401 North Main Street, Kenansville, NC, Zip 28349–8801, Mailing Address: P.O. Box 278, 28349–0278, tel. 910/296–0941; Jeffery Dial, Interim President

VIDANT MEDICAL CENTER, 2100 Stantonsburg Road, Greenville, NC, Zip 27834–2818, Mailing Address: P.O. Box 6028, 27835–6028, tel. 252/847–4100; William Brian. Floyd, President

### MISSION HEALTH SYSTEM
**509 Biltmore Avenue, Asheville, NC Zip 28801–4601; tel. 828/213–1111; Greg Lowe, President, North Carolina Division**

ANGEL MEDICAL CENTER, 120 Riverview Street, Franklin, NC, Zip 28734–2612, Mailing Address: P.O. Box 1209, 28744–0569, tel. 828/524–8411; Karen S. Gorby, R.N., MSN, FACHE, Chief Executive Officer and Chief Nursing Officer

ASHEVILLE SPECIALTY HOSPITAL, 428 Biltmore Avenue, 4th Floor, Asheville, NC, Zip 28801–4502; tel. 828/213–5400; Julie A. Dikos, President and Chief Executive Officer

BLUE RIDGE REGIONAL HOSPITAL, 125 Hospital Drive, Spruce Pine, NC, Zip 28777–3035; tel. 828/765–4201; Tonia Hale, R.N., Chief Executive Officer and Chief Nursing Officer

CAREPARTNERS HEALTH SERVICES, 68 Sweeten Creek Road, Asheville, NC, Zip 28803–2318, Mailing Address: P.O. Box 15025, 28813–0025, tel. 828/277–4800; Tracy Buchanan, Chief Executive Officer and President

HIGHLANDS–CASHIERS HOSPITAL, 190 Hospital Drive, Highlands, NC, Zip 28741–7600, P O Drawer 190, 28741–0190, tel. 828/526–1200; Jacqueline Medland, MS, Ph.D., President and Chief Nursing Officer

MCDOWELL HOSPITAL, 430 Rankin Drive, Marion, NC, Zip 28752–6568, Mailing Address: P.O. Box 730, 28752–0730, tel. 828/659–5000; Carol C. Wolfenbarger, FACHE, MSN, President

MISSION HOSPITAL, 509 Biltmore Avenue, Asheville, NC, Zip 28801–4690; tel. 828/213–1111; Chad Patrick, Chief Executive Officer

TRANSYLVANIA REGIONAL HOSPITAL, 260 Hospital Drive, Brevard, NC, Zip 28712–3378; tel. 828/884–9111; Michele Pilon, President and Chief Nursing Officer

### WNC HEALTH NETWORK, INC.
**1200 Ridgefield Boulevard Suite 200, Asheville, NC Zip 28806–2280; tel. 828/667–8220; Heather Gates, Executive Director**

ADVENTHEALTH HENDERSONVILLE, 100 Hospital Drive, Hendersonville, NC, Zip 28792–5272; tel. 828/684–8501; Cory Reeves, President and Chief Executive Officer

ANGEL MEDICAL CENTER, 120 Riverview Street, Franklin, NC, Zip 28734–2612, Mailing Address: P.O. Box 1209, 28744–0569, tel. 828/524–8411; Karen S. Gorby, R.N., MSN, FACHE, Chief Executive Officer and Chief Nursing Officer

BLUE RIDGE REGIONAL HOSPITAL, 125 Hospital Drive, Spruce Pine, NC, Zip 28777–3035; tel. 828/765–4201; Tonia Hale, R.N., Chief Executive Officer and Chief Nursing Officer

CAREPARTNERS HEALTH SERVICES, 68 Sweeten Creek Road, Asheville, NC, Zip 28803–2318, Mailing Address: P.O. Box 15025, 28813–0025, tel. 828/277–4800; Tracy Buchanan, Chief Executive Officer and President

CHARLES GEORGE VETERANS AFFAIRS MEDICAL CENTER, 1100 Tunnel Road, Asheville, NC, Zip 28805–2087; tel. 828/298–7911; Cynthia Breyfogle, FACHE, Director

CHEROKEE INDIAN HOSPITAL, 1 Hospital Road, Cherokee, NC, Zip 28719; tel. 828/497–9163; Casey Cooper, Chief Executive Officer

ERLANGER WESTERN CAROLINA HOSPITAL, 3990 U S Highway 64 East Alt, Murphy, NC, Zip 28906–7917; tel. 828/837–8161; Mark E. Kimball, Chief Executive Officer

HARRIS REGIONAL HOSPITAL, 68 Hospital Road, Sylva, NC, Zip 28779–2722; tel. 828/586–7000; Steve Heatherly, Chief Executive Officer

HAYWOOD REGIONAL MEDICAL CENTER, 262 Leroy George Drive, Clyde, NC, Zip 28721–7430; tel. 828/456–7311; Chris Fensterle, Interim Chief Executive Officer

HIGHLANDS–CASHIERS HOSPITAL, 190 Hospital Drive, Highlands, NC, Zip 28741–7600, P O Drawer 190, 28741–0190, tel. 828/526–1200; Jacqueline Medland, MS, Ph.D., President and Chief Nursing Officer

MARGARET R. PARDEE MEMORIAL HOSPITAL, 800 North Justice Street, Hendersonville, NC, Zip 28791–3410; tel. 828/696–1000; James M. Kirby, II., President and Chief Executive Officer

MCDOWELL HOSPITAL, 430 Rankin Drive, Marion, NC, Zip 28752–6568, Mailing Address: P.O. Box 730, 28752–0730, tel. 828/659–5000; Carol C. Wolfenbarger, FACHE, MSN, President

MISSION HOSPITAL, 509 Biltmore Avenue, Asheville, NC, Zip 28801–4690; tel. 828/213–1111; Chad Patrick, Chief Executive Officer

RUTHERFORD REGIONAL HEALTH SYSTEM, 288 South Ridgecrest Avenue, Rutherfordton, NC, Zip 28139–2838; tel. 828/286–5000; Rebecca Segal, Chief Executive Officer

ST. LUKE'S HOSPITAL, 101 Hospital Drive, Columbus, NC, Zip 28722–6418; tel. 828/894–3311; Michelle Fortune, R.N., Chief Executive Officer

SWAIN COMMUNITY HOSPITAL, 45 Plateau Street, Bryson City, NC, Zip 28713–4200; tel. 828/488–2155; Steve Heatherly, Chief Executive Officer

TRANSYLVANIA REGIONAL HOSPITAL, 260 Hospital Drive, Brevard, NC, Zip 28712–3378; tel. 828/884–9111; Michele Pilon, President and Chief Nursing Officer

## NORTH DAKOTA

### NORTHLAND HEALTHCARE ALLIANCE
**2223 East Rosser Avenue, Bismarck, ND Zip 58501–4949; tel. 701/250–0709; Timothy Cox, President**

ASHLEY MEDICAL CENTER, 612 North Center Avenue, Ashley, ND, Zip 58413–7013, Mailing Address: P.O. Box 450, 58413–0450, tel. 701/288–3433; Eric Heupel, Interim Chief Executive Officer

CHI ST. ALEXIUS HEALTH – DICKINSON MEDICAL CENTER, 2500 Fairway Street, Dickinson, ND, Zip 58601–4399; tel. 701/456–4000; DeeAnna Opstedahl, R.N., Interim President

CHI ST. ALEXIUS HEALTH–GARRISON MEMORIAL HOSPITAL, 407 Third Avenue SE, Garrison, ND, Zip 58540–7235; tel. 701/463–2275; Tod Graeber, Administrator

CHI ST. ALEXIUS HEALTH–TURTLE LAKE HOSPITAL, 220 Fifth Avenue, Turtle Lake, ND, Zip 58575–4005, Mailing Address: P.O. Box 280, 58575–0280, tel. 701/448–2331; Tod Graeber, Administrator

CHI ST. ALEXIUS HEALTH, 900 East Broadway, Bismarck, ND, Zip 58501–4586, Mailing Address: P.O. Box 5510, 58506–5510, tel. 701/530–7000; Kurt Schley, Chief Executive Officer

LINTON HOSPITAL, 518 North Broadway, Linton, ND, Zip 58552–7308, Mailing Address: P.O. Box 850, 58552–0850, tel. 701/254–4511; Robert O. Black, Chief Executive Officer

MCKENZIE COUNTY HEALTHCARE SYSTEM, 516 North Main Street, Watford City, ND, Zip 58854–7310; tel. 701/842–3000; Daniel R. Kelly, Chief Executive Officer

MOBRIDGE REGIONAL HOSPITAL, 1401 Tenth Avenue West, Mobridge, SD, Zip 57601–1106, Mailing Address: P.O. Box 580, 57601–0580, tel. 605/845–3692; John J. Ayoub, FACHE, Chief Executive Officer

PRESENTATION MEDICAL CENTER, 213 Second Avenue NE, Rolla, ND, Zip 58367–7153, Mailing Address: P.O. Box 759, 58367–0759, tel. 701/477–3161; Chris Albertson, Chief Executive Officer and President

SAKAKAWEA MEDICAL CENTER, 510 Eighth Avenue NE, Hazen, ND, Zip 58545–4637; tel. 701/748–2225; Darrold Bertsch, Chief Executive Officer

SOUTH CENTRAL HEALTH, 1007 Fourth Avenue South, Wishek, ND, Zip 58495–7527, Mailing Address: P.O. Box 647, 58495–0647, tel. 701/452–2326; Beverly Vilhauer, Chief Executive Officer

SOUTHWEST HEALTHCARE SERVICES, 802 2nd Street Northwest, Bowman, ND, Zip 58623–4483, P O Drawer 'C', 58623, tel. 701/523–5265; Jerry Wiesner, Administrator and Chief Executive Officer

WEST RIVER REGIONAL MEDICAL CENTER, 1000 Highway 12, Hettinger, ND, Zip 58639–7530; tel. 701/567–4561; Matthew Shahan, Chief Executive Officer

### SANFORD HEALTH NETWORK – FARGO MARKET
**736 Broadway North, Route 1000, Fargo, ND Zip 58102–4421; tel. 701/234–6951; Bruce Viessman, Vice President Operations**

BOZEMAN HEALTH, 915 Highland Boulevard, Bozeman, MT, Zip 59715–6902; tel. 406/585–5000; Kathryn Bertany, M.D., President

JAMESTOWN REGIONAL MEDICAL CENTER, 2422 20th Street SW, Jamestown, ND, Zip 58401–6201; tel. 701/252–1050; Michael Delfs, President and Chief Executive Officer

KITTSON MEMORIAL HEALTHCARE CENTER, 1010 South Birch Street, Hallock, MN, Zip 56728–4215, Mailing Address: P.O. Box 700, 56728–0700, tel. 218/843–3612; Gabriel Mooney, Chief Executive Officer

LIBERTY MEDICAL CENTER, 315 West Madison Avenue, Chester, MT, Zip 59522, Mailing Address: P.O. Box 705, 59522–0705, tel. 406/759–5181; Matthew Waller, Chief Executive Officer

MAHNOMEN HEALTH CENTER, 414 West Jefferson Avenue, Mahnomen, MN, Zip 56557–4912, Mailing Address: P.O. Box 396, 56557–0396, tel. 218/935–2511; Dale K. Kruger, Chief Executive Officer

MCKENZIE COUNTY HEALTHCARE SYSTEM, 516 North Main Street, Watford City, ND, Zip 58854–7310; tel. 701/842–3000; Daniel R. Kelly, Chief Executive Officer

NORTHWOOD DEACONESS HEALTH CENTER, 4 North Park Street, Northwood, ND, Zip 58267–4102, Mailing Address: P.O. Box 190, 58267–0190, tel. 701/587–6060; Pete Antonson, Chief Executive Officer

PERHAM HEALTH, 1000 Coney Street West, Perham, MN, Zip 56573–1108; tel. 218/347–4500; Chuck Hofius, Chief Executive Officer

RIVERVIEW HEALTH, 323 South Minnesota Street, Crookston, MN, Zip 56716–1601; tel. 218/281–9200; Carrie Michalski, President and Chief Executive Officer

SANFORD BAGLEY MEDICAL CENTER, 203 Fourth Street NW, Bagley, MN, Zip 56621–8307; tel. 218/694–6501; Robert Belanger, Administrator Director

SANFORD BEMIDJI MEDICAL CENTER, 1300 Anne Street NW, Bemidji, MN, Zip 56601–5103; tel. 218/751–5430; Susan Jarvis, President

SANFORD MAYVILLE MEDICAL CENTER, 42 Sixth Avenue SE, Mayville, ND, Zip 58257–1598; tel. 701/786–3800; Jac McTaggart, Chief Executive Officer

SANFORD MEDICAL CENTER BISMARCK, 300 North Seventh Street, Bismarck, ND, Zip 58501–4439, Mailing Address: P.O. Box 5525, 58506–5525, tel. 701/323–6000; Michael LeBeau, President

SANFORD MEDICAL CENTER THIEF RIVER FALLS, 3001 Sanford Parkway, Thief River Falls, MN, Zip 56701–2700; tel. 218/681–4747; Brian J. Carlson, FACHE, Executive Director

SANFORD THIEF RIVER FALLS BEHAVIORAL HEALTH CENTER, 120 LaBree Avenue South, Thief River Falls, MN, Zip 56701–2819, 3001 Sanford Parkway, 56701–2819, tel. 218/683–4349; Brian J. Carlson, FACHE, Chief Executive Officer

SANFORD WHEATON MEDICAL CENTER, 401 12th Street North, Wheaton, MN, Zip 56296–1099; tel. 320/563–8226; Chelsie Falk, Senior Director

SIDNEY HEALTH CENTER, 216 14th Avenue SW, Sidney, MT, Zip 59270–3586; tel. 406/488–2100; Jennifer Doty, Chief Executive Officer

## OHIO

### CLEVELAND HEALTH NETWORK
**6000 West Creek Road, Suite 20, Independence, OH Zip 44131–2139; tel. 216/986–1100; Fred M. DeGrandis, President**

AKRON CHILDREN'S HOSPITAL, One Perkins Square, Akron, OH, Zip 44308–1063; tel. 330/543–1000; Grace Wakulchik, R.N., MSN, President and Chief Executive Officer

ASHTABULA COUNTY MEDICAL CENTER, 2420 Lake Avenue, Ashtabula, OH, Zip 44004–4954; tel. 440/997–2262; Michael J. Habowski, President and Chief Executive Officer

CLEVELAND CLINIC CHILDREN'S HOSPITAL FOR REHABILITATION, 2801 Martin Luther King Jr Drive, Cleveland, OH, Zip 44104–3865; tel. 216/448–6400; Michelle Marks, D.O., Medical Director

CLEVELAND CLINIC FAIRVIEW HOSPITAL, 18101 Lorain Avenue, Cleveland, OH, Zip 44111–5656; tel. 216/476–7000; Neil Smith, D.O., President

CLEVELAND CLINIC, MEDINA HOSPITAL, 1000 East Washington Street, Medina, OH, Zip 44256–2170; tel. 330/725–1000; Richard K. Shewbridge, President

CLEVELAND CLINIC, 9500 Euclid Avenue, Cleveland, OH, Zip 44195–5108; tel. 216/444–2200; Tomislav Mihaljevic, M.D., President and Chief Executive Officer

EUCLID HOSPITAL, 18901 Lake Shore Boulevard, Euclid, OH, Zip 44119–1090; tel. 216/531–9000; Teresa Dews, M.D., President

FIRELANDS REGIONAL HEALTH SYSTEM, 1111 Hayes Avenue, Sandusky, OH, Zip 44870–3323; tel. 419/557–7400; Daniel J. Moncher, Interim President and Chief Executive Officer

FISHER–TITUS MEDICAL CENTER, 272 Benedict Avenue, Norwalk, OH, Zip 44857–2374; tel. 419/668–8101; Brent Burkey, M.D., President and Chief Executive Officer

HILLCREST HOSPITAL, 6780 Mayfield Road, Cleveland, OH, Zip 44124–2203; tel. 440/312–4500; Richard Parker, M.D., President, Hillcrest Hospital

LUTHERAN HOSPITAL, 1730 West 25th Street, Cleveland, OH, Zip 44113–3170; tel. 216/696–4300; Donald A. Malone, Jr., M.D., President

MARYMOUNT HOSPITAL, 12300 McCracken Road, Garfield Heights, OH, Zip 44125–2975; tel. 216/581–0500; Daniel Napierkowski, M.D., President

METROHEALTH MEDICAL CENTER, 2500 MetroHealth Drive, Cleveland, OH, Zip 44109–1998; tel. 216/778–7800; Akram Boutros, M.D., FACHE, President and Chief Executive Officer

SOUTH POINTE HOSPITAL, 20000 Harvard Road, Warrensville Heights, OH, Zip 44122–6805; tel. 216/491–6000; Margaret McKenzie, M.D., President

SUMMA HEALTH SYSTEM, 525 East Market Street, Akron, OH, Zip 44304–1619; tel. 330/375–3000; David Custodio, M.D., President Summa Akron City and St. Thomas Campuses

UH ELYRIA MEDICAL CENTER, 630 East River Street, Elyria, OH, Zip 44035–5902; tel. 440/329–7500; Kristi M. Sink, President

UNIVERSITY HOSPITALS PARMA MEDICAL CENTER, 7007 Powers Boulevard, Parma, OH, Zip 44129–5495; tel. 440/743–3000; Brian Monter, MSN, R.N., President

WESTERN RESERVE HOSPITAL, 1900 23rd Street, Cuyahoga Falls, OH, Zip 44223–1499; tel. 330/971–7000; Robert Kent, D.O., President and Chief Executive Officer

### MERCY HEALTH – SOUTHWEST OHIO
**4600 McAuley Place, Cincinnati, OH Zip 45242; tel. 513/981–6000; John M. Starcher, President and Chief Executive Officer**

MERCY HEALTH – ANDERSON HOSPITAL, 7500 State Road, Cincinnati, OH, Zip 45255–2492; tel. 513/624–4500; Ken James, President and Chief Executive Officer of East Market

MERCY HEALTH – CLERMONT HOSPITAL, 3000 Hospital Drive, Batavia, OH, Zip 45103–1921; tel. 513/732–8200; Shane Knisley, President

MERCY HEALTH – FAIRFIELD HOSPITAL, 3000 Mack Road, Fairfield, OH, Zip 45014–5335; tel. 513/870–7000; Justin Krueger, FACHE, President

MERCY HEALTH – WEST HOSPITAL, 3300 Mercy Health Boulevard, Cincinnati, OH, Zip 45211–1103; tel. 513/215–5000; Michael Kramer, Chief Executive Officer

THE JEWISH HOSPITAL – MERCY HEALTH, 4777 East Galbraith Road, Cincinnati, OH, Zip 45236–2725; tel. 513/686–3000; Patricia Davis–Hagens, R.N., Central Market Leader and President

### PREMIER HEALTH
**110 North Main Street, Suite 390, Dayton, OH Zip 45402–3720; tel. 937/499–9401; Mary H. Boosalis, President and Chief Executive Officer**

ATRIUM MEDICAL CENTER, One Medical Center Drive, Middletown, OH, Zip 45005–1066; tel. 513/424–2111; Michael Uhl, President

MIAMI VALLEY HOSPITAL, One Wyoming Street, Dayton, OH, Zip 45409–2793; tel. 937/208–8000; Michael J. Maiberger, President

UPPER VALLEY MEDICAL CENTER, 3130 North County Road 25A, Troy, OH, Zip 45373–1309; tel. 937/440–4000; Thomas Parker, President

### THE OHIO STATE HEALTH NETWORK
**660 Ackerman Road, Suite 601F, Columbus, OH Zip 43202–4500; tel. 614/293–4425; Thomas Blincoe, Executive Director**

AVITA ONTARIO HOSPITAL, 715 Richland Mall, Ontario, OH, Zip 44906–3802; tel. 567/307–7666; Jerome Morasko, President and Chief Executive Officer

BUCYRUS HOSPITAL, 629 North Sandusky Avenue, Bucyrus, OH, Zip 44820–1821; tel. 419/562–4677; Jerome Morasko, Chief Executive Officer

FAYETTE COUNTY MEMORIAL HOSPITAL, 1430 Columbus Avenue, Washington Court House, OH, Zip 43160–1791; tel. 740/335–1210; D Michael. Diener, Chief Executive Officer

GALION HOSPITAL, 269 Portland Way South, Galion, OH, Zip 44833–2399; tel. 419/468–4841; Jerome Morasko, President and Chief Executive Officer

HIGHLAND DISTRICT HOSPITAL, 1275 North High Street, Hillsboro, OH, Zip 45133–8273; tel. 937/393–6100; Randal P. Lennartz, CPA, President and Chief Executive Officer

HOCKING VALLEY COMMUNITY HOSPITAL, 601 State Route 664 North, Logan, OH, Zip 43138–8541, Mailing Address: P.O. Box 966, 43138–0966, tel. 740/380–8000; Stacey Gabriel, R.N., President and Chief Executive Officer

MADISON HEALTH, 210 North Main Street, London, OH, Zip 43140–1115; tel. 740/845–7000; Dana E. Engle, Chief Executive Officer

MARY RUTAN HEALTH, 205 Palmer Avenue, Bellefontaine, OH, Zip 43311–2281; tel. 937/592–4015; Mandy C. Goble, President and Chief Executive Officer

MERCER HEALTH, 800 West Main Street, Coldwater, OH, Zip 45828–1698; tel. 419/678–2341; Lisa R. Klenke, R.N., Chief Executive Officer

OHIO STATE UNIVERSITY WEXNER MEDICAL CENTER, 410 West 10th Avenue, Columbus, OH, Zip 43210–1240; tel. 614/293–8000; David P. McQuaid, FACHE, Chief Operating Officer

WVU MEDICINE – BARNESVILLE HOSPITAL, 639 West Main Street, Barnesville, OH, Zip 43713–1039, Mailing Address: P.O. Box 309, 43713–0309, tel. 740/425–3941; David D. Phillips, Chief Executive Officer and Administrator

WAYNE HEALTHCARE, 835 Sweitzer Street, Greenville, OH, Zip 45331–1077; tel. 937/548–1141; Wayne G. Deschambeau, President and Chief Executive Officer

WILSON MEMORIAL HOSPITAL, 915 West Michigan Street, Sidney, OH, Zip 45365–2491; tel. 937/498–2311; Mark Klosterman, FACHE, President and Chief Executive Officer

WYANDOT MEMORIAL HOSPITAL, 885 North Sandusky Avenue, Upper Sandusky, OH, Zip 43351–1098; tel. 419/294–4991; Ty Shaull, President and Chief Executive Officer

### TRIHEALTH
**619 Oak Street, Cincinnati, OH Zip 45206; tel. 513/569–6507; Mark C. Clement, President and Chief Executive Officer**

BETHESDA NORTH HOSPITAL, 10500 Montgomery Road, Cincinnati, OH, Zip 45242–4402; tel. 513/865–1111; Mark C. Clement, President

GOOD SAMARITAN HOSPITAL, 375 Dixmyth Avenue, Cincinnati, OH, Zip 45220–2489; tel. 513/862–1400; Jamie Easterling, Executive Director, Operations

MCCULLOUGH–HYDE MEMORIAL HOSPITAL/TRIHEALTH, 110 North Poplar Street, Oxford, OH, Zip 45056–1292; tel. 513/523–2111; Brett Kirkpatrick, Executive Director

TRIHEALTH EVENDALE HOSPITAL, 3155 Glendale Milford Road, Cincinnati, OH, Zip 45241–3134; tel. 513/454–2222; Kelvin Hanger, Chief Executive Officer

## OKLAHOMA

### ALLIANCEHEALTH OKLAHOMA
**5300 North Grand Boulevard, Oklahoma City, OK Zip 73112–5647; tel. 405/815–3900; Clay Franklin, Market Chief Executive Officer**

ALLIANCEHEALTH CLINTON, 100 North 30th Street, Clinton, OK, Zip 73601–3117; tel. 580/323–2363; Landon E. Hise, Chief Executive Officer

ALLIANCEHEALTH DURANT, 1800 University Boulevard, Durant, OK, Zip 74701–3006, Mailing Address: P.O. Box 1207, 74702–1207, tel. 580/924–3080; Kevin Samrow, Chief Executive Officer

ALLIANCEHEALTH MADILL, 901 South Fifth Avenue, Madill, OK, Zip 73446–3640, Mailing Address: P.O. Box 827, 73446–0827, tel. 580/795–3384; Kevin Samrow, Chief Executive Officer

ALLIANCEHEALTH MIDWEST, 2825 Parklawn Drive, Midwest City, OK, Zip 73110–4258; tel. 405/610–4411; Clay Franklin, Chief Executive Officer

ALLIANCEHEALTH PONCA CITY, 1900 North 14th Street, Ponca City, OK, Zip 74601–2099; tel. 580/765–3321; Christopher Mendoza, Chief Executive Officer

ALLIANCEHEALTH SEMINOLE, 2401 Wrangler Boulevard, Seminole, OK, Zip 74868–1917; tel. 405/303–4000; Damon Brown, Interim Chief Executive Officer

ALLIANCEHEALTH WOODWARD, 900 17th Street, Woodward, OK, Zip 73801–2448; tel. 580/256–5511; Landon E. Hise, Interim Chief Executive Officer

INTEGRIS DEACONESS, 5501 North Portland Avenue, Oklahoma City, OK, Zip 73112–2099; tel. 405/604–6000; Rex Van Meter, President

### MERCY HEALTH SYSTEM OF OKLAHOMA
**4300 West Memorial Road, Oklahoma City, OK Zip 73120–8304; tel. 405/752–3756; Diana Smalley, President and Chief Executive Officer**

ARBUCKLE MEMORIAL HOSPITAL, 2011 West Broadway Street, Sulphur, OK, Zip 73086–4221, Mailing Address: P.O. Box 1109, 73086–8109, tel. 580/622–2161; Jeremy A. Jones, Chief Executive Officer

MERCY HEALTH LOVE COUNTY, 300 Wanda Street, Marietta, OK, Zip 73448–1200; tel. 580/276–3347; Richard Barker, Administrator and Chief Executive Officer

MERCY HOSPITAL ADA, 430 North Monte Vista, Ada, OK, Zip 74820–4610; tel. 580/332–2323; Terence Farrell, President

MERCY HOSPITAL ARDMORE, 1011 14th Avenue NW, Ardmore, OK, Zip 73401–1828; tel. 580/223–5400; Daryle Voss, FACHE, President and Chief Executive Officer

MERCY HOSPITAL HEALDTON, 3462 Hospital Road, Healdton, OK, Zip 73438–6124, Mailing Address: P.O. Box 928, 73438–0928, tel. 580/229–0701; Nichole Barrett, R.N., Interim Administrator

MERCY HOSPITAL KINGFISHER, 1000 Hospital Cirle, Kingfisher, OK, Zip 73750–5002, Mailing Address: P.O. Box 59, 73750–0059, tel. 405/375–3141; Brian Denton, Administrator

MERCY HOSPITAL LOGAN COUNTY, 200 South Academy Road, Guthrie, OK, Zip 73044–8727, Mailing Address: P.O. Box 1017, 73044–1017, tel. 405/282–6700; Bobby Stitt, R.N., Administrator

MERCY HOSPITAL OKLAHOMA CITY, 4300 West Memorial Road, Oklahoma City, OK, Zip 73120–8362; tel. 405/755–1515; Jim Gebhart, Jr., FACHE, President

MERCY HOSPITAL TISHOMINGO, 1000 South Byrd Street, Tishomingo, OK, Zip 73460–3299; tel. 580/371–2327; Lori McMillin, Administrator

MERCY HOSPITAL WATONGA, 500 North Clarence Nash Boulevard, Watonga, OK, Zip 73772–2845, Mailing Address: P.O. Box 370, 73772–0370, tel. 580/623–7211; Bobby Stitt, R.N., Administrator

MERCY REHABILITATION HOSPITAL OKLAHOMA CITY, 5401 West Memorial Rd, Oklahoma City, OK, Zip 73142–2026; tel. 405/384–5211; Thomas Elliott, President

OKLAHOMA HEART HOSPITAL SOUTH CAMPUS, 5200 East I–240 Service Road, Oklahoma City, OK, Zip 73135; tel. 405/628–6000; John Harvey, M.D., Chief Executive Officer

OKLAHOMA HEART HOSPITAL, 4050 West Memorial Road, Oklahoma City, OK, Zip 73120–8382; tel. 405/608–3200; John Harvey, M.D., Chief Executive Officer

OKLAHOMA STATE UNIVERSITY MEDICAL CENTER, 744 West Ninth Street, Tulsa, OK, Zip 74127–9020; tel. 918/599–1000; Lynn A. Sund, Interim Administrator

SEILING REGIONAL MEDICAL CENTER, Highway 60 NE, Seiling, OK, Zip 73663, Mailing Address: P.O. Box 720, 73663–0720, tel. 580/922–7361; Miranda Walz–Allen, Chief Executive Officer

## PENNSYLVANIA

### ALLEGHENY HEALTH NETWORK
**30 Isabella Street, Suite 300, Pittsburgh, PA Zip 15212–5862; tel. 412/330–2400; Cynthia Hundorfean, President and Chief Executive Officer**

ALLEGHENY GENERAL HOSPITAL, 320 East North Avenue, Pittsburgh, PA, Zip 15212–4756; tel. 412/359–3131; David S. Parda, M.D., President

ALLEGHENY VALLEY HOSPITAL , 1301 Carlisle Street, Natrona Heights, PA, Zip 15065–1152; tel. 724/224–5100; Vicenta Gaspar–Yoo, M.D., President and Chief Executive Officer

CANONSBURG HOSPITAL, 100 Medical Boulevard, Canonsburg, PA, Zip 15317–9762; tel. 724/745–6100; Chong Park, M.D., President

FORBES HOSPITAL, 2570 Haymaker Road, Monroeville, PA, Zip 15146–3513; tel. 412/858–2000; Mark Rubino, M.D., President

JEFFERSON HOSPITAL, 565 Coal Valley Road, Jefferson Hills, PA, Zip 15025–3703, Box 18119, Pittsburgh, 15236–0119, tel. 412/469–5000; Chong Park, M.D., President

SAINT VINCENT HOSPITAL, 232 West 25th Street, Erie, PA, Zip 16544–0002; tel. 814/452–5000; Christopher Clark, D.O., President and Chief Executive Officer

WEST PENN HOSPITAL, 4800 Friendship Avenue, Pittsburgh, PA, Zip 15224–1722; tel. 412/578–5000; Ronald J. Andro, R.N., MS, President and Chief Executive Officer

WESTFIELD MEMORIAL HOSPITAL, 189 East Main Street, Westfield, NY, Zip 14787–1195; tel. 716/326–4921; Karen Surkala, President

### BRIDGES HEALTH PARTNERS
**500 Commonwealth Drive, Warrendale, PA Zip 15086–7516; tel. 724/300–8105; Tom Boggs, President**

BUTLER HEALTH SYSTEM, 1 Hospital Way, Butler, PA, Zip 16001–4697; tel. 724/283–6666; Ken DeFurio, President and Chief Executive Officer

EXCELA FRICK HOSPITAL, 508 South Church Street, Mount Pleasant, PA, Zip 15666–1790; tel. 724/547–1500; John Sphon, Chief Executive Officer

EXCELA HEALTH WESTMORELAND HOSPITAL, 532 West Pittsburgh Street, Greensburg, PA, Zip 15601–2282; tel. 724/832–4000; John Sphon, Chief Executive Officer

EXCELA LATROBE AREA HOSPITAL, One Mellon Way, Latrobe, PA, Zip 15650–1096; tel. 724/537–1000; John Sphon, Chief Executive Officer

ST. CLAIR HOSPITAL, 1000 Bower Hill Road, Pittsburgh, PA, Zip 15243–1873; tel. 412/942–4000; James M. Collins, President and Chief Executive Officer

WASHINGTON HEALTH SYSTEM GREENE, 350 Bonar Avenue, Waynesburg, PA, Zip 15370–1608; tel. 724/627–3101; Terry Wiltrout, President

WASHINGTON HOSPITAL, 155 Wilson Avenue, Washington, PA, Zip 15301–3398; tel. 724/225–7000; Brook Ward, President and Chief Executive Officer

### COMMONWEALTH HEALTH
**575 North River Street, Wilkes Barre, PA Zip 18764–0999; tel. 570/829–8111; Cornelio R. Catena, Market President and Chief Executive Officer, Wilkes–Barre General Hospital**

BERWICK HOSPITAL CENTER, 701 East 16th Street, Berwick, PA, Zip 18603–2397; tel. 570/759–5000; Thomas Neal, Chief Executive Officer

FIRST HOSPITAL WYOMING VALLEY, 562 Wyoming Avenue, Kingston, PA, Zip 18704–3721; tel. 570/552–3900; Christine Mathews, Interim President and Chief Executive Officer, Chief Nursing Officer

MOSES TAYLOR HOSPITAL, 700 Quincy Avenue, Scranton, PA, Zip 18510–1724; tel. 570/770–5000; Michael L. Brown, President and Chief Executive Officer

REGIONAL HOSPITAL OF SCRANTON, 746 Jefferson Avenue, Scranton, PA, Zip 18510–1624; tel. 570/348–7100; Michael L. Brown, Chief Executive Officer

TYLER MEMORIAL HOSPITAL, 5950 State Route 6, Tunkhannock, PA, Zip 18657–7905; tel. 570/836–2161; Ann Marie. Stevens, R.N., Chief Executive Officer

WILKES–BARRE GENERAL HOSPITAL, 575 North River Street, Wilkes–Barre, PA, Zip 18764–0001; tel. 570/829–8111; Cornelio R. Catena, President and Chief Executive Officer

### PENN HIGHLANDS HEALTHCARE
**204 Hospital Avenue, DuBois, PA Zip 15801–0447; tel. 814/375–6430; Steven M. Fontaine, System Chief Executive Officer**

PENN HIGHLANDS BROOKVILLE , 100 Hospital Road, Brookville, PA, Zip 15825–1367; tel. 814/849–2312; Julianne Peer, President

PENN HIGHLANDS CLEARFIELD, 809 Turnpike Avenue, Clearfield, PA, Zip 16830–1232, Mailing Address: P.O. Box 992, 16830–0992, tel. 814/765–5341; Rhonda Halstead, President

PENN HIGHLANDS DUBOIS, 100 Hospital Avenue, DuBois, PA, Zip 15801–1440, Mailing Address: P.O. Box 447, 15801–0447, tel. 814/371–2200; John Sutika, President

PENN HIGHLANDS ELK, 763 Johnsonburg Road, Saint Marys, PA, Zip 15857–3498; tel. 814/788–8000; Bradley Chapman, President

### VANTAGE HEALTHCARE NETWORK, INC.
**18282 Technology Drive, Suite 202, Meadville, PA Zip 16335–8378; tel. 814/337–0000; David Petrarca, Director Retail Operations**

CLARION HOSPITAL, One Hospital Drive, Clarion, PA, Zip 16214–8501; tel. 814/226–9500; Steven T. Davis, Chief Executive Officer

MEADVILLE MEDICAL CENTER, 751 Liberty Street, Meadville, PA, Zip 16335–2559; tel. 814/333–5000; Philip E. Pandolph, FACHE, Chief Executive Officer

PENN HIGHLANDS BROOKVILLE , 100 Hospital Road, Brookville, PA, Zip 15825–1367; tel. 814/849–2312; Julianne Peer, President

PENN HIGHLANDS ELK, 763 Johnsonburg Road, Saint Marys, PA, Zip 15857–3498; tel. 814/788–8000; Bradley Chapman, President

PUNXSUTAWNEY AREA HOSPITAL, 81 Hillcrest Drive, Punxsutawney, PA, Zip 15767–2616; tel. 814/938–1800; Daniel D. Blough, Jr., Chief Executive Officer

TITUSVILLE AREA HOSPITAL, 406 West Oak Street, Titusville, PA, Zip 16354–1404; tel. 814/827–1851; Lee M. Clinton, FACHE, President and Chief Executive Officer

UPMC BEDFORD, 10455 Lincoln Highway, Everett, PA, Zip 15537–7046; tel. 814/623–6161; Jan E. Fisher, President

UPMC HAMOT, 201 State Street, Erie, PA, Zip 16550–0002; tel. 814/877–6000; David Gibbons, President

UPMC JAMESON , 1211 Wilmington Avenue, New Castle, PA, Zip 16105–2516; tel. 724/658–9001; Robert Charles. Jackson, Jr., President

UPMC KANE, 4372 Route 6, Kane, PA, Zip 16735–3060; tel. 814/837–8585; Mark Papalia, President

UPMC MCKEESPORT, 1500 Fifth Avenue, McKeesport, PA, Zip 15132–2422; tel. 412/664–2000; Mark O'Hern, President

UPMC NORTHWEST, 100 Fairfield Drive, Seneca, PA, Zip 16346–2130; tel. 814/676–7600; Brian Durniok, President

UPMC PASSAVANT, 9100 Babcock Boulevard, Pittsburgh, PA, Zip 15237–5815; tel. 412/748–6700; Susan E. Hoolahan, R.N., MSN, President

UPMC ST. MARGARET, 815 Freeport Road, Pittsburgh, PA, Zip 15215–3301; tel. 412/784–4000; David J. Patton, President

WARREN GENERAL HOSPITAL, Two Crescent Park West, Warren, PA, Zip 16365–0068, Mailing Address: P.O. Box 68, 16365–0068, tel. 814/723–4973; Richard Allen, Chief Executive Officer

## SOUTH DAKOTA

**REGIONAL HEALTH**
**353 Fairmont Boulevard, Rapid City, SD Zip 57701–7375; tel. 605/719–1000; Brent R. Phillips, President and Chief Executive Officer**

MONUMENT HEALTH CUSTER HOSPITAL, 1039 Montgomery Street, Custer, SD, Zip 57730–1397; tel. 605/673–2229; Mark C. Schmidt, President

MONUMENT HEALTH LEAD–DEADWOOD HOSPITAL, 61 Charles Street, Deadwood, SD, Zip 57732–1303; tel. 605/717–6000; Mark C. Schmidt, President

MONUMENT HEALTH RAPID CITY HOSPITAL, 353 Fairmont Boulevard, Rapid City, SD, Zip 57701–7393, Mailing Address: P.O. Box 6000, 57709–6000, tel. 605/755–1000; John Pierce, Acting President

MONUMENT HEALTH SPEARFISH HOSPITAL, 1440 North Main Street, Spearfish, SD, Zip 57783–1504; tel. 605/644–4000; Thomas Worsley, Chief Executive Officer

MONUMENT HEALTH STURGIS HOSPITAL, 2140 Junction Avenue, Sturgis, SD, Zip 57785–2452; tel. 605/720–2400; Mark Schulte, FACHE, President

PHILIP HEALTH SERVICES, 503 West Pine Street, Philip, SD, Zip 57567–3300, Mailing Address: P.O. Box 790, 57567–0790, tel. 605/859–2511; Jeremy Schultes, Administrator and Chief Executive Officer

WESTON COUNTY HEALTH SERVICES, 1124 Washington Boulevard, Newcastle, WY, Zip 82701–2972; tel. 307/746–4491; Maureen K. Cadwell, Chief Executive Officer

**SANFORD HEALTH NETWORK – SIOUX FALLS MARKET**
**1305 West 18th Street, Route 6145, Sioux Falls, SD Zip 57105–0401; tel. 605/328–5513; Eric C. Hilmoe, Vice President Operations**

COMMUNITY MEMORIAL HOSPITAL, 809 Jackson Street, Burke, SD, Zip 57523–2065, Mailing Address: P.O. Box 319, 57523–0319, tel. 605/775–2621; Mistie Sachtjen, Chief Executive Officer

DOUGLAS COUNTY MEMORIAL HOSPITAL, 708 Eighth Street, Armour, SD, Zip 57313–2102; tel. 605/724–2159; Heath Brouwer, Administrator

MURRAY COUNTY MEDICAL CENTER, 2042 Juniper Avenue, Slayton, MN, Zip 56172–1017; tel. 507/836–6111; Michael Ladevich, FACHE, Interim Chief Executive Officer

ORANGE CITY AREA HEALTH SYSTEM, 1000 Lincoln Circle SE, Orange City, IA, Zip 51041–1862; tel. 712/737–4984; Martin W. Guthmiller, Chief Executive Officer

ORTONVILLE AREA HEALTH SERVICES, 450 Eastvold Avenue, Ortonville, MN, Zip 56278–1133; tel. 320/839–2502; David Rogers, Chief Executive Officer

PIONEER MEMORIAL HOSPITAL AND HEALTH SERVICES, 315 North Washington Street, Viborg, SD, Zip 57070–2002, Mailing Address: P.O. Box 368, 57070–0368, tel. 605/326–5161; Thomas V. Richter, Chief Executive Officer

SANFORD ABERDEEN MEDICAL CENTER, 2905 3rd Avenue SE, Aberdeen, SD, Zip 57401–5420; tel. 605/626–4200; Ashley M. Erickson, Chief Executive Officer

SANFORD CANBY MEDICAL CENTER, 112 St Olaf Avenue South, Canby, MN, Zip 56220–1433; tel. 507/223–7277; Lori Sisk, R.N., Chief Executive Officer

SANFORD CANTON–INWOOD MEDICAL CENTER, 440 North Hiawatha Drive, Canton, SD, Zip 57013–5800; tel. 605/764–1400; Scott C. Larson, Chief Executive Officer

SANFORD CHAMBERLAIN MEDICAL CENTER, 300 South Byron Boulevard, Chamberlain, SD, Zip 57325–9741; tel. 605/234–5511; Erica Peterson, Chief Executive Officer

SANFORD CLEAR LAKE MEDICAL CENTER, 701 Third Avenue South, Clear Lake, SD, Zip 57226–2016; tel. 605/874–2141; Lori Sisk, R.N., Chief Executive Officer

SANFORD HILLSBORO MEDICAL CENTER, 12 Third Street SE, Hillsboro, ND, Zip 58045–4840, Mailing Address: P.O. Box 609, 58045–0609, tel. 701/636–3200; Jac McTaggart, Chief Executive Officer

SANFORD JACKSON MEDICAL CENTER, 1430 North Highway, Jackson, MN, Zip 56143–1093; tel. 507/847–2420; Dawn Schnell, Chief Nursing Officer and Interim Senior Director

SANFORD LUVERNE MEDICAL CENTER, 1600 North Kniss Avenue, Luverne, MN, Zip 56156–1067; tel. 507/283–2321; Tammy Loosbrock, Senior Director

SANFORD SHELDON MEDICAL CENTER, 118 North Seventh Avenue, Sheldon, IA, Zip 51201–1235, Mailing Address: P.O. Box 250, 51201–0250, tel. 712/324–5041; Richard E. Nordahl, Senior Director

SANFORD TRACY MEDICAL CENTER, 251 Fifth Street East, Tracy, MN, Zip 56175–1536; tel. 507/629–8400; Stacy Barstad, Chief Executive Officer

SANFORD USD MEDICAL CENTER, 1305 West 18th Street, Sioux Falls, SD, Zip 57105–0496, Mailing Address: P.O. Box 5039, 57117–5039, tel. 605/333–1000; Paul A. Hanson, FACHE, President

SANFORD VERMILLION MEDICAL CENTER, 20 South Plum Street, Vermillion, SD, Zip 57069–3346; tel. 605/677–3500; Timothy J. Tracy, Senior Director

SANFORD WESTBROOK MEDICAL CENTER, 920 Bell Avenue, Westbrook, MN, Zip 56183–9669, Mailing Address: P.O. Box 188, 56183–0188, tel. 507/274–6121; Stacy Barstad, Chief Executive Officer

SANFORD WORTHINGTON MEDICAL CENTER, 1018 Sixth Avenue, Worthington, MN, Zip 56187–2202, Mailing Address: P.O. Box 997, 56187–0997, tel. 507/372–2941; Jennifer . Weg, MS, R.N., Executive Director

WEST HOLT MEDICAL SERVICES, 406 West Neely Street, Atkinson, NE, Zip 68713–4801; tel. 402/925–2811; Ashley Rivera, Chief Executive Officer

WINDOM AREA HEALTH, 2150 Hospital Drive, Windom, MN, Zip 56101–0339, Mailing Address: P.O. Box 339, 56101–0339, tel. 507/831–2400; Shelby Medina, Chief Executive Officer

WINNER REGIONAL HEALTHCARE CENTER, 745 East Eighth Street, Winner, SD, Zip 57580–2631; tel. 605/842–7100; Kevin Coffey, Chief Executive Officer

## TENNESSEE

**TRISTAR HEALTH**
**110 Winners Circle, First Floor, Brentwood, TN Zip 37027–5070; tel. 615/886–4900; Stephen Corbeil, President**

CARTERSVILLE MEDICAL CENTER, 960 Joe Frank Harris Parkway, Cartersville, GA, Zip 30120–2129; tel. 770/382–1530; J. Christopher. Mosley, Chief Executive Officer

EASTSIDE MEDICAL CENTER, 1700 Medical Way, Snellville, GA, Zip 30078–2195; tel. 770/979–0200; Trent Lind, Chief Executive Officer

PARKRIDGE MEDICAL CENTER, 2333 McCallie Avenue, Chattanooga, TN, Zip 37404–3258; tel. 423/698–6061; Thomas H. Ozburn, Chief Executive Officer

REDMOND REGIONAL MEDICAL CENTER, 501 Redmond Road, Rome, GA, Zip 30165–1415, Mailing Address: P.O. Box 107001, 30164–7001, tel. 706/291–0291; John Quinlivan, Chief Executive Officer

TRISTAR ASHLAND CITY MEDICAL CENTER, 313 North Main Street, Ashland City, TN, Zip 37015–1347; tel. 615/792–3030; Darrell White, R.N., Administrator and Chief Nursing Officer

TRISTAR CENTENNIAL MEDICAL CENTER, 2300 Patterson Street, Nashville, TN, Zip 37203–1528; tel. 615/342–1000; Scott A. Cihak, President and Chief Executive Officer

TRISTAR GREENVIEW REGIONAL HOSPITAL, 1801 Ashley Circle, Bowling Green, KY, Zip 42104–3362; tel. 270/793–1000; Michael Sherrod, Chief Executive Officer

TRISTAR HENDERSONVILLE MEDICAL CENTER, 355 New Shackle Island Road, Hendersonville, TN, Zip 37075–2479; tel. 615/338–1000; Regina Bartlett, Chief Executive Officer

TRISTAR HORIZON MEDICAL CENTER, 111 Highway 70 East, Dickson, TN, Zip 37055–2080; tel. 615/446–0446; Jason E. Boyd, Chief Executive Officer

TRISTAR SKYLINE MEDICAL CENTER, 3441 Dickerson Pike, Nashville, TN, Zip 37207–2539; tel. 615/769–2000; Dustin Greene, Chief Executive Officer

TRISTAR SOUTHERN HILLS MEDICAL CENTER, 391 Wallace Road, Nashville, TN, Zip 37211–4859, 3441 Dickerson Pike, 37207, tel. 615/781–4000; Joanna J. Conley, FACHE, Chief Executive Officer

TRISTAR STONECREST MEDICAL CENTER, 200 StoneCrest Boulevard, Smyrna, TN, Zip 37167–6810; tel. 615/768–2000; Louis Caputo, Chief Executive Officer

TRISTAR SUMMIT MEDICAL CENTER, 5655 Frist Boulevard, Hermitage, TN, Zip 37076–2053; tel. 615/316–3000; Brian Marger, Chief Executive Officer

## TEXAS

**LITTLE RIVER HEALTHCARE**
**1700 Brazos Avenue, Rockdale, TX Zip 76567–2517; tel. 512/446–4500; Jeffrey Madison, FACHE, Chief Executive Officer**

**Section B**

CAMERON HOSPITAL, 806 North Crockett Avenue, Cameron, TX, Zip 76520–2553; tel. 254/605–1300; Troy Zinn, Chief Executive Officer

**METHODIST HEALTHCARE SYSTEM**
**8109 Fredericksburg Road, San Antonio, TX Zip 78229–3311; tel. 210/575–0355; Allen Harrison, Chief Executive Officer**

METHODIST AMBULATORY SURGERY HOSPITAL – NORTHWEST, 9150 Huebner Road, Suite 100, San Antonio, TX, Zip 78240–1545; tel. 210/575–5000; Scott Rausch, Chief Executive Officer

METHODIST HOSPITAL, 7700 Floyd Curl Drive, San Antonio, TX, Zip 78229–3993; tel. 210/575–4000; Daniel Miller, FACHE, Chief Executive Officer

METHODIST STONE OAK HOSPITAL, 1139 E Sonterra Boulevard, San Antonio, TX, Zip 78258–4347, 1139 East Sonterra Boulevard, 78258–4347, tel. 210/638–2100; Marc Strode, Chief Executive Officer

**REGIONAL HEALTHCARE ALLIANCE**
**530 South Beckham Avenue, Tyler, TX Zip 75702–8310; tel. 903/531–4449; John Webb, President**

BAYLOR UNIVERSITY MEDICAL CENTER, 3500 Gaston Avenue, Dallas, TX, Zip 75246–2088; tel. 214/820–0111; Steven R. Newton, FACHE, President

CHRISTUS MOTHER FRANCES HOSPITAL – JACKSONVILLE, 2026 South Jackson, Jacksonville, TX, Zip 75766–5822; tel. 903/541–4500; Barry D. Lofquist, Chief Executive Officer

CHRISTUS MOTHER FRANCES HOSPITAL – SULPHUR SPRINGS, 115 Airport Road, Sulphur Springs, TX, Zip 75482–2105; tel. 903/885–7671; Paul Harvey, President and Chief Executive Officer

CHRISTUS MOTHER FRANCES HOSPITAL – TYLER, 800 East Dawson Street, Tyler, TX, Zip 75701–2036; tel. 903/593–8441; Jason J. Proctor, Chief Executive Officer

CHRISTUS TRINITY MOTHER FRANCES REHABILITATION HOSPITAL, A PARTNER OF ENCOMPASS HEALTH, 3131 Troup Highway, Tyler, TX, Zip 75701–8352; tel. 903/510–7000; Sharla Anderson, Chief Executive Officer

CHILDREN'S MEDICAL CENTER DALLAS, 1935 Medical District Drive, Pavilion, 3rd Floor, Dallas, TX, Zip 75235–7701; tel. 214/456–7000; David T. Berry, President

NACOGDOCHES MEDICAL CENTER, 4920 NE Stallings Drive, Nacogdoches, TX, Zip 75965–1200; tel. 936/569–9481; Jeff Patterson, Chief Executive Officer

PALESTINE REGIONAL MEDICAL CENTER–EAST, 2900 South Loop 256, Palestine, TX, Zip 75801–6958; tel. 903/731–1000; Roy Finch, Chief Executive Officer

PARIS REGIONAL MEDICAL CENTER, 865 Deshong Drive, Paris, TX, Zip 75460–9313, Mailing Address: P.O. Box 9070, 75461–9070, tel. 903/785–4521; Steve Hyde, Chief Executive Officer

TITUS REGIONAL MEDICAL CENTER, 2001 North Jefferson Avenue, Mount Pleasant, TX, Zip 75455–2398; tel. 903/577–6000; Terry Scoggin, Chief Executive Officer

TYLER CONTINUECARE HOSPITAL, 800 East Dawson, 4th Floor, Tyler, TX, Zip 75701–2036; tel. 903/531–4080; Stephanie Hyde, R.N., MSN, Chief Executive Officer

UT HEALTH HENDERSON, 300 Wilson Street, Henderson, TX, Zip 75652–5956; tel. 903/657–7541; Mark Leitner, FACHE, Administrator

UT HEALTH NORTH CAMPUS TYLER, 11937 Highway 271, Tyler, TX, Zip 75708–3154; tel. 903/877–7777; Cody Boyd, Chief Executive Officer

**ST. DAVID'S HEALTH NETWORK**
**98 San Jacinto Boulevard, Austin, TX Zip 78701–4082; tel. 512/708–9700; David Huffstutler, President and Chief Executive Officer**

ST. DAVID'S MEDICAL CENTER, 919 East 32nd Street, Austin, TX, Zip 78705–2709, Mailing Address: P.O. Box 4039, 78765–4039, tel. 512/476–7111; Todd E. Steward, FACHE, Chief Executive Officer

ST. DAVID'S NORTH AUSTIN MEDICAL CENTER, 12221 North MoPac Expressway, Austin, TX, Zip 78758–2496; tel. 512/901–1000; Thomas W. Jackson, Chief Executive Officer

ST. DAVID'S ROUND ROCK MEDICAL CENTER, 2400 Round Rock Avenue, Round Rock, TX, Zip 78681–4097; tel. 512/341–1000; Jeremy Barclay, Chief Executive Officer

ST. DAVID'S SOUTH AUSTIN MEDICAL CENTER, 901 West Ben White Boulevard, Austin, TX, Zip 78704–6903; tel. 512/447–2211; Todd E. Steward, FACHE, Chief Executive Officer

**THE HOSPITALS OF PROVIDENCE**
**2001 North Oregon Street, El Paso, TX Zip 79902–3320; tel. 915/577–6625; Nicholas R. Tejeda, FACHE, Market Chief Executive Officer**

THE HOSPITALS OF PROVIDENCE EAST CAMPUS, 3280 Joe Battle Boulevard, El Paso, TX, Zip 79938–2622; tel. 915/832–2000; Monica Vargas–Mahar, FACHE, Chief Executive Officer

THE HOSPITALS OF PROVIDENCE MEMORIAL CAMPUS, 2001 North Oregon Street, El Paso, TX, Zip 79902–3368; tel. 915/577–6625; Nicholas R. Tejeda, FACHE, Market Chief Executive Officer

THE HOSPITALS OF PROVIDENCE SIERRA CAMPUS, 1625 Medical Center Drive, El Paso, TX, Zip 79902–5005; tel. 915/747–4000; Rob J. Anderson, Chief Executive Officer

THE HOSPITALS OF PROVIDENCE TRANSMOUNTAIN CAMPUS, 2000 Transmountain Road, El Paso, TX, Zip 79911; tel. 915/877–8300; Tasha Hopper, Chief Executive Officer

## VERMONT

**THE UNIVERSITY OF VERMONT HEALTH NETWORK**
**111 Colchester Avenue, Burlington, VT Zip 05401–1473; tel. 802/847–3983; John R. Brumsted, M.D., President and Chief Executive Officer**

THE UNIVERSITY OF VERMONT HEALTH NETWORK CENTRAL VERMONT MEDICAL CENTER, 130 Fisher Road, Berlin, VT, Zip 05602–9516, Mailing Address: P.O. Box 547, Barre, 05641–0547, tel. 802/371–4100; Anna T. Noonan, President and Chief Operating Officer

THE UNIVERSITY OF VERMONT HEALTH NETWORK ELIZABETHTOWN COMMUNITY HOSPITAL, 75 Park Street, Elizabethtown, NY, Zip 12932, Mailing Address: P.O. Box 277, 12932–0277, tel. 518/873–6377; John R. Remillard, President

THE UNIVERSITY OF VERMONT HEALTH NETWORK–CHAMPLAIN VALLEY PHYSICIANS HOSPITAL, 75 Beekman Street, Plattsburgh, NY, Zip 12901–1438; tel. 518/561–2000; Michelle LeBeau, President and Chief Operating Officer

UNIVERSITY OF VERMONT MEDICAL CENTER, 111 Colchester Avenue, Burlington, VT, Zip 05401–1473; tel. 802/847–0000; Stephen Leffler, M.D., President and Chief Operating Officer

## VIRGINIA

**VIRGINIA HEALTH NETWORK**
**7400 Beaufont Springs Drive, Suite 505, Richmond, VA Zip 23225–5521; tel. 804/320–3837; James Brittain, President**

AUGUSTA HEALTH, 78 Medical Center Drive, Fishersville, VA, Zip 22939–2332, Mailing Address: P.O. Box 1000, 22939–1000, tel. 540/932–4000; Mary N. Mannix, FACHE, President and Chief Executive Officer

BATH COMMUNITY HOSPITAL, 106 Park Drive, Hot Springs, VA, Zip 24445–2921, Mailing Address: P.O. Box Z, 24445–0750, tel. 540/839–7000; Kathy Landreth, Chief Executive Officer

BON SECOURS MARY IMMACULATE HOSPITAL, 2 Bernardine Drive, Newport News, VA, Zip 23602–4499; tel. 757/886–6000; Darlene Stephenson, Chief Executive Officer

BON SECOURS MARYVIEW MEDICAL CENTER, 3636 High Street, Portsmouth, VA, Zip 23707–3270; tel. 757/398–2200; Paul Gaden, Chief Executive Officer

BON SECOURS MEMORIAL REGIONAL MEDICAL CENTER, 8260 Atlee Road, Mechanicsville, VA, Zip 23116–1844; tel. 804/764–6000; Leigh Sewell, Chief Executive Officer

BON SECOURS ST. FRANCIS MEDICAL CENTER, 13710 St Francis Boulevard, Midlothian, VA, Zip 23114–3267; tel. 804/594–7300; Chris Accashian, Chief Executive Officer

BON SECOURS ST. MARY'S HOSPITAL, 5801 Bremo Road, Richmond, VA, Zip 23226–1907; tel. 804/285–2011; Francine Barr, R.N., MS, Chief Executive Officer

BON SECOURS–DEPAUL MEDICAL CENTER, 150 Kingsley Lane, Norfolk, VA, Zip 23505–4650; tel. 757/889–5000; Paul Gaden, Chief Executive Officer

BON SECOURS–RICHMOND COMMUNITY HOSPITAL, 1500 North 28th Street, Richmond, VA, Zip 23223–5396, Mailing Address: P.O. Box 27184, 23261–7184, tel. 804/225–1700; Leigh Sewell, Chief Executive Officer

BUCHANAN GENERAL HOSPITAL, 1535 Slate Creek Road, Grundy, VA, Zip 24614–6974; tel. 276/935–1000; Robert D. Ruchti, Chief Executive Officer

CARILION FRANKLIN MEMORIAL HOSPITAL, 180 Floyd Avenue, Rocky Mount, VA, Zip 24151–1389; tel. 540/483–5277; Carl T. Cline, Vice President, Carilion Clinic and Hospital Administrator

CARILION GILES COMMUNITY HOSPITAL, 159 Hartley Way, Pearisburg, VA, Zip 24134–2471; tel. 540/921–6000; William Flattery, Vice President and Administrator Western Division

CARILION NEW RIVER VALLEY MEDICAL CENTER, 2900 Lamb Circle, Christiansburg, VA, Zip 24073–6344, Mailing Address: P.O. Box 5, Radford, 24143–0005, tel. 540/731–2000; William Flattery, Vice President and Administrator Western Division

CARILION ROANOKE MEMORIAL HOSPITAL, 1906 Belleview Avenue Southeast, Roanoke, VA, Zip 24014–1838, Mailing Address: P.O. Box 13367, 24033–3367, tel. 540/981–7000; Steven C. Arner, President

CARILION STONEWALL JACKSON HOSPITAL, 1 Health Circle, Lexington, VA, Zip 24450–2492; tel. 540/458–3300; Greg T. Madsen, Chief Executive Officer

CARILION TAZEWELL COMMUNITY HOSPITAL, 388 Ben Bolt Avenue, Tazewell, VA, Zip 24651–9700; tel. 276/988–8700; Alicia Bales, Senior Director, Chief Executive Officer and Chief Nursing Officer

CENTRA BEDFORD MEMORIAL HOSPITAL, 1613 Oakwood Street, Bedford, VA, Zip 24523–1213; tel. 540/586–2441; Patti Jurkus, Vice President and Chief Executive Officer

CENTRA SOUTHSIDE COMMUNITY HOSPITAL, 800 Oak Street, Farmville, VA, Zip 23901–1199; tel. 434/392–8811; Thomas Angelo, Chief Executive Officer

CHESAPEAKE REGIONAL MEDICAL CENTER, 736 Battlefield Boulevard North, Chesapeake, VA, Zip 23320–4941, Mailing Address: P.O. Box 2028, 23327–2028, tel. 757/312–8121; Reese Jackson, President and Chief Executive Officer

CHILDREN'S HOSPITAL OF RICHMOND AT VCU–BROOK ROAD CAMPUS, 2924 Brook Road, Richmond, VA, Zip 23220–1298; tel. 804/321–7474; Elias Neujahr, Chief Executive Officer

CHILDREN'S HOSPITAL OF THE KING'S DAUGHTERS, 601 Children's Lane, Norfolk, VA, Zip 23507–1910; tel. 757/668–7000; James D. Dahling, President and Chief Executive Officer

CHIPPENHAM HOSPITAL, 7101 Jahnke Road, Richmond, VA, Zip 23225–4044; tel. 804/483–0000; William Lunn, M.D., Chief Executive Officer

CLINCH VALLEY MEDICAL CENTER, 6801 Governor G C Peery Highway, Richlands, VA, Zip 24641–2194; tel. 276/596–6000; Peter Mulkey, Chief Executive Officer

COASTAL VIRGINIA REHABILITATION, 245 Chesapeake Avenue, Newport News, VA, Zip 23607–6038; tel. 757/928–8000; Daniel Ballin, Administrator

DOMINION HOSPITAL, 2960 Sleepy Hollow Road, Falls Church, VA, Zip 22044–2030; tel. 703/536–2000; Lee Higginbotham, Chief Executive Officer

ENCOMPASS HEALTH REHABILITATION HOSPITAL OF RICHMOND, 5700 Fitzhugh Avenue, Richmond, VA, Zip 23226–1800; tel. 804/288–5700; Vivian White, Chief Executive Officer

FAUQUIER HOSPITAL, 500 Hospital Drive, Warrenton, VA, Zip 20186–3099; tel. 540/316–5000; Chad Melton, Chief Executive Officer

HENRICO DOCTORS' HOSPITAL, 1602 Skipwith Road, Richmond, VA, Zip 23229–5205; tel. 804/289–4500; Ryan Jensen, Chief Executive Officer

INOVA ALEXANDRIA HOSPITAL, 4320 Seminary Road, Alexandria, VA, Zip 22304–1535; tel. 703/504–3167; Rina Bansal, M.D., President

INOVA FAIR OAKS HOSPITAL, 3600 Joseph Siewick Drive, Fairfax, VA, Zip 22033–1798; tel. 703/391–3600; Donald Brideau, M.D., Chief Executive Officer

INOVA FAIRFAX HOSPITAL, 3300 Gallows Road, Falls Church, VA, Zip 22042–3300; tel. 703/776–4001; Susan T. Carroll, FACHE, Acting President

INOVA LOUDOUN HOSPITAL, 44045 Riverside Parkway, Leesburg, VA, Zip 20176–5101, Mailing Address: P.O. Box 6000, 20177–0600, tel. 703/858–6000; Deborah Addo, Chief Executive Officer

INOVA MOUNT VERNON HOSPITAL, 2501 Parker's Lane, Alexandria, VA, Zip 22306–3209; tel. 703/664–7000; Joseph Pina, M.D., Chief Executive Officer

JOHN RANDOLPH MEDICAL CENTER, 411 West Randolph Road, Hopewell, VA, Zip 23860–2938; tel. 804/541–1600; Joseph Mazzo, Chief Executive Officer

JOHNSTON MEMORIAL HOSPITAL, 16000 Johnston Memorial Drive, Abingdon, VA, Zip 24211–7659; tel. 276/258–1000; John Jeter, Chief Executive Officer

LEWISGALE HOSPITAL ALLEGHANY, One ARH Lane, Low Moor, VA, Zip 24457, Mailing Address: P.O. Box 7, 24457–0007, tel. 540/862–6011; William Windham, Chief Executive Officer

LEWISGALE HOSPITAL PULASKI, 2400 Lee Highway, Pulaski, VA, Zip 24301–2326, Mailing Address: P.O. Box 759, 24301–0759, tel. 540/994–8100; Sean Pressman, Chief Executive Officer

MARY WASHINGTON HOSPITAL, 1001 Sam Perry Boulevard, Fredericksburg, VA, Zip 22401–3354; tel. 540/741–1100; Michael P. McDermott, M.D., President and Chief Executive Officer

MOUNTAIN VIEW REGIONAL MEDICAL CENTER, 310 Third Street NE, Norton, VA, Zip 24273–1137; tel. 276/679–9100; Mark T. Leonard, Interim Chief Executive Officer

NORTHERN REGIONAL HOSPITAL, 830 Rockford Street, Mount Airy, NC, Zip 27030–5365, Mailing Address: P.O. Box 1101, 27030–1101, tel. 336/719–7000; Chris A. Lumsden, President and Chief Executive Officer

NOVANT HEALTH UVA HEALTH SYSTEM CULPEPER MEDICAL CENTER, 501 Sunset Lane, Culpeper, VA, Zip 22701–3917, Mailing Address: P.O. Box 592, 22701–0500, tel. 540/829–4100; Jeff Hetmanski, President and Chief Operating Officer

NOVANT HEALTH UVA HEALTH SYSTEM PRINCE WILLIAM MEDICAL CENTER, 8700 Sudley Road, Manassas, VA, Zip 20110–4418, Mailing Address: P.O. Box 2610, 20108–0867, tel. 703/369–8000; Stephen Smith, President and Chief Operating Officer

RAPPAHANNOCK GENERAL HOSPITAL, 101 Harris Drive, Kilmarnock, VA, Zip 22482–3880, Mailing Address: P.O. Box 1449, 22482–1449, tel. 804/435–8000; Chris Accashian, Chief Executive Officer

RESTON HOSPITAL CENTER, 1850 Town Center Parkway, Reston, VA, Zip 20190–3219; tel. 703/689–9000; John A. Deardorff, President and Chief Executive, Northern Virginia Market

RIVERSIDE REGIONAL MEDICAL CENTER, 500 J Clyde Morris Boulevard, Newport News, VA, Zip 23601–1929; tel. 757/594–2000; Michael J. Doucette, Senior Vice President and Administrator

RIVERSIDE SHORE MEMORIAL HOSPITAL, 20480 Market Street, Onancock, VA, Zip 23417–4309, Mailing Address: P.O. Box 430, 23417, tel. 757/302–2100; John Peterman, Vice President and Administrator

RIVERSIDE TAPPAHANNOCK HOSPITAL, 618 Hospital Road, Tappahannock, VA, Zip 22560–5000; tel. 804/443–3311; Elizabeth J. Martin, Hospital President

RIVERSIDE WALTER REED HOSPITAL, 7519 Hospital Drive, Gloucester, VA, Zip 23061–4178, Mailing Address: P.O. Box 1130, 23061–1130, tel. 804/693–8800; Esther Muscari. Desimini, Interim Administrator

RUSSELL COUNTY MEDICAL CENTER, 58 Carroll Street, Lebanon, VA, Zip 24266, Mailing Address: P.O. Box 3600, 24266–0200, tel. 276/883–8000; Stephen K. Givens, Assistant Vice President and Administrator

SOVAH HEALTH–MARTINSVILLE, 320 Hospital Drive, Martinsville, VA, Zip 24112–1981, Mailing Address: P.O. Box 4788, 24115–4788, tel. 276/666–7200; Alan Larson, Market President

SENTARA CAREPLEX HOSPITAL, 3000 Coliseum Drive, Hampton, VA, Zip 23666–5963; tel. 757/736–1000; Kirkpatrick Conley, President

SENTARA LEIGH HOSPITAL, 830 Kempsville Road, Norfolk, VA, Zip 23502–3920; tel. 757/261–6000; Joanne Inman, President

SENTARA MARTHA JEFFERSON HOSPITAL, 500 Martha Jefferson Drive, Charlottesville, VA, Zip 22911–4668; tel. 434/654–7000; Jonathan S. Davis, FACHE, President

SENTARA NORFOLK GENERAL HOSPITAL, 600 Gresham Drive, Norfolk, VA, Zip 23507–1904; tel. 757/388–3000; Jessica Melton, Interim President

SENTARA NORTHERN VIRGINIA MEDICAL CENTER, 2300 Opitz Boulevard, Woodbridge, VA, Zip 22191–3399; tel. 703/523–1000; Katherine Johnson, Ph.D., President

SENTARA OBICI HOSPITAL, 2800 Godwin Boulevard, Suffolk, VA, Zip 23434–8038; tel. 757/934–4000; Coleen F. Santa Ana, President

SENTARA PRINCESS ANNE HOSPITAL, 2025 Glenn Mitchell Drive, Virginia Beach, VA, Zip 23456–0178; tel. 757/507–1000; Paul Gaden, Chief Executive Officer

SENTARA VIRGINIA BEACH GENERAL HOSPITAL, 1060 First Colonial Road, Virginia Beach, VA, Zip 23454–3002; tel. 757/395–8000; Elwood Bernard. Boone, III., FACHE, President

SENTARA WILLIAMSBURG REGIONAL MEDICAL CENTER, 100 Sentara Circle, Williamsburg, VA, Zip 23188–5713; tel. 757/984–6000; David J. Masterson, President

SHELTERING ARMS REHABILITATION HOSPITAL, 8254 Atlee Road, Mechanicsville, VA, Zip 23116–1844; tel. 804/764–1000; Mary A. Zweifel, MS, President and Chief Executive Officer

SMYTH COUNTY COMMUNITY HOSPITAL , 245 Medical Park Drive, Marion, VA, Zip 24354, Mailing Address: P.O. Box 880, 24354–0880, tel. 276/378–1000; James E. Tyler, Chief Executive Officer

SOUTHAMPTON MEMORIAL HOSPITAL, 100 Fairview Drive, Franklin, VA, Zip 23851–1238, Mailing Address: P.O. Box 817, 23851–0817, tel. 757/569–6100; Kimberly W. Marks, Chief Executive Officer

SOUTHERN VIRGINIA REGIONAL MEDICAL CENTER, 727 North Main Street, Emporia, VA, Zip 23847–1274; tel. 434/348–4400; Wilson A. Thomas, Chief Executive Officer

SOUTHSIDE REGIONAL MEDICAL CENTER, 200 Medical Park Boulevard, Petersburg, VA, Zip 23805–9274; tel. 804/765–5000; Trent Nobles, Chief Executive Officer

TWIN COUNTY REGIONAL HEALTHCARE, 200 Hospital Drive, Galax, VA, Zip 24333–2227; tel. 276/236–8181; Dale Alward, Chief Executive Officer

UVA ENCOMPASS HEALTH REHABILITATION HOSPITAL, 515 Ray C Hunt Drive, Charlottesville, VA, Zip 22903–2981; tel. 434/244–2000; Louis Collier, Chief Executive Officer

UNIVERSITY OF VIRGINIA MEDICAL CENTER, 1215 Lee Street, Charlottesville, VA, Zip 22908–0001, Mailing Address: P.O. Box 800809, 22908–0809, tel. 434/924–0211; Craig Kent, Interim Chief Executive Officer

VCU HEALTH COMMUNITY MEMORIAL HOSPITAL, 125 Buena Vista Circle, South Hill, VA, Zip 23970–1431, Mailing Address: P.O. Box 90, 23970–0090, tel. 434/447–3151; W Scott. Burnette, Chief Executive Officer

VCU MEDICAL CENTER, 1250 East Marshall Street, Richmond, VA, Zip 23298–5051, Mailing Address: P.O. Box 980510, 23298–0510, tel. 804/828–9000; Ron Clark, M.D., Interim Chief Executive Officer

VIRGINIA HOSPITAL CENTER, 1701 North George Mason Drive, Arlington, VA, Zip 22205–3698; tel. 703/558–5000; James B. Cole, President and Chief Executive Officer

WYTHE COUNTY COMMUNITY HOSPITAL, 600 West Ridge Road, Wytheville, VA, Zip 24382–1099; tel. 276/228–0200; Joseph Wilkins, Chief Executive Officer

## WASHINGTON

**GROUP HEALTH COOPERATIVE**
**320 Westlake Avenue North, Suite 100, Seattle, WA Zip 98109–5233; tel. 206/448–5083; Scott Armstrong, Chief Executive Officer**

ASTRIA SUNNYSIDE HOSPITAL, 1016 Tacoma Avenue, Sunnyside, WA, Zip 98944–2263, Mailing Address: P.O. Box 719, 98944–0719, tel. 509/837–1500; Brian P. Gibbons, Jr., Chief Executive Officer

ASTRIA TOPPENISH HOSPITAL, 502 West Fourth Avenue, Toppenish, WA, Zip 98948–1616, Mailing Address: P.O. Box 672, 98948–0672, tel. 509/865–3105; Michael J. Arno, President

CASCADE VALLEY HOSPITAL , 330 South Stillaguamish Avenue, Arlington, WA, Zip 98223–1642; tel. 360/435–2133; Brian K. Ivie, President and Chief Executive Officer

COLUMBIA COUNTY HEALTH SYSTEM, 1012 South Third Street, Dayton, WA, Zip 99328–1696; tel. 509/382–2531; Shane McGuire, Chief Executive Officer

ISLAND HOSPITAL, 1211 24th Street, Anacortes, WA, Zip 98221–2562; tel. 360/299–1300; Charles Hall, Chief Executive Officer

KADLEC REGIONAL MEDICAL CENTER, 888 Swift Boulevard, Richland, WA, Zip 99352–3514; tel. 509/946–4611; Reza Kaleel, Chief Executive

KAISER PERMANENTE CAPITOL HILL CAMPUS, 201 16th Avenue East, Seattle, WA, Zip 98112–5226; tel. 206/326–3000; Carol M. Taylor, R.N., Regional Director Clinical Operations

KITTITAS VALLEY HEALTHCARE, 603 South Chestnut Street, Ellensburg, WA, Zip 98926–3875; tel. 509/962–7302; Julie Petersen, CPA, Chief Executive Officer

KOOTENAI HEALTH, 2003 Kootenai Health Way, Coeur D'Alene, ID, Zip 83814–2677; tel. 208/625–4000; Jon Ness, Chief Executive Officer

LOURDES MEDICAL CENTER, 520 North Fourth Avenue, Pasco, WA, Zip 99301–5257; tel. 509/547–7704; John Serle, FACHE, President and Chief Executive Officer

MULTICARE DEACONESS HOSPITAL, 800 West Fifth Avenue, Spokane, WA, Zip 99204–2803, Mailing Address: P.O. Box 248, 99210–0248, tel. 509/458–5800; Gregory George. Repetti, III., FACHE, President

MULTICARE MARY BRIDGE CHILDREN'S HOSPITAL AND HEALTH CENTER, 317 Martin Luther King Jr Way, Tacoma, WA, Zip 98405–4234, Mailing Address: P.O. Box 5299, 98415–0299, tel. 253/403–1400; Jeffrey S. Poltawsky, President and Market Leader

MULTICARE VALLEY HOSPITAL , 12606 East Mission Avenue, Spokane Valley, WA, Zip 99216–1090; tel. 509/924–6650; Gregory George. Repetti, III., FACHE, Chief Executive Officer

NORTHWEST SPECIALTY HOSPITAL, 1593 East Polston Avenue, Post Falls, ID, Zip 83854–5326; tel. 208/262–2300; Rick Rasmussen, Chief Executive Officer

OVERLAKE MEDICAL CENTER, 1035 116th Avenue NE, Bellevue, WA, Zip 98004–4604; tel. 425/688–5000; J. Michael. Marsh, President and Chief Executive Officer

PEACEHEALTH ST. JOSEPH MEDICAL CENTER, 2901 Squalicum Parkway, Bellingham, WA, Zip 98225–1851; tel. 360/734–5400; Charles Prosper, Chief Executive NW

PEACEHEALTH UNITED GENERAL MEDICAL CENTER, 2000 Hospital Drive, Sedro-Woolley, WA, Zip 98284–4327; tel. 360/856–6021; Christopher Johnston, Chief Administrative Officer

PROSSER MEMORIAL HEALTH, 723 Memorial Street, Prosser, WA, Zip 99350–1524; tel. 509/786–2222; Craig J. Marks, FACHE, Chief Executive Officer

PROVIDENCE CENTRALIA HOSPITAL, 914 S Scheuber RD, Centralia, WA, Zip 98531–9027, 914 South Scheuber Road, 98531–9027, tel. 360/736–2803; Darin Goss, FACHE, Site Administrator

PROVIDENCE HOLY FAMILY HOSPITAL, 5633 North Lidgerwood Street, Spokane, WA, Zip 99208–1224; tel. 509/482–0111; Peggy M. Currie, R.N., Chief Operating Officer

PROVIDENCE REGIONAL MEDICAL CENTER EVERETT, 1321 Colby Avenue, Everett, WA, Zip 98201–1665, Mailing Address: P.O. Box 1147, 98206–1147, tel. 425/261–2000; Kim Williams, R.N., MS, Chief Executive Officer

PROVIDENCE SACRED HEART MEDICAL CENTER & CHILDREN'S HOSPITAL, 101 West Eighth Avenue, Spokane, WA, Zip 99204–2364, Mailing Address: P.O. Box 2555, 99220–2555, tel. 509/474–3131; Peggy M. Currie, R.N., Chief Operating Officer

PROVIDENCE ST. MARY MEDICAL CENTER, 401 W Poplar Street, Walla Walla, WA, Zip 99362–2846, Mailing Address: P.O. Box 1477, 99362–0312, tel. 509/897–3320; Susan Blackburn, Chief Administrative Officer

PULLMAN REGIONAL HOSPITAL, 835 SE Bishop Boulevard, Pullman, WA, Zip 99163–5512; tel. 509/332–2541; Scott K. Adams, FACHE, Chief Executive Officer

SEATTLE CHILDREN'S HOSPITAL, 4800 Sand Point Way NE, Seattle, WA, Zip 98105–3901, Mailing Address: P.O. Box 5371, 98145–5005, tel. 206/987–2000; Jeff Sperring, M.D., Chief Executive Officer

SKAGIT VALLEY HOSPITAL, 300 Hospital Parkway, Mount Vernon, WA, Zip 98273, Mailing Address: P.O. Box 1376, 98273–1376, tel. 360/424–4111; Brian K. Ivie, President and Chief Executive Officer

ST. FRANCIS HOSPITAL, 34515 Ninth Avenue South, Federal Way, WA, Zip 98003–6799; tel. 253/944–8100; Dino Johnson, R.N., Chief Operating Officer

ST. JOSEPH MEDICAL CENTER, 1717 South 'J' Street, Tacoma, WA, Zip 98405–3004, Mailing Address: P.O. Box 2197, 98401–2197, tel. 253/426–4101; Tim O'Haver, President

ST. MICHAEL MEDICAL CENTER, 2520 Cherry Avenue, Bremerton, WA, Zip 98310–4229; tel. 360/744–3911; David W. Schultz, FACHE, President, Peninsula Region

TRIOS HEALTH, 900 South Auburn Street, Kennewick, WA, Zip 99336–5621, Mailing Address: P.O. Box 6128, 99336–0128, tel. 509/586–6111; John H. Solheim, Chief Executive Officer

VIRGINIA MASON MEDICAL CENTER, 1100 Ninth Avenue, Seattle, WA, Zip 98101–2756, Mailing Address: P.O. Box 900, 98111–0900, tel. 206/223–6600; Suzanne Anderson, President

VIRGINIA MASON MEMORIAL, 2811 Tieton Drive, Yakima, WA, Zip 98902–3761; tel. 509/575–8000; Carole Peet, R.N., MSN, Chief Executive Officer

WHIDBEYHEALTH, 101 North Main Street, Coupeville, WA, Zip 98239–3413; tel. 360/678–5151; Ron Telles, Interim Chief Executive Officer

WHITMAN HOSPITAL AND MEDICAL CENTER, 1200 West Fairview Street, Colfax, WA, Zip 99111–9579; tel. 509/397–3435; Hank Hanigan, FACHE, Chief Executive Officer

**LINCOLN COUNTY HEALTH DEPARTMENT**
**90 Nichols Street, Davenport, WA Zip 99122–9729; tel. 509/725–1001; Ed Dzedzy, Public Health Administration**

LINCOLN HOSPITAL, 10 Nicholls Street, Davenport, WA, Zip 99122–9729; tel. 509/725–7101; Tyson Lacy, Chief Executive Officer and Superintendent

ODESSA MEMORIAL HEALTHCARE CENTER, 502 East Amende Drive, Odessa, WA, Zip 99159–7003, Mailing Address: P.O. Box 368, 99159–0368, tel. 509/982–2611; Emmett Schuster, Interim Chief Executive Officer

## WEST VIRGINIA

**HEALTH PARTNERS NETWORK, INC.**
**1000 Technology Drive, Suite 2320, Fairmont, WV Zip 26554–8834; tel. 304/368–2740; William G. MacLean, Executive Director**

BROADDUS HOSPITAL, 1 Healthcare Drive, Philippi, WV, Zip 26416–9405, Mailing Address: P.O. Box 930, 26416–0930, tel. 304/457–1760; Dana L. Gould, Chief Executive Officer

CAMDEN CLARK MEDICAL CENTER, 800 Garfield Avenue, Parkersburg, WV, Zip 26101–5378, Mailing Address: P.O. Box 718, 26102–0718, tel. 304/424–2111; Steve Altmiller, President and Chief Executive Officer

DAVIS MEDICAL CENTER, Gorman Avenue and Reed Street, Elkins, WV, Zip 26241, Mailing Address: P.O. Box 1484, 26241–1484, tel. 304/636–3300; Vance Jackson, FACHE, Chief Executive Officer

ENCOMPASS HEALTH REHABILITATION HOSPITAL OF MORGANTOWN, 1160 Van Voorhis Road, Morgantown, WV, Zip 26505–3437; tel. 304/598–1100; Tracy Vinciguerra, Chief Executive Officer

GRAFTON CITY HOSPITAL, 1 Hospital Plaza, Grafton, WV, Zip 26354–1283; tel. 304/265–0400; George C. Boyles, Interim President and Chief Administrative Officer

MINNIE HAMILTON HEALTHCARE CENTER, 186 Hospital Drive, Grantsville, WV, Zip 26147–7100; tel. 304/354–9244; Steve Whited, Chief Executive Officer

ST. JOSEPH'S HOSPITAL OF BUCKHANNON, 1 Amalia Drive, Buckhannon, WV, Zip 26201–2276; tel. 304/473–2000; Skip Gjolberg, FACHE, Administrator

STONEWALL JACKSON MEMORIAL HOSPITAL, 230 Hospital Plaza, Weston, WV, Zip 26452–8558; tel. 304/269–8000; Avah Stalnaker, Chief Executive Officer

UNITED HOSPITAL CENTER, 327 Medical Park Drive, Bridgeport, WV, Zip 26330–9006; tel. 681/342–1000; Michael C. Tillman, President and Chief Executive Officer

WEBSTER COUNTY MEMORIAL HOSPITAL, 324 Miller Mountain Drive, Webster Springs, WV, Zip 26288–1087, Mailing Address: P.O. Box 312, 26288–0312, tel. 304/847–5682; Jim Parker, FACHE, Chief Executive Officer

WEST VIRGINIA UNIVERSITY HOSPITALS, 1 Medical Center Drive, Morgantown, WV, Zip 26506–4749; tel. 304/598–4000; Albert L. Wright, Jr., President and Chief Executive Officer

**PARTNERS IN HEALTH NETWORK, INC.**
**405 Capitol Street, Suite 505, Charleston, WV Zip 25301–1783; tel. 304/388–7385; Robert D. Whitler, Executive Director**

BOONE MEMORIAL HOSPITAL, 701 Madison Avenue, Madison, WV, Zip 25130–1699; tel. 304/369–1230; Virgil Underwood, Chief Executive Officer

BRAXTON COUNTY MEMORIAL HOSPITAL, 100 Hoylman DR, Gassaway, WV, Zip 26624–9318, 100 Hoylman Drive, 26624–9318, tel. 304/364–5156; Karen L. Bowling, MSN, R.N., Interim Chief Executive Officer

CHARLESTON AREA MEDICAL CENTER, 501 Morris Street, Charleston, WV, Zip 25301–1300, Mailing Address: P.O. Box 1547, 25326–1547, tel. 304/388–5432; David L. Ramsey, President and Chief Executive Officer

CHARLESTON SURGICAL HOSPITAL, 1306 Kanawha Boulevard East, Charleston, WV, Zip 25301–3001, Mailing Address: P.O. Box 2271, 25328–2271, tel. 304/343–4371; Christina Arvon, Administrator and Chief Executive Officer

HIGHLAND HOSPITAL, 300 56th Street SE, Charleston, WV, Zip 25304–2361, Mailing Address: P.O. Box 4107, 25364–4107, tel. 304/926–1600; Cynthia A. Persily, Ph.D., R.N., Chief Executive Officer

JACKSON GENERAL HOSPITAL, 122 Pinnell Street, Ripley, WV, Zip 25271–9101, Mailing Address: P.O. Box 720, 25271–0720, tel. 304/372–2731; Stephanie McCoy, President and Chief Executive Officer

MINNIE HAMILTON HEALTHCARE CENTER, 186 Hospital Drive, Grantsville, WV, Zip 26147–7100; tel. 304/354–9244; Steve Whited, Chief Executive Officer

MONTGOMERY GENERAL HOSPITAL, 401 Sixth Avenue, Montgomery, WV, Zip 25136–2116, Mailing Address: P.O. Box 270, 25136–0270, tel. 304/442–5151; Vickie Lynn. Gay, Chief Executive Officer

POCAHONTAS MEMORIAL HOSPITAL, 150 Duncan Road, Buckeye, WV, Zip 24924; tel. 304/799–7400; Mary Beth Barr, R.N., Chief Executive Officer

ROANE GENERAL HOSPITAL, 200 Hospital Drive, Spencer, WV, Zip 25276–1050; tel. 304/927–4444; Douglas E. Bentz, Chief Executive Officer

STONEWALL JACKSON MEMORIAL HOSPITAL, 230 Hospital Plaza, Weston, WV, Zip 26452–8558; tel. 304/269–8000; Avah Stalnaker, Chief Executive Officer

SUMMERSVILLE REGIONAL MEDICAL CENTER, 400 Fairview Heights Road, Summersville, WV, Zip 26651–9308; tel. 304/872–2891; Karen L. Bowling, MSN, R.N., Interim Chief Executive Officer

WEBSTER COUNTY MEMORIAL HOSPITAL, 324 Miller Mountain Drive, Webster Springs, WV, Zip 26288–1087, Mailing Address: P.O. Box 312, 26288–0312, tel. 304/847–5682; Jim Parker, FACHE, Chief Executive Officer

## WISCONSIN

**ASCENSION WISCONSIN**
**1506 South Oneida Street, Appleton, WI Zip 54915–1305; tel. 920/831–8912; Monica Hilt, President and Chief Executive Officer**

ASCENSION CALUMET HOSPITAL, 614 Memorial Drive, Chilton, WI, Zip 53014–1597; tel. 920/849–2386; Jenny Derks, Chief Administrative Officer

ASCENSION NORTHEAST WISCONSIN MERCY HOSPITAL , 500 South Oakwood Road, Oshkosh, WI, Zip 54904–7944; tel. 920/223–2000; Denise Parrish, Interim Chief Administrative Officer

ASCENSION NORTHEAST WISCONSIN ST. ELIZABETH HOSPITAL, 1506 South Oneida Street, Appleton, WI, Zip 54915–1305; tel. 920/738–2000; Monica Hilt, President and Regional Vice President

**ASPIRUS, INC.**
**2200 Westwood Drive, Wausau, WI Zip 54401–7806; tel. 715/847–2118; Matthew Heywood, President and Chief Executive Officer**

ASPIRUS IRON RIVER HOSPITALS & CLINICS, INC., 1400 West Ice Lake Road, Iron River, MI, Zip 49935–9526; tel. 906/265–6121; Connie L. Koutouzos, R.N., MSN, Chief Executive Officer

ASPIRUS IRONWOOD HOSPITALS & CLINICS, INC., N10561 Grand View Lane, Ironwood, MI, Zip 49938–9622; tel. 906/932–2525; Paula L. Chermside, Chief Executive Officer

ASPIRUS KEWEENAW HOSPITAL, INC., 205 Osceola Street, Laurium, MI, Zip 49913–2134; tel. 906/337–6500; Christine K. Harff, UP Regional President

ASPIRUS LANGLADE HOSPITAL, 112 East Fifth Avenue, Antigo, WI, Zip 54409–2796; tel. 715/623–2331; Andrew J. Barth, Executive Director

ASPIRUS MEDFORD HOSPITAL & CLINICS, INC., 135 South Gibson Street, Medford, WI, Zip 54451; tel. 715/748–8100; Dale Hustedt, President

ASPIRUS ONTONAGON HOSPITAL, INC., 601 South Seventh Street, Ontonagon, MI, Zip 49953–1459; tel. 906/884–8000; Dylan Taylor, Chief Administrative Officer

ASPIRUS RIVERVIEW HOSPITAL AND CLINICS, INC., 410 Dewey Street, Wisconsin Rapids, WI, Zip 54494–4715, Mailing Address: P.O. Box 8080, 54495–8080, tel. 715/423–6060; Todd Burch, Chief Executive Officer

ASPIRUS WAUSAU HOSPITAL, INC., 333 Pine Ridge Boulevard, Wausau, WI, Zip 54401–4187; tel. 715/847–2121; Darrell Lentz, President

**COLUMBIA ST. MARY'S**
**2025 East Newport Avenue, Milwaukee, WI Zip 53211–2906; tel. 414/961–3300; Travis Andersen, President and Chief Executive Officer**

ASCENSION COLUMBIA ST. MARY'S HOSPITAL MILWAUKEE, 2301 North Lake Drive, Milwaukee, WI, Zip 53211–4508; tel. 414/291–1000; Travis Andersen, Chief Executive Officer

ASCENSION COLUMBIA ST. MARY'S HOSPITAL OZAUKEE, 13111 North Port Washington Road, Mequon, WI, Zip 53097–2416; tel. 262/243–7300; Kelly Elkins, President and Chief Executive Officer

ASCENSION COLUMBIA ST. MARY'S MILWAUKEE HOSPITAL, 2323 North Lake Drive, Milwaukee, WI, Zip 53211–4508, 2301 North Lake Drive, 53211–4508, tel. 414/585–1000; Kelly Elkins, President and Chief Executive Officer

**COMMUNITY HEALTH NETWORK, INC.**
**225 Memorial Drive, Berlin, WI Zip 54923–1243; tel. 920/361–5580**

THEDA CARE MEDICAL CENTER – WILD ROSE, 601 Grove Avenue, Wild Rose, WI, Zip 54984–6903, Mailing Address: P.O. Box 243, 54984–0243, tel. 920/622–3257; Tammy Bending, Vice President

THEDACARE MEDICAL CENTER–BERLIN, 225 Memorial Drive, Berlin, WI, Zip 54923–1295; tel. 920/361–1313; Tammy Bending, Vice President, Critical Access Hospital

**GUNDERSEN HEALTH SYSTEM**
**1900 South Avenue, La Crosse, WI Zip 54601–5467; tel. 608/782–7300; Scott W. Rathgaber, M.D., Chief Executive Officer**

GUNDERSEN BOSCOBEL AREA HOSPITAL AND CLINICS, 205 Parker Street, Boscobel, WI, Zip 53805–1698; tel. 608/375–4112; David Hartberg, Chief Executive Officer

GUNDERSEN LUTHERAN MEDICAL CENTER, 1900 South Avenue, La Crosse, WI, Zip 54601–5467; tel. 608/782–7300; Scott W. Rathgaber, M.D., Chief Executive Officer

GUNDERSEN MOUNDVIEW HOSPITAL & CLINICS, 402 West Lake Street, Friendship, WI, Zip 53934–9699, Mailing Address: P.O. Box 40, 53934–0040, tel. 608/339–3331; Francisco Perez–Guerra, Chief Executive Officer

GUNDERSEN PALMER LUTHERAN HOSPITAL AND CLINICS, 112 Jefferson Street, West Union, IA, Zip 52175–1022; tel. 563/422–3811; Patrice Kuennen, Chief Executive Officer

GUNDERSEN ST. JOSEPH'S HOSPITAL AND CLINICS, 400 Water Avenue, Hillsboro, WI, Zip 54634–9054, Mailing Address: P.O. Box 527, 54634–0527, tel. 608/489–8000; Robin Nelson, Interim Chief Executive Officer

GUNDERSEN TRI–COUNTY HOSPITAL AND CLINICS, 18601 Lincoln Street, Whitehall, WI, Zip 54773–8605; tel. 715/538–4361; Joni Olson, Chief Executive Officer

**Section B**

## ALLIANCE OF INDEPENDENT ACADEMIC MEDICAL CENTERS

233 East Erie Street, Ste 306, Chicago, IL Zip 60611; tel. 312/836–3712; Kimberly Pierce–Boggs, Executive Director

### ARIZONA
**Scottsdale**
Alliance
HonorHealth

### CALIFORNIA
**Colton**
Alliance
Arrowhead Regional Medical Center

**Los Angeles**
Alliance
Cedars–Sinai Medical Center

**Oakland**
Alliance
Kaiser Permanente Oakland Medical Center

### COLORADO
**Aurora**
Alliance
Medical Center of Aurora

**Denver**
Alliance
v/St. Luke's Medical Center

Rose Medical Center

Saint Joseph Hospital

**Englewood**
Alliance
Swedish Medical Center

**Lone Tree**
Alliance
Sky Ridge Medical Center

**Thornton**
Alliance
North Suburban Medical Center

### CONNECTICUT
**Hartford**
Alliance
Saint Francis Hospital and Medical Center

### DELAWARE
**Newark**
Alliance
ChristianaCare

### FLORIDA
**Hollywood**
Alliance
Memorial Healthcare System

**Orange Park**
Alliance
Orange Park Medical Center

**Orlando**
Alliance
AdventHealth Orlando

Orlando Regional Medical Center

### GEORGIA
**Macon**
Alliance
Coliseum Medical Centers

### ILLINOIS
**Chicago**
Alliance
Advocate Illinois Masonic Medical Center

**Oak Lawn**
Alliance
Advocate Christ Medical Center

**Park Ridge**
Alliance
Advocate Lutheran General Hospital

**Peoria**
Alliance
OSF Saint Francis Medical Center

### INDIANA
**Indianapolis**
Alliance
Community Health Network

### IOWA
**West Des Moines**
Alliance
UnityPoint Health

### LOUISIANA
**Baton Rouge**
Alliance
Our Lady of the Lake Regional Medical Center

**New Orleans**
Alliance
Ochsner Health

### MAINE
**Portland**
Alliance
Maine Medical Center

### MARYLAND
**Baltimore**
Alliance
Sinai Hospital of Baltimore

### MASSACHUSETTS
**Burlington**
Alliance
Lahey Hospital & Medical Center, Burlington

**Springfield**
Alliance
Baystate Medical Center

### MICHIGAN
**Grand Rapids**
Alliance
Mercy Health Saint Mary's

**Lansing**
Alliance
Sparrow Hospital

**Rochester**
Alliance
Ascension Crittenton Hospital Medical Center

### MINNESOTA
**Bloomington**
Alliance
HealthPartners

### MONTANA
**Billings**
Alliance
Billings Clinic

### NEW JERSEY
**Brick Township**
Alliance
Hackensack Meridian Health Ocean Medical Center

**Holmdel**
Alliance
Hackensack Meridian Health Bayshore Community Hospital

**Livingston**
Alliance
Saint Barnabas Medical Center

**Long Branch**
Alliance
Monmouth Medical Center, Long Branch Campus

**Manahawkin**
Alliance
Hackensack Meridian Health Southern Ocean Medical Center**Neptune**

Alliance
Hackensack Meridian Health Jersey Shore University Medical Center

**Newark**
Alliance
Newark Beth Israel Medical Center

**Perth Amboy**
Alliance
Hackensack Meridian Health Raritan Bay Medical Center

**Phillipsburg**
Alliance
St. Luke's Hospital – Warren Campus

**Red Bank**
Alliance
Hackensack Meridian Health Riverview Medical Center

### NEW YORK
**Brooklyn**
Alliance
Maimonides Medical Center

**Cooperstown**
Alliance
Bassett Medical Center

### NORTH CAROLINA
**Charlotte**
Alliance
Atrium Health's Carolinas Medical Center

### OHIO
**Akron**
Alliance
Cleveland Clinic Akron General

**Cincinnati**
Alliance
Christ Hospital

TriHealth Evendale Hospital

**Cleveland**
Alliance
Cleveland Clinic

**Columbus**
Alliance
OhioHealth Grant Medical Center

OhioHealth Riverside Methodist Hospital

### OREGON
**Hood River**
Alliance
Providence Hood River Memorial Hospital

**Milwaukie**
Alliance
Providence Milwaukie Hospital

**Portland**
Alliance
Providence Portland Medical Center

Providence St. Vincent Medical Center

### PENNSYLVANIA
**Bethlehem**
Alliance
St. Luke's University Hospital – Bethlehem Campus

**Philadelphia**
Alliance
Einstein Medical Center Philadelphia

**Sayre**
Alliance
Guthrie Robert Packer Hospital

**Wynnewood**
Alliance
Lankenau Medical Center

**York**
Alliance
WellSpan York Hospital

**SOUTH CAROLINA**
**Charleston**
Alliance
Trident Medical Center

**Myrtle Beach**
Alliance
Grand Strand Medical Center

**TEXAS**
**Dallas**
Alliance
Baylor Scott & White Health

**Fort Worth**
Alliance
JPS Health Network

**Lubbock**
Alliance
Covenant Children's Hospital
Covenant Medical Center

**WASHINGTON**
**Seattle**
Alliance
Kaiser Permanente Capitol Hill Campus
Swedish Medical Center–Cherry Hill Campus
Swedish Medical Center–First Hill
Virginia Mason Medical Center

**WEST VIRGINIA**
**Charleston**
Alliance
Charleston Area Medical Center

**WISCONSIN**
**Marshfield**
Alliance
Marshfield Medical Center

## CAPSTONE HEALTH ALLIANCE
1200 Ridgefield Boulevard, Suite 200, Asheville, NC Zip 28806; tel. 828/418–5050; Tim Bugg, President and Chief Executive Officer

**ALABAMA**
**Butler**
Alliance
Choctaw General Hospital

**Dothan**
Alliance
Southeast Alabama Medical Center

**Eufaula**
Alliance
Medical Center Barbour

**Opelika**
Alliance
East Alabama Medical Center

**Wedowee**
Alliance
Tanner Medical Center/East Alabama

**ARKANSAS**
**Batesville**
Alliance
White River Medical Center

**Calico Rock**
Alliance
Izard County Medical Center

**Fordyce**
Alliance
Dallas County Medical Center

**Harrison**
Alliance
North Arkansas Regional Medical Center

**Mountain View**
Alliance
Stone County Medical Center

**Pine Bluff**
Alliance
Jefferson Regional Medical Center

**DELAWARE**
**Lewes**
Alliance
Beebe Healthcare

**GEORGIA**
**Bremen**
Alliance
Higgins General Hospital

**Carrollton**
Alliance
Tanner Medical Center–Carrollton

**Jesup**
Alliance
Wayne Memorial Hospital

**Lagrange**
Alliance
Wellstar West Georgia Medical Center

**Savannah**
Alliance
Candler Hospital
St. Joseph's Hospital

**Villa Rica**
Alliance
Tanner Medical Center–Villa Rica

**ILLINOIS**
**Centreville**
Alliance
Touchette Regional Hospital

**Chicago**
Alliance
Loretto Hospital
Norwegian American Hospital
Thorek Memorial Hospital

**Dixon**
Alliance
Katherine Shaw Bethea Hospital

**Elmhurst**
Alliance
Elmhurst Hospital

**Hoopeston**
Alliance
Carle Hoopeston Regional Health Center

**Kankakee**
Alliance
Riverside Medical Center

**Naperville**
Alliance
Edward Hospital
Linden Oaks Hospital

**Urbana**
Alliance
Carle Foundation Hospital

**INDIANA**
**Greenfield**
Alliance
Hancock Regional Hospital

**Rushville**
Alliance
Rush Memorial Hospital

**KANSAS**
**Manhattan**
Alliance
Manhattan Surgical

**KENTUCKY**
**Albany**
Alliance
The Medical Center Albany

**Bowling Green**
Alliance
Commonwealth Regional Specialty Hospital
Medical Center at Bowling Green

**Danville**
Alliance
Ephraim McDowell Regional Medical Center

**Edgewood**
Alliance
St. Elizabeth Edgewood

**Florence**
Alliance
St. Elizabeth Florence

**Fort Thomas**
Alliance
St. Elizabeth Fort Thomas

**Franklin**
Alliance
Medical Center at Franklin

**Glasgow**
Alliance
T. J. Samson Community Hospital

**Henderson**
Alliance
Methodist Hospital

**Horse Cave**
Alliance
The Medical Center at Caverna

**Morganfield**
Alliance
Methodist Hospital Union County

**Murray**
Alliance
Murray–Calloway County Hospital

**Scottsville**
Alliance
Medical Center at Scottsville

**Stanford**
Alliance
Ephraim McDowell Fort Logan Hospital

**Williamstown**
Alliance
St. Elizabeth Grant

**LOUISIANA**
**Abbeville**
Alliance
Abbeville General Hospital

**Baton Rouge**
Alliance
Baton Rouge General Medical Center
Baton Rouge Rehabilitation Hospital
The NeuroMedical Center Rehabilitation Hospital
The Spine Hospital of Louisiana at The NeuroMedical Center
Woman's Hospital

**Breaux Bridge**
Alliance
St. Martin Hospital

**Bunkie**
Alliance
Bunkie General Hospital

**Church Point**
Alliance
Acadia–St. Landry Hospital

**Columbia**
Alliance
Citizens Medical Center

**Crowley**
Alliance
Acadia General Hospital

**Delhi**
Alliance
Richland Parish Hospital–Delhi

**Hammond**
Alliance
North Oaks Medical Center
North Oaks Rehabilitation Hospital

**Houma**
Alliance
Terrebonne General Medical Center

**Jennings**
Alliance
Jennings American Legion Hospital

**Kaplan**
Alliance
Abrom Kaplan Memorial Hospital

**Kinder**
Alliance
Allen Parish Community Healthcare

**Lafayette**
Alliance
Lafayette General Medical Center
Lafayette General Surgical Hospital
Louisiana Extended Care Hospital of Lafayette
University Hospital & Clinics

**Marrero**
Alliance
Bridgepoint Continuing Care Hospital

**Monroe**
Alliance
Specialty Hospital

**Natchitoches**
Alliance
Louisiana Extended Care Hospital of Natchitoches

**New Iberia**
Alliance
Iberia Medical Center

**New Orleans**
Alliance
Ochsner Extended Care Hospital

**Opelousas**
Alliance
St. Landry Extended Care Hospital

**Rayville**
Alliance
Richardson Medical Center

**West Monroe**
Alliance
Louisiana Extended Care Hospital of West Monroe

**Winnsboro**
Alliance
Franklin Medical Center

**MARYLAND**
**Annapolis**
Alliance
Anne Arundel Medical Center

**Baltimore**
Alliance
Greater Baltimore Medical Center
Levindale Hebrew Hospital and Nursing
Mercy Medical Center
Sinai Hospital of Baltimore

**Berlin**
Alliance
Atlantic General Hospital

**Cumberland**
Alliance
Western Maryland Regional Medical Center

**Elkton**
Alliance
Union Hospital

**Frederick**
Alliance
Frederick Health

**Lanham**
Alliance
Doctors Community Hospital

**Randallstown**
Alliance
Northwest Hospital

**Salisbury**
Alliance
TidalHealth Peninsula

**Westminster**
Alliance
Carroll Hospital Center

**MICHIGAN**
**Ypsilanti**
Alliance
Forest Health Medical Center

**MINNESOTA**
**Blue Earth**
Alliance
United Hospital District

**MISSISSIPPI**
**Bay Springs**
Alliance
Jasper General Hospital

**Carthage**
Alliance
Baptist Medical Center Leake

**Charleston**
Alliance
Tallahatchie General Hospital

**De Kalb**
Alliance
John C. Stennis Memorial Hospital

**Jackson**
Alliance
Mississippi Baptist Medical Center

**Kosciusko**
Alliance
Baptist Medical Center Attala

**Laurel**
Alliance
South Central Regional Medical Center

**Louisville**
Alliance
Winston Medical Center

**Magee**
Alliance
Magee General Hospital

**Mendenhall**
Alliance
Simpson General Hospital

**Meridian**
Alliance
Rush Foundation Hospital

**Morton**
Alliance
Scott Regional Hospital

**Quitman**
Alliance
H. C. Watkins Memorial Hospital

**Ruleville**
Alliance
North Sunflower Medical Center

**Union**
Alliance
Laird Hospital

**Water Valley**
Alliance
Yalobusha General Hospital

**Yazoo City**
Alliance
Baptist Medical Center Yazoo

**NEBRASKA**
**Kearney**
Alliance
Kearney Regional Medical Center

**NORTH CAROLINA**
**Asheville**
Alliance
Asheville Specialty Hospital
CarePartners Health Services
Mission Hospital

**Boone**
Alliance
Watauga Medical Center

**Brevard**
Alliance
Transylvania Regional Hospital

**Bryson City**
Alliance
Swain Community Hospital

**Cherokee**
Alliance
Cherokee Indian Hospital

**Clyde**
Alliance
Haywood Regional Medical Center

**Columbus**
Alliance
St. Luke's Hospital

**Dunn**
Alliance
Harnett Health System

**Elizabeth City**
Alliance
Sentara Albemarle Medical Center

**Elizabethtown**
Alliance
Cape Fear Valley – Bladen County Hospital

**Fayetteville**
Alliance
Cape Fear Valley Medical Center
Highsmith–Rainey Specialty Hospital

**Franklin**
Alliance
Angel Medical Center

**Gastonia**
Alliance
CaroMont Regional Medical Center

**Goldsboro**
Alliance
Wayne UNC Health Care

**Hendersonville**
Alliance
AdventHealth Hendersonville
Margaret R. Pardee Memorial Hospital

**Hickory**
Alliance
Catawba Valley Medical Center

**Highlands**
Alliance
Highlands–Cashiers Hospital

**Marion**
Alliance
McDowell Hospital

**Morehead City**
Alliance
Carteret Health Care

**Newland**
Alliance
Charles A. Cannon Memorial Hospital

**Oxford**
Alliance
Granville Health System

**Pinehurst**
Alliance
FirstHealth Moore Regional Hospital

**Raeford**
Alliance
Hoke Hospital

**Roanoke Rapids**
Alliance
Vidant North Hospital

**Spruce Pine**
Alliance
Blue Ridge Regional Hospital

**Statesville**
Alliance
Iredell Health System

**Troy**
Alliance
FirstHealth Montgomery Memorial Hospital

**NORTH DAKOTA**
**Cavalier**
Alliance
Pembina County Memorial Hospital and Wedgewood Manor

**OHIO**
**Amherst**
Alliance
Specialty Hospital of Lorain

**Bowling Green**
Alliance
Wood County Hospital

**Cleveland**
Alliance
Grace Hospital

**Cuyahoga Falls**
Alliance
Western Reserve Hospital

**Salem**
Alliance
Salem Regional Medical Center

**Steubenville**
Alliance
Life Line Hospital

**PENNSYLVANIA**
**Corry**
Alliance
LECOM Corry Memorial Hospital

**Erie**
Alliance
LECOM Health Millcreek Community Hospital

**Kittanning**
Alliance
ACMH Hospital

**Langhorne**
Alliance
Barix Clinics of Pennsylvania

**Meadville**
Alliance
Meadville Medical Center

**State College**
Alliance
Mount Nittany Medical Center

**Titusville**
Alliance
Titusville Area Hospital

**Tyrone**
Alliance
Tyrone Hospital

**Windber**
Alliance
Chan Soon–Shiong Medical Center

**SOUTH CAROLINA**
**Conway**
Alliance
Conway Medical Center

**West Columbia**
Alliance
Lexington Medical Center

**TENNESSEE**
**Crossville**
Alliance
Cumberland Medical Center

**Elizabethton**
Alliance
Sycamore Shoals Hospital

**Erwin**
Alliance
Unicoi County Memorial Hospital

**Johnson City**
Alliance
Franklin Woods Community Hospital
Johnson City Medical Center
Quillen Rehabilitation Hospital

**Kingsport**
Alliance
Indian Path Community Hospital

**Knoxville**
Alliance
University of Tennessee Medical Center

**Maryville**
Alliance
Blount Memorial Hospital

**Mountain City**
Alliance
Johnson County Community Hospital

**TEXAS**
**The Woodlands**
Alliance
Woodlands Specialty Hospital

**VIRGINIA**
**Abingdon**
Alliance
Johnston Memorial Hospital

**Chesapeake**
Alliance
Chesapeake Regional Medical Center

**Christiansburg**
Alliance
Carilion New River Valley Medical Center

**Clintwood**
Alliance
Dickenson Community Hospital

**Front Royal**
Alliance
Valley Health – Warren Memorial Hospital

**Gloucester**
Alliance
Riverside Walter Reed Hospital

**Grundy**
Alliance
Buchanan General Hospital

**Lebanon**
Alliance
Russell County Medical Center

**Lexington**
Alliance
Carilion Stonewall Jackson Hospital

**Luray**
Alliance
Valley Health – Page Memorial Hospital

**Marion**
Alliance
Smyth County Community Hospital

**Newport News**
Alliance
Riverside Regional Medical Center

**Norton**
Alliance
Norton Community Hospital

**Onancock**
Alliance
Riverside Shore Memorial Hospital

**Pearisburg**
Alliance
Carilion Giles Community Hospital

**Roanoke**
Alliance
Carilion Roanoke Memorial Hospital

**Rocky Mount**
Alliance
Carilion Franklin Memorial Hospital

**South Hill**
Alliance
VCU Health Community Memorial Hospital

**Tappahannock**
Alliance
Riverside Tappahannock Hospital

**Tazewell**
Alliance
Carilion Tazewell Community Hospital

**Williamsburg**
Alliance
Riverside Doctors' Hospital Williamsburg

**Winchester**
Alliance
Valley Health – Winchester Medical Center

**Woodstock**
Alliance
Valley Health – Shenandoah Memorial Hospital

**WEST VIRGINIA**
**Berkeley Springs**
Alliance
Valley Health – War Memorial Hospital

**Charleston**
Alliance
Saint Francis Hospital

**Elkins**
Alliance
Davis Medical Center

**Huntington**
Alliance
Cabell Huntington Hospital
St. Mary's Medical Center

**Kingwood**
Alliance
Preston Memorial Hospital

**Morgantown**
Alliance
Mon Health Medical Center

**Point Pleasant**
Alliance
Pleasant Valley Hospital

**Romney**
Alliance
Valley Health – Hampshire Memorial Hospital

**South Charleston**
Alliance
Thomas Memorial Hospital

## CATHOLIC CEO HEALTHCARE CONNECTION

50 South Main Street, Suite 200, Naperville, IL Zip 60540–5484; tel. 630/352–2220; Roger N. Butler, Executive Director

**COLORADO**
**Broomfield**
Alliance
SCL Health

**ILLINOIS**
**Peoria**
Alliance
OSF Healthcare

**Springfield**
Alliance
HSHS Hospital Sisters Health System

**LOUISIANA**
**Baton Rouge**
Alliance
Franciscan Missionaries of Our Lady Health System, Inc.

**MARYLAND**
**Marriottsville**
Alliance
Bon Secours Mercy Health

**MISSOURI**
**Chesterfield**
Alliance
Mercy

Section B

## Saint Louis
Alliance
Ascension Healthcare

SSM Health

## OHIO
### Cincinnati
Alliance
Mercy Health

## SOUTH DAKOTA
### Sioux Falls
Alliance
Avera Health

## TEXAS
### Irving
Alliance
CHRISTUS Health

## WASHINGTON
### Renton
Alliance
Providence St. Joseph Health

### Vancouver
Alliance
PeaceHealth

## WISCONSIN
### Manitowoc
Alliance
Franciscan Sisters of Christian Charity Sponsored Ministries, Inc.

# HEALTH ENTERPRISES COOPERATIVE
5825 Dry Creek Lane NE, Cedar Rapids, IA Zip 52402–1225; tel. 319/368–3619; Judy L. Sadler, President and Chief Executive Officer

## IOWA
### Ames
Alliance
Mary Greeley Medical Center

### Chariton
Alliance
Lucas County Health Center

### Charles City
Alliance
Floyd County Medical Center

### Cherokee
Alliance
Cherokee Regional Medical Center

### Davenport
Alliance
Genesis Health System

### Denison
Alliance
Crawford County Memorial Hospital

### Des Moines
Alliance
Broadlawns Medical Center

### Fairfield
Alliance
Jefferson County Health Center

### Grinnell
Alliance
UnityPoint Health – Grinnell Regional Medical Center

### Guthrie Center
Alliance
Guthrie County Hospital

### Humboldt
Alliance
Humboldt County Memorial Hospital

### Ida Grove
Alliance
Horn Memorial Hospital

### Independence
Alliance
Buchanan County Health Center

### Iowa City
Alliance
MercyOne Iowa City Medical Center

### Manchester
Alliance
Regional Medical Center

### Maquoketa
Alliance
Jackson County Regional Health Center

### Marshalltown
Alliance
UnityPoint Health – Marshalltown

### Mount Pleasant
Alliance
Henry County Health Center

### Newton
Alliance
MercyOne Newton Medical Center

### Oskaloosa
Alliance
Mahaska Health Partnership

### Pella
Alliance
Pella Regional Health Center

### Pocahontas
Alliance
Pocahontas Community Hospital

### Sac City
Alliance
Loring Hospital

### Waukon
Alliance
Veterans Memorial Hospital

### Waverly
Alliance
Waverly Health Center

### West Burlington
Alliance
Great River Medical Center

## MISSOURI
### Bethany
Alliance
Harrison County Community Hospital

### Fairfax
Alliance
Community Hospital–Fairfax

# HOSPITAL NETWORK VENTURES, LLC
6212 American Avenue, Portage, MI Zip 49002; tel. 269/329–3200; Gregory L. Hedegore, President and Chief Executive Officer

## MICHIGAN
### Allegan
Alliance
Ascension Allegan Hospital

### Kalamazoo
Alliance
Bronson Healthcare Group

Bronson Methodist Hospital

### Marshall
Alliance
Oaklawn Hospital

### Sturgis
Alliance
Sturgis Hospital

# HOSPITAL SHARED SERVICES ASSOCIATION
P O Box 19741, Seattle, WA Zip 98109–6741; tel. 206/399–0865; Joe McNamee, Executive Director

## OREGON
### Salem
Alliance
Oregon State Hospital

## WASHINGTON
### Bellevue
Alliance
Overlake Medical Center

### Chelan
Alliance
Lake Chelan Community Hospital and Clinics

### Clarkston
Alliance
Tri–State Memorial Hospital

### Davenport
Alliance
Lincoln Hospital

### Edmonds
Alliance
Swedish/Edmonds

### Ephrata
Alliance
Columbia Basin Hospital

### Grand Coulee
Alliance
Coulee Medical Center

### Kirkland
Alliance
EvergreenHealth

### Medical Lake
Alliance
Eastern State Hospital

### Moses Lake
Alliance
Samaritan Healthcare

### Mount Vernon
Alliance
Skagit Valley Hospital

### Newport
Alliance
Newport Hospital and Health Services

### Odessa
Alliance
Odessa Memorial Healthcare Center

### Othello
Alliance
Othello Community Hospital

### Prosser
Alliance
Prosser Memorial Health

### Pullman
Alliance
Pullman Regional Hospital

### Quincy
Alliance
Quincy Valley Medical Center

### Republic
Alliance
Ferry County Memorial Hospital

### Ritzville
Alliance
East Adams Rural Healthcare

### Tacoma
Alliance
Western State Hospital

### Tonasket
Alliance
North Valley Hospital

# KENTUCKY HEALTH COLLABORATIVE
651 Perimeter Drive, Suite 650, Lexington, KY Zip 40517–4134; tel. 859/286–3107; David Zimba, Managing Director

## KENTUCKY
### Bowling Green
Alliance
Medical Center at Bowling Green

Danville
Alliance
Ephraim McDowell Health

Edgewood
Alliance
St. Elizabeth Healthcare

Lexington
Alliance
Appalachian Regional Healthcare, Inc.
University of Kentucky Albert B. Chandler Hospital

Louisville
Alliance
Baptist Health
Norton Healthcare

Morehead
Alliance
St. Claire HealthCare

Owensboro
Alliance
Owensboro Health

## TENNESSEE

Brentwood
Alliance
LifePoint Health

## MEDI–SOTA, INC.
1280 Locust Street Suite 16, Dawson, MN Zip 56232–2375; tel. 320/769–2269; Deb Ranallo, Executive Director

## MINNESOTA

Appleton
Alliance
Appleton Area Health Services

Arlington
Alliance
Ridgeview Sibley Medical Center

Benson
Alliance
Swift County – Benson Health Services

Blue Earth
Alliance
United Hospital District

Canby
Alliance
Sanford Canby Medical Center

Dawson
Alliance
Johnson Memorial Health Services

Elbow Lake
Alliance
Prairie Ridge Hospital and Health Services

Glencoe
Alliance
Glencoe Regional Health

Glenwood
Alliance
Glacial Ridge Health System

Graceville
Alliance
Essentia Health–Graceville

Granite Falls
Alliance
Avera Granite Falls Health Center

Hendricks
Alliance
Hendricks Community Hospital Association

Litchfield
Alliance
Meeker Memorial Hospital

Madelia
Alliance
Madelia Community Hospital

Madison
Alliance
Madison Healthcare Services

Mahnomen
Alliance
Mahnomen Health Center

Marshall
Alliance
Avera Marshall Regional Medical Center

Montevideo
Alliance
CCM Health

Olivia
Alliance
RC Hospital and Clinics

Ortonville
Alliance
Ortonville Area Health Services

Paynesville
Alliance
CentraCare Health–Paynesville

Perham
Alliance
Perham Health

Pipestone
Alliance
Pipestone County Medical Center Avera

Redwood Falls
Alliance
Carris Health – Redwood

Saint Peter
Alliance
River's Edge Hospital and Clinic

Slayton
Alliance
Murray County Medical Center

Sleepy Eye
Alliance
Sleepy Eye Medical Center

Staples
Alliance
Lakewood Health System

Tracy
Alliance
Sanford Tracy Medical Center

Tyler
Alliance
Avera Tyler Hospital

Wadena
Alliance
Tri–County Hospital

Willmar
Alliance
Rice Memorial Hospital

Windom
Alliance
Windom Area Health

## NORTHWEST KANSAS HEALTH ALLIANCE
2220 Canterbury Drive, Hays, KS Zip 67601–2370; tel. 785/623–2300; Edward Herrman, R.N., FACHE, President and Chief Executive Officer

## KANSAS

Ashland
Alliance
Ashland Health Center

Atwood
Alliance
Rawlins County Health Center

Beloit
Alliance
Mitchell County Hospital Health Systems

Colby
Alliance
Citizens Medical Center

Dighton
Alliance
Lane County Hospital

Dodge City
Alliance
Western Plains Medical Complex

Ellsworth
Alliance
Ellsworth County Medical Center

Garden City
Alliance
St. Catherine Hospital

Goodland
Alliance
Goodland Regional Medical Center

Great Bend
Alliance
University of Kansas Health System Great Bend Campus

Greensburg
Alliance
Kiowa County Memorial Hospital

Hill City
Alliance
Graham County Hospital

Hoisington
Alliance
Clara Barton Hospital

Hoxie
Alliance
Sheridan County Health Complex

Hutchinson
Alliance
Hutchinson Regional Medical Center

Jetmore
Alliance
Hodgeman County Health Center

Kinsley
Alliance
Edwards County Medical Center

La Crosse
Alliance
Rush County Memorial Hospital

Larned
Alliance
University of Kansas Health System Pawnee Valley Campus

Lawrence
Alliance
LMH Health

Leoti
Alliance
Wichita County Health Center

Lincoln
Alliance
Lincoln County Hospital

Lyons
Alliance
Hospital District No 1 of Rice County

Minneola
Alliance
Minneola District Hospital

Ness City
Alliance
Ness County Hospital District No 2

Norton
Alliance
Norton County Hospital

Oakley
Alliance
Logan County Hospital

Oberlin
Alliance
Decatur Health Systems

Osborne
Alliance
Osborne County Memorial Hospital

Ottawa
Alliance
AdventHealth Ottawa

Section B

**Phillipsburg**
Alliance
Phillips County Health Systems

**Plainville**
Alliance
Rooks County Health Center

**Quinter**
Alliance
Gove County Medical Center

**Ransom**
Alliance
Grisell Memorial Hospital District One

**Russell**
Alliance
Russell Regional Hospital

**Saint Francis**
Alliance
Cheyenne County Hospital

**Salina**
Alliance
Salina Regional Health Center

**Satanta**
Alliance
Satanta District Hospital and Long Term Care

**Scott City**
Alliance
Scott County Hospital

**Smith Center**
Alliance
Smith County Memorial Hospital

**Stafford**
Alliance
Stafford County Hospital

**Tribune**
Alliance
Greeley County Health Services

**Wakeeney**
Alliance
Trego County–Lemke Memorial Hospital

## OHSU PARTNERS
3303 SW Bond Avenue, Suite 6100,
Mail Code: CH6P, Portland, OR
Zip 97239–4501; tel. 503/494–4036;
Peter F. Rapp, Chief Executive Officer

### OREGON
**Hillsboro**
Alliance
Tuality Healthcare

**Salem**
Alliance
Salem Health

## PANDION SOURCING & CONSULTING REGIONAL CORPORATION
3445 Winton Place, Suite 222,
Rochester, NY Zip 14623–2950;
tel. 888/732–4282; Travis Heider,
President and Chief Executive Officer

### GEORGIA
**Fort Oglethorpe**
Alliance
CHI Memorial Hospital – Georgia

### NEW JERSEY
**Berkeley Heights**
Alliance
Runnells Center for Rehabilitation and Healthcare

**Newark**
Alliance
Columbus Hospital LTACH

### NEW YORK
**Batavia**
Alliance
United Memorial Medical Center

**Bath**
Alliance
Bath Veterans Affairs Medical Center
Ira Davenport Memorial Hospital

**Buffalo**
Alliance
Erie County Medical Center
Roswell Park Comprehensive Cancer Center
Sisters of Charity Hospital of Buffalo

**Canandaigua**
Alliance
F. F. Thompson Hospital

**Clifton Springs**
Alliance
Clifton Springs Hospital and Clinic

**Corning**
Alliance
Guthrie Corning Hospital

**Dansville**
Alliance
Nicholas H. Noyes Memorial Hospital

**Dunkirk**
Alliance
Brooks Memorial Hospital

**Elmira**
Alliance
Arnot Ogden Medical Center

**Geneva**
Alliance
Geneva General Hospital

**Hornell**
Alliance
St. James Hospital

**Ithaca**
Alliance
Cayuga Medical Center at Ithaca

**Jamestown**
Alliance
UPMC Chautauqua

**Kenmore**
Alliance
Kenmore Mercy Hospital

**Lewiston**
Alliance
Mount St. Mary's Hospital and Health Center

**Montour Falls**
Alliance
Schuyler Hospital

**Newark**
Alliance
Newark–Wayne Community Hospital

**Niagara Falls**
Alliance
Niagara Falls Memorial Medical Center

**Olean**
Alliance
Olean General Hospital

**Penn Yan**
Alliance
Soldiers and Sailors Memorial Hospital

**Rochester**
Alliance
Highland Hospital
Rochester General Hospital
Strong Memorial Hospital of the University of Rochester
Unity Hospital

**Springville**
Alliance
Bertrand Chaffee Hospital

**Wellsville**
Alliance
Jones Memorial Hospital

## PANDION SOURCING NATIONAL LLC
3445 Winton Place, Suite 222,
Rochester, NY Zip 14623–2950;
tel. 888/732–4282; Travis Heider,
President and Chief Executive Officer

### GEORGIA
**Fort Oglethorpe**
Alliance
CHI Memorial Hospital – Georgia

### NEW JERSEY
**Berkeley Heights**
Alliance
Runnells Center for Rehabilitation and Healthcare

**Newark**
Alliance
Columbus Hospital LTACH

### NEW YORK
**Dansville**
Alliance
Nicholas H. Noyes Memorial Hospital

**Geneva**
Alliance
Geneva General Hospital

**Lockport**
Alliance
Eastern Niagara Hospital

**Penn Yan**
Alliance
Soldiers and Sailors Memorial Hospital

**Springville**
Alliance
Bertrand Chaffee Hospital

**Wellsville**
Alliance
Jones Memorial Hospital

## PENNANT HEALTH ALLIANCE
2122 Health Drive SW Suite 100,
Wyoming, MI Zip 49519–9698;
tel. 616/252–6800; Michael D. Faas,
Chief Executive Officer

### MICHIGAN
**Ann Arbor**
Alliance
Michigan Medicine

**Cadillac**
Alliance
Munson Healthcare Cadillac Hospital

**Grand Rapids**
Alliance
Mary Free Bed Rehabilitation Hospital
Mercy Health Saint Mary's

**Grayling**
Alliance
Munson Healthcare Grayling Hospital

**Wyoming**
Alliance
Metro Health – University of Michigan Health

## PREMIER, INC.
13034 Ballantyne Corporate Place,
Charlotte, NC Zip 28277–1498;
tel. 704/816–5353; Susan DeVore,
President and Chief Executive Officer

### ALABAMA
**Dothan**
Alliance
Southeast Alabama Medical Center

**Opelika**
Alliance
East Alabama Medical Center

### ARIZONA
**Phoenix**
Alliance
Banner Health

**Scottsdale**
Alliance
HonorHealth

## ARKANSAS

**Batesville**
Alliance
White River Medical Center

**Pine Bluff**
Alliance
Jefferson Regional Medical Center

## CALIFORNIA

**Fresno**
Alliance
Community Medical Centers

**Loma Linda**
Alliance
Loma Linda University Medical Center

**Los Angeles**
Alliance
Verity Health System

**Mountain View**
Alliance
El Camino Hospital

**Rancho Mirage**
Alliance
Eisenhower Health

**Roseville**
Alliance
Adventist Health

## CONNECTICUT

**Hartford**
Alliance
Saint Francis Hospital and Medical Center

**Waterbury**
Alliance
Saint Mary's Hospital

## DELAWARE

**Dover**
Alliance
Bayhealth Medical Center

**Lewes**
Alliance
Beebe Healthcare

## FLORIDA

**Altamonte Springs**
Alliance
AdventHealth

**Clearwater**
Alliance
BayCare Health System

**Coral Gables**
Alliance
Baptist Health South Florida

**Dunedin**
Alliance
BayCare Alliant Hospital

**Jacksonville**
Alliance
Baptist Health

Nemours

**Miami Beach**
Alliance
Mount Sinai Medical Center

**Tampa**
Alliance
H. Lee Moffitt Cancer Center and Research Institute

**Vero Beach**
Alliance
Cleveland Clinic Indian River Hospital

**Winter Haven**
Alliance
Winter Haven Hospital

## GEORGIA

**Carrollton**
Alliance
Tanner Medical Center–Carrollton

**Lagrange**
Alliance
Wellstar West Georgia Medical Center

**Savannah**
Alliance
Memorial Health

St. Joseph's Hospital

## HAWAII

**Honolulu**
Alliance
Kuakini Medical Center

## ILLINOIS

**Chicago**
Alliance
Mount Sinai Hospital

**Harvey**
Alliance
Ingalls Memorial Hospital

**Naperville**
Alliance
Edward Hospital

**Peoria**
Alliance
UnityPoint Health – Peoria

**Urbana**
Alliance
Carle Foundation Hospital

## INDIANA

**Gary**
Alliance
Methodist Hospitals

## KENTUCKY

**Ashland**
Alliance
King's Daughters Medical Center

**Bowling Green**
Alliance
Commonwealth Regional Specialty Hospital

**Danville**
Alliance
Ephraim McDowell Regional Medical Center

**Edgewood**
Alliance
St. Elizabeth Edgewood

**Glasgow**
Alliance
T. J. Samson Community Hospital

**Henderson**
Alliance
Methodist Hospital

**Louisville**
Alliance
Alliant Management Services

Baptist Health

Norton Healthcare

**Murray**
Alliance
Murray–Calloway County Hospital

## LOUISIANA

**Baton Rouge**
Alliance
Woman's Hospital

**Hammond**
Alliance
North Oaks Health System

**Houma**
Alliance
Terrebonne General Medical Center

**Lafayette**
Alliance
Lafayette General Medical Center

**Marrero**
Alliance
West Jefferson Medical Center

## MAINE

**Lewiston**
Alliance
Central Maine Medical Center

## MARYLAND

**Annapolis**
Alliance
Anne Arundel Medical Center

**Baltimore**
Alliance
Greater Baltimore Medical Center

Johns Hopkins Health System

Mercy Medical Center

Sinai Hospital of Baltimore

**Cumberland**
Alliance
Western Maryland Regional Medical Center

**Elkton**
Alliance
Union Hospital

**Frederick**
Alliance
Frederick Health

**Gaithersburg**
Alliance
Adventist HealthCare

**Hagerstown**
Alliance
Meritus Medical Center

**Lanham**
Alliance
Doctors Community Hospital

**Marriottsville**
Alliance
Bon Secours Mercy Health

**Randallstown**
Alliance
Northwest Hospital

**Salisbury**
Alliance
TidalHealth Peninsula

**Westminster**
Alliance
Carroll Hospital Center

## MASSACHUSETTS

**Boston**
Alliance
Tufts Medical Center

**Fall River**
Alliance
Southcoast Hospitals Group

**Springfield**
Alliance
Baystate Health, Inc.

## MICHIGAN

**Detroit**
Alliance
Henry Ford Health System

**Grand Blanc**
Alliance
McLaren Health Care Corporation

**Jackson**
Alliance
Henry Ford Allegiance Health

## MINNESOTA

**Minneapolis**
Alliance
M Health Fairview

## MISSISSIPPI

**Laurel**
Alliance
South Central Regional Medical Center

**Meridian**
Alliance
Rush Health Systems

## MISSOURI

**Saint Joseph**
Alliance
Mosaic Life Care at St. Joseph – Medical Center

Section B

## Alliances

**Saint Louis**
Alliance
  SSM Health

## MONTANA

**Billings**
Alliance
  Billings Clinic

## NEW MEXICO

**Albuquerque**
Alliance
  Presbyterian Healthcare Services

## NEW YORK

**Rochester**
Alliance
  Pandion Sourcing National LLC

  Rochester Regional Health

## NORTH CAROLINA

**Asheboro**
Alliance
  Randolph Hospital

**Boone**
Alliance
  Watauga Medical Center

**Charlotte**
Alliance
  Atrium Health

**Fayetteville**
Alliance
  Cape Fear Valley Health System

**Gastonia**
Alliance
  CaroMont Regional Medical Center

**Goldsboro**
Alliance
  Wayne UNC Health Care

**Greensboro**
Alliance
  Moses H. Cone Memorial Hospital

**Hendersonville**
Alliance
  Margaret R. Pardee Memorial Hospital

**Hickory**
Alliance
  Catawba Valley Medical Center

**Kinston**
Alliance
  UNC Lenoir Healthcare

**Lumberton**
Alliance
  Southeastern Health

**Morehead City**
Alliance
  Carteret Health Care

**Pinehurst**
Alliance
  FirstHealth of the Carolinas

**Roanoke Rapids**
Alliance
  Vidant North Hospital

**Statesville**
Alliance
  Iredell Health System

## OHIO

**Akron**
Alliance
  Summa Health System

**Cincinnati**
Alliance
  Mercy Health

**Cleveland**
Alliance
  University Hospitals

**Elyria**
Alliance
  UH Elyria Medical Center

**Kettering**
Alliance
  Kettering Medical Center

**Middleburg Heights**
Alliance
  Southwest General Health Center

**Parma**
Alliance
  University Hospitals Parma Medical Center

**Sandusky**
Alliance
  Firelands Regional Health System

## OKLAHOMA

**Tulsa**
Alliance
  Saint Francis Hospital

## OREGON

**Salem**
Alliance
  Salem Hospital

## PENNSYLVANIA

**Beaver**
Alliance
  Heritage Valley Health System

**Bethlehem**
Alliance
  St. Luke's University Health Network

**Danville**
Alliance
  Geisinger

**King of Prussia**
Alliance
  Universal Health Services, Inc.

**Philadelphia**
Alliance
  Einstein Healthcare Network

**Washington**
Alliance
  Washington Hospital

## SOUTH CAROLINA

**Anderson**
Alliance
  AnMed Health Medical Center

**Conway**
Alliance
  Conway Medical Center

**Greenwood**
Alliance
  Self Regional Healthcare

**West Columbia**
Alliance
  Lexington Medical Center

## SOUTH DAKOTA

**Rapid City**
Alliance
  Monument Health Rapid City Hospital

**Sioux Falls**
Alliance
  Avera Health

## TENNESSEE

**Crossville**
Alliance
  Cumberland Medical Center

**Knoxville**
Alliance
  University of Tennessee Medical Center

**Maryville**
Alliance
  Blount Memorial Hospital

## TEXAS

**Arlington**
Alliance
  Texas Health Resources

**Dallas**
Alliance
  Methodist Health System

  University of Texas Southwestern Medical Center

**Galveston**
Alliance
  University of Texas Medical Branch

**Houston**
Alliance
  Harris Health System

  University of Texas M.D. Anderson Cancer Center

**Lubbock**
Alliance
  University Medical Center

## VIRGINIA

**Abingdon**
Alliance
  Johnston Memorial Hospital

**Chesapeake**
Alliance
  Chesapeake Regional Medical Center

**Falls Church**
Alliance
  Inova Health System

**Marion**
Alliance
  Smyth County Community Hospital

**Newport News**
Alliance
  Riverside Health System

**Roanoke**
Alliance
  Carilion Clinic

**South Hill**
Alliance
  VCU Health Community Memorial Hospital

**Winchester**
Alliance
  Valley Health System

## WASHINGTON

**Seattle**
Alliance
  Kaiser Permanente Capitol Hill Campus

**Vancouver**
Alliance
  PeaceHealth

## WEST VIRGINIA

**Elkins**
Alliance
  Davis Medical Center

**Huntington**
Alliance
  Cabell Huntington Hospital

**Morgantown**
Alliance
  Mon Health Medical Center

**Parkersburg**
Alliance
  Camden Clark Medical Center

**Point Pleasant**
Alliance
  Pleasant Valley Hospital

**South Charleston**
Alliance
  Thomas Memorial Hospital

**Weirton**
Alliance
  Weirton Medical Center

## THE NEW JERSEY COUNCIL OF TEACHING HOSPITALS

154 West State Street, Trenton, NJ Zip 8608; tel. 609/656–9600; Deborah S. Briggs, President

## NEW JERSEY

**Camden**
Alliance
Cooper University Health Care

**Hackensack**
Alliance
Hackensack Meridian Health Hackensack University
Medical Center

**Marlton**
Alliance
Weisman Children's Rehabilitation Hospital

**Montclair**
Alliance
Hackensack Meridian Health Mountainside Medical
Center

**Morristown**
Alliance
Atlantic Health System
Morristown Medical Center

**New Brunswick**
Alliance
Children's Specialized Hospital

**North Bergen**
Alliance
Hackensack Meridian Health Palisades Medical Center

**Paterson**
Alliance
St. Joseph's University Medical Center

**Summit**
Alliance
Overlook Medical Center

## UNITED IROQUOIS SHARED SERVICES, INC.

15 Executive Park Drive, Clifton Park,
NY Zip 12065–5631; tel. 518/383–
5060; Gary J. Fitzgerald, President

## NEW YORK

**Albany**
Alliance
St. Peter's Hospital

**Alexandria Bay**
Alliance
River Hospital

**Amsterdam**
Alliance
St. Mary's Healthcare

**Auburn**
Alliance
Auburn Community Hospital

**Binghamton**
Alliance
Our Lady of Lourdes Memorial Hospital, Inc.
United Health Services Hospitals–Binghamton

**Buffalo**
Alliance
Roswell Park Comprehensive Cancer Center

**Carthage**
Alliance
Carthage Area Hospital

**Cobleskill**
Alliance
Cobleskill Regional Hospital

**Cooperstown**
Alliance
Bassett Medical Center

**Cortland**
Alliance
Guthrie Cortland Regional Medical Center

**Cuba**
Alliance
Cuba Memorial Hospital

**Delhi**
Alliance
O'Connor Hospital

**Elizabethtown**
Alliance
The University of Vermont Health Network
Elizabethtown Community Hospital

**Glens Falls**
Alliance
Glens Falls Hospital

**Glenville**
Alliance
Conifer Park

**Gloversville**
Alliance
Nathan Littauer Hospital and Nursing Home

**Hamilton**
Alliance
Community Memorial Hospital

**Hudson**
Alliance
Columbia Memorial Hospital

**Ithaca**
Alliance
Cayuga Medical Center at Ithaca

**Little Falls**
Alliance
Little Falls Hospital

**Lowville**
Alliance
Lewis County General Hospital

**Malone**
Alliance
The University of Vermont Health Network – Alice Hyde
Medical Center

**Margaretville**
Alliance
Margaretville Hospital

**Massena**
Alliance
Massena Hospital, Inc.

**Norwich**
Alliance
UHS Chenango Memorial Hospital

**Ogdensburg**
Alliance
Claxton–Hepburn Medical Center

**Olean**
Alliance
Olean General Hospital

**Oneida**
Alliance
Oneida Healthcare

**Oneonta**
Alliance
Aurelia Osborn Fox Memorial Hospital

**Oswego**
Alliance
Oswego Hospital

**Plattsburgh**
Alliance
The University of Vermont Health Network–Champlain
Valley Physicians Hospital

**Potsdam**
Alliance
Canton–Potsdam Hospital

**Rome**
Alliance
Rome Memorial Hospital

**Saranac Lake**
Alliance
Adirondack Health

**Saratoga Springs**
Alliance
Saratoga Hospital

**Schenectady**
Alliance
Ellis Hospital
Sunnyview Rehabilitation Hospital

**Springville**
Alliance
Bertrand Chaffee Hospital

**Star Lake**
Alliance
Clifton–Fine Hospital

**Syracuse**
Alliance
Crouse Health
Upstate University Hospital

**Troy**
Alliance
Samaritan Hospital – Main Campus

**Utica**
Alliance
Faxton St. Luke's Healthcare
St. Elizabeth Medical Center

**Walton**
Alliance
UHS Delaware Valley Hospital

**Watertown**
Alliance
Samaritan Medical Center

## VANTAGE HEALTHCARE NETWORK, INC.

18282 Technology Drive, Suite 202,
Meadville, PA Zip 16335; tel. 814/337–
0000; David Petrarca, Director Retail
Operations

## PENNSYLVANIA

**Corry**
Alliance
LECOM Corry Memorial Hospital

**DuBois**
Alliance
Penn Highlands DuBois

**Erie**
Alliance
LECOM Health Millcreek Community Hospital
Saint Vincent Hospital

**Farrell**
Alliance
UPMC Horizon

**Kane**
Alliance
UPMC Kane

**Kittanning**
Alliance
ACMH Hospital

**Meadville**
Alliance
Meadville Medical Center

**Saint Marys**
Alliance
Penn Highlands Elk

**Seneca**
Alliance
UPMC Northwest

**Titusville**
Alliance
Titusville Area Hospital

**Warren**
Alliance
Warren General Hospital

## VIZIENT, INC.

290 East John Carpenter Freeway,
Irving, TX Zip 75062–2730;
tel. 972/830–0000; Curtis W.
Nonomaque, President and Chief
Executive Officer

## ALABAMA

**Alexander City**
Alliance
Russell Medical

# Alliances

**Anniston**
Alliance
RMC Anniston

**Athens**
Alliance
Athens–Limestone Hospital

**Atmore**
Alliance
Atmore Community Hospital

**Bay Minette**
Alliance
North Baldwin Infirmary

**Bessemer**
Alliance
Medical West

**Birmingham**
Alliance
University of Alabama Hospital

**Boaz**
Alliance
Marshall Medical Center South

**Brewton**
Alliance
D. W. McMillan Memorial Hospital

**Decatur**
Alliance
Decatur Morgan Hospital

**Fairhope**
Alliance
Thomas Hospital

**Fayette**
Alliance
Fayette Medical Center

**Guntersville**
Alliance
Marshall Health System

Marshall Medical Center North

**Huntsville**
Alliance
Huntsville Hospital

**Mobile**
Alliance
Mobile Infirmary Medical Center

USA Health Children's & Women's Hospital

USA Health University Hospital

**Montgomery**
Alliance
Baptist Medical Center East

Baptist Medical Center South

**Opp**
Alliance
Mizell Memorial Hospital

**Ozark**
Alliance
Dale Medical Center

**Prattville**
Alliance
Prattville Baptist Hospital

**Red Bay**
Alliance
Red Bay Hospital

**Scottsboro**
Alliance
Highlands Medical Center

**Sheffield**
Alliance
Helen Keller Hospital

**Tuscaloosa**
Alliance
DCH Health System

DCH Regional Medical Center

**Union Springs**
Alliance
Bullock County Hospital

## ALASKA

**Anchorage**
Alliance
Providence Alaska Medical Center

St. Elias Specialty Hospital

**Cordova**
Alliance
Cordova Community Medical Center

**Kodiak**
Alliance
Providence Kodiak Island Medical Center

**Seward**
Alliance
Providence Seward Medical Center

**Valdez**
Alliance
Providence Valdez Medical Center

**Wrangell**
Alliance
Wrangell Medical Center

## AMERICAN SAMOA

**Pago Pago**
Alliance
Lyndon B. Johnson Tropical Medical Center

## ARIZONA

**Benson**
Alliance
Benson Hospital

**Bisbee**
Alliance
Copper Queen Community Hospital

**Flagstaff**
Alliance
Flagstaff Medical Center

**Green Valley**
Alliance
Santa Cruz Valley Regional Hospital

**Kingman**
Alliance
Kingman Regional Medical Center

**Phoenix**
Alliance
Mayo Clinic Hospital

Valleywise Health

**Safford**
Alliance
Mt. Graham Regional Medical Center

**Tucson**
Alliance
Banner – University Medical Center South

Banner – University Medical Center Tucson

TMC HealthCare

**Willcox**
Alliance
Northern Cochise Community Hospital

## ARKANSAS

**Arkadelphia**
Alliance
Baptist Health Medical Center–Arkadelphia

**Booneville**
Alliance
Mercy Hospital Booneville

**Clinton**
Alliance
Ozark Health Medical Center

**Conway**
Alliance
Conway Regional Medical Center

**Fayetteville**
Alliance
Washington Regional Medical Center

**Heber Springs**
Alliance
Baptist Health Medical Center–Heber Springs

**Hot Springs**
Alliance
CHI St. Vincent Hot Springs

**Jonesboro**
Alliance
NEA Baptist Memorial Hospital

St. Bernards Medical Center

**Little Rock**
Alliance
Baptist Health Extended Care Hospital

Baptist Health Medical Center–Little Rock

Baptist Health

CHI St. Vincent Infirmary Medical Center

**Malvern**
Alliance
Baptist Health Medical Center–Hot Spring County

**Morrilton**
Alliance
CHI St. Vincent Morrilton

**North Little Rock**
Alliance
Baptist Health Medical Center – North Little Rock

**Paragould**
Alliance
Arkansas Methodist Medical Center

**Piggott**
Alliance
Piggott Community Hospital

**Stuttgart**
Alliance
Baptist Health Medical Center–Stuttgart

**Walnut Ridge**
Alliance
Lawrence Memorial Hospital

**Wynne**
Alliance
CrossRidge Community Hospital

## CALIFORNIA

**Alameda**
Alliance
Alameda Hospital

**Antioch**
Alliance
Kaiser Permanente Antioch Medical Center

**Arcadia**
Alliance
Methodist Hospital of Southern California

**Auburn**
Alliance
Sutter Auburn Faith Hospital

**Bakersfield**
Alliance
Kern Medical

**Berkeley**
Alliance
Alta Bates Medical Center–Herrick Campus

Alta Bates Summit Medical Center–Alta Bates Campus

**Burbank**
Alliance
Providence Saint Joseph Medical Center

**Burlingame**
Alliance
Mills–Peninsula Health Services

**Castro Valley**
Alliance
Eden Medical Center

**Colton**
Alliance
Arrowhead Regional Medical Center

**Concord**
Alliance
John Muir Medical Center, Concord

**Covina**
Alliance
  Emanate Health Inter–Community Hospital
  Emanate Health

**Crescent City**
Alliance
  Sutter Coast Hospital

**Davis**
Alliance
  Sutter Davis Hospital

**Downey**
Alliance
  PIH Health Hospital – Downey
  Rancho Los Amigos National Rehabilitation Center

**El Centro**
Alliance
  El Centro Regional Medical Center

**Escondido**
Alliance
  Palomar Health
  Palomar Medical Center Escondido

**Fairfield**
Alliance
  NorthBay Medical Center

**Fremont**
Alliance
  Kaiser Permanente Fremont Medical Center
  Washington Hospital Healthcare System

**French Camp**
Alliance
  San Joaquin General Hospital

**Fresno**
Alliance
  Community Medical Centers
  Saint Agnes Medical Center

**Glendora**
Alliance
  Emanate Health Foothill Presbyterian Hospital

**Jackson**
Alliance
  Sutter Amador Hospital

**King City**
Alliance
  Mee Memorial Hospital

**Lakeport**
Alliance
  Sutter Lakeside Hospital

**Lancaster**
Alliance
  Antelope Valley Hospital

**Los Angeles**
Alliance
  Cedars–Sinai Medical Center
  LAC+USC Medical Center
  Martin Luther King, Jr. Community Hospital
  Ronald Reagan UCLA Medical Center
  Stewart & Lynda Resnick Neuropsychiatric Hospital
  at UCLA
  USC Norris Comprehensive Cancer Center

**Los Banos**
Alliance
  Memorial Hospital Los Banos

**Manteca**
Alliance
  Kaiser Permanente Manteca Medical Center

**Marina Del Rey**
Alliance
  Marina Del Rey Hospital

**Mariposa**
Alliance
  John C. Fremont Healthcare District

**Martinez**
Alliance
  Contra Costa Regional Medical Center

**Menlo Park**
Alliance
  Menlo Park Surgical Hospital

**Mission Hills**
Alliance
  Providence Holy Cross Medical Center

**Modesto**
Alliance
  Memorial Medical Center

**Monterey**
Alliance
  Community Hospital of the Monterey Peninsula

**Moreno Valley**
Alliance
  Riverside University Health System–Medical Center

**Mountain View**
Alliance
  El Camino Hospital

**Novato**
Alliance
  Novato Community Hospital

**Oakland**
Alliance
  Alta Bates Summit Medical Center – Summit Campus
  Highland Hospital
  Kaiser Permanente Oakland Medical Center

**Oceanside**
Alliance
  Tri–City Medical Center

**Ojai**
Alliance
  Ojai Valley Community Hospital

**Orange**
Alliance
  UCI Medical Center

**Palo Alto**
Alliance
  Lucile Packard Children's Hospital Stanford
  Stanford Health Care

**Pleasanton**
Alliance
  Stanford Health Care – ValleyCare

**Pomona**
Alliance
  Pomona Valley Hospital Medical Center

**Porterville**
Alliance
  Sierra View Medical Center

**Portola**
Alliance
  Eastern Plumas Health Care

**Poway**
Alliance
  Palomar Medical Center Poway

**Redlands**
Alliance
  Redlands Community Hospital

**Redwood City**
Alliance
  Kaiser Permanente Redwood City Medical Center

**Roseville**
Alliance
  Kaiser Permanente Roseville Medical Center
  Sutter Roseville Medical Center

**Sacramento**
Alliance
  Kaiser Permanente Sacramento Medical Center
  Kaiser Permanente South Sacramento Medical Center
  Shriners Hospitals for Children–Northern California
  Sutter Center for Psychiatry
  Sutter Health
  Sutter Medical Center, Sacramento
  University of California, Davis Medical Center

**Salinas**
Alliance
  Natividad Medical Center

**San Diego**
Alliance
  Scripps Health
  UC San Diego Medical Center–Hillcrest

**San Francisco**
Alliance
  California Pacific Medical Center–Davies Campus
  California Pacific Medical Center–St. Luke's Campus
  California Pacific Medical Center
  Chinese Hospital
  Kaiser Permanente San Francisco Medical Center
  UCSF Medical Center
  Zuckerberg San Francisco General Hospital and
  Trauma Center

**San Jose**
Alliance
  Kaiser Permanente San Jose Medical Center
  Santa Clara Valley Medical Center

**San Leandro**
Alliance
  San Leandro Hospital

**San Mateo**
Alliance
  San Mateo Medical Center

**San Pedro**
Alliance
  Providence Little Company of Mary Medical Center
  San Pedro

**San Rafael**
Alliance
  Kaiser Permanente San Rafael Medical Center

**Santa Barbara**
Alliance
  Cottage Health
  Goleta Valley Cottage Hospital
  Santa Barbara Cottage Hospital

**Santa Clara**
Alliance
  Kaiser Permanente Santa Clara Medical Center

**Santa Cruz**
Alliance
  Sutter Maternity and Surgery Center of Santa Cruz

**Santa Monica**
Alliance
  Providence Saint John's Health Center
  UCLA Medical Center–Santa Monica

**Santa Rosa**
Alliance
  Kaiser Permanente Santa Rosa Medical Center
  Sutter Santa Rosa Regional Hospital

**Solvang**
Alliance
  Santa Ynez Valley Cottage Hospital

**South San Francisco**
Alliance
  Kaiser Permanente South San Francisco

**Stockton**
Alliance
  Dameron Hospital

**Sylmar**
Alliance
  LAC–Olive View–UCLA Medical Center

**Tarzana**
Alliance
  Providence Tarzana Medical Center

**Torrance**
Alliance
  Harbor–UCLA Medical Center
  Providence Little Company of Mary Medical Center –
  Torrance
  Torrance Memorial Medical Center

## Alliances

**Tracy**
Alliance
Sutter Tracy Community Hospital

**Vacaville**
Alliance
Kaiser Permanente Vacaville Medical Center

**Vallejo**
Alliance
Kaiser Permanente Vallejo Medical Center
Sutter Solano Medical Center

**Ventura**
Alliance
Community Memorial Hospital

**Walnut Creek**
Alliance
John Muir Health
John Muir Medical Center, Walnut Creek
Kaiser Permanente Walnut Creek Medical Center

**Whittier**
Alliance
PIH Health Hospital – Whittier

**Yuba City**
Alliance
Sutter Surgical Hospital – North Valley

### COLORADO

**Alamosa**
Alliance
San Luis Valley Health

**Aurora**
Alliance
University of Colorado Hospital

**Boulder**
Alliance
Boulder Community Health

**Canon City**
Alliance
St. Thomas More Hospital

**Colorado Springs**
Alliance
Penrose–St. Francis Health Services
UCHealth Memorial Hospital

**Denver**
Alliance
Denver Health
National Jewish Health

**Durango**
Alliance
Mercy Regional Medical Center

**Englewood**
Alliance
Craig Hospital

**Estes Park**
Alliance
Estes Park Medical Center

**Fort Collins**
Alliance
UCHealth Poudre Valley Hospital

**Grand Junction**
Alliance
St. Mary's Hospital and Medical Center

**Gunnison**
Alliance
Gunnison Valley Hospital

**La Jara**
Alliance
San Luis Valley Health Conejos County Hospital

**Lakewood**
Alliance
St. Anthony Hospital

**Loveland**
Alliance
UCHealth Medical Center of the Rockies

**Pueblo**
Alliance
St. Mary–Corwin Medical Center

**Steamboat Springs**
Alliance
UCHealth Yampa Valley Medical Center

**Westminster**
Alliance
St. Anthony North Health Campus

**Yuma**
Alliance
Yuma District Hospital

### CONNECTICUT

**Bridgeport**
Alliance
Bridgeport Hospital

**Bristol**
Alliance
Bristol Health

**Danbury**
Alliance
Danbury Hospital

**Farmington**
Alliance
UConn, John Dempsey Hospital

**Greenwich**
Alliance
Greenwich Hospital

**Hartford**
Alliance
Hartford Hospital
Saint Francis Hospital and Medical Center

**Manchester**
Alliance
Manchester Memorial Hospital

**Middletown**
Alliance
Connecticut Valley Hospital
Middlesex Hospital

**New Haven**
Alliance
Connecticut Mental Health Center
Yale New Haven Health
Yale–New Haven Hospital

**New London**
Alliance
Lawrence + Memorial Hospital

**Norwalk**
Alliance
Norwalk Hospital

**Putnam**
Alliance
Day Kimball Hospital

**Stamford**
Alliance
Stamford Hospital

**Torrington**
Alliance
Charlotte Hungerford Hospital

**Vernon**
Alliance
Rockville General Hospital

### DELAWARE

**Wilmington**
Alliance
St. Francis Hospital

### DISTRICT OF COLUMBIA

**Washington**
Alliance
Howard University Hospital
MedStar Georgetown University Hospital
MedStar Washington Hospital Center
Sibley Memorial Hospital

### FLORIDA

**Apalachicola**
Alliance
George E. Weems Memorial Hospital

**Boca Raton**
Alliance
Boca Raton Regional Hospital

**Boynton Beach**
Alliance
Bethesda Hospital East

**Clermont**
Alliance
South Lake Hospital

**Cocoa Beach**
Alliance
Health First Cape Canaveral Hospital

**Coral Gables**
Alliance
Baptist Health South Florida, Doctors Hospital

**Daytona Beach**
Alliance
Halifax Health Medical Center of Daytona Beach

**Gainesville**
Alliance
UF Health Shands Hospital

**Gulf Breeze**
Alliance
Gulf Breeze Hospital

**Homestead**
Alliance
Baptist Health South Florida, Homestead Hospital

**Jacksonville**
Alliance
Mayo Clinic Hospital in Florida

**Jay**
Alliance
Jay Hospital

**Lakeland**
Alliance
Lakeland Regional Health Medical Center

**Leesburg**
Alliance
Leesburg Regional Medical Center

**Melbourne**
Alliance
Health First Holmes Regional Medical Center

**Miami**
Alliance
Baptist Health South Florida, Baptist Hospital of Miami
Baptist Health South Florida, West Kendall Baptist Hospital
Jackson Health System

**Milton**
Alliance
West Florida Community Care Center

**Naples**
Alliance
NCH Baker Hospital

**Ocoee**
Alliance
Health Central Hospital

**Orlando**
Alliance
Orlando Health
Orlando Regional Medical Center

**Palm Bay**
Alliance
Health First Palm Bay Hospital

**Panama City**
Alliance
Bay Medical Sacred Heart

**Pensacola**
Alliance
Baptist Health Care Corporation
Baptist Hospital

**Perry**
Alliance
Doctor's Memorial Hospital

**Rockledge**
Alliance
  Health First, Inc.

**Stuart**
Alliance
  Cleveland Clinic Martin North Hospital

**Tallahassee**
Alliance
  Tallahassee Memorial HealthCare

**Tampa**
Alliance
  H. Lee Moffitt Cancer Center and Research Institute
  Shriners Hospitals for Children–Tampa
  Tampa General Hospital

**Tavernier**
Alliance
  Baptist Health South Florida, Mariners Hospital

**The Villages**
Alliance
  The Villages Regional Hospital

**Titusville**
Alliance
  Parrish Medical Center

**Vero Beach**
Alliance
  Cleveland Clinic Indian River Hospital

**Weston**
Alliance
  Cleveland Clinic Florida

## GEORGIA
**Adel**
Alliance
  Southwell Medical

**Albany**
Alliance
  Phoebe Putney Health System
  Phoebe Putney Memorial Hospital

**Americus**
Alliance
  Phoebe Sumter Medical Center

**Athens**
Alliance
  Piedmont Athens Regional Medical Center
  St. Mary's Health Care System

**Atlanta**
Alliance
  Emory Saint Joseph's Hospital of Atlanta
  Emory University Hospital Midtown
  Emory University Hospital
  Grady Memorial Hospital
  Northside Hospital
  Wellstar Atlanta Medical Center

**Augusta**
Alliance
  Augusta University Medical Center
  Charlie Norwood Veterans Affairs Medical Center
  University Hospital

**Austell**
Alliance
  WellStar Cobb Hospital

**Braselton**
Alliance
  Northeast Georgia Medical Center Braselton

**Brunswick**
Alliance
  Southeast Georgia Health System Brunswick Campus
  Southeast Georgia Health System

**Bryon**
Alliance
  Medical Center of Peach County, Navicent Health

**Cairo**

**Alliance**
  Grady General Hospital

**Camilla**
Alliance
  Mitchell County Hospital

**Canton**
Alliance
  Northside Hospital–Cherokee

**Cedartown**
Alliance
  Polk Medical Center

**Claxton**
Alliance
  Evans Memorial Hospital

**Columbus**
Alliance
  Columbus Regional Healthcare System
  Columbus Specialty Hospital
  Piedmont Columbus Regional Midtown
  Piedmont Columbus Regional Northside

**Cordele**
Alliance
  Crisp Regional Hospital

**Cumming**
Alliance
  Northside Hospital–Forsyth

**Cuthbert**
Alliance
  Southwest Georgia Regional Medical Center

**Dalton**
Alliance
  Hamilton Medical Center

**Decatur**
Alliance
  Emory Long–Term Acute Care

**Douglas**
Alliance
  Coffee Regional Medical Center

**Douglasville**
Alliance
  WellStar Douglas Hospital

**Eatonton**
Alliance
  Putnam General Hospital

**Fitzgerald**
Alliance
  Dorminy Medical Center

**Gainesville**
Alliance
  Northeast Georgia Medical Center

**Hiram**
Alliance
  WellStar Paulding Hospital

**Homerville**
Alliance
  Clinch Memorial Hospital

**Jackson**
Alliance
  Wellstar Sylvan Grove Hospital

**Johns Creek**
Alliance
  Emory Johns Creek Hospital

**Lakeland**
Alliance
  South Georgia Medical Center Lanier Campus

**Lawrenceville**
Alliance
  Northside Hospital – Gwinnett

**Lithonia**
Alliance
  Emory Hillandale Hospital

**Macon**
Alliance
  Medical Center, Navicent Health
  Rehabilitation Hospital, Navicent Health

**Marietta**
Alliance
  WellStar Health System
  WellStar Kennestone Hospital
  WellStar Windy Hill Hospital

**Moultrie**
Alliance
  Colquitt Regional Medical Center

**Nashville**
Alliance
  South Georgia Medical Center Berrien Campus

**Newnan**
Alliance
  Southeastern Regional Medical Center

**Perry**
Alliance
  Perry Hospital

**Quitman**
Alliance
  Brooks County Hospital

**Riverdale**
Alliance
  Southern Regional Medical Center

**Rome**
Alliance
  Floyd Medical Center

**Roswell**
Alliance
  Wellstar North Fulton Hospital

**Saint Marys**
Alliance
  Southeast Georgia Health System Camden Campus

**Sandersville**
Alliance
  Washington County Regional Medical Center

**Savannah**
Alliance
  Memorial Health

**Swainsboro**
Alliance
  Emanuel Medical Center

**Sylvester**
Alliance
  Phoebe Worth Medical Center

**Thomasville**
Alliance
  Archbold Medical Center
  John D. Archbold Memorial Hospital

**Thomson**
Alliance
  University Hospital McDuffie

**Tifton**
Alliance
  Tift Regional Medical Center

**Valdosta**
Alliance
  South Georgia Medical Center

**Warm Springs**
Alliance
  Roosevelt Warm Springs Rehabilitation Hospital – Rehab
  Roosevelt Warm Springs Rehabilitation and Specialty Hospitals – LTAC

**Warner Robins**
Alliance
  Houston Medical Center

**Waycross**
Alliance
  Memorial Satilla Health

## GUAM
**Dededo**
Alliance
  Guam Regional Medical City

## HAWAII
**Aiea**
Alliance
  Pali Momi Medical Center

**Section B**

# Alliances

**Ewa Beach**
Alliance
Sutter Health Kahi Mohala

**Honolulu**
Alliance
Kaiser Permanente Medical Center

Queen's Health Systems

Shriners Hospitals for Children–Honolulu

Straub Medical Center

The Queen's Medical Center

**Kamuela**
Alliance
Queen's North Hawaii Community Hospital

**Kaunakakai**
Alliance
Molokai General Hospital

**Wahiawa**
Alliance
Wahiawa General Hospital

## IDAHO
**American Falls**
Alliance
Power County Hospital District

**Blackfoot**
Alliance
Bingham Memorial Hospital

**Boise**
Alliance
Saint Alphonsus Regional Medical Center

St. Luke's Health System

**Bonners Ferry**
Alliance
Boundary Community Hospital

**Cascade**
Alliance
Cascade Medical Center

**Coeur D'Alene**
Alliance
Kootenai Health

**Cottonwood**
Alliance
St. Mary's Hospital

**Emmett**
Alliance
Valor Health

**Orofino**
Alliance
Clearwater Valley Hospital and Clinics

**Preston**
Alliance
Franklin County Medical Center

**Rupert**
Alliance
Minidoka Memorial Hospital

**Sandpoint**
Alliance
Bonner General Health

**Weiser**
Alliance
Weiser Memorial Hospital

## ILLINOIS
**Alton**
Alliance
Alton Memorial Hospital

**Arlington Heights**
Alliance
Northwest Community Healthcare

**Aurora**
Alliance
Rush–Copley Medical Center

**Barrington**
Alliance
Advocate Good Shepherd Hospital

**Belleville**
Alliance
Memorial Hospital

**Bloomington**
Alliance
OSF St. Joseph Medical Center

**Canton**
Alliance
Graham Hospital Association

**Carbondale**
Alliance
Memorial Hospital of Carbondale

Southern Illinois Healthcare

**Chester**
Alliance
Memorial Hospital

**Chicago**
Alliance
AMITA Health Resurrection Medical Center

Advocate Illinois Masonic Medical Center

Advocate Trinity Hospital

Ann & Robert H. Lurie Children's Hospital of Chicago

John H. Stroger Jr. Hospital of Cook County

La Rabida Children's Hospital

Louis A. Weiss Memorial Hospital

Mercy Hospital and Medical Center

Methodist Hospital of Chicago

Northwestern Memorial Hospital

Norwegian American Hospital

Provident Hospital of Cook County

Rush University Medical Center

Shriners Hospitals for Children–Chicago

Swedish Covenant Hospital

University of Chicago Medical Center

University of Illinois Hospital & Health Sciences System

**Decatur**
Alliance
Decatur Memorial Hospital

**Downers Grove**
Alliance
Advocate Good Samaritan Hospital

**Eldorado**
Alliance
Ferrell Hospital

**Elgin**
Alliance
Advocate Sherman Hospital

**Elmhurst**
Alliance
Elmhurst Hospital

**Evanston**
Alliance
NorthShore University Health System

**Evergreen Park**
Alliance
OSF Healthcare Little Company of Mary Medical Center

**Freeport**
Alliance
FHN Memorial Hospital

**Galesburg**
Alliance
OSF St. Mary Medical Center

**Geneva**
Alliance
Northwestern Medicine Delnor Hospital

**Greenville**
Alliance
HSHS Holy Family Hospital in Greenville

**Harvey**
Alliance
Ingalls Memorial Hospital

**Hazel Crest**
Alliance
Advocate South Suburban Hospital

**Herrin**
Alliance
Herrin Hospital

**Hinsdale**
Alliance
AMITA Health Adventist Medical Center – Hinsdale

RML Specialty Hospital

**Hoffman Estates**
Alliance
AMITA Health Alexian Brothers Behavioral Health Hospital

**Jacksonville**
Alliance
Passavant Area Hospital

**Jerseyville**
Alliance
Jersey Community Hospital

**Joliet**
Alliance
AMITA Health Saint Joseph Medical Center

**Kewanee**
Alliance
OSF Saint Luke Medical Center

**Lake Forest**
Alliance
Northwestern Medicine Lake Forest Hospital

**Libertyville**
Alliance
Advocate Condell Medical Center

**Lincoln**
Alliance
Abraham Lincoln Memorial Hospital

**Macomb**
Alliance
McDonough District Hospital

**Maryville**
Alliance
Anderson Hospital

**Mattoon**
Alliance
Sarah Bush Lincoln Health Center

**Maywood**
Alliance
Loyola University Medical Center

**McHenry**
Alliance
Northwestern Medicine McHenry

**Monticello**
Alliance
Kirby Medical Center

**Murphysboro**
Alliance
St. Joseph Memorial Hospital

**New Lenox**
Alliance
Silver Cross Hospital

**Oak Lawn**
Alliance
Advocate Christ Medical Center

**Oak Park**
Alliance
Rush Oak Park Hospital

**Palos Heights**
Alliance
Palos Health

**Park Ridge**
Alliance
Advocate Lutheran General Hospital

**Peoria**
Alliance
OSF Saint Francis Medical Center

UnityPoint Health – Peoria

**Pittsfield**
Alliance
Illini Community Hospital

**Pontiac**
Alliance
OSF Saint James – John W. Albrecht Medical Center

**Quincy**
Alliance
Blessing Hospital

**Rock Island**
Alliance
UnityPoint Health – Trinity Rock Island

**Rockford**
Alliance
OSF Saint Anthony Medical Center
SwedishAmerican – A Division of UW Health

**Rushville**
Alliance
Sarah D. Culbertson Memorial Hospital

**Salem**
Alliance
Salem Township Hospital

**Shelbyville**
Alliance
HSHS Good Shepherd Hospital

**Shiloh**
Alliance
Memorial Hospital East

**Springfield**
Alliance
Memorial Health System
Memorial Medical Center

**Taylorville**
Alliance
Taylorville Memorial Hospital

**Urbana**
Alliance
Carle Foundation Hospital

**Winfield**
Alliance
Northwestern Medicine Central DuPage Hospital

**INDIANA**
**Anderson**
Alliance
Community Hospital Anderson

**Angola**
Alliance
Cameron Memorial Community Hospital

**Auburn**
Alliance
Parkview DeKalb Hospital

**Avon**
Alliance
Indiana University Health West Hospital

**Batesville**
Alliance
Margaret Mary Health

**Bedford**
Alliance
Indiana University Health Bedford Hospital

**Bloomington**
Alliance
Indiana University Health Bloomington Hospital

**Carmel**
Alliance
Indiana University Health North Hospital

**Clinton**
Alliance
Union Hospital Clinton

**Columbia City**
Alliance
Parkview Whitley Hospital

**Columbus**
Alliance
Columbus Regional Hospital

**Danville**
Alliance
Hendricks Regional Health

**Elkhart**
Alliance
Elkhart General Hospital

**Evansville**
Alliance
Deaconess Health System
Deaconess Midtown Hospital

**Fort Wayne**
Alliance
Parkview Ortho Hospital
Parkview Health
Parkview Regional Medical Center

**Frankfort**
Alliance
Indiana University Health Methodist Hospital

**Franklin**
Alliance
Johnson Memorial Hospital

**Goshen**
Alliance
Goshen Health

**Hartford City**
Alliance
Indiana University Health Blackford Hospital

**Huntington**
Alliance
Parkview Huntington Hospital

**Indianapolis**
Alliance
Community Health Network
Community Hospital East
Community Hospital North
Community Hospital South
Eskenazi Health
Indiana University Health University Hospital

**Jasper**
Alliance
Memorial Hospital and Health Care Center

**Kendallville**
Alliance
Parkview Noble Hospital

**Knox**
Alliance
Starke Hospital

**Kokomo**
Alliance
Community Howard Regional Health

**La Porte**
Alliance
La Porte Hospital

**LaGrange**
Alliance
Parkview LaGrange Hospital

**Lafayette**
Alliance
Indiana University Health Arnett Hospital

**Logansport**
Alliance
Logansport Memorial Hospital

**Madison**
Alliance
King's Daughters' Health

**Marion**
Alliance
Marion General Hospital

**Monticello**
Alliance
Indiana University Health White Memorial Hospital

**Muncie**
Alliance
Indiana University Health Ball Memorial Hospital

**New Albany**
Alliance
Baptist Health Floyd
Southern Indiana Rehabilitation Hospital

**New Castle**
Alliance
Henry Community Health

**Newburgh**
Alliance
The Women's Hospital

**Noblesville**
Alliance
Riverview Health

**Paoli**
Alliance
Indiana University Health Paoli Hospital

**Portland**
Alliance
Indiana University Health Jay Hospital

**Richmond**
Alliance
Reid Health

**Rochester**
Alliance
Woodlawn Hospital

**Seymour**
Alliance
Schneck Medical Center

**Shelbyville**
Alliance
Major Hospital

**South Bend**
Alliance
Healthwin Hospital
Memorial Hospital of South Bend

**Terre Haute**
Alliance
Union Hospital

**Tipton**
Alliance
Indiana University Health Tipton Hospital

**Vincennes**
Alliance
Good Samaritan Hospital

**Wabash**
Alliance
Parkview Wabash Hospital

**IOWA**
**Anamosa**
Alliance
UnityPoint Health – Jones Regional Medical Center

**Atlantic**
Alliance
Cass County Health System

**Bettendorf**
Alliance
UnityPoint Health – Trinity Bettendorf

**Cedar Rapids**
Alliance
UnityPoint Health – St. Luke's Hospital

**Centerville**
Alliance
MercyOne Centerville Medical Center

**Clarinda**
Alliance
Clarinda Regional Health Center

**Clinton**
Alliance
MercyOne Clinton Medical Center

**Corning**
Alliance
CHI Health Mercy Corning

**Council Bluffs**
Alliance
Methodist Jennie Edmundson Hospital

# Alliances

**Decorah**
Alliance
  Winneshiek Medical Center

**Des Moines**
Alliance
  MercyOne Des Moines Medical Center

**Dubuque**
Alliance
  MercyOne Dubuque Medical Center
  UnityPoint Health – Finley Hospital

**Fort Dodge**
Alliance
  UnityPoint Health – Trinity Regional Medical Center

**Grundy Center**
Alliance
  Grundy County Memorial Hospital

**Guttenberg**
Alliance
  Guttenberg Municipal Hospital and Clinics

**Hamburg**
Alliance
  George C. Grape Community Hospital

**Hampton**
Alliance
  Franklin General Hospital

**Harlan**
Alliance
  Myrtue Medical Center

**Iowa City**
Alliance
  University of Iowa Hospitals and Clinics

**Iowa Falls**
Alliance
  Hansen Family Hospital

**Jefferson**
Alliance
  Greene County Medical Center

**Keokuk**
Alliance
  UnityPoint Health–Keokuk

**Keosauqua**
Alliance
  Van Buren County Hospital

**Lake City**
Alliance
  Stewart Memorial Community Hospital

**Le Mars**
Alliance
  Floyd Valley Healthcare

**Marengo**
Alliance
  Compass Memorial Healthcare

**Mason City**
Alliance
  MercyOne North Iowa Medical Center

**Missouri Valley**
Alliance
  CHI Health Missouri Valley

**Muscatine**
Alliance
  UnityPoint Health – Trinity Muscatine

**Nevada**
Alliance
  Story County Medical Center

**New Hampton**
Alliance
  MercyOne New Hampton Medical Center

**Orange City**
Alliance
  Orange City Area Health System

**Osceola**
Alliance
  Clarke County Hospital

**Pella**
Alliance
  Pella Regional Health Center

**Red Oak**
Alliance
  Montgomery County Memorial Hospital

**Sheldon**
Alliance
  Sanford Sheldon Medical Center

**Shenandoah**
Alliance
  Shenandoah Medical Center

**Sigourney**
Alliance
  Keokuk County Health Center

**Sioux City**
Alliance
  MercyOne Siouxland Medical Center
  UnityPoint Health – St. Lukes's Sioux City

**Sumner**
Alliance
  Community Memorial Hospital

**Waverly**
Alliance
  Waverly Health Center

**West Des Moines**
Alliance
  UnityPoint Health – Methodist West Hospital

**West Union**
Alliance
  Gundersen Palmer Lutheran Hospital and Clinics

## KANSAS

**Abilene**
Alliance
  Memorial Health System

**Ashland**
Alliance
  Ashland Health Center

**Atchison**
Alliance
  Atchison Hospital

**Atwood**
Alliance
  Rawlins County Health Center

**Belleville**
Alliance
  Republic County Hospital

**Beloit**
Alliance
  Mitchell County Hospital Health Systems

**Clay Center**
Alliance
  Clay County Medical Center

**Colby**
Alliance
  Citizens Medical Center

**Coldwater**
Alliance
  Comanche County Hospital

**Concordia**
Alliance
  Cloud County Health Center

**Dighton**
Alliance
  Lane County Hospital

**El Dorado**
Alliance
  Susan B. Allen Memorial Hospital

**Ellinwood**
Alliance
  Ellinwood District Hospital

**Ellsworth**
Alliance
  Ellsworth County Medical Center

**Emporia**
Alliance
  Newman Regional Health

**Fredonia**
Alliance
  Fredonia Regional Hospital

**Garden City**
Alliance
  St. Catherine Hospital

**Garnett**
Alliance
  Anderson County Hospital

**Girard**
Alliance
  Girard Medical Center

**Goodland**
Alliance
  Goodland Regional Medical Center

**Great Bend**
Alliance
  University of Kansas Health System Great Bend Campus

**Greensburg**
Alliance
  Kiowa County Memorial Hospital

**Hays**
Alliance
  Hays Medical Center

**Herington**
Alliance
  Herington Municipal Hospital

**Hiawatha**
Alliance
  Hiawatha Community Hospital

**Hill City**
Alliance
  Graham County Hospital

**Hoisington**
Alliance
  Clara Barton Hospital

**Hoxie**
Alliance
  Sheridan County Health Complex

**Junction City**
Alliance
  Geary Community Hospital

**Kansas City**
Alliance
  The University of Kansas Hospital

**La Crosse**
Alliance
  Rush County Memorial Hospital

**Larned**
Alliance
  University of Kansas Health System Pawnee Valley Campus

**Lawrence**
Alliance
  LMH Health

**Leavenworth**
Alliance
  Saint Luke's Cushing Hospital

**Lincoln**
Alliance
  Lincoln County Hospital

**Lindsborg**
Alliance
  Lindsborg Community Hospital

**Mankato**
Alliance
  Jewell County Hospital

**Medicine Lodge**
Alliance
  Medicine Lodge Memorial Hospital

**Minneapolis**
Alliance
  Ottawa County Health Center

**Minneola**
Alliance
  Minneola District Hospital

**Ness City**
Alliance
  Ness County Hospital District No 2

**Norton**
Alliance
  Norton County Hospital

**Oakley**
Alliance
  Logan County Hospital

**Overland Park**
Alliance
  Menorah Medical Center
  Overland Park Regional Medical Center
  Saint Luke's South Hospital

**Parsons**
Alliance
  Labette Health

**Phillipsburg**
Alliance
  Phillips County Health Systems

**Plainville**
Alliance
  Rooks County Health Center

**Pratt**
Alliance
  Pratt Regional Medical Center

**Quinter**
Alliance
  Gove County Medical Center

**Ransom**
Alliance
  Grisell Memorial Hospital District One

**Russell**
Alliance
  Russell Regional Hospital

**Sabetha**
Alliance
  Sabetha Community Hospital

**Saint Francis**
Alliance
  Cheyenne County Hospital

**Salina**
Alliance
  Salina Regional Health Center
  Salina Surgical Hospital

**Satanta**
Alliance
  Satanta District Hospital and Long Term Care

**Scott City**
Alliance
  Scott County Hospital

**Smith Center**
Alliance
  Smith County Memorial Hospital

**Stafford**
Alliance
  Stafford County Hospital

**Topeka**
Alliance
  Stormont Vail Health

**Wakeeney**
Alliance
  Trego County–Lemke Memorial Hospital

**Wichita**
Alliance
  Great Plains Health Alliance, Inc.
  Kansas Spine & Specialty Hospital

## KENTUCKY

**Bardstown**
Alliance
  CHI Flaget Memorial Hospital

**Berea**
Alliance
  CHI Saint Joseph Berea

**Cynthiana**
Alliance
  Harrison Memorial Hospital

**Florence**
Alliance
  St. Elizabeth Florence

**Lexington**
Alliance
  CHI Saint Joseph East
  CHI Saint Joseph Health
  Eastern State Hospital
  University of Kentucky Albert B. Chandler Hospital

**London**
Alliance
  CHI Saint Joseph London

**Louisville**
Alliance
  UofL Health – Jewish Hospital
  UofL Health – Peace Hospital
  UofL Health – UofL Hospital

**Martin**
Alliance
  ARH Our Lady of the Way

**Morehead**
Alliance
  St. Claire HealthCare

**Mount Sterling**
Alliance
  Saint Joseph Mount Sterling

**Mount Vernon**
Alliance
  Rockcastle Regional Hospital and Respiratory Care Center

**Owensboro**
Alliance
  Owensboro Health Regional Hospital

**Pikeville**
Alliance
  Pikeville Medical Center

**Shelbyville**
Alliance
  UofL Health – Shelbyville Hospital

## LOUISIANA

**Baton Rouge**
Alliance
  Franciscan Missionaries of Our Lady Health System, Inc.
  Ochsner Medical Center – Baton Rouge
  Our Lady of the Lake Regional Medical Center

**Bogalusa**
Alliance
  Our Lady of the Angels Hospital

**Church Point**
Alliance
  Acadia–St. Landry Hospital

**Covington**
Alliance
  St. Tammany Health System

**De Ridder**
Alliance
  Beauregard Health System

**Ferriday**
Alliance
  Riverland Medical Center

**Jennings**
Alliance
  Jennings American Legion Hospital

**Kenner**
Alliance
  Ochsner Medical Center – Kenner

**Lafayette**
Alliance
  Lafayette General Medical Center
  Our Lady of Lourdes Regional Medical Center

**Lake Charles**
Alliance
  Lake Charles Memorial Hospital

**Mansfield**
Alliance
  De Soto Regional Health System

**Monroe**
Alliance
  Ochsner LSU Health Shreveport – Monroe Medical Center
  St. Francis Medical Center

**Napoleonville**
Alliance
  Assumption Community Hospital

**Natchitoches**
Alliance
  Natchitoches Regional Medical Center

**New Iberia**
Alliance
  Iberia Medical Center

**New Orleans**
Alliance
  Touro Infirmary

**Raceland**
Alliance
  Ochsner St. Anne General Hospital

**Shreveport**
Alliance
  Ochsner LSU Health Shreveport – Academic Medical Center
  Shriners Hospitals for Children–Shreveport
  Willis–Knighton Health System
  Willis–Knighton Medical Center

**Slidell**
Alliance
  Ochsner Medical Center – North Shore

**Springhill**
Alliance
  Springhill Medical Center

**Sulphur**
Alliance
  West Calcasieu Cameron Hospital

**Vivian**
Alliance
  North Caddo Medical Center

## MAINE

**Augusta**
Alliance
  MaineGeneral Medical Center–Augusta Campus
  MaineGeneral Medical Center

**Bangor**
Alliance
  Northern Light Eastern Maine Medical Center
  The Acadia Hospital

**Bar Harbor**
Alliance
  Mount Desert Island Hospital

**Belfast**
Alliance
  Waldo County General Hospital

**Biddeford**
Alliance
  Southern Maine Health Care – Biddeford Medical Center

**Blue Hill**
Alliance
  Northern Light Blue Hill Hospital

**Brewer**
Alliance
  Northern Light Health

**Brunswick**
Alliance
  Mid Coast Hospital

**Damariscotta**
Alliance
  LincolnHealth

**Dover–Foxcroft**
Alliance
  Mayo Regional Hospital

Section B

**Ellsworth**
Alliance
  Northern Light Maine Coast Hospital

**Farmington**
Alliance
  Franklin Memorial Hospital

**Fort Kent**
Alliance
  Northern Maine Medical Center

**Greenville**
Alliance
  Northern Light CA Dean Hospital

**Houlton**
Alliance
  Houlton Regional Hospital

**Machias**
Alliance
  Down East Community Hospital

**Millinocket**
Alliance
  Millinocket Regional Hospital

**Norway**
Alliance
  Stephens Memorial Hospital

**Pittsfield**
Alliance
  Northern Light Sebasticook Valley Hospital

**Portland**
Alliance
  Maine Medical Center

  Northern Light Mercy Hospital

**Presque Isle**
Alliance
  The Aroostook Medical Center

**Rockport**
Alliance
  Pen Bay Medical Center

**Skowhegan**
Alliance
  Redington–Fairview General Hospital

**Waterville**
Alliance
  Northern Light Inland Hospital

**Westbrook**
Alliance
  Spring Harbor Hospital

## MARYLAND
**Baltimore**
Alliance
  Greater Baltimore Medical Center

  Johns Hopkins Bayview Medical Center

  Johns Hopkins Hospital

  MedStar Franklin Square Medical Center

  MedStar Good Samaritan Hospital

  MedStar Harbor Hospital

  MedStar Union Memorial Hospital

  Mercy Medical Center

  Mt. Washington Pediatric Hospital

  University of Maryland Medical Center Midtown Campus

  University of Maryland Medical Center

  University of Maryland Rehabilitation & Orthopaedic Institute

**Bel Air**
Alliance
  University of Maryland Upper Chesapeake Medical Center

**Bethesda**
Alliance
  Suburban Hospital

**Cambridge**
Alliance
  University of Maryland Shore Medical Center at Dorchester

**Chestertown**
Alliance
  University of Maryland Shore Medical Center at Chestertown

**Cheverly**
Alliance
  University of Maryland Capital Region Health Prince George's Hospital Center

**Clinton**
Alliance
  MedStar Southern Maryland Hospital Center

**Columbia**
Alliance
  Howard County General Hospital

  MedStar Health

**Easton**
Alliance
  University of Maryland Shore Medical Center at Easton

**Elkton**
Alliance
  Union Hospital

**Glen Burnie**
Alliance
  University of Maryland Baltimore Washington Medical Center

**Hagerstown**
Alliance
  Meritus Medical Center

**Havre De Grace**
Alliance
  University of Maryland Harford Memorial Hospital

**La Plata**
Alliance
  University of Maryland Charles Regional Medical Center

**Leonardtown**
Alliance
  MedStar St. Mary's Hospital

**Olney**
Alliance
  MedStar Montgomery Medical Center

**Prince Frederick**
Alliance
  CalvertHealth Medical Center

**Randallstown**
Alliance
  Northwest Hospital

**Rockville**
Alliance
  Adventist Healthcare Shady Grove Medical Center

**Silver Spring**
Alliance
  Holy Cross Hospital

## MASSACHUSETTS
**Athol**
Alliance
  Athol Hospital

**Ayer**
Alliance
  Nashoba Valley Medical Center

**Belmont**
Alliance
  McLean Hospital

**Beverly**
Alliance
  Beverly Hospital

**Boston**
Alliance
  Beth Israel Deaconess Medical Center

  Boston Medical Center

  Brigham and Women's Faulkner Hospital

  Brigham and Women's Hospital

  Carney Hospital

  Dana–Farber Cancer Institute

  Mass General Brigham

  Massachusetts Eye and Ear

  Massachusetts General Hospital

  Shriners Hospitals for Children–Boston

  Tufts Medical Center

**Brighton**
Alliance
  St. Elizabeth's Medical Center

**Brockton**
Alliance
  Good Samaritan Medical Center

  Signature Healthcare Brockton Hospital

**Burlington**
Alliance
  Lahey Hospital & Medical Center, Burlington

**Cambridge**
Alliance
  Cambridge Health Alliance

  Mount Auburn Hospital

  Spaulding Hospital for Continuing Medical Care Cambridge

**Charlestown**
Alliance
  Spaulding Rehabilitation Hospital

**Concord**
Alliance
  Emerson Hospital

**East Sandwich**
Alliance
  Spaulding Rehabilitation Hospital Cape Cod

**Fall River**
Alliance
  Saint Anne's Hospital

**Gardner**
Alliance
  Heywood Hospital

**Greenfield**
Alliance
  Baystate Franklin Medical Center

**Holyoke**
Alliance
  Holyoke Medical Center

**Hyannis**
Alliance
  Cape Cod Healthcare, Inc.

**Leominster**
Alliance
  UMass Memorial HealthAlliance–Clinton Hospital

**Lowell**
Alliance
  Lowell General Hospital

**Marlborough**
Alliance
  UMass Memorial–Marlborough Hospital

**Melrose**
Alliance
  Melrose–Wakefield Hospital

**Methuen**
Alliance
  Holy Family Hospital

**Milton**
Alliance
  Beth Israel Deaconess Hospital–Milton

**Nantucket**
Alliance
  Nantucket Cottage Hospital

**Newton Lower Falls**
Alliance
Newton–Wellesley Hospital

**Northampton**
Alliance
Cooley Dickinson Hospital

**Norwood**
Alliance
Norwood Hospital

**Oak Bluffs**
Alliance
Martha's Vineyard Hospital

**Palmer**
Alliance
Baystate Wing Hospital

**Plymouth**
Alliance
Beth Israel Deaconess Hospital Plymouth

**Salem**
Alliance
North Shore Medical Center

**South Weymouth**
Alliance
South Shore Hospital

**Southbridge**
Alliance
Harrington Hospital

**Springfield**
Alliance
Baystate Medical Center
Shriners Hospitals for Children–Springfield

**Taunton**
Alliance
Morton Hospital and Medical Center

**Winchester**
Alliance
Winchester Hospital

**Worcester**
Alliance
UMass Memorial Medical Center

**MICHIGAN**
**Alma**
Alliance
MidMichigan Medical Center–Gratiot

**Alpena**
Alliance
MidMichigan Medical Center – Alpena

**Ann Arbor**
Alliance
Michigan Medicine

**Battle Creek**
Alliance
Bronson Battle Creek Hospital

**Bay City**
Alliance
McLaren Bay Region
McLaren Bay Special Care

**Big Rapids**
Alliance
Spectrum Health Big Rapids Hospital

**Cadillac**
Alliance
Munson Healthcare Cadillac Hospital

**Carson City**
Alliance
Sparrow Carson Hospital

**Cass City**
Alliance
Hills & Dales General Hospital

**Chelsea**
Alliance
St. Joseph Mercy Chelsea

**Coldwater**
Alliance
ProMedica Coldwater Regional Hospital

**Dearborn**
Alliance
Beaumont Hospital – Dearborn

**Detroit**
Alliance
Henry Ford Hospital

**Farmington Hills**
Alliance
Beaumont Hospital – Farmington Hills

**Flint**
Alliance
McLaren Flint

**Fremont**
Alliance
Spectrum Health Gerber Memorial

**Grand Haven**
Alliance
North Ottawa Community Hospital

**Grand Rapids**
Alliance
Mary Free Bed Rehabilitation Hospital
Pine Rest Christian Mental Health Services
Spectrum Health – Butterworth Hospital
Spectrum Health

**Grayling**
Alliance
Munson Healthcare Grayling Hospital

**Greenville**
Alliance
Spectrum Health United Hospital

**Grosse Pointe**
Alliance
Beaumont Hospital – Grosse Pointe

**Hastings**
Alliance
Spectrum Health Pennock

**Holland**
Alliance
Holland Hospital

**Ionia**
Alliance
Sparrow Ionia Hospital

**Iron River**
Alliance
Aspirus Iron River Hospitals & Clinics, Inc.

**Ironwood**
Alliance
Aspirus Ironwood Hospitals & Clinics, Inc.

**Kalamazoo**
Alliance
Bronson Healthcare Group
Bronson Methodist Hospital

**Lansing**
Alliance
Sparrow Hospital
Sparrow Specialty Hospital

**Laurium**
Alliance
Aspirus Keweenaw Hospital, Inc.

**Ludington**
Alliance
Spectrum Health Ludington Hospital

**Marlette**
Alliance
Marlette Regional Hospital

**Marshall**
Alliance
Oaklawn Hospital

**Midland**
Alliance
MidMichigan Medical Center–Midland

**Monroe**
Alliance
ProMedica Monroe Regional Hospital

**Mount Clemens**
Alliance
McLaren Macomb

**Mount Pleasant**
Alliance
McLaren Central Michigan

**Muskegon**
Alliance
Mercy Health Hackley Campus

**Ontonagon**
Alliance
Aspirus Ontonagon Hospital, Inc.

**Paw Paw**
Alliance
Bronson LakeView Hospital

**Petoskey**
Alliance
McLaren Northern Michigan

**Pontiac**
Alliance
McLaren Oakland
St. Joseph Mercy Oakland

**Port Huron**
Alliance
McLaren Port Huron

**Reed City**
Alliance
Spectrum Health Reed City Hospital

**Royal Oak**
Alliance
Beaumont Hospital – Royal Oak

**Saginaw**
Alliance
Covenant Healthcare

**Saint Johns**
Alliance
Sparrow Clinton Hospital

**Saint Joseph**
Alliance
Spectrum Health Lakeland

**Sheridan**
Alliance
Sheridan Community Hospital

**South Haven**
Alliance
Bronson South Haven Hospital

**Taylor**
Alliance
Beaumont Hospital – Taylor

**Tecumseh**
Alliance
ProMedica Herrick Hospital

**Trenton**
Alliance
Beaumont Hospital – Trenton

**Troy**
Alliance
Beaumont Hospital – Troy

**Watervliet**
Alliance
Lakeland Hospital, Watervliet

**Wayne**
Alliance
Beaumont Hospital, Wayne

**West Branch**
Alliance
MidMichigan Medical Center – West Branch

**Wyoming**
Alliance
Metro Health – University of Michigan Health

**Zeeland**
Alliance
Spectrum Health Zeeland Community Hospital

**MINNESOTA**
**Ada**
Alliance
Essentia Health–Ada

# Alliances

**Albert Lea**
Alliance
Mayo Clinic Health System – Albert Lea and Austin

**Arlington**
Alliance
Ridgeview Sibley Medical Center

**Aurora**
Alliance
Essentia Health Northern Pines Medical Center

**Bagley**
Alliance
Sanford Bagley Medical Center

**Baudette**
Alliance
CHI LakeWood Health

**Bemidji**
Alliance
Sanford Bemidji Medical Center

**Benson**
Alliance
Swift County – Benson Health Services

**Blue Earth**
Alliance
United Hospital District

**Brainerd**
Alliance
Essentia Health–St. Joseph's Medical Center

**Buffalo**
Alliance
Buffalo Hospital

**Burnsville**
Alliance
Fairview Ridges Hospital

**Cambridge**
Alliance
Cambridge Medical Center

**Canby**
Alliance
Sanford Canby Medical Center

**Cannon Falls**
Alliance
Mayo Clinic Health System in Cannon Falls

**Coon Rapids**
Alliance
Mercy Hospital

**Crookston**
Alliance
RiverView Health

**Deer River**
Alliance
Essentia Health–Deer River

**Detroit Lakes**
Alliance
Essentia Health St. Mary's – Detroit Lakes

**Duluth**
Alliance
Essentia Health Duluth

Essentia Health St. Mary's Medical Center

Essentia Health

St. Luke's Hospital

**Fairmont**
Alliance
Mayo Clinic Health System in Fairmont

**Faribault**
Alliance
District One Hospital

**Fergus Falls**
Alliance
Lake Region Healthcare

**Fosston**
Alliance
Essentia Health–Fosston

**Glencoe**
Alliance
Glencoe Regional Health

**Graceville**
Alliance
Essentia Health–Graceville

**Grand Rapids**
Alliance
Grand Itasca Clinic and Hospital

**Granite Falls**
Alliance
Avera Granite Falls Health Center

**Hallock**
Alliance
Kittson Memorial Healthcare Center

**Hastings**
Alliance
Regina Hospital

**Hutchinson**
Alliance
Hutchinson Health

**Jackson**
Alliance
Sanford Jackson Medical Center

**Lake City**
Alliance
Mayo Clinic Health System in Lake City

**Little Falls**
Alliance
CHI St. Gabriel's Health

**Long Prairie**
Alliance
CentraCare – Long Prairie

**Luverne**
Alliance
Sanford Luverne Medical Center

**Madelia**
Alliance
Madelia Community Hospital

**Mahnomen**
Alliance
Mahnomen Health Center

**Mankato**
Alliance
Mayo Clinic Health System in Mankato

**Maple Grove**
Alliance
Maple Grove Hospital

**Melrose**
Alliance
CentraCare – Melrose

**Minneapolis**
Alliance
Abbott Northwestern Hospital

Allina Health

Hennepin Healthcare

**Monticello**
Alliance
CentraCare – Monticello

**New Prague**
Alliance
Mayo Clinic Health System in New Prague

**New Ulm**
Alliance
New Ulm Medical Center

**Ortonville**
Alliance
Ortonville Area Health Services

**Owatonna**
Alliance
Owatonna Hospital

**Park Rapids**
Alliance
CHI St. Joseph's Health

**Paynesville**
Alliance
CentraCare Health–Paynesville

**Perham**
Alliance
Perham Health

**Princeton**
Alliance
Fairview Northland Medical Center

**Red Wing**
Alliance
Mayo Clinic Health System in Red Wing

**Redwood Falls**
Alliance
Carris Health – Redwood

**Robbinsdale**
Alliance
North Memorial Health Hospital

**Rochester**
Alliance
Mayo Clinic Hospital – Rochester

Mayo Clinic

**Roseau**
Alliance
LifeCare Medical Center

**Saint Cloud**
Alliance
CentraCare Health

St. Cloud Hospital

**Saint James**
Alliance
Mayo Clinic Health System in Saint James

**Saint Paul**
Alliance
Regions Hospital

United Hospital

**Sandstone**
Alliance
Essentia Health Sandstone

**Sauk Centre**
Alliance
CentraCare Health–Sauk Centre

**Shakopee**
Alliance
St. Francis Regional Medical Center

**Slayton**
Alliance
Murray County Medical Center

**Stillwater**
Alliance
Lakeview Hospital

**Thief River Falls**
Alliance
Sanford Medical Center Thief River Falls

Sanford Thief River Falls Behavioral Health Center

**Tracy**
Alliance
Sanford Tracy Medical Center

**Two Harbors**
Alliance
Lake View Hospital

**Virginia**
Alliance
Essentia Health–Virginia

**Waconia**
Alliance
Ridgeview Medical Center

**Warren**
Alliance
North Valley Health Center

**Waseca**
Alliance
Mayo Clinic Health System in Waseca

**Westbrook**
Alliance
Sanford Westbrook Medical Center

**Wheaton**
Alliance
Sanford Wheaton Medical Center

**Willmar**
Alliance
Rice Memorial Hospital

**Windom**
Alliance
  Windom Area Health

**Worthington**
Alliance
  Sanford Worthington Medical Center

**Wyoming**
Alliance
  Fairview Lakes Health Services

## MISSISSIPPI

**Booneville**
Alliance
  Baptist Memorial Hospital–Booneville

**Columbia**
Alliance
  Marion General Hospital

**Columbus**
Alliance
  Baptist Memorial Hospital–Golden Triangle

**Corinth**
Alliance
  Magnolia Regional Health Center

**Greenville**
Alliance
  Delta Regional Medical Center

**Greenwood**
Alliance
  Greenwood Leflore Hospital

**Grenada**
Alliance
  University of Mississippi Medical Center Grenada

**Gulfport**
Alliance
  Memorial Hospital at Gulfport

**Hattiesburg**
Alliance
  Forrest General Hospital

**Indianola**
Alliance
  South Sunflower County Hospital

**Jackson**
Alliance
  St. Dominic–Jackson Memorial Hospital
  University of Mississippi Medical Center

**Leakesville**
Alliance
  Greene County Hospital

**Lexington**
Alliance
  University of Mississippi Medical Center Holmes County

**Lucedale**
Alliance
  George Regional Hospital

**Magnolia**
Alliance
  Beacham Memorial Hospital

**McComb**
Alliance
  Southwest Mississippi Regional Medical Center

**Meridian**
Alliance
  Anderson Regional Health System South
  Anderson Regional Health System

**Monticello**
Alliance
  Lawrence County Hospital

**New Albany**
Alliance
  Baptist Memorial Hospital–Union County

**Olive Branch**
Alliance
  Methodist Healthcare Olive Branch Hospital

**Oxford**
Alliance
  Baptist Memorial Hospital–North Mississippi

**Pascagoula**
Alliance
  Singing River Health System

**Philadelphia**
Alliance
  Neshoba County General Hospital

**Picayune**
Alliance
  Highland Community Hospital

**Prentiss**
Alliance
  Jefferson Davis Community Hospital

**Southaven**
Alliance
  Baptist Memorial Hospital–Desoto

**Starkville**
Alliance
  OCH Regional Medical Center

**Tupelo**
Alliance
  North Mississippi Health Services, Inc.

**Tylertown**
Alliance
  Walthall County General Hospital

## MISSOURI

**Appleton City**
Alliance
  Ellett Memorial Hospital

**Belton**
Alliance
  Belton Regional Medical Center

**Bolivar**
Alliance
  Citizens Memorial Hospital

**Bonne Terre**
Alliance
  Parkland Health Center–Bonne Terre

**Branson**
Alliance
  Cox Medical Center Branson

**Brookfield**
Alliance
  Pershing Memorial Hospital

**Cameron**
Alliance
  Cameron Regional Medical Center

**Cape Girardeau**
Alliance
  Saint Francis Medical Center

**Chillicothe**
Alliance
  Hedrick Medical Center

**Clinton**
Alliance
  Golden Valley Memorial Healthcare

**Columbia**
Alliance
  Boone Hospital Center
  University of Missouri Health Care

**Farmington**
Alliance
  Parkland Health Center – Farmington Community

**Independence**
Alliance
  Centerpoint Medical Center

**Jefferson City**
Alliance
  Capital Region Medical Center

**Joplin**
Alliance
  Freeman Health System
  Freeman Hospital East

**Kansas City**
Alliance
  Children's Mercy Hospital Kansas City
  Research Medical Center
  Saint Luke's Health System
  Saint Luke's Hospital of Kansas City
  Saint Luke's North Hospital – Barry Road
  Truman Medical Center–Hospital Hill
  Truman Medical Center–Lakewood

**Lamar**
Alliance
  Cox Barton County Memorial Hospital

**Lee's Summit**
Alliance
  Lee's Summit Medical Center
  Saint Luke's East Hospital

**Lexington**
Alliance
  Lafayette Regional Health Center

**Liberty**
Alliance
  Liberty Hospital

**Macon**
Alliance
  Samaritan Hospital

**Marshall**
Alliance
  Fitzgibbon Hospital

**Milan**
Alliance
  Sullivan County Memorial Hospital

**Monett**
Alliance
  Cox Monett Hospital

**Neosho**
Alliance
  Freeman Neosho Hospital

**O'Fallon**
Alliance
  Progress West Hospital

**Osage Beach**
Alliance
  Lake Regional Health System

**Potosi**
Alliance
  Washington County Memorial Hospital

**Saint Louis**
Alliance
  BJC HealthCare
  Barnes–Jewish Hospital
  Barnes–Jewish West County Hospital
  Christian Hospital
  Missouri Baptist Medical Center
  Shriners Hospitals for Children–St. Louis
  St. Louis Children's Hospital

**Saint Peters**
Alliance
  Barnes–Jewish St. Peters Hospital

**Salem**
Alliance
  Salem Memorial District Hospital

**Sikeston**
Alliance
  Missouri Delta Medical Center

**Springfield**
Alliance
  Cox Medical Center North
  Cox Medical Centers
  CoxHealth

**Ste Genevieve**
Alliance
  Ste. Genevieve County Memorial Hospital

**Section B**

**Sullivan**
Alliance
Missouri Baptist Sullivan Hospital

**Trenton**
Alliance
Wright Memorial Hospital

**Warrensburg**
Alliance
Western Missouri Medical Center

## MONTANA

**Anaconda**
Alliance
Community Hospital of Anaconda

**Bozeman**
Alliance
Bozeman Health

**Columbus**
Alliance
Stillwater Billings Clinic

**Conrad**
Alliance
Pondera Medical Center

**Deer Lodge**
Alliance
Deer Lodge Medical Center

**Ennis**
Alliance
Madison Valley Medical Center

**Hamilton**
Alliance
Marcus Daly Memorial Hospital

**Helena**
Alliance
St. Peter's Hospital

**Kalispell**
Alliance
Kalispell Regional Healthcare

The HealthCenter

**Libby**
Alliance
Cabinet Peaks Medical Center

**Missoula**
Alliance
Providence St. Patrick Hospital

**Philipsburg**
Alliance
Granite County Medical Center

**Plains**
Alliance
Clark Fork Valley Hospital

**Polson**
Alliance
Providence St. Joseph Medical Center

**Ronan**
Alliance
St. Luke Community Healthcare

**Sidney**
Alliance
Sidney Health Center

**Townsend**
Alliance
Broadwater Health Center

**White Sulphur Springs**
Alliance
Mountainview Medical Center

## NEBRASKA

**Alliance**
Alliance
Box Butte General Hospital

**Alma**
Alliance
Harlan County Health System

**Atkinson**
Alliance
West Holt Medical Services

**Beatrice**
Alliance
Beatrice Community Hospital and Health Center

**Bellevue**
Alliance
Nebraska Medicine – Bellevue

**Blair**
Alliance
Memorial Community Hospital and Health System

**Bridgeport**
Alliance
Morrill County Community Hospital

**Broken Bow**
Alliance
Jennie M. Melham Memorial Medical Center

**Columbus**
Alliance
Columbus Community Hospital

**Crete**
Alliance
Crete Area Medical Center

**Falls City**
Alliance
Community Medical Center, Inc.

**Franklin**
Alliance
Franklin County Memorial Hospital

**Gordon**
Alliance
Gordon Memorial Health Services

**Grand Island**
Alliance
CHI Health Saint Francis

**Hastings**
Alliance
Mary Lanning Healthcare

**Kearney**
Alliance
CHI Health Good Samaritan

**Lexington**
Alliance
Lexington Regional Health Center

**Lincoln**
Alliance
Bryan Health

Bryan Medical Center

CHI Health Nebraska Heart

CHI Health St Elizabeth

Madonna Rehabilitation Hospital

**Lynch**
Alliance
Niobrara Valley Hospital

**Minden**
Alliance
Kearney County Health Services

**Nebraska City**
Alliance
CHI Health St. Mary's

**Neligh**
Alliance
Antelope Memorial Hospital

**Norfolk**
Alliance
Faith Regional Health Services

**O'Neill**
Alliance
Avera St. Anthony's Hospital

**Omaha**
Alliance
CHI Health Creighton University Medical Center – Bergan Mercy

CHI Health Immanuel

CHI Health Lakeside

Nebraska Medicine – Nebraska Medical Center

Nebraska Methodist Health System, Inc.

Nebraska Methodist Hospital

OrthoNebraska Hospital

**Ord**
Alliance
Valley County Health System

**Oshkosh**
Alliance
Regional West Garden County

**Osmond**
Alliance
Osmond General Hospital

**Papillion**
Alliance
CHI Health Midlands

**Plainview**
Alliance
CHI Health Plainview

**Schuyler**
Alliance
CHI Health Schuyler

**Scottsbluff**
Alliance
Regional West Medical Center

**York**
Alliance
York General

## NEVADA

**Las Vegas**
Alliance
Sunrise Hospital and Medical Center

University Medical Center

## NEW HAMPSHIRE

**Claremont**
Alliance
Valley Regional Hospital

**Colebrook**
Alliance
Upper Connecticut Valley Hospital

**Dover**
Alliance
Wentworth–Douglass Hospital

**Keene**
Alliance
Cheshire Medical Center

**Lancaster**
Alliance
Weeks Medical Center

**Lebanon**
Alliance
Alice Peck Day Memorial Hospital

Dartmouth–Hitchcock Medical Center

**Nashua**
Alliance
Southern New Hampshire Medical Center

**New London**
Alliance
New London Hospital

**North Conway**
Alliance
Memorial Hospital

**Peterborough**
Alliance
Monadnock Community Hospital

**Plymouth**
Alliance
Speare Memorial Hospital

**Woodsville**
Alliance
Cottage Hospital

**NEW JERSEY**
**Atlantic City**
Alliance
AtlantiCare Regional Medical Center

**Camden**
Alliance
Cooper University Health Care

**Cape May Court House**
Alliance
Cape Regional Health System

**Denville**
Alliance
Saint Clare's Denville Hospital

**Edison**
Alliance
Hackensack Meridian Health JFK Medical Center

**Elmer**
Alliance
Inspira Medical Center–Elmer

**Flemington**
Alliance
Hunterdon Healthcare

**Hamilton**
Alliance
Robert Wood Johnson University Hospital at Hamilton

**Marlton**
Alliance
Virtua Marlton

**Morristown**
Alliance
Morristown Medical Center

**Mount Holly**
Alliance
Virtua Memorial

**Mullica Hill**
Alliance
Inspira Health Network

**New Brunswick**
Alliance
Robert Wood Johnson University Hospital

**Newark**
Alliance
University Hospital

**Newton**
Alliance
Newton Medical Center

**Pomona**
Alliance
Bacharach Institute for Rehabilitation

**Pompton Plains**
Alliance
Chilton Medical Center

**Rahway**
Alliance
Robert Wood Johnson University Hospital Rahway

**Ridgewood**
Alliance
Valley Hospital

**Somers Point**
Alliance
Shore Medical Center

**Summit**
Alliance
Overlook Medical Center

**Trenton**
Alliance
Capital Health

**Vineland**
Alliance
Inspira Medical Center–Vineland

**Voorhees**
Alliance
Virtua Voorhees

**Woodbury**
Alliance
Inspira Medical Center–Woodbury

**NEW MEXICO**
**Albuquerque**
Alliance
University of New Mexico Hospitals

**Farmington**
Alliance
San Juan Regional Medical Center

**Gallup**
Alliance
Rehoboth McKinley Christian Health Care Services

**Rio Rancho**
Alliance
UNM Sandoval Regional Medical Center, Inc.

**Santa Fe**
Alliance
CHRISTUS St. Vincent Regional Medical Center

**NEW YORK**
**Albany**
Alliance
Albany Medical Center

St. Peter's Hospital

**Alexandria Bay**
Alliance
River Hospital

**Binghamton**
Alliance
United Health Services Hospitals–Binghamton

**Bronx**
Alliance
Montefiore Medical Center

NYC Health + Hospitals / Jacobi

NYC Health + Hospitals / North Central Bronx

**Brooklyn**
Alliance
Brooklyn Hospital Center

NYC Health + Hospitals / Coney Island

NYC Health + Hospitals / Woodhull

New York Community Hospital

NewYork–Presbyterian Brooklyn Methodist Hospital

SUNY Downstate–University Hospital of Brooklyn

**Buffalo**
Alliance
Erie County Medical Center

Roswell Park Comprehensive Cancer Center

**Canandaigua**
Alliance
F. F. Thompson Hospital

**Cooperstown**
Alliance
Bassett Medical Center

**Corning**
Alliance
Guthrie Corning Hospital

**Cortlandt Manor**
Alliance
New York–Presbyterian/Hudson Valley Hospital

**Elizabethtown**
Alliance
The University of Vermont Health Network
Elizabethtown Community Hospital

**Elmhurst**
Alliance
NYC Health + Hospitals / Elmhurst

**Flushing**
Alliance
New York–Presbyterian Queens

**Geneva**
Alliance
Finger Lakes Health

**Hamilton**
Alliance
Community Memorial Hospital

**Ithaca**
Alliance
Cayuga Medical Center at Ithaca

**Jamaica**
Alliance
NYC Health + Hospitals / Queens

**Jamestown**
Alliance
UPMC Chautauqua

**Malone**
Alliance
The University of Vermont Health Network – Alice Hyde
Medical Center

**Montour Falls**
Alliance
Schuyler Hospital

**Mount Vernon**
Alliance
Montefiore Mount Vernon

**New Rochelle**
Alliance
Montefiore New Rochelle

**New York**
Alliance
Gracie Square Hospital

Lenox Hill Hospital

NYC Health + Hospitals / Bellevue

NYC Health + Hospitals / Harlem

NYC Health + Hospitals / Henry J Carter Specialty
Hospital and Medical Center

NYU Langone Hospitals

New York–Presbyterian Hospital

New York–Presbyterian/Columbia University Medical
Center

Rockefeller University Hospital

The Mount Sinai Hospital

**Norwich**
Alliance
UHS Chenango Memorial Hospital

**Nyack**
Alliance
Montefiore Nyack Hospital

**Ogdensburg**
Alliance
Claxton–Hepburn Medical Center

**Plattsburgh**
Alliance
The University of Vermont Health Network–Champlain
Valley Physicians Hospital

**Riverhead**
Alliance
Peconic Bay Medical Center

**Rochester**
Alliance
Highland Hospital

Strong Memorial Hospital of the University of
Rochester

University of Rochester Medical Center

**Sleepy Hollow**
Alliance
Phelps Memorial Hospital Center

**Staten Island**
Alliance
Staten Island University Hospital

**Stony Brook**
Alliance
Stony Brook University Hospital

**Syracuse**
Alliance
Crouse Health

Upstate University Hospital

**Valhalla**
Alliance
Westchester Medical Center

**Walton**
Alliance
UHS Delaware Valley Hospital

## NORTH CAROLINA

**Ahoskie**
Alliance
Vidant Roanoke–Chowan Hospital

**Bermuda Run**
Alliance
Wake Forest Baptist Health–Davie Medical Center

**Bolivia**
Alliance
Novant Health Brunswick Medical Center

**Cary**
Alliance
WakeMed Cary Hospital

**Chapel Hill**
Alliance
University of North Carolina Hospitals

**Charlotte**
Alliance
Atrium Health
Novant Health Charlotte Orthopaedic Hospital
Novant Health Presbyterian Medical Center

**Clinton**
Alliance
Sampson Regional Medical Center

**Dunn**
Alliance
Harnett Health System

**Durham**
Alliance
Duke Regional Hospital
Duke University Hospital

**Eden**
Alliance
UNC Rockingham Health Care

**Edenton**
Alliance
Vidant Chowan Hospital

**Elizabeth City**
Alliance
Sentara Albemarle Medical Center

**Elkin**
Alliance
Hugh Chatham Memorial Hospital

**Greenville**
Alliance
Vidant Medical Center

**Huntersville**
Alliance
Novant Health Huntersville Medical Center

**Jefferson**
Alliance
Ashe Memorial Hospital

**Kenansville**
Alliance
Vidant Duplin Hospital

**Lexington**
Alliance
Wake Forest Baptist Health–Lexington Medical Center

**Matthews**
Alliance
Novant Health Matthews Medical Center

**Morehead City**
Alliance
Carteret Health Care

**Nags Head**
Alliance
The Outer Banks Hospital

**New Bern**
Alliance
CarolinaEast Health System

**Raleigh**
Alliance
Duke Raleigh Hospital
UNC REX Health Care
WakeMed Health & Hospitals
WakeMed Raleigh Campus

**Roanoke Rapids**
Alliance
Vidant North Hospital

**Rocky Mount**
Alliance
Nash UNC Health Care

**Salisbury**
Alliance
Novant Health Rowan Medical Center

**Siler City**
Alliance
Chatham Hospital

**Sparta**
Alliance
Alleghany Memorial Hospital

**Tarboro**
Alliance
Vidant Edgecombe Hospital

**Thomasville**
Alliance
Novant Health Thomasville Medical Center

**Washington**
Alliance
Vidant Beaufort Hospital

**Wilson**
Alliance
Wilson Medical Center

**Windsor**
Alliance
Vidant Bertie Hospital

**Winston Salem**
Alliance
Novant Health

**Winston–Salem**
Alliance
Novant Health Forsyth Medical Center
Novant Health Medical Park Hospital
Wake Forest Baptist Medical Center

## NORTH DAKOTA

**Bismarck**
Alliance
Sanford Medical Center Bismarck

**Devils Lake**
Alliance
CHI St. Alexius Health Devils Lake Hospital

**Dickinson**
Alliance
CHI St. Alexius Health – Dickinson Medical Center

**Fargo**
Alliance
Sanford Medical Center Fargo

**Grand Forks**
Alliance
Altru Health System

**Hillsboro**
Alliance
Sanford Hillsboro Medical Center

**Jamestown**
Alliance
Jamestown Regional Medical Center

**Kenmare**
Alliance
Kenmare Community Hospital

**Lisbon**
Alliance
CHI Lisbon Health

**Mayville**
Alliance
Sanford Mayville Medical Center

**Mcville**
Alliance
Nelson County Health System

**Minot**
Alliance
Trinity Health

**Northwood**
Alliance
Northwood Deaconess Health Center

**Oakes**
Alliance
CHI Oakes Hospital

**Valley City**
Alliance
CHI Mercy Health

## OHIO

**Akron**
Alliance
Akron Children's Hospital
Cleveland Clinic Akron General

**Alliance**
Alliance
Alliance Community Hospital

**Ashland**
Alliance
UH Samaritan Medical Center

**Ashtabula**
Alliance
Ashtabula County Medical Center

**Athens**
Alliance
O'Bleness Memorial Hospital

**Barnesville**
Alliance
WVU Medicine – Barnesville Hospital

**Bellefontaine**
Alliance
Mary Rutan Hospital

**Bluffton**
Alliance
Bluffton Hospital

**Bucyrus**
Alliance
Bucyrus Hospital

**Cadiz**
Alliance
Harrison Community Hospital

**Cambridge**
Alliance
Southeastern Ohio Regional Medical Center

**Canton**
Alliance
Aultman Hospital

**Chardon**
Alliance
UH Geauga Medical Center

**Cincinnati**
Alliance
Christ Hospital
Cincinnati Children's Hospital Medical Center
Good Samaritan Hospital
Shriners Hospitals for Children – Cincinnati
The Jewish Hospital – Mercy Health
UC Health
University of Cincinnati Medical Center

**Circleville**
Alliance
OhioHealth Berger Hospital

**Cleveland**
Alliance
Cleveland Clinic Fairview Hospital

Cleveland Clinic

Lutheran Hospital

MetroHealth Medical Center

UH Cleveland Medical Center

**Coldwater**
Alliance
Mercer Health

**Columbus**
Alliance
Ohio State University Wexner Medical Center

OhioHealth Doctors Hospital

OhioHealth Grant Medical Center

OhioHealth Riverside Methodist Hospital

OhioHealth

**Conneaut**
Alliance
UH Conneaut Medical Center

**Copley**
Alliance
Edwin Shaw Rehab

**Coshocton**
Alliance
Coshocton Regional Medical Center

**Dayton**
Alliance
Miami Valley Hospital

**Defiance**
Alliance
ProMedica Defiance Regional Hospital

**Delaware**
Alliance
OhioHealth Grady Memorial Hospital

**Dover**
Alliance
Cleveland Clinic Union Hospital

**Dublin**
Alliance
OhioHealth Dublin Methodist Hospital

**Euclid**
Alliance
Euclid Hospital

**Findlay**
Alliance
Blanchard Valley Hospital

**Fostoria**
Alliance
ProMedica Fostoria Community Hospital

**Fremont**
Alliance
ProMedica Memorial Hospital

**Galion**
Alliance
Galion Hospital

**Garfield Heights**
Alliance
Marymount Hospital

**Geneva**
Alliance
UH Geneva Medical Center

**Greenville**
Alliance
Wayne HealthCare

**Hamilton**
Alliance
Fort Hamilton Hospital

**Kenton**
Alliance
OhioHealth Hardin Memorial Hospital

**Lima**
Alliance
Lima Memorial Health System

**Lodi**
Alliance
Cleveland Clinic Akron General Lodi Hospital

**Logan**
Alliance
Hocking Valley Community Hospital

**London**
Alliance
Madison Health

**Mansfield**
Alliance
OhioHealth MedCentral Mansfield Hospital

**Marion**
Alliance
OhioHealth Marion General Hospital

**Marysville**
Alliance
Memorial Health

**Mason**
Alliance
Lindner Center of HOPE

**Maumee**
Alliance
St. Luke's Hospital

**Medina**
Alliance
Cleveland Clinic, Medina Hospital

**Middleburg Heights**
Alliance
Southwest General Health Center

**Millersburg**
Alliance
Pomerene Hospital

**Mount Gilead**
Alliance
Morrow County Hospital

**New Albany**
Alliance
Mount Carmel New Albany Surgical Hospital

**Newark**
Alliance
Licking Memorial Hospital

**Norwalk**
Alliance
Fisher–Titus Medical Center

**Orrville**
Alliance
Aultman Orrville Hospital

**Paulding**
Alliance
Paulding County Hospital

**Portsmouth**
Alliance
Southern Ohio Medical Center

**Rock Creek**
Alliance
Glenbeigh Hospital and Outpatient Centers

**Shelby**
Alliance
OhioHealth MedCentral Shelby Hospital

**Sidney**
Alliance
Wilson Memorial Hospital

**Toledo**
Alliance
ProMedica Health System

ProMedica Toledo Hospital

The University of Toledo Medical Center

**Troy**
Alliance
Upper Valley Medical Center

**Upper Sandusky**
Alliance
Wyandot Memorial Hospital

**Van Wert**
Alliance
Van Wert County Hospital

**Warrensville Heights**
Alliance
South Pointe Hospital

**Washington Court House**
Alliance
Fayette County Memorial Hospital

**Westerville**
Alliance
Mount Carmel St. Ann's

**Westlake**
Alliance
UH St. John Medical Center

**Zanesville**
Alliance
Genesis HealthCare System

**OKLAHOMA**

**Altus**
Alliance
Jackson County Memorial Hospital

**Antlers**
Alliance
Pushmataha Hospital

**Atoka**
Alliance
Atoka County Medical Center

**Bethany**
Alliance
The Children's Center Rehabilitation Hospital

**Carnegie**
Alliance
Carnegie Tri–County Municipal Hospital

**Chickasha**
Alliance
Grady Memorial Hospital

**Duncan**
Alliance
Duncan Regional Hospital

**Edmond**
Alliance
INTEGRIS Health Edmond

**Elk City**
Alliance
Great Plains Regional Medical Center

**Enid**
Alliance
Integris Bass Baptist Health Center

**Grove**
Alliance
INTEGRIS Grove Hospital

**Hobart**
Alliance
Elkview General Hospital

**Hugo**
Alliance
Choctaw Memorial Hospital

**Lawton**
Alliance
Comanche County Memorial Hospital

**McAlester**
Alliance
McAlester Regional Health Center

**Miami**
Alliance
INTEGRIS Miami Hospital

**Norman**
Alliance
Norman Regional Health System

**Oklahoma City**
Alliance
INTEGRIS Baptist Medical Center

INTEGRIS Health

INTEGRIS Southwest Medical Center

Lakeside Women's Hospital

**Stillwater**
Alliance
Stillwater Medical Center

# Alliances

**Tahlequah**
Alliance
Northeastern Health System

**Waurika**
Alliance
Jefferson County Hospital

**Yukon**
Alliance
INTEGRIS Canadian Valley Hospital

## OREGON

**Forest Grove**
Alliance
Tuality Forest Grove Hospital

**Grants Pass**
Alliance
Asante Three Rivers Medical Center

**Hillsboro**
Alliance
Tuality Healthcare

**Hood River**
Alliance
Providence Hood River Memorial Hospital

**Medford**
Alliance
Asante Rogue Regional Medical Center

Providence Medford Medical Center

**Milwaukie**
Alliance
Providence Milwaukie Hospital

**Newberg**
Alliance
Providence Newberg Medical Center

**Ontario**
Alliance
Saint Alphonsus Medical Center – Ontario

**Oregon City**
Alliance
Providence Willamette Falls Medical Center

**Pendleton**
Alliance
CHI St. Anthony Hospital

**Portland**
Alliance
OHSU Hospital

Providence Portland Medical Center

Providence St. Vincent Medical Center

Shriners Hospitals for Children–Portland

**Roseburg**
Alliance
Mercy Medical Center

**Salem**
Alliance
Salem Hospital

**Seaside**
Alliance
Providence Seaside Hospital

**Silverton**
Alliance
Legacy Silverton Medical Center

**The Dalles**
Alliance
Mid–Columbia Medical Center

## PENNSYLVANIA

**Abington**
Alliance
Abington Jefferson Health

**Allentown**
Alliance
Lehigh Valley Hospital

**Brookville**
Alliance
Penn Highlands Brookville

**Bryn Mawr**
Alliance
Bryn Mawr Hospital

**Butler**
Alliance
Butler Health System

**Chambersburg**
Alliance
WellSpan Chambersburg Hospital

**Clearfield**
Alliance
Penn Highlands Clearfield

**Darby**
Alliance
Mercy Catholic Medical Center – Mercy Fitzgerald Campus

**Drexel Hill**
Alliance
Delaware County Memorial Hospital

**DuBois**
Alliance
Penn Highlands DuBois

**East Norriton**
Alliance
Einstein Medical Center Montgomery

**East Stroudsburg**
Alliance
Lehigh Valley Hospital – Pocono

**Ephrata**
Alliance
WellSpan Ephrata Community Hospital

**Gettysburg**
Alliance
WellSpan Gettysburg Hospital

**Greensburg**
Alliance
Excela Health Westmoreland Hospital

**Hanover**
Alliance
UPMC Hanover

**Harrisburg**
Alliance
PinnacleHealth at Community General Osteopathic Hospital

UPMC Pinnacle Harrisburg

**Hazleton**
Alliance
Lehigh Valley Hospital – Hazleton

**Hershey**
Alliance
Penn State Milton S. Hershey Medical Center

**Huntingdon**
Alliance
Penn Highlands Huntingdon

**Indiana**
Alliance
Indiana Regional Medical Center

**Jefferson Hills**
Alliance
Jefferson Hospital

**Lancaster**
Alliance
Penn Medicine Lancaster General Hospital

**Langhorne**
Alliance
St. Mary Medical Center

**Lansdale**
Alliance
Abington–Lansdale Hospital Jefferson Health

**Latrobe**
Alliance
Excela Latrobe Area Hospital

**Lebanon**
Alliance
WellSpan Good Samaritan Hospital

**Lehighton**
Alliance
St. Luke's – Lehighton Campus

**Malvern**
Alliance
Bryn Mawr Rehabilitation Hospital

**Meadowbrook**
Alliance
Holy Redeemer Hospital

**Media**
Alliance
Riddle Hospital

**Monongahela**
Alliance
Monongahela Valley Hospital

**Mount Pleasant**
Alliance
Excela Frick Hospital

**Muncy**
Alliance
UPMC Muncy

**New Castle**
Alliance
UPMC Jameson

**Paoli**
Alliance
Paoli Hospital

**Philadelphia**
Alliance
Children's Hospital of Philadelphia

Einstein Medical Center Philadelphia

Fox Chase Cancer Center–American Oncologic Hospital

Hospital of the University of Pennsylvania

Jefferson Health Northeast

Magee Rehabilitation Hospital

Penn Presbyterian Medical Center

Pennsylvania Hospital

Temple University Hospital – Jeanes Campus

Temple University Hospital

University of Pennsylvania Health System

**Pittsburgh**
Alliance
St. Clair Hospital

UPMC Presbyterian

**Pottsville**
Alliance
Lehigh Valley Hospital – Schuylkill

**Reading**
Alliance
Penn State Health St. Joseph

**Saint Marys**
Alliance
Penn Highlands Elk

**Sayre**
Alliance
Guthrie Clinic

Guthrie Robert Packer Hospital

**Sellersville**
Alliance
Grand View Health

**Towanda**
Alliance
Guthrie Towanda Memorial Hospital

**Troy**
Alliance
Guthrie Troy Community Hospital

**Uniontown**
Alliance
Uniontown Hospital

**Upland**
Alliance
Crozer–Chester Medical Center

**Waynesboro**
Alliance
Wellspan Waynesboro Hospital

**Wellsboro**
Alliance
  UPMC Wellsboro

**West Chester**
Alliance
  Chester County Hospital

**West Reading**
Alliance
  Reading Hospital

**Williamsport**
Alliance
  UPMC Susquehanna

  UPMC Williamsport

**Wynnewood**
Alliance
  Lankenau Medical Center

**York**
Alliance
  WellSpan Health

  WellSpan York Hospital

## RHODE ISLAND
**Newport**
Alliance
  Newport Hospital

**Providence**
Alliance
  Butler Hospital

  Care New England Health System

  Lifespan Corporation

  Miriam Hospital

  Rhode Island Hospital

  Women & Infants Hospital of Rhode Island

**Warwick**
Alliance
  Kent County Memorial Hospital

**Westerly**
Alliance
  Westerly Hospital

## SOUTH CAROLINA
**Charleston**
Alliance
  MUSC Health of Medical University of South Carolina

**Cheraw**
Alliance
  McLeod Health Cheraw

**Clinton**
Alliance
  Prisma Health Laurens County Hospital

**Columbia**
Alliance
  ContinueCARE Hospital at Palmetto Health Baptist

  Prisma Health Baptist Hospital

  Prisma Health Baptist Parkridge Hospital

  Prisma Health Richland Hospital

  Providence Hospital

**Darlington**
Alliance
  McLeod Health Darlington

**Dillon**
Alliance
  McLeod Health Dillon

**Easley**
Alliance
  Prisma Health Baptist Easley Hospital

**Florence**
Alliance
  McLeod Regional Medical Center

**Georgetown**
Alliance
  Tidelands Georgetown Memorial Hospital

**Greenville**
Alliance
  Prisma Health Greenville Memorial Hospital

  Prisma Health Patewood Hospital

  Shriners Hospitals for Children–Greenville

**Greenwood**
Alliance
  Self Regional Healthcare

**Greer**
Alliance
  Prisma Health Greer Memorial Hospital

**Loris**
Alliance
  McLeod Health Loris

**Murrells Inlet**
Alliance
  Tidelands Waccamaw Community Hospital

**Seneca**
Alliance
  Prisma Health Oconee Memorial Hospital

**Simpsonville**
Alliance
  Prisma Health Hillcrest Hospital

**Sumter**
Alliance
  Prisma Health Tuomey Hospital

**Travelers Rest**
Alliance
  Prisma Health North Greenville

## SOUTH DAKOTA
**Aberdeen**
Alliance
  Sanford Aberdeen Medical Center

**Armour**
Alliance
  Douglas County Memorial Hospital

**Burke**
Alliance
  Community Memorial Hospital

**Canton**
Alliance
  Sanford Canton–Inwood Medical Center

**Chamberlain**
Alliance
  Sanford Chamberlain Medical Center

**Clear Lake**
Alliance
  Sanford Clear Lake Medical Center

**Sioux Falls**
Alliance
  Sanford Health

  Sanford USD Medical Center

**Vermillion**
Alliance
  Sanford Vermillion Medical Center

**Viborg**
Alliance
  Pioneer Memorial Hospital and Health Services

**Watertown**
Alliance
  Prairie Lakes Healthcare System

**Webster**
Alliance
  Sanford Webster Medical Center

**Winner**
Alliance
  Winner Regional Healthcare Center

## TENNESSEE
**Chattanooga**
Alliance
  Erlanger Health System

  Erlanger North Hospital

**Collierville**
Alliance
  Baptist Memorial Hospital–Collierville

**Columbia**
Alliance
  Maury Regional Hospital

**Covington**
Alliance
  Baptist Memorial Hospital–Tipton

**Franklin**
Alliance
  Williamson Medical Center

**Harriman**
Alliance
  Roane Medical Center

**Huntingdon**
Alliance
  Baptist Memorial Hospital–Carroll County

**Knoxville**
Alliance
  Covenant Health

  Fort Sanders Regional Medical Center

  Parkwest Medical Center

  University of Tennessee Medical Center

**Lenoir City**
Alliance
  Fort Loudoun Medical Center

**Lewisburg**
Alliance
  Marshall Medical Center

**Memphis**
Alliance
  Baptist Memorial Health Care Corporation

  Baptist Memorial Hospital – Memphis

  Baptist Memorial Hospital for Women

  Methodist Healthcare Memphis Hospitals

  Regional One Health

  St. Jude Children's Research Hospital

**Morristown**
Alliance
  Morristown–Hamblen Healthcare System

**Nashville**
Alliance
  Vanderbilt University Medical Center

**Oak Ridge**
Alliance
  Methodist Medical Center of Oak Ridge

**Sevierville**
Alliance
  LeConte Medical Center

**Tazewell**
Alliance
  Claiborne Medical Center

**Union City**
Alliance
  Baptist Memorial Hospital–Union City

**Waynesboro**
Alliance
  Wayne Medical Center

## TEXAS
**Andrews**
Alliance
  Permian Regional Medical Center

**Baytown**
Alliance
  Houston Methodist Baytown Hospital

**Bellville**
Alliance
  Bellville Medical Center

**Dallas**
Alliance
  Baylor Scott & White Health

  Children's Medical Center Dallas

  Methodist Health System

  Parkland Health & Hospital System

# Alliances

**El Paso**
Alliance
  University Medical Center of El Paso

**Fort Worth**
Alliance
  JPS Health Network

**Galveston**
Alliance
  Shriners Hospitals for Children–Galveston

  University of Texas Medical Branch

**Houston**
Alliance
  Baylor St. Luke's Medical Center

  CHI St. Luke's Hospital – The Vintage Hospital

  Harris Health System

  Houston Methodist Hospital

  Houston Methodist West Hospital

  Houston Methodist Willowbrook Hospital

  Memorial Hermann – Texas Medical Center

  Memorial Hermann Greater Heights Hospital

  Memorial Hermann Health System

  Memorial Hermann Memorial City Medical Center

  Shriners Hospitals for Children–Houston

  TIRR Memorial Hermann

**Humble**
Alliance
  Memorial Hermann Northeast

**Katy**
Alliance
  Houston Methodist Continuing Care Hospital

  Memorial Hermann Katy Hospital

**Livingston**
Alliance
  CHI St. Luke's Health Memorial Livingston

**Lubbock**
Alliance
  Covenant Health System

  Covenant Medical Center–Lakeside

**Lufkin**
Alliance
  CHI St. Luke's Health Memorial Lufkin

**Midland**
Alliance
  Midland Memorial Hospital

**Pasadena**
Alliance
  CHI St. Luke's Health – Patients Medical Center

**Pearsall**
Alliance
  Frio Regional Hospital

**Plano**
Alliance
  Community Hospital Corporation

**San Antonio**
Alliance
  University Health System

**San Augustine**
Alliance
  CHI St. Luke's Health Memorial San Augustine

**Sugar Land**
Alliance
  Houston Methodist Sugar Land Hospital

  Memorial Hermann Sugar Land Hospital

**Sweeny**
Alliance
  Sweeny Community Hospital

**The Woodlands**
Alliance
  CHI St. Luke's Health–Lakeside Hospital

  CHI St. Luke's Health–The Woodlands Hospital

**Tyler**
Alliance
  CHRISTUS Mother Frances Hospital – Tyler

  UT Health North Campus Tyler

## UTAH
**Gunnison**
Alliance
  Gunnison Valley Hospital

**Provo**
Alliance
  Utah State Hospital

**Salt Lake City**
Alliance
  Shriners Hospitals for Children–Salt Lake City

  University of Utah Health

## VERMONT
**Bennington**
Alliance
  Southwestern Vermont Medical Center

**Berlin**
Alliance
  The University of Vermont Health Network Central Vermont Medical Center

**Brattleboro**
Alliance
  Brattleboro Memorial Hospital

  Brattleboro Retreat

**Burlington**
Alliance
  University of Vermont Medical Center

**Morrisville**
Alliance
  Copley Hospital

**Newport**
Alliance
  North Country Hospital and Health Center

**Rutland**
Alliance
  Rutland Regional Medical Center

**Saint Johnsbury**
Alliance
  Northeastern Vermont Regional Hospital

**Springfield**
Alliance
  Springfield Hospital

**Townshend**
Alliance
  Grace Cottage Hospital

**Windsor**
Alliance
  Mt. Ascutney Hospital and Health Center

## VIRGIN ISLANDS
**Saint Thomas**
Alliance
  Schneider Regional Medical Center

## VIRGINIA
**Bedford**
Alliance
  Centra Bedford Memorial Hospital

**Charlottesville**
Alliance
  Sentara Martha Jefferson Hospital

  UVA Encompass Health Rehabilitation Hospital

  University of Virginia Medical Center

**Culpeper**
Alliance
  Novant Health UVA Health System Culpeper Medical Center

**Farmville**
Alliance
  Centra Southside Community Hospital

**Fishersville**
Alliance
  Augusta Health

**Fredericksburg**
Alliance
  Mary Washington Hospital

**Hampton**
Alliance
  Sentara CarePlex Hospital

**Harrisonburg**
Alliance
  Sentara RMH Medical Center

**Lynchburg**
Alliance
  Centra Lynchburg General Hospital

**Manassas**
Alliance
  Novant Health UVA Health System Prince William Medical Center

**Norfolk**
Alliance
  Hospital for Extended Recovery

  Sentara Healthcare

  Sentara Leigh Hospital

  Sentara Norfolk General Hospital

**Richmond**
Alliance
  Children's Hospital of Richmond at VCU–Brook Road Campus

  VCU Medical Center

**South Boston**
Alliance
  Sentara Halifax Regional Hospital

**Stafford**
Alliance
  Stafford Hospital

**Suffolk**
Alliance
  Sentara Obici Hospital

**Virginia Beach**
Alliance
  Sentara Princess Anne Hospital

  Sentara Virginia Beach General Hospital

**Williamsburg**
Alliance
  Sentara Williamsburg Regional Medical Center

**Woodbridge**
Alliance
  Sentara Northern Virginia Medical Center

## WASHINGTON
**Aberdeen**
Alliance
  Grays Harbor Community Hospital

**Auburn**
Alliance
  MultiCare Auburn Medical Center

**Bellingham**
Alliance
  PeaceHealth St. Joseph Medical Center

**Bremerton**
Alliance
  St. Michael Medical Center

**Burien**
Alliance
  St. Anne Hospital

**Centralia**
Alliance
  Providence Centralia Hospital

**Chewelah**
Alliance
  Providence St. Joseph's Hospital

**Colfax**
Alliance
  Whitman Hospital and Medical Center

**Colville**
Alliance
  Providence Mount Carmel Hospital

**Dayton**
Alliance
Columbia County Health System

**Edmonds**
Alliance
Swedish/Edmonds

**Enumclaw**
Alliance
St. Elizabeth Hospital

**Everett**
Alliance
Providence Regional Medical Center Everett

**Gig Harbor**
Alliance
St. Anthony Hospital

**Ilwaco**
Alliance
Ocean Beach Hospital

**Issaquah**
Alliance
Swedish/Issaquah

**Lakewood**
Alliance
St. Clare Hospital

**Morton**
Alliance
Arbor Health, Morton Hospital

**Olympia**
Alliance
Providence St. Peter Hospital

**Pomeroy**
Alliance
Garfield County Public Hospital District

**Port Angeles**
Alliance
Olympic Medical Center

**Prosser**
Alliance
Prosser Memorial Health

**Puyallup**
Alliance
MultiCare Good Samaritan Hospital

**Renton**
Alliance
UW Medicine/Valley Medical Center

**Richland**
Alliance
Kadlec Regional Medical Center

**Seattle**
Alliance
Swedish Medical Center–Cherry Hill Campus

Swedish Medical Center–First Hill

UW Medicine/Harborview Medical Center

UW Medicine/Northwest Hospital & Medical Center

University of Washington Medical Center

**Spokane**
Alliance
Providence Holy Family Hospital

Providence Sacred Heart Medical Center & Children's Hospital

Shriners Hospitals for Children–Spokane

St. Luke's Rehabilitation Institute

**Tacoma**
Alliance
MultiCare Health System

MultiCare Tacoma General Hospital

St. Joseph Medical Center

**Walla Walla**
Alliance
Providence St. Mary Medical Center

**WEST VIRGINIA**
**Charleston**
Alliance
CAMC Women and Children's Hospital

Charleston Area Medical Center

**Gassaway**
Alliance
Braxton County Memorial Hospital

**Madison**
Alliance
Boone Memorial Hospital

**Martinsburg**
Alliance
Berkeley Medical Center

**Montgomery**
Alliance
Montgomery General Hospital

**Morgantown**
Alliance
West Virginia University Hospitals

**Princeton**
Alliance
Princeton Community Hospital

**Ranson**
Alliance
Jefferson Medical Center

**Ripley**
Alliance
Jackson General Hospital

**Spencer**
Alliance
Roane General Hospital

**WISCONSIN**
**Antigo**
Alliance
Aspirus Langlade Hospital

**Appleton**
Alliance
ThedaCare, Inc.

**Barron**
Alliance
Mayo Clinic Health System – Northland in Barron

**Beaver Dam**
Alliance
Marshfield Medical Center – Beaver Dam

**Beloit**
Alliance
Beloit Health System

**Bloomer**
Alliance
Mayo Clinic Health System – Chippewa Valley in Bloomer

**Boscobel**
Alliance
Gundersen Boscobel Area Hospital and Clinics

**Eau Claire**
Alliance
Mayo Clinic Health System in Eau Claire

**Friendship**
Alliance
Gundersen Moundview Hospital & Clinics

**Green Bay**
Alliance
Bellin Hospital

Bellin Psychiatric Center

**Hillsboro**
Alliance
Gundersen St. Joseph's Hospital and Clinics

**Hudson**
Alliance
Hudson Hospital and Clinic

**La Crosse**
Alliance
Gundersen Lutheran Medical Center

Mayo Clinic Health System – Franciscan Healthcare in La Crosse

**Madison**
Alliance
UnityPoint Health Meriter

University Hospital

**Marinette**
Alliance
Aurora Medical Center – Bay Area

**Medford**
Alliance
Aspirus Medford Hospital & Clinics, Inc.

**Menomonee Falls**
Alliance
Froedtert Menomonee Falls Hospital

**Menomonie**
Alliance
Mayo Clinic Health System – Red Cedar in Menomonie

**Milwaukee**
Alliance
Froedtert and the Medical College of Wisconsin
Froedtert Hospital

**Neenah**
Alliance
ThedaCare Regional Medical Center–Neenah

**Neillsville**
Alliance
Marshfield Medical Center – Neilsville

**New Richmond**
Alliance
Westfields Hospital and Clinic

**Oconomowoc**
Alliance
Oconomowoc Memorial Hospital

**Oconto**
Alliance
Bellin Health Oconto Hospital

**Osseo**
Alliance
Mayo Clinic Health System – Oakridge in Osseo

**Portage**
Alliance
Divine Savior Healthcare

**River Falls**
Alliance
River Falls Area Hospital

**Sparta**
Alliance
Mayo Clinic Health System – Franciscan Healthcare in Sparta

**Superior**
Alliance
Essentia Health St. Mary's Hospital of Superior

**Waukesha**
Alliance
ProHealth Care, Inc.

Waukesha Memorial Hospital

**Waupaca**
Alliance
ThedaCare Medical Center–Waupaca

**Wausau**
Alliance
Aspirus Wausau Hospital, Inc.

North Central Health Care

**West Bend**
Alliance
Froedtert West Bend Hospital

**Whitehall**
Alliance
Gundersen Tri–County Hospital and Clinics

**Wild Rose**
Alliance
Theda Care Medical Center – Wild Rose

**Wisconsin Rapids**
Alliance
Aspirus Riverview Hospital and Clinics, Inc.

# Alliances

## WYOMING

**Buffalo**
Alliance
  Johnson County Healthcare Center

**Casper**
Alliance
  Wyoming Medical Center

**Cheyenne**
Alliance
  Cheyenne Regional Medical Center

**Douglas**
Alliance
  Memorial Hospital of Converse County

**Laramie**
Alliance
  Ivinson Memorial Hospital

**Lusk**
Alliance
  Niobrara Community Hospital

**Sheridan**
Alliance
  Sheridan Memorial Hospital

## YANKEE ALLIANCE

138 River Road, Andover, MA
Zip 01810–1083; tel. 978/470–2000;
James W. Oliver, President and Chief
Executive Officer

### CALIFORNIA

**Long Beach**
Alliance
  College Medical Center

**Oceanside**
Alliance
  Tri–City Medical Center

### CONNECTICUT

**Derby**
Alliance
  Griffin Hospital

**Hartford**
Alliance
  Saint Francis Hospital and Medical Center

**New London**
Alliance
  Lawrence + Memorial Hospital

**Stafford Springs**
Alliance
  Johnson Memorial Hospital

### FLORIDA

**Coral Gables**
Alliance
  Baptist Health South Florida, Doctors Hospital

**Homestead**
Alliance
  Baptist Health South Florida, Homestead Hospital

**Miami Beach**
Alliance
  Mount Sinai Medical Center

**Miami**
Alliance
  Baptist Health South Florida, Baptist Hospital of Miami
  Baptist Health South Florida, South Miami Hospital
  Baptist Health South Florida, West Kendall Baptist Hospital

**Miramar**
Alliance
  Memorial Hospital Miramar

**Pembroke Pines**
Alliance
  Memorial Hospital Pembroke
  Memorial Hospital West

**South Miami**
Alliance
  Larkin Community Hospital–South Miami Campus

**Tavernier**
Alliance
  Baptist Health South Florida, Mariners Hospital

### ILLINOIS

**Geneva**
Alliance
  Northwestern Medicine Delnor Hospital

**Winfield**
Alliance
  Northwestern Medicine Central DuPage Hospital

### INDIANA

**Gary**
Alliance
  Methodist Hospitals

**Mishawaka**
Alliance
  Unity Medical & Surgical Hospital

### KENTUCKY

**Ashland**
Alliance
  King's Daughters Medical Center

**Benton**
Alliance
  Marshall County Hospital

**Corbin**
Alliance
  Baptist Health Corbin

**Elizabethtown**
Alliance
  Hardin Memorial Health

**La Grange**
Alliance
  Baptist Health La Grange

**Lexington**
Alliance
  Baptist Health Lexington

**Louisville**
Alliance
  Baptist Health Louisville

**Madisonville**
Alliance
  Baptist Health Madisonville

**Paducah**
Alliance
  Baptist Health Paducah

**Prestonsburg**
Alliance
  Highlands ARH Regional Medical Center

**Richmond**
Alliance
  Baptist Health Richmond

### MAINE

**Bangor**
Alliance
  St. Joseph Hospital

**Lewiston**
Alliance
  St. Mary's Regional Medical Center

### MASSACHUSETTS

**Attleboro**
Alliance
  Sturdy Memorial Hospital

**Boston**
Alliance
  Boston Medical Center
  New England Baptist Hospital
  Tufts Medical Center

**Brockton**
Alliance
  Signature Healthcare Brockton Hospital

**Burlington**
Alliance
  Lahey Hospital & Medical Center, Burlington

**Fall River**
Alliance
  Southcoast Hospitals Group

**Great Barrington**
Alliance
  Fairview Hospital

**Lowell**
Alliance
  Lowell General Hospital

**Milford**
Alliance
  Milford Regional Medical Center

**Newburyport**
Alliance
  Anna Jaques Hospital

**Oak Bluffs**
Alliance
  Martha's Vineyard Hospital

**Pittsfield**
Alliance
  Berkshire Medical Center

**Westfield**
Alliance
  Baystate Noble Hospital

**Winchester**
Alliance
  Winchester Hospital

### NEW HAMPSHIRE

**Concord**
Alliance
  Concord Hospital

**Exeter**
Alliance
  Exeter Hospital

**Franklin**
Alliance
  Franklin Regional Hospital

**Laconia**
Alliance
  Lakes Region General Hospital

**Manchester**
Alliance
  Catholic Medical Center
  Elliot Hospital

**Nashua**
Alliance
  St. Joseph Hospital

**North Conway**
Alliance
  Memorial Hospital

**Rochester**
Alliance
  Frisbie Memorial Hospital

**Salem**
Alliance
  Northeast Rehabilitation Hospital

### NEW YORK

**Batavia**
Alliance
  United Memorial Medical Center

**Bath**
Alliance
  Ira Davenport Memorial Hospital

**Elizabethtown**
Alliance
  The University of Vermont Health Network
  Elizabethtown Community Hospital

**Elmira**
Alliance
  Arnot Ogden Medical Center

**Glens Falls**
Alliance
  Glens Falls Hospital

**Gloversville**
Alliance
  Nathan Littauer Hospital and Nursing Home

**Plattsburgh**
Alliance
 The University of Vermont Health Network–Champlain Valley Physicians Hospital

**Warsaw**
Alliance
 Wyoming County Community Hospital

## OHIO
**Logan**
Alliance
 Hocking Valley Community Hospital

**Montpelier**
Alliance
 Community Hospitals and Wellness Centers–Montpelier

**Salem**
Alliance
 Salem Regional Medical Center

**Seaman**
Alliance
 Adams County Regional Medical Center

**Sidney**
Alliance
 Wilson Memorial Hospital

**Steubenville**
Alliance
 Life Line Hospital

## PENNSYLVANIA
**Honesdale**
Alliance
 Wayne Memorial Hospital

**Langhorne**
Alliance
 Barix Clinics of Pennsylvania

**Washington**
Alliance
 Advanced Surgical Hospital

## RHODE ISLAND
**Providence**
Alliance
 Roger Williams Medical Center

**Wakefield**
Alliance
 South County Hospital

**Westerly**
Alliance
 Westerly Hospital

## SOUTH CAROLINA
**Columbia**
Alliance
 Providence Hospital

**Fairfax**
Alliance
 Allendale County Hospital

## TEXAS
**Austin**
Alliance
 Arise Austin Medical Center

**Houston**
Alliance
 Nexus Children's Hospital Houston

**New Braunfels**
Alliance
 PAM Specialty Hospital of New Braunfels

**Plainview**
Alliance
 Covenant Hospital Plainview

## WEST VIRGINIA
**New Martinsville**
Alliance
 Wetzel County Hospital

**Section B**

# Abbreviations Used in the AHA Guide

**AB,** Army Base
**ACSW,** Academy of Certified Social Workers
**AEC,** Atomic Energy Commission
**AFB,** Air Force Base
**AHA,** American Hospital Association
**AK,** Alaska
**AL,** Alabama
**AODA,** Alcohol and Other Drug Abuse
**APO,** Army Post Office
**AR,** Arkansas
**A.R.T.,** Accredited Record Technician
**A.S.C.,** Ambulatory Surgical Center
**A.T.C.,** Alcoholism Treatment Center
**Ave.,** Avenue
**AZ,** Arizona

**B.A.,** Bachelor of Arts
**B.B.A.,** Bachelor of Business Administration
**B.C.,** British Columbia
**Blvd.,** Boulevard
**B.S.,** Bachelor of Science
**B.S.Ed.,** Bachelor of Science in Education
**B.S.H.S.,** Bachelor of Science in Health Studies
**B.S.N.,** Bachelor of Science in Nursing
**B.S.W.,** Bachelor of Science and Social Worker

**CA,** California; Controller of Accounts
**C.A.A.D.A.C.,** Certified Alcohol and Drug Abuse Counselor
**CAC,** Certified Alcoholism Counselor
**CAE,** Certified Association Executive
**CAP,** College of American Pathologists
**CAPA,** Certified Ambulatory Post Anesthesia
**C.A.S.,** Certificate of Advanced Study
**CCDC,** Certified Chemical Dependency Counselor
**C.D.,** Commander of the Order of Distinction
**CDR,** Commander
**CDS,** Chemical Dependency Specialist
**CFACHE,** Certified Fellow American College of Healthcare Executives
**CFRE,** Certified Fund Raising Executive
**C.G.,** Certified Gastroenterology
**CHC,** Certified Health Consultant
**CHE,** Certified Healthcare Executive
**C.L.D.,** Clinical Laboratory Director
**CLU,** Certified Life Underwriter, Chartered Life Underwriter
**CMA,** Certified Medical Assistant
**C.M.H.A.,** Certified Mental Health Administrator
**CNHA,** Certified Nursing Home Administrator
**CNM,** Certified Nurse Midwife
**CNOR,** Certified Operating Room Nurse
**C.N.S.,** Clinical Nurse Specialist
**CO,** Colorado; Commanding Officer
**COA,** Certified Ophthalmic Assistant
**COMT,** Commandant
**C.O.M.T.,** Certified Ophthalmic Medical Technician
**Conv.,** Conventions
**Corp.,** Corporation; Corporate
**C.O.T.,** Certified Ophthalmic Technician
**CPA,** Certified Public Accountant
**C.P.H.Q.,** Certified Professional in Health Care Quality
**CPM,** Certified Public Manager
**CRNA,** Certified Registered Nurse Anesthetist
**CRNH,** Certified Registered Nurse Hospice
**C.S.J.B,** Catholic Saint John the Baptist
**CSW,** Certified Social Worker
**CT,** Connecticut
**CWO,** Chief Warrant Officer

**D.B.A.,** Doctor of Business Administration
**DC,** District of Columbia
**D.D.,** Doctor of Divinity
**D.D.S.,** Doctor of Dental Surgery
**DE,** Delaware
**Diet,** Dietitian; Dietary; Dietetics
**D.M.D.,** Doctor of Dental Medicine
**D.MIN.,** Doctor of Ministry
**D.O.,** Doctor of Osteopathic Medicine and Surgery, Doctor of Osteopathy
**DPA,** Doctorate Public Administration
**D.P.M.,** Doctor of Podiatric Medicine
**Dr.,** Drive
**Dr.Ph.,** Doctor of Public Health
**D.Sc.,** Doctor of Science
**D.S.W.,** Doctor of Social Welfare
**D.V.M.,** Doctor of Veterinary Medicine

**E.,** East
**Ed.D.,** Doctor of Education
**Ed.S.,** Specialist in Education
**ENS,** Ensign
**Esq.,** Esquire
**Expwy.,** Expressway
**ext.,** extension

**FAAN,** Fellow of the American Academy of Nursing
**FACATA,** Fellow of the American College of Addiction Treatment Administrators
**FACHE,** Fellow of the American College of Healthcare Executives
**FACMGA,** Fellow of the American College of Medical Group Administrators
**FACP,** Fellow of the American College of Physicians
**FACS,** Fellow of the American College of Surgeons
**FAX,** Facsimile
**FL,** Florida
**FPO,** Fleet Post Office
**FRCPSC,** Fellow of the Royal College of Physicians and Surgeons of Canada
**FT,** Full-time

**GA,** Georgia
**Govt.,** Government; Governmental

**HHS,** Department of Health and Human Services
**HI,** Hawaii
**HM,** Helmsman
**HMO,** Health Maintenance Organization
**Hon.,** Honorable; Honorary
**H.S.A.,** Health System Administrator
**Hts.,** Heights
**Hwy.,** Highway

**IA,** Iowa
**ID,** Idaho
**IL,** Illinois
**IN,** Indiana
**Inc.,** Incorporated

**J.D.,** Doctor of Law
**J.P.,** Justice of the Peace
**Jr.,** Junior

**KS,** Kansas
**KY,** Kentucky

**LA,** Louisiana
**LCDR,** Lieutenant Commander
**LCSW,** Licensed Certified Social Worker
**L.H.D.,** Doctor of Humanities

**L.I.S.W.,** Licensed Independent Social Worker
**LL.D.,** Doctor of Laws
**L.L.P.,** Limited Licensed Practitioner
**L.M.H.C.,** Licensed Master of Health Care
**L.M.S.W.,** Licensed Master of Social Work
**L.N.H.A.,** Licensed Nursing Home Administrator
**L.P.C.,** Licensed Professional Counselor
**LPN,** Licensed Practical Nurse
**L.P.N.,** Licensed Practical Nurse
**L.S.W.,** Licensed Social Worker
**Lt.,** Lieutenant
**LTC,** Lieutenant Colonel
**Ltd.,** Limited
**LT.GEN.,** Lieutenant General
**LTJG,** Lieutenant (junior grade)

**MA,** Massachusetts
**M.A.,** Master of Arts
**Maj.,** Major
**M.B.,** Bachelor of Medicine
**M.B.A.,** Masters of Business Administration
**MC,** Medical Corps; Marine Corps
**M.C.,** Member of Congress
**MD,** Maryland
**M.D.,** Doctor of Medicine
**ME,** Maine
**M.Ed.,** Master of Education
**MFCC,** Marriage/Family/Child Counselor
**MHA,** Mental Health Association
**M.H.S.,** Masters in Health Science; Masters in Human Service
**MI,** Michigan
**MM,** Masters of Management
**MN,** Minnesota
**M.N.,** Master of Nursing
**MO,** Missouri
**M.P.A.,** Master of Public Administration; Master Public Affairs
**M.P.H.,** Master of Public Health
**M.P.S.,** Master of Professional Studies; Master of Public Science
**MS,** Mississippi
**M.S.,** Master of Science
**MSC,** Medical Service Corps
**M.S.D.,** Doctor of Medical Science
**MSHSA,** Master of Science Health Service Administration
**M.S.N.,** Master of Science in Nursing
**M.S.P.H.,** Master of Science in Public Health
**M.S.S.W.,** Master of Science in Social Work
**M.S.W.,** Master of Social Work
**MT,** Montana
**Mt.,** Mount

**N.,** North
**NC,** North Carolina
**N.C.A.D.C.,** National Certification of Alcohol and Drug Counselors
**ND,** North Dakota
**NE,** Nebraska
**NH,** New Hampshire
**NHA,** National Hearing Association; Nursing Home Administrator
**NJ,** New Jersey
**NM,** New Mexico
**NPA,** National Perinatal Association
**NV,** Nevada
**NY,** New York

**OCN,** Oncology Certified Nurse
**O.D.,** Doctor of Optometry
**O.F.M.,** Order Franciscan Monks, Order of Friars Minor
**OH,** Ohio
**OK,** Oklahoma
**OR,** Oregon

**O.R.,** Operating Room
**O.R.S.,** Operating Room Supervisor
**OSF,** Order of St. Francis

**PA,** Pennsylvania
**P.A.,** Professional Association
**P.C.,** Professional Corporation
**Pharm.D.,** Doctor of Pharmacy
**Ph.B.,** Bachelor of Philosophy
**Ph.D.,** Doctor of Philosophy
**PHS,** Public Health Service
**Pkwy.,** Parkway
**Pl.,** Place
**PR,** Puerto Rico
**PS,** Professional Services
**PSRO,** Professional Standards Review Organization

**RADM,** Rear Admiral
**RD,** Rural Delivery
**Rd.,** Road
**R.F.D.,** Rural Free Delivery
**RI,** Rhode Island
**R.M.,** Risk Manager
**R.N.,** Registered Nurse
**RNC,** Republican National Committee; Registered Nurse or Board Certified
**R.Ph.,** Registered Pharmacist
**RRA,** Registered Record Administrator
**R.S.M.,** Religious Sisters of Mercy
**Rte.,** Route

**S.,** South
**SC,** South Carolina
**S.C.,** Surgery Center
**SCAC,** Senior Certified Addiction Counselor
**Sc.D.,** Doctor of Science
**Sci.,** Science, Scientific
**SD,** South Dakota
**SHCC,** Statewide Health Coordinating Council

**Sgt.,** Sergeant
**SNA,** Surgical Nursing Assistant
**SNF,** Skilled Nursing Facility
**Sq.,** Square
**Sr.,** Senior, Sister
**St.,** Saint, Street
**Sta.,** Station
**Ste.,** Saint; Suite

**Tel.,** Telephone
**Terr.,** Terrace
**TN,** Tennessee
**Tpke.,** Turnpike
**Twp.,** Township
**TX,** Texas

**USA,** United States Army
**USAF,** United States Air Force
**USMC,** United States Marine Corps
**USN,** United States Navy
**USPHS,** United States Public Health Service
**UT,** Utah

**VA,** Virginia
**VADM,** Vice Admiral
**VI,** Virgin Islands
**Vlg.,** Village
**VT,** Vermont
**W.,** West

**WA,** Washington
**WI,** Wisconsin
**WV,** West Virginia
**WY,** Wyoming

# Index

Abbreviations Used in the AHA Guide, C1
Acknowledgements, v
AHA Offices, Officers, and Historical Data, ix
AHA Guide Hospital Listing Requirements, A2
Alliances, B175
    defined, B2
Ambulatory Centers and Home Care
    Agencies, A1112
Annual Survey, A5
Approval Codes, A3
Associate Members, A1112
    defined, A1112
Associated University Programs in Health
    Administration, A1108
Blue Cross Plans, A1112
Control and Service Classifications, A12
Explanation of Hospital Listings, A3
Facility Codes
    defined, A4
    numerically, A3
Health Care Professionals alphabetically, A877
Health Care Systems
    and their hospitals, B4
    defined, B2
    geographically, B150
    introduced, B2
    Statistics for Multihospital Health Care Systems
      and their Hospitals, B3
Hospital Listing Requirements, A2
Hospital Schools of Nursing, A1109

Hospitals in Areas Associated with the United States,
    by Area, A805
Hospitals in the United States, by state, A13
Index of Health Care Professionals, A877
Index of Hospitals, A814
Introduction, vi
    accredited Hospitals, A2
Membership Categories, A1106
Networks and their Hospitals, B159
    defined, B2
Nonhospital Preacute and Postacute Care Facilities,
    A1110
Nonreporting defined, A3
Other Associate Members, A1113
Other Institutional Members, A1107
    defined, A1107
Provisional Hospitals, A1111
Types of Hospitals, A2
    general, A2
    psychiatric, A2
    rehabilitation and chronic disease, A2
    special, A2
U.S. Government Hospitals Outside the United
    States, by Area, A813
Utilization Data, A3
    defined, A3
    expense, A3
    facilities, A4
    personnel, A3